**OPTUM**360°™

 D1284766

SAVE UP TO 25%*
when you renew your coding essentials.

Buy 1–2 items, save 15%
Buy 3–5 items, save 20%
Buy 6+ items, save 25%

ITEM #	TITLE INDICATE THE ITEMS YOU WISH TO PURCHASE	QUANTITY	PRICE PER PRODUCT	TOTAL

	Subtotal	
(AK, DE, HI, MT, NH & OR are exempt)	Sales Tax	
1 item $10.95 • 2–4 items $12.95 • 5+ CALL	Shipping & Handling	
	TOTAL AMOUNT ENCLOSED	

Save up to 25% when you renew.

 Visit **optumcoding.com** and enter the promo code below.

 Call **1-800-464-3649, option 1,** and mention the promo code below.

 Fax this order form with purchase order to **1-801-982-4033.**
Optum360 no longer accepts credit cards by fax.

PROMO CODE
FOBA16WA

Mail this order form with payment and/or purchase order to:
Optum360, PO Box 88050, Chicago, IL 60680-9920.
Optum360 no longer accepts credit cards by mail.

Name _____

Address _____

_____

Customer Number _____ Contact Number _____

○ CHECK ENCLOSED (PAYABLE TO OPTUM360)

○ BILL ME ○ P.O.# _____

( ) _____
Telephone

( ) _____
Fax

_____@_____
E-mail

Optum360 respects your right to privacy. We will not sell or rent your email address or fax number to anyone outside Optum360 and its business partners. If you would like to remove your name from Optum360 promotions, please call 1-800-464-3649, option 1.

*Discount does not include digital coding solutions, workers' comp or bookstore products.

PIONEER
THE NEW FRONTIER OF CODING

WITH A TRUSTED, INDUSTRY LEADER BY YOUR SIDE.

Navigate the changing landscape of coding and move forward with confidence.

With Optum360 tools and resources at your fingertips, you can open a world of opportunities and help build the foundation for greater efficiencies, financial gains, and competitive advantages. For over 30 years, our print resources have remained trusted tools for coding professionals, and our 2016 editions offer the same quality and reliability you have come to expect from us.

Eliminate roadblocks with web-based coding solutions.

ICD-10 will have 668 percent more codes than ICD-9. Web-based coding solutions can help you experience a smooth, successful transition with fast access to ICD-10 codes, data and mapping tools, and can easily be used in conjunction with our ICD-10 books. Learn more about EncoderPro.com and RevenueCyclePro.com today by visiting **optumcoding.com/transitions.**

The new frontier of coding awaits.
Save up to 25% on the ICD-10, CPT®, and HCPCS coding resources you need.

 Visit OptumCoding.com and enter promo code **00000AD3** to save 25%

 Call 1.800.464.3649, option 1 and mention promo code **00000AD3** to save 20%

ESSENTIALS CODING, BILLING & COMPLIANCE CONFERENCE

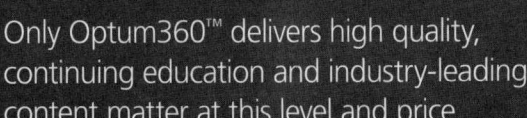

VISIT OPTUMCODING.COM/ESSENTIALS

Only Optum360™ delivers high quality, continuing education and industry-leading content matter at this level and price.

Whether you're looking for daily tips to help make your job just a little easier, or you want to keep your skills current and relevant in this ever-changing world of coding, billing and compliance, Optum360 Essentials is truly, well, essential.

REGISTER NOW!

VISIT
optumcoding.com/essentials

CALL
1-510-463-6073

EMAIL
optumECBC@streamlinevents.com

WHY ATTEND?

- Choose from up to 40 educational sessions, all created to be timely and relevant with what's currently happening in the industry.

- Earn as many as 16 CEUs approved by both AAPC and AHIMA.

- Learn from nationally recognized experts on medical coding, billing and compliance.

- Learn about the CPT® code updates firsthand.

- Stay current with updates on ICD-10-CM/PCS, HCPCS, DRG codes, HCC, PQRS, IPPS and OPPS.

- Focus on ICD-10 with specialty sessions dedicated to your practice.

- Attend vetted presentations that are reviewed and approved by legal and clinical experts.

- Network with a wide spectrum of medical professionals, from entry-level to expert understanding.

- Join user group sessions to learn about the latest in Digital Coding solutions.

CPT is a registered trademark of the American Medical Association.

Optum360™
ESSENTIALS
CODING, BILLING & COMPLIANCE CONFERENCE

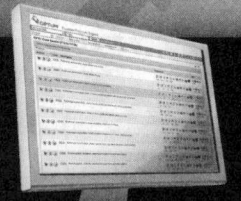
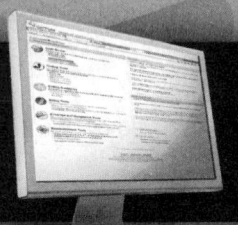

OPTUM360°™

Simplify your ordering.

Magnify your savings.

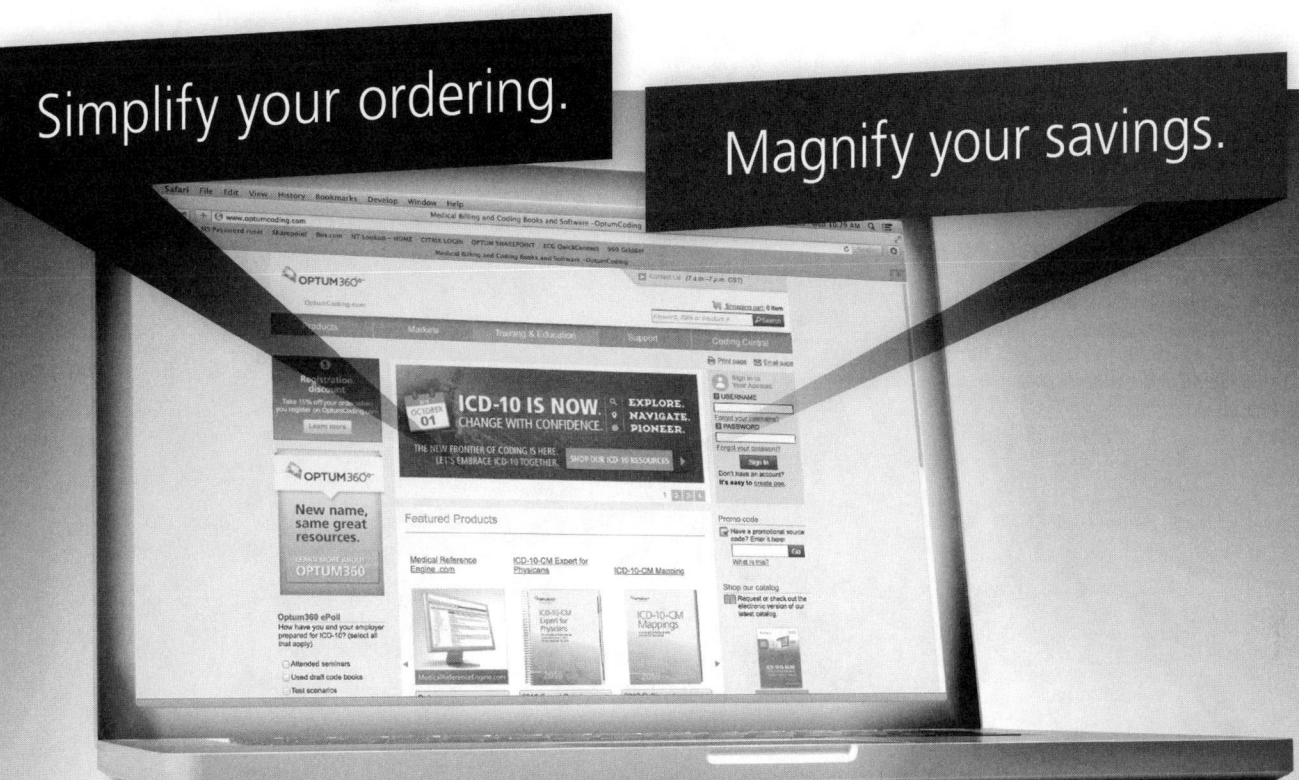

① Click.

Visit optumcoding.com

- Find the products you need quickly and easily.
- View all available formats and edition years on the same page.
- Chat live with a customer service representative.
- Visit Coding Central for expert resources including articles, *Inside Track to ICD-10* and coding scenarios to test your knowledge.
- View our catalog online. Utilize our interactive online catalog features to view product information quickly and easily.

② Register.

By registering, you'll be able to:

- Enjoy special promotions, discounts and automatic rewards.
- Get recommendations based on your order history.
- Check on shipment status and tracking.
- View order and payment history.
- Pay invoices.
- Manage your address book and ship orders to multiple locations.
- Renew your order with a single click.
- Compile a wish list of the products you want and purchase when you're ready.

③ Save.

Get 15% off your next order

Register for an account and receive a coupon via email for 15% off your next order.

Plus, save even more with our no-cost eRewards program.

Register for an account and you're automatically enrolled in our eRewards program, where you'll get a $50 coupon for every $500 you spend*. When logged in at optumcoding.com, the eRewards meter keeps track of purchases toward your next reward.

Visit us at optumcoding.com to register today!

OPTUM360°™

DRG Expert

A Comprehensive Guidebook to the
DRG Classification System
Using the ICD-10-CM and ICD-10-PCS Code Set

Changes effective with discharges on or after October 1, 2015

Grouper Version 33.0 effective 10/01/2015 – 09/30/2016

2016

5th Edition

Optum360 Notice

The *DRG Expert (I-10 Version)* has been prepared based upon subjective medical judgment and upon the information available as of the date of publication. This publication is designed to provide accurate and authoritative information in regard to the subject covered, and every reasonable effort has been made to ensure the accuracy of the information contained within these pages. However, the book does not replace the ICD-10-CM and ICD-10-PCS code books; it serves only as a guide. Optum360, its employees, agents, and staff make no representation or guarantee that this book is error-free or that the use of this book will prevent differences of opinion or disputes with Medicare as to the amounts that will be paid to providers of services, and will bear no responsibility for the results or consequences of its use.

Our Commitment to Accuracy

Optum360 is committed to producing accurate and reliable materials. To report corrections, please visit www.optumcoding.com/accuracy or email accuracy@optum.com. You can also reach customer service by calling 1.800.464.3649, option 1.

Copyright

Property of Optum360, LLC. Optum360 and the Optum360 logo are trademarks of Optum360, LLC. All other brand or product names are trademarks or registered trademarks of their respective owner.

© 2015 Optum360, LLC

All Rights Reserved. No part of this publication may be reproduced, transmitted, stored, or retrieved in any form or by any means without express written permission of the publisher, except as allowed by law.

Made in the USA.

ISBN 978-1-62254-184-3

Acknowledgments

Ken Kracker, *Product Manager*
Karen Schmidt, BSN, *Senior Director, Clinical Technical Editors*
Stacy Perry, *Manager, Desktop Publishing*
Lisa Singley, *Project Manager*
Karen Krawzik, RHIT, CCS, AHIMA-Approved ICD-10-CM/PCS Trainer, *Clinical Technical Editor*
Anita Schmidt, BS, RHIT, AHIMA-Approved ICD-10-CM/PCS Trainer, *Clinical Technical Editor*
Tracy Betzler, *Senior Desktop Publishing Specialist*
Hope M. Dunn, *Senior Desktop Publishing Specialist*
Katie Russell, *Desktop Publishing Specialist*
Kate Holden, *Editor*

Technical Editors

Karen Krawzik, RHIT, CCS, AHIMA-Approved ICD-10-CM/PCS Trainer

Ms. Krawzik has expertise in ICD-10-CM, ICD-9-CM, and CPT/HCPCS coding. Her coding experience includes inpatient, ambulatory surgery, and ancillary and emergency room records. She has served as a DRG analyst and auditor of commercial and government payer claims, and as a contract administrator. Most recently she was responsible for the conversion of the ICD-9-CM code set to ICD-10 and for analyzing audit results, identifying issues and trends, and developing remediation plans. Ms. Krawzik is credentialed by the American Health Information Management Association (AHIMA) as a Certified Coding Specialist (CCS) and is an AHIMA-approved ICD-10-CM/PCS trainer. She is an active member of AHIMA and the Missouri Health Information Management Association.

Anita Schmidt, BS, RHIT, AHIMA-Approved ICD-10-CM/PCS Trainer

Ms. Schmidt has expertise in Level I Adult and Pediatric Trauma hospital coding, specializing in ICD-9-CM, DRG, and CPT coding. Her experience includes analysis of medical record documentation and assignment of ICD-9-CM codes and DRGs, and CPT code assignments for same-day surgery cases. She has conducted coding training and auditing inclusive of DRG validation, conducted electronic health record training, and worked with clinical documentation specialists to identify documentation needs and potential areas for physician education. Ms. Schmidt is an active member of the American Health Information Management Association (AHIMA) and the Minnesota Health Information Management Association (MHIMA).

Summary of Changes for FY 2016

The Centers for Medicare and Medicaid Services has issued its final rule on changes to the hospital inpatient prospective payment system (IPPS) and Fiscal Year 2016 rates (*Federal Register,* August 17, 2015). The MS-DRGs are now considered Version 33.0 Medicare DRGs, and are effective for discharges occurring on or after October 1, 2015.

DRG and Code Changes

- Added 50 new ICD-10-PCS procedure codes.
- Added a new section X New Technology for classifying new technology procedures.
- Created seven new MS-DRGs in MDC 5: MS-DRG 268 (Aortic and Heart Assist Procedures Except Pulsation Balloon With MCC), MS-DRG 269 (Aortic and Heart Assist Procedures Except Pulsation Balloon Without MCC), MS-DRG 270 (Other Major Cardiovascular Procedures with MCC), MS-DRG 271 (Other Major Cardiovascular Procedures with CC), MS-DRG 272 (Other Major Cardiovascular Procedures without CC/MCC), MS-DRG 273 (Percutaneous Intracardiac Procedures with MCC), and MS-DRG 274 (Percutaneous Intracardiac Procedures Without MCC).
- Deleted MS-DRGs 237 and 238 (Major Cardiac Procedures With/Without MCC).
- Assigned ICD-10-PCS procedure code 02UG3JZ to new MS-DRGs 273 and 274 (Percutaneous Intracardiac Procedures with MCC; without MCC), and will continue to assign to MS-DRGs 231 and 232 (Coronary Bypass with PTCA With MCC; without MCC).
- Revised the titles for MS-DRGs 456-458 to Spinal Fusion Except Cervical with Spinal Curvature/Malignancy/Infection or Extensive Fusion with MCC, Spinal Fusion Except Cervical with Spinal Curvature/Malignancy/Infection or Extensive Fusion with CC, and Spinal Fusion Except Cervical with Spinal Curvature/Malignancy/Infection or Extensive Fusion without CC/MCC.
- Added code combinations that will depict joint revision procedures to MS-DRGs 466-468 (Revision of Hip or Knee Replacement with MCC, with CC, without CC/MCC) and MS-DRGs 628-630 (Other Endocrine, Nutritional and Metabolic O.R. Procedures with MCC; with CC; without CC/MCC).
- Changed nine ICD-10-PCS procedure codes to non-O.R. code status so that cases reporting this procedure code will group to the appropriate MS-DRG assignment, MS-DRG 775 (Vaginal Delivery without Complicating Diagnoses), in MDC 14.
- Added 43 ICD-10-CM diagnosis codes to the Manifestation Codes Not Allowed as Principal Diagnosis edit in the FY 2016 ICD-10 MCE Version 33.
- Revised MCE edit language for Procedure Inconsistent with Length of Stay (LOS) to read "The following procedure code should only be coded on claims with a length of stay greater than 4 days" which includes ICD-10-PCS code 5A1955Z (Respiratory ventilation, greater than 96 consecutive hours).
- Revised eight MS-DRG titles that reflected old ICD-9-CM terminology for mechanical ventilation of 96 hours by adding a *greater than* sign before the 96 and removing the "plus sign" after the 96 (MS-DRG 003 ECMO or Tracheostomy with Mechanical Ventilation >96 Hours or Principal Diagnosis Except Face, Mouth and Neck with Major O.R.; MS-DRG 004 Tracheostomy with Mechanical Ventilation >96 Hours or Principal Diagnosis Except Face, Mouth and Neck without Major O.R.; MS-DRG 207 Respiratory System Diagnosis with Ventilator Support >96 Hours; MS-DRG 870 Septicemia or Severe Sepsis with Mechanical Ventilation >96 Hours; MS-DRGs 871 and 872 Septicemia or Severe Sepsis without Mechanical Ventilation >96 Hours with MCC; without MCC; MS-DRG 927 Extensive Burns or Full Thickness Burns with Mechanical Ventilation >96 Hours with Skin Graft; and MS-DRG 933 Extensive Burns or Full Thickness Burns with Mechanical Ventilation >96 Hours without Skin Graft).
- Addressed ICD-10-MS-DRG replication issues by:
  - designating eight ICD-10-PCS codes describing the insertion of pressure sensor monitoring device as O.R. procedures and assigned them to MS-DRG 264 Other Circulatory System O.R. Procedures
  - assigning ICD-10-PCS codes 0LB[S,T]0ZZ (Excision of [right, left] ankle tendon, open approach) to MS-DRGs 579 – 581 (Other Skin, Subcutaneous Tissue and Breast Procedures with MCC; with CC; without CC/MCC).
  - assigning ICD-10-PCS code 0UBMXZZ (Excision of vulva, external approach) to MS-DRG 774 (Vaginal Delivery with Complicating Diagnoses) and MS-DRG 775 (Vaginal Delivery without Complicating Diagnoses).
- Revised the surgical hierarchy for MDC 5 Diseases and Disorders of the Circulatory System.
- Recalibrated the DRG relative weights as required by the Social Security Act.
- Added two ICD-10-CM codes to the list of principal diagnoses that can act as their own CC, N13.1 (Hydronephrosis with ureteral stricture, not elsewhere classified) and N13.2 (Hydronephrosis with renal and ureteral calculus obstruction).
- No revisions to the CC, MCC, or CC Excludes list for Fiscal Year 2016.

Contents

Numeric MS-DRG Listing

Numeric MS-DRG Listing

Numeric MS-DRG Listing

Numeric MS-DRG Listing

MS-DRG Listing by Major Diagnostic Category

MDC 6   Diseases And Disorders Of The Digestive System

SURGICAL

MEDICAL

MDC 7 Diseases And Disorders Of The Hepatobiliary System And Pancreas

SURGICAL

MEDICAL

MDC 8 Diseases And Disorders Of The Musculoskeletal System And Connective Tissue

SURGICAL

MDC 9   Diseases And Disorders Of The Skin, Subcutaneous Tissue And Breast

MS-DRG Listing by Major Diagnostic Category

MDC 18 Infectious And Parasitic Diseases, Systemic or Unspecified Sites

MDC 19 Mental Diseases And Disorders

MDC 20 Alcohol/Drug Use And Alcohol/Drug-Induced Organic Mental Disorders

MDC 21 Injuries, Poisonings And Toxic Effects Of Drugs

MDC 22 Burns

MDC 23 Factors Influencing Health Status And Other Contacts With Health Services

MS-DRG Listing by Major Diagnostic Category

MS-DRG Listing by Major Diagnostic Category

Introduction

The Medicare severity diagnosis-related group (MS-DRG) system organizes ICD-10 diagnosis and procedure codes into a complex, comprehensive system based on a few simple principles.

Understanding how the system works enables providers to recover the appropriate payment for inpatient services rendered in an acute care hospital facility, which is consistent with the intent of the federal government in devising the system. The *DRG Expert* helps providers understand ICD-10 MS-DRGs, thus ensuring appropriate payment.

DRG Expert Website

Optum360 maintains a website to accompany *DRG Expert*. Optum will post special reports, Centers for Medicare and Medicaid Services (CMS) information and updated data files on this website so that the information is available before the next book update. This website address is:

https://www.optumcoding.com/Product/Updates/DRG/

This website is available only to customers who purchase the *DRG Expert*, using the following password: **DRG16**

Available on eBook

The *DRG Expert* is available as an eBook for your convenience. The eBook version of *DRG Expert* contains a complete copy of this book including appendixes. In the eBook, appendix G includes a list of all ICD-10-CM diagnosis codes that are assigned to each MDC. They are listed in numeric order, beginning with MDC 1. Please note that there are no diagnosis codes for the Pre-MDC DRGs, since they are grouped according to procedure code.

Source of Information

Information in the book is the data posted by the Centers for Medicare and Medicaid Services (CMS) at https://www.cms.gov/Medicare/Medicare-Fee-for-Service-Payment/AcuteInpatientPPS/FY2016-IPPS-Final-Rule-Home-Page.html

This version of Optum360's *DRG Expert* reflects the ICD-10-CM/PCS MS-DRG version 33.0.

Basic Characteristics of MS-DRG Classification

An MS-DRG is one of 758 groups (version 33.0) that classify patients into clinically cohesive groups that demonstrate similar consumption of hospital resources and length-of-stay patterns. In 1983, Congress mandated a national inpatient prospective payment system (IPPS) for all Medicare inpatients. The following types of hospitals are excluded from the inpatient prospective payment system (IPPS):

- Psychiatric hospitals and units
- Rehabilitation hospitals and units
- Children's hospitals
- Long-term care hospitals
- Cancer hospitals
- Critical Access Hospitals

This IPPS uses MS-DRGs to determine hospital reimbursement. CMS administers the IPPS and issues all rules and changes with regard to MS-DRGs.

In addition to calculating reimbursement, MS-DRGs have two major functions. The first is to help evaluate the quality of care. Not only are critical pathways designed around MS-DRGs, but benchmarking and outcomes analysis can be launched using the MS-DRG clinical framework, and quality reviews can be performed to assess coding practices and physician documentation. Ongoing education of physicians, coders, clinical documentation specialists, nurses, and utilization review personnel can be guided by the results of MS-DRG analysis.

Second, MS-DRGs assist in evaluating utilization of services. Each MS-DRG represents the average resources needed to treat patients grouped to that MS-DRG relative to the national average of resources used to treat all Medicare patients. The MS-DRG assigned to each hospital inpatient stay also relates to the hospital case mix (i.e., the types of patients the hospital treats). A hospital's Medicare population case complexity is measured by calculation of the case-mix index, which is an average of all MS-DRG relative weights for the facility during a given period of time. The higher the case-mix index, the more complex the patient population and the higher the required level of resources utilized. Since severity is such an essential component of MS-DRG assignment and case-mix index calculation, documentation and code assignment to the highest degree of accuracy and specificity are of the utmost importance.

Medicare computes the case-mix adjustment for each fiscal year for all hospitals based upon the case-mix data received. This CMI is then used to adjust the hospital base rate, which is a factor in computing the total hospital payment under IPPS.

The formula for computing the hospital payment for each MS-DRG is as follows:

Relative Weight x Hospital Base Rate = Hospital Payment

The hospital case-mix complexity includes the following patient attributes:

- Severity of illness—the level of loss of function or mortality associated with disease
- Prognosis—defined as probable outcome of illness
- Treatment difficulty—patient management problems
- Need for intervention—severity of illness that would result due to lack of immediate or continuing care
- Resource intensity—volume and types of services required for patient management

The MS-DRG system was developed to relate case mix to resource utilization. Reimbursement is adjusted to reflect the resource utilization and does not take into consideration severity of illness, prognosis, treatment difficulty, or need for intervention.

Case mix and complexity can be analyzed and monitored in relation to cost and utilization of services. In addition, high-volume conditions and services can be identified and monitored, and MS-DRG trend analysis can aid in forecasting future staff and facility requirements. One important operating parameter is the CMI, which measures the cost of a hospital's Medicare patient mix in relation to the cost of all Medicare patients. A low case mix may indicate unnecessary revenue loss.

MS-DRG Assignment Process

MS-DRGs are assigned using the principal diagnosis, which in some cases may function as a complication/comorbidity (CC) or a major complication/comorbidity (MCC); secondary diagnoses, which include CCs and MCCs; surgical or other invasive procedures; sex of the patient;

and discharge status. One MS-DRG is assigned to each inpatient stay. Diagnoses and procedures are designated by ICD-10-CM and PCS codes. The following describes the typical decision process used to assign an MS-DRG to a case.

A case is assigned to one of 25 major diagnostic categories (MDC), which are mutually exclusive groups based on principal diagnosis. MS-DRG assignment is based upon the following considerations:

- Principal and secondary diagnosis and procedure codes
- Sex of the patient
- Discharge status

- Presence or absence of MCCs and/or presence or absence of CCs
- Birth weight for neonates

Each MDC is organized into one of two sections—surgical or medical. The surgical section classifies all surgical conditions based upon operating room procedures. The medical section classifies all diagnostic conditions based upon diagnosis codes. The majority of MDCs are organized by major body system and/or are associated with a particular medical specialty.

There are two groups of MS-DRGs that are not assigned to MDCs. First, there is the group that may be associated with all MDCs. This group includes MS-DRGs created specifically to report admissions into a facility that have been assigned invalid principal diagnoses (MS-DRG 998), have O.R. procedures unrelated to a principal diagnosis (MS-DRGs 981–983, 984–986, and 987–989), or are ungroupable principal diagnoses (MS-DRG 999). Although the scope is too broad for clinical analysis, the DRGs encompass clinically coherent cases.

Another group not assigned to MDCs is called Pre-MDC MS-DRGs, which consist of cases that are grouped by surgical procedure rather than principal diagnosis. The Pre-MDC MS-DRG group includes bone marrow and organ transplant cases as well as tracheostomy cases.

Further sorting of medical classifications is performed by principal diagnosis type and/or surgical classifications by type of surgery. Finally, the case is analyzed for the presence of MCCs and/or CCs as indicated by ICD-10-CM diagnosis codes, and an MS-DRG is assigned.

Each year, effective October 1 through September 30, MS-DRG assignments are adjusted based on relative weight (RW), arithmetic mean length of stay (AMLOS), and geometric mean length of stay (GMLOS). Annually, new ICD-10 codes will be incorporated into the existing MS-DRGs or new MS-DRGs will be added for the next fiscal year.

The information contained in this manual reflects the DRG classification system for Fiscal Year 2016, Grouper version 33.0.

Grouper Version	Effective Time Period
MS 33.0	10/01/2015 – 09/30/2016
MS 32.0	10/01/2014 – 09/30/2015
MS 31.0	10/01/2013 – 09/30/2014
MS 30.0	10/01/2012 – 09/30/2013
MS 29.0	10/01/2011 – 09/30/2012
MS 28.0	10/01/2010 – 09/30/2011
MS 27.0	10/01/2009 – 09/30/2010
MS 26.0	10/01/2008 – 09/30/2009
MS 25.0	10/01/2007 – 09/30/2008
CMS 24.0	10/01/2006 – 09/30/2007
CMS 23.0	10/01/2005 – 09/30/2006
CMS 22.0	10/01/2004 – 09/30/2005
CMS 21.0	10/01/2003 – 09/30/2004
CMS 20.0	10/01/2002 – 09/30/2003
CMS 19.0	10/01/2001 – 09/30/2002
CMS 18.0	10/01/2000 – 09/30/2001
CMS 17.0	10/01/1999 – 09/30/2000
CMS 16.0	10/01/1998 – 09/30/1999
CMS 15.0	10/01/1997 – 09/30/1998
CMS 14.0	10/01/1996 – 09/30/1997
CMS 13.0	10/01/1995 – 09/30/1996
CMS 12.0	10/01/1994 – 09/30/1995
CMS 11.0	10/01/1993 – 09/30/1994
CMS 10.0	10/01/1992 – 09/30/1993
CMS 9.0	10/01/1991 – 09/30/1992
CMS 8.0	10/01/1990 – 09/30/1991
CMS 7.0	10/01/1989 – 09/30/1990
CMS 6.0	10/01/1988 – 09/30/1989
CMS 5.0	10/01/1987 – 09/30/1988
CMS 4.0	10/01/1986 – 09/30/1987
CMS 3.0	05/01/1986 – 09/30/1986
CMS 2.0	10/01/1983 – 04/30/1986

Complications and Comorbidities

CMS developed lists of MCC and CC conditions for assignment of hospital cases to appropriate MS-DRGs. When a CC or MCC is present as a secondary diagnosis, it may affect assignment. With the conversion of MS-DRGs to ICD-10, it was recognized that certain ICD-10-CM diagnosis codes specify both an underlying condition and an acute manifestation or complication in one code. The MS-DRG assignment logic was modified to assign all ICD-10-CM codes that met this criterion to the appropriate "with MCC" or "with CC" MS-DRG by having the single ICD-10 code serve as principal diagnosis *and* as the CC or MCC. Appendix A lists principal diagnoses that are their own CC and their own MCC.

For certain principal diagnoses, conditions generally considered CCs are not seen as such because a closely related condition deemed a CC would result in duplicative or inconsistent coding.

Conversion of MS-DRGs to ICD-10

The conversion of MS-DRGs from ICD-9-CM to ICD-10-CM/PCS codes took 18 months of painstaking analysis and a trial run. The sheer number of ICD-10 codes and their greater specificity than ICD-9-CM codes meant that converting MS-DRGs to the new coding system would require more than just pressing a key. The final result is a new MS-DRG system that is clinically accurate as well as comprehensive.

Much of the conversion relied on the general equivalency mappings (GEMs) developed by the Centers for Medicare and Medicaid Services and the Centers for Disease Control and Prevention. GEMs translate from ICD-9-CM to ICD-10-CM/PCS codes and vice versa and are instrumental to providers and payers converting to the new coding system October 1, 2015. Inaccurate or incomplete GEMs would lead to failure of Grouper logic and much more work for anyone transitioning to ICD-10-CM/PCS codes.

One of the best gauges of success is how the conversion affected those who rely on MS-DRGs for reimbursement. Inaccuracies in the conversion would be evident in sizeable payment variances between ICD-10 and ICD-9-CM MS-DRGs.

The conversion passed the test with flying colors. There is a "high degree of consistency between the ICD-9-CM and I-10 version of MS-DRGs," according to a study entitled "Impact of the Transition to ICD-10 on Medicare Inpatient Hospital Payments." The authors of the study, Ronald Mills, Rhonda Butler, Richard Averill, Elizabeth McCullough, and Mona Bao, all of 3M Health Information Systems, found that overall Medicare payments would be increased only 0.05 percent under the conversion (based on 2009 data).

The study found that, under conversion, although some diagnosis and procedure codes are assigned to different MDCs than under ICD-9-CM MS-DRGs, the differences balance each other out for a net effect of close to zero.

Three Steps to Conversion

CMS decided to transition from MS-DRG version 26.0, which was based on ICD-9-CM, to an interim version, 27.0, based on ICD-10-CM/PCS, in three steps. The first step was to convert just one representative MDC. After ironing out the problems with this first attempt, the conversion team would then convert the entire set of MS-DRGs. Finally, the team would issue a final update of the MS-DRG Definitions Manual and MS-DRG grouping software.

Step 1—Converting a trial MDC: This was by far the most involved step in the process. The conversion team, consisting of physicians, clinical coders, researchers, MS-DRG analysts, and programmers, decided that the most comprehensive approach would be to devise MS-DRGs that process ICD-10-CM/PCS codes directly, rather than merely translating ICD-10 codes into ICD-9-CM codes so that existing applications could be used.

The team set out in 2006 to do a trial run of converting MS-DRGs to ICD-10 to pinpoint trouble spots before tackling the entire MS-DRG system. It chose MDC 6 Diseases and Disorders of the Digestive System as the guinea pig because it contains lists of codes for diseases and procedures of average complexity.

The conversion team worked nine months to translate the 11 diagnosis lists and 10 procedure lists in MDC 6 to ICD-10-CM/PCS codes. For the most part, it was possible to convert the codes automatically using GEMs. Some codes posed problems, however:

> **Challenge #1:** Some ICD-10-CM/PCS codes translated to two or more ICD-9-CM codes that appear on more than one mutually exclusive list.

> For example, ICD-10-CM code K22.8 (Other specified diseases of esophagus; includes hemorrhage of esophagus NOS) translates to ICD-9-CM code 530.82 (Esophageal hemorrhage) and 530.89 (Other diseases of esophagus), which are on two different mutually exclusive lists. If this translation were not altered, the programming logic would break down at this point since one code cannot be mutually exclusive to itself.

> **Solution:** In each such instance, the conversion team decided which ICD-9-CM code best reflected the ICD-10-CM/PCS code. The team weighed reporting frequency as well as specificity in its decision. In the case above, the team selected 530.89 as the best translation for ICD-10-CM code K22.8.

> **Challenge #2:** ICD-10-PCS codes are much more specific as to site than are ICD-9-CM codes. This means that hundreds of ICD-10-PCS codes may translate to one general ICD-9-CM code, resulting in inappropriate MS-DRG assignments.

> For example, 261 ICD-10-PCS codes translate to the general ICD-9-CM procedure code 92.27 (Implantation or insertion of

radioactive elements). Whereas 92.27 can appropriately appear in several MDCs because it does not indicate a body site, each ICD-10-PCS code can appear in only one MDC because of its site specificity. For the purposes of converting MDC 6, only a small portion of the 261 ICD-10-PCS codes specify body sites appropriately classified to the digestive system.

> **Solution:** For MDC 6, the conversion team selected only 21 ICD-10-PCS codes that could appropriately be assigned to the MS-DRG Other Digestive System O.R. Procedures (356–358).

> **Challenge #3:** In some cases, two or more ICD-10-CM/PCS codes must be used together to replicate the meaning of one ICD-9-CM code. Each ICD-10-CM/PCS code might translate to a separate ICD-9-CM code, and then the two or more together might translate to yet another ICD-9-CM code, all of which fall into mutually exclusive MS-DRGs. The team called these instances "code clusters."

> For example, ICD-10-PCS code 0DQ80ZZ (Repair small intestine, open approach) translates to ICD-9-CM code 46.79 (Other repair of intestine) which falls under MS-DRG 329–331 Major small and large bowel procedures; and 0WQFXZ2 (Repair abdominal wall, stoma, external approach) translates to 46.41 (Revision of stoma of small intestine), which fall under MS-DRG 347–349 Anal and stomal procedures. The two ICD-10-PCS codes used together, however, translate to 46.51 (Closure of stoma of small intestine), assigned to MS-DRG 344–346 Minor small and large bowel procedures.

> **Solution:** The team wrote programs to identify cases in which code clusters are required to completely replicate an MS-DRG list. In the example above, the assignment logic for MS-DRG 344–346 was altered so that the program looks for two ICD-10-PCS codes instead of just one ICD-9-CM code. The following is a partial list of MS-DRGs and surgical cases that required ICD-10-PCS code clusters to produce the same Grouper results:

> - Heart transplantation or implant of heart assist system
> - Simultaneous pancreas/kidney transplant
> - Craniotomy with major device implant
> - Neurostimulators
> - Cardiac defibrillators
> - Implant/replace subcutaneous cardiac device
> - Lead device pairs
> - Permanent cardiac pacemaker implant
> - Resection of abdominal aorta and other thoracic vessels with replacement

In September 2008, the conversion team presented the results of its test conversion of MDC 6 to the Coordination and Maintenance Committee. Its findings suggested that more than 90 percent of ICD-10-CM codes could be converted to MS-DRGs automatically using GEMs. Of the diagnosis codes, only 1 percent required clinical review because of a conflict, whereas 9 percent of procedure codes encountered problems that needed clinical resolution.

Step 2—Converting all MS-DRGs to ICD-10-CM/PCS: Converting the rest of the MDCs took nine months, the same amount of time it took the team to convert just MDC 6. The same problems encountered above cropped up again, with the same or similar resolutions.

It was at this point that the team instituted its "reverse look-up" in the index to ensure every clinical aspect of ICD-10-CM/PCS codes were reflected in their MS-DRG assignments. It searched for each ICD-10 code in the index and analyzed the entries, making sure that all clinical aspects of a code were reflected in the translation to MS-DRGs.

Conversion of the MCC/CC Lists

It was also at this point that the MCC and CC lists were converted—99.4 percent of the more than 5,000 ICD-9-CM codes were translated automatically into slightly more than 17,000 ICD-10-CM codes.

Two issues arose during the MCC/CC conversion. The first had to do with two mutually exclusive lists. In other words, a code cannot function as both an MCC and a CC for the MS-DRG logic to work. The translation program identified a list of codes referred to as "list conflicts." The entire conversion team reviewed these list conflicts, established conventions, and decided whether a code would be deemed an MCC or a CC.

The second issue had to do with certain ICD-10-CM diagnosis codes that specify both an underlying condition and an acute manifestation or complication in one code. In the ICD-9-CM system, there could be one code assigned for the principal diagnosis and one or more for a secondary diagnosis designated as a CC or MCC. In this case, the assignment logic was modified in order to assign all ICD-10-CM codes that met these criteria to the appropriate "with MCC" or "with CC" MS-DRG by having the single ICD-10-CM code describe the principal diagnosis as well as the CC or MCC.

GEM Translation

Throughout the second step of conversion, two general areas were identified where it was thought the GEM translations could be improved:

- ICD-10-CM diagnosis codes for injury and poisoning specifying subsequent encounter
- Translation of obstetrics codes

Both of the issues above were referred to the Cooperating Parties on ICD-9-CM, which published new guidelines to address subsequent encounter codes. The new guidelines ensured that those codes were assigned to appropriate aftercare MS-DRGs rather than being assigned to various injury and poisoning MS-DRGs, as was previously the case. Since the ICD-10-CM GEMs were revised and expanded for obstetrics codes, the MS-DRG logic for MDC 14 Pregnancy, Childbirth and the Puerperium was modified.

Gender-Specific Codes

The sex of the patient is not specified in ICD-10-CM as it was in ICD-9-CM. As a result, the assignment logic based on ICD-10-CM/PCS had to be modified to look for the patient's gender in the submitted data. The ICD-10-CM/PCS version will assign the same MS-DRG assignment as the ICD-9-CM version if the gender is obtained from the data.

Gender-Specific Example:

ICD-9-CM		ICD-10-CM	
625.6	Stress incontinence, female	N39.3	Stress incontinence (female) (male)
788.32	Stress incontinence, male	N39.3	Stress incontinence (female) (male)

Specific MS-DRG Conversion

Diseases and Disorders of the Circulatory System
Coronary Bypass, MS-DRGs 231–236

At the time of conversion, there were 232 ICD-10-PCS codes on the operating room procedure code list for MS-DRGs 231–236 Coronary Bypass, compared with nine ICD-9-CM procedure codes. The ICD-10 PCS codes are much more detailed compared with the ICD-9-CM procedure codes. The body part component of the I-10 code identifies the number of coronary artery sites bypassed to, and the qualifier component specifies the vessel bypassed from, in addition to specifying the approach used to reach the procedure site and the specific bypass graft material used in the procedure.

Cardiac Defibrillator Implant, MS-DRGs 222–227, 245, and 260–262

CMS created what it termed "ICD-10-PCS clusters" to replicate the MS-DRG logic for cardiac defibrillator implants. The Grouper logic was modified to look for a pair of ICD-10-PCS procedure codes that replace the previous ICD-9-CM code, 00.51 Implantation of cardiac resynchronization defibrillator, total system (CRT-D), which was assigned to MS-DRGs 222–227. In addition, the cardiac defibrillator implant DRGs share ICD-10-PCS codes to replicate the MS-DRG logic that existed before ICD-10-CM implementation. The table below shows cardiac defibrillator implantation codes.

ICD-9-CM		ICD-10-PCS		MS-DRGs
00.51	Implantation of cardiac resynchronization defibrillator, total system (CRT-D)	0JH60P5*	Insertion of cardiac resynchronization defibrillator pulse generator into chest subcutaneous tissue and fascia, open approach	MS-DRGs 222–227 Cardiac Defibrillator Implant
		AND 02HL3MZ	Insertion of cardiac lead into left ventricle, percutaneous approach	
00.54	Implantation or replacement of cardiac resynchronization defibrillator pulse generator device only (CRT-D)	0JH60P5*	Insertion of cardiac resynchronization defibrillator pulse generator into chest subcutaneous tissue and fascia, open approach	MS-DRG 245 AICD Generator Procedures
37.76	Replacement of transvenous atrial and/or ventricular lead(s) (electrode(s))	02HL3MZ	Insertion of cardiac lead into left ventricle, percutaneous approach	MS-DRGs 260–262 Cardiac Pacemaker Revision Except Device Replacement

* Invalid code effective 2012

Percutaneous Cardiovascular Procedures without Stent, MS-DRGs 250–251

At the time of conversion, there were 136 ICD-10-PCS codes on the operating room procedure code list for MS-DRGs 250–251 Percutaneous Cardiovascular Procedures without Stent, compared with eight ICD-9-CM procedure codes. The ICD-10 PCS codes are much more detailed compared with the ICD-9-CM procedure codes, providing greater specificity concerning the anatomic site and the operative technique and approach.

Cardiac Pacemaker Device Replacement, MS-DRGs 258–259

At the time of conversion, there were 14 ICD-10-PCS codes on the operating room procedure code list for MS-DRGs 258–259 Cardiac Pacemaker Device Replacement, compared with six ICD-9-CM procedure codes. The ICD-10-PCS codes are more specific about the anatomic site and the approach.

Acute Myocardial Infarction, MS-DRGs 280–285

The axis of classification used in ICD-9-CM pertaining to myocardial infarction (MI) codes specifying initial episode of care, subsequent episode of care, and unspecified episode of care has been discontinued in ICD-10-CM. MS-DRG assignments will no longer include MS-DRGs 314–316 Other Circulatory System Diagnoses because ICD-10-CM does not differentiate between initial and subsequent visits. The ICD-10-CM MI codes will be assigned to MS-DRGs 280–285 Acute Myocardial Infarction or MS-DRGs 222–227 Cardiac Defibrillator Implant with Acute MI/Heart Failure/Shock, depending on other codes assigned.

Heart Failure and Shock, MS-DRGs 291–293
At the time of conversion, there were only 20 ICD-10-CM codes on the principal diagnosis code list for MS-DRGs 291–293 Heart Failure and Shock, compared with 27 ICD-9-CM principal diagnosis codes. This is because ICD-10-CM does not use the terms "benign" and "malignant" to further classify the hypertensive component of hypertensive heart failure.

Atherosclerosis, MS-DRG 302
In ICD-10-CM there are now codes that specify both the underlying diagnosis of atherosclerosis and the current exacerbation of unstable angina. These replace the need for two ICD-9-CM codes to report the atherosclerosis as principal diagnosis and the unstable angina as the secondary diagnosis, which resulted in MS-DRG assignment 302 Atherosclerosis with MCC. In ICD-10-CM these codes are referred to as combination codes. The MS-DRG logic will be modified to assign any one of the ICD-10 CM combination codes (I25.7*) to the appropriate MS-DRG *with* MCC/CC, even if no secondary diagnoses are reported.

Angina Pectoris, MS-DRG 311
At the time of conversion, there were seven ICD-10-CM codes on the principal diagnosis code list for MS-DRG 311 Angina Pectoris, compared with six ICD-9-CM codes. In addition to the seven codes, there are other codes in ICD-10-CM (I25.7*) that specify angina as part of a combination code. They describe the underlying diagnosis of coronary artery atherosclerosis and the current exacerbation of angina. The combination codes were included in the list of codes for MS-DRGs 302–303 Atherosclerosis, not in MS-DRG 311 Angina Pectoris.

Diseases and Disorders of the Musculoskeletal System and Connective Tissue
Spinal Fusions, MS-DRGs 456–458
The ICD-10-PCS list of operating room procedure codes at the time of conversion included 240 spinal fusion codes, compared with the previous ICD-9-CM list of 13 codes. ICD-10 PCS specifies distinct body part values for single and multiple vertebral joints at each spinal level, as well as devices and materials used on a vertebral joint to render the joint immobile.

Wound Debridement, MS-DRGs 463–465
Wound debridement became problematic when converting MS-DRGs from ICD-9-CM to ICD-10-PCS. The ICD-9-CM procedure codes contained diagnosis information in them (for example 83.39 Excision of lesion of other soft tissue or 86.22 Excisional debridement of wound, infection, or burn). MS-DRGs 463–465 and 500–502 used that diagnosis information to differentiate themselves, thus making the conversion to I-10 difficult. In ICD-10-PCS the procedure code is more straightforward based on the root operation, "Excision." In its deliberations, CMS reviewed possible ICD-9-CM translations and their MS-DRG assignment, as well as frequency data. The final decision was to assign the ICD-10-PCS codes that replace 83.39 and 86.22 to MS-DRGs 463–465 Wound Debridement and Skin Graft Except Hand, for Musculo-Connective Tissue Disorders *only*.

Revision of Hip and Knee Replacements, MS-DRGs 466–468, 469–470, 480–482
Again it was necessary for CMS to create what it termed "ICD-10-PCS clusters" to replicate the MS-DRG logic for the revision of hip and knee replacements. The Grouper logic was modified to look for *both* the ICD-10-PCS procedure codes indicating removal (for example, 0SP90JZ), and replacement (for example, code 0SR90JZ). In ICD-10-PCS, the root operation term "removal" specifies taking out the previously implanted

prosthesis, and "replacement" specifies putting in the new prosthesis. Without the ICD-10-PCS code for removal, it would not be clear that a previous hip replacement was revised and the assignment logic would not assign the case to MS-DRGs 466–468.

For MS-DRGs 469–470 the list of ICD-10-PCS operating room procedure codes include only the codes for replacement of the hip joint (for example, code 0SR90JZ). For this reason, in this case there was a straightforward replacement of ICD-9-CM code 81.51, and the cases could be assigned to MS-DRGs 469–470.

For MS-DRGs 480–482 the list of ICD-10-PCS operating room procedure codes include only the codes for removal of the previously implanted hip prosthesis (for example, code 0SP90JZ). These codes replace ICD-9-CM code 80.05, and cases are assigned to MS-DRGs 480–482.

Note the similarity of the revision of hip and knee replacement DRGs to the cardiac defibrillator implant DRGs in the table below and how the DRGs share ICD-10-PCS codes to replicate the MS-DRG logic that existed before ICD-10-CM implementation.

ICD-10-PCS		MS-DRGs
0SR90JZ	Replacement of right hip joint with synthetic substitute, open approach	MS-DRGs 466–468 Revision of Hip or Knee Replacement
AND		
0SP90JZ	Removal of synthetic substitute from right hip joint, open approach	
0SR90JZ	Replacement of right hip joint with synthetic substitute, open approach	MS-DRGs 469–470 Major Joint Replacement or Reattachment of Lower Extremity
0SP90JZ	Removal of synthetic substitute from right hip joint, open approach	MS-DRGs 480–482 Hip and Femur Procedures Except Major Joint

Spinal Neurostimulator, MS-DRG 490
CMS reported that the implantation of spinal neurostimulator lead and pulse generator code pairs in ICD-9-CM converted to 30 ICD-10-PCS codes without any issues.

Fractures of the Femur, MS-DRGs 533–534
There were 273 ICD-10-CM principal diagnosis femur fracture codes on the principal diagnosis code list, compared with 14 ICD-9-CM codes. The ICD-10-CM codes provide greater specificity of fracture type, anatomic site, laterality, and encounter, and initial versus subsequent. There were no issues with the conversion to MS-DRGs.

Medical Back Problems, MS-DRGs 551–552
In the conversion, 1,132 ICD-10-CM codes replaced the 166 principal diagnosis codes in MS-DRGs 551–552. The ICD-10-CM codes better specify the region of the spine. The vertebral fracture codes more specifically identify site and fracture type. It should be noted that ICD-10-CM no longer includes the open dislocation as a combination code. In ICD-10-CM the dislocation is coded separately with a code also note that indicates that open wound of neck (S11-) should also be coded.

Pregnancy, Childbirth and the Puerperium
The conversion of the MS-DRGs for obstetrics proved to be challenging and, again, it was necessary to modify MS-DRG assignment logic. The MS-DRGs found in MDC 14 Pregnancy, Childbirth and the Puerperium were organized around the ICD-9-CM diagnosis codes that defined whether the patient delivered during the episode of care. The ICD-10-CM system classifies based on the trimester of the pregnancy and other

clinically relevant factors. MS-DRG assignment logic was modified to look for both a diagnosis code and a procedure code to assign to MS-DRGs 774–775, Vaginal Delivery. A diagnosis code alone does not specify that the patient delivered during the admission and if reported without a procedure code will be assigned to MS-DRG 781 Other Antepartum Diagnoses without Medical Complications.

Step 3—Updating the MS-DRG Grouper Software and Definitions Manual: This final step involved making final tweaks to MS-DRG grouping logic, as well as updating the ICD-10 MS-DRG Definitions Manual to version 28.0. The manual was posted in March of 2011 at http://www.cms.gov/ICD10/17_ICD10_MS_DRG_Conversion_Project.asp#TopOfPage.

Keys to a Financially Successful MS-DRG Program

CMS assigns each MS-DRG a relative weight based upon charge data for all Medicare inpatient hospital discharges. Each hospital has a customized base rate that adjusts payment commensurate with the hospital's cost of providing services. The type of hospital and the wage index for the geographic area determines the hospital base rate. MS-DRG relative weights and hospital base rates are adjusted yearly (effective October 1 through September 30) to reflect changes in health care resource consumption as well as economic factors. Payment is determined by multiplying the MS-DRG relative weight by the hospital base rate. The MS-DRG with the highest relative weight is the highest-paying MS-DRG. Regardless of actual costs incurred, the hospital receives only the calculated payment.

The MS-DRG payment system is based on averages. Payment is determined by the resource needs of the average Medicare patient for a given set of diseases or disorders. These resources include the length of stay and the number and intensity of services provided. Therefore, the more efficiently a provider delivers care, the greater the operating margin will be.

The keys to a financially successful program are:

- Decreased length of stay
- Decreased resource utilization (tests and procedures)
- Increased intensity of case-management services resulting in optimal length of stay for the patient and facility
- Increased preadmission testing
- Improved medical record documentation

The Physician's Role

Proper MS-DRG assignment requires a complete and thorough accounting of the following:

- Principal diagnosis
- Procedures
- Complications
- Comorbidities (all relevant pre-existing conditions)
- Signs and symptoms when diagnoses are not established
- Discharge status

Because MS-DRG assignment is based on documentation in the medical record, the record should:

- Be comprehensive and complete
- Include all diagnoses, procedures, complications, and comorbidities, as well as abnormal test results documented by the physician. It should also include any suspected conditions and what was done to investigate or evaluate them.
- Be timely

All dictation, signatures, etc., should be completed in the medical record as patient care is provided and must be:

- Legible
- Well documented

The information should be documented properly. With complete information in the medical record, coders can effectively analyze, code, and report the required information. This ensures that proper payment is received. For example, if the physician documents that a patient with a skull fracture was in a coma for less than one hour, MS-DRGs 085–087 may be assigned. If the physician documents that the coma lasted for more than one hour, MS-DRGs 082–084 may be assigned, with a resulting payment difference.

Physicians must be actively involved in the query process. They should respond to queries in a timely fashion and document their responses, as established by the process, to ensure they meet regulatory requirements and are maintained in some form in the permanent medical record.

DRG Expert Organization

Numeric MS-DRG Listing
This section is a numeric listing of all DRGs with MDC and page reference.

MS-DRG Listing by Major Diagnostic Category
The MDC List is a numerical listing of the MDCs with the category title. Each MDC then is separated into a surgical MS-DRG list and medical MS-DRG list for the MDC in numerical order. Also, the page reference for each MS-DRG is noted.

Introduction
The introduction addresses the basic characteristics of MS-DRG classification, a brief overview of the MS-DRG assignment process, including complications and comorbidities, a summary of the conversion of MS-DRGs to ICD-10, keys to a financially successful MS-DRG program, and the physician's role in proper MS-DRG assignment.

Definitions of the MS-DRGs
The book contains a list of the 25 MDCs. They are listed in numeric order, beginning with Pre MDC. Each MDC is divided into surgical and medical sections (when appropriate). Listed in each section are the applicable MS-DRGs and their associated diagnosis and/or procedure codes. Please note that there are no diagnosis codes for the Pre-MDC DRGs, since they are grouped according to procedure code. Beside each MS-DRG title is its GMLOS, AMLOS, and RW. Under each MS-DRG is a list of diagnosis and/or procedure codes that determine assignment of the case to that MS-DRG.

Indexes
Both the print and eBook versions of the *DRG Expert* allow you to locate a DRG by searching alphabetically (code narrative) by either disease or procedure and to search numerically (ICD-10-CM/PCS codes).

The Alphabetic Index to Diseases, Alphabetic Index to Procedures, Numeric Index to Diseases, and Numeric Index to Procedures are included in both the print and eBook versions.

Appendix A: Lists of Principal Diagnoses That Are Their Own CC and Their Own MCC

The MCC and CC lists were converted during the second stage of the conversion process—99.4 percent of the more than 5,000 ICD-9-CM codes were translated automatically into slightly more than 17,000 ICD-10-CM codes. At this time certain ICD-10-CM diagnosis codes that specify both an underlying condition and an acute manifestation or complication in one code were identified. The assignment logic was modified to assign all ICD-10-CM codes that met this criterion to the appropriate "with MCC" or "with CC" MS-DRG by having the single ICD-10 code serve as principal diagnosis *and* as the CC or MCC. The lists in this section represent principal diagnosis codes that are their own CC or their own MCC under the ICD-10-CM MS-DRGs.

Appendix B: Lists of CCs and MCCs

The Centers for Medicare & Medicaid Services (CMS) reviewed more than 13,500 diagnosis codes to determine which should be classified as CCs as part of their process to develop MS-DRGs. The agency then did an additional analysis to further refine secondary diagnoses into what is now known as major CCs (MCCs). An issue arose with these lists during the MCC/CC conversion process. It had to do with two mutually exclusive lists. In other words, a code cannot function as both an MCC and a CC for the MS-DRG logic to work. The translation program identified a list of codes referred to as "list conflicts." The entire conversion team reviewed the list conflicts, established conventions, and decided whether a code would be deemed an MCC or a CC. The lists in this section represent diagnosis codes designated as CCs and MCCs under the ICD-10-CM MS-DRGs.

Appendix C: MS-DRG Surgical Hierarchy Table

Since patients may be assigned to only one MS-DRG per admission, a tool was necessary to enable the evaluation of the relative resource consumption for cases involving multiple surgeries that individually group to different surgical MS-DRGs within an MDC. The surgical hierarchy table in this section reflects the relative resource requirements of the various surgical procedures of each MDC. Arranging the surgical MS-DRGs this way helps the user assign the MS-DRG that accurately reflects the resource utilization for multiple surgery cases and thereby assign the case to the highest surgical MS-DRG.

Appendix D: National Average Payment Table

This section lists all MS-DRGs in numerical order. Each MS-DRG is listed with the MS-DRG title, MDC number, and the average national payment.

The national average payment for each MS-DRG is calculated by multiplying the current RW of the MS-DRG and national average hospital Medicare base rate. The national average hospital Medicare base rate is the sum of the full update labor-related and nonlabor-related amounts published in the *Federal Register*, FY 2016 Final Rule, Table 1A. National Adjusted Operating Standardized Amounts; Labor/Nonlabor (if wage index greater than 1) or Table 1B. National Adjusted Operating Standardized Amounts; Labor/Nonlabor (if wage index less than or equal to 1).

Appendix E: Abbreviations

An all-inclusive list of abbreviations used in the bracketed code descriptions. Asterisk and complete codes use either the official CMS description of the category or the official CMS shortened version (60 characters).

Glossary of MS-DRG Terms

This section of the introduction contains definitions of terms associated with the MS-DRG classification system.

Instructions for Using *DRG Expert*

If the MS-DRG is known, use the "Numeric MS-DRG Listing," which lists MS-DRGs numerically. Locate the designated MS-DRG and check the MS-DRG title, the MDC into which the MS-DRG falls, and the reference page number. Turn to the referenced page for a complete list of codes that group to the MS-DRG, as well as the reimbursement data for the MS-DRG. Scan the list for codes with an asterisk (*) or brackets, the meaning of which is discussed in the steps below.

If the MDC to which the case groups is known but the specific MS-DRG is not, use the "MS-DRG Listed by Major Diagnostic Category" to locate potential MS-DRG selections. Find the MDC, determine whether the case is surgical or medical, scan the MS-DRG and title list, and then turn to the referenced page for further information.

If the MS-DRG is not known, follow the steps below to determine MS-DRG assignment:

1. Determine whether the case had an operating room procedure (certain operating room procedures do not qualify and do not appear in this book). If so, refer to either the alphabetic or numeric procedure index to locate all potential MS-DRG assignments.

   Look for the specific code or search by the general type of procedure (e.g., resection, transfer, division) or a more commonly used term (e.g., appendectomy).

   Example:.

   ØDTJ4ZZ   **Resection of appendix, percutaneous endoscopic approach**

2. If the case lacks an operating room procedure, look up the diagnosis by using either the alphabetic or numeric diagnosis index.

   To locate a diagnosis, look for the specific code, the condition, or main term, qualifier, then body site and qualifier, in that order.

   Example:

   S12.8XXA   **Fracture of other parts of neck, initial encounter**

3. In some cases it is necessary to scan the list for codes with an asterisk (*) or brackets. The asterisk indicates a sequence or range of codes, and all codes within that code category or subcategory are represented. See an ICD-10-CM/PCS code book for specific codes. Some of the ICD-10 codes appear in this book with brackets as a space-saving convention. The numbers in the brackets correspond to the appropriate, valid digits for the character where the brackets appear.

   Example:

   MØ5.44 [1,2,9] Rheumatoid myopathy with rheumatoid arthritis of [right, left, unspecified] hand

   6th character meanings for codes as indicated
   - 1   RIGHT
   - 2   LEFT
   - 9   UNSPECIFIED

4. Turn to the page(s) and review the MS-DRG descriptions. Determine which is the correct MS-DRG.

   Often a diagnosis or procedure code is assigned to more than one MS-DRG. Sometimes an MS-DRG entry does not have a full list of the codes that group to the particular MS-DRG, but instead refers to an MS-DRG entry that does contain the full list. The only difference in the assignment of either of the MS-DRGs is the presence or absence of an MCC

Be careful to examine all possible potential MS-DRG assignments when the MS-DRG title includes qualifiers such as "with MCC" versus "without MCC," "with CC" versus "without CC," and "with CC/MCC" versus "without CC/MCC."

5. Examine the medical record closely for the following considerations: the patient's principal diagnosis, secondary diagnoses, which include complication/comorbidities; surgical or other invasive procedures; sex of the patient and discharge status; and birth weight for neonates.

6. Documentation must support selection of the final MS-DRG.

Important Protocols of *DRG Expert*

More than one MS-DRG: Many diagnosis and procedure codes group to more than one MS-DRG. Be sure to check every MS-DRG referenced.

Asterisks: Some numeric codes are followed by an asterisk, which indicates that the ICD-10 code is incomplete and represents a sequence or range of codes. Refer to the ICD-10-CM or ICD-10-PCS code book(s) for the specific codes included in the code range.

Brackets: Some of the characters in ICD-10-CM or ICD-10-PCS codes are enclosed in brackets as a space-saving convention. The numbers or letters within the brackets correspond to all appropriate, valid characters for the character position where the bracket appears. For example:

S04.01[1,2,9]S Injury of optic nerve, [rt, lt, unsp] eye, sequela

The bracketed code above represents three distinct codes:

S04.011   Injury of optic nerve, right eye

S04.012   Injury of optic nerve, left eye

S04.019   Injury of optic nerve, unspecified eye

A complete MS-DRG title is necessary to understand the nature of the cases the MS-DRG comprises.

Example:

698   Other Kidney and Urinary Tract Diagnoses with MCC

699   Other Kidney and Urinary Tract Diagnoses with CC

700   Other Kidney and Urinary Tract Diagnoses without CC/MCC

The MS-DRG title must be reviewed to understand that correct MS-DRG assignment depends on two factors—the presence/absence of an MCC and/or CC and patient disposition. Review MS-DRGs that precede or follow the target MS-DRG, and determine how their narrative descriptions differ. It is possible another MS-DRG with a higher relative weight may be assigned appropriately.

A **red color bar** indicates a surgical DRG.

A **blue color bar** indicates a medical DRG.

A **green color bar** indicates an MCC.

A **purple color bar** indicates a CC.

A **yellow color bar** indicates a procedure proxy, whereby the inclusion of a specific procedure code acts as a proxy for the MCC or CC for the case. If the procedure code is assigned, the MCC or CC code typically required would not be necessary for grouping.

The symbol ● indicates a new MS-DRG.

The symbol ▲ indicates a revised MS-DRG title.

The symbol Ⓣ indicates an MS-DRG selected as a qualified discharge that may be paid as a transfer case.

The symbol SP indicates an MS-DRG that is subject to the special payment methodology.

The symbol PDxMCC indicates an ICD-10-CM diagnosis code that can serve as principal diagnosis *and* as the CC condition.

The symbol PDxCC indicates an ICD-10-CM diagnosis code that can serve as principal diagnosis *and* as the MCC condition.

PDxMCC PDxCC codes are not indicated with their respective symbols when the codes are included in an asterisk code or a bracketed code. Refer to appendix A for the complete lists of principal diagnoses that are their own CC and their own MCC.

The terms principal or secondary diagnosis indicate MS-DRGs that are based on specific principal or secondary diagnosis requirements.

Bold text **OR, AND, WITH, WITH ONE OF, WITH ALL OF** alerts the user to those complex MS-DRGs that have additional diagnosis or procedure qualifications.

SURGICAL

DRG 001 — Heart Transplant or Implant of Heart Assist System with MCC
GMLOS 29.4 AMLOS 38.8 RW 26.2466

Operating Room Procedures

02HA[0,3,4]QZ	Insert/Heart, [Opn, Perc, Perc Endo], Implantable Heart Assist Sys, NQ
02YA0Z[0,1,2]	Transplantation/Heart, Opn, No Dev, [Allogeneic, Syngeneic, Zooplastic]

OR

02HA0RS	Insert of Bivent Ext Heart Assist into Heart, Opn Appr
02HA0RZ	Insert of Ext Heart Assist into Heart, Opn Appr
02HA3RS	Insert of Bivent Ext Heart Assist into Heart, Perc Appr
02HA4RS	Insert Bivent Ext Heart Assist in Heart, Perc Endo
02HA4RZ	Insert of Ext Heart Assist into Heart, Perc Endo Appr
02WA[0,3,4][Q,R]Z	Rev/Heart, [Opn, Perc, Perc Endo], [Implantable Heart Assist Sys, Ext Heart Assist Sys], NQ

AND

02PA[0,3,4]RZ	Rmvl/Heart, [Opn, Perc, Perc Endo], Ext Heart Assist Sys, NQ

DRG 002 — Heart Transplant or Implant of Heart Assist System without MCC
GMLOS 16.6 AMLOS 20.0 RW 14.6448

Select operating room procedure OR any procedure combinations listed under DRG 001

▲DRG 003 — ECMO or Tracheostomy with Mechanical Ventilation >96 Hours or Principal Diagnosis Except Face, Mouth and Neck with Major O.R.
GMLOS 25.5 AMLOS 31.7 RW 17.6569 [T]

Operating Room Procedure

5A15223	Extracorporeal Membrane Oxygenation, Continuous

OR

Nonoperating Room Procedure

0B113[F,Z]4	Bypass/Trachea, Perc, [Tracheostomy Dev, No Dev], Cutaneous

OR

Operating Room Procedure

0B11[0,4][F,Z]4	Bypass/Trachea, [Opn, Perc Endo], [Tracheostomy Dev, No Dev], Cutaneous

AND EITHER

Principal Diagnosis

Any diagnosis EXCEPT mouth, larynx and pharynx disorders listed under DRG 011

OR

Nonoperating Room Procedure

5A1955Z	Respiratory Ventilation, > 96 Consecutive Hrs

AND

Operating Room Procedures

Any O.R. procedure not listed in DRGs 984-989

▲DRG 004 — Tracheostomy with Mechanical Ventilation >96 Hours or Principal Diagnosis Except Face, Mouth and Neck without Major O.R.
GMLOS 20.0 AMLOS 24.1 RW 10.9458 [T]

Operating Room Procedures

0B11[0,4][F,Z]4	Bypass/Trachea, [Opn, Perc Endo], [Tracheostomy Dev, No Dev], Cutaneous

OR

Nonoperating Room Procedure

0B113[F,Z]4	Bypass/Trachea, Perc, [Tracheostomy Dev, No Dev], Cutaneous

AND EITHER

Principal Diagnosis

Any diagnosis EXCEPT mouth, larynx and pharynx disorders listed under DRG 011

OR

Nonoperating Room Procedure

5A1955Z	Respiratory Ventilation, > 96 Consecutive Hrs

DRG 005 — Liver Transplant with MCC or Intestinal Transplant
GMLOS 15.3 AMLOS 21.0 RW 10.7263

Operating Room Procedures

0DY80Z[0,1,2]	Transplantation/Sm Intestine, Opn, No Dev, [Allogeneic, Syngeneic, Zooplastic]
0DYE0Z[0,1,2]	Transplantation/Lg Intestine, Opn, No Dev, [Allogeneic, Syngeneic, Zooplastic]
0FY00Z[0,1,2]	Transplantation/Liver, Opn, No Dev, [Allogeneic, Syngeneic, Zooplastic]

DRG 006 — Liver Transplant without MCC
GMLOS 7.9 AMLOS 8.8 RW 4.8330

Operating Room Procedures

0FY00Z[0,1,2]	Transplantation/Liver, Opn, No Dev, [Allogeneic, Syngeneic, Zooplastic]

DRG 007 — Lung Transplant
GMLOS 15.8 AMLOS 18.8 RW 9.7007

Operating Room Procedures

0BYC0Z[0,1,2]	Transplantation/Upr Lung Lobe, Rt, Opn, No Dev, [Allogeneic, Syngeneic, Zooplastic]
0BYD0Z[0,1,2]	Transplantation/Mid Lung Lobe, Rt, Opn, No Dev, [Allogeneic, Syngeneic, Zooplastic]
0BYF0Z[0,1,2]	Transplantation/Lwr Lung Lobe, Rt, Opn, No Dev, [Allogeneic, Syngeneic, Zooplastic]
0BYG0Z[0,1,2]	Transplantation/Upr Lung Lobe, Lt, Opn, No Dev, [Allogeneic, Syngeneic, Zooplastic]
0BYH0Z[0,1,2]	Transplantation/Lung Lingula, Opn, No Dev, [Allogeneic, Syngeneic, Zooplastic]
0BYJ0Z[0,1,2]	Transplantation/Lwr Lung Lobe, Lt, Opn, No Dev, [Allogeneic, Syngeneic, Zooplastic]
0BYK0Z[0,1,2]	Transplantation/Lung, Rt, Opn, No Dev, [Allogeneic, Syngeneic, Zooplastic]
0BYL0Z[0,1,2]	Transplantation/Lung, Lt, Opn, No Dev, [Allogeneic, Syngeneic, Zooplastic]
0BYM0Z[0,1,2]	Transplantation/Lungs, Bilat, Opn, No Dev, [Allogeneic, Syngeneic, Zooplastic]

DRG 008 — Simultaneous Pancreas/Kidney Transplant
GMLOS 9.8 AMLOS 11.4 RW 5.4338

Principal or Secondary Diagnosis

E08.0*	Diabetes d/t underlying condition w hyperosmolarity
E08.1*	Diabetes mellitus d/t underlying condition w ketoacidosis
E08.2*	Diabetes d/t underlying condition w kidney comp
E08.3*	Diabetes d/t underlying condition w ophthalmic comp
E08.4*	Diabetes d/t underlying condition w neurological comp
E08.5*	Diabetes d/t underlying condition w circulatory comp
E08.6*	Diabetes d/t underlying condition w oth comp
E08.8	Diabetes d/t underlying condition w unsp comp
E08.9	Diabetes d/t underlying condition w/o comp
E09.0*	Drug or chemical induced diabetes mellitus w hyperosmolarity
E09.1*	Drug or chemical induced diabetes mellitus with ketoacidosis
E09.2*	Drug/chem diabetes mellitus w kidney comp
E09.3*	Drug/chem diabetes mellitus w ophthalmic comp
E09.4*	Drug/chem diabetes mellitus w neurological comp

Pre MDC—SURGICAL

E09.5*	Drug/chem diabetes mellitus w circulatory comp
E09.6*	Drug/chem diabetes mellitus w oth comp
E09.8	Drug/chem diabetes mellitus w unsp comp
E09.9	Drug or chemical induced diabetes mellitus w/o comps
E10.1*	Type 1 diabetes mellitus with ketoacidosis
E10.2*	Type 1 diabetes mellitus with kidney comp
E10.3*	Type 1 diabetes mellitus with ophthalmic comp
E10.4*	Type 1 diabetes mellitus with neurological comp
E10.5*	Type 1 diabetes mellitus with circulatory comp
E10.6*	Type 1 diabetes mellitus with oth spec comp
E10.8	Type 1 diabetes mellitus with unsp comp
E10.9	Type 1 diabetes mellitus w/o comp
E11.0*	Type 2 diabetes mellitus with hyperosmolarity
E11.2*	Type 2 diabetes mellitus with kidney comp
E11.3*	Type 2 diabetes mellitus with ophthalmic comp
E11.4*	Type 2 diabetes mellitus with neurological comp
E11.5*	Type 2 diabetes mellitus with circulatory comp
E11.6*	Type 2 diabetes mellitus with oth spec comp
E11.8	Type 2 diabetes mellitus with unsp comp
E11.9	Type 2 diabetes mellitus w/o comp
E13.0*	Oth spec diabetes mellitus with hyperosmolarity
E13.1*	Oth spec diabetes mellitus with ketoacidosis
E13.2*	Oth spec diabetes mellitus with kidney comp
E13.3*	Oth diabetes mellitus with ophthalmic comp
E13.4*	Oth diabetes mellitus with neurological comp
E13.5*	Oth diabetes mellitus with circulatory comp
E13.6*	Oth diabetes mellitus with oth spec comp
E13.8	Oth diabetes mellitus with unsp comp
E13.9	Oth spec diabetes mellitus w/o comp
E89.1	Postprocedural hypoinsulinemia

AND

Principal or Secondary Diagnosis

I12.0	Hyp chr kidney dz w stage 5 chr kidney dz or ESRD
I13.11	Hyp hrt and chr kdny dis w/o hrt fail, w stg 5 chr kdny/ESRD
I13.2	Hyp hrt & chr kdny dis w hrt fail and w stg 5 chr kdny/ESRD
N18.1	Chr kidney dz, stage 1
N18.2	Chr kidney dz, stage 2 (mild)
N18.3	Chr kidney dz, stage 3 (mod)
N18.4	Chr kidney dz, stage 4 (severe)
N18.5	Chr kidney dz, stage 5
N18.6	End stage renal dz
N18.9	Chr kidney dz, unsp
Z94.0	Kidney transplant status
Z96.49	Presence of oth endocrine implants
Z96.89	Presence of oth spec functional implants
Z96.9	Presence of functional implant, unsp

AND

Operating Room Procedures

0TY00Z[0,1,2]	Transplantation/Kidney, Rt, Opn, No Dev, [Allogeneic, Syngeneic, Zooplastic]
0TY10Z[0,1,2]	Transplantation/Kidney, Lt, Opn, No Dev, [Allogeneic, Syngeneic, Zooplastic]

AND

Operating Room Procedures

0FYG*	Transplantation/Pancreas

DRG 009   Bone Marrow Transplant
         GMLOS 0.0   AMLOS 0.0   RW 0.0000

Omitted in October 2011 Grouper version.

DRG 010   Pancreas Transplant
         GMLOS 8.1   AMLOS 9.5   RW 4.3039

Principal or Secondary Diagnosis

E08.0*	Diabetes d/t underlying condition w hyperosmolarity
E08.1*	Diabetes mellitus d/t underlying condition w ketoacidosis
E08.2*	Diabetes d/t underlying condition w kidney comp
E08.3*	Diabetes d/t underlying condition w ophthalmic comp
E08.4*	Diabetes d/t underlying condition w neurological comp
E08.5*	Diabetes d/t underlying condition w circulatory comp
E08.6*	Diabetes d/t underlying condition w oth comp
E08.8	Diabetes d/t underlying condition w unsp comp
E08.9	Diabetes d/t underlying condition w/o comp
E09.0*	Drug or chemical induced diabetes mellitus w hyperosmolarity
E09.1*	Drug or chemical induced diabetes mellitus with ketoacidosis
E09.2*	Drug/chem diabetes mellitus w kidney comp

E09.3*	Drug/chem diabetes mellitus w ophthalmic comp
E09.4*	Drug/chem diabetes mellitus w neurological comp
E09.5*	Drug/chem diabetes mellitus w circulatory comp
E09.6*	Drug/chem diabetes mellitus w oth comp
E09.8	Drug/chem diabetes mellitus w unsp comp
E09.9	Drug or chemical induced diabetes mellitus w/o comp
E10.1*	Type 1 diabetes mellitus with ketoacidosis
E10.2*	Type 1 diabetes mellitus with kidney comp
E10.3*	Type 1 diabetes mellitus with ophthalmic comp
E10.4*	Type 1 diabetes mellitus with neurological comp
E10.5*	Type 1 diabetes mellitus with circulatory comp
E10.6*	Type 1 diabetes mellitus with oth spec comp
E10.8	Type 1 diabetes mellitus with unsp comp
E10.9	Type 1 diabetes mellitus w/o comp
E11.0*	Type 2 diabetes mellitus with hyperosmolarity
E11.2*	Type 2 diabetes mellitus with kidney comp
E11.3*	Type 2 diabetes mellitus with ophthalmic comp
E11.4*	Type 2 diabetes mellitus with neurological comp
E11.5*	Type 2 diabetes mellitus with circulatory comp
E11.6*	Type 2 diabetes mellitus with oth spec comp
E11.8	Type 2 diabetes mellitus with unsp comp
E11.9	Type 2 diabetes mellitus w/o comp
E13.0*	Oth spec diabetes mellitus with hyperosmolarity
E13.1*	Oth spec diabetes mellitus with ketoacidosis
E13.2*	Oth spec diabetes mellitus with kidney comp
E13.3*	Oth diabetes mellitus with ophthalmic comp
E13.4*	Oth diabetes mellitus with neurological comp
E13.5*	Oth diabetes mellitus with circulatory comp
E13.6*	Oth diabetes mellitus with oth spec comp
E13.8	Oth diabetes mellitus with unsp comp
E13.9	Oth spec diabetes mellitus w/o comp
E89.1	Postprocedural hypoinsulinemia

AND

Operating Room Procedures

0FYG*	Transplantation/Pancreas

DRG 011   Tracheostomy for Face, Mouth, and Neck Diagnoses with MCC
         GMLOS 11.3   AMLOS 13.8   RW 4.7501

Operating Room Procedures

0CTS[0,4,7,8]ZZ	Resect/Larynx, [Opn, Perc Endo, Via Natrl or Artfcl Opng, Via Natrl or Artfcl Opng Endo]

OR

Principal Diagnosis

A36.0	Pharyngeal diphtheria
A36.1	Nasopharyngeal diphtheria
A36.2	Laryngeal diphtheria
A54.5	Gonococcal pharyngitis
A56.4	Chlamydial infxn of pharynx
A66.5	Gangosa
A69.0	Necrotizing ulcerative stomatitis
A69.1	Oth Vincent's infections
B00.2	Herpesviral gingivostomatitis and pharyngotonsillitis
B08.5	Enteroviral vesicular pharyngitis
B37.0	Candidal stomatitis
B37.83	Candidal cheilitis
C00.0	Malig neoplasm of ext upr lip
C00.1	Malig neoplasm of ext lwr lip
C00.2	Malig neoplasm of ext lip, unsp
C00.3	Malig neoplasm of upr lip, inner aspect
C00.4	Malig neoplasm of lwr lip, inner aspect
C00.5	Malig neoplasm of lip, unsp, inner aspect
C00.6	Malig neoplasm of commissure of lip, unsp
C00.8	Malig neoplasm of overlapping sites of lip
C00.9	Malig neoplasm of lip, unsp
C01	Malig neoplasm of base of tongue
C02.0	Malig neoplasm of dorsal surface of tongue
C02.1	Malig neoplasm of border of tongue
C02.2	Malig neoplasm of ventral surface of tongue
C02.3	Malig neoplasm of ant two-thirds of tongue, part unsp
C02.4	Malig neoplasm of lingual tonsil
C02.8	Malig neoplasm of overlapping sites of tongue
C02.9	Malig neoplasm of tongue, unsp
C03.0	Malig neoplasm of upr gum
C03.1	Malig neoplasm of lwr gum
C03.9	Malig neoplasm of gum, unsp
C04.0	Malig neoplasm of ant floor of mouth
C04.1	Malig neoplasm of lat floor of mouth

Ⓣ Transfer DRG   ⓢⓟ Special Payment   * Code Range   6th and 7th Character of ZZ = No Device, No Qualifier ZX = No Device, Diagnostic

2   MS-DRG Version 33.0   © 2015 Optum360, LLC

C04.8	Malig neoplasm of overlapping sites of floor of mouth
C04.9	Malig neoplasm of floor of mouth, unsp
C05.0	Malig neoplasm of hard palate
C05.1	Malig neoplasm of soft palate
C05.2	Malig neoplasm of uvula
C05.8	Malig neoplasm of overlapping sites of palate
C05.9	Malig neoplasm of palate, unsp
C06.0	Malig neoplasm of cheek mucosa
C06.1	Malig neoplasm of vestibule of mouth
C06.2	Malig neoplasm of retromolar area
C06.8*	Malig neoplasm of ovrlp sites of and unsp parts of mouth
C06.9	Malig neoplasm of mouth, unsp
C07	Malig neoplasm of parotid gland
C08.0	Malig neoplasm of submandibular gland
C08.1	Malig neoplasm of sublingual gland
C08.9	Malig neoplasm of major salivary gland, unsp
C09.0	Malig neoplasm of tonsillar fossa
C09.1	Malig neoplasm of tonsillar pillar (ant) (posterior)
C09.8	Malig neoplasm of overlapping sites of tonsil
C09.9	Malig neoplasm of tonsil, unsp
C10.0	Malig neoplasm of vallecula
C10.1	Malig neoplasm of ant surface of epiglottis
C10.2	Malig neoplasm of lat wall of oropharynx
C10.3	Malig neoplasm of posterior wall of oropharynx
C10.4	Malig neoplasm of branchial cleft
C10.8	Malig neoplasm of overlapping sites of oropharynx
C10.9	Malig neoplasm of oropharynx, unsp
C11.0	Malig neoplasm of superior wall of nasopharynx
C11.1	Malig neoplasm of posterior wall of nasopharynx
C11.2	Malig neoplasm of lat wall of nasopharynx
C11.3	Malig neoplasm of ant wall of nasopharynx
C11.8	Malig neoplasm of overlapping sites of nasopharynx
C11.9	Malig neoplasm of nasopharynx, unsp
C12	Malig neoplasm of pyriform sinus
C13.0	Malig neoplasm of postcricoid region
C13.1	Malig neoplasm of aryepiglottic fold, hypopharyngeal aspect
C13.2	Malig neoplasm of posterior wall of hypopharynx
C13.8	Malig neoplasm of overlapping sites of hypopharynx
C13.9	Malig neoplasm of hypopharynx, unsp
C14.0	Malig neoplasm of pharynx, unsp
C14.2	Malig neoplasm of Waldeyer's ring
C14.8	Malig neoplm of ovrlp sites of lip, oral cavity and pharynx
C30.0	Malig neoplasm of nasal cavity
C30.1	Malig neoplasm of mid ear
C31.0	Malig neoplasm of maxillary sinus
C31.1	Malig neoplasm of ethmoidal sinus
C31.2	Malig neoplasm of frontal sinus
C31.3	Malig neoplasm of sphenoid sinus
C31.8	Malig neoplasm of overlapping sites of accessory sinuses
C31.9	Malig neoplasm of accessory sinus, unsp
C32.0	Malig neoplasm of glottis
C32.1	Malig neoplasm of supraglottis
C32.2	Malig neoplasm of subglottis
C32.3	Malig neoplasm of laryngeal cartilage
C32.8	Malig neoplasm of overlapping sites of larynx
C32.9	Malig neoplasm of larynx, unsp
C39.0	Malig neoplasm of upr respiratory tract, part unsp
C41.1	Malig neoplasm of mandible
C44.0*	Oth and unsp malig neoplasm of skin of lip
C46.2	Kaposi's sarcoma of palate
C73	Malig neoplasm of thyroid gland
C76.0	Malig neoplasm of head, face and neck
C77.0	Sec and unsp malig neoplasm of nodes of head, face and neck
C81.01	Nodlr lymphocy predom Hodgkin lymph, nodes of head, face, & nk
C81.11	Nodlr scler class Hodgkin lymph, nodes of head, face, and neck
C81.21	Mix cellular class Hodgkin lymph, nodes of head, face, and neck
C81.31	Lymphocy deplet class Hodgkin lymph, nodes of head, face, & nk
C81.41	Lymp-rich class Hodgkin lymph, nodes of head, face, and neck
C81.71	Oth class Hodgkin lymphoma, nodes of head, face, and neck
C81.91	Hodgkin lymphoma, unsp, lymph nodes of head, face, and neck
C82.01	Follicular lymphoma grade I, nodes of head, face, and neck
C82.11	Follicular lymphoma grade II, nodes of head, face, and neck
C82.21	Foliclar lymph grade III, unsp, nodes of head, face, and nk
C82.31	Foliclar lymphoma grade IIIa, nodes of head, face, and neck
C82.41	Foliclar lymphoma grade IIIb, nodes of head, face, and neck
C82.51	Diffuse folicl center lymph, nodes of head, face, and neck
C82.61	Cutan folicl center lymphoma, nodes of head, face, and neck
C82.81	Oth types of foliclar lymph, nodes of head, face, and neck
C82.91	Follicular lymphoma, unsp, nodes of head, face, and neck
C83.01	Sm cell B-cell lymphoma, nodes of head, face, and neck
C83.31	Diffuse large B-cell lymphoma, nodes of head, face, and neck
C83.51	Lymphoblastic lymphoma, nodes of head, face, and neck
C83.71	Burkitt lymphoma, lymph nodes of head, face, and neck
C83.81	Oth non-follic lymphoma, lymph nodes of head, face, and neck
C83.91	Non-follic lymphoma, unsp, nodes of head, face, and neck
C84.01	Mycosis fungoides, lymph nodes of head, face, and neck
C84.11	Sezary dz, lymph nodes of head, face, and neck
C84.91	Mature T/NK-cell lymph, unsp, nodes of head, face, and neck
C84.A1	Cutan T-cell lymphoma, unsp nodes of head, face, and neck
C84.Z1	Oth mature T/NK-cell lymph, nodes of head, face, and neck
C85.11	Unsp B-cell lymphoma, lymph nodes of head, face, and neck
C85.21	Mediastnl large B-cell lymph, nodes of head, face, and neck
C85.81	Oth types of non-hodg lymph, nodes of head, face, and neck
C85.91	Non-Hodgkin lymphoma, unsp, nodes of head, face, and neck
C86.0	Extranodal NK/T-cell lymphoma, nasal type
C91.40	Hairy cell leukemia not having achieved remission
C96.0	Multifocal and multisystemic Langerhans-cell histiocytosis
C96.2	Malig mast cell tumor
C96.9	Malig neoplm of lymphoid, hematpoetc and rel tissue, unsp
C96.A	Histiocytic sarcoma
D00.0*	Carcinoma in situ of lip, oral cavity and pharynx
D02.0	Carcinoma in situ of larynx
D10.0	Benign neoplasm of lip
D10.1	Benign neoplasm of tongue
D10.2	Benign neoplasm of floor of mouth
D10.3*	Oth and unsp parts of mouth
D10.4	Benign neoplasm of tonsil
D10.5	Benign neoplasm of oth parts of oropharynx
D10.6	Benign neoplasm of nasopharynx
D10.7	Benign neoplasm of hypopharynx
D10.9	Benign neoplasm of pharynx, unsp
D11.0	Benign neoplasm of parotid gland
D11.7	Benign neoplasm of oth major salivary glands
D11.9	Benign neoplasm of major salivary gland, unsp
D14.0	Benign neoplasm of mid ear, nasl cav and accessory sinuses
D14.1	Benign neoplasm of larynx
D16.4	Benign neoplasm of bones of skull and face
D16.5	Benign neoplasm of lwr jaw bone
D18.00	Hemangioma unsp site
D18.01	Hemangioma of skin and SQ tissue
D18.09	Hemangioma of oth sites
D34	Benign neoplasm of thyroid gland
D37.0*	Neoplasm of uncertain behav of lip, oral cavity and pharynx
D38.0	Neoplasm of uncertain behav of larynx
E03.4	Atrophy of thyroid (acquired)
E04.1	Nontoxic single thyroid nodule
E05.0*	Thyrotoxicosis with diffuse goiter
E05.1*	Thyrotoxicosis with txc single thyroid nodule
E05.2*	Thyrotoxicosis with txc multinodular goiter
E05.3*	Thyrotoxicosis from ectopic thyroid tissue
E05.4*	Thyrotoxicosis factitia
E05.8*	Oth thyrotoxicosis
E05.9*	Thyrotoxicosis, unsp
E06.0	Acute thyroiditis
E06.1	Subacute thyroiditis
E06.2	Chr thyroiditis with transient thyrotoxicosis
E06.3	Autoimmune thyroiditis
E06.4	Drug-induced thyroiditis
E06.5	Oth chr thyroiditis
E06.9	Thyroiditis, unsp
E07.89	Oth spec d/o of thyroid
E07.9	D/o of thyroid, unsp
E35	D/o of endocrine glands in dz classd elsw
G47.2*	Circadian rhythm sleep d/o
G47.3*	Sleep apnea
G47.5*	Parasomnia
G47.6*	Sleep related movement d/o
G47.8	Oth sleep d/o
J00	Acute nasopharyngitis [common cold]
J02.0	Streptococcal pharyngitis
J02.8	Acute pharyngitis d/t oth spec organisms
J02.9	Acute pharyngitis, unsp
J03.0*	Streptococcal tonsillitis
J03.8*	Acute tonsillitis d/t oth spec organisms
J03.9*	Acute tonsillitis, unsp
J04.0	Acute laryngitis
J04.2	Acute laryngotracheitis
J04.3*	Supraglottitis, unsp
J05.0	Acute obstructive laryngitis [croup]
J05.1*	Acute epiglottitis

Surgical   **Medical**   **CC Indicator**   **MCC Indicator**   **Procedure Proxy**   PDxMCC **PDx acts as own MCC**   PDxCC **PDx acts as own CC**

Pre MDC—SURGICAL

J06.0	Acute laryngopharyngitis	K08.1*	Complete loss of teeth
J06.9	Acute upr respiratory infxn, unsp	K08.2*	Atrophy of edentulous alveolar ridge
J31.1	Chr nasopharyngitis	K08.3	Retained dental root
J31.2	Chr pharyngitis	K08.4*	Partial loss of teeth
J34.2	Deviated nasal septum	K08.5*	Unsatisfactory restoration of tooth
J35.0*	Chr tonsillitis and adenoiditis	K08.8	Oth spec d/o of teeth and supporting structures
J35.1	Hypertrophy of tonsils	K08.9	D/o of teeth and supporting structures, unsp
J35.2	Hypertrophy of adenoids	K09.0	Developmental odontogenic cysts
J35.3	Hypertrophy of tonsils with hypertrophy of adenoids	K09.1	Developmental (nonodontogenic) cysts of oral region
J35.8	Oth chr dz of tonsils and adenoids	K09.8	Oth cysts of oral region, NEC
J35.9	Chr dz of tonsils and adenoids, unsp	K09.9	Cyst of oral region, unsp
J36	Peritonsillar abscess	K11.0	Atrophy of salivary gland
J37.0	Chr laryngitis	K11.1	Hypertrophy of salivary gland
J37.1	Chr laryngotracheitis	K11.2*	Sialoadenitis
J38.0*	Paralysis of vocal cords and larynx	K11.3	Abscess of salivary gland
J38.1	Polyp of vocal cord and larynx	K11.4	Fistula of salivary gland
J38.2	Nodules of vocal cords	K11.5	Sialolithiasis
J38.3	Oth dz of vocal cords	K11.6	Mucocele of salivary gland
J38.4	Edema of larynx	K11.7	Disturbances of salivary secretion
J38.5	Laryngeal spasm	K11.8	Oth dz of salivary glands
J38.6	Stenosis of larynx	K11.9	Dz of salivary gland, unsp
J38.7	Oth dz of larynx	K12.0	Recurrent oral aphthae
J39.0	Retropharyngeal and parapharyngeal abscess	K12.1	Oth forms of stomatitis
J39.1	Oth abscess of pharynx	K12.2	Cellulitis and abscess of mouth
J39.2	Oth dz of pharynx	K12.3*	Oral mucositis (ulcerative)
J39.3	Upr respiratory tract hypersensitivity reaction, site unsp	K13.0	Dz of lips
J39.8	Oth spec dz of upr respiratory tract	K13.1	Cheek and lip biting
J39.9	Dz of upr respiratory tract, unsp	K13.2*	Leukoplakia and oth disturb of oral epithelium, incl* tongue
J95.0*	Tracheostomy comp	K13.3	Hairy leukoplakia
J98.0*	Dz of bronchus, NEC	K13.4	Granuloma and granuloma-like lesions of oral mucosa
K00.0	Anodontia	K13.5	Oral submucous fibrosis
K00.1	Supernumerary teeth	K13.6	Irritative hyperplasia of oral mucosa
K00.2	Abnormalities of size and form of teeth	K13.7*	Oth and unsp lesions of oral mucosa
K00.3	Mottled teeth	K14.0	Glossitis
K00.4	Disturbances in tooth formation	K14.1	Geographic tongue
K00.5	Hereditary disturbances in tooth structure, NEC	K14.2	Median rhomboid glossitis
K00.6	Disturbances in tooth eruption	K14.3	Hypertrophy of tongue papillae
K00.7	Teething synd	K14.4	Atrophy of tongue papillae
K00.8	Oth d/o of tooth development	K14.5	Plicated tongue
K00.9	D/o of tooth development, unsp	K14.6	Glossodynia
K01.0	Embedded teeth	K14.8	Oth dz of tongue
K01.1	Impacted teeth	K14.9	Dz of tongue, unsp
K02.3	Arrested dental caries	L02.01	Cutaneous abscess of face
K02.5*	Dental caries on pit and fissure surface	L02.11	Cutaneous abscess of neck
K02.6*	Dental caries on smooth surface	L03.2*	Cellulitis and acute lymphangitis of face and neck
K02.7	Dental root caries	M26.0*	Major anomalies of jaw size
K02.9	Dental caries, unsp	M26.1*	Anomalies of jaw-cranial base relationship
K03.0	Excessive attrition of teeth	M26.2*	Anomalies of dental arch relationship
K03.1	Abrasion of teeth	M26.3*	Anomalies of tooth position of fully erupted tooth or teeth
K03.2	Erosion of teeth	M26.4	Malocclusion, unsp
K03.3	Path resorption of teeth	M26.5*	Dentofacial functional abnormalities
K03.4	Hypercementosis	M26.6*	Temporomandibular jt d/o
K03.5	Ankylosis of teeth	M26.7*	Dental alveolar anomalies
K03.6	Deposits [accretions] on teeth	M26.8*	Oth dentofacial anomalies
K03.7	Posteruptive color changes of dental hard tissues	M26.9	Dentofacial anomaly, unsp
K03.8*	Oth spec dz of hard tissues of teeth	M27.0	Developmental d/o of jaws
K03.9	Dz of hard tissues of teeth, unsp	M27.1	Giant cell granuloma, central
K04.0	Pulpitis	M27.2	Inflam conditions of jaws
K04.1	Necrosis of pulp	M27.3	Alveolitis of jaws
K04.2	Pulp degeneration	M27.4*	Oth and unsp cysts of jaw
K04.3	Abnormal hard tissue formation in pulp	M27.5*	Periradicular pathology assoc w previous endodontic tx
K04.4	Acute apical periodontitis of pulpal origin	M27.6*	Endosseous dental implant failure
K04.5	Chr apical periodontitis	M27.8	Oth spec dz of jaws
K04.6	Periapical abscess with sinus	M27.9	Dz of jaws, unsp
K04.7	Periapical abscess w/o sinus	Q31.0	Web of larynx
K04.8	Radicular cyst	Q31.1	Congenital subglottic stenosis
K04.9*	Oth and unsp dz of pulp and periapical tissues	Q31.2	Laryngeal hypoplasia
K05.0*	Acute gingivitis	Q31.3	Laryngocele
K05.1*	Chr gingivitis	Q31.5	Congenital laryngomalacia
K05.2*	Aggressive periodontitis	Q31.8	Oth congenital malformations of larynx
K05.3*	Chr periodontitis	Q31.9	Congenital malformation of larynx, unsp
K05.4	Periodontosis	Q32.0	Congenital tracheomalacia
K05.5	Oth periodontal dz	Q32.1	Oth congenital malformations of trachea
K05.6	Periodontal dz, unsp	Q32.2	Congenital bronchomalacia
K06.0	Gingival recession	Q32.3	Congenital stenosis of bronchus
K06.1	Gingival enlargement	Q32.4	Oth congenital malformations of bronchus
K06.2	Gingival & edentulous alveolar ridge lesions assoc w trauma	Q35.1	Cleft hard palate
K06.8	Oth disrd of gingiva and edentulous alveolar ridge	Q35.3	Cleft soft palate
K06.9	D/o of gingiva and edentulous alveolar ridge, unsp	Q35.5	Cleft hard palate with cleft soft palate
K08.0	Exfoliation of teeth d/t systemic causes	Q35.7	Cleft uvula

---

T **Transfer DRG**   SP **Special Payment**   * **Code Range**   **6th and 7th Character of ZZ = No Device, No Qualifier ZX = No Device, Diagnostic**

Q35.9	Cleft palate, unsp
Q36.0	Cleft lip, bilat
Q36.1	Cleft lip, median
Q36.9	Cleft lip, unilat
Q37.0	Cleft hard palate with bilat cleft lip
Q37.1	Cleft hard palate with unilat cleft lip
Q37.2	Cleft soft palate with bilat cleft lip
Q37.3	Cleft soft palate with unilat cleft lip
Q37.4	Cleft hard and soft palate with bilat cleft lip
Q37.5	Cleft hard and soft palate with unilat cleft lip
Q37.8	Unsp cleft palate with bilat cleft lip
Q37.9	Unsp cleft palate with unilat cleft lip
Q38.0	Congenital malformations of lips, NEC
Q38.1	Ankyloglossia
Q38.2	Macroglossia
Q38.3	Oth congenital malformations of tongue
Q38.4	Congenital malformations of salivary glands and ducts
Q38.6	Oth congenital malformations of mouth
Q38.7	Congenital pharyngeal pouch
Q38.8	Oth congenital malformations of pharynx
R04.1	Hemor from throat
R68.2	Dry mouth, unsp
R68.84	Jaw pain
S01.20XA	Unsp opn wnd of nose, init enc
S01.21XA	Lac w/o FB of nose, init enc
S01.22XA	Lac with FB of nose, init enc
S01.23XA	Punc wnd w/o FB of nose, init enc
S01.24XA	Punc wnd with FB of nose, init enc
S01.25XA	Opn bite of nose, init enc
S01.4[0,1,2,3,4,5]1A	Opn wnd of rt cheek and temporomandibular area, [unsp, lac w/o FB, lac w/ FB, punc w/o FB, punc w/ FB, bite], init enc
S01.4[0,1,2,3,4,5]2A	Opn wnd of lt cheek and temporomandibular area, [unsp, lac w/o FB, lac w/ FB, punc w/o FB, punc w/ FB, bite] init enc
S01.4[0,1,2,3,4,5]9A	[Unsp opn wnd, Lac w/o FB, Lac w/ FB, Punc w/o FB, Punc w/ FB, Bite] of unsp cheek and temporomandibular area, init enc
S01.5[0,1,2,3,4,5]1A	[Unsp opn wnd, Lac w/o FB, Lac w/ FB, Punc wnd w/o FB, Punc wnd w/ FB, Opn bite] of lip, init enc
S01.5[0,1,2,3,4,5]2A	[Unsp opn wnd, Lac w/o FB, Lac w/ FB, Punc wnd w/o FB, Punc wnd w/ FB, Opn bite] of oral cavity, init enc
S02.3XXA	Fx of orbital floor, init enc for clsd fx
S02.3XXB	Fx of orbital floor, init enc for opn fx
S02.400A	Malar fx unsp, init enc for clsd fx
S02.400B	Malar fx unsp, init enc for opn fx
S02.401A	Maxillary fx, unsp, init enc for clsd fx
S02.401B	Maxillary fx, unsp, init enc for opn fx
S02.402A	Zygomatic fx, unsp, init enc for clsd fx
S02.402B	Zygomatic fx, unsp, init enc for opn fx
S02.411A	LeFort I fx, init enc for clsd fx
S02.411B	LeFort I fx, init enc for opn fx
S02.412A	LeFort II fx, init enc for clsd fx
S02.412B	LeFort II fx, init enc for opn fx
S02.413A	LeFort III fx, init enc for clsd fx
S02.413B	LeFort III fx, init enc for opn fx
S02.42XA	Fx of alveolus of maxilla, init for clos fx
S02.42XB	Fx of alveolus of maxilla, init for opn fx
S02.600A	Fx of unsp part of body of mandible, init for clos fx
S02.600B	Fx of unsp part of body of mandible, init for opn fx
S02.609A	Fx of mandible, unsp, init enc for clsd fx
S02.609B	Fx of mandible, unsp, init enc for opn fx
S02.61XA	Fx of condylar process of mandible, init for clos fx
S02.61XB	Fx of condylar process of mandible, init for opn fx
S02.62XA	Fx of subcondylar process of mandible, init
S02.62XB	Fx of subcondylar process of mandible, init for opn fx
S02.63XA	Fx of coronoid process of mandible, init for clos fx
S02.63XB	Fx of coronoid process of mandible, init for opn fx
S02.64XA	Fx of ramus of mandible, init for clos fx
S02.64XB	Fx of ramus of mandible, init enc for opn fx
S02.65XA	Fx of angle of mandible, init for clos fx
S02.65XB	Fx of angle of mandible, init enc for opn fx
S02.66XA	Fx of symphysis of mandible, init for clos fx
S02.66XB	Fx of symphysis of mandible, init for opn fx
S02.67XA	Fx of alveolus of mandible, init for clos fx
S02.67XB	Fx of alveolus of mandible, init for opn fx
S02.69XA	Fx of mandible of oth site, init for clos fx
S02.69XB	Fx of mandible of oth site, init for opn fx
S02.8XXA	Fractures of oth skull and facial bones, init for clos fx
S02.8XXB	Fractures of oth skull and facial bones, init for opn fx
S02.92XA	Unsp fx of facial bones, init for clos fx
S02.92XB	Unsp fx of facial bones, init enc for opn fx
S03.0XXA	Disloc of jaw, init enc
S07.0XXA	Crushing inj of face, init enc
S07.1XXA	Crushing inj of skull, init enc
S07.8XXA	Crushing inj of oth parts of head, init enc
S07.9XXA	Crushing inj of head, part unsp, init enc
S08.811A	Complete traum amp of nose, init enc
S08.812A	Partial traum amp of nose, init enc
S09.0XXA	Inj of bld vessels of head, NEC, init enc
S09.10XA	Unsp inj of muscle and tndn of head, init enc
S09.11XA	Strain of muscle and tndn of head, init enc
S09.19XA	Oth inj of muscle and tndn of head, init enc
S09.8XXA	Oth spec injuries of head, init enc
S09.90XA	Unsp inj of head, init enc
S09.92XA	Unsp inj of nose, init enc
S09.93XA	Unsp inj of face, init enc
S11.011A	Lac w/o FB of larynx, init enc
S11.012A	Lac with FB of larynx, init enc
S11.013A	Punc wnd w/o FB of larynx, init enc
S11.014A	Punc wnd with FB of larynx, init enc
S11.015A	Opn bite of larynx, init enc
S11.019A	Unsp opn wnd of larynx, init enc
S11.021A	Lac w/o FB of trachea, init enc
S11.022A	Lac with FB of trachea, init enc
S11.023A	Punc wnd w/o FB of trachea, init enc
S11.024A	Punc wnd with FB of trachea, init enc
S11.025A	Opn bite of trachea, init enc
S11.029A	Unsp opn wnd of trachea, init enc
S11.031A	Lac w/o FB of vocal cord, init enc
S11.032A	Lac with FB of vocal cord, init enc
S11.033A	Punc wnd w/o FB of vocal cord, init enc
S11.034A	Punc wnd with FB of vocal cord, init enc
S11.035A	Opn bite of vocal cord, init enc
S11.039A	Unsp opn wnd of vocal cord, init enc
S11.10XA	Unsp opn wnd of thyroid gland, init enc
S11.11XA	Lac w/o FB of thyroid gland, init enc
S11.12XA	Lac with FB of thyroid gland, init enc
S11.13XA	Punc wnd w/o FB of thyroid gland, init
S11.14XA	Punc wnd w FB of thyroid gland, init enc
S11.15XA	Opn bite of thyroid gland, init enc
S11.20XA	Unsp opn wnd of pharynx and cervical esophagus, init
S11.21XA	Lac w/o fb of pharynx and cervical esophagus, init
S11.22XA	Lac w fb of pharynx and cervical esophagus, init
S11.23XA	Punc w/o fb of pharynx and cervical esophagus, init
S11.24XA	Punc w FB of pharynx and cervical esophagus, init
S11.25XA	Opn bite of pharynx and cervical esophagus, init enc
S11.80XA	Unsp opn wnd of oth part of neck, init enc
S11.81XA	Lac w/o FB of oth part of neck, init enc
S11.82XA	Lac w FB of oth part of neck, init enc
S11.83XA	Punc wnd w/o FB oth prt neck, init enc
S11.84XA	Punc wnd w FB oth prt neck, init enc
S11.85XA	Opn bite of oth spec part of neck, init enc
S11.89XA	Oth opn wnd of oth part of neck, init enc
S11.90XA	Unsp opn wnd of unsp part of neck, init enc
S11.91XA	Lac w/o FB of unsp part of neck, init
S11.92XA	Lac w FB of unsp part of neck, init enc
S11.93XA	Punc wnd w/o FB of unsp part of neck, init
S11.94XA	Punc wnd w FB of unsp part of neck, init
S11.95XA	Opn bite of unsp part of neck, init enc
S12.8XXA	Fx of oth parts of neck, init enc
S15.101A	Unsp inj of rt vert artery, init enc
S15.102A	Unsp inj of lt vert artery, init enc
S15.109A	Unsp inj of unsp vert artery, init enc
S15.111A	Minor lac of rt vert artery, init enc
S15.112A	Minor lac of lt vert artery, init enc
S15.119A	Minor lac of unsp vert artery, init enc
S15.121A	Major lac of rt vert artery, init enc
S15.122A	Major lac of lt vert artery, init enc
S15.129A	Major lac of unsp vert artery, init enc
S15.191A	Oth inj of rt vert artery, init enc
S15.192A	Oth spec inj of lt vert artery, init enc
S15.199A	Oth inj of unsp vert artery, init enc
S15.8XXA	Inj of oth bld vessels at neck lvl, init enc
S15.9XXA	Inj of unsp bld vessel at neck lvl, init enc
S16.2XXA	Lac of muscle, fascia and tndn at neck lvl, init
S16.8XXA	Inj muscle, fascia and tndn at neck lvl, init enc
S16.9XXA	Unsp inj of muscle, fascia and tndn at neck lvl, init
S17.0XXA	Crushing inj of larynx and trachea, init enc
S17.8XXA	Crushing inj of oth parts of neck, init enc
S17.9XXA	Crushing inj of neck, part unsp, init enc
S19.80XA	Oth injuries of unsp part of neck, init enc
S19.81XA	Oth spec injuries of larynx, init enc

Surgical   **Medical**   **CC Indicator**   **MCC Indicator**   **Procedure Proxy**   **PDxMCC PDx acts as own MCC**   **PDxCC PDx acts as own CC**

S19.82XA	Oth spec injuries of cervical trachea, init enc
S19.83XA	Oth spec injuries of vocal cord, init enc
S19.84XA	Oth spec injuries of thyroid gland, init enc
S19.85XA	Oth injuries of pharynx and cervical esophagus, init enc
S19.89XA	Oth injuries of oth spec part of neck, init enc
S19.9XXA	Unsp inj of neck, init enc
T17.200A	Unsp FB in pharynx causing asphyxiation, init
T17.208A	Unsp FB in pharynx causing oth inj, init enc
T17.210A	Gastric contents in pharynx causing asphyxiation, init
T17.218A	Gastric contents in pharynx causing oth inj, init enc
T17.220A	Food in pharynx causing asphyxiation, init enc
T17.228A	Food in pharynx causing oth inj, init enc
T17.290A	Oth foreign object in pharynx causing asphyxiation, init
T17.298A	Oth foreign object in pharynx causing oth inj, init
T17.300A	Unsp FB in larynx causing asphyxiation, init
T17.308A	Unsp FB in larynx causing oth inj, init enc
T17.310A	Gastric contents in larynx causing asphyxiation, init enc
T17.318A	Gastric contents in larynx causing oth inj, init enc
T17.320A	Food in larynx causing asphyxiation, init enc
T17.328A	Food in larynx causing oth inj, init enc
T17.390A	Oth foreign object in larynx causing asphyxiation, init
T17.398A	Oth foreign object in larynx causing oth inj, init enc
T18.0XXA	FB in mouth, init enc
T28.0XXA	Burn of mouth and pharynx, init enc
T28.5XXA	Corrosion of mouth and pharynx, init enc
Z85.21	Personal history of malig neoplasm of larynx
Z85.810	Personal history of malig neoplasm of tongue
Z85.818	Prsnl hx of malig neoplm of site of lip, oral cav, & pharynx
Z85.819	Prsnl hx of malig neoplm of unsp site lip,oral cav,& pharynx

AND EITHER

Nonoperating Room Procedures

| 0B113[F,Z]4 | Bypass/Trachea, Perc, [Tracheostomy Dev, No Dev], Cutaneous |

OR

Operating Room Procedures

| 0B11[0,4][F,Z]4 | Bypass/Trachea, [Opn, Perc Endo], [Tracheostomy Dev, No Dev], Cutaneous |

DRG 012   **Tracheostomy for Face, Mouth, and Neck Diagnoses with CC**
     GMLOS 8.4   AMLOS 9.8   RW 3.4047

Select principal diagnosis AND operating or nonoperating room procedures listed under DRG 011

DRG 013   **Tracheostomy for Face, Mouth, and Neck Diagnoses without CC/MCC**
     GMLOS 5.8   AMLOS 6.6   RW 2.1906

Select principal diagnosis AND operating or nonoperating room procedures listed under DRG 011

DRG 014   **Allogeneic Bone Marrow Transplant**
     GMLOS 22.7   AMLOS 27.5   RW 11.5928

Operating Room Procedures

3023[0,3]X0	Transfusion/Peripheral Vein, [Opn, Perc], Stem Cells, Cord Bld, Auto
3023[0,3][G,X,Y]1	Transfusion/Peripheral Vein, [Opn, Perc], [Bone Marrow, Stem Cells, Cord Bld, Stem Cells, Hematopoietic], Nonauto
3024[0,3]X0	Transfusion/Central Vein, [Opn, Perc], Stem Cells, Cord Bld, Auto
3024[0,3][G,X,Y]1	Transfusion/Central Vein, [Opn, Perc], [Bone Marrow, Stem Cells, Cord Bld, Stem Cells, Hematopoietic], Nonauto
3025[0,3]X0	Transfusion/Peripheral Artery, [Opn, Perc], Stem Cells, Cord Bld, Auto
3025[0,3][G,X,Y]1	Transfusion/Peripheral Artery, [Opn, Perc], [Bone Marrow, Stem Cells, Cord Bld, Stem Cells, Hematopoietic], Nonauto
3026[0,3]X0	Transfusion/Central Artery, [Opn, Perc], Stem Cells, Cord Bld, Auto
3026[0,3][G,X,Y]1	Transfusion/Central Artery, [Opn, Perc], [Bone Marrow, Stem Cells, Cord Bld, Stem Cells, Hematopoietic], Nonauto

---

DRG 015   **Autologous Bone Marrow Transplant**
     GMLOS 0.0   AMLOS 0.0   RW 0.0000

Omitted in October 2012 Grouper version

DRG 016   **Autologous Bone Marrow Transplant with CC/MCC**
     GMLOS 17.8   AMLOS 19.2   RW 6.1746

Operating Room Procedures

30230AZ	Transfusion of Embr Stem Cell into Periph Vein, Opn Appr
30230[G,Y]0	Transfusion/Peripheral Vein, Opn, [Bone Marrow, Stem Cells, Hematopoietic], Auto
30233AZ	Transfusion of Embr Stem Cell into Periph Vein, Perc Appr
30233[G,Y]0	Transfusion/Peripheral Vein, Perc, [Bone Marrow, Stem Cells, Hematopoietic], Auto
30240AZ	Transfusion of Embr Stem Cell into Central Vein, Opn Appr
30240[G,Y]0	Transfusion/Central Vein, Opn, [Bone Marrow, Stem Cells, Hematopoietic], Auto
30243AZ	Transfusion of Embr Stem Cell into Central Vein, Perc Appr
30243[G,Y]0	Transfusion/Central Vein, Perc, [Bone Marrow, Stem Cells, Hematopoietic], Auto
3025[0,3][G,Y]0	Transfusion/Peripheral Artery, [Opn, Perc], [Bone Marrow, Stem Cells, Hematopoietic], Auto
3026[0,3][G,Y]0	Transfusion/Central Artery, [Opn, Perc], [Bone Marrow, Stem Cells, Hematopoietic], Auto

---

DRG 017   **Autologous Bone Marrow Transplant without CC/MCC**
     GMLOS 10.0   AMLOS 12.8   RW 4.3721

Select operating room procedures listed under DRG 016

Pre MDC—SURGICAL

T Transfer DRG   SP Special Payment   * Code Range   6th and 7th Character of ZZ = No Device, No Qualifier ZX = No Device, Diagnostic

6   MS-DRG Version 33.0   © 2015 Optum360, LLC

SURGICAL

DRG 020 **Intracranial Vascular Procedures with Principal Diagnosis of Hemorrhage with MCC**

GMLOS 13.6   AMLOS 16.8   RW 9.7571

Principal Diagnosis

I60.0*   Nontraumatic subarach hemor from carotid siphon and bifurcation
I60.1*   Nontraumatic subarachnoid hemor from mid cerebral artery
I60.2*   Nontraumatic subarach hemor from ant communicating artery
I60.3*   Nontraumatic subarach hemor from posterior communicating artery
I60.4   Nontraumatic subarachnoid hemor from basilar artery
I60.5*   Nontraumatic subarachnoid hemor from vert artery
I60.6   Nontraumatic subarachnoid hemor from oth intracran art
I60.7   Nontraumatic subarachnoid hemor from unsp intracran art
I60.8   Oth nontraumatic subarachnoid hemor
I60.9   Nontraumatic subarachnoid hemor, unsp
I61.0   Nontraumatic intcrbl hemor in hemisphere, subcortical
I61.1   Nontraumatic intcrbl hemor in hemisphere, cortical
I61.2   Nontraumatic intracerebral hemor in hemisphere, unsp
I61.3   Nontraumatic intracerebral hemor in brain stem
I61.4   Nontraumatic intracerebral hemor in cerebellum
I61.5   Nontraumatic intracerebral hemor, intraventricular
I61.6   Nontraumatic intracerebral hemor, multi localized
I61.8   Oth nontraumatic intracerebral hemor
I61.9   Nontraumatic intracerebral hemor, unsp
I62.0*   Nontraumatic subdural hemor
I62.1   Nontraumatic extradural hemor
I62.9   Nontraumatic intracranial hemor, unsp

AND

Operating Room Procedures

031H0[9,A,J,K,Z]G Bypass/Common Carotid Artery, Rt, Opn, [Auto Venous Tissue, Auto Arterial Tissue, Synth Sub, Nonauto Tissue Sub, No Dev], Intracranial Artery
031J0[9,A,J,K,Z]G Bypass/Common Carotid Artery, Lt, Opn, [Auto Venous Tissue, Auto Arterial Tissue, Synth Sub, Nonauto Tissue Sub, No Dev], Intracranial Artery
031S0[9,A,J,K,Z]G Bypass/Temporal Artery, Rt, Opn, [Auto Venous Tissue, Auto Arterial Tissue, Synth Sub, Nonauto Tissue Sub, No Dev], Intracranial Artery
031T0[9,A,J,K,Z]G Bypass/Temporal Artery, Lt, Opn, [Auto Venous Tissue, Auto Arterial Tissue, Synth Sub, Nonauto Tissue Sub, No Dev], Intracranial Artery
035G[0,3,4]ZZ   Destr/Intracranial Artery, [Opn, Perc, Perc Endo]
03BG[0,3,4]ZZ   Exc/Intracranial Artery, [Opn, Perc, Perc Endo]
03CG[0,4]ZZ   Extir/Intracranial Artery, [Opn, Perc Endo]
03LG[0,3,4][B,C,D,Z]Z Occlsn/Intracranial Artery, [Opn, Perc, Perc Endo], [Bioactive Intralum Dev, Extralum Dev, Intralum Dev, No Dev], NQ
03LH[0,3,4][B,D]Z Occlsn/Common Carotid Artery, Rt, [Opn, Perc, Perc Endo], [Bioactive Intralum Dev, Intralum Dev], NQ
03LJ[0,3,4][B,D]Z Occlsn/Common Carotid Artery, Lt, [Opn, Perc, Perc Endo], [Bioactive Intralum Dev, Intralum Dev], NQ
03LK[0,3,4][B,C,D,Z]Z Occlsn/Int Carotid Artery, Rt, [Opn, Perc, Perc Endo], [Bioactive Intralum Dev, Extralum Dev, Intralum Dev, No Dev], NQ
03LL[0,3,4][B,C,D,Z]Z Occlsn/Int Carotid Artery, Lt, [Opn, Perc, Perc Endo], [Bioactive Intralum Dev, Extralum Dev, Intralum Dev, No Dev], NQ
03LM[0,3,4][B,D]Z Occlsn/Ext Carotid Artery, Rt, [Opn, Perc, Perc Endo], [Bioactive Intralum Dev, Intralum Dev], NQ
03LN[0,3,4][B,D]Z Occlsn/Ext Carotid Artery, Lt, [Opn, Perc, Perc Endo], [Bioactive Intralum Dev, Intralum Dev], NQ
03LP[0,3,4][B,D]Z Occlsn/Vert Artery, Rt, [Opn, Perc, Perc Endo], [Bioactive Intralum Dev, Intralum Dev], NQ
03LQ[0,3,4][B,D]Z Occlsn/Vert Artery, Lt, [Opn, Perc, Perc Endo], [Bioactive Intralum Dev, Intralum Dev], NQ
03LR[0,3,4]DZ   Occlsn/Face Artery, [Opn, Perc, Perc Endo], Intralum Dev, NQ
03LS[0,3,4]DZ   Occlsn/Temporal Artery, Rt, [Opn, Perc, Perc Endo], Intralum Dev, NQ
03LT[0,3,4]DZ   Occlsn/Temporal Artery, Lt, [Opn, Perc, Perc Endo], Intralum Dev, NQ

03RG[0,4][7,J,K]Z Replace/Intracranial Artery, [Opn, Perc Endo], [Auto Tissue Sub, Synth Sub, Nonauto Tissue Sub], NQ
03VG[0,3,4][B,C,D,Z]Z Restrict/Intracranial Artery, [Opn, Perc, Perc Endo], [Bioactive Intralum Dev, Extralum Dev, Intralum Dev, No Dev], NQ
03VH[0,3,4][B,D]Z Restrict/Common Carotid Artery, Rt, [Opn, Perc, Perc Endo], [Bioactive Intralum Dev, Intralum Dev], NQ
03VJ[0,3,4][B,D]Z Restrict/Common Carotid Artery, Lt, [Opn, Perc, Perc Endo], [Bioactive Intralum Dev, Intralum Dev], NQ
03VK[0,3,4][B,C,D]Z Restrict/Int Carotid Artery, Rt, [Opn, Perc, Perc Endo], [Bioactive Intralum Dev, Extralum Dev, Intralum Dev], NQ
03VL[0,3,4][B,C,D]Z Restrict/Int Carotid Artery, Lt, [Opn, Perc, Perc Endo], [Bioactive Intralum Dev, Extralum Dev, Intralum Dev], NQ
03VM[0,3,4][B,D]Z Restrict/Ext Carotid Artery, Rt, [Opn, Perc, Perc Endo], [Bioactive Intralum Dev, Intralum Dev], NQ
03VN[0,3,4][B,D]Z Restrict/Ext Carotid Artery, Lt, [Opn, Perc, Perc Endo], [Bioactive Intralum Dev, Intralum Dev], NQ
03VP[0,3,4][B,D]Z Restrict/Vert Artery, Rt, [Opn, Perc, Perc Endo], [Bioactive Intralum Dev, Intralum Dev], NQ
03VQ[0,3,4][B,D]Z Restrict/Vert Artery, Lt, [Opn, Perc, Perc Endo], [Bioactive Intralum Dev, Intralum Dev], NQ
03VR[0,3,4]DZ   Restrict/Face Artery, [Opn, Perc, Perc Endo], Intralum Dev, NQ
03VS[0,3,4]DZ   Restrict/Temporal Artery, Rt, [Opn, Perc, Perc Endo], Intralum Dev, NQ
03VT[0,3,4]DZ   Restrict/Temporal Artery, Lt, [Opn, Perc, Perc Endo], Intralum Dev, NQ
03VU[0,3,4]DZ   Restrict, Rt Thyroid Artery, Intralum Dev, [Opn, Perc, Perc Endo]
03VV[0,3,4]DZ   Restrict, Lt Thyroid Artery, Intralum Dev, [Opn, Perc, Perc Endo]
055L[0,3,4]ZZ   Destr/Intracranial Vein, [Opn, Perc, Perc Endo]
05BL[0,3,4]ZZ   Exc/Intracranial Vein, [Opn, Perc, Perc Endo]
05CL[0,4]ZZ   Extir/Intracranial Vein, [Opn, Perc Endo]
05LL[0,3,4][C,D,Z]Z Occlsn/Intracranial Vein, [Opn, Perc, Perc Endo], [Extralum Dev, Intralum Dev, No Dev], NQ
05RL[0,4][7,J,K]Z Replace/Intracranial Vein, [Opn, Perc Endo], [Auto Tissue Sub, Synth Sub, Nonauto Tissue Sub], NQ
05VL[0,3,4][C,D,Z]Z Restrict/Intracranial Vein, [Opn, Perc, Perc Endo], [Extralum Dev, Intralum Dev, No Dev], NQ

DRG 021 **Intracranial Vascular Procedures with Principal Diagnosis of Hemorrhage with CC**

GMLOS 12.3   AMLOS 13.7   RW 7.1549

Select principal diagnosis AND operating room procedures listed under DRG 020

DRG 022 **Intracranial Vascular Procedures with Principal Diagnosis of Hemorrhage without CC/MCC**

GMLOS 6.7   AMLOS 8.4   RW 4.9977

Select principal diagnosis AND operating room procedures listed under DRG 020

DRG 023 **Craniotomy with Major Device Implant/Acute Complex Central Nervous System Principal Diagnosis with MCC or Chemo Implant**

GMLOS 7.9   AMLOS 11.0   RW 5.3486   [T]

Operating Room Procedures

00160[7,J,K]B Bypass/Cerebral Ventricle, Opn, [Auto Tissue, Synth, Nonauto Tissue] Sub, Cerebral Cisterns
00163[7,J,K]B Bypass/Cerebral Ventricle, Perc, [Auto Tissue, Synth, Nonauto Tissue] Sub, Cerebral Cisterns
0050*   Destr/Brain
0051*   Destr/Cerebral Meninges
0052*   Destr/Dura Mater
0056*   Destr/Cerebral Ventricle
0057*   Destr/Cerebral Hemisphere
0058*   Destr/Basal Ganglia
0059*   Destr/Thalamus
005A*   Destr/Hypothalamus
005B*   Destr/Pons

Surgical   **Medical**   **CC Indicator**   **MCC Indicator**   **Procedure Proxy**   [PDxMCC] **PDx acts as own MCC**   [PDxCC] **PDx acts as own CC**

© 2015 Optum360, LLC   MS-DRG Version 33.0   7

Code	Description
005C*	Destr/Cerebellum
005D*	Destr/Medulla Oblongata
0080*	Div/Brain
0087*	Div/Cerebral Hemisphere
0088*	Div/Basal Ganglia
008P*	Div/Glossopharyngeal Nerve
00900ZX	Drain of Brain, Opn Appr, Diagnostic
0090[0,3,4][0,Z]Z	Drain/Brain, [Opn, Perc, Perc Endo], [Drain Dev, No Dev], NQ
00910ZX	Drain of Cerebral Meninges, Opn Appr, Diagnostic
00910[0,Z]Z	Drain/Cerebral Meninges, Opn, [Drain Dev, No Dev], NQ
00920ZX	Drain of Dura Mater, Opn Appr, Diagnostic
00920[0,Z]Z	Drain/Dura Mater, Opn, [Drain Dev, No Dev], NQ
00930ZX	Drain of Epidural Space, Opn Appr, Diagnostic
0093[0,3,4][0,Z]Z	Drain/Epidural Space, [Opn, Perc, Perc Endo], [Drain Dev, No Dev], NQ
00940ZX	Drain of Subdural Space, Opn Appr, Diagnostic
00940[0,Z]Z	Drain/Subdural Space, Opn, [Drain Dev, No Dev], NQ
00950ZX	Drain of Subarachnoid Space, Opn Appr, Diagnostic
00950[0,Z]Z	Drain/Subarachnoid Space, Opn, [Drain Dev, No Dev], NQ
00960ZX	Drain of Cerebral Ventricle, Opn Appr, Diagnostic
00960ZZ	Drain of Cerebral Ventricle, Opn Appr
0096[0,3,4]0Z	Drain/Cerebral Ventricle, [Opn, Perc, Perc Endo], Drain Dev, NQ
00970ZX	Drain of Cerebral Hemisphere, Opn Appr, Diagnostic
0097[0,3,4][0,Z]Z	Drain/Cerebral Hemisphere, [Opn, Perc, Perc Endo], [Drain Dev, No Dev], NQ
00980ZX	Drain of Basal Ganglia, Opn Appr, Diagnostic
0098[0,3,4][0,Z]Z	Drain/Basal Ganglia, [Opn, Perc, Perc Endo], [Drain Dev, No Dev], NQ
00990ZX	Drain of Thalamus, Opn Appr, Diagnostic
0099[0,3,4][0,Z]Z	Drain/Thalamus, [Opn, Perc, Perc Endo], [Drain Dev, No Dev], NQ
009A0ZX	Drain of Hypothalamus, Opn Appr, Diagnostic
009A[0,3,4][0,Z]Z	Drain/Hypothalamus, [Opn, Perc, Perc Endo], [Drain Dev, No Dev], NQ
009B0ZX	Drain of Pons, Opn Appr, Diagnostic
009B[0,3,4][0,Z]Z	Drain/Pons, [Opn, Perc, Perc Endo], [Drain Dev, No Dev], NQ
009C0ZX	Drain of Cerebellum, Opn Appr, Diagnostic
009C[0,3,4][0,Z]Z	Drain/Cerebellum, [Opn, Perc, Perc Endo], [Drain Dev, No Dev], NQ
009D0ZX	Drain of Medulla Oblongata, Opn Appr, Diagnostic
009D[0,3,4][0,Z]Z	Drain/Medulla Oblongata, [Opn, Perc, Perc Endo], [Drain Dev, No Dev], NQ
00B00ZX	Exc of Brain, Opn Appr, Diagnostic
00B0[0,3,4]ZZ	Exc/Brain, [Opn, Perc, Perc Endo]
00B10ZX	Exc of Cerebral Meninges, Opn Appr, Diagnostic
00B1[0,3,4]ZZ	Exc/Cerebral Meninges, [Opn, Perc, Perc Endo]
00B20ZX	Exc of Dura Mater, Opn Appr, Diagnostic
00B2[0,3,4]ZZ	Exc/Dura Mater, [Opn, Perc, Perc Endo]
00B60ZX	Exc of Cerebral Ventricle, Opn Appr, Diagnostic
00B6[0,3,4]ZZ	Exc/Cerebral Ventricle, [Opn, Perc, Perc Endo]
00B70ZX	Exc of Cerebral Hemisphere, Opn Appr, Diagnostic
00B7[0,3,4]ZZ	Exc/Cerebral Hemisphere, [Opn, Perc, Perc Endo]
00B80ZX	Exc of Basal Ganglia, Opn Appr, Diagnostic
00B8[0,3,4]ZZ	Exc/Basal Ganglia, [Opn, Perc, Perc Endo]
00B90ZX	Exc of Thalamus, Opn Appr, Diagnostic
00B9[0,3,4]ZZ	Exc/Thalamus, [Opn, Perc, Perc Endo]
00BA0ZX	Exc of Hypothalamus, Opn Appr, Diagnostic
00BA[0,3,4]ZZ	Exc/Hypothalamus, [Opn, Perc, Perc Endo]
00BB0ZX	Exc of Pons, Opn Appr, Diagnostic
00BB[0,3,4]ZZ	Exc/Pons, [Opn, Perc, Perc Endo]
00BC0ZX	Exc of Cerebellum, Opn Appr, Diagnostic
00BC[0,3,4]ZZ	Exc/Cerebellum, [Opn, Perc, Perc Endo]
00BD0ZX	Exc of Medulla Oblongata, Opn Appr, Diagnostic
00BD[0,3,4]ZZ	Exc/Medulla Oblongata, [Opn, Perc, Perc Endo]
00BN0ZZ	Exc of Acoustic Nerve, Opn Appr
00C0[0,3,4]ZZ	Extir/Brain, [Opn, Perc, Perc Endo]
00C1[0,3,4]ZZ	Extir/Cerebral Meninges, [Opn, Perc, Perc Endo]
00C2[0,3,4]ZZ	Extir/Dura Mater, [Opn, Perc, Perc Endo]
00C3[0,3,4]ZZ	Extir/Epidural Space, [Opn, Perc, Perc Endo]
00C4[0,3,4]ZZ	Extir/Subdural Space, [Opn, Perc, Perc Endo]
00C5[0,3,4]ZZ	Extir/Subarachnoid Space, [Opn, Perc, Perc Endo]
00C6[0,3,4]ZZ	Extir/Cerebral Ventricle, [Opn, Perc, Perc Endo]
00C7[0,3,4]ZZ	Extir/Cerebral Hemisphere, [Opn, Perc, Perc Endo]
00C8[0,3,4]ZZ	Extir/Basal Ganglia, [Opn, Perc, Perc Endo]
00C9[0,3,4]ZZ	Extir/Thalamus, [Opn, Perc, Perc Endo]
00CA[0,3,4]ZZ	Extir/Hypothalamus, [Opn, Perc, Perc Endo]
00CB[0,3,4]ZZ	Extir/Pons, [Opn, Perc, Perc Endo]
00CC[0,3,4]ZZ	Extir/Cerebellum, [Opn, Perc, Perc Endo]
00CD[0,3,4]ZZ	Extir/Medulla Oblongata, [Opn, Perc, Perc Endo]
00D1[0,3,4]ZZ	Extract/Cerebral Meninges, [Opn, Perc, Perc Endo]
00D2[0,3,4]ZZ	Extract/Dura Mater, [Opn, Perc, Perc Endo]
00F3[0,3,4]ZZ	Fragmn/Epidural Space, [Opn, Perc, Perc Endo]
00F4[0,3,4]ZZ	Fragmn/Subdural Space, [Opn, Perc, Perc Endo]
00F5[0,3,4]ZZ	Fragmn/Subarachnoid Space, [Opn, Perc, Perc Endo]
00F6[0,3,4]ZZ	Fragmn/Cerebral Ventricle, [Opn, Perc, Perc Endo]
00H0[0,3,4][2,3,M]Z	Insert/Brain, [Opn, Perc, Perc Endo], [Monitoring Dev, Inf Dev, Neurostimulator Lead], NQ
00H6[0,3,4][2,3,M]Z	Insert/Cerebral Ventricle, [Opn, Perc, Perc Endo], [Monitoring Dev, Inf Dev, Neurostimulator Lead], NQ
00J0[0,3,4]ZZ	Inspect/Brain, [Opn, Perc, Perc Endo]
00K0[0,3,4]ZZ	Map/Brain, [Opn, Perc, Perc Endo]
00K7[0,3,4]ZZ	Map/Cerebral Hemisphere, [Opn, Perc, Perc Endo]
00K8[0,3,4]ZZ	Map/Basal Ganglia, [Opn, Perc, Perc Endo]
00K9[0,3,4]ZZ	Map/Thalamus, [Opn, Perc, Perc Endo]
00KA[0,3,4]ZZ	Map/Hypothalamus, [Opn, Perc, Perc Endo]
00KB[0,3,4]ZZ	Map/Pons, [Opn, Perc, Perc Endo]
00KC[0,3,4]ZZ	Map/Cerebellum, [Opn, Perc, Perc Endo]
00KD[0,3,4]ZZ	Map/Medulla Oblongata, [Opn, Perc, Perc Endo]
00N0[0,3,4]ZZ	Rls/Brain, [Opn, Perc, Perc Endo]
00N1[0,3,4]ZZ	Rls/Cerebral Meninges, [Opn, Perc, Perc Endo]
00N2[0,3,4]ZZ	Rls/Dura Mater, [Opn, Perc, Perc Endo]
00N6[0,3,4]ZZ	Rls/Cerebral Ventricle, [Opn, Perc, Perc Endo]
00N7[0,3,4]ZZ	Rls/Cerebral Hemisphere, [Opn, Perc, Perc Endo]
00N8[0,3,4]ZZ	Rls/Basal Ganglia, [Opn, Perc, Perc Endo]
00N9[0,3,4]ZZ	Rls/Thalamus, [Opn, Perc, Perc Endo]
00NA[0,3,4]ZZ	Rls/Hypothalamus, [Opn, Perc, Perc Endo]
00NB[0,3,4]ZZ	Rls/Pons, [Opn, Perc, Perc Endo]
00NC[0,3,4]ZZ	Rls/Cerebellum, [Opn, Perc, Perc Endo]
00ND[0,3,4]ZZ	Rls/Medulla Oblongata, [Opn, Perc, Perc Endo]
00NK[0,3,4]ZZ	Rls/Trigeminal Nerve, [Opn, Perc, Perc Endo]
00P0[0,3,4][0,2,3,7,J,K,M]Z	Rmvl/Brain, [Opn, Perc, Perc Endo], [Drain Dev, Monitoring Dev, Inf Dev, Auto Tissue Sub, Synth Sub, Nonauto Tissue Sub, Neurostimulator Lead], NQ
00P6X[2,M]Z	Rmvl/Cerebral Ventricle, Ext, [Monitoring Dev, Neurostimulator Lead], NQ
00P6[0,3,4][0,2,3,M]Z	Rmvl/Cerebral Ventricle, [Opn, Perc, Perc Endo], [Drain Dev, Monitoring Dev, Inf Dev, Neurostimulator Lead], NQ
00Q0[0,3,4]ZZ	Rpr/Brain, [Opn, Perc, Perc Endo]
00Q1[0,3,4]ZZ	Rpr/Cerebral Meninges, [Opn, Perc, Perc Endo]
00Q2[0,3,4]ZZ	Rpr/Dura Mater, [Opn, Perc, Perc Endo]
00Q6[0,3,4]ZZ	Rpr/Cerebral Ventricle, [Opn, Perc, Perc Endo]
00Q7[0,3,4]ZZ	Rpr/Cerebral Hemisphere, [Opn, Perc, Perc Endo]
00Q8[0,3,4]ZZ	Rpr/Basal Ganglia, [Opn, Perc, Perc Endo]
00Q9[0,3,4]ZZ	Rpr/Thalamus, [Opn, Perc, Perc Endo]
00QA[0,3,4]ZZ	Rpr/Hypothalamus, [Opn, Perc, Perc Endo]
00QB[0,3,4]ZZ	Rpr/Pons, [Opn, Perc, Perc Endo]
00QC[0,3,4]ZZ	Rpr/Cerebellum, [Opn, Perc, Perc Endo]
00QD[0,3,4]ZZ	Rpr/Medulla Oblongata, [Opn, Perc, Perc Endo]
00T7[0,3,4]ZZ	Resect/Cerebral Hemisphere, [Opn, Perc, Perc Endo]
00U1[0,3,4][7,J,K]Z	Supl/Cerebral Meninges, [Opn, Perc, Perc Endo], [Auto Tissue Sub, Synth Sub, Nonauto Tissue Sub], NQ
00U2[0,3,4][7,J,K]Z	Supl/Dura Mater, [Opn, Perc, Perc Endo], [Auto Tissue Sub, Synth Sub, Nonauto Tissue Sub], NQ
00W0[0,3,4][0,2,3,7,J,K,M]Z	Rev/Brain, [Opn, Perc, Perc Endo], [Drain Dev, Monitoring Dev, Inf Dev, Auto Tissue Sub, Synth Sub, Nonauto Tissue Sub, Neurostimulator Lead], NQ
00W6[0,3,4][0,2,3,M]Z	Rev/Cerebral Ventricle, [Opn, Perc, Perc Endo], [Drain Dev, Monitoring Dev, Inf Dev, Neurostimulator Lead], NQ
031H0[9,A,J,K,Z]G	Bypass/Common Carotid Artery, Rt, Opn, [Auto Venous Tissue, Auto Arterial Tissue, Synth Sub, Nonauto Tissue Sub, No Dev], Intracranial Artery
031J0[9,A,J,K,Z]G	Bypass/Common Carotid Artery, Lt, Opn, [Auto Venous Tissue, Auto Arterial Tissue, Synth Sub, Nonauto Tissue Sub, No Dev], Intracranial Artery
031S0[9,A,J,K,Z]G	Bypass/Temporal Artery, Rt, Opn, [Auto Venous Tissue, Auto Arterial Tissue, Synth Sub, Nonauto Tissue Sub, No Dev], Intracranial Artery
031T0[9,A,J,K,Z]G	Bypass/Temporal Artery, Lt, Opn, [Auto Venous Tissue, Auto Arterial Tissue, Synth Sub, Nonauto Tissue Sub, No Dev], Intracranial Artery
035G[0,3,4]ZZ	Destr/Intracranial Artery, [Opn, Perc, Perc Endo]
037G[3,4][4,D,Z]Z	Dilation/Intracranial Artery, [Perc, Perc Endo], [Drug-eluting Intralum Dev, Intralum Dev, No Dev], NQ
03BG[0,3,4]ZZ	Exc/Intracranial Artery, [Opn, Perc, Perc Endo]
03CG[0,3,4]ZZ	Extir/Intracranial Artery, [Opn, Perc, Perc Endo]
03CH[3,4]ZZ	Extir/Common Carotid Artery, Rt, [Perc, Perc Endo]
03CJ[3,4]ZZ	Extir/Common Carotid Artery, Lt, [Perc, Perc Endo]
03CK[3,4]ZZ	Extir/Int Carotid Artery, Rt, [Perc, Perc Endo]
03CL[3,4]ZZ	Extir/Int Carotid Artery, Lt, [Perc, Perc Endo]
03CM[3,4]ZZ	Extir/Ext Carotid Artery, Rt, [Perc, Perc Endo]

[T] Transfer DRG   [SP] Special Payment   * Code Range   6th and 7th Character of ZZ = No Device, No Qualifier ZX = No Device, Diagnostic

8   MS-DRG Version 33.0   © 2015 Optum360, LLC

03CN[3,4]ZZ	Extir/Ext Carotid Artery, Lt, [Perc, Perc Endo]
03CP[3,4]ZZ	Extir/Vert Artery, Rt, [Perc, Perc Endo]
03CQ[3,4]ZZ	Extir/Vert Artery, Lt, [Perc, Perc Endo]
03CR[3,4]ZZ	Extir/Face Artery, [Perc, Perc Endo]
03CS[3,4]ZZ	Extir/Temporal Artery, Rt, [Perc, Perc Endo]
03CT[3,4]ZZ	Extir/Temporal Artery, Lt, [Perc, Perc Endo]
03CU[3,4]ZZ	Extir/Thyroid Artery, Rt, [Perc, Perc Endo]
03CV[3,4]ZZ	Extir/Thyroid Artery, Lt, [Perc, Perc Endo]
03LG[0,3,4][B,C,D,Z]Z	Occlsn/Intracranial Artery, [Opn, Perc, Perc Endo], [Bioactive Intralum Dev, Extralum Dev, Intralum Dev, No Dev], NQ
03LH[0,3,4][B,D]Z	Occlsn/Common Carotid Artery, Rt, [Opn, Perc, Perc Endo], [Bioactive Intralum Dev, Intralum Dev], NQ
03LJ[0,3,4][B,D]Z	Occlsn/Common Carotid Artery, Lt, [Opn, Perc, Perc Endo], [Bioactive Intralum Dev, Intralum Dev], NQ
03LK[0,3,4][B,C,D,Z]Z	Occlsn/Int Carotid Artery, Rt, [Opn, Perc, Perc Endo], [Bioactive Intralum Dev, Extralum Dev, Intralum Dev, No Dev], NQ
03LL[0,3,4][B,C,D,Z]Z	Occlsn/Int Carotid Artery, Lt, [Opn, Perc, Perc Endo], [Bioactive Intralum Dev, Extralum Dev, Intralum Dev, No Dev], NQ
03LM[0,3,4][B,D]Z	Occlsn/Ext Carotid Artery, Rt, [Opn, Perc, Perc Endo], [Bioactive Intralum Dev, Intralum Dev], NQ
03LN[0,3,4][B,D]Z	Occlsn/Ext Carotid Artery, Lt, [Opn, Perc, Perc Endo], [Bioactive Intralum Dev, Intralum Dev], NQ
03LP[0,3,4][B,D]Z	Occlsn/Vert Artery, Rt, [Opn, Perc, Perc Endo], [Bioactive Intralum Dev, Intralum Dev], NQ
03LQ[0,3,4][B,D]Z	Occlsn/Vert Artery, Lt, [Opn, Perc, Perc Endo], [Bioactive Intralum Dev, Intralum Dev], NQ
03LR[0,3,4]DZ	Occlsn/Face Artery, [Opn, Perc, Perc Endo], Intralum Dev, NQ
03LS[0,3,4]DZ	Occlsn/Temporal Artery, Rt, [Opn, Perc, Perc Endo], Intralum Dev, NQ
03LT[0,3,4]DZ	Occlsn/Temporal Artery, Lt, [Opn, Perc, Perc Endo], Intralum Dev, NQ
03RG[0,4][7,J,K]Z	Replace/Intracranial Artery, [Opn, Perc Endo], [Auto Tissue Sub, Synth Sub, Nonauto Tissue Sub], NQ
03VG[0,3,4][B,C,D,Z]Z	Restrict/Intracranial Artery, [Opn, Perc, Perc Endo], [Bioactive Intralum Dev, Extralum Dev, Intralum Dev, No Dev], NQ
03VH[0,3,4][B,D]Z	Restrict/Common Carotid Artery, Rt, [Opn, Perc, Perc Endo], [Bioactive Intralum Dev, Intralum Dev], NQ
03VJ[0,3,4][B,D]Z	Restrict/Common Carotid Artery, Lt, [Opn, Perc, Perc Endo], [Bioactive Intralum Dev, Intralum Dev], NQ
03VK[0,3,4][B,C,D]Z	Restrict/Int Carotid Artery, Rt, [Opn, Perc, Perc Endo], [Bioactive Intralum Dev, Extralum Dev, Intralum Dev], NQ
03VL[0,3,4][B,C,D]Z	Restrict/Int Carotid Artery, Lt, [Opn, Perc, Perc Endo], [Bioactive Intralum Dev, Extralum Dev, Intralum Dev], NQ
03VM[0,3,4][B,D]Z	Restrict/Ext Carotid Artery, Rt, [Opn, Perc, Perc Endo], [Bioactive Intralum Dev, Intralum Dev], NQ
03VN[0,3,4][B,D]Z	Restrict/Ext Carotid Artery, Lt, [Opn, Perc, Perc Endo], [Bioactive Intralum Dev, Intralum Dev], NQ
03VP[0,3,4][B,D]Z	Restrict/Vert Artery, Rt, [Opn, Perc, Perc Endo], [Bioactive Intralum Dev, Intralum Dev], NQ
03VQ[0,3,4][B,D]Z	Restrict/Vert Artery, Lt, [Opn, Perc, Perc Endo], [Bioactive Intralum Dev, Intralum Dev], NQ
03VR[0,3,4]DZ	Restrict/Face Artery, [Opn, Perc, Perc Endo], Intralum Dev, NQ
03VS[0,3,4]DZ	Restrict/Temporal Artery, Rt, [Opn, Perc, Perc Endo], Intralum Dev, NQ
03VT[0,3,4]DZ	Restrict/Temporal Artery, Lt, [Opn, Perc, Perc Endo], Intralum Dev, NQ
03VU[0,3,4]DZ	Restrict/Thyroid Artery, Rt, [Opn, Perc, Perc Endo], Intralum Dev, NQ
03VV[0,3,4]DZ	Restrict/Thyroid Artery, Lt, [Opn, Perc, Perc Endo], Intralum Dev, NQ
055L[0,3,4]ZZ	Destr/Intracranial Vein, [Opn, Perc, Perc Endo]
057L[3,4]DZ	Dilation/Intracranial Vein, [Perc, Perc Endo], Intralum Dev, NQ
05BL[0,3,4]ZZ	Exc/Intracranial Vein, [Opn, Perc, Perc Endo]
05CL[0,3,4]ZZ	Extir/Intracranial Vein, [Opn, Perc, Perc Endo]
05LL[0,3,4][C,D,Z]Z	Occlsn/Intracranial Vein, [Opn, Perc, Perc Endo], [Extralum Dev, Intralum Dev, No Dev], NQ
05RL[0,4][7,J,K]Z	Replace/Intracranial Vein, [Opn, Perc Endo], [Auto Tissue Sub, Synth Sub, Nonauto Tissue Sub], NQ
05VL[0,3,4][C,D,Z]Z	Restrict/Intracranial Vein, [Opn, Perc, Perc Endo], [Extralum Dev, Intralum Dev, No Dev], NQ
0G50[0,3,4]ZZ	Destr/Pituitary Gland, [Opn, Perc, Perc Endo]
0G51[0,3,4]ZZ	Destr/Pineal Body, [Opn, Perc, Perc Endo]
0G80[0,3,4]ZZ	Div/Pituitary Gland, [Opn, Perc, Perc Endo]
0G90[0,3,4]ZX	Drain/Pituitary Gland, [Opn, Perc, Perc Endo]
0G90[0,3,4][0,Z]Z	Drain/Pituitary Gland, [Opn, Perc, Perc Endo], [Drain Dev, No Dev], NQ

0G91[0,3,4]ZX	Drain/Pineal Body, [Opn, Perc, Perc Endo]
0G91[0,3,4][0,Z]Z	Drain/Pineal Body, [Opn, Perc, Perc Endo], [Drain Dev, No Dev], NQ
0GB0[0,3,4]Z[X,Z]	Exc/Pituitary Gland, [Opn, Perc, Perc Endo], No Dev, [Dx, NQ]
0GB1[0,3,4]Z[X,Z]	Exc/Pineal Body, [Opn, Perc, Perc Endo], No Dev, [Dx, NQ]
0GC0[0,3,4]ZZ	Extir/Pituitary Gland, [Opn, Perc, Perc Endo]
0GC1[0,3,4]ZZ	Extir/Pineal Body, [Opn, Perc, Perc Endo]
0GJ0[0,3,4]ZZ	Inspect/Pituitary Gland, [Opn, Perc, Perc Endo]
0GJ1[0,3,4]ZZ	Inspect/Pineal Body, [Opn, Perc, Perc Endo]
0GN0[0,3,4]ZZ	Rls/Pituitary Gland, [Opn, Perc, Perc Endo]
0GN1[0,3,4]ZZ	Rls/Pineal Body, [Opn, Perc, Perc Endo]
0GP0[0,3,4]0Z	Rmvl/Pituitary Gland, [Opn, Perc, Perc Endo], Drain Dev, NQ
0GP1[0,3,4]0Z	Rmvl/Pineal Body, [Opn, Perc, Perc Endo], Drain Dev, NQ
0GQ0[0,3,4]ZZ	Rpr/Pituitary Gland, [Opn, Perc, Perc Endo]
0GQ1[0,3,4]ZZ	Rpr/Pineal Body, [Opn, Perc, Perc Endo]
0GT0[0,4]ZZ	Resect/Pituitary Gland, [Opn, Perc Endo]
0GT1[0,4]ZZ	Resect/Pineal Body, [Opn, Perc Endo]
0GW0[0,3,4]0Z	Rev/Pituitary Gland, [Opn, Perc, Perc Endo], Drain Dev, NQ
0GW1[0,3,4]0Z	Rev/Pineal Body, [Opn, Perc, Perc Endo], Drain Dev, NQ
0N50[0,3,4]ZZ	Destr/Skull, [Opn, Perc, Perc Endo]
0N51[0,3,4]ZZ	Destr/Frontal Bone, Rt, [Opn, Perc, Perc Endo]
0N52[0,3,4]ZZ	Destr/Frontal Bone, Lt, [Opn, Perc, Perc Endo]
0N53[0,3,4]ZZ	Destr/Parietal Bone, Rt, [Opn, Perc, Perc Endo]
0N54[0,3,4]ZZ	Destr/Parietal Bone, Lt, [Opn, Perc, Perc Endo]
0N55[0,3,4]ZZ	Destr/Temporal Bone, Rt, [Opn, Perc, Perc Endo]
0N56[0,3,4]ZZ	Destr/Temporal Bone, Lt, [Opn, Perc, Perc Endo]
0N57[0,3,4]ZZ	Destr/Occipital Bone, Rt, [Opn, Perc, Perc Endo]
0N58[0,3,4]ZZ	Destr/Occipital Bone, Lt, [Opn, Perc, Perc Endo]
0N80[0,3,4]ZZ	Div/Skull, [Opn, Perc, Perc Endo]
0N81[0,3,4]ZZ	Div/Frontal Bone, Rt, [Opn, Perc, Perc Endo]
0N82[0,3,4]ZZ	Div/Frontal Bone, Lt, [Opn, Perc, Perc Endo]
0N83[0,3,4]ZZ	Div/Parietal Bone, Rt, [Opn, Perc, Perc Endo]
0N84[0,3,4]ZZ	Div/Parietal Bone, Lt, [Opn, Perc, Perc Endo]
0N850ZZ	Div of Rt Temporal Bone, Opn Appr
0N853ZZ	Div of Rt Temporal Bone, Perc Appr
0N854ZZ	Div of Rt Temporal Bone, Perc Endo Appr
0N86[0,3,4]ZZ	Div/Temporal Bone, Lt, [Opn, Perc, Perc Endo]
0N87[0,3,4]ZZ	Div/Occipital Bone, Rt, [Opn, Perc, Perc Endo]
0N88[0,3,4]ZZ	Div/Occipital Bone, Lt, [Opn, Perc, Perc Endo]
0N90[0,3,4]ZX	Drain/Skull, [Opn, Perc, Perc Endo]
0N90[0,3,4][0,Z]Z	Drain/Skull, [Opn, Perc, Perc Endo], [Drain Dev, No Dev], NQ
0N91[0,3,4]ZX	Drain/Frontal Bone, Rt, [Opn, Perc, Perc Endo]
0N91[0,3,4][0,Z]Z	Drain/Frontal Bone, Rt, [Opn, Perc, Perc Endo], [Drain Dev, No Dev], NQ
0N92[0,3,4]ZX	Drain/Frontal Bone, Lt, [Opn, Perc, Perc Endo]
0N92[0,3,4][0,Z]Z	Drain/Frontal Bone, Lt, [Opn, Perc, Perc Endo], [Drain Dev, No Dev], NQ
0N93[0,3,4]ZX	Drain/Parietal Bone, Rt, [Opn, Perc, Perc Endo]
0N93[0,3,4][0,Z]Z	Drain/Parietal Bone, Rt, [Opn, Perc, Perc Endo], [Drain Dev, No Dev], NQ
0N94[0,3,4]ZX	Drain/Parietal Bone, Lt, [Opn, Perc, Perc Endo]
0N94[0,3,4][0,Z]Z	Drain/Parietal Bone, Lt, [Opn, Perc, Perc Endo], [Drain Dev, No Dev], NQ
0N95*	Drain/Temporal Bone, Rt
0N96*	Drain/Temporal Bone, Lt
0N97*	Drain/Occipital Bone, Rt
0N9800Z	Drain of Lt Occipital Bone with Drain Dev, Opn Appr
0N980ZX	Drain of Lt Occipital Bone, Opn Appr, Diagnostic
0N980ZZ	Drain of Lt Occipital Bone, Opn Appr
0N9830Z	Drain of Lt Occipital Bone with Drain Dev, Perc Appr
0N983ZX	Drain of Lt Occipital Bone, Perc Appr, Diagn
0N983ZZ	Drain of Lt Occipital Bone, Perc Appr
0N9840Z	Drain of Lt Occipital Bone with Drain Dev, Perc Endo Appr
0N984ZX	Drain of Lt Occipital Bone, Perc Endo Appr, Diagn
0N984ZZ	Drain of Lt Occipital Bone, Perc Endo Appr
0NB0*	Exc/Skull
0NB1*	Exc/Frontal Bone, Rt
0NB2*	Exc/Frontal Bone, Lt
0NB3*	Exc/Parietal Bone, Rt
0NB4*	Exc/Parietal Bone, Lt
0NB5*	Exc/Temporal Bone, Rt
0NB6*	Exc/Temporal Bone, Lt
0NB7*	Exc/Occipital Bone, Rt
0NB8*	Exc/Occipital Bone, Lt
0NC1*	Extir/Frontal Bone, Rt
0NC2*	Extir/Frontal Bone, Lt
0NC3*	Extir/Parietal Bone, Rt
0NC4*	Extir/Parietal Bone, Lt
0NC5*	Extir/Temporal Bone, Rt
0NC6*	Extir/Temporal Bone, Lt

Surgical   **Medical**   **CC Indicator**   **MCC Indicator**   **Procedure Proxy**   PDxMCC **PDx acts as own MCC**   PDxCC **PDx acts as own CC**

MDC 1: Diseases And Disorders Of The Nervous System—SURGICAL

Code	Description
ØNC7*	Extir/Occipital Bone, Rt
ØNC8*	Extir/Occipital Bone, Lt
ØNHØ[Ø,3,4][4,M]Z	Insert/Skull, [Opn, Perc, Perc Endo], [Int Fix Dev, Bone Growth Stimulator], NQ
ØNH1*	Insert/Frontal Bone, Rt
ØNH2*	Insert/Frontal Bone, Lt
ØNH3*	Insert/Parietal Bone, Rt
ØNH4*	Insert/Parietal Bone, Lt
ØNH5[Ø,3,4]4Z	Insert/Temporal Bone, Rt, [Opn, Perc, Perc Endo], Int Fix Dev, NQ
ØNH6[Ø,3,4]4Z	Insert/Temporal Bone, Lt, [Opn, Perc, Perc Endo], Int Fix Dev, NQ
ØNH7*	Insert/Occipital Bone, Rt
ØNH8*	Insert/Occipital Bone, Lt
ØNJØ[Ø,3,4]ZZ	Inspect/Skull, [Opn, Perc, Perc Endo]
ØNN1*	Rls/Frontal Bone, Rt
ØNN2*	Rls/Frontal Bone, Lt
ØNN3*	Rls/Parietal Bone, Rt
ØNN4*	Rls/Parietal Bone, Lt
ØNN5*	Rls/Temporal Bone, Rt
ØNN6*	Rls/Temporal Bone, Lt
ØNN7*	Rls/Occipital Bone, Rt
ØNN8*	Rls/Occipital Bone, Lt
ØNPØØ5Z	Rmvl of Ext Fix from Skull, Opn Appr
ØNPØX4Z	Rmvl of Int Fix from Skull, Extern Appr
ØNPØXMZ	Rmvl of Bone Stim from Skull, Extern Appr
ØNPØXSZ	Rmvl of Hearing Device from Skull, Ext Appr
ØNPØ[Ø,3,4][Ø,4,7,J,K,M,S]Z	Rmvl/Skull, [Opn, Perc, Perc Endo], [Drain Dev, Int Fix Dev, Auto Tissue Sub, Synth Sub, Nonauto Tissue Sub, Bone Growth Stimulator, Hearing Dev], NQ
ØNQØ*	Repair/Skull
ØNQ1*	Repair/Frontal Bone, Rt
ØNQ2*	Repair/Frontal Bone, Lt
ØNQ3*	Repair/Parietal Bone, Rt
ØNQ4*	Repair/Parietal Bone, Lt
ØNQ5*	Repair/Temporal Bone, Rt
ØNQ6*	Repair/Temporal Bone, Lt
ØNQ7*	Repair/Occipital Bone, Rt
ØNQ8*	Repair/Occipital Bone, Lt
ØNRØ*	Replace/Skull
ØNR1*	Replace/Frontal Bone, Rt
ØNR2*	Replace/Frontal Bone, Lt
ØNR3*	Replace/Parietal Bone, Rt
ØNR4*	Replace/Parietal Bone, Lt
ØNR5*	Replace/Temporal Bone, Rt
ØNR6*	Replace/Temporal Bone, Lt
ØNR7*	Replace/Occipital Bone, Rt
ØNR8*	Replace/Occipital Bone, Lt
ØNSØ*	Repos/Skull
ØNS1*	Repos/Frontal Bone, Rt
ØNS2*	Repos/Frontal Bone, Lt
ØNS3*	Repos/Parietal Bone, Rt
ØNS4*	Repos/Parietal Bone, Lt
ØNS5*	Repos/Temporal Bone, Rt
ØNS6*	Repos/Temporal Bone, Lt
ØNS7*	Repos/Occipital Bone, Rt
ØNS8*	Repos/Occipital Bone, Lt
ØNT1ØZZ	Resect of Rt Frontal Bone, Opn Appr
ØNT2ØZZ	Resect of Lt Frontal Bone, Opn Appr
ØNT3ØZZ	Resect of Rt Parietal Bone, Opn Appr
ØNT4ØZZ	Resect of Lt Parietal Bone, Opn Appr
ØNT5ØZZ	Resect of Rt Temporal Bone, Opn Appr
ØNT6ØZZ	Resect of Lt Temporal Bone, Opn Appr
ØNT7ØZZ	Resect of Rt Occipital Bone, Opn Appr
ØNT8ØZZ	Resect of Lt Occipital Bone, Opn Appr
ØNUØ*	Supl/Skull
ØNU1*	Supl/Frontal Bone, Rt
ØNU2*	Supl/Frontal Bone, Lt
ØNU3Ø7Z	Supl Rt Parietal Bone with Autol Sub, Opn Appr
ØNU3ØJZ	Supl Rt Parietal Bone with Synth Sub, Opn Appr
ØNU3ØKZ	Supl Rt Parietal Bone with Nonaut Sub, Opn Appr
ØNU337Z	Supl Rt Parietal Bone with Autol Sub, Perc Appr
ØNU33JZ	Supl Rt Parietal Bone with Synth Sub, Perc Appr
ØNU33KZ	Supl Rt Parietal Bone with Nonaut Sub, Perc Appr
ØNU347Z	Supl Rt Parietal Bone w Autol Sub, Perc Endo
ØNU34JZ	Supl Rt Parietal Bone w Synth Sub, Perc Endo
ØNU34KZ	Supl Rt Parietal Bone w Nonaut Sub, Perc Endo
ØNU4*	Supl/Parietal Bone, Lt
ØNU5*	Supl/Temporal Bone, Rt
ØNU6*	Supl/Temporal Bone, Lt
ØNU7*	Supl/Occipital Bone, Rt
ØNU8*	Supl/Occipital Bone, Lt
ØNWØØØZ	Rev of Drain Device in Skull, Opn Appr
ØNWØØ4Z	Rev of Int Fix Device in Skull, Opn Appr
ØNWØØ5Z	Rev of Ext Fix Device in Skull, Opn Appr
ØNWØØ7Z	Rev of Autol Sub in Skull, Opn Appr
ØNWØØJZ	Rev of Synth Sub in Skull, Opn Appr
ØNWØØKZ	Rev of Nonaut Sub in Skull, Opn Appr
ØNWØØMZ	Rev of Bone Growth Stimulator in Skull, Opn Appr
ØNWØØNZ	Rev of Neurostim in Skull, Opn Appr
ØNWØØSZ	Rev of Hearing Device in Skull, Opn Appr
ØNWØ3ØZ	Rev of Drain Device in Skull, Perc Appr
ØNWØ34Z	Rev of Int Fix Device in Skull, Perc Appr
ØNWØ35Z	Rev of Ext Fix Device in Skull, Perc Appr
ØNWØ37Z	Rev of Autol Sub in Skull, Perc Appr
ØNWØ3JZ	Rev of Synth Sub in Skull, Perc Appr
ØNWØ3KZ	Rev of Nonaut Sub in Skull, Perc Appr
ØNWØ3MZ	Rev of Bone Growth Stimulator in Skull, Perc Appr
ØNWØ3SZ	Rev of Hearing Device in Skull, Perc Appr
ØNWØ4ØZ	Rev of Drain Device in Skull, Perc Endo Appr
ØNWØ44Z	Rev of Int Fix in Skull, Perc Endo Appr
ØNWØ45Z	Rev of Ext Fix in Skull, Perc Endo Appr
ØNWØ47Z	Rev of Autol Sub in Skull, Perc Endo Appr
ØNWØ4JZ	Rev of Synth Sub in Skull, Perc Endo Appr
ØNWØ4KZ	Rev of Nonaut Sub in Skull, Perc Endo Appr
ØNWØ4MZ	Rev of Bone Stim in Skull, Perc Endo Appr
ØNWØ4SZ	Rev of Hearing Device in Skull, Perc Endo Appr
ØW91ØZX	Drain of Cranial Cavity, Opn Appr, Diagnostic
ØW91Ø[Ø,Z]Z	Drain/Cranial Cavity, Opn, [Drain Dev, No Dev], NQ
ØWC1[Ø,3,4]ZZ	Extir/Cranial Cavity, [Opn, Perc, Perc Endo]
ØWF1[Ø,3,4]ZZ	Fragmn/Cranial Cavity, [Opn, Perc, Perc Endo]
ØWH1[Ø,3,4]YZ	Insert/Cranial Cavity, [Opn, Perc, Perc Endo], Oth Dev, NQ
ØWJ1*	Inspect/Cranial Cavity
ØWP1[Ø,3,4][Ø,1,J,Y]Z	Rmvl/Cranial Cavity, [Opn, Perc, Perc Endo], [Drain Dev, Radioact Elmt, Synth Sub, Oth Dev], NQ
ØWW1[Ø,3,4][Ø,1,3,J,Y]Z	Rev/Cranial Cavity, [Opn, Perc, Perc Endo], [Drain Dev, Radioact Elmt, Inf Dev, Synth Sub, Oth Dev], NQ
DØYØKZZ	Laser Interstitial Thermal Therapy of Brain
DØY1KZZ	Laser Interstitial Thermal Therapy of Brain Stem

AND

Acute Complex CNS Principal Diagnosis

Code	Description
AØ2.21	Salmonella meningitis
AØ6.6	Amebic brain abscess
A17.Ø	Tuberculous meningitis
A17.1	Meningeal tuberculoma
A17.8*	Oth tuberculosis of nervous sys
A27.8*	Oth forms of leptospirosis
A39.Ø	Meningococcal meningitis
A39.81	Meningococcal encephalitis
A51.41	Secondary syphilitic meningitis
A52.13	Late syphilitic meningitis
A52.14	Late syphilitic encephalitis
A54.81	Gonococcal meningitis
A8Ø.Ø	Acute paralytic poliomyelitis, vaccine-associated
A8Ø.1	Acute paralytic poliomyelitis, wild virus, imported
A8Ø.2	Acute paralytic poliomyelitis, wild virus, indigenous
A8Ø.3*	Acute paralytic poliomyelitis, oth and unsp
A8Ø.9	Acute poliomyelitis, unsp
A82.Ø	Sylvatic rabies
A82.1	Urban rabies
A82.9	Rabies, unsp
A83.Ø	Japanese encephalitis
A83.1	Western equine encephalitis
A83.2	Eastern equine encephalitis
A83.3	St Louis encephalitis
A83.4	Australian encephalitis
A83.5	California encephalitis
A83.6	Rocio virus dz
A83.8	Oth mosquito-borne viral encephalitis
A83.9	Mosquito-borne viral encephalitis, unsp
A84.Ø	Far Eastern tick-borne encephalitis
A84.1	Central European tick-borne encephalitis
A84.8	Oth tick-borne viral encephalitis
A84.9	Tick-borne viral encephalitis, unsp
A85.Ø	Arthropod-borne viral encephalitis, unsp
A92.2	Venezuelan equine fever
BØØ.3	Herpesviral meningitis
BØØ.4	Herpesviral encephalitis
BØØ.82	Herpes simplex myelitis

Ⓣ **Transfer DRG**   ⓈⓅ **Special Payment**   * **Code Range**   **6th and 7th Character of ZZ = No Device, No Qualifier ZX = No Device, Diagnostic**

B01.12	Varicella myelitis
B02.24	Postherpetic myelitis
B05.0	Measles complicated by encephalitis
B10.0*	Oth human herpesvirus encephalitis
B26.1	Mumps meningitis
B26.2	Mumps encephalitis
B37.5	Candidal meningitis
B38.4	Coccidioidomycosis meningitis
B45.1	Cerebral cryptococcosis `PDxMCC`
B58.2	Toxoplasma meningoencephalitis
G00.0	Hemophilus meningitis
G00.1	Pneumococcal meningitis
G00.2	Streptococcal meningitis
G00.3	Staphylococcal meningitis
G00.8	Oth bacterial meningitis
G00.9	Bacterial meningitis, unsp
G01	Meningitis in bacterial dz classified elsw
G02	Meningitis in oth infec/parastc dz classd elsw
G04.0*	Acute disseminated encephalitis & encephalomyelitis (ADEM)
G04.2	Bacterial meningoencephalitis and meningomyelitis, NEC
G04.3*	Acute necrotizing hemorrhagic encephalopathy
G04.8*	Oth encephalitis, myelitis and encephalomyelitis
G04.9*	Encephalitis, myelitis and encephalomyelitis, unsp
G05.3	Encephalitis and encephalomyelitis in dz classd elsw
G05.4	Myelitis in dz classified elsw
G06.0	Intracranial abscess and granuloma
G06.1	Intraspinal abscess and granulomadue
G06.2	Extradural and subdural abscess, unsp
G07	Intcrn & intraspinal abscs & granuloma in dis classd elsw
G08	Intracranial and intraspinal phlebitis and thrombophlebitis
G37.3	Acute transv myelitis in demyelinating dz of cnsl
G37.4	Subacute necrotizing myelitis of central nervous sys
G92	Txc encephalopathy
I60.0*	Nontraumatic subarach hemor from carotid siphon and bifurcation
I60.1*	Nontraumatic subarachnoid hemor from mid cerebral artery
I60.2*	Nontraumatic subarach hemor from ant communicating artery
I60.3*	Ntrm subarach hemor from posterior communicating artery
I60.4	Nontraumatic subarachnoid hemor from basilar artery
I60.5*	Nontraumatic subarachnoid hemor from vert artery
I60.6	Nontraumatic subarachnoid hemor from oth intracran art
I60.7	Nontraumatic subarachnoid hemor from unsp intracran art
I60.8	Oth nontraumatic subarachnoid hemor
I60.9	Nontraumatic subarachnoid hemor, unsp
I61.0	Nontraumatic intcrbl hemor in hemisphere, subcortical
I61.1	Nontraumatic intcrbl hemor in hemisphere, cortical
I61.2	Nontraumatic intracerebral hemor in hemisphere, unsp
I61.3	Nontraumatic intracerebral hemor in brain stem
I61.4	Nontraumatic intracerebral hemor in cerebellum
I61.5	Nontraumatic intracerebral hemor, intraventricular
I61.6	Nontraumatic intracerebral hemor, multi localized
I61.8	Oth nontraumatic intracerebral hemor
I61.9	Nontraumatic intracerebral hemor, unsp
I62.9	Nontraumatic intracranial hemor, unsp
I63.0*	Cerebral infarction d/t thrombosis of precerb arteries
I63.1*	Cerebral infarction d/t embolism of precerebral arteries
I63.2*	Cerebral infrc d/t unsp occlsn or stenosis of precerb art
I63.3*	Cerebral infarction d/t thrombosis of cerebral arteries
I63.4*	Cerebral infarction d/t embolism of cerebral arteries
I63.5*	Cerebral infrc d/t unsp occlsn or stenosis of cerebral art
I63.6	Cerebral infrc d/t cerebral venous thombos, nonpyogenic
I63.8	Oth cerebral infarction
I63.9	Cerebral infarction, unsp
S06.370A	Contus/lac/hem crblm w/o LOC, init
S06.371A	Contus/lac/hem crblm w LOC of 30 min or less, init
S06.372A	Contus/lac/hem crblm w LOC of 31-59 min, init
S06.373A	Contus/lac/hem crblm w LOC of 1-5 hrs 59 min, init
S06.374A	Contus/lac/hem crblm w LOC of 6 hrs to 24 hrs, init
S06.375A	Contus/lac/hem crblm w LOC >24 hr w ret consc lev, init
S06.376A	Contus/lac/hem crblm w LOC >24 hr w/o consc w surv, init
S06.377A	Contus/lac/hem crblm w LOC w dth d/t brain inj bf consc,init
S06.378A	Contus/lac/hem crblm w LOC w dth d/t oth cause bf consc,init
S06.379A	Contus/lac/hem crblm w LOC of unsp dur, init
S06.380A	Contus/lac/hem brainstem w/o LOC, init
S06.381A	Contus/lac/hem brainstem w LOC of 30 min or less, init
S06.382A	Contus/lac/hem brainstem w LOC of 31-59 min, init
S06.383A	Contus/lac/hem brainstem w LOC of 1-5 hrs 59 min, init
S06.384A	Contus/lac/hem brainstem w LOC of 6 hrs to 24 hrs, init
S06.385A	Contus/lac/hem brainstem w LOC >24 hr w ret consc lev, init
S06.386A	Contus/lac/hem brnst w LOC >24 hr w/o ret consc w surv, init
S06.387A	Contus/lac/hem brnst w LOC w dth d/t brain inj bf consc,init

S06.388A	Contus/lac/hem brnst w LOC w dth d/t oth cause bf consc,init
S06.389A	Contus/lac/hem brainstem w LOC of unsp dur, init
S06.3[1,2,3]0A	Contsn and lac of [rt, lt, unsp] cerebrum w/o LOC, init enc
S06.3[1,2,3]1A	Contsn and lac, [Rt, Lt, Unsp] cerebrum w/ LOC, 30 min or less, init enc
S06.3[1,2,3]2A	Contsn and lac of [rt, unsp] cerebrum w/ LOC, 31 to 59 min, init enc
S06.3[1,2,3]3A	Contsn and lac of [rt, lt, unsp] cerebrum w/ LOC, 1 to 5 hrs 59 min, init enc
S06.3[1,2,3]4A	Contsn and lac of [rt, lt, unsp] cerebrum w/ LOC, 6 to 24 hrs, init enc
S06.3[1,2,3]5A	Contsn and lac of [rt, lt, unsp] cerebrum w/ LOC > 24 hrs w/ return to pre-existing conscious lvl, init enc
S06.3[1,2,3]6A	Contsn and lac of [rt, lt, unsp] cerebrum w/ LOC > 24 hrs w/o return to pre-existing conscious lvl, w/ patient surviving, init enc
S06.3[1,2,3]7A	Contsn and lac of [rt, lt, unsp] cerebrum w/ LOC, any dur, w/ death d/t brain inj prior to regain cnscness, init enc
S06.3[1,2,3]8A	Contsn and lac of [rt, lt, unsp] cerebrum w/ LOC, any dur w/ death d/t oth cause prior to regain cnscness, init enc
S06.3[1,2,3]9A	Contsn and lac of [rt, lt, unsp] cerebrum w/ LOC, unsp dur, init enc
S06.3[4,5,6]0A	Traum hemor of [rt, lt, unsp] cerebrum w/o LOC, init enc
S06.3[4,5,6]1A	Traum hemor of [rt, lt, unsp] cerebrum w/ LOC, 30 min or less, init enc
S06.3[4,5,6]2A	Traum hemor of [rt, lt, unsp] cerebrum w/ LOC, 31 to 59 min, init enc
S06.3[4,5,6]3A	Traum hemor of [rt, lt, unsp] rt cerebrum w/ LOC, 1 to 5 hrs 59 min, init enc
S06.3[4,5,6]4A	Traum hemor of [rt, lt, unsp] cerebrum w/ LOC, 6 to 24 hrs, init enc
S06.3[4,5,6]5A	Traum hemor of [rt, lt, unsp] cerebrum w/ LOC, > 24 hrs w/ return to pre-existing conscious lvl, init enc
S06.3[4,5,6]6A	Traum hemor of [rt, lt, unsp] cerebrum w/ LOC, > 24 hrs w/o return to pre-existing conscious lvl w/ patient surviving, init enc
S06.3[4,5,6]7A	Traum hemor of [rt, lt, unsp] cerebrum w/ LOC, any dur w/ death d/t brain inj prior to regain cnscness, init enc
S06.3[4,5,6]8A	Traum hemor of [rt, lt, unsp] cerebrum w/ LOC, any dur w/ death d/t oth cause prior to regain cnscness, init enc
S06.3[4,5,6]9A	Traum hemor of [rt, lt, unsp] cerebrum w/ LOC, unsp dur, init enc
S06.6X0A	Traum subrac hem w/o LOC, init
S06.6X1A	Traum subrac hem w LOC of 30 min or less, init
S06.6X2A	Traum subrac hem w LOC of 31-59 min, init
S06.6X3A	Traum subrac hem w LOC of 1-5 hrs 59 min, init
S06.6X4A	Traum subrac hem w LOC of 6 hrs to 24 hrs, init
S06.6X5A	Traum subrac hem w LOC >24 hr w ret consc lev, init
S06.6X6A	Traum subrac hem w LOC >24 hr w/o ret consc w surv, init
S06.6X7A	Traum subrac hem w LOC w death d/t brain inj bf consc, init
S06.6X8A	Traum subrac hem w LOC w death d/t oth cause bf consc, init
S06.6X9A	Traum subrac hem w LOC of unsp dur, init

OR

The following procedure combination

00H0[0,3,4]MZ	Insert/Brain, [Opn, Perc, Perc Endo], Neurostimulator Lead, NQ
00H6[0,3,4]MZ	Insert/Cerebral Ventricle, [Opn, Perc, Perc Endo], Neurostimulator Lead, NQ

AND

0JH6[0,3][D,E]Z	Insert of Multi Array [Stimulator Generator, Rechargeable Stimulator Generator] into Chest SQ Tissue & Fascia, [Opn, Perc] Appr
0JH7[0,3][D,E]Z	Insert of Multi Array [Stimulator Generator, Rechargeable Stimulator Generator] into Back SQ Tissue & Fascia, [Opn, Perc] Appr
0JH8[0,3][D,E]Z	Insert of Multi Array [Stimulator Generator, Rechargeable Stimulator Generator] into Abd SQ Tissue & Fascia, [Opn, Perc] Appr
0NH00NZ	Insert of Neurostim into Skull, Opn Appr

OR

Nonoperating Room Procedure

3E0Q[3,7]05	Introduction/Cranial Cavity and Brain, [Perc, Via Natrl or Artfcl Opng], Antineoplastic, Oth Antineoplastic

MDC 1: Diseases And Disorders Of The Nervous System—SURGICAL

DRG 024   **Craniotomy with Major Device Implant/Acute Complex Central Nervous System Principal Diagnosis without MCC**

       GMLOS 4.2   **AMLOS 5.9**   **RW 3.7976**   T

Operating Room Procedures

00160[7,J,K]B	Bypass/Cerebral Ventricle, Opn, [Auto Tissue, Synth, Nonauto Tissue] Sub, Cerebral Cisterns
00163[7,J,K]B	Bypass/Cerebral Ventricle, Perc, [Auto Tissue, Synth, Nonauto Tissue] Sub, Cerebral Cisterns
0050[0,3,4]ZZ	Destr/Brain, [Opn, Perc, Perc Endo]
0051[0,3,4]ZZ	Destr/Cerebral Meninges, [Opn, Perc, Perc Endo]
0052[0,3,4]ZZ	Destr/Dura Mater, [Opn, Perc, Perc Endo]
0056[0,3,4]ZZ	Destr/Cerebral Ventricle, [Opn, Perc, Perc Endo]
0057[0,3,4]ZZ	Destr/Cerebral Hemisphere, [Opn, Perc, Perc Endo]
0058[0,3,4]ZZ	Destr/Basal Ganglia, [Opn, Perc, Perc Endo]
0059[0,3,4]ZZ	Destr/Thalamus, [Opn, Perc, Perc Endo]
005A[0,3,4]ZZ	Destr/Hypothalamus, [Opn, Perc, Perc Endo]
005B[0,3,4]ZZ	Destr/Pons, [Opn, Perc, Perc Endo]
005C[0,3,4]ZZ	Destr/Cerebellum, [Opn, Perc, Perc Endo]
005D[0,3,4]ZZ	Destr/Medulla Oblongata, [Opn, Perc, Perc Endo]
0080[0,3,4]ZZ	Div/Brain, [Opn, Perc, Perc Endo]
0087[0,3,4]ZZ	Div/Cerebral Hemisphere, [Opn, Perc, Perc Endo]
0088[0,3,4]ZZ	Div/Basal Ganglia, [Opn, Perc, Perc Endo]
008P[0,3,4]ZZ	Div/Glossopharyngeal Nerve, [Opn, Perc, Perc Endo]
00900ZX	Drain of Brain, Opn Appr, Diagnostic
0090[0,3,4][0,Z]Z	Drain/Brain, [Opn, Perc, Perc Endo], [Drain Dev, No Dev], NQ
00910ZX	Drain of Cerebral Meninges, Opn Appr, Diagnostic
00910[0,Z]Z	Drain/Cerebral Meninges, Opn, [Drain Dev, No Dev], NQ
00920ZX	Drain of Dura Mater, Opn Appr, Diagnostic
00920[0,Z]Z	Drain/Dura Mater, Opn, [Drain Dev, No Dev], NQ
00930ZX	Drain of Epidural Space, Opn Appr, Diagnostic
0093[0,3,4][0,Z]Z	Drain/Epidural Space, [Opn, Perc, Perc Endo], [Drain Dev, No Dev], NQ
00940ZX	Drain of Subdural Space, Opn Appr, Diagnostic
00940[0,Z]Z	Drain/Subdural Space, Opn, [Drain Dev, No Dev], NQ
00950ZX	Drain of Subarachnoid Space, Opn Appr, Diagnostic
00950[0,Z]Z	Drain/Subarachnoid Space, Opn, [Drain Dev, No Dev], NQ
00960ZX	Drain of Cerebral Ventricle, Opn Appr, Diagnostic
00960[0,Z]Z	Drain/Cerebral Ventricle, Opn, [Drain Dev, No Dev], NQ
009630Z	Drain of Cerebral Ventricle with Drain Dev, Perc Appr
009640Z	Drain of Cereb Ventricle with Drain Dev, Perc Endo Appr
00970ZX	Drain of Cerebral Hemisphere, Opn Appr, Diagnostic
0097[0,3,4][0,Z]Z	Drain/Cerebral Hemisphere, [Opn, Perc, Perc Endo], [Drain Dev, No Dev], NQ
00980ZX	Drain of Basal Ganglia, Opn Appr, Diagnostic
0098[0,3,4][0,Z]Z	Drain/Basal Ganglia, [Opn, Perc, Perc Endo], [Drain Dev, No Dev], NQ
00990ZX	Drain of Thalamus, Opn Appr, Diagnostic
0099[0,3,4][0,Z]Z	Drain/Thalamus, [Opn, Perc, Perc Endo], [Drain Dev, No Dev], NQ
009A0ZX	Drain of Hypothalamus, Opn Appr, Diagnostic
009A[0,3,4][0,Z]Z	Drain/Hypothalamus, [Opn, Perc, Perc Endo], [Drain Dev, No Dev], NQ
009B0ZX	Drain of Pons, Opn Appr, Diagnostic
009B[0,3,4][0,Z]Z	Drain/Pons, [Opn, Perc, Perc Endo], [Drain Dev, No Dev], NQ
009C0ZX	Drain of Cerebellum, Opn Appr, Diagnostic
009C[0,3,4][0,Z]Z	Drain/Cerebellum, [Opn, Perc, Perc Endo], [Drain Dev, No Dev], NQ
009D0ZX	Drain of Medulla Oblongata, Opn Appr, Diagnostic
009D[0,3,4][0,Z]Z	Drain/Medulla Oblongata, [Opn, Perc, Perc Endo], [Drain Dev, No Dev], NQ
00B00ZX	Exc of Brain, Opn Appr, Diagnostic
00B0[0,3,4]ZZ	Exc/Brain, [Opn, Perc, Perc Endo]
00B10ZX	Exc of Cerebral Meninges, Opn Appr, Diagnostic
00B1[0,3,4]ZZ	Exc/Cerebral Meninges, [Opn, Perc, Perc Endo]
00B20ZX	Exc of Dura Mater, Opn Appr, Diagnostic
00B2[0,3,4]ZZ	Exc/Dura Mater, [Opn, Perc, Perc Endo]
00B60ZX	Exc of Cerebral Ventricle, Opn Appr, Diagnostic
00B6[0,3,4]ZZ	Exc/Cerebral Ventricle, [Opn, Perc, Perc Endo]
00B70ZX	Exc of Cerebral Hemisphere, Opn Appr, Diagnostic
00B7[0,3,4]ZZ	Exc/Cerebral Hemisphere, [Opn, Perc, Perc Endo]
00B80ZX	Exc of Basal Ganglia, Opn Appr, Diagnostic
00B8[0,3,4]ZZ	Exc/Basal Ganglia, [Opn, Perc, Perc Endo]
00B90ZX	Exc of Thalamus, Opn Appr, Diagnostic
00B9[0,3,4]ZZ	Exc/Thalamus, [Opn, Perc, Perc Endo]
00BA0ZX	Exc of Hypothalamus, Opn Appr, Diagnostic
00BA[0,3,4]ZZ	Exc/Hypothalamus, [Opn, Perc, Perc Endo]
00BB0ZX	Exc of Pons, Opn Appr, Diagnostic
00BB[0,3,4]ZZ	Exc/Pons, [Opn, Perc, Perc Endo]
00BC0ZX	Exc of Cerebellum, Opn Appr, Diagnostic
00BC[0,3,4]ZZ	Exc/Cerebellum, [Opn, Perc, Perc Endo]
00BD0ZX	Exc of Medulla Oblongata, Opn Appr, Diagnostic
00BD[0,3,4]ZZ	Exc/Medulla Oblongata, [Opn, Perc, Perc Endo]
00BN0ZZ	Exc of Acoustic Nerve, Opn Appr
00C0[0,3,4]ZZ	Extir/Brain, [Opn, Perc, Perc Endo]
00C1[0,3,4]ZZ	Extir/Cerebral Meninges, [Opn, Perc, Perc Endo]
00C2[0,3,4]ZZ	Extir/Dura Mater, [Opn, Perc, Perc Endo]
00C3[0,3,4]ZZ	Extir/Epidural Space, [Opn, Perc, Perc Endo]
00C4[0,3,4]ZZ	Extir/Subdural Space, [Opn, Perc, Perc Endo]
00C5[0,3,4]ZZ	Extir/Subarachnoid Space, [Opn, Perc, Perc Endo]
00C6[0,3,4]ZZ	Extir/Cerebral Ventricle, [Opn, Perc, Perc Endo]
00C7[0,3,4]ZZ	Extir/Cerebral Hemisphere, [Opn, Perc, Perc Endo]
00C8[0,3,4]ZZ	Extir/Basal Ganglia, [Opn, Perc, Perc Endo]
00C9[0,3,4]ZZ	Extir/Thalamus, [Opn, Perc, Perc Endo]
00CA[0,3,4]ZZ	Extir/Hypothalamus, [Opn, Perc, Perc Endo]
00CB[0,3,4]ZZ	Extir/Pons, [Opn, Perc, Perc Endo]
00CC[0,3,4]ZZ	Extir/Cerebellum, [Opn, Perc, Perc Endo]
00CD[0,3,4]ZZ	Extir/Medulla Oblongata, [Opn, Perc, Perc Endo]
00D1[0,3,4]ZZ	Extract/Cerebral Meninges, [Opn, Perc, Perc Endo]
00D2[0,3,4]ZZ	Extract/Dura Mater, [Opn, Perc, Perc Endo]
00F3[0,3,4]ZZ	Fragmn/Epidural Space, [Opn, Perc, Perc Endo]
00F4[0,3,4]ZZ	Fragmn/Subdural Space, [Opn, Perc, Perc Endo]
00F5[0,3,4]ZZ	Fragmn/Subarachnoid Space, [Opn, Perc, Perc Endo]
00F6[0,3,4]ZZ	Fragmn/Cerebral Ventricle, [Opn, Perc, Perc Endo]
00H0[0,3,4][2,3,M]Z	Insert/Brain, [Opn, Perc, Perc Endo], [Monitoring Dev, Inf Dev, Neurostimulator Lead], NQ
00H6[0,3,4][2,3,M]Z	Insert/Cerebral Ventricle, [Opn, Perc, Perc Endo], [Monitoring Dev, Inf Dev, Neurostimulator Lead], NQ
00J0[0,3,4]ZZ	Inspect/Brain, [Opn, Perc, Perc Endo]
00K0[0,3,4]ZZ	Map/Brain, [Opn, Perc, Perc Endo]
00K7[0,3,4]ZZ	Map/Cerebral Hemisphere, [Opn, Perc, Perc Endo]
00K8[0,3,4]ZZ	Map/Basal Ganglia, [Opn, Perc, Perc Endo]
00K9[0,3,4]ZZ	Map/Thalamus, [Opn, Perc, Perc Endo]
00KA[0,3,4]ZZ	Map/Hypothalamus, [Opn, Perc, Perc Endo]
00KB[0,3,4]ZZ	Map/Pons, [Opn, Perc, Perc Endo]
00KC[0,3,4]ZZ	Map/Cerebellum, [Opn, Perc, Perc Endo]
00KD[0,3,4]ZZ	Map/Medulla Oblongata, [Opn, Perc, Perc Endo]
00N0[0,3,4]ZZ	Rls/Brain, [Opn, Perc, Perc Endo]
00N1[0,3,4]ZZ	Rls/Cerebral Meninges, [Opn, Perc, Perc Endo]
00N2[0,3,4]ZZ	Rls/Dura Mater, [Opn, Perc, Perc Endo]
00N6[0,3,4]ZZ	Rls/Cerebral Ventricle, [Opn, Perc, Perc Endo]
00N7[0,3,4]ZZ	Rls/Cerebral Hemisphere, [Opn, Perc, Perc Endo]
00N8[0,3,4]ZZ	Rls/Basal Ganglia, [Opn, Perc, Perc Endo]
00N9[0,3,4]ZZ	Rls/Thalamus, [Opn, Perc, Perc Endo]
00NA[0,3,4]ZZ	Rls/Hypothalamus, [Opn, Perc, Perc Endo]
00NB[0,3,4]ZZ	Rls/Pons, [Opn, Perc, Perc Endo]
00NC[0,3,4]ZZ	Rls/Cerebellum, [Opn, Perc, Perc Endo]
00ND[0,3,4]ZZ	Rls/Medulla Oblongata, [Opn, Perc, Perc Endo]
00NK[0,3,4]ZZ	Rls/Trigeminal Nerve, [Opn, Perc, Perc Endo]
00P0[0,3,4][0,2,3,7,J,K,M]Z	Rmvl/Brain, [Opn, Perc, Perc Endo], [Drain Dev, Monitoring Dev, Inf Dev, Auto Tissue Sub, Synth Sub, Nonauto Tissue Sub, Neurostimulator Lead], NQ
00P6X[2,M]Z	Rmvl/Cerebral Ventricle, Ext, [Monitoring Dev, Neurostimulator Lead], NQ
00P6[0,3,4][0,2,3,M]Z	Rmvl/Cerebral Ventricle, [Opn, Perc, Perc Endo], [Drain Dev, Monitoring Dev, Inf Dev, Neurostimulator Lead], NQ
00Q0[0,3,4]ZZ	Rpr/Brain, [Opn, Perc, Perc Endo]
00Q1[0,3,4]ZZ	Rpr/Cerebral Meninges, [Opn, Perc, Perc Endo]
00Q2[0,3,4]ZZ	Rpr/Dura Mater, [Opn, Perc, Perc Endo]
00Q6[0,3,4]ZZ	Rpr/Cerebral Ventricle, [Opn, Perc, Perc Endo]
00Q7[0,3,4]ZZ	Rpr/Cerebral Hemisphere, [Opn, Perc, Perc Endo]
00Q8[0,3,4]ZZ	Rpr/Basal Ganglia, [Opn, Perc, Perc Endo]
00Q9[0,3,4]ZZ	Rpr/Thalamus, [Opn, Perc, Perc Endo]
00QA[0,3,4]ZZ	Rpr/Hypothalamus, [Opn, Perc, Perc Endo]
00QB[0,3,4]ZZ	Rpr/Pons, [Opn, Perc, Perc Endo]
00QC[0,3,4]ZZ	Rpr/Cerebellum, [Opn, Perc, Perc Endo]
00QD[0,3,4]ZZ	Rpr/Medulla Oblongata, [Opn, Perc, Perc Endo]
00T7[0,3,4]ZZ	Resect/Cerebral Hemisphere, [Opn, Perc, Perc Endo]
00U1[0,3,4][7,J,K]Z	Supl/Cerebral Meninges, [Opn, Perc, Perc Endo], [Auto Tissue Sub, Synth Sub, Nonauto Tissue Sub], NQ
00U2[0,3,4][7,J,K]Z	Supl/Dura Mater, [Opn, Perc, Perc Endo], [Auto Tissue Sub, Synth Sub, Nonauto Tissue Sub], NQ
00W0[0,3,4][0,2,3,7,J,K,M]Z	Rev/Brain, [Opn, Perc, Perc Endo], [Drain Dev, Monitoring Dev, Inf Dev, Auto Tissue Sub, Synth Sub, Nonauto Tissue Sub, Neurostimulator Lead], NQ
00W6[0,3,4][0,2,3,M]Z	Rev/Cerebral Ventricle, [Opn, Perc, Perc Endo], [Drain Dev, Monitoring Dev, Inf Dev, Neurostimulator Lead], NQ
031H0[9,A,J,K,Z]G	Bypass/Common Carotid Artery, Rt, Opn, [Auto Venous Tissue, Auto Arterial Tissue, Synth Sub, Nonauto Tissue Sub, No Dev], Intracranial Artery

---

T **Transfer DRG**   SP **Special Payment**   * **Code Range**   **6th and 7th Character of ZZ = No Device, No Qualifier ZX = No Device, Diagnostic**

MS-DRG Version 33.0

031J0[9,A,J,K,Z]G Bypass/Common Carotid Artery, Lt, Opn, [Auto Venous Tissue, Auto Arterial Tissue, Synth Sub, Nonauto Tissue Sub, No Dev], Intracranial Artery

031S0[9,A,J,K,Z]G Bypass/Temporal Artery, Rt, Opn, [Auto Venous Tissue, Auto Arterial Tissue, Synth Sub, Nonauto Tissue Sub, No Dev], Intracranial Artery

031T0[9,A,J,K,Z]G Bypass/Temporal Artery, Lt, Opn, [Auto Venous Tissue, Auto Arterial Tissue, Synth Sub, Nonauto Tissue Sub, No Dev], Intracranial Artery

035G[0,3,4]ZZ Destr/Intracranial Artery, [Opn, Perc, Perc Endo]

037G[3,4][4,D,Z]Z Dilation/Intracranial Artery, [Perc, Perc Endo], [Drug-eluting Intralum Dev, Intralum Dev, No Dev], NQ

03BG[0,3,4]ZZ Exc/Intracranial Artery, [Opn, Perc, Perc Endo]

03CG[0,3,4]ZZ Extir/Intracranial Artery, [Opn, Perc, Perc Endo]

03CH[3,4]ZZ Extir/Common Carotid Artery, Rt, [Perc, Perc Endo]

03CJ[3,4]ZZ Extir/Common Carotid Artery, Lt, [Perc, Perc Endo]

03CK[3,4]ZZ Extir/Int Carotid Artery, Rt, [Perc, Perc Endo]

03CL[3,4]ZZ Extir/Int Carotid Artery, Lt, [Perc, Perc Endo]

03CM[3,4]ZZ Extir/Ext Carotid Artery, Rt, [Perc, Perc Endo]

03CN[3,4]ZZ Extir/Ext Carotid Artery, Lt, [Perc, Perc Endo]

03CP[3,4]ZZ Extir/Vert Artery, Rt, [Perc, Perc Endo]

03CQ[3,4]ZZ Extir/Vert Artery, Lt, [Perc, Perc Endo]

03CR[3,4]ZZ Extir/Face Artery, [Perc, Perc Endo]

03CS[3,4]ZZ Extir/Temporal Artery, Rt, [Perc, Perc Endo]

03CT[3,4]ZZ Extir/Temporal Artery, Lt, [Perc, Perc Endo]

03CU[3,4]ZZ Extir/Thyroid Artery, Rt, [Perc, Perc Endo]

03CV[3,4]ZZ Extir/Thyroid Artery, Lt, [Perc, Perc Endo]

03LG[0,3,4][B,C,D,Z]Z Occlsn/Intracranial Artery, [Opn, Perc, Perc Endo], [Bioactive Intralum Dev, Extralum Dev, Intralum Dev, No Dev], NQ

03LH[0,3,4][B,D]Z Occlsn/Common Carotid Artery, Rt, [Opn, Perc, Perc Endo], [Bioactive Intralum Dev, Intralum Dev], NQ

03LJ[0,3,4][B,D]Z Occlsn/Common Carotid Artery, Lt, [Opn, Perc, Perc Endo], [Bioactive Intralum Dev, Intralum Dev], NQ

03LK[0,3,4][B,C,D,Z]Z Occlsn/Int Carotid Artery, Rt, [Opn, Perc, Perc Endo], [Bioactive Intralum Dev, Extralum Dev, Intralum Dev, No Dev], NQ

03LL[0,3,4][B,C,D,Z]Z Occlsn/Int Carotid Artery, Lt, [Opn, Perc, Perc Endo], [Bioactive Intralum Dev, Extralum Dev, Intralum Dev, No Dev], NQ

03LM[0,3,4][B,D]Z Occlsn/Ext Carotid Artery, Rt, [Opn, Perc, Perc Endo], [Bioactive Intralum Dev, Intralum Dev], NQ

03LN[0,3,4][B,D]Z Occlsn/Ext Carotid Artery, Lt, [Opn, Perc, Perc Endo], [Bioactive Intralum Dev, Intralum Dev], NQ

03LP[0,3,4][B,D]Z Occlsn/Vert Artery, Rt, [Opn, Perc, Perc Endo], [Bioactive Intralum Dev, Intralum Dev], NQ

03LQ[0,3,4][B,D]Z Occlsn/Vert Artery, Lt, [Opn, Perc, Perc Endo], [Bioactive Intralum Dev, Intralum Dev], NQ

03LR[0,3,4]DZ Occlsn/Face Artery, [Opn, Perc, Perc Endo], Intralum Dev, NQ

03LS[0,3,4]DZ Occlsn/Temporal Artery, Rt, [Opn, Perc, Perc Endo], Intralum Dev, NQ

03LT[0,3,4]DZ Occlsn/Temporal Artery, Lt, [Opn, Perc, Perc Endo], Intralum Dev, NQ

03RG[0,4][7,J,K]Z Replace/Intracranial Artery, [Opn, Perc, Perc Endo], [Auto Tissue Sub, Synth Sub, Nonauto Tissue Sub], NQ

03VG[0,3,4][B,C,D,Z]Z Restrict/Intracranial Artery, [Opn, Perc, Perc Endo], [Bioactive Intralum Dev, Extralum Dev, Intralum Dev, No Dev], NQ

03VH[0,3,4][B,D]Z Restrict/Common Carotid Artery, Rt, [Opn, Perc, Perc Endo], [Bioactive Intralum Dev, Intralum Dev], NQ

03VJ[0,3,4][B,D]Z Restrict/Common Carotid Artery, Lt, [Opn, Perc, Perc Endo], [Bioactive Intralum Dev, Intralum Dev], NQ

03VK[0,3,4][B,C,D]Z Restrict/Int Carotid Artery, Rt, [Opn, Perc, Perc Endo], [Bioactive Intralum Dev, Extralum Dev, Intralum Dev], NQ

03VL[0,3,4][B,C,D]Z Restrict/Int Carotid Artery, Lt, [Opn, Perc, Perc Endo], [Bioactive Intralum Dev, Extralum Dev, Intralum Dev], NQ

03VM[0,3,4][B,D]Z Restrict/Ext Carotid Artery, Rt, [Opn, Perc, Perc Endo], [Bioactive Intralum Dev, Intralum Dev], NQ

03VN[0,3,4][B,D]Z Restrict/Ext Carotid Artery, Lt, [Opn, Perc, Perc Endo], [Bioactive Intralum Dev, Intralum Dev], NQ

03VP[0,3,4][B,D]Z Restrict/Vert Artery, Rt, [Opn, Perc, Perc Endo], [Bioactive Intralum Dev, Intralum Dev], NQ

03VQ[0,3,4][B,D]Z Restrict/Vert Artery, Lt, [Opn, Perc, Perc Endo], [Bioactive Intralum Dev, Intralum Dev], NQ

03VR[0,3,4]DZ Restrict/Face Artery, [Opn, Perc, Perc Endo], Intralum Dev, NQ

03VS[0,3,4]DZ Restrict/Temporal Artery, Rt, [Opn, Perc, Perc Endo], Intralum Dev, NQ

03VT[0,3,4]DZ Restrict/Temporal Artery, Lt, [Opn, Perc, Perc Endo], Intralum Dev, NQ

03VU[0,3,4]DZ Restrict/Thyroid Artery, Rt, [Opn, Perc, Perc Endo], Intralum Dev, NQ

03VV[0,3,4]DZ Restrict/Thyroid Artery, Lt, [Opn, Perc, Perc Endo], Intralum Dev, NQ

055L[0,3,4]ZZ Destr/Intracranial Vein, [Opn, Perc, Perc Endo]

057L[3,4]DZ Dilation/Intracranial Vein, [Perc, Perc Endo], Intralum Dev, NQ

05BL[0,3,4]ZZ Exc/Intracranial Vein, [Opn, Perc, Perc Endo]

05CL[0,3,4]ZZ Extir/Intracranial Vein, [Opn, Perc, Perc Endo]

05LL[0,3,4][C,D,Z]Z Occlsn/Intracranial Vein, [Opn, Perc, Perc Endo], [Extralum Dev, Intralum Dev, No Dev], NQ

05RL[0,4][7,J,K]Z Replace/Intracranial Vein, [Opn, Perc, Perc Endo], [Auto Tissue Sub, Synth Sub, Nonauto Tissue Sub], NQ

05VL[0,3,4][C,D,Z]Z Restrict/Intracranial Vein, [Opn, Perc, Perc Endo], [Extralum Dev, Intralum Dev, No Dev], NQ

0G50[0,3,4]ZZ Destr/Pituitary Gland, [Opn, Perc, Perc Endo]

0G51[0,3,4]ZZ Destr/Pineal Body, [Opn, Perc, Perc Endo]

0G80[0,3,4]ZZ Div/Pituitary Gland, [Opn, Perc, Perc Endo]

0G90[0,3,4]ZX Drain/Pituitary Gland, [Opn, Perc, Perc Endo]

0G90[0,3,4][0,Z]Z Drain/Pituitary Gland, [Opn, Perc, Perc Endo], [Drain Dev, No Dev], NQ

0G91[0,3,4]ZX Drain/Pineal Body, [Opn, Perc, Perc Endo]

0G91[0,3,4][0,Z]Z Drain/Pineal Body, [Opn, Perc, Perc Endo], [Drain Dev, No Dev], NQ

0GB0[0,3,4]Z[X,Z] Exc/Pituitary Gland, [Opn, Perc, Perc Endo], No Dev, [Dx, NQ]

0GB1[0,3,4]Z[X,Z] Exc/Pineal Body, [Opn, Perc, Perc Endo], No Dev, [Dx, NQ]

0GC0[0,3,4]ZZ Extir/Pituitary Gland, [Opn, Perc, Perc Endo]

0GC1[0,3,4]ZZ Extir/Pineal Body, [Opn, Perc, Perc Endo]

0GJ0[0,3,4]ZZ Inspect/Pituitary Gland, [Opn, Perc, Perc Endo]

0GJ1[0,3,4]ZZ Inspect/Pineal Body, [Opn, Perc, Perc Endo]

0GN0[0,3,4]ZZ Rls/Pituitary Gland, [Opn, Perc, Perc Endo]

0GN1[0,3,4]ZZ Rls/Pineal Body, [Opn, Perc, Perc Endo]

0GP0[0,3,4]0Z Rmvl/Pituitary Gland, [Opn, Perc, Perc Endo], Drain Dev, NQ

0GP1[0,3,4]0Z Rmvl/Pineal Body, [Opn, Perc, Perc Endo], Drain Dev, NQ

0GQ0[0,3,4]ZZ Rpr/Pituitary Gland, [Opn, Perc, Perc Endo]

0GQ1[0,3,4]ZZ Rpr/Pineal Body, [Opn, Perc, Perc Endo]

0GT0[0,4]ZZ Resect/Pituitary Gland, [Opn, Perc, Perc Endo]

0GT1[0,4]ZZ Resect/Pineal Body, [Opn, Perc Endo]

0GW0[0,3,4]0Z Rev/Pituitary Gland, [Opn, Perc, Perc Endo], Drain Dev, NQ

0GW1[0,3,4]0Z Rev/Pineal Body, [Opn, Perc, Perc Endo], Drain Dev, NQ

0N50[0,3,4]ZZ Destr/Skull, [Opn, Perc, Perc Endo]

0N51[0,3,4]ZZ Destr/Frontal Bone, Rt, [Opn, Perc, Perc Endo]

0N52[0,3,4]ZZ Destr/Frontal Bone, Lt, [Opn, Perc, Perc Endo]

0N53[0,3,4]ZZ Destr/Parietal Bone, Rt, [Opn, Perc, Perc Endo]

0N54[0,3,4]ZZ Destr/Parietal Bone, Lt, [Opn, Perc, Perc Endo]

0N55[0,3,4]ZZ Destr/Temporal Bone, Rt, [Opn, Perc, Perc Endo]

0N56[0,3,4]ZZ Destr/Temporal Bone, Lt, [Opn, Perc, Perc Endo]

0N57[0,3,4]ZZ Destr/Occipital Bone, Rt, [Opn, Perc, Perc Endo]

0N58[0,3,4]ZZ Destr/Occipital Bone, Lt, [Opn, Perc, Perc Endo]

0N80[0,3,4]ZZ Div/Skull, [Opn, Perc, Perc Endo]

0N81[0,3,4]ZZ Div/Frontal Bone, Rt, [Opn, Perc, Perc Endo]

0N82[0,3,4]ZZ Div/Frontal Bone, Lt, [Opn, Perc, Perc Endo]

0N83[0,3,4]ZZ Div/Parietal Bone, Rt, [Opn, Perc, Perc Endo]

0N84[0,3,4]ZZ Div/Parietal Bone, Lt, [Opn, Perc, Perc Endo]

0N85[0,3,4]ZZ Div/Temporal Bone, Rt, [Opn, Perc, Perc Endo]

0N86[0,3,4]ZZ Div/Temporal Bone, Lt, [Opn, Perc, Perc Endo]

0N87[0,3,4]ZZ Div/Occipital Bone, Rt, [Opn, Perc, Perc Endo]

0N88[0,3,4]ZZ Div/Occipital Bone, Lt, [Opn, Perc, Perc Endo]

0N90[0,3,4]ZX Drain/Skull, [Opn, Perc, Perc Endo]

0N90[0,3,4][0,Z]Z Drain/Skull, [Opn, Perc, Perc Endo], [Drain Dev, No Dev], NQ

0N91[0,3,4]ZX Drain/Frontal Bone, Rt, [Opn, Perc, Perc Endo]

0N91[0,3,4][0,Z]Z Drain/Frontal Bone, Rt, [Opn, Perc, Perc Endo], [Drain Dev, No Dev], NQ

0N92[0,3,4]ZX Drain/Frontal Bone, Lt, [Opn, Perc, Perc Endo]

0N92[0,3,4][0,Z]Z Drain/Frontal Bone, Lt, [Opn, Perc, Perc Endo], [Drain Dev, No Dev], NQ

0N93[0,3,4]ZX Drain/Parietal Bone, Rt, [Opn, Perc, Perc Endo]

0N93[0,3,4][0,Z]Z Drain/Parietal Bone, Rt, [Opn, Perc, Perc Endo], [Drain Dev, No Dev], NQ

0N94[0,3,4]ZX Drain/Parietal Bone, Lt, [Opn, Perc, Perc Endo]

0N94[0,3,4][0,Z]Z Drain/Parietal Bone, Lt, [Opn, Perc, Perc Endo], [Drain Dev, No Dev], NQ

0N95[0,3,4]ZX Drain/Temporal Bone, Rt, [Opn, Perc, Perc Endo]

0N95[0,3,4][0,Z]Z Drain/Temporal Bone, Rt, [Opn, Perc, Perc Endo], [Drain Dev, No Dev], NQ

0N96[0,3,4]ZX Drain/Temporal Bone, Lt, [Opn, Perc, Perc Endo]

0N96[0,3,4][0,Z]Z Drain/Temporal Bone, Lt, [Opn, Perc, Perc Endo], [Drain Dev, No Dev], NQ

0N97[0,3,4]ZX Drain/Occipital Bone, Rt, [Opn, Perc, Perc Endo]

0N97[0,3,4][0,Z]Z Drain/Occipital Bone, Rt, [Opn, Perc, Perc Endo], [Drain Dev, No Dev], NQ

Surgical   **Medical**   **CC Indicator**   **MCC Indicator**   **Procedure Proxy**   **PDxMCC PDx acts as own MCC**   **PDxCC PDx acts as own CC**

ØN98[Ø,3,4]ZX   Drain/Occipital Bone, Lt, [Opn, Perc, Perc Endo]
ØN98[Ø,3,4][Ø,Z]Z   Drain/Occipital Bone, Lt, [Opn, Perc, Perc Endo], [Drain Dev, No Dev], NQ
ØNBØ[Ø,3,4]Z[X,Z]   Exc/Skull, [Opn, Perc, Perc Endo], No Dev, [Dx, NQ]
ØNB1[Ø,3,4]Z[X,Z]   Exc/Frontal Bone, Rt, [Opn, Perc, Perc Endo], No Dev, [Dx, NQ]
ØNB2[Ø,3,4]Z[X,Z]   Exc/Frontal Bone, Lt, [Opn, Perc, Perc Endo], No Dev, [Dx, NQ]
ØNB3[Ø,3,4]Z[X,Z]   Exc/Parietal Bone, Rt, [Opn, Perc, Perc Endo], No Dev, [Dx, NQ]
ØNB4[Ø,3,4]Z[X,Z]   Exc/Parietal Bone, Lt, [Opn, Perc, Perc Endo], No Dev, [Dx, NQ]
ØNB5[Ø,3,4]Z[X,Z]   Exc/Temporal Bone, Rt, [Opn, Perc, Perc Endo], No Dev, [Dx, NQ]
ØNB6[Ø,3,4]Z[X,Z]   Exc/Temporal Bone, Lt, [Opn, Perc, Perc Endo], No Dev, [Dx, NQ]
ØNB7[Ø,3,4]Z[X,Z]   Exc/Occipital Bone, Rt, [Opn, Perc, Perc Endo], No Dev, [Dx, NQ]
ØNB8[Ø,3,4]Z[X,Z]   Exc/Occipital Bone, Lt, [Opn, Perc, Perc Endo], No Dev, [Dx, NQ]
ØNC1[Ø,3,4]ZZ   Extir/Frontal Bone, Rt, [Opn, Perc, Perc Endo]
ØNC2[Ø,3,4]ZZ   Extir/Frontal Bone, Lt, [Opn, Perc, Perc Endo]
ØNC3[Ø,3,4]ZZ   Extir/Parietal Bone, Rt, [Opn, Perc, Perc Endo]
ØNC4[Ø,3,4]ZZ   Extir/Parietal Bone, Lt, [Opn, Perc, Perc Endo]
ØNC5[Ø,3,4]ZZ   Extir/Temporal Bone, Rt, [Opn, Perc, Perc Endo]
ØNC6[Ø,3,4]ZZ   Extir/Temporal Bone, Lt, [Opn, Perc, Perc Endo]
ØNC7[Ø,3,4]ZZ   Extir/Occipital Bone, Rt, [Opn, Perc, Perc Endo]
ØNC8[Ø,3,4]ZZ   Extir/Occipital Bone, Lt, [Opn, Perc, Perc Endo]
ØNHØ[Ø,3,4][4,M]Z   Insert/Skull, [Opn, Perc, Perc Endo], [Int Fix Dev, Bone Growth Stimulator], NQ
ØNH1[Ø,3,4]4Z   Insert/Frontal Bone, Rt, [Opn, Perc, Perc Endo], Int Fix Dev, NQ
ØNH2[Ø,3,4]4Z   Insert/Frontal Bone, Lt, [Opn, Perc, Perc Endo], Int Fix Dev, NQ
ØNH3[Ø,3,4]4Z   Insert/Parietal Bone, Rt, [Opn, Perc, Perc Endo], Int Fix Dev, NQ
ØNH4[Ø,3,4]4Z   Insert/Parietal Bone, Lt, [Opn, Perc, Perc Endo], Int Fix Dev, NQ
ØNH5[Ø,3,4]4Z   Insert/Temporal Bone, Rt, [Opn, Perc, Perc Endo], Int Fix Dev, NQ
ØNH6[Ø,3,4]4Z   Insert/Temporal Bone, Lt, [Opn, Perc, Perc Endo], Int Fix Dev, NQ
ØNH7[Ø,3,4]4Z   Insert/Occipital Bone, Rt, [Opn, Perc, Perc Endo], Int Fix Dev, NQ
ØNH8[Ø,3,4]4Z   Insert/Occipital Bone, Lt, [Opn, Perc, Perc Endo], Int Fix Dev, NQ
ØNJØ[Ø,3,4]ZZ   Inspect/Skull, [Opn, Perc, Perc Endo]
ØNN1[Ø,3,4]ZZ   Rls/Frontal Bone, Rt, [Opn, Perc, Perc Endo]
ØNN2[Ø,3,4]ZZ   Rls/Frontal Bone, Lt, [Opn, Perc, Perc Endo]
ØNN3[Ø,3,4]ZZ   Rls/Parietal Bone, Rt, [Opn, Perc, Perc Endo]
ØNN4[Ø,3,4]ZZ   Rls/Parietal Bone, Lt, [Opn, Perc, Perc Endo]
ØNN5[Ø,3,4]ZZ   Rls/Temporal Bone, Rt, [Opn, Perc, Perc Endo]
ØNN6[Ø,3,4]ZZ   Rls/Temporal Bone, Lt, [Opn, Perc, Perc Endo]
ØNN7[Ø,3,4]ZZ   Rls/Occipital Bone, Rt, [Opn, Perc, Perc Endo]
ØNN8[Ø,3,4]ZZ   Rls/Occipital Bone, Lt, [Opn, Perc, Perc Endo]
ØNPØØ5Z   Rmvl of Ext Fix from Skull, Opn Appr
ØNPØX[4,M,S]Z   Rmvl/Skull, Ext, [Int Fix Dev, Bone Growth Stimulator, Bone Conduction Hearing Dev], NQ
ØNPØ[Ø,3,4][Ø,4,7,J,K,M,S]Z   Rmvl/Skull, [Opn, Perc, Perc Endo], [Drain Dev, Int Fix Dev, Auto Tissue Sub, Synth Sub, Nonauto Tissue Sub, Bone Growth Stimulator, Hearing Dev], NQ
ØNQØ[Ø,3,4,X]ZZ   Rpr/Skull, [Opn, Perc, Perc Endo, Ext]
ØNQ1[Ø,3,4,X]ZZ   Rpr/Frontal Bone, Rt, [Opn, Perc, Perc Endo, Ext]
ØNQ2[Ø,3,4,X]ZZ   Rpr/Frontal Bone, Lt, [Opn, Perc, Perc Endo, Ext]
ØNQ3[Ø,3,4,X]ZZ   Rpr/Parietal Bone, Rt, [Opn, Perc, Perc Endo, Ext]
ØNQ4[Ø,3,4,X]ZZ   Rpr/Parietal Bone, Lt, [Opn, Perc, Perc Endo, Ext]
ØNQ5[Ø,3,4,X]ZZ   Rpr/Temporal Bone, Rt, [Opn, Perc, Perc Endo, Ext]
ØNQ6[Ø,3,4,X]ZZ   Rpr/Temporal Bone, Lt, [Opn, Perc, Perc Endo, Ext]
ØNQ7[Ø,3,4,X]ZZ   Rpr/Occipital Bone, Rt, [Opn, Perc, Perc Endo, Ext]
ØNQ8[Ø,3,4,X]ZZ   Rpr/Occipital Bone, Lt, [Opn, Perc, Perc Endo, Ext]
ØNRØ[Ø,3,4][7,J,K]Z   Replace/Skull, [Opn, Perc, Perc Endo], [Auto Tissue Sub, Synth Sub, Nonauto Tissue Sub], NQ
ØNR1[Ø,3,4][7,J,K]Z   Replace/Frontal Bone, Rt, [Opn, Perc, Perc Endo], [Auto Tissue Sub, Synth Sub, Nonauto Tissue Sub], NQ
ØNR2[Ø,3,4][7,J,K]Z   Replace/Frontal Bone, Lt, [Opn, Perc, Perc Endo], [Auto Tissue Sub, Synth Sub, Nonauto Tissue Sub], NQ
ØNR3[Ø,3,4][7,J,K]Z   Replace/Parietal Bone, Rt, [Opn, Perc, Perc Endo], [Auto Tissue Sub, Synth Sub, Nonauto Tissue Sub], NQ
ØNR4[Ø,3,4][7,J,K]Z   Replace/Parietal Bone, Lt, [Opn, Perc, Perc Endo], [Auto Tissue Sub, Synth Sub, Nonauto Tissue Sub], NQ
ØNR5[Ø,3,4][7,J,K]Z   Replace/Temporal Bone, Rt, [Opn, Perc, Perc Endo], [Auto Tissue Sub, Synth Sub, Nonauto Tissue Sub], NQ
ØNR6[Ø,3,4][7,J,K]Z   Replace/Temporal Bone, Lt, [Opn, Perc, Perc Endo], [Auto Tissue Sub, Synth Sub, Nonauto Tissue Sub], NQ
ØNR7[Ø,3,4][7,J,K]Z   Replace/Occipital Bone, Rt, [Opn, Perc, Perc Endo], [Auto Tissue Sub, Synth Sub, Nonauto Tissue Sub], NQ
ØNR8[Ø,3,4][7,J,K]Z   Replace/Occipital Bone, Lt, [Opn, Perc, Perc Endo], [Auto Tissue Sub, Synth Sub, Nonauto Tissue Sub], NQ
ØNSØXZZ   Repos Skull, Ext Appr

ØNSØ[Ø,3,4][4,5,Z]Z   Repos/Skull, [Opn, Perc, Perc Endo], [Int Fix Dev, Ext Fix Dev, No Dev], NQ
ØNS1[Ø,3,4,X]ZZ   Repos/Frontal Bone, Rt, [Opn, Perc, Perc Endo, Ext]
ØNS1[Ø,3,4]4Z   Repos/Frontal Bone, Rt, [Opn, Perc, Perc Endo], Int Fix Dev, NQ
ØNS2[Ø,3,4,X]ZZ   Repos/Frontal Bone, Lt, [Opn, Perc, Perc Endo, Ext]
ØNS2[Ø,3,4]4Z   Repos/Frontal Bone, Lt, [Opn, Perc, Perc Endo], Int Fix Dev, NQ
ØNS3[Ø,3,4,X]ZZ   Repos/Parietal Bone, Rt, [Opn, Perc, Perc Endo, Ext]
ØNS3[Ø,3,4]4Z   Repos/Parietal Bone, Rt, [Opn, Perc, Perc Endo], Int Fix Dev, NQ
ØNS4[Ø,3,4,X]ZZ   Repos/Parietal Bone, Lt, [Opn, Perc, Perc Endo, Ext]
ØNS4[Ø,3,4]4Z   Repos/Parietal Bone, Lt, [Opn, Perc, Perc Endo], Int Fix Dev, NQ
ØNS5[Ø,3,4,X]ZZ   Repos/Temporal Bone, Rt, [Opn, Perc, Perc Endo, Ext]
ØNS5[Ø,3,4]4Z   Repos/Temporal Bone, Rt, [Opn, Perc, Perc Endo], Int Fix Dev, NQ
ØNS6[Ø,3,4,X]ZZ   Repos/Temporal Bone, Lt, [Opn, Perc, Perc Endo, Ext]
ØNS6[Ø,3,4]4Z   Repos/Temporal Bone, Lt, [Opn, Perc, Perc Endo], Int Fix Dev, NQ
ØNS7[Ø,3,4,X]ZZ   Repos/Occipital Bone, Rt, [Opn, Perc, Perc Endo, Ext]
ØNS7[Ø,3,4]4Z   Repos/Occipital Bone, Rt, [Opn, Perc, Perc Endo], Int Fix Dev, NQ
ØNS8[Ø,3,4,X]ZZ   Repos/Occipital Bone, Lt, [Opn, Perc, Perc Endo, Ext]
ØNS8[Ø,3,4]4Z   Repos/Occipital Bone, Lt, [Opn, Perc, Perc Endo], Int Fix Dev, NQ
ØNT1ØZZ   Resect of Rt Frontal Bone, Opn Appr
ØNT2ØZZ   Resect of Lt Frontal Bone, Opn Appr
ØNT3ØZZ   Resect of Rt Parietal Bone, Opn Appr
ØNT4ØZZ   Resect of Lt Parietal Bone, Opn Appr
ØNT5ØZZ   Resect of Rt Temporal Bone, Opn Appr
ØNT6ØZZ   Resect of Lt Temporal Bone, Opn Appr
ØNT7ØZZ   Resect of Rt Occipital Bone, Opn Appr
ØNT8ØZZ   Resect of Lt Occipital Bone, Opn Appr
ØNUØ[Ø,3,4][7,J,K]Z   Supl/Skull, [Opn, Perc, Perc Endo], [Auto Tissue Sub, Synth Sub, Nonauto Tissue Sub], NQ
ØNU1[Ø,3,4][7,J,K]Z   Supl/Frontal Bone, Rt, [Opn, Perc, Perc Endo], [Auto Tissue Sub, Synth Sub, Nonauto Tissue Sub], NQ
ØNU2[Ø,3,4][7,J,K]Z   Supl/Frontal Bone, Lt, [Opn, Perc, Perc Endo], [Auto Tissue Sub, Synth Sub, Nonauto Tissue Sub], NQ
ØNU3[Ø,3,4][7,J,K]Z   Supl/Parietal Bone, Rt, [Opn, Perc, Perc Endo], [Auto Tissue Sub, Synth Sub, Nonauto Tissue Sub], NQ
ØNU4[Ø,3,4][7,J,K]Z   Supl/Parietal Bone, Lt, [Opn, Perc, Perc Endo], [Auto Tissue Sub, Synth Sub, Nonauto Tissue Sub], NQ
ØNU5[Ø,3,4][7,J,K]Z   Supl/Temporal Bone, Rt, [Opn, Perc, Perc Endo], [Auto Tissue Sub, Synth Sub, Nonauto Tissue Sub], NQ
ØNU6[Ø,3,4][7,J,K]Z   Supl/Temporal Bone, Lt, [Opn, Perc, Perc Endo], [Auto Tissue Sub, Synth Sub, Nonauto Tissue Sub], NQ
ØNU7[Ø,3,4][7,J,K]Z   Supl/Occipital Bone, Rt, [Opn, Perc, Perc Endo], [Auto Tissue Sub, Synth Sub, Nonauto Tissue Sub], NQ
ØNU8[Ø,3,4][7,J,K]Z   Supl/Occipital Bone, Lt, [Opn, Perc, Perc Endo], [Auto Tissue Sub, Synth Sub, Nonauto Tissue Sub], NQ
ØNWØØNZ   Rev of Neurostim in Skull, Opn Appr
ØNWØ[Ø,3,4][Ø,4,5,7,J,K,M,S]Z   Rev/Skull, [Opn, Perc, Perc Endo], [Drain Dev, Int Fix Dev, Ext Fix Dev, Auto Tissue Sub, Synth Sub, Nonauto Tissue Sub, Bone Growth Stimulator, Bone Conduction Hearing Dev], NQ
ØW91ØZX   Drain of Cranial Cavity, Opn Appr, Diagnostic
ØW91Ø[Ø,Z]Z   Drain/Cranial Cavity, Opn, [Drain Dev, No Dev], NQ
ØWC1[Ø,3,4]ZZ   Extir/Cranial Cavity, [Opn, Perc, Perc Endo]
ØWF1[Ø,3,4]ZZ   Fragmn/Cranial Cavity, [Opn, Perc, Perc Endo]
ØWH1[Ø,3,4]YZ   Insert/Cranial Cavity, [Opn, Perc, Perc Endo], Oth Dev, NQ
ØWJ1[Ø,3,4]ZZ   Inspect/Cranial Cavity, [Opn, Perc, Perc Endo]
ØWP1[Ø,3,4][Ø,1,J,Y]Z   Rmvl/Cranial Cavity, [Opn, Perc, Perc Endo], [Drain Dev, Radioact Elmt, Synth Sub, Oth Dev], NQ
ØWW1[Ø,3,4][Ø,1,3,J,Y]Z   Rev/Cranial Cavity, [Opn, Perc, Perc Endo], [Drain Dev, Radioact Elmt, Inf Dev, Synth Sub, Oth Dev], NQ
DØYØKZZ   Laser Interstitial Thermal Therapy of Brain
DØY1KZZ   Laser Interstitial Thermal Therapy of Brain Stem

AND

Acute Complex CNS Principal Diagnosis

AØ2.21	Salmonella meningitis
AØ6.6	Amebic brain abscess
A17.Ø	Tuberculous meningitis
A17.1	Meningeal tuberculoma
A17.8*	Oth tuberculosis of nervous sys
A27.8*	Oth forms of leptospirosis
A39.Ø	Meningococcal meningitis
A39.81	Meningococcal encephalitis
A51.41	Secondary syphilitic meningitis
A52.13	Late syphilitic meningitis
A52.14	Late syphilitic encephalitis
A54.81	Gonococcal meningitis

[T] Transfer DRG   [SP] Special Payment   * Code Range   6th and 7th Character of ZZ = No Device, No Qualifier ZX = No Device, Diagnostic

14   MS-DRG Version 33.0   © 2015 Optum360, LLC

Code	Description
A80.0	Acute paralytic poliomyelitis, vaccine-associated
A80.1	Acute paralytic poliomyelitis, wild virus, imported
A80.2	Acute paralytic poliomyelitis, wild virus, indigenous
A80.3*	Acute paralytic poliomyelitis, oth and unsp
A80.9	Acute poliomyelitis, unsp
A82.0	Sylvatic rabies
A82.1	Urban rabies
A82.9	Rabies, unsp
A83.0	Japanese encephalitis
A83.1	Western equine encephalitis
A83.2	Eastern equine encephalitis
A83.3	St Louis encephalitis
A83.4	Australian encephalitis
A83.5	California encephalitis
A83.6	Rocio virus dz
A83.8	Oth mosquito-borne viral encephalitis
A83.9	Mosquito-borne viral encephalitis, unsp
A84.0	Far Eastern tick-borne encephalitis
A84.1	Central European tick-borne encephalitis
A84.8	Oth tick-borne viral encephalitis
A84.9	Tick-borne viral encephalitis, unsp
A85.2	Arthropod-borne viral encephalitis, unsp
A92.2	Venezuelan equine fever
B00.3	Herpesviral meningitis
B00.4	Herpesviral encephalitis
B00.82	Herpes simplex myelitis
B01.12	Varicella myelitis
B02.24	Postherpetic myelitis
B05.0	Measles complicated by encephalitis
B10.0*	Oth human herpesvirus encephalitis
B26.1	Mumps meningitis
B26.2	Mumps encephalitis
B37.5	Candidal meningitis
B38.4	Coccidioidomycosis meningitis
B45.1	Cerebral cryptococcosis **PDxMCC**
B58.2	Toxoplasma meningoencephalitis
G00.0	Hemophilus meningitis
G00.1	Pneumococcal meningitis
G00.2	Streptococcal meningitis
G00.3	Staphylococcal meningitis
G00.8	Oth bacterial meningitis
G00.9	Bacterial meningitis, unsp
G01	Meningitis in bacterial dz classified elsw
G02	Meningitis in oth infec/parastc dz classd elsw
G04.0*	Acute disseminated encephalitis and encephalomyelitis (ADEM)
G04.2	Bacterial meningoencephalitis and meningomyelitis, NEC
G04.3*	Acute necrotizing hemorrhagic encephalopathy
G04.8*	Oth encephalitis, myelitis and encephalomyelitis
G04.9*	Encephalitis, myelitis and encephalomyelitis, unsp
G05.3	Encephalitis and encephalomyelitis in dz classd elsw
G05.4	Myelitis in dz classified elsw
G06.0	Intracranial abscess and granuloma
G06.1	Intraspinal abscess and granuloma
G06.2	Extradural and subdural abscess, unsp
G07	Intcrn & intraspinal abscs & granuloma in dis classd elsw
G08	Intracranial and intraspinal phlebitis and thrombophlebitis
G37.3	Acute transv myelitis in demyelinating dz of cnsl
G37.4	Subacute necrotizing myelitis of central nervous sys
G92	Txc encephalopathy
I60.0*	Ntrm subarach hemor from carotid siphon and bifurcation
I60.1*	Ntrm subarachnoid hemor from mid cerebral artery
I60.2*	Ntrm subarach hemor from ant communicating artery
I60.3*	Ntrm subarach hemor from posterior communicating artery
I60.4	Nontraumatic subarachnoid hemor from basilar artery
I60.5*	Nontraumatic subarachnoid hemor from vert artery
I60.6	Nontraumatic subarachnoid hemor from oth intracran art
I60.7	Nontraumatic subarachnoid hemor from unsp intracran art
I60.8	Oth nontraumatic subarachnoid hemor
I60.9	Nontraumatic subarachnoid hemor, unsp
I61.0	Nontraumatic intcrbl hemor in hemisphere, subcortical
I61.1	Nontraumatic intcrbl hemor in hemisphere, cortical
I61.2	Nontraumatic intracerebral hemor in hemisphere, unsp
I61.3	Nontraumatic intracerebral hemor in brain stem
I61.4	Nontraumatic intracerebral hemor in cerebellum
I61.5	Nontraumatic intracerebral hemor, intraventricular
I61.6	Nontraumatic intracerebral hemor, multi localized
I61.8	Oth nontraumatic intracerebral hemor
I61.9	Nontraumatic intracerebral hemor, unsp
I62.9	Nontraumatic intracranial hemor, unsp
I63.0*	Cerebral infarction d/t thrombosis of precerb arteries
I63.1*	Cerebral infarction d/t embolism of precerebral arteries
I63.2*	Cerebral infrc d/t unsp occlsn or stenosis of precerb art
I63.3*	Cerebral infarction d/t thrombosis of cerebral arteries
I63.4*	Cerebral infarction d/t embolism of cerebral arteries
I63.5*	Cerebral infrc d/t unsp occlsn or stenosis of cerebral art
I63.6	Cerebral infrc d/t cerebral venous thrombos, nonpyogenic
I63.8	Oth cerebral infarction
I63.9	Cerebral infarction, unsp
S06.370A	Contus/lac/hem crblm w/o LOC, init
S06.371A	Contus/lac/hem crblm w LOC of 30 min or less, init
S06.372A	Contus/lac/hem crblm w LOC of 31-59 min, init
S06.373A	Contus/lac/hem crblm w LOC of 1-5 hrs 59 min, init
S06.374A	Contus/lac/hem crblm w LOC of 6 hrs to 24 hrs, init
S06.375A	Contus/lac/hem crblm w LOC >24 hr w ret consc lev, init
S06.376A	Contus/lac/hem crblm w LOC >24 hr w/o ret consc w surv, init
S06.377A	Contus/lac/hem crblm w LOC w dth d/t brain inj bf consc,init
S06.378A	Contus/lac/hem crblm w LOC w dth d/t oth cause bf consc,init
S06.379A	Contus/lac/hem crblm w LOC of unsp dur, init
S06.380A	Contus/lac/hem brainstem w/o LOC, init
S06.381A	Contus/lac/hem brainstem w LOC of 30 min or less, init
S06.382A	Contus/lac/hem brainstem w LOC of 31-59 min, init
S06.383A	Contus/lac/hem brainstem w LOC of 1-5 hrs 59 min, init
S06.384A	Contus/lac/hem brainstem w LOC of 6 hrs to 24 hrs, init
S06.385A	Contus/lac/hem brainstem w LOC >24 hr w ret consc lev, init
S06.386A	Contus/lac/hem brnst w LOC >24 hr w/o ret consc w surv, init
S06.387A	Contus/lac/hem brnst w LOC w dth d/t brain inj bf consc,init
S06.388A	Contus/lac/hem brnst w LOC w dth d/t oth cause bf consc,init
S06.389A	Contus/lac/hem brainstem w LOC of unsp dur, init
S06.3[1,2,3]0A	Contsn and lac of [rt, lt, unsp] cerebrum w/o LOC, init enc
S06.3[1,2,3]1A	Contsn and lac, [Rt, Lt, Unsp] cerebrum w/ LOC, 30 min or less, init enc
S06.3[1,2,3]2A	Contsn and lac of [rt, lt, unsp] cerebrum w/ LOC, 31 to 59 min, init enc
S06.3[1,2,3]3A	Contsn and lac of [rt, lt, unsp] cerebrum w/ LOC, 1 to 5 hrs 59 min, init enc
S06.3[1,2,3]4A	Contsn and lac of [rt, lt, unsp] cerebrum w/ LOC, 6 to 24 hrs, init enc
S06.3[1,2,3]5A	Contsn and lac of [rt, lt, unsp] cerebrum w/ LOC > 24 hrs w/ return to pre-existing conscious lvl, init enc
S06.3[1,2,3]6A	Contsn and lac of [rt, lt, unsp] cerebrum w/ LOC > 24 hrs w/o return to pre-existing conscious lvl, w/ patient surviving, init enc
S06.3[1,2,3]7A	Contsn and lac of [rt, lt, unsp] cerebrum w/ LOC, any dur, w/ death d/t brain inj prior to regain cnscness, init enc
S06.3[1,2,3]8A	Contsn and lac of [rt, lt, unsp] cerebrum w/ LOC, any dur w/ death d/t oth cause prior to regain cnscness, init enc
S06.3[1,2,3]9A	Contsn and lac of [rt, lt, unsp] cerebrum w/ LOC, unsp dur, init enc
S06.3[4,5,6]0A	Traum hemor of [rt, lt, unsp] cerebrum w/o LOC, init enc
S06.3[4,5,6]1A	Traum hemor of [rt, lt, unsp] cerebrum w/ LOC, 30 min or less, init enc
S06.3[4,5,6]2A	Traum hemor of [rt, lt, unsp] cerebrum w/ LOC, 31 to 59 min, init enc
S06.3[4,5,6]3A	Traum hemor of [rt, lt, unsp] rt cerebrum w/ LOC, 1 to 5 hrs 59 min, init enc
S06.3[4,5,6]4A	Traum hemor of [rt, lt, unsp] cerebrum w/ LOC, 6 to 24 hrs, init enc
S06.3[4,5,6]5A	Traum hemor of [rt, lt, unsp] cerebrum w/ LOC, > 24 hrs w/ return to pre-existing conscious lvl, init enc
S06.3[4,5,6]6A	Traum hemor of [rt, lt, unsp] cerebrum w/ LOC, > 24 hrs w/o return to pre-existing conscious lvl w/ patient surviving, init enc
S06.3[4,5,6]7A	Traum hemor of [rt, lt, unsp] cerebrum w/ LOC, any dur w/ death d/t brain inj prior to regain cnscness, init enc
S06.3[4,5,6]8A	Traum hemor of [rt, lt, unsp] cerebrum w/ LOC, any dur w/ death d/t oth cause prior to regain cnscness, init enc
S06.3[4,5,6]9A	Traum hemor of [rt, lt, unsp] cerebrum w/ LOC, unsp dur, init enc
S06.6X0A	Traum subrac hem w/o LOC, init
S06.6X1A	Traum subrac hem w LOC of 30 min or less, init
S06.6X2A	Traum subrac hem w LOC of 31-59 min, init
S06.6X3A	Traum subrac hem w LOC of 1-5 hrs 59 min, init
S06.6X4A	Traum subrac hem w LOC of 6 hrs to 24 hrs, init
S06.6X5A	Traum subrac hem w LOC >24 hr w ret consc lev, init
S06.6X6A	Traum subrac hem w LOC >24 hr w/o ret consc w surv, init
S06.6X7A	Traum subrac hem w LOC w death d/t brain inj bf consc, init
S06.6X8A	Traum subrac hem w LOC w death d/t oth cause bf consc, init
S06.6X9A	Traum subrac hem w LOC of unsp dur, init

Surgical   **Medical**   **CC Indicator**   **MCC Indicator**   **Procedure Proxy**   **PDxMCC** PDx acts as own MCC   **PDxCC** PDx acts as own CC

OR

One of

00H0[0,3,4]MZ	Insert/Brain, [Opn, Perc, Perc Endo], Neurostimulator Lead, NQ
00H6[0,3,4]MZ	Insert/Cerebral Ventricle, [Opn, Perc, Perc Endo], Neurostimulator Lead, NQ

AND

One of

0JH6[0,3][D,E]Z	Insert of Multi Array [Stimulator Generator, Rechargeable Stimulator Generator] into Chest SQ Tissue & Fascia, [Opn, Perc] Appr
0JH7[0,3][D,E]Z	Insert of Multi Array [Stimulator Generator, Rechargeable Stimulator Generator] into Back SQ Tissue & Fascia, [Opn, Perc] Appr
0JH8[0,3][D,E]Z	Insert of Multi Array [Stimulator Generator, Rechargeable Stimulator Generator] into Abd SQ Tissue & Fascia, [Opn, Perc] Appr
0NH00NZ	Insert of Neurostim into Skull, Opn Appr

DRG 025 Craniotomy and Endovascular Intracranial Procedures with MCC

GMLOS 7.2   **AMLOS 9.3**   **RW 4.2965**   T

Operating Room Procedures

00160[7,J,K]B	Bypass/Cerebral Ventricle, Opn, [Auto Tissue, Synth, Nonauto Tissue] Sub, Cerebral Cisterns
00163[7,J,K]B	Bypass/Cerebral Ventricle, Perc, [Auto Tissue, Synth, Nonauto Tissue] Sub, Cerebral Cisterns
0050[0,3,4]ZZ	Destr/Brain, [Opn, Perc, Perc Endo]
0051[0,3,4]ZZ	Destr/Cerebral Meninges, [Opn, Perc, Perc Endo]
0052[0,3,4]ZZ	Destr/Dura Mater, [Opn, Perc, Perc Endo]
0056[0,3,4]ZZ	Destr/Cerebral Ventricle, [Opn, Perc, Perc Endo]
0057[0,3,4]ZZ	Destr/Cerebral Hemisphere, [Opn, Perc, Perc Endo]
0058[0,3,4]ZZ	Destr/Basal Ganglia, [Opn, Perc, Perc Endo]
0059[0,3,4]ZZ	Destr/Thalamus, [Opn, Perc, Perc Endo]
005A[0,3,4]ZZ	Destr/Hypothalamus, [Opn, Perc, Perc Endo]
005B[0,3,4]ZZ	Destr/Pons, [Opn, Perc, Perc Endo]
005C[0,3,4]ZZ	Destr/Cerebellum, [Opn, Perc, Perc Endo]
005D[0,3,4]ZZ	Destr/Medulla Oblongata, [Opn, Perc, Perc Endo]
0080[0,3,4]ZZ	Div/Brain, [Opn, Perc, Perc Endo]
0087[0,3,4]ZZ	Div/Cerebral Hemisphere, [Opn, Perc, Perc Endo]
0088[0,3,4]ZZ	Div/Basal Ganglia, [Opn, Perc, Perc Endo]
008P[0,3,4]ZZ	Div/Glossopharyngeal Nerve, [Opn, Perc, Perc Endo]
00900ZX	Drain of Brain, Opn Appr, Diagnostic
0090[0,3,4][0,Z]Z	Drain/Brain, [Opn, Perc, Perc Endo], [Drain Dev, No Dev], NQ
00910ZX	Drain of Cerebral Meninges, Opn Appr, Diagnostic
00910[0,Z]Z	Drain/Cerebral Meninges, Opn, [Drain Dev, No Dev], NQ
00920ZX	Drain of Dura Mater, Opn Appr, Diagnostic
00920[0,Z]Z	Drain/Dura Mater, Opn, [Drain Dev, No Dev], NQ
00930ZX	Drain of Epidural Space, Opn Appr, Diagnostic
0093[0,3,4][0,Z]Z	Drain/Epidural Space, [Opn, Perc, Perc Endo], [Drain Dev, No Dev], NQ
00940ZX	Drain of Subdural Space, Opn Appr, Diagnostic
00940[0,Z]Z	Drain/Subdural Space, Opn, [Drain Dev, No Dev], NQ
00950ZX	Drain of Subarachnoid Space, Opn Appr, Diagnostic
00950[0,Z]Z	Drain/Subarachnoid Space, Opn, [Drain Dev, No Dev], NQ
00960ZX	Drain of Cerebral Ventricle, Opn Appr, Diagnostic
00960[0,Z]Z	Drain/Cerebral Ventricle, Opn, [Drain Dev, No Dev], NQ
009630Z	Drain of Cerebral Ventricle with Drain Dev, Perc Appr
009640Z	Drain of Cereb Ventricle with Drain Dev, Perc Endo Appr
00970ZX	Drain of Cerebral Hemisphere, Opn Appr, Diagnostic
0097[0,3,4][0,Z]Z	Drain/Cerebral Hemisphere, [Opn, Perc, Perc Endo], [Drain Dev, No Dev], NQ
00980ZX	Drain of Basal Ganglia, Opn Appr, Diagnostic
0098[0,3,4][0,Z]Z	Drain/Basal Ganglia, [Opn, Perc, Perc Endo], [Drain Dev, No Dev], NQ
00990ZX	Drain of Thalamus, Opn Appr, Diagnostic
0099[0,3,4][0,Z]Z	Drain/Thalamus, [Opn, Perc, Perc Endo], [Drain Dev, No Dev], NQ
009A0ZX	Drain of Hypothalamus, Opn Appr, Diagnostic
009A[0,3,4][0,Z]Z	Drain/Hypothalamus, [Opn, Perc, Perc Endo], [Drain Dev, No Dev], NQ
009B0ZX	Drain of Pons, Opn Appr, Diagnostic
009B[0,3,4][0,Z]Z	Drain/Pons, [Opn, Perc, Perc Endo], [Drain Dev, No Dev], NQ
009C0ZX	Drain of Cerebellum, Opn Appr, Diagnostic
009C[0,3,4][0,Z]Z	Drain/Cerebellum, [Opn, Perc, Perc Endo], [Drain Dev, No Dev], NQ
009D0ZX	Drain of Medulla Oblongata, Opn Appr, Diagnostic
009D[0,3,4][0,Z]Z	Drain/Medulla Oblongata, [Opn, Perc, Perc Endo], [Drain Dev, No Dev], NQ
00B00ZX	Exc of Brain, Opn Appr, Diagnostic
00B0[0,3,4]ZZ	Exc/Brain, [Opn, Perc, Perc Endo]
00B10ZX	Exc of Cerebral Meninges, Opn Appr, Diagnostic
00B1[0,3,4]ZZ	Exc/Cerebral Meninges, [Opn, Perc, Perc Endo]
00B20ZX	Exc of Dura Mater, Opn Appr, Diagnostic
00B2[0,3,4]ZZ	Exc/Dura Mater, [Opn, Perc, Perc Endo]
00B60ZX	Exc of Cerebral Ventricle, Opn Appr, Diagnostic
00B6[0,3,4]ZZ	Exc/Cerebral Ventricle, [Opn, Perc, Perc Endo]
00B70ZX	Exc of Cerebral Hemisphere, Opn Appr, Diagnostic
00B7[0,3,4]ZZ	Exc/Cerebral Hemisphere, [Opn, Perc, Perc Endo]
00B80ZX	Exc of Basal Ganglia, Opn Appr, Diagnostic
00B8[0,3,4]ZZ	Exc/Basal Ganglia, [Opn, Perc, Perc Endo]
00B90ZX	Exc of Thalamus, Opn Appr, Diagnostic
00B9[0,3,4]ZZ	Exc/Thalamus, [Opn, Perc, Perc Endo]
00BA0ZX	Exc of Hypothalamus, Opn Appr, Diagnostic
00BA[0,3,4]ZZ	Exc/Hypothalamus, [Opn, Perc, Perc Endo]
00BB0ZX	Exc of Pons, Opn Appr, Diagnostic
00BB[0,3,4]ZZ	Exc/Pons, [Opn, Perc, Perc Endo]
00BC0ZX	Exc of Cerebellum, Opn Appr, Diagnostic
00BC[0,3,4]ZZ	Exc/Cerebellum, [Opn, Perc, Perc Endo]
00BD0ZX	Exc of Medulla Oblongata, Opn Appr, Diagnostic
00BD[0,3,4]ZZ	Exc/Medulla Oblongata, [Opn, Perc, Perc Endo]
00BN0ZZ	Exc of Acoustic Nerve, Opn Appr
00C0[0,3,4]ZZ	Extir/Brain, [Opn, Perc, Perc Endo]
00C1[0,3,4]ZZ	Extir/Cerebral Meninges, [Opn, Perc, Perc Endo]
00C2[0,3,4]ZZ	Extir/Dura Mater, [Opn, Perc, Perc Endo]
00C3[0,3,4]ZZ	Extir/Epidural Space, [Opn, Perc, Perc Endo]
00C4[0,3,4]ZZ	Extir/Subdural Space, [Opn, Perc, Perc Endo]
00C5[0,3,4]ZZ	Extir/Subarachnoid Space, [Opn, Perc, Perc Endo]
00C6[0,3,4]ZZ	Extir/Cerebral Ventricle, [Opn, Perc, Perc Endo]
00C7[0,3,4]ZZ	Extir/Cerebral Hemisphere, [Opn, Perc, Perc Endo]
00C8[0,3,4]ZZ	Extir/Basal Ganglia, [Opn, Perc, Perc Endo]
00C9[0,3,4]ZZ	Extir/Thalamus, [Opn, Perc, Perc Endo]
00CA[0,3,4]ZZ	Extir/Hypothalamus, [Opn, Perc, Perc Endo]
00CB[0,3,4]ZZ	Extir/Pons, [Opn, Perc, Perc Endo]
00CC[0,3,4]ZZ	Extir/Cerebellum, [Opn, Perc, Perc Endo]
00CD[0,3,4]ZZ	Extir/Medulla Oblongata, [Opn, Perc, Perc Endo]
00D1[0,3,4]ZZ	Extract/Cerebral Meninges, [Opn, Perc, Perc Endo]
00D2[0,3,4]ZZ	Extract/Dura Mater, [Opn, Perc, Perc Endo]
00F3[0,3,4]ZZ	Fragmn/Epidural Space, [Opn, Perc, Perc Endo]
00F4[0,3,4]ZZ	Fragmn/Subdural Space, [Opn, Perc, Perc Endo]
00F5[0,3,4]ZZ	Fragmn/Subarachnoid Space, [Opn, Perc, Perc Endo]
00F6[0,3,4]ZZ	Fragmn/Cerebral Ventricle, [Opn, Perc, Perc Endo]
00H0[0,3,4][2,3,M]Z	Insert/Brain, [Opn, Perc, Perc Endo], [Monitoring Dev, Inf Dev, Neurostimulator Lead], NQ
00H6[0,3,4][2,3,M]Z	Insert/Cerebral Ventricle, [Opn, Perc, Perc Endo], [Monitoring Dev, Inf Dev, Neurostimulator Lead], NQ
00J0[0,3,4]ZZ	Inspect/Brain, [Opn, Perc, Perc Endo]
00K0[0,3,4]ZZ	Map/Brain, [Opn, Perc, Perc Endo]
00K7[0,3,4]ZZ	Map/Cerebral Hemisphere, [Opn, Perc, Perc Endo]
00K8[0,3,4]ZZ	Map/Basal Ganglia, [Opn, Perc, Perc Endo]
00K9[0,3,4]ZZ	Map/Thalamus, [Opn, Perc, Perc Endo]
00KA[0,3,4]ZZ	Map/Hypothalamus, [Opn, Perc, Perc Endo]
00KB[0,3,4]ZZ	Map/Pons, [Opn, Perc, Perc Endo]
00KC[0,3,4]ZZ	Map/Cerebellum, [Opn, Perc, Perc Endo]
00KD[0,3,4]ZZ	Map/Medulla Oblongata, [Opn, Perc, Perc Endo]
00N0[0,3,4]ZZ	Rls/Brain, [Opn, Perc, Perc Endo]
00N1[0,3,4]ZZ	Rls/Cerebral Meninges, [Opn, Perc, Perc Endo]
00N2[0,3,4]ZZ	Rls/Dura Mater, [Opn, Perc, Perc Endo]
00N6[0,3,4]ZZ	Rls/Cerebral Ventricle, [Opn, Perc, Perc Endo]
00N7[0,3,4]ZZ	Rls/Cerebral Hemisphere, [Opn, Perc, Perc Endo]
00N8[0,3,4]ZZ	Rls/Basal Ganglia, [Opn, Perc, Perc Endo]
00N9[0,3,4]ZZ	Rls/Thalamus, [Opn, Perc, Perc Endo]
00NA[0,3,4]ZZ	Rls/Hypothalamus, [Opn, Perc, Perc Endo]
00NB[0,3,4]ZZ	Rls/Pons, [Opn, Perc, Perc Endo]
00NC[0,3,4]ZZ	Rls/Cerebellum, [Opn, Perc, Perc Endo]
00ND[0,3,4]ZZ	Rls/Medulla Oblongata, [Opn, Perc, Perc Endo]
00NK[0,3,4]ZZ	Rls/Trigeminal Nerve, [Opn, Perc, Perc Endo]
00P0[0,3,4][0,2,3,7,J,K,M]Z	Rmvl/Brain, [Opn, Perc, Perc Endo], [Drain Dev, Monitoring Dev, Inf Dev, Auto Tissue Sub, Synth Sub, Nonauto Tissue Sub, Neurostimulator Lead], NQ
00P6X[2,M]Z	Rmvl/Cerebral Ventricle, Ext, [Monitoring Dev, Neurostimulator Lead], NQ
00P6[0,3,4][0,2,3,M]Z	Rmvl/Cerebral Ventricle, [Opn, Perc, Perc Endo], [Drain Dev, Monitoring Dev, Inf Dev, Neurostimulator Lead], NQ
00Q0[0,3,4]ZZ	Rpr/Brain, [Opn, Perc, Perc Endo]
00Q1[0,3,4]ZZ	Rpr/Cerebral Meninges, [Opn, Perc, Perc Endo]
00Q2[0,3,4]ZZ	Rpr/Dura Mater, [Opn, Perc, Perc Endo]

T **Transfer DRG**   SP **Special Payment**   * **Code Range**   **6th and 7th Character of ZZ = No Device, No Qualifier ZX = No Device, Diagnostic**

00Q6[0,3,4]ZZ   Rpr/Cerebral Ventricle, [Opn, Perc, Perc Endo]
00Q7[0,3,4]ZZ   Rpr/Cerebral Hemisphere, [Opn, Perc, Perc Endo]
00Q8[0,3,4]ZZ   Rpr/Basal Ganglia, [Opn, Perc, Perc Endo]
00Q9[0,3,4]ZZ   Rpr/Thalamus, [Opn, Perc, Perc Endo]
00QA[0,3,4]ZZ   Rpr/Hypothalamus, [Opn, Perc, Perc Endo]
00QB[0,3,4]ZZ   Rpr/Pons, [Opn, Perc, Perc Endo]
00QC[0,3,4]ZZ   Rpr/Cerebellum, [Opn, Perc, Perc Endo]
00QD[0,3,4]ZZ   Rpr/Medulla Oblongata, [Opn, Perc, Perc Endo]
00T7[0,3,4]ZZ   Resect/Cerebral Hemisphere, [Opn, Perc, Perc Endo]
00U1[0,3,4][7,J,K]Z Supl/Cerebral Meninges, [Opn, Perc, Perc Endo], [Auto Tissue Sub, Synth Sub, Nonauto Tissue Sub], NQ
00U2[0,3,4][7,J,K]Z Supl/Dura Mater, [Opn, Perc, Perc Endo], [Auto Tissue Sub, Synth Sub, Nonauto Tissue Sub], NQ
00W0[0,3,4][0,2,3,7,J,K,M]Z Rev/Brain, [Opn, Perc, Perc Endo], [Drain Dev, Monitoring Dev, Inf Dev, Auto Tissue Sub, Synth Sub, Nonauto Tissue Sub, Neurostimulator Lead], NQ
00W6[0,3,4][0,2,3,M]Z Rev/Cerebral Ventricle, [Opn, Perc, Perc Endo], [Drain Dev, Monitoring Dev, Inf Dev, Neurostimulator Lead], NQ
031H0[9,A,J,K,Z]G Bypass/Common Carotid Artery, Rt, Opn, [Auto Venous Tissue, Auto Arterial Tissue, Synth Sub, Nonauto Tissue Sub, No Dev], Intracranial Artery
031J0[9,A,J,K,Z]G Bypass/Common Carotid Artery, Lt, Opn, [Auto Venous Tissue, Auto Arterial Tissue, Synth Sub, Nonauto Tissue Sub, No Dev], Intracranial Artery
031S0[9,A,J,K,Z]G Bypass/Temporal Artery, Rt, Opn, [Auto Venous Tissue, Auto Arterial Tissue, Synth Sub, Nonauto Tissue Sub, No Dev], Intracranial Artery
031T0[9,A,J,K,Z]G Bypass/Temporal Artery, Lt, Opn, [Auto Venous Tissue, Auto Arterial Tissue, Synth Sub, Nonauto Tissue Sub, No Dev], Intracranial Artery
035G[0,3,4]ZZ   Destr/Intracranial Artery, [Opn, Perc, Perc Endo]
037G[3,4][4,D,Z]Z Dilation/Intracranial Artery, [Perc, Perc Endo], [Drug-eluting Intralum Dev, Intralum Dev, No Dev], NQ
03BG[0,3,4]ZZ   Exc/Intracranial Artery, [Opn, Perc, Perc Endo]
03CG[0,3,4]ZZ   Extir/Intracranial Artery, [Opn, Perc, Perc Endo]
03CH[3,4]ZZ   Extir/Common Carotid Artery, Rt, [Perc, Perc Endo]
03CJ[3,4]ZZ   Extir/Common Carotid Artery, Lt, [Perc, Perc Endo]
03CK[3,4]ZZ   Extir/Int Carotid Artery, Rt, [Perc, Perc Endo]
03CL[3,4]ZZ   Extir/Int Carotid Artery, Lt, [Perc, Perc Endo]
03CM[3,4]ZZ   Extir/Ext Carotid Artery, Rt, [Perc, Perc Endo]
03CN[3,4]ZZ   Extir/Ext Carotid Artery, Lt, [Perc, Perc Endo]
03CP[3,4]ZZ   Extir/Vert Artery, Rt, [Perc, Perc Endo]
03CQ[3,4]ZZ   Extir/Vert Artery, Lt, [Perc, Perc Endo]
03CR[3,4]ZZ   Extir/Face Artery, [Perc, Perc Endo]
03CS[3,4]ZZ   Extir/Temporal Artery, Rt, [Perc, Perc Endo]
03CT[3,4]ZZ   Extir/Temporal Artery, Lt, [Perc, Perc Endo]
03CU[3,4]ZZ   Extir/Thyroid Artery, Rt, [Perc, Perc Endo]
03CV[3,4]ZZ   Extir/Thyroid Artery, Lt, [Perc, Perc Endo]
03LG[0,3,4][B,C,D,Z]Z Occlsn/Intracranial Artery, [Opn, Perc, Perc Endo], [Bioactive Intralum Dev, Extralum Dev, Intralum Dev, No Dev], NQ
03LH[0,3,4][B,D]Z Occlsn/Common Carotid Artery, Rt, [Opn, Perc, Perc Endo], [Bioactive Intralum Dev, Intralum Dev], NQ
03LJ[0,3,4][B,D]Z Occlsn/Common Carotid Artery, Lt, [Opn, Perc, Perc Endo], [Bioactive Intralum Dev, Intralum Dev], NQ
03LK[0,3,4][B,C,D,Z]Z Occlsn/Int Carotid Artery, Rt, [Opn, Perc, Perc Endo], [Bioactive Intralum Dev, Extralum Dev, Intralum Dev], NQ
03LL[0,3,4][B,C,D,Z]Z Occlsn/Int Carotid Artery, Lt, [Opn, Perc, Perc Endo], [Bioactive Intralum Dev, Extralum Dev, Intralum Dev], NQ
03LM[0,3,4][B,D]Z Occlsn/Ext Carotid Artery, Rt, [Opn, Perc, Perc Endo], [Bioactive Intralum Dev, Intralum Dev], NQ
03LN[0,3,4][B,D]Z Occlsn/Ext Carotid Artery, Lt, [Opn, Perc, Perc Endo], [Bioactive Intralum Dev, Intralum Dev], NQ
03LP[0,3,4][B,D]Z Occlsn/Vert Artery, Rt, [Opn, Perc, Perc Endo], [Bioactive Intralum Dev, Intralum Dev], NQ
03LQ[0,3,4][B,D]Z Occlsn/Vert Artery, Lt, [Opn, Perc, Perc Endo], [Bioactive Intralum Dev, Intralum Dev], NQ
03LR[0,3,4]DZ Occlsn/Face Artery, [Opn, Perc, Perc Endo], Intralum Dev, NQ
03LS[0,3,4]DZ Occlsn/Temporal Artery, Rt, [Opn, Perc, Perc Endo], Intralum Dev, NQ
03LT[0,3,4]DZ Occlsn/Temporal Artery, Lt, [Opn, Perc, Perc Endo], Intralum Dev, NQ
03RG[0,4][7,J,K]Z Replace/Intracranial Artery, [Opn, Perc Endo], [Auto Tissue Sub, Synth Sub, Nonauto Tissue Sub], NQ
03VG[0,3,4][B,C,D,Z]Z Restrict/Intracranial Artery, [Opn, Perc, Perc Endo], [Bioactive Intralum Dev, Extralum Dev, Intralum Dev, No Dev], NQ

03VH[0,3,4][B,D]Z Restrict/Common Carotid Artery, Rt, [Opn, Perc, Perc Endo], [Bioactive Intralum Dev, Intralum Dev], NQ
03VJ[0,3,4][B,D]Z Restrict/Common Carotid Artery, Lt, [Opn, Perc, Perc Endo], [Bioactive Intralum Dev, Intralum Dev], NQ
03VK[0,3,4][B,C,D]Z Restrict/Int Carotid Artery, Rt, [Opn, Perc, Perc Endo], [Bioactive Intralum Dev, Extralum Dev, Intralum Dev], NQ
03VL[0,3,4][B,C,D]Z Restrict/Int Carotid Artery, Lt, [Opn, Perc, Perc Endo], [Bioactive Intralum Dev, Extralum Dev, Intralum Dev], NQ
03VM[0,3,4][B,D]Z Restrict/Ext Carotid Artery, Rt, [Opn, Perc, Perc Endo], [Bioactive Intralum Dev, Intralum Dev], NQ
03VN[0,3,4][B,D]Z Restrict/Ext Carotid Artery, Lt, [Opn, Perc, Perc Endo], [Bioactive Intralum Dev, Intralum Dev], NQ
03VP[0,3,4][B,D]Z Restrict/Vert Artery, Rt, [Opn, Perc, Perc Endo], [Bioactive Intralum Dev, Intralum Dev], NQ
03VQ[0,3,4][B,D]Z Restrict/Vert Artery, Lt, [Opn, Perc, Perc Endo], [Bioactive Intralum Dev, Intralum Dev], NQ
03VR[0,3,4]DZ Restrict/Face Artery, [Opn, Perc, Perc Endo], Intralum Dev, NQ
03VS[0,3,4]DZ Restrict/Temporal Artery, Rt, [Opn, Perc, Perc Endo], Intralum Dev, NQ
03VT[0,3,4]DZ Restrict/Temporal Artery, Lt, [Opn, Perc, Perc Endo], Intralum Dev, NQ
03VU[0,3,4]DZ Restrict/Thyroid Artery, Rt, [Opn, Perc, Perc Endo], Intralum Dev, NQ
03VV[0,3,4]DZ Restrict/Thyroid Artery, Lt, [Opn, Perc, Perc Endo], Intralum Dev, NQ
055L[0,3,4]ZZ   Destr/Intracranial Vein, [Opn, Perc, Perc Endo]
057L[3,4]DZ   Dilation/Intracranial Vein, [Perc, Perc Endo], Intralum Dev, NQ
05BL[0,3,4]ZZ   Exc/Intracranial Vein, [Opn, Perc, Perc Endo]
05CL[0,3,4]ZZ   Extir/Intracranial Vein, [Opn, Perc, Perc Endo]
05LL[0,3,4][C,D,Z]Z Occlsn/Intracranial Vein, [Opn, Perc, Perc Endo], [Extralum Dev, Intralum Dev, No Dev], NQ
05RL[0,4][7,J,K]Z Replace/Intracranial Vein, [Opn, Perc, Perc Endo], [Auto Tissue Sub, Synth Sub, Nonauto Tissue Sub], NQ
05VL[0,3,4][C,D,Z]Z Restrict/Intracranial Vein, [Opn, Perc, Perc Endo], [Extralum Dev, Intralum Dev, No Dev], NQ
0G50[0,3,4]ZZ   Destr/Pituitary Gland, [Opn, Perc, Perc Endo]
0G51[0,3,4]ZZ   Destr/Pineal Body, [Opn, Perc, Perc Endo]
0G80[0,3,4]ZZ   Div/Pituitary Gland, [Opn, Perc, Perc Endo]
0G90[0,3,4]ZX   Drain/Pituitary Gland, [Opn, Perc, Perc Endo]
0G90[0,3,4][0,Z]Z Drain/Pituitary Gland, [Opn, Perc, Perc Endo], [Drain Dev, No Dev], NQ
0G91[0,3,4]ZX   Drain/Pineal Body, [Opn, Perc, Perc Endo]
0G91[0,3,4][0,Z]Z Drain/Pineal Body, [Opn, Perc, Perc Endo], [Drain Dev, No Dev], NQ
0GB0[0,3,4]Z[X,Z] Exc/Pituitary Gland, [Opn, Perc, Perc Endo], No Dev, [Dx, NQ]
0GB1[0,3,4]Z[X,Z] Exc/Pineal Body, [Opn, Perc, Perc Endo], No Dev, [Dx, NQ]
0GC0[0,3,4]ZZ   Extir/Pituitary Gland, [Opn, Perc, Perc Endo]
0GC1[0,3,4]ZZ   Extir/Pineal Body, [Opn, Perc, Perc Endo]
0GJ0[0,3,4]ZZ   Inspect/Pituitary Gland, [Opn, Perc, Perc Endo]
0GJ1[0,3,4]ZZ   Inspect/Pineal Body, [Opn, Perc, Perc Endo]
0GN0[0,3,4]ZZ   Rls/Pituitary Gland, [Opn, Perc, Perc Endo]
0GN1[0,3,4]ZZ   Rls/Pineal Body, [Opn, Perc, Perc Endo]
0GP0[0,3,4]0Z   Rmvl/Pituitary Gland, [Opn, Perc, Perc Endo], Drain Dev, NQ
0GP1[0,3,4]0Z   Rmvl/Pineal Body, [Opn, Perc, Perc Endo], Drain Dev, NQ
0GQ0[0,3,4]ZZ   Rpr/Pituitary Gland, [Opn, Perc, Perc Endo]
0GQ1[0,3,4]ZZ   Rpr/Pineal Body, [Opn, Perc, Perc Endo]
0GT0[0,4]ZZ   Resect/Pituitary Gland, [Opn, Perc Endo]
0GT1[0,4]ZZ   Resect/Pineal Body, [Opn, Perc Endo]
0GW0[0,3,4]0Z   Rev/Pituitary Gland, [Opn, Perc, Perc Endo], Drain Dev, NQ
0GW1[0,3,4]0Z   Rev/Pineal Body, [Opn, Perc, Perc Endo], Drain Dev, NQ
0N50[0,3,4]ZZ   Destr/Skull, [Opn, Perc, Perc Endo]
0N51[0,3,4]ZZ   Destr/Frontal Bone, Rt, [Opn, Perc, Perc Endo]
0N52[0,3,4]ZZ   Destr/Frontal Bone, Lt, [Opn, Perc, Perc Endo]
0N53[0,3,4]ZZ   Destr/Parietal Bone, Rt, [Opn, Perc, Perc Endo]
0N54[0,3,4]ZZ   Destr/Parietal Bone, Lt, [Opn, Perc, Perc Endo]
0N55[0,3,4]ZZ   Destr/Temporal Bone, Rt, [Opn, Perc, Perc Endo]
0N56[0,3,4]ZZ   Destr/Temporal Bone, Lt, [Opn, Perc, Perc Endo]
0N57[0,3,4]ZZ   Destr/Occipital Bone, Rt, [Opn, Perc, Perc Endo]
0N58[0,3,4]ZZ   Destr/Occipital Bone, Lt, [Opn, Perc, Perc Endo]
0N80[0,3,4]ZZ   Div/Skull, [Opn, Perc, Perc Endo]
0N81[0,3,4]ZZ   Div/Frontal Bone, Rt, [Opn, Perc, Perc Endo]
0N82[0,3,4]ZZ   Div/Frontal Bone, Lt, [Opn, Perc, Perc Endo]
0N83[0,3,4]ZZ   Div/Parietal Bone, Rt, [Opn, Perc, Perc Endo]
0N84[0,3,4]ZZ   Div/Parietal Bone, Lt, [Opn, Perc, Perc Endo]
0N85[0,3,4]ZZ   Div/Temporal Bone, Rt, [Opn, Perc, Perc Endo]
0N86[0,3,4]ZZ   Div/Temporal Bone, Lt, [Opn, Perc, Perc Endo]
0N87[0,3,4]ZZ   Div/Occipital Bone, Rt, [Opn, Perc, Perc Endo]
0N88[0,3,4]ZZ   Div/Occipital Bone, Lt, [Opn, Perc, Perc Endo]
0N90[0,3,4]ZX   Drain/Skull, [Opn, Perc, Perc Endo]
0N90[0,3,4][0,Z]Z Drain/Skull, [Opn, Perc, Perc Endo], [Drain Dev, No Dev], NQ

| Surgical | Medical | CC Indicator | MCC Indicator | Procedure Proxy | PDx MCC PDx acts as own MCC | PDx CC PDx acts as own CC |

MDC 1: Diseases And Disorders Of The Nervous System—SURGICAL

Code	Description
ØN91[Ø,3,4]ZX	Drain/Frontal Bone, Rt, [Opn, Perc, Perc Endo]
ØN91[Ø,3,4][Ø,Z]Z	Drain/Frontal Bone, Rt, [Opn, Perc, Perc Endo], [Drain Dev, No Dev], NQ
ØN92[Ø,3,4]ZX	Drain/Frontal Bone, Lt, [Opn, Perc, Perc Endo]
ØN92[Ø,3,4][Ø,Z]Z	Drain/Frontal Bone, Lt, [Opn, Perc, Perc Endo], [Drain Dev, No Dev], NQ
ØN93[Ø,3,4]ZX	Drain/Parietal Bone, Rt, [Opn, Perc, Perc Endo]
ØN93[Ø,3,4][Ø,Z]Z	Drain/Parietal Bone, Rt, [Opn, Perc, Perc Endo], [Drain Dev, No Dev], NQ
ØN94[Ø,3,4]ZX	Drain/Parietal Bone, Lt, [Opn, Perc, Perc Endo]
ØN94[Ø,3,4][Ø,Z]Z	Drain/Parietal Bone, Lt, [Opn, Perc, Perc Endo], [Drain Dev, No Dev], NQ
ØN95[Ø,3,4]ZX	Drain/Temporal Bone, Rt, [Opn, Perc, Perc Endo]
ØN95[Ø,3,4][Ø,Z]Z	Drain/Temporal Bone, Rt, [Opn, Perc, Perc Endo], [Drain Dev, No Dev], NQ
ØN96[Ø,3,4]ZX	Drain/Temporal Bone, Lt, [Opn, Perc, Perc Endo]
ØN96[Ø,3,4][Ø,Z]Z	Drain/Temporal Bone, Lt, [Opn, Perc, Perc Endo], [Drain Dev, No Dev], NQ
ØN97[Ø,3,4]ZX	Drain/Occipital Bone, Rt, [Opn, Perc, Perc Endo]
ØN97[Ø,3,4][Ø,Z]Z	Drain/Occipital Bone, Rt, [Opn, Perc, Perc Endo], [Drain Dev, No Dev], NQ
ØN98[Ø,3,4]ZX	Drain/Occipital Bone, Lt, [Opn, Perc, Perc Endo]
ØN98[Ø,3,4][Ø,Z]Z	Drain/Occipital Bone, Lt, [Opn, Perc, Perc Endo], [Drain Dev, No Dev], NQ
ØNBØ[Ø,3,4]Z[X,Z]	Exc/Skull, [Opn, Perc, Perc Endo], No Dev, [Dx, NQ]
ØNB1[Ø,3,4]Z[X,Z]	Exc/Frontal Bone, Rt, [Opn, Perc, Perc Endo], No Dev, [Dx, NQ]
ØNB2[Ø,3,4]Z[X,Z]	Exc/Frontal Bone, Lt, [Opn, Perc, Perc Endo], No Dev, [Dx, NQ]
ØNB3[Ø,3,4]Z[X,Z]	Exc/Parietal Bone, Rt, [Opn, Perc, Perc Endo], No Dev, [Dx, NQ]
ØNB4[Ø,3,4]Z[X,Z]	Exc/Parietal Bone, Lt, [Opn, Perc, Perc Endo], No Dev, [Dx, NQ]
ØNB5[Ø,3,4]Z[X,Z]	Exc/Temporal Bone, Rt, [Opn, Perc, Perc Endo], No Dev, [Dx, NQ]
ØNB6[Ø,3,4]Z[X,Z]	Exc/Temporal Bone, Lt, [Opn, Perc, Perc Endo], No Dev, [Dx, NQ]
ØNB7[Ø,3,4]Z[X,Z]	Exc/Occipital Bone, Rt, [Opn, Perc, Perc Endo], No Dev, [Dx, NQ]
ØNB8[Ø,3,4]Z[X,Z]	Exc/Occipital Bone, Lt, [Opn, Perc, Perc Endo], No Dev, [Dx, NQ]
ØNC1[Ø,3,4]ZZ	Extir/Frontal Bone, Rt, [Opn, Perc, Perc Endo]
ØNC2[Ø,3,4]ZZ	Extir/Frontal Bone, Lt, [Opn, Perc, Perc Endo]
ØNC3[Ø,3,4]ZZ	Extir/Parietal Bone, Rt, [Opn, Perc, Perc Endo]
ØNC4[Ø,3,4]ZZ	Extir/Parietal Bone, Lt, [Opn, Perc, Perc Endo]
ØNC5[Ø,3,4]ZZ	Extir/Temporal Bone, Rt, [Opn, Perc, Perc Endo]
ØNC6[Ø,3,4]ZZ	Extir/Temporal Bone, Lt, [Opn, Perc, Perc Endo]
ØNC7[Ø,3,4]ZZ	Extir/Occipital Bone, Rt, [Opn, Perc, Perc Endo]
ØNC8[Ø,3,4]ZZ	Extir/Occipital Bone, Lt, [Opn, Perc, Perc Endo]
ØNHØ[Ø,3,4][4,M]Z	Insert/Skull, [Opn, Perc, Perc Endo], [Int Fix Dev, Bone Growth Stimulator], NQ
ØNH1[Ø,3,4]4Z	Insert/Frontal Bone, Rt, [Opn, Perc, Perc Endo], Int Fix Dev, NQ
ØNH2[Ø,3,4]4Z	Insert/Frontal Bone, Lt, [Opn, Perc, Perc Endo], Int Fix Dev, NQ
ØNH3[Ø,3,4]4Z	Insert/Parietal Bone, Rt, [Opn, Perc, Perc Endo], Int Fix Dev, NQ
ØNH4[Ø,3,4]4Z	Insert/Parietal Bone, Lt, [Opn, Perc, Perc Endo], Int Fix Dev, NQ
ØNH5[Ø,3,4]4Z	Insert/Temporal Bone, Rt, [Opn, Perc, Perc Endo], Int Fix Dev, NQ
ØNH6[Ø,3,4]4Z	Insert/Temporal Bone, Lt, [Opn, Perc, Perc Endo], Int Fix Dev, NQ
ØNH7[Ø,3,4]4Z	Insert/Occipital Bone, Rt, [Opn, Perc, Perc Endo], Int Fix Dev, NQ
ØNH8[Ø,3,4]4Z	Insert/Occipital Bone, Lt, [Opn, Perc, Perc Endo], Int Fix Dev, NQ
ØNJØ[Ø,3,4]ZZ	Inspect/Skull, [Opn, Perc, Perc Endo]
ØNN1[Ø,3,4]ZZ	Rls/Frontal Bone, Rt, [Opn, Perc, Perc Endo]
ØNN2[Ø,3,4]ZZ	Rls/Frontal Bone, Lt, [Opn, Perc, Perc Endo]
ØNN3[Ø,3,4]ZZ	Rls/Parietal Bone, Rt, [Opn, Perc, Perc Endo]
ØNN4[Ø,3,4]ZZ	Rls/Parietal Bone, Lt, [Opn, Perc, Perc Endo]
ØNN5[Ø,3,4]ZZ	Rls/Temporal Bone, Rt, [Opn, Perc, Perc Endo]
ØNN6[Ø,3,4]ZZ	Rls/Temporal Bone, Lt, [Opn, Perc, Perc Endo]
ØNN7[Ø,3,4]ZZ	Rls/Occipital Bone, Rt, [Opn, Perc, Perc Endo]
ØNN8[Ø,3,4]ZZ	Rls/Occipital Bone, Lt, [Opn, Perc, Perc Endo]
ØNP005Z	Rmvl of Ext Fix from Skull, Opn Appr
ØNPØX[4,M,S]Z	Rmvl/Skull, Ext, [Int Fix Dev, Bone Growth Stimulator, Bone Conduction Hearing Dev], NQ
ØNPØ[Ø,3,4][Ø,4,7,J,K,M,S]Z	Rmvl/Skull, [Opn, Perc, Perc Endo], [Drain Dev, Int Fix Dev, Auto Tissue Sub, Synth Sub, Nonauto Tissue Sub, Bone Growth Stimulator, Hearing Dev], NQ
ØNQØ[Ø,3,4,X]ZZ	Rpr/Skull, [Opn, Perc, Perc Endo, Ext]
ØNQ1[Ø,3,4,X]ZZ	Rpr/Frontal Bone, Rt, [Opn, Perc, Perc Endo, Ext]
ØNQ2[Ø,3,4,X]ZZ	Rpr/Frontal Bone, Lt, [Opn, Perc, Perc Endo, Ext]
ØNQ3[Ø,3,4,X]ZZ	Rpr/Parietal Bone, Rt, [Opn, Perc, Perc Endo, Ext]
ØNQ4[Ø,3,4,X]ZZ	Rpr/Parietal Bone, Lt, [Opn, Perc, Perc Endo, Ext]
ØNQ5[Ø,3,4,X]ZZ	Rpr/Temporal Bone, Rt, [Opn, Perc, Perc Endo, Ext]
ØNQ6[Ø,3,4,X]ZZ	Rpr/Temporal Bone, Lt, [Opn, Perc, Perc Endo, Ext]
ØNQ7[Ø,3,4,X]ZZ	Rpr/Occipital Bone, Rt, [Opn, Perc, Perc Endo, Ext]
ØNQ8[Ø,3,4,X]ZZ	Rpr/Occipital Bone, Lt, [Opn, Perc, Perc Endo, Ext]
ØNRØ[Ø,3,4][7,J,K]Z	Replace/Skull, [Opn, Perc, Perc Endo], [Auto Tissue Sub, Synth Sub, Nonauto Tissue Sub], NQ
ØNR1[Ø,3,4][7,J,K]Z	Replace/Frontal Bone, Rt, [Opn, Perc, Perc Endo], [Auto Tissue Sub, Synth Sub, Nonauto Tissue Sub], NQ
ØNR2[Ø,3,4][7,J,K]Z	Replace/Frontal Bone, Lt, [Opn, Perc, Perc Endo], [Auto Tissue Sub, Synth Sub, Nonauto Tissue Sub], NQ
ØNR3[Ø,3,4][7,J,K]Z	Replace/Parietal Bone, Rt, [Opn, Perc, Perc Endo], [Auto Tissue Sub, Synth Sub, Nonauto Tissue Sub], NQ
ØNR4[Ø,3,4][7,J,K]Z	Replace/Parietal Bone, Lt, [Opn, Perc, Perc Endo], [Auto Tissue Sub, Synth Sub, Nonauto Tissue Sub], NQ
ØNR5[Ø,3,4][7,J,K]Z	Replace/Temporal Bone, Rt, [Opn, Perc, Perc Endo], [Auto Tissue Sub, Synth Sub, Nonauto Tissue Sub], NQ
ØNR6[Ø,3,4][7,J,K]Z	Replace/Temporal Bone, Lt, [Opn, Perc, Perc Endo], [Auto Tissue Sub, Synth Sub, Nonauto Tissue Sub], NQ
ØNR7[Ø,3,4][7,J,K]Z	Replace/Occipital Bone, Rt, [Opn, Perc, Perc Endo], [Auto Tissue Sub, Synth Sub, Nonauto Tissue Sub], NQ
ØNR8[Ø,3,4][7,J,K]Z	Replace/Occipital Bone, Lt, [Opn, Perc, Perc Endo], [Auto Tissue Sub, Synth Sub, Nonauto Tissue Sub], NQ
ØNSØXZZ	Repos Skull, Ext Appr
ØNSØ[Ø,3,4][4,5,Z]Z	Repos/Skull, [Opn, Perc, Perc Endo], [Int Fix Dev, Ext Fix Dev, No Dev], NQ
ØNS1[Ø,3,4,X]ZZ	Repos/Frontal Bone, Rt, [Opn, Perc, Perc Endo, Ext]
ØNS1[Ø,3,4]4Z	Repos/Frontal Bone, Rt, [Opn, Perc, Perc Endo], Int Fix Dev, NQ
ØNS2[Ø,3,4,X]ZZ	Repos/Frontal Bone, Lt, [Opn, Perc, Perc Endo, Ext]
ØNS2[Ø,3,4]4Z	Repos/Frontal Bone, Lt, [Opn, Perc, Perc Endo], Int Fix Dev, NQ
ØNS3[Ø,3,4,X]ZZ	Repos/Parietal Bone, Rt, [Opn, Perc, Perc Endo, Ext]
ØNS3[Ø,3,4]4Z	Repos/Parietal Bone, Rt, [Opn, Perc, Perc Endo], Int Fix Dev, NQ
ØNS4[Ø,3,4,X]ZZ	Repos/Parietal Bone, Lt, [Opn, Perc, Perc Endo, Ext]
ØNS4[Ø,3,4]4Z	Repos/Parietal Bone, Lt, [Opn, Perc, Perc Endo], Int Fix Dev, NQ
ØNS5[Ø,3,4,X]ZZ	Repos/Temporal Bone, Rt, [Opn, Perc, Perc Endo, Ext]
ØNS5[Ø,3,4]4Z	Repos/Temporal Bone, Rt, [Opn, Perc, Perc Endo], Int Fix Dev, NQ
ØNS6[Ø,3,4,X]ZZ	Repos/Temporal Bone, Lt, [Opn, Perc, Perc Endo, Ext]
ØNS6[Ø,3,4]4Z	Repos/Temporal Bone, Lt, [Opn, Perc, Perc Endo], Int Fix Dev, NQ
ØNS7[Ø,3,4,X]ZZ	Repos/Occipital Bone, Rt, [Opn, Perc, Perc Endo, Ext]
ØNS7[Ø,3,4]4Z	Repos/Occipital Bone, Rt, [Opn, Perc, Perc Endo], Int Fix Dev, NQ
ØNS8[Ø,3,4,X]ZZ	Repos/Occipital Bone, Lt, [Opn, Perc, Perc Endo, Ext]
ØNS8[Ø,3,4]4Z	Repos/Occipital Bone, Lt, [Opn, Perc, Perc Endo], Int Fix Dev, NQ
ØNT10ZZ	Resect of Rt Frontal Bone, Opn Appr
ØNT20ZZ	Resect of Lt Frontal Bone, Opn Appr
ØNT30ZZ	Resect of Rt Parietal Bone, Opn Appr
ØNT40ZZ	Resect of Lt Parietal Bone, Opn Appr
ØNT50ZZ	Resect of Rt Temporal Bone, Opn Appr
ØNT60ZZ	Resect of Lt Temporal Bone, Opn Appr
ØNT70ZZ	Resect of Rt Occipital Bone, Opn Appr
ØNT80ZZ	Resect of Lt Occipital Bone, Opn Appr
ØNUØ[Ø,3,4][7,J,K]Z	Supl/Skull, [Opn, Perc, Perc Endo], [Auto Tissue Sub, Synth Sub, Nonauto Tissue Sub], NQ
ØNU1[Ø,3,4][7,J,K]Z	Supl/Frontal Bone, Rt, [Opn, Perc, Perc Endo], [Auto Tissue Sub, Synth Sub, Nonauto Tissue Sub], NQ
ØNU2[Ø,3,4][7,J,K]Z	Supl/Frontal Bone, Lt, [Opn, Perc, Perc Endo], [Auto Tissue Sub, Synth Sub, Nonauto Tissue Sub], NQ
ØNU3[Ø,3,4][7,J,K]Z	Supl/Parietal Bone, Rt, [Opn, Perc, Perc Endo], [Auto Tissue Sub, Synth Sub, Nonauto Tissue Sub], NQ
ØNU4[Ø,3,4][7,J,K]Z	Supl/Parietal Bone, Lt, [Opn, Perc, Perc Endo], [Auto Tissue Sub, Synth Sub, Nonauto Tissue Sub], NQ
ØNU5[Ø,3,4][7,J,K]Z	Supl/Temporal Bone, Rt, [Opn, Perc, Perc Endo], [Auto Tissue Sub, Synth Sub, Nonauto Tissue Sub], NQ
ØNU6[Ø,3,4][7,J,K]Z	Supl/Temporal Bone, Lt, [Opn, Perc, Perc Endo], [Auto Tissue Sub, Synth Sub, Nonauto Tissue Sub], NQ
ØNU7[Ø,3,4][7,J,K]Z	Supl/Occipital Bone, Rt, [Opn, Perc, Perc Endo], [Auto Tissue Sub, Synth Sub, Nonauto Tissue Sub], NQ
ØNU8[Ø,3,4][7,J,K]Z	Supl/Occipital Bone, Lt, [Opn, Perc, Perc Endo], [Auto Tissue Sub, Synth Sub, Nonauto Tissue Sub], NQ
ØNWØØNZ	Rev of Neurostim in Skull, Opn Appr
ØNWØ[Ø,3,4][Ø,4,5,7,J,K,M,S]Z	Rev/Skull, [Opn, Perc, Perc Endo], [Drain Dev, Int Fix Dev, Ext Fix Dev, Auto Tissue Sub, Synth Sub, Nonauto Tissue Sub, Bone Growth Stimulator, Bone Conduction Hearing Dev], NQ
ØW910ZX	Drain of Cranial Cavity, Opn Appr, Diagnostic
ØW910[Ø,Z]Z	Drain/Cranial Cavity, Opn, [Drain Dev, No Dev], NQ
ØWC1[Ø,3,4]ZZ	Extir/Cranial Cavity, [Opn, Perc, Perc Endo]
ØWF1[Ø,3,4]ZZ	Fragmn/Cranial Cavity, [Opn, Perc, Perc Endo]
ØWH1[Ø,3,4]YZ	Insert/Cranial Cavity, [Opn, Perc, Perc Endo], Oth Dev, NQ
ØWJ1[Ø,3,4]ZZ	Inspect/Cranial Cavity, [Opn, Perc, Perc Endo]

ØWP1[Ø,3,4][Ø,1,J,Y]Z Rmvl/Cranial Cavity, [Opn, Perc, Perc Endo], [Drain Dev, Radioact Elmt, Synth Sub, Oth Dev], NQ
ØWW1[Ø,3,4][Ø,1,3,J,Y]Z Rev/Cranial Cavity, [Opn, Perc, Perc Endo], [Drain Dev, Radioact Elmt, Inf Dev, Synth Sub, Oth Dev], NQ
DØYØKZZ   Laser Interstitial Thermal Therapy of Brain
DØY1KZZ   Laser Interstitial Thermal Therapy of Brain Stem

DRG 026 Craniotomy and Endovascular Intracranial Procedures with CC

GMLOS 4.6   **AMLOS 6.1**   **RW 2.9958**   [T]

Select operating room procedures listed under DRG 025

DRG 027 Craniotomy and Endovascular Intracranial Procedures without CC/MCC

GMLOS 2.4   **AMLOS 3.1**   **RW 2.2835**   [T]

Select operating room procedures listed under DRG 025

DRG 028 Spinal Procedures with MCC

GMLOS 9.3   **AMLOS 11.7**   **RW 5.3695**   [SP]

Operating Room Procedures

ØØ1U[Ø,3][7,J,K][4,6,7,9] Bypass/Spinal Canal, [Opn, Perc], [Auto Tissue Sub, Synth Sub, Nonauto Tissue Sub], [Pleural Cavity, Peritoneal Cavity, Urinary Tract, Fallopian Tube]
ØØ5T[Ø,3,4]ZZ   Destr/Spinal Meninges, [Opn, Perc, Perc Endo]
ØØ5W[Ø,3,4]ZZ   Destr/Cervical Spinal Cord, [Opn, Perc, Perc Endo]
ØØ5X[Ø,3,4]ZZ   Destr/Thoracic Spinal Cord, [Opn, Perc, Perc Endo]
ØØ5Y[Ø,3,4]ZZ   Destr/Lumbar Spinal Cord, [Opn, Perc, Perc Endo]
ØØ8W[Ø,3,4]ZZ   Div/Cervical Spinal Cord, [Opn, Perc, Perc Endo]
ØØ8X[Ø,3,4]ZZ   Div/Thoracic Spinal Cord, [Opn, Perc, Perc Endo]
ØØ8Y[Ø,3,4]ZZ   Div/Lumbar Spinal Cord, [Opn, Perc, Perc Endo]
ØØ9T[Ø,3,4]ZX   Drain/Spinal Meninges, [Opn, Perc, Perc Endo]
ØØ9T[Ø,3,4][Ø,Z]Z Drain/Spinal Meninges, [Opn, Perc, Perc Endo], [Drain Dev, No Dev], NQ
ØØ9UØØZ   Drain of Spinal Canal with Drain Device, Opn Appr
ØØ9UØZX   Drain of Spinal Canal, Opn Appr, Diagnostic
ØØ9UØZZ   Drain of Spinal Canal, Opn Appr
ØØ9W[Ø,3,4]ZX   Drain/Cervical Spinal Cord, [Opn, Perc, Perc Endo]
ØØ9W[Ø,3,4][Ø,Z]Z Drain/Cervical Spinal Cord, [Opn, Perc, Perc Endo], [Drain Dev, No Dev], NQ
ØØ9X[Ø,3,4]ZX   Drain/Thoracic Spinal Cord, [Opn, Perc, Perc Endo]
ØØ9X[Ø,3,4][Ø,Z]Z Drain/Thoracic Spinal Cord, [Opn, Perc, Perc Endo], [Drain Dev, No Dev], NQ
ØØ9Y[Ø,3,4]ZX   Drain/Lumbar Spinal Cord, [Opn, Perc, Perc Endo]
ØØ9Y[Ø,3,4][Ø,Z]Z Drain/Lumbar Spinal Cord, [Opn, Perc, Perc Endo], [Drain Dev, No Dev], NQ
ØØBT[Ø,3,4]Z[X,Z] Exc/Spinal Meninges, [Opn, Perc, Perc Endo], No Dev, [Dx, NQ]
ØØBW[Ø,3,4]Z[X,Z] Exc/Cervical Spinal Cord, [Opn, Perc, Perc Endo], No Dev, [Dx, NQ]
ØØBX[Ø,3,4]Z[X,Z] Exc/Thoracic Spinal Cord, [Opn, Perc, Perc Endo], No Dev, [Dx, NQ]
ØØBY[Ø,3,4]Z[X,Z] Exc/Lumbar Spinal Cord, [Opn, Perc, Perc Endo], No Dev, [Dx, NQ]
ØØCT[Ø,3,4]ZZ   Extir/Spinal Meninges, [Opn, Perc, Perc Endo]
ØØCW[Ø,3,4]ZZ   Extir/Cervical Spinal Cord, [Opn, Perc, Perc Endo]
ØØCX[Ø,3,4]ZZ   Extir/Thoracic Spinal Cord, [Opn, Perc, Perc Endo]
ØØCY[Ø,3,4]ZZ   Extir/Lumbar Spinal Cord, [Opn, Perc, Perc Endo]
ØØDT[Ø,3,4]ZZ   Extract/Spinal Meninges, [Opn, Perc, Perc Endo]
ØØFU[Ø,3,4,X]ZZ Fragmn/Spinal Canal, [Opn, Perc, Perc Endo, Ext]
ØØHU[Ø,3,4][2,M]Z Insert/Spinal Canal, [Opn, Perc, Perc Endo], [Monitoring Dev, Neurostimulator Lead], NQ
ØØHV[Ø,3,4][2,M]Z Insert/Spinal Cord, [Opn, Perc, Perc Endo], [Monitoring Dev, Neurostimulator Lead], NQ
ØØJU[Ø,3,4]ZZ   Inspect/Spinal Canal, [Opn, Perc, Perc Endo]
ØØJV[Ø,3,4]ZZ   Inspect/Spinal Cord, [Opn, Perc, Perc Endo]
ØØNT[Ø,3,4]ZZ   Rls/Spinal Meninges, [Opn, Perc, Perc Endo]
ØØNW[Ø,3,4]ZZ   Rls/Cervical Spinal Cord, [Opn, Perc, Perc Endo]
ØØNX[Ø,3,4]ZZ   Rls/Thoracic Spinal Cord, [Opn, Perc, Perc Endo]
ØØNY[Ø,3,4]ZZ   Rls/Lumbar Spinal Cord, [Opn, Perc, Perc Endo]
ØØPU[Ø,3,4][Ø,2,3,J,M]Z Rmvl/Spinal Canal, [Opn, Perc, Perc Endo], [Drain Dev, Monitoring Dev, Inf Dev, Synth Sub, Neurostimulator Lead], NQ
ØØPV[Ø,3,4][Ø,2,3,7,J,K,M]Z Rmvl/Spinal Cord, [Opn, Perc, Perc Endo], [Drain Dev, Monitoring Dev, Inf Dev, Auto Tissue Sub, Synth Sub, Nonauto Tissue Sub, Neurostimulator Lead], NQ
ØØQT[Ø,3,4]ZZ   Rpr/Spinal Meninges, [Opn, Perc, Perc Endo]
ØØQW[Ø,3,4]ZZ   Rpr/Cervical Spinal Cord, [Opn, Perc, Perc Endo]
ØØQX[Ø,3,4]ZZ   Rpr/Thoracic Spinal Cord, [Opn, Perc, Perc Endo]

ØØQY[Ø,3,4]ZZ   Rpr/Lumbar Spinal Cord, [Opn, Perc, Perc Endo]
ØØSW[Ø,3,4]ZZ   Repos/Cervical Spinal Cord, [Opn, Perc, Perc Endo]
ØØSX[Ø,3,4]ZZ   Repos/Thoracic Spinal Cord, [Opn, Perc, Perc Endo]
ØØSY[Ø,3,4]ZZ   Repos/Lumbar Spinal Cord, [Opn, Perc, Perc Endo]
ØØUT[Ø,3,4][7,J,K]ZSupl/Spinal Meninges, [Opn, Perc, Perc Endo], [Auto Tissue Sub, Synth Sub, Nonauto Tissue Sub], NQ
ØØWU[Ø,3,4][Ø,2,3,J,M]Z Rev/Spinal Canal, [Opn, Perc, Perc Endo], [Drain Dev, Monitoring Dev, Inf Dev, Synth Sub, Neurostimulator Lead], NQ
ØØWV[Ø,3,4][Ø,2,3,7,J,K,M]Z Rev/Spinal Cord, [Opn, Perc, Perc Endo], [Drain Dev, Monitoring Dev, Inf Dev, Auto Tissue Sub, Synth Sub, Nonauto Tissue Sub, Neurostimulator Lead], NQ
Ø151[Ø,4]ZZ   Destr/Cervical Nerve, [Opn, Perc Endo]
Ø158[Ø,4]ZZ   Destr/Thoracic Nerve, [Opn, Perc Endo]
Ø15B[Ø,4]ZZ   Destr/Lumbar Nerve, [Opn, Perc Endo]
Ø15R[Ø,4]ZZ   Destr/Sacral Nerve, [Opn, Perc Endo]
Ø181[Ø,3,4]ZZ   Div/Cervical Nerve, [Opn, Perc, Perc Endo]
Ø188[Ø,3,4]ZZ   Div/Thoracic Nerve, [Opn, Perc, Perc Endo]
Ø18B[Ø,3,4]ZZ   Div/Lumbar Nerve, [Opn, Perc, Perc Endo]
Ø18R[Ø,3,4]ZZ   Div/Sacral Nerve, [Opn, Perc, Perc Endo]
ØPBØ[Ø,3,4]ZZ   Exc/Sternum, [Opn, Perc, Perc Endo]
ØPB1[Ø,3,4]ZZ   Exc/Rib, Rt, [Opn, Perc, Perc Endo]
ØPB2[Ø,3,4]ZZ   Exc/Rib, Lt, [Opn, Perc, Perc Endo]
ØPB5[Ø,3,4]ZZ   Exc/Scapula, Rt, [Opn, Perc, Perc Endo]
ØPB6[Ø,3,4]ZZ   Exc/Scapula, Lt, [Opn, Perc, Perc Endo]
ØPB7[Ø,3,4]ZZ   Exc/Glenoid Cavity, Rt, [Opn, Perc, Perc Endo]
ØPB8[Ø,3,4]ZZ   Exc/Glenoid Cavity, Lt, [Opn, Perc, Perc Endo]
ØPB9[Ø,3,4]ZZ   Exc/Clavicle, Rt, [Opn, Perc, Perc Endo]
ØPBB[Ø,3,4]ZZ   Exc/Clavicle, Lt, [Opn, Perc, Perc Endo]
ØPS3XZZ   Repos Cervical Vertebra, Ext Appr
ØPS3[Ø,3,4]4Z   Repos/Cervical Vertebra, [Opn, Perc, Perc Endo], Int Fix Dev, NQ
ØPS3[Ø,4]ZZ   Repos/Cervical Vertebra, [Opn, Perc Endo]
ØPS4XZZ   Repos Thoracic Vertebra, Ext Appr
ØPS4[Ø,3,4]4Z   Repos/Thoracic Vertebra, [Opn, Perc, Perc Endo], Int Fix Dev, NQ
ØPS4[Ø,4]ZZ   Repos/Thoracic Vertebra, [Opn, Perc Endo]
ØPT[Ø,1,2,5,6,7,8,9,B]ØZZ Resect [Sternum, Rt rib, Lt rib, Rt scapula, Lt scapula, Rt glenoid cavity, Lt glenoid cavity, Rt clavicle, Lt clavicle], Opn
ØQSØXZZ   Repos Lumbar Vertebra, Ext Appr
ØQSØ[Ø,3,4]4Z   Repos/Lumbar Vertebra, [Opn, Perc, Perc Endo], Int Fix Dev, NQ
ØQSØ[Ø,4]ZZ   Repos/Lumbar Vertebra, [Opn, Perc Endo]
ØQS1XZZ   Repos Sacrum, Ext Appr
ØQS1[Ø,3,4]4Z   Repos/Sacrum, [Opn, Perc, Perc Endo], Int Fix Dev, NQ
ØQS1[Ø,4]ZZ   Repos/Sacrum, [Opn, Perc Endo]
ØQSS[Ø,3,4,X]ZZ Repos/Coccyx, [Opn, Perc, Perc Endo, Ext]
ØQSS[Ø,3,4]4Z   Repos/Coccyx, [Opn, Perc, Perc Endo], Int Fix Dev, NQ
ØR5[3,5,9,B]ØZZ Destr [Cervical, Cervicothoracic, Thoracic, Thoracolumbar] Vert Disc, Opn
ØRBØ[Ø,3,4]ZZ   Exc/Occipital-cervical Jt, [Opn, Perc, Perc Endo]
ØRB1[Ø,3,4]ZZ   Exc/Cervical Vert Jt, [Opn, Perc, Perc Endo]
ØRB3[Ø,3,4]ZZ   Exc/Cervical Vert Disc, [Opn, Perc, Perc Endo]
ØRB4[Ø,3,4]ZZ   Exc/Cervicothoracic Vert Jt, [Opn, Perc, Perc Endo]
ØRB5[Ø,3,4]ZZ   Exc/Cervicothoracic Vert Disc, [Opn, Perc, Perc Endo]
ØRB6[Ø,3,4]ZZ   Exc/Thoracic Vert Jt, [Opn, Perc, Perc Endo]
ØRB9[Ø,3,4]ZZ   Exc/Thoracic Vert Disc, [Opn, Perc, Perc Endo]
ØRBA[Ø,3,4]ZZ   Exc/Thoracolumbar Vert Jt, [Opn, Perc, Perc Endo]
ØRBB[Ø,3,4]ZZ   Exc/Thoracolumbar Vert Disc, [Opn, Perc, Perc Endo]
ØRGØ[Ø,3,4][7,A,J,K,Z][Ø,1,J] Fusion/Occipital-cervical Jt, [Opn, Perc, Perc Endo], [Auto Tissue Sub, Interbody Fusion Dev, Synth Sub, Nonauto Tissue Sub, No Dev], [Ant Appr, Ant Column, Post Appr, Post Column, Post Appr, Ant Column]
ØRG1[Ø,3,4][7,A,J,K,Z][Ø,1,J] Fusion/ Cervical Vert Jt, [Opn, Perc, Perc Endo], [Auto Tissue Sub, Interbody Fusion Dev, Synth Sub, Nonauto Tissue Sub, No Dev], [Ant Appr, Ant Column, Post Appr, Post Column, Post Appr, Ant Column]
ØRG2[Ø,3,4][7,A,J,K,Z][Ø,1,J] Fusion/Cervical Vert Jts, 2 or more, [Opn, Perc, Perc Endo], [Auto Tissue Sub, Interbody Fusion Dev, Synth Sub, Nonauto Tissue Sub, No Dev], [Ant Appr, Ant Column, Post Appr, Post Column, Post Appr, Ant Column]
ØRG4[Ø,3,4][7,A,J,K,Z][Ø,1,J] Fusion/Cervicothoracic Vert Jt, [Opn, Perc, Perc Endo], [Auto Tissue Sub, Interbody Fusion Dev, Synth Sub, Nonauto Tissue Sub, No Dev], [Ant Appr, Ant Column, Post Appr, Post Column, Post Appr, Ant Column]
ØRG6[Ø,3,4][7,A,J,K,Z][Ø,1,J] Fusion/Thoracic Vert Jt, [Opn, Perc, Perc Endo], [Auto Tissue Sub, Interbody Fusion Dev, Synth Sub, Nonauto Tissue Sub, No Dev], [Ant Appr, Ant Column, Post Appr, Post Column, Post Appr, Ant Column]

Surgical   **Medical**   **CC Indicator**   **MCC Indicator**   **Procedure Proxy**   [PDxMCC] **PDx acts as own MCC**   [PDxCC] **PDx acts as own CC**

MDC 1: Diseases And Disorders Of The Nervous System—SURGICAL

ØRG7[Ø,3,4][7,A,J,K,Z][Ø,1,J] Fusion/Thoracic Vert Jts, 2 to 7, [Opn, Perc, Perc Endo], [Auto Tissue Sub, Interbody Fusion Dev, Synth Sub, Nonauto Tissue Sub, No Dev], [Ant Appr, Ant Column, Post Appr, Post Column, Ant Column]

ØRG8[Ø,3,4][7,A,J,K,Z][Ø,1,J] Fusion/Thoracic Vert Jts, 8 or more, [Opn, Perc, Perc Endo], [Auto Tissue Sub, Interbody Fusion Dev, Synth Sub, Nonauto Tissue Sub, No Dev], [Ant Appr, Ant Column, Post Appr, Post Column, Ant Column]

ØRGA[Ø,3,4][7,A,J,K,Z][Ø,1,J] Fusion/Thoracolumbar Vert Jt, [Opn, Perc, Perc Endo], [Auto Tissue Sub, Interbody Fusion Dev, Synth Sub, Nonauto Tissue Sub, No Dev], [Ant Appr, Ant Column, Post Appr, Post Column, Ant Column]

ØRHØ[Ø,3,4][B,C,D]Z Insert/Occipital-cervical Jt, [Opn, Perc, Perc Endo], [Spinal Stabliz Dev, Interspinous Process, Spinal Stabliz Dev, Pedicle-Based, Spinal Stabliz Dev, Facet Replace], NQ

ØRH1[Ø,3,4][B,C,D]Z Insert/Cervical Vert Jt, [Opn, Perc, Perc Endo], [Spinal Stabliz Dev, Interspinous Process, Spinal Stabliz Dev, Pedicle-Based, Spinal Stabliz Dev, Facet Replace], NQ

ØRH4[Ø,3,4][B,C,D]Z Insert/Cervicothoracic Vert Jt, [Opn, Perc, Perc Endo], [Spinal Stabliz Dev, Interspinous Process, Spinal Stabliz Dev, Pedicle-Based, Spinal Stabliz Dev, Facet Replace], NQ

ØRH6[Ø,3,4][B,C,D]Z Insert/Thoracic Vert Jt, [Opn, Perc, Perc Endo], [Spinal Stabliz Dev, Interspinous Process, Spinal Stabliz Dev, Pedicle-Based, Spinal Stabliz Dev, Facet Replace], NQ

ØRHA[Ø,3,4][B,C,D]Z Insert/Thoracolumbar Vert Jt, [Opn, Perc, Perc Endo], [Spinal Stabliz Dev, Interspinous Process, Spinal Stabliz Dev, Pedicle-Based, Spinal Stabliz Dev, Facet Replace], NQ

ØRQ[3,9,B]ØZZ Rpr [Cervical, Thoracic, Thoracolumbar] Vert Disc, Opn
ØRR3ØJZ Replace of Cerv Disc with Synth Sub, Opn Appr
ØRR5ØJZ Replace of C-thor Disc with Synth Sub, Opn Appr
ØRR9ØJZ Replace of Thor Disc with Synth Sub, Opn Appr
ØRRBØJZ Replace of T-lum Disc with Synth Sub, Opn Appr
ØRT[3,4,5,9,B]ØZZ Resect [Cervical Vert Disc, Cervicothoracic Vert Jt, Cervicothoracic Vert Disc, Thoracic Vert Disc, Thoracolumbar Vert Disc], Opn

ØRUØ[Ø,3,4]JZ Supl/Occipital-cervical Jt, [Opn, Perc, Perc Endo], Synth Sub, NQ
ØRU1[Ø,3,4]JZ Supl/Cervical Vert Jt, [Opn, Perc, Perc Endo], Synth Sub, NQ
ØRU3[Ø,3,4][7,J,K]Z Supl/Cervical Vert Disc, [Opn, Perc, Perc Endo], [Auto Tissue Sub, Synth Sub, Nonauto Tissue Sub], NQ
ØRU4[Ø,3,4]JZ Supl/Cervicothoracic Vert Jt, [Opn, Perc, Perc Endo], Synth Sub, NQ
ØRU5[Ø,3,4]JZ Supl/Cervicothoracic Vert Disc, [Opn, Perc, Perc Endo], Synth Sub, NQ
ØRU6[Ø,3,4]JZ Supl/Thoracic Vert Jt, [Opn, Perc, Perc Endo], Synth Sub, NQ
ØRU9[Ø,3,4][7,J,K]Z Supl/Thoracic Vert Disc, [Opn, Perc, Perc Endo], [Auto Tissue Sub, Synth Sub, Nonauto Tissue Sub], NQ
ØRUA[Ø,3,4]JZ Supl/Thoracolumbar Vert Jt, [Opn, Perc, Perc Endo], Synth Sub, NQ
ØRUB[Ø,3,4][7,J,K]Z Supl/Thoracolumbar Vert Disc, [Opn, Perc, Perc Endo], [Auto Tissue Sub, Synth Sub, Nonauto Tissue Sub], NQ
ØRW3[Ø,3,4]JZ Rev/Cervical Vert Disc, [Opn, Perc, Perc Endo], Synth Sub, NQ
ØRW5[Ø,3,4]JZ Rev/Cervicothoracic Vert Disc, [Opn, Perc, Perc Endo], Synth Sub, NQ
ØRW9[Ø,3,4]JZ Rev/Thoracic Vert Disc, [Opn, Perc, Perc Endo], Synth Sub, NQ
ØRWB[Ø,3,4]JZ Rev/Thoracolumbar Vert Disc, [Opn, Perc, Perc Endo], Synth Sub, NQ
ØS52[Ø,3,4]ZZ Destr/Lumbar Vert Disc, [Opn, Perc, Perc Endo]
ØS54[Ø,3,4]ZZ Destr/Lumbosacral Disc, [Opn, Perc, Perc Endo]
ØSBØ[Ø,3,4]ZZ Exc/Lumbar Vert Jt, [Opn, Perc, Perc Endo]
ØSB2[Ø,3,4]ZZ Exc/Lumbar Vert Disc, [Opn, Perc, Perc Endo]
ØSB3[Ø,3,4]ZZ Exc/Lumbosacral Jt, [Opn, Perc, Perc Endo]
ØSB4[Ø,3,4]ZZ Exc/Lumbosacral Disc, [Opn, Perc, Perc Endo]
ØSB5[Ø,3,4]ZZ Exc/Sacrococcygeal Jt, [Opn, Perc, Perc Endo]
ØSB6[Ø,3,4]ZZ Exc/Coccygeal Jt, [Opn, Perc, Perc Endo]
ØSB7[Ø,3,4]ZZ Exc/Sacroiliac Jt, Rt, [Opn, Perc, Perc Endo]
ØSB8[Ø,3,4]ZZ Exc/Sacroiliac Jt, Lt, [Opn, Perc, Perc Endo]
ØSGØ* Fusion/Lumbar Vert Jt
ØSG1* Fusion/Lumbar Vert Jts, 2 or more
ØSG3* Fusion/Lumbosacral Jt
ØSG5* Fusion/Sacrococcygeal Jt
ØSG6* Fusion/Coccygeal Jt
ØSG7* Fusion/Sacroiliac Jt, Rt
ØSG8* Fusion/Sacroiliac Jt, Lt
ØSHØ[Ø,3,4][B,C,D]Z Insert/Lumbar Vert Jt, [Opn, Perc, Perc Endo], [Spinal Stabliz Dev, Interspinous Process, Spinal Stabliz Dev, Pedicle-Based, Spinal Stabliz Dev, Facet Replace], NQ
ØSH3[Ø,3,4][B,C,D]Z Insert/Lumbosacral Jt, [Opn, Perc, Perc Endo], [Spinal Stabliz Dev, Interspinous Process, Spinal Stabliz Dev, Pedicle-Based, Spinal Stabliz Dev, Facet Replace], NQ

ØSQ[2,4]ØZZ Rpr [Lumbar Vert Disc, Lumbosacral Disc], Opn
ØSR2ØJZ Replace of Lum Disc with Synth Sub, Opn Appr
ØSR4ØJZ Replace of Lumsac Disc with Synth Sub, Opn Appr
ØST[2,4]ØZZ Resect [Lumbar Vert Disc, Lumbosacral Disc], Opn
ØSUØ[Ø,3,4]JZ Supl/Lumbar Vert Jt, [Opn, Perc, Perc Endo], Synth Sub, NQ
ØSU2[Ø,3,4][7,J,K]Z Supl/Lumbar Vert Disc, [Opn, Perc, Perc Endo], [Auto Tissue Sub, Synth Sub, Nonauto Tissue Sub], NQ
ØSU3[Ø,3,4]JZ Supl/Lumbosacral Jt, [Opn, Perc, Perc Endo], Synth Sub, NQ
ØSU4[Ø,3,4][7,J,K]Z Supl/Lumbosacral Disc, [Opn, Perc, Perc Endo], [Auto Tissue Sub, Synth Sub, Nonauto Tissue Sub], NQ
ØSU5[Ø,3,4]JZ Supl/Sacrococcygeal Jt, [Opn, Perc, Perc Endo], Synth Sub, NQ
ØSU6[Ø,3,4]JZ Supl/Coccygeal Jt, [Opn, Perc, Perc Endo], Synth Sub, NQ
ØSW2[Ø,3,4]JZ Rev/Lumbar Vert Disc, [Opn, Perc, Perc Endo], Synth Sub, NQ
ØSW4[Ø,3,4]JZ Rev/Lumbosacral Disc, [Opn, Perc, Perc Endo], Synth Sub, NQ

DRG 029   Spinal Procedures with CC or Spinal Neurostimulator
GMLOS 4.8   AMLOS 6.2   RW 3.Ø548   [SP]

Select operating room procedures listed under DRG 028

OR

Any of the following procedure combinations

ØJH6[Ø,3][B,C,D,E]Z Insert/SQ Tissue & Fascia, Chest, [Opn, Perc], [Stimulator Generator, Single Array, Stimulator Generator, Single Array Rechargeable, Stimulator Generator, Multi Array, Stimulator Generator, Multi Array Rechargeable], NQ
ØJH7[Ø,3][B,C,D,E]Z Insert/SQ Tissue & Fascia, Back, [Opn, Perc], [Stimulator Generator, Single Array, Stimulator Generator, Single Array Rechargeable, Stimulator Generator, Multi Array, Stimulator Generator, Multi Array Rechargeable], NQ
ØJH8[Ø,3][B,C,D,E]Z Insert/SQ Tissue & Fascia, Abd, [Opn, Perc], [Stimulator Generator, Single Array, Stimulator Generator, Single Array Rechargeable, Stimulator Generator, Multi Array, Stimulator Generator, Multi Array Rechargeable], NQ

AND

ØØHU[Ø,3,4]MZ Insert/Spinal Canal, [Opn, Perc, Perc Endo], Neurostimulator Lead, NQ
ØØHV[Ø,3,4]MZ Insert/Spinal Cord, [Opn, Perc, Perc Endo], Neurostimulator Lead, NQ

DRG 030   Spinal Procedures without CC/MCC
GMLOS 2.6   AMLOS 3.3   RW 1.7982   [SP]

Select operating room procedures listed under DRG 028

DRG 031   Ventricular Shunt Procedures with MCC
GMLOS 7.4   AMLOS 1Ø.3   RW 3.7834   [T]

Operating Room Procedures

ØØ16[Ø,3][7,J,K][Ø,1,2,3,4,5,6,7,8] Bypass/Cerebral Ventricle, [Opn, Perc], [Auto Tissue Sub, Synth Sub, Nonauto Tissue Sub], [Nasopharynx, Mastoid Sinus, Atrium, Bld Vessel, Pleural Cavity, Intestine, Peritoneal Cavity, Urinary Tract, Bone Marrow]
ØØP6[Ø,3,4]JZ Rmvl/Cerebral Ventricle, [Opn, Perc, Perc Endo], Synth Sub, NQ
ØØW6[Ø,3,4]JZ Rev/Cerebral Ventricle, [Opn, Perc, Perc Endo], Synth Sub, NQ
ØW11* Bypass/Cranial Cavity

DRG 032   Ventricular Shunt Procedures with CC
GMLOS 3.3   AMLOS 4.7   RW 2.Ø352   [T]

Select operating room procedures listed under DRG 031

DRG 033   Ventricular Shunt Procedures without CC/MCC
GMLOS 2.Ø   AMLOS 2.5   RW 1.5734   [T]

Select operating room procedures listed under DRG 031

DRG 034   Carotid Artery Stent Procedure with MCC
GMLOS 4.8   AMLOS 7.1   RW 3.6851   [T]

Operating Room Procedures

037H[3,4][4,D,Z]Z Dilation/Common Carotid Artery, Rt, [Perc, Perc Endo], [Drug-eluting Intralum Dev, Intralum Dev, No Dev], NQ
037J[3,4][4,D,Z]Z Dilation/Common Carotid Artery, Lt, [Perc, Perc Endo], [Drug-eluting Intralum Dev, Intralum Dev, No Dev], NQ
037K[3,4][4,D,Z]Z Dilation/Int Carotid Artery, Rt, [Perc, Perc Endo], [Drug-eluting Intralum Dev, Intralum Dev, No Dev], NQ

[T] **Transfer DRG**   [SP] **Special Payment**   * **Code Range**   **6th and 7th Character of ZZ = No Device, No Qualifier ZX = No Device, Diagnostic**

037L[3,4][4,D,Z]Z Dilation/Int Carotid Artery, Lt, [Perc, Perc Endo], [Drug-eluting Intralum Dev, Intralum Dev, No Dev], NQ
037M[3,4][4,D,Z]Z Dilation/Ext Carotid Artery, Rt, [Perc, Perc Endo], [Drug-eluting Intralum Dev, Intralum Dev, No Dev], NQ
037N[3,4][4,D,Z]Z Dilation/Ext Carotid Artery, Lt, [Perc, Perc Endo], [Drug-eluting Intralum Dev, Intralum Dev, No Dev], NQ
037P[3,4][4,D,Z]Z Dilation/Vert Artery, Rt, [Perc, Perc Endo], [Drug-eluting Intralum Dev, Intralum Dev, No Dev], NQ
037Q[3,4][4,D,Z]Z Dilation/Vert Artery, Lt, [Perc, Perc Endo], [Drug-eluting Intralum Dev, Intralum Dev, No Dev], NQ
057M[3,4]DZ Dilation/Int Jugular Vein, Rt, [Perc, Perc Endo], Intralum Dev, NQ
057N[3,4]DZ Dilation/Int Jugular Vein, Lt, [Perc, Perc Endo], Intralum Dev, NQ
057P[3,4]DZ Dilation/Ext Jugular Vein, Rt, [Perc, Perc Endo], Intralum Dev, NQ
057Q[3,4]DZ Dilation/Ext Jugular Vein, Lt, [Perc, Perc Endo], Intralum Dev, NQ
057R[3,4]DZ Dilation/Vert Vein, Rt, [Perc, Perc Endo], Intralum Dev, NQ
057S[3,4]DZ Dilation/Vert Vein, Lt, [Perc, Perc Endo], Intralum Dev, NQ
057T[3,4]DZ Dilation/Face Vein, Rt, [Perc, Perc Endo], Intralum Dev, NQ
AND

Nonoperating Room Procedure

037H[3,4]DZ Dilation/Common Carotid Artery, Rt, [Perc, Perc Endo], Intralum Dev, NQ
037J[3,4]DZ Dilation/Common Carotid Artery, Lt, [Perc, Perc Endo], Intralum Dev, NQ
037K[3,4]DZ Dilation/Int Carotid Artery, Rt, [Perc, Perc Endo], Intralum Dev, NQ
037L[3,4]DZ Dilation/Int Carotid Artery, Lt, [Perc, Perc Endo], Intralum Dev, NQ
037M[3,4]DZ Dilation/Ext Carotid Artery, Rt, [Perc, Perc Endo], Intralum Dev, NQ
037N[3,4]DZ Dilation/Ext Carotid Artery, Lt, [Perc, Perc Endo], Intralum Dev, NQ

DRG 035 **Carotid Artery Stent Procedure with CC**
     GMLOS 2.1   AMLOS 3.2   RW 2.3048

Select operating AND nonoperating room procedures listed under DRG 034

DRG 036 **Carotid Artery Stent Procedure without CC/MCC**
     GMLOS 1.3   AMLOS 1.5   RW 1.7180

Select operating AND nonoperating room procedures listed under DRG 034

DRG 037 **Extracranial Procedures with MCC**
     GMLOS 5.3   AMLOS 7.8   RW 3.0888

Operating Room Procedures

021W[0,4][9,A,J,K,Z][B,D] Bypass/Thoracic Aorta, [Opn, Perc Endo], [Auto Venous Tissue, Auto Arterial Tissue, Synth Sub, Nonauto Tissue Sub, No Dev], [Subclavian, Carotid]
03150[9,A,J,K,Z]0 Bypass/Axillary Artery, Rt, Opn, [Auto Venous Tissue, Auto Arterial Tissue, Synth Sub, Nonauto Tissue Sub, No Dev], Upr Arm Artery, Rt
03160[9,A,J,K,Z]1 Bypass/Axillary Artery, Lt, Opn, [Auto Venous Tissue, Auto Arterial Tissue, Synth Sub, Nonauto Tissue Sub, No Dev], Upr Arm Artery, Lt
031H0[9,A,J,K,Z]J Bypass Rt Common Carotid Artery, Opn, to Rt Extracranial Artery [Auto Venous Tissue, Auto Arterial Tissue, Synth Sub, Nonauto Tissue Sub, NQ]
031J0[9,A,J,K,Z]K Bypass Lt Common Carotid Artery, Opn, to Lt Extracranial Artery [Auto Venous Tissue, Auto Arterial Tissue, Synth Sub, Nonauto Tissue Sub, NQ]
031K0[9,A,J,K,Z]J Bypass Rt Int Carotid Artery, Opn, to Rt Extracranial Artery [Auto Venous Tissue, Auto Arterial Tissue, Synth Sub, Nonauto Tissue Sub, NQ]
031L0[9,A,J,K,Z]K Bypass Lt Int Carotid Artery, Opn, to Lt Extracranial Artery [Auto Venous Tissue, Auto Arterial Tissue, Synth Sub, Nonauto Tissue Sub, NQ]
031M0[9,A,J,K,Z]J Bypass Rt Ext Carotid Artery, Opn, to Rt Extracranial Artery [Auto Venous Tissue, Auto Arterial Tissue, Synth Sub, Nonauto Tissue Sub, NQ]

031N0[9,A,J,K,Z]K Bypass Lt Ext Carotid Artery, Opn, to Lt Extracranial Artery [Auto Venous Tissue, Auto Arterial Tissue, Synth Sub, Nonauto Tissue Sub, NQ]
035H* Destr/Common Carotid Artery, Rt
035J* Destr/Common Carotid Artery, Lt
035K* Destr/Int Carotid Artery, Rt
035L* Destr/Int Carotid Artery, Lt
035M* Destr/Ext Carotid Artery, Rt
035N* Destr/Ext Carotid Artery, Lt
035P* Destr/Vert Artery, Rt
035Q* Destr/Vert Artery, Lt
035R* Destr/Face Artery
035S* Destr/Temporal Artery, Rt
035T* Destr/Temporal Artery, Lt
035U* Destr/Thyroid Artery, Rt
035V* Destr/Thyroid Artery, Lt
03733[4,D,Z]Z Dilation/Subclavian Artery, Rt, Perc, [Drug-eluting Intralum Dev, Intralum Dev, No Dev], NQ
03743[4,D,Z]Z Dilation/Subclavian Artery, Lt, Perc, [Drug-eluting Intralum Dev, Intralum Dev, No Dev], NQ
03773[4,D,Z]Z Dilation/Brachial Artery, Rt, Perc, [Drug-eluting Intralum Dev, Intralum Dev, No Dev], NQ
03783[4,D,Z]Z Dilation/Brachial Artery, Lt, Perc, [Drug-eluting Intralum Dev, Intralum Dev, No Dev], NQ
03793[4,D,Z]Z Dilation/Ulnar Artery, Rt, Perc, [Drug-eluting Intralum Dev, Intralum Dev, No Dev], NQ
037A3[4,D,Z]Z Dilation/Ulnar Artery, Lt, Perc, [Drug-eluting Intralum Dev, Intralum Dev, No Dev], NQ
037H[3,4][4,D,Z]Z Dilation/Common Carotid Artery, Rt, [Perc, Perc Endo], [Drug-eluting Intralum Dev, Intralum Dev, No Dev], NQ
037J[3,4][4,D,Z]Z Dilation/Common Carotid Artery, Lt, [Perc, Perc Endo], [Drug-eluting Intralum Dev, Intralum Dev, No Dev], NQ
037K[3,4][4,D,Z]Z Dilation/Int Carotid Artery, Rt, [Perc, Perc Endo], [Drug-eluting Intralum Dev, Intralum Dev, No Dev], NQ
037L[3,4][4,D,Z]Z Dilation/Int Carotid Artery, Lt, [Perc, Perc Endo], [Drug-eluting Intralum Dev, Intralum Dev, No Dev], NQ
037M[3,4][4,D,Z]Z Dilation/Ext Carotid Artery, Rt, [Perc, Perc Endo], [Drug-eluting Intralum Dev, Intralum Dev, No Dev], NQ
037N[3,4][4,D,Z]Z Dilation/Ext Carotid Artery, Lt, [Perc, Perc Endo], [Drug-eluting Intralum Dev, Intralum Dev, No Dev], NQ
037P[3,4][4,D,Z]Z Dilation/Vert Artery, Rt, [Perc, Perc Endo], [Drug-eluting Intralum Dev, Intralum Dev, No Dev], NQ
037Q[3,4][4,D,Z]Z Dilation/Vert Artery, Lt, [Perc, Perc Endo], [Drug-eluting Intralum Dev, Intralum Dev, No Dev], NQ
037Y3[4,D,Z]Z Dilation/Upr Artery, Perc, [Drug-eluting Intralum Dev, Intralum Dev, No Dev], NQ
03BH[0,3,4]ZZ Exc/Common Carotid Artery, Rt, [Opn, Perc, Perc Endo]
03BJ[0,3,4]ZZ Exc/Common Carotid Artery, Lt, [Opn, Perc, Perc Endo]
03BK[0,3,4]ZZ Exc/Int Carotid Artery, Rt, [Opn, Perc, Perc Endo]
03BL[0,3,4]ZZ Exc/Int Carotid Artery, Lt, [Opn, Perc, Perc Endo]
03BM[0,3,4]ZZ Exc/Ext Carotid Artery, Rt, [Opn, Perc, Perc Endo]
03BN[0,3,4]ZZ Exc/Ext Carotid Artery, Lt, [Opn, Perc, Perc Endo]
03BP[0,3,4]ZZ Exc/Vert Artery, Rt, [Opn, Perc, Perc Endo]
03BQ[0,3,4]ZZ Exc/Vert Artery, Lt, [Opn, Perc, Perc Endo]
03BR[0,3,4]ZZ Exc/Face Artery, [Opn, Perc, Perc Endo]
03BS[0,3,4]ZZ Exc/Temporal Artery, Rt, [Opn, Perc, Perc Endo]
03BT[0,3,4]ZZ Exc/Temporal Artery, Lt, [Opn, Perc, Perc Endo]
03BU[0,3,4]ZZ Exc/Thyroid Artery, Rt, [Opn, Perc, Perc Endo]
03BV[0,3,4]ZZ Exc/Thyroid Artery, Lt, [Opn, Perc, Perc Endo]
03CY* Extir/Upr Artery
03C[H,J,K,L,M,N]0ZZ Extir [Rt Common Carotid, Lt Common Carotid, Rt Int Carotid, Lt Int Carotid, Rt Ext Carotid, Lt Ext Carotid] Artery, Opn
03C[P,Q,R,S,T,U,V]0ZZ Extir [Rt Vert, Lt Vert, Face, Rt Temporal, Lt Temporal, Rt Thyroid, Lt Thyroid] Artery, Opn
03QH* Repair/Common Carotid Artery, Rt
03QJ* Repair/Common Carotid Artery, Lt
03QK* Repair/Int Carotid Artery, Rt
03QL* Repair/Int Carotid Artery, Lt
03QM* Repair/Ext Carotid Artery, Rt
03QN* Repair/Ext Carotid Artery, Lt
03QP* Repair/Vert Artery, Rt
03QQ* Repair/Vert Artery, Lt
03QR* Repair/Face Artery
03QS* Repair/Temporal Artery, Rt
03QT* Repair/Temporal Artery, Lt
03SH* Repos/Common Carotid Artery, Rt
03SJ* Repos/Common Carotid Artery, Lt
03SK* Repos/Int Carotid Artery, Rt
03SL* Repos/Int Carotid Artery, Lt

Surgical   **Medical**   **CC Indicator**   **MCC Indicator**   **Procedure Proxy**   **PDxMCC** **PDx acts as own MCC**   **PDxCC** **PDx acts as own CC**

Code	Description
03SM*	Repos/Ext Carotid Artery, Rt
03SN*	Repos/Ext Carotid Artery, Lt
03SP*	Repos/Vert Artery, Rt
03SQ*	Repos/Vert Artery, Lt
03SR*	Repos/Face Artery
03SS*	Repos/Temporal Artery, Rt
03ST*	Repos/Temporal Artery, Lt
03UH[0,3,4][7,J]Z	Supl/Common Carotid Artery, Rt, [Opn, Perc, Perc Endo], [Auto Tissue Sub, Synth Sub], NQ
03UJ[0,3,4][7,J]Z	Supl/Common Carotid Artery, Lt, [Opn, Perc, Perc Endo], [Auto Tissue Sub, Synth Sub], NQ
03UK[0,3,4][7,J]Z	Supl/Int Carotid Artery, Rt, [Opn, Perc, Perc Endo], [Auto Tissue Sub, Synth Sub], NQ
03UL[0,3,4][7,J]Z	Supl/Int Carotid Artery, Lt, [Opn, Perc, Perc Endo], [Auto Tissue Sub, Synth Sub], NQ
03UM[0,3,4][7,J]Z	Supl/Ext Carotid Artery, Rt, [Opn, Perc, Perc Endo], [Auto Tissue Sub, Synth Sub], NQ
03UN[0,3,4][7,J]Z	Supl/Ext Carotid Artery, Lt, [Opn, Perc, Perc Endo], [Auto Tissue Sub, Synth Sub], NQ
03UP[0,3,4][7,J]Z	Supl/Vert Artery, Rt, [Opn, Perc, Perc Endo], [Auto Tissue Sub, Synth Sub], NQ
03UQ[0,3,4][7,J]Z	Supl/Vert Artery, Lt, [Opn, Perc, Perc Endo], [Auto Tissue Sub, Synth Sub], NQ
041K[0,4][9,A,J,K,Z][H,J,K,L]	Bypass/Femor Artery, Rt, [Opn, Perc Endo], [Auto Venous Tissue, Auto Arterial Tissue, Synth Sub, Nonauto Tissue Sub, No Dev], [Femor Artery, Rt, Femor Artery, Lt, Femor Arteries, Bilat, Popliteal Artery]
041L[0,4][9,A,J,K,Z][H,J,K,L]	Bypass/Femor Artery, Lt, [Opn, Perc Endo], [Auto Venous Tissue, Auto Arterial Tissue, Synth Sub, Nonauto Tissue Sub, No Dev], [Femor Artery, Rt, Femor Artery, Lt, Femor Arteries, Bilat, Popliteal Artery]
04703[4,D,Z]Z	Dilation/Abd Aorta, Perc, [Drug-eluting Intralum Dev, Intralum Dev, No Dev], NQ
04713[4,D,Z]Z	Dilation/Celiac Artery, Perc, [Drug-eluting Intralum Dev, Intralum Dev, No Dev], NQ
04723[4,D,Z]Z	Dilation/Gastric Artery, Perc, [Drug-eluting Intralum Dev, Intralum Dev, No Dev], NQ
04733[4,D,Z]Z	Dilation/Hepatic Artery, Perc, [Drug-eluting Intralum Dev, Intralum Dev, No Dev], NQ
04743[4,D,Z]Z	Dilation/Splenic Artery, Perc, [Drug-eluting Intralum Dev, Intralum Dev, No Dev], NQ
04753[4,D,Z]Z	Dilation/Superior Mesenteric Artery, Perc, [Drug-eluting Intralum Dev, Intralum Dev, No Dev], NQ
04763[4,D,Z]Z	Dilation/Colic Artery, Rt, Perc, [Drug-eluting Intralum Dev, Intralum Dev, No Dev], NQ
04773[4,D,Z]Z	Dilation/Colic Artery, Lt, Perc, [Drug-eluting Intralum Dev, Intralum Dev, No Dev], NQ
04783[4,D,Z]Z	Dilation/Colic Artery, Mid, Perc, [Drug-eluting Intralum Dev, Intralum Dev, No Dev], NQ
04793[4,D,Z]Z	Dilation/Renal Artery, Rt, Perc, [Drug-eluting Intralum Dev, Intralum Dev, No Dev], NQ
047A3[4,D,Z]Z	Dilation/Renal Artery, Lt, Perc, [Drug-eluting Intralum Dev, Intralum Dev, No Dev], NQ
047B3[4,D,Z]Z	Dilation/Inferior Mesenteric Artery, Perc, [Drug-eluting Intralum Dev, Intralum Dev, No Dev], NQ
047C3[4,D,Z]Z	Dilation/Common Iliac Artery, Rt, Perc, [Drug-eluting Intralum Dev, Intralum Dev, No Dev], NQ
047D3[4,D,Z]Z	Dilation/Common Iliac Artery, Lt, Perc, [Drug-eluting Intralum Dev, Intralum Dev, No Dev], NQ
047E3[4,D,Z]Z	Dilation/Int Iliac Artery, Rt, Perc, [Drug-eluting Intralum Dev, Intralum Dev, No Dev], NQ
047F3[4,D,Z]Z	Dilation/Int Iliac Artery, Lt, Perc, [Drug-eluting Intralum Dev, Intralum Dev, No Dev], NQ
047H3[4,D,Z]Z	Dilation/Ext Iliac Artery, Rt, Perc, [Drug-eluting Intralum Dev, Intralum Dev, No Dev], NQ
047J3[4,D,Z]Z	Dilation/Ext Iliac Artery, Lt, Perc, [Drug-eluting Intralum Dev, Intralum Dev, No Dev], NQ
047K041	Dilation Rt Fem Art w Drug-elut Intralum, Drug Blln, Opn
047K0D1	Dilation Rt Fem Art w Intralum Dev, Drug Blln, Opn
047K0Z1	Dilation of Rt Fem Art using Drug Blln, Opn Appr
047K341	Dilation Rt Fem Art w Drug-elut Intralum, Drug Blln, Perc
047K3D1	Dilation Rt Fem Art w Intralum Dev, Drug Blln, Perc
047K3Z1	Dilation of Rt Fem Art using Drug Blln, Perc Appr
047K3[4,D,Z]Z	Dilation/Femor Artery, Rt, Perc, [Drug-eluting Intralum Dev, Intralum Dev, No Dev], NQ
047K441	Dilation Rt Fem Art w Drug-elut Intralum, Drug Blln, Perc Endo
047K4D1	Dilation Rt Fem Art w Intralum Dev, Drug Blln, Perc Endo
047K4Z1	Dilation of Rt Fem Art using Drug Blln, Perc Endo Appr
047L041	Dilation Lt Fem Art w Drug-elut Intralum, Drug Blln, Opn
047L0D1	Dilation Lt Fem Art w Intralum Dev, Drug Blln, Opn
047L0Z1	Dilation of Lt Fem Art using Drug Blln, Opn Appr
047L341	Dilation Lt Fem Art w Drug-elut Intralum, Drug Blln, Perc
047L3D1	Dilation Lt Fem Art w Intralum Dev, Drug Blln, Perc
047L3Z1	Dilation of Lt Fem Art using Drug Blln, Perc Appr
047L3[4,D,Z]Z	Dilation/Femor Artery, Lt, Perc, [Drug-eluting Intralum Dev, Intralum Dev, No Dev], NQ
047L441	Dilation Lt Fem Art w Drug-elut Intralum, Drug Blln, Perc Endo
047L4D1	Dilation Lt Fem Art w Intralum Dev, Drug Blln, Perc Endo
047L4Z1	Dilation of Lt Fem Art using Drug Blln, Perc Endo Appr
047M041	Dilation Rt Popl Art w Drug-elut Intralum, Drug Blln, Opn
047M0D1	Dilation Rt Popl Art w Intralum Dev, Drug Blln, Opn
047M0Z1	Dilation of Rt Popl Art using Drug Blln, Opn Appr
047M341	Dilation Rt Popl Art w Drug-elut Intralum, Drug Blln, Perc
047M3D1	Dilation Rt Popl Art w Intralum Dev, Drug Blln, Perc
047M3Z1	Dilation of Rt Popl Art using Drug Blln, Perc Appr
047M441	Dilation Rt Popl Art w Drug-elut Intralum, Drug Blln, Perc Endo
047M4D1	Dilation Rt Popl Art w Intralum Dev, Drug Blln, Perc Endo
047M4Z1	Dilation of Rt Popl Art using Drug Blln, Perc Endo Appr
047N041	Dilation Lt Popl Art w Drug-elut Intralum, Drug Blln, Opn
047N0D1	Dilation Lt Popl Art w Intralum Dev, Drug Blln, Opn
047N0Z1	Dilation of Lt Popl Art using Drug Blln, Opn Appr
047N341	Dilation Lt Popl Art w Drug-elut Intralum, Drug Blln, Perc
047N3D1	Dilation Lt Popl Art w Intralum Dev, Drug Blln, Perc
047N3Z1	Dilation of Lt Popl Art using Drug Blln, Perc Appr
047N441	Dilation Lt Popl Art w Drug-elut Intralum, Drug Blln, Perc Endo
047N4D1	Dilation Lt Popl Art w Intralum Dev, Drug Blln, Perc Endo
047N4Z1	Dilation of Lt Popl Art using Drug Blln, Perc Endo Appr
047Y3[4,D,Z]Z	Dilation/Lwr Artery, Perc, [Drug-eluting Intralum Dev, Intralum Dev, No Dev], NQ
04CY*	Extir/Lwr Artery
04V0[0,3,4]DJ	Restrict/Abd Aorta, [Opn, Perc, Perc Endo], Intralum Dev, Temporary
055M*	Destr/Int Jugular Vein, Rt
055N*	Destr/Int Jugular Vein, Lt
055P*	Destr/Ext Jugular Vein, Rt
055Q*	Destr/Ext Jugular Vein, Lt
055R*	Destr/Vert Vein, Rt
055S*	Destr/Vert Vein, Lt
055T*	Destr/Face Vein, Rt
055V*	Destr/Face Vein, Lt
05793[D,Z]Z	Dilation/Brachial Vein, Rt, Perc, [Intralum Dev, No Dev], NQ
057A3[D,Z]Z	Dilation/Brachial Vein, Lt, Perc, [Intralum Dev, No Dev], NQ
057B3[D,Z]Z	Dilation/Basilic Vein, Rt, Perc, [Intralum Dev, No Dev], NQ
057C3[D,Z]Z	Dilation/Basilic Vein, Lt, Perc, [Intralum Dev, No Dev], NQ
057D3[D,Z]Z	Dilation/Cephalic Vein, Rt, Perc, [Intralum Dev, No Dev], NQ
057F3[D,Z]Z	Dilation/Cephalic Vein, Lt, Perc, [Intralum Dev, No Dev], NQ
057M[3,4]DZ	Dilation/Int Jugular Vein, Rt, [Perc, Perc Endo], Intralum Dev, NQ
057N[3,4]DZ	Dilation/Int Jugular Vein, Lt, [Perc, Perc Endo], Intralum Dev, NQ
057P[3,4]DZ	Dilation/Ext Jugular Vein, Rt, [Perc, Perc Endo], Intralum Dev, NQ
057Q[3,4]DZ	Dilation/Ext Jugular Vein, Lt, [Perc, Perc Endo], Intralum Dev, NQ
057R[3,4]DZ	Dilation/Vert Vein, Rt, [Perc, Perc Endo], Intralum Dev, NQ
057S[3,4]DZ	Dilation/Vert Vein, Lt, [Perc, Perc Endo], Intralum Dev, NQ
057T[3,4]DZ	Dilation/Face Vein, Rt, [Perc, Perc Endo], Intralum Dev, NQ
05BM[0,3,4]ZZ	Exc/Int Jugular Vein, Rt, [Opn, Perc, Perc Endo]
05BN[0,3,4]ZZ	Exc/Int Jugular Vein, Lt, [Opn, Perc, Perc Endo]
05BP[0,3,4]ZZ	Exc/Ext Jugular Vein, Rt, [Opn, Perc, Perc Endo]
05BQ[0,3,4]ZZ	Exc/Ext Jugular Vein, Lt, [Opn, Perc, Perc Endo]
05BR[0,3,4]ZZ	Exc/Vert Vein, Rt, [Opn, Perc, Perc Endo]
05BS[0,3,4]ZZ	Exc/Vert Vein, Lt, [Opn, Perc, Perc Endo]
05BT[0,3,4]ZZ	Exc/Face Vein, Rt, [Opn, Perc, Perc Endo]
05BV[0,3,4]ZZ	Exc/Face Vein, Lt, [Opn, Perc, Perc Endo]
05QR*	Repair/Vert Vein, Rt
05QS*	Repair/Vert Vein, Lt
05UR[0,3,4][7,J]Z	Supl/Vert Vein, Rt, [Opn, Perc, Perc Endo], [Auto Tissue Sub, Synth Sub], NQ
05US[0,3,4][7,J]Z	Supl/Vert Vein, Lt, [Opn, Perc, Perc Endo], [Auto Tissue Sub, Synth Sub], NQ
0653*	Destr/Esophageal Vein
06703[D,Z]Z	Dilation/Inferior Vena Cava, Perc, [Intralum Dev, No Dev], NQ
06B3[0,3,4]ZZ	Exc/Esophageal Vein, [Opn, Perc, Perc Endo]
3E03[0,3]TZ	Introduction/Peripheral Vein, [Opn, Perc], Destr Agent, NQ
3E04[0,3]TZ	Introduction/Central Vein, [Opn, Perc], Destr Agent, NQ

T Transfer DRG   SP Special Payment   * Code Range   6th and 7th Character of ZZ = No Device, No Qualifier ZX = No Device, Diagnostic

DRG 038 **Extracranial Procedures with CC**
GMLOS 2.3   AMLOS 3.2   RW 1.5560

Select operating room procedures listed under DRG 037

DRG 039 **Extracranial Procedures without CC/MCC**
GMLOS 1.3   AMLOS 1.6   RW 1.0609

Select operating room procedures listed under DRG 037

DRG 040 **Peripheral/Cranial Nerve and Other Nervous System Procedures with MCC**
GMLOS 8.2   AMLOS 10.8   RW 3.8044   SP

Operating Room Procedures

008F*	Div/Olfactory Nerve
008G*	Div/Optic Nerve
008H*	Div/Oculomotor Nerve
008J*	Div/Trochlear Nerve
008K*	Div/Trigeminal Nerve
008L*	Div/Abducens Nerve
008M*	Div/Facial Nerve
008N*	Div/Acoustic Nerve
008Q*	Div/Vagus Nerve
008R*	Div/Accessory Nerve
008S*	Div/Hypoglossal Nerve
009F0ZX	Drain of Olfactory Nerve, Opn Appr, Diagnostic
009F[0,3,4][0,Z]Z	Drain/Olfactory Nerve, [Opn, Perc, Perc Endo], [Drain Dev, No Dev], NQ
009G0ZX	Drain of Optic Nerve, Opn Appr, Diagnostic
009G[0,3,4][0,Z]Z	Drain/Optic Nerve, [Opn, Perc, Perc Endo], [Drain Dev, No Dev], NQ
009H0ZX	Drain of Oculomotor Nerve, Opn Appr, Diagnostic
009H[0,3,4][0,Z]Z	Drain/Oculomotor Nerve, [Opn, Perc, Perc Endo], [Drain Dev, No Dev], NQ
009J0ZX	Drain of Trochlear Nerve, Opn Appr, Diagnostic
009J[0,3,4][0,Z]Z	Drain/Trochlear Nerve, [Opn, Perc, Perc Endo], [Drain Dev, No Dev], NQ
009K0ZX	Drain of Trigeminal Nerve, Opn Appr, Diagnostic
009K[0,3,4][0,Z]Z	Drain/Trigeminal Nerve, [Opn, Perc, Perc Endo], [Drain Dev, No Dev], NQ
009L0ZX	Drain of Abducens Nerve, Opn Appr, Diagnostic
009L[0,3,4][0,Z]Z	Drain/Abducens Nerve, [Opn, Perc, Perc Endo], [Drain Dev, No Dev], NQ
009M0ZX	Drain of Facial Nerve, Opn Appr, Diagnostic
009M[0,3,4][0,Z]Z	Drain/Facial Nerve, [Opn, Perc, Perc Endo], [Drain Dev, No Dev], NQ
009N0ZX	Drain of Acoustic Nerve, Opn Appr, Diagnostic
009N[0,3,4][0,Z]Z	Drain/Acoustic Nerve, [Opn, Perc, Perc Endo], [Drain Dev, No Dev], NQ
009P0ZX	Drain of Glossopharyngeal Nerve, Opn Appr, Diagn
009P[0,3,4][0,Z]Z	Drain/Glossopharyngeal Nerve, [Opn, Perc, Perc Endo], [Drain Dev, No Dev], NQ
009Q0ZX	Drain of Vagus Nerve, Opn Appr, Diagnostic
009Q[0,3,4][0,Z]Z	Drain/Vagus Nerve, [Opn, Perc, Perc Endo], [Drain Dev, No Dev], NQ
009R0ZX	Drain of Accessory Nerve, Opn Appr, Diagnostic
009R[0,3,4][0,Z]Z	Drain/Accessory Nerve, [Opn, Perc, Perc Endo], [Drain Dev, No Dev], NQ
009S0ZX	Drain of Hypoglossal Nerve, Opn Appr, Diagnostic
009S[0,3,4][0,Z]Z	Drain/Hypoglossal Nerve, [Opn, Perc, Perc Endo], [Drain Dev, No Dev], NQ
00BF0ZX	Exc of Olfactory Nerve, Opn Appr, Diagnostic
00BF[0,3,4]ZZ	Exc/Olfactory Nerve, [Opn, Perc, Perc Endo]
00BG0ZX	Exc of Optic Nerve, Opn Appr, Diagnostic
00BG[0,3,4]ZZ	Exc/Optic Nerve, [Opn, Perc, Perc Endo]
00BH0ZX	Exc of Oculomotor Nerve, Opn Appr, Diagnostic
00BH[0,3,4]ZZ	Exc/Oculomotor Nerve, [Opn, Perc, Perc Endo]
00BJ0ZX	Exc of Trochlear Nerve, Opn Appr, Diagnostic
00BJ[0,3,4]ZZ	Exc/Trochlear Nerve, [Opn, Perc, Perc Endo]
00BK0ZX	Exc of Trigeminal Nerve, Opn Appr, Diagnostic
00BK[0,3,4]ZZ	Exc/Trigeminal Nerve, [Opn, Perc, Perc Endo]
00BL0ZX	Exc of Abducens Nerve, Opn Appr, Diagnostic
00BL[0,3,4]ZZ	Exc/Abducens Nerve, [Opn, Perc, Perc Endo]
00BM0ZX	Exc of Facial Nerve, Opn Appr, Diagnostic
00BM[0,3,4]ZZ	Exc/Facial Nerve, [Opn, Perc, Perc Endo]
00BN0ZX	Exc of Acoustic Nerve, Opn Appr, Diagnostic
00BN[3,4]ZZ	Exc/Acoustic Nerve, [Perc, Perc Endo]
00BP0ZX	Exc of Glossopharyngeal Nerve, Opn Appr, Diagn
00BP[0,3,4]ZZ	Exc/Glossopharyngeal Nerve, [Opn, Perc, Perc Endo]
00BQ0ZX	Exc of Vagus Nerve, Opn Appr, Diagnostic
00BQ[0,3,4]ZZ	Exc/Vagus Nerve, [Opn, Perc, Perc Endo]
00BR0ZX	Exc of Accessory Nerve, Opn Appr, Diagnostic
00BR[0,3,4]ZZ	Exc/Accessory Nerve, [Opn, Perc, Perc Endo]
00BS0ZX	Exc of Hypoglossal Nerve, Opn Appr, Diagnostic
00BS[0,3,4]ZZ	Exc/Hypoglossal Nerve, [Opn, Perc, Perc Endo]
00CF*	Extir/Olfactory Nerve
00CG*	Extir/Optic Nerve
00CH*	Extir/Oculomotor Nerve
00CJ*	Extir/Trochlear Nerve
00CK*	Extir/Trigeminal Nerve
00CL*	Extir/Abducens Nerve
00CM*	Extir/Facial Nerve
00CN*	Extir/Acoustic Nerve
00CP*	Extir/Glossopharyngeal Nerve
00CQ*	Extir/Vagus Nerve
00CR*	Extir/Accessory Nerve
00CS*	Extir/Hypoglossal Nerve
00DF*	Extract/Olfactory Nerve
00DG*	Extract/Optic Nerve
00DH*	Extract/Oculomotor Nerve
00DJ*	Extract/Trochlear Nerve
00DK*	Extract/Trigeminal Nerve
00DL*	Extract/Abducens Nerve
00DM*	Extract/Facial Nerve
00DN*	Extract/Acoustic Nerve
00DP*	Extract/Glossopharyngeal Nerve
00DQ*	Extract/Vagus Nerve
00DR*	Extract/Accessory Nerve
00DS*	Extract/Hypoglossal Nerve
00HE*	Insert/Cranial Nerve
00JE*	Inspect/Cranial Nerve
00NF*	Rls/Olfactory Nerve
00NG*	Rls/Optic Nerve
00NH*	Rls/Oculomotor Nerve
00NJ*	Rls/Trochlear Nerve
00NL*	Rls/Abducens Nerve
00NM*	Rls/Facial Nerve
00NN*	Rls/Acoustic Nerve
00NP*	Rls/Glossopharyngeal Nerve
00NQ*	Rls/Vagus Nerve
00NR*	Rls/Accessory Nerve
00NS*	Rls/Hypoglossal Nerve
00PEXMZ	Rmvl of Neuro Lead from Cranial Nrv, Extern Appr
00PE[0,3,4][0,2,3,7,M]Z	Rmvl/Cranial Nerve, [Opn, Perc, Perc Endo], [Drain Dev, Monitoring Dev, Inf Dev, Auto Tissue Sub, Neurostimulator Lead], NQ
00QF*	Repair/Olfactory Nerve
00QG*	Repair/Optic Nerve
00QH*	Repair/Oculomotor Nerve
00QJ*	Repair/Trochlear Nerve
00QK*	Repair/Trigeminal Nerve
00QL*	Repair/Abducens Nerve
00QM*	Repair/Facial Nerve
00QN*	Repair/Acoustic Nerve
00QP*	Repair/Glossopharyngeal Nerve
00QQ*	Repair/Vagus Nerve
00QR*	Repair/Accessory Nerve
00QS*	Repair/Hypoglossal Nerve
00SF*	Repos/Olfactory Nerve
00SG*	Repos/Optic Nerve
00SH*	Repos/Oculomotor Nerve
00SJ*	Repos/Trochlear Nerve
00SK*	Repos/Trigeminal Nerve
00SL*	Repos/Abducens Nerve
00SM*	Repos/Facial Nerve
00SN*	Repos/Acoustic Nerve
00SP*	Repos/Glossopharyngeal Nerve
00SQ*	Repos/Vagus Nerve
00SR*	Repos/Accessory Nerve
00SS*	Repos/Hypoglossal Nerve
00UF*	Supl/Olfactory Nerve
00UG*	Supl/Optic Nerve
00UH*	Supl/Oculomotor Nerve
00UJ*	Supl/Trochlear Nerve
00UK*	Supl/Trigeminal Nerve
00UL*	Supl/Abducens Nerve
00UM*	Supl/Facial Nerve
00UN*	Supl/Acoustic Nerve

Surgical	Medical	CC Indicator	MCC Indicator	Procedure Proxy	PDxMCC PDx acts as own MCC	PDxCC PDx acts as own CC

Code	Description
00UP*	Supl/Glossopharyngeal Nerve
00UQ*	Supl/Vagus Nerve
00UR*	Supl/Accessory Nerve
00US*	Supl/Hypoglossal Nerve
00WE[0,3,4][0,2,3,7,M]Z	Rev/Cranial Nerve, [Opn, Perc, Perc Endo], [Drain Dev, Monitoring Dev, Inf Dev, Auto Tissue Sub, Neurostimulator Lead], NQ
00X*	Central Nervous Sys, Transfer
015K*	Destr/Head and Neck Sympathetic Nerve
015L*	Destr/Thoracic Sympathetic Nerve
015M*	Destr/Abd Sympathetic Nerve
015N*	Destr/Lumbar Sympathetic Nerve
015P*	Destr/Sacral Sympathetic Nerve
0180*	Div/Cervical Plexus
0182*	Div/Phrenic Nerve
0183*	Div/Brachial Plexus
0184*	Div/Ulnar Nerve
0185*	Div/Median Nerve
0186*	Div/Radial Nerve
0189*	Div/Lumbar Plexus
018A*	Div/Lumbosacral Plexus
018C*	Div/Pudendal Nerve
018D*	Div/Femor Nerve
018F*	Div/Sciatic Nerve
018G*	Div/Tibial Nerve
018H*	Div/Peroneal Nerve
018K*	Div/Head and Neck Sympathetic Nerve
018L*	Div/Thoracic Sympathetic Nerve
018M*	Div/Abd Sympathetic Nerve
018N*	Div/Lumbar Sympathetic Nerve
018P*	Div/Sacral Sympathetic Nerve
018Q*	Div/Sacral Plexus
0190ZX	Drain of Cervical Plexus, Opn Appr, Diagnostic
0190[0,3,4][0,Z]Z	Drain/Cervical Plexus, [Opn, Perc, Perc Endo], [Drain Dev, No Dev], NQ
0191ZX	Drain of Cervical Nerve, Opn Appr, Diagnostic
0191[0,3,4][0,Z]Z	Drain/Cervical Nerve, [Opn, Perc, Perc Endo], [Drain Dev, No Dev], NQ
0192ZX	Drain of Phrenic Nerve, Opn Appr, Diagnostic
0192[0,3,4][0,Z]Z	Drain/Phrenic Nerve, [Opn, Perc, Perc Endo], [Drain Dev, No Dev], NQ
0193ZX	Drain of Brachial Plexus, Opn Appr, Diagnostic
0193[0,3,4][0,Z]Z	Drain/Brachial Plexus, [Opn, Perc, Perc Endo], [Drain Dev, No Dev], NQ
0194ZX	Drain of Ulnar Nerve, Opn Appr, Diagnostic
0194[0,3,4][0,Z]Z	Drain/Ulnar Nerve, [Opn, Perc, Perc Endo], [Drain Dev, No Dev], NQ
0195ZX	Drain of Median Nerve, Opn Appr, Diagnostic
0195[0,3,4][0,Z]Z	Drain/Median Nerve, [Opn, Perc, Perc Endo], [Drain Dev, No Dev], NQ
0196ZX	Drain of Radial Nerve, Opn Appr, Diagnostic
0196[0,3,4][0,Z]Z	Drain/Radial Nerve, [Opn, Perc, Perc Endo], [Drain Dev, No Dev], NQ
0198ZX	Drain of Thoracic Nerve, Opn Appr, Diagnostic
0198[0,3,4][0,Z]Z	Drain/Thoracic Nerve, [Opn, Perc, Perc Endo], [Drain Dev, No Dev], NQ
0199ZX	Drain of Lumbar Plexus, Opn Appr, Diagnostic
0199[0,3,4][0,Z]Z	Drain/Lumbar Plexus, [Opn, Perc, Perc Endo], [Drain Dev, No Dev], NQ
019A0ZX	Drain of Lumbosacral Plexus, Opn Appr, Diagnostic
019A[0,3,4][0,Z]Z	Drain/Lumbosacral Plexus, [Opn, Perc, Perc Endo], [Drain Dev, No Dev], NQ
019B0ZX	Drain of Lumbar Nerve, Opn Appr, Diagnostic
019B[0,3,4][0,Z]Z	Drain/Lumbar Nerve, [Opn, Perc, Perc Endo], [Drain Dev, No Dev], NQ
019C0ZX	Drain of Pudendal Nerve, Opn Appr, Diagnostic
019C[0,3,4][0,Z]Z	Drain/Pudendal Nerve, [Opn, Perc, Perc Endo], [Drain Dev, No Dev], NQ
019D0ZX	Drain of Femor Nerve, Opn Appr, Diagnostic
019D[0,3,4][0,Z]Z	Drain/Femor Nerve, [Opn, Perc, Perc Endo], [Drain Dev, No Dev], NQ
019F0ZX	Drain of Sciatic Nerve, Opn Appr, Diagnostic
019F[0,3,4][0,Z]Z	Drain/Sciatic Nerve, [Opn, Perc, Perc Endo], [Drain Dev, No Dev], NQ
019G0ZX	Drain of Tibial Nerve, Opn Appr, Diagnostic
019G[0,3,4][0,Z]Z	Drain/Tibial Nerve, [Opn, Perc, Perc Endo], [Drain Dev, No Dev], NQ
019H0ZX	Drain of Peroneal Nerve, Opn Appr, Diagnostic
019H[0,3,4][0,Z]Z	Drain/Peroneal Nerve, [Opn, Perc, Perc Endo], [Drain Dev, No Dev], NQ
019K*	Drain/Head and Neck Sympathetic Nerve
019L*	Drain/Thoracic Sympathetic Nerve
019M*	Drain/Abd Sympathetic Nerve
019N*	Drain/Lumbar Sympathetic Nerve
019P*	Drain/Sacral Sympathetic Nerve
019Q0ZX	Drain of Sacral Plexus, Opn Appr, Diagnostic
019Q[0,3,4][0,Z]Z	Drain/Sacral Plexus, [Opn, Perc, Perc Endo], [Drain Dev, No Dev], NQ
019R0ZX	Drain of Sacral Nerve, Opn Appr, Diagnostic
019R[0,3,4][0,Z]Z	Drain/Sacral Nerve, [Opn, Perc, Perc Endo], [Drain Dev, No Dev], NQ
01B00ZX	Exc of Cervical Plexus, Opn Appr, Diagnostic
01B0[0,3,4]ZZ	Exc/Cervical Plexus, [Opn, Perc, Perc Endo]
01B10ZX	Exc of Cervical Nerve, Opn Appr, Diagnostic
01B1[0,3,4]ZZ	Exc/Cervical Nerve, [Opn, Perc, Perc Endo]
01B20ZX	Exc of Phrenic Nerve, Opn Appr, Diagnostic
01B2[0,3,4]ZZ	Exc/Phrenic Nerve, [Opn, Perc, Perc Endo]
01B30ZX	Exc of Brachial Plexus, Opn Appr, Diagnostic
01B3[0,3,4]ZZ	Exc/Brachial Plexus, [Opn, Perc, Perc Endo]
01B40ZX	Exc of Ulnar Nerve, Opn Appr, Diagnostic
01B4[0,3,4]ZZ	Exc/Ulnar Nerve, [Opn, Perc, Perc Endo]
01B50ZX	Exc of Median Nerve, Opn Appr, Diagnostic
01B5[0,3,4]ZZ	Exc/Median Nerve, [Opn, Perc, Perc Endo]
01B60ZX	Exc of Radial Nerve, Opn Appr, Diagnostic
01B6[0,3,4]ZZ	Exc/Radial Nerve, [Opn, Perc, Perc Endo]
01B80ZX	Exc of Thoracic Nerve, Opn Appr, Diagnostic
01B8[0,3,4]ZZ	Exc/Thoracic Nerve, [Opn, Perc, Perc Endo]
01B90ZX	Exc of Lumbar Plexus, Opn Appr, Diagnostic
01B9[0,3,4]ZZ	Exc/Lumbar Plexus, [Opn, Perc, Perc Endo]
01BA0ZX	Exc of Lumbosacral Plexus, Opn Appr, Diagnostic
01BA[0,3,4]ZZ	Exc/Lumbosacral Plexus, [Opn, Perc, Perc Endo]
01BB0ZX	Exc of Lumbar Nerve, Opn Appr, Diagnostic
01BB[0,3,4]ZZ	Exc/Lumbar Nerve, [Opn, Perc, Perc Endo]
01BC0ZX	Exc of Pudendal Nerve, Opn Appr, Diagnostic
01BC[0,3,4]ZZ	Exc/Pudendal Nerve, [Opn, Perc, Perc Endo]
01BD0ZX	Exc of Femor Nerve, Opn Appr, Diagnostic
01BD[0,3,4]ZZ	Exc/Femor Nerve, [Opn, Perc, Perc Endo]
01BF0ZX	Exc of Sciatic Nerve, Opn Appr, Diagnostic
01BF[0,3,4]ZZ	Exc/Sciatic Nerve, [Opn, Perc, Perc Endo]
01BG0ZX	Exc of Tibial Nerve, Opn Appr, Diagnostic
01BG[0,3,4]ZZ	Exc/Tibial Nerve, [Opn, Perc, Perc Endo]
01BH0ZX	Exc of Peroneal Nerve, Opn Appr, Diagnostic
01BH[0,3,4]ZZ	Exc/Peroneal Nerve, [Opn, Perc, Perc Endo]
01BK*	Exc/Head and Neck Sympathetic Nerve
01BL*	Exc/Thoracic Sympathetic Nerve
01BM*	Exc/Abd Sympathetic Nerve
01BN*	Exc/Lumbar Sympathetic Nerve
01BP*	Exc/Sacral Sympathetic Nerve
01BQ0ZX	Exc of Sacral Plexus, Opn Appr, Diagnostic
01BQ[0,3,4]ZZ	Exc/Sacral Plexus, [Opn, Perc, Perc Endo]
01BR0ZX	Exc of Sacral Nerve, Opn Appr, Diagnostic
01BR[0,3,4]ZZ	Exc/Sacral Nerve, [Opn, Perc, Perc Endo]
01C*	Peripheral Nervous Sys, Extir
01D*	Peripheral Nervous Sys, Extract
01H*	Peripheral Nervous Sys, Insert
01J*	Peripheral Nervous Sys, Inspect
01N*	Peripheral Nervous Sys, Rls
01PYXMZ	Rmvl of Neuro Lead from Periph Nrv, Extern Appr
01PY[0,3,4][0,2,7,M]Z	Rmvl/Peripheral Nerve, [Opn, Perc, Perc Endo], [Drain Dev, Monitoring Dev, Auto Tissue Sub, Neurostimulator Lead], NQ
01Q*	Peripheral Nervous Sys, Repair
01S*	Peripheral Nervous Sys, Repos
01U*	Peripheral Nervous Sys, Supl
01WY[0,3,4][0,2,7,M]Z	Rev/Peripheral Nerve, [Opn, Perc, Perc Endo], [Drain Dev, Monitoring Dev, Auto Tissue Sub, Neurostimulator Lead], NQ
01X*	Peripheral Nervous Sys, Transfer
02H63[J,M]Z	Insert/Atrium, Rt, Perc, [Cardiac Lead, Pacemaker, Cardiac Lead], NQ
02H73[J,M]Z	Insert/Atrium, Lt, Perc, [Cardiac Lead, Pacemaker, Cardiac Lead], NQ
02HK3JZ	Insert of Pacemaker Lead into Rt Ventricle, Perc Appr
02HL3JZ	Insert of Pacemaker Lead into Lt Ventricle, Perc Appr
02HN[0,3,4][J,M]Z	Insert/Pericardium, [Opn, Perc, Perc Endo], [Cardiac Lead, Pacemaker, Cardiac Lead], NQ
02HV[0,3,4][2,D]Z	Insert/Superior Vena Cava, [Opn, Perc, Perc Endo], [Monitoring Dev, Intralum Dev], NQ
02LV*	Occlsn/Superior Vena Cava
02PA[0,3,4,X]MZ	Rmvl/Heart, [Opn, Perc, Perc Endo, Ext], Cardiac Lead, NQ
02VV*	Restrict/Superior Vena Cava
02WA[0,3,4]MZ	Rev/Heart, [Opn, Perc, Perc Endo], Cardiac Lead, NQ

Ⓣ **Transfer DRG**   ⓈⓅ **Special Payment**   * **Code Range**   **6th and 7th Character of ZZ = No Device, No Qualifier ZX = No Device, Diagnostic**

24   MS-DRG Version 33.0   © 2015 Optum360, LLC

Code	Description
039S[0,3,4]ZX	Drain/Temporal Artery, Rt, [Opn, Perc, Perc Endo]
039T[0,3,4]ZX	Drain/Temporal Artery, Lt, [Opn, Perc, Perc Endo]
03BS[0,3,4]ZX	Exc/Temporal Artery, Rt, [Opn, Perc, Perc Endo]
03BT[0,3,4]ZX	Exc/Temporal Artery, Lt, [Opn, Perc, Perc Endo]
03LH[0,3,4][C,Z]Z	Occlsn/Common Carotid Artery, Rt, [Opn, Perc, Perc Endo], [Extralum Dev, No Dev], NQ
03LJ[0,3,4][C,Z]Z	Occlsn/Common Carotid Artery, Lt, [Opn, Perc, Perc Endo], [Extralum Dev, No Dev], NQ
03LM[0,3,4][C,Z]Z	Occlsn/Ext Carotid Artery, Rt, [Opn, Perc, Perc Endo], [Extralum Dev, No Dev], NQ
03LN[0,3,4][C,Z]Z	Occlsn/Ext Carotid Artery, Lt, [Opn, Perc, Perc Endo], [Extralum Dev, No Dev], NQ
03LP[0,3,4][C,Z]Z	Occlsn/Vert Artery, Rt, [Opn, Perc, Perc Endo], [Extralum Dev, No Dev], NQ
03LQ[0,3,4][C,Z]Z	Occlsn/Vert Artery, Lt, [Opn, Perc, Perc Endo], [Extralum Dev, No Dev], NQ
03LR[0,3,4][C,Z]Z	Occlsn/Face Artery, [Opn, Perc, Perc Endo], [Extralum Dev, No Dev], NQ
03LS[0,3,4][C,Z]Z	Occlsn/Temporal Artery, Rt, [Opn, Perc, Perc Endo], [Extralum Dev, No Dev], NQ
03LT[0,3,4][C,Z]Z	Occlsn/Temporal Artery, Lt, [Opn, Perc, Perc Endo], [Extralum Dev, No Dev], NQ
03RH*	Replace/Common Carotid Artery, Rt
03RJ*	Replace/Common Carotid Artery, Lt
03RK*	Replace/Int Carotid Artery, Rt
03RL*	Replace/Int Carotid Artery, Lt
03RM*	Replace/Ext Carotid Artery, Rt
03RN*	Replace/Ext Carotid Artery, Lt
03RP*	Replace/Vert Artery, Rt
03RQ*	Replace/Vert Artery, Lt
03RR*	Replace/Face Artery
03RS*	Replace/Temporal Artery, Rt
03RT*	Replace/Temporal Artery, Lt
03RU*	Replace/Thyroid Artery, Rt
03RV*	Replace/Thyroid Artery, Lt
05CM*	Extir/Int Jugular Vein, Rt
05CN*	Extir/Int Jugular Vein, Lt
05CP*	Extir/Ext Jugular Vein, Rt
05CQ*	Extir/Ext Jugular Vein, Lt
05CR*	Extir/Vert Vein, Rt
05CS*	Extir/Vert Vein, Lt
05CT*	Extir/Face Vein, Rt
05CV*	Extir/Face Vein, Lt
05HY[0,3,4]2Z	Insert/Upr Vein, [Opn, Perc, Perc Endo], Monitoring Dev, NQ
05LM*	Occlsn/Int Jugular Vein, Rt
05LN*	Occlsn/Int Jugular Vein, Lt
05LP*	Occlsn/Ext Jugular Vein, Rt
05LQ*	Occlsn/Ext Jugular Vein, Lt
05LR*	Occlsn/Vert Vein, Rt
05LS*	Occlsn/Vert Vein, Lt
05LT*	Occlsn/Face Vein, Rt
05LV*	Occlsn/Face Vein, Lt
05RM*	Replace/Int Jugular Vein, Rt
05RN*	Replace/Int Jugular Vein, Lt
05RP*	Replace/Ext Jugular Vein, Rt
05RQ*	Replace/Ext Jugular Vein, Lt
05RR*	Replace/Vert Vein, Rt
05RS*	Replace/Vert Vein, Lt
05RT*	Replace/Face Vein, Rt
05RV*	Replace/Face Vein, Lt
0693[0,3,4][0,Z]Z	Drain/Esophageal Vein, [Opn, Perc, Perc Endo], [Drain Dev, No Dev], NQ
06C3*	Extir/Esophageal Vein
06H0[0,3,4]DZ	Insert/Inferior Vena Cava, [Opn, Perc, Perc Endo], Intralum Dev, NQ
06L0*	Occlsn/Inferior Vena Cava
06R3*	Replace/Esophageal Vein
06V0*	Restrict/Inferior Vena Cava
075M*	Destr/Thymus
0790[0,3,4]ZX	Drain/Lymphatic, Head, [Opn, Perc, Perc Endo]
0791[0,3,4]ZX	Drain/Lymphatic, Rt Neck, [Opn, Perc, Perc Endo]
0792[0,3,4]ZX	Drain/Lymphatic, Lt Neck, [Opn, Perc, Perc Endo]
0793[0,3,4]ZX	Drain/Lymphatic, Rt Upr Extr, [Opn, Perc, Perc Endo]
0794[0,3,4]ZX	Drain/Lymphatic, Lt Upr Extr, [Opn, Perc, Perc Endo]
0795[0,3,4]ZX	Drain/Lymphatic, Rt Axillary, [Opn, Perc, Perc Endo]
0796[0,3,4]ZX	Drain/Lymphatic, Lt Axillary, [Opn, Perc, Perc Endo]
0797[0,3,4]ZX	Drain/Lymphatic, Thorax, [Opn, Perc, Perc Endo]
0798[0,3,4]ZX	Drain/Lymphatic, Int Mammary, Rt, [Opn, Perc, Perc Endo]
0799[0,3,4]ZX	Drain/Lymphatic, Int Mammary, Lt, [Opn, Perc, Perc Endo]
079B[0,3,4]ZX	Drain/Lymphatic, Mesenteric, [Opn, Perc, Perc Endo]
079C[0,3,4]ZX	Drain/Lymphatic, Pelvis, [Opn, Perc, Perc Endo]
079D[0,3,4]ZX	Drain/Lymphatic, Aortic, [Opn, Perc, Perc Endo]
079F[0,3,4]ZX	Drain/Lymphatic, Rt Lwr Extr, [Opn, Perc, Perc Endo]
079G[0,3,4]ZX	Drain/Lymphatic, Lt Lwr Extr, [Opn, Perc, Perc Endo]
079H[0,3,4]ZX	Drain/Lymphatic, Rt Inguinal, [Opn, Perc, Perc Endo]
079J[0,3,4]ZX	Drain/Lymphatic, Lt Inguinal, [Opn, Perc, Perc Endo]
079K[0,3,4]ZX	Drain/Thoracic Duct, [Opn, Perc, Perc Endo]
079L[0,3,4]ZX	Drain/Cisterna Chyli, [Opn, Perc, Perc Endo]
079M4ZZ	Drain of Thymus, Perc Endo Appr
07B0[0,3,4]ZX	Exc/Lymphatic, Head, [Opn, Perc, Perc Endo]
07B1[0,3,4]ZX	Exc/Lymphatic, Rt Neck, [Opn, Perc, Perc Endo]
07B2[0,3,4]ZX	Exc/Lymphatic, Lt Neck, [Opn, Perc, Perc Endo]
07B3[0,3,4]ZX	Exc/Lymphatic, Rt Upr Extr, [Opn, Perc, Perc Endo]
07B4[0,3,4]ZX	Exc/Lymphatic, Lt Upr Extr, [Opn, Perc, Perc Endo]
07B5[0,3,4]ZX	Exc/Lymphatic, Rt Axillary, [Opn, Perc, Perc Endo]
07B6[0,3,4]ZX	Exc/Lymphatic, Lt Axillary, [Opn, Perc, Perc Endo]
07B7[0,3,4]ZX	Exc/Lymphatic, Thorax, [Opn, Perc, Perc Endo]
07B8[0,3,4]ZX	Exc/Lymphatic, Int Mammary, Rt, [Opn, Perc, Perc Endo]
07B9[0,3,4]ZX	Exc/Lymphatic, Int Mammary, Lt, [Opn, Perc, Perc Endo]
07BB[0,3,4]ZX	Exc/Lymphatic, Mesenteric, [Opn, Perc, Perc Endo]
07BC[0,3,4]ZX	Exc/Lymphatic, Pelvis, [Opn, Perc, Perc Endo]
07BD[0,3,4]ZX	Exc/Lymphatic, Aortic, [Opn, Perc, Perc Endo]
07BF[0,3,4]ZX	Exc/Lymphatic, Rt Lwr Extr, [Opn, Perc, Perc Endo]
07BG[0,3,4]ZX	Exc/Lymphatic, Lt Lwr Extr, [Opn, Perc, Perc Endo]
07BH[0,3,4]ZX	Exc/Lymphatic, Rt Inguinal, [Opn, Perc, Perc Endo]
07BJ[0,3,4]ZX	Exc/Lymphatic, Lt Inguinal, [Opn, Perc, Perc Endo]
07BK[0,3,4]ZX	Exc/Thoracic Duct, [Opn, Perc, Perc Endo]
07BL[0,3,4]ZX	Exc/Cisterna Chyli, [Opn, Perc, Perc Endo]
07BM[0,3,4]ZZ	Exc/Thymus, [Opn, Perc, Perc Endo]
07CM4ZZ	Extir of Matter from Thymus, Perc Endo Appr
07JM[3,4]ZZ	Inspect/Thymus, [Perc, Perc Endo]
07NM4ZZ	Rls Thymus, Perc Endo Appr
07QM4ZZ	Repair Thymus, Perc Endo Appr
07TM*	Resect/Thymus
08H0[3,X]1Z	Insert/Eye, Rt, [Perc, Ext], Radioact Elmt, NQ
08H1[3,X]1Z	Insert/Eye, Lt, [Perc, Ext], Radioact Elmt, NQ
08NN*	Rls/Upr Eyelid, Rt
08NP*	Rls/Upr Eyelid, Lt
08NQ*	Rls/Lwr Eyelid, Rt
08NR*	Rls/Lwr Eyelid, Lt
08SN*	Repos/Upr Eyelid, Rt
08SP*	Repos/Upr Eyelid, Lt
08SQ*	Repos/Lwr Eyelid, Rt
08SR*	Repos/Lwr Eyelid, Lt
09QN*	Repair/Nasopharynx
09RN*	Replace/Nasopharynx
09UN*	Supl/Nasopharynx
0CQ2*	Repair/Hard Palate
0CQ3*	Repair/Soft Palate
0CQM*	Repair/Pharynx
0CR2*	Replace/Hard Palate
0CR3*	Replace/Soft Palate
0CRM*	Replace/Pharynx
0CS2*	Repos/Hard Palate
0CS3*	Repos/Soft Palate
0CU2XJZ	Supl Hard Palate with Synth Sub, Extern Appr
0CU2[0,3,X][7,K]Z	Supl/Hard Palate, [Opn, Perc, Ext], [Auto Tissue Sub, Nonauto Tissue Sub], NQ
0CU3*	Supl/Soft Palate
0CUM*	Supl/Pharynx
0DH6[0,3,4]MZ	Insert/Stomach, [Opn, Perc, Perc Endo], Stimulator Lead, NQ
0DP6[0,3,4]MZ	Rmvl/Stomach, [Opn, Perc, Perc Endo], Stimulator Lead, NQ
0DPR*	Rmvl/Anal Sphincter
0DWW[0,3,4]JZ	Rev/Peritoneum, [Opn, Perc, Perc Endo], Synth Sub, NQ
0H8[0,1,4,5,6,7,8,A]XZZ	Div [Scalp, Face, Neck, Chest, Back, Abd, Buttock, Genitalia] Skin, Ext
0H8[B,C,D,E,F,G]XZZ	Div [Rt Upr Arm, Lt Upr Arm, Rt Lwr Arm, Lt Lwr Arm, Rt Hand, Lt Hand], Ext
0H8[H,J,K,L,M,N]XZZ	Div [Rt Upr Leg, Lt Upr Leg, Rt Lwr Leg, Lt Lwr Leg, Rt Foot, Lt Foot], Ext
0HB[0,1,4,5,6,7,8,A]XZZ	Exc [Scalp, Face, Neck, Chest, Back, Abd, Buttock, Genitalia] Skin, Ext
0HB[B,C,D,E,F,G]XZZ	Exc of Skin of [Rt Upr Arm, Lt Upr Arm, Rt Lwr Arm, Lt Lwr Arm, Rt Hand, Lt Hand], Ext
0HB[H,J,K,L,M,N]XZZ	Exc of Skin of [Rt Upr Leg, Lt Upr Leg, Rt Lwr Leg, Lt Lwr Leg, Rt Foot, Lt Foot], Ext
0HR0*	Replace/Skin, Scalp
0HR1*	Replace/Skin, Face
0HR4*	Replace/Skin, Neck
0HR5*	Replace/Skin, Chest

Surgical   **Medical**   **CC Indicator**   **MCC Indicator**   **Procedure Proxy**   **PDxMCC** PDx acts as own MCC   **PDxCC** PDx acts as own CC

ØHR6*	Replace/Skin, Back
ØHR7*	Replace/Skin, Abd
ØHR8*	Replace/Skin, Buttock
ØHRA*	Replace/Skin, Genitalia
ØHRB*	Replace/Skin, Rt Upr Arm
ØHRC*	Replace/Skin, Lt Upr Arm
ØHRD*	Replace/Skin, Rt Lwr Arm
ØHRE*	Replace/Skin, Lt Lwr Arm
ØHRF*	Replace/Skin, Rt Hand
ØHRG*	Replace/Skin, Lt Hand
ØHRH*	Replace/Skin, Rt Upr Leg
ØHRJ*	Replace/Skin, Lt Upr Leg
ØHRK*	Replace/Skin, Rt Lwr Leg
ØHRL*	Replace/Skin, Lt Lwr Leg
ØHRM*	Replace/Skin, Rt Foot
ØHRN*	Replace/Skin, Lt Foot
ØHX[Ø,1,4,5,6,7,8,9,A]XZZ	Transfer [Scalp, Face, Neck, Chest, Back, Abd, Buttock, Perineum, Genitalia] Skin, Ext
ØHX[B,C,D,E,F,G]XZZ	Transfer [Rt Upr Arm, Lt Upr Arm, Rt Lwr Arm, Lt Lwr Arm, Rt Hand, Lt Hand], Ext
ØHX[H,J,K,L,M,N]XZZ	Transfer [Rt Upr Leg, Lt Upr Leg, Rt Lwr Leg, Lt Lwr Leg, Rt Foot, Lt Foot], Ext
ØJ8Ø*	Div/SQ Tissue & Fascia, Scalp
ØJ84*	Div/SQ Tissue & Fascia, Ant Neck
ØJ85*	Div/SQ Tissue & Fascia, Posterior Neck
ØJ86*	Div/SQ Tissue & Fascia, Chest
ØJ87*	Div/SQ Tissue & Fascia, Back
ØJ88*	Div/SQ Tissue & Fascia, Abd
ØJ89*	Div/SQ Tissue & Fascia, Buttock
ØJ8B*	Div/SQ Tissue & Fascia, Perineum
ØJ8C*	Div/SQ Tissue & Fascia, Pelvic Region
ØJ8D*	Div/SQ Tissue & Fascia, Rt Upr Arm
ØJ8F*	Div/SQ Tissue & Fascia, Lt Upr Arm
ØJ8G*	Div/SQ Tissue & Fascia, Rt Lwr Arm
ØJ8H*	Div/SQ Tissue & Fascia, Lt Lwr Arm
ØJ8L*	Div/SQ Tissue & Fascia, Rt Upr Leg
ØJ8M*	Div/SQ Tissue & Fascia, Lt Upr Leg
ØJ8N*	Div/SQ Tissue & Fascia, Rt Lwr Leg
ØJ8P*	Div/SQ Tissue & Fascia, Lt Lwr Leg
ØJ8Q*	Div/SQ Tissue & Fascia, Rt Foot
ØJ8R*	Div/SQ Tissue & Fascia, Lt Foot
ØJ8S*	Div/SQ Tissue & Fascia, Head and Neck
ØJ8T*	Div/SQ Tissue & Fascia, Trunk
ØJ8V*	Div/SQ Tissue & Fascia, Upr Extr
ØJ8W*	Div/SQ Tissue & Fascia, Lwr Extr
ØJB[Ø,1,4,5,6]ØZZ	Exc of SQ Tissue & Fascia of [Scalp, Face, Ant Neck, Post Neck, Chest], Opn
ØJB[7,8,9,B,C]ØZZ	Exc of SQ Tissue & Fascia of [Back, Abd, Buttock, Perineum, Pelvic Rgn], Opn
ØJB[D,F,G,H]ØZZ	Exc of SQ Tissue & Fascia of [Rt Upr Arm, Lt Upr Arm, Rt Lwr Arm, Lt Lwr Arm], Opn
ØJB[L,M,N,P,Q,R]ØZZ	Exc of SQ Tissue & Fascia of [Rt Upr Leg, Lt Upr Leg, Rt Lwr Leg, Lt Lwr Leg, Rt Foot, Lt Foot], Opn
ØJDØ*	Extract/SQ Tissue & Fascia, Scalp
ØJD1*	Extract/SQ Tissue & Fascia, Face
ØJD4*	Extract/SQ Tissue & Fascia, Ant Neck
ØJD5*	Extract/SQ Tissue & Fascia, Posterior Neck
ØJD6*	Extract/SQ Tissue & Fascia, Chest
ØJD7*	Extract/SQ Tissue & Fascia, Back
ØJD8*	Extract/SQ Tissue & Fascia, Abd
ØJD9*	Extract/SQ Tissue & Fascia, Buttock
ØJDB*	Extract/SQ Tissue & Fascia, Perineum
ØJDC*	Extract/SQ Tissue & Fascia, Pelvic Region
ØJDD*	Extract/SQ Tissue & Fascia, Rt Upr Arm
ØJDF*	Extract/SQ Tissue & Fascia, Lt Upr Arm
ØJDG*	Extract/SQ Tissue & Fascia, Rt Lwr Arm
ØJDH*	Extract/SQ Tissue & Fascia, Lt Lwr Arm
ØJDL*	Extract/SQ Tissue & Fascia, Rt Upr Leg
ØJDM*	Extract/SQ Tissue & Fascia, Lt Upr Leg
ØJDN*	Extract/SQ Tissue & Fascia, Rt Lwr Leg
ØJDP*	Extract/SQ Tissue & Fascia, Lt Lwr Leg
ØJDQ*	Extract/SQ Tissue & Fascia, Rt Foot
ØJDR*	Extract/SQ Tissue & Fascia, Lt Foot
ØJHØ*	Insert/SQ Tissue & Fascia, Scalp
ØJH1*	Insert/SQ Tissue & Fascia, Face
ØJH4*	Insert/SQ Tissue & Fascia, Ant Neck
ØJH5*	Insert/SQ Tissue & Fascia, Posterior Neck

ØJH6[Ø,3][B,C,D,E,M,N,P,V]Z	Insert/SQ Tissue & Fascia, Chest, [Opn, Perc], [Stimulator Generator, Single Array, Stimulator Generator, Single Array Rechargeable, Stimulator Generator, Multi Array, Stimulator Generator, Multi Array Rechargeable, Stimulator Generator, Tissue Expander, Cardiac Rhythm Related Dev, Inf Dev, Pump], NQ
ØJH7*	Insert/SQ Tissue & Fascia, Back
ØJH8[Ø,3][B,C,D,E,M,N,P,V]Z	Insert/SQ Tissue & Fascia, Abd, [Opn, Perc], [Stimulator Generator, Single Array, Stimulator Generator, Single Array Rechargeable, Stimulator Generator, Multi Array, Stimulator Generator, Multi Array Rechargeable, Stimulator Generator, Tissue Expander, Cardiac Rhythm Related Dev, Inf Dev, Pump], NQ
ØJH9*	Insert/SQ Tissue & Fascia, Buttock
ØJHB*	Insert/SQ Tissue & Fascia, Perineum
ØJHC*	Insert/SQ Tissue & Fascia, Pelvic Region
ØJHD[Ø,3]NZ	Insert/SQ Tissue & Fascia, Rt Upr Arm, [Opn, Perc], Tissue Expander, NQ
ØJHF[Ø,3]NZ	Insert/SQ Tissue & Fascia, Lt Upr Arm, [Opn, Perc], Tissue Expander, NQ
ØJHG[Ø,3]NZ	Insert/SQ Tissue & Fascia, Rt Lwr Arm, [Opn, Perc], Tissue Expander, NQ
ØJHH[Ø,3]NZ	Insert/SQ Tissue & Fascia, Lt Lwr Arm, [Opn, Perc], Tissue Expander, NQ
ØJHJ*	Insert/SQ Tissue & Fascia, Rt Hand
ØJHK*	Insert/SQ Tissue & Fascia, Lt Hand
ØJHL[Ø,3]NZ	Insert/SQ Tissue & Fascia, Rt Upr Leg, [Opn, Perc], Tissue Expander, NQ
ØJHM[Ø,3]NZ	Insert/SQ Tissue & Fascia, Lt Upr Leg, [Opn, Perc], Tissue Expander, NQ
ØJHN[Ø,3]NZ	Insert/SQ Tissue & Fascia, Rt Lwr Leg, [Opn, Perc], Tissue Expander, NQ
ØJHP[Ø,3]NZ	Insert/SQ Tissue & Fascia, Lt Lwr Leg, [Opn, Perc], Tissue Expander, NQ
ØJHQ*	Insert/SQ Tissue & Fascia, Rt Foot
ØJHR*	Insert/SQ Tissue & Fascia, Lt Foot
ØJHT[Ø,3]VZ	Insert/SQ Tissue & Fascia, Trunk, [Opn, Perc], Inf Pump, NQ
ØJPT[Ø,3]PZ	Rmvl/SQ Tissue & Fascia, Trunk, [Opn, Perc], Cardiac Rhythm Related Dev, NQ
ØJQØ*	Repair/SQ Tissue & Fascia, Scalp
ØJQJ*	Repair/SQ Tissue & Fascia, Rt Hand
ØJQK*	Repair/SQ Tissue & Fascia, Lt Hand
ØJRJØ7Z	Replace of Rt Hand SQ/Fascia with Autol Sub, Opn Appr
ØJRJ[Ø,3][J,K]Z	Replace/SQ Tissue & Fascia, Rt Hand, [Opn, Perc], [Synth Sub, Nonauto Tissue Sub], NQ
ØJRKØ7Z	Replace of Lt Hand SQ/Fascia with Autol Sub, Opn Appr
ØJRK[Ø,3][J,K]Z	Replace/SQ Tissue & Fascia, Lt Hand, [Opn, Perc], [Synth Sub, Nonauto Tissue Sub], NQ
ØJUJ*	Supl/SQ Tissue & Fascia, Rt Hand
ØJUK*	Supl/SQ Tissue & Fascia, Lt Hand
ØJWT[Ø,3]PZ	Rev/SQ Tissue & Fascia, Trunk, [Opn, Perc], Cardiac Rhythm Related Dev, NQ
ØJXØ[Ø,3]Z[B,C]	Transfer/SQ Tissue & Fascia, Scalp, [Opn, Perc], No Dev, [Skin and SQ Tissue, Skin, SQ Tissue & Fascia]
ØJX1[Ø,3]Z[B,C]	Transfer/SQ Tissue & Fascia, Face, [Opn, Perc], No Dev, [Skin and SQ Tissue, Skin, SQ Tissue & Fascia]
ØJX4[Ø,3]Z[B,C]	Transfer/SQ Tissue & Fascia, Ant Neck, [Opn, Perc], No Dev, [Skin and SQ Tissue, Skin, SQ Tissue & Fascia]
ØJX5[Ø,3]Z[B,C]	Transfer/SQ Tissue & Fascia, Post Neck, [Opn, Perc], No Dev, [Skin and SQ Tissue, Skin, SQ Tissue & Fascia]
ØJX6[Ø,3]Z[B,C]	Transfer/SQ Tissue & Fascia, Chest, [Opn, Perc], No Dev, [Skin and SQ Tissue, Skin, SQ Tissue & Fascia]
ØJX7[Ø,3]Z[B,C]	Transfer/SQ Tissue & Fascia, Back, [Opn, Perc], No Dev, [Skin and SQ Tissue, Skin, SQ Tissue & Fascia]
ØJX8[Ø,3]Z[B,C]	Transfer/SQ Tissue & Fascia, Abd, [Opn, Perc], No Dev, [Skin and SQ Tissue, Skin, SQ Tissue & Fascia]
ØJX9[Ø,3]Z[B,C]	Transfer/SQ Tissue & Fascia, Buttock, [Opn, Perc], No Dev, [Skin and SQ Tissue, Skin, SQ Tissue & Fascia]
ØJXB[Ø,3]Z[B,C]	Transfer/SQ Tissue & Fascia, Perineum, [Opn, Perc], No Dev, [Skin and SQ Tissue, Skin, SQ Tissue & Fascia]
ØJXC[Ø,3]Z[B,C]	Transfer/SQ Tissue & Fascia, Genitalia, [Opn, Perc], No Dev, [Skin and SQ Tissue, Skin, SQ Tissue & Fascia]
ØJXD[Ø,3]Z[B,C]	Transfer/SQ Tissue & Fascia, Rt Upr Arm, [Opn, Perc], No Dev, [Skin and SQ Tissue, Skin, SQ Tissue & Fascia]
ØJXF[Ø,3]Z[B,C]	Transfer/SQ Tissue & Fascia, Lt Upr Arm, [Opn, Perc], No Dev, [Skin and SQ Tissue, Skin, SQ Tissue & Fascia]
ØJXG[Ø,3]Z[B,C]	Transfer/SQ Tissue & Fascia, Rt Lwr Arm, [Opn, Perc], No Dev, [Skin and SQ Tissue, Skin, SQ Tissue & Fascia]
ØJXH[Ø,3]Z[B,C]	Transfer/SQ Tissue & Fascia, Lt Lwr Arm, [Opn, Perc], No Dev, [Skin and SQ Tissue, Skin, SQ Tissue & Fascia]

T Transfer DRG   SP Special Payment   * Code Range   6th and 7th Character of ZZ = No Device, No Qualifier ZX = No Device, Diagnostic

MS-DRG Version 33.0

© 2015 Optum360, LLC

Code	Description
ØJXJ[Ø,3]ZZ	Transfer/SQ Tissue & Fascia, Rt Hand, [Opn, Perc]
ØJXL[Ø,3]Z[B,C]	Transfer/SQ Tissue & Fascia, Rt Upr Leg, [Opn, Perc], No Dev, [Skin and SQ Tissue, Skin, SQ Tissue & Fascia]
ØJXM[Ø,3]Z[B,C]	Transfer/SQ Tissue & Fascia, Lt Upr Leg, [Opn, Perc], No Dev, [Skin and SQ Tissue, Skin, SQ Tissue & Fascia]
ØJXN[Ø,3]Z[B,C]	Transfer/SQ Tissue & Fascia, Rt Lwr Leg, [Opn, Perc], No Dev, [Skin and SQ Tissue, Skin, SQ Tissue & Fascia]
ØJXP[Ø,3]Z[B,C]	Transfer/SQ Tissue & Fascia, Lt Lwr Leg, [Opn, Perc], No Dev, [Skin and SQ Tissue, Skin, SQ Tissue & Fascia]
ØJXQ[Ø,3]Z[B,C]	Transfer/SQ Tissue & Fascia, Rt Foot, [Opn, Perc], No Dev, [Skin and SQ Tissue, Skin, SQ Tissue & Fascia]
ØJXR[Ø,3]Z[B,C]	Transfer/SQ Tissue & Fascia, Lt Foot, [Opn, Perc], No Dev, [Skin and SQ Tissue, Skin, SQ Tissue & Fascia]
ØK8Ø*	Div/Head Muscle
ØK81*	Div/Facial Muscle
ØK82*	Div/Neck Muscle, Rt
ØK83*	Div/Neck Muscle, Lt
ØK85*	Div/Shldr Muscle, Rt
ØK86*	Div/Shldr Muscle, Lt
ØK87*	Div/Upr Arm Muscle, Rt
ØK88*	Div/Upr Arm Muscle, Lt
ØK89*	Div/Lwr Arm and Wrist Muscle, Rt
ØK8B*	Div/Lwr Arm and Wrist Muscle, Lt
ØK8F*	Div/Trunk Muscle, Rt
ØK8G*	Div/Trunk Muscle, Lt
ØK8H*	Div/Thorax Muscle, Rt
ØK8J*	Div/Thorax Muscle, Lt
ØK8K*	Div/Abd Muscle, Rt
ØK8L*	Div/Abd Muscle, Lt
ØK8M*	Div/Perineum Muscle
ØK8N*	Div/Hip Muscle, Rt
ØK8P*	Div/Hip Muscle, Lt
ØK8Q*	Div/Upr Leg Muscle, Rt
ØK8R*	Div/Upr Leg Muscle, Lt
ØK8S*	Div/Lwr Leg Muscle, Rt
ØK8T*	Div/Lwr Leg Muscle, Lt
ØK8V*	Div/Foot Muscle, Rt
ØK8W*	Div/Foot Muscle, Lt
ØK9[Ø,1,2,3,4,5,6]ØZX	Drain [Head, Facial, Rt neck, Lt Neck, Rt Shldr, Lt Shldr] Muscle, Opn
ØK9[7,8,9,B,C,D]ØZX	Drain [Rt Upr Arm, Lt Upr Arm, Rt Lwr Arm and Wrist, Lt Lwr Arm and Wrist, Rt Hand, Lt Hand] Muscle, Opn
ØK9[F,G,H,J,K,L,M,N,P]ØZX	Drain [Rt Trunk, Lt Trunk, Rt Thorax, Lt Thorax, Rt Abd, Lt Abd, Perineum, Rt Hip, Lt Hip] Muscle, Opn
ØK9[Q,R,S,T,V,W]ØZX	Drain [Rt Upr Leg, Lt Upr Leg, Rt Lwr Leg, Lt Lwr Leg, Rt Foot, Lt Foot] Muscle, Opn
ØKBØØZX	Exc of Head Muscle, Opn Appr, Diagnostic
ØKBØ[Ø,3,4]ZZ	Exc/Head Muscle, [Opn, Perc, Perc Endo]
ØKB1ØZX	Exc of Facial Muscle, Opn Appr, Diagnostic
ØKB1[Ø,3,4]ZZ	Exc/Facial Muscle, [Opn, Perc, Perc Endo]
ØKB2ØZX	Exc of Rt Neck Muscle, Opn Appr, Diagnostic
ØKB2[Ø,3,4]ZZ	Exc/Neck Muscle, Rt, [Opn, Perc, Perc Endo]
ØKB3ØZX	Exc of Lt Neck Muscle, Opn Appr, Diagnostic
ØKB3[Ø,3,4]ZZ	Exc/Neck Muscle, Lt, [Opn, Perc, Perc Endo]
ØKB4ØZX	Exc of Tongue/Palate/Phar Muscle, Opn Appr, Diagn
ØKB4[Ø,3,4]ZZ	Exc/Tongue, Palate, Pharynx Muscle, [Opn, Perc, Perc Endo]
ØKB5ØZX	Exc of Rt Shldr Muscle, Opn Appr, Diagnostic
ØKB5[Ø,3,4]ZZ	Exc/Shldr Muscle, Rt, [Opn, Perc, Perc Endo]
ØKB6ØZX	Exc of Lt Shldr Muscle, Opn Appr, Diagnostic
ØKB6[Ø,3,4]ZZ	Exc/Shldr Muscle, Lt, [Opn, Perc, Perc Endo]
ØKB7ØZX	Exc of Rt Upr Arm Muscle, Opn Appr, Diagn
ØKB7[Ø,3,4]ZZ	Exc/Upr Arm Muscle, Rt, [Opn, Perc, Perc Endo]
ØKB8ØZX	Exc of Lt Upr Arm Muscle, Opn Appr, Diagnostic
ØKB8[Ø,3,4]ZZ	Exc/Upr Arm Muscle, Lt, [Opn, Perc, Perc Endo]
ØKB9ØZX	Exc of Rt Low Arm & Wrist Muscle, Opn Appr, Diagn
ØKB9[Ø,3,4]ZZ	Exc/Lwr Arm and Wrist Muscle, Rt, [Opn, Perc, Perc Endo]
ØKBBØZX	Exc of Lt Low Arm & Wrist Muscle, Opn Appr, Diagn
ØKBB[Ø,3,4]ZZ	Exc/Lwr Arm and Wrist Muscle, Lt, [Opn, Perc, Perc Endo]
ØKBFØZX	Exc of Rt Trunk Muscle, Opn Appr, Diagnostic
ØKBF[Ø,3,4]ZZ	Exc/Trunk Muscle, Rt, [Opn, Perc, Perc Endo]
ØKBGØZX	Exc of Lt Trunk Muscle, Opn Appr, Diagnostic
ØKBG[Ø,3,4]ZZ	Exc/Trunk Muscle, Lt, [Opn, Perc, Perc Endo]
ØKBHØZX	Exc of Rt Thorax Muscle, Opn Appr, Diagnostic
ØKBH[Ø,3,4]ZZ	Exc/Thorax Muscle, Rt, [Opn, Perc, Perc Endo]
ØKBJØZX	Exc of Lt Thorax Muscle, Opn Appr, Diagnostic
ØKBJ[Ø,3,4]ZZ	Exc/Thorax Muscle, Lt, [Opn, Perc, Perc Endo]
ØKBKØZX	Exc of Rt Abd Muscle, Opn Appr, Diagnostic
ØKBK[Ø,3,4]ZZ	Exc/Abd Muscle, Rt, [Opn, Perc, Perc Endo]
ØKBLØZX	Exc of Lt Abd Muscle, Opn Appr, Diagnostic
ØKBL[Ø,3,4]ZZ	Exc/Abd Muscle, Lt, [Opn, Perc, Perc Endo]
ØKBMØZX	Exc of Perineum Muscle, Opn Appr, Diagnostic
ØKBM[Ø,3,4]ZZ	Exc/Perineum Muscle, [Opn, Perc, Perc Endo]
ØKBNØZX	Exc of Rt Hip Muscle, Opn Appr, Diagnostic
ØKBN[Ø,3,4]ZZ	Exc/Hip Muscle, Rt, [Opn, Perc, Perc Endo]
ØKBPØZX	Exc of Lt Hip Muscle, Opn Appr, Diagnostic
ØKBP[Ø,3,4]ZZ	Exc/Hip Muscle, Lt, [Opn, Perc, Perc Endo]
ØKBQØZX	Exc of Rt Upr Leg Muscle, Opn Appr, Diagn
ØKBQ[Ø,3,4]ZZ	Exc/Upr Leg Muscle, Rt, [Opn, Perc, Perc Endo]
ØKBRØZX	Exc of Lt Upr Leg Muscle, Opn Appr, Diagnostic
ØKBR[Ø,3,4]ZZ	Exc/Upr Leg Muscle, Lt, [Opn, Perc, Perc Endo]
ØKBSØZX	Exc of Rt Lwr Leg Muscle, Opn Appr, Diagnostic
ØKBS[Ø,3,4]ZZ	Exc/Lwr Leg Muscle, Rt, [Opn, Perc, Perc Endo]
ØKBTØZX	Exc of Lt Lwr Leg Muscle, Opn Appr, Diagnostic
ØKBT[Ø,3,4]ZZ	Exc/Lwr Leg Muscle, Lt, [Opn, Perc, Perc Endo]
ØKBVØZX	Exc of Rt Foot Muscle, Opn Appr, Diagnostic
ØKBV[Ø,3,4]ZZ	Exc/Foot Muscle, Rt, [Opn, Perc, Perc Endo]
ØKBWØZX	Exc of Lt Foot Muscle, Opn Appr, Diagnostic
ØKBW[Ø,3,4]ZZ	Exc/Foot Muscle, Lt, [Opn, Perc, Perc Endo]
ØKB[C,D]ØZX	Exc [Rt Hand, Lt Hand] Muscle, Opn
ØKH*	Muscles, Insert
ØKM*	Muscles, Reattach
ØKPX[Ø,3,4]MZ	Rmvl/Upr Muscle, [Opn, Perc, Perc Endo], Stimulator Lead, NQ
ØKPY[Ø,3,4]MZ	Rmvl/Lwr Muscle, [Opn, Perc, Perc Endo], Stimulator Lead, NQ
ØKQØ*	Repair/Head Muscle
ØKQ1*	Repair/Facial Muscle
ØKQ2*	Repair/Neck Muscle, Rt
ØKQ3*	Repair/Neck Muscle, Lt
ØKQ4*	Repair/Tongue, Palate, Pharynx Muscle
ØKQ5*	Repair/Shldr Muscle, Rt
ØKQ6*	Repair/Shldr Muscle, Lt
ØKQ7*	Repair/Upr Arm Muscle, Rt
ØKQ8*	Repair/Upr Arm Muscle, Lt
ØKQ9*	Repair/Lwr Arm and Wrist Muscle, Rt
ØKQB*	Repair/Lwr Arm and Wrist Muscle, Lt
ØKQF*	Repair/Trunk Muscle, Rt
ØKQG*	Repair/Trunk Muscle, Lt
ØKQH*	Repair/Thorax Muscle, Rt
ØKQJ*	Repair/Thorax Muscle, Lt
ØKQK*	Repair/Abd Muscle, Rt
ØKQL*	Repair/Abd Muscle, Lt
ØKQM*	Repair/Perineum Muscle
ØKQN*	Repair/Hip Muscle, Rt
ØKQP*	Repair/Hip Muscle, Lt
ØKQS*	Repair/Lwr Leg Muscle, Rt
ØKQT*	Repair/Lwr Leg Muscle, Lt
ØKQV*	Repair/Foot Muscle, Rt
ØKQW*	Repair/Foot Muscle, Lt
ØKS*	Muscles, Repos
ØKTØ*	Resect/Head Muscle
ØKT1*	Resect/Facial Muscle
ØKT2*	Resect/Neck Muscle, Rt
ØKT3*	Resect/Neck Muscle, Lt
ØKT4*	Resect/Tongue, Palate, Pharynx Muscle
ØKT5*	Resect/Shldr Muscle, Rt
ØKT6*	Resect/Shldr Muscle, Lt
ØKT7*	Resect/Upr Arm Muscle, Rt
ØKT8*	Resect/Upr Arm Muscle, Lt
ØKT9*	Resect/Lwr Arm and Wrist Muscle, Rt
ØKTB*	Resect/Lwr Arm and Wrist Muscle, Lt
ØKTF*	Resect/Trunk Muscle, Rt
ØKTG*	Resect/Trunk Muscle, Lt
ØKTH*	Resect/Thorax Muscle, Rt
ØKTJ*	Resect/Thorax Muscle, Lt
ØKTK*	Resect/Abd Muscle, Rt
ØKTL*	Resect/Abd Muscle, Lt
ØKTM*	Resect/Perineum Muscle
ØKTN*	Resect/Hip Muscle, Rt
ØKTP*	Resect/Hip Muscle, Lt
ØKTQ*	Resect/Upr Leg Muscle, Rt
ØKTR*	Resect/Upr Leg Muscle, Lt
ØKTS*	Resect/Lwr Leg Muscle, Rt
ØKTT*	Resect/Lwr Leg Muscle, Lt
ØKTV*	Resect/Foot Muscle, Rt
ØKTW*	Resect/Foot Muscle, Lt
ØKU*	Muscles, Supl
ØKXØ*	Transfer/Head Muscle
ØKX1*	Transfer/Facial Muscle
ØKX2*	Transfer/Neck Muscle, Rt
ØKX3*	Transfer/Neck Muscle, Lt
ØKX4*	Transfer/Tongue, Palate, Pharynx Muscle

Surgical   **Medical**   **CC Indicator**   **MCC Indicator**   **Procedure Proxy**   **PDxMCC** PDx acts as own MCC   **PDxCC** PDx acts as own CC

MDC 1: Diseases And Disorders Of The Nervous System—SURGICAL

MDC 1: Diseases And Disorders Of The Nervous System—SURGICAL

Code	Description
ØKX5*	Transfer/Shldr Muscle, Rt
ØKX6*	Transfer/Shldr Muscle, Lt
ØKX7*	Transfer/Upr Arm Muscle, Rt
ØKX8*	Transfer/Upr Arm Muscle, Lt
ØKX9*	Transfer/Lwr Arm and Wrist Muscle, Rt
ØKXB*	Transfer/Lwr Arm and Wrist Muscle, Lt
ØKXC*	Transfer/Hand Muscle, Rt
ØKXD*	Transfer/Hand Muscle, Lt
ØKXF*	Transfer/Trunk Muscle, Rt
ØKXG*	Transfer/Trunk Muscle, Lt
ØKXH[Ø,4]Z[Ø,1,2]	Transfer/Thorax Muscle, Rt, [Opn, Perc Endo], No Dev, [Skin, SQ Tissue, Skin and SQ Tissue]
ØKXJ[Ø,4]Z[Ø,1,2]	Transfer/Thorax Muscle, Lt, [Opn, Perc Endo], No Dev, [Skin, SQ Tissue, Skin and SQ Tissue]
ØKXK[Ø,4]Z[Ø,1,2,Z]	Transfer/Abd Muscle, Rt, [Opn, Perc Endo], No Dev, [Skin, SQ Tissue, Skin and SQ Tissue, NQ]
ØKXL[Ø,4]Z[Ø,1,2,Z]	Transfer/Abd Muscle, Lt, [Opn, Perc Endo], No Dev, [Skin, SQ Tissue, Skin and SQ Tissue, NQ]
ØKXM*	Transfer/Perineum Muscle
ØKXN*	Transfer/Hip Muscle, Rt
ØKXP*	Transfer/Hip Muscle, Lt
ØKXQ*	Transfer/Upr Leg Muscle, Rt
ØKXR*	Transfer/Upr Leg Muscle, Lt
ØKXS*	Transfer/Lwr Leg Muscle, Rt
ØKXT*	Transfer/Lwr Leg Muscle, Lt
ØKXV*	Transfer/Foot Muscle, Rt
ØKXW*	Transfer/Foot Muscle, Lt
ØL8Ø*	Div/Head and Neck Tndn
ØL81*	Div/Shldr Tndn, Rt
ØL82*	Div/Shldr Tndn, Lt
ØL83*	Div/Upr Arm Tndn, Rt
ØL84*	Div/Upr Arm Tndn, Lt
ØL85*	Div/Lwr Arm and Wrist Tndn, Rt
ØL86*	Div/Lwr Arm and Wrist Tndn, Lt
ØL89*	Div/Trunk Tndn, Rt
ØL8B*	Div/Trunk Tndn, Lt
ØL8C*	Div/Thorax Tndn, Rt
ØL8D*	Div/Thorax Tndn, Lt
ØL8F*	Div/Abd Tndn, Rt
ØL8G*	Div/Abd Tndn, Lt
ØL8H*	Div/Perineum Tndn
ØL8L*	Div/Upr Leg Tndn, Rt
ØL8M*	Div/Upr Leg Tndn, Lt
ØL8Q*	Div/Knee Tndn, Rt
ØL8R*	Div/Knee Tndn, Lt
ØL8S*	Div/Ankle Tndn, Rt
ØL8T*	Div/Ankle Tndn, Lt
ØL8V*	Div/Foot Tndn, Rt
ØL8W*	Div/Foot Tndn, Lt
ØLBØ[Ø,3,4]ZZ	Exc/Head and Neck Tndn, [Opn, Perc, Perc Endo]
ØLB1[Ø,3,4]ZZ	Exc/Shldr Tndn, Rt, [Opn, Perc, Perc Endo]
ØLB2[Ø,3,4]ZZ	Exc/Shldr Tndn, Lt, [Opn, Perc, Perc Endo]
ØLB3[Ø,3,4]ZZ	Exc/Upr Arm Tndn, Rt, [Opn, Perc, Perc Endo]
ØLB4[Ø,3,4]ZZ	Exc/Upr Arm Tndn, Lt, [Opn, Perc, Perc Endo]
ØLB5[Ø,3,4]ZZ	Exc/Lwr Arm and Wrist Tndn, Rt, [Opn, Perc, Perc Endo]
ØLB6[Ø,3,4]ZZ	Exc/Lwr Arm and Wrist Tndn, Lt, [Opn, Perc, Perc Endo]
ØLB9[Ø,3,4]ZZ	Exc/Trunk Tndn, Rt, [Opn, Perc, Perc Endo]
ØLBB[Ø,3,4]ZZ	Exc/Trunk Tndn, Lt, [Opn, Perc, Perc Endo]
ØLBC[Ø,3,4]ZZ	Exc/Thorax Tndn, Rt, [Opn, Perc, Perc Endo]
ØLBD[Ø,3,4]ZZ	Exc/Thorax Tndn, Lt, [Opn, Perc, Perc Endo]
ØLBF[Ø,3,4]ZZ	Exc/Abd Tndn, Rt, [Opn, Perc, Perc Endo]
ØLBG[Ø,3,4]ZZ	Exc/Abd Tndn, Lt, [Opn, Perc, Perc Endo]
ØLBH[Ø,3,4]ZZ	Exc/Perineum Tndn, [Opn, Perc, Perc Endo]
ØLBJ[Ø,3,4]ZZ	Exc/Hip Tndn, Rt, [Opn, Perc, Perc Endo]
ØLBK[Ø,3,4]ZZ	Exc/Hip Tndn, Lt, [Opn, Perc, Perc Endo]
ØLBL[Ø,3,4]ZZ	Exc/Upr Leg Tndn, Rt, [Opn, Perc, Perc Endo]
ØLBM[Ø,3,4]ZZ	Exc/Upr Leg Tndn, Lt, [Opn, Perc, Perc Endo]
ØLBN[Ø,3,4]ZZ	Exc/Lwr Leg Tndn, Rt, [Opn, Perc, Perc Endo]
ØLBP[Ø,3,4]ZZ	Exc/Lwr Leg Tndn, Lt, [Opn, Perc, Perc Endo]
ØLBQ[Ø,3,4]ZZ	Exc/Knee Tndn, Rt, [Opn, Perc, Perc Endo]
ØLBR[Ø,3,4]ZZ	Exc/Knee Tndn, Lt, [Opn, Perc, Perc Endo]
ØLBS[Ø,3,4]ZZ	Exc/Ankle Tndn, Rt, [Opn, Perc, Perc Endo]
ØLBT[Ø,3,4]ZZ	Exc/Ankle Tndn, Lt, [Opn, Perc, Perc Endo]
ØLBV[Ø,3,4]ZZ	Exc/Foot Tndn, Rt, [Opn, Perc, Perc Endo]
ØLBW[Ø,3,4]ZZ	Exc/Foot Tndn, Lt, [Opn, Perc, Perc Endo]
ØLM*	Tndns, Reattach
ØLQØ*	Repair/Head and Neck Tndn
ØLQ3*	Repair/Upr Arm Tndn, Rt
ØLQ4*	Repair/Upr Arm Tndn, Lt
ØLQ5*	Repair/Lwr Arm and Wrist Tndn, Rt
ØLQ6*	Repair/Lwr Arm and Wrist Tndn, Lt
ØLQ7*	Repair/Hand Tndn, Rt
ØLQ8*	Repair/Hand Tndn, Lt
ØLQ9*	Repair/Trunk Tndn, Rt
ØLQB*	Repair/Trunk Tndn, Lt
ØLQC*	Repair/Thorax Tndn, Rt
ØLQD*	Repair/Thorax Tndn, Lt
ØLQF*	Repair/Abd Tndn, Rt
ØLQG*	Repair/Abd Tndn, Lt
ØLQH*	Repair/Perineum Tndn
ØLQJ*	Repair/Hip Tndn, Rt
ØLQK*	Repair/Hip Tndn, Lt
ØLQL*	Repair/Upr Leg Tndn, Rt
ØLQM*	Repair/Upr Leg Tndn, Lt
ØLQN*	Repair/Lwr Leg Tndn, Rt
ØLQP*	Repair/Lwr Leg Tndn, Lt
ØLQV*	Repair/Foot Tndn, Rt
ØLQW*	Repair/Foot Tndn, Lt
ØLR7*	Replace/Hand Tndn, Rt
ØLR8*	Replace/Hand Tndn, Lt
ØLS*	Tndns, Repos
ØLU7*	Supl/Hand Tndn, Rt
ØLU8*	Supl/Hand Tndn, Lt
ØLX*	Tndns, Transfer
ØNHØØNZ	Insert of Neurostim into Skull, Opn Appr
ØNPØØNZ	Rmvl of Neurostim from Skull, Opn Appr
ØRQN*	Repair/Wrist Jt, Rt
ØRQP*	Repair/Wrist Jt, Lt
ØRQQ*	Repair/Carpal Jt, Rt
ØRQR*	Repair/Carpal Jt, Lt
ØRQS*	Repair/Metacarpocarpal Jt, Rt
ØRQT*	Repair/Metacarpocarpal Jt, Lt
ØRQU*	Repair/Metacarpophalangeal Jt, Rt
ØRQV*	Repair/Metacarpophalangeal Jt, Lt
ØRQW*	Repair/Finger Phalangeal Jt, Rt
ØRQX*	Repair/Finger Phalangeal Jt, Lt
ØRRQ*	Replace/Carpal Jt, Rt
ØRRR*	Replace/Carpal Jt, Lt
ØRRS*	Replace/Metacarpocarpal Jt, Rt
ØRRT*	Replace/Metacarpocarpal Jt, Lt
ØRRU*	Replace/Metacarpophalangeal Jt, Rt
ØRRV*	Replace/Metacarpophalangeal Jt, Lt
ØRRW*	Replace/Finger Phalangeal Jt, Rt
ØRRX*	Replace/Finger Phalangeal Jt, Lt
ØRUN*	Supl/Wrist Jt, Rt
ØRUP*	Supl/Wrist Jt, Lt
ØRUQ*	Supl/Carpal Jt, Rt
ØRUR*	Supl/Carpal Jt, Lt
ØRUS*	Supl/Metacarpocarpal Jt, Rt
ØRUT*	Supl/Metacarpocarpal Jt, Lt
ØRUU*	Supl/Metacarpophalangeal Jt, Rt
ØRUV*	Supl/Metacarpophalangeal Jt, Lt
ØRUW*	Supl/Finger Phalangeal Jt, Rt
ØRUX*	Supl/Finger Phalangeal Jt, Lt
ØW9J[Ø,4][Ø,Z]Z	Drain/Pelvic Cavity, [Opn, Perc Endo], [Drain Dev, No Dev], NQ
ØWBØ[Ø,3,4,X]ZZ	Exc/Head, [Opn, Perc, Perc Endo, Ext]
ØWB2[Ø,3,4,X]ZZ	Exc/Face, [Opn, Perc, Perc Endo, Ext]
ØWB4[Ø,3,4,X]ZZ	Exc/Upr Jaw, [Opn, Perc, Perc Endo, Ext]
ØWB5[Ø,3,4,X]ZZ	Exc/Lwr Jaw, [Opn, Perc, Perc Endo, Ext]
ØWB6[Ø,3,4,X]ZZ	Exc/Neck, [Opn, Perc, Perc Endo, Ext]
ØWBK[Ø,3,4,X]ZZ	Exc/Upr Back, [Opn, Perc, Perc Endo, Ext]
ØWBL[Ø,3,4,X]ZZ	Exc/Lwr Back, [Opn, Perc, Perc Endo, Ext]
ØWBM[Ø,3,4,X]ZZ	Exc/Perineum, Male, [Opn, Perc, Perc Endo, Ext]
ØWHØ[Ø,3,4]1Z	Insert/Head, [Opn, Perc, Perc Endo], Radioact Elmt, NQ
ØWH1[Ø,3,4]1Z	Insert/Cranial Cavity, [Opn, Perc, Perc Endo], Radioact Elmt, NQ
ØWH2[Ø,3,4]1Z	Insert/Face, [Opn, Perc, Perc Endo], Radioact Elmt, NQ
ØWU2[Ø,4]7Z	Supl/Face, [Opn, Perc Endo], Auto Tissue Sub, NQ
ØWU4[Ø,4]7Z	Supl/Upr Jaw, [Opn, Perc Endo], Auto Tissue Sub, NQ
ØWU5[Ø,4]7Z	Supl/Lwr Jaw, [Opn, Perc Endo], Auto Tissue Sub, NQ
ØXB2[Ø,3,4]ZZ	Exc/Shldr Rgn, Rt, [Opn, Perc, Perc Endo]
ØXB3[Ø,3,4]ZZ	Exc/Shldr Rgn, Lt, [Opn, Perc, Perc Endo]
ØXB4[Ø,3,4]ZZ	Exc/Axilla, Rt, [Opn, Perc, Perc Endo]
ØXB5[Ø,3,4]ZZ	Exc/Axilla, Lt, [Opn, Perc, Perc Endo]
ØXB6[Ø,3,4]ZZ	Exc/Upr Extr, Rt, [Opn, Perc, Perc Endo]
ØXB7[Ø,3,4]ZZ	Exc/Upr Extr, Lt, [Opn, Perc, Perc Endo]
ØXB8[Ø,3,4]ZZ	Exc/Upr Arm, Rt, [Opn, Perc, Perc Endo]
ØXB9[Ø,3,4]ZZ	Exc/Upr Arm, Lt, [Opn, Perc, Perc Endo]
ØXBB[Ø,3,4]ZZ	Exc/Elbow Rgn, Rt, [Opn, Perc, Perc Endo]
ØXBC[Ø,3,4]ZZ	Exc/Elbow Rgn, Lt, [Opn, Perc, Perc Endo]

T Transfer DRG   SP Special Payment   * Code Range   6th and 7th Character of ZZ = No Device, No Qualifier ZX = No Device, Diagnostic

ØXBD[Ø,3,4]ZZ	Exc/Lwr Arm, Rt, [Opn, Perc, Perc Endo]
ØXBF[Ø,3,4]ZZ	Exc/Lwr Arm, Lt, [Opn, Perc, Perc Endo]
ØXBG[Ø,3,4]ZZ	Exc/Wrist Rgn, Rt, [Opn, Perc, Perc Endo]
ØXBH[Ø,3,4]ZZ	Exc/Wrist Rgn, Lt, [Opn, Perc, Perc Endo]
ØXBJ[Ø,3,4]ZZ	Exc/Hand, Rt, [Opn, Perc, Perc Endo]
ØXBK[Ø,3,4]ZZ	Exc/Hand, Lt, [Opn, Perc, Perc Endo]
ØXQJ*	Repair/Hand, Rt
ØXQK*	Repair/Hand, Lt
ØXQL*	Repair/Thumb, Rt
ØXQM*	Repair/Thumb, Lt
ØXQN*	Repair/Index Finger, Rt
ØXQP*	Repair/Index Finger, Lt
ØXQQ*	Repair/Mid Finger, Rt
ØXQR*	Repair/Mid Finger, Lt
ØXQS*	Repair/Ring Finger, Rt
ØXQT*	Repair/Ring Finger, Lt
ØXQV*	Repair/Little Finger, Rt
ØXQW*	Repair/Little Finger, Lt
ØXR*	Anatomical Regions, Upr Extremities, Replace
ØXUJ[Ø,4]7Z	Supl/Hand, Rt, [Opn, Perc Endo], Auto Tissue Sub, NQ
ØXUK[Ø,4]7Z	Supl/Hand, Lt, [Opn, Perc Endo], Auto Tissue Sub, NQ
ØXUL[Ø,4]7Z	Supl/Thumb, Rt, [Opn, Perc Endo], Auto Tissue Sub, NQ
ØXUM[Ø,4]7Z	Supl/Thumb, Lt, [Opn, Perc Endo], Auto Tissue Sub, NQ
ØXUN[Ø,4]7Z	Supl/Index Finger, Rt, [Opn, Perc Endo], Auto Tissue Sub, NQ
ØXUP[Ø,4]7Z	Supl/Index Finger, Lt, [Opn, Perc Endo], Auto Tissue Sub, NQ
ØXUQ[Ø,4]7Z	Supl/Mid Finger, Rt, [Opn, Perc Endo], Auto Tissue Sub, NQ
ØXUR[Ø,4]7Z	Supl/Mid Finger, Lt, [Opn, Perc Endo], Auto Tissue Sub, NQ
ØXUS[Ø,4]7Z	Supl/Ring Finger, Rt, [Opn, Perc Endo], Auto Tissue Sub, NQ
ØXUT[Ø,4]7Z	Supl/Ring Finger, Lt, [Opn, Perc Endo], Auto Tissue Sub, NQ
ØXUV[Ø,4]7Z	Supl/Little Finger, Rt, [Opn, Perc Endo], Auto Tissue Sub, NQ
ØXUW[Ø,4]7Z	Supl/Little Finger, Lt, [Opn, Perc Endo], Auto Tissue Sub, NQ
ØXX*	Anatomical Regions, Upr Extremities, Transfer
ØY6C*	Detach/Upr Leg, Rt
ØY6D*	Detach/Upr Leg, Lt
ØY6FØZZ	Detach at Rt Knee Region, Opn Appr
ØY6GØZZ	Detach at Lt Knee Region, Opn Appr
ØY6H*	Detach/Lwr Leg, Rt
ØY6J*	Detach/Lwr Leg, Lt
ØY6M*	Detach/Foot, Rt
ØY6N*	Detach/Foot, Lt
ØY6P*	Detach/1st Toe, Rt
ØY6Q*	Detach/1st Toe, Lt
ØY6R*	Detach/2nd Toe, Rt
ØY6S*	Detach/2nd Toe, Lt
ØY6T*	Detach/3rd Toe, Rt
ØY6U*	Detach/3rd Toe, Lt
ØY6V*	Detach/4th Toe, Rt
ØY6W*	Detach/4th Toe, Lt
ØY6X*	Detach/5th Toe, Rt
ØY6Y*	Detach/5th Toe, Lt
ØYBØ[Ø,3,4]ZZ	Exc/Buttock, Rt, [Opn, Perc, Perc Endo]
ØYB1[Ø,3,4]ZZ	Exc/Buttock, Lt, [Opn, Perc, Perc Endo]
ØYB9[Ø,3,4]ZZ	Exc/Lwr Extr, Rt, [Opn, Perc, Perc Endo]
ØYBB[Ø,3,4]ZZ	Exc/Lwr Extr, Lt, [Opn, Perc, Perc Endo]
ØYBC[Ø,3,4]ZZ	Exc/Upr Leg, Rt, [Opn, Perc, Perc Endo]
ØYBD[Ø,3,4]ZZ	Exc/Upr Leg, Lt, [Opn, Perc, Perc Endo]
ØYBF[Ø,3,4]ZZ	Exc/Knee Rgn, Rt, [Opn, Perc, Perc Endo]
ØYBG[Ø,3,4]ZZ	Exc/Knee Rgn, Lt, [Opn, Perc, Perc Endo]
ØYBH[Ø,3,4]ZZ	Exc/Lwr Leg, Rt, [Opn, Perc, Perc Endo]
ØYBJ[Ø,3,4]ZZ	Exc/Lwr Leg, Lt, [Opn, Perc, Perc Endo]
ØYBK[Ø,3,4]ZZ	Exc/Ankle Rgn, Rt, [Opn, Perc, Perc Endo]
ØYBL[Ø,3,4]ZZ	Exc/Ankle Rgn, Lt, [Opn, Perc, Perc Endo]
ØYBM[Ø,3,4]ZZ	Exc/Foot, Rt, [Opn, Perc, Perc Endo]
ØYBN[Ø,3,4]ZZ	Exc/Foot, Lt, [Opn, Perc, Perc Endo]

OR

Ø2H4[Ø,4][J,M]Z	Insert/Coronary Vein, [Opn, Perc Endo], [Cardiac Lead, Pacemaker, Cardiac Lead], NQ
Ø2H6[Ø,3,4]JZ	Insert/Atrium, Rt, [Opn, Perc, Perc Endo], Cardiac Lead, Pacemaker, NQ
Ø2H6[Ø,4]MZ	Insert/Atrium, Rt, [Opn, Perc Endo], Cardiac Lead, NQ
Ø2H7[Ø,3,4]JZ	Insert/Atrium, Lt, [Opn, Perc, Perc Endo], Cardiac Lead, Pacemaker, NQ
Ø2H7[Ø,4]MZ	Insert/Atrium, Lt, [Opn, Perc Endo], Cardiac Lead, NQ
Ø2HK[Ø,3,4][J,M]Z	Insert/Ventricle, Rt, [Opn, Perc, Perc Endo], [Cardiac Lead, Pacemaker, Cardiac Lead], NQ
Ø2HL[Ø,3,4][J,M]Z	Insert/Ventricle, Lt, [Opn, Perc, Perc Endo], [Cardiac Lead, Pacemaker, Cardiac Lead], NQ

AND	
ØJH6[Ø,3][4,5,P]Z	Insert/SQ Tissue & Fascia, Chest, [Opn, Perc], [Pacemaker, Single Chamber, Pacemaker, Single Chamber Rate Responsive, Cardiac Rhythm Related Dev], NQ
ØJH8[Ø,3][4,5,P]Z	Insert/SQ Tissue & Fascia, Abd, [Opn, Perc], [Pacemaker, Single Chamber, Pacemaker, Single Chamber Rate Responsive, Cardiac Rhythm Related Dev], NQ

OR

Ø2H4[Ø,4][J,M]Z	Insert/Coronary Vein, [Opn, Perc Endo], [Cardiac Lead, Pacemaker, Cardiac Lead], NQ
Ø2H6[Ø,3,4]JZ	Insert/Atrium, Rt, [Opn, Perc, Perc Endo], Cardiac Lead, Pacemaker, NQ
Ø2H6[Ø,4]MZ	Insert/Atrium, Rt, [Opn, Perc Endo], Cardiac Lead, NQ
Ø2H7[Ø,3,4]JZ	Insert/Atrium, Lt, [Opn, Perc, Perc Endo], Cardiac Lead, Pacemaker, NQ
Ø2H7[Ø,4]MZ	Insert/Atrium, Lt, [Opn, Perc Endo], Cardiac Lead, NQ
Ø2HK[Ø,3,4][J,M]Z	Insert/Ventricle, Rt, [Opn, Perc, Perc Endo], [Cardiac Lead, Pacemaker, Cardiac Lead], NQ
Ø2HL[Ø,3,4][J,M]Z	Insert/Ventricle, Lt, [Opn, Perc, Perc Endo], [Cardiac Lead, Pacemaker, Cardiac Lead], NQ

AND	
ØJH6[Ø,3][4,5,6]Z	Insert/SQ Tissue & Fascia, Chest, [Opn, Perc], [Pacemaker, Single Chamber, Pacemaker, Single Chamber Rate Responsive, Pacemaker, Dual Chamber], NQ
ØJH8[Ø,3][4,5,6]Z	Insert/SQ Tissue & Fascia, Abd, [Opn, Perc], [Pacemaker, Single Chamber, Pacemaker, Single Chamber Rate Responsive, Pacemaker, Dual Chamber], NQ
AND	
ØJPT[Ø,3]PZ	Rmvl/SQ Tissue & Fascia, Trunk, [Opn, Perc], Cardiac Rhythm Related Dev, NQ

OR

Ø2HK[3,4][J,M]Z	Insert/Ventricle, Rt, [Perc, Perc Endo], [Cardiac Lead, Pacemaker, Cardiac Lead], NQ
Ø2HL[Ø,3,4][J,M]Z	Insert/Ventricle, Lt, [Opn, Perc, Perc Endo], [Cardiac Lead, Pacemaker, Cardiac Lead], NQ

AND	
ØJH6[Ø,3][4,5,6]Z	Insert/SQ Tissue & Fascia, Chest, [Opn, Perc], [Pacemaker, Single Chamber, Pacemaker, Single Chamber Rate Responsive, Pacemaker, Dual Chamber], NQ
ØJH8[Ø,3][4,5,6]Z	Insert/SQ Tissue & Fascia, Abd, [Opn, Perc], [Pacemaker, Single Chamber, Pacemaker, Single Chamber Rate Responsive, Pacemaker, Dual Chamber], NQ
AND	
ØJPT[Ø,3]PZ	Rmvl/SQ Tissue & Fascia, Trunk, [Opn, Perc], Cardiac Rhythm Related Dev, NQ

OR

Ø2HK3JZ	Insert of Pacemaker Lead into Rt Ventricle, Perc Appr
Ø2HL3JZ	Insert of Pacemaker Lead into Lt Ventricle, Perc Appr

AND	
ØJH6[Ø,3][6,P]Z	Insert/SQ Tissue & Fascia, Chest, [Opn, Perc], [Pacemaker, Dual Chamber, Cardiac Rhythm Related Dev], NQ
ØJH8[Ø,3][6,P]Z	Insert/SQ Tissue & Fascia, Abd, [Opn, Perc], [Pacemaker, Dual Chamber, Cardiac Rhythm Related Dev], NQ

OR

Ø2H64MZ	Insert of Cardiac Lead into Rt Atrium, Perc Endo Appr
Ø2H6[3,4]JZ	Insert/Atrium, Rt, [Perc, Perc Endo], Cardiac Lead, Pacemaker, NQ
Ø2H7[Ø,3,4]JZ	Insert/Atrium, Lt, [Opn, Perc, Perc Endo], Cardiac Lead, Pacemaker, NQ
Ø2H7[Ø,4]MZ	Insert/Atrium, Lt, [Opn, Perc Endo], Cardiac Lead, NQ
Ø2HK[Ø,3,4][J,M]Z	Insert/Ventricle, Rt, [Opn, Perc, Perc Endo], [Cardiac Lead, Pacemaker, Cardiac Lead], NQ
Ø2HL[Ø,3,4][J,M]Z	Insert/Ventricle, Lt, [Opn, Perc, Perc Endo], [Cardiac Lead, Pacemaker, Cardiac Lead], NQ

AND	
ØJH6[Ø,3][4,5,6]Z	Insert/SQ Tissue & Fascia, Chest, [Opn, Perc], [Pacemaker, Single Chamber, Pacemaker, Single Chamber Rate Responsive, Pacemaker, Dual Chamber], NQ
ØJH8[Ø,3][4,5,6]Z	Insert/SQ Tissue & Fascia, Abd, [Opn, Perc], [Pacemaker, Single Chamber, Pacemaker, Single Chamber Rate Responsive, Pacemaker, Dual Chamber], NQ
AND	
ØJPT[Ø,3]PZ	Rmvl/SQ Tissue & Fascia, Trunk, [Opn, Perc], Cardiac Rhythm Related Dev, NQ

OR

Ø2HN[Ø,3,4][J,M]Z	Insert/Pericardium, [Opn, Perc, Perc Endo], [Cardiac Lead, Pacemaker, Cardiac Lead], NQ

Surgical   **Medical**   **CC Indicator**   **MCC Indicator**   **Procedure Proxy**   **PDxMCC PDx acts as own MCC**   **PDxCC PDx acts as own CC**

AND

ØJH6[Ø,3][4,5,6,P]Z Insert/SQ Tissue & Fascia, Chest, [Opn, Perc], [Pacemaker, Single Chamber, Pacemaker, Single Chamber Rate Responsive, Pacemaker, Dual Chamber, Cardiac Rhythm Related Dev], NQ

ØJH8[Ø,3][4,5,6,P]Z Insert/SQ Tissue & Fascia, Abd, [Opn, Perc], [Pacemaker, Single Chamber, Pacemaker, Single Chamber Rate Responsive, Pacemaker, Dual Chamber, Cardiac Rhythm Related Dev], NQ

OR

02HN[Ø,3,4][J,M]Z Insert/Pericardium, [Opn, Perc, Perc Endo], [Cardiac Lead, Pacemaker, Cardiac Lead], NQ

AND

ØJH6[Ø,3][4,5,6]Z Insert/SQ Tissue & Fascia, Chest, [Opn, Perc], [Pacemaker, Single Chamber, Pacemaker, Single Chamber Rate Responsive, Pacemaker, Dual Chamber], NQ

ØJH8[Ø,3][4,5,6]Z Insert/SQ Tissue & Fascia, Abd, [Opn, Perc], [Pacemaker, Single Chamber, Pacemaker, Single Chamber Rate Responsive, Pacemaker, Dual Chamber], NQ

AND

ØJPT[Ø,3]PZ Rmvl/SQ Tissue & Fascia, Trunk, [Opn, Perc], Cardiac Rhythm Related Dev, NQ

OR

02H63MZ Insert of Cardiac Lead into Rt Atrium, Perc Appr
02H73MZ Insert of Cardiac Lead into Lt Atrium, Perc Appr

AND

ØJH6[Ø,3]PZ Insert/SQ Tissue & Fascia, Chest, [Opn, Perc], Cardiac Rhythm Related Dev, NQ

ØJH8[Ø,3]PZ Insert/SQ Tissue & Fascia, Abd, [Opn, Perc], Cardiac Rhythm Related Dev, NQ

OR

02H63MZ Insert of Cardiac Lead into Rt Atrium, Perc Appr
02H73MZ Insert of Cardiac Lead into Lt Atrium, Perc Appr

AND

ØJH6[Ø,3][4,5,6]Z Insert/SQ Tissue & Fascia, Chest, [Opn, Perc], [Pacemaker, Single Chamber, Pacemaker, Single Chamber Rate Responsive, Pacemaker, Dual Chamber], NQ

ØJH8[Ø,3][4,5,6]Z Insert/SQ Tissue & Fascia, Abd, [Opn, Perc], [Pacemaker, Single Chamber, Pacemaker, Single Chamber Rate Responsive, Pacemaker, Dual Chamber], NQ

AND

ØJPT[Ø,3]PZ Rmvl/SQ Tissue & Fascia, Trunk, [Opn, Perc], Cardiac Rhythm Related Dev, NQ

OR

02H63JZ Insert of Pacemaker Lead into Rt Atrium, Perc Appr
02H73JZ Insert of Pacemaker Lead into Lt Atrium, Perc Appr
02HK3JZ Insert of Pacemaker Lead into Rt Ventricle, Perc Appr
02HL3JZ Insert of Pacemaker Lead into Lt Ventricle, Perc Appr

AND

02PA[Ø,3,4,X]MZ Rmvl/Heart, [Opn, Perc, Perc Endo, Ext], Cardiac Lead, NQ

AND

ØJH6[Ø,3]PZ Insert/SQ Tissue & Fascia, Chest, [Opn, Perc], Cardiac Rhythm Related Dev, NQ

ØJH8[Ø,3]PZ Insert/SQ Tissue & Fascia, Abd, [Opn, Perc], Cardiac Rhythm Related Dev, NQ

OR

02H63JZ Insert of Pacemaker Lead into Rt Atrium, Perc Appr
02H73JZ Insert of Pacemaker Lead into Lt Atrium, Perc Appr
02HK3JZ Insert of Pacemaker Lead into Rt Ventricle, Perc Appr
02HL3JZ Insert of Pacemaker Lead into Lt Ventricle, Perc Appr

AND

02PA[Ø,3,4,X]MZ Rmvl/Heart, [Opn, Perc, Perc Endo, Ext], Cardiac Lead, NQ

AND

ØJH6[Ø,3][4,5,6]Z Insert/SQ Tissue & Fascia, Chest, [Opn, Perc], [Pacemaker, Single Chamber, Pacemaker, Single Chamber Rate Responsive, Pacemaker, Dual Chamber], NQ

ØJH8[Ø,3][4,5,6]Z Insert/SQ Tissue & Fascia, Abd, [Opn, Perc], [Pacemaker, Single Chamber, Pacemaker, Single Chamber Rate Responsive, Pacemaker, Dual Chamber], NQ

AND

ØJPT[Ø,3]PZ Rmvl/SQ Tissue & Fascia, Trunk, [Opn, Perc], Cardiac Rhythm Related Dev, NQ

OR

Nonoperating Room Procedures

DØ2Ø[D,H,J]ZZ Stereotactic Radiosurgery/Brain, [Stereotactic Oth Photon Radiosurgery, Stereotactic Particulate Radiosurgery, Stereotactic Gamma Beam Radiosurgery], None, None

DØ21[D,H,J]ZZ Stereotactic Radiosurgery/Brain Stem, [Stereotactic Oth Photon Radiosurgery, Stereotactic Particulate Radiosurgery, Stereotactic Gamma Beam Radiosurgery], None, None

DØ26[D,H,J]ZZ Stereotactic Radiosurgery/Spinal Cord, [Stereotactic Oth Photon Radiosurgery, Stereotactic Particulate Radiosurgery, Stereotactic Gamma Beam Radiosurgery], None, None

DØ27[D,H,J]ZZ Stereotactic Radiosurgery/Peripheral Nerve, [Stereotactic Oth Photon Radiosurgery, Stereotactic Particulate Radiosurgery, Stereotactic Gamma Beam Radiosurgery], None, None

D72Ø[D,H,J]ZZ Stereotactic Radiosurgery/Bone Marrow, [Stereotactic Oth Photon Radiosurgery, Stereotactic Particulate Radiosurgery, Stereotactic Gamma Beam Radiosurgery], None, None

D721[D,H,J]ZZ Stereotactic Radiosurgery/Thymus, [Stereotactic Oth Photon Radiosurgery, Stereotactic Particulate Radiosurgery, Stereotactic Gamma Beam Radiosurgery], None, None

D722[D,H,J]ZZ Stereotactic Radiosurgery/Spleen, [Stereotactic Oth Photon Radiosurgery, Stereotactic Particulate Radiosurgery, Stereotactic Gamma Beam Radiosurgery], None, None

D723[D,H,J]ZZ Stereotactic Radiosurgery/Lymphatics, Neck, [Stereotactic Oth Photon Radiosurgery, Stereotactic Particulate Radiosurgery, Stereotactic Gamma Beam Radiosurgery], None, None

D724[D,H,J]ZZ Stereotactic Radiosurgery/Lymphatics, Axillary, [Stereotactic Oth Photon Radiosurgery, Stereotactic Particulate Radiosurgery, Stereotactic Gamma Beam Radiosurgery], None, None

D725[D,H,J]ZZ Stereotactic Radiosurgery/Lymphatics, Thorax, [Stereotactic Oth Photon Radiosurgery, Stereotactic Particulate Radiosurgery, Stereotactic Gamma Beam Radiosurgery], None, None

D726[D,H,J]ZZ Stereotactic Radiosurgery/Lymphatics, Abd, [Stereotactic Oth Photon Radiosurgery, Stereotactic Particulate Radiosurgery, Stereotactic Gamma Beam Radiosurgery], None, None

D727[D,H,J]ZZ Stereotactic Radiosurgery/Lymphatics, Pelvis, [Stereotactic Oth Photon Radiosurgery, Stereotactic Particulate Radiosurgery, Stereotactic Gamma Beam Radiosurgery], None, None

D728[D,H,J]ZZ Stereotactic Radiosurgery/Lymphatics, Inguinal, [Stereotactic Oth Photon Radiosurgery, Stereotactic Particulate Radiosurgery, Stereotactic Gamma Beam Radiosurgery], None, None

D82Ø[D,H,J]ZZ Stereotactic Radiosurgery/Eye, [Stereotactic Oth Photon Radiosurgery, Stereotactic Particulate Radiosurgery, Stereotactic Gamma Beam Radiosurgery], None, None

D92Ø[D,H,J]ZZ Stereotactic Radiosurgery/Ear, [Stereotactic Oth Photon Radiosurgery, Stereotactic Particulate Radiosurgery, Stereotactic Gamma Beam Radiosurgery], None, None

D921[D,H,J]ZZ Stereotactic Radiosurgery/Nose, [Stereotactic Oth Photon Radiosurgery, Stereotactic Particulate Radiosurgery, Stereotactic Gamma Beam Radiosurgery], None, None

D924[D,H,J]ZZ Stereotactic Radiosurgery/Mouth, [Stereotactic Oth Photon Radiosurgery, Stereotactic Particulate Radiosurgery, Stereotactic Gamma Beam Radiosurgery], None, None

D925[D,H,J]ZZ Stereotactic Radiosurgery/Tongue, [Stereotactic Oth Photon Radiosurgery, Stereotactic Particulate Radiosurgery, Stereotactic Gamma Beam Radiosurgery], None, None

D926[D,H,J]ZZ Stereotactic Radiosurgery/Salivary Glands, [Stereotactic Oth Photon Radiosurgery, Stereotactic Particulate Radiosurgery, Stereotactic Gamma Beam Radiosurgery], None, None

D927[D,H,J]ZZ Stereotactic Radiosurgery/Sinuses, [Stereotactic Oth Photon Radiosurgery, Stereotactic Particulate Radiosurgery, Stereotactic Gamma Beam Radiosurgery], None, None

D928[D,H,J]ZZ Stereotactic Radiosurgery/Hard Palate, [Stereotactic Oth Photon Radiosurgery, Stereotactic Particulate Radiosurgery, Stereotactic Gamma Beam Radiosurgery], None, None

D929[D,H,J]ZZ Stereotactic Radiosurgery/Soft Palate, [Stereotactic Oth Photon Radiosurgery, Stereotactic Particulate Radiosurgery, Stereotactic Gamma Beam Radiosurgery], None, None

D92B[D,H,J]ZZ Stereotactic Radiosurgery/Larynx, [Stereotactic Oth Photon Radiosurgery, Stereotactic Particulate Radiosurgery, Stereotactic Gamma Beam Radiosurgery], None, None

D92C[D,H,J]ZZ Stereotactic Radiosurgery/Pharynx, [Stereotactic Oth Photon Radiosurgery, Stereotactic Particulate Radiosurgery, Stereotactic Gamma Beam Radiosurgery], None, None

D92D[D,H,J]ZZ Stereotactic Radiosurgery/Nasopharynx, [Stereotactic Oth Photon Radiosurgery, Stereotactic Particulate Radiosurgery, Stereotactic Gamma Beam Radiosurgery], None, None

DB2Ø[D,H,J]ZZ Stereotactic Radiosurgery/Trachea, [Stereotactic Oth Photon Radiosurgery, Stereotactic Particulate Radiosurgery, Stereotactic Gamma Beam Radiosurgery], None, None

---

Ⓣ **Transfer DRG** 　Ⓢᴾ **Special Payment** 　***Code Range** 　**6th and 7th Character of ZZ = No Device, No Qualifier ZX = No Device, Diagnostic**

DB21[D,H,J]ZZ Stereotactic Radiosurgery/Bronchus, [Stereotactic Oth Photon Radiosurgery, Stereotactic Particulate Radiosurgery, Stereotactic Gamma Beam Radiosurgery], None, None
DB22[D,H,J]ZZ Stereotactic Radiosurgery/Lung, [Stereotactic Oth Photon Radiosurgery, Stereotactic Particulate Radiosurgery, Stereotactic Gamma Beam Radiosurgery], None, None
DB25[D,H,J]ZZ Stereotactic Radiosurgery/Pleura, [Stereotactic Oth Photon Radiosurgery, Stereotactic Particulate Radiosurgery, Stereotactic Gamma Beam Radiosurgery], None, None
DB26[D,H,J]ZZ Stereotactic Radiosurgery/Mediastinum, [Stereotactic Oth Photon Radiosurgery, Stereotactic Particulate Radiosurgery, Stereotactic Gamma Beam Radiosurgery], None, None
DB27[D,H,J]ZZ Stereotactic Radiosurgery/Chest Wall, [Stereotactic Oth Photon Radiosurgery, Stereotactic Particulate Radiosurgery, Stereotactic Gamma Beam Radiosurgery], None, None
DB28[D,H,J]ZZ Stereotactic Radiosurgery/Diaphragm, [Stereotactic Oth Photon Radiosurgery, Stereotactic Particulate Radiosurgery, Stereotactic Gamma Beam Radiosurgery], None, None
DD20[D,H,J]ZZ Stereotactic Radiosurgery/Esophagus, [Stereotactic Oth Photon Radiosurgery, Stereotactic Particulate Radiosurgery, Stereotactic Gamma Beam Radiosurgery], None, None
DD21[D,H,J]ZZ Stereotactic Radiosurgery/Stomach, [Stereotactic Oth Photon Radiosurgery, Stereotactic Particulate Radiosurgery, Stereotactic Gamma Beam Radiosurgery], None, None
DD22[D,H,J]ZZ Stereotactic Radiosurgery/Duodenum, [Stereotactic Oth Photon Radiosurgery, Stereotactic Particulate Radiosurgery, Stereotactic Gamma Beam Radiosurgery], None, None
DD23[D,H,J]ZZ Stereotactic Radiosurgery/Jejunum, [Stereotactic Oth Photon Radiosurgery, Stereotactic Particulate Radiosurgery, Stereotactic Gamma Beam Radiosurgery], None, None
DD24[D,H,J]ZZ Stereotactic Radiosurgery/Ileum, [Stereotactic Oth Photon Radiosurgery, Stereotactic Particulate Radiosurgery, Stereotactic Gamma Beam Radiosurgery], None, None
DD25[D,H,J]ZZ Stereotactic Radiosurgery/Colon, [Stereotactic Oth Photon Radiosurgery, Stereotactic Particulate Radiosurgery, Stereotactic Gamma Beam Radiosurgery], None, None
DD27[D,H,J]ZZ Stereotactic Radiosurgery/Rectum, [Stereotactic Oth Photon Radiosurgery, Stereotactic Particulate Radiosurgery, Stereotactic Gamma Beam Radiosurgery], None, None
DF20[D,H,J]ZZ Stereotactic Radiosurgery/Liver, [Stereotactic Oth Photon Radiosurgery, Stereotactic Particulate Radiosurgery, Stereotactic Gamma Beam Radiosurgery], None, None
DF21[D,H,J]ZZ Stereotactic Radiosurgery/Gallbladder, [Stereotactic Oth Photon Radiosurgery, Stereotactic Particulate Radiosurgery, Stereotactic Gamma Beam Radiosurgery], None, None
DF22[D,H,J]ZZ Stereotactic Radiosurgery/Bile Ducts, [Stereotactic Oth Photon Radiosurgery, Stereotactic Particulate Radiosurgery, Stereotactic Gamma Beam Radiosurgery], None, None
DF23[D,H,J]ZZ Stereotactic Radiosurgery/Pancreas, [Stereotactic Oth Photon Radiosurgery, Stereotactic Particulate Radiosurgery, Stereotactic Gamma Beam Radiosurgery], None, None
DG20[D,H,J]ZZ Stereotactic Radiosurgery/Pituitary Gland, [Stereotactic Oth Photon Radiosurgery, Stereotactic Particulate Radiosurgery, Stereotactic Gamma Beam Radiosurgery], None, None
DG21[D,H,J]ZZ Stereotactic Radiosurgery/Pineal Body, [Stereotactic Oth Photon Radiosurgery, Stereotactic Particulate Radiosurgery, Stereotactic Gamma Beam Radiosurgery], None, None
DG22[D,H,J]ZZ Stereotactic Radiosurgery/Adrenal Glands, [Stereotactic Oth Photon Radiosurgery, Stereotactic Particulate Radiosurgery, Stereotactic Gamma Beam Radiosurgery], None, None
DG24[D,H,J]ZZ Stereotactic Radiosurgery/Parathyroid Glands, [Stereotactic Oth Photon Radiosurgery, Stereotactic Particulate Radiosurgery, Stereotactic Gamma Beam Radiosurgery], None, None
DG25[D,H,J]ZZ Stereotactic Radiosurgery/Thyroid, [Stereotactic Oth Photon Radiosurgery, Stereotactic Particulate Radiosurgery, Stereotactic Gamma Beam Radiosurgery], None, None
DM20[D,H,J]ZZ Stereotactic Radiosurgery/Breast, Lt, [Stereotactic Oth Photon Radiosurgery, Stereotactic Particulate Radiosurgery, Stereotactic Gamma Beam Radiosurgery], None, None
DM21[D,H,J]ZZ Stereotactic Radiosurgery/Breast, Rt, [Stereotactic Oth Photon Radiosurgery, Stereotactic Particulate Radiosurgery, Stereotactic Gamma Beam Radiosurgery], None, None
DT20[D,H,J]ZZ Stereotactic Radiosurgery/Kidney, [Stereotactic Oth Photon Radiosurgery, Stereotactic Particulate Radiosurgery, Stereotactic Gamma Beam Radiosurgery], None, None
DT21[D,H,J]ZZ Stereotactic Radiosurgery/Ureter, [Stereotactic Oth Photon Radiosurgery, Stereotactic Particulate Radiosurgery, Stereotactic Gamma Beam Radiosurgery], None, None

DT22[D,H,J]ZZ Stereotactic Radiosurgery/Bladder, [Stereotactic Oth Photon Radiosurgery, Stereotactic Particulate Radiosurgery, Stereotactic Gamma Beam Radiosurgery], None, None
DT23[D,H,J]ZZ Stereotactic Radiosurgery/Urethra, [Stereotactic Oth Photon Radiosurgery, Stereotactic Particulate Radiosurgery, Stereotactic Gamma Beam Radiosurgery], None, None
DU20[D,H,J]ZZ Stereotactic Radiosurgery/Ovary, [Stereotactic Oth Photon Radiosurgery, Stereotactic Particulate Radiosurgery, Stereotactic Gamma Beam Radiosurgery], None, None
DU21[D,H,J]ZZ Stereotactic Radiosurgery/Cervix, [Stereotactic Oth Photon Radiosurgery, Stereotactic Particulate Radiosurgery, Stereotactic Gamma Beam Radiosurgery], None, None
DU22[D,H,J]ZZ Stereotactic Radiosurgery/Uterus, [Stereotactic Oth Photon Radiosurgery, Stereotactic Particulate Radiosurgery, Stereotactic Gamma Beam Radiosurgery], None, None
DV20[D,H,J]ZZ Stereotactic Radiosurgery/Prostate, [Stereotactic Oth Photon Radiosurgery, Stereotactic Particulate Radiosurgery, Stereotactic Gamma Beam Radiosurgery], None, None
DV21[D,H,J]ZZ Stereotactic Radiosurgery/Testis, [Stereotactic Oth Photon Radiosurgery, Stereotactic Particulate Radiosurgery, Stereotactic Gamma Beam Radiosurgery], None, None
DW21[D,H,J]ZZ Stereotactic Radiosurgery/Head and Neck, [Stereotactic Oth Photon Radiosurgery, Stereotactic Particulate Radiosurgery, Stereotactic Gamma Beam Radiosurgery], None, None
DW22[D,H,J]ZZ Stereotactic Radiosurgery/Chest, [Stereotactic Oth Photon Radiosurgery, Stereotactic Particulate Radiosurgery, Stereotactic Gamma Beam Radiosurgery], None, None
DW23[D,H,J]ZZ Stereotactic Radiosurgery/Abd, [Stereotactic Oth Photon Radiosurgery, Stereotactic Particulate Radiosurgery, Stereotactic Gamma Beam Radiosurgery], None, None
DW26[D,H,J]ZZ Stereotactic Radiosurgery/Pelvic Rgn, [Stereotactic Oth Photon Radiosurgery, Stereotactic Particulate Radiosurgery, Stereotactic Gamma Beam Radiosurgery], None, None

DRG 041 — Peripheral/Cranial Nerve and Other Nervous System Procedures with CC or Peripheral Neurostimulator

GMLOS 4.7   AMLOS 6.0   RW 2.1354   [SP]

Select operating room procedures or procedure combinations listed under DRG 040

OR

Any of the following procedures

0JH6[0,3][B,C,D,E]Z Insert/SQ Tissue & Fascia, Chest, [Opn, Perc], [Stimulator Generator, Single Array, Stimulator Generator, Single Array Rechargeable, Stimulator Generator, Multi Array, Stimulator Generator, Multi Array Rechargeable], NQ
0JH7[0,3][B,C,D,E]Z Insert/SQ Tissue & Fascia, Back, [Opn, Perc], [Stimulator Generator, Single Array, Stimulator Generator, Single Array Rechargeable, Stimulator Generator, Multi Array, Stimulator Generator, Multi Array Rechargeable], NQ
0JH8[0,3][B,C,D,E]Z Insert/SQ Tissue & Fascia, Abd, [Opn, Perc], [Stimulator Generator, Single Array, Stimulator Generator, Single Array Rechargeable, Stimulator Generator, Multi Array, Stimulator Generator, Multi Array Rechargeable], NQ

AND

00HE[0,3,4]MZ Insert/Cranial Nerve, [Opn, Perc, Perc Endo], Neurostimulator Lead, NQ
01HY[0,3,4]MZ Insert/Peripheral Nerve, [Opn, Perc, Perc Endo], Neurostimulator Lead, NQ
0DH6[0,3,4]MZ Insert/Stomach, [Opn, Perc, Perc Endo], Stimulator Lead, NQ

DRG 042 — Peripheral/Cranial Nerve and Other Nervous System Procedures without CC/MCC

GMLOS 2.7   AMLOS 3.5   RW 1.9242   [SP]

Select operating room procedures or procedure combinations listed under DRG 040

MDC 1: Diseases And Disorders Of The Nervous System—SURGICAL

MDC 1: Diseases And Disorders Of The Nervous System—MEDICAL

MEDICAL

DRG 052   Spinal Disorders and Injuries with CC/MCC
GMLOS 4.1   AMLOS 5.4   RW 1.4915

Principal Diagnosis

G04.1	Tropical spastic paraplegia
G80.0	Spastic quadriplegic cerebral palsy
G80.1	Spastic diplegic cerebral palsy
G80.2	Spastic hemiplegic cerebral palsy
G82*	Paraplegia (paraparesis) and quadriplegia (quadriparesis)
G83.0	Diplegia of upr limbs
R53.2	Functional quadriplegia
S14.0XX[A,S]	Concussion and edema of cervical spinal cord, [init enc, seq]
S14.10[1,2,3,4,5,6,7,8,9][A,S]	Unsp inj at [C1, C2, C3, C4, C5, C6, C7, C8, unsp] lvl of cervical spinal cord [init enc, seq]
S14.11[1,2,3,4,5,6,7,8,9][A,S]	Complete lesion at [C1, C2, C3, C4, C5, C6, C7, C8, unsp] lvl of cervical spinal cord, [init enc, seq]
S14.12[1,2,3,4,5,6,7,8,9][A,S]	Central cord synd at [C1, C2, C3, C4, C5, C6, C7, C8, unsp] lvl of cervical spinal cord, [init enc, seq]
S14.13[1,2,3,4,5,6,7,8,9][A,S]	Ant cord synd at [C1, C2, C3, C4, C5, C6, C7, C8, unsp] lvl of cervical spinal cord, [init enc, seq]
S14.14[1,2,3,4,5,6,7,8,9][A,S]	Brown-Sequard synd at [C1, C2, C3, C4, C5, C6, C7, C8, unsp] lvl of cervical spinal cord, [init enc, seq]
S14.15[1,2,3,4,5,6,7,8,9][A,S]	Oth incomplete lesion at [C1, C2, C3, C4, C5, C6, C7, C8, unsp] lvl of cervical spinal cord, [init enc, seq]
S24.0XX[A,S]	Concussion and edema of thoracic spinal cord, [init enc, seq]
S24.10[1,2,3,4,9][A,S]	Unsp inj at [T1, T2-T6, T7-T10, T11-T12, unsp] lvl of thoracic spinal cord, [init enc, seq]
S24.11[1,2,3,4,9][A,S]	Complete lesion at [T1, T2-T6, T7-T10, T11-T12, unsp] lvl of thoracic spinal cord, [init enc, seq]
S24.13[1,2,3,4,9][A,S]	Ant cord synd at [T1, T2-T6, T7-T10, T11-T12, unsp] lvl of thoracic spinal cord, [init enc, seq]
S24.14[1,2,3,4,9][A,S]	Brown-Sequard synd at [T1, T2-T6, T7-T10, T11-T12, unsp] lvl of thoracic spinal cord, [init enc, seq]
S24.15[1,2,3,4,9][A,S]	Oth incomplete inj at [T1, T2-T6, T7-T10, T11-T12, unsp] lvl of thoracic spinal cord, [init enc, seq]
S34.0[1,2]X[A,S]	Concussion and edema of [lumbar, sacral] spinal cord, [init enc, seq]
S34.10[1,2,3,4,5,9][A,S]	Unsp inj to [L1, L2, L3, L4, L5, unsp] lvl of lumbar spinal cord, [init enc, seq]
S34.11[1,2,3,4,5,9][A,S]	Complete lesion inj to [L1, L2, L3, L4, L5, unsp] lvl of lumbar spinal cord, [init enc, seq]
S34.12[1,2,3,4,5,9][A,S]	Incomplete lesion to [L1, L2, L3, L4, L5, unsp] lvl of lumbar spinal cord, [init enc, seq]
S34.13[1,2,9][A,S]	[Complete lesion, Incomplete lesion, Unsp inj] to sacral spinal cord, [init enc, seq]
S34.3XXA	Inj of cauda equina, init enc

DRG 053   Spinal Disorders and Injuries without CC/MCC
GMLOS 2.8   AMLOS 3.4   RW 0.8625

Select principal diagnosis listed under DRG 052

DRG 054   Nervous System Neoplasms with MCC
GMLOS 4.0   AMLOS 5.4   RW 1.3570   T

Principal Diagnosis

C70*	Malig neoplasm of meninges
C71*	Malig neoplasm of brain
C72*	Malig neoplm of spinal cord, cranial nerves and oth prt cnsl
C75.3	Malig neoplasm of pineal gland
C75.4	Malig neoplasm of carotid body
C75.5	Malig neoplasm of aortic body and oth paraganglia
C79.3*	Secondary malig neoplasm of brain and cerebral meninges
C79.4*	Secondary malig neoplasm of and unsp parts of nervous sys
D32*	Benign neoplasm of meninges
D33*	Benign neoplasm of brain and oth prt central nervous sys
D35.4	Benign neoplasm of pineal gland
D35.5	Benign neoplasm of carotid body
D35.6	Benign neoplasm of aortic body and oth paraganglia
D42*	Neoplasm of uncertain behav of meninges
D43*	Neoplasm of uncertain behav of brain and cnsl
D44.5	Neoplasm of uncertain behav of pineal gland
D44.6	Neoplasm of uncertain behav of carotid body
D44.7	Neoplasm of uncertain behav of aortic body and oth paraganglia

D49.6	Neoplasm of unsp behav of brain

DRG 055   Nervous System Neoplasms without MCC
GMLOS 3.0   AMLOS 4.1   RW 1.0401   T

Select principal diagnosis listed under DRG 054

DRG 056   Degenerative Nervous System Disorders with MCC
GMLOS 5.2   AMLOS 7.2   RW 1.8513   T

Principal Diagnosis

A52.10	Symptomatic neurosyphilis, unsp
A52.11	Tabes dorsalis
A52.12	Oth cerebrospinal syphilis
A52.15	Late syphilitic neuropathy
A52.16	Charcot's arthropathy (tabetic)
A52.17	General paresis
A52.19	Oth symptomatic neurosyphilis
A52.3	Neurosyphilis, unsp
A81*	Atypical virus infections of central nervous sys
E75.0*	GM2 gangliosidosis
E75.1*	Oth and unsp gangliosidosis
E75.23	Krabbe dz
E75.25	Metachromatic leukodystrophy
E75.29	Oth sphingolipidosis
E75.4	Neuronal ceroid lipofuscinosis
F07.89	Oth personality & behavrl d/o d/t known physiol cond
F48.2	Pseudobulbar affect
F84.2	Rett's synd
G10	Huntington's dz
G12*	Spinal muscular atrophy and related syndromes
G13.2	Systemic atrophy primarily affecting the cnsl in myxedema
G13.8	Systemic atrophy affected cnsl in oth dz classd elsw
G20	Parkinson's dz
G21.1*	Oth drug-induced secondary parkinsonism
G21.2	Secondary parkinsonism d/t oth ext agents
G21.3	Postencephalitic parkinsonism
G21.4	Vascular parkinsonism
G21.8	Oth secondary parkinsonism
G21.9	Secondary parkinsonism, unsp
G23*	Oth degenerative dz of basal ganglia
G24.1	Genetic torsion dystonia
G25.4	Drug-induced chorea
G25.5	Oth chorea
G25.7*	Oth and unsp drug induced movement d/o
G25.81	Restless legs synd
G25.89	Oth spec extrapyramidal and movement d/o
G25.9	Extrapyramidal and movement d/o, unsp
G26	Extrapyramidal and movement d/o in dz classd elsw
G30*	Alzheimer's dz
G31*	Oth degenerative dz of nervous sys, NEC
G70.0*	Myasthenia gravis
G70.80	Lambert-Eaton synd, unsp
G70.81	Lambert-Eaton synd in dz classified elsw
G71.1	Lambert-Eaton synd in neoplastic dz
G73.3	Myasthenic syndromes in oth dz classified elsw
G80.3	Athetoid cerebral palsy
G81*	Hemiplegia and hemiparesis
G90.3	Multi-sys degeneration of the autonomic nervous sys
G91*	Hydrocephalus
G94	Oth d/o of brain in dz classified elsw
G95.0	Syringomyelia and syringobulbia
H57.01	Argyll Robertson pupil, atypical
I67.3	Progressive vascular leukoencephalopathy
I69*	Sequelae of cerebrovascular dz

DRG 057   Degenerative Nervous System Disorders without MCC
GMLOS 3.7   AMLOS 5.0   RW 1.0716   T

Select prinicpal diagnosis listed under DRG 056

DRG 058   Multiple Sclerosis and Cerebellar Ataxia with MCC
GMLOS 5.5   AMLOS 7.3   RW 1.7198

Prinicpal Diagnosis

G11*	Hereditary ataxia
G32.81	Cerebellar ataxia in dz classified elsw
G35	Multi sclerosis

T **Transfer DRG**   SP **Special Payment**   * **Code Range**   **6th and 7th Character of ZZ = No Device, No Qualifier ZX = No Device, Diagnostic**

G36*	Oth acute disseminated demyelination
G37.0	Diffuse sclerosis of central nervous sys
G37.1	Central demyelination of corpus callosum
G37.2	Central pontine myelinolysis
G37.5	Concentric sclerosis [Balo] of central nervous sys
G37.8	Oth demyelinating dz of central nervous sys
G37.9	Demyelinating dz of central nervous sys, unsp

DRG 059 Multiple Sclerosis and Cerebellar Ataxia with CC
GMLOS 3.7   AMLOS 4.5   RW 1.0134

Select principal diagnosis listed under DRG 058

DRG 060 Multiple Sclerosis and Cerebellar Ataxia without CC/MCC
GMLOS 3.1   AMLOS 3.7   RW 0.8130

Select principal diagnosis listed under DRG 058

DRG 061 Acute Ischemic Stroke with Use of Thrombolytic Agent with MCC
GMLOS 5.4   AMLOS 7.1   RW 2.6843

Prinicpal Diagnosis

I63*	Cerebral infarction

AND

Nonoperating Room Procedure

3E03[0,3]17	Introduction/Peripheral Vein, [Opn, Perc], Thrombolytic, Oth Thrombolytic
3E04[0,3]17	Introduction/Central Vein, [Opn, Perc], Thrombolytic, Oth Thrombolytic
3E05[0,3]17	Introduction/Peripheral Artery, [Opn, Perc], Thrombolytic, Oth Thrombolytic
3E06[0,3]17	Introduction/Central Artery, [Opn, Perc], Thrombolytic, Oth Thrombolytic
3E08[0,3]17	Introduction/Heart, [Opn, Perc], Thrombolytic, Oth Thrombolytic

DRG 062 Acute Ischemic Stroke with Use of Thrombolytic Agent with CC
GMLOS 3.9   AMLOS 4.6   RW 1.8918

Select principal diagnosis AND nonoperating room procedure listed under DRG 061

DRG 063 Acute Ischemic Stroke with Use of Thrombolytic Agent without CC/MCC
GMLOS 2.9   AMLOS 3.2   RW 1.5238

Select principal diagnosis AND nonoperating room procedure listed under DRG 061

DRG 064 Intracranial Hemorrhage or Cerebral Infarction with MCC
GMLOS 4.5   AMLOS 6.1   RW 1.7326   [T]

Principal Diagnosis

I60*	Nontraumatic subarachnoid hemor
I61*	Nontraumatic intracerebral hemor
I62*	Oth and unsp nontraumatic intracranial hemor
I63*	Cerebral infarction

DRG 065 Intracranial Hemorrhage or Cerebral Infarction with CC or tPA in 24 Hours
GMLOS 3.3   AMLOS 4.1   RW 1.0593   [T]

Select principal diagnosis listed under DRG 064

AND

Secondary Diagnosis

Z92.82	S/p admn tPA in diff fac w/n last 24 hr bef adm to crnt fac

DRG 066 Intracranial Hemorrhage or Cerebral Infarction without CC/MCC
GMLOS 2.4   AMLOS 2.8   RW 0.7574   [T]

Select principal diagnosis listed under DRG 064

DRG 067 Nonspecific Cerebrovascular Accident and Precerebral Occlusion without Infarction with MCC
GMLOS 4.0   AMLOS 5.0   RW 1.4338

Principal Diagnosis

I65*	Occlsn and stenosis of precerb art, not rslt in cereb infrc
I66*	Occlsn and stenosis of cereb art, not rslt in cerebral infrc

DRG 068 Nonspecific Cerebrovascular Accident and Precerebral Occlusion without Infarction without MCC
GMLOS 2.4   AMLOS 2.9   RW 0.8731

Select principal diagnosis listed under DRG 067

DRG 069 Transient Ischemia
GMLOS 2.1   AMLOS 2.5   RW 0.7227

Principal Diagnosis

G45.0	Vertebro-basilar artery synd
G45.1	Carotid artery synd (hemispheric)
G45.2	Multi and bilat precerebral artery syndromes
G45.8	Oth transient cerebral ischemic attacks and related synd
G45.9	Transient cerebral ischemic attack, unsp
G46.0	Mid cerebral artery synd
G46.1	Ant cerebral artery synd
G46.2	Posterior cerebral artery synd
I67.81	Acute cerebrovascular insufficiency
I67.82	Cerebral ischemia
I67.841	Reversible cerebrovascular vasoconstriction synd
I67.848	Oth cerebrovascular vasospasm and vasoconstriction
I67.89	Oth cerebrovascular dz

DRG 070 Nonspecific Cerebrovascular Disorders with MCC
GMLOS 4.7   AMLOS 6.3   RW 1.6283   [T]

Principal Diagnosis

G32.89	Oth degeneratv d/o of nervous sys in dis classd elsw
G45.4	Transient global amnesia
G46.3	Brain stem stroke synd
G46.4	Cerebellar stroke synd
G46.5	Pure motor lacunar synd
G46.6	Pure sensory lacunar synd
G46.7	Oth lacunar syndromes
G46.8	Oth vascular syndromes of brain in cerebrovascular dz
G93.4*	Oth and unsp encephalopathy
G93.81	Temporal sclerosis
G93.89	Oth spec d/o of brain
G93.9	D/o of brain, unsp
G96.8	Oth spec d/o of central nervous sys
G96.9	D/o of central nervous sys, unsp
G98*	Oth d/o of nervous sys NEC
G99.8	Oth disrd of nervous sys in dz classified elsw
I67.2	Cerebral atherosclerosis
I67.83	Posterior reversible encephalopathy synd
I67.9	Cerebrovascular dz, unsp
I68.0	Cerebral amyloid angiopathy
I68.8	Oth cerebrovascular d/o in dz classd elsw

DRG 071 Nonspecific Cerebrovascular Disorders with CC
GMLOS 3.5   AMLOS 4.4   RW 1.0079   [T]

Select principal diagnosis listed under DRG 070

DRG 072 Nonspecific Cerebrovascular Disorders without CC/MCC
GMLOS 2.4   AMLOS 3.0   RW 0.7329   [T]

Select principal diagnosis listed under DRG 070

DRG 073 Cranial and Peripheral Nerve Disorders with MCC
GMLOS 3.8   AMLOS 5.2   RW 1.3359

Principal Diagnosis

B02.0	Zoster encephalitis
B02.21	Postherpetic geniculate ganglionitis
B02.22	Postherpetic trigeminal neuralgia
B02.23	Postherpetic polyneuropathy
B02.29	Oth postherpetic nervous sys involvement

Surgical	Medical	CC Indicator	MCC Indicator	Procedure Proxy	PDxMCC PDx acts as own MCC	PDxCC PDx acts as own CC

B06.00	Rubella with neurological comp, unsp
B26.84	Mumps polyneuropathy
E08.4*	Diabetes d/t underlying condition w neurological comp
E08.610	Diabetes d/t undrl cond w diabetic neuropathic arthrop
E09.4*	Drug/chem diabetes mellitus w neurological comp
E09.610	Drug/chem diabetes w diabetic neuropathic arthropathy
E10.4*	Type 1 diabetes mellitus with neurological comp
E10.610	Type 1 diabetes mellitus w diabetic neuropathic arthropathy
E11.4*	Type 2 diabetes mellitus with neurological comp
E11.610	Type 2 diabetes mellitus w diabetic neuropathic arthropathy
E13.4*	Oth diabetes mellitus with neurological comp
E13.610	Oth diabetes mellitus with diabetic neuropathic arthropathy
G13.0	Paraneoplastic neuromyopathy and neuropathy
G13.1	Oth systemic atrophy affected cnsl in neoplastic dz
G50*	D/o of trigeminal nerve
G51*	Facial nerve d/o
G52*	D/o of oth cranial nerves
G53	Cranial nerve d/o in dz classified elsw
G54*	Nerve root and plexus d/o
G55	Nerve root and plexus compressions in dz classd elsw
G56*	Mononeuropathies of upr limb
G57*	Mononeuropathies of lwr limb
G58*	Oth mononeuropathies
G59	Mononeuropathy in dz classified elsw
G60.0	Hereditary motor and sensory neuropathy
G60.2	Neuropathy in association with hereditary ataxia
G60.3	Idiopathic progressive neuropathy
G60.8	Oth hereditary and idiopathic neuropathies
G60.9	Hereditary and idiopathic neuropathy, unsp
G61.1	Serum neuropathy
G61.8*	Oth inflam polyneuropathies
G61.9	Inflam polyneuropathy, unsp
G62*	Oth and unsp polyneuropathies
G63	Polyneuropathy in dz classified elsw
G64	Oth d/o of peripheral nervous sys
G65*	Sequelae of inflam and txc polyneuropathies
G70.1	Txc myoneural d/o
G70.2	Congenital and developmental myasthenia
G70.89	Oth spec myoneural d/o
G70.9	Myoneural d/o, unsp
G83.4	Cauda equina synd
G90.0*	Idiopathic peripheral autonomic neuropathy
G90.2	Horner's synd
G90.4	Autonomic dysreflexia
G90.5*	Complex regional pain synd I (CRPS I)
G90.8	Oth d/o of autonomic nervous sys
G90.9	D/o of the autonomic nervous sys, unsp
G99.0	Autonomic neuropathy in dz classified elsw
M21.33[1,2,9]	Wrist drop, [Rt, Lt, Unsp] Wrist
M21.53[1,2,9]	Acquired clawfoot, [rt, lt, unsp] foot
M21.5[1,2][1,2,9]	Acquired [clawhand, clubhand], [rt, lt, unsp] hand
M34.83	Systemic sclerosis with polyneuropathy
M53.0	Cervicocranial synd
M53.1	Cervicobrachial synd
M54.1[0,1,2,3,8]	Radiculopathy, [unsp, occipito-atlanto-axial, cervical, cervicothoracic, sacral and sacrococcygeal] rgn
M79.2	Neuralgia and neuritis, unsp
S04.1[0,1,2]XA	Inj of oculomotor nerve, [unsp, rt, lt] side, init enc
S04.2[0,1,2]XA	Inj of trochlear nerve, [unsp, rt, lt] side, init enc
S04.3[0,1,2]XA	Inj of trigeminal nerve, [unsp, rt, lt] side, init enc
S04.4[0,1,2]XA	Inj of abducent nerve, [unsp, rt, lt] side, init enc
S04.5[0,1,2]XA	Inj of facial nerve, [unsp, rt, lt] side, init enc
S04.7[0,1,2]XA	Inj of accessory nerve, [unsp, rt, lt] side, init enc
S04.81[1,2,9]A	Inj of olfactory (1st) nerve, [rt, lt, unsp] side, init enc
S04.89[1,2,9]A	Inj of oth cranial nerves, [rt, lt, unsp] side, init enc
S04.9XXA	Inj of unsp cranial nerve, init enc
S14.2XXA	Inj of nerve root of cervical spine, init enc
S14.3XXA	Inj of brachial plexus, init enc
S14.4XXA	Inj of peripheral nerves of neck, init enc
S14.5XXA	Inj of cervical sympathetic nerves, init enc
S14.8XXA	Inj of oth spec nerves of neck, init enc
S14.9XXA	Inj of unsp nerves of neck, init enc
S24.2XXA	Inj of nerve root of thoracic spine, init enc
S24.3XXA	Inj of peripheral nerves of thorax, init enc
S24.4XXA	Inj of thoracic sympathetic nervous sys, init enc
S24.8XXA	Inj of oth spec nerves of thorax, init enc
S24.9XXA	Inj of unsp nerve of thorax, init enc
S34.2[1,2]XA	Inj of nerve root of [lumbar, sacral] spine, init enc
S34.4XXA	Inj of lumbosacral plexus, init enc
S34.5XXA	Inj of lumbar, sacral and pelvic sympathetic nerves, init

S34.6XXA	Inj prph nerve(s) at abd, low back and pelvis lvl, init
S34.8XXA	Inj of nerves at abd, low back and pelvis lvl, init
S34.9XXA	Inj unsp nerves at abd, low back and pelvis lvl, init
S44.0[0,1,2]XA	Inj of ulnar nerve at upr arm lvl, [unsp, rt, lt] arm, init enc
S44.1[0,1,2]XA	Inj of median nerve at upr arm lvl, [unsp, rt, lt] arm, init enc
S44.2[0,1,2]XA	Inj of radial nerve at upr arm lvl, [unsp, rt, lt] arm, init enc
S44.3[0,1,2]XA	Inj of axillary nerve at upr arm lvl, [unsp, rt, lt] arm, init enc
S44.4[0,1,2]XA	Inj of musculocutaneous nerve at upr arm lvl, [unsp, rt, lt] arm, init enc
S44.5[0,1,2]XA	Inj of cutaneous sensory nerve at shldr and upr arm lvl, [unsp, rt, lt] arm, init enc
S44.8X1A	Inj of nerves at shldr/up arm, rt arm, init
S44.8X2A	Inj of nerves at shldr/up arm, lt arm, init
S44.8X9A	Inj of nerves at shldr/up arm, unsp arm, init
S44.9[0,1,2]XA	Inj of unsp nerve at shldr and upr arm lvl, [unsp, rt, lt] arm, init enc
S54.0[0,1,2]XA	Inj of ulnar nerve at forearm lvl, [unsp, rt, lt] arm, init enc
S54.1[0,1,2]XA	Inj of median nerve at forearm lvl, [unsp, rt, lt] arm, init enc
S54.2[0,1,2]XA	Inj of radial nerve at forearm lvl, [unsp, rt, lt] arm, init enc
S54.3[0,1,2]XA	Inj of cutaneous sensory nerve at forearm lvl, [unsp, rt, lt] arm, init enc
S54.8X1A	Unsp inj of oth nerves at forearm lvl, rt arm, init
S54.8X2A	Unsp inj of oth nerves at forearm lvl, lt arm, init
S54.8X9A	Unsp inj of oth nerves at forearm lvl, unsp arm, init
S54.9[0,1,2]XA	Inj of unsp nerve at forearm lvl, [unsp, rt, lt] arm, init enc
S64.0[0,1,2]XA	Inj of ulnar nerve at wrist and hand lvl of [unsp, rt, lt] arm, init enc
S64.1[0,1,2]XA	Inj of median nerve at wrist and hand lvl of [unsp, rt, lt] arm, init enc
S64.2[0,1,2]XA	Inj of radial nerve at wrist and hand lvl of [unsp, rt, lt] arm, init enc
S64.3[0,1,2]XA	Inj of digital nerve of [unsp, rt, lt] thumb, init enc
S64.40XA	Inj of digital nerve of unsp finger, init enc
S64.49[0,1,2,3,4,5,6,7,8]A	Inj of digital nerve of [rt index, lt index, rt mid, lt mid, rt ring, lt ring, rt little, lt little, oth] finger, init enc
S64.8X1A	Inj of nerves at wrist and hand lvl of rt arm, init
S64.8X2A	Inj of oth nerves at wrist and hand lvl of lt arm, init
S64.8X9A	Inj of nerves at wrist and hand lvl of unsp arm, init
S64.9[0,1,2]XA	Inj of unsp nerve at wrist and hand lvl of [unsp, rt, lt] arm, init enc
S74.0[0,1,2]XA	Inj of sciatic nerve at hip & thigh lvl, [unsp, rt, lt] leg, init enc
S74.1[0,1,2]XA	Inj of femor nerve at hip & thigh lvl, [unsp, rt, lt] leg, init enc
S74.2[0,1,2]XA	Inj of cutaneous sensory nerve at hip & thigh lvl, [unsp, rt, lt] leg, init enc
S74.8X1A	Inj of oth nerves at hip & thigh lvl, rt leg, init
S74.8X2A	Inj of oth nerves at hip & thigh lvl, lt leg, init
S74.8X9A	Inj of oth nerves at hip & thigh lvl, unsp leg, init
S74.9[0,1,2]XA	Inj of unsp nerve at hip & thigh lvl, [unsp, rt, lt] leg, init enc
S84.0[0,1,2]XA	Inj of tibial nerve at lwr leg lvl, [unsp, rt, lt] leg, init enc
S84.1[0,1,2]XA	Inj of peroneal nerve at lwr leg lvl, [unsp, rt, lt] leg, init enc
S84.2[0,1,2]XA	Inj of cutaneous sensory nerve at lwr leg lvl, [unsp, rt, lt] leg, init enc
S84.801A	Inj of oth nerves at lwr leg lvl, rt leg, init
S84.802A	Inj of oth nerves at lwr leg lvl, lt leg, init
S84.809A	Inj of oth nerves at lwr leg lvl, unsp leg, init
S84.9[0,1,2]XA	Inj of unsp nerve at lwr leg lvl, [unsp, rt, lt] leg, init enc
S94.0[0,1,2]XA	Inj of lat plantar nerve, [unsp, rt, lt] leg, init enc
S94.1[0,1,2]XA	Inj of med plantar nerve, [unsp, rt, lt] leg, init enc
S94.2[0,1,2]XA	Inj of deep peroneal nerve at ankle and foot lvl, [unsp, rt, lt] leg, init enc
S94.3[0,1,2]XA	Inj of cutaneous sensory nerve at ankle and foot lvl, [unsp, rt, lt] leg, init enc
S94.8X1A	Inj of nerves at ankle and foot lvl, rt leg, init
S94.8X2A	Inj of oth nerves at ankle and foot lvl, lt leg, init
S94.8X9A	Inj of oth nerves at ankle and foot lvl, unsp leg, init
S94.9[0,1,2]XA	Inj of unsp nerve at ankle and foot lvl, [unsp leg, rt, lt], init enc

DRG 074   Cranial and Peripheral Nerve Disorders without MCC

GMLOS 3.0	AMLOS 3.8	RW 0.9063

Select principal diagnosis listed under DRG 073

DRG 075   Viral Meningitis with CC/MCC

GMLOS 5.3	AMLOS 6.7	RW 1.6917

Principal Diagnosis

A87*	Viral meningitis
A88.0	Enteroviral exanthematous fever [Boston exanthem]
B00.3	Herpesviral meningitis

T Transfer DRG   SP Special Payment   * Code Range   6th and 7th Character of ZZ = No Device, No Qualifier ZX = No Device, Diagnostic

B02.1　　　　Zoster meningitis
B26.1　　　　Mumps meningitis
G03.2　　　　Benign recurrent meningitis [Mollaret]

DRG 076　Viral Meningitis without CC/MCC
　　　GMLOS 2.9　　　AMLOS 3.4　　　RW 0.8302

Select principal diagnosis listed under DRG 075

DRG 077　Hypertensive Encephalopathy with MCC
　　　GMLOS 4.4　　　AMLOS 5.6　　　RW 1.5448

Principal Diagnosis

I67.4　　　　Hypertensive encephalopathy

DRG 078　Hypertensive Encephalopathy with CC
　　　GMLOS 3.1　　　AMLOS 3.9　　　RW 0.9676

Select principal diagnosis listed under DRG 077

DRG 079　Hypertensive Encephalopathy without CC/MCC
　　　GMLOS 2.3　　　AMLOS 2.8　　　RW 0.6862

Select principal diagnosis listed under DRG 077

DRG 080　Nontraumatic Stupor and Coma with MCC
　　　GMLOS 3.7　　　AMLOS 5.1　　　RW 1.2159

Principal Diagnosis

E03.5　　　　Myxedema coma
G93.5　　　　Compression of brain
G93.6　　　　Cerebral edema
G93.82　　　Brain death
R40.0　　　　Somnolence
R40.1　　　　Stupor
R40.20　　　Unsp coma
R40.211[0,1,2,3,4] Coma scale, eyes opn, never [unsp time, in the field (EMT or ambulance), at arrival to ED, at hospital admission, 24 hrs or more after hospital admission]
R40.212[0,1,2,3,4] Coma scale, eyes opn, to pain [unsp time, in the field (EMT or ambulance), at arrival to ED, at hospital admission, 24 hrs or more after hospital admission]
R40.221[0,1,2,3,4] Coma scale, best verbal response, none [unsp time, in the field (EMT or ambulance), at arrival to ED, at hospital admission, 24 hrs or more after hospital admission]
R40.222[0,1,2,3,4] Coma scale, best verbal response, incomprehensible words [unsp time, in the field (EMT or ambulance), at arrival to ED, at hospital admission, 24 hrs or more after hospital admission]
R40.231[0,1,2,3,4] Coma scale, best motor response, none [unsp time, in the field (EMT or ambulance), at arrival to ED, at hospital admission, 24 hrs or more after hospital admission]
R40.232[0,1,2,3,4] Coma scale, best motor response, extension [unsp time, in the field (EMT or ambulance), at arrival to ED, at hospital admission, 24 hrs or more after hospital admission
R40.234[0,1,2,3,4] Coma scale, best motor response, flexion w/drawal [unsp time, in the field (EMT or ambulance), at arrival to ED, at hospital admission, 24 hrs or more after hospital admission
R40.3　　　　Persistent vegetative state

DRG 081　Nontraumatic Stupor and Coma without MCC
　　　GMLOS 2.7　　　AMLOS 3.5　　　RW 0.7651

Select principal diagnosis listed under DRG 080

DRG 082　Traumatic Stupor and Coma, Coma Greater Than One Hour with MCC
　　　GMLOS 3.4　　　AMLOS 5.8　　　RW 2.0170

Principal Diagnosis of Traumatic Stupor and Coma > 1 Hour

S06.1X[3,4,5,6]A　Traum cerebral edema w/ LOC of [1 hr to 5 hrs 59 min, 6 hrs to 24 hrs, > 24 hrs w/ return to pre-existing conscious lvl, > 24 hrs w/o return to pre-existing conscious lvl patient surviving], init enc
S06.1X[7,8,9]A　Traum cerebral edema w/ LOC of [any dur w/ death d/t brain inj prior to regain cnscness, any dur w/ death d/t oth cause prior to regain cnscness, unsp dur], init enc

S06.2X[3,4,5,6]A　Diffuse traum brain inj w/ LOC of [1 hr to 5 hrs 59 min, 6 hrs to 24 hrs, > 24 hrs w/ return to pre-existing conscious lvl, > 24 hrs w/o return to pre-existing conscious lvl patient surviving], init enc
S06.2X[7,8,9]A　Diffuse traum brain inj w/ LOC of [any dur w/ death d/t brain inj prior to regain cnscness, any dur w/ death d/t oth cause prior to regain cnscness, unsp dur], init enc
S06.30[3,4,5,6]A　Unsp focal traum brain inj w/ LOC of [1 hr to 5 hrs 59 min, 6 hrs to 24 hrs, > 24 hrs w/ return to pre-existing conscious lvl, > 24 hrs w/o return to pre-existing conscious lvl patient surviving], init enc
S06.30[7,8,9]A　Unsp focal traum brain inj w/ LOC of [any dur w/ death d/t brain inj prior to regain cnscness, any dur w/ death d/t oth cause prior to regain cnscness, unsp dur], init enc
S06.31[3,4,5,6]A　Contsn and lac of rt cerebrum w/ LOC of [1 hr to 5 hrs 59 min, 6 hrs to 24 hrs, > 24 hrs w/ return to pre-existing conscious lvl, > 24 hrs w/o return to pre-existing conscious lvl patient surviving], init enc
S06.31[7,8,9]A　Contsn and lac of rt cerebrum w/ LOC of [any dur w/ death d/t brain inj prior to regain cnscness, any dur w/ death d/t oth cause prior to regain cnscness, unsp dur], init enc
S06.32[3,4,5,6]A　Contsn and lac of lt cerebrum w/ LOC of [1 hr to 5 hrs 59 min, 6 hrs to 24 hrs, > 24 hrs w/ return to pre-existing conscious lvl, > 24 hrs w/o return to pre-existing conscious lvl patient surviving], init enc
S06.32[7,8,9]A　Contsn and lac of lt cerebrum w/ LOC of [any dur w/ death d/t brain inj prior to regain cnscness, any dur w/ death d/t oth cause prior to regain cnscness, unsp dur], init enc
S06.33[3,4,5,6]A　Contsn and lac of cerebrum, unsp, w/ LOC of [1 hr to 5 hrs 59 min, 6 hrs to 24 hrs, > 24 hrs w/ return to pre-existing conscious lvl, > 24 hrs w/o return to pre-existing conscious lvl patient surviving], init enc
S06.33[7,8,9]A　Contsn and lac of cerebrum, unsp, w/ LOC of [any dur w/ death d/t brain inj prior to regain cnscness, any dur w/ death d/t oth cause prior to regain cnscness, unsp dur], init enc
S06.34[3,4,5,6]A　Traum hemor of rt cerebrum w/ LOC of [1 hr to 5 hrs 59 min, 6 hrs to 24 hrs, > 24 hrs w/ return to pre-existing conscious lvl, > 24 hrs w/o return to pre-existing conscious lvl patient surviving], init enc
S06.34[7,8,9]A　Traum hemor of rt cerebrum w/ LOC of [any dur w/ death d/t brain inj prior to regain cnscness, any dur w/ death d/t oth cause prior to regain cnscness, unsp dur], init enc
S06.35[3,4,5,6]A　Traum hemor of lt cerebrum w/ LOC of [1 hr to 5 hrs 59 min, 6 hrs to 24 hrs, > 24 hrs w/ return to pre-existing conscious lvl, > 24 hrs w/o return to pre-existing conscious lvl patient surviving], init enc
S06.35[7,8,9]A　Traum hemor of lt cerebrum w/ LOC of [any dur w/ death d/t brain inj prior to regain cnscness, any dur w/ death d/t oth cause prior to regain cnscness, unsp dur], init enc
S06.36[3,4,5,6]A　Traum hemor of cerebrum, unsp, w/ LOC of [1 hr to 5 hrs 59 min, 6 hrs to 24 hrs, > 24 hrs w/ return to pre-existing conscious lvl, > 24 hrs w/o return to pre-existing conscious lvl patient surviving], init enc
S06.36[7,8,9]A　Traum hemor of cerebrum, unsp, w/ LOC of [any dur w/ death d/t brain inj prior to regain cnscness, any dur w/ death d/t oth cause prior to regain cnscness, unsp dur], init enc
S06.37[3,4,5,6]A　Contsn, lac and hemor of cerebellum w/ LOC of [1 hr to 5 hrs 59 min, 6 hrs to 24 hrs, > 24 hrs w/ return to pre-existing conscious lvl, > 24 hrs w/o return to pre-existing conscious lvl patient surviving], init enc
S06.37[7,8,9]A　Contsn, lac, and hemor of cerebellum w/ LOC of [any dur w/ death d/t brain inj prior to regain cnscness, any dur w/ death d/t oth cause prior to regain cnscness, unsp dur], init enc
S06.38[3,4,5,6]A　Contsn, lac and hemor of brainstem w/ LOC of [1 hr to 5 hrs 59 min, 6 hrs to 24 hrs, > 24 hrs w/ return to pre-existing conscious lvl, > 24 hrs w/o return to pre-existing conscious lvl patient surviving], init enc
S06.38[7,8,9]A　Contsn, lac, and hemor of brainstem w/ LOC of [any dur w/ death d/t brain inj prior to regain cnscness, any dur w/ death d/t oth cause prior to regain cnscness, unsp dur], init enc
S06.4X[3,4,5,6]A　Epidural hemor w/ LOC of [1 hr to 5 hrs 59 min, 6 hrs to 24 hrs, > 24 hrs w/ return to pre-existing conscious lvl, > 24 hrs w/o return to pre-existing conscious lvl pt surviving], init enc
S06.4X[7,8,9]A　Epidural hemor w/ LOC of [any dur w/ death d/t brain inj prior to regain cnscness, any dur w/ death d/t oth cause prior to regain cnscness, unsp dur], init enc
S06.5X[3,4,5,6]A　Traum subdural hemor w/ LOC of [1 hr to 5 hrs 59 min, 6 hrs to 24 hrs, > 24 hrs w/ return to pre-existing conscious lvl, > 24 hrs w/o return to pre-existing conscious lvl patient surviving], init enc

S06.5X[7,8,9]A	Traum subdural hemor w/ LOC of [any dur w/ death d/t brain inj prior to regain cnscness, any dur w/ death d/t oth cause prior to regain cnscness, unsp dur], init enc
S06.6X[3,4,5,6]A	Traum subarachnoid hemor w/ LOC of [1 hr to 5 hrs 59 min, 6 hrs to 24 hrs, > 24 hrs w/ return to pre-existing conscious lvl, > 24 hrs w/o return to pre-existing conscious lvl patient surviving], init enc
S06.6X[7,8,9]A	Traum subarachnoid hemor w/ LOC of [any dur w/ death d/t brain inj prior to regain cnscness, any dur w/ death d/t oth cause prior to regain cnscness, unsp dur], init enc
S06.81[3,4,5,6]A	Inj of rt int carotid artery, intracranial portion, NEC w/ LOC of [1 hr to 5 hrs 59 min, 6 hrs to 24 hrs, > 24 hrs w/ return to pre-existing conscious lvl, > 24 hrs w/o return to pre-existing conscious lvl patient surviving], init enc
S06.81[7,8,9]A	Inj of rt int carotid artery, intracranial portion, NEC w/ LOC of [any dur w/ death d/t brain inj prior to regain cnscness, any dur w/ death d/t oth cause prior to regain cnscness, unsp dur], init enc
S06.82[3,4,5,6]A	Inj of lt int carotid artery, intracranial portion, NEC w/ LOC of [1 hr to 5 hrs 59 min, 6 hrs to 24 hrs, > 24 hrs w/ return to pre-existing conscious lvl, > 24 hrs w/o return to pre-existing conscious lvl patient surviving], init enc
S06.82[7,8,9]A	Inj of lt int carotid artery, intracranial portion, NEC w/ LOC of [any dur w/ death d/t brain inj prior to regain cnscness, any dur w/ death d/t oth cause prior to regain cnscness, unsp dur], init enc
S06.89[3,4,5,6]A	Oth intracranial inj w/ LOC of [1 hr to 5 hrs 59 min, 6 hrs to 24 hrs, > 24 hrs w/ return to pre-existing conscious lvl, > 24 hrs w/o return to pre-existing conscious lvl patient surviving], init enc
S06.89[7,8,9]A	Oth spec intracranial inj w/ LOC of [any dur w/ death d/t brain inj prior to regain cnscness, any dur w/ death d/t oth cause prior to regain cnscness, unsp dur], init enc
S06.9X[3,4,5,6]A	Unsp intracranial inj w/ LOC of [1 hr to 5 hrs 59 min, 6 hrs to 24 hrs, >24 hrs w/ return to pre-existing conscious lvl, > 24 hrs w/o return to pre-existing conscious lvl patient surviving], init enc
S06.9X[7,8,9]A	Unsp intracranial inj w/ LOC of [any dur w/ death d/t brain inj prior to regain cnscness, any dur w/ death d/t oth cause prior to regain cnscness, unsp dur], init enc

OR

Principal Diagnosis of Traumatic Stupor and Coma

S02.0XX[A,B]	Fx of vault of skull, init enc for [clsd, opn] fx
S02.10X[A,B]	Unsp fx of base of skull, init enc for [clsd, opn] fx
S02.11[0,1,2,3]A	[Type I, Type II, Type III, unsp] occipital condyle fx, init enc for clsd fx
S02.11[0,1,2,3]B	[Type I, Type II, Type III, unsp] occipital condyle fx, init enc for opn fx
S02.11[8,9]A	[Oth, Unsp] fx of occiput, init enc for clsd fx
S02.11[8,9]B	[Oth, Unsp] fx of occiput, init enc for opn fx
S02.19X[A,B]	Oth fx of base of skull, init enc for [clsd, opn] fx
S02.91X[A,B]	Unsp fx of skull, init enc for [clsd, opn] fx
S06.1X0A	Traum cerebral edema w/o LOC, init `PDx MCC`
S06.1X[1,2,3,4]A	Traum cerebral edema w/ LOC of [30 min or less, 31 min to 59 min, 1 hr to 5 hrs 59 min, 6 hrs to 24 hrs], init enc
S06.1X[5,6]A	Traum cerebral edema w/ LOC > 24 hrs [w/ return to pre-existing conscious lvl, w/o return to pre-existing conscious lvl w/ patient surviving], init enc
S06.1X[7,8,9]A	Traum cerebral edema w/ LOC of [any dur w/ death d/t brain inj prior to regain cnscness, any dur w/ death d/t oth cause prior to regain cnscness, unsp dur], init enc
S06.2X0A	Diffuse TBI w/o LOC, init
S06.2X[1,2,3,4]A	Diffuse traum brain inj w/ LOC of [30 min or less, 31 min to 59 min, 1 hr to 5 hrs 59 min, 6 hrs to 24 hrs], init enc
S06.2X[5,6]A	Diffuse traum brain inj w/ LOC > 24 hrs [w/ return to pre-existing conscious lvl, w/o return to pre-existing conscious lvl w/ patient surviving], init enc
S06.2X[7,8,9]A	Diffuse traum brain inj w/ LOC of [any dur w/ death d/t brain inj prior to regain cnscness, any dur w/ death d/t oth cause prior to regain cnscness, unsp dur], init enc
S06.300A	Unsp focal TBI w/o LOC, init
S06.30[1,2,3,4]A	Unsp focal traum brain inj w/ LOC of [30 min or less, 31 min to 59 min, 1 hr to 5 hrs 59 min, 6 hrs to 24 hrs], init enc
S06.30[5,6]A	Unsp focal traum brain inj w/ LOC > 24 hrs [w/ return to pre-existing conscious lvl, w/o return to pre-existing conscious lvl w/ patient surviving], init enc
S06.30[7,8,9]A	Unsp focal traum brain inj w/ LOC of [any dur w/ death d/t brain inj prior to regain cnscness, any dur w/ death d/t oth cause prior to regain cnscness, unsp dur], init enc

S06.310A	Contus/lac rt cerebrum w/o LOC, init
S06.31[1,2,3,4]A	Contsn and lac of rt cerebrum w/ LOC of [30 min to 59 min, 1 hr to 5 hrs 59 min, 6 hrs to 24 hrs], init enc
S06.31[5,6]A	Contsn and lac of rt cerebrum w/ LOC > 24 hrs [w/ return to pre-existing conscious lvl, w/o return to pre-existing conscious lvl w/ patient surviving], init enc
S06.31[7,8,9]A	Contsn and lac of rt cerebrum w/ LOC of [any dur w/ death d/t brain inj prior to regain cnscness, any dur w/ death d/t oth cause prior to regain cnscness, unsp dur], init enc
S06.320A	Contus/lac lt cerebrum w/o LOC, init
S06.32[1,2,3,4]A	Contsn and lac of lt cerebrum w/ LOC of [30 min or less, 31 min to 59 min, 1 hr to 5 hrs 59 min, 6 hrs to 24 hrs], init enc
S06.32[5,6]A	Contsn and lac of lt cerebrum w/ LOC > 24 hrs [w/ return to pre-existing conscious lvl, w/o return to pre-existing conscious lvl w/ patient surviving], init enc
S06.32[7,8,9]A	Contsn and lac of lt cerebrum w/ LOC of [any dur w/ death d/t brain inj prior to regain cnscness, any dur w/ death d/t oth cause prior to regain cnscness, unsp dur], init enc
S06.330A	Contus/lac cereb, w/o LOC, init
S06.33[1,2,3,4]A	Contsn and lac of cerebrum, unsp, w/ LOC of [30 min or less, 31 min to 59 min, 1 hr to 5 hrs 59 min, 6 hrs to 24 hrs], init enc
S06.33[5,6]A	Contsn and lac of cerebrum, unsp, w/ LOC > 24 hrs [w/ return to pre-existing conscious lvl, w/o return to pre-existing conscious lvl w/ patient surviving], init enc
S06.33[7,8,9]A	Contsn and lac of cerebrum, unsp, w/ LOC of [any dur w/ death d/t brain inj prior to regain cnscness, any dur w/ death d/t oth cause prior to regain cnscness, unsp dur], init enc
S06.340A	Traum hemor rt cerebrum w/o LOC, init
S06.34[1,2,3,4]A	Traum hemor of rt cerebrum w/ LOC of [30 min or less, 31 min to 59 min, 1 hr to 5 hrs 59 min, 6 hrs to 24 hrs], init enc
S06.34[5,6]A	Traum hemor of rt cerebrum w/ LOC > 24 hrs [w/ return to pre-existing conscious lvl, w/o return to pre-existing conscious lvl w/ patient surviving], init enc
S06.34[7,8,9]A	Traum hemor of rt cerebrum w/ LOC of [any dur w/ death d/t brain inj prior to regain cnscness, any dur w/ death d/t oth cause prior to regain cnscness, unsp dur], init enc
S06.350A	Traum hemor lt cerebrum w/o LOC, init
S06.35[1,2,3,4]A	Traum hemor of lt cerebrum w/ LOC of [30 min or less, 31 min to 59 min, 1 hr to 5 hrs 59 min, 6 hrs to 24 hrs], init enc
S06.35[5,6]A	Traum hemor of lt cerebrum w/ LOC > 24 hrs [w/ return to pre-existing conscious lvl, w/o return to pre-existing conscious lvl w/ patient surviving], init enc
S06.35[7,8,9]A	Traum hemor of lt cerebrum w/ LOC of [any dur w/ death d/t brain inj prior to regain cnscness, any dur w/ death d/t oth cause prior to regain cnscness, unsp dur], init enc
S06.360A	Traum hemor cereb, w/o LOC, init
S06.36[1,2,3,4]A	Traum hemor of cerebrum, unsp, w/ LOC of [30 min or less, 31 min to 59 min, 1 hr to 5 hrs 59 min, 6 hrs to 24 hrs], init enc
S06.36[5,6]A	Traum hemor of cerebrum, unsp, w/ LOC > 24 hrs [w/ return to pre-existing conscious lvl, w/o return to pre-existing conscious lvl w/ patient surviving], init enc
S06.36[7,8,9]A	Traum hemor of cerebrum, unsp, w/ LOC of [any dur w/ death d/t brain inj prior to regain cnscness, any dur w/ death d/t oth cause prior to regain cnscness, unsp dur], init enc
S06.370A	Contus/lac/hem crblm w/o LOC, init
S06.37[1,2,3,4]A	Contsn, lac, and hemor of cerebellum w/ LOC of [30 min or less, 31 min to 59 min, 1 hr to 5 hrs 59 min, 6 hrs to 24 hrs], init enc
S06.37[5,6]A	Contsn, lac, and hemor of cerebellum w/ LOC > 24 hrs [w/ return to pre-existing conscious lvl, w/o return to pre-existing conscious lvl w/ patient surviving], init enc
S06.37[7,8,9]A	Contsn, lac, and hemor of cerebellum w/ LOC of [any dur w/ death d/t brain inj prior to regain cnscness, any dur w/ death d/t oth cause prior to regain cnscness, unsp dur], init enc
S06.380A	Contus/lac/hem brainstem w/o LOC, init
S06.38[1,2,3,4]A	Contsn, lac, and hemor of brainstem w/ LOC of [30 min or less, 31 min to 59 min, 1 hr to 5 hrs 59 min, 6 hrs to 24 hrs], init enc
S06.38[5,6]A	Contsn, lac, and hemor of brainstem w/ LOC > 24 hrs [w/ return to pre-existing conscious lvl, w/o return to pre-existing conscious lvl w/ patient surviving], init enc
S06.38[7,8,9]A	Contsn, lac, and hemor of brainstem w/ LOC of [any dur w/ death d/t brain inj prior to regain cnscness, any dur w/ death d/t oth cause prior to regain cnscness, unsp dur], init enc
S06.4X0A	Epidural hemor w/o LOC, init enc
S06.4X[1,2,3,4]A	Epidural hemor w/ LOC of [30 min or less, 31 min to 59 min, 1 hr to 5 hrs 59 min, 6 hrs to 24 hrs], init enc
S06.4X[5,6]A	Epidural hemor w/ LOC > 24 hrs [w/ return to pre-existing conscious lvl, w/o return to pre-existing conscious lvl w/ patient surviving], init enc

---

T **Transfer DRG**   SP **Special Payment**   * **Code Range**   **6th and 7th Character of ZZ = No Device, No Qualifier ZX = No Device, Diagnostic**

MS-DRG Version 33.0

© 2015 Optum360, LLC

S06.4X[7,8,9]A   Epidural hemor w/ LOC of [any dur w/ death d/t brain inj prior to regain cnscness, any dur w/ death d/t oth cause prior to regain cnscness, unsp dur], init enc

S06.5X0A   Traum subdr hem w/o LOC, init

S06.5X[1,2,3,4]A   Traum subdural hemor w/ LOC of [30 min or less, 31 min to 59 min, 1 hr to 5 hrs 59 min, 6 hrs to 24 hrs], init enc

S06.5X[5,6]A   Traum subdural hemor w/ LOC > 24 hrs [w/ return to pre-existing conscious lvl, w/o return to pre-existing conscious lvl w/ patient surviving], init enc

S06.5X[7,8,9]A   Traum subdural hemor w/ LOC of [any dur w/ death d/t brain inj prior to regain cnscness, any dur w/ death d/t oth cause prior to regain cnscness, unsp dur], init enc

S06.6X0A   Traum subrac hem w/o LOC, init

S06.6X[1,2,3,4]A   Traum subarachnoid hemor w/ LOC of [30 min or less, 31 min to 59 min, 1 hr to 5 hrs 59 min, 6 hrs to 24 hrs], init enc

S06.6X[5,6]A   Traum subarachnoid hemor w/ LOC > 24 hrs [w/ return to pre-existing conscious lvl, w/o return to pre-existing conscious lvl w/ patient surviving], init enc

S06.6X[7,8,9]A   Traum subarachnoid hemor w/ LOC of [any dur w/ death d/t brain inj prior to regain cnscness, any dur w/ death d/t oth cause prior to regain cnscness, unsp dur], init enc

S06.810A   Inj of Rt int carotid, intcr w/o LOC, init

S06.81[1,2,3,4]A   Inj of rt int carotid artery, intracranial portion, NEC, w/ LOC of [30 min or less, 31 min to 59 min, 1 hr to 5 hrs 59 min, 6 hrs to 24 hrs], init enc

S06.81[5,6]A   Inj of rt int carotid artery, intracranial portion, NEC, w/ LOC > 24 hrs [w/ return to pre-existing conscious lvl, w/o return to pre-existing conscious lvl w/ patient surviving], init enc

S06.81[7,8,9]A   Inj of rt int carotid artery, intracranial portion, NEC w/ LOC of [any dur w/ death d/t brain inj prior to regain cnscness, any dur w/ death d/t oth cause prior to regain cnscness, unsp dur], init enc

S06.820A   Inj of Lt int carotid, intcr w/o LOC, init

S06.82[1,2,3,4]A   Inj of lt int carotid artery, intracranial portion, NEC, w/ LOC of [30 min or less, 31 min to 59 min, 1 hr to 5 hrs 59 min, 6 hrs to 24 hrs], init enc

S06.82[5,6]A   Inj of lt int carotid artery, intracranial portion, NEC, w/ LOC > 24 hrs [w/ return to pre-existing conscious lvl, w/o return to pre-existing conscious lvl w/ patient surviving], init enc

S06.82[7,8,9]A   Inj of lt int carotid artery, intracranial portion, NEC w/ LOC of [any dur w/ death d/t brain inj prior to regain cnscness, any dur w/ death d/t oth cause prior to regain cnscness, unsp dur], init enc

S06.890A   Intcran inj w/o LOC, init enc

S06.89[1,2,3,4]A   Oth spec intracranial inj w/ LOC of [30 min or less, 31 min to 5 hrs 59 min, 6 hrs to 24 hrs], init enc

S06.89[5,6]A   Oth spec intracranial inj w/ LOC > 24 hrs [w/ return to pre-existing conscious lvl, w/o return to pre-existing conscious lvl w/ patient surviving], init enc

S06.89[7,8,9]A   Oth spec intracranial inj w/ LOC of [any dur w/ death d/t brain inj prior to regain cnscness, any dur w/ death d/t oth cause prior to regain cnscness, unsp dur], init enc

S06.9X0A   Unsp intracranial inj w/o LOC, init

S06.9X[1,2,3,4]A   Unsp intracranial inj w/ LOC of [30 min or less, 31 min to 59 min, 1 hr to 5 hrs 59 min, 6 hrs to 24 hrs], init enc

S06.9X[5,6]A   Unsp intracranial inj w/ LOC > 24 hrs [w/ return to pre-existing conscious lvl, w/o return to pre-existing conscious lvl w/ patient surviving], init enc

S06.9X[7,8,9]A   Unsp intracranial inj w/ LOC of [any dur w/ death d/t brain inj prior to regain cnscness, any dur w/ death d/t oth cause prior to regain cnscness, unsp dur], init enc

AND

Secondary Diagnosis of Traumatic Stupor and Coma > 1 Hour

Select from above list of diagnoses with description of loss of consciousness greater than one hour or of unsp duration

DRG 083   Traumatic Stupor and Coma, Coma Greater Than One Hour with CC

GMLOS 3.3   AMLOS 4.3   RW 1.3006

Select principal diagnosis of coma greater than one hour OR principal diagnosis of traumatic stupor AND a secondary diagnosis of coma greater than one hour listed under DRG 082

DRG 084   Traumatic Stupor and Coma, Coma Greater Than One Hour without CC/MCC

GMLOS 2.1   AMLOS 2.6   RW 0.8469

Select principal diagnosis of coma greater than one hour OR principal diagnosis of traumatic stupor AND a secondary diagnosis of coma greater than one hour listed under DRG 082

DRG 085   Traumatic Stupor and Coma, Coma Less Than One Hour with MCC

GMLOS 4.7   AMLOS 6.6   RW 2.0357   ⊤

Principal Diagnosis of Traumatic Stupor and Coma < 1 Hour

S02.0XX[A,B]   Fx of vault of skull, init enc for [clsd, opn] fx

S02.10X[A,B]   Unsp fx of base of skull, init enc for [clsd, opn] fx

S02.11[0,1,2,3]A   [Type I, Type II, Type III, unsp] occipital condyle fx, init enc for clsd fx

S02.11[0,1,2,3]B   [Type I, Type II, Type III, unsp] occipital condyle fx, init enc for opn fx

S02.11[8,9]A   [Oth, Unsp] fx of occiput, init enc for clsd fx

S02.11[8,9]B   [Oth, Unsp] fx of occiput, init enc for opn fx

S02.19X[A,B]   Oth fx of base of skull, init enc for [clsd, opn] fx

S02.91X[A,B]   Unsp fx of skull, init enc for [clsd, opn] fx

S06.1X0A   Traum cerebral edema w/o LOC, init   PDx MCC

S06.1X1A   Traum cerebral edema w LOC of 30 min or less, init   PDx MCC

S06.1X2A   Traum cerebral edema w LOC of 31-59 min, init   PDx MCC

S06.2X0A   Diffuse TBI w/o LOC, init

S06.2X1A   Diffuse TBI w LOC of 30 min or less, init

S06.2X2A   Diffuse TBI w LOC of 31-59 min, init

S06.300A   Unsp focal TBI w/o LOC, init

S06.301A   Unsp focal TBI w LOC of 30 min or less, init

S06.302A   Unsp focal TBI w LOC of 31-59 min, init

S06.310A   Contus/lac rt cerebrum w/o LOC, init

S06.311A   Contus/lac rt cerebrum w LOC of 30 min or less, init

S06.312A   Contus/lac rt cerebrum w LOC of 31-59 min, init

S06.320A   Contus/lac lt cerebrum w/o LOC, init

S06.321A   Contus/lac lt cerebrum w LOC of 30 min or less, init

S06.322A   Contus/lac lt cerebrum w LOC of 31-59 min, init

S06.330A   Contus/lac cereb, w/o LOC, init

S06.331A   Contus/lac cereb, w LOC of 30 min or less, init

S06.332A   Contus/lac cereb, w LOC of 31-59 min, init

S06.340A   Traum hemor rt cerebrum w/o LOC, init

S06.341A   Traum hemor rt cerebrum w LOC of 30 min or less, init

S06.342A   Traum hemor rt cerebrum w LOC of 31-59 min, init

S06.350A   Traum hemor lt cerebrum w/o LOC, init

S06.351A   Traum hemor lt cerebrum w LOC of 30 min or less, init

S06.352A   Traum hemor lt cerebrum w LOC of 31-59 min, init

S06.360A   Traum hemor cereb, w/o LOC, init

S06.361A   Traum hemor cereb, w LOC of 30 min or less, init

S06.362A   Traum hemor cereb, w LOC of 31-59 min, init

S06.370A   Contus/lac/hem crblm w/o LOC, init

S06.371A   Contus/lac/hem crblm w LOC of 30 min or less, init

S06.372A   Contus/lac/hem crblm w LOC of 31-59 min, init

S06.379A   Contus/lac/hem crblm w LOC of unsp dur, init

S06.380A   Contus/lac/hem brainstem w/o LOC, init

S06.381A   Contus/lac/hem brainstem w LOC of 30 min or less, init

S06.382A   Contus/lac/hem brainstem w LOC of 31-59 min, init

S06.389A   Contus/lac/hem brainstem w LOC of unsp dur, init

S06.4X0A   Epidural hemor w/o LOC, init enc

S06.4X1A   Epidural hemor w LOC of 30 min or less, init

S06.4X2A   Epidural hemor w LOC of 31-59 min, init

S06.5X0A   Traum subdr hem w/o LOC, init

S06.5X1A   Traum subdr hem w LOC of 30 min or less, init

S06.5X2A   Traum subdr hem w LOC of 31-59 min, init

S06.6X0A   Traum subrac hem w/o LOC, init

S06.6X1A   Traum subrac hem w LOC of 30 min or less, init

S06.6X2A   Traum subrac hem w LOC of 31-59 min, init

S06.810A   Inj of Rt int carotid, intcr w/o LOC, init

S06.811A   Inj Rt int carotid, intcr w LOC of 30 min or less, init

S06.812A   Inj of Rt int carotid, intcr w LOC of 31-59 min, init

S06.820A   Inj of Lt int carotid, intcr w/o LOC, init

S06.821A   Inj Lt int carotid, intcr w LOC of 30 min or less, init

S06.822A   Inj of Lt int carotid, intcr w LOC of 31-59 min, init

S06.890A   Intcran inj w/o LOC, init enc

S06.891A   Intcran inj w LOC of 30 min or less, init

S06.892A   Intcran inj w LOC of 31-59 min, init

S06.9X0A   Unsp intracranial inj w/o LOC, init

S06.9X1A   Unsp intracranial inj w LOC of 30 min or less, init

S06.9X2A   Unsp intracranial inj w LOC of 31-59 min, init

Surgical   **Medical**   **CC Indicator**   **MCC Indicator**   **Procedure Proxy**   PDx MCC **PDx acts as own MCC**   PDx CC **PDx acts as own CC**

MDC 1: Diseases And Disorders Of The Nervous System—MEDICAL

DRG 086	Traumatic Stupor and Coma, Coma Less Than One Hour with CC			
	GMLOS 3.3	AMLOS 4.1	RW 1.1394	T

Select principal diagnosis listed under DRG 085

DRG 087	Traumatic Stupor and Coma, Coma Less Than One Hour without CC/MCC			
	GMLOS 2.2	AMLOS 2.7	RW 0.7918	T

Select principal diagnosis listed under DRG 085

DRG 088	Concussion with MCC		
	GMLOS 3.7	AMLOS 4.7	RW 1.3653

Principal Diagnosis

S06.0X0A	Concussion without LOC, init enc
S06.0X[1,2,3,4]A	Concussion w/ LOC of [30 min or less, 31 min to 59 min, 1 hr to 5 hrs 59 min, 6 hrs to 24 hrs], init enc
S06.0X[5,6]A	Concussion w/ LOC > 24 hrs [w/, w/o] return to pre-existing conscious lvl, init enc
S06.0X[7,8,9]A	Concussion w/ LOC of [any dur w/ death d/t brain inj prior to regain cnscness, any dur w/ death d/t oth cause prior to regain cnscness, unsp dur], init enc

DRG 089	Concussion with CC		
	GMLOS 2.8	AMLOS 3.4	RW 0.9759

Select principal diagnosis listed under DRG 088

DRG 090	Concussion without CC/MCC		
	GMLOS 1.9	AMLOS 2.3	RW 0.7394

Select principal diagnosis listed under DRG 088

DRG 091	Other Disorders of Nervous System with MCC			
	GMLOS 4.2	AMLOS 5.8	RW 1.5880	T

Principal Diagnosis

A88.1	Epidemic vertigo
B90.0	Sequelae of central nervous sys tuberculosis
B91	Sequelae of poliomyelitis
B94.1	Sequelae of viral encephalitis
D18.02	Hemangioma of intracranial structures
F80.81	Childhood onset fluency d/o
F95*	Tic d/o
G08	Intracranial and intraspinal phlebitis and thrombophlebitis
G09	Sequelae of inflam dz of central nervous sys
G14	Postpolio synd
G21.0	Malig neuroleptic synd
G24.0*	Drug induced dystonia
G24.2	Idiopathic nonfamilial dystonia
G24.3	Spasmodic torticollis
G24.4	Idiopathic orofacial dystonia
G24.8	Oth dystonia
G24.9	Dystonia, unsp
G25.0	Essential tremor
G25.1	Drug-induced tremor
G25.2	Oth spec forms of tremor
G25.3	Myoclonus
G25.6*	Drug induced tics and oth tics of organic origin
G25.82	Stiff-man synd
G25.83	Benign shuddering attacks
G32.0	Subac comb degeneration of spinal cord in dis classd elsw
G47.2*	Circadian rhythm sleep d/o
G47.31	Primary central sleep apnea
G47.35	Congenital central alveolar hypoventilation synd
G47.37	Central sleep apnea in conditions classified elsw
G47.4*	Narcolepsy and cataplexy
G47.51	Confusional arousals
G47.53	Recurrent isolated sleep paralysis
G47.61	Periodic limb movement d/o
G47.62	Sleep related leg cramps
G60.1	Refsum's dz
G71*	Primary d/o of muscles
G72.0	Drug-induced myopathy
G72.1	Alcoholic myopathy
G72.2	Myopathy d/t oth txc agents

G72.3	Periodic paralysis
G72.8*	Oth spec myopathies
G72.9	Myopathy, unsp
G73.7	Myopathy in dz classified elsw
G80.4	Ataxic cerebral palsy
G80.8	Oth cerebral palsy
G80.9	Cerebral palsy, unsp
G83.1*	Monoplegia of lwr limb
G83.2*	Monoplegia of upr limb
G83.3*	Monoplegia, unsp
G83.5	Locked-in state
G83.8*	Oth spec paralytic syndromes
G83.9	Paralytic synd, unsp
G89.0	Central pain synd
G89.2*	Chr pain, NEC
G89.4	Chr pain synd
G90.1	Familial dysautonomia [Riley-Day]
G92	Txc encephalopathy
G93.0	Cerebral cysts
G93.1	Anoxic brain damage, NEC
G93.7	Reye's synd
G95.1*	Vascular myelopathies
G95.2*	Oth and unsp cord compression
G95.8*	Oth spec dz of spinal cord
G95.9	Dz of spinal cord, unsp
G96.0	Cerebrospinal fluid leak
G96.12	Meningeal adhesions (cerebral) (spinal)
G96.19	Oth d/o of meninges, NEC
G97.0	Cerebrospinal fluid leak from spinal punc
G97.2	Intracranial hypotension following ventricular shunting
G97.3*	Intraop hemor/hemtom of a nervous sys org comp a procedure
G97.8*	Oth intraop and postproc comp and d/o of nervous sys
G99.2	Myelopathy in dz classified elsw
H47.10	Unsp papilledema
H47.11	Papilledema associated with increased intracranial pressure
H47.14[1,2,3,9]	Foster-Kennedy synd, [rt, lt, bilat, unsp] eye
H47.4*	D/o of optic chiasm
H47.5*	D/o of oth visual pathways
H47.6*	D/o of visual cortex
H47.9	Unsp d/o of visual pathways
H51.2*	Internuclear ophthalmoplegia
I67.1	Cerebral aneurysm, nonruptured
I67.5	Moyamoya dz
I67.6	Nonpyogenic thrombosis of intracranial venous sys
I97.81[0,1]	Intraoperative cerebrovascular infarction during [cardiac, oth] surgery
I97.82[0,1]	Postprocedural cerebrovascular infarction during [cardiac, oth] surgery
P91.2	Neonatal cerebral leukomalacia
Q00*	Anencephaly and similar malformations
Q01*	Encephalocele
Q02	Microcephaly
Q03*	Congenital hydrocephalus
Q04*	Oth congenital malformations of brain
Q05*	Spina bifida
Q06*	Oth congenital malformations of spinal cord
Q07*	Oth congenital malformations of nervous sys
Q28.2	Arteriovenous malformation of cerebral vessels
Q28.3	Oth malformations of cerebral vessels
Q76.0	Spina bifida occulta
Q85.0*	Neurofibromatosis (nonmalignant)
Q85.1	Tuberous sclerosis
R20*	Disturbances of skin sensation
R25*	Abnormal involuntary movements
R26.0	Ataxic gait
R26.1	Paralytic gait
R26.8*	Oth abnormalities of gait and mobility
R26.9	Unsp abnormalities of gait and mobility
R27*	Oth lack of coordination
R29.1	Meningismus
R29.2	Abnormal reflex
R29.3	Abnormal posture
R29.5	Transient paralysis
R29.6	Repeated falls
R29.810	Facial weakness
R29.818	Oth symptoms and signs involving the nervous sys
R29.890	Loss of height
R29.9*	Unsp symptoms & signs involving the nervous and ms systems

T Transfer DRG   SP Special Payment   * Code Range   6th and 7th Character of ZZ = No Device, No Qualifier ZX = No Device, Diagnostic

38   MS-DRG Version 33.0   © 2015 Optum360, LLC

Code	Description
R41.4	Neurologic neglect synd
R41.842	Visuospatial deficit
R43*	Disturbances of smell and taste
R47*	Speech disturbances, NEC
R83*	Abnormal findings in cerebrospinal fluid
R90.81	Abnormal echoencephalogram
R90.82	White matter dz, unsp
R93.0	Abnormal findings on dx imaging of skull and head, NEC
R94.0*	Abnormal results of function studies of cnsl
R94.130	Abnormal response to nerve stimulation, unsp
R94.1[1,2,3]8	Abnormal results of oth function studies of [eye, ear and oth special senses, peripheral nervous sys]
S02.0XXS	Fx of vault of skull, seq
S02.10XS	Unsp fx of base of skull, seq
S02.11[0,1,2,3]S	[Type I, Type II, Type III, Unsp] occipital condyle fx, seq
S02.11[8,9]S	[Oth, Unsp] fx of occiput, seq
S02.19XS	Oth fx of base of skull, seq
S02.2XXS	Fx of nasal bones, seq
S02.3XXS	Fx of orbital floor, seq
S02.40[0,1,2]S	[Malar, Maxillary, Zygomatic] fx, unsp
S02.41[1,2,3]S	LeFort [I, II, III] fx, seq
S02.42XS	Fx of alveolus of maxilla, seq
S02.5XXS	Fx of tooth (Traum), seq
S02.600S	Fx of unsp part of body of mandible, seq
S02.609S	Fx of mandible, unsp, seq
S02.6[1,2,3]XS	Fx of [condylar, subcondylar, coronoid] process of mandible
S02.6[4,5,6,7,9]XS	Fx of [ramus, angle, symphysis, alveolus, oth spec site] of mandible
S02.8XXS	Fractures of oth spec skull and facial bones, seq
S02.91XS	Unsp fx of skull, seq
S02.92XS	Unsp fx of facial bones, seq
S04.01[1,2,9]S	Inj of optic nerve, [rt, lt, unsp] eye, seq
S04.02X[A,S]	Inj of optic chiasm, [init enc, seq]
S04.03[1,2,9]A	Inj of optic tract and pathways, [rt, lt, unsp] eye, init enc
S04.03[1,2,9]S	Inj of optic tract and pathways, [rt, lt, unsp] eye, seq
S04.04[1,2,9]A	Inj of visual cortex, [rt, lt, unsp] eye, init enc
S04.04[1,2,9]S	Inj of visual cortex, [rt, lt, unsp] eye, seq
S04.1[0,1,2]XS	Inj of oculomotor nerve, [unsp, rt, lt] side, seq
S04.2[0,1,2]XS	Inj of trochlear nerve, [unsp, rt, lt] side, seq
S04.3[0,1,2]XS	Inj of trigeminal nerve, [unsp, rt, lt] side, seq
S04.4[0,1,2]XS	Inj of abducent nerve, [unsp, rt, lt] side, seq
S04.5[0,1,2]XS	Inj of facial nerve, [unsp, rt, lt] side, seq
S04.6[0,1,2]XS	Inj of acoustic nerve, [unsp, rt, lt] side, seq
S04.7[0,1,2]XS	Inj of accessory nerve, [unsp, rt, lt] side, seq
S04.81[1,2,9]S	Inj of olfactory (1st) nerve, [rt, lt, unsp] side, seq
S04.89[1,2,9]S	Inj of oth cranial nerves, [rt, lt, unsp] side, seq
S04.9XXS	Inj of unsp cranial nerve, seq
S06.0X0S	Concussion without LOC, seq
S06.0X[1,2,3,4]S	Concussion w/ LOC of [30 min or less, 31-59 min, 1 hr to 5 hrs 59 min, 6 hrs to 24 hrs], seq
S06.0X[5,6]S	Concussion w/ LOC of [> 24 hrs w/ return to pre-existing conscious lvl, > 24 hrs w/o return to pre-existing conscious lvl w/ patient surviving], seq
S06.0X[7,8,9]S	Concussion w/ LOC of [any dur w/ death d/t brain inj prior to regain cnscness, any dur w/ death d/t oth cause prior to regain cnscness, unsp dur], seq
S06.1X0S	Traum cerebral edema w/o LOC, seq
S06.1X[1,2,3,4]S	Traum cerebral edema w/ LOC of [30 min or less, 31-59 min, 1 hr to 5 hrs 59 min, 6 hrs to 24 hrs], seq
S06.1X[5,6]S	Traum cerebral edema w/ LOC of [> 24 hrs w/ return to pre-existing conscious lvl, > 24 hrs w/o return to pre-existing conscious lvl w/ patient surviving], seq
S06.1X[7,8,9]S	Traum cerebral edema w/ LOC of [any dur w/ death d/t brain inj prior to regain cnscness, any dur w/ death d/t oth cause prior to regain cnscness, unsp dur], seq
S06.2X0S	Diffuse TBI w/o LOC, seq
S06.2X[1,2,3,4]S	Diffuse traum brain inj w/ LOC of [30 min or less, 31-59 min, 1 hr to 5 hrs 59 min, 6 hrs to 24 hrs], seq
S06.2X[5,6]S	Diffuse traum brain inj w/ LOC of [> 24 hrs w/ return to pre-existing conscious lvl, > 24 hrs w/o return to pre-existing conscious lvl w/ patient surviving], seq
S06.2X[7,8,9]S	Diffuse traum brain inj w/ LOC of [any dur w/ death d/t brain inj prior to regain cnscness, any dur w/ death d/t oth cause prior to regain cnscness, unsp dur], seq
S06.300S	Unsp focal TBI w/o LOC, seq
S06.30[1,2,3,4]S	Unsp focal traum brain inj w/ LOC of [30 min or less, 31-59 min, 1 hr to 5 hrs 59 min, 6 hrs to 24 hrs], seq
S06.30[5,6]S	Unsp focal traum brain inj w/ LOC of [> 24 hrs w/ return to pre-existing conscious lvl, > 24 hrs w/o return to pre-existing conscious lvl w/ patient surviving], seq
S06.30[7,8,9]S	Unsp focal traum brain inj w/ LOC of [any dur w/ death d/t brain inj prior to regain cnscness, any dur w/ death d/t oth cause prior to regain cnscness, unsp dur], seq
S06.310S	Contus/lac rt cerebrum w/o LOC, seq
S06.31[1,2,3,4]S	Contsn and lac of rt cerebrum w/ LOC of [30 min or less, 31-59 min, 1 hr to 5 hrs 59 min, 6 hrs to 24 hrs], seq
S06.31[5,6]S	Contsn and lac of rt cerebrum w/ LOC of [> 24 hrs w/ return to pre-existing conscious lvl, > 24 hrs w/o return to pre-existing conscious lvl w/ patient surviving], seq
S06.31[7,8,9]S	Contsn and lac of rt cerebrum w/ LOC of [any dur w/ death d/t brain inj prior to regain cnscness, any dur w/ death d/t oth cause prior to regain cnscness, unsp dur], seq
S06.320S	Contus/lac lt cerebrum w/o LOC, seq
S06.32[1,2,3,4]S	Contsn and lac of lt cerebrum w/ LOC of [30 min or less, 31-59 min, 1 hr to 5 hrs 59 min, 6 hrs to 24 hrs], seq
S06.32[5,6]S	Contsn and lac of lt cerebrum w/ LOC of [> 24 hrs w/ return to pre-existing conscious lvl, > 24 hrs w/o return to pre-existing conscious lvl w/ patient surviving], seq
S06.32[7,8,9]S	Contsn and lac of lt cerebrum w/ LOC of [any dur w/ death d/t brain inj prior to regain cnscness, any dur w/ death d/t oth cause prior to regain cnscness, unsp dur], seq
S06.330S	Contus/lac cereb, w/o LOC, seq
S06.33[1,2,3,4]S	Contsn and lac of cerebrum, unsp, w/ LOC of [30 min or less, 31-59 min, 1 hr to 5 hrs 59 min, 6 hrs to 24 hrs], seq
S06.33[5,6]S	Contsn and lac of cerebrum, unsp, w/ LOC of [> 24 hrs w/ return to pre-existing conscious lvl, > 24 hrs w/o return to pre-existing conscious lvl w/ patient surviving], seq
S06.33[7,8,9]S	Contsn and lac of cerebrum, unsp, w/ LOC of [any dur w/ death d/t brain inj prior to regain cnscness, any dur w/ death d/t oth cause prior to regain cnscness, unsp dur], seq
S06.340S	Traum hemor rt cerebrum w/o LOC, seq
S06.34[1,2,3,4]S	Traum hemor of rt cerebrum w/ LOC of [30 min or less, 31-59 min, 1 hr to 5 hrs 59 min, 6 hrs to 24 hrs], seq
S06.34[5,6]S	Traum hemor of rt cerebrum w/ LOC of [> 24 hrs w/ return to pre-existing conscious lvl, > 24 hrs w/o return to pre-existing conscious lvl w/ patient surviving], seq
S06.34[7,8,9]S	Traum hemor of rt cerebrum w/ LOC of [any dur w/ death d/t brain inj prior to regain cnscness, any dur w/ death d/t oth cause prior to regain cnscness, unsp dur], seq
S06.350S	Traum hemor lt cerebrum w/o LOC, seq
S06.35[1,2,3,4]S	Traum hemor of lt cerebrum w/ LOC of [30 min or less, 31-59 min, 1 hr to 5 hrs 59 min, 6 hrs to 24 hrs], seq
S06.35[5,6]S	Traum hemor of lt cerebrum w/ LOC of [> 24 hrs w/ return to pre-existing conscious lvl, > 24 hrs w/o return to pre-existing conscious lvl w/ patient surviving], seq
S06.35[7,8,9]S	Traum hemor of lt cerebrum w/ LOC of [any dur w/ death d/t brain inj prior to regain cnscness, any dur w/ death d/t oth cause prior to regain cnscness, unsp dur], seq
S06.360S	Traum hemor cereb, w/o LOC, seq
S06.36[1,2,3,4]S	Traum hemor of cerebrum, unsp, w/ LOC of [30 min or less, 31-59 min, 1 hr to 5 hrs 59 min, 6 hrs to 24 hrs], seq
S06.36[5,6]S	Traum hemor of cerebrum, unsp, w/ LOC of [> 24 hrs w/ return to pre-existing conscious lvl, > 24 hrs w/o return to pre-existing conscious lvl w/ patient surviving], seq
S06.36[7,8,9]S	Traum hemor of cerebrum, unsp, w/ LOC of [any dur w/ death d/t brain inj prior to regain cnscness, any dur w/ death d/t oth cause prior to regain cnscness, unsp dur], seq
S06.370S	Contus/lac/hem crblm w/o LOC, seq
S06.37[1,2,3,4]S	Contsn, lac and hemor of cerebellum w/ LOC of [30 min or less, 31-59 min, 1 hr to 5 hrs 59 min, 6 hrs to 24 hrs], seq
S06.37[5,6]S	Contsn, lac and hemor of cerebellum w/ LOC of [> 24 hrs w/ return to pre-existing conscious lvl, > 24 hrs w/o return to pre-existing conscious lvl w/ patient surviving], seq
S06.37[7,8,9]S	Contsn, lac and hemor of cerebellum w/ LOC of [any dur w/ death d/t brain inj prior to regain cnscness, any dur w/ death d/t oth cause prior to regain cnscness, unsp dur], seq
S06.380S	Contus/lac/hem brainstem w/o LOC, seq
S06.38[1,2,3,4]S	Contsn, lac and hemor of brainstem w/ LOC of [30 min or less, 31-59 min, 1 hr to 5 hrs 59 min, 6 hrs to 24 hrs], seq
S06.38[5,6]S	Contsn, lac and hemor of brainstem w/ LOC of [> 24 hrs w/ return to pre-existing conscious lvl, > 24 hrs w/o return to pre-existing conscious lvl w/ patient surviving], seq
S06.38[7,8,9]S	Contsn, lac and hemor of brainstem w/ LOC of [any dur w/ death d/t brain inj prior to regain cnscness, any dur w/ death d/t oth cause prior to regain cnscness, unsp dur], seq
S06.4X0S	Epidural hemor without LOC, seq
S06.4X[1,2,3,4]S	Epidural hemor w/ LOC of [30 min or less, 31-59 min, 1 hr to 5 hrs 59 min, 6 hrs to 24 hrs], seq

Surgical   **Medical**   **CC Indicator**   **MCC Indicator**   **Procedure Proxy**   **PDxMCC** PDx acts as own MCC   **PDxCC** PDx acts as own CC

© 2015 Optum360, LLC   MS-DRG Version 33.0   39

MDC 1: Diseases And Disorders Of The Nervous System—MEDICAL

S06.4X[5,6]S	Epidural hemor w/ LOC of [> 24 hrs w/ return to pre-existing conscious lvl, > 24 hrs w/o return to pre-existing conscious lvl w/ patient surviving], seq
S06.4X[7,8,9]S	Epidural hemor w/ LOC of [any dur w/ death d/t brain inj prior to regain cnscness, any dur w/ death d/t oth cause prior to regain cnscness, unsp dur], seq
S06.5X0S	Traum subdr hem w/o LOC, seq
S06.5X[1,2,3,4]S	Traum subdural hemor w/ LOC of [30 min or less, 31-59 min, 1 hr to 5 hrs 59 min, 6 hrs to 24 hrs], seq
S06.5X[5,6]S	Traum subdural hemor w/ LOC of [> 24 hrs w/ return to pre-existing conscious lvl, > 24 hrs w/o return to pre-existing conscious lvl w/ patient surviving], seq
S06.5X[7,8,9]S	Traum subdural hemor w/ LOC of [any dur w/ death d/t brain inj prior to regain cnscness, any dur w/ death d/t oth cause prior to regain cnscness, unsp dur], seq
S06.6X0S	Traum subrac hem w/o LOC, seq
S06.6X[1,2,3,4]S	Traum subarachnoid hemor w/ LOC of [30 min or less, 31-59 min, 1 hr to 5 hrs 59 min, 6 hrs to 24 hrs], seq
S06.6X[5,6]S	Traum subarachnoid hemor w/ LOC of [> 24 hrs w/ return to pre-existing conscious lvl, > 24 hrs w/o return to pre-existing conscious lvl w/ patient surviving], seq
S06.6X[7,8,9]S	Traum subarachnoid hemor w/ LOC of [any dur w/ death d/t brain inj prior to regain cnscness, any dur w/ death d/t oth cause prior to regain cnscness, unsp dur], seq
S06.810S	Inj of Rt int carotid, intcr w/o LOC, seq
S06.81[1,2,3,4]S	Inj of rt int carotid artery, intracranial portion, NEC w/ LOC of [30 min or less, 31-59 min, 1 hr to 5 hrs 59 min, 6 hrs to 24 hrs], seq
S06.81[5,6]S	Inj of rt int carotid artery, intracranial portion, NEC w/ LOC of [> 24 hrs w/ return to pre-existing conscious lvl, > 24 hrs w/o return to pre-existing conscious lvl w/ patient surviving], seq
S06.81[7,8,9]S	Inj of rt int carotid artery, intracranial portion, NEC w/ LOC of [any dur w/ death d/t brain inj prior to regain cnscness, any dur w/ death d/t oth cause prior to regain cnscness, unsp dur], seq
S06.820S	Inj of Lt int carotid, intcr w/o LOC, seq
S06.82[1,2,3,4]S	Inj of lt int carotid artery, intracranial portion, NEC w/ LOC of [30 min or less, 31-59 min, 1 hr to 5 hrs 59 min, 6 hrs to 24 hrs], seq
S06.82[5,6]S	Inj of lt int carotid artery, intracranial portion, NEC w/ LOC of > 24 hrs [w/ return to pre-existing conscious lvl, w/o return to pre-existing conscious lvl w/ patient surviving], seq
S06.82[7,8,9]S	Inj of lt int carotid artery, intracranial portion, NEC w/ LOC of [any dur w/ death d/t brain inj prior to regain cnscness, any dur w/ death d/t oth cause prior to regain cnscness, unsp dur], seq
S06.890S	Oth intracranial inj w/o LOC, seq
S06.89[1,2,3,4]S	Oth spec intracranial inj w/ LOC of [30 min or less, 31-59 min, 1 hr to 5 hrs 59 min, 6 hrs to 24 hrs], seq
S06.89[5,6]S	Oth spec intracranial inj w/ LOC of > 24 hrs [w/ return to pre-existing conscious lvl, w/o return to pre-existing conscious lvl w/ patient surviving], seq
S06.89[7,8,9]S	Oth spec intracranial inj w/ LOC of [any dur w/ death d/t brain inj prior to regain cnscness, any dur w/ death d/t oth cause prior to regain cnscness, unsp dur], seq
S06.9X0S	Unsp intracranial inj w/o LOC, seq
S06.9X[1,2,3,4]S	Unsp intracranial inj w/ LOC of [30 min or less, 31-59 min, 1 hr to 5 hrs 59 min, 6 hrs to 24 hrs], seq
S06.9X[5,6]S	Unsp intracranial inj w/ LOC of > 24 hrs [w/ return to pre-existing conscious lvl, w/o return to pre-existing conscious lvl w/ patient surviving], seq
S06.9X[7,8,9]S	Unsp intracranial inj w/ LOC of [any dur w/ death d/t brain inj prior to regain cnscness, any dur w/ death d/t oth cause prior to regain cnscness, unsp dur], seq
S14.2XXS	Inj of nerve root of cervical spine, seq
S14.3XXS	Inj of brachial plexus, seq
S14.4XXS	Inj of peripheral nerves of neck, seq
S14.5XXS	Inj of cervical sympathetic nerves, seq
S14.8XXS	Inj of oth spec nerves of neck, seq
S14.9XXS	Inj of unsp nerves of neck, seq
S24.2XXS	Inj of nerve root of thoracic spine, seq
S24.3XXS	Inj of peripheral nerves of thorax, seq
S24.4XXS	Inj of thoracic sympathetic nervous sys, seq
S24.8XXS	Inj of oth spec nerves of thorax, seq
S24.9XXS	Inj of unsp nerve of thorax, seq
S34.2[1,2]XS	Inj of nerve root of [lumbar, sacral] spine, seq
S34.3XXS	Inj of cauda equina, seq
S34.4XXS	Inj of lumbosacral plexus, seq
S34.5XXS	Inj lumbar, sacral and pelvic sympathetic nerves, seq
S34.6XXS	Inj prph nerve(s) at abd, low back and pelvis lvl, seq

S34.8XXS	Inj nerves at abd, low back and pelvis lvl, seq
S34.9XXS	Inj unsp nerves at abd, low back and pelvis lvl, seq
S44.0[0,1,2]XS	Inj of ulnar nerve at upr arm lvl, [unsp, rt, lt] arm, seq
S44.1[0,1,2]XS	Inj of median nerve at upr arm lvl, [unsp, rt, lt] arm, seq
S44.2[0,1,2]XS	Inj of radial nerve at upr arm lvl, [unsp, rt, lt] arm, seq
S44.3[0,1,2]XS	Inj of axillary nerve at upr arm lvl, [unsp, rt, lt] arm, seq
S44.4[0,1,2]XS	Inj of musculocutaneous nerve at upr arm lvl, [unsp, rt, lt] arm, seq
S44.5[0,1,2]XS	Inj of cutaneous sensory nerve at shldr and upr arm lvl, [unsp, rt, lt] arm, seq
S44.8X[1,2,9]S	Inj of oth nerves at shldr and upr arm lvl, [unsp, rt, lt] arm, seq
S44.9[0,1,2]XS	Inj of unsp nerve at shldr and upr arm lvl, [unsp, rt, lt] arm, seq
S54.0[0,1,2]XS	Inj of ulnar nerve at forearm lvl, [unsp, rt, lt] arm, seq
S54.1[0,1,2]XS	Inj of median nerve at forearm lvl, [unsp, rt, lt] arm, seq
S54.2[0,1,2]XS	Inj of radial nerve at forearm lvl, [unsp, rt, lt] arm, seq
S54.3[0,1,2]XS	Inj of cutaneous sensory nerve at forearm lvl, [unsp, rt, lt] arm, seq
S54.8X[1,2,9]S	Inj of oth nerves at forearm lvl, [unsp, rt, lt] arm, seq
S54.9[0,1,2]XS	Inj of unsp nerve at forearm lvl, [unsp, rt, lt] arm, seq
S64.0[0,1,2]XS	Inj of ulnar nerve at wrist and hand lvl, [unsp, rt, lt] arm, seq
S64.1[0,1,2]XS	Inj of median nerve at wrist and hand lvl, [unsp, rt, lt] arm, seq
S64.2[0,1,2]XS	Inj of radial nerve at wrist and hand lvl, [unsp, rt, lt] arm, seq
S64.3[0,1,2]XS	Inj of digital nerve of thumb, [unsp, rt, lt] arm, seq
S64.40XS	Inj of digital nerve of unsp finger, seq
S64.49[0,1,2,3,4,5,6,7,8]S	Inj of digital nerve of [rt index, lt index, rt mid, lt mid, rt ring, lt ring, rt little, lt little, unsp] finger, seq
S64.8X[1,2,9]S	Inj of oth nerves at wrist and hand lvl, [unsp, rt, lt] arm, seq
S64.9[0,1,2]XS	Inj of unsp nerve at wrist and hand lvl, [unsp, rt, lt] arm, seq
S74.0[0,1,2]XS	Inj of sciatic nerve at hip & thigh lvl, [unsp, rt, lt] leg, seq
S74.1[0,1,2]XS	Inj of femor nerve at hip & thigh lvl, [unsp, rt, lt] leg, seq
S74.2[0,1,2]XS	Inj of cutaneous sensory nerve at hip & thigh lvl, [unsp, rt, lt] leg, seq
S74.8X[1,2,9]S	Inj of oth nerves at hip & thigh lvl, [unsp, rt, lt] leg, seq
S74.9[0,1,2]XS	Inj of unsp nerve at hip & thigh lvl, [unsp, rt, lt] leg, seq
S84.0[0,1,2]XS	Inj of tibial nerve at lwr leg lvl, [unsp, rt, lt] leg, seq
S84.1[0,1,2]XS	Inj of peroneal nerve at lwr leg lvl, [unsp, rt, lt] leg, seq
S84.2[0,1,2]XS	Inj of cutaneous sensory nerve at lwr leg lvl, [unsp, rt, lt] leg, seq
S84.80[1,2,9]S	Inj of oth nerves at lwr leg lvl, [unsp, rt, lt] leg, seq
S84.9[0,1,2]XS	Inj of unsp nerve at lwr leg lvl, [unsp, rt, lt] leg, seq
S94.0[0,1,2]XS	Inj of lat plantar nerve, [unsp, rt, lt] leg, seq
S94.1[0,1,2]XS	Inj of med plantar nerve, [unsp, rt, lt] leg, seq
S94.2[0,1,2]XS	Inj of deep peroneal nerve at ankle and foot lvl, [unsp, rt, lt] leg, seq
S94.3[0,1,2]XS	Inj of cutaneous sensory nerve at ankle and foot lvl, [unsp, rt, lt] leg, seq
S94.8X[1,2,9]S	Inj of oth nerves at ankle and foot lvl, [unsp, rt, lt] leg, seq
S94.9[0,1,2]XS	Inj of unsp nerve at ankle and foot lvl, [unsp, rt, lt] leg, seq
T85.09XA	Mech compl of ventricular intracranial shunt, init
T85.0[1,2,3]XA	[Breakdown (mech), Displac, Leakage] of ventricular intracranial (communicating) shunt, init enc
T85.11[0,1,2,8]A	Breakdown (mech) of implanted electronic neurostimulator (electrode) of [brain, peripheral nerve, spinal cord, oth nervous sys], init enc
T85.12[0,1,2,8]A	Displac of implanted electronic neurostimulator (electrode) of [brain, peripheral nerve, spinal cord, oth nervous sys], init enc
T85.19[0,1,2,9]A	Oth mech comp of implanted electronic neurostimulator (electrode) of [brain, peripheral nerve, spinal cord, oth nervous sys], init enc
Z45.3*	Enc for adjust and mgmt of implnt dev of the specl senses
Z45.4*	Enc for adjust and mgmt of implanted nervous sys device
Z46.2	Enc for fit/adjst of dev rel to nrv sys and specl senses

DRG 092 **Other Disorders of Nervous System with CC**

GMLOS 3.1	AMLOS 3.8	RW 0.9075	T

Select principal diagnosis listed under DRG 091

DRG 093 **Other Disorders of Nervous System without CC/MCC**

GMLOS 2.2	AMLOS 2.7	RW 0.6981	T

Select principal diagnosis listed under DRG 091

T **Transfer DRG**   SP **Special Payment**   * **Code Range**   **6th and 7th Character of ZZ = No Device, No Qualifier ZX = No Device, Diagnostic**

40   MS-DRG Version 33.0   © 2015 Optum360, LLC

DRG 094   Bacterial and Tuberculous Infections of Nervous System with MCC

GMLOS 8.2   AMLOS 10.7   RW 3.4429

Principal Diagnosis

A02.21	Salmonella meningitis
A17.0	Tuberculous meningitis
A17.1	Meningeal tuberculoma
A17.8*	Oth tuberculosis of nervous sys
A39.0	Meningococcal meningitis
A39.81	Meningococcal encephalitis
A54.81	Gonococcal meningitis
G00*	Bacterial meningitis, NEC
G01	Meningitis in bacterial dz classified elsw
G04.2	Bacterial meningoencephalitis and meningomyelitis, NEC
G06*	Intracranial and intraspinal abscess and granuloma
G07	Intcrn & intraspinal abscs & granuloma in dis classd elsw
G61.0	Guillain-Barre synd

DRG 095   Bacterial and Tuberculous Infections of Nervous System with CC

GMLOS 5.7   AMLOS 7.2   RW 2.3282

Select principal diagnosis listed under DRG 094

DRG 096   Bacterial and Tuberculous Infections of Nervous System without CC/MCC

GMLOS 4.8   AMLOS 5.7   RW 2.1855

Select principal diagnosis listed under DRG 094

DRG 097   Nonbacterial Infections of Nervous System Except Viral Meningitis with MCC

GMLOS 8.1   AMLOS 10.6   RW 3.1221

Principal Diagnosis

A06.6	Amebic brain abscess
A27.8*	Oth forms of leptospirosis
A50.45	Juvenile general paresis
A50.49	Oth late congenital neurosyphilis
A50.4[0,1,2,3]	Late congenital [unsp neurosyphilis, syphilitic meningitis, syphilitic encephalitis, syphilitic polyneuropathy]
A51.41	Secondary syphilitic meningitis
A52.13	Late syphilitic meningitis
A52.14	Late syphilitic encephalitis
A52.2	Asymptomatic neurosyphilis
A80.0	Acute paralytic poliomyelitis, vaccine-associated
A80.1	Acute paralytic poliomyelitis, wild virus, imported
A80.2	Acute paralytic poliomyelitis, wild virus, indigenous
A80.3*	Acute paralytic poliomyelitis, oth and unsp
A80.9	Acute poliomyelitis, unsp
A82*	Rabies
A83*	Mosquito-borne viral encephalitis
A84*	Tick-borne viral encephalitis
A85*	Oth viral encephalitis, NEC
A86	Unsp viral encephalitis
A88.8	Oth spec viral infections of central nervous sys
A89	Unsp viral infxn of central nervous sys
A92.2	Venezuelan equine fever
B00.4	Herpesviral encephalitis
B00.82	Herpes simplex myelitis
B01.1*	Varicella encephalitis, myelitis and encephalomyelitis
B02.24	Postherpetic myelitis
B05.0	Measles complicated by encephalitis
B06.01	Rubella encephalitis
B06.02	Rubella meningitis
B06.09	Oth neurological comp of rubella
B10.0*	Oth human herpesvirus encephalitis
B26.2	Mumps encephalitis
B37.5	Candidal meningitis
B38.4	Coccidioidomycosis meningitis
B45.1	Cerebral cryptococcosis [PDx MCC]
B58.2	Toxoplasma meningoencephalitis
G02	Meningitis in oth infec/parastc dz classd elsw
G03.0	Nonpyogenic meningitis
G03.1	Chr meningitis
G03.8	Meningitis d/t oth spec causes
G03.9	Meningitis, unsp

G04.0*	Acute disseminated encephalitis & encephalomyelitis (ADEM)
G04.3*	Acute necrotizing hemorrhagic encephalopathy
G04.8*	Oth encephalitis, myelitis and encephalomyelitis
G04.9*	Encephalitis, myelitis and encephalomyelitis, unsp
G05*	Encphlts, myelitis & encephalomyelitis in dis classd elsw
G37.3	Acute transv myelitis in demyelinating dz of cnsl
G37.4	Subacute necrotizing myelitis of central nervous sys

DRG 098   Nonbacterial Infections of Nervous System Except Viral Meningitis with CC

GMLOS 5.7   AMLOS 7.3   RW 1.8410

Select principal diagnosis listed under DRG 097

DRG 099   Nonbacterial Infections of Nervous System Except Viral Meningitis without CC/MCC

GMLOS 4.1   AMLOS 5.0   RW 1.2570

Select principal diagnosis listed under DRG 097

DRG 100   Seizures with MCC

GMLOS 4.2   AMLOS 5.6   RW 1.5639   [T]

Principal Diagnosis

G40*	Epilepsy and recurrent seizures
R56*	Convulsions, NEC

DRG 101   Seizures without MCC

GMLOS 2.6   AMLOS 3.3   RW 0.7942   [T]

Select principal diagnosis listed under DRG 100

DRG 102   Headaches with MCC

GMLOS 3.1   AMLOS 4.2   RW 1.0685

Principal Diagnosis

F07.81	Postconcussional synd
G43*	Migraine
G44*	Oth headache syndromes
G93.2	Benign intracranial hypertension
G97.1	Oth reaction to spinal and lumbar punc
I67.7	Cerebral arteritis, NEC
I68.2	Cerebral arteritis in oth dz classified elsw
R51	Headache

DRG 103   Headaches without MCC

GMLOS 2.3   AMLOS 2.9   RW 0.7199

Select principal diagnosis listed under DRG 102

MDC 1: Diseases And Disorders Of The Nervous System—MEDICAL

Surgical   Medical   CC Indicator   MCC Indicator   Procedure Proxy   [PDxMCC] PDx acts as own MCC   [PDxCC] PDx acts as own CC

SURGICAL

DRG 113   Orbital Procedures with CC/MCC

GMLOS 4.0	AMLOS 5.8	RW 2.0118

Operating Room Procedures

Code	Description
089[0,1]XZX	Drain of [Rt, Lt] Eye, Ext Appr, Dx
08B0[0,3,X]ZX	Exc/Eye, Rt, [Opn, Perc, Ext]
08B1[0,3,X]ZX	Exc/Eye, Lt, [Opn, Perc, Ext]
08J[J,K]XZZ	Inspect of [Rt, Lt] Lens, Ext Appr
08P00[3,J]Z	Rmvl/Eye, Rt, Opn, [Inf Dev, Synth Sub], NQ
08P10[3,J]Z	Rmvl/Eye, Lt, Opn, [Inf Dev, Synth Sub], NQ
08Q[0,1]XZZ	Rpr [Rt, Lt] Eye, Ext Appr
08R00[7,J]Z	Replace/Eye, Rt, Opn, [Auto Tissue Sub, Synth Sub], NQ
08R03[7,K]Z	Replace/Eye, Rt, Perc, [Auto Tissue Sub, Nonauto Tissue Sub], NQ
08R10[7,J]Z	Replace/Eye, Lt, Opn, [Auto Tissue Sub, Synth Sub], NQ
08R13[7,K]Z	Replace/Eye, Lt, Perc, [Auto Tissue Sub, Nonauto Tissue Sub], NQ
08T[0,1]XZZ	Resect of [Rt, Lt] Eye, Ext Appr
08W0[0,3]JZ	Rev/Eye, Rt, [Opn, Perc], Synth Sub, NQ
08W1[0,3]JZ	Rev/Eye, Lt, [Opn, Perc], Synth Sub, NQ
0J81*	Div/SQ Tissue & Fascia, Face
0JR1[0,3][7,K]Z	Replace/SQ Tissue & Fascia, Face, [Opn, Perc], [Auto Tissue Sub, Nonauto Tissue Sub], NQ
0N8P*	Div/Orbit, Rt
0N8Q*	Div/Orbit, Lt
0N9P[0,3,4]0Z	Drain/Orbit, Rt, [Opn, Perc, Perc Endo], Drain Dev, NQ
0N9P[0,3,4]ZX	Drain/Orbit, Rt, [Opn, Perc, Perc Endo]
0N9P[0,4]ZZ	Drain/Orbit, Rt, [Opn, Perc Endo]
0N9Q[0,3,4]0Z	Drain/Orbit, Lt, [Opn, Perc, Perc Endo], Drain Dev, NQ
0N9Q[0,3,4]ZX	Drain/Orbit, Lt, [Opn, Perc, Perc Endo]
0N9Q[0,4]ZZ	Drain/Orbit, Lt, [Opn, Perc Endo]
0NBP*	Exc/Orbit, Rt
0NBQ*	Exc/Orbit, Lt
0NPW[0,3,4]JZ	Rmvl/Facial Bone, [Opn, Perc, Perc Endo], Synth Sub, NQ
0NQP*	Repair/Orbit, Rt
0NQQ*	Repair/Orbit, Lt
0NRC[0,3,4]JZ	Replace/Sphenoid Bone, Rt, [Opn, Perc, Perc Endo], Synth Sub, NQ
0NRD[0,3,4]JZ	Replace/Sphenoid Bone, Lt, [Opn, Perc, Perc Endo], Synth Sub, NQ
0NRF[0,3,4]JZ	Replace/Ethmoid Bone, Rt, [Opn, Perc, Perc Endo], Synth Sub, NQ
0NRG[0,3,4]JZ	Replace/Ethmoid Bone, Lt, [Opn, Perc, Perc Endo], Synth Sub, NQ
0NRH[0,3,4]JZ	Replace/Lacrimal Bone, Rt, [Opn, Perc, Perc Endo], Synth Sub, NQ
0NRJ[0,3,4]JZ	Replace/Lacrimal Bone, Lt, [Opn, Perc, Perc Endo], Synth Sub, NQ
0NRK[0,3,4]JZ	Replace/Palatine Bone, Rt, [Opn, Perc, Perc Endo], Synth Sub, NQ
0NRL[0,3,4]JZ	Replace/Palatine Bone, Lt, [Opn, Perc, Perc Endo], Synth Sub, NQ
0NRM[0,3,4]JZ	Replace/Zygomatic Bone, Rt, [Opn, Perc, Perc Endo], Synth Sub, NQ
0NRN[0,3,4]JZ	Replace/Zygomatic Bone, Lt, [Opn, Perc, Perc Endo], Synth Sub, NQ
0NRP[0,3,4][7,J]Z	Replace/Orbit, Rt, [Opn, Perc, Perc Endo], [Auto Tissue Sub, Synth Sub], NQ
0NRQ[0,3,4][7,J]Z	Replace/Orbit, Lt, [Opn, Perc, Perc Endo], [Auto Tissue Sub, Synth Sub], NQ
0NRX[0,3,4]JZ	Replace/Hyoid Bone, [Opn, Perc, Perc Endo], Synth Sub, NQ
0NSC0[4,Z]Z	Repos/Sphenoid Bone, Rt, Opn, [Int Fix Dev, No Dev], NQ
0NSD0[4,Z]Z	Repos/Sphenoid Bone, Lt, Opn, [Int Fix Dev, No Dev], NQ
0NSF0[4,Z]Z	Repos/Ethmoid Bone, Rt, Opn, [Int Fix Dev, No Dev], NQ
0NSG0[4,Z]Z	Repos/Ethmoid Bone, Lt, Opn, [Int Fix Dev, No Dev], NQ
0NSH0[4,Z]Z	Repos/Lacrimal Bone, Rt, Opn, [Int Fix Dev, No Dev], NQ
0NSJ0[4,Z]Z	Repos/Lacrimal Bone, Lt, Opn, [Int Fix Dev, No Dev], NQ
0NSK0[4,Z]Z	Repos/Palatine Bone, Rt, Opn, [Int Fix Dev, No Dev], NQ
0NSL0[4,Z]Z	Repos/Palatine Bone, Lt, Opn, [Int Fix Dev, No Dev], NQ
0NSP0[4,Z]Z	Repos/Orbit, Rt, Opn, [Int Fix Dev, No Dev], NQ
0NSQ0[4,Z]Z	Repos/Orbit, Lt, Opn, [Int Fix Dev, No Dev], NQ
0NSX0[4,Z]Z	Repos/Hyoid Bone, Opn, [Int Fix Dev, No Dev], NQ
0NUC[0,3,4]JZ	Supl/Sphenoid Bone, Rt, [Opn, Perc, Perc Endo], Synth Sub, NQ
0NUD[0,3,4]JZ	Supl/Sphenoid Bone, Lt, [Opn, Perc, Perc Endo], Synth Sub, NQ
0NUF[0,3,4]JZ	Supl/Ethmoid Bone, Rt, [Opn, Perc, Perc Endo], Synth Sub, NQ
0NUG[0,3,4]JZ	Supl/Ethmoid Bone, Lt, [Opn, Perc, Perc Endo], Synth Sub, NQ
0NUH[0,3,4]JZ	Supl/Lacrimal Bone, Rt, [Opn, Perc, Perc Endo], Synth Sub, NQ
0NUJ[0,3,4]JZ	Supl/Lacrimal Bone, Lt, [Opn, Perc, Perc Endo], Synth Sub, NQ
0NUK[0,3,4]JZ	Supl/Palatine Bone, Rt, [Opn, Perc, Perc Endo], Synth Sub, NQ
0NUL[0,3,4]JZ	Supl/Palatine Bone, Lt, [Opn, Perc, Perc Endo], Synth Sub, NQ
0NUM[0,3,4]JZ	Supl/Zygomatic Bone, Rt, [Opn, Perc, Perc Endo], Synth Sub, NQ
0NUN[0,3,4]JZ	Supl/Zygomatic Bone, Lt, [Opn, Perc, Perc Endo], Synth Sub, NQ
0NUP[0,3,4]JZ	Supl/Orbit, Rt, [Opn, Perc, Perc Endo], Synth Sub, NQ
0NUQ[0,3,4]JZ	Supl/Orbit, Lt, [Opn, Perc, Perc Endo], Synth Sub, NQ
0NUX[0,3,4]JZ	Supl/Hyoid Bone, [Opn, Perc, Perc Endo], Synth Sub, NQ
0WQ2XZZ	Repair Face, Ext Appr

DRG 114   Orbital Procedures without CC/MCC

GMLOS 2.4	AMLOS 2.9	RW 1.2094

Select operating room procedures listed under DRG 113

DRG 115   Extraocular Procedures Except Orbit

GMLOS 3.5	AMLOS 4.5	RW 1.3151

Operating Room Procedures

Code	Description
039S[0,3,4]ZX	Drain/Temporal Artery, Rt, [Opn, Perc, Perc Endo]
039T[0,3,4]ZX	Drain/Temporal Artery, Lt, [Opn, Perc, Perc Endo]
03BS[0,3,4]ZX	Exc/Temporal Artery, Rt, [Opn, Perc, Perc Endo]
03BT[0,3,4]ZX	Exc/Temporal Artery, Lt, [Opn, Perc, Perc Endo]
081X*	Bypass/Lacrimal Duct, Rt
081Y*	Bypass/Lacrimal Duct, Lt
085L*	Destr/Extraocular Muscle, Rt
085M*	Destr/Extraocular Muscle, Lt
085N*	Destr/Upr Eyelid, Rt
085P*	Destr/Upr Eyelid, Lt
085Q*	Destr/Lwr Eyelid, Rt
085R*	Destr/Lwr Eyelid, Lt
085V*	Destr/Lacrimal Gland, Rt
085W*	Destr/Lacrimal Gland, Lt
085X*	Destr/Lacrimal Duct, Rt
085Y*	Destr/Lacrimal Duct, Lt
085[0,1,6,7,8,9]XZZ	Destr of [Rt Eye, Lt Eye, Rt Sclera, Lt Sclera, Rt Cornea, Lt Cornea], Ext Appr
085[S,T]XZZ	Destr of [Rt, Lt] Conjunctiva, Ext Appr
087*	Eye, Dilation
0890X[0,Z]Z	Drain/Eye, Rt, Ext, [Drain Dev, No Dev], NQ
0891X[0,Z]Z	Drain/Eye, Lt, Ext, [Drain Dev, No Dev], NQ
0896X[0,Z]Z	Drain/Sclera, Rt, Ext, [Drain Dev, No Dev], NQ
0897X[0,Z]Z	Drain/Sclera, Lt, Ext, [Drain Dev, No Dev], NQ
089L*	Drain/Extraocular Muscle, Rt
089M*	Drain/Extraocular Muscle, Lt
089N[0,3,X]ZX	Drain/Upr Eyelid, Rt, [Opn, Perc, Ext]
089P[0,3,X]ZX	Drain/Upr Eyelid, Lt, [Opn, Perc, Ext]
089Q[0,3,X]ZX	Drain/Lwr Eyelid, Rt, [Opn, Perc, Ext]
089R[0,3,X]ZX	Drain/Lwr Eyelid, Lt, [Opn, Perc, Ext]
089S*	Drain/Conjunctiva, Rt
089T*	Drain/Conjunctiva, Lt
089V*	Drain/Lacrimal Gland, Rt
089W*	Drain/Lacrimal Gland, Lt
089X*	Drain/Lacrimal Duct, Rt
089Y*	Drain/Lacrimal Duct, Lt
089[8,9]XZX	Drain of [Rt, Lt] Cornea, Ext Appr, Dx
08B0[0,3,X]ZZ	Exc/Eye, Rt, [Opn, Perc, Ext]
08B1[0,3,X]ZZ	Exc/Eye, Lt, [Opn, Perc, Ext]
08B8*	Exc/Cornea, Rt
08B9*	Exc/Cornea, Lt
08BL*	Exc/Extraocular Muscle, Rt
08BM*	Exc/Extraocular Muscle, Lt
08BN*	Exc/Upr Eyelid, Rt
08BP*	Exc/Upr Eyelid, Lt
08BQ*	Exc/Lwr Eyelid, Rt
08BR*	Exc/Lwr Eyelid, Lt

T Transfer DRG   SP Special Payment   * Code Range   6th and 7th Character of ZZ = No Device, No Qualifier ZX = No Device, Diagnostic

Code	Description
08BS*	Exc/Conjunctiva, Rt
08BT*	Exc/Conjunctiva, Lt
08BV*	Exc/Lacrimal Gland, Rt
08BW*	Exc/Lacrimal Gland, Lt
08BX*	Exc/Lacrimal Duct, Rt
08BY*	Exc/Lacrimal Duct, Lt
08B[6,7]XZZ	Exc of [Rt, Lt] Sclera, Ext Appr
08CL[0,3]ZZ	Extir/Extraocular Muscle, Rt, [Opn, Perc]
08CM[0,3]ZZ	Extir/Extraocular Muscle, Lt, [Opn, Perc]
08CV[0,3]ZZ	Extir/Lacrimal Gland, Rt, [Opn, Perc]
08CW[0,3]ZZ	Extir/Lacrimal Gland, Lt, [Opn, Perc]
08CX*	Extir/Lacrimal Duct, Rt
08CY*	Extir/Lacrimal Duct, Lt
08C[8,9]XZZ	Extir of Matter from [Rt, Lt] Cornea, Ext Appr
08C[S,T]XZZ	Extir of Matter from [Rt, Lt] Conjunctiva, Ext Appr
08D8*	Extract/Cornea, Rt
08D9*	Extract/Cornea, Lt
08H0[3,X]3Z	Insert/Eye, Rt, [Perc, Ext], Inf Dev, NQ
08H1[3,X]3Z	Insert/Eye, Lt, [Perc, Ext], Inf Dev, NQ
08JL*	Inspect/Extraocular Muscle, Rt
08JM*	Inspect/Extraocular Muscle, Lt
08J[0,1]XZZ	Inspect of [Rt, Lt] Eye, Ext Appr
08L*	Eye, Occlsn
08M*	Eye, Reattach
08NL*	Rls/Extraocular Muscle, Rt
08NM*	Rls/Extraocular Muscle, Lt
08NN*	Rls/Upr Eyelid, Rt
08NP*	Rls/Upr Eyelid, Lt
08NQ*	Rls/Lwr Eyelid, Rt
08NR*	Rls/Lwr Eyelid, Lt
08NV*	Rls/Lacrimal Gland, Rt
08NW*	Rls/Lacrimal Gland, Lt
08NX*	Rls/Lacrimal Duct, Rt
08NY*	Rls/Lacrimal Duct, Lt
08N[0,1,6,7]XZZ	Rls [Rt Eye, Lt Eye, Rt Sclera, Lt Sclera], Ext Appr
08N[S,T]XZZ	Rls [Rt, Lt] Conjunctiva, Ext Appr
08P00[0,1,7,C,D,K]Z	Rmvl/Eye, Rt, Opn, [Drain Dev, Radioact Elmt, Auto Tissue Sub, Extralum Dev, Intralum Dev, Nonauto Tissue Sub], NQ
08P0X[1,7,K]Z	Rmvl/Eye, Rt, Ext, [Radioact Elmt, Auto Tissue Sub, Nonauto Tissue Sub], NQ
08P0[3,7,8][0,1,3,7,C,D,J,K]Z	Rmvl/Eye, Rt, [Perc, Via Natrl or Artfcl Opng, Via Natrl or Artfcl Opng Endo], [Drain Dev, Radioact Elmt, Inf Dev, Auto Tissue Sub, Extralum Dev, Intralum Dev, Synth Sub, Nonauto Tissue Sub], NQ
08P10[0,1,7,C,D,K]Z	Rmvl/Eye, Lt, Opn, [Drain Dev, Radioact Elmt, Auto Tissue Sub, Extralum Dev, Intralum Dev, Nonauto Tissue Sub], NQ
08P1X[7,K]Z	Rmvl/Eye, Lt, Ext, [Auto Tissue Sub, Nonauto Tissue Sub], NQ
08P1[3,7,8][0,1,3,7,C,D,J,K]Z	Rmvl/Eye, Lt, [Perc, Via Natrl or Artfcl Opng, Via Natrl or Artfcl Opng Endo], [Drain Dev, Radioact Elmt, Inf Dev, Auto Tissue Sub, Extralum Dev, Intralum Dev, Synth Sub, Nonauto Tissue Sub], NQ
08PL*	Rmvl/Extraocular Muscle, Rt
08PM*	Rmvl/Extraocular Muscle, Lt
08QL*	Repair/Extraocular Muscle, Rt
08QM*	Repair/Extraocular Muscle, Lt
08QV0ZZ	Repair Rt Lacrimal Gland, Opn Appr
08QV3ZZ	Repair Rt Lacrimal Gland, Perc Appr
08QW*	Repair/Lacrimal Gland, Lt
08QX*	Repair/Lacrimal Duct, Rt
08QY*	Repair/Lacrimal Duct, Lt
08Q[S,T]XZZ	Rpr [Rt, Lt] Conjunctiva, Ext Appr
08R00KZ	Replace of Rt Eye with Nonaut Sub, Opn Appr
08R03JZ	Replace of Rt Eye with Synth Sub, Perc Appr
08R10KZ	Replace of Lt Eye with Nonaut Sub, Opn Appr
08R13JZ	Replace of Lt Eye with Synth Sub, Perc Appr
08R6*	Replace/Sclera, Rt
08R7*	Replace/Sclera, Lt
08RN*	Replace/Upr Eyelid, Rt
08RP*	Replace/Upr Eyelid, Lt
08RQ*	Replace/Lwr Eyelid, Rt
08RR*	Replace/Lwr Eyelid, Lt
08RS*	Replace/Conjunctiva, Rt
08RT*	Replace/Conjunctiva, Lt
08RX*	Replace/Lacrimal Duct, Rt
08RY*	Replace/Lacrimal Duct, Lt
08R[8,9]X7Z	Replace of [Rt, Lt] Cornea w/ Auto Tissue Sub, Ext Appr
08SL*	Repos/Extraocular Muscle, Rt
08SM*	Repos/Extraocular Muscle, Lt
08SN*	Repos/Upr Eyelid, Rt
08SP*	Repos/Upr Eyelid, Lt
08SQ*	Repos/Lwr Eyelid, Rt
08SR*	Repos/Lwr Eyelid, Lt
08SV*	Repos/Lacrimal Gland, Rt
08SW*	Repos/Lacrimal Gland, Lt
08SX*	Repos/Lacrimal Duct, Rt
08SY*	Repos/Lacrimal Duct, Lt
08TL*	Resect/Extraocular Muscle, Rt
08TM*	Resect/Extraocular Muscle, Lt
08TN*	Resect/Upr Eyelid, Rt
08TP*	Resect/Upr Eyelid, Lt
08TQ*	Resect/Lwr Eyelid, Rt
08TR*	Resect/Lwr Eyelid, Lt
08TV*	Resect/Lacrimal Gland, Rt
08TW*	Resect/Lacrimal Gland, Lt
08TX*	Resect/Lacrimal Duct, Rt
08TY*	Resect/Lacrimal Duct, Lt
08U0*	Supl/Eye, Rt
08U1*	Supl/Eye, Lt
08UL*	Supl/Extraocular Muscle, Rt
08UM*	Supl/Extraocular Muscle, Lt
08UN*	Supl/Upr Eyelid, Rt
08UP*	Supl/Upr Eyelid, Lt
08UQ*	Supl/Lwr Eyelid, Rt
08UR*	Supl/Lwr Eyelid, Lt
08UX*	Supl/Lacrimal Duct, Rt
08UY*	Supl/Lacrimal Duct, Lt
08U[8,9]X7Z	Supl [Rt, Lt] Cornea w/ Auto Tissue Sub, Ext Appr
08V*	Eye, Restrict
08W0[0,3,7,8][0,3,7,C,D,K]Z	Rev/Eye, Rt, [Opn, Perc, Via Natrl or Artfcl Opng, Via Natrl or Artfcl Opng Endo], [Drain Dev, Inf Dev, Auto Tissue Sub, Extralum Dev, Intralum Dev, Nonauto Tissue Sub], NQ
08W0[7,8]JZ	Rev/Eye, Rt, [Via Natrl or Artfcl Opng, Via Natrl or Artfcl Opng Endo], Synth Sub, NQ
08W1[0,3,7,8][0,3,7,C,D,K]Z	Rev/Eye, Lt, [Opn, Perc, Via Natrl or Artfcl Opng, Via Natrl or Artfcl Opng Endo], [Drain Dev, Inf Dev, Auto Tissue Sub, Extralum Dev, Intralum Dev, Nonauto Tissue Sub], NQ
08W1[7,8]JZ	Rev/Eye, Lt, [Via Natrl or Artfcl Opng, Via Natrl or Artfcl Opng Endo], Synth Sub, NQ
08WL*	Rev/Extraocular Muscle, Rt
08WM*	Rev/Extraocular Muscle, Lt
08X*	Eye, Transfer
0HB0XZZ	Exc of Scalp Skin, Ext Appr
0HB1XZZ	Exc of Face Skin, Ext Appr
0HB4XZZ	Exc of Neck Skin, Ext Appr
0HB5XZZ	Exc of Chest Skin, Ext Appr
0HB6XZZ	Exc of Back Skin, Ext Appr
0HB7XZZ	Exc of Abd Skin, Ext Appr
0HB8XZZ	Exc of Buttock Skin, Ext Appr
0HBAXZZ	Exc of Genitalia Skin, Ext Appr
0HBBXZZ	Exc of Rt Upr Arm Skin, Ext Appr
0HBCXZZ	Exc of Lt Upr Arm Skin, Ext Appr
0HBDXZZ	Exc of Rt Lwr Arm Skin, Ext Appr
0HBEXZZ	Exc of Lt Lwr Arm Skin, Ext Appr
0HBFXZZ	Exc of Rt Hand Skin, Ext Appr
0HBGXZZ	Exc of Lt Hand Skin, Ext Appr
0HBHXZZ	Exc of Rt Upr Leg Skin, Ext Appr
0HBJXZZ	Exc of Lt Upr Leg Skin, Ext Appr
0HBKXZZ	Exc of Rt Lwr Leg Skin, Ext Appr
0HBLXZZ	Exc of Lt Lwr Leg Skin, Ext Appr
0HBMXZZ	Exc of Rt Foot Skin, Ext Appr
0HBNXZZ	Exc of Lt Foot Skin, Ext Appr
0JB00ZZ	Exc of Scalp SQ/Fascia, Opn Appr
0JB10ZZ	Exc of Face SQ/Fascia, Opn Appr
0JB40ZZ	Exc of Ant Neck SQ/Fascia, Opn Appr
0JB50ZZ	Exc of Post Neck SQ/Fascia, Opn Appr
0JB60ZZ	Exc of Chest SQ/Fascia, Opn Appr
0JB70ZZ	Exc of Back SQ/Fascia, Opn Appr
0JB80ZZ	Exc of Abd SQ/Fascia, Opn Appr
0JB90ZZ	Exc of Buttock SQ/Fascia, Opn Appr
0JBB0ZZ	Exc of Perineum SQ/Fascia, Opn Appr
0JBC0ZZ	Exc of Pelvic SQ/Fascia, Opn Appr
0JBD0ZZ	Exc of Rt Up Arm SQ/Fascia, Opn Appr
0JBF0ZZ	Exc of Lt Up Arm SQ/Fascia, Opn Appr
0JBG0ZZ	Exc of Rt Low Arm SQ/Fascia, Opn Appr
0JBH0ZZ	Exc of Lt Low Arm SQ/Fascia, Opn Appr
0JBL0ZZ	Exc of Rt Up Leg SQ/Fascia, Opn Appr
0JBM0ZZ	Exc of Lt Up Leg SQ/Fascia, Opn Appr
0JBN0ZZ	Exc of Rt Low Leg SQ/Fascia, Opn Appr
0JBP0ZZ	Exc of Lt Low Leg SQ/Fascia, Opn Appr
0JBQ0ZZ	Exc of Rt Foot SQ/Fascia, Opn Appr

MDC 2: Diseases And Disorders Of The Eye—SURGICAL

Surgical   **Medical**   **CC Indicator**   **MCC Indicator**   **Procedure Proxy**   PDxMCC **PDx acts as own MCC**   PDxCC **PDx acts as own CC**

ØJBRØZZ	Exc of Lt Foot SQ/Fascia, Opn Appr
ØKS1*	Repos/Facial Muscle
ØWBØ[Ø,3,4,X]ZZ	Exc/Head, [Opn, Perc, Perc Endo, Ext]
ØWB2[Ø,3,4,X]ZZ	Exc/Face, [Opn, Perc, Perc Endo, Ext]
3EØC3[3,H,K,M,T]Z	Introduction/Eye, Perc, [Anti-inflam, Radioact Substance, Oth Dx Substance, Pigment, Destr Agent], NQ
3EØC729	Introduction of Oth Anti-infective into Eye, Via Opng
3EØC7GC	Introduction of Oth Therap Subst into Eye, Via Opng
3EØC7SF	Introduction of Oth Gas into Eye, Via Opng
3EØC7[3,B,H,K,M,T]Z	Introduction/Eye, Via Natrl or Artfcl Opng, [Anti-inflam, Local Anesthetic, Radioact Substance, Oth Dx Substance, Pigment, Destr Agent], NQ
3EØCX29	Introduction of Oth Anti-infect into Eye, Extern Appr
3EØCXGC	Introduction of Oth Therap Subst into Eye, Extern Appr
3EØCX[3,B,H,K,M,T]Z	Introduction/Eye, Ext, [Anti-inflam, Local Anesthetic, Radioact Substance, Oth Dx Substance, Pigment, Destr Agent], NQ

DRG 116   Intraocular Procedures with CC/MCC
GMLOS 3.5   AMLOS 5.2   RW 1.5Ø15

Operating Room Procedures

Ø812*	Bypass/Ant Chamber, Rt
Ø813*	Bypass/Ant Chamber, Lt
Ø85A*	Destr/Choroid, Rt
Ø85B*	Destr/Choroid, Lt
Ø85[2,3,4,5]3ZZ	Destr of [Rt Ant Chamber, Lt Ant Chamber, Rt Vitreous, Lt Vitreous], Perc
Ø85[C,D,E,F,G,H,J,K]3ZZ	Destr of [Rt Iris, Lt Iris, Rt Retina, Lt Retina, Rt Retinal Vessel, Lt Retinal Vessel, Rt Lens, Lt Lens], Perc Appr
Ø892*	Drain/Ant Chamber, Rt
Ø893*	Drain/Ant Chamber, Lt
Ø894*	Drain/Vitreous, Rt
Ø895*	Drain/Vitreous, Lt
Ø898X[Ø,Z]Z	Drain/Cornea, Rt, Ext, [Drain Dev, No Dev], NQ
Ø899X[Ø,Z]Z	Drain/Cornea, Lt, Ext, [Drain Dev, No Dev], NQ
Ø89A*	Drain/Choroid, Rt
Ø89B*	Drain/Choroid, Lt
Ø89C*	Drain/Iris, Rt
Ø89D*	Drain/Iris, Lt
Ø89E*	Drain/Retina, Rt
Ø89F*	Drain/Retina, Lt
Ø89G*	Drain/Retinal Vessel, Rt
Ø89H*	Drain/Retinal Vessel, Lt
Ø89J*	Drain/Lens, Rt
Ø89K*	Drain/Lens, Lt
Ø89[6,7]XZX	Drain of [Rt, Lt] Sclera, Ext Appr, Dx
Ø8B4*	Exc/Vitreous, Rt
Ø8B5*	Exc/Vitreous, Lt
Ø8BA*	Exc/Choroid, Rt
Ø8BB*	Exc/Choroid, Lt
Ø8BC*	Exc/Iris, Rt
Ø8BD*	Exc/Iris, Lt
Ø8BE*	Exc/Retina, Rt
Ø8BF*	Exc/Retina, Lt
Ø8BJ*	Exc/Lens, Rt
Ø8BK*	Exc/Lens, Lt
Ø8B[6,7]XZX	Exc of [Rt, Lt] Sclera, Ext Appr, Dx
Ø8C4*	Extir/Vitreous, Rt
Ø8C5*	Extir/Vitreous, Lt
Ø8CA*	Extir/Choroid, Rt
Ø8CB*	Extir/Choroid, Lt
Ø8CC*	Extir/Iris, Rt
Ø8CD*	Extir/Iris, Lt
Ø8CE*	Extir/Retina, Rt
Ø8CF*	Extir/Retina, Lt
Ø8CG*	Extir/Retinal Vessel, Rt
Ø8CH*	Extir/Retinal Vessel, Lt
Ø8CJ*	Extir/Lens, Rt
Ø8CK*	Extir/Lens, Lt
Ø8C[Ø,1]XZZ	Extir of Matter from [Rt, Lt] Eye, Ext Appr
Ø8C[2,3]3ZZ	Extir of Matter from [Rt, Lt] Ant Chamber, Perc Appr
Ø8C[L,M]XZZ	Extir of Matter from [Rt, Lt] Extraocular Muscle, Ext Appr
Ø8C[V,W]XZZ	Extir of Matter from [Rt, Lt] Lacrimal Gland, Ext Appr
Ø8D[J,K]3ZZ	Extract of [Rt, Lt] Lens, Perc Appr
Ø8F[4,5]3ZZ	Fragmn in [Rt, Lt] Vitreous, Perc Appr
Ø8HØ[3,X]1Z	Insert/Eye, Rt, [Perc, Ext], Radioact Elmt, NQ
Ø8H1[3,X]1Z	Insert/Eye, Lt, [Perc, Ext], Radioact Elmt, NQ
Ø8H[Ø,1]Ø5Z	Insert/Eye, [Rt, Lt], Opn, Epiretinal Visual Prosthesis, NQ

Ø8N23ZZ	Rls Rt Ant Chamber, Perc Appr
Ø8N33ZZ	Rls Lt Ant Chamber, Perc Appr
Ø8N43ZZ	Rls Rt Vitreous, Perc Appr
Ø8N53ZZ	Rls Lt Vitreous, Perc Appr
Ø8N8XZZ	Rls Rt Cornea, Ext Appr
Ø8N9XZZ	Rls Lt Cornea, Ext Appr
Ø8NA*	Rls/Choroid, Rt
Ø8NB*	Rls/Choroid, Lt
Ø8N[C,D,E,F,G,H,J,K]3ZZ	Rls [Rt Iris, Lt Iris, Rt Retina, Lt Retina, Rt Retinal Vessel, Lt Retinal Vessel, Rt Lens, Lt Lens], Perc Appr
Ø8P[Ø,1]XJZ	Rmvl of Synth Sub from [Rt, Lt] Eye, Ext Appr
Ø8P[J,K]3JZ	Rmvl of Synth Sub from [Rt, Lt] Lens, Perc Appr
Ø8Q23ZZ	Repair Rt Ant Chamber, Perc Appr
Ø8Q33ZZ	Repair Lt Ant Chamber, Perc Appr
Ø8Q43ZZ	Repair Rt Vitreous, Perc Appr
Ø8Q53ZZ	Repair Lt Vitreous, Perc Appr
Ø8Q6XZZ	Repair Rt Sclera, Ext Appr
Ø8Q7XZZ	Repair Lt Sclera, Ext Appr
Ø8Q8XZZ	Repair Rt Cornea, Ext Appr
Ø8Q9XZZ	Repair Lt Cornea, Ext Appr
Ø8QA*	Repair/Choroid, Rt
Ø8QB*	Repair/Choroid, Lt
Ø8Q[C,D,E,F,G,H,J,K]3ZZ	Rpr [Rt Iris, Lt Iris, Rt Retina, Lt Retina, Rt Retinal Vessel, Lt Retinal Vessel, Rt Lens, Lt Lens], Perc Appr
Ø8R4*	Replace/Vitreous, Rt
Ø8R5*	Replace/Vitreous, Lt
Ø8R837Z	Replace of Rt Cornea with Autol Sub, Perc Appr
Ø8R8[3,X][J,K]Z	Replace/Cornea, Rt, [Perc, Ext], [Synth Sub, Nonauto Tissue Sub], NQ
Ø8R937Z	Replace of Lt Cornea with Autol Sub, Perc Appr
Ø8R9[3,X][J,K]Z	Replace/Cornea, Lt, [Perc, Ext], [Synth Sub, Nonauto Tissue Sub], NQ
Ø8RA*	Replace/Choroid, Rt
Ø8RB*	Replace/Choroid, Lt
Ø8RC*	Replace/Iris, Rt
Ø8RD*	Replace/Iris, Lt
Ø8RG*	Replace/Retinal Vessel, Rt
Ø8RH*	Replace/Retinal Vessel, Lt
Ø8RJ*	Replace/Lens, Rt
Ø8RK*	Replace/Lens, Lt
Ø8S[C,D,G,H,J,K]3ZZ	Repos [Rt Iris, Lt Iris, Rt Retinal Vessel, Lt Retinal Vessel, Rt Lens, Lt Lens], Perc
Ø8T43ZZ	Resect of Rt Vitreous, Perc Appr
Ø8T53ZZ	Resect of Lt Vitreous, Perc Appr
Ø8T8XZZ	Resect of Rt Cornea, Ext Appr
Ø8T9XZZ	Resect of Lt Cornea, Ext Appr
Ø8TC3ZZ	Resect of Rt Iris, Perc Appr
Ø8TD3ZZ	Resect of Lt Iris, Perc Appr
Ø8TJ3ZZ	Resect of Rt Lens, Perc Appr
Ø8TK3ZZ	Resect of Lt Lens, Perc Appr
Ø8U8[Ø,3,X][J,K]Z	Supl/Cornea, Rt, [Opn, Perc, Ext], [Synth Sub, Nonauto Tissue Sub], NQ
Ø8U8[Ø,3]7Z	Supl/Cornea, Rt, [Opn, Perc], Auto Tissue Sub, NQ
Ø8U9[Ø,3,X][J,K]Z	Supl/Cornea, Lt, [Opn, Perc, Ext], [Synth Sub, Nonauto Tissue Sub], NQ
Ø8U9[Ø,3]7Z	Supl/Cornea, Lt, [Opn, Perc], Auto Tissue Sub, NQ
Ø8UC*	Supl/Iris, Rt
Ø8UD*	Supl/Iris, Lt
Ø8UE*	Supl/Retina, Rt
Ø8UF*	Supl/Retina, Lt
Ø8UG*	Supl/Retinal Vessel, Rt
Ø8UH*	Supl/Retinal Vessel, Lt
Ø8W[J,K]3JZ	Rev of Synth Sub in [Rt, Lt] Lens, Perc Appr
3EØC3BZ	Introduction of Local Anesthetic into Eye, Perc Appr
3EØC3GC	Introduction of Oth Therap Subst into Eye, Perc Appr
3EØC[3,X]SF	Introduction/Eye, [Perc, Ext], Gas, Oth Gas

DRG 117   Intraocular Procedures without CC/MCC
GMLOS 2.Ø   AMLOS 2.5   RW Ø.834Ø

Select operating room procedures listed under DRG 116

T Transfer DRG   SP Special Payment   * Code Range   6th and 7th Character of ZZ = No Device, No Qualifier ZX = No Device, Diagnostic

44   MS-DRG Version 33.0   © 2015 Optum360, LLC

(left margin) **MDC 2: Diseases And Disorders Of The Eye—SURGICAL**

MEDICAL

DRG 121   Acute Major Eye Infections with CC/MCC
GMLOS 3.8   AMLOS 4.7   RW 0.9934

Principal Diagnosis

H04.01[1,2,3,9]	Acute dacryoadenitis, [rt, lt, bilat, unsp] lacrimal gland
H04.3[2,3][1,2,3,9]	Acute [dacryocystitis, lacrimal canaliculitis] of [rt, lt, bilat, unsp] lacrimal passage
H05.0[1,2,3,4][1,2,3,9]	[Cellulitis, Osteomyelitis, Periostitis, Tenonitis] of [rt, lt, bilat, unsp] orbit
H16.03[1,2,3,9]	Corneal ulcer w/ hypopyon, [rt, lt, bilat, unsp] eye
H16.0[0,1][1,2,3,9]	[Unsp, Central] corneal ulcer, [rt, lt, bilat, unsp] eye
H16.0[6,7][1,2,3,9]	[Mycotic, Perforated] corneal ulcer, [rt, lt, bilat, unsp] eye
H16.31[1,2,3,9]	Corneal abscess, [rt, lt, bilat, unsp] eye
H21.33[1,2,3,9]	Parasitic cyst of iris, ciliary body or ant chamber, [rt, lt, bilat, unsp] eye
H33.12[1,2,3,9]	Parasitic cyst of retina, [rt, lt, bilat, unsp] eye
H44.0*	Purulent endophthalmitis
H44.12[1,2,3,9]	Parasitic endophthalmitis, unsp, [rt, lt, bilat, unsp] eye
H44.19	Oth endophthalmitis

DRG 122   Acute Major Eye Infections without CC/MCC
GMLOS 3.0   AMLOS 3.6   RW 0.5850

Select principal diagnosis listed under DRG 121

DRG 123   Neurological Eye Disorders
GMLOS 2.1   AMLOS 2.6   RW 0.7171

Prinicpal Diagnosis

A39.82	Meningococcal retrobulbar neuritis
G45.3	Amaurosis fugax
H02.4[0,2,3][1,2,3,9]	[Unsp, Myogenic, Paralytic] ptosis of [rt, lt, bilat, unsp] eyelid
H02.59	Oth d/o affecting eyelid function
H05.21[1,2,3,9]	Displac (lat) of globe, [rt, lt, bilat, unsp] eye
H05.2[5,6][1,2,3,9]	[Intermittent, Pulsating] exophthalmos, [rt, lt, bilat, unsp] eye
H05.82[1,2,3,9]	Myopathy of extraocular muscles, [rt, lt, bilat, unsp] orbit
H34*	Retinal vascular occlusions
H40.12*	Low-tension glaucoma
H46*	Optic neuritis
H47.0*	D/o of optic nerve, NEC
H47.20	Unsp optic atrophy
H47.21[1,2,3,9]	Primary optic atrophy, [rt, lt, bilat, unsp] eye
H47.22	Hereditary optic atrophy
H47.29[1,2,3,9]	Oth optic atrophy, [rt, lt, bilat, unsp] eye
H47.3[2,3][1,2,3,9]	[Drusen, Pseudopapilledema] of optic disc, [rt, lt, bilat, unsp] eye
H49.0*	Third [oculomotor] nerve palsy
H49.1*	Fourth [trochlear] nerve palsy
H49.2*	Sixth [abducent] nerve palsy
H49.3*	Total (ext) ophthalmoplegia
H49.4*	Progressive ext ophthalmoplegia
H49.88[1,2,3,9]	Oth paralytic strabismus, [rt, lt, bilat, unsp] eye
H49.9	Unsp paralytic strabismus
H50.89	Oth spec strabismus
H51.8	Oth spec d/o of binocular movement
H52.51[1,2,3,9]	Int ophthalmoplegia (complete) (total), [rt, lt, bilat, unsp] eye
H53.1[2,3][1,2,3,9]	[Transient, Sudden] visual loss, [rt, lt, bilat, unsp] eye
H53.2	Diplopia
H53.40	Unsp visual field defects
H53.41[1,2,3,9]	Scotoma involving central area, [rt, lt, bilat, unsp] eye
H53.43[1,2,3,9]	Sector or arcuate defects, [rt, lt, bilat, unsp] eye
H53.45[1,2,3,9]	Oth localized visual field defect, [rt, lt, bilat, unsp] eye
H53.46[1,2,9]	Homonymous bilat field defects, [rt, lt, unsp] side
H53.47	Heteronymous bilat field defects
H53.48[1,2,3,9]	Generalized contraction of visual field, [rt, lt, bilat, unsp] eye
H53.52	Acquired color vision deficiency
H55.0[0,2,4]	[Unsp, Latent, Dissociated] nystagmus
H55.81	Saccadic eye movements
H57.00	Unsp anomaly of pupillary function
H57.02	Anisocoria
H57.03	Miosis
H57.04	Mydriasis
H57.05[1,2,3,9]	Tonic pupil, [rt, lt, bilat, unsp] eye
H57.09	Oth anomalies of pupillary function

DRG 124   Other Disorders of the Eye with MCC
GMLOS 3.8   AMLOS 5.1   RW 1.2163

Principal Diagnosis

A18.5*	Tuberculosis of eye
A36.86	Diphtheritic conjunctivitis
A50.31	Late congenital syphilitic interstitial keratitis
A51.43	Secondary syphilitic oculopathy
A52.71	Late syphilitic oculopathy
A54.3*	Gonococcal infxn of eye
A71*	Trachoma
A74.0	Chlamydial conjunctivitis
B00.5*	Herpesviral ocular dz
B02.3*	Zoster ocular dz
B05.81	Measles keratitis and keratoconjunctivitis
B30*	Viral conjunctivitis
B58.01	Toxoplasma chorioretinitis
B58.09	Oth toxoplasma oculopathy
B60.1[2,3]	[Conjunctivitis, Keratoconjunctivitis] d/t Acanthamoeba
B94.0	Sequelae of trachoma
C43.1*	Malig melanoma of eyelid, incl* canthus
C44.1*	Oth and unsp malig neoplasm skin/ eyelid, incl* canthus
C69*	Malig neoplasm of eye and adnexa
D03.1*	Melanoma in situ of eyelid, incl* canthus
D04.1*	Carcinoma in situ of skin of eyelid, incl* canthus
D09.2*	Carcinoma in situ of eye
D22.1*	Melanocytic nevi of eyelid, incl* canthus
D23.1*	Oth benign neoplasm of skin of eyelid, incl* canthus
D31*	Benign neoplasm of eye and adnexa
E08.3*	Diabetes d/t underlying condition w ophthalmic comp
E09.3*	Drug/chem diabetes mellitus w ophthalmic comp
E10.3*	Type 1 diabetes mellitus with ophthalmic comp
E11.3*	Type 2 diabetes mellitus with ophthalmic comp
E13.3*	Oth diabetes mellitus with ophthalmic comp
E50.0	Vitamin A deficiency with conjunctival xerosis
E50.1	Vitamin A deficiency w Bitot's spot and conjunctival xerosis
E50.2	Vitamin A deficiency with corneal xerosis
E50.3	Vitamin A deficiency with corneal ulceration and xerosis
E50.4	Vitamin A deficiency with keratomalacia
E50.5	Vitamin A deficiency with night blindness
E50.6	Vitamin A deficiency with xerophthalmic scars of cornea
E50.7	Oth ocular manifestations of vitamin A deficiency
G24.5	Blepharospasm
H00*	Hordeolum and chalazion
H01*	Oth inflam of eyelid
H02.0*	Entropion and trichiasis of eyelid
H02.1*	Ectropion of eyelid
H02.2*	Lagophthalmos
H02.3*	Blepharochalasis
H02.41[1,2,3,9]	Mech ptosis of [rt, lt, bilat, unsp] eyelid
H02.51*	Abnormal innervation synd
H02.52*	Blepharophimosis
H02.53*	Eyelid retraction
H02.7*	Oth and unsp degeneratv d/o of eyelid and perioculr area
H02.8*	Oth spec d/o of eyelid
H02.9	Unsp d/o of eyelid
H04.03[1,2,3,9]	Chr enlgment of [rt, lt, bilat, unsp] lacrimal gland
H04.0[0,2][1,2,3,9]	[Unsp, Chr] dacryoadenitis, [rt, lt, bilat, unsp] lacrimal gland
H04.1*	Oth d/o of lacrimal gland
H04.2*	Epiphora
H04.3[0,1][1,2,3,9]	[Unsp, Phlegmonous] dacryocystitis of [rt, lt, bilat, unsp] lacrimal passage
H04.4*	Chr inflam of lacrimal passages
H04.5*	Stenosis and insufficiency of lacrimal passages
H04.6*	Oth changes of lacrimal passages
H04.8*	Oth d/o of lacrimal sys
H04.9	D/o of lacrimal sys, unsp
H05.00	Unsp acute inflam of orbit
H05.1*	Chr inflam d/o of orbit
H05.20	Unsp exophthalmos
H05.24[1,2,3,9]	Constant exophthalmos, [rt, lt, bilat, unsp] eye
H05.2[2,3][1,2,3,9]	[Edema, Hemor] of [rt, lt, bilat, unsp] orbit
H05.3*	Deformity of orbit
H05.4*	Enophthalmos
H05.5*	Retained (old) fb following penetrating wnd of orbit
H05.81[1,2,3,9]	Cyst of [rt, lt, bilat, unsp] orbit
H05.89	Oth d/o of orbit
H05.9	Unsp d/o of orbit
H10*	Conjunctivitis
H11*	Oth d/o of conjunctiva

Surgical   **Medical**   **CC Indicator**   **MCC Indicator**   **Procedure Proxy**   **PDxMCC PDx acts as own MCC**   **PDxCC PDx acts as own CC**

© 2015 Optum360, LLC   MS-DRG Version 33.0   **45**

MDC 2: Diseases And Disorders Of The Eye—MEDICAL

H15*	D/o of sclera	H50.9	Unsp strabismus
H16.0[2,4,5][1,2,3,9]	[Ring, Marginal, Mooren's] corneal ulcer, [rt, lt, bilat, unsp] eye	H51.0	Palsy (spasm) of conjugate gaze
H16.1*	Oth and unsp superf keratitis without conjunctivitis	H51.1*	Convergence insufficiency and excess
		H51.9	Unsp d/o of binocular movement
H16.2*	Keratoconjunctivitis	H52.0*	Hypermetropia
H16.30[1,2,3,9]	Unsp interstitial keratitis, [rt, lt, bilat, unsp] eye	H52.1*	Myopia
H16.3[2,3,9][1,2,3,9]	[Diffuse interstitial, Sclerosing, Oth interstitial and deep] keratitis, [rt, lt, bilat, unsp] eye	H52.2*	Astigmatism
		H52.3*	Anisometropia and aniseikonia
H16.4*	Corneal neovascularization	H52.4	Presbyopia
H16.8	Oth keratitis	H52.52*	Paresis of accommodation
H16.9	Unsp keratitis	H52.53*	Spasm of accommodation
H17*	Corneal scars and opacities	H52.6	Oth d/o of refraction
H18*	Oth d/o of cornea	H52.7	Unsp d/o of refraction
H20*	Iridocyclitis	H53.0*	Amblyopia ex anopsia
H21.0*	Hyphema	H53.10	Unsp subjective visual disturbances
H21.1*	Oth vascular d/o of iris and ciliary body	H53.11	Day blindness
H21.2*	Degeneration of iris and ciliary body	H53.14[1,2,3,9]	Visual discomfort, [rt, lt, bilat, unsp] eye
H21.3[0,1,2][1,2,3,9]	[Idiopathic, Exudative, Implantation] cysts of iris, ciliary body or ant chamber, [rt, lt, bilat, unsp] eye	H53.15	Visual distortions of shape and size
		H53.16	Psychophysical visual disturbances
H21.3[4,5][1,2,3,9]	[Primary, Exudative] cyst of pars plana, [rt, lt, bilat, unsp] eye	H53.19	Oth subjective visual disturbances
H21.4*	Pupillary membranes	H53.3*	Oth and unsp d/o of binocular vision
H21.5*	Oth and unsp adhes and disruptions of iris and ciliary body	H53.42*	Scotoma of blind spot area
		H53.50	Unsp color vision deficiencies
H21.8*	Oth spec d/o of iris and ciliary body	H53.51	Achromatopsia
H21.9	Unsp d/o of iris and ciliary body	H53.53	Deuteranomaly
H22	D/o of iris and ciliary body in dz classd elsw	H53.54	Protanomaly
H25*	Age-related cataract	H53.55	Tritanomaly
H26*	Oth cataract	H53.59	Oth color vision deficiencies
H27*	Oth d/o of lens	H53.6*	Night blindness
H28	Cataract in dz classified elsw	H53.7*	Vision sensitivity deficiencies
H30*	Chorioretinal inflam	H53.8	Oth visual disturbances
H31*	Oth d/o of choroid	H53.9	Unsp visual disturbance
H32	Chorioretinal d/o in dz classified elsw	H54*	Blindness and low vision
H33.0*	Retinal detach with retinal break	H55.0[1,3,9]	[Congenital, Visual deprivation, Oth forms] nystagmus
H33.10[1,2,3,9]	Unsp retinoschisis, [rt, lt, bilat, unsp] eye	H55.89	Oth irregular eye movements
H33.11[1,2,3,9]	Cyst of ora serrata, [rt, lt, bilat, unsp] eye	H57.1*	Ocular pain
H33.19[1,2,3,9]	Oth retinoschisis and retinal cysts, [rt, lt, bilat, unsp] eye	H57.8	Oth spec d/o of eye and adnexa
		H57.9	Unsp d/o of eye and adnexa
H33.2*	Serous retinal detach	H59.02*	Cataract (lens) fragments in eye following cataract surgery
H33.3*	Retinal breaks without detach		
H33.4*	Traction detach of retina	H59.4*	Inflam (infxn) of postprocedural bleb
H33.8	Oth retinal detachments	Q10*	Congenital malform of eyelid, lacrimal apparatus and orbit
H35*	Oth retinal d/o		
H36	Retinal d/o in dz classified elsw	Q11*	Anophthalmos, microphthalmos and macrophthalmos
H40.0*	Glaucoma suspect		
H40.10*	Unsp opn-angle glaucoma	Q12*	Congenital lens malformations
H40.11*	Primary opn-angle glaucoma	Q13*	Congenital malformations of ant segment of eye
H40.13*	Pigmentary glaucoma	Q14*	Congenital malformations of posterior segment of eye
H40.14*	Capsular glaucoma with pseudoexfoliation of lens	Q15*	Oth congenital malformations of eye
H40.15*	Residual stage of opn-angle glaucoma	R44.1	Visual hallucinations
H40.2*	Primary angle-closure glaucoma	R48.3	Visual agnosia
H40.3*	Glaucoma secondary to eye trauma	R94.110	Abnormal electro-oculogram [EOG]
H40.4*	Glaucoma secondary to eye inflam	R94.111	Abnormal electroretinogram [ERG]
H40.5*	Glaucoma secondary to oth eye d/o	R94.112	Abnormal visually evoked potential [VEP]
H40.6*	Glaucoma secondary to drugs	R94.113	Abnormal oculomotor study
H40.8*	Oth glaucoma	S00.1[0,1,2]XA	Contsn of [unsp, rt, lt] eyelid and periocular area, init enc
H40.9	Unsp glaucoma	S00.20[1,2,9]A	Unsp superf inj of [rt, lt, unsp] eyelid and periocular area, init enc
H42	Glaucoma in dz classified elsw		
H43*	D/o of vitreous body	S00.21[1,2,9]A	Abrasion of [rt, lt, unsp] eyelid and periocular area, init enc
H44.11*	Panuveitis	S00.22[1,2,9]A	Blister (nonthermal) of [rt, lt, unsp] eyelid and periocular area, init enc
H44.13*	Sympathetic uveitis		
H44.2*	Degenerative myopia	S00.24[1,2,9]A	Ext constriction of [rt, lt, unsp] eyelid and periocular area, init enc
H44.3*	Oth and unsp degenerative d/o of globe		
H44.4*	Hypotony of eye	S00.25[1,2,9]A	Superf FB of [rt, lt, unsp] eyelid and periocular area, init enc
H44.5*	Degenerated conditions of globe	S00.26[1,2,9]A	Insect bite (nonvenomous) of [rt, lt, unsp] eyelid and periocular area, init enc
H44.6*	Retained (old) intraocular FB, magnetic		
H44.7*	Retained (old) intraocular FB, nonmagnetic	S00.27[1,2,9]A	Oth superf bite of [rt, lt, unsp] eyelid and periocular area, init enc
H44.8*	Oth d/o of globe		
H44.9	Unsp d/o of globe	S01.10[1,2,9]A	Unsp opn wnd of [rt, lt, unsp] eyelid and periocular area, init enc
H47.12	Papilledema associated with decreased ocular pressure		
		S01.11[1,2,9]A	Lac w/o FB of [rt, lt, unsp] eyelid and periocular area, init enc
H47.13	Papilledema associated with retinal d/o	S01.12[1,2,9]A	Lac w/ FB of [rt, lt, unsp] eyelid and periocular area, init enc
H47.23*	Glaucomatous optic atrophy	S01.13[1,2,9]A	Punc wnd w/o FB of [rt, lt, unsp] eyelid and periocular area, init enc
H47.31*	Coloboma of optic disc		
H47.39*	Oth d/o of optic disc	S01.14[1,2,9]A	Punc wnd w/ FB of [rt, lt, unsp] eyelid and periocular area, init enc
H50.0*	Esotropia		
H50.1*	Exotropia	S01.15[1,2,9]A	Opn bite of [rt, lt, unsp] eyelid and periocular area, init enc
H50.2*	Vertical strabismus	S02.3XX[A,B]	Fx of orbital floor, init enc for [clsd, opn] fx
H50.3*	Intermittent heterotropia	S04.01[1,2,9]A	Inj of optic nerve, [rt, lt, unsp] eye, init enc
H50.4*	Oth and unsp heterotropia	S05.0[0,1,2]XA	Inj of conjunctiva and corneal abrasion w/o FB, [unsp, rt, lt] eye, init enc
H50.5*	Heterophoria		
H50.6*	Mechanical strabismus	S05.1[0,1,2]XA	Contsn of eyeball and orbital tissues, [unsp, rt, lt] eye, init enc
H50.81[1,2]	Duane's synd, [rt, lt] eye		

T **Transfer DRG**   SP **Special Payment**   * **Code Range**   **6th and 7th Character of ZZ = No Device, No Qualifier ZX = No Device, Diagnostic**

S05.2[0,1,2]XA   Ocular lac and rupture w/ prolapse or loss of intraocular tissue, [unsp, rt, lt] eye, init enc
S05.3[0,1,2]XA   Ocular lac w/o prolapse or loss of intraocular tissue, [unsp, rt, lt] eye, init enc
S05.4[0,1,2]XA   Penetrating wnd of orbit w/ or w/o FB, [unsp, rt, lt] eye, init enc
S05.5[0,1,2]XA   Penetrating wnd w/ FB of [unsp, rt, lt] eyeball, init enc
S05.6[0,1,2]XA   Penetrating wnd w/o FB of [unsp, rt, lt] eyeball, init enc
S05.7[0,1,2]XA   Avulsion of [unsp, rt, lt] eye, init enc
S05.8X[1,2,9]A   Oth injuries of [rt, lt, unsp] eye and orbit, init enc
S05.9[0,1,2]XA   Unsp inj of [unsp, rt, lt] eye and orbit, init enc
T15.0[0,1,2]XA   FB in cornea, [unsp, rt, lt] eye, init enc
T15.1[0,1,2]XA   FB in conjunctival sac, [unsp, rt, lt] eye, init enc
T15.8[0,1,2]XA   FB in oth and multi parts of ext eye, [unsp, rt, lt] eye, init enc
T15.9[0,1,2]XA   FB on ext eye, part unsp, [unsp, rt, lt] eye, init enc
T26.0[0,1,2]XA   Burn of [unsp, rt, lt] eyelid and periocular area, init enc
T26.1[0,1,2]XA   Burn of cornea and conjunctival sac, [unsp, rt, lt] eye, init enc
T26.2[0,1,2]XA   Burn w/ resulting rupture and destr of [unsp, rt, lt] eyeball, init enc
T26.3[0,1,2]XA   Burns of oth spec parts of [unsp, rt, lt] eye and adnexa, init enc
T26.4[0,1,2]XA   Burn of [unsp, rt, lt] eye and adnexa, part unsp, init enc
T26.5[0,1,2]XA   Corrosion of [unsp, rt, lt] eyelid and periocular area, init enc
T26.6[0,1,2]XA   Corrosion of cornea and conjunctival sac, [unsp, rt, lt] eye, init enc
T26.7[0,1,2]XA   Corrosion w/ resulting rupture and destr of [unsp, rt, lt] eyeball, init enc
T26.8[0,1,2]XA   Corrosions of oth spec parts of [unsp, rt, lt] eye and adnexa, init enc
T26.9[0,1,2]XA   Corrosion of [unsp, rt, lt] eye and adnexa, part unsp, init enc
T49.5X[1,2,3,4]A Poison by ophthalmological drugs and preparations, [accid (unintentional), intentional self-harm, assault, undetermined], init enc
T85.2[1,2,9]XA   [Breakdown (mech), Displac, Oth mech comp] of intraocular lens, init enc
T85.3[1,2,9]8A   [Breakdown (mech), Displac, Oth mech comp] of oth ocular prosthetic devs, implants and grafts, init enc
T86.84[0,1]   Corneal transplant [rejection, failure]
Z90.01   Acquired absence of eye
Z94.7   Corneal transplant status
Z96.1   Presence of intraocular lens
Z97.0   Presence of artfcl eye

DRG 125   Other Disorders of the Eye without MCC

GMLOS 2.5   AMLOS 3.2   RW 0.7256

Select principal diagnosis listed under DRG 124

MDC 2: Diseases And Disorders Of The Eye—MEDICAL

MDC 3
Diseases And Disorders Of The Ear, Nose, Mouth And Throat

SURGICAL

DRG 129 Major Head and Neck Procedures with CC/MCC or Major Device
GMLOS 3.7 AMLOS 5.2 RW 2.2292

Operating Room Procedures

Code	Description
07T0*	Resect/Lymphatic, Head
07T1*	Resect/Lymphatic, Rt Neck
07T2*	Resect/Lymphatic, Lt Neck
07T3*	Resect/Lymphatic, Rt Upr Extr
07T4*	Resect/Lymphatic, Lt Upr Extr
07T7*	Resect/Lymphatic, Thorax
07T8*	Resect/Lymphatic, Int Mammary, Rt
07T9*	Resect/Lymphatic, Int Mammary, Lt
07TB*	Resect/Lymphatic, Mesenteric
07TF*	Resect/Lymphatic, Rt Lwr Extr
07TG*	Resect/Lymphatic, Lt Lwr Extr
09HD[0,3,4][5,6,S]Z	Insert/Inner Ear, Rt, [Opn, Perc, Perc Endo], [Hearing Dev, Single Channel Cochlear Prosthesis, Hearing Dev, Multi Channel Cochlear Prosthesis, Hearing Dev], NQ
09HE[0,3,4][5,6,S]Z	Insert/Inner Ear, Lt, [Opn, Perc, Perc Endo], [Hearing Dev, Single Channel Cochlear Prosthesis, Hearing Dev, Multi Channel Cochlear Prosthesis, Hearing Dev], NQ
0CBS[0,3,4,7,8]ZZ	Exc/Larynx, [Opn, Perc, Perc Endo, Via Natrl or Artfcl Opng, Via Natrl or Artfcl Opng Endo]
0CT2*	Resect/Hard Palate
0CT7*	Resect/Tongue
0NBT[0,3,4]ZZ	Exc/Mandible, Rt, [Opn, Perc, Perc Endo]
0NBV[0,3,4]ZZ	Exc/Mandible, Lt, [Opn, Perc, Perc Endo]
0NRT*	Replace/Mandible, Rt
0NRV*	Replace/Mandible, Lt
0NT[T,V]0ZZ	Resect of [Rt, Lt] Mandible, Opn Appr

OR

Major Device Implant Operating Room Procedures

Code	Description
09HD[0,3,4][5,6,S]Z	Insert/Inner Ear, Rt, [Opn, Perc, Perc Endo], [Hearing Dev, Single Channel Cochlear Prosthesis, Hearing Dev, Multi Channel Cochlear Prosthesis, Hearing Dev], NQ
09HE[0,3,4][5,6,S]Z	Insert/Inner Ear, Lt, [Opn, Perc, Perc Endo], [Hearing Dev, Single Channel Cochlear Prosthesis, Hearing Dev, Multi Channel Cochlear Prosthesis, Hearing Dev], NQ

DRG 130 Major Head and Neck Procedures without CC/MCC
GMLOS 2.3 AMLOS 2.8 RW 1.3596

Operating Room Procedures

Code	Description
07T0*	Resect/Lymphatic, Head
07T1*	Resect/Lymphatic, Rt Neck
07T2*	Resect/Lymphatic, Lt Neck
07T3*	Resect/Lymphatic, Rt Upr Extr
07T4*	Resect/Lymphatic, Lt Upr Extr
07T7*	Resect/Lymphatic, Thorax
07T8*	Resect/Lymphatic, Int Mammary, Rt
07T9*	Resect/Lymphatic, Int Mammary, Lt
07TB*	Resect/Lymphatic, Mesenteric
07TF*	Resect/Lymphatic, Rt Lwr Extr
07TG*	Resect/Lymphatic, Lt Lwr Extr
09HD[0,3,4][5,6,S]Z	Insert/Inner Ear, Rt, [Opn, Perc, Perc Endo], [Hearing Dev, Single Channel Cochlear Prosthesis, Hearing Dev, Multi Channel Cochlear Prosthesis, Hearing Dev], NQ
09HE[0,3,4][5,6,S]Z	Insert/Inner Ear, Lt, [Opn, Perc, Perc Endo], [Hearing Dev, Single Channel Cochlear Prosthesis, Hearing Dev, Multi Channel Cochlear Prosthesis, Hearing Dev], NQ
0CBS[0,3,4,7,8]ZZ	Exc/Larynx, [Opn, Perc, Perc Endo, Via Natrl or Artfcl Opng, Via Natrl or Artfcl Opng Endo]
0CT2*	Resect/Hard Palate
0CT7*	Resect/Tongue
0NBT[0,3,4]ZZ	Exc/Mandible, Rt, [Opn, Perc, Perc Endo]
0NBV[0,3,4]ZZ	Exc/Mandible, Lt, [Opn, Perc, Perc Endo]
0NRT*	Replace/Mandible, Rt
0NRV*	Replace/Mandible, Lt
0NT[T,V]0ZZ	Resect of [Rt, Lt] Mandible, Opn Appr

DRG 131 Cranial/Facial Procedures with CC/MCC
GMLOS 4.3 AMLOS 6.0 RW 2.4094

Operating Room Procedures

Code	Description
00J00ZZ	Inspect of Brain, Opn Appr
08Q[0,1]XZZ	Rpr [Rt, Lt] Eye, Ext Appr
08T[0,1]XZZ	Resect of [Rt, Lt] Eye, Ext Appr
09TK*	Resect/Nose
0J81*	Div/SQ Tissue & Fascia, Face
0JR107Z	Replace of Face SQ/Fascia with Autol Sub, Opn Appr
0JR1[0,3]KZ	Replace/SQ Tissue & Fascia, Face, [Opn, Perc], Nonauto Tissue Sub, NQ
0N5*	Head and Facial Bones, Destr
0N8P*	Div/Orbit, Rt
0N8Q*	Div/Orbit, Lt
0N9P[0,3,4]0Z	Drain/Orbit, Rt, [Opn, Perc, Perc Endo], Drain Dev, NQ
0N9P[0,4]ZZ	Drain/Orbit, Rt, [Opn, Perc Endo]
0N9Q[0,3,4]0Z	Drain/Orbit, Lt, [Opn, Perc, Perc Endo], Drain Dev, NQ
0N9Q[0,4]ZZ	Drain/Orbit, Lt, [Opn, Perc Endo]
0NB0[0,3,4]ZZ	Exc/Skull, [Opn, Perc, Perc Endo]
0NB1[0,3,4]ZZ	Exc/Frontal Bone, Rt, [Opn, Perc, Perc Endo]
0NB2[0,3,4]ZZ	Exc/Frontal Bone, Lt, [Opn, Perc, Perc Endo]
0NB3[0,3,4]ZZ	Exc/Parietal Bone, Rt, [Opn, Perc, Perc Endo]
0NB4[0,3,4]ZZ	Exc/Parietal Bone, Lt, [Opn, Perc, Perc Endo]
0NB5[0,3,4]ZZ	Exc/Temporal Bone, Rt, [Opn, Perc, Perc Endo]
0NB6[0,3,4]ZZ	Exc/Temporal Bone, Lt, [Opn, Perc, Perc Endo]
0NB7[0,3,4]ZZ	Exc/Occipital Bone, Rt, [Opn, Perc, Perc Endo]
0NB8[0,3,4]ZZ	Exc/Occipital Bone, Lt, [Opn, Perc, Perc Endo]
0NBB[0,3,4]ZZ	Exc/Nasal Bone, [Opn, Perc, Perc Endo]
0NBC[0,3,4]ZZ	Exc/Sphenoid Bone, Rt, [Opn, Perc, Perc Endo]
0NBD[0,3,4]ZZ	Exc/Sphenoid Bone, Lt, [Opn, Perc, Perc Endo]
0NBF[0,3,4]ZZ	Exc/Ethmoid Bone, Rt, [Opn, Perc, Perc Endo]
0NBG[0,3,4]ZZ	Exc/Ethmoid Bone, Lt, [Opn, Perc, Perc Endo]
0NBH[0,3,4]ZZ	Exc/Lacrimal Bone, Rt, [Opn, Perc, Perc Endo]
0NBJ[0,3,4]ZZ	Exc/Lacrimal Bone, Lt, [Opn, Perc, Perc Endo]
0NBK[0,3,4]ZZ	Exc/Palatine Bone, Rt, [Opn, Perc, Perc Endo]
0NBL[0,3,4]ZZ	Exc/Palatine Bone, Lt, [Opn, Perc, Perc Endo]
0NBM[0,3,4]ZZ	Exc/Zygomatic Bone, Rt, [Opn, Perc, Perc Endo]
0NBN[0,3,4]ZZ	Exc/Zygomatic Bone, Lt, [Opn, Perc, Perc Endo]
0NBP[0,3,4]ZZ	Exc/Orbit, Rt, [Opn, Perc, Perc Endo]
0NBQ[0,3,4]ZZ	Exc/Orbit, Lt, [Opn, Perc, Perc Endo]
0NBR[0,3,4]ZZ	Exc/Maxilla, Rt, [Opn, Perc, Perc Endo]
0NBS[0,3,4]ZZ	Exc/Maxilla, Lt, [Opn, Perc, Perc Endo]
0NBX[0,3,4]ZZ	Exc/Hyoid Bone, [Opn, Perc, Perc Endo]
0NC1*	Extir/Frontal Bone, Rt
0NC2*	Extir/Frontal Bone, Lt
0NC3*	Extir/Parietal Bone, Rt
0NC4*	Extir/Parietal Bone, Lt
0NC5*	Extir/Temporal Bone, Rt
0NC6*	Extir/Temporal Bone, Lt
0NC7*	Extir/Occipital Bone, Rt
0NC8*	Extir/Occipital Bone, Lt
0NH1*	Insert/Frontal Bone, Rt
0NH2*	Insert/Frontal Bone, Lt
0NH3*	Insert/Parietal Bone, Rt
0NH4*	Insert/Parietal Bone, Lt
0NH5[0,3,4]4Z	Insert/Temporal Bone, Rt, [Opn, Perc, Perc Endo], Int Fix Dev, NQ
0NH6[0,3,4]4Z	Insert/Temporal Bone, Lt, [Opn, Perc, Perc Endo], Int Fix Dev, NQ
0NH7*	Insert/Occipital Bone, Rt
0NH8*	Insert/Occipital Bone, Lt
0NJB[0,3,4]ZZ	Inspect/Nasal Bone, [Opn, Perc, Perc Endo]
0NJW[0,3,4]ZZ	Inspect/Facial Bone, [Opn, Perc, Perc Endo]
0NN1*	Rls/Frontal Bone, Rt
0NN2*	Rls/Frontal Bone, Lt
0NN3*	Rls/Parietal Bone, Rt
0NN4*	Rls/Parietal Bone, Lt
0NN5*	Rls/Temporal Bone, Rt
0NN6*	Rls/Temporal Bone, Lt
0NN7*	Rls/Occipital Bone, Rt
0NN8*	Rls/Occipital Bone, Lt
0NNC*	Rls/Sphenoid Bone, Rt
0NND*	Rls/Sphenoid Bone, Lt
0NNF*	Rls/Ethmoid Bone, Rt

T Transfer DRG   SP Special Payment   * Code Range   6th and 7th Character of ZZ = No Device, No Qualifier ZX = No Device, Diagnostic

Code	Description
ØNNG*	Rls/Ethmoid Bone, Lt
ØNNH*	Rls/Lacrimal Bone, Rt
ØNNJ*	Rls/Lacrimal Bone, Lt
ØNNK*	Rls/Palatine Bone, Rt
ØNNL*	Rls/Palatine Bone, Lt
ØNNM*	Rls/Zygomatic Bone, Rt
ØNNN*	Rls/Zygomatic Bone, Lt
ØNNP*	Rls/Orbit, Rt
ØNNQ*	Rls/Orbit, Lt
ØNNR*	Rls/Maxilla, Rt
ØNNS*	Rls/Maxilla, Lt
ØNNT*	Rls/Mandible, Rt
ØNNV*	Rls/Mandible, Lt
ØNPØ[Ø,3,4]JZ	Rmvl/Skull, [Opn, Perc, Perc Endo], Synth Sub, NQ
ØNPW[Ø,3,4,X]4Z	Rmvl/Facial Bone, [Opn, Perc, Perc Endo, Ext], Int Fix Dev, NQ
ØNQØ*	Repair/Skull
ØNQ1*	Repair/Frontal Bone, Rt
ØNQ2*	Repair/Frontal Bone, Lt
ØNQ3*	Repair/Parietal Bone, Rt
ØNQ4*	Repair/Parietal Bone, Lt
ØNQ5*	Repair/Temporal Bone, Rt
ØNQ6*	Repair/Temporal Bone, Lt
ØNQ7*	Repair/Occipital Bone, Rt
ØNQ8*	Repair/Occipital Bone, Lt
ØNQC*	Repair/Sphenoid Bone, Rt
ØNQD*	Repair/Sphenoid Bone, Lt
ØNQF*	Repair/Ethmoid Bone, Rt
ØNQG*	Repair/Ethmoid Bone, Lt
ØNQH*	Repair/Lacrimal Bone, Rt
ØNQJ*	Repair/Lacrimal Bone, Lt
ØNQK*	Repair/Palatine Bone, Rt
ØNQL*	Repair/Palatine Bone, Lt
ØNQM*	Repair/Zygomatic Bone, Rt
ØNQN*	Repair/Zygomatic Bone, Lt
ØNQP*	Repair/Orbit, Rt
ØNQQ*	Repair/Orbit, Lt
ØNQR*	Repair/Maxilla, Rt
ØNQS*	Repair/Maxilla, Lt
ØNQT*	Repair/Mandible, Rt
ØNQV*	Repair/Mandible, Lt
ØNQX*	Repair/Hyoid Bone
ØNRØ*	Replace/Skull
ØNR1*	Replace/Frontal Bone, Rt
ØNR2*	Replace/Frontal Bone, Lt
ØNR3*	Replace/Parietal Bone, Rt
ØNR4*	Replace/Parietal Bone, Lt
ØNR5*	Replace/Temporal Bone, Rt
ØNR6*	Replace/Temporal Bone, Lt
ØNR7*	Replace/Occipital Bone, Rt
ØNR8*	Replace/Occipital Bone, Lt
ØNRC*	Replace/Sphenoid Bone, Rt
ØNRD*	Replace/Sphenoid Bone, Lt
ØNRF*	Replace/Ethmoid Bone, Rt
ØNRG*	Replace/Ethmoid Bone, Lt
ØNRH*	Replace/Lacrimal Bone, Rt
ØNRJ*	Replace/Lacrimal Bone, Lt
ØNRK*	Replace/Palatine Bone, Rt
ØNRL*	Replace/Palatine Bone, Lt
ØNRM*	Replace/Zygomatic Bone, Rt
ØNRN*	Replace/Zygomatic Bone, Lt
ØNRP*	Replace/Orbit, Rt
ØNRQ*	Replace/Orbit, Lt
ØNRR*	Replace/Maxilla, Rt
ØNRS*	Replace/Maxilla, Lt
ØNRX*	Replace/Hyoid Bone
ØNSØ*	Repos/Skull
ØNS1*	Repos/Frontal Bone, Rt
ØNS2*	Repos/Frontal Bone, Lt
ØNS3*	Repos/Parietal Bone, Rt
ØNS4*	Repos/Parietal Bone, Lt
ØNS5*	Repos/Temporal Bone, Rt
ØNS6*	Repos/Temporal Bone, Lt
ØNS7*	Repos/Occipital Bone, Rt
ØNS8*	Repos/Occipital Bone, Lt
ØNSBØ[4,Z]Z	Repos/Nasal Bone, Opn, [Int Fix Dev, No Dev], NQ
ØNSCØ[4,Z]Z	Repos/Sphenoid Bone, Rt, Opn, [Int Fix Dev, No Dev], NQ
ØNSDØ[4,Z]Z	Repos/Sphenoid Bone, Lt, Opn, [Int Fix Dev, No Dev], NQ
ØNSFØ[4,Z]Z	Repos/Ethmoid Bone, Rt, Opn, [Int Fix Dev, No Dev], NQ
ØNSGØ[4,Z]Z	Repos/Ethmoid Bone, Lt, Opn, [Int Fix Dev, No Dev], NQ
ØNSHØ[4,Z]Z	Repos/Lacrimal Bone, Rt, Opn, [Int Fix Dev, No Dev], NQ
ØNSJØ[4,Z]Z	Repos/Lacrimal Bone, Lt, Opn, [Int Fix Dev, No Dev], NQ
ØNSKØ[4,Z]Z	Repos/Palatine Bone, Rt, Opn, [Int Fix Dev, No Dev], NQ
ØNSLØ[4,Z]Z	Repos/Palatine Bone, Lt, Opn, [Int Fix Dev, No Dev], NQ
ØNSMØ[4,Z]Z	Repos/Zygomatic Bone, Rt, Opn, [Int Fix Dev, No Dev], NQ
ØNSNØ[4,Z]Z	Repos/Zygomatic Bone, Lt, Opn, [Int Fix Dev, No Dev], NQ
ØNSPØ[4,Z]Z	Repos/Orbit, Rt, Opn, [Int Fix Dev, No Dev], NQ
ØNSQØ[4,Z]Z	Repos/Orbit, Lt, Opn, [Int Fix Dev, No Dev], NQ
ØNSRØ[4,5,Z]Z	Repos/Maxilla, Rt, Opn, [Int Fix Dev, Ext Fix Dev, No Dev], NQ
ØNSSØ[4,5,Z]Z	Repos/Maxilla, Lt, Opn, [Int Fix Dev, Ext Fix Dev, No Dev], NQ
ØNSTØ[4,5,Z]Z	Repos/Mandible, Rt, Opn, [Int Fix Dev, Ext Fix Dev, No Dev], NQ
ØNSVØ[4,5,Z]Z	Repos/Mandible, Lt, Opn, [Int Fix Dev, Ext Fix Dev, No Dev], NQ
ØNSXØ[4,Z]Z	Repos/Hyoid Bone, Opn, [Int Fix Dev, No Dev], NQ
ØNTBØZZ	Resect of Nasal Bone, Opn Appr
ØNTXØZZ	Resect of Hyoid Bone, Opn Appr
ØNT[1,2]ØZZ	Resect of [Rt, Lt] Frontal Bone, Opn Appr
ØNT[3,4]ØZZ	Resect of [Rt, Lt] Parietal Bone, Opn Appr
ØNT[5,6]ØZZ	Resect of [Rt, Lt] Temporal Bone, Opn Appr
ØNT[7,8]ØZZ	Resect of [Rt, Lt] Occipital Bone, Opn Appr
ØNT[C,D]ØZZ	Resect of [Rt, Lt] Sphenoid Bone, Opn Appr
ØNT[F,G]ØZZ	Resect of [Rt, Lt] Ethmoid Bone, Opn Appr
ØNT[H,J]ØZZ	Resect of [Rt, Lt] Lacrimal Bone, Opn Appr
ØNT[K,L]ØZZ	Resect of [Rt, Lt] Palatine Bone, Opn Appr
ØNT[M,N]ØZZ	Resect of [Rt, Lt] Zygomatic Bone, Opn Appr
ØNT[P,Q]ØZZ	Resect of [Rt, Lt] Orbit, Opn Appr
ØNT[R,S]ØZZ	Resect of [Rt, Lt] Maxilla, Opn Appr
ØNUØ*	Supl/Skull
ØNU1*	Supl/Frontal Bone, Rt
ØNU2*	Supl/Frontal Bone, Lt
ØNU3*	Supl/Parietal Bone, Rt
ØNU4*	Supl/Parietal Bone, Lt
ØNU5*	Supl/Temporal Bone, Rt
ØNU6*	Supl/Temporal Bone, Lt
ØNU7*	Supl/Occipital Bone, Rt
ØNU8*	Supl/Occipital Bone, Lt
ØNUC*	Supl/Sphenoid Bone, Rt
ØNUD*	Supl/Sphenoid Bone, Lt
ØNUF*	Supl/Ethmoid Bone, Rt
ØNUG*	Supl/Ethmoid Bone, Lt
ØNUH*	Supl/Lacrimal Bone, Rt
ØNUJ*	Supl/Lacrimal Bone, Lt
ØNUK*	Supl/Palatine Bone, Rt
ØNUL*	Supl/Palatine Bone, Lt
ØNUM*	Supl/Zygomatic Bone, Rt
ØNUN*	Supl/Zygomatic Bone, Lt
ØNUP*	Supl/Orbit, Rt
ØNUQ*	Supl/Orbit, Lt
ØNUR*	Supl/Maxilla, Rt
ØNUS*	Supl/Maxilla, Lt
ØNUT*	Supl/Mandible, Rt
ØNUV*	Supl/Mandible, Lt
ØNUX*	Supl/Hyoid Bone
ØR5C*	Destr/Temporomandibular Jt, Rt
ØR5D*	Destr/Temporomandibular Jt, Lt
ØRBC[Ø,3,4]ZZ	Exc/Temporomandibular Jt, Rt, [Opn, Perc, Perc Endo]
ØRBD[Ø,3,4]ZZ	Exc/Temporomandibular Jt, Lt, [Opn, Perc, Perc Endo]
ØRCC*	Extir/Temporomandibular Jt, Rt
ØRCD*	Extir/Temporomandibular Jt, Lt
ØRGC*	Fusion/Temporomandibular Jt, Rt
ØRGD*	Fusion/Temporomandibular Jt, Lt
ØRJC[Ø,3,4]ZZ	Inspect/Temporomandibular Jt, Rt, [Opn, Perc, Perc Endo]
ØRJD[Ø,3,4]ZZ	Inspect/Temporomandibular Jt, Lt, [Opn, Perc, Perc Endo]
ØRNC[Ø,3,4]ZZ	Rls/Temporomandibular Jt, Rt, [Opn, Perc, Perc Endo]
ØRND[Ø,3,4]ZZ	Rls/Temporomandibular Jt, Lt, [Opn, Perc, Perc Endo]
ØRPC[Ø,3,4,X]4Z	Rmvl/Temporomandibular Jt, Rt, [Opn, Perc, Perc Endo, Ext], Int Fix Dev, NQ
ØRPD[Ø,3,4,X]4Z	Rmvl/Temporomandibular Jt, Lt, [Opn, Perc, Perc Endo, Ext], Int Fix Dev, NQ
ØRSCØ[4,Z]Z	Repos/Temporomandibular Jt, Rt, Opn, [Int Fix Dev, No Dev], NQ
ØRSDØ[4,Z]Z	Repos/Temporomandibular Jt, Lt, Opn, [Int Fix Dev, No Dev], NQ
ØRT[C,D]ØZZ	Resect of [Rt, Lt] Temporomandibular Jt, Opn Appr
ØW04*	Alter/Upr Jaw
ØW05*	Alter/Lwr Jaw
ØW91Ø[Ø,Z]Z	Drain/Cranial Cavity, Opn, [Drain Dev, No Dev], NQ
ØWC1[Ø,3,4]ZZ	Extir/Cranial Cavity, [Opn, Perc, Perc Endo]
ØWJ1ØZZ	Inspect of Cranial Cavity, Opn Appr
ØWU4*	Supl/Upr Jaw
ØWU5*	Supl/Lwr Jaw

Surgical   **Medical**   **CC Indicator**   **MCC Indicator**   **Procedure Proxy**   **PDxMCC** PDx acts as own MCC   **PDxCC** PDx acts as own CC

MDC 3: Diseases And Disorders Of The Ear, Nose, Mouth And Throat—SURGICAL

DRG 132	**Cranial/Facial Procedures without CC/MCC**

| GMLOS 2.2 | AMLOS 2.8 | RW 1.4401 |

Select operating room procedures listed under DRG 131

DRG 133	**Other Ear, Nose, Mouth and Throat O.R. Procedures with CC/MCC**

| GMLOS 3.8 | AMLOS 5.5 | RW 1.8573 |

Operating Room Procedures

008F*	Div/Olfactory Nerve
008G*	Div/Optic Nerve
008H*	Div/Oculomotor Nerve
008J*	Div/Trochlear Nerve
008K*	Div/Trigeminal Nerve
008L*	Div/Abducens Nerve
008M*	Div/Facial Nerve
008N*	Div/Acoustic Nerve
008P*	Div/Glossopharyngeal Nerve
008Q*	Div/Vagus Nerve
008R*	Div/Accessory Nerve
008S*	Div/Hypoglossal Nerve
009[F,G,H,J]0ZX	Drain of [Olfactory, Optic, Oculomotor, Trochlear] Nerve, Opn, Dx
009[K,L,M,N]0ZX	Drain of [Trigeminal, Abducens, Facial, Acoustic] Nerve, Opn, Dx
009[P,Q,R,S]0ZX	Drain of [Glossopharyngeal, Vagus, Accessory, Hypoglossal] Nerve, Opn, Dx
00BF0ZX	Exc of Olfactory Nerve, Opn Appr, Diagnostic
00BF[0,3,4]ZZ	Exc/Olfactory Nerve, [Opn, Perc, Perc Endo]
00BG0ZX	Exc of Optic Nerve, Opn Appr, Diagnostic
00BG[0,3,4]ZZ	Exc/Optic Nerve, [Opn, Perc, Perc Endo]
00BH0ZX	Exc of Oculomotor Nerve, Opn Appr, Diagnostic
00BH[0,3,4]ZZ	Exc/Oculomotor Nerve, [Opn, Perc, Perc Endo]
00BJ0ZX	Exc of Trochlear Nerve, Opn Appr, Diagnostic
00BJ[0,3,4]ZZ	Exc/Trochlear Nerve, [Opn, Perc, Perc Endo]
00BK0ZX	Exc of Trigeminal Nerve, Opn Appr, Diagnostic
00BK[0,3,4]ZZ	Exc/Trigeminal Nerve, [Opn, Perc, Perc Endo]
00BL0ZX	Exc of Abducens Nerve, Opn Appr, Diagnostic
00BL[0,3,4]ZZ	Exc/Abducens Nerve, [Opn, Perc, Perc Endo]
00BM0ZX	Exc of Facial Nerve, Opn Appr, Diagnostic
00BM[0,3,4]ZZ	Exc/Facial Nerve, [Opn, Perc, Perc Endo]
00BN0ZX	Exc of Acoustic Nerve, Opn Appr, Diagnostic
00BN[0,3,4]ZZ	Exc/Acoustic Nerve, [Opn, Perc, Perc Endo]
00BP0ZX	Exc of Glossopharyngeal Nerve, Opn Appr, Diagn
00BP[0,3,4]ZZ	Exc/Glossopharyngeal Nerve, [Opn, Perc, Perc Endo]
00BQ0ZX	Exc of Vagus Nerve, Opn Appr, Diagnostic
00BQ[0,3,4]ZZ	Exc/Vagus Nerve, [Opn, Perc, Perc Endo]
00BR0ZX	Exc of Accessory Nerve, Opn Appr, Diagnostic
00BR[0,3,4]ZZ	Exc/Accessory Nerve, [Opn, Perc, Perc Endo]
00BS0ZX	Exc of Hypoglossal Nerve, Opn Appr, Diagnostic
00BS[0,3,4]ZZ	Exc/Hypoglossal Nerve, [Opn, Perc, Perc Endo]
00DF*	Extract/Olfactory Nerve
00DG*	Extract/Optic Nerve
00DH*	Extract/Oculomotor Nerve
00DJ*	Extract/Trochlear Nerve
00DK*	Extract/Trigeminal Nerve
00DL*	Extract/Abducens Nerve
00DM*	Extract/Facial Nerve
00DN*	Extract/Acoustic Nerve
00DP*	Extract/Glossopharyngeal Nerve
00DQ*	Extract/Vagus Nerve
00DR*	Extract/Accessory Nerve
00DS*	Extract/Hypoglossal Nerve
00HE[0,3,4]MZ	Insert/Cranial Nerve, [Opn, Perc, Perc Endo], Neurostimulator Lead, NQ
00NF*	Rls/Olfactory Nerve
00NG*	Rls/Optic Nerve
00NH*	Rls/Oculomotor Nerve
00NJ*	Rls/Trochlear Nerve
00NK*	Rls/Trigeminal Nerve
00NL*	Rls/Abducens Nerve
00NM*	Rls/Facial Nerve
00NN*	Rls/Acoustic Nerve
00NP*	Rls/Glossopharyngeal Nerve
00NQ*	Rls/Vagus Nerve
00NR*	Rls/Accessory Nerve
00NS*	Rls/Hypoglossal Nerve

00PE[0,3,4,X]MZ	Rmvl/Cranial Nerve, [Opn, Perc, Perc Endo, Ext], Neurostimulator Lead, NQ
00QF*	Repair/Olfactory Nerve
00QG*	Repair/Optic Nerve
00QH*	Repair/Oculomotor Nerve
00QJ*	Repair/Trochlear Nerve
00QK*	Repair/Trigeminal Nerve
00QL*	Repair/Abducens Nerve
00QM*	Repair/Facial Nerve
00QN*	Repair/Acoustic Nerve
00QP*	Repair/Glossopharyngeal Nerve
00QQ*	Repair/Vagus Nerve
00QR*	Repair/Accessory Nerve
00QS*	Repair/Hypoglossal Nerve
00XR[0,4]Z[M,S]	Transfer/Accessory Nerve, [Opn, Perc Endo], No Dev, [Facial Nerve, Hypoglossal Nerve]
00XS[0,4]ZM	Transfer/Hypoglossal Nerve, [Opn, Perc Endo], No Dev, Facial Nerve
015K*	Destr/Head and Neck Sympathetic Nerve
01BK[0,3,4]ZZ	Exc/Head and Neck Sympathetic Nerve, [Opn, Perc, Perc Endo]
01DK*	Extract/Head and Neck Sympathetic Nerve
01HY[0,3,4]MZ	Insert/Peripheral Nerve, [Opn, Perc, Perc Endo], Neurostimulator Lead, NQ
01PY[0,3,4,X]MZ	Rmvl/Peripheral Nerve, [Opn, Perc, Perc Endo, Ext], Neurostimulator Lead, NQ
02J[A,Y]4ZZ	Inspect of [Heart, Great Vessel], Perc Endo Appr
039S[0,3,4]ZX	Drain/Temporal Artery, Rt, [Opn, Perc, Perc Endo]
039T[0,3,4]ZX	Drain/Temporal Artery, Lt, [Opn, Perc, Perc Endo]
03BH[0,3,4]ZZ	Exc/Common Carotid Artery, Rt, [Opn, Perc, Perc Endo]
03BJ[0,3,4]ZZ	Exc/Common Carotid Artery, Lt, [Opn, Perc, Perc Endo]
03BK[0,3,4]ZZ	Exc/Int Carotid Artery, Rt, [Opn, Perc, Perc Endo]
03BL[0,3,4]ZZ	Exc/Int Carotid Artery, Lt, [Opn, Perc, Perc Endo]
03BM[0,3,4]ZZ	Exc/Ext Carotid Artery, Rt, [Opn, Perc, Perc Endo]
03BN[0,3,4]ZZ	Exc/Ext Carotid Artery, Lt, [Opn, Perc, Perc Endo]
03BP[0,3,4]ZZ	Exc/Vert Artery, Rt, [Opn, Perc, Perc Endo]
03BQ[0,3,4]ZZ	Exc/Vert Artery, Lt, [Opn, Perc, Perc Endo]
03BR[0,3,4]ZZ	Exc/Face Artery, [Opn, Perc, Perc Endo]
03BS*	Exc/Temporal Artery, Rt
03BT*	Exc/Temporal Artery, Lt
03BU[0,3,4]ZZ	Exc/Thyroid Artery, Rt, [Opn, Perc, Perc Endo]
03BV[0,3,4]ZZ	Exc/Thyroid Artery, Lt, [Opn, Perc, Perc Endo]
03C[H,J,K,L,M,N]0ZZ	Extir [Rt Common Carotid, Lt Common Carotid, Rt Int Carotid, Lt Int Carotid, Rt Ext Carotid, Lt Ext Carotid] Artery, Opn
03C[P,Q,R,S,T,U,V]0ZZ	Extir [Rt Vert, Lt Vert, Face, Rt Temporal, Lt Temporal, Rt Thyroid, Lt Thyroid] Artery, Opn
03H2[0,3,4]DZ	Insert/Innominate Artery, [Opn, Perc, Perc Endo], Intralum Dev, NQ
03HJ[0,3,4]DZ	Insert/Common Carotid Artery, Lt, [Opn, Perc, Perc Endo], Intralum Dev, NQ
03HK[0,3,4]DZ	Insert/Int Carotid Artery, Rt, [Opn, Perc, Perc Endo], Intralum Dev, NQ
03HM[0,3,4]DZ	Insert/Ext Carotid Artery, Rt, [Opn, Perc, Perc Endo], Intralum Dev, NQ
03HN[0,3,4]DZ	Insert/Ext Carotid Artery, Lt, [Opn, Perc, Perc Endo], Intralum Dev, NQ
03HP[0,3,4]DZ	Insert/Vert Artery, Rt, [Opn, Perc, Perc Endo], Intralum Dev, NQ
03HQ[0,3,4]DZ	Insert/Vert Artery, Lt, [Opn, Perc, Perc Endo], Intralum Dev, NQ
03HR[0,3,4]DZ	Insert/Face Artery, [Opn, Perc, Perc Endo], Intralum Dev, NQ
03HS[0,3,4]DZ	Insert/Temporal Artery, Rt, [Opn, Perc, Perc Endo], Intralum Dev, NQ
03HT[0,3,4]DZ	Insert/Temporal Artery, Lt, [Opn, Perc, Perc Endo], Intralum Dev, NQ
03HU[0,3,4]DZ	Insert/Thyroid Artery, Rt, [Opn, Perc, Perc Endo], Intralum Dev, NQ
03HV[0,3,4]DZ	Insert/Thyroid Artery, Lt, [Opn, Perc, Perc Endo], Intralum Dev, NQ
03HY[0,3,4]DZ	Insert/Upr Artery, [Opn, Perc, Perc Endo], Intralum Dev, NQ
03LH[0,3,4][C,Z]Z	Occlsn/Common Carotid Artery, Rt, [Opn, Perc, Perc Endo], [Extralum Dev, No Dev], NQ
03LJ[0,3,4][C,Z]Z	Occlsn/Common Carotid Artery, Lt, [Opn, Perc, Perc Endo], [Extralum Dev, No Dev], NQ
03LM[0,3,4][C,Z]Z	Occlsn/Ext Carotid Artery, Rt, [Opn, Perc, Perc Endo], [Extralum Dev, No Dev], NQ
03LN[0,3,4][C,Z]Z	Occlsn/Ext Carotid Artery, Lt, [Opn, Perc, Perc Endo], [Extralum Dev, No Dev], NQ
03LP[0,3,4][C,Z]Z	Occlsn/Vert Artery, Rt, [Opn, Perc, Perc Endo], [Extralum Dev, No Dev], NQ
03LQ[0,3,4][C,Z]Z	Occlsn/Vert Artery, Lt, [Opn, Perc, Perc Endo], [Extralum Dev, No Dev], NQ

| T Transfer DRG | SP Special Payment | * Code Range | 6th and 7th Character of ZZ = No Device, No Qualifier ZX = No Device, Diagnostic |

03LR[0,3,4][C,Z]Z	Occlsn/Face Artery, [Opn, Perc, Perc Endo], [Extralum Dev, No Dev], NQ
03LS[0,3,4][C,Z]Z	Occlsn/Temporal Artery, Rt, [Opn, Perc, Perc Endo], [Extralum Dev, No Dev], NQ
03LT[0,3,4][C,Z]Z	Occlsn/Temporal Artery, Lt, [Opn, Perc, Perc Endo], [Extralum Dev, No Dev], NQ
05BM[0,4]ZZ	Exc/Int Jugular Vein, Rt, [Opn, Perc Endo]
05BN[0,4]ZZ	Exc/Int Jugular Vein, Lt, [Opn, Perc Endo]
05BP[0,4]ZZ	Exc/Ext Jugular Vein, Rt, [Opn, Perc Endo]
05BQ[0,4]ZZ	Exc/Ext Jugular Vein, Lt, [Opn, Perc Endo]
05BR[0,4]ZZ	Exc/Vert Vein, Rt, [Opn, Perc Endo]
05BS[0,4]ZZ	Exc/Vert Vein, Lt, [Opn, Perc Endo]
05BT[0,4]ZZ	Exc/Face Vein, Rt, [Opn, Perc Endo]
05BV[0,4]ZZ	Exc/Face Vein, Lt, [Opn, Perc Endo]
05CM*	Extir/Int Jugular Vein, Rt
05CN*	Extir/Int Jugular Vein, Lt
05CP*	Extir/Ext Jugular Vein, Rt
05CQ*	Extir/Ext Jugular Vein, Lt
05CR*	Extir/Vert Vein, Rt
05CS*	Extir/Vert Vein, Lt
05CT*	Extir/Face Vein, Rt
05CV*	Extir/Face Vein, Lt
05HM[0,3,4]DZ	Insert/Int Jugular Vein, Rt, [Opn, Perc, Perc Endo], Intralum Dev, NQ
05HN[0,3,4]DZ	Insert/Int Jugular Vein, Lt, [Opn, Perc, Perc Endo], Intralum Dev, NQ
05HP[0,3,4]DZ	Insert/Ext Jugular Vein, Rt, [Opn, Perc, Perc Endo], Intralum Dev, NQ
05HQ[0,3,4]DZ	Insert/Ext Jugular Vein, Lt, [Opn, Perc, Perc Endo], Intralum Dev, NQ
05HR[0,3,4]DZ	Insert/Vert Vein, Rt, [Opn, Perc, Perc Endo], Intralum Dev, NQ
05HS[0,3,4]DZ	Insert/Vert Vein, Lt, [Opn, Perc, Perc Endo], Intralum Dev, NQ
05HT[0,3,4]DZ	Insert/Face Vein, Rt, [Opn, Perc, Perc Endo], Intralum Dev, NQ
05HV[0,3,4]DZ	Insert/Face Vein, Lt, [Opn, Perc, Perc Endo], Intralum Dev, NQ
05HY[0,3,4][2,D]Z	Insert/Upr Vein, [Opn, Perc, Perc Endo], [Monitoring Dev, Intralum Dev], NQ
05LM*	Occlsn/Int Jugular Vein, Rt
05LN*	Occlsn/Int Jugular Vein, Lt
05LP*	Occlsn/Ext Jugular Vein, Rt
05LQ*	Occlsn/Ext Jugular Vein, Lt
05LR*	Occlsn/Vert Vein, Rt
05LS*	Occlsn/Vert Vein, Lt
05LT*	Occlsn/Face Vein, Rt
05LV*	Occlsn/Face Vein, Lt
0693[0,3,4][0,Z]Z	Drain/Esophageal Vein, [Opn, Perc, Perc Endo], [Drain Dev, No Dev], NQ
06C3*	Extir/Esophageal Vein
06H3[0,3,4]DZ	Insert/Esophageal Vein, [Opn, Perc, Perc Endo], Intralum Dev, NQ
06HY[0,3,4]DZ	Insert/Lwr Vein, [Opn, Perc, Perc Endo], Intralum Dev, NQ
0790[0,3,4]ZX	Drain/Lymphatic, Head, [Opn, Perc, Perc Endo]
0791[0,3,4]ZX	Drain/Lymphatic, Rt Neck, [Opn, Perc, Perc Endo]
0792[0,3,4]ZX	Drain/Lymphatic, Lt Neck, [Opn, Perc, Perc Endo]
07B0[0,3,4]ZX	Exc/Lymphatic, Head, [Opn, Perc, Perc Endo]
07B0[0,4]ZZ	Exc/Lymphatic, Head, [Opn, Perc Endo]
07B1*	Exc/Lymphatic, Rt Neck
07B2*	Exc/Lymphatic, Lt Neck
07B5[0,3,4]ZZ	Exc/Lymphatic, Rt Axillary, [Opn, Perc, Perc Endo]
07B6[0,3,4]ZZ	Exc/Lymphatic, Lt Axillary, [Opn, Perc, Perc Endo]
081X*	Bypass/Lacrimal Duct, Rt
081Y*	Bypass/Lacrimal Duct, Lt
087*	Eye, Dilation
089X[0,3,7,8]ZX	Drain/Lacrimal Duct, Rt, [Opn, Perc, Via Natrl or Artfcl Opng, Via Natrl or Artfcl Opng Endo]
089Y[0,3,7,8]ZX	Drain/Lacrimal Duct, Lt, [Opn, Perc, Via Natrl or Artfcl Opng, Via Natrl or Artfcl Opng Endo]
08BX[0,3,7,8]ZX	Exc/Lacrimal Duct, Rt, [Opn, Perc, Via Natrl or Artfcl Opng, Via Natrl or Artfcl Opng Endo]
08BY[0,3,7,8]ZX	Exc/Lacrimal Duct, Lt, [Opn, Perc, Via Natrl or Artfcl Opng, Via Natrl or Artfcl Opng Endo]
08J[0,1]XZZ	Inspect of [Rt, Lt] Eye, Ext Appr
08NX*	Rls/Lacrimal Duct, Rt
08NY*	Rls/Lacrimal Duct, Lt
08SX*	Repos/Lacrimal Duct, Rt
08SY*	Repos/Lacrimal Duct, Lt
08TX*	Resect/Lacrimal Duct, Rt
08TY*	Resect/Lacrimal Duct, Lt
08V*	Eye, Restrict
090*	Ear, Nose, Sinus, Alter
091*	Ear, Nose, Sinus, Bypass

0957*	Destr/Tympanic Membrane, Rt
0958*	Destr/Tympanic Membrane, Lt
095L*	Destr/Nasal Turbinate
095N*	Destr/Nasopharynx
095[5,6]0ZZ	Destr of [Rt, Lt] Mid Ear, Opn Appr
095[9,A,D,E]0ZZ	Destr of [Rt Auditory Ossicle, Lt Auditory Ossicle, Rt Inner Ear, Lt Inner Ear], Opn Appr
098*	Ear, Nose, Sinus, Div
099500Z	Drain of Rt Mid Ear with Drain Dev, Opn Appr
09950ZX	Drain of Rt Mid Ear, Opn Appr, Diagnostic
099600Z	Drain of Lt Mid Ear with Drain Dev, Opn Appr
09960ZX	Drain of Lt Mid Ear, Opn Appr, Diagnostic
0997[0,3,4,7,8]0Z	Drain/Tympanic Membrane, Rt, [Opn, Perc, Perc Endo, Via Natrl or Artfcl Opng, Via Natrl or Artfcl Opng Endo], Drain Dev, NQ
0997[0,3,4,7,8]ZX	Drain/Tympanic Membrane, Rt, [Opn, Perc, Perc Endo, Via Natrl or Artfcl Opng, Via Natrl or Artfcl Opng Endo]
0998[0,3,4,7,8]0Z	Drain/Tympanic Membrane, Lt, [Opn, Perc, Perc Endo, Via Natrl or Artfcl Opng, Via Natrl or Artfcl Opng Endo], Drain Dev, NQ
0998[0,3,4,7,8]ZX	Drain/Tympanic Membrane, Lt, [Opn, Perc, Perc Endo, Via Natrl or Artfcl Opng, Via Natrl or Artfcl Opng Endo]
0999*	Drain/Auditory Ossicle, Rt
099A*	Drain/Auditory Ossicle, Lt
099B[0,3,4]ZX	Drain/Mastoid Sinus, Rt, [Opn, Perc, Perc Endo]
099C[0,3,4]ZX	Drain/Mastoid Sinus, Lt, [Opn, Perc, Perc Endo]
099D*	Drain/Inner Ear, Rt
099E*	Drain/Inner Ear, Lt
099F[0,3,4,7,8]ZX	Drain/Eustachian Tube, Rt, [Opn, Perc, Perc Endo, Via Natrl or Artfcl Opng, Via Natrl or Artfcl Opng Endo]
099G[0,3,4,7,8]ZX	Drain/Eustachian Tube, Lt, [Opn, Perc, Perc Endo, Via Natrl or Artfcl Opng, Via Natrl or Artfcl Opng Endo]
099N[0,3,4,7,8][0,Z]Z	Drain/Nasopharynx, [Opn, Perc, Perc Endo, Via Natrl or Artfcl Opng, Via Natrl or Artfcl Opng Endo], [Drain Dev, No Dev], NQ
09B5*	Exc/Mid Ear, Rt
09B6*	Exc/Mid Ear, Lt
09B7*	Exc/Tympanic Membrane, Rt
09B8*	Exc/Tympanic Membrane, Lt
09B9*	Exc/Auditory Ossicle, Rt
09BA*	Exc/Auditory Ossicle, Lt
09BB[0,3,4]ZX	Exc/Mastoid Sinus, Rt, [Opn, Perc, Perc Endo]
09BC[0,3,4]ZX	Exc/Mastoid Sinus, Lt, [Opn, Perc, Perc Endo]
09BD*	Exc/Inner Ear, Rt
09BE*	Exc/Inner Ear, Lt
09BL[0,3,4,7,8]ZX	Exc/Nasal Turbinate, [Opn, Perc, Perc Endo, Via Natrl or Artfcl Opng, Via Natrl or Artfcl Opng Endo]
09BM[0,3,4]ZZ	Exc/Nasal Septum, [Opn, Perc, Perc Endo]
09BN[0,3,4,7,8]ZZ	Exc/Nasopharynx, [Opn, Perc, Perc Endo, Via Natrl or Artfcl Opng, Via Natrl or Artfcl Opng Endo]
09CN*	Extir/Nasopharynx
09C[5,6,9,A,D,E]0ZZ	Extir of Matter from [Rt Mid Ear, Lt Mid Ear, Rt Auditory Ossicle, Lt Auditory Ossicle, Rt Inner Ear, Lt Inner Ear], Opn Appr
09D7*	Extract/Tympanic Membrane, Rt
09D8*	Extract/Tympanic Membrane, Lt
09DL*	Extract/Nasal Turbinate
09DM*	Extract/Nasal Septum
09D[9,A]0ZZ	Extract, [Rt Auditory Ossicle, Lt Auditory Ossicle], Opn
09HD[0,3,4]4Z	Insert/Inner Ear, Rt, [Opn, Perc, Perc Endo], Hearing Dev, Bone Conduction, NQ
09HE[0,3,4]4Z	Insert/Inner Ear, Lt, [Opn, Perc, Perc Endo], Hearing Dev, Bone Conduction, NQ
09J7[0,3,4,7,X]ZZ	Inspect/Tympanic Membrane, Rt, [Opn, Perc, Perc Endo, Via Natrl or Artfcl Opng, Ext]
09J8[0,3,4,7,X]ZZ	Inspect/Tympanic Membrane, Lt, [Opn, Perc, Perc Endo, Via Natrl or Artfcl Opng, Ext]
09JD*	Inspect/Inner Ear, Rt
09JE*	Inspect/Inner Ear, Lt
09M*	Ear, Nose, Sinus, Reattach
09N0*	Rls/Ext Ear, Rt
09N1*	Rls/Ext Ear, Lt
09N3*	Rls/Ext Auditory Canal, Rt
09N4*	Rls/Ext Auditory Canal, Lt
09N7*	Rls/Tympanic Membrane, Rt
09N8*	Rls/Tympanic Membrane, Lt
09NB*	Rls/Mastoid Sinus, Rt
09NC*	Rls/Mastoid Sinus, Lt
09NN*	Rls/Nasopharynx
09N[5,6]0ZZ	Rls, [Rt Mid Ear, Lt Mid Ear], Opn

MDC 3: Diseases And Disorders Of The Ear, Nose, Mouth And Throat—SURGICAL

MDC 3: Diseases And Disorders Of The Ear, Nose, Mouth And Throat—SURGICAL

09N[9,A]ØZZ	Rls [Rt, Lt] Auditory Ossicle, Opn Appr
09N[D,E]ØZZ	Rls [Rt, Lt] Inner Ear, Opn Appr
09PD*	Rmvl/Inner Ear, Rt
09PE*	Rmvl/Inner Ear, Lt
09PH00Z	Rmvl of Drain Device from Rt Ear, Opn Appr
09PHØDZ	Rmvl of Intralum Device from Rt Ear, Opn Appr
09PH37Z	Rmvl of Autol Sub from Rt Ear, Perc Appr
09PH3DZ	Rmvl of Intralum Device from Rt Ear, Perc Appr
09PH47Z	Rmvl of Autol Sub from Rt Ear, Perc Endo Appr
09PH4DZ	Rmvl of Intralum Dev from Rt Ear, Perc Endo Appr
09PH[Ø,7,8][7,J,K]Z	Rmvl/Ear, Rt, [Opn, Via Natrl or Artfcl Opng, Via Natrl or Artfcl Opng Endo], [Auto Tissue Sub, Synth Sub, Nonauto Tissue Sub], NQ
09PJ00Z	Rmvl of Drain Device from Lt Ear, Opn Appr
09PJØDZ	Rmvl of Intralum Device from Lt Ear, Opn Appr
09PJ37Z	Rmvl of Autol Sub from Lt Ear, Perc Appr
09PJ3DZ	Rmvl of Intralum Device from Lt Ear, Perc Appr
09PJ47Z	Rmvl of Autol Sub from Lt Ear, Perc Endo Appr
09PJ4DZ	Rmvl of Intralum Dev from Lt Ear, Perc Endo Appr
09PJ[Ø,7,8][7,J,K]Z	Rmvl/Ear, Lt, [Opn, Via Natrl or Artfcl Opng, Via Natrl or Artfcl Opng Endo], [Auto Tissue Sub, Synth Sub, Nonauto Tissue Sub], NQ
09Q0[Ø,3,4]ZZ	Rpr/Ext Ear, Rt, [Opn, Perc, Perc Endo]
09Q1[Ø,3,4]ZZ	Rpr/Ext Ear, Lt, [Opn, Perc, Perc Endo]
09Q2[Ø,3,4]ZZ	Rpr/Ext Ear, Bilat, [Opn, Perc, Perc Endo]
09Q3[Ø,3,4,7,8]ZZ	Rpr/Ext Auditory Canal, Rt, [Opn, Perc, Perc Endo, Via Natrl or Artfcl Opng, Via Natrl or Artfcl Opng Endo]
09Q4[Ø,3,4,7,8]ZZ	Rpr/Ext Auditory Canal, Lt, [Opn, Perc, Perc Endo, Via Natrl or Artfcl Opng, Via Natrl or Artfcl Opng Endo]
09Q7*	Repair/Tympanic Membrane, Rt
09Q8*	Repair/Tympanic Membrane, Lt
09QK*	Repair/Nose
09QL*	Repair/Nasal Turbinate
09QM*	Repair/Nasal Septum
09QN*	Repair/Nasopharynx
09Q[5,6]ØZZ	Rpr, [Rt Mid Ear, Lt Mid Ear], Opn
09Q[9,A,D,E]ØZZ	Rpr [Rt Auditory Ossicle, Lt Auditory Ossicle, Rt Inner Ear, Lt Inner Ear], Opn Appr
09R*	Ear, Nose, Sinus, Replace
09S0*	Repos/Ext Ear, Rt
09S1*	Repos/Ext Ear, Lt
09S2*	Repos/Ext Ear, Bilat
09S7*	Repos/Tympanic Membrane, Rt
09S8*	Repos/Tympanic Membrane, Lt
09S9*	Repos/Auditory Ossicle, Rt
09SA*	Repos/Auditory Ossicle, Lt
09SK*	Repos/Nose
09SL*	Repos/Nasal Turbinate
09SM*	Repos/Nasal Septum
09TØ*	Resect/Ext Ear, Rt
09T1*	Resect/Ext Ear, Lt
09T7*	Resect/Tympanic Membrane, Rt
09T8*	Resect/Tympanic Membrane, Lt
09TL*	Resect/Nasal Turbinate
09TM*	Resect/Nasal Septum
09TN*	Resect/Nasopharynx
09T[5,6]ØZZ	Resect of [Rt, Lt] Mid Ear, Opn Appr
09T[9,A,D,E]ØZZ	Resect of [Rt Auditory Ossicle, Lt Auditory Ossicle, Rt Inner Ear, Lt Inner Ear], Opn Appr
09U*	Ear, Nose, Sinus, Supl
09W7*	Rev/Tympanic Membrane, Rt
09W8*	Rev/Tympanic Membrane, Lt
09W9*	Rev/Auditory Ossicle, Rt
09WA*	Rev/Auditory Ossicle, Lt
09WD*	Rev/Inner Ear, Rt
09WE*	Rev/Inner Ear, Lt
09WH3[Ø,7]Z	Rev/Ear, Rt, Perc, [Drain Dev, Auto Tissue Sub], NQ
09WH4[Ø,7]Z	Rev/Ear, Rt, Perc Endo, [Drain Dev, Auto Tissue Sub], NQ
09WH[Ø,3,4]DZ	Rev/Ear, Rt, [Opn, Perc, Perc Endo], Intralum Dev, NQ
09WH[Ø,7,8][Ø,7,J,K]Z	Rev/Ear, Rt, [Opn, Via Natrl or Artfcl Opng, Via Natrl or Artfcl Opng Endo], [Drain Dev, Auto Tissue Sub, Synth Sub, Nonauto Tissue Sub], NQ
09WJ3[Ø,7]Z	Rev/Ear, Lt, Perc, [Drain Dev, Auto Tissue Sub], NQ
09WJ4[Ø,7]Z	Rev/Ear, Lt, Perc Endo, [Drain Dev, Auto Tissue Sub], NQ
09WJ[Ø,3,4]DZ	Rev/Ear, Lt, [Opn, Perc, Perc Endo], Intralum Dev, NQ
09WJ[Ø,7,8][Ø,7,J,K]Z	Rev/Ear, Lt, [Opn, Via Natrl or Artfcl Opng, Via Natrl or Artfcl Opng Endo], [Drain Dev, Auto Tissue Sub, Synth Sub, Nonauto Tissue Sub], NQ
ØB51*	Destr/Trachea
ØB52*	Destr/Carina

ØB71*	Dilation/Trachea
ØB72*	Dilation/Carina
ØB9[1,2]ØZX	Drain of [Trachea, Carina], Opn Appr, Dx
ØBB1ØZX	Exc of Trachea, Opn Appr, Diagnostic
ØBB1[Ø,3,4,7,8]ZZ	Exc/Trachea, [Opn, Perc, Perc Endo, Via Natrl or Artfcl Opng, Via Natrl or Artfcl Opng Endo]
ØBB2ØZX	Exc of Carina, Opn Appr, Diagnostic
ØBB2[Ø,3,4,7,8]ZZ	Exc/Carina, [Opn, Perc, Perc Endo, Via Natrl or Artfcl Opng, Via Natrl or Artfcl Opng Endo]
ØBF1[Ø,3,4,7,8]ZZ	Fragmn/Trachea, [Opn, Perc, Perc Endo, Via Natrl or Artfcl Opng, Via Natrl or Artfcl Opng Endo]
ØBF2[Ø,3,4,7,8]ZZ	Fragmn/Carina, [Opn, Perc, Perc Endo, Via Natrl or Artfcl Opng, Via Natrl or Artfcl Opng Endo]
ØBL1*	Occlsn/Trachea
ØBL2*	Occlsn/Carina
ØBM[1,2]ØZZ	Reattach of [Trachea, Carina], Opn Appr
ØBN1*	Rls/Trachea
ØBN2*	Rls/Carina
ØBQ1*	Repair/Trachea
ØBQ2*	Repair/Carina
ØBS[1,2]ØZZ	Repos [Trachea, Carina], Opn Appr
ØBT1*	Resect/Trachea
ØBT2*	Resect/Carina
ØBU1*	Supl/Trachea
ØBU2*	Supl/Carina
ØBV1*	Restrict/Trachea
ØBV2*	Restrict/Carina
ØBW1[Ø,3,4]FZ	Rev/Trachea, [Opn, Perc, Perc Endo], Tracheostomy Dev, NQ
ØC5M*	Destr/Pharynx
ØC5P*	Destr/Tonsils
ØC5Q*	Destr/Adenoids
ØC5R*	Destr/Epiglottis
ØC5S*	Destr/Larynx
ØC5T*	Destr/Vocal Cord, Rt
ØC5V*	Destr/Vocal Cord, Lt
ØC7S*	Dilation/Larynx
ØC9M[Ø,3,4,7,8][Ø,Z]Z	Drain/Pharynx, [Opn, Perc, Perc Endo, Via Natrl or Artfcl Opng, Via Natrl or Artfcl Opng Endo], [Drain Dev, No Dev], NQ
ØC9P*	Drain/Tonsils
ØC9Q*	Drain/Adenoids
ØC9RØZX	Drain of Epiglottis, Opn Appr, Diagnostic
ØC9R[Ø,3,4,7,8][Ø,Z]Z	Drain/Epiglottis, [Opn, Perc, Perc Endo, Via Natrl or Artfcl Opng, Via Natrl or Artfcl Opng Endo], [Drain Dev, No Dev], NQ
ØC9SØZX	Drain of Larynx, Opn Appr, Diagnostic
ØC9S[Ø,3,4,7,8][Ø,Z]Z	Drain/Larynx, [Opn, Perc, Perc Endo, Via Natrl or Artfcl Opng, Via Natrl or Artfcl Opng Endo], [Drain Dev, No Dev], NQ
ØC9TØZX	Drain of Rt Vocal Cord, Opn Appr, Diagnostic
ØC9T[Ø,3,4,7,8][Ø,Z]Z	Drain/Vocal Cord, Rt, [Opn, Perc, Perc Endo, Via Natrl or Artfcl Opng, Via Natrl or Artfcl Opng Endo], [Drain Dev, No Dev], NQ
ØC9VØZX	Drain of Lt Vocal Cord, Opn Appr, Diagnostic
ØC9V[Ø,3,4,7,8][Ø,Z]Z	Drain/Vocal Cord, Lt, [Opn, Perc, Perc Endo, Via Natrl or Artfcl Opng, Via Natrl or Artfcl Opng Endo], [Drain Dev, No Dev], NQ
ØCBM[Ø,3,4,7,8]ZZ	Exc/Pharynx, [Opn, Perc, Perc Endo, Via Natrl or Artfcl Opng, Via Natrl or Artfcl Opng Endo]
ØCBP*	Exc/Tonsils
ØCBQ*	Exc/Adenoids
ØCBRØZX	Exc of Epiglottis, Opn Appr, Diagnostic
ØCBR[Ø,3,4,7,8]ZZ	Exc/Epiglottis, [Opn, Perc, Perc Endo, Via Natrl or Artfcl Opng, Via Natrl or Artfcl Opng Endo]
ØCBSØZX	Exc of Larynx, Opn Appr, Diagnostic
ØCBTØZX	Exc of Rt Vocal Cord, Opn Appr, Diagnostic
ØCBT[Ø,3,4,7,8]ZZ	Exc/Vocal Cord, Rt, [Opn, Perc, Perc Endo, Via Natrl or Artfcl Opng, Via Natrl or Artfcl Opng Endo]
ØCBVØZX	Exc of Lt Vocal Cord, Opn Appr, Diagnostic
ØCBV[Ø,3,4,7,8]ZZ	Exc/Vocal Cord, Lt, [Opn, Perc, Perc Endo, Via Natrl or Artfcl Opng, Via Natrl or Artfcl Opng Endo]
ØCCM[Ø,3,4]ZZ	Extir/Pharynx, [Opn, Perc, Perc Endo]
ØCCP[Ø,3]ZZ	Extir/Tonsils, [Opn, Perc]
ØCCQØZZ	Extir of Matter from Adenoids, Opn Appr
ØCCQ3ZZ	Extir of Matter from Adenoids, Perc Appr
ØCCR*	Extir/Epiglottis
ØCCS[Ø,3,4]ZZ	Extir/Larynx, [Opn, Perc, Perc Endo]
ØCCT*	Extir/Vocal Cord, Rt
ØCCV*	Extir/Vocal Cord, Lt
ØCDT*	Extract/Vocal Cord, Rt
ØCDV*	Extract/Vocal Cord, Lt
ØCH7*	Insert/Tongue
ØCNM*	Rls/Pharynx

T Transfer DRG   SP Special Payment   * Code Range   6th and 7th Character of ZZ = No Device, No Qualifier ZX = No Device, Diagnostic

ØCNP*	Rls/Tonsils
ØCNQ*	Rls/Adenoids
ØCNR*	Rls/Epiglottis
ØCNS*	Rls/Larynx
ØCNT*	Rls/Vocal Cord, Rt
ØCNV*	Rls/Vocal Cord, Lt
ØCPS[Ø,3,7,8][Ø,7,D,J,K]Z	Rmvl/Larynx, [Opn, Perc, Via Natrl or Artfcl Opng, Via Natrl or Artfcl Opng Endo], [Drain Dev, Auto Tissue Sub, Intralum Dev, Synth Sub, Nonauto Tissue Sub], NQ
ØCPY[7,8][1,7,J,K]Z	Rmvl/Mouth and Throat, [Via Natrl or Artfcl Opng, Via Natrl or Artfcl Opng Endo], [Radioact Elmt, Auto Tissue Sub, Synth Sub, Nonauto Tissue Sub], NQ
ØCQ2*	Repair/Hard Palate
ØCQ3*	Repair/Soft Palate
ØCQM*	Repair/Pharynx
ØCQP*	Repair/Tonsils
ØCQQ*	Repair/Adenoids
ØCQR*	Repair/Epiglottis
ØCQS*	Repair/Larynx
ØCQT*	Repair/Vocal Cord, Rt
ØCQV*	Repair/Vocal Cord, Lt
ØCR2*	Replace/Hard Palate
ØCR3*	Replace/Soft Palate
ØCRM*	Replace/Pharynx
ØCRR*	Replace/Epiglottis
ØCRS*	Replace/Larynx
ØCRT*	Replace/Vocal Cord, Rt
ØCRV*	Replace/Vocal Cord, Lt
ØCS2*	Repos/Hard Palate
ØCS3*	Repos/Soft Palate
ØCSR*	Repos/Epiglottis
ØCST*	Repos/Vocal Cord, Rt
ØCSV*	Repos/Vocal Cord, Lt
ØCTM*	Resect/Pharynx
ØCTP*	Resect/Tonsils
ØCTQ*	Resect/Adenoids
ØCTR*	Resect/Epiglottis
ØCTT*	Resect/Vocal Cord, Rt
ØCTV*	Resect/Vocal Cord, Lt
ØCU2XJZ	Supl Hard Palate with Synth Sub, Extern Appr
ØCU2[Ø,3,X][7,K]Z	Supl/Hard Palate, [Opn, Perc, Ext], [Auto Tissue Sub, Nonauto Tissue Sub], NQ
ØCU3*	Supl/Soft Palate
ØCUM*	Supl/Pharynx
ØCUR*	Supl/Epiglottis
ØCUS*	Supl/Larynx
ØCUT*	Supl/Vocal Cord, Rt
ØCUV*	Supl/Vocal Cord, Lt
ØCWS[Ø,3,7,8][Ø,7,D,J,K]Z	Rev/Larynx, [Opn, Perc, Via Natrl or Artfcl Opng, Via Natrl or Artfcl Opng Endo], [Drain Dev, Auto Tissue Sub, Intralum Dev, Synth Sub, Nonauto Tissue Sub], NQ
ØCWY[7,8][Ø,1,7,D,J,K]Z	Rev/Mouth and Throat, [Via Natrl or Artfcl Opng, Via Natrl or Artfcl Opng Endo], [Drain Dev, Radioact Elmt, Auto Tissue Sub, Intralum Dev, Synth Sub, Nonauto Tissue Sub], NQ
ØD113J4	Bypass Up Esophag to Cutan with Synth Sub, Perc Appr
ØD11[Ø,4,8][7,J,K,Z][4,6]	Bypass/Esophagus, Upr, [Opn, Perc Endo, Via Natrl or Artfcl Opng Endo], [Auto Tissue Sub, Synth Sub, Nonauto Tissue Sub, No Dev], [Cutaneous, Stomach]
ØD123J4	Bypass Mid Esophag to Cutan with Synth Sub, Perc Appr
ØD12[Ø,4,8][7,J,K,Z][4,6]	Bypass/Esophagus, Mid, [Opn, Perc Endo, Via Natrl or Artfcl Opng Endo], [Auto Tissue Sub, Synth Sub, Nonauto Tissue Sub, No Dev], [Cutaneous, Stomach]
ØD133J4	Bypass Low Esophag to Cutan with Synth Sub, Perc Appr
ØD13[Ø,4,8][7,J,K,Z][4,6]	Bypass/Esophagus, Lwr, [Opn, Perc Endo, Via Natrl or Artfcl Opng Endo], [Auto Tissue Sub, Synth Sub, Nonauto Tissue Sub, No Dev], [Cutaneous, Stomach]
ØD15*	Bypass/Esophagus
ØD51[Ø,3,7]ZZ	Destr/Esophagus, Upr, [Opn, Perc, Via Natrl or Artfcl Opng]
ØD52[Ø,3,7]ZZ	Destr/Esophagus, Mid, [Opn, Perc, Via Natrl or Artfcl Opng]
ØD53[Ø,3,7]ZZ	Destr/Esophagus, Lwr, [Opn, Perc, Via Natrl or Artfcl Opng]
ØD54[Ø,3,7]ZZ	Destr/Esophagogastric Junction, [Opn, Perc, Via Natrl or Artfcl Opng]
ØD55[Ø,3,7]ZZ	Destr/Esophagus, [Opn, Perc, Via Natrl or Artfcl Opng]
ØD84*	Div/Esophagogastric Junction
ØD9[1,2,3,4,5]ØZX	Drain of [Upr Esophagus, Mid Esophagus, Lwr Esophagus, Esophagogastric Junction, Esophagus], Opn Appr, Dx
ØDB1ØZX	Exc of Upr Esophagus, Opn Appr, Diagnostic
ØDB1[Ø,3,7]ZZ	Exc/Esophagus, Upr, [Opn, Perc, Via Natrl or Artfcl Opng]
ØDB2ØZX	Exc of Mid Esophagus, Opn Appr, Diagnostic
ØDB2[Ø,3,7]ZZ	Exc/Esophagus, Mid, [Opn, Perc, Via Natrl or Artfcl Opng]

ØDB3ØZX	Exc of Lwr Esophagus, Opn Appr, Diagnostic
ØDB3[Ø,3,7]ZZ	Exc/Esophagus, Lwr, [Opn, Perc, Via Natrl or Artfcl Opng]
ØDB4ØZX	Exc of Esophagogastric Junction, Opn Appr, Diagn
ØDB5ØZX	Exc of Esophagus, Opn Appr, Diagnostic
ØDB5[Ø,3,7]ZZ	Exc/Esophagus, [Opn, Perc, Via Natrl or Artfcl Opng]
ØDH6[Ø,3,4]MZ	Insert/Stomach, [Opn, Perc, Perc Endo], Stimulator Lead, NQ
ØDJ04ZZ	Inspect of Upr Intestinal Tract, Perc Endo Appr
ØDN5*	Rls/Esophagus
ØDP6[Ø,3,4]MZ	Rmvl/Stomach, [Opn, Perc, Perc Endo], Stimulator Lead, NQ
ØDPR*	Rmvl/Anal Sphincter
ØDQ5*	Repair/Esophagus
ØDR5*	Replace/Esophagus
ØDT1*	Resect/Esophagus, Upr
ØDT2*	Resect/Esophagus, Mid
ØDT3*	Resect/Esophagus, Lwr
ØDT5*	Resect/Esophagus
ØDU1*	Supl/Esophagus, Upr
ØDU2*	Supl/Esophagus, Mid
ØDU3*	Supl/Esophagus, Lwr
ØDU5*	Supl/Esophagus
ØDX*	Gastrointestinal Sys, Transfer
ØF9[Ø,1,2]ØZX	Drain of [Liver, Rt Lobe Liver, Lt Lobe Liver], Opn Appr, Dx
ØFB[Ø,1,2]ØZX	Exc of [Liver, Rt Lobe Liver, Lt Lobe Liver], Opn Appr, Dx
ØG9GØ[Ø,Z]Z	Drain/Thyroid Gland Lobe, Lt, Opn, [Drain Dev, No Dev], NQ
ØG9HØ[Ø,Z]Z	Drain/Thyroid Gland Lobe, Rt, Opn, [Drain Dev, No Dev], NQ
ØG9KØ[Ø,Z]Z	Drain/Thyroid Gland, Opn, [Drain Dev, No Dev], NQ
ØG9LØ[Ø,Z]Z	Drain/Superior Parathyroid Gland, Rt, Opn, [Drain Dev, No Dev], NQ
ØG9MØ[Ø,Z]Z	Drain/Superior Parathyroid Gland, Lt, Opn, [Drain Dev, No Dev], NQ
ØG9NØ[Ø,Z]Z	Drain/Inferior Parathyroid Gland, Rt, Opn, [Drain Dev, No Dev], NQ
ØG9PØ[Ø,Z]Z	Drain/Inferior Parathyroid Gland, Lt, Opn, [Drain Dev, No Dev], NQ
ØG9QØ[Ø,Z]Z	Drain/Parathyroid Glands, Multi, Opn, [Drain Dev, No Dev], NQ
ØG9RØ[Ø,Z]Z	Drain/Parathyroid Gland, Opn, [Drain Dev, No Dev], NQ
ØGCG*	Extir/Thyroid Gland Lobe, Lt
ØGCH*	Extir/Thyroid Gland Lobe, Rt
ØGCK*	Extir/Thyroid Gland
ØGCL*	Extir/Superior Parathyroid Gland, Rt
ØGCM*	Extir/Superior Parathyroid Gland, Lt
ØGCN*	Extir/Inferior Parathyroid Gland, Rt
ØGCP*	Extir/Inferior Parathyroid Gland, Lt
ØGCQ*	Extir/Parathyroid Glands, Multi
ØGCR*	Extir/Parathyroid Gland
ØGH*	Endocrine Sys, Insert
ØGJ[K,R,S]ØZZ	Inspect of [Thyroid Gland, Parathyroid Gland, Endocrine Gland], Opn
ØGPK[Ø,3,4]ØZ	Rmvl/Thyroid Gland, [Opn, Perc, Perc Endo], Drain Dev, NQ
ØGPR[Ø,3,4]ØZ	Rmvl/Parathyroid Gland, [Opn, Perc, Perc Endo], Drain Dev, NQ
ØGWK[Ø,3,4]ØZ	Rev/Thyroid Gland, [Opn, Perc, Perc Endo], Drain Dev, NQ
ØGWR[Ø,3,4]ØZ	Rev/Parathyroid Gland, [Opn, Perc, Perc Endo], Drain Dev, NQ
ØH8[Ø,1,4]XZZ	Div of [Scalp, Face, Neck] Skin, Ext Appr
ØHB[Ø,1,4,5]XZZ	Exc of Skin of [Scalp, Face, Neck, Chest], Ext
ØHB[6,7,8,A]XZZ	Exc of Skin of [Back, Abd, Buttock, Genitalia], Ext
ØHB[B,C,D,E,F,G]XZZ	Exc of Skin of [Rt Upr Arm, Lt Upr Arm, Rt Lwr Arm, Lt Lwr Arm, Rt Hand, Lt Hand], Ext
ØHB[H,J,K,L,M,N]XZZ	Exc of Skin of [Rt Upr Leg, Lt Upr Leg, Rt Lwr Leg, Lt Lwr Leg, Rt Foot, Lt Foot], Ext
ØHM[1,2,3,4,9]XZZ	Reattach of [Face, Rt Ear, Lt Ear, Neck, Perineum] Skin, Ext Appr
ØHN[Ø,1,2,3,4]XZZ	Rls of Skin of [Scalp, Face, Rt Ear, Lt Ear, Neck], Ext
ØHRØ*	Replace/Skin, Scalp
ØHR1*	Replace/Skin, Face
ØHR2*	Replace/Skin, Rt Ear
ØHR3*	Replace/Skin, Lt Ear
ØHR4*	Replace/Skin, Neck
ØHR5XK[3,4]	Replace/Skin, Chest, Ext, Nonauto Tissue Sub, [Full Thickness, Partial Thickness]
ØHR6XK[3,4]	Replace/Skin, Back, Ext, Nonauto Tissue Sub, [Full Thickness, Partial Thickness]
ØHR7XK[3,4]	Replace/Skin, Abd, Ext, Nonauto Tissue Sub, [Full Thickness, Partial Thickness]
ØHR8XK[3,4]	Replace/Skin, Buttock, Ext, Nonauto Tissue Sub, [Full Thickness, Partial Thickness]
ØHX*	Skin and Breast, Transfer
ØJ01*	Alter/SQ Tissue & Fascia, Face
ØJB00ZZ	Exc of Scalp SQ/Fascia, Opn Appr
ØJB1[Ø,3]ZZ	Exc/SQ Tissue & Fascia, Face, [Opn, Perc]

Surgical   **Medical**   **CC Indicator**   **MCC Indicator**   **Procedure Proxy**   PDxMCC **PDx acts as own MCC**   PDxCC **PDx acts as own CC**

© 2015 Optum360, LLC   MS-DRG Version 33.0   53

MDC 3: Diseases And Disorders Of The Ear, Nose, Mouth And Throat—SURGICAL

Code	Description
ØJB[4,5,6]ØZZ	Exc of [Ant Neck, Post Neck, Chest] SQ Tissue & Fascia, Opn Appr
ØJB[7,8,9,B,C]ØZZ	Exc of SQ Tissue & Fascia of [Back, Abd, Buttock, Perineum, Pelvic Rgn], Opn
ØJB[D,F,G,H]ØZZ	Exc of SQ Tissue & Fascia of [Rt Upr Arm, Lt Upr Arm, Rt Lwr Arm, Lt Lwr Arm], Opn
ØJB[L,M,N,P,Q,R]ØZZ	Exc of SQ Tissue & Fascia of [Rt Upr Leg, Lt Upr Leg, Rt Lwr Leg, Lt Lwr Leg, Rt Foot, Lt Foot], Opn
ØJHØ*	Insert/SQ Tissue & Fascia, Scalp
ØJH1*	Insert/SQ Tissue & Fascia, Face
ØJH4*	Insert/SQ Tissue & Fascia, Ant Neck
ØJH5*	Insert/SQ Tissue & Fascia, Posterior Neck
ØJR[Ø,1,4,5,6]37Z	Replace of [Scalp, Face, Ant Neck, Post Neck, Chest] SQ Tissue & Fascia w/ Auto Tissue Sub, Perc Appr
ØJR[7,8,9,B,C]37Z	Replace of [Back, Abd, Buttock, Perineum, Pelvic Rgn] SQ Tissue & Fascia w/ Auto Tissue Sub, Perc Appr
ØJR[D,F,G,H,J,K]37Z	Replace of [Rt Upr Arm, Lt Upr Arm, Rt Lwr Arm, Lt Lwr Arm, Rt Hand, Lt Hand] SQ Tissue & Fascia w/ Auto Tissue Sub, Perc Appr
ØJR[L,M,N,P,Q,R]37Z	Replace of SQ Tissue & Fascia of [Rt Upr Leg, Lt Upr Leg, Rt Lwr Leg, Lt Lwr Leg, Rt Foot, Lt Foot] w/ Auto Tissue Sub, Perc
ØJXØ[Ø,3]Z[B,C]	Transfer/SQ Tissue & Fascia, Scalp, [Opn, Perc], No Dev, [Skin and SQ Tissue, Skin, SQ Tissue & Fascia]
ØJX1[Ø,3]Z[B,C]	Transfer/SQ Tissue & Fascia, Face, [Opn, Perc], No Dev, [Skin and SQ Tissue, Skin, SQ Tissue & Fascia]
ØJX4[Ø,3]Z[B,C]	Transfer/SQ Tissue & Fascia, Ant Neck, [Opn, Perc], No Dev, [Skin and SQ Tissue, Skin, SQ Tissue & Fascia]
ØJX5[Ø,3]Z[B,C]	Transfer/SQ Tissue & Fascia, Post Neck, [Opn, Perc], No Dev, [Skin and SQ Tissue, Skin, SQ Tissue & Fascia]
ØK84*	Div/Tongue, Palate, Pharynx Muscle
ØK9Ø[Ø,3,4]ØZ	Drain/Head Muscle, [Opn, Perc, Perc Endo], Drain Dev, NQ
ØK9Ø[Ø,4]ZZ	Drain/Head Muscle, [Opn, Perc Endo]
ØK91[Ø,3,4]ØZ	Drain/Facial Muscle, [Opn, Perc, Perc Endo], Drain Dev, NQ
ØK91[Ø,4]ZZ	Drain/Facial Muscle, [Opn, Perc Endo]
ØK92[Ø,3,4]ØZ	Drain/Neck Muscle, Rt, [Opn, Perc, Perc Endo], Drain Dev, NQ
ØK92[Ø,4]ZZ	Drain/Neck Muscle, Rt, [Opn, Perc Endo]
ØK93[Ø,3,4]ØZ	Drain/Neck Muscle, Lt, [Opn, Perc, Perc Endo], Drain Dev, NQ
ØK93[Ø,4]ZZ	Drain/Neck Muscle, Lt, [Opn, Perc Endo]
ØKCØ*	Extir/Head Muscle
ØKC1*	Extir/Facial Muscle
ØKC2*	Extir/Neck Muscle, Rt
ØKC3*	Extir/Neck Muscle, Lt
ØN8C*	Div/Sphenoid Bone, Rt
ØN8D*	Div/Sphenoid Bone, Lt
ØN8F*	Div/Ethmoid Bone, Rt
ØN8G*	Div/Ethmoid Bone, Lt
ØN8H*	Div/Lacrimal Bone, Rt
ØN8J*	Div/Lacrimal Bone, Lt
ØN8K*	Div/Palatine Bone, Rt
ØN8L*	Div/Palatine Bone, Lt
ØN8M*	Div/Zygomatic Bone, Rt
ØN8N*	Div/Zygomatic Bone, Lt
ØN8R*	Div/Maxilla, Rt
ØN8S*	Div/Maxilla, Lt
ØN8T*	Div/Mandible, Rt
ØN8V*	Div/Mandible, Lt
ØN8X*	Div/Hyoid Bone
ØN9C*	Drain/Sphenoid Bone, Rt
ØN9D*	Drain/Sphenoid Bone, Lt
ØN9F*	Drain/Ethmoid Bone, Rt
ØN9G*	Drain/Ethmoid Bone, Lt
ØN9H*	Drain/Lacrimal Bone, Rt
ØN9J*	Drain/Lacrimal Bone, Lt
ØN9K*	Drain/Palatine Bone, Rt
ØN9L*	Drain/Palatine Bone, Lt
ØN9M*	Drain/Zygomatic Bone, Rt
ØN9N*	Drain/Zygomatic Bone, Lt
ØN9R[Ø,3,4]ZX	Drain/Maxilla, Rt, [Opn, Perc, Perc Endo]
ØN9S[Ø,3,4]ZX	Drain/Maxilla, Lt, [Opn, Perc, Perc Endo]
ØN9T[Ø,3,4]ZX	Drain/Mandible, Rt, [Opn, Perc, Perc Endo]
ØN9V[Ø,3,4]ZX	Drain/Mandible, Lt, [Opn, Perc, Perc Endo]
ØN9X*	Drain/Hyoid Bone
ØN9[P,Q]3ZZ	Drain of [Rt, Lt] Orbit, Perc Appr
ØNBC[Ø,3,4]ZX	Exc/Sphenoid Bone, Rt, [Opn, Perc, Perc Endo]
ØNBD[Ø,3,4]ZX	Exc/Sphenoid Bone, Lt, [Opn, Perc, Perc Endo]
ØNBF[Ø,3,4]ZX	Exc/Ethmoid Bone, Rt, [Opn, Perc, Perc Endo]
ØNBG[Ø,3,4]ZX	Exc/Ethmoid Bone, Lt, [Opn, Perc, Perc Endo]
ØNBH[Ø,3,4]ZX	Exc/Lacrimal Bone, Rt, [Opn, Perc, Perc Endo]
ØNBJ[Ø,3,4]ZX	Exc/Lacrimal Bone, Lt, [Opn, Perc, Perc Endo]
ØNBK[Ø,3,4]ZX	Exc/Palatine Bone, Rt, [Opn, Perc, Perc Endo]
ØNBL[Ø,3,4]ZX	Exc/Palatine Bone, Lt, [Opn, Perc, Perc Endo]
ØNBM[Ø,3,4]ZX	Exc/Zygomatic Bone, Rt, [Opn, Perc, Perc Endo]
ØNBN[Ø,3,4]ZX	Exc/Zygomatic Bone, Lt, [Opn, Perc, Perc Endo]
ØNBX[Ø,3,4]ZX	Exc/Hyoid Bone, [Opn, Perc, Perc Endo]
ØNCC*	Extir/Sphenoid Bone, Rt
ØNCD*	Extir/Sphenoid Bone, Lt
ØNCF*	Extir/Ethmoid Bone, Rt
ØNCG*	Extir/Ethmoid Bone, Lt
ØNCH*	Extir/Lacrimal Bone, Rt
ØNCJ*	Extir/Lacrimal Bone, Lt
ØNCK*	Extir/Palatine Bone, Rt
ØNCL*	Extir/Palatine Bone, Lt
ØNCM*	Extir/Zygomatic Bone, Rt
ØNCN*	Extir/Zygomatic Bone, Lt
ØNCP*	Extir/Orbit, Rt
ØNCQ*	Extir/Orbit, Lt
ØNCX*	Extir/Hyoid Bone
ØNH5[Ø,3,4]SZ	Insert/Temporal Bone, Rt, [Opn, Perc, Perc Endo], Bone Conduction Hearing Dev, NQ
ØNH6[Ø,3,4]SZ	Insert/Temporal Bone, Lt, [Opn, Perc, Perc Endo], Bone Conduction Hearing Dev, NQ
ØNHC*	Insert/Sphenoid Bone, Rt
ØNHD*	Insert/Sphenoid Bone, Lt
ØNHF*	Insert/Ethmoid Bone, Rt
ØNHG*	Insert/Ethmoid Bone, Lt
ØNHH*	Insert/Lacrimal Bone, Rt
ØNHJ*	Insert/Lacrimal Bone, Lt
ØNHK*	Insert/Palatine Bone, Rt
ØNHL*	Insert/Palatine Bone, Lt
ØNHM*	Insert/Zygomatic Bone, Rt
ØNHN*	Insert/Zygomatic Bone, Lt
ØNHP*	Insert/Orbit, Rt
ØNHQ*	Insert/Orbit, Lt
ØNHR*	Insert/Maxilla, Rt
ØNHS*	Insert/Maxilla, Lt
ØNHT*	Insert/Mandible, Rt
ØNHV*	Insert/Mandible, Lt
ØNHW*	Insert/Facial Bone
ØNHX*	Insert/Hyoid Bone
ØNPW[Ø,3,4][Ø,7,K,M]Z	Rmvl/Facial Bone, [Opn, Perc, Perc Endo], [Drain Dev, Auto Tissue Sub, Nonauto Tissue Sub, Bone Growth Stimulator], NQ
ØNQB*	Repair/Nasal Bone
ØNRB*	Replace/Nasal Bone
ØNUB*	Supl/Nasal Bone
ØNWW[Ø,3,4][Ø,4,7,J,K,M]Z	Rev/Facial Bone, [Opn, Perc, Perc Endo], [Drain Dev, Int Fix Dev, Auto Tissue Sub, Synth Sub, Nonauto Tissue Sub, Bone Growth Stimulator], NQ
ØP53*	Destr/Cervical Vertebra
ØP93[Ø,3,4]ZX	Drain/Cervical Vertebra, [Opn, Perc, Perc Endo]
ØPB3*	Exc/Cervical Vertebra
ØPB4[Ø,3,4]ZZ	Exc/Thoracic Vertebra, [Opn, Perc, Perc Endo]
ØPBR[Ø,3,4]ZZ	Exc/Thumb Phalanx, Rt, [Opn, Perc, Perc Endo]
ØPBS[Ø,3,4]ZZ	Exc/Thumb Phalanx, Lt, [Opn, Perc, Perc Endo]
ØPBT[Ø,3,4]ZZ	Exc/Finger Phalanx, Rt, [Opn, Perc, Perc Endo]
ØPBV[Ø,3,4]ZZ	Exc/Finger Phalanx, Lt, [Opn, Perc, Perc Endo]
ØPSØØ[4,Z]Z	Repos/Sternum, Opn, [Int Fix Dev, No Dev], NQ
ØPS1Ø[4,Z]Z	Repos/Rib, Rt, Opn, [Int Fix Dev, No Dev], NQ
ØPS2Ø[4,Z]Z	Repos/Rib, Lt, Opn, [Int Fix Dev, No Dev], NQ
ØPS5Ø[4,Z]Z	Repos/Scapula, Rt, Opn, [Int Fix Dev, No Dev], NQ
ØPS6Ø[4,Z]Z	Repos/Scapula, Lt, Opn, [Int Fix Dev, No Dev], NQ
ØPS7Ø[4,Z]Z	Repos/Glenoid Cavity, Rt, Opn, [Int Fix Dev, No Dev], NQ
ØPS8Ø[4,Z]Z	Repos/Glenoid Cavity, Lt, Opn, [Int Fix Dev, No Dev], NQ
ØPS9Ø[4,Z]Z	Repos/Clavicle, Rt, Opn, [Int Fix Dev, No Dev], NQ
ØPSBØ[4,Z]Z	Repos/Clavicle, Lt, Opn, [Int Fix Dev, No Dev], NQ
ØPT[R,S,T,V]ØZZ	Resect of [Rt Thumb, Lt Thumb, Rt Finger, Lt Finger] Phalanx, Opn Appr
ØQBØ[Ø,3,4]ZZ	Exc/Lumbar Vertebra, [Opn, Perc, Perc Endo]
ØQB1[Ø,3,4]ZZ	Exc/Sacrum, [Opn, Perc, Perc Endo]
ØQB2[Ø,3,4]ZZ	Exc/Pelvic Bone, Rt, [Opn, Perc, Perc Endo]
ØQB3[Ø,3,4]ZZ	Exc/Pelvic Bone, Lt, [Opn, Perc, Perc Endo]
ØQB4[Ø,3,4]ZZ	Exc/Acetab, Rt, [Opn, Perc, Perc Endo]
ØQB5[Ø,3,4]ZZ	Exc/Acetab, Lt, [Opn, Perc, Perc Endo]
ØQBQ[Ø,3,4]ZZ	Exc/Toe Phalanx, Rt, [Opn, Perc, Perc Endo]
ØQBR[Ø,3,4]ZZ	Exc/Toe Phalanx, Lt, [Opn, Perc, Perc Endo]
ØQBS[Ø,3,4]ZZ	Exc/Coccyx, [Opn, Perc, Perc Endo]
ØQS2Ø[4,Z]Z	Repos/Pelvic Bone, Rt, Opn, [Int Fix Dev, No Dev], NQ
ØQS3Ø[4,Z]Z	Repos/Pelvic Bone, Lt, Opn, [Int Fix Dev, No Dev], NQ
ØQS4Ø[4,Z]Z	Repos/Acetab, Rt, Opn, [Int Fix Dev, No Dev], NQ
ØQS5Ø[4,Z]Z	Repos/Acetab, Lt, Opn, [Int Fix Dev, No Dev], NQ

Ⓣ **Transfer DRG**   ⓈⓅ **Special Payment**   * **Code Range**   6th and 7th Character of ZZ = No Device, No Qualifier ZX = No Device, Diagnostic

54   MS-DRG Version 33.0   © 2015 Optum360, LLC

0QSD0[4,Z]Z	Repos/Patella, Rt, Opn, [Int Fix Dev, No Dev], NQ
0QSF0[4,Z]Z	Repos/Patella, Lt, Opn, [Int Fix Dev, No Dev], NQ
0QT[2,3,4,5]0ZZ	Resect of [Rt Pelvic Bone, Lt Pelvic Bone, Rt Acetab, Lt Acetab], Opn Appr
0QT[Q,R,S]0ZZ	Resect of [Rt Toe Phalanx, Lt Toe Phalanx, Coccyx], Opn Appr
0R9C*	Drain/Temporomandibular Jt, Rt
0R9D*	Drain/Temporomandibular Jt, Lt
0RBC[0,3,4]ZX	Exc/Temporomandibular Jt, Rt, [Opn, Perc, Perc Endo]
0RBD[0,3,4]ZX	Exc/Temporomandibular Jt, Lt, [Opn, Perc, Perc Endo]
0RHC[0,3,4][3,4]Z	Insert/Temporomandibular Jt, Rt, [Opn, Perc, Perc Endo], [Inf Dev, Int Fix Dev], NQ
0RHD[0,3,4][3,4]Z	Insert/Temporomandibular Jt, Lt, [Opn, Perc, Perc Endo], [Inf Dev, Int Fix Dev], NQ
0RPC[0,3,4][0,3,7,J,K]Z	Rmvl/Temporomandibular Jt, Rt, [Opn, Perc, Perc Endo], [Drain Dev, Inf Dev, Auto Tissue Sub, Synth Sub, Nonauto Tissue Sub], NQ
0RPD[0,3,4][0,3,7,J,K]Z	Rmvl/Temporomandibular Jt, Lt, [Opn, Perc, Perc Endo], [Drain Dev, Inf Dev, Auto Tissue Sub, Synth Sub, Nonauto Tissue Sub], NQ
0RQC[0,3,4]ZZ	Rpr/Temporomandibular Jt, Rt, [Opn, Perc, Perc Endo]
0RQD[0,3,4]ZZ	Rpr/Temporomandibular Jt, Lt, [Opn, Perc, Perc Endo]
0RRC*	Replace/Temporomandibular Jt, Rt
0RRD*	Replace/Temporomandibular Jt, Lt
0RUC*	Supl/Temporomandibular Jt, Rt
0RUD*	Supl/Temporomandibular Jt, Lt
0RWC[0,3,4][0,3,4,7,8,J,K]Z	Rev/Temporomandibular Jt, Rt, [Opn, Perc, Perc Endo], [Drain Dev, Inf Dev, Int Fix Dev, Auto Tissue Sub, Spacer, Synth Sub, Nonauto Tissue Sub], NQ
0RWD[0,3,4][0,3,4,7,8,J,K]Z	Rev/Temporomandibular Jt, Lt, [Opn, Perc, Perc Endo], [Drain Dev, Inf Dev, Int Fix Dev, Auto Tissue Sub, Spacer, Synth Sub, Nonauto Tissue Sub], NQ
0W02*	Alter/Face
0W06*	Alter/Neck
0W30*	Control/Head
0W31*	Control/Cranial Cavity
0W32*	Control/Face
0W33[0,3,4]ZZ	Control/Oral Cavity and Throat, [Opn, Perc, Perc Endo]
0W34*	Control/Upr Jaw
0W35*	Control/Lwr Jaw
0W36*	Control/Neck
0W96[0,3,4][0,Z]Z	Drain/Neck, [Opn, Perc, Perc Endo], [Drain Dev, No Dev], NQ
0WB0[0,3,4,X]ZZ	Exc/Head, [Opn, Perc, Perc Endo, Ext]
0WB2[0,3,4,X]ZZ	Exc/Face, [Opn, Perc, Perc Endo, Ext]
0WB4[0,3,4,X]ZZ	Exc/Upr Jaw, [Opn, Perc, Perc Endo, Ext]
0WB5[0,3,4,X]ZZ	Exc/Lwr Jaw, [Opn, Perc, Perc Endo, Ext]
0WB6XZ2	Exc of Neck, Stoma, Ext Appr
0WB6[0,3,4,X]ZZ	Exc/Neck, [Opn, Perc, Perc Endo, Ext]
0WH3[0,3,4]1Z	Insert/Oral Cavity and Throat, [Opn, Perc, Perc Endo], Radioact Elmt, NQ
0WH4[0,3,4]1Z	Insert/Upr Jaw, [Opn, Perc, Perc Endo], Radioact Elmt, NQ
0WH5[0,3,4]1Z	Insert/Lwr Jaw, [Opn, Perc, Perc Endo], Radioact Elmt, NQ
0WH6[0,3,4]1Z	Insert/Neck, [Opn, Perc, Perc Endo], Radioact Elmt, NQ
0WJ60ZZ	Inspect of Neck, Opn Appr
0WJ[C,D]4ZZ	Inspect of [Mediastinum Pericardial Cavity], Perc Endo Appr
0WM[2,4,5,6]0ZZ	Reattach of [Face, Upr Jaw, Lwr Jaw, Neck], Opn Appr
0WQ2*	Repair/Face
0WQ4*	Repair/Upr Jaw
0WQ5*	Repair/Lwr Jaw
0WQ6*	Repair/Neck
0WU2[0,4][J,K]Z	Supl/Face, [Opn, Perc Endo], [Synth Sub, Nonauto Tissue Sub], NQ
0WU6[0,4][J,K]Z	Supl/Neck, [Opn, Perc Endo], [Synth Sub, Nonauto Tissue Sub], NQ
3E0B[3,7,X]29	Introduction/Ear, [Perc, Via Natrl or Artfcl Opng, Ext], Anti-infective, Oth Anti-infective
3E0B[3,7,X]GC	Introduction/Ear, [Perc, Via Natrl or Artfcl Opng, Ext], Oth Therapeutic Substance, Oth Substance
3E0B[3,7,X][3,B,H,K,T]Z	Introduction/Ear, [Perc, Via Natrl or Artfcl Opng, Ext], [Anti-inflam, Local Anesthetic, Radioact Substance, Oth Dx Substance, Destr Agent], NQ

DRG 134 Other Ear, Nose, Mouth and Throat O.R. Procedures without CC/MCC

GMLOS 1.9   **AMLOS 2.4**   **RW 1.0635**

Select operating room procedures listed under DRG 133

DRG 135 Sinus and Mastoid Procedures with CC/MCC

GMLOS 4.1   **AMLOS 5.6**   **RW 1.9100**

Operating Room Procedures

095B*	Destr/Mastoid Sinus, Rt
095C*	Destr/Mastoid Sinus, Lt
095P*	Destr/Accessory Sinus
095Q*	Destr/Maxillary Sinus, Rt
095R*	Destr/Maxillary Sinus, Lt
095S*	Destr/Frontal Sinus, Rt
095T*	Destr/Frontal Sinus, Lt
095U*	Destr/Ethmoid Sinus, Rt
095V*	Destr/Ethmoid Sinus, Lt
095W*	Destr/Sphenoid Sinus, Rt
095X*	Destr/Sphenoid Sinus, Lt
099B[0,3,4][0,Z]Z	Drain/Mastoid Sinus, Rt, [Opn, Perc, Perc Endo], [Drain Dev, No Dev], NQ
099C[0,3,4][0,Z]Z	Drain/Mastoid Sinus, Lt, [Opn, Perc, Perc Endo], [Drain Dev, No Dev], NQ
099P0ZX	Drain of Accessory Sinus, Opn Appr, Diagnostic
099P0[0,Z]Z	Drain/Accessory Sinus, Opn, [Drain Dev, No Dev], NQ
099Q0ZX	Drain of Rt Maxillary Sinus, Opn Appr, Diagnostic
099Q0[0,Z]Z	Drain/Maxillary Sinus, Rt, Opn, [Drain Dev, No Dev], NQ
099R0ZX	Drain of Lt Maxillary Sinus, Opn Appr, Diagnostic
099R0[0,Z]Z	Drain/Maxillary Sinus, Lt, Opn, [Drain Dev, No Dev], NQ
099S0ZX	Drain of Rt Frontal Sinus, Opn Appr, Diagnostic
099S0[0,Z]Z	Drain/Frontal Sinus, Rt, Opn, [Drain Dev, No Dev], NQ
099T0ZX	Drain of Lt Frontal Sinus, Opn Appr, Diagnostic
099T0[0,Z]Z	Drain/Frontal Sinus, Lt, Opn, [Drain Dev, No Dev], NQ
099U0ZX	Drain of Rt Ethmoid Sinus, Opn Appr, Diagnostic
099U0[0,Z]Z	Drain/Ethmoid Sinus, Rt, Opn, [Drain Dev, No Dev], NQ
099V0ZX	Drain of Lt Ethmoid Sinus, Opn Appr, Diagnostic
099V0[0,Z]Z	Drain/Ethmoid Sinus, Lt, Opn, [Drain Dev, No Dev], NQ
099W0ZX	Drain of Rt Sphenoid Sinus, Opn Appr, Diagnostic
099W0[0,Z]Z	Drain/Sphenoid Sinus, Rt, Opn, [Drain Dev, No Dev], NQ
099X0ZX	Drain of Lt Sphenoid Sinus, Opn Appr, Diagnostic
099X0[0,Z]Z	Drain/Sphenoid Sinus, Lt, Opn, [Drain Dev, No Dev], NQ
09BB[0,3,4]ZZ	Exc/Mastoid Sinus, Rt, [Opn, Perc, Perc Endo]
09BC[0,3,4]ZZ	Exc/Mastoid Sinus, Lt, [Opn, Perc, Perc Endo]
09BP0ZX	Exc of Accessory Sinus, Opn Appr, Diagnostic
09BP[0,3,4]ZZ	Exc/Accessory Sinus, [Opn, Perc, Perc Endo]
09BQ0ZX	Exc of Rt Maxillary Sinus, Opn Appr, Diagnostic
09BQ[0,3,4]ZZ	Exc/Maxillary Sinus, Rt, [Opn, Perc, Perc Endo]
09BR0ZX	Exc of Lt Maxillary Sinus, Opn Appr, Diagnostic
09BR[0,3,4]ZZ	Exc/Maxillary Sinus, Lt, [Opn, Perc, Perc Endo]
09BS0ZX	Exc of Rt Frontal Sinus, Opn Appr, Diagnostic
09BS[0,3,4]ZZ	Exc/Frontal Sinus, Rt, [Opn, Perc, Perc Endo]
09BT0ZX	Exc of Lt Frontal Sinus, Opn Appr, Diagnostic
09BT[0,3,4]ZZ	Exc/Frontal Sinus, Lt, [Opn, Perc, Perc Endo]
09BU0ZX	Exc of Rt Ethmoid Sinus, Opn Appr, Diagnostic
09BU[0,3,4]ZZ	Exc/Ethmoid Sinus, Rt, [Opn, Perc, Perc Endo]
09BV0ZX	Exc of Lt Ethmoid Sinus, Opn Appr, Diagnostic
09BV[0,3,4]ZZ	Exc/Ethmoid Sinus, Lt, [Opn, Perc, Perc Endo]
09BW0ZX	Exc of Rt Sphenoid Sinus, Opn Appr, Diagnostic
09BW[0,3,4]ZZ	Exc/Sphenoid Sinus, Rt, [Opn, Perc, Perc Endo]
09BX0ZX	Exc of Lt Sphenoid Sinus, Opn Appr, Diagnostic
09BX[0,3,4]ZZ	Exc/Sphenoid Sinus, Lt, [Opn, Perc, Perc Endo]
09CB*	Extir/Mastoid Sinus, Rt
09CC*	Extir/Mastoid Sinus, Lt
09CP*	Extir/Accessory Sinus
09CQ*	Extir/Maxillary Sinus, Rt
09CR*	Extir/Maxillary Sinus, Lt
09CS*	Extir/Frontal Sinus, Rt
09CT*	Extir/Frontal Sinus, Lt
09CU*	Extir/Ethmoid Sinus, Rt
09CV*	Extir/Ethmoid Sinus, Lt
09CW*	Extir/Sphenoid Sinus, Rt
09CX*	Extir/Sphenoid Sinus, Lt
09DB*	Extract/Mastoid Sinus, Rt
09DC*	Extract/Mastoid Sinus, Lt
09DP*	Extract/Accessory Sinus
09DQ*	Extract/Maxillary Sinus, Rt
09DR*	Extract/Maxillary Sinus, Lt
09DS*	Extract/Frontal Sinus, Rt
09DT*	Extract/Frontal Sinus, Lt
09DU*	Extract/Ethmoid Sinus, Rt
09DV*	Extract/Ethmoid Sinus, Lt
09DW*	Extract/Sphenoid Sinus, Rt
09DX*	Extract/Sphenoid Sinus, Lt
09NP*	Rls/Accessory Sinus

MDC 3: Diseases And Disorders Of The Ear, Nose, Mouth And Throat—SURGICAL

Surgical   **Medical**   **CC Indicator**   **MCC Indicator**   **Procedure Proxy**   **PDxMCC** PDx acts as own MCC   **PDxCC** PDx acts as own CC

MDC 3: Diseases And Disorders Of The Ear, Nose, Mouth And Throat—SURGICAL

09NQ*	Rls/Maxillary Sinus, Rt
09NR*	Rls/Maxillary Sinus, Lt
09NS*	Rls/Frontal Sinus, Rt
09NT*	Rls/Frontal Sinus, Lt
09NU*	Rls/Ethmoid Sinus, Rt
09NV*	Rls/Ethmoid Sinus, Lt
09NW*	Rls/Sphenoid Sinus, Rt
09NX*	Rls/Sphenoid Sinus, Lt
09PY[0,3,4]0Z	Rmvl/Sinus, [Opn, Perc, Perc Endo], Drain Dev, NQ
09QB*	Repair/Mastoid Sinus, Rt
09QC*	Repair/Mastoid Sinus, Lt
09QP*	Repair/Accessory Sinus
09QQ*	Repair/Maxillary Sinus, Rt
09QR*	Repair/Maxillary Sinus, Lt
09QS*	Repair/Frontal Sinus, Rt
09QT*	Repair/Frontal Sinus, Lt
09QU*	Repair/Ethmoid Sinus, Rt
09QV*	Repair/Ethmoid Sinus, Lt
09QW*	Repair/Sphenoid Sinus, Rt
09QX*	Repair/Sphenoid Sinus, Lt
09TB*	Resect/Mastoid Sinus, Rt
09TC*	Resect/Mastoid Sinus, Lt
09TP*	Resect/Accessory Sinus
09TQ*	Resect/Maxillary Sinus, Rt
09TR*	Resect/Maxillary Sinus, Lt
09TS*	Resect/Frontal Sinus, Rt
09TT*	Resect/Frontal Sinus, Lt
09TU*	Resect/Ethmoid Sinus, Rt
09TV*	Resect/Ethmoid Sinus, Lt
09TW*	Resect/Sphenoid Sinus, Rt
09TX*	Resect/Sphenoid Sinus, Lt
09WY[0,3,4]0Z	Rev/Sinus, [Opn, Perc, Perc Endo], Drain Dev, NQ

DRG 136   Sinus and Mastoid Procedures without CC/MCC
GMLOS 1.9   AMLOS 2.6   RW 1.1905

Select operating room procedures listed under DRG 135

DRG 137   Mouth Procedures with CC/MCC
GMLOS 3.8   AMLOS 5.0   RW 1.4261

Operating Room Procedures

0C0*	Mouth and Throat, Alter
0C50*	Destr/Upr Lip
0C51*	Destr/Lwr Lip
0C52*	Destr/Hard Palate
0C53*	Destr/Soft Palate
0C54*	Destr/Buccal Mucosa
0C57*	Destr/Tongue
0C5N*	Destr/Uvula
0C90[0,3,X][0,Z]Z	Drain/Upr Lip, [Opn, Perc, Ext], [Drain Dev, No Dev], NQ
0C91[0,3,X][0,Z]Z	Drain/Lwr Lip, [Opn, Perc, Ext], [Drain Dev, No Dev], NQ
0C92*	Drain/Hard Palate
0C93*	Drain/Soft Palate
0C94[0,3,X][0,Z]Z	Drain/Buccal Mucosa, [Opn, Perc, Ext], [Drain Dev, No Dev], NQ
0C970ZX	Drain of Tongue, Opn Appr, Diagnostic
0C97[0,3,X][0,Z]Z	Drain/Tongue, [Opn, Perc, Ext], [Drain Dev, No Dev], NQ
0C9N*	Drain/Uvula
0CB0[0,3,X]ZZ	Exc/Upr Lip, [Opn, Perc, Ext]
0CB1[0,3,X]ZZ	Exc/Lwr Lip, [Opn, Perc, Ext]
0CB2*	Exc/Hard Palate
0CB3*	Exc/Soft Palate
0CB4[0,3,X]ZZ	Exc/Buccal Mucosa, [Opn, Perc, Ext]
0CB70ZX	Exc of Tongue, Opn Appr, Diagnostic
0CB7[0,3,X]ZZ	Exc/Tongue, [Opn, Perc, Ext]
0CBN*	Exc/Uvula
0CC0[0,3]ZZ	Extir/Upr Lip, [Opn, Perc]
0CC1[0,3]ZZ	Extir/Lwr Lip, [Opn, Perc]
0CC2[0,3]ZZ	Extir/Hard Palate, [Opn, Perc]
0CC3[0,3]ZZ	Extir/Soft Palate, [Opn, Perc]
0CC4[0,3]ZZ	Extir/Buccal Mucosa, [Opn, Perc]
0CC7[0,3]ZZ	Extir/Tongue, [Opn, Perc]
0CCN[0,3]ZZ	Extir/Uvula, [Opn, Perc]
0CM[0,1,3,7,N]0ZZ	Reattach of [Upr Lip, Lwr Lip, Soft Palate, Tongue, Uvula], Opn Appr
0CN2*	Rls/Hard Palate
0CN3*	Rls/Soft Palate
0CN4*	Rls/Buccal Mucosa
0CNN*	Rls/Uvula

0CPY[0,3][0,1,7,D,J,K]Z	Rmvl/Mouth and Throat, [Opn, Perc], [Drain Dev, Radioact Elmt, Auto Tissue Sub, Intralum Dev, Synth Sub, Nonauto Tissue Sub], NQ
0CQ0[0,3]ZZ	Rpr/Upr Lip, [Opn, Perc]
0CQ1[0,3]ZZ	Rpr/Lwr Lip, [Opn, Perc]
0CQ4*	Repair/Buccal Mucosa
0CQ7*	Repair/Tongue
0CQN*	Repair/Uvula
0CR0*	Replace/Upr Lip
0CR1*	Replace/Lwr Lip
0CR4*	Replace/Buccal Mucosa
0CR5*	Replace/Upr Gingiva
0CR6*	Replace/Lwr Gingiva
0CR7*	Replace/Tongue
0CRN*	Replace/Uvula
0CS0*	Repos/Upr Lip
0CS1*	Repos/Lwr Lip
0CS7*	Repos/Tongue
0CSN*	Repos/Uvula
0CT0*	Resect/Upr Lip
0CT1*	Resect/Lwr Lip
0CT3*	Resect/Soft Palate
0CTN*	Resect/Uvula
0CU0*	Supl/Upr Lip
0CU1*	Supl/Lwr Lip
0CU4*	Supl/Buccal Mucosa
0CU5*	Supl/Upr Gingiva
0CU6*	Supl/Lwr Gingiva
0CU7*	Supl/Tongue
0CUN*	Supl/Uvula
0CWY37Z	Rev of Autol Sub in Mouth/Throat, Perc Appr
0CWY[0,3][0,1,D,J,K]Z	Rev/Mouth and Throat, [Opn, Perc], [Drain Dev, Radioact Elmt, Intralum Dev, Synth Sub, Nonauto Tissue Sub], NQ
0CX*	Mouth and Throat, Transfer
0J910ZZ	Drain of Face SQ/Fascia, Opn Appr
0J91[0,3]0Z	Drain/SQ Tissue & Fascia, Face, [Opn, Perc], Drain Dev, NQ
0NNX*	Rls/Hyoid Bone
0W92[0,3,4][0,Z]Z	Drain/Face, [Opn, Perc, Perc Endo], [Drain Dev, No Dev], NQ
0W93[0,3,4][0,Z]Z	Drain/Oral Cavity and Throat, [Opn, Perc, Perc Endo], [Drain Dev, No Dev], NQ
0W94[0,3,4][0,Z]Z	Drain/Upr Jaw, [Opn, Perc, Perc Endo], [Drain Dev, No Dev], NQ
0W95[0,3,4][0,Z]Z	Drain/Lwr Jaw, [Opn, Perc, Perc Endo], [Drain Dev, No Dev], NQ
0WC3[0,3,4]ZZ	Extir/Oral Cavity and Throat, [Opn, Perc, Perc Endo]
0WF3[0,3,4]ZZ	Fragmn/Oral Cavity and Throat, [Opn, Perc, Perc Endo]
0WH3[0,3,4][3,Y]Z	Insert/Oral Cavity and Throat, [Opn, Perc, Perc Endo], [Inf Dev, Oth Dev], NQ

DRG 138   Mouth Procedures without CC/MCC
GMLOS 2.0   AMLOS 2.5   RW 0.8272

Select operating room procedures listed under DRG 137

DRG 139   Salivary Gland Procedures
GMLOS 1.6   AMLOS 2.2   RW 0.9828

Operating Room Procedures

0C58*	Destr/Parotid Gland, Rt
0C59*	Destr/Parotid Gland, Lt
0C5B*	Destr/Parotid Duct, Rt
0C5C*	Destr/Parotid Duct, Lt
0C5D*	Destr/Sublingual Gland, Rt
0C5F*	Destr/Sublingual Gland, Lt
0C5G*	Destr/Submaxillary Gland, Rt
0C5H*	Destr/Submaxillary Gland, Lt
0C5J*	Destr/Minor Salivary Gland
0C9J0ZX	Drain of Minor Salivary Gland, Opn Appr, Diagnostic
0C9[8,9]0ZX	Drain of [Rt, Lt] Parotid Gland, Opn Appr, Dx
0C9[B,C]0ZX	Drain of [Rt, Lt] Parotid Duct, Opn Appr, Dx
0C9[D,F]0ZX	Drain of [Rt, Lt] Sublingual Gland, Opn Appr, Dx
0C9[G,H]0ZX	Drain of [Rt, Lt] Submaxillary Gland, Opn Appr, Dx
0CB80ZX	Exc of Rt Parotid Gland, Opn Appr, Diagnostic
0CB8[0,3]ZZ	Exc/Parotid Gland, Rt, [Opn, Perc]
0CB90ZX	Exc of Lt Parotid Gland, Opn Appr, Diagnostic
0CB9[0,3]ZZ	Exc/Parotid Gland, Lt, [Opn, Perc]
0CBB0ZX	Exc of Rt Parotid Duct, Opn Appr, Diagnostic
0CBB[0,3]ZZ	Exc/Parotid Duct, Rt, [Opn, Perc]
0CBC0ZX	Exc of Lt Parotid Duct, Opn Appr, Diagnostic
0CBC[0,3]ZZ	Exc/Parotid Duct, Lt, [Opn, Perc]
0CBD0ZX	Exc of Rt Sublingual Gland, Opn Appr, Diagn

Ⓣ **Transfer DRG**   ⓢ�ᴾ **Special Payment**   * **Code Range**   **6th and 7th Character of ZZ = No Device, No Qualifier ZX = No Device, Diagnostic**

ØCBD[Ø,3]ZZ	Exc/Sublingual Gland, Rt, [Opn, Perc]
ØCBFØZX	Exc of Lt Sublingual Gland, Opn Appr, Diagnostic
ØCBF[Ø,3]ZZ	Exc/Sublingual Gland, Lt, [Opn, Perc]
ØCBGØZX	Exc of Rt Submaxillary Gland, Opn Appr, Diagn
ØCBG[Ø,3]ZZ	Exc/Submaxillary Gland, Rt, [Opn, Perc]
ØCBHØZX	Exc of Lt Submaxillary Gland, Opn Appr, Diagn
ØCBH[Ø,3]ZZ	Exc/Submaxillary Gland, Lt, [Opn, Perc]
ØCBJØZX	Exc of Minor Salivary Gland, Opn Appr, Diagnostic
ØCBJ[Ø,3]ZZ	Exc/Minor Salivary Gland, [Opn, Perc]
ØCL*	Mouth and Throat, Occlsn
ØCN8*	Rls/Parotid Gland, Rt
ØCN9*	Rls/Parotid Gland, Lt
ØCNB*	Rls/Parotid Duct, Rt
ØCNC*	Rls/Parotid Duct, Lt
ØCND*	Rls/Sublingual Gland, Rt
ØCNF*	Rls/Sublingual Gland, Lt
ØCNG*	Rls/Submaxillary Gland, Rt
ØCNH*	Rls/Submaxillary Gland, Lt
ØCNJ*	Rls/Minor Salivary Gland
ØCQ8*	Repair/Parotid Gland, Rt
ØCQ9*	Repair/Parotid Gland, Lt
ØCQB*	Repair/Parotid Duct, Rt
ØCQC*	Repair/Parotid Duct, Lt
ØCQD*	Repair/Sublingual Gland, Rt
ØCQF*	Repair/Sublingual Gland, Lt
ØCQG*	Repair/Submaxillary Gland, Rt
ØCQH*	Repair/Submaxillary Gland, Lt
ØCQJ*	Repair/Minor Salivary Gland
ØCRB*	Replace/Parotid Duct, Rt
ØCRC*	Replace/Parotid Duct, Lt
ØCSB*	Repos/Parotid Duct, Rt
ØCSC*	Repos/Parotid Duct, Lt
ØCTJØZZ	Resect of Minor Salivary Gland, Opn Appr
ØCT[8,9]ØZZ	Resect of [Rt, Lt] Parotid Gland, Opn Appr
ØCT[B,C]ØZZ	Resect of [Rt, Lt] Parotid Duct, Opn Appr
ØCT[D,F]ØZZ	Resect of [Rt, Lt] Sublingual Gland, Opn Appr
ØCT[G,H]ØZZ	Resect of [Rt, Lt] Submaxillary Gland, Opn Appr
ØCV*	Mouth and Throat, Restrict

MEDICAL

DRG 146   Ear, Nose, Mouth and Throat Malignancy with MCC
GMLOS 5.7   AMLOS 8.0   RW 1.8740

Principal Diagnosis

C00*	Malig neoplasm of lip
C01	Malig neoplasm of base of tongue
C02*	Malig neoplasm of oth and unsp parts of tongue
C03*	Malig neoplasm of gum
C04*	Malig neoplasm of floor of mouth
C05*	Malig neoplasm of palate
C06*	Malig neoplasm of oth and unsp parts of mouth
C07	Malig neoplasm of parotid gland
C08*	Malig neoplasm of oth and unsp major salivary glands
C09*	Malig neoplasm of tonsil
C10*	Malig neoplasm of oropharynx
C11*	Malig neoplasm of nasopharynx
C12	Malig neoplasm of pyriform sinus
C13*	Malig neoplasm of hypopharynx
C14*	Malig neoplasm of sites in the lip, oral cavity and pharynx
C30*	Malig neoplasm of nasal cavity and mid ear
C31*	Malig neoplasm of accessory sinuses
C32*	Malig neoplasm of larynx
C39.Ø	Malig neoplasm of upr respiratory tract, part unsp
C46.2	Kaposi's sarcoma of palate
C76.Ø	Malig neoplasm of head, face and neck
D00.0*	Carcinoma in situ of lip, oral cavity and pharynx
D02.0	Carcinoma in situ of larynx
D37.0*	Neoplasm of uncertain behav of lip, oral cavity and pharynx
D38.0	Neoplasm of uncertain behav of larynx

DRG 147   Ear, Nose, Mouth and Throat Malignancy with CC
GMLOS 3.9   AMLOS 5.2   RW 1.2419

Select principal diagnosis listed under DRG 146

DRG 148   Ear, Nose, Mouth and Throat Malignancy without CC/MCC
GMLOS 2.2   AMLOS 2.8   RW 0.8094

Select principal diagnosis listed under DRG 146

DRG 149   Dysequilibrium
GMLOS 2.1   AMLOS 2.5   RW 0.6707

Principal Diagnosis

H81*	D/o of vestibular function
H82*	Vertiginous syndromes in dz classified elsw
H83.0*	Labyrinthitis
H83.2*	Labyrinthine dysfunction
H83.8*	Oth spec dz of inner ear
H83.9*	Unsp dz of inner ear
R42	Dizziness and giddiness
T75.3XXA	Motion sickness, init enc

DRG 150   Epistaxis with MCC
GMLOS 3.6   AMLOS 4.7   RW 1.2560

Principal Diagnosis

R04.0	Epistaxis

DRG 151   Epistaxis without MCC
GMLOS 2.3   AMLOS 2.8   RW 0.7033

Select principal diagnosis listed under DRG 150

DRG 152   Otitis Media and Upr Respiratory Infection with MCC
GMLOS 3.4   AMLOS 4.3   RW 1.0612

Principal Diagnosis

A54.5	Gonococcal pharyngitis
A56.4	Chlamydial infxn of pharynx
A69.1	Oth Vincent's infections
B05.3	Measles complicated by otitis media
B08.5	Enteroviral vesicular pharyngitis
H61.00[1,2,3,9]	Unsp perichondritis of [rt, lt, bilat, unsp] ext ear
H65*	Nonsuppurative otitis media
H66*	Suppurative and unsp otitis media
H67*	Otitis media in dz classified elsw
H68.0*	Eustachian salpingitis
H70.0*	Acute mastoiditis
H70.1*	Chr mastoiditis
H70.2*	Petrositis
H70.9*	Unsp mastoiditis
H73.0*	Acute myringitis
H73.1*	Chr myringitis
H73.2*	Unsp myringitis
J00	Acute nasopharyngitis [common cold]
J01*	Acute sinusitis
J02*	Acute pharyngitis
J03*	Acute tonsillitis
J04.0	Acute laryngitis
J04.2	Acute laryngotracheitis
J04.3*	Supraglottitis, unsp
J05*	Acute obstructive laryngitis [croup] and epiglottitis
J06*	Acute upr resp infections of multi and unsp sites
J11.1	Flu d/t unidentified flu virus w oth resp manifest
J30*	Vasomotor and allergic rhinitis
J31*	Chr rhinitis, nasopharyngitis and pharyngitis
J32*	Chr sinusitis
J35.0*	Chr tonsillitis and adenoiditis
J36	Peritonsillar abscess
J37*	Chr laryngitis and laryngotracheitis
J39.0	Retropharyngeal and parapharyngeal abscess
J39.1	Oth abscess of pharynx
J39.3	Upr respiratory tract hypersensitivity reaction, site unsp
J39.9	Dz of upr respiratory tract, unsp
T70.0XXA	Otitic barotrauma, init enc
T70.1XXA	Sinus barotrauma, init enc

DRG 153   Otitis Media and Upper Respiratory Infection without MCC
GMLOS 2.5   AMLOS 3.0   RW 0.7042

Select principal diagnosis listed under DRG 152

Surgical	Medical	CC Indicator	MCC Indicator	Procedure Proxy	PDxMCC PDx acts as own MCC	PDxCC PDx acts as own CC

MDC 3: Diseases And Disorders Of The Ear, Nose, Mouth And Throat—MEDICAL

DRG 154 Other Ear, Nose, Mouth and Throat Diagnoses with MCC
GMLOS 4.0   AMLOS 5.4   RW 1.4090

Principal Diagnosis

A18.6	Tuberculosis of (inner) (mid) ear
A36.0	Pharyngeal diphtheria
A36.1	Nasopharyngeal diphtheria
A36.2	Laryngeal diphtheria
A66.5	Gangosa
B00.1	Herpesviral vesicular dermatitis
B37.84	Candidal otitis externa
D10.4	Benign neoplasm of tonsil
D10.5	Benign neoplasm of oth parts of oropharynx
D10.6	Benign neoplasm of nasopharynx
D10.7	Benign neoplasm of hypopharynx
D10.9	Benign neoplasm of pharynx, unsp
D11*	Benign neoplasm of major salivary glands
D14.0	Benign neoplasm of mid ear, nasl cav and accessory sinuses
D14.1	Benign neoplasm of larynx
G47.30	Sleep apnea, unsp
G47.33	Obstructive sleep apnea (adult) (pediatric)
G47.34	Idio sleep related nonobstructive alveolar hypoventilation
G47.36	Sleep related hypoventilation in conditions classd elsw
G47.39	Oth sleep apnea
G47.50	Parasomnia, unsp
G47.52	REM sleep behav d/o
G47.54	Parasomnia in conditions classified elsw
G47.59	Oth parasomnia
G47.63	Sleep related bruxism
G47.69	Oth sleep related movement d/o
G47.8	Oth sleep d/o
H60*	Otitis externa
H61.1*	Noninfective d/o of pinna
H61.2*	Impacted cerumen
H61.3*	Acquired stenosis of ext ear canal
H61.8*	Oth spec d/o of ext ear
H61.9*	D/o of ext ear, unsp
H62*	D/o of ext ear in dz classified elsw
H68.1*	Obstruction of Eustachian tube
H69*	Oth and unsp d/o of Eustachian tube
H70.8*	Oth mastoiditis and related conditions
H71*	Cholesteatoma of mid ear
H72*	Perforation of tympanic membrane
H73.8*	Oth spec d/o of tympanic membrane
H73.9*	Unsp d/o of tympanic membrane
H74*	Oth d/o of mid ear mastoid
H75*	Oth d/o of mid ear and mastoid in dz classd elsw
H80*	Otosclerosis
H83.1*	Labyrinthine fistula
H83.3*	Noise effects on inner ear
H90*	Conductive and sensorineural hearing loss
H91*	Oth and unsp hearing loss
H92*	Otalgia and effusion of ear
H93.0*	Degenerative and vascular d/o of ear
H93.1*	Tinnitus
H93.21[1,2,3,9]	Auditory recruitment, [rt, lt, bilat, unsp] ear
H93.22[1,2,3,9]	Diplacusis, [rt, lt, bilat, unsp] ear
H93.23[1,2,3,9]	Hyperacusis, [rt, lt, bilat, unsp] ear
H93.24[1,2,3,9]	Temporary auditory threshold shift, [rt, lt, bilat, unsp] ear
H93.29[1,2,3,9]	Oth abnormal auditory perceptions, [rt, lt, bilat, unsp] ear
H93.3*	D/o of acoustic nerve
H93.8*	Oth spec d/o of ear
H93.9*	Unsp d/o of ear
H94*	Oth d/o of ear in dz classified elsw
H95.0*	Recurrent cholesteatoma of postmastoidectomy cavity
H95.1*	Oth d/o of ear/mastd following mastoidectomy
J33*	Nasal polyp
J34*	Oth and unsp d/o of nose and nasal sinuses
J35.1	Hypertrophy of tonsils
J35.2	Hypertrophy of adenoids
J35.3	Hypertrophy of tonsils with hypertrophy of adenoids
J35.8	Oth chr dz of tonsils and adenoids
J35.9	Chr dz of tonsils and adenoids, unsp
J38*	Dz of vocal cords and larynx, NEC
J39.2	Oth dz of pharynx
K11*	Dz of salivary glands
M95.0	Acquired deformity of nose
M95.1*	Cauliflwr ear
Q16*	Congenital malform of ear causing impairment of hearing
Q17*	Oth congenital malformations of ear

Q18.0	Sinus, fistula and cyst of branchial cleft
Q18.1	Preauricular sinus and cyst
Q18.2	Oth branchial cleft malformations
Q18.8	Oth spec congenital malformations of face and neck
Q30*	Congenital malformations of nose
Q31*	Congenital malformations of larynx
Q32*	Congenital malformations of trachea and bronchus
Q38.4	Congenital malformations of salivary glands and ducts
Q38.7	Congenital pharyngeal pouch
Q38.8	Oth congenital malformations of pharynx
R04.1	Hemor from throat
R06.5	Mouth breathing
R06.7	Sneezing
R07.0	Pain in throat
R09.81	Nasal congestion
R09.82	Postnasal drip
R19.6	Halitosis
R49*	Voice and resonance d/o
R68.2	Dry mouth, unsp
R94.120	Abnormal auditory function study
R94.121	Abnormal vestibular function study
S01.20XA	Unsp opn wnd of nose, init enc
S01.25XA	Opn bite of nose, init enc
S01.2[1,2]XA	Lac [w/o, w/] FB of nose, init enc
S01.2[3,4]XA	Punc wnd [w/o, w/] FB of nose, init enc
S01.3[0,1,2,3,4,5][1,2,9]A	[Unsp opn wnd, Lac w/o FB, Lac w/ FB, Punc wnd w/o FB, Punc wnd w/ FB, Opn bite] of [rt, lt, unsp] ear, init enc
S02.2XX[A,B]	Fx of nasal bones, init enc for [clsd, opn] fx
S04.6[0,1,2]XA	Inj of acoustic nerve, [unsp, rt, lt] side, init enc
S08.11[1,2,9]A	Complete traum amp of [rt, lt, unsp] ear, init enc
S08.121A	Partial Traum amp of rt ear, init enc
S08.122A	Partial Traum amp of lt ear, init enc
S08.129A	Partial Traum amp of unsp ear, init enc
S08.81[1,2]A	[Complete, Partial] traum amp of nose, init enc
S09.2[0,1,2]XA	Traum rupture of [unsp, rt, lt] ear drum, init enc
S09.30[1,2,9]A	Unsp inj of [rt, lt, unsp] mid and inner ear, init enc
S09.31[1,2,3,9]A	Primary blast inj of [rt, lt, bilat, unsp] ear, init enc
S09.39[1,2,9]A	Oth spec inj of [rt, lt, unsp] mid and inner ear, init enc
S09.91XA	Unsp inj of ear, init enc
S11.015A	Opn bite of larynx, init enc
S11.019A	Unsp opn wnd of larynx, init enc
S11.01[1,2]A	Lac [w/o, w/] FB of larynx, init enc
S11.01[3,4]A	Punc wnd [w/o, w/] FB of larynx, init enc
S11.035A	Opn bite of vocal cord, init enc
S11.039A	Unsp opn wnd of vocal cord, init enc
S11.03[1,2]A	Lac [w/o, w/] FB of vocal cord, init enc
S11.03[3,4]A	Punc wnd [w/o, w/] FB of vocal cord, init enc
S11.20XA	Unsp opn wnd of pharynx and cervical esophagus, init
S11.25XA	Opn bite of pharynx and cervical esophagus, init enc
S11.2[1,2]XA	Lac [w/o, w/] FB of pharynx and cervical esophagus, init enc
S11.2[3,4]XA	Punc wnd [w/o, w/] FB of pharynx and cervical esophagus, init enc
S12.8XXA	Fx of oth parts of neck, init enc
T16.1XXA	FB in rt ear, init enc
T16.2XXA	FB in lt ear, init enc
T16.9XXA	FB in ear, unsp ear, init enc
T17.0XXA	FB in nasal sinus, init enc
T17.1XXA	FB in nostril, init enc
T17.20[0,8]A	Unsp FB in pharynx causing [asphyxiation, oth inj], init enc
T17.21[0,8]A	Gastric contents in pharynx causing [asphyxiation, oth inj], init enc
T17.22[0,8]A	Food in pharynx causing [asphyxiation, oth inj], init enc
T17.29[0,8]A	Oth foreign object in pharynx causing [asphyxiation, oth inj], init enc
T17.30[0,8]A	Unsp FB in larynx causing [asphyxiation, oth inj], init enc
T17.31[0,8]A	Gastric contents in larynx causing [asphyxiation, oth inj], init enc
T17.32[0,8]A	Food in larynx causing [asphyxiation, oth inj], init enc
T17.39[0,8]A	Oth foreign object in larynx causing [asphyxiation, oth inj], init enc
T28.0XXA	Burn of mouth and pharynx, init enc
T28.5XXA	Corrosion of mouth and pharynx, init enc

DRG 155 Other Ear, Nose, Mouth and Throat Diagnoses with CC
GMLOS 3.1   AMLOS 3.8   RW 0.8733

Select principal diagnosis listed under DRG 154

Ⓣ **Transfer DRG**   ⓢ **Special Payment**   * **Code Range**   **6th and 7th Character of ZZ = No Device, No Qualifier ZX = No Device, Diagnostic**

DRG 156   **Other Ear, Nose, Mouth and Throat Diagnoses without CC/MCC**

         GMLOS 2.3   AMLOS 2.8   RW 0.6662

Select principal diagnosis listed under DRG 154

DRG 157   **Dental and Oral Diseases with MCC**

         GMLOS 4.5   AMLOS 6.1   RW 1.4949

Principal Diagnosis

Code	Description
A69.0	Necrotizing ulcerative stomatitis
B00.2	Herpesviral gingivostomatitis and pharyngotonsillitis
B37.0	Candidal stomatitis
B37.83	Candidal cheilitis
D10.0	Benign neoplasm of lip
D10.1	Benign neoplasm of tongue
D10.2	Benign neoplasm of floor of mouth
D10.3*	Oth and unsp parts of mouth
D16.5	Benign neoplasm of lwr jaw bone
K00*	D/o of tooth development and eruption
K01*	Embedded and impacted teeth
K02*	Dental caries
K03*	Oth dz of hard tissues of teeth
K04*	Dz of pulp and periapical tissues
K05*	Gingivitis and periodontal dz
K06*	Oth d/o of gingiva and edentulous alveolar ridge
K08*	Oth d/o of teeth and supporting structures
K09*	Cysts of oral region, NEC
K12*	Stomatitis and related lesions
K13*	Oth dz of lip and oral mucosa
K14*	Dz of tongue
M26*	Dentofacial anomalies [incl* malocclusion]
M27*	Oth dz of jaws
Q18.4	Macrostomia
Q18.5	Microstomia
Q18.6	Macrocheilia
Q18.7	Microcheilia
Q35*	Cleft palate
Q36*	Cleft lip
Q37*	Cleft palate with cleft lip
Q38.0	Congenital malformations of lips, NEC
Q38.1	Ankyloglossia
Q38.2	Macroglossia
Q38.3	Oth congenital malformations of tongue
Q38.6	Oth congenital malformations of mouth
R68.84	Jaw pain
S01.50[1,2]A	Unsp opn wnd of [lip, oral cavity] init enc
S01.51[1,2]A	Lac w/o FB of [lip, oral cavity] init enc
S01.52[1,2]A	Lac w/ FB of [lip, oral cavity] init enc
S01.53[1,2]A	Punc wnd w/o FB of [lip, oral cavity] init enc
S01.54[1,2]A	Punc wnd w/ FB of [lip, oral cavity] init enc
S01.55[1,2]A	Opn bite of [lip, oral cavity], init enc
S02.400[A,B]	Malar fx unsp, init enc for [clsd, opn] fx
S02.401[A,B]	Maxillary fx, unsp, init enc for [clsd, opn] fx
S02.402[A,B]	Zygomatic fx, unsp, init enc for [clsd, opn] fx
S02.411[A,B]	LeFort I fx, init enc for [clsd, opn] fx
S02.412[A,B]	LeFort II fx, init enc for [clsd, opn] fx
S02.413[A,B]	LeFort III fx, init enc for [clsd, opn] fx
S02.5XX[A,B]	Fx of tooth (traum), init enc for [clsd, opn] fx
S02.600[A,B]	Fx of unsp part of body of mandible, init enc for [clsd, opn] fx
S02.609[A,B]	Fx of mandible, unsp, init enc for [clsd, opn] fx
S02.61X[A,B]	Fx of condylar process of mandible, init enc for [clsd, opn] fx
S02.62X[A,B]	Fx of subcondylar process of mandible, init enc for [clsd, opn] fx
S02.63X[A,B]	Fx of coronoid process of mandible, init enc for [clsd, opn] fx
S02.64X[A,B]	Fx of ramus of mandible, init enc for [clsd, opn] fx
S02.65X[A,B]	Fx of angle of mandible, init enc for [clsd, opn] fx
S02.66X[A,B]	Fx of symphysis of mandible, init enc for [clsd, opn] fx
S02.67X[A,B]	Fx of alveolus of mandible, init enc for [clsd, opn] fx
S02.69X[A,B]	Fx of mandible of oth spec site, init enc for [clsd, opn] fx
S03.0XXA	Disloc of jaw, init enc
S03.2XXA	Disloc of tooth, init enc
S03.4XXA	Sprain of jaw, init enc
T18.0XXA	FB in mouth, init enc

DRG 158   **Dental and Oral Diseases with CC**

         GMLOS 3.0   AMLOS 3.8   RW 0.8582

Select principal diagnosis listed under DRG 157

DRG 159   **Dental and Oral Diseases without CC/MCC**

         GMLOS 2.1   AMLOS 2.6   RW 0.6176

Select principal diagnosis listed under DRG 157

MDC 3: Diseases And Disorders Of The Ear, Nose, Mouth And Throat—MEDICAL

Surgical   Medical   CC Indicator   MCC Indicator   Procedure Proxy   **PDxMCC** PDx acts as own MCC   **PDxCC** PDx acts as own CC

MDC 4
Diseases And Disorders Of The Respiratory System

SURGICAL

DRG 163 Major Chest Procedures with MCC
GMLOS 10.5   AMLOS 12.8   RW 5.0016   [T]

Operating Room Procedures

Code	Description
025N*	Destr/Pericardium
025P*	Destr/Pulmn Trunk
025Q*	Destr/Pulmn Artery, Rt
025R*	Destr/Pulmn Artery, Lt
025S*	Destr/Pulmn Vein, Rt
025T*	Destr/Pulmn Vein, Lt
025V*	Destr/Superior Vena Cava
025W*	Destr/Thoracic Aorta
02BN*	Exc/Pericardium
02BP[0,3,4]ZZ	Exc/Pulmn Trunk, [Opn, Perc, Perc Endo]
02BQ[0,3,4]ZZ	Exc/Pulmn Artery, Rt, [Opn, Perc, Perc Endo]
02BR[0,3,4]ZZ	Exc/Pulmn Artery, Lt, [Opn, Perc, Perc Endo]
02BS[0,3,4]ZZ	Exc/Pulmn Vein, Rt, [Opn, Perc, Perc Endo]
02BT[0,3,4]ZZ	Exc/Pulmn Vein, Lt, [Opn, Perc, Perc Endo]
02BV[0,3,4]ZZ	Exc/Superior Vena Cava, [Opn, Perc, Perc Endo]
02BW3ZZ	Exc of Thoracic Aorta, Perc Appr
02CN*	Extir/Pericardium
02CP*	Extir/Pulmn Trunk
02CQ*	Extir/Pulmn Artery, Rt
02CR*	Extir/Pulmn Artery, Lt
02CS*	Extir/Pulmn Vein, Rt
02CT*	Extir/Pulmn Vein, Lt
02CV*	Extir/Superior Vena Cava
02HN[0,3,4][0,2]Z	Insert/Pericardium, [Opn, Perc, Perc Endo], [Monitoring Dev, Pressure Sensor, Monitoring Dev], NQ
02JA0ZZ	Inspect of Heart, Opn Appr
02JY0ZZ	Inspect of Great Vessel, Opn Appr
02NN*	Rls/Pericardium
02QA0ZZ	Repair Heart, Opn Appr
02RP*	Replace/Pulmn Trunk
02RQ*	Replace/Pulmn Artery, Rt
02RR*	Replace/Pulmn Artery, Lt
02RS*	Replace/Pulmn Vein, Rt
02RT*	Replace/Pulmn Vein, Lt
02RV*	Replace/Superior Vena Cava
02RW*	Replace/Thoracic Aorta
02TN*	Resect/Pericardium
0350*	Destr/Int Mammary Artery, Rt
0351*	Destr/Int Mammary Artery, Lt
0352*	Destr/Innominate Artery
0353*	Destr/Subclavian Artery, Rt
0354*	Destr/Subclavian Artery, Lt
03B0[0,3,4]ZZ	Exc/Int Mammary Artery, Rt, [Opn, Perc, Perc Endo]
03B1[0,3,4]ZZ	Exc/Int Mammary Artery, Lt, [Opn, Perc, Perc Endo]
03B2[0,3,4]ZZ	Exc/Innominate Artery, [Opn, Perc, Perc Endo]
03B3[0,3,4]ZZ	Exc/Subclavian Artery, Rt, [Opn, Perc, Perc Endo]
03B4[0,3,4]ZZ	Exc/Subclavian Artery, Lt, [Opn, Perc, Perc Endo]
03C0*	Extir/Int Mammary Artery, Rt
03C1*	Extir/Int Mammary Artery, Lt
03C2*	Extir/Innominate Artery
03C3*	Extir/Subclavian Artery, Rt
03C4*	Extir/Subclavian Artery, Lt
03L2*	Occlsn/Innominate Artery
03L3*	Occlsn/Subclavian Artery, Rt
03L4*	Occlsn/Subclavian Artery, Lt
03R0*	Replace/Int Mammary Artery, Rt
03R1*	Replace/Int Mammary Artery, Lt
03R2*	Replace/Innominate Artery
03R3*	Replace/Subclavian Artery, Rt
03R4*	Replace/Subclavian Artery, Lt
0550*	Destr/Azygos Vein
0551*	Destr/Hemiazygos Vein
0553*	Destr/Innominate Vein, Rt
0554*	Destr/Innominate Vein, Lt
0555*	Destr/Subclavian Vein, Rt
0556*	Destr/Subclavian Vein, Lt
05B0[0,3,4]ZZ	Exc/Azygos Vein, [Opn, Perc, Perc Endo]
05B1[0,3,4]ZZ	Exc/Hemiazygos Vein, [Opn, Perc, Perc Endo]
05B3[0,3,4]ZZ	Exc/Innominate Vein, Rt, [Opn, Perc, Perc Endo]
05B4[0,3,4]ZZ	Exc/Innominate Vein, Lt, [Opn, Perc, Perc Endo]
05B5[0,3,4]ZZ	Exc/Subclavian Vein, Rt, [Opn, Perc, Perc Endo]
05B6[0,3,4]ZZ	Exc/Subclavian Vein, Lt, [Opn, Perc, Perc Endo]
05C0*	Extir/Azygos Vein
05C1*	Extir/Hemiazygos Vein
05C3*	Extir/Innominate Vein, Rt
05C4*	Extir/Innominate Vein, Lt
05C5*	Extir/Subclavian Vein, Rt
05C6*	Extir/Subclavian Vein, Lt
05L3*	Occlsn/Innominate Vein, Rt
05L4*	Occlsn/Innominate Vein, Lt
05L5*	Occlsn/Subclavian Vein, Rt
05L6*	Occlsn/Subclavian Vein, Lt
05R0*	Replace/Azygos Vein
05R1*	Replace/Hemiazygos Vein
05R3*	Replace/Innominate Vein, Rt
05R4*	Replace/Innominate Vein, Lt
05R5*	Replace/Subclavian Vein, Rt
05R6*	Replace/Subclavian Vein, Lt
075K*	Destr/Thoracic Duct
075L*	Destr/Cisterna Chyli
075M*	Destr/Thymus
079K[0,3,4][0,Z]Z	Drain/Thoracic Duct, [Opn, Perc, Perc Endo], [Drain Dev, No Dev], NQ
079L[0,3,4][0,Z]Z	Drain/Cisterna Chyli, [Opn, Perc, Perc Endo], [Drain Dev, No Dev], NQ
079M*	Drain/Thymus
07B8[0,3,4]ZZ	Exc/Lymphatic, Int Mammary, Rt, [Opn, Perc, Perc Endo]
07B9[0,3,4]ZZ	Exc/Lymphatic, Int Mammary, Lt, [Opn, Perc, Perc Endo]
07BK[0,3,4]ZZ	Exc/Thoracic Duct, [Opn, Perc, Perc Endo]
07BL[0,3,4]ZZ	Exc/Cisterna Chyli, [Opn, Perc, Perc Endo]
07BM*	Exc/Thymus
07CM*	Extir/Thymus
07JM[0,4]ZZ	Inspect/Thymus, [Opn, Perc Endo]
07LK*	Occlsn/Thoracic Duct
07LL*	Occlsn/Cisterna Chyli
07NK*	Rls/Thoracic Duct
07NL*	Rls/Cisterna Chyli
07NM*	Rls/Thymus
07PK[0,3,4][0,3,C,D]Z	Rmvl/Thoracic Duct, [Opn, Perc, Perc Endo], [Drain Dev, Inf Dev, Extralum Dev, Intralum Dev], NQ
07PL[0,3,4][0,3,C,D]Z	Rmvl/Cisterna Chyli, [Opn, Perc, Perc Endo], [Drain Dev, Inf Dev, Extralum Dev, Intralum Dev], NQ
07PM[0,3,4][0,3]Z	Rmvl/Thymus, [Opn, Perc, Perc Endo], [Drain Dev, Inf Dev], NQ
07QK*	Repair/Thoracic Duct
07QL*	Repair/Cisterna Chyli
07QM*	Repair/Thymus
07SM0ZZ	Repos Thymus, Opn Appr
07TD*	Resect/Lymphatic, Aortic
07TK*	Resect/Thoracic Duct
07TL*	Resect/Cisterna Chyli
07TM*	Resect/Thymus
07UK*	Supl/Thoracic Duct
07UL*	Supl/Cisterna Chyli
07VK*	Restrict/Thoracic Duct
07VL*	Restrict/Cisterna Chyli
07WK[0,3,4][0,3,C,D]Z	Rev/Thoracic Duct, [Opn, Perc, Perc Endo], [Drain Dev, Inf Dev, Extralum Dev, Intralum Dev], NQ
07WL[0,3,4][0,3,C,D]Z	Rev/Cisterna Chyli, [Opn, Perc, Perc Endo], [Drain Dev, Inf Dev, Extralum Dev, Intralum Dev], NQ
07WM[0,3,4][0,3]Z	Rev/Thymus, [Opn, Perc, Perc Endo], [Drain Dev, Inf Dev], NQ
07YM*	Transplantation/Thymus
0B53[0,3,7,8]ZZ	Destr/Main Bronchus, Rt, [Opn, Perc, Via Natrl or Artfcl Opng, Via Natrl or Artfcl Opng Endo]
0B54[0,3,7,8]ZZ	Destr/Upr Lobe Bronchus, Rt, [Opn, Perc, Via Natrl or Artfcl Opng, Via Natrl or Artfcl Opng Endo]
0B55[0,3,7,8]ZZ	Destr/Mid Lobe Bronchus, Rt, [Opn, Perc, Via Natrl or Artfcl Opng, Via Natrl or Artfcl Opng Endo]
0B56[0,3,7,8]ZZ	Destr/Lwr Lobe Bronchus, Rt, [Opn, Perc, Via Natrl or Artfcl Opng, Via Natrl or Artfcl Opng Endo]
0B57[0,3,7,8]ZZ	Destr/Main Bronchus, Lt, [Opn, Perc, Via Natrl or Artfcl Opng, Via Natrl or Artfcl Opng Endo]

[T] **Transfer DRG**   [SP] **Special Payment**   * **Code Range**   6th and 7th Character of ZZ = No Device, No QUALIFIER ZX = No Device, Diagnostic

0B58[0,3,7,8]ZZ	Destr/Upr Lobe Bronchus, Lt, [Opn, Perc, Via Natrl or Artfcl Opng, Via Natrl or Artfcl Opng Endo]
0B59[0,3,7,8]ZZ	Destr/Lingula Bronchus, [Opn, Perc, Via Natrl or Artfcl Opng, Via Natrl or Artfcl Opng Endo]
0B5B[0,3,7,8]ZZ	Destr/Lwr Lobe Bronchus, Lt, [Opn, Perc, Via Natrl or Artfcl Opng, Via Natrl or Artfcl Opng Endo]
0B5C[0,4,7]ZZ	Destr/Upr Lung Lobe, Rt, [Opn, Perc Endo, Via Natrl or Artfcl Opng]
0B5D[0,4,7]ZZ	Destr/Mid Lung Lobe, Rt, [Opn, Perc Endo, Via Natrl or Artfcl Opng]
0B5F[0,4,7]ZZ	Destr/Lwr Lung Lobe, Rt, [Opn, Perc Endo, Via Natrl or Artfcl Opng]
0B5G[0,4,7]ZZ	Destr/Upr Lung Lobe, Lt, [Opn, Perc Endo, Via Natrl or Artfcl Opng]
0B5H[0,4,7]ZZ	Destr/Lung Lingula, [Opn, Perc Endo, Via Natrl or Artfcl Opng]
0B5J[0,4,7]ZZ	Destr/Lwr Lung Lobe, Lt, [Opn, Perc Endo, Via Natrl or Artfcl Opng]
0B5K[0,4,7]ZZ	Destr/Lung, Rt, [Opn, Perc Endo, Via Natrl or Artfcl Opng]
0B5L[0,4,7]ZZ	Destr/Lung, Lt, [Opn, Perc Endo, Via Natrl or Artfcl Opng]
0B5M[0,4,7]ZZ	Destr/Lungs, Bilat, [Opn, Perc Endo, Via Natrl or Artfcl Opng]
0B5N*	Destr/Pleura, Rt
0B5P*	Destr/Pleura, Lt
0B5R*	Destr/Diaphragm, Rt
0B5S*	Destr/Diaphragm, Lt
0B930ZX	Drain of Rt Main Bronchus, Opn Appr, Diagnostic
0B93[0,3,4,7,8][0,Z]Z	Drain/Main Bronchus, Rt, [Opn, Perc, Perc Endo, Via Natrl or Artfcl Opng, Via Natrl or Artfcl Opng Endo], [Drain Dev, No Dev], NQ
0B940ZX	Drain of Rt Upr Lobe Bronchus, Opn Appr, Diagn
0B94[0,3,4,7,8][0,Z]Z	Drain/Upr Lobe Bronchus, Rt, [Opn, Perc, Perc Endo, Via Natrl or Artfcl Opng, Via Natrl or Artfcl Opng Endo], [Drain Dev, No Dev], NQ
0B950ZX	Drain of Rt Mid Lobe Bronchus, Opn Appr, Diagn
0B95[0,3,4,7,8][0,Z]Z	Drain/Mid Lobe Bronchus, Rt, [Opn, Perc, Perc Endo, Via Natrl or Artfcl Opng, Via Natrl or Artfcl Opng Endo], [Drain Dev, No Dev], NQ
0B960ZX	Drain of Rt Lwr Lobe Bronchus, Opn Appr, Diagn
0B96[0,3,4,7,8][0,Z]Z	Drain/Lwr Lobe Bronchus, Rt, [Opn, Perc, Perc Endo, Via Natrl or Artfcl Opng, Via Natrl or Artfcl Opng Endo], [Drain Dev, No Dev], NQ
0B970ZX	Drain of Lt Main Bronchus, Opn Appr, Diagnostic
0B97[0,3,4,7,8][0,Z]Z	Drain/Main Bronchus, Lt, [Opn, Perc, Perc Endo, Via Natrl or Artfcl Opng, Via Natrl or Artfcl Opng Endo], [Drain Dev, No Dev], NQ
0B980ZX	Drain of Lt Upr Lobe Bronchus, Opn Appr, Diagn
0B98[0,3,4,7,8][0,Z]Z	Drain/Upr Lobe Bronchus, Lt, [Opn, Perc, Perc Endo, Via Natrl or Artfcl Opng, Via Natrl or Artfcl Opng Endo], [Drain Dev, No Dev], NQ
0B990ZX	Drain of Lingula Bronchus, Opn Appr, Diagnostic
0B99[0,3,4,7,8][0,Z]Z	Drain/Lingula Bronchus, [Opn, Perc, Perc Endo, Via Natrl or Artfcl Opng, Via Natrl or Artfcl Opng Endo], [Drain Dev, No Dev], NQ
0B9B0ZX	Drain of Lt Lwr Lobe Bronchus, Opn Appr, Diagn
0B9B[0,3,4,7,8][0,Z]Z	Drain/Lwr Lobe Bronchus, Lt, [Opn, Perc, Perc Endo, Via Natrl or Artfcl Opng, Via Natrl or Artfcl Opng Endo], [Drain Dev, No Dev], NQ
0B9C0ZX	Drain of Rt Upr Lung Lobe, Opn Appr, Diagnostic
0B9C0[0,Z]Z	Drain/Upr Lung Lobe, Rt, Opn, [Drain Dev, No Dev], NQ
0B9D0ZX	Drain of Rt Mid Lung Lobe, Opn Appr, Diagn
0B9D0[0,Z]Z	Drain/Mid Lung Lobe, Rt, Opn, [Drain Dev, No Dev], NQ
0B9F0ZX	Drain of Rt Lwr Lung Lobe, Opn Appr, Diagnostic
0B9F0[0,Z]Z	Drain/Lwr Lung Lobe, Rt, Opn, [Drain Dev, No Dev], NQ
0B9G0ZX	Drain of Lt Upr Lung Lobe, Opn Appr, Diagnostic
0B9G0[0,Z]Z	Drain/Upr Lung Lobe, Lt, Opn, [Drain Dev, No Dev], NQ
0B9H0ZX	Drain of Lung Lingula, Opn Appr, Diagnostic
0B9H0[0,Z]Z	Drain/Lung Lingula, Opn, [Drain Dev, No Dev], NQ
0B9J0ZX	Drain of Lt Lwr Lung Lobe, Opn Appr, Diagnostic
0B9J0[0,Z]Z	Drain/Lwr Lung Lobe, Lt, Opn, [Drain Dev, No Dev], NQ
0B9K0ZX	Drain of Rt Lung, Opn Appr, Diagnostic
0B9K0[0,Z]Z	Drain/Lung, Rt, Opn, [Drain Dev, No Dev], NQ
0B9L0ZX	Drain of Lt Lung, Opn Appr, Diagnostic
0B9L0[0,Z]Z	Drain/Lung, Lt, Opn, [Drain Dev, No Dev], NQ
0B9M0ZX	Drain of Bilat Lungs, Opn Appr, Diagnostic
0B9M0[0,Z]Z	Drain/Lungs, Bilat, Opn, [Drain Dev, No Dev], NQ
0B9R*	Drain/Diaphragm, Rt
0B9S*	Drain/Diaphragm, Lt
0BB30ZX	Exc of Rt Main Bronchus, Opn Appr, Diagnostic
0BB3[0,3,7]ZZ	Exc/Main Bronchus, Rt, [Opn, Perc, Via Natrl or Artfcl Opng]
0BB40ZX	Exc of Rt Upr Lobe Bronchus, Opn Appr, Diagn

0BB4[0,3,7]ZZ	Exc/Upr Lobe Bronchus, Rt, [Opn, Perc, Via Natrl or Artfcl Opng]
0BB50ZX	Exc of Rt Mid Lobe Bronchus, Opn Appr, Diagn
0BB5[0,3,7]ZZ	Exc/Mid Lobe Bronchus, Rt, [Opn, Perc, Via Natrl or Artfcl Opng]
0BB60ZX	Exc of Rt Lwr Lobe Bronchus, Opn Appr, Diagn
0BB6[0,3,7]ZZ	Exc/Lwr Lobe Bronchus, Rt, [Opn, Perc, Via Natrl or Artfcl Opng]
0BB70ZX	Exc of Lt Main Bronchus, Opn Appr, Diagnostic
0BB7[0,3,7]ZZ	Exc/Main Bronchus, Lt, [Opn, Perc, Via Natrl or Artfcl Opng]
0BB80ZX	Exc of Lt Upr Lobe Bronchus, Opn Appr, Diagn
0BB8[0,3,7]ZZ	Exc/Upr Lobe Bronchus, Lt, [Opn, Perc, Via Natrl or Artfcl Opng]
0BB90ZX	Exc of Lingula Bronchus, Opn Appr, Diagnostic
0BB9[0,3,7]ZZ	Exc/Lingula Bronchus, [Opn, Perc, Via Natrl or Artfcl Opng]
0BBB0ZX	Exc of Lt Lwr Lobe Bronchus, Opn Appr, Diagn
0BBB[0,3,7]ZZ	Exc/Lwr Lobe Bronchus, Lt, [Opn, Perc, Via Natrl or Artfcl Opng]
0BBC0ZX	Exc of Rt Upr Lung Lobe, Opn Appr, Diagnostic
0BBC[0,3,4,7]ZZ	Exc/Upr Lung Lobe, Rt, [Opn, Perc, Perc Endo, Via Natrl or Artfcl Opng]
0BBD0ZX	Exc of Rt Mid Lung Lobe, Opn Appr, Diagn
0BBD[0,3,4,7]ZZ	Exc/Mid Lung Lobe, Rt, [Opn, Perc, Perc Endo, Via Natrl or Artfcl Opng]
0BBF0ZX	Exc of Rt Lwr Lung Lobe, Opn Appr, Diagnostic
0BBF[0,3,4,7]ZZ	Exc/Lwr Lung Lobe, Rt, [Opn, Perc, Perc Endo, Via Natrl or Artfcl Opng]
0BBG0ZX	Exc of Lt Upr Lung Lobe, Opn Appr, Diagnostic
0BBG[0,3,4,7]ZZ	Exc/Upr Lung Lobe, Lt, [Opn, Perc, Perc Endo, Via Natrl or Artfcl Opng]
0BBH0ZX	Exc of Lung Lingula, Opn Appr, Diagnostic
0BBH[0,3,4,7]ZZ	Exc/Lung Lingula, [Opn, Perc, Perc Endo, Via Natrl or Artfcl Opng]
0BBJ0ZX	Exc of Lt Lwr Lung Lobe, Opn Appr, Diagnostic
0BBJ[0,3,4,7]ZZ	Exc/Lwr Lung Lobe, Lt, [Opn, Perc, Perc Endo, Via Natrl or Artfcl Opng]
0BBK0ZX	Exc of Rt Lung, Opn Appr, Diagnostic
0BBK[0,3,4,7]ZZ	Exc/Lung, Rt, [Opn, Perc, Perc Endo, Via Natrl or Artfcl Opng]
0BBL0ZX	Exc of Lt Lung, Opn Appr, Diagnostic
0BBL[0,3,4,7]ZZ	Exc/Lung, Lt, [Opn, Perc, Perc Endo, Via Natrl or Artfcl Opng]
0BBM0ZX	Exc of Bilat Lungs, Opn Appr, Diagnostic
0BBM[0,3,7]ZZ	Exc/Lungs, Bilat, [Opn, Perc, Via Natrl or Artfcl Opng]
0BBN[0,3,4]ZZ	Exc/Pleura, Rt, [Opn, Perc, Perc Endo]
0BBP[0,3,4]ZZ	Exc/Pleura, Lt, [Opn, Perc, Perc Endo]
0BBR*	Exc/Diaphragm, Rt
0BBS*	Exc/Diaphragm, Lt
0BC3[0,3,4]ZZ	Extir/Main Bronchus, Rt, [Opn, Perc, Perc Endo]
0BC4[0,3,4]ZZ	Extir/Upr Lobe Bronchus, Rt, [Opn, Perc, Perc Endo]
0BC5[0,3,4]ZZ	Extir/Mid Lobe Bronchus, Rt, [Opn, Perc, Perc Endo]
0BC6[0,3,4]ZZ	Extir/Lwr Lobe Bronchus, Rt, [Opn, Perc, Perc Endo]
0BC7[0,3,4]ZZ	Extir/Main Bronchus, Lt, [Opn, Perc, Perc Endo]
0BC8[0,3,4]ZZ	Extir/Upr Lobe Bronchus, Lt, [Opn, Perc, Perc Endo]
0BC9[0,3,4]ZZ	Extir/Lingula Bronchus, [Opn, Perc, Perc Endo]
0BCB[0,3,4]ZZ	Extir/Lwr Lobe Bronchus, Lt, [Opn, Perc, Perc Endo]
0BCC*	Extir/Upr Lung Lobe, Rt
0BCD*	Extir/Mid Lung Lobe, Rt
0BCF*	Extir/Lwr Lung Lobe, Rt
0BCG*	Extir/Upr Lung Lobe, Lt
0BCH*	Extir/Lung Lingula
0BCJ*	Extir/Lwr Lung Lobe, Lt
0BCK*	Extir/Lung, Rt
0BCL*	Extir/Lung, Lt
0BCM*	Extir/Lungs, Bilat
0BCR*	Extir/Diaphragm, Rt
0BCS*	Extir/Diaphragm, Lt
0BD*	Respiratory Sys, Extract
0BF1[0,3,4,7,8]ZZ	Fragmn/Trachea, [Opn, Perc, Perc Endo, Via Natrl or Artfcl Opng, Via Natrl or Artfcl Opng Endo]
0BF2[0,3,4,7,8]ZZ	Fragmn/Carina, [Opn, Perc, Perc Endo, Via Natrl or Artfcl Opng, Via Natrl or Artfcl Opng Endo]
0BF3[0,3,4,7,8]ZZ	Fragmn/Main Bronchus, Rt, [Opn, Perc, Perc Endo, Via Natrl or Artfcl Opng, Via Natrl or Artfcl Opng Endo]
0BF4[0,3,4,7,8]ZZ	Fragmn/Upr Lobe Bronchus, Rt, [Opn, Perc, Perc Endo, Via Natrl or Artfcl Opng, Via Natrl or Artfcl Opng Endo]
0BF5[0,3,4,7,8]ZZ	Fragmn/Mid Lobe Bronchus, Rt, [Opn, Perc, Perc Endo, Via Natrl or Artfcl Opng, Via Natrl or Artfcl Opng Endo]
0BF6[0,3,4,7,8]ZZ	Fragmn/Lwr Lobe Bronchus, Rt, [Opn, Perc, Perc Endo, Via Natrl or Artfcl Opng, Via Natrl or Artfcl Opng Endo]
0BF7[0,3,4,7,8]ZZ	Fragmn/Main Bronchus, Lt, [Opn, Perc, Perc Endo, Via Natrl or Artfcl Opng, Via Natrl or Artfcl Opng Endo]

Surgical　　**Medical**　　**CC Indicator**　　**MCC Indicator**　　**Procedure Proxy**　　PDxMCC **PDx acts as own MCC**　　PDxCC **PDx acts as own CC**

© 2015 Optum360, LLC　　　　MS-DRG Version 33.0　　　　**61**

MDC 4: Diseases And Disorders Of The Respiratory System—SURGICAL

ØBF8[Ø,3,4,7,8]ZZ	Fragmn/Upr Lobe Bronchus, Lt, [Opn, Perc, Perc Endo, Via Natrl or Artfcl Opng, Via Natrl or Artfcl Opng Endo]
ØBF9[Ø,3,4,7,8]ZZ	Fragmn/Lingula Bronchus, [Opn, Perc, Perc Endo, Via Natrl or Artfcl Opng, Via Natrl or Artfcl Opng Endo]
ØBFB[Ø,3,4,7,8]ZZ	Fragmn/Lwr Lobe Bronchus, Lt, [Opn, Perc, Perc Endo, Via Natrl or Artfcl Opng, Via Natrl or Artfcl Opng Endo]
ØBHØ[Ø,3,4][2,3,D]Z	Insert/Tracheobronchial Tree, [Opn, Perc, Perc Endo], [Monitoring Dev, Inf Dev, Intralum Dev], NQ
ØBH3[Ø,3,4,7]GZ	Insert/Main Bronchus, Rt, [Opn, Perc, Perc Endo, Via Natrl or Artfcl Opng], Endobronchial Valve, NQ
ØBH4[Ø,3,4,7]GZ	Insert/Upr Lobe Bronchus, Rt, [Opn, Perc, Perc Endo, Via Natrl or Artfcl Opng], Endobronchial Valve, NQ
ØBH5[Ø,3,4,7]GZ	Insert/Mid Lobe Bronchus, Rt, [Opn, Perc, Perc Endo, Via Natrl or Artfcl Opng], Endobronchial Valve, NQ
ØBH6[Ø,3,4,7]GZ	Insert/Lwr Lobe Bronchus, Rt, [Opn, Perc, Perc Endo, Via Natrl or Artfcl Opng], Endobronchial Valve, NQ
ØBH7[Ø,3,4,7]GZ	Insert/Main Bronchus, Lt, [Opn, Perc, Perc Endo, Via Natrl or Artfcl Opng], Endobronchial Valve, NQ
ØBH8[Ø,3,4,7]GZ	Insert/Upr Lobe Bronchus, Lt, [Opn, Perc, Perc Endo, Via Natrl or Artfcl Opng], Endobronchial Valve, NQ
ØBH9[Ø,3,4,7]GZ	Insert/Lingula Bronchus, [Opn, Perc, Perc Endo, Via Natrl or Artfcl Opng], Endobronchial Valve, NQ
ØBHB[Ø,3,4,7]GZ	Insert/Lwr Lobe Bronchus, Lt, [Opn, Perc, Perc Endo, Via Natrl or Artfcl Opng], Endobronchial Valve, NQ
ØBHK[Ø,3,4,7,8][2,3]Z	Insert/Lung, Rt, [Opn, Perc, Perc Endo, Via Natrl or Artfcl Opng, Via Natrl or Artfcl Opng Endo], [Monitoring Dev, Inf Dev], NQ
ØBHL[Ø,3,4,7,8][2,3]Z	Insert/Lung, Lt, [Opn, Perc, Perc Endo, Via Natrl or Artfcl Opng, Via Natrl or Artfcl Opng Endo], [Monitoring Dev, Inf Dev], NQ
ØBHR*	Insert/Diaphragm, Rt
ØBHS*	Insert/Diaphragm, Lt
ØBL3*	Occlsn/Main Bronchus, Rt
ØBL4*	Occlsn/Upr Lobe Bronchus, Rt
ØBL5*	Occlsn/Mid Lobe Bronchus, Rt
ØBL6*	Occlsn/Lwr Lobe Bronchus, Rt
ØBL7*	Occlsn/Main Bronchus, Lt
ØBL8*	Occlsn/Upr Lobe Bronchus, Lt
ØBL9*	Occlsn/Lingula Bronchus
ØBLB*	Occlsn/Lwr Lobe Bronchus, Lt
ØBM*	Respiratory Sys, Reattach
ØBN3*	Rls/Main Bronchus, Rt
ØBN4*	Rls/Upr Lobe Bronchus, Rt
ØBN5*	Rls/Mid Lobe Bronchus, Rt
ØBN6*	Rls/Lwr Lobe Bronchus, Rt
ØBN7*	Rls/Main Bronchus, Lt
ØBN8*	Rls/Upr Lobe Bronchus, Lt
ØBN9*	Rls/Lingula Bronchus
ØBNB*	Rls/Lwr Lobe Bronchus, Lt
ØBNC*	Rls/Upr Lung Lobe, Rt
ØBND*	Rls/Mid Lung Lobe, Rt
ØBNF*	Rls/Lwr Lung Lobe, Rt
ØBNG*	Rls/Upr Lung Lobe, Lt
ØBNH*	Rls/Lung Lingula
ØBNJ*	Rls/Lwr Lung Lobe, Lt
ØBNK*	Rls/Lung, Rt
ØBNL*	Rls/Lung, Lt
ØBNM*	Rls/Lungs, Bilat
ØBNR*	Rls/Diaphragm, Rt
ØBNS*	Rls/Diaphragm, Lt
ØBP07[Ø,1,2,D]Z	Rmvl/Tracheobronchial Tree, Via Natrl or Artfcl Opng, [Drain Dev, Radioact Elmt, Monitoring Dev, Intralum Dev], NQ
ØBP08[Ø,1,2,D]Z	Rmvl/Tracheobronchial Tree, Via Natrl or Artfcl Opng Endo, [Drain Dev, Radioact Elmt, Monitoring Dev, Intralum Dev], NQ
ØBPØ[Ø,3,4][Ø,1,2,C,D,J,K]Z	Rmvl/Tracheobronchial Tree, [Opn, Perc, Perc Endo], [Drain Dev, Radioact Elmt, Monitoring Dev, Extralum Dev, Intralum Dev, Synth Sub, Nonauto Tissue Sub], NQ
ØBPK[Ø,3,4,7,8][Ø,1,2,3]Z	Rmvl/Lung, Rt, [Opn, Perc, Perc Endo, Via Natrl or Artfcl Opng, Via Natrl or Artfcl Opng Endo], [Drain Dev, Radioact Elmt, Monitoring Dev, Inf Dev], NQ
ØBPL[Ø,3,4,7,8][Ø,1,2,3]Z	Rmvl/Lung, Lt, [Opn, Perc, Perc Endo, Via Natrl or Artfcl Opng, Via Natrl or Artfcl Opng Endo], [Drain Dev, Radioact Elmt, Monitoring Dev, Inf Dev], NQ
ØBPT[Ø,3,4,7,8][Ø,2,7,J,K,M]Z	Rmvl/Diaphragm, [Opn, Perc, Perc Endo, Via Natrl or Artfcl Opng, Via Natrl or Artfcl Opng Endo], [Drain Dev, Monitoring Dev, Auto Tissue Sub, Synth Sub, Nonauto Tissue Sub, Diaphragmatic Pacemaker Lead], NQ
ØBQ*	Respiratory Sys, Repair
ØBS*	Respiratory Sys, Repos
ØBT1*	Resect/Trachea
ØBT2*	Resect/Carina
ØBT3*	Resect/Main Bronchus, Rt
ØBT4*	Resect/Upr Lobe Bronchus, Rt
ØBT5*	Resect/Mid Lobe Bronchus, Rt
ØBT6*	Resect/Lwr Lobe Bronchus, Rt
ØBT7*	Resect/Main Bronchus, Lt
ØBT8*	Resect/Upr Lobe Bronchus, Lt
ØBT9*	Resect/Lingula Bronchus
ØBTB*	Resect/Lwr Lobe Bronchus, Lt
ØBTC*	Resect/Upr Lung Lobe, Rt
ØBTD*	Resect/Mid Lung Lobe, Rt
ØBTF*	Resect/Lwr Lung Lobe, Rt
ØBTG*	Resect/Upr Lung Lobe, Lt
ØBTH*	Resect/Lung Lingula
ØBTJ*	Resect/Lwr Lung Lobe, Lt
ØBTK*	Resect/Lung, Rt
ØBTL*	Resect/Lung, Lt
ØBTM*	Resect/Lungs, Bilat
ØBU*	Respiratory Sys, Supl
ØBV*	Respiratory Sys, Restrict
ØBW07[Ø,2,D]Z	Rev/Tracheobronchial Tree, Via Natrl or Artfcl Opng, [Drain Dev, Monitoring Dev, Intralum Dev], NQ
ØBW08[Ø,2,D]Z	Rev/Tracheobronchial Tree, Via Natrl or Artfcl Opng Endo, [Drain Dev, Monitoring Dev, Intralum Dev], NQ
ØBWØ[Ø,3,4][Ø,2,C,D,J,K]Z	Rev/Tracheobronchial Tree, [Opn, Perc, Perc Endo], [Drain Dev, Monitoring Dev, Extralum Dev, Intralum Dev, Synth Sub, Nonauto Tissue Sub], NQ
ØBWK[Ø,3,4,7,8][Ø,2,3]Z	Rev/Lung, Rt, [Opn, Perc, Perc Endo, Via Natrl or Artfcl Opng, Via Natrl or Artfcl Opng Endo], [Drain Dev, Monitoring Dev, Inf Dev], NQ
ØBWL[Ø,3,4,7,8][Ø,2,3]Z	Rev/Lung, Lt, [Opn, Perc, Perc Endo, Via Natrl or Artfcl Opng, Via Natrl or Artfcl Opng Endo], [Drain Dev, Monitoring Dev, Inf Dev], NQ
ØBWT[Ø,3,4,7,8][Ø,2,7,J,K,M]Z	Rev/Diaphragm, [Opn, Perc, Perc Endo, Via Natrl or Artfcl Opng, Via Natrl or Artfcl Opng Endo], [Drain Dev, Monitoring Dev, Auto Tissue Sub, Synth Sub, Nonauto Tissue Sub, Diaphragmatic Pacemaker Lead], NQ
ØDQ5*	Repair/Esophagus
ØW33[7,8,X]ZZ	Control/Oral Cavity and Throat, [Via Natrl or Artfcl Opng, Via Natrl or Artfcl Opng Endo, Ext]
ØW38*	Control/Chest Wall
ØW39*	Control/Pleural Cavity, Rt
ØW3B*	Control/Pleural Cavity, Lt
ØW3D*	Control/Pericardial Cavity
ØW3Q*	Control/Respiratory Tract
ØW9DØZX	Drain of Pericardial Cavity, Opn Appr, Diagnostic
ØW9DØ[Ø,Z]Z	Drain/Pericardial Cavity, Opn, [Drain Dev, No Dev], NQ
ØWBC[Ø,3,4]ZZ	Exc/Mediastinum, [Opn, Perc, Perc Endo]
ØWCD[Ø,3,4]ZZ	Extir/Pericardial Cavity, [Opn, Perc, Perc Endo]
ØWHD[Ø,3,4][3,Y]Z	Insert/Pericardial Cavity, [Opn, Perc, Perc Endo], [Inf Dev, Oth Dev], NQ
ØWJ90ZZ	Inspect of Rt Pleural Cavity, Opn Appr
ØWJB0ZZ	Inspect of Lt Pleural Cavity, Opn Appr
ØWJC0ZZ	Inspect of Mediastinum, Opn Appr
ØWJQ0ZZ	Inspect of Respiratory Tract, Opn Appr
ØWPD[Ø,3,4][Ø,1,3,Y]Z	Rmvl/Pericardial Cavity, [Opn, Perc, Perc Endo], [Drain Dev, Radioact Elmt, Inf Dev, Oth Dev], NQ
ØWU8*	Supl/Chest Wall
ØWWD[Ø,3,4][Ø,1,3,Y]Z	Rev/Pericardial Cavity, [Opn, Perc, Perc Endo], [Drain Dev, Radioact Elmt, Inf Dev, Oth Dev], NQ
DØY6KZZ	Laser Interstitial Thermal Therapy of Spinal Cord
DØY7KZZ	Laser Interstitial Thermal Therapy of Peripheral Nerve
DBYØKZZ	Laser Interstitial Thermal Therapy of Trachea
DBY1KZZ	Laser Interstitial Thermal Therapy of Bronchus
DBY2KZZ	Laser Interstitial Thermal Therapy of Lung
DBY5KZZ	Laser Interstitial Thermal Therapy of Pleura
DBY6KZZ	Laser Interstitial Thermal Therapy of Mediastinum
DBY7KZZ	Laser Interstitial Thermal Therapy of Chest Wall
DBY8KZZ	Laser Interstitial Thermal Therapy of Diaphragm
DDYØKZZ	Laser Interstitial Thermal Therapy of Esophagus
DDY1KZZ	Laser Interstitial Thermal Therapy of Stomach
DDY2KZZ	Laser Interstitial Thermal Therapy of Duodenum
DDY3KZZ	Laser Interstitial Thermal Therapy of Jejunum
DDY4KZZ	Laser Interstitial Thermal Therapy of Ileum
DDY5KZZ	Laser Interstitial Thermal Therapy of Colon
DDY7KZZ	Laser Interstitial Thermal Therapy of Rectum
DDY8KZZ	Laser Interstitial Thermal Therapy of Anus
DFY1KZZ	Laser Interstitial Thermal Therapy of Gallbladder
DFY2KZZ	Laser Interstitial Thermal Therapy of Bile Ducts
DFY3KZZ	Laser Interstitial Thermal Therapy of Pancreas

[T] **Transfer DRG**   [SP] **Special Payment**   *** Code Range**   **6th and 7th Character of ZZ = No Device, No Qualifier ZX = No Device, Diagnostic**

DGY2KZZ	Laser Interstitial Thermal Therapy of Adrenal Glands
DMY0KZZ	Laser Interstitial Thermal Therapy of Lt Breast
DMY1KZZ	Laser Interstitial Thermal Therapy of Rt Breast
DVY0KZZ	Laser Interstitial Thermal Therapy of Prostate

DRG 164 Major Chest Procedures with CC
GMLOS 5.3   AMLOS 6.4   RW 2.5822   [T]

Select operating room procedures listed under DRG 163

DRG 165 Major Chest Procedures without CC/MCC
GMLOS 3.1   AMLOS 3.8   RW 1.8148   [T]

Select operating room procedures listed under DRG 163

DRG 166 Other Respiratory System O.R. Procedures with MCC
GMLOS 8.5   AMLOS 10.9   RW 3.6796   [T]

Operating Room Procedures

0008Q*	Div/Vagus Nerve
02HV[0,3,4][2,D]Z	Insert/Superior Vena Cava, [Opn, Perc, Perc Endo], [Monitoring Dev, Intralum Dev], NQ
02J[A,Y]4ZZ	Inspect of [Heart, Great Vessel], Perc Endo Appr
02LV*	Occlsn/Superior Vena Cava
02QP*	Repair/Pulmn Trunk
02QQ*	Repair/Pulmn Artery, Rt
02QR*	Repair/Pulmn Artery, Lt
02QW*	Repair/Thoracic Aorta
02VV*	Restrict/Superior Vena Cava
03150[9,A,J,K,Z]0	Bypass/Axillary Artery, Rt, Opn, [Auto Venous Tissue, Auto Arterial Tissue, Synth Sub, Nonauto Tissue Sub, No Dev], Upr Arm Artery, Rt
03160[9,A,J,K,Z]1	Bypass/Axillary Artery, Lt, Opn, [Auto Venous Tissue, Auto Arterial Tissue, Synth Sub, Nonauto Tissue Sub, No Dev], Upr Arm Artery, Lt
031H0[9,A,J,K,Z]J	Bypass Rt Common Carotid Artery, Opn, to Rt Extracranial Artery [Auto Venous Tissue, Auto Arterial Tissue, Synth Sub, Nonauto Tissue Sub, NQ]
031J0[9,A,J,K,Z]K	Bypass Lt Common Carotid Artery, Opn, to Lt Extracranial Artery [Auto Venous Tissue, Auto Arterial Tissue, Synth Sub, Nonauto Tissue Sub, NQ]
031K0[9,A,J,K,Z]J	Bypass Rt Int Carotid Artery, Opn, to Rt Extracranial Artery [Auto Venous Tissue, Auto Arterial Tissue, Synth Sub, Nonauto Tissue Sub, NQ]
031L0[9,A,J,K,Z]K	Bypass Lt Int Carotid Artery, Opn, to Lt Extracranial Artery [Auto Venous Tissue, Auto Arterial Tissue, Synth Sub, Nonauto Tissue Sub, NQ]
031M0[9,A,J,K,Z]J	Bypass Rt Ext Carotid Artery, Opn, to Rt Extracranial Artery [Auto Venous Tissue, Auto Arterial Tissue, Synth Sub, Nonauto Tissue Sub, NQ]
031N0[9,A,J,K,Z]K	Bypass Lt Ext Carotid Artery, Opn, to Lt Extracranial Artery [Auto Venous Tissue, Auto Arterial Tissue, Synth Sub, Nonauto Tissue Sub, NQ]
03733[4,D,Z]Z	Dilation/Subclavian Artery, Rt, Perc, [Drug-eluting Intralum Dev, Intralum Dev, No Dev], NQ
03743[4,D,Z]Z	Dilation/Subclavian Artery, Lt, Perc, [Drug-eluting Intralum Dev, Intralum Dev, No Dev], NQ
03773[4,D,Z]Z	Dilation/Brachial Artery, Rt, Perc, [Drug-eluting Intralum Dev, Intralum Dev, No Dev], NQ
03783[4,D,Z]Z	Dilation/Brachial Artery, Lt, Perc, [Drug-eluting Intralum Dev, Intralum Dev, No Dev], NQ
03793[4,D,Z]Z	Dilation/Ulnar Artery, Rt, Perc, [Drug-eluting Intralum Dev, Intralum Dev, No Dev], NQ
037A3[4,D,Z]Z	Dilation/Ulnar Artery, Lt, Perc, [Drug-eluting Intralum Dev, Intralum Dev, No Dev], NQ
037Y3[4,D,Z]Z	Dilation/Upr Artery, Perc, [Drug-eluting Intralum Dev, Intralum Dev, No Dev], NQ
039S[0,3,4]ZX	Drain/Temporal Artery, Rt, [Opn, Perc, Perc Endo]
039T[0,3,4]ZX	Drain/Temporal Artery, Lt, [Opn, Perc, Perc Endo]
03BS[0,3,4]ZX	Exc/Temporal Artery, Rt, [Opn, Perc, Perc Endo]
03BT[0,3,4]ZX	Exc/Temporal Artery, Lt, [Opn, Perc, Perc Endo]
03H0[0,3,4]DZ	Insert/Int Mammary Artery, Rt, [Opn, Perc, Perc Endo], Intralum Dev, NQ
03H1[0,3,4]DZ	Insert/Int Mammary Artery, Lt, [Opn, Perc, Perc Endo], Intralum Dev, NQ
03H3[0,3,4]DZ	Insert/Subclavian Artery, Rt, [Opn, Perc, Perc Endo], Intralum Dev, NQ
03H4[0,3,4]DZ	Insert/Subclavian Artery, Lt, [Opn, Perc, Perc Endo], Intralum Dev, NQ

03H5[0,3,4]DZ	Insert/Axillary Artery, Rt, [Opn, Perc, Perc Endo], Intralum Dev, NQ
03H6[0,3,4]DZ	Insert/Axillary Artery, Lt, [Opn, Perc, Perc Endo], Intralum Dev, NQ
03Q0*	Repair/Int Mammary Artery, Rt
03Q1*	Repair/Int Mammary Artery, Lt
03Q2*	Repair/Innominate Artery
03Q3*	Repair/Subclavian Artery, Rt
03Q4*	Repair/Subclavian Artery, Lt
041K[0,4][9,A,J,K,Z][H,J,K,L]	Bypass/Femor Artery, Rt, [Opn, Perc Endo], [Auto Venous Tissue, Auto Arterial Tissue, Synth Sub, Nonauto Tissue Sub, No Dev], [Femor Artery, Rt, Femor Artery, Lt, Femor Arteries, Bilat, Popliteal Artery]
041L[0,4][9,A,J,K,Z][H,J,K,L]	Bypass/Femor Artery, Lt, [Opn, Perc Endo], [Auto Venous Tissue, Auto Arterial Tissue, Synth Sub, Nonauto Tissue Sub, No Dev], [Femor Artery, Rt, Femor Artery, Lt, Femor Arteries, Bilat, Popliteal Artery]
04703[4,D,Z]Z	Dilation/Abd Aorta, Perc, [Drug-eluting Intralum Dev, Intralum Dev, No Dev], NQ
04713[4,D,Z]Z	Dilation/Celiac Artery, Perc, [Drug-eluting Intralum Dev, Intralum Dev, No Dev], NQ
04723[4,D,Z]Z	Dilation/Gastric Artery, Perc, [Drug-eluting Intralum Dev, Intralum Dev, No Dev], NQ
04733[4,D,Z]Z	Dilation/Hepatic Artery, Perc, [Drug-eluting Intralum Dev, Intralum Dev, No Dev], NQ
04743[4,D,Z]Z	Dilation/Splenic Artery, Perc, [Drug-eluting Intralum Dev, Intralum Dev, No Dev], NQ
04753[4,D,Z]Z	Dilation/Superior Mesenteric Artery, Perc, [Drug-eluting Intralum Dev, Intralum Dev, No Dev], NQ
04763[4,D,Z]Z	Dilation/Colic Artery, Rt, Perc, [Drug-eluting Intralum Dev, Intralum Dev, No Dev], NQ
04773[4,D,Z]Z	Dilation/Colic Artery, Lt, Perc, [Drug-eluting Intralum Dev, Intralum Dev, No Dev], NQ
04783[4,D,Z]Z	Dilation/Colic Artery, Mid, Perc, [Drug-eluting Intralum Dev, Intralum Dev, No Dev], NQ
04793[4,D,Z]Z	Dilation/Renal Artery, Rt, Perc, [Drug-eluting Intralum Dev, Intralum Dev, No Dev], NQ
047A3[4,D,Z]Z	Dilation/Renal Artery, Lt, Perc, [Drug-eluting Intralum Dev, Intralum Dev, No Dev], NQ
047B3[4,D,Z]Z	Dilation/Inferior Mesenteric Artery, Perc, [Drug-eluting Intralum Dev, Intralum Dev, No Dev], NQ
047C3[4,D,Z]Z	Dilation/Common Iliac Artery, Rt, Perc, [Drug-eluting Intralum Dev, Intralum Dev, No Dev], NQ
047D3[4,D,Z]Z	Dilation/Common Iliac Artery, Lt, Perc, [Drug-eluting Intralum Dev, Intralum Dev, No Dev], NQ
047E3[4,D,Z]Z	Dilation/Int Iliac Artery, Rt, Perc, [Drug-eluting Intralum Dev, Intralum Dev, No Dev], NQ
047F3[4,D,Z]Z	Dilation/Int Iliac Artery, Lt, Perc, [Drug-eluting Intralum Dev, Intralum Dev, No Dev], NQ
047H3[4,D,Z]Z	Dilation/Ext Iliac Artery, Rt, Perc, [Drug-eluting Intralum Dev, Intralum Dev, No Dev], NQ
047J3[4,D,Z]Z	Dilation/Ext Iliac Artery, Lt, Perc, [Drug-eluting Intralum Dev, Intralum Dev, No Dev], NQ
047K041	Dilation Rt Fem Art w Drug-elut Intralum, Drug Blln, Opn
047K0D1	Dilation Rt Fem Art w Intralum Dev, Drug Blln, Opn
047K0Z1	Dilation of Rt Fem Art using Drug Blln, Opn Appr
047K341	Dilation Rt Fem Art w Drug-elut Intralum, Drug Blln, Perc
047K3D1	Dilation Rt Fem Art w Intralum Dev, Drug Blln, Perc
047K3Z1	Dilation of Rt Fem Art using Drug Blln, Perc Appr
047K3[4,D,Z]Z	Dilation/Femor Artery, Rt, Perc, [Drug-eluting Intralum Dev, Intralum Dev, No Dev], NQ
047K441	Dilation Rt Fem Art w Drug-elut Intralum, Drug Blln, Perc Endo
047K4D1	Dilation Rt Fem Art w Intralum Dev, Drug Blln, Perc Endo
047K4Z1	Dilation of Rt Fem Art using Drug Blln, Perc Endo Appr
047L041	Dilation Lt Fem Art w Drug-elut Intralum, Drug Blln, Opn
047L0D1	Dilation Lt Fem Art w Intralum Dev, Drug Blln, Opn
047L0Z1	Dilation of Lt Fem Art using Drug Blln, Opn Appr
047L341	Dilation Lt Fem Art w Drug-elut Intralum, Drug Blln, Perc
047L3D1	Dilation Lt Fem Art w Intralum Dev, Drug Blln, Perc
047L3Z1	Dilation of Lt Fem Art using Drug Blln, Perc Appr
047L3[4,D,Z]Z	Dilation/Femor Artery, Lt, Perc, [Drug-eluting Intralum Dev, Intralum Dev, No Dev], NQ
047L441	Dilation Lt Fem Art w Drug-elut Intralum, Drug Blln, Perc Endo
047L4D1	Dilation Lt Fem Art w Intralum Dev, Drug Blln, Perc Endo
047L4Z1	Dilation of Lt Fem Art using Drug Blln, Perc Endo Appr
047M041	Dilation Rt Popl Art w Drug-elut Intralum, Drug Blln, Opn
047M0D1	Dilation Rt Popl Art w Intralum Dev, Drug Blln, Opn
047M0Z1	Dilation of Rt Popl Art using Drug Blln, Opn Appr
047M341	Dilation Rt Popl Art w Drug-elut Intralum, Drug Blln, Perc
047M3D1	Dilation Rt Popl Art w Intralum Dev, Drug Blln, Perc

Surgical	**Medical**	**CC Indicator**	**MCC Indicator**	**Procedure Proxy**	**PDxMCC** PDx acts as own MCC **PDxCC** PDx acts as own CC

MDC 4: Diseases And Disorders Of The Respiratory System—SURGICAL

047M3Z1	Dilation of Rt Popl Art using Drug Blln, Perc Appr
047M441	Dilation Rt Popl Art w Drug-elut Intralum, Drug Blln, Perc Endo
047M4D1	Dilation Rt Popl Art w Intralum Dev, Drug Blln, Perc Endo
047M4Z1	Dilation of Rt Popl Art using Drug Blln, Perc Endo Appr
047N041	Dilation Lt Popl Art w Drug-elut Intralum, Drug Blln, Opn
047N0D1	Dilation Lt Popl Art w Intralum Dev, Drug Blln, Opn
047N0Z1	Dilation of Lt Popl Art using Drug Blln, Opn Appr
047N341	Dilation Lt Popl Art w Drug-elut Intralum, Drug Blln, Perc
047N3D1	Dilation Lt Popl Art w Intralum Dev, Drug Blln, Perc
047N3Z1	Dilation of Lt Popl Art using Drug Blln, Perc Appr
047N441	Dilation Lt Popl Art w Drug-elut Intralum, Drug Blln, Perc Endo
047N4D1	Dilation Lt Popl Art w Intralum Dev, Drug Blln, Perc Endo
047N4Z1	Dilation of Lt Popl Art using Drug Blln, Perc Endo Appr
047Y3[4,D,Z]Z	Dilation/Lwr Artery, Perc, [Drug-eluting Intralum Dev, Intralum Dev, No Dev], NQ
05793[D,Z]Z	Dilation/Brachial Vein, Rt, Perc, [Intralum Dev, No Dev], NQ
057A3[D,Z]Z	Dilation/Brachial Vein, Lt, Perc, [Intralum Dev, No Dev], NQ
057B3[D,Z]Z	Dilation/Basilic Vein, Rt, Perc, [Intralum Dev, No Dev], NQ
057C3[D,Z]Z	Dilation/Basilic Vein, Lt, Perc, [Intralum Dev, No Dev], NQ
057D3[D,Z]Z	Dilation/Cephalic Vein, Rt, Perc, [Intralum Dev, No Dev], NQ
057F3[D,Z]Z	Dilation/Cephalic Vein, Lt, Perc, [Intralum Dev, No Dev], NQ
05H0[0,3,4]DZ	Insert/Azygos Vein, [Opn, Perc, Perc Endo], Intralum Dev, NQ
05H1[0,3,4]DZ	Insert/Hemiazygos Vein, [Opn, Perc, Perc Endo], Intralum Dev, NQ
05H3[0,3,4]DZ	Insert/Innominate Vein, Rt, [Opn, Perc, Perc Endo], Intralum Dev, NQ
05H4[0,3,4]DZ	Insert/Innominate Vein, Lt, [Opn, Perc, Perc Endo], Intralum Dev, NQ
05H5[0,3,4]DZ	Insert/Subclavian Vein, Rt, [Opn, Perc, Perc Endo], Intralum Dev, NQ
05H6[0,3,4]DZ	Insert/Subclavian Vein, Lt, [Opn, Perc, Perc Endo], Intralum Dev, NQ
05HY[0,3,4]DZ	Insert/Upr Vein, [Opn, Perc, Perc Endo], Intralum Dev, NQ
06703[D,Z]Z	Dilation/Inferior Vena Cava, Perc, [Intralum Dev, No Dev], NQ
06H0[0,3,4]DZ	Insert/Inferior Vena Cava, [Opn, Perc, Perc Endo], Intralum Dev, NQ
06HY[0,3,4]DZ	Insert/Lwr Vein, [Opn, Perc, Perc Endo], Intralum Dev, NQ
06L0*	Occlsn/Inferior Vena Cava
06V0*	Restrict/Inferior Vena Cava
0797[0,3,4]ZX	Drain/Lymphatic, Thorax, [Opn, Perc, Perc Endo]
079K[0,3,4]ZX	Drain/Thoracic Duct, [Opn, Perc, Perc Endo]
07B1[0,3,4]ZZ	Exc/Lymphatic, Rt Neck, [Opn, Perc, Perc Endo]
07B2[0,3,4]ZZ	Exc/Lymphatic, Lt Neck, [Opn, Perc, Perc Endo]
07B5[0,3,4]ZZ	Exc/Lymphatic, Rt Axillary, [Opn, Perc, Perc Endo]
07B6[0,3,4]ZZ	Exc/Lymphatic, Lt Axillary, [Opn, Perc, Perc Endo]
07B7[0,4]ZZ	Exc/Lymphatic, Thorax, [Opn, Perc Endo]
07BH[0,3,4]ZZ	Exc/Lymphatic, Rt Inguinal, [Opn, Perc, Perc Endo]
07BJ[0,3,4]ZZ	Exc/Lymphatic, Lt Inguinal, [Opn, Perc, Perc Endo]
07BK[0,3,4]ZX	Exc/Thoracic Duct, [Opn, Perc, Perc Endo]
07JP0ZZ	Inspect of Spleen, Opn Appr
07T0*	Resect/Lymphatic, Head
07T1*	Resect/Lymphatic, Rt Neck
07T2*	Resect/Lymphatic, Lt Neck
07T3*	Resect/Lymphatic, Rt Upr Extr
07T4*	Resect/Lymphatic, Lt Upr Extr
07T7*	Resect/Lymphatic, Thorax
07T8*	Resect/Lymphatic, Int Mammary, Rt
07T9*	Resect/Lymphatic, Int Mammary, Lt
07TB*	Resect/Lymphatic, Mesenteric
07TF*	Resect/Lymphatic, Rt Lwr Extr
07TG*	Resect/Lymphatic, Lt Lwr Extr
0B51*	Destr/Trachea
0B52*	Destr/Carina
0B5[C,D,F]3ZZ	Destr of Rt [Upr, Mid, Lwr] Lung Lobe, Perc Appr
0B5[G,H,J]3ZZ	Destr of [Lt Upr Lung Lobe, Lung Lingula, Lt Lwr Lung Lobe], Perc Appr
0B5[K,L,M]3ZZ	Destr of [Rt, Lt, Bilat] Lung, Perc Appr
0B71*	Dilation/Trachea
0B72*	Dilation/Carina
0B910ZX	Drain of Trachea, Opn Appr, Diagnostic
0B91[0,3,4,7,8][0,Z]Z	Drain/Trachea, [Opn, Perc, Perc Endo, Via Natrl or Artfcl Opng, Via Natrl or Artfcl Opng Endo], [Drain Dev, No Dev], NQ
0B920ZX	Drain of Carina, Opn Appr, Diagnostic
0B92[0,3,4,7,8][0,Z]Z	Drain/Carina, [Opn, Perc, Perc Endo, Via Natrl or Artfcl Opng, Via Natrl or Artfcl Opng Endo], [Drain Dev, No Dev], NQ
0B9C8ZX	Drain of Rt Upr Lung Lobe, Endo, Diagn
0B9C[3,4,7,8][0,Z]Z	Drain/Upr Lung Lobe, Rt, [Perc, Perc Endo, Via Natrl or Artfcl Opng, Via Natrl or Artfcl Opng Endo], [Drain Dev, No Dev], NQ
0B9D8ZX	Drain of Rt Mid Lung Lobe, Endo, Diagn
0B9D[3,4,7,8][0,Z]Z	Drain/Mid Lung Lobe, Rt, [Perc, Perc Endo, Via Natrl or Artfcl Opng, Via Natrl or Artfcl Opng Endo], [Drain Dev, No Dev], NQ
0B9F8ZX	Drain of Rt Lwr Lung Lobe, Endo, Diagn
0B9F[3,4,7,8][0,Z]Z	Drain/Lwr Lung Lobe, Rt, [Perc, Perc Endo, Via Natrl or Artfcl Opng, Via Natrl or Artfcl Opng Endo], [Drain Dev, No Dev], NQ
0B9G8ZX	Drain of Lt Upr Lung Lobe, Endo, Diagn
0B9G[3,4,7,8][0,Z]Z	Drain/Upr Lung Lobe, Lt, [Perc, Perc Endo, Via Natrl or Artfcl Opng, Via Natrl or Artfcl Opng Endo], [Drain Dev, No Dev], NQ
0B9H8ZX	Drain of Lung Lingula, Endo, Diagn
0B9H[3,4,7,8][0,Z]Z	Drain/Lung Lingula, [Perc, Perc Endo, Via Natrl or Artfcl Opng, Via Natrl or Artfcl Opng Endo], [Drain Dev, No Dev], NQ
0B9J8ZX	Drain of Lt Lwr Lung Lobe, Endo, Diagn
0B9J[3,4,7,8][0,Z]Z	Drain/Lwr Lung Lobe, Lt, [Perc, Perc Endo, Via Natrl or Artfcl Opng, Via Natrl or Artfcl Opng Endo], [Drain Dev, No Dev], NQ
0B9K8ZX	Drain of Rt Lung, Endo, Diagn
0B9K[3,4,7,8][0,Z]Z	Drain/Lung, Rt, [Perc, Perc Endo, Via Natrl or Artfcl Opng, Via Natrl or Artfcl Opng Endo], [Drain Dev, No Dev], NQ
0B9L8ZX	Drain of Lt Lung, Endo, Diagn
0B9L[3,4,7,8][0,Z]Z	Drain/Lung, Lt, [Perc, Perc Endo, Via Natrl or Artfcl Opng, Via Natrl or Artfcl Opng Endo], [Drain Dev, No Dev], NQ
0B9M8ZX	Drain of Bilat Lungs, Endo, Diagn
0B9M[3,4,7,8][0,Z]Z	Drain/Lungs, Bilat, [Perc, Perc Endo, Via Natrl or Artfcl Opng, Via Natrl or Artfcl Opng Endo], [Drain Dev, No Dev], NQ
0B9N4[0,Z]Z	Drain/Pleura, Rt, Perc Endo, [Drain Dev, No Dev], NQ
0B9P4[0,Z]Z	Drain/Pleura, Lt, Perc Endo, [Drain Dev, No Dev], NQ
0BB10ZX	Exc of Trachea, Opn Appr, Diagnostic
0BB1[0,3,4,7,8]ZZ	Exc/Trachea, [Opn, Perc, Perc Endo, Via Natrl or Artfcl Opng, Via Natrl or Artfcl Opng Endo]
0BB20ZX	Exc of Carina, Opn Appr, Diagnostic
0BB2[0,3,4,7,8]ZZ	Exc/Carina, [Opn, Perc, Perc Endo, Via Natrl or Artfcl Opng, Via Natrl or Artfcl Opng Endo]
0BBC[4,7,8]ZX	Exc/Upr Lung Lobe, Rt, [Perc Endo, Via Natrl or Artfcl Opng, Via Natrl or Artfcl Opng Endo]
0BBD[4,7,8]ZX	Exc/Mid Lung Lobe, Rt, [Perc Endo, Via Natrl or Artfcl Opng, Via Natrl or Artfcl Opng Endo]
0BBF[4,7,8]ZX	Exc/Lwr Lung Lobe, Rt, [Perc Endo, Via Natrl or Artfcl Opng, Via Natrl or Artfcl Opng Endo]
0BBG[4,7,8]ZX	Exc/Upr Lung Lobe, Lt, [Perc Endo, Via Natrl or Artfcl Opng, Via Natrl or Artfcl Opng Endo]
0BBH[4,7,8]ZX	Exc/Lung Lingula, [Perc Endo, Via Natrl or Artfcl Opng, Via Natrl or Artfcl Opng Endo]
0BBJ[4,7,8]ZX	Exc/Lwr Lung Lobe, Lt, [Perc Endo, Via Natrl or Artfcl Opng, Via Natrl or Artfcl Opng Endo]
0BBK[4,7,8]ZX	Exc/Lung, Rt, [Perc Endo, Via Natrl or Artfcl Opng, Via Natrl or Artfcl Opng Endo]
0BBL[4,7,8]ZX	Exc/Lung, Lt, [Perc Endo, Via Natrl or Artfcl Opng, Via Natrl or Artfcl Opng Endo]
0BBM[4,7,8]ZX	Exc/Lungs, Bilat, [Perc Endo, Via Natrl or Artfcl Opng Endo]
0BB[N,P]4ZX	Exc of [Rt, Lt] Pleura, Perc Endo Appr, Dx
0BC1[0,3,4]ZZ	Extir/Trachea, [Opn, Perc, Perc Endo]
0BC2[0,3,4]ZZ	Extir/Carina, [Opn, Perc, Perc Endo]
0BH0[0,3,4,7,8]1Z	Insert/Tracheobronchial Tree, [Opn, Perc, Perc Endo, Via Natrl or Artfcl Opng, Via Natrl or Artfcl Opng Endo], Radioact Elmt, NQ
0BH1[0,3,4,7,8]DZ	Insert/Trachea, [Opn, Perc, Perc Endo, Via Natrl or Artfcl Opng, Via Natrl or Artfcl Opng Endo], Intralum Dev, NQ
0BH1[0,7,8]2Z	Insert/Trachea, [Opn, Via Natrl or Artfcl Opng, Via Natrl or Artfcl Opng Endo], Monitoring Dev, NQ
0BHK[0,3,4,7,8]1Z	Insert/Lung, Rt, [Opn, Perc, Perc Endo, Via Natrl or Artfcl Opng, Via Natrl or Artfcl Opng Endo], Radioact Elmt, NQ
0BHL[0,3,4,7,8]1Z	Insert/Lung, Lt, [Opn, Perc, Perc Endo, Via Natrl or Artfcl Opng, Via Natrl or Artfcl Opng Endo], Radioact Elmt, NQ
0BJ0[0,3,4,7,X]ZZ	Inspect/Tracheobronchial Tree, [Opn, Perc, Perc Endo, Via Natrl or Artfcl Opng, Ext]
0BJ10ZZ	Inspect of Trachea, Opn Appr
0BJK[0,3,4,7,X]ZZ	Inspect/Lung, Rt, [Opn, Perc, Perc Endo, Via Natrl or Artfcl Opng, Ext]
0BJL[0,3,4,7,X]ZZ	Inspect/Lung, Lt, [Opn, Perc, Perc Endo, Via Natrl or Artfcl Opng, Ext]
0BJQ*	Inspect/Pleura
0BJT*	Inspect/Diaphragm
0BL1*	Occlsn/Trachea
0BL2*	Occlsn/Carina
0BN1*	Rls/Trachea
0BN2*	Rls/Carina
0BNN*	Rls/Pleura, Rt
0BNP*	Rls/Pleura, Lt
0BP00[3,7]Z	Rmvl/Tracheobronchial Tree, Opn, [Inf Dev, Auto Tissue Sub], NQ

T Transfer DRG   SP Special Payment   * Code Range   6th and 7th Character of ZZ = No Device, No Qualifier ZX = No Device, Diagnostic

64   MS-DRG Version 33.0   © 2015 Optum360, LLC

ØBP03[3,7]Z	Rmvl/Tracheobronchial Tree, Perc, [Inf Dev, Auto Tissue Sub], NQ
ØBP04[3,7]Z	Rmvl/Tracheobronchial Tree, Perc Endo, [Inf Dev, Auto Tissue Sub], NQ
ØBPØ[7,8][3,7,C,J,K]Z	Rmvl/Tracheobronchial Tree, [Via Natrl or Artfcl Opng, Via Natrl or Artfcl Opng Endo], [Inf Dev, Auto Tissue Sub, Extralum Dev, Synth Sub, Nonauto Tissue Sub], NQ
ØBP1[0,3,4,7,8][0,2,7,C,D,F,J,K]Z	Rmvl/Trachea, [Opn, Perc, Perc Endo, Via Natrl or Artfcl Opng, Via Natrl or Artfcl Opng Endo], [Drain Dev, Monitoring Dev, Auto Tissue Sub, Extralum Dev, Intralum Dev, Tracheostomy Dev, Synth Sub, Nonauto Tissue Sub], NQ
ØBTR*	Resect/Diaphragm, Rt
ØBTS*	Resect/Diaphragm, Lt
ØBW00[3,7]Z	Rev/Tracheobronchial Tree, Opn, [Inf Dev, Auto Tissue Sub], NQ
ØBW03[3,7]Z	Rev/Tracheobronchial Tree, Perc, [Inf Dev, Auto Tissue Sub], NQ
ØBW04[3,7]Z	Rev/Tracheobronchial Tree, Perc Endo, [Inf Dev, Auto Tissue Sub], NQ
ØBWØ[7,8][3,7,C,J,K]Z	Rev/Tracheobronchial Tree, [Via Natrl or Artfcl Opng, Via Natrl or Artfcl Opng Endo], [Inf Dev, Auto Tissue Sub, Extralum Dev, Synth Sub, Nonauto Tissue Sub], NQ
ØBW1[0,3,4,7,8][0,2,7,C,D,F,J,K]Z	Rev/Trachea, [Opn, Perc, Perc Endo, Via Natrl or Artfcl Opng, Via Natrl or Artfcl Opng Endo], [Drain Dev, Monitoring Dev, Auto Tissue Sub, Extralum Dev, Intralum Dev, Tracheostomy Dev, Synth Sub, Nonauto Tissue Sub], NQ
ØC5R*	Destr/Epiglottis
ØC5S*	Destr/Larynx
ØC5T*	Destr/Vocal Cord, Rt
ØC5V*	Destr/Vocal Cord, Lt
ØC7S*	Dilation/Larynx
ØC9[R,S,T,V]ØZX	Drain of [Epiglottis, Larynx, Rt Vocal Cord, Lt Vocal Cord], Opn Appr, Dx
ØCBRØZX	Exc of Epiglottis, Opn Appr, Diagnostic
ØCBR[0,3,4,7,8]ZZ	Exc/Epiglottis, [Opn, Perc, Perc Endo, Via Natrl or Artfcl Opng, Via Natrl or Artfcl Opng Endo]
ØCBSØZX	Exc of Larynx, Opn Appr, Diagnostic
ØCBS[0,3,4,7,8]ZZ	Exc/Larynx, [Opn, Perc, Perc Endo, Via Natrl or Artfcl Opng, Via Natrl or Artfcl Opng Endo]
ØCBTØZX	Exc of Rt Vocal Cord, Opn Appr, Diagnostic
ØCBT[0,3,4,7,8]ZZ	Exc/Vocal Cord, Rt, [Opn, Perc, Perc Endo, Via Natrl or Artfcl Opng, Via Natrl or Artfcl Opng Endo]
ØCBVØZX	Exc of Lt Vocal Cord, Opn Appr, Diagnostic
ØCBV[0,3,4,7,8]ZZ	Exc/Vocal Cord, Lt, [Opn, Perc, Perc Endo, Via Natrl or Artfcl Opng, Via Natrl or Artfcl Opng Endo]
ØCDT*	Extract/Vocal Cord, Rt
ØCDV*	Extract/Vocal Cord, Lt
ØCNR*	Rls/Epiglottis
ØCNS*	Rls/Larynx
ØCNT*	Rls/Vocal Cord, Rt
ØCNV*	Rls/Vocal Cord, Lt
ØCPS[0,3,7,8]JZ	Rmvl/Larynx, [Opn, Perc, Via Natrl or Artfcl Opng, Via Natrl or Artfcl Opng Endo], Synth Sub, NQ
ØCQR*	Repair/Epiglottis
ØCQS*	Repair/Larynx
ØCQT*	Repair/Vocal Cord, Rt
ØCQV*	Repair/Vocal Cord, Lt
ØCRR*	Replace/Epiglottis
ØCRS*	Replace/Larynx
ØCRT*	Replace/Vocal Cord, Rt
ØCRV*	Replace/Vocal Cord, Lt
ØCSR*	Repos/Epiglottis
ØCST*	Repos/Vocal Cord, Rt
ØCSV*	Repos/Vocal Cord, Lt
ØCTR*	Resect/Epiglottis
ØCTT*	Resect/Vocal Cord, Rt
ØCTV*	Resect/Vocal Cord, Lt
ØCUR*	Supl/Epiglottis
ØCUS*	Supl/Larynx
ØCUT*	Supl/Vocal Cord, Rt
ØCUV*	Supl/Vocal Cord, Lt
ØDJ[0,6,D,U,V,W]ØZZ	Inspect of [Upr Intestinal Tract, Stomach, Lwr Intestinal Tract, Omentum, Mesentery, Peritoneum], Opn Appr
ØF9ØØZX	Drain of Liver, Opn Appr, Diagnostic
ØF91ØZX	Drain of Rt Lobe Liver, Opn Appr, Diagnostic
ØF92ØZX	Drain of Lt Lobe Liver, Opn Appr, Diagnostic
ØFBØØZX	Exc of Liver, Opn Appr, Diagnostic
ØFB1ØZX	Exc of Rt Lobe Liver, Opn Appr, Diagnostic
ØFB2ØZX	Exc of Lt Lobe Liver, Opn Appr, Diagnostic
ØFJØØZZ	Inspect of Liver, Opn Appr

ØHB[0,1,4,5]XZZ	Exc of Skin of [Scalp, Face, Neck, Chest], Ext
ØHB[6,7,8,A]XZZ	Exc of Skin of [Back, Abd, Buttock, Genitalia], Ext
ØHB[B,C,D,E,F,G]XZZ	Exc of Skin of [Rt Upr Arm, Lt Upr Arm, Rt Lwr Arm, Lt Lwr Arm, Rt Hand, Lt Hand], Ext
ØHB[H,J,K,L,M,N]XZZ	Exc of Skin of [Rt Upr Leg, Lt Upr Leg, Rt Lwr Leg, Lt Lwr Leg, Rt Foot, Lt Foot], Ext
ØHR[5,6,7]X74	Replace of [Chest, Back, Abd] Skin w/ Auto Tissue Sub, Partial Thickness, Ext Appr
ØJB[0,1,4,5,6]ØZZ	Exc of SQ Tissue & Fascia of [Scalp, Face, Ant Neck, Post Neck, Chest], Opn
ØJB[7,8,9,B,C]ØZZ	Exc of SQ Tissue & Fascia of [Back, Abd, Buttock, Perineum, Pelvic Rgn], Opn
ØJB[D,F,G,H]ØZZ	Exc of SQ Tissue & Fascia of [Rt Upr Arm, Lt Upr Arm, Rt Lwr Arm, Lt Lwr Arm], Opn
ØJB[L,M,N,P,Q,R]ØZZ	Exc of SQ Tissue & Fascia of [Rt Upr Leg, Lt Upr Leg, Rt Lwr Leg, Lt Lwr Leg, Rt Foot, Lt Foot], Opn
ØJH6[0,3]VZ	Insert/SQ Tissue & Fascia, Chest, [Opn, Perc], Inf Pump, NQ
ØJH7[0,3]VZ	Insert/SQ Tissue & Fascia, Back, [Opn, Perc], Inf Pump, NQ
ØJH8[0,3]VZ	Insert/SQ Tissue & Fascia, Abd, [Opn, Perc], Inf Pump, NQ
ØJHT[0,3]VZ	Insert/SQ Tissue & Fascia, Trunk, [Opn, Perc], Inf Pump, NQ
ØK9[H,J]ØZX	Drain of [Rt, Lt] Thorax Muscle, Opn Appr, Dx
ØKB[H,J]ØZX	Exc of [Rt, Lt] Thorax Muscle, Opn Appr, Dx
ØP50*	Destr/Sternum
ØP51*	Destr/Rib, Rt
ØP52*	Destr/Rib, Lt
ØP55*	Destr/Scapula, Rt
ØP56*	Destr/Scapula, Lt
ØP57*	Destr/Glenoid Cavity, Rt
ØP58*	Destr/Glenoid Cavity, Lt
ØP59*	Destr/Clavicle, Rt
ØP5B*	Destr/Clavicle, Lt
ØP80*	Div/Sternum
ØP81*	Div/Rib, Rt
ØP82*	Div/Rib, Lt
ØP85*	Div/Scapula, Rt
ØP86*	Div/Scapula, Lt
ØP87*	Div/Glenoid Cavity, Rt
ØP88*	Div/Glenoid Cavity, Lt
ØP89*	Div/Clavicle, Rt
ØP8B*	Div/Clavicle, Lt
ØP90[0,3,4]ZX	Drain/Sternum, [Opn, Perc, Perc Endo]
ØP91[0,3,4]ZX	Drain/Rib, Rt, [Opn, Perc, Perc Endo]
ØP92[0,3,4]ZX	Drain/Rib, Lt, [Opn, Perc, Perc Endo]
ØP94[0,3,4]ZX	Drain/Thoracic Vertebra, [Opn, Perc, Perc Endo]
ØP95[0,3,4]ZX	Drain/Scapula, Rt, [Opn, Perc, Perc Endo]
ØP96[0,3,4]ZX	Drain/Scapula, Lt, [Opn, Perc, Perc Endo]
ØP97[0,3,4]ZX	Drain/Glenoid Cavity, Rt, [Opn, Perc, Perc Endo]
ØP98[0,3,4]ZX	Drain/Glenoid Cavity, Lt, [Opn, Perc, Perc Endo]
ØP99[0,3,4]ZX	Drain/Clavicle, Rt, [Opn, Perc, Perc Endo]
ØP9B[0,3,4]ZX	Drain/Clavicle, Lt, [Opn, Perc, Perc Endo]
ØPBØ*	Exc/Sternum
ØPB1*	Exc/Rib, Rt
ØPB2*	Exc/Rib, Lt
ØPB4[0,3,4]ZX	Exc/Thoracic Vertebra, [Opn, Perc, Perc Endo]
ØPB5*	Exc/Scapula, Rt
ØPB6*	Exc/Scapula, Lt
ØPB7*	Exc/Glenoid Cavity, Rt
ØPB8*	Exc/Glenoid Cavity, Lt
ØPB9*	Exc/Clavicle, Rt
ØPBB*	Exc/Clavicle, Lt
ØPCØ*	Extir/Sternum
ØPC1*	Extir/Rib, Rt
ØPC2*	Extir/Rib, Lt
ØPC5*	Extir/Scapula, Rt
ØPC6*	Extir/Scapula, Lt
ØPC7*	Extir/Glenoid Cavity, Rt
ØPC8*	Extir/Glenoid Cavity, Lt
ØPC9*	Extir/Clavicle, Rt
ØPCB*	Extir/Clavicle, Lt
ØPHØ*	Insert/Sternum
ØPH1*	Insert/Rib, Rt
ØPH2*	Insert/Rib, Lt
ØPH5*	Insert/Scapula, Rt
ØPH6*	Insert/Scapula, Lt
ØPH7*	Insert/Glenoid Cavity, Rt
ØPH8*	Insert/Glenoid Cavity, Lt
ØPH9*	Insert/Clavicle, Rt
ØPHB*	Insert/Clavicle, Lt
ØPHY*	Insert/Upr Bone
ØPJY[0,3,4]ZZ	Inspect/Upr Bone, [Opn, Perc, Perc Endo]

Surgical   **Medical**   **CC Indicator**   **MCC Indicator**   **Procedure Proxy**   PDxMCC **PDx acts as own MCC**   PDxCC **PDx acts as own CC**

MDC 4: Diseases And Disorders Of The Respiratory System—SURGICAL

ØPNØ*	Rls/Sternum
ØPN1*	Rls/Rib, Rt
ØPN2*	Rls/Rib, Lt
ØPN5*	Rls/Scapula, Rt
ØPN6*	Rls/Scapula, Lt
ØPN7*	Rls/Glenoid Cavity, Rt
ØPN8*	Rls/Glenoid Cavity, Lt
ØPN9*	Rls/Clavicle, Rt
ØPNB*	Rls/Clavicle, Lt
ØPQØ*	Repair/Sternum
ØPQ1*	Repair/Rib, Rt
ØPQ2*	Repair/Rib, Lt
ØPQ5*	Repair/Scapula, Rt
ØPQ6*	Repair/Scapula, Lt
ØPQ7*	Repair/Glenoid Cavity, Rt
ØPQ8*	Repair/Glenoid Cavity, Lt
ØPQ9*	Repair/Clavicle, Rt
ØPQB*	Repair/Clavicle, Lt
ØPRØ[Ø,3,4]JZ	Replace/Sternum, [Opn, Perc, Perc Endo], Synth Sub, NQ
ØPR1[Ø,3,4]JZ	Replace/Rib, Rt, [Opn, Perc, Perc Endo], Synth Sub, NQ
ØPR2[Ø,3,4]JZ	Replace/Rib, Lt, [Opn, Perc, Perc Endo], Synth Sub, NQ
ØPR5[Ø,3,4]JZ	Replace/Scapula, Rt, [Opn, Perc, Perc Endo], Synth Sub, NQ
ØPR6[Ø,3,4]JZ	Replace/Scapula, Lt, [Opn, Perc, Perc Endo], Synth Sub, NQ
ØPR7[Ø,3,4]JZ	Replace/Glenoid Cavity, Rt, [Opn, Perc, Perc Endo], Synth Sub, NQ
ØPR8[Ø,3,4]JZ	Replace/Glenoid Cavity, Lt, [Opn, Perc, Perc Endo], Synth Sub, NQ
ØPR9[Ø,3,4]JZ	Replace/Clavicle, Rt, [Opn, Perc, Perc Endo], Synth Sub, NQ
ØPRB[Ø,3,4]JZ	Replace/Clavicle, Lt, [Opn, Perc, Perc Endo], Synth Sub, NQ
ØPSØ[Ø,3,4]ØZ	Repos/Sternum, [Opn, Perc, Perc Endo], Int Fix Dev, Rigid Plate, NQ
ØPT[Ø,1,2,5,6]ØZZ	Resect of [Sternum, Rt Rib, Lt Rib, Rt Scapula, Lt Scapula], Opn Appr
ØPT[7,8,9,B]ØZZ	Resect of [Rt Glenoid Cavity, Lt Glenoid Cavity, Rt Clavicle, Lt Clavicle], Opn Appr
ØPUØ[Ø,3,4]JZ	Supl/Sternum, [Opn, Perc, Perc Endo], Synth Sub, NQ
ØPU1[Ø,3,4]JZ	Supl/Rib, Rt, [Opn, Perc, Perc Endo], Synth Sub, NQ
ØPU2[Ø,3,4]JZ	Supl/Rib, Lt, [Opn, Perc, Perc Endo], Synth Sub, NQ
ØPU5[Ø,3,4]JZ	Supl/Scapula, Rt, [Opn, Perc, Perc Endo], Synth Sub, NQ
ØPU6[Ø,3,4]JZ	Supl/Scapula, Lt, [Opn, Perc, Perc Endo], Synth Sub, NQ
ØPU7[Ø,3,4]JZ	Supl/Glenoid Cavity, Rt, [Opn, Perc, Perc Endo], Synth Sub, NQ
ØPU8[Ø,3,4]JZ	Supl/Glenoid Cavity, Lt, [Opn, Perc, Perc Endo], Synth Sub, NQ
ØPU9[Ø,3,4]JZ	Supl/Clavicle, Rt, [Opn, Perc, Perc Endo], Synth Sub, NQ
ØPUB[Ø,3,4]JZ	Supl/Clavicle, Lt, [Opn, Perc, Perc Endo], Synth Sub, NQ
ØW19[Ø,4]J[9,B,J]	Bypass/Pleural Cavity, Rt, [Opn, Perc Endo], Synth Sub, [Pleural Cavity, Rt, Pleural Cavity, Lt, Pelvic Cavity]
ØW1B[Ø,4]J[9,B,J]	Bypass/Pleural Cavity, Lt, [Opn, Perc Endo], Synth Sub, [Pleural Cavity, Rt, Pleural Cavity, Lt, Pelvic Cavity]
ØW9CØZX	Drain of Mediastinum, Opn Appr, Diagnostic
ØW9C[Ø,3,4][Ø,Z]Z	Drain/Mediastinum, [Opn, Perc, Perc Endo], [Drain Dev, No Dev], NQ
ØWB6XZ2	Exc of Neck, Stoma, Ext Appr
ØWB8[Ø,3,4,X]ZZ	Exc/Chest Wall, [Opn, Perc, Perc Endo, Ext]
ØWBCØZX	Exc of Mediastinum, Opn Appr, Diagnostic
ØWCC[Ø,3,4]ZZ	Extir/Mediastinum, [Opn, Perc, Perc Endo]
ØWCQ[7,8]ZZ	Extir/Respiratory Tract, [Via Natrl or Artfcl Opng, Via Natrl or Artfcl Opng Endo]
ØWF9[Ø,3,4]ZZ	Fragmn/Pleural Cavity, Rt, [Opn, Perc, Perc Endo]
ØWFB[Ø,3,4]ZZ	Fragmn/Pleural Cavity, Lt, [Opn, Perc, Perc Endo]
ØWFC[Ø,3,4]ZZ	Fragmn/Mediastinum, [Opn, Perc, Perc Endo]
ØWFQ[Ø,3,4,7,8]ZZ	Fragmn/Respiratory Tract, [Opn, Perc, Perc Endo, Via Natrl or Artfcl Opng, Via Natrl or Artfcl Opng Endo]
ØWH8[Ø,3,4]1Z	Insert/Chest Wall, [Opn, Perc, Perc Endo], Radioact Elmt, NQ
ØWH9[Ø,3,4]1Z	Insert/Pleural Cavity, Rt, [Opn, Perc, Perc Endo], Radioact Elmt, NQ
ØWHB[Ø,3,4]1Z	Insert/Pleural Cavity, Lt, [Opn, Perc, Perc Endo], Radioact Elmt, NQ
ØWHC[Ø,3,4][3,Y]Z	Insert/Mediastinum, [Opn, Perc, Perc Endo], [Inf Dev, Oth Dev], NQ
ØWHQ[Ø,3,4,7,8]1Z	Insert/Respiratory Tract, [Opn, Perc, Perc Endo, Via Natrl or Artfcl Opng, Via Natrl or Artfcl Opng Endo], Radioact Elmt, NQ
ØWHQ[3,4]3Z	Insert/Respiratory Tract, [Perc, Perc Endo], Inf Dev, NQ
ØWHQ[3,4]YZ	Insert/Respiratory Tract, [Perc, Perc Endo], Oth Dev, NQ
ØWJ8[Ø,3,4]ZZ	Inspect/Chest Wall, [Opn, Perc, Perc Endo]
ØWJ9[3,4]ZZ	Inspect/Pleural Cavity, Rt, [Perc, Perc Endo]
ØWJB[3,4]ZZ	Inspect/Pleural Cavity, Lt, [Perc, Perc Endo]
ØWJC[3,4]ZZ	Inspect/Mediastinum, [Perc, Perc Endo]
ØWJD4ZZ	Inspect of Pericardial Cavity, Perc Endo Appr
ØWJGØZZ	Inspect of Peritoneal Cavity, Opn Appr
ØWJJØZZ	Inspect of Pelvic Cavity, Opn Appr
ØWJPØZZ	Inspect of Gastrointestinal Tract, Opn Appr
ØWJQ[3,4,7,8]ZZ	Inspect/Respiratory Tract, [Perc, Perc Endo, Via Natrl or Artfcl Opng, Via Natrl or Artfcl Opng Endo]
ØWJRØZZ	Inspect of Genitourinary Tract, Opn Appr
ØWM8ØZZ	Reattach of Chest Wall, Opn Appr
ØWPC[Ø,3,4][Ø,1,3,7,J,K,Y]Z	Rmvl/Mediastinum, [Opn, Perc, Perc Endo], [Drain Dev, Radioact Elmt, Inf Dev, Auto Tissue Sub, Synth Sub, Nonauto Tissue Sub, Oth Dev], NQ
ØWPQ81Z	Rmvl of Radioact Elmt from Respiratory Tract, Endo
ØWPQ[3,4,7][1,3,Y]Z	Rmvl/Respiratory Tract, [Perc, Perc Endo, Via Natrl or Artfcl Opng], [Radioact Elmt, Inf Dev, Oth Dev], NQ
ØWQ6XZ2	Repair Neck, Stoma, Ext Appr
ØWQ8*	Repair/Chest Wall
ØWQC*	Repair/Mediastinum
ØWUC*	Supl/Mediastinum
ØWWC[Ø,3,4][Ø,1,3,7,J,K,Y]Z	Rev/Mediastinum, [Opn, Perc, Perc Endo], [Drain Dev, Radioact Elmt, Inf Dev, Auto Tissue Sub, Synth Sub, Nonauto Tissue Sub, Oth Dev], NQ
ØWWQ[3,4,7,8][1,3,Y]Z	Rev/Respiratory Tract, [Perc, Perc Endo, Via Natrl or Artfcl Opng, Via Natrl or Artfcl Opng Endo], [Radioact Elmt, Inf Dev, Oth Dev], NQ

DRG 167   Other Respiratory System O.R. Procedures with CC
    GMLOS 5.Ø   AMLOS 6.2   RW 1.9367   T

Select operating room procedures listed under DRG 166

DRG 168   Other Respiratory System O.R. Procedures without CC/MCC
    GMLOS 2.9   AMLOS 3.8   RW 1.295Ø   T

Select operating room procedures listed under DRG 166

MEDICAL

DRG 175   Pulmonary Embolism with MCC
    GMLOS 4.9   AMLOS 5.9   RW 1.4839   T

Principal Diagnosis

I26.Ø1	Septic pulmn embolism with acute cor pulmonale	PDxMCC
I26.Ø2	Saddle embolus of pulmn artery with acute cor pulmonale	PDxMCC
I26.Ø9	Oth pulmn embolism with acute cor pulmonale	PDxMCC
I26.9Ø	Septic pulmn embolism w/o acute cor pulmonale	
I26.92	Saddle embolus of pulmn artery w/o acute cor pulmonale	
I26.99	Oth pulmn embolism w/o acute cor pulmonale	
I27.82	Chr pulmn embolism	
T79.ØXXA	Air embolism (traum), init enc	
T79.1XXA	Fat embolism (traum), init enc	
T8Ø.ØXXA	Air embolism fol inf, tranfs and theraputc inject, init	

DRG 176   Pulmonary Embolism without MCC
    GMLOS 3.3   AMLOS 4.Ø   RW Ø.9375   T

Select principal diagnosis listed under DRG 175

DRG 177   Respiratory Infections and Inflammations with MCC
    GMLOS 6.Ø   AMLOS 7.4   RW 1.9Ø33   T

Principal Diagnosis

J1Ø.ØØ	Flu d/t oth ident flu virus w unsp type of pneumonia
J1Ø.Ø1	Flu d/t oth ident flu virus w same oth ident flu virus pn
J1Ø.Ø8	Flu d/t oth ident flu virus w oth pneumonia
J11.ØØ	Flu d/t unidentified flu virus w unsp type of pneumonia
J11.Ø8	Flu d/t unidentified flu virus w spec pneumonia

AND

Secondary Diagnosis

A48.1	Legionnaires' dz
J15.Ø	Pneumonia d/t Klebsiella pneumoniae
J15.1	Pneumonia d/t Pseudomonas
J15.2*	Pneumonia d/t staphylococcus
J15.5	Pneumonia d/t Escherichia coli
J15.6	Pneumonia d/t oth aerobic Gram-negative bacteria
J15.8	Pneumonia d/t oth spec bacteria

T **Transfer DRG**   SP **Special Payment**   * **Code Range**   **6th and 7th Character of ZZ = No Device, No Qualifier ZX = No Device, Diagnostic**

OR

Principal Diagnosis

A02.22	Salmonella pneumonia
A06.5	Amebic lung abscess
A15*	Respiratory tuberculosis
A20.2	Pneumonic plague
A21.2	Pulmn tularemia
A22.1	Pulmn anthrax
A31.0	Pulmn mycobacterial infxn
A42.0	Pulmn actinomycosis
A43.0	Pulmn nocardiosis
A48.1	Legionnaires' dz
A52.72	Syphilis of lung and bronchus
B01.2	Varicella pneumonia
B05.2	Measles complicated by pneumonia
B25.0	Cytomegaloviral pneumonitis PDx MCC
B37.1	Pulmn candidiasis
B38.0	Acute pulmn coccidioidomycosis
B38.1	Chr pulmn coccidioidomycosis
B38.2	Pulmn coccidioidomycosis, unsp
B39.0	Acute pulmn histoplasmosis capsulati
B39.1	Chr pulmn histoplasmosis capsulati
B39.2	Pulmn histoplasmosis capsulati, unsp
B44.0	Invasive pulmn aspergillosis PDx MCC
B58.3	Pulmn toxoplasmosis
B59	Pneumocystosis
B66.4	Paragonimiasis
B67.1	Echinococcus granulosus infxn of lung
E84.0	Cystic fibrosis with pulmn manifestations
J15.0	Pneumonia d/t Klebsiella pneumoniae
J15.1	Pneumonia d/t Pseudomonas
J15.2*	Pneumonia d/t staphylococcus
J15.5	Pneumonia d/t Escherichia coli
J15.6	Pneumonia d/t oth aerobic Gram-negative bacteria
J15.8	Pneumonia d/t oth spec bacteria
J17	Pneumonia in dz classified elsw
J69*	Pneumonitis d/t solids and liquids
J85*	Abscess of lung and mediastinum
J86*	Pyothorax
J98.5	Dz of mediastinum, NEC
R76.1*	Nonspecific reaction to test for tuberculosis

DRG 178 **Respiratory Infections and Inflammations with CC**

GMLOS 4.8   AMLOS 5.8   RW 1.3575   T

Select principal diagnosis or principal diagnosis and secondary diagnosis combinations listed under DRG 177

DRG 179 **Respiratory Infections and Inflammations without CC/MCC**

GMLOS 3.6   AMLOS 4.3   RW 0.9659   T

Select principal diagnosis or principal diagnosis and secondary diagnosis combinations listed under DRG 177

DRG 180 **Respiratory Neoplasms with MCC**

GMLOS 5.2   AMLOS 6.7   RW 1.6767

Principal Diagnosis

C33	Malig neoplasm of trachea
C34*	Malig neoplasm of bronchus and lung
C38.1	Malig neoplasm of ant mediastinum
C38.2	Malig neoplasm of posterior mediastinum
C38.3	Malig neoplasm of mediastinum, part unsp
C38.4	Malig neoplasm of pleura
C38.8	Malig neoplm of ovrlp sites of heart, mediastinum and pleura
C39.9	Malig neoplasm of lwr respiratory tract, part unsp
C45.0	Mesothelioma of pleura
C46.5*	Kaposi's sarcoma of lung
C76.1	Malig neoplasm of thorax
C78.0*	Secondary malig neoplasm of lung
C78.1	Secondary malig neoplasm of mediastinum
C78.2	Secondary malig neoplasm of pleura
C78.3*	Secondary malig neoplasm of and unsp respiratory organs
C7A.090	Malig carcinoid tumor of the bronchus and lung
D02.1	Carcinoma in situ of trachea
D02.2*	Carcinoma in situ of bronchus and lung
D02.3	Carcinoma in situ of oth parts of respiratory sys
D02.4	Carcinoma in situ of respiratory sys, unsp

D14.2	Benign neoplasm of trachea
D14.3*	Benign neoplasm of bronchus and lung
D14.4	Benign neoplasm of respiratory sys, unsp
D15.2	Benign neoplasm of mediastinum
D15.7	Benign neoplasm of oth spec intrathoracic organs
D15.9	Benign neoplasm of intrathoracic organ, unsp
D16.7	Benign neoplasm of ribs, sternum and clavicle
D17.4	Benign lipomatous neoplasm of intrathoracic organs
D19.0	Benign neoplasm of mesothelial tissue of pleura
D38.1	Neoplasm of uncertain behav of trachea, bronchus and lung
D38.2	Neoplasm of uncertain behav of pleura
D38.3	Neoplasm of uncertain behav of mediastinum
D38.4	Neoplasm of uncertain behav of thymus
D38.5	Neoplasm of uncertain behav of oth respiratory organs
D38.6	Neoplasm of uncertain behav of respiratory organ, unsp
D3A.090	Benign carcinoid tumor of the bronchus and lung
D49.1	Neoplasm of unsp behav of respiratory sys
J91.0	Malig pleural effusion

DRG 181 **Respiratory Neoplasms with CC**

GMLOS 3.7   AMLOS 4.8   RW 1.1775

Select principal diagnosis listed under DRG 180

DRG 182 **Respiratory Neoplasms without CC/MCC**

GMLOS 2.6   AMLOS 3.3   RW 0.8553

Select principal diagnosis listed under DRG 180

DRG 183 **Major Chest Trauma with MCC**

GMLOS 4.7   AMLOS 5.8   RW 1.4723

Principal Diagnosis

M99.18	Sublux complex (vert) of rib cage
S11.025A	Opn bite of trachea, init enc
S11.029A	Unsp opn wnd of trachea, init enc
S11.02[1,2]A	Lac [w/o, w/] FB of trachea, init enc
S11.02[3,4]A	Punc wnd [w/o, w/] FB of trachea, init enc
S22.20X[A,B]	Unsp fx of sternum, init enc for [clsd, opn] fx
S22.21X[A,B]	Fx of manubrium, init enc for [clsd, opn] fx
S22.22X[A,B]	Fx of body of sternum, init enc for [clsd, opn] fx
S22.23X[A,B]	Sternal manubrial dissociation, init enc for [clsd, opn] fx
S22.24X[A,B]	Fx of xiphoid process, init enc for [clsd, opn] fx
S22.3[1,2,9]XB	Fx of one rib, [rt, lt, unsp] side, init enc for opn fx
S22.41X[A,B]	Multi fxs of ribs, rt side, init enc for [clsd, opn] fx
S22.42X[A,B]	Multi fxs of ribs, lt side, init enc for [clsd, opn] fx
S22.43X[A,B]	Multi fxs of ribs, bilat, init enc for [clsd, opn] fx
S22.49X[A,B]	Multi fxs of ribs, unsp side, init enc for [clsd, opn] fx
S22.5XX[A,B]	Flail chest, init enc for [clsd, opn] fx
S27.33[1,2,9]A	Lac of lung, [unilat, bilat, unsp], init enc
S27.40[1,2,9]A	Unsp inj of bronchus, [unilat, bilat, unsp], init enc
S27.41[1,2,9]A	Primary blast inj of bronchus, [unilat, bilat, unsp], init enc
S27.42[1,2,9]A	Contsn of bronchus, [unilat, bilat, unsp], init enc
S27.43[1,2,9]A	Lac of bronchus, [unilat, bilat, unsp], init enc
S27.49[1,2,9]A	Oth inj of bronchus, [unilat, bilat, unsp], init enc
S27.80[2,3,8,9]A	[Contsn, Lac, Oth inj, Unsp inj] of diaphragm, init enc
S43.20[1,2,3]A	Unsp sublux of [rt, lt, unsp] sternoclavicular jt, init enc
S43.20[4,5,6]A	Unsp disloc of [rt, lt, unsp] sternoclavicular jt, init enc
S43.21[1,2,3]A	Ant sublux of [rt, lt, unsp] sternoclavicular jt, init enc
S43.21[4,5,6]A	Ant disloc of [rt, lt, unsp] sternoclavicular jt, init enc
S43.22[1,2,3]A	Post sublux of [rt, lt, unsp] sternoclavicular jt, init enc
S43.22[4,5,6]A	Post disloc of [rt, lt, unsp] sternoclavicular jt, init enc

---

DRG 184 **Major Chest Trauma with CC**

GMLOS 3.4   AMLOS 4.0   RW 1.0125

Select principal diagnosis listed under DRG 183

Surgical   Medical   CC Indicator   MCC Indicator   Procedure Proxy   PDx MCC PDx acts as own MCC   PDx CC PDx acts as own CC

MDC 4: Diseases And Disorders Of The Respiratory System—MEDICAL

DRG 185   Major Chest Trauma without CC/MCC
GMLOS 2.5   AMLOS 2.9   RW 0.7182

Select principal diagnosis listed under DRG 183

DRG 186   Pleural Effusion with MCC
GMLOS 4.7   AMLOS 6.1   RW 1.5734   T

Principal Diagnosis

J90	Pleural effusion, NEC
J91.8	Pleural effusion in oth conditions classified elsw
J94.0	Chylous effusion
J94.2	Hemothorax
J94.8	Oth spec pleural conditions

DRG 187   Pleural Effusion with CC
GMLOS 3.5   AMLOS 4.4   RW 1.0835   T

Select principal diagnosis listed under DRG 186

DRG 188   Pleural Effusion without CC/MCC
GMLOS 2.7   AMLOS 3.3   RW 0.7860   T

Select principal diagnosis listed under DRG 186

DRG 189   Pulmonary Edema and Respiratory Failure
GMLOS 3.9   AMLOS 5.0   RW 1.2265

Principal Diagnosis

J18.2	Hypostatic pneumonia, unsp organism
J68.1	Pulmn edema d/t chemicals, gases, fumes and vapors
J81*	Pulmn edema
J95.1	Acute pulmn insufficiency following thoracic surgery
J95.2	Acute pulmn insufficiency following nonthoracic surgery
J95.3	Chr pulmn insufficiency following surgery
J95.82*	Postprocedural respiratory failure
J96*	Respiratory failure, NEC

DRG 190   Chronic Obstructive Pulmonary Disease with MCC
GMLOS 4.0   AMLOS 4.9   RW 1.1578   T

Principal Diagnosis

J41.1	Mucopurulent chr bronchitis
J41.8	Mixed simple and mucopurulent chr bronchitis
J42	Unsp chr bronchitis
J43*	Emphysema
J44*	Oth chr obstructive pulmn dz
J47*	Bronchiectasis
J68.4	Chr resp cond d/t chemicals, gases, fumes and vapors
J68.8	Oth resp cond d/t chemicals, gases, fumes and vapors
J68.9	Unsp resp cond d/t chemicals, gases, fumes and vapors
Q33.4	Congenital bronchiectasis

DRG 191   Chronic Obstructive Pulmonary Disease with CC
GMLOS 3.3   AMLOS 4.0   RW 0.9321   T

Select principal diagnosis listed under DRG 190

DRG 192   Chronic Obstructive Pulmonary Disease without CC/MCC
GMLOS 2.7   AMLOS 3.3   RW 0.7313   T

Select principal diagnosis listed under DRG 190

DRG 193   Simple Pneumonia and Pleurisy with MCC
GMLOS 4.8   AMLOS 5.8   RW 1.4261   T

Principal Diagnosis

B33.0	Epidemic myalgia
J09.X[1,2]	flu d/t identified novel flu A virus w/ [pneumonia, oth respiratory manifestations]
J10.00	Flu d/t oth ident flu virus w unsp type of pneumonia
J10.01	Flu d/t oth ident flu virus w same oth ident flu virus pn
J10.08	Flu d/t oth ident flu virus w oth pneumonia
J10.1	Flu d/t oth ident flu virus w oth resp manifest
J11.0*	Flu d/t unidentified flu virus with pneumonia
J12*	Viral pneumonia, NEC
J13	Pneumonia d/t Streptococcus pneumoniae

J14	Pneumonia d/t Hemophilus influenzae
J15.3	Pneumonia d/t streptococcus, group B
J15.4	Pneumonia d/t oth streptococci
J15.7	Pneumonia d/t Mycoplasma pneumoniae
J15.9	Unsp bacterial pneumonia
J16*	Pneumonia d/t oth infectious organisms, NEC
J18.0	Bronchopneumonia, unsp organism
J18.1	Lobar pneumonia, unsp organism
J18.8	Oth pneumonia, unsp organism
J18.9	Pneumonia, unsp organism
J92*	Pleural plaque
J94.1	Fibrothorax
J94.9	Pleural condition, unsp
R09.1	Pleurisy

DRG 194   Simple Pneumonia and Pleurisy with CC
GMLOS 3.7   AMLOS 4.4   RW 0.9695   T

Select principal diagnosis listed under DRG 193

DRG 195   Simple Pneumonia and Pleurisy without CC/MCC
GMLOS 2.8   AMLOS 3.3   RW 0.7111   T

Select principal diagnosis listed under DRG 193

DRG 196   Interstitial Lung Disease with MCC
GMLOS 5.2   AMLOS 6.6   RW 1.6315   T

Principal Diagnosis

B44.81	Allergic bronchopulmonary aspergillosis	
B90.9	Sequelae of respiratory and unsp tuberculosis	
D86*	Sarcoidosis	
J60	Coalworker's pneumoconiosis	
J61	Pneumoconiosis d/t asbestos and oth mineral fibers	
J62*	Pneumoconiosis d/t dust containing silica	
J63*	Pneumoconiosis d/t oth inorganic dusts	
J64	Unsp pneumoconiosis	
J65	Pneumoconiosis associated with tuberculosis	
J66*	Airway dz d/t specific organic dust	
J67*	Hypersensitivity pneumonitis d/t organic dust	
J70.1	Chr and oth pulmn manifestations d/t radiation	
J82	Pulmn eosinophilia, NEC	
J84*	Oth interstitial pulmn dz	
J99	Respiratory d/o in dz classified elsw	
M05.1*	Rheumatoid lung dz with rheumatoid arthritis	
M34.81	Systemic sclerosis with lung involvement	PDx CC
P27*	Chr respiratory dz origin in the perinatal period	

DRG 197   Interstitial Lung Disease with CC
GMLOS 3.6   AMLOS 4.4   RW 1.0406   T

Select principal diagnosis listed under DRG 196

DRG 198   Interstitial Lung Disease without CC/MCC
GMLOS 2.8   AMLOS 3.4   RW 0.7775   T

Select principal diagnosis listed under DRG 196

DRG 199   Pneumothorax with MCC
GMLOS 5.7   AMLOS 7.2   RW 1.7503

Principal Diagnosis

J93*	Pneumothorax and air leak
J95.81*	Postprocedural pneumothorax and air leak
J98.2	Interstitial emphysema
S27.0XXA	Traum pneumothorax, init enc
S27.1XXA	Traum hemothorax, init enc
S27.2XXA	Traum hemopneumothorax, init enc
T79.7XXA	Traum SQ emphysema, init enc

DRG 200   Pneumothorax with CC
GMLOS 3.5   AMLOS 4.5   RW 1.0443

Select principal diagnosis listed under DRG 199

T Transfer DRG   SP Special Payment   * Code Range   6th and 7th Character of ZZ = No Device, No Qualifier ZX = No Device, Diagnostic

DRG 201 Pneumothorax without CC/MCC

| GMLOS 2.7 | AMLOS 3.3 | RW 0.7354 |

Select principal diagnosis listed under DRG 199

DRG 202 Bronchitis and Asthma with CC/MCC

| GMLOS 3.1 | AMLOS 3.8 | RW 0.8980 |

Principal Diagnosis

A37*	Whooping cough
J04.1*	Acute tracheitis
J20*	Acute bronchitis
J21*	Acute bronchiolitis
J39.8	Oth spec dz of upr respiratory tract
J40	Bronchitis, not spec as acute or chr
J41.0	Simple chr bronchitis
J45*	Asthma
J98.0*	Dz of bronchus, NEC

DRG 203 Bronchitis and Asthma without CC/MCC

| GMLOS 2.5 | AMLOS 3.0 | RW 0.6697 |

Select principal diagnosis listed under DRG 202

DRG 204 Respiratory Signs and Symptoms

| GMLOS 2.2 | AMLOS 2.8 | RW 0.7291 |

Principal Diagnosis

G47.32	High altitude periodic breathing
J80	Acute respiratory distress synd
R04.2	Hemoptysis
R04.8*	Hemor from oth sites in respiratory passages
R04.9	Hemor from respiratory passages, unsp
R05	Cough
R06.0*	Dyspnea
R06.1	Stridor
R06.2	Wheezing
R06.3	Periodic breathing
R06.4	Hyperventilation
R06.6	Hiccough
R06.8*	Oth abnormalities of breathing
R06.9	Unsp abnormalities of breathing
R07.1	Chest pain on breathing
R07.81	Pleurodynia
R09.3	Abnormal sputum
R22.2	Localized swelling, mass and lump, trunk
R91.8	Oth nonspecific abnormal finding of lung field

DRG 205 Other Respiratory System Diagnoses with MCC

| GMLOS 4.1 | AMLOS 5.4 | RW 1.4478 | [T] |

Principal Diagnosis

E66.2	Morbid (severe) obesity with alveolar hypoventilation
J22	Unsp acute lwr respiratory infxn
J68.[0,2,3]	[Bronchitis and pneumonitis, Upr respiratory inflam NEC, Oth acute and subacute respiratory conditions] d/t chemicals, gases, fumes and vapors
J70.0	Acute pulmn manifestations d/t radiation
J70.[2,3,4]	[Acute, Chr, Unsp] drug-induced interstitial lung d/os
J70.[5,8,9]	Respiratory conditions d/t [smoke inhalation, oth spec ext agents, unsp ext agents]
J95.0*	Tracheostomy comp
J95.4	Chemical pneumonitis d/t anesthesia
J95.5	Postprocedural subglottic stenosis
J95.84	Transfusion-related acute lung inj (TRALI)
J95.851	Ventilator associated pneumonia
J95.859	Oth comp of respirator [ventilator]
J95.88	Oth intraoperative comp of respiratory sys, NEC
J95.89	Oth postproc comp and d/o of resp sys, NEC
J98.1*	Pulmn collapse
J98.3	Compensatory emphysema
J98.4	Oth d/o of lung
J98.6	D/o of diaphragm
J98.8	Oth spec respiratory d/o
J98.9	Respiratory d/o, unsp
K76.81	Hepatopulmonary synd
M94.0	Chondrocostal junction synd [Tietze]
Q33.0	Congenital cystic lung

Q33.1	Accessory lobe of lung
Q33.2	Sequestration of lung
Q33.3	Agenesis of lung
Q33.5	Ectopic tissue in lung
Q33.6	Congenital hypoplasia and dysplasia of lung
Q33.8	Oth congenital malformations of lung
Q33.9	Congenital malformation of lung, unsp
Q34*	Oth congenital malformations of respiratory sys
Q67.6	Pectus excavatum
Q67.7	Pectus carinatum
Q76.6	Oth congenital malformations of ribs
Q76.7	Congenital malformation of sternum
Q76.8	Oth congenital malformations of bony thorax
Q76.9	Congenital malformation of bony thorax, unsp
Q77.2	Short rib synd
Q79.0	Congenital diaphragmatic hernia
Q79.1	Oth congenital malformations of diaphragm
R09.0*	Asphyxia and hypoxemia
R09.2	Respiratory arrest
R68.3	Clubbing of fingers
R91.1	Solitary pulmn nodule
R94.2	Abnormal results of pulmn function studies
S22.3[1,2,9]XA	Fx of one rib, [rt, lt, unsp] side, init enc for clsd fx
S23.41XA	Sprain of ribs, init enc
S23.42[0,1]A	Sprain of [sternoclavicular (jt) (lgmt), chondrosternal jt], init enc
S23.42[8,9]A	[Oth, Unsp] sprain of sternum, init enc
S26.02[0,1,2]S	[Mild, Mod, Major] lac of heart w/ hemopericardium, seq
S26.09XS	Oth inj of heart with hemopericardium, seq
S26.0[0,1]XS	[Unsp inj, Contsn] of heart w/ hemopericardium, seq
S26.1[0,1,2,9]XS	[Unsp inj, Contsn, Lac, Oth inj] of heart w/o hemopericardium, seq
S26.9[0,1,2,9]XS	[Unsp inj, Contsn, Lac, Oth inj] of heart, unsp w/ or w/o hemopericardium, seq
S27.301[A,S]	Unsp inj of lung, unilat, [init enc, seq]
S27.302[A,S]	Unsp inj of lung, bilat, [init enc, seq]
S27.309[A,S]	Unsp inj of lung, unsp, [init enc, seq]
S27.311[A,S]	Primary blast inj of lung, unilat, [init enc, seq]
S27.312[A,S]	Primary blast inj of lung, bilat, [init enc, seq]
S27.319[A,S]	Primary blast inj of lung, unsp, [init enc, seq]
S27.321[A,S]	Contsn of lung, unilat, [init enc, seq]
S27.322[A,S]	Contsn of lung, bilat, [init enc, seq]
S27.329[A,S]	Contsn of lung, unsp, [init enc, seq]
S27.33[1,2,9]S	Lac of lung, [unilat, bilat, unsp], seq
S27.391[A,S]	Oth injuries of lung, unilat, [init enc, seq]
S27.392[A,S]	Oth injuries of lung, bilat, [init enc, seq]
S27.399[A,S]	Oth injuries of lung, unsp, [init enc, seq]
S27.40[1,2,9]S	Unsp inj of bronchus, [unilat, bilat, unsp], seq
S27.41[1,2,9]S	Primary blast inj of bronchus, [unilat, bilat, unsp], seq
S27.42[1,2,9]S	Contsn of bronchus, [unilat, bilat, unsp], seq
S27.43[1,2,9]S	Lac of bronchus, [unilat, bilat, unsp], seq
S27.49[1,2,9]S	Oth inj of bronchus, [unilat, bilat, unsp], seq
S27.50X[A,S]	Unsp inj of thoracic trachea, [init enc, seq]
S27.51X[A,S]	Primary blast inj of thoracic trachea, [init enc, seq]
S27.52X[A,S]	Contsn of thoracic trachea, [init enc, seq]
S27.53X[A,S]	Lac of thoracic trachea, [init enc, seq]
S27.59X[A,S]	Oth inj of thoracic trachea, [init enc, seq]
S27.60X[A,S]	Unsp inj of pleura, [init enc, seq]
S27.63X[A,S]	Lac of pleura, [init enc, seq]
S27.69X[A,S]	Oth inj of pleura, [init enc, seq]
S27.80[2,3,8,9]S	[Contsn, Lac, Oth inj, Unsp inj] of diaphragm, seq
S27.81[2,3,8,9]S	[Contsn, Lac, Oth inj, Unsp inj] of esophagus, seq
S27.892[A,S]	Contsn of oth spec intrathoracic organs, [init enc, seq]
S27.893[A,S]	Lac of oth spec intrathoracic organs, [init enc, seq]
S27.898[A,S]	Oth inj of oth spec intrathoracic organs, [init enc, seq]
S27.899[A,S]	Unsp inj of oth spec intrathoracic organs, [init enc, seq]
S27.9XXS	Inj of unsp intrathoracic organ, seq
S27.[0,1,2]XXS	Traum [pneumothorax, hemothorax, hemopneumothorax], seq
T17.40[0,8]A	Unsp FB in trachea causing [asphyxiation, oth inj], init enc
T17.41[0,8]A	Gastric contents in trachea causing [asphyxiation, oth inj], init enc
T17.42[0,8]A	Food in trachea causing [asphyxiation, oth inj], init enc
T17.49[0,8]A	Oth foreign object in trachea causing [asphyxiation, oth inj], init enc
T17.50[0,8]A	Unsp FB in bronchus causing [asphyxiation, oth inj], init enc
T17.51[0,8]A	Gastric contents in bronchus causing [asphyxiation, oth inj], init enc
T17.52[0,8]A	Food in bronchus causing [asphyxiation, oth inj], init enc

MDC 4: Diseases And Disorders Of The Respiratory System—MEDICAL

T17.59[0,8]A	Oth foreign object in bronchus causing [asphyxiation, oth inj], init enc
T17.80[0,8]A	Unsp FB in oth parts of respiratory tract causing [asphyxiation, oth inj], init enc
T17.81[0,8]A	Gastric contents in oth parts of respiratory tract causing [asphyxiation, oth inj], init enc
T17.82[0,8]A	Food in oth parts of respiratory tract causing [asphyxiation, oth inj], init enc
T17.89[0,8]A	Oth foreign object in oth parts of respiratory tract causing [asphyxiation, oth inj], init enc
T17.90[0,8]A	Unsp FB in respiratory tract, part unsp causing [asphyxiation, oth inj], init enc
T17.91[0,8]A	Gastric contents in respiratory tract, part unsp causing [asphyxiation, oth inj], init enc
T17.92[0,8]A	Food in respiratory tract, part unsp causing [asphyxiation, oth inj], init enc
T17.99[0,8]A	Oth foreign object in respiratory tract, part unsp [in causing asphyxiation, causing oth inj], init enc
T27.[0,1,2,3]XXA	Burn [of larynx and trachea, involving larynx and trachea w/ lung, of oth parts of respiratory tract, respiratory tract part unsp], init enc
T27.[4,5,6,7]XXA	Corrosion [of larynx and trachea, involving larynx and trachea w/ lung, of oth parts of respiratory tract, respiratory tract part unsp], init enc
T86.81[0,1,2]	Lung transplant [rejection, failure, infxn]
T86.81[8,9]	[Oth, Unsp] comps of lung transplant
Z43.0	Enc for attention to tracheostomy
Z90.2	Acquired absence of lung [part of]
Z94.2	Lung transplant status

DRG 206   Other Respiratory System Diagnoses without MCC

| GMLOS 2.5 | AMLOS 3.2 | RW 0.8164 | T |

Select principal diagnosis listed under DRG 205

▲DRG 207   Respiratory System Diagnosis with Ventilator Support >96 Hours

| GMLOS 12.2 | AMLOS 14.1 | RW 5.3498 | T |

Select principal diagnosis from MDC 4

AND

Nonoperating Room Procedure

| 5A1955Z | Respiratory Ventilation, > 96 Consecutive Hrs |

DRG 208   Respiratory System Diagnosis with Ventilator Support <96 Hours

| GMLOS 4.9 | AMLOS 6.7 | RW 2.3055 |

Select principal diagnosis from MDC 4

AND

Nonoperating Room Procedures

| 5A1935Z | Respiratory Ventilation, < 24 Consecutive Hrs |
| 5A1945Z | Respiratory Ventilation, 24-96 Consecutive Hrs |

SURGICAL

DRG 215   Other Heart Assist System Implant
GMLOS 12.0	AMLOS 18.4	RW 15.8738

Operating Room Procedures

02HA0RS	Insert of Bivent Ext Heart Assist into Heart, Opn Appr
02HA0RZ	Insert of Ext Heart Assist into Heart, Opn Appr
02HA3RS	Insert of Bivent Ext Heart Assist into Heart, Perc Appr
02HA3RZ	Insert of Ext Heart Assist into Heart, Perc Appr
02HA4RS	Insert Bivent Ext Heart Assist in Heart, Perc Endo
02HA4RZ	Insert of Ext Heart Assist into Heart, Perc Endo Appr
02WA0JZ	Rev of Synth Sub in Heart, Opn Appr
02WA0QZ	Rev of Implant Heart Assist in Heart, Opn Appr
02WA0RZ	Rev of Ext Heart Assist in Heart, Opn Appr
02WA3QZ	Rev of Implant Heart Assist in Heart, Perc Appr
02WA3RZ	Rev of Ext Heart Assist in Heart, Perc Appr
02WA4QZ	Revise of Implant Heart Assist in Heart, Perc Endo Appr
02WA4RZ	Rev of Ext Heart Assist in Heart, Perc Endo Appr

DRG 216   Cardiac Valve and Other Major Cardiothoracic Procedures with Cardiac Catheterization with MCC
GMLOS 12.7	AMLOS 15.5	RW 9.4642	SP

Operating Room Procedures

027F0[4,D,Z]Z	Dilation/Aortic Valve, Opn, [Drug-eluting Intralum Dev, Intralum Dev, No Dev], NQ
027G0[4,D,Z]Z	Dilation/Mitral Valve, Opn, [Drug-eluting Intralum Dev, Intralum Dev, No Dev], NQ
027H0[4,D,Z]Z	Dilation/Pulmn Valve, Opn, [Drug-eluting Intralum Dev, Intralum Dev, No Dev], NQ
027J0[4,D,Z]Z	Dilation/Tricuspid Valve, Opn, [Drug-eluting Intralum Dev, Intralum Dev, No Dev], NQ
02NF0ZZ	Rls Aortic Valve, Opn Appr
02NG0ZZ	Rls Mitral Valve, Opn Appr
02NH0ZZ	Rls Pulmn Valve, Opn Appr
02NJ0ZZ	Rls Tricuspid Valve, Opn Appr
02QF*	Repair/Aortic Valve
02QG*	Repair/Mitral Valve
02QH*	Repair/Pulmn Valve
02QJ*	Repair/Tricuspid Valve
02RF07Z	Replace of Aortic Valve with Autol Sub, Opn Appr
02RF08Z	Replace of Aortic Valve with Zooplastic, Opn Appr
02RF0JZ	Replace of Aortic Valve with Synth Sub, Opn Appr
02RF0KZ	Replace of Aortic Valve with Nonaut Sub, Opn Appr
02RF47Z	Replace of Aortic Valve with Autol Sub, Perc Endo Appr
02RF48Z	Replace of Aortic Valve with Zooplastic, Perc Endo Appr
02RF4JZ	Replace of Aortic Valve with Synth Sub, Perc Endo Appr
02RF4KZ	Replace of Aortic Valve with Nonaut Sub, Perc Endo Appr
02RG[0,3,4][7,8,J,K]Z	Replace/Mitral Valve, [Opn, Perc, Perc Endo], [Auto Tissue Sub, Zooplastic Tissue, Synth Sub, Nonauto Tissue Sub], NQ
02RH07Z	Replace of Pulmn Valve with Autol Sub, Opn Appr
02RH08Z	Replace of Pulm Valve with Zooplastic, Opn Appr
02RH0JZ	Replace of Pulm Valve with Synth Sub, Opn Appr
02RH0KZ	Replace of Pulm Valve with Nonaut Sub, Opn Appr
02RH47Z	Replace of Pulm Valve with Autol Sub, Perc Endo Appr
02RH48Z	Replace of Pulm Valve with Zooplastic, Perc Endo Appr
02RH4JZ	Replace of Pulm Valve with Synth Sub, Perc Endo Appr
02RH4KZ	Replace of Pulm Valve with Nonaut Sub, Perc Endo Appr
02RJ*	Replace/Tricuspid Valve
02RP[0,4][7,8,J,K]Z	Replace/Pulmn Trunk, [Opn, Perc Endo], [Auto Tissue Sub, Zooplastic Tissue, Synth Sub, Nonauto Tissue Sub], NQ
02RQ[0,4][7,8,J,K]Z	Replace/Pulmn Artery, Rt, [Opn, Perc Endo], [Auto Tissue Sub, Zooplastic Tissue, Synth Sub, Nonauto Tissue Sub], NQ
02RR[0,4][7,8,J,K]Z	Replace/Pulmn Artery, Lt, [Opn, Perc Endo], [Auto Tissue Sub, Zooplastic Tissue, Synth Sub, Nonauto Tissue Sub], NQ
02RS[0,4][7,8,J,K]Z	Replace/Pulmn Vein, Rt, [Opn, Perc Endo], [Auto Tissue Sub, Zooplastic Tissue, Synth Sub, Nonauto Tissue Sub], NQ
02RT[0,4][7,8,J,K]Z	Replace/Pulmn Vein, Lt, [Opn, Perc Endo], [Auto Tissue Sub, Zooplastic Tissue, Synth Sub, Nonauto Tissue Sub], NQ
02RV[0,4][7,8,J,K]Z	Replace/Superior Vena Cava, [Opn, Perc Endo], [Auto Tissue Sub, Zooplastic Tissue, Synth Sub, Nonauto Tissue Sub], NQ
02RW[0,4][7,8,J,K]Z	Replace/Thoracic Aorta, [Opn, Perc Endo], [Auto Tissue Sub, Zooplastic Tissue, Synth Sub, Nonauto Tissue Sub], NQ
02UF*	Supl/Aortic Valve
02UG07Z	Supl Mitral Valve with Autol Sub, Opn Appr
02UG08Z	Supl Mitral Valve with Zooplastic, Opn Appr
02UG0JZ	Supl Mitral Valve with Synth Sub, Opn Appr
02UG0KZ	Supl Mitral Valve with Nonaut Sub, Opn Appr
02UG37Z	Supl Mitral Valve with Autol Sub, Perc Appr
02UG38Z	Supl Mitral Valve with Zooplastic, Perc Appr
02UG3KZ	Supl Mitral Valve with Nonaut Sub, Perc Appr
02UG47Z	Supl Mitral Valve with Autol Sub, Perc Endo Appr
02UG48Z	Supl Mitral Valve with Zooplastic, Perc Endo Appr
02UG4JZ	Supl Mitral Valve with Synth Sub, Perc Endo Appr
02UG4KZ	Supl Mitral Valve with Nonaut Sub, Perc Endo Appr
02UH*	Supl/Pulmn Valve
02UJ*	Supl/Tricuspid Valve
02UW[3,4]JZ	Supl/Thoracic Aorta, [Perc, Perc Endo], Synth Sub, NQ
02VW[0,3,4]DZ	Restrict/Thoracic Aorta, [Opn, Perc, Perc Endo], Intralum Dev, NQ
03R0[0,4][7,J,K]Z	Replace/Int Mammary Artery, Rt, [Opn, Perc Endo], [Auto Tissue Sub, Synth Sub, Nonauto Tissue Sub], NQ
03R1[0,4][7,J,K]Z	Replace/Int Mammary Artery, Lt, [Opn, Perc Endo], [Auto Tissue Sub, Synth Sub, Nonauto Tissue Sub], NQ
03R2[0,4][7,J,K]Z	Replace/Innominate Artery, [Opn, Perc Endo], [Auto Tissue Sub, Synth Sub, Nonauto Tissue Sub], NQ
03R3[0,4][7,J,K]Z	Replace/Subclavian Artery, Rt, [Opn, Perc Endo], [Auto Tissue Sub, Synth Sub, Nonauto Tissue Sub], NQ
03R4[0,4][7,J,K]Z	Replace/Subclavian Artery, Lt, [Opn, Perc Endo], [Auto Tissue Sub, Synth Sub, Nonauto Tissue Sub], NQ
05R0[0,4][7,J,K]Z	Replace/Azygos Vein, [Opn, Perc Endo], [Auto Tissue Sub, Synth Sub, Nonauto Tissue Sub], NQ
05R1[0,4][7,J,K]Z	Replace/Hemiazygos Vein, [Opn, Perc Endo], [Auto Tissue Sub, Synth Sub, Nonauto Tissue Sub], NQ
05R3[0,4][7,J,K]Z	Replace/Innominate Vein, Rt, [Opn, Perc Endo], [Auto Tissue Sub, Synth Sub, Nonauto Tissue Sub], NQ
05R4[0,4][7,J,K]Z	Replace/Innominate Vein, Lt, [Opn, Perc Endo], [Auto Tissue Sub, Synth Sub, Nonauto Tissue Sub], NQ
05R5[0,4][7,J,K]Z	Replace/Subclavian Vein, Rt, [Opn, Perc Endo], [Auto Tissue Sub, Synth Sub, Nonauto Tissue Sub], NQ
05R6[0,4][7,J,K]Z	Replace/Subclavian Vein, Lt, [Opn, Perc Endo], [Auto Tissue Sub, Synth Sub, Nonauto Tissue Sub], NQ
5A02[1,2]1[6,D]	Assistance/Cardiac, [Intermittent, Continuous], Output, [Oth Pump, Impeller Pump]

AND

Nonoperating Room Procedures

4A023FZ	Measurement of Cardiac Rhythm, Perc Appr
4A02[0,3]N[6,7,8]	Measurement/Cardiac, [Opn, Perc], Sampling and Pressure, [Rt Heart, Lt Heart, Bilat]
B20*	Imaging, Heart, Plain Radiography
B210[0,1,Y]ZZ	Fluoroscopy/Coronary Artery, Single, [High Osmolar, Low Osmolar, Oth Contrast], None, None
B211[0,1,Y]ZZ	Fluoroscopy/Coronary Arteries, Multi, [High Osmolar, Low Osmolar, Oth Contrast], None, None
B212[0,1,Y]ZZ	Fluoroscopy/Coronary Artery Bypass Graft, Single, [High Osmolar, Low Osmolar, Oth Contrast], None, None
B213[0,1,Y]ZZ	Fluoroscopy/Coronary Artery Bypass Grafts, Multi, [High Osmolar, Low Osmolar, Oth Contrast], None, None
B214*	Fluoroscopy/Heart, Rt
B215*	Fluoroscopy/Heart, Lt
B216*	Fluoroscopy/Heart, Rt and Lt
B217*	Fluoroscopy/Int Mammary Bypass Graft, Rt
B218*	Fluoroscopy/Int Mammary Bypass Graft, Lt
B21F*	Fluoroscopy/Bypass Graft, Oth

DRG 217   Cardiac Valve and Other Major Cardiothoracic Procedures with Cardiac Catheterization with CC
GMLOS 8.5	AMLOS 9.7	RW 6.2576	SP

Select operating room procedures AND nonoperating room procedures listed under DRG 216

Surgical	Medical	CC Indicator	MCC Indicator	Procedure Proxy	PDxMCC PDx acts as own MCC	PDxCC PDx acts as own CC

MDC 5: Diseases And Disorders Of The Circulatory System—SURGICAL

DRG 218 Cardiac Valve and Other Major Cardiothoracic Procedures with Cardiac Catheterization without CC/MCC
GMLOS 6.5   AMLOS 7.2   RW 5.4815   [SP]

Select operating room procedures AND nonoperating room procedures listed under DRG 216

DRG 219 Cardiac Valve and Other Major Cardiothoracic Procedures without Cardiac Catheterization with MCC
GMLOS 9.6   AMLOS 11.5   RW 7.5590   [SP]

Operating Room Procedures

027F0[4,D,Z]Z	Dilation/Aortic Valve, Opn, [Drug-eluting Intralum Dev, Intralum Dev, No Dev], NQ
027G0[4,D,Z]Z	Dilation/Mitral Valve, Opn, [Drug-eluting Intralum Dev, Intralum Dev, No Dev], NQ
027H0[4,D,Z]Z	Dilation/Pulmn Valve, Opn, [Drug-eluting Intralum Dev, Intralum Dev, No Dev], NQ
027J0[4,D,Z]Z	Dilation/Tricuspid Valve, Opn, [Drug-eluting Intralum Dev, Intralum Dev, No Dev], NQ
02NF0ZZ	Rls Aortic Valve, Opn Appr
02NG0ZZ	Rls Mitral Valve, Opn Appr
02NH0ZZ	Rls Pulmn Valve, Opn Appr
02NJ0ZZ	Rls Tricuspid Valve, Opn Appr
02QF*	Repair/Aortic Valve
02QG*	Repair/Mitral Valve
02QH*	Repair/Pulmn Valve
02QJ*	Repair/Tricuspid Valve
02RF07Z	Replace of Aortic Valve with Autol Sub, Opn Appr
02RF08Z	Replace of Aortic Valve with Zooplastic, Opn Appr
02RF0JZ	Replace of Aortic Valve with Synth Sub, Opn Appr
02RF0KZ	Replace of Aortic Valve with Nonaut Sub, Opn Appr
02RF47Z	Replace of Aortic Valve with Autol Sub, Perc Endo Appr
02RF48Z	Replace of Aortic Valve with Zooplastic, Perc Endo Appr
02RF4JZ	Replace of Aortic Valve with Synth Sub, Perc Endo Appr
02RF4KZ	Replace of Aortic Valve with Nonaut Sub, Perc Endo Appr
02RG[0,3,4][7,8,J,K]Z	Replace/Mitral Valve, [Opn, Perc, Perc Endo], [Auto Tissue Sub, Zooplastic Tissue, Synth Sub, Nonauto Tissue Sub], NQ
02RH07Z	Replace of Pulmn Valve with Autol Sub, Opn Appr
02RH08Z	Replace of Pulm Valve with Zooplastic, Opn Appr
02RH0JZ	Replace of Pulm Valve with Synth Sub, Opn Appr
02RH0KZ	Replace of Pulm Valve with Nonaut Sub, Opn Appr
02RH47Z	Replace of Pulm Valve with Autol Sub, Perc Endo Appr
02RH48Z	Replace of Pulm Valve with Zooplastic, Perc Endo Appr
02RH4JZ	Replace of Pulm Valve with Synth Sub, Perc Endo Appr
02RH4KZ	Replace of Pulm Valve with Nonaut Sub, Perc Endo Appr
02RJ*	Replace/Tricuspid Valve
02RP[0,4][7,8,J,K]Z	Replace/Pulmn Trunk, [Opn, Perc Endo], [Auto Tissue Sub, Zooplastic Tissue, Synth Sub, Nonauto Tissue Sub], NQ
02RQ[0,4][7,8,J,K]Z	Replace/Pulmn Artery, Rt, [Opn, Perc Endo], [Auto Tissue Sub, Zooplastic Tissue, Synth Sub, Nonauto Tissue Sub], NQ
02RR[0,4][7,8,J,K]Z	Replace/Pulmn Artery, Lt, [Opn, Perc Endo], [Auto Tissue Sub, Zooplastic Tissue, Synth Sub, Nonauto Tissue Sub], NQ
02RS[0,4][7,8,J,K]Z	Replace/Pulmn Vein, Rt, [Opn, Perc Endo], [Auto Tissue Sub, Zooplastic Tissue, Synth Sub, Nonauto Tissue Sub], NQ
02RT[0,4][7,8,J,K]Z	Replace/Pulmn Vein, Lt, [Opn, Perc Endo], [Auto Tissue Sub, Zooplastic Tissue, Synth Sub, Nonauto Tissue Sub], NQ
02RV[0,4][7,8,J,K]Z	Replace/Superior Vena Cava, [Opn, Perc Endo], [Auto Tissue Sub, Zooplastic Tissue, Synth Sub, Nonauto Tissue Sub], NQ
02RW[0,4][7,8,J,K]Z	Replace/Thoracic Aorta, [Opn, Perc Endo], [Auto Tissue Sub, Zooplastic Tissue, Synth Sub, Nonauto Tissue Sub], NQ
02UF*	Supl/Aortic Valve
02UG07Z	Supl Mitral Valve with Autol Sub, Opn Appr
02UG08Z	Supl Mitral Valve with Zooplastic, Opn Appr
02UG0JZ	Supl Mitral Valve with Synth Sub, Opn Appr
02UG0KZ	Supl Mitral Valve with Nonaut Sub, Opn Appr
02UG37Z	Supl Mitral Valve with Autol Sub, Perc Appr
02UG38Z	Supl Mitral Valve with Zooplastic, Perc Appr
02UG3KZ	Supl Mitral Valve with Nonaut Sub, Perc Appr
02UG47Z	Supl Mitral Valve with Autol Sub, Perc Endo Appr
02UG48Z	Supl Mitral Valve with Zooplastic, Perc Endo Appr
02UG4JZ	Supl Mitral Valve with Synth Sub, Perc Endo Appr
02UG4KZ	Supl Mitral Valve with Nonaut Sub, Perc Endo Appr
02UH*	Supl/Pulmn Valve
02UJ*	Supl/Tricuspid Valve
02UW[3,4]JZ	Supl/Thoracic Aorta, [Perc, Perc Endo], Synth Sub, NQ
02VW[0,3,4]DZ	Restrict/Thoracic Aorta, [Opn, Perc, Perc Endo], Intralum Dev, NQ

03R0[0,4][7,J,K]Z	Replace/Int Mammary Artery, Rt, [Opn, Perc Endo], [Auto Tissue Sub, Synth Sub, Nonauto Tissue Sub], NQ
03R1[0,4][7,J,K]Z	Replace/Int Mammary Artery, Lt, [Opn, Perc Endo], [Auto Tissue Sub, Synth Sub, Nonauto Tissue Sub], NQ
03R2[0,4][7,J,K]Z	Replace/Innominate Artery, [Opn, Perc Endo], [Auto Tissue Sub, Synth Sub, Nonauto Tissue Sub], NQ
03R3[0,4][7,J,K]Z	Replace/Subclavian Artery, Rt, [Opn, Perc Endo], [Auto Tissue Sub, Synth Sub, Nonauto Tissue Sub], NQ
03R4[0,4][7,J,K]Z	Replace/Subclavian Artery, Lt, [Opn, Perc Endo], [Auto Tissue Sub, Synth Sub, Nonauto Tissue Sub], NQ
05R0[0,4][7,J,K]Z	Replace/Azygos Vein, [Opn, Perc Endo], [Auto Tissue Sub, Synth Sub, Nonauto Tissue Sub], NQ
05R1[0,4][7,J,K]Z	Replace/Hemiazygos Vein, [Opn, Perc Endo], [Auto Tissue Sub, Synth Sub, Nonauto Tissue Sub], NQ
05R3[0,4][7,J,K]Z	Replace/Innominate Vein, Rt, [Opn, Perc Endo], [Auto Tissue Sub, Synth Sub, Nonauto Tissue Sub], NQ
05R4[0,4][7,J,K]Z	Replace/Innominate Vein, Lt, [Opn, Perc Endo], [Auto Tissue Sub, Synth Sub, Nonauto Tissue Sub], NQ
05R5[0,4][7,J,K]Z	Replace/Subclavian Vein, Rt, [Opn, Perc Endo], [Auto Tissue Sub, Synth Sub, Nonauto Tissue Sub], NQ
05R6[0,4][7,J,K]Z	Replace/Subclavian Vein, Lt, [Opn, Perc Endo], [Auto Tissue Sub, Synth Sub, Nonauto Tissue Sub], NQ
5A02116	Assist with Cardiac Output using Oth Pump, Intermittent
5A0211D	Assist with Cardiac Output using Impeller Pump, Intermittent
5A02216	Assistance with Cardiac Output using Oth Pump, Continuous
5A0221D	Assist with Cardiac Output using Impeller Pump, Continuous

DRG 220 Cardiac Valve and Other Major Cardiothoracic Procedures without Cardiac Catheterization with CC
GMLOS 6.5   AMLOS 7.1   RW 5.1074   [SP]

Select operating room procedures listed under DRG 219

DRG 221 Cardiac Valve and Other Major Cardiothoracic Procedures without Cardiac Catheterization without CC/MCC
GMLOS 4.8   AMLOS 5.4   RW 4.5406   [SP]

Select operating room procedures listed under DRG 219

DRG 222 Cardiac Defibrillator Implant with Cardiac Catheterization with Acute Myocardial Infarction/Heart Failure/Shock with MCC
GMLOS 10.2   AMLOS 12.1   RW 8.5188

Principal Diagnosis

I09.81	Rheumatic heart failure
I11.0	Hypertensive heart dz with heart failure
I13.0	Hyp hrt & chr kdny dis w hrt fail and stg 1-4/unsp chr kdny
I13.2	Hyp hrt & chr kdny dis w hrt fail and w stg 5 chr kdny/ESRD
I21*	STEMI & NSTEMI mocard infrc
I22*	Subsq STEMI & NSTEMI mocard infrc
I50*	Heart failure
R57.0	Cardiogenic shock
R57.9	Shock, unsp

AND

Operating Room Procedures

0JH6[0,3]9Z	Insert/SQ Tissue & Fascia, Chest, [Opn, Perc], Cardiac Resynchronization Defibrillator Pulse Generator, NQ
0JH8[0,3]9Z	Insert/SQ Tissue & Fascia, Abd, [Opn, Perc], Cardiac Resynchronization Defibrillator Pulse Generator, NQ

AND

02HK[0,3,4]KZ	Insert/Ventricle, Rt, [Opn, Perc, Perc Endo], Cardiac Lead, Defibrillator, NQ
02HL[0,3,4]KZ	Insert/Ventricle, Lt, [Opn, Perc, Perc Endo], Cardiac Lead, Defibrillator, NQ

OR

0JH6[0,3]AZ	Insert/SQ Tissue & Fascia, Chest, [Opn, Perc], Contractility Modulation Dev, NQ
0JH8[0,3]AZ	Insert/SQ Tissue & Fascia, Abd, [Opn, Perc], Contractility Modulation Dev, NQ

AND

02HL[0,3,4]MZ	Insert/Ventricle, Lt, [Opn, Perc, Perc Endo], Cardiac Lead, NQ

OR

0JH6[0,3]8Z	Insert/SQ Tissue & Fascia, Chest, [Opn, Perc], Defibrillator Generator, NQ

[T] **Transfer DRG**   [SP] **Special Payment**   * **Code Range**   6th and 7th Character of ZZ = No Device, No Qualifier ZX = No Device, Diagnostic

ØJH8[0,3]8Z   Insert/SQ Tissue & Fascia, Abd, [Opn, Perc], Defibrillator Generator, NQ
AND
02H6[0,3,4]KZ   Insert/Atrium, Rt, [Opn, Perc, Perc Endo], Cardiac Lead, Defibrillator, NQ
02H7[0,3,4]KZ   Insert/Atrium, Lt, [Opn, Perc, Perc Endo], Cardiac Lead, Defibrillator, NQ
02HK[0,3,4]KZ   Insert/Ventricle, Rt, [Opn, Perc, Perc Endo], Cardiac Lead, Defibrillator, NQ
02HL[0,3,4]KZ   Insert/Ventricle, Lt, [Opn, Perc, Perc Endo], Cardiac Lead, Defibrillator, NQ

OR
ØJH6[0,3]9Z   Insert/SQ Tissue & Fascia, Chest, [Opn, Perc], Cardiac Resynchronization Defibrillator Pulse Generator, NQ
ØJH8[0,3]9Z   Insert/SQ Tissue & Fascia, Abd, [Opn, Perc], Cardiac Resynchronization Defibrillator Pulse Generator, NQ
AND
02H40KZ   Insert of Defibrillator Lead into Cor Vein, Opn Appr
02H43[J,K,M]Z   Insert/Coronary Vein, Perc, [Cardiac Lead, Pacemaker, Cardiac Lead, Defibrillator, Cardiac Lead], NQ
02H44KZ   Insert of Defib Lead into Cor Vein, Perc Endo Appr
02H6[0,3,4]KZ   Insert/Atrium, Rt, [Opn, Perc, Perc Endo], Cardiac Lead, Defibrillator, NQ
02H7[0,3,4]KZ   Insert/Atrium, Lt, [Opn, Perc, Perc Endo], Cardiac Lead, Defibrillator, NQ
02HK[0,3,4]KZ   Insert/Ventricle, Rt, [Opn, Perc, Perc Endo], Cardiac Lead, Defibrillator, NQ
02HL[0,3,4]KZ   Insert/Ventricle, Lt, [Opn, Perc, Perc Endo], Cardiac Lead, Defibrillator, NQ
02HN[0,3,4][J,K,M]Z Insert/Pericardium, [Opn, Perc, Perc Endo], [Cardiac Lead, Pacemaker, Cardiac Lead, Defibrillator, Cardiac Lead], NQ

OR
ØJH6[0,3]8Z   Insert/SQ Tissue & Fascia, Chest, [Opn, Perc], Defibrillator Generator, NQ
ØJH8[0,3]8Z   Insert/SQ Tissue & Fascia, Abd, [Opn, Perc], Defibrillator Generator, NQ
AND
02H4[0,4]KZ   Insert/Coronary Vein, [Opn, Perc Endo], Cardiac Lead, Defibrillator, NQ
02H6[0,3,4]KZ   Insert/Atrium, Rt, [Opn, Perc, Perc Endo], Cardiac Lead, Defibrillator, NQ
02H7[0,3,4]KZ   Insert/Atrium, Lt, [Opn, Perc, Perc Endo], Cardiac Lead, Defibrillator, NQ
02HK[0,3,4]KZ   Insert/Ventricle, Rt, [Opn, Perc, Perc Endo], Cardiac Lead, Defibrillator, NQ
02HL[0,3,4]KZ   Insert/Ventricle, Lt, [Opn, Perc, Perc Endo], Cardiac Lead, Defibrillator, NQ
02HN[0,3,4][J,K,M]ZInsert/Pericardium, [Opn, Perc, Perc Endo], [Cardiac Lead, Pacemaker, Cardiac Lead, Defibrillator, Cardiac Lead], NQ

AND

Nonoperating Room Procedures
4A02[0,3]N[6,7,8] Measurement/Cardiac, [Opn, Perc], Sampling and Pressure, [Rt Heart, Lt Heart, Bilat]
B20*   Imaging, Heart, Plain Radiography
B210[0,1,Y]ZZ   Fluoroscopy/Coronary Artery, Single, [High Osmolar, Low Osmolar, Oth Contrast], None, None
B211[0,1,Y]ZZ   Fluoroscopy/Coronary Arteries, Multi, [High Osmolar, Low Osmolar, Oth Contrast], None, None
B212[0,1,Y]ZZ   Fluoroscopy/Coronary Artery Bypass Graft, Single, [High Osmolar, Low Osmolar, Oth Contrast], None, None
B213[0,1,Y]ZZ   Fluoroscopy/Coronary Artery Bypass Grafts, Multi, [High Osmolar, Low Osmolar, Oth Contrast], None, None
B214*   Fluoroscopy/Heart, Rt
B215*   Fluoroscopy/Heart, Lt
B216*   Fluoroscopy/Heart, Rt and Lt
B217*   Fluoroscopy/Int Mammary Bypass Graft, Rt
B218*   Fluoroscopy/Int Mammary Bypass Graft, Lt
B21F*   Fluoroscopy/Bypass Graft, Oth

DRG 223   Cardiac Defibrillator Implant with Cardiac Catheterization with Acute Myocardial Infarction/Heart Failure/Shock without MCC

| GMLOS 5.4 | AMLOS 6.6 | RW 6.4026 |

Select principal diagnosis AND operating room procedure combinations AND nonoperating room procedures listed under DRG 222

DRG 224   Cardiac Defibrillator Implant with Cardiac Catheterization without Acute Myocardial Infarction/Heart Failure/Shock with MCC

| GMLOS 8.0 | AMLOS 9.9 | RW 7.6140 |

Select any principal diagnosis listed under MDC 5 excluding acute myocardial infarction, heart failure and shock

Select operating room procedure combinations AND nonoperating room procedures listed under DRG 222

DRG 225   Cardiac Defibrillator Implant with Cardiac Catheterization without Acute Myocardial Infarction/Heart Failure/Shock without MCC

| GMLOS 4.1 | AMLOS 4.9 | RW 5.8561 |

Select any principal diagnosis listed under MDC 5 excluding acute myocardial infarction, heart failure and shock

Select operating room procedure combinations AND nonoperating room procedures listed under DRG 222

DRG 226   Cardiac Defibrillator Implant without Cardiac Catheterization with MCC

| GMLOS 6.8 | AMLOS 8.9 | RW 6.9737 |

Operating Room Procedures
ØJH6[0,3]9Z   Insert/SQ Tissue & Fascia, Chest, [Opn, Perc], Cardiac Resynchronization Defibrillator Pulse Generator, NQ
ØJH8[0,3]9Z   Insert/SQ Tissue & Fascia, Abd, [Opn, Perc], Cardiac Resynchronization Defibrillator Pulse Generator, NQ
AND
02HK[0,3,4]KZ   Insert/Ventricle, Rt, [Opn, Perc, Perc Endo], Cardiac Lead, Defibrillator, NQ
02HL[0,3,4]KZ   Insert/Ventricle, Lt, [Opn, Perc, Perc Endo], Cardiac Lead, Defibrillator, NQ

OR
ØJH6[0,3]AZ   Insert/SQ Tissue & Fascia, Chest, [Opn, Perc], Contractility Modulation Dev, NQ
ØJH8[0,3]AZ   Insert/SQ Tissue & Fascia, Abd, [Opn, Perc], Contractility Modulation Dev, NQ
AND
02HL[0,3,4]MZ   Insert/Ventricle, Lt, [Opn, Perc, Perc Endo], Cardiac Lead, NQ

OR
ØJH6[0,3]8Z   Insert/SQ Tissue & Fascia, Chest, [Opn, Perc], Defibrillator Generator, NQ
ØJH8[0,3]8Z   Insert/SQ Tissue & Fascia, Abd, [Opn, Perc], Defibrillator Generator, NQ
AND
02H6[0,3,4]KZ   Insert/Atrium, Rt, [Opn, Perc, Perc Endo], Cardiac Lead, Defibrillator, NQ
02H7[0,3,4]KZ   Insert/Atrium, Lt, [Opn, Perc, Perc Endo], Cardiac Lead, Defibrillator, NQ
02HK[0,3,4]KZ   Insert/Ventricle, Rt, [Opn, Perc, Perc Endo], Cardiac Lead, Defibrillator, NQ
02HL[0,3,4]KZ   Insert/Ventricle, Lt, [Opn, Perc, Perc Endo], Cardiac Lead, Defibrillator, NQ

OR
ØJH6[0,3]9Z   Insert/SQ Tissue & Fascia, Chest, [Opn, Perc], Cardiac Resynchronization Defibrillator Pulse Generator, NQ
ØJH8[0,3]9Z   Insert/SQ Tissue & Fascia, Abd, [Opn, Perc], Cardiac Resynchronization Defibrillator Pulse Generator, NQ
AND
02H40KZ   Insert of Defibrillator Lead into Cor Vein, Opn Appr
02H43[J,K,M]Z   Insert/Coronary Vein, Perc, [Cardiac Lead, Pacemaker, Cardiac Lead, Defibrillator, Cardiac Lead], NQ
02H44KZ   Insert of Defib Lead into Cor Vein, Perc Endo Appr
02H6[0,3,4]KZ   Insert/Atrium, Rt, [Opn, Perc, Perc Endo], Cardiac Lead, Defibrillator, NQ
02H7[0,3,4]KZ   Insert/Atrium, Lt, [Opn, Perc, Perc Endo], Cardiac Lead, Defibrillator, NQ
02HK[0,3,4]KZ   Insert/Ventricle, Rt, [Opn, Perc, Perc Endo], Cardiac Lead, Defibrillator, NQ
02HL[0,3,4]KZ   Insert/Ventricle, Lt, [Opn, Perc, Perc Endo], Cardiac Lead, Defibrillator, NQ
02HN[0,3,4][J,K,M]Z Insert/Pericardium, [Opn, Perc, Perc Endo], [Cardiac Lead, Pacemaker, Cardiac Lead, Defibrillator, Cardiac Lead], NQ

Surgical   **Medical**   **CC Indicator**   **MCC Indicator**   **Procedure Proxy**   **PDx MCC** PDx acts as own MCC   **PDx CC** PDx acts as own CC

© 2015 Optum360, LLC   MS-DRG Version 33.0   73

OR

ØJH6[Ø,3]8Z	Insert/SQ Tissue & Fascia, Chest, [Opn, Perc], Defibrillator Generator, NQ
ØJH8[Ø,3]8Z	Insert/SQ Tissue & Fascia, Abd, [Opn, Perc], Defibrillator Generator, NQ

AND

02H4[Ø,4]KZ	Insert/Coronary Vein, [Opn, Perc Endo], Cardiac Lead, Defibrillator, NQ
02H6[Ø,3,4]KZ	Insert/Atrium, Rt, [Opn, Perc, Perc Endo], Cardiac Lead, Defibrillator, NQ
02H7[Ø,3,4]KZ	Insert/Atrium, Lt, [Opn, Perc, Perc Endo], Cardiac Lead, Defibrillator, NQ
02HK[Ø,3,4]KZ	Insert/Ventricle, Rt, [Opn, Perc, Perc Endo], Cardiac Lead, Defibrillator, NQ
02HL[Ø,3,4]KZ	Insert/Ventricle, Lt, [Opn, Perc, Perc Endo], Cardiac Lead, Defibrillator, NQ
02HN[Ø,3,4][J,K,M]Z	Insert/Pericardium, [Opn, Perc, Perc Endo], [Cardiac Lead, Pacemaker, Cardiac Lead, Defibrillator, Cardiac Lead], NQ

DRG 227 Cardiac Defibrillator Implant without Cardiac Catheterization without MCC

GMLOS 3.1   AMLOS 4.3   RW 5.4816

Select operating room procedure combinations listed under DRG 226

DRG 228 Other Cardiothoracic Procedures with MCC

GMLOS 10.8   AMLOS 12.8   RW 6.9512

Operating Room Procedures

0216[Ø,4][9,A,J,K,Z][P,Q,R]	Bypass/Atrium, Rt, [Opn, Perc Endo], [Auto Venous Tissue, Auto Arterial Tissue, Synth Sub, Nonauto Tissue Sub, No Dev], [Pulmn Trunk, Pulmn Artery, Rt, Pulmn Artery, Lt]
0217[Ø,4][9,A,J,K,Z][P,Q,R]	Bypass/Atrium, Lt, [Opn, Perc Endo], [Auto Venous Tissue, Auto Arterial Tissue, Synth Sub, Nonauto Tissue Sub, No Dev], [Pulmn Trunk, Pulmn Artery, Rt, Pulmn Artery, Lt]
021K09[P,Q,R]	Bypass/Ventricle, Rt, Opn, Auto Venous Tissue, [Pulmn Trunk, Pulmn Artery, Rt, Pulmn Artery, Lt]
021K0A[P,Q,R]	Bypass/Ventricle, Rt, Opn, Auto Arterial Tissue, [Pulmn Trunk, Pulmn Artery, Rt, Pulmn Artery, Lt]
021K0J[P,Q,R]	Bypass/Ventricle, Rt, Opn, Synth Sub, [Pulmn Trunk, Pulmn Artery, Rt, Pulmn Artery, Lt]
021K0K[P,Q,R]	Bypass/Ventricle, Rt, Opn, Nonauto Tissue Sub, [Pulmn Trunk, Pulmn Artery, Rt, Pulmn Artery, Lt]
021K0Z[5,8,9,C,F,P,Q,R,W]	Bypass/Ventricle, Rt, Opn, No Dev, [Coronary Circulation, Int Mammary, Rt, Int Mammary, Lt, Thoracic Artery, Abd Artery, Pulmn Trunk, Pulmn Artery, Rt, Pulmn Artery, Lt, Aorta]
021K49[P,Q,R]	Bypass/Ventricle, Rt, Perc Endo, Auto Venous Tissue, [Pulmn Trunk, Pulmn Artery, Rt, Pulmn Artery, Lt]
021K4A[P,Q,R]	Bypass/Ventricle, Rt, Perc Endo, Auto Arterial Tissue, [Pulmn Trunk, Pulmn Artery, Rt, Pulmn Artery, Lt]
021K4J[P,Q,R]	Bypass/Ventricle, Rt, Perc Endo, Synth Sub, [Pulmn Trunk, Pulmn Artery, Rt, Pulmn Artery, Lt]
021K4K[P,Q,R]	Bypass/Ventricle, Rt, Perc Endo, Nonauto Tissue Sub, [Pulmn Trunk, Pulmn Artery, Rt, Pulmn Artery, Lt]
021K4Z[5,8,9,C,F,P,Q,R,W]	Bypass/Ventricle, Rt, Perc Endo, No Dev, [Coronary Circulation, Int Mammary, Rt, Int Mammary, Lt, Thoracic Artery, Abd Artery, Pulmn Trunk, Pulmn Artery, Rt, Pulmn Artery, Lt, Aorta]
021L09[P,Q,R]	Bypass/Ventricle, Lt, Opn, Auto Venous Tissue, [Pulmn Trunk, Pulmn Artery, Rt, Pulmn Artery, Lt]
021L0A[P,Q,R]	Bypass/Ventricle, Lt, Opn, Auto Arterial Tissue, [Pulmn Trunk, Pulmn Artery, Rt, Pulmn Artery, Lt]
021L0J[P,Q,R]	Bypass/Ventricle, Lt, Opn, Synth Sub, [Pulmn Trunk, Pulmn Artery, Rt, Pulmn Artery, Lt]
021L0K[P,Q,R]	Bypass/Ventricle, Lt, Opn, Nonauto Tissue Sub, [Pulmn Trunk, Pulmn Artery, Rt, Pulmn Artery, Lt]
021L0Z[5,8,9,C,F,P,Q,R,W]	Bypass/Ventricle, Lt, Opn, No Dev, [Coronary Circulation, Int Mammary, Rt, Int Mammary, Lt, Thoracic Artery, Abd Artery, Pulmn Trunk, Pulmn Artery, Rt, Pulmn Artery, Lt, Aorta]
021L49[P,Q,R]	Bypass/Ventricle, Lt, Perc Endo, Auto Venous Tissue, [Pulmn Trunk, Pulmn Artery, Rt, Pulmn Artery, Lt]
021L4A[P,Q,R]	Bypass/Ventricle, Lt, Perc Endo, Auto Arterial Tissue, [Pulmn Trunk, Pulmn Artery, Rt, Pulmn Artery, Lt]
021L4J[P,Q,R]	Bypass/Ventricle, Lt, Perc Endo, Synth Sub, [Pulmn Trunk, Pulmn Artery, Rt, Pulmn Artery, Lt]
021L4K[P,Q,R]	Bypass/Ventricle, Lt, Perc Endo, Nonauto Tissue Sub, [Pulmn Trunk, Pulmn Artery, Rt, Pulmn Artery, Lt]

021L4Z[5,8,9,C,F,P,Q,R,W]	Bypass/Ventricle, Lt, Perc Endo, No Dev, [Coronary Circulation, Int Mammary, Rt, Int Mammary, Lt, Thoracic Artery, Abd Artery, Pulmn Trunk, Pulmn Artery, Rt, Pulmn Artery, Lt, Aorta]
0254[Ø,3,4]ZZ	Destr/Coronary Vein, [Opn, Perc, Perc Endo]
0255[Ø,4]ZZ	Destr/Atrial Septum, [Opn, Perc Endo]
0256[Ø,4]ZZ	Destr/Atrium, Rt, [Opn, Perc Endo]
0257[Ø,4]ZZ	Destr/Atrium, Lt, [Opn, Perc Endo]
0258[Ø,4]ZZ	Destr/Conduction Mech, [Opn, Perc Endo]
0259[Ø,4]ZZ	Destr/Chordae Tendineae, [Opn, Perc Endo]
025D[Ø,3,4]ZZ	Destr/Papillary Muscle, [Opn, Perc, Perc Endo]
025F[Ø,4]ZZ	Destr/Aortic Valve, [Opn, Perc Endo]
025G[Ø,4]ZZ	Destr/Mitral Valve, [Opn, Perc Endo]
025H[Ø,4]ZZ	Destr/Pulmn Valve, [Opn, Perc Endo]
025J[Ø,4]ZZ	Destr/Tricuspid Valve, [Opn, Perc Endo]
025K[Ø,4]ZZ	Destr/Ventricle, Rt, [Opn, Perc Endo]
025L[Ø,4]ZZ	Destr/Ventricle, Lt, [Opn, Perc Endo]
025M[Ø,4]ZZ	Destr/Ventricular Septum, [Opn, Perc Endo]
0270Ø[4,D,T,Z][6,Z]	Dilation/Coronary Artery, One Site, Opn, [Drug-eluting Intralum Dev, Intralum Dev, Radioact Intralum Dev, No Dev], [Bifurcation, NQ]
0271Ø[4,D,T,Z][6,Z]	Dilation/Coronary Artery, Two Sites, Opn, [Drug-eluting Intralum Dev, Intralum Dev, Radioact Intralum Dev, No Dev], [Bifurcation, NQ]
0272Ø[4,D,T,Z][6,Z]	Dilation/Coronary Artery, Three Sites, Opn, [Drug-eluting Intralum Dev, Intralum Dev, Radioact Intralum Dev, No Dev], [Bifurcation, NQ]
0273Ø[4,D,T,Z][6,Z]	Dilation/Coronary Artery, Four or More Sites, Opn, [Drug-eluting Intralum Dev, Intralum Dev, Radioact Intralum Dev, No Dev], [Bifurcation, NQ]
0289[Ø,3,4]ZZ	Div/Chordae Tendineae, [Opn, Perc, Perc Endo]
028D[Ø,3,4]ZZ	Div/Papillary Muscle, [Opn, Perc, Perc Endo]
02B4[Ø,3,4]ZZ	Exc/Coronary Vein, [Opn, Perc, Perc Endo]
02B5[Ø,4]ZZ	Exc/Atrial Septum, [Opn, Perc Endo]
02B6[Ø,4]ZZ	Exc/Atrium, Rt, [Opn, Perc Endo]
02B7[Ø,4]ZZ	Exc/Atrium, Lt, [Opn, Perc Endo]
02B8[Ø,4]ZZ	Exc/Conduction Mech, [Opn, Perc Endo]
02B9[Ø,4]ZZ	Exc/Chordae Tendineae, [Opn, Perc Endo]
02BD[Ø,3,4]ZZ	Exc/Papillary Muscle, [Opn, Perc, Perc Endo]
02BF[Ø,4]ZZ	Exc/Aortic Valve, [Opn, Perc Endo]
02BG[Ø,4]ZZ	Exc/Mitral Valve, [Opn, Perc Endo]
02BH[Ø,4]ZZ	Exc/Pulmn Valve, [Opn, Perc Endo]
02BJ[Ø,4]ZZ	Exc/Tricuspid Valve, [Opn, Perc Endo]
02BK[Ø,3,4]ZZ	Exc/Ventricle, Rt, [Opn, Perc, Perc Endo]
02BL[Ø,3,4]ZZ	Exc/Ventricle, Lt, [Opn, Perc, Perc Endo]
02BM[Ø,4]ZZ	Exc/Ventricular Septum, [Opn, Perc Endo]
02C00ZZ	Extir of Matter from 1 Cor Art, Opn Appr
02C10ZZ	Extir of Matter from 2 Cor Art, Opn Appr
02C20ZZ	Extir of Matter from 3 Cor Art, Opn Appr
02C30ZZ	Extir of Matter from 4+ Cor Art, Opn Appr
02C4[Ø,3,4]ZZ	Extir/Coronary Vein, [Opn, Perc, Perc Endo]
02C5[Ø,3,4]ZZ	Extir/Atrial Septum, [Opn, Perc, Perc Endo]
02C6[Ø,3,4]ZZ	Extir/Atrium, Rt, [Opn, Perc, Perc Endo]
02C7[Ø,3,4]ZZ	Extir/Atrium, Lt, [Opn, Perc, Perc Endo]
02C8[Ø,3,4]ZZ	Extir/Conduction Mech, [Opn, Perc, Perc Endo]
02C9[Ø,3,4]ZZ	Extir/Chordae Tendineae, [Opn, Perc, Perc Endo]
02CD[Ø,3,4]ZZ	Extir/Papillary Muscle, [Opn, Perc, Perc Endo]
02CF0ZZ	Extir of Matter from Aortic Valve, Opn Appr
02CG0ZZ	Extir of Matter from Mitral Valve, Opn Appr
02CH0ZZ	Extir of Matter from Pulmn Valve, Opn Appr
02CJ0ZZ	Extir of Matter from Tricuspid Valve, Opn Appr
02CK[Ø,3,4]ZZ	Extir/Ventricle, Rt, [Opn, Perc, Perc Endo]
02CL[Ø,3,4]ZZ	Extir/Ventricle, Lt, [Opn, Perc, Perc Endo]
02CM[Ø,3,4]ZZ	Extir/Ventricular Septum, [Opn, Perc, Perc Endo]
02H4[Ø,3,4][2,3,D]Z	Insert/Coronary Vein, [Opn, Perc, Perc Endo], [Monitoring Dev, Inf Dev, Intralum Dev], NQ
02H603Z	Insert of Inf Device into Rt Atrium, Opn Appr
02H60DZ	Insert of Intralum Dev into Rt Atrium, Opn Appr
02H63DZ	Insert of Intralum Dev into Rt Atrium, Perc Appr
02H643Z	Insert of Inf Dev into Rt Atrium, Perc Endo Appr
02H64DZ	Insert of Intralum Dev into Rt Atrium, Perc Endo Appr
02H6[Ø,3,4]2Z	Insert of Monitoring Dev into Rt Atrium, [Opn, Perc, Perc Endo]
02H7[Ø,3,4][2,3,D]Z	Insert/Atrium, Lt, [Opn, Perc, Perc Endo], [Monitoring Dev, Inf Dev, Intralum Dev], NQ
02HK03Z	Insert of Inf Device into Rt Ventricle, Opn Appr
02HK0DZ	Insert of Intralum Dev into Rt Ventricle, Opn Appr
02HK3DZ	Insert of Intralum Dev into Rt Ventricle, Perc Appr
02HK43Z	Insert of Inf Dev into Rt Ventricle, Perc Endo Appr
02HK4DZ	Insert of Intralum Dev into Rt Ventricle, Perc Endo Appr

---

⊤ Transfer DRG   SP Special Payment   * Code Range   6th and 7th Character of ZZ = No Device, No Qualifier ZX = No Device, Diagnostic

74   MS-DRG Version 33.0   © 2015 Optum360, LLC

02HL[0,3,4][2,3,D]Z Insert/Ventricle, Lt, [Opn, Perc, Perc Endo], [Monitoring Dev, Inf Dev, Intralum Dev], NQ
02N5[0,3,4]ZZ Rls/Atrial Septum, [Opn, Perc, Perc Endo]
02N6[0,3,4]ZZ Rls/Atrium, Rt, [Opn, Perc, Perc Endo]
02N7[0,3,4]ZZ Rls/Atrium, Lt, [Opn, Perc, Perc Endo]
02N9[0,3,4]ZZ Rls/Chordae Tendineae, [Opn, Perc, Perc Endo]
02ND[0,3,4]ZZ Rls/Papillary Muscle, [Opn, Perc, Perc Endo]
02NK[0,3,4]ZZ Rls/Ventricle, Rt, [Opn, Perc, Perc Endo]
02NL[0,3,4]ZZ Rls/Ventricle, Lt, [Opn, Perc, Perc Endo]
02NM[0,3,4]ZZ Rls/Ventricular Septum, [Opn, Perc, Perc Endo]
02PA[0,3,4][2,3,7,8,C,D,J,K]Z Rmvl/Heart, [Opn, Perc, Perc Endo], [Monitoring Dev, Inf Dev, Auto Tissue Sub, Zooplastic Tissue, Extralum Dev, Intralum Dev, Synth Sub, Nonauto Tissue Sub], NQ
02Q0[0,3,4]ZZ Rpr/Coronary Artery, One Site, [Opn, Perc, Perc Endo]
02Q1[0,3,4]ZZ Rpr/Coronary Artery, Two Sites, [Opn, Perc, Perc Endo]
02Q2[0,3,4]ZZ Rpr/Coronary Artery, Three Sites, [Opn, Perc, Perc Endo]
02Q3[0,3,4]ZZ Rpr/Coronary Artery, Four or More Sites, [Opn, Perc, Perc Endo]
02Q4[0,3,4]ZZ Rpr/Coronary Vein, [Opn, Perc, Perc Endo]
02Q5[0,3,4]ZZ Rpr/Atrial Septum, [Opn, Perc, Perc Endo]
02Q9[0,3,4]ZZ Rpr/Chordae Tendineae, [Opn, Perc, Perc Endo]
02QB[0,3,4]ZZ Rpr/Heart, Rt, [Opn, Perc, Perc Endo]
02QC[0,3,4]ZZ Rpr/Heart, Lt, [Opn, Perc, Perc Endo]
02QD[0,3,4]ZZ Rpr/Papillary Muscle, [Opn, Perc, Perc Endo]
02QM[0,3,4]ZZ Rpr/Ventricular Septum, [Opn, Perc, Perc Endo]
02R9[0,4][7,8,J,K]Z Replace/Chordae Tendineae, [Opn, Perc, Perc Endo], [Auto Tissue Sub, Zooplastic Tissue, Synth Sub, Nonauto Tissue Sub], NQ
02RD[0,4][7,8,J,K]Z Replace/Papillary Muscle, [Opn, Perc Endo], [Auto Tissue Sub, Zooplastic Tissue, Synth Sub, Nonauto Tissue Sub], NQ
02RK[0,4][7,K]Z Replace/Ventricle, Rt, [Opn, Perc Endo], [Auto Tissue Sub, Nonauto Tissue Sub], NQ
02RL[0,4][7,K]Z Replace/Ventricle, Lt, [Opn, Perc Endo], [Auto Tissue Sub, Nonauto Tissue Sub], NQ
02RM[0,4][7,J,K]Z Replace/Ventricular Septum, [Opn, Perc Endo], [Auto Tissue Sub, Synth Sub, Nonauto Tissue Sub], NQ
02T5[0,3,4]ZZ Resect/Atrial Septum, [Opn, Perc, Perc Endo]
02T8[0,4]ZZ Resect/Conduction Mech, [Opn, Perc Endo]
02T9[0,3,4]ZZ Resect/Chordae Tendineae, [Opn, Perc, Perc Endo]
02TD[0,3,4]ZZ Resect/Papillary Muscle, [Opn, Perc, Perc Endo]
02TH[0,3,4]ZZ Resect/Pulmn Valve, [Opn, Perc, Perc Endo]
02TM[0,3,4]ZZ Resect/Ventricular Septum, [Opn, Perc, Perc Endo]
02U50JZ Supl Atrial Septum with Synth Sub, Opn Appr
02U5[0,3,4][7,8,K]Z Supl/Atrial Septum, [Opn, Perc, Perc Endo], [Auto Tissue Sub, Zooplastic Tissue, Nonauto Tissue Sub], NQ
02U60[7,8,K]Z Supl/Atrium, Rt, Opn, [Auto Tissue Sub, Zooplastic Tissue, Nonauto Tissue Sub], NQ
02U7[0,3,4][7,8,K]Z Supl/Atrium, Lt, [Opn, Perc, Perc Endo], [Auto Tissue Sub, Zooplastic Tissue, Nonauto Tissue Sub], NQ
02U9[0,3,4][7,8,J,K]Z Supl/Chordae Tendineae, [Opn, Perc, Perc Endo], [Auto Tissue Sub, Zooplastic Tissue, Synth Sub, Nonauto Tissue Sub], NQ
02UD[0,3,4][7,8,J,K]Z Supl/Papillary Muscle, [Opn, Perc, Perc Endo], [Auto Tissue Sub, Zooplastic Tissue, Synth Sub, Nonauto Tissue Sub], NQ
02UK[0,3,4]KZ Supl/Ventricle, Rt, [Opn, Perc, Perc Endo], Nonauto Tissue Sub, NQ
02UL[0,3,4]KZ Supl/Ventricle, Lt, [Opn, Perc, Perc Endo], Nonauto Tissue Sub, NQ
02UM[0,3,4][7,J,K]Z Supl/Ventricular Septum, [Opn, Perc, Perc Endo], [Auto Tissue Sub, Synth Sub, Nonauto Tissue Sub], NQ
02UM[3,4]8Z Supl/Ventricular Septum, [Perc, Perc Endo], Zooplastic Tissue, NQ
02W5[0,4]JZ Rev/Atrial Septum, [Opn, Perc Endo], Synth Sub, NQ
02WA[0,3,4][2,3,7,8,C,D,K]Z Rev/Heart, [Opn, Perc, Perc Endo], [Monitoring Dev, Inf Dev, Auto Tissue Sub, Zooplastic Tissue, Extralum Dev, Intralum Dev, Nonauto Tissue Sub], NQ
02WA[3,4]JZ Rev/Heart, [Perc, Perc Endo], Synth Sub, NQ
02WF[0,4][7,8,J,K]Z Rev/Aortic Valve, [Opn, Perc Endo], [Auto Tissue Sub, Zooplastic Tissue, Synth Sub, Nonauto Tissue Sub], NQ
02WG[0,4][7,8,J,K]Z Rev/Mitral Valve, [Opn, Perc Endo], [Auto Tissue Sub, Zooplastic Tissue, Synth Sub, Nonauto Tissue Sub], NQ
02WH[0,4][7,8,J,K]Z Rev/Pulmn Valve, [Opn, Perc Endo], [Auto Tissue Sub, Zooplastic Tissue, Synth Sub, Nonauto Tissue Sub], NQ
02WJ[0,4][7,8,J,K]Z Rev/Tricuspid Valve, [Opn, Perc Endo], [Auto Tissue Sub, Zooplastic Tissue, Synth Sub, Nonauto Tissue Sub], NQ
02WM[0,4]JZ Rev/Ventricular Septum, [Opn, Perc Endo], Synth Sub, NQ

DRG 229 **Other Cardiothoracic Procedures with CC**
GMLOS 6.5 AMLOS 7.4 RW 4.5589

Select operating room procedures listed under DRG 228

DRG 230 **Other Cardiothoracic Procedures without CC/MCC**
GMLOS 4.3 AMLOS 4.9 RW 4.3018

Select operating room procedures listed under DRG 228

DRG 231 **Coronary Bypass with PTCA with MCC**
GMLOS 9.9 AMLOS 11.7 RW 7.8056

Operating Room Procedures
0210[0,4][9,A,J,K,Z][3,8,9,C,F] Bypass/Coronary Artery, One Site, [Opn, Perc Endo], [Auto Venous Tissue, Auto Arterial Tissue, Synth Sub, Nonauto Tissue Sub, No Dev], [Coronary Artery, Int Mammary, Rt, Int Mammary, Lt, Thoracic Artery, Abd Artery]
0210[0,4][9,A,J,K]W Bypass/Coronary Artery, One Site, [Opn, Perc Endo], [Auto Venous Tissue, Auto Arterial Tissue, Synth Sub, Nonauto Tissue Sub], Aorta
0211[0,4][9,A,J,K,Z][3,8,9,C,F] Bypass/Coronary Artery, Two Sites, [Opn, Perc Endo], [Auto Venous Tissue, Auto Arterial Tissue, Synth Sub, Nonauto Tissue Sub, No Dev], [Coronary Artery, Int Mammary, Rt, Int Mammary, Lt, Thoracic Artery, Abd Artery]
0211[0,4][9,A,J,K]W Bypass/Coronary Artery, Two Sites, [Opn, Perc Endo], [Auto Venous Tissue, Auto Arterial Tissue, Synth Sub, Nonauto Tissue Sub], Aorta
0212[0,4][9,A,J,K,Z][3,8,9,C,F] Bypass/Coronary Artery, Three Sites, [Opn, Perc Endo], [Auto Venous Tissue, Auto Arterial Tissue, Synth Sub, Nonauto Tissue Sub, No Dev], [Coronary Artery, Int Mammary, Rt, Int Mammary, Lt, Thoracic Artery, Abd Artery]
0212[0,4][9,A,J,K]W Bypass/Coronary Artery, Three Sites, [Opn, Perc Endo], [Auto Venous Tissue, Auto Arterial Tissue, Synth Sub, Nonauto Tissue Sub], Aorta
0213[0,4][9,A,J,K,Z][3,8,9,C,F] Bypass/Coronary Artery, Four or More Sites, [Opn, Perc Endo], [Auto Venous Tissue, Auto Arterial Tissue, Synth Sub, Nonauto Tissue Sub, No Dev], [Coronary Artery, Int Mammary, Rt, Int Mammary, Lt, Thoracic Artery, Abd Artery]
0213[0,4][9,A,J,K]W Bypass/Coronary Artery, Four or More Sites, [Opn, Perc Endo], [Auto Venous Tissue, Auto Arterial Tissue, Synth Sub, Nonauto Tissue Sub], Aorta

AND
0270[3,4][4,D,T,Z][6,Z] Dilation/Coronary Artery, One Site, [Perc, Perc Endo], [Drug-eluting Intralum Dev, Intralum Dev, Radioact Intralum Dev, No Dev], [Bifurcation, NQ]
0271[3,4][4,D,T,Z][6,Z] Dilation/Coronary Artery, Two Sites, [Perc, Perc Endo], [Drug-eluting Intralum Dev, Intralum Dev, Radioact Intralum Dev, No Dev], [Bifurcation, NQ]
0272[3,4][4,D,T,Z][6,Z] Dilation/Coronary Artery, Three Sites, [Perc, Perc Endo], [Drug-eluting Intralum Dev, Intralum Dev, Radioact Intralum Dev, No Dev], [Bifurcation, NQ]
0273[3,4][4,D,T,Z][6,Z] Dilation/Coronary Artery, Four or More Sites, [Perc, Perc Endo], [Drug-eluting Intralum Dev, Intralum Dev, Radioact Intralum Dev, No Dev], [Bifurcation, NQ]
027F[3,4][4,D,Z]Z Dilation/Aortic Valve, [Perc, Perc Endo], [Drug-eluting Intralum Dev, Intralum Dev, No Dev], NQ
027G[3,4][4,D,Z]Z Dilation/Mitral Valve, [Perc, Perc Endo], [Drug-eluting Intralum Dev, Intralum Dev, No Dev], NQ
027H[3,4][4,D,Z]Z Dilation/Pulmn Valve, [Perc, Perc Endo], [Drug-eluting Intralum Dev, Intralum Dev, No Dev], NQ
027J[3,4][4,D,Z]Z Dilation/Tricuspid Valve, [Perc, Perc Endo], [Drug-eluting Intralum Dev, Intralum Dev, No Dev], NQ
02C03ZZ Extir of Matter from 1 Cor Art, Perc Appr
02C13ZZ Extir of Matter from 2 Cor Art, Perc Appr
02C23ZZ Extir of Matter from 3 Cor Art, Perc Appr
02C33ZZ Extir of Matter from 4+ Cor Art, Perc Appr
02UG3JZ Supl Mitral Valve with Synth Sub, Perc Appr
X2C0361 Extirpate matter from 1 Cor Art, Orbit Athrect, New Tech 1
X2C1361 Extirpate matter from 2 Cor Art, Orbit Athrect, New Tech 1
X2C2361 Extirpate matter from 3 Cor Art, Orbit Athrect, New Tech 1
X2C3361 Extirpate matter from 4+ Cor Art, Orbit Athrect, New Tech 1

DRG 232 **Coronary Bypass with PTCA without MCC**
GMLOS 7.9 AMLOS 8.6 RW 5.7779

Select operating room procedure combinations listed under DRG 231

Surgical **Medical** **CC Indicator** **MCC Indicator** **Procedure Proxy** PDxMCC PDx acts as own MCC PDxCC PDx acts as own CC

MDC 5: Diseases And Disorders Of The Circulatory System—SURGICAL

DRG 233　Coronary Bypass with Cardiac Catheterization with MCC
　　　　GMLOS 11.6　　　AMLOS 13.0　　　RW 7.3581　　[T]

Operating Room Procedures

0210[0,4][9,A,J,K,Z][3,8,9,C,F] Bypass/Coronary Artery, One Site, [Opn, Perc Endo], [Auto Venous Tissue, Auto Arterial Tissue, Synth Sub, Nonauto Tissue Sub, No Dev], [Coronary Artery, Int Mammary, Rt, Int Mammary, Lt, Thoracic Artery, Abd Artery]

0210[0,4][9,A,J,K]W Bypass/Coronary Artery, One Site, [Opn, Perc Endo], [Auto Venous Tissue, Auto Arterial Tissue, Synth Sub, Nonauto Tissue Sub], Aorta

0211[0,4][9,A,J,K,Z][3,8,9,C,F] Bypass/Coronary Artery, Two Sites, [Opn, Perc Endo], [Auto Venous Tissue, Auto Arterial Tissue, Synth Sub, Nonauto Tissue Sub, No Dev], [Coronary Artery, Int Mammary, Rt, Int Mammary, Lt, Thoracic Artery, Abd Artery]

0211[0,4][9,A,J,K]W Bypass/Coronary Artery, Two Sites, [Opn, Perc Endo], [Auto Venous Tissue, Auto Arterial Tissue, Synth Sub, Nonauto Tissue Sub], Aorta

0212[0,4][9,A,J,K,Z][3,8,9,C,F] Bypass/Coronary Artery, Three Sites, [Opn, Perc Endo], [Auto Venous Tissue, Auto Arterial Tissue, Synth Sub, Nonauto Tissue Sub, No Dev], [Coronary Artery, Int Mammary, Rt, Int Mammary, Lt, Thoracic Artery, Abd Artery]

0212[0,4][9,A,J,K]W Bypass/Coronary Artery, Three Sites, [Opn, Perc Endo], [Auto Venous Tissue, Auto Arterial Tissue, Synth Sub, Nonauto Tissue Sub], Aorta

0213[0,4][9,A,J,K,Z][3,8,9,C,F] Bypass/Coronary Artery, Four or More Sites, [Opn, Perc Endo], [Auto Venous Tissue, Auto Arterial Tissue, Synth Sub, Nonauto Tissue Sub, No Dev], [Coronary Artery, Int Mammary, Rt, Int Mammary, Lt, Thoracic Artery, Abd Artery]

0213[0,4][9,A,J,K]W Bypass/Coronary Artery, Four or More Sites, [Opn, Perc Endo], [Auto Venous Tissue, Auto Arterial Tissue, Synth Sub, Nonauto Tissue Sub], Aorta

AND

Nonoperating Room Procedures

4A02[0,3]N[6,7,8] Measurement/Cardiac, [Opn, Perc], Sampling and Pressure, [Rt Heart, Lt Heart, Bilat]
B20* Imaging, Heart, Plain Radiography
B210[0,1,Y]ZZ Fluoroscopy/Coronary Artery, Single, [High Osmolar, Low Osmolar, Oth Contrast], None, None
B211[0,1,Y]ZZ Fluoroscopy/Coronary Arteries, Multi, [High Osmolar, Low Osmolar, Oth Contrast], None, None
B212[0,1,Y]ZZ Fluoroscopy/Coronary Artery Bypass Graft, Single, [High Osmolar, Low Osmolar, Oth Contrast], None, None
B213[0,1,Y]ZZ Fluoroscopy/Coronary Artery Bypass Grafts, Multi, [High Osmolar, Low Osmolar, Oth Contrast], None, None
B214* Fluoroscopy/Heart, Rt
B215* Fluoroscopy/Heart, Lt
B216* Fluoroscopy/Heart, Rt and Lt
B217* Fluoroscopy/Int Mammary Bypass Graft, Rt
B218* Fluoroscopy/Int Mammary Bypass Graft, Lt
B21F* Fluoroscopy/Bypass Graft, Oth

DRG 234　Coronary Bypass with Cardiac Catheterization without MCC
　　　　GMLOS 8.0　　　AMLOS 8.6　　　RW 4.9076　　[T]

Select operating room procedure combinations listed under DRG 233

DRG 235　Coronary Bypass without Cardiac Catheterization with MCC
　　　　GMLOS 8.9　　　AMLOS 10.3　　　RW 5.8103　　[T]

Operating Room Procedures

0210[0,4][9,A,J,K,Z][3,8,9,C,F] Bypass/Coronary Artery, One Site, [Opn, Perc Endo], [Auto Venous Tissue, Auto Arterial Tissue, Synth Sub, Nonauto Tissue Sub, No Dev], [Coronary Artery, Int Mammary, Rt, Int Mammary, Lt, Thoracic Artery, Abd Artery]

0210[0,4][9,A,J,K]W Bypass/Coronary Artery, One Site, [Opn, Perc Endo], [Auto Venous Tissue, Auto Arterial Tissue, Synth Sub, Nonauto Tissue Sub], Aorta

0211[0,4][9,A,J,K,Z][3,8,9,C,F] Bypass/Coronary Artery, Two Sites, [Opn, Perc Endo], [Auto Venous Tissue, Auto Arterial Tissue, Synth Sub, Nonauto Tissue Sub, No Dev], [Coronary Artery, Int Mammary, Rt, Int Mammary, Lt, Thoracic Artery, Abd Artery]

0211[0,4][9,A,J,K]W Bypass/Coronary Artery, Two Sites, [Opn, Perc Endo], [Auto Venous Tissue, Auto Arterial Tissue, Synth Sub, Nonauto Tissue Sub], Aorta

0212[0,4][9,A,J,K,Z][3,8,9,C,F] Bypass/Coronary Artery, Three Sites, [Opn, Perc Endo], [Auto Venous Tissue, Auto Arterial Tissue, Synth Sub, Nonauto Tissue Sub, No Dev], [Coronary Artery, Int Mammary, Rt, Int Mammary, Lt, Thoracic Artery, Abd Artery]

0212[0,4][9,A,J,K]W Bypass/Coronary Artery, Three Sites, [Opn, Perc Endo], [Auto Venous Tissue, Auto Arterial Tissue, Synth Sub, Nonauto Tissue Sub], Aorta

0213[0,4][9,A,J,K,Z][3,8,9,C,F] Bypass/Coronary Artery, Four or More Sites, [Opn, Perc Endo], [Auto Venous Tissue, Auto Arterial Tissue, Synth Sub, Nonauto Tissue Sub, No Dev], [Coronary Artery, Int Mammary, Rt, Int Mammary, Lt, Thoracic Artery, Abd Artery]

0213[0,4][9,A,J,K]W Bypass/Coronary Artery, Four or More Sites, [Opn, Perc Endo], [Auto Venous Tissue, Auto Arterial Tissue, Synth Sub, Nonauto Tissue Sub], Aorta

DRG 236　Coronary Bypass without Cardiac Catheterization without MCC
　　　　GMLOS 6.0　　　AMLOS 6.5　　　RW 3.8013　　[T]

Select operating room procedures listed under DRG 235

DRG 237　Major Cardiovascular Procedures with MCC
　　　　GMLOS 0.0　　　AMLOS 0.0　　　RW 0.0000

Omitted in October 2016 Grouper version.

DRG 238　Major Cardiac Procedures without MCC
　　　　GMLOS 0.0　　　AMLOS 0.0　　　RW 0.0000

Omitted in October 2016 Grouper version.

DRG 239　Amputation for Circulatory System Disorders Except Upper Limb and Toe with MCC
　　　　GMLOS 10.5　　　AMLOS 13.4　　　RW 4.8380　　[T]

Operating Room Procedures

0Y620ZZ Detach at Rt Hindquarter, Opn Appr
0Y630ZZ Detach at Lt Hindquarter, Opn Appr
0Y640ZZ Detach at Bilat Hindquarter, Opn Appr
0Y670ZZ Detach at Rt Femor Region, Opn Appr
0Y680ZZ Detach at Lt Femor Region, Opn Appr
0Y6C* Detach/Upr Leg, Rt
0Y6D* Detach/Upr Leg, Lt
0Y6F0ZZ Detach at Rt Knee Region, Opn Appr
0Y6G0ZZ Detach at Lt Knee Region, Opn Appr
0Y6H* Detach/Lwr Leg, Rt
0Y6J* Detach/Lwr Leg, Lt
0Y6M* Detach/Foot, Rt
0Y6N* Detach/Foot, Lt

DRG 240　Amputation for Circulatory System Disorders Except Upper Limb and Toe with CC
　　　　GMLOS 7.0　　　AMLOS 8.5　　　RW 2.6835　　[T]

Select operating room procedures listed under DRG 239

DRG 241　Amputation for Circulatory System Disorders Except Upper Limb and Toe without CC/MCC
　　　　GMLOS 4.5　　　AMLOS 5.3　　　RW 1.4476　　[T]

Select operating room procedures listed under DRG 239

DRG 242　Permanent Cardiac Pacemaker Implant with MCC
　　　　GMLOS 5.7　　　AMLOS 7.4　　　RW 3.7836　　[T]

Any of the following procedure combinations

0JH6[0,3]7Z Insert/SQ Tissue & Fascia, Chest, [Opn, Perc], Cardiac Resynchronization Pacemaker Pulse Generator, NQ
0JH8[0,3]7Z Insert/SQ Tissue & Fascia, Abd, [Opn, Perc], Cardiac Resynchronization Pacemaker Pulse Generator, NQ
AND
02HK[0,3,4]JZ Insert/Ventricle, Rt, [Opn, Perc, Perc Endo], Cardiac Lead, Pacemaker, NQ
02HL[0,3,4]JZ Insert/Ventricle, Lt, [Opn, Perc, Perc Endo], Cardiac Lead, Pacemaker, NQ

[T] **Transfer DRG**　　　[SP] **Special Payment**　　　* **Code Range**　　　6th and 7th Character of ZZ = No Device, No Qualifier ZX = No Device, Diagnostic

OR

ØJH6[Ø,3][4,5,P]Z	Insert/SQ Tissue & Fascia, Chest, [Opn, Perc], [Pacemaker, Single Chamber, Pacemaker, Single Chamber Rate Responsive, Cardiac Rhythm Related Dev], NQ
ØJH8[Ø,3][4,5,P]Z	Insert/SQ Tissue & Fascia, Abd, [Opn, Perc], [Pacemaker, Single Chamber, Pacemaker, Single Chamber Rate Responsive, Cardiac Rhythm Related Dev], NQ

AND

02H4[Ø,4][J,M]Z	Insert/Coronary Vein, [Opn, Perc Endo], [Cardiac Lead, Pacemaker, Cardiac Lead], NQ
02H6[Ø,3,4]JZ	Insert/Atrium, Rt, [Opn, Perc, Perc Endo], Cardiac Lead, Pacemaker, NQ
02H6[Ø,4]MZ	Insert/Atrium, Rt, [Opn, Perc Endo], Cardiac Lead, NQ
02H7[Ø,3,4]JZ	Insert/Atrium, Lt, [Opn, Perc, Perc Endo], Cardiac Lead, Pacemaker, NQ
02H7[Ø,4]MZ	Insert/Atrium, Lt, [Opn, Perc Endo], Cardiac Lead, NQ
02HK[Ø,3,4][J,M]Z	Insert/Ventricle, Rt, [Opn, Perc, Perc Endo], [Cardiac Lead, Pacemaker, Cardiac Lead], NQ
02HL[Ø,3,4][J,M]Z	Insert/Ventricle, Lt, [Opn, Perc, Perc Endo], [Cardiac Lead, Pacemaker, Cardiac Lead], NQ

OR

ØJH6[Ø,3][4,5,6]Z	Insert/SQ Tissue & Fascia, Chest, [Opn, Perc], [Pacemaker, Single Chamber, Pacemaker, Single Chamber Rate Responsive, Pacemaker, Dual Chamber], NQ
ØJH8[Ø,3][4,5,6]Z	Insert/SQ Tissue & Fascia, Abd, [Opn, Perc], [Pacemaker, Single Chamber, Pacemaker, Single Chamber Rate Responsive, Pacemaker, Dual Chamber], NQ

AND

ØJPT[Ø,3]PZ	Rmvl/SQ Tissue & Fascia, Trunk, [Opn, Perc], Cardiac Rhythm Related Dev, NQ

AND

02H4[Ø,4][J,M]Z	Insert/Coronary Vein, [Opn, Perc Endo], [Cardiac Lead, Pacemaker, Cardiac Lead], NQ
02H6[Ø,3,4]JZ	Insert/Atrium, Rt, [Opn, Perc, Perc Endo], Cardiac Lead, Pacemaker, NQ
02H6[Ø,4]MZ	Insert/Atrium, Rt, [Opn, Perc Endo], Cardiac Lead, NQ
02H7[Ø,3,4]JZ	Insert/Atrium, Lt, [Opn, Perc, Perc Endo], Cardiac Lead, Pacemaker, NQ
02H7[Ø,4]MZ	Insert/Atrium, Lt, [Opn, Perc Endo], Cardiac Lead, NQ
02HK[Ø,3,4][J,M]Z	Insert/Ventricle, Rt, [Opn, Perc, Perc Endo], [Cardiac Lead, Pacemaker, Cardiac Lead], NQ
02HL[Ø,3,4][J,M]Z	Insert/Ventricle, Lt, [Opn, Perc, Perc Endo], [Cardiac Lead, Pacemaker, Cardiac Lead], NQ

OR

ØJH6[Ø,3][4,5,6]Z	Insert/SQ Tissue & Fascia, Chest, [Opn, Perc], [Pacemaker, Single Chamber, Pacemaker, Single Chamber Rate Responsive, Pacemaker, Dual Chamber], NQ
ØJH8[Ø,3][4,5,6]Z	Insert/SQ Tissue & Fascia, Abd, [Opn, Perc], [Pacemaker, Single Chamber, Pacemaker, Single Chamber Rate Responsive, Pacemaker, Dual Chamber], NQ

AND

ØJPT[Ø,3]PZ	Rmvl/SQ Tissue & Fascia, Trunk, [Opn, Perc], Cardiac Rhythm Related Dev, NQ

AND

02HK[3,4][J,M]Z	Insert/Ventricle, Rt, [Perc, Perc Endo], [Cardiac Lead, Pacemaker, Cardiac Lead], NQ
02HL[Ø,3,4][J,M]Z	Insert/Ventricle, Lt, [Opn, Perc, Perc Endo], [Cardiac Lead, Pacemaker, Cardiac Lead], NQ

OR

ØJH6[Ø,3][6,7,P]Z	Insert/SQ Tissue & Fascia, Chest, [Opn, Perc], [Pacemaker, Dual Chamber, Cardiac Resynchronization Pacemaker Pulse Generator, Cardiac Rhythm Related Dev], NQ
ØJH8[Ø,3][6,7,P]Z	Insert/SQ Tissue & Fascia, Abd, [Opn, Perc], [Pacemaker, Dual Chamber, Cardiac Resynchronization Pacemaker Pulse Generator, Cardiac Rhythm Related Dev], NQ

AND

02HK3JZ	Insert of Pacemaker Lead into Rt Ventricle, Perc Appr
02HL3JZ	Insert of Pacemaker Lead into Lt Ventricle, Perc Appr

OR

ØJH6[Ø,3][4,5,6]Z	Insert/SQ Tissue & Fascia, Chest, [Opn, Perc], [Pacemaker, Single Chamber, Pacemaker, Single Chamber Rate Responsive, Pacemaker, Dual Chamber], NQ
ØJH8[Ø,3][4,5,6]Z	Insert/SQ Tissue & Fascia, Abd, [Opn, Perc], [Pacemaker, Single Chamber, Pacemaker, Single Chamber Rate Responsive, Pacemaker, Dual Chamber], NQ

AND

ØJPT[Ø,3]PZ	Rmvl/SQ Tissue & Fascia, Trunk, [Opn, Perc], Cardiac Rhythm Related Dev, NQ

AND

02H64MZ	Insert of Cardiac Lead into Rt Atrium, Perc Endo Appr
02H6[3,4]JZ	Insert/Atrium, Rt, [Perc, Perc Endo], Cardiac Lead, Pacemaker, NQ
02H7[Ø,3,4]JZ	Insert/Atrium, Lt, [Opn, Perc, Perc Endo], Cardiac Lead, Pacemaker, NQ
02H7[Ø,4]MZ	Insert/Atrium, Lt, [Opn, Perc Endo], Cardiac Lead, NQ
02HK[Ø,3,4][J,M]Z	Insert/Ventricle, Rt, [Opn, Perc, Perc Endo], [Cardiac Lead, Pacemaker, Cardiac Lead], NQ
02HL[Ø,3,4][J,M]Z	Insert/Ventricle, Lt, [Opn, Perc, Perc Endo], [Cardiac Lead, Pacemaker, Cardiac Lead], NQ

OR

ØJH6[Ø,3][4,5,6,7,P]Z	Insert/SQ Tissue & Fascia, Chest, [Opn, Perc], [Pacemaker, Single Chamber, Pacemaker, Single Chamber Rate Responsive, Pacemaker, Dual Chamber, Cardiac Resynchronization Pacemaker Pulse Generator, Cardiac Rhythm Related Dev], NQ
ØJH8[Ø,3][4,5,6,7,P]Z	Insert/SQ Tissue & Fascia, Abd, [Opn, Perc], [Pacemaker, Single Chamber, Pacemaker, Single Chamber Rate Responsive, Pacemaker, Dual Chamber, Cardiac Resynchronization Pacemaker Pulse Generator, Cardiac Rhythm Related Dev], NQ

AND

02HN[Ø,3,4][J,M]Z	Insert/Pericardium, [Opn, Perc, Perc Endo], [Cardiac Lead, Pacemaker, Cardiac Lead], NQ

OR

ØJH6[Ø,3][4,5,6]Z	Insert/SQ Tissue & Fascia, Chest, [Opn, Perc], [Pacemaker, Single Chamber, Pacemaker, Single Chamber Rate Responsive, Pacemaker, Dual Chamber], NQ
ØJH8[Ø,3][4,5,6]Z	Insert/SQ Tissue & Fascia, Abd, [Opn, Perc], [Pacemaker, Single Chamber, Pacemaker, Single Chamber Rate Responsive, Pacemaker, Dual Chamber], NQ

AND

ØJPT[Ø,3]PZ	Rmvl/SQ Tissue & Fascia, Trunk, [Opn, Perc], Cardiac Rhythm Related Dev, NQ

AND

02HN[Ø,3,4][J,M]Z	Insert/Pericardium, [Opn, Perc, Perc Endo], [Cardiac Lead, Pacemaker, Cardiac Lead], NQ

OR

ØJH6[Ø,3][7,P]Z	Insert/SQ Tissue & Fascia, Chest, [Opn, Perc], [Cardiac Resynchronization Pacemaker Pulse Generator, Cardiac Rhythm Related Dev], NQ
ØJH8[Ø,3][7,P]Z	Insert/SQ Tissue & Fascia, Abd, [Opn, Perc], [Cardiac Resynchronization Pacemaker Pulse Generator, Cardiac Rhythm Related Dev], NQ

AND

02H63MZ	Insert of Cardiac Lead into Rt Atrium, Perc Appr
02H73MZ	Insert of Cardiac Lead into Lt Atrium, Perc Appr

OR

ØJH6[Ø,3][7,P]Z	Insert/SQ Tissue & Fascia, Chest, [Opn, Perc], [Cardiac Resynchronization Pacemaker Pulse Generator, Cardiac Rhythm Related Dev], NQ
ØJH8[Ø,3][7,P]Z	Insert/SQ Tissue & Fascia, Abd, [Opn, Perc], [Cardiac Resynchronization Pacemaker Pulse Generator, Cardiac Rhythm Related Dev], NQ

AND

02H63JZ	Insert of Pacemaker Lead into Rt Atrium, Perc Appr
02H73JZ	Insert of Pacemaker Lead into Lt Atrium, Perc Appr
02HK3JZ	Insert of Pacemaker Lead into Rt Ventricle, Perc Appr
02HL3JZ	Insert of Pacemaker Lead into Lt Ventricle, Perc Appr

AND

02PA[Ø,3,4,X]MZ	Rmvl/Heart, [Opn, Perc, Perc Endo, Ext], Cardiac Lead, NQ

OR

ØJH6[Ø,3][4,5,6]Z	Insert/SQ Tissue & Fascia, Chest, [Opn, Perc], [Pacemaker, Single Chamber, Pacemaker, Single Chamber Rate Responsive, Pacemaker, Dual Chamber], NQ
ØJH8[Ø,3][4,5,6]Z	Insert/SQ Tissue & Fascia, Abd, [Opn, Perc], [Pacemaker, Single Chamber, Pacemaker, Single Chamber Rate Responsive, Pacemaker, Dual Chamber], NQ

AND

ØJPT[Ø,3]PZ	Rmvl/SQ Tissue & Fascia, Trunk, [Opn, Perc], Cardiac Rhythm Related Dev, NQ

AND

02H63MZ	Insert of Cardiac Lead into Rt Atrium, Perc Appr
02H73MZ	Insert of Cardiac Lead into Lt Atrium, Perc Appr

OR

ØJH6[Ø,3][4,5,6]Z	Insert/SQ Tissue & Fascia, Chest, [Opn, Perc], [Pacemaker, Single Chamber, Pacemaker, Single Chamber Rate Responsive, Pacemaker, Dual Chamber], NQ

Surgical	**Medical**	**CC Indicator**	**MCC Indicator**	**Procedure Proxy**	**PDxMCC** PDx acts as own MCC	**PDxCC** PDx acts as own CC

MDC 5: Diseases And Disorders Of The Circulatory System—SURGICAL

ØJH8[Ø,3][4,5,6]Z　Insert/SQ Tissue & Fascia, Abd, [Opn, Perc], [Pacemaker, Single Chamber, Pacemaker, Single Chamber Rate Responsive, Pacemaker, Dual Chamber], NQ
AND
ØJPT[Ø,3]PZ　Rmvl/SQ Tissue & Fascia, Trunk, [Opn, Perc], Cardiac Rhythm Related Dev, NQ
AND
02H63JZ　Insert of Pacemaker Lead into Rt Atrium, Perc Appr
02H73JZ　Insert of Pacemaker Lead into Lt Atrium, Perc Appr
02HK3JZ　Insert of Pacemaker Lead into Rt Ventricle, Perc Appr
02HL3JZ　Insert of Pacemaker Lead into Lt Ventricle, Perc Appr
AND
02PA[Ø,3,4,X]MZ　Rmvl/Heart, [Opn, Perc, Perc Endo, Ext], Cardiac Lead, NQ
OR
ØJH6[Ø,3]7Z　Insert/SQ Tissue & Fascia, Chest, [Opn, Perc], Cardiac Resynchronization Pacemaker Pulse Generator, NQ
ØJH8[Ø,3]7Z　Insert/SQ Tissue & Fascia, Abd, [Opn, Perc], Cardiac Resynchronization Pacemaker Pulse Generator, NQ
AND
02H43KZ　Insert of Defibrillator Lead into Cor Vein, Perc Appr
02H4[Ø,3,4][J,M]Z　Insert/Coronary Vein, [Opn, Perc, Perc Endo], [Cardiac Lead, Pacemaker, Cardiac Lead], NQ
02H6[Ø,3,4]JZ　Insert/Atrium, Rt, [Opn, Perc, Perc Endo], Cardiac Lead, Pacemaker, NQ
02H6[Ø,4]MZ　Insert/Atrium, Rt, [Opn, Perc Endo], Cardiac Lead, NQ
02H7[Ø,3,4]JZ　Insert/Atrium, Lt, [Opn, Perc, Perc Endo], Cardiac Lead, Pacemaker, NQ
02H7[Ø,4]MZ　Insert/Atrium, Lt, [Opn, Perc Endo], Cardiac Lead, NQ
02HK[Ø,3,4][J,M]Z　Insert/Ventricle, Rt, [Opn, Perc, Perc Endo], [Cardiac Lead, Pacemaker, Cardiac Lead], NQ
02HL[Ø,3,4][J,M]Z　Insert/Ventricle, Lt, [Opn, Perc, Perc Endo], [Cardiac Lead, Pacemaker, Cardiac Lead], NQ

DRG 243　Permanent Cardiac Pacemaker Implant with CC
GMLOS 3.6　　　AMLOS 4.4　　　RW 2.6444　　[T]

Select operating room procedure combinations listed under DRG 242

DRG 244　Permanent Cardiac Pacemaker Implant without CC/MCC
GMLOS 2.5　　　AMLOS 2.9　　　RW 2.1394　　[T]

Select operating room procedure combinations listed under DRG 242

DRG 245　AICD Generator Procedures
GMLOS 4.Ø　　　AMLOS 5.5　　　RW 4.6864

Operating Room Procedures
ØJH6[Ø,3][8,9,A]Z　Insert/SQ Tissue & Fascia, Chest, [Opn, Perc], [Defibrillator Generator, Cardiac Resynchronization Defibrillator Pulse Generator, Contractility Modulation Dev], NQ
ØJH8[Ø,3][8,9,A]Z　Insert/SQ Tissue & Fascia, Abd, [Opn, Perc], [Defibrillator Generator, Cardiac Resynchronization Defibrillator Pulse Generator, Contractility Modulation Dev], NQ

DRG 246　Percutaneous Cardiovascular Procedure with Drug-Eluting Stent with MCC or 4+ Vessels/Stents
GMLOS 4.1　　　AMLOS 5.5　　　RW 3.2494

Operating Room Procedures
027Ø[3,4][4,D,T][6,Z]　Dilation/Coronary Artery, One Site, [Perc, Perc Endo], [Drug-eluting Intralum Dev, Intralum Dev, Radioact Intralum Dev], [Bifurcation, NQ]
0271[3,4][4,D,T][6,Z]　Dilation/Coronary Artery, Two Sites, [Perc, Perc Endo], [Drug-eluting Intralum Dev, Intralum Dev, Radioact Intralum Dev], [Bifurcation, NQ]
0272[3,4][4,D,T][6,Z]　Dilation/Coronary Artery, Three Sites, [Perc, Perc Endo], [Drug-eluting Intralum Dev, Intralum Dev, Radioact Intralum Dev], [Bifurcation, NQ]
0273[3,4][4,D,T][6,Z]　Dilation/Coronary Artery, Four or More Sites, [Perc, Perc Endo], [Drug-eluting Intralum Dev, Intralum Dev, Radioact Intralum Dev], [Bifurcation, NQ]
02CØ[3,4]ZZ　Extir/Coronary Artery, One Site, [Perc, Perc Endo]
02C1[3,4]ZZ　Extir/Coronary Artery, Two Sites, [Perc, Perc Endo]
02C2[3,4]ZZ　Extir/Coronary Artery, Three Sites, [Perc, Perc Endo]
02C3[3,4]ZZ　Extir/Coronary Artery, Four or More Sites, [Perc, Perc Endo]
X2CØ361　Extirpate matter from 1 Cor Art, Orbit Athrect, New Tech 1
X2C1361　Extirpate matter from 2 Cor Art, Orbit Athrect, New Tech 1

X2C2361　Extirpate matter from 3 Cor Art, Orbit Athrect, New Tech 1
X2C3361　Extirpate matter from 4+ Cor Art, Orbit Athrect, New Tech 1
OR

Nonoperating Room Procedures
02K80ZZ　Map Conduction Mechanism, Opn Appr
AND

Nonoperating Room Procedures
027Ø[Ø,3,4]4[6,Z]　Dilation/Coronary Artery, One Site, [Opn, Perc, Perc Endo], Drug-eluting Intralum Dev, [Bifurcation, NQ]
0271[Ø,3,4]4[6,Z]　Dilation/Coronary Artery, Two Sites, [Opn, Perc, Perc Endo], Drug-eluting Intralum Dev, [Bifurcation, NQ]
0272[Ø,3,4]4[6,Z]　Dilation/Coronary Artery, Three Sites, [Opn, Perc, Perc Endo], Drug-eluting Intralum Dev, [Bifurcation, NQ]
0273[Ø,3,4]4[6,Z]　Dilation/Coronary Artery, Four or More Sites, [Opn, Perc, Perc Endo], Drug-eluting Intralum Dev, [Bifurcation, NQ]

OR

Operating Room Procedures
ØWHCØ1Z　Insert of Radioact Elem into Mediastinum, Opn Appr
ØWHC31Z　Insert of Radioact Elem into Mediastinum, Perc Appr
ØWHC41Z　Insert of Radioact Elem into Mediastinum, Perc Endo Appr
ØWHDØ1Z　Insert of Radioact Elem into Pericard Cav, Opn Appr
ØWHD31Z　Insert of Radioact Elem into Pericard Cav, Perc Appr
ØWHD41Z　Insert Radioact Elem in Pericard Cav, Perc Endo
OR

Any combination of codes in the next four lists adding up to four or more vessels/stents

One Stent
027Ø[Ø,3,4][4,D,T][6,Z]　Dilation/Coronary Artery, One Site, [Opn, Perc, Perc Endo], [Drug-eluting Intralum Dev, Intralum Dev, Radioact Intralum Dev], [Bifurcation, NQ]

Two Stents
0271[Ø,3,4][4,D,T][6,Z]　Dilation/Coronary Artery, Two Sites, [Opn, Perc, Perc Endo], [Drug-eluting Intralum Dev, Intralum Dev, Radioact Intralum Dev], [Bifurcation, NQ]

Three Stents
0272[Ø,3,4][4,D,T][6,Z]　Dilation/Coronary Artery, Three Sites, [Opn, Perc, Perc Endo], [Drug-eluting Intralum Dev, Intralum Dev, Radioact Intralum Dev], [Bifurcation, NQ]

Four or more Stents
0273[Ø,3,4][4,D,T][6,Z]　Dilation/Coronary Artery, Four or More Sites, [Opn, Perc, Perc Endo], [Drug-eluting Intralum Dev, Intralum Dev, Radioact Intralum Dev], [Bifurcation, NQ]

DRG 247　Percutaneous Cardiovascular Procedure with Drug-Eluting Stent without MCC
GMLOS 2.2　　　AMLOS 2.7　　　RW 2.13Ø7

Operating Room Procedures
027Ø[3,4][4,D,T][6,Z]　Dilation/Coronary Artery, One Site, [Perc, Perc Endo], [Drug-eluting Intralum Dev, Intralum Dev, Radioact Intralum Dev], [Bifurcation, NQ]
0271[3,4][4,D,T][6,Z]　Dilation/Coronary Artery, Two Sites, [Perc, Perc Endo], [Drug-eluting Intralum Dev, Intralum Dev, Radioact Intralum Dev], [Bifurcation, NQ]
0272[3,4][4,D,T][6,Z]　Dilation/Coronary Artery, Three Sites, [Perc, Perc Endo], [Drug-eluting Intralum Dev, Intralum Dev, Radioact Intralum Dev], [Bifurcation, NQ]
0273[3,4][4,D,T][6,Z]　Dilation/Coronary Artery, Four or More Sites, [Perc, Perc Endo], [Drug-eluting Intralum Dev, Intralum Dev, Radioact Intralum Dev], [Bifurcation, NQ]
02CØ[3,4]ZZ　Extir/Coronary Artery, One Site, [Perc, Perc Endo]
02C1[3,4]ZZ　Extir/Coronary Artery, Two Sites, [Perc, Perc Endo]
02C2[3,4]ZZ　Extir/Coronary Artery, Three Sites, [Perc, Perc Endo]
02C3[3,4]ZZ　Extir/Coronary Artery, Four or More Sites, [Perc, Perc Endo]
X2CØ361　Extirpate matter from 1 Cor Art, Orbit Athrect, New Tech 1
X2C1361　Extirpate matter from 2 Cor Art, Orbit Athrect, New Tech 1
X2C2361　Extirpate matter from 3 Cor Art, Orbit Athrect, New Tech 1
X2C3361　Extirpate matter from 4+ Cor Art, Orbit Athrect, New Tech 1
OR

Nonoperating Room Procedures
02K80ZZ　Map Conduction Mechanism, Opn Appr

[T] **Transfer DRG**　　[SP] **Special Payment**　　***Code Range**　　**6th and 7th Character of ZZ = No Device, No Qualifier　ZX = No Device, Diagnostic**

AND

Nonoperating Room Procedures

0270[0,3,4]4[6,Z] Dilation/Coronary Artery, One Site, [Opn, Perc, Perc Endo], Drug-eluting Intralum Dev, [Bifurcation, NQ]
0271[0,3,4]4[6,Z] Dilation/Coronary Artery, Two Sites, [Opn, Perc, Perc Endo], Drug-eluting Intralum Dev, [Bifurcation, NQ]
0272[0,3,4]4[6,Z] Dilation/Coronary Artery, Three Sites, [Opn, Perc, Perc Endo], Drug-eluting Intralum Dev, [Bifurcation, NQ]
0273[0,3,4]4[6,Z] Dilation/Coronary Artery, Four or More Sites, [Opn, Perc, Perc Endo], Drug-eluting Intralum Dev, [Bifurcation, NQ]

OR

Operating Room Procedures

0270[0,3,4][4,D,T][6,Z] Dilation/Coronary Artery, One Site, [Opn, Perc, Perc Endo], [Drug-eluting Intralum Dev, Intralum Dev, Radioact Intralum Dev], [Bifurcation, NQ]
0271[0,3,4][4,D,T][6,Z] Dilation/Coronary Artery, Two Sites, [Opn, Perc, Perc Endo], [Drug-eluting Intralum Dev, Intralum Dev, Radioact Intralum Dev], [Bifurcation, NQ]
0272[0,3,4][4,D,T][6,Z] Dilation/Coronary Artery, Three Sites, [Opn, Perc, Perc Endo], [Drug-eluting Intralum Dev, Intralum Dev, Radioact Intralum Dev], [Bifurcation, NQ]

OR

Operating Room Procedures

0WHC01Z Insert of Radioact Elem into Mediastinum, Opn Appr
0WHC31Z Insert of Radioact Elem into Mediastinum, Perc Appr
0WHC41Z Insert of Radioact Elem into Mediastinum, Perc Endo Appr
0WHD01Z Insert of Radioact Elem into Pericard Cav, Opn Appr
0WHD31Z Insert of Radioact Elem into Pericard Cav, Perc Appr
0WHD41Z Insert Radioact Elem in Pericard Cav, Perc Endo

DRG 248 **Percutaneous Cardiovascular Procedure with Non Drug-Eluting Stent with MCC or 4+ Vessels/Stents**

GMLOS 4.8   AMLOS 6.3   RW 3.0696

Operating Room Procedures

0270[3,4][4,D,T][6,Z] Dilation/Coronary Artery, One Site, [Perc, Perc Endo], [Drug-eluting Intralum Dev, Intralum Dev, Radioact Intralum Dev], [Bifurcation, NQ]
0271[3,4][4,D,T][6,Z] Dilation/Coronary Artery, Two Sites, [Perc, Perc Endo], [Drug-eluting Intralum Dev, Intralum Dev, Radioact Intralum Dev], [Bifurcation, NQ]
0272[3,4][4,D,T][6,Z] Dilation/Coronary Artery, Three Sites, [Perc, Perc Endo], [Drug-eluting Intralum Dev, Intralum Dev, Radioact Intralum Dev], [Bifurcation, NQ]
0273[3,4][4,D,T][6,Z] Dilation/Coronary Artery, Four or More Sites, [Perc, Perc Endo], [Drug-eluting Intralum Dev, Intralum Dev, Radioact Intralum Dev], [Bifurcation, NQ]
02C0[3,4]ZZ Extir/Coronary Artery, One Site, [Perc, Perc Endo]
02C1[3,4]ZZ Extir/Coronary Artery, Two Sites, [Perc, Perc Endo]
02C2[3,4]ZZ Extir/Coronary Artery, Three Sites, [Perc, Perc Endo]
02C3[3,4]ZZ Extir/Coronary Artery, Four or More Sites, [Perc, Perc Endo]
X2C0361 Extirpate matter from 1 Cor Art, Orbit Athrect, New Tech 1
X2C1361 Extirpate matter from 2 Cor Art, Orbit Athrect, New Tech 1
X2C2361 Extirpate matter from 3 Cor Art, Orbit Athrect, New Tech 1
X2C3361 Extirpate matter from 4+ Cor Art, Orbit Athrect, New Tech 1

OR

Nonoperating Room Procedures

02K80ZZ Map Conduction Mechanism, Opn Appr
AND

Nonoperating Room Procedures

0270[0,3,4][D,T][6,Z] Dilation/Coronary Artery, One Site, [Opn, Perc, Perc Endo], [Intralum Dev, Radioact Intralum Dev], [Bifurcation, NQ]
0271[0,3,4][D,T][6,Z] Dilation/Coronary Artery, Two Sites, [Opn, Perc, Perc Endo], [Intralum Dev, Radioact Intralum Dev], [Bifurcation, NQ]
0272[0,3,4][D,T][6,Z] Dilation/Coronary Artery, Three Sites, [Opn, Perc, Perc Endo], [Intralum Dev, Radioact Intralum Dev], [Bifurcation, NQ]
0273[0,3,4][D,T][6,Z] Dilation/Coronary Artery, Four or More Sites, [Opn, Perc, Perc Endo], [Intralum Dev, Radioact Intralum Dev], [Bifurcation, NQ]

OR

Operating Room Procedures

0WHC[0,3,4]1Z Insert/Mediastinum, [Opn, Perc, Perc Endo], Radioact Elmt, NQ

0WHD[0,3,4]1Z Insert/Pericardial Cavity, [Opn, Perc, Perc Endo], Radioact Elmt, NQ

OR

Any combination of codes in the next four lists adding up to four or more vessels/stents

One Stent

0270[0,3,4][4,D,T][6,Z] Dilation/Coronary Artery, One Site, [Opn, Perc, Perc Endo], [Drug-eluting Intralum Dev, Intralum Dev, Radioact Intralum Dev], [Bifurcation, NQ]

Two Stents

0271[0,3,4][4,D,T][6,Z] Dilation/Coronary Artery, Two Sites, [Opn, Perc, Perc Endo], [Drug-eluting Intralum Dev, Intralum Dev, Radioact Intralum Dev], [Bifurcation, NQ]

Three Stents

0272[0,3,4][4,D,T][6,Z] Dilation/Coronary Artery, Three Sites, [Opn, Perc, Perc Endo], [Drug-eluting Intralum Dev, Intralum Dev, Radioact Intralum Dev], [Bifurcation, NQ]

Four or more Stents

0273[0,3,4][4,D,T][6,Z] Dilation/Coronary Artery, Four or More Sites, [Opn, Perc, Perc Endo], [Drug-eluting Intralum Dev, Intralum Dev, Radioact Intralum Dev], [Bifurcation, NQ]

DRG 249 **Percutaneous Cardiovascular Procedure with Non Drug-Eluting Stent without MCC**

GMLOS 2.5   AMLOS 3.1   RW 1.9140

Operating Room Procedures

0270[3,4][4,D,T][6,Z] Dilation/Coronary Artery, One Site, [Perc, Perc Endo], [Drug-eluting Intralum Dev, Intralum Dev, Radioact Intralum Dev], [Bifurcation, NQ]
0271[3,4][4,D,T][6,Z] Dilation/Coronary Artery, Two Sites, [Perc, Perc Endo], [Drug-eluting Intralum Dev, Intralum Dev, Radioact Intralum Dev], [Bifurcation, NQ]
0272[3,4][4,D,T][6,Z] Dilation/Coronary Artery, Three Sites, [Perc, Perc Endo], [Drug-eluting Intralum Dev, Intralum Dev, Radioact Intralum Dev], [Bifurcation, NQ]
0273[3,4][4,D,T][6,Z] Dilation/Coronary Artery, Four or More Sites, [Perc, Perc Endo], [Drug-eluting Intralum Dev, Intralum Dev, Radioact Intralum Dev], [Bifurcation, NQ]
02C0[3,4]ZZ Extir/Coronary Artery, One Site, [Perc, Perc Endo]
02C1[3,4]ZZ Extir/Coronary Artery, Two Sites, [Perc, Perc Endo]
02C2[3,4]ZZ Extir/Coronary Artery, Three Sites, [Perc, Perc Endo]
02C3[3,4]ZZ Extir/Coronary Artery, Four or More Sites, [Perc, Perc Endo]
X2C0361 Extirpate matter from 1 Cor Art, Orbit Athrect, New Tech 1
X2C1361 Extirpate matter from 2 Cor Art, Orbit Athrect, New Tech 1
X2C2361 Extirpate matter from 3 Cor Art, Orbit Athrect, New Tech 1
X2C3361 Extirpate matter from 4+ Cor Art, Orbit Athrect, New Tech 1
OR

Nonoperating Room Procedures

02K80ZZ Map Conduction Mechanism, Opn Appr
AND

Operating Room Procedures

0WHC[0,3,4]1Z Insert/Mediastinum, [Opn, Perc, Perc Endo], Radioact Elmt, NQ
0WHD[0,3,4]1Z Insert/Pericardial Cavity, [Opn, Perc, Perc Endo], Radioact Elmt, NQ

OR

Nonoperating Room Procedures

0270[0,3,4][D,T][6,Z] Dilation/Coronary Artery, One Site, [Opn, Perc, Perc Endo], [Intralum Dev, Radioact Intralum Dev], [Bifurcation, NQ]
0271[0,3,4][D,T][6,Z] Dilation/Coronary Artery, Two Sites, [Opn, Perc, Perc Endo], [Intralum Dev, Radioact Intralum Dev], [Bifurcation, NQ]
0272[0,3,4][D,T][6,Z] Dilation/Coronary Artery, Three Sites, [Opn, Perc, Perc Endo], [Intralum Dev, Radioact Intralum Dev], [Bifurcation, NQ]
0273[0,3,4][D,T][6,Z] Dilation/Coronary Artery, Four or More Sites, [Opn, Perc, Perc Endo], [Intralum Dev, Radioact Intralum Dev], [Bifurcation, NQ]

OR

Operating Room Procedures

0270[0,3,4][4,D,T][6,Z] Dilation/Coronary Artery, One Site, [Opn, Perc, Perc Endo], [Drug-eluting Intralum Dev, Intralum Dev, Radioact Intralum Dev], [Bifurcation, NQ]

Surgical	Medical	CC Indicator	MCC Indicator	Procedure Proxy	PDxMCC PDx acts as own MCC	PDxCC PDx acts as own CC

0271[0,3,4][4,D,T][6,Z] Dilation/Coronary Artery, Two Sites, [Opn, Perc, Perc Endo], [Drug-eluting Intralum Dev, Intralum Dev, Radioact Intralum Dev], [Bifurcation, NQ]
0272[0,3,4][4,D,T][6,Z] Dilation/Coronary Artery, Three Sites, [Opn, Perc, Perc Endo], [Drug-eluting Intralum Dev, Intralum Dev, Radioact Intralum Dev], [Bifurcation, NQ]

DRG 250 Percutaneous Cardiovascular Procedure without Coronary Artery Stent with MCC

GMLOS 4.2   AMLOS 5.7   RW 2.6975

Operating Room Procedures

0270[3,4]Z[6,Z]	Dilation/Coronary Artery, One Site, [Perc, Perc Endo], No Dev, [Bifurcation, NQ]
0271[3,4]Z[6,Z]	Dilation/Coronary Artery, Two Sites, [Perc, Perc Endo], No Dev, [Bifurcation, NQ]
0272[3,4]Z[6,Z]	Dilation/Coronary Artery, Three Sites, [Perc, Perc Endo], No Dev, [Bifurcation, NQ]
0273[3,4]Z[6,Z]	Dilation/Coronary Artery, Four or More Sites, [Perc, Perc Endo], No Dev, [Bifurcation, NQ]
02C0[3,4]ZZ	Extir/Coronary Artery, One Site, [Perc, Perc Endo]
02C1[3,4]ZZ	Extir/Coronary Artery, Two Sites, [Perc, Perc Endo]
02C2[3,4]ZZ	Extir/Coronary Artery, Three Sites, [Perc, Perc Endo]
02C3[3,4]ZZ	Extir/Coronary Artery, Four or More Sites, [Perc, Perc Endo]
X2C0361	Extirpate matter from 1 Cor Art, Orbit Athrect, New Tech 1
X2C1361	Extirpate matter from 2 Cor Art, Orbit Athrect, New Tech 1
X2C2361	Extirpate matter from 3 Cor Art, Orbit Athrect, New Tech 1
X2C3361	Extirpate matter from 4+ Cor Art, Orbit Athrect, New Tech 1

OR

Nonoperating Room Procedures

02570ZK	Destr of Lt Atrial Appendage, Opn Appr
02B70ZK	Exc of Lt Atrial Appendage, Opn Appr
02K80ZZ	Map Conduction Mechanism, Opn Appr
02L70CK	Occlsn of LAA with Extralum Dev, Opn Appr
02L70DK	Occlsn of LAA with Intralum Dev, Opn Appr
02L70ZK	Occlsn of Lt Atrial Appendage, Opn Appr
02U73JZ	Supl Lt Atrium with Synth Sub, Perc Appr
02U74JZ	Supl Lt Atrium with Synth Sub, Perc Endo Appr

DRG 251 Percutaneous Cardiovascular Procedure without Coronary Artery Stent without MCC

GMLOS 2.4   AMLOS 2.9   RW 1.6863

Select operating room procedures OR nonoperating room procedures listed under DRG 250

DRG 252 Other Vascular Procedures with MCC

GMLOS 5.5   AMLOS 7.9   RW 3.2872

Operating Room Procedures

00HE[0,3,4]MZ	Insert/Cranial Nerve, [Opn, Perc, Perc Endo], Neurostimulator Lead, NQ
01HY[0,3,4]MZ	Insert/Peripheral Nerve, [Opn, Perc, Perc Endo], Neurostimulator Lead, NQ
027P*	Dilation/Pulmn Trunk
027Q*	Dilation/Pulmn Artery, Rt
027R[0,3,4][4,D,Z]Z	Dilation/Pulmn Artery, Lt, [Opn, Perc, Perc Endo], [Drug-eluting Intralum Dev, Intralum Dev, No Dev], NQ
027S*	Dilation/Pulmn Vein, Rt
027T*	Dilation/Pulmn Vein, Lt
027V*	Dilation/Superior Vena Cava
027W*	Dilation/Thoracic Aorta
02BP[0,3,4]ZX	Exc/Pulmn Trunk, [Opn, Perc, Perc Endo]
02BQ[0,3,4]ZX	Exc/Pulmn Artery, Rt, [Opn, Perc, Perc Endo]
02BR[0,3,4]ZX	Exc/Pulmn Artery, Lt, [Opn, Perc, Perc Endo]
02BS[0,3,4]ZX	Exc/Pulmn Vein, Rt, [Opn, Perc, Perc Endo]
02BT[0,3,4]ZX	Exc/Pulmn Vein, Lt, [Opn, Perc, Perc Endo]
02BV[0,3,4]ZX	Exc/Superior Vena Cava, [Opn, Perc, Perc Endo]
02BW[0,3,4]ZX	Exc/Thoracic Aorta, [Opn, Perc, Perc Endo]
02HV[0,3,4][2,D]Z	Insert/Superior Vena Cava, [Opn, Perc, Perc Endo], [Monitoring Dev, Intralum Dev], NQ
02LV*	Occlsn/Superior Vena Cava
02NP*	Rls/Pulmn Trunk
02NQ*	Rls/Pulmn Artery, Rt
02NR*	Rls/Pulmn Artery, Lt
02NS*	Rls/Pulmn Vein, Rt
02NT*	Rls/Pulmn Vein, Lt

02NV*	Rls/Superior Vena Cava
02NW*	Rls/Thoracic Aorta
02QP*	Repair/Pulmn Trunk
02QQ*	Repair/Pulmn Artery, Rt
02QR*	Repair/Pulmn Artery, Lt
02S*	Heart and Great Vessels, Repos
02UP*	Supl/Pulmn Trunk
02UQ*	Supl/Pulmn Artery, Rt
02UR*	Supl/Pulmn Artery, Lt
02US*	Supl/Pulmn Vein, Rt
02UT*	Supl/Pulmn Vein, Lt
02UV*	Supl/Superior Vena Cava
02UW0JZ	Supl Thoracic Aorta with Synth Sub, Opn Appr
02UW[0,3,4][7,8,K]Z	Supl/Thoracic Aorta, [Opn, Perc, Perc Endo], [Auto Tissue Sub, Zooplastic Tissue, Nonauto Tissue Sub], NQ
02VP[0,3,4]CZ	Restrict/Pulmn Trunk, [Opn, Perc, Perc Endo], Extralum Dev, NQ
02VR0CT	Restrict of Ductus Arterio with Extralum Dev, Opn Appr
02VR3CT	Restrict of Ductus Arterio with Extralum Dev, Perc Appr
02VR4CT	Restrict Ductus Arterio w Extralum Dev, Perc Endo
02VS[0,3,4]CZ	Restrict/Pulmn Vein, Rt, [Opn, Perc, Perc Endo], Extralum Dev, NQ
02VT[0,3,4]CZ	Restrict/Pulmn Vein, Lt, [Opn, Perc, Perc Endo], Extralum Dev, NQ
02VV*	Restrict/Superior Vena Cava
02VW[0,3,4]CZ	Restrict/Thoracic Aorta, [Opn, Perc, Perc Endo], Extralum Dev, NQ
0312*	Bypass/Innominate Artery
0313[0,9,A,J,K,Z][0,1,2,3,4,5,6,7,8,9,B,C,D,F,J,K]	Bypass/Subclavian Artery, Rt, Opn, [Auto Venous Tissue, Auto Arterial Tissue, Synth Sub, Nonauto Tissue Sub, No Dev], [Rt Upr Arm Artery, Lt Upr Arm Artery, Bilat Upr Arm Artery, Rt Lwr Arm Artery, Lt Lwr Arm Artery, Bilat Lwr Arm Artery, Rt Upr Leg Artery, Lt Upr Leg Artery, Bilat Upr Leg Artery, Rt Lwr Leg Artery, Lt Lwr Leg Artery, Bilat Lwr Leg Artery, Upr Arm Vein, Lwr Arm Vein, Rt Extracranial Artery, Lt Extracranial Artery]
0314[0,9,A,J,K,Z][0,1,2,3,4,5,6,7,8,9,B,C,D,F,J,K]	Bypass/Subclavian Artery, Lt, Opn, [Auto Venous Tissue, Auto Arterial Tissue, Synth Sub, Nonauto Tissue Sub, No Dev], [Upr Arm Artery, Rt, Upr Arm Artery, Lt, Upr Arm Artery, Bilat, Lwr Arm Artery, Rt, Lwr Arm Artery, Lt, Lwr Arm Artery, Bilat, Upr Leg Artery, Rt, Upr Leg Artery, Lt, Upr Leg Artery, Bilat, Lwr Leg Artery, Rt, Lwr Leg Artery, Lt, Lwr Leg Artery, Bilat, Upr Arm Vein, Lwr Arm Vein, Extracranial Artery, Rt, Extracranial Artery, Lt]
0315*	Bypass/Axillary Artery, Rt
0316*	Bypass/Axillary Artery, Lt
0317[0,9,A,J,K,Z][0,3]	Bypass/Brachial Artery, Rt, Opn, [Auto Venous Tissue, Auto Arterial Tissue, Synth Sub, Nonauto Tissue Sub, No Dev], [Upr Arm Artery, Rt, Lwr Arm Artery, Rt]
0318[0,9,A,J,K,Z][1,4]	Bypass/Brachial Artery, Lt, Opn, [Auto Venous Tissue, Auto Arterial Tissue, Synth Sub, Nonauto Tissue Sub, No Dev], [Upr Arm Artery, Lt, Lwr Arm Artery, Lt]
0319[0,9,A,J,K,Z]3	Bypass/Ulnar Artery, Rt, Opn, [Auto Venous Tissue, Auto Arterial Tissue, Synth Sub, Nonauto Tissue Sub, No Dev], Lwr Arm Artery, Rt
031A0[0,9,A,J,K,Z]4	Bypass/Ulnar Artery, Lt, Opn, [Auto Venous Tissue, Auto Arterial Tissue, Synth Sub, Nonauto Tissue Sub, No Dev], Lwr Arm Artery, Lt
031B0[0,9,A,J,K,Z]3	Bypass/Radial Artery, Rt, Opn, [Auto Venous Tissue, Auto Arterial Tissue, Synth Sub, Nonauto Tissue Sub, No Dev], Lwr Arm Artery, Rt
031C0[0,9,A,J,K,Z]4	Bypass/Radial Artery, Lt, Opn, [Auto Venous Tissue, Auto Arterial Tissue, Synth Sub, Nonauto Tissue Sub, No Dev], Lwr Arm Artery, Lt
031G*	Bypass/Intracranial Artery
031H0[0,9,A,J,K,Z]J	Bypass/Common Carotid Artery, Rt, Opn, [Auto Venous Tissue, Auto Arterial Tissue, Synth Sub, Nonauto Tissue Sub, No Dev], Extracranial Artery, Rt
031J0[0,9,A,J,K,Z]K	Bypass/Common Carotid Artery, Lt, Opn, [Auto Venous Tissue, Auto Arterial Tissue, Synth Sub, Nonauto Tissue Sub, No Dev], Extracranial Artery, Lt
031K0[0,9,A,J,K,Z]J	Bypass/Int Carotid Artery, Rt, Opn, [Auto Venous Tissue, Auto Arterial Tissue, Synth Sub, Nonauto Tissue Sub, No Dev], Extracranial Artery, Rt
031L0[0,9,A,J,K,Z]K	Bypass/Int Carotid Artery, Lt, Opn, [Auto Venous Tissue, Auto Arterial Tissue, Synth Sub, Nonauto Tissue Sub, No Dev], Extracranial Artery, Lt
031M0[0,9,A,J,K,Z]J	Bypass/Ext Carotid Artery, Rt, Opn, [Auto Venous Tissue, Auto Arterial Tissue, Synth Sub, Nonauto Tissue Sub, No Dev], Extracranial Artery, Rt

MDC 5: Diseases And Disorders Of The Circulatory System—SURGICAL

Ⓣ **Transfer DRG**   ⓢⓟ **Special Payment**   * **Code Range**   **6th and 7th Character of ZZ = No Device, No Qualifier ZX = No Device, Diagnostic**

Code	Description
031N0[9,A,J,K,Z]K	Bypass/Ext Carotid Artery, Lt, Opn, [Auto Venous Tissue, Auto Arterial Tissue, Synth Sub, Nonauto Tissue Sub, No Dev], Extracranial Artery, Lt
0355*	Destr/Axillary Artery, Rt
0356*	Destr/Axillary Artery, Lt
0357*	Destr/Brachial Artery, Rt
0358*	Destr/Brachial Artery, Lt
0359*	Destr/Ulnar Artery, Rt
035A*	Destr/Ulnar Artery, Lt
035B*	Destr/Radial Artery, Rt
035C*	Destr/Radial Artery, Lt
035D*	Destr/Hand Artery, Rt
035F*	Destr/Hand Artery, Lt
035H*	Destr/Common Carotid Artery, Rt
035J*	Destr/Common Carotid Artery, Lt
035K*	Destr/Int Carotid Artery, Rt
035L*	Destr/Int Carotid Artery, Lt
035M*	Destr/Ext Carotid Artery, Rt
035N*	Destr/Ext Carotid Artery, Lt
035P*	Destr/Vert Artery, Rt
035Q*	Destr/Vert Artery, Lt
035R*	Destr/Face Artery
035S*	Destr/Temporal Artery, Rt
035T*	Destr/Temporal Artery, Lt
035U*	Destr/Thyroid Artery, Rt
035V*	Destr/Thyroid Artery, Lt
035Y*	Destr/Upr Artery
037*	Upr Arteries, Dilation
0390[0,3,4]ZX	Drain/Int Mammary Artery, Rt, [Opn, Perc, Perc Endo]
0391[0,3,4]ZX	Drain/Int Mammary Artery, Lt, [Opn, Perc, Perc Endo]
0392[0,3,4]ZX	Drain/Innominate Artery, [Opn, Perc, Perc Endo]
0393[0,3,4]ZX	Drain/Subclavian Artery, Rt, [Opn, Perc, Perc Endo]
0394[0,3,4]ZX	Drain/Subclavian Artery, Lt, [Opn, Perc, Perc Endo]
0395[0,3,4]ZX	Drain/Axillary Artery, Rt, [Opn, Perc, Perc Endo]
0396[0,3,4]ZX	Drain/Axillary Artery, Lt, [Opn, Perc, Perc Endo]
0397[0,3,4]ZX	Drain/Brachial Artery, Rt, [Opn, Perc, Perc Endo]
0398[0,3,4]ZX	Drain/Brachial Artery, Lt, [Opn, Perc, Perc Endo]
0399[0,3,4]ZX	Drain/Ulnar Artery, Rt, [Opn, Perc, Perc Endo]
039A[0,3,4]ZX	Drain/Ulnar Artery, Lt, [Opn, Perc, Perc Endo]
039B[0,3,4]ZX	Drain/Radial Artery, Rt, [Opn, Perc, Perc Endo]
039C[0,3,4]ZX	Drain/Radial Artery, Lt, [Opn, Perc, Perc Endo]
039D[0,3,4]ZX	Drain/Hand Artery, Rt, [Opn, Perc, Perc Endo]
039F[0,3,4]ZX	Drain/Hand Artery, Lt, [Opn, Perc, Perc Endo]
039G[0,3,4]ZX	Drain/Intracranial Artery, [Opn, Perc, Perc Endo]
039H[0,3,4]ZX	Drain/Common Carotid Artery, Rt, [Opn, Perc, Perc Endo]
039J[0,3,4]ZX	Drain/Common Carotid Artery, Lt, [Opn, Perc, Perc Endo]
039K[0,3,4]ZX	Drain/Int Carotid Artery, Rt, [Opn, Perc, Perc Endo]
039L[0,3,4]ZX	Drain/Int Carotid Artery, Lt, [Opn, Perc, Perc Endo]
039M[0,3,4]ZX	Drain/Ext Carotid Artery, Rt, [Opn, Perc, Perc Endo]
039N[0,3,4]ZX	Drain/Ext Carotid Artery, Lt, [Opn, Perc, Perc Endo]
039P[0,3,4]ZX	Drain/Vert Artery, Rt, [Opn, Perc, Perc Endo]
039Q[0,3,4]ZX	Drain/Vert Artery, Lt, [Opn, Perc, Perc Endo]
039R[0,3,4]ZX	Drain/Face Artery, [Opn, Perc, Perc Endo]
039S[0,3,4]ZX	Drain/Temporal Artery, Rt, [Opn, Perc, Perc Endo]
039T[0,3,4]ZX	Drain/Temporal Artery, Lt, [Opn, Perc, Perc Endo]
039U[0,3,4]ZX	Drain/Thyroid Artery, Rt, [Opn, Perc, Perc Endo]
039V[0,3,4]ZX	Drain/Thyroid Artery, Lt, [Opn, Perc, Perc Endo]
039Y[0,3,4]ZX	Drain/Upr Artery, [Opn, Perc, Perc Endo]
03B0[0,3,4]ZX	Exc/Int Mammary Artery, Rt, [Opn, Perc, Perc Endo]
03B1[0,3,4]ZX	Exc/Int Mammary Artery, Lt, [Opn, Perc, Perc Endo]
03B2[0,3,4]ZX	Exc/Innominate Artery, [Opn, Perc, Perc Endo]
03B3[0,3,4]ZX	Exc/Subclavian Artery, Rt, [Opn, Perc, Perc Endo]
03B4[0,3,4]ZX	Exc/Subclavian Artery, Lt, [Opn, Perc, Perc Endo]
03B5*	Exc/Axillary Artery, Rt
03B6*	Exc/Axillary Artery, Lt
03B7*	Exc/Brachial Artery, Rt
03B8*	Exc/Brachial Artery, Lt
03B9*	Exc/Ulnar Artery, Rt
03BA*	Exc/Ulnar Artery, Lt
03BB*	Exc/Radial Artery, Rt
03BC*	Exc/Radial Artery, Lt
03BD*	Exc/Hand Artery, Rt
03BF*	Exc/Hand Artery, Lt
03BG[0,3,4]ZX	Exc/Intracranial Artery, [Opn, Perc, Perc Endo]
03BH*	Exc/Common Carotid Artery, Rt
03BJ*	Exc/Common Carotid Artery, Lt
03BK*	Exc/Int Carotid Artery, Rt
03BL*	Exc/Int Carotid Artery, Lt
03BM*	Exc/Ext Carotid Artery, Rt
03BN*	Exc/Ext Carotid Artery, Lt
03BP*	Exc/Vert Artery, Rt
03BQ*	Exc/Vert Artery, Lt
03BR*	Exc/Face Artery
03BS*	Exc/Temporal Artery, Rt
03BT*	Exc/Temporal Artery, Lt
03BU*	Exc/Thyroid Artery, Rt
03BV*	Exc/Thyroid Artery, Lt
03BY*	Exc/Upr Artery
03C5*	Extir/Axillary Artery, Rt
03C6*	Extir/Axillary Artery, Lt
03C7*	Extir/Brachial Artery, Rt
03C8*	Extir/Brachial Artery, Lt
03C9*	Extir/Ulnar Artery, Rt
03CA*	Extir/Ulnar Artery, Lt
03CB*	Extir/Radial Artery, Rt
03CC*	Extir/Radial Artery, Lt
03CD*	Extir/Hand Artery, Rt
03CF*	Extir/Hand Artery, Lt
03CG3ZZ	Extir of Matter from Intracran Art, Perc Appr
03CR0ZZ	Extir of Matter from Face Artery, Opn Appr
03CY*	Extir/Upr Artery
03C[H,J]0ZZ	Extir of Matter from [Rt, Lt] Common Carotid Artery, Opn Appr
03C[K,L]0ZZ	Extir of Matter from [Rt, Lt] Int Carotid Artery, Opn Appr
03C[M,N]0ZZ	Extir of Matter from [Rt, Lt] Ext Carotid Artery, Opn Appr
03C[P,Q]0ZZ	Extir of Matter from [Rt, Lt] Vert Artery, Opn Appr
03C[S,T]0ZZ	Extir of Matter from [Rt, Lt] Temporal Artery, Opn Appr
03C[U,V]0ZZ	Extir of Matter from [Rt, Lt] Thyroid Artery, Opn Appr
03H0[0,3,4]DZ	Insert/Int Mammary Artery, Rt, [Opn, Perc, Perc Endo], Intralum Dev, NQ
03H1[0,3,4]DZ	Insert/Int Mammary Artery, Lt, [Opn, Perc, Perc Endo], Intralum Dev, NQ
03H2[0,3,4]DZ	Insert/Innominate Artery, [Opn, Perc, Perc Endo], Intralum Dev, NQ
03H3[0,3,4]DZ	Insert/Subclavian Artery, Rt, [Opn, Perc, Perc Endo], Intralum Dev, NQ
03H4[0,3,4]DZ	Insert/Subclavian Artery, Lt, [Opn, Perc, Perc Endo], Intralum Dev, NQ
03H5[0,3,4]DZ	Insert/Axillary Artery, Rt, [Opn, Perc, Perc Endo], Intralum Dev, NQ
03H6[0,3,4]DZ	Insert/Axillary Artery, Lt, [Opn, Perc, Perc Endo], Intralum Dev, NQ
03H7[0,3,4]DZ	Insert/Brachial Artery, Rt, [Opn, Perc, Perc Endo], Intralum Dev, NQ
03H8[0,3,4]DZ	Insert/Brachial Artery, Lt, [Opn, Perc, Perc Endo], Intralum Dev, NQ
03H9[0,3,4]DZ	Insert/Ulnar Artery, Rt, [Opn, Perc, Perc Endo], Intralum Dev, NQ
03HA[0,3,4]DZ	Insert/Ulnar Artery, Lt, [Opn, Perc, Perc Endo], Intralum Dev, NQ
03HB[0,3,4]DZ	Insert/Radial Artery, Rt, [Opn, Perc, Perc Endo], Intralum Dev, NQ
03HC[0,3,4]DZ	Insert/Radial Artery, Lt, [Opn, Perc, Perc Endo], Intralum Dev, NQ
03HD[0,3,4]DZ	Insert/Hand Artery, Rt, [Opn, Perc, Perc Endo], Intralum Dev, NQ
03HF[0,3,4]DZ	Insert/Hand Artery, Lt, [Opn, Perc, Perc Endo], Intralum Dev, NQ
03HG[0,3,4]DZ	Insert/Intracranial Artery, [Opn, Perc, Perc Endo], Intralum Dev, NQ
03HH[0,3,4]DZ	Insert/Common Carotid Artery, Rt, [Opn, Perc, Perc Endo], Intralum Dev, NQ
03HJ[0,3,4]DZ	Insert/Common Carotid Artery, Lt, [Opn, Perc, Perc Endo], Intralum Dev, NQ
03HK[0,3,4][D,M]Z	Insert/Int Carotid Artery, Rt, [Opn, Perc, Perc Endo], [Intralum Dev, Stimulator Lead], NQ
03HL[0,3,4][D,M]Z	Insert/Int Carotid Artery, Lt, [Opn, Perc, Perc Endo], [Intralum Dev, Stimulator Lead], NQ
03HM[0,3,4]DZ	Insert/Ext Carotid Artery, Rt, [Opn, Perc, Perc Endo], Intralum Dev, NQ
03HN[0,3,4]DZ	Insert/Ext Carotid Artery, Lt, [Opn, Perc, Perc Endo], Intralum Dev, NQ
03HP[0,3,4]DZ	Insert/Vert Artery, Rt, [Opn, Perc, Perc Endo], Intralum Dev, NQ
03HQ[0,3,4]DZ	Insert/Vert Artery, Lt, [Opn, Perc, Perc Endo], Intralum Dev, NQ
03HR[0,3,4]DZ	Insert/Face Artery, [Opn, Perc, Perc Endo], Intralum Dev, NQ
03HS[0,3,4]DZ	Insert/Temporal Artery, Rt, [Opn, Perc, Perc Endo], Intralum Dev, NQ
03HT[0,3,4]DZ	Insert/Temporal Artery, Lt, [Opn, Perc, Perc Endo], Intralum Dev, NQ
03HU[0,3,4]DZ	Insert/Thyroid Artery, Rt, [Opn, Perc, Perc Endo], Intralum Dev, NQ

Surgical **Medical** **CC Indicator** **MCC Indicator** **Procedure Proxy** **PDxMCC** **PDx acts as own MCC** **PDxCC** **PDx acts as own CC**

MDC 5: Diseases And Disorders Of The Circulatory System—SURGICAL

MDC 5: Diseases And Disorders Of The Circulatory System—SURGICAL

Code	Description
03HV[0,3,4]DZ	Insert/Thyroid Artery, Lt, [Opn, Perc, Perc Endo], Intralum Dev, NQ
03HY[0,3,4][2,D]Z	Insert/Upr Artery, [Opn, Perc, Perc Endo], [Monitoring Dev, Intralum Dev], NQ
03JY[0,3]ZZ	Inspect/Upr Artery, [Opn, Perc]
03L5[0,3,4][C,D,Z]Z	Occlsn/Axillary Artery, Rt, [Opn, Perc, Perc Endo], [Extralum Dev, Intralum Dev, No Dev], NQ
03L6[0,3,4][C,D,Z]Z	Occlsn/Axillary Artery, Lt, [Opn, Perc, Perc Endo], [Extralum Dev, Intralum Dev, No Dev], NQ
03L7[0,3,4][C,D,Z]Z	Occlsn/Brachial Artery, Rt, [Opn, Perc, Perc Endo], [Extralum Dev, Intralum Dev, No Dev], NQ
03L8[0,3,4][C,D,Z]Z	Occlsn/Brachial Artery, Lt, [Opn, Perc, Perc Endo], [Extralum Dev, Intralum Dev, No Dev], NQ
03L9[0,3,4][C,D,Z]Z	Occlsn/Ulnar Artery, Rt, [Opn, Perc, Perc Endo], [Extralum Dev, Intralum Dev, No Dev], NQ
03LA[0,3,4][C,D,Z]Z	Occlsn/Ulnar Artery, Lt, [Opn, Perc, Perc Endo], [Extralum Dev, Intralum Dev, No Dev], NQ
03LB[0,3,4][C,D,Z]Z	Occlsn/Radial Artery, Rt, [Opn, Perc, Perc Endo], [Extralum Dev, Intralum Dev, No Dev], NQ
03LC[0,3,4][C,D,Z]Z	Occlsn/Radial Artery, Lt, [Opn, Perc, Perc Endo], [Extralum Dev, Intralum Dev, No Dev], NQ
03LD[0,3,4][C,D,Z]Z	Occlsn/Hand Artery, Rt, [Opn, Perc, Perc Endo], [Extralum Dev, Intralum Dev, No Dev], NQ
03LF[0,3,4][C,D,Z]Z	Occlsn/Hand Artery, Lt, [Opn, Perc, Perc Endo], [Extralum Dev, Intralum Dev, No Dev], NQ
03LH[0,3,4][C,Z]Z	Occlsn/Common Carotid Artery, Rt, [Opn, Perc, Perc Endo], [Extralum Dev, No Dev], NQ
03LJ[0,3,4][C,Z]Z	Occlsn/Common Carotid Artery, Lt, [Opn, Perc, Perc Endo], [Extralum Dev, No Dev], NQ
03LK[0,3,4][C,Z]Z	Occlsn/Int Carotid Artery, Rt, [Opn, Perc, Perc Endo], [Extralum Dev, No Dev], NQ
03LL[0,3,4][C,Z]Z	Occlsn/Int Carotid Artery, Lt, [Opn, Perc, Perc Endo], [Extralum Dev, No Dev], NQ
03LM[0,3,4][C,Z]Z	Occlsn/Ext Carotid Artery, Rt, [Opn, Perc, Perc Endo], [Extralum Dev, No Dev], NQ
03LN[0,3,4][C,Z]Z	Occlsn/Ext Carotid Artery, Lt, [Opn, Perc, Perc Endo], [Extralum Dev, No Dev], NQ
03LP[0,3,4][C,Z]Z	Occlsn/Vert Artery, Rt, [Opn, Perc, Perc Endo], [Extralum Dev, No Dev], NQ
03LQ[0,3,4][C,Z]Z	Occlsn/Vert Artery, Lt, [Opn, Perc, Perc Endo], [Extralum Dev, No Dev], NQ
03LR[0,3,4][C,Z]Z	Occlsn/Face Artery, [Opn, Perc, Perc Endo], [Extralum Dev, No Dev], NQ
03LS[0,3,4][C,Z]Z	Occlsn/Temporal Artery, Rt, [Opn, Perc, Perc Endo], [Extralum Dev, No Dev], NQ
03LT[0,3,4][C,Z]Z	Occlsn/Temporal Artery, Lt, [Opn, Perc, Perc Endo], [Extralum Dev, No Dev], NQ
03LY[0,3,4][C,D,Z]Z	Occlsn/Upr Artery, [Opn, Perc, Perc Endo], [Extralum Dev, Intralum Dev, No Dev], NQ
03N*	Upr Arteries, Rls
03PY[0,3,4][0,2,3,C,D,M]Z	Rmvl/Upr Artery, [Opn, Perc, Perc Endo], [Drain Dev, Monitoring Dev, Inf Dev, Extralum Dev, Intralum Dev, Stimulator Lead], NQ
03Q*	Upr Arteries, Repair
03R5*	Replace/Axillary Artery, Rt
03R6*	Replace/Axillary Artery, Lt
03R7*	Replace/Brachial Artery, Rt
03R8*	Replace/Brachial Artery, Lt
03R9*	Replace/Ulnar Artery, Rt
03RA*	Replace/Ulnar Artery, Lt
03RB*	Replace/Radial Artery, Rt
03RC*	Replace/Radial Artery, Lt
03RD*	Replace/Hand Artery, Rt
03RF*	Replace/Hand Artery, Lt
03RH*	Replace/Common Carotid Artery, Rt
03RJ*	Replace/Common Carotid Artery, Lt
03RK*	Replace/Int Carotid Artery, Rt
03RL*	Replace/Int Carotid Artery, Lt
03RM*	Replace/Ext Carotid Artery, Rt
03RN*	Replace/Ext Carotid Artery, Lt
03RP*	Replace/Vert Artery, Rt
03RQ*	Replace/Vert Artery, Lt
03RR*	Replace/Face Artery
03RS*	Replace/Temporal Artery, Rt
03RT*	Replace/Temporal Artery, Lt
03RU*	Replace/Thyroid Artery, Rt
03RV*	Replace/Thyroid Artery, Lt
03RY*	Replace/Upr Artery
03S*	Upr Arteries, Repos
03U*	Upr Arteries, Supl

Code	Description
03V0[0,3,4]CZ	Restrict/Int Mammary Artery, Rt, [Opn, Perc, Perc Endo], Extralum Dev, NQ
03V1[0,3,4]CZ	Restrict/Int Mammary Artery, Lt, [Opn, Perc, Perc Endo], Extralum Dev, NQ
03V2[0,3,4]CZ	Restrict/Innominate Artery, [Opn, Perc, Perc Endo], Extralum Dev, NQ
03V3[0,3,4]CZ	Restrict/Subclavian Artery, Rt, [Opn, Perc, Perc Endo], Extralum Dev, NQ
03V4[0,3,4]CZ	Restrict/Subclavian Artery, Lt, [Opn, Perc, Perc Endo], Extralum Dev, NQ
03V5[0,3,4]CZ	Restrict/Axillary Artery, Rt, [Opn, Perc, Perc Endo], Extralum Dev, NQ
03V6[0,3,4]CZ	Restrict/Axillary Artery, Lt, [Opn, Perc, Perc Endo], Extralum Dev, NQ
03V7[0,3,4]CZ	Restrict/Brachial Artery, Rt, [Opn, Perc, Perc Endo], Extralum Dev, NQ
03V8[0,3,4]CZ	Restrict/Brachial Artery, Lt, [Opn, Perc, Perc Endo], Extralum Dev, NQ
03V9[0,3,4]CZ	Restrict/Ulnar Artery, Rt, [Opn, Perc, Perc Endo], Extralum Dev, NQ
03VA[0,3,4]CZ	Restrict/Ulnar Artery, Lt, [Opn, Perc, Perc Endo], Extralum Dev, NQ
03VB[0,3,4]CZ	Restrict/Radial Artery, Rt, [Opn, Perc, Perc Endo], Extralum Dev, NQ
03VC[0,3,4]CZ	Restrict/Radial Artery, Lt, [Opn, Perc, Perc Endo], Extralum Dev, NQ
03VD[0,3,4]CZ	Restrict/Hand Artery, Rt, [Opn, Perc, Perc Endo], Extralum Dev, NQ
03VF[0,3,4]CZ	Restrict/Hand Artery, Lt, [Opn, Perc, Perc Endo], Extralum Dev, NQ
03VG[0,3,4]CZ	Restrict/Intracranial Artery, [Opn, Perc, Perc Endo], Extralum Dev, NQ
03VH[0,3,4]CZ	Restrict/Common Carotid Artery, Rt, [Opn, Perc, Perc Endo], Extralum Dev, NQ
03VJ[0,3,4]CZ	Restrict/Common Carotid Artery, Lt, [Opn, Perc, Perc Endo], Extralum Dev, NQ
03VK[0,3,4]CZ	Restrict/Int Carotid Artery, Rt, [Opn, Perc, Perc Endo], Extralum Dev, NQ
03VL[0,3,4]CZ	Restrict/Int Carotid Artery, Lt, [Opn, Perc, Perc Endo], Extralum Dev, NQ
03VM[0,3,4]CZ	Restrict/Ext Carotid Artery, Rt, [Opn, Perc, Perc Endo], Extralum Dev, NQ
03VN[0,3,4]CZ	Restrict/Ext Carotid Artery, Lt, [Opn, Perc, Perc Endo], Extralum Dev, NQ
03VP[0,3,4]CZ	Restrict/Vert Artery, Rt, [Opn, Perc, Perc Endo], Extralum Dev, NQ
03VQ[0,3,4]CZ	Restrict/Vert Artery, Lt, [Opn, Perc, Perc Endo], Extralum Dev, NQ
03VR[0,3,4]CZ	Restrict/Face Artery, [Opn, Perc, Perc Endo], Extralum Dev, NQ
03VS[0,3,4]CZ	Restrict/Temporal Artery, Rt, [Opn, Perc, Perc Endo], Extralum Dev, NQ
03VT[0,3,4]CZ	Restrict/Temporal Artery, Lt, [Opn, Perc, Perc Endo], Extralum Dev, NQ
03VU[0,3,4]CZ	Restrict/Thyroid Artery, Rt, [Opn, Perc, Perc Endo], Extralum Dev, NQ
03VV[0,3,4]CZ	Restrict/Thyroid Artery, Lt, [Opn, Perc, Perc Endo], Extralum Dev, NQ
03VY[0,3,4]CZ	Restrict/Upr Artery, [Opn, Perc, Perc Endo], Extralum Dev, NQ
03WY[0,3,4][0,2,3,7,C,D,J,K,M]Z	Rev/Upr Artery, [Opn, Perc, Perc Endo], [Drain Dev, Monitoring Dev, Inf Dev, Auto Tissue Sub, Extralum Dev, Intralum Dev, Synth Sub, Nonauto Tissue Sub, Stimulator Lead], NQ
041K*	Bypass/Femor Artery, Rt
041L*	Bypass/Femor Artery, Lt
041M*	Bypass/Popliteal Artery, Rt
041N*	Bypass/Popliteal Artery, Lt
045K*	Destr/Femor Artery, Rt
045L*	Destr/Femor Artery, Lt
045M*	Destr/Popliteal Artery, Rt
045N*	Destr/Popliteal Artery, Lt
045P*	Destr/Ant Tibial Artery, Rt
045Q*	Destr/Ant Tibial Artery, Lt
045R*	Destr/Posterior Tibial Artery, Rt
045S*	Destr/Posterior Tibial Artery, Lt
045T*	Destr/Peroneal Artery, Rt
045U*	Destr/Peroneal Artery, Lt
045V*	Destr/Foot Artery, Rt
045W*	Destr/Foot Artery, Lt
045Y*	Destr/Lwr Artery
047*	Lwr Arteries, Dilation

Ⓣ **Transfer DRG**   ⓈⓅ **Special Payment**   * **Code Range**   **6th and 7th Character of ZZ = No Device, No Qualifier ZX = No Device, Diagnostic**

MDC 5: Diseases And Disorders Of The Circulatory System—SURGICAL

Code	Description
047K041	Dilation Rt Fem Art w Drug-elut Intralum, Drug Blln, Opn
047K0D1	Dilation Rt Fem Art w Intralum Dev, Drug Blln, Opn
047K0Z1	Dilation of Rt Fem Art using Drug Blln, Opn Appr
047K341	Dilation Rt Fem Art w Drug-elut Intralum, Drug Blln, Perc
047K3D1	Dilation Rt Fem Art w Intralum Dev, Drug Blln, Perc
047K3Z1	Dilation of Rt Fem Art using Drug Blln, Perc Appr
047K441	Dilation Rt Fem Art w Drug-elut Intralum, Drug Blln, Perc Endo
047K4D1	Dilation Rt Fem Art w Intralum Dev, Drug Blln, Perc Endo
047K4Z1	Dilation of Rt Fem Art using Drug Blln, Perc Endo Appr
047L041	Dilation Lt Fem Art w Drug-elut Intralum, Drug Blln, Opn
047L0D1	Dilation Lt Fem Art w Intralum Dev, Drug Blln, Opn
047L0Z1	Dilation of Lt Fem Art using Drug Blln, Opn Appr
047L341	Dilation Lt Fem Art w Drug-elut Intralum, Drug Blln, Perc
047L3D1	Dilation Lt Fem Art w Intralum Dev, Drug Blln, Perc
047L3Z1	Dilation of Lt Fem Art using Drug Blln, Perc Appr
047L441	Dilation Lt Fem Art w Drug-elut Intralum, Drug Blln, Perc Endo
047L4D1	Dilation Lt Fem Art w Intralum Dev, Drug Blln, Perc Endo
047L4Z1	Dilation of Lt Fem Art using Drug Blln, Perc Endo Appr
047M041	Dilation Rt Popl Art w Drug-elut Intralum, Drug Blln, Opn
047M0D1	Dilation Rt Popl Art w Intralum Dev, Drug Blln, Opn
047M0Z1	Dilation of Rt Popl Art using Drug Blln, Opn Appr
047M341	Dilation Rt Popl Art w Drug-elut Intralum, Drug Blln, Perc
047M3D1	Dilation Rt Popl Art w Intralum Dev, Drug Blln, Perc
047M3Z1	Dilation of Rt Popl Art using Drug Blln, Perc Appr
047M441	Dilation Rt Popl Art w Drug-elut Intralum, Drug Blln, Perc Endo
047M4D1	Dilation Rt Popl Art w Intralum Dev, Drug Blln, Perc Endo
047M4Z1	Dilation of Rt Popl Art using Drug Blln, Perc Endo Appr
047N041	Dilation Lt Popl Art w Drug-elut Intralum, Drug Blln, Opn
047N0D1	Dilation Lt Popl Art w Intralum Dev, Drug Blln, Opn
047N0Z1	Dilation of Lt Popl Art using Drug Blln, Opn Appr
047N341	Dilation Lt Popl Art w Drug-elut Intralum, Drug Blln, Perc
047N3D1	Dilation Lt Popl Art w Intralum Dev, Drug Blln, Perc
047N3Z1	Dilation of Lt Popl Art using Drug Blln, Perc Appr
047N441	Dilation Lt Popl Art w Drug-elut Intralum, Drug Blln, Perc Endo
047N4D1	Dilation Lt Popl Art w Intralum Dev, Drug Blln, Perc Endo
047N4Z1	Dilation of Lt Popl Art using Drug Blln, Perc Endo Appr
0490[0,3,4]ZX	Drain/Abd Aorta, [Opn, Perc, Perc Endo]
0491[0,3,4]ZX	Drain/Celiac Artery, [Opn, Perc, Perc Endo]
0492[0,3,4]ZX	Drain/Gastric Artery, [Opn, Perc, Perc Endo]
0493[0,3,4]ZX	Drain/Hepatic Artery, [Opn, Perc, Perc Endo]
0494[0,3,4]ZX	Drain/Splenic Artery, [Opn, Perc, Perc Endo]
0495[0,3,4]ZX	Drain/Superior Mesenteric Artery, [Opn, Perc, Perc Endo]
0496[0,3,4]ZX	Drain/Colic Artery, Rt, [Opn, Perc, Perc Endo]
0497[0,3,4]ZX	Drain/Colic Artery, Lt, [Opn, Perc, Perc Endo]
0498[0,3,4]ZX	Drain/Colic Artery, Mid, [Opn, Perc, Perc Endo]
0499[0,3,4]ZX	Drain/Renal Artery, Rt, [Opn, Perc, Perc Endo]
049A[0,3,4]ZX	Drain/Renal Artery, Lt, [Opn, Perc, Perc Endo]
049B[0,3,4]ZX	Drain/Inferior Mesenteric Artery, [Opn, Perc, Perc Endo]
049C[0,3,4]ZX	Drain/Common Iliac Artery, Rt, [Opn, Perc, Perc Endo]
049D[0,3,4]ZX	Drain/Common Iliac Artery, Lt, [Opn, Perc, Perc Endo]
049E[0,3,4]ZX	Drain/Int Iliac Artery, Rt, [Opn, Perc, Perc Endo]
049F[0,3,4]ZX	Drain/Int Iliac Artery, Lt, [Opn, Perc, Perc Endo]
049H[0,3,4]ZX	Drain/Ext Iliac Artery, Rt, [Opn, Perc, Perc Endo]
049J[0,3,4]ZX	Drain/Ext Iliac Artery, Lt, [Opn, Perc, Perc Endo]
049K[0,3,4]ZX	Drain/Femor Artery, Rt, [Opn, Perc, Perc Endo]
049L[0,3,4]ZX	Drain/Femor Artery, Lt, [Opn, Perc, Perc Endo]
049M[0,3,4]ZX	Drain/Popliteal Artery, Rt, [Opn, Perc, Perc Endo]
049N[0,3,4]ZX	Drain/Popliteal Artery, Lt, [Opn, Perc, Perc Endo]
049P[0,3,4]ZX	Drain/Ant Tibial Artery, Rt, [Opn, Perc, Perc Endo]
049Q[0,3,4]ZX	Drain/Ant Tibial Artery, Lt, [Opn, Perc, Perc Endo]
049R[0,3,4]ZX	Drain/Post Tibial Artery, Rt, [Opn, Perc, Perc Endo]
049S[0,3,4]ZX	Drain/Post Tibial Artery, Lt, [Opn, Perc, Perc Endo]
049T[0,3,4]ZX	Drain/Peroneal Artery, Rt, [Opn, Perc, Perc Endo]
049U[0,3,4]ZX	Drain/Peroneal Artery, Lt, [Opn, Perc, Perc Endo]
049V[0,3,4]ZX	Drain/Foot Artery, Rt, [Opn, Perc, Perc Endo]
049W[0,3,4]ZX	Drain/Foot Artery, Lt, [Opn, Perc, Perc Endo]
049Y[0,3,4]ZX	Drain/Lwr Artery, [Opn, Perc, Perc Endo]
04B0[0,3,4]ZX	Exc/Abd Aorta, [Opn, Perc, Perc Endo]
04B1[0,3,4]ZX	Exc/Celiac Artery, [Opn, Perc, Perc Endo]
04B2[0,3,4]ZX	Exc/Gastric Artery, [Opn, Perc, Perc Endo]
04B3[0,3,4]ZX	Exc/Hepatic Artery, [Opn, Perc, Perc Endo]
04B4[0,3,4]ZX	Exc/Splenic Artery, [Opn, Perc, Perc Endo]
04B5[0,3,4]ZX	Exc/Superior Mesenteric Artery, [Opn, Perc, Perc Endo]
04B6[0,3,4]ZX	Exc/Colic Artery, Rt, [Opn, Perc, Perc Endo]
04B7[0,3,4]ZX	Exc/Colic Artery, Lt, [Opn, Perc, Perc Endo]
04B8[0,3,4]ZX	Exc/Colic Artery, Mid, [Opn, Perc, Perc Endo]
04B9[0,3,4]ZX	Exc/Renal Artery, Rt, [Opn, Perc, Perc Endo]
04BA[0,3,4]ZX	Exc/Renal Artery, Lt, [Opn, Perc, Perc Endo]
04BB[0,3,4]ZX	Exc/Inferior Mesenteric Artery, [Opn, Perc, Perc Endo]
04BC[0,3,4]ZX	Exc/Common Iliac Artery, Rt, [Opn, Perc, Perc Endo]
04BD[0,3,4]ZX	Exc/Common Iliac Artery, Lt, [Opn, Perc, Perc Endo]
04BE[0,3,4]ZX	Exc/Int Iliac Artery, Rt, [Opn, Perc, Perc Endo]
04BF[0,3,4]ZX	Exc/Int Iliac Artery, Lt, [Opn, Perc, Perc Endo]
04BH[0,3,4]ZX	Exc/Ext Iliac Artery, Rt, [Opn, Perc, Perc Endo]
04BJ[0,3,4]ZX	Exc/Ext Iliac Artery, Lt, [Opn, Perc, Perc Endo]
04BK*	Exc/Femor Artery, Rt
04BL*	Exc/Femor Artery, Lt
04BM*	Exc/Popliteal Artery, Rt
04BN*	Exc/Popliteal Artery, Lt
04BP*	Exc/Ant Tibial Artery, Rt
04BQ*	Exc/Ant Tibial Artery, Lt
04BR*	Exc/Posterior Tibial Artery, Rt
04BS*	Exc/Posterior Tibial Artery, Lt
04BT*	Exc/Peroneal Artery, Rt
04BU*	Exc/Peroneal Artery, Lt
04BV*	Exc/Foot Artery, Rt
04BW*	Exc/Foot Artery, Lt
04BY*	Exc/Lwr Artery
04CK*	Extir/Femor Artery, Rt
04CL*	Extir/Femor Artery, Lt
04CM*	Extir/Popliteal Artery, Rt
04CN*	Extir/Popliteal Artery, Lt
04CP*	Extir/Ant Tibial Artery, Rt
04CQ*	Extir/Ant Tibial Artery, Lt
04CR*	Extir/Posterior Tibial Artery, Rt
04CS*	Extir/Posterior Tibial Artery, Lt
04CT*	Extir/Peroneal Artery, Rt
04CU*	Extir/Peroneal Artery, Lt
04CV*	Extir/Foot Artery, Rt
04CW*	Extir/Foot Artery, Lt
04CY*	Extir/Lwr Artery
04H0[0,3,4]DZ	Insert/Abd Aorta, [Opn, Perc, Perc Endo], Intralum Dev, NQ
04H1[0,3,4]DZ	Insert/Celiac Artery, [Opn, Perc, Perc Endo], Intralum Dev, NQ
04H2[0,3,4]DZ	Insert/Gastric Artery, [Opn, Perc, Perc Endo], Intralum Dev, NQ
04H3[0,3,4]DZ	Insert/Hepatic Artery, [Opn, Perc, Perc Endo], Intralum Dev, NQ
04H4[0,3,4]DZ	Insert/Splenic Artery, [Opn, Perc, Perc Endo], Intralum Dev, NQ
04H5[0,3,4]DZ	Insert/Superior Mesenteric Artery, [Opn, Perc, Perc Endo], Intralum Dev, NQ
04H6[0,3,4]DZ	Insert/Colic Artery, Rt, [Opn, Perc, Perc Endo], Intralum Dev, NQ
04H7[0,3,4]DZ	Insert/Colic Artery, Lt, [Opn, Perc, Perc Endo], Intralum Dev, NQ
04H8[0,3,4]DZ	Insert/Colic Artery, Mid, [Opn, Perc, Perc Endo], Intralum Dev, NQ
04H9[0,3,4]DZ	Insert/Renal Artery, Rt, [Opn, Perc, Perc Endo], Intralum Dev, NQ
04HA[0,3,4]DZ	Insert/Renal Artery, Lt, [Opn, Perc, Perc Endo], Intralum Dev, NQ
04HB[0,3,4]DZ	Insert/Inferior Mesenteric Artery, [Opn, Perc, Perc Endo], Intralum Dev, NQ
04HC[0,3,4]DZ	Insert/Common Iliac Artery, Rt, [Opn, Perc, Perc Endo], Intralum Dev, NQ
04HD[0,3,4]DZ	Insert/Common Iliac Artery, Lt, [Opn, Perc, Perc Endo], Intralum Dev, NQ
04HE[0,3,4]DZ	Insert/Int Iliac Artery, Rt, [Opn, Perc, Perc Endo], Intralum Dev, NQ
04HF[0,3,4]DZ	Insert/Int Iliac Artery, Lt, [Opn, Perc, Perc Endo], Intralum Dev, NQ
04HH[0,3,4]DZ	Insert/Ext Iliac Artery, Rt, [Opn, Perc, Perc Endo], Intralum Dev, NQ
04HJ[0,3,4]DZ	Insert/Ext Iliac Artery, Lt, [Opn, Perc, Perc Endo], Intralum Dev, NQ
04HK[0,3,4]DZ	Insert/Femor Artery, Rt, [Opn, Perc, Perc Endo], Intralum Dev, NQ
04HL[0,3,4]DZ	Insert/Femor Artery, Lt, [Opn, Perc, Perc Endo], Intralum Dev, NQ
04HM[0,3,4]DZ	Insert/Popliteal Artery, Rt, [Opn, Perc, Perc Endo], Intralum Dev, NQ
04HN[0,3,4]DZ	Insert/Popliteal Artery, Lt, [Opn, Perc, Perc Endo], Intralum Dev, NQ
04HP[0,3,4]DZ	Insert/Ant Tibial Artery, Rt, [Opn, Perc, Perc Endo], Intralum Dev, NQ
04HQ[0,3,4]DZ	Insert/Ant Tibial Artery, Lt, [Opn, Perc, Perc Endo], Intralum Dev, NQ
04HR[0,3,4]DZ	Insert/Post Tibial Artery, Rt, [Opn, Perc, Perc Endo], Intralum Dev, NQ
04HS[0,3,4]DZ	Insert/Post Tibial Artery, Lt, [Opn, Perc, Perc Endo], Intralum Dev, NQ

04HT[Ø,3,4]DZ	Insert/Peroneal Artery, Rt, [Opn, Perc, Perc Endo], Intralum Dev, NQ
04HU[Ø,3,4]DZ	Insert/Peroneal Artery, Lt, [Opn, Perc, Perc Endo], Intralum Dev, NQ
04HV[Ø,3,4]DZ	Insert/Foot Artery, Rt, [Opn, Perc, Perc Endo], Intralum Dev, NQ
04HW[Ø,3,4]DZ	Insert/Foot Artery, Lt, [Opn, Perc, Perc Endo], Intralum Dev, NQ
04HY[Ø,3,4][2,D]Z	Insert/Lwr Artery, [Opn, Perc, Perc Endo], [Monitoring Dev, Intralum Dev], NQ
04JY[Ø,3]ZZ	Inspect/Lwr Artery, [Opn, Perc]
04LK[Ø,3,4][C,D,Z]Z	Occlsn/Femor Artery, Rt, [Opn, Perc, Perc Endo], [Extralum Dev, Intralum Dev, No Dev], NQ
04LL[Ø,3,4][C,D,Z]Z	Occlsn/Femor Artery, Lt, [Opn, Perc, Perc Endo], [Extralum Dev, Intralum Dev, No Dev], NQ
04LM[Ø,3,4][C,D,Z]Z	Occlsn/Popliteal Artery, Rt, [Opn, Perc, Perc Endo], [Extralum Dev, Intralum Dev, No Dev], NQ
04LN[Ø,3,4][C,D,Z]Z	Occlsn/Popliteal Artery, Lt, [Opn, Perc, Perc Endo], [Extralum Dev, Intralum Dev, No Dev], NQ
04LP[Ø,3,4][C,D,Z]Z	Occlsn/Ant Tibial Artery, Rt, [Opn, Perc, Perc Endo], [Extralum Dev, Intralum Dev, No Dev], NQ
04LQ[Ø,3,4][C,D,Z]Z	Occlsn/Ant Tibial Artery, Lt, [Opn, Perc, Perc Endo], [Extralum Dev, Intralum Dev, No Dev], NQ
04LR[Ø,3,4][C,D,Z]Z	Occlsn/Post Tibial Artery, Rt, [Opn, Perc, Perc Endo], [Extralum Dev, Intralum Dev, No Dev], NQ
04LS[Ø,3,4][C,D,Z]Z	Occlsn/Post Tibial Artery, Lt, [Opn, Perc, Perc Endo], [Extralum Dev, Intralum Dev, No Dev], NQ
04LT[Ø,3,4][C,D,Z]Z	Occlsn/Peroneal Artery, Rt, [Opn, Perc, Perc Endo], [Extralum Dev, Intralum Dev, No Dev], NQ
04LU[Ø,3,4][C,D,Z]Z	Occlsn/Peroneal Artery, Lt, [Opn, Perc, Perc Endo], [Extralum Dev, Intralum Dev, No Dev], NQ
04LV[Ø,3,4][C,D,Z]Z	Occlsn/Foot Artery, Rt, [Opn, Perc, Perc Endo], [Extralum Dev, Intralum Dev, No Dev], NQ
04LW[Ø,3,4][C,D,Z]Z	Occlsn/Foot Artery, Lt, [Opn, Perc, Perc Endo], [Extralum Dev, Intralum Dev, No Dev], NQ
04LY[Ø,3,4][C,D,Z]Z	Occlsn/Lwr Artery, [Opn, Perc, Perc Endo], [Extralum Dev, Intralum Dev, No Dev], NQ
04N*	Lwr Arteries, Rls
04PY[Ø,3,4][Ø,2,3,7,C,D,J,K]Z	Rmvl/Lwr Artery, [Opn, Perc, Perc Endo], [Drain Dev, Monitoring Dev, Inf Dev, Auto Tissue Sub, Extralum Dev, Intralum Dev, Synth Sub, Nonauto Tissue Sub], NQ
04Q*	Lwr Arteries, Repair
04RK*	Replace/Femor Artery, Rt
04RL*	Replace/Femor Artery, Lt
04RM*	Replace/Popliteal Artery, Rt
04RN*	Replace/Popliteal Artery, Lt
04RP*	Replace/Ant Tibial Artery, Rt
04RQ*	Replace/Ant Tibial Artery, Lt
04RR*	Replace/Posterior Tibial Artery, Rt
04RS*	Replace/Posterior Tibial Artery, Lt
04RT*	Replace/Peroneal Artery, Rt
04RU*	Replace/Peroneal Artery, Lt
04RV*	Replace/Foot Artery, Rt
04RW*	Replace/Foot Artery, Lt
04RY*	Replace/Lwr Artery
04S*	Lwr Arteries, Repos
04UØØJZ	Supl Abd Aorta with Synth Sub, Opn Appr
04UØ[Ø,3,4][7,K]Z	Supl/Abd Aorta, [Opn, Perc, Perc Endo], [Auto Tissue Sub, Nonauto Tissue Sub], NQ
04U1*	Supl/Celiac Artery
04U2*	Supl/Gastric Artery
04U3*	Supl/Hepatic Artery
04U4*	Supl/Splenic Artery
04U5*	Supl/Superior Mesenteric Artery
04U6*	Supl/Colic Artery, Rt
04U7*	Supl/Colic Artery, Lt
04U8*	Supl/Colic Artery, Mid
04U9*	Supl/Renal Artery, Rt
04UA*	Supl/Renal Artery, Lt
04UB*	Supl/Inferior Mesenteric Artery
04UC*	Supl/Common Iliac Artery, Rt
04UD*	Supl/Common Iliac Artery, Lt
04UE*	Supl/Int Iliac Artery, Rt
04UF*	Supl/Int Iliac Artery, Lt
04UH*	Supl/Ext Iliac Artery, Rt
04UJ*	Supl/Ext Iliac Artery, Lt
04UK*	Supl/Femor Artery, Rt
04UL*	Supl/Femor Artery, Lt
04UM*	Supl/Popliteal Artery, Rt
04UN*	Supl/Popliteal Artery, Lt
04UP*	Supl/Ant Tibial Artery, Rt

04UQ*	Supl/Ant Tibial Artery, Lt
04UR*	Supl/Posterior Tibial Artery, Rt
04US*	Supl/Posterior Tibial Artery, Lt
04UT*	Supl/Peroneal Artery, Rt
04UU*	Supl/Peroneal Artery, Lt
04UV*	Supl/Foot Artery, Rt
04UW*	Supl/Foot Artery, Lt
04UY*	Supl/Lwr Artery
04VØ[Ø,3,4]CZ	Restrict/Abd Aorta, [Opn, Perc, Perc Endo], Extralum Dev, NQ
04VØ[Ø,3,4]DJ	Restrict/Abd Aorta, [Opn, Perc, Perc Endo], Intralum Dev, Temporary
04V1[Ø,3,4]CZ	Restrict/Celiac Artery, [Opn, Perc, Perc Endo], Extralum Dev, NQ
04V2[Ø,3,4]CZ	Restrict/Gastric Artery, [Opn, Perc, Perc Endo], Extralum Dev, NQ
04V3[Ø,3,4]CZ	Restrict/Hepatic Artery, [Opn, Perc, Perc Endo], Extralum Dev, NQ
04V4[Ø,3,4]CZ	Restrict/Splenic Artery, [Opn, Perc, Perc Endo], Extralum Dev, NQ
04V5[Ø,3,4]CZ	Restrict/Superior Mesenteric Artery, [Opn, Perc, Perc Endo], Extralum Dev, NQ
04V6[Ø,3,4]CZ	Restrict/Colic Artery, Rt, [Opn, Perc, Perc Endo], Extralum Dev, NQ
04V7[Ø,3,4]CZ	Restrict/Colic Artery, Lt, [Opn, Perc, Perc Endo], Extralum Dev, NQ
04V8[Ø,3,4]CZ	Restrict/Colic Artery, Mid, [Opn, Perc, Perc Endo], Extralum Dev, NQ
04V9[Ø,3,4]CZ	Restrict/Renal Artery, Rt, [Opn, Perc, Perc Endo], Extralum Dev, NQ
04VA[Ø,3,4]CZ	Restrict/Renal Artery, Lt, [Opn, Perc, Perc Endo], Extralum Dev, NQ
04VB[Ø,3,4]CZ	Restrict/Inferior Mesenteric Artery, [Opn, Perc, Perc Endo], Extralum Dev, NQ
04VC[Ø,3,4]CZ	Restrict/Common Iliac Artery, Rt, [Opn, Perc, Perc Endo], Extralum Dev, NQ
04VD[Ø,3,4]CZ	Restrict/Common Iliac Artery, Lt, [Opn, Perc, Perc Endo], Extralum Dev, NQ
04VE[Ø,3,4]CZ	Restrict/Int Iliac Artery, Rt, [Opn, Perc, Perc Endo], Extralum Dev, NQ
04VF[Ø,3,4]CZ	Restrict/Int Iliac Artery, Lt, [Opn, Perc, Perc Endo], Extralum Dev, NQ
04VH[Ø,3,4]CZ	Restrict/Ext Iliac Artery, Rt, [Opn, Perc, Perc Endo], Extralum Dev, NQ
04VJ[Ø,3,4]CZ	Restrict/Ext Iliac Artery, Lt, [Opn, Perc, Perc Endo], Extralum Dev, NQ
04VK[Ø,3,4]CZ	Restrict/Femor Artery, Rt, [Opn, Perc, Perc Endo], Extralum Dev, NQ
04VL[Ø,3,4]CZ	Restrict/Femor Artery, Lt, [Opn, Perc, Perc Endo], Extralum Dev, NQ
04VM[Ø,3,4]CZ	Restrict/Popliteal Artery, Rt, [Opn, Perc, Perc Endo], Extralum Dev, NQ
04VN[Ø,3,4]CZ	Restrict/Popliteal Artery, Lt, [Opn, Perc, Perc Endo], Extralum Dev, NQ
04VP[Ø,3,4]CZ	Restrict/Ant Tibial Artery, Rt, [Opn, Perc, Perc Endo], Extralum Dev, NQ
04VQ[Ø,3,4]CZ	Restrict/Ant Tibial Artery, Lt, [Opn, Perc, Perc Endo], Extralum Dev, NQ
04VR[Ø,3,4]CZ	Restrict/Post Tibial Artery, Rt, [Opn, Perc, Perc Endo], Extralum Dev, NQ
04VS[Ø,3,4]CZ	Restrict/Post Tibial Artery, Lt, [Opn, Perc, Perc Endo], Extralum Dev, NQ
04VT[Ø,3,4]CZ	Restrict/Peroneal Artery, Rt, [Opn, Perc, Perc Endo], Extralum Dev, NQ
04VU[Ø,3,4]CZ	Restrict/Peroneal Artery, Lt, [Opn, Perc, Perc Endo], Extralum Dev, NQ
04VV[Ø,3,4]CZ	Restrict/Foot Artery, Rt, [Opn, Perc, Perc Endo], Extralum Dev, NQ
04VW[Ø,3,4]CZ	Restrict/Foot Artery, Lt, [Opn, Perc, Perc Endo], Extralum Dev, NQ
04VY[Ø,3,4]CZ	Restrict/Lwr Artery, [Opn, Perc, Perc Endo], Extralum Dev, NQ
04WY[Ø,3,4][Ø,2,3,7,C,D,J,K]Z	Rev/Lwr Artery, [Opn, Perc, Perc Endo], [Drain Dev, Monitoring Dev, Inf Dev, Auto Tissue Sub, Extralum Dev, Intralum Dev, Synth Sub, Nonauto Tissue Sub], NQ
0517*	Bypass/Axillary Vein, Rt
0518*	Bypass/Axillary Vein, Lt
0519*	Bypass/Brachial Vein, Rt
051A*	Bypass/Brachial Vein, Lt
051B*	Bypass/Basilic Vein, Rt
051C*	Bypass/Basilic Vein, Lt
051D*	Bypass/Cephalic Vein, Rt

T Transfer DRG   SP Special Payment   * Code Range   6th and 7th Character of ZZ = No Device, No Qualifier ZX = No Device, Diagnostic

051F*	Bypass/Cephalic Vein, Lt
051G*	Bypass/Hand Vein, Rt
051H*	Bypass/Hand Vein, Lt
051L*	Bypass/Intracranial Vein
051M*	Bypass/Int Jugular Vein, Rt
051N*	Bypass/Int Jugular Vein, Lt
051P*	Bypass/Ext Jugular Vein, Rt
051Q*	Bypass/Ext Jugular Vein, Lt
051R*	Bypass/Vert Vein, Rt
051S*	Bypass/Vert Vein, Lt
051T*	Bypass/Face Vein, Rt
051V*	Bypass/Face Vein, Lt
0557*	Destr/Axillary Vein, Rt
0558*	Destr/Axillary Vein, Lt
0559*	Destr/Brachial Vein, Rt
055A*	Destr/Brachial Vein, Lt
055B*	Destr/Basilic Vein, Rt
055C*	Destr/Basilic Vein, Lt
055D*	Destr/Cephalic Vein, Rt
055F*	Destr/Cephalic Vein, Lt
055G*	Destr/Hand Vein, Rt
055H*	Destr/Hand Vein, Lt
055M*	Destr/Int Jugular Vein, Rt
055N*	Destr/Int Jugular Vein, Lt
055P*	Destr/Ext Jugular Vein, Rt
055Q*	Destr/Ext Jugular Vein, Lt
055R*	Destr/Vert Vein, Rt
055S*	Destr/Vert Vein, Lt
055T*	Destr/Face Vein, Rt
055V*	Destr/Face Vein, Lt
055Y*	Destr/Upr Vein
057*	Upr Veins, Dilation
0590[0,3,4]ZX	Drain/Azygos Vein, [Opn, Perc, Perc Endo]
0591[0,3,4]ZX	Drain/Hemiazygos Vein, [Opn, Perc, Perc Endo]
0593[0,3,4]ZX	Drain/Innominate Vein, Rt, [Opn, Perc, Perc Endo]
0594[0,3,4]ZX	Drain/Innominate Vein, Lt, [Opn, Perc, Perc Endo]
0595[0,3,4]ZX	Drain/Subclavian Vein, Rt, [Opn, Perc, Perc Endo]
0596[0,3,4]ZX	Drain/Subclavian Vein, Lt, [Opn, Perc, Perc Endo]
0597[0,3,4]ZX	Drain/Axillary Vein, Rt, [Opn, Perc, Perc Endo]
0598[0,3,4]ZX	Drain/Axillary Vein, Lt, [Opn, Perc, Perc Endo]
0599[0,3,4]ZX	Drain/Brachial Vein, Rt, [Opn, Perc, Perc Endo]
059A[0,3,4]ZX	Drain/Brachial Vein, Lt, [Opn, Perc, Perc Endo]
059B[0,3,4]ZX	Drain/Basilic Vein, Rt, [Opn, Perc, Perc Endo]
059C[0,3,4]ZX	Drain/Basilic Vein, Lt, [Opn, Perc, Perc Endo]
059D[0,3,4]ZX	Drain/Cephalic Vein, Rt, [Opn, Perc, Perc Endo]
059F[0,3,4]ZX	Drain/Cephalic Vein, Lt, [Opn, Perc, Perc Endo]
059G[0,3,4]ZX	Drain/Hand Vein, Rt, [Opn, Perc, Perc Endo]
059H[0,3,4]ZX	Drain/Hand Vein, Lt, [Opn, Perc, Perc Endo]
059L[0,3,4]ZX	Drain/Intracranial Vein, [Opn, Perc, Perc Endo]
059M[0,3,4]ZX	Drain/Int Jugular Vein, Rt, [Opn, Perc, Perc Endo]
059N[0,3,4]ZX	Drain/Int Jugular Vein, Lt, [Opn, Perc, Perc Endo]
059P[0,3,4]ZX	Drain/Ext Jugular Vein, Rt, [Opn, Perc, Perc Endo]
059Q[0,3,4]ZX	Drain/Ext Jugular Vein, Lt, [Opn, Perc, Perc Endo]
059R[0,3,4]ZX	Drain/Vert Vein, Rt, [Opn, Perc, Perc Endo]
059S[0,3,4]ZX	Drain/Vert Vein, Lt, [Opn, Perc, Perc Endo]
059T[0,3,4]ZX	Drain/Face Vein, Rt, [Opn, Perc, Perc Endo]
059V[0,3,4]ZX	Drain/Face Vein, Lt, [Opn, Perc, Perc Endo]
059Y[0,3,4]ZX	Drain/Upr Vein, [Opn, Perc, Perc Endo]
05B0[0,3,4]ZX	Exc/Azygos Vein, [Opn, Perc, Perc Endo]
05B1[0,3,4]ZX	Exc/Hemiazygos Vein, [Opn, Perc, Perc Endo]
05B3[0,3,4]ZX	Exc/Innominate Vein, Rt, [Opn, Perc, Perc Endo]
05B4[0,3,4]ZX	Exc/Innominate Vein, Lt, [Opn, Perc, Perc Endo]
05B5[0,3,4]ZX	Exc/Subclavian Vein, Rt, [Opn, Perc, Perc Endo]
05B6[0,3,4]ZX	Exc/Subclavian Vein, Lt, [Opn, Perc, Perc Endo]
05B7*	Exc/Axillary Vein, Rt
05B8*	Exc/Axillary Vein, Lt
05B9*	Exc/Brachial Vein, Rt
05BA*	Exc/Brachial Vein, Lt
05BB*	Exc/Basilic Vein, Rt
05BC*	Exc/Basilic Vein, Lt
05BD*	Exc/Cephalic Vein, Rt
05BF*	Exc/Cephalic Vein, Lt
05BG*	Exc/Hand Vein, Rt
05BH*	Exc/Hand Vein, Lt
05BL[0,3,4]ZX	Exc/Intracranial Vein, [Opn, Perc, Perc Endo]
05BM*	Exc/Int Jugular Vein, Rt
05BN*	Exc/Int Jugular Vein, Lt
05BP*	Exc/Ext Jugular Vein, Rt
05BQ*	Exc/Ext Jugular Vein, Lt
05BR*	Exc/Vert Vein, Rt

05BS*	Exc/Vert Vein, Lt
05BT*	Exc/Face Vein, Rt
05BV*	Exc/Face Vein, Lt
05BY*	Exc/Upr Vein
05C7*	Extir/Axillary Vein, Rt
05C8*	Extir/Axillary Vein, Lt
05C9*	Extir/Brachial Vein, Rt
05CA*	Extir/Brachial Vein, Lt
05CB*	Extir/Basilic Vein, Rt
05CC*	Extir/Basilic Vein, Lt
05CD*	Extir/Cephalic Vein, Rt
05CF*	Extir/Cephalic Vein, Lt
05CG*	Extir/Hand Vein, Rt
05CH*	Extir/Hand Vein, Lt
05CL3ZZ	Extir of Matter from Intracranial Vein, Perc Appr
05CM*	Extir/Int Jugular Vein, Rt
05CN*	Extir/Int Jugular Vein, Lt
05CP*	Extir/Ext Jugular Vein, Rt
05CQ*	Extir/Ext Jugular Vein, Lt
05CR*	Extir/Vert Vein, Rt
05CS*	Extir/Vert Vein, Lt
05CT*	Extir/Face Vein, Rt
05CV*	Extir/Face Vein, Lt
05CY*	Extir/Upr Vein
05H0[0,3,4]DZ	Insert/Azygos Vein, [Opn, Perc, Perc Endo], Intralum Dev, NQ
05H1[0,3,4]DZ	Insert/Hemiazygos Vein, [Opn, Perc, Perc Endo], Intralum Dev, NQ
05H3[0,3,4]DZ	Insert/Innominate Vein, Rt, [Opn, Perc, Perc Endo], Intralum Dev, NQ
05H4[0,3,4]DZ	Insert/Innominate Vein, Lt, [Opn, Perc, Perc Endo], Intralum Dev, NQ
05H5[0,3,4]DZ	Insert/Subclavian Vein, Rt, [Opn, Perc, Perc Endo], Intralum Dev, NQ
05H6[0,3,4]DZ	Insert/Subclavian Vein, Lt, [Opn, Perc, Perc Endo], Intralum Dev, NQ
05H7[0,3,4]DZ	Insert/Axillary Vein, Rt, [Opn, Perc, Perc Endo], Intralum Dev, NQ
05H8[0,3,4]DZ	Insert/Axillary Vein, Lt, [Opn, Perc, Perc Endo], Intralum Dev, NQ
05H9[0,3,4]DZ	Insert/Brachial Vein, Rt, [Opn, Perc, Perc Endo], Intralum Dev, NQ
05HA[0,3,4]DZ	Insert/Brachial Vein, Lt, [Opn, Perc, Perc Endo], Intralum Dev, NQ
05HB[0,3,4]DZ	Insert/Basilic Vein, Rt, [Opn, Perc, Perc Endo], Intralum Dev, NQ
05HC[0,3,4]DZ	Insert/Basilic Vein, Lt, [Opn, Perc, Perc Endo], Intralum Dev, NQ
05HD[0,3,4]DZ	Insert/Cephalic Vein, Rt, [Opn, Perc, Perc Endo], Intralum Dev, NQ
05HF[0,3,4]DZ	Insert/Cephalic Vein, Lt, [Opn, Perc, Perc Endo], Intralum Dev, NQ
05HG[0,3,4]DZ	Insert/Hand Vein, Rt, [Opn, Perc, Perc Endo], Intralum Dev, NQ
05HH[0,3,4]DZ	Insert/Hand Vein, Lt, [Opn, Perc, Perc Endo], Intralum Dev, NQ
05HL[0,3,4]DZ	Insert/Intracranial Vein, [Opn, Perc, Perc Endo], Intralum Dev, NQ
05HM[0,3,4]DZ	Insert/Int Jugular Vein, Rt, [Opn, Perc, Perc Endo], Intralum Dev, NQ
05HN[0,3,4]DZ	Insert/Int Jugular Vein, Lt, [Opn, Perc, Perc Endo], Intralum Dev, NQ
05HP[0,3,4]DZ	Insert/Ext Jugular Vein, Rt, [Opn, Perc, Perc Endo], Intralum Dev, NQ
05HQ[0,3,4]DZ	Insert/Ext Jugular Vein, Lt, [Opn, Perc, Perc Endo], Intralum Dev, NQ
05HR[0,3,4]DZ	Insert/Vert Vein, Rt, [Opn, Perc, Perc Endo], Intralum Dev, NQ
05HS[0,3,4]DZ	Insert/Vert Vein, Lt, [Opn, Perc, Perc Endo], Intralum Dev, NQ
05HT[0,3,4]DZ	Insert/Face Vein, Rt, [Opn, Perc, Perc Endo], Intralum Dev, NQ
05HV[0,3,4]DZ	Insert/Face Vein, Lt, [Opn, Perc, Perc Endo], Intralum Dev, NQ
05HY[0,3,4][2,D]Z	Insert/Upr Vein, [Opn, Perc, Perc Endo], [Monitoring Dev, Intralum Dev], NQ
05JY[0,3,4]ZZ	Inspect/Upr Vein, [Opn, Perc, Perc Endo]
05L7[0,3,4][C,D,Z]Z	Occlsn/Axillary Vein, Rt, [Opn, Perc, Perc Endo], [Extralum Dev, Intralum Dev, No Dev], NQ
05L8[0,3,4][C,D,Z]Z	Occlsn/Axillary Vein, Lt, [Opn, Perc, Perc Endo], [Extralum Dev, Intralum Dev, No Dev], NQ
05L9[0,3,4][C,D,Z]Z	Occlsn/Brachial Vein, Rt, [Opn, Perc, Perc Endo], [Extralum Dev, Intralum Dev, No Dev], NQ
05LA[0,3,4][C,D,Z]Z	Occlsn/Brachial Vein, Lt, [Opn, Perc, Perc Endo], [Extralum Dev, Intralum Dev, No Dev], NQ
05LB[0,3,4][C,D,Z]Z	Occlsn/Basilic Vein, Rt, [Opn, Perc, Perc Endo], [Extralum Dev, Intralum Dev, No Dev], NQ
05LC[0,3,4][C,D,Z]Z	Occlsn/Basilic Vein, Lt, [Opn, Perc, Perc Endo], [Extralum Dev, Intralum Dev, No Dev], NQ

Surgical **Medical** **CC Indicator** **MCC Indicator** **Procedure Proxy** PDxMCC **PDx acts as own MCC** PDxCC **PDx acts as own CC**

MDC 5: Diseases And Disorders Of The Circulatory System—SURGICAL

MDC 5: Diseases And Disorders Of The Circulatory System—SURGICAL

05LD[0,3,4][C,D,Z]Z	Occlsn/Cephalic Vein, Rt, [Opn, Perc, Perc Endo], [Extralum Dev, Intralum Dev, No Dev], NQ
05LF[0,3,4][C,D,Z]Z	Occlsn/Cephalic Vein, Lt, [Opn, Perc, Perc Endo], [Extralum Dev, Intralum Dev, No Dev], NQ
05LG[0,3,4][C,D,Z]Z	Occlsn/Hand Vein, Rt, [Opn, Perc, Perc Endo], [Extralum Dev, Intralum Dev, No Dev], NQ
05LH[0,3,4][C,D,Z]Z	Occlsn/Hand Vein, Lt, [Opn, Perc, Perc Endo], [Extralum Dev, Intralum Dev, No Dev], NQ
05LM*	Occlsn/Int Jugular Vein, Rt
05LN*	Occlsn/Int Jugular Vein, Lt
05LP*	Occlsn/Ext Jugular Vein, Rt
05LQ*	Occlsn/Ext Jugular Vein, Lt
05LR*	Occlsn/Vert Vein, Rt
05LS*	Occlsn/Vert Vein, Lt
05LT*	Occlsn/Face Vein, Rt
05LV*	Occlsn/Face Vein, Lt
05LY[0,3,4][C,D,Z]Z	Occlsn/Upr Vein, [Opn, Perc, Perc Endo], [Extralum Dev, Intralum Dev, No Dev], NQ
05N*	Upr Veins, Rls
05PY[0,3,4][0,2,3,7,C,D,J,K]Z	Rmvl/Upr Vein, [Opn, Perc, Perc Endo], [Drain Dev, Monitoring Dev, Inf Dev, Auto Tissue Sub, Extralum Dev, Intralum Dev, Synth Sub, Nonauto Tissue Sub], NQ
05QY*	Repair/Upr Vein
05R7*	Replace/Axillary Vein, Rt
05R8*	Replace/Axillary Vein, Lt
05R9*	Replace/Brachial Vein, Rt
05RA*	Replace/Brachial Vein, Lt
05RB*	Replace/Basilic Vein, Rt
05RC*	Replace/Basilic Vein, Lt
05RD*	Replace/Cephalic Vein, Rt
05RF*	Replace/Cephalic Vein, Lt
05RG*	Replace/Hand Vein, Rt
05RH*	Replace/Hand Vein, Lt
05RM*	Replace/Int Jugular Vein, Rt
05RN*	Replace/Int Jugular Vein, Lt
05RP*	Replace/Ext Jugular Vein, Rt
05RQ*	Replace/Ext Jugular Vein, Lt
05RR*	Replace/Vert Vein, Rt
05RS*	Replace/Vert Vein, Lt
05RT*	Replace/Face Vein, Rt
05RV*	Replace/Face Vein, Lt
05RY*	Replace/Upr Vein
05S*	Upr Veins, Repos
05U*	Upr Veins, Supl
05V0[0,3,4]CZ	Restrict/Azygos Vein, [Opn, Perc, Perc Endo], Extralum Dev, NQ
05V1[0,3,4]CZ	Restrict/Hemiazygos Vein, [Opn, Perc, Perc Endo], Extralum Dev, NQ
05V3[0,3,4]CZ	Restrict/Innominate Vein, Rt, [Opn, Perc, Perc Endo], Extralum Dev, NQ
05V4[0,3,4]CZ	Restrict/Innominate Vein, Lt, [Opn, Perc, Perc Endo], Extralum Dev, NQ
05V5[0,3,4]CZ	Restrict/Subclavian Vein, Rt, [Opn, Perc, Perc Endo], Extralum Dev, NQ
05V6[0,3,4]CZ	Restrict/Subclavian Vein, Lt, [Opn, Perc, Perc Endo], Extralum Dev, NQ
05V7[0,3,4]CZ	Restrict/Axillary Vein, Rt, [Opn, Perc, Perc Endo], Extralum Dev, NQ
05V8[0,3,4]CZ	Restrict/Axillary Vein, Lt, [Opn, Perc, Perc Endo], Extralum Dev, NQ
05V9[0,3,4]CZ	Restrict/Brachial Vein, Rt, [Opn, Perc, Perc Endo], Extralum Dev, NQ
05VA[0,3,4]CZ	Restrict/Brachial Vein, Lt, [Opn, Perc, Perc Endo], Extralum Dev, NQ
05VB[0,3,4]CZ	Restrict/Basilic Vein, Rt, [Opn, Perc, Perc Endo], Extralum Dev, NQ
05VC[0,3,4]CZ	Restrict/Basilic Vein, Lt, [Opn, Perc, Perc Endo], Extralum Dev, NQ
05VD[0,3,4]CZ	Restrict/Cephalic Vein, Rt, [Opn, Perc, Perc Endo], Extralum Dev, NQ
05VF[0,3,4]CZ	Restrict/Cephalic Vein, Lt, [Opn, Perc, Perc Endo], Extralum Dev, NQ
05VG[0,3,4]CZ	Restrict/Hand Vein, Rt, [Opn, Perc, Perc Endo], Extralum Dev, NQ
05VH[0,3,4]CZ	Restrict/Hand Vein, Lt, [Opn, Perc, Perc Endo], Extralum Dev, NQ
05VL[0,3,4]CZ	Restrict/Intracranial Vein, [Opn, Perc, Perc Endo], Extralum Dev, NQ
05VM[0,3,4]CZ	Restrict/Int Jugular Vein, Rt, [Opn, Perc, Perc Endo], Extralum Dev, NQ
05VN[0,3,4]CZ	Restrict/Int Jugular Vein, Lt, [Opn, Perc, Perc Endo], Extralum Dev, NQ
05VP[0,3,4]CZ	Restrict/Ext Jugular Vein, Rt, [Opn, Perc, Perc Endo], Extralum Dev, NQ
05VQ[0,3,4]CZ	Restrict/Ext Jugular Vein, Lt, [Opn, Perc, Perc Endo], Extralum Dev, NQ
05VR[0,3,4]CZ	Restrict/Vert Vein, Rt, [Opn, Perc, Perc Endo], Extralum Dev, NQ
05VS[0,3,4]CZ	Restrict/Vert Vein, Lt, [Opn, Perc, Perc Endo], Extralum Dev, NQ
05VT[0,3,4]CZ	Restrict/Face Vein, Rt, [Opn, Perc, Perc Endo], Extralum Dev, NQ
05VV[0,3,4]CZ	Restrict/Face Vein, Lt, [Opn, Perc, Perc Endo], Extralum Dev, NQ
05VY[0,3,4]CZ	Restrict/Upr Vein, [Opn, Perc, Perc Endo], Extralum Dev, NQ
05WY[0,3,4][0,2,3,7,C,D,J,K]Z	Rev/Upr Vein, [Opn, Perc, Perc Endo], [Drain Dev, Monitoring Dev, Inf Dev, Auto Tissue Sub, Extralum Dev, Intralum Dev, Synth Sub, Nonauto Tissue Sub], NQ
0613*	Bypass/Esophageal Vein
061C*	Bypass/Common Iliac Vein, Rt
061D*	Bypass/Common Iliac Vein, Lt
061F*	Bypass/Ext Iliac Vein, Rt
061G*	Bypass/Ext Iliac Vein, Lt
061H*	Bypass/Hypogastric Vein, Rt
061M*	Bypass/Femor Vein, Rt
061N*	Bypass/Femor Vein, Lt
061P*	Bypass/Greater Saphenous Vein, Rt
061Q*	Bypass/Greater Saphenous Vein, Lt
061R*	Bypass/Lesser Saphenous Vein, Rt
061S*	Bypass/Lesser Saphenous Vein, Lt
061T*	Bypass/Foot Vein, Rt
061V*	Bypass/Foot Vein, Lt
0653*	Destr/Esophageal Vein
067*	Lwr Veins, Dilation
0690[0,3,4]ZX	Drain/Inferior Vena Cava, [Opn, Perc, Perc Endo]
0691[0,3,4]ZX	Drain/Splenic Vein, [Opn, Perc, Perc Endo]
0692[0,3,4]ZX	Drain/Gastric Vein, [Opn, Perc, Perc Endo]
0693*	Drain/Esophageal Vein
0694[0,3,4]ZX	Drain/Hepatic Vein, [Opn, Perc, Perc Endo]
0695[0,3,4]ZX	Drain/Superior Mesenteric Vein, [Opn, Perc, Perc Endo]
0696[0,3,4]ZX	Drain/Inferior Mesenteric Vein, [Opn, Perc, Perc Endo]
0697[0,3,4]ZX	Drain/Colic Vein, [Opn, Perc, Perc Endo]
0698[0,3,4]ZX	Drain/Portal Vein, [Opn, Perc, Perc Endo]
0699[0,3,4]ZX	Drain/Renal Vein, Rt, [Opn, Perc, Perc Endo]
069B[0,3,4]ZX	Drain/Renal Vein, Lt, [Opn, Perc, Perc Endo]
069C[0,3,4]ZX	Drain/Common Iliac Vein, Rt, [Opn, Perc, Perc Endo]
069D[0,3,4]ZX	Drain/Common Iliac Vein, Lt, [Opn, Perc, Perc Endo]
069F[0,3,4]ZX	Drain/Ext Iliac Vein, Rt, [Opn, Perc, Perc Endo]
069G[0,3,4]ZX	Drain/Ext Iliac Vein, Lt, [Opn, Perc, Perc Endo]
069H[0,3,4]ZX	Drain/Hypogastric Vein, Rt, [Opn, Perc, Perc Endo]
069J[0,3,4]ZX	Drain/Hypogastric Vein, Lt, [Opn, Perc, Perc Endo]
069M[0,3,4]ZX	Drain/Femor Vein, Rt, [Opn, Perc, Perc Endo]
069N[0,3,4]ZX	Drain/Femor Vein, Lt, [Opn, Perc, Perc Endo]
069P[0,3,4]ZX	Drain/Greater Saphenous Vein, Rt, [Opn, Perc, Perc Endo]
069Q[0,3,4]ZX	Drain/Greater Saphenous Vein, Lt, [Opn, Perc, Perc Endo]
069R[0,3,4]ZX	Drain/Lesser Saphenous Vein, Rt, [Opn, Perc, Perc Endo]
069S[0,3,4]ZX	Drain/Lesser Saphenous Vein, Lt, [Opn, Perc, Perc Endo]
069T[0,3,4]ZX	Drain/Foot Vein, Rt, [Opn, Perc, Perc Endo]
069V[0,3,4]ZX	Drain/Foot Vein, Lt, [Opn, Perc, Perc Endo]
069Y[0,3,4]ZX	Drain/Lwr Vein, [Opn, Perc, Perc Endo]
06B0[0,3,4]ZX	Exc/Inferior Vena Cava, [Opn, Perc, Perc Endo]
06B1[0,3,4]ZX	Exc/Splenic Vein, [Opn, Perc, Perc Endo]
06B2[0,3,4]ZX	Exc/Gastric Vein, [Opn, Perc, Perc Endo]
06B3*	Exc/Esophageal Vein
06B4[0,3,4]ZX	Exc/Hepatic Vein, [Opn, Perc, Perc Endo]
06B5[0,3,4]ZX	Exc/Superior Mesenteric Vein, [Opn, Perc, Perc Endo]
06B6[0,3,4]ZX	Exc/Inferior Mesenteric Vein, [Opn, Perc, Perc Endo]
06B7[0,3,4]ZX	Exc/Colic Vein, [Opn, Perc, Perc Endo]
06B8[0,3,4]ZX	Exc/Portal Vein, [Opn, Perc, Perc Endo]
06B9[0,3,4]ZX	Exc/Renal Vein, Rt, [Opn, Perc, Perc Endo]
06BB[0,3,4]ZX	Exc/Renal Vein, Lt, [Opn, Perc, Perc Endo]
06BC[0,3,4]ZX	Exc/Common Iliac Vein, Rt, [Opn, Perc, Perc Endo]
06BD[0,3,4]ZX	Exc/Common Iliac Vein, Lt, [Opn, Perc, Perc Endo]
06BF[0,3,4]ZX	Exc/Ext Iliac Vein, Rt, [Opn, Perc, Perc Endo]
06BG[0,3,4]ZX	Exc/Ext Iliac Vein, Lt, [Opn, Perc, Perc Endo]
06BH[0,3,4]ZX	Exc/Hypogastric Vein, Rt, [Opn, Perc, Perc Endo]
06BJ[0,3,4]ZX	Exc/Hypogastric Vein, Lt, [Opn, Perc, Perc Endo]
06BM[0,3,4]ZX	Exc/Femor Vein, Rt, [Opn, Perc, Perc Endo]
06BN[0,3,4]ZX	Exc/Femor Vein, Lt, [Opn, Perc, Perc Endo]
06BP[0,3,4]ZX	Exc/Greater Saphenous Vein, Rt, [Opn, Perc, Perc Endo]
06BQ[0,3,4]ZX	Exc/Greater Saphenous Vein, Lt, [Opn, Perc, Perc Endo]

T Transfer DRG   SP Special Payment   * Code Range   6th and 7th Character of ZZ = No Device, No Qualifier ZX = No Device, Diagnostic

06BR[0,3,4]ZX   Exc/Lesser Saphenous Vein, Rt, [Opn, Perc, Perc Endo]
06BS[0,3,4]ZX   Exc/Lesser Saphenous Vein, Lt, [Opn, Perc, Perc Endo]
06BT[0,3,4]ZX   Exc/Foot Vein, Rt, [Opn, Perc, Perc Endo]
06BV[0,3,4]ZX   Exc/Foot Vein, Lt, [Opn, Perc, Perc Endo]
06BY[0,3,4]Z[X,Z]   Exc/Lwr Vein, [Opn, Perc, Perc Endo], No Dev, [Dx, NQ]
06C3*   Extir/Esophageal Vein
06CY*   Extir/Lwr Vein
06H0[0,3,4]DZ   Insert/Inferior Vena Cava, [Opn, Perc, Perc Endo], Intralum Dev, NQ
06H1[0,3,4]DZ   Insert/Splenic Vein, [Opn, Perc, Perc Endo], Intralum Dev, NQ
06H2[0,3,4]DZ   Insert/Gastric Vein, [Opn, Perc, Perc Endo], Intralum Dev, NQ
06H3[0,3,4]DZ   Insert/Esophageal Vein, [Opn, Perc, Perc Endo], Intralum Dev, NQ
06H4[0,3,4]DZ   Insert/Hepatic Vein, [Opn, Perc, Perc Endo], Intralum Dev, NQ
06H5[0,3,4]DZ   Insert/Superior Mesenteric Vein, [Opn, Perc, Perc Endo], Intralum Dev, NQ
06H6[0,3,4]DZ   Insert/Inferior Mesenteric Vein, [Opn, Perc, Perc Endo], Intralum Dev, NQ
06H7[0,3,4]DZ   Insert/Colic Vein, [Opn, Perc, Perc Endo], Intralum Dev, NQ
06H8[0,3,4]DZ   Insert/Portal Vein, [Opn, Perc, Perc Endo], Intralum Dev, NQ
06H9[0,3,4]DZ   Insert/Renal Vein, Rt, [Opn, Perc, Perc Endo], Intralum Dev, NQ
06HB[0,3,4]DZ   Insert/Renal Vein, Lt, [Opn, Perc, Perc Endo], Intralum Dev, NQ
06HC[0,3,4]DZ   Insert/Common Iliac Vein, Rt, [Opn, Perc, Perc Endo], Intralum Dev, NQ
06HD[0,3,4]DZ   Insert/Common Iliac Vein, Lt, [Opn, Perc, Perc Endo], Intralum Dev, NQ
06HF[0,3,4]DZ   Insert/Ext Iliac Vein, Rt, [Opn, Perc, Perc Endo], Intralum Dev, NQ
06HG[0,3,4]DZ   Insert/Ext Iliac Vein, Lt, [Opn, Perc, Perc Endo], Intralum Dev, NQ
06HH[0,3,4]DZ   Insert/Hypogastric Vein, Rt, [Opn, Perc, Perc Endo], Intralum Dev, NQ
06HJ[0,3,4]DZ   Insert/Hypogastric Vein, Lt, [Opn, Perc, Perc Endo], Intralum Dev, NQ
06HM[0,3,4]DZ   Insert/Femor Vein, Rt, [Opn, Perc, Perc Endo], Intralum Dev, NQ
06HN[0,3,4]DZ   Insert/Femor Vein, Lt, [Opn, Perc, Perc Endo], Intralum Dev, NQ
06HP[0,3,4]DZ   Insert/Greater Saphenous Vein, Rt, [Opn, Perc, Perc Endo], Intralum Dev, NQ
06HQ[0,3,4]DZ   Insert/Greater Saphenous Vein, Lt, [Opn, Perc, Perc Endo], Intralum Dev, NQ
06HR[0,3,4]DZ   Insert/Lesser Saphenous Vein, Rt, [Opn, Perc, Perc Endo], Intralum Dev, NQ
06HS[0,3,4]DZ   Insert/Lesser Saphenous Vein, Lt, [Opn, Perc, Perc Endo], Intralum Dev, NQ
06HT[0,3,4]DZ   Insert/Foot Vein, Rt, [Opn, Perc, Perc Endo], Intralum Dev, NQ
06HV[0,3,4]DZ   Insert/Foot Vein, Lt, [Opn, Perc, Perc Endo], Intralum Dev, NQ
06HY[0,3,4]DZ   Insert/Lwr Vein, [Opn, Perc, Perc Endo], Intralum Dev, NQ
06JY[0,3,4]ZZ   Inspect/Lwr Vein, [Opn, Perc, Perc Endo]
06L0*   Occlsn/Inferior Vena Cava
06LY[0,3,4][C,Z]Z   Occlsn/Lwr Vein, [Opn, Perc, Perc Endo], [Extralum Dev, No Dev], NQ
06N*   Lwr Veins, Rls
06PY[0,3,4][7,J,K]Z   Rmvl/Lwr Vein, [Opn, Perc, Perc Endo], [Auto Tissue Sub, Synth Sub, Nonauto Tissue Sub], NQ
06QY*   Repair/Lwr Vein
06R3*   Replace/Esophageal Vein
06S*   Lwr Veins, Repos
06U*   Lwr Veins, Supl
06V0*   Restrict/Inferior Vena Cava
06V1[0,3,4]CZ   Restrict/Splenic Vein, [Opn, Perc, Perc Endo], Extralum Dev, NQ
06V2[0,3,4]CZ   Restrict/Gastric Vein, [Opn, Perc, Perc Endo], Extralum Dev, NQ
06V3[0,3,4]CZ   Restrict/Esophageal Vein, [Opn, Perc, Perc Endo], Extralum Dev, NQ
06V4[0,3,4]CZ   Restrict/Hepatic Vein, [Opn, Perc, Perc Endo], Extralum Dev, NQ
06V5[0,3,4]CZ   Restrict/Superior Mesenteric Vein, [Opn, Perc, Perc Endo], Extralum Dev, NQ
06V6[0,3,4]CZ   Restrict/Inferior Mesenteric Vein, [Opn, Perc, Perc Endo], Extralum Dev, NQ
06V7[0,3,4]CZ   Restrict/Colic Vein, [Opn, Perc, Perc Endo], Extralum Dev, NQ
06V8[0,3,4]CZ   Restrict/Portal Vein, [Opn, Perc, Perc Endo], Extralum Dev, NQ
06V9[0,3,4]CZ   Restrict/Renal Vein, Rt, [Opn, Perc, Perc Endo], Extralum Dev, NQ
06VB[0,3,4]CZ   Restrict/Renal Vein, Lt, [Opn, Perc, Perc Endo], Extralum Dev, NQ
06VC[0,3,4]CZ   Restrict/Common Iliac Vein, Rt, [Opn, Perc, Perc Endo], Extralum Dev, NQ

06VD[0,3,4]CZ   Restrict/Common Iliac Vein, Lt, [Opn, Perc, Perc Endo], Extralum Dev, NQ
06VF[0,3,4]CZ   Restrict/Ext Iliac Vein, Rt, [Opn, Perc, Perc Endo], Extralum Dev, NQ
06VG[0,3,4]CZ   Restrict/Ext Iliac Vein, Lt, [Opn, Perc, Perc Endo], Extralum Dev, NQ
06VH[0,3,4]CZ   Restrict/Hypogastric Vein, Rt, [Opn, Perc, Perc Endo], Extralum Dev, NQ
06VJ[0,3,4]CZ   Restrict/Hypogastric Vein, Lt, [Opn, Perc, Perc Endo], Extralum Dev, NQ
06VM[0,3,4]CZ   Restrict/Femor Vein, Rt, [Opn, Perc, Perc Endo], Extralum Dev, NQ
06VN[0,3,4]CZ   Restrict/Femor Vein, Lt, [Opn, Perc, Perc Endo], Extralum Dev, NQ
06VP[0,3,4]CZ   Restrict/Greater Saphenous Vein, Rt, [Opn, Perc, Perc Endo], Extralum Dev, NQ
06VQ[0,3,4]CZ   Restrict/Greater Saphenous Vein, Lt, [Opn, Perc, Perc Endo], Extralum Dev, NQ
06VR[0,3,4]CZ   Restrict/Lesser Saphenous Vein, Rt, [Opn, Perc, Perc Endo], Extralum Dev, NQ
06VS[0,3,4]CZ   Restrict/Lesser Saphenous Vein, Lt, [Opn, Perc, Perc Endo], Extralum Dev, NQ
06VT[0,3,4]CZ   Restrict/Foot Vein, Rt, [Opn, Perc, Perc Endo], Extralum Dev, NQ
06VV[0,3,4]CZ   Restrict/Foot Vein, Lt, [Opn, Perc, Perc Endo], Extralum Dev, NQ
06VY[0,3,4]CZ   Restrict/Lwr Vein, [Opn, Perc, Perc Endo], Extralum Dev, NQ
06WY[0,3,4][7,J,K]Z   Rev/Lwr Vein, [Opn, Perc, Perc Endo], [Auto Tissue Sub, Synth Sub, Nonauto Tissue Sub], NQ
0DH6[0,3,4]MZ   Insert/Stomach, [Opn, Perc, Perc Endo], Stimulator Lead, NQ
0JH6[0,3]MZ   Insert/SQ Tissue & Fascia, Chest, [Opn, Perc], Stimulator Generator, NQ
0JH7[0,3]MZ   Insert/SQ Tissue & Fascia, Back, [Opn, Perc], Stimulator Generator, NQ
0JH8[0,3]MZ   Insert/SQ Tissue & Fascia, Abd, [Opn, Perc], Stimulator Generator, NQ
0JWT[0,3,X]MZ   Rev/SQ Tissue & Fascia, Trunk, [Opn, Perc, Ext], Stimulator Generator, NQ
0W3C*   Control/Mediastinum

DRG 253   Other Vascular Procedures with CC
GMLOS 4.3   AMLOS 5.7   RW 2.6028

Select operating room procedures listed under DRG 252

DRG 254   Other Vascular Procedures without CC/MCC
GMLOS 2.4   AMLOS 3.0   RW 1.7232

Select operating room procedures listed under DRG 252

DRG 255   Upper Limb and Toe Amputation for Circulatory System Disorders with MCC
GMLOS 6.8   AMLOS 8.6   RW 2.6202   [T]

Operating Room Procedures
0X6*   Anatomical Regions, Upr Extremities, Detach
0Y6P*   Detach/1st Toe, Rt
0Y6Q*   Detach/1st Toe, Lt
0Y6R*   Detach/2nd Toe, Rt
0Y6S*   Detach/2nd Toe, Lt
0Y6T*   Detach/3rd Toe, Rt
0Y6U*   Detach/3rd Toe, Lt
0Y6V*   Detach/4th Toe, Rt
0Y6W*   Detach/4th Toe, Lt
0Y6X*   Detach/5th Toe, Rt
0Y6Y*   Detach/5th Toe, Lt

DRG 256   Upper Limb and Toe Amputation for Circulatory System Disorders with CC
GMLOS 5.3   AMLOS 6.4   RW 1.6241   [T]

Select operating room procedures listed under DRG 255

Surgical   **Medical**   **CC Indicator**   **MCC Indicator**   **Procedure Proxy**   PDxMCC PDx acts as own MCC   PDxCC PDx acts as own CC

MDC 5: Diseases And Disorders Of The Circulatory System—SURGICAL

DRG 257   Upper Limb and Toe Amputation for Circulatory System Disorders without CC/MCC
GMLOS 3.4   AMLOS 4.1   RW 1.0844   T

Select operating room procedures listed under DRG 255

DRG 258   Cardiac Pacemaker Device Replacement with MCC
GMLOS 4.9   AMLOS 6.3   RW 2.8590

Operating Room Procedures

0JH6[0,3][7,P]Z	Insert/SQ Tissue & Fascia, Chest, [Opn, Perc], [Cardiac Resynchronization Pacemaker Pulse Generator, Cardiac Rhythm Related Dev], NQ
0JH8[0,3][7,P]Z	Insert/SQ Tissue & Fascia, Abd, [Opn, Perc], [Cardiac Resynchronization Pacemaker Pulse Generator, Cardiac Rhythm Related Dev], NQ

OR

0JH6[0,3]4Z	Insert/SQ Tissue & Fascia, Chest, [Opn, Perc], Pacemaker, Single Chamber, NQ
0JH8[0,3]4Z	Insert/SQ Tissue & Fascia, Abd, [Opn, Perc], Pacemaker, Single Chamber, NQ
	AND
0JPT[0,3]PZ	Rmvl/SQ Tissue & Fascia, Trunk, [Opn, Perc], Cardiac Rhythm Related Dev, NQ

OR

0JH6[0,3]5Z	Insert/SQ Tissue & Fascia, Chest, [Opn, Perc], Pacemaker, Single Chamber Rate Responsive, NQ
0JH8[0,3]5Z	Insert/SQ Tissue & Fascia, Abd, [Opn, Perc], Pacemaker, Single Chamber Rate Responsive, NQ
	AND
0JPT[0,3]PZ	Rmvl/SQ Tissue & Fascia, Trunk, [Opn, Perc], Cardiac Rhythm Related Dev, NQ

OR

0JH6[0,3]6Z	Insert/SQ Tissue & Fascia, Chest, [Opn, Perc], Pacemaker, Dual Chamber, NQ
0JH8[0,3]6Z	Insert/SQ Tissue & Fascia, Abd, [Opn, Perc], Pacemaker, Dual Chamber, NQ
	AND
0JPT[0,3]PZ	Rmvl/SQ Tissue & Fascia, Trunk, [Opn, Perc], Cardiac Rhythm Related Dev, NQ

OR

Operating Room Procedures

0JH6[0,3]0Z	Insert/SQ Tissue & Fascia, Chest, [Opn, Perc], Monitoring Dev, Hemodynamic, NQ
0JH8[0,3]0Z	Insert/SQ Tissue & Fascia, Abd, [Opn, Perc], Monitoring Dev, Hemodynamic, NQ

DRG 259   Cardiac Pacemaker Device Replacement without MCC
GMLOS 2.9   AMLOS 3.6   RW 1.9456

Select operating room procedures OR procedure combinations listed under DRG 258

DRG 260   Cardiac Pacemaker Revision Except Device Replacement with MCC
GMLOS 7.6   AMLOS 10.3   RW 3.7299

Operating Room Procedures

02H63MZ	Insert of Cardiac Lead into Rt Atrium, Perc Appr
02H73MZ	Insert of Cardiac Lead into Lt Atrium, Perc Appr
02HN[0,3,4][J,M]Z	Insert/Pericardium, [Opn, Perc, Perc Endo], [Cardiac Lead, Pacemaker, Cardiac Lead], NQ
02PA[0,3,4,X]MZ	Rmvl/Heart, [Opn, Perc, Perc Endo, Ext], Cardiac Lead, NQ
02WA[0,3,4]MZ	Rev/Heart, [Opn, Perc, Perc Endo], Cardiac Lead, NQ
0JPT[0,3]PZ	Rmvl/SQ Tissue & Fascia, Trunk, [Opn, Perc], Cardiac Rhythm Related Dev, NQ
0JWT[0,3]PZ	Rev/SQ Tissue & Fascia, Trunk, [Opn, Perc], Cardiac Rhythm Related Dev, NQ

OR

02H63JZ	Insert of Pacemaker Lead into Rt Atrium, Perc Appr
02H73JZ	Insert of Pacemaker Lead into Lt Atrium, Perc Appr
02HK3JZ	Insert of Pacemaker Lead into Rt Ventricle, Perc Appr
02HL3JZ	Insert of Pacemaker Lead into Lt Ventricle, Perc Appr
	AND
02PA[0,3,4,X]MZ	Rmvl/Heart, [Opn, Perc, Perc Endo, Ext], Cardiac Lead, NQ

OR

Operating Room Procedures

02HK[0,3,4][0,2]Z	Insert/Ventricle, Rt, [Opn, Perc, Perc Endo], [Monitoring Dev, Pressure Sensor, Monitoring Dev], NQ

OR

Operating Room Procedures

0JH6[0,3]0Z	Insert/SQ Tissue & Fascia, Chest, [Opn, Perc], Monitoring Dev, Hemodynamic, NQ
0JH8[0,3]0Z	Insert/SQ Tissue & Fascia, Abd, [Opn, Perc], Monitoring Dev, Hemodynamic, NQ

DRG 261   Cardiac Pacemaker Revision Except Device Replacement with CC
GMLOS 3.5   AMLOS 4.4   RW 1.8639

Select operating room procedures OR procedure combinations listed under DRG 260

DRG 262   Cardiac Pacemaker Revision Except Device Replacement without CC/MCC
GMLOS 2.5   AMLOS 3.0   RW 1.5125

Select operating room procedures OR procedure combinations listed under DRG 260

DRG 263   Vein Ligation and Stripping
GMLOS 4.1   AMLOS 6.2   RW 2.0854

Operating Room Procedures

02QS*	Repair/Pulmn Vein, Rt
02QT*	Repair/Pulmn Vein, Lt
02QV*	Repair/Superior Vena Cava
05D*	Upr Veins, Extract
05Q0*	Repair/Azygos Vein
05Q1*	Repair/Hemiazygos Vein
05Q3*	Repair/Innominate Vein, Rt
05Q4*	Repair/Innominate Vein, Lt
05Q5*	Repair/Subclavian Vein, Rt
05Q6*	Repair/Subclavian Vein, Lt
05Q7*	Repair/Axillary Vein, Rt
05Q8*	Repair/Axillary Vein, Lt
05Q9*	Repair/Brachial Vein, Rt
05QA*	Repair/Brachial Vein, Lt
05QB*	Repair/Basilic Vein, Rt
05QC*	Repair/Basilic Vein, Lt
05QD*	Repair/Cephalic Vein, Rt
05QF*	Repair/Cephalic Vein, Lt
05QG*	Repair/Hand Vein, Rt
05QH*	Repair/Hand Vein, Lt
05QL*	Repair/Intracranial Vein
05QM*	Repair/Int Jugular Vein, Rt
05QN*	Repair/Int Jugular Vein, Lt
05QP*	Repair/Ext Jugular Vein, Rt
05QQ*	Repair/Ext Jugular Vein, Lt
05QR*	Repair/Vert Vein, Rt
05QS*	Repair/Vert Vein, Lt
05QT*	Repair/Face Vein, Rt
05QV*	Repair/Face Vein, Lt
065M*	Destr/Femor Vein, Rt
065N*	Destr/Femor Vein, Lt
065P*	Destr/Greater Saphenous Vein, Rt
065Q*	Destr/Greater Saphenous Vein, Lt
065R*	Destr/Lesser Saphenous Vein, Rt
065S*	Destr/Lesser Saphenous Vein, Lt
065T*	Destr/Foot Vein, Rt
065V*	Destr/Foot Vein, Lt
065Y[0,3,4]ZZ	Destr/Lwr Vein, [Opn, Perc, Perc Endo]
06BM[0,3,4]ZZ	Exc/Femor Vein, Rt, [Opn, Perc, Perc Endo]
06BN[0,3,4]ZZ	Exc/Femor Vein, Lt, [Opn, Perc, Perc Endo]
06BP[0,3,4]ZZ	Exc/Greater Saphenous Vein, Rt, [Opn, Perc, Perc Endo]
06BQ[0,3,4]ZZ	Exc/Greater Saphenous Vein, Lt, [Opn, Perc, Perc Endo]
06BR[0,3,4]ZZ	Exc/Lesser Saphenous Vein, Rt, [Opn, Perc, Perc Endo]
06BS[0,3,4]ZZ	Exc/Lesser Saphenous Vein, Lt, [Opn, Perc, Perc Endo]
06BT[0,3,4]ZZ	Exc/Foot Vein, Rt, [Opn, Perc, Perc Endo]
06BV[0,3,4]ZZ	Exc/Foot Vein, Lt, [Opn, Perc, Perc Endo]
06CM*	Extir/Femor Vein, Rt
06CN*	Extir/Femor Vein, Lt

T Transfer DRG   SP Special Payment   * Code Range   6th and 7th Character of ZZ = No Device, No Qualifier ZX = No Device, Diagnostic

06CP*	Extir/Greater Saphenous Vein, Rt
06CQ*	Extir/Greater Saphenous Vein, Lt
06CR*	Extir/Lesser Saphenous Vein, Rt
06CS*	Extir/Lesser Saphenous Vein, Lt
06CT*	Extir/Foot Vein, Rt
06CV*	Extir/Foot Vein, Lt
06D*	Lwr Veins, Extract
06HY[0,3,4]2Z	Insert/Lwr Vein, [Opn, Perc, Perc Endo], Monitoring Dev, NQ
06LM[0,3,4][C,D,Z]Z	Occlsn/Femor Vein, Rt, [Opn, Perc, Perc Endo], [Extralum Dev, Intralum Dev, No Dev], NQ
06LN[0,3,4][C,D,Z]Z	Occlsn/Femor Vein, Lt, [Opn, Perc, Perc Endo], [Extralum Dev, Intralum Dev, No Dev], NQ
06LP[0,3,4][C,D,Z]Z	Occlsn/Greater Saphenous Vein, Rt, [Opn, Perc, Perc Endo], [Extralum Dev, Intralum Dev, No Dev], NQ
06LQ[0,3,4][C,D,Z]Z	Occlsn/Greater Saphenous Vein, Lt, [Opn, Perc, Perc Endo], [Extralum Dev, Intralum Dev, No Dev], NQ
06LR[0,3,4][C,D,Z]Z	Occlsn/Lesser Saphenous Vein, Rt, [Opn, Perc, Perc Endo], [Extralum Dev, Intralum Dev, No Dev], NQ
06LS[0,3,4][C,D,Z]Z	Occlsn/Lesser Saphenous Vein, Lt, [Opn, Perc, Perc Endo], [Extralum Dev, Intralum Dev, No Dev], NQ
06LT[0,3,4][C,D,Z]Z	Occlsn/Foot Vein, Rt, [Opn, Perc, Perc Endo], [Extralum Dev, Intralum Dev, No Dev], NQ
06LV[0,3,4][C,D,Z]Z	Occlsn/Foot Vein, Lt, [Opn, Perc, Perc Endo], [Extralum Dev, Intralum Dev, No Dev], NQ
06LY[0,3,4]DZ	Occlsn/Lwr Vein, [Opn, Perc, Perc Endo], Intralum Dev, NQ
06PY[0,3,4][0,2,3,C,D]Z	Rmvl/Lwr Vein, [Opn, Perc, Perc Endo], [Drain Dev, Monitoring Dev, Inf Dev, Extralum Dev, Intralum Dev], NQ
06Q0*	Repair/Inferior Vena Cava
06Q1*	Repair/Splenic Vein
06Q2*	Repair/Gastric Vein
06Q3*	Repair/Esophageal Vein
06Q4*	Repair/Hepatic Vein
06Q5*	Repair/Superior Mesenteric Vein
06Q6*	Repair/Inferior Mesenteric Vein
06Q7*	Repair/Colic Vein
06Q8*	Repair/Portal Vein
06Q9*	Repair/Renal Vein, Rt
06QB*	Repair/Renal Vein, Lt
06QC*	Repair/Common Iliac Vein, Rt
06QD*	Repair/Common Iliac Vein, Lt
06QF*	Repair/Ext Iliac Vein, Rt
06QG*	Repair/Ext Iliac Vein, Lt
06QH*	Repair/Hypogastric Vein, Rt
06QJ*	Repair/Hypogastric Vein, Lt
06QM*	Repair/Femor Vein, Rt
06QN*	Repair/Femor Vein, Lt
06QP*	Repair/Greater Saphenous Vein, Rt
06QQ*	Repair/Greater Saphenous Vein, Lt
06QR*	Repair/Lesser Saphenous Vein, Rt
06QS*	Repair/Lesser Saphenous Vein, Lt
06QT*	Repair/Foot Vein, Rt
06QV*	Repair/Foot Vein, Lt
06RM*	Replace/Femor Vein, Rt
06RN*	Replace/Femor Vein, Lt
06RP*	Replace/Greater Saphenous Vein, Rt
06RQ*	Replace/Greater Saphenous Vein, Lt
06RR*	Replace/Lesser Saphenous Vein, Rt
06RS*	Replace/Lesser Saphenous Vein, Lt
06RT*	Replace/Foot Vein, Rt
06RV*	Replace/Foot Vein, Lt
06RY*	Replace/Lwr Vein
06WY[0,3,4][0,2,3,C,D]Z	Rev/Lwr Vein, [Opn, Perc, Perc Endo], [Drain Dev, Monitoring Dev, Inf Dev, Extralum Dev, Intralum Dev], NQ
3E03[0,3]TZ	Introduction/Peripheral Vein, [Opn, Perc], Destr Agent, NQ
3E04[0,3]TZ	Introduction/Central Vein, [Opn, Perc], Destr Agent, NQ

DRG 264   Other Circulatory System O.R. Procedures

GMLOS 5.8   AMLOS 8.3   RW 2.8080   [T]

Operating Room Procedures

015K*	Destr/Head and Neck Sympathetic Nerve
015L*	Destr/Thoracic Sympathetic Nerve
015M*	Destr/Abd Sympathetic Nerve
015N*	Destr/Lumbar Sympathetic Nerve
015P*	Destr/Sacral Sympathetic Nerve
018K*	Div/Head and Neck Sympathetic Nerve
018L*	Div/Thoracic Sympathetic Nerve
018M*	Div/Abd Sympathetic Nerve
018N*	Div/Lumbar Sympathetic Nerve

018P*	Div/Sacral Sympathetic Nerve
019K[0,3,4][0,Z]Z	Drain/Head and Neck Sympathetic Nerve, [Opn, Perc, Perc Endo], [Drain Dev, No Dev], NQ
019L[0,3,4][0,Z]Z	Drain/Thoracic Sympathetic Nerve, [Opn, Perc, Perc Endo], [Drain Dev, No Dev], NQ
019M[0,3,4][0,Z]Z	Drain/Abd Sympathetic Nerve, [Opn, Perc, Perc Endo], [Drain Dev, No Dev], NQ
019N[0,3,4][0,Z]Z	Drain/Lumbar Sympathetic Nerve, [Opn, Perc, Perc Endo], [Drain Dev, No Dev], NQ
019P[0,3,4][0,Z]Z	Drain/Sacral Sympathetic Nerve, [Opn, Perc, Perc Endo], [Drain Dev, No Dev], NQ
01BK[0,3,4]ZZ	Exc/Head and Neck Sympathetic Nerve, [Opn, Perc, Perc Endo]
01BL[0,3,4]ZZ	Exc/Thoracic Sympathetic Nerve, [Opn, Perc, Perc Endo]
01BM[0,3,4]ZZ	Exc/Abd Sympathetic Nerve, [Opn, Perc, Perc Endo]
01BN[0,3,4]ZZ	Exc/Lumbar Sympathetic Nerve, [Opn, Perc, Perc Endo]
01BP[0,3,4]ZZ	Exc/Sacral Sympathetic Nerve, [Opn, Perc, Perc Endo]
01CK*	Extir/Head and Neck Sympathetic Nerve
01CL*	Extir/Thoracic Sympathetic Nerve
01CM*	Extir/Abd Sympathetic Nerve
01CN*	Extir/Lumbar Sympathetic Nerve
01CP*	Extir/Sacral Sympathetic Nerve
01DK*	Extract/Head and Neck Sympathetic Nerve
01DL*	Extract/Thoracic Sympathetic Nerve
01DM*	Extract/Abd Sympathetic Nerve
01DN*	Extract/Lumbar Sympathetic Nerve
01DP*	Extract/Sacral Sympathetic Nerve
02H4[0,3,4]0Z	Insert/Coronary Vein, [Opn, Perc, Perc Endo], Monitoring Dev, Pressure Sensor, NQ
02H6[0,3,4]0Z	Insert/Atrium, Rt, [Opn, Perc, Perc Endo], Monitoring Dev, Pressure Sensor, NQ
02H7[0,3,4]0Z	Insert/Atrium, Lt, [Opn, Perc, Perc Endo], Monitoring Dev, Pressure Sensor, NQ
02HL[0,3,4]0Z	Insert/Ventricle, Lt, [Opn, Perc, Perc Endo], Monitoring Dev, Pressure Sensor, NQ
02HQ00Z	Insert of Pressure Sens into Rt Pulm Art, Opn Appr
02HQ30Z	Insert of Pressure Sens into Rt Pulm Art, Perc Appr
02HQ40Z	Insert of Pressure Sens into Rt Pulm Art, Perc Endo Appr
02HR00Z	Insert of Pressure Sens into Lt Pulm Art, Opn Appr
02HR30Z	Insert of Pressure Sens into Lt Pulm Art, Perc Appr
02HR40Z	Insert of Pressure Sens into Lt Pulm Art, Perc Endo Appr
02HS[0,3,4]0Z	Insert/Pulmn Vein, Rt, [Opn, Perc, Perc Endo], Monitoring Dev, Pressure Sensor, NQ
02HT[0,3,4]0Z	Insert/Pulmn Vein, Lt, [Opn, Perc, Perc Endo], Monitoring Dev, Pressure Sensor, NQ
02HV[0,3,4]0Z	Insert/Superior Vena Cava, [Opn, Perc, Perc Endo], Monitoring Dev, Pressure Sensor, NQ
02JA[0,4]ZZ	Inspect/Heart, [Opn, Perc Endo]
02JY0ZZ	Inspect of Great Vessel, Opn Appr
02JY4ZZ	Inspect of Great Vessel, Perc Endo Appr
0317O[9,A,J,K,Z][D,F]	Bypass/Brachial Artery, Rt, Opn, [Auto Venous Tissue, Auto Arterial Tissue, Synth Sub, Nonauto Tissue Sub, No Dev], [Upr Arm Vein, Lwr Arm Vein]
0318O[9,A,J,K,Z][D,F]	Bypass/Brachial Artery, Lt, Opn, [Auto Venous Tissue, Auto Arterial Tissue, Synth Sub, Nonauto Tissue Sub, No Dev], [Upr Arm Vein, Lwr Arm Vein]
0319O[9,A,J,K,Z]F	Bypass/Ulnar Artery, Rt, Opn, [Auto Venous Tissue, Auto Arterial Tissue, Synth Sub, Nonauto Tissue Sub, No Dev], Lwr Arm Vein
031A0[9,A,J,K,Z]F	Bypass/Ulnar Artery, Lt, Opn, [Auto Venous Tissue, Auto Arterial Tissue, Synth Sub, Nonauto Tissue Sub, No Dev], Lwr Arm Vein
031B0[9,A,J,K,Z]F	Bypass/Radial Artery, Rt, Opn, [Auto Venous Tissue, Auto Arterial Tissue, Synth Sub, Nonauto Tissue Sub, No Dev], Lwr Arm Vein
031C0[9,A,J,K,Z]F	Bypass/Radial Artery, Lt, Opn, [Auto Venous Tissue, Auto Arterial Tissue, Synth Sub, Nonauto Tissue Sub, No Dev], Lwr Arm Vein
03PY[0,3,4][7,J,K]Z	Rmvl/Upr Artery, [Opn, Perc, Perc Endo], [Auto Tissue Sub, Synth Sub, Nonauto Tissue Sub], NQ
0790[0,3,4]ZX	Drain/Lymphatic, Head, [Opn, Perc, Perc Endo]
0791[0,3,4]ZX	Drain/Lymphatic, Rt Neck, [Opn, Perc, Perc Endo]
0792[0,3,4]ZX	Drain/Lymphatic, Lt Neck, [Opn, Perc, Perc Endo]
0793[0,3,4]ZX	Drain/Lymphatic, Rt Upr Extr, [Opn, Perc, Perc Endo]
0794[0,3,4]ZX	Drain/Lymphatic, Lt Upr Extr, [Opn, Perc, Perc Endo]
0795[0,3,4]ZX	Drain/Lymphatic, Rt Axillary, [Opn, Perc, Perc Endo]
0796[0,3,4]ZX	Drain/Lymphatic, Lt Axillary, [Opn, Perc, Perc Endo]
0797[0,3,4]ZX	Drain/Lymphatic, Thorax, [Opn, Perc, Perc Endo]
0798[0,3,4]ZX	Drain/Lymphatic, Int Mammary, Rt, [Opn, Perc, Perc Endo]
0799[0,3,4]ZX	Drain/Lymphatic, Int Mammary, Lt, [Opn, Perc, Perc Endo]
079B[0,3,4]ZX	Drain/Lymphatic, Mesenteric, [Opn, Perc, Perc Endo]

Surgical   **Medical**   **CC Indicator**   **MCC Indicator**   **Procedure Proxy**   PDxMCC **PDx acts as own MCC**   PDxCC **PDx acts as own CC**

MDC 5: Diseases And Disorders Of The Circulatory System—SURGICAL

Code	Description
079C[0,3,4]ZX	Drain/Lymphatic, Pelvis, [Opn, Perc, Perc Endo]
079D[0,3,4]ZX	Drain/Lymphatic, Aortic, [Opn, Perc, Perc Endo]
079F[0,3,4]ZX	Drain/Lymphatic, Rt Lwr Extr, [Opn, Perc, Perc Endo]
079G[0,3,4]ZX	Drain/Lymphatic, Lt Lwr Extr, [Opn, Perc, Perc Endo]
079H[0,3,4]ZX	Drain/Lymphatic, Rt Inguinal, [Opn, Perc, Perc Endo]
079J[0,3,4]ZX	Drain/Lymphatic, Lt Inguinal, [Opn, Perc, Perc Endo]
079K[0,3,4]ZX	Drain/Thoracic Duct, [Opn, Perc, Perc Endo]
079L[0,3,4]ZX	Drain/Cisterna Chyli, [Opn, Perc, Perc Endo]
07B0[0,3,4]ZX	Exc/Lymphatic, Head, [Opn, Perc, Perc Endo]
07B1*	Exc/Lymphatic, Rt Neck
07B2*	Exc/Lymphatic, Lt Neck
07B3[0,3,4]ZX	Exc/Lymphatic, Rt Upr Extr, [Opn, Perc, Perc Endo]
07B3[0,4]ZZ	Exc/Lymphatic, Rt Upr Extr, [Opn, Perc Endo]
07B4[0,3,4]ZX	Exc/Lymphatic, Lt Upr Extr, [Opn, Perc, Perc Endo]
07B4[0,4]ZZ	Exc/Lymphatic, Lt Upr Extr, [Opn, Perc Endo]
07B5*	Exc/Lymphatic, Rt Axillary
07B6*	Exc/Lymphatic, Lt Axillary
07B7[0,3,4]ZX	Exc/Lymphatic, Thorax, [Opn, Perc, Perc Endo]
07B7[0,4]ZZ	Exc/Lymphatic, Thorax, [Opn, Perc Endo]
07B8[0,3,4]ZX	Exc/Lymphatic, Int Mammary, Rt, [Opn, Perc, Perc Endo]
07B9[0,3,4]ZX	Exc/Lymphatic, Int Mammary, Lt, [Opn, Perc, Perc Endo]
07BB[0,3,4]ZX	Exc/Lymphatic, Mesenteric, [Opn, Perc, Perc Endo]
07BC[0,3,4]ZX	Exc/Lymphatic, Pelvis, [Opn, Perc, Perc Endo]
07BD[0,3,4]ZX	Exc/Lymphatic, Aortic, [Opn, Perc, Perc Endo]
07BF[0,3,4]ZX	Exc/Lymphatic, Rt Lwr Extr, [Opn, Perc, Perc Endo]
07BF[0,4]ZZ	Exc/Lymphatic, Rt Lwr Extr, [Opn, Perc Endo]
07BG[0,3,4]ZX	Exc/Lymphatic, Lt Lwr Extr, [Opn, Perc, Perc Endo]
07BG[0,4]ZZ	Exc/Lymphatic, Lt Lwr Extr, [Opn, Perc Endo]
07BH*	Exc/Lymphatic, Rt Inguinal
07BJ*	Exc/Lymphatic, Lt Inguinal
07BK[0,3,4]ZX	Exc/Thoracic Duct, [Opn, Perc, Perc Endo]
07BL[0,3,4]ZX	Exc/Cisterna Chyli, [Opn, Perc, Perc Endo]
07JP0ZZ	Inspect of Spleen, Opn Appr
07TP*	Resect/Spleen
09QKXZZ	Repair Nose, Ext Appr
09RK07Z	Replace of Nose with Autol Sub, Opn Appr
0B9C[0,8]ZX	Drain/Upr Lung Lobe, Rt, [Opn, Via Natrl or Artfcl Opng Endo]
0B9D[0,8]ZX	Drain/Mid Lung Lobe, Rt, [Opn, Via Natrl or Artfcl Opng Endo]
0B9F[0,8]ZX	Drain/Lwr Lung Lobe, Rt, [Opn, Via Natrl or Artfcl Opng Endo]
0B9G[0,8]ZX	Drain/Upr Lung Lobe, Lt, [Opn, Via Natrl or Artfcl Opng Endo]
0B9H[0,8]ZX	Drain/Lung Lingula, [Opn, Via Natrl or Artfcl Opng Endo]
0B9J[0,8]ZX	Drain/Lwr Lung Lobe, Lt, [Opn, Via Natrl or Artfcl Opng Endo]
0B9K[0,8]ZX	Drain/Lung, Rt, [Opn, Via Natrl or Artfcl Opng Endo]
0B9L[0,8]ZX	Drain/Lung, Lt, [Opn, Via Natrl or Artfcl Opng Endo]
0B9M[0,8]ZX	Drain/Lungs, Bilat, [Opn, Via Natrl or Artfcl Opng Endo]
0BBC[0,4,7,8]ZX	Exc/Upr Lung Lobe, Rt, [Opn, Perc Endo, Via Natrl or Artfcl Opng, Via Natrl or Artfcl Opng Endo]
0BBD[0,4,7,8]ZX	Exc/Mid Lung Lobe, Rt, [Opn, Perc Endo, Via Natrl or Artfcl Opng, Via Natrl or Artfcl Opng Endo]
0BBF[0,4,7,8]ZX	Exc/Lwr Lung Lobe, Rt, [Opn, Perc Endo, Via Natrl or Artfcl Opng, Via Natrl or Artfcl Opng Endo]
0BBG[0,4,7,8]ZX	Exc/Upr Lung Lobe, Lt, [Opn, Perc Endo, Via Natrl or Artfcl Opng, Via Natrl or Artfcl Opng Endo]
0BBH[0,4,7,8]ZX	Exc/Lung Lingula, [Opn, Perc Endo, Via Natrl or Artfcl Opng, Via Natrl or Artfcl Opng Endo]
0BBJ[0,4,7,8]ZX	Exc/Lwr Lung Lobe, Lt, [Opn, Perc Endo, Via Natrl or Artfcl Opng, Via Natrl or Artfcl Opng Endo]
0BBK[0,4,7,8]ZX	Exc/Lung, Rt, [Opn, Perc Endo, Via Natrl or Artfcl Opng, Via Natrl or Artfcl Opng Endo]
0BBL[0,4,7,8]ZX	Exc/Lung, Lt, [Opn, Perc Endo, Via Natrl or Artfcl Opng, Via Natrl or Artfcl Opng Endo]
0BBM[0,4,7,8]ZX	Exc/Lungs, Bilat, [Opn, Perc Endo, Via Natrl or Artfcl Opng, Via Natrl or Artfcl Opng Endo]
0BJ[0,K,L]4ZZ	Inspect of [Tracheobronchial Tree, Rt Lung, Lt Lung], Perc Endo
0BQ1*	Repair/Trachea
0BW1[0,3,4]FZ	Rev/Trachea, [Opn, Perc, Perc Endo], Tracheostomy Dev, NQ
0C57*	Destr/Tongue
0D16[0,4,8][7,J,K,Z][9,A,B,L]	Bypass/Stomach, [Opn, Perc Endo, Via Natrl or Artfcl Opng Endo], [Auto Tissue Sub, Synth Sub, Nonauto Tissue Sub, No Dev], [Duodenum, Jejunum, Ileum, Transv Colon]
0D1A8[7,J,K]H	Bypass/Jejunum, Via Natrl or Artfcl Opng Endo, [Auto Tissue Sub, Synth Sub, Nonauto Tissue Sub], Cecum
0D1B8[7,J,K]H	Bypass/Ileum, Via Natrl or Artfcl Opng Endo, [Auto Tissue Sub, Synth Sub, Nonauto Tissue Sub], Cecum
0D1K[0,4,8]Z4	Bypass/Ascending Colon, [Opn, Perc Endo, Via Natrl or Artfcl Opng Endo], No Dev, Cutaneous
0D1L[0,4,8]Z4	Bypass/Transv Colon, [Opn, Perc Endo, Via Natrl or Artfcl Opng Endo], No Dev, Cutaneous
0D9P0ZX	Drain of Rectum, Opn Appr, Diagnostic
0DB6[0,3,4,7,8]Z3	Exc/Stomach, [Opn, Perc, Perc Endo, Via Natrl or Artfcl Opng, Via Natrl or Artfcl Opng Endo], No Dev, Vertical
0DB6[0,3,7]ZZ	Exc/Stomach, [Opn, Perc, Via Natrl or Artfcl Opng]
0DB8[0,4]ZZ	Exc/Sm Intestine, [Opn, Perc Endo]
0DBE[0,3,4]ZZ	Exc/Lg Intestine, [Opn, Perc, Perc Endo]
0DBF[0,3,4]ZZ	Exc/Lg Intestine, Rt, [Opn, Perc, Perc Endo]
0DBG[0,3,4]ZZ	Exc/Lg Intestine, Lt, [Opn, Perc, Perc Endo]
0DBH[0,3,4]ZZ	Exc/Cecum, [Opn, Perc, Perc Endo]
0DBK[0,3,4]ZZ	Exc/Ascending Colon, [Opn, Perc, Perc Endo]
0DBL[0,3,4]ZZ	Exc/Transv Colon, [Opn, Perc, Perc Endo]
0DBM[0,3,4]ZZ	Exc/Descending Colon, [Opn, Perc, Perc Endo]
0DBN[0,3,4]ZZ	Exc/Sigmoid Colon, [Opn, Perc, Perc Endo]
0DBP0ZX	Exc of Rectum, Opn Appr, Diagnostic
0DBP[0,3,4,7]ZZ	Exc/Rectum, [Opn, Perc, Perc Endo, Via Natrl or Artfcl Opng]
0DJ[0,6,D,U,V,W]0ZZ	Inspect of [Upr Intestinal Tract, Stomach, Lwr Intestinal Tract, Omentum, Mesentery, Peritoneum], Opn Appr
0DT6*	Resect/Stomach
0DT7*	Resect/Stomach, Pylorus
0DT9*	Resect/Duodenum
0DTA*	Resect/Jejunum
0DTB*	Resect/Ileum
0DTC*	Resect/Ileocecal Valve
0DTE*	Resect/Large Intestine
0DTF*	Resect/Large Intestine, Rt
0DTG*	Resect/Large Intestine, Lt
0DTH*	Resect/Cecum
0DTJ[0,7,8]ZZ	Resect/Appendix, [Opn, Via Natrl or Artfcl Opng, Via Natrl or Artfcl Opng Endo]
0DTK*	Resect/Ascending Colon
0DTL*	Resect/Transv Colon
0DTM*	Resect/Descending Colon
0DTP[0,4]ZZ	Resect/Rectum, [Opn, Perc Endo]
0DWW[0,3,4]JZ	Rev/Peritoneum, [Opn, Perc, Perc Endo], Synth Sub, NQ
0F9[0,1,2]0ZX	Drain of [Liver, Rt Lobe Liver, Lt Lobe Liver], Opn Appr, Dx
0FB[0,1,2]0ZX	Exc of [Liver, Rt Lobe Liver, Lt Lobe Liver], Opn Appr, Dx
0FJ00ZZ	Inspect of Liver, Opn Appr
0H8[0,1,4,5,6]XZZ	Div of Skin of [Scalp, Face, Neck, Chest, Back], Ext
0H8[7,8,A]XZZ	Div of [Abd, Buttock, Genitalia] Skin, Ext Appr
0H8[B,C,D,E]XZZ	Div of [Rt Upr Arm, Lt Upr Arm, Rt Lwr Arm, Lt Lwr Arm] Skin, Ext Appr
0H8[H,J,K,L,M,N]XZZ	Div [Rt Upr Leg, Lt Upr Leg, Rt Lwr Leg, Lt Lwr Leg, Rt Foot, Lt Foot], Ext
0HB[0,1,4,5]XZZ	Exc of Skin of [Scalp, Face, Neck, Chest], Ext
0HB[6,7,8,A]XZZ	Exc of Skin of [Back, Abd, Buttock, Genitalia], Ext
0HB[B,C,D,E,F,G]XZZ	Exc of Skin of [Rt Upr Arm, Lt Upr Arm, Rt Lwr Arm, Lt Lwr Arm, Rt Hand, Lt Hand], Ext
0HB[H,J,K,L,M,N]XZZ	Exc of Skin of [Rt Upr Leg, Lt Upr Leg, Rt Lwr Leg, Lt Lwr Leg, Rt Foot, Lt Foot], Ext
0HR0XK[3,4]	Replace/Skin, Scalp, Ext, Nonauto Tissue Sub, [Full Thickness, Partial Thickness]
0HR1XK[3,4]	Replace/Skin, Face, Ext, Nonauto Tissue Sub, [Full Thickness, Partial Thickness]
0HR4XK[3,4]	Replace/Skin, Neck, Ext, Nonauto Tissue Sub, [Full Thickness, Partial Thickness]
0HR5*	Replace/Skin, Chest
0HR6*	Replace/Skin, Back
0HR7*	Replace/Skin, Abd
0HR8*	Replace/Skin, Buttock
0HRA*	Replace/Skin, Genitalia
0HRB*	Replace/Skin, Rt Upr Arm
0HRC*	Replace/Skin, Lt Upr Arm
0HRD*	Replace/Skin, Rt Lwr Arm
0HRE*	Replace/Skin, Lt Lwr Arm
0HRF*	Replace/Skin, Rt Hand
0HRG*	Replace/Skin, Lt Hand
0HRH*	Replace/Skin, Rt Upr Leg
0HRJ*	Replace/Skin, Lt Upr Leg
0HRK*	Replace/Skin, Rt Lwr Leg
0HRL*	Replace/Skin, Lt Lwr Leg
0HRM*	Replace/Skin, Rt Foot
0HRN*	Replace/Skin, Lt Foot
0HX[0,1,4,5,6,7,8,9,A]XZZ	Transfer [Scalp, Face, Neck, Chest, Back, Abd, Buttock, Perineum, Genitalia] Skin, Ext
0HX[B,C,D,E,F,G]XZZ	Transfer [Rt Upr Arm, Lt Upr Arm, Rt Lwr Arm, Lt Lwr Arm, Rt Hand, Lt Hand], Ext
0HX[H,J,K,L,M,N]XZZ	Transfer [Rt Upr Leg, Lt Upr Leg, Rt Lwr Leg, Lt Lwr Leg, Rt Foot, Lt Foot], Ext
0JB[0,1,4,5,6]0ZZ	Exc of SQ Tissue & Fascia of [Scalp, Face, Ant Neck, Post Neck, Chest], Opn

---

T Transfer DRG   SP Special Payment   * Code Range   **6th and 7th Character of ZZ = No Device, No Qualifier ZX = No Device, Diagnostic**

ØJB[7,8,9,B,C]ØZZ	Exc of SQ Tissue & Fascia of [Back, Abd, Buttock, Perineum, Pelvic Rgn], Opn
ØJB[D,F,G,H]ØZZ	Exc of SQ Tissue & Fascia of [Rt Upr Arm, Lt Upr Arm, Rt Lwr Arm, Lt Lwr Arm], Opn
ØJB[L,M,N,P,Q,R]ØZZ	Exc of SQ Tissue & Fascia of [Rt Upr Leg, Lt Upr Leg, Rt Lwr Leg, Lt Lwr Leg, Rt Foot, Lt Foot], Opn
ØJHØ*	Insert/SQ Tissue & Fascia, Scalp
ØJH1*	Insert/SQ Tissue & Fascia, Face
ØJH4*	Insert/SQ Tissue & Fascia, Ant Neck
ØJH5*	Insert/SQ Tissue & Fascia, Posterior Neck
ØJH6[Ø,3][N,V]Z	Insert/SQ Tissue & Fascia, Chest, [Opn, Perc], [Tissue Expander, Inf Pump], NQ
ØJH7[Ø,3][N,V]Z	Insert/SQ Tissue & Fascia, Back, [Opn, Perc], [Tissue Expander, Inf Pump], NQ
ØJH8[Ø,3][N,V]Z	Insert/SQ Tissue & Fascia, Abd, [Opn, Perc], [Tissue Expander, Inf Pump], NQ
ØJH9*	Insert/SQ Tissue & Fascia, Buttock
ØJHB*	Insert/SQ Tissue & Fascia, Perineum
ØJHC*	Insert/SQ Tissue & Fascia, Pelvic Region
ØJHD[Ø,3]NZ	Insert/SQ Tissue & Fascia, Rt Upr Arm, [Opn, Perc], Tissue Expander, NQ
ØJHF[Ø,3]NZ	Insert/SQ Tissue & Fascia, Lt Upr Arm, [Opn, Perc], Tissue Expander, NQ
ØJHG[Ø,3]NZ	Insert/SQ Tissue & Fascia, Rt Lwr Arm, [Opn, Perc], Tissue Expander, NQ
ØJHH[Ø,3]NZ	Insert/SQ Tissue & Fascia, Lt Lwr Arm, [Opn, Perc], Tissue Expander, NQ
ØJHL[Ø,3]NZ	Insert/SQ Tissue & Fascia, Rt Upr Leg, [Opn, Perc], Tissue Expander, NQ
ØJHM[Ø,3]NZ	Insert/SQ Tissue & Fascia, Lt Upr Leg, [Opn, Perc], Tissue Expander, NQ
ØJHN[Ø,3]NZ	Insert/SQ Tissue & Fascia, Rt Lwr Leg, [Opn, Perc], Tissue Expander, NQ
ØJHP[Ø,3]NZ	Insert/SQ Tissue & Fascia, Lt Lwr Leg, [Opn, Perc], Tissue Expander, NQ
ØJHQ*	Insert/SQ Tissue & Fascia, Rt Foot
ØJHR*	Insert/SQ Tissue & Fascia, Lt Foot
ØJHT[Ø,3]VZ	Insert/SQ Tissue & Fascia, Trunk, [Opn, Perc], Inf Pump, NQ
ØJXØ[Ø,3]Z[B,C]	Transfer/SQ Tissue & Fascia, Scalp, [Opn, Perc], No Dev, [Skin and SQ Tissue, Skin, SQ Tissue & Fascia]
ØJX1[Ø,3]Z[B,C]	Transfer/SQ Tissue & Fascia, Face, [Opn, Perc], No Dev, [Skin and SQ Tissue, Skin, SQ Tissue & Fascia]
ØJX4[Ø,3]Z[B,C]	Transfer/SQ Tissue & Fascia, Ant Neck, [Opn, Perc], No Dev, [Skin and SQ Tissue, Skin, SQ Tissue & Fascia]
ØJX5[Ø,3]Z[B,C]	Transfer/SQ Tissue & Fascia, Post Neck, [Opn, Perc], No Dev, [Skin and SQ Tissue, Skin, SQ Tissue & Fascia]
ØJX6[Ø,3]Z[B,C]	Transfer/SQ Tissue & Fascia, Chest, [Opn, Perc], No Dev, [Skin and SQ Tissue, Skin, SQ Tissue & Fascia]
ØJX7[Ø,3]Z[B,C]	Transfer/SQ Tissue & Fascia, Back, [Opn, Perc], No Dev, [Skin and SQ Tissue, Skin, SQ Tissue & Fascia]
ØJX8[Ø,3]Z[B,C]	Transfer/SQ Tissue & Fascia, Abd, [Opn, Perc], No Dev, [Skin and SQ Tissue, Skin, SQ Tissue & Fascia]
ØJX9[Ø,3]Z[B,C]	Transfer/SQ Tissue & Fascia, Buttock, [Opn, Perc], No Dev, [Skin and SQ Tissue, Skin, SQ Tissue & Fascia]
ØJXB[Ø,3]Z[B,C]	Transfer/SQ Tissue & Fascia, Perineum, [Opn, Perc], No Dev, [Skin and SQ Tissue, Skin, SQ Tissue & Fascia]
ØJXC[Ø,3]Z[B,C]	Transfer/SQ Tissue & Fascia, Genitalia, [Opn, Perc], No Dev, [Skin and SQ Tissue, Skin, SQ Tissue & Fascia]
ØJXD[Ø,3]Z[B,C]	Transfer/SQ Tissue & Fascia, Rt Upr Arm, [Opn, Perc], No Dev, [Skin and SQ Tissue, Skin, SQ Tissue & Fascia]
ØJXF[Ø,3]Z[B,C]	Transfer/SQ Tissue & Fascia, Lt Upr Arm, [Opn, Perc], No Dev, [Skin and SQ Tissue, Skin, SQ Tissue & Fascia]
ØJXG[Ø,3]Z[B,C]	Transfer/SQ Tissue & Fascia, Rt Lwr Arm, [Opn, Perc], No Dev, [Skin and SQ Tissue, Skin, SQ Tissue & Fascia]
ØJXH[Ø,3]Z[B,C]	Transfer/SQ Tissue & Fascia, Lt Lwr Arm, [Opn, Perc], No Dev, [Skin and SQ Tissue, Skin, SQ Tissue & Fascia]
ØJXL[Ø,3]Z[B,C]	Transfer/SQ Tissue & Fascia, Rt Upr Leg, [Opn, Perc], No Dev, [Skin and SQ Tissue, Skin, SQ Tissue & Fascia]
ØJXM[Ø,3]Z[B,C]	Transfer/SQ Tissue & Fascia, Lt Upr Leg, [Opn, Perc], No Dev, [Skin and SQ Tissue, Skin, SQ Tissue & Fascia]
ØJXN[Ø,3]Z[B,C]	Transfer/SQ Tissue & Fascia, Rt Lwr Leg, [Opn, Perc], No Dev, [Skin and SQ Tissue, Skin, SQ Tissue & Fascia]
ØJXP[Ø,3]Z[B,C]	Transfer/SQ Tissue & Fascia, Lt Lwr Leg, [Opn, Perc], No Dev, [Skin and SQ Tissue, Skin, SQ Tissue & Fascia]
ØJXQ[Ø,3]Z[B,C]	Transfer/SQ Tissue & Fascia, Rt Foot, [Opn, Perc], No Dev, [Skin and SQ Tissue, Skin, SQ Tissue & Fascia]
ØJXR[Ø,3]Z[B,C]	Transfer/SQ Tissue & Fascia, Lt Foot, [Opn, Perc], No Dev, [Skin and SQ Tissue, Skin, SQ Tissue & Fascia]
ØPHØ[Ø,3,4]ØZ	Insert/Sternum, [Opn, Perc, Perc Endo], Int Fix Dev, Rigid Plate, NQ
ØPSØ[Ø,3,4]ØZ	Repos/Sternum, [Opn, Perc, Perc Endo], Int Fix Dev, Rigid Plate, NQ
ØW1G[Ø,3,4]J4	Bypass/Peritoneal Cavity, [Opn, Perc, Perc Endo], Synth Sub, Cutaneous
ØW3Ø*	Control/Head
ØW31*	Control/Cranial Cavity
ØW32*	Control/Face
ØW33*	Control/Oral Cavity and Throat
ØW34*	Control/Upr Jaw
ØW35*	Control/Lwr Jaw
ØW36*	Control/Neck
ØW38*	Control/Chest Wall
ØW39*	Control/Pleural Cavity, Rt
ØW3B*	Control/Pleural Cavity, Lt
ØW3D*	Control/Pericardial Cavity
ØW3F*	Control/Abd Wall
ØW3G3ZZ	Control Bleeding in Peritoneal Cavity, Perc Appr
ØW3G4ZZ	Control Bleeding in Peritoneal Cavity, Perc Endo Appr
ØW3H[3,4]ZZ	Control/Retroperitoneum, [Perc, Perc Endo]
ØW3J*	Control/Pelvic Cavity
ØW3K*	Control/Upr Back
ØW3L*	Control/Lwr Back
ØW3M*	Control/Perineum, Male
ØW3N*	Control/Perineum, Female
ØW3P[3,4]ZZ	Control/Gastrointestinal Tract, [Perc, Perc Endo]
ØW3Q*	Control/Respiratory Tract
ØW3R*	Control/Genitourinary Tract
ØW9CØZX	Drain of Mediastinum, Opn Appr, Diagnostic
ØW9C[Ø,3,4][Ø,Z]Z	Drain/Mediastinum, [Opn, Perc, Perc Endo], [Drain Dev, No Dev], NQ
ØW9FØ[Ø,Z]Z	Drain/Abd Wall, Opn, [Drain Dev, No Dev], NQ
ØW9GØ[Ø,Z]Z	Drain/Peritoneal Cavity, Opn, [Drain Dev, No Dev], NQ
ØW9H[Ø,3,4][Ø,Z]Z	Drain/Retroperitoneum, [Opn, Perc, Perc Endo], [Drain Dev, No Dev], NQ
ØW9J[Ø,4][Ø,Z]Z	Drain/Pelvic Cavity, [Opn, Perc Endo], [Drain Dev, No Dev], NQ
ØWBØ[Ø,3,4,X]ZZ	Exc/Head, [Opn, Perc, Perc Endo, Ext]
ØWB2[Ø,3,4,X]ZZ	Exc/Face, [Opn, Perc, Perc Endo, Ext]
ØWB4[Ø,3,4,X]ZZ	Exc/Upr Jaw, [Opn, Perc, Perc Endo, Ext]
ØWB5[Ø,3,4,X]ZZ	Exc/Lwr Jaw, [Opn, Perc, Perc Endo, Ext]
ØWB6XZ2	Exc of Neck, Stoma, Ext Appr
ØWB6[Ø,3,4,X]ZZ	Exc/Neck, [Opn, Perc, Perc Endo, Ext]
ØWBCØZX	Exc of Mediastinum, Opn Appr, Diagnostic
ØWBK[Ø,3,4,X]ZZ	Exc/Upr Back, [Opn, Perc, Perc Endo, Ext]
ØWBL[Ø,3,4,X]ZZ	Exc/Lwr Back, [Opn, Perc, Perc Endo, Ext]
ØWBM[Ø,3,4,X]ZZ	Exc/Perineum, Male, [Opn, Perc, Perc Endo, Ext]
ØWCC[Ø,3,4]ZZ	Extir/Mediastinum, [Opn, Perc, Perc Endo]
ØWCJ[Ø,3,4]ZZ	Extir/Pelvic Cavity, [Opn, Perc, Perc Endo]
ØWCP[Ø,3,4]ZZ	Extir/Gastrointestinal Tract, [Opn, Perc, Perc Endo]
ØWCR[Ø,3,4]ZZ	Extir/Genitourinary Tract, [Opn, Perc, Perc Endo]
ØWHC*	Insert/Mediastinum
ØWHD[Ø,3,4]1Z	Insert/Pericardial Cavity, [Opn, Perc, Perc Endo], Radioact Elmt, NQ
ØWJ9[Ø,4]ZZ	Inspect/Pleural Cavity, Rt, [Opn, Perc Endo]
ØWJB[Ø,4]ZZ	Inspect/Pleural Cavity, Lt, [Opn, Perc Endo]
ØWJC*	Inspect/Mediastinum
ØWJD4ZZ	Inspect of Pericardial Cavity, Perc Endo Appr
ØWJQØZZ	Inspect of Respiratory Tract, Opn Appr
ØWJQ4ZZ	Inspect of Respiratory Tract, Perc Endo Appr
ØWJRØZZ	Inspect of Genitourinary Tract, Opn Appr
ØWJ[F,G,H,J,P]ØZZ	Inspect of [Abd Wall, Peritoneal Cavity, Retroperitoneum, Pelvic Cavity, Gastrointestinal Tract], Perc Endo Appr
ØWPC[Ø,3,4][Ø,1,3,7,J,K,Y]Z	Rmvl/Mediastinum, [Opn, Perc, Perc Endo], [Drain Dev, Radioact Elmt, Inf Dev, Auto Tissue Sub, Synth Sub, Nonauto Tissue Sub, Oth Dev], NQ
ØWQ6XZ2	Repair Neck, Stoma, Ext Appr
ØWWC[Ø,3,4][Ø,1,3,7,J,K,Y]Z	Rev/Mediastinum, [Opn, Perc, Perc Endo], [Drain Dev, Radioact Elmt, Inf Dev, Auto Tissue Sub, Synth Sub, Nonauto Tissue Sub, Oth Dev], NQ
ØX3*	Anatomical Regions, Upr Extremities, Control
ØXB2[Ø,3,4]ZZ	Exc/Shldr Rgn, Rt, [Opn, Perc, Perc Endo]
ØXB3[Ø,3,4]ZZ	Exc/Shldr Rgn, Lt, [Opn, Perc, Perc Endo]
ØXB4[Ø,3,4]ZZ	Exc/Axilla, Rt, [Opn, Perc, Perc Endo]
ØXB5[Ø,3,4]ZZ	Exc/Axilla, Lt, [Opn, Perc, Perc Endo]
ØXB6[Ø,3,4]ZZ	Exc/Upr Extr, Rt, [Opn, Perc, Perc Endo]
ØXB7[Ø,3,4]ZZ	Exc/Upr Extr, Lt, [Opn, Perc, Perc Endo]
ØXB8[Ø,3,4]ZZ	Exc/Upr Arm, Rt, [Opn, Perc, Perc Endo]
ØXB9[Ø,3,4]ZZ	Exc/Upr Arm, Lt, [Opn, Perc, Perc Endo]
ØXBB[Ø,3,4]ZZ	Exc/Elbow Rgn, Rt, [Opn, Perc, Perc Endo]
ØXBC[Ø,3,4]ZZ	Exc/Elbow Rgn, Lt, [Opn, Perc, Perc Endo]
ØXBD[Ø,3,4]ZZ	Exc/Lwr Arm, Rt, [Opn, Perc, Perc Endo]

Surgical   **Medical**   **CC Indicator**   **MCC Indicator**   **Procedure Proxy**   **PDx MCC** **PDx acts as own MCC**   **PDx CC** **PDx acts as own CC**

MDC 5: Diseases And Disorders Of The Circulatory System—SURGICAL

0XBF[0,3,4]ZZ	Exc/Lwr Arm, Lt, [Opn, Perc, Perc Endo]
0XBG[0,3,4]ZZ	Exc/Wrist Rgn, Rt, [Opn, Perc, Perc Endo]
0XBH[0,3,4]ZZ	Exc/Wrist Rgn, Lt, [Opn, Perc, Perc Endo]
0XBJ[0,3,4]ZZ	Exc/Hand, Rt, [Opn, Perc, Perc Endo]
0XBK[0,3,4]ZZ	Exc/Hand, Lt, [Opn, Perc, Perc Endo]
0XUJ[0,4]7Z	Supl/Hand, Rt, [Opn, Perc Endo], Auto Tissue Sub, NQ
0XUK[0,4]7Z	Supl/Hand, Lt, [Opn, Perc Endo], Auto Tissue Sub, NQ
0XUL[0,4]7Z	Supl/Thumb, Rt, [Opn, Perc Endo], Auto Tissue Sub, NQ
0XUM[0,4]7Z	Supl/Thumb, Lt, [Opn, Perc Endo], Auto Tissue Sub, NQ
0XUN[0,4]7Z	Supl/Index Finger, Rt, [Opn, Perc Endo], Auto Tissue Sub, NQ
0XUP[0,4]7Z	Supl/Index Finger, Lt, [Opn, Perc Endo], Auto Tissue Sub, NQ
0XUQ[0,4]7Z	Supl/Mid Finger, Rt, [Opn, Perc Endo], Auto Tissue Sub, NQ
0XUR[0,4]7Z	Supl/Mid Finger, Lt, [Opn, Perc Endo], Auto Tissue Sub, NQ
0XUS[0,4]7Z	Supl/Ring Finger, Rt, [Opn, Perc Endo], Auto Tissue Sub, NQ
0XUT[0,4]7Z	Supl/Ring Finger, Lt, [Opn, Perc Endo], Auto Tissue Sub, NQ
0XUV[0,4]7Z	Supl/Little Finger, Rt, [Opn, Perc Endo], Auto Tissue Sub, NQ
0XUW[0,4]7Z	Supl/Little Finger, Lt, [Opn, Perc Endo], Auto Tissue Sub, NQ
0Y3*	Anatomical Regions, Lwr Extremities, Control
0Y95[0,3,4][0,Z]Z	Drain/Inguinal Rgn, Rt, [Opn, Perc, Perc Endo], [Drain Dev, No Dev], NQ
0Y96[0,3,4][0,Z]Z	Drain/Inguinal Rgn, Lt, [Opn, Perc, Perc Endo], [Drain Dev, No Dev], NQ
0YB0[0,3,4]ZZ	Exc/Buttock, Rt, [Opn, Perc, Perc Endo]
0YB1[0,3,4]ZZ	Exc/Buttock, Lt, [Opn, Perc, Perc Endo]
0YB9[0,3,4]ZZ	Exc/Lwr Extr, Rt, [Opn, Perc, Perc Endo]
0YBB[0,3,4]ZZ	Exc/Lwr Extr, Lt, [Opn, Perc, Perc Endo]
0YBC[0,3,4]ZZ	Exc/Upr Leg, Rt, [Opn, Perc, Perc Endo]
0YBD[0,3,4]ZZ	Exc/Upr Leg, Lt, [Opn, Perc, Perc Endo]
0YBF[0,3,4]ZZ	Exc/Knee Rgn, Rt, [Opn, Perc, Perc Endo]
0YBG[0,3,4]ZZ	Exc/Knee Rgn, Lt, [Opn, Perc, Perc Endo]
0YBH[0,3,4]ZZ	Exc/Lwr Leg, Rt, [Opn, Perc, Perc Endo]
0YBJ[0,3,4]ZZ	Exc/Lwr Leg, Lt, [Opn, Perc, Perc Endo]
0YBK[0,3,4]ZZ	Exc/Ankle Rgn, Rt, [Opn, Perc, Perc Endo]
0YBL[0,3,4]ZZ	Exc/Ankle Rgn, Lt, [Opn, Perc, Perc Endo]
0YBM[0,3,4]ZZ	Exc/Foot, Rt, [Opn, Perc, Perc Endo]
0YBN[0,3,4]ZZ	Exc/Foot, Lt, [Opn, Perc, Perc Endo]
0YJ50ZZ	Inspect of Rt Inguinal Region, Opn Appr
0YJ60ZZ	Inspect of Lt Inguinal Region, Opn Appr
0YJ70ZZ	Inspect of Rt Femor Region, Opn Appr
0YJA0ZZ	Inspect of Bilat Inguinal Region, Opn Appr

OR

Any of the following procedure combinations

02HK[0,3,4][0,2]Z	Insert/Ventricle, Rt, [Opn, Perc, Perc Endo], [Monitoring Dev, Pressure Sensor, Monitoring Dev], NQ

AND

0JH6[0,3]0Z	Insert/SQ Tissue & Fascia, Chest, [Opn, Perc], Monitoring Dev, Hemodynamic, NQ
0JH8[0,3]0Z	Insert/SQ Tissue & Fascia, Abd, [Opn, Perc], Monitoring Dev, Hemodynamic, NQ

DRG 265   AICD Lead Procedures
GMLOS 3.1   AMLOS 4.5   RW 2.9681

Operating Room Procedures

02H40KZ	Insert of Defibrillator Lead into Cor Vein, Opn Appr
02H43[J,K,M]Z	Insert/Coronary Vein, Perc, [Cardiac Lead, Pacemaker, Cardiac Lead, Defibrillator, Cardiac Lead], NQ
02H44KZ	Insert of Defib Lead into Cor Vein, Perc Endo Appr
02H6[0,3,4]KZ	Insert/Atrium, Rt, [Opn, Perc, Perc Endo], Cardiac Lead, Defibrillator, NQ
02H7[0,3,4]KZ	Insert/Atrium, Lt, [Opn, Perc, Perc Endo], Cardiac Lead, Defibrillator, NQ
02HK[0,3,4]KZ	Insert/Ventricle, Rt, [Opn, Perc, Perc Endo], Cardiac Lead, Defibrillator, NQ
02HL[0,3,4]KZ	Insert/Ventricle, Lt, [Opn, Perc, Perc Endo], Cardiac Lead, Defibrillator, NQ
02HN[0,3,4]KZ	Insert/Pericardium, [Opn, Perc, Perc Endo], Cardiac Lead, Defibrillator, NQ

DRG 266   Endovascular Cardiac Valve Replacement with MCC
GMLOS 7.3   AMLOS 9.5   RW 8.5986   [SP]

Operating Room Procedures

02RF3[7,8,J,K]H	Replace/Aortic Valve, Perc, [Auto Tissue Sub, Zooplastic Tissue, Synth Sub, Nonauto Tissue Sub], Transapical
02RF3[7,8,J,K]Z	Replace/Aortic Valve, [Opn, Perc, Perc Endo], [Auto Tissue Sub, Zooplastic Tissue, Synth Sub, Nonauto Tissue Sub], NQ

02RG3[7,8,J,K]H	Replace/Mitral Valve, Perc, [Auto Tissue Sub, Zooplastic Tissue, Synth Sub, Nonauto Tissue Sub], Transapical
02RH3[7,8,J,K]H	Replace/Pulmn Valve, Perc, [Auto Tissue Sub, Zooplastic Tissue, Synth Sub, Nonauto Tissue Sub], Transapical
02RH3[7,8,J,K]Z	Replace/Pulmn Valve, [Opn, Perc, Perc Endo], [Auto Tissue Sub, Zooplastic Tissue, Synth Sub, Nonauto Tissue Sub], NQ

DRG 267   Endovascular Cardiac Valve Replacement without MCC
GMLOS 4.4   AMLOS 5.2   RW 6.5575   [SP]

Select operating room procedures listed under DRG 266

●DRG 268   Aortic and Heart Assist Procedures Except Pulsation Balloon with MCC
GMLOS 6.9   AMLOS 9.9   RW 6.2807

Operating Room Procedures

02BW[0,4]ZZ	Exc/Thoracic Aorta, [Opn, Perc Endo]
02CW[0,3,4]ZZ	Extir/Thoracic Aorta, [Opn, Perc, Perc Endo]
02PA[0,3,4][Q,R]Z	Rmvl/Heart, [Opn, Perc, Perc Endo], [Implantable Heart Assist Sys, Ext Heart Assist Sys], NQ
02QW[0,3,4]ZZ	Rpr/Thoracic Aorta, [Opn, Perc, Perc Endo]
02UA0JZ	Supl Heart with Synth Sub, Opn Appr
02UA3JZ	Supl Heart with Synth Sub, Perc Appr
02UA4JZ	Supl Heart with Synth Sub, Perc Endo Appr
0410O[9,A,J,K,Z]3	Bypass Abd Aorta to Rt Renal Artery w/ [Auto Venous Tissue, Auto Arterial Tissue, Synth Sub, Nonauto Tissue Sub, No Dev], Opn
0410O[9,A,J,K,Z]4	Bypass Abd Aorta to Lt Renal Artery w/ [Auto Venous Tissue, Auto Arterial Tissue, Synth Sub, Nonauto Tissue Sub, No Dev], Opn
0410O[9,A,J,K,Z]5	Bypass Abd Aorta to Bilat Renal Artery w/ [Auto Venous Tissue, Auto Arterial Tissue, Synth Sub, Nonauto Tissue Sub, No Dev], Opn
0410+[9,A,J,K,Z]3	Bypass Abd Aorta to Rt Renal Artery w/ [Auto Venous Tissue, Auto Arterial Tissue, Synth Sub, Nonauto Tissue Sub, No Dev], Perc Endo
0410+[9,A,J,K,Z]4	Bypass Abd Aorta to Lt Renal Artery w/ [Auto Venous Tissue, Auto Arterial Tissue, Synth Sub, Nonauto Tissue Sub, No Dev], Perc Endo
0410+[9,A,J,K,Z]5	Bypass Abd Aorta to Bilat Renal Artery w/ [Auto Venous Tissue, Auto Arterial Tissue, Synth Sub, Nonauto Tissue Sub, No Dev], Perc Endo
0450[0,3,4]ZZ	Destr/Abd Aorta, [Opn, Perc, Perc Endo]
04B0[0,3,4]ZZ	Exc/Abd Aorta, [Opn, Perc, Perc Endo]
04C0[0,3,4]ZZ	Extir/Abd Aorta, [Opn, Perc, Perc Endo]
04L0[0,3,4][C,D,Z]Z	Occlsn/Abd Aorta, [Opn, Perc, Perc Endo], [Extralum Dev, Intralum Dev, No Dev], NQ
04R0[0,4][7,J,K]Z	Replace/Abd Aorta, [Opn, Perc, Perc Endo], [Auto Tissue Sub, Synth Sub, Nonauto Tissue Sub], NQ
04U03JZ	Supl Abd Aorta with Synth Sub, Perc Appr
04U04JZ	Supl Abd Aorta with Synth Sub, Perc Endo Appr
04V03DZ	Restrict of Abd Aorta with Intralum Dev, Perc Appr
04V04DZ	Restrict of Abd Aorta with Intralum Dev, Perc Endo Appr

●DRG 269   Aortic and Heart Assist Procedures Except Pulsation Balloon without MCC
GMLOS 1.9   AMLOS 2.6   RW 3.9041

Select operating room procedures listed under DRG 268

●DRG 270   Other Major Cardiovascular Procedures with MCC
GMLOS 6.5   AMLOS 9.3   RW 4.7349

Operating Room Procedures

0216[0,4]Z7	Bypass/Atrium, Rt, [Opn, Perc Endo], No Dev, Atrium, Lt
021V[0,4][9,A,J,K,Z][P,Q,R]	Bypass/Superior Vena Cava, [Opn, Perc Endo], [Auto Venous Tissue, Auto Arterial Tissue, Synth Sub, Nonauto Tissue Sub, No Dev], [Pulmn Trunk, Pulmn Artery, Rt, Pulmn Artery, Lt]
021W[0,4][9,A,J,K,Z][B,D,P,Q,R]	Bypass/Thoracic Aorta, [Opn, Perc Endo], [Auto Venous Tissue, Auto Arterial Tissue, Synth Sub, Nonauto Tissue Sub, No Dev], [Subclavian, Carotid, Pulmn Trunk, Pulmn Artery, Rt, Pulmn Artery, Lt]
025N[0,3,4]ZZ	Destr/Pericardium, [Opn, Perc, Perc Endo]
025P[0,3,4]ZZ	Destr/Pulmn Trunk, [Opn, Perc, Perc Endo]
025Q[0,3,4]ZZ	Destr/Pulmn Artery, Rt, [Opn, Perc, Perc Endo]
025R[0,3,4]ZZ	Destr/Pulmn Artery, Lt, [Opn, Perc, Perc Endo]

[T] **Transfer DRG**   [SP] **Special Payment**   * **Code Range**   **6th and 7th Character of ZZ = No Device, No Qualifier ZX = No Device, Diagnostic**

025S[0,3,4]ZZ	Destr/Pulmn Vein, Rt, [Opn, Perc, Perc Endo]
025T[0,3,4]ZZ	Destr/Pulmn Vein, Lt, [Opn, Perc, Perc Endo]
025V[0,3,4]ZZ	Destr/Superior Vena Cava, [Opn, Perc, Perc Endo]
025W[0,3,4]ZZ	Destr/Thoracic Aorta, [Opn, Perc, Perc Endo]
027K[0,3,4][4,D,Z]Z	Dilation/Ventricle, Rt, [Opn, Perc, Perc Endo], [Drug-eluting Intralum Dev, Intralum Dev, No Dev], NQ
027R[0,3,4][4,D,Z]T	Dilation/Pulmn Artery, Lt, [Opn, Perc, Perc Endo], [Drug-eluting Intralum Dev, Intralum Dev, No Dev], Ductus Arteriosus
0288[0,3,4]ZZ	Div/Conduction Mech, [Opn, Perc, Perc Endo]
02BN[0,3,4]Z[X,Z]	Exc/Pericardium, [Opn, Perc, Perc Endo], No Dev, [Dx, NQ]
02BP[0,3,4]ZZ	Exc/Pulmn Trunk, [Opn, Perc, Perc Endo]
02BQ[0,3,4]ZZ	Exc/Pulmn Artery, Rt, [Opn, Perc, Perc Endo]
02BR[0,3,4]ZZ	Exc/Pulmn Artery, Lt, [Opn, Perc, Perc Endo]
02BS[0,3,4]ZZ	Exc/Pulmn Vein, Rt, [Opn, Perc, Perc Endo]
02BT[0,3,4]ZZ	Exc/Pulmn Vein, Lt, [Opn, Perc, Perc Endo]
02BV[0,3,4]ZZ	Exc/Superior Vena Cava, [Opn, Perc, Perc Endo]
02BW3ZZ	Exc of Thoracic Aorta, Perc Appr
02CF[3,4]ZZ	Extir/Aortic Valve, [Perc, Perc Endo]
02CG[3,4]ZZ	Extir/Mitral Valve, [Perc, Perc Endo]
02CH[3,4]ZZ	Extir/Pulmn Valve, [Perc, Perc Endo]
02CJ[3,4]ZZ	Extir/Tricuspid Valve, [Perc, Perc Endo]
02CN[0,3,4]ZZ	Extir/Pericardium, [Opn, Perc, Perc Endo]
02CP[0,3,4]ZZ	Extir/Pulmn Trunk, [Opn, Perc, Perc Endo]
02CQ[0,3,4]ZZ	Extir/Pulmn Artery, Rt, [Opn, Perc, Perc Endo]
02CR[0,3,4]ZZ	Extir/Pulmn Artery, Lt, [Opn, Perc, Perc Endo]
02CS[0,3,4]ZZ	Extir/Pulmn Vein, Rt, [Opn, Perc, Perc Endo]
02CT[0,3,4]ZZ	Extir/Pulmn Vein, Lt, [Opn, Perc, Perc Endo]
02CV[0,3,4]ZZ	Extir/Superior Vena Cava, [Opn, Perc, Perc Endo]
02FN[0,3,4]ZZ	Fragmn/Pericardium, [Opn, Perc, Perc Endo]
02HN[0,3,4][0,2]Z	Insert/Pericardium, [Opn, Perc, Perc Endo], [Monitoring Dev, Pressure Sensor, Monitoring Dev], NQ
02HP[0,3,4]DZ	Insert/Pulmn Trunk, [Opn, Perc, Perc Endo], Intralum Dev, NQ
02HQ[0,3,4]DZ	Insert/Pulmn Artery, Rt, [Opn, Perc, Perc Endo], Intralum Dev, NQ
02HR[0,3,4]DZ	Insert/Pulmn Artery, Lt, [Opn, Perc, Perc Endo], Intralum Dev, NQ
02HS[0,3,4][2,D]Z	Insert/Pulmn Vein, Rt, [Opn, Perc, Perc Endo], [Monitoring Dev, Intralum Dev], NQ
02HT[0,3,4][2,D]Z	Insert/Pulmn Vein, Lt, [Opn, Perc, Perc Endo], [Monitoring Dev, Intralum Dev], NQ
02HW[0,3,4][2,D]Z	Insert/Thoracic Aorta, [Opn, Perc, Perc Endo], [Monitoring Dev, Intralum Dev], NQ
02LR[0,3,4][C,D,Z]T	Occlsn/Pulmn Artery, Lt, [Opn, Perc, Perc Endo], [Extralum Dev, Intralum Dev, No Dev], Ductus Arteriosus
02LS[0,3,4][C,D,Z]Z	Occlsn/Pulmn Artery, Rt, [Opn, Perc, Perc Endo], [Extralum Dev, Intralum Dev, No Dev], NQ
02LT[0,3,4][C,D,Z]Z	Occlsn/Pulmn Vein, Lt, [Opn, Perc, Perc Endo], [Extralum Dev, Intralum Dev, No Dev], NQ
02N4[0,3,4]ZZ	Rls/Coronary Vein, [Opn, Perc, Perc Endo]
02N8[0,3,4]ZZ	Rls/Conduction Mech, [Opn, Perc, Perc Endo]
02NF[3,4]ZZ	Rls/Aortic Valve, [Perc, Perc Endo]
02NG[3,4]ZZ	Rls/Mitral Valve, [Perc, Perc Endo]
02NH[3,4]ZZ	Rls/Pulmn Valve, [Perc, Perc Endo]
02NJ[3,4]ZZ	Rls/Tricuspid Valve, [Perc, Perc Endo]
02NN[0,3,4]ZZ	Rls/Pericardium, [Opn, Perc, Perc Endo]
02PY[0,3,4][2,3,7,8,C,D,J,K]Z	Rmvl/Great Vessel, [Opn, Perc, Perc Endo], [Monitoring Dev, Inf Dev, Auto Tissue Sub, Zooplastic Tissue, Extralum Dev, Intralum Dev, Synth Sub, Nonauto Tissue Sub], NQ
02Q6[0,3,4]ZZ	Rpr/Atrium, Rt, [Opn, Perc, Perc Endo]
02Q7[0,3,4]ZZ	Rpr/Atrium, Lt, [Opn, Perc, Perc Endo]
02Q8[0,3,4]ZZ	Rpr/Conduction Mech, [Opn, Perc, Perc Endo]
02QA[0,3,4]ZZ	Rpr/Heart, [Opn, Perc, Perc Endo]
02QK[0,3,4]ZZ	Rpr/Ventricle, Rt, [Opn, Perc, Perc Endo]
02QL[0,3,4]ZZ	Rpr/Ventricle, Lt, [Opn, Perc, Perc Endo]
02QN[0,3,4]ZZ	Rpr/Pericardium, [Opn, Perc, Perc Endo]
02R5[0,4][7,8,J,K]Z	Replace/Atrial Septum, [Opn, Perc Endo], [Auto Tissue Sub, Zooplastic Tissue, Synth Sub, Nonauto Tissue Sub], NQ
02R6[0,4][7,8,J,K]Z	Replace/Atrium, Rt, [Opn, Perc Endo], [Auto Tissue Sub, Zooplastic Tissue, Synth Sub, Nonauto Tissue Sub], NQ
02R7[0,4][7,8,J,K]Z	Replace/Atrium, Lt, [Opn, Perc Endo], [Auto Tissue Sub, Zooplastic Tissue, Synth Sub, Nonauto Tissue Sub], NQ
02RK[0,4][8,J]Z	Replace/Ventricle, Rt, [Opn, Perc Endo], [Zooplastic Tissue, Synth Sub], NQ
02RL[0,4][8,J]Z	Replace/Ventricle, Lt, [Opn, Perc Endo], [Zooplastic Tissue, Synth Sub], NQ
02RM[0,4]8Z	Replace/Ventricular Septum, [Opn, Perc Endo], Zooplastic Tissue, NQ

02RN[0,4][7,8,J,K]Z	Replace/Pericardium, [Opn, Perc Endo], [Auto Tissue Sub, Zooplastic Tissue, Synth Sub, Nonauto Tissue Sub], NQ
02TN[0,3,4]ZZ	Resect/Pericardium, [Opn, Perc, Perc Endo]
02U60JZ	Supl Rt Atrium with Synth Sub, Opn Appr
02U6[3,4][7,8,J,K]Z	Supl/Atrium, Rt, [Perc, Perc Endo], [Auto Tissue Sub, Zooplastic Tissue, Synth Sub, Nonauto Tissue Sub], NQ
02U70JZ	Supl Lt Atrium with Synth Sub, Opn Appr
02UA[0,3,4][7,8,K]Z	Supl/Heart, [Opn, Perc, Perc Endo], [Auto Tissue Sub, Zooplastic Tissue, Nonauto Tissue Sub], NQ
02UK[0,3,4][7,8,J]Z	Supl/Ventricle, Rt, [Opn, Perc, Perc Endo], [Auto Tissue Sub, Zooplastic Tissue, Synth Sub], NQ
02UL[0,3,4][7,8,J]Z	Supl/Ventricle, Lt, [Opn, Perc, Perc Endo], [Auto Tissue Sub, Zooplastic Tissue, Synth Sub], NQ
02UM08Z	Supl Ventricular Septum with Zooplastic, Opn Appr
02UN[0,3,4][7,8,J,K]Z	Supl/Pericardium, [Opn, Perc, Perc Endo], [Auto Tissue Sub, Zooplastic Tissue, Synth Sub, Nonauto Tissue Sub], NQ
02VA[0,3,4][C,Z]Z	Restrict/Heart, [Opn, Perc, Perc Endo], [Extralum Dev, No Dev], NQ
02VP[0,3,4][D,Z]Z	Restrict/Pulmn Trunk, [Opn, Perc, Perc Endo], [Intralum Dev, No Dev], NQ
02VQ[0,3,4]CZ	Restrict/Pulmn Artery, Rt, [Opn, Perc, Perc Endo], Extralum Dev, NQ
02VQ[0,3,4][D,Z]Z	Restrict/Pulmn Artery, Rt, [Opn, Perc, Perc Endo], [Intralum Dev, No Dev], NQ
02VR0CZ	Restrict of Lt Pulm Art with Extralum Dev, Opn Appr
02VR0DT	Restrict of Ductus Arterio with Intralum Dev, Opn Appr
02VR0DZ	Restrict of Lt Pulm Art with Intralum Dev, Opn Appr
02VR0ZT	Restrict of Ductus Arteriosus, Opn Appr
02VR0ZZ	Restrict of Lt Pulmn Artery, Opn Appr
02VR3CZ	Restrict of Lt Pulm Art with Extralum Dev, Perc Appr
02VR3DT	Restrict of Ductus Arterio with Intralum Dev, Perc Appr
02VR3DZ	Restrict of Lt Pulm Art with Intralum Dev, Perc Appr
02VR3ZT	Restrict of Ductus Arteriosus, Perc Appr
02VR3ZZ	Restrict of Lt Pulmn Artery, Perc Appr
02VR4CZ	Restrict of Lt Pulm Art with Extralum Dev, Perc Endo Appr
02VR4DT	Restrict Ductus Arterio w Intralum Dev, Perc Endo
02VR4DZ	Restrict of Lt Pulm Art with Intralum Dev, Perc Endo Appr
02VR4ZT	Restrict of Ductus Arteriosus, Perc Endo Appr
02VR4ZZ	Restrict of Lt Pulmn Artery, Perc Endo Appr
02VS[0,3,4][D,Z]Z	Restrict/Pulmn Vein, Rt, [Opn, Perc, Perc Endo], [Intralum Dev, No Dev], NQ
02VT[0,3,4][D,Z]Z	Restrict/Pulmn Vein, Lt, [Opn, Perc, Perc Endo], [Intralum Dev, No Dev], NQ
02VW[0,3,4]ZZ	Restrict/Thoracic Aorta, [Opn, Perc, Perc Endo]
02WY[0,3,4][2,3,7,8,C,D,J,K]Z	Rev/Great Vessel, [Opn, Perc, Perc Endo], [Monitoring Dev, Inf Dev, Auto Tissue Sub, Zooplastic Tissue, Extralum Dev, Intralum Dev, Synth Sub, Nonauto Tissue Sub], NQ
03130[9,A,J,K,Z][M,N]	Bypass/Subclavian Artery, Rt, Opn, [Auto Venous Tissue, Auto Arterial Tissue, Synth Sub, Nonauto Tissue Sub, No Dev], [Pulmn Artery, Rt, Pulmn Artery, Lt]
03140[9,A,J,K,Z][M,N]	Bypass/Subclavian Artery, Lt, Opn, [Auto Venous Tissue, Auto Arterial Tissue, Synth Sub, Nonauto Tissue Sub, No Dev], [Pulmn Artery, Rt, Pulmn Artery, Lt]
0350[0,3,4]ZZ	Destr/Int Mammary Artery, Rt, [Opn, Perc, Perc Endo]
0351[0,3,4]ZZ	Destr/Int Mammary Artery, Lt, [Opn, Perc, Perc Endo]
0352[0,3,4]ZZ	Destr/Innominate Artery, [Opn, Perc, Perc Endo]
0353[0,3,4]ZZ	Destr/Subclavian Artery, Rt, [Opn, Perc, Perc Endo]
0354[0,3,4]ZZ	Destr/Subclavian Artery, Lt, [Opn, Perc, Perc Endo]
03B0[0,3,4]ZZ	Exc/Int Mammary Artery, Rt, [Opn, Perc, Perc Endo]
03B1[0,3,4]ZZ	Exc/Int Mammary Artery, Lt, [Opn, Perc, Perc Endo]
03B2[0,3,4]ZZ	Exc/Innominate Artery, [Opn, Perc, Perc Endo]
03B3[0,3,4]ZZ	Exc/Subclavian Artery, Rt, [Opn, Perc, Perc Endo]
03B4[0,3,4]ZZ	Exc/Subclavian Artery, Lt, [Opn, Perc, Perc Endo]
03C0[0,3,4]ZZ	Extir/Int Mammary Artery, Rt, [Opn, Perc, Perc Endo]
03C1[0,3,4]ZZ	Extir/Int Mammary Artery, Lt, [Opn, Perc, Perc Endo]
03C2[0,3,4]ZZ	Extir/Innominate Artery, [Opn, Perc, Perc Endo]
03C3[0,3,4]ZZ	Extir/Subclavian Artery, Rt, [Opn, Perc, Perc Endo]
03C4[0,3,4]ZZ	Extir/Subclavian Artery, Lt, [Opn, Perc, Perc Endo]
03L0[0,3,4][C,D,Z]Z	Occlsn/Int Mammary Artery, Rt, [Opn, Perc, Perc Endo], [Extralum Dev, Intralum Dev, No Dev], NQ
03L1[0,3,4][C,D,Z]Z	Occlsn/Int Mammary Artery, Lt, [Opn, Perc, Perc Endo], [Extralum Dev, Intralum Dev, No Dev], NQ
03L2[0,3,4][C,D,Z]Z	Occlsn/Innominate Artery, [Opn, Perc, Perc Endo], [Extralum Dev, Intralum Dev, No Dev], NQ
03L3[0,3,4][C,D,Z]Z	Occlsn/Subclavian Artery, Rt, [Opn, Perc, Perc Endo], [Extralum Dev, Intralum Dev, No Dev], NQ
03L4[0,3,4][C,D,Z]Z	Occlsn/Subclavian Artery, Lt, [Opn, Perc, Perc Endo], [Extralum Dev, Intralum Dev, No Dev], NQ

MDC 5: Diseases And Disorders Of The Circulatory System—SURGICAL

Surgical	**Medical**	**CC Indicator**	**MCC Indicator**	**Procedure Proxy**	**PDxMCC** PDx acts as own MCC **PDxCC** PDx acts as own CC

MDC 5: Diseases And Disorders Of The Circulatory System—SURGICAL

03LG[0,3,4][B,D]Z Occlsn/Intracranial Artery, [Opn, Perc, Perc Endo], [Bioactive Intralum Dev, Intralum Dev], NQ

03LH[0,3,4][B,D]Z Occlsn/Common Carotid Artery, Rt, [Opn, Perc, Perc Endo], [Bioactive Intralum Dev, Intralum Dev], NQ

03LJ[0,3,4][B,D]Z Occlsn/Common Carotid Artery, Lt, [Opn, Perc, Perc Endo], [Bioactive Intralum Dev, Intralum Dev], NQ

03LK[0,3,4][B,D]Z Occlsn/Int Carotid Artery, Rt, [Opn, Perc, Perc Endo], [Bioactive Intralum Dev, Intralum Dev], NQ

03LL[0,3,4][B,D]Z Occlsn/Int Carotid Artery, Lt, [Opn, Perc, Perc Endo], [Bioactive Intralum Dev, Intralum Dev], NQ

03LM[0,3,4][B,D]Z Occlsn/Ext Carotid Artery, Rt, [Opn, Perc, Perc Endo], [Bioactive Intralum Dev, Intralum Dev], NQ

03LN[0,3,4][B,D]Z Occlsn/Ext Carotid Artery, Lt, [Opn, Perc, Perc Endo], [Bioactive Intralum Dev, Intralum Dev], NQ

03LP[0,3,4][B,D]Z Occlsn/Vert Artery, Rt, [Opn, Perc, Perc Endo], [Bioactive Intralum Dev, Intralum Dev], NQ

03LQ[0,3,4][B,D]Z Occlsn/Vert Artery, Lt, [Opn, Perc, Perc Endo], [Bioactive Intralum Dev, Intralum Dev], NQ

03LR[0,3,4]DZ Occlsn/Face Artery, [Opn, Perc, Perc Endo], Intralum Dev, NQ

03LS[0,3,4]DZ Occlsn/Temporal Artery, Rt, [Opn, Perc, Perc Endo], Intralum Dev, NQ

03LT[0,3,4]DZ Occlsn/Temporal Artery, Lt, [Opn, Perc, Perc Endo], Intralum Dev, NQ

03V0[0,3,4][D,Z]Z Restrict/Int Mammary Artery, Rt, [Opn, Perc, Perc Endo], [Intralum Dev, No Dev], NQ

03V1[0,3,4][D,Z]Z Restrict/Int Mammary Artery, Lt, [Opn, Perc, Perc Endo], [Intralum Dev, No Dev], NQ

03V2[0,3,4][D,Z]Z Restrict/Innominate Artery, [Opn, Perc, Perc Endo], [Intralum Dev, No Dev], NQ

03V3[0,3,4][D,Z]Z Restrict/Subclavian Artery, Rt, [Opn, Perc, Perc Endo], [Intralum Dev, No Dev], NQ

03V4[0,3,4][D,Z]Z Restrict/Subclavian Artery, Lt, [Opn, Perc, Perc Endo], [Intralum Dev, No Dev], NQ

03V5[0,3,4][D,Z]Z Restrict/Axillary Artery, Rt, [Opn, Perc, Perc Endo], [Intralum Dev, No Dev], NQ

03V6[0,3,4][D,Z]Z Restrict/Axillary Artery, Lt, [Opn, Perc, Perc Endo], [Intralum Dev, No Dev], NQ

03V7[0,3,4][D,Z]Z Restrict/Brachial Artery, Rt, [Opn, Perc, Perc Endo], [Intralum Dev, No Dev], NQ

03V8[0,3,4][D,Z]Z Restrict/Brachial Artery, Lt, [Opn, Perc, Perc Endo], [Intralum Dev, No Dev], NQ

03V9[0,3,4][D,Z]Z Restrict/Ulnar Artery, Rt, [Opn, Perc, Perc Endo], [Intralum Dev, No Dev], NQ

03VA[0,3,4][D,Z]Z Restrict/Ulnar Artery, Lt, [Opn, Perc, Perc Endo], [Intralum Dev, No Dev], NQ

03VB[0,3,4][D,Z]Z Restrict/Radial Artery, Rt, [Opn, Perc, Perc Endo], [Intralum Dev, No Dev], NQ

03VC[0,3,4][D,Z]Z Restrict/Radial Artery, Lt, [Opn, Perc, Perc Endo], [Intralum Dev, No Dev], NQ

03VD[0,3,4][D,Z]Z Restrict/Hand Artery, Rt, [Opn, Perc, Perc Endo], [Intralum Dev, No Dev], NQ

03VF[0,3,4][D,Z]Z Restrict/Hand Artery, Lt, [Opn, Perc, Perc Endo], [Intralum Dev, No Dev], NQ

03VG[0,3,4][B,D,Z]Z Restrict/Intracranial Artery, [Opn, Perc, Perc Endo], [Bioactive Intralum Dev, Intralum Dev, No Dev], NQ

03VH[0,3,4][B,D,Z]Z Restrict/Common Carotid Artery, Rt, [Opn, Perc, Perc Endo], [Bioactive Intralum Dev, Intralum Dev, No Dev], NQ

03VJ[0,3,4][B,D,Z]Z Restrict/Common Carotid Artery, Lt, [Opn, Perc, Perc Endo], [Bioactive Intralum Dev, Intralum Dev, No Dev], NQ

03VK[0,3,4][B,D,Z]Z Restrict/Int Carotid Artery, Rt, [Opn, Perc, Perc Endo], [Bioactive Intralum Dev, Intralum Dev, No Dev], NQ

03VL[0,3,4][B,D,Z]Z Restrict/Int Carotid Artery, Lt, [Opn, Perc, Perc Endo], [Bioactive Intralum Dev, Intralum Dev, No Dev], NQ

03VM[0,3,4][B,D,Z]Z Restrict/Ext Carotid Artery, Rt, [Opn, Perc, Perc Endo], [Bioactive Intralum Dev, Intralum Dev, No Dev], NQ

03VN[0,3,4][B,D,Z]Z Restrict/Ext Carotid Artery, Lt, [Opn, Perc, Perc Endo], [Bioactive Intralum Dev, Intralum Dev, No Dev], NQ

03VP[0,3,4][B,D,Z]Z Restrict/Vert Artery, Rt, [Opn, Perc, Perc Endo], [Bioactive Intralum Dev, Intralum Dev, No Dev], NQ

03VQ[0,3,4][B,D,Z]Z Restrict/Vert Artery, Lt, [Opn, Perc, Perc Endo], [Bioactive Intralum Dev, Intralum Dev, No Dev], NQ

03VR[0,3,4][D,Z]Z Restrict/Face Artery, [Opn, Perc, Perc Endo], [Intralum Dev, No Dev], NQ

03VS[0,3,4][D,Z]Z Restrict/Temporal Artery, Rt, [Opn, Perc, Perc Endo], [Intralum Dev, No Dev], NQ

03VT[0,3,4][D,Z]Z Restrict/Temporal Artery, Lt, [Opn, Perc, Perc Endo], [Intralum Dev, No Dev], NQ

03VU[0,3,4][D,Z]Z Restrict/Thyroid Artery, Rt, [Opn, Perc, Perc Endo], [Intralum Dev, No Dev], NQ

03VV[0,3,4][D,Z]Z Restrict/Thyroid Artery, Lt, [Opn, Perc, Perc Endo], [Intralum Dev, No Dev], NQ

03VY[0,3,4][D,Z]Z Restrict/Upr Artery, [Opn, Perc, Perc Endo], [Intralum Dev, No Dev], NQ

0410090 Bypass Abd Aorta to Abd Aorta with Autol Vn, Opn Appr

0410091 Bypass Abd Aorta to Celiac Art with Autol Vn, Opn Appr

0410092 Bypass Abd Aorta to Mesent Art with Autol Vn, Opn Appr

0410096 Bypass Abd Aorta to Rt Com Ilia with Autol Vn, Opn Appr

0410097 Bypass Abd Aorta to Lt Com Ilia with Autol Vn, Opn Appr

0410098 Bypass Abd Aorta to Bilat Com Ilia with Autol Vn, Opn Appr

0410099 Bypass Abd Aorta to Rt Int Ilia with Autol Vn, Opn Appr

041009B Bypass Abd Aorta to Lt Int Ilia with Autol Vn, Opn Appr

041009C Bypass Abd Aorta to Bilat Int Ilia with Autol Vn, Opn Appr

041009D Bypass Abd Aorta to Rt Ext Ilia with Autol Vn, Opn Appr

041009F Bypass Abd Aorta to Lt Ext Ilia with Autol Vn, Opn Appr

041009G Bypass Abd Aorta to Bilat Ext Ilia with Autol Vn, Opn Appr

041009H Bypass Abd Aorta to Rt Femor A with Autol Vn, Opn Appr

041009J Bypass Abd Aorta to Lt Femor A with Autol Vn, Opn Appr

041009K Bypass Abd Aorta to Bilat Femor A with Autol Vn, Opn Appr

041009Q Bypass Abd Aorta to Low Ex Art with Autol Vn, Opn Appr

041009R Bypass Abd Aorta to Low Art with Autol Vn, Opn Appr

04100A0 Bypass Abd Aorta to Abd Aorta with Autol Art, Opn Appr

04100A1 Bypass Abd Aorta to Celiac Art with Autol Art, Opn Appr

04100A2 Bypass Abd Aorta to Mesent Art with Autol Art, Opn Appr

04100A6 Bypass Abd Aorta to Rt Com Ilia with Autol Art, Opn Appr

04100A7 Bypass Abd Aorta to Lt Com Ilia with Autol Art, Opn Appr

04100A8 Bypass Abd Aorta to Bilat Com Ilia with Autol Art, Opn Appr

04100A9 Bypass Abd Aorta to Rt Int Ilia with Autol Art, Opn Appr

04100AB Bypass Abd Aorta to Lt Int Ilia with Autol Art, Opn Appr

04100AC Bypass Abd Aorta to Bilat Int Ilia with Autol Art, Opn Appr

04100AD Bypass Abd Aorta to Rt Ext Ilia with Autol Art, Opn Appr

04100AF Bypass Abd Aorta to Lt Ext Ilia with Autol Art, Opn Appr

04100AG Bypass Abd Aorta to Bilat Ext Ilia with Autol Art, Opn Appr

04100AH Bypass Abd Aorta to Rt Femor A with Autol Art, Opn Appr

04100AJ Bypass Abd Aorta to Lt Femor A with Autol Art, Opn Appr

04100AK Bypass Abd Aorta to Bilat Femor A with Autol Art, Opn Appr

04100AQ Bypass Abd Aorta to Low Ex Art with Autol Art, Opn Appr

04100AR Bypass Abd Aorta to Low Art with Autol Art, Opn Appr

04100J0 Bypass Abd Aorta to Abd Aorta with Synth Sub, Opn Appr

04100J1 Bypass Abd Aorta to Celiac Art with Synth Sub, Opn Appr

04100J2 Bypass Abd Aorta to Mesent Art with Synth Sub, Opn Appr

04100J6 Bypass Abd Aorta to Rt Com Ilia with Synth Sub, Opn Appr

04100J7 Bypass Abd Aorta to Lt Com Ilia with Synth Sub, Opn Appr

04100J8 Bypass Abd Aorta to Bilat Com Ilia with Synth Sub, Opn Appr

04100J9 Bypass Abd Aorta to Rt Int Ilia with Synth Sub, Opn Appr

04100JB Bypass Abd Aorta to Lt Int Ilia with Synth Sub, Opn Appr

04100JC Bypass Abd Aorta to Bilat Int Ilia with Synth Sub, Opn Appr

04100JD Bypass Abd Aorta to Rt Ext Ilia with Synth Sub, Opn Appr

04100JF Bypass Abd Aorta to Lt Ext Ilia with Synth Sub, Opn Appr

04100JG Bypass Abd Aorta to Bilat Ext Ilia with Synth Sub, Opn Appr

04100JH Bypass Abd Aorta to Rt Femor A with Synth Sub, Opn Appr

04100JJ Bypass Abd Aorta to Lt Femor A with Synth Sub, Opn Appr

04100JK Bypass Abd Aorta to Bilat Femor A with Synth Sub, Opn Appr

04100JQ Bypass Abd Aorta to Low Ex Art with Synth Sub, Opn Appr

04100JR Bypass Abd Aorta to Low Art with Synth Sub, Opn Appr

04100K0 Bypass Abd Aorta to Abd Aorta with Nonaut Sub, Opn Appr

04100K1 Bypass Abd Aorta to Celiac Art w Nonaut Sub, Opn

04100K2 Bypass Abd Aorta to Mesent Art w Nonaut Sub, Opn

04100K6 Bypass Abd Aorta to Rt Com Ilia w Nonaut Sub, Opn

04100K7 Bypass Abd Aorta to Lt Com Ilia w Nonaut Sub, Opn

04100K8 Bypass Abd Aorta to Bilat Com Ilia w Nonaut Sub, Opn

04100K9 Bypass Abd Aorta to Rt Int Ilia w Nonaut Sub, Opn

04100KB Bypass Abd Aorta to Lt Int Ilia w Nonaut Sub, Opn

04100KC Bypass Abd Aorta to Bilat Int Ilia w Nonaut Sub, Opn

04100KD Bypass Abd Aorta to Rt Ext Ilia w Nonaut Sub, Opn

04100KF Bypass Abd Aorta to Lt Ext Ilia w Nonaut Sub, Opn

04100KG Bypass Abd Aorta to Bilat Ext Ilia w Nonaut Sub, Opn

04100KH Bypass Abd Aorta to Rt Femor A with Nonaut Sub, Opn Appr

04100KJ Bypass Abd Aorta to Lt Femor A with Nonaut Sub, Opn Appr

04100KK Bypass Abd Aorta to Bilat Femor A with Nonaut Sub, Opn Appr

04100KQ Bypass Abd Aorta to Low Ex Art w Nonaut Sub, Opn

04100KR Bypass Abd Aorta to Low Art with Nonaut Sub, Opn Appr

04100Z0 Bypass Abd Aorta to Abd Aorta, Opn Appr

04100Z1 Bypass Abd Aorta to Celiac Artery, Opn Appr

04100Z2 Bypass Abd Aorta to Mesenteric Artery, Opn Appr

04100Z6 Bypass Abd Aorta to Rt Com Ilia, Opn Appr

04100Z7 Bypass Abd Aorta to Lt Com Ilia, Opn Appr

04100Z8 Bypass Abd Aorta to Bilat Com Ilia, Opn Appr

04100Z9 Bypass Abd Aorta to Rt Int Ilia, Opn Appr

T **Transfer DRG**   SP **Special Payment**   * **Code Range**   **6th and 7th Character of ZZ = No Device, No Qualifier ZX = No Device, Diagnostic**

04100ZB	Bypass Abd Aorta to Lt Int Ilia, Opn Appr
04100ZC	Bypass Abd Aorta to Bilat Int Ilia, Opn Appr
04100ZD	Bypass Abd Aorta to Rt Ext Ilia, Opn Appr
04100ZF	Bypass Abd Aorta to Lt Ext Ilia, Opn Appr
04100ZG	Bypass Abd Aorta to Bilat Ext Ilia, Opn Appr
04100ZH	Bypass Abd Aorta to Rt Femor A, Opn Appr
04100ZJ	Bypass Abd Aorta to Lt Femor Artery, Opn Appr
04100ZK	Bypass Abd Aorta to Bilat Femor A, Opn Appr
04100ZQ	Bypass Abd Aorta to Low Ex Art, Opn Appr
04100ZR	Bypass Abd Aorta to Lwr Artery, Opn Appr
0410490	Bypass Abd Aorta to Abd Aorta w Autol Vn, Perc Endo
0410491	Bypass Abd Aorta to Celiac Art w Autol Vn, Perc Endo
0410492	Bypass Abd Aorta to Mesent Art w Autol Vn, Perc Endo
0410496	Bypass Abd Aorta to Rt Com Ilia w Autol Vn, Perc Endo
0410497	Bypass Abd Aorta to Lt Com Ilia w Autol Vn, Perc Endo
0410498	Bypass Abd Aorta to Bilat Com Ilia w Autol Vn, Perc Endo
0410499	Bypass Abd Aorta to Rt Int Ilia w Autol Vn, Perc Endo
041049B	Bypass Abd Aorta to Lt Int Ilia w Autol Vn, Perc Endo
041049C	Bypass Abd Aorta to Bilat Int Ilia w Autol Vn, Perc Endo
041049D	Bypass Abd Aorta to Rt Ext Ilia w Autol Vn, Perc Endo
041049F	Bypass Abd Aorta to Lt Ext Ilia w Autol Vn, Perc Endo
041049G	Bypass Abd Aorta to Bilat Ext Ilia w Autol Vn, Perc Endo
041049H	Bypass Abd Aorta to Rt Femor A w Autol Vn, Perc Endo
041049J	Bypass Abd Aorta to Lt Femor A w Autol Vn, Perc Endo
041049K	Bypass Abd Aorta to Bilat Femor A w Autol Vn, Perc Endo
041049Q	Bypass Abd Aorta to Low Ex Art w Autol Vn, Perc Endo
041049R	Bypass Abd Aorta to Low Art w Autol Vn, Perc Endo
04104A0	Bypass Abd Aorta to Abd Aorta w Autol Art, Perc Endo
04104A1	Bypass Abd Aorta to Celiac Art w Autol Art, Perc Endo
04104A2	Bypass Abd Aorta to Mesent Art w Autol Art, Perc Endo
04104A6	Bypass Abd Aorta to Rt Com Ilia w Autol Art, Perc Endo
04104A7	Bypass Abd Aorta to Lt Com Ilia w Autol Art, Perc Endo
04104A8	Bypass Abd Aorta to Bilat Com Ilia w Autol Art, Perc Endo
04104A9	Bypass Abd Aorta to Rt Int Ilia w Autol Art, Perc Endo
04104AB	Bypass Abd Aorta to Lt Int Ilia w Autol Art, Perc Endo
04104AC	Bypass Abd Aorta to Bilat Int Ilia w Autol Art, Perc Endo
04104AD	Bypass Abd Aorta to Rt Ext Ilia w Autol Art, Perc Endo
04104AF	Bypass Abd Aorta to Lt Ext Ilia w Autol Art, Perc Endo
04104AG	Bypass Abd Aorta to Bilat Ext Ilia w Autol Art, Perc Endo
04104AH	Bypass Abd Aorta to Rt Femor A w Autol Art, Perc Endo
04104AJ	Bypass Abd Aorta to Lt Femor A w Autol Art, Perc Endo
04104AK	Bypass Abd Aorta to Bilat Femor A w Autol Art, Perc Endo
04104AQ	Bypass Abd Aorta to Low Ex Art w Autol Art, Perc Endo
04104AR	Bypass Abd Aorta to Low Art w Autol Art, Perc Endo
04104J0	Bypass Abd Aorta to Abd Aorta w Synth Sub, Perc Endo
04104J1	Bypass Abd Aorta to Celiac Art w Synth Sub, Perc Endo
04104J2	Bypass Abd Aorta to Mesent Art w Synth Sub, Perc Endo
04104J6	Bypass Abd Aorta to Rt Com Ilia w Synth Sub, Perc Endo
04104J7	Bypass Abd Aorta to Lt Com Ilia w Synth Sub, Perc Endo
04104J8	Bypass Abd Aorta to Bilat Com Ilia w Synth Sub, Perc Endo
04104J9	Bypass Abd Aorta to Rt Int Ilia w Synth Sub, Perc Endo
04104JB	Bypass Abd Aorta to Lt Int Ilia w Synth Sub, Perc Endo
04104JC	Bypass Abd Aorta to Bilat Int Ilia w Synth Sub, Perc Endo
04104JD	Bypass Abd Aorta to Rt Ext Ilia w Synth Sub, Perc Endo
04104JF	Bypass Abd Aorta to Lt Ext Ilia w Synth Sub, Perc Endo
04104JG	Bypass Abd Aorta to Bilat Ext Ilia w Synth Sub, Perc Endo
04104JH	Bypass Abd Aorta to Rt Femor A w Synth Sub, Perc Endo
04104JJ	Bypass Abd Aorta to Lt Femor A w Synth Sub, Perc Endo
04104JK	Bypass Abd Aorta to Bilat Femor A w Synth Sub, Perc Endo
04104JQ	Bypass Abd Aorta to Low Ex Art w Synth Sub, Perc Endo
04104JR	Bypass Abd Aorta to Low Art w Synth Sub, Perc Endo
04104K0	Bypass Abd Aorta to Abd Aorta w Nonaut Sub, Perc Endo
04104K1	Bypass Abd Aorta to Celiac Art w Nonaut Sub, Perc Endo
04104K2	Bypass Abd Aorta to Mesent Art w Nonaut Sub, Perc Endo
04104K6	Bypass Abd Aorta to Rt Com Ilia w Nonaut Sub, Perc Endo
04104K7	Bypass Abd Aorta to Lt Com Ilia w Nonaut Sub, Perc Endo
04104K8	Bypass Abd Aorta to Bilat Com Ilia w Nonaut Sub, Perc Endo
04104K9	Bypass Abd Aorta to Rt Int Ilia w Nonaut Sub, Perc Endo
04104KB	Bypass Abd Aorta to Lt Int Ilia w Nonaut Sub, Perc Endo
04104KC	Bypass Abd Aorta to Bilat Int Ilia w Nonaut Sub, Perc Endo
04104KD	Bypass Abd Aorta to Rt Ext Ilia w Nonaut Sub, Perc Endo
04104KF	Bypass Abd Aorta to Lt Ext Ilia w Nonaut Sub, Perc Endo
04104KG	Bypass Abd Aorta to Bilat Ext Ilia w Nonaut Sub, Perc Endo
04104KH	Bypass Abd Aorta to Rt Femor A w Nonaut Sub, Perc Endo
04104KJ	Bypass Abd Aorta to Lt Femor A w Nonaut Sub, Perc Endo
04104KK	Bypass Abd Aorta to Bilat Femor A w Nonaut Sub, Perc Endo
04104KQ	Bypass Abd Aorta to Low Ex Art w Nonaut Sub, Perc Endo
04104KR	Bypass Abd Aorta to Low Art w Nonaut Sub, Perc Endo
04104Z0	Bypass Abd Aorta to Abd Aorta, Perc Endo Appr
04104Z1	Bypass Abd Aorta to Celiac Artery, Perc Endo Appr

04104Z2	Bypass Abd Aorta to Mesent Art, Perc Endo Appr
04104Z6	Bypass Abd Aorta to Rt Com Ilia, Perc Endo Appr
04104Z7	Bypass Abd Aorta to Lt Com Ilia, Perc Endo Appr
04104Z8	Bypass Abd Aorta to Bilat Com Ilia, Perc Endo Appr
04104Z9	Bypass Abd Aorta to Rt Int Ilia, Perc Endo Appr
04104ZB	Bypass Abd Aorta to Lt Int Ilia, Perc Endo Appr
04104ZC	Bypass Abd Aorta to Bilat Int Ilia, Perc Endo Appr
04104ZD	Bypass Abd Aorta to Rt Ext Ilia, Perc Endo Appr
04104ZF	Bypass Abd Aorta to Lt Ext Ilia, Perc Endo Appr
04104ZG	Bypass Abd Aorta to Bilat Ext Ilia, Perc Endo Appr
04104ZH	Bypass Abd Aorta to Rt Femor A, Perc Endo Appr
04104ZJ	Bypass Abd Aorta to Lt Femor A, Perc Endo Appr
04104ZK	Bypass Abd Aorta to Bilat Femor A, Perc Endo Appr
04104ZQ	Bypass Abd Aorta to Low Ex Art, Perc Endo Appr
04104ZR	Bypass Abd Aorta to Lwr Artery, Perc Endo Appr
0414[0,4][9,A,J,K,Z][3,4,5]	Bypass/Splenic Artery, [Opn, Perc Endo], [Auto Venous Tissue, Auto Arterial Tissue, Synth Sub, Nonauto Tissue Sub, No Dev], [Renal Artery, Rt, Renal Artery, Lt, Renal Artery, Bilat]
041C*	Bypass/Common Iliac Artery, Rt
041D*	Bypass/Common Iliac Artery, Lt
041E*	Bypass/Int Iliac Artery, Rt
041F*	Bypass/Int Iliac Artery, Lt
041H*	Bypass/Ext Iliac Artery, Rt
041J*	Bypass/Ext Iliac Artery, Lt
0451[0,3,4]ZZ	Destr/Celiac Artery, [Opn, Perc, Perc Endo]
0452[0,3,4]ZZ	Destr/Gastric Artery, [Opn, Perc, Perc Endo]
0453[0,3,4]ZZ	Destr/Hepatic Artery, [Opn, Perc, Perc Endo]
0454[0,3,4]ZZ	Destr/Splenic Artery, [Opn, Perc, Perc Endo]
0455[0,3,4]ZZ	Destr/Superior Mesenteric Artery, [Opn, Perc, Perc Endo]
0456[0,3,4]ZZ	Destr/Colic Artery, Rt, [Opn, Perc, Perc Endo]
0457[0,3,4]ZZ	Destr/Colic Artery, Lt, [Opn, Perc, Perc Endo]
0458[0,3,4]ZZ	Destr/Colic Artery, Mid, [Opn, Perc, Perc Endo]
0459[0,3,4]ZZ	Destr/Renal Artery, Rt, [Opn, Perc, Perc Endo]
045A[0,3,4]ZZ	Destr/Renal Artery, Lt, [Opn, Perc, Perc Endo]
045B[0,3,4]ZZ	Destr/Inferior Mesenteric Artery, [Opn, Perc, Perc Endo]
045C[0,3,4]ZZ	Destr/Common Iliac Artery, Rt, [Opn, Perc, Perc Endo]
045D[0,3,4]ZZ	Destr/Common Iliac Artery, Lt, [Opn, Perc, Perc Endo]
045E[0,3,4]ZZ	Destr/Int Iliac Artery, Rt, [Opn, Perc, Perc Endo]
045F[0,3,4]ZZ	Destr/Int Iliac Artery, Lt, [Opn, Perc, Perc Endo]
045H[0,3,4]ZZ	Destr/Ext Iliac Artery, Rt, [Opn, Perc, Perc Endo]
045J[0,3,4]ZZ	Destr/Ext Iliac Artery, Lt, [Opn, Perc, Perc Endo]
04B1[0,3,4]ZZ	Exc/Celiac Artery, [Opn, Perc, Perc Endo]
04B2[0,3,4]ZZ	Exc/Gastric Artery, [Opn, Perc, Perc Endo]
04B3[0,3,4]ZZ	Exc/Hepatic Artery, [Opn, Perc, Perc Endo]
04B4[0,3,4]ZZ	Exc/Splenic Artery, [Opn, Perc, Perc Endo]
04B5[0,3,4]ZZ	Exc/Superior Mesenteric Artery, [Opn, Perc, Perc Endo]
04B6[0,3,4]ZZ	Exc/Colic Artery, Rt, [Opn, Perc, Perc Endo]
04B7[0,3,4]ZZ	Exc/Colic Artery, Lt, [Opn, Perc, Perc Endo]
04B8[0,3,4]ZZ	Exc/Colic Artery, Mid, [Opn, Perc, Perc Endo]
04B9[0,3,4]ZZ	Exc/Renal Artery, Rt, [Opn, Perc, Perc Endo]
04BA[0,3,4]ZZ	Exc/Renal Artery, Lt, [Opn, Perc, Perc Endo]
04BB[0,3,4]ZZ	Exc/Inferior Mesenteric Artery, [Opn, Perc, Perc Endo]
04BC[0,3,4]ZZ	Exc/Common Iliac Artery, Rt, [Opn, Perc, Perc Endo]
04BD[0,3,4]ZZ	Exc/Common Iliac Artery, Lt, [Opn, Perc, Perc Endo]
04BE[0,3,4]ZZ	Exc/Int Iliac Artery, Rt, [Opn, Perc, Perc Endo]
04BF[0,3,4]ZZ	Exc/Int Iliac Artery, Lt, [Opn, Perc, Perc Endo]
04BH[0,3,4]ZZ	Exc/Ext Iliac Artery, Rt, [Opn, Perc, Perc Endo]
04BJ[0,3,4]ZZ	Exc/Ext Iliac Artery, Lt, [Opn, Perc, Perc Endo]
04C1[0,3,4]ZZ	Extir/Celiac Artery, [Opn, Perc, Perc Endo]
04C2[0,3,4]ZZ	Extir/Gastric Artery, [Opn, Perc, Perc Endo]
04C3[0,3,4]ZZ	Extir/Hepatic Artery, [Opn, Perc, Perc Endo]
04C4[0,3,4]ZZ	Extir/Splenic Artery, [Opn, Perc, Perc Endo]
04C5[0,3,4]ZZ	Extir/Superior Mesenteric Artery, [Opn, Perc, Perc Endo]
04C6[0,3,4]ZZ	Extir/Colic Artery, Rt, [Opn, Perc, Perc Endo]
04C7[0,3,4]ZZ	Extir/Colic Artery, Lt, [Opn, Perc, Perc Endo]
04C8[0,3,4]ZZ	Extir/Colic Artery, Mid, [Opn, Perc, Perc Endo]
04C9[0,3,4]ZZ	Extir/Renal Artery, Rt, [Opn, Perc, Perc Endo]
04CA[0,3,4]ZZ	Extir/Renal Artery, Lt, [Opn, Perc, Perc Endo]
04CB[0,3,4]ZZ	Extir/Inferior Mesenteric Artery, [Opn, Perc, Perc Endo]
04CC[0,3,4]ZZ	Extir/Common Iliac Artery, Rt, [Opn, Perc, Perc Endo]
04CD[0,3,4]ZZ	Extir/Common Iliac Artery, Lt, [Opn, Perc, Perc Endo]
04CE[0,3,4]ZZ	Extir/Int Iliac Artery, Rt, [Opn, Perc, Perc Endo]
04CF[0,3,4]ZZ	Extir/Int Iliac Artery, Lt, [Opn, Perc, Perc Endo]
04CH[0,3,4]ZZ	Extir/Ext Iliac Artery, Rt, [Opn, Perc, Perc Endo]
04CJ[0,3,4]ZZ	Extir/Ext Iliac Artery, Lt, [Opn, Perc, Perc Endo]
04L1[0,3,4][C,D,Z]Z	Occlsn/Celiac Artery, [Opn, Perc, Perc Endo], [Extralum Dev, Intralum Dev, No Dev], NQ
04L2[0,3,4][C,Z]Z	Occlsn/Gastric Artery, [Opn, Perc, Perc Endo], [Extralum Dev, No Dev], NQ
04L2[0,4]DZ	Occlsn/Gastric Artery, [Opn, Perc Endo], Intralum Dev, NQ

Surgical   **Medical**   **CC Indicator**   **MCC Indicator**   **Procedure Proxy**   **PDxMCC** PDx acts as own MCC   **PDxCC** PDx acts as own CC

MDC 5: Diseases And Disorders Of The Circulatory System—SURGICAL

04L3[0,3,4][C,D,Z]Z Occlsn/Hepatic Artery, [Opn, Perc, Perc Endo], [Extralum Dev, Intralum Dev, No Dev], NQ

04L4[0,3,4][C,D,Z]Z Occlsn/Splenic Artery, [Opn, Perc, Perc Endo], [Extralum Dev, Intralum Dev, No Dev], NQ

04L5[0,3,4][C,D,Z]Z Occlsn/Superior Mesenteric Artery, [Opn, Perc, Perc Endo], [Extralum Dev, Intralum Dev, No Dev], NQ

04L6[0,3,4][C,D,Z]Z Occlsn/Colic Artery, Rt, [Opn, Perc, Perc Endo], [Extralum Dev, Intralum Dev, No Dev], NQ

04L7[0,3,4][C,D,Z]Z Occlsn/Colic Artery, Lt, [Opn, Perc, Perc Endo], [Extralum Dev, Intralum Dev, No Dev], NQ

04L8[0,3,4][C,D,Z]Z Occlsn/Colic Artery, Mid, [Opn, Perc, Perc Endo], [Extralum Dev, Intralum Dev, No Dev], NQ

04L9[0,3,4][C,D,Z]Z Occlsn/Renal Artery, Rt, [Opn, Perc, Perc Endo], [Extralum Dev, Intralum Dev, No Dev], NQ

04LA[0,3,4][C,D,Z]Z Occlsn/Renal Artery, Lt, [Opn, Perc, Perc Endo], [Extralum Dev, Intralum Dev, No Dev], NQ

04LB[0,3,4][C,D,Z]Z Occlsn/Inferior Mesenteric Artery, [Opn, Perc, Perc Endo], [Extralum Dev, Intralum Dev, No Dev], NQ

04LC[0,3,4][C,D,Z]Z Occlsn/Common Iliac Artery, Rt, [Opn, Perc, Perc Endo], [Extralum Dev, Intralum Dev, No Dev], NQ

04LD[0,3,4][C,D,Z]ZOcclsn/Common Iliac Artery, Lt, [Opn, Perc, Perc Endo], [Extralum Dev, Intralum Dev, No Dev], NQ

04LE[0,3,4][C,D,Z]Z Occlsn/Int Iliac Artery, Rt, [Opn, Perc, Perc Endo], [Extralum Dev, Intralum Dev, No Dev], NQ

04LF[0,3,4][C,D,Z]Z Occlsn/Int Iliac Artery, Lt, [Opn, Perc, Perc Endo], [Extralum Dev, Intralum Dev, No Dev], NQ

04LH[0,3,4][C,D,Z]Z Occlsn/Ext Iliac Artery, Rt, [Opn, Perc, Perc Endo], [Extralum Dev, Intralum Dev, No Dev], NQ

04LJ[0,3,4][C,D,Z]Z Occlsn/Ext Iliac Artery, Lt, [Opn, Perc, Perc Endo], [Extralum Dev, Intralum Dev, No Dev], NQ

04R1[0,4][7,J,K]Z Replace/Celiac Artery, [Opn, Perc Endo], [Auto Tissue Sub, Synth Sub, Nonauto Tissue Sub], NQ

04R2[0,4][7,J,K]Z Replace/Gastric Artery, [Opn, Perc Endo], [Auto Tissue Sub, Synth Sub, Nonauto Tissue Sub], NQ

04R3[0,4][7,J,K]Z Replace/Hepatic Artery, [Opn, Perc Endo], [Auto Tissue Sub, Synth Sub, Nonauto Tissue Sub], NQ

04R4[0,4][7,J,K]Z Replace/Splenic Artery, [Opn, Perc Endo], [Auto Tissue Sub, Synth Sub, Nonauto Tissue Sub], NQ

04R5[0,4][7,J,K]Z Replace/Superior Mesenteric Artery, [Opn, Perc Endo], [Auto Tissue Sub, Synth Sub, Nonauto Tissue Sub], NQ

04R6[0,4][7,J,K]Z Replace/Colic Artery, Rt, [Opn, Perc Endo], [Auto Tissue Sub, Synth Sub, Nonauto Tissue Sub], NQ

04R7[0,4][7,J,K]Z Replace/Colic Artery, Lt, [Opn, Perc Endo], [Auto Tissue Sub, Synth Sub, Nonauto Tissue Sub], NQ

04R8[0,4][7,J,K]Z Replace/Colic Artery, Mid, [Opn, Perc Endo], [Auto Tissue Sub, Synth Sub, Nonauto Tissue Sub], NQ

04R9[0,4][7,J,K]Z Replace/Renal Artery, Rt, [Opn, Perc Endo], [Auto Tissue Sub, Synth Sub, Nonauto Tissue Sub], NQ

04RA[0,4][7,J,K]Z Replace/Renal Artery, Lt, [Opn, Perc Endo], [Auto Tissue Sub, Synth Sub, Nonauto Tissue Sub], NQ

04RB[0,4][7,J,K]Z Replace/Inferior Mesenteric Artery, [Opn, Perc Endo], [Auto Tissue Sub, Synth Sub, Nonauto Tissue Sub], NQ

04RC[0,4][7,J,K]Z Replace/Common Iliac Artery, Rt, [Opn, Perc Endo], [Auto Tissue Sub, Synth Sub, Nonauto Tissue Sub], NQ

04RD[0,4][7,J,K]Z Replace/Common Iliac Artery, Lt, [Opn, Perc Endo], [Auto Tissue Sub, Synth Sub, Nonauto Tissue Sub], NQ

04RE[0,4][7,J,K]Z Replace/Int Iliac Artery, Rt, [Opn, Perc Endo], [Auto Tissue Sub, Synth Sub, Nonauto Tissue Sub], NQ

04RF[0,4][7,J,K]Z Replace/Int Iliac Artery, Lt, [Opn, Perc Endo], [Auto Tissue Sub, Synth Sub, Nonauto Tissue Sub], NQ

04RH[0,4][7,J,K]Z Replace/Ext Iliac Artery, Rt, [Opn, Perc Endo], [Auto Tissue Sub, Synth Sub, Nonauto Tissue Sub], NQ

04RJ[0,4][7,J,K]Z Replace/Ext Iliac Artery, Lt, [Opn, Perc Endo], [Auto Tissue Sub, Synth Sub, Nonauto Tissue Sub], NQ

04V00DZ Restrict of Abd Aorta with Intralum Dev, Opn Appr

04V00ZZ Restrict of Abd Aorta, Opn Appr

04V03ZZ Restrict of Abd Aorta, Perc Appr

04V04ZZ Restrict of Abd Aorta, Perc Endo Appr

04V1[0,3,4][D,Z]Z Restrict/Celiac Artery, [Opn, Perc, Perc Endo], [Intralum Dev, No Dev], NQ

04V2[0,3,4][D,Z]Z Restrict/Gastric Artery, [Opn, Perc, Perc Endo], [Intralum Dev, No Dev], NQ

04V3[0,3,4][D,Z]Z Restrict/Hepatic Artery, [Opn, Perc, Perc Endo], [Intralum Dev, No Dev], NQ

04V4[0,3,4][D,Z]Z Restrict/Splenic Artery, [Opn, Perc, Perc Endo], [Intralum Dev, No Dev], NQ

04V5[0,3,4][D,Z]Z Restrict/Superior Mesenteric Artery, [Opn, Perc, Perc Endo], [Intralum Dev, No Dev], NQ

04V6[0,3,4][D,Z]Z Restrict/Colic Artery, Rt, [Opn, Perc, Perc Endo], [Intralum Dev, No Dev], NQ

04V7[0,3,4][D,Z]Z Restrict/Colic Artery, Lt, [Opn, Perc, Perc Endo], [Intralum Dev, No Dev], NQ

04V8[0,3,4][D,Z]Z Restrict/Colic Artery, Mid, [Opn, Perc, Perc Endo], [Intralum Dev, No Dev], NQ

04V9[0,3,4][D,Z]Z Restrict/Renal Artery, Rt, [Opn, Perc, Perc Endo], [Intralum Dev, No Dev], NQ

04VA[0,3,4][D,Z]Z Restrict/Renal Artery, Lt, [Opn, Perc, Perc Endo], [Intralum Dev, No Dev], NQ

04VB[0,3,4][D,Z]Z Restrict/Inferior Mesenteric Artery, [Opn, Perc, Perc Endo], [Intralum Dev, No Dev], NQ

04VC[0,3,4][D,Z]Z Restrict/Common Iliac Artery, Rt, [Opn, Perc, Perc Endo], [Intralum Dev, No Dev], NQ

04VD[0,3,4][D,Z]Z Restrict/Common Iliac Artery, Lt, [Opn, Perc, Perc Endo], [Intralum Dev, No Dev], NQ

04VE[0,3,4][D,Z]Z Restrict/Int Iliac Artery, Rt, [Opn, Perc, Perc Endo], [Intralum Dev, No Dev], NQ

04VF[0,3,4][D,Z]Z Restrict/Int Iliac Artery, Lt, [Opn, Perc, Perc Endo], [Intralum Dev, No Dev], NQ

04VH[0,3,4][D,Z]Z Restrict/Ext Iliac Artery, Rt, [Opn, Perc, Perc Endo], [Intralum Dev, No Dev], NQ

04VJ[0,3,4][D,Z]Z Restrict/Ext Iliac Artery, Lt, [Opn, Perc, Perc Endo], [Intralum Dev, No Dev], NQ

04VK[0,3,4][D,Z]Z Restrict/Femor Artery, Rt, [Opn, Perc, Perc Endo], [Intralum Dev, No Dev], NQ

04VL[0,3,4][D,Z]Z Restrict/Femor Artery, Lt, [Opn, Perc, Perc Endo], [Intralum Dev, No Dev], NQ

04VM[0,3,4][D,Z]Z Restrict/Popliteal Artery, Rt, [Opn, Perc, Perc Endo], [Intralum Dev, No Dev], NQ

04VN[0,3,4][D,Z]Z Restrict/Popliteal Artery, Lt, [Opn, Perc, Perc Endo], [Intralum Dev, No Dev], NQ

04VP[0,3,4][D,Z]Z Restrict/Ant Tibial Artery, Rt, [Opn, Perc, Perc Endo], [Intralum Dev, No Dev], NQ

04VQ[0,3,4][D,Z]Z Restrict/Ant Tibial Artery, Lt, [Opn, Perc, Perc Endo], [Intralum Dev, No Dev], NQ

04VR[0,3,4][D,Z]Z Restrict/Post Tibial Artery, Rt, [Opn, Perc, Perc Endo], [Intralum Dev, No Dev], NQ

04VS[0,3,4][D,Z]Z Restrict/Post Tibial Artery, Lt, [Opn, Perc, Perc Endo], [Intralum Dev, No Dev], NQ

04VT[0,3,4][D,Z]Z Restrict/Peroneal Artery, Rt, [Opn, Perc, Perc Endo], [Intralum Dev, No Dev], NQ

04VU[0,3,4][D,Z]Z Restrict/Peroneal Artery, Lt, [Opn, Perc, Perc Endo], [Intralum Dev, No Dev], NQ

04VV[0,3,4][D,Z]Z Restrict/Foot Artery, Rt, [Opn, Perc, Perc Endo], [Intralum Dev, No Dev], NQ

04VW[0,3,4][D,Z]ZRestrict/Foot Artery, Lt, [Opn, Perc, Perc Endo], [Intralum Dev, No Dev], NQ

04VY[0,3,4][D,Z]Z Restrict/Lwr Artery, [Opn, Perc, Perc Endo], [Intralum Dev, No Dev], NQ

0510[0,4][7,9,A,J,K,Z]Y Bypass/Azygos Vein, [Opn, Perc Endo], [Auto Tissue Sub, Auto Venous Tissue, Auto Arterial Tissue, Synth Sub, Nonauto Tissue Sub, No Dev], Upr Vein

0511[0,4][7,9,A,J,K,Z]Y Bypass/Hemiazygos Vein, [Opn, Perc Endo], [Auto Tissue Sub, Auto Venous Tissue, Auto Arterial Tissue, Synth Sub, Nonauto Tissue Sub, No Dev], Upr Vein

0513[0,4][7,9,A,J,K,Z]Y Bypass/Innominate Vein, Rt, [Opn, Perc Endo], [Auto Tissue Sub, Auto Venous Tissue, Auto Arterial Tissue, Synth Sub, Nonauto Tissue Sub, No Dev], Upr Vein

0514[0,4][7,9,A,J,K,Z]Y Bypass/Innominate Vein, Lt, [Opn, Perc Endo], [Auto Tissue Sub, Auto Venous Tissue, Auto Arterial Tissue, Synth Sub, Nonauto Tissue Sub, No Dev], Upr Vein

0515[0,4][7,9,A,J,K,Z]Y Bypass/Subclavian Vein, Rt, [Opn, Perc Endo], [Auto Tissue Sub, Auto Venous Tissue, Auto Arterial Tissue, Synth Sub, Nonauto Tissue Sub, No Dev], Upr Vein

0516[0,4][7,9,A,J,K,Z]Y Bypass/Subclavian Vein, Lt, [Opn, Perc Endo], [Auto Tissue Sub, Auto Venous Tissue, Auto Arterial Tissue, Synth Sub, Nonauto Tissue Sub, No Dev], Upr Vein

0550[0,3,4]ZZ Destr/Azygos Vein, [Opn, Perc, Perc Endo]

0551[0,3,4]ZZ Destr/Hemiazygos Vein, [Opn, Perc, Perc Endo]

0553[0,3,4]ZZ Destr/Innominate Vein, Rt, [Opn, Perc, Perc Endo]

0554[0,3,4]ZZ Destr/Innominate Vein, Lt, [Opn, Perc, Perc Endo]

0555[0,3,4]ZZ Destr/Subclavian Vein, Rt, [Opn, Perc, Perc Endo]

0556[0,3,4]ZZ Destr/Subclavian Vein, Lt, [Opn, Perc, Perc Endo]

05B0[0,3,4]ZZ Exc/Azygos Vein, [Opn, Perc, Perc Endo]

05B1[0,3,4]ZZ Exc/Hemiazygos Vein, [Opn, Perc, Perc Endo]

05B3[0,3,4]ZZ Exc/Innominate Vein, Rt, [Opn, Perc, Perc Endo]

05B4[0,3,4]ZZ Exc/Innominate Vein, Lt, [Opn, Perc, Perc Endo]

05B5[0,3,4]ZZ Exc/Subclavian Vein, Rt, [Opn, Perc, Perc Endo]

05B6[0,3,4]ZZ Exc/Subclavian Vein, Lt, [Opn, Perc, Perc Endo]

05C0[0,3,4]ZZ Extir/Azygos Vein, [Opn, Perc, Perc Endo]

05C1[0,3,4]ZZ Extir/Hemiazygos Vein, [Opn, Perc, Perc Endo]

T Transfer DRG SP Special Payment * Code Range **6th and 7th Character of ZZ = No Device, No Qualifier ZX = No Device, Diagnostic**

05C3[0,3,4]ZZ   Extir/Innominate Vein, Rt, [Opn, Perc, Perc Endo]
05C4[0,3,4]ZZ   Extir/Innominate Vein, Lt, [Opn, Perc, Perc Endo]
05C5[0,3,4]ZZ   Extir/Subclavian Vein, Rt, [Opn, Perc, Perc Endo]
05C6[0,3,4]ZZ   Extir/Subclavian Vein, Lt, [Opn, Perc, Perc Endo]
05L0[0,3,4][C,D,Z]Z Occlsn/Azygos Vein, [Opn, Perc, Perc Endo], [Extralum Dev, Intralum Dev, No Dev], NQ
05L1[0,3,4][C,D,Z]Z Occlsn/Hemiazygos Vein, [Opn, Perc, Perc Endo], [Extralum Dev, Intralum Dev, No Dev], NQ
05L3[0,3,4][C,D,Z]Z Occlsn/Innominate Vein, Rt, [Opn, Perc, Perc Endo], [Extralum Dev, Intralum Dev, No Dev], NQ
05L4[0,3,4][C,D,Z]Z Occlsn/Innominate Vein, Lt, [Opn, Perc, Perc Endo], [Extralum Dev, Intralum Dev, No Dev], NQ
05L5[0,3,4][C,D,Z]Z Occlsn/Subclavian Vein, Rt, [Opn, Perc, Perc Endo], [Extralum Dev, Intralum Dev, No Dev], NQ
05L6[0,3,4][C,D,Z]Z Occlsn/Subclavian Vein, Lt, [Opn, Perc, Perc Endo], [Extralum Dev, Intralum Dev, No Dev], NQ
05V0[0,3,4][D,Z]Z Restrict/Azygos Vein, [Opn, Perc, Perc Endo], [Intralum Dev, No Dev], NQ
05V1[0,3,4][D,Z]Z Restrict/Hemiazygos Vein, [Opn, Perc, Perc Endo], [Intralum Dev, No Dev], NQ
05V3[0,3,4][D,Z]Z Restrict/Innominate Vein, Rt, [Opn, Perc, Perc Endo], [Intralum Dev, No Dev], NQ
05V4[0,3,4][D,Z]Z Restrict/Innominate Vein, Lt, [Opn, Perc, Perc Endo], [Intralum Dev, No Dev], NQ
05V5[0,3,4][D,Z]Z Restrict/Subclavian Vein, Rt, [Opn, Perc, Perc Endo], [Intralum Dev, No Dev], NQ
05V6[0,3,4][D,Z]Z Restrict/Subclavian Vein, Lt, [Opn, Perc, Perc Endo], [Intralum Dev, No Dev], NQ
05V7[0,3,4][D,Z]Z Restrict/Axillary Vein, Rt, [Opn, Perc, Perc Endo], [Intralum Dev, No Dev], NQ
05V8[0,3,4][D,Z]Z Restrict/Axillary Vein, Lt, [Opn, Perc, Perc Endo], [Intralum Dev, No Dev], NQ
05V9[0,3,4][D,Z]Z Restrict/Brachial Vein, Rt, [Opn, Perc, Perc Endo], [Intralum Dev, No Dev], NQ
05VA[0,3,4][D,Z]Z Restrict/Brachial Vein, Lt, [Opn, Perc, Perc Endo], [Intralum Dev, No Dev], NQ
05VB[0,3,4][D,Z]Z Restrict/Basilic Vein, Rt, [Opn, Perc, Perc Endo], [Intralum Dev, No Dev], NQ
05VC[0,3,4][D,Z]Z Restrict/Basilic Vein, Lt, [Opn, Perc, Perc Endo], [Intralum Dev, No Dev], NQ
05VD[0,3,4][D,Z]Z Restrict/Cephalic Vein, Rt, [Opn, Perc, Perc Endo], [Intralum Dev, No Dev], NQ
05VF[0,3,4][D,Z]Z Restrict/Cephalic Vein, Lt, [Opn, Perc, Perc Endo], [Intralum Dev, No Dev], NQ
05VG[0,3,4][D,Z]Z Restrict/Hand Vein, Rt, [Opn, Perc, Perc Endo], [Intralum Dev, No Dev], NQ
05VH[0,3,4][D,Z]Z Restrict/Hand Vein, Lt, [Opn, Perc, Perc Endo], [Intralum Dev, No Dev], NQ
05VL[0,3,4][D,Z]Z Restrict/Intracranial Vein, [Opn, Perc, Perc Endo], [Intralum Dev, No Dev], NQ
05VM[0,3,4][D,Z]Z Restrict/Int Jugular Vein, Rt, [Opn, Perc, Perc Endo], [Intralum Dev, No Dev], NQ
05VN[0,3,4][D,Z]Z Restrict/Int Jugular Vein, Lt, [Opn, Perc, Perc Endo], [Intralum Dev, No Dev], NQ
05VP[0,3,4][D,Z]Z Restrict/Ext Jugular Vein, Rt, [Opn, Perc, Perc Endo], [Intralum Dev, No Dev], NQ
05VQ[0,3,4][D,Z]Z Restrict/Ext Jugular Vein, Lt, [Opn, Perc, Perc Endo], [Intralum Dev, No Dev], NQ
05VR[0,3,4][D,Z]Z Restrict/Vert Vein, Rt, [Opn, Perc, Perc Endo], [Intralum Dev, No Dev], NQ
05VS[0,3,4][D,Z]Z Restrict/Vert Vein, Lt, [Opn, Perc, Perc Endo], [Intralum Dev, No Dev], NQ
05VT[0,3,4][D,Z]Z Restrict/Face Vein, Rt, [Opn, Perc, Perc Endo], [Intralum Dev, No Dev], NQ
05VV[0,3,4][D,Z]Z Restrict/Face Vein, Lt, [Opn, Perc, Perc Endo], [Intralum Dev, No Dev], NQ
05VY[0,3,4][D,Z]Z Restrict/Upr Vein, [Opn, Perc, Perc Endo], [Intralum Dev, No Dev], NQ
0610*   Bypass/Inferior Vena Cava
0611*   Bypass/Splenic Vein
0612*   Bypass/Gastric Vein
0614*   Bypass/Hepatic Vein
0615*   Bypass/Superior Mesenteric Vein
0616*   Bypass/Inferior Mesenteric Vein
0617*   Bypass/Colic Vein
0618*   Bypass/Portal Vein
0619*   Bypass/Renal Vein, Rt
061B*   Bypass/Renal Vein, Lt
061J*   Bypass/Hypogastric Vein, Lt
0650[0,3,4]ZZ   Destr/Inferior Vena Cava, [Opn, Perc, Perc Endo]

0651[0,3,4]ZZ   Destr/Splenic Vein, [Opn, Perc, Perc Endo]
0652[0,3,4]ZZ   Destr/Gastric Vein, [Opn, Perc, Perc Endo]
0654[0,3,4]ZZ   Destr/Hepatic Vein, [Opn, Perc, Perc Endo]
0655[0,3,4]ZZ   Destr/Superior Mesenteric Vein, [Opn, Perc, Perc Endo]
0656[0,3,4]ZZ   Destr/Inferior Mesenteric Vein, [Opn, Perc, Perc Endo]
0657[0,3,4]ZZ   Destr/Colic Vein, [Opn, Perc, Perc Endo]
0658[0,3,4]ZZ   Destr/Portal Vein, [Opn, Perc, Perc Endo]
0659[0,3,4]ZZ   Destr/Renal Vein, Rt, [Opn, Perc, Perc Endo]
065B[0,3,4]ZZ   Destr/Renal Vein, Lt, [Opn, Perc, Perc Endo]
065C[0,3,4]ZZ   Destr/Common Iliac Vein, Rt, [Opn, Perc, Perc Endo]
065D[0,3,4]ZZ   Destr/Common Iliac Vein, Lt, [Opn, Perc, Perc Endo]
065F[0,3,4]ZZ   Destr/Ext Iliac Vein, Rt, [Opn, Perc, Perc Endo]
065G[0,3,4]ZZ   Destr/Ext Iliac Vein, Lt, [Opn, Perc, Perc Endo]
065H[0,3,4]ZZ   Destr/Hypogastric Vein, Rt, [Opn, Perc, Perc Endo]
065J[0,3,4]ZZ   Destr/Hypogastric Vein, Lt, [Opn, Perc, Perc Endo]
06B0[0,3,4]ZZ   Exc/Inferior Vena Cava, [Opn, Perc, Perc Endo]
06B1[0,3,4]ZZ   Exc/Splenic Vein, [Opn, Perc, Perc Endo]
06B2[0,3,4]ZZ   Exc/Gastric Vein, [Opn, Perc, Perc Endo]
06B4[0,3,4]ZZ   Exc/Hepatic Vein, [Opn, Perc, Perc Endo]
06B5[0,3,4]ZZ   Exc/Superior Mesenteric Vein, [Opn, Perc, Perc Endo]
06B6[0,3,4]ZZ   Exc/Inferior Mesenteric Vein, [Opn, Perc, Perc Endo]
06B7[0,3,4]ZZ   Exc/Colic Vein, [Opn, Perc, Perc Endo]
06B8[0,3,4]ZZ   Exc/Portal Vein, [Opn, Perc, Perc Endo]
06B9[0,3,4]ZZ   Exc/Renal Vein, Rt, [Opn, Perc, Perc Endo]
06BB[0,3,4]ZZ   Exc/Renal Vein, Lt, [Opn, Perc, Perc Endo]
06BC[0,3,4]ZZ   Exc/Common Iliac Vein, Rt, [Opn, Perc, Perc Endo]
06BD[0,3,4]ZZ   Exc/Common Iliac Vein, Lt, [Opn, Perc, Perc Endo]
06BF[0,3,4]ZZ   Exc/Ext Iliac Vein, Rt, [Opn, Perc, Perc Endo]
06BG[0,3,4]ZZ   Exc/Ext Iliac Vein, Lt, [Opn, Perc, Perc Endo]
06BH[0,3,4]ZZ   Exc/Hypogastric Vein, Rt, [Opn, Perc, Perc Endo]
06BJ[0,3,4]ZZ   Exc/Hypogastric Vein, Lt, [Opn, Perc, Perc Endo]
06C0[0,3,4]ZZ   Extir/Inferior Vena Cava, [Opn, Perc, Perc Endo]
06C1[0,3,4]ZZ   Extir/Splenic Vein, [Opn, Perc, Perc Endo]
06C2[0,3,4]ZZ   Extir/Gastric Vein, [Opn, Perc, Perc Endo]
06C4[0,3,4]ZZ   Extir/Hepatic Vein, [Opn, Perc, Perc Endo]
06C5[0,3,4]ZZ   Extir/Superior Mesenteric Vein, [Opn, Perc, Perc Endo]
06C6[0,3,4]ZZ   Extir/Inferior Mesenteric Vein, [Opn, Perc, Perc Endo]
06C7[0,3,4]ZZ   Extir/Colic Vein, [Opn, Perc, Perc Endo]
06C8[0,3,4]ZZ   Extir/Portal Vein, [Opn, Perc, Perc Endo]
06C9[0,3,4]ZZ   Extir/Renal Vein, Rt, [Opn, Perc, Perc Endo]
06CB[0,3,4]ZZ   Extir/Renal Vein, Lt, [Opn, Perc, Perc Endo]
06CC[0,3,4]ZZ   Extir/Common Iliac Vein, Rt, [Opn, Perc, Perc Endo]
06CD[0,3,4]ZZ   Extir/Common Iliac Vein, Lt, [Opn, Perc, Perc Endo]
06CF[0,3,4]ZZ   Extir/Ext Iliac Vein, Rt, [Opn, Perc, Perc Endo]
06CG[0,3,4]ZZ   Extir/Ext Iliac Vein, Lt, [Opn, Perc, Perc Endo]
06CH[0,3,4]ZZ   Extir/Hypogastric Vein, Rt, [Opn, Perc, Perc Endo]
06CJ[0,3,4]ZZ   Extir/Hypogastric Vein, Lt, [Opn, Perc, Perc Endo]
06L1[0,3,4][C,D,Z]Z Occlsn/Splenic Vein, [Opn, Perc, Perc Endo], [Extralum Dev, Intralum Dev, No Dev], NQ
06L2[0,3,4][C,D,Z]Z Occlsn/Gastric Vein, [Opn, Perc, Perc Endo], [Extralum Dev, Intralum Dev, No Dev], NQ
06L3[0,3,4][C,D,Z]Z Occlsn/Esophageal Vein, [Opn, Perc, Perc Endo], [Extralum Dev, Intralum Dev, No Dev], NQ
06L4[0,3,4][C,D,Z]Z Occlsn/Hepatic Vein, [Opn, Perc, Perc Endo], [Extralum Dev, Intralum Dev, No Dev], NQ
06L5[0,3,4][C,D,Z]Z Occlsn/Superior Mesenteric Vein, [Opn, Perc, Perc Endo], [Extralum Dev, Intralum Dev, No Dev], NQ
06L6[0,3,4][C,D,Z]Z Occlsn/Inferior Mesenteric Vein, [Opn, Perc, Perc Endo], [Extralum Dev, Intralum Dev, No Dev], NQ
06L7[0,3,4][C,D,Z]Z Occlsn/Colic Vein, [Opn, Perc, Perc Endo], [Extralum Dev, Intralum Dev, No Dev], NQ
06L8[0,3,4][C,D,Z]Z Occlsn/Portal Vein, [Opn, Perc, Perc Endo], [Extralum Dev, Intralum Dev, No Dev], NQ
06L9[0,3,4][C,D,Z]Z Occlsn/Renal Vein, Rt, [Opn, Perc, Perc Endo], [Extralum Dev, Intralum Dev, No Dev], NQ
06LB[0,3,4][C,D,Z]Z Occlsn/Renal Vein, Lt, [Opn, Perc, Perc Endo], [Extralum Dev, Intralum Dev, No Dev], NQ
06LC[0,3,4][C,D,Z]Z Occlsn/Common Iliac Vein, Rt, [Opn, Perc, Perc Endo], [Extralum Dev, Intralum Dev, No Dev], NQ
06LD[0,3,4][C,D,Z]Z Occlsn/Common Iliac Vein, Lt, [Opn, Perc, Perc Endo], [Extralum Dev, Intralum Dev, No Dev], NQ
06LF[0,3,4][C,D,Z]Z Occlsn/Ext Iliac Vein, Rt, [Opn, Perc, Perc Endo], [Extralum Dev, Intralum Dev, No Dev], NQ
06LG[0,3,4][C,D,Z]Z Occlsn/Ext Iliac Vein, Lt, [Opn, Perc, Perc Endo], [Extralum Dev, Intralum Dev, No Dev], NQ
06LH[0,3,4][C,D,Z]Z Occlsn/Hypogastric Vein, Rt, [Opn, Perc, Perc Endo], [Extralum Dev, Intralum Dev, No Dev], NQ
06LJ[0,3,4][C,D,Z]Z Occlsn/Hypogastric Vein, Lt, [Opn, Perc, Perc Endo], [Extralum Dev, Intralum Dev, No Dev], NQ

Surgical   **Medical**   **CC Indicator**   **MCC Indicator**   **Procedure Proxy**   PDxMCC **PDx acts as own MCC**   PDxCC **PDx acts as own CC**

MDC 5: Diseases And Disorders Of The Circulatory System—SURGICAL

06R0[0,4][7,J,K]Z Replace/Inferior Vena Cava, [Opn, Perc Endo], [Auto Tissue Sub, Synth Sub, Nonauto Tissue Sub], NQ
06R1[0,4][7,J,K]Z Replace/Splenic Vein, [Opn, Perc Endo], [Auto Tissue Sub, Synth Sub, Nonauto Tissue Sub], NQ
06R2[0,4][7,J,K]Z Replace/Gastric Vein, [Opn, Perc Endo], [Auto Tissue Sub, Synth Sub, Nonauto Tissue Sub], NQ
06R4[0,4][7,J,K]Z Replace/Hepatic Vein, [Opn, Perc Endo], [Auto Tissue Sub, Synth Sub, Nonauto Tissue Sub], NQ
06R5[0,4][7,J,K]Z Replace/Superior Mesenteric Vein, [Opn, Perc Endo], [Auto Tissue Sub, Synth Sub, Nonauto Tissue Sub], NQ
06R6[0,4][7,J,K]Z Replace/Inferior Mesenteric Vein, [Opn, Perc Endo], [Auto Tissue Sub, Synth Sub, Nonauto Tissue Sub], NQ
06R7[0,4][7,J,K]Z Replace/Colic Vein, [Opn, Perc Endo], [Auto Tissue Sub, Synth Sub, Nonauto Tissue Sub], NQ
06R8[0,4][7,J,K]Z Replace/Portal Vein, [Opn, Perc Endo], [Auto Tissue Sub, Synth Sub, Nonauto Tissue Sub], NQ
06R9[0,4][7,J,K]Z Replace/Renal Vein, Rt, [Opn, Perc Endo], [Auto Tissue Sub, Synth Sub, Nonauto Tissue Sub], NQ
06RB[0,4][7,J,K]Z Replace/Renal Vein, Lt, [Opn, Perc Endo], [Auto Tissue Sub, Synth Sub, Nonauto Tissue Sub], NQ
06RC[0,4][7,J,K]Z Replace/Common Iliac Vein, Rt, [Opn, Perc Endo], [Auto Tissue Sub, Synth Sub, Nonauto Tissue Sub], NQ
06RD[0,4][7,J,K]Z Replace/Common Iliac Vein, Lt, [Opn, Perc Endo], [Auto Tissue Sub, Synth Sub, Nonauto Tissue Sub], NQ
06RF[0,4][7,J,K]Z Replace/Ext Iliac Vein, Rt, [Opn, Perc Endo], [Auto Tissue Sub, Synth Sub, Nonauto Tissue Sub], NQ
06RG[0,4][7,J,K]Z Replace/Ext Iliac Vein, Lt, [Opn, Perc Endo], [Auto Tissue Sub, Synth Sub, Nonauto Tissue Sub], NQ
06RH[0,4][7,J,K]Z Replace/Hypogastric Vein, Rt, [Opn, Perc Endo], [Auto Tissue Sub, Synth Sub, Nonauto Tissue Sub], NQ
06RJ[0,4][7,J,K]Z Replace/Hypogastric Vein, Lt, [Opn, Perc Endo], [Auto Tissue Sub, Synth Sub, Nonauto Tissue Sub], NQ
06V1[0,3,4][D,Z]Z Restrict/Splenic Vein, [Opn, Perc, Perc Endo], [Intralum Dev, No Dev], NQ
06V2[0,3,4][D,Z]Z Restrict/Gastric Vein, [Opn, Perc, Perc Endo], [Intralum Dev, No Dev], NQ
06V3[0,3,4][D,Z]Z Restrict/Esophageal Vein, [Opn, Perc, Perc Endo], [Intralum Dev, No Dev], NQ
06V4[0,3,4][D,Z]Z Restrict/Hepatic Vein, [Opn, Perc, Perc Endo], [Intralum Dev, No Dev], NQ
06V5[0,3,4][D,Z]Z Restrict/Superior Mesenteric Vein, [Opn, Perc, Perc Endo], [Intralum Dev, No Dev], NQ
06V6[0,3,4][D,Z]Z Restrict/Inferior Mesenteric Vein, [Opn, Perc, Perc Endo], [Intralum Dev, No Dev], NQ
06V7[0,3,4][D,Z]Z Restrict/Colic Vein, [Opn, Perc, Perc Endo], [Intralum Dev, No Dev], NQ
06V8[0,3,4][D,Z]Z Restrict/Portal Vein, [Opn, Perc, Perc Endo], [Intralum Dev, No Dev], NQ
06V9[0,3,4][D,Z]Z Restrict/Renal Vein, Rt, [Opn, Perc, Perc Endo], [Intralum Dev, No Dev], NQ
06VB[0,3,4][D,Z]Z Restrict/Renal Vein, Lt, [Opn, Perc, Perc Endo], [Intralum Dev, No Dev], NQ
06VC[0,3,4][D,Z]Z Restrict/Common Iliac Vein, Rt, [Opn, Perc, Perc Endo], [Intralum Dev, No Dev], NQ
06VD[0,3,4][D,Z]Z Restrict/Common Iliac Vein, Lt, [Opn, Perc, Perc Endo], [Intralum Dev, No Dev], NQ
06VF[0,3,4][D,Z]Z Restrict/Ext Iliac Vein, Rt, [Opn, Perc, Perc Endo], [Intralum Dev, No Dev], NQ
06VG[0,3,4][D,Z]Z Restrict/Ext Iliac Vein, Lt, [Opn, Perc, Perc Endo], [Intralum Dev, No Dev], NQ
06VH[0,3,4][D,Z]Z Restrict/Hypogastric Vein, Rt, [Opn, Perc, Perc Endo], [Intralum Dev, No Dev], NQ
06VJ[0,3,4][D,Z]Z Restrict/Hypogastric Vein, Lt, [Opn, Perc, Perc Endo], [Intralum Dev, No Dev], NQ
06VM[0,3,4][D,Z]Z Restrict/Femor Vein, Rt, [Opn, Perc, Perc Endo], [Intralum Dev, No Dev], NQ
06VN[0,3,4][D,Z]Z Restrict/Femor Vein, Lt, [Opn, Perc, Perc Endo], [Intralum Dev, No Dev], NQ
06VP[0,3,4][D,Z]Z Restrict/Greater Saphenous Vein, Rt, [Opn, Perc, Perc Endo], [Intralum Dev, No Dev], NQ
06VQ[0,3,4][D,Z]Z Restrict/Greater Saphenous Vein, Lt, [Opn, Perc, Perc Endo], [Intralum Dev, No Dev], NQ
06VR[0,3,4][D,Z]Z Restrict/Lesser Saphenous Vein, Rt, [Opn, Perc, Perc Endo], [Intralum Dev, No Dev], NQ
06VS[0,3,4][D,Z]Z Restrict/Lesser Saphenous Vein, Lt, [Opn, Perc, Perc Endo], [Intralum Dev, No Dev], NQ
06VT[0,3,4][D,Z]Z Restrict/Foot Vein, Rt, [Opn, Perc, Perc Endo], [Intralum Dev, No Dev], NQ
06VV[0,3,4][D,Z]Z Restrict/Foot Vein, Lt, [Opn, Perc, Perc Endo], [Intralum Dev, No Dev], NQ

06VY[0,3,4][D,Z]Z Restrict/Lwr Vein, [Opn, Perc, Perc Endo], [Intralum Dev, No Dev], NQ
0W9D0ZX Drain of Pericardial Cavity, Opn Appr, Diagnostic
0W9D0[0,Z]Z Drain/Pericardial Cavity, Opn, [Drain Dev, No Dev], NQ
0WCD[0,3,4]ZZ Extir/Pericardial Cavity, [Opn, Perc, Perc Endo]
0WFD[0,3,4,X]ZZ Fragmn/Pericardial Cavity, [Opn, Perc, Perc Endo, Ext]
0WHD[0,3,4][3,Y]Z Insert/Pericardial Cavity, [Opn, Perc, Perc Endo], [Inf Dev, Oth Dev], NQ
0WPD[0,3,4][0,1,3,Y]Z Rmvl/Pericardial Cavity, [Opn, Perc, Perc Endo], [Drain Dev, Radioact Elmt, Inf Dev, Oth Dev], NQ
0WWD[0,3,4][0,1,3,Y]Z Rev/Pericardial Cavity, [Opn, Perc, Perc Endo], [Drain Dev, Radioact Elmt, Inf Dev, Oth Dev], NQ
5A02[1,2]10 Assistance/Cardiac, [Intermittent, Continuous], Output, Balloon Pump

●DRG 271 Other Major Cardiovascular Procedures with CC
GMLOS 4.5   AMLOS 6.0   RW 3.1426

Select operating room procedures listed under DRG 270

●DRG 272 Other Major Cardiovascular Procedures without CC/MCC
GMLOS 2.3   AMLOS 3.1   RW 2.2508

Select operating room procedures listed under DRG 270

●DRG 273 Percutaneous Intracardiac Procedures with MCC
GMLOS 6.0   AMLOS 8.0   RW 3.5499   SP

Operating Room Procedures

Code	Description
02553ZZ	Destr of Atrial Septum, Perc Appr
02563ZZ	Destr of Rt Atrium, Perc Appr
02573ZZ	Destr of Lt Atrium, Perc Appr
02583ZZ	Destr of Conduction Mechanism, Perc Appr
02593ZZ	Destr of Chordae Tendineae, Perc Appr
025F3ZZ	Destr of Aortic Valve, Perc Appr
025G3ZZ	Destr of Mitral Valve, Perc Appr
025H3ZZ	Destr of Pulmn Valve, Perc Appr
025J3ZZ	Destr of Tricuspid Valve, Perc Appr
025K3ZZ	Destr of Rt Ventricle, Perc Appr
025L3ZZ	Destr of Lt Ventricle, Perc Appr
025M3ZZ	Destr of Ventricular Septum, Perc Appr
027F[3,4][4,D,Z]Z	Dilation/Aortic Valve, [Perc, Perc Endo], [Drug-eluting Intralum Dev, Intralum Dev, No Dev], NQ
027G[3,4][4,D,Z]Z	Dilation/Mitral Valve, [Perc, Perc Endo], [Drug-eluting Intralum Dev, Intralum Dev, No Dev], NQ
027H[3,4][4,D,Z]Z	Dilation/Pulmn Valve, [Perc, Perc Endo], [Drug-eluting Intralum Dev, Intralum Dev, No Dev], NQ
027J[3,4][4,D,Z]Z	Dilation/Tricuspid Valve, [Perc, Perc Endo], [Drug-eluting Intralum Dev, Intralum Dev, No Dev], NQ
02B53ZZ	Exc of Atrial Septum, Perc Appr
02B63ZZ	Exc of Rt Atrium, Perc Appr
02B73ZZ	Exc of Lt Atrium, Perc Appr
02B83ZZ	Exc of Conduction Mechanism, Perc Appr
02B93ZZ	Exc of Chordae Tendineae, Perc Appr
02BF3ZZ	Exc of Aortic Valve, Perc Appr
02BG3ZZ	Exc of Mitral Valve, Perc Appr
02BH3ZZ	Exc of Pulmn Valve, Perc Appr
02BJ3ZZ	Exc of Tricuspid Valve, Perc Appr
02BM3ZZ	Exc of Ventricular Septum, Perc Appr
02T83ZZ	Resect of Conduction Mechanism, Perc Appr
02U5[3,4]JZ	Supl/Atrial Septum, [Perc, Perc Endo], Synth Sub, NQ
02UG3JZ	Supl Mitral Valve with Synth Sub, Perc Appr

OR

Nonoperating Room Procedures

Code	Description
02573ZK	Destr of Lt Atrial Appendage, Perc Appr
02574ZK	Destr of Lt Atrial Appendage, Perc Endo Appr
02B73ZK	Exc of Lt Atrial Appendage, Perc Appr
02B74ZK	Exc of Lt Atrial Appendage, Perc Endo Appr
02K83ZZ	Map Conduction Mechanism, Perc Appr
02K84ZZ	Map Conduction Mechanism, Perc Endo Appr
02L73CK	Occlsn of LAA with Extralum Dev, Perc Appr
02L73DK	Occlsn of LAA with Intralum Dev, Perc Appr
02L73ZK	Occlsn of Lt Atrial Appendage, Perc Appr
02L74CK	Occlsn of LAA with Extralum Dev, Perc Endo Appr
02L74DK	Occlsn of LAA with Intralum Dev, Perc Endo Appr
02L74ZK	Occlsn of Lt Atrial Appendage, Perc Endo Appr
4A023FZ	Measurement of Cardiac Rhythm, Perc Appr

T Transfer DRG   SP Special Payment   * Code Range   6th and 7th Character of ZZ = No Device, No Qualifier ZX = No Device, Diagnostic

●**DRG 274   Percutaneous Intracardiac Procedures without MCC**
        GMLOS 2.7   AMLOS 3.4   RW 2.4197   [SP]

Select operating room procedures OR nonoperating room procedures listed under DRG 273

MEDICAL

DRG 280   Acute Myocardial Infarction, Discharged Alive with MCC
        GMLOS 4.5   AMLOS 5.8   RW 1.6971   [T]

Principal or Secondary Diagnosis
I21*   STEMI & NSTEMI mocard infrc
I22*   Subsq STEMI & NSTEMI mocard infrc

DRG 281   Acute Myocardial Infarction, Discharged Alive with CC
        GMLOS 2.9   AMLOS 3.6   RW 1.0232   [T]

Select Principal or Secondary Diagnosis listed under DRG 280

DRG 282   Acute Myocardial Infarction, Discharged Alive without CC/MCC
        GMLOS 2.0   AMLOS 2.4   RW 0.7557   [T]

Select Principal or Secondary Diagnosis listed under DRG 280

DRG 283   Acute Myocardial Infarction, Expired with MCC
        GMLOS 2.9   AMLOS 4.6   RW 1.6613

Select Principal or Secondary Diagnosis listed under DRG 280

DRG 284   Acute Myocardial Infarction, Expired with CC
        GMLOS 1.8   AMLOS 2.5   RW 0.7827

Select Principal or Secondary Diagnosis listed under DRG 280

DRG 285   Acute Myocardial Infarction, Expired without CC/MCC
        GMLOS 1.4   AMLOS 1.6   RW 0.5473

Select Principal or Secondary Diagnosis listed under DRG 280

DRG 286   Circulatory Disorders Except Acute Myocardial Infarction, with Cardiac Catheterization with MCC
        GMLOS 5.1   AMLOS 6.9   RW 2.1775

Select any principal diagnosis listed under MDC 5 excluding AMI
AND

Nonoperating Room Procedures
4A02[0,3]N[6,7,8] Measurement/Cardiac, [Opn, Perc], Sampling and Pressure, [Rt Heart, Lt Heart, Bilat]
B20*   Imaging, Heart, Plain Radiography
B210[0,1,Y]ZZ   Fluoroscopy/Coronary Artery, Single, [High Osmolar, Low Osmolar, Oth Contrast], None, None
B211[0,1,Y]ZZ   Fluoroscopy/Coronary Arteries, Multi, [High Osmolar, Low Osmolar, Oth Contrast], None, None
B212[0,1,Y]ZZ   Fluoroscopy/Coronary Artery Bypass Graft, Single, [High Osmolar, Low Osmolar, Oth Contrast], None, None
B213[0,1,Y]ZZ   Fluoroscopy/Coronary Artery Bypass Grafts, Multi, [High Osmolar, Low Osmolar, Oth Contrast], None, None
B214*   Fluoroscopy/Heart, Rt
B215*   Fluoroscopy/Heart, Lt
B216*   Fluoroscopy/Heart, Rt and Lt
B217*   Fluoroscopy/Int Mammary Bypass Graft, Rt
B218*   Fluoroscopy/Int Mammary Bypass Graft, Lt
B21F*   Fluoroscopy/Bypass Graft, Oth

DRG 287   Circulatory Disorders Except Acute Myocardial Infarction, with Cardiac Catheterization without MCC
        GMLOS 2.5   AMLOS 3.3   RW 1.1562

Select any principal diagnosis listed under MDC 5 excluding AMI
AND

Select any nonoperating procedure listed under DRG 286

DRG 288   Acute and Subacute Endocarditis with MCC
        GMLOS 7.5   AMLOS 9.5   RW 2.7933   [T]

Principal Diagnosis
A39.51   Meningococcal endocarditis
A52.03   Syphilitic endocarditis
B37.6   Candidal endocarditis
I33.0   Acute and subacute infective endocarditis
I33.9   Acute and subacute endocarditis, unsp

DRG 289   Acute and Subacute Endocarditis with CC
        GMLOS 5.6   AMLOS 6.9   RW 1.6969   [T]

Select principal diagnosis listed under DRG 288

DRG 290   Acute and Subacute Endocarditis without CC/MCC
        GMLOS 3.7   AMLOS 4.4   RW 1.0546   [T]

Select principal diagnosis listed under DRG 288

DRG 291   Heart Failure and Shock with MCC
        GMLOS 4.6   AMLOS 5.8   RW 1.4809   [T]

Principal Diagnosis
I09.81   Rheumatic heart failure
I11.0   Hypertensive heart dz with heart failure
I13.0   Hyp hrt & chr kdny dis w hrt fail and stg 1-4/unsp chr kdny
I13.2   Hyp hrt & chr kdny dis w hrt fail and w stg 5 chr kdny/ESRD
I50*   Heart failure
R57.0   Cardiogenic shock
R57.9   Shock, unsp

DRG 292   Heart Failure and Shock with CC
        GMLOS 3.6   AMLOS 4.4   RW 0.9707   [T]

Select principal diagnosis listed under DRG 291

DRG 293   Heart Failure and Shock without CC/MCC
        GMLOS 2.6   AMLOS 3.1   RW 0.6737   [T]

Select principal diagnosis listed under DRG 291

DRG 294   Deep Vein Thrombophlebitis with CC/MCC
        GMLOS 3.8   AMLOS 4.7   RW 0.9826

Principal Diagnosis
I80.1*   Phlebitis and thrombophlebitis of Femor vein
I80.2*   Phlbts and thombophlb of and unsp deep vessels of low extrm
I80.3   Phlebitis and thrombophlebitis of lwr extremities, unsp
I82.22[0,1]   [Acute, Chr] embolism and thrombosis of inferior vena cava

DRG 295   Deep Vein Thrombophlebitis without CC/MCC
        GMLOS 3.2   AMLOS 3.7   RW 0.7427

Select principal diagnosis listed under DRG 294

DRG 296   Cardiac Arrest, Unexplained with MCC
        GMLOS 1.9   AMLOS 2.8   RW 1.2864

Principal Diagnosis
I46*   Cardiac arrest

DRG 297   Cardiac Arrest, Unexplained with CC
        GMLOS 1.3   AMLOS 1.6   RW 0.6488

Select principal diagnosis listed under DRG 296

DRG 298   Cardiac Arrest, Unexplained without CC/MCC
        GMLOS 1.1   AMLOS 1.2   RW 0.4477

Select principal diagnosis listed under DRG 296

MDC 5: Diseases And Disorders Of The Circulatory System—MEDICAL

| Surgical | Medical | CC Indicator | MCC Indicator | Procedure Proxy | PDxMCC PDx acts as own MCC | PDxCC PDx acts as own CC |

DRG 299   **Peripheral Vascular Disorders with MCC**

       GMLOS 4.3   AMLOS 5.6   RW 1.4216   T

Principal Diagnosis

E08.5*	Diabetes d/t underlying condition w circulatory comp
E09.5*	Drug/chem diabetes mellitus w circulatory comp
E10.5*	Type 1 diabetes mellitus with circulatory comp
E11.5*	Type 2 diabetes mellitus with circulatory comp
E13.5*	Oth diabetes mellitus with circulatory comp
I67.0	Dissection of cerebral arteries, nonruptured
I70.0	Atherosclerosis of aorta
I70.2*	Atherosclerosis of native arteries of the extremities
I70.3*	Athscl unsp type bypass graft(s) of the extremities
I70.4*	Athscl auto vein bypass graft(s) of the extremities
I70.5*	Athscl nonauto bio bypass graft(s) of the extremities
I70.6*	Athscl nonbiological bypass graft(s) of the extremities
I70.7*	Athscl type of bypass graft(s) of the extremities
I70.8	Atherosclerosis of oth arteries
I70.9*	Oth and unsp atherosclerosis
I71*	Aortic aneurysm and dissection
I72.[0,1,3,4,8,9]	Aneurysm of [carotid, upr extr, iliac, lwr extr, oth spec, unsp] artery
I73.1	Thromboangiitis obliterans [Buerger's dz]
I73.8*	Oth spec peripheral vascular dz
I73.9	Peripheral vascular dz, unsp
I74*	Arterial embolism and thrombosis
I75.0*	Atheroembolism of extremities
I75.89	Atheroembolism of oth site
I76	Septic arterial embolism
I77.0	Arteriovenous fistula, acquired
I77.1	Stricture of artery
I77.2	Rupture of artery
I77.3	Arterial fibromuscular dysplasia
I77.5	Necrosis of artery
I77.7[1,2,4,9]	Dissection of [carotid, iliac, vert, oth] artery
I77.8*	Oth spec d/o of arteries and arterioles
I77.9	D/o of arteries and arterioles, unsp
I78.0	Hereditary hemorrhagic telangiectasia
I78.8	Oth dz of capillaries
I78.9	Dz of capillaries, unsp
I79*	D/o of art, arterioles and capilare in dis classd elsw
I80.0*	Phlebitis and thombophlb of superf vessels of low extrm
I80.[8,9]	Phlebitis and thrombophlebitis of [oth, unsp] site(s)
I82.1	Thrombophlebitis migrans
I82.21[0,1]	[Acute, Chr] embolism and thrombosis of superior vena cava
I82.29[0,1]	[Acute, Chr] embolism and thrombosis of oth thoracic veins
I82.4*	Acute embolism and thrombosis of deep veins of low extrm
I82.5*	Chr embolism and thrombosis of deep veins of low extrm
I82.6*	Acute embolism and thrombosis of veins of upr extr
I82.7*	Chr embolism and thrombosis of veins of upr extr
I82.8*	Embolism and thrombosis of oth spec veins
I82.9*	Embolism and thrombosis of unsp vein
I82.A*	Embolism and thrombosis of axillary vein
I82.B*	Embolism and thrombosis of subclavian vein
I82.C*	Embolism and thrombosis of int jugular vein
I83.0*	Varicose veins of lwr extremities with ulcer
I83.1*	Varicose veins of lwr extremities with inflam
I83.2*	Varicose veins of lwr extremities w ulc and inflam
I83.8*	Varicose veins of lwr extremities with oth comp
I83.9*	Asymptomatic varicose veins of lwr extremities
I86.0	Sublingual varices
I86.4	Gastric varices
I86.8	Varicose veins of oth spec sites
I87.0*	Postthrombotic synd
I87.1	Compression of vein
I87.2	Venous insufficiency (chr) (peripheral)
I87.3*	Chr venous hypertension (idiopathic)
I96	Gangrene, NEC
M31.8	Oth spec necrotizing vasculopathies
M31.9	Necrotizing vasculopathy, unsp
Q26.5	Anomalous portal venous connection
Q26.6	Portal vein-hepatic artery fistula
Q27*	Oth congenital malformations of peripheral vascular sys
Q28.[0,1]	[Arteriovenous, Oth] malformation(s) of precerebral vessels
Q28.[8,9]	[Oth spec, Unsp] congenital malformations of circulatory sys
S09.0XXS	Inj of bld vessels of head, NEC, seq
S15.00[1,2,9]S	Unsp inj of [rt, lt, unsp] carotid artery, seq
S15.01[1,2,9]S	Minor lac of [rt, lt, unsp] carotid artery, seq
S15.02[1,2,9]S	Major lac of [rt, lt, unsp] carotid artery, seq
S15.09[1,2,9]S	Oth spec inj of [rt, lt, unsp] carotid artery, seq
S15.10[1,2,9]S	Unsp inj of [rt, lt, unsp] vert artery, seq
S15.11[1,2,9]S	Minor lac of [rt, lt, unsp] vert artery, seq
S15.12[1,2,9]S	Major lac of [rt, lt, unsp] vert artery, seq
S15.19[1,2,9]S	Oth spec inj of [rt, lt, unsp] vert artery, seq
S15.20[1,2,9]S	Unsp inj of [rt, lt, unsp] ext jugular vein, seq
S15.21[1,2,9]S	Minor lac of [rt, lt, unsp] ext jugular vein, seq
S15.22[1,2,9]S	Major lac of [rt, lt, unsp] ext jugular vein, seq
S15.29[1,2,9]S	Oth spec inj of [rt, lt, unsp] ext jugular vein, seq
S15.30[1,2,9]S	Unsp inj of [rt, lt, unsp] int jugular vein, seq
S15.31[1,2,9]S	Minor lac of [rt, lt, unsp] int jugular vein, seq
S15.32[1,2,9]S	Major lac of [rt, lt, unsp] int jugular vein, seq
S15.39[1,2,9]S	Oth spec inj of [rt, lt, unsp] int jugular vein, seq
S15.[8,9]XXS	Inj of [oth, unsp] spec bld vessel(s) at neck lvl, seq
S25.0[0,1,2,9]XS	[Unsp inj, Minor lac, Major lac, Oth spec inj] of thoracic aorta, seq
S25.10[1,2,9]S	Unsp inj of [rt, lt, unsp] innominate or subclavian artery, seq
S25.11[1,2,9]S	Minor lac of [rt, lt, unsp] innominate or subclavian artery, seq
S25.12[1,2,9]S	Major lac of [rt, lt, unsp] innominate or subclavian artery, seq
S25.19[1,2,9]S	Oth spec inj of [rt, lt, unsp] innominate or subclavian artery, seq
S25.2[0,1,2,9]XS	[Unsp inj, Minor lac, Major lac, Oth spec inj] of superior vena cava, seq
S25.30[1,2,9]S	Unsp inj of [rt, lt, unsp] innominate or subclavian vein, seq
S25.31[1,2,9]S	Minor lac of [rt, lt, unsp] innominate or subclavian vein, seq
S25.32[1,2,9]S	Major lac of [rt, lt, unsp] innominate or subclavian vein, seq
S25.39[1,2,9]S	Oth spec inj of [rt, lt, unsp] innominate or subclavian vein, seq
S25.40[1,2,9]S	Unsp inj of [rt, lt, unsp] pulmn bld vessels, seq
S25.41[1,2,9]S	Minor lac of [rt, lt, unsp] pulmn bld vessels, seq
S25.42[1,2,9]S	Major lac of [rt, lt, unsp] pulmn bld vessels, seq
S25.49[1,2,9]S	Oth spec inj of [rt, lt, unsp] pulmn bld vessels, seq
S25.50[1,2,9]S	Unsp inj of intercostal bld vessels, [rt, lt, unsp] side, seq
S25.51[1,2,9]S	Lac of intercostal bld vessels, [rt, lt, unsp] side, seq
S25.59[1,2,9]S	Oth spec inj of intercostal bld vessels, [rt, lt, unsp] side, seq
S25.80[1,2,9]S	Unsp inj of oth bld vessels of thorax, [rt, lt, unsp] side, seq
S25.81[1,2,9]S	Lac of oth bld vessels of thorax, [rt, lt, unsp] side, seq
S25.89[1,2,9]S	Oth spec inj of oth bld vessels of thorax, [rt, lt, unsp] side, seq
S25.9[0,1,9]XS	[Unsp inj, Lac, Oth spec inj] of unsp bld vessel of thorax, seq
S35.0[0,1,2,9]XS	[Unsp inj, Minor lac, Major lac, Oth spec inj] of abd aorta, seq
S35.1[0,1,2,9]XS	[Unsp inj, Minor lac, Major lac, Oth spec inj] of inferior vena cava, seq
S35.21[1,2,8,9]S	[Minor lac, Major lac, Oth inj, Unsp inj] of celiac artery, seq
S35.22[1,2,8,9]S	[Minor lac, Major lac, Oth inj, Unsp inj] of superior mesenteric artery, seq
S35.23[1,2,8,9]S	[Minor lac, Major lac, Oth inj, Unsp inj] of inferior mesenteric artery, seq
S35.29[1,2,8,9]S	[Minor lac, Major lac, Oth inj, Unsp inj] of branches of celiac and mesenteric artery, seq
S35.31[1,8,9]S	[Lac, Oth spec inj, Unsp inj] of portal vein, seq
S35.32[1,8,9]S	[Lac, Oth spec inj, Unsp inj] of splenic vein, seq
S35.33[1,8,9]S	[Lac, Oth spec inj, Unsp inj] of superior mesenteric vein, seq
S35.34[1,8,9]S	[Lac, Oth spec inj, Unsp inj] of inferior mesenteric, seq
S35.40[1,2,3]S	Unsp inj of [rt, lt, unsp] renal artery, seq
S35.40[4,5,6]S	Unsp inj of [rt, lt, unsp] renal vein, seq
S35.41[1,2,3]S	Lac of [rt, lt, unsp] renal artery, seq
S35.41[4,5,6]S	Lac of [rt, lt, unsp] renal vein, seq
S35.49[1,2,3]S	Oth spec inj of [rt, lt, unsp] renal artery, seq
S35.49[4,5,6]S	Oth spec inj of [rt, lt, unsp] renal vein, seq
S35.50XS	Inj of unsp iliac bld vessel(s), seq
S35.51[1,2,3]S	Inj of [rt, lt, unsp] iliac artery, seq
S35.51[4,5,6]S	Inj of [rt, lt, unsp] iliac vein, seq
S35.53[1,2,3]S	Inj of [rt, lt, unsp] uterine artery, seq
S35.53[4,5,6]S	Inj of [rt, lt, unsp] uterine vein, seq
S35.59XS	Inj of oth iliac bld vessels, seq
S35.8X[1,8,9]S	[Lac, Oth spec inj, Unsp inj] of oth bld vessels at abd, lwr back and pelvis lvl, seq
S35.9[0,1,9]XS	[Unsp inj, Lac, Oth spec inj] of unsp bld vessel at abd, lwr back and pelvis lvl, seq
S45.00[1,2,9]S	Unsp inj of axillary artery, [rt, lt, unsp] side, seq
S45.01[1,2,9]S	Lac of axillary artery, [rt, lt, unsp] side, seq
S45.09[1,2,9]S	Oth spec inj of axillary artery, [rt, lt, unsp] side, seq
S45.10[1,2,9]S	Unsp inj of brachial artery, [rt, lt, unsp] side, seq
S45.11[1,2,9]S	Lac of brachial artery, [rt, lt, unsp] side, seq
S45.19[1,2,9]S	Oth spec inj of brachial artery, [rt, lt, unsp] side, seq
S45.20[1,2,9]S	Unsp inj of axillary or brachial vein, [rt, lt, unsp] side, seq
S45.21[1,2,9]S	Lac of axillary or brachial vein, [rt, lt, unsp] side, seq
S45.29[1,2,9]S	Oth spec inj of axillary or brachial vein, [rt, lt, unsp] side, seq
S45.30[1,2,9]S	Unsp inj of superf vein at shldr and upr arm lvl, [rt, lt, unsp] arm, seq
S45.31[1,2,9]S	Lac of superf vein at shldr and upr arm lvl, [rt, lt, unsp] arm, seq

---

T **Transfer DRG**   SP **Special Payment**   * **Code Range**   **6th and 7th Character of ZZ = No Device, No Qualifier ZX = No Device, Diagnostic**

Code	Description	Code	Description
S45.39[1,2,9]S	Oth spec inj of superf vein at shldr and upr arm lvl, [rt, lt, unsp] arm, seq	S75.20[1,2,9]S	Unsp inj of greater saphenous vein at hip & thigh lvl, [rt, lt, unsp] leg, seq
S45.80[1,2,9]S	Unsp inj of oth spec bld vessels at shldr and upr arm lvl, [rt, lt, unsp] arm, seq	S75.21[1,2,9]S	Minor lac of greater saphenous vein at hip & thigh lvl, [rt, lt, unsp] leg, seq
S45.81[1,2,9]S	Lac of oth spec bld vessels at shldr and upr arm lvl, [rt, lt, unsp] arm, seq	S75.22[1,2,9]S	Major lac of greater saphenous vein at hip & thigh lvl, [rt, lt, unsp] leg, seq
S45.89[1,2,9]S	Oth spec inj of oth spec bld vessels at shldr and upr arm lvl, [rt, lt, unsp] arm, seq	S75.29[1,2,9]S	Oth spec inj of greater saphenous vein at hip & thigh lvl, [rt, lt, unsp] leg, seq
S45.90[1,2,9]S	Unsp inj of unsp bld vessels at shldr and upr arm lvl, [rt, lt, unsp] arm, seq	S75.80[1,2,9]S	Unsp inj of oth bld vessels at hip & thigh lvl, [rt, lt, unsp] leg, seq
S45.91[1,2,9]S	Lac of unsp bld vessels at shldr and upr arm lvl, [rt, lt, unsp] arm, seq	S75.81[1,2,9]S	Lac of oth bld vessels at hip & thigh lvl, [rt, lt, unsp] leg, seq
S45.99[1,2,9]S	Oth spec inj of unsp bld vessels at shldr and upr arm lvl, [rt, lt, unsp] arm, seq	S75.89[1,2,9]S	Oth spec inj of oth bld vessels at hip & thigh lvl, [rt, lt, unsp] leg, seq
S55.00[1,2,9]S	Unsp inj of ulnar artery at forearm lvl, [rt, lt, unsp] arm, seq	S75.90[1,2,9]S	Unsp inj of unsp bld vessel at hip & thigh lvl, [rt, lt, unsp] leg, seq
S55.01[1,2,9]S	Lac of ulnar artery at forearm lvl, [rt, lt, unsp] arm, seq	S75.91[1,2,9]S	Lac of unsp bld vessel at hip & thigh lvl, [rt, lt, unsp] leg, seq
S55.09[1,2,9]S	Oth spec inj of ulnar artery at forearm lvl, [rt, lt, unsp] arm, seq	S75.99[1,2,9]S	Oth spec inj of unsp bld vessel at hip & thigh lvl, [rt, lt, unsp] leg, seq
S55.10[1,2,9]S	Unsp inj of radial artery at forearm lvl, [rt, lt, unsp] arm, seq	S85.00[1,2,9]S	Unsp inj of popliteal artery, [rt, lt, unsp] leg, seq
S55.11[1,2,9]S	Lac of radial artery at forearm lvl, [rt, lt, unsp] arm, seq	S85.01[1,2,9]S	Lac of popliteal artery, [rt, lt, unsp] leg, seq
S55.19[1,2,9]S	Oth spec inj of radial artery at forearm lvl, [rt, lt, unsp] arm, seq	S85.09[1,2,9]S	Oth spec inj of popliteal artery, [rt, lt, unsp] leg, seq
S55.20[1,2,9]S	Unsp inj of vein at forearm lvl, [rt, lt, unsp] arm, seq	S85.10[1,2,9]S	Unsp inj of unsp tibial artery, [rt, lt, unsp] leg, seq
S55.21[1,2,9]S	Lac of vein at forearm lvl, [rt, lt, unsp] arm, seq	S85.11[1,2,9]S	Lac of unsp tibial artery, [rt, lt, unsp] leg, seq
S55.29[1,2,9]S	Oth spec inj of vein at forearm lvl, [rt, lt, unsp] arm, seq	S85.12[1,2,9]S	Oth spec inj of unsp tibial artery, [rt, lt, unsp] leg, seq
S55.80[1,2,9]S	Unsp inj of oth bld vessels at forearm lvl, [rt, lt, unsp] arm, seq	S85.13[1,2,9]S	Unsp inj of ant tibial artery, [rt, lt, unsp] leg, seq
S55.81[1,2,9]S	Lac of oth bld vessels at forearm lvl, [rt, lt, unsp] arm, seq	S85.14[1,2,9]S	Lac of ant tibial artery, [rt, lt, unsp] leg, seq
S55.89[1,2,9]S	Oth spec inj of oth bld vessels at forearm lvl, [rt, lt, unsp] arm, seq	S85.15[1,2,9]S	Oth spec inj of ant tibial artery, [rt, lt, unsp] leg, seq
S55.90[1,2,9]S	Unsp inj of unsp bld vessel at forearm lvl, [rt, lt, unsp] arm, seq	S85.16[1,2,9]S	Unsp inj of post tibial artery, [rt, lt, unsp] leg, seq
S55.91[1,2,9]S	Lac of unsp bld vessel at forearm lvl, [rt, lt, unsp] arm, seq	S85.17[1,2,9]S	Lac of post tibial artery, [rt, lt, unsp] leg, seq
S55.99[1,2,9]S	Oth spec inj of unsp bld vessel at forearm lvl, [rt, lt, unsp] arm, seq	S85.18[1,2,9]S	Oth spec inj of post tibial artery, [rt, lt, unsp] leg, seq
S65.00[1,2,9]S	Unsp inj of ulnar artery at wrist and hand lvl of [rt, lt, unsp] arm, seq	S85.20[1,2,9]S	Unsp inj of peroneal artery, [rt, lt, unsp] leg, seq
S65.01[1,2,9]S	Lac of ulnar artery at wrist and hand lvl of [rt, lt, unsp] arm, seq	S85.21[1,2,9]S	Lac of peroneal artery, [rt, lt, unsp] leg, seq
S65.09[1,2,9]S	Oth spec inj of ulnar artery at wrist and hand lvl of [rt, lt, unsp] arm, seq	S85.29[1,2,9]S	Oth spec inj of peroneal artery, [rt, lt, unsp] leg, seq
S65.10[1,2,9]S	Unsp inj of radial artery at wrist and hand lvl of [rt, lt, unsp] arm, seq	S85.30[1,2,9]S	Unsp inj of greater saphenous vein at lwr leg lvl, [rt, lt, unsp] leg, seq
S65.11[1,2,9]S	Lac of radial artery at wrist and hand lvl of [rt, lt, unsp] arm, seq	S85.31[1,2,9]S	Lac of greater saphenous vein at lwr leg lvl, [rt, lt, unsp] leg, seq
S65.19[1,2,9]S	Oth spec inj of radial artery at wrist and hand lvl of [rt, lt, unsp] arm, seq	S85.39[1,2,9]S	Oth spec inj of greater saphenous vein at lwr leg lvl, [rt, lt, unsp] leg, seq
S65.20[1,2,9]S	Unsp inj of superf palmar arch of [rt, lt, unsp] hand, seq	S85.40[1,2,9]S	Unsp inj of lesser saphenous vein at lwr leg lvl, [rt, lt, unsp] leg, seq
S65.21[1,2,9]S	Lac of superf palmar arch of [rt, lt, unsp] hand, seq	S85.41[1,2,9]S	Lac of lesser saphenous vein at lwr leg lvl, [rt, lt, unsp] leg, seq
S65.29[1,2,9]S	Oth spec inj of superf palmar arch of [rt, lt, unsp] hand, seq	S85.49[1,2,9]S	Oth spec inj of lesser saphenous vein at lwr leg lvl, [rt, lt, unsp] leg, seq
S65.30[1,2,9]S	Unsp inj of deep palmar arch of [rt, lt, unsp] hand, seq	S85.50[1,2,9]S	Unsp inj of popliteal vein, [rt, lt, unsp] leg, seq
S65.31[1,2,9]S	Lac of deep palmar arch of [rt, lt, unsp] hand, seq	S85.51[1,2,9]S	Lac of popliteal vein, [rt, lt, unsp] leg, seq
S65.39[1,2,9]S	Oth spec inj of deep palmar arch of [rt, lt, unsp] hand, seq	S85.59[1,2,9]S	Oth spec inj of popliteal vein, [rt, lt, unsp] leg, seq
S65.40[1,2,9]S	Unsp inj of bld vessel of [rt, lt, unsp] thumb, seq	S85.80[1,2,9]S	Unsp inj of oth bld vessels at lwr leg lvl, [rt, lt, unsp] leg, seq
S65.41[1,2,9]S	Lac of bld vessel of [rt, lt, unsp] thumb, seq	S85.81[1,2,9]S	Lac of oth bld vessels at lwr leg lvl, [rt, lt, unsp] leg, seq
S65.49[1,2,9]S	Oth spec inj of bld vessel of [rt, lt, unsp] thumb, seq	S85.89[1,2,9]S	Oth spec inj of oth bld vessels at lwr leg lvl, [rt, lt, unsp] leg, seq
S65.50[0,1,2,3,4,5,6,7,8,9]S	Unsp inj of bld vessel of [rt index, lt index, rt mid, lt mid, rt ring, lt ring, rt little, lt little, oth, unsp] finger, seq	S85.90[1,2,9]S	Unsp inj of unsp bld vessel at lwr leg lvl, [rt, lt, unsp] leg, seq
S65.51[0,1,2,3,4,5,6,7,8,9]S	Lac of bld vessel of [rt index, lt index, rt mid, lt mid, rt ring, lt ring, rt little, lt little, oth, unsp] finger, seq	S85.91[1,2,9]S	Lac of unsp bld vessel at lwr leg lvl, [rt, lt, unsp] leg, seq
S65.59[0,1,2,3,4,5,6,7,8,9]S	Oth spec inj of bld vessel of [rt index, lt index, rt mid, lt mid, rt ring, lt ring, rt little, lt little, oth, unsp] finger, seq	S85.99[1,2,9]S	Oth spec inj of unsp bld vessel at lwr leg lvl, [rt, lt, unsp] leg, seq
S65.80[1,2,9]S	Unsp inj of oth bld vessels at wrist and hand lvl of [rt, lt, unsp] arm, seq	S95.00[1,2,9]S	Unsp inj of dorsal artery of [rt, lt, unsp] foot, seq
S65.81[1,2,9]S	Lac of oth bld vessels at wrist and hand lvl of [rt, lt, unsp] arm, seq	S95.01[1,2,9]S	Lac of dorsal artery of [rt, lt, unsp] foot, seq
		S95.09[1,2,9]S	Oth spec inj of dorsal artery of [rt, lt, unsp] foot, seq
S65.89[1,2,9]S	Oth spec inj of oth bld vessels at wrist and hand lvl of [rt, lt, unsp] arm, seq	S95.10[1,2,9]S	Unsp inj of plantar artery of [rt, lt, unsp] foot, seq
		S95.11[1,2,9]S	Lac of plantar artery of [rt, lt, unsp] foot, seq
S65.90[1,2,9]S	Unsp inj of unsp bld vessel at wrist and hand lvl of [rt, lt, unsp] arm, seq	S95.19[1,2,9]S	Oth spec inj of plantar artery of [rt, lt, unsp] foot, seq
		S95.20[1,2,9]S	Unsp inj of dorsal vein of [rt, lt, unsp] foot, seq
S65.91[1,2,9]S	Lac of unsp bld vessel at wrist and hand lvl of [rt, lt, unsp] arm, seq	S95.21[1,2,9]S	Lac of dorsal vein of [rt, lt, unsp] foot, seq
		S95.29[1,2,9]S	Oth spec inj of dorsal vein of [rt, lt, unsp] foot, seq
S65.99[1,2,9]S	Oth spec inj of unsp bld vessel at wrist and hand lvl of [rt, lt, unsp] arm, seq	S95.80[1,2,9]S	Unsp inj of oth bld vessels at ankle and foot lvl, [rt, lt, unsp] leg, seq
S75.00[1,2,9]S	Unsp inj of femor artery, [rt, lt, unsp] leg, seq	S95.81[1,2,9]S	Lac of oth bld vessels at ankle and foot lvl, [rt, lt, unsp] leg, seq
S75.01[1,2,9]S	Minor lac of femor artery, [rt, lt, unsp] leg, seq	S95.89[1,2,9]S	Oth spec inj of oth bld vessels at ankle and foot lvl, [rt, lt, unsp] leg, seq
S75.02[1,2,9]S	Major lac of femor artery, [rt, lt, unsp] leg, seq		
S75.09[1,2,9]S	Oth spec inj of femor artery, [rt, lt, unsp] leg, seq	S95.90[1,2,9]S	Unsp inj of unsp bld vessel at ankle and foot lvl, [rt, lt, unsp] leg, seq
S75.10[1,2,9]S	Unsp inj of femor vein at hip & thigh lvl, [rt, lt, unsp] leg, seq	S95.91[1,2,9]S	Lac of unsp bld vessel at ankle and foot lvl, [rt, lt, unsp] leg, seq
S75.11[1,2,9]S	Minor lac of femor vein at hip & thigh lvl, [rt, lt, unsp] leg, seq		
S75.12[1,2,9]S	Major lac of femor vein at hip & thigh lvl, [rt, lt, unsp] leg, seq	S95.99[1,2,9]S	Oth spec inj of unsp bld vessel at ankle and foot lvl, [rt, lt, unsp] leg, seq
S75.19[1,2,9]S	Oth spec inj of femor vein at hip & thigh lvl, [rt, lt, unsp] leg, seq	T81.71[8,9]A	Comp of [oth, unsp] artery following a procedure, NEC, init enc
		T81.72XA	Comp of vein following a procedure, NEC, init

Surgical **Medical** **CC Indicator** **MCC Indicator** **Procedure Proxy** **PDxMCC PDx acts as own MCC** **PDxCC PDx acts as own CC**

MDC 5: Diseases And Disorders Of The Circulatory System—MEDICAL

DRG 300	**Peripheral Vascular Disorders with CC**			
	GMLOS 3.5	AMLOS 4.4	RW 0.9994	T

Select principal diagnosis listed under DRG 299

DRG 301	**Peripheral Vascular Disorders without CC/MCC**			
	GMLOS 2.6	AMLOS 3.2	RW 0.7023	T

Select principal diagnosis listed under DRG 299

DRG 302	**Atherosclerosis with MCC**		
	GMLOS 2.9	AMLOS 3.9	RW 1.0590

Principal Diagnosis

I25.1*	Atherosclerotic heart dz of native coronary artery
I25.2	Old myocardial infarction
I25.5	Ischemic cardiomyopathy
I25.6	Silent myocardial ischemia
I25.7*	Athscl CABG and cor art of transplanted heart w ang pctrs
I25.8*	Oth forms of chr ischemic heart dz
I25.9	Chr ischemic heart dz, unsp
I51.3	Intracardiac thrombosis, NEC
I51.7	Cardiomegaly
I51.89	Oth ill-defined heart dz
I51.9	Heart dz, unsp
I52	Oth heart d/o in dz classified elsw
I87.8	Oth spec d/o of veins
I87.9	D/o of vein, unsp
I99*	Oth and unsp d/o of circulatory sys
R93.1	Abnormal findings on dx imaging of heart and cor circ
R93.8	Abnormal findings on diagnostic imaging of body structures

DRG 303	**Atherosclerosis without MCC**		
	GMLOS 2.0	AMLOS 2.4	RW 0.6427

Select principal diagnosis listed under DRG 302

DRG 304	**Hypertension with MCC**		
	GMLOS 3.3	AMLOS 4.1	RW 1.0109

Principal Diagnosis

I10	Essential (primary) hypertension
I11.9	Hypertensive heart dz w/o heart failure
I13.10	Hyp hrt & chr kdny dis w/o hrt fail, w stg 1-4/unsp chr kdny
I15*	Secondary hypertension
N26.2	Page kidney

DRG 305	**Hypertension without MCC**		
	GMLOS 2.2	AMLOS 2.6	RW 0.6626

Select principal diagnosis listed under DRG 304

DRG 306	**Cardiac Congenital and Valvular Disorders with MCC**		
	GMLOS 4.0	AMLOS 5.4	RW 1.4029

Principal Diagnosis

A52.01	Syphilitic aneurysm of aorta
A52.02	Syphilitic aortitis
B33.21	Viral endocarditis
I01.1	Acute rheumatic endocarditis
I05*	Rheumatic mitral valve dz
I06*	Rheumatic aortic valve dz
I07*	Rheumatic tricuspid valve dz
I08*	Multi valve dz
I09.1	Rheumatic dz of endocardium, valve unsp
I09.89	Oth spec rheumatic heart dz
I23.4	Rupture of chord tendne as current comp following AMI
I23.5	Rupture of papillary muscle as current comp following AMI
I34*	Nonrheumatic mitral valve d/o
I35*	Nonrheumatic aortic valve d/o
I36*	Nonrheumatic tricuspid valve d/o
I37*	Nonrheumatic pulmn valve d/o
I38	Endocarditis, valve unsp
I39	Endocarditis and heart valve d/o in dis classd elsw
I51.1	Rupture of chordae tendineae, NEC
I51.2	Rupture of papillary muscle, NEC
Q20*	Congenital malformations of cardiac chambers and connections

Q21*	Congenital malformations of cardiac septa
Q22*	Congenital malformations of pulmn and tricuspid valves
Q23*	Congenital malformations of aortic and mitral valves
Q24.0	Dextrocardia
Q24.1	Levocardia
Q24.2	Cor triatriatum
Q24.3	Pulmn infundibular stenosis
Q24.4	Congenital subaortic stenosis
Q24.5	Malformation of coronary vessels
Q24.8	Oth spec congenital malformations of heart
Q24.9	Congenital malformation of heart, unsp
Q25*	Congenital malformations of great arteries
Q26.0	Congenital stenosis of vena cava
Q26.1	Persistent lt superior vena cava
Q26.2	Total anomalous pulmn venous connection
Q26.3	Partial anomalous pulmn venous connection
Q26.4	Anomalous pulmn venous connection, unsp
Q26.8	Oth congenital malformations of great veins
Q26.9	Congenital malformation of great vein, unsp
Q87.4*	Marfan's synd
R01.0	Benign and innocent cardiac murmurs
R01.1	Cardiac murmur, unsp
T82.0[1,2,3,9]XA	[Breakdown (mech), Displac, Leakage, Oth mech] comp of heart valve prosthesis, init enc

DRG 307	**Cardiac Congenital and Valvular Disorders without MCC**		
	GMLOS 2.5	AMLOS 3.2	RW 0.8044

Select principal diagnosis listed under DRG 306

DRG 308	**Cardiac Arrhythmia and Conduction Disorders with MCC**		
	GMLOS 3.8	AMLOS 4.8	RW 1.2150

Principal Diagnosis

I44*	Atrioventricular and lt bundle-branch block
I45*	Oth conduction d/o
I47*	Paroxysmal tachycardia
I48*	Atrial fibrillation and flutter
I49*	Oth cardiac arrhythmias
Q24.6	Congenital heart block
R00.0	Tachycardia, unsp
R00.1	Bradycardia, unsp
R00.2	Palpitations
T82.110A	Breakdown (mech) of cardiac electrode, init enc
T82.111A	Breakdown of cardiac pulse generator (battery), init
T82.120A	Displac of cardiac electrode, init enc
T82.121A	Displac of cardiac pulse generator (battery), init
T82.190A	Mech compl of cardiac electrode, init enc
T82.191A	Mech compl of cardiac pulse generator (battery), init enc

DRG 309	**Cardiac Arrhythmia and Conduction Disorders with CC**		
	GMLOS 2.6	AMLOS 3.3	RW 0.7851

Select principal diagnosis listed under DRG 308

DRG 310	**Cardiac Arrhythmia and Conduction Disorders without CC/MCC**		
	GMLOS 2.0	AMLOS 2.3	RW 0.5608

Select principal diagnosis listed under DRG 308

DRG 311	**Angina Pectoris**		
	GMLOS 1.8	AMLOS 2.3	RW 0.6091

Principal Diagnosis

I20*	Angina pectoris
I24.0	Acute coronary thrombosis not resulting in myocardial infrc
I24.8	Oth forms of acute ischemic heart dz
I24.9	Acute ischemic heart dz, unsp

DRG 312	**Syncope and Collapse**		
	GMLOS 2.4	AMLOS 2.9	RW 0.7630

Principal Diagnosis

I95.1	Orthostatic hypotension
I95.2	Hypotension d/t drugs
I95.3	Hypotension of hemodialysis
I95.81	Postprocedural hypotension
R55	Syncope and collapse

T Transfer DRG   SP Special Payment   * Code Range   6th and 7th Character of ZZ = No Device, No Qualifier ZX = No Device, Diagnostic

102   MS-DRG Version 33.0   © 2015 Optum360, LLC

DRG 313 Chest Pain
GMLOS 1.8   AMLOS 2.2   RW 0.6621

Principal Diagnosis

R07.2	Precordial pain
R07.82	Intercostal pain
R07.89	Oth chest pain
R07.9	Chest pain, unsp

DRG 314 Other Circulatory System Diagnoses with MCC
GMLOS 4.9   AMLOS 6.7   RW 1.9334   [T]

Principal Diagnosis

A36.81	Diphtheritic cardiomyopathy
A39.5[0,2,3]	Meningococcal [carditis unsp, myocarditis, pericarditis]
A52.00	Cardiovascular syphilis, unsp
A52.04	Syphilitic cerebral arteritis
A52.05	Oth cerebrovascular syphilis
A52.06	Oth syphilitic heart involvement
A52.09	Oth cardiovascular syphilis
A54.83	Gonococcal heart infxn
B33.2[0,2,3]	Viral [carditis unsp, myocarditis, pericarditis]
B57.0	Acute Chagas' dz with heart involvement
B57.2	Chagas' dz (chr) with heart involvement
B58.81	Toxoplasma myocarditis
C38.0	Malig neoplasm of heart
C45.2	Mesothelioma of pericardium
D15.1	Benign neoplasm of heart
D18.0[0,9]	Hemangioma [unsp, oth] site
I01.0	Acute rheumatic pericarditis
I01.2	Acute rheumatic myocarditis
I01.8	Oth acute rheumatic heart dz
I01.9	Acute rheumatic heart dz, unsp
I02*	Rheumatic chorea
I09.0	Rheumatic myocarditis
I09.2	Chr rheumatic pericarditis
I09.9	Rheumatic heart dz, unsp
I23.0	Hemopericardium as current comp following AMI
I23.1	Atrial septal defect as current comp following AMI
I23.2	Ventricular septal defect as current comp following AMI
I23.3	Rupture of card wall w/o hemoperic as current comp fol AMI
I23.6	Thombos of atrium/auric append/ventr as current comp fol AMI
I23.7	Postinfarction angina
I23.8	Oth current comp following AMI
I24.1	Dressler's synd
I25.3	Aneurysm of heart
I25.4*	Coronary artery aneurysm and dissection
I27.0	Primary pulmn hypertension
I27.1	Kyphoscoliotic heart dz
I27.2	Oth secondary pulmn hypertension
I27.81	Cor pulmonale (chr)
I27.89	Oth spec pulmn heart dz
I27.9	Pulmn heart dz, unsp
I28*	Oth dz of pulmn vessels
I30*	Acute pericarditis
I31*	Oth dz of pericardium
I32	Pericarditis in dz classified elsw
I40*	Acute myocarditis
I41	Myocarditis in dz classified elsw
I42*	Cardiomyopathy
I43	Cardiomyopathy in dz classified elsw
I51.0	Cardiac septal defect, acquired
I51.4	Myocarditis, unsp
I51.5	Myocardial degeneration
I51.81	Takotsubo synd
I95.0	Idiopathic hypotension
I95.89	Oth hypotension
I95.9	Hypotension, unsp
I97.0	Postcardiotomy synd
I97.1*	Oth postprocedural cardiac functional disturbances
I97.7*	Intraoperative cardiac functional disturbances
I97.88	Oth intraoperative comp of the circ sys, NEC
I97.89	Oth postproc comp and d/o of the circ sys, NEC
R00.8	Oth abnormalities of heart beat
R00.9	Unsp abnormalities of heart beat
R01.2	Oth cardiac sounds
R03*	Abnormal bld-pressure reading, w/o diagnosis
R09.89	Oth symptoms and signs involving the circ and resp systems

R58	Hemor, NEC
R94.3*	Abnormal results of cardiovascular function studies
S26.02[0,1,2]A	[Mild, Mod, Major] lac of heart w/ hemopericardium, init enc
S26.09XA	Oth inj of heart with hemopericardium, init enc
S26.0[0,1]XA	[Unsp inj, Contsn] of heart w/ hemopericardium, init enc
S26.1[0,1,2,9]XA	[Unsp inj, Contsn, Lac, Oth inj] of heart w/o hemopericardium, init enc
S26.9[0,1,2,9]XA	[Unsp inj, Contsn, Lac, Oth inj] of heart, unsp w/ or w/o hemopericardium, init enc
T80.1XXA	Vascular comp fol infusn, tranfs and theraputc inject, init
T80.21[1,2,8,9]A	[Bldstream, Local, Oth, Unsp] infxn d/t central venous catheter, init enc
T80.810A	Extravasation of vesicant antineoplastic chemotherapy, init
T80.818A	Extravasation of oth vesicant agent, init enc
T80.90XA	Unsp comp following inf and therapeutic injection, init
T82.118A	Breakdown (mech) of cardiac electronic device, init
T82.119A	Breakdown of unsp cardiac electronic device, init
T82.128A	Displac of oth cardiac electronic device, init enc
T82.129A	Displac of unsp cardiac electronic device, init enc
T82.198A	Mech compl of oth cardiac electronic device, init enc
T82.199A	Mech compl of unsp cardiac device, init enc
T82.21[1,2,3,8]A	[Breakdown (mech), Displac, Leakage, Oth mech comp] of coronary artery bypass graft, init enc
T82.22[1,2,3,8]A	[Breakdown (mech), Displac, Leakage, Oth mech comp] of biological heart valve graft, init enc
T82.3[1,2,3,9][0,1,2,8,9]A	[Breakdown (mech), Displac, Leakage, Oth mech comp] of [aortic (bifurcation) graft (replace), carotid arterial graft (bypass), femor arterial graft (bypass), oth vascular grafts, unsp vascular graft], init enc
T82.4[1,2,3,9]XA	[Breakdown (mech), Displac, Leakage, Oth mech comp] of vascular dialysis catheter, init enc
T82.51[0,1,2,3,4,5,8,9]A	Breakdown (mech) of [surgically created arteriovenous fistula, surgically created arteriovenous shunt, artfcl heart, balloon (counterpulsation) dev, inf catheter, umbrella dev, oth cardiac/vascular dev, unsp cardiac/vascular dev], init enc
T82.52[0,1,2,3,4,5,8,9]A	Displac of [surgically created arteriovenous fistula, surgically created arteriovenous shunt, artfcl heart, balloon (counterpulsation) dev, inf catheter, umbrella dev, oth cardiac/vascular dev, unsp cardiac/vascular dev], init enc
T82.53[0,1,2,3,4,5,8,9]A	Leakage of [surgically created arteriovenous fistula, surgically created arteriovenous shunt, artfcl heart, balloon (counterpulsation) dev, inf catheter, umbrella dev, oth cardiac/vascular dev, unsp cardiac/vascular dev], init enc
T82.59[0,1,2,3,4,5,8,9]A	Oth mech comp of [surgically created arteriovenous fistula, surgically created arteriovenous shunt, artfcl heart, balloon (counterpulsation) dev, inf catheter, umbrella dev, oth cardiac/vascular dev, unsp cardiac/vascular dev], init enc
T82.6XXA	Infect/inflm reaction d/t cardiac valve prosthesis, init
T82.7XXA	Infect/inflm react d/t oth cardi/vasc dev/implnt/grft, init
T82.81[7,8]A	Embolism of [cardiac, vascular] prosthetic devs, implants and grafts, init enc
T82.82[7,8]A	Fibrosis of [cardiac, vascular] prosthetic devs, implants and grafts, init enc
T82.83[7,8]A	Hemor of [cardiac, vascular] prosthetic devs, implants and grafts, init enc
T82.84[7,8]A	Pain from [cardiac, vascular] prosthetic devs, implants and grafts, init enc
T82.85[7,8]A	Stenosis of [cardiac, vascular] prosthetic devs, implants and grafts, init enc
T82.86[7,8]A	Thrombosis of [cardiac, vascular] prosthetic devs, implants and grafts, init enc
T82.89[7,8]A	Oth spec comp of [cardiac, vascular] prosthetic devs, implants and grafts, init enc
T82.9XXA	Unsp comp of cardiac and vascular prosth dev/grft, init
T86.2*	Comp of heart transplant
T86.3*	Comp of heart-lung transplant
Z45.0*	Enc for adjustment and management of cardiac device
Z94.1	Heart transplant status
Z94.3	Heart and lungs transplant status PDxCC
Z95.2	Presence of prosthetic heart valve
Z95.3	Presence of xenogenic heart valve
Z95.4	Presence of oth heart-valve replace
Z95.81[1,2]	Presence of [heart assist dev, fully implantable artfcl heart]
Z95.820	Peripheral vascular angioplasty status w implants and grafts
Z95.828	Presence of oth vascular implants and grafts

Surgical   **Medical**   **CC Indicator**   **MCC Indicator**   **Procedure Proxy**   PDxMCC **PDx acts as own MCC**   PDxCC **PDx acts as own CC**

© 2015 Optum360, LLC   MS-DRG Version 33.0   103

DRG 315 **Other Circulatory System Diagnoses with CC**
GMLOS 3.1   AMLOS 3.9   RW 0.9722   T

Select principal diagnosis listed under DRG 314

DRG 316 **Other Circulatory System Diagnoses without CC/MCC**
GMLOS 2.0   AMLOS 2.5   RW 0.6498   T

Select principal diagnosis listed under DRG 314

MDC 5: Diseases And Disorders Of The Circulatory System—MEDICAL

T Transfer DRG   SP Special Payment   * Code Range   6th and 7th Character of ZZ = No Device, No Qualifier ZX = No Device, Diagnostic

104   MS-DRG Version 33.0   © 2015 Optum360, LLC

MDC 6
Diseases And Disorders Of The Digestive System

SURGICAL

DRG 326   Stomach, Esophageal and Duodenal Procedures with MCC
GMLOS 11.0   AMLOS 14.2   RW 5.4452   T

Operating Room Procedures

008Q*	Div/Vagus Nerve
02BP3ZZ	Exc of Pulmn Trunk, Perc Appr
02B[Q,R]3ZZ	Exc of [Rt, Lt] Pulmn Artery, Perc Appr
02B[S,T]3ZZ	Exc of [Rt, Lt] Pulmn Vein, Perc Appr
02B[V,W]3ZZ	Exc of [Superior Vena Cava, Thoracic Aorta], Perc Appr
03B03ZZ	Exc of Rt Int Mammary Artery, Perc Appr
03B13ZZ	Exc of Lt Int Mammary Artery, Perc Appr
03B23ZZ	Exc of Innominate Artery, Perc Appr
03B33ZZ	Exc of Rt Subclavian Artery, Perc Appr
03B43ZZ	Exc of Lt Subclavian Artery, Perc Appr
03L2*	Occlsn/Innominate Artery
03L3*	Occlsn/Subclavian Artery, Rt
03L4*	Occlsn/Subclavian Artery, Lt
05L3*	Occlsn/Innominate Vein, Rt
05L4*	Occlsn/Innominate Vein, Lt
05L5*	Occlsn/Subclavian Vein, Rt
05L6*	Occlsn/Subclavian Vein, Lt
0610[0,4][J,Z][5,6,Y]	Bypass/Inferior Vena Cava, [Opn, Perc Endo], [Synth Sub, No Dev], [Superior Mesenteric Vein, Inferior Mesenteric Vein, Lwr Vein]
0611[0,4][J,Z][9,B,Y]	Bypass/Splenic Vein, [Opn, Perc Endo], [Synth Sub, No Dev], [Renal Vein, Rt, Renal Vein, Lt, Lwr Vein]
0618[0,4][J,Z][9,B,Y]	Bypass/Portal Vein, [Opn, Perc Endo], [Synth Sub, No Dev], [Renal Vein, Rt, Renal Vein, Lt, Lwr Vein]
06L2[0,3,4]ZZ	Occlsn/Gastric Vein, [Opn, Perc, Perc Endo]
06L3[0,3,4]ZZ	Occlsn/Esophageal Vein, [Opn, Perc, Perc Endo]
095N*	Destr/Nasopharynx
09BN[0,3,4,7,8]ZZ	Exc/Nasopharynx, [Opn, Perc, Perc Endo, Via Natrl or Artfcl Opng, Via Natrl or Artfcl Opng Endo]
09TN*	Resect/Nasopharynx
0BQR*	Repair/Diaphragm, Rt
0BQS*	Repair/Diaphragm, Lt
0BUR*	Supl/Diaphragm, Rt
0BUS*	Supl/Diaphragm, Lt
0C5M*	Destr/Pharynx
0CBM[0,3,4,7,8]ZZ	Exc/Pharynx, [Opn, Perc, Perc Endo, Via Natrl or Artfcl Opng, Via Natrl or Artfcl Opng Endo]
0CTM*	Resect/Pharynx
0D11*	Bypass/Esophagus, Upr
0D12*	Bypass/Esophagus, Mid
0D13*	Bypass/Esophagus, Lwr
0D15*	Bypass/Esophagus
0D16[0,4,8][7,J,K,Z][9,A,B,L]	Bypass/Stomach, [Opn, Perc Endo, Via Natrl or Artfcl Opng Endo], [Auto Tissue Sub, Synth Sub, Nonauto Tissue Sub, No Dev], [Duodenum, Jejunum, Ileum, Transv Colon]
0D51[0,3,7]ZZ	Destr/Esophagus, Upr, [Opn, Perc, Via Natrl or Artfcl Opng]
0D52[0,3,7]ZZ	Destr/Esophagus, Mid, [Opn, Perc, Via Natrl or Artfcl Opng]
0D53[0,3,7]ZZ	Destr/Esophagus, Lwr, [Opn, Perc, Via Natrl or Artfcl Opng]
0D54[0,3,7]ZZ	Destr/Esophagogastric Junction, [Opn, Perc, Via Natrl or Artfcl Opng]
0D55[0,3,7]ZZ	Destr/Esophagus, [Opn, Perc, Via Natrl or Artfcl Opng]
0D56[0,3,7]ZZ	Destr/Stomach, [Opn, Perc, Via Natrl or Artfcl Opng]
0D57[0,3,7]ZZ	Destr/Stomach, Pylorus, [Opn, Perc, Via Natrl or Artfcl Opng]
0D59[0,3,7]ZZ	Destr/Duodenum, [Opn, Perc, Via Natrl or Artfcl Opng]
0D71[0,3,4][D,Z]Z	Dilation/Esophagus, Upr, [Opn, Perc, Perc Endo], [Intralum Dev, No Dev], NQ
0D72[0,3,4][D,Z]Z	Dilation/Esophagus, Mid, [Opn, Perc, Perc Endo], [Intralum Dev, No Dev], NQ
0D73[0,3,4][D,Z]Z	Dilation/Esophagus, Lwr, [Opn, Perc, Perc Endo], [Intralum Dev, No Dev], NQ
0D74[0,3,4][D,Z]Z	Dilation/Esophagogastric Junction, [Opn, Perc, Perc Endo], [Intralum Dev, No Dev], NQ
0D75[0,3,4][D,Z]Z	Dilation/Esophagus, [Opn, Perc, Perc Endo], [Intralum Dev, No Dev], NQ
0D76*	Dilation/Stomach
0D770ZZ	Dilation of Stomach, Pylorus, Opn Appr
0D773ZZ	Dilation of Stomach, Pylorus, Perc Appr
0D774ZZ	Dilation of Stomach, Pylorus, Perc Endo Appr
0D777ZZ	Dilation of Stomach, Pylorus, Via Opng
0D77[0,3,7]DZ	Dilation/Stomach, Pylorus, [Opn, Perc, Via Natrl or Artfcl Opng], Intralum Dev, NQ
0D84*	Div/Esophagogastric Junction
0D87[0,3,4,7,8]ZZ	Div/Stomach, Pylorus, [Opn, Perc, Perc Endo, Via Natrl or Artfcl Opng, Via Natrl or Artfcl Opng Endo]
0D910ZX	Drain of Upr Esophagus, Opn Appr, Diagnostic
0D91[0,3,4,7,8][0,Z]Z	Drain/Esophagus, Upr, [Opn, Perc, Perc Endo, Via Natrl or Artfcl Opng, Via Natrl or Artfcl Opng Endo], [Drain Dev, No Dev], NQ
0D920ZX	Drain of Mid Esophagus, Opn Appr, Diagnostic
0D92[0,3,4,7,8][0,Z]Z	Drain/Esophagus, Mid, [Opn, Perc, Perc Endo, Via Natrl or Artfcl Opng, Via Natrl or Artfcl Opng Endo], [Drain Dev, No Dev], NQ
0D930ZX	Drain of Lwr Esophagus, Opn Appr, Diagnostic
0D93[0,3,4,7,8][0,Z]Z	Drain/Esophagus, Lwr, [Opn, Perc, Perc Endo, Via Natrl or Artfcl Opng, Via Natrl or Artfcl Opng Endo], [Drain Dev, No Dev], NQ
0D940ZX	Drain of Esophagogastric Junction, Opn Appr, Diagn
0D94[0,3,4,7,8][0,Z]Z	Drain/Esophagogastric Junction, [Opn, Perc, Perc Endo, Via Natrl or Artfcl Opng, Via Natrl or Artfcl Opng Endo], [Drain Dev, No Dev], NQ
0D950ZX	Drain of Esophagus, Opn Appr, Diagnostic
0D95[0,3,4,7,8][0,Z]Z	Drain/Esophagus, [Opn, Perc, Perc Endo, Via Natrl or Artfcl Opng, Via Natrl or Artfcl Opng Endo], [Drain Dev, No Dev], NQ
0D960ZX	Drain of Stomach, Opn Appr, Diagnostic
0D96[0,3,4,7,8]ZZ	Drain/Stomach, [Opn, Perc, Perc Endo, Via Natrl or Artfcl Opng, Via Natrl or Artfcl Opng Endo]
0D96[0,3,4]0Z	Drain/Stomach, [Opn, Perc, Perc Endo], Drain Dev, NQ
0D970ZX	Drain of Stomach, Pylorus, Opn Appr, Diagnostic
0D97[0,3,4,7,8]ZZ	Drain/Stomach, Pylorus, [Opn, Perc, Perc Endo, Via Natrl or Artfcl Opng, Via Natrl or Artfcl Opng Endo]
0D97[0,3,4]0Z	Drain/Stomach, Pylorus, [Opn, Perc, Perc Endo], Drain Dev, NQ
0D99[0,3,4,7,8]ZZ	Drain/Duodenum, [Opn, Perc, Perc Endo, Via Natrl or Artfcl Opng, Via Natrl or Artfcl Opng Endo]
0D99[0,3,4]0Z	Drain/Duodenum, [Opn, Perc, Perc Endo], Drain Dev, NQ
0DB10ZX	Exc of Upr Esophagus, Opn Appr, Diagnostic
0DB1[0,3,7]ZZ	Exc/Esophagus, Upr, [Opn, Perc, Via Natrl or Artfcl Opng]
0DB20ZX	Exc of Mid Esophagus, Opn Appr, Diagnostic
0DB2[0,3,7]ZZ	Exc/Esophagus, Mid, [Opn, Perc, Via Natrl or Artfcl Opng]
0DB30ZX	Exc of Lwr Esophagus, Opn Appr, Diagnostic
0DB3[0,3,7]ZZ	Exc/Esophagus, Lwr, [Opn, Perc, Via Natrl or Artfcl Opng]
0DB40ZX	Exc of Esophagogastric Junction, Opn Appr, Diagn
0DB4[0,3,4,7]ZZ	Exc/Esophagogastric Junction, [Opn, Perc, Perc Endo, Via Natrl or Artfcl Opng]
0DB50ZX	Exc of Esophagus, Opn Appr, Diagnostic
0DB5[0,3,7]ZZ	Exc/Esophagus, [Opn, Perc, Via Natrl or Artfcl Opng]
0DB60ZX	Exc of Stomach, Opn Appr, Diagnostic
0DB6[0,3,4,7,8]Z3	Exc/Stomach, [Opn, Perc, Perc Endo, Via Natrl or Artfcl Opng, Via Natrl or Artfcl Opng Endo], No Dev, Vertical
0DB6[0,3,7]ZZ	Exc/Stomach, [Opn, Perc, Via Natrl or Artfcl Opng]
0DB70ZX	Exc of Stomach, Pylorus, Opn Appr, Diagnostic
0DB7[0,3,7]ZZ	Exc/Stomach, Pylorus, [Opn, Perc, Via Natrl or Artfcl Opng]
0DB9[0,3]ZZ	Exc/Duodenum, [Opn, Perc]
0DC1[0,3,4]ZZ	Extir/Esophagus, Upr, [Opn, Perc, Perc Endo]
0DC2[0,3,4]ZZ	Extir/Esophagus, Mid, [Opn, Perc, Perc Endo]
0DC3[0,3,4]ZZ	Extir/Esophagus, Lwr, [Opn, Perc, Perc Endo]
0DC4[0,3,4]ZZ	Extir/Esophagogastric Junction, [Opn, Perc, Perc Endo]
0DC5[0,3,4]ZZ	Extir/Esophagus, [Opn, Perc, Perc Endo]
0DC6[0,3,4]ZZ	Extir/Stomach, [Opn, Perc, Perc Endo]
0DC7[0,3,4]ZZ	Extir/Stomach, Pylorus, [Opn, Perc, Perc Endo]
0DC9[0,3,4]ZZ	Extir/Duodenum, [Opn, Perc, Perc Endo]
0DF5[0,3,4,7,8]ZZ	Fragmn/Esophagus, [Opn, Perc, Perc Endo, Via Natrl or Artfcl Opng, Via Natrl or Artfcl Opng Endo]
0DF6[0,3,4,7,8]ZZ	Fragmn/Stomach, [Opn, Perc, Perc Endo, Via Natrl or Artfcl Opng, Via Natrl or Artfcl Opng Endo]
0DH502Z	Insert of Monitoring Device into Esophagus, Opn Appr
0DH503Z	Insert of Inf Device into Esophagus, Opn Appr
0DH532Z	Insert of Monitoring Device into Esophagus, Perc Appr
0DH533Z	Insert of Inf Device into Esophagus, Perc Appr
0DH542Z	Insert of Monitor Dev into Esophag, Perc Endo Appr
0DH543Z	Insert of Inf Dev into Esophag, Perc Endo Appr
0DH572Z	Insert of Monitoring Device into Esophagus, Via Opng
0DH573Z	Insert of Inf Device into Esophagus, Via Opng

ØDH582Z	Insert of Monitoring Device into Esophagus, Endo
ØDH583Z	Insert of Inf Device into Esophagus, Endo
ØDH6ØUZ	Insert of Feeding Device into Stomach, Opn Appr
ØDH6[Ø,3,4,7,8][2,3,D]Z	Insert/Stomach, [Opn, Perc, Perc Endo, Via Natrl or Artfcl Opng, Via Natrl or Artfcl Opng Endo], [Monitoring Dev, Inf Dev, Intralum Dev], NQ
ØDH9[Ø,3,4,7,8][2,3]Z	Insert/Duodenum, [Opn, Perc, Perc Endo, Via Natrl or Artfcl Opng, Via Natrl or Artfcl Opng Endo], [Monitoring Dev, Inf Dev], NQ
ØDJ[Ø,6]4ZZ	Inspect of [Upr Intestinal Tract, Stomach], Perc Endo Appr
ØDL6*	Occlsn/Stomach
ØDL7*	Occlsn/Stomach, Pylorus
ØDM5*	Reattach/Esophagus
ØDM6*	Reattach/Stomach
ØDN1*	Rls/Esophagus, Upr
ØDN2*	Rls/Esophagus, Mid
ØDN3*	Rls/Esophagus, Lwr
ØDN4*	Rls/Esophagogastric Junction
ØDN5*	Rls/Esophagus
ØDN6*	Rls/Stomach
ØDN7*	Rls/Stomach, Pylorus
ØDP57DZ	Rmvl of Intralum Device from Esophagus, Via Opng
ØDP58DZ	Rmvl of Intralum Device from Esophagus, Endo
ØDP5[Ø,3,4][1,2,3,U]Z	Rmvl/Esophagus, [Opn, Perc, Perc Endo], [Radioact Elmt, Monitoring Dev, Inf Dev, Feeding Dev], NQ
ØDP64[Ø,2,7,D,J,K,U]Z	Rmvl/Stomach, Perc Endo, [Drain Dev, Monitoring Dev, Auto Tissue Sub, Intralum Dev, Synth Sub, Nonauto Tissue Sub, Feeding Dev], NQ
ØDP6[Ø,3,7,8][Ø,2,3,7,C,J,K,U]Z	Rmvl/Stomach, [Opn, Perc, Via Natrl or Artfcl Opng, Via Natrl or Artfcl Opng Endo], [Drain Dev, Monitoring Dev, Inf Dev, Auto Tissue Sub, Extralum Dev, Synth Sub, Nonauto Tissue Sub, Feeding Dev], NQ
ØDP6[Ø,3]DZ	Rmvl/Stomach, [Opn, Perc], Intralum Dev, NQ
ØDQ1*	Repair/Esophagus, Upr
ØDQ2*	Repair/Esophagus, Mid
ØDQ3*	Repair/Esophagus, Lwr
ØDQ4*	Repair/Esophagogastric Junction
ØDQ5*	Repair/Esophagus
ØDQ6*	Repair/Stomach
ØDQ7*	Repair/Stomach, Pylorus
ØDQ9*	Repair/Duodenum
ØDR5*	Replace/Esophagus
ØDS5*	Repos/Esophagus
ØDS6ØZZ	Repos Stomach, Opn Appr
ØDS64ZZ	Repos Stomach, Perc Endo Appr
ØDS67ZZ	Repos Stomach, Via Natrl or Artfcl Opng
ØDS68ZZ	Repos Stomach, Endo
ØDT1*	Resect/Esophagus, Upr
ØDT2*	Resect/Esophagus, Mid
ØDT3*	Resect/Esophagus, Lwr
ØDT4*	Resect/Esophagogastric Junction
ØDT5*	Resect/Esophagus
ØDT6*	Resect/Stomach
ØDT7*	Resect/Stomach, Pylorus
ØDU1*	Supl/Esophagus, Upr
ØDU2*	Supl/Esophagus, Mid
ØDU3*	Supl/Esophagus, Lwr
ØDU4*	Supl/Esophagogastric Junction
ØDU5*	Supl/Esophagus
ØDU6*	Supl/Stomach
ØDU7*	Supl/Stomach, Pylorus
ØDV1*	Restrict/Esophagus, Upr
ØDV2*	Restrict/Esophagus, Mid
ØDV3*	Restrict/Esophagus, Lwr
ØDV4*	Restrict/Esophagogastric Junction
ØDV5*	Restrict/Esophagus
ØDV67ZZ	Restrict of Stomach, Via Natrl or Artfcl Opng
ØDV68ZZ	Restrict of Stomach, Endo
ØDV6[Ø,3,4][C,D,Z]Z	Restrict/Stomach, [Opn, Perc, Perc Endo], [Extralum Dev, Intralum Dev, No Dev], NQ
ØDV7*	Restrict/Stomach, Pylorus
ØDWØ4UZ	Revise of Feeding Dev in Up Intest Tract, Perc Endo Appr
ØDW5[7,8]DZ	Rev/Esophagus, [Via Natrl or Artfcl Opng, Via Natrl or Artfcl Opng Endo], Intralum Dev, NQ
ØDW64[Ø,2,7,D,J,K,M,U]Z	Rev/Stomach, Perc Endo, [Drain Dev, Monitoring Dev, Auto Tissue Sub, Intralum Dev, Synth Sub, Nonauto Tissue Sub, Stimulator Lead, Feeding Dev], NQ

ØDW6[Ø,3,7,8][Ø,2,3,7,C,D,J,K,U]Z	Rev/Stomach, [Opn, Perc, Via Natrl or Artfcl Opng, Via Natrl or Artfcl Opng Endo], [Drain Dev, Monitoring Dev, Inf Dev, Auto Tissue Sub, Extralum Dev, Intralum Dev, Synth Sub, Nonauto Tissue Sub, Feeding Dev], NQ
ØDW6[Ø,3]MZ	Rev/Stomach, [Opn, Perc], Stimulator Lead, NQ
ØDX*	Gastrointestinal Sys, Transfer
ØDY6*	Transplantation/Stomach
ØF8G[Ø,3]ZZ	Div/Pancreas, [Opn, Perc]
ØFCCØZZ	Extir of Matter from Ampulla of Vater, Opn Appr
ØFQC*	Repair/Ampulla of Vater
ØK84*	Div/Tongue, Palate, Pharynx Muscle
ØWQ6XZ2	Repair Neck, Stoma, Ext Appr
OR	
ØFTGØZZ	Resect of Pancreas, Opn Appr
AND	
ØDT9ØZZ	Resect of Duodenum, Opn Appr

DRG 327   Stomach, Esophageal and Duodenal Procedures with CC

GMLOS 5.7   AMLOS 7.5   RW 2.6399   [T]

Select operating room procedures OR procedure combination listed under DRG 326

DRG 328   Stomach, Esophageal and Duodenal Procedures without CC/MCC

GMLOS 2.5   AMLOS 3.3   RW 1.5154   [T]

Select operating room procedures OR procedure combination listed under DRG 326

DRG 329   Major Small and Large Bowel Procedures with MCC

GMLOS 11.5   AMLOS 14.2   RW 5.Ø7Ø9   [T]

Operating Room Procedures

ØD19*	Bypass/Duodenum
ØD1A*	Bypass/Jejunum
ØD1B*	Bypass/Ileum
ØD1H*	Bypass/Cecum
ØD1K*	Bypass/Ascending Colon
ØD1L*	Bypass/Transv Colon
ØD1M*	Bypass/Descending Colon
ØD1N*	Bypass/Sigmoid Colon
ØD78[Ø,3,4]ZZ	Dilation/Sm Intestine, [Opn, Perc, Perc Endo]
ØD79[Ø,3,4]ZZ	Dilation/Duodenum, [Opn, Perc, Perc Endo]
ØD7A[Ø,3,4]ZZ	Dilation/Jejunum, [Opn, Perc, Perc Endo]
ØD7B[Ø,3,4]ZZ	Dilation/Ileum, [Opn, Perc, Perc Endo]
ØD7C[Ø,3,4]ZZ	Dilation/Ileocecal Valve, [Opn, Perc, Perc Endo]
ØD7E[Ø,3,4]ZZ	Dilation/Lg Intestine, [Opn, Perc, Perc Endo]
ØD7F[Ø,3,4]ZZ	Dilation/Lg Intestine, Rt, [Opn, Perc, Perc Endo]
ØD7G[Ø,3,4]ZZ	Dilation/Lg Intestine, Lt, [Opn, Perc, Perc Endo]
ØD7H[Ø,3,4]ZZ	Dilation/Cecum, [Opn, Perc, Perc Endo]
ØD7K[Ø,3,4]ZZ	Dilation/Ascending Colon, [Opn, Perc, Perc Endo]
ØD7L[Ø,3,4]ZZ	Dilation/Transv Colon, [Opn, Perc, Perc Endo]
ØD7M[Ø,3,4]ZZ	Dilation/Descending Colon, [Opn, Perc, Perc Endo]
ØD7N[Ø,3,4]ZZ	Dilation/Sigmoid Colon, [Opn, Perc, Perc Endo]
ØD7P[Ø,3,4][D,Z]Z	Dilation/Rectum, [Opn, Perc, Perc Endo], [Intralum Dev, No Dev], NQ
ØD9P[Ø,3,4]ØZ	Drain/Rectum, [Opn, Perc, Perc Endo], Drain Dev, NQ
ØDB8[Ø,4]ZZ	Exc/Sm Intestine, [Opn, Perc Endo]
ØDBE[Ø,3,4]ZZ	Exc/Lg Intestine, [Opn, Perc, Perc Endo]
ØDBF[Ø,3,4]ZZ	Exc/Lg Intestine, Rt, [Opn, Perc, Perc Endo]
ØDBG[Ø,3,4]ZZ	Exc/Lg Intestine, Lt, [Opn, Perc, Perc Endo]
ØDBH[Ø,3,4]ZZ	Exc/Cecum, [Opn, Perc, Perc Endo]
ØDBK[Ø,3,4]ZZ	Exc/Ascending Colon, [Opn, Perc, Perc Endo]
ØDBL[Ø,3,4]ZZ	Exc/Transv Colon, [Opn, Perc, Perc Endo]
ØDBM[Ø,3,4]ZZ	Exc/Descending Colon, [Opn, Perc, Perc Endo]
ØDBN[Ø,3,4]ZZ	Exc/Sigmoid Colon, [Opn, Perc, Perc Endo]
ØDF8[Ø,3,4,7,8]ZZ	Fragmn/Sm Intestine, [Opn, Perc, Perc Endo, Via Natrl or Artfcl Opng, Via Natrl or Artfcl Opng Endo]
ØDF9[Ø,3,4,7,8]ZZ	Fragmn/Duodenum, [Opn, Perc, Perc Endo, Via Natrl or Artfcl Opng, Via Natrl or Artfcl Opng Endo]
ØDFA[Ø,3,4,7,8]ZZ	Fragmn/Jejunum, [Opn, Perc, Perc Endo, Via Natrl or Artfcl Opng, Via Natrl or Artfcl Opng Endo]
ØDFB[Ø,3,4,7,8]ZZ	Fragmn/Ileum, [Opn, Perc, Perc Endo, Via Natrl or Artfcl Opng, Via Natrl or Artfcl Opng Endo]
ØDFE[Ø,3,4,7,8]ZZ	Fragmn/Lg Intestine, [Opn, Perc, Perc Endo, Via Natrl or Artfcl Opng, Via Natrl or Artfcl Opng Endo]

[T] **Transfer DRG**   [SP] **Special Payment**   *** Code Range**   **6th and 7th Character of ZZ = No Device, No Qualifier ZX = No Device, Diagnostic**

106   MS-DRG Version 33.0   © 2015 Optum360, LLC

ØDFF[Ø,3,4,7,8]ZZ Fragmn/Lg Intestine, Rt, [Opn, Perc, Perc Endo, Via Natrl or Artfcl Opng, Via Natrl or Artfcl Opng Endo]
ØDFG[Ø,3,4,7,8]ZZ Fragmn/Lg Intestine, Lt, [Opn, Perc, Perc Endo, Via Natrl or Artfcl Opng, Via Natrl or Artfcl Opng Endo]
ØDFH[Ø,3,4,7,8]ZZ Fragmn/Cecum, [Opn, Perc, Perc Endo, Via Natrl or Artfcl Opng, Via Natrl or Artfcl Opng Endo]
ØDFK[Ø,3,4,7,8]ZZ Fragmn/Ascending Colon, [Opn, Perc, Perc Endo, Via Natrl or Artfcl Opng, Via Natrl or Artfcl Opng Endo]
ØDFL[Ø,3,4,7,8]ZZ Fragmn/Transv Colon, [Opn, Perc, Perc Endo, Via Natrl or Artfcl Opng, Via Natrl or Artfcl Opng Endo]
ØDFM[Ø,3,4,7,8]ZZ Fragmn/Descending Colon, [Opn, Perc, Perc Endo, Via Natrl or Artfcl Opng, Via Natrl or Artfcl Opng Endo]
ØDFN[Ø,3,4,7,8]ZZ Fragmn/Sigmoid Colon, [Opn, Perc, Perc Endo, Via Natrl or Artfcl Opng, Via Natrl or Artfcl Opng Endo]
ØDL8* Occlsn/Sm Intestine
ØDL9* Occlsn/Duodenum
ØDLA* Occlsn/Jejunum
ØDLB* Occlsn/Ileum
ØDLC* Occlsn/Ileocecal Valve
ØDLE* Occlsn/Large Intestine
ØDLF* Occlsn/Large Intestine, Rt
ØDLG* Occlsn/Large Intestine, Lt
ØDLH* Occlsn/Cecum
ØDLK* Occlsn/Ascending Colon
ØDLL* Occlsn/Transv Colon
ØDLM* Occlsn/Descending Colon
ØDLN* Occlsn/Sigmoid Colon
ØDM8* Reattach/Sm Intestine
ØDM9* Reattach/Duodenum
ØDMA* Reattach/Jejunum
ØDMB* Reattach/Ileum
ØDME* Reattach/Large Intestine
ØDMF* Reattach/Large Intestine, Rt
ØDMG* Reattach/Large Intestine, Lt
ØDMH* Reattach/Cecum
ØDMK* Reattach/Ascending Colon
ØDML* Reattach/Transv Colon
ØDMM* Reattach/Descending Colon
ØDMN* Reattach/Sigmoid Colon
ØDMP* Reattach/Rectum
ØDNC[7,8]ZZ Rls/Ileocecal Valve, [Via Natrl or Artfcl Opng, Via Natrl or Artfcl Opng Endo]
ØDQ8* Repair/Sm Intestine
ØDQA* Repair/Jejunum
ØDQB* Repair/Ileum
ØDQC* Repair/Ileocecal Valve
ØDQE* Repair/Large Intestine
ØDQF[3,4,7,8]ZZ Rpr/Lg Intestine, Rt, [Perc, Perc Endo, Via Natrl or Artfcl Opng, Via Natrl or Artfcl Opng Endo]
ØDQG[3,4,7,8]ZZ Rpr/Lg Intestine, Lt, [Perc, Perc Endo, Via Natrl or Artfcl Opng, Via Natrl or Artfcl Opng Endo]
ØDQH* Repair/Cecum
ØDQK* Repair/Ascending Colon
ØDQL[3,4,7,8]ZZ Rpr/Transv Colon, [Perc, Perc Endo, Via Natrl or Artfcl Opng, Via Natrl or Artfcl Opng Endo]
ØDQM[3,4,7,8]ZZ Rpr/Descending Colon, [Perc, Perc Endo, Via Natrl or Artfcl Opng, Via Natrl or Artfcl Opng Endo]
ØDQN* Repair/Sigmoid Colon
ØDQP* Repair/Rectum
ØDSB[Ø,4,7,8]ZZ Repos/Ileum, [Opn, Perc Endo, Via Natrl or Artfcl Opng, Via Natrl or Artfcl Opng Endo]
ØDSH[Ø,4,7,8]ZZ Repos/Cecum, [Opn, Perc Endo, Via Natrl or Artfcl Opng, Via Natrl or Artfcl Opng Endo]
ØDSP[Ø,4,7,8]ZZ Repos/Rectum, [Opn, Perc Endo, Via Natrl or Artfcl Opng, Via Natrl or Artfcl Opng Endo]
ØDT8* Resect/Sm Intestine
ØDT9* Resect/Duodenum
ØDTA* Resect/Jejunum
ØDTB* Resect/Ileum
ØDTC* Resect/Ileocecal Valve
ØDTE* Resect/Large Intestine
ØDTF* Resect/Large Intestine, Rt
ØDTG* Resect/Large Intestine, Lt
ØDTH* Resect/Cecum
ØDTK* Resect/Ascending Colon
ØDTL* Resect/Transv Colon
ØDTM* Resect/Descending Colon
ØDTN* Resect/Sigmoid Colon
ØDU8* Supl/Sm Intestine
ØDU9* Supl/Duodenum

ØDUA* Supl/Jejunum
ØDUB* Supl/Ileum
ØDUC* Supl/Ileocecal Valve
ØDUE* Supl/Large Intestine
ØDUF* Supl/Large Intestine, Rt
ØDUG* Supl/Large Intestine, Lt
ØDUH* Supl/Cecum
ØDUK* Supl/Ascending Colon
ØDUL* Supl/Transv Colon
ØDUM* Supl/Descending Colon
ØDUN* Supl/Sigmoid Colon
ØDV8* Restrict/Sm Intestine
ØDV9* Restrict/Duodenum
ØDVA* Restrict/Jejunum
ØDVB* Restrict/Ileum
ØDVC* Restrict/Ileocecal Valve
ØDVE* Restrict/Large Intestine
ØDVF* Restrict/Large Intestine, Rt
ØDVG* Restrict/Large Intestine, Lt
ØDVH* Restrict/Cecum
ØDVK* Restrict/Ascending Colon
ØDVL* Restrict/Transv Colon
ØDVM* Restrict/Descending Colon
ØDVN* Restrict/Sigmoid Colon
ØDW8* Rev/Sm Intestine
ØDWE* Rev/Large Intestine
ØJQC* Repair/SQ Tissue & Fascia, Pelvic Region
ØJUC* Supl/SQ Tissue & Fascia, Pelvic Region
ØUQG[Ø,3,4]ZZ Rpr/Vagina, [Opn, Perc, Perc Endo]

DRG 330 Major Small and Large Bowel Procedures with CC
GMLOS 7.Ø   AMLOS 8.2   RW 2.5511   T

Select operating room procedures listed under DRG 329

DRG 331 Major Small and Large Bowel Procedures without CC/MCC
GMLOS 4.1   AMLOS 4.6   RW 1.6491   T

Select operating room procedures listed under DRG 329

DRG 332 Rectal Resection with MCC
GMLOS 1Ø.2   AMLOS 12.4   RW 4.557Ø   T

Operating Room Procedures
ØDBP[Ø,4]ZZ Exc/Rectum, [Opn, Perc Endo]
ØDHQ[Ø,3,4]LZ Insert/Anus, [Opn, Perc, Perc Endo], Artfcl Sphincter, NQ
ØDPQ* Rmvl/Anus
ØDTP* Resect/Rectum
ØDWQ* Rev/Anus
OR
ØTTBØZZ Resect of Bladder, Opn Appr

With all of the following
ØTTDØZZ Resect of Urethra, Opn Appr
ØUT2ØZZ Resect of Bilat Ovaries, Opn Appr
ØUT7ØZZ Resect of Bilat Fallopian Tubes, Opn Appr
ØUT9ØZZ Resect of Uterus, Opn Appr
ØUTCØZZ Resect of Cervix, Opn Appr
ØUTGØZZ Resect of Vagina, Opn Appr

DRG 333 Rectal Resection with CC
GMLOS 6.Ø   AMLOS 7.1   RW 2.4254   T

Select operating room procedures OR procedure combination listed under DRG 332

DRG 334 Rectal Resection without CC/MCC
GMLOS 3.5   AMLOS 4.1   RW 1.648Ø   T

Select operating room procedures OR procedure combination listed under DRG 332

DRG 335 Peritoneal Adhesiolysis with MCC
GMLOS 1Ø.4   AMLOS 12.6   RW 4.1261   T

Operating Room Procedures
ØDN8[Ø,3,4]ZZ Rls/Sm Intestine, [Opn, Perc, Perc Endo]
ØDN9[Ø,3,4]ZZ Rls/Duodenum, [Opn, Perc, Perc Endo]

Surgical   Medical   CC Indicator   MCC Indicator   Procedure Proxy   PDxMCC PDx acts as own MCC   PDxCC PDx acts as own CC

MDC 6: Diseases And Disorders Of The Digestive System—SURGICAL

ØDNA[Ø,3,4]ZZ　　Rls/Jejunum, [Opn, Perc, Perc Endo]
ØDNB[Ø,3,4]ZZ　　Rls/Ileum, [Opn, Perc, Perc Endo]
ØDNC[Ø,3,4]ZZ　　Rls/Ileocecal Valve, [Opn, Perc, Perc Endo]
ØDNE[Ø,3,4]ZZ　　Rls/Lg Intestine, [Opn, Perc, Perc Endo]
ØDNF[Ø,3,4]ZZ　　Rls/Lg Intestine, Rt, [Opn, Perc, Perc Endo]
ØDNG[Ø,3,4]ZZ　　Rls/Lg Intestine, Lt, [Opn, Perc, Perc Endo]
ØDNH[Ø,3,4]ZZ　　Rls/Cecum, [Opn, Perc, Perc Endo]
ØDNJ[Ø,3,4]ZZ　　Rls/Appendix, [Opn, Perc, Perc Endo]
ØDNK[Ø,3,4]ZZ　　Rls/Ascending Colon, [Opn, Perc, Perc Endo]
ØDNL[Ø,3,4]ZZ　　Rls/Transv Colon, [Opn, Perc, Perc Endo]
ØDNM[Ø,3,4]ZZ　　Rls/Descending Colon, [Opn, Perc, Perc Endo]
ØDNN[Ø,3,4]ZZ　　Rls/Sigmoid Colon, [Opn, Perc, Perc Endo]
ØDNS*　　　　　　Rls/Greater Omentum
ØDNT*　　　　　　Rls/Lesser Omentum
ØDNV*　　　　　　Rls/Mesentery
ØDNW*　　　　　　Rls/Peritoneum
ØFN*　　　　　　　Hepatobiliary Sys and Pancreas, Rls

DRG 336　Peritoneal Adhesiolysis with CC
GMLOS 6.7　　　　AMLOS 8.1　　　　RW 2.334Ø　　　Ⓣ

Select operating room procedures listed under DRG 335

DRG 337　Peritoneal Adhesiolysis without CC/MCC
GMLOS 4.Ø　　　　AMLOS 4.9　　　　RW 1.5675　　　Ⓣ

Select operating room procedures listed under DRG 335

DRG 338　Appendectomy with Complicated Principal Diagnosis with MCC
GMLOS 7.5　　　　AMLOS 9.Ø　　　　RW 2.9719

Principal Diagnosis

C18.1　　　　　　Malig neoplasm of appendix
C7A.Ø2Ø　　　　Malig carcinoid tumor of the appendix
K35.2　　　　　　Acute appendicitis with generalized peritonitis
K35.3　　　　　　Acute appendicitis with localized peritonitis
AND

Operating Room Procedures

ØD5J*　　　　　　Destr/Appendix
ØD9J*　　　　　　Drain/Appendix
ØDBJ*　　　　　　Exc/Appendix
ØDCJ*　　　　　　Extir/Appendix
ØDFJ[Ø,3,4,7,8]ZZ　Fragmn/Appendix, [Opn, Perc, Perc Endo, Via Natrl or Artfcl Opng, Via Natrl or Artfcl Opng Endo]
ØDNJ[7,8]ZZ　　Rls/Appendix, [Via Natrl or Artfcl Opng, Via Natrl or Artfcl Opng Endo]
ØDQJ*　　　　　　Repair/Appendix
ØDTJ*　　　　　　Resect/Appendix

DRG 339　Appendectomy with Complicated Principal Diagnosis with CC
GMLOS 4.8　　　　AMLOS 5.8　　　　RW 1.7693

Select principal diagnosis AND operating room procedure listed under DRG 338

DRG 340　Appendectomy with Complicated Principal Diagnosis without CC/MCC
GMLOS 2.9　　　　AMLOS 3.4　　　　RW 1.1773

Select principal diagnosis AND operating room procedure listed under DRG 338

DRG 341　Appendectomy without Complicated Principal Diagnosis with MCC
GMLOS 4.5　　　　AMLOS 6.2　　　　RW 2.1523

Operating Room Procedures

ØD5J*　　　　　　Destr/Appendix
ØD9J*　　　　　　Drain/Appendix
ØDBJ*　　　　　　Exc/Appendix
ØDCJ*　　　　　　Extir/Appendix
ØDFJ[Ø,3,4,7,8]ZZ　Fragmn/Appendix, [Opn, Perc, Perc Endo, Via Natrl or Artfcl Opng, Via Natrl or Artfcl Opng Endo]
ØDNJ[7,8]ZZ　　Rls/Appendix, [Via Natrl or Artfcl Opng, Via Natrl or Artfcl Opng Endo]
ØDQJ*　　　　　　Repair/Appendix
ØDTJ*　　　　　　Resect/Appendix

DRG 342　Appendectomy without Complicated Principal Diagnosis with CC
GMLOS 2.7　　　　AMLOS 3.5　　　　RW 1.3275

Select operating room procedures listed under DRG 341

DRG 343　Appendectomy without Complicated Principal Diagnosis without CC/MCC
GMLOS 1.7　　　　AMLOS 2.Ø　　　　RW 1.ØØ99

Select operating room procedures listed under DRG 341

DRG 344　Minor Small and Large Bowel Procedures with MCC
GMLOS 8.Ø　　　　AMLOS 1Ø.2　　　　RW 3.1Ø29

Operating Room Procedures

ØD58*　　　　　　Destr/Sm Intestine
ØD5A*　　　　　　Destr/Jejunum
ØD5B*　　　　　　Destr/Ileum
ØD5C*　　　　　　Destr/Ileocecal Valve
ØD5E[Ø,3,7]ZZ　Destr/Lg Intestine, [Opn, Perc, Via Natrl or Artfcl Opng]
ØD5F[Ø,3,7]ZZ　Destr/Lg Intestine, Rt, [Opn, Perc, Via Natrl or Artfcl Opng]
ØD5G[Ø,3,7]ZZ　Destr/Lg Intestine, Lt, [Opn, Perc, Via Natrl or Artfcl Opng]
ØD5H[Ø,3,7]ZZ　Destr/Cecum, [Opn, Perc, Via Natrl or Artfcl Opng]
ØD5K[Ø,3,7]ZZ　Destr/Ascending Colon, [Opn, Perc, Via Natrl or Artfcl Opng]
ØD5L[Ø,3,7]ZZ　Destr/Transv Colon, [Opn, Perc, Via Natrl or Artfcl Opng]
ØD5M[Ø,3,7]ZZ　Destr/Descending Colon, [Opn, Perc, Via Natrl or Artfcl Opng]
ØD5N[Ø,3,7]ZZ　Destr/Sigmoid Colon, [Opn, Perc, Via Natrl or Artfcl Opng]
ØD98ØZX　　　　Drain of Sm Intestine, Opn Appr, Diagnostic
ØD98[Ø,3,4,7,8]ZZ　Drain/Sm Intestine, [Opn, Perc, Perc Endo, Via Natrl or Artfcl Opng, Via Natrl or Artfcl Opng Endo]
ØD98[Ø,3,4]ØZ　Drain/Sm Intestine, [Opn, Perc, Perc Endo], Drain Dev, NQ
ØD99ØZX　　　　Drain of Duodenum, Opn Appr, Diagnostic
ØD9AØZX　　　　Drain of Jejunum, Opn Appr, Diagnostic
ØD9A[Ø,3,4,7,8]ZZ　Drain/Jejunum, [Opn, Perc, Perc Endo, Via Natrl or Artfcl Opng, Via Natrl or Artfcl Opng Endo]
ØD9A[Ø,3,4]ØZ　Drain/Jejunum, [Opn, Perc, Perc Endo], Drain Dev, NQ
ØD9BØZX　　　　Drain of Ileum, Opn Appr, Diagnostic
ØD9B[Ø,3,4,7,8]ZZ　Drain/Ileum, [Opn, Perc, Perc Endo, Via Natrl or Artfcl Opng, Via Natrl or Artfcl Opng Endo]
ØD9B[Ø,3,4]ØZ　Drain/Ileum, [Opn, Perc, Perc Endo], Drain Dev, NQ
ØD9CØZX　　　　Drain of Ileocecal Valve, Opn Appr, Diagnostic
ØD9C[Ø,3,4,7,8][Ø,Z]Z　Drain/Ileocecal Valve, [Opn, Perc, Perc Endo, Via Natrl or Artfcl Opng, Via Natrl or Artfcl Opng Endo], [Drain Dev, No Dev], NQ
ØD9EØZX　　　　Drain of Large Intestine, Opn Appr, Diagnostic
ØD9E[Ø,3,4,7,8]ZZ　Drain/Lg Intestine, [Opn, Perc, Perc Endo, Via Natrl or Artfcl Opng, Via Natrl or Artfcl Opng Endo]
ØD9E[Ø,3,4]ØZ　Drain/Lg Intestine, [Opn, Perc, Perc Endo], Drain Dev, NQ
ØD9FØZX　　　　Drain of Rt Large Intestine, Opn Appr, Diagnostic
ØD9F[Ø,3,4,7,8]ZZ　Drain/Lg Intestine, Rt, [Opn, Perc, Perc Endo, Via Natrl or Artfcl Opng, Via Natrl or Artfcl Opng Endo]
ØD9F[Ø,3,4]ØZ　Drain/Lg Intestine, Rt, [Opn, Perc, Perc Endo], Drain Dev, NQ
ØD9GØZX　　　　Drain of Lt Large Intestine, Opn Appr, Diagnostic
ØD9G[Ø,3,4,7,8]ZZ　Drain/Lg Intestine, Lt, [Opn, Perc, Perc Endo, Via Natrl or Artfcl Opng, Via Natrl or Artfcl Opng Endo]
ØD9G[Ø,3,4]ØZ　Drain/Lg Intestine, Lt, [Opn, Perc, Perc Endo], Drain Dev, NQ
ØD9HØZX　　　　Drain of Cecum, Opn Appr, Diagnostic
ØD9H[Ø,3,4,7,8]ZZ　Drain/Cecum, [Opn, Perc, Perc Endo, Via Natrl or Artfcl Opng, Via Natrl or Artfcl Opng Endo]
ØD9H[Ø,3,4]ØZ　Drain/Cecum, [Opn, Perc, Perc Endo], Drain Dev, NQ
ØD9KØZX　　　　Drain of Ascending Colon, Opn Appr, Diagnostic
ØD9K[Ø,3,4,7,8]ZZ　Drain/Ascending Colon, [Opn, Perc, Perc Endo, Via Natrl or Artfcl Opng, Via Natrl or Artfcl Opng Endo]
ØD9K[Ø,3,4]ØZ　Drain/Ascending Colon, [Opn, Perc, Perc Endo], Drain Dev, NQ
ØD9LØZX　　　　Drain of Transv Colon, Opn Appr, Diagnostic
ØD9L[Ø,3,4,7,8]ZZ　Drain/Transv Colon, [Opn, Perc, Perc Endo, Via Natrl or Artfcl Opng, Via Natrl or Artfcl Opng Endo]
ØD9L[Ø,3,4]ØZ　Drain/Transv Colon, [Opn, Perc, Perc Endo], Drain Dev, NQ
ØD9MØZX　　　　Drain of Descending Colon, Opn Appr, Diagnostic
ØD9M[Ø,3,4,7,8]ZZ　Drain/Descending Colon, [Opn, Perc, Perc Endo, Via Natrl or Artfcl Opng, Via Natrl or Artfcl Opng Endo]
ØD9M[Ø,3,4]ØZ　Drain/Descending Colon, [Opn, Perc, Perc Endo], Drain Dev, NQ
ØD9NØZX　　　　Drain of Sigmoid Colon, Opn Appr, Diagnostic

Ⓣ **Transfer DRG**　　　　ⓈⓅ **Special Payment**　　　　* **Code Range**　　　　**6th and 7th Character of ZZ = No Device, No Qualifier ZX = No Device, Diagnostic**

Code	Description
0D9N[0,3,4,7,8]ZZ	Drain/Sigmoid Colon, [Opn, Perc, Perc Endo, Via Natrl or Artfcl Opng, Via Natrl or Artfcl Opng Endo]
0D9N[0,3,4]0Z	Drain/Sigmoid Colon, [Opn, Perc, Perc Endo], Drain Dev, NQ
0D9P0ZX	Drain of Rectum, Opn Appr, Diagnostic
0D9P[0,3,4,7,8]ZZ	Drain/Rectum, [Opn, Perc, Perc Endo, Via Natrl or Artfcl Opng, Via Natrl or Artfcl Opng Endo]
0DBH0ZX	Exc of Cecum, Opn Appr, Diagnostic
0DBP0ZX	Exc of Rectum, Opn Appr, Diagnostic
0DB[8,9,A,B,C]0ZX	Exc of [Sm Intestine, Duodenum, Jejunum, Ileum, Ileocecal Valve], Opn Appr, Dx
0DB[E,F,G]0ZX	Exc of [Lg, Rt Lg, Lt Lg] Intestine, Opn Appr, Dx
0DB[K,L,M,N]0ZX	Exc of [Ascending, Transv, Descending, Sigmoid] Colon, Opn Appr, Dx
0DC8[0,3,4]ZZ	Extir/Sm Intestine, [Opn, Perc, Perc Endo]
0DCA[0,3,4]ZZ	Extir/Jejunum, [Opn, Perc, Perc Endo]
0DCB[0,3,4]ZZ	Extir/Ileum, [Opn, Perc, Perc Endo]
0DCC[0,3,4]ZZ	Extir/Ileocecal Valve, [Opn, Perc, Perc Endo]
0DCE[0,3,4]ZZ	Extir/Lg Intestine, [Opn, Perc, Perc Endo]
0DCF[0,3,4]ZZ	Extir/Lg Intestine, Rt, [Opn, Perc, Perc Endo]
0DCG[0,3,4]ZZ	Extir/Lg Intestine, Lt, [Opn, Perc, Perc Endo]
0DCH[0,3,4]ZZ	Extir/Cecum, [Opn, Perc, Perc Endo]
0DCK[0,3,4]ZZ	Extir/Ascending Colon, [Opn, Perc, Perc Endo]
0DCL[0,3,4]ZZ	Extir/Transv Colon, [Opn, Perc, Perc Endo]
0DCM[0,3,4]ZZ	Extir/Descending Colon, [Opn, Perc, Perc Endo]
0DCN[0,3,4]ZZ	Extir/Sigmoid Colon, [Opn, Perc, Perc Endo]
0DCP[0,3,4]ZZ	Extir/Rectum, [Opn, Perc, Perc Endo]
0DH8[0,3,4,7,8][2,3]Z	Insert/Sm Intestine, [Opn, Perc, Perc Endo, Via Natrl or Artfcl Opng, Via Natrl or Artfcl Opng Endo], [Monitoring Dev, Inf Dev], NQ
0DHA[0,3,4,7,8][2,3]Z	Insert/Jejunum, [Opn, Perc, Perc Endo, Via Natrl or Artfcl Opng, Via Natrl or Artfcl Opng Endo], [Monitoring Dev, Inf Dev], NQ
0DHB[0,3,4,7,8][2,3]Z	Insert/Ileum, [Opn, Perc, Perc Endo, Via Natrl or Artfcl Opng, Via Natrl or Artfcl Opng Endo], [Monitoring Dev, Inf Dev], NQ
0DJD4ZZ	Inspect of Lwr Intestinal Tract, Perc Endo Appr
0DP0[0,3,4,7,8][0,2,3,7,C,D,J,K,U]Z	Rmvl/Upr Intestinal Tract, [Opn, Perc, Perc Endo, Via Natrl or Artfcl Opng, Via Natrl or Artfcl Opng Endo], [Drain Dev, Monitoring Dev, Inf Dev, Auto Tissue Sub, Extralum Dev, Intralum Dev, Synth Sub, Nonauto Tissue Sub, Feeding Dev], NQ
0DPD[0,3,4,7,8][0,2,3,7,C,D,J,K,U]Z	Rmvl/Lwr Intestinal Tract, [Opn, Perc, Perc Endo, Via Natrl or Artfcl Opng, Via Natrl or Artfcl Opng Endo], [Drain Dev, Monitoring Dev, Inf Dev, Auto Tissue Sub, Extralum Dev, Intralum Dev, Synth Sub, Nonauto Tissue Sub, Feeding Dev], NQ
0DPP[0,3,4]1Z	Rmvl/Rectum, [Opn, Perc, Perc Endo], Radioact Elmt, NQ
0DS9[0,4,7,8]ZZ	Repos/Duodenum, [Opn, Perc Endo, Via Natrl or Artfcl Opng, Via Natrl or Artfcl Opng Endo]
0DSA[0,4,7,8]ZZ	Repos/Jejunum, [Opn, Perc Endo, Via Natrl or Artfcl Opng, Via Natrl or Artfcl Opng Endo]
0DSK[0,4,7,8]ZZ	Repos/Ascending Colon, [Opn, Perc Endo, Via Natrl or Artfcl Opng, Via Natrl or Artfcl Opng Endo]
0DSL[0,4,7,8]ZZ	Repos/Transv Colon, [Opn, Perc Endo, Via Natrl or Artfcl Opng, Via Natrl or Artfcl Opng Endo]
0DSM[0,4,7,8]ZZ	Repos/Descending Colon, [Opn, Perc Endo, Via Natrl or Artfcl Opng, Via Natrl or Artfcl Opng Endo]
0DSN[0,4,7,8]ZZ	Repos/Sigmoid Colon, [Opn, Perc Endo, Via Natrl or Artfcl Opng, Via Natrl or Artfcl Opng Endo]
0DW0[0,3,4,7,8][0,2,3,7,C,D,J,K]Z	Rev/Upr Intestinal Tract, [Opn, Perc, Perc Endo, Via Natrl or Artfcl Opng, Via Natrl or Artfcl Opng Endo], [Drain Dev, Monitoring Dev, Inf Dev, Auto Tissue Sub, Extralum Dev, Intralum Dev, Synth Sub, Nonauto Tissue Sub], NQ
0DW0[0,3,7,8]UZ	Rev/Upr Intestinal Tract, [Opn, Perc, Via Natrl or Artfcl Opng, Via Natrl or Artfcl Opng Endo], Feeding Dev, NQ
0DWD[0,3,4,7,8][0,2,3,7,C,D,J,K,U]Z	Rev/Lwr Intestinal Tract, [Opn, Perc, Perc Endo, Via Natrl or Artfcl Opng, Via Natrl or Artfcl Opng Endo], [Drain Dev, Monitoring Dev, Inf Dev, Auto Tissue Sub, Extralum Dev, Intralum Dev, Synth Sub, Nonauto Tissue Sub, Feeding Dev], NQ
0TQ6*	Repair/Ureter, Rt
0TQ7*	Repair/Ureter, Lt
0TQB*	Repair/Bladder
0UQ9*	Repair/Uterus
0UQM*	Repair/Vulva

OR

Code	Description
0WQFXZ2	Repair Abd Wall, Stoma, Ext Appr

AND

Code	Description
0DQ80ZZ	Repair Sm Intestine, Opn Appr
0DQ90ZZ	Repair Duodenum, Opn Appr

Code	Description
0DQA0ZZ	Repair Jejunum, Opn Appr
0DQB0ZZ	Repair Ileum, Opn Appr
0DQE0ZZ	Repair Large Intestine, Opn Appr
0DQF0ZZ	Repair Rt Large Intestine, Opn Appr
0DQG0ZZ	Repair Lt Large Intestine, Opn Appr
0DQH0ZZ	Repair Cecum, Opn Appr
0DQK0ZZ	Repair Ascending Colon, Opn Appr
0DQL0ZZ	Repair Transv Colon, Opn Appr
0DQM0ZZ	Repair Descending Colon, Opn Appr
0DQN0ZZ	Repair Sigmoid Colon, Opn Appr

DRG 345 — Minor Small and Large Bowel Procedures with CC
GMLOS 5.2   AMLOS 6.1   RW 1.6268

Select operating room procedures OR procedure combinations listed under DRG 344

DRG 346 — Minor Small and Large Bowel Procedures without CC/MCC
GMLOS 3.7   AMLOS 4.2   RW 1.2143

Select operating room procedures OR procedure combinations listed under DRG 344

DRG 347 — Anal and Stomal Procedures with MCC
GMLOS 6.1   AMLOS 8.3   RW 2.4457

Operating Room Procedures

Code	Description
065Y[0,3,4]ZC	Destr/Lwr Vein, [Opn, Perc, Perc Endo], No Dev, Hemorrhoidal Plexus
06BY[0,3,4]ZC	Exc/Lwr Vein, [Opn, Perc, Perc Endo], No Dev, Hemorrhoidal Plexus
06LY[0,3,4][C,D,Z]C	Occlsn/Lwr Vein, [Opn, Perc, Perc Endo], [Extralum Dev, Intralum Dev, No Dev], Hemorrhoidal Plexus
0D5Q[0,3,7,X]ZZ	Destr/Anus, [Opn, Perc, Via Natrl or Artfcl Opng, Ext]
0D5R[0,3]ZZ	Destr/Anal Sphincter, [Opn, Perc]
0D7Q[0,3,4][D,Z]Z	Dilation/Anus, [Opn, Perc, Perc Endo], [Intralum Dev, No Dev], NQ
0D8R*	Div/Anal Sphincter
0D9Q[0,3,4,7,8,X][0,Z]Z	Drain/Anus, [Opn, Perc, Perc Endo, Via Natrl or Artfcl Opng, Via Natrl or Artfcl Opng Endo, Ext], [Drain Dev, No Dev], NQ
0D9R[0,3,4][0,Z]Z	Drain/Anal Sphincter, [Opn, Perc, Perc Endo], [Drain Dev, No Dev], NQ
0DB8[3,7,8]ZZ	Exc/Sm Intestine, [Perc, Via Natrl or Artfcl Opng, Via Natrl or Artfcl Opng Endo]
0DBA[0,3,4,7,8]ZZ	Exc/Jejunum, [Opn, Perc, Perc Endo, Via Natrl or Artfcl Opng, Via Natrl or Artfcl Opng Endo]
0DBB[0,3,4,7,8]ZZ	Exc/Ileum, [Opn, Perc, Perc Endo, Via Natrl or Artfcl Opng, Via Natrl or Artfcl Opng Endo]
0DBC[0,3,4,7,8]ZZ	Exc/Ileocecal Valve, [Opn, Perc, Perc Endo, Via Natrl or Artfcl Opng, Via Natrl or Artfcl Opng Endo]
0DBE7ZZ	Exc of Large Intestine, Via Opng
0DBF7ZZ	Exc of Rt Large Intestine, Via Opng
0DBG7ZZ	Exc of Lt Large Intestine, Via Opng
0DBH7ZZ	Exc of Cecum, Via Natrl or Artfcl Opng
0DBK7ZZ	Exc of Ascending Colon, Via Opng
0DBL7ZZ	Exc of Transv Colon, Via Opng
0DBM7ZZ	Exc of Descending Colon, Via Opng
0DBN7ZZ	Exc of Sigmoid Colon, Via Natrl or Artfcl Opng
0DBP[3,7]ZZ	Exc/Rectum, [Perc, Via Natrl or Artfcl Opng]
0DBQ[0,3,4,7,8,X]ZZ	Exc/Anus, [Opn, Perc, Perc Endo, Via Natrl or Artfcl Opng, Via Natrl or Artfcl Opng Endo, Ext]
0DBR[0,3,4]ZZ	Exc/Anal Sphincter, [Opn, Perc, Perc Endo]
0DCQ[0,3,4]ZZ	Extir/Anus, [Opn, Perc, Perc Endo]
0DCR*	Extir/Anal Sphincter
0DFP[0,3,4,7,8]ZZ	Fragmn/Rectum, [Opn, Perc, Perc Endo, Via Natrl or Artfcl Opng, Via Natrl or Artfcl Opng Endo]
0DFQ[0,3,4,7,8]ZZ	Fragmn/Anus, [Opn, Perc, Perc Endo, Via Natrl or Artfcl Opng, Via Natrl or Artfcl Opng Endo]
0DHQ[0,3,4,7,8]DZ	Insert/Anus, [Opn, Perc, Perc Endo, Via Natrl or Artfcl Opng, Via Natrl or Artfcl Opng Endo], Intralum Dev, NQ
0DHR*	Insert/Anal Sphincter
0DLP*	Occlsn/Rectum
0DLQ*	Occlsn/Anus
0DNP*	Rls/Rectum
0DNQ*	Rls/Anus
0DNR*	Rls/Anal Sphincter
0DQQ*	Repair/Anus
0DQR*	Repair/Anal Sphincter

| Surgical | Medical | CC Indicator | MCC Indicator | Procedure Proxy | PDxMCC PDx acts as own MCC | PDxCC PDx acts as own CC |

MDC 6: Diseases And Disorders Of The Digestive System—SURGICAL

ØDRR*	Replace/Anal Sphincter
ØDSQ*	Repos/Anus
ØDTQ*	Resect/Anus
ØDTR*	Resect/Anal Sphincter
ØDUP*	Supl/Rectum
ØDUQ*	Supl/Anus
ØDUR*	Supl/Anal Sphincter
ØDVP*	Restrict/Rectum
ØDVQ*	Restrict/Anus
ØDWR*	Rev/Anal Sphincter
ØH89XZZ	Div of Perineum Skin, Ext Appr
ØW3P7ZZ	Control Bleeding in Gastrointestinal Tract, Via Opng
ØWQFXZ2	Repair Abd Wall, Stoma, Ext Appr

DRG 348   Anal and Stomal Procedures with CC
GMLOS 4.Ø   AMLOS 5.1   RW 1.4486

Select operating room procedures listed under DRG 347

DRG 349   Anal and Stomal Procedures without CC/MCC
GMLOS 2.4   AMLOS 2.9   RW Ø.9265

Select operating room procedures listed under DRG 347

DRG 350   Inguinal and Femor Hernia Procedures with MCC
GMLOS 5.6   AMLOS 7.6   RW 2.4982

Operating Room Procedures

ØYQ5[Ø,3,4]ZZ	Rpr/Inguinal Rgn, Rt, [Opn, Perc, Perc Endo]
ØYQ6[Ø,3,4]ZZ	Rpr/Inguinal Rgn, Lt, [Opn, Perc, Perc Endo]
ØYQ7[Ø,3,4]ZZ	Rpr/Femor Rgn, Rt, [Opn, Perc, Perc Endo]
ØYQ8[Ø,3,4]ZZ	Rpr/Femor Rgn, Lt, [Opn, Perc, Perc Endo]
ØYQA[Ø,3,4]ZZ	Rpr/Inguinal Rgn, Bilat, [Opn, Perc, Perc Endo]
ØYQE[Ø,3,4]ZZ	Rpr/Femor Rgn, Bilat, [Opn, Perc, Perc Endo]
ØYU5*	Supl/Inguinal Region, Rt
ØYU6*	Supl/Inguinal Region, Lt
ØYU7*	Supl/Femor Region, Rt
ØYU8*	Supl/Femor Region, Lt
ØYUA*	Supl/Inguinal Region, Bilat
ØYUE*	Supl/Femor Region, Bilat

DRG 351   Inguinal and Femor Hernia Procedures with CC
GMLOS 3.4   AMLOS 4.3   RW 1.411Ø

Select operating room procedures listed under DRG 350

DRG 352   Inguinal and Femoral Hernia Procedures without CC/MCC
GMLOS 2.1   AMLOS 2.6   RW Ø.9764

Select operating room procedures listed under DRG 350

DRG 353   Hernia Procedures Except Inguinal and Femoral with MCC
GMLOS 6.2   AMLOS 8.1   RW 2.9142

Operating Room Procedures

ØDQS*	Repair/Greater Omentum
ØDQT*	Repair/Lesser Omentum
ØWMFØZZ	Reattach of Abd Wall, Opn Appr
ØWQF[Ø,3,4,X]ZZ	Rpr/Abd Wall, [Opn, Perc, Perc Endo, Ext]
ØWUF*	Supl/Abd Wall

DRG 354   Hernia Procedures Except Inguinal and Femoral with CC
GMLOS 3.9   AMLOS 4.8   RW 1.664Ø

Select operating room procedures listed under DRG 353

DRG 355   Hernia Procedures Except Inguinal and Femoral without CC/MCC
GMLOS 2.5   AMLOS 3.Ø   RW 1.2366

Select operating room procedures listed under DRG 353

DRG 356   Other Digestive System O.R. Procedures with MCC
GMLOS 8.2   AMLOS 10.9   RW 3.7588   [T]

Operating Room Procedures

02BW[Ø,4]ZZ	Exc/Thoracic Aorta, [Opn, Perc Endo]
02CW*	Extir/Thoracic Aorta
02HV[Ø,3,4][2,D]Z	Insert/Superior Vena Cava, [Opn, Perc, Perc Endo], [Monitoring Dev, Intralum Dev], NQ
02LV*	Occlsn/Superior Vena Cava
02VV*	Restrict/Superior Vena Cava
Ø319ØZF	Bypass Rt Ulnar Artery to Lwr Arm Vein, Opn Appr
Ø31AØZF	Bypass Lt Ulnar Artery to Lwr Arm Vein, Opn Appr
Ø31BØZF	Bypass Rt Radial Artery to Lwr Arm Vein, Opn Appr
Ø31CØZF	Bypass Lt Radial Artery to Lwr Arm Vein, Opn Appr
Ø31[3,4]ØZD	Bypass [Rt, Lt] Subclavian Artery to Upr Arm Vein, Opn Appr
Ø31[5,6]ØZD	Bypass [Rt, Lt] Axillary Artery to Upr Arm Vein, Opn Appr
Ø31[7,8]ØZD	Bypass [Rt, Lt] Brachial Artery to Upr Arm Vein, Opn Appr
Ø3733[4,D,Z]Z	Dilation/Subclavian Artery, Rt, Perc, [Drug-eluting Intralum Dev, Intralum Dev, No Dev], NQ
Ø3743[4,D,Z]Z	Dilation/Subclavian Artery, Lt, Perc, [Drug-eluting Intralum Dev, Intralum Dev, No Dev], NQ
Ø3773[4,D,Z]Z	Dilation/Brachial Artery, Rt, Perc, [Drug-eluting Intralum Dev, Intralum Dev, No Dev], NQ
Ø3783[4,D,Z]Z	Dilation/Brachial Artery, Lt, Perc, [Drug-eluting Intralum Dev, Intralum Dev, No Dev], NQ
Ø3793[4,D,Z]Z	Dilation/Ulnar Artery, Rt, Perc, [Drug-eluting Intralum Dev, Intralum Dev, No Dev], NQ
Ø37A3[4,D,Z]Z	Dilation/Ulnar Artery, Lt, Perc, [Drug-eluting Intralum Dev, Intralum Dev, No Dev], NQ
Ø37Y3[4,D,Z]Z	Dilation/Upr Artery, Perc, [Drug-eluting Intralum Dev, Intralum Dev, No Dev], NQ
Ø3CY*	Extir/Upr Artery
Ø3QY*	Repair/Upr Artery
Ø41ØØ[J,Z][1,2]	Bypass/Abd Aorta, Opn, [Synth Sub, No Dev], [Celiac Artery, Mesenteric Artery]
Ø41C[Ø,4][J,Z][3,4,5]	Bypass/Common Iliac Artery, Rt, [Opn, Perc Endo], [Synth Sub, No Dev], [Renal Artery, Rt, Renal Artery, Lt, Renal Artery, Bilat]
Ø41D[Ø,7][J,Z][3,4,5]	Bypass/Common Iliac Artery, Lt, [Opn, Perc Endo], [Synth Sub, No Dev], [Renal Artery, Rt, Renal Artery, Lt, Renal Artery, Bilat]
Ø45Ø*	Destr/Abd Aorta
Ø47Ø3[4,D,Z]Z	Dilation/Abd Aorta, Perc, [Drug-eluting Intralum Dev, Intralum Dev, No Dev], NQ
Ø4713[4,D,Z]Z	Dilation/Celiac Artery, Perc, [Drug-eluting Intralum Dev, Intralum Dev, No Dev], NQ
Ø4723[4,D,Z]Z	Dilation/Gastric Artery, Perc, [Drug-eluting Intralum Dev, Intralum Dev, No Dev], NQ
Ø4733[4,D,Z]Z	Dilation/Hepatic Artery, Perc, [Drug-eluting Intralum Dev, Intralum Dev, No Dev], NQ
Ø4743[4,D,Z]Z	Dilation/Splenic Artery, Perc, [Drug-eluting Intralum Dev, Intralum Dev, No Dev], NQ
Ø4753[4,D,Z]Z	Dilation/Superior Mesenteric Artery, Perc, [Drug-eluting Intralum Dev, Intralum Dev, No Dev], NQ
Ø4763[4,D,Z]Z	Dilation/Colic Artery, Rt, Perc, [Drug-eluting Intralum Dev, Intralum Dev, No Dev], NQ
Ø4773[4,D,Z]Z	Dilation/Colic Artery, Lt, Perc, [Drug-eluting Intralum Dev, Intralum Dev, No Dev], NQ
Ø4783[4,D,Z]Z	Dilation/Colic Artery, Mid, Perc, [Drug-eluting Intralum Dev, Intralum Dev, No Dev], NQ
Ø4793[4,D,Z]Z	Dilation/Renal Artery, Rt, Perc, [Drug-eluting Intralum Dev, Intralum Dev, No Dev], NQ
Ø47A3[4,D,Z]Z	Dilation/Renal Artery, Lt, Perc, [Drug-eluting Intralum Dev, Intralum Dev, No Dev], NQ
Ø47B3[4,D,Z]Z	Dilation/Inferior Mesenteric Artery, Perc, [Drug-eluting Intralum Dev, Intralum Dev, No Dev], NQ
Ø47C3[4,D,Z]Z	Dilation/Common Iliac Artery, Rt, Perc, [Drug-eluting Intralum Dev, Intralum Dev, No Dev], NQ
Ø47D3[4,D,Z]Z	Dilation/Common Iliac Artery, Lt, Perc, [Drug-eluting Intralum Dev, Intralum Dev, No Dev], NQ
Ø47E3[4,D,Z]Z	Dilation/Int Iliac Artery, Rt, Perc, [Drug-eluting Intralum Dev, Intralum Dev, No Dev], NQ
Ø47F3[4,D,Z]Z	Dilation/Int Iliac Artery, Lt, Perc, [Drug-eluting Intralum Dev, Intralum Dev, No Dev], NQ
Ø47H3[4,D,Z]Z	Dilation/Ext Iliac Artery, Rt, Perc, [Drug-eluting Intralum Dev, Intralum Dev, No Dev], NQ
Ø47J3[4,D,Z]Z	Dilation/Ext Iliac Artery, Lt, Perc, [Drug-eluting Intralum Dev, Intralum Dev, No Dev], NQ
Ø47KØ41	Dilation Rt Fem Art w Drug-elut Intralum, Drug Blln, Opn
Ø47KØD1	Dilation Rt Fem Art w Intralum Dev, Drug Blln, Opn

[T] **Transfer DRG**   [SP] **Special Payment**   * **Code Range**   **6th and 7th Character of ZZ = No Device, No Qualifier ZX = No Device, Diagnostic**

110   MS-DRG Version 33.0   © 2015 Optum360, LLC

047KØZ1	Dilation of Rt Fem Art using Drug Blln, Opn Appr
047K341	Dilation Rt Fem Art w Drug-elut Intralum, Drug Blln, Perc
047K3D1	Dilation Rt Fem Art w Intralum Dev, Drug Blln, Perc
047K3Z1	Dilation of Rt Fem Art using Drug Blln, Perc Appr
047K3[4,D,Z]Z	Dilation/Femor Artery, Rt, Perc, [Drug-eluting Intralum Dev, Intralum Dev, No Dev], NQ
047K441	Dilation Rt Fem Art w Drug-elut Intralum, Drug Blln, Perc Endo
047K4D1	Dilation Rt Fem Art w Intralum Dev, Drug Blln, Perc Endo
047K4Z1	Dilation of Rt Fem Art using Drug Blln, Perc Endo Appr
047LØ41	Dilation Lt Fem Art w Drug-elut Intralum, Drug Blln, Opn
047LØD1	Dilation Lt Fem Art w Intralum Dev, Drug Blln, Opn
047LØZ1	Dilation of Lt Fem Art using Drug Blln, Opn Appr
047L341	Dilation Lt Fem Art w Drug-elut Intralum, Drug Blln, Perc
047L3D1	Dilation Lt Fem Art w Intralum Dev, Drug Blln, Perc
047L3Z1	Dilation of Lt Fem Art using Drug Blln, Perc Appr
047L3[4,D,Z]Z	Dilation/Femor Artery, Lt, Perc, [Drug-eluting Intralum Dev, Intralum Dev, No Dev], NQ
047L441	Dilation Lt Fem Art w Drug-elut Intralum, Drug Blln, Perc Endo
047L4D1	Dilation Lt Fem Art w Intralum Dev, Drug Blln, Perc Endo
047L4Z1	Dilation of Lt Fem Art using Drug Blln, Perc Endo Appr
047MØ41	Dilation Rt Popl Art w Drug-elut Intralum, Drug Blln, Opn
047MØD1	Dilation Rt Popl Art w Intralum Dev, Drug Blln, Opn
047MØZ1	Dilation of Rt Popl Art using Drug Blln, Opn Appr
047M341	Dilation Rt Popl Art w Drug-elut Intralum, Drug Blln, Perc
047M3D1	Dilation Rt Popl Art w Intralum Dev, Drug Blln, Perc
047M3Z1	Dilation of Rt Popl Art using Drug Blln, Perc Appr
047M441	Dilation Rt Popl Art w Drug-elut Intralum, Drug Blln, Perc Endo
047M4D1	Dilation Rt Popl Art w Intralum Dev, Drug Blln, Perc Endo
047M4Z1	Dilation of Rt Popl Art using Drug Blln, Perc Endo Appr
047NØ41	Dilation Lt Popl Art w Drug-elut Intralum, Drug Blln, Opn
047NØD1	Dilation Lt Popl Art w Intralum Dev, Drug Blln, Opn
047NØZ1	Dilation of Lt Popl Art using Drug Blln, Opn Appr
047N341	Dilation Lt Popl Art w Drug-elut Intralum, Drug Blln, Perc
047N3D1	Dilation Lt Popl Art w Intralum Dev, Drug Blln, Perc
047N3Z1	Dilation of Lt Popl Art using Drug Blln, Perc Appr
047N441	Dilation Lt Popl Art w Drug-elut Intralum, Drug Blln, Perc Endo
047N4D1	Dilation Lt Popl Art w Intralum Dev, Drug Blln, Perc Endo
047N4Z1	Dilation of Lt Popl Art using Drug Blln, Perc Endo Appr
047Y3[4,D,Z]Z	Dilation/Lwr Artery, Perc, [Drug-eluting Intralum Dev, Intralum Dev, No Dev], NQ
04BØ[Ø,3,4]ZZ	Exc/Abd Aorta, [Opn, Perc, Perc Endo]
04CØ*	Extir/Abd Aorta
04C1*	Extir/Celiac Artery
04C2*	Extir/Gastric Artery
04C3*	Extir/Hepatic Artery
04C4*	Extir/Splenic Artery
04C5*	Extir/Superior Mesenteric Artery
04C6*	Extir/Colic Artery, Rt
04C7*	Extir/Colic Artery, Lt
04C8*	Extir/Colic Artery, Mid
04C9*	Extir/Renal Artery, Rt
04CA*	Extir/Renal Artery, Lt
04CB*	Extir/Inferior Mesenteric Artery
04CC*	Extir/Common Iliac Artery, Rt
04CD*	Extir/Common Iliac Artery, Lt
04CE*	Extir/Int Iliac Artery, Rt
04CF*	Extir/Int Iliac Artery, Lt
04CH*	Extir/Ext Iliac Artery, Rt
04CJ*	Extir/Ext Iliac Artery, Lt
04CY*	Extir/Lwr Artery
04HØ[Ø,3,4]DZ	Insert/Abd Aorta, [Opn, Perc, Perc Endo], Intralum Dev, NQ
04LØ*	Occlsn/Abd Aorta
04L1*	Occlsn/Celiac Artery
04L2[Ø,3,4][C,Z]Z	Occlsn/Gastric Artery, [Opn, Perc, Perc Endo], [Extralum Dev, No Dev], NQ
04L2[Ø,4]DZ	Occlsn/Gastric Artery, [Opn, Perc Endo], Intralum Dev, NQ
04L3*	Occlsn/Hepatic Artery
04L4*	Occlsn/Splenic Artery
04L5*	Occlsn/Superior Mesenteric Artery
04L6*	Occlsn/Colic Artery, Rt
04L7*	Occlsn/Colic Artery, Lt
04L8*	Occlsn/Colic Artery, Mid
04L9*	Occlsn/Renal Artery, Rt
04LA*	Occlsn/Renal Artery, Lt
04LB*	Occlsn/Inferior Mesenteric Artery
04LC[Ø,3,4][C,Z]Z	Occlsn/Common Iliac Artery, Rt, [Opn, Perc, Perc Endo], [Extralum Dev, No Dev], NQ
04LD[Ø,3,4][C,Z]Z	Occlsn/Common Iliac Artery, Lt, [Opn, Perc, Perc Endo], [Extralum Dev, No Dev], NQ

04LE[Ø,3,4][C,Z]Z	Occlsn/Int Iliac Artery, Rt, [Opn, Perc, Perc Endo], [Extralum Dev, No Dev], NQ
04LF[Ø,3,4][C,Z]Z	Occlsn/Int Iliac Artery, Lt, [Opn, Perc, Perc Endo], [Extralum Dev, No Dev], NQ
04LH[Ø,3,4][C,Z]Z	Occlsn/Ext Iliac Artery, Rt, [Opn, Perc, Perc Endo], [Extralum Dev, No Dev], NQ
04LJ[Ø,3,4][C,Z]Z	Occlsn/Ext Iliac Artery, Lt, [Opn, Perc, Perc Endo], [Extralum Dev, No Dev], NQ
04NØ[Ø,4]ZZ	Rls/Abd Aorta, [Opn, Perc Endo]
04N1[Ø,4]ZZ	Rls/Celiac Artery, [Opn, Perc Endo]
04N2[Ø,4]ZZ	Rls/Gastric Artery, [Opn, Perc Endo]
04N3[Ø,4]ZZ	Rls/Hepatic Artery, [Opn, Perc Endo]
04N4[Ø,4]ZZ	Rls/Splenic Artery, [Opn, Perc Endo]
04N5[Ø,4]ZZ	Rls/Superior Mesenteric Artery, [Opn, Perc Endo]
04N6[Ø,4]ZZ	Rls/Colic Artery, Rt, [Opn, Perc Endo]
04N7[Ø,4]ZZ	Rls/Colic Artery, Lt, [Opn, Perc Endo]
04N8[Ø,4]ZZ	Rls/Colic Artery, Mid, [Opn, Perc Endo]
04N9[Ø,4]ZZ	Rls/Renal Artery, Rt, [Opn, Perc Endo]
04NA[Ø,4]ZZ	Rls/Renal Artery, Lt, [Opn, Perc Endo]
04NB[Ø,4]ZZ	Rls/Inferior Mesenteric Artery, [Opn, Perc Endo]
04NC[Ø,4]ZZ	Rls/Common Iliac Artery, Rt, [Opn, Perc Endo]
04ND[Ø,4]ZZ	Rls/Common Iliac Artery, Lt, [Opn, Perc Endo]
04NE[Ø,4]ZZ	Rls/Int Iliac Artery, Rt, [Opn, Perc Endo]
04NF[Ø,4]ZZ	Rls/Int Iliac Artery, Lt, [Opn, Perc Endo]
04NH[Ø,4]ZZ	Rls/Ext Iliac Artery, Rt, [Opn, Perc Endo]
04NJ[Ø,4]ZZ	Rls/Ext Iliac Artery, Lt, [Opn, Perc Endo]
04QY*	Repair/Lwr Artery
05793[D,Z]Z	Dilation/Brachial Vein, Rt, Perc, [Intralum Dev, No Dev], NQ
057A3[D,Z]Z	Dilation/Brachial Vein, Lt, Perc, [Intralum Dev, No Dev], NQ
057B3[D,Z]Z	Dilation/Basilic Vein, Rt, Perc, [Intralum Dev, No Dev], NQ
057C3[D,Z]Z	Dilation/Basilic Vein, Lt, Perc, [Intralum Dev, No Dev], NQ
057D3[D,Z]Z	Dilation/Cephalic Vein, Rt, Perc, [Intralum Dev, No Dev], NQ
057F3[D,Z]Z	Dilation/Cephalic Vein, Lt, Perc, [Intralum Dev, No Dev], NQ
05CY*	Extir/Upr Vein
05HY[Ø,3,4]DZ	Insert/Upr Vein, [Opn, Perc, Perc Endo], Intralum Dev, NQ
05QY*	Repair/Upr Vein
06703[D,Z]Z	Dilation/Inferior Vena Cava, Perc, [Intralum Dev, No Dev], NQ
06CY*	Extir/Lwr Vein
06HØ[Ø,3,4]DZ	Insert/Inferior Vena Cava, [Opn, Perc, Perc Endo], Intralum Dev, NQ
06H1[Ø,3,4]DZ	Insert/Splenic Vein, [Opn, Perc, Perc Endo], Intralum Dev, NQ
06H2[Ø,3,4]DZ	Insert/Gastric Vein, [Opn, Perc, Perc Endo], Intralum Dev, NQ
06H3[Ø,3,4]DZ	Insert/Esophageal Vein, [Opn, Perc, Perc Endo], Intralum Dev, NQ
06H4[Ø,3,4]DZ	Insert/Hepatic Vein, [Opn, Perc, Perc Endo], Intralum Dev, NQ
06H5[Ø,3,4]DZ	Insert/Superior Mesenteric Vein, [Opn, Perc, Perc Endo], Intralum Dev, NQ
06H6[Ø,3,4]DZ	Insert/Inferior Mesenteric Vein, [Opn, Perc, Perc Endo], Intralum Dev, NQ
06H7[Ø,3,4]DZ	Insert/Colic Vein, [Opn, Perc, Perc Endo], Intralum Dev, NQ
06H8[Ø,3,4]DZ	Insert/Portal Vein, [Opn, Perc, Perc Endo], Intralum Dev, NQ
06HY[Ø,3,4]DZ	Insert/Lwr Vein, [Opn, Perc, Perc Endo], Intralum Dev, NQ
06LØ*	Occlsn/Inferior Vena Cava
06L1*	Occlsn/Splenic Vein
06L2[Ø,3,4][C,D]Z	Occlsn/Gastric Vein, [Opn, Perc, Perc Endo], [Extralum Dev, Intralum Dev], NQ
06L3[Ø,3,4][C,D]Z	Occlsn/Esophageal Vein, [Opn, Perc, Perc Endo], [Extralum Dev, Intralum Dev], NQ
06L4*	Occlsn/Hepatic Vein
06L5*	Occlsn/Superior Mesenteric Vein
06L6*	Occlsn/Inferior Mesenteric Vein
06L7*	Occlsn/Colic Vein
06L8*	Occlsn/Portal Vein
06L9*	Occlsn/Renal Vein, Rt
06LB*	Occlsn/Renal Vein, Lt
06LC[Ø,3,4][C,Z]Z	Occlsn/Common Iliac Vein, Rt, [Opn, Perc, Perc Endo], [Extralum Dev, No Dev], NQ
06LD[Ø,3,4][C,Z]Z	Occlsn/Common Iliac Vein, Lt, [Opn, Perc, Perc Endo], [Extralum Dev, No Dev], NQ
06LF[Ø,3,4][C,Z]Z	Occlsn/Ext Iliac Vein, Rt, [Opn, Perc, Perc Endo], [Extralum Dev, No Dev], NQ
06LG[Ø,3,4][C,Z]Z	Occlsn/Ext Iliac Vein, Lt, [Opn, Perc, Perc Endo], [Extralum Dev, No Dev], NQ
06LH*	Occlsn/Hypogastric Vein, Rt
06LJ*	Occlsn/Hypogastric Vein, Lt
06NØ[Ø,4]ZZ	Rls/Inferior Vena Cava, [Opn, Perc Endo]
06N1[Ø,4]ZZ	Rls/Splenic Vein, [Opn, Perc Endo]
06N2[Ø,4]ZZ	Rls/Gastric Vein, [Opn, Perc Endo]
06N3[Ø,4]ZZ	Rls/Esophageal Vein, [Opn, Perc Endo]
06N4[Ø,4]ZZ	Rls/Hepatic Vein, [Opn, Perc Endo]

MDC 6: Diseases And Disorders Of The Digestive System—SURGICAL

Surgical   **Medical**   **CC Indicator**   **MCC Indicator**   **Procedure Proxy**   **PDx MCC** **PDx acts as own MCC**   **PDx CC** **PDx acts as own CC**

MDC 6: Diseases And Disorders Of The Digestive System—SURGICAL

06N5[0,4]ZZ	Rls/Superior Mesenteric Vein, [Opn, Perc Endo]
06N6[0,4]ZZ	Rls/Inferior Mesenteric Vein, [Opn, Perc Endo]
06N7[0,4]ZZ	Rls/Colic Vein, [Opn, Perc Endo]
06N8[0,4]ZZ	Rls/Portal Vein, [Opn, Perc Endo]
06N9[0,4]ZZ	Rls/Renal Vein, Rt, [Opn, Perc Endo]
06NB[0,4]ZZ	Rls/Renal Vein, Lt, [Opn, Perc Endo]
06NC[0,4]ZZ	Rls/Common Iliac Vein, Rt, [Opn, Perc Endo]
06ND[0,4]ZZ	Rls/Common Iliac Vein, Lt, [Opn, Perc Endo]
06NF[0,4]ZZ	Rls/Ext Iliac Vein, Rt, [Opn, Perc Endo]
06NG[0,4]ZZ	Rls/Ext Iliac Vein, Lt, [Opn, Perc Endo]
06NH[0,4]ZZ	Rls/Hypogastric Vein, Rt, [Opn, Perc Endo]
06NJ[0,4]ZZ	Rls/Hypogastric Vein, Lt, [Opn, Perc Endo]
06QY*	Repair/Lwr Vein
06V0*	Restrict/Inferior Vena Cava
079B[0,3,4]ZX	Drain/Lymphatic, Mesenteric, [Opn, Perc, Perc Endo]
079C[0,3,4]ZX	Drain/Lymphatic, Pelvis, [Opn, Perc, Perc Endo]
079D[0,3,4]ZX	Drain/Lymphatic, Aortic, [Opn, Perc, Perc Endo]
079L[0,3,4]ZX	Drain/Cisterna Chyli, [Opn, Perc, Perc Endo]
07B1[0,3,4]ZZ	Exc/Lymphatic, Rt Neck, [Opn, Perc, Perc Endo]
07B2[0,3,4]ZZ	Exc/Lymphatic, Lt Neck, [Opn, Perc, Perc Endo]
07B5[0,3,4]ZZ	Exc/Lymphatic, Rt Axillary, [Opn, Perc, Perc Endo]
07B6[0,3,4]ZZ	Exc/Lymphatic, Lt Axillary, [Opn, Perc, Perc Endo]
07BB*	Exc/Lymphatic, Mesenteric
07BC*	Exc/Lymphatic, Pelvis
07BD*	Exc/Lymphatic, Aortic
07BH[0,3,4]ZZ	Exc/Lymphatic, Rt Inguinal, [Opn, Perc, Perc Endo]
07BJ[0,3,4]ZZ	Exc/Lymphatic, Lt Inguinal, [Opn, Perc, Perc Endo]
07BL[0,3,4]ZX	Exc/Cisterna Chyli, [Opn, Perc, Perc Endo]
07JN[0,3,4]ZZ	Inspect/Lymphatic, [Opn, Perc, Perc Endo]
07JP0ZZ	Inspect of Spleen, Opn Appr
07T0*	Resect/Lymphatic, Head
07T3*	Resect/Lymphatic, Rt Upr Extr
07T4*	Resect/Lymphatic, Lt Upr Extr
07T5*	Resect/Lymphatic, Rt Axillary
07T6*	Resect/Lymphatic, Lt Axillary
07T7*	Resect/Lymphatic, Thorax
07T8*	Resect/Lymphatic, Int Mammary, Rt
07T9*	Resect/Lymphatic, Int Mammary, Lt
07TB*	Resect/Lymphatic, Mesenteric
07TC*	Resect/Lymphatic, Pelvis
07TD*	Resect/Lymphatic, Aortic
07TF*	Resect/Lymphatic, Rt Lwr Extr
07TG*	Resect/Lymphatic, Lt Lwr Extr
07TH*	Resect/Lymphatic, Rt Inguinal
07TJ*	Resect/Lymphatic, Lt Inguinal
07TP*	Resect/Spleen
0D5S*	Destr/Greater Omentum
0D5T*	Destr/Lesser Omentum
0D5V*	Destr/Mesentery
0D5W*	Destr/Peritoneum
0D9S00Z	Drain of Greater Omentum with Drain Dev, Opn Appr
0D9S0ZZ	Drain of Greater Omentum, Opn Appr
0D9S[0,3,4]ZX	Drain/Greater Omentum, [Opn, Perc, Perc Endo]
0D9T00Z	Drain of Lesser Omentum with Drain Dev, Opn Appr
0D9T0ZZ	Drain of Lesser Omentum, Opn Appr
0D9T[0,3,4]ZX	Drain/Lesser Omentum, [Opn, Perc, Perc Endo]
0D9V00Z	Drain of Mesentery with Drain Device, Opn Appr
0D9V0ZZ	Drain of Mesentery, Opn Appr
0D9V[0,3,4]ZX	Drain/Mesentery, [Opn, Perc, Perc Endo]
0D9W00Z	Drain of Peritoneum with Drain Device, Opn Appr
0D9W0ZZ	Drain of Peritoneum, Opn Appr
0D9W[0,3,4]ZX	Drain/Peritoneum, [Opn, Perc, Perc Endo]
0DBS0ZX	Exc of Greater Omentum, Opn Appr, Diagnostic
0DBS[0,3,4]ZZ	Exc/Greater Omentum, [Opn, Perc, Perc Endo]
0DBT0ZX	Exc of Lesser Omentum, Opn Appr, Diagnostic
0DBT[0,3,4]ZZ	Exc/Lesser Omentum, [Opn, Perc, Perc Endo]
0DBV0ZX	Exc of Mesentery, Opn Appr, Diagnostic
0DBV[0,3,4]ZZ	Exc/Mesentery, [Opn, Perc, Perc Endo]
0DBW0ZX	Exc of Peritoneum, Opn Appr, Diagnostic
0DBW[0,3,4]ZZ	Exc/Peritoneum, [Opn, Perc, Perc Endo]
0DCS*	Extir/Greater Omentum
0DCT*	Extir/Lesser Omentum
0DCV*	Extir/Mesentery
0DCW*	Extir/Peritoneum
0DH5[0,3,4,7,8]1Z	Insert/Esophagus, [Opn, Perc, Perc Endo, Via Natrl or Artfcl Opng, Via Natrl or Artfcl Opng Endo], Radioact Elmt, NQ
0DHP[0,3,4,7,8]1Z	Insert/Rectum, [Opn, Perc, Perc Endo, Via Natrl or Artfcl Opng, Via Natrl or Artfcl Opng Endo], Radioact Elmt, NQ
0DJU[0,3,4]ZZ	Inspect/Omentum, [Opn, Perc, Perc Endo]
0DJV[0,3,4]ZZ	Inspect/Mesentery, [Opn, Perc, Perc Endo]
0DJW[0,3,4]ZZ	Inspect/Peritoneum, [Opn, Perc, Perc Endo]
0DJ[0,6,D]0ZZ	Inspect of [Upr Intestinal Tract, Stomach, Lwr Intestinal Tract], Opn Appr
0DPU*	Rmvl/Omentum
0DPV*	Rmvl/Mesentery
0DPW*	Rmvl/Peritoneum
0DQV*	Repair/Mesentery
0DQW*	Repair/Peritoneum
0DRS*	Replace/Greater Omentum
0DRT*	Replace/Lesser Omentum
0DRV*	Replace/Mesentery
0DRW*	Replace/Peritoneum
0DTS*	Resect/Greater Omentum
0DTT*	Resect/Lesser Omentum
0DUS*	Supl/Greater Omentum
0DUT*	Supl/Lesser Omentum
0DUV*	Supl/Mesentery
0DUW*	Supl/Peritoneum
0DWU[0,3,4][7,J,K]Z	Rev/Omentum, [Opn, Perc, Perc Endo], [Auto Tissue Sub, Synth Sub, Nonauto Tissue Sub], NQ
0DWV[0,3,4][7,J,K]Z	Rev/Mesentery, [Opn, Perc, Perc Endo], [Auto Tissue Sub, Synth Sub, Nonauto Tissue Sub], NQ
0DWW[0,3,4][7,J,K]Z	Rev/Peritoneum, [Opn, Perc, Perc Endo], [Auto Tissue Sub, Synth Sub, Nonauto Tissue Sub], NQ
0F14[0,4][D,Z][3,B]	Bypass/Gallbladder, [Opn, Perc Endo], [Intralum Dev, No Dev], [Duodenum, Sm Intestine]
0F15[0,4][D,Z][3,4,B]	Bypass/Hepatic Duct, Rt, [Opn, Perc Endo], [Intralum Dev, No Dev], [Duodenum, Stomach, Sm Intestine]
0F16[0,4][D,Z][3,4,B]	Bypass/Hepatic Duct, Lt, [Opn, Perc Endo], [Intralum Dev, No Dev], [Duodenum, Stomach, Sm Intestine]
0F18[0,4][D,Z][3,B]	Bypass/Cystic Duct, [Opn, Perc Endo], [Intralum Dev, No Dev], [Duodenum, Sm Intestine]
0F19[0,4][D,Z][3,B]	Bypass/Common Bile Duct, [Opn, Perc Endo], [Intralum Dev, No Dev], [Duodenum, Sm Intestine]
0F50*	Destr/Liver
0F51*	Destr/Liver, Rt Lobe
0F52*	Destr/Liver, Lt Lobe
0F55[0,3,7]ZZ	Destr/Hepatic Duct, Rt, [Opn, Perc, Via Natrl or Artfcl Opng]
0F56[0,3,7]ZZ	Destr/Hepatic Duct, Lt, [Opn, Perc, Via Natrl or Artfcl Opng]
0F58[0,3,7]ZZ	Destr/Cystic Duct, [Opn, Perc, Via Natrl or Artfcl Opng]
0F59[0,3,7]ZZ	Destr/Common Bile Duct, [Opn, Perc, Via Natrl or Artfcl Opng]
0F5C[0,3,7]ZZ	Destr/Ampulla of Vater, [Opn, Perc, Via Natrl or Artfcl Opng]
0F7C[0,3,4,7][D,Z]Z	Dilation/Ampulla of Vater, [Opn, Perc, Perc Endo, Via Natrl or Artfcl Opng], [Intralum Dev, No Dev], NQ
0F7D[0,3,7]DZ	Dilation/Pancreatic Duct, [Opn, Perc, Via Natrl or Artfcl Opng], Intralum Dev, NQ
0F7D[0,3]ZZ	Dilation/Pancreatic Duct, [Opn, Perc]
0F7F[0,3,7]DZ	Dilation/Pancreatic Duct, Accessory, [Opn, Perc, Via Natrl or Artfcl Opng], Intralum Dev, NQ
0F7F[0,3]ZZ	Dilation/Pancreatic Duct, Accessory, [Opn, Perc]
0F940Z[X,Z]	Drain/Gallbladder, Opn, No Dev, [Dx, NQ]
0F950ZX	Drain of Rt Hepatic Duct, Opn Appr, Diagnostic
0F95[0,3,4,7,8][0,Z]Z	Drain/Hepatic Duct, Rt, [Opn, Perc, Perc Endo, Via Natrl or Artfcl Opng, Via Natrl or Artfcl Opng Endo], [Drain Dev, No Dev], NQ
0F960ZX	Drain of Lt Hepatic Duct, Opn Appr, Diagnostic
0F96[0,3,4,7,8][0,Z]Z	Drain/Hepatic Duct, Lt, [Opn, Perc, Perc Endo, Via Natrl or Artfcl Opng, Via Natrl or Artfcl Opng Endo], [Drain Dev, No Dev], NQ
0F980ZX	Drain of Cystic Duct, Opn Appr, Diagnostic
0F98[0,3,4,7,8][0,Z]Z	Drain/Cystic Duct, [Opn, Perc, Perc Endo, Via Natrl or Artfcl Opng, Via Natrl or Artfcl Opng Endo], [Drain Dev, No Dev], NQ
0F9[0,1,2]0ZX	Drain of [Liver, Rt Lobe Liver, Lt Lobe Liver], Opn Appr, Dx
0F9[9,C,D,F,G]0ZX	Drain of [Common Bile Duct, Ampulla of Vater, Pancreatic Duct, Accessory Pancreatic Duct, Pancreas], Opn Appr, Dx
0FB0[0,4]ZX	Exc/Liver, [Opn, Perc Endo]
0FB1[0,4]ZX	Exc/Liver, Rt Lobe, [Opn, Perc Endo]
0FB2[0,4]ZX	Exc/Liver, Lt Lobe, [Opn, Perc Endo]
0FB40ZX	Exc of Gallbladder, Opn Appr, Diagnostic
0FB50ZX	Exc of Rt Hepatic Duct, Opn Appr, Diagnostic
0FB5[0,3,7]ZZ	Exc/Hepatic Duct, Rt, [Opn, Perc, Via Natrl or Artfcl Opng]
0FB60ZX	Exc of Lt Hepatic Duct, Opn Appr, Diagnostic
0FB6[0,3,7]ZZ	Exc/Hepatic Duct, Lt, [Opn, Perc, Via Natrl or Artfcl Opng]
0FB80ZX	Exc of Cystic Duct, Opn Appr, Diagnostic
0FB90ZX	Exc of Common Bile Duct, Opn Appr, Diagnostic
0FB9[0,3,7]ZZ	Exc/Common Bile Duct, [Opn, Perc, Via Natrl or Artfcl Opng]
0FBC0ZX	Exc of Ampulla of Vater, Opn Appr, Diagnostic
0FBC[0,3,7]ZZ	Exc/Ampulla of Vater, [Opn, Perc, Via Natrl or Artfcl Opng]
0FB[D,F,G]0ZX	Exc of [Pancreatic Duct, Accessory Pancreatic Duct, Pancreas], Opn Appr, Dx

---

T Transfer DRG   SP Special Payment   * Code Range   6th and 7th Character of ZZ = No Device, No Qualifier ZX = No Device, Diagnostic

0FHB[0,3,7]DZ	Insert/Hepatobiliary Duct, [Opn, Perc, Via Natrl or Artfcl Opng], Intralum Dev, NQ
0FHD[0,3,7]DZ	Insert/Pancreatic Duct, [Opn, Perc, Via Natrl or Artfcl Opng], Intralum Dev, NQ
0FJ0[0,3,4]ZZ	Inspect/Liver, [Opn, Perc, Perc Endo]
0FJ4[0,3,4]ZZ	Inspect/Gallbladder, [Opn, Perc, Perc Endo]
0FJD*	Inspect/Pancreatic Duct
0FJG[0,3,4]ZZ	Inspect/Pancreas, [Opn, Perc, Perc Endo]
0FLD*	Occlsn/Pancreatic Duct
0FLF*	Occlsn/Pancreatic Duct, Accessory
0FT4*	Resect/Gallbladder
0FT5*	Resect/Hepatic Duct, Rt
0FT6*	Resect/Hepatic Duct, Lt
0FT8*	Resect/Cystic Duct
0FT9*	Resect/Common Bile Duct
0FTC*	Resect/Ampulla of Vater
0FUD[3,4]7Z	Supl/Pancreatic Duct, [Perc, Perc Endo], Auto Tissue Sub, NQ
0H8[0,1,4,5,6,7,8,A]XZZ	Div [Scalp, Face, Neck, Chest, Back, Abd, Buttock, Genitalia] Skin, Ext
0H8[B,C,D,E]XZZ	Div of [Rt Upr Arm, Lt Upr Arm, Rt Lwr Arm, Lt Lwr Arm] Skin, Ext Appr
0H8[H,J,K,L,M,N]XZZ	Div of Skin of [Rt Upr Leg, Lt Upr Leg, Rt Lwr Leg, Lt Lwr Leg, Rt Foot, Lt Foot], Ext
0HB0XZZ	Exc of Scalp Skin, Ext Appr
0HB1XZZ	Exc of Face Skin, Ext Appr
0HB4XZZ	Exc of Neck Skin, Ext Appr
0HB5XZZ	Exc of Chest Skin, Ext Appr
0HB6XZZ	Exc of Back Skin, Ext Appr
0HB7XZZ	Exc of Abd Skin, Ext Appr
0HB8XZZ	Exc of Buttock Skin, Ext Appr
0HBAXZZ	Exc of Genitalia Skin, Ext Appr
0HBBXZZ	Exc of Rt Upr Arm Skin, Ext Appr
0HBCXZZ	Exc of Lt Upr Arm Skin, Ext Appr
0HBDXZZ	Exc of Rt Lwr Arm Skin, Ext Appr
0HBEXZZ	Exc of Lt Lwr Arm Skin, Ext Appr
0HBFXZZ	Exc of Rt Hand Skin, Ext Appr
0HBGXZZ	Exc of Lt Hand Skin, Ext Appr
0HBHXZZ	Exc of Rt Upr Leg Skin, Ext Appr
0HBJXZZ	Exc of Lt Upr Leg Skin, Ext Appr
0HBKXZZ	Exc of Rt Lwr Leg Skin, Ext Appr
0HBLXZZ	Exc of Lt Lwr Leg Skin, Ext Appr
0HBMXZZ	Exc of Rt Foot Skin, Ext Appr
0HBNXZZ	Exc of Lt Foot Skin, Ext Appr
0HR5XJZ	Replace of Chest Skin with Synth Sub, Extern Appr
0HR5X[7,J][3,4]	Replace/Skin, Chest, Ext, [Auto Tissue Sub, Synth Sub], [Full Thickness, Partial Thickness]
0HR6XJZ	Replace of Back Skin with Synth Sub, Extern Appr
0HR6X[7,J][3,4]	Replace/Skin, Back, Ext, [Auto Tissue Sub, Synth Sub], [Full Thickness, Partial Thickness]
0HR7XJZ	Replace of Abd Skin with Synth Sub, Extern Appr
0HR7X[7,J][3,4]	Replace/Skin, Abd, Ext, [Auto Tissue Sub, Synth Sub], [Full Thickness, Partial Thickness]
0HR8X73	Replace Buttock Skin w Autol Sub, Full Thick, Extern
0HR8XJ[3,4,Z]	Replace/Skin, Buttock, Ext, Synth Sub, [Full Thickness, Partial Thickness, NQ]
0HX[0,1,4,5,6,7,8,9,A]XZZ	Transfer [Scalp, Face, Neck, Chest, Back, Abd, Buttock, Perineum, Genitalia] Skin, Ext
0HX[B,C,D,E,F,G]XZZ	Transfer [Rt Upr Arm, Lt Upr Arm, Rt Lwr Arm, Lt Lwr Arm, Rt Hand, Lt Hand], Ext
0HX[H,J,K,L,M,N]XZZ	Transfer [Rt Upr Leg, Lt Upr Leg, Rt Lwr Leg, Lt Lwr Leg, Rt Foot, Lt Foot], Ext
0JB[0,1,4,5,6]0ZZ	Exc of SQ Tissue & Fascia of [Scalp, Face, Ant Neck, Post Neck, Chest], Opn
0JB[7,8,9,B,C]0ZZ	Exc of SQ Tissue & Fascia of [Back, Abd, Buttock, Perineum, Pelvic Rgn], Opn
0JB[D,F,G,H]0ZZ	Exc of SQ Tissue & Fascia of [Rt Upr Arm, Lt Upr Arm, Rt Lwr Arm, Lt Lwr Arm], Opn
0JB[L,M,N,P,Q,R]0ZZ	Exc of SQ Tissue & Fascia of [Rt Upr Leg, Lt Upr Leg, Rt Lwr Leg, Lt Lwr Leg, Rt Foot, Lt Foot], Opn
0JH0*	Insert/SQ Tissue & Fascia, Scalp
0JH1*	Insert/SQ Tissue & Fascia, Face
0JH4*	Insert/SQ Tissue & Fascia, Ant Neck
0JH5*	Insert/SQ Tissue & Fascia, Posterior Neck
0JH6[0,3][N,V]Z	Insert/SQ Tissue & Fascia, Chest, [Opn, Perc], [Tissue Expander, Inf Pump], NQ
0JH7[0,3][N,V]Z	Insert/SQ Tissue & Fascia, Back, [Opn, Perc], [Tissue Expander, Inf Pump], NQ
0JH8[0,3][N,V]Z	Insert/SQ Tissue & Fascia, Abd, [Opn, Perc], [Tissue Expander, Inf Pump], NQ
0JHT[0,3]VZ	Insert/SQ Tissue & Fascia, Trunk, [Opn, Perc], Inf Pump, NQ
0JX0[0,3]Z[B,C]	Transfer/SQ Tissue & Fascia, Scalp, [Opn, Perc], No Dev, [Skin and SQ Tissue, Skin, SQ Tissue & Fascia]
0JX1[0,3]Z[B,C]	Transfer/SQ Tissue & Fascia, Face, [Opn, Perc], No Dev, [Skin and SQ Tissue, Skin, SQ Tissue & Fascia]
0JX4[0,3]Z[B,C]	Transfer/SQ Tissue & Fascia, Ant Neck, [Opn, Perc], No Dev, [Skin and SQ Tissue, Skin, SQ Tissue & Fascia]
0JX5[0,3]Z[B,C]	Transfer/SQ Tissue & Fascia, Post Neck, [Opn, Perc], No Dev, [Skin and SQ Tissue, Skin, SQ Tissue & Fascia]
0JX6[0,3]Z[B,C]	Transfer/SQ Tissue & Fascia, Chest, [Opn, Perc], No Dev, [Skin and SQ Tissue, Skin, SQ Tissue & Fascia]
0JX7[0,3]Z[B,C]	Transfer/SQ Tissue & Fascia, Back, [Opn, Perc], No Dev, [Skin and SQ Tissue, Skin, SQ Tissue & Fascia]
0JX8[0,3]Z[B,C]	Transfer/SQ Tissue & Fascia, Abd, [Opn, Perc], No Dev, [Skin and SQ Tissue, Skin, SQ Tissue & Fascia]
0JX9[0,3]Z[B,C]	Transfer/SQ Tissue & Fascia, Buttock, [Opn, Perc], No Dev, [Skin and SQ Tissue, Skin, SQ Tissue & Fascia]
0JXB[0,3]Z[B,C]	Transfer/SQ Tissue & Fascia, Perineum, [Opn, Perc], No Dev, [Skin and SQ Tissue, Skin, SQ Tissue & Fascia]
0JXC[0,3]Z[B,C]	Transfer/SQ Tissue & Fascia, Genitalia, [Opn, Perc], No Dev, [Skin and SQ Tissue, Skin, SQ Tissue & Fascia]
0JXD[0,3]Z[B,C]	Transfer/SQ Tissue & Fascia, Rt Upr Arm, [Opn, Perc], No Dev, [Skin and SQ Tissue, Skin, SQ Tissue & Fascia]
0JXF[0,3]Z[B,C]	Transfer/SQ Tissue & Fascia, Lt Upr Arm, [Opn, Perc], No Dev, [Skin and SQ Tissue, Skin, SQ Tissue & Fascia]
0JXG[0,3]Z[B,C]	Transfer/SQ Tissue & Fascia, Rt Lwr Arm, [Opn, Perc], No Dev, [Skin and SQ Tissue, Skin, SQ Tissue & Fascia]
0JXH[0,3]Z[B,C]	Transfer/SQ Tissue & Fascia, Lt Lwr Arm, [Opn, Perc], No Dev, [Skin and SQ Tissue, Skin, SQ Tissue & Fascia]
0JXL[0,3]Z[B,C]	Transfer/SQ Tissue & Fascia, Rt Upr Leg, [Opn, Perc], No Dev, [Skin and SQ Tissue, Skin, SQ Tissue & Fascia]
0JXM[0,3]Z[B,C]	Transfer/SQ Tissue & Fascia, Lt Upr Leg, [Opn, Perc], No Dev, [Skin and SQ Tissue, Skin, SQ Tissue & Fascia]
0JXN[0,3]Z[B,C]	Transfer/SQ Tissue & Fascia, Rt Lwr Leg, [Opn, Perc], No Dev, [Skin and SQ Tissue, Skin, SQ Tissue & Fascia]
0JXP[0,3]Z[B,C]	Transfer/SQ Tissue & Fascia, Lt Lwr Leg, [Opn, Perc], No Dev, [Skin and SQ Tissue, Skin, SQ Tissue & Fascia]
0JXQ[0,3]Z[B,C]	Transfer/SQ Tissue & Fascia, Rt Foot, [Opn, Perc], No Dev, [Skin and SQ Tissue, Skin, SQ Tissue & Fascia]
0JXR[0,3]Z[B,C]	Transfer/SQ Tissue & Fascia, Lt Foot, [Opn, Perc], No Dev, [Skin and SQ Tissue, Skin, SQ Tissue & Fascia]
0W1G[0,3,4]J4	Bypass/Peritoneal Cavity, [Opn, Perc, Perc Endo], Synth Sub, Cutaneous
0W1G[0,4]JY	Bypass/Peritoneal Cavity, [Opn, Perc Endo], Synth Sub, Lwr Vein
0W3F*	Control/Abd Wall
0W3G[3,4]ZZ	Control/Peritoneal Cavity, [Perc, Perc Endo]
0W3H*	Control/Retroperitoneum
0W3J*	Control/Pelvic Cavity
0W3P[0,3,4]ZZ	Control/Gastrointestinal Tract, [Opn, Perc, Perc Endo]
0W9F00Z	Drain of Abd Wall with Drain Dev, Opn Appr
0W9F0ZZ	Drain of Abd Wall, Opn Appr
0W9F[0,3,4]ZX	Drain/Abd Wall, [Opn, Perc, Perc Endo]
0W9G00Z	Drain of Peritoneal Cavity with Drain Dev, Opn Appr
0W9G0ZZ	Drain of Peritoneal Cavity, Opn Appr
0W9G[0,3,4]ZX	Drain/Peritoneal Cavity, [Opn, Perc, Perc Endo]
0W9H*	Drain/Retroperitoneum
0W9J[0,3,4]ZX	Drain/Pelvic Cavity, [Opn, Perc, Perc Endo]
0W9J[0,4]0Z	Drain/Pelvic Cavity, [Opn, Perc Endo], Drain Dev, NQ
0W9J[0,4]ZZ	Drain/Pelvic Cavity, [Opn, Perc Endo]
0WBF*	Exc/Abd Wall
0WBH0ZX	Exc of Retroperitoneum, Opn Appr, Diagnostic
0WCG[0,3,4]ZZ	Extir/Peritoneal Cavity, [Opn, Perc, Perc Endo]
0WCJ[0,3,4]ZZ	Extir/Pelvic Cavity, [Opn, Perc, Perc Endo]
0WCP[0,3,4]ZZ	Extir/Gastrointestinal Tract, [Opn, Perc, Perc Endo]
0WCR[0,3,4]ZZ	Extir/Genitourinary Tract, [Opn, Perc, Perc Endo]
0WFG[0,3,4]ZZ	Fragmn/Peritoneal Cavity, [Opn, Perc, Perc Endo]
0WHF*	Insert/Abd Wall
0WHG*	Insert/Peritoneal Cavity
0WHH[0,3,4][3,Y]Z	Insert/Retroperitoneum, [Opn, Perc, Perc Endo], [Inf Dev, Oth Dev], NQ
0WHJ[0,3,4][3,Y]Z	Insert/Pelvic Cavity, [Opn, Perc, Perc Endo], [Inf Dev, Oth Dev], NQ
0WHP03Z	Insert of Inf Device into GI Tract, Opn Appr
0WHP[0,3,4,7,8]1Z	Insert/Gastrointestinal Tract, [Opn, Perc, Perc Endo, Via Natrl or Artfcl Opng, Via Natrl or Artfcl Opng Endo], Radioact Elmt, NQ
0WJF[0,3,4]ZZ	Inspect/Abd Wall, [Opn, Perc, Perc Endo]
0WJG*	Inspect/Peritoneal Cavity
0WJH*	Inspect/Retroperitoneum
0WJJ*	Inspect/Pelvic Cavity

Surgical	**Medical**	**CC Indicator**	**MCC Indicator**	**Procedure Proxy**	PDxMCC **PDx acts as own MCC** PDxCC **PDx acts as own CC**

© 2015 Optum360, LLC   MS-DRG Version 33.0   **113**

MDC 6: Diseases And Disorders Of The Digestive System—SURGICAL

MDC 6: Diseases And Disorders Of The Digestive System—MEDICAL

ØWJP*　　　　　Inspect/Gastrointestinal Tract
ØWJR*　　　　　Inspect/Genitourinary Tract
ØWPF[Ø,3,4][Ø,1,3,7,J,K,Y]Z Rmvl/Abd Wall, [Opn, Perc, Perc Endo], [Drain Dev, Radioact Elmt, Inf Dev, Auto Tissue Sub, Synth Sub, Nonauto Tissue Sub, Oth Dev], NQ
ØWPG[Ø,3,4][Ø,1,3,J,Y]Z Rmvl/Peritoneal Cavity, [Opn, Perc, Perc Endo], [Drain Dev, Radioact Elmt, Inf Dev, Synth Sub, Oth Dev], NQ
ØWPH[Ø,3,4][Ø,1,3,Y]Z Rmvl/Retroperitoneum, [Opn, Perc, Perc Endo], [Drain Dev, Radioact Elmt, Inf Dev, Oth Dev], NQ
ØWPPØ[1,3,Y]Z　Rmvl/Gastrointestinal Tract, Opn, [Radioact Elmt, Inf Dev, Oth Dev], NQ
ØWWF[Ø,3,4][Ø,1,3,7,J,K,Y]Z Rev/Abd Wall, [Opn, Perc, Perc Endo], [Drain Dev, Radioact Elmt, Inf Dev, Auto Tissue Sub, Synth Sub, Nonauto Tissue Sub, Oth Dev], NQ
ØWWG[Ø,3,4][Ø,1,3,J,Y]Z Rev/Peritoneal Cavity, [Opn, Perc, Perc Endo], [Drain Dev, Radioact Elmt, Inf Dev, Synth Sub, Oth Dev], NQ
ØWWH[Ø,3,4][Ø,1,3,Y]Z Rev/Retroperitoneum, [Opn, Perc, Perc Endo], [Drain Dev, Radioact Elmt, Inf Dev, Oth Dev], NQ
ØWWJ[Ø,3,4][Ø,1,3,J,Y]Z Rev/Pelvic Cavity, [Opn, Perc, Perc Endo], [Drain Dev, Radioact Elmt, Inf Dev, Synth Sub, Oth Dev], NQ
ØWWPØ[1,3,Y]Z　Rev/Gastrointestinal Tract, Opn, [Radioact Elmt, Inf Dev, Oth Dev], NQ
ØY35*　　　　　Control/Inguinal Region, Rt
ØY36*　　　　　Control/Inguinal Region, Lt
ØY95*　　　　　Drain/Inguinal Region, Rt
ØY96*　　　　　Drain/Inguinal Region, Lt
ØYB5*　　　　　Exc/Inguinal Region, Rt
ØYB6*　　　　　Exc/Inguinal Region, Lt
ØYB7*　　　　　Exc/Femor Region, Rt
ØYB8*　　　　　Exc/Femor Region, Lt
ØYJ5[Ø,3,4]ZZ　Inspect/Inguinal Rgn, Rt, [Opn, Perc, Perc Endo]
ØYJ6[Ø,3,4]ZZ　Inspect/Inguinal Rgn, Lt, [Opn, Perc, Perc Endo]
ØYJ7[Ø,3,4]ZZ　Inspect/Femor Rgn, Rt, [Opn, Perc, Perc Endo]
ØYJ8[3,4]ZZ　　Inspect/Femor Rgn, Lt, [Perc, Perc Endo]
ØYJA[Ø,3,4]ZZ　Inspect/Inguinal Rgn, Bilat, [Opn, Perc, Perc Endo]
ØYJE[3,4]ZZ　　Inspect/Femor Rgn, Bilat, [Perc, Perc Endo]
4AØC[3,4,7,8]5Z Measurement/Biliary, [Perc, Perc Endo, Via Natrl or Artfcl Opng, Via Natrl or Artfcl Opng Endo], Flow, NQ
4AØC[3,4,7]BZ　Measurement/Biliary, [Perc, Perc Endo, Via Natrl or Artfcl Opng], Pressure, NQ
DFYØKZZ　　　Laser Interstitial Thermal Therapy of Liver

DRG 357　Other Digestive System O.R. Procedures with CC
GMLOS 5.1　　　　AMLOS 6.6　　　　RW 2.Ø8Ø1　　　T

Select operating room procedures listed under DRG 356

DRG 358　Other Digestive System O.R. Procedures without CC/MCC
GMLOS 3.1　　　　AMLOS 3.8　　　　RW 1.3515　　　T

Select operating room procedures listed under DRG 356

MEDICAL

DRG 368　Major Esophageal Disorders with MCC
GMLOS 4.8　　　　AMLOS 6.1　　　　RW 1.7848

Principal Diagnosis

B37.81　　　　　Candidal esophagitis
I85.Ø*　　　　　Esophageal varices
I85.11　　　　　Secondary esophageal varices with bleeding
K22.3　　　　　Perforation of esophagus
K22.6　　　　　Gastro-esophageal lac-hemor synd
Q39*　　　　　Congenital malformations of esophagus
S27.81[2,3,8,9]A　[Contsn, Lac, Oth inj, Unsp inj] of esophagus (thoracic part), init enc
T28.1XXA　　　Burn of esophagus, init enc
T28.6XXA　　　Corrosion of esophagus, init enc

DRG 369　Major Esophageal Disorders with CC
GMLOS 3.4　　　　AMLOS 4.1　　　　RW 1.Ø63Ø

Select principal diagnosis listed under DRG 368

DRG 370　Major Esophageal Disorders without CC/MCC
GMLOS 2.4　　　　AMLOS 2.9　　　　RW Ø.7355

Select principal diagnosis listed under DRG 368

DRG 371　Major Gastrointestinal Disorders and Peritoneal Infections with MCC
GMLOS 5.8　　　　AMLOS 7.5　　　　RW 1.7854　　　T

Principal Diagnosis

AØØ*　　　　　Cholera
AØ2.Ø　　　　　Salmonella enteritis
AØ3*　　　　　Shigellosis
AØ4*　　　　　Oth bacterial intestinal infections
AØ5.Ø　　　　　Foodborne staphylococcal intoxication
AØ5.2　　　　　Foodborne Clostridium perfringens intoxication
AØ5.3　　　　　Foodborne Vibrio parahaemolyticus intoxication
AØ5.4　　　　　Foodborne Bacillus cereus intoxication
AØ5.5　　　　　Foodborne Vibrio vulnificus intoxication
AØ5.8　　　　　Oth spec bacterial foodborne intoxications
AØ6.Ø　　　　　Acute amebic dysentery
AØ6.1　　　　　Chr intestinal amebiasis
AØ6.2　　　　　Amebic nondysenteric colitis
AØ7*　　　　　Oth protozoal intestinal dz
A18.3*　　　　　Tuberculosis of intestines, peritoneum and mesenteric glands
A18.83　　　　　Tuberculosis of digestive tract organs, NEC
A21.3　　　　　Gastrointestinal tularemia
A22.2　　　　　Gastrointestinal anthrax
A42.1　　　　　Abd actinomycosis
A54.85　　　　　Gonococcal peritonitis
B69*　　　　　Cysticercosis
B7Ø.1　　　　　Sparganosis
B71*　　　　　Oth cestode infections
B76*　　　　　Hookworm dz
K35.2　　　　　Acute appendicitis with generalized peritonitis
K35.3　　　　　Acute appendicitis with localized peritonitis
K63.Ø　　　　　Abscess of intestine
K65.Ø　　　　　Generalized (acute) peritonitis
K65.1　　　　　Peritoneal abscess
K65.2　　　　　Spontaneous bacterial peritonitis
K65.8　　　　　Oth peritonitis
K65.9　　　　　Peritonitis, unsp
K67　　　　　　D/o of peritoneum in infectious dz classd elsw
K68.12　　　　　Psoas muscle abscess
K68.19　　　　　Oth retroperitoneal abscess
K68.9　　　　　Oth d/o of retroperitoneum

DRG 372　Major Gastrointestinal Disorders and Peritoneal Infections with CC
GMLOS 4.4　　　　AMLOS 5.4　　　　RW 1.1Ø9Ø　　　T

Select principal diagnosis listed under DRG 371

DRG 373　Major Gastrointestinal Disorders and Peritoneal Infections without CC/MCC
GMLOS 3.3　　　　AMLOS 3.9　　　　RW Ø.7817　　　T

Select principal diagnosis listed under DRG 371

DRG 374　Digestive Malignancy with MCC
GMLOS 5.9　　　　AMLOS 7.9　　　　RW 2.Ø345　　　T

Principal Diagnosis

C15*　　　　　Malig neoplasm of esophagus
C16*　　　　　Malig neoplasm of stomach
C17*　　　　　Malig neoplasm of sm intestine
C18*　　　　　Malig neoplasm of colon
C19　　　　　　Malig neoplasm of rectosigmoid junction
C2Ø　　　　　　Malig neoplasm of rectum
C21*　　　　　Malig neoplasm of anus and anal canal
C26.Ø　　　　　Malig neoplasm of intestinal tract, part unsp
C26.9　　　　　Malig neoplasm of ill-defined sites within the dgstv sys
C45.1　　　　　Mesothelioma of peritoneum
C46.4　　　　　Kaposi's sarcoma of gastrointestinal sites
C48.1　　　　　Malig neoplasm of spec parts of peritoneum
C48.2　　　　　Malig neoplasm of peritoneum, unsp
C48.8　　　　　Malig neoplasm of ovrlp sites of retroperiton and peritoneum
C76.2　　　　　Malig neoplasm of abd

T Transfer DRG　　　SP Special Payment　　　* Code Range　　　6th and 7th Character of ZZ = No Device, No Qualifier　ZX = No Device, Diagnostic

C78.4	Secondary malig neoplasm of sm intestine
C78.5	Secondary malig neoplasm of large intestine and rectum
C78.6	Secondary malig neoplasm of retroperiton and peritoneum
C78.8*	Secondary malig neoplasm of and unsp digestive organs
C7A.01[0,1,2,9]	Malig carcinoid tumor of the [duodenum, jejunum, ileum, sm intestine unsp]
C7A.02[0,1,2,3,4,5,6,9]	Malig carcinoid tumor of the [appendix, cecum, ascending colon, transv colon, descending colon, sigmoid colon, rectum, lg intestine unsp]
C7A.09[2,4,5,6]	Malig carcinoid tumor of the [stomach, forgut NOS, midgut NOS, hindgut NOS]
C7B.04	Secondary carcinoid tumors of peritoneum
D00.1	Carcinoma in situ of esophagus
D00.2	Carcinoma in situ of stomach
D01.0	Carcinoma in situ of colon
D01.1	Carcinoma in situ of rectosigmoid junction
D01.2	Carcinoma in situ of rectum
D01.3	Carcinoma in situ of anus and anal canal
D01.4*	Carcinoma in situ of oth and unsp parts of intestine
D01.7	Carcinoma in situ of oth spec digestive organs
D01.9	Carcinoma in situ of digestive organ, unsp
D37.1	Neoplasm of uncertain behav of stomach
D37.2	Neoplasm of uncertain behav of sm intestine
D37.3	Neoplasm of uncertain behav of appendix
D37.4	Neoplasm of uncertain behav of colon
D37.5	Neoplasm of uncertain behav of rectum
D37.8	Neoplasm of uncertain behav of oth digestive organs
D37.9	Neoplasm of uncertain behav of digestive organ, unsp
D48.3	Neoplasm of uncertain behav of retroperitoneum
D48.4	Neoplasm of uncertain behav of peritoneum
D49.0	Neoplasm of unsp behav of digestive sys

DRG 375   Digestive Malignancy with CC
GMLOS 4.0   AMLOS 5.1   RW 1.2302   T

Select principal diagnosis listed under DRG 374

DRG 376   Digestive Malignancy without CC/MCC
GMLOS 2.8   AMLOS 3.5   RW 0.9093   T

Select principal diagnosis listed under DRG 374

DRG 377   GI Hemorrhage with MCC
GMLOS 4.7   AMLOS 5.9   RW 1.7509   T

Principal Diagnosis

K25.0	Acute gastric ulcer with hemor
K25.2	Acute gastric ulcer with both hemor and perforation
K25.4	Chr or unsp gastric ulcer with hemor
K25.6	Chr or unsp gastric ulcer w both hemor and perf
K26.0	Acute duodenal ulcer with hemor
K26.2	Acute duodenal ulcer with both hemor and perforation
K26.4	Chr or unsp duodenal ulcer with hemor
K26.6	Chr or unsp duodenal ulcer w both hemor and perf
K27.0	Acute peptic ulcer, site unsp, with hemor
K27.2	Acute peptic ulcer, site unsp, w both hemor and perf
K27.4	Chr or unsp peptic ulcer, site unsp, with hemor
K27.6	Chr or unsp peptic ulcer, site unsp, w both hemor and perf
K28.0	Acute gastrojejunal ulcer with hemor
K28.2	Acute gastrojejunal ulcer w both hemor and perforation
K28.4	Chr or unsp gastrojejunal ulcer with hemor
K28.6	Chr or unsp gastrojejunal ulcer w both hemor and perf
K29.01	Acute gastritis with bleeding
K29.21	Alcoholic gastritis with bleeding
K29.31	Chr superf gastritis with bleeding
K29.41	Chr atrophic gastritis with bleeding
K29.51	Unsp chr gastritis with bleeding
K29.61	Oth gastritis with bleeding
K29.71	Gastritis, unsp, with bleeding
K29.81	Duodenitis with bleeding
K29.91	Gastroduodenitis, unsp, with bleeding
K31.811	Angiodysplasia of stomach and duodenum with bleeding
K31.82	Dieulafoy lesion (hemorrhagic) of stomach and duodenum
K55.21	Angiodysplasia of colon with hemor
K57.01	Dvtrcli of sm int w perforation and abscess w bleeding PDxCC
K57.1[1,3]	[Diverticulosis, Diverticulitis] of sm intestine w/o perforation or abscess w/ bleeding
K57.21	Dvtrcli of lg int w perforation and abscess w bleeding PDxCC

K57.3[1,3]	[Diverticulosis, Diverticulitis] of lg intestine w/o perforation or abscess w/ bleeding
K57.41	Dvtrcli of both sm and lg int w perf and abscess w bleed PDxCC
K57.5[1,3]	[Diverticulosis, Diverticulitis] of both sm and lg intestine w/o perforation or abscess w/ bleeding
K57.81	Dvtrcli of intest, part unsp, w perf and abscess w bleeding PDxCC
K57.9[1,3]	[Diverticulosis, Diverticulitis] of intestine, part unsp, w/o perforation or abscess w/ bleeding
K62.5	Hemor of anus and rectum
K92.0	Hematemesis
K92.1	Melena
K92.2	Gastrointestinal hemor, unsp

DRG 378   GI Hemorrhage with CC
GMLOS 3.2   AMLOS 3.8   RW 0.9949   T

Select principal diagnosis listed under DRG 377

DRG 379   GI Hemorrhage without CC/MCC
GMLOS 2.3   AMLOS 2.7   RW 0.6712   T

Select principal diagnosis listed under DRG 377

DRG 380   Complicated Peptic Ulcer with MCC
GMLOS 5.3   AMLOS 7.0   RW 1.9549   T

Principal Diagnosis

E16.4	Increased secretion of gastrin
K22.1*	Ulcer of esophagus
K22.7*	Barrett's esophagus
K25.1	Acute gastric ulcer with perforation
K25.5	Chr or unsp gastric ulcer with perforation
K26.1	Acute duodenal ulcer with perforation
K26.5	Chr or unsp duodenal ulcer with perforation
K27.1	Acute peptic ulcer, site unsp, with perforation
K27.5	Chr or unsp peptic ulcer, site unsp, with perforation
K28.1	Acute gastrojejunal ulcer with perforation
K28.3	Acute gastrojejunal ulcer w/o hemor or perforation
K28.5	Chr or unsp gastrojejunal ulcer with perforation
K28.7	Chr gastrojejunal ulcer w/o hemor or perforation
K28.9	Gastrojejunal ulcer, unsp as acute or chr, w/o hemor or perf
K31.1	Adult hypertrophic pyloric stenosis
K31.5	Obstruction of duodenum
Q43.0	Meckel's diverticulum (disp) (hypertrophic)

DRG 381   Complicated Peptic Ulcer with CC
GMLOS 3.5   AMLOS 4.2   RW 1.0690   T

Select principal diagnosis listed under DRG 380

DRG 382   Complicated Peptic Ulcer without CC/MCC
GMLOS 2.7   AMLOS 3.3   RW 0.8238   T

Select principal diagnosis listed under DRG 380

DRG 383   Uncomplicated Peptic Ulcer with MCC
GMLOS 4.2   AMLOS 5.1   RW 1.3545

Principal Diagnosis

K25.3	Acute gastric ulcer w/o hemor or perforation
K25.7	Chr gastric ulcer w/o hemor or perforation
K25.9	Gastric ulcer, unsp as acute or chr, w/o hemor or perf
K26.3	Acute duodenal ulcer w/o hemor or perforation
K26.7	Chr duodenal ulcer w/o hemor or perforation
K26.9	Duodenal ulcer, unsp as acute or chr, w/o hemor or perf
K27.3	Acute peptic ulcer, site unsp, w/o hemor or perforation
K27.7	Chr peptic ulcer, site unsp, w/o hemor or perf
K27.9	Peptic ulc, site unsp, unsp as ac or chr, w/o hemor or perf

DRG 384   Uncomplicated Peptic Ulcer without MCC
GMLOS 2.8   AMLOS 3.3   RW 0.8481

Select principal diagnosis listed under DRG 383

Surgical	Medical	CC Indicator	MCC Indicator	Procedure Proxy	PDxMCC PDx acts as own MCC	PDxCC PDx acts as own CC

DRG 385   Inflammatory Bowel Disease with MCC
GMLOS 5.7   AMLOS 7.5   RW 1.7195

Principal Diagnosis

K50*	Crohn's dz [regional enteritis]
K51*	Ulcerative colitis

DRG 386   Inflammatory Bowel Disease with CC
GMLOS 3.8   AMLOS 4.8   RW 0.9996

Select principal diagnosis listed under DRG 385

DRG 387   Inflammatory Bowel Disease without CC/MCC
GMLOS 3.0   AMLOS 3.6   RW 0.7379

Select principal diagnosis listed under DRG 385

DRG 388   GI Obstruction with MCC
GMLOS 5.2   AMLOS 6.8   RW 1.5813   [T]

Principal Diagnosis

K56*	Paralytic ileus and intestinal obstruction w/o hernia

DRG 389   GI Obstruction with CC
GMLOS 3.5   AMLOS 4.3   RW 0.8707   [T]

Select principal diagnosis listed under DRG 388

DRG 390   GI Obstruction without CC/MCC
GMLOS 2.7   AMLOS 3.1   RW 0.6067   [T]

Select principal diagnosis listed under DRG 388

DRG 391   Esophagitis, Gastroenteritis and Miscellaneous Digestive Disorders with MCC
GMLOS 3.8   AMLOS 5.0   RW 1.1925

Principal Diagnosis

A05.9	Bacterial foodborne intoxication, unsp
A08*	Viral and oth spec intestinal infections
A09	Infectious gastroenteritis and colitis, unsp
B37.82	Candidal enteritis
B68*	Taeniasis
B70.0	Diphyllobothriasis
B77*	Ascariasis
B78.0	Intestinal strongyloidiasis
B78.7	Disseminated strongyloidiasis
B78.9	Strongyloidiasis, unsp
B79	Trichuriasis
B80	Enterobiasis
B81.0	Anisakiasis
B81.1	Intestinal capillariasis
B81.2	Trichostrongyliasis
B81.3	Intestinal angiostrongyliasis
B81.8	Oth spec intestinal helminthiases
B82*	Unsp intestinal parasitism
D18.03	Hemangioma of intra-abd structures
E73*	Lactose intolerance
E74.1*	D/o of fructose metabolism
E74.3*	Oth d/o of intestinal carbohydrate absorption
I77.4	Celiac artery compression synd
K20*	Esophagitis
K21*	Gastro-esophageal reflux dz
K22.0	Achalasia of cardia
K22.2	Esophageal obstruction
K22.4	Dyskinesia of esophagus
K22.5	Diverticulum of esophagus, acquired
K22.8	Oth spec dz of esophagus
K22.9	Dz of esophagus, unsp
K23	D/o of esophagus in dz classified elsw
K29.[0,2,3,4,5,6,7]0	[Acute, Alcoholic, Chr superf, Chr atropic, Unsp chr, Oth, Unsp] gastritis w/o bleeding
K29.[8,9]0	[Duodenitis, Unsp gastroduodenitis] w/o bleeding
K30	Functional dyspepsia
K31.0	Acute dilatation of stomach
K31.2	Hourglass stricture and stenosis of stomach
K31.3	Pylorospasm, NEC

K31.4	Gastric diverticulum
K31.6	Fistula of stomach and duodenum
K31.819	Angiodysplasia of stomach and duodenum w/o bleeding
K31.83	Achlorhydria
K31.84	Gastroparesis
K31.89	Oth dz of stomach and duodenum
K31.9	Dz of stomach and duodenum, unsp
K44.0	Diaphragmatic hernia with obstruction, w/o gangrene
K44.9	Diaphragmatic hernia w/o obstruction or gangrene
K52.2	Allergic and dietetic gastroenteritis and colitis
K52.8*	Oth spec noninfective gastroenteritis and colitis
K52.9	Noninfective gastroenteritis and colitis, unsp
K57.00	Dvtrcli of sm int w perforation and abscess w/o bleeding **PDxCC**
K57.1[0,2]	[Diverticulosis, Diverticulitis] of sm intestine w/ perforation and abscess w/o bleeding
K57.20	Dvtrcli of lg int w perforation and abscess w/o bleeding **PDxCC**
K57.3[0,2]	[Diverticulosis, Diverticulitis] of lg intestine w/o perforation or abscess w/o bleeding
K57.40	Dvtrcli of both sm and lg int w perf and abscs w/o bleed **PDxCC**
K57.5[0,2]	[Diverticulosis, Diverticulitis] of both sm and lg intestine w/o perforation or abscess w/o bleeding
K57.80	Dvtrcli of intest, part unsp, w perf and abscess w/o bleed **PDxCC**
K57.9[0,2]	[Diverticulosis, Diverticulitis] of intestine, part unsp, w/o perforation or abscess w/o bleeding
K58*	Irritable bowel synd
K59.0*	Constipation
K59.1	Functional diarrhea
K59.2	Neurogenic bowel, NEC
K59.4	Anal spasm
K59.8	Oth spec functional intestinal d/o
K59.9	Functional intestinal d/o, unsp
K90.0	Celiac dz
K90.1	Tropical sprue
K90.2	Blind loop synd, NEC
K90.3	Pancreatic steatorrhea
K90.4	Malabsorption d/t intolerance, NEC
K90.89	Oth intestinal malabsorption
K90.9	Intestinal malabsorption, unsp
K91.0	Vomiting following gastrointestinal surgery
K91.1	Postgastric surgery syndromes
K91.2	Postsurgical malabsorption, NEC
K92.81	Gastrointestinal mucositis (ulcerative)
N80.5	Endometriosis of intestine
R10*	Abd and pelvic pain
R11.0	Nausea
R11.10	Vomiting, unsp
R11.11	Vomiting w/o nausea
R11.12	Projectile vomiting
R11.14	Bilious vomiting
R11.2	Nausea with vomiting, unsp
R12	Heartburn
R13*	Aphagia and dysphagia
R14*	Flatulence and related conditions
R15*	Fecal incontinence
R19.0*	Intra-abd and pelvic swelling, mass and lump
R19.1*	Abnormal bowel sounds
R19.2	Visible peristalsis
R19.4	Change in bowel habit
R19.5	Oth fecal abnormalities
R19.7	Diarrhea, unsp
R19.8	Oth symptoms and signs involving the dgstv sys and abd
R93.3	Abnormal findings on dx imaging of prt digestive tract
R93.5	Abn findings on dx imaging of abd regions, incl* retroperiton

DRG 392   Esophagitis, Gastroenteritis and Miscellaneous Digestive Disorders without MCC
GMLOS 2.7   AMLOS 3.3   RW 0.7400

Select principal diagnosis listed under DRG 391

DRG 393   Other Digestive System Diagnoses with MCC
GMLOS 4.6   AMLOS 6.3   RW 1.6335

Principal Diagnosis

A51.1	Primary anal syphilis
A54.6	Gonococcal infxn of anus and rectum
A56.3	Chlamydial infxn of anus and rectum
B00.81	Herpesviral hepatitis

[T] **Transfer DRG**   [SP] **Special Payment**   * **Code Range**   **6th and 7th Character of ZZ = No Device, No Qualifier ZX = No Device, Diagnostic**

D12*	Benign neoplasm of colon, rectum, anus and anal canal
D13.0	Benign neoplasm of esophagus
D13.1	Benign neoplasm of stomach
D13.2	Benign neoplasm of duodenum
D13.3*	Benign neoplasm of oth and unsp parts of sm intestine
D13.9	Benign neoplasm of ill-defined sites within the dgstv sys
D17.5	Benign lipomatous neoplasm of intra-abd organs
D17.71	Benign lipomatous neoplasm of kidney
D19.1	Benign neoplasm of mesothelial tissue of peritoneum
D20*	Benign neoplm of soft tissue of retroperiton and peritoneum
D3A.01[0,1,2,9]	Benign carcinoid tumor of the [duodenum, jejunum, ileum, unsp portion of sm intestine]
D3A.02[0,1,2,3,4,5,6,9]	Benign carcinoid tumor of the [appendix, cecum, ascending colon, descending colon, sigmoid colon, rectum, unsp portion of lg intestine]
D3A.09[2,4,5,6]	Benign carcinoid tumor of the [stomach, foregut NOS, midgut NOS, hindgut NOS]
E84.19	Cystic fibrosis with oth intestinal manifestations
I85.10	Secondary esophageal varices w/o bleeding
I88.0	Nonspecific mesenteric lymphadenitis
K31.7	Polyp of stomach and duodenum
K35.8*	Oth and unsp acute appendicitis
K36	Oth appendicitis
K37	Unsp appendicitis
K38*	Oth dz of appendix
K40*	Inguinal hernia
K41*	Femor hernia
K42*	Umbilical hernia
K43*	Ventral hernia
K44.1	Diaphragmatic hernia with gangrene
K45*	Oth abd hernia
K46*	Unsp abd hernia
K52.0	Gastroenteritis and colitis d/t radiation
K52.1	Txc gastroenteritis and colitis
K55.0	Acute vascular d/o of intestine
K55.1	Chr vascular d/o of intestine
K55.20	Angiodysplasia of colon w/o hemor
K55.8	Oth vascular d/o of intestine
K55.9	Vascular d/o of intestine, unsp
K59.3	Megacolon, NEC
K60*	Fissure and fistula of anal and rectal regions
K61*	Abscess of anal and rectal regions
K62.0	Anal polyp
K62.1	Rectal polyp
K62.2	Anal prolapse
K62.3	Rectal prolapse
K62.4	Stenosis of anus and rectum
K62.6	Ulcer of anus and rectum
K62.7	Radiation proctitis
K62.8*	Oth spec dz of anus and rectum
K62.9	Dz of anus and rectum, unsp
K63.1	Perforation of intestine (nontraumatic)
K63.2	Fistula of intestine
K63.3	Ulcer of intestine
K63.4	Enteroptosis
K63.5	Polyp of colon
K63.8*	Oth spec dz of intestine
K63.9	Dz of intestine, unsp
K64*	Hemorrhoids and perianal venous thrombosis
K65.3	Choleperitonitis
K65.4	Sclerosing mesenteritis
K66*	Oth d/o of peritoneum
K90.81	Whipple's dz
K91.3	Postprocedural intestinal obstruction
K91.81	Oth intraoperative comp of digestive sys
K91.82	Postprocedural hepatic failure
K91.83	Postprocedural hepatorenal synd
K91.850	Pouchitis
K91.858	Oth comp of intestinal pouch
K91.86	Retained cholelithiasis following cholecystectomy
K91.89	Oth postprocedural comp and d/o of dgstv sys
K92.89	Oth spec dz of the digestive sys
K92.9	Dz of digestive sys, unsp
K94*	Comp of artfcl openings of the digestive sys
K95*	Comp of bariatric procedures
N82.2	Fistula of vagina to sm intestine
N82.3	Fistula of vagina to large intestine
N82.4	Oth female intestinal-genital tract fistulae
N99.4	Postprocedural pelvic peritoneal adhesions
Q38.5	Congenital malformations of palate, NEC

Q40*	Oth congenital malformations of upr alimentary tract
Q41*	Congenital absence, atresia and stenosis of sm intestine
Q42*	Congenital absence, atresia and stenosis of large intestine
Q43.1	Hirschsprung's dz
Q43.2	Oth congenital functional d/o of colon
Q43.3	Congenital malformations of intestinal fix
Q43.4	Duplication of intestine
Q43.5	Ectopic anus
Q43.6	Congenital fistula of rectum and anus
Q43.7	Persistent cloaca
Q43.8	Oth spec congenital malformations of intestine
Q43.9	Congenital malformation of intestine, unsp
Q45.8	Oth spec congenital malformations of digestive sys
Q45.9	Congenital malformation of digestive sys, unsp
Q79.2	Exomphalos
Q79.3	Gastroschisis
Q79.4	Prune belly synd
Q79.5*	Oth congenital malformations of abd wall
Q89.3	Situs inversus
Q89.4	Conjoined twins
R11.13	Vomiting of fecal matter
R19.3*	Abd rigidity
R85.61*	Abnormal cytologic smear of anus
R85.8[1,2]	Anal [high, low] risk human papillomavirus (HPV) DNA test positive
S31.60[0,1,2,3,4,5,9]A	Unsp opn wnd of abd wall, [rt upr quadrant, lt upr quadrant, epigastric rgn, rt lwr quadrant, lt lwr quadrant, periumbilic rgn, unsp quadrant] w/ penetration into peritoneal cavity, init enc
S31.61[0,1,2,3,4,5,9]A	Lac w/o FB of abd wall, [rt upr quadrant, lt upr quadrant, epigastric rgn, rt lwr quadrant, lt lwr quadrant, periumbilic rgn, unsp quadrant] w/ penetration into peritoneal cavity, init enc
S31.62[0,1,2,3,4,5,9]A	Lac w/ FB of abd wall, [rt upr quadrant, lt upr quadrant, epigastric rgn, rt lwr quadrant, lt lwr quadrant, periumbilic rgn, unsp quadrant] w/ penetration into peritoneal cavity, init enc
S31.63[0,1,2,3,4,5,9]A	Punc wnd w/o FB of abd wall, [rt upr quadrant, lt upr quadrant, epigastric rgn, rt lwr quadrant, lt lwr quadrant, periumbilic rgn, unsp quadrant] w/ penetration into peritoneal cavity, init enc
S31.64[0,1,2,3,4,5,9]A	Punc wnd w/ FB of abd wall, [rt upr quadrant, lt upr quadrant, epigastric rgn, rt lwr quadrant, lt lwr quadrant, periumbilic rgn, unsp quadrant] w/ penetration into peritoneal cavity, init enc
S31.65[0,1,2,3,4,5,9]A	Opn bite of abd wall, [rt upr quadrant, lt upr quadrant, epigastric rgn, rt lwr quadrant, lt lwr quadrant, periumbilic rgn, unsp quadrant] w/ penetration into peritoneal cavity, init enc
S36.00XS	Unsp inj of spleen, seq
S36.02[0,1,9]S	[Minor, Major, Unsp] contsn of spleen, seq
S36.03[0,1,2,9]S	[Superf (capsular), Mod, Major, Unsp] lac of spleen, seq
S36.09XS	Oth inj of spleen, seq
S36.112S	Contsn of liver, seq
S36.113S	Lac of liver, unsp degree, seq
S36.11[4,5,6]S	[Minor, Mod, Major] lac of liver, seq
S36.11[8,9]S	[Oth, Unsp] inj of liver, seq
S36.12[2,3,8,9]S	[Contsn, Lac, Oth inj, Unsp inj] of gallbladder, seq
S36.13XS	Inj of bile duct, seq
S36.20[0,1,2,9]S	Unsp inj of [head, body, tail, unsp part] of pancreas, seq
S36.22[0,1,2,9]S	Contsn of [head, body, tail, unsp part] of pancreas, seq
S36.23[0,1,2,9]S	Lac of [head, body, tail, unsp part] of pancreas, unsp degree, seq
S36.24[0,1,2,9]S	Minor lac of [head, body, tail, unsp part] of pancreas, seq
S36.25[0,1,2,9]S	Mod lac of [head, body, tail, unsp part] of pancreas, seq
S36.26[0,1,2,9]S	Major lac of [head, body, tail, unsp part] of pancreas, seq
S36.29[0,1,2,9]S	Oth inj of [head, body, tail, unsp part] of pancreas, seq
S36.30X[A,S]	Unsp inj of stomach, [init enc, seq]
S36.32X[A,S]	Contsn of stomach, [init enc, seq]
S36.33X[A,S]	Lac of stomach, [init enc, seq]
S36.39X[A,S]	Oth inj of stomach, [init enc, seq]
S36.400[A,S]	Unsp inj of duodenum, [init enc, seq]
S36.408[A,S]	Unsp inj of oth part of sm intestine, [init enc, seq]
S36.409[A,S]	Unsp inj of unsp part of sm intestine, [init enc, seq]
S36.410[A,S]	Primary blast inj of duodenum, [init enc, seq]
S36.418[A,S]	Primary blast inj of oth part of sm intestine, [init enc, seq]
S36.419[A,S]	Primary blast inj of unsp part of sm intestine, [init enc, seq]
S36.420[A,S]	Contsn of duodenum, [init enc, seq]
S36.428[A,S]	Contsn of oth part of sm intestine, [init enc, seq]
S36.429[A,S]	Contsn of unsp part of sm intestine, [init enc, seq]

Surgical   **Medical**   **CC Indicator**   **MCC Indicator**   **Procedure Proxy**   **PDxMCC PDx acts as own MCC**   **PDxCC PDx acts as own CC**

MDC 6: Diseases And Disorders Of The Digestive System—MEDICAL

S36.430[A,S]	Lac of duodenum, [init enc, seq]
S36.438[A,S]	Lac of oth part of sm intestine, [init enc, seq]
S36.439[A,S]	Lac of unsp part of sm intestine, [init enc, seq]
S36.490[A,S]	Oth inj of duodenum, [init enc, seq]
S36.498[A,S]	Oth inj of oth part of sm intestine, [init enc, seq]
S36.499[A,S]	Oth inj of unsp part of sm intestine, [init enc, seq]
S36.500[A,S]	Unsp inj of ascending [rt] colon, [init enc, seq]
S36.501[A,S]	Unsp inj of transv colon, [init enc, seq]
S36.502[A,S]	Unsp inj of descending [lt] colon, [init enc, seq]
S36.503[A,S]	Unsp inj of sigmoid colon, [init enc, seq]
S36.508[A,S]	Unsp inj of oth part of colon, [init enc, seq]
S36.509[A,S]	Unsp inj of unsp part of colon, [init enc, seq]
S36.510[A,S]	Primary blast inj of ascending [rt] colon, [init enc, seq]
S36.511[A,S]	Primary blast inj of transv colon, [init enc, seq]
S36.512[A,S]	Primary blast inj of descending [lt] colon, [init enc, seq]
S36.513[A,S]	Primary blast inj of sigmoid colon, [init enc, seq]
S36.518[A,S]	Primary blast inj of oth part of colon, [init enc, seq]
S36.519[A,S]	Primary blast inj of unsp part of colon, [init enc, seq]
S36.520[A,S]	Contsn of ascending [rt] colon, [init enc, seq]
S36.521[A,S]	Contsn of transv colon, [init enc, seq]
S36.522[A,S]	Contsn of descending [lt] colon, [init enc, seq]
S36.523[A,S]	Contsn of sigmoid colon, [init enc, seq]
S36.528[A,S]	Contsn of oth part of colon, [init enc, seq]
S36.529[A,S]	Contsn of unsp part of colon, [init enc, seq]
S36.530[A,S]	Lac of ascending [rt] colon, [init enc, seq]
S36.531[A,S]	Lac of transv colon, [init enc, seq]
S36.532[A,S]	Lac of descending [lt] colon, [init enc, seq]
S36.533[A,S]	Lac of sigmoid colon, [init enc, seq]
S36.538[A,S]	Lac of oth part of colon, [init enc, seq]
S36.539[A,S]	Lac of unsp part of colon, [init enc, seq]
S36.590[A,S]	Oth inj of ascending [rt] colon, [init enc, seq]
S36.591[A,S]	Oth inj of transv colon, [init enc, seq]
S36.592[A,S]	Oth inj of descending [lt] colon, [init enc, seq]
S36.593[A,S]	Oth inj of sigmoid colon, [init enc, seq]
S36.598[A,S]	Oth inj of oth part of colon, [init enc, seq]
S36.599[A,S]	Oth inj of unsp part of colon, [init enc, seq]
S36.60X[A,S]	Unsp inj of rectum, [init enc, seq]
S36.61X[A,S]	Primary blast inj of rectum, [init enc, seq]
S36.62X[A,S]	Contsn of rectum, [init enc, seq]
S36.63X[A,S]	Lac of rectum, [init enc, seq]
S36.69X[A,S]	Oth inj of rectum, [init enc, seq]
S36.81X[A,S]	Inj of peritoneum, [init enc, seq]
S36.89[2,3,8,9]S	[Contsn, Lac, Oth inj, Unsp inj] of oth intra-abd organs, seq
S36.90X[A,S]	Unsp inj of unsp intra-abd organ, [init enc, seq]
S36.92X[A,S]	Contsn of unsp intra-abd organ, [init enc, seq]
S36.93X[A,S]	Lac of unsp intra-abd organ, [init enc, seq]
S36.99X[A,S]	Oth inj of unsp intra-abd organ, [init enc, seq]
S37.00[1,2,9]S	Unsp inj of [rt, lt, unsp] kidney, seq
S37.01[1,2,9]S	Minor contsn of [rt, lt, unsp] kidney, seq
S37.02[1,2,9]S	Major contsn of [rt, lt, unsp] kidney, seq
S37.03[1,2,9]S	Lac of [rt, lt, unsp] kidney, unsp degree, seq
S37.04[1,2,9]S	Minor lac of [rt, lt, unsp] kidney, seq
S37.05[1,2,9]S	Mod lac of [rt, lt, unsp] kidney, seq
S37.06[1,2,9]S	Major lac of [rt, lt, unsp] kidney, seq
S37.09[1,2,9]S	Oth inj of [rt, lt, unsp] kidney, seq
T18.10[0,8]A	Unsp FB in esophagus causing [compression of trachea, oth inj], init enc
T18.11[0,8]A	Gastric contents in esophagus causing [compression of trachea, oth inj], init enc
T18.12[0,8]A	Food in esophagus causing [compression of trachea, oth inj], init enc
T18.19[0,8]A	Oth FB in esophagus causing [compression of trachea, oth inj], init enc
T18.[2,3,4,5,8,9]XXA	FB in [stomach, sm intestine, colon, anus and rectum, oth parts of alimentary tract, unsp part of alimentary tract], init enc
T28.[2,7]XXA	[Burn, Corrosion] of oth parts of alimentary tract, init enc
T81.710A	Comp of mesent art following a procedure, NEC, init
Z43.1	Enc for attention to gastrostomy
Z43.2	Enc for attention to ileostomy
Z43.3	Enc for attention to colostomy
Z43.4	Enc for attn to oth artif openings of digestive tract
Z46.51	Enc for fitting and adjustment of gastric lap band
Z46.59	Enc for fit/adjst of GI appliance and device

DRG 394 **Other Digestive System Diagnoses with CC**

GMLOS 3.3   AMLOS 4.2   RW 0.9502

Select principal diagnosis listed under DRG 393

DRG 395 **Other Digestive System Diagnoses without CC/MCC**

GMLOS 2.4   AMLOS 2.9   RW 0.6756

Select principal diagnosis listed under DRG 393

T Transfer DRG   SP Special Payment   * Code Range   6th and 7th Character of ZZ = No Device, No Qualifier ZX = No Device, Diagnostic

118   MS-DRG Version 33.0   © 2015 Optum360, LLC

SURGICAL

DRG 405   Pancreas, Liver and Shunt Procedures with MCC
| GMLOS 10.5 | AMLOS 14.2 | RW 5.5888 | [T] |

Operating Room Procedures

0610[0,4][J,Z][5,6,Y]	Bypass/Inferior Vena Cava, [Opn, Perc Endo], [Synth Sub, No Dev], [Superior Mesenteric Vein, Inferior Mesenteric Vein, Lwr Vein]
0611[0,4][J,Z][9,B,Y]	Bypass/Splenic Vein, [Opn, Perc Endo], [Synth Sub, No Dev], [Renal Vein, Rt, Renal Vein, Lt, Lwr Vein]
0618[0,4][J,Z][9,B,Y]	Bypass/Portal Vein, [Opn, Perc Endo], [Synth Sub, No Dev], [Renal Vein, Rt, Renal Vein, Lt, Lwr Vein]
0F1D*	Bypass/Pancreatic Duct
0F1F*	Bypass/Pancreatic Duct, Accessory
0F1G*	Bypass/Pancreas
0F50*	Destr/Liver
0F51*	Destr/Liver, Rt Lobe
0F52*	Destr/Liver, Lt Lobe
0F5D[0,3,7]ZZ	Destr/Pancreatic Duct, [Opn, Perc, Via Natrl or Artfcl Opng]
0F5F[0,3,7]ZZ	Destr/Pancreatic Duct, Accessory, [Opn, Perc, Via Natrl or Artfcl Opng]
0F5G[0,3]ZZ	Destr/Pancreas, [Opn, Perc]
0F7D[0,3,7][D,Z]Z	Dilation/Pancreatic Duct, [Opn, Perc, Via Natrl or Artfcl Opng], [Intralum Dev, No Dev], NQ
0F7F[0,3,7][D,Z]Z	Dilation/Pancreatic Duct, Accessory, [Opn, Perc, Via Natrl or Artfcl Opng], [Intralum Dev, No Dev], NQ
0F8*	Hepatobiliary Sys and Pancreas, Div
0F900[0,Z]Z	Drain/Liver, Opn, [Drain Dev, No Dev], NQ
0F910[0,Z]Z	Drain/Liver, Rt Lobe, Opn, [Drain Dev, No Dev], NQ
0F920[0,Z]Z	Drain/Liver, Lt Lobe, Opn, [Drain Dev, No Dev], NQ
0F9970Z	Drain of Common Bile Duct with Drain Dev, Via Opng
0F9D[0,3,4,7,8]ZZ	Drain/Pancreatic Duct, [Opn, Perc, Perc Endo, Via Natrl or Artfcl Opng, Via Natrl or Artfcl Opng Endo]
0F9D[0,3,4,7]0Z	Drain/Pancreatic Duct, [Opn, Perc, Perc Endo, Via Natrl or Artfcl Opng], Drain Dev, NQ
0F9F[0,3,4,7,8]ZZ	Drain/Pancreatic Duct, Accessory, [Opn, Perc, Perc Endo, Via Natrl or Artfcl Opng, Via Natrl or Artfcl Opng Endo]
0F9F[0,3,4,7]0Z	Drain/Pancreatic Duct, Accessory, [Opn, Perc, Perc Endo, Via Natrl or Artfcl Opng], Drain Dev, NQ
0F9G[0,3,4][0,Z]Z	Drain/Pancreas, [Opn, Perc, Perc Endo], [Drain Dev, No Dev], NQ
0FB0[0,3,4]ZZ	Exc/Liver, [Opn, Perc, Perc Endo]
0FB1[0,3,4]ZZ	Exc/Liver, Rt Lobe, [Opn, Perc, Perc Endo]
0FB2[0,3,4]ZZ	Exc/Liver, Lt Lobe, [Opn, Perc, Perc Endo]
0FBD[0,3,7]ZZ	Exc/Pancreatic Duct, [Opn, Perc, Via Natrl or Artfcl Opng]
0FBF[0,3,7]ZZ	Exc/Pancreatic Duct, Accessory, [Opn, Perc, Via Natrl or Artfcl Opng]
0FBG[0,3,4]ZZ	Exc/Pancreas, [Opn, Perc, Perc Endo]
0FC0*	Extir/Liver
0FC1*	Extir/Liver, Rt Lobe
0FC2*	Extir/Liver, Lt Lobe
0FCC0ZZ	Extir of Matter from Ampulla of Vater, Opn Appr
0FCD[0,7]ZZ	Extir/Pancreatic Duct, [Opn, Via Natrl or Artfcl Opng]
0FCF[0,7]ZZ	Extir/Pancreatic Duct, Accessory, [Opn, Via Natrl or Artfcl Opng]
0FCG*	Extir/Pancreas
0FFD[0,3,4,7,8]ZZ	Fragmn/Pancreatic Duct, [Opn, Perc, Perc Endo, Via Natrl or Artfcl Opng, Via Natrl or Artfcl Opng Endo]
0FFF[0,3,4,7,8]ZZ	Fragmn/Pancreatic Duct, Accessory, [Opn, Perc, Perc Endo, Via Natrl or Artfcl Opng, Via Natrl or Artfcl Opng Endo]
0FH0[0,3,4]2Z	Insert/Liver, [Opn, Perc, Perc Endo], Monitoring Dev, NQ
0FH1[0,3,4]2Z	Insert/Liver, Rt Lobe, [Opn, Perc, Perc Endo], Monitoring Dev, NQ
0FH2[0,3,4]2Z	Insert/Liver, Lt Lobe, [Opn, Perc, Perc Endo], Monitoring Dev, NQ
0FHD[0,3,4,7,8]2Z	Insert/Pancreatic Duct, [Opn, Perc, Perc Endo, Via Natrl or Artfcl Opng, Via Natrl or Artfcl Opng Endo], Monitoring Dev, NQ
0FHD[0,3,7]DZ	Insert/Pancreatic Duct, [Opn, Perc, Via Natrl or Artfcl Opng], Intralum Dev, NQ
0FHG[0,3,4]2Z	Insert/Pancreas, [Opn, Perc, Perc Endo], Monitoring Dev, NQ
0FLD*	Occlsn/Pancreatic Duct
0FLF*	Occlsn/Pancreatic Duct, Accessory
0FM0*	Reattach/Liver
0FM1*	Reattach/Liver, Rt Lobe
0FM2*	Reattach/Liver, Lt Lobe
0FMD*	Reattach/Pancreatic Duct
0FMF*	Reattach/Pancreatic Duct, Accessory
0FMG*	Reattach/Pancreas
0FP0[0,3,4][0,2,3]Z	Rmvl/Liver, [Opn, Perc, Perc Endo], [Drain Dev, Monitoring Dev, Inf Dev], NQ
0FPD[0,3,4,7,8][0,1,2,3,7,C,D,J,K]Z	Rmvl/Pancreatic Duct, [Opn, Perc, Perc Endo, Via Natrl or Artfcl Opng, Via Natrl or Artfcl Opng Endo], [Drain Dev, Radioact Elmt, Monitoring Dev, Inf Dev, Auto Tissue Sub, Extralum Dev, Intralum Dev, Synth Sub, Nonauto Tissue Sub], NQ
0FPGXDZ	Rmvl of Intralum Dev from Pancreas, Extern Appr
0FPG[0,3,4][0,2,3,D]Z	Rmvl/Pancreas, [Opn, Perc, Perc Endo], [Drain Dev, Monitoring Dev, Inf Dev, Intralum Dev], NQ
0FQ0*	Repair/Liver
0FQ1*	Repair/Liver, Rt Lobe
0FQ2*	Repair/Liver, Lt Lobe
0FQC*	Repair/Ampulla of Vater
0FQD*	Repair/Pancreatic Duct
0FQF*	Repair/Pancreatic Duct, Accessory
0FQG*	Repair/Pancreas
0FRD*	Replace/Pancreatic Duct
0FRF*	Replace/Pancreatic Duct, Accessory
0FS0*	Repos/Liver
0FSD*	Repos/Pancreatic Duct
0FSF*	Repos/Pancreatic Duct, Accessory
0FSG*	Repos/Pancreas
0FT0*	Resect/Liver
0FT1*	Resect/Liver, Rt Lobe
0FT2*	Resect/Liver, Lt Lobe
0FTD[0,7]ZZ	Resect/Pancreatic Duct, [Opn, Via Natrl or Artfcl Opng]
0FTF[0,7]ZZ	Resect/Pancreatic Duct, Accessory, [Opn, Via Natrl or Artfcl Opng]
0FTG*	Resect/Pancreas
0FUD*	Supl/Pancreatic Duct
0FUF*	Supl/Pancreatic Duct, Accessory
0FVD*	Restrict/Pancreatic Duct
0FVF*	Restrict/Pancreatic Duct, Accessory
0FW0[0,3,4][0,2,3]Z	Rev/Liver, [Opn, Perc, Perc Endo], [Drain Dev, Monitoring Dev, Inf Dev], NQ
0FWD[0,3,4,7,8][0,2,3,7,C,D,J,K]Z	Rev/Pancreatic Duct, [Opn, Perc, Perc Endo, Via Natrl or Artfcl Opng, Via Natrl or Artfcl Opng Endo], [Drain Dev, Monitoring Dev, Inf Dev, Auto Tissue Sub, Extralum Dev, Intralum Dev, Synth Sub, Nonauto Tissue Sub], NQ
0FWG[0,3,4][0,2,3,D]Z	Rev/Pancreas, [Opn, Perc, Perc Endo], [Drain Dev, Monitoring Dev, Inf Dev, Intralum Dev], NQ
0FYG*	Transplantation/Pancreas
0W1G[0,4]JY	Bypass/Peritoneal Cavity, [Opn, Perc Endo], Synth Sub, Lwr Vein
DFY0KZZ	Laser Interstitial Thermal Therapy of Liver

DRG 406   Pancreas, Liver and Shunt Procedures with CC
| GMLOS 5.9 | AMLOS 7.4 | RW 2.8075 | [T] |

Select operating room procedures listed under DRG 405

DRG 407   Pancreas, Liver and Shunt Procedures without CC/MCC
| GMLOS 4.1 | AMLOS 5.0 | RW 2.0026 | [T] |

Select operating room procedures listed under DRG 405

DRG 408   Biliary Tract Procedures Except Only Cholecystectomy with or without C.D.E. with MCC
| GMLOS 9.6 | AMLOS 11.6 | RW 3.6476 |

Operating Room Procedures

0F14*	Bypass/Gallbladder
0F15*	Bypass/Hepatic Duct, Rt
0F16*	Bypass/Hepatic Duct, Lt
0F18*	Bypass/Cystic Duct

| Surgical | Medical | CC Indicator | MCC Indicator | Procedure Proxy | PDxMCC PDx acts as own MCC | PDxCC PDx acts as own CC |

MDC 7: Diseases And Disorders Of The Hepatobiliary System And Pancreas—SURGICAL

ØF19*	Bypass/Common Bile Duct
ØF55[Ø,3,7]ZZ	Destr/Hepatic Duct, Rt, [Opn, Perc, Via Natrl or Artfcl Opng]
ØF56[Ø,3,7]ZZ	Destr/Hepatic Duct, Lt, [Opn, Perc, Via Natrl or Artfcl Opng]
ØF58[Ø,3,7]ZZ	Destr/Cystic Duct, [Opn, Perc, Via Natrl or Artfcl Opng]
ØF59[Ø,3,7]ZZ	Destr/Common Bile Duct, [Opn, Perc, Via Natrl or Artfcl Opng]
ØF5C[Ø,3,7]ZZ	Destr/Ampulla of Vater, [Opn, Perc, Via Natrl or Artfcl Opng]
ØF75ØDZ	Dilation of Rt Hepatic Duct with Intralum Dev, Opn Appr
ØF75[Ø,7]ZZ	Dilation/Hepatic Duct, Rt, [Opn, Via Natrl or Artfcl Opng]
ØF76ØDZ	Dilation of Lt Hepatic Duct with Intralum Dev, Opn Appr
ØF76[Ø,7]ZZ	Dilation/Hepatic Duct, Lt, [Opn, Via Natrl or Artfcl Opng]
ØF78ØDZ	Dilation of Cystic Duct with Intralum Dev, Opn Appr
ØF78[Ø,7]ZZ	Dilation/Cystic Duct, [Opn, Via Natrl or Artfcl Opng]
ØF79ØDZ	Dilation of Com Bile Duct with Intralum Dev, Opn Appr
ØF79[Ø,7]ZZ	Dilation/Common Bile Duct, [Opn, Via Natrl or Artfcl Opng]
ØF7C[Ø,3,4,7][D,Z]Z	Dilation/Ampulla of Vater, [Opn, Perc, Perc Endo, Via Natrl or Artfcl Opng], [Intralum Dev, No Dev], NQ
ØF94ØZZ	Drain of Gallbladder, Opn Appr
ØF94[Ø,3]ØZ	Drain/Gallbladder, [Opn, Perc], Drain Dev, NQ
ØF95[Ø,3,4,7,8][Ø,Z]Z	Drain/Hepatic Duct, Rt, [Opn, Perc, Perc Endo, Via Natrl or Artfcl Opng, Via Natrl or Artfcl Opng Endo], [Drain Dev, No Dev], NQ
ØF96[Ø,3,4,7,8][Ø,Z]Z	Drain/Hepatic Duct, Lt, [Opn, Perc, Perc Endo, Via Natrl or Artfcl Opng, Via Natrl or Artfcl Opng Endo], [Drain Dev, No Dev], NQ
ØF98[Ø,3,4,7,8][Ø,Z]Z	Drain/Cystic Duct, [Opn, Perc, Perc Endo, Via Natrl or Artfcl Opng, Via Natrl or Artfcl Opng Endo], [Drain Dev, No Dev], NQ
ØF9C[Ø,3,7][Ø,Z]Z	Drain/Ampulla of Vater, [Opn, Perc, Via Natrl or Artfcl Opng], [Drain Dev, No Dev], NQ
ØFB5[Ø,3,7]ZZ	Exc/Hepatic Duct, Rt, [Opn, Perc, Via Natrl or Artfcl Opng]
ØFB6[Ø,3,7]ZZ	Exc/Hepatic Duct, Lt, [Opn, Perc, Via Natrl or Artfcl Opng]
ØFB8[Ø,3,7]ZZ	Exc/Cystic Duct, [Opn, Perc, Via Natrl or Artfcl Opng]
ØFB9[Ø,3,7]ZZ	Exc/Common Bile Duct, [Opn, Perc, Via Natrl or Artfcl Opng]
ØFBC[Ø,3,7]ZZ	Exc/Ampulla of Vater, [Opn, Perc, Via Natrl or Artfcl Opng]
ØFC4*	Extir/Gallbladder
ØFC8ØZZ	Extir of Matter from Cystic Duct, Opn Appr
ØFCC[3,7]ZZ	Extir/Ampulla of Vater, [Perc, Via Natrl or Artfcl Opng]
ØFC[5,6]ØZZ	Extir of Matter from [Rt, Lt] Hepatic Duct, Opn Appr
ØFF4[Ø,3,4,7]ZZ	Fragmn/Gallbladder, [Opn, Perc, Perc Endo, Via Natrl or Artfcl Opng]
ØFF5[Ø,3,4,7]ZZ	Fragmn/Hepatic Duct, Rt, [Opn, Perc, Perc Endo, Via Natrl or Artfcl Opng]
ØFF6[Ø,3,4,7]ZZ	Fragmn/Hepatic Duct, Lt, [Opn, Perc, Perc Endo, Via Natrl or Artfcl Opng]
ØFF8[Ø,3,4,7]ZZ	Fragmn/Cystic Duct, [Opn, Perc, Perc Endo, Via Natrl or Artfcl Opng]
ØFF9[Ø,3,4,7]ZZ	Fragmn/Common Bile Duct, [Opn, Perc, Perc Endo, Via Natrl or Artfcl Opng]
ØFFC[Ø,3,4,7]ZZ	Fragmn/Ampulla of Vater, [Opn, Perc, Perc Endo, Via Natrl or Artfcl Opng]
ØFH4[Ø,3,4]2Z	Insert/Gallbladder, [Opn, Perc, Perc Endo], Monitoring Dev, NQ
ØFHB[Ø,3,4,7,8]2Z	Insert/Hepatobiliary Duct, [Opn, Perc, Perc Endo, Via Natrl or Artfcl Opng, Via Natrl or Artfcl Opng Endo], Monitoring Dev, NQ
ØFHB[Ø,3,7]DZ	Insert/Hepatobiliary Duct, [Opn, Perc, Via Natrl or Artfcl Opng], Intralum Dev, NQ
ØFL5Ø[C,D,Z]Z	Occlsn/Hepatic Duct, Rt, Opn, [Extralum Dev, Intralum Dev, No Dev], NQ
ØFL6Ø[C,D,Z]Z	Occlsn/Hepatic Duct, Lt, Opn, [Extralum Dev, Intralum Dev, No Dev], NQ
ØFL8Ø[C,D,Z]Z	Occlsn/Cystic Duct, Opn, [Extralum Dev, Intralum Dev, No Dev], NQ
ØFL9Ø[C,D,Z]Z	Occlsn/Common Bile Duct, Opn, [Extralum Dev, Intralum Dev, No Dev], NQ
ØFLC*	Occlsn/Ampulla of Vater
ØFM4ØZZ	Reattach of Gallbladder, Opn Appr
ØFM5ØZZ	Reattach of Rt Hepatic Duct, Opn Appr
ØFM6ØZZ	Reattach of Lt Hepatic Duct, Opn Appr
ØFM8ØZZ	Reattach of Cystic Duct, Opn Appr
ØFM9ØZZ	Reattach of Common Bile Duct, Opn Appr
ØFMC*	Reattach/Ampulla of Vater
ØFP4[Ø,3,4][Ø,2,3,D]Z	Rmvl/Gallbladder, [Opn, Perc, Perc Endo], [Drain Dev, Monitoring Dev, Inf Dev, Intralum Dev], NQ
ØFPB[Ø,3,4,7,8][Ø,1,2,3,7,C,D,J,K]Z	Rmvl/Hepatobiliary Duct, [Opn, Perc, Perc Endo, Via Natrl or Artfcl Opng, Via Natrl or Artfcl Opng Endo], [Drain Dev, Radioact Elmt, Monitoring Dev, Inf Dev, Auto Tissue Sub, Extralum Dev, Intralum Dev, Synth Sub, Nonauto Tissue Sub], NQ
ØFQ4*	Repair/Gallbladder
ØFQ5*	Repair/Hepatic Duct, Rt
ØFQ6*	Repair/Hepatic Duct, Lt

ØFQ8*	Repair/Cystic Duct
ØFQ9*	Repair/Common Bile Duct
ØFR5*	Replace/Hepatic Duct, Rt
ØFR6*	Replace/Hepatic Duct, Lt
ØFR8*	Replace/Cystic Duct
ØFR9*	Replace/Common Bile Duct
ØFRC*	Replace/Ampulla of Vater
ØFS4*	Repos/Gallbladder
ØFS5*	Repos/Hepatic Duct, Rt
ØFS6*	Repos/Hepatic Duct, Lt
ØFS8*	Repos/Cystic Duct
ØFS9*	Repos/Common Bile Duct
ØFSC*	Repos/Ampulla of Vater
ØFT5*	Resect/Hepatic Duct, Rt
ØFT6*	Resect/Hepatic Duct, Lt
ØFT8*	Resect/Cystic Duct
ØFT9*	Resect/Common Bile Duct
ØFTC*	Resect/Ampulla of Vater
ØFU5*	Supl/Hepatic Duct, Rt
ØFU6*	Supl/Hepatic Duct, Lt
ØFU8*	Supl/Cystic Duct
ØFU9*	Supl/Common Bile Duct
ØFUC*	Supl/Ampulla of Vater
ØFV5Ø[C,D,Z]Z	Restrict/Hepatic Duct, Rt, Opn, [Extralum Dev, Intralum Dev, No Dev], NQ
ØFV6Ø[C,D,Z]Z	Restrict/Hepatic Duct, Lt, Opn, [Extralum Dev, Intralum Dev, No Dev], NQ
ØFV8Ø[C,D,Z]Z	Restrict/Cystic Duct, Opn, [Extralum Dev, Intralum Dev, No Dev], NQ
ØFV9Ø[C,D,Z]Z	Restrict/Common Bile Duct, Opn, [Extralum Dev, Intralum Dev, No Dev], NQ
ØFVC*	Restrict/Ampulla of Vater
ØFW4[Ø,3,4][Ø,2,3,D]Z	Rev/Gallbladder, [Opn, Perc, Perc Endo], [Drain Dev, Monitoring Dev, Inf Dev, Intralum Dev], NQ
ØFWB[Ø,3,4,7,8][Ø,2,3,7,C,D,J,K]Z	Rev/Hepatobiliary Duct, [Opn, Perc, Perc Endo, Via Natrl or Artfcl Opng, Via Natrl or Artfcl Opng Endo], [Drain Dev, Monitoring Dev, Inf Dev, Auto Tissue Sub, Extralum Dev, Intralum Dev, Synth Sub, Nonauto Tissue Sub], NQ

OR

ØF99ØZZ	Drain of Common Bile Duct, Opn Appr
ØF99[Ø,3,4]ØZ	Drain/Common Bile Duct, [Opn, Perc, Perc Endo], Drain Dev, NQ
ØFC9ØZZ	Extir of Matter from Common Bile Duct, Opn Appr
ØFJB*	Inspect/Hepatobiliary Duct

WITHOUT

ØF54*	Destr/Gallbladder
ØFB4[Ø,3,4]ZZ	Exc/Gallbladder, [Opn, Perc, Perc Endo]
ØFT4*	Resect/Gallbladder

DRG 409 **Biliary Tract Procedures Except Only Cholecystectomy with or without C.D.E. with CC**

GMLOS 6.6 AMLOS 7.9 RW 2.4648

Select operating room procedures listed under DRG 408

DRG 410 **Biliary Tract Procedures Except Only Cholecystectomy with or without C.D.E. without CC/MCC**

GMLOS 4.5 AMLOS 5.2 RW 1.5576

Select operating room procedures listed under DRG 408

DRG 411 **Cholecystectomy with C.D.E. with MCC**

GMLOS 8.9 AMLOS 11.Ø RW 3.5782

Operating Room Procedures

ØF99ØZZ	Drain of Common Bile Duct, Opn Appr
ØF99[Ø,3,4]ØZ	Drain/Common Bile Duct, [Opn, Perc, Perc Endo], Drain Dev, NQ
ØFC9ØZZ	Extir of Matter from Common Bile Duct, Opn Appr
ØFJB*	Inspect/Hepatobiliary Duct

AND

ØF54*	Destr/Gallbladder
ØFB4[Ø,3,4]ZZ	Exc/Gallbladder, [Opn, Perc, Perc Endo]
ØFT4*	Resect/Gallbladder

Ⓣ **Transfer DRG**   ⓈⓅ **Special Payment**   * **Code Range**   **6th and 7th Character of ZZ = No Device, No Qualifier ZX = No Device, Diagnostic**

120   MS-DRG Version 33.0   © 2015 Optum360, LLC

DRG 412   **Cholecystectomy with C.D.E. with CC**

     GMLOS 6.6   **AMLOS 7.6**   **RW 2.4981**

Select operating room procedure combinations listed under DRG 411

DRG 413   **Cholecystectomy with C.D.E. without CC/MCC**

     GMLOS 4.1   **AMLOS 5.0**   **RW 1.7996**

Select operating room procedure combinations listed under DRG 411

DRG 414   **Cholecystectomy Except by Laparoscope without C.D.E. with MCC**

     GMLOS 8.5   **AMLOS 10.3**   **RW 3.5283**   [T]

Operating Room Procedures

0F54[0,3]ZZ	Destr/Gallbladder, [Opn, Perc]
0FB4[0,3]ZZ	Exc/Gallbladder, [Opn, Perc]
0FT40ZZ	Resect of Gallbladder, Opn Appr

DRG 415   **Cholecystectomy Except by Laparoscope without C.D.E. with CC**

     GMLOS 5.5   **AMLOS 6.4**   **RW 2.0071**   [T]

Select operating room procedures listed under DRG 414

DRG 416   **Cholecystectomy Except by Laparoscope without C.D.E. without CC/MCC**

     GMLOS 3.4   **AMLOS 4.0**   **RW 1.3342**   [T]

Select operating room procedures listed under DRG 414

DRG 417   **Laparoscopic Cholecystectomy without C.D.E. with MCC**

     GMLOS 5.8   **AMLOS 7.2**   **RW 2.4734**

Operating Room Procedures

0F544ZZ	Destr of Gallbladder, Perc Endo Appr
0FB44ZZ	Exc of Gallbladder, Perc Endo Appr
0FT44ZZ	Resect of Gallbladder, Perc Endo Appr

DRG 418   **Laparoscopic Cholecystectomy without C.D.E. with CC**

     GMLOS 3.9   **AMLOS 4.7**   **RW 1.6584**

Select operating room procedures listed under DRG 417

DRG 419   **Laparoscopic Cholecystectomy without C.D.E. without CC/MCC**

     GMLOS 2.5   **AMLOS 3.0**   **RW 1.2540**

Select operating room procedures listed under DRG 417

DRG 420   **Hepatobiliary Diagnostic Procedures with MCC**

     GMLOS 8.1   **AMLOS 11.1**   **RW 3.6609**

Operating Room Procedures

07JP0ZZ	Inspect of Spleen, Opn Appr
0D9S[0,3,4]ZX	Drain/Greater Omentum, [Opn, Perc, Perc Endo]
0D9T[0,3,4]ZX	Drain/Lesser Omentum, [Opn, Perc, Perc Endo]
0D9V[0,3,4]ZX	Drain/Mesentery, [Opn, Perc, Perc Endo]
0D9W[0,3,4]ZX	Drain/Peritoneum, [Opn, Perc, Perc Endo]
0DB[S,T,V,W]0ZX	Exc of [Greater Omentum, Lesser Omentum, Mesentery, Peritoneum], Opn Appr, Dx
0DJ00ZZ	Inspect of Upr Intestinal Tract, Opn Appr
0DJ6[0,4]ZZ	Inspect/Stomach, [Opn, Perc Endo]
0DJD0ZZ	Inspect of Lwr Intestinal Tract, Opn Appr
0DJU[0,3,4]ZZ	Inspect/Omentum, [Opn, Perc, Perc Endo]
0DJV[0,3,4]ZZ	Inspect/Mesentery, [Opn, Perc, Perc Endo]
0DJW[0,3,4]ZZ	Inspect/Peritoneum, [Opn, Perc, Perc Endo]
0F9[0,1,2]0ZX	Drain of [Liver, Rt Lobe Liver, Lt Lobe Liver], Opn Appr, Dx
0F9[4,5,6,8]0ZX	Drain of [Gallbladder, Rt Hepatic Duct, Lt Hepatic Duct, Cystic Duct], Opn Appr, Dx
0F9[9,C,D,F,G]0ZX	Drain of [Common Bile Duct, Ampulla of Vater, Pancreatic Duct, Accessory Pancreatic Duct, Pancreas], Opn Appr, Dx
0FB0[0,4]ZX	Exc/Liver, [Opn, Perc Endo]
0FB1[0,4]ZX	Exc/Liver, Rt Lobe, [Opn, Perc Endo]
0FB2[0,4]ZX	Exc/Liver, Lt Lobe, [Opn, Perc Endo]
0FB[4,5,6,8,9,C]0ZX	Exc of [Gallbladder, Rt Hepatic Duct, Lt Hepatic Duct, Cystic Duct, Common Bile Duct, Ampulla of Vater], Opn Appr, Dx

0FB[D,F,G]0ZX	Exc of [Pancreatic Duct, Accessory Pancreatic Duct, Pancreas], Opn Appr, Dx
0FJ0[0,3,4]ZZ	Inspect/Liver, [Opn, Perc, Perc Endo]
0FJ4[0,3,4]ZZ	Inspect/Gallbladder, [Opn, Perc, Perc Endo]
0FJD*	Inspect/Pancreatic Duct
0FJG[0,3,4]ZZ	Inspect/Pancreas, [Opn, Perc, Perc Endo]
0W9G00Z	Drain of Peritoneal Cavity with Drain Dev, Opn Appr
0W9G0ZZ	Drain of Peritoneal Cavity, Opn Appr
0W9G[0,3,4]ZX	Drain/Peritoneal Cavity, [Opn, Perc, Perc Endo]
0W9H[0,3,4]ZX	Drain/Retroperitoneum, [Opn, Perc, Perc Endo]
0W9J[0,3,4]ZX	Drain/Pelvic Cavity, [Opn, Perc, Perc Endo]
0WBH0ZX	Exc of Retroperitoneum, Opn Appr, Diagnostic
0WC[J,P,R]0ZZ	Extir of Matter from [Pelvic Cavity, Gastrointestinal Tract, Genitourinary Tract], Opn Appr
0WJF[3,4]ZZ	Inspect/Abd Wall, [Perc, Perc Endo]
0WJG*	Inspect/Peritoneal Cavity
0WJH[3,4]ZZ	Inspect/Retroperitoneum, [Perc, Perc Endo]
0WJJ*	Inspect/Pelvic Cavity
0WJP*	Inspect/Gastrointestinal Tract
0WJR*	Inspect/Genitourinary Tract
0Y95[0,3,4]ZX	Drain/Inguinal Rgn, Rt, [Opn, Perc, Perc Endo]
0Y96[0,3,4]ZX	Drain/Inguinal Rgn, Lt, [Opn, Perc, Perc Endo]
0YB5[0,3,4]ZX	Exc/Inguinal Rgn, Rt, [Opn, Perc, Perc Endo]
0YB6[0,3,4]ZX	Exc/Inguinal Rgn, Lt, [Opn, Perc, Perc Endo]
0YB7[0,3,4]ZX	Exc/Femor Rgn, Rt, [Opn, Perc, Perc Endo]
0YB8[0,3,4]ZX	Exc/Femor Rgn, Lt, [Opn, Perc, Perc Endo]
0YJ5[3,4]ZZ	Inspect/Inguinal Rgn, Rt, [Perc, Perc Endo]
0YJ6[3,4]ZZ	Inspect/Inguinal Rgn, Lt, [Perc, Perc Endo]
0YJ7[3,4]ZZ	Inspect/Femor Rgn, Rt, [Perc, Perc Endo]
0YJ8[3,4]ZZ	Inspect/Femor Rgn, Lt, [Perc, Perc Endo]
0YJA[3,4]ZZ	Inspect/Inguinal Rgn, Bilat, [Perc, Perc Endo]
0YJE[3,4]ZZ	Inspect/Femor Rgn, Bilat, [Perc, Perc Endo]
4A0C[3,4,7,8]5Z	Measurement/Biliary, [Perc, Perc Endo, Via Natrl or Artfcl Opng, Via Natrl or Artfcl Opng Endo], Flow, NQ
4A0C[3,4,7]BZ	Measurement/Biliary, [Perc, Perc Endo, Via Natrl or Artfcl Opng], Pressure, NQ
BF03[0,1,Y]ZZ	Plain Radiography/Gallbladder and Bile Ducts, [High Osmolar, Low Osmolar, Oth Contrast], None, None
BF0C[0,1,Y]ZZ	Plain Radiography of Hepatobiliary Sys, All using [High Osmolar, Low Osmolar, Oth] Contrast

DRG 421   **Hepatobiliary Diagnostic Procedures with CC**

     GMLOS 4.1   **AMLOS 5.3**   **RW 1.7451**

Select operating room procedures listed under DRG 420

DRG 422   **Hepatobiliary Diagnostic Procedures without CC/MCC**

     GMLOS 2.8   **AMLOS 3.4**   **RW 1.2941**

Select operating room procedures listed under DRG 420

DRG 423   **Other Hepatobiliary or Pancreas O.R. Procedures with MCC**

     GMLOS 9.8   **AMLOS 13.4**   **RW 4.2650**

Operating Room Procedures

008W*	Div/Cervical Spinal Cord
008X*	Div/Thoracic Spinal Cord
008Y*	Div/Lumbar Spinal Cord
00PV[0,3,4][0,2,3,7,J,K]Z	Rmvl/Spinal Cord, [Opn, Perc, Perc Endo], [Drain Dev, Monitoring Dev, Inf Dev, Auto Tissue Sub, Synth Sub, Nonauto Tissue Sub], NQ
00WV[0,3,4][0,2,3,7,J,K,M]Z	Rev/Spinal Cord, [Opn, Perc, Perc Endo], [Drain Dev, Monitoring Dev, Inf Dev, Auto Tissue Sub, Synth Sub, Nonauto Tissue Sub, Neurostimulator Lead], NQ
02HV[0,3,4][2,D]Z	Insert/Superior Vena Cava, [Opn, Perc, Perc Endo], [Monitoring Dev, Intralum Dev], NQ
02LV*	Occlsn/Superior Vena Cava
02VV*	Restrict/Superior Vena Cava
03150[9,A,J,K,Z]0	Bypass/Axillary Artery, Rt, Opn, [Auto Venous Tissue, Auto Arterial Tissue, Synth Sub, Nonauto Tissue Sub, No Dev], Upr Arm Artery, Rt
03160[9,A,J,K,Z]1	Bypass/Axillary Artery, Lt, Opn, [Auto Venous Tissue, Auto Arterial Tissue, Synth Sub, Nonauto Tissue Sub, No Dev], Upr Arm Artery, Lt
031H0[9,A,J,K,Z]J	Bypass/Common Carotid Artery, Rt, Opn, [Auto Venous Tissue, Auto Arterial Tissue, Synth Sub, Nonauto Tissue Sub, No Dev], Extracranial Artery, Rt

---

Surgical   **Medical**   **CC Indicator**   **MCC Indicator**   **Procedure Proxy**   **PDxMCC PDx acts as own MCC**   **PDxCC PDx acts as own CC**

MS-DRG Version 33.0

MDC 7: Diseases And Disorders Of The Hepatobiliary System And Pancreas—SURGICAL

031J0[9,A,J,K,Z]K	Bypass Lt Common Carotid Artery, Opn, to Lt Extracranial Artery [Auto Venous Tissue, Auto Arterial Tissue, Synth Sub, Nonauto Tissue Sub, NQ]
031K0[9,A,J,K,Z]J	Bypass Rt Int Carotid Artery, Opn, to Rt Extracranial Artery [Auto Venous Tissue, Auto Arterial Tissue, Synth Sub, Nonauto Tissue Sub, NQ]
031L0[9,A,J,K,Z]K	Bypass Lt Int Carotid Artery, Opn, to Lt Extracranial Artery [Auto Venous Tissue, Auto Arterial Tissue, Synth Sub, Nonauto Tissue Sub, NQ]
031M0[9,A,J,K,Z]J	Bypass Rt Ext Carotid Artery, Opn, to Rt Extracranial Artery [Auto Venous Tissue, Auto Arterial Tissue, Synth Sub, Nonauto Tissue Sub, NQ]
031N0[9,A,J,K,Z]K	Bypass Lt Ext Carotid Artery, Opn, to Lt Extracranial Artery [Auto Venous Tissue, Auto Arterial Tissue, Synth Sub, Nonauto Tissue Sub, NQ]
03733[4,D,Z]Z	Dilation/Subclavian Artery, Rt, Perc, [Drug-eluting Intralum Dev, Intralum Dev, No Dev], NQ
03743[4,D,Z]Z	Dilation/Subclavian Artery, Lt, Perc, [Drug-eluting Intralum Dev, Intralum Dev, No Dev], NQ
03773[4,D,Z]Z	Dilation/Brachial Artery, Rt, Perc, [Drug-eluting Intralum Dev, Intralum Dev, No Dev], NQ
03783[4,D,Z]Z	Dilation/Brachial Artery, Lt, Perc, [Drug-eluting Intralum Dev, Intralum Dev, No Dev], NQ
03793[4,D,Z]Z	Dilation/Ulnar Artery, Rt, Perc, [Drug-eluting Intralum Dev, Intralum Dev, No Dev], NQ
037A3[4,D,Z]Z	Dilation/Ulnar Artery, Lt, Perc, [Drug-eluting Intralum Dev, Intralum Dev, No Dev], NQ
037Y3[4,D,Z]Z	Dilation/Upr Artery, Perc, [Drug-eluting Intralum Dev, Intralum Dev, No Dev], NQ
03CY*	Extir/Upr Artery
03QY*	Repair/Upr Artery
041K[0,4][9,A,J,K,Z][H,J,K,L]	Bypass/Femor Artery, Rt, [Opn, Perc Endo], [Auto Venous Tissue, Auto Arterial Tissue, Synth Sub, Nonauto Tissue Sub, No Dev], [Femor Artery, Rt, Femor Artery, Lt, Femor Arteries, Bilat, Popliteal Artery]
041L[0,4][9,A,J,K,Z][H,J,K,L]	Bypass/Femor Artery, Lt, [Opn, Perc Endo], [Auto Venous Tissue, Auto Arterial Tissue, Synth Sub, Nonauto Tissue Sub, No Dev], [Femor Artery, Rt, Femor Artery, Lt, Femor Arteries, Bilat, Popliteal Artery]
04703[4,D,Z]Z	Dilation/Abd Aorta, Perc, [Drug-eluting Intralum Dev, Intralum Dev, No Dev], NQ
04713[4,D,Z]Z	Dilation/Celiac Artery, Perc, [Drug-eluting Intralum Dev, Intralum Dev, No Dev], NQ
04723[4,D,Z]Z	Dilation/Gastric Artery, Perc, [Drug-eluting Intralum Dev, Intralum Dev, No Dev], NQ
04733[4,D,Z]Z	Dilation/Hepatic Artery, Perc, [Drug-eluting Intralum Dev, Intralum Dev, No Dev], NQ
04743[4,D,Z]Z	Dilation/Splenic Artery, Perc, [Drug-eluting Intralum Dev, Intralum Dev, No Dev], NQ
04753[4,D,Z]Z	Dilation/Superior Mesenteric Artery, Perc, [Drug-eluting Intralum Dev, Intralum Dev, No Dev], NQ
04763[4,D,Z]Z	Dilation/Colic Artery, Rt, Perc, [Drug-eluting Intralum Dev, Intralum Dev, No Dev], NQ
04773[4,D,Z]Z	Dilation/Colic Artery, Lt, Perc, [Drug-eluting Intralum Dev, Intralum Dev, No Dev], NQ
04783[4,D,Z]Z	Dilation/Colic Artery, Mid, Perc, [Drug-eluting Intralum Dev, Intralum Dev, No Dev], NQ
04793[4,D,Z]Z	Dilation/Renal Artery, Rt, Perc, [Drug-eluting Intralum Dev, Intralum Dev, No Dev], NQ
047A3[4,D,Z]Z	Dilation/Renal Artery, Lt, Perc, [Drug-eluting Intralum Dev, Intralum Dev, No Dev], NQ
047B3[4,D,Z]Z	Dilation/Inferior Mesenteric Artery, Perc, [Drug-eluting Intralum Dev, Intralum Dev, No Dev], NQ
047C3[4,D,Z]Z	Dilation/Common Iliac Artery, Rt, Perc, [Drug-eluting Intralum Dev, Intralum Dev, No Dev], NQ
047D3[4,D,Z]Z	Dilation/Common Iliac Artery, Lt, Perc, [Drug-eluting Intralum Dev, Intralum Dev, No Dev], NQ
047E3[4,D,Z]Z	Dilation/Int Iliac Artery, Rt, Perc, [Drug-eluting Intralum Dev, Intralum Dev, No Dev], NQ
047F3[4,D,Z]Z	Dilation/Int Iliac Artery, Lt, Perc, [Drug-eluting Intralum Dev, Intralum Dev, No Dev], NQ
047H3[4,D,Z]Z	Dilation/Ext Iliac Artery, Rt, Perc, [Drug-eluting Intralum Dev, Intralum Dev, No Dev], NQ
047J3[4,D,Z]Z	Dilation/Ext Iliac Artery, Lt, Perc, [Drug-eluting Intralum Dev, Intralum Dev, No Dev], NQ
047K041	Dilation Rt Fem Art w Drug-elut Intralum, Drug Blln, Opn
047K0D1	Dilation Rt Fem Art w Intralum Dev, Drug Blln, Opn
047K0Z1	Dilation of Rt Fem Art using Drug Blln, Opn Appr
047K341	Dilation Rt Fem Art w Drug-elut Intralum, Drug Blln, Perc
047K3D1	Dilation Rt Fem Art w Intralum Dev, Drug Blln, Perc

047K3Z1	Dilation of Rt Fem Art using Drug Blln, Perc Appr
047K3[4,D,Z]Z	Dilation/Femor Artery, Rt, Perc, [Drug-eluting Intralum Dev, Intralum Dev, No Dev], NQ
047K441	Dilation Rt Fem Art w Drug-elut Intralum, Drug Blln, Perc Endo
047K4D1	Dilation Rt Fem Art w Intralum Dev, Drug Blln, Perc Endo
047K4Z1	Dilation of Rt Fem Art using Drug Blln, Perc Endo Appr
047L041	Dilation Lt Fem Art w Drug-elut Intralum, Drug Blln, Opn
047L0D1	Dilation Lt Fem Art w Intralum Dev, Drug Blln, Opn
047L0Z1	Dilation of Lt Fem Art using Drug Blln, Opn Appr
047L341	Dilation Lt Fem Art w Drug-elut Intralum, Drug Blln, Perc
047L3D1	Dilation Lt Fem Art w Intralum Dev, Drug Blln, Perc
047L3Z1	Dilation of Lt Fem Art using Drug Blln, Perc Appr
047L3[4,D,Z]Z	Dilation/Femor Artery, Lt, Perc, [Drug-eluting Intralum Dev, Intralum Dev, No Dev], NQ
047L441	Dilation Lt Fem Art w Drug-elut Intralum, Drug Blln, Perc Endo
047L4D1	Dilation Lt Fem Art w Intralum Dev, Drug Blln, Perc Endo
047L4Z1	Dilation of Lt Fem Art using Drug Blln, Perc Endo Appr
047M041	Dilation Rt Popl Art w Drug-elut Intralum, Drug Blln, Opn
047M0D1	Dilation Rt Popl Art w Intralum Dev, Drug Blln, Opn
047M0Z1	Dilation of Rt Popl Art using Drug Blln, Opn Appr
047M341	Dilation Rt Popl Art w Drug-elut Intralum, Drug Blln, Perc
047M3D1	Dilation Rt Popl Art w Intralum Dev, Drug Blln, Perc
047M3Z1	Dilation of Rt Popl Art using Drug Blln, Perc Appr
047M441	Dilation Rt Popl Art w Drug-elut Intralum, Drug Blln, Perc Endo
047M4D1	Dilation Rt Popl Art w Intralum Dev, Drug Blln, Perc Endo
047M4Z1	Dilation of Rt Popl Art using Drug Blln, Perc Endo Appr
047N041	Dilation Lt Popl Art w Drug-elut Intralum, Drug Blln, Opn
047N0D1	Dilation Lt Popl Art w Intralum Dev, Drug Blln, Opn
047N0Z1	Dilation of Lt Popl Art using Drug Blln, Opn Appr
047N341	Dilation Lt Popl Art w Drug-elut Intralum, Drug Blln, Perc
047N3D1	Dilation Lt Popl Art w Intralum Dev, Drug Blln, Perc
047N3Z1	Dilation of Lt Popl Art using Drug Blln, Perc Appr
047N441	Dilation Lt Popl Art w Drug-elut Intralum, Drug Blln, Perc Endo
047N4D1	Dilation Lt Popl Art w Intralum Dev, Drug Blln, Perc Endo
047N4Z1	Dilation of Lt Popl Art using Drug Blln, Perc Endo Appr
047Y3[4,D,Z]Z	Dilation/Lwr Artery, Perc, [Drug-eluting Intralum Dev, Intralum Dev, No Dev], NQ
04CY*	Extir/Lwr Artery
04QY*	Repair/Lwr Artery
05793[D,Z]Z	Dilation/Brachial Vein, Rt, Perc, [Intralum Dev, No Dev], NQ
057A3[D,Z]Z	Dilation/Brachial Vein, Lt, Perc, [Intralum Dev, No Dev], NQ
057B3[D,Z]Z	Dilation/Basilic Vein, Rt, Perc, [Intralum Dev, No Dev], NQ
057C3[D,Z]Z	Dilation/Basilic Vein, Lt, Perc, [Intralum Dev, No Dev], NQ
057D3[D,Z]Z	Dilation/Cephalic Vein, Rt, Perc, [Intralum Dev, No Dev], NQ
057F3[D,Z]Z	Dilation/Cephalic Vein, Lt, Perc, [Intralum Dev, No Dev], NQ
05CY*	Extir/Upr Vein
05QY*	Repair/Upr Vein
06703[D,Z]Z	Dilation/Inferior Vena Cava, Perc, [Intralum Dev, No Dev], NQ
06CY*	Extir/Lwr Vein
06H0[0,3,4]DZ	Insert/Inferior Vena Cava, [Opn, Perc, Perc Endo], Intralum Dev, NQ
06L0*	Occlsn/Inferior Vena Cava
06L2[0,3,4]ZZ	Occlsn/Gastric Vein, [Opn, Perc, Perc Endo]
06L3[0,3,4]ZZ	Occlsn/Esophageal Vein, [Opn, Perc, Perc Endo]
06QY*	Repair/Lwr Vein
06V0*	Restrict/Inferior Vena Cava
079B[0,3,4]ZX	Drain/Lymphatic, Mesenteric, [Opn, Perc, Perc Endo]
079C[0,3,4]ZX	Drain/Lymphatic, Pelvis, [Opn, Perc, Perc Endo]
079D[0,3,4]ZX	Drain/Lymphatic, Aortic, [Opn, Perc, Perc Endo]
079L[0,3,4]ZX	Drain/Cisterna Chyli, [Opn, Perc, Perc Endo]
07BB[0,3,4]ZX	Exc/Lymphatic, Mesenteric, [Opn, Perc, Perc Endo]
07BC[0,3,4]ZX	Exc/Lymphatic, Pelvis, [Opn, Perc, Perc Endo]
07BD[0,3,4]ZX	Exc/Lymphatic, Aortic, [Opn, Perc, Perc Endo]
07BL[0,3,4]ZX	Exc/Cisterna Chyli, [Opn, Perc, Perc Endo]
0D16[0,4,8][7,J,K,Z][9,A,B,L]	Bypass/Stomach, [Opn, Perc Endo, Via Natrl or Artfcl Opng Endo], [Auto Tissue Sub, Synth Sub, Nonauto Tissue Sub, No Dev], [Duodenum, Jejunum, Ileum, Transv Colon]
0D59[0,3,7]ZZ	Destr/Duodenum, [Opn, Perc, Via Natrl or Artfcl Opng]
0D5S*	Destr/Greater Omentum
0D5T*	Destr/Lesser Omentum
0D5V*	Destr/Mesentery
0D5W*	Destr/Peritoneum
0D96[0,3,4,7,8]ZZ	Drain/Stomach, [Opn, Perc, Perc Endo, Via Natrl or Artfcl Opng, Via Natrl or Artfcl Opng Endo]
0D96[0,3,4]0Z	Drain/Stomach, [Opn, Perc, Perc Endo], Drain Dev, NQ
0D99[0,3,4,7,8]ZZ	Drain/Duodenum, [Opn, Perc, Perc Endo, Via Natrl or Artfcl Opng, Via Natrl or Artfcl Opng Endo]
0D99[0,3,4]0Z	Drain/Duodenum, [Opn, Perc, Perc Endo], Drain Dev, NQ
0DB7[0,3,7]ZZ	Exc/Stomach, Pylorus, [Opn, Perc, Via Natrl or Artfcl Opng]
0DB9[0,3]ZZ	Exc/Duodenum, [Opn, Perc]

T Transfer DRG   SP Special Payment   * Code Range   **6th and 7th Character of ZZ = No Device, No Qualifier ZX = No Device, Diagnostic**

0DBS[0,3,4]ZZ   Exc/Greater Omentum, [Opn, Perc, Perc Endo]
0DBT[0,3,4]ZZ   Exc/Lesser Omentum, [Opn, Perc, Perc Endo]
0DBV[0,3,4]ZZ   Exc/Mesentery, [Opn, Perc, Perc Endo]
0DBW[0,3,4]ZZ   Exc/Peritoneum, [Opn, Perc, Perc Endo]
0DC6[0,3,4]ZZ   Extir/Stomach, [Opn, Perc, Perc Endo]
0DC9[0,3,4]ZZ   Extir/Duodenum, [Opn, Perc, Perc Endo]
0DH9[0,3,4,7,8][2,3]Z   Insert/Duodenum, [Opn, Perc, Perc Endo, Via Natrl or Artfcl Opng, Via Natrl or Artfcl Opng Endo], [Monitoring Dev, Inf Dev], NQ
0DL8*   Occlsn/Sm Intestine
0DL9*   Occlsn/Duodenum
0DN8[0,3,4]ZZ   Rls/Sm Intestine, [Opn, Perc, Perc Endo]
0DN9[0,3,4]ZZ   Rls/Duodenum, [Opn, Perc, Perc Endo]
0DNA[0,3,4]ZZ   Rls/Jejunum, [Opn, Perc, Perc Endo]
0DNB[0,3,4]ZZ   Rls/Ileum, [Opn, Perc, Perc Endo]
0DNC[0,3,4]ZZ   Rls/Ileocecal Valve, [Opn, Perc, Perc Endo]
0DNE[0,3,4]ZZ   Rls/Lg Intestine, [Opn, Perc, Perc Endo]
0DNF[0,3,4]ZZ   Rls/Lg Intestine, Rt, [Opn, Perc, Perc Endo]
0DNG[0,3,4]ZZ   Rls/Lg Intestine, Lt, [Opn, Perc, Perc Endo]
0DNH[0,3,4]ZZ   Rls/Cecum, [Opn, Perc, Perc Endo]
0DNJ[0,3,4]ZZ   Rls/Appendix, [Opn, Perc, Perc Endo]
0DNK[0,3,4]ZZ   Rls/Ascending Colon, [Opn, Perc, Perc Endo]
0DNL[0,3,4]ZZ   Rls/Transv Colon, [Opn, Perc, Perc Endo]
0DNM[0,3,4]ZZ   Rls/Descending Colon, [Opn, Perc, Perc Endo]
0DNN[0,3,4]ZZ   Rls/Sigmoid Colon, [Opn, Perc, Perc Endo]
0DNS*   Rls/Greater Omentum
0DNT*   Rls/Lesser Omentum
0DNV*   Rls/Mesentery
0DNW*   Rls/Peritoneum
0DQ6[0,3,7,8]ZZ   Rpr/Stomach, [Opn, Perc, Via Natrl or Artfcl Opng, Via Natrl or Artfcl Opng Endo]
0DQV*   Repair/Mesentery
0DQW*   Repair/Peritoneum
0DRS*   Replace/Greater Omentum
0DRT*   Replace/Lesser Omentum
0DRV*   Replace/Mesentery
0DRW*   Replace/Peritoneum
0DS6[7,8]ZZ   Repos/Stomach, [Via Natrl or Artfcl Opng, Via Natrl or Artfcl Opng Endo]
0DSB[0,4,7,8]ZZ   Repos/Ileum, [Opn, Perc Endo, Via Natrl or Artfcl Opng, Via Natrl or Artfcl Opng Endo]
0DSH[0,4,7,8]ZZ   Repos/Cecum, [Opn, Perc Endo, Via Natrl or Artfcl Opng, Via Natrl or Artfcl Opng Endo]
0DTS*   Resect/Greater Omentum
0DTT*   Resect/Lesser Omentum
0DUS*   Supl/Greater Omentum
0DUT*   Supl/Lesser Omentum
0DUV*   Supl/Mesentery
0DUW*   Supl/Peritoneum
0DW04UZ   Revise of Feeding Dev in Up Intest Tract, Perc Endo Appr
0DWW[0,3,4]JZ   Rev/Peritoneum, [Opn, Perc, Perc Endo], Synth Sub, NQ
0FN*   Hepatobiliary Sys and Pancreas, Rls
0HB[0,1,4,5,6,7,8,A]XZZ   Exc [Scalp, Face, Neck, Chest, Back, Abd, Buttock, Genitalia] Skin, Ext
0HB[B,C,D,E,F,G]XZZ   Exc of Skin of [Rt Upr Arm, Lt Upr Arm, Rt Lwr Arm, Lt Lwr Arm, Rt Hand, Lt Hand], Ext
0HB[H,J,K,L,M,N]XZZ   Exc of Skin of [Rt Upr Leg, Lt Upr Leg, Rt Lwr Leg, Lt Lwr Leg, Rt Foot, Lt Foot], Ext
0JB[0,1,4,5,6]0ZZ   Exc of SQ Tissue & Fascia of [Scalp, Face, Ant Neck, Post Neck, Chest], Opn
0JB[7,8,9,B,C]0ZZ   Exc of SQ Tissue & Fascia of [Back, Abd, Buttock, Perineum, Pelvic Rgn], Opn
0JB[D,F,G,H]0ZZ   Exc of SQ Tissue & Fascia of [Rt Upr Arm, Lt Upr Arm, Rt Lwr Arm, Lt Lwr Arm], Opn
0JB[L,M,N,P,Q,R]0ZZ   Exc of SQ Tissue & Fascia of [Rt Upr Leg, Lt Upr Leg, Rt Lwr Leg, Lt Lwr Leg, Rt Foot, Lt Foot], Opn
0JH6[0,3]VZ   Insert/SQ Tissue & Fascia, Chest, [Opn, Perc], Inf Pump, NQ
0JH7[0,3]VZ   Insert/SQ Tissue & Fascia, Back, [Opn, Perc], Inf Pump, NQ
0JH8[0,3]VZ   Insert/SQ Tissue & Fascia, Abd, [Opn, Perc], Inf Pump, NQ
0JHT[0,3]VZ   Insert/SQ Tissue & Fascia, Trunk, [Opn, Perc], Inf Pump, NQ
0W1G[0,3,4]J4   Bypass/Peritoneal Cavity, [Opn, Perc, Perc Endo], Synth Sub, Cutaneous
0W3F*   Control/Abd Wall
0W3G[3,4]ZZ   Control/Peritoneal Cavity, [Perc, Perc Endo]
0W3H*   Control/Retroperitoneum
0W3J*   Control/Pelvic Cavity
0W3P[0,3,4]ZZ   Control/Gastrointestinal Tract, [Opn, Perc, Perc Endo]
0W9F0[0,Z]Z   Drain/Abd Wall, Opn, [Drain Dev, No Dev], NQ
0W9H[0,3,4][0,Z]Z   Drain/Retroperitoneum, [Opn, Perc, Perc Endo], [Drain Dev, No Dev], NQ

0W9J[0,4][0,Z]Z   Drain/Pelvic Cavity, [Opn, Perc Endo], [Drain Dev, No Dev], NQ
0WCJ[3,4]ZZ   Extir/Pelvic Cavity, [Perc, Perc Endo]
0WCP[3,4]ZZ   Extir/Gastrointestinal Tract, [Perc, Perc Endo]
0WCR[3,4]ZZ   Extir/Genitourinary Tract, [Perc, Perc Endo]
0WFG[0,3,4]ZZ   Fragmn/Peritoneal Cavity, [Opn, Perc, Perc Endo]
0WJ[F,H]0ZZ   Inspect of [Abd Wall, Retroperitoneum], Opn Appr
0WMF0ZZ   Reattach of Abd Wall, Opn Appr
0WQF[3,4,X]ZZ   Rpr/Abd Wall, [Perc, Perc Endo, Ext]
0Y35*   Control/Inguinal Region, Rt
0Y36*   Control/Inguinal Region, Lt
0Y95[0,3,4][0,Z]Z   Drain/Inguinal Rgn, Rt, [Opn, Perc, Perc Endo], [Drain Dev, No Dev], NQ
0Y96[0,3,4][0,Z]Z   Drain/Inguinal Rgn, Lt, [Opn, Perc, Perc Endo], [Drain Dev, No Dev], NQ
0YJ50ZZ   Inspect of Rt Inguinal Region, Opn Appr
0YJ60ZZ   Inspect of Lt Inguinal Region, Opn Appr
0YJ70ZZ   Inspect of Rt Femor Region, Opn Appr
0YJA0ZZ   Inspect of Bilat Inguinal Region, Opn Appr

DRG 424   Other Hepatobiliary or Pancreas O.R. Procedures with CC
GMLOS 6.0   AMLOS 8.0   RW 2.3049

Select operating room procedures listed under DRG 423

DRG 425   Other Hepatobiliary or Pancreas O.R. Procedures without CC/MCC
GMLOS 3.6   AMLOS 4.8   RW 1.6000

Select operating room procedures listed under DRG 423

MEDICAL

DRG 432   Cirrhosis and Alcoholic Hepatitis with MCC
GMLOS 4.7   AMLOS 6.1   RW 1.6567

Principal Diagnosis

K70.1*   Alcoholic hepatitis
K70.2   Alcoholic fibrosis and sclerosis of liver
K70.3*   Alcoholic cirrhosis of liver
K70.4*   Alcoholic hepatic failure
K70.9   Alcoholic liver dz, unsp
K74.0   Hepatic fibrosis
K74.3   Primary biliary cirrhosis
K74.4   Secondary biliary cirrhosis
K74.5   Biliary cirrhosis, unsp
K74.6*   Oth and unsp cirrhosis of liver

DRG 433   Cirrhosis and Alcoholic Hepatitis with CC
GMLOS 3.2   AMLOS 4.0   RW 0.9164

Select principal diagnosis listed under DRG 432

DRG 434   Cirrhosis and Alcoholic Hepatitis without CC/MCC
GMLOS 2.3   AMLOS 2.7   RW 0.6235

Select principal diagnosis listed under DRG 432

DRG 435   Malignancy of Hepatobiliary System or Pancreas with MCC
GMLOS 5.1   AMLOS 6.6   RW 1.7476

Principal Diagnosis

C22*   Malig neoplasm of liver and intrahepatic bile ducts
C23   Malig neoplasm of gallbladder
C24*   Malig neoplasm of oth and unsp parts of biliary tract
C25*   Malig neoplasm of pancreas
C78.7   Secondary malig neoplasm of liver and intrahepatic bile duct
C7B.02   Secondary carcinoid tumors of liver
D01.5   Carcinoma in situ of liver, gallbladder and bile ducts
D37.6   Neoplasm of uncertain behav of liver, GB & bile duct

DRG 436   Malignancy of Hepatobiliary System or Pancreas with CC
GMLOS 3.8   AMLOS 4.9   RW 1.1686

Select principal diagnosis listed under DRG 435

| Surgical | Medical | CC Indicator | MCC Indicator | Procedure Proxy | PDxMCC PDx acts as own MCC | PDxCC PDx acts as own CC |

MDC 7: Diseases And Disorders Of The Hepatobiliary System And Pancreas—MEDICAL

DRG 437 Malignancy of Hepatobiliary System or Pancreas without CC/MCC
GMLOS 2.7 AMLOS 3.4 RW 0.9051

Select principal diagnosis listed under DRG 435

DRG 438 Disorders of Pancreas Except Malignancy with MCC
GMLOS 4.9 AMLOS 6.7 RW 1.6612

Principal Diagnosis

B25.2	Cytomegaloviral pancreatitis	PDxMCC
B26.3	Mumps pancreatitis	
D13.6	Benign neoplasm of pancreas	
K85*	Acute pancreatitis	
K86*	Oth dz of pancreas	
Q45.0	Agenesis, aplasia and hypoplasia of pancreas	
Q45.1	Annular pancreas	
Q45.2	Congenital pancreatic cyst	
Q45.3	Oth congenital malformations of pancreas and pancreatic duct	
S36.20[0,1,2,9]A	Unsp inj of [head, body, tail, unsp part] of pancreas, init enc	
S36.22[0,1,2,9]A	Contsn of [head, body, tail, unsp part] of pancreas, init enc	
S36.23[0,1,2,9]A	Lac of [head, body, tail, unsp part] of pancreas, unsp degree, init enc	
S36.24[0,1,2,9]A	Minor lac of [head, body, tail, unsp part] of pancreas, init enc	
S36.25[0,1,2,9]A	Mod lac of [head, body, tail, unsp part] of pancreas, init enc	
S36.26[0,1,2,9]A	Major lac of [head, body, tail, unsp part] of pancreas, init enc	
S36.29[0,1,2,9]A	Oth inj of [head, body, tail, unsp part] of pancreas, init enc	
T86.89[0,1,2]	Oth transplanted tissue [rejection, failure, infxn]	
T86.89[8,9]	[Oth, Unsp] comp of oth transplanted tissue	
Z94.83	Pancreas transplant status	

DRG 439 Disorders of Pancreas Except Malignancy with CC
GMLOS 3.5 AMLOS 4.3 RW 0.8823

Select principal diagnosis listed under DRG 438

DRG 440 Disorders of Pancreas Except Malignancy without CC/MCC
GMLOS 2.6 AMLOS 3.1 RW 0.6368

Select principal diagnosis listed under DRG 438

DRG 441 Disorders of Liver Except Malignancy, Cirrhosis, Alcoholic Hepatitis with MCC
GMLOS 5.0 AMLOS 6.8 RW 1.8767 [T]

Principal Diagnosis

A06.4	Amebic liver abscess	
A51.45	Secondary syphilitic hepatitis	
A52.74	Syphilis of liver and oth viscera	
B15*	Acute hepatitis A	
B16*	Acute hepatitis B	
B17*	Oth acute viral hepatitis	
B18*	Chr viral hepatitis	
B19*	Unsp viral hepatitis	
B25.1	Cytomegaloviral hepatitis	PDxCC
B26.81	Mumps hepatitis	
B58.1	Toxoplasma hepatitis	
B65.1	Schistosomiasis d/t Schistosoma mansoni	
B66.0	Opisthorchiasis	
B66.1	Clonorchiasis	
B66.3	Fascioliasis	
B66.5	Fasciolopsiasis	
B67.0	Echinococcus granulosus infxn of liver	
B67.5	Echinococcus multilocularis infxn of liver	
B67.8	Echinococcosis, unsp, of liver	
D13.4	Benign neoplasm of liver	
D13.5	Benign neoplasm of extrahepatic bile ducts	
E80.4	Gilbert synd	
E80.5	Crigler-Najjar synd	
E80.6	Oth d/o of bilirubin metabolism	
E80.7	D/o of bilirubin metabolism, unsp	
I81	Portal vein thrombosis	
I82.0	Budd-Chiari synd	
K70.0	Alcoholic fatty liver	
K71*	Txc liver dz	
K72*	Hepatic failure, NEC	
K73*	Chr hepatitis, NEC	

K74.1	Hepatic sclerosis
K74.2	Hepatic fibrosis with hepatic sclerosis
K75*	Oth inflam liver dz
K76.0	Fatty (change of) liver, NEC
K76.1	Chr passive congestion of liver
K76.2	Central hemorrhagic necrosis of liver
K76.3	Infarction of liver
K76.4	Peliosis hepatis
K76.5	Hepatic veno-occlusive dz
K76.6	Portal hypertension
K76.7	Hepatorenal synd
K76.89	Oth spec dz of liver
K76.9	Liver dz, unsp
K77	Liver d/o in dz classified elsw
Q44.0	Agenesis, aplasia and hypoplasia of gallbladder
Q44.1	Oth congenital malformations of gallbladder
Q44.4	Choledochal cyst
Q44.5	Oth congenital malformations of bile ducts
Q44.6	Cystic dz of liver
Q44.7	Oth congenital malformations of liver
R16.0	Hepatomegaly, NEC
R16.2	Hepatomegaly with splenomegaly, NEC
R17	Unsp jaundice
R82.2	Biliuria
R94.5	Abnormal results of liver function studies
S36.112A	Contsn of liver, init enc
S36.11[3,4,5,6]A	[Lac unsp degree, Minor lac, Mod lac, Major lac] of liver, init enc
S36.11[8,9]A	[Oth, unsp] inj of liver, init enc
T86.4*	Comp of liver transplant
Z22.5*	Carrier of viral hepatitis
Z52.6	Liver donor
Z94.4	Liver transplant status

DRG 442 Disorders of Liver Except Malignancy, Cirrhosis, Alcoholic Hepatitis with CC
GMLOS 3.4 AMLOS 4.3 RW 0.9371 [T]

Select principal diagnosis listed under DRG 441

DRG 443 Disorders of Liver Except Malignancy, Cirrhosis, Alcoholic Hepatitis without CC/MCC
GMLOS 2.5 AMLOS 3.1 RW 0.6545 [T]

Select principal diagnosis listed under DRG 441

DRG 444 Disorders of the Biliary Tract with MCC
GMLOS 4.5 AMLOS 5.9 RW 1.5895

Principal Diagnosis

K80*	Cholelithiasis
K81*	Cholecystitis
K82*	Oth dz of gallbladder
K83*	Oth dz of biliary tract
K87	D/o of GB, biliary trac and pancreas in dis classd elsw
K91.5	Postcholecystectomy synd
Q44.2	Atresia of bile ducts
Q44.3	Congenital stenosis and stricture of bile ducts
R93.2	Abnormal findings on dx imaging of liver and biliary tract
S36.122A	Contsn of gallbladder, init enc
S36.123A	Lac of gallbladder, init enc
S36.128A	Oth inj of gallbladder, init enc
S36.129A	Unsp inj of gallbladder, init enc
S36.13XA	Inj of bile duct, init enc

DRG 445 Disorders of the Biliary Tract with CC
GMLOS 3.3 AMLOS 4.0 RW 1.0553

Select principal diagnosis listed under DRG 444

DRG 446 Disorders of the Biliary Tract without CC/MCC
GMLOS 2.4 AMLOS 2.8 RW 0.7633

Select principal diagnosis listed under DRG 444

[T] **Transfer DRG**   [SP] **Special Payment**   * **Code Range**   6th and 7th Character of ZZ = No Device, No Qualifier ZX = No Device, Diagnostic

SURGICAL

DRG 453 Combined Anterior/Posterior Spinal Fusion with MCC
GMLOS 9.2 AMLOS 11.3 RW 11.4304

Operating Room Procedures

ØRG1[Ø,3,4][7,A,J,K,Z]Ø Fusion/Cervical Vert Jt, [Opn, Perc, Perc Endo], [Auto Tissue Sub, Interbody Fusion Dev, Synth Sub, Nonauto Tissue Sub, No Dev], Ant Appr, Ant Column

ØRG2[Ø,3,4][7,A,J,K,Z]Ø Fusion/Cervical Vert Jts, 2 or more, [Opn, Perc, Perc Endo], [Auto Tissue Sub, Interbody Fusion Dev, Synth Sub, Nonauto Tissue Sub, No Dev], Ant Appr, Ant Column

ØRG4[Ø,3,4][7,A,J,K,Z]Ø Fusion/Cervicothoracic Vert Jt, [Opn, Perc, Perc Endo], [Auto Tissue Sub, Interbody Fusion Dev, Synth Sub, Nonauto Tissue Sub, No Dev], Ant Appr, Ant Column

ØRG6[Ø,3,4][7,A,J,K,Z]Ø Fusion/Thoracic Vert Jt, [Opn, Perc, Perc Endo], [Auto Tissue Sub, Interbody Fusion Dev, Synth Sub, Nonauto Tissue Sub, No Dev], Ant Appr, Ant Column

ØRG7[Ø,3,4][7,A,J,K,Z]Ø Fusion/Thoracic Vert Jts, 2 to 7, [Opn, Perc, Perc Endo], [Auto Tissue Sub, Interbody Fusion Dev, Synth Sub, Nonauto Tissue Sub, No Dev], Ant Appr, Ant Column

ØRG8[Ø,3,4][7,A,J,K,Z]Ø Fusion/Thoracic Vert Jts, 8 or more, [Opn, Perc, Perc Endo], [Auto Tissue Sub, Interbody Fusion Dev, Synth Sub, Nonauto Tissue Sub, No Dev], Ant Appr, Ant Column

ØRGA[Ø,3,4][7,A,J,K,Z]Ø Fusion/Thoracolumbar Vert Jt, [Opn, Perc, Perc Endo], [Auto Tissue Sub, Interbody Fusion Dev, Synth Sub, Nonauto Tissue Sub, No Dev], Ant Appr, Ant Column

ØSGØ[Ø,3,4][7,A,J,K,Z]Ø Fusion/Lumbar Vert Jt, [Opn, Perc, Perc Endo], [Auto Tissue Sub, Interbody Fusion Dev, Synth Sub, Nonauto Tissue Sub, No Dev], Ant Appr, Ant Column

ØSG1[Ø,3,4][7,A,J,K,Z]Ø Fusion/Lumbar Vert Jts, 2 or more, [Opn, Perc, Perc Endo], [Auto Tissue Sub, Interbody Fusion Dev, Synth Sub, Nonauto Tissue Sub, No Dev], Ant Appr, Ant Column

ØSG3[Ø,3,4][7,A,J,K,Z]Ø Fusion/Lumbosacral Jt, [Opn, Perc, Perc Endo], [Auto Tissue Sub, Interbody Fusion Dev, Synth Sub, Nonauto Tissue Sub, No Dev], Ant Appr, Ant Column

AND

Operating Room Procedures

ØRG1[Ø,3,4][7,A,J,K,Z][1,J] Fusion/Cervical Vert Jt, [Opn, Perc, Perc Endo], [Auto Tissue Sub, Interbody Fusion Dev, Synth Sub, Nonauto Tissue Sub, No Dev], [Post Appr, Post Column, Post Appr, Ant Column]

ØRG2[Ø,3,4][7,A,J,K,Z][1,J] Fusion/Cervical Vert Jts, 2 or more, [Opn, Perc, Perc Endo], [Auto Tissue Sub, Interbody Fusion Dev, Synth Sub, Nonauto Tissue Sub, No Dev], [Post Appr, Post Column, Post Appr, Ant Column]

ØRG4[Ø,3,4][7,A,J,K,Z][1,J] Fusion/Cervicothoracic Vert Jt, [Opn, Perc, Perc Endo], [Auto Tissue Sub, Interbody Fusion Dev, Synth Sub, Nonauto Tissue Sub, No Dev], [Post Appr, Post Column, Post Appr, Ant Column]

ØRG6[Ø,3,4][7,A,J,K,Z][1,J] Fusion/Thoracic Vert Jt, [Opn, Perc, Perc Endo], [Auto Tissue Sub, Interbody Fusion Dev, Synth Sub, Nonauto Tissue Sub, No Dev], [Post Appr, Post Column, Post Appr, Ant Column]

ØRG7[Ø,3,4][7,A,J,K,Z][1,J] Fusion/Thoracic Vert Jts, 2 to 7, [Opn, Perc, Perc Endo], [Auto Tissue Sub, Interbody Fusion Dev, Synth Sub, Nonauto Tissue Sub, No Dev], [Post Appr, Post Column, Post Appr, Ant Column]

ØRG8[Ø,3,4][7,A,J,K,Z][1,J] Fusion/Thoracic Vert Jts, 8 or more, [Opn, Perc, Perc Endo], [Auto Tissue Sub, Interbody Fusion Dev, Synth Sub, Nonauto Tissue Sub, No Dev], [Post Appr, Post Column, Post Appr, Ant Column]

ØRGA[Ø,3,4][7,A,J,K,Z][1,J] Fusion/Thoracolumbar Vert Jt, [Opn, Perc, Perc Endo], [Auto Tissue Sub, Interbody Fusion Dev, Synth Sub, Nonauto Tissue Sub, No Dev], [Post Appr, Post Column, Post Appr, Ant Column]

ØSGØ[Ø,3,4][7,A,J,K,Z][1,J] Fusion/Lumbar Vert Jt, [Opn, Perc, Perc Endo], [Auto Tissue Sub, Interbody Fusion Dev, Synth Sub, Nonauto Tissue Sub, No Dev], [Post Appr, Post Column, Post Appr, Ant Column]

ØSG1[Ø,3,4][7,A,J,K,Z][1,J] Fusion/Lumbar Vert Jts, 2 or more, [Opn, Perc, Perc Endo], [Auto Tissue Sub, Interbody Fusion Dev, Synth Sub, Nonauto Tissue Sub, No Dev], [Post Appr, Post Column, Post Appr, Ant Column]

ØSG3[Ø,3,4][7,A,J,K,Z][1,J] Fusion/Lumbosacral Jt, [Opn, Perc, Perc Endo], [Auto Tissue Sub, Interbody Fusion Dev, Synth Sub, Nonauto Tissue Sub, No Dev], [Post Appr, Post Column, Post Appr, Ant Column]

ØSG7* Fusion/Sacroiliac Jt, Rt
ØSG8* Fusion/Sacroiliac Jt, Lt

DRG 454 Combined Anterior/Posterior Spinal Fusion with CC
GMLOS 4.9 AMLOS 5.8 RW 8.Ø698

Select operating room procedure combinations listed under DRG 453

DRG 455 Combined Anterior/Posterior Spinal Fusion without CC/MCC
GMLOS 3.Ø AMLOS 3.4 RW 6.1934

Select operating room procedure combinations listed under DRG 453

▲DRG 456 Spinal Fusion Except Cervical with Spinal Curvature/Malignancy/Infection or Extensive Fusions with MCC
GMLOS 9.8 AMLOS 12.Ø RW 9.4Ø61

Principal Diagnosis

Code	Description
A18.Ø1	Tuberculosis of spine
C41.2	Malig neoplasm of vert column
C79.5*	Secondary malig neoplasm of bone and bone marrow
C7B.Ø3	Secondary carcinoid tumors of bone
D16.6	Benign neoplasm of vert column
D48.Ø	Neoplasm of uncertain behav of bone/artic cartl
D49.2	Neoplasm of unsp behav of bone, soft tissue, and skin
M4Ø.Ø*	Postural kyphosis
M4Ø.2*	Oth and unsp kyphosis
M4Ø.3*	Flatback synd
M4Ø.4*	Postural lordosis
M4Ø.5*	Lordosis, unsp
M41.Ø*	Infantile idiopathic scoliosis
M41.1*	Juvenile and adolescent idiopathic scoliosis
M41.2*	Oth idiopathic scoliosis
M41.3*	Thoracogenic scoliosis
M41.8*	Oth forms of scoliosis
M41.9	Scoliosis, unsp
M42.Ø*	Juvenile osteochondrosis of spine
M43.8*	Oth spec deforming dorsopathies
M43.9	Deforming dorsopathy, unsp
M46.2*	Osteomyelitis of vertebra
M48.5[Ø,1,2,3,4,5,6,7,8]XA	Collapsed vertebra, NEC, [unsp, occipito-atlanto-axial, cervical, cervicothoracic, thoracic, thoracolumbar, lumbar, lumbosacral, sacral and sacrococcygeal] rgn, init enc for fx
M8Ø.Ø8XA	Age-rel osteopor w current path fx, vertebra(e), init
M8Ø.88XA	Oth osteopor w current path fx, vertebra(e), init
M84.58XA	Path fx in neoplastic dz, oth site, init
M84.68XA	Path fx in oth dz, oth site, init for fx
M86.Ø8	Acute hematogenous osteomyelitis, oth sites
M86.18	Oth acute osteomyelitis, oth site
M86.28	Subacute osteomyelitis, oth site
M86.38	Chr multifocal osteomyelitis, oth site
M86.48	Chr osteomyelitis with draining sinus, oth site
M86.58	Oth chr hematogenous osteomyelitis, oth site
M86.68	Oth chr osteomyelitis, oth site
M86.8X8	Oth osteomyelitis, oth site
M96.2	Postradiation kyphosis
M96.3	Postlaminectomy kyphosis
M96.4	Postsurgical lordosis
M96.5	Postradiation scoliosis

Q67.5	Congenital deformity of spine
Q76.3	Congenital scoliosis d/t congenital bony malformation
Q76.42*	Congenital lordosis
Q78.0	Osteogenesis imperfecta

OR

Secondary Diagnosis

M40.1*	Oth secondary kyphosis
M40.5*	Lordosis, unsp
M41.4*	Neuromuscular scoliosis
M41.5*	Oth secondary scoliosis
M43.8X9	Oth spec deforming dorsopathies, site unsp

AND

Operating Room Procedures

0RG6*	Fusion/Thoracic Vert Jt
0RG7*	Fusion/Thoracic Vert Jts, 2 to 7
0RG8*	Fusion/Thoracic Vert Jts, 8 or more
0RGA*	Fusion/Thoracolumbar Vert Jt
0SG0*	Fusion/Lumbar Vert Jt
0SG1*	Fusion/Lumbar Vert Jts, 2 or more
0SG3*	Fusion/Lumbosacral Jt
0SG5*	Fusion/Sacrococcygeal Jt
0SG6*	Fusion/Coccygeal Jt
0SG7*	Fusion/Sacroiliac Jt, Rt
0SG8*	Fusion/Sacroiliac Jt, Lt

OR

Operating Room Procedures

0RG8*	Fusion/Thoracic Vert Jts, 8 or more

OR

Operating Room Procedures

0RG7*	Fusion/Thoracic Vert Jts, 2 to 7

AND

Operating Room Procedures

0SG1*	Fusion/Lumbar Vert Jts, 2 or more

▲**DRG 457   Spinal Fusion Except Cervical with Spinal Curvature/Malignancy/Infection or Extensive Fusions with CC**

GMLOS 5.5	AMLOS 6.5	RW 7.0741

Select principal OR secondary diagnosis AND operating room procedures listed under DRG 456

▲**DRG 458   Spinal Fusion Except Cervical with Spinal Curvature/ Malignancy/Infection or Extensive Fusions without CC/MCC**

GMLOS 3.3	AMLOS 3.7	RW 5.2986

Select principal OR secondary diagnosis AND operating room procedures listed under DRG 456

DRG 459   Spinal Fusion Except Cervical with MCC

GMLOS 6.7	AMLOS 8.3	RW 6.5455	T

Operating Room Procedures

0RG6*	Fusion/Thoracic Vert Jt
0RG7*	Fusion/Thoracic Vert Jts, 2 to 7
0RG8*	Fusion/Thoracic Vert Jts, 8 or more
0RGA*	Fusion/Thoracolumbar Vert Jt
0SG0*	Fusion/Lumbar Vert Jt
0SG1*	Fusion/Lumbar Vert Jts, 2 or more
0SG3*	Fusion/Lumbosacral Jt
0SG5*	Fusion/Sacrococcygeal Jt
0SG6*	Fusion/Coccygeal Jt
0SG7*	Fusion/Sacroiliac Jt, Rt
0SG8*	Fusion/Sacroiliac Jt, Lt

DRG 460   Spinal Fusion Except Cervical without MCC

GMLOS 2.9	AMLOS 3.4	RW 3.9717	T

Select operating room procedures listed under DRG 459

DRG 461   Bilateral or Multiple Major Joint Procedures of Lower Extremity with MCC

GMLOS 6.3	AMLOS 8.2	RW 5.0977

Any combination of two or more of the following Operating Room Procedures

0SR9*	Replace/Hip Jt, Rt
0SRA*	Replace/Hip Jt, Acetabular Surface, Rt
0SRB*	Replace/Hip Jt, Lt
0SRC*	Replace/Knee Jt, Rt
0SRD*	Replace/Knee Jt, Lt
0SRE*	Replace/Hip Jt, Acetabular Surface, Lt
0SRF*	Replace/Ankle Jt, Rt
0SRG*	Replace/Ankle Jt, Lt
0SRR*	Replace/Hip Jt, Femor Surface, Rt
0SRS*	Replace/Hip Jt, Femor Surface, Lt
0SRT*	Replace/Knee Jt, Femor Surface, Rt
0SRU*	Replace/Knee Jt, Femor Surface, Lt
0SRV*	Replace/Knee Jt, Tibial Surface, Rt
0SRW*	Replace/Knee Jt, Tibial Surface, Lt
0SU90BZ	Supl Rt Hip Jt with Resurf Dev, Opn Appr
0SUA0BZ	Supl Rt Hip Jt, Acetab with Resurf Dev, Opn Appr
0SUB0BZ	Supl Lt Hip Jt with Resurf Dev, Opn Appr
0SUE0BZ	Supl Lt Hip Jt, Acetab with Resurf Dev, Opn Appr
0SUR0BZ	Supl Rt Hip Jt, Femor with Resurf Dev, Opn Appr
0SUS0BZ	Supl Lt Hip Jt, Femor with Resurf Dev, Opn Appr

DRG 462   Bilateral or Multiple Major Joint Procedures of Lower Extremity without MCC

GMLOS 3.2	AMLOS 3.5	RW 3.2145

Select any combination of two or more procedures listed under DRG 461

DRG 463   Wound Debridement and Skin Graft Except Hand, for Musculo-Connective Tissue Disorders with MCC

GMLOS 10.2	AMLOS 13.4	RW 5.1028	T

Operating Room Procedures

0H8[0,1,4,5,6,7,8,A]XZZ	Div [Scalp, Face, Neck, Chest, Back, Abd, Buttock, Genitalia] Skin, Ext
0H8[B,C,D,E]XZZ	Div of [Rt Upr Arm, Lt Upr Arm, Rt Lwr Arm, Lt Lwr Arm] Skin, Ext Appr
0H8[H,J,K,L,M,N]XZZ	Div [Rt Upr Leg, Lt Upr Leg, Rt Lwr Leg, Lt Lwr Leg, Rt Foot, Lt Foot], Ext
0HB[0,1,4,5,6,7,8,A]XZZ	Exc [Scalp, Face, Neck, Chest, Back, Abd, Buttock, Genitalia] Skin, Ext
0HB[B,C,D,E,F,G]XZZ	Exc of Skin of [Rt Upr Arm, Lt Upr Arm, Rt Lwr Arm, Lt Lwr Arm, Rt Hand, Lt Hand], Ext
0HB[H,J,K,L,M,N]XZZ	Exc of Skin of [Rt Upr Leg, Lt Upr Leg, Rt Lwr Leg, Lt Lwr Leg, Rt Foot, Lt Foot], Ext
0HR0*	Replace/Skin, Scalp
0HR1*	Replace/Skin, Face
0HR4*	Replace/Skin, Neck
0HR5*	Replace/Skin, Chest
0HR6*	Replace/Skin, Back
0HR7*	Replace/Skin, Abd
0HR8*	Replace/Skin, Buttock
0HRA*	Replace/Skin, Genitalia
0HRB*	Replace/Skin, Rt Upr Arm
0HRC*	Replace/Skin, Lt Upr Arm
0HRD*	Replace/Skin, Rt Lwr Arm
0HRE*	Replace/Skin, Lt Lwr Arm
0HRH*	Replace/Skin, Rt Upr Leg
0HRJ*	Replace/Skin, Lt Upr Leg
0HRK*	Replace/Skin, Rt Lwr Leg
0HRL*	Replace/Skin, Lt Lwr Leg
0HRM*	Replace/Skin, Rt Foot
0HRN*	Replace/Skin, Lt Foot
0HX[0,1,4,5,6,7,8,9,A]XZZ	Transfer [Scalp, Face, Neck, Chest, Back, Abd, Buttock, Perineum, Genitalia] Skin, Ext
0HX[B,C,D,E,F,G]XZZ	Transfer [Rt Upr Arm, Lt Upr Arm, Rt Lwr Arm, Lt Lwr Arm, Rt Hand], Ext
0HX[H,J,K,L,M,N]XZZ	Transfer [Rt Upr Leg, Lt Upr Leg, Rt Lwr Leg, Lt Lwr Leg, Rt Foot, Lt Foot], Ext
0JB[0,1,4,5,6]0ZZ	Exc of SQ Tissue & Fascia of [Scalp, Face, Ant Neck, Post Neck, Chest], Opn
0JB[7,8,9,B,C]0ZZ	Exc of SQ Tissue & Fascia of [Back, Abd, Buttock, Perineum, Pelvic Rgn], Opn

---

T **Transfer DRG**   SP **Special Payment**   * **Code Range**   **6th and 7th Character of ZZ = No Device, No Qualifier ZX = No Device, Diagnostic**

Code	Description
0JB[D,F,G,H]0ZZ	Exc of SQ Tissue & Fascia of [Rt Upr Arm, Lt Upr Arm, Rt Lwr Arm, Lt Lwr Arm], Opn
0JB[L,M,N,P,Q,R]0ZZ	Exc of SQ Tissue & Fascia of [Rt Upr Leg, Lt Upr Leg, Rt Lwr Leg, Lt Lwr Leg, Rt Foot, Lt Foot], Opn
0JH0*	Insert/SQ Tissue & Fascia, Scalp
0JH1*	Insert/SQ Tissue & Fascia, Face
0JH4*	Insert/SQ Tissue & Fascia, Ant Neck
0JH5*	Insert/SQ Tissue & Fascia, Posterior Neck
0JH6[0,3]NZ	Insert/SQ Tissue & Fascia, Chest, [Opn, Perc], Tissue Expander, NQ
0JH7[0,3]NZ	Insert/SQ Tissue & Fascia, Back, [Opn, Perc], Tissue Expander, NQ
0JH8[0,3]NZ	Insert/SQ Tissue & Fascia, Abd, [Opn, Perc], Tissue Expander, NQ
0JH9*	Insert/SQ Tissue & Fascia, Buttock
0JHB*	Insert/SQ Tissue & Fascia, Perineum
0JHC*	Insert/SQ Tissue & Fascia, Pelvic Region
0JHD[0,3]NZ	Insert/SQ Tissue & Fascia, Rt Upr Arm, [Opn, Perc], Tissue Expander, NQ
0JHF[0,3]NZ	Insert/SQ Tissue & Fascia, Lt Upr Arm, [Opn, Perc], Tissue Expander, NQ
0JHG[0,3]NZ	Insert/SQ Tissue & Fascia, Rt Lwr Arm, [Opn, Perc], Tissue Expander, NQ
0JHH[0,3]NZ	Insert/SQ Tissue & Fascia, Lt Lwr Arm, [Opn, Perc], Tissue Expander, NQ
0JHL[0,3]NZ	Insert/SQ Tissue & Fascia, Rt Upr Leg, [Opn, Perc], Tissue Expander, NQ
0JHM[0,3]NZ	Insert/SQ Tissue & Fascia, Lt Upr Leg, [Opn, Perc], Tissue Expander, NQ
0JHN[0,3]NZ	Insert/SQ Tissue & Fascia, Rt Lwr Leg, [Opn, Perc], Tissue Expander, NQ
0JHP[0,3]NZ	Insert/SQ Tissue & Fascia, Lt Lwr Leg, [Opn, Perc], Tissue Expander, NQ
0JHQ*	Insert/SQ Tissue & Fascia, Rt Foot
0JHR*	Insert/SQ Tissue & Fascia, Lt Foot
0JX0[0,3]Z[B,C]	Transfer/SQ Tissue & Fascia, Scalp, [Opn, Perc], No Dev, [Skin and SQ Tissue, Skin, SQ Tissue & Fascia]
0JX1[0,3]Z[B,C]	Transfer/SQ Tissue & Fascia, Face, [Opn, Perc], No Dev, [Skin and SQ Tissue, Skin, SQ Tissue & Fascia]
0JX4[0,3]Z[B,C]	Transfer/SQ Tissue & Fascia, Ant Neck, [Opn, Perc], No Dev, [Skin and SQ Tissue, Skin, SQ Tissue & Fascia]
0JX5[0,3]Z[B,C]	Transfer/SQ Tissue & Fascia, Post Neck, [Opn, Perc], No Dev, [Skin and SQ Tissue, Skin, SQ Tissue & Fascia]
0JX6[0,3]Z[B,C]	Transfer/SQ Tissue & Fascia, Chest, [Opn, Perc], No Dev, [Skin and SQ Tissue, Skin, SQ Tissue & Fascia]
0JX7[0,3]Z[B,C]	Transfer/SQ Tissue & Fascia, Back, [Opn, Perc], No Dev, [Skin and SQ Tissue, Skin, SQ Tissue & Fascia]
0JX8[0,3]Z[B,C]	Transfer/SQ Tissue & Fascia, Abd, [Opn, Perc], No Dev, [Skin and SQ Tissue, Skin, SQ Tissue & Fascia]
0JX9[0,3]Z[B,C]	Transfer/SQ Tissue & Fascia, Buttock, [Opn, Perc], No Dev, [Skin and SQ Tissue, Skin, SQ Tissue & Fascia]
0JXB[0,3]Z[B,C]	Transfer/SQ Tissue & Fascia, Perineum, [Opn, Perc], No Dev, [Skin and SQ Tissue, Skin, SQ Tissue & Fascia]
0JXC[0,3]Z[B,C]	Transfer/SQ Tissue & Fascia, Genitalia, [Opn, Perc], No Dev, [Skin and SQ Tissue, Skin, SQ Tissue & Fascia]
0JXD[0,3]Z[B,C]	Transfer/SQ Tissue & Fascia, Rt Upr Arm, [Opn, Perc], No Dev, [Skin and SQ Tissue, Skin, SQ Tissue & Fascia]
0JXF[0,3]Z[B,C]	Transfer/SQ Tissue & Fascia, Lt Upr Arm, [Opn, Perc], No Dev, [Skin and SQ Tissue, Skin, SQ Tissue & Fascia]
0JXG[0,3]Z[B,C]	Transfer/SQ Tissue & Fascia, Rt Lwr Arm, [Opn, Perc], No Dev, [Skin and SQ Tissue, Skin, SQ Tissue & Fascia]
0JXH[0,3]Z[B,C]	Transfer/SQ Tissue & Fascia, Lt Lwr Arm, [Opn, Perc], No Dev, [Skin and SQ Tissue, Skin, SQ Tissue & Fascia]
0JXL[0,3]Z[B,C]	Transfer/SQ Tissue & Fascia, Rt Upr Leg, [Opn, Perc], No Dev, [Skin and SQ Tissue, Skin, SQ Tissue & Fascia]
0JXM[0,3]Z[B,C]	Transfer/SQ Tissue & Fascia, Lt Upr Leg, [Opn, Perc], No Dev, [Skin and SQ Tissue, Skin, SQ Tissue & Fascia]
0JXN[0,3]Z[B,C]	Transfer/SQ Tissue & Fascia, Rt Lwr Leg, [Opn, Perc], No Dev, [Skin and SQ Tissue, Skin, SQ Tissue & Fascia]
0JXP[0,3]Z[B,C]	Transfer/SQ Tissue & Fascia, Lt Lwr Leg, [Opn, Perc], No Dev, [Skin and SQ Tissue, Skin, SQ Tissue & Fascia]
0JXQ[0,3]Z[B,C]	Transfer/SQ Tissue & Fascia, Rt Foot, [Opn, Perc], No Dev, [Skin and SQ Tissue, Skin, SQ Tissue & Fascia]
0JXR[0,3]Z[B,C]	Transfer/SQ Tissue & Fascia, Lt Foot, [Opn, Perc], No Dev, [Skin and SQ Tissue, Skin, SQ Tissue & Fascia]
0SP909Z	Rmvl of Liner from Rt Hip Jt, Opn Appr
0SP9[0,3,4]JZ	Rmvl/Hip Jt, Rt, [Opn, Perc, Perc Endo], Synth Sub, NQ
0SPB09Z	Rmvl of Liner from Lt Hip Jt, Opn Appr
0SPB[0,3,4]JZ	Rmvl/Hip Jt, Lt, [Opn, Perc, Perc Endo], Synth Sub, NQ
0SPC09Z	Rmvl of Liner from Rt Knee Jt, Opn Appr
0SPC[0,3,4]JZ	Rmvl/Knee Jt, Rt, [Opn, Perc, Perc Endo], Synth Sub, NQ
0SPD09Z	Rmvl of Liner from Lt Knee Jt, Opn Appr
0SPD[0,3,4]JZ	Rmvl/Knee Jt, Lt, [Opn, Perc, Perc Endo], Synth Sub, NQ
0WU0[0,4]7Z	Supl/Head, [Opn, Perc Endo], Auto Tissue Sub, NQ
0WU2[0,4]7Z	Supl/Face, [Opn, Perc Endo], Auto Tissue Sub, NQ
0WU6[0,4]7Z	Supl/Neck, [Opn, Perc Endo], Auto Tissue Sub, NQ
0WUK[0,4]7Z	Supl/Upr Back, [Opn, Perc Endo], Auto Tissue Sub, NQ
0WUL[0,4]7Z	Supl/Lwr Back, [Opn, Perc Endo], Auto Tissue Sub, NQ
0XU2[0,4]7Z	Supl/Shldr Rgn, Rt, [Opn, Perc Endo], Auto Tissue Sub, NQ
0XU3[0,4]7Z	Supl/Shldr Rgn, Lt, [Opn, Perc Endo], Auto Tissue Sub, NQ
0XU4[0,4]7Z	Supl/Axilla, Rt, [Opn, Perc Endo], Auto Tissue Sub, NQ
0XU5[0,4]7Z	Supl/Axilla, Lt, [Opn, Perc Endo], Auto Tissue Sub, NQ
0XU6[0,4]7Z	Supl/Upr Extr, Rt, [Opn, Perc Endo], Auto Tissue Sub, NQ
0XU7[0,4]7Z	Supl/Upr Extr, Lt, [Opn, Perc Endo], Auto Tissue Sub, NQ
0XU8[0,4]7Z	Supl/Upr Arm, Rt, [Opn, Perc Endo], Auto Tissue Sub, NQ
0XU9[0,4]7Z	Supl/Upr Arm, Lt, [Opn, Perc Endo], Auto Tissue Sub, NQ
0XUB[0,4]7Z	Supl/Elbow Rgn, Rt, [Opn, Perc Endo], Auto Tissue Sub, NQ
0XUC[0,4]7Z	Supl/Elbow Rgn, Lt, [Opn, Perc Endo], Auto Tissue Sub, NQ
0XUD[0,4]7Z	Supl/Lwr Arm, Rt, [Opn, Perc Endo], Auto Tissue Sub, NQ
0XUF[0,4]7Z	Supl/Lwr Arm, Lt, [Opn, Perc Endo], Auto Tissue Sub, NQ
0XUG[0,4]7Z	Supl/Wrist Rgn, Rt, [Opn, Perc Endo], Auto Tissue Sub, NQ
0XUH[0,4]7Z	Supl/Wrist Rgn, Lt, [Opn, Perc Endo], Auto Tissue Sub, NQ

DRG 464 Wound Debridement and Skin Graft Except Hand, for Musculo-Connective Tissue Disorders with CC

GMLOS 6.2	AMLOS 7.8	RW 3.0937	T

Select operating room procedures listed under DRG 463

DRG 465 Wound Debridement and Skin Graft Except Hand, for Musculo-Connective Tissue Disorders without CC/MCC

GMLOS 3.8	AMLOS 4.7	RW 1.9349	T

Select operating room procedures listed under DRG 463

DRG 466 Revision of Hip or Knee Replacement with MCC

GMLOS 6.6	AMLOS 8.1	RW 5.0394	T

Operating Room Procedures

Code	Description
0SW9[0,3,4]JZ	Rev/Hip Jt, Rt, [Opn, Perc, Perc Endo], Synth Sub, NQ
0SWB[0,3,4]JZ	Rev/Hip Jt, Lt, [Opn, Perc, Perc Endo], Synth Sub, NQ
0SWC[0,3,4]JZ	Rev/Knee Jt, Rt, [Opn, Perc, Perc Endo], Synth Sub, NQ
0SWD[0,3,4]JZ	Rev/Knee Jt, Lt, [Opn, Perc, Perc Endo], Synth Sub, NQ

OR

0SR90[1,2,3,4,J][9,A,Z]	Replace/Hip Jt, Rt, Opn, [Synth Sub, Metal, Synth Sub, Metal on Polyethylene, Synth Sub, Ceramic, Synth Sub, Ceramic on Polyethylene, Synth Sub], [Cemented, Uncemented, NQ]

AND

0SP908Z	Rmvl of Spacer from Rt Hip Jt, Opn Appr
0SP909Z	Rmvl of Liner from Rt Hip Jt, Opn Appr
0SP90BZ	Rmvl of Resurfacing Device from Rt Hip Jt, Opn Appr
0SP90JZ	Rmvl of Synth Sub from Rt Hip Jt, Opn Appr
0SP948Z	Rmvl of Spacer from Rt Hip Jt, Perc Endo Appr
0SP94JZ	Rmvl of Synth Sub from Rt Hip Jt, Perc Endo Appr

OR

0SRA0[0,1,3,J][9,A,Z]	Replace/Hip Jt, Acetabular Surface, Rt, Opn, [Synth Sub, Polyethylene, Synth Sub, Metal, Synth Sub, Ceramic, Synth Sub], [Cemented, Uncemented, NQ]

AND

0SP908Z	Rmvl of Spacer from Rt Hip Jt, Opn Appr
0SP909Z	Rmvl of Liner from Rt Hip Jt, Opn Appr
0SP90BZ	Rmvl of Resurfacing Device from Rt Hip Jt, Opn Appr
0SP90JZ	Rmvl of Synth Sub from Rt Hip Jt, Opn Appr
0SP948Z	Rmvl of Spacer from Rt Hip Jt, Perc Endo Appr
0SP94JZ	Rmvl of Synth Sub from Rt Hip Jt, Perc Endo Appr

OR

0SRR0[1,3,J][9,A,Z]	Replace/Hip Jt, Femor Surface, Rt, Opn, [Synth Sub, Metal, Synth Sub, Ceramic, Synth Sub], [Cemented, Uncemented, NQ]

AND

0SP908Z	Rmvl of Spacer from Rt Hip Jt, Opn Appr
0SP909Z	Rmvl of Liner from Rt Hip Jt, Opn Appr
0SP90BZ	Rmvl of Resurfacing Device from Rt Hip Jt, Opn Appr
0SP90JZ	Rmvl of Synth Sub from Rt Hip Jt, Opn Appr
0SP948Z	Rmvl of Spacer from Rt Hip Jt, Perc Endo Appr
0SP94JZ	Rmvl of Synth Sub from Rt Hip Jt, Perc Endo Appr

Surgical **Medical** **CC Indicator** **MCC Indicator** **Procedure Proxy** PDxMCC **PDx acts as own MCC** PDxCC **PDx acts as own CC**

OR

ØSU9Ø9Z	Supl Rt Hip Jt with Liner, Opn Appr
ØSUAØ9Z	Supl Rt Hip Jt, Acetab with Liner, Opn Appr
ØSURØ9Z	Supl Rt Hip Jt, Femor with Liner, Opn Appr
AND	
ØSP9Ø8Z	Rmvl of Spacer from Rt Hip Jt, Opn Appr
ØSP9Ø9Z	Rmvl of Liner from Rt Hip Jt, Opn Appr
ØSP9ØBZ	Rmvl of Resurfacing Device from Rt Hip Jt, Opn Appr
ØSP948Z	Rmvl of Spacer from Rt Hip Jt, Perc Endo Appr
ØSP94JZ	Rmvl of Synth Sub from Rt Hip Jt, Perc Endo Appr

OR

ØSRBØ[1,2,3,4,J][9,A,Z] Replace/Hip Jt, Lt, Opn, [Synth Sub, Metal, Synth Sub, Metal on Polyethylene, Synth Sub, Ceramic, Synth Sub, Ceramic on Polyethylene, Synth Sub], [Cemented, Uncemented, NQ]

AND	
ØSPBØ8Z	Rmvl of Spacer from Lt Hip Jt, Opn Appr
ØSPBØ9Z	Rmvl of Liner from Lt Hip Jt, Opn Appr
ØSPBØBZ	Rmvl of Resurfacing Device from Lt Hip Jt, Opn Appr
ØSPBØJZ	Rmvl of Synth Sub from Lt Hip Jt, Opn Appr
ØSPB48Z	Rmvl of Spacer from Lt Hip Jt, Perc Endo Appr
ØSPB4JZ	Rmvl of Synth Sub from Lt Hip Jt, Perc Endo Appr

OR

ØSREØ[Ø,1,3,J][9,A,Z] Replace/Hip Jt, Acetabular Surface, Lt, Opn, [Synth Sub, Polyethylene, Synth Sub, Metal, Synth Sub, Ceramic, Synth Sub], [Cemented, Uncemented, NQ]

AND	
ØSPBØ8Z	Rmvl of Spacer from Lt Hip Jt, Opn Appr
ØSPBØ9Z	Rmvl of Liner from Lt Hip Jt, Opn Appr
ØSPBØBZ	Rmvl of Resurfacing Device from Lt Hip Jt, Opn Appr
ØSPBØJZ	Rmvl of Synth Sub from Lt Hip Jt, Opn Appr
ØSPB48Z	Rmvl of Spacer from Lt Hip Jt, Perc Endo Appr
ØSPB4JZ	Rmvl of Synth Sub from Lt Hip Jt, Perc Endo Appr

OR

ØSRSØ[1,3,J][9,A,Z] Replace/Hip Jt, Femor Surface, Lt, Opn, [Synth Sub, Metal, Synth Sub, Ceramic, Synth Sub], [Cemented, Uncemented, NQ]

AND	
ØSPBØ8Z	Rmvl of Spacer from Lt Hip Jt, Opn Appr
ØSPBØ9Z	Rmvl of Liner from Lt Hip Jt, Opn Appr
ØSPBØBZ	Rmvl of Resurfacing Device from Lt Hip Jt, Opn Appr
ØSPBØJZ	Rmvl of Synth Sub from Lt Hip Jt, Opn Appr
ØSPB48Z	Rmvl of Spacer from Lt Hip Jt, Perc Endo Appr
ØSPB4JZ	Rmvl of Synth Sub from Lt Hip Jt, Perc Endo Appr

OR

ØSUBØ9Z	Supl Lt Hip Jt with Liner, Opn Appr
ØSUEØ9Z	Supl Lt Hip Jt, Acetab with Liner, Opn Appr
ØSUSØ9Z	Supl Lt Hip Jt, Femor with Liner, Opn Appr
AND	
ØSPBØ8Z	Rmvl of Spacer from Lt Hip Jt, Opn Appr
ØSPBØ9Z	Rmvl of Liner from Lt Hip Jt, Opn Appr
ØSPBØBZ	Rmvl of Resurfacing Device from Lt Hip Jt, Opn Appr
ØSPB48Z	Rmvl of Spacer from Lt Hip Jt, Perc Endo Appr
ØSPB4JZ	Rmvl of Synth Sub from Lt Hip Jt, Perc Endo Appr

OR

ØSRCØJ[9,A,Z] Replace/Knee Jt, Rt, Opn, Synth Sub, [Cemented, Uncemented, NQ]

AND	
ØSPCØ9Z	Rmvl of Liner from Rt Knee Jt, Opn Appr
ØSPCØJZ	Rmvl of Synth Sub from Rt Knee Jt, Opn Appr
ØSPC4JZ	Rmvl of Synth Sub from Rt Knee Jt, Perc Endo Appr

OR

ØSRTØJ[9,A,Z] Replace/Knee Jt, Femor Surface, Rt, Opn, Synth Sub, [Cemented, Uncemented, NQ]

AND	
ØSPCØ9Z	Rmvl of Liner from Rt Knee Jt, Opn Appr
ØSPDØJZ	Rmvl of Synth Sub from Lt Knee Jt, Opn Appr

OR

ØSRVØJ[9,A,Z] Replace/Knee Jt, Tibial Surface, Rt, Opn, Synth Sub, [Cemented, Uncemented, NQ]

AND	
ØSPCØ9Z	Rmvl of Liner from Rt Knee Jt, Opn Appr
ØSPCØJZ	Rmvl of Synth Sub from Rt Knee Jt, Opn Appr

OR

ØSRTØJ9	Replace Rt Knee Jt, Femor w Synth Sub, Cement, Opn
ØSRTØJA	Replace Rt Knee Jt, Femor w Synth Sub, Uncement, Opn
ØSRVØJ9	Replace Rt Knee Jt, Tibial w Synth Sub, Cement, Opn

ØSRVØJA	Replace Rt Knee Jt, Tibial w Synth Sub, Uncement, Opn
AND	
ØSPC4JZ	Rmvl of Synth Sub from Rt Knee Jt, Perc Endo Appr

OR

ØSRDØJ[9,A,Z] Replace/Knee Jt, Lt, Opn, Synth Sub, [Cemented, Uncemented, NQ]

AND	
ØSPDØ9Z	Rmvl of Liner from Lt Knee Jt, Opn Appr
ØSPDØJZ	Rmvl of Synth Sub from Lt Knee Jt, Opn Appr
ØSPD4JZ	Rmvl of Synth Sub from Lt Knee Jt, Perc Endo Appr

OR

ØSRUØJ[9,A,Z] Replace/Knee Jt, Femor Surface, Lt, Opn, Synth Sub, [Cemented, Uncemented, NQ]

AND	
ØSPDØ9Z	Rmvl of Liner from Lt Knee Jt, Opn Appr
ØSPDØJZ	Rmvl of Synth Sub from Lt Knee Jt, Opn Appr

OR

ØSRWØJ[9,A,Z] Replace/Knee Jt, Tibial Surface, Lt, Opn, Synth Sub, [Cemented, Uncemented, NQ]

AND	
ØSPDØ9Z	Rmvl of Liner from Lt Knee Jt, Opn Appr
ØSPDØJZ	Rmvl of Synth Sub from Lt Knee Jt, Opn Appr
ØSPD4JZ	Rmvl of Synth Sub from Lt Knee Jt, Perc Endo Appr

OR

ØSRUØJ9	Replace Lt Knee Jt, Femor w Synth Sub, Cement, Opn
ØSRUØJA	Replace Lt Knee Jt, Femor w Synth Sub, Uncement, Opn
AND	
ØSPD4JZ	Rmvl of Synth Sub from Lt Knee Jt, Perc Endo Appr

DRG 467   Revision of Hip or Knee Replacement with CC

GMLOS 3.7	AMLOS 4.3	RW 3.4376	T

Select operating room procedures or procedure combinations listed under DRG 466

DRG 468   Revision of Hip or Knee Replacement without CC/MCC

GMLOS 2.7	AMLOS 3.0	RW 2.7513	T

Select operating room procedures or procedure combinations listed under DRG 466

DRG 469   Major Joint Replacement or Reattachment of Lower Extremity with MCC

GMLOS 5.9	AMLOS 7.0	RW 3.2962	T

Operating Room Procedures

ØSR9*	Replace/Hip Jt, Rt
ØSRA*	Replace/Hip Jt, Acetabular Surface, Rt
ØSRB*	Replace/Hip Jt, Lt
ØSRC*	Replace/Knee Jt, Rt
ØSRD*	Replace/Knee Jt, Lt
ØSRE*	Replace/Hip Jt, Acetabular Surface, Lt
ØSRF*	Replace/Ankle Jt, Rt
ØSRG*	Replace/Ankle Jt, Lt
ØSRR*	Replace/Hip Jt, Femor Surface, Rt
ØSRS*	Replace/Hip Jt, Femor Surface, Lt
ØSRT*	Replace/Knee Jt, Femor Surface, Rt
ØSRU*	Replace/Knee Jt, Femor Surface, Lt
ØSRV*	Replace/Knee Jt, Tibial Surface, Rt
ØSRW*	Replace/Knee Jt, Tibial Surface, Lt
ØSU[9,A]ØBZ	Supl Rt Hip Jt [w/ Resurfacing Dev, Acetabular Surface w/ Resurfacing Dev], Opn Appr
ØSU[B,E]ØBZ	Supl Lt Hip Jt [w/ Resurfacing Dev, Acetabular Surface w/ Resurfacing Dev], Opn Appr
ØSU[R,S]ØBZ	Supl [Rt, Lt] Hip Jt, Femor Surface w/ Resurfacing Dev, Opn Appr
ØYM[7,8]ØZZ	Reattach of [Rt, Lt] Femor Rgn, Opn Appr
ØYM[C,D]ØZZ	Reattach of [Rt, Lt] Upr Leg, Opn Appr
ØYM[F,G]ØZZ	Reattach of [Rt, Lt] Knee Rgn, Opn Appr
ØYM[H,J]ØZZ	Reattach of [Rt, Lt] Lwr Leg, Opn Appr
ØYM[K,L]ØZZ	Reattach of [Rt, Lt] Ankle Rgn, Opn Appr
ØYM[M,N]ØZZ	Reattach of [Rt, Lt] Foot, Opn Appr

T Transfer DRG   SP Special Payment   * Code Range   6th and 7th Character of ZZ = No Device, No Qualifier ZX = No Device, Diagnostic

DRG 470　Major Joint Replacement or Reattachment of Lower Extremity without MCC

GMLOS 2.8　　　AMLOS 3.1　　　RW 2.0816　　[T]

Select operating room procedures listed under DRG 469

DRG 471　Cervical Spinal Fusion with MCC

GMLOS 6.2　　　AMLOS 8.6　　　RW 4.9033

Operating Room Procedures

ØRGØ*	Fusion/Occipital-cervical Jt
ØRG1*	Fusion/Cervical Vert Jt
ØRG2*	Fusion/Cervical Vert Jts, 2 or more
ØRG4*	Fusion/Cervicothoracic Vert Jt

DRG 472　Cervical Spinal Fusion with CC

GMLOS 2.4　　　AMLOS 3.3　　　RW 2.9051

Select operating room procedures listed under DRG 471

DRG 473　Cervical Spinal Fusion without CC/MCC

GMLOS 1.5　　　AMLOS 1.8　　　RW 2.2650

Select operating room procedures listed under DRG 471

DRG 474　Amputation for Musculoskeletal System and Connective Tissue Disorders with MCC

GMLOS 8.7　　　AMLOS 11.0　　　RW 3.6260　　[T]

Operating Room Procedures

ØX68*	Detach/Upr Arm, Rt
ØX69*	Detach/Upr Arm, Lt
ØX6D*	Detach/Lwr Arm, Rt
ØX6F*	Detach/Lwr Arm, Lt
ØX6J*	Detach/Hand, Rt
ØX6K*	Detach/Hand, Lt
ØX6[Ø,1]ØZZ	Detach at [Rt, Lt] Forequarter, Opn Appr
ØX6[2,3]ØZZ	Detach at [Rt, Lt] Shldr Rgn, Opn Appr
ØX6[B,C]ØZZ	Detach at [Rt, Lt] Elbow Rgn, Opn Appr
ØY6C*	Detach/Upr Leg, Rt
ØY6D*	Detach/Upr Leg, Lt
ØY6H*	Detach/Lwr Leg, Rt
ØY6J*	Detach/Lwr Leg, Lt
ØY6M*	Detach/Foot, Rt
ØY6N*	Detach/Foot, Lt
ØY6[2,3,4]ØZZ	Detach at [Rt, Lt, Bilat] Hindquarter, Opn Appr
ØY6[7,8]ØZZ	Detach at [Rt, Lt] Femor Rgn, Opn Appr
ØY6[F,G]ØZZ	Detach at [Rt, Lt] Knee Rgn, Opn Appr

DRG 475　Amputation for Musculoskeletal System and Connective Tissue Disorders with CC

GMLOS 5.7　　　AMLOS 7.2　　　RW 2.1001　　[T]

Select operating room procedures listed under DRG 474

DRG 476　Amputation for Musculoskeletal System and Connective Tissue Disorders without CC/MCC

GMLOS 3.1　　　AMLOS 3.9　　　RW 1.1427　　[T]

Select operating room procedures listed under DRG 474

DRG 477　Biopsies of Musculoskeletal System and Connective Tissue with MCC

GMLOS 8.3　　　AMLOS 10.2　　　RW 3.1211　　[SP]

Operating Room Procedures

ØMJX[Ø,3,4]ZZ	Inspect/Upr Bursa & Lgmt, [Opn, Perc, Perc Endo]
ØMJY[Ø,3,4]ZZ	Inspect/Lwr Bursa & Lgmt, [Opn, Perc, Perc Endo]
ØN9Ø[Ø,3,4]ZX	Drain/Skull, [Opn, Perc, Perc Endo]
ØN91[Ø,3,4]ZX	Drain/Frontal Bone, Rt, [Opn, Perc, Perc Endo]
ØN92[Ø,3,4]ZX	Drain/Frontal Bone, Lt, [Opn, Perc, Perc Endo]
ØN93[Ø,3,4]ZX	Drain/Parietal Bone, Rt, [Opn, Perc, Perc Endo]
ØN94[Ø,3,4]ZX	Drain/Parietal Bone, Lt, [Opn, Perc, Perc Endo]
ØN95[Ø,3,4]ZX	Drain/Temporal Bone, Rt, [Opn, Perc, Perc Endo]
ØN96[Ø,3,4]ZX	Drain/Temporal Bone, Lt, [Opn, Perc, Perc Endo]
ØN97[Ø,3,4]ZX	Drain/Occipital Bone, Rt, [Opn, Perc, Perc Endo]

ØN98[Ø,3,4]ZX	Drain/Occipital Bone, Lt, [Opn, Perc, Perc Endo]
ØN9C[Ø,3,4]ZX	Drain/Sphenoid Bone, Rt, [Opn, Perc, Perc Endo]
ØN9D[Ø,3,4]ZX	Drain/Sphenoid Bone, Lt, [Opn, Perc, Perc Endo]
ØN9F[Ø,3,4]ZX	Drain/Ethmoid Bone, Rt, [Opn, Perc, Perc Endo]
ØN9G[Ø,3,4]ZX	Drain/Ethmoid Bone, Lt, [Opn, Perc, Perc Endo]
ØN9H[Ø,3,4]ZX	Drain/Lacrimal Bone, Rt, [Opn, Perc, Perc Endo]
ØN9J[Ø,3,4]ZX	Drain/Lacrimal Bone, Lt, [Opn, Perc, Perc Endo]
ØN9K[Ø,3,4]ZX	Drain/Palatine Bone, Rt, [Opn, Perc, Perc Endo]
ØN9L[Ø,3,4]ZX	Drain/Palatine Bone, Lt, [Opn, Perc, Perc Endo]
ØN9M[Ø,3,4]ZX	Drain/Zygomatic Bone, Rt, [Opn, Perc, Perc Endo]
ØN9N[Ø,3,4]ZX	Drain/Zygomatic Bone, Lt, [Opn, Perc, Perc Endo]
ØN9R[Ø,3,4]ZX	Drain/Maxilla, Rt, [Opn, Perc, Perc Endo]
ØN9S[Ø,3,4]ZX	Drain/Maxilla, Lt, [Opn, Perc, Perc Endo]
ØN9T[Ø,3,4]ZX	Drain/Mandible, Rt, [Opn, Perc, Perc Endo]
ØN9V[Ø,3,4]ZX	Drain/Mandible, Lt, [Opn, Perc, Perc Endo]
ØN9X[Ø,3,4]ZX	Drain/Hyoid Bone, [Opn, Perc, Perc Endo]
ØNBØ[Ø,3,4]ZX	Exc/Skull, [Opn, Perc, Perc Endo]
ØNB1[Ø,3,4]ZX	Exc/Frontal Bone, Rt, [Opn, Perc, Perc Endo]
ØNB2[Ø,3,4]ZX	Exc/Frontal Bone, Lt, [Opn, Perc, Perc Endo]
ØNB3[Ø,3,4]ZX	Exc/Parietal Bone, Rt, [Opn, Perc, Perc Endo]
ØNB4[Ø,3,4]ZX	Exc/Parietal Bone, Lt, [Opn, Perc, Perc Endo]
ØNB5[Ø,3,4]ZX	Exc/Temporal Bone, Rt, [Opn, Perc, Perc Endo]
ØNB6[Ø,3,4]ZX	Exc/Temporal Bone, Lt, [Opn, Perc, Perc Endo]
ØNB7[Ø,3,4]ZX	Exc/Occipital Bone, Rt, [Opn, Perc, Perc Endo]
ØNB8[Ø,3,4]ZX	Exc/Occipital Bone, Lt, [Opn, Perc, Perc Endo]
ØNBC[Ø,3,4]ZX	Exc/Sphenoid Bone, Rt, [Opn, Perc, Perc Endo]
ØNBD[Ø,3,4]ZX	Exc/Sphenoid Bone, Lt, [Opn, Perc, Perc Endo]
ØNBF[Ø,3,4]ZX	Exc/Ethmoid Bone, Rt, [Opn, Perc, Perc Endo]
ØNBG[Ø,3,4]ZX	Exc/Ethmoid Bone, Lt, [Opn, Perc, Perc Endo]
ØNBH[Ø,3,4]ZX	Exc/Lacrimal Bone, Rt, [Opn, Perc, Perc Endo]
ØNBJ[Ø,3,4]ZX	Exc/Lacrimal Bone, Lt, [Opn, Perc, Perc Endo]
ØNBK[Ø,3,4]ZX	Exc/Palatine Bone, Rt, [Opn, Perc, Perc Endo]
ØNBL[Ø,3,4]ZX	Exc/Palatine Bone, Lt, [Opn, Perc, Perc Endo]
ØNBM[Ø,3,4]ZX	Exc/Zygomatic Bone, Rt, [Opn, Perc, Perc Endo]
ØNBN[Ø,3,4]ZX	Exc/Zygomatic Bone, Lt, [Opn, Perc, Perc Endo]
ØNBX[Ø,3,4]ZX	Exc/Hyoid Bone, [Opn, Perc, Perc Endo]
ØNJØ[Ø,3,4]ZZ	Inspect/Skull, [Opn, Perc, Perc Endo]
ØNJB[Ø,3,4]ZZ	Inspect/Nasal Bone, [Opn, Perc, Perc Endo]
ØNJW[Ø,3,4]ZZ	Inspect/Facial Bone, [Opn, Perc, Perc Endo]
ØP9Ø[Ø,3,4]ZX	Drain/Sternum, [Opn, Perc, Perc Endo]
ØP91[Ø,3,4]ZX	Drain/Rib, Rt, [Opn, Perc, Perc Endo]
ØP92[Ø,3,4]ZX	Drain/Rib, Lt, [Opn, Perc, Perc Endo]
ØP93[Ø,3,4]ZX	Drain/Cervical Vertebra, [Opn, Perc, Perc Endo]
ØP94[Ø,3,4]ZX	Drain/Thoracic Vertebra, [Opn, Perc, Perc Endo]
ØP95[Ø,3,4]ZX	Drain/Scapula, Rt, [Opn, Perc, Perc Endo]
ØP96[Ø,3,4]ZX	Drain/Scapula, Lt, [Opn, Perc, Perc Endo]
ØP97[Ø,3,4]ZX	Drain/Glenoid Cavity, Rt, [Opn, Perc, Perc Endo]
ØP98[Ø,3,4]ZX	Drain/Glenoid Cavity, Lt, [Opn, Perc, Perc Endo]
ØP99[Ø,3,4]ZX	Drain/Clavicle, Rt, [Opn, Perc, Perc Endo]
ØP9B[Ø,3,4]ZX	Drain/Clavicle, Lt, [Opn, Perc, Perc Endo]
ØP9C[Ø,3,4]ZX	Drain/Humeral Head, Rt, [Opn, Perc, Perc Endo]
ØP9D[Ø,3,4]ZX	Drain/Humeral Head, Lt, [Opn, Perc, Perc Endo]
ØP9F[Ø,3,4]ZX	Drain/Humeral Shaft, Rt, [Opn, Perc, Perc Endo]
ØP9G[Ø,3,4]ZX	Drain/Humeral Shaft, Lt, [Opn, Perc, Perc Endo]
ØP9H[Ø,3,4]ZX	Drain/Radius, Rt, [Opn, Perc, Perc Endo]
ØP9J[Ø,3,4]ZX	Drain/Radius, Lt, [Opn, Perc, Perc Endo]
ØP9K[Ø,3,4]ZX	Drain/Ulna, Rt, [Opn, Perc, Perc Endo]
ØP9L[Ø,3,4]ZX	Drain/Ulna, Lt, [Opn, Perc, Perc Endo]
ØP9R[Ø,3,4]ZX	Drain/Thumb Phalanx, Rt, [Opn, Perc, Perc Endo]
ØP9S[Ø,3,4]ZX	Drain/Thumb Phalanx, Lt, [Opn, Perc, Perc Endo]
ØP9T[Ø,3,4]ZX	Drain/Finger Phalanx, Rt, [Opn, Perc, Perc Endo]
ØP9V[Ø,3,4]ZX	Drain/Finger Phalanx, Lt, [Opn, Perc, Perc Endo]
ØPBØ[Ø,3,4]ZX	Exc/Sternum, [Opn, Perc, Perc Endo]
ØPB1[Ø,3,4]ZX	Exc/Rib, Rt, [Opn, Perc, Perc Endo]
ØPB2[Ø,3,4]ZX	Exc/Rib, Lt, [Opn, Perc, Perc Endo]
ØPB3[Ø,3,4]ZX	Exc/Cervical Vertebra, [Opn, Perc, Perc Endo]
ØPB4[Ø,3,4]ZX	Exc/Thoracic Vertebra, [Opn, Perc, Perc Endo]
ØPB5[Ø,3,4]ZX	Exc/Scapula, Rt, [Opn, Perc, Perc Endo]
ØPB6[Ø,3,4]ZX	Exc/Scapula, Lt, [Opn, Perc, Perc Endo]
ØPB7[Ø,3,4]ZX	Exc/Glenoid Cavity, Rt, [Opn, Perc, Perc Endo]
ØPB8[Ø,3,4]ZX	Exc/Glenoid Cavity, Lt, [Opn, Perc, Perc Endo]
ØPB9[Ø,3,4]ZX	Exc/Clavicle, Rt, [Opn, Perc, Perc Endo]
ØPBB[Ø,3,4]ZX	Exc/Clavicle, Lt, [Opn, Perc, Perc Endo]
ØPBC[Ø,3,4]ZX	Exc/Humeral Head, Rt, [Opn, Perc, Perc Endo]
ØPBD[Ø,3,4]ZX	Exc/Humeral Head, Lt, [Opn, Perc, Perc Endo]
ØPBF[Ø,3,4]ZX	Exc/Humeral Shaft, Rt, [Opn, Perc, Perc Endo]
ØPBG[Ø,3,4]ZX	Exc/Humeral Shaft, Lt, [Opn, Perc, Perc Endo]
ØPBH[Ø,3,4]ZX	Exc/Radius, Rt, [Opn, Perc, Perc Endo]
ØPBJ[Ø,3,4]ZX	Exc/Radius, Lt, [Opn, Perc, Perc Endo]
ØPBK[Ø,3,4]ZX	Exc/Ulna, Rt, [Opn, Perc, Perc Endo]

Surgical　　**Medical**　　**CC Indicator**　　**MCC Indicator**　　**Procedure Proxy**　　[PDxMCC] **PDx acts as own MCC**　　[PDxCC] **PDx acts as own CC**

ØPBL[Ø,3,4]ZX	Exc/Ulna, Lt, [Opn, Perc, Perc Endo]
ØPBR[Ø,3,4]ZX	Exc/Thumb Phalanx, Rt, [Opn, Perc, Perc Endo]
ØPBS[Ø,3,4]ZX	Exc/Thumb Phalanx, Lt, [Opn, Perc, Perc Endo]
ØPBT[Ø,3,4]ZX	Exc/Finger Phalanx, Rt, [Opn, Perc, Perc Endo]
ØPBV[Ø,3,4]ZX	Exc/Finger Phalanx, Lt, [Opn, Perc, Perc Endo]
ØPJY[Ø,3,4]ZZ	Inspect/Upr Bone, [Opn, Perc, Perc Endo]
ØQ9Ø[Ø,3,4]ZX	Drain/Lumbar Vertebra, [Opn, Perc, Perc Endo]
ØQ91[Ø,3,4]ZX	Drain/Sacrum, [Opn, Perc, Perc Endo]
ØQ92[Ø,3,4]ZX	Drain/Pelvic Bone, Rt, [Opn, Perc, Perc Endo]
ØQ93[Ø,3,4]ZX	Drain/Pelvic Bone, Lt, [Opn, Perc, Perc Endo]
ØQ94[Ø,3,4]ZX	Drain/Acetab, Rt, [Opn, Perc, Perc Endo]
ØQ95[Ø,3,4]ZX	Drain/Acetab, Lt, [Opn, Perc, Perc Endo]
ØQ96[Ø,3,4]ZX	Drain/Upr Femur, Rt, [Opn, Perc, Perc Endo]
ØQ97[Ø,3,4]ZX	Drain/Upr Femur, Lt, [Opn, Perc, Perc Endo]
ØQ98[Ø,3,4]ZX	Drain/Femor Shaft, Rt, [Opn, Perc, Perc Endo]
ØQ99[Ø,3,4]ZX	Drain/Femor Shaft, Lt, [Opn, Perc, Perc Endo]
ØQ9B[Ø,3,4]ZX	Drain/Lwr Femur, Rt, [Opn, Perc, Perc Endo]
ØQ9C[Ø,3,4]ZX	Drain/Lwr Femur, Lt, [Opn, Perc, Perc Endo]
ØQ9D[Ø,3,4]ZX	Drain/Patella, Rt, [Opn, Perc, Perc Endo]
ØQ9F[Ø,3,4]ZX	Drain/Patella, Lt, [Opn, Perc, Perc Endo]
ØQ9G[Ø,3,4]ZX	Drain/Tibia, Rt, [Opn, Perc, Perc Endo]
ØQ9H[Ø,3,4]ZX	Drain/Tibia, Lt, [Opn, Perc, Perc Endo]
ØQ9J[Ø,3,4]ZX	Drain/Fibula, Rt, [Opn, Perc, Perc Endo]
ØQ9K[Ø,3,4]ZX	Drain/Fibula, Lt, [Opn, Perc, Perc Endo]
ØQ9L[Ø,3,4]ZX	Drain/Tarsal, Rt, [Opn, Perc, Perc Endo]
ØQ9M[Ø,3,4]ZX	Drain/Tarsal, Lt, [Opn, Perc, Perc Endo]
ØQ9N[Ø,3,4]ZX	Drain/Metatarsal, Rt, [Opn, Perc, Perc Endo]
ØQ9P[Ø,3,4]ZX	Drain/Metatarsal, Lt, [Opn, Perc, Perc Endo]
ØQ9Q[Ø,3,4]ZX	Drain/Toe Phalanx, Rt, [Opn, Perc, Perc Endo]
ØQ9R[Ø,3,4]ZX	Drain/Toe Phalanx, Lt, [Opn, Perc, Perc Endo]
ØQ9S[Ø,3,4]ZX	Drain/Coccyx, [Opn, Perc, Perc Endo]
ØQBØ[Ø,3,4]ZX	Exc/Lumbar Vertebra, [Opn, Perc, Perc Endo]
ØQB1[Ø,3,4]ZX	Exc/Sacrum, [Opn, Perc, Perc Endo]
ØQB2[Ø,3,4]ZX	Exc/Pelvic Bone, Rt, [Opn, Perc, Perc Endo]
ØQB3[Ø,3,4]ZX	Exc/Pelvic Bone, Lt, [Opn, Perc, Perc Endo]
ØQB4[Ø,3,4]ZX	Exc/Acetab, Rt, [Opn, Perc, Perc Endo]
ØQB5[Ø,3,4]ZX	Exc/Acetab, Lt, [Opn, Perc, Perc Endo]
ØQB6[Ø,3,4]ZX	Exc/Upr Femur, Rt, [Opn, Perc, Perc Endo]
ØQB7[Ø,3,4]ZX	Exc/Upr Femur, Lt, [Opn, Perc, Perc Endo]
ØQB8[Ø,3,4]ZX	Exc/Femor Shaft, Rt, [Opn, Perc, Perc Endo]
ØQB9[Ø,3,4]ZX	Exc/Femor Shaft, Lt, [Opn, Perc, Perc Endo]
ØQBB[Ø,3,4]ZX	Exc/Lwr Femur, Rt, [Opn, Perc, Perc Endo]
ØQBC[Ø,3,4]ZX	Exc/Lwr Femur, Lt, [Opn, Perc, Perc Endo]
ØQBD[Ø,3,4]ZX	Exc/Patella, Rt, [Opn, Perc, Perc Endo]
ØQBF[Ø,3,4]ZX	Exc/Patella, Lt, [Opn, Perc, Perc Endo]
ØQBG[Ø,3,4]ZX	Exc/Tibia, Rt, [Opn, Perc, Perc Endo]
ØQBH[Ø,3,4]ZX	Exc/Tibia, Lt, [Opn, Perc, Perc Endo]
ØQBJ[Ø,3,4]ZX	Exc/Fibula, Rt, [Opn, Perc, Perc Endo]
ØQBK[Ø,3,4]ZX	Exc/Fibula, Lt, [Opn, Perc, Perc Endo]
ØQBL[Ø,3,4]ZX	Exc/Tarsal, Rt, [Opn, Perc, Perc Endo]
ØQBM[Ø,3,4]ZX	Exc/Tarsal, Lt, [Opn, Perc, Perc Endo]
ØQBN[Ø,3,4]ZX	Exc/Metatarsal, Rt, [Opn, Perc, Perc Endo]
ØQBP[Ø,3,4]ZX	Exc/Metatarsal, Lt, [Opn, Perc, Perc Endo]
ØQBQ[Ø,3,4]ZX	Exc/Toe Phalanx, Rt, [Opn, Perc, Perc Endo]
ØQBR[Ø,3,4]ZX	Exc/Toe Phalanx, Lt, [Opn, Perc, Perc Endo]
ØQBS[Ø,3,4]ZX	Exc/Coccyx, [Opn, Perc, Perc Endo]
ØQJYØZZ	Inspect of Lwr Bone, Opn Appr
ØQJY3ZZ	Inspect of Lwr Bone, Perc Appr
ØQJY4ZZ	Inspect of Lwr Bone, Perc Endo Appr
ØR9C[Ø,3,4]ZX	Drain/Temporomandibular Jt, Rt, [Opn, Perc, Perc Endo]
ØR9D[Ø,3,4]ZX	Drain/Temporomandibular Jt, Lt, [Opn, Perc, Perc Endo]
ØRBC[Ø,3,4]ZX	Exc/Temporomandibular Jt, Rt, [Opn, Perc, Perc Endo]
ØRBD[Ø,3,4]ZX	Exc/Temporomandibular Jt, Lt, [Opn, Perc, Perc Endo]
ØRJC[Ø,3,4]ZZ	Inspect/Temporomandibular Jt, Rt, [Opn, Perc, Perc Endo]
ØRJD[Ø,3,4]ZZ	Inspect/Temporomandibular Jt, Lt, [Opn, Perc, Perc Endo]
ØRJ[Ø,1,3]3ZZ	Inspect of [Occipital-cervical Jt, Cervical Vert Jt, Cervical Vert Disc], Perc Appr
ØRJ[4,5,6,9]3ZZ	Inspect of [Cervicothoracic Vert Jt, Cervicothoracic Vert Disc, Thoracic Vert Jt, Thoracic Vert Disc], Perc Appr
ØRJ[A,B]3ZZ	Inspect of [Thoracolumbar Vert Jt, Thoracolumbar Vert Disc], Perc Appr
ØRJ[E,F]3ZZ	Inspect of [Rt Sternoclavicular Jt, Lt Sternoclavicular Jt], Perc Appr
ØRJ[G,H]3ZZ	Inspect of [Rt Acromioclavicular Jt, Lt Acromioclavicular Jt], Perc Appr
ØRJ[J,K,L,M]3ZZ	Inspect of [Rt Shldr Jt, Lt Shldr Jt, Rt Elbow Jt, Lt Elbow Jt], Perc Appr
ØRJ[N,P,Q,R]3ZZ	Inspect of [Rt Wrist Jt, Lt Wrist Jt, Rt Carpal Jt, Lt Carpal Jt], Perc Appr

ØRJ[S,T]3ZZ	Inspect of [Rt Metacarpocarpal Jt, Lt Metacarpocarpal Jt], Perc Appr
ØRJ[U,V]3ZZ	Inspect of [Rt Metacarpophalangeal Jt, Lt Metacarpophalangeal Jt], Perc Appr
ØRJ[W,X]3ZZ	Inspect of [Rt Finger Phalangeal Jt, Lt Finger Phalangeal Jt], Perc Appr
ØSJØ3ZZ	Inspect of Lumbar Vert Jt, Perc Appr
ØSJ2[3,4]ZZ	Inspect/Lumbar Vert Disc, [Perc, Perc Endo]
ØSJ33ZZ	Inspect of Lumbosacral Jt, Perc Appr
ØSJ4[3,4]ZZ	Inspect/Lumbosacral Disc, [Perc, Perc Endo]
ØSJ[5,6]3ZZ	Inspect of [Sacrococcygeal, Coccygeal] Jt, Perc Appr
ØSJ[7,8,9,B]3ZZ	Inspect of [Rt Sacroiliac, Lt Sacroiliac, Rt Hip, Lt Hip] Jt, Perc Appr
ØSJ[C,D,F,G,H,J]3ZZ	Inspect of [Rt Knee, Lt Knee, Rt Ankle, Lt Ankle, Rt Tarsal, Lt Tarsal] Jt, Perc Appr
ØSJ[K,L]3ZZ	Inspect of [Rt Metatarsal-Tarsal, Lt Metatarsal-Tarsal] Jt, Perc Appr
ØSJ[M,N]3ZZ	Inspect of [Rt Metatarsal-Phalangeal, Lt Metatarsal-Phalangeal] Jt, Perc Appr
ØSJ[P,Q]3ZZ	Inspect of [Rt Toe Phalangeal Jt, Lt Toe Phalangeal Jt], Perc Appr

DRG 478   **Biopsies of Musculoskeletal System and Connective Tissue with CC**

GMLOS 5.4	AMLOS 6.6	RW 2.1992	SP

Select operating room procedures listed under DRG 477

DRG 479   **Biopsies of Musculoskeletal System and Connective Tissue without CC/MCC**

GMLOS 3.5	AMLOS 4.3	RW 1.7158	SP

Select operating room procedures listed under DRG 477

DRG 480   **Hip and Femur Procedures Except Major Joint with MCC**

GMLOS 6.7	AMLOS 7.9	RW 2.999Ø	SP

Operating Room Procedures

ØL8J*	Div/Hip Tndn, Rt
ØL8K*	Div/Hip Tndn, Lt
ØM9[L,M]4ZZ	Drain of [Rt, Lt] Hip Bursa & Lgmt, Perc Endo Appr
ØQ86*	Div/Upr Femur, Rt
ØQ87*	Div/Upr Femur, Lt
ØQ88*	Div/Femor Shaft, Rt
ØQ89*	Div/Femor Shaft, Lt
ØQ8B*	Div/Lwr Femur, Rt
ØQ8C*	Div/Lwr Femur, Lt
ØQC6*	Extir/Upr Femur, Rt
ØQC7*	Extir/Upr Femur, Lt
ØQC8*	Extir/Femor Shaft, Rt
ØQC9*	Extir/Femor Shaft, Lt
ØQCB*	Extir/Lwr Femur, Rt
ØQCC*	Extir/Lwr Femur, Lt
ØQH6[Ø,3,4][4,5,6,B,C,D]Z	Insert/Upr Femur, Rt, [Opn, Perc, Perc Endo], [Int Fix Dev, Ext Fix Dev, Int Fix Dev, Intramedullary Int Fix Dev, Ext Fix Dev, Monop, Ext Fix Dev, Ring, Ext Fix Dev, Hybrid], NQ
ØQH7[Ø,3,4][4,5,6,B,C,D]Z	Insert/Upr Femur, Lt, [Opn, Perc, Perc Endo], [Int Fix Dev, Ext Fix Dev, Int Fix Dev, Intramedullary Int Fix Dev, Ext Fix Dev, Monop, Ext Fix Dev, Ring, Ext Fix Dev, Hybrid], NQ
ØQH8[Ø,3,4][4,5,6,B,C,D]Z	Insert/Femor Shaft, Rt, [Opn, Perc, Perc Endo], [Int Fix Dev, Ext Fix Dev, Int Fix Dev, Intramedullary Int Fix Dev, Ext Fix Dev, Monop, Ext Fix Dev, Ring, Ext Fix Dev, Hybrid], NQ
ØQH9[Ø,3,4][4,5,6,B,C,D]Z	Insert/Femor Shaft, Lt, [Opn, Perc, Perc Endo], [Int Fix Dev, Ext Fix Dev, Int Fix Dev, Intramedullary Int Fix Dev, Ext Fix Dev, Monop, Ext Fix Dev, Ring, Ext Fix Dev, Hybrid], NQ
ØQHB[Ø,3,4][4,5,6,B,C,D]Z	Insert/Lwr Femur, Rt, [Opn, Perc, Perc Endo], [Int Fix Dev, Ext Fix Dev, Int Fix Dev, Intramedullary Int Fix Dev, Ext Fix Dev, Monop, Ext Fix Dev, Ring, Ext Fix Dev, Hybrid], NQ
ØQHC[Ø,3,4][4,5,6,B,C,D]Z	Insert/Lwr Femur, Lt, [Opn, Perc, Perc Endo], [Int Fix Dev, Ext Fix Dev, Int Fix Dev, Intramedullary Int Fix Dev, Ext Fix Dev, Monop, Ext Fix Dev, Ring, Ext Fix Dev, Hybrid], NQ
ØQN6*	Rls/Upr Femur, Rt
ØQN7*	Rls/Upr Femur, Lt
ØQN8*	Rls/Femor Shaft, Rt
ØQN9*	Rls/Femor Shaft, Lt
ØQNB*	Rls/Lwr Femur, Rt
ØQNC*	Rls/Lwr Femur, Lt
ØQQ6*	Repair/Upr Femur, Rt
ØQQ7*	Repair/Upr Femur, Lt

| T | Transfer DRG | SP | Special Payment | * Code Range | **6th and 7th Character of ZZ = No Device, No Qualifier ZX = No Device, Diagnostic** |

ØQQ8*	Repair/Femor Shaft, Rt
ØQQ9*	Repair/Femor Shaft, Lt
ØQQB*	Repair/Lwr Femur, Rt
ØQQC*	Repair/Lwr Femur, Lt
ØQR6*	Replace/Upr Femur, Rt
ØQR7*	Replace/Upr Femur, Lt
ØQR8*	Replace/Femor Shaft, Rt
ØQR9*	Replace/Femor Shaft, Lt
ØQRB*	Replace/Lwr Femur, Rt
ØQRC*	Replace/Lwr Femur, Lt
ØQS6ØZZ	Repos Rt Upr Femur, Opn Appr
ØQS6[Ø,3,4][4,5,6,B,C,D]Z	Repos/Upr Femur, Rt, [Opn, Perc, Perc Endo], [Int Fix Dev, Ext Fix Dev, Int Fix Dev, Intramedullary Int Fix Dev, Ext Fix Dev, Monop, Ext Fix Dev, Ring, Ext Fix Dev, Hybrid], NQ
ØQS7ØZZ	Repos Lt Upr Femur, Opn Appr
ØQS7[Ø,3,4][4,5,6,B,C,D]Z	Repos/Upr Femur, Lt, [Opn, Perc, Perc Endo], [Int Fix Dev, Ext Fix Dev, Int Fix Dev, Intramedullary Int Fix Dev, Ext Fix Dev, Monop, Ext Fix Dev, Ring, Ext Fix Dev, Hybrid], NQ
ØQS8ØZZ	Repos Rt Femor Shaft, Opn Appr
ØQS8[Ø,3,4][4,5,6,B,C,D]Z	Repos/Femor Shaft, Rt, [Opn, Perc, Perc Endo], [Int Fix Dev, Ext Fix Dev, Int Fix Dev, Intramedullary Int Fix Dev, Ext Fix Dev, Monop, Ext Fix Dev, Ring, Ext Fix Dev, Hybrid], NQ
ØQS9ØZZ	Repos Lt Femor Shaft, Opn Appr
ØQS9[Ø,3,4][4,5,6,B,C,D]Z	Repos/Femor Shaft, Lt, [Opn, Perc, Perc Endo], [Int Fix Dev, Ext Fix Dev, Int Fix Dev, Intramedullary Int Fix Dev, Ext Fix Dev, Monop, Ext Fix Dev, Ring, Ext Fix Dev, Hybrid], NQ
ØQSBØZZ	Repos Rt Lwr Femur, Opn Appr
ØQSB[Ø,3,4][4,5,6,B,C,D]Z	Repos/Lwr Femur, Rt, [Opn, Perc, Perc Endo], [Int Fix Dev, Ext Fix Dev, Int Fix Dev, Intramedullary Int Fix Dev, Ext Fix Dev, Monop, Ext Fix Dev, Ring, Ext Fix Dev, Hybrid], NQ
ØQSCØZZ	Repos Lt Lwr Femur, Opn Appr
ØQSC[Ø,3,4][4,5,6,B,C,D]Z	Repos/Lwr Femur, Lt, [Opn, Perc, Perc Endo], [Int Fix Dev, Ext Fix Dev, Int Fix Dev, Intramedullary Int Fix Dev, Ext Fix Dev, Monop, Ext Fix Dev, Ring, Ext Fix Dev, Hybrid], NQ
ØQT[6,7]ØZZ	Resect of [Rt, Lt] Upr Femur, Opn Appr
ØQT[8,9]ØZZ	Resect of [Rt, Lt] Femor Shaft, Opn Appr
ØQT[B,C]ØZZ	Resect of [Rt, Lt] Lwr Femur, Opn Appr
ØQU6*	Supl/Upr Femur, Rt
ØQU7*	Supl/Upr Femur, Lt
ØQU8*	Supl/Femor Shaft, Rt
ØQU9*	Supl/Femor Shaft, Lt
ØQUB*	Supl/Lwr Femur, Rt
ØQUC*	Supl/Lwr Femur, Lt
ØS99Ø[Ø,Z]Z	Drain/Hip Jt, Rt, Opn, [Drain Dev, No Dev], NQ
ØS9BØ[Ø,Z]Z	Drain/Hip Jt, Lt, Opn, [Drain Dev, No Dev], NQ
ØSB9[Ø,3,4]ZZ	Exc/Hip Jt, Rt, [Opn, Perc, Perc Endo]
ØSBB[Ø,3,4]ZZ	Exc/Hip Jt, Lt, [Opn, Perc, Perc Endo]
ØSC9*	Extir/Hip Jt, Rt
ØSCB*	Extir/Hip Jt, Lt
ØSG9*	Fusion/Hip Jt, Rt
ØSGB*	Fusion/Hip Jt, Lt
ØSH9[Ø,3,4][4,5]Z	Insert/Hip Jt, Rt, [Opn, Perc, Perc Endo], [Int Fix Dev, Ext Fix Dev], NQ
ØSHB[Ø,3,4][4,5]Z	Insert/Hip Jt, Lt, [Opn, Perc, Perc Endo], [Int Fix Dev, Ext Fix Dev], NQ
ØSJ[9,B]ØZZ	Inspect of [Rt, Lt] Hip Jt, Opn Appr
ØSN9[Ø,3,4]ZZ	Rls/Hip Jt, Rt, [Opn, Perc, Perc Endo]
ØSNB[Ø,3,4]ZZ	Rls/Hip Jt, Lt, [Opn, Perc, Perc Endo]
ØSP90BZ	Rmvl of Resurfacing Device from Rt Hip Jt, Opn Appr
ØSP9[Ø,3,4][Ø,3,4,5,7,K]Z	Rmvl/Hip Jt, Rt, [Opn, Perc, Perc Endo], [Drain Dev, Inf Dev, Int Fix Dev, Ext Fix Dev, Auto Tissue Sub, Nonauto Tissue Sub], NQ
ØSPBØBZ	Rmvl of Resurfacing Device from Lt Hip Jt, Opn Appr
ØSPB[Ø,3,4][Ø,3,4,5,7,K]Z	Rmvl/Hip Jt, Lt, [Opn, Perc, Perc Endo], [Drain Dev, Inf Dev, Int Fix Dev, Ext Fix Dev, Auto Tissue Sub, Nonauto Tissue Sub], NQ
ØSQ9*	Repair/Hip Jt, Rt
ØSQB*	Repair/Hip Jt, Lt
ØSS90[4,5,Z]Z	Repos Hip Jt, Rt, Opn, [Int Fix Dev, Ext Fix Dev, No Dev], NQ
ØSSB0[4,5,Z]Z	Repos/Hip Jt, Lt, Opn, [Int Fix Dev, Ext Fix Dev, No Dev], NQ
ØST[9,B]ØZZ	Resect of [Rt, Lt] Hip Jt, Opn Appr
ØSW90[Ø,3,4,5,7,8,9,B,K]Z	Rev/Hip Jt, Rt, Opn, [Drain Dev, Inf Dev, Int Fix Dev, Ext Fix Dev, Auto Tissue Sub, Spacer, Liner, Resurfacing Dev, Nonauto Tissue Sub], NQ
ØSW93[Ø,3,4,5,7,8,K]Z	Rev/Hip Jt, Rt, Perc, [Drain Dev, Inf Dev, Int Fix Dev, Ext Fix Dev, Auto Tissue Sub, Spacer, Nonauto Tissue Sub], NQ
ØSW94[Ø,3,4,5,7,8,K]Z	Rev/Hip Jt, Rt, Perc Endo, [Drain Dev, Inf Dev, Int Fix Dev, Ext Fix Dev, Auto Tissue Sub, Spacer, Nonauto Tissue Sub], NQ

ØSWBØ[Ø,3,4,5,7,8,9,B,K]Z	Rev/Hip Jt, Lt, Opn, [Drain Dev, Inf Dev, Int Fix Dev, Ext Fix Dev, Auto Tissue Sub, Spacer, Liner, Resurfacing Dev, Nonauto Tissue Sub], NQ
ØSWB3[Ø,3,4,5,7,8,K]Z	Rev/Hip Jt, Lt, Perc, [Drain Dev, Inf Dev, Int Fix Dev, Ext Fix Dev, Auto Tissue Sub, Spacer, Nonauto Tissue Sub], NQ
ØSWB4[Ø,3,4,5,7,8,K]Z	Rev/Hip Jt, Lt, Perc Endo, [Drain Dev, Inf Dev, Int Fix Dev, Ext Fix Dev, Auto Tissue Sub, Spacer, Nonauto Tissue Sub], NQ

DRG 481 Hip and Femur Procedures Except Major Joint with CC

GMLOS 4.6	AMLOS 5.0	RW 1.979Ø	SP

Select operating room procedures listed under DRG 480

DRG 482 Hip and Femur Procedures Except Major Joint without CC/MCC

GMLOS 3.7	AMLOS 4.0	RW 1.6228	SP

Select operating room procedures listed under DRG 480

DRG 483 Major Joint/Limb Reattachment Procedure of Upper Extremities

GMLOS 1.9	AMLOS 2.3	RW 2.4127

Operating Room Procedures

ØRRE*	Replace/Sternoclavicular Jt, Rt
ØRRF*	Replace/Sternoclavicular Jt, Lt
ØRRG*	Replace/Acromioclavicular Jt, Rt
ØRRH*	Replace/Acromioclavicular Jt, Lt
ØRRJ*	Replace/Shldr Jt, Rt
ØRRK*	Replace/Shldr Jt, Lt
ØRRL*	Replace/Elbow Jt, Rt
ØRRM*	Replace/Elbow Jt, Lt
ØRRN*	Replace/Wrist Jt, Rt
ØRRP*	Replace/Wrist Jt, Lt
ØXM[Ø,1]ØZZ	Reattach of [Rt, Lt] Forequarter, Opn Appr
ØXM[2,3]ØZZ	Reattach of [Rt, Lt] Shldr Rgn, Opn Appr
ØXM[4,5]ØZZ	Reattach of [Rt, Lt] Axilla, Opn Appr
ØXM[6,7]ØZZ	Reattach of [Rt, Lt] Upr Extr, Opn Appr
ØXM[8,9]ØZZ	Reattach of [Rt, Lt] Upr Arm, Opn Appr
ØXM[B,C]ØZZ	Reattach of [Rt, Lt] Elbow Rgn, Opn Appr
ØXM[D,F]ØZZ	Reattach of [Rt, Lt] Lwr Arm, Opn Appr
ØXM[G,H]ØZZ	Reattach of [Rt, Lt] Wrist Rgn, Opn Appr
ØXM[J,K]ØZZ	Reattach of [Rt, Lt] Hand, Opn Appr

DRG 484 Major Joint/Limb Reattachment Procedures of Upper Extremity without CC/MCC

GMLOS 0.0	AMLOS 0.0	RW 0.0000

Omitted in October 2015 Grouper version.

DRG 485 Knee Procedures with Principal Diagnosis of Infection with MCC

GMLOS 8.1	AMLOS 9.8	RW 3.2132

Principal Diagnosis

MØØ.Ø6*	Staphylococcal arthritis, knee
MØØ.16[1,2,9]	Pneumococcal arthritis, [rt, lt, unsp] knee
MØØ.26[1,2,9]	Oth streptococcal arthritis, [rt, lt, unsp] knee
MØØ.86[1,2,9]	Arthritis d/t oth bacteria, [rt, lt, unsp] knee
M86.Ø6[1,2,9]	Acute hematogenous osteomyelitis, [rt, lt, unsp] tibia & fibula
M86.16[1,2,9]	Oth acute osteomyelitis, [rt, lt, unsp] tibia & fibula
M86.26[1,2,9]	Subacute osteomyelitis, [rt, lt, unsp] tibia & fibula
M86.36[1,2,9]	Chr multifocal osteomyelitis, [rt, lt, unsp] tibia & fibula
M86.46[1,2,9]	Chr osteomyelitis w/ draining sinus, [rt, lt, unsp] tibia & fibula
M86.56[1,2,9]	Oth chr hematogenous osteomyelitis, [rt, lt, unsp] tibia & fibula
M86.66[1,2,9]	Oth chr osteomyelitis, [rt, lt, unsp] tibia & fibula
M86.8X6	Oth osteomyelitis, lwr leg
M86.9	Osteomyelitis, unsp
T84.5[Ø,1,2,3,4,9]XA	Infxn and inflam reaction d/t [unsp int jt, int rt hip, int lt hip, int rt knee, int lt knee, oth int jt] prosthesis, init enc
T84.60XA	Infect/inflm reaction d/t int fix of unsp site, init
T84.629A	Infect/inflm react d/t int fix of unsp bone of leg, init
T84.62[Ø,1]A	Infxn and inflam reaction d/t int fix dev of [rt, lt] femur, init enc
T84.62[2,3]A	Infxn and inflam reaction d/t int fix dev of [rt, lt] tibia, init enc
T84.62[4,5]A	Infxn and inflam reaction d/t int fix dev of [rt, lt] fibula, init enc
T84.63XA	Infect/inflm reaction d/t int fix of spine, init
T84.69XA	Infect/inflm reaction d/t int fix of site, init

Surgical   **Medical**   **CC Indicator**   **MCC Indicator**   **Procedure Proxy**   **PDxMCC** PDx acts as own MCC   **PDxCC** PDx acts as own CC

T84.7XXA   Infect/inflm react d/t oth int orth prosth dev/grft, init
AND

Operating Room Procedures

ØM9N[3,4]ØZ	Drain/Knee Bursa & Lgmt, Rt, [Perc, Perc Endo], Drain Dev, NQ
ØM9P[3,4]ØZ	Drain/Knee Bursa & Lgmt, Lt, [Perc, Perc Endo], Drain Dev, NQ
ØMQN*	Repair/Knee Bursa & Lgmt, Rt
ØMQP*	Repair/Knee Bursa & Lgmt, Lt
ØQ8D*	Div/Patella, Rt
ØQ8F*	Div/Patella, Lt
ØQBD[Ø,3,4]ZZ	Exc/Patella, Rt, [Opn, Perc, Perc Endo]
ØQBF[Ø,3,4]ZZ	Exc/Patella, Lt, [Opn, Perc, Perc Endo]
ØQCD*	Extir/Patella, Rt
ØQCF*	Extir/Patella, Lt
ØQHD*	Insert/Patella, Rt
ØQHF*	Insert/Patella, Lt
ØQND*	Rls/Patella, Rt
ØQNF*	Rls/Patella, Lt
ØQQD[Ø,4,X]ZZ	Rpr/Patella, Rt, [Opn, Perc Endo, Ext]
ØQQF[Ø,4,X]ZZ	Rpr/Patella, Lt, [Opn, Perc Endo, Ext]
ØQRD*	Replace/Patella, Rt
ØQRF*	Replace/Patella, Lt
ØQSD[Ø,3,4]5Z	Repos/Patella, Rt, [Opn, Perc, Perc Endo], Ext Fix Dev, NQ
ØQSF[Ø,3,4]5Z	Repos/Patella, Lt, [Opn, Perc, Perc Endo], Ext Fix Dev, NQ
ØQT[D,F]ØZZ	Resect of [Rt, Lt] Patella, Opn Appr
ØQUD*	Supl/Patella, Rt
ØQUF*	Supl/Patella, Lt
ØS9CØ[Ø,Z]Z	Drain/Knee Jt, Rt, Opn, [Drain Dev, No Dev], NQ
ØS9DØ[Ø,Z]Z	Drain/Knee Jt, Lt, Opn, [Drain Dev, No Dev], NQ
ØSBC[Ø,3,4]ZZ	Exc/Knee Jt, Rt, [Opn, Perc, Perc Endo]
ØSBD[Ø,3,4]ZZ	Exc/Knee Jt, Lt, [Opn, Perc, Perc Endo]
ØSCC*	Extir/Knee Jt, Rt
ØSCD*	Extir/Knee Jt, Lt
ØSGC*	Fusion/Knee Jt, Rt
ØSGD*	Fusion/Knee Jt, Lt
ØSHC[Ø,3,4][4,5]Z	Insert/Knee Jt, Rt, [Opn, Perc, Perc Endo], [Int Fix Dev, Ext Fix Dev], NQ
ØSHD[Ø,3,4][4,5]Z	Insert/Knee Jt, Lt, [Opn, Perc, Perc Endo], [Int Fix Dev, Ext Fix Dev], NQ
ØSJ[C,D]ØZZ	Inspect of [Rt, Lt] Knee Jt, Opn Appr
ØSNC[Ø,3,4]ZZ	Rls/Knee Jt, Rt, [Opn, Perc, Perc Endo]
ØSND[Ø,3,4]ZZ	Rls/Knee Jt, Lt, [Opn, Perc, Perc Endo]
ØSPC[Ø,3,4][Ø,3,4,5,7,K]Z	Rmvl/Knee Jt, Rt, [Opn, Perc, Perc Endo], [Drain Dev, Inf Dev, Int Fix Dev, Ext Fix Dev, Auto Tissue Sub, Nonauto Tissue Sub], NQ
ØSPD[Ø,3,4][Ø,3,4,5,7,K]Z	Rmvl/Knee Jt, Lt, [Opn, Perc, Perc Endo], [Drain Dev, Inf Dev, Int Fix Dev, Ext Fix Dev, Auto Tissue Sub, Nonauto Tissue Sub], NQ
ØSQC*	Repair/Knee Jt, Rt
ØSQD*	Repair/Knee Jt, Lt
ØSSCØ[4,5,Z]Z	Repos/Knee Jt, Rt, Opn, [Int Fix Dev, Ext Fix Dev, No Dev], NQ
ØSSDØ[4,5,Z]Z	Repos/Knee Jt, Lt, Opn, [Int Fix Dev, Ext Fix Dev, No Dev], NQ
ØST[C,D]ØZZ	Resect of [Rt, Lt] Knee Jt, Opn Appr
ØSWCØ9Z	Rev of Liner in Rt Knee Jt, Opn Appr
ØSWC[Ø,3,4][Ø,3,4,5,7,8,K]Z	Rev/Knee Jt, Rt, [Opn, Perc, Perc Endo], [Drain Dev, Inf Dev, Int Fix Dev, Ext Fix Dev, Auto Tissue Sub, Spacer, Nonauto Tissue Sub], NQ
ØSWDØ9Z	Rev of Liner in Lt Knee Jt, Opn Appr
ØSWD[Ø,3,4][Ø,3,4,5,7,8,K]Z	Rev/Knee Jt, Lt, [Opn, Perc, Perc Endo], [Drain Dev, Inf Dev, Int Fix Dev, Ext Fix Dev, Auto Tissue Sub, Spacer, Nonauto Tissue Sub], NQ
XR2GØ21	Monitor Rt Knee Jt w Intraop Knee Sens, Opn, New Tech 1
XR2HØ21	Monitor Lt Knee Jt w Intraop Knee Sens, Opn, New Tech 1

OR

ØSUVØ9Z	Supl Rt Knee Jt, Tibial with Liner, Opn Appr

AND

ØSPCØ9Z	Rmvl of Liner from Rt Knee Jt, Opn Appr

OR

ØSUWØ9Z	Supl Lt Knee Jt, Tibial with Liner, Opn Appr

AND

ØSPDØ9Z	Rmvl of Liner from Lt Knee Jt, Opn Appr

DRG 486   Knee Procedures with Principal Diagnosis of Infection with CC

GMLOS 5.4   AMLOS 6.2   RW 2.0690

Select principal diagnosis AND operating room procedures or procedure combinations listed under DRG 485

DRG 487   Knee Procedures with Principal Diagnosis of Infection without CC/MCC

GMLOS 3.9   AMLOS 4.5   RW 1.5484

Select principal diagnosis AND operating room procedures or procedure combinations listed under DRG 485

DRG 488   Knee Procedures without Principal Diagnosis of Infection with CC/MCC

GMLOS 3.4   AMLOS 4.2   RW 1.7591   T

Select only operating room procedures or procedure combinations under DRG 485

DRG 489   Knee Procedures without Principal Diagnosis of Infection without CC/MCC

GMLOS 2.3   AMLOS 2.6   RW 1.2991   T

Select only operating room procedures or procedure combinations under DRG 485

DRG 490   Back and Neck Procedures Except Spinal Fusion with CC/MCC or Disc Device/Neurostimulator

GMLOS 0.0   AMLOS 0.0   RW 0.0000

Omitted in October 2015 Grouper version.

DRG 491   Back and Neck Procedures Except Spinal Fusion without CC/MCC

GMLOS 0.0   AMLOS 0.0   RW 0.0000

Omitted in October 2015 Grouper version.

DRG 492   Lower Extremity and Humerus Procedures Except Hip, Foot, Femur with MCC

GMLOS 6.2   AMLOS 7.6   RW 3.1585   SP

Operating Room Procedures

ØM5Q*	Destr/Ankle Bursa & Lgmt, Rt
ØM5R*	Destr/Ankle Bursa & Lgmt, Lt
ØM9Q[3,4]ØZ	Drain/Ankle Bursa & Lgmt, Rt, [Perc, Perc Endo], Drain Dev, NQ
ØM9R[3,4]ØZ	Drain/Ankle Bursa & Lgmt, Lt, [Perc, Perc Endo], Drain Dev, NQ
ØP8C*	Div/Humeral Head, Rt
ØP8D*	Div/Humeral Head, Lt
ØP8F*	Div/Humeral Shaft, Rt
ØP8G*	Div/Humeral Shaft, Lt
ØPBC[Ø,3,4]ZZ	Exc/Humeral Head, Rt, [Opn, Perc, Perc Endo]
ØPBD[Ø,3,4]ZZ	Exc/Humeral Head, Lt, [Opn, Perc, Perc Endo]
ØPBF[Ø,3,4]ZZ	Exc/Humeral Shaft, Rt, [Opn, Perc, Perc Endo]
ØPBG[Ø,3,4]ZZ	Exc/Humeral Shaft, Lt, [Opn, Perc, Perc Endo]
ØPCC*	Extir/Humeral Head, Rt
ØPCD*	Extir/Humeral Head, Lt
ØPCF*	Extir/Humeral Shaft, Rt
ØPCG*	Extir/Humeral Shaft, Lt
ØPHC[Ø,3,4][4,5,6,B,C,D]Z	Insert/Humeral Head, Rt, [Opn, Perc, Perc Endo], [Int Fix Dev, Ext Fix Dev, Int Fix Dev, Intramedullary Int Fix Dev, Ext Fix Dev, Monop, Ext Fix Dev, Ring, Ext Fix Dev, Hybrid], NQ
ØPHD[Ø,3,4][4,5,6,B,C,D]Z	Insert/Humeral Head, Lt, [Opn, Perc, Perc Endo], [Int Fix Dev, Ext Fix Dev, Int Fix Dev, Intramedullary Int Fix Dev, Ext Fix Dev, Monop, Ext Fix Dev, Ring, Ext Fix Dev, Hybrid], NQ
ØPHF[Ø,3,4][4,5,6,B,C,D]Z	Insert/Humeral Shaft, Rt, [Opn, Perc, Perc Endo], [Int Fix Dev, Ext Fix Dev, Int Fix Dev, Intramedullary Int Fix Dev, Ext Fix Dev, Monop, Ext Fix Dev, Ring, Ext Fix Dev, Hybrid], NQ
ØPHG[Ø,3,4][4,5,6,B,C,D]Z	Insert/Humeral Shaft, Lt, [Opn, Perc, Perc Endo], [Int Fix Dev, Ext Fix Dev, Int Fix Dev, Intramedullary Int Fix Dev, Ext Fix Dev, Monop, Ext Fix Dev, Ring, Ext Fix Dev, Hybrid], NQ
ØPNC*	Rls/Humeral Head, Rt
ØPND*	Rls/Humeral Head, Lt
ØPNF*	Rls/Humeral Shaft, Rt
ØPNG*	Rls/Humeral Shaft, Lt

T **Transfer DRG**   SP **Special Payment**   * **Code Range**   **6th and 7th Character of ZZ = No Device, No Qualifier ZX = No Device, Diagnostic**

0PQC*	Repair/Humeral Head, Rt
0PQD*	Repair/Humeral Head, Lt
0PQF*	Repair/Humeral Shaft, Rt
0PQG*	Repair/Humeral Shaft, Lt
0PRC[0,3,4][7,K]Z	Replace/Humeral Head, Rt, [Opn, Perc, Perc Endo], [Auto Tissue Sub, Nonauto Tissue Sub], NQ
0PRC[3,4]JZ	Replace/Humeral Head, Rt, [Perc, Perc Endo], Synth Sub, NQ
0PRD[0,3,4][7,K]Z	Replace/Humeral Head, Lt, [Opn, Perc, Perc Endo], [Auto Tissue Sub, Nonauto Tissue Sub], NQ
0PRD[3,4]JZ	Replace/Humeral Head, Lt, [Perc, Perc Endo], Synth Sub, NQ
0PRF*	Replace/Humeral Shaft, Rt
0PRG*	Replace/Humeral Shaft, Lt
0PSC0ZZ	Repos Rt Humeral Head, Opn Appr
0PSC[0,3,4][4,5,6,B,C,D]Z	Repos/Humeral Head, Rt, [Opn, Perc, Perc Endo], [Int Fix Dev, Ext Fix Dev, Int Fix Dev, Intramedullary Int Fix Dev, Ext Fix Dev, Monop, Ext Fix Dev, Ring, Ext Fix Dev, Hybrid], NQ
0PSD0ZZ	Repos Lt Humeral Head, Opn Appr
0PSD[0,3,4][4,5,6,B,C,D]Z	Repos/Humeral Head, Lt, [Opn, Perc, Perc Endo], [Int Fix Dev, Ext Fix Dev, Int Fix Dev, Intramedullary Int Fix Dev, Ext Fix Dev, Monop, Ext Fix Dev, Ring, Ext Fix Dev, Hybrid], NQ
0PSF0ZZ	Repos Rt Humeral Shaft, Opn Appr
0PSF[0,3,4][4,5,6,B,C,D]Z	Repos/Humeral Shaft, Rt, [Opn, Perc, Perc Endo], [Int Fix Dev, Ext Fix Dev, Int Fix Dev, Intramedullary Int Fix Dev, Ext Fix Dev, Monop, Ext Fix Dev, Ring, Ext Fix Dev, Hybrid], NQ
0PSG0ZZ	Repos Lt Humeral Shaft, Opn Appr
0PSG[0,3,4][4,5,6,B,C,D]Z	Repos/Humeral Shaft, Lt, [Opn, Perc, Perc Endo], [Int Fix Dev, Ext Fix Dev, Int Fix Dev, Intramedullary Int Fix Dev, Ext Fix Dev, Monop, Ext Fix Dev, Ring, Ext Fix Dev, Hybrid], NQ
0PT[C,D]0ZZ	Resect of [Rt, Lt] Humeral Head, Opn Appr
0PT[F,G]0ZZ	Resect of [Rt, Lt] Humeral Shaft, Opn Appr
0PUC*	Supl/Humeral Head, Rt
0PUD*	Supl/Humeral Head, Lt
0PUF*	Supl/Humeral Shaft, Rt
0PUG*	Supl/Humeral Shaft, Lt
0Q8G*	Div/Tibia, Rt
0Q8H*	Div/Tibia, Lt
0Q8J*	Div/Fibula, Rt
0Q8K*	Div/Fibula, Lt
0QBG[0,3,4]ZZ	Exc/Tibia, Rt, [Opn, Perc, Perc Endo]
0QBH[0,3,4]ZZ	Exc/Tibia, Lt, [Opn, Perc, Perc Endo]
0QBJ[0,3,4]ZZ	Exc/Fibula, Rt, [Opn, Perc, Perc Endo]
0QBK[0,3,4]ZZ	Exc/Fibula, Lt, [Opn, Perc, Perc Endo]
0QCG*	Extir/Tibia, Rt
0QCH*	Extir/Tibia, Lt
0QCJ*	Extir/Fibula, Rt
0QCK*	Extir/Fibula, Lt
0QHG[0,3,4][4,5,6,B,C,D]Z	Insert/Tibia, Rt, [Opn, Perc, Perc Endo], [Int Fix Dev, Ext Fix Dev, Int Fix Dev, Intramedullary Int Fix Dev, Ext Fix Dev, Monop, Ext Fix Dev, Ring, Ext Fix Dev, Hybrid], NQ
0QHH[0,3,4][4,5,6,B,C,D]Z	Insert/Tibia, Lt, [Opn, Perc, Perc Endo], [Int Fix Dev, Ext Fix Dev, Int Fix Dev, Intramedullary Int Fix Dev, Ext Fix Dev, Monop, Ext Fix Dev, Ring, Ext Fix Dev, Hybrid], NQ
0QHJ[0,3,4][4,5,6,B,C,D]Z	Insert/Fibula, Rt, [Opn, Perc, Perc Endo], [Int Fix Dev, Ext Fix Dev, Int Fix Dev, Intramedullary Int Fix Dev, Ext Fix Dev, Monop, Ext Fix Dev, Ring, Ext Fix Dev, Hybrid], NQ
0QHK[0,3,4][4,5,6,B,C,D]Z	Insert/Fibula, Lt, [Opn, Perc, Perc Endo], [Int Fix Dev, Ext Fix Dev, Int Fix Dev, Intramedullary Int Fix Dev, Ext Fix Dev, Monop, Ext Fix Dev, Ring, Ext Fix Dev, Hybrid], NQ
0QNG*	Rls/Tibia, Rt
0QNH*	Rls/Tibia, Lt
0QNJ*	Rls/Fibula, Rt
0QNK*	Rls/Fibula, Lt
0QQG*	Repair/Tibia, Rt
0QQH*	Repair/Tibia, Lt
0QQJ*	Repair/Fibula, Rt
0QQK*	Repair/Fibula, Lt
0QRG*	Replace/Tibia, Rt
0QRH*	Replace/Tibia, Lt
0QRJ*	Replace/Fibula, Rt
0QRK*	Replace/Fibula, Lt
0QSG0ZZ	Repos Rt Tibia, Opn Appr
0QSG[0,3,4][4,5,6,B,C,D]Z	Repos/Tibia, Rt, [Opn, Perc, Perc Endo], [Int Fix Dev, Ext Fix Dev, Int Fix Dev, Intramedullary Int Fix Dev, Ext Fix Dev, Monop, Ext Fix Dev, Ring, Ext Fix Dev, Hybrid], NQ
0QSH0ZZ	Repos Lt Tibia, Opn Appr
0QSH[0,3,4][4,5,6,B,C,D]Z	Repos/Tibia, Lt, [Opn, Perc, Perc Endo], [Int Fix Dev, Ext Fix Dev, Int Fix Dev, Intramedullary Int Fix Dev, Ext Fix Dev, Monop, Ext Fix Dev, Ring, Ext Fix Dev, Hybrid], NQ
0QSJ0ZZ	Repos Rt Fibula, Opn Appr

0QSJ[0,3,4][4,5,6,B,C,D]Z	Repos/Fibula, Rt, [Opn, Perc, Perc Endo], [Int Fix Dev, Ext Fix Dev, Int Fix Dev, Intramedullary Int Fix Dev, Ext Fix Dev, Monop, Ext Fix Dev, Ring, Ext Fix Dev, Hybrid], NQ
0QSK0ZZ	Repos Lt Fibula, Opn Appr
0QSK[0,3,4][4,5,6,B,C,D]Z	Repos/Fibula, Lt, [Opn, Perc, Perc Endo], [Int Fix Dev, Ext Fix Dev, Int Fix Dev, Intramedullary Int Fix Dev, Ext Fix Dev, Monop, Ext Fix Dev, Ring, Ext Fix Dev, Hybrid], NQ
0QT[G,H,J,K]0ZZ	Resect of [Rt Tibia, Lt Tibia, Rt Fibula, Lt Fibula], Opn Appr
0QUG*	Supl/Tibia, Rt
0QUH*	Supl/Tibia, Lt
0QUJ*	Supl/Fibula, Rt
0QUK*	Supl/Fibula, Lt
0S5F*	Destr/Ankle Jt, Rt
0S5G*	Destr/Ankle Jt, Lt
0S9F0[0,Z]Z	Drain/Ankle Jt, Rt, Opn, [Drain Dev, No Dev], NQ
0S9G0[0,Z]Z	Drain/Ankle Jt, Lt, Opn, [Drain Dev, No Dev], NQ
0SBF[0,3,4]ZZ	Exc/Ankle Jt, Rt, [Opn, Perc, Perc Endo]
0SBG[0,3,4]ZZ	Exc/Ankle Jt, Lt, [Opn, Perc, Perc Endo]
0SCF*	Extir/Ankle Jt, Rt
0SCG*	Extir/Ankle Jt, Lt
0SGF*	Fusion/Ankle Jt, Rt
0SGG*	Fusion/Ankle Jt, Lt
0SHF[0,3,4][4,5]Z	Insert/Ankle Jt, Rt, [Opn, Perc, Perc Endo], [Int Fix Dev, Ext Fix Dev], NQ
0SHG[0,3,4][4,5]Z	Insert/Ankle Jt, Lt, [Opn, Perc, Perc Endo], [Int Fix Dev, Ext Fix Dev], NQ
0SJ[F,G]0ZZ	Inspect of [Rt, Lt] Ankle Jt, Opn Appr
0SNF[0,3,4]ZZ	Rls/Ankle Jt, Rt, [Opn, Perc, Perc Endo]
0SNG[0,3,4]ZZ	Rls/Ankle Jt, Lt, [Opn, Perc, Perc Endo]
0SPF[0,3,4][0,3,4,5,7,K]Z	Rmvl/Ankle Jt, Rt, [Opn, Perc, Perc Endo], [Drain Dev, Inf Dev, Int Fix Dev, Ext Fix Dev, Auto Tissue Sub, Nonauto Tissue Sub], NQ
0SPG[0,3,4][0,3,4,5,7,K]Z	Rmvl/Ankle Jt, Lt, [Opn, Perc, Perc Endo], [Drain Dev, Inf Dev, Int Fix Dev, Ext Fix Dev, Auto Tissue Sub, Nonauto Tissue Sub], NQ
0SQF*	Repair/Ankle Jt, Rt
0SQG*	Repair/Ankle Jt, Lt
0SSF0[4,5,Z]Z	Repos/Ankle Jt, Rt, Opn, [Int Fix Dev, Ext Fix Dev, No Dev], NQ
0SSG0[4,5,Z]Z	Repos/Ankle Jt, Lt, Opn, [Int Fix Dev, Ext Fix Dev, No Dev], NQ
0ST[F,G]0ZZ	Resect of [Rt, Lt] Ankle Jt, Opn Appr
0SWF[0,3,4][0,3,4,5,7,8,K]Z	Rev/Ankle Jt, Rt, [Opn, Perc, Perc Endo], [Drain Dev, Inf Dev, Int Fix Dev, Ext Fix Dev, Auto Tissue Sub, Spacer, Nonauto Tissue Sub], NQ
0SWG[0,3,4][0,3,4,5,7,8,K]Z	Rev/Ankle Jt, Lt, [Opn, Perc, Perc Endo], [Drain Dev, Inf Dev, Int Fix Dev, Ext Fix Dev, Auto Tissue Sub, Spacer, Nonauto Tissue Sub], NQ

DRG 493 **Lower Extremity and Humerus Procedures Except Hip, Foot, Femur with CC**

GMLOS 3.9   AMLOS 4.6   RW 2.0557   [SP]

Select operating room procedures listed under DRG 492

DRG 494 **Lower Extremity and Humerus Procedures Except Hip, Foot, Femur without CC/MCC**

GMLOS 2.7   AMLOS 3.1   RW 1.5796   [SP]

Select operating room procedures listed under DRG 492

DRG 495 **Local Excision and Rmvl Internal Fixation Devices Except Hip and Femur with MCC**

GMLOS 7.3   AMLOS 9.3   RW 3.0151   [SP]

Operating Room Procedures

0M50*	Destr/Head and Neck Bursa & Lgmt
0M51*	Destr/Shldr Bursa & Lgmt, Rt
0M52*	Destr/Shldr Bursa & Lgmt, Lt
0M53*	Destr/Elbow Bursa & Lgmt, Rt
0M54*	Destr/Elbow Bursa & Lgmt, Lt
0M59*	Destr/Upr Extr Bursa & Lgmt, Rt
0M5B*	Destr/Upr Extr Bursa & Lgmt, Lt
0M5C*	Destr/Trunk Bursa & Lgmt, Rt
0M5D*	Destr/Trunk Bursa & Lgmt, Lt
0M5F*	Destr/Thorax Bursa & Lgmt, Rt
0M5G*	Destr/Thorax Bursa & Lgmt, Lt
0M5H*	Destr/Abd Bursa & Lgmt, Rt
0M5J*	Destr/Abd Bursa & Lgmt, Lt
0M5K*	Destr/Perineum Bursa & Lgmt

Surgical   **Medical**   **CC Indicator**   **MCC Indicator**   **Procedure Proxy**   PDxMCC **PDx acts as own MCC**   PDxCC **PDx acts as own CC**

MDC 8: Diseases And Disorders Of The Musculoskeletal System And Connective Tissue—SURGICAL

ØM5N*	Destr/Knee Bursa & Lgmt, Rt
ØM5P*	Destr/Knee Bursa & Lgmt, Lt
ØM5V*	Destr/Lwr Extr Bursa & Lgmt, Rt
ØM5W*	Destr/Lwr Extr Bursa & Lgmt, Lt
ØN5B*	Destr/Nasal Bone
ØN5C*	Destr/Sphenoid Bone, Rt
ØN5D*	Destr/Sphenoid Bone, Lt
ØN5F*	Destr/Ethmoid Bone, Rt
ØN5G*	Destr/Ethmoid Bone, Lt
ØN5H*	Destr/Lacrimal Bone, Rt
ØN5J*	Destr/Lacrimal Bone, Lt
ØN5K*	Destr/Palatine Bone, Rt
ØN5L*	Destr/Palatine Bone, Lt
ØN5M*	Destr/Zygomatic Bone, Rt
ØN5N*	Destr/Zygomatic Bone, Lt
ØN5P*	Destr/Orbit, Rt
ØN5Q*	Destr/Orbit, Lt
ØN5R*	Destr/Maxilla, Rt
ØN5S*	Destr/Maxilla, Lt
ØN5T*	Destr/Mandible, Rt
ØN5V*	Destr/Mandible, Lt
ØN5X*	Destr/Hyoid Bone
ØNPWØØZ	Rmvl of Drain Device from Facial Bone, Opn Appr
ØNPWØ4Z	Rmvl of Int Fix from Facial Bone, Opn Appr
ØNPWØ7Z	Rmvl of Autol Sub from Facial Bone, Opn Appr
ØNPWØKZ	Rmvl of Nonaut Sub from Facial Bone, Opn Appr
ØNPWØMZ	Rmvl of Bone Stim from Facial Bone, Opn Appr
ØNPW3ØZ	Rmvl of Drain Device from Facial Bone, Perc Appr
ØNPW34Z	Rmvl of Int Fix from Facial Bone, Perc Appr
ØNPW37Z	Rmvl of Autol Sub from Facial Bone, Perc Appr
ØNPW3KZ	Rmvl of Nonaut Sub from Facial Bone, Perc Appr
ØNPW3MZ	Rmvl of Bone Stim from Facial Bone, Perc Appr
ØNPW4ØZ	Rmvl of Drain Dev from Facial Bone, Perc Endo Appr
ØNPW44Z	Rmvl of Int Fix from Facial Bone, Perc Endo Appr
ØNPW47Z	Rmvl of Autol Sub from Facial Bone, Perc Endo Appr
ØNPW4KZ	Rmvl of Nonaut Sub from Facial Bone, Perc Endo Appr
ØNPW4MZ	Rmvl of Bone Stim from Facial Bone, Perc Endo Appr
ØNPWX4Z	Rmvl of Int Fix from Facial Bone, Extern Appr
ØP5Ø*	Destr/Sternum
ØP51*	Destr/Rib, Rt
ØP52*	Destr/Rib, Lt
ØP54*	Destr/Thoracic Vertebra
ØP55*	Destr/Scapula, Rt
ØP56*	Destr/Scapula, Lt
ØP57*	Destr/Glenoid Cavity, Rt
ØP58*	Destr/Glenoid Cavity, Lt
ØP59*	Destr/Clavicle, Rt
ØP5B*	Destr/Clavicle, Lt
ØP5C*	Destr/Humeral Head, Rt
ØP5D*	Destr/Humeral Head, Lt
ØP5F*	Destr/Humeral Shaft, Rt
ØP5G*	Destr/Humeral Shaft, Lt
ØP5H*	Destr/Radius, Rt
ØP5J*	Destr/Radius, Lt
ØP5K*	Destr/Ulna, Rt
ØP5L*	Destr/Ulna, Lt
ØP5R*	Destr/Thumb Phalanx, Rt
ØP5S*	Destr/Thumb Phalanx, Lt
ØP5T*	Destr/Finger Phalanx, Rt
ØP5V*	Destr/Finger Phalanx, Lt
ØP9Ø[Ø,3,4][Ø,Z]Z	Drain/Sternum, [Opn, Perc, Perc Endo], [Drain Dev, No Dev], NQ
ØP91[Ø,3,4][Ø,Z]Z	Drain/Rib, Rt, [Opn, Perc, Perc Endo], [Drain Dev, No Dev], NQ
ØP92[Ø,3,4][Ø,Z]Z	Drain/Rib, Lt, [Opn, Perc, Perc Endo], [Drain Dev, No Dev], NQ
ØP93[Ø,3,4][Ø,Z]Z	Drain/Cervical Vertebra, [Opn, Perc, Perc Endo], [Drain Dev, No Dev], NQ
ØP94[Ø,3,4][Ø,Z]Z	Drain/Thoracic Vertebra, [Opn, Perc, Perc Endo], [Drain Dev, No Dev], NQ
ØP95[Ø,3,4][Ø,Z]Z	Drain/Scapula, Rt, [Opn, Perc, Perc Endo], [Drain Dev, No Dev], NQ
ØP96[Ø,3,4][Ø,Z]Z	Drain/Scapula, Lt, [Opn, Perc, Perc Endo], [Drain Dev, No Dev], NQ
ØP97[Ø,3,4][Ø,Z]Z	Drain/Glenoid Cavity, Rt, [Opn, Perc, Perc Endo], [Drain Dev, No Dev], NQ
ØP98[Ø,3,4][Ø,Z]Z	Drain/Glenoid Cavity, Lt, [Opn, Perc, Perc Endo], [Drain Dev, No Dev], NQ
ØP99[Ø,3,4][Ø,Z]Z	Drain/Clavicle, Rt, [Opn, Perc, Perc Endo], [Drain Dev, No Dev], NQ
ØP9B[Ø,3,4][Ø,Z]Z	Drain/Clavicle, Lt, [Opn, Perc, Perc Endo], [Drain Dev, No Dev], NQ

ØP9C[Ø,3,4][Ø,Z]Z	Drain/Humeral Head, Rt, [Opn, Perc, Perc Endo], [Drain Dev, No Dev], NQ
ØP9D[Ø,3,4][Ø,Z]Z	Drain/Humeral Head, Lt, [Opn, Perc, Perc Endo], [Drain Dev, No Dev], NQ
ØP9F[Ø,3,4][Ø,Z]Z	Drain/Humeral Shaft, Rt, [Opn, Perc, Perc Endo], [Drain Dev, No Dev], NQ
ØP9G[Ø,3,4][Ø,Z]Z	Drain/Humeral Shaft, Lt, [Opn, Perc, Perc Endo], [Drain Dev, No Dev], NQ
ØP9H[Ø,3,4][Ø,Z]Z	Drain/Radius, Rt, [Opn, Perc, Perc Endo], [Drain Dev, No Dev], NQ
ØP9J[Ø,3,4][Ø,Z]Z	Drain/Radius, Lt, [Opn, Perc, Perc Endo], [Drain Dev, No Dev], NQ
ØP9K[Ø,3,4][Ø,Z]Z	Drain/Ulna, Rt, [Opn, Perc, Perc Endo], [Drain Dev, No Dev], NQ
ØP9L[Ø,3,4][Ø,Z]Z	Drain/Ulna, Lt, [Opn, Perc, Perc Endo], [Drain Dev, No Dev], NQ
ØP9R[Ø,3,4][Ø,Z]Z	Drain/Thumb Phalanx, Rt, [Opn, Perc, Perc Endo], [Drain Dev, No Dev], NQ
ØP9S[Ø,3,4][Ø,Z]Z	Drain/Thumb Phalanx, Lt, [Opn, Perc, Perc Endo], [Drain Dev, No Dev], NQ
ØP9T[Ø,3,4][Ø,Z]Z	Drain/Finger Phalanx, Rt, [Opn, Perc, Perc Endo], [Drain Dev, No Dev], NQ
ØP9V[Ø,3,4][Ø,Z]Z	Drain/Finger Phalanx, Lt, [Opn, Perc, Perc Endo], [Drain Dev, No Dev], NQ
ØPPØ[Ø,3,4][4,7,J,K]Z	Rmvl/Sternum, [Opn, Perc, Perc Endo], [Int Fix Dev, Auto Tissue Sub, Synth Sub, Nonauto Tissue Sub], NQ
ØPP1[Ø,3,4][4,7,J,K]Z	Rmvl/Rib, Rt, [Opn, Perc, Perc Endo], [Int Fix Dev, Auto Tissue Sub, Synth Sub, Nonauto Tissue Sub], NQ
ØPP2[Ø,3,4][4,7,J,K]Z	Rmvl/Rib, Lt, [Opn, Perc, Perc Endo], [Int Fix Dev, Auto Tissue Sub, Synth Sub, Nonauto Tissue Sub], NQ
ØPP3[Ø,3,4][4,7,J,K]Z	Rmvl/Cervical Vertebra, [Opn, Perc, Perc Endo], [Int Fix Dev, Auto Tissue Sub, Synth Sub, Nonauto Tissue Sub], NQ
ØPP4[Ø,3,4][4,7,J,K]Z	Rmvl/Thoracic Vertebra, [Opn, Perc, Perc Endo], [Int Fix Dev, Auto Tissue Sub, Synth Sub, Nonauto Tissue Sub], NQ
ØPP5[Ø,3,4][4,7,J,K]Z	Rmvl/Scapula, Rt, [Opn, Perc, Perc Endo], [Int Fix Dev, Auto Tissue Sub, Synth Sub, Nonauto Tissue Sub], NQ
ØPP6[Ø,3,4][4,7,J,K]Z	Rmvl/Scapula, Lt, [Opn, Perc, Perc Endo], [Int Fix Dev, Auto Tissue Sub, Synth Sub, Nonauto Tissue Sub], NQ
ØPP7[Ø,3,4][4,7,J,K]Z	Rmvl/Glenoid Cavity, Rt, [Opn, Perc, Perc Endo], [Int Fix Dev, Auto Tissue Sub, Synth Sub, Nonauto Tissue Sub], NQ
ØPP8[Ø,3,4][4,7,J,K]Z	Rmvl/Glenoid Cavity, Lt, [Opn, Perc, Perc Endo], [Int Fix Dev, Auto Tissue Sub, Synth Sub, Nonauto Tissue Sub], NQ
ØPP9[Ø,3,4][4,7,J,K]Z	Rmvl/Clavicle, Rt, [Opn, Perc, Perc Endo], [Int Fix Dev, Auto Tissue Sub, Synth Sub, Nonauto Tissue Sub], NQ
ØPPB[Ø,3,4][4,7,J,K]Z	Rmvl/Clavicle, Lt, [Opn, Perc, Perc Endo], [Int Fix Dev, Auto Tissue Sub, Synth Sub, Nonauto Tissue Sub], NQ
ØPPC[Ø,3,4][4,5,7,J,K]Z	Rmvl/Humeral Head, Rt, [Opn, Perc, Perc Endo], [Int Fix Dev, Ext Fix Dev, Auto Tissue Sub, Synth Sub, Nonauto Tissue Sub], NQ
ØPPD[Ø,3,4][4,5,7,J,K]Z	Rmvl/Humeral Head, Lt, [Opn, Perc, Perc Endo], [Int Fix Dev, Ext Fix Dev, Auto Tissue Sub, Synth Sub, Nonauto Tissue Sub], NQ
ØPPF[Ø,3,4][4,5,7,J,K]Z	Rmvl/Humeral Shaft, Rt, [Opn, Perc, Perc Endo], [Int Fix Dev, Ext Fix Dev, Auto Tissue Sub, Synth Sub, Nonauto Tissue Sub], NQ
ØPPG[Ø,3,4][4,5,7,J,K]Z	Rmvl/Humeral Shaft, Lt, [Opn, Perc, Perc Endo], [Int Fix Dev, Ext Fix Dev, Auto Tissue Sub, Synth Sub, Nonauto Tissue Sub], NQ
ØPPH[Ø,3,4][4,5,7,J,K]Z	Rmvl/Radius, Rt, [Opn, Perc, Perc Endo], [Int Fix Dev, Ext Fix Dev, Auto Tissue Sub, Synth Sub, Nonauto Tissue Sub], NQ
ØPPJ[Ø,3,4][4,5,7,J,K]Z	Rmvl/Radius, Lt, [Opn, Perc, Perc Endo], [Int Fix Dev, Ext Fix Dev, Auto Tissue Sub, Synth Sub, Nonauto Tissue Sub], NQ
ØPPK[Ø,3,4][4,5,7,J,K]Z	Rmvl/Ulna, Rt, [Opn, Perc, Perc Endo], [Int Fix Dev, Ext Fix Dev, Auto Tissue Sub, Synth Sub, Nonauto Tissue Sub], NQ
ØPPL[Ø,3,4][4,5,7,J,K]Z	Rmvl/Ulna, Lt, [Opn, Perc, Perc Endo], [Int Fix Dev, Ext Fix Dev, Auto Tissue Sub, Synth Sub, Nonauto Tissue Sub], NQ
ØPPM[Ø,3,4][4,5,7,J,K]Z	Rmvl/Carpal, Rt, [Opn, Perc, Perc Endo], [Int Fix Dev, Ext Fix Dev, Auto Tissue Sub, Synth Sub, Nonauto Tissue Sub], NQ
ØPPN[Ø,3,4][4,5,7,J,K]Z	Rmvl/Carpal, Lt, [Opn, Perc, Perc Endo], [Int Fix Dev, Ext Fix Dev, Auto Tissue Sub, Synth Sub, Nonauto Tissue Sub], NQ
ØPPP[Ø,3,4][4,5,7,J,K]Z	Rmvl/Metacarpal, Rt, [Opn, Perc, Perc Endo], [Int Fix Dev, Ext Fix Dev, Auto Tissue Sub, Synth Sub, Nonauto Tissue Sub], NQ
ØPPQ[Ø,3,4][4,5,7,J,K]Z	Rmvl/Metacarpal, Lt, [Opn, Perc, Perc Endo], [Int Fix Dev, Ext Fix Dev, Auto Tissue Sub, Synth Sub, Nonauto Tissue Sub], NQ
ØPPR[Ø,3,4][4,5,7,J,K]Z	Rmvl/Thumb Phalanx, Rt, [Opn, Perc, Perc Endo], [Int Fix Dev, Ext Fix Dev, Auto Tissue Sub, Synth Sub, Nonauto Tissue Sub], NQ
ØPPS[Ø,3,4][4,5,7,J,K]Z	Rmvl/Thumb Phalanx, Lt, [Opn, Perc, Perc Endo], [Int Fix Dev, Ext Fix Dev, Auto Tissue Sub, Synth Sub, Nonauto Tissue Sub], NQ

Ⓣ **Transfer DRG**   Ⓢᴾ **Special Payment**   * **Code Range**   **6th and 7th Character of ZZ = No Device, No Qualifier ZX = No Device, Diagnostic**

0PPT[0,3,4][4,5,7,J,K]Z Rmvl/Finger Phalanx, Rt, [Opn, Perc, Perc Endo], [Int Fix Dev, Ext Fix Dev, Auto Tissue Sub, Synth Sub, Nonauto Tissue Sub], NQ

0PPV[0,3,4][4,5,7,J,K]Z Rmvl/Finger Phalanx, Lt, [Opn, Perc, Perc Endo], [Int Fix Dev, Ext Fix Dev, Auto Tissue Sub, Synth Sub, Nonauto Tissue Sub], NQ

0PPY[0,3,4][0,M]Z Rmvl/Upr Bone, [Opn, Perc, Perc Endo], [Drain Dev, Bone Growth Stimulator], NQ

0PW0[0,3,4][4,7,J,K]Z Rev/Sternum, [Opn, Perc, Perc Endo], [Int Fix Dev, Auto Tissue Sub, Synth Sub, Nonauto Tissue Sub], NQ

0PW1[0,3,4][4,7,J,K]Z Rev/Rib, Rt, [Opn, Perc, Perc Endo], [Int Fix Dev, Auto Tissue Sub, Synth Sub, Nonauto Tissue Sub], NQ

0PW2[0,3,4][4,7,J,K]Z Rev/Rib, Lt, [Opn, Perc, Perc Endo], [Int Fix Dev, Auto Tissue Sub, Synth Sub, Nonauto Tissue Sub], NQ

0PW3[0,3,4][4,7,J,K]Z Rev/Cervical Vertebra, [Opn, Perc, Perc Endo], [Int Fix Dev, Auto Tissue Sub, Synth Sub, Nonauto Tissue Sub], NQ

0PW4[0,3,4][4,7,J,K]Z Rev/Thoracic Vertebra, [Opn, Perc, Perc Endo], [Int Fix Dev, Auto Tissue Sub, Synth Sub, Nonauto Tissue Sub], NQ

0PW5[0,3,4][4,7,J,K]Z Rev/Scapula, Rt, [Opn, Perc, Perc Endo], [Int Fix Dev, Auto Tissue Sub, Synth Sub, Nonauto Tissue Sub], NQ

0PW6[0,3,4][4,7,J,K]Z Rev/Scapula, Lt, [Opn, Perc, Perc Endo], [Int Fix Dev, Auto Tissue Sub, Synth Sub, Nonauto Tissue Sub], NQ

0PW7[0,3,4][4,7,J,K]Z Rev/Glenoid Cavity, Rt, [Opn, Perc, Perc Endo], [Int Fix Dev, Auto Tissue Sub, Synth Sub, Nonauto Tissue Sub], NQ

0PW8[0,3,4][4,7,J,K]Z Rev/Glenoid Cavity, Lt, [Opn, Perc, Perc Endo], [Int Fix Dev, Auto Tissue Sub, Synth Sub, Nonauto Tissue Sub], NQ

0PW9[0,3,4][4,7,J,K]Z Rev/Clavicle, Rt, [Opn, Perc, Perc Endo], [Int Fix Dev, Auto Tissue Sub, Synth Sub, Nonauto Tissue Sub], NQ

0PWB[0,3,4][4,7,J,K]Z Rev/Clavicle, Lt, [Opn, Perc, Perc Endo], [Int Fix Dev, Auto Tissue Sub, Synth Sub, Nonauto Tissue Sub], NQ

0PWC[0,3,4][4,5,7,J,K]Z Rev/Humeral Head, Rt, [Opn, Perc, Perc Endo], [Int Fix Dev, Ext Fix Dev, Auto Tissue Sub, Synth Sub, Nonauto Tissue Sub], NQ

0PWD[0,3,4][4,5,7,J,K]Z Rev/Humeral Head, Lt, [Opn, Perc, Perc Endo], [Int Fix Dev, Ext Fix Dev, Auto Tissue Sub, Synth Sub, Nonauto Tissue Sub], NQ

0PWF[0,3,4][4,5,7,J,K]Z Rev/Humeral Shaft, Rt, [Opn, Perc, Perc Endo], [Int Fix Dev, Ext Fix Dev, Auto Tissue Sub, Synth Sub, Nonauto Tissue Sub], NQ

0PWG[0,3,4][4,5,7,J,K]Z Rev/Humeral Shaft, Lt, [Opn, Perc, Perc Endo], [Int Fix Dev, Ext Fix Dev, Auto Tissue Sub, Synth Sub, Nonauto Tissue Sub], NQ

0PWH[0,3,4][4,5,7,J,K]Z Rev/Radius, Rt, [Opn, Perc, Perc Endo], [Int Fix Dev, Ext Fix Dev, Auto Tissue Sub, Synth Sub, Nonauto Tissue Sub], NQ

0PWJ[0,3,4][4,5,7,J,K]Z Rev/Radius, Lt, [Opn, Perc, Perc Endo], [Int Fix Dev, Ext Fix Dev, Auto Tissue Sub, Synth Sub, Nonauto Tissue Sub], NQ

0PWK[0,3,4][4,5,7,J,K]Z Rev/Ulna, Rt, [Opn, Perc, Perc Endo], [Int Fix Dev, Ext Fix Dev, Auto Tissue Sub, Synth Sub, Nonauto Tissue Sub], NQ

0PWL[0,3,4][4,5,7,J,K]Z Rev/Ulna, Lt, [Opn, Perc, Perc Endo], [Int Fix Dev, Ext Fix Dev, Auto Tissue Sub, Synth Sub, Nonauto Tissue Sub], NQ

0PWR[0,3,4][4,5,7,J,K]Z Rev/Thumb Phalanx, Rt, [Opn, Perc, Perc Endo], [Int Fix Dev, Ext Fix Dev, Auto Tissue Sub, Synth Sub, Nonauto Tissue Sub], NQ

0PWS[0,3,4][4,5,7,J,K]Z Rev/Thumb Phalanx, Lt, [Opn, Perc, Perc Endo], [Int Fix Dev, Ext Fix Dev, Auto Tissue Sub, Synth Sub, Nonauto Tissue Sub], NQ

0PWT[0,3,4][4,5,7,J,K]Z Rev/Finger Phalanx, Rt, [Opn, Perc, Perc Endo], [Int Fix Dev, Ext Fix Dev, Auto Tissue Sub, Synth Sub, Nonauto Tissue Sub], NQ

0PWV[0,3,4][4,5,7,J,K]Z Rev/Finger Phalanx, Lt, [Opn, Perc, Perc Endo], [Int Fix Dev, Ext Fix Dev, Auto Tissue Sub, Synth Sub, Nonauto Tissue Sub], NQ

0PWY[0,3,4][0,M]Z Rev/Upr Bone, [Opn, Perc, Perc Endo], [Drain Dev, Bone Growth Stimulator], NQ

0Q50*   Destr/Lumbar Vertebra
0Q51*   Destr/Sacrum
0Q52*   Destr/Pelvic Bone, Rt
0Q53*   Destr/Pelvic Bone, Lt
0Q54*   Destr/Acetabulum, Rt
0Q55*   Destr/Acetabulum, Lt
0Q5D*   Destr/Patella, Rt
0Q5F*   Destr/Patella, Lt
0Q5G*   Destr/Tibia, Rt
0Q5H*   Destr/Tibia, Lt
0Q5J*   Destr/Fibula, Rt
0Q5K*   Destr/Fibula, Lt
0Q5Q*   Destr/Toe Phalanx, Rt
0Q5R*   Destr/Toe Phalanx, Lt
0Q5S*   Destr/Coccyx

0Q90[0,3,4][0,Z]Z Drain/Lumbar Vertebra, [Opn, Perc, Perc Endo], [Drain Dev, No Dev], NQ

0Q91[0,3,4][0,Z]Z Drain/Sacrum, [Opn, Perc, Perc Endo], [Drain Dev, No Dev], NQ

0Q92[0,3,4][0,Z]Z Drain/Pelvic Bone, Rt, [Opn, Perc, Perc Endo], [Drain Dev, No Dev], NQ

0Q93[0,3,4][0,Z]Z Drain/Pelvic Bone, Lt, [Opn, Perc, Perc Endo], [Drain Dev, No Dev], NQ

0Q94[0,3,4][0,Z]Z Drain/Acetab, Rt, [Opn, Perc, Perc Endo], [Drain Dev, No Dev], NQ

0Q95[0,3,4][0,Z]Z Drain/Acetab, Lt, [Opn, Perc, Perc Endo], [Drain Dev, No Dev], NQ

0Q9D[0,3,4][0,Z]Z Drain/Patella, Rt, [Opn, Perc, Perc Endo], [Drain Dev, No Dev], NQ

0Q9F[0,3,4][0,Z]Z Drain/Patella, Lt, [Opn, Perc, Perc Endo], [Drain Dev, No Dev], NQ

0Q9G[0,3,4][0,Z]Z Drain/Tibia, Rt, [Opn, Perc, Perc Endo], [Drain Dev, No Dev], NQ

0Q9H[0,3,4][0,Z]Z Drain/Tibia, Lt, [Opn, Perc, Perc Endo], [Drain Dev, No Dev], NQ

0Q9J[0,3,4][0,Z]Z Drain/Fibula, Rt, [Opn, Perc, Perc Endo], [Drain Dev, No Dev], NQ

0Q9K[0,3,4][0,Z]Z Drain/Fibula, Lt, [Opn, Perc, Perc Endo], [Drain Dev, No Dev], NQ

0Q9Q[0,3,4][0,Z]Z Drain/Toe Phalanx, Rt, [Opn, Perc, Perc Endo], [Drain Dev, No Dev], NQ

0Q9R[0,3,4][0,Z]Z Drain/Toe Phalanx, Lt, [Opn, Perc, Perc Endo], [Drain Dev, No Dev], NQ

0Q9S[0,3,4][0,Z]Z Drain/Coccyx, [Opn, Perc, Perc Endo], [Drain Dev, No Dev], NQ

0QP0[0,3,4][4,7,J,K]Z Rmvl/Lumbar Vertebra, [Opn, Perc, Perc Endo], [Int Fix Dev, Auto Tissue Sub, Synth Sub, Nonauto Tissue Sub], NQ

0QP1[0,3,4][4,7,J,K]Z Rmvl/Sacrum, [Opn, Perc, Perc Endo], [Int Fix Dev, Auto Tissue Sub, Synth Sub, Nonauto Tissue Sub], NQ

0QP2[0,3,4][4,5,7,J,K]Z Rmvl/Pelvic Bone, Rt, [Opn, Perc, Perc Endo], [Int Fix Dev, Ext Fix Dev, Auto Tissue Sub, Synth Sub, Nonauto Tissue Sub], NQ

0QP3[0,3,4][4,5,7,J,K]Z Rmvl/Pelvic Bone, Lt, [Opn, Perc, Perc Endo], [Int Fix Dev, Ext Fix Dev, Auto Tissue Sub, Synth Sub, Nonauto Tissue Sub], NQ

0QP4[0,3,4][4,7,J,K]Z Rmvl/Acetab, Rt, [Opn, Perc, Perc Endo], [Int Fix Dev, Auto Tissue Sub, Synth Sub, Nonauto Tissue Sub], NQ

0QP5[0,3,4][4,7,J,K]Z Rmvl/Acetab, Lt, [Opn, Perc, Perc Endo], [Int Fix Dev, Auto Tissue Sub, Synth Sub, Nonauto Tissue Sub], NQ

0QPD[0,3,4][4,5,7,J,K]Z Rmvl/Patella, Rt, [Opn, Perc, Perc Endo], [Int Fix Dev, Ext Fix Dev, Auto Tissue Sub, Synth Sub, Nonauto Tissue Sub], NQ

0QPF[0,3,4][4,5,7,J,K]Z Rmvl/Patella, Lt, [Opn, Perc, Perc Endo], [Int Fix Dev, Ext Fix Dev, Auto Tissue Sub, Synth Sub, Nonauto Tissue Sub], NQ

0QPG[0,3,4][4,5,7,J,K]Z Rmvl/Tibia, Rt, [Opn, Perc, Perc Endo], [Int Fix Dev, Ext Fix Dev, Auto Tissue Sub, Synth Sub, Nonauto Tissue Sub], NQ

0QPH[0,3,4][4,5,7,J,K]Z Rmvl/Tibia, Lt, [Opn, Perc, Perc Endo], [Int Fix Dev, Ext Fix Dev, Auto Tissue Sub, Synth Sub, Nonauto Tissue Sub], NQ

0QPJ[0,3,4][4,5,7,J,K]Z Rmvl/Fibula, Rt, [Opn, Perc, Perc Endo], [Int Fix Dev, Ext Fix Dev, Auto Tissue Sub, Synth Sub, Nonauto Tissue Sub], NQ

0QPK[0,3,4][4,5,7,J,K]Z Rmvl/Fibula, Lt, [Opn, Perc, Perc Endo], [Int Fix Dev, Ext Fix Dev, Auto Tissue Sub, Synth Sub, Nonauto Tissue Sub], NQ

0QPL[0,3,4][4,5,7,J,K]Z Rmvl/Tarsal, Rt, [Opn, Perc, Perc Endo], [Int Fix Dev, Ext Fix Dev, Auto Tissue Sub, Synth Sub, Nonauto Tissue Sub], NQ

0QPM[0,3,4][4,5,7,J,K]Z Rmvl/Tarsal, Lt, [Opn, Perc, Perc Endo], [Int Fix Dev, Ext Fix Dev, Auto Tissue Sub, Synth Sub, Nonauto Tissue Sub], NQ

0QPN[0,3,4][4,5,7,J,K]Z Rmvl/Metatarsal, Rt, [Opn, Perc, Perc Endo], [Int Fix Dev, Ext Fix Dev, Auto Tissue Sub, Synth Sub, Nonauto Tissue Sub], NQ

0QPP[0,3,4][4,5,7,J,K]Z Rmvl/Metatarsal, Lt, [Opn, Perc, Perc Endo], [Int Fix Dev, Ext Fix Dev, Auto Tissue Sub, Synth Sub, Nonauto Tissue Sub], NQ

0QPQ[0,3,4][4,5,7,J,K]Z Rmvl/Toe Phalanx, Rt, [Opn, Perc, Perc Endo], [Int Fix Dev, Ext Fix Dev, Auto Tissue Sub, Synth Sub, Nonauto Tissue Sub], NQ

0QPR[0,3,4][4,5,7,J,K]Z Rmvl/Toe Phalanx, Lt, [Opn, Perc, Perc Endo], [Int Fix Dev, Ext Fix Dev, Auto Tissue Sub, Synth Sub, Nonauto Tissue Sub], NQ

0QPS[0,3,4][4,7,J,K]Z Rmvl/Coccyx, [Opn, Perc, Perc Endo], [Int Fix Dev, Auto Tissue Sub, Synth Sub, Nonauto Tissue Sub], NQ

0QPY[0,3,4][0,M]Z Rmvl/Lwr Bone, [Opn, Perc, Perc Endo], [Drain Dev, Bone Growth Stimulator], NQ

0QW0[0,3,4][4,7,J,K]Z Rev/Lumbar Vertebra, [Opn, Perc, Perc Endo], [Int Fix Dev, Auto Tissue Sub, Synth Sub, Nonauto Tissue Sub], NQ

0QW1[0,3,4][4,7,J,K]Z Rev/Sacrum, [Opn, Perc, Perc Endo], [Int Fix Dev, Auto Tissue Sub, Synth Sub, Nonauto Tissue Sub], NQ

0QW2[0,3,4][4,5,7,J,K]Z Rev/Pelvic Bone, Rt, [Opn, Perc, Perc Endo], [Int Fix Dev, Ext Fix Dev, Auto Tissue Sub, Synth Sub, Nonauto Tissue Sub], NQ

Surgical   **Medical**   **CC Indicator**   **MCC Indicator**   **Procedure Proxy**   PDxMCC **PDx acts as own MCC**   PDxCC **PDx acts as own CC**

MDC 8: Diseases And Disorders Of The Musculoskeletal System And Connective Tissue—SURGICAL

0QW3[0,3,4][4,5,7,J,K]Z Rev/Pelvic Bone, Lt, [Opn, Perc, Perc Endo], [Int Fix Dev, Ext Fix Dev, Auto Tissue Sub, Synth Sub, Nonauto Tissue Sub], NQ
0QW4[0,3,4][4,7,J,K]Z Rev/Acetab, Rt, [Opn, Perc, Perc Endo], [Int Fix Dev, Auto Tissue Sub, Synth Sub, Nonauto Tissue Sub], NQ
0QW5[0,3,4][4,7,J,K]Z Rev/Acetab, Lt, [Opn, Perc, Perc Endo], [Int Fix Dev, Auto Tissue Sub, Synth Sub, Nonauto Tissue Sub], NQ
0QWD[0,3,4][4,5,7,J,K]Z Rev/Patella, Rt, [Opn, Perc, Perc Endo], [Int Fix Dev, Ext Fix Dev, Auto Tissue Sub, Synth Sub, Nonauto Tissue Sub], NQ
0QWF[0,3,4][4,5,7,J,K]Z Rev/Patella, Lt, [Opn, Perc, Perc Endo], [Int Fix Dev, Ext Fix Dev, Auto Tissue Sub, Synth Sub, Nonauto Tissue Sub], NQ
0QWG[0,3,4][4,5,7,J,K]Z Rev/Tibia, Rt, [Opn, Perc, Perc Endo], [Int Fix Dev, Ext Fix Dev, Auto Tissue Sub, Synth Sub, Nonauto Tissue Sub], NQ
0QWH[0,3,4][4,5,7,J,K]Z Rev/Tibia, Lt, [Opn, Perc, Perc Endo], [Int Fix Dev, Ext Fix Dev, Auto Tissue Sub, Synth Sub, Nonauto Tissue Sub], NQ
0QWJ[0,3,4][4,5,7,J,K]Z Rev/Fibula, Rt, [Opn, Perc, Perc Endo], [Int Fix Dev, Ext Fix Dev, Auto Tissue Sub, Synth Sub, Nonauto Tissue Sub], NQ
0QWK[0,3,4][4,5,7,J,K]Z Rev/Fibula, Lt, [Opn, Perc, Perc Endo], [Int Fix Dev, Ext Fix Dev, Auto Tissue Sub, Synth Sub, Nonauto Tissue Sub], NQ
0QWQ[0,3,4][4,5,7,J,K]Z Rev/Toe Phalanx, Rt, [Opn, Perc, Perc Endo], [Int Fix Dev, Ext Fix Dev, Auto Tissue Sub, Synth Sub, Nonauto Tissue Sub], NQ
0QWR[0,3,4][4,5,7,J,K]Z Rev/Toe Phalanx, Lt, [Opn, Perc, Perc Endo], [Int Fix Dev, Ext Fix Dev, Auto Tissue Sub, Synth Sub, Nonauto Tissue Sub], NQ
0QWS[0,3,4][4,7,J,K]Z Rev/Coccyx, [Opn, Perc, Perc Endo], [Int Fix Dev, Auto Tissue Sub, Synth Sub, Nonauto Tissue Sub], NQ
0QWY[0,3,4][0,M]Z Rev/Lwr Bone, [Opn, Perc, Perc Endo], [Drain Dev, Bone Growth Stimulator], NQ
0R50* Destr/Occipital-cervical Jt
0R51* Destr/Cervical Vert Jt
0R54* Destr/Cervicothoracic Vert Jt
0R56* Destr/Thoracic Vert Jt
0R5A* Destr/Thoracolumbar Vert Jt
0R5C* Destr/Temporomandibular Jt, Rt
0R5D* Destr/Temporomandibular Jt, Lt
0R5E* Destr/Sternoclavicular Jt, Rt
0R5F* Destr/Sternoclavicular Jt, Lt
0R5G* Destr/Acromioclavicular Jt, Rt
0R5H* Destr/Acromioclavicular Jt, Lt
0R5J* Destr/Shldr Jt, Rt
0R5K* Destr/Shldr Jt, Lt
0R5L* Destr/Elbow Jt, Rt
0R5M* Destr/Elbow Jt, Lt
0RBC[0,3,4]ZZ Exc/Temporomandibular Jt, Rt, [Opn, Perc, Perc Endo]
0RBD[0,3,4]ZZ Exc/Temporomandibular Jt, Lt, [Opn, Perc, Perc Endo]
0RP0[0,3,4]JZ Rmvl/Occipital-cervical Jt, [Opn, Perc, Perc Endo], Synth Sub, NQ
0RP1[0,3,4]JZ Rmvl/Cervical Vert Jt, [Opn, Perc, Perc Endo], Synth Sub, NQ
0RP3[0,3,4]JZ Rmvl/Cervical Vert Disc, [Opn, Perc, Perc Endo], Synth Sub, NQ
0RP4[0,3,4]JZ Rmvl/Cervicothoracic Vert Jt, [Opn, Perc, Perc Endo], Synth Sub, NQ
0RP5[0,3,4]JZ Rmvl/Cervicothoracic Vert Disc, [Opn, Perc, Perc Endo], Synth Sub, NQ
0RP6[0,3,4]JZ Rmvl/Thoracic Vert Jt, [Opn, Perc, Perc Endo], Synth Sub, NQ
0RP9[0,3,4]JZ Rmvl/Thoracic Vert Disc, [Opn, Perc, Perc Endo], Synth Sub, NQ
0RPA[0,3,4]JZ Rmvl/Thoracolumbar Vert Jt, [Opn, Perc, Perc Endo], Synth Sub, NQ
0RPB[0,3,4]JZ Rmvl/Thoracolumbar Vert Disc, [Opn, Perc, Perc Endo], Synth Sub, NQ
0RPC00Z Rmvl of Drain Dev from Rt Temporomandib Jt, Opn Appr
0RPC03Z Remove Inf Dev from Rt Temporomandib Jt, Opn
0RPC04Z Rmvl of Int Fix from Rt Temporomandib Jt, Opn Appr
0RPC07Z Rmvl of Autol Sub from Rt Temporomandib Jt, Opn Appr
0RPC0JZ Rmvl of Synth Sub from Rt Temporomandib Jt, Opn Appr
0RPC0KZ Rmvl of Nonaut Sub from Rt Temporomandib Jt, Opn Appr
0RPC30Z Rmvl of Drain Dev from Rt Temporomandib Jt, Perc Appr
0RPC33Z Remove Inf Dev from Rt Temporomandib Jt, Perc
0RPC34Z Rmvl of Int Fix from Rt Temporomandib Jt, Perc Appr
0RPC37Z Rmvl of Autol Sub from Rt Temporomandib Jt, Perc Appr
0RPC3JZ Rmvl of Synth Sub from Rt Temporomandib Jt, Perc Appr
0RPC3KZ Rmvl of Nonaut Sub from Rt Temporomandib Jt, Perc Appr
0RPC40Z Remove Drain Dev from Rt Temporomandib Jt, Perc Endo
0RPC43Z Remove Inf Dev from Rt Temporomandib Jt, Perc Endo
0RPC44Z Remove Int Fix from Rt Temporomandib Jt, Perc Endo
0RPC47Z Remove Autol Sub from Rt Temporomandib Jt, Perc Endo
0RPC4JZ Remove Synth Sub from Rt Temporomandib Jt, Perc Endo
0RPC4KZ Remove Nonaut Sub from Rt Temporomandib Jt, Perc Endo
0RPCX4Z Rmvl of Int Fix from Rt Temporomandib Jt, Extern Appr
0RPD00Z Rmvl of Drain Dev from Lt Temporomandib Jt, Opn Appr

0RPD03Z Remove Inf Dev from Lt Temporomandib Jt, Opn
0RPD04Z Rmvl of Int Fix from Lt Temporomandib Jt, Opn Appr
0RPD07Z Rmvl of Autol Sub from Lt Temporomandib Jt, Opn Appr
0RPD0JZ Rmvl of Synth Sub from Lt Temporomandib Jt, Opn Appr
0RPD0KZ Rmvl of Nonaut Sub from Lt Temporomandib Jt, Opn Appr
0RPD30Z Rmvl of Drain Dev from Lt Temporomandib Jt, Perc Appr
0RPD33Z Remove Inf Dev from Lt Temporomandib Jt, Perc
0RPD34Z Rmvl of Int Fix from Lt Temporomandib Jt, Perc Appr
0RPD37Z Rmvl of Autol Sub from Lt Temporomandib Jt, Perc Appr
0RPD3JZ Rmvl of Synth Sub from Lt Temporomandib Jt, Perc Appr
0RPD3KZ Rmvl of Nonaut Sub from Lt Temporomandib Jt, Perc Appr
0RPD40Z Remove Drain Dev from Lt Temporomandib Jt, Perc Endo
0RPD43Z Remove Inf Dev from Lt Temporomandib Jt, Perc Endo
0RPD44Z Remove Int Fix from Lt Temporomandib Jt, Perc Endo
0RPD47Z Remove Autol Sub from Lt Temporomandib Jt, Perc Endo
0RPD4JZ Remove Synth Sub from Lt Temporomandib Jt, Perc Endo
0RPD4KZ Remove Nonaut Sub from Lt Temporomandib Jt, Perc Endo
0RPDX4Z Rmvl of Int Fix from Lt Temporomandib Jt, Extern Appr
0RPE[0,3,4]JZ Rmvl/Sternoclavicular Jt, Rt, [Opn, Perc, Perc Endo], Synth Sub, NQ
0RPF[0,3,4]JZ Rmvl/Sternoclavicular Jt, Lt, [Opn, Perc, Perc Endo], Synth Sub, NQ
0RPG[0,3,4]JZ Rmvl/Acromioclavicular Jt, Rt, [Opn, Perc, Perc Endo], Synth Sub, NQ
0RPH[0,3,4]JZ Rmvl/Acromioclavicular Jt, Lt, [Opn, Perc, Perc Endo], Synth Sub, NQ
0RPJ[0,3,4]JZ Rmvl/Shldr Jt, Rt, [Opn, Perc, Perc Endo], Synth Sub, NQ
0RPK[0,3,4]JZ Rmvl/Shldr Jt, Lt, [Opn, Perc, Perc Endo], Synth Sub, NQ
0RPL[0,3,4]JZ Rmvl/Elbow Jt, Rt, [Opn, Perc, Perc Endo], Synth Sub, NQ
0RPM[0,3,4]JZ Rmvl/Elbow Jt, Lt, [Opn, Perc, Perc Endo], Synth Sub, NQ
0RPN[0,3,4]JZ Rmvl/Wrist Jt, Rt, [Opn, Perc, Perc Endo], Synth Sub, NQ
0RPP[0,3,4]JZ Rmvl/Wrist Jt, Lt, [Opn, Perc, Perc Endo], Synth Sub, NQ
0RPQ[0,3,4]JZ Rmvl/Carpal Jt, Rt, [Opn, Perc, Perc Endo], Synth Sub, NQ
0RPR[0,3,4]JZ Rmvl/Carpal Jt, Lt, [Opn, Perc, Perc Endo], Synth Sub, NQ
0RPS[0,3,4]JZ Rmvl/Metacarpocarpal Jt, Rt, [Opn, Perc, Perc Endo], Synth Sub, NQ
0RPT[0,3,4]JZ Rmvl/Metacarpocarpal Jt, Lt, [Opn, Perc, Perc Endo], Synth Sub, NQ
0RPU[0,3,4]JZ Rmvl/Metacarpophalangeal Jt, Rt, [Opn, Perc, Perc Endo], Synth Sub, NQ
0RPV[0,3,4]JZ Rmvl/Metacarpophalangeal Jt, Lt, [Opn, Perc, Perc Endo], Synth Sub, NQ
0RPW[0,3,4]JZ Rmvl/Finger Phalangeal Jt, Rt, [Opn, Perc, Perc Endo], Synth Sub, NQ
0RPX[0,3,4]JZ Rmvl/Finger Phalangeal Jt, Lt, [Opn, Perc, Perc Endo], Synth Sub, NQ
0S50* Destr/Lumbar Vert Jt
0S53* Destr/Lumbosacral Jt
0S55* Destr/Sacrococcygeal Jt
0S56* Destr/Coccygeal Jt
0S57* Destr/Sacroiliac Jt, Rt
0S58* Destr/Sacroiliac Jt, Lt
0S5C* Destr/Knee Jt, Rt
0S5D* Destr/Knee Jt, Lt
0SP0[0,3,4]JZ Rmvl/Lumbar Vert Jt, [Opn, Perc, Perc Endo], Synth Sub, NQ
0SP2[0,3,4]JZ Rmvl/Lumbar Vert Disc, [Opn, Perc, Perc Endo], Synth Sub, NQ
0SP3[0,3,4]JZ Rmvl/Lumbosacral Jt, [Opn, Perc, Perc Endo], Synth Sub, NQ
0SP4[0,3,4]JZ Rmvl/Lumbosacral Disc, [Opn, Perc, Perc Endo], Synth Sub, NQ
0SP5[0,3,4]JZ Rmvl/Sacrococcygeal Jt, [Opn, Perc, Perc Endo], Synth Sub, NQ
0SP6[0,3,4]JZ Rmvl/Coccygeal Jt, [Opn, Perc, Perc Endo], Synth Sub, NQ
0SP7[0,3,4]JZ Rmvl/Sacroiliac Jt, Rt, [Opn, Perc, Perc Endo], Synth Sub, NQ
0SP8[0,3,4]JZ Rmvl/Sacroiliac Jt, Lt, [Opn, Perc, Perc Endo], Synth Sub, NQ
0SPF[0,3,4]JZ Rmvl/Ankle Jt, Rt, [Opn, Perc, Perc Endo], Synth Sub, NQ
0SPG[0,3,4]JZ Rmvl/Ankle Jt, Lt, [Opn, Perc, Perc Endo], Synth Sub, NQ
0SPH[0,3,4]JZ Rmvl/Tarsal Jt, Rt, [Opn, Perc, Perc Endo], Synth Sub, NQ
0SPJ[0,3,4]JZ Rmvl/Tarsal Jt, Lt, [Opn, Perc, Perc Endo], Synth Sub, NQ
0SPK[0,3,4]JZ Rmvl/Metatarsal-Tarsal Jt, Rt, [Opn, Perc, Perc Endo], Synth Sub, NQ
0SPL[0,3,4]JZ Rmvl/Metatarsal-Tarsal Jt, Lt, [Opn, Perc, Perc Endo], Synth Sub, NQ
0SPM[0,3,4]JZ Rmvl/Metatarsal-Phalangeal Jt, Rt, [Opn, Perc, Perc Endo], Synth Sub, NQ
0SPN[0,3,4]JZ Rmvl/Metatarsal-Phalangeal Jt, Lt, [Opn, Perc, Perc Endo], Synth Sub, NQ
0SPP[0,3,4]JZ Rmvl/Toe Phalangeal Jt, Rt, [Opn, Perc, Perc Endo], Synth Sub, NQ
0SPQ[0,3,4]JZ Rmvl/Toe Phalangeal Jt, Lt, [Opn, Perc, Perc Endo], Synth Sub, NQ
0WB8[0,3,4,X]ZZ Exc/Chest Wall, [Opn, Perc, Perc Endo, Ext]

T Transfer DRG SP Special Payment * Code Range 6th and 7th Character of ZZ = No Device, No Qualifier ZX = No Device, Diagnostic

DRG 496 **Local Excision and Removal Internal Fixation Devices Except Hip and Femur with CC**
GMLOS 4.0   AMLOS 5.1   RW 1.7451 [SP]

Select operating room procedures listed under DRG 495

DRG 497 **Local Excision and Removal Internal Fixation Devices Except Hip and Femur without CC/MCC**
GMLOS 2.1   AMLOS 2.6   RW 1.2436 [SP]

Select operating room procedures listed under DRG 495

DRG 498 **Local Excision and Removal Internal Fixation Devices of Hip and Femur with CC/MCC**
GMLOS 5.4   AMLOS 7.3   RW 2.2492

Operating Room Procedures

0M5L*	Destr/Hip Bursa & Lgmt, Rt
0M5M*	Destr/Hip Bursa & Lgmt, Lt
0Q56*	Destr/Upr Femur, Rt
0Q57*	Destr/Upr Femur, Lt
0Q58*	Destr/Femor Shaft, Rt
0Q59*	Destr/Femor Shaft, Lt
0Q5B*	Destr/Lwr Femur, Rt
0Q5C*	Destr/Lwr Femur, Lt
0Q96[0,3,4][0,Z]Z	Drain/Upr Femur, Rt, [Opn, Perc, Perc Endo], [Drain Dev, No Dev], NQ
0Q97[0,3,4][0,Z]Z	Drain/Upr Femur, Lt, [Opn, Perc, Perc Endo], [Drain Dev, No Dev], NQ
0Q98[0,3,4][0,Z]Z	Drain/Femor Shaft, Rt, [Opn, Perc, Perc Endo], [Drain Dev, No Dev], NQ
0Q99[0,3,4][0,Z]Z	Drain/Femor Shaft, Lt, [Opn, Perc, Perc Endo], [Drain Dev, No Dev], NQ
0Q9B[0,3,4][0,Z]Z	Drain/Lwr Femur, Rt, [Opn, Perc, Perc Endo], [Drain Dev, No Dev], NQ
0Q9C[0,3,4][0,Z]Z	Drain/Lwr Femur, Lt, [Opn, Perc, Perc Endo], [Drain Dev, No Dev], NQ
0QB6[0,3,4]ZZ	Exc/Upr Femur, Rt, [Opn, Perc, Perc Endo]
0QB7[0,3,4]ZZ	Exc/Upr Femur, Lt, [Opn, Perc, Perc Endo]
0QB8[0,3,4]ZZ	Exc/Femor Shaft, Rt, [Opn, Perc, Perc Endo]
0QB9[0,3,4]ZZ	Exc/Femor Shaft, Lt, [Opn, Perc, Perc Endo]
0QBB[0,3,4]ZZ	Exc/Lwr Femur, Rt, [Opn, Perc, Perc Endo]
0QBC[0,3,4]ZZ	Exc/Lwr Femur, Lt, [Opn, Perc, Perc Endo]
0QP6[0,3,4][4,5,7,J,K]Z	Rmvl/Upr Femur, Rt, [Opn, Perc, Perc Endo], [Int Fix Dev, Ext Fix Dev, Auto Tissue Sub, Synth Sub, Nonauto Tissue Sub], NQ
0QP7[0,3,4][4,5,7,J,K]Z	Rmvl/Upr Femur, Lt, [Opn, Perc, Perc Endo], [Int Fix Dev, Ext Fix Dev, Auto Tissue Sub, Synth Sub, Nonauto Tissue Sub], NQ
0QP8[0,3,4][4,5,7,J,K]Z	Rmvl/Femor Shaft, Rt, [Opn, Perc, Perc Endo], [Int Fix Dev, Ext Fix Dev, Auto Tissue Sub, Synth Sub, Nonauto Tissue Sub], NQ
0QP9[0,3,4][4,5,7,J,K]Z	Rmvl/Femor Shaft, Lt, [Opn, Perc, Perc Endo], [Int Fix Dev, Ext Fix Dev, Auto Tissue Sub, Synth Sub, Nonauto Tissue Sub], NQ
0QPB[0,3,4][4,5,7,J,K]Z	Rmvl/Lwr Femur, Rt, [Opn, Perc, Perc Endo], [Int Fix Dev, Ext Fix Dev, Auto Tissue Sub, Synth Sub, Nonauto Tissue Sub], NQ
0QPC[0,3,4][4,5,7,J,K]Z	Rmvl/Lwr Femur, Lt, [Opn, Perc, Perc Endo], [Int Fix Dev, Ext Fix Dev, Auto Tissue Sub, Synth Sub, Nonauto Tissue Sub], NQ
0QW6[0,3,4][4,5,7,J,K]Z	Rev/Upr Femur, Rt, [Opn, Perc, Perc Endo], [Int Fix Dev, Ext Fix Dev, Auto Tissue Sub, Synth Sub, Nonauto Tissue Sub], NQ
0QW7[0,3,4][4,5,7,J,K]Z	Rev/Upr Femur, Lt, [Opn, Perc, Perc Endo], [Int Fix Dev, Ext Fix Dev, Auto Tissue Sub, Synth Sub, Nonauto Tissue Sub], NQ
0QW8[0,3,4][4,5,7,J,K]Z	Rev/Femor Shaft, Rt, [Opn, Perc, Perc Endo], [Int Fix Dev, Ext Fix Dev, Auto Tissue Sub, Synth Sub, Nonauto Tissue Sub], NQ
0QW9[0,3,4][4,5,7,J,K]Z	Rev/Femor Shaft, Lt, [Opn, Perc, Perc Endo], [Int Fix Dev, Ext Fix Dev, Auto Tissue Sub, Synth Sub, Nonauto Tissue Sub], NQ
0QWB[0,3,4][4,5,7,J,K]Z	Rev/Lwr Femur, Rt, [Opn, Perc, Perc Endo], [Int Fix Dev, Ext Fix Dev, Auto Tissue Sub, Synth Sub, Nonauto Tissue Sub], NQ
0QWC[0,3,4][4,5,7,J,K]Z	Rev/Lwr Femur, Lt, [Opn, Perc, Perc Endo], [Int Fix Dev, Ext Fix Dev, Auto Tissue Sub, Synth Sub, Nonauto Tissue Sub], NQ

0S59*	Destr/Hip Jt, Rt
0S5B*	Destr/Hip Jt, Lt

DRG 499 **Local Excision and Removal Internal Fixation Devices of Hip and Femur without CC/MCC**
GMLOS 2.2   AMLOS 2.7   RW 1.0512

Select operating room procedures listed under DRG 498

DRG 500 **Soft Tissue Procedures with MCC**
GMLOS 7.4   AMLOS 10.1   RW 3.2024 [SP]

Operating Room Procedures

0J80*	Div/SQ Tissue & Fascia, Scalp
0J84*	Div/SQ Tissue & Fascia, Ant Neck
0J85*	Div/SQ Tissue & Fascia, Posterior Neck
0J86*	Div/SQ Tissue & Fascia, Chest
0J87*	Div/SQ Tissue & Fascia, Back
0J88*	Div/SQ Tissue & Fascia, Abd
0J89*	Div/SQ Tissue & Fascia, Buttock
0J8B*	Div/SQ Tissue & Fascia, Perineum
0J8C*	Div/SQ Tissue & Fascia, Pelvic Region
0J8D*	Div/SQ Tissue & Fascia, Rt Upr Arm
0J8F*	Div/SQ Tissue & Fascia, Lt Upr Arm
0J8G*	Div/SQ Tissue & Fascia, Rt Lwr Arm
0J8H*	Div/SQ Tissue & Fascia, Lt Lwr Arm
0J8L*	Div/SQ Tissue & Fascia, Rt Upr Leg
0J8M*	Div/SQ Tissue & Fascia, Lt Upr Leg
0J8N*	Div/SQ Tissue & Fascia, Rt Lwr Leg
0J8P*	Div/SQ Tissue & Fascia, Lt Lwr Leg
0J8Q*	Div/SQ Tissue & Fascia, Rt Foot
0J8R*	Div/SQ Tissue & Fascia, Lt Foot
0J8S*	Div/SQ Tissue & Fascia, Head and Neck
0J8T*	Div/SQ Tissue & Fascia, Trunk
0J8V*	Div/SQ Tissue & Fascia, Upr Extr
0J8W*	Div/SQ Tissue & Fascia, Lwr Extr
0J9[0,4,5]0ZZ	Drain of SQ Tissue & Fascia of [Scalp, Ant Neck, Post Neck], Opn
0J9[6,7,8,9,B,C]0ZZ	Drain of SQ Tissue & Fascia of [Chest, Back, Abd, Buttock, Perineum, Pelvic Rgn], Opn
0J9[D,F,G,H]0ZZ	Drain/SQ Tissue & Fascia, [Rt Upr Arm, Lt Upr Arm, Rt Lwr Arm, Lt Lwr Arm], Opn
0J9[L,M,N,P,Q,R]0ZZ	Drain of SQ Tissue & Fascia of [Rt Upr Leg, Lt Upr Leg, Rt Lwr Leg, Lt Lwr Leg, Rt Foot, Lt Foot], Opn
0JD0*	Extract/SQ Tissue & Fascia, Scalp
0JD1*	Extract/SQ Tissue & Fascia, Face
0JD4*	Extract/SQ Tissue & Fascia, Ant Neck
0JD5*	Extract/SQ Tissue & Fascia, Posterior Neck
0JD6*	Extract/SQ Tissue & Fascia, Chest
0JD7*	Extract/SQ Tissue & Fascia, Back
0JD8*	Extract/SQ Tissue & Fascia, Abd
0JD9*	Extract/SQ Tissue & Fascia, Buttock
0JDB*	Extract/SQ Tissue & Fascia, Perineum
0JDC*	Extract/SQ Tissue & Fascia, Pelvic Region
0JDD*	Extract/SQ Tissue & Fascia, Rt Upr Arm
0JDF*	Extract/SQ Tissue & Fascia, Lt Upr Arm
0JDG*	Extract/SQ Tissue & Fascia, Rt Lwr Arm
0JDH*	Extract/SQ Tissue & Fascia, Lt Lwr Arm
0JDL*	Extract/SQ Tissue & Fascia, Rt Upr Leg
0JDM*	Extract/SQ Tissue & Fascia, Lt Upr Leg
0JDN*	Extract/SQ Tissue & Fascia, Rt Lwr Leg
0JDP*	Extract/SQ Tissue & Fascia, Lt Lwr Leg
0JDQ*	Extract/SQ Tissue & Fascia, Rt Foot
0JDR*	Extract/SQ Tissue & Fascia, Lt Foot
0JN0[0,3]ZZ	Rls/SQ Tissue & Fascia, Scalp, [Opn, Perc]
0JN1[0,3]ZZ	Rls/SQ Tissue & Fascia, Face, [Opn, Perc]
0JN4[0,3]ZZ	Rls/SQ Tissue & Fascia, Ant Neck, [Opn, Perc]
0JN5[0,3]ZZ	Rls/SQ Tissue & Fascia, Post Neck, [Opn, Perc]
0JN6[0,3]ZZ	Rls/SQ Tissue & Fascia, Chest, [Opn, Perc]
0JN7[0,3]ZZ	Rls/SQ Tissue & Fascia, Back, [Opn, Perc]
0JN8[0,3]ZZ	Rls/SQ Tissue & Fascia, Abd, [Opn, Perc]
0JN9[0,3]ZZ	Rls/SQ Tissue & Fascia, Buttock, [Opn, Perc]
0JNB[0,3]ZZ	Rls/SQ Tissue & Fascia, Perineum, [Opn, Perc]
0JNC[0,3]ZZ	Rls/SQ Tissue & Fascia, Genitalia, [Opn, Perc]
0JND[0,3]ZZ	Rls/SQ Tissue & Fascia, Rt Upr Arm, [Opn, Perc]
0JNF[0,3]ZZ	Rls/SQ Tissue & Fascia, Lt Upr Arm, [Opn, Perc]
0JNG[0,3]ZZ	Rls/SQ Tissue & Fascia, Rt Lwr Arm, [Opn, Perc]
0JNH[0,3]ZZ	Rls/SQ Tissue & Fascia, Lt Lwr Arm, [Opn, Perc]
0JNL[0,3]ZZ	Rls/SQ Tissue & Fascia, Rt Upr Leg, [Opn, Perc]

Surgical   **Medical**   **CC Indicator**   **MCC Indicator**   **Procedure Proxy**   [PDxMCC] **PDx acts as own MCC**   [PDxCC] **PDx acts as own CC**

0JNM[0,3]ZZ	Rls/SQ Tissue & Fascia, Lt Upr Leg, [Opn, Perc]
0JNN[0,3]ZZ	Rls/SQ Tissue & Fascia, Rt Lwr Leg, [Opn, Perc]
0JNP[0,3]ZZ	Rls/SQ Tissue & Fascia, Lt Lwr Leg, [Opn, Perc]
0JNQ[0,3]ZZ	Rls/SQ Tissue & Fascia, Rt Foot, [Opn, Perc]
0JNR[0,3]ZZ	Rls/SQ Tissue & Fascia, Lt Foot, [Opn, Perc]
0JQ0*	Repair/SQ Tissue & Fascia, Scalp
0JQ1*	Repair/SQ Tissue & Fascia, Face
0JQ4*	Repair/SQ Tissue & Fascia, Ant Neck
0JQ5*	Repair/SQ Tissue & Fascia, Posterior Neck
0JQ6*	Repair/SQ Tissue & Fascia, Chest
0JQ7*	Repair/SQ Tissue & Fascia, Back
0JQ8*	Repair/SQ Tissue & Fascia, Abd
0JQ9*	Repair/SQ Tissue & Fascia, Buttock
0JQB*	Repair/SQ Tissue & Fascia, Perineum
0JQC*	Repair/SQ Tissue & Fascia, Pelvic Region
0JQD*	Repair/SQ Tissue & Fascia, Rt Upr Arm
0JQF*	Repair/SQ Tissue & Fascia, Lt Upr Arm
0JQG*	Repair/SQ Tissue & Fascia, Rt Lwr Arm
0JQH*	Repair/SQ Tissue & Fascia, Lt Lwr Arm
0JQL*	Repair/SQ Tissue & Fascia, Rt Upr Leg
0JQM*	Repair/SQ Tissue & Fascia, Lt Upr Leg
0JQN*	Repair/SQ Tissue & Fascia, Rt Lwr Leg
0JQP*	Repair/SQ Tissue & Fascia, Lt Lwr Leg
0JQQ*	Repair/SQ Tissue & Fascia, Rt Foot
0JQR*	Repair/SQ Tissue & Fascia, Lt Foot
0JR0*	Replace/SQ Tissue & Fascia, Scalp
0JR1*	Replace/SQ Tissue & Fascia, Face
0JR4*	Replace/SQ Tissue & Fascia, Ant Neck
0JR5*	Replace/SQ Tissue & Fascia, Posterior Neck
0JR6*	Replace/SQ Tissue & Fascia, Chest
0JR7*	Replace/SQ Tissue & Fascia, Back
0JR8*	Replace/SQ Tissue & Fascia, Abd
0JR9*	Replace/SQ Tissue & Fascia, Buttock
0JRB*	Replace/SQ Tissue & Fascia, Perineum
0JRC*	Replace/SQ Tissue & Fascia, Pelvic Region
0JRD*	Replace/SQ Tissue & Fascia, Rt Upr Arm
0JRF*	Replace/SQ Tissue & Fascia, Lt Upr Arm
0JRG*	Replace/SQ Tissue & Fascia, Rt Lwr Arm
0JRH*	Replace/SQ Tissue & Fascia, Lt Lwr Arm
0JRL*	Replace/SQ Tissue & Fascia, Rt Upr Leg
0JRM*	Replace/SQ Tissue & Fascia, Lt Upr Leg
0JRN*	Replace/SQ Tissue & Fascia, Rt Lwr Leg
0JRP*	Replace/SQ Tissue & Fascia, Lt Lwr Leg
0JRQ*	Replace/SQ Tissue & Fascia, Rt Foot
0JRR*	Replace/SQ Tissue & Fascia, Lt Foot
0JU0*	Supl/SQ Tissue & Fascia, Scalp
0JU1*	Supl/SQ Tissue & Fascia, Face
0JU4*	Supl/SQ Tissue & Fascia, Ant Neck
0JU5*	Supl/SQ Tissue & Fascia, Posterior Neck
0JU6*	Supl/SQ Tissue & Fascia, Chest
0JU7*	Supl/SQ Tissue & Fascia, Back
0JU8*	Supl/SQ Tissue & Fascia, Abd
0JU9*	Supl/SQ Tissue & Fascia, Buttock
0JUB*	Supl/SQ Tissue & Fascia, Perineum
0JUC*	Supl/SQ Tissue & Fascia, Pelvic Region
0JUD*	Supl/SQ Tissue & Fascia, Rt Upr Arm
0JUF*	Supl/SQ Tissue & Fascia, Lt Upr Arm
0JUG*	Supl/SQ Tissue & Fascia, Rt Lwr Arm
0JUH*	Supl/SQ Tissue & Fascia, Lt Lwr Arm
0JUL*	Supl/SQ Tissue & Fascia, Rt Upr Leg
0JUM*	Supl/SQ Tissue & Fascia, Lt Upr Leg
0JUN*	Supl/SQ Tissue & Fascia, Rt Lwr Leg
0JUP*	Supl/SQ Tissue & Fascia, Lt Lwr Leg
0JUQ*	Supl/SQ Tissue & Fascia, Rt Foot
0JUR*	Supl/SQ Tissue & Fascia, Lt Foot
0JX0[0,3]ZZ	Transfer/SQ Tissue & Fascia, Scalp, [Opn, Perc]
0JX1[0,3]ZZ	Transfer/SQ Tissue & Fascia, Face, [Opn, Perc]
0JX4[0,3]ZZ	Transfer/SQ Tissue & Fascia, Ant Neck, [Opn, Perc]
0JX5[0,3]ZZ	Transfer/SQ Tissue & Fascia, Post Neck, [Opn, Perc]
0JX6[0,3]ZZ	Transfer/SQ Tissue & Fascia, Chest, [Opn, Perc]
0JX7[0,3]ZZ	Transfer/SQ Tissue & Fascia, Back, [Opn, Perc]
0JX8[0,3]ZZ	Transfer/SQ Tissue & Fascia, Abd, [Opn, Perc]
0JX9[0,3]ZZ	Transfer/SQ Tissue & Fascia, Buttock, [Opn, Perc]
0JXB[0,3]ZZ	Transfer/SQ Tissue & Fascia, Perineum, [Opn, Perc]
0JXC[0,3]ZZ	Transfer/SQ Tissue & Fascia, Genitalia, [Opn, Perc]
0JXD[0,3]ZZ	Transfer/SQ Tissue & Fascia, Rt Upr Arm, [Opn, Perc]
0JXF[0,3]ZZ	Transfer/SQ Tissue & Fascia, Lt Upr Arm, [Opn, Perc]
0JXG[0,3]ZZ	Transfer/SQ Tissue & Fascia, Rt Lwr Arm, [Opn, Perc]
0JXH[0,3]ZZ	Transfer/SQ Tissue & Fascia, Lt Lwr Arm, [Opn, Perc]
0JXJ[0,3]ZZ	Transfer/SQ Tissue & Fascia, Rt Hand, [Opn, Perc]

0JXK[0,3]ZZ	Transfer/SQ Tissue & Fascia, Lt Hand, [Opn, Perc]
0JXL[0,3]ZZ	Transfer/SQ Tissue & Fascia, Rt Upr Leg, [Opn, Perc]
0JXM[0,3]ZZ	Transfer/SQ Tissue & Fascia, Lt Upr Leg, [Opn, Perc]
0JXN[0,3]ZZ	Transfer/SQ Tissue & Fascia, Rt Lwr Leg, [Opn, Perc]
0JXP[0,3]ZZ	Transfer/SQ Tissue & Fascia, Lt Lwr Leg, [Opn, Perc]
0JXQ[0,3]ZZ	Transfer/SQ Tissue & Fascia, Rt Foot, [Opn, Perc]
0JXR[0,3]ZZ	Transfer/SQ Tissue & Fascia, Lt Foot, [Opn, Perc]
0K50*	Destr/Head Muscle
0K51*	Destr/Facial Muscle
0K52*	Destr/Neck Muscle, Rt
0K53*	Destr/Neck Muscle, Lt
0K54*	Destr/Tongue, Palate, Pharynx Muscle
0K55*	Destr/Shldr Muscle, Rt
0K56*	Destr/Shldr Muscle, Lt
0K57*	Destr/Upr Arm Muscle, Rt
0K58*	Destr/Upr Arm Muscle, Lt
0K59*	Destr/Lwr Arm and Wrist Muscle, Rt
0K5B*	Destr/Lwr Arm and Wrist Muscle, Lt
0K5F*	Destr/Trunk Muscle, Rt
0K5G*	Destr/Trunk Muscle, Lt
0K5H*	Destr/Thorax Muscle, Rt
0K5J*	Destr/Thorax Muscle, Lt
0K5K*	Destr/Abd Muscle, Rt
0K5L*	Destr/Abd Muscle, Lt
0K5M*	Destr/Perineum Muscle
0K5N*	Destr/Hip Muscle, Rt
0K5P*	Destr/Hip Muscle, Lt
0K5Q*	Destr/Upr Leg Muscle, Rt
0K5R*	Destr/Upr Leg Muscle, Lt
0K5S*	Destr/Lwr Leg Muscle, Rt
0K5T*	Destr/Lwr Leg Muscle, Lt
0K5V*	Destr/Foot Muscle, Rt
0K5W*	Destr/Foot Muscle, Lt
0K80*	Div/Head Muscle
0K81*	Div/Facial Muscle
0K82*	Div/Neck Muscle, Rt
0K83*	Div/Neck Muscle, Lt
0K85*	Div/Shldr Muscle, Rt
0K86*	Div/Shldr Muscle, Lt
0K87*	Div/Upr Arm Muscle, Rt
0K88*	Div/Upr Arm Muscle, Lt
0K89*	Div/Lwr Arm and Wrist Muscle, Rt
0K8B*	Div/Lwr Arm and Wrist Muscle, Lt
0K8F*	Div/Trunk Muscle, Rt
0K8G*	Div/Trunk Muscle, Lt
0K8H*	Div/Thorax Muscle, Rt
0K8J*	Div/Thorax Muscle, Lt
0K8K*	Div/Abd Muscle, Rt
0K8L*	Div/Abd Muscle, Lt
0K8M*	Div/Perineum Muscle
0K8N*	Div/Hip Muscle, Rt
0K8P*	Div/Hip Muscle, Lt
0K8Q*	Div/Upr Leg Muscle, Rt
0K8R*	Div/Upr Leg Muscle, Lt
0K8S*	Div/Lwr Leg Muscle, Rt
0K8T*	Div/Lwr Leg Muscle, Lt
0K8V*	Div/Foot Muscle, Rt
0K8W*	Div/Foot Muscle, Lt
0K90[0,3,4]0Z	Drain/Head Muscle, [Opn, Perc, Perc Endo], Drain Dev, NQ
0K90[0,3,4]ZX	Drain/Head Muscle, [Opn, Perc, Perc Endo]
0K90[0,4]ZZ	Drain/Head Muscle, [Opn, Perc Endo]
0K91[0,3,4]0Z	Drain/Facial Muscle, [Opn, Perc, Perc Endo], Drain Dev, NQ
0K91[0,3,4]ZX	Drain/Facial Muscle, [Opn, Perc, Perc Endo]
0K91[0,4]ZZ	Drain/Facial Muscle, [Opn, Perc Endo]
0K92[0,3,4]0Z	Drain/Neck Muscle, Rt, [Opn, Perc, Perc Endo], Drain Dev, NQ
0K92[0,3,4]ZX	Drain/Neck Muscle, Rt, [Opn, Perc, Perc Endo]
0K92[0,4]ZZ	Drain/Neck Muscle, Rt, [Opn, Perc Endo]
0K93[0,3,4]0Z	Drain/Neck Muscle, Lt, [Opn, Perc, Perc Endo], Drain Dev, NQ
0K93[0,3,4]ZX	Drain/Neck Muscle, Lt, [Opn, Perc, Perc Endo]
0K93[0,4]ZZ	Drain/Neck Muscle, Lt, [Opn, Perc Endo]
0K94[0,3,4]0Z	Drain/Tongue, Palate, Pharynx Muscle, [Opn, Perc, Perc Endo], Drain Dev, NQ
0K94[0,3,4]ZX	Drain/Tongue, Palate, Pharynx Muscle, [Opn, Perc, Perc Endo]
0K94[0,4]ZZ	Drain/Tongue, Palate, Pharynx Muscle, [Opn, Perc Endo]
0K95[0,3,4]0Z	Drain/Shldr Muscle, Rt, [Opn, Perc, Perc Endo], Drain Dev, NQ
0K95[0,3,4]ZX	Drain/Shldr Muscle, Rt, [Opn, Perc, Perc Endo]
0K95[0,4]ZZ	Drain/Shldr Muscle, Rt, [Opn, Perc Endo]
0K96[0,3,4]0Z	Drain/Shldr Muscle, Lt, [Opn, Perc, Perc Endo], Drain Dev, NQ
0K96[0,3,4]ZX	Drain/Shldr Muscle, Lt, [Opn, Perc, Perc Endo]
0K96[0,4]ZZ	Drain/Shldr Muscle, Lt, [Opn, Perc Endo]

Ⓣ **Transfer DRG**　　ⓈⓅ **Special Payment**　　***Code Range**　　**6th and 7th Character of ZZ = No Device, No Qualifier ZX = No Device, Diagnostic**

Code	Description
ØK97[Ø,3,4]ØZ	Drain/Upr Arm Muscle, Rt, [Opn, Perc, Perc Endo], Drain Dev, NQ
ØK97[Ø,3,4]ZX	Drain/Upr Arm Muscle, Rt, [Opn, Perc, Perc Endo]
ØK97[Ø,4]ZZ	Drain/Upr Arm Muscle, Rt, [Opn, Perc Endo]
ØK98[Ø,3,4]ØZ	Drain/Upr Arm Muscle, Lt, [Opn, Perc, Perc Endo], Drain Dev, NQ
ØK98[Ø,3,4]ZX	Drain/Upr Arm Muscle, Lt, [Opn, Perc, Perc Endo]
ØK98[Ø,4]ZZ	Drain/Upr Arm Muscle, Lt, [Opn, Perc Endo]
ØK99[Ø,3,4]ØZ	Drain/Lwr Arm and Wrist Muscle, Rt, [Opn, Perc, Perc Endo], Drain Dev, NQ
ØK99[Ø,3,4]ZX	Drain/Lwr Arm and Wrist Muscle, Rt, [Opn, Perc, Perc Endo]
ØK99[Ø,4]ZZ	Drain/Lwr Arm and Wrist Muscle, Rt, [Opn, Perc Endo]
ØK9B[Ø,3,4]ØZ	Drain/Lwr Arm and Wrist Muscle, Lt, [Opn, Perc, Perc Endo], Drain Dev, NQ
ØK9B[Ø,3,4]ZX	Drain/Lwr Arm and Wrist Muscle, Lt, [Opn, Perc, Perc Endo]
ØK9B[Ø,4]ZZ	Drain/Lwr Arm and Wrist Muscle, Lt, [Opn, Perc Endo]
ØK9C[Ø,3,4]ZX	Drain/Hand Muscle, Rt, [Opn, Perc, Perc Endo]
ØK9D[Ø,3,4]ZX	Drain/Hand Muscle, Lt, [Opn, Perc, Perc Endo]
ØK9F[Ø,3,4]ØZ	Drain/Trunk Muscle, Rt, [Opn, Perc, Perc Endo], Drain Dev, NQ
ØK9F[Ø,3,4]ZX	Drain/Trunk Muscle, Rt, [Opn, Perc, Perc Endo]
ØK9F[Ø,4]ZZ	Drain/Trunk Muscle, Rt, [Opn, Perc Endo]
ØK9G[Ø,3,4]ØZ	Drain/Trunk Muscle, Lt, [Opn, Perc, Perc Endo], Drain Dev, NQ
ØK9G[Ø,3,4]ZX	Drain/Trunk Muscle, Lt, [Opn, Perc, Perc Endo]
ØK9G[Ø,4]ZZ	Drain/Trunk Muscle, Lt, [Opn, Perc Endo]
ØK9H[Ø,3,4]ØZ	Drain/Thorax Muscle, Rt, [Opn, Perc, Perc Endo], Drain Dev, NQ
ØK9H[Ø,3,4]ZX	Drain/Thorax Muscle, Rt, [Opn, Perc, Perc Endo]
ØK9H[Ø,4]ZZ	Drain/Thorax Muscle, Rt, [Opn, Perc Endo]
ØK9J[Ø,3,4]ØZ	Drain/Thorax Muscle, Lt, [Opn, Perc, Perc Endo], Drain Dev, NQ
ØK9J[Ø,3,4]ZX	Drain/Thorax Muscle, Lt, [Opn, Perc, Perc Endo]
ØK9J[Ø,4]ZZ	Drain/Thorax Muscle, Lt, [Opn, Perc Endo]
ØK9K[Ø,3,4]ØZ	Drain/Abd Muscle, Rt, [Opn, Perc, Perc Endo], Drain Dev, NQ
ØK9K[Ø,3,4]ZX	Drain/Abd Muscle, Rt, [Opn, Perc, Perc Endo]
ØK9K[Ø,4]ZZ	Drain/Abd Muscle, Rt, [Opn, Perc Endo]
ØK9L[Ø,3,4]ØZ	Drain/Abd Muscle, Lt, [Opn, Perc, Perc Endo], Drain Dev, NQ
ØK9L[Ø,3,4]ZX	Drain/Abd Muscle, Lt, [Opn, Perc, Perc Endo]
ØK9L[Ø,4]ZZ	Drain/Abd Muscle, Lt, [Opn, Perc Endo]
ØK9M[Ø,3,4]ØZ	Drain/Perineum Muscle, [Opn, Perc, Perc Endo], Drain Dev, NQ
ØK9M[Ø,3,4]ZX	Drain/Perineum Muscle, [Opn, Perc, Perc Endo]
ØK9M[Ø,4]ZZ	Drain/Perineum Muscle, [Opn, Perc Endo]
ØK9N[Ø,3,4]ØZ	Drain/Hip Muscle, Rt, [Opn, Perc, Perc Endo], Drain Dev, NQ
ØK9N[Ø,3,4]ZX	Drain/Hip Muscle, Rt, [Opn, Perc, Perc Endo]
ØK9N[Ø,4]ZZ	Drain/Hip Muscle, Rt, [Opn, Perc Endo]
ØK9P[Ø,3,4]ØZ	Drain/Hip Muscle, Lt, [Opn, Perc, Perc Endo], Drain Dev, NQ
ØK9P[Ø,3,4]ZX	Drain/Hip Muscle, Lt, [Opn, Perc, Perc Endo]
ØK9P[Ø,4]ZZ	Drain/Hip Muscle, Lt, [Opn, Perc Endo]
ØK9Q[Ø,3,4]ØZ	Drain/Upr Leg Muscle, Rt, [Opn, Perc, Perc Endo], Drain Dev, NQ
ØK9Q[Ø,3,4]ZX	Drain/Upr Leg Muscle, Rt, [Opn, Perc, Perc Endo]
ØK9Q[Ø,4]ZZ	Drain/Upr Leg Muscle, Rt, [Opn, Perc Endo]
ØK9R[Ø,3,4]ØZ	Drain/Upr Leg Muscle, Lt, [Opn, Perc, Perc Endo], Drain Dev, NQ
ØK9R[Ø,3,4]ZX	Drain/Upr Leg Muscle, Lt, [Opn, Perc, Perc Endo]
ØK9R[Ø,4]ZZ	Drain/Upr Leg Muscle, Lt, [Opn, Perc Endo]
ØK9S[Ø,3,4]ØZ	Drain/Lwr Leg Muscle, Rt, [Opn, Perc, Perc Endo], Drain Dev, NQ
ØK9S[Ø,3,4]ZX	Drain/Lwr Leg Muscle, Rt, [Opn, Perc, Perc Endo]
ØK9S[Ø,4]ZZ	Drain/Lwr Leg Muscle, Rt, [Opn, Perc Endo]
ØK9T[Ø,3,4]ØZ	Drain/Lwr Leg Muscle, Lt, [Opn, Perc, Perc Endo], Drain Dev, NQ
ØK9T[Ø,3,4]ZX	Drain/Lwr Leg Muscle, Lt, [Opn, Perc, Perc Endo]
ØK9T[Ø,4]ZZ	Drain/Lwr Leg Muscle, Lt, [Opn, Perc Endo]
ØK9V[Ø,3,4]ØZ	Drain/Foot Muscle, Rt, [Opn, Perc, Perc Endo], Drain Dev, NQ
ØK9V[Ø,3,4]ZX	Drain/Foot Muscle, Rt, [Opn, Perc, Perc Endo]
ØK9V[Ø,4]ZZ	Drain/Foot Muscle, Rt, [Opn, Perc Endo]
ØK9W[Ø,3,4]ØZ	Drain/Foot Muscle, Lt, [Opn, Perc, Perc Endo], Drain Dev, NQ
ØK9W[Ø,3,4]ZX	Drain/Foot Muscle, Lt, [Opn, Perc, Perc Endo]
ØK9W[Ø,4]ZZ	Drain/Foot Muscle, Lt, [Opn, Perc Endo]
ØKBØ*	Exc/Head Muscle
ØKB1*	Exc/Facial Muscle
ØKB2*	Exc/Neck Muscle, Rt
ØKB3*	Exc/Neck Muscle, Lt
ØKB4*	Exc/Tongue, Palate, Pharynx Muscle
ØKB5*	Exc/Shldr Muscle, Rt
ØKB6*	Exc/Shldr Muscle, Lt
ØKB7*	Exc/Upr Arm Muscle, Rt
ØKB8*	Exc/Upr Arm Muscle, Lt
ØKB9*	Exc/Lwr Arm and Wrist Muscle, Rt
ØKBB*	Exc/Lwr Arm and Wrist Muscle, Lt
ØKBC[Ø,3,4]ZX	Exc/Hand Muscle, Rt, [Opn, Perc, Perc Endo]
ØKBD[Ø,3,4]ZX	Exc/Hand Muscle, Lt, [Opn, Perc, Perc Endo]
ØKBF*	Exc/Trunk Muscle, Rt
ØKBG*	Exc/Trunk Muscle, Lt
ØKBH*	Exc/Thorax Muscle, Rt
ØKBJ*	Exc/Thorax Muscle, Lt
ØKBK*	Exc/Abd Muscle, Rt
ØKBL*	Exc/Abd Muscle, Lt
ØKBM*	Exc/Perineum Muscle
ØKBN*	Exc/Hip Muscle, Rt
ØKBP*	Exc/Hip Muscle, Lt
ØKBQ*	Exc/Upr Leg Muscle, Rt
ØKBR*	Exc/Upr Leg Muscle, Lt
ØKBS*	Exc/Lwr Leg Muscle, Rt
ØKBT*	Exc/Lwr Leg Muscle, Lt
ØKBV*	Exc/Foot Muscle, Rt
ØKBW*	Exc/Foot Muscle, Lt
ØKCØ*	Extir/Head Muscle
ØKC1*	Extir/Facial Muscle
ØKC2*	Extir/Neck Muscle, Rt
ØKC3*	Extir/Neck Muscle, Lt
ØKC4*	Extir/Tongue, Palate, Pharynx Muscle
ØKC5*	Extir/Shldr Muscle, Rt
ØKC6*	Extir/Shldr Muscle, Lt
ØKC7*	Extir/Upr Arm Muscle, Rt
ØKC8*	Extir/Upr Arm Muscle, Lt
ØKC9*	Extir/Lwr Arm and Wrist Muscle, Rt
ØKCB*	Extir/Lwr Arm and Wrist Muscle, Lt
ØKCF*	Extir/Trunk Muscle, Rt
ØKCG*	Extir/Trunk Muscle, Lt
ØKCH*	Extir/Thorax Muscle, Rt
ØKCJ*	Extir/Thorax Muscle, Lt
ØKCK*	Extir/Abd Muscle, Rt
ØKCL*	Extir/Abd Muscle, Lt
ØKCM*	Extir/Perineum Muscle
ØKCN*	Extir/Hip Muscle, Rt
ØKCP*	Extir/Hip Muscle, Lt
ØKCQ*	Extir/Upr Leg Muscle, Rt
ØKCR*	Extir/Upr Leg Muscle, Lt
ØKCS*	Extir/Lwr Leg Muscle, Rt
ØKCT*	Extir/Lwr Leg Muscle, Lt
ØKCV*	Extir/Foot Muscle, Rt
ØKCW*	Extir/Foot Muscle, Lt
ØKH*	Muscles, Insert
ØKJX[Ø,3,4]ZZ	Inspect/Upr Muscle, [Opn, Perc, Perc Endo]
ØKJY[Ø,3,4]ZZ	Inspect/Lwr Muscle, [Opn, Perc, Perc Endo]
ØKMØ*	Reattach/Head Muscle
ØKM1*	Reattach/Facial Muscle
ØKM2*	Reattach/Neck Muscle, Rt
ØKM3*	Reattach/Neck Muscle, Lt
ØKM4*	Reattach/Tongue, Palate, Pharynx Muscle
ØKM5*	Reattach/Shldr Muscle, Rt
ØKM6*	Reattach/Shldr Muscle, Lt
ØKM7*	Reattach/Upr Arm Muscle, Rt
ØKM8*	Reattach/Upr Arm Muscle, Lt
ØKM9*	Reattach/Lwr Arm and Wrist Muscle, Rt
ØKMB*	Reattach/Lwr Arm and Wrist Muscle, Lt
ØKMF*	Reattach/Trunk Muscle, Rt
ØKMG*	Reattach/Trunk Muscle, Lt
ØKMH*	Reattach/Thorax Muscle, Rt
ØKMJ*	Reattach/Thorax Muscle, Lt
ØKMK*	Reattach/Abd Muscle, Rt
ØKML*	Reattach/Abd Muscle, Lt
ØKMM*	Reattach/Perineum Muscle
ØKMN*	Reattach/Hip Muscle, Rt
ØKMP*	Reattach/Hip Muscle, Lt
ØKMQ*	Reattach/Upr Leg Muscle, Rt
ØKMR*	Reattach/Upr Leg Muscle, Lt
ØKMS*	Reattach/Lwr Leg Muscle, Rt
ØKMT*	Reattach/Lwr Leg Muscle, Lt
ØKMV*	Reattach/Foot Muscle, Rt
ØKMW*	Reattach/Foot Muscle, Lt
ØKNØ[Ø,3,4]ZZ	Rls/Head Muscle, [Opn, Perc, Perc Endo]
ØKN1[Ø,3,4]ZZ	Rls/Facial Muscle, [Opn, Perc, Perc Endo]
ØKN2[Ø,3,4]ZZ	Rls/Neck Muscle, Rt, [Opn, Perc, Perc Endo]
ØKN3[Ø,3,4]ZZ	Rls/Neck Muscle, Lt, [Opn, Perc, Perc Endo]
ØKN4[Ø,3,4]ZZ	Rls/Tongue, Palate, Pharynx Muscle, [Opn, Perc, Perc Endo]
ØKN5[Ø,3,4]ZZ	Rls/Shldr Muscle, Rt, [Opn, Perc, Perc Endo]
ØKN6[Ø,3,4]ZZ	Rls/Shldr Muscle, Lt, [Opn, Perc, Perc Endo]
ØKN7[Ø,3,4]ZZ	Rls/Upr Arm Muscle, Rt, [Opn, Perc, Perc Endo]
ØKN8[Ø,3,4]ZZ	Rls/Upr Arm Muscle, Lt, [Opn, Perc, Perc Endo]
ØKN9[Ø,3,4]ZZ	Rls/Lwr Arm and Wrist Muscle, Rt, [Opn, Perc, Perc Endo]

Surgical   **Medical**   **CC Indicator**   **MCC Indicator**   **Procedure Proxy**   **PDxMCC** **PDx acts as own MCC**   **PDxCC** **PDx acts as own CC**

0KNB[0,3,4]ZZ	Rls/Lwr Arm and Wrist Muscle, Lt, [Opn, Perc, Perc Endo]
0KNF[0,3,4]ZZ	Rls/Trunk Muscle, Rt, [Opn, Perc, Perc Endo]
0KNG[0,3,4]ZZ	Rls/Trunk Muscle, Lt, [Opn, Perc, Perc Endo]
0KNH[0,3,4]ZZ	Rls/Thorax Muscle, Rt, [Opn, Perc, Perc Endo]
0KNJ[0,3,4]ZZ	Rls/Thorax Muscle, Lt, [Opn, Perc, Perc Endo]
0KNK[0,3,4]ZZ	Rls/Abd Muscle, Rt, [Opn, Perc, Perc Endo]
0KNL[0,3,4]ZZ	Rls/Abd Muscle, Lt, [Opn, Perc, Perc Endo]
0KNM[0,3,4]ZZ	Rls/Perineum Muscle, [Opn, Perc, Perc Endo]
0KNN[0,3,4]ZZ	Rls/Hip Muscle, Rt, [Opn, Perc, Perc Endo]
0KNP[0,3,4]ZZ	Rls/Hip Muscle, Lt, [Opn, Perc, Perc Endo]
0KNQ[0,3,4]ZZ	Rls/Upr Leg Muscle, Rt, [Opn, Perc, Perc Endo]
0KNR[0,3,4]ZZ	Rls/Upr Leg Muscle, Lt, [Opn, Perc, Perc Endo]
0KNS[0,3,4]ZZ	Rls/Lwr Leg Muscle, Rt, [Opn, Perc, Perc Endo]
0KNT[0,3,4]ZZ	Rls/Lwr Leg Muscle, Lt, [Opn, Perc, Perc Endo]
0KNV[0,3,4]ZZ	Rls/Foot Muscle, Rt, [Opn, Perc, Perc Endo]
0KNW[0,3,4]ZZ	Rls/Foot Muscle, Lt, [Opn, Perc, Perc Endo]
0KPX[0,3,4][0,7,J,K,M]Z	Rmvl/Upr Muscle, [Opn, Perc, Perc Endo], [Drain Dev, Auto Tissue Sub, Synth Sub, Nonauto Tissue Sub, Stimulator Lead], NQ
0KPY[0,3,4][0,7,J,K,M]Z	Rmvl/Lwr Muscle, [Opn, Perc, Perc Endo], [Drain Dev, Auto Tissue Sub, Synth Sub, Nonauto Tissue Sub, Stimulator Lead], NQ
0KQ0*	Repair/Head Muscle
0KQ1*	Repair/Facial Muscle
0KQ2*	Repair/Neck Muscle, Rt
0KQ3*	Repair/Neck Muscle, Lt
0KQ4*	Repair/Tongue, Palate, Pharynx Muscle
0KQ5*	Repair/Shldr Muscle, Rt
0KQ6*	Repair/Shldr Muscle, Lt
0KQ7*	Repair/Upr Arm Muscle, Rt
0KQ8*	Repair/Upr Arm Muscle, Lt
0KQ9*	Repair/Lwr Arm and Wrist Muscle, Rt
0KQB*	Repair/Lwr Arm and Wrist Muscle, Lt
0KQF*	Repair/Trunk Muscle, Rt
0KQG*	Repair/Trunk Muscle, Lt
0KQH*	Repair/Thorax Muscle, Rt
0KQJ*	Repair/Thorax Muscle, Lt
0KQK*	Repair/Abd Muscle, Rt
0KQL*	Repair/Abd Muscle, Lt
0KQM*	Repair/Perineum Muscle
0KQN*	Repair/Hip Muscle, Rt
0KQP*	Repair/Hip Muscle, Lt
0KQQ*	Repair/Upr Leg Muscle, Rt
0KQR*	Repair/Upr Leg Muscle, Lt
0KQS*	Repair/Lwr Leg Muscle, Rt
0KQT*	Repair/Lwr Leg Muscle, Lt
0KQV*	Repair/Foot Muscle, Rt
0KQW*	Repair/Foot Muscle, Lt
0KS0*	Repos/Head Muscle
0KS1*	Repos/Facial Muscle
0KS2*	Repos/Neck Muscle, Rt
0KS3*	Repos/Neck Muscle, Lt
0KS4*	Repos/Tongue, Palate, Pharynx Muscle
0KS5*	Repos/Shldr Muscle, Rt
0KS6*	Repos/Shldr Muscle, Lt
0KS7*	Repos/Upr Arm Muscle, Rt
0KS8*	Repos/Upr Arm Muscle, Lt
0KS9*	Repos/Lwr Arm and Wrist Muscle, Rt
0KSB*	Repos/Lwr Arm and Wrist Muscle, Lt
0KSF*	Repos/Trunk Muscle, Rt
0KSG*	Repos/Trunk Muscle, Lt
0KSH*	Repos/Thorax Muscle, Rt
0KSJ*	Repos/Thorax Muscle, Lt
0KSK*	Repos/Abd Muscle, Rt
0KSL*	Repos/Abd Muscle, Lt
0KSM*	Repos/Perineum Muscle
0KSN*	Repos/Hip Muscle, Rt
0KSP*	Repos/Hip Muscle, Lt
0KSQ*	Repos/Upr Leg Muscle, Rt
0KSR*	Repos/Upr Leg Muscle, Lt
0KSS*	Repos/Lwr Leg Muscle, Rt
0KST*	Repos/Lwr Leg Muscle, Lt
0KSV*	Repos/Foot Muscle, Rt
0KSW*	Repos/Foot Muscle, Lt
0KT0*	Resect/Head Muscle
0KT1*	Resect/Facial Muscle
0KT2*	Resect/Neck Muscle, Rt
0KT3*	Resect/Neck Muscle, Lt
0KT4*	Resect/Tongue, Palate, Pharynx Muscle
0KT5*	Resect/Shldr Muscle, Rt
0KT6*	Resect/Shldr Muscle, Lt
0KT7*	Resect/Upr Arm Muscle, Rt
0KT8*	Resect/Upr Arm Muscle, Lt
0KT9*	Resect/Lwr Arm and Wrist Muscle, Rt
0KTB*	Resect/Lwr Arm and Wrist Muscle, Lt
0KTF*	Resect/Trunk Muscle, Rt
0KTG*	Resect/Trunk Muscle, Lt
0KTH*	Resect/Thorax Muscle, Rt
0KTJ*	Resect/Thorax Muscle, Lt
0KTK*	Resect/Abd Muscle, Rt
0KTL*	Resect/Abd Muscle, Lt
0KTM*	Resect/Perineum Muscle
0KTN*	Resect/Hip Muscle, Rt
0KTP*	Resect/Hip Muscle, Lt
0KTQ*	Resect/Upr Leg Muscle, Rt
0KTR*	Resect/Upr Leg Muscle, Lt
0KTS*	Resect/Lwr Leg Muscle, Rt
0KTT*	Resect/Lwr Leg Muscle, Lt
0KTV*	Resect/Foot Muscle, Rt
0KTW*	Resect/Foot Muscle, Lt
0KU0*	Supl/Head Muscle
0KU1*	Supl/Facial Muscle
0KU2*	Supl/Neck Muscle, Rt
0KU3*	Supl/Neck Muscle, Lt
0KU4*	Supl/Tongue, Palate, Pharynx Muscle
0KU5*	Supl/Shldr Muscle, Rt
0KU6*	Supl/Shldr Muscle, Lt
0KU7*	Supl/Upr Arm Muscle, Rt
0KU8*	Supl/Upr Arm Muscle, Lt
0KU9*	Supl/Lwr Arm and Wrist Muscle, Rt
0KUB*	Supl/Lwr Arm and Wrist Muscle, Lt
0KUF*	Supl/Trunk Muscle, Rt
0KUG*	Supl/Trunk Muscle, Lt
0KUH*	Supl/Thorax Muscle, Rt
0KUJ*	Supl/Thorax Muscle, Lt
0KUK*	Supl/Abd Muscle, Rt
0KUL*	Supl/Abd Muscle, Lt
0KUM*	Supl/Perineum Muscle
0KUN*	Supl/Hip Muscle, Rt
0KUP*	Supl/Hip Muscle, Lt
0KUQ*	Supl/Upr Leg Muscle, Rt
0KUR*	Supl/Upr Leg Muscle, Lt
0KUS*	Supl/Lwr Leg Muscle, Rt
0KUT*	Supl/Lwr Leg Muscle, Lt
0KUV*	Supl/Foot Muscle, Rt
0KUW*	Supl/Foot Muscle, Lt
0KWX[0,3,4][0,7,J,K,M]Z	Rev/Upr Muscle, [Opn, Perc, Perc Endo], [Drain Dev, Auto Tissue Sub, Synth Sub, Nonauto Tissue Sub, Stimulator Lead], NQ
0KWY[0,3,4][0,7,J,K,M]Z	Rev/Lwr Muscle, [Opn, Perc, Perc Endo], [Drain Dev, Auto Tissue Sub, Synth Sub, Nonauto Tissue Sub, Stimulator Lead], NQ
0KX0*	Transfer/Head Muscle
0KX1*	Transfer/Facial Muscle
0KX2*	Transfer/Neck Muscle, Rt
0KX3*	Transfer/Neck Muscle, Lt
0KX4*	Transfer/Tongue, Palate, Pharynx Muscle
0KX5*	Transfer/Shldr Muscle, Rt
0KX6*	Transfer/Shldr Muscle, Lt
0KX7*	Transfer/Upr Arm Muscle, Rt
0KX8*	Transfer/Upr Arm Muscle, Lt
0KX9*	Transfer/Lwr Arm and Wrist Muscle, Rt
0KXB*	Transfer/Lwr Arm and Wrist Muscle, Lt
0KXF*	Transfer/Trunk Muscle, Rt
0KXG*	Transfer/Trunk Muscle, Lt
0KXH[0,4]Z[0,1,2]	Transfer/Thorax Muscle, Rt, [Opn, Perc Endo], No Dev, [Skin, SQ Tissue, Skin and SQ Tissue]
0KXJ[0,4]Z[0,1,2]	Transfer/Thorax Muscle, Lt, [Opn, Perc Endo], No Dev, [Skin, SQ Tissue, Skin and SQ Tissue]
0KXK[0,4]Z[0,1,2,Z]	Transfer/Abd Muscle, Rt, [Opn, Perc Endo], No Dev, [Skin, SQ Tissue, Skin and SQ Tissue, NQ]
0KXL[0,4]Z[0,1,2,Z]	Transfer/Abd Muscle, Lt, [Opn, Perc Endo], No Dev, [Skin, SQ Tissue, Skin and SQ Tissue, NQ]
0KXM*	Transfer/Perineum Muscle
0KXN*	Transfer/Hip Muscle, Rt
0KXP*	Transfer/Hip Muscle, Lt
0KXQ*	Transfer/Upr Leg Muscle, Rt
0KXR*	Transfer/Upr Leg Muscle, Lt
0KXS*	Transfer/Lwr Leg Muscle, Rt
0KXT*	Transfer/Lwr Leg Muscle, Lt

T **Transfer DRG**   SP **Special Payment**   * **Code Range**   **6th and 7th Character of ZZ = No Device, No Qualifier ZX = No Device, Diagnostic**

0KXV*	Transfer/Foot Muscle, Rt	
0KXW*	Transfer/Foot Muscle, Lt	
0L50*	Destr/Head and Neck Tndn	
0L51*	Destr/Shldr Tndn, Rt	
0L52*	Destr/Shldr Tndn, Lt	
0L53*	Destr/Upr Arm Tndn, Rt	
0L54*	Destr/Upr Arm Tndn, Lt	
0L55*	Destr/Lwr Arm and Wrist Tndn, Rt	
0L56*	Destr/Lwr Arm and Wrist Tndn, Lt	
0L59*	Destr/Trunk Tndn, Rt	
0L5B*	Destr/Trunk Tndn, Lt	
0L5C*	Destr/Thorax Tndn, Rt	
0L5D*	Destr/Thorax Tndn, Lt	
0L5F*	Destr/Abd Tndn, Rt	
0L5G*	Destr/Abd Tndn, Lt	
0L5H*	Destr/Perineum Tndn	
0L5J*	Destr/Hip Tndn, Rt	
0L5K*	Destr/Hip Tndn, Lt	
0L5L*	Destr/Upr Leg Tndn, Rt	
0L5M*	Destr/Upr Leg Tndn, Lt	
0L5N*	Destr/Lwr Leg Tndn, Rt	
0L5P*	Destr/Lwr Leg Tndn, Lt	
0L5Q*	Destr/Knee Tndn, Rt	
0L5R*	Destr/Knee Tndn, Lt	
0L5S*	Destr/Ankle Tndn, Rt	
0L5T*	Destr/Ankle Tndn, Lt	
0L5V*	Destr/Foot Tndn, Rt	
0L5W*	Destr/Foot Tndn, Lt	
0L80*	Div/Head and Neck Tndn	
0L81*	Div/Shldr Tndn, Rt	
0L82*	Div/Shldr Tndn, Lt	
0L83*	Div/Upr Arm Tndn, Rt	
0L84*	Div/Upr Arm Tndn, Lt	
0L85*	Div/Lwr Arm and Wrist Tndn, Rt	
0L86*	Div/Lwr Arm and Wrist Tndn, Lt	
0L89*	Div/Trunk Tndn, Rt	
0L8B*	Div/Trunk Tndn, Lt	
0L8C*	Div/Thorax Tndn, Rt	
0L8D*	Div/Thorax Tndn, Lt	
0L8F*	Div/Abd Tndn, Rt	
0L8G*	Div/Abd Tndn, Lt	
0L8H*	Div/Perineum Tndn	
0L8L*	Div/Upr Leg Tndn, Rt	
0L8M*	Div/Upr Leg Tndn, Lt	
0L8Q*	Div/Knee Tndn, Rt	
0L8R*	Div/Knee Tndn, Lt	
0L8S*	Div/Ankle Tndn, Rt	
0L8T*	Div/Ankle Tndn, Lt	
0L8V*	Div/Foot Tndn, Rt	
0L8W*	Div/Foot Tndn, Lt	
0L90*	Drain/Head and Neck Tndn	
0L91*	Drain/Shldr Tndn, Rt	
0L92*	Drain/Shldr Tndn, Lt	
0L93*	Drain/Upr Arm Tndn, Rt	
0L94*	Drain/Upr Arm Tndn, Lt	
0L95*	Drain/Lwr Arm and Wrist Tndn, Rt	
0L96*	Drain/Lwr Arm and Wrist Tndn, Lt	
0L97[0,3,4]ZX	Drain/Hand Tndn, Rt, [Opn, Perc, Perc Endo]	
0L98[0,3,4]ZX	Drain/Hand Tndn, Lt, [Opn, Perc, Perc Endo]	
0L99*	Drain/Trunk Tndn, Rt	
0L9B*	Drain/Trunk Tndn, Lt	
0L9C*	Drain/Thorax Tndn, Rt	
0L9D*	Drain/Thorax Tndn, Lt	
0L9F*	Drain/Abd Tndn, Rt	
0L9G*	Drain/Abd Tndn, Lt	
0L9H*	Drain/Perineum Tndn	
0L9J*	Drain/Hip Tndn, Rt	
0L9K*	Drain/Hip Tndn, Lt	
0L9L*	Drain/Upr Leg Tndn, Rt	
0L9M*	Drain/Upr Leg Tndn, Lt	
0L9N*	Drain/Lwr Leg Tndn, Rt	
0L9P*	Drain/Lwr Leg Tndn, Lt	
0L9Q*	Drain/Knee Tndn, Rt	
0L9R*	Drain/Knee Tndn, Lt	
0L9S*	Drain/Ankle Tndn, Rt	
0L9T*	Drain/Ankle Tndn, Lt	
0L9V*	Drain/Foot Tndn, Rt	
0L9W*	Drain/Foot Tndn, Lt	
0LB0*	Exc/Head and Neck Tndn	
0LB1*	Exc/Shldr Tndn, Rt	
0LB2*	Exc/Shldr Tndn, Lt	
0LB3*	Exc/Upr Arm Tndn, Rt	
0LB4*	Exc/Upr Arm Tndn, Lt	
0LB5*	Exc/Lwr Arm and Wrist Tndn, Rt	
0LB6*	Exc/Lwr Arm and Wrist Tndn, Lt	
0LB7[0,3,4]ZX	Exc/Hand Tndn, Rt, [Opn, Perc, Perc Endo]	
0LB8[0,3,4]ZX	Exc/Hand Tndn, Lt, [Opn, Perc, Perc Endo]	
0LB9*	Exc/Trunk Tndn, Rt	
0LBB*	Exc/Trunk Tndn, Lt	
0LBC*	Exc/Thorax Tndn, Rt	
0LBD*	Exc/Thorax Tndn, Lt	
0LBF*	Exc/Abd Tndn, Rt	
0LBG*	Exc/Abd Tndn, Lt	
0LBH*	Exc/Perineum Tndn	
0LBJ*	Exc/Hip Tndn, Rt	
0LBK*	Exc/Hip Tndn, Lt	
0LBL*	Exc/Upr Leg Tndn, Rt	
0LBM*	Exc/Upr Leg Tndn, Lt	
0LBN*	Exc/Lwr Leg Tndn, Rt	
0LBP*	Exc/Lwr Leg Tndn, Lt	
0LBQ*	Exc/Knee Tndn, Rt	
0LBR*	Exc/Knee Tndn, Lt	
0LBS*	Exc/Ankle Tndn, Rt	
0LBT*	Exc/Ankle Tndn, Lt	
0LBV*	Exc/Foot Tndn, Rt	
0LBW*	Exc/Foot Tndn, Lt	
0LC0*	Extir/Head and Neck Tndn	
0LC1*	Extir/Shldr Tndn, Rt	
0LC2*	Extir/Shldr Tndn, Lt	
0LC3*	Extir/Upr Arm Tndn, Rt	
0LC4*	Extir/Upr Arm Tndn, Lt	
0LC5*	Extir/Lwr Arm and Wrist Tndn, Rt	
0LC6*	Extir/Lwr Arm and Wrist Tndn, Lt	
0LC9*	Extir/Trunk Tndn, Rt	
0LCB*	Extir/Trunk Tndn, Lt	
0LCC*	Extir/Thorax Tndn, Rt	
0LCD*	Extir/Thorax Tndn, Lt	
0LCF*	Extir/Abd Tndn, Rt	
0LCG*	Extir/Abd Tndn, Lt	
0LCH*	Extir/Perineum Tndn	
0LCJ*	Extir/Hip Tndn, Rt	
0LCK*	Extir/Hip Tndn, Lt	
0LCL*	Extir/Upr Leg Tndn, Rt	
0LCM*	Extir/Upr Leg Tndn, Lt	
0LCN*	Extir/Lwr Leg Tndn, Rt	
0LCP*	Extir/Lwr Leg Tndn, Lt	
0LCQ*	Extir/Knee Tndn, Rt	
0LCR*	Extir/Knee Tndn, Lt	
0LCS*	Extir/Ankle Tndn, Rt	
0LCT*	Extir/Ankle Tndn, Lt	
0LCV*	Extir/Foot Tndn, Rt	
0LCW*	Extir/Foot Tndn, Lt	
0LJY0ZZ	Inspect of Lwr Tndn, Opn Appr	
0LJY3ZZ	Inspect of Lwr Tndn, Perc Appr	
0LJY4ZZ	Inspect of Lwr Tndn, Perc Endo Appr	
0LM0*	Reattach/Head and Neck Tndn	
0LM1*	Reattach/Shldr Tndn, Rt	
0LM2*	Reattach/Shldr Tndn, Lt	
0LM3*	Reattach/Upr Arm Tndn, Rt	
0LM4*	Reattach/Upr Arm Tndn, Lt	
0LM5*	Reattach/Lwr Arm and Wrist Tndn, Rt	
0LM6*	Reattach/Lwr Arm and Wrist Tndn, Lt	
0LM9*	Reattach/Trunk Tndn, Rt	
0LMB*	Reattach/Trunk Tndn, Lt	
0LMC*	Reattach/Thorax Tndn, Rt	
0LMD*	Reattach/Thorax Tndn, Lt	
0LMF*	Reattach/Abd Tndn, Rt	
0LMG*	Reattach/Abd Tndn, Lt	
0LMH*	Reattach/Perineum Tndn	
0LMJ*	Reattach/Hip Tndn, Rt	
0LMK*	Reattach/Hip Tndn, Lt	
0LML*	Reattach/Upr Leg Tndn, Rt	
0LMM*	Reattach/Upr Leg Tndn, Lt	
0LMN*	Reattach/Lwr Leg Tndn, Rt	
0LMP*	Reattach/Lwr Leg Tndn, Lt	
0LMQ*	Reattach/Knee Tndn, Rt	
0LMR*	Reattach/Knee Tndn, Lt	
0LMS*	Reattach/Ankle Tndn, Rt	
0LMT*	Reattach/Ankle Tndn, Lt	
0LMV*	Reattach/Foot Tndn, Rt	

Surgical   **Medical**   **CC Indicator**   **MCC Indicator**   **Procedure Proxy**   PDxMCC **PDx acts as own MCC**   PDxCC **PDx acts as own CC**

ØLMW*	Reattach/Foot Tndn, Lt
ØLN0[Ø,3,4]ZZ	Rls/Head and Neck Tndn, [Opn, Perc, Perc Endo]
ØLN1[Ø,3,4]ZZ	Rls/Shldr Tndn, Rt, [Opn, Perc, Perc Endo]
ØLN2[Ø,3,4]ZZ	Rls/Shldr Tndn, Lt, [Opn, Perc, Perc Endo]
ØLN3[Ø,3,4]ZZ	Rls/Upr Arm Tndn, Rt, [Opn, Perc, Perc Endo]
ØLN4[Ø,3,4]ZZ	Rls/Upr Arm Tndn, Lt, [Opn, Perc, Perc Endo]
ØLN5[Ø,3,4]ZZ	Rls/Lwr Arm and Wrist Tndn, Rt, [Opn, Perc, Perc Endo]
ØLN6[Ø,3,4]ZZ	Rls/Lwr Arm and Wrist Tndn, Lt, [Opn, Perc, Perc Endo]
ØLN9[Ø,3,4]ZZ	Rls/Trunk Tndn, Rt, [Opn, Perc, Perc Endo]
ØLNB[Ø,3,4]ZZ	Rls/Trunk Tndn, Lt, [Opn, Perc, Perc Endo]
ØLNC[Ø,3,4]ZZ	Rls/Thorax Tndn, Rt, [Opn, Perc, Perc Endo]
ØLND[Ø,3,4]ZZ	Rls/Thorax Tndn, Lt, [Opn, Perc, Perc Endo]
ØLNF[Ø,3,4]ZZ	Rls/Abd Tndn, Rt, [Opn, Perc, Perc Endo]
ØLNG[Ø,3,4]ZZ	Rls/Abd Tndn, Lt, [Opn, Perc, Perc Endo]
ØLNH[Ø,3,4]ZZ	Rls/Perineum Tndn, [Opn, Perc, Perc Endo]
ØLNJ[Ø,3,4]ZZ	Rls/Hip Tndn, Rt, [Opn, Perc, Perc Endo]
ØLNK[Ø,3,4]ZZ	Rls/Hip Tndn, Lt, [Opn, Perc, Perc Endo]
ØLNL[Ø,3,4]ZZ	Rls/Upr Leg Tndn, Rt, [Opn, Perc, Perc Endo]
ØLNM[Ø,3,4]ZZ	Rls/Upr Leg Tndn, Lt, [Opn, Perc, Perc Endo]
ØLNN[Ø,3,4]ZZ	Rls/Lwr Leg Tndn, Rt, [Opn, Perc, Perc Endo]
ØLNP[Ø,3,4]ZZ	Rls/Lwr Leg Tndn, Lt, [Opn, Perc, Perc Endo]
ØLNQ[Ø,3,4]ZZ	Rls/Knee Tndn, Rt, [Opn, Perc, Perc Endo]
ØLNR[Ø,3,4]ZZ	Rls/Knee Tndn, Lt, [Opn, Perc, Perc Endo]
ØLNS[Ø,3,4]ZZ	Rls/Ankle Tndn, Rt, [Opn, Perc, Perc Endo]
ØLNT[Ø,3,4]ZZ	Rls/Ankle Tndn, Lt, [Opn, Perc, Perc Endo]
ØLNV[Ø,3,4]ZZ	Rls/Foot Tndn, Rt, [Opn, Perc, Perc Endo]
ØLNW[Ø,3,4]ZZ	Rls/Foot Tndn, Lt, [Opn, Perc, Perc Endo]
ØLPX[Ø,3,4][Ø,7,J,K]Z	Rmvl/Upr Tndn, [Opn, Perc, Perc Endo], [Drain Dev, Auto Tissue Sub, Synth Sub, Nonauto Tissue Sub], NQ
ØLPY[Ø,3,4][Ø,7,J,K]Z	Rmvl/Lwr Tndn, [Opn, Perc, Perc Endo], [Drain Dev, Auto Tissue Sub, Synth Sub, Nonauto Tissue Sub], NQ
ØLQ0*	Repair/Head and Neck Tndn
ØLQ3*	Repair/Upr Arm Tndn, Rt
ØLQ4*	Repair/Upr Arm Tndn, Lt
ØLQ5*	Repair/Lwr Arm and Wrist Tndn, Rt
ØLQ6*	Repair/Lwr Arm and Wrist Tndn, Lt
ØLQ9*	Repair/Trunk Tndn, Rt
ØLQB*	Repair/Trunk Tndn, Lt
ØLQC*	Repair/Thorax Tndn, Rt
ØLQD*	Repair/Thorax Tndn, Lt
ØLQF*	Repair/Abd Tndn, Rt
ØLQG*	Repair/Abd Tndn, Lt
ØLQH*	Repair/Perineum Tndn
ØLQJ*	Repair/Hip Tndn, Rt
ØLQK*	Repair/Hip Tndn, Lt
ØLQL*	Repair/Upr Leg Tndn, Rt
ØLQM*	Repair/Upr Leg Tndn, Lt
ØLQN*	Repair/Lwr Leg Tndn, Rt
ØLQP*	Repair/Lwr Leg Tndn, Lt
ØLQQ*	Repair/Knee Tndn, Rt
ØLQR*	Repair/Knee Tndn, Lt
ØLQS*	Repair/Ankle Tndn, Rt
ØLQT*	Repair/Ankle Tndn, Lt
ØLQV*	Repair/Foot Tndn, Rt
ØLQW*	Repair/Foot Tndn, Lt
ØLR0*	Replace/Head and Neck Tndn
ØLR1*	Replace/Shldr Tndn, Rt
ØLR2*	Replace/Shldr Tndn, Lt
ØLR3*	Replace/Upr Arm Tndn, Rt
ØLR4*	Replace/Upr Arm Tndn, Lt
ØLR5*	Replace/Lwr Arm and Wrist Tndn, Rt
ØLR6*	Replace/Lwr Arm and Wrist Tndn, Lt
ØLR9*	Replace/Trunk Tndn, Rt
ØLRB*	Replace/Trunk Tndn, Lt
ØLRC*	Replace/Thorax Tndn, Rt
ØLRD*	Replace/Thorax Tndn, Lt
ØLRF*	Replace/Abd Tndn, Rt
ØLRG*	Replace/Abd Tndn, Lt
ØLRH*	Replace/Perineum Tndn
ØLRJ*	Replace/Hip Tndn, Rt
ØLRK*	Replace/Hip Tndn, Lt
ØLRL*	Replace/Upr Leg Tndn, Rt
ØLRM*	Replace/Upr Leg Tndn, Lt
ØLRN*	Replace/Lwr Leg Tndn, Rt
ØLRP*	Replace/Lwr Leg Tndn, Lt
ØLRQ*	Replace/Knee Tndn, Rt
ØLRR*	Replace/Knee Tndn, Lt
ØLRS*	Replace/Ankle Tndn, Rt
ØLRT*	Replace/Ankle Tndn, Lt
ØLRV*	Replace/Foot Tndn, Rt
ØLRW*	Replace/Foot Tndn, Lt
ØLS0*	Repos/Head and Neck Tndn
ØLS1*	Repos/Shldr Tndn, Rt
ØLS2*	Repos/Shldr Tndn, Lt
ØLS3*	Repos/Upr Arm Tndn, Rt
ØLS4*	Repos/Upr Arm Tndn, Lt
ØLS5*	Repos/Lwr Arm and Wrist Tndn, Rt
ØLS6*	Repos/Lwr Arm and Wrist Tndn, Lt
ØLS9*	Repos/Trunk Tndn, Rt
ØLSB*	Repos/Trunk Tndn, Lt
ØLSC*	Repos/Thorax Tndn, Rt
ØLSD*	Repos/Thorax Tndn, Lt
ØLSF*	Repos/Abd Tndn, Rt
ØLSG*	Repos/Abd Tndn, Lt
ØLSH*	Repos/Perineum Tndn
ØLSJ*	Repos/Hip Tndn, Rt
ØLSK*	Repos/Hip Tndn, Lt
ØLSL*	Repos/Upr Leg Tndn, Rt
ØLSM*	Repos/Upr Leg Tndn, Lt
ØLSN*	Repos/Lwr Leg Tndn, Rt
ØLSP*	Repos/Lwr Leg Tndn, Lt
ØLSQ*	Repos/Knee Tndn, Rt
ØLSR*	Repos/Knee Tndn, Lt
ØLSS*	Repos/Ankle Tndn, Rt
ØLST*	Repos/Ankle Tndn, Lt
ØLSV*	Repos/Foot Tndn, Rt
ØLSW*	Repos/Foot Tndn, Lt
ØLT0*	Resect/Head and Neck Tndn
ØLT1*	Resect/Shldr Tndn, Rt
ØLT2*	Resect/Shldr Tndn, Lt
ØLT3*	Resect/Upr Arm Tndn, Rt
ØLT4*	Resect/Upr Arm Tndn, Lt
ØLT5*	Resect/Lwr Arm and Wrist Tndn, Rt
ØLT6*	Resect/Lwr Arm and Wrist Tndn, Lt
ØLT9*	Resect/Trunk Tndn, Rt
ØLTB*	Resect/Trunk Tndn, Lt
ØLTC*	Resect/Thorax Tndn, Rt
ØLTD*	Resect/Thorax Tndn, Lt
ØLTF*	Resect/Abd Tndn, Rt
ØLTG*	Resect/Abd Tndn, Lt
ØLTH*	Resect/Perineum Tndn
ØLTJ*	Resect/Hip Tndn, Rt
ØLTK*	Resect/Hip Tndn, Lt
ØLTL*	Resect/Upr Leg Tndn, Rt
ØLTM*	Resect/Upr Leg Tndn, Lt
ØLTN*	Resect/Lwr Leg Tndn, Rt
ØLTP*	Resect/Lwr Leg Tndn, Lt
ØLTQ*	Resect/Knee Tndn, Rt
ØLTR*	Resect/Knee Tndn, Lt
ØLTS*	Resect/Ankle Tndn, Rt
ØLTT*	Resect/Ankle Tndn, Lt
ØLTV*	Resect/Foot Tndn, Rt
ØLTW*	Resect/Foot Tndn, Lt
ØLU0*	Supl/Head and Neck Tndn
ØLU1*	Supl/Shldr Tndn, Rt
ØLU2*	Supl/Shldr Tndn, Lt
ØLU3*	Supl/Upr Arm Tndn, Rt
ØLU4*	Supl/Upr Arm Tndn, Lt
ØLU5*	Supl/Lwr Arm and Wrist Tndn, Rt
ØLU6*	Supl/Lwr Arm and Wrist Tndn, Lt
ØLU9*	Supl/Trunk Tndn, Rt
ØLUB*	Supl/Trunk Tndn, Lt
ØLUC*	Supl/Thorax Tndn, Rt
ØLUD*	Supl/Thorax Tndn, Lt
ØLUF*	Supl/Abd Tndn, Rt
ØLUG*	Supl/Abd Tndn, Lt
ØLUH*	Supl/Perineum Tndn
ØLUJ*	Supl/Hip Tndn, Rt
ØLUK*	Supl/Hip Tndn, Lt
ØLUL*	Supl/Upr Leg Tndn, Rt
ØLUM*	Supl/Upr Leg Tndn, Lt
ØLUN*	Supl/Lwr Leg Tndn, Rt
ØLUP*	Supl/Lwr Leg Tndn, Lt
ØLUQ*	Supl/Knee Tndn, Rt
ØLUR*	Supl/Knee Tndn, Lt
ØLUS*	Supl/Ankle Tndn, Rt
ØLUT*	Supl/Ankle Tndn, Lt
ØLUV*	Supl/Foot Tndn, Rt
ØLUW*	Supl/Foot Tndn, Lt

[T] **Transfer DRG** [SP] **Special Payment** * **Code Range** **6th and 7th Character of ZZ = No Device, No Qualifier ZX = No Device, Diagnostic**

0LWX[0,3,4][0,7,J,K]Z	Rev/Upr Tndn, [Opn, Perc, Perc Endo], [Drain Dev, Auto Tissue Sub, Synth Sub, Nonauto Tissue Sub], NQ
0LWY[0,3,4][0,7,J,K]Z	Rev/Lwr Tndn, [Opn, Perc, Perc Endo], [Drain Dev, Auto Tissue Sub, Synth Sub, Nonauto Tissue Sub], NQ
0LX0*	Transfer/Head and Neck Tndn
0LX1*	Transfer/Shldr Tndn, Rt
0LX2*	Transfer/Shldr Tndn, Lt
0LX3*	Transfer/Upr Arm Tndn, Rt
0LX4*	Transfer/Upr Arm Tndn, Lt
0LX5*	Transfer/Lwr Arm and Wrist Tndn, Rt
0LX6*	Transfer/Lwr Arm and Wrist Tndn, Lt
0LX9*	Transfer/Trunk Tndn, Rt
0LXB*	Transfer/Trunk Tndn, Lt
0LXC*	Transfer/Thorax Tndn, Rt
0LXD*	Transfer/Thorax Tndn, Lt
0LXF*	Transfer/Abd Tndn, Rt
0LXG*	Transfer/Abd Tndn, Lt
0LXH*	Transfer/Perineum Tndn
0LXJ*	Transfer/Hip Tndn, Rt
0LXK*	Transfer/Hip Tndn, Lt
0LXL*	Transfer/Upr Leg Tndn, Rt
0LXM*	Transfer/Upr Leg Tndn, Lt
0LXN*	Transfer/Lwr Leg Tndn, Rt
0LXP*	Transfer/Lwr Leg Tndn, Lt
0LXQ*	Transfer/Knee Tndn, Rt
0LXR*	Transfer/Knee Tndn, Lt
0LXS*	Transfer/Ankle Tndn, Rt
0LXT*	Transfer/Ankle Tndn, Lt
0LXV*	Transfer/Foot Tndn, Rt
0LXW*	Transfer/Foot Tndn, Lt
0M80*	Div/Head and Neck Bursa & Lgmt
0M81*	Div/Shldr Bursa & Lgmt, Rt
0M82*	Div/Shldr Bursa & Lgmt, Lt
0M83*	Div/Elbow Bursa & Lgmt, Rt
0M84*	Div/Elbow Bursa & Lgmt, Lt
0M89*	Div/Upr Extr Bursa & Lgmt, Rt
0M8B*	Div/Upr Extr Bursa & Lgmt, Lt
0M8C*	Div/Trunk Bursa & Lgmt, Rt
0M8D*	Div/Trunk Bursa & Lgmt, Lt
0M8F*	Div/Thorax Bursa & Lgmt, Rt
0M8G*	Div/Thorax Bursa & Lgmt, Lt
0M8H*	Div/Abd Bursa & Lgmt, Rt
0M8J*	Div/Abd Bursa & Lgmt, Lt
0M8K*	Div/Perineum Bursa & Lgmt
0M8L*	Div/Hip Bursa & Lgmt, Rt
0M8M*	Div/Hip Bursa & Lgmt, Lt
0M8N*	Div/Knee Bursa & Lgmt, Rt
0M8P*	Div/Knee Bursa & Lgmt, Lt
0M8Q*	Div/Ankle Bursa & Lgmt, Rt
0M8R*	Div/Ankle Bursa & Lgmt, Lt
0M8S*	Div/Foot Bursa & Lgmt, Rt
0M8T*	Div/Foot Bursa & Lgmt, Lt
0M8V*	Div/Lwr Extr Bursa & Lgmt, Rt
0M8W*	Div/Lwr Extr Bursa & Lgmt, Lt
0M900[0,Z]Z	Drain/Head and Neck Bursa & Lgmt, Opn, [Drain Dev, No Dev], NQ
0M910[0,Z]Z	Drain/Shldr Bursa & Lgmt, Rt, Opn, [Drain Dev, No Dev], NQ
0M920[0,Z]Z	Drain/Shldr Bursa & Lgmt, Lt, Opn, [Drain Dev, No Dev], NQ
0M930[0,Z]Z	Drain/Elbow Bursa & Lgmt, Rt, Opn, [Drain Dev, No Dev], NQ
0M940[0,Z]Z	Drain/Elbow Bursa & Lgmt, Lt, Opn, [Drain Dev, No Dev], NQ
0M9900Z	Drain of Rt Up Extrem Bursa/Lig with Drain Dev, Opn Appr
0M990ZX	Drain of Rt Up Extrem Bursa/Lig, Opn Appr, Diagn
0M990ZZ	Drain of Rt Up Extrem Bursa/Lig, Opn Appr
0M993ZX	Drain of Rt Up Extrem Bursa/Lig, Perc Appr, Diagn
0M994ZX	Drain of Rt Up Extrem Bursa/Lig, Perc Endo Appr, Diagn
0M9B00Z	Drain of Lt Up Extrem Bursa/Lig with Drain Dev, Opn Appr
0M9B0ZX	Drain of Lt Up Extrem Bursa/Lig, Opn Appr, Diagn
0M9B0ZZ	Drain of Lt Up Extrem Bursa/Lig, Opn Appr
0M9B3ZX	Drain of Lt Up Extrem Bursa/Lig, Perc Appr, Diagn
0M9B4ZX	Drain of Lt Up Extrem Bursa/Lig, Perc Endo Appr, Diagn
0M9C0[0,Z]Z	Drain/Trunk Bursa & Lgmt, Rt, Opn, [Drain Dev, No Dev], NQ
0M9D0[0,Z]Z	Drain/Trunk Bursa & Lgmt, Lt, Opn, [Drain Dev, No Dev], NQ
0M9F0[0,Z]Z	Drain/Thorax Bursa & Lgmt, Rt, Opn, [Drain Dev, No Dev], NQ
0M9G0[0,Z]Z	Drain/Thorax Bursa & Lgmt, Lt, Opn, [Drain Dev, No Dev], NQ
0M9H00Z	Drain of Rt Abd Bursa/Lig with Drain Dev, Opn Appr
0M9H0ZZ	Drain of Rt Abd Bursa & Lgmt, Opn Appr
0M9H[0,3,4]ZX	Drain/Abd Bursa & Lgmt, Rt, [Opn, Perc, Perc Endo]
0M9J00Z	Drain of Lt Abd Bursa/Lig with Drain Dev, Opn Appr
0M9J0ZZ	Drain of Lt Abd Bursa & Lgmt, Opn Appr
0M9J[0,3,4]ZX	Drain/Abd Bursa & Lgmt, Lt, [Opn, Perc, Perc Endo]
0M9K00Z	Drain of Perineum Bursa/Lig with Drain Dev, Opn Appr
0M9K0ZZ	Drain of Perineum Bursa & Lgmt, Opn Appr
0M9K[0,3,4]ZX	Drain/Perineum Bursa & Lgmt, [Opn, Perc, Perc Endo]
0M9L0[0,Z]Z	Drain/Hip Bursa & Lgmt, Rt, Opn, [Drain Dev, No Dev], NQ
0M9M0[0,Z]Z	Drain/Hip Bursa & Lgmt, Lt, Opn, [Drain Dev, No Dev], NQ
0M9N0[0,Z]Z	Drain/Knee Bursa & Lgmt, Rt, Opn, [Drain Dev, No Dev], NQ
0M9P0[0,Z]Z	Drain/Knee Bursa & Lgmt, Lt, Opn, [Drain Dev, No Dev], NQ
0M9Q0[0,Z]Z	Drain/Ankle Bursa & Lgmt, Rt, Opn, [Drain Dev, No Dev], NQ
0M9R0[0,Z]Z	Drain/Ankle Bursa & Lgmt, Lt, Opn, [Drain Dev, No Dev], NQ
0M9S0[0,Z]Z	Drain/Foot Bursa & Lgmt, Rt, Opn, [Drain Dev, No Dev], NQ
0M9T0[0,Z]Z	Drain/Foot Bursa & Lgmt, Lt, Opn, [Drain Dev, No Dev], NQ
0M9V00Z	Drain Rt Low Extrem Bursa/Lig w Drain Dev, Opn
0M9V0ZZ	Drain of Rt Low Extrem Bursa/Lig, Opn Appr
0M9V[0,3,4]ZX	Drain/Lwr Extr Bursa & Lgmt, Rt, [Opn, Perc, Perc Endo]
0M9W00Z	Drain Lt Low Extrem Bursa/Lig w Drain Dev, Opn
0M9W0ZZ	Drain of Lt Low Extrem Bursa/Lig, Opn Appr
0M9W[0,3,4]ZX	Drain/Lwr Extr Bursa & Lgmt, Lt, [Opn, Perc, Perc Endo]
0MB0[0,3,4]ZZ	Exc/Head and Neck Bursa & Lgmt, [Opn, Perc, Perc Endo]
0MB1[0,3,4]ZZ	Exc/Shldr Bursa & Lgmt, Rt, [Opn, Perc, Perc Endo]
0MB2[0,3,4]ZZ	Exc/Shldr Bursa & Lgmt, Lt, [Opn, Perc, Perc Endo]
0MB3[0,3,4]ZZ	Exc/Elbow Bursa & Lgmt, Rt, [Opn, Perc, Perc Endo]
0MB4[0,3,4]ZZ	Exc/Elbow Bursa & Lgmt, Lt, [Opn, Perc, Perc Endo]
0MB5[0,3,4]ZZ	Exc/Wrist Bursa & Lgmt, Rt, [Opn, Perc, Perc Endo]
0MB6[0,3,4]ZZ	Exc/Wrist Bursa & Lgmt, Lt, [Opn, Perc, Perc Endo]
0MB90ZX	Exc of Rt Up Extrem Bursa/Lig, Opn Appr, Diagn
0MB90ZZ	Exc of Rt Up Extrem Bursa/Lig, Opn Appr
0MB93ZX	Exc of Rt Up Extrem Bursa/Lig, Perc Appr, Diagn
0MB93ZZ	Exc of Rt Up Extrem Bursa/Lig, Perc Appr
0MB94ZZ	Exc of Rt Up Extrem Bursa/Lig, Perc Endo Appr
0MBB[0,3,4]ZZ	Exc/Upr Extr Bursa & Lgmt, Lt, [Opn, Perc, Perc Endo]
0MBC[0,3,4]ZZ	Exc/Trunk Bursa & Lgmt, Rt, [Opn, Perc, Perc Endo]
0MBD[0,3,4]ZZ	Exc/Trunk Bursa & Lgmt, Lt, [Opn, Perc, Perc Endo]
0MBF[0,3,4]ZZ	Exc/Thorax Bursa & Lgmt, Rt, [Opn, Perc, Perc Endo]
0MBG[0,3,4]ZZ	Exc/Thorax Bursa & Lgmt, Lt, [Opn, Perc, Perc Endo]
0MBH*	Exc/Abd Bursa & Lgmt, Rt
0MBJ*	Exc/Abd Bursa & Lgmt, Lt
0MBK*	Exc/Perineum Bursa & Lgmt
0MBL[0,3,4]ZZ	Exc/Hip Bursa & Lgmt, Rt, [Opn, Perc, Perc Endo]
0MBM[0,3,4]ZZ	Exc/Hip Bursa & Lgmt, Lt, [Opn, Perc, Perc Endo]
0MBN[0,3,4]ZZ	Exc/Knee Bursa & Lgmt, Rt, [Opn, Perc, Perc Endo]
0MBP[0,3,4]ZZ	Exc/Knee Bursa & Lgmt, Lt, [Opn, Perc, Perc Endo]
0MBQ[0,3,4]ZZ	Exc/Ankle Bursa & Lgmt, Rt, [Opn, Perc, Perc Endo]
0MBR[0,3,4]ZZ	Exc/Ankle Bursa & Lgmt, Lt, [Opn, Perc, Perc Endo]
0MBS[0,3,4]ZZ	Exc/Foot Bursa & Lgmt, Rt, [Opn, Perc, Perc Endo]
0MBT[0,3,4]ZZ	Exc/Foot Bursa & Lgmt, Lt, [Opn, Perc, Perc Endo]
0MBV*	Exc/Lwr Extr Bursa & Lgmt, Rt
0MBW*	Exc/Lwr Extr Bursa & Lgmt, Lt
0MC0*	Extir/Head and Neck Bursa & Lgmt
0MC1*	Extir/Shldr Bursa & Lgmt, Rt
0MC2*	Extir/Shldr Bursa & Lgmt, Lt
0MC3*	Extir/Elbow Bursa & Lgmt, Rt
0MC4*	Extir/Elbow Bursa & Lgmt, Lt
0MC9*	Extir/Upr Extr Bursa & Lgmt, Rt
0MCB*	Extir/Upr Extr Bursa & Lgmt, Lt
0MCC*	Extir/Trunk Bursa & Lgmt, Rt
0MCD*	Extir/Trunk Bursa & Lgmt, Lt
0MCF*	Extir/Thorax Bursa & Lgmt, Rt
0MCG*	Extir/Thorax Bursa & Lgmt, Lt
0MCH*	Extir/Abd Bursa & Lgmt, Rt
0MCJ*	Extir/Abd Bursa & Lgmt, Lt
0MCK*	Extir/Perineum Bursa & Lgmt
0MCL*	Extir/Hip Bursa & Lgmt, Rt
0MCM*	Extir/Hip Bursa & Lgmt, Lt
0MCN*	Extir/Knee Bursa & Lgmt, Rt
0MCP*	Extir/Knee Bursa & Lgmt, Lt
0MCQ*	Extir/Ankle Bursa & Lgmt, Rt
0MCR*	Extir/Ankle Bursa & Lgmt, Lt
0MCS*	Extir/Foot Bursa & Lgmt, Rt
0MCT*	Extir/Foot Bursa & Lgmt, Lt
0MCV*	Extir/Lwr Extr Bursa & Lgmt, Rt
0MCW*	Extir/Lwr Extr Bursa & Lgmt, Lt
0MD0*	Extract/Head and Neck Bursa & Lgmt
0MD1*	Extract/Shldr Bursa & Lgmt, Rt
0MD2*	Extract/Shldr Bursa & Lgmt, Lt
0MD3*	Extract/Elbow Bursa & Lgmt, Rt
0MD4*	Extract/Elbow Bursa & Lgmt, Lt
0MD5*	Extract/Wrist Bursa & Lgmt, Rt
0MD6*	Extract/Wrist Bursa & Lgmt, Lt
0MD9*	Extract/Upr Extr Bursa & Lgmt, Rt
0MDB*	Extract/Upr Extr Bursa & Lgmt, Lt

Surgical	Medical	CC Indicator	MCC Indicator	Procedure Proxy	PDxMCC PDx acts as own MCC	PDxCC PDx acts as own CC

ØMDC*	Extract/Trunk Bursa & Lgmt, Rt		ØMT5*	Resect/Wrist Bursa & Lgmt, Rt
ØMDD*	Extract/Trunk Bursa & Lgmt, Lt		ØMT6*	Resect/Wrist Bursa & Lgmt, Lt
ØMDF*	Extract/Thorax Bursa & Lgmt, Rt		ØMT9*	Resect/Upr Extr Bursa & Lgmt, Rt
ØMDG*	Extract/Thorax Bursa & Lgmt, Lt		ØMTB*	Resect/Upr Extr Bursa & Lgmt, Lt
ØMDH*	Extract/Abd Bursa & Lgmt, Rt		ØMTC*	Resect/Trunk Bursa & Lgmt, Rt
ØMDJ*	Extract/Abd Bursa & Lgmt, Lt		ØMTD*	Resect/Trunk Bursa & Lgmt, Lt
ØMDK*	Extract/Perineum Bursa & Lgmt		ØMTF*	Resect/Thorax Bursa & Lgmt, Rt
ØMDL*	Extract/Hip Bursa & Lgmt, Rt		ØMTG*	Resect/Thorax Bursa & Lgmt, Lt
ØMDM*	Extract/Hip Bursa & Lgmt, Lt		ØMTH*	Resect/Abd Bursa & Lgmt, Rt
ØMDN*	Extract/Knee Bursa & Lgmt, Rt		ØMTJ*	Resect/Abd Bursa & Lgmt, Lt
ØMDP*	Extract/Knee Bursa & Lgmt, Lt		ØMTK*	Resect/Perineum Bursa & Lgmt
ØMDQ*	Extract/Ankle Bursa & Lgmt, Rt		ØMTL*	Resect/Hip Bursa & Lgmt, Rt
ØMDR*	Extract/Ankle Bursa & Lgmt, Lt		ØMTM*	Resect/Hip Bursa & Lgmt, Lt
ØMDS*	Extract/Foot Bursa & Lgmt, Rt		ØMTN*	Resect/Knee Bursa & Lgmt, Rt
ØMDT*	Extract/Foot Bursa & Lgmt, Lt		ØMTP*	Resect/Knee Bursa & Lgmt, Lt
ØMDV*	Extract/Lwr Extr Bursa & Lgmt, Rt		ØMTQ*	Resect/Ankle Bursa & Lgmt, Rt
ØMDW*	Extract/Lwr Extr Bursa & Lgmt, Lt		ØMTR*	Resect/Ankle Bursa & Lgmt, Lt
ØMN0*	Rls/Head and Neck Bursa & Lgmt		ØMTS*	Resect/Foot Bursa & Lgmt, Rt
ØMN1*	Rls/Shldr Bursa & Lgmt, Rt		ØMTT*	Resect/Foot Bursa & Lgmt, Lt
ØMN2*	Rls/Shldr Bursa & Lgmt, Lt		ØMTV*	Resect/Lwr Extr Bursa & Lgmt, Rt
ØMN3*	Rls/Elbow Bursa & Lgmt, Rt		ØMTW*	Resect/Lwr Extr Bursa & Lgmt, Lt
ØMN4*	Rls/Elbow Bursa & Lgmt, Lt		ØMU9*	Supl/Upr Extr Bursa & Lgmt, Rt
ØMN5*	Rls/Wrist Bursa & Lgmt, Rt		ØMUB*	Supl/Upr Extr Bursa & Lgmt, Lt
ØMN6*	Rls/Wrist Bursa & Lgmt, Lt		ØMUV*	Supl/Lwr Extr Bursa & Lgmt, Rt
ØMN9*	Rls/Upr Extr Bursa & Lgmt, Rt		ØMUW*	Supl/Lwr Extr Bursa & Lgmt, Lt
ØMNB*	Rls/Upr Extr Bursa & Lgmt, Lt		ØMWX[Ø,3,4][Ø,7,J,K]Z	Rev/Upr Bursa & Lgmt, [Opn, Perc, Perc Endo], [Drain Dev, Auto Tissue Sub, Synth Sub, Nonauto Tissue Sub], NQ
ØMNC*	Rls/Trunk Bursa & Lgmt, Rt			
ØMND*	Rls/Trunk Bursa & Lgmt, Lt		ØMWY[Ø,3,4][Ø,7,J,K]Z	Rev/Lwr Bursa & Lgmt, [Opn, Perc, Perc Endo], [Drain Dev, Auto Tissue Sub, Synth Sub, Nonauto Tissue Sub], NQ
ØMNF*	Rls/Thorax Bursa & Lgmt, Rt			
ØMNG*	Rls/Thorax Bursa & Lgmt, Lt		ØMX*	Bursa & Lgmt, Transfer
ØMNH*	Rls/Abd Bursa & Lgmt, Rt		ØWB0[Ø,3,4,X]ZZ	Exc/Head, [Opn, Perc, Perc Endo, Ext]
ØMNJ*	Rls/Abd Bursa & Lgmt, Lt		ØWB2[Ø,3,4,X]ZZ	Exc/Face, [Opn, Perc, Perc Endo, Ext]
ØMNK*	Rls/Perineum Bursa & Lgmt		ØWB4[Ø,3,4,X]ZZ	Exc/Upr Jaw, [Opn, Perc, Perc Endo, Ext]
ØMNL*	Rls/Hip Bursa & Lgmt, Rt		ØWB5[Ø,3,4,X]ZZ	Exc/Lwr Jaw, [Opn, Perc, Perc Endo, Ext]
ØMNM*	Rls/Hip Bursa & Lgmt, Lt		ØWB6[Ø,3,4,X]ZZ	Exc/Neck, [Opn, Perc, Perc Endo, Ext]
ØMNN*	Rls/Knee Bursa & Lgmt, Rt		ØWBF0ZZ	Exc of Abd Wall, Opn Appr
ØMNP*	Rls/Knee Bursa & Lgmt, Lt		ØWBF3ZZ	Exc of Abd Wall, Perc Appr
ØMNQ*	Rls/Ankle Bursa & Lgmt, Rt		ØWBF4ZZ	Exc of Abd Wall, Perc Endo Appr
ØMNR*	Rls/Ankle Bursa & Lgmt, Lt		ØWBFXZ2	Exc of Abd Wall, Stoma, Ext Appr
ØMNS*	Rls/Foot Bursa & Lgmt, Rt		ØWBFXZZ	Exc of Abd Wall, Ext Appr
ØMNT*	Rls/Foot Bursa & Lgmt, Lt		ØWBK[Ø,3,4,X]ZZ	Exc/Upr Back, [Opn, Perc, Perc Endo, Ext]
ØMNV*	Rls/Lwr Extr Bursa & Lgmt, Rt		ØWBL[Ø,3,4,X]ZZ	Exc/Lwr Back, [Opn, Perc, Perc Endo, Ext]
ØMNW*	Rls/Lwr Extr Bursa & Lgmt, Lt		ØWBM[Ø,3,4,X]ZZ	Exc/Perineum, Male, [Opn, Perc, Perc Endo, Ext]
ØMPX[Ø,3,4][7,K]Z	Rmvl/Upr Bursa & Lgmt, [Opn, Perc, Perc Endo], [Auto Tissue Sub, Nonauto Tissue Sub], NQ		ØXB2[Ø,3,4]ZZ	Exc/Shldr Rgn, Rt, [Opn, Perc, Perc Endo]
			ØXB3[Ø,3,4]ZZ	Exc/Shldr Rgn, Lt, [Opn, Perc, Perc Endo]
ØMPY[Ø,3,4][7,K]Z	Rmvl/Lwr Bursa & Lgmt, [Opn, Perc, Perc Endo], [Auto Tissue Sub, Nonauto Tissue Sub], NQ		ØXB4[Ø,3,4]ZZ	Exc/Axilla, Rt, [Opn, Perc, Perc Endo]
			ØXB5[Ø,3,4]ZZ	Exc/Axilla, Lt, [Opn, Perc, Perc Endo]
ØMQ0*	Repair/Head and Neck Bursa & Lgmt		ØXB6[Ø,3,4]ZZ	Exc/Upr Extr, Rt, [Opn, Perc, Perc Endo]
ØMQ1*	Repair/Shldr Bursa & Lgmt, Rt		ØXB7[Ø,3,4]ZZ	Exc/Upr Extr, Lt, [Opn, Perc, Perc Endo]
ØMQ2*	Repair/Shldr Bursa & Lgmt, Lt		ØXB8[Ø,3,4]ZZ	Exc/Upr Arm, Rt, [Opn, Perc, Perc Endo]
ØMQ3*	Repair/Elbow Bursa & Lgmt, Rt		ØXB9[Ø,3,4]ZZ	Exc/Upr Arm, Lt, [Opn, Perc, Perc Endo]
ØMQ4*	Repair/Elbow Bursa & Lgmt, Lt		ØXBB[Ø,3,4]ZZ	Exc/Elbow Rgn, Rt, [Opn, Perc, Perc Endo]
ØMQ5*	Repair/Wrist Bursa & Lgmt, Rt		ØXBC[Ø,3,4]ZZ	Exc/Elbow Rgn, Lt, [Opn, Perc, Perc Endo]
ØMQ6*	Repair/Wrist Bursa & Lgmt, Lt		ØXBD[Ø,3,4]ZZ	Exc/Lwr Arm, Rt, [Opn, Perc, Perc Endo]
ØMQ7*	Repair/Hand Bursa & Lgmt, Rt		ØXBF[Ø,3,4]ZZ	Exc/Lwr Arm, Lt, [Opn, Perc, Perc Endo]
ØMQ8*	Repair/Hand Bursa & Lgmt, Lt		ØXBG[Ø,3,4]ZZ	Exc/Wrist Rgn, Rt, [Opn, Perc, Perc Endo]
ØMQ9*	Repair/Upr Extr Bursa & Lgmt, Rt		ØXBH[Ø,3,4]ZZ	Exc/Wrist Rgn, Lt, [Opn, Perc, Perc Endo]
ØMQB*	Repair/Upr Extr Bursa & Lgmt, Lt		ØXBJ[Ø,3,4]ZZ	Exc/Hand, Rt, [Opn, Perc, Perc Endo]
ØMQC*	Repair/Trunk Bursa & Lgmt, Rt		ØXBK[Ø,3,4]ZZ	Exc/Hand, Lt, [Opn, Perc, Perc Endo]
ØMQD*	Repair/Trunk Bursa & Lgmt, Lt		ØXJJ[3,4]ZZ	Inspect/Hand, Rt, [Perc, Perc Endo]
ØMQF*	Repair/Thorax Bursa & Lgmt, Rt		ØXJK[3,4]ZZ	Inspect/Hand, Lt, [Perc, Perc Endo]
ØMQG*	Repair/Thorax Bursa & Lgmt, Lt		ØYB0[Ø,3,4]ZZ	Exc/Buttock, Rt, [Opn, Perc, Perc Endo]
ØMQH*	Repair/Abd Bursa & Lgmt, Rt		ØYB1[Ø,3,4]ZZ	Exc/Buttock, Lt, [Opn, Perc, Perc Endo]
ØMQJ*	Repair/Abd Bursa & Lgmt, Lt		ØYB5[Ø,3,4]ZZ	Exc/Inguinal Rgn, Rt, [Opn, Perc, Perc Endo]
ØMQK*	Repair/Perineum Bursa & Lgmt		ØYB6[Ø,3,4]ZZ	Exc/Inguinal Rgn, Lt, [Opn, Perc, Perc Endo]
ØMQL*	Repair/Hip Bursa & Lgmt, Rt		ØYB7[Ø,3,4]ZZ	Exc/Femor Rgn, Rt, [Opn, Perc, Perc Endo]
ØMQM*	Repair/Hip Bursa & Lgmt, Lt		ØYB8[Ø,3,4]ZZ	Exc/Femor Rgn, Lt, [Opn, Perc, Perc Endo]
ØMQQ*	Repair/Ankle Bursa & Lgmt, Rt		ØYB9[Ø,3,4]ZZ	Exc/Lwr Extr, Rt, [Opn, Perc, Perc Endo]
ØMQR*	Repair/Ankle Bursa & Lgmt, Lt		ØYBB[Ø,3,4]ZZ	Exc/Lwr Extr, Lt, [Opn, Perc, Perc Endo]
ØMQV*	Repair/Lwr Extr Bursa & Lgmt, Rt		ØYBC[Ø,3,4]ZZ	Exc/Upr Leg, Rt, [Opn, Perc, Perc Endo]
ØMQW*	Repair/Lwr Extr Bursa & Lgmt, Lt		ØYBD[Ø,3,4]ZZ	Exc/Upr Leg, Lt, [Opn, Perc, Perc Endo]
ØMS9*	Repos/Upr Extr Bursa & Lgmt, Rt		ØYBF[Ø,3,4]ZZ	Exc/Knee Rgn, Rt, [Opn, Perc, Perc Endo]
ØMSB*	Repos/Upr Extr Bursa & Lgmt, Lt		ØYBG[Ø,3,4]ZZ	Exc/Knee Rgn, Lt, [Opn, Perc, Perc Endo]
ØMSV*	Repos/Lwr Extr Bursa & Lgmt, Rt		ØYBH[Ø,3,4]ZZ	Exc/Lwr Leg, Rt, [Opn, Perc, Perc Endo]
ØMSW*	Repos/Lwr Extr Bursa & Lgmt, Lt		ØYBJ[Ø,3,4]ZZ	Exc/Lwr Leg, Lt, [Opn, Perc, Perc Endo]
ØMT0*	Resect/Head and Neck Bursa & Lgmt		ØYBK[Ø,3,4]ZZ	Exc/Ankle Rgn, Rt, [Opn, Perc, Perc Endo]
ØMT1*	Resect/Shldr Bursa & Lgmt, Rt		ØYBL[Ø,3,4]ZZ	Exc/Ankle Rgn, Lt, [Opn, Perc, Perc Endo]
ØMT2*	Resect/Shldr Bursa & Lgmt, Lt		ØYBM[Ø,3,4]ZZ	Exc/Foot, Rt, [Opn, Perc, Perc Endo]
ØMT3*	Resect/Elbow Bursa & Lgmt, Rt		ØYBN[Ø,3,4]ZZ	Exc/Foot, Lt, [Opn, Perc, Perc Endo]
ØMT4*	Resect/Elbow Bursa & Lgmt, Lt			

Ⓣ **Transfer DRG**   ⓈⓅ **Special Payment**   * **Code Range**   **6th and 7th Character of ZZ = No Device, No Qualifier ZX = No Device, Diagnostic**

144   MS-DRG Version 33.0   © 2015 Optum360, LLC

DRG 501   Soft Tissue Procedures with CC
  GMLOS 4.3   AMLOS 5.4   RW 1.6064   [SP]

Select operating room procedures listed under DRG 500

DRG 502   Soft Tissue Procedures without CC/MCC
  GMLOS 2.4   AMLOS 2.9   RW 1.1752   [SP]

Select operating room procedures listed under DRG 500

DRG 503   Foot Procedures with MCC
  GMLOS 6.7   AMLOS 8.1   RW 2.2679

Operating Room Procedures

Ø1NG*	Rls/Tibial Nerve
ØL8N*	Div/Lwr Leg Tndn, Rt
ØL8P*	Div/Lwr Leg Tndn, Lt
ØM5S*	Destr/Foot Bursa & Lgmt, Rt
ØM5T*	Destr/Foot Bursa & Lgmt, Lt
ØM9S[3,4]ØZ	Drain/Foot Bursa & Lgmt, Rt, [Perc, Perc Endo], Drain Dev, NQ
ØM9T[3,4]ØZ	Drain/Foot Bursa & Lgmt, Lt, [Perc, Perc Endo], Drain Dev, NQ
ØMQS*	Repair/Foot Bursa & Lgmt, Rt
ØMQT*	Repair/Foot Bursa & Lgmt, Lt
ØQ5L*	Destr/Tarsal, Rt
ØQ5M*	Destr/Tarsal, Lt
ØQ5N*	Destr/Metatarsal, Rt
ØQ5P*	Destr/Metatarsal, Lt
ØQ8L*	Div/Tarsal, Rt
ØQ8M*	Div/Tarsal, Lt
ØQ8N*	Div/Metatarsal, Rt
ØQ8P*	Div/Metatarsal, Lt
ØQ9L[Ø,3,4][Ø,Z]Z	Drain/Tarsal, Rt, [Opn, Perc, Perc Endo], [Drain Dev, No Dev], NQ
ØQ9M[Ø,3,4][Ø,Z]Z	Drain/Tarsal, Lt, [Opn, Perc, Perc Endo], [Drain Dev, No Dev], NQ
ØQ9N[Ø,3,4][Ø,Z]Z	Drain/Metatarsal, Rt, [Opn, Perc, Perc Endo], [Drain Dev, No Dev], NQ
ØQ9P[Ø,3,4][Ø,Z]Z	Drain/Metatarsal, Lt, [Opn, Perc, Perc Endo], [Drain Dev, No Dev], NQ
ØQBL[Ø,3,4]ZZ	Exc/Tarsal, Rt, [Opn, Perc, Perc Endo]
ØQBM[Ø,3,4]ZZ	Exc/Tarsal, Lt, [Opn, Perc, Perc Endo]
ØQBN[Ø,3,4]ZZ	Exc/Metatarsal, Rt, [Opn, Perc, Perc Endo]
ØQBP[Ø,3,4]ZZ	Exc/Metatarsal, Lt, [Opn, Perc, Perc Endo]
ØQCL*	Extir/Tarsal, Rt
ØQCM*	Extir/Tarsal, Lt
ØQCN*	Extir/Metatarsal, Rt
ØQCP*	Extir/Metatarsal, Lt
ØQHL*	Insert/Tarsal, Rt
ØQHM*	Insert/Tarsal, Lt
ØQHN*	Insert/Metatarsal, Rt
ØQHP*	Insert/Metatarsal, Lt
ØQNL*	Rls/Tarsal, Rt
ØQNM*	Rls/Tarsal, Lt
ØQNN*	Rls/Metatarsal, Rt
ØQNP*	Rls/Metatarsal, Lt
ØQQL*	Repair/Tarsal, Rt
ØQQM*	Repair/Tarsal, Lt
ØQQN*	Repair/Metatarsal, Rt
ØQQP*	Repair/Metatarsal, Lt
ØQRL*	Replace/Tarsal, Rt
ØQRM*	Replace/Tarsal, Lt
ØQRN*	Replace/Metatarsal, Rt
ØQRP*	Replace/Metatarsal, Lt
ØQSLØZZ	Repos Rt Tarsal, Opn Appr
ØQSL[Ø,3,4][4,5]Z	Repos/Tarsal, Rt, [Opn, Perc, Perc Endo], [Int Fix Dev, Ext Fix Dev], NQ
ØQSMØZZ	Repos Lt Tarsal, Opn Appr
ØQSM[Ø,3,4][4,5]Z	Repos/Tarsal, Lt, [Opn, Perc, Perc Endo], [Int Fix Dev, Ext Fix Dev], NQ
ØQSNØZZ	Repos Rt Metatarsal, Opn Appr
ØQSN[Ø,3,4][4,5]Z	Repos/Metatarsal, Rt, [Opn, Perc, Perc Endo], [Int Fix Dev, Ext Fix Dev], NQ
ØQSPØZZ	Repos Lt Metatarsal, Opn Appr
ØQSP[Ø,3,4][4,5]Z	Repos/Metatarsal, Lt, [Opn, Perc, Perc Endo], [Int Fix Dev, Ext Fix Dev], NQ
ØQSQØZZ	Repos Rt Toe Phalanx, Opn Appr
ØQSQ[Ø,3,4]4Z	Repos/Toe Phalanx, Rt, [Opn, Perc, Perc Endo], Int Fix Dev, NQ
ØQSRØZZ	Repos Lt Toe Phalanx, Opn Appr
ØQSR[Ø,3,4]4Z	Repos/Toe Phalanx, Lt, [Opn, Perc, Perc Endo], Int Fix Dev, NQ

ØQT[L,M]ØZZ	Resect of [Rt, Lt] Tarsal, Opn Appr
ØQT[N,P]ØZZ	Resect of [Rt, Lt] Metatarsal, Opn Appr
ØQUL*	Supl/Tarsal, Rt
ØQUM*	Supl/Tarsal, Lt
ØQUN*	Supl/Metatarsal, Rt
ØQUP*	Supl/Metatarsal, Lt
ØQWL[Ø,3,4][4,5,7,J,K]Z	Rev/Tarsal, Rt, [Opn, Perc, Perc Endo], [Int Fix Dev, Ext Fix Dev, Auto Tissue Sub, Synth Sub, Nonauto Tissue Sub], NQ
ØQWM[Ø,3,4][4,5,7,J,K]Z	Rev/Tarsal, Lt, [Opn, Perc, Perc Endo], [Int Fix Dev, Ext Fix Dev, Auto Tissue Sub, Synth Sub, Nonauto Tissue Sub], NQ
ØQWN[Ø,3,4][4,5,7,J,K]Z	Rev/Metatarsal, Rt, [Opn, Perc, Perc Endo], [Int Fix Dev, Ext Fix Dev, Auto Tissue Sub, Synth Sub, Nonauto Tissue Sub], NQ
ØQWP[Ø,3,4][4,5,7,J,K]Z	Rev/Metatarsal, Lt, [Opn, Perc, Perc Endo], [Int Fix Dev, Ext Fix Dev, Auto Tissue Sub, Synth Sub, Nonauto Tissue Sub], NQ
ØS5H*	Destr/Tarsal Jt, Rt
ØS5J*	Destr/Tarsal Jt, Lt
ØS5K*	Destr/Metatarsal-Tarsal Jt, Rt
ØS5L*	Destr/Metatarsal-Tarsal Jt, Lt
ØS5M*	Destr/Metatarsal-Phalangeal Jt, Rt
ØS5N*	Destr/Metatarsal-Phalangeal Jt, Lt
ØS5P*	Destr/Toe Phalangeal Jt, Rt
ØS5Q*	Destr/Toe Phalangeal Jt, Lt
ØS9HØ[Ø,Z]Z	Drain/Tarsal Jt, Rt, Opn, [Drain Dev, No Dev], NQ
ØS9JØ[Ø,Z]Z	Drain/Tarsal Jt, Lt, Opn, [Drain Dev, No Dev], NQ
ØS9KØ[Ø,Z]Z	Drain/Metatarsal-Tarsal Jt, Rt, Opn, [Drain Dev, No Dev], NQ
ØS9LØ[Ø,Z]Z	Drain/Metatarsal-Tarsal Jt, Lt, Opn, [Drain Dev, No Dev], NQ
ØS9MØ[Ø,Z]Z	Drain/Metatarsal-Phalangeal Jt, Rt, Opn, [Drain Dev, No Dev], NQ
ØS9NØ[Ø,Z]Z	Drain/Metatarsal-Phalangeal Jt, Lt, Opn, [Drain Dev, No Dev], NQ
ØS9PØ[Ø,Z]Z	Drain/Toe Phalangeal Jt, Rt, Opn, [Drain Dev, No Dev], NQ
ØS9QØ[Ø,Z]Z	Drain/Toe Phalangeal Jt, Lt, Opn, [Drain Dev, No Dev], NQ
ØSBH[Ø,3,4]ZZ	Exc/Tarsal Jt, Rt, [Opn, Perc, Perc Endo]
ØSBJ[Ø,3,4]ZZ	Exc/Tarsal Jt, Lt, [Opn, Perc, Perc Endo]
ØSBK[Ø,3,4]ZZ	Exc/Metatarsal-Tarsal Jt, Rt, [Opn, Perc, Perc Endo]
ØSBL[Ø,3,4]ZZ	Exc/Metatarsal-Tarsal Jt, Lt, [Opn, Perc, Perc Endo]
ØSBM[Ø,3,4]ZZ	Exc/Metatarsal-Phalangeal Jt, Rt, [Opn, Perc, Perc Endo]
ØSBN[Ø,3,4]ZZ	Exc/Metatarsal-Phalangeal Jt, Lt, [Opn, Perc, Perc Endo]
ØSBP[Ø,3,4]ZZ	Exc/Toe Phalangeal Jt, Rt, [Opn, Perc, Perc Endo]
ØSBQ[Ø,3,4]ZZ	Exc/Toe Phalangeal Jt, Lt, [Opn, Perc, Perc Endo]
ØSCH*	Extir/Tarsal Jt, Rt
ØSCJ*	Extir/Tarsal Jt, Lt
ØSCK*	Extir/Metatarsal-Tarsal Jt, Rt
ØSCL*	Extir/Metatarsal-Tarsal Jt, Lt
ØSCM*	Extir/Metatarsal-Phalangeal Jt, Rt
ØSCN*	Extir/Metatarsal-Phalangeal Jt, Lt
ØSCP*	Extir/Toe Phalangeal Jt, Rt
ØSCQ*	Extir/Toe Phalangeal Jt, Lt
ØSGH*	Fusion/Tarsal Jt, Rt
ØSGJ*	Fusion/Tarsal Jt, Lt
ØSGK*	Fusion/Metatarsal-Tarsal Jt, Rt
ØSGL*	Fusion/Metatarsal-Tarsal Jt, Lt
ØSGM*	Fusion/Metatarsal-Phalangeal Jt, Rt
ØSGN*	Fusion/Metatarsal-Phalangeal Jt, Lt
ØSGP*	Fusion/Toe Phalangeal Jt, Rt
ØSGQ*	Fusion/Toe Phalangeal Jt, Lt
ØSHH[Ø,3,4][4,5]Z	Insert/Tarsal Jt, Rt, [Opn, Perc, Perc Endo], [Int Fix Dev, Ext Fix Dev], NQ
ØSHJ[Ø,3,4][4,5]Z	Insert/Tarsal Jt, Lt, [Opn, Perc, Perc Endo], [Int Fix Dev, Ext Fix Dev], NQ
ØSHK[Ø,3,4][4,5]Z	Insert/Metatarsal-Tarsal Jt, Rt, [Opn, Perc, Perc Endo], [Int Fix Dev, Ext Fix Dev], NQ
ØSHL[Ø,3,4][4,5]Z	Insert/Metatarsal-Tarsal Jt, Lt, [Opn, Perc, Perc Endo], [Int Fix Dev, Ext Fix Dev], NQ
ØSHM[Ø,3,4][4,5]Z	Insert/Metatarsal-Phalangeal Jt, Rt, [Opn, Perc, Perc Endo], [Int Fix Dev, Ext Fix Dev], NQ
ØSHN[Ø,3,4][4,5]Z	Insert/Metatarsal-Phalangeal Jt, Lt, [Opn, Perc, Perc Endo], [Int Fix Dev, Ext Fix Dev], NQ
ØSHP[Ø,3,4][4,5]Z	Insert/Toe Phalangeal Jt, Rt, [Opn, Perc, Perc Endo], [Int Fix Dev, Ext Fix Dev], NQ
ØSHQ[Ø,3,4][4,5]Z	Insert/Toe Phalangeal Jt, Lt, [Opn, Perc, Perc Endo], [Int Fix Dev, Ext Fix Dev], NQ
ØSJ[H,J]ØZZ	Inspect of [Rt, Lt] Tarsal Jt, Opn Appr
ØSJ[K,L]ØZZ	Inspect of [Rt, Lt] Metatarsal-Tarsal Jt, Opn Appr
ØSJ[M,N]ØZZ	Inspect of [Rt, Lt] Metatarsal-Phalangeal Jt, Opn Appr
ØSJ[P,Q]ØZZ	Inspect of [Rt, Lt] Toe Phalangeal Jt, Opn Appr
ØSNH[Ø,3,4]ZZ	Rls/Tarsal Jt, Rt, [Opn, Perc, Perc Endo]
ØSNJ[Ø,3,4]ZZ	Rls/Tarsal Jt, Lt, [Opn, Perc, Perc Endo]

Surgical	**Medical**	**CC Indicator**	**MCC Indicator**	**Procedure Proxy**	**[PDxMCC] PDx acts as own MCC**	**[PDxCC] PDx acts as own CC**

MDC 8: Diseases And Disorders Of The Musculoskeletal System And Connective Tissue—SURGICAL

ØSNK[Ø,3,4]ZZ   Rls/Metatarsal-Tarsal Jt, Rt, [Opn, Perc, Perc Endo]
ØSNL[Ø,3,4]ZZ   Rls/Metatarsal-Tarsal Jt, Lt, [Opn, Perc, Perc Endo]
ØSNM[Ø,3,4]ZZ   Rls/Metatarsal-Phalangeal Jt, Rt, [Opn, Perc, Perc Endo]
ØSNN[Ø,3,4]ZZ   Rls/Metatarsal-Phalangeal Jt, Lt, [Opn, Perc, Perc Endo]
ØSNP[Ø,3,4]ZZ   Rls/Toe Phalangeal Jt, Rt, [Opn, Perc, Perc Endo]
ØSNQ[Ø,3,4]ZZ   Rls/Toe Phalangeal Jt, Lt, [Opn, Perc, Perc Endo]
ØSPH[Ø,3,4][Ø,3,4,5,7,K]Z Rmvl/Tarsal Jt, Rt, [Opn, Perc, Perc Endo], [Drain Dev, Inf Dev, Int Fix Dev, Ext Fix Dev, Auto Tissue Sub, Nonauto Tissue Sub], NQ
ØSPJ[Ø,3,4][Ø,3,4,5,7,K]Z Rmvl/Tarsal Jt, Lt, [Opn, Perc, Perc Endo], [Drain Dev, Inf Dev, Int Fix Dev, Ext Fix Dev, Auto Tissue Sub, Nonauto Tissue Sub], NQ
ØSPK[Ø,3,4][Ø,3,4,5,7,K]Z Rmvl/Metatarsal-Tarsal Jt, Rt, [Opn, Perc, Perc Endo], [Drain Dev, Inf Dev, Int Fix Dev, Ext Fix Dev, Auto Tissue Sub, Nonauto Tissue Sub], NQ
ØSPL[Ø,3,4][Ø,3,4,5,7,K]Z Rmvl/Metatarsal-Tarsal Jt, Lt, [Opn, Perc, Perc Endo], [Drain Dev, Inf Dev, Int Fix Dev, Ext Fix Dev, Auto Tissue Sub, Nonauto Tissue Sub], NQ
ØSPM[Ø,3,4][Ø,3,4,5,7,K]Z Rmvl/Metatarsal-Phalangeal Jt, Rt, [Opn, Perc, Perc Endo], [Drain Dev, Inf Dev, Int Fix Dev, Ext Fix Dev, Auto Tissue Sub, Nonauto Tissue Sub], NQ
ØSPN[Ø,3,4][Ø,3,4,5,7,K]Z Rmvl/Metatarsal-Phalangeal Jt, Lt, [Opn, Perc, Perc Endo], [Drain Dev, Inf Dev, Int Fix Dev, Ext Fix Dev, Auto Tissue Sub, Nonauto Tissue Sub], NQ
ØSPP[Ø,3,4][Ø,3,4,5,7,K]Z Rmvl/Toe Phalangeal Jt, Rt, [Opn, Perc, Perc Endo], [Drain Dev, Inf Dev, Int Fix Dev, Ext Fix Dev, Auto Tissue Sub, Nonauto Tissue Sub], NQ
ØSPQ[Ø,3,4][Ø,3,4,5,7,K]Z Rmvl/Toe Phalangeal Jt, Lt, [Opn, Perc, Perc Endo], [Drain Dev, Inf Dev, Int Fix Dev, Ext Fix Dev, Auto Tissue Sub, Nonauto Tissue Sub], NQ
ØSRH*   Replace/Tarsal Jt, Rt
ØSRJ*   Replace/Tarsal Jt, Lt
ØSRK*   Replace/Metatarsal-Tarsal Jt, Rt
ØSRL*   Replace/Metatarsal-Tarsal Jt, Lt
ØSRM*   Replace/Metatarsal-Phalangeal Jt, Rt
ØSRN*   Replace/Metatarsal-Phalangeal Jt, Lt
ØSRP*   Replace/Toe Phalangeal Jt, Rt
ØSRQ*   Replace/Toe Phalangeal Jt, Lt
ØSSHØ[4,5,Z]Z   Repos/Tarsal Jt, Rt, Opn, [Int Fix Dev, Ext Fix Dev, No Dev], NQ
ØSSJØ[4,5,Z]Z   Repos/Tarsal Jt, Lt, Opn, [Int Fix Dev, Ext Fix Dev, No Dev], NQ
ØSSKØ[4,5,Z]Z   Repos/Metatarsal-Tarsal Jt, Rt, Opn, [Int Fix Dev, Ext Fix Dev, No Dev], NQ
ØSSLØ[4,5,Z]Z   Repos/Metatarsal-Tarsal Jt, Lt, Opn, [Int Fix Dev, Ext Fix Dev, No Dev], NQ
ØSSMØ[4,5,Z]Z   Repos/Metatarsal-Phalangeal Jt, Rt, Opn, [Int Fix Dev, Ext Fix Dev, No Dev], NQ
ØSSNØ[4,5,Z]Z   Repos/Metatarsal-Phalangeal Jt, Lt, Opn, [Int Fix Dev, Ext Fix Dev, No Dev], NQ
ØSSPØ[4,5,Z]Z   Repos/Toe Phalangeal Jt, Rt, Opn, [Int Fix Dev, Ext Fix Dev, No Dev], NQ
ØSSQØ[4,5,Z]Z   Repos/Toe Phalangeal Jt, Lt, Opn, [Int Fix Dev, Ext Fix Dev, No Dev], NQ
ØST[H,J]ØZZ   Resect of [Rt, Lt] Tarsal Jt, Opn Appr
ØST[K,L]ØZZ   Resect of [Rt Metatarsal-Tarsal Jt, Lt Metatarsal-Tarsal Jt], Opn
ØST[M,N]ØZZ   Resect of [Rt Metatarsal-Phalangeal Jt, Rt Metatarsal-Phalangeal Jt], Opn
ØST[P,Q]ØZZ   Resect of [Rt Toe Phalangeal Jt, Lt Toe Phalangeal Jt], Opn
ØSWH[Ø,3,4][Ø,3,4,5,7,8,K]Z Rev/Tarsal Jt, Rt, [Opn, Perc, Perc Endo], [Drain Dev, Inf Dev, Int Fix Dev, Ext Fix Dev, Auto Tissue Sub, Spacer, Nonauto Tissue Sub], NQ
ØSWJ[Ø,3,4][Ø,3,4,5,7,8,K]Z Rev/Tarsal Jt, Lt, [Opn, Perc, Perc Endo], [Drain Dev, Inf Dev, Int Fix Dev, Ext Fix Dev, Auto Tissue Sub, Spacer, Nonauto Tissue Sub], NQ
ØSWK[Ø,3,4][Ø,3,4,5,7,8,K]Z Rev/Metatarsal-Tarsal Jt, Rt, [Opn, Perc, Perc Endo], [Drain Dev, Inf Dev, Int Fix Dev, Ext Fix Dev, Auto Tissue Sub, Spacer, Nonauto Tissue Sub], NQ
ØSWL[Ø,3,4][Ø,3,4,5,7,8,K]Z Rev/Metatarsal-Tarsal Jt, Lt, [Opn, Perc, Perc Endo], [Drain Dev, Inf Dev, Int Fix Dev, Ext Fix Dev, Auto Tissue Sub, Spacer, Nonauto Tissue Sub], NQ
ØSWM[Ø,3,4][Ø,3,4,5,7,8,K]Z Rev/Metatarsal-Phalangeal Jt, Rt, [Opn, Perc, Perc Endo], [Drain Dev, Inf Dev, Int Fix Dev, Ext Fix Dev, Auto Tissue Sub, Spacer, Nonauto Tissue Sub], NQ
ØSWN[Ø,3,4][Ø,3,4,5,7,8,K]Z Rev/Metatarsal-Phalangeal Jt, Lt, [Opn, Perc, Perc Endo], [Drain Dev, Inf Dev, Int Fix Dev, Ext Fix Dev, Auto Tissue Sub, Spacer, Nonauto Tissue Sub], NQ
ØSWP[Ø,3,4][Ø,3,4,5,7,8,K]Z Rev/Toe Phalangeal Jt, Rt, [Opn, Perc, Perc Endo], [Drain Dev, Inf Dev, Int Fix Dev, Ext Fix Dev, Auto Tissue Sub, Spacer, Nonauto Tissue Sub], NQ

ØSWQ[Ø,3,4][Ø,3,4,5,7,8,K]Z Rev/Toe Phalangeal Jt, Lt, [Opn, Perc, Perc Endo], [Drain Dev, Inf Dev, Int Fix Dev, Ext Fix Dev, Auto Tissue Sub, Spacer, Nonauto Tissue Sub], NQ
ØY6P*   Detach/1st Toe, Rt
ØY6Q*   Detach/1st Toe, Lt
ØY6R*   Detach/2nd Toe, Rt
ØY6S*   Detach/2nd Toe, Lt
ØY6T*   Detach/3rd Toe, Rt
ØY6U*   Detach/3rd Toe, Lt
ØY6V*   Detach/4th Toe, Rt
ØY6W*   Detach/4th Toe, Lt
ØY6X*   Detach/5th Toe, Rt
ØY6Y*   Detach/5th Toe, Lt
ØYM[P,Q]ØZZ   Reattach of [Rt, Lt] 1st Toe, Opn Appr
ØYM[R,S]ØZZ   Reattach of [Rt, Lt] 2nd Toe, Opn Appr
ØYM[T,U]ØZZ   Reattach of [Rt, Lt] 3rd Toe, Opn Appr
ØYM[V,W]ØZZ   Reattach of [Rt, Lt] 4th Toe, Opn Appr
ØYM[X,Y]ØZZ   Reattach of [Rt, Lt] 5th Toe, Opn Appr

DRG 504   **Foot Procedures with CC**

GMLOS 5.Ø   AMLOS 5.9   RW 1.5941

Select operating room procedures listed under DRG 503

DRG 505   **Foot Procedures without CC/MCC**

GMLOS 2.9   AMLOS 3.5   RW 1.259Ø

Select operating room procedures listed under DRG 503

DRG 506   **Major Thumb or Joint Procedures**

GMLOS 3.4   AMLOS 4.3   RW 1.349Ø

Operating Room Procedures

ØM95ØØZ   Drain of Rt Wrist Bursa/Lig with Drain Dev, Opn Appr
ØM95ØZZ   Drain of Rt Wrist Bursa & Lgmt, Opn Appr
ØM953ØZ   Drain of Rt Wrist Bursa/Lig with Drain Dev, Perc Appr
ØM954ØZ   Drain Rt Wrist Bursa/Lig w Drain Dev, Perc Endo
ØM96ØØZ   Drain of Lt Wrist Bursa/Lig with Drain Dev, Opn Appr
ØM96ØZZ   Drain of Lt Wrist Bursa & Lgmt, Opn Appr
ØM963ØZ   Drain of Lt Wrist Bursa/Lig with Drain Dev, Perc Appr
ØM964ØZ   Drain Lt Wrist Bursa/Lig w Drain Dev, Perc Endo
ØMC5*   Extir/Wrist Bursa & Lgmt, Rt
ØMC6*   Extir/Wrist Bursa & Lgmt, Lt
ØR9NØ[Ø,Z]Z   Drain/Wrist Jt, Rt, Opn, [Drain Dev, No Dev], NQ
ØR9PØ[Ø,Z]Z   Drain/Wrist Jt, Lt, Opn, [Drain Dev, No Dev], NQ
ØR9QØ[Ø,Z]Z   Drain/Carpal Jt, Rt, Opn, [Drain Dev, No Dev], NQ
ØR9RØ[Ø,Z]Z   Drain/Carpal Jt, Lt, Opn, [Drain Dev, No Dev], NQ
ØR9SØ[Ø,Z]Z   Drain/Metacarpocarpal Jt, Rt, Opn, [Drain Dev, No Dev], NQ
ØR9TØ[Ø,Z]Z   Drain/Metacarpocarpal Jt, Lt, Opn, [Drain Dev, No Dev], NQ
ØR9UØ[Ø,Z]Z   Drain/Metacarpophalangeal Jt, Rt, Opn, [Drain Dev, No Dev], NQ
ØR9VØ[Ø,Z]Z   Drain/Metacarpophalangeal Jt, Lt, Opn, [Drain Dev, No Dev], NQ
ØR9WØ[Ø,Z]Z   Drain/Finger Phalangeal Jt, Rt, Opn, [Drain Dev, No Dev], NQ
ØR9XØ[Ø,Z]Z   Drain/Finger Phalangeal Jt, Lt, Opn, [Drain Dev, No Dev], NQ
ØRCN*   Extir/Wrist Jt, Rt
ØRCP*   Extir/Wrist Jt, Lt
ØRCQ*   Extir/Carpal Jt, Rt
ØRCR*   Extir/Carpal Jt, Lt
ØRCS*   Extir/Metacarpocarpal Jt, Rt
ØRCT*   Extir/Metacarpocarpal Jt, Lt
ØRCU*   Extir/Metacarpophalangeal Jt, Rt
ØRCV*   Extir/Metacarpophalangeal Jt, Lt
ØRCW*   Extir/Finger Phalangeal Jt, Rt
ØRCX*   Extir/Finger Phalangeal Jt, Lt
ØRHN[Ø,3,4][4,5]Z Insert/Wrist Jt, Rt, [Opn, Perc, Perc Endo], [Int Fix Dev, Ext Fix Dev], NQ
ØRHP[Ø,3,4][4,5]Z Insert/Wrist Jt, Lt, [Opn, Perc, Perc Endo], [Int Fix Dev, Ext Fix Dev], NQ
ØRHQ[Ø,3,4][4,5]Z Insert/Carpal Jt, Rt, [Opn, Perc, Perc Endo], [Int Fix Dev, Ext Fix Dev], NQ
ØRHR[Ø,3,4][4,5]Z Insert/Carpal Jt, Lt, [Opn, Perc, Perc Endo], [Int Fix Dev, Ext Fix Dev], NQ
ØRHS[Ø,3,4][4,5]Z Insert/Metacarpocarpal Jt, Rt, [Opn, Perc, Perc Endo], [Int Fix Dev, Ext Fix Dev], NQ
ØRHT[Ø,3,4][4,5]Z Insert/Metacarpocarpal Jt, Lt, [Opn, Perc, Perc Endo], [Int Fix Dev, Ext Fix Dev], NQ
ØRHU[Ø,3,4][4,5]Z Insert/Metacarpophalangeal Jt, Rt, [Opn, Perc, Perc Endo], [Int Fix Dev, Ext Fix Dev], NQ

T Transfer DRG   SP Special Payment   * Code Range   6th and 7th Character of ZZ = No Device, No Qualifier   ZX = No Device, Diagnostic

146   MS-DRG Version 33.0   © 2015 Optum360, LLC

ØRHV[Ø,3,4][4,5]Z Insert/Metacarpophalangeal Jt, Lt, [Opn, Perc, Perc Endo], [Int Fix Dev, Ext Fix Dev], NQ

ØRHW[Ø,3,4][4,5]Z Insert/Finger Phalangeal Jt, Rt, [Opn, Perc, Perc Endo], [Int Fix Dev, Ext Fix Dev], NQ

ØRHX[Ø,3,4][4,5]Z Insert/Finger Phalangeal Jt, Lt, [Opn, Perc, Perc Endo], [Int Fix Dev, Ext Fix Dev], NQ

ØRJ[N,P,Q,R]ØZZ Inspect of [Rt Wrist Jt, Lt Wrist Jt, Rt Carpal Jt, Lt Carpal Jt], Opn Appr

ØRJ[S,T]ØZZ Inspect of [Rt Metacarpocarpal Jt, Lt Metacarpocarpal Jt], Opn Appr

ØRJ[U,V]ØZZ Inspect of [Rt Metacarpophalangeal Jt, Lt Metacarpophalangeal Jt], Opn Appr

ØRJ[W,X]ØZZ Inspect of [Rt Finger Phalangeal Jt, Lt Finger Phalangeal Jt], Opn Appr

ØRPN[Ø,3,4][Ø,3,4,5,7,K]Z Rmvl/Wrist Jt, Rt, [Opn, Perc, Perc Endo], [Drain Dev, Inf Dev, Int Fix Dev, Ext Fix Dev, Auto Tissue Sub, Nonauto Tissue Sub], NQ

ØRPP[Ø,3,4][Ø,3,4,5,7,K]Z Rmvl/Wrist Jt, Lt, [Opn, Perc, Perc Endo], [Drain Dev, Inf Dev, Int Fix Dev, Ext Fix Dev, Auto Tissue Sub, Nonauto Tissue Sub], NQ

ØRPQ[Ø,3,4][Ø,3,4,5,7,K]Z Rmvl/Carpal Jt, Rt, [Opn, Perc, Perc Endo], [Drain Dev, Inf Dev, Int Fix Dev, Ext Fix Dev, Auto Tissue Sub, Nonauto Tissue Sub], NQ

ØRPR[Ø,3,4][Ø,3,4,5,7,K]ZRmvl/Carpal Jt, Lt, [Opn, Perc, Perc Endo], [Drain Dev, Inf Dev, Int Fix Dev, Ext Fix Dev, Auto Tissue Sub, Nonauto Tissue Sub], NQ

ØRPS[Ø,3,4][Ø,3,4,5,7,K]Z Rmvl/Metacarpocarpal Jt, Rt, [Opn, Perc, Perc Endo], [Drain Dev, Inf Dev, Int Fix Dev, Ext Fix Dev, Auto Tissue Sub, Nonauto Tissue Sub], NQ

ØRPT[Ø,3,4][Ø,3,4,5,7,K]Z Rmvl/Metacarpocarpal Jt, Lt, [Opn, Perc, Perc Endo], [Drain Dev, Inf Dev, Int Fix Dev, Ext Fix Dev, Auto Tissue Sub, Nonauto Tissue Sub], NQ

ØRPU[Ø,3,4][Ø,3,4,5,7,K]Z Rmvl/Metacarpophalangeal Jt, Rt, [Opn, Perc, Perc Endo], [Drain Dev, Inf Dev, Int Fix Dev, Ext Fix Dev, Auto Tissue Sub, Nonauto Tissue Sub], NQ

ØRPV[Ø,3,4][Ø,3,4,5,7,K]Z Rmvl/Metacarpophalangeal Jt, Lt, [Opn, Perc, Perc Endo], [Drain Dev, Inf Dev, Int Fix Dev, Ext Fix Dev, Auto Tissue Sub, Nonauto Tissue Sub], NQ

ØRPW[Ø,3,4][Ø,3,4,5,7,K]Z Rmvl/Finger Phalangeal Jt, Rt, [Opn, Perc, Perc Endo], [Drain Dev, Inf Dev, Int Fix Dev, Ext Fix Dev, Auto Tissue Sub, Nonauto Tissue Sub], NQ

ØRPX[Ø,3,4][Ø,3,4,5,7,K]Z Rmvl/Finger Phalangeal Jt, Lt, [Opn, Perc, Perc Endo], [Drain Dev, Inf Dev, Int Fix Dev, Ext Fix Dev, Auto Tissue Sub, Nonauto Tissue Sub], NQ

ØRQN* Repair/Wrist Jt, Rt
ØRQP* Repair/Wrist Jt, Lt
ØRQQ* Repair/Carpal Jt, Rt
ØRQR* Repair/Carpal Jt, Lt
ØRQS* Repair/Metacarpocarpal Jt, Rt
ØRQT* Repair/Metacarpocarpal Jt, Lt
ØRQU* Repair/Metacarpophalangeal Jt, Rt
ØRQV* Repair/Metacarpophalangeal Jt, Lt
ØRQW* Repair/Finger Phalangeal Jt, Rt
ØRQX* Repair/Finger Phalangeal Jt, Lt
ØRRQ* Replace/Carpal Jt, Rt
ØRRR* Replace/Carpal Jt, Lt
ØRRS* Replace/Metacarpocarpal Jt, Rt
ØRRT* Replace/Metacarpocarpal Jt, Lt
ØRRU* Replace/Metacarpophalangeal Jt, Rt
ØRRV* Replace/Metacarpophalangeal Jt, Lt
ØRRW* Replace/Finger Phalangeal Jt, Rt
ØRRX* Replace/Finger Phalangeal Jt, Lt
ØRUN* Supl/Wrist Jt, Rt
ØRUP* Supl/Wrist Jt, Lt
ØRUQ* Supl/Carpal Jt, Rt
ØRUR* Supl/Carpal Jt, Lt
ØRUS* Supl/Metacarpocarpal Jt, Rt
ØRUT* Supl/Metacarpocarpal Jt, Lt
ØRUU* Supl/Metacarpophalangeal Jt, Rt
ØRUV* Supl/Metacarpophalangeal Jt, Lt
ØRUW* Supl/Finger Phalangeal Jt, Rt
ØRUX* Supl/Finger Phalangeal Jt, Lt

ØRWN[Ø,3,4][Ø,3,4,5,7,8,K]Z Rev/Wrist Jt, Rt, [Opn, Perc, Perc Endo], [Drain Dev, Inf Dev, Int Fix Dev, Ext Fix Dev, Auto Tissue Sub, Spacer, Nonauto Tissue Sub], NQ

ØRWP[Ø,3,4][Ø,3,4,5,7,8,K]Z Rev/Wrist Jt, Lt, [Opn, Perc, Perc Endo], [Drain Dev, Inf Dev, Int Fix Dev, Ext Fix Dev, Auto Tissue Sub, Spacer, Nonauto Tissue Sub], NQ

ØRWQ[Ø,3,4][Ø,3,4,5,7,8,K]Z Rev/Carpal Jt, Rt, [Opn, Perc, Perc Endo], [Drain Dev, Inf Dev, Int Fix Dev, Ext Fix Dev, Auto Tissue Sub, Spacer, Nonauto Tissue Sub], NQ

ØRWR[Ø,3,4][Ø,3,4,5,7,8,K]Z Rev/Carpal Jt, Lt, [Opn, Perc, Perc Endo], [Drain Dev, Inf Dev, Int Fix Dev, Ext Fix Dev, Auto Tissue Sub, Spacer, Nonauto Tissue Sub], NQ

ØRWS[Ø,3,4][Ø,3,4,5,7,8,K]Z Rev/Metacarpocarpal Jt, Rt, [Opn, Perc, Perc Endo], [Drain Dev, Inf Dev, Int Fix Dev, Ext Fix Dev, Auto Tissue Sub, Spacer, Nonauto Tissue Sub], NQ

ØRWT[Ø,3,4][Ø,3,4,5,7,8,K]Z Rev/Metacarpocarpal Jt, Lt, [Opn, Perc, Perc Endo], [Drain Dev, Inf Dev, Int Fix Dev, Ext Fix Dev, Auto Tissue Sub, Spacer, Nonauto Tissue Sub], NQ

ØRWU[Ø,3,4][Ø,3,4,5,7,8,K]Z Rev/Metacarpophalangeal Jt, Rt, [Opn, Perc, Perc Endo], [Drain Dev, Inf Dev, Int Fix Dev, Ext Fix Dev, Auto Tissue Sub, Spacer, Nonauto Tissue Sub], NQ

ØRWV[Ø,3,4][Ø,3,4,5,7,8,K]Z Rev/Metacarpophalangeal Jt, Lt, [Opn, Perc, Perc Endo], [Drain Dev, Inf Dev, Int Fix Dev, Ext Fix Dev, Auto Tissue Sub, Spacer, Nonauto Tissue Sub], NQ

ØRWW[Ø,3,4][Ø,3,4,5,7,8,K]Z Rev/Finger Phalangeal Jt, Rt, [Opn, Perc, Perc Endo], [Drain Dev, Inf Dev, Int Fix Dev, Ext Fix Dev, Auto Tissue Sub, Spacer, Nonauto Tissue Sub], NQ

ØRWX[Ø,3,4][Ø,3,4,5,7,8,K]Z Rev/Finger Phalangeal Jt, Lt, [Opn, Perc, Perc Endo], [Drain Dev, Inf Dev, Int Fix Dev, Ext Fix Dev, Auto Tissue Sub, Spacer, Nonauto Tissue Sub], NQ

ØXRLØ7N Replace of Rt Thumb with Rt Toe, Autol Sub, Opn Appr
ØXRLØ7P Replace of Rt Thumb with Lt Toe, Autol Sub, Opn Appr
ØXRL47N Replace of Rt Thumb with Rt Toe, Autol Sub, Perc Endo Appr
ØXRL47P Replace of Rt Thumb with Lt Toe, Autol Sub, Perc Endo Appr
ØXRMØ7N Replace of Lt Thumb with Rt Toe, Autol Sub, Opn Appr
ØXRMØ7P Replace of Lt Thumb with Lt Toe, Autol Sub, Opn Appr
ØXRM47N Replace of Lt Thumb with Rt Toe, Autol Sub, Perc Endo Appr
ØXRM47P Replace of Lt Thumb with Lt Toe, Autol Sub, Perc Endo Appr
ØXXNØZL Transfer Rt Index Finger to Rt Thumb, Opn Appr
ØXXPØZM Transfer Lt Index Finger to Lt Thumb, Opn Appr

DRG 507	Major Shoulder or Elbow Joint Procedures with CC/MCC		
GMLOS 4.3	AMLOS 5.3	RW 1.8698	

Operating Room Procedures

ØM9[1,2,3,4]4ZZ Drain of [Rt Shldr, Lt Shldr, Rt Elbow, Lt Elbow] Bursa & Lgmt, Perc Endo Appr

ØR9EØ[Ø,Z]Z Drain/Sternoclavicular Jt, Rt, Opn, [Drain Dev, No Dev], NQ
ØR9FØ[Ø,Z]Z Drain/Sternoclavicular Jt, Lt, Opn, [Drain Dev, No Dev], NQ
ØR9GØ[Ø,Z]Z Drain/Acromioclavicular Jt, Rt, Opn, [Drain Dev, No Dev], NQ
ØR9HØ[Ø,Z]Z Drain/Acromioclavicular Jt, Lt, Opn, [Drain Dev, No Dev], NQ
ØR9JØ[Ø,Z]Z Drain/Shldr Jt, Rt, Opn, [Drain Dev, No Dev], NQ
ØR9KØ[Ø,Z]Z Drain/Shldr Jt, Lt, Opn, [Drain Dev, No Dev], NQ
ØR9LØ[Ø,Z]Z Drain/Elbow Jt, Rt, Opn, [Drain Dev, No Dev], NQ
ØR9MØ[Ø,Z]Z Drain/Elbow Jt, Lt, Opn, [Drain Dev, No Dev], NQ
ØRCE* Extir/Sternoclavicular Jt, Rt
ØRCF* Extir/Sternoclavicular Jt, Lt
ØRCG* Extir/Acromioclavicular Jt, Rt
ØRCH* Extir/Acromioclavicular Jt, Lt
ØRCJ* Extir/Shldr Jt, Rt
ØRCK* Extir/Shldr Jt, Lt
ØRCL* Extir/Elbow Jt, Rt
ØRCM* Extir/Elbow Jt, Lt
ØRGE* Fusion/Sternoclavicular Jt, Rt
ØRGF* Fusion/Sternoclavicular Jt, Lt
ØRGG* Fusion/Acromioclavicular Jt, Rt
ØRGH* Fusion/Acromioclavicular Jt, Lt
ØRGJ* Fusion/Shldr Jt, Rt
ØRGK* Fusion/Shldr Jt, Lt
ØRGL* Fusion/Elbow Jt, Rt
ØRGM* Fusion/Elbow Jt, Lt

ØRHE[Ø,3,4]4Z Insert/Sternoclavicular Jt, Rt, [Opn, Perc, Perc Endo], Int Fix Dev, NQ
ØRHF[Ø,3,4]4Z Insert/Sternoclavicular Jt, Lt, [Opn, Perc, Perc Endo], Int Fix Dev, NQ
ØRHG[Ø,3,4]4Z Insert/Acromioclavicular Jt, Rt, [Opn, Perc, Perc Endo], Int Fix Dev, NQ
ØRHH[Ø,3,4]4Z Insert/Acromioclavicular Jt, Lt, [Opn, Perc, Perc Endo], Int Fix Dev, NQ
ØRHJ[Ø,3,4]4Z Insert/Shldr Jt, Rt, [Opn, Perc, Perc Endo], Int Fix Dev, NQ
ØRHK[Ø,3,4]4Z Insert/Shldr Jt, Lt, [Opn, Perc, Perc Endo], Int Fix Dev, NQ
ØRHL[Ø,3,4][4,5]Z Insert/Elbow Jt, Rt, [Opn, Perc, Perc Endo], [Int Fix Dev, Ext Fix Dev], NQ
ØRHM[Ø,3,4][4,5]Z Insert/Elbow Jt, Lt, [Opn, Perc, Perc Endo], [Int Fix Dev, Ext Fix Dev], NQ

Surgical　　**Medical**　　**CC Indicator**　　**MCC Indicator**　　**Procedure Proxy**　　[PDxMCC] PDx acts as own MCC　　[PDxCC] PDx acts as own CC

MDC 8: Diseases And Disorders Of The Musculoskeletal System And Connective Tissue—SURGICAL

ØRJ[E,F]ØZZ — Inspect of [Rt Sternoclavicular Jt, Lt Sternoclavicular Jt], Opn Appr

ØRJ[G,H]ØZZ — Inspect of [Rt Acromioclavicular Jt, Lt Acromioclavicular Jt], Opn Appr

ØRJ[J,K,L,M]ØZZ — Inspect of [Rt Shldr Jt, Lt Shldr Jt, Rt Elbow Jt, Lt Elbow Jt], Opn Appr

ØRPE[Ø,3,4][Ø,3,4,7,K]Z Rmvl/Sternoclavicular Jt, Rt, [Opn, Perc, Perc Endo], [Drain Dev, Inf Dev, Int Fix Dev, Auto Tissue Sub, Nonauto Tissue Sub], NQ

ØRPF[Ø,3,4][Ø,3,4,7,K]Z Rmvl/Sternoclavicular Jt, Lt, [Opn, Perc, Perc Endo], [Drain Dev, Inf Dev, Int Fix Dev, Auto Tissue Sub, Nonauto Tissue Sub], NQ

ØRPG[Ø,3,4][Ø,3,4,7,K]Z Rmvl/Acromioclavicular Jt, Rt, [Opn, Perc, Perc Endo], [Drain Dev, Inf Dev, Int Fix Dev, Auto Tissue Sub, Nonauto Tissue Sub], NQ

ØRPH[Ø,3,4][Ø,3,4,7,K]Z Rmvl/Acromioclavicular Jt, Lt, [Opn, Perc, Perc Endo], [Drain Dev, Inf Dev, Int Fix Dev, Auto Tissue Sub, Nonauto Tissue Sub], NQ

ØRPJ[Ø,3,4][Ø,3,4,7,K]Z Rmvl/Shldr Jt, Rt, [Opn, Perc, Perc Endo], [Drain Dev, Inf Dev, Int Fix Dev, Auto Tissue Sub, Nonauto Tissue Sub], NQ

ØRPK[Ø,3,4][Ø,3,4,7,K]Z Rmvl/Shldr Jt, Lt, [Opn, Perc, Perc Endo], [Drain Dev, Inf Dev, Int Fix Dev, Auto Tissue Sub, Nonauto Tissue Sub], NQ

ØRPL[Ø,3,4][Ø,3,4,5,7,K]Z Rmvl/Elbow Jt, Rt, [Opn, Perc, Perc Endo], [Drain Dev, Inf Dev, Int Fix Dev, Ext Fix Dev, Auto Tissue Sub, Nonauto Tissue Sub], NQ

ØRPM[Ø,3,4][Ø,3,4,5,7,K]Z Rmvl/Elbow Jt, Lt, [Opn, Perc, Perc Endo], [Drain Dev, Inf Dev, Int Fix Dev, Ext Fix Dev, Auto Tissue Sub, Nonauto Tissue Sub], NQ

ØRQE* — Repair/Sternoclavicular Jt, Rt
ØRQF* — Repair/Sternoclavicular Jt, Lt
ØRQG* — Repair/Acromioclavicular Jt, Rt
ØRQH* — Repair/Acromioclavicular Jt, Lt
ØRQJ* — Repair/Shldr Jt, Rt
ØRQK* — Repair/Shldr Jt, Lt
ØRQL* — Repair/Elbow Jt, Rt
ØRQM* — Repair/Elbow Jt, Lt
ØRUE* — Supl/Sternoclavicular Jt, Rt
ØRUF* — Supl/Sternoclavicular Jt, Lt
ØRUG* — Supl/Acromioclavicular Jt, Rt
ØRUH* — Supl/Acromioclavicular Jt, Lt
ØRUJ* — Supl/Shldr Jt, Rt
ØRUK* — Supl/Shldr Jt, Lt
ØRUL* — Supl/Elbow Jt, Rt
ØRUM* — Supl/Elbow Jt, Lt

ØRWE[Ø,3,4][Ø,3,4,7,8,J,K]Z Rev/Sternoclavicular Jt, Rt, [Opn, Perc, Perc Endo], [Drain Dev, Inf Dev, Int Fix Dev, Auto Tissue Sub, Spacer, Synth Sub, Nonauto Tissue Sub], NQ

ØRWF[Ø,3,4][Ø,3,4,7,8,J,K]Z Rev/Sternoclavicular Jt, Lt, [Opn, Perc, Perc Endo], [Drain Dev, Inf Dev, Int Fix Dev, Auto Tissue Sub, Spacer, Synth Sub, Nonauto Tissue Sub], NQ

ØRWG[Ø,3,4][Ø,3,4,7,8,K]Z Rev/Acromioclavicular Jt, Rt, [Opn, Perc, Perc Endo], [Drain Dev, Inf Dev, Int Fix Dev, Auto Tissue Sub, Spacer, Nonauto Tissue Sub], NQ

ØRWH[Ø,3,4][Ø,3,4,7,8,K]Z Rev/Acromioclavicular Jt, Lt, [Opn, Perc, Perc Endo], [Drain Dev, Inf Dev, Int Fix Dev, Auto Tissue Sub, Spacer, Nonauto Tissue Sub], NQ

ØRWJ[Ø,3,4][Ø,3,4,7,8,K]Z Rev/Shldr Jt, Rt, [Opn, Perc, Perc Endo], [Drain Dev, Inf Dev, Int Fix Dev, Auto Tissue Sub, Spacer, Nonauto Tissue Sub], NQ

ØRWK[Ø,3,4][Ø,3,4,7,8,K]Z Rev/Shldr Jt, Lt, [Opn, Perc, Perc Endo], [Drain Dev, Inf Dev, Int Fix Dev, Auto Tissue Sub, Spacer, Nonauto Tissue Sub], NQ

ØRWL[Ø,3,4][Ø,3,4,5,7,8,K]Z Rev/Elbow Jt, Rt, [Opn, Perc, Perc Endo], [Drain Dev, Inf Dev, Int Fix Dev, Ext Fix Dev, Auto Tissue Sub, Spacer, Nonauto Tissue Sub], NQ

ØRWM[Ø,3,4][Ø,3,4,5,7,8,K]Z Rev/Elbow Jt, Lt, [Opn, Perc, Perc Endo], [Drain Dev, Inf Dev, Int Fix Dev, Ext Fix Dev, Auto Tissue Sub, Spacer, Nonauto Tissue Sub], NQ

DRG 508   Major Shoulder or Elbow Joint Procedures without CC/MCC
GMLOS 2.2   AMLOS 2.7   RW 1.6134

Select operating room procedures listed under DRG 507

DRG 509   Arthroscopy
GMLOS 3.4   AMLOS 4.8   RW 1.6562

Operating Room Procedures

ØRJ[Ø,1,3]4ZZ — Inspect of [Occipital-cervical Jt, Cervical Vert Jt, Cervical Vert Disc], Perc Endo

ØRJ[4,5,6,9]4ZZ — Inspect of [Cervicothoracic Vert Jt, Cervicothoracic Vert Disc, Thoracic Vert Jt, Thoracic Vert Disc], Perc Endo

ØRJ[A,B]4ZZ — Inspect of [Thoracolumbar Vert Jt, Thoracolumbar Vert Disc], Perc Endo

ØRJ[E,F]4ZZ — Inspect of [Rt Sternoclavicular Jt, Lt Sternoclavicular Jt], Perc Endo

ØRJ[G,H]4ZZ — Inspect of [Rt Acromioclavicular Jt, Lt Acromioclavicular Jt], Perc Endo

ØRJ[J,K,L,M]4ZZ — Inspect of [Rt Shldr Jt, Lt Shldr Jt, Rt Elbow Jt, Lt Elbow Jt], Perc Endo

ØRJ[N,P,Q,R]4ZZ — Inspect of [Rt Wrist Jt, Lt Wrist Jt, Rt Carpal Jt, Lt Carpal Jt], Perc Endo

ØRJ[S,T]4ZZ — Inspect of [Rt Metacarpocarpal Jt, Lt Metacarpocarpal Jt], Perc Endo

ØRJ[U,V]4ZZ — Inspect of [Rt Metacarpophalangeal Jt, Lt Metacarpophalangeal Jt], Perc Endo

ØRJ[W,X]4ZZ — Inspect of [Rt Finger Phalangeal Jt, Lt Finger Phalangeal Jt], Perc Endo

ØSJ[Ø,3,5,6]4ZZ — Inspect of [Lumbar Vert, Lumbosacral, Sacrococcygeal, Coccygeal] Jt, Perc Endo

ØSJ[7,8,9,B]4ZZ — Inspect of [Rt Sacroiliac, Lt Sacroiliac, Rt Hip Jt, Lt Hip] Jt, Perc Endo

ØSJ[C,D,F,G,H,J]4ZZ Inspect of [Rt Knee, Lt Knee, Rt Ankle, Lt Ankle, Rt Tarsal, Lt Tarsal] Jt, Perc Endo

ØSJ[K,L]4ZZ — Inspect of [Rt Metatarsal-Tarsal, Lt Metatarsal-Tarsal] Jt, Perc Endo

ØSJ[M,N]4ZZ — Inspect of [Rt Metatarsal-Phalangeal, Lt Metatarsal-Phalangeal] Jt, Perc Endo

ØSJ[P,Q]4ZZ — Inspect of [Rt Toe Phalangeal, Lt Toe Phalangeal] Jt, Perc Endo

DRG 510   Shoulder, Elbow or Forearm Procedures, Except Major Joint Procedures with MCC
GMLOS 4.8   AMLOS 5.9   RW 2.442Ø   [T]

Operating Room Procedures

ØLQ1* — Repair/Shldr Tndn, Rt
ØLQ2* — Repair/Shldr Tndn, Lt
ØP8H* — Div/Radius, Rt
ØP8J* — Div/Radius, Lt
ØP8K* — Div/Ulna, Rt
ØP8L* — Div/Ulna, Lt
ØPBH[Ø,3,4]ZZ — Exc/Radius, Rt, [Opn, Perc, Perc Endo]
ØPBJ[Ø,3,4]ZZ — Exc/Radius, Lt, [Opn, Perc, Perc Endo]
ØPBK[Ø,3,4]ZZ — Exc/Ulna, Rt, [Opn, Perc, Perc Endo]
ØPBL[Ø,3,4]ZZ — Exc/Ulna, Lt, [Opn, Perc, Perc Endo]
ØPCH* — Extir/Radius, Rt
ØPCJ* — Extir/Radius, Lt
ØPCK* — Extir/Ulna, Rt
ØPCL* — Extir/Ulna, Lt

ØPHH[Ø,3,4][4,5,6,B,C,D]Z Insert/Radius, Rt, [Opn, Perc, Perc Endo], [Int Fix Dev, Ext Fix Dev, Int Fix Dev, Intramedullary Int Fix Dev, Ext Fix Dev, Monop, Ext Fix Dev, Ring, Ext Fix Dev, Hybrid], NQ

ØPHJ[Ø,3,4][4,5,6,B,C,D]Z Insert/Radius, Lt, [Opn, Perc, Perc Endo], [Int Fix Dev, Ext Fix Dev, Int Fix Dev, Intramedullary Int Fix Dev, Ext Fix Dev, Monop, Ext Fix Dev, Ring, Ext Fix Dev, Hybrid], NQ

ØPHK[Ø,3,4][4,5,6,B,C,D]Z Insert/Ulna, Rt, [Opn, Perc, Perc Endo], [Int Fix Dev, Ext Fix Dev, Int Fix Dev, Intramedullary Int Fix Dev, Ext Fix Dev, Monop, Ext Fix Dev, Ring, Ext Fix Dev, Hybrid], NQ

ØPHL[Ø,3,4][4,5,6,B,C,D]Z Insert/Ulna, Lt, [Opn, Perc, Perc Endo], [Int Fix Dev, Ext Fix Dev, Int Fix Dev, Intramedullary Int Fix Dev, Ext Fix Dev, Monop, Ext Fix Dev, Ring, Ext Fix Dev, Hybrid], NQ

ØPNH* — Rls/Radius, Rt
ØPNJ* — Rls/Radius, Lt
ØPNK* — Rls/Ulna, Rt
ØPNL* — Rls/Ulna, Lt
ØPQH* — Repair/Radius, Rt
ØPQJ* — Repair/Radius, Lt
ØPQK* — Repair/Ulna, Rt
ØPQL* — Repair/Ulna, Lt
ØPRH* — Replace/Radius, Rt
ØPRJ* — Replace/Radius, Lt
ØPRK* — Replace/Ulna, Rt
ØPRL* — Replace/Ulna, Lt

[T] Transfer DRG   [SP] Special Payment   * Code Range   6th and 7th Character of ZZ = No Device, No Qualifier ZX = No Device, Diagnostic

148   MS-DRG Version 33.0   © 2015 Optum360, LLC

0PSH0ZZ	Repos Rt Radius, Opn Appr
0PSH[0,3,4][4,5,6,B,C,D]Z	Repos/Radius, Rt, [Opn, Perc, Perc Endo], [Int Fix Dev, Ext Fix Dev, Int Fix Dev, Intramedullary Int Fix Dev, Ext Fix Dev, Monop, Ext Fix Dev, Ring, Ext Fix Dev, Hybrid], NQ
0PSJ0ZZ	Repos Lt Radius, Opn Appr
0PSJ[0,3,4][4,5,6,B,C,D]Z	Repos/Radius, Lt, [Opn, Perc, Perc Endo], [Int Fix Dev, Ext Fix Dev, Int Fix Dev, Intramedullary Int Fix Dev, Ext Fix Dev, Monop, Ext Fix Dev, Ring, Ext Fix Dev, Hybrid], NQ
0PSK0ZZ	Repos Rt Ulna, Opn Appr
0PSK[0,3,4][4,5,6,B,C,D]Z	Repos/Ulna, Rt, [Opn, Perc, Perc Endo], [Int Fix Dev, Ext Fix Dev, Int Fix Dev, Intramedullary Int Fix Dev, Ext Fix Dev, Monop, Ext Fix Dev, Ring, Ext Fix Dev, Hybrid], NQ
0PSL0ZZ	Repos Lt Ulna, Opn Appr
0PSL[0,3,4][4,5,6,B,C,D]Z	Repos/Ulna, Lt, [Opn, Perc, Perc Endo], [Int Fix Dev, Ext Fix Dev, Int Fix Dev, Intramedullary Int Fix Dev, Ext Fix Dev, Monop, Ext Fix Dev, Ring, Ext Fix Dev, Hybrid], NQ
0PT[H,J,K,L]0ZZ	Resect of [Rt Radius, Lt Radius, Rt Ulna, Lt Ulna], Opn Appr
0PUH*	Supl/Radius, Rt
0PUJ*	Supl/Radius, Lt
0PUK*	Supl/Ulna, Rt
0PUL*	Supl/Ulna, Lt
0RBE[0,3,4]ZZ	Exc/Sternoclavicular Jt, Rt, [Opn, Perc, Perc Endo]
0RBF[0,3,4]ZZ	Exc/Sternoclavicular Jt, Lt, [Opn, Perc, Perc Endo]
0RBG[0,3,4]ZZ	Exc/Acromioclavicular Jt, Rt, [Opn, Perc, Perc Endo]
0RBH[0,3,4]ZZ	Exc/Acromioclavicular Jt, Lt, [Opn, Perc, Perc Endo]
0RBJ[0,3,4]ZZ	Exc/Shldr Jt, Rt, [Opn, Perc, Perc Endo]
0RBK[0,3,4]ZZ	Exc/Shldr Jt, Lt, [Opn, Perc, Perc Endo]
0RBL[0,3,4]ZZ	Exc/Elbow Jt, Rt, [Opn, Perc, Perc Endo]
0RBM[0,3,4]ZZ	Exc/Elbow Jt, Lt, [Opn, Perc, Perc Endo]
0RNE[0,3,4]ZZ	Rls/Sternoclavicular Jt, Rt, [Opn, Perc, Perc Endo]
0RNF[0,3,4]ZZ	Rls/Sternoclavicular Jt, Lt, [Opn, Perc, Perc Endo]
0RNG[0,3,4]ZZ	Rls/Acromioclavicular Jt, Rt, [Opn, Perc, Perc Endo]
0RNH[0,3,4]ZZ	Rls/Acromioclavicular Jt, Lt, [Opn, Perc, Perc Endo]
0RNJ[0,3,4]ZZ	Rls/Shldr Jt, Rt, [Opn, Perc, Perc Endo]
0RNK[0,3,4]ZZ	Rls/Shldr Jt, Lt, [Opn, Perc, Perc Endo]
0RNL[0,3,4]ZZ	Rls/Elbow Jt, Rt, [Opn, Perc, Perc Endo]
0RNM[0,3,4]ZZ	Rls/Elbow Jt, Lt, [Opn, Perc, Perc Endo]
0RSE0[4,Z]Z	Repos/Sternoclavicular Jt, Rt, Opn, [Int Fix Dev, No Dev], NQ
0RSF0[4,Z]Z	Repos/Sternoclavicular Jt, Lt, Opn, [Int Fix Dev, No Dev], NQ
0RSG0[4,Z]Z	Repos/Acromioclavicular Jt, Rt, Opn, [Int Fix Dev, No Dev], NQ
0RSH0[4,Z]Z	Repos/Acromioclavicular Jt, Lt, Opn, [Int Fix Dev, No Dev], NQ
0RSJ0[4,Z]Z	Repos/Shldr Jt, Rt, Opn, [Int Fix Dev, No Dev], NQ
0RSK0[4,Z]Z	Repos/Shldr Jt, Lt, Opn, [Int Fix Dev, No Dev], NQ
0RSL0[4,5,Z]Z	Repos/Elbow Jt, Rt, Opn, [Int Fix Dev, Ext Fix Dev, No Dev], NQ
0RSM0[4,5,Z]Z	Repos/Elbow Jt, Lt, Opn, [Int Fix Dev, Ext Fix Dev, No Dev], NQ
0RT[E,F]0ZZ	Resect of [Rt, Lt] Sternoclavicular Jt, Opn Appr
0RT[G,H]0ZZ	Resect of [Rt, Lt] Acromioclavicular Jt, Opn Appr
0RT[J,K,L,M]0ZZ	Resect of [Rt Shldr, Lt Shldr, Rt Elbow, Lt Elbow] Jt, Opn Appr

DRG 511　Shoulder, Elbow or Forearm Procedures, Except Major Joint Procedures with CC

GMLOS 3.3	AMLOS 3.9	RW 1.7018	T

Select operating room procedures listed under DRG 510

DRG 512　Shoulder, Elbow or Forearm Procedures, Except Major Joint Procedures without CC/MCC

GMLOS 2.1	AMLOS 2.5	RW 1.3531	T

Select operating room procedures listed under DRG 510

DRG 513　Hand or Wrist Procedures, Except Major Thumb or Joint Procedures with CC/MCC

GMLOS 3.8	AMLOS 4.9	RW 1.5025

Operating Room Procedures

01N5*	Rls/Median Nerve
0H8[F,G]XZZ	Div of [Rt, Lt] Hand Skin, Ext Appr
0HRF*	Replace/Skin, Rt Hand
0HRG*	Replace/Skin, Lt Hand
0J8J*	Div/SQ Tissue & Fascia, Rt Hand
0J8K*	Div/SQ Tissue & Fascia, Lt Hand
0J9J[0,3][0,Z]Z	Drain/SQ Tissue & Fascia, Rt Hand, [Opn, Perc], [Drain Dev, No Dev], NQ
0J9K[0,3][0,Z]Z	Drain/SQ Tissue & Fascia, Lt Hand, [Opn, Perc], [Drain Dev, No Dev], NQ
0JBJ[0,3]ZZ	Exc/SQ Tissue & Fascia, Rt Hand, [Opn, Perc]
0JBK[0,3]ZZ	Exc/SQ Tissue & Fascia, Lt Hand, [Opn, Perc]

0JDJ*	Extract/SQ Tissue & Fascia, Rt Hand
0JDK*	Extract/SQ Tissue & Fascia, Lt Hand
0JHJ*	Insert/SQ Tissue & Fascia, Rt Hand
0JHK*	Insert/SQ Tissue & Fascia, Lt Hand
0JNJ[0,3]ZZ	Rls/SQ Tissue & Fascia, Rt Hand, [Opn, Perc]
0JNK[0,3]ZZ	Rls/SQ Tissue & Fascia, Lt Hand, [Opn, Perc]
0JQJ*	Repair/SQ Tissue & Fascia, Rt Hand
0JQK*	Repair/SQ Tissue & Fascia, Lt Hand
0JRJ07Z	Replace of Rt Hand SQ/Fascia with Autol Sub, Opn Appr
0JRJ0JZ	Replace of Rt Hand SQ/Fascia with Synth Sub, Opn Appr
0JRJ0KZ	Replace Rt Hand SQ/Fascia w Nonaut Sub, Opn
0JRJ3JZ	Replace of Rt Hand SQ/Fascia with Synth Sub, Perc Appr
0JRJ3KZ	Replace Rt Hand SQ/Fascia w Nonaut Sub, Perc
0JRK07Z	Replace of Lt Hand SQ/Fascia with Autol Sub, Opn Appr
0JRK0JZ	Replace of Lt Hand SQ/Fascia with Synth Sub, Opn Appr
0JRK0KZ	Replace Lt Hand SQ/Fascia w Nonaut Sub, Opn
0JRK3JZ	Replace of Lt Hand SQ/Fascia with Synth Sub, Perc Appr
0JRK3KZ	Replace Lt Hand SQ/Fascia w Nonaut Sub, Perc
0JUJ*	Supl/SQ Tissue & Fascia, Rt Hand
0JUK*	Supl/SQ Tissue & Fascia, Lt Hand
0JXJ[0,3]Z[B,C]	Transfer/SQ Tissue & Fascia, Rt Hand, [Opn, Perc], No Dev, [Skin and SQ Tissue, Skin, SQ Tissue & Fascia]
0JXK[0,3]Z[B,C]	Transfer/SQ Tissue & Fascia, Lt Hand, [Opn, Perc], No Dev, [Skin and SQ Tissue, Skin, SQ Tissue & Fascia]
0K5C*	Destr/Hand Muscle, Rt
0K5D*	Destr/Hand Muscle, Lt
0K8C*	Div/Hand Muscle, Rt
0K8D*	Div/Hand Muscle, Lt
0K9C00Z	Drain of Rt Hand Muscle with Drain Dev, Opn Appr
0K9C0ZZ	Drain of Rt Hand Muscle, Opn Appr
0K9C30Z	Drain of Rt Hand Muscle with Drain Dev, Perc Appr
0K9C40Z	Drain of Rt Hand Muscle with Drain Dev, Perc Endo Appr
0K9D00Z	Drain of Lt Hand Muscle with Drain Dev, Opn Appr
0K9D0ZZ	Drain of Lt Hand Muscle, Opn Appr
0K9D30Z	Drain of Lt Hand Muscle with Drain Dev, Perc Appr
0K9D40Z	Drain of Lt Hand Muscle with Drain Dev, Perc Endo Appr
0KBC[0,3,4]ZZ	Exc/Hand Muscle, Rt, [Opn, Perc, Perc Endo]
0KBD[0,3,4]ZZ	Exc/Hand Muscle, Lt, [Opn, Perc, Perc Endo]
0KCC*	Extir/Hand Muscle, Rt
0KCD*	Extir/Hand Muscle, Lt
0KMC*	Reattach/Hand Muscle, Rt
0KMD*	Reattach/Hand Muscle, Lt
0KNC[0,3,4]ZZ	Rls/Hand Muscle, Rt, [Opn, Perc, Perc Endo]
0KND[0,3,4]ZZ	Rls/Hand Muscle, Lt, [Opn, Perc, Perc Endo]
0KQC*	Repair/Hand Muscle, Rt
0KQD*	Repair/Hand Muscle, Lt
0KSC*	Repos/Hand Muscle, Rt
0KSD*	Repos/Hand Muscle, Lt
0KTC*	Resect/Hand Muscle, Rt
0KTD*	Resect/Hand Muscle, Lt
0KUC*	Supl/Hand Muscle, Rt
0KUD*	Supl/Hand Muscle, Lt
0KXC*	Transfer/Hand Muscle, Rt
0KXD*	Transfer/Hand Muscle, Lt
0L57*	Destr/Hand Tndn, Rt
0L58*	Destr/Hand Tndn, Lt
0L87*	Div/Hand Tndn, Rt
0L88*	Div/Hand Tndn, Lt
0L9700Z	Drain of Rt Hand Tndn with Drain Dev, Opn Appr
0L970ZZ	Drain of Rt Hand Tndn, Opn Appr
0L9730Z	Drain of Rt Hand Tndn with Drain Dev, Perc Appr
0L9740Z	Drain of Rt Hand Tndn with Drain Dev, Perc Endo Appr
0L9800Z	Drain of Lt Hand Tndn with Drain Dev, Opn Appr
0L980ZZ	Drain of Lt Hand Tndn, Opn Appr
0L9830Z	Drain of Lt Hand Tndn with Drain Dev, Perc Appr
0L9840Z	Drain of Lt Hand Tndn with Drain Dev, Perc Endo Appr
0LB7[0,3,4]ZZ	Exc/Hand Tndn, Rt, [Opn, Perc, Perc Endo]
0LB8[0,3,4]ZZ	Exc/Hand Tndn, Lt, [Opn, Perc, Perc Endo]
0LC7*	Extir/Hand Tndn, Rt
0LC8*	Extir/Hand Tndn, Lt
0LJX0ZZ	Inspect of Upr Tndn, Opn Appr
0LJX3ZZ	Inspect of Upr Tndn, Perc Appr
0LJX4ZZ	Inspect of Upr Tndn, Perc Endo Appr
0LM7*	Reattach/Hand Tndn, Rt
0LM8*	Reattach/Hand Tndn, Lt
0LN7[0,3,4]ZZ	Rls/Hand Tndn, Rt, [Opn, Perc, Perc Endo]
0LN8[0,3,4]ZZ	Rls/Hand Tndn, Lt, [Opn, Perc, Perc Endo]
0LQ7*	Repair/Hand Tndn, Rt
0LQ8*	Repair/Hand Tndn, Lt
0LR7*	Replace/Hand Tndn, Rt

ØLR8*	Replace/Hand Tndn, Lt
ØLS7*	Repos/Hand Tndn, Rt
ØLS8*	Repos/Hand Tndn, Lt
ØLT7*	Resect/Hand Tndn, Rt
ØLT8*	Resect/Hand Tndn, Lt
ØLU7*	Supl/Hand Tndn, Rt
ØLU8*	Supl/Hand Tndn, Lt
ØLX7*	Transfer/Hand Tndn, Rt
ØLX8*	Transfer/Hand Tndn, Lt
ØM55*	Destr/Wrist Bursa & Lgmt, Rt
ØM56*	Destr/Wrist Bursa & Lgmt, Lt
ØM57*	Destr/Hand Bursa & Lgmt, Rt
ØM58*	Destr/Hand Bursa & Lgmt, Lt
ØM87*	Div/Hand Bursa & Lgmt, Rt
ØM88*	Div/Hand Bursa & Lgmt, Lt
ØM97Ø[Ø,Z]Z	Drain/Hand Bursa & Lgmt, Rt, Opn, [Drain Dev, No Dev], NQ
ØM98Ø[Ø,Z]Z	Drain/Hand Bursa & Lgmt, Lt, Opn, [Drain Dev, No Dev], NQ
ØMB7[Ø,3,4]ZZ	Exc/Hand Bursa & Lgmt, Rt, [Opn, Perc, Perc Endo]
ØMB8[Ø,3,4]ZZ	Exc/Hand Bursa & Lgmt, Lt, [Opn, Perc, Perc Endo]
ØMC7*	Extir/Hand Bursa & Lgmt, Rt
ØMC8*	Extir/Hand Bursa & Lgmt, Lt
ØMD7*	Extract/Hand Bursa & Lgmt, Rt
ØMD8*	Extract/Hand Bursa & Lgmt, Lt
ØMN7*	Rls/Hand Bursa & Lgmt, Rt
ØMN8*	Rls/Hand Bursa & Lgmt, Lt
ØMT7*	Resect/Hand Bursa & Lgmt, Rt
ØMT8*	Resect/Hand Bursa & Lgmt, Lt
ØP5M*	Destr/Carpal, Rt
ØP5N*	Destr/Carpal, Lt
ØP5P*	Destr/Metacarpal, Rt
ØP5Q*	Destr/Metacarpal, Lt
ØP8M*	Div/Carpal, Rt
ØP8N*	Div/Carpal, Lt
ØP8P*	Div/Metacarpal, Rt
ØP8Q*	Div/Metacarpal, Lt
ØP9M*	Drain/Carpal, Rt
ØP9N*	Drain/Carpal, Lt
ØP9P*	Drain/Metacarpal, Rt
ØP9Q*	Drain/Metacarpal, Lt
ØPBM*	Exc/Carpal, Rt
ØPBN*	Exc/Carpal, Lt
ØPBP*	Exc/Metacarpal, Rt
ØPBQ*	Exc/Metacarpal, Lt
ØPCM*	Extir/Carpal, Rt
ØPCN*	Extir/Carpal, Lt
ØPCP*	Extir/Metacarpal, Rt
ØPCQ*	Extir/Metacarpal, Lt
ØPHM*	Insert/Carpal, Rt
ØPHN*	Insert/Carpal, Lt
ØPHP*	Insert/Metacarpal, Rt
ØPHQ*	Insert/Metacarpal, Lt
ØPNM*	Rls/Carpal, Rt
ØPNN*	Rls/Carpal, Lt
ØPNP*	Rls/Metacarpal, Rt
ØPNQ*	Rls/Metacarpal, Lt
ØPQM*	Repair/Carpal, Rt
ØPQN*	Repair/Carpal, Lt
ØPQP*	Repair/Metacarpal, Rt
ØPQQ*	Repair/Metacarpal, Lt
ØPRM*	Replace/Carpal, Rt
ØPRN*	Replace/Carpal, Lt
ØPRP*	Replace/Metacarpal, Rt
ØPRQ*	Replace/Metacarpal, Lt
ØPSMØZZ	Repos Rt Carpal, Opn Appr
ØPSM[Ø,3,4][4,5]Z	Repos/Carpal, Rt, [Opn, Perc, Perc Endo], [Int Fix Dev, Ext Fix Dev], NQ
ØPSNØZZ	Repos Lt Carpal, Opn Appr
ØPSN[Ø,3,4][4,5]Z	Repos/Carpal, Lt, [Opn, Perc, Perc Endo], [Int Fix Dev, Ext Fix Dev], NQ
ØPSPØZZ	Repos Rt Metacarpal, Opn Appr
ØPSP[Ø,3,4][4,5]Z	Repos/Metacarpal, Rt, [Opn, Perc, Perc Endo], [Int Fix Dev, Ext Fix Dev], NQ
ØPSQØZZ	Repos Lt Metacarpal, Opn Appr
ØPSQ[Ø,3,4][4,5]Z	Repos/Metacarpal, Lt, [Opn, Perc, Perc Endo], [Int Fix Dev, Ext Fix Dev], NQ
ØPSRØZZ	Repos Rt Thumb Phalanx, Opn Appr
ØPSR[Ø,3,4]4Z	Repos/Thumb Phalanx, Rt, [Opn, Perc, Perc Endo], Int Fix Dev, NQ
ØPSSØZZ	Repos Lt Thumb Phalanx, Opn Appr

ØPSS[Ø,3,4]4Z	Repos/Thumb Phalanx, Lt, [Opn, Perc, Perc Endo], Int Fix Dev, NQ
ØPSTØZZ	Repos Rt Finger Phalanx, Opn Appr
ØPST[Ø,3,4]4Z	Repos/Finger Phalanx, Rt, [Opn, Perc, Perc Endo], Int Fix Dev, NQ
ØPSVØZZ	Repos Lt Finger Phalanx, Opn Appr
ØPSV[Ø,3,4]4Z	Repos/Finger Phalanx, Lt, [Opn, Perc, Perc Endo], Int Fix Dev, NQ
ØPT[M,N,P,Q]ØZZ	Resect of [Rt Carpal, Lt Carpal, Rt Metacarpal, Lt Metacarpal], Opn Appr
ØPUM*	Supl/Carpal, Rt
ØPUN*	Supl/Carpal, Lt
ØPUP*	Supl/Metacarpal, Rt
ØPUQ*	Supl/Metacarpal, Lt
ØPWM[Ø,3,4][4,5,7,J,K]Z	Rev/Carpal, Rt, [Opn, Perc, Perc Endo], [Int Fix Dev, Ext Fix Dev, Auto Tissue Sub, Synth Sub, Nonauto Tissue Sub], NQ
ØPWN[Ø,3,4][4,5,7,J,K]Z	Rev/Carpal, Lt, [Opn, Perc, Perc Endo], [Int Fix Dev, Ext Fix Dev, Auto Tissue Sub, Synth Sub, Nonauto Tissue Sub], NQ
ØPWP[Ø,3,4][4,5,7,J,K]Z	Rev/Metacarpal, Rt, [Opn, Perc, Perc Endo], [Int Fix Dev, Ext Fix Dev, Auto Tissue Sub, Synth Sub, Nonauto Tissue Sub], NQ
ØPWQ[Ø,3,4][4,5,7,J,K]Z	Rev/Metacarpal, Lt, [Opn, Perc, Perc Endo], [Int Fix Dev, Ext Fix Dev, Auto Tissue Sub, Synth Sub, Nonauto Tissue Sub], NQ
ØR5N*	Destr/Wrist Jt, Rt
ØR5P*	Destr/Wrist Jt, Lt
ØR5Q*	Destr/Carpal Jt, Rt
ØR5R*	Destr/Carpal Jt, Lt
ØR5S*	Destr/Metacarpocarpal Jt, Rt
ØR5T*	Destr/Metacarpocarpal Jt, Lt
ØR5U*	Destr/Metacarpophalangeal Jt, Rt
ØR5V*	Destr/Metacarpophalangeal Jt, Lt
ØR5W*	Destr/Finger Phalangeal Jt, Rt
ØR5X*	Destr/Finger Phalangeal Jt, Lt
ØRBN[Ø,3,4]ZZ	Exc/Wrist Jt, Rt, [Opn, Perc, Perc Endo]
ØRBP[Ø,3,4]ZZ	Exc/Wrist Jt, Lt, [Opn, Perc, Perc Endo]
ØRBQ[Ø,3,4]ZZ	Exc/Carpal Jt, Rt, [Opn, Perc, Perc Endo]
ØRBR[Ø,3,4]ZZ	Exc/Carpal Jt, Lt, [Opn, Perc, Perc Endo]
ØRBS[Ø,3,4]ZZ	Exc/Metacarpocarpal Jt, Rt, [Opn, Perc, Perc Endo]
ØRBT[Ø,3,4]ZZ	Exc/Metacarpocarpal Jt, Lt, [Opn, Perc, Perc Endo]
ØRBU[Ø,3,4]ZZ	Exc/Metacarpophalangeal Jt, Rt, [Opn, Perc, Perc Endo]
ØRBV[Ø,3,4]ZZ	Exc/Metacarpophalangeal Jt, Lt, [Opn, Perc, Perc Endo]
ØRBW[Ø,3,4]ZZ	Exc/Finger Phalangeal Jt, Rt, [Opn, Perc, Perc Endo]
ØRBX[Ø,3,4]ZZ	Exc/Finger Phalangeal Jt, Lt, [Opn, Perc, Perc Endo]
Ørgn*	Fusion/Wrist Jt, Rt
ØRGP*	Fusion/Wrist Jt, Lt
ØRGQ*	Fusion/Carpal Jt, Rt
ØRGR*	Fusion/Carpal Jt, Lt
ØRGS*	Fusion/Metacarpocarpal Jt, Rt
ØRGT*	Fusion/Metacarpocarpal Jt, Lt
ØRGU*	Fusion/Metacarpophalangeal Jt, Rt
ØRGV*	Fusion/Metacarpophalangeal Jt, Lt
ØRGW*	Fusion/Finger Phalangeal Jt, Rt
ØRGX*	Fusion/Finger Phalangeal Jt, Lt
ØRNN[Ø,3,4]ZZ	Rls/Wrist Jt, Rt, [Opn, Perc, Perc Endo]
ØRNP[Ø,3,4]ZZ	Rls/Wrist Jt, Lt, [Opn, Perc, Perc Endo]
ØRNQ[Ø,3,4]ZZ	Rls/Carpal Jt, Rt, [Opn, Perc, Perc Endo]
ØRNR[Ø,3,4]ZZ	Rls/Carpal Jt, Lt, [Opn, Perc, Perc Endo]
ØRNS[Ø,3,4]ZZ	Rls/Metacarpocarpal Jt, Rt, [Opn, Perc, Perc Endo]
ØRNT[Ø,3,4]ZZ	Rls/Metacarpocarpal Jt, Lt, [Opn, Perc, Perc Endo]
ØRNU[Ø,3,4]ZZ	Rls/Metacarpophalangeal Jt, Rt, [Opn, Perc, Perc Endo]
ØRNV[Ø,3,4]ZZ	Rls/Metacarpophalangeal Jt, Lt, [Opn, Perc, Perc Endo]
ØRNW[Ø,3,4]ZZ	Rls/Finger Phalangeal Jt, Rt, [Opn, Perc, Perc Endo]
ØRNX[Ø,3,4]ZZ	Rls/Finger Phalangeal Jt, Lt, [Opn, Perc, Perc Endo]
ØRSNØ[4,5,Z]Z	Repos/Wrist Jt, Rt, Opn, [Int Fix Dev, Ext Fix Dev, No Dev], NQ
ØRSPØ[4,5,Z]Z	Repos/Wrist Jt, Lt, Opn, [Int Fix Dev, Ext Fix Dev, No Dev], NQ
ØRSQØ[4,5,Z]Z	Repos/Carpal Jt, Rt, Opn, [Int Fix Dev, Ext Fix Dev, No Dev], NQ
ØRSRØ[4,5,Z]Z	Repos/Carpal Jt, Lt, Opn, [Int Fix Dev, Ext Fix Dev, No Dev], NQ
ØRSSØ[4,5,Z]Z	Repos/Metacarpocarpal Jt, Rt, Opn, [Int Fix Dev, Ext Fix Dev, No Dev], NQ
ØRSTØ[4,5,Z]Z	Repos/Metacarpocarpal Jt, Lt, Opn, [Int Fix Dev, Ext Fix Dev, No Dev], NQ
ØRSUØ[4,5,Z]Z	Repos/Metacarpophalangeal Jt, Rt, Opn, [Int Fix Dev, Ext Fix Dev, No Dev], NQ
ØRSVØ[4,5,Z]Z	Repos/Metacarpophalangeal Jt, Lt, Opn, [Int Fix Dev, Ext Fix Dev, No Dev], NQ
ØRSWØ[4,5,Z]Z	Repos/Finger Phalangeal Jt, Rt, Opn, [Int Fix Dev, Ext Fix Dev, No Dev], NQ
ØRSXØ[4,5,Z]Z	Repos/Finger Phalangeal Jt, Lt, Opn, [Int Fix Dev, Ext Fix Dev, No Dev], NQ

T Transfer DRG   SP Special Payment   * Code Range   6th and 7th Character of ZZ = No Device, No Qualifier ZX = No Device, Diagnostic

MS-DRG Version 33.0

ØRT[N,P]ØZZ	Resect of [Rt, Lt] Wrist Jt, Opn Appr
ØRT[Q,R]ØZZ	Resect of [Rt, Lt] Carpal Jt, Opn Appr
ØRT[S,T]ØZZ	Resect of [Rt, Lt] Metacarpocarpal Jt, Opn Appr
ØRT[U,V]ØZZ	Resect of [Rt, Lt] Metacarpophalangeal Jt, Opn Appr
ØRT[W,X]ØZZ	Resect of [Rt, Lt] Finger Phalangeal Jt, Opn Appr
ØX6L*	Detach/Thumb, Rt
ØX6M*	Detach/Thumb, Lt
ØX6N*	Detach/Index Finger, Rt
ØX6P*	Detach/Index Finger, Lt
ØX6Q*	Detach/Mid Finger, Rt
ØX6R*	Detach/Mid Finger, Lt
ØX6S*	Detach/Ring Finger, Rt
ØX6T*	Detach/Ring Finger, Lt
ØX6V*	Detach/Little Finger, Rt
ØX6W*	Detach/Little Finger, Lt
ØXM[L,M]ØZZ	Reattach of [Rt, Lt] Thumb, Opn Appr
ØXM[N,P]ØZZ	Reattach of [Rt, Lt] Index Finger, Opn Appr
ØXM[Q,R]ØZZ	Reattach of [Rt, Lt] Mid Finger, Opn Appr
ØXM[S,T]ØZZ	Reattach of [Rt, Lt] Ring Finger, Opn Appr
ØXM[V,W]ØZZ	Reattach of [Rt, Lt] Little Finger, Opn Appr
ØXUJ[Ø,4]7Z	Supl/Hand, Rt, [Opn, Perc Endo], Auto Tissue Sub, NQ
ØXUK[Ø,4]7Z	Supl/Hand, Lt, [Opn, Perc Endo], Auto Tissue Sub, NQ
ØXUL[Ø,4]7Z	Supl/Thumb, Rt, [Opn, Perc Endo], Auto Tissue Sub, NQ
ØXUM[Ø,4]7Z	Supl/Thumb, Lt, [Opn, Perc Endo], Auto Tissue Sub, NQ
ØXUN[Ø,4]7Z	Supl/Index Finger, Rt, [Opn, Perc Endo], Auto Tissue Sub, NQ
ØXUP[Ø,4]7Z	Supl/Index Finger, Lt, [Opn, Perc Endo], Auto Tissue Sub, NQ
ØXUQ[Ø,4]7Z	Supl/Mid Finger, Rt, [Opn, Perc Endo], Auto Tissue Sub, NQ
ØXUR[Ø,4]7Z	Supl/Mid Finger, Lt, [Opn, Perc Endo], Auto Tissue Sub, NQ
ØXUS[Ø,4]7Z	Supl/Ring Finger, Rt, [Opn, Perc Endo], Auto Tissue Sub, NQ
ØXUT[Ø,4]7Z	Supl/Ring Finger, Lt, [Opn, Perc Endo], Auto Tissue Sub, NQ
ØXUV[Ø,4]7Z	Supl/Little Finger, Rt, [Opn, Perc Endo], Auto Tissue Sub, NQ
ØXUW[Ø,4]7Z	Supl/Little Finger, Lt, [Opn, Perc Endo], Auto Tissue Sub, NQ

DRG 514   Hand or Wrist Procedures, Except Major Thumb or Joint Procedures without CC/MCC

GMLOS 2.3   AMLOS 2.8   RW 0.9055

Select operating room procedures listed under DRG 513

DRG 515   Other Musculoskeletal System and Connective Tissue O.R. Procedures with MCC

GMLOS 7.0   AMLOS 8.9   RW 3.1862   [SP]

Operating Room Procedures

008F*	Div/Olfactory Nerve
008G*	Div/Optic Nerve
008H*	Div/Oculomotor Nerve
008J*	Div/Trochlear Nerve
008L*	Div/Abducens Nerve
008M*	Div/Facial Nerve
008N*	Div/Acoustic Nerve
008R*	Div/Accessory Nerve
008S*	Div/Hypoglossal Nerve
009[F,G,H,J]ØZZ	Drain of [Olfactory, Optic, Oculomotor, Trochlear] Nerve, Opn, Dx
009[K,L,M,N]ØZX	Drain of [Trigeminal, Abducens, Facial, Acoustic] Nerve, Opn, Dx
009[P,Q,R,S]ØZX	Drain of [Glossopharyngeal, Vagus, Accessory, Hypoglossal] Nerve, Opn, Dx
00BFØZX	Exc of Olfactory Nerve, Opn Appr, Diagnostic
00BF[Ø,3,4]ZZ	Exc/Olfactory Nerve, [Opn, Perc, Perc Endo]
00BGØZX	Exc of Optic Nerve, Opn Appr, Diagnostic
00BG[Ø,3,4]ZZ	Exc/Optic Nerve, [Opn, Perc, Perc Endo]
00BHØZX	Exc of Oculomotor Nerve, Opn Appr, Diagnostic
00BH[Ø,3,4]ZZ	Exc/Oculomotor Nerve, [Opn, Perc, Perc Endo]
00BJØZX	Exc of Trochlear Nerve, Opn Appr, Diagnostic
00BJ[Ø,3,4]ZZ	Exc/Trochlear Nerve, [Opn, Perc, Perc Endo]
00BKØZX	Exc of Trigeminal Nerve, Opn Appr, Diagnostic
00BK[Ø,3,4]ZZ	Exc/Trigeminal Nerve, [Opn, Perc, Perc Endo]
00BLØZX	Exc of Abducens Nerve, Opn Appr, Diagnostic
00BL[Ø,3,4]ZZ	Exc/Abducens Nerve, [Opn, Perc, Perc Endo]
00BMØZX	Exc of Facial Nerve, Opn Appr, Diagnostic
00BM[Ø,3,4]ZZ	Exc/Facial Nerve, [Opn, Perc, Perc Endo]
00BNØZX	Exc of Acoustic Nerve, Opn Appr, Diagnostic
00BN[3,4]ZZ	Exc/Acoustic Nerve, [Perc, Perc Endo]
00BPØZX	Exc of Glossopharyngeal Nerve, Opn Appr, Diagn
00BP[Ø,3,4]ZZ	Exc/Glossopharyngeal Nerve, [Opn, Perc, Perc Endo]
00BQØZX	Exc of Vagus Nerve, Opn Appr, Diagnostic
00BQ[Ø,3,4]ZZ	Exc/Vagus Nerve, [Opn, Perc, Perc Endo]
00BRØZX	Exc of Accessory Nerve, Opn Appr, Diagnostic
00BR[Ø,3,4]ZZ	Exc/Accessory Nerve, [Opn, Perc, Perc Endo]
00BSØZX	Exc of Hypoglossal Nerve, Opn Appr, Diagnostic
00BS[Ø,3,4]ZZ	Exc/Hypoglossal Nerve, [Opn, Perc, Perc Endo]
00DF*	Extract/Olfactory Nerve
00DG*	Extract/Optic Nerve
00DH*	Extract/Oculomotor Nerve
00DJ*	Extract/Trochlear Nerve
00DK*	Extract/Trigeminal Nerve
00DL*	Extract/Abducens Nerve
00DM*	Extract/Facial Nerve
00DN*	Extract/Acoustic Nerve
00DP*	Extract/Glossopharyngeal Nerve
00DQ*	Extract/Vagus Nerve
00DR*	Extract/Accessory Nerve
00DS*	Extract/Hypoglossal Nerve
00HE[Ø,3,4]MZ	Insert/Cranial Nerve, [Opn, Perc, Perc Endo], Neurostimulator Lead, NQ
00PE[Ø,3,4,X]MZ	Rmvl/Cranial Nerve, [Opn, Perc, Perc Endo, Ext], Neurostimulator Lead, NQ
0180*	Div/Cervical Plexus
0182*	Div/Phrenic Nerve
0183*	Div/Brachial Plexus
0184*	Div/Ulnar Nerve
0185*	Div/Median Nerve
0186*	Div/Radial Nerve
0189*	Div/Lumbar Plexus
018A*	Div/Lumbosacral Plexus
018C*	Div/Pudendal Nerve
018D*	Div/Femor Nerve
018F*	Div/Sciatic Nerve
018G*	Div/Tibial Nerve
018H*	Div/Peroneal Nerve
018Q*	Div/Sacral Plexus
019[0,1,2,3]ØZX	Drain of [Cervical Plexus, Cervical Nerve, Phrenic Nerve, Brachial Plexus], Opn, Dx
019[4,5,6,8]ØZX	Drain of [Ulnar, Median, Radial, Thoracic] Nerve, Opn, Dx
019[9,A,B,C]ØZX	Drain of [Lumbar Plexus, Lumbosacral Plexus, Lumbar Nerve, Pudenal Nerve], Opn, Dx
019[D,F,G,H]ØZX	Drain of [Femor, Sciatic, Tibial, Peroneal] Nerve, Opn, Dx
019[Q,R]ØZX	Drain of [Sacral Plexus, Sacral Nerve], Opn, Dx
01B00ZX	Exc of Cervical Plexus, Opn Appr, Diagnostic
01B0[Ø,3,4]ZZ	Exc/Cervical Plexus, [Opn, Perc, Perc Endo]
01B10ZX	Exc of Cervical Nerve, Opn Appr, Diagnostic
01B1[Ø,3,4]ZZ	Exc/Cervical Nerve, [Opn, Perc, Perc Endo]
01B20ZX	Exc of Phrenic Nerve, Opn Appr, Diagnostic
01B2[Ø,3,4]ZZ	Exc/Phrenic Nerve, [Opn, Perc, Perc Endo]
01B30ZX	Exc of Brachial Plexus, Opn Appr, Diagnostic
01B3[Ø,3,4]ZZ	Exc/Brachial Plexus, [Opn, Perc, Perc Endo]
01B40ZX	Exc of Ulnar Nerve, Opn Appr, Diagnostic
01B4[Ø,3,4]ZZ	Exc/Ulnar Nerve, [Opn, Perc, Perc Endo]
01B50ZX	Exc of Median Nerve, Opn Appr, Diagnostic
01B5[Ø,3,4]ZZ	Exc/Median Nerve, [Opn, Perc, Perc Endo]
01B60ZX	Exc of Radial Nerve, Opn Appr, Diagnostic
01B6[Ø,3,4]ZZ	Exc/Radial Nerve, [Opn, Perc, Perc Endo]
01B80ZX	Exc of Thoracic Nerve, Opn Appr, Diagnostic
01B8[Ø,3,4]ZZ	Exc/Thoracic Nerve, [Opn, Perc, Perc Endo]
01B90ZX	Exc of Lumbar Plexus, Opn Appr, Diagnostic
01B9[Ø,3,4]ZZ	Exc/Lumbar Plexus, [Opn, Perc, Perc Endo]
01BA0ZX	Exc of Lumbosacral Plexus, Opn Appr, Diagnostic
01BA[Ø,3,4]ZZ	Exc/Lumbosacral Plexus, [Opn, Perc, Perc Endo]
01BB0ZX	Exc of Lumbar Nerve, Opn Appr, Diagnostic
01BB[Ø,3,4]ZZ	Exc/Lumbar Nerve, [Opn, Perc, Perc Endo]
01BC0ZX	Exc of Pudendal Nerve, Opn Appr, Diagnostic
01BC[Ø,3,4]ZZ	Exc/Pudendal Nerve, [Opn, Perc, Perc Endo]
01BD0ZX	Exc of Femor Nerve, Opn Appr, Diagnostic
01BD[Ø,3,4]ZZ	Exc/Femor Nerve, [Opn, Perc, Perc Endo]
01BF0ZX	Exc of Sciatic Nerve, Opn Appr, Diagnostic
01BF[Ø,3,4]ZZ	Exc/Sciatic Nerve, [Opn, Perc, Perc Endo]
01BG0ZX	Exc of Tibial Nerve, Opn Appr, Diagnostic
01BG[Ø,3,4]ZZ	Exc/Tibial Nerve, [Opn, Perc, Perc Endo]
01BH0ZX	Exc of Peroneal Nerve, Opn Appr, Diagnostic
01BH[Ø,3,4]ZZ	Exc/Peroneal Nerve, [Opn, Perc, Perc Endo]
01BQ0ZX	Exc of Sacral Plexus, Opn Appr, Diagnostic
01BQ[Ø,3,4]ZZ	Exc/Sacral Plexus, [Opn, Perc, Perc Endo]
01BR0ZX	Exc of Sacral Nerve, Opn Appr, Diagnostic
01BR[Ø,3,4]ZZ	Exc/Sacral Nerve, [Opn, Perc, Perc Endo]
01DØ*	Extract/Cervical Plexus
01D1*	Extract/Cervical Nerve
01D2*	Extract/Phrenic Nerve

Surgical   **Medical**   **CC Indicator**   **MCC Indicator**   **Procedure Proxy**   [PDxMCC] **PDx acts as own MCC**   [PDxCC] **PDx acts as own CC**

01D3*	Extract/Brachial Plexus	04733[4,D,Z]Z	Dilation/Hepatic Artery, Perc, [Drug-eluting Intralum Dev, Intralum Dev, No Dev], NQ
01D4*	Extract/Ulnar Nerve		
01D5*	Extract/Median Nerve	04743[4,D,Z]Z	Dilation/Splenic Artery, Perc, [Drug-eluting Intralum Dev, Intralum Dev, No Dev], NQ
01D6*	Extract/Radial Nerve		
01D8*	Extract/Thoracic Nerve	04753[4,D,Z]Z	Dilation/Superior Mesenteric Artery, Perc, [Drug-eluting Intralum Dev, Intralum Dev, No Dev], NQ
01D9*	Extract/Lumbar Plexus		
01DA*	Extract/Lumbosacral Plexus	04763[4,D,Z]Z	Dilation/Colic Artery, Rt, Perc, [Drug-eluting Intralum Dev, Intralum Dev, No Dev], NQ
01DB*	Extract/Lumbar Nerve		
01DC*	Extract/Pudendal Nerve	04773[4,D,Z]Z	Dilation/Colic Artery, Lt, Perc, [Drug-eluting Intralum Dev, Intralum Dev, No Dev], NQ
01DD*	Extract/Femor Nerve		
01DF*	Extract/Sciatic Nerve	04783[4,D,Z]Z	Dilation/Colic Artery, Mid, Perc, [Drug-eluting Intralum Dev, Intralum Dev, No Dev], NQ
01DG*	Extract/Tibial Nerve		
01DH*	Extract/Peroneal Nerve	04793[4,D,Z]Z	Dilation/Renal Artery, Rt, Perc, [Drug-eluting Intralum Dev, Intralum Dev, No Dev], NQ
01DQ*	Extract/Sacral Plexus		
01DR*	Extract/Sacral Nerve	047A3[4,D,Z]Z	Dilation/Renal Artery, Lt, Perc, [Drug-eluting Intralum Dev, Intralum Dev, No Dev], NQ
01HY[0,3,4]MZ	Insert/Peripheral Nerve, [Opn, Perc, Perc Endo], Neurostimulator Lead, NQ	047B3[4,D,Z]Z	Dilation/Inferior Mesenteric Artery, Perc, [Drug-eluting Intralum Dev, Intralum Dev, No Dev], NQ
01N0*	Rls/Cervical Nerve		
01N1*	Rls/Cervical Nerve	047C3[4,D,Z]Z	Dilation/Common Iliac Artery, Rt, Perc, [Drug-eluting Intralum Dev, Intralum Dev, No Dev], NQ
01N2*	Rls/Phrenic Nerve		
01N3*	Rls/Brachial Plexus	047D3[4,D,Z]Z	Dilation/Common Iliac Artery, Lt, Perc, [Drug-eluting Intralum Dev, Intralum Dev, No Dev], NQ
01N4*	Rls/Ulnar Nerve		
01N6*	Rls/Radial Nerve	047E3[4,D,Z]Z	Dilation/Int Iliac Artery, Rt, Perc, [Drug-eluting Intralum Dev, Intralum Dev, No Dev], NQ
01N8*	Rls/Thoracic Nerve		
01N9*	Rls/Lumbar Plexus	047F3[4,D,Z]Z	Dilation/Int Iliac Artery, Lt, Perc, [Drug-eluting Intralum Dev, Intralum Dev, No Dev], NQ
01NA*	Rls/Lumbosacral Plexus		
01NB*	Rls/Lumbar Nerve	047H3[4,D,Z]Z	Dilation/Ext Iliac Artery, Rt, Perc, [Drug-eluting Intralum Dev, Intralum Dev, No Dev], NQ
01NC*	Rls/Pudendal Nerve		
01ND*	Rls/Femor Nerve	047J3[4,D,Z]Z	Dilation/Ext Iliac Artery, Lt, Perc, [Drug-eluting Intralum Dev, Intralum Dev, No Dev], NQ
01NF*	Rls/Sciatic Nerve		
01NH*	Rls/Peroneal Nerve	047K041	Dilation Rt Fem Art w Drug-elut Intralum, Drug Blln, Opn
01NQ*	Rls/Sacral Plexus	047K0D1	Dilation Rt Fem Art w Intralum Dev, Drug Blln, Opn
01NR*	Rls/Sacral Nerve	047K0Z1	Dilation of Rt Fem Art using Drug Blln, Opn Appr
01PY[0,3,4,X]MZ	Rmvl/Peripheral Nerve, [Opn, Perc, Perc Endo, Ext], Neurostimulator Lead, NQ	047K341	Dilation Rt Fem Art w Drug-elut Intralum, Drug Blln, Perc
		047K3D1	Dilation Rt Fem Art w Intralum Dev, Drug Blln, Perc
01Q0*	Repair/Cervical Plexus	047K3Z1	Dilation of Rt Fem Art using Drug Blln, Perc Appr
01Q1*	Repair/Cervical Nerve	047K3[4,D,Z]Z	Dilation/Femor Artery, Rt, Perc, [Drug-eluting Intralum Dev, Intralum Dev, No Dev], NQ
01Q2*	Repair/Phrenic Nerve		
01Q3*	Repair/Brachial Plexus	047K441	Dilation Rt Fem Art w Drug-elut Intralum, Drug Blln, Perc Endo
01Q4*	Repair/Ulnar Nerve	047K4D1	Dilation Rt Fem Art w Intralum Dev, Drug Blln, Perc Endo
01Q5*	Repair/Median Nerve	047K4Z1	Dilation of Rt Fem Art using Drug Blln, Perc Endo Appr
01Q6*	Repair/Radial Nerve	047L041	Dilation Lt Fem Art w Drug-elut Intralum, Drug Blln, Opn
01Q8*	Repair/Thoracic Nerve	047L0D1	Dilation Lt Fem Art w Intralum Dev, Drug Blln, Opn
01Q9*	Repair/Lumbar Plexus	047L0Z1	Dilation of Lt Fem Art using Drug Blln, Opn Appr
01QA*	Repair/Lumbosacral Plexus	047L341	Dilation Lt Fem Art w Drug-elut Intralum, Drug Blln, Perc
01QB*	Repair/Lumbar Nerve	047L3D1	Dilation Lt Fem Art w Intralum Dev, Drug Blln, Perc
01QC*	Repair/Pudendal Nerve	047L3Z1	Dilation of Lt Fem Art using Drug Blln, Perc Appr
01QD*	Repair/Femor Nerve	047L3[4,D,Z]Z	Dilation/Femor Artery, Lt, Perc, [Drug-eluting Intralum Dev, Intralum Dev, No Dev], NQ
01QF*	Repair/Sciatic Nerve		
01QG*	Repair/Tibial Nerve	047L441	Dilation Lt Fem Art w Drug-elut Intralum, Drug Blln, Perc Endo
01QH*	Repair/Peroneal Nerve	047L4D1	Dilation Lt Fem Art w Intralum Dev, Drug Blln, Perc Endo
01QQ*	Repair/Sacral Plexus	047L4Z1	Dilation of Lt Fem Art using Drug Blln, Perc Endo Appr
02HV[0,3,4][2,D]Z	Insert/Superior Vena Cava, [Opn, Perc, Perc Endo], [Monitoring Dev, Intralum Dev], NQ	047M041	Dilation Rt Popl Art w Drug-elut Intralum, Drug Blln, Opn
		047M0D1	Dilation Rt Popl Art w Intralum Dev, Drug Blln, Opn
02LV*	Occlsn/Superior Vena Cava	047M0Z1	Dilation of Rt Popl Art using Drug Blln, Opn Appr
02VV*	Restrict/Superior Vena Cava	047M341	Dilation Rt Popl Art w Drug-elut Intralum, Drug Blln, Perc
03733[4,D,Z]Z	Dilation/Subclavian Artery, Rt, Perc, [Drug-eluting Intralum Dev, Intralum Dev, No Dev], NQ	047M3D1	Dilation Rt Popl Art w Intralum Dev, Drug Blln, Perc
		047M3Z1	Dilation of Rt Popl Art using Drug Blln, Perc Appr
03743[4,D,Z]Z	Dilation/Subclavian Artery, Lt, Perc, [Drug-eluting Intralum Dev, Intralum Dev, No Dev], NQ	047M441	Dilation Rt Popl Art w Drug-elut Intralum, Drug Blln, Perc Endo
		047M4D1	Dilation Rt Popl Art w Intralum Dev, Drug Blln, Perc Endo
03773[4,D,Z]Z	Dilation/Brachial Artery, Rt, Perc, [Drug-eluting Intralum Dev, Intralum Dev, No Dev], NQ	047M4Z1	Dilation of Rt Popl Art using Drug Blln, Perc Endo Appr
		047N041	Dilation Lt Popl Art w Drug-elut Intralum, Drug Blln, Opn
03783[4,D,Z]Z	Dilation/Brachial Artery, Lt, Perc, [Drug-eluting Intralum Dev, Intralum Dev, No Dev], NQ	047N0D1	Dilation Lt Popl Art w Intralum Dev, Drug Blln, Opn
		047N0Z1	Dilation of Lt Popl Art using Drug Blln, Opn Appr
03793[4,D,Z]Z	Dilation/Ulnar Artery, Rt, Perc, [Drug-eluting Intralum Dev, Intralum Dev, No Dev], NQ	047N341	Dilation Lt Popl Art w Drug-elut Intralum, Drug Blln, Perc
		047N3D1	Dilation Lt Popl Art w Intralum Dev, Drug Blln, Perc
037A3[4,D,Z]Z	Dilation/Ulnar Artery, Lt, Perc, [Drug-eluting Intralum Dev, Intralum Dev, No Dev], NQ	047N3Z1	Dilation of Lt Popl Art using Drug Blln, Perc Appr
		047N441	Dilation Lt Popl Art w Drug-elut Intralum, Drug Blln, Perc Endo
037Y3[4,D,Z]Z	Dilation/Upr Artery, Perc, [Drug-eluting Intralum Dev, Intralum Dev, No Dev], NQ	047N4D1	Dilation Lt Popl Art w Intralum Dev, Drug Blln, Perc Endo
		047N4Z1	Dilation of Lt Popl Art using Drug Blln, Perc Endo Appr
039S[0,3,4]ZX	Drain/Temporal Artery, Rt, [Opn, Perc, Perc Endo]	047Y3[4,D,Z]Z	Dilation/Lwr Artery, Perc, [Drug-eluting Intralum Dev, Intralum Dev, No Dev], NQ
039T[0,3,4]ZX	Drain/Temporal Artery, Lt, [Opn, Perc, Perc Endo]		
03BS[0,3,4]ZX	Exc/Temporal Artery, Rt, [Opn, Perc, Perc Endo]	05793[D,Z]Z	Dilation/Brachial Vein, Rt, Perc, [Intralum Dev, No Dev], NQ
03BT[0,3,4]ZX	Exc/Temporal Artery, Lt, [Opn, Perc, Perc Endo]	057A3[D,Z]Z	Dilation/Brachial Vein, Lt, Perc, [Intralum Dev, No Dev], NQ
04703[4,D,Z]Z	Dilation/Abd Aorta, Perc, [Drug-eluting Intralum Dev, Intralum Dev, No Dev], NQ	057B3[D,Z]Z	Dilation/Basilic Vein, Rt, Perc, [Intralum Dev, No Dev], NQ
		057C3[D,Z]Z	Dilation/Basilic Vein, Lt, Perc, [Intralum Dev, No Dev], NQ
04713[4,D,Z]Z	Dilation/Celiac Artery, Perc, [Drug-eluting Intralum Dev, Intralum Dev, No Dev], NQ	057D3[D,Z]Z	Dilation/Cephalic Vein, Rt, Perc, [Intralum Dev, No Dev], NQ
		057F3[D,Z]Z	Dilation/Cephalic Vein, Lt, Perc, [Intralum Dev, No Dev], NQ
04723[4,D,Z]Z	Dilation/Gastric Artery, Perc, [Drug-eluting Intralum Dev, Intralum Dev, No Dev], NQ	06703[D,Z]Z	Dilation/Inferior Vena Cava, Perc, [Intralum Dev, No Dev], NQ

⊤ **Transfer DRG**   ⑤⑲ **Special Payment**   * **Code Range**   **6th and 7th Character of ZZ = No Device, No Qualifier ZX = No Device, Diagnostic**

06H0[0,3,4]DZ	Insert/Inferior Vena Cava, [Opn, Perc, Perc Endo], Intralum Dev, NQ
06L0*	Occlsn/Inferior Vena Cava
06V0*	Restrict/Inferior Vena Cava
0790[0,3,4]ZX	Drain/Lymphatic, Head, [Opn, Perc, Perc Endo]
0791[0,3,4]ZX	Drain/Lymphatic, Rt Neck, [Opn, Perc, Perc Endo]
0792[0,3,4]ZX	Drain/Lymphatic, Lt Neck, [Opn, Perc, Perc Endo]
0793[0,3,4]ZX	Drain/Lymphatic, Rt Upr Extr, [Opn, Perc, Perc Endo]
0794[0,3,4]ZX	Drain/Lymphatic, Lt Upr Extr, [Opn, Perc, Perc Endo]
0795[0,3,4]ZX	Drain/Lymphatic, Rt Axillary, [Opn, Perc, Perc Endo]
0796[0,3,4]ZX	Drain/Lymphatic, Lt Axillary, [Opn, Perc, Perc Endo]
0797[0,3,4]ZX	Drain/Lymphatic, Thorax, [Opn, Perc, Perc Endo]
0798[0,3,4]ZX	Drain/Lymphatic, Int Mammary, Rt, [Opn, Perc, Perc Endo]
0799[0,3,4]ZX	Drain/Lymphatic, Int Mammary, Lt, [Opn, Perc, Perc Endo]
079B[0,3,4]ZX	Drain/Lymphatic, Mesenteric, [Opn, Perc, Perc Endo]
079C[0,3,4]ZX	Drain/Lymphatic, Pelvis, [Opn, Perc, Perc Endo]
079D[0,3,4]ZX	Drain/Lymphatic, Aortic, [Opn, Perc, Perc Endo]
079F[0,3,4]ZX	Drain/Lymphatic, Rt Lwr Extr, [Opn, Perc, Perc Endo]
079G[0,3,4]ZX	Drain/Lymphatic, Lt Lwr Extr, [Opn, Perc, Perc Endo]
079H[0,3,4]ZX	Drain/Lymphatic, Rt Inguinal, [Opn, Perc, Perc Endo]
079J[0,3,4]ZX	Drain/Lymphatic, Lt Inguinal, [Opn, Perc, Perc Endo]
079K[0,3,4]ZX	Drain/Thoracic Duct, [Opn, Perc, Perc Endo]
079L[0,3,4]ZX	Drain/Cisterna Chyli, [Opn, Perc, Perc Endo]
07B0[0,3,4]ZX	Exc/Lymphatic, Head, [Opn, Perc, Perc Endo]
07B1*	Exc/Lymphatic, Rt Neck
07B2*	Exc/Lymphatic, Lt Neck
07B3[0,3,4]ZX	Exc/Lymphatic, Rt Upr Extr, [Opn, Perc, Perc Endo]
07B3[0,4]ZZ	Exc/Lymphatic, Rt Upr Extr, [Opn, Perc, Perc Endo]
07B4[0,3,4]ZX	Exc/Lymphatic, Lt Upr Extr, [Opn, Perc, Perc Endo]
07B4[0,4]ZZ	Exc/Lymphatic, Lt Upr Extr, [Opn, Perc, Perc Endo]
07B5*	Exc/Lymphatic, Rt Axillary
07B6*	Exc/Lymphatic, Lt Axillary
07B7[0,3,4]ZX	Exc/Lymphatic, Thorax, Rt, [Opn, Perc, Perc Endo]
07B7[0,4]ZZ	Exc/Lymphatic, Thorax, [Opn, Perc, Perc Endo]
07B8[0,3,4]ZX	Exc/Lymphatic, Int Mammary, Rt, [Opn, Perc, Perc Endo]
07B9[0,3,4]ZX	Exc/Lymphatic, Int Mammary, Lt, [Opn, Perc, Perc Endo]
07BB[0,3,4]ZX	Exc/Lymphatic, Mesenteric, [Opn, Perc, Perc Endo]
07BC[0,3,4]ZX	Exc/Lymphatic, Pelvis, [Opn, Perc, Perc Endo]
07BD[0,3,4]ZX	Exc/Lymphatic, Aortic, [Opn, Perc, Perc Endo]
07BF[0,3,4]ZX	Exc/Lymphatic, Rt Lwr Extr, [Opn, Perc, Perc Endo]
07BF[0,4]ZZ	Exc/Lymphatic, Rt Lwr Extr, [Opn, Perc, Perc Endo]
07BG[0,3,4]ZX	Exc/Lymphatic, Lt Lwr Extr, [Opn, Perc, Perc Endo]
07BG[0,4]ZZ	Exc/Lymphatic, Lt Lwr Extr, [Opn, Perc, Perc Endo]
07BH*	Exc/Lymphatic, Rt Inguinal
07BJ*	Exc/Lymphatic, Lt Inguinal
07BK[0,3,4]ZX	Exc/Thoracic Duct, [Opn, Perc, Perc Endo]
07BL[0,3,4]ZX	Exc/Cisterna Chyli, [Opn, Perc, Perc Endo]
07BP[0,3,4]ZZ	Exc/Spleen, [Opn, Perc, Perc Endo]
07T5*	Resect/Lymphatic, Rt Axillary
07T6*	Resect/Lymphatic, Lt Axillary
07T8*	Resect/Lymphatic, Int Mammary, Rt
07T9*	Resect/Lymphatic, Int Mammary, Lt
07TC*	Resect/Lymphatic, Pelvis
07TD*	Resect/Lymphatic, Aortic
07TH*	Resect/Lymphatic, Rt Inguinal
07TJ*	Resect/Lymphatic, Lt Inguinal
07TP*	Resect/Spleen
08T[0,1]XZZ	Resect of [Rt, Lt] Eye, Ext Appr
090K*	Alter/Nose
09BQ[0,3,4]ZZ	Exc/Maxillary Sinus, Rt, [Opn, Perc, Perc Endo]
09BR[0,3,4]ZZ	Exc/Maxillary Sinus, Lt, [Opn, Perc, Perc Endo]
09MKXZZ	Reattach of Nose, Ext Appr
09QK*	Repair/Nose
09QM*	Repair/Nasal Septum
09RK*	Replace/Nose
09RM*	Replace/Nasal Septum
09SK*	Repos/Nose
09SM*	Repos/Nasal Septum
09TQ*	Resect/Maxillary Sinus, Rt
09TR*	Resect/Maxillary Sinus, Lt
09UK*	Supl/Nose
09UM*	Supl/Nasal Septum
0B5R*	Destr/Diaphragm, Rt
0B5S*	Destr/Diaphragm, Lt
0B9[C,D,F,G,H]0ZX	Drain, [Rt Upr Lung Lobe, Rt Mid Lung Lobe, Rt Lwr Lung Lobe, Lt Upr Lung Lobe, Lung Lingula], Opn Appr, Dx
0B9[J,K,L,M]0ZX	Drain, [Lt Lwr Lung Lobe, Rt Lung, Lt Lung, Bilat Lungs], Opn Appr, Dx
0BBC[0,4]ZX	Exc/Upr Lung Lobe, Rt, [Opn, Perc Endo]
0BBD[0,4]ZX	Exc/Mid Lung Lobe, Rt, [Opn, Perc Endo]
0BBF[0,4]ZX	Exc/Lwr Lung Lobe, Rt, [Opn, Perc Endo]
0BBG[0,4]ZX	Exc/Upr Lung Lobe, Lt, [Opn, Perc Endo]
0BBH[0,4]ZX	Exc/Lung Lingula, [Opn, Perc Endo]
0BBJ[0,4]ZX	Exc/Lwr Lung Lobe, Lt, [Opn, Perc Endo]
0BBK[0,4]ZX	Exc/Lung, Rt, [Opn, Perc Endo]
0BBL[0,4]ZX	Exc/Lung, Lt, [Opn, Perc Endo]
0BBM0ZX	Exc of Bilat Lungs, Opn Appr, Diagnostic
0BBR[0,3,4]ZZ	Exc/Diaphragm, Rt, [Opn, Perc, Perc Endo]
0BBS[0,3,4]ZZ	Exc/Diaphragm, Lt, [Opn, Perc, Perc Endo]
0DH6[0,3,4]MZ	Insert/Stomach, [Opn, Perc, Perc Endo], Stimulator Lead, NQ
0DP6[0,3,4]MZ	Rmvl/Stomach, [Opn, Perc, Perc Endo], Stimulator Lead, NQ
0DPR*	Rmvl/Anal Sphincter
0F9[0,1,2]0ZX	Drain of [Liver, Rt Lobe Liver, Lt Lobe Liver], Opn Appr, Dx
0FB[0,1,2]0ZX	Exc of [Liver, Rt Lobe Liver, Lt Lobe Liver], Opn Appr, Dx
0G9L[0,3,4]ZX	Drain/Superior Parathyroid Gland, Rt, [Opn, Perc, Perc Endo]
0G9M[0,3,4]ZX	Drain/Superior Parathyroid Gland, Lt, [Opn, Perc, Perc Endo]
0G9N[0,3,4]ZX	Drain/Inferior Parathyroid Gland, Rt, [Opn, Perc, Perc Endo]
0G9P[0,3,4]ZX	Drain/Inferior Parathyroid Gland, Lt, [Opn, Perc, Perc Endo]
0G9Q[0,3,4]ZX	Drain/Parathyroid Glands, Multi, [Opn, Perc, Perc Endo]
0G9R[0,3,4]ZX	Drain/Parathyroid Gland, [Opn, Perc, Perc Endo]
0GBL[0,3,4]ZX	Exc/Superior Parathyroid Gland, Rt, [Opn, Perc, Perc Endo]
0GBM[0,3,4]ZX	Exc/Superior Parathyroid Gland, Lt, [Opn, Perc, Perc Endo]
0GBN[0,3,4]ZX	Exc/Inferior Parathyroid Gland, Rt, [Opn, Perc, Perc Endo]
0GBP[0,3,4]ZX	Exc/Inferior Parathyroid Gland, Lt, [Opn, Perc, Perc Endo]
0GBQ[0,3,4]ZX	Exc/Parathyroid Glands, Multi, [Opn, Perc, Perc Endo]
0GBR[0,3,4]ZX	Exc/Parathyroid Gland, [Opn, Perc, Perc Endo]
0GJK[3,4]ZZ	Inspect/Thyroid Gland, [Perc, Perc Endo]
0GJR[3,4]ZZ	Inspect/Parathyroid Gland, [Perc, Perc Endo]
0GJS3ZZ	Inspect of Endocrine Gland, Perc Appr
0GJS4ZZ	Inspect of Endocrine Gland, Perc Endo Appr
0JH6[0,3]VZ	Insert/SQ Tissue & Fascia, Chest, [Opn, Perc], Inf Pump, NQ
0JH7[0,3]VZ	Insert/SQ Tissue & Fascia, Back, [Opn, Perc], Inf Pump, NQ
0JH8[0,3]VZ	Insert/SQ Tissue & Fascia, Abd, [Opn, Perc], Inf Pump, NQ
0JHT[0,3]VZ	Insert/SQ Tissue & Fascia, Trunk, [Opn, Perc], Inf Pump, NQ
0M90[3,4]0Z	Drain/Head and Neck Bursa & Lgmt, [Perc, Perc Endo], Drain Dev, NQ
0MM*	Bursa & Lgmt, Reattach
0MPX[0,3,4][0,J]Z	Rmvl/Upr Bursa & Lgmt, [Opn, Perc, Perc Endo], [Drain Dev, Synth Sub], NQ
0MPY[0,3,4][0,J]Z	Rmvl/Lwr Bursa & Lgmt, [Opn, Perc, Perc Endo], [Drain Dev, Synth Sub], NQ
0MS0*	Repos/Head and Neck Bursa & Lgmt
0MS1*	Repos/Shldr Bursa & Lgmt, Rt
0MS2*	Repos/Shldr Bursa & Lgmt, Lt
0MS3*	Repos/Elbow Bursa & Lgmt, Rt
0MS4*	Repos/Elbow Bursa & Lgmt, Lt
0MS5*	Repos/Wrist Bursa & Lgmt, Rt
0MS6*	Repos/Wrist Bursa & Lgmt, Lt
0MS7*	Repos/Hand Bursa & Lgmt, Rt
0MS8*	Repos/Hand Bursa & Lgmt, Lt
0MSC*	Repos/Trunk Bursa & Lgmt, Rt
0MSD*	Repos/Trunk Bursa & Lgmt, Lt
0MSF*	Repos/Thorax Bursa & Lgmt, Rt
0MSG*	Repos/Thorax Bursa & Lgmt, Lt
0MSH*	Repos/Abd Bursa & Lgmt, Rt
0MSJ*	Repos/Abd Bursa & Lgmt, Lt
0MSK*	Repos/Perineum Bursa & Lgmt
0MSL*	Repos/Hip Bursa & Lgmt, Rt
0MSM*	Repos/Hip Bursa & Lgmt, Lt
0MSN*	Repos/Knee Bursa & Lgmt, Rt
0MSP*	Repos/Knee Bursa & Lgmt, Lt
0MSQ*	Repos/Ankle Bursa & Lgmt, Rt
0MSR*	Repos/Ankle Bursa & Lgmt, Lt
0MSS*	Repos/Foot Bursa & Lgmt, Rt
0MST*	Repos/Foot Bursa & Lgmt, Lt
0MU0*	Supl/Head and Neck Bursa & Lgmt
0MU1*	Supl/Shldr Bursa & Lgmt, Rt
0MU2*	Supl/Shldr Bursa & Lgmt, Lt
0MU3*	Supl/Elbow Bursa & Lgmt, Rt
0MU4*	Supl/Elbow Bursa & Lgmt, Lt
0MU5*	Supl/Wrist Bursa & Lgmt, Rt
0MU6*	Supl/Wrist Bursa & Lgmt, Lt
0MU7*	Supl/Hand Bursa & Lgmt, Rt
0MU8*	Supl/Hand Bursa & Lgmt, Lt
0MUC*	Supl/Trunk Bursa & Lgmt, Rt
0MUD*	Supl/Trunk Bursa & Lgmt, Lt
0MUF*	Supl/Thorax Bursa & Lgmt, Rt
0MUG*	Supl/Thorax Bursa & Lgmt, Lt
0MUH*	Supl/Abd Bursa & Lgmt, Rt
0MUJ*	Supl/Abd Bursa & Lgmt, Lt

Surgical   **Medical**   **CC Indicator**   **MCC Indicator**   **Procedure Proxy**   PDxMCC **PDx acts as own MCC**   PDxCC **PDx acts as own CC**

MDC 8: Diseases And Disorders Of The Musculoskeletal System And Connective Tissue—SURGICAL

MDC 8: Diseases And Disorders Of The Musculoskeletal System And Connective Tissue—SURGICAL

Code	Description
0MUK*	Supl/Perineum Bursa & Lgmt
0MUL*	Supl/Hip Bursa & Lgmt, Rt
0MUM*	Supl/Hip Bursa & Lgmt, Lt
0MUN*	Supl/Knee Bursa & Lgmt, Rt
0MUP*	Supl/Knee Bursa & Lgmt, Lt
0MUQ*	Supl/Ankle Bursa & Lgmt, Rt
0MUR*	Supl/Ankle Bursa & Lgmt, Lt
0MUS*	Supl/Foot Bursa & Lgmt, Rt
0MUT*	Supl/Foot Bursa & Lgmt, Lt
0N50*	Destr/Skull
0N51*	Destr/Frontal Bone, Rt
0N52*	Destr/Frontal Bone, Lt
0N53*	Destr/Parietal Bone, Rt
0N54*	Destr/Parietal Bone, Lt
0N55*	Destr/Temporal Bone, Rt
0N56*	Destr/Temporal Bone, Lt
0N57*	Destr/Occipital Bone, Rt
0N58*	Destr/Occipital Bone, Lt
0NB0[0,3,4]ZZ	Exc/Skull, [Opn, Perc, Perc Endo]
0NB1[0,3,4]ZZ	Exc/Frontal Bone, Rt, [Opn, Perc, Perc Endo]
0NB2[0,3,4]ZZ	Exc/Frontal Bone, Lt, [Opn, Perc, Perc Endo]
0NB3[0,3,4]ZZ	Exc/Parietal Bone, Rt, [Opn, Perc, Perc Endo]
0NB4[0,3,4]ZZ	Exc/Parietal Bone, Lt, [Opn, Perc, Perc Endo]
0NB5[0,3,4]ZZ	Exc/Temporal Bone, Rt, [Opn, Perc, Perc Endo]
0NB6[0,3,4]ZZ	Exc/Temporal Bone, Lt, [Opn, Perc, Perc Endo]
0NB7[0,3,4]ZZ	Exc/Occipital Bone, Rt, [Opn, Perc, Perc Endo]
0NB8[0,3,4]ZZ	Exc/Occipital Bone, Lt, [Opn, Perc, Perc Endo]
0NBB[0,3,4]ZZ	Exc/Nasal Bone, [Opn, Perc, Perc Endo]
0NBC[0,3,4]ZZ	Exc/Sphenoid Bone, Rt, [Opn, Perc, Perc Endo]
0NBD[0,3,4]ZZ	Exc/Sphenoid Bone, Lt, [Opn, Perc, Perc Endo]
0NBF[0,3,4]ZZ	Exc/Ethmoid Bone, Rt, [Opn, Perc, Perc Endo]
0NBG[0,3,4]ZZ	Exc/Ethmoid Bone, Lt, [Opn, Perc, Perc Endo]
0NBH[0,3,4]ZZ	Exc/Lacrimal Bone, Rt, [Opn, Perc, Perc Endo]
0NBJ[0,3,4]ZZ	Exc/Lacrimal Bone, Lt, [Opn, Perc, Perc Endo]
0NBK[0,3,4]ZZ	Exc/Palatine Bone, Rt, [Opn, Perc, Perc Endo]
0NBL[0,3,4]ZZ	Exc/Palatine Bone, Lt, [Opn, Perc, Perc Endo]
0NBM[0,3,4]ZZ	Exc/Zygomatic Bone, Rt, [Opn, Perc, Perc Endo]
0NBN[0,3,4]ZZ	Exc/Zygomatic Bone, Lt, [Opn, Perc, Perc Endo]
0NBR[0,3,4]ZZ	Exc/Maxilla, Rt, [Opn, Perc, Perc Endo]
0NBS[0,3,4]ZZ	Exc/Maxilla, Lt, [Opn, Perc, Perc Endo]
0NBT[0,3,4]ZZ	Exc/Mandible, Rt, [Opn, Perc, Perc Endo]
0NBV[0,3,4]ZZ	Exc/Mandible, Lt, [Opn, Perc, Perc Endo]
0NBX[0,3,4]ZZ	Exc/Hyoid Bone, [Opn, Perc, Perc Endo]
0NH0[0,3,4]4Z	Insert/Skull, [Opn, Perc, Perc Endo], Int Fix Dev, NQ
0NH1*	Insert/Frontal Bone, Rt
0NH2*	Insert/Frontal Bone, Lt
0NH3*	Insert/Parietal Bone, Rt
0NH4*	Insert/Parietal Bone, Lt
0NH5[0,3,4]4Z	Insert/Temporal Bone, Rt, [Opn, Perc, Perc Endo], Int Fix Dev, NQ
0NH6[0,3,4]4Z	Insert/Temporal Bone, Lt, [Opn, Perc, Perc Endo], Int Fix Dev, NQ
0NH7*	Insert/Occipital Bone, Rt
0NH8*	Insert/Occipital Bone, Lt
0NN1*	Rls/Frontal Bone, Rt
0NN2*	Rls/Frontal Bone, Lt
0NN3*	Rls/Parietal Bone, Rt
0NN4*	Rls/Parietal Bone, Lt
0NN5*	Rls/Temporal Bone, Rt
0NN6*	Rls/Temporal Bone, Lt
0NN7*	Rls/Occipital Bone, Rt
0NN8*	Rls/Occipital Bone, Lt
0NP0[0,3,4]JZ	Rmvl/Skull, [Opn, Perc, Perc Endo], Synth Sub, NQ
0NQ0*	Repair/Skull
0NQ1*	Repair/Frontal Bone, Rt
0NQ2*	Repair/Frontal Bone, Lt
0NQ3*	Repair/Parietal Bone, Rt
0NQ4*	Repair/Parietal Bone, Lt
0NQ5*	Repair/Temporal Bone, Rt
0NQ6*	Repair/Temporal Bone, Lt
0NQ7*	Repair/Occipital Bone, Rt
0NQ8*	Repair/Occipital Bone, Lt
0NQB*	Repair/Nasal Bone
0NQR*	Repair/Maxilla, Rt
0NQS*	Repair/Maxilla, Lt
0NQT*	Repair/Mandible, Rt
0NQV*	Repair/Mandible, Lt
0NR0*	Replace/Skull
0NR1*	Replace/Frontal Bone, Rt
0NR2*	Replace/Frontal Bone, Lt
0NR3*	Replace/Parietal Bone, Rt
0NR4*	Replace/Parietal Bone, Lt
0NR5*	Replace/Temporal Bone, Rt
0NR6*	Replace/Temporal Bone, Lt
0NR7*	Replace/Occipital Bone, Rt
0NR8*	Replace/Occipital Bone, Lt
0NRB*	Replace/Nasal Bone
0NRC[0,3,4]JZ	Replace/Sphenoid Bone, Rt, [Opn, Perc, Perc Endo], Synth Sub, NQ
0NRD[0,3,4]JZ	Replace/Sphenoid Bone, Lt, [Opn, Perc, Perc Endo], Synth Sub, NQ
0NRF[0,3,4]JZ	Replace/Ethmoid Bone, Rt, [Opn, Perc, Perc Endo], Synth Sub, NQ
0NRG[0,3,4]JZ	Replace/Ethmoid Bone, Lt, [Opn, Perc, Perc Endo], Synth Sub, NQ
0NRH[0,3,4]JZ	Replace/Lacrimal Bone, Rt, [Opn, Perc, Perc Endo], Synth Sub, NQ
0NRJ[0,3,4]JZ	Replace/Lacrimal Bone, Lt, [Opn, Perc, Perc Endo], Synth Sub, NQ
0NRK[0,3,4]JZ	Replace/Palatine Bone, Rt, [Opn, Perc, Perc Endo], Synth Sub, NQ
0NRL[0,3,4]JZ	Replace/Palatine Bone, Lt, [Opn, Perc, Perc Endo], Synth Sub, NQ
0NRM[0,3,4]JZ	Replace/Zygomatic Bone, Rt, [Opn, Perc, Perc Endo], Synth Sub, NQ
0NRN[0,3,4]JZ	Replace/Zygomatic Bone, Lt, [Opn, Perc, Perc Endo], Synth Sub, NQ
0NRT*	Replace/Mandible, Rt
0NRV*	Replace/Mandible, Lt
0NRX[0,3,4]JZ	Replace/Hyoid Bone, [Opn, Perc, Perc Endo], Synth Sub, NQ
0NS0*	Repos/Skull
0NS1*	Repos/Frontal Bone, Rt
0NS2*	Repos/Frontal Bone, Lt
0NS3*	Repos/Parietal Bone, Rt
0NS4*	Repos/Parietal Bone, Lt
0NS5*	Repos/Temporal Bone, Rt
0NS6*	Repos/Temporal Bone, Lt
0NS7*	Repos/Occipital Bone, Rt
0NS8*	Repos/Occipital Bone, Lt
0NSB0[4,Z]Z	Repos/Nasal Bone, Opn, [Int Fix Dev, No Dev], NQ
0NSC0[4,Z]Z	Repos/Sphenoid Bone, Rt, Opn, [Int Fix Dev, No Dev], NQ
0NSD0[4,Z]Z	Repos/Sphenoid Bone, Lt, Opn, [Int Fix Dev, No Dev], NQ
0NSF0[4,Z]Z	Repos/Ethmoid Bone, Rt, Opn, [Int Fix Dev, No Dev], NQ
0NSG0[4,Z]Z	Repos/Ethmoid Bone, Lt, Opn, [Int Fix Dev, No Dev], NQ
0NSH0[4,Z]Z	Repos/Lacrimal Bone, Rt, Opn, [Int Fix Dev, No Dev], NQ
0NSJ0[4,Z]Z	Repos/Lacrimal Bone, Lt, Opn, [Int Fix Dev, No Dev], NQ
0NSK0[4,Z]Z	Repos/Palatine Bone, Rt, Opn, [Int Fix Dev, No Dev], NQ
0NSL0[4,Z]Z	Repos/Palatine Bone, Lt, Opn, [Int Fix Dev, No Dev], NQ
0NSM0[4,Z]Z	Repos/Zygomatic Bone, Rt, Opn, [Int Fix Dev, No Dev], NQ
0NSN0[4,Z]Z	Repos/Zygomatic Bone, Lt, Opn, [Int Fix Dev, No Dev], NQ
0NSP0[4,Z]Z	Repos/Orbit, Rt, Opn, [Int Fix Dev, No Dev], NQ
0NSQ0[4,Z]Z	Repos/Orbit, Lt, Opn, [Int Fix Dev, No Dev], NQ
0NSR0[4,5,Z]Z	Repos/Maxilla, Rt, Opn, [Int Fix Dev, Ext Fix Dev, No Dev], NQ
0NSS0[4,5,Z]Z	Repos/Maxilla, Lt, Opn, [Int Fix Dev, Ext Fix Dev, No Dev], NQ
0NST0[4,5,Z]Z	Repos/Mandible, Rt, Opn, [Int Fix Dev, Ext Fix Dev, No Dev], NQ
0NSV0[4,5,Z]Z	Repos/Mandible, Lt, Opn, [Int Fix Dev, Ext Fix Dev, No Dev], NQ
0NSX0[4,Z]Z	Repos/Hyoid Bone, Opn, [Int Fix Dev, No Dev], NQ
0NT*	Head and Facial Bones, Resect
0NU0*	Supl/Skull
0NU1*	Supl/Frontal Bone, Rt
0NU2*	Supl/Frontal Bone, Lt
0NU3*	Supl/Parietal Bone, Rt
0NU4*	Supl/Parietal Bone, Lt
0NU5*	Supl/Temporal Bone, Rt
0NU6*	Supl/Temporal Bone, Lt
0NU7*	Supl/Occipital Bone, Rt
0NU8*	Supl/Occipital Bone, Lt
0NUB*	Supl/Nasal Bone
0NUC[0,3,4]JZ	Supl/Sphenoid Bone, Rt, [Opn, Perc, Perc Endo], Synth Sub, NQ
0NUD[0,3,4]JZ	Supl/Sphenoid Bone, Lt, [Opn, Perc, Perc Endo], Synth Sub, NQ
0NUF[0,3,4]JZ	Supl/Ethmoid Bone, Rt, [Opn, Perc, Perc Endo], Synth Sub, NQ
0NUG[0,3,4]JZ	Supl/Ethmoid Bone, Lt, [Opn, Perc, Perc Endo], Synth Sub, NQ
0NUH[0,3,4]JZ	Supl/Lacrimal Bone, Rt, [Opn, Perc, Perc Endo], Synth Sub, NQ
0NUJ[0,3,4]JZ	Supl/Lacrimal Bone, Lt, [Opn, Perc, Perc Endo], Synth Sub, NQ
0NUK[0,3,4]JZ	Supl/Palatine Bone, Rt, [Opn, Perc, Perc Endo], Synth Sub, NQ
0NUL[0,3,4]JZ	Supl/Palatine Bone, Lt, [Opn, Perc, Perc Endo], Synth Sub, NQ
0NUM[0,3,4]JZ	Supl/Zygomatic Bone, Rt, [Opn, Perc, Perc Endo], Synth Sub, NQ

T Transfer DRG   SP Special Payment   * Code Range   6th and 7th Character of ZZ = No Device, No Qualifier ZX = No Device, Diagnostic

Code	Description
ØNUN[Ø,3,4]JZ	Supl/Zygomatic Bone, Lt, [Opn, Perc, Perc Endo], Synth Sub, NQ
ØNUT*	Supl/Mandible, Rt
ØNUV*	Supl/Mandible, Lt
ØNUX[Ø,3,4]JZ	Supl/Hyoid Bone, [Opn, Perc, Perc Endo], Synth Sub, NQ
ØP8Ø*	Div/Sternum
ØP81*	Div/Rib, Rt
ØP82*	Div/Rib, Lt
ØP83*	Div/Cervical Vertebra
ØP84*	Div/Thoracic Vertebra
ØP85*	Div/Scapula, Rt
ØP86*	Div/Scapula, Lt
ØP87*	Div/Glenoid Cavity, Rt
ØP88*	Div/Glenoid Cavity, Lt
ØP89*	Div/Clavicle, Rt
ØP8B*	Div/Clavicle, Lt
ØP8R*	Div/Thumb Phalanx, Rt
ØP8S*	Div/Thumb Phalanx, Lt
ØP8T*	Div/Finger Phalanx, Rt
ØP8V*	Div/Finger Phalanx, Lt
ØPBØ[Ø,3,4]ZZ	Exc/Sternum, [Opn, Perc, Perc Endo]
ØPB1[Ø,3,4]ZZ	Exc/Rib, Rt, [Opn, Perc, Perc Endo]
ØPB2[Ø,3,4]ZZ	Exc/Rib, Lt, [Opn, Perc, Perc Endo]
ØPB3[Ø,3,4]ZZ	Exc/Cervical Vertebra, [Opn, Perc, Perc Endo]
ØPB4[Ø,3,4]ZZ	Exc/Thoracic Vertebra, [Opn, Perc, Perc Endo]
ØPB5[Ø,3,4]ZZ	Exc/Scapula, Rt, [Opn, Perc, Perc Endo]
ØPB6[Ø,3,4]ZZ	Exc/Scapula, Lt, [Opn, Perc, Perc Endo]
ØPB7[Ø,3,4]ZZ	Exc/Glenoid Cavity, Rt, [Opn, Perc, Perc Endo]
ØPB8[Ø,3,4]ZZ	Exc/Glenoid Cavity, Lt, [Opn, Perc, Perc Endo]
ØPB9[Ø,3,4]ZZ	Exc/Clavicle, Rt, [Opn, Perc, Perc Endo]
ØPBB[Ø,3,4]ZZ	Exc/Clavicle, Lt, [Opn, Perc, Perc Endo]
ØPBR[Ø,3,4]ZZ	Exc/Thumb Phalanx, Rt, [Opn, Perc, Perc Endo]
ØPBS[Ø,3,4]ZZ	Exc/Thumb Phalanx, Lt, [Opn, Perc, Perc Endo]
ØPBT[Ø,3,4]ZZ	Exc/Finger Phalanx, Rt, [Opn, Perc, Perc Endo]
ØPBV[Ø,3,4]ZZ	Exc/Finger Phalanx, Lt, [Opn, Perc, Perc Endo]
ØPCØ*	Extir/Sternum
ØPC1*	Extir/Rib, Rt
ØPC2*	Extir/Rib, Lt
ØPC3*	Extir/Cervical Vertebra
ØPC4*	Extir/Thoracic Vertebra
ØPC5*	Extir/Scapula, Rt
ØPC6*	Extir/Scapula, Lt
ØPC7*	Extir/Glenoid Cavity, Rt
ØPC8*	Extir/Glenoid Cavity, Lt
ØPC9*	Extir/Clavicle, Rt
ØPCB*	Extir/Clavicle, Lt
ØPCR*	Extir/Thumb Phalanx, Rt
ØPCS*	Extir/Thumb Phalanx, Lt
ØPCT*	Extir/Finger Phalanx, Rt
ØPCV*	Extir/Finger Phalanx, Lt
ØPHØ*	Insert/Sternum
ØPH1*	Insert/Rib, Rt
ØPH2*	Insert/Rib, Lt
ØPH3*	Insert/Cervical Vertebra
ØPH4*	Insert/Thoracic Vertebra
ØPH5*	Insert/Scapula, Rt
ØPH6*	Insert/Scapula, Lt
ØPH7*	Insert/Glenoid Cavity, Rt
ØPH8*	Insert/Glenoid Cavity, Lt
ØPH9*	Insert/Clavicle, Rt
ØPHB*	Insert/Clavicle, Lt
ØPHR*	Insert/Thumb Phalanx, Rt
ØPHS*	Insert/Thumb Phalanx, Lt
ØPHT*	Insert/Finger Phalanx, Rt
ØPHV*	Insert/Finger Phalanx, Lt
ØPHY*	Insert/Upr Bone
ØPNØ*	Rls/Sternum
ØPN1*	Rls/Rib, Rt
ØPN2*	Rls/Rib, Lt
ØPN3*	Rls/Cervical Vertebra
ØPN4*	Rls/Thoracic Vertebra
ØPN5*	Rls/Scapula, Rt
ØPN6*	Rls/Scapula, Lt
ØPN7*	Rls/Glenoid Cavity, Rt
ØPN8*	Rls/Glenoid Cavity, Lt
ØPN9*	Rls/Clavicle, Rt
ØPNB*	Rls/Clavicle, Lt
ØPNR*	Rls/Thumb Phalanx, Rt
ØPNS*	Rls/Thumb Phalanx, Lt
ØPNT*	Rls/Finger Phalanx, Rt
ØPNV*	Rls/Finger Phalanx, Lt
ØPQØ*	Repair/Sternum
ØPQ1*	Repair/Rib, Rt
ØPQ2*	Repair/Rib, Lt
ØPQ3*	Repair/Cervical Vertebra
ØPQ4*	Repair/Thoracic Vertebra
ØPQ5*	Repair/Scapula, Rt
ØPQ6*	Repair/Scapula, Lt
ØPQ7*	Repair/Glenoid Cavity, Rt
ØPQ8*	Repair/Glenoid Cavity, Lt
ØPQ9*	Repair/Clavicle, Rt
ØPQB*	Repair/Clavicle, Lt
ØPQR*	Repair/Thumb Phalanx, Rt
ØPQS*	Repair/Thumb Phalanx, Lt
ØPQT*	Repair/Finger Phalanx, Rt
ØPQV*	Repair/Finger Phalanx, Lt
ØPRØ*	Replace/Sternum
ØPR1*	Replace/Rib, Rt
ØPR2*	Replace/Rib, Lt
ØPR3*	Replace/Cervical Vertebra
ØPR4*	Replace/Thoracic Vertebra
ØPR5*	Replace/Scapula, Rt
ØPR6*	Replace/Scapula, Lt
ØPR7*	Replace/Glenoid Cavity, Rt
ØPR8*	Replace/Glenoid Cavity, Lt
ØPR9*	Replace/Clavicle, Rt
ØPRB*	Replace/Clavicle, Lt
ØPRR*	Replace/Thumb Phalanx, Rt
ØPRS*	Replace/Thumb Phalanx, Lt
ØPRT*	Replace/Finger Phalanx, Rt
ØPRV*	Replace/Finger Phalanx, Lt
ØPSØØZZ	Repos Sternum, Opn Appr
ØPSØ[Ø,3,4][Ø,4]Z	Repos/Sternum, [Opn, Perc, Perc Endo], [Int Fix Dev, Rigid Plate, Int Fix Dev], NQ
ØPS1ØZZ	Repos Rt Rib, Opn Appr
ØPS1[Ø,3,4]4Z	Repos/Rib, Rt, [Opn, Perc, Perc Endo], Int Fix Dev, NQ
ØPS2ØZZ	Repos Lt Rib, Opn Appr
ØPS2[Ø,3,4]4Z	Repos/Rib, Lt, [Opn, Perc, Perc Endo], Int Fix Dev, NQ
ØPS33ZZ	Repos Cervical Vertebra, Perc Appr
ØPS5ØZZ	Repos Rt Scapula, Opn Appr
ØPS5[Ø,3,4]4Z	Repos/Scapula, Rt, [Opn, Perc, Perc Endo], Int Fix Dev, NQ
ØPS6ØZZ	Repos Lt Scapula, Opn Appr
ØPS6[Ø,3,4]4Z	Repos/Scapula, Lt, [Opn, Perc, Perc Endo], Int Fix Dev, NQ
ØPS7ØZZ	Repos Rt Glenoid Cavity, Opn Appr
ØPS7[Ø,3,4]4Z	Repos/Glenoid Cavity, Rt, [Opn, Perc, Perc Endo], Int Fix Dev, NQ
ØPS8ØZZ	Repos Lt Glenoid Cavity, Opn Appr
ØPS8[Ø,3,4]4Z	Repos/Glenoid Cavity, Lt, [Opn, Perc, Perc Endo], Int Fix Dev, NQ
ØPS9ØZZ	Repos Rt Clavicle, Opn Appr
ØPS9[Ø,3,4]4Z	Repos/Clavicle, Rt, [Opn, Perc, Perc Endo], Int Fix Dev, NQ
ØPSBØZZ	Repos Lt Clavicle, Opn Appr
ØPSB[Ø,3,4]4Z	Repos/Clavicle, Lt, [Opn, Perc, Perc Endo], Int Fix Dev, NQ
ØPSR[Ø,3,4]5Z	Repos/Thumb Phalanx, Rt, [Opn, Perc, Perc Endo], Ext Fix Dev, NQ
ØPSS[Ø,3,4]5Z	Repos/Thumb Phalanx, Lt, [Opn, Perc, Perc Endo], Ext Fix Dev, NQ
ØPST[Ø,3,4]5Z	Repos/Finger Phalanx, Rt, [Opn, Perc, Perc Endo], Ext Fix Dev, NQ
ØPSV[Ø,3,4]5Z	Repos/Finger Phalanx, Lt, [Opn, Perc, Perc Endo], Ext Fix Dev, NQ
ØPT[Ø,1,2,5,6]ØZZ	Resect of [Sternum, Rt Rib, Lt Rib, Rt Scapula, Lt Scapula], Opn Appr
ØPT[7,8,9,B]ØZZ	Resect of [Rt Glenoid Cavity, Lt Glenoid Cavity, Rt Clavicle, Lt Clavicle], Opn Appr
ØPT[R,S,T,V]ØZZ	Resect of [Rt Thumb, Lt Thumb, Rt Finger, Lt Finger] Phalanx, Opn Appr
ØPUØ*	Supl/Sternum
ØPU1*	Supl/Rib, Rt
ØPU2*	Supl/Rib, Lt
ØPU3Ø7Z	Supl Cervical Vertebra with Autol Sub, Opn Appr
ØPU3ØJZ	Supl Cervical Vertebra with Synth Sub, Opn Appr
ØPU3ØKZ	Supl Cervical Vertebra with Nonaut Sub, Opn Appr
ØPU337Z	Supl Cervical Vertebra with Autol Sub, Perc Appr
ØPU33JZ	Supl Cervical Vertebra with Synth Sub, Perc Appr
ØPU33KZ	Supl Cervical Vertebra with Nonaut Sub, Perc Appr
ØPU347Z	Supl Cervcal Vertebra w Autol Sub, Perc Endo
ØPU34JZ	Supl Cervcal Vertebra w Synth Sub, Perc Endo
ØPU34KZ	Supl Cervcal Vertebra w Nonaut Sub, Perc Endo
ØPU4*	Supl/Thoracic Vertebra

Surgical   **Medical**   CC Indicator   MCC Indicator   Procedure Proxy   PDxMCC PDx acts as own MCC   PDxCC PDx acts as own CC

MDC 8: Diseases And Disorders Of The Musculoskeletal System And Connective Tissue—SURGICAL

MDC 8: Diseases And Disorders Of The Musculoskeletal System And Connective Tissue—SURGICAL

Code	Description
0PU5*	Supl/Scapula, Rt
0PU6*	Supl/Scapula, Lt
0PU7*	Supl/Glenoid Cavity, Rt
0PU8*	Supl/Glenoid Cavity, Lt
0PU9*	Supl/Clavicle, Rt
0PUB*	Supl/Clavicle, Lt
0PUR*	Supl/Thumb Phalanx, Rt
0PUS*	Supl/Thumb Phalanx, Lt
0PUT*	Supl/Finger Phalanx, Rt
0PUV*	Supl/Finger Phalanx, Lt
0Q80*	Div/Lumbar Vertebra
0Q81*	Div/Sacrum
0Q82*	Div/Pelvic Bone, Rt
0Q83*	Div/Pelvic Bone, Lt
0Q84*	Div/Acetabulum, Rt
0Q85*	Div/Acetabulum, Lt
0Q8Q*	Div/Toe Phalanx, Rt
0Q8R*	Div/Toe Phalanx, Lt
0Q8S*	Div/Coccyx
0QB0[0,3,4]ZZ	Exc/Lumbar Vertebra, [Opn, Perc, Perc Endo]
0QB1[0,3,4]ZZ	Exc/Sacrum, [Opn, Perc, Perc Endo]
0QB2[0,3,4]ZZ	Exc/Pelvic Bone, Rt, [Opn, Perc, Perc Endo]
0QB3[0,3,4]ZZ	Exc/Pelvic Bone, Lt, [Opn, Perc, Perc Endo]
0QB4[0,3,4]ZZ	Exc/Acetab, Rt, [Opn, Perc, Perc Endo]
0QB5[0,3,4]ZZ	Exc/Acetab, Lt, [Opn, Perc, Perc Endo]
0QBQ[0,3,4]ZZ	Exc/Toe Phalanx, Rt, [Opn, Perc, Perc Endo]
0QBR[0,3,4]ZZ	Exc/Toe Phalanx, Lt, [Opn, Perc, Perc Endo]
0QBS[0,3,4]ZZ	Exc/Coccyx, [Opn, Perc, Perc Endo]
0QC0*	Extir/Lumbar Vertebra
0QC1*	Extir/Sacrum
0QC2*	Extir/Pelvic Bone, Rt
0QC3*	Extir/Pelvic Bone, Lt
0QC4*	Extir/Acetabulum, Rt
0QC5*	Extir/Acetabulum, Lt
0QCQ*	Extir/Toe Phalanx, Rt
0QCR*	Extir/Toe Phalanx, Lt
0QCS*	Extir/Coccyx
0QH0*	Insert/Lumbar Vertebra
0QH1*	Insert/Sacrum
0QH2*	Insert/Pelvic Bone, Rt
0QH3*	Insert/Pelvic Bone, Lt
0QH4*	Insert/Acetabulum, Rt
0QH5*	Insert/Acetabulum, Lt
0QHQ*	Insert/Toe Phalanx, Rt
0QHR*	Insert/Toe Phalanx, Lt
0QHS*	Insert/Coccyx
0QHY*	Insert/Lwr Bone
0QN0*	Rls/Lumbar Vertebra
0QN1*	Rls/Sacrum
0QN2*	Rls/Pelvic Bone, Rt
0QN3*	Rls/Pelvic Bone, Lt
0QN4*	Rls/Acetabulum, Rt
0QN5*	Rls/Acetabulum, Lt
0QNQ*	Rls/Toe Phalanx, Rt
0QNR*	Rls/Toe Phalanx, Lt
0QNS*	Rls/Coccyx
0QQ0*	Repair/Lumbar Vertebra
0QQ1*	Repair/Sacrum
0QQ2*	Repair/Pelvic Bone, Rt
0QQ3*	Repair/Pelvic Bone, Lt
0QQ4*	Repair/Acetabulum, Rt
0QQ5*	Repair/Acetabulum, Lt
0QQQ*	Repair/Toe Phalanx, Rt
0QQR*	Repair/Toe Phalanx, Lt
0QQS*	Repair/Coccyx
0QQ[D,F]3ZZ	Rpr [Rt, Lt] Patella, Perc Appr
0QR0*	Replace/Lumbar Vertebra
0QR1*	Replace/Sacrum
0QR2*	Replace/Pelvic Bone, Rt
0QR3*	Replace/Pelvic Bone, Lt
0QR4*	Replace/Acetabulum, Rt
0QR5*	Replace/Acetabulum, Lt
0QRQ*	Replace/Toe Phalanx, Rt
0QRR*	Replace/Toe Phalanx, Lt
0QRS*	Replace/Coccyx
0QS20ZZ	Repos Rt Pelvic Bone, Opn Appr
0QS2[0,3,4][4,5]Z	Repos/Pelvic Bone, Rt, [Opn, Perc, Perc Endo], [Int Fix Dev, Ext Fix Dev], NQ
0QS30ZZ	Repos Lt Pelvic Bone, Opn Appr

Code	Description
0QS3[0,3,4][4,5]Z	Repos/Pelvic Bone, Lt, [Opn, Perc, Perc Endo], [Int Fix Dev, Ext Fix Dev], NQ
0QS40ZZ	Repos Rt Acetabulum, Opn Appr
0QS4[0,3,4]4Z	Repos/Acetab, Rt, [Opn, Perc, Perc Endo], Int Fix Dev, NQ
0QS50ZZ	Repos Lt Acetabulum, Opn Appr
0QS5[0,3,4]4Z	Repos/Acetab, Lt, [Opn, Perc, Perc Endo], Int Fix Dev, NQ
0QSD0ZZ	Repos Rt Patella, Opn Appr
0QSD[0,3,4]4Z	Repos/Patella, Rt, [Opn, Perc, Perc Endo], Int Fix Dev, NQ
0QSF0ZZ	Repos Lt Patella, Opn Appr
0QSF[0,3,4]4Z	Repos/Patella, Lt, [Opn, Perc, Perc Endo], Int Fix Dev, NQ
0QSQ[0,3,4]5Z	Repos/Toe Phalanx, Rt, [Opn, Perc, Perc Endo], Ext Fix Dev, NQ
0QSR[0,3,4]5Z	Repos/Toe Phalanx, Lt, [Opn, Perc, Perc Endo], Ext Fix Dev, NQ
0QT[2,3,4,5]0ZZ	Resect of [Rt Pelvic Bone, Lt Pelvic Bone, Rt Acetab, Lt Acetab], Opn Appr
0QT[Q,R,S]0ZZ	Resect of [Rt Toe Phalanx, Lt Toe Phalanx, Coccyx], Opn Appr
0QU0*	Supl/Lumbar Vertebra
0QU1*	Supl/Sacrum
0QU2*	Supl/Pelvic Bone, Rt
0QU3*	Supl/Pelvic Bone, Lt
0QU4*	Supl/Acetabulum, Rt
0QU5*	Supl/Acetabulum, Lt
0QUQ*	Supl/Toe Phalanx, Rt
0QUR*	Supl/Toe Phalanx, Lt
0QUS*	Supl/Coccyx
0R900[0,Z]Z	Drain/Occipital-cervical Jt, Opn, [Drain Dev, No Dev], NQ
0R910[0,Z]Z	Drain/Cervical Vert Jt, Opn, [Drain Dev, No Dev], NQ
0R930[0,Z]Z	Drain/Cervical Vert Disc, Opn, [Drain Dev, No Dev], NQ
0R940[0,Z]Z	Drain/Cervicothoracic Vert Jt, Opn, [Drain Dev, No Dev], NQ
0R950[0,Z]Z	Drain/Cervicothoracic Vert Disc, Opn, [Drain Dev, No Dev], NQ
0R960[0,Z]Z	Drain/Thoracic Vert Jt, Opn, [Drain Dev, No Dev], NQ
0R990[0,Z]Z	Drain/Thoracic Vert Disc, Opn, [Drain Dev, No Dev], NQ
0R9A0[0,Z]Z	Drain/Thoracolumbar Vert Jt, Opn, [Drain Dev, No Dev], NQ
0R9B0[0,Z]Z	Drain/Thoracolumbar Vert Disc, Opn, [Drain Dev, No Dev], NQ
0RC0*	Extir/Occipital-cervical Jt
0RC1*	Extir/Cervical Vert Jt
0RC3*	Extir/Cervical Vert Disc
0RC4*	Extir/Cervicothoracic Vert Jt
0RC5*	Extir/Cervicothoracic Vert Disc
0RC6*	Extir/Thoracic Vert Jt
0RC9*	Extir/Thoracic Vert Disc
0RCA*	Extir/Thoracolumbar Vert Jt
0RCB*	Extir/Thoracolumbar Vert Disc
0RCC*	Extir/Temporomandibular Jt, Rt
0RCD*	Extir/Temporomandibular Jt, Lt
0RGC*	Fusion/Temporomandibular Jt, Rt
0RGD*	Fusion/Temporomandibular Jt, Lt
0RH0[0,3,4]4Z	Insert/Occipital-cervical Jt, [Opn, Perc, Perc Endo], Int Fix Dev, NQ
0RH1[0,3,4]4Z	Insert/Cervical Vert Jt, [Opn, Perc, Perc Endo], Int Fix Dev, NQ
0RH4[0,3,4]4Z	Insert/Cervicothoracic Vert Jt, [Opn, Perc, Perc Endo], Int Fix Dev, NQ
0RH6[0,3,4]4Z	Insert/Thoracic Vert Jt, [Opn, Perc, Perc Endo], Int Fix Dev, NQ
0RHA[0,3,4]4Z	Insert/Thoracolumbar Vert Jt, [Opn, Perc, Perc Endo], Int Fix Dev, NQ
0RJ00ZZ	Inspect of Occipital-cervical Jt, Opn Appr
0RJ[1,3]0ZZ	Inspect of Cervical Vert [Jt, Disc], Opn Appr
0RJ[4,5]0ZZ	Inspect of Cervicothoracic Vert [Jt, Disc], Opn Appr
0RJ[6,9]0ZZ	Inspect of Thoracic Vert [Jt, Disc], Opn Appr
0RJ[A,B]0ZZ	Inspect of Thoracolumbar Vert [Jt, Disc], Opn Appr
0RP0[0,3,4][0,3,4,7,A,K]Z	Rmvl/Occipital-cervical Jt, [Opn, Perc, Perc Endo], [Drain Dev, Inf Dev, Int Fix Dev, Auto Tissue Sub, Interbody Fusion Dev, Nonauto Tissue Sub], NQ
0RP1[0,3,4][0,3,4,7,A,K]Z	Rmvl/Cervical Vert Jt, [Opn, Perc, Perc Endo], [Drain Dev, Inf Dev, Int Fix Dev, Auto Tissue Sub, Interbody Fusion Dev, Nonauto Tissue Sub], NQ
0RP3[0,3,4][0,3,7,K]Z	Rmvl/Cervical Vert Disc, [Opn, Perc, Perc Endo], [Drain Dev, Inf Dev, Auto Tissue Sub, Nonauto Tissue Sub], NQ
0RP4[0,3,4][0,3,4,7,A,K]Z	Rmvl/Cervicothoracic Vert Jt, [Opn, Perc, Perc Endo], [Drain Dev, Inf Dev, Int Fix Dev, Auto Tissue Sub, Interbody Fusion Dev, Nonauto Tissue Sub], NQ
0RP5[0,3,4][0,3,7,K]Z	Rmvl/Cervicothoracic Vert Disc, [Opn, Perc, Perc Endo], [Drain Dev, Inf Dev, Auto Tissue Sub, Nonauto Tissue Sub], NQ
0RP6[0,3,4][0,3,4,7,A,K]Z	Rmvl/Thoracic Vert Jt, [Opn, Perc, Perc Endo], [Drain Dev, Inf Dev, Int Fix Dev, Auto Tissue Sub, Interbody Fusion Dev, Nonauto Tissue Sub], NQ
0RP9[0,3,4][0,3,7,K]Z	Rmvl/Thoracic Vert Disc, [Opn, Perc, Perc Endo], [Drain Dev, Inf Dev, Auto Tissue Sub, Nonauto Tissue Sub], NQ
0RPA[0,3,4][0,3,4,7,A,K]Z	Rmvl/Thoracolumbar Vert Jt, [Opn, Perc, Perc Endo], [Drain Dev, Inf Dev, Int Fix Dev, Auto Tissue Sub, Interbody Fusion Dev, Nonauto Tissue Sub], NQ

T **Transfer DRG**   SP **Special Payment**   * **Code Range**   **6th and 7th Character of ZZ = No Device, No Qualifier ZX = No Device, Diagnostic**

ØRPB[Ø,3,4][Ø,3,7,K]Z Rmvl/Thoracolumbar Vert Disc, [Opn, Perc, Perc Endo], [Drain Dev, Inf Dev, Auto Tissue Sub, Nonauto Tissue Sub], NQ
ØRQØ* Repair/Occipital-cervical Jt
ØRQ1* Repair/Cervical Vert Jt
ØRQ3[3,4,X]ZZ Rpr/Cervical Vert Disc, [Perc, Perc Endo, Ext]
ØRQ4* Repair/Cervicothoracic Vert Jt
ØRQ5* Repair/Cervicothoracic Vert Disc
ØRQ6* Repair/Thoracic Vert Jt
ØRQ9[3,4,X]ZZ Rpr/Thoracic Vert Disc, [Perc, Perc Endo, Ext]
ØRQA* Repair/Thoracolumbar Vert Jt
ØRQB[3,4,X]ZZ Rpr/Thoracolumbar Vert Disc, [Perc, Perc Endo, Ext]
ØRQC[Ø,3,4]ZZ Rpr/Temporomandibular Jt, Rt, [Opn, Perc, Perc Endo]
ØRQD[Ø,3,4]ZZ Rpr/Temporomandibular Jt, Lt, [Opn, Perc, Perc Endo]
ØRRØØ[7,J,K]Z Replace/Occipital-cervical Jt, Opn, [Auto Tissue Sub, Synth Sub, Nonauto Tissue Sub], NQ
ØRR1Ø[7,J,K]Z Replace/Cervical Vert Jt, Opn, [Auto Tissue Sub, Synth Sub, Nonauto Tissue Sub], NQ
ØRR3Ø[7,K]Z Replace/Cervical Vert Disc, Opn, [Auto Tissue Sub, Nonauto Tissue Sub], NQ
ØRR4Ø[7,J,K]Z Replace/Cervicothoracic Vert Jt, Opn, [Auto Tissue Sub, Synth Sub, Nonauto Tissue Sub], NQ
ØRR5Ø[7,K]Z Replace/Cervicothoracic Vert Disc, Opn, [Auto Tissue Sub, Nonauto Tissue Sub], NQ
ØRR6Ø[7,J,K]Z Replace/Thoracic Vert Jt, Opn, [Auto Tissue Sub, Synth Sub, Nonauto Tissue Sub], NQ
ØRR9Ø[7,K]Z Replace/Thoracic Vert Disc, Opn, [Auto Tissue Sub, Nonauto Tissue Sub], NQ
ØRRAØ[7,J,K]Z Replace/Thoracolumbar Vert Jt, Opn, [Auto Tissue Sub, Synth Sub, Nonauto Tissue Sub], NQ
ØRRBØ[7,K]Z Replace/Thoracolumbar Vert Disc, Opn, [Auto Tissue Sub, Nonauto Tissue Sub], NQ
ØRRC* Replace/Temporomandibular Jt, Rt
ØRRD* Replace/Temporomandibular Jt, Lt
ØRSØØ[4,Z]Z Repos/Occipital-cervical Jt, Opn, [Int Fix Dev, No Dev], NQ
ØRS1Ø[4,Z]Z Repos/Cervical Vert Jt, Opn, [Int Fix Dev, No Dev], NQ
ØRS4Ø[4,Z]Z Repos/Cervicothoracic Vert Jt, Opn, [Int Fix Dev, No Dev], NQ
ØRS6Ø[4,Z]Z Repos/Thoracic Vert Jt, Opn, [Int Fix Dev, No Dev], NQ
ØRSAØ[4,Z]Z Repos/Thoracolumbar Vert Jt, Opn, [Int Fix Dev, No Dev], NQ
ØRSCØ[4,Z]Z Repos/Temporomandibular Jt, Rt, Opn, [Int Fix Dev, No Dev], NQ
ØRSDØ[4,Z]Z Repos/Temporomandibular Jt, Lt, Opn, [Int Fix Dev, No Dev], NQ
ØRT[C,D]ØZZ Resect of [Rt, Lt] Temporomandibular Jt, Opn Appr
ØRUØ[Ø,3,4][7,K]Z Supl/Occipital-cervical Jt, [Opn, Perc, Perc Endo], [Auto Tissue Sub, Nonauto Tissue Sub], NQ
ØRU1[Ø,3,4][7,K]Z Supl/Cervical Vert Jt, [Opn, Perc, Perc Endo], [Auto Tissue Sub, Nonauto Tissue Sub], NQ
ØRU4[Ø,3,4][7,K]Z Supl/Cervicothoracic Vert Jt, [Opn, Perc, Perc Endo], [Auto Tissue Sub, Nonauto Tissue Sub], NQ
ØRU5[Ø,3,4][7,K]Z Supl/Cervicothoracic Vert Disc, [Opn, Perc, Perc Endo], [Auto Tissue Sub, Nonauto Tissue Sub], NQ
ØRU6[Ø,3,4][7,K]Z Supl/Thoracic Vert Jt, [Opn, Perc, Perc Endo], [Auto Tissue Sub, Nonauto Tissue Sub], NQ
ØRUA[Ø,3,4][7,K]Z Supl/Thoracolumbar Vert Jt, [Opn, Perc, Perc Endo], [Auto Tissue Sub, Nonauto Tissue Sub], NQ
ØRUC* Supl/Temporomandibular Jt, Rt
ØRUD* Supl/Temporomandibular Jt, Lt
ØRWØ[Ø,3,4][Ø,3,4,7,8,A,J,K]Z Rev/Occipital-cervical Jt, [Opn, Perc, Perc Endo], [Drain Dev, Inf Dev, Int Fix Dev, Auto Tissue Sub, Spacer, Interbody Fusion Dev, Synth Sub, Nonauto Tissue Sub], NQ
ØRW1[Ø,3,4][Ø,3,4,7,8,A,J,K]Z Rev/Cervical Vert Jt, [Opn, Perc, Perc Endo], [Drain Dev, Inf Dev, Int Fix Dev, Auto Tissue Sub, Spacer, Interbody Fusion Dev, Synth Sub, Nonauto Tissue Sub], NQ
ØRW3[Ø,3,4][Ø,3,7,K]Z Rev/Cervical Vert Disc, [Opn, Perc, Perc Endo], [Drain Dev, Inf Dev, Auto Tissue Sub, Nonauto Tissue Sub], NQ
ØRW4[Ø,3,4][Ø,3,4,7,8,A,J,K]Z Rev/Cervicothoracic Vert Jt, [Opn, Perc, Perc Endo], [Drain Dev, Inf Dev, Int Fix Dev, Auto Tissue Sub, Spacer, Interbody Fusion Dev, Synth Sub, Nonauto Tissue Sub], NQ
ØRW5[Ø,3,4][Ø,3,7,K]Z Rev/Cervicothoracic Vert Disc, [Opn, Perc, Perc Endo], [Drain Dev, Inf Dev, Auto Tissue Sub, Nonauto Tissue Sub], NQ
ØRW6[Ø,3,4][Ø,3,4,7,8,A,J,K]Z Rev/Thoracic Vert Jt, [Opn, Perc, Perc Endo], [Drain Dev, Inf Dev, Int Fix Dev, Auto Tissue Sub, Spacer, Interbody Fusion Dev, Synth Sub, Nonauto Tissue Sub], NQ
ØRW9[Ø,3,4][Ø,3,7,K]Z Rev/Thoracic Vert Disc, [Opn, Perc, Perc Endo], [Drain Dev, Inf Dev, Auto Tissue Sub, Nonauto Tissue Sub], NQ
ØRWA[Ø,3,4][Ø,3,4,7,8,A,J,K]ZRev/Thoracolumbar Vert Jt, [Opn, Perc, Perc Endo], [Drain Dev, Inf Dev, Int Fix Dev, Auto Tissue Sub, Spacer, Interbody Fusion Dev, Synth Sub, Nonauto Tissue Sub], NQ
ØRWB[Ø,3,4][Ø,3,7,K]Z Rev/Thoracolumbar Vert Disc, [Opn, Perc, Perc Endo], [Drain Dev, Inf Dev, Auto Tissue Sub, Nonauto Tissue Sub], NQ

ØRWG[Ø,3,4]JZ Rev/Acromioclavicular Jt, Rt, [Opn, Perc, Perc Endo], Synth Sub, NQ
ØRWH[Ø,3,4]JZ Rev/Acromioclavicular Jt, Lt, [Opn, Perc, Perc Endo], Synth Sub, NQ
ØRWJ[Ø,3,4]JZ Rev/Shldr Jt, Rt, [Opn, Perc, Perc Endo], Synth Sub, NQ
ØRWK[Ø,3,4]JZ Rev/Shldr Jt, Lt, [Opn, Perc, Perc Endo], Synth Sub, NQ
ØRWL[Ø,3,4]JZ Rev/Elbow Jt, Rt, [Opn, Perc, Perc Endo], Synth Sub, NQ
ØRWM[Ø,3,4]JZ Rev/Elbow Jt, Lt, [Opn, Perc, Perc Endo], Synth Sub, NQ
ØRWN[Ø,3,4]JZ Rev/Wrist Jt, Rt, [Opn, Perc, Perc Endo], Synth Sub, NQ
ØRWP[Ø,3,4]JZ Rev/Wrist Jt, Lt, [Opn, Perc, Perc Endo], Synth Sub, NQ
ØRWQ[Ø,3,4]JZ Rev/Carpal Jt, Rt, [Opn, Perc, Perc Endo], Synth Sub, NQ
ØRWR[Ø,3,4]JZ Rev/Carpal Jt, Lt, [Opn, Perc, Perc Endo], Synth Sub, NQ
ØRWS[Ø,3,4]JZ Rev/Metacarpocarpal Jt, Rt, [Opn, Perc, Perc Endo], Synth Sub, NQ
ØRWT[Ø,3,4]JZ Rev/Metacarpocarpal Jt, Lt, [Opn, Perc, Perc Endo], Synth Sub, NQ
ØRWU[Ø,3,4]JZ Rev/Metacarpophalangeal Jt, Rt, [Opn, Perc, Perc Endo], Synth Sub, NQ
ØRWV[Ø,3,4]JZ Rev/Metacarpophalangeal Jt, Lt, [Opn, Perc, Perc Endo], Synth Sub, NQ
ØRWW[Ø,3,4]JZ Rev/Finger Phalangeal Jt, Rt, [Opn, Perc, Perc Endo], Synth Sub, NQ
ØRWX[Ø,3,4]JZ Rev/Finger Phalangeal Jt, Lt, [Opn, Perc, Perc Endo], Synth Sub, NQ
ØS9ØØ[Ø,Z]Z Drain/Lumbar Vert Jt, Opn, [Drain Dev, No Dev], NQ
ØS92Ø[Ø,Z]Z Drain/Lumbar Vert Disc, Opn, [Drain Dev, No Dev], NQ
ØS93Ø[Ø,Z]Z Drain/Lumbosacral Jt, Opn, [Drain Dev, No Dev], NQ
ØS94Ø[Ø,Z]Z Drain/Lumbosacral Disc, Opn, [Drain Dev, No Dev], NQ
ØS95Ø[Ø,Z]Z Drain/Sacrococcygeal Jt, Opn, [Drain Dev, No Dev], NQ
ØS96Ø[Ø,Z]Z Drain/Coccygeal Jt, Opn, [Drain Dev, No Dev], NQ
ØS97Ø[Ø,Z]Z Drain/Sacroiliac Jt, Rt, Opn, [Drain Dev, No Dev], NQ
ØS98Ø[Ø,Z]Z Drain/Sacroiliac Jt, Lt, Opn, [Drain Dev, No Dev], NQ
ØSCØ* Extir/Lumbar Vert Jt
ØSC2* Extir/Lumbar Vert Disc
ØSC3* Extir/Lumbosacral Jt
ØSC4* Extir/Lumbosacral Disc
ØSC5* Extir/Sacrococcygeal Jt
ØSC6* Extir/Coccygeal Jt
ØSC7* Extir/Sacroiliac Jt, Rt
ØSC8* Extir/Sacroiliac Jt, Lt
ØSHØ[Ø,3,4]4Z Insert/Lumbar Vert Jt, [Opn, Perc, Perc Endo], Int Fix Dev, NQ
ØSH3[Ø,3,4]4Z Insert/Lumbosacral Jt, [Opn, Perc, Perc Endo], Int Fix Dev, NQ
ØSH5[Ø,3,4]4Z Insert/Sacrococcygeal Jt, [Opn, Perc, Perc Endo], Int Fix Dev, NQ
ØSH6[Ø,3,4]4Z Insert/Coccygeal Jt, [Opn, Perc, Perc Endo], Int Fix Dev, NQ
ØSH7[Ø,3,4]4Z Insert/Sacroiliac Jt, Rt, [Opn, Perc, Perc Endo], Int Fix Dev, NQ
ØSH8[Ø,3,4]4Z Insert/Sacroiliac Jt, Lt, [Opn, Perc, Perc Endo], Int Fix Dev, NQ
ØSJ[Ø,2]ØZZ Inspect of Lumbar Vert [Jt, Disc], Opn Appr
ØSJ[3,4]ØZZ Inspect of Lumbosacral [Jt, Disc], Opn Appr
ØSJ[5,6]ØZZ Inspect of [Sacrococcygeal, Coccygeal] Jt, Opn Appr
ØSJ[7,8]ØZZ Inspect of [Rt, Lt] Sacroiliac Jt, Opn Appr
ØSPØ[Ø,3,4][Ø,3,4,7,A,K]Z Rmvl/Lumbar Vert Jt, [Opn, Perc, Perc Endo], [Drain Dev, Inf Dev, Int Fix Dev, Auto Tissue Sub, Interbody Fusion Dev, Nonauto Tissue Sub], NQ
ØSP2[Ø,3,4][Ø,3,7,K]Z Rmvl/Lumbar Vert Disc, [Opn, Perc, Perc Endo], [Drain Dev, Inf Dev, Auto Tissue Sub, Nonauto Tissue Sub], NQ
ØSP3[Ø,3,4][Ø,3,4,7,A,K]Z Rmvl/Lumbosacral Jt, [Opn, Perc, Perc Endo], [Drain Dev, Inf Dev, Int Fix Dev, Auto Tissue Sub, Interbody Fusion Dev, Nonauto Tissue Sub], NQ
ØSP4[Ø,3,4][Ø,3,7,K]Z Rmvl/Lumbosacral Disc, [Opn, Perc, Perc Endo], [Drain Dev, Inf Dev, Auto Tissue Sub, Nonauto Tissue Sub], NQ
ØSP5[Ø,3,4][Ø,3,4,7,K]Z Rmvl/Sacrococcygeal Jt, [Opn, Perc, Perc Endo], [Drain Dev, Inf Dev, Int Fix Dev, Auto Tissue Sub, Nonauto Tissue Sub], NQ
ØSP6[Ø,3,4][Ø,3,4,7,K]Z Rmvl/Coccygeal Jt, [Opn, Perc, Perc Endo], [Drain Dev, Inf Dev, Int Fix Dev, Auto Tissue Sub, Nonauto Tissue Sub], NQ
ØSP7[Ø,3,4][Ø,3,4,7,K]Z Rmvl/Sacroiliac Jt, Rt, [Opn, Perc, Perc Endo], [Drain Dev, Inf Dev, Int Fix Dev, Auto Tissue Sub, Nonauto Tissue Sub], NQ
ØSP8[Ø,3,4][Ø,3,4,7,K]Z Rmvl/Sacroiliac Jt, Lt, [Opn, Perc, Perc Endo], [Drain Dev, Inf Dev, Int Fix Dev, Auto Tissue Sub, Nonauto Tissue Sub], NQ
ØSQØ* Repair/Lumbar Vert Jt
ØSQ2[3,4,X]ZZ Rpr/Lumbar Vert Disc, [Perc, Perc Endo, Ext]
ØSQ3* Repair/Lumbosacral Jt
ØSQ4[3,4,X]ZZ Rpr/Lumbosacral Disc, [Perc, Perc Endo, Ext]
ØSQ5* Repair/Sacrococcygeal Jt
ØSQ6* Repair/Coccygeal Jt
ØSQ7* Repair/Sacroiliac Jt, Rt
ØSQ8* Repair/Sacroiliac Jt, Lt
ØSQH* Repair/Tarsal Jt, Rt
ØSQJ* Repair/Tarsal Jt, Lt

Surgical　　**Medical**　　CC Indicator　　MCC Indicator　　Procedure Proxy　　PDxMCC **PDx acts as own MCC**　　PDxCC **PDx acts as own CC**

Code	Description
ØSQK*	Repair/Metatarsal-Tarsal Jt, Rt
ØSQL*	Repair/Metatarsal-Tarsal Jt, Lt
ØSQM*	Repair/Metatarsal-Phalangeal Jt, Rt
ØSQN*	Repair/Metatarsal-Phalangeal Jt, Lt
ØSQP*	Repair/Toe Phalangeal Jt, Rt
ØSQQ*	Repair/Toe Phalangeal Jt, Lt
ØSR00[7,J,K]Z	Replace/Lumbar Vert Jt, Opn, [Auto Tissue Sub, Synth Sub, Nonauto Tissue Sub], NQ
ØSR20[7,J,K]Z	Replace/Lumbar Vert Disc, Opn, [Auto Tissue Sub, Nonauto Tissue Sub], NQ
ØSR30[7,J,K]Z	Replace/Lumbosacral Jt, Opn, [Auto Tissue Sub, Synth Sub, Nonauto Tissue Sub], NQ
ØSR40[7,K]Z	Replace/Lumbosacral Disc, Opn, [Auto Tissue Sub, Nonauto Tissue Sub], NQ
ØSR5*	Replace/Sacrococcygeal Jt
ØSR6*	Replace/Coccygeal Jt
ØSR7*	Replace/Sacroiliac Jt, Rt
ØSR8*	Replace/Sacroiliac Jt, Lt
ØSS00[4,Z]Z	Repos/Lumbar Vert Jt, Opn, [Int Fix Dev, No Dev], NQ
ØSS30[4,Z]Z	Repos/Lumbosacral Jt, Opn, [Int Fix Dev, No Dev], NQ
ØSS50[4,Z]Z	Repos/Sacrococcygeal Jt, Opn, [Int Fix Dev, No Dev], NQ
ØSS60[4,Z]Z	Repos/Coccygeal Jt, Opn, [Int Fix Dev, No Dev], NQ
ØSS70[4,Z]Z	Repos/Sacroiliac Jt, Rt, Opn, [Int Fix Dev, No Dev], NQ
ØSS80[4,Z]Z	Repos/Sacroiliac Jt, Lt, Opn, [Int Fix Dev, No Dev], NQ
ØST[5,6]ØZZ	Resect of [Sacrococcygeal, Coccygeal] Jt, Opn Appr
ØST[7,8]ØZZ	Resect of [Rt, Lt] Sacroiliac Jt, Opn Appr
ØSU0[Ø,3,4][7,K]Z	Supl/Lumbar Vert Jt, [Opn, Perc, Perc Endo], [Auto Tissue Sub, Nonauto Tissue Sub], NQ
ØSU3[Ø,3,4][7,K]Z	Supl/Lumbosacral Jt, [Opn, Perc, Perc Endo], [Auto Tissue Sub, Nonauto Tissue Sub], NQ
ØSU5[Ø,3,4][7,K]Z	Supl/Sacrococcygeal Jt, [Opn, Perc, Perc Endo], [Auto Tissue Sub, Nonauto Tissue Sub], NQ
ØSU6[Ø,3,4][7,K]Z	Supl/Coccygeal Jt, [Opn, Perc, Perc Endo], [Auto Tissue Sub, Nonauto Tissue Sub], NQ
ØSU7*	Supl/Sacroiliac Jt, Rt
ØSU8*	Supl/Sacroiliac Jt, Lt
ØSU9Ø9Z	Supl Rt Hip Jt with Liner, Opn Appr
ØSU9[Ø,3,4][7,J,K]Z	Supl/Hip Jt, Rt, [Opn, Perc, Perc Endo], [Auto Tissue Sub, Synth Sub, Nonauto Tissue Sub], NQ
ØSUAØ9Z	Supl Rt Hip Jt, Acetab with Liner, Opn Appr
ØSUBØ9Z	Supl Lt Hip Jt with Liner, Opn Appr
ØSUB[Ø,3,4][7,J,K]Z	Supl/Hip Jt, Lt, [Opn, Perc, Perc Endo], [Auto Tissue Sub, Synth Sub, Nonauto Tissue Sub], NQ
ØSUC*	Supl/Knee Jt, Rt
ØSUD*	Supl/Knee Jt, Lt
ØSUEØ9Z	Supl Lt Hip Jt, Acetab with Liner, Opn Appr
ØSUF*	Supl/Ankle Jt, Rt
ØSUG*	Supl/Ankle Jt, Lt
ØSUH*	Supl/Tarsal Jt, Rt
ØSUJ*	Supl/Tarsal Jt, Lt
ØSUK*	Supl/Metatarsal-Tarsal Jt, Rt
ØSUL*	Supl/Metatarsal-Tarsal Jt, Lt
ØSUM*	Supl/Metatarsal-Phalangeal Jt, Rt
ØSUN*	Supl/Metatarsal-Phalangeal Jt, Lt
ØSUP*	Supl/Toe Phalangeal Jt, Rt
ØSUQ*	Supl/Toe Phalangeal Jt, Lt
ØSU[R,S]Ø9Z	Supl [Rt, Lt] Hip Jt, Femor Surface w/ Liner, Opn Appr
ØSU[T,U]Ø9Z	Supl [Rt, Lt] Knee Jt, Femor Surface w/ Liner, Opn Appr
ØSU[V,W]Ø9Z	Supl [Rt, Lt] Knee Jt, Tibial Surface w/ Liner, Opn Appr
ØSW0[Ø,3,4][Ø,3,4,7,8,A,J,K]Z	Rev/Lumbar Vert Jt, [Opn, Perc, Perc Endo], [Drain Dev, Inf Dev, Int Fix Dev, Auto Tissue Sub, Spacer, Interbody Fusion Dev, Synth Sub, Nonauto Tissue Sub], NQ
ØSW2[Ø,3,4][Ø,3,7,K]Z	Rev/Lumbar Vert Disc, [Opn, Perc, Perc Endo], [Drain Dev, Inf Dev, Auto Tissue Sub, Nonauto Tissue Sub], NQ
ØSW3[Ø,3,4][Ø,3,4,7,8,A,J,K]Z	Rev/Lumbosacral Jt, [Opn, Perc, Perc Endo], [Drain Dev, Inf Dev, Int Fix Dev, Auto Tissue Sub, Spacer, Interbody Fusion Dev, Synth Sub, Nonauto Tissue Sub], NQ
ØSW4[Ø,3,4][Ø,3,7,K]Z	Rev/Lumbosacral Disc, [Opn, Perc, Perc Endo], [Drain Dev, Inf Dev, Auto Tissue Sub, Nonauto Tissue Sub], NQ
ØSW5[Ø,3,4][Ø,3,4,7,8,J,K]Z	Rev/Sacrococcygeal Jt, [Opn, Perc, Perc Endo], [Drain Dev, Inf Dev, Int Fix Dev, Auto Tissue Sub, Spacer, Synth Sub, Nonauto Tissue Sub], NQ
ØSW6[Ø,3,4][Ø,3,4,7,8,J,K]Z	Rev/Coccygeal Jt, [Opn, Perc, Perc Endo], [Drain Dev, Inf Dev, Int Fix Dev, Auto Tissue Sub, Spacer, Synth Sub, Nonauto Tissue Sub], NQ
ØSW7[Ø,3,4][Ø,3,4,7,8,J,K]Z	Rev/Sacroiliac Jt, Rt, [Opn, Perc, Perc Endo], [Drain Dev, Inf Dev, Int Fix Dev, Auto Tissue Sub, Spacer, Synth Sub, Nonauto Tissue Sub], NQ
ØSW8[Ø,3,4][Ø,3,4,7,8,J,K]Z	Rev/Sacroiliac Jt, Lt, [Opn, Perc, Perc Endo], [Drain Dev, Inf Dev, Int Fix Dev, Auto Tissue Sub, Spacer, Synth Sub, Nonauto Tissue Sub], NQ
ØSWF[Ø,3,4]JZ	Rev/Ankle Jt, Rt, [Opn, Perc, Perc Endo], Synth Sub, NQ
ØSWG[Ø,3,4]JZ	Rev/Ankle Jt, Lt, [Opn, Perc, Perc Endo], Synth Sub, NQ
ØSWH[Ø,3,4]JZ	Rev/Tarsal Jt, Rt, [Opn, Perc, Perc Endo], Synth Sub, NQ
ØSWJ[Ø,3,4]JZ	Rev/Tarsal Jt, Lt, [Opn, Perc, Perc Endo], Synth Sub, NQ
ØSWK[Ø,3,4]JZ	Rev/Metatarsal-Tarsal Jt, Rt, [Opn, Perc, Perc Endo], Synth Sub, NQ
ØSWL[Ø,3,4]JZ	Rev/Metatarsal-Tarsal Jt, Lt, [Opn, Perc, Perc Endo], Synth Sub, NQ
ØSWM[Ø,3,4]JZ	Rev/Metatarsal-Phalangeal Jt, Rt, [Opn, Perc, Perc Endo], Synth Sub, NQ
ØSWN[Ø,3,4]JZ	Rev/Metatarsal-Phalangeal Jt, Lt, [Opn, Perc, Perc Endo], Synth Sub, NQ
ØSWP[Ø,3,4]JZ	Rev/Toe Phalangeal Jt, Rt, [Opn, Perc, Perc Endo], Synth Sub, NQ
ØSWQ[Ø,3,4]JZ	Rev/Toe Phalangeal Jt, Lt, [Opn, Perc, Perc Endo], Synth Sub, NQ
ØT9[Ø,1]ØZX	Drain of [Rt, Lt] Kidney, Opn Appr, Dx
ØT9[3,4]ØZX	Drain of [Rt, Lt] Kidney Pelvis, Opn Appr, Dx
ØTB[Ø,1]ØZX	Exc of [Rt, Lt] Kidney, Opn Appr, Dx
ØTB[3,4]ØZX	Exc of [Rt, Lt] Kidney Pelvis, Opn Appr, Dx
ØVTC*	Resect/Testes, Bilat
ØW04*	Alter/Upr Jaw
ØW05*	Alter/Lwr Jaw
ØW38*	Control/Chest Wall
ØW3F*	Control/Abd Wall
ØW3K*	Control/Upr Back
ØW3L*	Control/Lwr Back
ØWBH[Ø,3,4]ZZ	Exc/Retroperitoneum, [Opn, Perc, Perc Endo]
ØWJ6[3,4]ZZ	Inspect/Neck, [Perc, Perc Endo]
ØWM8ØZZ	Reattach of Chest Wall, Opn Appr
ØWQ8*	Repair/Chest Wall
ØWU4*	Supl/Upr Jaw
ØWU5*	Supl/Lwr Jaw
ØWU8[Ø,4]JZ	Supl/Chest Wall, [Opn, Perc Endo], Synth Sub, NQ
ØX3*	Anatomical Regions, Upr Extremities, Control
ØY3*	Anatomical Regions, Lwr Extremities, Control
ØYM[2,3,4]ØZZ	Reattach of [Rt, Lt, Bilat] Hindquarter, Opn Appr
ØYM[5,6]ØZZ	Reattach of [Rt, Lt] Inguinal Rgn, Opn Appr
ØYM[9,B]ØZZ	Reattach of [Rt, Lt] Lwr Extr, Opn Appr

OR

ØQSS3ZZ	Repos Coccyx, Perc Appr

AND

ØQUS3JZ	Supl Coccyx with Synth Sub, Perc Appr

OR

ØPS33ZZ	Repos Cervical Vertebra, Perc Appr

AND

ØPU33JZ	Supl Cervical Vertebra with Synth Sub, Perc Appr

OR

ØPS43ZZ	Repos Thoracic Vertebra, Perc Appr

AND

ØPU43JZ	Supl Thoracic Vertebra with Synth Sub, Perc Appr

OR

ØQSØ3ZZ	Repos Lumbar Vertebra, Perc Appr

AND

ØQUØ3JZ	Supl Lumbar Vertebra with Synth Sub, Perc Appr

OR

ØQS13ZZ	Repos Sacrum, Perc Appr

AND

ØQU13JZ	Supl Sacrum with Synth Sub, Perc Appr

OR

Nonoperating Room Procedures

FØDZ8ZZ	Prosthesis Device Fitting
FØDZ9[E,F,U,Z]Z	Adaptive,Supportive or Protective Devs Dev Fitting using [Orthosis, Assistive, Adaptive, Supportive or Protective Equipment, Prosthesis, No Dev]

DRG 516　**Other Musculoskeletal System and Connective Tissue O.R. Procedures with CC**

GMLOS 4.3	AMLOS 5.3	RW 2.Ø67Ø	SP

Select operating room procedures, procedure combinations or nonoperating room procedures listed under DRG 515

T Transfer DRG　　SP Special Payment　　* Code Range　　6th and 7th Character of ZZ = No Device, No Qualifier ZX = No Device, Diagnostic

158　　　　　　　　　　　　　　　MS-DRG Version 33.0　　　　　　　　　　　© 2015 Optum360, LLC

DRG 517   Other Musculoskeletal System and Connective Tissue O.R. Procedures without CC/MCC
GMLOS 2.6   AMLOS 3.2   RW 1.7716   SP

Select operating room procedures, procedure combinations or nonoperating room procedures listed under DRG 515

DRG 518   Back and Neck Procedures Except Spinal Fusion with MCC or Disc Device/Neurostimulator
GMLOS 3.8   AMLOS 5.8   RW 2.9249   SP

Operating Room Procedures

005T*	Destr/Spinal Meninges
005W*	Destr/Cervical Spinal Cord
005X*	Destr/Thoracic Spinal Cord
005Y*	Destr/Lumbar Spinal Cord
009T*	Drain/Spinal Meninges
009U00Z	Drain of Spinal Canal with Drain Device, Opn Appr
009U0ZX	Drain of Spinal Canal, Opn Appr, Diagnostic
009U0ZZ	Drain of Spinal Canal, Opn Appr
009W*	Drain/Cervical Spinal Cord
009X*	Drain/Thoracic Spinal Cord
009Y*	Drain/Lumbar Spinal Cord
00BT*	Exc/Spinal Meninges
00BW*	Exc/Cervical Spinal Cord
00BX*	Exc/Thoracic Spinal Cord
00BY*	Exc/Lumbar Spinal Cord
00DT*	Extract/Spinal Meninges
00FU*	Fragmn/Spinal Canal
00HU[0,3,4][2,M]Z	Insert/Spinal Canal, [Opn, Perc, Perc Endo], [Monitoring Dev, Neurostimulator Lead], NQ
00HV[0,3,4][2,M]Z	Insert/Spinal Cord, [Opn, Perc, Perc Endo], [Monitoring Dev, Neurostimulator Lead], NQ
00JU*	Inspect/Spinal Canal
00JV*	Inspect/Spinal Cord
00NT*	Rls/Spinal Meninges
00NW*	Rls/Cervical Spinal Cord
00NX*	Rls/Thoracic Spinal Cord
00NY*	Rls/Lumbar Spinal Cord
00PU[0,3,4][0,2,3,J,M]Z	Rmvl/Spinal Canal, [Opn, Perc, Perc Endo], [Drain Dev, Monitoring Dev, Inf Dev, Synth Sub, Neurostimulator Lead], NQ
00PV[0,3,4]MZ	Rmvl/Spinal Cord, [Opn, Perc, Perc Endo], Neurostimulator Lead, NQ
00QT*	Repair/Spinal Meninges
00QW*	Repair/Cervical Spinal Cord
00QX*	Repair/Thoracic Spinal Cord
00QY*	Repair/Lumbar Spinal Cord
00SW*	Repos/Cervical Spinal Cord
00SX*	Repos/Thoracic Spinal Cord
00SY*	Repos/Lumbar Spinal Cord
00UT*	Supl/Spinal Meninges
00WU[0,3,4][0,2,3,J,M]Z	Rev/Spinal Canal, [Opn, Perc, Perc Endo], [Drain Dev, Monitoring Dev, Inf Dev, Synth Sub, Neurostimulator Lead], NQ
0151[0,4]ZZ	Destr/Cervical Nerve, [Opn, Perc Endo]
0158[0,4]ZZ	Destr/Thoracic Nerve, [Opn, Perc Endo]
015B[0,4]ZZ	Destr/Lumbar Nerve, [Opn, Perc Endo]
015R[0,4]ZZ	Destr/Sacral Nerve, [Opn, Perc Endo]
0181*	Div/Cervical Nerve
0188*	Div/Thoracic Nerve
018B*	Div/Lumbar Nerve
018R*	Div/Sacral Nerve
0PS3XZZ	Repos Cervical Vertebra, Ext Appr
0PS3[0,3,4]4Z	Repos/Cervical Vertebra, [Opn, Perc, Perc Endo], Int Fix Dev, NQ
0PS3[0,4]ZZ	Repos/Cervical Vertebra, [Opn, Perc Endo]
0PS4XZZ	Repos Thoracic Vertebra, Ext Appr
0PS4[0,3,4]4Z	Repos/Thoracic Vertebra, [Opn, Perc, Perc Endo], Int Fix Dev, NQ
0PS4[0,4]ZZ	Repos/Thoracic Vertebra, [Opn, Perc Endo]
0QS004Z	Repos Lumbar Vertebra with Int Fix, Opn Appr
0QS00ZZ	Repos Lumbar Vertebra, Opn Appr
0QS034Z	Repos Lumbar Vertebra with Int Fix, Perc Appr
0QS044Z	Repos Lumbar Vertebra with Int Fix, Perc Endo Appr
0QS04ZZ	Repos Lumbar Vertebra, Perc Endo Appr
0QS0XZZ	Repos Lumbar Vertebra, Ext Appr
0QS1XZZ	Repos Sacrum, Ext Appr
0QS1[0,3,4]4Z	Repos/Sacrum, [Opn, Perc, Perc Endo], Int Fix Dev, NQ
0QS1[0,4]ZZ	Repos/Sacrum, [Opn, Perc Endo]
0QSS*	Repos/Coccyx
0R5[3,5,9,B]0ZZ	Destr [Cervical, Cervicothoracic, Thoracic, Thoracolumbar] Vert Disc, Opn
0RB0[0,3,4]ZZ	Exc/Occipital-cervical Jt, [Opn, Perc, Perc Endo]
0RB1[0,3,4]ZZ	Exc/Cervical Vert Jt, [Opn, Perc, Perc Endo]
0RB3[0,3,4]ZZ	Exc/Cervical Vert Disc, [Opn, Perc, Perc Endo]
0RB4[0,3,4]ZZ	Exc/Cervicothoracic Vert Jt, [Opn, Perc, Perc Endo]
0RB5[0,3,4]ZZ	Exc/Cervicothoracic Vert Disc, [Opn, Perc, Perc Endo]
0RB6[0,3,4]ZZ	Exc/Thoracic Vert Jt, [Opn, Perc, Perc Endo]
0RB9[0,3,4]ZZ	Exc/Thoracic Vert Disc, [Opn, Perc, Perc Endo]
0RBA[0,3,4]ZZ	Exc/Thoracolumbar Vert Jt, [Opn, Perc, Perc Endo]
0RBB[0,3,4]ZZ	Exc/Thoracolumbar Vert Disc, [Opn, Perc, Perc Endo]
0RH0[0,3,4][B,C,D]Z	Insert/Occipital-cervical Jt, [Opn, Perc, Perc Endo], [Spinal Stabliz Dev, Interspinous Process, Spinal Stabliz Dev, Pedicle-Based, Spinal Stabliz Dev, Facet Replace], NQ
0RH1[0,3,4][B,C,D]Z	Insert/Cervical Vert Jt, [Opn, Perc, Perc Endo], [Spinal Stabliz Dev, Interspinous Process, Spinal Stabliz Dev, Pedicle-Based, Spinal Stabliz Dev, Facet Replace], NQ
0RH4[0,3,4][B,C,D]Z	Insert/Cervicothoracic Vert Jt, [Opn, Perc, Perc Endo], [Spinal Stabliz Dev, Interspinous Process, Spinal Stabliz Dev, Pedicle-Based, Spinal Stabliz Dev, Facet Replace], NQ
0RH6[0,3,4][B,C,D]Z	Insert/Thoracic Vert Jt, [Opn, Perc, Perc Endo], [Spinal Stabliz Dev, Interspinous Process, Spinal Stabliz Dev, Pedicle-Based, Spinal Stabliz Dev, Facet Replace], NQ
0RHA[0,3,4][B,C,D]Z	Insert/Thoracolumbar Vert Jt, [Opn, Perc, Perc Endo], [Spinal Stabliz Dev, Interspinous Process, Spinal Stabliz Dev, Pedicle-Based, Spinal Stabliz Dev, Facet Replace], NQ
0RQ[3,9,B]0ZZ	Rpr [Cervical, Thoracic, Thoracolumbar] Vert Disc, Opn
0RR30JZ	Replace of Cerv Disc with Synth Sub, Opn Appr
0RR50JZ	Replace of C-thor Disc with Synth Sub, Opn Appr
0RR90JZ	Replace of Thor Disc with Synth Sub, Opn Appr
0RRB0JZ	Replace of T-lum Disc with Synth Sub, Opn Appr
0RT[3,4,5,9,B]0ZZ	Resect [Cervical Vert Disc, Cervicothoracic Vert Jt, Cervicothoracic Vert Disc, Thoracic Vert Disc, Thoracolumbar Vert Disc], Opn
0RU00JZ	Supl Occip Jt with Synth Sub, Opn Appr
0RU03JZ	Supl Occip Jt with Synth Sub, Perc Appr
0RU04JZ	Supl Occip Jt with Synth Sub, Perc Endo Appr
0RU10JZ	Supl Cerv Jt with Synth Sub, Opn Appr
0RU13JZ	Supl Cerv Jt with Synth Sub, Perc Appr
0RU14JZ	Supl Cerv Jt with Synth Sub, Perc Endo Appr
0RU3*	Supl/Cervical Vert Disc
0RU40JZ	Supl C-thor Jt with Synth Sub, Opn Appr
0RU43JZ	Supl C-thor Jt with Synth Sub, Perc Appr
0RU44JZ	Supl C-thor Jt with Synth Sub, Perc Endo Appr
0RU5[0,3,4]JZ	Supl/Cervicothoracic Vert Disc, [Opn, Perc, Perc Endo], Synth Sub, NQ
0RU60JZ	Supl Thor Jt with Synth Sub, Opn Appr
0RU63JZ	Supl Thor Jt with Synth Sub, Perc Appr
0RU64JZ	Supl Thor Jt with Synth Sub, Perc Endo Appr
0RU9*	Supl/Thoracic Vert Disc
0RUA0JZ	Supl T-lum Jt with Synth Sub, Opn Appr
0RUA3JZ	Supl T-lum Jt with Synth Sub, Perc Appr
0RUA4JZ	Supl T-lum Jt with Synth Sub, Perc Endo Appr
0RUB*	Supl/Thoracolumbar Vert Disc
0RW3[0,3,4]JZ	Rev/Cervical Vert Disc, [Opn, Perc, Perc Endo], Synth Sub, NQ
0RW5[0,3,4]JZ	Rev/Cervicothoracic Vert Disc, [Opn, Perc, Perc Endo], Synth Sub, NQ
0RW9[0,3,4]JZ	Rev/Thoracic Vert Disc, [Opn, Perc, Perc Endo], Synth Sub, NQ
0RWB[0,3,4]JZ	Rev/Thoracolumbar Vert Disc, [Opn, Perc, Perc Endo], Synth Sub, NQ
0S52*	Destr/Lumbar Vert Disc
0S54*	Destr/Lumbosacral Disc
0SB0[0,3,4]ZZ	Exc/Lumbar Vert Jt, [Opn, Perc, Perc Endo]
0SB2[0,3,4]ZZ	Exc/Lumbar Vert Disc, [Opn, Perc, Perc Endo]
0SB3[0,3,4]ZZ	Exc/Lumbosacral Jt, [Opn, Perc, Perc Endo]
0SB4[0,3,4]ZZ	Exc/Lumbosacral Disc, [Opn, Perc, Perc Endo]
0SB5[0,3,4]ZZ	Exc/Sacrococcygeal Jt, [Opn, Perc, Perc Endo]
0SB6[0,3,4]ZZ	Exc/Coccygeal Jt, [Opn, Perc, Perc Endo]
0SB7[0,3,4]ZZ	Exc/Sacroiliac Jt, Rt, [Opn, Perc, Perc Endo]
0SB8[0,3,4]ZZ	Exc/Sacroiliac Jt, Lt, [Opn, Perc, Perc Endo]
0SH0[0,3,4][B,C,D]Z	Insert/Lumbar Vert Jt, [Opn, Perc, Perc Endo], [Spinal Stabliz Dev, Interspinous Process, Spinal Stabliz Dev, Pedicle-Based, Spinal Stabliz Dev, Facet Replace], NQ
0SH3[0,3,4][B,C,D]Z	Insert/Lumbosacral Jt, [Opn, Perc, Perc Endo], [Spinal Stabliz Dev, Interspinous Process, Spinal Stabliz Dev, Pedicle-Based, Spinal Stabliz Dev, Facet Replace], NQ
0SQ[2,4]0ZZ	Rpr [Lumbar Vert Disc, Lumbosacral Disc], Opn
0SR20JZ	Replace of Lum Disc with Synth Sub, Opn Appr

Surgical   Medical   CC Indicator   MCC Indicator   Procedure Proxy   PDxMCC PDx acts as own MCC   PDxCC PDx acts as own CC

MDC 8: Diseases And Disorders Of The Musculoskeletal System And Connective Tissue—SURGICAL

ØSR4ØJZ	Replace of Lumsac Disc with Synth Sub, Opn Appr
ØST[2,4]ØZZ	Resect [Lumbar Vert Disc, Lumbosacral Disc], Opn
ØSUØØJZ	Supl Lum Jt with Synth Sub, Opn Appr
ØSUØ3JZ	Supl Lum Jt with Synth Sub, Perc Appr
ØSUØ4JZ	Supl Lum Jt with Synth Sub, Perc Endo Appr
ØSU2*	Supl/Lumbar Vert Disc
ØSU3ØJZ	Supl Lumbosacral Jt with Synth Sub, Opn Appr
ØSU33JZ	Supl Lumbosacral Jt with Synth Sub, Perc Appr
ØSU34JZ	Supl Lumsac Jt with Synth Sub, Perc Endo Appr
ØSU4*	Supl/Lumbosacral Disc
ØSU5[Ø,3,4]JZ	Supl/Sacrococcygeal Jt, [Opn, Perc, Perc Endo], Synth Sub, NQ
ØSU6[Ø,3,4]JZ	Supl/Coccygeal Jt, [Opn, Perc, Perc Endo], Synth Sub, NQ
ØSW2[Ø,3,4]JZ	Rev/Lumbar Vert Disc, [Opn, Perc, Perc Endo], Synth Sub, NQ
ØSW4[Ø,3,4]JZ	Rev/Lumbosacral Disc, [Opn, Perc, Perc Endo], Synth Sub, NQ

OR

ØRHØ[Ø,3,4][B,C,D]Z	Insert/Occipital-cervical Jt, [Opn, Perc, Perc Endo], [Spinal Stabliz Dev, Interspinous Process, Spinal Stabliz Dev, Pedicle-Based, Spinal Stabliz Dev, Facet Replace], NQ
ØRH1[Ø,3,4][B,C,D]Z	Insert/Cervical Vert Jt, [Opn, Perc, Perc Endo], [Spinal Stabliz Dev, Interspinous Process, Spinal Stabliz Dev, Pedicle-Based, Spinal Stabliz Dev, Facet Replace], NQ
ØRH4[Ø,3,4][B,C,D]Z	Insert/Cervicothoracic Vert Jt, [Opn, Perc, Perc Endo], [Spinal Stabliz Dev, Interspinous Process, Spinal Stabliz Dev, Pedicle-Based, Spinal Stabliz Dev, Facet Replace], NQ
ØRH6[Ø,3,4][B,C,D]Z	Insert/Thoracic Vert Jt, [Opn, Perc, Perc Endo], [Spinal Stabliz Dev, Interspinous Process, Spinal Stabliz Dev, Pedicle-Based, Spinal Stabliz Dev, Facet Replace], NQ
ØRHA[Ø,3,4][B,C,D]Z	Insert/Thoracolumbar Vert Jt, [Opn, Perc, Perc Endo], [Spinal Stabliz Dev, Interspinous Process, Spinal Stabliz Dev, Pedicle-Based, Spinal Stabliz Dev, Facet Replace], NQ
ØRR3ØJZ	Replace of Cerv Disc with Synth Sub, Opn Appr
ØRR5ØJZ	Replace of C-thor Disc with Synth Sub, Opn Appr
ØRUØ[Ø,3,4]JZ	Supl/Occipital-cervical Jt, [Opn, Perc, Perc Endo], Synth Sub, NQ
ØRU1[Ø,3,4]JZ	Supl/Cervical Vert Jt, [Opn, Perc, Perc Endo], Synth Sub, NQ
ØRU4[Ø,3,4]JZ	Supl/Cervicothoracic Vert Jt, [Opn, Perc, Perc Endo], Synth Sub, NQ
ØRU5[Ø,3,4]JZ	Supl/Cervicothoracic Vert Disc, [Opn, Perc, Perc Endo], Synth Sub, NQ
ØRU6[Ø,3,4]JZ	Supl/Thoracic Vert Jt, [Opn, Perc, Perc Endo], Synth Sub, NQ
ØRUA[Ø,3,4]JZ	Supl/Thoracolumbar Vert Jt, [Opn, Perc, Perc Endo], Synth Sub, NQ
ØSHØ[Ø,3,4][B,C,D]Z	Insert/Lumbar Vert Jt, [Opn, Perc, Perc Endo], [Spinal Stabliz Dev, Interspinous Process, Spinal Stabliz Dev, Pedicle-Based, Spinal Stabliz Dev, Facet Replace], NQ
ØSH3[Ø,3,4][B,C,D]Z	Insert/Lumbosacral Jt, [Opn, Perc, Perc Endo], [Spinal Stabliz Dev, Interspinous Process, Spinal Stabliz Dev, Pedicle-Based, Spinal Stabliz Dev, Facet Replace], NQ
ØSR2ØJZ	Replace of Lum Disc with Synth Sub, Opn Appr
ØSR4ØJZ	Replace of Lumsac Disc with Synth Sub, Opn Appr
ØSUØ[Ø,3,4]JZ	Supl/Lumbar Vert Jt, [Opn, Perc, Perc Endo], Synth Sub, NQ
ØSU3[Ø,3,4]JZ	Supl/Lumbosacral Jt, [Opn, Perc, Perc Endo], Synth Sub, NQ
ØSU5[Ø,3,4]JZ	Supl/Sacrococcygeal Jt, [Opn, Perc, Perc Endo], Synth Sub, NQ
ØSU6[Ø,3,4]JZ	Supl/Coccygeal Jt, [Opn, Perc, Perc Endo], Synth Sub, NQ

OR

ØJH6[Ø,3][B,C,D,E]Z	Insert/SQ Tissue & Fascia, Chest, [Opn, Perc], [Stimulator Generator, Single Array, Stimulator Generator, Single Array Rechargeable, Stimulator Generator, Multi Array, Stimulator Generator, Multi Array Rechargeable], NQ
ØJH7[Ø,3][B,C,D,E]Z	Insert/SQ Tissue & Fascia, Back, [Opn, Perc], [Stimulator Generator, Single Array, Stimulator Generator, Single Array Rechargeable, Stimulator Generator, Multi Array, Stimulator Generator, Multi Array Rechargeable], NQ
ØJH8[Ø,3][B,C,D,E]Z	Insert/SQ Tissue & Fascia, Abd, [Opn, Perc], [Stimulator Generator, Single Array, Stimulator Generator, Single Array Rechargeable, Stimulator Generator, Multi Array, Stimulator Generator, Multi Array Rechargeable], NQ

AND

ØØHU[Ø,3,4]MZ	Insert/Spinal Canal, [Opn, Perc, Perc Endo], Neurostimulator Lead, NQ
ØØHV[Ø,3,4]MZ	Insert/Spinal Cord, [Opn, Perc, Perc Endo], Neurostimulator Lead, NQ

DRG 519 · Back and Neck Procedures Except Spinal Fusion with CC

GMLOS 3.1	AMLOS 4.Ø	RW 1.68Ø5 · SP

Operating Room Procedures

ØØ5T*	Destr/Spinal Meninges
ØØ5W*	Destr/Cervical Spinal Cord

ØØ5X*	Destr/Thoracic Spinal Cord
ØØ5Y*	Destr/Lumbar Spinal Cord
ØØ9T*	Drain/Spinal Meninges
ØØ9UØØZ	Drain of Spinal Canal with Drain Device, Opn Appr
ØØ9UØZX	Drain of Spinal Canal, Opn Appr, Diagnostic
ØØ9UØZZ	Drain of Spinal Canal, Opn Appr
ØØ9W*	Drain/Cervical Spinal Cord
ØØ9X*	Drain/Thoracic Spinal Cord
ØØ9Y*	Drain/Lumbar Spinal Cord
ØØBT*	Exc/Spinal Meninges
ØØBW*	Exc/Cervical Spinal Cord
ØØBX*	Exc/Thoracic Spinal Cord
ØØBY*	Exc/Lumbar Spinal Cord
ØØDT*	Extract/Spinal Meninges
ØØFU*	Fragmn/Spinal Canal
ØØHU[Ø,3,4][2,M]Z	Insert/Spinal Canal, [Opn, Perc, Perc Endo], [Monitoring Dev, Neurostimulator Lead], NQ
ØØHV[Ø,3,4][2,M]Z	Insert/Spinal Cord, [Opn, Perc, Perc Endo], [Monitoring Dev, Neurostimulator Lead], NQ
ØØJU*	Inspect/Spinal Canal
ØØJV*	Inspect/Spinal Cord
ØØNT*	Rls/Spinal Meninges
ØØNW*	Rls/Cervical Spinal Cord
ØØNX*	Rls/Thoracic Spinal Cord
ØØNY*	Rls/Lumbar Spinal Cord
ØØPU[Ø,3,4][Ø,2,3,J,M]Z	Rmvl/Spinal Canal, [Opn, Perc, Perc Endo], [Drain Dev, Monitoring Dev, Inf Dev, Synth Sub, Neurostimulator Lead], NQ
ØØPV[Ø,3,4]MZ	Rmvl/Spinal Cord, [Opn, Perc, Perc Endo], Neurostimulator Lead, NQ
ØØQT*	Repair/Spinal Meninges
ØØQW*	Repair/Cervical Spinal Cord
ØØQX*	Repair/Thoracic Spinal Cord
ØØQY*	Repair/Lumbar Spinal Cord
ØØSW*	Repos/Cervical Spinal Cord
ØØSX*	Repos/Thoracic Spinal Cord
ØØSY*	Repos/Lumbar Spinal Cord
ØØUT*	Supl/Spinal Meninges
ØØWU[Ø,3,4][Ø,2,3,J,M]Z	Rev/Spinal Canal, [Opn, Perc, Perc Endo], [Drain Dev, Monitoring Dev, Inf Dev, Synth Sub, Neurostimulator Lead], NQ
Ø151[Ø,4]ZZ	Destr/Cervical Nerve, [Opn, Perc Endo]
Ø158[Ø,4]ZZ	Destr/Thoracic Nerve, [Opn, Perc Endo]
Ø15B[Ø,4]ZZ	Destr/Lumbar Nerve, [Opn, Perc Endo]
Ø15R[Ø,4]ZZ	Destr/Sacral Nerve, [Opn, Perc Endo]
Ø181*	Div/Cervical Nerve
Ø188*	Div/Thoracic Nerve
Ø18B*	Div/Lumbar Nerve
Ø18R*	Div/Sacral Nerve
ØPS3XZZ	Repos Cervical Vertebra, Ext Appr
ØPS3[Ø,3,4]4Z	Repos/Cervical Vertebra, [Opn, Perc, Perc Endo], Int Fix Dev, NQ
ØPS3[Ø,4]ZZ	Repos/Cervical Vertebra, [Opn, Perc Endo]
ØPS4XZZ	Repos Thoracic Vertebra, Ext Appr
ØPS4[Ø,3,4]4Z	Repos/Thoracic Vertebra, [Opn, Perc, Perc Endo], Int Fix Dev, NQ
ØPS4[Ø,4]ZZ	Repos/Thoracic Vertebra, [Opn, Perc Endo]
ØQSØXZZ	Repos Lumbar Vertebra, Ext Appr
ØQSØ[Ø,3,4]4Z	Repos/Lumbar Vertebra, [Opn, Perc, Perc Endo], Int Fix Dev, NQ
ØQSØ[Ø,4]ZZ	Repos/Lumbar Vertebra, [Opn, Perc Endo]
ØQS1XZZ	Repos Sacrum, Ext Appr
ØQS1[Ø,3,4]4Z	Repos/Sacrum, [Opn, Perc, Perc Endo], Int Fix Dev, NQ
ØQS1[Ø,4]ZZ	Repos/Sacrum, [Opn, Perc Endo]
ØQSS*	Repos/Coccyx
ØR5[3,5,9,B]ØZZ	Destr [Cervical, Cervicothoracic, Thoracic, Thoracolumbar] Vert Disc, Opn
ØRBØ[Ø,3,4]ZZ	Exc/Occipital-cervical Jt, [Opn, Perc, Perc Endo]
ØRB1[Ø,3,4]ZZ	Exc/Cervical Vert Jt, [Opn, Perc, Perc Endo]
ØRB3[Ø,3,4]ZZ	Exc/Cervical Vert Disc, [Opn, Perc, Perc Endo]
ØRB4[Ø,3,4]ZZ	Exc/Cervicothoracic Vert Jt, [Opn, Perc, Perc Endo]
ØRB5[Ø,3,4]ZZ	Exc/Cervicothoracic Vert Disc, [Opn, Perc, Perc Endo]
ØRB6[Ø,3,4]ZZ	Exc/Thoracic Vert Jt, [Opn, Perc, Perc Endo]
ØRB9[Ø,3,4]ZZ	Exc/Thoracic Vert Disc, [Opn, Perc, Perc Endo]
ØRBA[Ø,3,4]ZZ	Exc/Thoracolumbar Vert Jt, [Opn, Perc, Perc Endo]
ØRBB[Ø,3,4]ZZ	Exc/Thoracolumbar Vert Disc, [Opn, Perc, Perc Endo]
ØRHØ[Ø,3,4][B,C,D]Z	Insert/Occipital-cervical Jt, [Opn, Perc, Perc Endo], [Spinal Stabliz Dev, Interspinous Process, Spinal Stabliz Dev, Pedicle-Based, Spinal Stabliz Dev, Facet Replace], NQ

⊤ **Transfer DRG**	SP **Special Payment**	* **Code Range**	**6th and 7th Character of ZZ = No Device, No Qualifier ZX = No Device, Diagnostic**

ØRH1[Ø,3,4][B,C,D]Z Insert/Cervical Vert Jt, [Opn, Perc, Perc Endo], [Spinal Stabliz Dev, Interspinous Process, Spinal Stabliz Dev, Pedicle-Based, Spinal Stabliz Dev, Facet Replace], NQ

ØRH4[Ø,3,4][B,C,D]Z Insert/Cervicothoracic Vert Jt, [Opn, Perc, Perc Endo], [Spinal Stabliz Dev, Interspinous Process, Spinal Stabliz Dev, Pedicle-Based, Spinal Stabliz Dev, Facet Replace], NQ

ØRH6[Ø,3,4][B,C,D]Z Insert/Thoracic Vert Jt, [Opn, Perc, Perc Endo], [Spinal Stabliz Dev, Interspinous Process, Spinal Stabliz Dev, Pedicle-Based, Spinal Stabliz Dev, Facet Replace], NQ

ØRHA[Ø,3,4][B,C,D]Z Insert/Thoracolumbar Vert Jt, [Opn, Perc, Perc Endo], [Spinal Stabliz Dev, Interspinous Process, Spinal Stabliz Dev, Pedicle-Based, Spinal Stabliz Dev, Facet Replace], NQ

ØRQ[3,9,B]ØZZ Rpr [Cervical, Thoracic, Thoracolumbar] Vert Disc, Opn
ØRR3ØJZ Replace of Cerv Disc with Synth Sub, Opn Appr
ØRR5ØJZ Replace of C-thor Disc with Synth Sub, Opn Appr
ØRR9ØJZ Replace of Thor Disc with Synth Sub, Opn Appr
ØRRBØJZ Replace of T-lum Disc with Synth Sub, Opn Appr
ØRT[3,4,5,9,B]ØZZ Resect [Cervical Vert Disc, Cervicothoracic Vert Jt, Cervicothoracic Vert Disc, Thoracic Vert Disc, Thoracolumbar Vert Disc], Opn

ØRUØ[Ø,3,4]JZ Supl/Occipital-cervical Jt, [Opn, Perc, Perc Endo], Synth Sub, NQ
ØRU1[Ø,3,4]JZ Supl/Cervical Vert Jt, [Opn, Perc, Perc Endo], Synth Sub, NQ
ØRU3* Supl/Cervical Vert Disc
ØRU4[Ø,3,4]JZ Supl/Cervicothoracic Vert Jt, [Opn, Perc, Perc Endo], Synth Sub, NQ
ØRU5[Ø,3,4]JZ Supl/Cervicothoracic Vert Disc, [Opn, Perc, Perc Endo], Synth Sub, NQ
ØRU6[Ø,3,4]JZ Supl/Thoracic Vert Jt, [Opn, Perc, Perc Endo], Synth Sub, NQ
ØRU9* Supl/Thoracic Vert Disc
ØRUA[Ø,3,4]JZ Supl/Thoracolumbar Vert Jt, [Opn, Perc, Perc Endo], Synth Sub, NQ
ØRUB* Supl/Thoracolumbar Vert Disc
ØRW3[Ø,3,4]JZ Rev/Cervical Vert Disc, [Opn, Perc, Perc Endo], Synth Sub, NQ
ØRW5[Ø,3,4]JZ Rev/Cervicothoracic Vert Disc, [Opn, Perc, Perc Endo], Synth Sub, NQ
ØRW9[Ø,3,4]JZ Rev/Thoracic Vert Disc, [Opn, Perc, Perc Endo], Synth Sub, NQ
ØRWB[Ø,3,4]JZ Rev/Thoracolumbar Vert Disc, [Opn, Perc, Perc Endo], Synth Sub, NQ
ØS52* Destr/Lumbar Vert Disc
ØS54* Destr/Lumbosacral Disc
ØSBØ[Ø,3,4]ZZ Exc/Lumbar Vert Jt, [Opn, Perc, Perc Endo]
ØSB2[Ø,3,4]ZZ Exc/Lumbar Vert Disc, [Opn, Perc, Perc Endo]
ØSB3[Ø,3,4]ZZ Exc/Lumbosacral Jt, [Opn, Perc, Perc Endo]
ØSB4[Ø,3,4]ZZ Exc/Lumbosacral Disc, [Opn, Perc, Perc Endo]
ØSB5[Ø,3,4]ZZ Exc/Sacrococcygeal Jt, [Opn, Perc, Perc Endo]
ØSB6[Ø,3,4]ZZ Exc/Coccygeal Jt, [Opn, Perc, Perc Endo]
ØSB7[Ø,3,4]ZZ Exc/Sacroiliac Jt, Rt, [Opn, Perc, Perc Endo]
ØSB8[Ø,3,4]ZZ Exc/Sacroiliac Jt, Lt, [Opn, Perc, Perc Endo]
ØSHØ[Ø,3,4][B,C,D]Z Insert/Lumbar Vert Jt, [Opn, Perc, Perc Endo], [Spinal Stabliz Dev, Interspinous Process, Spinal Stabliz Dev, Pedicle-Based, Spinal Stabliz Dev, Facet Replace], NQ

ØSH3[Ø,3,4][B,C,D]Z Insert/Lumbosacral Jt, [Opn, Perc, Perc Endo], [Spinal Stabliz Dev, Interspinous Process, Spinal Stabliz Dev, Pedicle-Based, Spinal Stabliz Dev, Facet Replace], NQ

ØSQ[2,4]ØZZ Rpr [Lumbar Vert Disc, Lumbosacral Disc], Opn
ØSR2ØJZ Replace of Lum Disc with Synth Sub, Opn Appr
ØSR4ØJZ Replace of Lumsac Disc with Synth Sub, Opn Appr
ØST[2,4]ØZZ Resect [Lumbar Vert Disc, Lumbosacral Disc], Opn
ØSUØ[Ø,3,4]JZ Supl/Lumbar Vert Jt, [Opn, Perc, Perc Endo], Synth Sub, NQ
ØSU2* Supl/Lumbar Vert Disc
ØSU3[Ø,3,4]JZ Supl/Lumbosacral Jt, [Opn, Perc, Perc Endo], Synth Sub, NQ
ØSU4* Supl/Lumbosacral Disc
ØSU5[Ø,3,4]JZ Supl/Sacrococcygeal Jt, [Opn, Perc, Perc Endo], Synth Sub, NQ
ØSU6[Ø,3,4]JZ Supl/Coccygeal Jt, [Opn, Perc, Perc Endo], Synth Sub, NQ
ØSW2[Ø,3,4]JZ Rev/Lumbar Vert Disc, [Opn, Perc, Perc Endo], Synth Sub, NQ
ØSW4[Ø,3,4]JZ Rev/Lumbosacral Disc, [Opn, Perc, Perc Endo], Synth Sub, NQ

DRG 520   Back and Neck Procedures Except Spinal Fusion without CC/MCC

| GMLOS 1.9 | AMLOS 2.3 | RW 1.1812 | SP |

Select operating room procedures listed under DRG 519

MEDICAL

DRG 533   Fractures of Femur with MCC

| GMLOS 4.5 | AMLOS 6.Ø | RW 1.443Ø | T |

Principal Diagnosis

S72.3Ø[1,2,9][A,B,C] Unsp fx of shaft of [rt, lt, unsp] femur, init enc for [clsd fx, opn fx type I or II, opn fx type IIIA, IIIB, or IIIC]

S72.32[1,2,3][A,B,C] Disp transv fx of shaft of [rt, lt, unsp] femur, init enc for [clsd fx, opn fx type I or II, opn fx type IIIA, IIIB, or IIIC]

S72.32[4,5,6][A,B,C] Nondisp transv fx of shaft of [rt, lt, unsp] femur, init enc for [clsd fx, opn fx type I or II, opn fx type IIIA, IIIB, or IIIC]

S72.33[1,2,3][A,B,C] Disp oblique fx of shaft of [rt, lt, unsp] femur, init enc for [clsd fx, opn fx type I or II , opn fx type IIIA, IIIB, or IIIC]

S72.33[4,5,6][A,B,C] Nondisp oblique fx of shaft of [rt, lt, unsp] femur, init enc for [clsd fx, opn fx type I or II, opn fx type IIIA, IIIB, or IIIC]

S72.34[1,2,3][A,B,C] Disp spiral fx of shaft of [rt, lt, unsp] femur, init enc for [clsd fx, opn fx type I or II, opn fx type IIIA, IIIB, or IIIC]

S72.34[4,5,6][A,B,C] Nondisp spiral fx of shaft of [rt, lt, unsp] femur, init enc for [clsd fx, opn fx type I or II, opn fx type IIIA, IIIB, or IIIC]

S72.35[1,2,3][A,B,C] Disp comm fx of shaft of [rt, lt, unsp] femur, init enc for [clsd fx, opn fx type I or II, opn fx type IIIA, IIIB, or IIIC]

S72.35[4,5,6][A,B,C] Nondisp comm fx of shaft of femur [rt, lt, unsp], init enc for [clsd fx, opn fx type I or II or NOS, opn fx type IIIA, IIIB, or IIIC]

S72.36[1,2,3][A,B,C] Disp seg fx of shaft of [rt, lt, unsp] femur, init enc for [clsd fx, opn fx type I or II, opn fx type IIIA, IIIB, or IIIC]

S72.36[4,5,6][A,B,C] Nondisp seg fx of shaft of [rt, lt, unsp] femur, init enc for [clsd fx, opn fx type I or II, opn fx type IIIA, IIIB, or IIIC]

S72.39[1,2,9][A,B,C] Oth fx of shaft of [rt, lt, unsp] femur, init enc for [clsd fx, opn fx type I or II, opn fx type IIIA, IIIB, or IIIC]

S72.4Ø[1,2,9][A,B,C] Unsp fx of lwr end of [rt, lt, unsp] femur, init enc for [clsd fx, opn fx type I or II, opn fx type IIIA, IIIB, or IIIC]

S72.41[1,2,3][A,B,C] Disp unsp condyle fx of lwr end of [rt, lt, unsp] femur, init enc for [clsd fx, opn fx type I or II, opn fx type IIIA, IIIB, or IIIC]

S72.41[4,5,6][A,B,C] Nondisp unsp condyle fx of lwr end of [rt, lt, unsp] femur, init enc for [clsd fx, opn fx type I or II, opn fx type IIIA, IIIB, or IIIC]

S72.42[1,2,3][A,B,C] Disp fx of lat condyle of [rt, lt, unsp] femur, init enc for [clsd fx, opn fx type I or II, opn fx type IIIA, IIIB, or IIIC]

S72.42[4,5,6][A,B,C] Nondisp fx of lat condyle of [rt, lt, unsp] femur, init enc for [clsd fx, opn fx type I or II, opn fx type IIIA, IIIB, or IIIC]

S72.43[1,2,3][A,B,C] Disp fx of med condyle of [rt, lt, unsp] femur, init enc for [clsd fx, opn fx type I or II, opn fx type IIIA, IIIB, or IIIC]

S72.43[4,5,6][A,B,C] Nondisp fx of med condyle of [rt, lt, unsp] femur, init enc for [clsd fx, opn fx type I or II, opn fx type IIIA, IIIB, or IIIC]

S72.44[1,2,3][A,B,C] Disp fx of lwr epiphysis (separation) of [rt, lt, unsp] femur, init enc for [clsd fx, opn fx type I or II, opn fx type IIIA, IIIB, or IIIC]

S72.44[4,5,6][A,B,C] Nondisp fx of lwr epiphysis (separation) of [rt, lt, unsp] femur, init enc for [clsd fx, opn fx type I or II, opn fx type IIIA, IIIB, or IIIC]

S72.45[1,2,3][A,B,C] Disp supracondylar fx w/o intracondylar extension of lwr end of [rt, lt, unsp] femur, init enc for [clsd fx, opn fx type I or II, opn fx type IIIA, IIIB, or IIIC]

S72.45[4,5,6][A,B,C] Nondisp supracondylar fx w/o intracondylar extension of lwr end of [rt, lt, unsp] femur, init enc for [clsd fx, opn fx type I or II, opn fx type IIIA, IIIB, or IIIC]

S72.46[1,2,3][A,B,C] Disp supracondylar fx w/ intracondylar extension of lwr end of [rt, lt, unsp] femur, init enc for [clsd fx, opn fx type I or II, opn fx type IIIA, IIIB, or IIIC]

S72.46[4,5,6][A,B,C] Nondisp supracondylar fx w/ intracondylar extension of lwr end of [rt, lt, unsp] femur, init enc for [clsd fx, opn fx type I or II, opn fx type IIIA, IIIB, or IIIC]

S72.47[1,2,9]A Torus fx of lwr end of [rt, lt, unsp] femur, init enc for clsd fx

S72.49[1,2,9][A,B,C] Oth fx of lwr end of [rt, lt, unsp] femur, init enc for [clsd fx, opn fx type I or II, opn fx type IIIA, IIIB, or IIIC]

S72.8X[1,2,9][A,B,C] Oth fx of [rt, lt, unsp] femur, init enc for [clsd fx, opn fx type I or II, opn fx type IIIA, IIIB, or IIIC]

S72.9[Ø,1,2]X[A,B,C] Unsp fx of [unsp, rt lt] femur, init enc for [clsd fx, opn fx type I or II, opn fx type IIIA, IIIB, or IIIC]

S79.1Ø[1,2,9]A Unsp physeal fx of lwr end of [rt, lt, unsp] femur, inital enc for clsd fx

S79.11[1,2,9]A Salter-Harris Type I physeal fx of lwr end of femur [rt, lt, unsp] inital enc for clsd fx

S79.12[1,2,9]A Salter-Harris Type II physeal fx of lwr end of femur [rt, lt, unsp] inital enc for clsd fx

S79.13[1,2,9]A Salter-Harris Type III physeal fx of lwr end of femur [rt, lt, unsp] inital enc for clsd fx

---

Surgical   Medical   CC Indicator   MCC Indicator   Procedure Proxy   PDxMCC PDx acts as own MCC   PDxCC PDx acts as own CC

S79.14[1,2,9]A   Salter-Harris Type IV physeal fx of lwr end of femur [rt, lt, unsp] inital enc for clsd fx
S79.19[1,2,9]A   Oth physeal fx of lwr end of [rt, lt, unsp] femur, inital enc for clsd fx

DRG 534   Fractures of Femur without MCC
GMLOS 2.9   AMLOS 3.5   RW 0.7353   ⊤

Select principal diagnosis listed under DRG 533

DRG 535   Fractures of Hip and Pelvis with MCC
GMLOS 4.0   AMLOS 5.1   RW 1.2235   ⊤

Principal Diagnosis

S32.30[1,2,9][A,B]   Unsp fx of [rt, lt, unsp] ilium, init enc for [clsd, opn] fx
S32.31[1,2,3][A,B]   Disp avulsion fx of ilium [rt, lt, unsp] init enc for [clsd fx, opn fx]
S32.31[4,5,6][A,B]   Nondisp avulsion fx of ilium [rt, lt, unsp] init enc for [clsd fx, opn fx]
S32.39[1,2,9][A,B]   Oth fx of ilium [rt, lt, unsp] init enc for [clsd, opn] fx
S32.40[1,2,9][A,B]   Unsp fx of acetab [rt, lt, unsp] init enc for [clsd, opn] fx
S32.41[1,2,3][A,B]   Disp fx of ant wall of acetab [rt, lt, unsp] init enc for [clsd fx, opn fx]
S32.41[4,5,6][A,B]   Nondisp fx of ant wall of acetab [rt, lt, unsp] init enc for [clsd fx, opn fx]
S32.42[1,2,3][A,B]   Disp fx of post wall of [rt, lt, unsp] acetab, init enc for [clsd, opn] fx
S32.42[4,5,6][A,B]   Nondisp fx of post wall of acetab [rt, lt, unsp] init enc for [clsd fx, opn fx]
S32.43[1,2,3][A,B]   Disp fx of ant column [iliopubic] of acetab [rt, lt, unsp] init enc for [clsd fx, opn fx]
S32.43[4,5,6][A,B]   Nondisp fx of ant column [iliopubic] of acetab [rt, lt, unsp] init enc for [clsd fx, opn fx
S32.44[1,2,3][A,B]   Disp fx of post column [ilioischial] of acetab [rt, lt, unsp] init enc for [clsd fx, opn fx]
S32.44[4,5,6][A,B]   Nondisp fx of post column [ilioischial] of acetab [rt, lt, unsp] init enc for [clsd fx, opn fx]
S32.45[1,2,3][A,B]   Disp transv fx of acetab [rt, lt, unsp] init enc for [clsd fx, opn fx]
S32.45[4,5,6][A,B]   Nondisp transv fx of acetab [rt, lt, unsp] init enc for [clsd fx, opn fx]
S32.46[1,2,3][A,B]   Disp associated transv-post fx of acetab [rt, lt, unsp] init enc for [clsd fx, opn fx]
S32.46[4,5,6][A,B]   Nondisp associated transv-post fx of acetab [rt, lt, unsp] init enc for [clsd, opn] fx
S32.47[1,2,3][A,B]   Disp fx of med wall of acetab [rt, lt, unsp] init enc for [clsd fx, opn fx]
S32.47[4,5,6][A,B]   Nondisp fx of med wall of [rt, lt, unsp] acetab, init enc for [clsd, opn] fx
S32.48[1,2,3][A,B]   Disp dome fx of [rt, lt, unsp] acetab, init enc for [clsd, opn] fx
S32.48[4,5,6][A,B]   Nondisp dome fx of [rt, lt, unsp] acetab, init enc for [clsd, opn] fx
S32.49[1,2,9][A,B]   Oth spec fx of [rt, lt, unsp] acetab, init enc for [clsd, opn] fx
S32.50[1,2,9][A,B]   Unsp fx of pubis [rt, lt, unsp] init enc for [clsd, opn] fx
S32.51[1,2,9][A,B]   Fx of superior rim of pubis [rt, lt, unsp] init enc for [clsd, opn] fx
S32.59[1,2,9][A,B]   Oth spec fx of pubis [rt, lt, unsp] init enc for [clsd, opn] fx
S32.60[1,2,9][A,B]   Unsp fx of ischium [rt, lt, unsp], init enc for [clsd, opn] fx
S32.61[1,2,3][A,B]   Disp avulsion fx of ischium [rt, lt, unsp] init enc for [clsd fx, opn fx]
S32.61[4,5,6][A,B]   Nondisp avulsion fx of ischium [rt, lt, unsp] init enc for [clsd fx, opn fx]
S32.69[1,2,9][A,B]   Oth spec fx of ischium [rt, lt, unsp] init enc for [clsd, opn] fx
S32.81[0,1][A,B]   Multi fxs of pelvis w/ [stable, unstable] disruption of pelvic ring, init enc for [clsd, opn] fx
S32.82X[A,B]   Multi fxs of pelvis w/o disruption of pelvic ring, init enc for [clsd, opn] fx
S32.89X[A,B]   Fx of oth parts of pelvis, init enc for [clsd, opn] fx
S32.9XX[A,B]   Fx of unsp parts of lumbosacral spine and pelvis, init enc for [clsd, opn] fx
S72.00[1,2,9][A,B,C]   Fx of unsp part of neck of [rt, lt, unsp] femur, init enc for [clsd fx, opn fx type I or II, opn fx type IIIA, IIIB, or IIIC]
S72.01[1,2,9][A,B,C]   Unsp intracapsular fx of [rt, lt, unsp] femur, init enc for [clsd fx, opn fx type I or II, opn fx type IIIA, IIIB, or IIIC]
S72.02[1,2,3][A,B,C]   Disp fx of epiphysis (separation) (upr) of [rt, lt, unsp] femur, init enc for [clsd fx, opn fx type I or II or NOS, or opn fx type IIIA, IIIB, or IIIC]
S72.02[4,5,6][A,B,C]   Nondisp fx of epiphysis (separation) (upr) of [rt, lt, unsp] femur, init enc for [clsd fx, opn fx type I or II or NOS, or opn fx type IIIA, IIIB, or IIIC]

S72.03[1,2,3][A,B,C]   Disp midcervical fx of [rt, lt, unsp] femur, init enc for [clsd fx, opn fx type I or II or NOS, or opn fx type IIIA, IIIB, or IIIC]
S72.03[4,5,6][A,B,C]   Nondisp midcervical fx of [rt, lt, unsp] femur, init enc for [clsd fx, opn fx type I or II or NOS, or opn fx type IIIA, IIIB, or IIIC]
S72.04[1,2,3][A,B,C]   Disp fx of base of neck of [rt, lt, unsp] femur, init enc for opn fx type [I or II, IIIA IIIB or IIIC]
S72.04[4,5,6][A,B,C]   Nondisp fx of base of neck of [rt, lt, unsp] femur, init enc for opn fx type [I or II, IIIA IIIB or IIIC]
S72.05[1,2,9][A,B,C]   Unsp fx of head of [rt, lt, unsp] femur, init enc for [clsd fx, opn fx type I or II, opn fx type IIIA, IIIB, or IIIC]
S72.06[1,2,3][A,B,C]   Disp articular fx of head of [rt, lt, unsp] femur, init enc for fx [clsd, opn fx type I or II or NOS, or opn fx type IIIA, IIIB, or IIIC]
S72.06[4,5,6][A,B,C]   Nondisp articular fx of head of femur [rt, lt, unsp] init enc for fx [clsd, opn fx type I or II or NOS, or opn fx type IIIA, IIIB, or IIIC]
S72.09[1,2,9][A,B,C]   Oth fx of head and neck of [rt, lt, unsp] femur, init enc for [clsd fx, opn fx type I or II, opn fx type IIIA, IIIB, or IIIC]
S72.10[1,2,9][A,B,C]   Unsp trochanteric fx of [rt, lt, unsp] femur, init enc for [clsd fx, opn fx type I or II, opn fx type IIIA, IIIB, or IIIC]
S72.11[1,2,3][A,B,C]   Disp fx of greater trochanter of [rt, lt, unsp] femur, init enc for fx [clsd, opn fx type I or II or NOS, or opn fx type IIIA, IIIB, or IIIC]
S72.11[4,5,6][A,B,C]   Nondisp fx of greater trochanter of femur [rt, lt, unsp] init enc for fx [clsd, opn fx type I or II or NOS, or opn fx type IIIA, IIIB, or IIIC]
S72.12[1,2,3][A,B,C]   Disp fx of lesser trochanter of [rt, lt, unsp] femur, init enc for [clsd fx, opn fx type I or II or NOS, or opn fx type IIIA, IIIB, or IIIC]
S72.12[4,5,6][A,B,C]   Nondisp fx of lesser trochanter of [rt, lt, unsp] femur, init enc for [clsd fx, opn fx type I or II or NOS, or opn fx type IIIA, IIIB, or IIIC]
S72.13[1,2,3][A,B,C]   Disp apophyseal fx of [rt, lt, unsp] femur, init enc for [clsd fx, opn fx type I or II or NOS, or opn fx type IIIA, IIIB, or IIIC]
S72.13[4,5,6][A,B,C]   Nondisp apophyseal fx of [rt, lt, unsp] femur, init enc for [clsd fx, opn fx type I or II or NOS, or opn fx type IIIA, IIIB, or IIIC]
S72.14[1,2,3][A,B,C]   Disp intertrochanteric fx of [rt, lt, unsp] femur, init enc for [clsd fx, opn fx type I or II or NOS, or opn fx type IIIA, IIIB, or IIIC]
S72.14[4,5,6][A,B,C]   Nondisp intertrochanteric fx of [rt, lt, unsp] femur, init enc for [clsd fx, opn fx type I or II or NOS, or opn fx type IIIA, IIIB, or IIIC]
S72.2[1,2,3]X[A,B,C]   Disp subtrochanteric fx of [rt, lt, unsp] femur, init enc for [clsd fractrure, opn fx type I or II or NOS, or opn fx type IIIA, IIIB, or IIIC]
S72.2[4,5,6]X[A,B,C]   Nondisp subtrochanteric fx of [rt, lt, unsp] femur, init enc for [clsd fractrure, opn fx type I or II or NOS, or opn fx type IIIA, IIIB, or IIIC]
S79.00[1,2,9]A   Unsp physeal fx of upr end of [rt, lt, unsp] femur, init enc for clsd fx
S79.01[1,2,9]A   Salter-Harris Type I physeal fx of upr end of [rt, lt, unsp] femur, init enc for clsd fx
S79.09[1,2,9]A   Oth physeal fx of upr end of [rt, lt, unsp] femur, init enc for clsd fx

DRG 536   Fractures of Hip and Pelvis without MCC
GMLOS 3.0   AMLOS 3.4   RW 0.7241   ⊤

Select principal diagnosis listed under DRG 535

DRG 537   Sprains, Strains, and Dislocations of Hip, Pelvis and Thigh with CC/MCC
GMLOS 3.3   AMLOS 3.9   RW 0.9046

Principal Diagnosis

S33.4XXA   Traum rupture of symphysis pubis, init enc
S73.00[1,2,3]A   Unsp sublux of [rt, lt, unsp] hip, init enc
S73.00[4,5,6]A   Unsp disloc of [rt, lt, unsp] hip, init enc
S73.01[1,2,3]A   Post sublux of [rt, lt, unsp] hip, init enc
S73.01[4,5,6]A   Post disloc of [rt, lt, unsp] hip, init enc
S73.02[1,2,3]A   Obturator sublux of [rt, lt, unsp] hip, init enc
S73.02[4,5,6]A   Obturator disloc of [rt, lt, unsp] hip, init enc
S73.03[1,2,3]A   Oth ant sublux of [rt, lt, unsp] hip, init enc
S73.03[4,5,6]A   Oth ant disloc of [rt, lt, unsp] hip, init enc
S73.04[1,2,3]A   Central sublux of [rt, lt, unsp] hip, init enc
S73.04[4,5,6]A   Central disloc of [rt, lt, unsp] hip, init enc
S73.10[1,2,9]A   Unsp sprain of [rt, lt, unsp] hip, init enc
S73.11[1,2,9]A   Iliofemoral lgmt sprain of hip [rt, lt, unsp] init enc
S73.12[1,2,9]A   Ischiocapsular (lgmt) sprain of hip [rt, lt, unsp] init enc

---

⊤ **Transfer DRG**   ⑤ᴾ **Special Payment**   * **Code Range**   **6th and 7th Character of ZZ = No Device, No Qualifier ZX = No Device, Diagnostic**

S73.19[1,2,9]A	Oth sprain of [rt, lt, unsp] hip, init enc
S76.01[1,2,9]A	Strain of muscle, fascia and tndn of hip [rt, lt, unsp] init enc
S76.11[1,2,9]A	Strain of [rt, lt, unsp] quadriceps muscle, fascia and tndn, init enc
S76.21[1,2,9]A	Strain of adductor muscle, fascia and tndn of thigh [rt, lt, unsp] init enc
S76.31[1,2,9]A	Strain of muscle, fascia and tndn of of the post muscle group at thigh lvl [rt, lt, unsp] init enc
S76.811A	Strain of musc/fasc/tend at thigh lvl, rt thigh, init
S76.812A	Strain of musc/fasc/tend at thigh lvl, lt thigh, init
S76.819A	Strain of musc/fasc/tend at thigh lvl, unsp thigh, init
S76.91[1,2,9]A	Strain of unsp muscles, fascia and tndns at thigh lvl [rt, lt, unsp] init enc

DRG 538 Sprains, Strains, and Dislocations of Hip, Pelvis and Thigh without CC/MCC
GMLOS 2.5　　　**AMLOS 2.9**　　　**RW 0.6282**

Select principal diagnosis listed under DRG 537

DRG 539 Osteomyelitis with MCC
GMLOS 6.0　　　**AMLOS 7.8**　　　**RW 1.8365**　　[T]

Principal Diagnosis

A02.24	Salmonella osteomyelitis
A18.0[1,3]	Tuberculosis of [spine, oth bones]
A51.46	Secondary syphilitic osteopathy
A52.77	Syphilis of bone and jt
A54.41	Gonococcal spondylopathy
M46.2*	Osteomyelitis of vertebra
M46.3*	infxn of intervertebral disc (pyogenic)
M86*	Osteomyelitis

DRG 540 Osteomyelitis with CC
GMLOS 4.7　　　**AMLOS 5.9**　　　**RW 1.2832**　　[T]

Select principal diagnosis listed under DRG 539

DRG 541 Osteomyelitis without CC/MCC
GMLOS 3.4　　　**AMLOS 4.3**　　　**RW 0.9098**　　[T]

Select principal diagnosis listed under DRG 539

DRG 542 Pathological Fractures and Musculoskeletal and Connective Tissue Malignancy with MCC
GMLOS 5.7　　　**AMLOS 7.5**　　　**RW 1.9100**　　[T]

Principal Diagnosis

C40*	Malig neoplasm of bone and articular cartilage of limbs
C41*	Malig neoplasm of bone/artic cartl of and unsp sites
C47*	Malig neoplasm of prph nerves and autonomic nervous sys
C49*	Malig neoplasm of oth connective and soft tissue
C79.5*	Secondary malig neoplasm of bone and bone marrow
C7B.03	Secondary carcinoid tumors of bone
D48.0	Neoplasm of uncertain behav of bone/artic cartl
M30.1	Polyarteritis with lung involvement [Churg-Strauss]
M31.2	Lethal midline granuloma
M31.3*	Wegener's granulomatosis
M48.4[0,1,2,3,4,5,6,7,8]XA	Fatigue fx of vertebra, [unsp, occipito-atlanto-axial, cervical, cervicothoracic, thoracic, thoraccolumbar, lumbar, lumbosacral, sacral and sacrococcygeal] rgn, init enc for fx
M48.5[0,1,2,3,4,5,6,7,8]XA	Collapsed vertebra, NEC, [unsp, occipito-atlanto-axial, cervical, cervicothoracic, thoracic, thoracolumbar, lumbar, lumbosacral, sacral and sacrococcygeal] rgn, init enc for fx
M80.00XA	Age-rel osteopor w current path fx, unsp site, init
M80.01[1,2,9]A	Age-related osteoporosis w/ current path fx, [rt, lt, unsp] shldr, init enc for fx
M80.02[1,2,9]A	Age-related osteoporosis w/ current path fx, [rt, lt, unsp] humerus, init enc for fx
M80.03[1,2,9]A	Age-related osteoporosis w/ current path fx, [rt, lt, unsp] forearm, init enc for fx
M80.04[1,2,9]A	Age-related osteoporosis w/ current path fx, [rt, lt, unsp] hand, init enc for fx
M80.05[1,2,9]A	Age-related osteoporosis w/ current path fx, [rt, lt, unsp] femur, init enc for fx
M80.06[1,2,9]A	Age-related osteoporosis w/ current path fx, [rt, lt, unsp] lwr leg, init enc for fx

M80.07[1,2,9]A	Age-related osteoporosis w/ current path fx, [rt, lt, unsp] ankle and foot, init enc for fx
M80.08XA	Age-rel osteopor w current path fx, vertebra(e), init
M80.80XA	Oth osteopor w current path fx, unsp site, init
M80.81[1,2,9]A	Oth osteoporosis w/ current path fx, [rt, lt, unsp] shldr, init enc for fx
M80.82[1,2,9]A	Oth osteoporosis w/ current path fx, [rt, lt, unsp] humerus, init enc for fx
M80.83[1,2,9]A	Oth osteoporosis w/ current path fx, [rt, lt, unsp] forearm, init enc for fx
M80.84[1,2,9]A	Oth osteoporosis w/ current path fx, [rt, lt, unsp] hand, init enc for fx
M80.85[1,2,9]A	Oth osteoporosis w/ current path fx, [rt, lt, unsp] femur, init enc for fx
M80.86[1,2,9]A	Oth osteoporosis w/ current path fx, [rt, lt, unsp] lwr leg, init enc for fx
M80.87[1,2,9]A	Oth osteoporosis w/ current path fx, [rt, lt, unsp] ankle and foot, init enc for fx
M80.88XA	Oth osteopor w current path fx, vertebra(e), init
M84.30XA	Stress fx, unsp site, init enc for fx
M84.31[1,2,9]A	Stress fx, [rt, lt, unsp] shldr, init enc for fx
M84.32[1,2,9]A	Stress fx, [rt, lt, unsp] humerus, init enc for fx
M84.33[1,2,3,4,9]A	Stress fx, [rt ulna, lt ulna, rt radius, lt radius, unsp radius and ulna], init enc for fx
M84.34[1,2,3,4,5,6]A	Stress fx, [rt hand, lt hand, unsp hand, rt finger(s), lt finger(s), unsp finger(s)], init enc for fx
M84.35[0,1,2,3,9]A	Stress fx, [pelvis, rt femur, lt femur, unsp femur], init enc for fx
M84.36[1,2,3,4,9]A	Stress fx, [rt tibia, lt tibia, rt fibula, lt fibula, unsp tibia & fibula], init enc for fx
M84.37[1,2,3,4,5,6,7,8,9]A	Stress fx, [rt ankle, lt ankle, unsp ankle, rt foot, lt foot, unsp foot, rt toe(s), lt toe(s), unsp toe(s)], init enc for fx
M84.38XA	Stress fx, oth site, init enc for fx
M84.40XA	Path fx, unsp site, init enc for fx
M84.41[1,2,9]A	Path fx, [rt, lt, unsp] shldr, init enc for fx
M84.42[1,2,9]A	Path fx, [rt, lt, unsp] humerus, init enc for fx
M84.43[1,2,3,4,9]A	Path fx, [rt ulna, lt ulna, rt radius, lt radius, unsp radius and ulna], init enc for fx
M84.44[1,2,3,4,5,6]A	Path fx, [rt hand, lt hand, unsp hand, rt finger(s), lt finger(s), unsp finger(s)], init enc for fx
M84.45[1,2,3,4,9]A	Path fx, [rt femur, lt femur, unsp femur, pelvis, unsp hip], init enc for fx
M84.46[1,2,3,4,9]A	Path fx, [rt tibia, lt tibia, rt fibula, lt fibula, unsp tibia & fibula], init enc for fx
M84.47[1,2,3,4,5,6,7,8,9]A	Path fx [rt ankle, lt ankle, unsp ankle, rt foot, lt foot, unsp foot, rt toe(s), lt toe(s), unsp toe(s)], init enc for fx
M84.48XA	Path fx, oth site, init enc for fx
M84.50XA	Path fx in neoplastic dz, unsp site, init
M84.51[1,2,9]A	Path fx in neoplastic dz, [rt, lt, unsp] shldr, init enc for fx
M84.52[1,2,9]A	Path fx in neoplastic dz, [rt, lt, unsp] humerus, init enc for fx
M84.53[1,2,3,4,9]A	Path fx in neoplastic dz, [rt ulna, lt ulna, rt radius, lt radius, unsp ulna and radius], init enc for fx
M84.54[1,2,9]A	Path fx in neoplastic dz, [rt, lt, unsp] hand, init enc for fx
M84.55[0,1,2,3,9]A	Path fx in neoplastic dz, [pelvis, rt femur, lt femur, unsp femur, unsp hip], init enc for fx
M84.56[1,2,3,4,9]A	Path fx in neoplastic dz, [rt tibia, lt tibia, rt fibula, lt fibula, unsp tibia & fibula], init enc for fx
M84.57[1,2,3,4,5,6]A	Path fx in neoplastic dz, [rt ankle, lt ankle, unsp ankle, rt foot, lt foot, unsp foot], init enc for fx
M84.58XA	Path fx in neoplastic dz, oth site, init
M84.60XA	Path fx in oth dz, unsp site, init for fx
M84.61[1,2,9]A	Path fx in oth dz, [rt, lt, unsp] shldr, init enc for fx
M84.62[1,2,9]A	Path fx in oth dz, [rt, lt, unsp] humerus, init enc for fx
M84.63[1,2,3,4,9]A	Path fx in oth dz, [rt ulna, lt ulna, lt radius, unsp ulna and radius], init enc for fx
M84.64[1,2,9]A	Path fx in oth dz, [rt, lt, unsp] hand, init enc for fx
M84.65[0,1,2,3,9]A	Path fx in oth dz, [pelvis, rt femur, lt femur, unsp femur, hip NOS], init enc for fx
M84.66[1,2,3,4,9]A	Path fx in oth dz, [rt tibia, lt tibia, rt fibula, lt fibula, unsp tibia & fibula], init enc for fx
M84.671A	Path fx in oth dz, rt ankle, init
M84.672A	Path fx in oth dz, lt ankle, init
M84.673A	Path fx in oth dz, unsp ankle, init
M84.674A	Path fx in oth dz, rt foot, init
M84.675A	Path fx in oth dz, lt foot, init for fx
M84.676A	Path fx in oth dz, unsp foot, init for fx
M84.68XA	Path fx in oth dz, oth site, init for fx

Surgical　　**Medical**　　**CC Indicator**　　**MCC Indicator**　　**Procedure Proxy**　　[PDxMCC] **PDx acts as own MCC**　　[PDxCC] **PDx acts as own CC**

MDC 8: Diseases And Disorders Of The Musculoskeletal System And Connective Tissue—MEDICAL

DRG 543   Pathological Fractures and Musculoskeletal and Connective Tissue Malignancy with CC

| GMLOS 4.0 | AMLOS 5.0 | RW 1.1171 | [T] |

Select principal diagnosis listed under DRG 542

DRG 544   Pathological Fractures and Musculoskeletal and Connective Tissue Malignancy without CC/MCC

| GMLOS 3.1 | AMLOS 3.5 | RW 0.7805 | [T] |

Select principal diagnosis listed under DRG 542

DRG 545   Connective Tissue Disorders with MCC

| GMLOS 5.9 | AMLOS 8.3 | RW 2.4409 | [T] |

Principal Diagnosis

D89.82	Autoimmune lymphoproliferative synd [ALPS]
E85*	Amyloidosis
G72.4*	Inflam and immune myopathies, NEC
I00	Rheumatic fever w/o heart involvement
I73.0*	Raynaud's synd
I77.6	Arteritis, unsp
L40.5*	Arthropathic psoriasis
M02.3*	Reiter's dz
M05.0*	Felty's synd
M05.2*	Rheumatoid vasculitis with rheumatoid arthritis
M05.3*	Rheumatoid heart dz with rheumatoid arthritis
M05.4*	Rheumatoid myopathy with rheumatoid arthritis
M05.5*	Rheumatoid polyneuropathy with rheumatoid arthritis
M05.6*	Rheumatoid arthritis w involvement of oth organs and systems
M05.7*	Rheumatoid arthritis w rheumatoid factor w/o org/sys involv
M05.8*	Oth rheumatoid arthritis with rheumatoid factor
M05.9	Rheumatoid arthritis with rheumatoid factor, unsp
M06.0*	Rheumatoid arthritis w/o rheumatoid factor
M06.1	Adult-onset Still's dz
M06.2*	Rheumatoid bursitis
M06.3*	Rheumatoid nodule
M06.8*	Oth spec rheumatoid arthritis
M06.9	Rheumatoid arthritis, unsp
M08*	Juvenile arthritis
M30.0	Polyarteritis nodosa
M30.2	Juvenile polyarteritis
M30.3	Mucocutaneous lymph node synd [Kawasaki]
M30.8	Oth conditions related to polyarteritis nodosa
M31.0	Hypersensitivity angiitis
M31.1	Thrombotic microangiopathy
M31.4	Aortic arch synd [Takayasu]
M31.5	Giant cell arteritis with polymyalgia rheumatica
M31.6	Oth giant cell arteritis
M31.7	Microscopic polyangiitis
M32*	Systemic lupus erythematosus (SLE)
M33*	Dermatopolymyositis
M34.0	Progressive systemic sclerosis
M34.1	CR(E)ST synd
M34.2	Systemic sclerosis induced by drug and chemical
M34.82	Systemic sclerosis with myopathy [PDxCC]
M34.89	Oth systemic sclerosis
M34.9	Systemic sclerosis, unsp
M35.0*	Sicca synd [Sjogren]
M35.1	Oth overlap syndromes
M35.2	Behcet's dz
M35.3	Polymyalgia rheumatica
M35.5	Multifocal fibrosclerosis
M35.8	Oth spec systemic involvement of connective tissue
M35.9	Systemic involvement of connective tissue, unsp
M36.0	Dermato(poly)myositis in neoplastic dz
M36.8	Systemic d/o of conn tiss in oth dz classd elsw
M45*	Ankylosing spondylitis
M48.8*	Oth spec spondylopathies

DRG 546   Connective Tissue Disorders with CC

| GMLOS 3.8 | AMLOS 4.8 | RW 1.1645 | [T] |

Select principal diagnosis listed under DRG 545

DRG 547   Connective Tissue Disorders without CC/MCC

| GMLOS 2.7 | AMLOS 3.3 | RW 0.7882 | [T] |

Select principal diagnosis listed under DRG 545

DRG 548   Septic Arthritis with MCC

| GMLOS 6.0 | AMLOS 7.4 | RW 1.8733 |

Principal Diagnosis

A02.23	Salmonella arthritis
A18.02	Tuberculous arthritis of oth jts
A18.09	Oth musculoskeletal tuberculosis
A39.8[3,4]	[Meningococcal, Postmeningococcal] arthritis
A54.4[0,2,3,9]	Gonococcal [infxn of musculoskeletal sys unsp, arthritis, osteomyelitis, oth musculoskeletal tissue]
A66.6	Bone and jt lesions of yaws
M00.00	Staphylococcal arthritis, unsp jt
M00.011	Staphylococcal arthritis, rt shldr
M00.012	Staphylococcal arthritis, lt shldr
M00.019	Staphylococcal arthritis, unsp shldr
M00.021	Staphylococcal arthritis, rt elbow
M00.022	Staphylococcal arthritis, lt elbow
M00.029	Staphylococcal arthritis, unsp elbow
M00.031	Staphylococcal arthritis, rt wrist
M00.032	Staphylococcal arthritis, lt wrist
M00.039	Staphylococcal arthritis, unsp wrist
M00.041	Staphylococcal arthritis, rt hand
M00.042	Staphylococcal arthritis, lt hand
M00.049	Staphylococcal arthritis, unsp hand
M00.051	Staphylococcal arthritis, rt hip
M00.052	Staphylococcal arthritis, lt hip
M00.059	Staphylococcal arthritis, unsp hip
M00.061	Staphylococcal arthritis, rt knee
M00.062	Staphylococcal arthritis, lt knee
M00.069	Staphylococcal arthritis, unsp knee
M00.071	Staphylococcal arthritis, rt ankle and foot
M00.072	Staphylococcal arthritis, lt ankle and foot
M00.079	Staphylococcal arthritis, unsp ankle and foot
M00.08	Staphylococcal arthritis, vertebrae
M00.09	Staphylococcal polyarthritis
M00.1*	Pneumococcal arthritis and polyarthritis
M00.2*	Oth streptococcal arthritis and polyarthritis
M00.8*	Arthritis and polyarthritis d/t oth bacteria
M00.9	Pyogenic arthritis, unsp
M01*	Direct infect of jt in infec/parastc dis classd elsw
M02.8*	Oth reactive arthropathies

DRG 549   Septic Arthritis with CC

| GMLOS 4.2 | AMLOS 5.3 | RW 1.1824 |

Select principal diagnosis listed under DRG 548

DRG 550   Septic Arthritis without CC/MCC

| GMLOS 2.9 | AMLOS 3.6 | RW 0.8129 |

Select principal diagnosis listed under DRG 548

DRG 551   Medical Back Problems with MCC

| GMLOS 4.6 | AMLOS 5.9 | RW 1.5573 | [T] |

Principal Diagnosis

M25.78	Osteophyte, vertebrae
M40*	Kyphosis and lordosis
M41*	Scoliosis
M43.0*	Spondylolysis
M43.1*	Spondylolisthesis
M43.2*	Fusion of spine
M43.6	Torticollis
M43.8*	Oth spec deforming dorsopathies
M43.9	Deforming dorsopathy, unsp
M46.0*	Spinal enthesopathy
M46.1	Sacroiliitis, NEC
M46.4*	Discitis, unsp
M46.5*	Oth infective spondylopathies
M46.8*	Oth spec inflam spondylopathies
M46.9*	Unsp inflam spondylopathy
M47*	Spondylosis
M48.0*	Spinal stenosis

[T] Transfer DRG   [SP] Special Payment   * Code Range   6th and 7th Character of ZZ = No Device, No Qualifier ZX = No Device, Diagnostic

M48.1*	Ankylosing hyperostosis [Forestier]
M48.2*	Kissing spine
M48.3*	Traum spondylopathy
M48.4[0,1,2,3,4,5,6,7,8]XS	Fatigue fx of vertebra, [unsp, occipito-atlanto-axial, cervical, cervicothoracic, thoracic, thoracolumbar, lumbar, lumbosacral, sacral and sacrococcygeal] rgn, seq of fx
M48.5[0,1,2,3,4,5,6,7,8]XS	Collapsed vertebra, NEC, [unsp, occipito-atlanto-axial, cervical, cervicothoracic, thoracic, thoracolumbar, lumbar, lumbosacral, sacral and sacrococcygeal] rgn, seq
M48.9	Spondylopathy, unsp
M49*	Spondylopathies in dz classified elsw
M50.0*	Cervical disc d/o with myelopathy
M50.10	Cervical disc d/o w radiculopathy, unsp cervical region
M50.11	Cerv disc d/o w radiculopathy, high cervical region
M50.12	Cervical disc d/o w radiculopathy, mid-cervical region
M50.13	Cervical disc d/o w radiculopathy, cervicothor region
M50.2*	Oth cervical disc displac
M50.3*	Oth cervical disc degeneration
M50.8*	Oth cervical disc d/o
M50.9*	Cervical disc d/o, unsp
M51*	Thoracic, thoracolum, and lumbosacral intvrt disc d/o
M53.2X[7,8]	Spinal instabilities, [lumbosacral, sacral and sacrococcygeal] rgn
M53.3	Sacrococcygeal d/o, NEC
M53.8*	Oth spec dorsopathies
M53.9	Dorsopathy, unsp
M54.0[3,4,5,6,7,8,9]	Panniculitis affecting rgns of neck and back [cervicothoracic, thoracic, thoracolumbar, lumbar, lumbosacral, sacral and sacrococcygeal, multi] rgn(s)
M54.1[4,5,6,7]	Radiculopathy [thoracic, thoracolumbar, lumbar, lumbosacral] rgn
M54.2	Cervicalgia
M54.3*	Sciatica
M54.4*	Lumbago with sciatica
M54.5	Low back pain
M54.6	Pain in thoracic spine
M54.8*	Oth dorsalgia
M54.9	Dorsalgia, unsp
M62.830	Muscle spasm of back
M80.08XS	Age-rel osteopor w current path fx, verteb, seq
M80.88XS	Oth osteopor w current path fx, vertebra(e), seq
M84.350S	Stress fx, pelvis, seq
M84.454S	Path fx, pelvis, seq
M84.550S	Path fx in neoplastic dz, pelvis, seq
M84.58XS	Path fx in neoplastic dz, oth site, seq
M84.650S	Path fx in oth dz, pelvis, seq
M96.1	Postlaminectomy synd, NEC
M96.2	Postradiation kyphosis
M96.3	Postlaminectomy kyphosis
M96.4	Postsurgical lordosis
M96.5	Postradiation scoliosis
M99.0[1,2,3,4]	Seg and somatic dysfunction of [head rgn, thoracic rgn, lumbar rgn, sacral rgn]
M99.1[0,1,2,3,4,5]	Sublux complex (vert) of [head rgn, cervical rgn, thoracic rgn, lumbar rgn, pelvic rgn]
M99.2*	Sublux stenosis of neural canal
M99.3*	Osseous stenosis of neural canal
M99.4*	Connective tissue stenosis of neural canal
M99.5*	Intervertebral disc stenosis of neural canal
M99.6*	Osseous and sublux stenosis of intervertebral foramina
M99.7*	Connective tiss and disc stenosis of intervertebral foramina
M99.8[3,4]	Oth biomech lesions [lumbar rgn, sacral rgn]
Q76.2	Congenital spondylolisthesis
Q76.41[1,2,3,4,5,9]	Congenital kyphosis [occipito-atlanto-axial, cervical, cervicothoracic, thoracic, thoracolumbar, unsp] rgn
Q76.49	Oth congenital malform of spine, not associated w scoliosis
R29.891	Ocular torticollis
S12.00[0,1][A,B,S]	Unsp [disp, nondisp] fx of 1st cervical vertebra, [init enc for clsd fx, init enc for opn fx, seq]
S12.03[0,1][A,B,S]	Post arch fx of 1st cervical vertebra [disp, nondisp] init enc for fx [clsd, opn, seq]
S12.04[0,1][A,B,S]	Lat mass fx of 1st cervical vertebra [disp, nondisp] init enc for fx [clsd, opn, seq]
S12.09[0,1][A,B,S]	Oth fx of 1st cervical vertebra [disp, nondisp] init enc for fx [clsd, opn, seq]
S12.0[1,2]X[A,B,S]	Burst fx of 1st cervical vertebra, [stable, unstable], [init enc for clsd fx, init enc for opn fx, seq]
S12.10[0,1][A,B,S]	Unsp disp fx of 2nd cervical vertebra [disp, nondisp] init enc for fx [clsd, opn, seq]
S12.11[0,1,2][A,B,S]	Type II dens fx [ant disp, post disp, nondisp] init enc for fx [clsd, opn, seq]
S12.12[0,1][A,B,S]	Oth dens fx [disp, nondisp] init enc for fx [clsd, opn, seq]
S12.13[0,1][A,B,S]	Unsp traum [disp, nondisp] spondylolisthesis of 2nd cervical vertebra, init enc for fx [clsd, opn, seq]
S12.14X[A,B,S]	Type III traum spondylolisthesis of 2nd cervical vertebra, init enc for fx [clsd, opn, seq]
S12.15[0,1][A,B,S]	Oth traum spondylolisthesis of 2nd cervical vertebra [disp, nondisp] init enc for fx [clsd, opn, seq]
S12.19[0,1][A,B,S]	Oth fx of 2nd cervical vertebra [disp, nondisp] init enc for fx [clsd, opn, seq]
S12.20[0,1][A,B,S]	Unsp fx of 3rd cervical vertebra [disp, nondisp] init enc for fx [clsd, opn, seq]
S12.23[0,1][A,B,S]	Unsp traum spondylolisthesis of 3rd cervical vertebra, [disp, nondisp], [init enc for clsd fx, init enc for opn fx, seq]
S12.24X[A,B,S]	Type III traum spondylolisthesis of 3rd cervical vertebra, init enc for fx [clsd, opn, seq]
S12.25[0,1][A,B,S]	Oth traum spondylolisthesis of 3rd cervical vertebra [disp, nondisp] init enc for fx [clsd, opn, seq]
S12.29[0,1][A,B,S]	Oth fx of 3rd cervical vertebra [disp, nondisp] init enc for fx [clsd, opn, seq]
S12.30[0,1][A,B,S]	Unsp fx of 4th cervical vertebra. [disp, nondisp], [init enc for clsd fx, init enc for opn fx, seq]
S12.33[0,1][A,B,S]	Unsp traum spondylolisthesis of 4th cervical vertebra [disp, nondisp] init enc for fx [clsd, opn, seq]
S12.34X[A,B,S]	Type III traum spondylolisthesis of 4th cervical vertebra, init enc for fx [clsd, opn, seq]
S12.35[0,1][A,B,S]	Oth traum spondylolisthesis of 4th cervical vertebra [disp, nondisp] init enc for fx [clsd, opn, seq]
S12.39[0,1][A,B,S]	Oth fx of 4th cervical vertebra [disp, nondisp] init enc for fx [clsd, opn, seq]
S12.40[0,1][A,B,S]	Unsp fx of 5th cervical vertebra [disp, nondisp] init enc for fx [clsd, opn, seq]
S12.43[0,1][A,B,S]	Unsp traum spondylolisthesis of 5th cervical vertebra [disp, nondisp] init enc for fx [clsd, opn, seq]
S12.44X[A,B,S]	Type III traum spondylolisthesis of 5th cervical vertebra, init enc for fx [clsd, opn, seq]
S12.45[0,1][A,B,S]	Oth traum spondylolisthesis of 5th cervical vertebra [disp, nondisp] init enc for fx [clsd, opn, seq]
S12.49[0,1][A,B,S]	Oth fx of 5th cervical vertebra [disp, nondisp] init enc for fx [clsd, opn, seq]
S12.50[0,1][A,B,S]	Unsp fx of 6th cervical vertebra [disp, nondisp] init enc for fx [clsd, opn, seq]
S12.53[0,1][A,B,S]	Unsp traum spondylolisthesis of 6th cervical vertebra [disp, nondisp] init enc for fx [clsd, opn, seq]
S12.54X[A,B,S]	Type III traum spondylolisthesis of 6th cervical vertebra, init enc for fx [clsd, opn, seq]
S12.55[0,1][A,B,S]	Oth traum spondylolisthesis of 6th cervical vertebra [disp, nondisp] init enc for fx [clsd, opn, seq]
S12.59[0,1][A,B,S]	Oth [disp, nondisp] fx of 6th cervical vertebra, [init enc for clsd fx, init enc for opn fx, seq]
S12.60[0,1][A,B,S]	Unsp fx of 6th cervical vertebra [disp, nondisp] init enc for fx [clsd, opn, seq]
S12.63[0,1][A,B,S]	Unsp traum spondylolisthesis of 7th cervical vertebra, [disp, nondisp], [init enc for clsd fx, init enc for opn fx, seq]
S12.64X[A,B,S]	Type III traum spondylolisthesis of 7th cervical vertebra init enc for fx [clsd, opn, seq]
S12.65[0,1][A,B,S]	Oth traum spondylolisthesis of 7th cervical vertebra [disp, nondisp] init enc for fx [clsd, opn, seq]
S12.69[0,1][A,B,S]	Oth [disp, nondisp] fx of 7th cervical vertebra, [init enc for clsd fx, init enc for opn fx, seq]
S12.8XXS	Fx of oth parts of neck, seq
S12.9XX[A,S]	Fx of neck, unsp, [init enc for clsd fx, seq]
S13.0XXA	Traum rupture of cervical intervertebral disc, init
S13.10[0,1]A	[Sublux, Disloc] of unsp cervical vertebrae, init enc
S13.11[0,1]A	[Sublux, Disloc] of C0/C1 cervical vertebrae, init enc
S13.12[0,1]A	[Sublux, Disloc] of C1/C2 cervical vertebrae, init enc
S13.13[0,1]A	[Sublux, Disloc] of C2/C3 cervical vertebrae, init enc
S13.14[0,1]A	[Sublux, Disloc] of C3/C4 cervical vertebrae, init enc
S13.15[0,1]A	[Sublux, Disloc] of C4/C5 cervical vertebrae, init enc
S13.16[0,1]A	[Sublux, Disloc] of C5/C6 cervical vertebrae, init enc
S13.17[0,1]A	[Sublux, Disloc] of C6/C7 cervical vertebrae, init enc
S13.18[0,1]A	[Sublux, Disloc] of C7/T1 cervical vertebrae, init enc
S13.2[0,9]XA	Disloc of [unsp, oth] parts of neck, init enc
S13.4XXA	Sprain of lgmt of cervical spine, init enc
S13.8XXA	Sprain of jts and lgmt of oth prt neck, init enc
S13.9XXA	Sprain of jts and lgmt of unsp parts of neck, init
S16.1XXA	Strain of muscle, fascia and tndn at neck lvl, init

Surgical   **Medical**   **CC Indicator**   **MCC Indicator**   **Procedure Proxy**   PDxMCC **PDx acts as own MCC**   PDxCC **PDx acts as own CC**

MDC 8: Diseases And Disorders Of The Musculoskeletal System And Connective Tissue—MEDICAL

S22.00[0,1,2,8,9][A,B,S] [Wedge compression, Stable burst, Unstable burst, Oth, Unsp] fx of unsp thoracic vertebra, [init enc for clsd fx, init enc for opn fx, seq]
S22.01[0,1,2,8,9][A,B,S] [Wedge compression, Stable burst, Unstable burst, Oth, Unsp] fx of 1st thoracic vertebra, [init enc for clsd fx, init enc for opn fx, seq]
S22.02[0,1,2,8,9][A,B,S] [Wedge compression, Stable burst, Unstable burst, Oth, Unsp] fx of 2nd thoracic vertebra, [init enc for clsd fx, init enc for opn fx, seq]
S22.03[0,1,2,8,9][A,B,S] [Wedge compression, Stable burst, Unstable burst, Oth, Unsp] fx of 3rd thoracic vertebra, [init enc for clsd fx, init enc for opn fx, seq]
S22.04[0,1,2,8,9][A,B,S] [Wedge compression, Stable burst, Unstable burst, Oth, Unsp] fx of 4th thoracic vertebra, [init enc for clsd fx, init enc for opn fx, seq]
S22.05[0,1,2,8,9][A,B,S] [Wedge compression, Stable burst, Unstable burst, Oth, Unsp] fx of T5-T6 vertebra, [init enc for clsd fx, init enc for opn fx, seq]
S22.06[0,1,2,8,9][A,B,S] [Wedge compression, Stable burst, Unstable burst, Oth, Unsp] fx of T7-T8 thoracic vertebra, [init enc for clsd fx, init enc for opn fx, seq]
S22.07[0,1,2,8,9][A,B,S] [Wedge compression, Stable burst, Unstable burst, Oth, Unsp] fx of T9-T10 thoracic vertebra, [init enc for clsd fx, init enc for opn fx, seq]
S22.08[0,1,2,8,9][A,B,S] [Wedge compression, Stable burst, Unstable burst, Oth, Unsp] fx of T11-T12 thoracic vertebra, [init enc for clsd fx, init enc for opn fx, seq]
S22.20XS   Unsp fx of sternum, seq
S22.21XS   Fx of manubrium, seq
S22.22XS   Fx of body of sternum, seq
S22.23XS   Sternal manubrial dissociation, seq
S22.24XS   Fx of xiphoid process, seq
S22.3[1,2,9]XS   Fx of one rib, [rt, lt, unsp] side, seq
S22.4[1,2,3,9]XS   Multi fxs of ribs, [rt, lt, bilat, unsp] side, seq
S22.5XXS   Flail chest, seq
S22.9XXS   Fx of bony thorax, part unsp, seq
S23.0XXA   Traum rupture of thoracic intervertebral disc, init
S23.10[0,1]A   [Sublux, Disloc] of unsp thoracic vertebra, init enc
S23.11[0,1]A   [Sublux, Disloc] of T1/T2 thoracic vertebrae, init enc
S23.12[0,1]A   [Sublux, Disloc] of T2/T3 thoracic vertebrae, init enc
S23.12[2,3]A   [Sublux, Disloc] of T3/T4 thoracic vertebrae, init enc
S23.13[0,1]A   [Sublux, Disloc] of T4/T5 thoracic vertebrae, init enc
S23.13[2,3]A   [Sublux, Disloc] of T5/T6 thoracic vertebrae, init enc
S23.14[0,1]A   [Sublux, Disloc] of T6/T7 thoracic vertebrae, init enc
S23.14[2,3]A   [Sublux, Disloc] of T7/T8 thoracic vertebrae, init enc
S23.15[0,1]A   [Sublux, Disloc] of T8/T9 thoracic vertebrae, init enc
S23.15[2,3]A   [Sublux, Disloc] of T9/T10 thoracic vertebrae, init enc
S23.16[0,1]A   [Sublux, Disloc] of T10/T11 thoracic vertebrae, init enc
S23.16[2,3]A   Sublux and disloc of T11/T12 thoracic vertebra [sublux, disloc] init enc
S23.17[0,1]A   [Sublux, Disloc] of T12/L1 thoracic vertebrae, init enc
S23.20XA   Disloc of unsp part of thorax, init enc
S23.29XA   Disloc of oth parts of thorax, init enc
S23.3XXA   Sprain of lgmt of thoracic spine, init enc
S23.8XXA   Sprain of oth spec parts of thorax, init enc
S23.9XXA   Sprain of unsp parts of thorax, init enc
S32.00[0,1,2,8,9][A,B,S] Fx of unsp lumbar vertebra [wedge compression fx, stable burst fx, unstable burst fx, oth fx, unsp fx] [init enc for fx [clsd,opn], seq]
S32.01[0,1,2,8,9][A,B,S] Fx of 1st lumbar vertebra [wedge compression fx, stable burst fx, unstable burst fx, oth fx, unsp fx] [init enc for fx [clsd,opn], seq]
S32.02[0,1,2,8,9][A,B,S] Fx of 2nd lumbar vertebra [wedge compression fx, stable burst fx, unstable burst fx, oth fx, unsp fx] [init enc for fx [clsd,opn], seq]
S32.03[0,1,2,8,9][A,B,S] Fx of 3rd lumbar vertebra [wedge compression fx, stable burst fx, unstable burst fx, oth fx, unsp fx] [init enc for fx [clsd,opn], seq]
S32.04[0,1,2,8,9][A,B,S] Fx of 4th lumbar vertebra [wedge compression fx, stable burst fx, unstable burst fx, oth fx, unsp fx] [init enc for fx [clsd,opn], seq]
S32.05[0,1,2,8,9][A,B,S] Fx of 5th lumbar vertebra [wedge compression fx, stable burst fx, unstable burst fx, unsp fx] init enc for fx [clsd, opn, seq]
S32.10X[A,B,S]   Unsp fx of sacrum init enc for fx [clsd, opn], seq]
S32.11[0,1,2,9][A,B,S] Zone I fx of sacrum [nondisp, minimally disp, severely disp, unsp] init enc for fx [clsd, opn], seq]
S32.12[0,1,2,9][A,B,S] Zone II fx of sacrum [nondisp, minimally disp, severely disp, unsp] init enc for fx [clsd, opn], seq]

S32.13[0,1,2,9][A,B,S] Zone III fx of sacrum [nondisp, minimally disp, severely disp, unsp] init enc for fx [clsd, opn], seq]
S32.1[4,5,6,7,9]X[A,B,S] Fx of sacrum [type 1, type 2, type 3, type 4, oth] init enc for fx [clsd, opn, seq]
S32.2XX[A,B,S]   Fx of coccyx, [init enc for clsd fx, init enc for opn fx, seq]
S32.30[1,2,9]S   Unsp fx of [rt, lt, unsp] ilium, seq
S32.31[1,2,3]S   Disp avulsion fx of [rt, lt, unsp] ilium, seq
S32.31[4,5,6]S   Nondisp avulsion fx of [rt, lt, unsp] ilium, seq
S32.39[1,2,9]S   Oth fx of [rt, lt, unsp] ilium, seq
S32.40[1,2,9]S   Unsp fx of [rt, lt, unsp] acetab, seq
S32.41[1,2,3]S   Disp fx of ant wall of [rt, lt, unsp] acetab, seq
S32.41[4,5,6]S   Nondisp fx of ant wall of [rt, lt, unsp] acetab, seq
S32.42[1,2,3]S   Disp fx of post wall of [rt, lt, unsp] acetab, seq
S32.42[4,5,6]S   Nondisp fx of post wall of [rt, lt, unsp] acetab, seq
S32.43[1,2,3]S   Disp fx of ant column (iliopubic) of [rt, lt, unsp] acetab, seq
S32.43[4,5,6]S   Nondisp fx of ant column (iliopubic) of [rt, lt, unsp] acetab, seq
S32.44[1,2,3]S   Disp fx of post column (ilioischial) of [rt, lt, unsp] acetab, seq
S32.44[4,5,6]S   Nondisp fx of post column (ilioischial) of [rt, lt, unsp] acetab, seq
S32.45[1,2,3]S   Disp transv fx of [rt, lt, unsp] acetab, seq
S32.45[4,5,6]S   Nondisp transv fx of [rt, lt, unsp] acetab, seq
S32.46[1,2,3]S   Disp associated transv-post fx of [rt, lt, unsp] acetab, seq
S32.46[4,5,6]S   Nondisp associated transv-post fx of [rt, lt, unsp] acetab, seq
S32.47[1,2,3]S   Disp fx of med wall of [rt, lt, unsp] acetab, seq
S32.47[4,5,6]S   Nondisp fx of med wall of [rt, lt, unsp] acetab, seq
S32.48[1,2,3]S   Disp dome fx of [rt, lt, unsp] acetab, seq
S32.48[4,5,6]S   Nondisp dome fx of [rt, lt, unsp] acetab, seq
S32.49[1,2,9]S   Oth spec fx of [rt, lt, unsp] acetab, seq
S32.50[1,2,9]S   Unsp fx of [rt, lt, unsp] pubis, seq
S32.51[1,2,9]S   Fx of superior rim of [rt, lt, unsp] pubis, seq
S32.59[1,2,9]S   Oth spec fx of [rt, lt, unsp] pubis, seq
S32.60[1,2,9]S   Unsp fx of [rt, lt, unsp] ischium, seq
S32.61[1,2,3]S   Disp avulsion fx of ischium [rt, lt, unsp] init enc for fx, seq
S32.61[4,5,6]S   Nondisp avulsion fx of ischium [rt, lt, unsp] init enc for fx, seq]
S32.69[1,2,9]S   Oth spec fx of ischium [rt, lt, unsp] init enc for fx, seq
S32.81[0,1]S   Multi fxs of pelvis w/ disruption of pelvic ring [stable, unstable] init enc for fx, seq
S32.82XS   Multi fx of pelvis w/o disrupt of pelvic ring, seq
S32.89XS   Fx of oth parts of pelvis, seq
S32.9XXS   Fx unsp parts of lumbosacral spine & pelvis, seq
S33.0XXA   Traum rupture of lumbar intervertebral disc, init enc
S33.10[0,1]A   Sublux and disloc of lumbar vertebra [sublux, disloc] init enc
S33.11[0,1]A   Sublux and disloc of L1/L2 lumbar vertebra [sublux, disloc] init enc
S33.12[0,1]A   Sublux and disloc of L2/L3 lumbar vertebra [sublux, disloc] init enc
S33.13[0,1]A   Sublux and disloc of L3/L4 lumbar vertebra [sublux, disloc] init enc
S33.14[0,1]A   Sublux and disloc of L4/L5 lumbar vertebra [sublux, disloc] init enc
S33.2XXA   Disloc of sacroiliac and sacrococcygeal jt, init
S33.[5,6,8,9]XXA   Sprain of [lgmts of lumbar spine, sacroiliac jt, oth parts of lumbar spine and pelvis, unsp parts of lumbar spine and pelvis] init enc

DRG 552   Medical Back Problems without MCC
         GMLOS 3.1   AMLOS 3.7   RW 0.8648   [T]

Select principal diagnosis listed under DRG 551

DRG 553   Bone Diseases and Arthropathies with MCC
         GMLOS 4.1   AMLOS 5.3   RW 1.2287

Principal Diagnosis
B06.82   Rubella arthritis
E55.0   Rickets, active
E64.3   Sequelae of rickets
M02.0*   Arthropathy following intestinal bypass
M02.1*   Postdysenteric arthropathy
M02.2*   Postimmunization arthropathy
M02.9   Reactive arthropathy, unsp
M06.4   Inflam polyarthropathy
M07*   Enteropathic arthropathies
M10.0*   Idiopathic gout
M10.1*   Lead-induced gout
M10.2*   Drug-induced gout
M10.4*   Oth secondary gout
M10.9   Gout, unsp
M11*   Oth crystal arthropathies

[T] **Transfer DRG**   [SP] **Special Payment**   * **Code Range**   6th and 7th Character of ZZ = No Device, No Qualifier ZX = No Device, Diagnostic

166   MS-DRG Version 33.0   © 2015 Optum360, LLC

M12*	Oth and unsp arthropathy
M13*	Oth arthritis
M14*	Arthropathies in oth dz classified elsw
M15*	Polyosteoarthritis
M16*	Osteoarthritis of hip
M17*	Osteoarthritis of knee
M18*	Osteoarthritis of first carpometacarpal jt
M19*	Oth and unsp osteoarthritis
M1A.0*	Idiopathic chr gout
M1A.2*	Drug-induced chr gout
M1A.3*	Chr gout d/t renal impairment
M1A.4*	Oth secondary chr gout
M1A.9*	Chr gout, unsp
M24.6*	Ankylosis of jt
M25.0*	Hemarthrosis
M36.1	Arthropathy in neoplastic dz
M36.2	Hemophilic arthropathy
M36.3	Arthropathy in oth bld d/o
M36.4	Arthropathy in hypersensitivity reactions classd elsw
M42*	Spinal osteochondrosis
M81*	Osteoporosis w/o current Path fx
M83*	Adult osteomalacia
M85.0*	Fibrous dysplasia (monostotic)
M85.3*	Osteitis condensans
M85.4*	Solitary bone cyst
M85.5*	Aneurysmal bone cyst
M85.6*	Oth cyst of bone
M87*	Osteonecrosis
M88*	Osteitis deformans [Paget's dz of bone]
M89.4*	Oth hypertrophic osteoarthropathy
M89.7*	Major osseous defect
M90*	Osteopathies in dz classified elsw
M91*	Juvenile osteochondrosis of hip and pelvis
M92*	Oth juvenile osteochondrosis
M93*	Oth osteochondropathies
M94.2*	Chondromalacia

DRG 554 Bone Diseases and Arthropathies without MCC
GMLOS 2.8　　AMLOS 3.4　　RW 0.7337

Select principal diagnosis listed under DRG 553

DRG 555 Signs and Symptoms of Musculoskeletal System and Connective Tissue with MCC
GMLOS 3.7　　AMLOS 5.0　　RW 1.2656

Principal Diagnosis

M25.1*	Fistula of jt
M25.5*	Pain in jt
M25.6*	Stiffness of jt, NEC
M25.8*	Oth spec jt d/o
M25.9	Jt d/o, unsp
M60.8*	Oth myositis
M60.9	Myositis, unsp
M62.4*	Contracture of muscle
M62.81	Muscle weakness (generalized)
M62.831	Muscle spasm of calf
M62.838	Oth muscle spasm
M70.8*	Oth soft tissue d/o related to use/pressure
M70.9*	Unsp soft tissue d/o related to use/pressure
M79.0	Rheumatism, unsp
M79.1	Myalgia
M79.6*	Pain in limb, hand, foot, fingers and toes
M79.7	Fibromyalgia
M79.8*	Oth spec soft tissue d/o
M79.9	Soft tissue d/o, unsp
M99.0[0,5,6,7,8,9]	Seg and somatic dysfunction [head rgn, pelvic rgn, lwr extr, upr extr, rib cage, abd and oth rgns]
R26.2	Difficulty in walking, NEC
R29.4	Clicking hip
R29.898	Oth symptoms and signs involving the musculoskeletal sys

DRG 556 Signs and Symptoms of Musculoskeletal System and Connective Tissue without MCC
GMLOS 2.6　　AMLOS 3.2　　RW 0.7440

Select principal diagnosis listed under DRG 555

DRG 557 Tendonitis, Myositis and Bursitis with MCC
GMLOS 4.8　　AMLOS 6.0　　RW 1.4295　[T]

Principal Diagnosis

A52.78	Syphilis of oth musculoskeletal tissue
M24.2*	D/o of lgmt
M25.70	Osteophyte, unsp jt
M25.71[1,2,9]	Osteophyte, [rt, lt, unsp] shldr
M25.72[1,2,9]	Osteophyte, [rt, lt, unsp] elbow
M25.73[1,2,9]	Osteophyte, [rt, lt, unsp] wrist
M25.74[1,2,9]	Osteophyte, [rt, lt, unsp] hand
M25.75[1,2,9]	Osteophyte, [rt, lt, unsp] hip
M25.76[1,2,9]	Osteophyte, [rt, lt, unsp] knee
M25.77[1,2,3]	Osteophyte, [rt, lt, unsp] ankle
M25.77[4,5,6]	Osteophyte, [rt, lt, unsp] foot
M35.4	Diffuse (eosinophilic) fasciitis
M35.7	Hypermobility synd
M60.0*	Infective myositis
M60.1*	Interstitial myositis
M60.2*	FB granuloma of soft tissue, NEC
M61*	Calcification and ossification of muscle
M62.0*	Separation of muscle (nontraumatic)
M62.1*	Oth rupture of muscle (nontraumatic)
M62.2*	Nontraumatic ischemic infarction of muscle
M62.3	Immobility synd (paraplegic)
M62.5*	Muscle wasting and atrophy, NEC
M62.82	Rhabdomyolysis
M62.89	Oth spec d/o of muscle
M62.9	D/o of muscle, unsp
M63*	D/o of muscle in dz classified elsw
M65*	Synovitis and tenosynovitis
M66*	Spontaneous rupture of synovium and tndn
M67*	Oth d/o of synovium and tndn
M70.0*	Crepitant synovitis (acute) (chr) of hand and wrist
M70.1*	Bursitis of hand
M70.2*	Olecranon bursitis
M70.3*	Oth bursitis of elbow
M70.4*	Prepatellar bursitis
M70.5*	Oth bursitis of knee
M70.6*	Trochanteric bursitis
M70.7*	Oth bursitis of hip
M71*	Oth bursopathies
M72*	Fibroblastic d/o
M75*	Shldr lesions
M76*	Enthesopathies, lwr limb, excluding foot
M77.0*	Medial epicondylitis
M77.1*	Lat epicondylitis
M77.2*	Periarthritis of wrist
M77.4*	Metatarsalgia
M77.5*	Oth enthesopathy of foot
M77.8	Oth enthesopathies, NEC
M77.9	Enthesopathy, unsp
M79.A*	Nontraumatic compartment synd

DRG 558 Tendonitis, Myositis and Bursitis without MCC
GMLOS 3.3　　AMLOS 3.9　　RW 0.8457　[T]

Select principal diagnosis listed under DRG 557

DRG 559 Aftercare, Musculoskeletal System and Connective Tissue with MCC
GMLOS 5.0　　AMLOS 7.0　　RW 1.9202　[T]

Principal Diagnosis

M48.40X[D,G]	Fatigue fx of vertebra, site unsp, subsq enc for fx w/ [routine, delayed] healing
M48.41X[D,G]	Fatigue fx of vertebra, occipito-atlanto-axial rgn, subsq enc for fx w/ [routine, delayed] healing
M48.48X[D,G]	Fatigue fx of vertebra, sacral and sacrococcygeal rgn, subsq enc for fx w/ [routine, delayed] healing
M48.4[2,3]X[D,G]	Fatigue fx of vertebra, [cervical, cervicothoracic] rgn, subsq enc for fx w/ [routine, delayed] healing
M48.4[4,5]X[D,G]	Fatigue fx of vertebra, [thoracic, thoracolumbar] rgn, subsq enc for fx w/ [routine, delayed] healing
M48.4[6,7]X[D,G]	Fatigue fx of vertebra, [lumbar, lumbosacral] rgn, subsq enc for fx w/ [routine, delayed] healing
M48.50X[D,G]	Collapsed vertebra, NEC, site unsp, subsq enc for fx w/ [routine, delayed] healing

Surgical	**Medical**	**CC Indicator**	**MCC Indicator**	**Procedure Proxy**	**PDxMCC** PDx acts as own MCC	**PDxCC** PDx acts as own CC

MDC 8: Diseases And Disorders Of The Musculoskeletal System And Connective Tissue—MEDICAL

M48.51X[D,G]	Collapsed vertebra, NEC, occipito-atlanto-axial rgn, subsq enc for fx w/ [routine, delayed] healing
M48.58X[D,G]	Collapsed vertebra, NEC, sacral and sacrococcygeal rgn, subsq enc for fx w/ [routine, delayed] healing
M48.5[2,3]X[D,G]	Collapsed vertebra, NEC, [cervical, cervicothoracic] rgn, subsq enc for fx w/ [routine, delayed] healing
M48.5[4,5]X[D,G]	Collapsed vertebra, NEC, [thoracic, thoracolumbar] rgn, subsq enc for fx w/ [routine, delayed] healing
M48.5[6,7]X[D,G]	Collapsed vertebra, NEC, [lumbar, lumbosacral] rgn, subsq enc for fx w/ [routine, delayed] healing
M80.00X[D,G,S]	Age-related osteoporosis w/ current path fx, unsp site, [subsq enc for fx w/ routine healing, subsq enc for fx w/ delayed healing, seq]
M80.01[1,2,9][D,G,S]	Age-related osteoporosis w/ current path fx, [rt, lt, unsp] shldr, [subsq enc for fx w/ routine healing, subsq enc for fx w/ delayed healing, seq]
M80.02[1,2,9][D,G,S]	Age-related osteoporosis w/ current path fx, [rt, lt, unsp] humerus, [subsq enc for fx w/ routine healing, subsq enc for fx w/ delayed healing, seq]
M80.03[1,2,9][D,G,S]	Age-related osteoporosis w/ current path fx, [rt, lt, unsp] forearm, [subsq enc for fx w/ routine healing, subsq enc for fx w/ delayed healing, seq]
M80.04[1,2,9][D,G,S]	Age-related osteoporosis w/ current path fx, [rt, lt, unsp] hand, [subsq enc for fx w/ routine healing, subsq enc for fx w/ delayed healing, seq]
M80.05[1,2,9][D,G,S]	Age-related osteoporosis w/ current path fx, [rt, lt, unsp] femur, [subsq enc for fx w/ routine healing, subsq enc for fx w/ delayed healing, seq]
M80.06[1,2,9][D,G,S]	Age-related osteoporosis w/ current path fx, [rt, lt, unsp] lwr leg, [subsq enc for fx w/ routine healing, subsq enc for fx w/ delayed healing, seq]
M80.07[1,2,9][D,G,S]	Age-related osteoporosis w/ current path fx, [rt, lt, unsp] ankle and foot, [subsq enc for fx w/ routine healing, subsq enc for fx w/ delayed healing, seq]
M80.08X[D,G]	Age-related osteoporosis w/ current path fx, vertebra(e), [subsq enc for fx w/ routine healing, subsq enc for fx w/ delayed healing]
M80.80X[D,G,S]	Oth osteoporosis w/ current path fx, unsp site, [subsq enc for fx w/ routine healing, subsq enc for fx w/ delayed healing, seq]
M80.81[1,2,9][D,G,S]	Oth osteoporosis w/ current path fx, [rt, lt, unsp] shldr, [subsq enc for fx w/ routine healing, subsq enc for fx w/ delayed healing, seq]
M80.82[1,2,9][D,G,S]	Oth osteoporosis w/ current path fx, [rt, lt, unsp] humerus, [subsq enc for fx w/ routine healing, subsq enc for fx w/ delayed healing, seq]
M80.83[1,2,9][D,G,S]	Oth osteoporosis w/ current path fx, [rt, lt, unsp] forearm, [subsq enc for fx w/ routine healing, subsq enc for fx w/ delayed healing, seq]
M80.84[1,2,9][D,G,S]	Oth osteoporosis w/ current path fx, [rt, lt, unsp] hand, [subsq enc for fx w/ routine healing, subsq enc for fx w/ delayed healing, seq]
M80.85[1,2,9][D,G,S]	Oth osteoporosis w/ current path fx, [rt, lt, unsp] femur, [subsq enc for fx w/ routine healing, subsq enc for fx w/ delayed healing, seq]
M80.86[1,2,9][D,G,S]	Oth osteoporosis w/ current path fx, [rt, lt, unsp] lwr leg, [subsq enc for fx w/ routine healing, subsq enc for fx w/ delayed healing, seq]
M80.87[1,2,9][D,G,S]	Oth osteoporosis w/ current path fx, [rt, lt, unsp] ankle and foot, [subsq enc for fx w/ routine healing, subsq enc for fx w/ delayed healing, seq]
M80.88X[D,G]	Oth osteoporosis w/ current path fx, vertebra(e), [subsq enc for fx w/ routine healing, subsq enc for fx w/ delayed healing]
M84.30X[D,G,S]	Stress fx, unsp site, [subsq enc for fx w/ routine healing, subsq enc for fx w/ delayed healing, seq]
M84.31[1,2,9][D,G,S]	Stress fx, [rt, lt, unsp] shldr, [subsq enc for fx w/ routine healing, subsq enc for fx w/ delayed healing, seq]
M84.32[1,2,9][D,G,S]	Stress fx, [rt, lt, unsp] humerus, [subsq enc for fx w/ routine healing, subsq enc for fx w/ delayed healing, seq]
M84.33[1,2,3,4,9][D,G,S]	Stress fx, [rt ulna, lt ulna, rt radius, lt radius, unsp ulna and radius], [subsq enc for fx w/ routine healing, subsq enc for fx w/ delayed healing, seq]
M84.34[1,2,3][D,G,S]	Stress fx, [rt, lt, unsp] hand, [subsq enc for fx w/ routine healing, subsq enc for fx w/ delayed healing, seq]
M84.34[4,5,6][D,G,S]	Stress fx, [rt, lt, unsp] fingers, [subsq enc for fx w/ routine healing, subsq enc for fx w/ delayed healing, seq]
M84.350[D,G]	Stress fx, pelvis, subsq enc for fx w/ [routine, delayed] healing
M84.359[D,G,S]	Stress fx, unsp hip, [subsq enc for fx w/ routine healing, subsq enc for fx w/ delayed healing, seq]
M84.35[1,2,3][D,G,S]	Stress fx, [rt, lt, unsp] femur, [subsq enc for fx w/ routine healing, subsq enc for fx w/ delayed healing, seq]
M84.36[1,2,3,4,9][D,G,S]	Stress fx, [rt tibia, lt tibia, rt fibula, lt fibula, unsp tibia & fibula], [subsq enc for fx w/ routine healing, subsq enc for fx w/ delayed healing, seq]
M84.37[1,2,3][D,G,S]	Stress fx, [rt, lt, unsp] ankle, [subsq enc for fx w/ routine healing, subsq enc for fx w/ delayed healing, seq]
M84.37[4,5,6][D,G,S]	Stress fx, [rt, lt, unsp] foot, [subsq enc for fx w/ routine healing, subsq enc for fx w/ delayed healing, seq]
M84.37[7,8,9][D,G,S]	Stress fx, [rt, lt, unsp] toes, [subsq enc for fx w/ routine healing, subsq enc for fx w/ delayed healing, seq]
M84.38X[D,G,S]	Stress fx, oth site, [subsq enc for fx w/ routine healing, subsq enc for fx w/ delayed healing, seq]
M84.40X[D,G,S]	Path fx, unsp site, [subsq enc for fx w/ routine healing, subsq enc for fx w/ delayed healing, seq]
M84.41[1,2,9][D,G,S]	Path fx, [rt, lt, unsp] shldr, [subsq enc for fx w/ routine healing, subsq enc for fx w/ delayed healing, seq]
M84.42[1,2,9][D,G,S]	Path fx, [rt, lt, unsp] humerus, [subsq enc for fx w/ routine healing, subsq enc for fx w/ delayed healing, seq]
M84.43[1,2,3,4,9][D,G,S]	Path fx, [rt ulna, lt ulna, rt radius, lt radius, unsp ulna and radius], [subsq enc for fx w/ routine healing, subsq enc for fx w/ delayed healing, seq]
M84.44[1,2,3][D,G,S]	Path fx, [rt, lt, unsp] hand, [subsq enc for fx w/ routine healing, subsq enc for fx w/ delayed healing, seq]
M84.44[4,5,6][D,G,S]	Path fx, [rt, lt, unsp] fingers, [subsq enc for fx w/ routine healing, subsq enc for fx w/ delayed healing, seq]
M84.454[D,G]	Path fx, pelvis, [subsq enc for fx w/ routine healing, subsq enc for fx w/ delayed healing]
M84.459[D,G,S]	Path fx, unsp hip, [subsq enc for fx w/ routine healing, subsq enc for fx w/ delayed healing, seq]
M84.45[1,2,3][D,G,S]	Path fx, [rt, lt, unsp] femur, [subsq enc for fx w/ routine healing, subsq enc for fx w/ delayed healing, seq]
M84.46[1,2,3,4,9][D,G,S]	Path fx, [rt tibia, lt tibia, rt fibula, lt fibula, unsp tibia & fibula], [subsq enc for fx w/ routine healing, subsq enc for fx w/ delayed healing, seq]
M84.47[1,2,3][D,G,S]	Path fx, [rt, lt, unsp] ankle, [subsq enc for fx w/ routine healing, subsq enc for fx w/ delayed healing, seq]
M84.47[4,5,6][D,G,S]	Path fx, [rt, lt, unsp] foot, [subsq enc for fx w/ routine healing, subsq enc for fx w/ delayed healing, seq]
M84.47[7,8,9][D,G,S]	Path fx, [rt, lt, unsp] toes, [subsq enc for fx w/ routine healing, subsq enc for fx w/ delayed healing, seq]
M84.48X[D,G,S]	Path fx, oth site, [subsq enc for fx w/ routine healing, subsq enc for fx w/ delayed healing, seq]
M84.50X[D,G,S]	Path fx in neoplastic dz, unsp site, [subsq enc for fx w/ routine healing, subsq enc for fx w/ delayed healing, seq]
M84.51[1,2,9][D,G,S]	Path fx in neoplastic dz, [rt, lt, unsp] shldr, [subsq enc for fx w/ routine healing, subsq enc for fx w/ delayed healing, seq]
M84.52[1,2,9][D,G,S]	Path fx in neoplastic dz, [rt, lt, unsp] humerus, [subsq enc for fx w/ routine healing, subsq enc for fx w/ delayed healing, seq]
M84.53[1,2,3,4,9][D,G,S]	Path fx in neoplastic dz, [rt ulna, lt ulna, rt radius, lt radius, unsp ulna and radius], [subsq enc for fx w/ routine healing, subsq enc for fx w/ delayed healing, seq]
M84.54[1,2,9][D,G,S]	Path fx in neoplastic dz, [rt, lt, unsp] hand, [subsq enc for fx w/ routine healing, subsq enc for fx w/ delayed healing, seq]
M84.550[D,G]	Path fx in neoplastic dz, pelvis, subsq enc for fx w/ [routine, delayed] healing
M84.559[D,G,S]	Path fx in neoplastic dz, unsp hip, [subsq enc for fx w/ routine healing, subsq enc for fx w/ delayed healing, seq]
M84.55[1,2,3][D,G,S	Path fx in neoplastic dz, [rt, lt, unsp] femur, [subsq enc for fx w/ routine healing, subsq enc for fx w/ delayed healing, seq]
M84.56[1,2,3,4,9][D,G,S]	Path fx in neoplastic dz, [rt tibia, lt tibia, rt fibula, lt fibula, unsp tibia & fibula], [subsq enc for fx w/ routine healing, subsq enc for fx w/ delayed healing, seq]
M84.57[1,2,3][D,G,S]	Path fx in neoplastic dz, [rt, lt, unsp] ankle, [subsq enc for fx w/ routine healing, subsq enc for fx w/ delayed healing, seq]
M84.57[4,5,6][D,G,S]	Path fx in neoplastic dz, [rt, lt, unsp] foot, [subsq enc for fx w/ routine healing, subsq enc for fx w/ delayed healing, seq]
M84.58XD	Path fx in neopltc dis, oth site, subs for fx w routn heal
M84.58XG	Path fx in neopltc dis, oth site, subs for fx w delay heal
M84.60X[D,G,S]	Path fx in oth dz, unsp site, [subsq enc for fx w/ routine healing, subsq enc for fx w/ delayed healing, seq]
M84.61[1,2,9][D,G,S]	Path fx in oth dz, [rt, lt, unsp] shldr, [subsq enc for fx w/ routine healing, subsq enc for fx w/ delayed healing, seq]
M84.62[1,2,9][D,G,S]	Path fx in oth dz, [rt, lt, unsp] humerus, [subsq enc for fx w/ routine healing, subsq enc for fx w/ delayed healing, seq]
M84.63[1,2,3,4,9][D,G,S]	Path fx in oth dz, [rt ulna, lt ulna, rt radius, lt radius, unsp ulna and radius], [subsq enc for fx w/ routine healing, subsq enc for fx w/ delayed healing, seq]

Ⓣ **Transfer DRG**   ⓢ **Special Payment**   * **Code Range**   **6th and 7th Character of ZZ = No Device, No Qualifier ZX = No Device, Diagnostic**

M84.64[1,2,9][D,G,S]	Path fx in oth dz, [rt, lt, unsp] hand, [subsq enc for fx w/ routine healing, subsq enc for fx w/ delayed healing, seq]
M84.650[D,G]	Path fx in oth dz, pelvis, subsq enc for fx w/ [routine, delayed] healing
M84.659[D,G,S]	Path fx in oth dz, unsp hip, [subsq enc for fx w/ routine healing, subsq enc for fx w/ delayed healing, seq]
M84.65[1,2,3][D,G,S]	Path fx in oth dz, [rt, lt, unsp] femur, [subsq enc for fx w/ routine healing, subsq enc for fx w/ delayed healing, seq]
M84.66[1,2,3,4,9][D,G,S]	Path fx in oth dz, [rt tibia, lt tibia, rt fibula, lt fibula, unsp tibia & fibula], [subsq enc for fx w/ routine healing, subsq enc for fx w/ delayed healing, seq]
M84.67[1,2,3][D,G,S]	Path fx in oth dz, [rt, lt, unsp] ankle, [subsq enc for fx w/ routine healing, subsq enc for fx w/ delayed healing, seq]
M84.67[4,5,6][D,G,S]	Path fx in oth dz, [rt, lt, unsp] foot, [subsq enc for fx w/ routine healing, subsq enc for fx w/ delayed healing, seq]
M84.68X[D,G,S]	Path fx in oth dz, oth site, [subsq enc for fx w/ routine healing, subsq enc for fx w/ delayed healing, seq]
M96.0	Pseudarthrosis after fusion or arthrodesis
M96.6[2,3][1,2,9]	Fx of [humerus, radius or ulna] following insert of orthopedic implant, jt prosthesis, or bone plate, [rt, lt, unspecified] arm
M96.6[5,9]	Fx of [pelvis, oth bone] following insert of orthopedic implant, jt prosthesis, or bone plate
M96.6[6,7][1,2,9]	Fx of [femur, tibia or fibula] following insert of orthopedic implant, jt prosthesis, or bone plate, [rt, lt, unspecified] leg
S02.0XX[D,G]	Fx of vault of skull, subsq enc for fx w/ [routine, delayed] healing
S02.10X[D,G]	Unsp fx of base of skull, subsq enc for fx w/ [routine, delayed] healing
S02.11[0,1,2,3][D,G]	[Type I, Type II, Type III, Unsp] occipital condyle fx, subsq enc for fx w/ [routine, delayed] healing
S02.11[8,9][D,G]	[Oth, Unsp] fx of occiput, subsq enc for fx w/ [routine, delayed] healing
S02.19X[D,G]	Oth fx of base of skull, subsq enc for fx w/ [routine, delayed] healing
S02.40[0,1,2][D,G]	[Malar, Maxillary, Zygomatic] fx unsp, subsq enc for fx w/ [routine, delayed] healing
S02.41[1,2,3][D,G]	LeFort [I, II, III] fx, subsq enc for fx w/ [routine, delayed] healing
S02.42X[D,G]	Fx of alveolus of maxilla, subsq enc for fx w/ [routine, delayed] healing
S02.5XX[D,G]	Fx of tooth (traum), subsq enc for fx w/ [routine, delayed] healing
S02.600[D,G]	Fx of unsp part of body of mandible, subsq enc for fx w/ [routine, delayed] healing
S02.609[D,G]	Fx of mandible, unsp, subsq enc for fx w/ [routine, delayed] healing
S02.6[1,2,3]X[D,G]	Fx of [condylar, subcondylar, coronoid] process of mandible, subsq enc for fx w/ [routine, delayed] healing
S02.6[4,5,6,7,9]X[D,G]	Fx of [ramus, angle, symphysis, alveolus, oth spec site] of mandible, subsq enc for fx w/ [routine, delayed] healing
S02.8XX[D,G]	Fxs of oth spec skull and facial bones, subsq enc for fx w/ [routine, delayed] healing
S02.9[1,2]X[D,G]	Unsp fx of [skull, facial bones], subsq enc for fx w/ [routine, delayed] healing
S02.[2,3]XX[D,G]	Fx of [nasal bones, orbital floor], subsq enc for fx w/ [routine, delayed] healing
S12.00[0,1][D,G]	Unsp [disp, nondisp] fx of 1st cervical vertebra, subsq enc for fx w/ [routine, delayed] healing
S12.03[0,1][D,G]	[Disp, Nondisp] post arch fx of 1st cervical vertebra, subsq enc for fx w/ [routine, delayed] healing
S12.04[0,1][D,G]	[Disp, Nondisp] lat mass fx of 1st cervical vertebra, subsq enc for fx w/ [routine, delayed] healing
S12.09[0,1][D,G]	Oth [disp, nondisp] fx of 1st cervical vertebra, subsq enc for fx w/ [routine, delayed] healing
S12.0[1,2]X[D,G]	[Stable, Unstable] burst fx of 1st cervical vertebra, subsq enc for fx w/ [routine, delayed] healing
S12.10[0,1][D,G]	Unsp [disp, nondisp] fx of 2nd cervical vertebra, subsq enc for fx w/ [routine, delayed] healing
S12.11[0,1,2][D,G]	[Ant disp, Post disp, Nondisp] Type II dens fx, subsq enc for fx w/ [routine, delayed] healing
S12.12[0,1][D,G]	Oth [disp, nondisp] dens fx, subsq enc for fx w/ [routine, delayed] healing
S12.13[0,1][D,G]	Unsp traum [disp, nondisp] spondylolisthesis of 2nd cervical vertebra, subsq enc for fx w/ [routine, delayed] healing
S12.14X[D,G]	Type III traum spondylolisthesis of 2nd cervical vertebra, subsq enc for fx w/ [routine, delayed] healing
S12.15[0,1][D,G]	Oth traum [disp, nondisp] spondylolisthesis of 2nd cervical vertebra, subsq enc for fx w/ [routine, delayed] healing
S12.19[0,1][D,G]	Oth [disp, nondisp] fx of 2nd cervical vertebra, subsq enc for fx w/ [routine, delayed] healing
S12.20[0,1][D,G]	Unsp [disp, nondisp] fx of 3rd cervical vertebra, subsq enc for fx w/ [routine, delayed] healing
S12.23[0,1][D,G]	Unsp traum [disp, nondisp] spondylolisthesis of 3rd cervical vertebra, subsq enc for fx w/ [routine, delayed] healing
S12.24X[D,G]	Type III traum spondylolisthesis of 3rd cervical vertebra, subsq enc for fx w/ [routine, delayed] healing
S12.25[0,1][D,G]	Oth traum [disp, nondisp] spondylolisthesis of 3rd cervical vertebra, subsq enc for fx w/ [routine, delayed] healing
S12.29[0,1][D,G]	Oth [disp, nondisp] fx of 3rd cervical vertebra, subsq enc for fx w/ [routine, delayed] healing
S12.30[0,1][D,G]	Unsp [disp, nondisp] fx of 4th cervical vertebra, subsq enc for fx w/ [routine, delayed] healing
S12.33[0,1][D,G]	Unsp traum [disp, nondisp] spondylolisthesis of 4th cervical vertebra, subsq enc for fx w/ [routine, delayed] healing
S12.34X[D,G]	Type III traum spondylolisthesis of 4th cervical vertebra, subsq enc for fx w/ [routine, delayed] healing
S12.35[0,1][D,G]	Oth traum [disp, nondisp] spondylolisthesis of 4th cervical vertebra, subsq enc for fx w/ [routine, delayed] healing
S12.39[0,1][D,G]	Oth [disp, nondisp] fx of 4th cervical vertebra, subsq enc for fx w/ [routine, delayed] healing
S12.40[0,1][D,G]	Unsp [disp, nondisp] fx of 5th cervical vertebra, subsq enc for fx w/ [routine, delayed] healing
S12.43[0,1][D,G]	Unsp traum [disp, nondisp] spondylolisthesis of 5th cervical vertebra, subsq enc for fx w/ [routine, delayed] healing
S12.44X[D,G]	Type III traum spondylolisthesis of 5th cervical vertebra, subsq enc for fx w/ [routine, delayed] healing
S12.45[0,1][D,G]	Oth traum [disp, nondisp] spondylolisthesis of 5th cervical vertebra, subsq enc for fx w/ [routine, delayed] healing
S12.49[0,1][D,G]	Oth [disp, nondisp] fx of 5th cervical vertebra, subsq enc for fx w/ [routine, delayed] healing
S12.50[0,1][D,G]	Unsp [disp, nondisp] fx of 6th cervical vertebra, subsq enc for fx w/ [routine, delayed] healing
S12.53[0,1][D,G]	Unsp traum [disp, nondisp] spondylolisthesis of 6th cervical vertebra, subsq enc for fx w/ [routine, delayed] healing
S12.54X[D,G]	Type III traum spondylolisthesis of 6th cervical vertebra, subsq enc for fx w/ [routine, delayed] healing
S12.55[0,1][D,G]	Oth traum [disp, nondisp] spondylolisthesis of 6th cervical vertebra, subsq enc for fx w/ [routine, delayed] healing
S12.59[0,1][D,G]	Oth [disp, nondisp] fx of 6th cervical vertebra, subsq enc for fx w/ [routine, delayed] healing
S12.60[0,1][D,G]	Unsp [disp, nondisp] fx of 7th cervical vertebra, subsq enc for fx w/ [routine, delayed] healing
S12.63[0,1][D,G]	Unsp traum [disp, nondisp] spondylolisthesis of 7th cervical vertebra, subsq enc for fx w/ [routine, delayed] healing
S12.64X[D,G]	Type III traum spondylolisthesis of 7th cervical vertebra, subsq enc for fx w/ [routine, delayed] healing
S12.65[0,1][D,G]	Oth traum [disp, nondisp] spondylolisthesis of 7th cervical vertebra, subsq enc for fx w/ [routine, delayed] healing
S12.69[0,1][D,G]	Oth [disp, nondisp] fx of 7th cervical vertebra, subsq enc for fx w/ [routine, delayed] healing
S12.[8,9]XXD	Fx of [oth parts of neck, neck unsp], subsq enc
S22.00[0,1,2,8,9][D,G]	[Wedge compression, Stable burst, Unstable burst, Oth, Unsp] fx of unsp thoracic vertebra, subsq enc for fx w/ [routine, delayed] healing
S22.01[0,1,2,8,9][D,G]	[Wedge compression, Stable burst, Unstable burst, Oth, Unsp] fx of 1st thoracic vertebra, subsq enc for fx w/ [routine, delayed] healing
S22.02[0,1,2,8,9][D,G]	[Wedge compression, Stable burst, Unstable burst, Oth, Unsp] fx of 2nd thoracic vertebra, subsq enc for fx w/ [routine, delayed] healing
S22.03[0,1,2,8,9][D,G]	[Wedge compression, Stable burst, Unstable burst, Oth, Unsp] fx of 3rd thoracic vertebra, subsq enc for fx w/ [routine, delayed] healing
S22.04[0,1,2,8,9][D,G]	[Wedge compression, Stable burst, Unstable burst, Oth, Unsp] fx of 4th thoracic vertebra, subsq enc for fx w/ [routine, delayed] healing
S22.05[0,1,2,8,9][D,G]	[Wedge compression, Stable burst, Unstable burst, Oth, Unsp] fx of T5-T6 vertebra, subsq enc for fx w/ [routine, delayed] healing
S22.06[0,1,2,8,9][D,G]	[Wedge compression, Stable burst, Unstable burst, Oth, Unsp] fx of T7-T8 vertebra, subsq enc for fx w/ [routine, delayed] healing
S22.07[0,1,2,8,9][D,G]	[Wedge compression, Stable burst, Unstable burst, Oth, Unsp] fx of T9-T10 vertebra, subsq enc for fx w/ [routine, delayed] healing
S22.08[0,1,2,8,9][D,G]	[Wedge compression, Stable burst, Unstable burst, Oth, Unsp] fx of T11-T12 vertebra, subsq enc for fx w/ [routine, delayed] healing
S22.20X[D,G]	Unsp fx of sternum, subsq enc for fx w/ [routine, delayed] healing

Surgical **Medical** **CC Indicator** **MCC Indicator** **Procedure Proxy** **PDxMCC** PDx acts as own MCC **PDxCC** PDx acts as own CC

Code	Description
S22.21X[D,G]	Fx of manubrium, subsq enc for fx w/ [routine, delayed] healing
S22.22X[D,G]	Fx of body of sternum, subsq enc for fx w/ [routine, delayed] healing
S22.23X[D,G]	Sternal manubrial dissociation, subsq enc for fx w/ [routine, delayed] healing
S22.24X[D,G]	Fx of xiphoid process, subsq enc for fx w/ [routine, delayed] healing
S22.3[1,2,9]X[D,G]	Fx of one rib, [rt, lt, unsp] side, subsq enc for fx w/ [routine, delayed] healing
S22.4[1,2,3,9]X[D,G]	Multi fxs of ribs, [rt, lt, bilat, unsp] side, subsq enc for fx w/ [routine, delayed] healing
S22.5XX[D,G]	Flail chest, subsq enc for fx w/ [routine, delayed] healing
S22.9XX[D,G]	Fx of bony thorax, part unsp, subsq enc for fx w/ [routine, delayed] healing
S32.00[0,1,2,8,9][D,G]	[Wedge compression, Stable burst, Unstable burst, Oth, Unsp] fx of unsp lumbar vertebra, subsq enc for fx w/ [routine, delayed] healing
S32.01[0,1,2,8,9][D,G]	[Wedge compression, Stable burst, Unstable burst, Oth, Unsp] fx of 1st lumbar vertebra, subsq enc for fx w/ [routine, delayed] healing
S32.02[0,1,2,8,9][D,G]	[Wedge compression, Stable burst, Unstable burst, Oth, Unsp] fx of 2nd lumbar vertebra, subsq enc for fx w/ [routine, delayed] healing
S32.03[0,1,2,8,9][D,G]	[Wedge compression, Stable burst, Unstable burst, Oth, Unsp] fx of 3rd lumbar vertebra, subsq enc for fx w/ [routine, delayed] healing
S32.04[0,1,2,8,9][D,G]	[Wedge compression, Stable burst, Unstable burst, Oth, Unsp] fx of 4th lumbar vertebra, subsq enc for fx w/ [routine, delayed] healing
S32.05[0,1,2,8,9][D,G]	[Wedge compression, Stable burst, Unstable burst, Oth, Unsp] fx of 5th lumbar vertebra, subsq enc for fx w/ [routine, delayed] healing
S32.10X[D,G]	Unsp fx of sacrum, subsq enc for fx w/ [routine, delayed] healing
S32.11[0,1,2,9][D,G]	[Nondisp, Minimally disp, Severely disp, Unsp] Zone I fx of sacrum, subsq enc for fx w/ [routine, delayed] healing
S32.12[0,1,2,9][D,G]	[Nondisp, Minimally disp, Severely disp, Unpsecified] Zone II fx of sacrum, subsq enc for fx w/ [routine, delayed] healing
S32.13[0,1,2,9][D,G]	[Nondisp, Minimally disp, Severely disp, Unpsecified] Zone III fx of sacrum, subsq enc for fx w/ [routine, delayed] healing
S32.1[4,5,6,7,9]X[D,G]	[Type 1, Type 2, Type 3, Type 4, Oth] fx of sacrum, subsq enc for fx w/ [routine, delayed] healing
S32.2XX[D,G]	Fx of coccyx, subsq enc for fx w/ [routine, delayed] healing
S32.30[1,2,9][D,G]	Unsp fx of [rt, lt, unsp] ilium, subsq enc for fx w/ [routine, delayed] healing
S32.31[1,2,3][D,G]	Disp avulsion fx of [rt, lt, unsp] ilium, subsq enc for fx w/ [routine, delayed] healing
S32.31[4,5,6][D,G]	Nondisp avulsion fx of [rt, lt, unsp] ilium, subsq enc for fx w/ [routine, delayed] healing
S32.39[1,2,9][D,G]	Oth fx of [rt, lt, unsp] ilium, subsq enc for fx w/ [routine, delayed] healing
S32.40[1,2,9][D,G]	Unsp fx of [rt, lt, unsp] acetab, subsq enc for fx w/ [routine, delayed] healing
S32.41[1,2,3][D,G]	Disp fx of ant wall of [rt, lt, unsp] acetab, subsq enc for fx w/ [routine, delayed] healing
S32.41[4,5,6][D,G]	Nondisp fx of ant wall of [rt, lt, unsp] acetab, subsq enc for fx w/ [routine, delayed] healing
S32.42[1,2,3][D,G]	Disp fx of post wall of [rt, lt, unsp] acetab, subsq enc for fx w/ [routine, delayed] healing
S32.42[4,5,6][D,G]	Nondisp fx of post wall of [rt, lt, unsp] acetab, subsq enc for fx w/ [routine, delayed] healing
S32.43[1,2,3][D,G]	Disp fx of ant column (iliopubic) of [rt, lt, unsp] acetab, subsq enc for fx w/ [routine, delayed] healing
S32.43[4,5,6][D,G]	Nondisp fx of ant column (iliopubic) of [rt, lt, unsp] acetab, subsq enc for fx w/ [routine, delayed] healing
S32.44[1,2,3][D,G]	Disp fx of post column (ilioischial) of [rt, lt, unsp] acetab, subsq enc for fx w/ [routine, delayed] healing
S32.44[4,5,6][D,G]	Nondisp fx of post column (ilioischial) of [rt, lt, unsp] acetab, subsq enc for fx w/ [routine, delayed] healing
S32.45[1,2,3][D,G]	Disp transv fx of [rt, lt, unsp] acetab, subsq enc for fx w/ [routine, delayed] healing
S32.45[4,5,6][D,G]	Nondisp transv fx of [rt, lt, unsp] acetab, subsq enc for fx w/ [routine, delayed] healing
S32.46[1,2,3][D,G]	Disp associated transv-post fx of [rt, lt, unsp] acetab, subsq enc for fx w/ [routine, delayed] healing
S32.46[4,5,6][D,G]	Nondisp associated transv-post fx of [rt, lt, unsp] acetab, subsq enc for fx w/ [routine, delayed] healing
S32.47[1,2,3][D,G]	Disp fx of med wall of [rt, lt, unsp] acetab, subsq enc for fx w/ [routine, delayed] healing
S32.47[4,5,6][D,G]	Nondisp fx of med wall of [rt, lt, unsp] acetab, subsq enc for fx w/ [routine, delayed] healing
S32.48[1,2,3][D,G]	Disp dome fx of [rt, lt, unsp] acetab, subsq enc for fx w/ [routine, delayed] healing
S32.48[4,5,6][D,G]	Nondisp dome fx of [rt, lt, unsp] acetab, subsq enc for fx w/ [routine, delayed] healing
S32.49[1,2,9][D,G]	Oth spec fx of [rt, lt, unsp] acetab, subsq enc for fx w/ [routine, delayed] healing
S32.50[1,2,9][D,G]	Unsp fx of [rt, lt, unsp] pubis, subsq enc for fx w/ [routine, delayed] healing
S32.51[1,2,9][D,G]	Fx of superior rim of [rt, lt, unsp] pubis, subsq enc for fx w/ [routine, delayed] healing
S32.59[1,2,9][D,G]	Oth spec fx of [rt, lt, unsp] pubis, subsq enc for fx w/ [routine, delayed] healing
S32.60[1,2,9][D,G]	Unsp fx of [rt, lt, unsp] ischium, subsq enc for fx w/ [routine, delayed] healing
S32.61[1,2,3][D,G]	Disp avulsion fx of [rt, lt, unsp] ischium, subsq enc for fx w/ [routine, delayed] healing
S32.61[4,5,6][D,G]	Nondisp avulsion fx of [rt, lt, unsp] ischium, subsq enc for fx w/ [routine, delayed] healing
S32.69[1,2,9][D,G]	Oth spec fx of [rt, lt, unsp] ischium, subsq enc for fx w/ [routine, delayed] healing
S32.81[0,1][D,G]	Multi fxs of pelvis w/ [stable, unstable] disruption of pelvic ring, subsq enc for fx w/ [routine, delayed] healing
S32.82X[D,G]	Multi fxs of pelvis w/o disruption of pelvic ring, subsq enc for fx w/ [routine, delayed] healing
S32.89X[D,G]	Fx of oth parts of pelvis, subsq enc for fx w/ [routine, delayed] healing
S32.9XX[D,G]	Fx of unsp parts of lumbosacral spine and pelvis, subsq enc for fx w/ [routine, delayed] healing
S42.00[1,2,9][D,G,S]	Fx of unsp part of [rt, lt, unsp] clavicle, [subsq enc for fx w/ routine healing, subsq enc for fx w/ delayed healing, seq]
S42.01[1,2,3][D,G,S]	Ant disp fx of sternal end of [rt, lt, unsp] clavicle, [subsq enc for fx w/ routine healing, subsq enc for fx w/ delayed healing, seq]
S42.01[4,5,6][D,G,S]	Post disp fx of sternal end of [rt, lt, unsp] clavicle, [subsq enc for fx w/ routine healing, subsq enc for fx w/ delayed healing, seq]
S42.01[7,8,9][D,G,S]	Nondisp fx of sternal end of [rt, lt, unsp] clavicle, [subsq enc for fx w/ routine healing, subsq enc for fx w/ delayed healing, seq]
S42.02[1,2,3][D,G,S]	Disp fx of shaft of [rt, lt, unsp] clavicle, [subsq enc for fx w/ routine healing, subsq enc for fx w/ delayed healing, seq]
S42.02[4,5,6][D,G,S]	Nondisp fx of shaft of [rt, lt, unsp] clavicle, [subsq enc for fx w/ routine healing, subsq enc for fx w/ delayed healing, seq]
S42.03[1,2,3][D,G,S]	Disp fx of lat end of [rt, lt, unsp] clavicle, [subsq enc for fx w/ routine healing, subsq enc for fx w/ delayed healing, seq]
S42.03[4,5,6][D,G,S]	Nondisp fx of lat end of [rt, lt, unsp] clavicle, [subsq enc for fx w/ routine healing, subsq enc for fx w/ delayed healing, seq]
S42.10[1,2,9][D,G,S]	Fx of unsp part of scapula, [rt, lt, unsp] shldr, [subsq enc for fx w/ routine healing, subsq enc for fx w/ delayed healing, seq]
S42.11[1,2,3][D,G,S]	Disp fx of body of scapula, [rt, lt, unsp] shldr, [subsq enc for fx w/ routine healing, subsq enc for fx w/ delayed healing, seq]
S42.11[4,5,6][D,G,S]	Nondisp fx of body of scapula, [rt, lt, unsp] shldr, [subsq enc for fx w/ routine healing, subsq enc for fx w/ delayed healing, seq]
S42.12[1,2,3][D,G,S]	Disp fx of acromial process, [rt, lt, unsp] shldr, [subsq enc for fx w/ routine healing, subsq enc for fx w/ delayed healing, seq]
S42.12[4,5,6][D,G,S]	Nondisp fx of acromial process, [rt, lt, unsp] shldr, [subsq enc for fx w/ routine healing, subsq enc for fx w/ delayed healing, seq]
S42.13[1,2,3][D,G,S]	Disp fx of coracoid process, [rt, lt, unsp] shldr, [subsq enc for fx w/ routine healing, subsq enc for fx w/ delayed healing, seq]
S42.13[4,5,6][D,G,S]	Nondisp fx of coracoid process, [rt, lt, unsp] shldr, [subsq enc for fx w/ routine healing, subsq enc for fx w/ delayed healing, seq]
S42.14[1,2,3][D,G,S]	Disp fx of glenoid cavity of scapula, [rt, lt, unsp] shldr, [subsq enc for fx w/ routine healing, subsq enc for fx w/ delayed healing, seq]
S42.14[4,5,6][D,G,S]	Nondisp fx of glenoid cavity of scapula, [rt, lt, unsp] shldr, [subsq enc for fx w/ routine healing, subsq enc for fx w/ delayed healing, seq]
S42.15[1,2,3][D,G,S]	Disp fx of neck of scapula, [rt, lt, unsp] shldr, [subsq enc for fx w/ routine healing, subsq enc for fx w/ delayed healing, seq]

⊤ **Transfer DRG**   Ȿᴾ **Special Payment**   * **Code Range**   **6th and 7th Character of ZZ = No Device, No Qualifier ZX = No Device, Diagnostic**

170   MS-DRG Version 33.0   © 2015 Optum360, LLC

S42.15[4,5,6][D,G,S] Nondisp fx of neck of scapula, [rt, lt, unsp] shldr, [subsq enc for fx w/ routine healing, subsq enc for fx w/ delayed healing, seq]

S42.19[1,2,9][D,G,S] Fx of oth part of scapula, [rt, lt, unsp] shldr, [subsq enc for fx w/ routine healing, subsq enc for fx w/ delayed healing, seq]

S42.20[1,2,9][D,G,S] Unsp fx of upr end of [rt, lt, unsp] humerus, [subsq enc for fx w/ routine healing, subsq enc for fx w/ delayed healing, seq]

S42.21[1,2,3][D,G,S] Unsp disp fx of surgical neck of [rt, lt, unsp] humerus, [subsq enc for fx w/ routine healing, subsq enc for fx w/ delayed healing, seq]

S42.21[4,5,6][D,G,S] Unsp nondisp fx of surgical neck of [rt, lt, unsp] humerus, [subsq enc for fx w/ routine healing, subsq enc for fx w/ delayed healing, seq]

S42.22[1,2,3][D,G,S] Two-part disp fx of surgical neck of [rt, lt, unsp] humerus, [subsq enc for fx w/ routine healing, subsq enc for fx w/ delayed healing, seq]

S42.22[4,5,6][D,G,S] Two-part nondisp fx of surgical neck of [rt, lt, unsp] humerus, [subsq enc for fx w/ routine healing, subsq enc for fx w/ delayed healing, seq]

S42.23[1,2,9][D,G,S] Three-part fx of surgical neck of [rt, lt, unsp] humerus, [subsq enc for fx w/ routine healing, subsq enc for fx w/ delayed healing, seq]

S42.24[1,2,9][D,G,S] Four-part fx of surgical neck of [rt, lt, unsp] humerus, [subsq enc for fx w/ routine healing, subsq enc for fx w/ delayed healing, seq]

S42.25[1,2,3][D,G,S] Disp fx of greater tuberosity of [rt, lt, unsp] humerus, [subsq enc for fx w/ routine healing, subsq enc for fx w/ delayed healing, seq]

S42.25[4,5,6][D,G,S] Nondisp fx of greater tuberosity of [rt, lt, unsp] humerus, [subsq enc for fx w/ routine healing, subsq enc for fx w/ delayed healing, seq]

S42.26[1,2,3][D,G,S] Disp fx of lesser tuberosity of [rt, lt, unsp] humerus, [subsq enc for fx w/ routine healing, subsq enc for fx w/ delayed healing, seq]

S42.26[4,5,6][D,G,S] Nondisp fx of lesser tuberosity of [rt, lt, unsp] humerus, [subsq enc for fx w/ routine healing, subsq enc for fx w/ delayed healing, seq]

S42.27[1,2,9][D,G,S] Torus fx of upr end of [rt, lt, unsp] humerus, [subsq enc for fx w/ routine healing, subsq enc for fx w/ delayed healing, seq]

S42.29[1,2,3][D,G,S] Oth disp fx of upr end of [rt, lt, unsp] humerus, [subsq enc for fx w/ routine healing, subsq enc for fx w/ delayed healing, seq]

S42.29[4,5,6][D,G,S] Oth nondisp fx of upr end of [rt, lt, unsp] humerus, [subsq enc for fx w/ routine healing, subsq enc for fx w/ delayed healing, seq]

S42.30[1,2,9][D,G,S] Unsp fx of shaft of [rt, lt, unsp] humerus, [subsq enc for fx w/ routine healing, subsq enc for fx w/ delayed healing, seq]

S42.31[1,2,9][D,G,S] Greenstick fx of shaft of [rt, lt, unsp] humerus, [subsq enc for fx w/ routine healing, subsq enc for fx w/ delayed healing, seq]

S42.32[1,2,3][D,G,S] Disp transv fx of shaft of [rt, lt, unsp] humerus, [subsq enc for fx w/ routine healing, subsq enc for fx w/ delayed healing, seq]

S42.32[4,5,6][D,G,S] Nondisp transv fx of shaft of [rt, lt, unsp] humerus, [subsq enc for fx w/ routine healing, subsq enc for fx w/ delayed healing, seq]

S42.33[1,2,3][D,G,S] Disp oblique fx of shaft of [rt, lt, unsp] humerus, [subsq enc for fx w/ routine healing, subsq enc for fx w/ delayed healing, seq]

S42.33[4,5,6][D,G,S] Nondisp oblique fx of shaft of [rt, lt, unsp] humerus, [subsq enc for fx w/ routine healing, subsq enc for fx w/ delayed healing, seq]

S42.34[1,2,3][D,G,S] Disp spiral fx of shaft of [rt, lt, unsp] humerus, [subsq enc for fx w/ routine healing, subsq enc for fx w/ delayed healing, seq]

S42.34[4,5,6][D,G,S] Nondisp spiral fx of shaft of [rt, lt, unsp] humerus, [subsq enc for fx w/ routine healing, subsq enc for fx w/ delayed healing, seq]

S42.35[1,2,3][D,G,S] Disp comm fx of shaft of [rt, lt, unsp] humerus, [subsq enc for fx w/ routine healing, subsq enc for fx w/ delayed healing, seq]

S42.35[4,5,6][D,G,S] Nondisp comm fx of shaft of [rt, lt, unsp] humerus, [subsq enc for fx w/ routine healing, subsq enc for fx w/ delayed healing, seq]

S42.36[1,2,3][D,G,S] Disp seg fx of shaft of [rt, lt, unsp] humerus, [subsq enc for fx w/ routine healing, subsq enc for fx w/ delayed healing, seq]

S42.36[4,5,6][D,G,S] Nondisp seg fx of shaft of [rt, lt, unsp] humerus, [subsq enc for fx w/ routine healing, subsq enc for fx w/ delayed healing, seq]

S42.39[1,2,9][D,G,S] Oth fx of shaft of [rt, lt, unsp] humerus, [subsq enc for fx w/ routine healing, subsq enc for fx w/ delayed healing, seq]

S42.40[1,2,9][D,G,S] Unsp fx of lwr end of [rt, lt, unsp] humerus, [subsq enc for fx w/ routine healing, subsq enc for fx w/ delayed healing, seq]

S42.41[1,2,3][D,G,S] Disp simple supracondylar fx w/o intercondylar fx of [rt, lt, unsp] humerus, [subsq enc for fx w/ routine healing, subsq enc for fx w/ delayed healing, seq]

S42.41[4,5,6][D,G,S] Nondisp simple supracondylar fx w/o intercondylar fx of [rt, lt, unsp] humerus, [subsq enc for fx w/ routine healing, subsq enc for fx w/ delayed healing, seq]

S42.42[1,2,3][D,G,S] Disp comm supracondylar fx w/o intercondylar fx of [rt, lt, unsp] humerus, [subsq enc for fx w/ routine healing, subsq enc for fx w/ delayed healing, seq]

S42.42[4,5,6][D,G,S] Nondisp comm supracondylar fx w/o intercondylar fx of [rt, lt, unsp] humerus, [subsq enc for fx w/ routine healing, subsq enc for fx w/ delayed healing, seq]

S42.43[1,2,3][D,G,S] Disp fx (avulsion) of lat epicondyle of [rt, lt, unsp] humerus, [subsq enc for fx w/ routine healing, subsq enc for fx w/ delayed healing, seq]

S42.43[4,5,6][D,G,S] Nondisp fx (avulsion) of lat epicondyle of [rt, lt, unsp] humerus, [subsq enc for fx w/ routine healing, subsq enc for fx w/ delayed healing, seq]

S42.44[1,2,3][D,G,S] Disp fx (avulsion) of med epicondyle of [rt, lt, unsp] humerus, [subsq enc for fx w/ routine healing, subsq enc for fx w/ delayed healing, seq]

S42.44[4,5,6][D,G,S] Nondisp fx (avulsion) of med epicondyle of [rt, lt, unsp] humerus, [subsq enc for fx w/ routine healing, subsq enc for fx w/ delayed healing, seq]

S42.44[7,8,9][D,G,S] Incarcerated fx (avulsion) of med epicondyle of [rt, lt, unsp] humerus, [subsq enc for fx w/ routine healing, subsq enc for fx w/ delayed healing, seq]

S42.45[1,2,3][D,G,S] Disp fx of lat condyle of [rt, lt, unsp] humerus, [subsq enc for fx w/ routine healing, subsq enc for fx w/ delayed healing, seq]

S42.45[4,5,6][D,G,S]Nondisp fx of lat condyle of [rt, lt, unsp] humerus, [subsq enc for fx w/ routine healing, subsq enc for fx w/ delayed healing, seq]

S42.46[1,2,3][D,G,S] Disp fx of med condyle of [rt, lt, unsp] humerus, [subsq enc for fx w/ routine healing, subsq enc for fx w/ delayed healing, seq]

S42.46[4,5,6][D,G,S] Nondisp fx of med condyle of [rt, lt, unsp] humerus, [subsq enc for fx w/ routine healing, subsq enc for fx w/ delayed healing, seq]

S42.47[1,2,3][D,G,S] Disp transcondylar fx of [rt, lt, unsp] humerus, [subsq enc for fx w/ routine healing, subsq enc for fx w/ delayed healing, seq]

S42.47[4,5,6][D,G,S] Nondisp transcondylar fx of [rt, lt, unsp] humerus, [subsq enc for fx w/ routine healing, subsq enc for fx w/ delayed healing, seq]

S42.48[1,2,9][D,G,S] Torus fx of lwr end of [rt, lt, unsp] humerus, [subsq enc for fx w/ routine healing, subsq enc for fx w/ delayed healing, seq]

S42.49[1,2,3][D,G,S] Oth disp fx of lwr end of [rt, lt, unsp] humerus, [subsq enc for fx w/ routine healing, subsq enc for fx w/ delayed healing, seq]

S42.49[4,5,6][D,G,S] Oth nondisp fx of lwr end of [rt, lt, unsp] humerus, [subsq enc for fx w/ routine healing, subsq enc for fx w/ delayed healing, seq]

S42.9[0,1,2]X[D,G,S] Fx of [unsp, rt, lt] shldr girdle, part unsp, [subsq enc for fx w/ routine healing, subsq enc for fx w/ delayed healing, seq]

S48.0[1,2][1,2,9]S [Complete, Partial] traum amp at [rt, lt, unsp] shldr jt, seq

S48.1[1,2][1,2,9]S [Complete, Partial] traum amp at lvl between [rt, lt, unsp] shldr and elbow, seq

S48.9[1,2][1,2,9]S [Complete, Partial] traum amp of [rt, lt, unsp] shldr and upr arm, lvl unsp, seq

S49.00[1,2,9][D,G,S] Unsp physeal fx of upr end of humerus, [rt, lt, unsp] arm, [subsq enc for fx w/ routine healing, subsq enc for fx w/ delayed healing, seq]

S49.01[1,2,9][D,G,S] Salter-Harris Type I physeal fx of upr end of humerus, [rt, lt, unsp] arm, [subsq enc for fx w/ routine healing, subsq enc for fx w/ delayed healing, seq]

S49.02[1,2,9][D,G,S] Salter-Harris Type II physeal fx of upr end of humerus, [rt, lt, unsp] arm, [subsq enc for fx w/ routine healing, subsq enc for fx w/ delayed healing, seq]

S49.03[1,2,9][D,G,S] Salter-Harris Type III physeal fx of upr end of humerus, [rt, lt, unsp] arm, [subsq enc for fx w/ routine healing, subsq enc for fx w/ delayed healing, seq]

S49.04[1,2,9][D,G,S] Salter-Harris Type IV physeal fx of upr end of humerus, [rt, lt, unsp] arm, [subsq enc for fx w/ routine healing, subsq enc for fx w/ delayed healing, seq]

Surgical **Medical** **CC Indicator** **MCC Indicator** **Procedure Proxy** **PDxMCC** PDx acts as own MCC **PDxCC** PDx acts as own CC

S49.09[1,2,9][D,G,S] Oth physeal fx of upr end of humerus, [rt, lt, unsp] arm, [subsq enc for fx w/ routine healing, subsq enc for fx w/ delayed healing, seq]

S49.10[1,2,9][D,G,S] Unsp physeal fx of lwr end of humerus, [rt, lt, unsp] arm, [subsq enc for fx w/ routine healing, subsq enc for fx w/ delayed healing, seq]

S49.11[1,2,9][D,G,S] Salter-Harris Type I physeal fx of lwr end of humerus, [rt, lt, unsp] arm, [subsq enc for fx w/ routine healing, subsq enc for fx w/ delayed healing, seq]

S49.12[1,2,9][D,G,S] Salter-Harris Type II physeal fx of lwr end of humerus, [rt, lt, unsp] arm, [subsq enc for fx w/ routine healing, subsq enc for fx w/ delayed healing, seq]

S49.13[1,2,9][D,G,S] Salter-Harris Type III physeal fx of lwr end of humerus, [rt, lt, unsp] arm, [subsq enc for fx w/ routine healing, subsq enc for fx w/ delayed healing, seq]

S49.14[1,2,9][D,G,S] Salter-Harris Type IV physeal fx of lwr end of humerus, [rt, lt, unsp] arm, [subsq enc for fx w/ routine healing, subsq enc for fx w/ delayed healing, seq]

S49.19[1,2,9][D,G,S] Oth physeal fx of lwr end of humerus, [rt, lt, unsp] arm, [subsq enc for fx w/ routine healing, subsq enc for fx w/ delayed healing, seq]

S52.00[1,2,9][D,E,F,G,H,J,S] Unsp fx of upr end of [rt, lt, unsp] ulna, [subsq enc for clsd fx w/ routine healing, subsq enc for opn fx type I or II w/ routine healing, subsq enc for opn fx type IIIA, IIIB, or IIIC w/ routine healing, subsq enc for clsd fx w/ delayed healing, subsq enc for opn fx type I or II w/ delayed healing, subsq enc for opn fx type IIIA, IIIB, or IIIC w/ delayed healing, seq]

S52.01[1,2,9][D,G,S] Torus fx of upr end of [rt, lt, unsp] ulna, [subsq enc for fx w/ routine healing, subsq enc for fx w/ delayed healing, seq]

S52.02[1,2,3][D,E,F,G,H,J,S] Disp fx of olecranon process w/o intraarticular extension of [rt, lt, unsp] ulna, [subsq enc for clsd fx w/ routine healing, subsq enc for opn fx type I or II w/ routine healing, subsq enc for opn fx type IIIA, IIIB, or IIIC w/ routine healing, subsq enc for clsd fx w/ delayed healing, subsq enc for opn fx type I or II w/ delayed healing, subsq enc for opn fx type IIIA, IIIB, or IIIC w/ delayed healing, seq]

S52.02[4,5,6][D,E,F,G,H,J,S] Nondisp fx of olecranon process w/o intraarticular extension of [rt, lt, unsp] ulna, [subsq enc for clsd fx w/ routine healing, subsq enc for opn fx type I or II w/ routine healing, subsq enc for opn fx type IIIA, IIIB, or IIIC w/ routine healing, subsq enc for clsd fx w/ delayed healing, subsq enc for opn fx type I or II w/ delayed healing, subsq enc for opn fx type IIIA, IIIB, or IIIC w/ delayed healing, seq]

S52.03[1,2,3][D,E,F,G,H,J,S] Disp fx of olecranon process w/ intraarticular extension of [rt, lt, unsp] ulna, [subsq enc for clsd fx w/ routine healing, subsq enc for opn fx type I or II w/ routine healing, subsq enc for opn fx type IIIA, IIIB, or IIIC w/ routine healing, subsq enc for clsd fx w/ delayed healing, subsq enc for opn fx type I or II w/ delayed healing, subsq enc for opn fx type IIIA, IIIB, or IIIC w/ delayed healing, seq]

S52.03[4,5,6][D,E,F,G,H,J,S] Nondisp fx of olecranon process w/ intraarticular extension of [rt, lt, unsp] ulna, [subsq enc for clsd fx w/ routine healing, subsq enc for opn fx type I or II w/ routine healing, subsq enc for opn fx type IIIA, IIIB, or IIIC w/ routine healing, subsq enc for clsd fx w/ delayed healing, subsq enc for opn fx type I or II w/ delayed healing, subsq enc for opn fx type IIIA, IIIB, or IIIC w/ delayed healing, seq]

S52.04[1,2,3][D,E,F,G,H,J,S] Disp fx of coronoid process of [rt, lt, unsp] ulna, [subsq enc for clsd fx w/ routine healing, subsq enc for opn fx type I or II w/ routine healing, subsq enc for opn fx type IIIA, IIIB, or IIIC w/ routine healing, subsq enc for clsd fx w/ delayed healing, subsq enc for opn fx type I or II w/ delayed healing, subsq enc for opn fx type IIIA, IIIB, or IIIC w/ delayed healing, seq]

S52.04[4,5,6][D,E,F,G,H,J,S] Nondisp fx of coronoid process of [rt, lt, unsp] ulna, [subsq enc for clsd fx w/ routine healing, subsq enc for opn fx type I or II w/ routine healing, subsq enc for opn fx type IIIA, IIIB, or IIIC w/ delayed healing, subsq enc for opn fx type I or II w/ delayed healing, subsq enc for opn fx type IIIA, IIIB, or IIIC w/ delayed healing, seq]

S52.09[1,2,9][D,E,F,G,H,J,S] Oth fx of upr end of [rt, lt, unsp] ulna, [subsq enc for clsd fx w/ routine healing, subsq enc for opn fx type I or II w/ routine healing, subsq enc for opn fx type IIIA, IIIB, or IIIC w/ routine healing, subsq enc for clsd fx w/ delayed healing, subsq enc for opn fx type I or II w/ delayed healing, subsq enc for opn fx type IIIA, IIIB, or IIIC w/ delayed healing, seq]

S52.10[1,2,9][D,E,F,G,H,J,S] Unsp fx of upr end of [rt, lt, unsp] ulna, [subsq enc for clsd fx w/ routine healing, subsq enc for opn fx type I or II w/ routine healing, subsq enc for opn fx type IIIA, IIIB, or IIIC w/ routine healing, subsq enc for clsd fx w/ delayed healing, subsq enc for opn fx type I or II w/ delayed healing, subsq enc for opn fx type IIIA, IIIB, or IIIC w/ delayed healing, seq]

S52.11[1,2,9][D,G,S] Torus fx of upr end of [rt, lt, unsp] radius, [subsq enc for fx w/ routine healing, subsq enc for fx w/ delayed healing, seq]

S52.12[1,2,3][D,E,F,G,H,J,S] Disp fx of head of [rt, lt, unsp] radius, [subsq enc for clsd fx w/ routine healing, subsq enc for opn fx type I or II w/ routine healing, subsq enc for opn fx type IIIA, IIIB, or IIIC w/ routine healing, subsq enc for clsd fx w/ delayed healing, subsq enc for opn fx type I or II w/ delayed healing, subsq enc for opn fx type IIIA, IIIB, or IIIC w/ delayed healing, seq]

S52.12[4,5,6][D,E,F,G,H,J,S] Nondisp fx of head of [rt, lt, unsp] radius, [subsq enc for clsd fx w/ routine healing, subsq enc for opn fx type I or II w/ routine healing, subsq enc for opn fx type IIIA, IIIB, or IIIC w/ routine healing, subsq enc for clsd fx w/ delayed healing, subsq enc for opn fx type I or II w/ delayed healing, subsq enc for opn fx type IIIA, IIIB, or IIIC w/ delayed healing, seq]

S52.13[1,2,3][D,E,F,G,H,J,S] Disp fx of neck of [rt, lt, unsp] radius, [subsq enc for clsd fx w/ routine healing, subsq enc for opn fx type I or II w/ routine healing, subsq enc for opn fx type IIIA, IIIB, or IIIC w/ routine healing, subsq enc for clsd fx w/ delayed healing, subsq enc for opn fx type I or II w/ delayed healing, subsq enc for opn fx type IIIA, IIIB, or IIIC w/ delayed healing, seq]

S52.13[4,5,6][D,E,F,G,H,J,S] Nondisp fx of neck of [rt, lt, unsp] radius, [subsq enc for clsd fx w/ routine healing, subsq enc for opn fx type I or II w/ routine healing, subsq enc for opn fx type IIIA, IIIB, or IIIC w/ routine healing, subsq enc for clsd fx w/ delayed healing, subsq enc for opn fx type I or II w/ delayed healing, subsq enc for opn fx type IIIA, IIIB, or IIIC w/ delayed healing, seq]

S52.18[1,2,9][D,E,F,G,H,J,S] Oth fx of upr end of [rt, lt, unsp] radius, [subsq enc for clsd fx w/ routine healing, subsq enc for opn fx type I or II w/ routine healing, subsq enc for opn fx type IIIA, IIIB, or IIIC w/ routine healing, subsq enc for clsd fx w/ delayed healing, subsq enc for opn fx type I or II w/ delayed healing, subsq enc for opn fx type IIIA, IIIB, or IIIC w/ delayed healing, seq]

S52.20[1,2,9][D,E,F,G,H,J,S] Unsp fx of shaft of [rt, lt, unsp] radius, [subsq enc for clsd fx w/ routine healing, subsq enc for opn fx type I or II w/ routine healing, subsq enc for opn fx type IIIA, IIIB, or IIIC w/ routine healing, subsq enc for clsd fx w/ delayed healing, subsq enc for opn fx type I or II w/ delayed healing, subsq enc for opn fx type IIIA, IIIB, or IIIC w/ delayed healing, seq]

S52.21[1,2,9][D,G,S] Greenstick fx of shaft of [rt, lt, unsp] ulna, [subsq enc for fx w/ routine healing, subsq enc for fx w/ delayed healing, seq]

S52.22[1,2,3][D,E,F,G,H,J,S] Disp transv fx of shaft of [rt, lt, unsp] ulna, [subsq enc for clsd fx w/ routine healing, subsq enc for opn fx type I or II w/ routine healing, subsq enc for opn fx type IIIA, IIIB, or IIIC w/ routine healing, subsq enc for clsd fx w/ delayed healing, subsq enc for opn fx type I or II w/ delayed healing, subsq enc for opn fx type IIIA, IIIB, or IIIC w/ delayed healing, seq]

S52.22[4,5,6][D,E,F,G,H,J,S] Nondisp transv fx of shaft of [rt, lt, unsp] ulna, [subsq enc for clsd fx w/ routine healing, subsq enc for opn fx type I or II w/ routine healing, subsq enc for opn fx type IIIA, IIIB, or IIIC w/ routine healing, subsq enc for clsd fx w/ delayed healing, subsq enc for opn fx type I or II w/ delayed healing, subsq enc for opn fx type IIIA, IIIB, or IIIC w/ delayed healing, seq]

S52.23[1,2,3][D,E,F,G,H,J,S] Disp oblique fx of shaft of [rt, lt, unsp] ulna, [subsq enc for clsd fx w/ routine healing, subsq enc for opn fx type I or II w/ routine healing, subsq enc for opn fx type IIIA, IIIB, or IIIC w/ routine healing, subsq enc for clsd fx w/ delayed healing, subsq enc for opn fx type I or II w/ delayed healing, subsq enc for opn fx type IIIA, IIIB, or IIIC w/ delayed healing, seq]

S52.23[4,5,6][D,E,F,G,H,J,S] Nondisp oblique fx of shaft of [rt, lt, unsp] ulna, [subsq enc for clsd fx w/ routine healing, subsq enc for opn fx type I or II w/ routine healing, subsq enc for opn fx type IIIA, IIIB, or IIIC w/ routine healing, subsq enc for clsd fx w/ delayed healing, subsq enc for opn fx type I or II w/ delayed healing, subsq enc for opn fx type IIIA, IIIB, or IIIC w/ delayed healing, seq]

S52.24[1,2,3][D,E,F,G,H,J,S] Disp spiral fx of shaft of [rt, lt, unsp] ulna, [subsq enc for clsd fx w/ routine healing, subsq enc for opn fx type I or II w/ routine healing, subsq enc for opn fx type IIIA, IIIB, or IIIC w/ routine healing, subsq enc for clsd fx w/ delayed healing, subsq enc for opn fx type I or II w/ delayed healing, subsq enc for opn fx type IIIA, IIIB, or IIIC w/ delayed healing, seq]

T Transfer DRG   SP Special Payment   * Code Range   6th and 7th Character of ZZ = No Device, No Qualifier ZX = No Device, Diagnostic

172   MS-DRG Version 33.0   © 2015 Optum360, LLC

S52.24[4,5,6][D,E,F,G,H,J,S] Nondisp spiral fx of shaft of [rt, lt, unsp] ulna, [subsq enc for clsd fx w/ routine healing, subsq enc for opn fx type I or II w/ routine healing, subsq enc for opn fx type IIIA, IIIB, or IIIC w/ routine healing, subsq enc for clsd fx w/ delayed healing, subsq enc for opn fx type I or II w/ delayed healing, subsq enc for opn fx type IIIA, IIIB, or IIIC w/ delayed healing, seq]

S52.25[1,2,3][D,E,F,G,H,J,S] Disp comm fx of shaft of [rt, lt, unsp] ulna, [subsq enc for clsd fx w/ routine healing, subsq enc for opn fx type I or II w/ routine healing, subsq enc for opn fx type IIIA, IIIB, or IIIC w/ routine healing, subsq enc for clsd fx w/ delayed healing, subsq enc for opn fx type I or II w/ delayed healing, subsq enc for opn fx type IIIA, IIIB, or IIIC w/ delayed healing, seq]

S52.25[4,5,6][D,E,F,G,H,J,S] Nondisp comm fx of shaft of [rt, lt, unsp] ulna, [subsq enc for clsd fx w/ routine healing, subsq enc for opn fx type I or II w/ routine healing, subsq enc for opn fx type IIIA, IIIB, or IIIC w/ routine healing, subsq enc for clsd fx w/ delayed healing, subsq enc for opn fx type I or II w/ delayed healing, subsq enc for opn fx type IIIA, IIIB, or IIIC w/ delayed healing, seq]

S52.26[1,2,3][D,E,F,G,H,J,S] Disp seg fx of shaft of [rt, lt, unsp] ulna, [subsq enc for clsd fx w/ routine healing, subsq enc for opn fx type I or II w/ routine healing, subsq enc for opn fx type IIIA, IIIB, or IIIC w/ routine healing, subsq enc for clsd fx w/ delayed healing, subsq enc for opn fx type I or II w/ delayed healing, subsq enc for opn fx type IIIA, IIIB, or IIIC w/ delayed healing, seq]

S52.26[4,5,6][D,E,F,G,H,J,S] Nondisp seg fx of shaft of [rt, lt, unsp] ulna, [subsq enc for clsd fx w/ routine healing, subsq enc for opn fx type I or II w/ routine healing, subsq enc for opn fx type IIIA, IIIB, or IIIC w/ routine healing, subsq enc for clsd fx w/ delayed healing, subsq enc for opn fx type I or II w/ delayed healing, subsq enc for opn fx type IIIA, IIIB, or IIIC w/ delayed healing, seq]

S52.27[1,2,9][D,E,F,G,H,J,S] Monteggia's fx of [rt, lt, unsp] ulna, [subsq enc for clsd fx w/ routine healing, subsq enc for opn fx type I or II w/ routine healing, subsq enc for opn fx type I or II w/ routine healing, subsq enc for clsd fx w/ delayed healing, subsq enc for opn fx type I or II w/ delayed healing, subsq enc for opn fx type IIIA, IIIB, or IIIC w/ delayed healing, seq]

S52.28[1,2,3][D,E,F,G,H,J,S] Bent bone of [rt, lt, unsp] ulna, [subsq enc for clsd fx w/ routine healing, subsq enc for opn fx type I or II w/ routine healing, subsq enc for opn fx type I or II w/ routine healing, subsq enc for clsd fx w/ delayed healing, subsq enc for opn fx type I or II w/ delayed healing, subsq enc for opn fx type IIIA, IIIB, or IIIC w/ delayed healing, seq]

S52.29[1,2,9][D,E,F,G,H,J,S] Oth fx of shaft of [rt, lt, unsp] ulna, [subsq enc for clsd fx w/ routine healing, subsq enc for opn fx type I or II w/ routine healing, subsq enc for opn fx type I or II w/ routine healing, subsq enc for clsd fx w/ delayed healing, subsq enc for opn fx type I or II w/ delayed healing, subsq enc for opn fx type IIIA, IIIB, or IIIC w/ delayed healing, seq]

S52.30[1,2,9][D,E,F,G,H,J,S] Unsp fx of shaft of [rt, lt, unsp] ulna, [subsq enc for clsd fx w/ routine healing, subsq enc for opn fx type I or II w/ routine healing, subsq enc for opn fx type I or II w/ routine healing, subsq enc for clsd fx w/ delayed healing, subsq enc for opn fx type I or II w/ delayed healing, subsq enc for opn fx type IIIA, IIIB, or IIIC w/ delayed healing, seq]

S52.31[1,2,9][D,G,S] Greenstick fx of shaft of radius, [rt, lt, unsp] arm, [subsq enc for fx w/ routine healing, subsq enc for fx w/ delayed healing, seq]

S52.32[1,2,3][D,E,F,G,H,J,S] Disp transv fx of shaft of [rt, lt, unsp] radius, [subsq enc for clsd fx w/ routine healing, subsq enc for opn fx type I or II w/ routine healing, subsq enc for opn fx type I or II w/ routine healing, subsq enc for clsd fx w/ delayed healing, subsq enc for opn fx type I or II w/ delayed healing, subsq enc for opn fx type IIIA, IIIB, or IIIC w/ delayed healing, seq]

S52.32[4,5,6][D,E,F,G,H,J,S] Nondisp transv fx of shaft of [rt, lt, unsp] radius, [subsq enc for clsd fx w/ routine healing, subsq enc for opn fx type I or II w/ routine healing, subsq enc for opn fx type I or II w/ routine healing, subsq enc for clsd fx w/ delayed healing, subsq enc for opn fx type I or II w/ delayed healing, subsq enc for opn fx type IIIA, IIIB, or IIIC w/ delayed healing, seq]

S52.33[1,2,3][D,E,F,G,H,J,S] Disp oblique fx of shaft of [rt, lt, unsp] radius, [subsq enc for clsd fx w/ routine healing, subsq enc for opn fx type I or II w/ routine healing, subsq enc for opn fx type I or II w/ routine healing, subsq enc for clsd fx w/ delayed healing, subsq enc for opn fx type I or II w/ delayed healing, subsq enc for opn fx type IIIA, IIIB, or IIIC w/ delayed healing, seq]

S52.33[4,5,6][D,E,F,G,H,J,S] Nondisp oblique fx of shaft of [rt, lt, unsp] radius, [subsq enc for clsd fx w/ routine healing, subsq enc for opn fx type I or II w/ routine healing, subsq enc for opn fx type I or II w/ routine healing, subsq enc for clsd fx w/ delayed healing, subsq enc for opn fx type I or II w/ delayed healing, subsq enc for opn fx type IIIA, IIIB, or IIIC w/ delayed healing, seq]

S52.34[1,2,3][D,E,F,G,H,J,S] Disp spiral fx of shaft of [rt, lt, unsp] radius, [subsq enc for clsd fx w/ routine healing, subsq enc for opn fx type I or II w/ routine healing, subsq enc for opn fx type I or II w/ routine healing, subsq enc for clsd fx w/ delayed healing, subsq enc for opn fx type I or II w/ delayed healing, subsq enc for opn fx type IIIA, IIIB, or IIIC w/ delayed healing, seq]

S52.34[4,5,6][D,E,F,G,H,J,S] Nondisp spiral fx of shaft of [rt, lt, unsp] radius, [subsq enc for clsd fx w/ routine healing, subsq enc for opn fx type I or II w/ routine healing, subsq enc for opn fx type I or II w/ routine healing, subsq enc for clsd fx w/ delayed healing, subsq enc for opn fx type I or II w/ delayed healing, subsq enc for opn fx type IIIA, IIIB, or IIIC w/ delayed healing, seq]

S52.35[1,2,3][D,E,F,G,H,J,S] Disp comm fx of shaft of [rt, lt, unsp] radius, [subsq enc for clsd fx w/ routine healing, subsq enc for opn fx type I or II w/ routine healing, subsq enc for opn fx type I or II w/ routine healing, subsq enc for clsd fx w/ delayed healing, subsq enc for opn fx type I or II w/ delayed healing, subsq enc for opn fx type IIIA, IIIB, or IIIC w/ delayed healing, seq]

S52.35[4,5,6][D,E,F,G,H,J,S] Nondisp comm fx of shaft of [rt, lt, unsp] radius, [subsq enc for clsd fx w/ routine healing, subsq enc for opn fx type I or II w/ routine healing, subsq enc for opn fx type I or II w/ routine healing, subsq enc for clsd fx w/ delayed healing, subsq enc for opn fx type I or II w/ delayed healing, subsq enc for opn fx type IIIA, IIIB, or IIIC w/ delayed healing, seq]

S52.36[1,2,3][D,E,F,G,H,J,S] Disp seg fx of shaft of [rt, lt, unsp] radius, [subsq enc for clsd fx w/ routine healing, subsq enc for opn fx type I or II w/ routine healing, subsq enc for opn fx type I or II w/ routine healing, subsq enc for clsd fx w/ delayed healing, subsq enc for opn fx type IIIA, IIIB, or IIIC w/ delayed healing, seq]

S52.36[4,5,6][D,E,F,G,H,J,S] Nondisp seg fx of shaft of [rt, lt, unsp] radius, [subsq enc for clsd fx w/ routine healing, subsq enc for opn fx type I or II w/ routine healing, subsq enc for opn fx type I or II w/ routine healing, subsq enc for clsd fx w/ delayed healing, subsq enc for opn fx type I or II w/ delayed healing, subsq enc for opn fx type IIIA, IIIB, or IIIC w/ delayed healing, seq]

S52.37[1,2,9][D,E,F,G,H,J,S] Galeazzi's fx of [rt, lt, unsp] radius, [subsq enc for clsd fx w/ routine healing, subsq enc for opn fx type I or II w/ routine healing, subsq enc for opn fx type I or II w/ routine healing, subsq enc for clsd fx w/ delayed healing, subsq enc for opn fx type I or II w/ delayed healing, subsq enc for opn fx type IIIA, IIIB, or IIIC w/ delayed healing, seq]

S52.38[1,2,9][D,E,F,G,H,J,S] Bent bone of [rt, lt, unsp] radius, [subsq enc for clsd fx w/ routine healing, subsq enc for opn fx type I or II w/ routine healing, subsq enc for opn fx type I or II w/ routine healing, subsq enc for clsd fx w/ delayed healing, subsq enc for opn fx type I or II w/ delayed healing, subsq enc for opn fx type IIIA, IIIB, or IIIC w/ delayed healing, seq]

S52.39[1,2,9][D,E,F,G,H,J,S] Oth fx of shaft of [rt, lt, unsp] radius, [subsq enc for clsd fx w/ routine healing, subsq enc for opn fx type I or II w/ routine healing, subsq enc for opn fx type I or II w/ routine healing, subsq enc for clsd fx w/ delayed healing, subsq enc for opn fx type I or II w/ delayed healing, subsq enc for opn fx type IIIA, IIIB, or IIIC w/ delayed healing, seq]

S52.50[1,2,9][D,E,F,G,H,J,S] Unsp fx of lwr end of [rt, lt, unsp] radius, [subsq enc for clsd fx w/ routine healing, subsq enc for opn fx type I or II w/ routine healing, subsq enc for opn fx type I or II w/ routine healing, subsq enc for clsd fx w/ delayed healing, subsq enc for opn fx type I or II w/ delayed healing, subsq enc for opn fx type IIIA, IIIB, or IIIC w/ delayed healing, seq]

S52.51[1,2,3][D,E,F,G,H,J,S] Disp fx of [rt, lt, unsp] radial styloid process, [subsq enc for clsd fx w/ routine healing, subsq enc for opn fx type I or II w/ routine healing, subsq enc for opn fx type I or II w/ routine healing, subsq enc for clsd fx w/ delayed healing, subsq enc for opn fx type I or II w/ delayed healing, subsq enc for opn fx type IIIA, IIIB, or IIIC w/ delayed healing, seq]

S52.51[4,5,6][D,E,F,G,H,J,S] Nondisp fx of [rt, lt, unsp] radial styloid process, [subsq enc for clsd fx w/ routine healing, subsq enc for opn fx type I or II w/ routine healing, subsq enc for opn fx type I or II w/ routine healing, subsq enc for clsd fx w/ delayed healing, subsq enc for opn fx type I or II w/ delayed healing, subsq enc for opn fx type IIIA, IIIB, or IIIC w/ delayed healing, seq]

S52.52[1,2,9][D,G,S] Torus fx of lwr end of [rt, lt, unsp] radius, [subsq enc for fx w/ routine healing, subsq enc for fx w/ delayed healing, seq]

Surgical   **Medical**   **CC Indicator**   **MCC Indicator**   **Procedure Proxy**   **PDxMCC** PDx acts as own MCC   **PDxCC** PDx acts as own CC

S52.53[1,2,9][D,E,F,G,H,J,S] Colles' fx of [rt, lt, unsp] radius, [subsq enc for clsd fx w/ routine healing, subsq enc for opn fx type I or II w/ routine healing, subsq enc for opn fx type I or II w/ routine healing, subsq enc for clsd fx w/ delayed healing, subsq enc for opn fx type I or II w/ delayed healing, subsq enc for opn fx type IIIA, IIIB, or IIIC w/ delayed healing, seq]

S52.54[1,2,9][D,E,F,G,H,J,S] Smith's fx of [rt, lt, unsp] radius, [subsq enc for clsd fx w/ routine healing, subsq enc for opn fx type I or II w/ routine healing, subsq enc for opn fx type I or II w/ routine healing, subsq enc for clsd fx w/ delayed healing, subsq enc for opn fx type I or II w/ delayed healing, subsq enc for opn fx type IIIA, IIIB, or IIIC w/ delayed healing, seq]

S52.55[1,2,9][D,E,F,G,H,J,S] Oth extraarticular fx of lwr end of [rt, lt, unsp] radius, [subsq enc for clsd fx w/ routine healing, subsq enc for opn fx type I or II w/ routine healing, subsq enc for opn fx type IIIA, IIIB, or IIIC w/ routine healing, subsq enc for clsd fx w/ delayed healing, subsq enc for opn fx type I or II w/ delayed healing, subsq enc for opn fx type I or II w/ delayed healing, seq]

S52.56[1,2,9][D,E,F,G,H,J,S] Barton's fx of [rt, lt, unsp] radius, [subsq enc for clsd fx w/ routine healing, subsq enc for opn fx type I or II w/ routine healing, subsq enc for opn fx type IIIA, IIIB, or IIIC w/ routine healing, subsq enc for clsd fx w/ delayed healing, subsq enc for opn fx type I or II w/ delayed healing, subsq enc for opn fx type I or II w/ delayed healing, seq]

S52.57[1,2,9][D,E,F,G,H,J,S] Oth intraarticular fx of lwr end of [rt, lt, unsp] radius, [subsq enc for clsd fx w/ routine healing, subsq enc for opn fx type I or II w/ routine healing, subsq enc for opn fx type IIIA, IIIB, or IIIC w/ routine healing, subsq enc for clsd fx w/ delayed healing, subsq enc for opn fx type I or II w/ delayed healing, subsq enc for opn fx type I or II w/ delayed healing, seq]

S52.59[1,2,9][D,E,F,G,H,J,S] Oth fxs of lwr end of [rt, lt, unsp] radius, [subsq enc for clsd fx w/ routine healing, subsq enc for opn fx type I or II w/ routine healing, subsq enc for opn fx type IIIA, IIIB, or IIIC w/ routine healing, subsq enc for clsd fx w/ delayed healing, subsq enc for opn fx type I or II w/ delayed healing, subsq enc for opn fx type I or II w/ delayed healing, seq]

S52.60[1,2,9][D,E,F,G,H,J,S] Unsp fx of lwr end of [rt, lt, unsp] ulna, [subsq enc for clsd fx w/ routine healing, subsq enc for opn fx type I or II w/ routine healing, subsq enc for opn fx type IIIA, IIIB, or IIIC w/ routine healing, subsq enc for clsd fx w/ delayed healing, subsq enc for opn fx type I or II w/ delayed healing, subsq enc for opn fx type I or II w/ delayed healing, seq]

S52.61[1,2,3][D,E,F,G,H,J,S] Disp fx of [rt, lt, unsp] ulna styloid process, [subsq enc for clsd fx w/ routine healing, subsq enc for opn fx type I or II w/ routine healing, subsq enc for opn fx type IIIA, IIIB, or IIIC w/ routine healing, subsq enc for clsd fx w/ delayed healing, subsq enc for opn fx type I or II w/ delayed healing, subsq enc for opn fx type I or II w/ delayed healing, seq]

S52.61[4,5,6][D,E,F,G,H,J,S] Nondisp fx of [rt, lt, unsp] ulna styloid process, [subsq enc for clsd fx w/ routine healing, subsq enc for opn fx type I or II w/ routine healing, subsq enc for opn fx type IIIA, IIIB, or IIIC w/ routine healing, subsq enc for clsd fx w/ delayed healing, subsq enc for opn fx type I or II w/ delayed healing, subsq enc for opn fx type I or II w/ delayed healing, seq]

S52.62[1,2,9][D,G,S] Torus fx of lwr end of [rt, lt, unsp] ulna, [subsq enc for fx w/ routine healing, subsq enc for fx w/ delayed healing, seq]

S52.69[1,2,9][D,E,F,G,H,J,S] Oth fx of lwr end of [rt, lt, unsp] ulna, [subsq enc for clsd fx w/ routine healing, subsq enc for opn fx type I or II w/ routine healing, subsq enc for opn fx type IIIA, IIIB, or IIIC w/ routine healing, subsq enc for clsd fx w/ delayed healing, subsq enc for opn fx type I or II w/ delayed healing, subsq enc for opn fx type I or II w/ delayed healing, seq]

S52.9[0,1,2]X[D,E,F,G,H,J,S] Unspecified fx of [unsp, rt, lt] forearm, [subsq enc for clsd fx w/ routine healing, subsq enc for opn fx type I or II w/ routine healing, subsq enc for opn fx type IIIA, IIIB, or IIIC w/ routine healing, subsq enc for clsd fx w/ delayed healing, subsq enc for opn fx type I or II w/ delayed healing, subsq enc for opn fx type I or II w/ delayed healing, seq]

S58.0[1,2][1,2,9]S [Complete, Partial] traum amp at elbow lvl, [rt, lt, unsp] arm, seq

S58.1[1,2][1,2,9]S [Complete, Partial] traum amp at lvl between elbow and wrist, [rt, lt, unsp] arm, seq

S58.9[1,2][1,2,9]S [Complete, Partial] traum amp of [rt, lt, unsp] forearm, lvl unsp, seq

S59.00[1,2,9][D,G,S] Unsp physeal fx of lwr end of ulna, [rt, lt, unsp] arm, [subsq enc for fx w/ routine healing, subsq enc for fx w/ delayed healing, seq]

S59.01[1,2,9][D,G,S] Salter-Harris Type I physeal fx of lwr end of ulna, [rt, lt, unsp] arm, [subsq enc for fx w/ routine healing, subsq enc for fx w/ delayed healing, seq]

S59.02[1,2,9][D,G,S] Salter-Harris Type II physeal fx of lwr end of ulna, [rt, lt, unsp] arm, [subsq enc for fx w/ routine healing, subsq enc for fx w/ delayed healing, seq]

S59.03[1,2,9][D,G,S] Salter-Harris Type III physeal fx of lwr end of ulna, [rt, lt, unsp] arm, [subsq enc for fx w/ routine healing, subsq enc for fx w/ delayed healing, seq]

S59.04[1,2,9][D,G,S] Salter-Harris Type IV physeal fx of lwr end of ulna, [rt, lt, unsp] arm, [subsq enc for fx w/ routine healing, subsq enc for fx w/ delayed healing, seq]

S59.09[1,2,9][D,G,S] Oth physeal fx of lwr end of ulna, [rt, lt, unsp] arm, [subsq enc for fx w/ routine healing, subsq enc for fx w/ delayed healing, seq]

S59.10[1,2,9][D,G,S] Unsp physeal fx of upr end of radius, [rt, lt, unsp] arm, [subsq enc for fx w/ routine healing, subsq enc for fx w/ delayed healing, seq]

S59.11[1,2,9][D,G,S] Salter-Harris Type I physeal fx of upr end of radius, [rt, lt, unsp] arm, [subsq enc for fx w/ routine healing, subsq enc for fx w/ delayed healing, seq]

S59.12[1,2,9][D,G,S] Salter-Harris Type II physeal fx of upr end of radius, [rt, lt, unsp] arm, [subsq enc for fx w/ routine healing, subsq enc for fx w/ delayed healing, seq]

S59.13[1,2,9][D,G,S] Salter-Harris Type III physeal fx of upr end of radius, [rt, lt, unsp] arm, [subsq enc for fx w/ routine healing, subsq enc for fx w/ delayed healing, seq]

S59.14[1,2,9][D,G,S] Salter-Harris Type IV physeal fx of upr end of radius, [rt, lt, unsp] arm, [subsq enc for fx w/ routine healing, subsq enc for fx w/ delayed healing, seq]

S59.19[1,2,9][D,G,S] Oth physeal fx of upr end of radius, [rt, lt, unsp] arm, [subsq enc for fx w/ routine healing, subsq enc for fx w/ delayed healing, seq]

S59.20[1,2,9][D,G,S] Unsp physeal fx of lwr end of radius, [rt, lt, unsp] arm, [subsq enc for fx w/ routine healing, subsq enc for fx w/ delayed healing, seq]

S59.21[1,2,9][D,G,S] Salter-Harris Type I physeal fx of lwr end of radius, [rt, lt, unsp] arm, [subsq enc for fx w/ routine healing, subsq enc for fx w/ delayed healing, seq]

S59.22[1,2,9][D,G,S] Salter-Harris Type II physeal fx of lwr end of radius, [rt, lt, unsp] arm, [subsq enc for fx w/ routine healing, subsq enc for fx w/ delayed healing, seq]

S59.23[1,2,9][D,G,S] Salter-Harris Type III physeal fx of lwr end of radius, [rt, lt, unsp] arm, [subsq enc for fx w/ routine healing, subsq enc for fx w/ delayed healing, seq]

S59.24[1,2,9][D,G,S] Salter-Harris Type IV physeal fx of lwr end of radius, [rt, lt, unsp] arm, [subsq enc for fx w/ routine healing, subsq enc for fx w/ delayed healing, seq]

S59.29[1,2,9][D,G,S] Oth physeal fx of lwr end of radius, [rt, lt, unsp] arm, [subsq enc for fx w/ routine healing, subsq enc for fx w/ delayed healing, seq]

S62.00[1,2,9][D,G,S] Unsp fx of navicular (scaphoid) bone of [rt, lt, unsp] wrist, [subsq enc for fx w/ routine healing, subsq enc for fx w/ delayed healing, seq]

S62.01[1,2,3][D,G,S] Disp fx of distal pole of navicular (scaphoid) bone of [rt, lt, unsp] wrist, [subsq enc for fx w/ routine healing, subsq enc for fx w/ delayed healing, seq]

S62.01[4,5,6][D,G,S] Nondisp fx of distal pole of navicular (scaphoid) bone of [rt, lt, unsp] wrist, [subsq enc for fx w/ routine healing, subsq enc for fx w/ delayed healing, seq]

S62.02[1,2,3][D,G,S] Disp fx of mid 3rd of navicular (scaphoid) bone of [rt, lt, unsp] wrist, [subsq enc for fx w/ routine healing, subsq enc for fx w/ delayed healing, seq]

S62.02[4,5,6][D,G,S] Nondisp fx of mid 3rd of navicular (scaphoid) bone of [rt, lt, unsp] wrist, [subsq enc for fx w/ routine healing, subsq enc for fx w/ delayed healing, seq]

S62.03[1,2,3][D,G,S] Disp fx of proximal 3rd of navicular (scaphoid) bone of [rt, lt, unsp] wrist, [subsq enc for fx w/ routine healing, subsq enc for fx w/ delayed healing, seq]

S62.03[4,5,6][D,G,S] Nondisp fx of proximal 3rd of navicular (scaphoid) bone of [rt, lt, unsp] wrist, [subsq enc for fx w/ routine healing, subsq enc for fx w/ delayed healing, seq]

S62.10[1,2,9][D,G,S] Fx of unsp carpal bone, [rt, lt, unsp] wrist, [subsq enc for fx w/ routine healing, subsq enc for fx w/ delayed healing, seq]

S62.11[1,2,3][D,G,S] Disp fx of triquetrum (cuneiform) bone of [rt, lt, unsp] wrist, [subsq enc for fx w/ routine healing, subsq enc for fx w/ delayed healing, seq]

S62.11[4,5,6][D,G,S] Nondisp fx of triquetrum (cuneiform) bone of [rt, lt, unsp] wrist, [subsq enc for fx w/ routine healing, subsq enc for fx w/ delayed healing, seq]

S62.12[1,2,3][D,G,S] Disp fx of lunate (semilunar), [rt, lt, unsp] wrist, [subsq enc for fx w/ routine healing, subsq enc for fx w/ delayed healing, seq]

T Transfer DRG　　　SP Special Payment　　　* Code Range　　　6th and 7th Character of ZZ = No Device, No Qualifier ZX = No Device, Diagnostic

174　　　　　　　　　　　　　　　　　　MS-DRG Version 33.0　　　　　　　　　　　　　© 2015 Optum360, LLC

S62.12[4,5,6][D,G,S] Nondisp fx of lunate (semilunar), [rt, lt, unsp] wrist, [subsq enc for fx w/ routine healing, subsq enc for fx w/ delayed healing, seq]

S62.13[1,2,3][D,G,S] Disp fx of capitate (os magnum) bone, [rt, lt, unsp] wrist, [subsq enc for fx w/ routine healing, subsq enc for fx w/ delayed healing, seq]

S62.13[4,5,6][D,G,S] Nondisp fx of capitate (os magnum) bone, [rt, lt, unsp] wrist, [subsq enc for fx w/ routine healing, subsq enc for fx w/ delayed healing, seq]

S62.14[1,2,3][D,G,S] Disp fx of body of hamate (unciform) bone, [rt, lt, unsp] wrist, [subsq enc for fx w/ routine healing, subsq enc for fx w/ delayed healing, seq]

S62.14[4,5,6][D,G,S] Nondisp fx of body of hamate (unciform) bone, [rt, lt, unsp] wrist, [subsq enc for fx w/ routine healing, subsq enc for fx w/ delayed healing, seq]

S62.15[1,2,3][D,G,S] Disp fx of hook process of hamate (unciform) bone, [rt, lt, unsp] wrist, [subsq enc for fx w/ routine healing, subsq enc for fx w/ delayed healing, seq]

S62.15[4,5,6][D,G,S] Nondisp fx of hook process of hamate (unciform) bone, [rt, lt, unsp] wrist, [subsq enc for fx w/ routine healing, subsq enc for fx w/ delayed healing, seq]

S62.16[1,2,3][D,G,S] Disp fx of pisiform, [rt, lt, unsp] wrist, [subsq enc for fx w/ routine healing, subsq enc for fx w/ delayed healing, seq]

S62.16[4,5,6][D,G,S] Nondisp fx of pisiform, [rt, lt, unsp] wrist, [subsq enc for fx w/ routine healing, subsq enc for fx w/ delayed healing, seq]

S62.17[1,2,3][D,G,S] Disp fx of trapezium (lgr multangular), [rt, lt, unsp] wrist, [subsq enc for fx w/ routine healing, subsq enc for fx w/ delayed healing, seq]

S62.17[4,5,6][D,G,S] Nondisp fx of trapezium (lgr multangular), [rt, lt, unsp] wrist, [subsq enc for fx w/ routine healing, subsq enc for fx w/ delayed healing, seq]

S62.18[1,2,3][D,G,S] Disp fx of trapezoid (smer multangular), [rt, lt, unsp] wrist, [subsq enc for fx w/ routine healing, subsq enc for fx w/ delayed healing, seq]

S62.18[4,5,6][D,G,S] Nondisp fx of trapezoid (smer multangular), [rt, lt, unsp] wrist, [subsq enc for fx w/ routine healing, subsq enc for fx w/ delayed healing, seq]

S62.20[1,2,9][D,G,S] Unsp fx of 1st metacarpal bone, [rt, lt, unsp] hand, [subsq enc for fx w/ routine healing, subsq enc for fx w/ delayed healing, seq]

S62.21[1,2,3][D,G,S] Bennett's fx, [rt, lt, unsp] hand, [subsq enc for fx w/ routine healing, subsq enc for fx w/ delayed healing, seq]

S62.22[1,2,3][D,G,S] Disp Rolando's fx, [rt, lt, unsp] hand, [subsq enc for fx w/ routine healing, subsq enc for fx w/ delayed healing, seq]

S62.22[4,5,6][D,G,S] Nondisp Rolando's fx, [rt, lt, unsp] hand, [subsq enc for fx w/ routine healing, subsq enc for fx w/ delayed healing, seq]

S62.23[1,2,3][D,G,S] Oth disp fx of base of 1st metacarpal bone, [rt, lt, unsp] hand, [subsq enc for fx w/ routine healing, subsq enc for fx w/ delayed healing, seq]

S62.23[4,5,6][D,G,S] Oth nondisp fx of base of 1st metacarpal bone, [rt, lt, unsp] hand, [subsq enc for fx w/ routine healing, subsq enc for fx w/ delayed healing, seq]

S62.24[1,2,3][D,G,S] Disp fx of shaft of 1st metacarpal bone, [rt, lt, unsp] hand, [subsq enc for fx w/ routine healing, subsq enc for fx w/ delayed healing, seq]

S62.24[4,5,6][D,G,S] Nondisp fx of shaft of 1st metacarpal bone, [rt, lt, unsp] hand, [subsq enc for fx w/ routine healing, subsq enc for fx w/ delayed healing, seq]

S62.25[1,2,3][D,G,S] Disp fx of neck of 1st metacarpal bone, [rt, lt, unsp] hand, [subsq enc for fx w/ routine healing, subsq enc for fx w/ delayed healing, seq]

S62.25[4,5,6][D,G,S] Nondisp fx of neck of 1st metacarpal bone, [rt, lt, unsp] hand, [subsq enc for fx w/ routine healing, subsq enc for fx w/ delayed healing, seq]

S62.29[1,2,9][D,G,S] Oth fx of 1st metacarpal bone, [rt, lt, unsp] hand, [subsq enc for fx w/ routine healing, subsq enc for fx w/ delayed healing, seq]

S62.30[0,1][D,G,S] Unsp fx of 2nd metacarpal bone, [rt, lt] hand, [subsq enc for fx w/ routine healing, subsq enc for fx w/ delayed healing, seq]

S62.30[2,3][D,G,S] Unsp fx of 3rd metacarpal bone, [rt, lt] hand, [subsq enc for fx w/ routine healing, subsq enc for fx w/ delayed healing, seq]

S62.30[4,5][D,G,S] Unsp fx of 4th metacarpal bone, [rt, lt] hand, [subsq enc for fx w/ routine healing, subsq enc for fx w/ delayed healing, seq]

S62.30[6,7][D,G,S] Unsp fx of 5th metacarpal bone, [rt, lt] hand, [subsq enc for fx w/ routine healing, subsq enc for fx w/ delayed healing, seq]

S62.30[8,9][D,G,S] Unsp fx of [oth, unsp] metacarpal bone, [subsq enc for fx w/ routine healing, subsq enc for fx w/ delayed healing, seq]

S62.31[0,1][D,G,S] Disp fx of base of 2nd metacarpal bone, [rt, lt] hand, [subsq enc for fx w/ routine healing, subsq enc for fx w/ delayed healing, seq]

S62.31[2,3][D,G,S] Disp fx of base of 3rd metacarpal bone, [rt, lt] hand, [subsq enc for fx w/ routine healing, subsq enc for fx w/ delayed healing, seq]

S62.31[4,5][D,G,S] Disp fx of base of 4th metacarpal bone, [rt, lt] hand, [subsq enc for fx w/ routine healing, subsq enc for fx w/ delayed healing, seq]

S62.31[6,7][D,G,S] Disp fx of base of 5th metacarpal bone, [rt, lt] hand, [subsq enc for fx w/ routine healing, subsq enc for fx w/ delayed healing, seq]

S62.31[8,9][D,G,S] Disp fx of base of [oth, unsp] metacarpal bone, [subsq enc for fx w/ routine healing, subsq enc for fx w/ delayed healing, seq]

S62.32[0,1][D,G,S] Disp fx of shaft of 2nd metacarpal bone, [rt, lt] hand, [subsq enc for fx w/ routine healing, subsq enc for fx w/ delayed healing, seq]

S62.32[2,3][D,G,S] Disp fx of shaft of 3rd metacarpal bone, [rt, lt] hand, [subsq enc for fx w/ routine healing, subsq enc for fx w/ delayed healing, seq]

S62.32[4,5][D,G,S] Disp fx of shaft of 4th metacarpal bone, [rt, lt] hand, [subsq enc for fx w/ routine healing, subsq enc for fx w/ delayed healing, seq]

S62.32[6,7][D,G,S] Disp fx of shaft of 5th metacarpal bone, [rt, lt] hand, [subsq enc for fx w/ routine healing, subsq enc for fx w/ delayed healing, seq]

S62.32[8,9][D,G,S] Disp fx of shaft of [oth, unsp] metacarpal bone, [subsq enc for fx w/ routine healing, subsq enc for fx w/ delayed healing, seq]

S62.33[0,1][D,G,S] Disp fx of neck of 2nd metacarpal bone, [rt, lt] hand, [subsq enc for fx w/ routine healing, subsq enc for fx w/ delayed healing, seq]

S62.33[2,3][D,G,S] Disp fx of neck of 3rd metacarpal bone, [rt, lt] hand, [subsq enc for fx w/ routine healing, subsq enc for fx w/ delayed healing, seq]

S62.33[4,5][D,G,S] Disp fx of neck of 4th metacarpal bone, [rt, lt] hand, [subsq enc for fx w/ routine healing, subsq enc for fx w/ delayed healing, seq]

S62.33[6,7][D,G,S] Disp fx of neck of 5th metacarpal bone, [rt, lt] hand, [subsq enc for fx w/ routine healing, subsq enc for fx w/ delayed healing, seq]

S62.33[8,9][D,G,S] Disp fx of neck of [oth, unsp] metacarpal bone, [subsq enc for fx w/ routine healing, subsq enc for fx w/ delayed healing, seq]

S62.34[0,1][D,G,S] Nondisp fx of base of 2nd metacarpal bone, [rt, lt] hand, [subsq enc for fx w/ routine healing, subsq enc for fx w/ delayed healing, seq]

S62.34[2,3][D,G,S] Nondisp fx of base of 3rd metacarpal bone, [rt, lt] hand, [subsq enc for fx w/ routine healing, subsq enc for fx w/ delayed healing, seq]

S62.34[4,5][D,G,S] Nondisp fx of base of 4th metacarpal bone, [rt, lt] hand, [subsq enc for fx w/ routine healing, subsq enc for fx w/ delayed healing, seq]

S62.34[6,7][D,G,S] Nondisp fx of base of 5th metacarpal bone, [rt, lt] hand, [subsq enc for fx w/ routine healing, subsq enc for fx w/ delayed healing, seq]

S62.34[8,9][D,G,S] Nondisp fx of base of [oth, unsp] metacarpal bone, [subsq enc for fx w/ routine healing, subsq enc for fx w/ delayed healing, seq]

S62.35[0,1][D,G,S] Nondisp fx of shaft of 2nd metacarpal bone, [rt, lt] hand, [subsq enc for fx w/ routine healing, subsq enc for fx w/ delayed healing, seq]

S62.35[2,3][D,G,S] Nondisp fx of shaft of 3rd metacarpal bone, [rt, lt] hand, [subsq enc for fx w/ routine healing, subsq enc for fx w/ delayed healing, seq]

S62.35[4,5][D,G,S] Nondisp fx of shaft of 4th metacarpal bone, [rt, lt] hand, [subsq enc for fx w/ routine healing, subsq enc for fx w/ delayed healing, seq]

S62.35[6,7][D,G,S] Nondisp fx of shaft of 5th metacarpal bone, [rt, lt] hand, [subsq enc for fx w/ routine healing, subsq enc for fx w/ delayed healing, seq]

S62.35[8,9][D,G,S] Nondisp fx of shaft of [oth, unsp] metacarpal bone, [subsq enc for fx w/ routine healing, subsq enc for fx w/ delayed healing, seq]

S62.36[0,1][D,G,S] Nondisp fx of neck of 2nd metacarpal bone, [rt, lt] hand, [subsq enc for fx w/ routine healing, subsq enc for fx w/ delayed healing, seq]

S62.36[2,3][D,G,S] Nondisp fx of neck of 3rd metacarpal bone, [rt, lt] hand, [subsq enc for fx w/ routine healing, subsq enc for fx w/ delayed healing, seq]

Surgical   **Medical**   **CC Indicator**   **MCC Indicator**   **Procedure Proxy**   PDxMCC **PDx acts as own MCC**   PDxCC **PDx acts as own CC**

S62.36[4,5][D,G,S] Nondisp fx of neck of 4th metacarpal bone, [rt, lt] hand, [subsq enc for fx w/ routine healing, subsq enc for fx w/ delayed healing, seq]

S62.36[6,7][D,G,S] Nondisp fx of neck of 5th metacarpal bone, [rt, lt] hand, [subsq enc for fx w/ routine healing, subsq enc for fx w/ delayed healing, seq]

S62.36[8,9][D,G,S] Nondisp fx of neck of [oth, unsp] metacarpal bone, [subsq enc for fx w/ routine healing, subsq enc for fx w/ delayed healing, seq]

S62.39[0,1][D,G,S] Oth fx of 2nd metacarpal bone, [rt, lt] hand, [subsq enc for fx w/ routine healing, subsq enc for fx w/ delayed healing, seq]

S62.39[2,3][D,G,S] Oth fx of 3rd metacarpal bone, [rt, lt] hand, [subsq enc for fx w/ routine healing, subsq enc for fx w/ delayed healing, seq]

S62.39[4,5][D,G,S] Oth fx of of 4th metacarpal bone, [rt, lt] hand, [subsq enc for fx w/ routine healing, subsq enc for fx w/ delayed healing, seq]

S62.39[6,7][D,G,S] Oth fx of of 5th metacarpal bone, [rt, lt] hand, [subsq enc for fx w/ routine healing, subsq enc for fx w/ delayed healing, seq]

S62.39[8,9][D,G,S] Oth fx of [oth, unsp] metacarpal bone, [subsq enc for fx w/ routine healing, subsq enc for fx w/ delayed healing, seq]

S62.50[1,2,9][D,G,S] Fx of unsp phalanx of [rt, lt, unsp] thumb, [subsq enc for fx w/ routine healing, subsq enc for fx w/ delayed healing, seq]

S62.51[1,2,3][D,G,S] Disp fx of proximal phalanx of [rt, lt, unsp] thumb, [subsq enc for fx w/ routine healing, subsq enc for fx w/ delayed healing, seq]

S62.51[4,5,6][D,G,S] Nondisp fx of proximal phalanx of [rt, lt, unsp] thumb, [subsq enc for fx w/ routine healing, subsq enc for fx w/ delayed healing, seq]

S62.52[1,2,3][D,G,S] Disp fx of distal phalanx of [rt, lt, unsp] thumb, [subsq enc for fx w/ routine healing, subsq enc for fx w/ delayed healing, seq]

S62.52[4,5,6][D,G,S] Nondisp fx of distal phalanx of [rt, lt, unsp] thumb, [subsq enc for fx w/ routine healing, subsq enc for fx w/ delayed healing, seq]

S62.60[0,1][D,G,S] Fx of unsp phalanx of [rt, lt] index finger, [subsq enc for fx w/ routine healing, subsq enc for fx w/ delayed healing, seq]

S62.60[2,3][D,G,S] Fx of unsp phalanx of [rt, lt] mid finger, [subsq enc for fx w/ routine healing, subsq enc for fx w/ delayed healing, seq]

S62.60[4,5][D,G,S] Fx of unsp phalanx of [rt, lt] ring finger, [subsq enc for fx w/ routine healing, subsq enc for fx w/ delayed healing, seq]

S62.60[6,7][D,G,S] Fx of unsp phalanx of [rt, lt] little finger, [subsq enc for fx w/ routine healing, subsq enc for fx w/ delayed healing, seq]

S62.60[8,9][D,G,S] Fx of unsp phalanx of [oth, unsp] finger, [subsq enc for fx w/ routine healing, subsq enc for fx w/ delayed healing, seq]

S62.61[0,1][D,G,S] Disp fx of proximal phalanx of [rt, lt] index finger, [subsq enc for fx w/ routine healing, subsq enc for fx w/ delayed healing, seq]

S62.61[2,3][D,G,S] Disp fx of proximal phalanx of [rt, lt] mid finger, [subsq enc for fx w/ routine healing, subsq enc for fx w/ delayed healing, seq]

S62.61[4,5][D,G,S] Disp fx of proximal phalanx of [rt, lt] ring finger, [subsq enc for fx w/ routine healing, subsq enc for fx w/ delayed healing, seq]

S62.61[6,7][D,G,S] Disp fx of proximal phalanx of [rt, lt] little finger, [subsq enc for fx w/ routine healing, subsq enc for fx w/ delayed healing, seq]

S62.61[8,9][D,G,S] Disp fx of proximal phalanx of [oth, unsp] finger, [subsq enc for fx w/ routine healing, subsq enc for fx w/ delayed healing, seq]

S62.62[0,1][D,G,S] Disp fx of med phalanx of [rt, lt] index finger, [subsq enc for fx w/ routine healing, subsq enc for fx w/ delayed healing, seq]

S62.62[2,3][D,G,S] Disp fx of med phalanx of [rt, lt] mid finger, [subsq enc for fx w/ routine healing, subsq enc for fx w/ delayed healing, seq]

S62.62[4,5][D,G,S] Disp fx of med phalanx of [rt, lt] ring finger, [subsq enc for fx w/ routine healing, subsq enc for fx w/ delayed healing, seq]

S62.62[6,7][D,G,S] Disp fx of med phalanx of [rt, lt] little finger, [subsq enc for fx w/ routine healing, subsq enc for fx w/ delayed healing, seq]

S62.62[8,9][D,G,S] Disp fx of med phalanx of [oth, unsp] finger, [subsq enc for fx w/ routine healing, subsq enc for fx w/ delayed healing, seq]

S62.63[0,1][D,G,S] Disp fx of distal phalanx of [rt, lt] index finger, [subsq enc for fx w/ routine healing, subsq enc for fx w/ delayed healing, seq]

S62.63[2,3][D,G,S] Disp fx of distal phalanx of [rt, lt] mid finger, [subsq enc for fx w/ routine healing, subsq enc for fx w/ delayed healing, seq]

S62.63[4,5][D,G,S] Disp fx of distal phalanx of [rt, lt] ring finger, [subsq enc for fx w/ routine healing, subsq enc for fx w/ delayed healing, seq]

S62.63[6,7][D,G,S] Disp fx of distal phalanx of [rt, lt] little finger, [subsq enc for fx w/ routine healing, subsq enc for fx w/ delayed healing, seq]

S62.63[8,9][D,G,S] Disp fx of distal phalanx of [oth, unsp] finger, [subsq enc for fx w/ routine healing, subsq enc for fx w/ delayed healing, seq]

S62.64[0,1][D,G,S] Nondisp fx of proximal phalanx of [rt, lt] index finger, [subsq enc for fx w/ routine healing, subsq enc for fx w/ delayed healing, seq]

S62.64[2,3][D,G,S] Nondisp fx of proximal phalanx of [rt, lt] mid finger, [subsq enc for fx w/ routine healing, subsq enc for fx w/ delayed healing, seq]

S62.64[4,5][D,G,S] Nondisp fx of proximal phalanx of [rt, lt] ring finger, [subsq enc for fx w/ routine healing, subsq enc for fx w/ delayed healing, seq]

S62.64[6,7][D,G,S] Nondisp fx of proximal phalanx of [rt, lt] little finger, [subsq enc for fx w/ routine healing, subsq enc for fx w/ delayed healing, seq]

S62.64[8,9][D,G,S] Nondisp fx of proximal phalanx of [oth, unsp] finger, [subsq enc for fx w/ routine healing, subsq enc for fx w/ delayed healing, seq]

S62.65[0,1][D,G,S] Nondisp fx of med phalanx of [rt, lt] index finger, [subsq enc for fx w/ routine healing, subsq enc for fx w/ delayed healing, seq]

S62.65[2,3][D,G,S] Nondisp fx of med phalanx of [rt, lt] mid finger, [subsq enc for fx w/ routine healing, subsq enc for fx w/ delayed healing, seq]

S62.65[4,5][D,G,S] Nondisp fx of med phalanx of [rt, lt] ring finger, [subsq enc for fx w/ routine healing, subsq enc for fx w/ delayed healing, seq]

S62.65[6,7][D,G,S] Nondisp fx of med phalanx of [rt, lt] little finger, [subsq enc for fx w/ routine healing, subsq enc for fx w/ delayed healing, seq]

S62.65[8,9][D,G,S] Nondisp fx of med phalanx of [oth, unsp] finger, [subsq enc for fx w/ routine healing, subsq enc for fx w/ delayed healing, seq]

S62.66[0,1][D,G,S] Nondisp fx of distal phalanx of [rt, lt] index finger, [subsq enc for fx w/ routine healing, subsq enc for fx w/ delayed healing, seq]

S62.66[2,3][D,G,S] Nondisp fx of distal phalanx of [rt, lt] mid finger, [subsq enc for fx w/ routine healing, subsq enc for fx w/ delayed healing, seq]

S62.66[4,5][D,G,S] Nondisp fx of distal phalanx of [rt, lt] ring finger, [subsq enc for fx w/ routine healing, subsq enc for fx w/ delayed healing, seq]

S62.66[6,7][D,G,S] Nondisp fx of distal phalanx of [rt, lt] little finger, [subsq enc for fx w/ routine healing, subsq enc for fx w/ delayed healing, seq]

S62.66[8,9][D,G,S] Nondisp fx of distal phalanx of [oth, unsp] finger, [subsq enc for fx w/ routine healing, subsq enc for fx w/ delayed healing, seq]

S62.9[0,1,2]X[D,G,S] Unsp fx of [unsp, rt, lt] wrist and hand, [subsq enc for fx w/ routine healing, subsq enc for fx w/ delayed healing, seq]

S68.0[1,2][1,2,9]S [Complete, Partial] traum metacarpophalangeal amp of [rt, lt, unsp] thumb, seq

S68.11[0,1,2,3,4,5,6,7,8,9]SComplete traum metacarpophalangeal amp of [rt index, lt index, rt mid, lt mid, rt ring, lt ring, rt little, lt little, oth, unsp] finger, seq

S68.12[0,1,2,3,4,5,6,7,8,9]SPartial traum metacarpophalangeal amp of [rt index, lt index, rt mid, lt mid, rt ring, lt ring, rt little, lt little, oth, unsp] finger, seq

S68.4[1,2][1,2,9]S [Complete, Partial] traum amp of [rt, lt, unsp] hand at wrist lvl, seq

S68.5[1,2][1,2,9]S [Complete, Partial] traum transphalangeal amp of [rt, lt, unsp] thumb, seq

S68.61[0,1,2,3,4,5,6,7,8,9]SComplete traum transphalangeal amp of [rt index, lt index, rt mid, lt mid, rt ring, lt ring, rt little, lt little, oth, unsp] finger, seq

S68.62[0,1,2,3,4,5,6,7,8,9]S Partial traum transphalangeal amp of [rt index, lt index, rt mid, lt mid, rt ring, lt ring, rt little, lt little, oth, unsp] finger, seq

S68.7[1,2][1,2,9]S [Complete, Partial] traum transmetacarpal amp of [rt, lt, unsp] hand, seq

S72.00[1,2,9][D,E,F,G,H,J,S] Fx of unsp part of neck of [rt, lt, unsp] femur, [subsq enc for clsd fx w/ routine healing, subsq enc for opn fx type I or II w/ routine healing, subsq enc for opn fx type IIIA, IIIB, or IIIC w/ routine healing, subsq enc for clsd fx w/ delayed healing, subsq enc for opn fx type I or II w/ delayed healing, subsq enc for opn fx type IIIA, IIIB, or IIIC w/ delayed healing, seq]

S72.01[1,2,9][D,E,F,G,H,J,S] Unsp intracapsular fx of [rt, lt, unsp] femur, [subsq enc for clsd fx w/ routine healing, subsq enc for opn fx type I or II w/ routine healing, subsq enc for opn fx type IIIA, IIIB, or IIIC w/ routine healing, subsq enc for clsd fx w/ delayed healing, subsq enc for opn fx type I or II w/ delayed healing, subsq enc for opn fx type IIIA, IIIB, or IIIC w/ delayed healing, seq]

| T | Transfer DRG | SP | Special Payment | * Code Range | 6th and 7th Character of ZZ = No Device, No Qualifier ZX = No Device, Diagnostic |

S72.02[1,2,3][D,E,F,G,H,J,S] Disp fx of epiphysis (separation) (upr) of [rt, lt, unsp] femur, [subsq enc for clsd fx w/ routine healing, subsq enc for opn fx type I or II w/ routine healing, subsq enc for opn fx type IIIA, IIIB, or IIIC w/ routine healing, subsq enc for clsd fx w/ delayed healing, subsq enc for opn fx type I or II w/ delayed healing, subsq enc for opn fx type IIIA, IIIB, or IIIC w/ delayed healing, seq]

S72.02[4,5,6][D,E,F,G,H,J,S] Nondisp fx of epiphysis (separation) (upr) of [rt, lt, unsp] femur, [subsq enc for clsd fx w/ routine healing, subsq enc for opn fx type I or II w/ routine healing, subsq enc for opn fx type IIIA, IIIB, or IIIC w/ routine healing, subsq enc for clsd fx w/ delayed healing, subsq enc for opn fx type I or II w/ delayed healing, subsq enc for opn fx type IIIA, IIIB, or IIIC w/ delayed healing, seq]

S72.03[1,2,3][D,E,F,G,H,J,S] Disp midcervical fx of [rt, lt, unsp] femur, [subsq enc for clsd fx w/ routine healing, subsq enc for opn fx type I or II w/ routine healing, subsq enc for opn fx type IIIA, IIIB, or IIIC w/ routine healing, subsq enc for clsd fx w/ delayed healing, subsq enc for opn fx type I or II w/ delayed healing, subsq enc for opn fx type IIIA, IIIB, or IIIC w/ delayed healing, seq]

S72.03[4,5,6][D,E,F,G,H,J,S] Nondisp midcervical fx of [rt, lt, unsp] femur, [subsq enc for clsd fx w/ routine healing, subsq enc for opn fx type I or II w/ routine healing, subsq enc for opn fx type IIIA, IIIB, or IIIC w/ routine healing, subsq enc for clsd fx w/ delayed healing, subsq enc for opn fx type I or II w/ delayed healing, subsq enc for opn fx type IIIA, IIIB, or IIIC w/ delayed healing, seq]

S72.04[1,2,3][D,E,F,G,H,J,S] Disp fx of base of neck of [rt, lt, unsp] femur, [subsq enc for clsd fx w/ routine healing, subsq enc for opn fx type I or II w/ routine healing, subsq enc for opn fx type IIIA, IIIB, or IIIC w/ routine healing, subsq enc for clsd fx w/ delayed healing, subsq enc for opn fx type I or II w/ delayed healing, subsq enc for opn fx type IIIA, IIIB, or IIIC w/ delayed healing, seq]

S72.04[4,5,6][D,E,F,G,H,J,S] Nondisp fx of base of neck of [rt, lt, unsp] femur, [subsq enc for clsd fx w/ routine healing, subsq enc for opn fx type I or II w/ routine healing, subsq enc for opn fx type IIIA, IIIB, or IIIC w/ routine healing, subsq enc for clsd fx w/ delayed healing, subsq enc for opn fx type I or II w/ delayed healing, subsq enc for opn fx type IIIA, IIIB, or IIIC w/ delayed healing, seq]

S72.05[1,2,9][D,E,F,G,H,J,S] Unsp fx of head of [rt, lt, unsp] femur, [subsq enc for clsd fx w/ routine healing, subsq enc for opn fx type I or II w/ routine healing, subsq enc for opn fx type IIIA, IIIB, or IIIC w/ routine healing, subsq enc for clsd fx w/ delayed healing, subsq enc for opn fx type I or II w/ delayed healing, subsq enc for opn fx type IIIA, IIIB, or IIIC w/ delayed healing, seq]

S72.06[1,2,3][D,E,F,G,H,J,S] Disp articular fx of head of [rt, lt, unsp] femur, [subsq enc for clsd fx w/ routine healing, subsq enc for opn fx type I or II w/ routine healing, subsq enc for opn fx type IIIA, IIIB, or IIIC w/ routine healing, subsq enc for clsd fx w/ delayed healing, subsq enc for opn fx type I or II w/ delayed healing, subsq enc for opn fx type IIIA, IIIB, or IIIC w/ delayed healing, seq]

S72.06[4,5,6][D,E,F,G,H,J,S] Nondisp articular fx of head of [rt, lt, unsp] femur, [subsq enc for clsd fx w/ routine healing, subsq enc for opn fx type I or II w/ routine healing, subsq enc for opn fx type IIIA, IIIB, or IIIC w/ routine healing, subsq enc for clsd fx w/ delayed healing, subsq enc for opn fx type I or II w/ delayed healing, subsq enc for opn fx type IIIA, IIIB, or IIIC w/ delayed healing, seq]

S72.09[1,2,9][D,E,F,G,H,J,S] Oth fx of head and neck of [rt, lt, unsp] femur, [subsq enc for clsd fx w/ routine healing, subsq enc for opn fx type I or II w/ routine healing, subsq enc for opn fx type IIIA, IIIB, or IIIC w/ routine healing, subsq enc for clsd fx w/ delayed healing, subsq enc for opn fx type I or II w/ delayed healing, subsq enc for opn fx type IIIA, IIIB, or IIIC w/ delayed healing, seq]

S72.10[1,2,9][D,E,F,G,H,J,S] Unsp trochanteric fx of [rt, lt, unsp] femur, [subsq enc for clsd fx w/ routine healing, subsq enc for opn fx type I or II w/ routine healing, subsq enc for opn fx type IIIA, IIIB, or IIIC w/ routine healing, subsq enc for clsd fx w/ delayed healing, subsq enc for opn fx type I or II w/ delayed healing, subsq enc for opn fx type IIIA, IIIB, or IIIC w/ delayed healing, seq]

S72.11[1,2,3][D,E,F,G,H,J,S] Disp fx of greater trochanter of [rt, lt, unsp] femur, [subsq enc for clsd fx w/ routine healing, subsq enc for opn fx type I or II w/ routine healing, subsq enc for opn fx type IIIA, IIIB, or IIIC w/ routine healing, subsq enc for clsd fx w/ delayed healing, subsq enc for opn fx type I or II w/ delayed healing, subsq enc for opn fx type IIIA, IIIB, or IIIC w/ delayed healing, seq]

S72.11[4,5,6][D,E,F,G,H,J,S] Nondisp fx of greater trochanter of [rt, lt, unsp] femur, [subsq enc for clsd fx w/ routine healing, subsq enc for opn fx type I or II w/ routine healing, subsq enc for opn fx type IIIA, IIIB, or IIIC w/ routine healing, subsq enc for clsd fx w/ delayed healing, subsq enc for opn fx type I or II w/ delayed healing, subsq enc for opn fx type IIIA, IIIB, or IIIC w/ delayed healing, seq]

S72.12[1,2,3][D,E,F,G,H,J,S] Disp fx of lesser trochanter of [rt, lt, unsp] femur, [subsq enc for clsd fx w/ routine healing, subsq enc for opn fx type I or II w/ routine healing, subsq enc for opn fx type IIIA, IIIB, or IIIC w/ routine healing, subsq enc for clsd fx w/ delayed healing, subsq enc for opn fx type I or II w/ delayed healing, subsq enc for opn fx type IIIA, IIIB, or IIIC w/ delayed healing, seq]

S72.12[4,5,6][D,E,F,G,H,J,S] Nondisp fx of lesser trochanter of [rt, lt, unsp] femur, [subsq enc for clsd fx w/ routine healing, subsq enc for opn fx type I or II w/ routine healing, subsq enc for opn fx type IIIA, IIIB, or IIIC w/ routine healing, subsq enc for clsd fx w/ delayed healing, subsq enc for opn fx type I or II w/ delayed healing, subsq enc for opn fx type IIIA, IIIB, or IIIC w/ delayed healing, seq]

S72.13[1,2,3][D,E,F,G,H,J,S] Disp apophyseal fx of [rt, lt, unsp] femur, [subsq enc for clsd fx w/ routine healing, subsq enc for opn fx type I or II w/ routine healing, subsq enc for opn fx type IIIA, IIIB, or IIIC w/ routine healing, subsq enc for clsd fx w/ delayed healing, subsq enc for opn fx type I or II w/ delayed healing, subsq enc for opn fx type IIIA, IIIB, or IIIC w/ delayed healing, seq]

S72.13[4,5,6][D,E,F,G,H,J,S] Nondisp apophyseal fx of [rt, lt, unsp] femur, [subsq enc for clsd fx w/ routine healing, subsq enc for opn fx type I or II w/ routine healing, subsq enc for opn fx type IIIA, IIIB, or IIIC w/ routine healing, subsq enc for clsd fx w/ delayed healing, subsq enc for opn fx type I or II w/ delayed healing, subsq enc for opn fx type IIIA, IIIB, or IIIC w/ delayed healing, seq]

S72.14[1,2,3][D,E,F,G,H,J,S] Disp intertrochanteric fx of [rt, lt, unsp] femur, [subsq enc for clsd fx w/ routine healing, subsq enc for opn fx type I or II w/ routine healing, subsq enc for opn fx type IIIA, IIIB, or IIIC w/ routine healing, subsq enc for clsd fx w/ delayed healing, subsq enc for opn fx type I or II w/ delayed healing, subsq enc for opn fx type IIIA, IIIB, or IIIC w/ delayed healing, seq]

S72.14[4,5,6][D,E,F,G,H,J,S] Nondisp intertrochanteric fx of [rt, lt, unsp] femur, [subsq enc for clsd fx w/ routine healing, subsq enc for opn fx type I or II w/ routine healing, subsq enc for opn fx type IIIA, IIIB, or IIIC w/ routine healing, subsq enc for clsd fx w/ delayed healing, subsq enc for opn fx type I or II w/ delayed healing, subsq enc for opn fx type IIIA, IIIB, or IIIC w/ delayed healing, seq]

S72.2[1,2,3]X[D,E,F,G,H,J,S] Disp subtrochanteric fx of [rt, lt, unsp] femur, [subsq enc for clsd fx w/ routine healing, subsq enc for opn fx type I or II w/ routine healing, subsq enc for opn fx type IIIA, IIIB, or IIIC w/ routine healing, subsq enc for clsd fx w/ delayed healing, subsq enc for opn fx type I or II w/ delayed healing, subsq enc for opn fx type IIIA, IIIB, or IIIC w/ delayed healing, seq]

S72.2[4,5,6]X[D,E,F,G,H,J,S] Nondisp subtrochanteric fx of [rt, lt, unsp] femur, [subsq enc for clsd fx w/ routine healing, subsq enc for opn fx type I or II w/ routine healing, subsq enc for opn fx type IIIA, IIIB, or IIIC w/ routine healing, subsq enc for clsd fx w/ delayed healing, subsq enc for opn fx type I or II w/ delayed healing, subsq enc for opn fx type IIIA, IIIB, or IIIC w/ delayed healing, seq]

S72.30[1,2,9][D,E,F,G,H,J,S] Unsp fx of shaft of [rt, lt, unsp] femur, [subsq enc for clsd fx w/ routine healing, subsq enc for opn fx type I or II w/ routine healing, subsq enc for opn fx type IIIA, IIIB, or IIIC w/ routine healing, subsq enc for clsd fx w/ delayed healing, subsq enc for opn fx type I or II w/ delayed healing, subsq enc for opn fx type IIIA, IIIB, or IIIC w/ delayed healing, seq]

S72.32[1,2,3][D,E,F,G,H,J,S] Disp transv fx of shaft of [rt, lt, unsp] femur, [subsq enc for clsd fx w/ routine healing, subsq enc for opn fx type I or II w/ routine healing, subsq enc for opn fx type IIIA, IIIB, or IIIC w/ routine healing, subsq enc for clsd fx w/ delayed healing, subsq enc for opn fx type I or II w/ delayed healing, subsq enc for opn fx type IIIA, IIIB, or IIIC w/ delayed healing, seq]

S72.32[4,5,6][D,E,F,G,H,J,S] Nondisp transv fx of shaft of [rt, lt, unsp] femur, [subsq enc for clsd fx w/ routine healing, subsq enc for opn fx type I or II w/ routine healing, subsq enc for opn fx type IIIA, IIIB, or IIIC w/ routine healing, subsq enc for clsd fx w/ delayed healing, subsq enc for opn fx type I or II w/ delayed healing, subsq enc for opn fx type IIIA, IIIB, or IIIC w/ delayed healing, seq]

S72.33[1,2,3][D,E,F,G,H,J,S] Disp oblique fx of shaft of [rt, lt, unsp] femur, [subsq enc for clsd fx w/ routine healing, subsq enc for opn fx type I or II w/ routine healing, subsq enc for opn fx type IIIA, IIIB, or IIIC w/ routine healing, subsq enc for clsd fx w/ delayed healing, subsq enc for opn fx type I or II w/ delayed healing, subsq enc for opn fx type IIIA, IIIB, or IIIC w/ delayed healing, seq]

S72.33[4,5,6][D,E,F,G,H,J,S] Nondisp oblique fx of shaft of [rt, lt, unsp] femur, [subsq enc for clsd fx w/ routine healing, subsq enc for opn fx type I or II w/ routine healing, subsq enc for opn fx type IIIA, IIIB, or IIIC w/ routine healing, subsq enc for clsd fx w/ delayed healing, subsq enc for opn fx type I or II w/ delayed healing, subsq enc for opn fx type IIIA, IIIB, or IIIC w/ delayed healing, seq]

S72.34[1,2,3][D,E,F,G,H,J,S] Disp spiral fx of shaft of [rt, lt, unsp] femur, [subsq enc for clsd fx w/ routine healing, subsq enc for opn fx type I or II w/ routine healing, subsq enc for opn fx type IIIA, IIIB, or IIIC w/ routine healing, subsq enc for clsd fx w/ delayed healing, subsq enc for opn fx type I or II w/ delayed healing, subsq enc for opn fx type IIIA, IIIB, or IIIC w/ delayed healing, seq]

S72.34[4,5,6][D,E,F,G,H,J,S] Nondisp spiral fx of shaft of [rt, lt, unsp] femur, [subsq enc for clsd fx w/ routine healing, subsq enc for opn fx type I or II w/ routine healing, subsq enc for opn fx type IIIA, IIIB, or IIIC w/ routine healing, subsq enc for clsd fx w/ delayed healing, subsq enc for opn fx type I or II w/ delayed healing, subsq enc for opn fx type IIIA, IIIB, or IIIC w/ delayed healing, seq]

S72.35[1,2,3][D,E,F,G,H,J,S] Disp comm fx of shaft of [rt, lt, unsp] femur, [subsq enc for clsd fx w/ routine healing, subsq enc for opn fx type I or II w/ routine healing, subsq enc for opn fx type IIIA, IIIB, or IIIC w/ routine healing, subsq enc for clsd fx w/ delayed healing, subsq enc for opn fx type I or II w/ delayed healing, subsq enc for opn fx type IIIA, IIIB, or IIIC w/ delayed healing, seq]

S72.35[4,5,6][D,E,F,G,H,J,S] Nondisp comm fx of shaft of [rt, lt, unsp] femur, [subsq enc for clsd fx w/ routine healing, subsq enc for opn fx type I or II w/ routine healing, subsq enc for opn fx type IIIA, IIIB, or IIIC w/ routine healing, subsq enc for clsd fx w/ delayed healing, subsq enc for opn fx type I or II w/ delayed healing, subsq enc for opn fx type IIIA, IIIB, or IIIC w/ delayed healing, seq]

S72.36[1,2,3][D,E,F,G,H,J,S] Disp seg fx of shaft of [rt, lt, unsp] femur, [subsq enc for clsd fx w/ routine healing, subsq enc for opn fx type I or II w/ routine healing, subsq enc for opn fx type IIIA, IIIB, or IIIC w/ routine healing, subsq enc for clsd fx w/ delayed healing, subsq enc for opn fx type I or II w/ delayed healing, subsq enc for opn fx type IIIA, IIIB, or IIIC w/ delayed healing, seq]

S72.36[4,5,6][D,E,F,G,H,J,S] Nondisp seg fx of shaft of [rt, lt, unsp] femur, [subsq enc for clsd fx w/ routine healing, subsq enc for opn fx type I or II w/ routine healing, subsq enc for opn fx type IIIA, IIIB, or IIIC w/ routine healing, subsq enc for clsd fx w/ delayed healing, subsq enc for opn fx type I or II w/ delayed healing, subsq enc for opn fx type IIIA, IIIB, or IIIC w/ delayed healing, seq]

S72.39[1,2,9][D,E,F,G,H,J,S] Oth fx of shaft of [rt, lt, unsp] femur, [subsq enc for clsd fx w/ routine healing, subsq enc for opn fx type I or II w/ routine healing, subsq enc for opn fx type IIIA, IIIB, or IIIC w/ routine healing, subsq enc for clsd fx w/ delayed healing, subsq enc for opn fx type I or II w/ delayed healing, subsq enc for opn fx type IIIA, IIIB, or IIIC w/ delayed healing, seq]

S72.40[1,2,9][D,E,F,G,H,J,S] Unsp fx of lwr end of [rt, lt, unsp] femur, [subsq enc for clsd fx w/ routine healing, subsq enc for opn fx type I or II w/ routine healing, subsq enc for opn fx type IIIA, IIIB, or IIIC w/ routine healing, subsq enc for clsd fx w/ delayed healing, subsq enc for opn fx type I or II w/ delayed healing, subsq enc for opn fx type IIIA, IIIB, or IIIC w/ delayed healing, seq]

S72.41[1,2,3][D,E,F,G,H,J,S] Disp unsp condyle fx of lwr end of [rt, lt, unsp] femur, [subsq enc for clsd fx w/ routine healing, subsq enc for opn fx type I or II w/ routine healing, subsq enc for opn fx type IIIA, IIIB, or IIIC w/ routine healing, subsq enc for clsd fx w/ delayed healing, subsq enc for opn fx type I or II w/ delayed healing, subsq enc for opn fx type IIIA, IIIB, or IIIC w/ delayed healing, seq]

S72.41[4,5,6][D,E,F,G,H,J,S] Nondisp unsp condyle fx of lwr end of [rt, lt, unsp] femur, [subsq enc for clsd fx w/ routine healing, subsq enc for opn fx type I or II w/ routine healing, subsq enc for opn fx type IIIA, IIIB, or IIIC w/ routine healing, subsq enc for clsd fx w/ delayed healing, subsq enc for opn fx type I or II w/ delayed healing, subsq enc for opn fx type IIIA, IIIB, or IIIC w/ delayed healing, seq]

S72.42[1,2,3][D,E,F,G,H,J,S] Disp fx of lat condyle of [rt, lt, unsp] femur, [subsq enc for clsd fx w/ routine healing, subsq enc for opn fx type I or II w/ routine healing, subsq enc for opn fx type IIIA, IIIB, or IIIC w/ routine healing, subsq enc for clsd fx w/ delayed healing, subsq enc for opn fx type I or II w/ delayed healing, subsq enc for opn fx type IIIA, IIIB, or IIIC w/ delayed healing, seq]

S72.42[4,5,6][D,E,F,G,H,J,S] Nondisp fx of lat condyle of [rt, lt, unsp] femur, [subsq enc for clsd fx w/ routine healing, subsq enc for opn fx type I or II w/ routine healing, subsq enc for opn fx type IIIA, IIIB, or IIIC w/ routine healing, subsq enc for clsd fx w/ delayed healing, subsq enc for opn fx type I or II w/ delayed healing, subsq enc for opn fx type IIIA, IIIB, or IIIC w/ delayed healing, seq]

S72.43[1,2,3][D,E,F,G,H,J,S] Disp fx of med condyle of [rt, lt, unsp] femur, [subsq enc for clsd fx w/ routine healing, subsq enc for opn fx type I or II w/ routine healing, subsq enc for opn fx type IIIA, IIIB, or IIIC w/ routine healing, subsq enc for clsd fx w/ delayed healing, subsq enc for opn fx type I or II w/ delayed healing, subsq enc for opn fx type IIIA, IIIB, or IIIC w/ delayed healing, seq]

S72.43[4,5,6][D,E,F,G,H,J,S] Nondisp fx of med condyle of [rt, lt, unsp] femur, [subsq enc for clsd fx w/ routine healing, subsq enc for opn fx type I or II w/ routine healing, subsq enc for opn fx type IIIA, IIIB, or IIIC w/ routine healing, subsq enc for clsd fx w/ delayed healing, subsq enc for opn fx type I or II w/ delayed healing, subsq enc for opn fx type IIIA, IIIB, or IIIC w/ delayed healing, seq]

S72.44[1,2,3][D,E,F,G,H,J,S] Disp fx of lwr epiphysis (separation) of [rt, lt, unsp] femur, [subsq enc for clsd fx w/ routine healing, subsq enc for opn fx type I or II w/ routine healing, subsq enc for opn fx type IIIA, IIIB, or IIIC w/ routine healing, subsq enc for clsd fx w/ delayed healing, subsq enc for opn fx type I or II w/ delayed healing, subsq enc for opn fx type I or II w/ delayed healing, seq]

S72.44[4,5,6][D,E,F,G,H,J,S] Nondisp fx of lwr epiphysis (separation) of [rt, lt, unsp] femur, [subsq enc for clsd fx w/ routine healing, subsq enc for opn fx type I or II w/ routine healing, subsq enc for opn fx type IIIA, IIIB, or IIIC w/ routine healing, subsq enc for clsd fx w/ delayed healing, subsq enc for opn fx type I or II w/ delayed healing, subsq enc for opn fx type I or II w/ delayed healing, seq]

S72.45[1,2,3][D,E,F,G,H,J,S] Disp supracondylar fx w/o intracondylar extension of lwr end of [rt, lt, unsp] femur, [subsq enc for clsd fx w/ routine healing, subsq enc for opn fx type I or II w/ routine healing, subsq enc for opn fx type IIIA, IIIB, or IIIC w/ routine healing, subsq enc for clsd fx w/ delayed healing, subsq enc for opn fx type I or II w/ delayed healing, subsq enc for opn fx type I or II w/ delayed healing, seq]

S72.45[4,5,6][D,E,F,G,H,J,S] Nondisp supracondylar fx w/o intracondylar extension of lwr end of [rt, lt, unsp] femur, [subsq enc for clsd fx w/ routine healing, subsq enc for opn fx type I or II w/ routine healing, subsq enc for opn fx type IIIA, IIIB, or IIIC w/ routine healing, subsq enc for clsd fx w/ delayed healing, subsq enc for opn fx type I or II w/ delayed healing, subsq enc for opn fx type I or II w/ delayed healing, seq]

S72.46[1,2,3][D,E,F,G,H,J,S] Disp supracondylar fx w/ intracondylar extension of lwr end of [rt, lt, unsp] femur, [subsq enc for clsd fx w/ routine healing, subsq enc for opn fx type I or II w/ routine healing, subsq enc for opn fx type IIIA, IIIB, or IIIC w/ routine healing, subsq enc for clsd fx w/ delayed healing, subsq enc for opn fx type I or II w/ delayed healing, subsq enc for opn fx type I or II w/ delayed healing, seq]

T Transfer DRG　　SP Special Payment　　* Code Range　　6th and 7th Character of ZZ = No Device, No Qualifier ZX = No Device, Diagnostic

S72.46[4,5,6][D,E,F,G,H,J,S] Nondisp supracondylar fx w/ intracondylar extension of lwr end of [rt, lt, unsp] femur, [subsq enc for clsd fx w/ routine healing, subsq enc for opn fx type I or II w/ routine healing, subsq enc for opn fx type IIIA, IIIB, or IIIC w/ routine healing, subsq enc for clsd fx w/ delayed healing, subsq enc for opn fx type I or II w/ delayed healing, subsq enc for opn fx type I or II w/ delayed healing, seq]

S72.47[1,2,9][D,G,S] Torus fx of lwr end of [rt, lt, unsp] femur, [subsq enc for fx w/ routine healing, subsq enc for fx w/ routine healing, seq]

S72.49[1,2,9][D,G,S] Oth fx of lwr end of [rt, lt, unsp] femur, [subsq enc for clsd fx w/ routine healing, subsq enc for opn fx type I or II w/ routine healing, subsq enc for opn fx type IIIA, IIIB, or IIIC w/ routine healing, subsq enc for clsd fx w/ delayed healing, subsq enc for opn fx type I or II w/ delayed healing, subsq enc for opn fx type I or II w/ delayed healing, seq]

S72.8X[1,2,9][D,E,F,G,H,J,S] Oth fx of [rt, lt, unsp] femur, [subsq enc for clsd fx w/ routine healing, subsq enc for opn fx type I or II w/ routine healing, subsq enc for opn fx type IIIA, IIIB, or IIIC w/ routine healing, subsq enc for clsd fx w/ delayed healing, subsq enc for opn fx type I or II w/ delayed healing, subsq enc for opn fx type I or II w/ delayed healing, seq]

S72.9[0,1,2]X[D,E,F,G,H,J,S] Unsp fx of [unsp, rt, lt] femur, [subsq enc for clsd fx w/ routine healing, subsq enc for opn fx type I or II w/ routine healing, subsq enc for opn fx type IIIA, IIIB, or IIIC w/ routine healing, subsq enc for clsd fx w/ delayed healing, subsq enc for opn fx type I or II w/ delayed healing, subsq enc for opn fx type IIIA, IIIB, or IIIC w/ delayed healing, seq]

S78.0[1,2][1,2,9]S [Complete, Partial] traum amp at [rt, lt, unsp] hip jt, seq

S78.1[1,2][1,2,9]S [Complete, Partial] traum amp at lvl between [rt, lt, unsp] hip and knee, seq

S78.9[1,2][1,2,9]S [Complete, Partial] traum amp at [rt, lt, unsp] hip & thigh, lvl unsp, seq

S79.00[1,2,9][D,G,S] Unsp physeal fx of upr end of [rt, lt, unsp] femur, [subsq enc for fx w/ routine healing, subsq enc for fx w/ delayed healing, seq]

S79.01[1,2,9][D,G,S] Salter-Harris Type I physeal fx of upr end of [rt, lt, unsp] femur, [subsq enc for fx w/ routine healing, subsq enc for fx w/ delayed healing, seq]

S79.09[1,2,9][D,G,S] Oth physeal fx of upr end of [rt, lt, unsp] femur, [subsq enc for fx w/ routine healing, subsq enc for fx w/ delayed healing, seq]

S79.10[1,2,9][D,G,S] Unsp physeal fx of lwr end of [rt, lt, unsp] femur, [subsq enc for fx w/ routine healing, subsq enc for fx w/ delayed healing, seq]

S79.11[1,2,9][D,G,S] Salter-Harris Type I physeal fx of lwr end of [rt, lt, unsp] femur, [subsq enc for fx w/ routine healing, subsq enc for fx w/ delayed healing, seq]

S79.12[1,2,9][D,G,S] Salter-Harris Type II physeal fx of lwr end of [rt, lt, unsp] femur, [subsq enc for fx w/ routine healing, subsq enc for fx w/ delayed healing, seq]

S79.13[1,2,9][D,G,S] Salter-Harris Type III physeal fx of lwr end of [rt, lt, unsp] femur, [subsq enc for fx w/ routine healing, subsq enc for fx w/ delayed healing, seq]

S79.14[1,2,9][D,G,S] Salter-Harris Type IV physeal fx of lwr end of [rt, lt, unsp] femur, [subsq enc for fx w/ routine healing, subsq enc for fx w/ delayed healing, seq]

S79.19[1,2,9][D,G,S] Oth physeal fx of lwr end of [rt, lt, unsp] femur, [subsq enc for fx w/ routine healing, subsq enc for fx w/ delayed healing, seq]

S82.00[1,2,9][D,E,F,G,H,J,S] Unsp fx of [rt, lt, unsp] patella, [subsq enc for clsd fx w/ routine healing, subsq enc for opn fx type I or II w/ routine healing, subsq enc for opn fx type IIIA, IIIB, or IIIC w/ routine healing, subsq enc for clsd fx w/ delayed healing, subsq enc for opn fx type I or II w/ delayed healing, subsq enc for opn fx type I or II w/ delayed healing, seq]

S82.01[1,2,3][D,E,F,G,H,J,S] Disp osteochondral fx of [rt, lt, unsp] patella, [subsq enc for clsd fx w/ routine healing, subsq enc for opn fx type I or II w/ routine healing, subsq enc for opn fx type IIIA, IIIB, or IIIC w/ routine healing, subsq enc for clsd fx w/ delayed healing, subsq enc for opn fx type I or II w/ delayed healing, subsq enc for opn fx type I or II w/ delayed healing, seq]

S82.01[4,5,6][D,E,F,G,H,J,S] Nondisp osteochondral fx of [rt, lt, unsp] patella, [subsq enc for clsd fx w/ routine healing, subsq enc for opn fx type I or II w/ routine healing, subsq enc for opn fx type IIIA, IIIB, or IIIC w/ routine healing, subsq enc for clsd fx w/ delayed healing, subsq enc for opn fx type I or II w/ delayed healing, subsq enc for opn fx type I or II w/ delayed healing, seq]

S82.02[1,2,3][D,E,F,G,H,J,S] Disp longitudinal fx of [rt, lt, unsp] patella, [subsq enc for clsd fx w/ routine healing, subsq enc for opn fx type I or II w/ routine healing, subsq enc for opn fx type IIIA, IIIB, or IIIC w/ routine healing, subsq enc for clsd fx w/ delayed healing, subsq enc for opn fx type I or II w/ delayed healing, subsq enc for opn fx type I or II w/ delayed healing, seq]

S82.02[4,5,6][D,E,F,G,H,J,S] Nondisp longitudinal fx of [rt, lt, unsp] patella, [subsq enc for clsd fx w/ routine healing, subsq enc for opn fx type I or II w/ routine healing, subsq enc for opn fx type IIIA, IIIB, or IIIC w/ routine healing, subsq enc for clsd fx w/ delayed healing, subsq enc for opn fx type I or II w/ delayed healing, subsq enc for opn fx type I or II w/ delayed healing, seq]

S82.03[1,2,3][D,E,F,G,H,J,S] Disp transv fx of [rt, lt, unsp] patella, [subsq enc for clsd fx w/ routine healing, subsq enc for opn fx type I or II w/ routine healing, subsq enc for opn fx type IIIA, IIIB, or IIIC w/ routine healing, subsq enc for clsd fx w/ delayed healing, subsq enc for opn fx type I or II w/ delayed healing, subsq enc for opn fx type I or II w/ delayed healing, seq]

S82.03[4,5,6][D,E,F,G,H,J,S] Nondisp transv fx of [rt, lt, unsp] patella, [subsq enc for clsd fx w/ routine healing, subsq enc for opn fx type I or II w/ routine healing, subsq enc for opn fx type IIIA, IIIB, or IIIC w/ routine healing, subsq enc for clsd fx w/ delayed healing, subsq enc for opn fx type I or II w/ delayed healing, subsq enc for opn fx type I or II w/ delayed healing, seq]

S82.04[1,2,3][D,E,F,G,H,J,S] Disp comm fx of [rt, lt, unsp] patella, [subsq enc for clsd fx w/ routine healing, subsq enc for opn fx type I or II w/ routine healing, subsq enc for opn fx type IIIA, IIIB, or IIIC w/ routine healing, subsq enc for clsd fx w/ delayed healing, subsq enc for opn fx type I or II w/ delayed healing, subsq enc for opn fx type I or II w/ delayed healing, seq]

S82.04[4,5,6][D,E,F,G,H,J,S] Nondisp comm fx of [rt, lt, unsp] patella, [subsq enc for clsd fx w/ routine healing, subsq enc for opn fx type I or II w/ routine healing, subsq enc for opn fx type IIIA, IIIB, or IIIC w/ routine healing, subsq enc for clsd fx w/ delayed healing, subsq enc for opn fx type I or II w/ delayed healing, subsq enc for opn fx type I or II w/ delayed healing, seq]

S82.09[1,2,9][D,E,F,G,H,J,S] Oth fx of [rt, lt, unsp] patella, [subsq enc for clsd fx w/ routine healing, subsq enc for opn fx type I or II w/ routine healing, subsq enc for opn fx type IIIA, IIIB, or IIIC w/ routine healing, subsq enc for clsd fx w/ delayed healing, subsq enc for opn fx type I or II w/ delayed healing, seq]

S82.10[1,2,9][D,E,F,G,H,J,S] Unsp fx of upr end of [rt, lt, unsp] tibia, [subsq enc for clsd fx w/ routine healing, subsq enc for opn fx type I or II w/ routine healing, subsq enc for opn fx type IIIA, IIIB, or IIIC w/ routine healing, subsq enc for clsd fx w/ delayed healing, subsq enc for opn fx type I or II w/ delayed healing, seq]

S82.11[1,2,3][D,E,F,G,H,J,S] Disp fx of [rt, lt, unsp] tibial spine, [subsq enc for clsd fx w/ routine healing, subsq enc for opn fx type I or II w/ routine healing, subsq enc for opn fx type IIIA, IIIB, or IIIC w/ routine healing, subsq enc for clsd fx w/ delayed healing, subsq enc for opn fx type I or II w/ delayed healing, subsq enc for opn fx type I or II w/ delayed healing, seq]

S82.11[4,5,6][D,E,F,G,H,J,S] Nondisp fx of [rt, lt, unsp] tibial spine, [subsq enc for clsd fx w/ routine healing, subsq enc for opn fx type I or II w/ routine healing, subsq enc for opn fx type IIIA, IIIB, or IIIC w/ routine healing, subsq enc for clsd fx w/ delayed healing, subsq enc for opn fx type I or II w/ delayed healing, seq]

S82.12[1,2,3][D,E,F,G,H,J,S] Disp fx of lat condyle of [rt, lt, unsp] tibia, [subsq enc for clsd fx w/ routine healing, subsq enc for opn fx type I or II w/ routine healing, subsq enc for opn fx type IIIA, IIIB, or IIIC w/ routine healing, subsq enc for clsd fx w/ delayed healing, subsq enc for opn fx type I or II w/ delayed healing, seq]

S82.12[4,5,6][D,E,F,G,H,J,S] Nondisp fx of lat condyle of [rt, lt, unsp] tibia, [subsq enc for clsd fx w/ routine healing, subsq enc for opn fx type I or II w/ routine healing, subsq enc for opn fx type IIIA, IIIB, or IIIC w/ routine healing, subsq enc for clsd fx w/ delayed healing, subsq enc for opn fx type I or II w/ delayed healing, seq]

S82.13[1,2,3][D,E,F,G,H,J,S] Disp fx of med condyle [rt, lt, unsp] tibia, [subsq enc for clsd fx w/ routine healing, subsq enc for opn fx type I or II w/ routine healing, subsq enc for opn fx type IIIA, IIIB, or IIIC w/ routine healing, subsq enc for clsd fx w/ delayed healing, subsq enc for opn fx type I or II w/ delayed healing, seq]

Surgical   **Medical**   **CC Indicator**   **MCC Indicator**   **Procedure Proxy**   PDx MCC **PDx acts as own MCC**   PDx CC **PDx acts as own CC**

S82.13[4,5,6][D,E,F,G,H,J,S] Nondisp fx of med condyle [rt, lt, unsp] tibia, [subsq enc for clsd fx w/ routine healing, subsq enc for opn fx type I or II w/ routine healing, subsq enc for opn fx type IIIA, IIIB, or IIIC w/ routine healing, subsq enc for clsd fx w/ delayed healing, subsq enc for opn fx type I or II w/ delayed healing, subsq enc for opn fx type I or II w/ delayed healing, seq]

S82.14[1,2,3][D,E,F,G,H,J,S] Disp bicondylar fx of [rt, lt, unsp] tibia, [subsq enc for clsd fx w/ routine healing, subsq enc for opn fx type I or II w/ routine healing, subsq enc for opn fx type IIIA, IIIB, or IIIC w/ routine healing, subsq enc for clsd fx w/ delayed healing, subsq enc for opn fx type I or II w/ delayed healing, subsq enc for opn fx type I or II w/ delayed healing, seq]

S82.14[4,5,6][D,E,F,G,H,J,S] Nondisp bicondylar fx of [rt, lt, unsp] tibia, [subsq enc for clsd fx w/ routine healing, subsq enc for opn fx type I or II w/ routine healing, subsq enc for opn fx type IIIA, IIIB, or IIIC w/ routine healing, subsq enc for clsd fx w/ delayed healing, subsq enc for opn fx type I or II w/ delayed healing, subsq enc for opn fx type I or II w/ delayed healing, seq]

S82.15[1,2,3][D,E,F,G,H,J,S] Disp fx of [rt, lt, unsp] tibial tuberosity, [subsq enc for clsd fx w/ routine healing, subsq enc for opn fx type I or II w/ routine healing, subsq enc for opn fx type IIIA, IIIB, or IIIC w/ routine healing, subsq enc for clsd fx w/ delayed healing, subsq enc for opn fx type I or II w/ delayed healing, subsq enc for opn fx type I or II w/ delayed healing, seq]

S82.15[4,5,6][D,E,F,G,H,J,S] Nondisp fx of [rt, lt, unsp] tibial tuberosity, [subsq enc for clsd fx w/ routine healing, subsq enc for opn fx type I or II w/ routine healing, subsq enc for opn fx type IIIA, IIIB, or IIIC w/ routine healing, subsq enc for clsd fx w/ delayed healing, subsq enc for opn fx type I or II w/ delayed healing, subsq enc for opn fx type I or II w/ delayed healing, seq]

S82.16[1,2,9][D,G,S] Torus fx of upr end of [rt, lt, unsp] tibia, [subsq enc for fx w/ routine healing, subsq enc for fx w/ delayed healing, seq]

S82.19[1,2,9][D,E,F,G,H,J,S] Oth fx of upr end of [rt, lt, unsp] tibia, [subsq enc for clsd fx w/ routine healing, subsq enc for opn fx type I or II w/ routine healing, subsq enc for opn fx type IIIA, IIIB, or IIIC w/ routine healing, subsq enc for clsd fx w/ delayed healing, subsq enc for opn fx type I or II w/ delayed healing, subsq enc for opn fx type I or II w/ delayed healing, seq]

S82.20[1,2,9][D,E,F,G,H,J,S] Unsp fx of shaft of [rt, lt, unsp] tibia, [subsq enc for clsd fx w/ routine healing, subsq enc for opn fx type I or II w/ routine healing, subsq enc for opn fx type IIIA, IIIB, or IIIC w/ routine healing, subsq enc for clsd fx w/ delayed healing, subsq enc for opn fx type I or II w/ delayed healing, subsq enc for opn fx type I or II w/ delayed healing, seq]

S82.22[1,2,3][D,E,F,G,H,J,S] Disp transv fx of shaft of [rt, lt, unsp] tibia, [subsq enc for clsd fx w/ routine healing, subsq enc for opn fx type I or II w/ routine healing, subsq enc for opn fx type IIIA, IIIB, or IIIC w/ routine healing, subsq enc for clsd fx w/ delayed healing, subsq enc for opn fx type I or II w/ delayed healing, subsq enc for opn fx type I or II w/ delayed healing, seq]

S82.22[4,5,6][D,E,F,G,H,J,S] Nondisp transv fx of shaft of [rt, lt, unsp] tibia, [subsq enc for clsd fx w/ routine healing, subsq enc for opn fx type I or II w/ routine healing, subsq enc for opn fx type IIIA, IIIB, or IIIC w/ routine healing, subsq enc for clsd fx w/ delayed healing, subsq enc for opn fx type I or II w/ delayed healing, subsq enc for opn fx type I or II w/ delayed healing, seq]

S82.23[1,2,3][D,E,F,G,H,J,S] Disp oblique fx of shaft of [rt, lt, unsp] tibia, [subsq enc for clsd fx w/ routine healing, subsq enc for opn fx type I or II w/ routine healing, subsq enc for opn fx type IIIA, IIIB, or IIIC w/ routine healing, subsq enc for clsd fx w/ delayed healing, subsq enc for opn fx type I or II w/ delayed healing, subsq enc for opn fx type IIIA, IIIB, or IIIC w/ delayed healing, seq]

S82.23[4,5,6][D,E,F,G,H,J,S] Nondisp oblique fx of shaft of [rt, lt, unsp] tibia, [subsq enc for clsd fx w/ routine healing, subsq enc for opn fx type I or II w/ routine healing, subsq enc for opn fx type IIIA, IIIB, or IIIC w/ routine healing, subsq enc for clsd fx w/ delayed healing, subsq enc for opn fx type I or II w/ delayed healing, subsq enc for opn fx type IIIA, IIIB, or IIIC w/ delayed healing, seq]

S82.24[1,2,3][D,E,F,G,H,J,S] Disp spiral fx of shaft of [rt, lt, unsp] tibia, [subsq enc for clsd fx w/ routine healing, subsq enc for opn fx type I or II w/ routine healing, subsq enc for opn fx type IIIA, IIIB, or IIIC w/ routine healing, subsq enc for clsd fx w/ delayed healing, subsq enc for opn fx type I or II w/ delayed healing, subsq enc for opn fx type IIIA, IIIB, or IIIC w/ delayed healing, seq]

S82.24[4,5,6][D,E,F,G,H,J,S] Nondisp spiral fx of shaft of [rt, lt, unsp] tibia, [subsq enc for clsd fx w/ routine healing, subsq enc for opn fx type I or II w/ routine healing, subsq enc for opn fx type IIIA, IIIB, or IIIC w/ routine healing, subsq enc for clsd fx w/ delayed healing, subsq enc for opn fx type I or II w/ delayed healing, subsq enc for opn fx type IIIA, IIIB, or IIIC w/ delayed healing, seq]

S82.25[1,2,3][D,E,F,G,H,J,S] Disp comm fx of shaft of [rt, lt, unsp] tibia, [subsq enc for clsd fx w/ routine healing, subsq enc for opn fx type I or II w/ routine healing, subsq enc for opn fx type IIIA, IIIB, or IIIC w/ routine healing, subsq enc for clsd fx w/ delayed healing, subsq enc for opn fx type I or II w/ delayed healing, subsq enc for opn fx type IIIA, IIIB, or IIIC w/ delayed healing, seq]

S82.25[4,5,6][D,E,F,G,H,J,S] Nondisp comm fx of shaft of [rt, lt, unsp] tibia, [subsq enc for clsd fx w/ routine healing, subsq enc for opn fx type I or II w/ routine healing, subsq enc for opn fx type IIIA, IIIB, or IIIC w/ routine healing, subsq enc for clsd fx w/ delayed healing, subsq enc for opn fx type I or II w/ delayed healing, subsq enc for opn fx type IIIA, IIIB, or IIIC w/ delayed healing, seq]

S82.26[1,2,3][D,E,F,G,H,J,S] Disp seg fx of shaft of [rt, lt, unsp] tibia, [subsq enc for clsd fx w/ routine healing, subsq enc for opn fx type I or II w/ routine healing, subsq enc for opn fx type IIIA, IIIB, or IIIC w/ routine healing, subsq enc for clsd fx w/ delayed healing, subsq enc for opn fx type I or II w/ delayed healing, subsq enc for opn fx type IIIA, IIIB, or IIIC w/ delayed healing, seq]

S82.26[4,5,6][D,E,F,G,H,J,S] Nondisp seg fx of shaft of [rt, lt, unsp] tibia, [subsq enc for clsd fx w/ routine healing, subsq enc for opn fx type I or II w/ routine healing, subsq enc for opn fx type IIIA, IIIB, or IIIC w/ routine healing, subsq enc for clsd fx w/ delayed healing, subsq enc for opn fx type I or II w/ delayed healing, subsq enc for opn fx type IIIA, IIIB, or IIIC w/ delayed healing, seq]

S82.29[1,2,9][D,E,F,G,H,J,S] Oth fx of shaft of [rt, lt, unsp] tibia, [subsq enc for clsd fx w/ routine healing, subsq enc for opn fx type I or II w/ routine healing, subsq enc for opn fx type IIIA, IIIB, or IIIC w/ routine healing, subsq enc for clsd fx w/ delayed healing, subsq enc for opn fx type I or II w/ delayed healing, subsq enc for opn fx type IIIA, IIIB, or IIIC w/ delayed healing, seq]

S82.30[1,2,9][D,E,F,G,H,J,S] Unsp fx of lwr end of [rt, lt, unsp] tibia, [subsq enc for clsd fx w/ routine healing, subsq enc for opn fx type I or II w/ routine healing, subsq enc for opn fx type IIIA, IIIB, or IIIC w/ routine healing, subsq enc for clsd fx w/ delayed healing, subsq enc for opn fx type I or II w/ delayed healing, subsq enc for opn fx type IIIA, IIIB, or IIIC w/ delayed healing, seq]

S82.31[1,2,9][D,G,S] Torus fx of lwr end of [rt, lt, unsp] tibia, [subsq enc for clsd fx w/ routine healing, subsq enc for clsd fx w/ delayed healing, seq]

S82.39[1,2,9][D,E,F,G,H,J,S] Oth fx of lwr end of[rt, lt, unsp] tibia, [subsq enc for clsd fx w/ routine healing, subsq enc for opn fx type I or II w/ routine healing, subsq enc for opn fx type IIIA, IIIB, or IIIC w/ routine healing, subsq enc for clsd fx w/ delayed healing, subsq enc for opn fx type I or II w/ delayed healing, subsq enc for opn fx type IIIA, IIIB, or IIIC w/ delayed healing, seq]

S82.40[1,2,9][D,E,F,G,H,J,S] Unsp fx of shaft of [rt, lt, unsp] fibula, [subsq enc for clsd fx w/ routine healing, subsq enc for opn fx type I or II w/ routine healing, subsq enc for opn fx type IIIA, IIIB, or IIIC w/ routine healing, subsq enc for clsd fx w/ delayed healing, subsq enc for opn fx type I or II w/ delayed healing, subsq enc for opn fx type IIIA, IIIB, or IIIC w/ delayed healing, seq]

S82.42[1,2,3][D,E,F,G,H,J,S] Disp transv fx of shaft of [rt, lt, unsp] fibula, [subsq enc for clsd fx w/ routine healing, subsq enc for opn fx type I or II w/ routine healing, subsq enc for opn fx type IIIA, IIIB, or IIIC w/ routine healing, subsq enc for clsd fx w/ delayed healing, subsq enc for opn fx type I or II w/ delayed healing, subsq enc for opn fx type IIIA, IIIB, or IIIC w/ delayed healing, seq]

S82.42[4,5,6][D,E,F,G,H,J,S] Nondisp transv fx of shaft of [rt, lt, unsp] fibula, [subsq enc for clsd fx w/ routine healing, subsq enc for opn fx type I or II w/ routine healing, subsq enc for opn fx type IIIA, IIIB, or IIIC w/ routine healing, subsq enc for clsd fx w/ delayed healing, subsq enc for opn fx type I or II w/ delayed healing, subsq enc for opn fx type IIIA, IIIB, or IIIC w/ delayed healing, seq]

T Transfer DRG   SP Special Payment   * Code Range   **6th and 7th Character of ZZ = No Device, No Qualifier ZX = No Device, Diagnostic**

180   MS-DRG Version 33.0   © 2015 Optum360, LLC

S82.43[1,2,3][D,E,F,G,H,J,S] Disp oblique fx of shaft of [rt, lt, unsp] fibula, [subsq enc for clsd fx w/ routine healing, subsq enc for opn fx type I or II w/ routine healing, subsq enc for opn fx type IIIA, IIIB, or IIIC w/ routine healing, subsq enc for clsd fx w/ delayed healing, subsq enc for opn fx type I or II w/ delayed healing, subsq enc for opn fx type IIIA, IIIB, or IIIC w/ delayed healing, seq]

S82.43[4,5,6][D,E,F,G,H,J,S] Nondisp oblique fx of shaft of [rt, lt, unsp] fibula, [subsq enc for clsd fx w/ routine healing, subsq enc for opn fx type I or II w/ routine healing, subsq enc for opn fx type IIIA, IIIB, or IIIC w/ routine healing, subsq enc for clsd fx w/ delayed healing, subsq enc for opn fx type I or II w/ delayed healing, subsq enc for opn fx type IIIA, IIIB, or IIIC w/ delayed healing, seq]

S82.44[1,2,3][D,E,F,G,H,J,S] Disp spiral fx of shaft of [rt, lt, unsp] fibula, [subsq enc for clsd fx w/ routine healing, subsq enc for opn fx type I or II w/ routine healing, subsq enc for opn fx type IIIA, IIIB, or IIIC w/ routine healing, subsq enc for clsd fx w/ delayed healing, subsq enc for opn fx type I or II w/ delayed healing, subsq enc for opn fx type IIIA, IIIB, or IIIC w/ delayed healing, seq]

S82.44[4,5,6][D,E,F,G,H,J,S] Nondisp spiral fx of shaft of [rt, lt, unsp] fibula, [subsq enc for clsd fx w/ routine healing, subsq enc for opn fx type I or II w/ routine healing, subsq enc for opn fx type IIIA, IIIB, or IIIC w/ routine healing, subsq enc for clsd fx w/ delayed healing, subsq enc for opn fx type I or II w/ delayed healing, subsq enc for opn fx type IIIA, IIIB, or IIIC w/ delayed healing, seq]

S82.45[1,2,3][D,E,F,G,H,J,S] Disp comm fx of shaft of [rt, lt, unsp] fibula, [subsq enc for clsd fx w/ routine healing, subsq enc for opn fx type I or II w/ routine healing, subsq enc for opn fx type IIIA, IIIB, or IIIC w/ routine healing, subsq enc for clsd fx w/ delayed healing, subsq enc for opn fx type I or II w/ delayed healing, subsq enc for opn fx type IIIA, IIIB, or IIIC w/ delayed healing, seq]

S82.45[4,5,6][D,E,F,G,H,J,S] Nondisp comm fx of shaft of [rt, lt, unsp] fibula, [subsq enc for clsd fx w/ routine healing, subsq enc for opn fx type I or II w/ routine healing, subsq enc for opn fx type IIIA, IIIB, or IIIC w/ routine healing, subsq enc for clsd fx w/ delayed healing, subsq enc for opn fx type I or II w/ delayed healing, subsq enc for opn fx type IIIA, IIIB, or IIIC w/ delayed healing, seq]

S82.46[1,2,3][D,E,F,G,H,J,S] Disp seg fx of shaft of [rt, lt, unsp] fibula, [subsq enc for clsd fx w/ routine healing, subsq enc for opn fx type I or II w/ routine healing, subsq enc for opn fx type IIIA, IIIB, or IIIC w/ routine healing, subsq enc for clsd fx w/ delayed healing, subsq enc for opn fx type I or II w/ delayed healing, subsq enc for opn fx type IIIA, IIIB, or IIIC w/ delayed healing, seq]

S82.46[4,5,6][D,E,F,G,H,J,S] Nondisp seg fx of shaft of [rt, lt, unsp] fibula, [subsq enc for clsd fx w/ routine healing, subsq enc for opn fx type I or II w/ routine healing, subsq enc for opn fx type IIIA, IIIB, or IIIC w/ routine healing, subsq enc for clsd fx w/ delayed healing, subsq enc for opn fx type I or II w/ delayed healing, subsq enc for opn fx type IIIA, IIIB, or IIIC w/ delayed healing, seq]

S82.49[1,2,9][D,E,F,G,H,J,S] Oth fx of shaft of [rt, lt, unsp] fibula, [subsq enc for clsd fx w/ routine healing, subsq enc for opn fx type I or II w/ routine healing, subsq enc for opn fx type IIIA, IIIB, or IIIC w/ routine healing, subsq enc for clsd fx w/ delayed healing, subsq enc for opn fx type I or II w/ delayed healing, subsq enc for opn fx type IIIA, IIIB, or IIIC w/ delayed healing, seq]

S82.5[1,2,3]X[D,E,F,G,H,J,S] Disp fx of med malleolus of [rt, lt, unsp] tibia, [subsq enc for clsd fx w/ routine healing, subsq enc for opn fx type I or II w/ routine healing, subsq enc for opn fx type IIIA, IIIB, or IIIC w/ routine healing, subsq enc for clsd fx w/ delayed healing, subsq enc for opn fx type I or II w/ delayed healing, subsq enc for opn fx type IIIA, IIIB, or IIIC w/ delayed healing, seq]

S82.5[4,5,6]X[D,E,F,G,H,J,S] Nondisp fx of med malleolus of [rt, lt, unsp] tibia, [subsq enc for clsd fx w/ routine healing, subsq enc for opn fx type I or II w/ routine healing, subsq enc for opn fx type IIIA, IIIB, or IIIC w/ routine healing, subsq enc for clsd fx w/ delayed healing, subsq enc for opn fx type I or II w/ delayed healing, subsq enc for opn fx type IIIA, IIIB, or IIIC w/ delayed healing, seq]

S82.6[1,2,3]X[D,E,F,G,H,J,S] Disp fx of lat malleolus of [rt, lt, unsp] fibula, [subsq enc for clsd fx w/ routine healing, subsq enc for opn fx type I or II w/ routine healing, subsq enc for opn fx type IIIA, IIIB, or IIIC w/ routine healing, subsq enc for clsd fx w/ delayed healing, subsq enc for opn fx type I or II w/ delayed healing, subsq enc for opn fx type IIIA, IIIB, or IIIC w/ delayed healing, seq]

S82.6[4,5,6]X[D,E,F,G,H,J,S] Nondisp fx of lat malleolus of [rt, lt, unsp] fibula, [subsq enc for clsd fx w/ routine healing, subsq enc for opn fx type I or II w/ routine healing, subsq enc for opn fx type IIIA, IIIB, or IIIC w/ routine healing, subsq enc for clsd fx w/ delayed healing, subsq enc for opn fx type I or II w/ delayed healing, subsq enc for opn fx type IIIA, IIIB, or IIIC w/ delayed healing, seq]

S82.81[1,2,9][D,G,S] Torus fx of upr end of [rt, lt, unsp] fibula, [subsq enc for clsd fx w/ routine healing, subsq enc for clsd fx w/ delayed healing, seq]

S82.82[1,2,9][D,G,S] Torus fx of lwr end of [rt, lt, unsp] fibula, [subsq enc for clsd fx w/ routine healing, subsq enc for clsd fx w/ delayed healing, seq]

S82.83[1,2,9][D,E,F,G,H,J,S] Oth fx of upr and lwr end of [rt, lt, unsp] fibula, [subsq enc for clsd fx w/ routine healing, subsq enc for opn fx type I or II w/ routine healing, subsq enc for opn fx type IIIA, IIIB, or IIIC w/ routine healing, subsq enc for clsd fx w/ delayed healing, subsq enc for opn fx type I or II w/ delayed healing, subsq enc for opn fx type IIIA, IIIB, or IIIC w/ delayed healing, seq]

S82.84[1,2,3][D,E,F,G,H,J,S] Disp bimalleolar fx of [rt, lt, unsp] lwr leg, [subsq enc for clsd fx w/ routine healing, subsq enc for opn fx type I or II w/ routine healing, subsq enc for opn fx type IIIA, IIIB, or IIIC w/ routine healing, subsq enc for clsd fx w/ delayed healing, subsq enc for opn fx type I or II w/ delayed healing, subsq enc for opn fx type IIIA, IIIB, or IIIC w/ delayed healing, seq]

S82.84[4,5,6][D,E,F,G,H,J,S] Nondisp bimalleolar fx of [rt, lt, unsp] lwr leg, [subsq enc for clsd fx w/ routine healing, subsq enc for opn fx type I or II w/ routine healing, subsq enc for opn fx type IIIA, IIIB, or IIIC w/ routine healing, subsq enc for clsd fx w/ delayed healing, subsq enc for opn fx type I or II w/ delayed healing, subsq enc for opn fx type IIIA, IIIB, or IIIC w/ delayed healing, seq]

S82.85[1,2,3][D,E,F,G,H,J,S] Disp trimalleolar fx of [rt, lt, unsp] lwr leg, [subsq enc for clsd fx w/ routine healing, subsq enc for opn fx type I or II w/ routine healing, subsq enc for opn fx type IIIA, IIIB, or IIIC w/ routine healing, subsq enc for clsd fx w/ delayed healing, subsq enc for opn fx type I or II w/ delayed healing, subsq enc for opn fx type IIIA, IIIB, or IIIC w/ delayed healing, seq]

S82.85[4,5,6][D,E,F,G,H,J,S] Nondisp trimalleolar fx of [rt, lt, unsp] lwr leg, [subsq enc for clsd fx w/ routine healing, subsq enc for opn fx type I or II w/ routine healing, subsq enc for opn fx type IIIA, IIIB, or IIIC w/ routine healing, subsq enc for clsd fx w/ delayed healing, subsq enc for opn fx type I or II w/ delayed healing, subsq enc for opn fx type IIIA, IIIB, or IIIC w/ delayed healing, seq]

S82.86[1,2,3][D,E,F,G,H,J,S] Disp Maisonneuve's fx of [rt, lt, unsp] leg, [subsq enc for clsd fx w/ routine healing, subsq enc for opn fx type I or II w/ routine healing, subsq enc for opn fx type IIIA, IIIB, or IIIC w/ routine healing, subsq enc for clsd fx w/ delayed healing, subsq enc for opn fx type I or II w/ delayed healing, subsq enc for opn fx type IIIA, IIIB, or IIIC w/ delayed healing, seq]

S82.86[4,5,6][D,E,F,G,H,J,S] Nondisp Maisonneuve's fx of [rt, lt, unsp] leg, [subsq enc for clsd fx w/ routine healing, subsq enc for opn fx type I or II w/ routine healing, subsq enc for opn fx type IIIA, IIIB, or IIIC w/ routine healing, subsq enc for clsd fx w/ delayed healing, subsq enc for opn fx type I or II w/ delayed healing, subsq enc for opn fx type IIIA, IIIB, or IIIC w/ delayed healing, seq]

S82.87[1,2,3][D,E,F,G,H,J,S] Disp pilon fx of [rt, lt, unsp] tibia, [subsq enc for clsd fx w/ routine healing, subsq enc for opn fx type I or II w/ routine healing, subsq enc for opn fx type IIIA, IIIB, or IIIC w/ routine healing, subsq enc for clsd fx w/ delayed healing, subsq enc for opn fx type I or II w/ delayed healing, subsq enc for opn fx type IIIA, IIIB, or IIIC w/ delayed healing, seq]

S82.87[4,5,6][D,E,F,G,H,J,S] Nondisp pilon fx of [rt, lt, unsp] tibia, [subsq enc for clsd fx w/ routine healing, subsq enc for opn fx type I or II w/ routine healing, subsq enc for opn fx type IIIA, IIIB, or IIIC w/ routine healing, subsq enc for clsd fx w/ delayed healing, subsq enc for opn fx type I or II w/ delayed healing, subsq enc for opn fx type IIIA, IIIB, or IIIC w/ delayed healing, seq]

Surgical　　**Medical**　　**CC Indicator**　　**MCC Indicator**　　**Procedure Proxy**　　**PDxMCC** PDx acts as own MCC　　**PDxCC** PDx acts as own CC

S82.89[1,2,9][D,E,F,G,H,J,S] Oth fx of [rt, lt, unsp] lwr leg, [subsq enc for clsd fx w/ routine healing, subsq enc for opn fx type I or II w/ routine healing, subsq enc for opn fx type IIIA, IIIB, or IIIC w/ routine healing, subsq enc for clsd fx w/ delayed healing, subsq enc for opn fx type I or II w/ delayed healing, subsq enc for opn fx type IIIA, IIIB, or IIIC w/ delayed healing, seq]

S82.9[0,1,2]X[D,E,F,G,H,J,S] Unsp fx of [rt, lt, unsp] lwr leg, [subsq enc for clsd fx w/ routine healing, subsq enc for opn fx type I or II w/ routine healing, subsq enc for opn fx type IIIA, IIIB, or IIIC w/ routine healing, subsq enc for clsd fx w/ delayed healing, subsq enc for opn fx type I or II w/ delayed healing, subsq enc for opn fx type IIIA, IIIB, or IIIC w/ delayed healing, seq]

S88.0[1,2][1,2,9]S [Complete, Partial] traum amp at knee lvl, [rt, lt, unsp] lwr leg, seq

S88.1[1,2][1,2,9]S [Complete, Partial] traum amp of [rt, lt, unsp] lwr leg, lvl unsp, seq

S88.9[1,2][1,2,9]S [Complete, Partial] traum amp at knee lvl, [rt, lt, unsp] lwr leg, seq

S89.00[1,2,9][D,G,S] Unsp physeal fx of upr end of [rt, lt, unsp] tibia, [subsq enc for fx w/ routine healing, subsq enc for fx w/ delayed healing, seq]

S89.01[1,2,9][D,G,S] Salter-Harris Type I physeal fx of upr end of [rt, lt, unsp] tibia, [subsq enc for fx w/ routine healing, subsq enc for fx w/ delayed healing, seq]

S89.02[1,2,9][D,G,S] Salter-Harris Type II physeal fx of upr end of [rt, lt, unsp] tibia, [subsq enc for fx w/ routine healing, subsq enc for fx w/ delayed healing, seq]

S89.03[1,2,9][D,G,S] Salter-Harris Type III physeal fx of upr end of [rt, lt, unsp] tibia, [subsq enc for fx w/ routine healing, subsq enc for fx w/ delayed healing, seq]

S89.04[1,2,9][D,G,S] Salter-Harris Type IV physeal fx of upr end of [rt, lt, unsp] tibia, [subsq enc for fx w/ routine healing, subsq enc for fx w/ delayed healing, seq]

S89.09[1,2,9][D,G,S] Oth physeal fx of upr end of [rt, lt, unsp] tibia, [subsq enc for fx w/ routine healing, subsq enc for fx w/ delayed healing, seq]

S89.10[1,2,9][D,G,S] Unsp physeal fx of lwr end of [rt, lt, unsp] tibia, [subsq enc for fx w/ routine healing, subsq enc for fx w/ delayed healing, seq]

S89.11[1,2,9][D,G,S] Salter-Harris Type I physeal fx of lwr end of [rt, lt, unsp] tibia, [subsq enc for fx w/ routine healing, subsq enc for fx w/ delayed healing, seq]

S89.12[1,2,9][D,G,S] Salter-Harris Type II physeal fx of lwr end of [rt, lt, unsp] tibia, [subsq enc for fx w/ routine healing, subsq enc for fx w/ delayed healing, seq]

S89.13[1,2,9][D,G,S] Salter-Harris Type III physeal fx of lwr end of [rt, lt, unsp] tibia, [subsq enc for fx w/ routine healing, subsq enc for fx w/ delayed healing, seq]

S89.14[1,2,9][D,G,S] Salter-Harris Type IV physeal fx of lwr end of [rt, lt, unsp] tibia, [subsq enc for fx w/ routine healing, subsq enc for fx w/ delayed healing, seq]

S89.19[1,2,9][D,G,S] Oth physeal fx of lwr end of [rt, lt, unsp] tibia, [subsq enc for fx w/ routine healing, subsq enc for fx w/ delayed healing, seq]

S89.20[1,2,9][D,G,S] Unsp physeal fx of upr end of [rt, lt, unsp] fibula, [subsq enc for fx w/ routine healing, subsq enc for fx w/ delayed healing, seq]

S89.21[1,2,9][D,G,S] Salter-Harris Type I physeal fx of upr end of [rt, lt, unsp] fibula, [subsq enc for fx w/ routine healing, subsq enc for fx w/ delayed healing, seq]

S89.22[1,2,9][D,G,S] Salter-Harris Type II physeal fx of upr end of [rt, lt, unsp] fibula, [subsq enc for fx w/ routine healing, subsq enc for fx w/ delayed healing, seq]

S89.29[1,2,9][D,G,S] Oth physeal fx of upr end of [rt, lt, unsp] fibula, [subsq enc for fx w/ routine healing, subsq enc for fx w/ delayed healing, seq]

S89.30[1,2,9][D,G,S] Unsp physeal fx of lwr end of [rt, lt, unsp] fibula, [subsq enc for fx w/ routine healing, subsq enc for fx w/ delayed healing, seq]

S89.31[1,2,9][D,G,S] Salter-Harris Type I physeal fx of lwr end of [rt, lt, unsp] fibula, [subsq enc for fx w/ routine healing, subsq enc for fx w/ delayed healing, seq]

S89.32[1,2,9][D,G,S] Salter-Harris Type II physeal fx of lwr end of [rt, lt, unsp] fibula, [subsq enc for fx w/ routine healing, subsq enc for fx w/ delayed healing, seq]

S89.39[1,2,9][D,G,S] Oth physeal fx of lwr end of [rt, lt, unsp] fibula, [subsq enc for fx w/ routine healing, subsq enc for fx w/ delayed healing, seq]

S92.00[1,2,9][D,G,S] Unsp fx of [rt, lt, unsp] calcaneus, [subsq enc for fx w/ routine healing, subsq enc for fx w/ delayed healing, seq]

S92.01[1,2,3][D,G,S] Disp fx of body of [rt, lt, unsp] calcaneus, [subsq enc for fx w/ routine healing, subsq enc for fx w/ delayed healing, seq]

S92.01[4,5,6][D,G,S] Nondisp fx of body of [rt, lt, unsp] calcaneus, [subsq enc for fx w/ routine healing, subsq enc for fx w/ delayed healing, seq]

S92.02[1,2,3][D,G,S] Disp fx of ant process of [rt, lt, unsp] calcaneus, [subsq enc for fx w/ routine healing, subsq enc for fx w/ delayed healing, seq]

S92.02[4,5,6][D,G,S] Nondisp fx of ant process of [rt, lt, unsp] calcaneus, [subsq enc for fx w/ routine healing, subsq enc for fx w/ delayed healing, seq]

S92.03[1,2,3][D,G,S] Disp avulsion fx of tuberosity of [rt, lt, unsp] calcaneus, [subsq enc for fx w/ routine healing, subsq enc for fx w/ delayed healing, seq]

S92.03[4,5,6][D,G,S] Nondisp avulsion fx of tuberosity of [rt, lt, unsp] calcaneus, [subsq enc for fx w/ routine healing, subsq enc for fx w/ delayed healing, seq]

S92.04[1,2,3][D,G,S] Disp oth fx of tuberosity of [rt, lt, unsp] calcaneus, [subsq enc for fx w/ routine healing, subsq enc for fx w/ delayed healing, seq]

S92.04[4,5,6][D,G,S] Nondisp oth fx of tuberosity of [rt, lt, unsp] calcaneus, [subsq enc for fx w/ routine healing, subsq enc for fx w/ delayed healing, seq]

S92.05[1,2,3][D,G,S] Disp oth extraarticular fx of [rt, lt, unsp] calcaneus, [subsq enc for fx w/ routine healing, subsq enc for fx w/ delayed healing, seq]

S92.05[4,5,6][D,G,S] Nondisp oth extraarticular fx of [rt, lt, unsp] calcaneus, [subsq enc for fx w/ routine healing, subsq enc for fx w/ delayed healing, seq]

S92.06[1,2,3][D,G,S] Disp intraarticular fx of [rt, lt, unsp] calcaneus, [subsq enc for fx w/ routine healing, subsq enc for fx w/ delayed healing, seq]

S92.06[4,5,6][D,G,S] Nondisp intraarticular fx of [rt, lt, unsp] calcaneus, [subsq enc for fx w/ routine healing, subsq enc for fx w/ delayed healing, seq]

S92.10[1,2,9][D,G,S] Unsp fx of [rt, lt, unsp] talus, [subsq enc for fx w/ routine healing, subsq enc for fx w/ delayed healing, seq]

S92.11[1,2,3][D,G,S] Disp fx of neck of [rt, lt, unsp] talus, [subsq enc for fx w/ routine healing, subsq enc for fx w/ delayed healing, seq]

S92.11[4,5,6][D,G,S] Nondisp fx of neck of [rt, lt, unsp] talus, [subsq enc for fx w/ routine healing, subsq enc for fx w/ delayed healing, seq]

S92.12[1,2,3][D,G,S] Disp fx of body of [rt, lt, unsp] talus, [subsq enc for fx w/ routine healing, subsq enc for fx w/ delayed healing, seq]

S92.12[4,5,6][D,G,S] Nondisp fx of body of [rt, lt, unsp] talus, [subsq enc for fx w/ routine healing, subsq enc for fx w/ delayed healing, seq]

S92.13[1,2,3][D,G,S] Disp fx of post process of [rt, lt, unsp] talus, [subsq enc for fx w/ routine healing, subsq enc for fx w/ delayed healing, seq]

S92.13[4,5,6][D,G,S] Nondisp fx of post process of [rt, lt, unsp] talus, [subsq enc for fx w/ routine healing, subsq enc for fx w/ delayed healing, seq]

S92.14[1,2,3][D,G,S] Disp dome fx of [rt, lt, unsp] talus, [subsq enc for fx w/ routine healing, subsq enc for fx w/ delayed healing, seq]

S92.14[4,5,6][D,G,S] Nondisp dome fx of [rt, lt, unsp] talus, [subsq enc for fx w/ routine healing, subsq enc for fx w/ delayed healing, seq]

S92.15[1,2,3][D,G,S] Disp avulsion fx (chip fx) of [rt, lt, unsp] talus, [subsq enc for fx w/ routine healing, subsq enc for fx w/ delayed healing, seq]

S92.15[4,5,6][D,G,S] Nondisp avulsion fx (chip fx) of [rt, lt, unsp] talus, [subsq enc for fx w/ routine healing, subsq enc for fx w/ delayed healing, seq]

S92.19[1,2,9][D,G,S] Oth fx of [rt, lt, unsp] talus, [subsq enc for fx w/ routine healing, subsq enc for fx w/ delayed healing, seq]

S92.20[1,2,9][D,G,S] Fx of unsp tarsal bone(s) of [rt, lt, unsp] foot, [subsq enc for fx w/ routine healing, subsq enc for fx w/ delayed healing, seq]

S92.21[1,2,3][D,G,S] Disp fx of cuboid bone of [rt, lt, unsp] foot, [subsq enc for fx w/ routine healing, subsq enc for fx w/ delayed healing, seq]

S92.21[4,5,6][D,G,S] Nondisp fx of cuboid bone of [rt, lt, unsp] foot, [subsq enc for fx w/ routine healing, subsq enc for fx w/ delayed healing, seq]

S92.22[1,2,3][D,G,S] Disp fx of lat cuneiform of [rt, lt, unsp] foot, [subsq enc for fx w/ routine healing, subsq enc for fx w/ delayed healing, seq]

S92.22[4,5,6][D,G,S] Nondisp fx of lat cuneiform of [rt, lt, unsp] foot, [subsq enc for fx w/ routine healing, subsq enc for fx w/ delayed healing, seq]

S92.23[1,2,3][D,G,S] Disp fx of intermediate cuneiform of [rt, lt, unsp] foot, [subsq enc for fx w/ routine healing, subsq enc for fx w/ delayed healing, seq]

Ⓣ **Transfer DRG**   ⓢⓅ **Special Payment**   * **Code Range**   **6th and 7th Character of ZZ = No Device, No Qualifier ZX = No Device, Diagnostic**

182   MS-DRG Version 33.0   © 2015 Optum360, LLC

S92.23[4,5,6][D,G,S] Nondisp fx of intermediate cuneiform of [rt, lt, unsp] foot, [subsq enc for fx w/ routine healing, subsq enc for fx w/ delayed healing, seq]

S92.24[1,2,3][D,G,S] Disp fx of med cuneiform of [rt, lt, unsp] foot, [subsq enc for fx w/ routine healing, subsq enc for fx w/ delayed healing, seq]

S92.24[4,5,6][D,G,S] Nondisp fx of med cuneiform of [rt, lt, unsp] foot, [subsq enc for fx w/ routine healing, subsq enc for fx w/ delayed healing, seq]

S92.25[1,2,3][D,G,S] Disp fx of navicular (scaphoid) of [rt, lt, unsp] foot, [subsq enc for fx w/ routine healing, subsq enc for fx w/ delayed healing, seq]

S92.25[4,5,6][D,G,S] Nondisp fx of navicular (scaphoid) of [rt, lt, unsp] foot, [subsq enc for fx w/ routine healing, subsq enc for fx w/ delayed healing, seq]

S92.30[1,2,9][D,G,S] Fx of unsp metatarsal bone(s), [rt, lt, unsp] foot, [subsq enc for fx w/ routine healing, subsq enc for fx w/ delayed healing, seq]

S92.31[1,2,3][D,G,S] Disp fx of 1st metatarsal bone, [rt, lt, unsp] foot, [subsq enc for fx w/ routine healing, subsq enc for fx w/ delayed healing, seq]

S92.31[4,5,6][D,G,S] Nondisp fx of 1st metatarsal bone, [rt, lt, unsp] foot, [subsq enc for fx w/ routine healing, subsq enc for fx w/ delayed healing, seq]

S92.32[1,2,3][D,G,S] Disp fx of 2nd metatarsal bone, [rt, lt, unsp] foot, [subsq enc for fx w/ routine healing, subsq enc for fx w/ delayed healing, seq]

S92.32[4,5,6][D,G,S] Nondisp fx of 2nd metatarsal bone, [rt, lt, unsp] foot, [subsq enc for fx w/ routine healing, subsq enc for fx w/ delayed healing, seq]

S92.33[1,2,3][D,G,S] Disp fx of 3rd metatarsal bone, [rt, lt, unsp] foot, [subsq enc for fx w/ routine healing, subsq enc for fx w/ delayed healing, seq]

S92.33[4,5,6][D,G,S] Nondisp fx of 3rd metatarsal bone, [rt, lt, unsp] foot, [subsq enc for fx w/ routine healing, subsq enc for fx w/ delayed healing, seq]

S92.34[1,2,3][D,G,S] Disp fx of 4th metatarsal bone, [rt, lt, unsp] foot, [subsq enc for fx w/ routine healing, subsq enc for fx w/ delayed healing, seq]

S92.34[4,5,6][D,G,S] Nondisp fx of 4th metatarsal bone, [rt, lt, unsp] foot, [subsq enc for fx w/ routine healing, subsq enc for fx w/ delayed healing, seq]

S92.35[1,2,3][D,G,S] Disp fx of 5th metatarsal bone, [rt, lt, unsp] foot, [subsq enc for fx w/ routine healing, subsq enc for fx w/ delayed healing, seq]

S92.35[4,5,6][D,G,S] Nondisp fx of 5th metatarsal bone, [rt, lt, unsp] foot, [subsq enc for fx w/ routine healing, subsq enc for fx w/ delayed healing, seq]

S92.40[1,2,3][D,G,S] Disp unsp fx of [rt, lt, unsp] great toe, [subsq enc for fx w/ routine healing, subsq enc for fx w/ delayed healing, seq]

S92.40[4,5,6][D,G,S] Nondisp unsp fx of [rt, lt, unsp] great toe, [subsq enc for fx w/ routine healing, subsq enc for fx w/ delayed healing, seq]

S92.41[1,2,3][D,G,S] Disp fx of proximal phalanx of [rt, lt, unsp] great toe, [subsq enc for fx w/ routine healing, subsq enc for fx w/ delayed healing, seq]

S92.41[4,5,6][D,G,S] Nondisp fx of proximal phalanx of [rt, lt, unsp] great toe, [subsq enc for fx w/ routine healing, subsq enc for fx w/ delayed healing, seq]

S92.42[1,2,3][D,G,S] Disp fx of distal phalanx of [rt, lt, unsp] great toe, [subsq enc for fx w/ routine healing, subsq enc for fx w/ delayed healing, seq]

S92.42[4,5,6][D,G,S] Nondisp fx of distal phalanx of [rt, lt, unsp] great toe, [subsq enc for fx w/ routine healing, subsq enc for fx w/ delayed healing, seq]

S92.49[1,2,9][D,G,S] Oth fx of [rt, lt, unsp] great toe, [subsq enc for fx w/ routine healing, subsq enc for fx w/ delayed healing, seq]

S92.50[1,2,3][D,G,S] Disp unsp fx of [rt, lt, unsp] lesser toe(s), [subsq enc for fx w/ routine healing, subsq enc for fx w/ delayed healing, seq]

S92.50[4,5,6][D,G,S] Nondisp unsp fx of [rt, lt, unsp] lesser toe(s), [subsq enc for fx w/ routine healing, subsq enc for fx w/ delayed healing, seq]

S92.51[1,2,3][D,G,S] Disp fx of proximal phalanx of [rt, lt, unsp] lesser toe(s), [subsq enc for fx w/ routine healing, subsq enc for fx w/ delayed healing, seq]

S92.51[4,5,6][D,G,S] Nondisp fx of proximal phalanx of [rt, lt, unsp] lesser toe(s), [subsq enc for fx w/ routine healing, subsq enc for fx w/ delayed healing, seq]

S92.52[1,2,3][D,G,S] Disp fx of med phalanx of [rt, lt, unsp] lesser toe(s), [subsq enc for fx w/ routine healing, subsq enc for fx w/ delayed healing, seq]

S92.52[4,5,6][D,G,S] Nondisp fx of med phalanx of [rt, lt, unsp] lesser toe(s), [subsq enc for fx w/ routine healing, subsq enc for fx w/ delayed healing, seq]

S92.53[1,2,3][D,G,S] Disp fx of distal phalanx of [rt, lt, unsp] lesser toe(s), [subsq enc for fx w/ routine healing, subsq enc for fx w/ delayed healing, seq]

S92.53[4,5,6][D,G,S] Nondisp fx of distal phalanx of [rt, lt, unsp] lesser toe(s), [subsq enc for fx w/ routine healing, subsq enc for fx w/ delayed healing, seq]

S92.59[1,2,9][D,G,S] Oth fx of [rt, lt, unsp] lesser toe(s), [subsq enc for fx w/ routine healing, subsq enc for fx w/ delayed healing, seq]

S92.90[1,2,9][D,G,S] Unsp fx of [rt, lt, unsp] foot, [subsq enc for fx w/ routine healing, subsq enc for fx w/ delayed healing, seq]

S92.91[1,2,9][D,G,S] Unsp fx of [rt, lt, unsp] toe(s), [subsq enc for fx w/ routine healing, subsq enc for fx w/ delayed healing, seq]

S98.0[1,2][1,2,9]S [Complete, Partial] traum amp of [rt, lt, unsp] foot at ankle lvl, seq

S98.1[1,2][1,2,9]S [Complete, Partial] traum amp of [rt, lt, unsp] great toe, seq

S98.1[3,4][1,2,9]S [Complete, Partial] traum amp of one [rt, lt, unsp] lesser toe, seq

S98.2[1,2][1,2,9]S [Complete, Partial] traum amp of two or more [rt, lt, unsp] lesser toes, seq

S98.3[1,2][1,2,9]S [Complete, Partial] traum amp of [rt, lt, unsp] midfoot, seq

S98.9[1,2][1,2,9]S [Complete, Partial] traum amp of [rt, lt, unsp] foot, lvl unsp, seq

T84.01[0,1,2,3,8,9]A Broken int [rt hip, lt hip, rt knee, lt knee, oth site, unsp site] prosthesis, init enc

T84.02[0,1]A Disloc of int [rt, lt] hip prosthesis, init enc

T84.02[2,3]A Instability of int [rt, lt] knee prosthesis, init enc

T84.02[8,9]A Disloc of [oth, unsp] int jt prosthesis, init enc

T84.03[0,1,2,3,8,9]A Mech loosening of [rt hip, lt hip, rt knee, lt knee, oth site, unsp site] prosthesis, init enc

T84.04[0,1][A,D] Periprosthetic fx around int prosthetic [rt, lt] hip jt, [init, subsq] enc

T84.04[2,3][A,D] Periprosthetic fx around int prosthetic [rt, lt] knee jt, [init, subsq] enc

T84.04[8,9][A,D] Periprosthetic fx around [oth, unsp] int prosthetic jt, [init, subsq] enc

T84.05[0,1,2,3,8,9]A Periprosthetic osteolysis [rt hip, lt hip, rt knee, lt knee, oth site, unsp site] prosthesis, init enc

T84.06[0,1,2,3,8,9]A Wear of articular bearing surface of int prosthetic [rt hip, lt hip, rt knee, lt knee, oth site, unsp site] jt, init enc

T84.09[0,1,2,3,8,9]A Oth mech comp of [rt hip, lt hip, rt knee, lt knee, oth jt, unsp jt] prosthesis, init enc

T84.11[0,1,2,3,4,5,6,7,9]A Breakdown (mech) of int fix dev of [rt humerus, lt humerus, bone of rt forearm, bone of lt forearm, rt femur, lt femur, bone of rt lwr leg, bone of lt lwr leg, unsp bone of limb], init enc

T84.12[0,1,2,3,4,5,6,7,9]A Displac of int fix dev of [rt humerus, lt humerus, bone of rt forearm, bone of lt forearm, rt femur, lt femur, bone of rt lwr leg, bone of lt lwr leg, unsp bone of limb], init enc

T84.19[0,1,2,3,4,5,6,7,9]A Oth mech comp of int fix dev of [rt humerus, lt humerus, bone of rt forearm, bone of lt forearm, rt femur, lt femur, bone of rt lwr leg, bone of lt lwr leg, unsp bone of limb], init enc

T84.21[0,3,6,8]A Breakdown (mech) of int fix dev of [bones of hand and fingers, bones of foot and toes, vertebrae, oth bones], init enc

T84.22[0,3,6,8]A Displac of int fix dev of [bones of hand and fingers, bones of foot and toes, vertebrae, oth bones], init enc

T84.29[0,3,6,8]A Oth mech comp of int fix dev of [bones of hand and fingers, bones of foot and toes, vertebrae, oth bones], init enc

T84.3[1,2,9][0,8]A [Breakdown (mech), Displac, Oth mech comp] of [electronic bone stimulator, oth bone dev(s), implants and grafts], init enc

T84.4[1,2,9][0,8]A [Breakdown (mech), Displac, Oth mech comp] of [muscle and tndn graft, oth int orthopedic dev(s), implants and graft], init enc

T84.5[0,1,2,3,4,9]XA Infxn and inflam reaction d/t [unsp int jt, int rt hip, int lt hip, int rt knee, int lt knee, oth int jt] prosthesis, init enc

T84.60XA Infect/inflm reaction d/t int fix of unsp site, init

T84.61[0,1,2,3,4,5,9]A Infxn and inflam reaction d/t int fix dev of [rt humerus, lt humerus, rt radius, lt radius, rt ulna, lt ulna, unsp bone of arm], init enc

T84.62[0,1,2,3,4,5,9]A Infxn and inflam reaction d/t int fix dev of [rt femur, lt femur, rt tibia, lt tibia, rt fibula, lt fibula, unsp bone of leg], init enc

T84.6[3,9]XA Infxn and inflam reaction d/t int fix dev of [spine, oth site], init enc

T84.7XXA Infect/inflm react d/t oth int orth prosth dev/grft, init

---

Surgical   **Medical**   **CC Indicator**   **MCC Indicator**   **Procedure Proxy**   PDxMCC **PDx acts as own MCC**   PDxCC **PDx acts as own CC**

T84.8[1,2,3,4,5,6,9]XA	[Embolism, Fibrosis, Hemor, Pain, Stenosis, Thrombosis, Oth spec comp] d/t int orthopedic prosthetic devs, implants and grafts, init enc
T84.9XXA	Unsp comp of int orthopedic prosth dev/grft, init
T87.0X[1,2,9]	Comps of reattached (part of) [rt, lt, unsp] upr extr
T87.1X[1,2,9]	Comps of reattached (part of) [rt, lt, unsp] lwr extr
T87.2	Comp of oth reattached body part
Z44.0[0,1,2][1,2,9]	Enc for fitting and adjustment of [unsp, complete, partial][rt, lt, unsp] artfcl arm
Z44.1[0,1,2][1,2,9]	Enc for fitting and adjustment of [unsp, complete, partial][rt, lt, unsp] artfcl leg
Z47.1	Aftercare following jt replace surgery
Z47.2	Enc for rmvl of int fix device
Z47.3*	Aftercare following explantation of jt prosthesis
Z47.89	Enc for oth orthopedic aftercare
Z47.8[1,2]	Enc for orthopedic aftercare following [surgical amp, scoliosis surgery]

DRG 560   Aftercare, Musculoskeletal System and Connective Tissue with CC

GMLOS 3.5	AMLOS 4.4	RW 1.0814	T

Select principal diagnosis listed under DRG 559

DRG 561   Aftercare, Musculoskeletal System and Connective Tissue without CC/MCC

GMLOS 2.1	AMLOS 2.6	RW 0.6842	T

Select principal diagnosis listed under DRG 559

DRG 562   Fracture, Sprain, Strain and Dislocation Except Femur, Hip, Pelvis and Thigh with MCC

GMLOS 4.2	AMLOS 5.3	RW 1.3662	T

Principal Diagnosis

M22*	D/o of patella
M23.0*	Cystic meniscus
M23.2*	Derangement of meniscus d/t old tear or inj
M23.3*	Oth meniscus derangements
M23.6*	Oth spontaneous disruption of lgmt(s) of knee
M23.8*	Oth int derangements of knee
M23.9*	Unsp int derangement of knee
M24.17[1,2,3]	Oth articular cartilage d/os, [rt, lt, unsp] ankle
M24.17[4,5,6]	Oth articular cartilage d/os, [rt, lt, unsp] foot
M24.1[1,2,3,4][1,2,9]	Oth articular cartilage d/os, [rt, lt, unsp] [shldr, elbow, wrist, hand]
M24.30	Path disloc of unsp jt, NEC
M24.37[1,2,3]	Path disloc of [rt, lt, unsp] ankle, NEC
M24.37[4,5,6]	Path disloc of [rt, lt, unsp] foot, NEC
M24.3[1,2,3,4,6][1,2,9]	Path disloc of [rt, lt, unsp] [shldr, elbow, wrist, hand, knee], NEC
M24.44[1,2,3]	Recurrent disloc,[rt, lt, unsp] hand
M24.44[4,5,6]	Recurrent disloc, [rt, lt, unsp] finger
M24.46[1,2,9]	Recurrent disloc, [rt, lt, unsp] knee
M24.47[1,2,3]	Recurrent disloc, [rt, lt, unsp] ankle
M24.47[4,5,6]	Recurrent disloc, [rt, lt, unsp] foot
M24.47[7,8,9]	Recurrent disloc, [rt, lt, unsp] toes
M24.4[1,2,3][1,2,9]	Recurrent disloc, [rt, lt, unsp] [shldr, elbow, wrist]
M99.1[6,7,9]	Sublux complex (vert) [lwr extr, upr extr, abd and oth rgns]
Q68.6	Discoid meniscus
S03.0XXS	Disloc of jaw, seq
S03.1XXA	Disloc of septal cartilage of nose, init enc
S03.1XXS	Disloc of septal cartilage of nose, seq
S03.4XXS	Sprain of jaw, seq
S03.8XXS	Sprain of jts and lgmt of oth parts of head, seq
S03.9XXA	Sprain of jts and lgmt of unsp parts of head, init
S03.9XXS	Sprain of jts and lgmt of unsp parts of head, seq
S09.11XS	Strain of muscle and tndn of head, seq
S13.0XXS	Traum rupture of cervical intervertebral disc, seq
S13.10[0,1]S	[Sublux, Disloc] of unsp cervical verterae, seq
S13.11[0,1]S	[Sublux, Disloc] of C0/C1 cervical verterae, seq
S13.12[0,1]S	[Sublux, Disloc] of C1/C2 cervical verterae, seq
S13.13[0,1]S	[Sublux, Disloc] of C2/C3 cervical verterae, seq
S13.14[0,1]S	[Sublux, Disloc] of C3/C4 cervical verterae, seq
S13.15[0,1]S	[Sublux, Disloc] of C4/C5 cervical verterae, seq
S13.16[0,1]S	[Sublux, Disloc] of C5/C6 cervical verterae, seq
S13.17[0,1]S	[Sublux, Disloc] of C6/C7 cervical verterae, seq
S13.18[0,1]S	[Sublux, Disloc] of C7/T1 cervical verterae, seq
S13.2[0,9]XS	Disloc of [unsp, oth] parts of neck, seq
S13.[4,5]XXS	Sprain of [lgmts of cervical spine, thyroid rgn], seq
S13.[8,9]XXS	Sprain of jts and lgmts, parts of neck {oth, unsp]
S16.1XXS	Strain of muscle and tndn at neck lvl, seq
S23.0XXS	Traum rupture of thoracic intervertebral disc, seq
S23.10[0,1]S	[Sublux, Disloc] of unsp thoracic vertebra, seq
S23.11[0,1]S	[Sublux, Disloc] of T1/T2 thoracic vertebra, seq
S23.12[0,1]S	[Sublux, Disloc] of T2/T3 thoracic vertebra, seq
S23.12[2,3]S	[Sublux, Disloc] of T3/T4 thoracic vertebra, seq
S23.13[0,1]S	[Sublux, Disloc] of T4/T5 thoracic vertebra, seq
S23.13[2,3]S	[Sublux, Disloc] of T5/T6 thoracic vertebra, seq
S23.14[0,1]S	[Sublux, Disloc] of T6/T7 thoracic vertebra, seq
S23.14[2,3]S	[Sublux, Disloc] of T7/T8 thoracic vertebra, seq
S23.15[0,1]S	[Sublux, Disloc] of T8/T9 thoracic vertebra, seq
S23.15[2,3]S	[Sublux, Disloc] of T9/T10 thoracic vertebra, seq
S23.16[0,1]S	[Sublux, Disloc] of T10/T11 thoracic vertebra, seq
S23.16[2,3]S	[Sublux, Disloc] of T11/T12 thoracic vertebra, seq
S23.17[0,1]S	[Sublux, Disloc] of T12/L1 thoracic vertebra, seq
S23.2[0,9]XS	Disloc of [unsp, oth] part of thorax, seq
S23.3XXS	Sprain of lgmt of thoracic spine, seq
S23.41XS	Sprain of ribs, seq
S23.42[0,1,8,9]S	Sprain of sternum [sternoclavicular (jt) (lgmt), chondrosternal jt, oth, unsp], seq
S23.[8,9]XXS	Sprain of oth parts of thorax [oth spec, unsp]
S29.01[1,2,9][A,S]	Strain of muscle and tndn of wall of thorax [front, back, unsp] [Init enc, seq]
S33.0XXS	Traum rupture of lumbar intervertebral disc, seq
S33.10[0,1]S	[Sublux, disloc] of unsp lumbar vertebra, seq
S33.11[0,1]S	[Sublux, disloc] of L1/L2 lumbar vertebra, seq
S33.12[0,1]S	[Sublux, disloc] of L2/L3 lumbar vertebra, seq
S33.13[0,1]S	[Sublux, disloc] of L3/L4 lumbar vertebra, seq
S33.14[0,1]S	[Sublux, disloc] of L4/L5 lumbar vertebra, seq
S33.2XXS	Disloc of sacroiliac and sacrococcygeal jt, seq
S33.3[0,9]X[A,S]	Disloc of of parts of lumbar spine and pelvis [unsp, oth] [Init enc, seq]
S33.4XXS	Traum rupture of symphysis pubis, seq
S33.[5,6,8,9]XXS	Sprain [lgmts of lumbar spine, sacroiliac jt, oth parts of lumbar spine and pelvis, unsp parts of lumbar spine and pelvis, seq
S39.01[1,2,3][A,S]	Strain of muscle, fascia, and tndn of [abd, lwr back, pelvis][init enc, seq]
S42.00[1,2,9][A,B]	Fx of unsp part of clavicle [rt, lt, unsp] init enc for fx [clsd, opn]
S42.01[1,2,3][A,B]	Ant disp fx of if sternal end of clavicle [rt, lt, unsp] init enc for fx [clsd, opn]
S42.01[4,5,6][A,B]	Post disp fx of if sternal end of clavicle [rt, lt, unsp] init enc for fx [clsd, opn
S42.01[7,8,9][A,B]	Nondisp fx of sternal end of clavicle [rt, lt, unsp] init enc for fx [clsd, opn]
S42.02[1,2,3][A,B]	Disp fx of shaft of clavicle [rt, lt, unsp] init enc for fx [clsd, opn]
S42.02[4,5,6][A,B]	Nondisp fx of shaft of clavicle [rt, lt, unsp] init enc for fx [clsd, opn]
S42.03[1,2,3][A,B]	Disp fx of lat end of clavicle [rt, lt, unsp] init enc for fx [clsd, opn]
S42.03[4,5,6][A,B]	Nondisp fx of lat end of clavicle [rt, lt, unsp] init enc for fx [clsd, opn]
S42.10[1,2,9][A,B]	Fx of unsp part of scapula, [rt, lt, unsp] shldr, init enc for [clsd, opn] fx
S42.12[1,2,3][A,B]	Disp fx of acromial process [rt, lt, unsp] init enc for fx [clsd, opn]
S42.12[4,5,6][A,B]	Nondisp fx of acromial process [rt, lt, unsp] init enc for fx [clsd, opn]
S42.13[1,2,3][A,B]	Disp fx of coracoid process of shldr [rt, lt, unsp] init enc for fx [clsd, opn]
S42.13[4,5,6][A,B]	Nondisp fx of coracoid process of shldr [rt, lt, unsp] init enc for fx [clsd, opn]
S42.14[1,2,3][A,B]	Disp fx of glenoid cavity of scapula [rt, lt, unsp] init enc for fx [clsd, opn]
S42.14[4,5,6][A,B]	Nondisp fx of glenoid cavity of scapula [rt, lt, unsp] init enc for fx [clsd, opn]
S42.15[1,2,3][A,B]	Nondisp fx of neck of scapula [rt, lt, unsp] init enc for fx [clsd, opn]
S42.15[4,5,6][A,B]	Nondisp fx of neck of scapula [rt, lt, unsp] init enc for fx [clsd, opn]
S42.20[1,2,9][A,B]	Unsp fx of upr end of [rt, lt, unsp] humerus, init enc for [clsd, opn] fx
S42.21[1,2,3][A,B]	Unsp disp fx of surgical neck of humerus [rt, lt, unsp] init enc for fx [clsd, opn]
S42.21[4,5,6][A,B]	Unsp nondisp fx of surgical neck of humerus [rt, lt, unsp] init enc for fx [clsd, opn]
S42.22[1,2,3][A,B]	Disp 2-part fx of surgical neck of humerus [rt, lt, unsp] init enc for fx, clsd, opn]

T Transfer DRG   SP Special Payment   * Code Range   6th and 7th Character of ZZ = No Device, No Qualifier ZX = No Device, Diagnostic

184   MS-DRG Version 33.0   © 2015 Optum360, LLC

S42.22[4,5,6][A,B] Nondisp 2-part fx of surgical neck of humerus [rt, lt, unsp] init enc for fx [clsd, opn]	S42.49[4,5,6][A,B] Oth nondisp fx of lwr end of humerus [rt, lt, unsp] init enc for fx [clsd, opn]
S42.23[1,2,9][A,B] 3-part fx of surgical neck of [rt, lt, unsp] humerus, init enc for [clsd, opn] fx	S42.9[0,1,2]X[A,B] Fx of [unsp, rt, lt] shldr girdle, part unsp, init enc for [clsd, opn]
S42.24[1,2,9][A,B] 4-part fx of surgical neck of [rt, lt, unsp] humerus, init enc for [clsd, opn] fx	S43.00[1,2,3][A,S] Unsp sublux of shldr jt [rt, lt, unsp] [init enc, seq]
S42.25[1,2,3][A,B] Disp fx of greater tuberosity of humerus [rt, lt, unsp] init enc for fx [clsd, opn]	S43.00[4,5,6][A,S] Unsp disloc of shldr jt [rt, lt, unsp] [init enc, seq]
S42.25[4,5,6][A,B] Nondisp fx of greater tuberosity of humerus [rt, lt, unsp] init enc for fx [clsd, opn]	S43.01[1,2,3][A,S] Ant sublux of humerus [rt, lt, unsp] [init enc, seq]
	S43.01[4,5,6][A,S] Ant disloc of humerus [rt, lt, unsp] [init enc, seq]
S42.26[1,2,3][A,B] Disp fx of lesser tuberosity of humerus [rt, lt, unsp] init enc for fx [clsd, opn]	S43.02[1,2,3][A,S] Post sublux of [rt, lt, unsp] humerus, [init enc, seq]
S42.26[4,5,6][A,B] Nondisp fx of lesser tuberosity of humerus [rt, lt, unsp] init enc for fx [clsd, opn]	S43.02[4,5,6][A,S] Post disloc of humerus [rt, lt, unsp] [init enc, seq]
S42.27[1,2,9]A Torus fx of upr end of humerus [rt, lt, unsp] init enc for clsd fx	S43.03[1,2,3][A,S] Inferior sublux of humerus [rt, lt, unsp] [init enc, seq]
S42.29[1,2,3][A,B] Oth disp fx of upr end of [rt, lt, unsp] humerus, init enc for [clsd, opn] fx	S43.03[4,5,6][A,S] Inferior disloc of humerus [rt, lt, unsp] [init enc, seq]
	S43.08[1,2,3][A,S] Oth sublux of shldr jt [rt, lt, unsp] [init enc, seq]
S42.29[4,5,6][A,B] Oth nondisp fx of upr end of humerus [rt, lt, unsp] init enc for clsd fx	S43.08[4,5,6][A,S] Oth disloc of shldr jt [rt, lt, unsp] [init enc, seq]
S42.30[1,2,9][A,B] Unsp fx of shaft of humerus [rt, lt, unsp] arm, init enc for [clsd, opn] fx	S43.10[1,2,9][A,S] Unsp disloc of acromioclavicular jt {rt, lt, unsp} [init enc, seq]
S42.31[1,2,9]A Greenstick fx of shaft of humerus, [rt, lt, unsp] arm, init enc for clsd fx	S43.11[1,2,9][A,S] Sublux of acromioclavicular jt {rt, lt, unsp} [init enc, seq]
S42.32[1,2,3][A,B] Disp transv fx of shaft of humerus [rt, lt, unsp] init enc for fx [clsd, opn]	S43.12[1,2,9][A,S] Disloc of acromioclavicular jt, 100%-200% displac {rt, lt, unsp} [init enc, seq]
S42.32[4,5,6][A,B] Nondisp transv fx of shaft of humerus [rt, lt, unsp] init enc for fx [clsd, opn]	S43.13[1,2,9][A,S] Disloc of acromioclavicular jt, > 200% displac {rt, lt, unsp} [init enc, seq]
S42.33[1,2,3][A,B] Disp oblique fx of shaft of humerus [rt, lt, unsp] init enc for fx [clsd, opn]	S43.14[1,2,9][A,S] Inferior disloc of acromioclavicular jt, > 200% displac {rt, lt, unsp} [init enc, seq]
S42.33[4,5,6][A,B] Nondisp oblique fx of shaft of humerus [rt, lt, unsp] init enc for fx [clsd, opn]	S43.15[1,2,9][A,S] Post disloc of acromioclavicular jt, > 200% displac {rt, lt, unsp} [init enc, seq]
S42.34[1,2,3][A,B] Disp spiral fx of shaft of humerus [rt, lt, unsp] init enc for fx [clsd, opn]	S43.20[1,2,3]S Unsp sublux of [rt, lt, unsp] sternoclavicular jt, seq
S42.34[4,5,6][A,B] Nondisp spiral fx of shaft of humerus [rt, lt, unsp] init enc for fx [clsd, opn]	S43.20[4,5,6]S Unsp disloc of [rt, lt, unsp] sternoclavicular jt, seq
	S43.21[1,2,3]S Ant sublux of [rt, lt, unsp] sternoclavicular jt, seq
S42.35[1,2,3][A,B] Disp comm fx of shaft of humerus [rt, lt, unsp] init enc for fx [clsd, opn]	S43.21[4,5,6]S Ant disloc of [rt, lt, unsp] sternoclavicular jt, seq
S42.35[4,5,6][A,B] Nondisp comm fx of shaft of humerus [rt, lt, unsp] init enc for fx [clsd, opn]	S43.22[1,2,3]S Post sublux of [rt, lt, unsp] sternoclavicular jt, seq
	S43.22[4,5,6]S Post disloc of [rt, lt, unsp] sternoclavicular jt, seq
S42.36[1,2,3][A,B] Disp seg fx of shaft of humerus [rt, lt, unsp] init enc for fx [clsd, opn]	S43.30[1,2,3][A,S] Sublux of unsp parts of shldr girdle [rt, lt, unsp] [init enc, seq]
S42.36[4,5,6][A,B] Nondisp seg fx of shaft of humerus [rt, lt, unsp] init enc for fx [clsd, opn]	S43.30[4,5,6][A,S] Disloc of unsp parts of shldr girdle [rt, lt, unsp] [init enc, seq]
	S43.31[1,2,3][A,S] Sublux of scapula [rt, lt, unsp] [init enc, seq]
S42.39[1,2,9][A,B] Oth fx of shaft of [rt, lt, unsp] humerus, init enc for [clsd, opn] fx	S43.31[4,5,6][A,S] Disloc of scapula [rt, lt, unsp] [init enc, seq]
S42.40[1,2,9][A,B] Unsp fx of lwr end of [rt, lt, unsp] humerus, init enc for [clsd, opn] fx	S43.39[1,2,3][A,S] Sublux of oth parts of shldr girdle [rt, lt, unsp] [init enc, seq]
	S43.39[4,5,6][A,S] Disloc of oth parts of shldr girdle [rt, lt, unsp] [init enc, seq]
S42.41[1,2,3][A,B] Disp simple supracondylar fx w/o intercondylar fx of humerus [rt, lt, unsp] init enc for fx [clsd, opn]	S43.40[1,2,9][A,S] Unsp sprain of shldr [rt, lt, unsp] [init enc, seq]
S42.41[4,5,6][A,B] Nondisp simple supracondylar fx w/o intercondylar fx of humerus [rt, lt, unsp] init enc for fx [clsd, opn]	S43.41[1,2,9][A,S] Sprain of coracohumeral (lgmt) [rt, lt, unsp] [init enc, seq]
S42.42[1,2,3][A,B] Disp comm supracondylar fx w/o intercondylar fx of humerus [rt, lt, unsp] init enc for fx [clsd, opn]	S43.42[1,2,9][A,S] Sprain of rotator cuff capsule [rt, lt, unsp] [init enc, seq]
S42.42[4,5,6][A,B] Nondisp comm supracondylar fx w/o intercondylar fx of humerus [rt, lt, unsp] init enc for fx [clsd, opn]	S43.43[1,2,9][A,S] Superior glenoid labrum lesion of shldr [rt, lt, unsp] [init enc, seq]
S42.43[1,2,3][A,B] Disp fx (avulsion) of lat epicondyle of humerus [rt, lt, unsp] init enc for fx [clsd, opn]	S43.49[1,2,9][A,S] Oth sprain of shldr jt [rt, lt, unsp] [init enc, seq]
	S43.5[0,1,2]X[A,S] Sprain of acromioclavicular jt [unsp, rt, lt] [init enc, seq]
S42.43[4,5,6][A,B] Nondisp fx (avulsion) of lat epicondyle of humerus [rt, lt, unsp] init enc for fx [clsd, opn]	S43.6[0,1,2]X[A,S] Sprain of [unsp, rt, lt] sternoclavicular jt, [init enc, seq]
S42.44[1,2,3][A,B] Disp fx (avulsion) of med epicondyle of humerus [rt, lt, unsp] init enc for fx [clsd, opn]	S43.8[0,1,2]X[A,S] Sprain of oth unsp parts of shldr girdle [unsp, rt, lt] [init enc, seq]
S42.44[4,5,6][A,B] Nondisp fx (avulsion) of med epicondyle of humerus [rt, lt, unsp] init enc for fx [clsd, opn]	S43.9[0,1,2]X[A,S] Sprain of unsp parts of shldr girdle [unsp, rt, lt]
S42.44[7,8,9][A,B] Incarcerated fx (avulsion) of med epicondyle of humerus [rt, lt, unsp] init enc for fx [clsd, opn]	S46.01[1,2,9][A,S] Strain of muscle(s) and tndn(s) of the rotator cuff of shldr [rt, lt, unsp] [init enc, seq]
S42.45[1,2,3][A,B] Disp fx of lat condyle of humerus [rt, lt, unsp] init enc for fx [clsd, opn]	S46.11[1,2,9][A,S] Strain of muscle, fascia and tndn of long head of biceps [rt, lt, unsp] [init enc, seq]
S42.45[4,5,6][A,B] Nondisp fx of lat condyle of humerus [rt, lt, unsp] init enc for fx [clsd, opn]	S46.21[1,2,9][A,S] Strain of muscle, fascia and tndn of oth parts of biceps [rt, lt, unsp] [init enc, seq]
S42.46[1,2,3][A,B] Disp fx of med condyle of humerus [rt, lt, unsp] init enc for fx [clsd, opn]	S46.31[1,2,9][A,S] Strain of muscle, fascia and tndn of triceps [rt, lt, unsp] [init enc, seq]
S42.46[4,5,6][A,B] Nondisp fx of med condyle of humerus [rt, lt, unsp] init enc for fx [clsd, opn]	S46.81[1,2,9][A,S] Strain of oth muscles, fascia and tndns at shldr and upr arm lvl, [rt, lt, unsp] arm, [init enc, seq]
S42.47[1,2,3][A,B] Disp transcondylar fx of humerus [rt, lt, unsp] init enc for fx [clsd, opn]	S46.91[1,2,9][A,S] Strain of unsp muscle, fascia and tndn at shldr and upr arm lvl [rt, lt, unsp] [init enc, seq]
S42.47[4,5,6][A,B] Nondisp transcondylar fx of humerus [rt, lt, unsp] init enc for fx [clsd, opn]	S49.00[1,2,9]A Unsp physeal fx of upr end of humerus [rt, lt, unsp], init enc for clsd fx
S42.48[1,2,9]A Torus fx of lwr end of [rt, lt, unsp] humerus, init enc for clsd fx	S49.01[1,2,9]A Salter-Harris Type I physeal fx of upr end of humerus [rt, lt, unsp], init enc for clsd fx
S42.49[1,2,3][A,B] Oth disp fx of lwr end of humerus [rt, lt, unsp] init enc for fx [clsd, opn]	S49.02[1,2,9]A Salter-Harris Type II physeal fx of upr end of [rt, lt, unsp] humerus, init enc for clsd fx
	S49.03[1,2,9]A Salter-Harris Type III physeal fx of upr end of humerus [rt, lt, unsp], init enc for clsd fx
	S49.04[1,2,9]A Salter-Harris Type IV physeal fx of upr end of humerus [rt, lt, unsp], init enc for clsd fx
	S49.09[1,2,9]A Oth physeal fx of upr end of humerus [rt, lt, unsp], init enc for clsd fx
	S49.10[1,2,9][A] Physeal fx of lwr end of humerus [rt, lt, unsp] init enc
	S49.11[1,2,9]A Salter-Harris Type I physeal fx of lwr end of humerus [rt, lt, unsp] init enc
	S49.12[1,2,9]A Salter-Harris Type II physeal fx of lwr end of [rt, lt, unsp] humerus, init enc
	S49.13[1,2,9]A Salter-Harris Type III physeal fx of lwr end of humerus [rt, lt, unsp] init enc
	S49.14[1,2,9]A Salter-Harris Type IV physeal fx of lwr end of humerus [rt, lt, unsp] init enc

Surgical   **Medical**   **CC Indicator**   **MCC Indicator**   **Procedure Proxy**   **PDxMCC PDx acts as own MCC**   **PDxCC PDx acts as own CC**

S49.19[1,2,9]A   Oth physeal fx of lwr end of humerus [rt, lt, unsp] init enc
S52.00[1,2,9][A,B,C] Unsp fx of upr end of [rt, lt, unsp] ulna, init enc for [clsd fx, opn fx type I or II, opn fx type IIIA, IIIB, or IIIC]
S52.01[1,2,9]A   Torus fx of upr end of [rt, lt, unsp] ulna, init enc for clsd fx
S52.02[1,2,3][A,B,C] Disp fx of olecranon process w/o intraarticular extension of ulna [rt, lt, unsp] init enc for fx [clsd fx, opn fx type I or II or opn fx NOS, opn fx type IIIA, IIIB, or IIIC]
S52.02[4,5,6][A,B,C] Nondisp fx of olecranon process w/o intraarticular extension of ulna [rt, lt, unsp] init enc for fx [clsd fx, opn fx type I or II or opn fx NOS, opn fx type IIIA, IIIB, or IIIC]
S52.03[1,2,3][A,B,C] Disp fx of olecranon process w/ intraarticular extension of ulna [rt, lt, unsp] init enc for fx [clsd fx, opn fx type I or II or opn fx NOS, opn fx type IIIA, IIIB, or IIIC]
S52.03[4,5,6][A,B,C] Nondisp fx of olecranon process w/ intraarticular extension of ulna [rt, lt, unsp] init enc for fx [clsd fx, opn fx type I or II or opn fx NOS, opn fx type IIIA, IIIB, or IIIC]
S52.04[1,2,3][A,B,C] Disp fx of coronoid process of ulna [rt, lt, unsp] init enc for fx [clsd fx, opn fx type I or II or opn fx NOS, opn fx type IIIA, IIIB, or IIIC]
S52.04[4,5,6][A,B,C] Nondisp fx of coronoid process of ulna [rt, lt, unsp] init enc for fx [clsd fx, opn fx type I or II or opn fx NOS, opn fx type IIIA, IIIB, or IIIC]
S52.09[1,2,9][A,B,C] Oth fx of upr end of [rt, lt, unsp] ulna, init enc for [clsd fx, opn fx type I or II, opn fx type IIIA, IIIB, or IIIC]
S52.10[1,2,9][A,B,C] Unsp fx of upr end of [rt, lt, unsp] radius, init enc for [clsd fx, opn fx type I or II, opn fx type IIIA, IIIB, or IIIC]
S52.11[1,2,9]A   Torus fx of upr end of [rt, lt, unsp] radius, init enc for clsd fx
S52.12[1,2,3][A,B,C] Disp fx of head of [rt, lt, unsp] radius, init enc for [clsd fx, opn fx type I or II or opn fx NOS, opn fx type IIIA, IIIB, or IIIC]
S52.12[4,5,6][A,B,C] Nondisp fx of head of radius [rt, lt, unsp] init enc for [clsd fx, opn fx type I or II or opn fx NOS, opn fx type IIIA, IIIB, or IIIC]
S52.13[1,2,3][A,B,C] Disp fx of neck of radius [rt, lt, unsp] init enc for [clsd fx, opn fx type I or II or opn fx NOS, opn fx type IIIA, IIIB, or IIIC]
S52.13[4,5,6][A,B,C] Nondisp fx of neck of radius [rt, lt, unsp] init enc for [clsd fx, opn fx type I or II or opn fx NOS, opn fx type IIIA, IIIB, or IIIC]
S52.18[1,2,9][A,B,C] Oth fx of upr end of [rt, lt, unsp] radius, init enc for [clsd fx, opn fx type I or II, opn fx type IIIA, IIIB, or IIIC]
S52.20[1,2,9][A,B,C] Unsp fx of shaft of [rt, lt, unsp] ulna, init enc for [clsd fx, opn fx type I or II, opn fx type IIIA, IIIB, or IIIC]
S52.21[1,2,9]A   Greenstick fx of shaft of [rt, lt, unsp] ulna, init enc for clsd fx
S52.22[1,2,3][A,B,C] Disp transv fx of ulna {rt, lt, unsp} init enc for [clsd fx, opn fx type I or II or opn fx NOS, opn fx type IIIA, IIIB, or IIIC]
S52.22[4,5,6][A,B,C] Nondisp transv fx of ulna {rt, lt, unsp} init enc for [clsd fx, opn fx type I or II or opn fx NOS, opn fx type IIIA, IIIB, or IIIC]
S52.23[1,2,3][A,B,C] Disp oblique fx of ulna [rt, lt, unsp] init enc for [clsd fx, opn fx type I or II or opn fx NOS, opn fx type IIIA, IIIB, or IIIC]
S52.23[4,5,6][A,B,C] Nondisp oblique fx of ulna [rt, lt, unsp} init enc for [clsd fx, opn fx type I or II or opn fx NOS, opn fx type IIIA, IIIB, or IIIC]
S52.24[1,2,3][A,B,C] Disp spiral fx of ulna [rt, lt, unsp} init enc for [clsd fx, opn fx type I or II or opn fx NOS, opn fx type IIIA, IIIB, or IIIC]
S52.24[4,5,6][A,B,C] Nondisp spiral fx of ulna [rt, lt, unsp} init enc for [clsd fx, opn fx type I or II or opn fx NOS, opn fx type IIIA, IIIB, or IIIC]
S52.25[1,2,3][A,B,C] Disp comm fx of ulna [rt, lt, unsp] init enc for [clsd fx, opn fx type I or II or opn fx NOS, opn fx type IIIA, IIIB, or IIIC]
S52.25[4,5,6][A,B,C] Nondisp comm fx of ulna [rt, lt, unsp] init enc for [clsd fx, opn fx type I or II or opn fx NOS, opn fx type IIIA, IIIB, or IIIC]
S52.26[1,2,3][A,B,C] Disp semental fx of shaft of ulna [rt, lt, unsp] init enc for [clsd fx, opn fx type I or II or opn fx NOS, opn fx type IIIA, IIIB, or IIIC]
S52.26[4,5,6][A,B,C] Nondisp semental fx of shaft of ulna [rt, lt, unsp} init enc for [clsd fx, opn fx type I or II or opn fx NOS, opn fx type IIIA, IIIB, or IIIC]
S52.27[1,2,9][A,B,C] Monteggia's fx of [rt, lt, unsp] ulna, init enc for [clsd fx, opn fx type I or II, opn fx type IIIA, IIIB, or IIIC]
S52.28[1,2,3][A,B,C] Bent bone of [rt, lt, unsp] ulna, init enc for [clsd fx, opn fx type I or II, opn fx type IIIA, IIIB, or IIIC]
S52.29[1,2,9][A,B,C] Oth fx of shaft of [rt, lt, unsp] ulna, init enc for [clsd fx, opn fx type I or II, opn fx type IIIA, IIIB, or IIIC]
S52.30[1,2,9][A,B,C] Unsp fx of shaft of [rt, lt, unsp] radius, init enc for [clsd fx, opn fx type I or II, opn fx type IIIA, IIIB, or IIIC]
S52.31[1,2,9]A   Greenstick fx of shaft of radius, [rt, lt, unsp] arm, init enc for clsd fx
S52.32[1,2,3][A,B,C] Disp transv fx of shaft of radius [rt, lt, unsp] init enc for [clsd fx, opn fx type I or II or opn fx NOS, opn fx type IIIA, IIIB, or IIIC]
S52.32[4,5,6][A,B,C] Nondisp transv fx of shaft of radius [rt, lt, unsp} init enc for [clsd fx, opn fx type I or II or opn fx NOS, opn fx type IIIA, IIIB, or IIIC]
S52.33[1,2,3][A,B,C] Disp oblique fx of shaft of radius [rt, lt, unsp] init enc for [clsd fx, opn fx type I or II or opn fx NOS, opn fx type IIIA, IIIB, or IIIC]

S52.33[4,5,6][A,B,C] Nondisp oblique fx of shaft of radius [rt, lt, unsp} init enc for [clsd fx, opn fx type I or II or opn fx NOS, opn fx type IIIA, IIIB, or IIIC]
S52.34[1,2,3][A,B,C] Disp spiral fx of shaft of radius [rt, lt, unsp} init enc for [clsd fx, opn fx type I or II or opn fx NOS, opn fx type IIIA, IIIB, or IIIC]
S52.34[4,5,6][A,B,C] Nondisp spiral fx of shaft of radius [rt, lt, unsp] init enc for [clsd fx, opn fx type I or II or opn fx NOS, opn fx type IIIA, IIIB, or IIIC]
S52.35[1,2,3][A,B,C] Disp comm fx of shaft of radius [rt, lt, unsp] init enc for [clsd fx, opn fx type I or II or opn fx NOS, opn fx type IIIA, IIIB, or IIIC]
S52.35[4,5,6][A,B,C] Nondisp comm fx of shaft of radius [rt, lt, unsp] init enc for [clsd fx, opn fx type I or II or opn fx NOS, opn fx type IIIA, IIIB, or IIIC]
S52.36[1,2,3][A,B,C] Disp seg fx of shaft of radius [rt, lt, unsp] init enc for [clsd fx, opn fx type I or II or opn fx NOS, opn fx type IIIA, IIIB, or IIIC]
S52.36[4,5,6][A,B,C] Nondisp seg fx of shaft of radius [rt, lt, unsp} init enc for [clsd fx, opn fx type I or II or opn fx NOS, opn fx type IIIA, IIIB, or IIIC]
S52.37[1,2,9][A,B,C] Galeazzi's fx of [rt, lt, unsp] radius, init enc for [clsd fx, opn fx type I or II, opn fx type IIIA, IIIB, or IIIC]
S52.38[1,2,9][A,B,C] Bent bone of [rt, lt, unsp] radius, init enc for [clsd fx, opn fx type I or II, opn fx type IIIA, IIIB, or IIIC]
S52.39[1,2,9][A,B,C] Oth fx of shaft of radius [rt, lt, unsp] arm, init enc for [clsd fx, opn fx type I or II, opn fx type IIIA, IIIB, or IIIC]
S52.50[1,2,9][A,B,C] Unsp fx of the lwr end of [rt, lt, unsp] radius, init enc for [clsd fx, opn fx type I or II, opn fx type IIIA, IIIB, or IIIC]
S52.51[1,2,3][A,B,C] Disp fx of [rt, lt, unsp] radial styloid process, init enc for [clsd fx, opn fx type I or II or opn fx NOS, opn fx type IIIA, IIIB, or IIIC]
S52.51[4,5,6][A,B,C] Nondisp fx of radial styloid process [rt, lt, unsp] init enc for [clsd fx, opn fx type I or II or opn fx NOS, opn fx type IIIA, IIIB, or IIIC]
S52.52[1,2,9]A   Torus fx of lwr end of [rt, lt, unsp] radius, init enc for clsd fx
S52.53[1,2,9][A,B,C] Colles' fx of [rt, lt, unsp] radius, init enc for [clsd fx, opn fx type I or II, opn fx type IIIA, IIIB, or IIIC]
S52.54[1,2,9][A,B,C] Smith's fx of [rt, lt, unsp] radius, init enc for [clsd fx, opn fx type I or II, opn fx type IIIA, IIIB, or IIIC]
S52.55[1,2,9][A,B,C] Oth extraarticular fx of lwr end of [rt, lt, unsp] radius, init enc for [clsd fx, opn fx type I or II, opn fx type IIIA, IIIB, or IIIC]
S52.56[1,2,9][A,B,C] Barton's fx of [rt, lt, unsp] radius, init enc for [clsd fx, opn fx type I or II, opn fx type IIIA, IIIB, or IIIC]
S52.57[1,2,9][A,B,C] Oth intraarticular fxs of lwr end of [rt, lt, unsp] radius, init enc for [clsd fx, opn fx type I or II, opn fx type IIIA, IIIB, or IIIC]
S52.59[1,2,9][A,B,C] Oth fxs of lwr end of [rt, lt, unsp] radius, init enc for [clsd fx, opn fx type I or II, opn fx type IIIA, IIIB, or IIIC]
S52.60[1,2,9][A,B,C] Unsp fx of lwr end of [rt, lt, unsp] ulna, init enc for [clsd fx, opn fx type I or II, opn fx type IIIA, IIIB, IIIC]
S52.61[1,2,3][A,B,C] Disp fx of ulna styloid process [rt, lt, unsp] init enc for fx [clsd, opn fx type I or II or opn fx NOS, opn fx type IIIA, IIIB, IIIC]
S52.61[4,5,6][A,B,C] Nondisp fx of ulna styloid process [rt, lt, unsp] init enc for fx [clsd, opn fx type I or II or opn fx NOS, opn fx type IIIA, IIIB, IIIC]
S52.62[1,2,9]A   Torus fx of lwr end of [rt, lt, unsp] ulna, init enc for clsd fx
S52.69[1,2,9][A,B,C] Oth fx of lwr end of [rt, lt, unsp] ulna, init enc for [clsd fx, opn fx type I or II, opn fx type IIIA, IIIB, or IIIC]
S52.9[0,1,2]X[A,B,C] Oth fx of [unsp, rt, lt] forearm, init enc for [clsd fx, opn fx type I or II, opn fx type IIIA, IIIB, IIIC]
S53.00[1,2,3][A,S]   Unsp sublux of radial head [unsp, rt, lt] [init enc, seq]
S53.00[4,5,6][A,S]   Unsp disloc of radial head [unsp, rt, lt] [init enc, seq]
S53.01[1,2,3][A,S]   Ant sublux of radial head [unsp, rt, lt] [init enc, seq]
S53.01[4,5,6][A,S]   Ant disloc of radial head [unsp, rt, lt] [init enc, seq]
S53.02[1,2,3][A,S]   Post sublux of [rt, lt, unsp] radial head, [init enc, seq]
S53.02[4,5,6][A,S]   Post disloc of radial head [unsp, rt, lt] [init enc, seq]
S53.03[1,2,3][A,S]   Nursemaid's elbow [unsp, rt, lt] [init enc, seq]
S53.09[1,2,3][A,S]   Oth sublux of radial head [unsp, rt, lt] [init enc, seq]
S53.09[4,5,6][A,S]   Oth disloc of radial head [unsp, rt, lt] [init enc, seq]
S53.10[1,2,3][A,S]   Unsp sublux of ulnohumeral jt [rt, lt, unsp] [init enc, seq]
S53.10[4,5,6][A,S]   Unsp disloc of ulnohumeral jt [rt, lt, unsp] [init enc, seq]
S53.11[1,2,3][A,S]   Ant sublux of ulnohumeral jt [rt, lt, unsp] [init enc, seq]
S53.11[4,5,6][A,S]   Ant disloc of ulnohumeral jt [rt, lt, unsp] [init enc, seq]
S53.12[1,2,3][A,S]   Post sublux of ulnohumeral jt [rt, lt, unsp] [init enc, seq]
S53.12[4,5,6][A,S]   Post disloc of ulnohumeral jt [rt, lt, unsp] [init enc, seq]
S53.13[1,2,3][A,S]   Med sublux of [rt, lt, unsp] ulnohumeral jt, [init enc, seq]
S53.13[4,5,6][A,S]   Med disloc of [rt, lt, unsp] ulnohumeral jt, [init enc, seq]
S53.14[1,2,3][A,S]   Lat sublux of [rt, lt, unsp] ulnohumeral jt, [init enc, seq]
S53.14[4,5,6][A,S]   Lat disloc of [rt, lt, unsp] ulnohumeral jt, [init enc, seq]
S53.19[1,2,3][A,S]   Oth sublux of [rt, lt, unsp] ulnohumeral jt, [init enc, seq]
S53.19[4,5,6][A,S]   Oth disloc of [rt, lt, unsp] ulnohumeral jt, [init enc, seq]
S53.2[0,1,2]X[A,S]   Traum rupture of [rt, lt, unsp] radial collat lgmt, [init enc, seq]
S53.3[0,1,2]X[A,S]   Traum rupture of [rt, lt, unsp] ulnar collat lgmt, [init enc, seq]
S53.40[1,2,9][A,S]   Sprain of [rt, lt, unsp] elbow, [init enc, seq]
S53.41[1,2,9][A,S]   Radiohumeral (jt) sprain [rt, lt, unsp] [init enc, seq]
S53.42[1,2,9][A,S]   Ulnohumeral (jt) sprain [rt, lt, unsp] [init enc, seq]

Ⓣ **Transfer DRG**   ⓈⓅ **Special Payment**   * **Code Range**   **6th and 7th Character of ZZ = No Device, No Qualifier ZX = No Device, Diagnostic**

S53.43[1,2,9][A,S]	Radial collat lgmt sprain [rt, lt, unsp] [init enc, seq]
S53.44[1,2,9][A,S]	Ulnar collat lgmt sprain [rt, lt, unsp] [init enc, seq]
S53.49[1,2,9][A,S]	Oth sprain of elbow [rt, lt, unsp] [init enc, seq]
S56.01[1,2,9][A,S]	Strain of flexor muscle, fascial and tndn of thumb at forearm lvl [rt, lt, unsp]][init enc, seq]
S56.119[A,S]	Strain of flexor muscle, fascia and tndn of [rt, lt] finger at forearm lvl, [init enc, seq]
S56.11[1,2][A,S]	Strain of flexor muscle, fascia and tndn of [rt, lt] index finger at forearm lvl, [init enc, seq]
S56.11[3,4][A,S]	Strain of flexor muscle, fascia and tndn of [rt, lt] mid finger at forearm lvl, [init enc, seq]
S56.11[5,6][A,S]	Strain of flexor muscle, fascia and tndn of [rt, lt] ring finger at forearm lvl, [init enc, seq]
S56.11[7,8][A,S]	Strain of flexor muscle, fascia and tndn of [rt, lt] little finger at forearm lvl, [init enc, seq]
S56.21[1,2,9][A,S]	Strain of oth flexor muscle, fascia and tndn at forearm lvl [rt, lt, unspifed] [init enc, seq]
S56.31[1,2,9][A,S]	Strain of extensor or abductor muscles, fascia and tndns of thumb at forearm lvl [rt, lt, unsp] [init enc, seq]
S56.419[A,S]	Strain of extensor muscle, fascia and tndn of unsp finger at forearm lvl [init enc, seq]
S56.41[1,2][A,S]	Strain of extensor muscle, fascia and tndn of index finger at forearm lvl [rt, lt] [init enc, seq]
S56.41[3,4][A,S]	Strain of extensor muscle, fascia and tndn of mid finger at forearm lvl [rt, lt] [init enc, seq]
S56.41[5,6][A,S]	Strain of extensor muscle, fascia and tndn of ring finger at forearm lvl [rt, lt] [init enc, seq]
S56.41[7,8][A,S]	Strain of extensor muscle, fascia and tndn of little finger at forearm lvl [rt, lt] [init enc, seq]
S56.51[1,2,9][A,S]	Strain of oth extensor muscle, fascia and tndn at forearm lvl, [rt, lt, unsp] arm, [init enc, seq]
S56.81[1,2,9][A,S]	Strain of oth muscles, fascia and tndns at forearm lvl, [rt, lt, unsp] arm, [init enc, seq]
S56.91[1,2,9][A,S]	Strain of unsp muscles, fascia and tndns at forearm lvl, [rt, lt, unsp] arm, [init enc, seq]
S59.00[1,2,9]A	Unsp physeal fx of lwr end of ulna [rt, lt, unsp] init enc
S59.01[1,2,9]A	Salter-Harris Type I physeal fx of lwr end of ulna [rt, lt, unsp] init enc
S59.02[1,2,9]A	Salter-Harris Type II physeal fx of lwr end of ulna [rt, lt, unsp] init enc
S59.03[1,2,9]A	Salter-Harris Type III physeal fx of lwr end of ulna [rt, lt, unsp] seq]
S59.04[1,2,9]A	Salter-Harris Type IV physeal fx of lwr end of ulna [rt, lt, unsp] init enc
S59.09[1,2,9]A	Oth physeal fx of lwr end of ulna [rt, lt, unsp] init enc
S59.10[1,2,9]A	Unsp physeal fx of upr end of radius [rt, lt, unsp] init enc
S59.11[1,2,9]A	Salter-Harris Type I physeal fx of upr end of radius [rt, lt, unsp] init enc
S59.12[1,2,9]A	Salter-Harris Type II physeal fx of upr end of radius [rt, lt, unsp] init enc
S59.13[1,2,9]A	Salter-Harris Type III physeal fx of upr end of radius [rt, lt, unsp] init enc
S59.14[1,2,9]A	Salter-Harris Type I physeal fx of upr end of radius [rt, lt, unsp] init enc
S59.19[1,2,9]A	Oth physeal fx of upr end of radius [rt, lt, unsp] init enc
S59.20[1,2,9]A	Unsp physeal fx of lwr end of radius [rt, lt, unsp] init enc
S59.21[1,2,9]A	Salter-Harris Type I physeal fx of lwr end of radius [rt, lt, unsp] init enc
S59.22[1,2,9]A	Salter-Harris Type II physeal fx of lwr end of radius [rt, lt, unsp] init enc
S59.23[1,2,9]A	Salter-Harris Type III physeal fx of lwr end of radius [rt, lt, unsp] init enc
S59.24[1,2,9]A	Salter-Harris Type IV physeal fx of lwr end of radius [rt, lt, unsp] init enc
S59.29[1,2,9]A	Oth physeal fx of lwr end of radius [rt, lt, unsp] init enc
S62.00[1,2,9][A,B]	Unsp fx of navicular [scaphoid] bone of [rt, lt, unsp] wrist, init enc for fx [clsd, opn] fx
S62.01[1,2,3][A,B]	Disp fx of distal pole of navicular [scaphoid] bone of wrist [rt, lt, unsp] init enc for fx [clsd, opn]
S62.01[4,5,6][A,B]	Nondisp fx of distal pole of navicular [scaphoid] bone of wrist [rt, lt, unsp] init enc for fx [clsd, opn]
S62.02[1,2,3][A,B]	Disp fx of mid 3rd of navicular [scaphoid] bone of wrist [rt, lt, unsp] init enc for fx [clsd, opn]
S62.02[4,5,6][A,B]	Nondisp fx of mid 3rd of navicular [scaphoid] bone of wrist [rt, lt, unsp] init enc for fx [clsd, opn]
S62.03[1,2,3][A,B]	Disp fx of proximal 3rd of navicular [scaphoid] bone of wrist [rt, lt, unsp] init enc for fx [clsd, opn]
S62.03[4,5,6][A,B]	Nondisp fx of proximal 3rd of navicular [scaphoid] bone of wrist [rt, lt, unsp] init enc for fx [clsd, opn]

S62.10[1,2,9][A,B]	Fx of unsp carpal bone, [rt, lt, unsp] wrist, init enc for [clsd, opn] fx
S62.11[1,2,3][A,B]	Disp fx of triquetrum [cuneiform] bone of wrist [rt, lt, unsp] init enc for fx [clsd, opn]
S62.11[4,5,6][A,B]	Nondisp fx of triquetrum [cuneiform] bone of wrist [rt, lt, unsp] init enc for fx [clsd, opn]
S62.12[1,2,3][A,B]	Disp fx of lunate [semilunar] bone of wrist [rt, lt, unsp] init enc for fx [clsd, opn]
S62.12[4,5,6][A,B]	Nondisp fx of lunate [semilunar] bone of wrist [rt, lt, unsp] init enc for fx [clsd, opn]
S62.13[1,2,3][A,B]	Disp fx of capitate [os magnum] bone of wrist [rt, lt, unsp] init enc for fx [clsd, opn]
S62.13[4,5,6][A,B]	Nondisp fx of capitate [os magnum] bone of wrist [rt, lt, unsp] init enc for fx [clsd, opn]
S62.14[1,2,3][A,B]	Disp fx of body of mate [unciform] bone of wrist [rt, lt, unsp] init enc for fx [clsd, opn]
S62.14[4,5,6][A,B]	Nondisp fx of body of hamate [unciform] bone of wrist [rt, lt, unsp] init enc for fx [clsd, opn]
S62.15[1,2,3][A,B]	Disp fx of hook process of hamate [unciform] bone of wrist [rt, lt, unsp] init enc for fx [clsd, opn]
S62.15[4,5,6][A,B]	Nondisp fx of hook process of hamate [unciform] bone of wrist [rt, lt, unsp] init enc for fx [clsd, opn]
S62.16[1,2,3][A,B]	Disp fx of pisiform bone of wrist [rt, lt, unsp] init enc for fx [clsd, opn]
S62.16[4,5,6][A,B]	Nondisp fx of pisiform bone of wrist [rt, lt, unsp] init enc for fx [clsd, opn]
S62.17[1,2,3][A,B]	Disp fx of trapezium [lgr multangular] bone of wrist [rt, lt, unsp] init enc for fx [clsd, opn]
S62.17[4,5,6][A,B]	Nondisp fx of trapezium [lgr multangular] bone of wrist [rt, lt, unsp] init enc for fx [clsd, opn]
S62.18[1,2,3][A,B]	Disp fx of trapezoid [smer multangular] bone of wrist [rt, lt, unsp] init enc for fx [clsd, opn]
S62.18[4,5,6][A,B]	Nondisp fx of trapezoid [smer multangular] bone of wrist [rt, lt, unsp] init enc for fx [clsd, opn]
S62.20[1,2,9][A,B]	Unsp fx of 1st metacarpal bone, [rt, lt, unsp] hand, init enc for [clsd, opn] fx
S62.21[1,2,3][A,B]	Bennett's fx, [rt, lt, unsp] hand, init enc for [clsd, opn] fx
S62.22[1,2,3][A,B]	Disp Rolando's fx of hand [rt, lt, unsp] init enc for fx [clsd, opn]
S62.22[4,5,6][A,B]	Nondisp Rolando's fx, [rt, lt, unsp] hand, init enc for [clsd, opn] fx
S62.23[1,2,3][A,B]	Oth disp fx of base of 1st metacarpal bone of hand [rt, lt, unsp] init enc for fx [clsd, opn]
S62.23[4,5,6][A,B]	Oth nondisp fx of base of 1st metacarpal bone of hand [rt, lt, unsp] init enc for fx [clsd, opn]
S62.24[1,2,3][A,B]	Disp fx of shaft of 1st metacarpal bone of hand [rt, lt, unsp] init enc for fx [clsd, opn]
S62.24[4,5,6][A,B]	Nondisp fx of shaft of 1st metacarpal bone of hand [rt, lt, unsp] init enc for fx [clsd, opn]
S62.25[1,2,3][A,B]	Disp fx of neck of 1st metacarpal bone of hand [rt, lt, unsp] init enc for fx [clsd, opn]
S62.25[4,5,6][A,B]	Nondisp fx of neck of 1st metacarpal bone of hand [rt, lt, unsp] init enc for fx [clsd, opn]
S62.29[1,2,9][A,B]	Oth fx of 1st metacarpal bone, [rt, lt, unsp] hand, init enc for [clsd, opn] fx
S62.30[0,1][A,B]	Unsp fx of 2nd metacarpal bone of [rt, lt] hand, init enc for fx [clsd, opn] fx
S62.30[2,3][A,B]	Unsp fx of 3rd metacarpal bone of [rt, lt] hand, init enc for [clsd, opn] fx
S62.30[4,5][A,B]	Unsp fx of 4th metacarpal bone of [rt, lt] hand, init enc for [clsd, opn] fx
S62.30[6,7][A,B]	Unsp fx of 5th metacarpal bone of [rt, lt] hand, init enc for [clsd, opn] fx
S62.30[8,9][A,B]	Unsp fx of oth metacarpal bone of [oth, unsp] hand, init enc for [clsd, opn] fx
S62.31[0,1][A,B]	Disp fx of base of 2nd metacarpal bone of hand [rt, lt] init enc for fx [clsd, opn]
S62.31[2,3][A,B]	Disp fx of base of 3rd metacarpal bone of hand [rt, lt] init enc for fx [clsd, opn]
S62.31[4,5][A,B]	Disp fx of base of 4th metacarpal bone of hand [rt, lt] init enc for fx [clsd, opn]
S62.31[6,7][A,B]	Disp fx of base of 5th metacarpal bone of hand [rt, lt] init enc for fx [clsd, opn]
S62.31[8,9][A,B]	Disp fx of base of metacarpal bone of hand [oth, unsp] init enc for fx [clsd, opn]
S62.32[0,1][A,B]	Disp fx of shaft of 2nd metacarpal bone of hand [rt, lt]] init enc for fx [clsd, opn]
S62.32[2,3][A,B]	Disp fx of shaft of 3rd metacarpal bone of hand [rt, lt]] init enc for fx [clsd, opn]
S62.32[4,5][A,B]	Disp fx of shaft of 4th metacarpal bone of hand [rt, lt] init enc for fx [clsd, opn]

Surgical   **Medical**   **CC Indicator**   **MCC Indicator**   **Procedure Proxy**   PDxMCC **PDx acts as own MCC**   PDxCC **PDx acts as own CC**

Code	Description
S62.32[6,7][A,B]	Disp fx of shaft of 5th metacarpal bone of hand [rt, lt] init enc for fx [clsd, opn]
S62.32[8,9][A,B]	Disp fx of shaft of metacarpal bone of hand [oth, unsp] init enc for fx [clsd, opn]
S62.33[0,1][A,B]	Disp fx of neck of 2nd metacarpal bone of hand [rt, lt] init enc for [clsd, opn] fx
S62.33[2,3][A,B]	Disp fx of neck of 3rd metacarpal bone of hand [rt, lt] init enc for fx [clsd, opn]
S62.33[4,5][A,B]	Disp fx of neck of 4th metacarpal bone of hand [rt, lt] init enc for fx [clsd, opn]
S62.33[6,7][A,B]	Disp fx of neck of 5th metacarpal bone of hand [rt, lt] init enc for fx [clsd, opn]
S62.33[8,9][A,B]	Disp fx of neck of metacarpal bone of hand [oth, unsp] init enc for fx [clsd, opn]
S62.34[0,1][A,B]	Nondisp fx of base of 2nd metacarpal bone, [rt, lt, unsp] hand, init enc for [clsd, opn] fx
S62.34[2,3][A,B]	Nondisp fx of base of 3rd metacarpal bone, [rt, lt, unsp] hand, init enc for [clsd, opn] fx
S62.34[4,5][A,B]	Nondisp fx of base of 4th metacarpal bone, [rt, lt, unsp] hand, init enc for [clsd, opn] fx
S62.34[6,7][A,B]	Nondisp fx of base of 5th metacarpal bone, [rt, lt, unsp] hand, init enc for [clsd, opn] fx
S62.34[8,9][A,B]	Nondisp fx of base of [oth,unsp] metacarpal bone, init enc for [clsd, opn] fx
S62.35[0,1][A,B]	Nondisp fx of shaft of 2nd metacarpal bone, [rt, lt, unsp] hand, init enc for [clsd, opn] fx
S62.35[2,3][A,B]	Nondisp fx of shaft of 3rd metacarpal bone, [rt, lt, unsp] hand, init enc for [clsd, opn] fx
S62.35[4,5][A,B]	Nondisp fx of shaft of 4th metacarpal bone, [rt, lt, unsp] hand, init enc for [clsd, opn] fx
S62.35[6,7][A,B]	Nondisp fx of shaft of 5th metacarpal bone, [rt, lt, unsp] hand, init enc for [clsd, opn] fx
S62.35[8,9][A,B]	Nondisp fx of shaft of [oth,unsp] metacarpal bone, init enc for [clsd, opn] fx
S62.36[0,1][A,B]	Nondisp fx of neck of 2nd metacarpal bone, [rt, lt, unsp] hand, init enc for [clsd, opn] fx
S62.36[2,3][A,B]	Nondisp fx of neck of 3rd metacarpal bone, [rt, lt, unsp] hand, init enc for [clsd, opn] fx
S62.36[4,5][A,B]	Nondisp fx of neck of 4th metacarpal bone, [rt, lt, unsp] hand, init enc for [clsd, opn] fx
S62.36[6,7][A,B]	Nondisp fx of neck of 5th metacarpal bone, [rt, lt, unsp] hand, init enc for [clsd, opn] fx
S62.36[8,9][A,B]	Nondisp fx of neck of [oth,unsp] metacarpal bone, init enc for [clsd, opn] fx
S62.39[0,1][A,B]	Oth fx of 2nd metacarpal bone, [rt, lt, unsp] hand, init enc for [clsd, opn] fx
S62.39[2,3][A,B]	Oth fx of 3rd metacarpal bone, [rt, lt, unsp] hand, init enc for [clsd, opn] fx
S62.39[4,5][A,B]	Oth fx of 4th metacarpal bone, [rt, lt, unsp] hand, init enc for [clsd, opn] fx
S62.39[6,7][A,B]	Oth fx of 5th metacarpal bone, [rt, lt, unsp] hand, init enc for [clsd, opn] fx
S62.39[8,9][A,B]	Oth fx of [oth,unsp] metacarpal bone, init enc for [clsd, opn] fx
S62.50[1,2,9][A,B]	Fx of unsp phalanx of [rt, lt, unsp] thumb, init enc for [clsd, opn] fx
S62.51[1,2,3][A,B]	Disp fx of proximal phalanx of [rt, lt, unsp] thumb, init enc for [clsd, opn] fx
S62.51[4,5,6][A,B]	Nondisp fx of proximal phalanx of [rt, lt, unsp] thumb, init enc for [clsd, opn] fx
S62.52[1,2,3][A,B]	Disp fx of distal phalanx of [rt, lt, unsp] thumb, init enc for [clsd, opn] fx
S62.52[4,5,6][A,B]	Nondisp fx of distal phalanx of [rt, lt, unsp] thumb, init enc for [clsd, opn] fx
S62.60[0,1][A,B]	Fx of unsp phalanx of [rt, lt] index finger, init enc for [clsd, opn] fx
S62.60[2,3][A,B]	Fx of unsp phalanx of [rt, lt] mid finger, init enc for [clsd, opn] fx
S62.60[4,5][A,B]	Fx of unsp phalanx of [rt, lt] ring finger, init enc for [clsd, opn] fx
S62.60[6,7][A,B]	Fx of unsp phalanx of [rt, lt] little finger, init enc for [clsd, opn] fx
S62.60[8,9][A,B]	Fx of unsp phalanx of [oth, unsp] finger, init enc for [clsd, opn] fx
S62.61[0,1][A,B]	Disp fx of proximal phalanx of [rt, lt] index finger, init enc for [clsd, opn] fx
S62.61[2,3][A,B]	Disp fx of proximal phalanx of [rt, lt] mid finger, init enc for [clsd, opn] fx
S62.61[4,5][A,B]	Disp fx proximal phalanx of [rt, lt] ring finger, init enc for [clsd, opn] fx
S62.61[6,7][A,B]	Disp fx proximal phalanx of [rt, lt] little finger, init enc for [clsd, opn] fx
S62.61[8,9][A,B]	Disp fx proximal phalanx of [oth, unsp] finger, init enc for [clsd, opn] fx
S62.62[0,1][A,B]	Disp fx of med phalanx of [rt, lt] index finger, init enc for [clsd, opn] fx
S62.62[2,3][A,B]	Disp fx of med phalanx of [rt, lt] mid finger, init enc for [clsd, opn] fx
S62.62[4,5][A,B]	Disp fx of med phalanx of [rt, lt] ring finger, init enc for [clsd, opn] fx
S62.62[6,7][A,B]	Disp fx of med phalanx of [rt, lt] little finger, init enc for [clsd, opn] fx
S62.62[8,9][A,B]	Disp fx of med phalanx of [oth, unsp] finger, init enc for [clsd, opn] fx
S62.63[0,1][A,B]	Disp fx of distal phalanx of [rt, lt] index finger, init enc for [clsd, opn] fx
S62.63[2,3][A,B]	Disp fx of distal phalanx of [rt, lt] mid finger, init enc for [clsd, opn] fx
S62.63[4,5][A,B]	Disp fx of distal phalanx of [rt, lt] ring finger, init enc for [clsd, opn] fx
S62.63[6,7][A,B]	Disp fx of distal phalanx of [rt, lt] little finger, init enc for [clsd, opn] fx
S62.63[8,9][A,B]	Disp fx of distal phalanx of [oth, unsp] finger, init enc for [clsd, opn] fx
S62.64[0,1][A,B]	Nondisp fx of proximal phalanx of [rt, lt] index finger, init enc for [clsd, opn] fx
S62.64[2,3][A,B]	Nondisp fx of proximal phalanx of [rt, lt] mid finger, init enc for [clsd, opn] fx
S62.64[4,5][A,B]	Nondisp fx of proximal phalanx of [rt, lt] ring finger, init enc for [clsd, opn] fx
S62.64[6,7][A,B]	Nondisp fx of proximal phalanx of [rt, lt] little finger, init enc for [clsd, opn] fx
S62.64[8,9][A,B]	Nondisp fx of proximal phalanx of [oth, unsp] finger, init enc for [clsd, opn] fx
S62.65[0,1][A,B]	Nondisp fx of med phalanx of [rt, lt] index finger, init enc for [clsd, opn] fx
S62.65[2,3][A,B]	Nondisp fx of med phalanx of [rt, lt] mid finger, init enc for [clsd, opn] fx
S62.65[4,5][A,B]	Nondisp fx of med phalanx of [rt, lt] ring finger, init enc for [clsd, opn] fx
S62.65[6,7][A,B]	Nondisp fx of med phalanx of [rt, lt] little finger, init enc for [clsd, opn] fx
S62.65[8,9][A,B]	Nondisp fx of med phalanx of [oth, unsp] finger, init enc for [clsd, opn] fx
S62.66[0,1][A,B]	Nondisp fx of distal phalanx of [rt, lt] index finger, init enc for [clsd, opn] fx
S62.66[2,3][A,B]	Nondisp fx of distal phalanx of [rt, lt] mid finger, init enc for [clsd, opn] fx
S62.66[4,5][A,B]	Nondisp fx of distal phalanx of [rt, lt] ring finger, init enc for [clsd, opn] fx
S62.66[6,7][A,B]	Nondisp fx of distal phalanx of [rt, lt] little finger, init enc for [clsd, opn] fx
S62.66[8,9][A,B]	Nondisp fx of distal phalanx of [oth, unsp] finger, init enc for [clsd, opn] fx
S62.9[0,1,2]X[A,B]	Unsp fx of [unsp, rt, lt] wrist and hand, init enc for [clsd, opn] fx
S63.00[1,2,3][A,S]	Unsp sublux of [rt, lt, unsp] wrist and hand, [init enc, seq]
S63.00[4,5,6][A,S]	Unsp disloc of [rt, lt, unsp] wrist and hand, [init enc, seq]
S63.01[1,2,3][A,S]	Sublux of distal radioulnar jt of [rt, lt, unsp] wrist, [init enc, seq]
S63.01[4,5,6][A,S]	Disloc of distal radioulnar jt of [rt, lt, unsp] wrist, [init enc, seq]
S63.02[1,2,3][A,S]	Sublux of radiocarpal jt of [rt, lt, unsp] wrist, [init enc, seq]
S63.02[4,5,6][A,S]	Disloc of radiocarpal jt of [rt, lt, unsp] wrist, [init enc, seq]
S63.03[1,2,3][A,S]	Sublux of midcarpal jt of [rt, lt, unsp] wrist, [init enc, seq]
S63.03[4,5,6][A,S]	Disloc of midcarpal jt of [rt, lt, unsp] wrist, [init enc, seq]
S63.04[1,2,3][A,S]	Sublux of carpometacarpal jt of [rt, lt, unsp] thumb, [init enc, seq]
S63.04[4,5,6][A,S]	Disloc of carpometacarpal jt of [rt, lt, unsp] thumb, [init enc, seq]
S63.05[1,2,3][A,S]	Sublux of oth carpometacarpal jt of [rt, lt, unsp] hand, [init enc, seq]
S63.05[4,5,6][A,S]	Disloc of oth carpometacarpal jt of [rt, lt, unsp] hand, [init enc, seq]
S63.06[1,2,3][A,S]	Sublux of metacarpal (bone), proximal end of [rt, lt, unsp] hand, [init enc, seq]
S63.06[4,5,6][A,S]	Disloc of metacarpal (bone), proximal end of [rt, lt, unsp] hand, [init enc, seq]
S63.07[1,2,3][A,S]	Sublux of distal end of [rt, lt, unsp] ulna, [init enc, seq]
S63.07[4,5,6][A,S]	Disloc of distal end of [rt, lt, unsp] ulna, [init enc, seq]
S63.09[1,2,3][A,S]	Oth sublux of [rt, lt, unsp] wrist and hand, [init enc, seq]

T Transfer DRG   SP Special Payment   * Code Range   6th and 7th Character of ZZ = No Device, No Qualifier ZX = No Device, Diagnostic

S63.Ø9[4,5,6][A,S] Oth disloc of [rt, lt, unsp] wrist and hand, [init enc, seq]
S63.1Ø[1,2,3][A,S] Unsp sublux of [rt, lt, unsp] thumb, [init enc, seq]
S63.1Ø[4,5,6][A,S] Unsp disloc of [rt, lt, unsp] thumb, [init enc, seq]
S63.11[1,2,3][A,S] Sublux of metacarpophalangeal jt of [rt, lt, unsp] thumb, [init enc, seq]
S63.11[4,5,6][A,S] Disloc of metacarpophalangeal jt of [rt, lt, unsp] thumb, [init enc, seq]
S63.12[1,2,3][A,S] Sublux of unsp interphalangeal jt of [rt, lt, unsp] thumb, [init enc, seq]
S63.12[4,5,6][A,S] Disloc of unsp interphalangeal jt of [rt, lt, unsp] thumb, [init enc, seq]
S63.13[1,2,3][A,S] Sublux of proximal interphalangeal jt of [rt, lt, unsp] thumb, [init enc, seq]
S63.13[4,5,6][A,S] Disloc of proximal interphalangeal jt of [rt, lt, unsp] thumb, [init enc, seq]
S63.14[1,2,3][A,S] Sublux of distal interphalangeal jt of [rt, lt, unsp] thumb, [init enc, seq]
S63.14[4,5,6][A,S] Disloc of distal interphalangeal jt of [rt, lt, unsp] thumb, [init enc, seq]
S63.2Ø[Ø,1][A,S] Unsp sublux of [rt, lt] index finger, [init enc, seq]
S63.2Ø[2,3][A,S] Unsp sublux of [rt, lt] mid finger, [init enc, seq]
S63.2Ø[4,5][A,S] Unsp sublux of [rt, lt] ring finger, [init enc, seq]
S63.2Ø[6,7][A,S] Unsp sublux of [rt, lt] little finger, [init enc, seq]
S63.2Ø[8,9][A,S] Unsp sublux of [oth, unsp] finger, [init enc, seq]
S63.21[Ø,1][A,S] Sublux of metacarpophalangeal jt of [rt, lt] index finger, [init enc, seq]
S63.21[2,3][A,S] Sublux of metacarpophalangeal jt of [rt, lt] mid finger, [init enc, seq]
S63.21[4,5][A,S] Sublux of metacarpophalangeal jt of [rt, lt] ring finger, [init enc, seq]
S63.21[6,7][A,S] Sublux of metacarpophalangeal jt of [rt, lt] little finger, [init enc, seq]
S63.21[8,9][A,S] Sublux of metacarpophalangeal jt of [oth, unsp] finger, [init enc, seq]
S63.22[Ø,1][A,S] Sublux of unsp interphalangeal jt of [rt, lt] index finger, [init enc, seq]
S63.22[2,3][A,S] Sublux of unsp interphalangeal jt of [rt, lt] mid finger, [init enc, seq]
S63.22[4,5][A,S] Sublux of unsp interphalangeal jt of [rt, lt] ring finger, [init enc, seq]
S63.22[6,7][A,S] Sublux of unsp interphalangeal jt of [rt, lt] little finger, [init enc, seq]
S63.22[8,9][A,S] Sublux of unsp interphalangeal jt of [oth, unsp] finger, [init enc, seq]
S63.23[Ø,1][A,S] Sublux of proximal interphalangeal jt of [rt, lt] index finger, [init enc, seq]
S63.23[2,3][A,S] Sublux of proximal interphalangeal jt of [rt, lt] mid finger, [init enc, seq]
S63.23[4,5][A,S] Sublux of proximal interphalangeal jt of [rt, lt] ring finger, [init enc, seq]
S63.23[6,7][A,S] Sublux of proximal interphalangeal jt of [rt, lt] little finger, [init enc, seq]
S63.23[8,9][A,S] Sublux of proximal interphalangeal jt of [oth, unsp] finger, [init enc, seq]
S63.24[Ø,1][A,S] Sublux of distal interphalangeal jt of [rt, lt] index finger, [init enc, seq]
S63.24[2,3][A,S] Sublux of distal interphalangeal jt of [rt, lt] mid finger, [init enc, seq]
S63.24[4,5][A,S] Sublux of distal interphalangeal jt of [rt, lt] ring finger, [init enc, seq]
S63.24[6,7][A,S] Sublux of distal interphalangeal jt of [rt, lt] little finger, [init enc, seq]
S63.24[8,9][A,S] Sublux of distal interphalangeal jt of [oth, unsp] finger, [init enc, seq]
S63.25[Ø,1][A,S] Unsp disloc of [rt, lt] index finger, [init enc, seq]
S63.25[2,3][A,S] Unsp disloc of [rt, lt] mid finger, [init enc, seq]
S63.25[4,5][A,S] Unsp disloc of [rt, lt] ring finger, [init enc, seq]
S63.25[6,7][A,S] Unsp disloc of [rt, lt] little finger, [init enc, seq]
S63.25[8,9][A,S] Unsp disloc of [oth, unsp] finger, [init enc, seq]
S63.26[Ø,1][A,S] Disloc of metacarpophalangeal jt of [rt, lt] index finger, [init enc, seq]
S63.26[2,3][A,S] Disloc of metacarpophalangeal jt of [rt, lt] mid finger, [init enc, seq]
S63.26[4,5][A,S] Disloc of metacarpophalangeal jt of [rt, lt] ring finger, [init enc, seq]
S63.26[6,7][A,S] Disloc of metacarpophalangeal jt of [rt, lt] little finger, [init enc, seq]
S63.26[8,9][A,S] Disloc of metacarpophalangeal jt of [oth, unsp] finger, [init enc, seq]

S63.27[Ø,1][A,S] Disloc of unsp interphalangeal jt of [rt, lt] index finger, [init enc, seq]
S63.27[2,3][A,S] Disloc of unsp interphalangeal jt of [rt, lt] mid finger, [init enc, seq]
S63.27[4,5][A,S] Disloc of unsp interphalangeal jt of [rt, lt] ring finger, [init enc, seq]
S63.27[6,7][A,S] Disloc of unsp interphalangeal jt of [rt, lt] little finger, [init enc, seq]
S63.27[8,9][A,S] Disloc of unsp interphalangeal jt of [oth, unsp] finger, [init enc, seq]
S63.28[Ø,1][A,S] Disloc of proximal interphalangeal jt of [rt, lt] index finger, [init enc, seq]
S63.28[2,3][A,S] Disloc of proximal interphalangeal jt of [rt, lt] mid finger, [init enc, seq]
S63.28[4,5][A,S] Disloc of proximal interphalangeal jt of [rt, lt] ring finger, [init enc, seq]
S63.28[6,7][A,S] Disloc of proximal interphalangeal jt of [rt, lt] little finger, [init enc, seq]
S63.28[8,9][A,S] Disloc of proximal interphalangeal jt of [oth, unsp] finger, [init enc, seq]
S63.29[Ø,1][A,S] Disloc of distal interphalangeal jt of [rt, lt] index finger, [init enc, seq]
S63.29[2,3][A,S] Disloc of distal interphalangeal jt of [rt, lt] mid finger, [init enc, seq]
S63.29[4,5][A,S] Disloc of distal interphalangeal jt of [rt, lt] ring finger, [init enc, seq]
S63.29[6,7][A,S] Disloc of distal interphalangeal jt of [rt, lt] little finger, [init enc, seq]
S63.29[8,9][A,S] Disloc of distal interphalangeal jt of [oth, unsp] finger, [init enc, seq]
S63.3Ø[1,2,9][A,S] Traum rupture of unsp lgmt of [rt, lt, unsp] wrist, [init enc, seq]
S63.31[1,2,9][A,S] Traum rupture of collat lgmt of [rt, lt, unsp] wrist, [init enc, seq]
S63.32[1,2,9][A,S] Traum rupture of radiocarpal lgmt of [rt, lt, unsp] wrist, [init enc, seq]
S63.33[1,2,9][A,S] Traum rupture of ulnocarpal lgmt of [rt, lt, unsp] wrist, [init enc, seq]
S63.39[1,2,9][A,S] Traum rupture of oth lgmt of [rt, lt, unsp] wrist, [init enc, seq]
S63.4Ø[Ø,1][A,S] Traum rupture of unsp lgmt of [rt, lt] index finger at metacarpophalangeal and interphalangeal jt, [init enc, seq]
S63.4Ø[2,3][A,S] Traum rupture of unsp lgmt of [rt, lt] mid finger at metacarpophalangeal and interphalangeal jt, [init enc, seq]
S63.4Ø[4,5][A,S] Traum rupture of unsp lgmt of [rt, lt] ring finger at metacarpophalangeal and interphalangeal jt, [init enc, seq]
S63.4Ø[6,7][A,S] Traum rupture of unsp lgmt of [rt, lt] little finger at metacarpophalangeal and interphalangeal jt, [init enc, seq]
S63.4Ø[8,9][A,S] Traum rupture of unsp lgmt of [oth, unsp] finger at metacarpophalangeal and interphalangeal jt, [init enc, seq]
S63.41[Ø,1][A,S] Traum rupture of collat lgmt of [rt, lt] index finger at metacarpophalangeal and interphalangeal jt, [init enc, seq]
S63.41[2,3][A,S] Traum rupture of collat lgmt of [rt, lt] mid finger at metacarpophalangeal and interphalangeal jt, [init enc, seq]
S63.41[4,5][A,S] Traum rupture of collat lgmt of [rt, lt] ring finger at metacarpophalangeal and interphalangeal jt, [init enc, seq]
S63.41[6,7][A,S] Traum rupture of collat lgmt of [rt, lt] little finger at metacarpophalangeal and interphalangeal jt, [init enc, seq]
S63.41[8,9][A,S] Traum rupture of collat lgmt of [oth, unsp] finger at metacarpophalangeal and interphalangeal jt, [init enc, seq]
S63.42[Ø,1][A,S] Traum rupture of palmar lgmt of [rt, lt] index finger at metacarpophalangeal and interphalangeal jt, [init enc, seq]
S63.42[2,3][A,S] Traum rupture of palmar lgmt of [rt, lt] mid finger at metacarpophalangeal and interphalangeal jt, [init enc, seq]
S63.42[4,5][A,S] Traum rupture of palmar lgmt of [rt, lt] ring finger at metacarpophalangeal and interphalangeal jt, [init enc, seq]
S63.42[6,7][A,S] Traum rupture of palmar lgmt of [rt, lt] little finger at metacarpophalangeal and interphalangeal jt, [init enc, seq]
S63.42[8,9][A,S] Traum rupture of palmar lgmt of [oth, unsp] finger at metacarpophalangeal and interphalangeal jt, [init enc, seq]
S63.43[Ø,1][A,S] Traum rupture of volar plate of [rt, lt] index finger at metacarpophalangeal and interphalangeal jt, [init enc, seq]
S63.43[2,3][A,S] Traum rupture of volar plate of [rt, lt] mid finger at metacarpophalangeal and interphalangeal jt, [init enc, seq]
S63.43[4,5][A,S] Traum rupture of volar plate of [rt, lt] ring finger at metacarpophalangeal and interphalangeal jt, [init enc, seq]
S63.43[6,7][A,S] Traum rupture of volar plate of [rt, lt] little finger at metacarpophalangeal and interphalangeal jt, [init enc, seq]
S63.43[8,9][A,S] Traum rupture of volar plate of [oth, unsp] finger at metacarpophalangeal and interphalangeal jt, [init enc, seq]
S63.49[Ø,1][A,S] Traum rupture of oth lgmt of [rt, lt] index finger at metacarpophalangeal and interphalangeal jt, [init enc, seq]

Surgical   **Medical**   **CC Indicator**   **MCC Indicator**   **Procedure Proxy**   **PDxMCC PDx acts as own MCC**   **PDxCC PDx acts as own CC**

S63.49[2,3][A,S] Traum rupture of oth lgmt of [rt, lt] mid finger at metacarpophalangeal and interphalangeal jt, [init enc, seq]

S63.49[4,5][A,S] Traum rupture of oth lgmt of [rt, lt] ring finger at metacarpophalangeal and interphalangeal jt, [init enc, seq]

S63.49[6,7][A,S] Traum rupture of oth lgmt of [rt, lt] little finger at metacarpophalangeal and interphalangeal jt, [init enc, seq]

S63.49[8,9][A,S] Traum rupture of oth lgmt of [oth, unsp] finger at metacarpophalangeal and interphalangeal jt, [init enc, seq]

S63.50[1,2,9][A,S] Unsp sprain of [rt, lt, unsp] wrist, [init enc, seq]

S63.51[1,2,9][A,S] Sprain of carpal jt of [rt, lt, unsp] wrist, [init enc, seq]

S63.52[1,2,9][A,S] Sprain of radiocarpal jt of [rt, lt, unsp] wrist, [init enc, seq]

S63.59[1,2,9][A,S] Oth spec sprain of [rt, lt, unsp] wrist, [init enc, seq]

S63.60[1,2,9][A,S] Unsp sprain of [rt, lt, unsp] thumb, [init enc, seq]

S63.61[0,1][A,S] Unsp sprain of [rt, lt] index finger, [init enc, seq]

S63.61[2,3][A,S] Unsp sprain of [rt, lt] mid finger, [init enc, seq]

S63.61[4,5][A,S] Unsp sprain of [rt, lt] ring finger, [init enc, seq]

S63.61[6,7][A,S] Unsp sprain of [rt, lt] little finger, [init enc, seq]

S63.61[8,9][A,S] Unsp sprain of [oth, unsp] finger, [init enc, seq]

S63.62[1,2,9][A,S] Sprain of interphalangeal jt of [rt, lt, unsp] thumb, [init enc, seq]

S63.63[0,1][A,S] Sprain of interphalangeal jt of [rt, lt] index finger, [init enc, seq]

S63.63[2,3][A,S] Sprain of interphalangeal jt of [rt, lt] mid finger, [init enc, seq]

S63.63[4,5][A,S] Sprain of interphalangeal jt of [rt, lt] ring finger, [init enc, seq]

S63.63[6,7][A,S] Sprain of interphalangeal jt of [rt, lt] little finger, [init enc, seq]

S63.63[8,9][A,S] Sprain of interphalangeal jt of [oth, unsp] finger, [init enc, seq]

S63.64[1,2,9][A,S] Sprain of metacarpophalangeal jt of [rt, lt, unsp] thumb, [init enc, seq]

S63.65[0,1][A,S] Sprain of metacarpophalangeal jt of [rt, lt] index finger, [init enc, seq]

S63.65[2,3][A,S] Sprain of metacarpophalangeal jt of [rt, lt] mid finger, [init enc, seq]

S63.65[4,5][A,S] Sprain of metacarpophalangeal jt of [rt, lt] ring finger, [init enc, seq]

S63.65[6,7][A,S] Sprain of metacarpophalangeal jt of [rt, lt] little finger, [init enc, seq]

S63.65[8,9][A,S] Sprain of metacarpophalangeal jt of [oth, unsp] finger, [init enc, seq]

S63.68[1,2,9][A,S] Oth sprain of [rt, lt, unsp] thumb, [init enc, seq]

S63.69[0,1][A,S] Oth sprain of [rt, lt] index finger, [init enc, seq]

S63.69[2,3][A,S] Oth sprain of [rt, lt] mid finger, [init enc, seq]

S63.69[4,5][A,S] Oth sprain of [rt, lt] ring finger, [init enc, seq]

S63.69[6,7][A,S] Oth sprain of [rt, lt] little finger, [init enc, seq]

S63.69[8,9][A,S] Oth sprain of [oth, unsp] finger, [init enc, seq]

S63.8X[1,2,9][A,S] Sprain of oth part of [rt, lt, unsp] wrist and hand, [init enc, seq]

S63.9[0,1,2]X[A,S] Sprain of unsp part of [unsp, rt, lt] wrist and hand, [init enc, seq]

S66.01[1,2,9][A,S] Strain of long flexor muscle, fascia and tndn of [rt, lt, unsp] thumb at wrist and hand lvl, [init enc, seq]

S66.11[0,1][A,S] Strain of flexor muscle, fascia and tndn of [rt, lt, unsp] index finger at wrist and hand lvl, [init enc, seq]

S66.11[2,3][A,S] Strain of flexor muscle, fascia and tndn of [rt, lt, unsp] mid finger at wrist and hand lvl, [init enc, seq]

S66.11[4,5][A,S] Strain of flexor muscle, fascia and tndn of [rt, lt, unsp] ring finger at wrist and hand lvl, [init enc, seq]

S66.11[6,7][A,S] Strain of flexor muscle, fascia and tndn of [rt, lt, unsp] little finger at wrist and hand lvl, [init enc, seq]

S66.11[8,9][A,S] Strain of flexor muscle, fascia and tndn of [oth, unsp] finger at wrist and hand lvl, [init enc, seq]

S66.21[1,2,9][A,S] Strain of extensor muscle, fascia and tndn of [rt, lt, unsp] thumb at wrist and hand lvl, [init enc, seq]

S66.31[0,1][A,S] Strain of extensor muscle, fascia and tndn of [rt, lt, unsp] index finger at wrist and hand lvl, [init enc, seq]

S66.31[2,3][A,S] Strain of extensor muscle, fascia and tndn of [rt, lt, unsp] mid finger at wrist and hand lvl, [init enc, seq]

S66.31[4,5][A,S] Strain of extensor muscle, fascia and tndn of [rt, lt, unsp] ring finger at wrist and hand lvl, [init enc, seq]

S66.31[6,7][A,S] Strain of extensor muscle, fascia and tndn of [rt, lt, unsp] little finger at wrist and hand lvl, [init enc, seq]

S66.31[8,9][A,S] Strain of extensor muscle, fascia and tndn of [oth, unsp] finger at wrist and hand lvl, [init enc, seq]

S66.41[1,2,9][A,S] Strain of intrinsic muscle, fascia and tndn of [rt, lt, unsp] thumb at wrist and hand lvl, [init enc, seq]

S66.51[0,1][A,S] Strain of intrinsic muscle, fascia and tndn of [rt, lt, unsp] index finger at wrist and hand lvl, [init enc, seq]

S66.51[2,3][A,S] Strain of intrinsic muscle, fascia and tndn of [rt, lt, unsp] mid finger at wrist and hand lvl, [init enc, seq]

S66.51[4,5][A,S] Strain of intrinsic muscle, fascia and tndn of [rt, lt, unsp] ring finger at wrist and hand lvl, [init enc, seq]

S66.51[6,7][A,S] Strain of intrinsic muscle, fascia and tndn of [rt, lt, unsp] little finger at wrist and hand lvl, [init enc, seq]

S66.51[8,9][A,S] Strain of intrinsic muscle, fascia and tndn of [oth, unsp] finger at wrist and hand lvl, [init enc, seq]

S66.[8,9]1[1,2,9][A,S] Strain of [oth spec, unsp] muscles, fascia and tndns at wrist and hand lvl, [rt, lt, unsp] hand, [init enc, seq]

S73.00[1,2,3]S Unsp sublux of [rt, lt, unsp] hip, seq

S73.00[4,5,6]S Unsp disloc of [rt, lt, unsp] hip, seq

S73.01[1,2,3]S Post sublux of [rt, lt, unsp] hip, seq

S73.01[4,5,6]S Post disloc of [rt, lt, unsp] hip, seq

S73.02[1,2,3]S Obturator sublux of [rt, lt, unsp] hip, seq

S73.02[4,5,6]S Obturator disloc of [rt, lt, unsp] hip, seq

S73.03[1,2,3]S Oth ant sublux of [rt, lt, unsp] hip, seq

S73.03[4,5,6]S Oth ant disloc of [rt, lt, unsp] hip, seq

S73.04[1,2,3]S Central sublux of [rt, lt, unsp] hip, seq

S73.04[4,5,6]S Central disloc of [rt, lt, unsp] hip, seq

S73.10[1,2,9]S Unsp sprain of [rt, lt, unsp] hip, seq

S73.1[1,2,9][1,2,9]S [Iliofemoral lgmt, Ischiocapsular lgmt, Oth] sprain of [rt, lt, unsp] hip, seq

S76.01[1,2,9]S Strain of muscle, fascia and tndn of [rt, lt, unsp] hip, seq

S76.11[1,2,9]S Strain of [rt, lt, unsp] quadriceps muscle, fascia and tndns, seq

S76.21[1,2,9]S Strain of adductor muscle, fasica and tndns of [rt, lt, unsp] thigh, seq

S76.31[1,2,9]S Strain of muscle, fasica and tndn of the post muscle group at thigh lvl, [rt, lt, unsp] thigh, seq

S76.81[1,2,9]S Strain of oth spec muscle, fasica and tndns at thigh lvl, [rt, lt, unsp] thigh, seq

S76.91[1,2,9]S Strain of unsp muscle, fasica and tndns at thigh lvl, [rt, lt, unsp] thigh, seq

S82.00[1,2,9][A,B,C] Unsp fx of [rt, lt, unsp] patella, init enc for [clsd fx, opn fx type I or II, opn fx type IIIA, IIIB, or IIIC]

S82.01[1,2,3][A,B,C] Disp osteochondral fx of [rt, lt, unsp] patella, [init enc for clsd fx, init enc for opn fx type I or II, init enc for opn fx type IIIA, IIIB, or IIIC]

S82.01[4,5,6][A,B,C] Nondisp osteochondral fx of [rt, lt, unsp] patella, [init enc for clsd fx, init enc for opn fx type I or II, init enc for opn fx type IIIA, IIIB, or IIIC]

S82.02[1,2,3][A,B,C] Disp longitudinal fx of [rt, lt, unsp] patella, [init enc for clsd fx, init enc for opn fx type I or II, init enc for opn fx type IIIA, IIIB, or IIIC]

S82.02[4,5,6][A,B,C] Nondisp longitudinal fx of [rt, lt, unsp] patella, [init enc for clsd fx, init enc for opn fx type I or II, init enc for opn fx type IIIA, IIIB, or IIIC]

S82.03[1,2,3][A,B,C] Disp transv fx of [rt, lt, unsp] patella, [init enc for clsd fx, init enc for opn fx type I or II, init enc for opn fx type IIIA, IIIB, or IIIC]

S82.03[4,5,6][A,B,C] Nondisp transv fx of [rt, lt, unsp] patella, [init enc for clsd fx, init enc for opn fx type I or II, init enc for opn fx type IIIA, IIIB, or IIIC]

S82.04[1,2,3][A,B,C] Disp comm fx of [rt, lt, unsp] patella, [init enc for clsd fx, init enc for opn fx type I or II, init enc for opn fx type IIIA, IIIB, or IIIC]

S82.04[4,5,6][A,B,C] Nondisp comm fx of [rt, lt, unsp] patella, [init enc for clsd fx, init enc for opn fx type I or II, init enc for opn fx type IIIA, IIIB, or IIIC]

S82.09[1,2,9][A,B,C] Oth fx of [rt, lt, unsp] patella, init enc for [clsd fx, opn fx type I or II, opn fx type IIIA, IIIB, or IIIC]

S82.10[1,2,9][A,B,C] Unsp fx of upr end of [rt, lt, unsp] tibia, init enc for [clsd fx, fx type I or II, opn fx type IIIA, IIIB, or IIIC]

S82.11[1,2,3][A,B,C] Disp fx of [rt, lt, unsp] tibial spine, [init enc for clsd fx, init enc for opn fx type I or II, init enc for opn fx type IIIA, IIIB, or IIIC]

S82.11[4,5,6][A,B,C] Nondisp fx of [rt, lt, unsp] tibial spine, [init enc for clsd fx, init enc for opn fx type I or II, init enc for opn fx type IIIA, IIIB, or IIIC]

S82.12[1,2,3][A,B,C] Disp fx of lat condyle of [rt, lt, unsp] tibia, [init enc for clsd fx, init enc for opn fx type I or II, init enc for opn fx type IIIA, IIIB, or IIIC]

S82.12[4,5,6][A,B,C] Nondisp fx of lat condyle of [rt, lt, unsp] tibia, [init enc for clsd fx, init enc for opn fx type I or II, init enc for opn fx type IIIA, IIIB, or IIIC]

S82.13[1,2,3][A,B,C] Disp fx of med condyle of [rt, lt, unsp] tibia, [init enc for clsd fx, init enc for opn fx type I or II, init enc for opn fx type IIIA, IIIB, or IIIC]

S82.13[4,5,6][A,B,C] Nondisp fx of med condyle of [rt, lt, unsp] tibia, [init enc for clsd fx, init enc for opn fx type I or II, init enc for opn fx type IIIA, IIIB, or IIIC]

S82.14[1,2,3][A,B,C] Disp bicondylar fx of [rt, lt, unsp] tibia, [init enc for clsd fx, init enc for opn fx type I or II, init enc for opn fx type IIIA, IIIB, or IIIC]

T Transfer DRG   SP Special Payment   * Code Range   6th and 7th Character of ZZ = No Device, No Qualifier ZX = No Device, Diagnostic

190   MS-DRG Version 33.0   © 2015 Optum360, LLC

S82.14[4,5,6][A,B,C] Nondisp bicondylar fx of [rt, lt, unsp] tibia, [init enc for clsd fx, init enc for opn fx type I or II, init enc for opn fx type IIIA, IIIB, or IIIC]

S82.15[1,2,3][A,B,C] Disp fx of [rt, lt, unsp] tibial tuberosity, [init enc for clsd fx, init enc for opn fx type I or II, init enc for opn fx type IIIA, IIIB, or IIIC]

S82.15[4,5,6][A,B,C] Nondisp fx of [rt, lt, unsp] tibial tuberosity, [init enc for clsd fx, init enc for opn fx type I or II, init enc for opn fx type IIIA, IIIB, or IIIC]

S82.16[1,2,9]A Torus fx of upr end of [rt, lt, unsp] tibia, init enc for clsd fx

S82.19[1,2,9][A,B,C] Oth fx of upr end of [rt, lt, unsp] tibia, init enc for [clsd fx, opn fx type I or II, opn fx type IIIA, IIIB, or IIIC]

S82.20[1,2,9][A,B,C] Unsp fx of shaft of [rt, lt, unsp] tibia, init enc for [clsd fx, opn fx type I or II, opn fx type IIIA, IIIB, or IIIC]

S82.22[1,2,3][A,B,C] Disp transv fx of shaft of [rt, lt, unsp] tibia, [init enc for clsd fx, init enc for opn fx type I or II, init enc for opn fx type IIIA, IIIB, or IIIC]

S82.22[4,5,6][A,B,C] Nondisp transv fx of shaft of [rt, lt, unsp] tibia, [init enc for clsd fx, init enc for opn fx type I or II, init enc for opn fx type IIIA, IIIB, or IIIC]

S82.23[1,2,3][A,B,C] Disp oblique fx of shaft of [rt, lt, unsp] tibia, [init enc for clsd fx, init enc for opn fx type I or II, init enc for opn fx type IIIA, IIIB, or IIIC]

S82.23[4,5,6][A,B,C] Nondisp oblique fx of shaft of [rt, lt, unsp] tibia, [init enc for clsd fx, init enc for opn fx type I or II, init enc for opn fx type IIIA, IIIB, or IIIC]

S82.24[1,2,3][A,B,C] Disp spiral fx of shaft of [rt, lt, unsp] tibia, [init enc for clsd fx, init enc for opn fx type I or II, init enc for opn fx type IIIA, IIIB, or IIIC]

S82.24[4,5,6][A,B,C] Nondisp spiral fx of shaft of [rt, lt, unsp] tibia, [init enc for clsd fx, init enc for opn fx type I or II, init enc for opn fx type IIIA, IIIB, or IIIC]

S82.25[1,2,3][A,B,C] Disp comm fx of shaft of [rt, lt, unsp] tibia, [init enc for clsd fx, init enc for opn fx type I or II, init enc for opn fx type IIIA, IIIB, or IIIC]

S82.25[4,5,6][A,B,C] Nondisp comm fx of shaft of [rt, lt, unsp] tibia, [init enc for clsd fx, init enc for opn fx type I or II, init enc for opn fx type IIIA, IIIB, or IIIC]

S82.26[1,2,3][A,B,C] Disp seg fx of shaft of [rt, lt, unsp] tibia, [init enc for clsd fx, init enc for opn fx type I or II, init enc for opn fx type IIIA, IIIB, or IIIC]

S82.26[4,5,6][A,B,C] Nondisp seg fx of shaft of [rt, lt, unsp] tibia, [init enc for clsd fx, init enc for opn fx type I or II, init enc for opn fx type IIIA, IIIB, or IIIC]

S82.29[1,2,9][A,B,C] Oth fx of shaft of [rt, lt, unsp] tibia, [init enc for clsd fx, init enc for opn fx type I or II, init enc for opn fx type IIIA, IIIB, or IIIC]

S82.30[1,2,9][A,B,C] Unsp fx of lwr end of [rt, lt, unsp] tibia, [init enc for clsd fx, init enc for opn fx type I or II, init enc for opn fx type IIIA, IIIB, or IIIC]

S82.31[1,2,9]A Torus fx of lwr end of [rt, lt, unsp] tibia, init enc for clsd fx

S82.39[1,2,9][A,B,C] Oth fx of lwr end of [rt, lt, unsp] tibia, [init enc for clsd fx, init enc for opn fx type I or II, init enc for opn fx type IIIA, IIIB, or IIIC]

S82.40[1,2,9][A,B,C] Unsp fx of shaft of [rt, lt, unsp] fibula, [init enc for clsd fx, init enc for opn fx type I or II, init enc for opn fx type IIIA, IIIB, or IIIC]

S82.42[1,2,3][A,B,C] Disp transv fx of shaft of [rt, lt, unsp] fibula, [init enc for clsd fx, init enc for opn fx type I or II, init enc for opn fx type IIIA, IIIB, or IIIC]

S82.42[4,5,6][A,B,C] Nondisp transv fx of shaft of [rt, lt, unsp] fibula, [init enc for clsd fx, init enc for opn fx type I or II, init enc for opn fx type IIIA, IIIB, or IIIC]

S82.43[1,2,3][A,B,C] Disp oblique fx of shaft of [rt, lt, unsp] fibula, [init enc for clsd fx, init enc for opn fx type I or II, init enc for opn fx type IIIA, IIIB, or IIIC]

S82.43[4,5,6][A,B,C] Nondisp oblique fx of shaft of [rt, lt, unsp] fibula, [init enc for clsd fx, init enc for opn fx type I or II, init enc for opn fx type IIIA, IIIB, or IIIC]

S82.44[1,2,3][A,B,C] Disp spiral fx of shaft of [rt, lt, unsp] fibula, [init enc for clsd fx, init enc for opn fx type I or II, init enc for opn fx type IIIA, IIIB, or IIIC]

S82.44[4,5,6][A,B,C] Nondisp spiral fx of shaft of [rt, lt, unsp] fibula, [init enc for clsd fx, init enc for opn fx type I or II, init enc for opn fx type IIIA, IIIB, or IIIC]

S82.45[1,2,3][A,B,C] Disp comm fx of shaft of [rt, lt, unsp] fibula, [init enc for clsd fx, init enc for opn fx type I or II, init enc for opn fx type IIIA, IIIB, or IIIC]

S82.45[4,5,6][A,B,C] Nondisp comm fx of shaft of [rt, lt, unsp] fibula, [init enc for clsd fx, init enc for opn fx type I or II, init enc for opn fx type IIIA, IIIB, or IIIC]

S82.46[1,2,3][A,B,C] Disp seg fx of shaft of [rt, lt, unsp] fibula, [init enc for clsd fx, init enc for opn fx type I or II, init enc for opn fx type IIIA, IIIB, or IIIC]

S82.46[4,5,6][A,B,C] Nondisp seg fx of shaft of [rt, lt, unsp] fibula, [init enc for clsd fx, init enc for opn fx type I or II, init enc for opn fx type IIIA, IIIB, or IIIC]

S82.49[1,2,9][A,B,C] Oth fx of shaft of [rt, lt, unsp] fibula, [init enc for clsd fx, init enc for opn fx type I or II, init enc for opn fx type IIIA, IIIB, or IIIC]

S82.5[1,2,3]X[A,B,C] Disp fx of med malleolus of [rt, lt, unsp] tibia, [init enc for clsd fx, init enc for opn fx type I or II, init enc for opn fx type I or II]

S82.5[4,5,6]X[A,B,C] Nondisp fx of med malleolus of [rt, lt, unsp] tibia, [init enc for clsd fx, init enc for opn fx type I or II, init enc for opn fx type I or II]

S82.6[1,2,3]X[A,B,C] Disp fx of lat malleolus of [rt, lt, unsp] tibia, [init enc for clsd fx, init enc for opn fx type I or II, init enc for opn fx type I or II]

S82.6[4,5,6]X[A,B,C] Nondisp fx of lat malleolus of [rt, lt, unsp] tibia, [init enc for clsd fx, init enc for opn fx type I or II, init enc for opn fx type I or II]

S82.83[1,2,9][A,B,C] Oth fx of upr and lwr end of [rt, lt, unsp] fibula, [init enc for clsd fx, init enc for opn fx type I or II, init enc for opn fx type IIIA, IIIB, or IIIC]

S82.84[1,2,3][A,B,C] Disp bimalleolar fx of [rt, lt, unsp] lwr leg, [init enc for clsd fx, init enc for opn fx type I or II, init enc for opn fx type I or II]

S82.84[4,5,6][A,B,C] Nondisp bimalleolar fx of [rt, lt, unsp] lwr leg, [init enc for clsd fx, init enc for opn fx type I or II, init enc for opn fx type I or II]

S82.85[1,2,3][A,B,C] Disp trimalleolar fx of [rt, lt, unsp] lwr leg, [init enc for clsd fx, init enc for opn fx type I or II, init enc for opn fx type I or II]

S82.85[4,5,6][A,B,C] Nondisp trimalleolar fx of [rt, lt, unsp] lwr leg, [init enc for clsd fx, init enc for opn fx type I or II, init enc for opn fx type I or II]

S82.86[1,2,3][A,B,C] Disp Maisonneuve's fx of [rt, lt, unsp] leg, [init enc for clsd fx, init enc for opn fx type I or II, init enc for opn fx type I or II]

S82.86[4,5,6][A,B,C] Nondisp Maisonneuve's fx of [rt, lt, unsp] leg, [init enc for clsd fx, init enc for opn fx type I or II, init enc for opn fx type I or II]

S82.87[1,2,3][A,B,C] Disp pilon fx of [rt, lt, unsp] tibia, [init enc for clsd fx, init enc for opn fx type I or II, init enc for opn fx type I or II]

S82.87[4,5,6][A,B,C] Nondisp pilon fx of [rt, lt, unsp] tibia, [init enc for clsd fx, init enc for opn fx type I or II, init enc for opn fx type I or II]

S82.89[1,2,9][A,B,C] Oth fx of [rt, lt, unsp] lwr leg, [init enc for clsd fx, init enc for opn fx type I or II, init enc for opn fx type I or II]

S82.8[1,2][1,2,9]A Torus fx of [upr, lwr] end of [rt, lt, unsp] fibula, init enc for clsd fx

S82.9[0,1,2]X[A,B,C] Unsp fx of [unsp, rt, lt] lwr leg, [init enc for clsd fx, init enc for opn fx type I or II, init enc for opn fx type I or II]

S83.00[1,2,3][A,S] Unsp sublux of [rt, lt, unsp] patella, [init enc, seq]

S83.00[4,5,6][A,S] Unsp disloc of [rt, lt, unsp] patella, [init enc, seq]

S83.01[1,2,3][A,S] Lat sublux of [rt, lt, unsp] patella, [init enc, seq]

S83.01[4,5,6][A,S] Lat disloc of [rt, lt, unsp] patella, [init enc, seq]

S83.09[1,2,3][A,S] Oth sublux of [rt, lt, unsp] patella, [init enc, seq]

S83.09[4,5,6][A,S] Oth disloc of [rt, lt, unsp] patella, [init enc, seq]

S83.10[1,2,3][A,S] Unsp sublux of [rt, lt, unsp] knee, [init enc, seq]

S83.10[4,5,6][A,S] Unsp disloc of [rt, lt, unsp] knee, [init enc, seq]

S83.11[1,2,3][A,S] Ant sublux of proximal end of tibia, [rt, lt, unsp] knee, [init enc, seq]

S83.11[4,5,6][A,S] Ant disloc of proximal end of tibia, [rt, lt, unsp] knee, [init enc, seq]

S83.12[1,2,3][A,S] Post sublux of proximal end of tibia, [rt, lt, unsp] knee, [init enc, seq]

S83.12[4,5,6][A,S] Post disloc of proximal end of tibia, [rt, lt, unsp] knee, [init enc, seq]

S83.13[1,2,3][A,S] Med sublux of proximal end of tibia, [rt, lt, unsp] knee, [init enc, seq]

S83.13[4,5,6][A,S] Med disloc of proximal end of tibia, [rt, lt, unsp] knee, [init enc, seq]

S83.14[1,2,3][A,S] Lat sublux of proximal end of tibia, [rt, lt, unsp] knee, [init enc, seq]

S83.14[4,5,6][A,S] Lat disloc of proximal end of tibia, [rt, lt, unsp] knee, [init enc, seq]

S83.19[1,2,3][A,S] Oth sublux of [rt, lt, unsp] knee, [init enc, seq]

S83.19[4,5,6][A,S] Oth disloc of [rt, lt, unsp] knee, [init enc, seq]

S83.20[0,1,2][A,S] Bucket-handle tear of unsp meniscus, current inj, [rt, lt, unsp] knee, [init enc, seq]

Surgical   **Medical**   **CC Indicator**   **MCC Indicator**   **Procedure Proxy**   PDxMCC **PDx acts as own MCC**   PDxCC **PDx acts as own CC**

© 2015 Optum360, LLC   MS-DRG Version 33.0   **191**

S83.20[3,4,5][A,S] Oth tear of unsp meniscus, current inj, [rt, lt, unsp] knee, [init enc, seq]

S83.20[6,7,9][A,S] Unsp tear of unsp meniscus, current inj, [rt, lt, unsp] knee, [init enc, seq]

S83.21[1,2,9][A,S] Bucket-handle tear of med meniscus, current inj, [rt, lt, unsp] knee, [init enc, seq]

S83.22[1,2,9][A,S] Peripheral tear of med meniscus, current inj, [rt, lt, unsp] knee, [init enc, seq]

S83.23[1,2,9][A,S] Complex tear of med meniscus, current inj, [rt, lt, unsp] knee, [init enc, seq]

S83.24[1,2,9][A,S] Oth tear of med meniscus, current inj, [rt, lt, unsp] knee, [init enc, seq]

S83.25[1,2,9][A,S] Bucket-handle tear of lat meniscus, current inj, [rt, lt, unsp] knee, [init enc, seq]

S83.26[1,2,9][A,S] Peripheral tear of lat meniscus, current inj, [rt, lt, unsp] knee, [init enc, seq]

S83.27[1,2,9][A,S] Complex tear of lat meniscus, current inj, [rt, lt, unsp] knee, [init enc, seq]

S83.28[1,2,9][A,S] Oth tear of lat meniscus, current inj, [rt, lt, unsp] knee, [init enc, seq]

S83.3[0,1,2]X[A,S] Tear of articular cartilage of [unsp, rt, lt] knee, current, [init enc, seq]

S83.40[1,2,9][A,S] Sprain of unsp collat lgmt of [rt, lt, unsp] knee, [init enc, seq]

S83.41[1,2,9][A,S] Sprain of med collat lgmt of [rt, lt, unsp] knee, [init enc, seq]

S83.42[1,2,9][A,S] Sprain of lat collat lgmt of [rt, lt, unsp] knee, [init enc, seq]

S83.50[1,2,9][A,S] Sprain of unsp cruciate lgmt of [rt, lt, unsp] knee, [init enc, seq]

S83.51[1,2,9][A,S] Sprain of ant cruciate lgmt of [rt, lt, unsp] knee, [init enc, seq]

S83.52[1,2,9][A,S] Sprain of post cruciate lgmt of [rt, lt, unsp] knee, [init enc, seq]

S83.6[0,1,2]X[A,S] Sprain of the superior tibiofibular jt and lgmt, [rt, lt, unsp] knee, [init enc, seq]

S83.8X[1,2,9][A,S] Sprain of oth spec parts of [rt, lt, unsp] knee, [init enc, seq]

S83.9[0,1,2]X[A,S] Sprain of unsp site of [unsp, rt, lt] knee, [init enc, seq]

S86.01[1,2,9][A,S] Strain of [rt, lt, unsp] Achilles tndn, [init enc, seq]

S86.11[1,2,9][A,S] Strain of oth muscle(s) and tndn(s) of post muscle group at lwr leg lvl, [rt, lt, unsp] leg, [init enc, seq]

S86.21[1,2,9][A,S] Strain of oth muscle(s) and tndn(s) of ant muscle group at lwr leg lvl, [rt, lt, unsp] leg, [init enc, seq]

S86.31[1,2,9][A,S] Strain of oth muscle(s) and tndn(s) of peroneal muscle group at lwr leg lvl, [rt, lt, unsp] leg, [init enc, seq]

S86.81[1,2,9][A,S] Strain of oth muscle(s) and tndn(s) at lwr leg lvl, [rt, lt, unsp] leg, [init enc, seq]

S86.91[1,2,9][A,S] Strain of unsp muscle(s) and tndn(s) at lwr leg lvl, [rt, lt, unsp] leg, [init enc, seq]

S89.00[1,2,9]A Unsp physeal fx of upr end of [rt, lt, unsp] tibia, init enc for clsd fx

S89.09[1,2,9]A Oth physeal fx of upr end of [rt, lt, unsp] tibia, init enc for clsd fx

S89.0[1,2,3,4][1,2,9]A Salter-Harris Type [I, II, III, IV] physeal fx of upr end of [rt, lt, unsp] tibia, init enc for clsd fx

S89.10[1,2,9]A Unsp physeal fx of lwr end of [rt, lt, unsp] tibia, init enc for clsd fx

S89.19[1,2,9]A Oth physeal fx of lwr end of [rt, lt, unsp] tibia, init enc for clsd fx

S89.1[1,2,3,4][1,2,9]A Salter-Harris Type [I, II, III, IV] physeal fx of lwr end of [rt, lt, unsp] tibia, init enc for clsd fx

S89.2[0,1,2,9][1,2,9]A [Unsp, Salter-Harris Type I, Salter-Harris Type II, Oth] physeal fx of upr end of [rt, lt, unsp] fibula, init enc for clsd fx

S89.3[0,1,2,9][1,2,9]A [Unsp, Salter-Harris Type I, Salter-Harris Type II, Oth] physeal fx of lwr end of [rt, lt, unsp] fibula, init enc for clsd fx

S92.00[1,2,9][A,B] Unsp fx of [rt, lt, unsp] calcaneus, init enc for [clsd, opn] fx

S92.01[1,2,3][A,B] Disp fx of body of [rt, lt, unsp] calcaneus, init enc for [clsd, opn] fx

S92.01[4,5,6][A,B] Nondisp fx of body of [rt, lt, unsp] calcaneus, init enc for [clsd, opn] fx

S92.02[1,2,3][A,B] Disp fx of ant process of [rt, lt, unsp] calcaneus, init enc for [clsd, opn] fx

S92.02[4,5,6][A,B] Nondisp fx of ant process of [rt, lt, unsp] calcaneus, init enc for [clsd, opn] fx

S92.03[1,2,3][A,B] Disp avulsion fx of tuberosity of [rt, lt, unsp] calcaneus, init enc for [clsd, opn] fx

S92.03[4,5,6][A,B] Nondisp avulsion fx of tuberosity of [rt, lt, unsp] calcaneus, init enc for [clsd, opn] fx

S92.04[1,2,3][A,B] Disp oth fx of tuberosity of [rt, lt, unsp] calcaneus, init enc for [clsd, opn] fx

S92.04[4,5,6][A,B] Nondisp oth fx of tuberosity of [rt, lt, unsp] calcaneus, init enc for [clsd, opn] fx

S92.05[1,2,3][A,B] Disp oth extraarticular fx of [rt, lt, unsp] calcaneus, init enc for [clsd, opn] fx

S92.05[4,5,6][A,B] Nondisp oth extraarticular fx of [rt, lt, unsp] calcaneus, init enc for [clsd, opn] fx

S92.06[1,2,3][A,B] Disp intraarticular fx of [rt, lt, unsp] calcaneus, init enc for [clsd, opn] fx

S92.06[4,5,6][A,B] Nondisp intraarticular fx of [rt, lt, unsp] calcaneus, init enc for [clsd, opn] fx

S92.10[1,2,9][A,B] Unsp fx of [rt, lt, unsp] talus, init enc for [clsd, opn] fx

S92.11[1,2,3][A,B] Disp fx of neck of [rt, lt, unsp] talus, init enc for [clsd, opn] fx

S92.11[4,5,6][A,B] Nondisp fx of neck of [rt, lt, unsp] talus, init enc for [clsd, opn] fx

S92.12[1,2,3][A,B] Disp fx of body of [rt, lt, unsp] talus, init enc for [clsd, opn] fx

S92.12[4,5,6][A,B] Nondisp fx of body of [rt, lt, unsp] talus, init enc for [clsd, opn] fx

S92.13[1,2,3][A,B] Disp fx of post process of [rt, lt, unsp] talus, init enc for [clsd, opn] fx

S92.13[4,5,6][A,B] Nondisp fx of post process of [rt, lt, unsp] talus, init enc for [clsd, opn] fx

S92.14[1,2,3][A,B] Disp dome fx of [rt, lt, unsp] talus, init enc for [clsd, opn] fx

S92.14[4,5,6][A,B] Nondisp dome fx of [rt, lt, unsp] talus, init enc for [clsd, opn] fx

S92.15[1,2,3][A,B] Disp avulsion fx (chip fx) of [rt, lt, unsp] talus, init enc for [clsd, opn] fx

S92.15[4,5,6][A,B] Nondisp avulsion fx (chip fx) of [rt, lt, unsp] talus, init enc for [clsd, opn] fx

S92.19[1,2,9][A,B] Oth fx of [rt, lt, unsp] talus, init enc for [clsd, opn] fx

S92.20[1,2,9][A,B] Fx of unsp tarsal bone(s) of [rt, lt, unsp] foot, init enc for [clsd, opn] fx

S92.21[1,2,3][A,B] Disp fx of cuboid bone of [rt, lt, unsp] foot, init enc for [clsd, opn] fx

S92.21[4,5,6][A,B] Nondisp fx of cuboid bone of [rt, lt, unsp] foot, init enc for [clsd, opn] fx

S92.22[1,2,3][A,B] Disp fx of lat cuneiform of [rt, lt, unsp] foot, init enc for [clsd, opn] fx

S92.22[4,5,6][A,B] Nondisp fx of lat cuneiform of [rt, lt, unsp] foot, init enc for [clsd, opn] fx

S92.23[1,2,3][A,B] Disp fx of intermediate cuneiform of [rt, lt, unsp] foot, init enc for [clsd, opn] fx

S92.23[4,5,6][A,B] Nondisp fx of intermediate cuneiform of [rt, lt, unsp] foot, init enc for [clsd, opn] fx

S92.24[1,2,3][A,B] Disp fx of med cuneiform of [rt, lt, unsp] foot, init enc for [clsd, opn] fx

S92.24[4,5,6][A,B] Nondisp fx of med cuneiform of [rt, lt, unsp] foot, init enc for [clsd, opn] fx

S92.25[1,2,3][A,B] Disp fx of navicular (scaphoid) of [rt, lt, unsp] foot, init enc for [clsd, opn] fx

S92.25[4,5,6][A,B] Nondisp fx of navicular (scaphoid) of [rt, lt, unsp] foot, init enc for [clsd, opn] fx

S92.30[1,2,9][A,B] Fx of unsp metatarsal bone(s), [rt, lt, unsp] foot, init enc for [clsd, opn] fx

S92.31[1,2,3][A,B] Disp fx of 1st metatarsal bone, [rt, lt, unsp] foot, init enc for [clsd, opn] fx

S92.31[4,5,6][A,B] Nondisp fx of 1st metatarsal bone, [rt, lt, unsp] foot, init enc for [clsd, opn] fx

S92.32[1,2,3][A,B] Disp fx of 2nd metatarsal bone, [rt, lt, unsp] foot, init enc for [clsd, opn] fx

S92.32[4,5,6][A,B] Nondisp fx of 2nd metatarsal bone, [rt, lt, unsp] foot, init enc for [clsd, opn] fx

S92.33[1,2,3][A,B] Disp fx of 3rd metatarsal bone, [rt, lt, unsp] foot, init enc for [clsd, opn] fx

S92.33[4,5,6][A,B] Nondisp fx of 3rd metatarsal bone, [rt, lt, unsp] foot, init enc for [clsd, opn] fx

S92.34[1,2,3][A,B] Disp fx of 4th metatarsal bone, [rt, lt, unsp] foot, init enc for [clsd, opn] fx

S92.34[4,5,6][A,B] Nondisp fx of 4th metatarsal bone, [rt, lt, unsp] foot, init enc for [clsd, opn] fx

S92.35[1,2,3][A,B] Disp fx of 5th metatarsal bone, [rt, lt, unsp] foot, init enc for [clsd, opn] fx

S92.35[4,5,6][A,B] Nondisp fx of 5th metatarsal bone, [rt, lt, unsp] foot, init enc for [clsd, opn] fx

S92.40[1,2,3][A,B] Disp unsp fx of [rt, lt, unsp] great toe, init enc for [clsd, opn] fx

S92.40[4,5,6][A,B] Nondisp unsp fx of [rt, lt, unsp] great toe, init enc for [clsd, opn] fx

S92.41[1,2,3][A,B] Disp fx of proximal phalanx of [rt, lt, unsp] great toe, init enc for [clsd, opn] fx

S92.41[4,5,6][A,B] Nondisp fx of proximal phalanx of [rt, lt, unsp] great toe, init enc for [clsd, opn] fx

S92.42[1,2,3][A,B] Disp fx of distal phalanx of [rt, lt, unsp] great toe, init enc for [clsd, opn] fx

S92.42[4,5,6][A,B] Nondisp fx of distal phalanx of [rt, lt, unsp] great toe, init enc for [clsd, opn] fx

S92.49[1,2,9][A,B] Oth fx of [rt, lt, unsp] great toe, init enc for [clsd, opn] fx

---

Ⓣ **Transfer DRG**　　Ⓢᴾ **Special Payment**　　＊ **Code Range**　　**6th and 7th Character of ZZ = No Device, No Qualifier ZX = No Device, Diagnostic**

S92.50[1,2,3][A,B] Disp unsp fx of [rt, lt, unsp] lesser toe(s), init enc for [clsd, opn] fx
S92.50[4,5,6][A,B] Nondisp unsp fx of [rt, lt, unsp] lesser toe(s), init enc for [clsd, opn] fx
S92.51[1,2,3][A,B] Disp fx of proximal phalanx of [rt, lt, unsp] lesser toe(s), init enc for [clsd, opn] fx
S92.51[4,5,6][A,B] Nondisp fx of proximal phalanx of [rt, lt, unsp] lesser toe(s), init enc for [clsd, opn] fx
S92.52[1,2,3][A,B] Disp fx of med phalanx of [rt, lt, unsp] lesser toe(s), init enc for [clsd, opn] fx
S92.52[4,5,6][A,B] Nondisp fx of med phalanx of [rt, lt, unsp] lesser toe(s), init enc for [clsd, opn] fx
S92.53[1,2,3][A,B] Disp fx of distal phalanx of [rt, lt, unsp] lesser toe(s), init enc for [clsd, opn] fx
S92.53[4,5,6][A,B] Nondisp fx of distal phalanx of [rt, lt, unsp] lesser toe(s), init enc for [clsd, opn] fx
S92.59[1,2,9][A,B] Oth fx of [rt, lt, unsp] lesser toe(s), init enc for [clsd, opn] fx
S92.90[1,2,9][A,B] Unsp fx of [rt, lt, unsp] foot, init enc for [clsd, opn] fx
S92.91[1,2,9][A,B] Unsp fx of [rt, lt, unsp] toe(s), init enc for [clsd, opn] fx
S93.0[1,2,3]X[A,S] Sublux of [rt, lt, unsp] ankle jt, [init enc, seq]
S93.0[4,5,6]X[A,S] Disloc of [rt, lt, unsp] ankle jt, [init enc, seq]
S93.10[1,2,3][A,S] Unsp sublux of [rt, lt, unsp] toe(s), [init enc, seq]
S93.10[4,5,6][A,S] Unsp disloc of [rt, lt, unsp] toe(s), [init enc, seq]
S93.119[A,S] Disloc of interphalangeal jt of unsp toe(s), [init enc, seq]
S93.11[1,2,3][A,S] Disloc of interphalangeal jt of [rt, lt, unsp] great toe, [init enc, seq]
S93.11[4,5,6][A,S] Disloc of interphalangeal jt of [rt, lt, unsp] lesser toe(s), [init enc, seq]
S93.129[A,S] Disloc of metatarsophalangeal jt of unsp toe(s), [init enc, seq]
S93.12[1,2,3][A,S] Disloc of metatarsophalangeal jt of [rt, lt, unsp] great toe, [init enc, seq]
S93.12[4,5,6][A,S] Disloc of metatarsophalangeal jt of [rt, lt, unsp] lesser toe(s), [init enc, seq]
S93.139[A,S] Sublux of interphalangeal jt of unsp toe(s), [init enc, seq]
S93.13[1,2,3][A,S] Sublux of interphalangeal jt of [rt, lt, unsp] great toe, [init enc, seq]
S93.13[4,5,6][A,S] Sublux of interphalangeal jt of [rt, lt, unsp] lesser toe(s), [init enc, seq]
S93.149[A,S] Sublux of metatarsophalangeal jt of unsp toe(s), [init enc, seq]
S93.14[1,2,3][A,S] Sublux of metatarsophalangeal jt of [rt, lt, unsp] great toe, [init enc, seq]
S93.14[4,5,6][A,S] Sublux of metatarsophalangeal jt of [rt, lt, unsp] lesser toe(s), [init enc, seq]
S93.30[1,2,3][A,S] Unsp sublux of [rt, lt, unsp] foot, [init enc, seq]
S93.30[4,5,6][A,S] Unsp disloc of [rt, lt, unsp] foot, [init enc, seq]
S93.31[1,2,3][A,S] Sublux of tarsal jt of [rt, lt, unsp] foot, [init enc, seq]
S93.31[4,5,6][A,S] Disloc of tarsal jt of [rt, lt, unsp] foot, [init enc, seq]
S93.32[1,2,3][A,S] Sublux of tarsometatarsal jt of [rt, lt, unsp] foot, [init enc, seq]
S93.32[4,5,6][A,S] Disloc of tarsometatarsal jt of [rt, lt, unsp] foot, [init enc, seq]
S93.33[1,2,3][A,S] Oth sublux of [rt, lt, unsp] foot, [init enc, seq]
S93.33[4,5,6][A,S] Oth disloc of [rt, lt, unsp] foot, [init enc, seq]
S93.40[1,2,9][A,S] Sprain of unsp lgmt of [rt, lt, unsp] ankle, [init enc, seq]
S93.41[1,2,9][A,S] Sprain of calcaneofibular lgmt of [rt, lt, unsp] ankle, [init enc, seq]
S93.42[1,2,9][A,S] Sprain of deltoid lgmt of [rt, lt, unsp] ankle, [init enc, seq]
S93.43[1,2,9][A,S] Sprain of tibiofibular lgmt of [rt, lt, unsp] ankle, [init enc, seq]
S93.49[1,2,9][A,S] Sprain of oth lgmt of [rt, lt, unsp] ankle, [init enc, seq]
S93.509[A,S] Unsp strain of unsp toe(s), [init enc, seq]
S93.50[1,2,3][A,S] Unsp strain of [rt, lt, unsp] great toe, [init enc, seq]
S93.50[4,5,6][A,S] Unsp strain of [rt, lt, unsp] lesser toe(s), [init enc, seq]
S93.519[A,S] Sprain of interphalangeal jt of unsp toe(s), [init enc, seq]
S93.51[1,2,3][A,S] Sprain of interphalangeal jt of [rt, lt, unsp] great toe, [init enc, seq]
S93.51[4,5,6][A,S] Sprain of interphalangeal jt of [rt, lt, unsp] lesser toe(s), [init enc, seq]
S93.529[A,S] Sprain of metatarsophalangeal jt of unsp toe(s), [init enc, seq]
S93.52[1,2,3][A,S] Sprain of metatarsophalangeal jt of [rt, lt, unsp] great toe, [init enc, seq]
S93.52[4,5,6][A,S] Sprain of metatarsophalangeal jt of [rt, lt, unsp] lesser toe(s), [init enc, seq]
S93.60[1,2,9][A,S] Unsp sprain of [rt, lt, unsp] foot, [init enc, seq]
S93.61[1,2,9][A,S] Sprain of tarsal lgmt of [rt, lt, unsp] foot, [init enc, seq]
S93.62[1,2,9][A,S] Sprain of tarsometatarsal lgmt of [rt, lt, unsp] foot, [init enc, seq]
S93.69[1,2,9][A,S] Oth sprain of [rt, lt, unsp] foot, [init enc, seq]
S96.01[1,2,9][A,S] Strain of muscle and tndn of long flexor muscle of toe at ankle and foot lvl, [rt, lt, unsp] foot, [init enc, seq]
S96.11[1,2,9][A,S] Strain of muscle and tndn of long extensor muscle of toe at ankle and foot lvl, [rt, lt, unsp] foot, [init enc, seq]

S96.21[1,2,9][A,S] Strain of intrinsic muscle and tndn at ankle and foot lvl, [rt, lt, unsp] foot, [init enc, seq]
S96.81[1,2,9][A,S] Strain of oth spec muscles and tndns at ankle and foot lvl, [rt, lt, unsp] foot, [init enc, seq]
S96.91[1,2,9][A,S] Strain of unsp muscle and tndn at ankle and foot lvl, [rt, lt, unsp] foot, [init enc, seq]

DRG 563   Fracture, Sprain, Strain and Dislocation Except Femur, Hip, Pelvis and Thigh without MCC

GMLOS 3.0   AMLOS 3.5   RW 0.7870   ⊺

Select principal diagnosis listed under DRG 562

DRG 564   Other Musculoskeletal System and Connective Tissue Diagnoses with MCC

GMLOS 4.7   AMLOS 6.1   RW 1.5225

Principal Diagnosis

B90.2 Sequelae of tuberculosis of bones and jts
D16.[0,1][0,1,2] Benign neoplasm of [scapula and long, short] bones of [unsp, rt, lt] upr limb
D16.[2,3][0,1,2] Benign neoplasm of [long, short] bones of [unsp, rt, lt] lwr limb
D16.[4,6,8,9] Benign neoplasm of [bones of skull and face, vert column, pelvic bones, sacrum and coccyx, unsp bone and articular cartilage]
D21.0 Benign neoplasm of connctv/soft tiss of head, face and neck
D21.1[0,1,2] Benign neoplasm of connective and oth soft tissue of [unsp, rt, lt] upr limb, incl* shldr
D21.2[0,1,2] Benign neoplasm of connective and oth soft tissue of [unsp, rt, lt] lwr limb, incl* hip
D21.[3,4,5,6,9] Benign neoplasm of connective and oth soft tissue of [thorax, abd, pelvis, unsp trunk, unsp connective and oth soft tissue]
D36.1[0,1,2,3,4,5,6,7] Benign neoplasm of peripheral nerves and autonomic nervous sys of [unsp site, face head and neck, upr limb incl* shldr, lwr limb incl* hip, thorax, abd, pelvis, unsp trunk]
D48.[1,2] Neoplasm of uncertain behav of [connective and oth soft tissue, peripheral nerves and autonomic nervous sys]
D49.2 Neoplasm of unsp behav of bone, soft tissue, and skin
E78.7[1,2] [Barth, Smith-Lemli-Opitz] synd
H61.03[1,2,3,9] Chondritis of [rt, lt, bilat, unsp] ext ear
H61.0[1,2][1,2,3,9] [Acute, Chr] perichondritis of [rt, lt, bilat, unsp] ext ear
M20.0[0,1,2,3,9][1,2,9] [Unsp, Mallet finger, Boutonniere, Swan-neck, Oth] deformity of [rt, lt, unsp] finger(s)
M20.4[0,1,2] Oth hammer toe(s) (acquired), [unsp, rt, lt] foot
M20.5X[1,2,9] Oth deformities of toe(s) (acquired), [rt, lt, unsp] foot
M20.6[0,1,2] Acquired deformities of toe(s), unsp, [unsp, rt, lt] foot
M20.[1,2,3][0,1,2] Hallux [valgus (acquired), rigidus, varus (acquired)], [unsp, rt, lt] foot
M21.00 Valgus deformity, NEC, unsp site
M21.0[2,5,6,7][1,2,9] Valgus deformity, NEC, [rt, lt, unsp] [elbow, hip, knee, ankle]
M21.10 Varus deformity, NEC, unsp site
M21.1[2,5,6,7][1,2,9] Varus deformity, NEC, [rt, lt, unsp] [elbow, hip, knee, ankle]
M21.20 Flexion deformity, unsp site
M21.2[1,2,3,4,5,6,7][1,2,9] Flexion deformity, [rt, lt, unsp] [shldr, elbow, wrist, finger jts, hip, knee, ankle and toes]
M21.37[1,2,9] Foot drop, [rt, lt, unsp] foot
M21.4[0,1,2] Flat foot (pes planus) (acquired), [unsp, rt, lt] foot
M21.54[1,2,9] Acquired clubfoot, [rt, lt, unsp] foot
M21.6X[1,2,9] Oth acquired deformities of [rt, lt, unsp] foot
M21.70 Unequal limb length (acquired), unsp site
M21.72[1,2,9] Unequal limb length (acquired), [rt, lt, unsp] humerus
M21.73[1,2,3,4,9] Unequal limb length (acquired), [rt ulna, lt ulna, rt radius, lt radius, unsp ulna and radius]
M21.75[1,2,9] Unequal limb length (acquired), [rt, lt, unsp] femur
M21.76[1,2,3,4,9] Unequal limb length (acquired), [rt tibia, lt tibia, rt fibula, lt fibula, unsp tibia & fibula]
M21.80 Oth spec acquired deformities of unsp limb
M21.8[2,3,5,6][1,2,9] Oth spec acquired deformities of [rt, lt, unsp] [upr arm, forearm, thigh, lwr leg]
M21.90 Unsp acquired deformity of unsp limb
M21.9[2,3,4,5,6][1,2,9] Unsp acquired deformity of [rt, lt, unsp] [upr arm, forearm, hand, thigh, lwr leg]
M23.4* Loose body in knee
M23.5* Chr instability of knee
M24.0* Loose body in jt
M24.10 Oth articular cartilage d/o, unsp site
M24.15[1,2,9] Oth articular cartilage d/os, [rt, lt, unsp] hip
M24.35[1,2,9] Path disloc of [rt, lt, unsp] hip, NEC

Surgical   **Medical**   **CC Indicator**   **MCC Indicator**   **Procedure Proxy**   PDxMCC **PDx acts as own MCC**   PDxCC **PDx acts as own CC**

Code	Description
M24.40	Recurrent disloc, unsp jt
M24.45[1,2,9]	Recurrent disloc, [rt, lt, unsp] hip
M24.5*	Contracture of jt
M24.7	Protrusio acetabuli
M24.8*	Oth specific jt derangements, NEC
M24.9	Jt derangement, unsp
M25.2*	Flail jt
M25.3*	Oth instability of jt
M25.4*	Effusion of jt
M43.3	Recurrent atlantoaxial disloc with myelopathy
M43.4	Oth recurrent atlantoaxial disloc
M43.5*	Oth recurrent vert disloc
M53.2X[1,2,3,4,5,6,9]	Spinal instabilities, [occipito-atlanto-axial, cervical, cervicothoracic, thoracic, thoracolumbar, lumbar, unsp] rgn
M77.3*	Calcaneal spur
M79.5	Residual FB in soft tissue
M80.00X[K,P]	Age-related osteoporosis w/ current path fx, unsp site, subsq enc for fx w/ [nonu, malu]
M80.01[1,2,9][K,P]	Age-related osteoporosis w/ current path fx, [rt, lt, unsp] shldr, subsq enc for fx w/ [nonu, malu]
M80.02[1,2,9][K,P]	Age-related osteoporosis w/ current path fx, [rt, lt, unsp] humerus, subsq enc for fx w/ [nonu, malu]
M80.03[1,2,9][K,P]	Age-related osteoporosis w/ current path fx, [rt, lt, unsp] forearm, subsq enc for fx w/ [nonu, malu]
M80.04[1,2,9][K,P]	Age-related osteoporosis w/ current path fx, [rt, lt, unsp] hand, subsq enc for fx w/ [nonu, malu]
M80.05[1,2,9][K,P]	Age-related osteoporosis w/ current path fx, [rt, lt, unsp] femur, subsq enc for fx w/ [nonu, malu]
M80.06[1,2,9][K,P]	Age-related osteoporosis w/ current path fx, [rt, lt, unsp] lwr leg, subsq enc for fx w/ [nonu, malu]
M80.07[1,2,9][K,P]	Age-related osteoporosis w/ current path fx, [rt, lt, unsp] ankle and foot, subsq enc for fx w/ [nonu, malu]
M80.08X[K,P]	Age-related osteoporosis w/ current path fx, vertebra(e), subsq enc for fx w/ [nonu, malu]
M80.80X[K,P]	Oth osteoporosis w/ current path fx, unsp site, subsq enc for fx w/ [nonu, malu]
M80.81[1,2,9][K,P]	Oth osteoporosis w/ current path fx, [rt, lt, unsp] shldr, subsq enc for fx w/ [nonu, malu]
M80.82[1,2,9][K,P]	Oth osteoporosis w/ current path fx, [rt, lt, unsp] humerus, subsq enc for fx w/ [nonu, malu]
M80.83[1,2,9][K,P]	Oth osteoporosis w/ current path fx, [rt, lt, unsp] forearm, subsq enc for fx w/ [nonu, malu]
M80.84[1,2,9][K,P]	Oth osteoporosis w/ current path fx, [rt, lt, unsp] hand, subsq enc for fx w/ [nonu, malu]
M80.85[1,2,9][K,P]	Oth osteoporosis w/ current path fx, [rt, lt, unsp] femur, subsq enc for fx w/ [nonu, malu]
M80.86[1,2,9][K,P]	Oth osteoporosis w/ current path fx, [rt, lt, unsp] lwr leg, subsq enc for fx w/ [nonu, malu]
M80.87[1,2,9][K,P]	Oth osteoporosis w/ current path fx, [rt, lt, unsp] ankle and foot, subsq enc for fx w/ [nonu, malu]
M80.88X[K,P]	Oth osteoporosis w/ current path fx, vertebra(e), subsq enc for fx w/ [nonu, malu]
M84.30X[K,P]	Stress fx, unsp site, subsq enc for fx w/ [nonu, malu]
M84.31[1,2,9][K,P]	Stress fx, [rt, lt, unsp] shldr, subsq enc for fx w/ [nonu, malu]
M84.32[1,2,9][K,P]	Stress fx, [rt, lt, unsp] humerus, subsq enc for fx w/ [nonu, malu]
M84.33[1,2,3,4,9][K,P]	Stress fx, [rt ulna, lt ulna, rt radius, lt radius, unsp ulna and radius], subsq enc for fx w/ [nonu, malu]
M84.34[1,2,3][K,P]	Stress fx, [rt, lt, unsp] hand, subsq enc for fx w/ [nonu, malu]
M84.34[4,5,6][K,P]	Stress fx, [rt, lt, unsp] finger(s), subsq enc for fx w/ [nonu, malu]
M84.350[K,P]	Stress fx, pelvis, subsq enc for fx w/ [nonu, malu]
M84.359[K,P]	Stress fx, hip, unsp, subsq enc for fx w/ [nonu, malu]
M84.35[1,2,3][K,P]	Stress fx, [rt, lt, unsp] femur, subsq enc for fx w/ [nonu, malu]
M84.36[1,2,3,4,9][K,P]	Stress fx, [rt tibia, lt tibia, rt fibula, lt fibula, unsp tibia & fibula], subsq enc for fx w/ [nonu, malu]
M84.37[1,2,3][K,P]	Stress fx, [rt, lt, unsp] ankle, subsq enc for fx w/ [nonu, malu]
M84.37[4,5,6][K,P]	Stress fx, [rt, lt, unsp] foot, subsq enc for fx w/ [nonu, malu]
M84.37[7,8,9][K,P]	Stress fx, [rt, lt, unsp] toe(s), subsq enc for fx w/ [nonu, malu]
M84.38X[K,P]	Stress fx, oth site, subsq enc for fx w/ [nonu, malu]
M84.40X[K,P]	Path fx, unsp site, subsq enc for fx w/ [nonu, malu]
M84.41[1,2,9][K,P]	Path fx, [rt, lt, unsp] shldr, subsq enc for fx w/ [nonu, malu]
M84.42[1,2,9][K,P]	Path fx, [rt, lt, unsp] humerus, subsq enc for fx w/ [nonu, malu]
M84.43[1,2,3,4,9][K,P]	Path fx, [rt ulna, lt ulna, rt radius, lt radius, unsp ulna and radius], subsq enc for fx w/ [nonu, malu]
M84.44[1,2,3][K,P]	Path fx, [rt, lt, unsp] hand, subsq enc for fx w/ [nonu, malu]
M84.44[4,5,6][K,P]	Path fx, [rt, lt, unsp] finger(s), subsq enc for fx w/ [nonu, malu]
M84.45[1,2,3][K,P]	Path fx, [rt, lt, unsp] femur, subsq enc for fx w/ [nonu, malu]
M84.45[4,9][K,P]	Path fx, [pelvis, unsp hip], subsq enc for fx w/ [nonu, malu]
M84.46[1,2,3,4,9][K,P]	Path fx, [rt tibia, lt tibia, rt fibula, lt fibula, unsp tibia & fibula], subsq enc for fx w/ [nonu, malu]
M84.47[1,2,3][K,P]	Path fx, [rt, lt, unsp] ankle, subsq enc for fx w/ [nonu, malu]
M84.47[4,5,6][K,P]	Path fx, [rt, lt, unsp] foot, subsq enc for fx w/ [nonu, malu]
M84.47[7,8,9][K,P]	Path fx, [rt, lt, unsp] toe(s), subsq enc for fx w/ [nonu, malu]
M84.48X[K,P]	Path fx, oth site, subsq enc for fx w/ [nonu, malu]
M84.50X[K,P]	Path fx in neoplastic dz, unsp site, subsq enc for fx w/ [nonu, malu]
M84.51[1,2,9][K,P]	Path fx in neoplastic dz, [rt, lt, unsp] shldr, subsq enc for fx w/ [nonu, malu]
M84.52[1,2,9][K,P]	Path fx in neoplastic dz, [rt, lt, unsp] humerus, subsq enc for fx w/ [nonu, malu]
M84.53[1,2,3,4,9][K,P]	Path fx in neoplastic dz, [rt ulna, lt ulna, rt radius, lt radius, unsp ulna and radius], subsq enc for fx w/ [nonu, malu]
M84.54[1,2,9][K,P]	Path fx in neoplastic dz, [rt, lt, unsp] hand, subsq enc for fx w/ [nonu, malu]
M84.550[K,P]	Path fx in neoplastic dz, pelvis, subsq enc for fx w/ [nonu, malu]
M84.559[K,P]	Path fx in neoplastic dz, hip, unsp, subsq enc for fx w/ [nonu, malu]
M84.55[1,2,3][K,P]	Path fx in neoplastic dz, [rt, lt, unsp] femur, subsq enc for fx w/ [nonu, malu]
M84.56[1,2,3,4,9][K,P]	Path fx in neoplastic dz, [rt tibia, lt tibia, rt fibula, lt fibula, unsp tibia & fibula], subsq enc for fx w/ [nonu, malu]
M84.57[1,2,3][K,P]	Path fx in neoplastic dz, [rt, lt, unsp] ankle, subsq enc for fx w/ [nonu, malu]
M84.57[4,5,6][K,P]	Path fx in neoplastic dz, [rt, lt, unsp] foot, subsq enc for fx w/ [nonu, malu]
M84.58X[K,P]	Path fx in neoplastic dz, vertebrae, subsq enc for fx w/ [nonu, malu]
M84.60X[K,P]	Path fx in oth dzs, unsp site, subsq enc for fx w/ [nonu, malu]
M84.61[1,2,9][K,P]	Path fx in oth dzs, [rt, lt, unsp] shldr, subsq enc for fx w/ [nonu, malu]
M84.62[1,2,9][K,P]	Path fx in oth dzs, [rt, lt, unsp] humerus, subsq enc for fx w/ [nonu, malu]
M84.63[1,2,3,4,9][K,P]	Path fx in oth dzs, [rt ulna, lt ulna, rt radius, lt radius, unsp ulna and radius], subsq enc for fx w/ [nonu, malu]
M84.64[1,2,9][K,P]	Path fx in oth dzs, [rt, lt, unsp] hand, subsq enc for fx w/ [nonu, malu]
M84.650[K,P]	Path fx in oth dzs, pelvis, subsq enc for fx w/ [nonu, malu]
M84.659[K,P]	Path fx in oth dzs, hip, unsp, subsq enc for fx w/ [nonu, malu]
M84.65[1,2,3][K,P]	Path fx in oth dzs, [rt, lt, unsp] femur, subsq enc for fx w/ [nonu, malu]
M84.66[1,2,3,4,9][K,P]	Path fx in oth dzs, [rt tibia, lt tibia, rt fibula, lt fibula, unsp tibia & fibula], subsq enc for fx w/ [nonu, malu]
M84.67[1,2,3][K,P]	Path fx in oth dzs, [rt, lt, unsp] ankle, subsq enc for fx w/ [nonu, malu]
M84.67[4,5,6][K,P]	Path fx in oth dzs, [rt, lt, unsp] foot, subsq enc for fx w/ [nonu, malu]
M84.68X[K,P]	Path fx in oth dz, oth site, subsq enc for fx w/ [nonu, malu]
M84.8*	Oth d/o of continuity of bone
M84.9	D/o of continuity of bone, unsp
M85.1*	Skeletal fluorosis
M85.2	Hyperostosis of skull
M85.8*	Oth spec d/o of bone density and structure
M85.9	D/o of bone density and structure, unsp
M89.0*	Algoneurodystrophy
M89.1*	Physeal arrest
M89.2*	Oth d/o of bone development and growth
M89.3*	Hypertrophy of bone
M89.5*	Osteolysis
M89.6*	Osteopathy after poliomyelitis
M89.8*	Oth spec d/o of bone
M89.9	D/o of bone, unsp
M94.1	Relapsing polychondritis
M94.3*	Chondrolysis
M94.8*	Oth spec d/o of cartilage
M94.9	D/o of cartilage, unsp
M95.2	Oth acquired deformity of head
M95.3	Acquired deformity of neck
M95.4	Acquired deformity of chest and rib
M95.5	Acquired deformity of pelvis
M95.8	Oth acquired deformities of musculoskeletal sys
M95.9	Acquired deformity of musculoskeletal sys, unsp
M99.8[0,1,2,5,6,7,8,9]	Oth biomech lesions of [head, cervical, thoracic, pelvic, lwr extr, upr extr, rib cage, abd and oth] rgn
M99.9	Biomechanical lesion, unsp
Q65*	Congenital deformities of hip
Q66*	Congenital deformities of feet
Q67.0	Congenital facial asymmetry

T Transfer DRG   SP Special Payment   * Code Range   6th and 7th Character of ZZ = No Device, No Qualifier ZX = No Device, Diagnostic

Q67.1	Congenital compression facies
Q67.2	Dolichocephaly
Q67.3	Plagiocephaly
Q67.4	Oth congenital deformities of skull, face and jaw
Q67.5	Congenital deformity of spine
Q67.8	Oth congenital deformities of chest
Q68.0	Congenital deformity of sternocleidomastoid muscle
Q68.1	Congenital deformity of finger(s) and hand
Q68.2	Congenital deformity of knee
Q68.3	Congenital bowing of femur
Q68.4	Congenital bowing of tibia & fibula
Q68.5	Congenital bowing of long bones of leg, unsp
Q68.8	Oth spec congenital musculoskeletal deformities
Q69*	Polydactyly
Q70*	Syndactyly
Q71*	Reduction defects of upr limb
Q72*	Reduction defects of lwr limb
Q73*	Reduction defects of unsp limb
Q74*	Oth congenital malformations of limb(s)
Q75*	Oth congenital malformations of skull and face bones
Q76.1	Klippel-Feil synd
Q76.3	Congenital scoliosis d/t congenital bony malformation
Q76.42[5,6,7,8,9]	Congenital lordosis, [thoracolumbar, lumbar, lumbosacral, sacral and sacrococcygeal, unsp] rgn
Q76.5	Cervical rib
Q77.0	Achondrogenesis
Q77.1	Thanatophoric short stature
Q77.3	Chondrodysplasia punctata
Q77.4	Achondroplasia
Q77.5	Diastrophic dysplasia
Q77.6	Chondroectodermal dysplasia
Q77.7	Spondyloepiphyseal dysplasia
Q77.[8,9]	[Oth, Unsp] osteochondrodysplasia w/ defects of growth of tubular bones and spine
Q78.0	Osteogenesis imperfecta
Q78.1	Polyostotic fibrous dysplasia
Q78.2	Osteopetrosis
Q78.3	Progressive diaphyseal dysplasia
Q78.4	Enchondromatosis
Q78.5	Metaphyseal dysplasia
Q78.6	Multi congenital exostoses
Q78.8	Oth spec osteochondrodysplasias
Q78.9	Osteochondrodysplasia, unsp
Q79.6	Ehlers-Danlos synd
Q79.[8,9]	[Oth, Unsp] congenital malformations of musculoskeletal sys
Q87.3	Congenital malformation syndromes involving early overgrowth
Q87.5	Oth congenital malformation syndromes w oth skeletal changes
Q87.8*	Oth congenital malformation syndromes, NEC
Q87.[0,1,2]	Congenital malformation synds predominantly [affecting facial appearance, associated w/ short stature, involving limbs]
Q89.7	Multi congenital malformations, NEC
Q89.8	Oth spec congenital malformations
R93.[6,7]	Abnormal findings on dx imaging of [limbs, oth parts of musculoskeletal sys]
R94.131	Abnormal electromyogram [EMG]
S02.0XXK	Fx of vault of skull, subs for fx w nonu
S02.10XK	Unsp fx of base of skull, subs for fx w nonu
S02.11[0,1,2,3]K	[Type I, Type II, Type III, Unsp] occipital condyle fx, subsq enc for fx w/ nonu
S02.11[8,9]K	[Oth, Unsp] fx of occiput, subsq enc for fx w/ nonu
S02.19XK	Oth fx of base of skull, subs for fx w nonu
S02.40[0,1,2]K	[Malar, Maxillary, Zygomatic] fx unsp, subsq enc for fx w/ nonu
S02.41[1,2,3]K	LeFort [I, II, III] fx, subsq enc for fx w/ nonu
S02.42X[A,B,K]	Fx of alveolus of maxilla, [init enc for clsd fx, init enc for opn fx, subsq enc for fx w/ nonu]
S02.5XXK	Fx of tooth (traum), subs for fx w nonu
S02.60[0,9]K	Fx of [unsp part of body of mandible, manible unsp], subsq enc for fx w/ nonu
S02.6[1,2,3,4,5,6,7,9]XK	Fx of [condylar process, subcondylar process, coronoid process, ramus, angle, symphysis, alveolus, oth spec site] of mandible, subsq enc for fx w/ nonu
S02.8XX[A,B,K]	Fxs of oth spec skull and facial bones, [init enc for clsd fx, init enc for opn fx, subsq enc for fx w/ nonu]
S02.91XK	Unsp fx of skull, subs enc for fx w nonu
S02.92X[A,B,K]	Unsp fx of facial bones, [init enc for clsd fx, init enc for opn fx, subsq enc for fx w/ nonu]
S02.[2,3]XXK	Fx of [nasal bones, orbital floor], subsq enc for fx w/ nonu

S03.8XXA	Sprain of jts and lgmt of oth prt head, init enc
S12.00[0,1]K	Unsp [disp, nondisp] fx of 1st cervical vertebra, subsq enc for fx w/ nonu
S12.03[0,1]K	[Disp, Nondisp] post arch fx of 1st cervical vertebra, subsq enc for fx w/ nonu
S12.04[0,1]K	[Disp, Nondisp] lat mass fx of 1st cervical vertebra, subsq enc for fx w/ nonu
S12.09[0,1]K	Oth [disp, nondisp] fx of 1st cervical vertebra, subsq enc for fx w/ nonu
S12.0[1,2]XK	[Stable, Unstable] burst fx of 1st cervical vertebra, subsq enc for fx w/ nonu
S12.10[0,1]K	Unsp [disp, undisp] fx of 2nd cervical vertebra, subsq enc for fx w/ nonu
S12.11[0,1,2]K	[Ant disp, Post disp, Nondisp] Type II dens fx, subsq enc for fx w/ nonu
S12.12[0,1]K	Oth [disp, nondisp] dens fx, subsq enc for fx w/ nonu
S12.13[0,1]K	Unsp traum [disp, nondisp] spondylolisthesis of 2nd cervical vertebra, subsq enc for fx w/ nonu
S12.14XK	Type III traum spondylolysis of 2nd cervcal vert, 7thK
S12.15[0,1]K	Oth traum [disp, nondisp] spondylolisthesis of 2nd cervical vertebra, subsq enc for fx w/ nonu
S12.19[0,1]K	Oth [disp, nondisp] fx of 2nd cervical vertebra, subsq enc for fx w/ nonu
S12.20[0,1]K	Unsp [disp, nondisp] fx of 3rd cervical vertebra, subsq enc for fx w/ nonu
S12.23[0,1]K	Unsp traum [disp, nondisp] spondylolisthesis of 3rd cervical vertebra, subsq enc for fx w/ nonu
S12.24XK	Type III traum spondylolysis of 3rd cervcal vert, 7thK
S12.25[0,1]K	Oth traum [disp, nondisp] spondylolisthesis of 3rd cervical vertebra, subsq enc for fx w/ nonu
S12.29[0,1]K	Oth [disp, nondisp] fx of 3rd cervical vertebra, subsq enc for fx w/ nonu
S12.30[0,1]K	Unsp [disp, nondisp] fx of 4th cervical vertebra, subsq enc for fx w/ nonu
S12.33[0,1]K	Unsp traum [disp, nondisp] spondylolisthesis of 4th cervical vertebra, subsq enc for fx w/ nonu
S12.34XK	Type III traum spondylolysis of 4th cervcal vert, 7thK
S12.35[0,1]K	Oth traum [disp, nondisp] spondylolisthesis of 4th cervical vertebra, subsq enc for fx w/ nonu
S12.39[0,1]K	Oth [disp, nondisp] fx of 4th cervical vertebra, subsq enc for fx w/ nonu
S12.40[0,1]K	Unsp [disp, nondisp] fx of 5th cervical vertebra, subsq enc for fx w/ nonu
S12.43[0,1]K	Unsp traum [disp, nondisp] spondylolisthesis of 5th cervical vertebra, subsq enc for fx w/ nonu
S12.44XK	Type III traum spondylolysis of 5th cervcal vert, 7thK
S12.45[0,1]K	Oth traum [disp, nondisp] spondylolisthesis of 5th cervical vertebra, subsq enc for fx w/ nonu
S12.49[0,1]K	Oth [disp, nondisp] fx of 5th cervical vertebra, subsq enc for fx w/ nonu
S12.50[0,1]K	Unsp [disp, nondisp] fx of 6th cervical vertebra, subsq enc for fx w/ nonu
S12.53[0,1]K	Unsp traum [disp, nondisp] spondylolisthesis of 6th cervical vertebra, subsq enc for fx w/ nonu
S12.54XK	Type III traum spondylolysis of sixth cervcal vert, 7thK
S12.55[0,1]K	Oth traum [disp, nondisp] spondylolisthesis of 6th cervical vertebra, subsq enc for fx w/ nonu
S12.59[0,1]K	Oth [disp, nondisp] fx of 6th cervical vertebra, subsq enc for fx w/ nonu
S12.60[0,1]K	Unsp [disp, nondisp] fx of 7th cervical vertebra, subsq enc for fx w/ nonu
S12.63[0,1]K	Unsp traum [disp, nondisp] spondylolisthesis of 7th cervical vertebra, subsq enc for fx w/ nonu
S12.64XK	Type III traum spondylolysis of 7th cervcal vert, 7thK
S12.65[0,1]K	Oth traum [disp, nondisp] spondylolisthesis of 7th cervical vertebra, subsq enc for fx w/ nonu
S12.69[0,1]K	Oth [disp, nondisp] fx of 7th cervical vertebra, subsq enc for fx w/ nonu
S13.5XXA	Sprain of thyroid region, init enc
S22.00[0,1,2,8,9]K	[Wedge compression, Stable burst, Unstable burst, Oth, Unsp] fx of unsp thoracic vertebra, subsq enc for fx w/ nonu
S22.01[0,1,2,8,9]K	[Wedge compression, Stable burst, Unstable burst, Oth, Unsp] fx of 1st thoracic vertebra, subsq enc for fx w/ nonu
S22.02[0,1,2,8,9]K	[Wedge compression, Stable burst, Unstable burst, Oth, Unsp] fx of 2nd thoracic vertebra, subsq enc for fx w/ nonu
S22.03[0,1,2,8,9]K	[Wedge compression, Stable burst, Unstable burst, Oth, Unsp] fx of 3rd thoracic vertebra, subsq enc for fx w/ nonu
S22.04[0,1,2,8,9]K	[Wedge compression, Stable burst, Unstable burst, Oth, Unsp] fx of 4th thoracic vertebra, subsq enc for fx w/ nonu

MDC 8: Diseases And Disorders Of The Musculoskeletal System And Connective Tissue—MEDICAL

Surgical	Medical	CC Indicator	MCC Indicator	Procedure Proxy	PDxMCC PDx acts as own MCC	PDxCC PDx acts as own CC

MDC 8: Diseases And Disorders Of The Musculoskeletal System And Connective Tissue—MEDICAL

S22.05[0,1,2,8,9]K [Wedge compression, Stable burst, Unstable burst, Oth, Unsp] fx of T5-T6 vertebra, subsq enc for fx w/ nonu

S22.06[0,1,2,8,9]K [Wedge compression, Stable burst, Unstable burst, Oth, Unsp] fx of T7-T8 vertebra, subsq enc for fx w/ nonu

S22.07[0,1,2,8,9]K [Wedge compression, Stable burst, Unstable burst, Oth, Unsp] fx of T9-T10 vertebra, subsq enc for fx w/ nonu

S22.08[0,1,2,8,9]K [Wedge compression, Stable burst, Unstable burst, Oth, Unsp] fx of T11-T12 vertebra, subsq enc for fx w/ nonu

S22.20XK Unsp fx of sternum, subs for fx w nonu

S22.23XK Sternal manubrial dissociation, subs for fx w nonu

S22.24XK Fx of xiphoid process, subs for fx w nonu

S22.2[1,2]XK Fx of [manubrium, body of sternum], subsq enc for fx w/ nonu

S22.3[1,2,9]XK Fx of one rib, [rt, lt, unsp] side, subsq enc for fx w/ nonu

S22.4[1,2,3,9]XK Multi fxs of ribs, [rt, lt, bilat, unsp] side, subsq enc for fx w/ nonu

S22.5XXK Flail chest, subsq enc for fx with nonu

S22.9XX[A,B,K] Fx of bony thorax, part unsp, [init enc for clsd fx, init enc for opn fx, subsq enc for fx w/ nonu]

S32.00[0,1,2,8,9]K [Wedge compression, Stable burst, Unstable burst, Oth, Unsp] fx of unsp lumbar vertebra, subsq enc for fx w/ nonu

S32.01[0,1,2,8,9]K [Wedge compression, Stable burst, Unstable burst, Oth, Unsp] fx of 1st lumbar vertebra, subsq enc for fx w/ nonu

S32.02[0,1,2,8,9]K [Wedge compression, Stable burst, Unstable burst, Oth, Unsp] fx of 2nd lumbar vertebra, subsq enc for fx w/ nonu

S32.03[0,1,2,8,9]K [Wedge compression, Stable burst, Unstable burst, Oth, Unsp] fx of 3rd lumbar vertebra, subsq enc for fx w/ nonu

S32.04[0,1,2,8,9]K [Wedge compression, Stable burst, Unstable burst, Oth, Unsp] fx of 4th lumbar vertebra, subsq enc for fx w/ nonu

S32.05[0,1,2,8,9]K [Wedge compression, Stable burst, Unstable burst, Oth, Unsp] fx of 5th lumbar vertebra, subsq enc for fx w/ nonu

S32.10XK Unsp fx of sacrum, subs enc for fx w nonu

S32.11[0,1,2,9]K [Nondisp, Minimally disp, Severely disp, Unsp] Zone I fx of sacrum, subsq enc for fx w/ nonu

S32.12[0,1,2,9]K [Nondisp, Minimally disp, Severely disp, Unsp] Zone II fx of sacrum, subsq enc for fx w/ nonu

S32.13[0,1,2,9]K [Nondisp, Minimally disp, Severely disp, Unsp] Zone III fx of sacrum, subsq enc for fx w/ nonu

S32.1[4,5,6,7,9]XK [Type 1, Type 2, Type 3, Type 4, Oth] fx of sacrum, subsq enc for fx w/ nonu

S32.2XXK Fx of coccyx, subs enc for fx with nonu

S32.30[1,2,9]K Unsp fx of [rt, lt, unsp] ilium, subsq enc for fx w/ nonu

S32.31[1,2,3]K Disp avulsion fx of [rt, lt, unsp] ilium, subsq enc for fx w/ nonu

S32.31[4,5,6]K Nondisp avulsion fx of [rt, lt, unsp] ilium, subsq enc for fx w/ nonu

S32.39[1,2,9]K Oth fx of [rt, lt, unsp] ilium, subsq enc for fx w/ nonu

S32.40[1,2,9]K Unsp fx of [rt, lt, unsp] acetab, subsq enc for fx w/ nonu

S32.41[1,2,3]K Disp fx of ant wall of [rt, lt, unsp] acetab, subsq enc for fx w/ nonu

S32.41[4,5,6]K Nondisp fx of ant wall of [rt, lt, unsp] acetab, subsq enc for fx w/ nonu

S32.42[1,2,3]K Disp fx of post wall of [rt, lt, unsp] acetab, subsq enc for fx w/ nonu

S32.42[4,5,6]K Nondisp fx of post wall of [rt, lt, unsp] acetab, subsq enc for fx w/ nonu

S32.43[1,2,3]K Disp fx of ant column (iliopubic) of [rt, lt, unsp] acetab, subsq enc for fx w/ nonu

S32.43[4,5,6]K Nondisp fx of ant column (iliopubic) of [rt, lt, unsp] acetab, subsq enc for fx w/ nonu

S32.44[1,2,3]K Disp fx of post column (ilioischial) of [rt, lt, unsp] acetab, subsq enc for fx w/ nonu

S32.44[4,5,6]K Nondisp fx of post column (ilioischial) of [rt, lt, unsp] acetab, subsq enc for fx w/ nonu

S32.45[1,2,3]K Disp transv fx of [rt, lt, unsp] acetab, subsq enc for fx w/ nonu

S32.45[4,5,6]K Nondisp transv fx of [rt, lt, unsp] acetab, subsq enc for fx w/ nonu

S32.46[1,2,3]K Disp associated transv-post fx of [rt, lt, unsp] acetab, subsq enc for fx w/ nonu

S32.46[4,5,6]K Nondisp associated transv-post fx of [rt, lt, unsp] acetab, subsq enc for fx w/ nonu

S32.47[1,2,3]K Disp fx of med wall of [rt, lt, unsp] acetab, subsq enc for fx w/ nonu

S32.47[4,5,6]K Nondisp fx of med wall of [rt, lt, unsp] acetab, subsq enc for fx w/ nonu

S32.48[1,2,3]K Disp dome fx of [rt, lt, unsp] acetab, subsq enc for fx w/ nonu

S32.48[4,5,6]K Nondisp dome fx of [rt, lt, unsp] acetab, subsq enc for fx w/ nonu

S32.49[1,2,9]K Oth spec fx of [rt, lt, unsp] acetab, subsq enc for fx w/ nonu

S32.50[1,2,9]K Unsp fx of [rt, lt, unsp] pubis, subsq enc for fx w/ nonu

S32.51[1,2,9]K Fx of superior rim of [rt, lt, unsp] pubis, subsq enc for fx w/ nonu

S32.59[1,2,9]K Oth spec fx of [rt, lt, unsp] pubis, subsq enc for fx w/ nonu

S32.60[1,2,9]K Unsp fx of [rt, lt, unsp] ischium, subsq enc for fx w/ nonu

S32.61[1,2,3]K Disp avulsion fx of [rt, lt, unsp] ischium, subsq enc for fx w/ nonu

S32.61[4,5,6]K Nondisp avulsion fx of [rt, lt, unsp] ischium, subsq enc for fx w/ nonu

S32.69[1,2,9]K Oth spec fx of [rt, lt, unsp] ischium, subsq enc for fx w/ nonu

S32.81[0,1]K Multi fxs of pelvis w/ [stable, unstable] disruption of pelvic ring, subsq enc for fx w/ nonu

S32.82XK Mult fx of pelv w/o disrupt of pelv ring, 7thK

S32.89XK Fx of oth parts of pelvis, subs for fx w nonu

S32.9XXK Fx unsp parts of lumbosacr spin & pelv, 7thK

S42.00[1,2,9][K,P] Fx of unsp part of [rt, lt, unsp] clavicle, subsq enc for fx w/ [nonu, malu]

S42.01[1,2,3][K,P] Ant disp fx of sternal end of [rt, lt, unsp] clavicle, subsq enc for fx w/ [nonu, malu]

S42.01[4,5,6][K,P] Post disp fx of sternal end of [rt, lt, unsp] clavicle, subsq enc for fx w/ [nonu, malu]

S42.01[7,8,9][K,P] Nondisp fx of sternal end of [rt, lt, unsp] clavicle, subsq enc for fx w/ [nonu, malu]

S42.02[1,2,3][K,P] Disp fx of shaft of [rt, lt, unsp] clavicle, subsq enc for fx w/ [nonu, malu]

S42.02[4,5,6][K,P] Nondisp fx of shaft of [rt, lt, unsp] clavicle, subsq enc for fx w/ [nonu, malu]

S42.03[1,2,3][K,P] Disp fx of lat end of [rt, lt, unsp] clavicle, subsq enc for fx w/ [nonu, malu]

S42.03[4,5,6][K,P] Nondisp fx of lat end of [rt, lt, unsp] clavicle, subsq enc for fx w/ [nonu, malu]

S42.10[1,2,9][K,P] Fx of unsp part of scapula, [rt, lt, unsp] shldr, subsq enc for fx w/ [nonu, malu]

S42.11[1,2,3][A,B,K,P] Disp fx of body of scapula, [rt, lt, unsp] shldr, [init enc for clsd fx, init enc for opn fx, subsq enc for fx w/ nonu, subsq enc for fx w/ malu]

S42.11[4,5,6][A,B,K,P] Nondisp fx of body of scapula, [rt, lt, unsp] shldr, [init enc for clsd fx, init enc for opn fx, subsq enc for fx w/ nonu, subsq enc for fx w/ malu]

S42.12[1,2,3][K,P] Disp fx of acromial process, [rt, lt, unsp] shldr, subsq enc for fx w/ [nonu, malu]

S42.12[4,5,6][K,P] Nondisp fx of acromial process, [rt, lt, unsp] shldr, subsq enc for fx w/ [nonu, malu]

S42.13[1,2,3][K,P] Disp fx of coracoid process, [rt, lt, unsp] shldr, subsq enc for fx w/ [nonu, malu]

S42.13[4,5,6][K,P] Nondisp fx of coracoid process, [rt, lt, unsp] shldr, subsq enc for fx w/ [nonu, malu]

S42.14[1,2,3][K,P] Disp fx of glenoid cavity of scapula, [rt, lt, unsp] shldr, subsq enc for fx w/ [nonu, malu]

S42.14[4,5,6][K,P] Nondisp fx of glenoid cavity of scapula, [rt, lt, unsp] shldr, subsq enc for fx w/ [nonu, malu]

S42.15[1,2,3][K,P] Disp fx of neck of scapula, [rt, lt, unsp] shldr, subsq enc for fx w/ [nonu, malu]

S42.15[4,5,6][K,P] Nondisp fx of neck of scapula, [rt, lt, unsp] shldr, subsq enc for fx w/ [nonu, malu]

S42.19[1,2,9][A,B,K,P] Fx of oth part of scapula, [rt, lt, unsp] shldr, [init enc for clsd fx, init enc for opn fx, subsq enc for fx w/ nonu, subsq enc for fx w/ malu]

S42.20[1,2,9][K,P] Unsp fx of upr end of [rt, lt, unsp] humerus, subsq enc for fx w/ [nonu, malu]

S42.21[1,2,3][K,P] Unsp disp fx of surgical neck of [rt, lt, unsp] humerus, subsq enc for fx w/ [nonu, malu]

S42.21[4,5,6][K,P] Unsp nondisp fx of surgical neck of [rt, lt, unsp] humerus, subsq enc for fx w/ [nonu, malu]

S42.22[1,2,3][K,P] Two-part disp fx of surgical neck of [rt, lt, unsp] humerus, subsq enc for fx w/ [nonu, malu]

S42.22[4,5,6][K,P] Two-part nondisp fx of surgical neck of [rt, lt, unsp] humerus, subsq enc for fx w/ [nonu, malu]

S42.23[1,2,9][K,P] Three-part disp fx of surgical neck of [rt, lt, unsp] humerus, subsq enc for fx w/ [nonu, malu]

S42.24[1,2,9][K,P] Four-part nondisp fx of surgical neck of [rt, lt, unsp] humerus, subsq enc for fx w/ [nonu, malu]

S42.25[1,2,3][K,P] Disp fx of greater tuberosity of [rt, lt, unsp] humerus, subsq enc for fx w/ [nonu, malu]

S42.25[4,5,6][K,P] Nondisp fx of greater tuberosity of [rt, lt, unsp] humerus, subsq enc for fx w/ [nonu, malu]

S42.26[1,2,3][K,P] Disp fx of lesser tuberosity of [rt, lt, unsp] humerus, subsq enc for fx w/ [nonu, malu]

S42.26[4,5,6][K,P] Nondisp fx of lesser tuberosity of [rt, lt, unsp] humerus, subsq enc for fx w/ [nonu, malu]

S42.27[1,2,9][K,P] Torus fx of upr end of [rt, lt, unsp] humerus, subsq enc for fx w/ [nonu, malu]

T Transfer DRG   SP Special Payment   * Code Range   6th and 7th Character of ZZ = No Device, No Qualifier ZX = No Device, Diagnostic

196   MS-DRG Version 33.0   © 2015 Optum360, LLC

S42.29[1,2,3][K,P] Oth disp fx of [rt, lt, unsp] humerus, subsq enc for fx w/ [nonu, malu]

S42.29[4,5,6][K,P] Oth nondisp fx of upr end of [rt, lt, unsp] humerus, subsq enc for fx w/ [nonu, malu]

S42.30[1,2,9][K,P] Unsp fx of shaft of humerus, [rt, lt, unsp] arm, subsq enc for fx w/ [nonu, malu]

S42.31[1,2,9][K,P] Greenstick fx of shaft of humerus, [rt, lt, unsp] arm, subsq enc for fx w/ [nonu, malu]

S42.32[1,2,3][K,P] Disp transv fx of shaft of humerus, [rt, lt, unsp] arm, subsq enc for fx w/ [nonu, malu]

S42.32[4,5,6][K,P] Nondisp transv fx of shaft of humerus, [rt, lt, unsp] arm, subsq enc for fx w/ [nonu, malu]

S42.33[1,2,3][K,P] Disp oblique fx of shaft of humerus, [rt, lt, unsp] arm, subsq enc for fx w/ [nonu, malu]

S42.33[4,5,6][K,P] Nondisp oblique fx of shaft of humerus, [rt, lt, unsp] arm, subsq enc for fx w/ [nonu, malu]

S42.34[1,2,3][K,P] Disp spiral fx of shaft of humerus, [rt, lt, unsp] arm, subsq enc for fx w/ [nonu, malu]

S42.34[4,5,6][K,P] Nondisp spiral fx of shaft of humerus, [rt, lt, unsp] arm, subsq enc for fx w/ [nonu, malu]

S42.35[1,2,3][K,P] Disp comm fx of shaft of humerus, [rt, lt, unsp] arm, subsq enc for fx w/ [nonu, malu]

S42.35[4,5,6][K,P] Nondisp comm fx of shaft of humerus, [rt, lt, unsp] arm, subsq enc for fx w/ [nonu, malu]

S42.36[1,2,3][K,P] Disp seg fx of shaft of humerus, [rt, lt, unsp] arm, subsq enc for fx w/ [nonu, malu]

S42.36[4,5,6][K,P] Nondisp seg fx of shaft of humerus, [rt, lt, unsp] arm, subsq enc for fx w/ [nonu, malu]

S42.39[1,2,9][K,P] Oth fx of shaft of [rt, lt, unsp] humerus, subsq enc for fx w/ [nonu, malu]

S42.40[1,2,9][K,P] Unsp fx of lwr end of [rt, lt, unsp] humerus, subsq enc for fx w/ [nonu, malu]

S42.41[1,2,3][K,P] Disp simple supracondylar fx w/o intercondylar fx of [rt, lt, unsp] humerus, subsq enc for fx w/ [nonu, malu]

S42.41[4,5,6][K,P] Nondisp simple supracondylar fx w/o intercondylar fx of [rt, lt, unsp] humerus, subsq enc for fx w/ [nonu, malu]

S42.42[1,2,3][K,P] Disp comm supracondylar fx w/o intercondylar fx of [rt, lt, unsp] humerus, subsq enc for fx w/ [nonu, malu]

S42.42[4,5,6][K,P] Nondisp comm supracondylar fx w/o intercondylar fx of [rt, lt, unsp] humerus, subsq enc for fx w/ [nonu, malu]

S42.43[1,2,3][K,P] Disp fx (avulsion) of lat epicondyle of [rt, lt, unsp] humerus, subsq enc for fx w/ [nonu, malu]

S42.43[4,5,6][K,P] Nondisp fx (avulsion) of lat epicondyle of [rt, lt, unsp] humerus, subsq enc for fx w/ [nonu, malu]

S42.44[1,2,3][K,P] Disp fx (avulsion) of med epicondyle of [rt, lt, unsp] humerus, subsq enc for fx w/ [nonu, malu]

S42.44[4,5,6][K,P] Nondisp fx (avulsion) of med epicondyle of [rt, lt, unsp] humerus, subsq enc for fx w/ [nonu, malu]

S42.44[7,8,9][K,P] Incarcerated fx (avulsion) of med epicondyle of [rt, lt, unsp] humerus, subsq enc for fx w/ [nonu, malu]

S42.45[1,2,3][K,P] Disp fx of lat condyle of [rt, lt, unsp] humerus, subsq enc for fx w/ [nonu, malu]

S42.45[4,5,6][K,P] Nondisp fx of lat condyle of [rt, lt, unsp] humerus, subsq enc for fx w/ [nonu, malu]

S42.46[1,2,3][K,P] Disp fx of med condyle of [rt, lt, unsp] humerus, subsq enc for fx w/ [nonu, malu]

S42.46[4,5,6][K,P] Nondisp fx of med condyle of [rt, lt, unsp] humerus, subsq enc for fx w/ [nonu, malu]

S42.47[1,2,3][K,P] Disp transcondylar fx of [rt, lt, unsp] humerus, subsq enc for fx w/ [nonu, malu]

S42.47[4,5,6][K,P] Nondisp transcondylar fx of [rt, lt, unsp] humerus, subsq enc for fx w/ [nonu, malu]

S42.48[1,2,9][K,P] Torus fx of lwr end of [rt, lt, unsp] humerus, subsq enc for fx w/ [nonu, malu]

S42.49[1,2,3][K,P] Oth disp fx of lwr end of [rt, lt, unsp] humerus, subsq enc for fx w/ [nonu, malu]

S42.49[4,5,6][K,P] Oth nondisp fx of lwr end of [rt, lt, unsp] humerus, subsq enc for fx w/ [nonu, malu]

S42.9[0,1,2]X[K,P] Fx of [unsp, rt, lt] shldr girdle, part unsp, subsq enc for fx w/ [nonu, malu]

S46.02[1,2,9]A Lac of muscle(s) and tndn(s) of the rotator cuff of [rt, lt, unsp] shldr, init enc

S46.32[1,2,9]A Lac of muscle, fascia and tndn of triceps, [rt, lt, unsp] arm, init enc

S46.[1,2]2[1,2,9]A Lac of muscle, fascia and tndn of [long head, oth parts] of biceps, [rt, lt, unsp] arm, init enc

S46.[8,9]2[1,2,9]A Lac of [oth, unsp] muscles, fascia and tndns at shldr and upr arm lvl, [rt, lt, unsp] arm, init enc

S49.00[1,2,9][K,P] Unsp physeal fx of upr end of humerus, [rt, lt, unsp] arm, subsq enc for fx w/ [nonu, malu]

S49.09[1,2,9][K,P] Oth physeal fx of upr end of humerus, [rt, lt, unsp] arm, subsq enc for fx w/ [nonu, malu]

S49.0[1,2,3,4][1,2,9][K,P] Salter-Harris Type [I, II, III, IV] physeal fx of upr end of humerus, [rt, lt, unsp] arm, subsq enc for fx w/ [nonu, malu]

S49.10[1,2,9][K,P] Unsp physeal fx of lwr end of humerus, [rt, lt, unsp] arm, subsq enc for fx w/ [nonu, malu]

S49.19[1,2,9][K,P] Oth physeal fx of lwr end of humerus, [rt, lt, unsp] arm, subsq enc for fx w/ [nonu, malu]

S49.1[1,2,3,4][1,2,9][K,P] Salter-Harris Type [I, II, III, IV] physeal fx of lwr end of humerus, [rt, lt, unsp] arm, subsq enc for fx w/ [nonu, malu]

S52.00[1,2,9][K,M,N,P,Q,R] Unsp fx of upr end of [rt, lt, unsp] ulna, subsq enc for [clsd fx w/ nonu, opn fx type I or II w/ nonu, opn fx type IIIA, IIIB, or IIIC w/ nonu, clsd fx w/ malu, opn fx type I or II w/ malu, opn fx type IIIA, IIIB, or IIIC w/ malu]

S52.01[1,2,9][K,P] Torus fx of upr end of [rt, lt, unsp] ulna, subsq enc for fx w/ [nonu, malu]

S52.02[1,2,3][K,M,N,P,Q,R] Disp fx of olecranon process w/o intraarticular extension of [rt, lt, unsp] ulna, subsq enc for [clsd fx w/ nonu, opn fx type I or II w/ nonu, opn fx type IIIA, IIIB, or IIIC w/ nonu, clsd fx w/ malu, opn fx type I or II w/ malu, opn fx type IIIA, IIIB, or IIIC w/ malu]

S52.02[4,5,6][K,M,N,P,Q,R] Nondisp fx of olecranon process w/o intraarticular extension of [rt, lt, unsp] ulna, subsq enc for [clsd fx w/ nonu, opn fx type I or II w/ nonu, opn fx type IIIA, IIIB, or IIIC w/ nonu, clsd fx w/ malu, opn fx type I or II w/ malu, opn fx type IIIA, IIIB, or IIIC w/ malu]

S52.03[1,2,3][K,M,N,P,Q,R] Disp fx of olecranon process w/ intraarticular extension of [rt, lt, unsp] ulna, subsq enc for [clsd fx w/ nonu, opn fx type I or II w/ nonu, opn fx type IIIA, IIIB, or IIIC w/ nonu, clsd fx w/ malu, opn fx type I or II w/ malu, opn fx type IIIA, IIIB, or IIIC w/ malu]

S52.03[4,5,6][K,M,N,P,Q,R] Nondisp fx of olecranon process w/ intraarticular extension of [rt, lt, unsp] ulna, subsq enc for [clsd fx w/ nonu, opn fx type I or II w/ nonu, opn fx type IIIA, IIIB, or IIIC w/ nonu, clsd fx w/ malu, opn fx type I or II w/ malu, opn fx type IIIA, IIIB, or IIIC w/ malu]

S52.04[1,2,3][K,M,N,P,Q,R] Disp fx of coronoid process of [rt, lt, unsp] ulna, subsq enc for [clsd fx w/ nonu, opn fx type I or II w/ nonu, opn fx type IIIA, IIIB, or IIIC w/ nonu, clsd fx w/ malu, opn fx type I or II w/ malu, opn fx type IIIA, IIIB, or IIIC w/ malu]

S52.04[4,5,6][K,M,N,P,Q,R] Nondisp fx of coronoid process of [rt, lt, unsp] ulna, subsq enc for [clsd fx w/ nonu, opn fx type I or II w/ nonu, opn fx type IIIA, IIIB, or IIIC w/ nonu, clsd fx w/ malu, opn fx type I or II w/ malu, opn fx type IIIA, IIIB, or IIIC w/ malu]

S52.09[1,2,9][K,M,N,P,Q,R] Oth fx of upr end of [rt, lt, unsp] ulna, subsq enc for [clsd fx w/ nonu, opn fx type I or II w/ nonu, opn fx type IIIA, IIIB, or IIIC w/ nonu, clsd fx w/ malu, opn fx type I or II w/ malu, opn fx type IIIA, IIIB, or IIIC w/ malu]

S52.10[1,2,9][K,M,N,P,Q,R] Unsp fx of upr end of [rt, lt, unsp] radius, subsq enc for [clsd fx w/ nonu, opn fx type I or II w/ nonu, opn fx type IIIA, IIIB, or IIIC w/ nonu, clsd fx w/ malu, opn fx type I or II w/ malu, opn fx type IIIA, IIIB, or IIIC w/ malu]

S52.11[1,2,9][K,P] Torus fx of upr end of [rt, lt, unsp] radius, subsq enc for fx w/ [nonu, malu]

S52.12[1,2,3][K,M,N,P,Q,R] Disp fx of head of [rt, lt, unsp] radius, subsq enc for [clsd fx w/ nonu, opn fx type I or II w/ nonu, opn fx type IIIA, IIIB, or IIIC w/ nonu, clsd fx w/ malu, opn fx type I or II w/ malu, opn fx type IIIA, IIIB, or IIIC w/ malu]

S52.12[4,5,6][K,M,N,P,Q,R] Nondisp fx of head of [rt, lt, unsp] radius, subsq enc for [clsd fx w/ nonu, opn fx type I or II w/ nonu, opn fx type IIIA, IIIB, or IIIC w/ nonu, clsd fx w/ malu, opn fx type I or II w/ malu, opn fx type IIIA, IIIB, or IIIC w/ malu]

S52.13[1,2,3][K,M,N,P,Q,R] Disp fx of neck of [rt, lt, unsp] radius, subsq enc for [clsd fx w/ nonu, opn fx type I or II w/ nonu, opn fx type IIIA, IIIB, or IIIC w/ nonu, clsd fx w/ malu, opn fx type I or II w/ malu, opn fx type IIIA, IIIB, or IIIC w/ malu]

S52.13[4,5,6][K,M,N,P,Q,R] Nondisp fx of neck of [rt, lt, unsp] radius, subsq enc for [clsd fx w/ nonu, opn fx type I or II w/ nonu, opn fx type IIIA, IIIB, or IIIC w/ nonu, clsd fx w/ malu, opn fx type I or II w/ malu, opn fx type IIIA, IIIB, or IIIC w/ malu]

S52.18[1,2,9][K,M,N,P,Q,R] Oth fx of upr end of [rt, lt, unsp] radius, subsq enc for [clsd fx w/ nonu, opn fx type I or II w/ nonu, opn fx type IIIA, IIIB, or IIIC w/ nonu, clsd fx w/ malu, opn fx type I or II w/ malu, opn fx type IIIA, IIIB, or IIIC w/ malu]

S52.20[1,2,9][K,M,N,P,Q,R] Unsp fx of shaft of [rt, lt, unsp] ulna, subsq enc for [clsd fx w/ nonu, opn fx type I or II w/ nonu, opn fx type IIIA, IIIB, or IIIC w/ nonu, clsd fx w/ malu, opn fx type I or II w/ malu, opn fx type IIIA, IIIB, or IIIC w/ malu]

S52.21[1,2,9][K,P] Greenstick fx of shaft of [rt, lt, unsp] ulna, subsq enc for fx w/ [nonu, malu]

Surgical   **Medical**   **CC Indicator**   **MCC Indicator**   **Procedure Proxy**   **PDxMCC** **PDx acts as own MCC**   **PDxCC** **PDx acts as own CC**

MDC 8: Diseases And Disorders Of The Musculoskeletal System And Connective Tissue—MEDICAL

S52.22[1,2,3][K,M,N,P,Q,R] Disp transv fx of shaft of [rt, lt, unsp] ulna, subsq enc for [clsd fx w/ nonu, opn fx type I or II w/ nonu, opn fx type IIIA, IIIB, or IIIC w/ nonu, clsd fx w/ malu, opn fx type I or II w/ malu, opn fx type IIIA, IIIB, or IIIC w/ malu]

S52.22[4,5,6][K,M,N,P,Q,R] Nondisp transv fx of shaft of [rt, lt, unsp] ulna, subsq enc for [clsd fx w/ nonu, opn fx type I or II w/ nonu, opn fx type IIIA, IIIB, or IIIC w/ nonu, clsd fx w/ malu, opn fx type I or II w/ malu, opn fx type IIIA, IIIB, or IIIC w/ malu]

S52.23[1,2,3][K,M,N,P,Q,R] Disp oblique fx of shaft of [rt, lt, unsp] ulna, subsq enc for [clsd fx w/ nonu, opn fx type I or II w/ nonu, opn fx type IIIA, IIIB, or IIIC w/ nonu, clsd fx w/ malu, opn fx type I or II w/ malu, opn fx type IIIA, IIIB, or IIIC w/ malu]

S52.23[4,5,6][K,M,N,P,Q,R] Nondisp oblique fx of shaft of [rt, lt, unsp] ulna, subsq enc for [clsd fx w/ nonu, opn fx type I or II w/ nonu, opn fx type IIIA, IIIB, or IIIC w/ nonu, clsd fx w/ malu, opn fx type I or II w/ malu, opn fx type IIIA, IIIB, or IIIC w/ malu]

S52.24[1,2,3][K,M,N,P,Q,R] Disp spiral fx of shaft of ulna, [rt, lt, unsp] arm, subsq enc for [clsd fx w/ nonu, opn fx type I or II w/ nonu, opn fx type IIIA, IIIB, or IIIC w/ nonu, clsd fx w/ malu, opn fx type I or II w/ malu, opn fx type IIIA, IIIB, or IIIC w/ malu]

S52.24[4,5,6][K,M,N,P,Q,R] Nondisp spiral fx of shaft of ulna, [rt, lt, unsp] arm, subsq enc for [clsd fx w/ nonu, opn fx type I or II w/ nonu, opn fx type IIIA, IIIB, or IIIC w/ nonu, clsd fx w/ malu, opn fx type I or II w/ malu, opn fx type IIIA, IIIB, or IIIC w/ malu]

S52.25[1,2,3][K,M,N,P,Q,R] Disp comm fx of shaft of ulna, [rt, lt, unsp] arm, subsq enc for [clsd fx w/ nonu, opn fx type I or II w/ nonu, opn fx type IIIA, IIIB, or IIIC w/ nonu, clsd fx w/ malu, opn fx type I or II w/ malu, opn fx type IIIA, IIIB, or IIIC w/ malu]

S52.25[4,5,6][K,M,N,P,Q,R] Nondisp comm fx of shaft of ulna, [rt, lt, unsp] arm, subsq enc for [clsd fx w/ nonu, opn fx type I or II w/ nonu, opn fx type IIIA, IIIB, or IIIC w/ nonu, clsd fx w/ malu, opn fx type I or II w/ malu, opn fx type IIIA, IIIB, or IIIC w/ malu]

S52.26[1,2,3][K,M,N,P,Q,R] Disp seg fx of shaft of ulna, [rt, lt, unsp] arm, subsq enc for [clsd fx w/ nonu, opn fx type I or II w/ nonu, opn fx type IIIA, IIIB, or IIIC w/ nonu, clsd fx w/ malu, opn fx type I or II w/ malu, opn fx type IIIA, IIIB, or IIIC w/ malu]

S52.26[4,5,6][K,M,N,P,Q,R] Nondisp seg fx of shaft of ulna, [rt, lt, unsp] arm, subsq enc for [clsd fx w/ nonu, opn fx type I or II w/ nonu, opn fx type IIIA, IIIB, or IIIC w/ nonu, clsd fx w/ malu, opn fx type I or II w/ malu, opn fx type IIIA, IIIB, or IIIC w/ malu]

S52.27[1,2,9][K,M,N,P,Q,R] Monteggia's fx of [rt, lt, unsp] ulna, subsq enc for [clsd fx w/ nonu, opn fx type I or II w/ nonu, opn fx type IIIA, IIIB, or IIIC w/ nonu, clsd fx w/ malu, opn fx type I or II w/ malu, opn fx type IIIA, IIIB, or IIIC w/ malu]

S52.28[1,2,3][K,M,N,P,Q,R] Bent bone of [rt, lt, unsp] ulna, subsq enc for [clsd fx w/ nonu, opn fx type I or II w/ nonu, opn fx type IIIA, IIIB, or IIIC w/ nonu, clsd fx w/ malu, opn fx type I or II w/ malu, opn fx type IIIA, IIIB, or IIIC w/ malu]

S52.29[1,2,9][K,M,N,P,Q,R] Oth fx of shaft of [rt, lt, unsp] ulna, subsq enc for [clsd fx w/ nonu, opn fx type I or II w/ nonu, opn fx type IIIA, IIIB, or IIIC w/ nonu, clsd fx w/ malu, opn fx type I or II w/ malu, opn fx type IIIA, IIIB, or IIIC w/ malu]

S52.30[1,2,9][K,M,N,P,Q,R] Unsp fx of shaft of [rt, lt, unsp] radius, subsq enc for [clsd fx w/ nonu, opn fx type I or II w/ nonu, opn fx type IIIA, IIIB, or IIIC w/ nonu, clsd fx w/ malu, opn fx type I or II w/ malu, opn fx type IIIA, IIIB, or IIIC w/ malu]

S52.31[1,2,9][K,P] Greenstick fx of shaft of radius, [rt, lt, unsp] arm, subsq enc for fx w/ [nonu, malu]

S52.32[1,2,3][K,M,N,P,Q,R] Disp transv fx of shaft of [rt, lt, unsp] radius, subsq enc for [clsd fx w/ nonu, opn fx type I or II w/ nonu, opn fx type IIIA, IIIB, or IIIC w/ nonu, clsd fx w/ malu, opn fx type I or II w/ malu, opn fx type IIIA, IIIB, or IIIC w/ malu]

S52.32[4,5,6][K,M,N,P,Q,R] Nondisp transv fx of shaft of [rt, lt, unsp] radius, subsq enc for [clsd fx w/ nonu, opn fx type I or II w/ nonu, opn fx type IIIA, IIIB, or IIIC w/ nonu, clsd fx w/ malu, opn fx type I or II w/ malu, opn fx type IIIA, IIIB, or IIIC w/ malu]

S52.33[1,2,3][K,M,N,P,Q,R] Disp oblique fx of shaft of [rt, lt, unsp] radius, subsq enc for [clsd fx w/ nonu, opn fx type I or II w/ nonu, opn fx type IIIA, IIIB, or IIIC w/ nonu, clsd fx w/ malu, opn fx type I or II w/ malu, opn fx type IIIA, IIIB, or IIIC w/ malu]

S52.33[4,5,6][K,M,N,P,Q,R] Nondisp oblique fx of shaft of [rt, lt, unsp] radius, subsq enc for [clsd fx w/ nonu, opn fx type I or II w/ nonu, opn fx type IIIA, IIIB, or IIIC w/ nonu, clsd fx w/ malu, opn fx type I or II w/ malu, opn fx type IIIA, IIIB, or IIIC w/ malu]

S52.34[1,2,3][K,M,N,P,Q,R] Disp spiral fx of shaft of radius, [rt, lt, unsp] arm, subsq enc for [clsd fx w/ nonu, opn fx type I or II w/ nonu, opn fx type IIIA, IIIB, or IIIC w/ nonu, clsd fx w/ malu, opn fx type I or II w/ malu, opn fx type IIIA, IIIB, or IIIC w/ malu]

S52.34[4,5,6][K,M,N,P,Q,R] Nondisp spiral fx of shaft of radius, [rt, lt, unsp] arm, subsq enc for [clsd fx w/ nonu, opn fx type I or II w/ nonu, opn fx type IIIA, IIIB, or IIIC w/ nonu, clsd fx w/ malu, opn fx type I or II w/ malu, opn fx type IIIA, IIIB, or IIIC w/ malu]

S52.35[1,2,3][K,M,N,P,Q,R] Disp comm fx of shaft of radius, [rt, lt, unsp] arm, subsq enc for [clsd fx w/ nonu, opn fx type I or II w/ nonu, opn fx type IIIA, IIIB, or IIIC w/ nonu, clsd fx w/ malu, opn fx type I or II w/ malu, opn fx type IIIA, IIIB, or IIIC w/ malu]

S52.35[4,5,6][K,M,N,P,Q,R] Nondisp comm fx of shaft of radius, [rt, lt, unsp] arm, subsq enc for [clsd fx w/ nonu, opn fx type I or II w/ nonu, opn fx type IIIA, IIIB, or IIIC w/ nonu, clsd fx w/ malu, opn fx type I or II w/ malu, opn fx type IIIA, IIIB, or IIIC w/ malu]

S52.36[1,2,3][K,M,N,P,Q,R] Disp seg fx of shaft of radius, [rt, lt, unsp] arm, subsq enc for [clsd fx w/ nonu, opn fx type I or II w/ nonu, opn fx type IIIA, IIIB, or IIIC w/ nonu, clsd fx w/ malu, opn fx type I or II w/ malu, opn fx type IIIA, IIIB, or IIIC w/ malu]

S52.36[4,5,6][K,M,N,P,Q,R] Nondisp seg fx of shaft of radius, [rt, lt, unsp] arm, subsq enc for [clsd fx w/ nonu, opn fx type I or II w/ nonu, opn fx type IIIA, IIIB, or IIIC w/ nonu, clsd fx w/ malu, opn fx type I or II w/ malu, opn fx type IIIA, IIIB, or IIIC w/ malu]

S52.37[1,2,9][K,M,N,P,Q,R] Galeazzi's fx of [rt, lt, unsp] radius, subsq enc for [clsd fx w/ nonu, opn fx type I or II w/ nonu, opn fx type IIIA, IIIB, or IIIC w/ nonu, clsd fx w/ malu, opn fx type I or II w/ malu, opn fx type IIIA, IIIB, or IIIC w/ malu]

S52.38[1,2,9][K,M,N,P,Q,R] Bent bone of [rt, lt, unsp] radius, subsq enc for [clsd fx w/ nonu, opn fx type I or II w/ nonu, opn fx type IIIA, IIIB, or IIIC w/ nonu, clsd fx w/ malu, opn fx type I or II w/ malu, opn fx type IIIA, IIIB, or IIIC w/ malu]

S52.39[1,2,9][K,M,N,P,Q,R] Oth fx of shaft of radius, [rt, lt, unsp] arm, subsq enc for [clsd fx w/ nonu, opn fx type I or II w/ nonu, opn fx type IIIA, IIIB, or IIIC w/ nonu, clsd fx w/ malu, opn fx type I or II w/ malu, opn fx type IIIA, IIIB, or IIIC w/ malu]

S52.50[1,2,9][K,M,N,P,Q,R] Unsp fx of the lwr end of [rt, lt, unsp] radius, subsq enc for [clsd fx w/ nonu, opn fx type I or II w/ nonu, opn fx type IIIA, IIIB, or IIIC w/ nonu, clsd fx w/ malu, opn fx type I or II w/ malu, opn fx type IIIA, IIIB, or IIIC w/ malu]

S52.51[1,2,3][K,M,N,P,Q,R] Disp fx of [rt, lt, unsp] radial styloid process, subsq enc for [clsd fx w/ nonu, opn fx type I or II w/ nonu, opn fx type IIIA, IIIB, or IIIC w/ nonu, clsd fx w/ malu, opn fx type I or II w/ malu, opn fx type IIIA, IIIB, or IIIC w/ malu]

S52.51[4,5,6][K,M,N,P,Q,R] Nondisp fx of [rt, lt, unsp] radial styloid process, subsq enc for [clsd fx w/ nonu, opn fx type I or II w/ nonu, opn fx type IIIA, IIIB, or IIIC w/ nonu, clsd fx w/ malu, opn fx type I or II w/ malu, opn fx type IIIA, IIIB, or IIIC w/ malu]

S52.52[1,2,9][K,P] Torus fx of lwr end of [rt, lt, unsp] radius, subsq enc for fx w/ [nonu, malu]

S52.53[1,2,9][K,M,N,P,Q,R] Colles' fx of [rt, lt, unsp] radius, subsq enc for [clsd fx w/ nonu, opn fx type I or II w/ nonu, opn fx type IIIA, IIIB, or IIIC w/ nonu, clsd fx w/ malu, opn fx type I or II w/ malu, opn fx type IIIA, IIIB, or IIIC w/ malu]

S52.54[1,2,9][K,M,N,P,Q,R] Smith's fx of [rt, lt, unsp] radius, subsq enc for [clsd fx w/ nonu, opn fx type I or II w/ nonu, opn fx type IIIA, IIIB, or IIIC w/ nonu, clsd fx w/ malu, opn fx type I or II w/ malu, opn fx type IIIA, IIIB, or IIIC w/ malu]

S52.55[1,2,9][K,M,N,P,Q,R] Oth extraarticular fx of lwr end of [rt, lt, unsp] radius, subsq enc for [clsd fx w/ nonu, opn fx type I or II w/ nonu, opn fx type IIIA, IIIB, or IIIC w/ nonu, clsd fx w/ malu, opn fx type I or II w/ malu, opn fx type IIIA, IIIB, or IIIC w/ malu]

S52.56[1,2,9][K,M,N,P,Q,R] Barton's fx of [rt, lt, unsp] radius, subsq enc for [clsd fx w/ nonu, opn fx type I or II w/ nonu, opn fx type IIIA, IIIB, or IIIC w/ nonu, clsd fx w/ malu, opn fx type I or II w/ malu, opn fx type IIIA, IIIB, or IIIC w/ malu]

S52.57[1,2,9][K,M,N,P,Q,R] Oth intraarticular fx of lwr end of [rt, lt, unsp] radius, subsq enc for [clsd fx w/ nonu, opn fx type I or II w/ nonu, opn fx type IIIA, IIIB, or IIIC w/ nonu, clsd fx w/ malu, opn fx type I or II w/ malu, opn fx type IIIA, IIIB, or IIIC w/ malu]

S52.59[1,2,9][K,M,N,P,Q,R] Oth fxs of lwr end of [rt, lt, unsp] radius, subsq enc for [clsd fx w/ nonu, opn fx type I or II w/ nonu, opn fx type IIIA, IIIB, or IIIC w/ nonu, clsd fx w/ malu, opn fx type I or II w/ malu, opn fx type IIIA, IIIB, or IIIC w/ malu]

S52.60[1,2,9][K,M,N,P,Q,R] Unsp fx of lwr end of [rt, lt, unsp] ulna, subsq enc for [clsd fx w/ nonu, opn fx type I or II w/ nonu, opn fx type IIIA, IIIB, or IIIC w/ nonu, clsd fx w/ malu, opn fx type I or II w/ malu, opn fx type IIIA, IIIB, or IIIC w/ malu]

S52.61[1,2,3][K,M,N,P,Q,R] Disp fx of [rt, lt, unsp] ulna styloid process, subsq enc for [clsd fx w/ nonu, opn fx type I or II w/ nonu, opn fx type IIIA, IIIB, or IIIC w/ nonu, clsd fx w/ malu, opn fx type I or II w/ malu, opn fx type IIIA, IIIB, or IIIC w/ malu]

[T] **Transfer DRG**   [SP] **Special Payment**   *** Code Range**   **6th and 7th Character of ZZ = No Device, No Qualifier ZX = No Device, Diagnostic**

S52.61[4,5,6][K,M,N,P,Q,R] Nondisp fx of [rt, lt, unsp] ulna styloid process, subsq enc for [clsd fx w/ nonu, opn fx type I or II w/ nonu, opn fx type IIIA, IIIB, or IIIC w/ nonu, clsd fx w/ malu, opn fx type I or II w/ malu, opn fx type IIIA, IIIB, or IIIC w/ malu]

S52.62[1,2,9][K,P] Torus fx of lwr end of [rt, lt, unsp] ulna, subsq enc for fx w/ [nonu, malu]

S52.69[1,2,9][K,M,N,P,Q,R] Oth fx of lwr end of [rt, lt, unsp] ulna, subsq enc for [clsd fx w/ nonu, opn fx type I or II w/ nonu, opn fx type IIIA, IIIB, or IIIC w/ nonu, clsd fx w/ malu, opn fx type I or II w/ malu, opn fx type IIIA, IIIB, or IIIC w/ malu]

S52.9[0,1,2]X[K,M,N,P,Q,R] Unsp fx of [unsp, rt, lt] forearm, subsq enc for [clsd fx w/ nonu, opn fx type I or II w/ nonu, opn fx type IIIA, IIIB, or IIIC w/ nonu, clsd fx w/ malu, opn fx type I or II w/ malu, opn fx type IIIA, IIIB, or IIIC w/ malu]

S56.02[1,2,9]A Lac of flexor muscle, fascia and tndn of [rt, lt, unsp] thumb at forearm lvl, init enc

S56.12[1,2,3,4,5,6,7,8,9]A Lac of flexor muscle, fascia and tndn of [rt index, lt index, rt mid, lt mid, rt ring, lt ring, rt little, lt little] finger at forearm lvl, init enc

S56.22[1,2,9]A Lac of oth flexor muscle, fascia and tndn at forearm lvl, [rt, lt, unsp] arm, init enc

S56.32[1,2,9]A Lac of extensor muscle, fascia and tndn of [rt, lt, unsp] thumb at forearm lvl, init enc

S56.42[1,2,3,4,5,6,7,8,9]A Lac of extensor muscle, fascia and tndn of [rt index, lt index, rt mid, lt mid, rt ring, lt ring, rt little, lt little] finger at forearm lvl, init enc

S56.52[1,2,9]A Lac of oth extensor muscle, fascia and tndn at forearm lvl, [rt, lt, unsp] arm, init enc

S56.[8,9]2[1,2,9]A Lac of [oth, unsp] muscles, fascia and tndns at forearm lvl, [rt, lt, unsp] arm, init enc

S59.00[1,2,9][K,P] Unsp physeal fx of lwr end of ulna, [rt, lt, unsp] arm, subsq enc for fx w/ [nonu, malu]

S59.09[1,2,9][K,P] Oth physeal fx of lwr end of ulna, [rt, lt, unsp] arm, subsq enc for fx w/ [nonu, malu]

S59.0[1,2,3,4][1,2,9][K,P] Salter-Harris Type [I, II, III, IV] physeal fx of lwr end of ulna, [rt, lt, unsp] arm, subsq enc for fx w/ [nonu, malu]

S59.10[1,2,9][K,P] Unsp physeal fx of upr end of ulna, [rt, lt, unsp] arm, subsq enc for fx w/ [nonu, malu]

S59.19[1,2,9][K,P] Oth physeal fx of upr end of ulna, [rt, lt, unsp] arm, subsq enc for fx w/ [nonu, malu]

S59.1[1,2,3,4][1,2,9][K,P] Salter-Harris Type [I, II, III, IV] physeal fx of upr end of ulna, [rt, lt, unsp] arm, subsq enc for fx w/ [nonu, malu]

S59.20[1,2,9][K,P] Unsp physeal fx of lwr end of radius, [rt, lt, unsp] arm, subsq enc for fx w/ [nonu, malu]

S59.29[1,2,9][K,P] Oth physeal fx of lwr end of radius, [rt, lt, unsp] arm, subsq enc for fx w/ [nonu, malu]

S59.2[1,2,3,4][1,2,9][K,P] Salter-Harris Type [I, II, III, IV] physeal fx of lwr end of radius, [rt, lt, unsp] arm, subsq enc for fx w/ [nonu, malu]

S62.00[1,2,9][K,P] Unsp fx of navicular (scaphoid) bone of [rt, lt, unsp] wrist, subsq enc for fx w/ [nonu, malu]

S62.01[1,2,3][K,P] Disp fx of distal pole of navicular (scaphoid) bone of [rt, lt, unsp] wrist, subsq enc for fx w/ [nonu, malu]

S62.01[4,5,6][K,P] Nondisp fx of distal pole of navicular (scaphoid) bone of [rt, lt, unsp] wrist, subsq enc for fx w/ [nonu, malu]

S62.02[1,2,3][K,P] Disp fx of mid 3rd of navicular (scaphoid) bone of [rt, lt, unsp] wrist, subsq enc for fx w/ [nonu, malu]

S62.02[4,5,6][K,P] Nondisp fx of mid 3rd of navicular (scaphoid) bone of [rt, lt, unsp] wrist, subsq enc for fx w/ [nonu, malu]

S62.03[1,2,3][K,P] Disp fx of proximal 3rd of navicular (scaphoid) bone of [rt, lt, unsp] wrist, subsq enc for fx w/ [nonu, malu]

S62.03[4,5,6][K,P] Nondisp fx of proximal 3rd of navicular (scaphoid) bone of [rt, lt, unsp] wrist, subsq enc for fx w/ [nonu, malu]

S62.10[1,2,9][K,P] Fx of unsp carpal bone, [rt, lt, unsp] wrist, subsq enc for fx w/ [nonu, malu]

S62.11[1,2,3][K,P] Disp fx of triquetrum (cuneiform) bone, [rt, lt, unsp] wrist, subsq enc for fx w/ [nonu, malu]

S62.11[4,5,6][K,P] Nondisp fx of triquetrum (cuneiform) bone, [rt, lt, unsp] wrist, subsq enc for fx w/ [nonu, malu]

S62.12[1,2,3][K,P] Disp fx of lunate (semilunar), [rt, lt, unsp] wrist, subsq enc for fx w/ [nonu, malu]

S62.12[4,5,6][K,P] Nondisp fx of lunate (semilunar), [rt, lt, unsp] wrist, subsq enc for fx w/ [nonu, malu]

S62.13[1,2,3][K,P] Disp fx of capitate (os magnum) bone, [rt, lt, unsp] wrist, subsq enc for fx w/ [nonu, malu]

S62.13[4,5,6][K,P] Nondisp fx of capitate (os magnum) bone, [rt, lt, unsp] wrist, subsq enc for fx w/ [nonu, malu]

S62.14[1,2,3][K,P] Disp fx of body of hamate (unciform) bone, [rt, lt, unsp] wrist, subsq enc for fx w/ [nonu, malu]

S62.14[4,5,6][K,P] Nondisp fx of body of hamate (unciform) bone, [rt, lt, unsp] wrist, subsq enc for fx w/ [nonu, malu]

S62.15[1,2,3][K,P] Disp fx of hook process of hamate (unciform) bone, [rt, lt, unsp] wrist, subsq enc for fx w/ [nonu, malu]

S62.15[4,5,6][K,P] Nondisp fx of hook process of hamate (unciform) bone, [rt, lt, unsp] wrist, subsq enc for fx w/ [nonu, malu]

S62.16[1,2,3][K,P] Disp fx of pisiform, [rt, lt, unsp] wrist, subsq enc for fx w/ [nonu, malu]

S62.16[4,5,6][K,P] Nondisp fx of pisiform, [rt, lt, unsp] wrist, subsq enc for fx w/ [nonu, malu]

S62.17[1,2,3][K,P] Disp fx of trapezium (lgr multangular), [rt, lt, unsp] wrist, subsq enc for fx w/ [nonu, malu]

S62.17[4,5,6][K,P] Nondisp fx of trapezium (lgr multangular), [rt, lt, unsp] wrist, subsq enc for fx w/ [nonu, malu]

S62.18[1,2,3][K,P] Disp fx of trapezoid (smer multangular), [rt, lt, unsp] wrist, subsq enc for fx w/ [nonu, malu]

S62.18[4,5,6][K,P] Nondisp fx of trapezoid (smer multangular), [rt, lt, unsp] wrist, subsq enc for fx w/ [nonu, malu]

S62.20[1,2,9][K,P] Unsp fx of 1st metacarpal bone, [rt, lt, unsp] hand, subsq enc for fx w/ [nonu, malu]

S62.21[1,2,3][K,P] Bennett's fx, [rt, lt, unsp] hand, subsq enc for fx w/ [nonu, malu]

S62.22[1,2,3][K,P] Disp Rolando's fx, [rt, lt, unsp] hand, subsq enc for fx w/ [nonu, malu]

S62.22[4,5,6][K,P] Nondisp Rolando's fx, [rt, lt, unsp] hand, subsq enc for fx w/ [nonu, malu]

S62.23[1,2,3][K,P] Oth disp fx of base of 1st metacarpal bone, [rt, lt, unsp] hand, subsq enc for fx w/ [nonu, malu]

S62.23[4,5,6][K,P] Oth nondisp fx of base of 1st metacarpal bone, [rt, lt, unsp] hand, subsq enc for fx w/ [nonu, malu]

S62.24[1,2,3][K,P] Disp fx of shaft of 1st metacarpal bone, [rt, lt, unsp] hand, subsq enc for fx w/ [nonu, malu]

S62.24[4,5,6][K,P] Nondisp fx of shaft of 1st metacarpal bone, [rt, lt, unsp] hand, subsq enc for fx w/ [nonu, malu]

S62.25[1,2,3][K,P] Disp fx of neck of 1st metacarpal bone, [rt, lt, unsp] hand, subsq enc for fx w/ [nonu, malu]

S62.25[4,5,6][K,P] Nondisp fx of neck of 1st metacarpal bone, [rt, lt, unsp] hand, subsq enc for fx w/ [nonu, malu]

S62.29[1,2,9][K,P] Oth fx of 1st metacarpal bone, [rt, lt, unsp] hand, subsq enc for fx w/ [nonu, malu]

S62.30[0,1][K,P] Unsp fx of 2nd metacarpal bone, [rt, lt] hand, subsq enc for fx w/ [nonu, malu]

S62.30[2,3][K,P] Unsp fx of 3rd metacarpal bone, [rt, lt] hand, subsq enc for fx w/ [nonu, malu]

S62.30[4,5][K,P] Unsp fx of 4th metacarpal bone, [rt, lt] hand, subsq enc for fx w/ [nonu, malu]

S62.30[6,7][K,P] Unsp fx of 5th metacarpal bone, [rt, lt] hand, subsq enc for fx w/ [nonu, malu]

S62.30[8,9][K,P] Unsp fx of [oth, unsp] metacarpal bone, subsq enc for fx w/ [nonu, malu]

S62.31[0,1][K,P] Disp fx of base of 2nd metacarpal bone, [rt, lt] hand, subsq enc for fx w/ [nonu, malu]

S62.31[2,3][K,P] Disp fx of base of 3rd metacarpal bone, [rt, lt] hand, subsq enc for fx w/ [nonu, malu]

S62.31[4,5][K,P] Disp fx of base of 4th metacarpal bone, [rt, lt] hand, subsq enc for fx w/ [nonu, malu]

S62.31[6,7][K,P] Disp fx of base of 5th metacarpal bone, [rt, lt] hand, subsq enc for fx w/ [nonu, malu]

S62.31[8,9][K,P] Disp fx of base of [oth, unsp] metacarpal bone, subsq enc for fx w/ [nonu, malu]

S62.32[0,1][K,P] Disp fx of shaft of 2nd metacarpal bone, [rt, lt] hand, subsq enc for fx w/ [nonu, malu]

S62.32[2,3][K,P] Disp fx of shaft of 3rd metacarpal bone, [rt, lt] hand, subsq enc for fx w/ [nonu, malu]

S62.32[4,5][K,P] Disp fx of shaft of 4th metacarpal bone, [rt, lt] hand, subsq enc for fx w/ [nonu, malu]

S62.32[6,7][K,P] Disp fx of shaft of 5th metacarpal bone, [rt, lt] hand, subsq enc for fx w/ [nonu, malu]

S62.32[8,9][K,P] Disp fx of shaft of [oth, unsp] metacarpal bone, subsq enc for fx w/ [nonu, malu]

S62.33[0,1][K,P] Disp fx of neck of 2nd metacarpal bone, [rt, lt] hand, subsq enc for fx w/ [nonu, malu]

S62.33[2,3][K,P] Disp fx of neck of 3rd metacarpal bone, [rt, lt] hand, subsq enc for fx w/ [nonu, malu]

S62.33[4,5][K,P] Disp fx of neck of 4th metacarpal bone, [rt, lt] hand, subsq enc for fx w/ [nonu, malu]

S62.33[6,7][K,P] Disp fx of neck of 5th metacarpal bone, [rt, lt] hand, subsq enc for fx w/ [nonu, malu]

S62.33[8,9][K,P] Disp fx of neck of [oth, unsp] metacarpal bone, subsq enc for fx w/ [nonu, malu]

S62.34[0,1][K,P] Nondisp fx of base of 2nd metacarpal bone, [rt, lt] hand, subsq enc for fx w/ [nonu, malu]

| Surgical | Medical | CC Indicator | MCC Indicator | Procedure Proxy | PDxMCC PDx acts as own MCC | PDxCC PDx acts as own CC |

MDC 8: Diseases And Disorders Of The Musculoskeletal System And Connective Tissue—MEDICAL

Code	Description
S62.34[2,3][K,P]	Nondisp fx of base of 3rd metacarpal bone, [rt, lt] hand, subsq enc for fx w/ [nonu, malu]
S62.34[4,5][K,P]	Nondisp fx of base of 4th metacarpal bone, [rt, lt] hand, subsq enc for fx w/ [nonu, malu]
S62.34[6,7][K,P]	Nondisp fx of base of 5th metacarpal bone, [rt, lt] hand, subsq enc for fx w/ [nonu, malu]
S62.34[8,9][K,P]	Nondisp fx of base of [oth, unsp] metacarpal bone, subsq enc for fx w/ [nonu, malu]
S62.35[0,1][K,P]	Nondisp fx of shaft of 2nd metacarpal bone, [rt, lt] hand, subsq enc for fx w/ [nonu, malu]
S62.35[2,3][K,P]	Nondisp fx of shaft of 3rd metacarpal bone, [rt, lt] hand, subsq enc for fx w/ [nonu, malu]
S62.35[4,5][K,P]	Nondisp fx of shaft of 4th metacarpal bone, [rt, lt] hand, subsq enc for fx w/ [nonu, malu]
S62.35[6,7][K,P]	Nondisp fx of shaft of 5th metacarpal bone, [rt, lt] hand, subsq enc for fx w/ [nonu, malu]
S62.35[8,9][K,P]	Nondisp fx of shaft of [oth, unsp] metacarpal bone, subsq enc for fx w/ [nonu, malu]
S62.36[0,1][K,P]	Nondisp fx of neck of 2nd metacarpal bone, [rt, lt] hand, subsq enc for fx w/ [nonu, malu]
S62.36[2,3][K,P]	Nondisp fx of neck of 3rd metacarpal bone, [rt, lt] hand, subsq enc for fx w/ [nonu, malu]
S62.36[4,5][K,P]	Nondisp fx of neck of 4th metacarpal bone, [rt, lt] hand, subsq enc for fx w/ [nonu, malu]
S62.36[6,7][K,P]	Nondisp fx of neck of 5th metacarpal bone, [rt, lt] hand, subsq enc for fx w/ [nonu, malu]
S62.36[8,9][K,P]	Nondisp fx of neck of [oth, unsp] metacarpal bone, subsq enc for fx w/ [nonu, malu]
S62.39[0,1][K,P]	Oth fx of 2nd metacarpal bone, [rt, lt] hand, subsq enc for fx w/ [nonu, malu]
S62.39[2,3][K,P]	Oth fx of 3rd metacarpal bone, [rt, lt] hand, subsq enc for fx w/ [nonu, malu]
S62.39[4,5][K,P]	Oth fx of 4th metacarpal bone, [rt, lt] hand, subsq enc for fx w/ [nonu, malu]
S62.39[6,7][K,P]	Oth fx of 5th metacarpal bone, [rt, lt] hand, subsq enc for fx w/ [nonu, malu]
S62.39[8,9][K,P]	Oth fx of [oth, unsp] metacarpal bone, subsq enc for fx w/ [nonu, malu]
S62.50[1,2,9][K,P]	Fx of unsp phalanx of [rt, lt, unsp] thumb, subsq enc for fx w/ [nonu, malu]
S62.51[1,2,3][K,P]	Disp fx of proximal phalanx of [rt, lt, unsp] thumb, subsq enc for fx w/ [nonu, malu]
S62.51[4,5,6][K,P]	Nondisp fx of proximal phalanx of [rt, lt, unsp] thumb, subsq enc for fx w/ [nonu, malu]
S62.52[1,2,3][K,P]	Disp fx of distal phalanx of [rt, lt, unsp] thumb, subsq enc for fx w/ [nonu, malu]
S62.52[4,5,6][K,P]	Nondisp fx of distal phalanx of [rt, lt, unsp] thumb, subsq enc for fx w/ [nonu, malu]
S62.60[0,1][K,P]	Fx of unsp phalanx of [rt, lt] index finger, subsq enc for fx w/ [nonu, malu]
S62.60[2,3][K,P]	Fx of unsp phalanx of [rt, lt] mid finger, subsq enc for fx w/ [nonu, malu]
S62.60[4,5][K,P]	Fx of unsp phalanx of [rt, lt] ring finger, subsq enc for fx w/ [nonu, malu]
S62.60[6,7][K,P]	Fx of unsp phalanx of [rt, lt] little finger, subsq enc for fx w/ [nonu, malu]
S62.60[8,9][K,P]	Fx of unsp phalanx of [oth, unsp] finger, subsq enc for fx w/ [nonu, malu]
S62.61[0,1][K,P]	Disp fx of proximal phalanx of [rt, lt] index finger, subsq enc for fx w/ [nonu, malu]
S62.61[2,3][K,P]	Disp fx of proximal phalanx of [rt, lt] mid finger, subsq enc for fx w/ [nonu, malu]
S62.61[4,5][K,P]	Disp fx of proximal phalanx of [rt, lt] ring finger, subsq enc for fx w/ [nonu, malu]
S62.61[6,7][K,P]	Disp fx of proximal phalanx of [rt, lt] little finger, subsq enc for fx w/ [nonu, malu]
S62.61[8,9][K,P]	Disp fx of proximal phalanx of [oth, unsp] finger, subsq enc for fx w/ [nonu, malu]
S62.62[0,1][K,P]	Disp fx of med phalanx of [rt, lt] index finger, subsq enc for fx w/ [nonu, malu]
S62.62[2,3][K,P]	Disp fx of med phalanx of [rt, lt] mid finger, subsq enc for fx w/ [nonu, malu]
S62.62[4,5][K,P]	Disp fx of med phalanx of [rt, lt] ring finger, subsq enc for fx w/ [nonu, malu]
S62.62[6,7][K,P]	Disp fx of med phalanx of [rt, lt] little finger, subsq enc for fx w/ [nonu, malu]
S62.62[8,9][K,P]	Disp fx of med phalanx of [oth, unsp] finger, subsq enc for fx w/ [nonu, malu]
S62.63[0,1][K,P]	Disp fx of distal phalanx of [rt, lt] index finger, subsq enc for fx w/ [nonu, malu]
S62.63[2,3][K,P]	Disp fx of distal phalanx of [rt, lt] mid finger, subsq enc for fx w/ [nonu, malu]
S62.63[4,5][K,P]	Disp fx of distal phalanx of [rt, lt] ring finger, subsq enc for fx w/ [nonu, malu]
S62.63[6,7][K,P]	Disp fx of distal phalanx of [rt, lt] little finger, subsq enc for fx w/ [nonu, malu]
S62.63[8,9][K,P]	Disp fx of distal phalanx of [oth, unsp] finger, subsq enc for fx w/ [nonu, malu]
S62.64[0,1][K,P]	Nondisp fx of proximal phalanx of [rt, lt] index finger, subsq enc for fx w/ [nonu, malu]
S62.64[2,3][K,P]	Nondisp fx of proximal phalanx of [rt, lt] mid finger, subsq enc for fx w/ [nonu, malu]
S62.64[4,5][K,P]	Nondisp fx of proximal phalanx of [rt, lt] ring finger, subsq enc for fx w/ [nonu, malu]
S62.64[6,7][K,P]	Nondisp fx of proximal phalanx of [rt, lt] little finger, subsq enc for fx w/ [nonu, malu]
S62.64[8,9][K,P]	Nondisp fx of proximal phalanx of [oth, unsp] finger, subsq enc for fx w/ [nonu, malu]
S62.65[0,1][K,P]	Nondisp fx of med phalanx of [rt, lt] index finger, subsq enc for fx w/ [nonu, malu]
S62.65[2,3][K,P]	Nondisp fx of med phalanx of [rt, lt] mid finger, subsq enc for fx w/ [nonu, malu]
S62.65[4,5][K,P]	Nondisp fx of med phalanx of [rt, lt] ring finger, subsq enc for fx w/ [nonu, malu]
S62.65[6,7][K,P]	Nondisp fx of med phalanx of [rt, lt] little finger, subsq enc for fx w/ [nonu, malu]
S62.65[8,9][K,P]	Nondisp fx of med phalanx of [oth, unsp] finger, subsq enc for fx w/ [nonu, malu]
S62.66[0,1][K,P]	Nondisp fx of distal phalanx of [rt, lt] index finger, subsq enc for fx w/ [nonu, malu]
S62.66[2,3][K,P]	Nondisp fx of distal phalanx of [rt, lt] mid finger, subsq enc for fx w/ [nonu, malu]
S62.66[4,5][K,P]	Nondisp fx of distal phalanx of [rt, lt] ring finger, subsq enc for fx w/ [nonu, malu]
S62.66[6,7][K,P]	Nondisp fx of distal phalanx of [rt, lt] little finger, subsq enc for fx w/ [nonu, malu]
S62.66[8,9][K,P]	Nondisp fx of distal phalanx of [oth, unsp] finger, subsq enc for fx w/ [nonu, malu]
S62.9[0,1,2]X[K,P]	Unsp fx of [unsp, rt, lt] wrist and hand, subsq enc for fx w/ [nonu, malu]
S66.02[1,2,9]A	Lac of long flexor muscle, fascia and tndn of [rt, lt, unsp] thumb at wrist and hand lvl, init enc
S66.12[0,1,2,3,4,5,6,7,8,9]A	Lac of flexor muscle, fascia and tndn of [rt index, lt index, rt mid, lt mid, rt ring, lt ring, rt little, lt little, oth, unsp] finger at wrist and hand lvl, init enc
S66.22[1,2,9]A	Lac of extensor muscle, fascia and tndn of [rt, lt, unsp] thumb at wrist and hand lvl, init enc
S66.32[0,1,2,3,4,5,6,7,8,9]A	Lac of extensor muscle, fascia and tndn of [rt index, lt index, rt mid, lt mid, rt ring, lt ring, rt little, lt little, oth, unsp] finger at wrist and hand lvl, init enc
S66.42[1,2,9]A	Lac of intrinsic muscle, fascia and tndn of [rt, lt, unsp] thumb at wrist and hand lvl, init enc
S66.52[0,1,2,3,4,5,6,7,8,9]A	Lac of intrinsic muscle, fascia and tndn of [rt index, lt index, rt mid, lt mid, rt ring, lt ring, rt little, lt little, oth, unsp] finger at wrist and hand lvl, init enc
S66.[8,9]2[1,2,9]A	Lac of [oth, unsp] spec muscles, fascia and tndns at wrist and hand lvl, [rt, lt, unsp] hand, init enc
S72.00[1,2,9][K,M,N,P,Q,R]	Fx of unsp part of neck of [rt, lt, unsp] femur, subsq enc for [clsd fx w/ nonu, opn fx type I or II w/ nonu, opn fx type IIIA, IIIB, or IIIC w/ nonu, clsd fx w/ malu, opn fx type I or II w/ malu, opn fx type IIIA, IIIB, or IIIC w/ malu]
S72.01[1,2,9][K,M,N,P,Q,R]	Unsp intracapsular fx of [rt, lt, unsp] femur, subsq enc for [clsd fx w/ nonu, opn fx type I or II w/ nonu, opn fx type IIIA, IIIB, or IIIC w/ nonu, clsd fx w/ malu, opn fx type I or II w/ malu, opn fx type IIIA, IIIB, or IIIC w/ malu]
S72.02[1,2,3][K,M,N,P,Q,R]	Disp fx of epiphysis (separation) (upr) of [rt, lt, unsp] femur, subsq enc for [clsd fx w/ nonu, opn fx type I or II w/ nonu, opn fx type IIIA, IIIB, or IIIC w/ nonu, clsd fx w/ malu, opn fx type I or II w/ malu, opn fx type IIIA, IIIB, or IIIC w/ malu]
S72.02[4,5,6][K,M,N,P,Q,R]	Nondisp fx of epiphysis (separation) (upr) of [rt, lt, unsp] femur, subsq enc for [clsd fx w/ nonu, opn fx type I or II w/ nonu, opn fx type IIIA, IIIB, or IIIC w/ nonu, clsd fx w/ malu, opn fx type I or II w/ malu, opn fx type IIIA, IIIB, or IIIC w/ malu]
S72.03[1,2,3][K,M,N,P,Q,R]	Disp midcervical fx of [rt, lt, unsp] femur, subsq enc for [clsd fx w/ nonu, opn fx type I or II w/ nonu, opn fx type IIIA, IIIB, or IIIC w/ nonu, clsd fx w/ malu, opn fx type I or II w/ malu, opn fx type IIIA, IIIB, or IIIC w/ malu]

[T] Transfer DRG   [SP] Special Payment   * Code Range   6th and 7th Character of ZZ = No Device, No Qualifier ZX = No Device, Diagnostic

200   MS-DRG Version 33.0   © 2015 Optum360, LLC

S72.03[4,5,6][K,M,N,P,Q,R] Nondisp midcervical fx of [rt, lt, unsp] femur, subsq enc for [clsd fx w/ nonu, opn fx type I or II w/ nonu, opn fx type IIIA, IIIB, or IIIC w/ nonu, clsd fx w/ malu, opn fx type I or II w/ malu, opn fx type IIIA, IIIB, or IIIC w/ malu]

S72.04[1,2,3][K,M,N,P,Q,R] Disp fx of base of neck of [rt, lt, unsp] femur, subsq enc for [clsd fx w/ nonu, opn fx type I or II w/ nonu, opn fx type IIIA, IIIB, or IIIC w/ nonu, clsd fx w/ malu, opn fx type I or II w/ malu, opn fx type IIIA, IIIB, or IIIC w/ malu]

S72.04[4,5,6][K,M,N,P,Q,R] Nondisp fx of base of neck of [rt, lt, unsp] femur, subsq enc for [clsd fx w/ nonu, opn fx type I or II w/ nonu, opn fx type IIIA, IIIB, or IIIC w/ nonu, clsd fx w/ malu, opn fx type I or II w/ malu, opn fx type IIIA, IIIB, or IIIC w/ malu]

S72.05[1,2,9][K,M,N,P,Q,R] Unsp fx of head of [rt, lt, unsp] femur, subsq enc for [clsd fx w/ nonu, opn fx type I or II w/ nonu, opn fx type IIIA, IIIB, or IIIC w/ nonu, clsd fx w/ malu, opn fx type I or II w/ malu, opn fx type IIIA, IIIB, or IIIC w/ malu]

S72.06[1,2,3][K,M,N,P,Q,R] Disp articular fx of head of [rt, lt, unsp] femur, subsq enc for [clsd fx w/ nonu, opn fx type I or II w/ nonu, opn fx type IIIA, IIIB, or IIIC w/ nonu, clsd fx w/ malu, opn fx type I or II w/ malu, opn fx type IIIA, IIIB, or IIIC w/ malu]

S72.06[4,5,6][K,M,N,P,Q,R] Nondisp articular fx of head of [rt, lt, unsp] femur, subsq enc for [clsd fx w/ nonu, opn fx type I or II w/ nonu, opn fx type IIIA, IIIB, or IIIC w/ nonu, clsd fx w/ malu, opn fx type I or II w/ malu, opn fx type IIIA, IIIB, or IIIC w/ malu]

S72.09[1,2,9][K,M,N,P,Q,R] Oth fx of head and neck of [rt, lt, unsp] femur, subsq enc for [clsd fx w/ nonu, opn fx type I or II w/ nonu, opn fx type IIIA, IIIB, or IIIC w/ nonu, clsd fx w/ malu, opn fx type I or II w/ malu, opn fx type IIIA, IIIB, or IIIC w/ malu]

S72.10[1,2,9][K,M,N,P,Q,R] Unsp trochanteric fx of [rt, lt, unsp] femur, subsq enc for [clsd fx w/ nonu, opn fx type I or II w/ nonu, opn fx type IIIA, IIIB, or IIIC w/ nonu, clsd fx w/ malu, opn fx type I or II w/ malu, opn fx type IIIA, IIIB, or IIIC w/ malu]

S72.11[1,2,3][K,M,N,P,Q,R] Disp fx of greater trochanter of [rt, lt, unsp] femur, subsq enc for [clsd fx w/ nonu, opn fx type I or II w/ nonu, opn fx type IIIA, IIIB, or IIIC w/ nonu, clsd fx w/ malu, opn fx type I or II w/ malu, opn fx type IIIA, IIIB, or IIIC w/ malu]

S72.11[4,5,6][K,M,N,P,Q,R] Nondisp fx of greater trochanter of [rt, lt, unsp] femur, subsq enc for [clsd fx w/ nonu, opn fx type I or II w/ nonu, opn fx type IIIA, IIIB, or IIIC w/ nonu, clsd fx w/ malu, opn fx type I or II w/ malu, opn fx type IIIA, IIIB, or IIIC w/ malu]

S72.12[1,2,3][K,M,N,P,Q,R] Disp fx of lesser trochanter of [rt, lt, unsp] femur, subsq enc for [clsd fx w/ nonu, opn fx type I or II w/ nonu, opn fx type IIIA, IIIB, or IIIC w/ nonu, clsd fx w/ malu, opn fx type I or II w/ malu, opn fx type IIIA, IIIB, or IIIC w/ malu]

S72.12[4,5,6][K,M,N,P,Q,R] Nondisp fx of lesser trochanter of [rt, lt, unsp] femur, subsq enc for [clsd fx w/ nonu, opn fx type I or II w/ nonu, opn fx type IIIA, IIIB, or IIIC w/ nonu, clsd fx w/ malu, opn fx type I or II w/ malu, opn fx type IIIA, IIIB, or IIIC w/ malu]

S72.13[1,2,3][K,M,N,P,Q,R] Disp apophyseal fx of [rt, lt, unsp] femur, subsq enc for [clsd fx w/ nonu, opn fx type I or II w/ nonu, opn fx type IIIA, IIIB, or IIIC w/ nonu, clsd fx w/ malu, opn fx type I or II w/ malu, opn fx type IIIA, IIIB, or IIIC w/ malu]

S72.13[4,5,6][K,M,N,P,Q,R] Nondisp apophyseal fx of [rt, lt, unsp] femur, subsq enc for [clsd fx w/ nonu, opn fx type I or II w/ nonu, opn fx type IIIA, IIIB, or IIIC w/ nonu, clsd fx w/ malu, opn fx type I or II w/ malu, opn fx type IIIA, IIIB, or IIIC w/ malu]

S72.14[1,2,3][K,M,N,P,Q,R] Disp intertrochanteric fx of [rt, lt, unsp] femur, subsq enc for [clsd fx w/ nonu, opn fx type I or II w/ nonu, opn fx type IIIA, IIIB, or IIIC w/ nonu, clsd fx w/ malu, opn fx type I or II w/ malu, opn fx type IIIA, IIIB, or IIIC w/ malu]

S72.14[4,5,6][K,M,N,P,Q,R] Nondisp intertrochanteric fx of [rt, lt, unsp] femur, subsq enc for [clsd fx w/ nonu, opn fx type I or II w/ nonu, opn fx type IIIA, IIIB, or IIIC w/ nonu, clsd fx w/ malu, opn fx type I or II w/ malu, opn fx type IIIA, IIIB, or IIIC w/ malu]

S72.2[1,2,3]X[K,M,N,P,Q,R] Disp subtrochanteric fx of [rt, lt, unsp] femur, subsq enc for [clsd fx w/ nonu, opn fx type I or II w/ nonu, opn fx type IIIA, IIIB, or IIIC w/ nonu, clsd fx w/ malu, opn fx type I or II w/ malu, opn fx type IIIA, IIIB, or IIIC w/ malu]

S72.2[4,5,6]X[K,M,N,P,Q,R] Nondisp subtrochanteric fx of [rt, lt, unsp] femur, subsq enc for [clsd fx w/ nonu, opn fx type I or II w/ nonu, opn fx type IIIA, IIIB, or IIIC w/ nonu, clsd fx w/ malu, opn fx type I or II w/ malu, opn fx type IIIA, IIIB, or IIIC w/ malu]

S72.30[1,2,9][K,M,N,P,Q,R] Unsp fx of shaft of [rt, lt, unsp] femur, subsq enc for [clsd fx w/ nonu, opn fx type I or II w/ nonu, opn fx type IIIA, IIIB, or IIIC w/ nonu, clsd fx w/ malu, opn fx type I or II w/ malu, opn fx type IIIA, IIIB, or IIIC w/ malu]

S72.32[1,2,3][K,M,N,P,Q,R] Disp transv fx of shaft of [rt, lt, unsp] femur, subsq enc for [clsd fx w/ nonu, opn fx type I or II w/ nonu, opn fx type IIIA, IIIB, or IIIC w/ nonu, clsd fx w/ malu, opn fx type I or II w/ malu, opn fx type IIIA, IIIB, or IIIC w/ malu]

S72.32[4,5,6][K,M,N,P,Q,R] Nondisp transv fx of shaft of [rt, lt, unsp] femur, subsq enc for [clsd fx w/ nonu, opn fx type I or II w/ nonu, opn fx type IIIA, IIIB, or IIIC w/ nonu, clsd fx w/ malu, opn fx type I or II w/ malu, opn fx type IIIA, IIIB, or IIIC w/ malu]

S72.33[1,2,3][K,M,N,P,Q,R] Disp oblique fx of shaft of [rt, lt, unsp] femur, subsq enc for [clsd fx w/ nonu, opn fx type I or II w/ nonu, opn fx type IIIA, IIIB, or IIIC w/ nonu, clsd fx w/ malu, opn fx type I or II w/ malu, opn fx type IIIA, IIIB, or IIIC w/ malu]

S72.33[4,5,6][K,M,N,P,Q,R] Nondisp oblique fx of shaft of [rt, lt, unsp] femur, subsq enc for [clsd fx w/ nonu, opn fx type I or II w/ nonu, opn fx type IIIA, IIIB, or IIIC w/ nonu, clsd fx w/ malu, opn fx type I or II w/ malu, opn fx type IIIA, IIIB, or IIIC w/ malu]

S72.34[1,2,3][K,M,N,P,Q,R] Disp spiral fx of shaft of [rt, lt, unsp] femur, subsq enc for [clsd fx w/ nonu, opn fx type I or II w/ nonu, opn fx type IIIA, IIIB, or IIIC w/ nonu, clsd fx w/ malu, opn fx type I or II w/ malu, opn fx type IIIA, IIIB, or IIIC w/ malu]

S72.34[4,5,6][K,M,N,P,Q,R] Nondisp spiral fx of shaft of [rt, lt, unsp] femur, subsq enc for [clsd fx w/ nonu, opn fx type I or II w/ nonu, opn fx type IIIA, IIIB, or IIIC w/ nonu, clsd fx w/ malu, opn fx type I or II w/ malu, opn fx type IIIA, IIIB, or IIIC w/ malu]

S72.35[1,2,3][K,M,N,P,Q,R] Disp comm fx of shaft of [rt, lt, unsp] femur, subsq enc for [clsd fx w/ nonu, opn fx type I or II w/ nonu, opn fx type IIIA, IIIB, or IIIC w/ nonu, clsd fx w/ malu, opn fx type I or II w/ malu, opn fx type IIIA, IIIB, or IIIC w/ malu]

S72.35[4,5,6][K,M,N,P,Q,R] Nondisp comm fx of shaft of [rt, lt, unsp] femur, subsq enc for [clsd fx w/ nonu, opn fx type I or II w/ nonu, opn fx type IIIA, IIIB, or IIIC w/ nonu, clsd fx w/ malu, opn fx type I or II w/ malu, opn fx type IIIA, IIIB, or IIIC w/ malu]

S72.36[1,2,3][K,M,N,P,Q,R] Disp seg fx of shaft of [rt, lt, unsp] femur, subsq enc for [clsd fx w/ nonu, opn fx type I or II w/ nonu, opn fx type IIIA, IIIB, or IIIC w/ nonu, clsd fx w/ malu, opn fx type I or II w/ malu, opn fx type IIIA, IIIB, or IIIC w/ malu]

S72.36[4,5,6][K,M,N,P,Q,R] Nondisp seg fx of shaft of [rt, lt, unsp] femur, subsq enc for [clsd fx w/ nonu, opn fx type I or II w/ nonu, opn fx type IIIA, IIIB, or IIIC w/ nonu, clsd fx w/ malu, opn fx type I or II w/ malu, opn fx type IIIA, IIIB, or IIIC w/ malu]

S72.39[1,2,9][K,M,N,P,Q,R] Oth fx of shaft of [rt, lt, unsp] femur, subsq enc for [clsd fx w/ nonu, opn fx type I or II w/ nonu, opn fx type IIIA, IIIB, or IIIC w/ nonu, clsd fx w/ malu, opn fx type I or II w/ malu, opn fx type IIIA, IIIB, or IIIC w/ malu]

S72.40[1,2,9][K,M,N,P,Q,R] Unsp fx of lwr end of [rt, lt, unsp] femur, subsq enc for [clsd fx w/ nonu, opn fx type I or II w/ nonu, opn fx type IIIA, IIIB, or IIIC w/ nonu, clsd fx w/ malu, opn fx type I or II w/ malu, opn fx type IIIA, IIIB, or IIIC w/ malu]

S72.41[1,2,3][K,M,N,P,Q,R] Disp unsp condyle fx of lwr end of [rt, lt, unsp] femur, subsq enc for [clsd fx w/ nonu, opn fx type I or II w/ nonu, opn fx type IIIA, IIIB, or IIIC w/ nonu, clsd fx w/ malu, opn fx type I or II w/ malu, opn fx type IIIA, IIIB, or IIIC w/ malu]

S72.41[4,5,6][K,M,N,P,Q,R] Nondisp unsp condyle fx of lwr end of [rt, lt, unsp] femur, subsq enc for [clsd fx w/ nonu, opn fx type I or II w/ nonu, opn fx type IIIA, IIIB, or IIIC w/ nonu, clsd fx w/ malu, opn fx type I or II w/ malu, opn fx type IIIA, IIIB, or IIIC w/ malu]

S72.42[1,2,3][K,M,N,P,Q,R] Disp fx of lat condyle of [rt, lt, unsp] femur, subsq enc for [clsd fx w/ nonu, opn fx type I or II w/ nonu, opn fx type IIIA, IIIB, or IIIC w/ nonu, clsd fx w/ malu, opn fx type I or II w/ malu, opn fx type IIIA, IIIB, or IIIC w/ malu]

S72.42[4,5,6][K,M,N,P,Q,R] Nondisp fx of lat condyle of [rt, lt, unsp] femur, subsq enc for [clsd fx w/ nonu, opn fx type I or II w/ nonu, opn fx type IIIA, IIIB, or IIIC w/ nonu, clsd fx w/ malu, opn fx type I or II w/ malu, opn fx type IIIA, IIIB, or IIIC w/ malu]

S72.43[1,2,3][K,M,N,P,Q,R] Disp fx of med condyle of [rt, lt, unsp] femur, subsq enc for [clsd fx w/ nonu, opn fx type I or II w/ nonu, opn fx type IIIA, IIIB, or IIIC w/ nonu, clsd fx w/ malu, opn fx type I or II w/ malu, opn fx type IIIA, IIIB, or IIIC w/ malu]

S72.43[4,5,6][K,M,N,P,Q,R] Nondisp fx of med condyle of [rt, lt, unsp] femur, subsq enc for [clsd fx w/ nonu, opn fx type I or II w/ nonu, opn fx type IIIA, IIIB, or IIIC w/ nonu, clsd fx w/ malu, opn fx type I or II w/ malu, opn fx type IIIA, IIIB, or IIIC w/ malu]

S72.44[1,2,3][K,M,N,P,Q,R] Disp fx of lwr epiphysis (separation) of [rt, lt, unsp] femur, subsq enc for [clsd fx w/ nonu, opn fx type I or II w/ nonu, opn fx type IIIA, IIIB, or IIIC w/ nonu, clsd fx w/ malu, opn fx type I or II w/ malu, opn fx type IIIA, IIIB, or IIIC w/ malu]

S72.44[4,5,6][K,M,N,P,Q,R] Nondisp fx of lwr epiphysis (separation) of [rt, lt, unsp] femur, subsq enc for [clsd fx w/ nonu, opn fx type I or II w/ nonu, opn fx type IIIA, IIIB, or IIIC w/ nonu, clsd fx w/ malu, opn fx type I or II w/ malu, opn fx type IIIA, IIIB, or IIIC w/ malu]

Surgical　　**Medical**　　**CC Indicator**　　**MCC Indicator**　　**Procedure Proxy**　　PDxMCC **PDx acts as own MCC**　　PDxCC **PDx acts as own CC**

© 2015 Optum360, LLC　　　　MS-DRG Version 33.0　　　　**201**

MDC 8: Diseases And Disorders Of The Musculoskeletal System And Connective Tissue—MEDICAL

S72.45[1,2,3][K,M,N,P,Q,R] Disp supracondylar fx w/o intracondylar extension of lwr end of [rt, lt, unsp] femur, subsq enc for [clsd fx w/ nonu, opn fx type I or II w/ nonu, opn fx type IIIA, IIIB, or IIIC w/ nonu, clsd fx w/ malu, opn fx type I or II w/ malu, opn fx type IIIA, IIIB, or IIIC w/ malu]

S72.45[4,5,6][K,M,N,P,Q,R] Nondisp supracondylar fx w/o intracondylar extension of lwr end of [rt, lt, unsp] femur, subsq enc for [clsd fx w/ nonu, opn fx type I or II w/ nonu, opn fx type IIIA, IIIB, or IIIC w/ nonu, clsd fx w/ malu, opn fx type I or II w/ malu, opn fx type IIIA, IIIB, or IIIC w/ malu]

S72.46[1,2,3][K,M,N,P,Q,R] Disp supracondylar fx w/ intracondylar extension of lwr end of [rt, lt, unsp] femur, subsq enc for [clsd fx w/ nonu, opn fx type I or II w/ nonu, opn fx type IIIA, IIIB, or IIIC w/ nonu, clsd fx w/ malu, opn fx type I or II w/ malu, opn fx type IIIA, IIIB, or IIIC w/ malu]

S72.46[4,5,6][K,M,N,P,Q,R] Nondisp supracondylar fx w/ intracondylar extension of lwr end of [rt, lt, unsp] femur, subsq enc for [clsd fx w/ nonu, opn fx type I or II w/ nonu, opn fx type IIIA, IIIB, or IIIC w/ nonu, clsd fx w/ malu, opn fx type I or II w/ malu, opn fx type IIIA, IIIB, or IIIC w/ malu]

S72.47[1,2,9][K,P] Torus fx of lwr end of [rt, lt, unsp] femur, subsq enc for fx w/ [nonu, malu]

S72.49[1,2,9][K,M,N,P,Q,R] Oth fx of lwr end of [rt, lt, unsp] femur, subsq enc for [clsd fx w/ nonu, opn fx type I or II w/ nonu, opn fx type IIIA, IIIB, or IIIC w/ nonu, clsd fx w/ malu, opn fx type I or II w/ malu, opn fx type IIIA, IIIB, or IIIC w/ malu]

S72.8X[1,2,9][K,M,N,P,Q,R] Oth fx of [rt, lt, unsp] femur, subsq enc for [clsd fx w/ nonu, opn fx type I or II w/ nonu, opn fx type IIIA, IIIB, or IIIC w/ nonu, clsd fx w/ malu, opn fx type I or II w/ malu, opn fx type IIIA, IIIB, or IIIC w/ malu]

S72.9[0,1,2]X[K,M,N,P,Q,R] Unsp fx of [unsp, rt, lt] femur, subsq enc for [clsd fx w/ nonu, opn fx type I or II w/ nonu, opn fx type IIIA, IIIB, or IIIC w/ nonu, clsd fx w/ malu, opn fx type I or II w/ malu, opn fx type IIIA, IIIB, or IIIC w/ malu]

S76.02[1,2,9]A Lac of muscle, fascia and tndn of [rt, lt, unsp] hip, init enc

S76.12[1,2,9]A Lac of [rt, lt, unsp] quadriceps muscle, fascia and tndn, init enc

S76.22[1,2,9]A Lac of adductor muscle, fascia and tndn of [rt, lt, unsp] thigh, init enc

S76.32[1,2,9]A Lac of muscle, fascia and tndn of the post muscle group at thigh lvl, [rt, lt, unsp] thigh, init enc

S76.82[1,2,9]A Lac of oth spec muscles, fascia and tndns at thigh lvl, [rt, lt, unsp] thigh, init enc

S76.92[1,2,9]A Lac of unsp muscles, fascia and tndns at thigh lvl, [rt, lt, unsp] thigh, init enc

S79.00[1,2,9][K,P] Unsp physeal fx of upr end of [rt, lt, unsp] femur, subsq enc for fx w/ [nonu, malu]

S79.01[1,2,9][K,P] Salter-Harris Type I physeal fx of upr end of [rt, lt, unsp] femur, subsq enc for fx w/ [nonu, malu]

S79.09[1,2,9][K,P] Oth physeal fx of upr end of [rt, lt, unsp] femur, subsq enc for fx w/ [nonu, malu]

S79.10[1,2,9][K,P] Unsp physeal fx of lwr end of [rt, lt, unsp] femur, subsq enc for fx w/ [nonu, malu]

S79.19[1,2,9][K,P] Oth physeal fx of lwr end of [rt, lt, unsp] femur, subsq enc for fx w/ [nonu, malu]

S79.1[1,2,3,4][1,2,9][K,P] Salter-Harris Type [I, II, III, IV] physeal fx of lwr end of [rt, lt, unsp] femur, subsq enc for fx w/ [nonu, malu]

S82.00[1,2,9][K,M,N,P,Q,R] Unsp fx of [rt, lt, unsp] patella, subsq enc for [clsd fx w/ nonu, opn fx type I or II w/ nonu, opn fx type IIIA, IIIB, or IIIC w/ nonu, clsd fx w/ malu, opn fx type I or II w/ malu, opn fx type I or II w/ malu]

S82.01[1,2,3][K,M,N,P,Q,R] Disp osteochondral fx of [rt, lt, unsp] patella, subsq enc for [clsd fx w/ nonu, opn fx type I or II w/ nonu, opn fx type IIIA, IIIB, or IIIC w/ nonu, clsd fx w/ malu, opn fx type I or II w/ malu, opn fx type I or II w/ malu]

S82.01[4,5,6][K,M,N,P,Q,R] Nondisp osteochondral fx of [rt, lt, unsp] patella, subsq enc for [clsd fx w/ nonu, opn fx type I or II w/ nonu, opn fx type IIIA, IIIB, or IIIC w/ nonu, clsd fx w/ malu, opn fx type I or II w/ malu, opn fx type I or II w/ malu]

S82.02[1,2,3][K,M,N,P,Q,R] Disp longitudinal fx of [rt, lt, unsp] patella, subsq enc for [clsd fx w/ nonu, opn fx type I or II w/ nonu, opn fx type IIIA, IIIB, or IIIC w/ nonu, clsd fx w/ malu, opn fx type I or II w/ malu, opn fx type I or II w/ malu]

S82.02[4,5,6][K,M,N,P,Q,R] Nondisp longitudinal fx of [rt, lt, unsp] patella, subsq enc for [clsd fx w/ nonu, opn fx type I or II w/ nonu, opn fx type IIIA, IIIB, or IIIC w/ nonu, clsd fx w/ malu, opn fx type I or II w/ malu, opn fx type I or II w/ malu]

S82.03[1,2,3][K,M,N,P,Q,R] Disp transv fx of [rt, lt, unsp] patella, subsq enc for [clsd fx w/ nonu, opn fx type I or II w/ nonu, opn fx type IIIA, IIIB, or IIIC w/ nonu, clsd fx w/ malu, opn fx type I or II w/ malu, opn fx type I or II w/ malu]

S82.03[4,5,6][K,M,N,P,Q,R] Nondisp transv fx of [rt, lt, unsp] patella, subsq enc for [clsd fx w/ nonu, opn fx type I or II w/ nonu, opn fx type IIIA, IIIB, or IIIC w/ nonu, clsd fx w/ malu, opn fx type I or II w/ malu]

S82.04[1,2,3][K,M,N,P,Q,R] Disp comm fx of [rt, lt, unsp] patella, subsq enc for [clsd fx w/ nonu, opn fx type I or II w/ nonu, opn fx type IIIA, IIIB, or IIIC w/ nonu, clsd fx w/ malu, opn fx type I or II w/ malu]

S82.04[4,5,6][K,M,N,P,Q,R] Nondisp comm fx of [rt, lt, unsp] patella, subsq enc for [clsd fx w/ nonu, opn fx type I or II w/ nonu, opn fx type IIIA, IIIB, or IIIC w/ nonu, clsd fx w/ malu, opn fx type I or II w/ malu]

S82.09[1,2,9][K,M,N,P,Q,R] Oth fx of [rt, lt, unsp] patella, subsq enc for [clsd fx w/ nonu, opn fx type I or II w/ nonu, opn fx type IIIA, IIIB, or IIIC w/ nonu, clsd fx w/ malu, opn fx type I or II w/ malu, opn fx type I or II w/ malu]

S82.10[1,2,9][K,M,N,P,Q,R] Unsp fx of upr end of [rt, lt, unsp] tibia, subsq enc for [clsd fx w/ nonu, opn fx type I or II w/ nonu, opn fx type IIIA, IIIB, or IIIC w/ nonu, clsd fx w/ malu, opn fx type I or II w/ malu, opn fx type I or II w/ malu]

S82.11[1,2,3][K,M,N,P,Q,R] Disp fx of [rt, lt, unsp] tibial spine, subsq enc for [clsd fx w/ nonu, opn fx type I or II w/ nonu, opn fx type IIIA, IIIB, or IIIC w/ nonu, clsd fx w/ malu, opn fx type I or II w/ malu, opn fx type I or II w/ malu]

S82.11[4,5,6][K,M,N,P,Q,R] Nondisp fx of [rt, lt, unsp] tibial spine, subsq enc for [clsd fx w/ nonu, opn fx type I or II w/ nonu, opn fx type IIIA, IIIB, or IIIC w/ nonu, clsd fx w/ malu, opn fx type I or II w/ malu, opn fx type I or II w/ malu]

S82.12[1,2,3][K,M,N,P,Q,R] Disp fx of lat condyle of [rt, lt, unsp] tibia, subsq enc for [clsd fx w/ nonu, opn fx type I or II w/ nonu, opn fx type IIIA, IIIB, or IIIC w/ nonu, clsd fx w/ malu, opn fx type I or II w/ malu, opn fx type I or II w/ malu]

S82.12[4,5,6][K,M,N,P,Q,R] Nondisp fx of lat condyle of [rt, lt, unsp] tibia, subsq enc for [clsd fx w/ nonu, opn fx type I or II w/ nonu, opn fx type IIIA, IIIB, or IIIC w/ nonu, clsd fx w/ malu, opn fx type I or II w/ malu, opn fx type I or II w/ malu]

S82.13[1,2,3][K,M,N,P,Q,R] Disp fx of med condyle of [rt, lt, unsp] tibia, subsq enc for [clsd fx w/ nonu, opn fx type I or II w/ nonu, opn fx type IIIA, IIIB, or IIIC w/ nonu, clsd fx w/ malu, opn fx type I or II w/ malu, opn fx type I or II w/ malu]

S82.13[4,5,6][K,M,N,P,Q,R] Nondisp fx of med condyle of [rt, lt, unsp] tibia, subsq enc for [clsd fx w/ nonu, opn fx type I or II w/ nonu, opn fx type IIIA, IIIB, or IIIC w/ nonu, clsd fx w/ malu, opn fx type I or II w/ malu, opn fx type I or II w/ malu]

S82.14[1,2,3][K,M,N,P,Q,R] Disp bicondylar fx of [rt, lt, unsp] tibia, subsq enc for [clsd fx w/ nonu, opn fx type I or II w/ nonu, opn fx type IIIA, IIIB, or IIIC w/ nonu, clsd fx w/ malu, opn fx type I or II w/ malu, opn fx type I or II w/ malu]

S82.14[4,5,6][K,M,N,P,Q,R] Nondisp bicondylar fx of [rt, lt, unsp] tibia, subsq enc for [clsd fx w/ nonu, opn fx type I or II w/ nonu, opn fx type IIIA, IIIB, or IIIC w/ nonu, clsd fx w/ malu, opn fx type I or II w/ malu, opn fx type I or II w/ malu]

S82.15[1,2,3][K,M,N,P,Q,R] Disp fx of [rt, lt, unsp] tibial tuberosity, subsq enc for [clsd fx w/ nonu, opn fx type I or II w/ nonu, opn fx type IIIA, IIIB, or IIIC w/ nonu, clsd fx w/ malu, opn fx type I or II w/ malu, opn fx type I or II w/ malu]

S82.15[4,5,6][K,M,N,P,Q,R] Nondisp fx of [rt, lt, unsp] tibial tuberosity, subsq enc for [clsd fx w/ nonu, opn fx type I or II w/ nonu, opn fx type IIIA, IIIB, or IIIC w/ nonu, clsd fx w/ malu, opn fx type I or II w/ malu, opn fx type I or II w/ malu]

S82.16[1,2,9][K,P] Torus fx of upr end of [rt, lt, unsp] tibia, subsq enc for fx w/ [nonu, malu]

S82.19[1,2,9][K,M,N,P,Q,R] Oth fx of upr end of [rt, lt, unsp] tibia, subsq enc for [clsd fx w/ nonu, opn fx type I or II w/ nonu, opn fx type IIIA, IIIB, or IIIC w/ nonu, clsd fx w/ malu, opn fx type I or II w/ malu, opn fx type I or II w/ malu]

S82.20[1,2,9][K,M,N,P,Q,R] Unsp fx of shaft of [rt, lt, unsp] tibia, subsq enc for [clsd fx w/ nonu, opn fx type I or II w/ nonu, opn fx type IIIA, IIIB, or IIIC w/ nonu, clsd fx w/ malu, opn fx type I or II w/ malu, opn fx type I or II w/ malu]

S82.22[1,2,3][K,M,N,P,Q,R] Disp transv fx of shaft of [rt, lt, unsp] tibia, subsq enc for [clsd fx w/ nonu, opn fx type I or II w/ nonu, opn fx type IIIA, IIIB, or IIIC w/ nonu, clsd fx w/ malu, opn fx type I or II w/ malu, opn fx type I or II w/ malu]

S82.22[4,5,6][K,M,N,P,Q,R] Nondisp transv fx of shaft of [rt, lt, unsp] tibia, subsq enc for [clsd fx w/ nonu, opn fx type I or II w/ nonu, opn fx type IIIA, IIIB, or IIIC w/ nonu, clsd fx w/ malu, opn fx type I or II w/ malu, opn fx type I or II w/ malu]

T **Transfer DRG**　　SP **Special Payment**　　* **Code Range**　　　**6th and 7th Character of ZZ = No Device, No Qualifier ZX = No Device, Diagnostic**

S82.23[1,2,3][K,M,N,P,Q,R] Disp oblique fx of shaft of [rt, lt, unsp] tibia, subsq enc for [clsd fx w/ nonu, opn fx type I or II w/ nonu, opn fx type IIIA, IIIB, or IIIC w/ nonu, clsd fx w/ malu, opn fx type I or II w/ malu]

S82.23[4,5,6][K,M,N,P,Q,R] Nondisp oblique fx of shaft of [rt, lt, unsp] tibia, subsq enc for [clsd fx w/ nonu, opn fx type I or II w/ nonu, opn fx type IIIA, IIIB, or IIIC w/ nonu, clsd fx w/ malu, opn fx type I or II w/ malu]

S82.24[1,2,3][K,M,N,P,Q,R] Disp spiral fx of shaft of [rt, lt, unsp] tibia, subsq enc for [clsd fx w/ nonu, opn fx type I or II w/ nonu, opn fx type IIIA, IIIB, or IIIC w/ nonu, clsd fx w/ malu, opn fx type I or II w/ malu]

S82.24[4,5,6][K,M,N,P,Q,R] Nondisp spiral fx of shaft of [rt, lt, unsp] tibia, subsq enc for [clsd fx w/ nonu, opn fx type I or II w/ nonu, opn fx type IIIA, IIIB, or IIIC w/ nonu, clsd fx w/ malu, opn fx type I or II w/ malu]

S82.25[1,2,3][K,M,N,P,Q,R] Disp comm fx of shaft of [rt, lt, unsp] tibia, subsq enc for [clsd fx w/ nonu, opn fx type I or II w/ nonu, opn fx type IIIA, IIIB, or IIIC w/ nonu, clsd fx w/ malu, opn fx type I or II w/ malu]

S82.25[4,5,6][K,M,N,P,Q,R] Nondisp comm fx of shaft of [rt, lt, unsp] tibia, subsq enc for [clsd fx w/ nonu, opn fx type I or II w/ nonu, opn fx type IIIA, IIIB, or IIIC w/ nonu, clsd fx w/ malu, opn fx type I or II w/ malu]

S82.26[1,2,3][K,M,N,P,Q,R] Disp seg fx of shaft of [rt, lt, unsp] tibia, subsq enc for [clsd fx w/ nonu, opn fx type I or II w/ nonu, opn fx type IIIA, IIIB, or IIIC w/ nonu, clsd fx w/ malu, opn fx type I or II w/ malu]

S82.26[4,5,6][K,M,N,P,Q,R] Nondisp seg fx of shaft of [rt, lt, unsp] tibia, subsq enc for [clsd fx w/ nonu, opn fx type I or II w/ nonu, opn fx type IIIA, IIIB, or IIIC w/ nonu, clsd fx w/ malu, opn fx type I or II w/ malu]

S82.29[1,2,9][K,M,N,P,Q,R] Oth fx of shaft of [rt, lt, unsp] tibia, subsq enc for [clsd fx w/ nonu, opn fx type I or II w/ nonu, opn fx type IIIA, IIIB, or IIIC w/ nonu, clsd fx w/ malu, opn fx type I or II w/ malu]

S82.30[1,2,9][K,M,N,P,Q,R] Unsp fx of lwr end of [rt, lt, unsp] tibia, subsq enc for [clsd fx w/ nonu, opn fx type I or II w/ nonu, opn fx type IIIA, IIIB, or IIIC w/ nonu, clsd fx w/ malu, opn fx type I or II w/ malu]

S82.31[1,2,9][K,P] Torus fx of lwr end of [rt, lt, unsp] tibia, subsq enc for clsd fx w/ [nonu, malu]

S82.39[1,2,9][K,M,N,P,Q,R] Oth fx of lwr end of [rt, lt, unsp] tibia, subsq enc for [clsd fx w/ nonu, opn fx type I or II w/ nonu, opn fx type IIIA, IIIB, or IIIC w/ nonu, clsd fx w/ malu, opn fx type I or II w/ malu]

S82.40[1,2,9][K,M,N,P,Q,R] Unsp fx of shaft of [rt, lt, unsp] fibula, subsq enc for [clsd fx w/ nonu, opn fx type I or II w/ nonu, opn fx type IIIA, IIIB, or IIIC w/ nonu, clsd fx w/ malu, opn fx type I or II w/ malu]

S82.42[1,2,3][K,M,N,P,Q,R] Disp transv fx of shaft of [rt, lt, unsp] fibula, subsq enc for [clsd fx w/ nonu, opn fx type I or II w/ nonu, opn fx type IIIA, IIIB, or IIIC w/ nonu, clsd fx w/ malu, opn fx type I or II w/ malu]

S82.42[4,5,6][K,M,N,P,Q,R] Nondisp transv fx of shaft of [rt, lt, unsp] fibula, subsq enc for [clsd fx w/ nonu, opn fx type I or II w/ nonu, opn fx type IIIA, IIIB, or IIIC w/ nonu, clsd fx w/ malu, opn fx type I or II w/ malu]

S82.43[1,2,3][K,M,N,P,Q,R] Disp oblique fx of shaft of [rt, lt, unsp] fibula, subsq enc for [clsd fx w/ nonu, opn fx type I or II w/ nonu, opn fx type IIIA, IIIB, or IIIC w/ nonu, clsd fx w/ malu, opn fx type I or II w/ malu]

S82.43[4,5,6][K,M,N,P,Q,R] Nondisp oblique fx of shaft of [rt, lt, unsp] fibula, subsq enc for [clsd fx w/ nonu, opn fx type I or II w/ nonu, opn fx type IIIA, IIIB, or IIIC w/ nonu, clsd fx w/ malu, opn fx type I or II w/ malu]

S82.44[1,2,3][K,M,N,P,Q,R] Disp spiral fx of shaft of [rt, lt, unsp] fibula, subsq enc for [clsd fx w/ nonu, opn fx type I or II w/ nonu, opn fx type IIIA, IIIB, or IIIC w/ nonu, clsd fx w/ malu, opn fx type I or II w/ malu]

S82.44[4,5,6][K,M,N,P,Q,R] Nondisp spiral fx of shaft of [rt, lt, unsp] fibula, subsq enc for [clsd fx w/ nonu, opn fx type I or II w/ nonu, opn fx type IIIA, IIIB, or IIIC w/ nonu, clsd fx w/ malu, opn fx type I or II w/ malu]

S82.45[1,2,3][K,M,N,P,Q,R] Disp comm fx of shaft of [rt, lt, unsp] fibula, subsq enc for [clsd fx w/ nonu, opn fx type I or II w/ nonu, opn fx type IIIA, IIIB, or IIIC w/ nonu, clsd fx w/ malu, opn fx type I or II w/ malu]

S82.45[4,5,6][K,M,N,P,Q,R] Nondisp comm fx of shaft of [rt, lt, unsp] fibula, subsq enc for [clsd fx w/ nonu, opn fx type I or II w/ nonu, opn fx type IIIA, IIIB, or IIIC w/ nonu, clsd fx w/ malu, opn fx type I or II w/ malu]

S82.46[1,2,3][K,M,N,P,Q,R] Disp seg fx of shaft of [rt, lt, unsp] fibula, subsq enc for [clsd fx w/ nonu, opn fx type I or II w/ nonu, opn fx type IIIA, IIIB, or IIIC w/ nonu, clsd fx w/ malu, opn fx type I or II w/ malu]

S82.46[4,5,6][K,M,N,P,Q,R] Nondisp seg fx of shaft of [rt, lt, unsp] fibula, subsq enc for [clsd fx w/ nonu, opn fx type I or II w/ nonu, opn fx type IIIA, IIIB, or IIIC w/ nonu, clsd fx w/ malu, opn fx type I or II w/ malu]

S82.49[1,2,9][K,M,N,P,Q,R] Oth fx of shaft of [rt, lt, unsp] fibula, subsq enc for [clsd fx w/ nonu, opn fx type I or II w/ nonu, opn fx type IIIA, IIIB, or IIIC w/ nonu, clsd fx w/ malu, opn fx type I or II w/ malu]

S82.5[1,2,3]X[K,M,N,P,Q,R] Disp fx of med malleolus of [rt, lt, unsp] tibia, subsq enc for [clsd fx w/ nonu, opn fx type I or II w/ nonu, opn fx type IIIA, IIIB, or IIIC w/ nonu, clsd fx w/ malu, opn fx type I or II w/ malu]

S82.5[4,5,6]X[K,M,N,P,Q,R] Nondisp fx of med malleolus of [rt, lt, unsp] tibia, subsq enc for [clsd fx w/ nonu, opn fx type I or II w/ nonu, opn fx type IIIA, IIIB, or IIIC w/ nonu, clsd fx w/ malu, opn fx type I or II w/ malu]

S82.6[1,2,3]X[K,M,N,P,Q,R] Disp fx of lat malleolus of [rt, lt, unsp] fibula, subsq enc for [clsd fx w/ nonu, opn fx type I or II w/ nonu, opn fx type IIIA, IIIB, or IIIC w/ nonu, clsd fx w/ malu, opn fx type I or II w/ malu]

S82.6[4,5,6]X[K,M,N,P,Q,R] Nondisp fx of lat malleolus of [rt, lt, unsp] fibula, subsq enc for [clsd fx w/ nonu, opn fx type I or II w/ nonu, opn fx type IIIA, IIIB, or IIIC w/ nonu, clsd fx w/ malu, opn fx type I or II w/ malu]

S82.83[1,2,9][K,M,N,P,Q,R] Oth fx of upr and lwr end of [rt, lt, unsp] fibula, subsq enc for [clsd fx w/ nonu, opn fx type I or II w/ nonu, opn fx type IIIA, IIIB, or IIIC w/ nonu, clsd fx w/ malu, opn fx type I or II w/ malu]

S82.84[1,2,3][K,M,N,P,Q,R] Disp bimalleolar fx of [rt, lt, unsp] lwr leg, subsq enc for [clsd fx w/ nonu, opn fx type I or II w/ nonu, opn fx type IIIA, IIIB, or IIIC w/ nonu, clsd fx w/ malu, opn fx type I or II w/ malu]

S82.84[4,5,6][K,M,N,P,Q,R] Nondisp bimalleolar fx of [rt, lt, unsp] lwr leg, subsq enc for [clsd fx w/ nonu, opn fx type I or II w/ nonu, opn fx type IIIA, IIIB, or IIIC w/ nonu, clsd fx w/ malu, opn fx type I or II w/ malu]

S82.85[1,2,3][K,M,N,P,Q,R] Disp trimalleolar fx of [rt, lt, unsp] lwr leg, subsq enc for [clsd fx w/ nonu, opn fx type I or II w/ nonu, opn fx type IIIA, IIIB, or IIIC w/ nonu, clsd fx w/ malu, opn fx type I or II w/ malu]

S82.85[4,5,6][K,M,N,P,Q,R] Nondisp trimalleolar fx of [rt, lt, unsp] lwr leg, subsq enc for [clsd fx w/ nonu, opn fx type I or II w/ nonu, opn fx type IIIA, IIIB, or IIIC w/ nonu, clsd fx w/ malu, opn fx type I or II w/ malu]

S82.86[1,2,3][K,M,N,P,Q,R] Disp Maisonneuve's fx of [rt, lt, unsp] leg, subsq enc for [clsd fx w/ nonu, opn fx type I or II w/ nonu, opn fx type IIIA, IIIB, or IIIC w/ nonu, clsd fx w/ malu, opn fx type I or II w/ malu]

S82.86[4,5,6][K,M,N,P,Q,R] Nondisp Maisonneuve's fx of [rt, lt, unsp] leg, subsq enc for [clsd fx w/ nonu, opn fx type I or II w/ nonu, opn fx type IIIA, IIIB, or IIIC w/ nonu, clsd fx w/ malu, opn fx type I or II w/ malu]

S82.87[1,2,3][K,M,N,P,Q,R] Disp pilon fx of [rt, lt, unsp] tibia, subsq enc for [clsd fx w/ nonu, opn fx type I or II w/ nonu, opn fx type IIIA, IIIB, or IIIC w/ nonu, clsd fx w/ malu, opn fx type I or II w/ malu]

S82.87[4,5,6][K,M,N,P,Q,R] Nondisp pilon fx of [rt, lt, unsp] tibia, subsq enc for [clsd fx w/ nonu, opn fx type I or II w/ nonu, opn fx type IIIA, IIIB, or IIIC w/ nonu, clsd fx w/ malu, opn fx type I or II w/ malu]

S82.89[1,2,9][K,M,N,P,Q,R] Oth fx of [rt, lt, unsp] lwr leg, subsq enc for [clsd fx w/ nonu, opn fx type I or II w/ nonu, opn fx type IIIA, IIIB, or IIIC w/ nonu, clsd fx w/ malu, opn fx type I or II w/ malu]

S82.8[1,2][1,2,9][K,P] Torus fx of [upr, lwr] end of [rt, lt, unsp] fibula, subsq enc for fx w/ [nonu, malu]

S82.9[0,1,2]X[K,M,N,P,Q,R] Unsp fx of [unsp, rt, lt] lwr leg, subsq enc for [clsd fx w/ nonu, opn fx type I or II w/ nonu, opn fx type IIIA, IIIB, or IIIC w/ nonu, clsd fx w/ malu, opn fx type I or II w/ malu]

S86.02[1,2,9]A Lac of [rt, lt, unsp] Achilles tndn, init enc

Surgical   **Medical**   **CC Indicator**   **MCC Indicator**   **Procedure Proxy**   **PDxMCC PDx acts as own MCC**   **PDxCC PDx acts as own CC**

S86.[1,2,3]2[1,2,9]ALac of oth muscle(s) and tndn(s) of [post, ant, peroneal] muscle group at lwr leg lvl, [rt, lt, unsp] leg, init enc

S86.[8,9]2[1,2,9]A Lac of [oth, unsp] muscle(s) and tndn(s) at lwr leg lvl, [rt, lt, unsp] leg, init enc

S89.00[1,2,9][K,P] Unsp physeal fx of upr end of [rt, lt, unsp] tibia, subsq enc for fx w/ [nonu, malu]

S89.09[1,2,9][K,P] Oth physeal fx of upr end of [rt, lt, unsp] tibia, subsq enc for fx w/ [nonu, malu]

S89.0[1,2,3,4][1,2,9][K,P]Salter-Harris Type [I, II, III, IV] physeal fx of upr end of [rt, lt, unsp] tibia, subsq enc for fx w/ [nonu, malu]

S89.10[1,2,9][K,P] Unsp physeal fx of lwr end of [rt, lt, unsp] tibia, subsq enc for fx w/ [nonu, malu]

S89.19[1,2,9][K,P] Oth physeal fx of lwr end of [rt, lt, unsp] tibia, subsq enc for fx w/ [nonu, malu]

S89.1[1,2,3,4][1,2,9][K,P]Salter-Harris Type [I, II, III, IV] physeal fx of lwr end of [rt, lt, unsp] tibia, subsq enc for fx w/ [nonu, malu]

S89.20[1,2,9][K,P] Unsp physeal fx of upr end of [rt, lt, unsp] fibula, subsq enc for fx w/ [nonu, malu]

S89.29[1,2,9][K,P] Oth physeal fx of upr end of [rt, lt, unsp] fibula, subsq enc for fx w/ [nonu, malu]

S89.2[1,2][1,2,9][K,P]Salter-Harris Type [I, II] physeal fx of upr end of [rt, lt, unsp] fibula, subsq enc for fx w/ [nonu, malu]

S89.30[1,2,9][K,P] Unsp physeal fx of lwr end of [rt, lt, unsp] fibula, subsq enc for fx w/ [nonu, malu]

S89.39[1,2,9][K,P] Oth physeal fx of lwr end of [rt, lt, unsp] fibula, subsq enc for fx w/ [nonu, malu]

S89.3[1,2][1,2,9][K,P] Salter-Harris Type [I, II] physeal fx of lwr end of [rt, lt, unsp] fibula, subsq enc for fx w/ [nonu, malu]

S92.00[1,2,9][K,P] Unsp fx of [rt, lt, unsp] calcaneus, subsq enc for fx w/ [nonu, malu]

S92.01[1,2,3][K,P] Disp fx of body of [rt, lt, unsp] calcaneus, subsq enc for fx w/ [nonu, malu]

S92.01[4,5,6][K,P] Nondisp fx of body of [rt, lt, unsp] calcaneus, subsq enc for fx w/ [nonu, malu]

S92.02[1,2,3][K,P] Disp fx of ant process of [rt, lt, unsp] calcaneus, subsq enc for fx w/ [nonu, malu]

S92.02[4,5,6][K,P] Nondisp fx of ant process of [rt, lt, unsp] calcaneus, subsq enc for fx w/ [nonu, malu]

S92.03[1,2,3][K,P] Disp avulsion fx of tuberosity of [rt, lt, unsp] calcaneus, subsq enc for fx w/ [nonu, malu]

S92.03[4,5,6][K,P] Nondisp avulsion fx of tuberosity of [rt, lt, unsp] calcaneus, subsq enc for fx w/ [nonu, malu]

S92.04[1,2,3][K,P] Disp oth fx of tuberosity of [rt, lt, unsp] calcaneus, subsq enc for fx w/ [nonu, malu]

S92.04[4,5,6][K,P] Nondisp oth fx of tuberosity of [rt, lt, unsp] calcaneus, subsq enc for fx w/ [nonu, malu]

S92.05[1,2,3][K,P] Disp oth extraarticular fx of [rt, lt, unsp] calcaneus, subsq enc for fx w/ [nonu, malu]

S92.05[4,5,6][K,P] Nondisp oth extraarticular fx of [rt, lt, unsp] calcaneus, subsq enc for fx w/ [nonu, malu]

S92.06[1,2,3][K,P] Disp intraarticular fx of [rt, lt, unsp] calcaneus, subsq enc for fx w/ [nonu, malu]

S92.06[4,5,6][K,P] Nondisp intraarticular fx of [rt, lt, unsp] calcaneus, subsq enc for fx w/ [nonu, malu]

S92.10[1,2,9][K,P] Unsp fx of [rt, lt, unsp] talus, subsq enc for fx w/ [nonu, malu]

S92.11[1,2,3][K,P] Disp fx of neck of [rt, lt, unsp] talus, subsq enc for fx w/ [nonu, malu]

S92.11[4,5,6][K,P] Nondisp fx of neck of [rt, lt, unsp] talus, subsq enc for fx w/ [nonu, malu]

S92.12[1,2,3][K,P] Disp fx of body of [rt, lt, unsp] talus, subsq enc for fx w/ [nonu, malu]

S92.12[4,5,6][K,P] Nondisp fx of body of [rt, lt, unsp] talus, subsq enc for fx w/ [nonu, malu]

S92.13[1,2,3][K,P] Disp fx of post process of [rt, lt, unsp] talus, subsq enc for fx w/ [nonu, malu]

S92.13[4,5,6][K,P] Nondisp fx of post process of [rt, lt, unsp] talus, subsq enc for fx w/ [nonu, malu]

S92.14[1,2,3][K,P] Disp dome fx of [rt, lt, unsp] talus, subsq enc for fx w/ [nonu, malu]

S92.14[4,5,6][K,P] Nondisp dome fx of [rt, lt, unsp] talus, subsq enc for fx w/ [nonu, malu]

S92.15[1,2,3][K,P] Disp avulsion fx (chip fx) of [rt, lt, unsp] talus, subsq enc for fx w/ [nonu, malu]

S92.15[4,5,6][K,P] Nondisp avulsion fx (chip fx) of [rt, lt, unsp] talus, subsq enc for fx w/ [nonu, malu]

S92.19[1,2,9][K,P] Oth fx of [rt, lt, unsp] talus, subsq enc for fx w/ [nonu, malu]

S92.20[1,2,9][K,P] Fx of unsp tarsal bone(s) of [rt, lt, unsp] foot, subsq enc for fx w/ [nonu, malu]

S92.21[1,2,3][K,P] Disp fx of cuboid bone of [rt, lt, unsp] foot, subsq enc for fx w/ [nonu, malu]

S92.21[4,5,6][K,P] Nondisp fx of cuboid bone of [rt, lt, unsp] foot, subsq enc for fx w/ [nonu, malu]

S92.22[1,2,3][K,P] Disp fx of lat cuneiform of [rt, lt, unsp] foot, subsq enc for fx w/ [nonu, malu]

S92.22[4,5,6][K,P] Nondisp fx of lat cuneiform of [rt, lt, unsp] foot, subsq enc for fx w/ [nonu, malu]

S92.23[1,2,3][K,P] Disp fx of intermediate cuneiform of [rt, lt, unsp] foot, subsq enc for fx w/ [nonu, malu]

S92.23[4,5,6][K,P] Nondisp fx of intermediate cuneiform of [rt, lt, unsp] foot, subsq enc for fx w/ [nonu, malu]

S92.24[1,2,3][K,P] Disp fx of med cuneiform of [rt, lt, unsp] foot, subsq enc for fx w/ [nonu, malu]

S92.24[4,5,6][K,P] Nondisp fx of med cuneiform of [rt, lt, unsp] foot, subsq enc for fx w/ [nonu, malu]

S92.25[1,2,3][K,P] Disp fx of navicular (scaphoid) of [rt, lt, unsp] foot, subsq enc for fx w/ [nonu, malu]

S92.25[4,5,6][K,P] Nondisp fx of navicular (scaphoid) of [rt, lt, unsp] foot, subsq enc for fx w/ [nonu, malu]

S92.30[1,2,9][K,P] Fx of unsp metatarsal bone(s) of [rt, lt, unsp] foot, subsq enc for fx w/ [nonu, malu]

S92.31[1,2,3][K,P] Disp fx of 1st metatarsal bone, [rt, lt, unsp] foot, subsq enc for fx w/ [nonu, malu]

S92.31[4,5,6][K,P] Nondisp fx of 1st metatarsal bone, [rt, lt, unsp] foot, subsq enc for fx w/ [nonu, malu]

S92.32[1,2,3][K,P] Disp fx of 2nd metatarsal bone, [rt, lt, unsp] foot, subsq enc for fx w/ [nonu, malu]

S92.32[4,5,6][K,P] Nondisp fx of 2nd metatarsal bone, [rt, lt, unsp] foot, subsq enc for fx w/ [nonu, malu]

S92.33[1,2,3][K,P] Disp fx of 3rd metatarsal bone, [rt, lt, unsp] foot, subsq enc for fx w/ [nonu, malu]

S92.33[4,5,6][K,P] Nondisp fx of 3rd metatarsal bone, [rt, lt, unsp] foot, subsq enc for fx w/ [nonu, malu]

S92.34[1,2,3][K,P] Disp fx of 4th metatarsal bone, [rt, lt, unsp] foot, subsq enc for fx w/ [nonu, malu]

S92.34[4,5,6][K,P] Nondisp fx of 4th metatarsal bone, [rt, lt, unsp] foot, subsq enc for fx w/ [nonu, malu]

S92.35[1,2,3][K,P] Disp fx of 5th metatarsal bone, [rt, lt, unsp] foot, subsq enc for fx w/ [nonu, malu]

S92.35[4,5,6][K,P] Nondisp fx of 5th metatarsal bone, [rt, lt, unsp] foot, subsq enc for fx w/ [nonu, malu]

S92.40[1,2,3][K,P] Disp unsp fx of [rt, lt, unsp] great toe, subsq enc for fx w/ [nonu, malu]

S92.40[4,5,6][K,P] Nondisp unsp fx of [rt, lt, unsp] great toe, subsq enc for fx w/ [nonu, malu]

S92.41[1,2,3][K,P] Disp fx of proximal phalanx of [rt, lt, unsp] great toe, subsq enc for fx w/ [nonu, malu]

S92.41[4,5,6][K,P] Nondisp fx of proximal phalanx of [rt, lt, unsp] great toe, subsq enc for fx w/ [nonu, malu]

S92.42[1,2,3][K,P] Disp fx of distal phalanx of [rt, lt, unsp] great toe, subsq enc for fx w/ [nonu, malu]

S92.42[4,5,6][K,P] Nondisp fx of distal phalanx of [rt, lt, unsp] great toe, subsq enc for fx w/ [nonu, malu]

S92.49[1,2,9][K,P] Oth fx of [rt, lt, unsp] great toe, subsq enc for fx w/ [nonu, malu]

S92.50[1,2,3][K,P] Disp unsp fx of [rt, lt, unsp] lesser toe(s), subsq enc for fx w/ [nonu, malu]

S92.50[4,5,6][K,P] Nondisp unsp fx of [rt, lt, unsp] lesser toe(s), subsq enc for fx w/ [nonu, malu]

S92.51[1,2,3][K,P] Disp fx of proximal phalanx [rt, lt, unsp] lesser toe(s), subsq enc for fx w/ [nonu, malu]

S92.51[4,5,6][K,P] Nondisp fx of proximal phalanx [rt, lt, unsp] lesser toe(s), subsq enc for fx w/ [nonu, malu]

S92.52[1,2,3][K,P] Disp fx of med phalanx [rt, lt, unsp] lesser toe(s), subsq enc for fx w/ [nonu, malu]

S92.52[4,5,6][K,P] Nondisp fx of med phalanx [rt, lt, unsp] lesser toe(s), subsq enc for fx w/ [nonu, malu]

S92.53[1,2,3][K,P] Disp fx of distal phalanx [rt, lt, unsp] lesser toe(s), subsq enc for fx w/ [nonu, malu]

S92.53[4,5,6][K,P] Nondisp fx of distal phalanx [rt, lt, unsp] lesser toe(s), subsq enc for fx w/ [nonu, malu]

S92.59[1,2,9][K,P] Oth fx of [rt, lt, unsp] lesser toe(s), subsq enc for fx w/ [nonu, malu]

S92.90[1,2,9][K,P] Unsp fx of [rt, lt, unsp] foot, subsq enc for fx w/ [nonu, malu]

S92.91[1,2,9][K,P] Unsp fx of [rt, lt, unsp] toe(s), subsq enc for fx w/ [nonu, malu]

S96.[0,1]2[1,2,9]A Lac of muscle and tndn of long [flexor, extensor] muscle of toe at ankle and foot lvl, [rt, lt, unsp] foot, init enc

S96.[2,8,9]2[1,2,9]A Lac of [intrinsic, oth, unsp] muscle and tndn at ankle and foot lvl, [rt, lt, unsp] foot, init enc

T79.6XXA Traum ischemia of muscle, init enc

T87.3* Neuroma of amp stump

☐ **Transfer DRG**   SP **Special Payment**   * **Code Range**   **6th and 7th Character of ZZ = No Device, No Qualifier ZX = No Device, Diagnostic**

204   MS-DRG Version 33.0   © 2015 Optum360, LLC

T87.4*	infxn of amp stump
T87.5*	Necrosis of amp stump
T87.8*	Oth comp of amp stump
T87.9	Unsp comp of amp stump
Z52.2*	Bone donor
Z94.6	Bone transplant status
Z96.6*	Presence of orthopedic jt implants
Z96.7	Presence of other bone and tndn implants
Z97.1*	Presence of artfcl limb (complete) (partial)

DRG 565 Other Musculoskeletal System and Connective Tissue Diagnoses with CC
GMLOS 3.5   AMLOS 4.3   RW 0.9598

Select principal diagnosis listed under DRG 564

DRG 566 Other Musculoskeletal System and Connective Tissue Diagnoses without CC/MCC
GMLOS 2.5   AMLOS 3.1   RW 0.7159

Select principal diagnosis listed under DRG 564

MDC 9
Diseases And Disorders Of The Skin, Subcutaneous Tissue And Breast

SURGICAL

DRG 570　Skin Debridement with MCC
GMLOS 7.0　　　AMLOS 9.2　　　RW 2.4504　　[T]

Operating Room Procedures

ØHBØXZZ	Exc of Scalp Skin, Ext Appr
ØHB1XZZ	Exc of Face Skin, Ext Appr
ØHB4XZZ	Exc of Neck Skin, Ext Appr
ØHB5XZZ	Exc of Chest Skin, Ext Appr
ØHB6XZZ	Exc of Back Skin, Ext Appr
ØHB7XZZ	Exc of Abd Skin, Ext Appr
ØHB8XZZ	Exc of Buttock Skin, Ext Appr
ØHBAXZZ	Exc of Genitalia Skin, Ext Appr
ØHBBXZZ	Exc of Rt Upr Arm Skin, Ext Appr
ØHBCXZZ	Exc of Lt Upr Arm Skin, Ext Appr
ØHBDXZZ	Exc of Rt Lwr Arm Skin, Ext Appr
ØHBEXZZ	Exc of Lt Lwr Arm Skin, Ext Appr
ØHBFXZZ	Exc of Rt Hand Skin, Ext Appr
ØHBGXZZ	Exc of Lt Hand Skin, Ext Appr
ØHBHXZZ	Exc of Rt Upr Leg Skin, Ext Appr
ØHBJXZZ	Exc of Lt Upr Leg Skin, Ext Appr
ØHBKXZZ	Exc of Rt Lwr Leg Skin, Ext Appr
ØHBLXZZ	Exc of Lt Lwr Leg Skin, Ext Appr
ØHBMXZZ	Exc of Rt Foot Skin, Ext Appr
ØHBNXZZ	Exc of Lt Foot Skin, Ext Appr
ØJBØØZZ	Exc of Scalp SQ/Fascia, Opn Appr
ØJB1ØZZ	Exc of Face SQ/Fascia, Opn Appr
ØJB4ØZZ	Exc of Ant Neck SQ/Fascia, Opn Appr
ØJB5ØZZ	Exc of Post Neck SQ/Fascia, Opn Appr
ØJB6ØZZ	Exc of Chest SQ/Fascia, Opn Appr
ØJB7ØZZ	Exc of Back SQ/Fascia, Opn Appr
ØJB8ØZZ	Exc of Abd SQ/Fascia, Opn Appr
ØJB9ØZZ	Exc of Buttock SQ/Fascia, Opn Appr
ØJBBØZZ	Exc of Perineum SQ/Fascia, Opn Appr
ØJBCØZZ	Exc of Pelvic SQ/Fascia, Opn Appr
ØJBDØZZ	Exc of Rt Up Arm SQ/Fascia, Opn Appr
ØJBFØZZ	Exc of Lt Up Arm SQ/Fascia, Opn Appr
ØJBGØZZ	Exc of Rt Low Arm SQ/Fascia, Opn Appr
ØJBHØZZ	Exc of Lt Low Arm SQ/Fascia, Opn Appr
ØJBLØZZ	Exc of Rt Up Leg SQ/Fascia, Opn Appr
ØJBMØZZ	Exc of Lt Up Leg SQ/Fascia, Opn Appr
ØJBNØZZ	Exc of Rt Low Leg SQ/Fascia, Opn Appr
ØJBPØZZ	Exc of Lt Low Leg SQ/Fascia, Opn Appr
ØJBQØZZ	Exc of Rt Foot SQ/Fascia, Opn Appr
ØJBRØZZ	Exc of Lt Foot SQ/Fascia, Opn Appr

DRG 571　Skin Debridement with CC
GMLOS 5.2　　　AMLOS 6.3　　　RW 1.4569　　[T]

Select operating room procedures listed under DRG 570

DRG 572　Skin Debridement without CC/MCC
GMLOS 3.7　　　AMLOS 4.5　　　RW 1.0391　　[T]

Select operating room procedures listed under DRG 570

DRG 573　Skin Graft for Skin Ulcer or Cellulitis with MCC
GMLOS 8.6　　　AMLOS 12.9　　　RW 3.9130　　[T]

Principal Diagnosis

LØ2.Ø1	Cutaneous abscess of face
LØ2.11	Cutaneous abscess of neck
LØ2.21[1,2,3,4,5,6,9]	Cutaneous abscess of [abd wall, back (any part, except buttock), chest wall, groin, perineum, umbilicus, trunk unsp]
LØ2.31	Cutaneous abscess of buttock
LØ2.41[1,2]	Cutaneous abscess of [rt, lt] axilla
LØ2.41[3,4,5,6,9]	Cutaneous abscess of [rt upr, lt upr, rt lwr, lt lwr, unsp] limb
LØ2.51[1,2,9]	Cutaneous abscess of [rt, lt, unsp] hand
LØ2.61[1,2,9]	Cutaneous abscess of [rt, lt, unsp] foot
LØ2.811	Cutaneous abscess of head [any part, except face]
LØ2.818	Cutaneous abscess of oth sites
LØ2.91	Cutaneous abscess, unsp
LØ3*	Cellulitis and acute lymphangitis
L89*	Pressure ulcer
L97*	Non-pressure chr ulcer of lwr limb, NEC
L98.3	Eosinophilic cellulitis [Wells]
L98.4*	Non-pressure chr ulcer of skin, NEC

AND

Operating Room Procedures

ØH8[Ø,1,4,5,6,7,8,A]XZZDiv	[Scalp, Face, Neck, Chest, Back, Abd, Buttock, Genitalia] Skin, Ext
ØH8[B,C,D,E,F,G]XZZDiv	of Skin of [Rt Upr Arm, Lt Upr Arm, Rt Lwr Arm, Lt Lwr Arm, Rt Hand, Lt Hand], Ext
ØH8[H,J,K,L,M,N]XZZDiv	[Rt Upr Leg, Lt Upr Leg, Rt Lwr Leg, Lt Lwr Leg, Rt Foot, Lt Foot], Ext
ØHRØ*	Replace/Skin, Scalp
ØHR1*	Replace/Skin, Face
ØHR4*	Replace/Skin, Neck
ØHR5*	Replace/Skin, Chest
ØHR6*	Replace/Skin, Back
ØHR7*	Replace/Skin, Abd
ØHR8*	Replace/Skin, Buttock
ØHRA*	Replace/Skin, Genitalia
ØHRB*	Replace/Skin, Rt Upr Arm
ØHRC*	Replace/Skin, Lt Upr Arm
ØHRD*	Replace/Skin, Rt Lwr Arm
ØHRE*	Replace/Skin, Lt Lwr Arm
ØHRF*	Replace/Skin, Rt Hand
ØHRG*	Replace/Skin, Lt Hand
ØHRH*	Replace/Skin, Rt Upr Leg
ØHRJ*	Replace/Skin, Lt Upr Leg
ØHRK*	Replace/Skin, Rt Lwr Leg
ØHRL*	Replace/Skin, Lt Lwr Leg
ØHRM*	Replace/Skin, Rt Foot
ØHRN*	Replace/Skin, Lt Foot
ØHRTX[7,K]Z	Replace/Breast, Rt, Ext, [Auto Tissue Sub, Nonauto Tissue Sub], NQ
ØHRUX[7,K]Z	Replace/Breast, Lt, Ext, [Auto Tissue Sub, Nonauto Tissue Sub], NQ
ØHRVX[7,K]Z	Replace/Breast, Bilat, Ext, [Auto Tissue Sub, Nonauto Tissue Sub], NQ
ØHX[Ø,1,4,5,6,7,8,9,A]XZZ Transfer	[Scalp, Face, Neck, Chest, Back, Abd, Perineum, Genitalia] Skin, Ext
ØHX[B,C,D,E,F,G]XZZ Transfer	[Rt Upr Arm, Lt Upr Arm, Rt Lwr Arm, Lt Lwr Arm, Rt Hand, Lt Hand], Ext
ØHX[H,J,K,L,M,N]XZZ Transfer	[Rt Upr Leg, Lt Upr Leg, Rt Lwr Leg, Lt Lwr Leg, Rt Foot, Lt Foot], Ext
ØJHØ*	Insert/SQ Tissue & Fascia, Scalp
ØJH1*	Insert/SQ Tissue & Fascia, Face
ØJH4*	Insert/SQ Tissue & Fascia, Ant Neck
ØJH5*	Insert/SQ Tissue & Fascia, Posterior Neck
ØJH6[Ø,3]NZ	Insert/SQ Tissue & Fascia, Chest, [Opn, Perc], Tissue Expander, NQ
ØJH7[Ø,3]NZ	Insert/SQ Tissue & Fascia, Back, [Opn, Perc], Tissue Expander, NQ
ØJH8[Ø,3]NZ	Insert/SQ Tissue & Fascia, Abd, [Opn, Perc], Tissue Expander, NQ
ØJH9*	Insert/SQ Tissue & Fascia, Buttock
ØJHB*	Insert/SQ Tissue & Fascia, Perineum
ØJHC*	Insert/SQ Tissue & Fascia, Pelvic Region
ØJHD[Ø,3]NZ	Insert/SQ Tissue & Fascia, Rt Upr Arm, [Opn, Perc], Tissue Expander, NQ
ØJHF[Ø,3]NZ	Insert/SQ Tissue & Fascia, Lt Upr Arm, [Opn, Perc], Tissue Expander, NQ
ØJHG[Ø,3]NZ	Insert/SQ Tissue & Fascia, Rt Lwr Arm, [Opn, Perc], Tissue Expander, NQ
ØJHH[Ø,3]NZ	Insert/SQ Tissue & Fascia, Lt Lwr Arm, [Opn, Perc], Tissue Expander, NQ
ØJHJ*	Insert/SQ Tissue & Fascia, Rt Hand

[T] Transfer DRG　　　[SP] Special Payment　　　* Code Range　　　6th and 7th Character of ZZ = No Device, No Qualifier ZX = No Device, Diagnostic

MS-DRG Version 33.0

ØJHK*	Insert/SQ Tissue & Fascia, Lt Hand
ØJHL[Ø,3]NZ	Insert/SQ Tissue & Fascia, Rt Upr Leg, [Opn, Perc], Tissue Expander, NQ
ØJHM[Ø,3]NZ	Insert/SQ Tissue & Fascia, Lt Upr Leg, [Opn, Perc], Tissue Expander, NQ
ØJHN[Ø,3]NZ	Insert/SQ Tissue & Fascia, Rt Lwr Leg, [Opn, Perc], Tissue Expander, NQ
ØJHP[Ø,3]NZ	Insert/SQ Tissue & Fascia, Lt Lwr Leg, [Opn, Perc], Tissue Expander, NQ
ØJHQ*	Insert/SQ Tissue & Fascia, Rt Foot
ØJHR*	Insert/SQ Tissue & Fascia, Lt Foot
ØJX0[Ø,3]Z[B,C]	Transfer/SQ Tissue & Fascia, Scalp, [Opn, Perc], No Dev, [Skin and SQ Tissue, Skin, SQ Tissue & Fascia]
ØJX1[Ø,3]Z[B,C]	Transfer/SQ Tissue & Fascia, Face, [Opn, Perc], No Dev, [Skin and SQ Tissue, Skin, SQ Tissue & Fascia]
ØJX4[Ø,3]Z[B,C]	Transfer/SQ Tissue & Fascia, Ant Neck, [Opn, Perc], No Dev, [Skin and SQ Tissue, Skin, SQ Tissue & Fascia]
ØJX5[Ø,3]Z[B,C]	Transfer/SQ Tissue & Fascia, Post Neck, [Opn, Perc], No Dev, [Skin and SQ Tissue, Skin, SQ Tissue & Fascia]
ØJX6[Ø,3]Z[B,C]	Transfer/SQ Tissue & Fascia, Chest, [Opn, Perc], No Dev, [Skin and SQ Tissue, Skin, SQ Tissue & Fascia]
ØJX7[Ø,3]Z[B,C]	Transfer/SQ Tissue & Fascia, Back, [Opn, Perc], No Dev, [Skin and SQ Tissue, Skin, SQ Tissue & Fascia]
ØJX8[Ø,3]Z[B,C]	Transfer/SQ Tissue & Fascia, Abd, [Opn, Perc], No Dev, [Skin and SQ Tissue, Skin, SQ Tissue & Fascia]
ØJX9[Ø,3]Z[B,C]	Transfer/SQ Tissue & Fascia, Buttock, [Opn, Perc], No Dev, [Skin and SQ Tissue, Skin, SQ Tissue & Fascia]
ØJXB[Ø,3]Z[B,C]	Transfer/SQ Tissue & Fascia, Perineum, [Opn, Perc], No Dev, [Skin and SQ Tissue, Skin, SQ Tissue & Fascia]
ØJXC[Ø,3]Z[B,C]	Transfer/SQ Tissue & Fascia, Genitalia, [Opn, Perc], No Dev, [Skin and SQ Tissue, Skin, SQ Tissue & Fascia]
ØJXD[Ø,3]Z[B,C]	Transfer/SQ Tissue & Fascia, Rt Upr Arm, [Opn, Perc], No Dev, [Skin and SQ Tissue, Skin, SQ Tissue & Fascia]
ØJXF[Ø,3]Z[B,C]	Transfer/SQ Tissue & Fascia, Lt Upr Arm, [Opn, Perc], No Dev, [Skin and SQ Tissue, Skin, SQ Tissue & Fascia]
ØJXG[Ø,3]Z[B,C]	Transfer/SQ Tissue & Fascia, Rt Lwr Arm, [Opn, Perc], No Dev, [Skin and SQ Tissue, Skin, SQ Tissue & Fascia]
ØJXH[Ø,3]Z[B,C]	Transfer/SQ Tissue & Fascia, Lt Lwr Arm, [Opn, Perc], No Dev, [Skin and SQ Tissue, Skin, SQ Tissue & Fascia]
ØJXJ[Ø,3]Z[B,C]	Transfer/SQ Tissue & Fascia, Rt Hand, [Opn, Perc], No Dev, [Skin and SQ Tissue, Skin, SQ Tissue & Fascia]
ØJXK[Ø,3]Z[B,C]	Transfer/SQ Tissue & Fascia, Lt Hand, [Opn, Perc], No Dev, [Skin and SQ Tissue, Skin, SQ Tissue & Fascia]
ØJXL[Ø,3]Z[B,C]	Transfer/SQ Tissue & Fascia, Rt Upr Leg, [Opn, Perc], No Dev, [Skin and SQ Tissue, Skin, SQ Tissue & Fascia]
ØJXM[Ø,3]Z[B,C]	Transfer/SQ Tissue & Fascia, Lt Upr Leg, [Opn, Perc], No Dev, [Skin and SQ Tissue, Skin, SQ Tissue & Fascia]
ØJXN[Ø,3]Z[B,C]	Transfer/SQ Tissue & Fascia, Rt Lwr Leg, [Opn, Perc], No Dev, [Skin and SQ Tissue, Skin, SQ Tissue & Fascia]
ØJXP[Ø,3]Z[B,C]	Transfer/SQ Tissue & Fascia, Lt Lwr Leg, [Opn, Perc], No Dev, [Skin and SQ Tissue, Skin, SQ Tissue & Fascia]
ØJXQ[Ø,3]Z[B,C]	Transfer/SQ Tissue & Fascia, Rt Foot, [Opn, Perc], No Dev, [Skin and SQ Tissue, Skin, SQ Tissue & Fascia]
ØJXR[Ø,3]Z[B,C]	Transfer/SQ Tissue & Fascia, Lt Foot, [Opn, Perc], No Dev, [Skin and SQ Tissue, Skin, SQ Tissue & Fascia]
ØKXH[Ø,4]ZZ	Transfer/Thorax Muscle, Rt, [Opn, Perc Endo]
ØKXJ[Ø,4]ZZ	Transfer/Thorax Muscle, Lt, [Opn, Perc Endo]
ØWB0[Ø,3,4,X]ZZ	Exc/Head, [Opn, Perc, Perc Endo, Ext]
ØWB2[Ø,3,4,X]ZZ	Exc/Face, [Opn, Perc, Perc Endo, Ext]
ØWB4[Ø,3,4,X]ZZ	Exc/Upr Jaw, [Opn, Perc, Perc Endo, Ext]
ØWB5[Ø,3,4,X]ZZ	Exc/Lwr Jaw, [Opn, Perc, Perc Endo, Ext]
ØWB6[Ø,3,4,X]ZZ	Exc/Neck, [Opn, Perc, Perc Endo, Ext]
ØWBK[Ø,3,4,X]ZZ	Exc/Upr Back, [Opn, Perc, Perc Endo, Ext]
ØWBL[Ø,3,4,X]ZZ	Exc/Lwr Back, [Opn, Perc, Perc Endo, Ext]
ØWBM[Ø,3,4,X]ZZ	Exc/Perineum, Male, [Opn, Perc, Perc Endo, Ext]
ØXB2[Ø,3,4]ZZ	Exc/Shldr Rgn, Rt, [Opn, Perc, Perc Endo]
ØXB3[Ø,3,4]ZZ	Exc/Shldr Rgn, Lt, [Opn, Perc, Perc Endo]
ØXB4[Ø,3,4]ZZ	Exc/Axilla, Rt, [Opn, Perc, Perc Endo]
ØXB5[Ø,3,4]ZZ	Exc/Axilla, Lt, [Opn, Perc, Perc Endo]
ØXB6[Ø,3,4]ZZ	Exc/Upr Extr, Rt, [Opn, Perc, Perc Endo]
ØXB7[Ø,3,4]ZZ	Exc/Upr Extr, Lt, [Opn, Perc, Perc Endo]
ØXB8[Ø,3,4]ZZ	Exc/Upr Arm, Rt, [Opn, Perc, Perc Endo]
ØXB9[Ø,3,4]ZZ	Exc/Upr Arm, Lt, [Opn, Perc, Perc Endo]
ØXBB[Ø,3,4]ZZ	Exc/Elbow Rgn, Rt, [Opn, Perc, Perc Endo]
ØXBC[Ø,3,4]ZZ	Exc/Elbow Rgn, Lt, [Opn, Perc, Perc Endo]
ØXBD[Ø,3,4]ZZ	Exc/Lwr Arm, Rt, [Opn, Perc, Perc Endo]
ØXBF[Ø,3,4]ZZ	Exc/Lwr Arm, Lt, [Opn, Perc, Perc Endo]
ØXBG[Ø,3,4]ZZ	Exc/Wrist Rgn, Rt, [Opn, Perc, Perc Endo]
ØXBH[Ø,3,4]ZZ	Exc/Wrist Rgn, Lt, [Opn, Perc, Perc Endo]
ØXBJ[Ø,3,4]ZZ	Exc/Hand, Rt, [Opn, Perc, Perc Endo]

ØXBK[Ø,3,4]ZZ	Exc/Hand, Lt, [Opn, Perc, Perc Endo]
ØXUJ[Ø,4]7Z	Supl/Hand, Rt, [Opn, Perc Endo], Auto Tissue Sub, NQ
ØXUK[Ø,4]7Z	Supl/Hand, Lt, [Opn, Perc Endo], Auto Tissue Sub, NQ
ØXUL[Ø,4]7Z	Supl/Thumb, Rt, [Opn, Perc Endo], Auto Tissue Sub, NQ
ØXUM[Ø,4]7Z	Supl/Thumb, Lt, [Opn, Perc Endo], Auto Tissue Sub, NQ
ØXUN[Ø,4]7Z	Supl/Index Finger, Rt, [Opn, Perc Endo], Auto Tissue Sub, NQ
ØXUP[Ø,4]7Z	Supl/Index Finger, Lt, [Opn, Perc Endo], Auto Tissue Sub, NQ
ØXUQ[Ø,4]7Z	Supl/Mid Finger, Rt, [Opn, Perc Endo], Auto Tissue Sub, NQ
ØXUR[Ø,4]7Z	Supl/Mid Finger, Lt, [Opn, Perc Endo], Auto Tissue Sub, NQ
ØXUS[Ø,4]7Z	Supl/Ring Finger, Rt, [Opn, Perc Endo], Auto Tissue Sub, NQ
ØXUT[Ø,4]7Z	Supl/Ring Finger, Lt, [Opn, Perc Endo], Auto Tissue Sub, NQ
ØXUV[Ø,4]7Z	Supl/Little Finger, Rt, [Opn, Perc Endo], Auto Tissue Sub, NQ
ØXUW[Ø,4]7Z	Supl/Little Finger, Lt, [Opn, Perc Endo], Auto Tissue Sub, NQ
ØYB0[Ø,3,4]ZZ	Exc/Buttock, Rt, [Opn, Perc, Perc Endo]
ØYB1[Ø,3,4]ZZ	Exc/Buttock, Lt, [Opn, Perc, Perc Endo]
ØYB9[Ø,3,4]ZZ	Exc/Lwr Extr, Rt, [Opn, Perc, Perc Endo]
ØYBB[Ø,3,4]ZZ	Exc/Lwr Extr, Lt, [Opn, Perc, Perc Endo]
ØYBC[Ø,3,4]ZZ	Exc/Upr Leg, Rt, [Opn, Perc, Perc Endo]
ØYBD[Ø,3,4]ZZ	Exc/Upr Leg, Lt, [Opn, Perc, Perc Endo]
ØYBF[Ø,3,4]ZZ	Exc/Knee Rgn, Rt, [Opn, Perc, Perc Endo]
ØYBG[Ø,3,4]ZZ	Exc/Knee Rgn, Lt, [Opn, Perc, Perc Endo]
ØYBH[Ø,3,4]ZZ	Exc/Lwr Leg, Rt, [Opn, Perc, Perc Endo]
ØYBJ[Ø,3,4]ZZ	Exc/Lwr Leg, Lt, [Opn, Perc, Perc Endo]
ØYBK[Ø,3,4]ZZ	Exc/Ankle Rgn, Rt, [Opn, Perc, Perc Endo]
ØYBL[Ø,3,4]ZZ	Exc/Ankle Rgn, Lt, [Opn, Perc, Perc Endo]
ØYBM[Ø,3,4]ZZ	Exc/Foot, Rt, [Opn, Perc, Perc Endo]
ØYBN[Ø,3,4]ZZ	Exc/Foot, Lt, [Opn, Perc, Perc Endo]

DRG 574   Skin Graft for Skin Ulcer or Cellulitis with CC
GMLOS 7.4   AMLOS 9.5   RW 2.8430   T

Select principal diagnosis AND operating room procedures listed under DRG 573

DRG 575   Skin Graft for Skin Ulcer or Cellulitis without CC/MCC
GMLOS 4.4   AMLOS 5.6   RW 1.6141   T

Select principal diagnosis AND operating room procedures listed under DRG 573

DRG 576   Skin Graft Except for Skin Ulcer or Cellulitis with MCC
GMLOS 8.9   AMLOS 13.6   RW 5.3493

Select only operating room procedures listed under DRG 573

DRG 577   Skin Graft Except for Skin Ulcer or Cellulitis with CC
GMLOS 4.4   AMLOS 6.4   RW 2.2579

Select only operating room procedures listed under DRG 573

DRG 578   Skin Graft Except for Skin Ulcer or Cellulitis without CC/MCC
GMLOS 2.6   AMLOS 3.7   RW 1.3812

Select only operating room procedures listed under DRG 573

DRG 579   Other Skin, Subcutaneous Tissue and Breast Procedures with MCC
GMLOS 7.Ø   AMLOS 9.1   RW 2.6848   T

Operating Room Procedures

Ø315Ø[9,A,J,K,Z]Ø	Bypass/Axillary Artery, Rt, Opn, [Auto Venous Tissue, Auto Arterial Tissue, Synth Sub, Nonauto Tissue Sub, No Dev], Upr Arm Artery, Rt
Ø316Ø[9,A,J,K,Z]1	Bypass/Axillary Artery, Lt, Opn, [Auto Venous Tissue, Auto Arterial Tissue, Synth Sub, Nonauto Tissue Sub, No Dev], Upr Arm Artery, Lt
Ø31HØ[9,A,J,K,Z]J	Bypass/Common Carotid Artery, Rt, Opn, [Auto Venous Tissue, Auto Arterial Tissue, Synth Sub, Nonauto Tissue Sub, No Dev], Extracranial Artery, Rt
Ø31JØ[9,A,J,K,Z]K	Bypass/Common Carotid Artery, Lt, Opn, [Auto Venous Tissue, Auto Arterial Tissue, Synth Sub, Nonauto Tissue Sub, No Dev], Extracranial Artery, Lt
Ø31KØ[9,A,J,K,Z]J	Bypass/Int Carotid Artery, Rt, Opn, [Auto Venous Tissue, Auto Arterial Tissue, Synth Sub, Nonauto Tissue Sub, No Dev], Extracranial Artery, Rt
Ø31LØ[9,A,J,K,Z]K	Bypass/Int Carotid Artery, Lt, Opn, [Auto Venous Tissue, Auto Arterial Tissue, Synth Sub, Nonauto Tissue Sub, No Dev], Extracranial Artery, Lt

---

Surgical   **Medical**   **CC Indicator**   **MCC Indicator**   **Procedure Proxy**   PDxMCC **PDx acts as own MCC**   PDxCC **PDx acts as own CC**

Ø31MØ[9,A,J,K,Z]J Bypass/Ext Carotid Artery, Rt, Opn, [Auto Venous Tissue, Arterial Tissue, Synth Sub, Nonauto Tissue Sub, No Dev], Extracranial Artery, Rt

Ø31NØ[9,A,J,K,Z]K Bypass/Ext Carotid Artery, Lt, Opn, [Auto Venous Tissue, Auto Arterial Tissue, Synth Sub, Nonauto Tissue Sub, No Dev], Extracranial Artery, Lt

Ø3733[4,D,Z]Z Dilation/Subclavian Artery, Rt, Perc, [Drug-eluting Intralum Dev, Intralum Dev, No Dev], NQ

Ø3743[4,D,Z]Z Dilation/Subclavian Artery, Lt, Perc, [Drug-eluting Intralum Dev, Intralum Dev, No Dev], NQ

Ø3773[4,D,Z]Z Dilation/Brachial Artery, Rt, Perc, [Drug-eluting Intralum Dev, Intralum Dev, No Dev], NQ

Ø3783[4,D,Z]Z Dilation/Brachial Artery, Lt, Perc, [Drug-eluting Intralum Dev, Intralum Dev, No Dev], NQ

Ø3793[4,D,Z]Z Dilation/Ulnar Artery, Rt, Perc, [Drug-eluting Intralum Dev, Intralum Dev, No Dev], NQ

Ø37A3[4,D,Z]Z Dilation/Ulnar Artery, Lt, Perc, [Drug-eluting Intralum Dev, Intralum Dev, No Dev], NQ

Ø37Y3[4,D,Z]Z Dilation/Upr Artery, Perc, [Drug-eluting Intralum Dev, Intralum Dev, No Dev], NQ

Ø3Q5[Ø,3,4]ZZ Rpr/Axillary Artery, Rt, [Opn, Perc, Perc Endo]
Ø3Q6[Ø,3,4]ZZ Rpr/Axillary Artery, Lt, [Opn, Perc, Perc Endo]
Ø3Q7[Ø,3,4]ZZ Rpr/Brachial Artery, Rt, [Opn, Perc, Perc Endo]
Ø3Q8[Ø,3,4]ZZ Rpr/Brachial Artery, Lt, [Opn, Perc, Perc Endo]
Ø3Q9[Ø,3,4]ZZ Rpr/Ulnar Artery, Rt, [Opn, Perc, Perc Endo]
Ø3QA[Ø,3,4]ZZ Rpr/Ulnar Artery, Lt, [Opn, Perc, Perc Endo]
Ø3QB[Ø,3,4]ZZ Rpr/Radial Artery, Rt, [Opn, Perc, Perc Endo]
Ø3QC[Ø,3,4]ZZ Rpr/Radial Artery, Lt, [Opn, Perc, Perc Endo]
Ø3QD[Ø,3,4]ZZ Rpr/Hand Artery, Rt, [Opn, Perc, Perc Endo]
Ø3QF[Ø,3,4]ZZ Rpr/Hand Artery, Lt, [Opn, Perc, Perc Endo]
Ø3S5[Ø,3,4]ZZ Repos/Axillary Artery, Rt, [Opn, Perc, Perc Endo]
Ø3S6[Ø,3,4]ZZ Repos/Axillary Artery, Lt, [Opn, Perc, Perc Endo]
Ø3S7[Ø,3,4]ZZ Repos/Brachial Artery, Rt, [Opn, Perc, Perc Endo]
Ø3S8[Ø,3,4]ZZ Repos/Brachial Artery, Lt, [Opn, Perc, Perc Endo]
Ø3S9[Ø,3,4]ZZ Repos/Ulnar Artery, Rt, [Opn, Perc, Perc Endo]
Ø3SA[Ø,3,4]ZZ Repos/Ulnar Artery, Lt, [Opn, Perc, Perc Endo]
Ø3SB[Ø,3,4]ZZ Repos/Radial Artery, Rt, [Opn, Perc, Perc Endo]
Ø3SC[Ø,3,4]ZZ Repos/Radial Artery, Lt, [Opn, Perc, Perc Endo]
Ø3SD[Ø,3,4]ZZ Repos/Hand Artery, Rt, [Opn, Perc, Perc Endo]
Ø3SF[Ø,3,4]ZZ Repos/Hand Artery, Lt, [Opn, Perc, Perc Endo]

Ø41Ø[Ø,4][9,A,J,K,Z][6,7,8,9,B,C,D,F,G,H,J,K,Q,R] Bypass/Abd Aorta, [Opn, Perc Endo], [Auto Venous Tissue, Auto Arterial Tissue, Synth Sub, Nonauto Tissue Sub, No Dev], [Common Iliac Artery, Rt, Common Iliac Artery, Lt, Common Iliac Arteries, Bilat, Int Iliac Artery, Rt, Int Iliac Artery, Lt, Int Iliac Arteries, Bilat, Ext Iliac Artery, Rt, Ext Iliac Artery, Lt, Ext Iliac Arteries, Bilat, Femor Artery, Rt, Femor Artery, Lt, Femor Arteries, Bilat, Lwr Extr Artery, Lwr Artery]

Ø41C[Ø,4][9,A,J,K,Z][H,J,K] Bypass/Common Iliac Artery, Rt, [Opn, Perc Endo], [Auto Venous Tissue, Auto Arterial Tissue, Synth Sub, Nonauto Tissue Sub, No Dev], [Femor Artery, Rt, Femor Artery, Lt, Femor Arteries, Bilat]

Ø41D[Ø,4][9,A,J,K,Z][H,J,K] Bypass/Common Iliac Artery, Lt, [Opn, Perc Endo], [Auto Venous Tissue, Auto Arterial Tissue, Synth Sub, Nonauto Tissue Sub, No Dev], [Femor Artery, Rt, Femor Artery, Lt, Femor Arteries, Bilat]

Ø41E[Ø,4][9,A,J,K,Z][H,J,K] Bypass/Int Iliac Artery, Rt, [Opn, Perc Endo], [Auto Venous Tissue, Auto Arterial Tissue, Synth Sub, Nonauto Tissue Sub, No Dev], [Femor Artery, Rt, Femor Artery, Lt, Femor Arteries, Bilat]

Ø41F[Ø,4][9,A,J,K,Z][H,J,K] Bypass/Int Iliac Artery, Lt, [Opn, Perc Endo], [Auto Venous Tissue, Auto Arterial Tissue, Synth Sub, Nonauto Tissue Sub, No Dev], [Femor Artery, Rt, Femor Artery, Lt, Femor Arteries, Bilat]

Ø41H[Ø,4][9,A,J,K,Z][H,J,K] Bypass/Ext Iliac Artery, Rt, [Opn, Perc Endo], [Auto Venous Tissue, Auto Arterial Tissue, Synth Sub, Nonauto Tissue Sub, No Dev], [Femor Artery, Rt, Femor Artery, Lt, Femor Arteries, Bilat]

Ø41J[Ø,4][9,A,J,K,Z][H,J,K] Bypass/Ext Iliac Artery, Lt, [Opn, Perc Endo], [Auto Venous Tissue, Auto Arterial Tissue, Synth Sub, Nonauto Tissue Sub, No Dev], [Femor Artery, Rt, Femor Artery, Lt, Femor Arteries, Bilat]

Ø41K[Ø,4][9,A,J,K,Z][H,J,K,L] Bypass/Femor Artery, Rt, [Opn, Perc Endo], [Auto Venous Tissue, Auto Arterial Tissue, Synth Sub, Nonauto Tissue Sub, No Dev], [Femor Artery, Rt, Femor Artery, Lt, Femor Arteries, Bilat, Popliteal Artery]

Ø41L[Ø,4][9,A,J,K,Z][H,J,K,L] Bypass/Femor Artery, Lt, [Opn, Perc Endo], [Auto Venous Tissue, Auto Arterial Tissue, Synth Sub, Nonauto Tissue Sub, No Dev], [Femor Artery, Rt, Femor Artery, Lt, Femor Arteries, Bilat, Popliteal Artery]

Ø47Ø3[4,D,Z]Z Dilation/Abd Aorta, Perc, [Drug-eluting Intralum Dev, Intralum Dev, No Dev], NQ

Ø4713[4,D,Z]Z Dilation/Celiac Artery, Perc, [Drug-eluting Intralum Dev, Intralum Dev, No Dev], NQ

Ø4723[4,D,Z]Z Dilation/Gastric Artery, Perc, [Drug-eluting Intralum Dev, Intralum Dev, No Dev], NQ

Ø4733[4,D,Z]Z Dilation/Hepatic Artery, Perc, [Drug-eluting Intralum Dev, Intralum Dev, No Dev], NQ

Ø4743[4,D,Z]Z Dilation/Splenic Artery, Perc, [Drug-eluting Intralum Dev, Intralum Dev, No Dev], NQ

Ø4753[4,D,Z]Z Dilation/Superior Mesenteric Artery, Perc, [Drug-eluting Intralum Dev, Intralum Dev, No Dev], NQ

Ø4763[4,D,Z]Z Dilation/Colic Artery, Rt, Perc, [Drug-eluting Intralum Dev, Intralum Dev, No Dev], NQ

Ø4773[4,D,Z]Z Dilation/Colic Artery, Lt, Perc, [Drug-eluting Intralum Dev, Intralum Dev, No Dev], NQ

Ø4783[4,D,Z]Z Dilation/Colic Artery, Mid, Perc, [Drug-eluting Intralum Dev, Intralum Dev, No Dev], NQ

Ø4793[4,D,Z]Z Dilation/Renal Artery, Rt, Perc, [Drug-eluting Intralum Dev, Intralum Dev, No Dev], NQ

Ø47A3[4,D,Z]Z Dilation/Renal Artery, Lt, Perc, [Drug-eluting Intralum Dev, Intralum Dev, No Dev], NQ

Ø47B3[4,D,Z]Z Dilation/Inferior Mesenteric Artery, Perc, [Drug-eluting Intralum Dev, Intralum Dev, No Dev], NQ

Ø47C3[4,D,Z]Z Dilation/Common Iliac Artery, Rt, Perc, [Drug-eluting Intralum Dev, Intralum Dev, No Dev], NQ

Ø47D3[4,D,Z]Z Dilation/Common Iliac Artery, Lt, Perc, [Drug-eluting Intralum Dev, Intralum Dev, No Dev], NQ

Ø47E3[4,D,Z]Z Dilation/Int Iliac Artery, Rt, Perc, [Drug-eluting Intralum Dev, Intralum Dev, No Dev], NQ

Ø47F3[4,D,Z]Z Dilation/Int Iliac Artery, Lt, Perc, [Drug-eluting Intralum Dev, Intralum Dev, No Dev], NQ

Ø47H3[4,D,Z]Z Dilation/Ext Iliac Artery, Rt, Perc, [Drug-eluting Intralum Dev, Intralum Dev, No Dev], NQ

Ø47J3[4,D,Z]Z Dilation/Ext Iliac Artery, Lt, Perc, [Drug-eluting Intralum Dev, Intralum Dev, No Dev], NQ

Ø47KØ41 Dilation Rt Fem Art w Drug-elut Intralum, Drug Blln, Opn
Ø47KØD1 Dilation Rt Fem Art w Intralum Dev, Drug Blln, Opn
Ø47KØZ1 Dilation of Rt Fem Art using Drug Blln, Opn Appr
Ø47K341 Dilation Rt Fem Art w Drug-elut Intralum, Drug Blln, Perc
Ø47K3D1 Dilation Rt Fem Art w Intralum Dev, Drug Blln, Perc
Ø47K3Z1 Dilation of Rt Fem Art using Drug Blln, Perc Appr
Ø47K3[4,D,Z]Z Dilation/Femor Artery, Rt, Perc, [Drug-eluting Intralum Dev, Intralum Dev, No Dev], NQ
Ø47K441 Dilation Rt Fem Art w Drug-elut Intralum, Drug Blln, Perc Endo
Ø47K4D1 Dilation Rt Fem Art w Intralum Dev, Drug Blln, Perc Endo
Ø47K4Z1 Dilation of Rt Fem Art using Drug Blln, Perc Endo Appr
Ø47LØ41 Dilation Lt Fem Art w Drug-elut Intralum, Drug Blln, Opn
Ø47LØD1 Dilation Lt Fem Art w Intralum Dev, Drug Blln, Opn
Ø47LØZ1 Dilation of Lt Fem Art using Drug Blln, Opn Appr
Ø47L341 Dilation Lt Fem Art w Drug-elut Intralum, Drug Blln, Perc
Ø47L3D1 Dilation Lt Fem Art w Intralum Dev, Drug Blln, Perc
Ø47L3Z1 Dilation of Lt Fem Art using Drug Blln, Perc Appr
Ø47L3[4,D,Z]Z Dilation/Femor Artery, Lt, Perc, [Drug-eluting Intralum Dev, Intralum Dev, No Dev], NQ
Ø47L441 Dilation Lt Fem Art w Drug-elut Intralum, Drug Blln, Perc Endo
Ø47L4D1 Dilation Lt Fem Art w Intralum Dev, Drug Blln, Perc Endo
Ø47L4Z1 Dilation of Lt Fem Art using Drug Blln, Perc Endo Appr
Ø47MØ41 Dilation Rt Popl Art w Drug-elut Intralum, Drug Blln, Opn
Ø47MØD1 Dilation Rt Popl Art w Intralum Dev, Drug Blln, Opn
Ø47MØZ1 Dilation of Rt Popl Art using Drug Blln, Opn Appr
Ø47M341 Dilation Rt Popl Art w Drug-elut Intralum, Drug Blln, Perc
Ø47M3D1 Dilation Rt Popl Art w Intralum Dev, Drug Blln, Perc
Ø47M3Z1 Dilation of Rt Popl Art using Drug Blln, Perc Appr
Ø47M441 Dilation Rt Popl Art w Drug-elut Intralum, Drug Blln, Perc Endo
Ø47M4D1 Dilation Rt Popl Art w Intralum Dev, Drug Blln, Perc Endo
Ø47M4Z1 Dilation of Rt Popl Art using Drug Blln, Perc Endo Appr
Ø47NØ41 Dilation Lt Popl Art w Drug-elut Intralum, Drug Blln, Opn
Ø47NØD1 Dilation Lt Popl Art w Intralum Dev, Drug Blln, Opn
Ø47NØZ1 Dilation of Lt Popl Art using Drug Blln, Opn Appr
Ø47N341 Dilation Lt Popl Art w Drug-elut Intralum, Drug Blln, Perc
Ø47N3D1 Dilation Lt Popl Art w Intralum Dev, Drug Blln, Perc
Ø47N3Z1 Dilation of Lt Popl Art using Drug Blln, Perc Appr
Ø47N441 Dilation Lt Popl Art w Drug-elut Intralum, Drug Blln, Perc Endo
Ø47N4D1 Dilation Lt Popl Art w Intralum Dev, Drug Blln, Perc Endo
Ø47N4Z1 Dilation of Lt Popl Art using Drug Blln, Perc Endo Appr
Ø47Y3[4,D,Z]Z Dilation/Lwr Artery, Perc, [Drug-eluting Intralum Dev, Intralum Dev, No Dev], NQ
Ø4QC[Ø,3,4]ZZ Rpr/Common Iliac Artery, Rt, [Opn, Perc, Perc Endo]
Ø4QD[Ø,3,4]ZZ Rpr/Common Iliac Artery, Lt, [Opn, Perc, Perc Endo]

T Transfer DRG   SP Special Payment   * Code Range   6th and 7th Character of ZZ = No Device, No Qualifier ZX = No Device, Diagnostic

04QE[0,3,4]ZZ	Rpr/Int Iliac Artery, Rt, [Opn, Perc, Perc Endo]
04QF[0,3,4]ZZ	Rpr/Int Iliac Artery, Lt, [Opn, Perc, Perc Endo]
04QH[0,3,4]ZZ	Rpr/Ext Iliac Artery, Rt, [Opn, Perc, Perc Endo]
04QJ[0,3,4]ZZ	Rpr/Ext Iliac Artery, Lt, [Opn, Perc, Perc Endo]
04QK[0,3,4]ZZ	Rpr/Femor Artery, Rt, [Opn, Perc, Perc Endo]
04QL[0,3,4]ZZ	Rpr/Femor Artery, Lt, [Opn, Perc, Perc Endo]
04QM[0,3,4]ZZ	Rpr/Popliteal Artery, Rt, [Opn, Perc, Perc Endo]
04QN[0,3,4]ZZ	Rpr/Popliteal Artery, Lt, [Opn, Perc, Perc Endo]
04QP[0,3,4]ZZ	Rpr/Ant Tibial Artery, Rt, [Opn, Perc, Perc Endo]
04QQ[0,3,4]ZZ	Rpr/Ant Tibial Artery, Lt, [Opn, Perc, Perc Endo]
04QR[0,3,4]ZZ	Rpr/Post Tibial Artery, Rt, [Opn, Perc, Perc Endo]
04QS[0,3,4]ZZ	Rpr/Post Tibial Artery, Lt, [Opn, Perc, Perc Endo]
04QT[0,3,4]ZZ	Rpr/Peroneal Artery, Rt, [Opn, Perc, Perc Endo]
04QU[0,3,4]ZZ	Rpr/Peroneal Artery, Lt, [Opn, Perc, Perc Endo]
04QV[0,3,4]ZZ	Rpr/Foot Artery, Rt, [Opn, Perc, Perc Endo]
04QW[0,3,4]ZZ	Rpr/Foot Artery, Lt, [Opn, Perc, Perc Endo]
04SK[0,3,4]ZZ	Repos/Femor Artery, Rt, [Opn, Perc, Perc Endo]
04SL[0,3,4]ZZ	Repos/Femor Artery, Lt, [Opn, Perc, Perc Endo]
04SM[0,3,4]ZZ	Repos/Popliteal Artery, Rt, [Opn, Perc, Perc Endo]
04SN[0,3,4]ZZ	Repos/Popliteal Artery, Lt, [Opn, Perc, Perc Endo]
04SP[0,3,4]ZZ	Repos/Ant Tibial Artery, Rt, [Opn, Perc, Perc Endo]
04SQ[0,3,4]ZZ	Repos/Ant Tibial Artery, Lt, [Opn, Perc, Perc Endo]
04SR[0,3,4]ZZ	Repos/Post Tibial Artery, Rt, [Opn, Perc, Perc Endo]
04SS[0,3,4]ZZ	Repos/Post Tibial Artery, Lt, [Opn, Perc, Perc Endo]
04ST[0,3,4]ZZ	Repos/Peroneal Artery, Rt, [Opn, Perc, Perc Endo]
04SU[0,3,4]ZZ	Repos/Peroneal Artery, Lt, [Opn, Perc, Perc Endo]
04SV[0,3,4]ZZ	Repos/Foot Artery, Rt, [Opn, Perc, Perc Endo]
04SW[0,3,4]ZZ	Repos/Foot Artery, Lt, [Opn, Perc, Perc Endo]
04SY[0,3,4]ZZ	Repos/Lwr Artery, [Opn, Perc, Perc Endo]
05793[D,Z]Z	Dilation/Brachial Vein, Rt, Perc, [Intralum Dev, No Dev], NQ
057A3[D,Z]Z	Dilation/Brachial Vein, Lt, Perc, [Intralum Dev, No Dev], NQ
057B3[D,Z]Z	Dilation/Basilic Vein, Rt, Perc, [Intralum Dev, No Dev], NQ
057C3[D,Z]Z	Dilation/Basilic Vein, Lt, Perc, [Intralum Dev, No Dev], NQ
057D3[D,Z]Z	Dilation/Cephalic Vein, Rt, Perc, [Intralum Dev, No Dev], NQ
057F3[D,Z]Z	Dilation/Cephalic Vein, Lt, Perc, [Intralum Dev, No Dev], NQ
05S7[0,3,4]ZZ	Repos/Axillary Vein, Rt, [Opn, Perc, Perc Endo]
05S8[0,3,4]ZZ	Repos/Axillary Vein, Lt, [Opn, Perc, Perc Endo]
05S9[0,3,4]ZZ	Repos/Brachial Vein, Rt, [Opn, Perc, Perc Endo]
05SA[0,3,4]ZZ	Repos/Brachial Vein, Lt, [Opn, Perc, Perc Endo]
05SB[0,3,4]ZZ	Repos/Basilic Vein, Rt, [Opn, Perc, Perc Endo]
05SC[0,3,4]ZZ	Repos/Basilic Vein, Lt, [Opn, Perc, Perc Endo]
05SD[0,3,4]ZZ	Repos/Cephalic Vein, Rt, [Opn, Perc, Perc Endo]
05SF[0,3,4]ZZ	Repos/Cephalic Vein, Lt, [Opn, Perc, Perc Endo]
05SG[0,3,4]ZZ	Repos/Hand Vein, Rt, [Opn, Perc, Perc Endo]
05SH[0,3,4]ZZ	Repos/Hand Vein, Lt, [Opn, Perc, Perc Endo]
06703[D,Z]Z	Dilation/Inferior Vena Cava, Perc, [Intralum Dev, No Dev], NQ
06SM[0,3,4]ZZ	Repos/Femor Vein, Rt, [Opn, Perc, Perc Endo]
06SN[0,3,4]ZZ	Repos/Femor Vein, Lt, [Opn, Perc, Perc Endo]
06SP[0,3,4]ZZ	Repos/Greater Saphenous Vein, Rt, [Opn, Perc, Perc Endo]
06SQ[0,3,4]ZZ	Repos/Greater Saphenous Vein, Lt, [Opn, Perc, Perc Endo]
06SR[0,3,4]ZZ	Repos/Lesser Saphenous Vein, Rt, [Opn, Perc, Perc Endo]
06SS[0,3,4]ZZ	Repos/Lesser Saphenous Vein, Lt, [Opn, Perc, Perc Endo]
06ST[0,3,4]ZZ	Repos/Foot Vein, Rt, [Opn, Perc, Perc Endo]
06SV[0,3,4]ZZ	Repos/Foot Vein, Lt, [Opn, Perc, Perc Endo]
06SY[0,3,4]ZZ	Repos/Lwr Vein, [Opn, Perc, Perc Endo]
0790[0,3,4]ZX	Drain/Lymphatic, Head, [Opn, Perc, Perc Endo]
0790[0,3,4][0,Z]Z	Drain/Lymphatic, Head, [Opn, Perc, Perc Endo], [Drain Dev, No Dev], NQ
0791[0,3,4]ZX	Drain/Lymphatic, Rt Neck, [Opn, Perc, Perc Endo]
0791[0,3,4][0,Z]Z	Drain/Lymphatic, Rt Neck, [Opn, Perc, Perc Endo], [Drain Dev, No Dev], NQ
0792[0,3,4]ZX	Drain/Lymphatic, Lt Neck, [Opn, Perc, Perc Endo]
0792[0,3,4][0,Z]Z	Drain/Lymphatic, Lt Neck, [Opn, Perc, Perc Endo], [Drain Dev, No Dev], NQ
0793[0,3,4]ZX	Drain/Lymphatic, Rt Upr Extr, [Opn, Perc, Perc Endo]
0793[0,3,4][0,Z]Z	Drain/Lymphatic, Rt Upr Extr, [Opn, Perc, Perc Endo], [Drain Dev, No Dev], NQ
0794[0,3,4]ZX	Drain/Lymphatic, Lt Upr Extr, [Opn, Perc, Perc Endo]
0794[0,3,4][0,Z]Z	Drain/Lymphatic, Lt Upr Extr, [Opn, Perc, Perc Endo], [Drain Dev, No Dev], NQ
0795[0,3,4]ZX	Drain/Lymphatic, Rt Axillary, [Opn, Perc, Perc Endo]
0795[0,3,4][0,Z]Z	Drain/Lymphatic, Rt Axillary, [Opn, Perc, Perc Endo], [Drain Dev, No Dev], NQ
0796[0,3,4]ZX	Drain/Lymphatic, Lt Axillary, [Opn, Perc, Perc Endo]
0796[0,3,4][0,Z]Z	Drain/Lymphatic, Lt Axillary, [Opn, Perc, Perc Endo], [Drain Dev, No Dev], NQ
0797[0,3,4]ZX	Drain/Lymphatic, Thorax, [Opn, Perc, Perc Endo]
0797[0,3,4][0,Z]Z	Drain/Lymphatic, Thorax, [Opn, Perc, Perc Endo], [Drain Dev, No Dev], NQ
0798[0,3,4]ZX	Drain/Lymphatic, Int Mammary, Rt, [Opn, Perc, Perc Endo]
0798[0,3,4][0,Z]Z	Drain/Lymphatic, Int Mammary, Rt, [Opn, Perc, Perc Endo], [Drain Dev, No Dev], NQ
0799[0,3,4]ZX	Drain/Lymphatic, Int Mammary, Lt, [Opn, Perc, Perc Endo]
0799[0,3,4][0,Z]Z	Drain/Lymphatic, Int Mammary, Lt, [Opn, Perc, Perc Endo], [Drain Dev, No Dev], NQ
079B[0,3,4]ZX	Drain/Lymphatic, Mesenteric, [Opn, Perc, Perc Endo]
079B[0,3,4][0,Z]Z	Drain/Lymphatic, Mesenteric, [Opn, Perc, Perc Endo], [Drain Dev, No Dev], NQ
079C[0,3,4]ZX	Drain/Lymphatic, Pelvis, [Opn, Perc, Perc Endo]
079C[0,3,4][0,Z]Z	Drain/Lymphatic, Pelvis, [Opn, Perc, Perc Endo], [Drain Dev, No Dev], NQ
079D[0,3,4]ZX	Drain/Lymphatic, Aortic, [Opn, Perc, Perc Endo]
079D[0,3,4][0,Z]Z	Drain/Lymphatic, Aortic, [Opn, Perc, Perc Endo], [Drain Dev, No Dev], NQ
079F[0,3,4]ZX	Drain/Lymphatic, Rt Lwr Extr, [Opn, Perc, Perc Endo]
079F[0,3,4][0,Z]Z	Drain/Lymphatic, Rt Lwr Extr, [Opn, Perc, Perc Endo], [Drain Dev, No Dev], NQ
079G[0,3,4]ZX	Drain/Lymphatic, Lt Lwr Extr, [Opn, Perc, Perc Endo]
079G[0,3,4][0,Z]Z	Drain/Lymphatic, Lt Lwr Extr, [Opn, Perc, Perc Endo], [Drain Dev, No Dev], NQ
079H[0,3,4]ZX	Drain/Lymphatic, Rt Inguinal, [Opn, Perc, Perc Endo]
079H[0,3,4][0,Z]Z	Drain/Lymphatic, Rt Inguinal, [Opn, Perc, Perc Endo], [Drain Dev, No Dev], NQ
079J[0,3,4]ZX	Drain/Lymphatic, Lt Inguinal, [Opn, Perc, Perc Endo]
079J[0,3,4][0,Z]Z	Drain/Lymphatic, Lt Inguinal, [Opn, Perc, Perc Endo], [Drain Dev, No Dev], NQ
079K[0,3,4]ZX	Drain/Thoracic Duct, [Opn, Perc, Perc Endo]
079L[0,3,4]ZX	Drain/Cisterna Chyli, [Opn, Perc, Perc Endo]
07B0[0,3,4]Z[X,Z]	Exc/Lymphatic, Head, [Opn, Perc, Perc Endo], No Dev, [Dx, NQ]
07B1[0,3,4]Z[X,Z]	Exc/Lymphatic, Rt Neck, [Opn, Perc, Perc Endo], No Dev, [Dx, NQ]
07B2[0,3,4]Z[X,Z]	Exc/Lymphatic, Lt Neck, [Opn, Perc, Perc Endo], No Dev, [Dx, NQ]
07B3[0,3,4]Z[X,Z]	Exc/Lymphatic, Rt Upr Extr, [Opn, Perc, Perc Endo], No Dev, [Dx, NQ]
07B4[0,3,4]Z[X,Z]	Exc/Lymphatic, Lt Upr Extr, [Opn, Perc, Perc Endo], No Dev, [Dx, NQ]
07B5[0,3,4]Z[X,Z]	Exc/Lymphatic, Rt Axillary, [Opn, Perc, Perc Endo], No Dev, [Dx, NQ]
07B6[0,3,4]Z[X,Z]	Exc/Lymphatic, Lt Axillary, [Opn, Perc, Perc Endo], No Dev, [Dx, NQ]
07B7[0,3,4]Z[X,Z]	Exc/Lymphatic, Thorax, [Opn, Perc, Perc Endo], No Dev, [Dx, NQ]
07B8[0,3,4]Z[X,Z]	Exc/Lymphatic, Int Mammary, Rt, [Opn, Perc, Perc Endo], No Dev, [Dx, NQ]
07B9[0,3,4]Z[X,Z]	Exc/Lymphatic, Int Mammary, Lt, [Opn, Perc, Perc Endo], No Dev, [Dx, NQ]
07BB[0,3,4]Z[X,Z]	Exc/Lymphatic, Mesenteric, [Opn, Perc, Perc Endo], No Dev, [Dx, NQ]
07BC[0,3,4]Z[X,Z]	Exc/Lymphatic, Pelvis, [Opn, Perc, Perc Endo], No Dev, [Dx, NQ]
07BD[0,3,4]Z[X,Z]	Exc/Lymphatic, Aortic, [Opn, Perc, Perc Endo], No Dev, [Dx, NQ]
07BF[0,3,4]Z[X,Z]	Exc/Lymphatic, Rt Lwr Extr, [Opn, Perc, Perc Endo], No Dev, [Dx, NQ]
07BG[0,3,4]Z[X,Z]	Exc/Lymphatic, Lt Lwr Extr, [Opn, Perc, Perc Endo], No Dev, [Dx, NQ]
07BH[0,3,4]Z[X,Z]	Exc/Lymphatic, Rt Inguinal, [Opn, Perc, Perc Endo], No Dev, [Dx, NQ]
07BJ[0,3,4]Z[X,Z]	Exc/Lymphatic, Lt Inguinal, [Opn, Perc, Perc Endo], No Dev, [Dx, NQ]
07BK[0,3,4]ZX	Exc/Thoracic Duct, [Opn, Perc, Perc Endo]
07BL[0,3,4]ZX	Exc/Cisterna Chyli, [Opn, Perc, Perc Endo]
07C0[0,3,4]ZZ	Extir/Lymphatic, Head, [Opn, Perc, Perc Endo]
07C1[0,3,4]ZZ	Extir/Lymphatic, Rt Neck, [Opn, Perc, Perc Endo]
07C2[0,3,4]ZZ	Extir/Lymphatic, Lt Neck, [Opn, Perc, Perc Endo]
07C3[0,3,4]ZZ	Extir/Lymphatic, Rt Upr Extr, [Opn, Perc, Perc Endo]
07C4[0,3,4]ZZ	Extir/Lymphatic, Lt Upr Extr, [Opn, Perc, Perc Endo]
07C5[0,3,4]ZZ	Extir/Lymphatic, Rt Axillary, [Opn, Perc, Perc Endo]
07C6[0,3,4]ZZ	Extir/Lymphatic, Lt Axillary, [Opn, Perc, Perc Endo]
07C7[0,3,4]ZZ	Extir/Lymphatic, Thorax, [Opn, Perc, Perc Endo]
07C8[0,3,4]ZZ	Extir/Lymphatic, Int Mammary, Rt, [Opn, Perc, Perc Endo]
07C9[0,3,4]ZZ	Extir/Lymphatic, Int Mammary, Lt, [Opn, Perc, Perc Endo]
07CB[0,3,4]ZZ	Extir/Lymphatic, Mesenteric, [Opn, Perc, Perc Endo]
07CC[0,3,4]ZZ	Extir/Lymphatic, Pelvis, [Opn, Perc, Perc Endo]
07CD[0,3,4]ZZ	Extir/Lymphatic, Aortic, [Opn, Perc, Perc Endo]
07CF[0,3,4]ZZ	Extir/Lymphatic, Rt Lwr Extr, [Opn, Perc, Perc Endo]
07CG[0,3,4]ZZ	Extir/Lymphatic, Lt Lwr Extr, [Opn, Perc, Perc Endo]
07CH[0,3,4]ZZ	Extir/Lymphatic, Rt Inguinal, [Opn, Perc, Perc Endo]
07CJ[0,3,4]ZZ	Extir/Lymphatic, Lt Inguinal, [Opn, Perc, Perc Endo]
07CK[0,3,4]ZZ	Extir/Thoracic Duct, [Opn, Perc, Perc Endo]

Surgical   **Medical**   **CC Indicator**   **MCC Indicator**   **Procedure Proxy**   PDxMCC **PDx acts as own MCC**   PDxCC **PDx acts as own CC**

MDC 9: Diseases And Disorders Of The Skin, Subcutaneous Tissue And Breast—SURGICAL

07CL[0,3,4]ZZ	Extir/Cisterna Chyli, [Opn, Perc, Perc Endo]
07JK[0,3,4]ZZ	Inspect/Thoracic Duct, [Opn, Perc, Perc Endo]
07JL[0,3,4]ZZ	Inspect/Cisterna Chyli, [Opn, Perc, Perc Endo]
07JN[0,3,4]ZZ	Inspect/Lymphatic, [Opn, Perc, Perc Endo]
07JP0ZZ	Inspect of Spleen, Opn Appr
07PN[0,3,4][0,3,C,D]Z	Rmvl/Lymphatic, [Opn, Perc, Perc Endo], [Drain Dev, Inf Dev, Extralum Dev, Intralum Dev], NQ
07T0[0,4]ZZ	Resect/Lymphatic, Head, [Opn, Perc Endo]
07T1[0,4]ZZ	Resect/Lymphatic, Rt Neck, [Opn, Perc Endo]
07T2[0,4]ZZ	Resect/Lymphatic, Lt Neck, [Opn, Perc Endo]
07T3[0,4]ZZ	Resect/Lymphatic, Rt Upr Extr, [Opn, Perc Endo]
07T4[0,4]ZZ	Resect/Lymphatic, Lt Upr Extr, [Opn, Perc Endo]
07T5[0,4]ZZ	Resect/Lymphatic, Rt Axillary, [Opn, Perc Endo]
07T6[0,4]ZZ	Resect/Lymphatic, Lt Axillary, [Opn, Perc Endo]
07T7[0,4]ZZ	Resect/Lymphatic, Thorax, [Opn, Perc Endo]
07T8[0,4]ZZ	Resect/Lymphatic, Int Mammary, Rt, [Opn, Perc Endo]
07T9[0,4]ZZ	Resect/Lymphatic, Int Mammary, Lt, [Opn, Perc Endo]
07TB[0,4]ZZ	Resect/Lymphatic, Mesenteric, [Opn, Perc Endo]
07TC[0,4]ZZ	Resect/Lymphatic, Pelvis, [Opn, Perc Endo]
07TD[0,4]ZZ	Resect/Lymphatic, Aortic, [Opn, Perc Endo]
07TF[0,4]ZZ	Resect/Lymphatic, Rt Lwr Extr, [Opn, Perc Endo]
07TG[0,4]ZZ	Resect/Lymphatic, Lt Lwr Extr, [Opn, Perc Endo]
07TH[0,4]ZZ	Resect/Lymphatic, Rt Inguinal, [Opn, Perc Endo]
07TJ[0,4]ZZ	Resect/Lymphatic, Lt Inguinal, [Opn, Perc Endo]
07WN[0,3,4][0,3,C,D]Z	Rev/Lymphatic, [Opn, Perc, Perc Endo], [Drain Dev, Inf Dev, Extralum Dev, Intralum Dev], NQ
085N[0,3,X]ZZ	Destr/Upr Eyelid, Rt, [Opn, Perc, Ext]
085P[0,3,X]ZZ	Destr/Upr Eyelid, Lt, [Opn, Perc, Ext]
085Q[0,3,X]ZZ	Destr/Lwr Eyelid, Rt, [Opn, Perc, Ext]
085R[0,3,X]ZZ	Destr/Lwr Eyelid, Lt, [Opn, Perc, Ext]
08B0[0,3,X]ZZ	Exc/Eye, Rt, [Opn, Perc, Ext]
08B1[0,3,X]ZZ	Exc/Eye, Lt, [Opn, Perc, Ext]
08BN[0,3,X]ZZ	Exc/Upr Eyelid, Rt, [Opn, Perc, Ext]
08BP[0,3,X]ZZ	Exc/Upr Eyelid, Lt, [Opn, Perc, Ext]
08BQ[0,3,X]ZZ	Exc/Lwr Eyelid, Rt, [Opn, Perc, Ext]
08BR[0,3,X]ZZ	Exc/Lwr Eyelid, Lt, [Opn, Perc, Ext]
08MNXZZ	Reattach of Rt Upr Eyelid, Ext Appr
08MPXZZ	Reattach of Lt Upr Eyelid, Ext Appr
08MQXZZ	Reattach of Rt Lwr Eyelid, Ext Appr
08MRXZZ	Reattach of Lt Lwr Eyelid, Ext Appr
08NN[0,3,X]ZZ	Rls/Upr Eyelid, Rt, [Opn, Perc, Ext]
08NP[0,3,X]ZZ	Rls/Upr Eyelid, Lt, [Opn, Perc, Ext]
08NQ[0,3,X]ZZ	Rls/Lwr Eyelid, Rt, [Opn, Perc, Ext]
08NR[0,3,X]ZZ	Rls/Lwr Eyelid, Lt, [Opn, Perc, Ext]
08QX[7,8]ZZ	Rpr/Lacrimal Duct, Rt, [Via Natrl or Artfcl Opng, Via Natrl or Artfcl Opng Endo]
08QY[7,8]ZZ	Rpr/Lacrimal Duct, Lt, [Via Natrl or Artfcl Opng, Via Natrl or Artfcl Opng Endo]
08RN[0,3,X][7,J,K]Z	Replace/Upr Eyelid, Rt, [Opn, Perc, Ext], [Auto Tissue Sub, Synth Sub, Nonauto Tissue Sub], NQ
08RP[0,3,X][7,J,K]Z	Replace/Upr Eyelid, Lt, [Opn, Perc, Ext], [Auto Tissue Sub, Synth Sub, Nonauto Tissue Sub], NQ
08RQ[0,3,X][7,J,K]Z	Replace/Lwr Eyelid, Rt, [Opn, Perc, Ext], [Auto Tissue Sub, Synth Sub, Nonauto Tissue Sub], NQ
08RR[0,3,X][7,J,K]Z	Replace/Lwr Eyelid, Lt, [Opn, Perc, Ext], [Auto Tissue Sub, Synth Sub, Nonauto Tissue Sub], NQ
08RX[0,3,7,8][7,J,K]Z	Replace/Lacrimal Duct, Rt, [Opn, Perc, Via Natrl or Artfcl Opng, Via Natrl or Artfcl Opng Endo], [Auto Tissue Sub, Synth Sub, Nonauto Tissue Sub], NQ
08RY[0,3,7,8][7,J,K]Z	Replace/Lacrimal Duct, Lt, [Opn, Perc, Via Natrl or Artfcl Opng, Via Natrl or Artfcl Opng Endo], [Auto Tissue Sub, Synth Sub, Nonauto Tissue Sub], NQ
08SN[0,3,X]ZZ	Repos/Upr Eyelid, Rt, [Opn, Perc, Ext]
08SP[0,3,X]ZZ	Repos/Upr Eyelid, Lt, [Opn, Perc, Ext]
08SQ[0,3,X]ZZ	Repos/Lwr Eyelid, Rt, [Opn, Perc, Ext]
08SR[0,3,X]ZZ	Repos/Lwr Eyelid, Lt, [Opn, Perc, Ext]
08TN[0,X]ZZ	Resect/Upr Eyelid, Rt, [Opn, Ext]
08TP[0,X]ZZ	Resect/Upr Eyelid, Lt, [Opn, Ext]
08TQ[0,X]ZZ	Resect/Lwr Eyelid, Rt, [Opn, Ext]
08TR[0,X]ZZ	Resect/Lwr Eyelid, Lt, [Opn, Ext]
08UN[0,3,X][7,J,K]Z	Supl/Upr Eyelid, Rt, [Opn, Perc, Ext], [Auto Tissue Sub, Synth Sub, Nonauto Tissue Sub], NQ
08UP[0,3,X][7,J,K]Z	Supl/Upr Eyelid, Lt, [Opn, Perc, Ext], [Auto Tissue Sub, Synth Sub, Nonauto Tissue Sub], NQ
08UQ[0,3,X][7,J,K]Z	Supl/Lwr Eyelid, Rt, [Opn, Perc, Ext], [Auto Tissue Sub, Synth Sub, Nonauto Tissue Sub], NQ
08UR[0,3,X][7,J,K]Z	Supl/Lwr Eyelid, Lt, [Opn, Perc, Ext], [Auto Tissue Sub, Synth Sub, Nonauto Tissue Sub], NQ

08UX[0,3,7,8][7,J,K]Z	Supl/Lacrimal Duct, Rt, [Opn, Perc, Via Natrl or Artfcl Opng, Via Natrl or Artfcl Opng Endo], [Auto Tissue Sub, Synth Sub, Nonauto Tissue Sub], NQ
08UY[0,3,7,8][7,J,K]Z	Supl/Lacrimal Duct, Lt, [Opn, Perc, Via Natrl or Artfcl Opng, Via Natrl or Artfcl Opng Endo], [Auto Tissue Sub, Synth Sub, Nonauto Tissue Sub], NQ
0900[0,3,4,X][7,J,K,Z]Z	Alter/Ext Ear, Rt, [Opn, Perc, Perc Endo, Ext], [Auto Tissue Sub, Synth Sub, Nonauto Tissue Sub, No Dev], NQ
0901[0,3,4,X][7,J,K,Z]Z	Alter/Ext Ear, Lt, [Opn, Perc, Perc Endo, Ext], [Auto Tissue Sub, Synth Sub, Nonauto Tissue Sub, No Dev], NQ
0902[0,3,4,X][7,J,K,Z]Z	Alter/Ext Ear, Bilat, [Opn, Perc, Perc Endo, Ext], [Auto Tissue Sub, Synth Sub, Nonauto Tissue Sub, No Dev], NQ
090K[0,3,4,X][7,J,K,Z]Z	Alter/Nose, [Opn, Perc, Perc Endo, Ext], [Auto Tissue Sub, Synth Sub, Nonauto Tissue Sub, No Dev], NQ
09DM[0,3,4]ZZ	Extract/Nasal Septum, [Opn, Perc, Perc Endo]
09MKXZZ	Reattach of Nose, Ext Appr
09N0[0,3,4,X]ZZ	Rls/Ext Ear, Rt, [Opn, Perc, Perc Endo, Ext]
09N1[0,3,4,X]ZZ	Rls/Ext Ear, Lt, [Opn, Perc, Perc Endo, Ext]
09N3[0,3,4,7,8,X]ZZ	Rls/Ext Auditory Canal, Rt, [Opn, Perc, Perc Endo, Via Natrl or Artfcl Opng, Via Natrl or Artfcl Opng Endo, Ext]
09N4[0,3,4,7,8,X]ZZ	Rls/Ext Auditory Canal, Lt, [Opn, Perc, Perc Endo, Via Natrl or Artfcl Opng, Via Natrl or Artfcl Opng Endo, Ext]
09Q0[0,3,4]ZZ	Rpr/Ext Ear, Rt, [Opn, Perc, Perc Endo]
09Q1[0,3,4]ZZ	Rpr/Ext Ear, Lt, [Opn, Perc, Perc Endo]
09Q2[0,3,4]ZZ	Rpr/Ext Ear, Bilat, [Opn, Perc, Perc Endo]
09Q3[0,3,4,7,8]ZZ	Rpr/Ext Auditory Canal, Rt, [Opn, Perc, Perc Endo, Via Natrl or Artfcl Opng, Via Natrl or Artfcl Opng Endo]
09Q4[0,3,4,7,8]ZZ	Rpr/Ext Auditory Canal, Lt, [Opn, Perc, Perc Endo, Via Natrl or Artfcl Opng, Via Natrl or Artfcl Opng Endo]
09QK[0,3,4,X]ZZ	Rpr/Nose, [Opn, Perc, Perc Endo, Ext]
09QL[0,3,4,7,8]ZZ	Rpr/Nasal Turbinate, [Opn, Perc, Perc Endo, Via Natrl or Artfcl Opng, Via Natrl or Artfcl Opng Endo]
09QM[0,3,4]ZZ	Rpr/Nasal Septum, [Opn, Perc, Perc Endo]
09R0[0,X][7,J,K]Z	Replace/Ext Ear, Rt, [Opn, Ext], [Auto Tissue Sub, Synth Sub, Nonauto Tissue Sub], NQ
09R1[0,X][7,J,K]Z	Replace/Ext Ear, Lt, [Opn, Ext], [Auto Tissue Sub, Synth Sub, Nonauto Tissue Sub], NQ
09R2[0,X][7,J,K]Z	Replace/Ext Ear, Bilat, [Opn, Ext], [Auto Tissue Sub, Synth Sub, Nonauto Tissue Sub], NQ
09RK[0,X][7,J,K]Z	Replace/Nose, [Opn, Ext], [Auto Tissue Sub, Synth Sub, Nonauto Tissue Sub], NQ
09RL[0,3,4,7,8][7,J,K]Z	Replace/Nasal Turbinate, [Opn, Perc, Perc Endo, Via Natrl or Artfcl Opng, Via Natrl or Artfcl Opng Endo], [Auto Tissue Sub, Synth Sub, Nonauto Tissue Sub], NQ
09RM[0,3,4][7,J,K]Z	Replace/Nasal Septum, [Opn, Perc, Perc Endo], [Auto Tissue Sub, Synth Sub, Nonauto Tissue Sub], NQ
09S0[0,4,X]ZZ	Repos/Ext Ear, Rt, [Opn, Perc Endo, Ext]
09S1[0,4,X]ZZ	Repos/Ext Ear, Lt, [Opn, Perc Endo, Ext]
09S2[0,4,X]ZZ	Repos/Ext Ear, Bilat, [Opn, Perc Endo, Ext]
09SK[0,4,X]ZZ	Repos/Nose, [Opn, Perc Endo, Ext]
09SM[0,4]ZZ	Repos/Nasal Septum, [Opn, Perc Endo]
09T0[0,4,X]ZZ	Resect/Ext Ear, Rt, [Opn, Perc Endo, Ext]
09T1[0,4,X]ZZ	Resect/Ext Ear, Lt, [Opn, Perc Endo, Ext]
09TK[0,4,X]ZZ	Resect/Nose, [Opn, Perc Endo, Ext]
09U0[0,X][7,J,K]Z	Supl/Ext Ear, Rt, [Opn, Ext], [Auto Tissue Sub, Synth Sub, Nonauto Tissue Sub], NQ
09U1[0,X][7,J,K]Z	Supl/Ext Ear, Lt, [Opn, Ext], [Auto Tissue Sub, Synth Sub, Nonauto Tissue Sub], NQ
09U2[0,X][7,J,K]Z	Supl/Ext Ear, Bilat, [Opn, Ext], [Auto Tissue Sub, Synth Sub, Nonauto Tissue Sub], NQ
09UK[0,X][7,J,K]Z	Supl/Nose, [Opn, Ext], [Auto Tissue Sub, Synth Sub, Nonauto Tissue Sub], NQ
09UL[0,3,4,7,8][7,J,K]Z	Supl/Nasal Turbinate, [Opn, Perc, Perc Endo, Via Natrl or Artfcl Opng, Via Natrl or Artfcl Opng Endo], [Auto Tissue Sub, Synth Sub, Nonauto Tissue Sub], NQ
09UM[0,3,4][7,J,K]Z	Supl/Nasal Septum, [Opn, Perc, Perc Endo], [Auto Tissue Sub, Synth Sub, Nonauto Tissue Sub], NQ
0BQ1[0,3,4,7,8]ZZ	Rpr/Trachea, [Opn, Perc, Perc Endo, Via Natrl or Artfcl Opng Endo]
0BW1[0,3,4]FZ	Rev/Trachea, [Opn, Perc, Perc Endo], Tracheostomy Dev, NQ
0C00X[7,J,K,Z]Z	Alter/Upr Lip, Ext, [Auto Tissue Sub, Synth Sub, Nonauto Tissue Sub, No Dev], NQ
0C01X[7,J,K,Z]Z	Alter/Lwr Lip, Ext, [Auto Tissue Sub, Synth Sub, Nonauto Tissue Sub, No Dev], NQ
0C50[0,3,X]ZZ	Destr/Upr Lip, [Opn, Perc, Ext]
0C51[0,3,X]ZZ	Destr/Lwr Lip, [Opn, Perc, Ext]
0C90[0,3,X][0,Z]Z	Drain/Upr Lip, [Opn, Perc, Ext], [Drain Dev, No Dev], NQ
0C91[0,3,X][0,Z]Z	Drain/Lwr Lip, [Opn, Perc, Ext], [Drain Dev, No Dev], NQ
0C94[0,3,X][0,Z]Z	Drain/Buccal Mucosa, [Opn, Perc, Ext], [Drain Dev, No Dev], NQ
0CB0[0,3,X]ZZ	Exc/Upr Lip, [Opn, Perc, Ext]

Ⓣ **Transfer DRG** 　Ⓢᴾ **Special Payment** 　*** Code Range** 　**6th and 7th Character of ZZ = No Device, No Qualifier ZX = No Device, Diagnostic**

0CB1[0,3,X]ZZ	Exc/Lwr Lip, [Opn, Perc, Ext]
0CC0[0,3]ZZ	Extir/Upr Lip, [Opn, Perc]
0CC1[0,3]ZZ	Extir/Lwr Lip, [Opn, Perc]
0CC4[0,3]ZZ	Extir/Buccal Mucosa, [Opn, Perc]
0CM00ZZ	Reattach of Upr Lip, Opn Appr
0CM10ZZ	Reattach of Lwr Lip, Opn Appr
0CM30ZZ	Reattach of Soft Palate, Opn Appr
0CN2[0,3,X]ZZ	Rls/Hard Palate, [Opn, Perc, Ext]
0CN3[0,3,X]ZZ	Rls/Soft Palate, [Opn, Perc, Ext]
0CN4[0,3,X]ZZ	Rls/Buccal Mucosa, [Opn, Perc, Ext]
0CPY[0,3][0,1,7,D,J,K]Z	Rmvl/Mouth and Throat, [Opn, Perc], [Drain Dev, Radioact Elmt, Auto Tissue Sub, Intralum Dev, Synth Sub, Nonauto Tissue Sub], NQ
0CQ0[0,3]ZZ	Rpr/Upr Lip, [Opn, Perc]
0CQ1[0,3]ZZ	Rpr/Lwr Lip, [Opn, Perc]
0CQ2[0,3,X]ZZ	Rpr/Hard Palate, [Opn, Perc, Ext]
0CQ3[0,3,X]ZZ	Rpr/Soft Palate, [Opn, Perc, Ext]
0CQ4[0,3,X]ZZ	Rpr/Buccal Mucosa, [Opn, Perc, Ext]
0CQM[0,3,4,7,8]ZZ	Rpr/Pharynx, [Opn, Perc, Perc Endo, Via Natrl or Artfcl Opng, Via Natrl or Artfcl Opng Endo]
0CR0[0,3,X][7,J,K]Z	Replace/Upr Lip, [Opn, Perc, Ext], [Auto Tissue Sub, Synth Sub, Nonauto Tissue Sub], NQ
0CR1[0,3,X][7,J,K]Z	Replace/Lwr Lip, [Opn, Perc, Ext], [Auto Tissue Sub, Synth Sub, Nonauto Tissue Sub], NQ
0CR2[0,3,X][7,J,K]Z	Replace/Hard Palate, [Opn, Perc, Ext], [Auto Tissue Sub, Synth Sub, Nonauto Tissue Sub], NQ
0CR3[0,3,X][7,J,K]Z	Replace/Soft Palate, [Opn, Perc, Ext], [Auto Tissue Sub, Synth Sub, Nonauto Tissue Sub], NQ
0CR4[0,3,X][7,J,K]Z	Replace/Buccal Mucosa, [Opn, Perc, Ext], [Auto Tissue Sub, Synth Sub, Nonauto Tissue Sub], NQ
0CS0[0,X]ZZ	Repos/Upr Lip, [Opn, Ext]
0CS1[0,X]ZZ	Repos/Lwr Lip, [Opn, Ext]
0CS2[0,X]ZZ	Repos/Hard Palate, [Opn, Ext]
0CS3[0,X]ZZ	Repos/Soft Palate, [Opn, Ext]
0CU0[0,3,X][7,J,K]Z	Supl/Upr Lip, [Opn, Perc, Ext], [Auto Tissue Sub, Synth Sub, Nonauto Tissue Sub], NQ
0CU1[0,3,X][7,J,K]Z	Supl/Lwr Lip, [Opn, Perc, Ext], [Auto Tissue Sub, Synth Sub, Nonauto Tissue Sub], NQ
0CU2[0,3,X][7,K]Z	Supl/Hard Palate, [Opn, Perc, Ext], [Auto Tissue Sub, Nonauto Tissue Sub], NQ
0CU3[0,3,X][7,J,K]Z	Supl/Soft Palate, [Opn, Perc, Ext], [Auto Tissue Sub, Synth Sub, Nonauto Tissue Sub], NQ
0CU4[0,3,X][7,J,K]Z	Supl/Buccal Mucosa, [Opn, Perc, Ext], [Auto Tissue Sub, Synth Sub, Nonauto Tissue Sub], NQ
0CWY37Z	Rev of Autol Sub in Mouth/Throat, Perc Appr
0CWY[0,3][0,1,D,J,K]Z	Rev/Mouth and Throat, [Opn, Perc], [Drain Dev, Radioact Elmt, Intralum Dev, Synth Sub, Nonauto Tissue Sub], NQ
0CX0[0,X]ZZ	Transfer/Upr Lip, [Opn, Ext]
0CX1[0,X]ZZ	Transfer/Lwr Lip, [Opn, Ext]
0CX3[0,X]ZZ	Transfer/Soft Palate, [Opn, Ext]
0CX4[0,X]ZZ	Transfer/Buccal Mucosa, [Opn, Ext]
0CX5[0,X]ZZ	Transfer/Upr Gingiva, [Opn, Ext]
0CX6[0,X]ZZ	Transfer/Lwr Gingiva, [Opn, Ext]
0D5Q[0,3,7,X]ZZ	Destr/Anus, [Opn, Perc, Via Natrl or Artfcl Opng, Ext]
0D5R[0,3]ZZ	Destr/Anal Sphincter, [Opn, Perc]
0D9Q[0,3,4,7,8,X][0,Z]Z	Drain/Anus, [Opn, Perc, Perc Endo, Via Natrl or Artfcl Opng, Via Natrl or Artfcl Opng Endo, Ext], [Drain Dev, No Dev], NQ
0DBP[3,7]ZZ	Exc/Rectum, [Perc, Via Natrl or Artfcl Opng]
0DBQ[0,3,4]ZZ	Exc/Anus, [Opn, Perc, Perc Endo]
0DHQ[0,3,4]LZ	Insert/Anus, [Opn, Perc, Perc Endo], Artfcl Sphincter, NQ
0DJ00ZZ	Inspect of Upr Intestinal Tract, Opn Appr
0DJ60ZZ	Inspect of Stomach, Opn Appr
0DJD0ZZ	Inspect of Lwr Intestinal Tract, Opn Appr
0DJU[0,4]ZZ	Inspect/Omentum, [Opn, Perc Endo]
0DJV[0,4]ZZ	Inspect/Mesentery, [Opn, Perc Endo]
0DJW[0,4]ZZ	Inspect/Peritoneum, [Opn, Perc Endo]
0DNP[0,3,4,7,8]ZZ	Rls/Rectum, [Opn, Perc, Perc Endo, Via Natrl or Artfcl Opng, Via Natrl or Artfcl Opng Endo]
0DNR[0,3,4]ZZ	Rls/Anal Sphincter, [Opn, Perc, Perc Endo]
0DPQ[0,3,4,7,8]LZ	Rmvl/Anus, [Opn, Perc, Perc Endo, Via Natrl or Artfcl Opng, Via Natrl or Artfcl Opng Endo], Artfcl Sphincter, NQ
0DQP[0,3,4,7,8]ZZ	Rpr/Rectum, [Opn, Perc, Perc Endo, Via Natrl or Artfcl Opng, Via Natrl or Artfcl Opng Endo]
0DQQ[0,3,4,7,8,X]ZZ	Rpr/Anus, [Opn, Perc, Perc Endo, Via Natrl or Artfcl Opng, Via Natrl or Artfcl Opng Endo, Ext]
0DQR[0,3,4]ZZ	Rpr/Anal Sphincter, [Opn, Perc, Perc Endo]
0DRR[0,4][7,J,K]Z	Replace/Anal Sphincter, [Opn, Perc Endo], [Auto Tissue Sub, Synth Sub, Nonauto Tissue Sub], NQ

0DUR[0,4][7,J,K]Z	Supl/Anal Sphincter, [Opn, Perc Endo], [Auto Tissue Sub, Synth Sub, Nonauto Tissue Sub], NQ
0DVQ[0,3,4,7,8,X][D,Z]Z	Restrict/Anus, [Opn, Perc, Perc Endo, Via Natrl or Artfcl Opng, Via Natrl or Artfcl Opng Endo, Ext], [Intralum Dev, No Dev], NQ
0DVQ[0,3,4,X]CZ	Restrict/Anus, [Opn, Perc, Perc Endo, Ext], Extralum Dev, NQ
0DWQ[0,3,4,7,8]LZ	Rev/Anus, [Opn, Perc, Perc Endo, Via Natrl or Artfcl Opng, Via Natrl or Artfcl Opng Endo], Artfcl Sphincter, NQ
0F900ZX	Drain of Liver, Opn Appr, Diagnostic
0F910ZX	Drain of Rt Lobe Liver, Opn Appr, Diagnostic
0F920ZX	Drain of Lt Lobe Liver, Opn Appr, Diagnostic
0FB0[0,4]ZX	Exc/Liver, [Opn, Perc Endo]
0FB1[0,4]ZX	Exc/Liver, Rt Lobe, [Opn, Perc Endo]
0FB2[0,4]ZX	Exc/Liver, Lt Lobe, [Opn, Perc Endo]
0FJ0[0,3,4]ZZ	Inspect/Liver, [Opn, Perc, Perc Endo]
0FJ44ZZ	Inspect of Gallbladder, Perc Endo Appr
0FJD4ZZ	Inspect of Pancreatic Duct, Perc Endo Appr
0FJG4ZZ	Inspect of Pancreas, Perc Endo Appr
0G50[0,3,4]ZZ	Destr/Pituitary Gland, [Opn, Perc, Perc Endo]
0G90[0,3,4][0,Z]Z	Drain/Pituitary Gland, [Opn, Perc, Perc Endo], [Drain Dev, No Dev], NQ
0G9G0[0,Z]Z	Drain/Thyroid Gland Lobe, Lt, Opn, [Drain Dev, No Dev], NQ
0G9H0[0,Z]Z	Drain/Thyroid Gland Lobe, Rt, Opn, [Drain Dev, No Dev], NQ
0G9K0[0,Z]Z	Drain/Thyroid Gland, Opn, [Drain Dev, No Dev], NQ
0G9L0[0,Z]Z	Drain/Superior Parathyroid Gland, Rt, Opn, [Drain Dev, No Dev], NQ
0G9M0[0,Z]Z	Drain/Superior Parathyroid Gland, Lt, Opn, [Drain Dev, No Dev], NQ
0G9N0[0,Z]Z	Drain/Inferior Parathyroid Gland, Rt, Opn, [Drain Dev, No Dev], NQ
0G9P0[0,Z]Z	Drain/Inferior Parathyroid Gland, Lt, Opn, [Drain Dev, No Dev], NQ
0G9Q0[0,Z]Z	Drain/Parathyroid Glands, Multi, Opn, [Drain Dev, No Dev], NQ
0G9R0[0,Z]Z	Drain/Parathyroid Gland, Opn, [Drain Dev, No Dev], NQ
0GB0[0,3,4]ZZ	Exc/Pituitary Gland, [Opn, Perc, Perc Endo]
0GC0[0,3,4]ZZ	Extir/Pituitary Gland, [Opn, Perc, Perc Endo]
0GCG[0,3,4]ZZ	Extir/Thyroid Gland Lobe, Lt, [Opn, Perc, Perc Endo]
0GCH[0,3,4]ZZ	Extir/Thyroid Gland Lobe, Rt, [Opn, Perc, Perc Endo]
0GCK[0,3,4]ZZ	Extir/Thyroid Gland, [Opn, Perc, Perc Endo]
0GCL[0,3,4]ZZ	Extir/Superior Parathyroid Gland, Rt, [Opn, Perc, Perc Endo]
0GCM[0,3,4]ZZ	Extir/Superior Parathyroid Gland, Lt, [Opn, Perc, Perc Endo]
0GCN[0,3,4]ZZ	Extir/Inferior Parathyroid Gland, Rt, [Opn, Perc, Perc Endo]
0GCP[0,3,4]ZZ	Extir/Inferior Parathyroid Gland, Lt, [Opn, Perc, Perc Endo]
0GCQ[0,3,4]ZZ	Extir/Parathyroid Glands, Multi, [Opn, Perc, Perc Endo]
0GCR[0,3,4]ZZ	Extir/Parathyroid Gland, [Opn, Perc, Perc Endo]
0GHS[0,3,4][2,3]Z	Insert/Endocrine Gland, [Opn, Perc, Perc Endo], [Monitoring Dev, Inf Dev], NQ
0GJK0ZZ	Inspect of Thyroid Gland, Opn Appr
0GJR0ZZ	Inspect of Parathyroid Gland, Opn Appr
0GJS0ZZ	Inspect of Endocrine Gland, Opn Appr
0GN0[0,3,4]ZZ	Rls/Pituitary Gland, [Opn, Perc, Perc Endo]
0GP0[0,3,4]0Z	Rmvl/Pituitary Gland, [Opn, Perc, Perc Endo], Drain Dev, NQ
0GPK[0,3,4]0Z	Rmvl/Thyroid Gland, [Opn, Perc, Perc Endo], Drain Dev, NQ
0GPR[0,3,4]0Z	Rmvl/Parathyroid Gland, [Opn, Perc, Perc Endo], Drain Dev, NQ
0GQ0[0,3,4]ZZ	Rpr/Pituitary Gland, [Opn, Perc, Perc Endo]
0GT0[0,4]ZZ	Resect/Pituitary Gland, [Opn, Perc Endo]
0GT2[0,4]ZZ	Resect/Adrenal Gland, Lt, [Opn, Perc Endo]
0GT3[0,4]ZZ	Resect/Adrenal Gland, Rt, [Opn, Perc Endo]
0GT4[0,4]ZZ	Resect/Adrenal Glands, Bilat, [Opn, Perc Endo]
0GW0[0,3,4]0Z	Rev/Pituitary Gland, [Opn, Perc, Perc Endo], Drain Dev, NQ
0GWK[0,3,4]0Z	Rev/Thyroid Gland, [Opn, Perc, Perc Endo], Drain Dev, NQ
0GWR[0,3,4]0Z	Rev/Parathyroid Gland, [Opn, Perc, Perc Endo], Drain Dev, NQ
0H89XZZ	Div of Perineum Skin, Ext Appr
0H99X[0,Z]Z	Drain/Skin, Perineum, Ext, [Drain Dev, No Dev], NQ
0HHT[0,3,7,8,X]1Z	Insert/Breast, Rt, [Opn, Perc, Via Natrl or Artfcl Opng, Via Natrl or Artfcl Opng Endo, Ext], Radioact Elmt, NQ
0HHU[0,3,7,8,X]1Z	Insert/Breast, Lt, [Opn, Perc, Via Natrl or Artfcl Opng, Via Natrl or Artfcl Opng Endo, Ext], Radioact Elmt, NQ
0HHV[0,3,7,8,X]1Z	Insert/Breast, Bilat, [Opn, Perc, Via Natrl or Artfcl Opng, Via Natrl or Artfcl Opng Endo, Ext], Radioact Elmt, NQ
0HHW[0,3,7,8,X]1Z	Insert/Nipple, Rt, [Opn, Perc, Via Natrl or Artfcl Opng, Via Natrl or Artfcl Opng Endo, Ext], Radioact Elmt, NQ
0HHX[0,3,7,8,X]1Z	Insert/Nipple, Lt, [Opn, Perc, Via Natrl or Artfcl Opng, Via Natrl or Artfcl Opng Endo, Ext], Radioact Elmt, NQ
0HM1XZZ	Reattach of Face Skin, Ext Appr
0HM2XZZ	Reattach of Rt Ear Skin, Ext Appr
0HM3XZZ	Reattach of Lt Ear Skin, Ext Appr
0HM4XZZ	Reattach of Neck Skin, Ext Appr
0HM5XZZ	Reattach of Chest Skin, Ext Appr
0HM6XZZ	Reattach of Back Skin, Ext Appr

Surgical   **Medical**   **CC Indicator**   **MCC Indicator**   **Procedure Proxy**   PDxMCC **PDx acts as own MCC**   PDxCC **PDx acts as own CC**

MDC 9: Diseases And Disorders Of The Skin, Subcutaneous Tissue And Breast—SURGICAL

Code	Description
ØHM7XZZ	Reattach of Abd Skin, Ext Appr
ØHM8XZZ	Reattach of Buttock Skin, Ext Appr
ØHM9XZZ	Reattach of Perineum Skin, Ext Appr
ØHMAXZZ	Reattach of Genitalia Skin, Ext Appr
ØHMBXZZ	Reattach of Rt Upr Arm Skin, Ext Appr
ØHMCXZZ	Reattach of Lt Upr Arm Skin, Ext Appr
ØHMDXZZ	Reattach of Rt Lwr Arm Skin, Ext Appr
ØHMEXZZ	Reattach of Lt Lwr Arm Skin, Ext Appr
ØHMFXZZ	Reattach of Rt Hand Skin, Ext Appr
ØHMGXZZ	Reattach of Lt Hand Skin, Ext Appr
ØHMHXZZ	Reattach of Rt Upr Leg Skin, Ext Appr
ØHMJXZZ	Reattach of Lt Upr Leg Skin, Ext Appr
ØHMKXZZ	Reattach of Rt Lwr Leg Skin, Ext Appr
ØHMLXZZ	Reattach of Lt Lwr Leg Skin, Ext Appr
ØHMMXZZ	Reattach of Rt Foot Skin, Ext Appr
ØHMNXZZ	Reattach of Lt Foot Skin, Ext Appr
ØHNØXZZ	Rls Scalp Skin, Ext Appr
ØHN1XZZ	Rls Face Skin, Ext Appr
ØHN2XZZ	Rls Rt Ear Skin, Ext Appr
ØHN3XZZ	Rls Lt Ear Skin, Ext Appr
ØHN4XZZ	Rls Neck Skin, Ext Appr
ØHN5XZZ	Rls Chest Skin, Ext Appr
ØHN6XZZ	Rls Back Skin, Ext Appr
ØHN7XZZ	Rls Abd Skin, Ext Appr
ØHN8XZZ	Rls Buttock Skin, Ext Appr
ØHN9XZZ	Rls Perineum Skin, Ext Appr
ØHNAXZZ	Rls Genitalia Skin, Ext Appr
ØHNBXZZ	Rls Rt Upr Arm Skin, Ext Appr
ØHNCXZZ	Rls Lt Upr Arm Skin, Ext Appr
ØHNDXZZ	Rls Rt Lwr Arm Skin, Ext Appr
ØHNEXZZ	Rls Lt Lwr Arm Skin, Ext Appr
ØHNFXZZ	Rls Rt Hand Skin, Ext Appr
ØHNGXZZ	Rls Lt Hand Skin, Ext Appr
ØHNHXZZ	Rls Rt Upr Leg Skin, Ext Appr
ØHNJXZZ	Rls Lt Upr Leg Skin, Ext Appr
ØHNKXZZ	Rls Rt Lwr Leg Skin, Ext Appr
ØHNLXZZ	Rls Lt Lwr Leg Skin, Ext Appr
ØHNMXZZ	Rls Rt Foot Skin, Ext Appr
ØHNNXZZ	Rls Lt Foot Skin, Ext Appr
ØHNQXZZ	Rls Finger Nail, Ext Appr
ØHNRXZZ	Rls Toe Nail, Ext Appr
ØHQQXZZ	Repair Finger Nail, Ext Appr
ØHQRXZZ	Repair Toe Nail, Ext Appr
ØHR2XJZ	Replace of Rt Ear Skin with Synth Sub, Extern Appr
ØHR2X[7,J,K][3,4]	Replace/Skin, Rt Ear, Ext, [Auto Tissue Sub, Synth Sub, Nonauto Tissue Sub], [Full Thickness, Partial Thickness]
ØHR3XJZ	Replace of Lt Ear Skin with Synth Sub, Extern Appr
ØHR3X[7,J,K][3,4]	Replace/Skin, Lt Ear, Ext, [Auto Tissue Sub, Synth Sub, Nonauto Tissue Sub], [Full Thickness, Partial Thickness]
ØHRQX[7,J,K]Z	Replace/Finger Nail, Ext, [Auto Tissue Sub, Synth Sub, Nonauto Tissue Sub], NQ
ØHRRX[7,J,K]Z	Replace/Toe Nail, Ext, [Auto Tissue Sub, Synth Sub, Nonauto Tissue Sub], NQ
ØHRSX[J,K]Z	Replace/Hair, Ext, [Synth Sub, Nonauto Tissue Sub], NQ
ØHX2XZZ	Transfer Rt Ear Skin, Ext Appr
ØHX3XZZ	Transfer Lt Ear Skin, Ext Appr
ØJ01[Ø,3]ZZ	Alter/SQ Tissue & Fascia, Face, [Opn, Perc]
ØJ04[Ø,3]ZZ	Alter/SQ Tissue & Fascia, Ant Neck, [Opn, Perc]
ØJ05[Ø,3]ZZ	Alter/SQ Tissue & Fascia, Post Neck, [Opn, Perc]
ØJ06[Ø,3]ZZ	Alter/SQ Tissue & Fascia, Chest, [Opn, Perc]
ØJ07[Ø,3]ZZ	Alter/SQ Tissue & Fascia, Back, [Opn, Perc]
ØJ08[Ø,3]ZZ	Alter/SQ Tissue & Fascia, Abd, [Opn, Perc]
ØJ09[Ø,3]ZZ	Alter/SQ Tissue & Fascia, Buttock, [Opn, Perc]
ØJ0D[Ø,3]ZZ	Alter/SQ Tissue & Fascia, Rt Upr Arm, [Opn, Perc]
ØJ0F[Ø,3]ZZ	Alter/SQ Tissue & Fascia, Lt Upr Arm, [Opn, Perc]
ØJ0G[Ø,3]ZZ	Alter/SQ Tissue & Fascia, Rt Lwr Arm, [Opn, Perc]
ØJ0H[Ø,3]ZZ	Alter/SQ Tissue & Fascia, Lt Lwr Arm, [Opn, Perc]
ØJ0L[Ø,3]ZZ	Alter/SQ Tissue & Fascia, Rt Upr Leg, [Opn, Perc]
ØJ0M[Ø,3]ZZ	Alter/SQ Tissue & Fascia, Lt Upr Leg, [Opn, Perc]
ØJ0N[Ø,3]ZZ	Alter/SQ Tissue & Fascia, Rt Lwr Leg, [Opn, Perc]
ØJ0P[Ø,3]ZZ	Alter/SQ Tissue & Fascia, Lt Lwr Leg, [Opn, Perc]
ØJ80[Ø,3]ZZ	Div/SQ Tissue & Fascia, Scalp, [Opn, Perc]
ØJ84[Ø,3]ZZ	Div/SQ Tissue & Fascia, Ant Neck, [Opn, Perc]
ØJ85[Ø,3]ZZ	Div/SQ Tissue & Fascia, Post Neck, [Opn, Perc]
ØJ86[Ø,3]ZZ	Div/SQ Tissue & Fascia, Chest, [Opn, Perc]
ØJ87[Ø,3]ZZ	Div/SQ Tissue & Fascia, Back, [Opn, Perc]
ØJ88[Ø,3]ZZ	Div/SQ Tissue & Fascia, Abd, [Opn, Perc]
ØJ89[Ø,3]ZZ	Div/SQ Tissue & Fascia, Buttock, [Opn, Perc]
ØJ8B[Ø,3]ZZ	Div/SQ Tissue & Fascia, Perineum, [Opn, Perc]
ØJ8C[Ø,3]ZZ	Div/SQ Tissue & Fascia, Genitalia, [Opn, Perc]
ØJ8D[Ø,3]ZZ	Div/SQ Tissue & Fascia, Rt Upr Arm, [Opn, Perc]
ØJ8F[Ø,3]ZZ	Div/SQ Tissue & Fascia, Lt Upr Arm, [Opn, Perc]
ØJ8G[Ø,3]ZZ	Div/SQ Tissue & Fascia, Rt Lwr Arm, [Opn, Perc]
ØJ8H[Ø,3]ZZ	Div/SQ Tissue & Fascia, Lt Lwr Arm, [Opn, Perc]
ØJ8J[Ø,3]ZZ	Div/SQ Tissue & Fascia, Rt Hand, [Opn, Perc]
ØJ8K[Ø,3]ZZ	Div/SQ Tissue & Fascia, Lt Hand, [Opn, Perc]
ØJ8L[Ø,3]ZZ	Div/SQ Tissue & Fascia, Rt Upr Leg, [Opn, Perc]
ØJ8M[Ø,3]ZZ	Div/SQ Tissue & Fascia, Lt Upr Leg, [Opn, Perc]
ØJ8N[Ø,3]ZZ	Div/SQ Tissue & Fascia, Rt Lwr Leg, [Opn, Perc]
ØJ8P[Ø,3]ZZ	Div/SQ Tissue & Fascia, Lt Lwr Leg, [Opn, Perc]
ØJ8Q[Ø,3]ZZ	Div/SQ Tissue & Fascia, Rt Foot, [Opn, Perc]
ØJ8R[Ø,3]ZZ	Div/SQ Tissue & Fascia, Lt Foot, [Opn, Perc]
ØJ8S[Ø,3]ZZ	Div/SQ Tissue & Fascia, Head and Neck, [Opn, Perc]
ØJ8T[Ø,3]ZZ	Div/SQ Tissue & Fascia, Trunk, [Opn, Perc]
ØJ8V[Ø,3]ZZ	Div/SQ Tissue & Fascia, Upr Extr, [Opn, Perc]
ØJ8W[Ø,3]ZZ	Div/SQ Tissue & Fascia, Lwr Extr, [Opn, Perc]
ØJ900ZZ	Drain of Scalp SQ/Fascia, Opn Appr
ØJ910ZZ	Drain of Face SQ/Fascia, Opn Appr
ØJ91[Ø,3]ØZ	Drain/SQ Tissue & Fascia, Face, [Opn, Perc], Drain Dev, NQ
ØJ940ZZ	Drain of Ant Neck SQ/Fascia, Opn Appr
ØJ950ZZ	Drain of Post Neck SQ/Fascia, Opn Appr
ØJ960ZZ	Drain of Chest SQ/Fascia, Opn Appr
ØJ970ZZ	Drain of Back SQ/Fascia, Opn Appr
ØJ980ZZ	Drain of Abd SQ/Fascia, Opn Appr
ØJ990ZZ	Drain of Buttock SQ/Fascia, Opn Appr
ØJ9B0ZZ	Drain of Perineum SQ/Fascia, Opn Appr
ØJ9C0ZZ	Drain of Pelvic SQ/Fascia, Opn Appr
ØJ9D0ZZ	Drain of Rt Up Arm SQ/Fascia, Opn Appr
ØJ9F0ZZ	Drain of Lt Up Arm SQ/Fascia, Opn Appr
ØJ9G0ZZ	Drain of Rt Low Arm SQ/Fascia, Opn Appr
ØJ9H0ZZ	Drain of Lt Low Arm SQ/Fascia, Opn Appr
ØJ9J[Ø,3][Ø,Z]Z	Drain/SQ Tissue & Fascia, Rt Hand, [Opn, Perc], [Drain Dev, No Dev], NQ
ØJ9K[Ø,3][Ø,Z]Z	Drain/SQ Tissue & Fascia, Lt Hand, [Opn, Perc], [Drain Dev, No Dev], NQ
ØJ9L0ZZ	Drain of Rt Up Leg SQ/Fascia, Opn Appr
ØJ9M0ZZ	Drain of Lt Up Leg SQ/Fascia, Opn Appr
ØJ9N0ZZ	Drain of Rt Low Leg SQ/Fascia, Opn Appr
ØJ9P0ZZ	Drain of Lt Low Leg SQ/Fascia, Opn Appr
ØJ9Q0ZZ	Drain of Rt Foot SQ/Fascia, Opn Appr
ØJ9R0ZZ	Drain of Lt Foot SQ/Fascia, Opn Appr
ØJBJ[Ø,3]ZZ	Exc/SQ Tissue & Fascia, Rt Hand, [Opn, Perc]
ØJBK[Ø,3]ZZ	Exc/SQ Tissue & Fascia, Lt Hand, [Opn, Perc]
ØJD0[Ø,3]ZZ	Extract/SQ Tissue & Fascia, Scalp, [Opn, Perc]
ØJD1[Ø,3]ZZ	Extract/SQ Tissue & Fascia, Face, [Opn, Perc]
ØJD4[Ø,3]ZZ	Extract/SQ Tissue & Fascia, Ant Neck, [Opn, Perc]
ØJD5[Ø,3]ZZ	Extract/SQ Tissue & Fascia, Post Neck, [Opn, Perc]
ØJD6[Ø,3]ZZ	Extract/SQ Tissue & Fascia, Chest, [Opn, Perc]
ØJD7[Ø,3]ZZ	Extract/SQ Tissue & Fascia, Back, [Opn, Perc]
ØJD8[Ø,3]ZZ	Extract/SQ Tissue & Fascia, Abd, [Opn, Perc]
ØJD9[Ø,3]ZZ	Extract/SQ Tissue & Fascia, Buttock, [Opn, Perc]
ØJDB[Ø,3]ZZ	Extract/SQ Tissue & Fascia, Perineum, [Opn, Perc]
ØJDC[Ø,3]ZZ	Extract/SQ Tissue & Fascia, Genitalia, [Opn, Perc]
ØJDD[Ø,3]ZZ	Extract/SQ Tissue & Fascia, Rt Upr Arm, [Opn, Perc]
ØJDF[Ø,3]ZZ	Extract/SQ Tissue & Fascia, Lt Upr Arm, [Opn, Perc]
ØJDG[Ø,3]ZZ	Extract/SQ Tissue & Fascia, Rt Lwr Arm, [Opn, Perc]
ØJDH[Ø,3]ZZ	Extract/SQ Tissue & Fascia, Lt Lwr Arm, [Opn, Perc]
ØJDL[Ø,3]ZZ	Extract/SQ Tissue & Fascia, Rt Upr Leg, [Opn, Perc]
ØJDM[Ø,3]ZZ	Extract/SQ Tissue & Fascia, Lt Upr Leg, [Opn, Perc]
ØJDN[Ø,3]ZZ	Extract/SQ Tissue & Fascia, Rt Lwr Leg, [Opn, Perc]
ØJDP[Ø,3]ZZ	Extract/SQ Tissue & Fascia, Lt Lwr Leg, [Opn, Perc]
ØJDQ[Ø,3]ZZ	Extract/SQ Tissue & Fascia, Rt Foot, [Opn, Perc]
ØJDR[Ø,3]ZZ	Extract/SQ Tissue & Fascia, Lt Foot, [Opn, Perc]
ØJH6[Ø,3]VZ	Insert/SQ Tissue & Fascia, Chest, [Opn, Perc], Inf Pump, NQ
ØJH7[Ø,3]VZ	Insert/SQ Tissue & Fascia, Back, [Opn, Perc], Inf Pump, NQ
ØJH8[Ø,3]VZ	Insert/SQ Tissue & Fascia, Abd, [Opn, Perc], Inf Pump, NQ
ØJHS[Ø,3]1Z	Insert/SQ Tissue & Fascia, Head and Neck, [Opn, Perc], Radioact Elmt, NQ
ØJHT[Ø,3][1,V]Z	Insert/SQ Tissue & Fascia, Trunk, [Opn, Perc], [Radioact Elmt, Inf Pump], NQ
ØJHV[Ø,3]1Z	Insert/SQ Tissue & Fascia, Upr Extr, [Opn, Perc], Radioact Elmt, NQ
ØJHW[Ø,3]1Z	Insert/SQ Tissue & Fascia, Lwr Extr, [Opn, Perc], Radioact Elmt, NQ
ØJQ0[Ø,3]ZZ	Rpr/SQ Tissue & Fascia, Scalp, [Opn, Perc]
ØJQ1[Ø,3]ZZ	Rpr/SQ Tissue & Fascia, Face, [Opn, Perc]
ØJQ4[Ø,3]ZZ	Rpr/SQ Tissue & Fascia, Ant Neck, [Opn, Perc]
ØJQ5[Ø,3]ZZ	Rpr/SQ Tissue & Fascia, Post Neck, [Opn, Perc]
ØJQ6[Ø,3]ZZ	Rpr/SQ Tissue & Fascia, Chest, [Opn, Perc]
ØJQ7[Ø,3]ZZ	Rpr/SQ Tissue & Fascia, Back, [Opn, Perc]

T Transfer DRG   SP Special Payment   * Code Range   6th and 7th Character of ZZ = No Device, No Qualifier ZX = No Device, Diagnostic

Code	Description
ØJQ8[Ø,3]ZZ	Rpr/SQ Tissue & Fascia, Abd, [Opn, Perc]
ØJQ9[Ø,3]ZZ	Rpr/SQ Tissue & Fascia, Buttock, [Opn, Perc]
ØJQB[Ø,3]ZZ	Rpr/SQ Tissue & Fascia, Perineum, [Opn, Perc]
ØJQC[Ø,3]ZZ	Rpr/SQ Tissue & Fascia, Genitalia, [Opn, Perc]
ØJQD[Ø,3]ZZ	Rpr/SQ Tissue & Fascia, Rt Upr Arm, [Opn, Perc]
ØJQF[Ø,3]ZZ	Rpr/SQ Tissue & Fascia, Lt Upr Arm, [Opn, Perc]
ØJQG[Ø,3]ZZ	Rpr/SQ Tissue & Fascia, Rt Lwr Arm, [Opn, Perc]
ØJQH[Ø,3]ZZ	Rpr/SQ Tissue & Fascia, Lt Lwr Arm, [Opn, Perc]
ØJQJ[Ø,3]ZZ	Rpr/SQ Tissue & Fascia, Rt Hand, [Opn, Perc]
ØJQK[Ø,3]ZZ	Rpr/SQ Tissue & Fascia, Lt Hand, [Opn, Perc]
ØJQL[Ø,3]ZZ	Rpr/SQ Tissue & Fascia, Rt Upr Leg, [Opn, Perc]
ØJQM[Ø,3]ZZ	Rpr/SQ Tissue & Fascia, Lt Upr Leg, [Opn, Perc]
ØJQN[Ø,3]ZZ	Rpr/SQ Tissue & Fascia, Rt Lwr Leg, [Opn, Perc]
ØJQP[Ø,3]ZZ	Rpr/SQ Tissue & Fascia, Lt Lwr Leg, [Opn, Perc]
ØJQQ[Ø,3]ZZ	Rpr/SQ Tissue & Fascia, Rt Foot, [Opn, Perc]
ØJQR[Ø,3]ZZ	Rpr/SQ Tissue & Fascia, Lt Foot, [Opn, Perc]
ØJRØ[Ø,3][7,J,K]Z	Replace/SQ Tissue & Fascia, Scalp, [Opn, Perc], [Auto Tissue Sub, Synth Sub, Nonauto Tissue Sub], NQ
ØJR1[Ø,3][7,J,K]Z	Replace/SQ Tissue & Fascia, Face, [Opn, Perc], [Auto Tissue Sub, Synth Sub, Nonauto Tissue Sub], NQ
ØJR4[Ø,3][7,J,K]Z	Replace/SQ Tissue & Fascia, Ant Neck, [Opn, Perc], [Auto Tissue Sub, Synth Sub, Nonauto Tissue Sub], NQ
ØJR5[Ø,3][7,J,K]Z	Replace/SQ Tissue & Fascia, Post Neck, [Opn, Perc], [Auto Tissue Sub, Synth Sub, Nonauto Tissue Sub], NQ
ØJR6[Ø,3][7,J,K]Z	Replace/SQ Tissue & Fascia, Chest, [Opn, Perc], [Auto Tissue Sub, Synth Sub, Nonauto Tissue Sub], NQ
ØJR7[Ø,3][7,J,K]Z	Replace/SQ Tissue & Fascia, Back, [Opn, Perc], [Auto Tissue Sub, Synth Sub, Nonauto Tissue Sub], NQ
ØJR8[Ø,3][7,J,K]Z	Replace/SQ Tissue & Fascia, Abd, [Opn, Perc], [Auto Tissue Sub, Synth Sub, Nonauto Tissue Sub], NQ
ØJR9[Ø,3][7,J,K]Z	Replace/SQ Tissue & Fascia, Buttock, [Opn, Perc], [Auto Tissue Sub, Synth Sub, Nonauto Tissue Sub], NQ
ØJRB[Ø,3][7,J,K]Z	Replace/SQ Tissue & Fascia, Perineum, [Opn, Perc], [Auto Tissue Sub, Synth Sub, Nonauto Tissue Sub], NQ
ØJRC[Ø,3][7,J,K]Z	Replace/SQ Tissue & Fascia, Genitalia, [Opn, Perc], [Auto Tissue Sub, Synth Sub, Nonauto Tissue Sub], NQ
ØJRD[Ø,3][7,J,K]Z	Replace/SQ Tissue & Fascia, Rt Upr Arm, [Opn, Perc], [Auto Tissue Sub, Synth Sub, Nonauto Tissue Sub], NQ
ØJRF[Ø,3][7,J,K]Z	Replace/SQ Tissue & Fascia, Lt Upr Arm, [Opn, Perc], [Auto Tissue Sub, Synth Sub, Nonauto Tissue Sub], NQ
ØJRG[Ø,3][7,J,K]Z	Replace/SQ Tissue & Fascia, Rt Lwr Arm, [Opn, Perc], [Auto Tissue Sub, Synth Sub, Nonauto Tissue Sub], NQ
ØJRH[Ø,3][7,J,K]Z	Replace/SQ Tissue & Fascia, Lt Lwr Arm, [Opn, Perc], [Auto Tissue Sub, Synth Sub, Nonauto Tissue Sub], NQ
ØJRJ[Ø,3][7,J,K]Z	Replace/SQ Tissue & Fascia, Rt Hand, [Opn, Perc], [Auto Tissue Sub, Synth Sub, Nonauto Tissue Sub], NQ
ØJRK[Ø,3][7,J,K]Z	Replace/SQ Tissue & Fascia, Lt Hand, [Opn, Perc], [Auto Tissue Sub, Synth Sub, Nonauto Tissue Sub], NQ
ØJRL[Ø,3][7,J,K]Z	Replace/SQ Tissue & Fascia, Rt Upr Leg, [Opn, Perc], [Auto Tissue Sub, Synth Sub, Nonauto Tissue Sub], NQ
ØJRM[Ø,3][7,J,K]Z	Replace/SQ Tissue & Fascia, Lt Upr Leg, [Opn, Perc], [Auto Tissue Sub, Synth Sub, Nonauto Tissue Sub], NQ
ØJRN[Ø,3][7,J,K]Z	Replace/SQ Tissue & Fascia, Rt Lwr Leg, [Opn, Perc], [Auto Tissue Sub, Synth Sub, Nonauto Tissue Sub], NQ
ØJRP[Ø,3][7,J,K]Z	Replace/SQ Tissue & Fascia, Lt Lwr Leg, [Opn, Perc], [Auto Tissue Sub, Synth Sub, Nonauto Tissue Sub], NQ
ØJRQ[Ø,3][7,J,K]Z	Replace/SQ Tissue & Fascia, Rt Foot, [Opn, Perc], [Auto Tissue Sub, Synth Sub, Nonauto Tissue Sub], NQ
ØJRR[Ø,3][7,J,K]Z	Replace/SQ Tissue & Fascia, Lt Foot, [Opn, Perc], [Auto Tissue Sub, Synth Sub, Nonauto Tissue Sub], NQ
ØJUØ[Ø,3][7,J,K]Z	Supl/SQ Tissue & Fascia, Scalp, [Opn, Perc], [Auto Tissue Sub, Synth Sub, Nonauto Tissue Sub], NQ
ØJU1[Ø,3][7,J,K]Z	Supl/SQ Tissue & Fascia, Face, [Opn, Perc], [Auto Tissue Sub, Synth Sub, Nonauto Tissue Sub], NQ
ØJU4[Ø,3][7,J,K]Z	Supl/SQ Tissue & Fascia, Ant Neck, [Opn, Perc], [Auto Tissue Sub, Synth Sub, Nonauto Tissue Sub], NQ
ØJU5[Ø,3][7,J,K]Z	Supl/SQ Tissue & Fascia, Post Neck, [Opn, Perc], [Auto Tissue Sub, Synth Sub, Nonauto Tissue Sub], NQ
ØJU6[Ø,3][7,J,K]Z	Supl/SQ Tissue & Fascia, Chest, [Opn, Perc], [Auto Tissue Sub, Synth Sub, Nonauto Tissue Sub], NQ
ØJU7[Ø,3][7,J,K]Z	Supl/SQ Tissue & Fascia, Back, [Opn, Perc], [Auto Tissue Sub, Synth Sub, Nonauto Tissue Sub], NQ
ØJU8[Ø,3][7,J,K]Z	Supl/SQ Tissue & Fascia, Abd, [Opn, Perc], [Auto Tissue Sub, Synth Sub, Nonauto Tissue Sub], NQ
ØJU9[Ø,3][7,J,K]Z	Supl/SQ Tissue & Fascia, Buttock, [Opn, Perc], [Auto Tissue Sub, Synth Sub, Nonauto Tissue Sub], NQ
ØJUB[Ø,3][7,J,K]Z	Supl/SQ Tissue & Fascia, Perineum, [Opn, Perc], [Auto Tissue Sub, Synth Sub, Nonauto Tissue Sub], NQ
ØJUC[Ø,3][7,J,K]Z	Supl/SQ Tissue & Fascia, Pelvic Rgn, [Opn, Perc], [Auto Tissue Sub, Synth Sub, Nonauto Tissue Sub], NQ
ØJUD[Ø,3][7,J,K]Z	Supl/SQ Tissue & Fascia, Rt Upr Arm, [Opn, Perc], [Auto Tissue Sub, Synth Sub, Nonauto Tissue Sub], NQ
ØJUF[Ø,3][7,J,K]Z	Supl/SQ Tissue & Fascia, Lt Upr Arm, [Opn, Perc], [Auto Tissue Sub, Synth Sub, Nonauto Tissue Sub], NQ
ØJUG[Ø,3][7,J,K]Z	Supl/SQ Tissue & Fascia, Rt Lwr Arm, [Opn, Perc], [Auto Tissue Sub, Synth Sub, Nonauto Tissue Sub], NQ
ØJUH[Ø,3][7,J,K]Z	Supl/SQ Tissue & Fascia, Lt Lwr Arm, [Opn, Perc], [Auto Tissue Sub, Synth Sub, Nonauto Tissue Sub], NQ
ØJUJ[Ø,3][7,J,K]Z	Supl/SQ Tissue & Fascia, Rt Hand, [Opn, Perc], [Auto Tissue Sub, Synth Sub, Nonauto Tissue Sub], NQ
ØJUK[Ø,3][7,J,K]Z	Supl/SQ Tissue & Fascia, Lt Hand, [Opn, Perc], [Auto Tissue Sub, Synth Sub, Nonauto Tissue Sub], NQ
ØJUL[Ø,3][7,J,K]Z	Supl/SQ Tissue & Fascia, Rt Upr Leg, [Opn, Perc], [Auto Tissue Sub, Synth Sub, Nonauto Tissue Sub], NQ
ØJUM[Ø,3][7,J,K]Z	Supl/SQ Tissue & Fascia, Lt Upr Leg, [Opn, Perc], [Auto Tissue Sub, Synth Sub, Nonauto Tissue Sub], NQ
ØJUN[Ø,3][7,J,K]Z	Supl/SQ Tissue & Fascia, Rt Lwr Leg, [Opn, Perc], [Auto Tissue Sub, Synth Sub, Nonauto Tissue Sub], NQ
ØJUP[Ø,3][7,J,K]Z	Supl/SQ Tissue & Fascia, Lt Lwr Leg, [Opn, Perc], [Auto Tissue Sub, Synth Sub, Nonauto Tissue Sub], NQ
ØJUQ[Ø,3][7,J,K]Z	Supl/SQ Tissue & Fascia, Rt Foot, [Opn, Perc], [Auto Tissue Sub, Synth Sub, Nonauto Tissue Sub], NQ
ØJUR[Ø,3][7,J,K]Z	Supl/SQ Tissue & Fascia, Lt Foot, [Opn, Perc], [Auto Tissue Sub, Synth Sub, Nonauto Tissue Sub], NQ
ØJWT[Ø,3]PZ	Rev/SQ Tissue & Fascia, Trunk, [Opn, Perc], Cardiac Rhythm Related Dev, NQ
ØJXØ[Ø,3]ZZ	Transfer/SQ Tissue & Fascia, Scalp, [Opn, Perc]
ØJX1[Ø,3]ZZ	Transfer/SQ Tissue & Fascia, Face, [Opn, Perc]
ØJX4[Ø,3]ZZ	Transfer/SQ Tissue & Fascia, Ant Neck, [Opn, Perc]
ØJX5[Ø,3]ZZ	Transfer/SQ Tissue & Fascia, Post Neck, [Opn, Perc]
ØJX6[Ø,3]ZZ	Transfer/SQ Tissue & Fascia, Chest, [Opn, Perc]
ØJX7[Ø,3]ZZ	Transfer/SQ Tissue & Fascia, Back, [Opn, Perc]
ØJX8[Ø,3]ZZ	Transfer/SQ Tissue & Fascia, Abd, [Opn, Perc]
ØJX9[Ø,3]ZZ	Transfer/SQ Tissue & Fascia, Buttock, [Opn, Perc]
ØJXB[Ø,3]ZZ	Transfer/SQ Tissue & Fascia, Perineum, [Opn, Perc]
ØJXC[Ø,3]ZZ	Transfer/SQ Tissue & Fascia, Genitalia, [Opn, Perc]
ØJXD[Ø,3]ZZ	Transfer/SQ Tissue & Fascia, Rt Upr Arm, [Opn, Perc]
ØJXF[Ø,3]ZZ	Transfer/SQ Tissue & Fascia, Lt Upr Arm, [Opn, Perc]
ØJXG[Ø,3]ZZ	Transfer/SQ Tissue & Fascia, Rt Lwr Arm, [Opn, Perc]
ØJXH[Ø,3]ZZ	Transfer/SQ Tissue & Fascia, Lt Lwr Arm, [Opn, Perc]
ØJXJ[Ø,3]ZZ	Transfer/SQ Tissue & Fascia, Rt Hand, [Opn, Perc]
ØJXL[Ø,3]ZZ	Transfer/SQ Tissue & Fascia, Rt Upr Leg, [Opn, Perc]
ØJXM[Ø,3]ZZ	Transfer/SQ Tissue & Fascia, Lt Upr Leg, [Opn, Perc]
ØJXN[Ø,3]ZZ	Transfer/SQ Tissue & Fascia, Rt Lwr Leg, [Opn, Perc]
ØJXP[Ø,3]ZZ	Transfer/SQ Tissue & Fascia, Lt Lwr Leg, [Opn, Perc]
ØJXQ[Ø,3]ZZ	Transfer/SQ Tissue & Fascia, Rt Foot, [Opn, Perc]
ØJXR[Ø,3]ZZ	Transfer/SQ Tissue & Fascia, Lt Foot, [Opn, Perc]
ØK5Ø[Ø,3,4]ZZ	Destr/Head Muscle, [Opn, Perc, Perc Endo]
ØK51[Ø,3,4]ZZ	Destr/Facial Muscle, [Opn, Perc, Perc Endo]
ØK52[Ø,3,4]ZZ	Destr/Neck Muscle, Rt, [Opn, Perc, Perc Endo]
ØK53[Ø,3,4]ZZ	Destr/Neck Muscle, Lt, [Opn, Perc, Perc Endo]
ØK54[Ø,3,4]ZZ	Destr/Tongue, Palate, Pharynx Muscle, [Opn, Perc, Perc Endo]
ØK55[Ø,3,4]ZZ	Destr/Shldr Muscle, Rt, [Opn, Perc, Perc Endo]
ØK56[Ø,3,4]ZZ	Destr/Shldr Muscle, Lt, [Opn, Perc, Perc Endo]
ØK57[Ø,3,4]ZZ	Destr/Upr Arm Muscle, Rt, [Opn, Perc, Perc Endo]
ØK58[Ø,3,4]ZZ	Destr/Upr Arm Muscle, Lt, [Opn, Perc, Perc Endo]
ØK59[Ø,3,4]ZZ	Destr/Lwr Arm and Wrist Muscle, Rt, [Opn, Perc, Perc Endo]
ØK5B[Ø,3,4]ZZ	Destr/Lwr Arm and Wrist Muscle, Lt, [Opn, Perc, Perc Endo]
ØK5F[Ø,3,4]ZZ	Destr/Trunk Muscle, Rt, [Opn, Perc, Perc Endo]
ØK5G[Ø,3,4]ZZ	Destr/Trunk Muscle, Lt, [Opn, Perc, Perc Endo]
ØK5H[Ø,3,4]ZZ	Destr/Thorax Muscle, Rt, [Opn, Perc, Perc Endo]
ØK5J[Ø,3,4]ZZ	Destr/Thorax Muscle, Lt, [Opn, Perc, Perc Endo]
ØK5K[Ø,3,4]ZZ	Destr/Abd Muscle, Rt, [Opn, Perc, Perc Endo]
ØK5L[Ø,3,4]ZZ	Destr/Abd Muscle, Lt, [Opn, Perc, Perc Endo]
ØK5M[Ø,3,4]ZZ	Destr/Perineum Muscle, [Opn, Perc, Perc Endo]
ØK5N[Ø,3,4]ZZ	Destr/Hip Muscle, Rt, [Opn, Perc, Perc Endo]
ØK5P[Ø,3,4]ZZ	Destr/Hip Muscle, Lt, [Opn, Perc, Perc Endo]
ØK5Q[Ø,3,4]ZZ	Destr/Upr Leg Muscle, Rt, [Opn, Perc, Perc Endo]
ØK5R[Ø,3,4]ZZ	Destr/Upr Leg Muscle, Lt, [Opn, Perc, Perc Endo]
ØK5S[Ø,3,4]ZZ	Destr/Lwr Leg Muscle, Rt, [Opn, Perc, Perc Endo]
ØK5T[Ø,3,4]ZZ	Destr/Lwr Leg Muscle, Lt, [Opn, Perc, Perc Endo]
ØK5V[Ø,3,4]ZZ	Destr/Foot Muscle, Rt, [Opn, Perc, Perc Endo]
ØK5W[Ø,3,4]ZZ	Destr/Foot Muscle, Lt, [Opn, Perc, Perc Endo]
ØK9ØØZX	Drain of Head Muscle, Opn Appr, Diagnostic
ØK9Ø[Ø,3,4]ØZ	Drain/Head Muscle, [Opn, Perc, Perc Endo], Drain Dev, NQ
ØK9Ø[Ø,4]ZZ	Drain/Head Muscle, [Opn, Perc Endo]
ØK91ØZX	Drain of Facial Muscle, Opn Appr, Diagnostic
ØK91[Ø,3,4]ØZ	Drain/Facial Muscle, [Opn, Perc, Perc Endo], Drain Dev, NQ
ØK91[Ø,4]ZZ	Drain/Facial Muscle, [Opn, Perc Endo]
ØK92ØZX	Drain of Rt Neck Muscle, Opn Appr, Diagnostic

Surgical   **Medical**   **CC Indicator**   **MCC Indicator**   **Procedure Proxy**   PDxMCC **PDx acts as own MCC**   PDxCC **PDx acts as own CC**

MDC 9: Diseases And Disorders Of The Skin, Subcutaneous Tissue And Breast—SURGICAL

MDC 9: Diseases And Disorders Of The Skin, Subcutaneous Tissue And Breast—SURGICAL

ØK92[Ø,3,4]ØZ	Drain/Neck Muscle, Rt, [Opn, Perc, Perc Endo], Drain Dev, NQ
ØK92[Ø,4]ZZ	Drain/Neck Muscle, Rt, [Opn, Perc Endo]
ØK93ØZX	Drain of Lt Neck Muscle, Opn Appr, Diagnostic
ØK93[Ø,3,4]ØZ	Drain/Neck Muscle, Lt, [Opn, Perc, Perc Endo], Drain Dev, NQ
ØK93[Ø,4]ZZ	Drain/Neck Muscle, Lt, [Opn, Perc Endo]
ØK94ØZX	Drain of Tongue/Palate/Phar Muscle, Opn Appr, Diagn
ØK94[Ø,3,4]ØZ	Drain/Tongue, Palate, Pharynx Muscle, [Opn, Perc, Perc Endo], Drain Dev, NQ
ØK94[Ø,4]ZZ	Drain/Tongue, Palate, Pharynx Muscle, [Opn, Perc Endo]
ØK95ØZX	Drain of Rt Shldr Muscle, Opn Appr, Diagnostic
ØK95[Ø,3,4]ØZ	Drain/Shldr Muscle, Rt, [Opn, Perc, Perc Endo], Drain Dev, NQ
ØK95[Ø,4]ZZ	Drain/Shldr Muscle, Rt, [Opn, Perc Endo]
ØK96ØZX	Drain of Lt Shldr Muscle, Opn Appr, Diagnostic
ØK96[Ø,3,4]ØZ	Drain/Shldr Muscle, Lt, [Opn, Perc, Perc Endo], Drain Dev, NQ
ØK96[Ø,4]ZZ	Drain/Shldr Muscle, Lt, [Opn, Perc Endo]
ØK97ØZX	Drain of Rt Upr Arm Muscle, Opn Appr, Diagn
ØK97[Ø,3,4]ØZ	Drain/Upr Arm Muscle, Rt, [Opn, Perc, Perc Endo], Drain Dev, NQ
ØK97[Ø,4]ZZ	Drain/Upr Arm Muscle, Rt, [Opn, Perc Endo]
ØK98ØZX	Drain of Lt Upr Arm Muscle, Opn Appr, Diagnostic
ØK98[Ø,3,4]ØZ	Drain/Upr Arm Muscle, Lt, [Opn, Perc, Perc Endo], Drain Dev, NQ
ØK98[Ø,4]ZZ	Drain/Upr Arm Muscle, Lt, [Opn, Perc Endo]
ØK99ØZX	Drain of Rt Low Arm & Wrist Muscle, Opn Appr, Diagn
ØK99[Ø,3,4]ØZ	Drain/Lwr Arm and Wrist Muscle, Rt, [Opn, Perc, Perc Endo], Drain Dev, NQ
ØK99[Ø,4]ZZ	Drain/Lwr Arm and Wrist Muscle, Rt, [Opn, Perc Endo]
ØK9BØZX	Drain of Lt Low Arm & Wrist Muscle, Opn Appr, Diagn
ØK9B[Ø,3,4]ØZ	Drain/Lwr Arm and Wrist Muscle, Lt, [Opn, Perc, Perc Endo], Drain Dev, NQ
ØK9B[Ø,4]ZZ	Drain/Lwr Arm and Wrist Muscle, Lt, [Opn, Perc Endo]
ØK9CØZX	Drain of Rt Hand Muscle, Opn Appr, Diagnostic
ØK9DØZX	Drain of Lt Hand Muscle, Opn Appr, Diagnostic
ØK9FØZX	Drain of Rt Trunk Muscle, Opn Appr, Diagnostic
ØK9F[Ø,3,4]ØZ	Drain/Trunk Muscle, Rt, [Opn, Perc, Perc Endo], Drain Dev, NQ
ØK9F[Ø,4]ZZ	Drain/Trunk Muscle, Rt, [Opn, Perc Endo]
ØK9GØZX	Drain of Lt Trunk Muscle, Opn Appr, Diagnostic
ØK9G[Ø,3,4]ØZ	Drain/Trunk Muscle, Lt, [Opn, Perc, Perc Endo], Drain Dev, NQ
ØK9G[Ø,4]ZZ	Drain/Trunk Muscle, Lt, [Opn, Perc Endo]
ØK9HØZX	Drain of Rt Thorax Muscle, Opn Appr, Diagnostic
ØK9H[Ø,3,4]ØZ	Drain/Thorax Muscle, Rt, [Opn, Perc, Perc Endo], Drain Dev, NQ
ØK9H[Ø,4]ZZ	Drain/Thorax Muscle, Rt, [Opn, Perc Endo]
ØK9JØZX	Drain of Lt Thorax Muscle, Opn Appr, Diagnostic
ØK9J[Ø,3,4]ØZ	Drain/Thorax Muscle, Lt, [Opn, Perc, Perc Endo], Drain Dev, NQ
ØK9J[Ø,4]ZZ	Drain/Thorax Muscle, Lt, [Opn, Perc Endo]
ØK9KØZX	Drain of Rt Abd Muscle, Opn Appr, Diagnostic
ØK9K[Ø,3,4]ØZ	Drain/Abd Muscle, Rt, [Opn, Perc, Perc Endo], Drain Dev, NQ
ØK9K[Ø,4]ZZ	Drain/Abd Muscle, Rt, [Opn, Perc Endo]
ØK9LØZX	Drain of Lt Abd Muscle, Opn Appr, Diagnostic
ØK9L[Ø,3,4]ØZ	Drain/Abd Muscle, Lt, [Opn, Perc, Perc Endo], Drain Dev, NQ
ØK9L[Ø,4]ZZ	Drain/Abd Muscle, Lt, [Opn, Perc Endo]
ØK9MØZX	Drain of Perineum Muscle, Opn Appr, Diagnostic
ØK9M[Ø,3,4]ØZ	Drain/Perineum Muscle, [Opn, Perc, Perc Endo], Drain Dev, NQ
ØK9M[Ø,4]ZZ	Drain/Perineum Muscle, [Opn, Perc Endo]
ØK9NØZX	Drain of Rt Hip Muscle, Opn Appr, Diagnostic
ØK9N[Ø,3,4]ØZ	Drain/Hip Muscle, Rt, [Opn, Perc, Perc Endo], Drain Dev, NQ
ØK9N[Ø,4]ZZ	Drain/Hip Muscle, Rt, [Opn, Perc Endo]
ØK9PØZX	Drain of Lt Hip Muscle, Opn Appr, Diagnostic
ØK9P[Ø,3,4]ØZ	Drain/Hip Muscle, Lt, [Opn, Perc, Perc Endo], Drain Dev, NQ
ØK9P[Ø,4]ZZ	Drain/Hip Muscle, Lt, [Opn, Perc Endo]
ØK9QØZX	Drain of Rt Upr Leg Muscle, Opn Appr, Diagn
ØK9Q[Ø,3,4]ØZ	Drain/Upr Leg Muscle, Rt, [Opn, Perc, Perc Endo], Drain Dev, NQ
ØK9Q[Ø,4]ZZ	Drain/Upr Leg Muscle, Rt, [Opn, Perc Endo]
ØK9RØZX	Drain of Lt Upr Leg Muscle, Opn Appr, Diagnostic
ØK9R[Ø,3,4]ØZ	Drain/Upr Leg Muscle, Lt, [Opn, Perc, Perc Endo], Drain Dev, NQ
ØK9R[Ø,4]ZZ	Drain/Upr Leg Muscle, Lt, [Opn, Perc Endo]
ØK9SØZX	Drain of Rt Lwr Leg Muscle, Opn Appr, Diagn
ØK9S[Ø,3,4]ØZ	Drain/Lwr Leg Muscle, Rt, [Opn, Perc, Perc Endo], Drain Dev, NQ
ØK9S[Ø,4]ZZ	Drain/Lwr Leg Muscle, Rt, [Opn, Perc Endo]
ØK9TØZX	Drain of Lt Lwr Leg Muscle, Opn Appr, Diagnostic
ØK9T[Ø,3,4]ØZ	Drain/Lwr Leg Muscle, Lt, [Opn, Perc, Perc Endo], Drain Dev, NQ
ØK9T[Ø,4]ZZ	Drain/Lwr Leg Muscle, Lt, [Opn, Perc Endo]
ØK9VØZX	Drain of Rt Foot Muscle, Opn Appr, Diagnostic
ØK9V[Ø,3,4]ØZ	Drain/Foot Muscle, Rt, [Opn, Perc, Perc Endo], Drain Dev, NQ
ØK9V[Ø,4]ZZ	Drain/Foot Muscle, Rt, [Opn, Perc Endo]
ØK9WØZX	Drain of Lt Foot Muscle, Opn Appr, Diagnostic

ØK9W[Ø,3,4]ØZ	Drain/Foot Muscle, Lt, [Opn, Perc, Perc Endo], Drain Dev, NQ
ØK9W[Ø,4]ZZ	Drain/Foot Muscle, Lt, [Opn, Perc Endo]
ØKBØØZX	Exc of Head Muscle, Opn Appr, Diagnostic
ØKBØ[Ø,3,4]ZZ	Exc/Head Muscle, [Opn, Perc, Perc Endo]
ØKB1ØZX	Exc of Facial Muscle, Opn Appr, Diagnostic
ØKB1[Ø,3,4]ZZ	Exc/Facial Muscle, [Opn, Perc, Perc Endo]
ØKB2ØZX	Exc of Rt Neck Muscle, Opn Appr, Diagnostic
ØKB2[Ø,3,4]ZZ	Exc/Neck Muscle, Rt, [Opn, Perc, Perc Endo]
ØKB3ØZX	Exc of Lt Neck Muscle, Opn Appr, Diagnostic
ØKB3[Ø,3,4]ZZ	Exc/Neck Muscle, Lt, [Opn, Perc, Perc Endo]
ØKB4ØZX	Exc of Tongue/Palate/Phar Muscle, Opn Appr, Diagn
ØKB4[Ø,3,4]ZZ	Exc/Tongue, Palate, Pharynx Muscle, [Opn, Perc, Perc Endo]
ØKB5ØZX	Exc of Rt Shldr Muscle, Opn Appr, Diagnostic
ØKB5[Ø,3,4]ZZ	Exc/Shldr Muscle, Rt, [Opn, Perc, Perc Endo]
ØKB6ØZX	Exc of Lt Shldr Muscle, Opn Appr, Diagnostic
ØKB6[Ø,3,4]ZZ	Exc/Shldr Muscle, Lt, [Opn, Perc, Perc Endo]
ØKB7ØZX	Exc of Rt Upr Arm Muscle, Opn Appr, Diagn
ØKB7[Ø,3,4]ZZ	Exc/Upr Arm Muscle, Rt, [Opn, Perc, Perc Endo]
ØKB8ØZX	Exc of Lt Upr Arm Muscle, Opn Appr, Diagnostic
ØKB8[Ø,3,4]ZZ	Exc/Upr Arm Muscle, Lt, [Opn, Perc, Perc Endo]
ØKB9ØZX	Exc of Rt Low Arm & Wrist Muscle, Opn Appr, Diagn
ØKB9[Ø,3,4]ZZ	Exc/Lwr Arm and Wrist Muscle, Rt, [Opn, Perc, Perc Endo]
ØKBBØZX	Exc of Lt Low Arm & Wrist Muscle, Opn Appr, Diagn
ØKBB[Ø,3,4]ZZ	Exc/Lwr Arm and Wrist Muscle, Lt, [Opn, Perc, Perc Endo]
ØKBCØZX	Exc of Rt Hand Muscle, Opn Appr, Diagnostic
ØKBDØZX	Exc of Lt Hand Muscle, Opn Appr, Diagnostic
ØKBFØZX	Exc of Rt Trunk Muscle, Opn Appr, Diagnostic
ØKBF[Ø,3,4]ZZ	Exc/Trunk Muscle, Rt, [Opn, Perc, Perc Endo]
ØKBGØZX	Exc of Lt Trunk Muscle, Opn Appr, Diagnostic
ØKBG[Ø,3,4]ZZ	Exc/Trunk Muscle, Lt, [Opn, Perc, Perc Endo]
ØKBHØZX	Exc of Rt Thorax Muscle, Opn Appr, Diagnostic
ØKBH[Ø,3,4]ZZ	Exc/Thorax Muscle, Rt, [Opn, Perc, Perc Endo]
ØKBJØZX	Exc of Lt Thorax Muscle, Opn Appr, Diagnostic
ØKBJ[Ø,3,4]ZZ	Exc/Thorax Muscle, Lt, [Opn, Perc, Perc Endo]
ØKBKØZX	Exc of Rt Abd Muscle, Opn Appr, Diagnostic
ØKBK[Ø,3,4]ZZ	Exc/Abd Muscle, Rt, [Opn, Perc, Perc Endo]
ØKBLØZX	Exc of Lt Abd Muscle, Opn Appr, Diagnostic
ØKBL[Ø,3,4]ZZ	Exc/Abd Muscle, Lt, [Opn, Perc, Perc Endo]
ØKBMØZX	Exc of Perineum Muscle, Opn Appr, Diagnostic
ØKBM[Ø,3,4]ZZ	Exc/Perineum Muscle, [Opn, Perc, Perc Endo]
ØKBNØZX	Exc of Rt Hip Muscle, Opn Appr, Diagnostic
ØKBN[Ø,3,4]ZZ	Exc/Hip Muscle, Rt, [Opn, Perc, Perc Endo]
ØKBPØZX	Exc of Lt Hip Muscle, Opn Appr, Diagnostic
ØKBP[Ø,3,4]ZZ	Exc/Hip Muscle, Lt, [Opn, Perc, Perc Endo]
ØKBQØZX	Exc of Rt Upr Leg Muscle, Opn Appr, Diagn
ØKBQ[Ø,3,4]ZZ	Exc/Upr Leg Muscle, Rt, [Opn, Perc, Perc Endo]
ØKBRØZX	Exc of Lt Upr Leg Muscle, Opn Appr, Diagnostic
ØKBR[Ø,3,4]ZZ	Exc/Upr Leg Muscle, Lt, [Opn, Perc, Perc Endo]
ØKBSØZX	Exc of Rt Lwr Leg Muscle, Opn Appr, Diagn
ØKBS[Ø,3,4]ZZ	Exc/Lwr Leg Muscle, Rt, [Opn, Perc, Perc Endo]
ØKBTØZX	Exc of Lt Lwr Leg Muscle, Opn Appr, Diagnostic
ØKBT[Ø,3,4]ZZ	Exc/Lwr Leg Muscle, Lt, [Opn, Perc, Perc Endo]
ØKBVØZX	Exc of Rt Foot Muscle, Opn Appr, Diagnostic
ØKBV[Ø,3,4]ZZ	Exc/Foot Muscle, Rt, [Opn, Perc, Perc Endo]
ØKBWØZX	Exc of Lt Foot Muscle, Opn Appr, Diagnostic
ØKBW[Ø,3,4]ZZ	Exc/Foot Muscle, Lt, [Opn, Perc, Perc Endo]
ØKCØ[Ø,3,4]ZZ	Extir/Head Muscle, [Opn, Perc, Perc Endo]
ØKC1[Ø,3,4]ZZ	Extir/Facial Muscle, [Opn, Perc, Perc Endo]
ØKC2[Ø,3,4]ZZ	Extir/Neck Muscle, Rt, [Opn, Perc, Perc Endo]
ØKC3[Ø,3,4]ZZ	Extir/Neck Muscle, Lt, [Opn, Perc, Perc Endo]
ØKC4[Ø,3,4]ZZ	Extir/Tongue, Palate, Pharynx Muscle, [Opn, Perc, Perc Endo]
ØKC5[Ø,3,4]ZZ	Extir/Shldr Muscle, Rt, [Opn, Perc, Perc Endo]
ØKC6[Ø,3,4]ZZ	Extir/Shldr Muscle, Lt, [Opn, Perc, Perc Endo]
ØKC7[Ø,3,4]ZZ	Extir/Upr Arm Muscle, Rt, [Opn, Perc, Perc Endo]
ØKC8[Ø,3,4]ZZ	Extir/Upr Arm Muscle, Lt, [Opn, Perc, Perc Endo]
ØKC9[Ø,3,4]ZZ	Extir/Lwr Arm and Wrist Muscle, Rt, [Opn, Perc, Perc Endo]
ØKCB[Ø,3,4]ZZ	Extir/Lwr Arm and Wrist Muscle, Lt, [Opn, Perc, Perc Endo]
ØKCF[Ø,3,4]ZZ	Extir/Trunk Muscle, Rt, [Opn, Perc, Perc Endo]
ØKCG[Ø,3,4]ZZ	Extir/Trunk Muscle, Lt, [Opn, Perc, Perc Endo]
ØKCH[Ø,3,4]ZZ	Extir/Thorax Muscle, Rt, [Opn, Perc, Perc Endo]
ØKCJ[Ø,3,4]ZZ	Extir/Thorax Muscle, Lt, [Opn, Perc, Perc Endo]
ØKCK[Ø,3,4]ZZ	Extir/Abd Muscle, Rt, [Opn, Perc, Perc Endo]
ØKCL[Ø,3,4]ZZ	Extir/Abd Muscle, Lt, [Opn, Perc, Perc Endo]
ØKCM[Ø,3,4]ZZ	Extir/Perineum Muscle, [Opn, Perc, Perc Endo]
ØKCN[Ø,3,4]ZZ	Extir/Hip Muscle, Rt, [Opn, Perc, Perc Endo]
ØKCP[Ø,3,4]ZZ	Extir/Hip Muscle, Lt, [Opn, Perc, Perc Endo]
ØKCQ[Ø,3,4]ZZ	Extir/Upr Leg Muscle, Rt, [Opn, Perc, Perc Endo]
ØKCR[Ø,3,4]ZZ	Extir/Upr Leg Muscle, Lt, [Opn, Perc, Perc Endo]
ØKCS[Ø,3,4]ZZ	Extir/Lwr Leg Muscle, Rt, [Opn, Perc, Perc Endo]
ØKCT[Ø,3,4]ZZ	Extir/Lwr Leg Muscle, Lt, [Opn, Perc, Perc Endo]

T **Transfer DRG**   SP **Special Payment**   * **Code Range**   **6th and 7th Character of ZZ = No Device, No Qualifier ZX = No Device, Diagnostic**

ØKCV[Ø,3,4]ZZ	Extir/Foot Muscle, Rt, [Opn, Perc, Perc Endo]
ØKCW[Ø,3,4]ZZ	Extir/Foot Muscle, Lt, [Opn, Perc, Perc Endo]
ØKNC[Ø,3,4]ZZ	Rls/Hand Muscle, Rt, [Opn, Perc, Perc Endo]
ØKND[Ø,3,4]ZZ	Rls/Hand Muscle, Lt, [Opn, Perc, Perc Endo]
ØKPX[Ø,3,4][Ø,7,J,K]Z	Rmvl/Upr Muscle, [Opn, Perc, Perc Endo], [Drain Dev, Auto Tissue Sub, Synth Sub, Nonauto Tissue Sub], NQ
ØKPY[Ø,3,4][Ø,7,J,K]Z	Rmvl/Lwr Muscle, [Opn, Perc, Perc Endo], [Drain Dev, Auto Tissue Sub, Synth Sub, Nonauto Tissue Sub], NQ
ØKQØ[Ø,3,4]ZZ	Rpr/Head Muscle, [Opn, Perc, Perc Endo]
ØKQ1[Ø,3,4]ZZ	Rpr/Facial Muscle, [Opn, Perc, Perc Endo]
ØKQ2[Ø,3,4]ZZ	Rpr/Neck Muscle, Rt, [Opn, Perc, Perc Endo]
ØKQ3[Ø,3,4]ZZ	Rpr/Neck Muscle, Lt, [Opn, Perc, Perc Endo]
ØKQ4[Ø,3,4]ZZ	Rpr/Tongue, Palate, Pharynx Muscle, [Opn, Perc, Perc Endo]
ØKQ5[Ø,3,4]ZZ	Rpr/Shldr Muscle, Rt, [Opn, Perc, Perc Endo]
ØKQ6[Ø,3,4]ZZ	Rpr/Shldr Muscle, Lt, [Opn, Perc, Perc Endo]
ØKQ7[Ø,3,4]ZZ	Rpr/Upr Arm Muscle, Rt, [Opn, Perc, Perc Endo]
ØKQ8[Ø,3,4]ZZ	Rpr/Upr Arm Muscle, Lt, [Opn, Perc, Perc Endo]
ØKQ9[Ø,3,4]ZZ	Rpr/Lwr Arm and Wrist Muscle, Rt, [Opn, Perc, Perc Endo]
ØKQB[Ø,3,4]ZZ	Rpr/Lwr Arm and Wrist Muscle, Lt, [Opn, Perc, Perc Endo]
ØKQF[Ø,3,4]ZZ	Rpr/Trunk Muscle, Rt, [Opn, Perc, Perc Endo]
ØKQG[Ø,3,4]ZZ	Rpr/Trunk Muscle, Lt, [Opn, Perc, Perc Endo]
ØKQH[Ø,3,4]ZZ	Rpr/Thorax Muscle, Rt, [Opn, Perc, Perc Endo]
ØKQJ[Ø,3,4]ZZ	Rpr/Thorax Muscle, Lt, [Opn, Perc, Perc Endo]
ØKQK[Ø,3,4]ZZ	Rpr/Abd Muscle, Rt, [Opn, Perc, Perc Endo]
ØKQL[Ø,3,4]ZZ	Rpr/Abd Muscle, Lt, [Opn, Perc, Perc Endo]
ØKQM[Ø,3,4]ZZ	Rpr/Perineum Muscle, [Opn, Perc, Perc Endo]
ØKQN[Ø,3,4]ZZ	Rpr/Hip Muscle, Rt, [Opn, Perc, Perc Endo]
ØKQP[Ø,3,4]ZZ	Rpr/Hip Muscle, Lt, [Opn, Perc, Perc Endo]
ØKQS[Ø,3,4]ZZ	Rpr/Lwr Leg Muscle, Rt, [Opn, Perc, Perc Endo]
ØKQT[Ø,3,4]ZZ	Rpr/Lwr Leg Muscle, Lt, [Opn, Perc, Perc Endo]
ØKQV[Ø,3,4]ZZ	Rpr/Foot Muscle, Rt, [Opn, Perc, Perc Endo]
ØKQW[Ø,3,4]ZZ	Rpr/Foot Muscle, Lt, [Opn, Perc, Perc Endo]
ØKTØ[Ø,4]ZZ	Resect/Head Muscle, [Opn, Perc Endo]
ØKT1[Ø,4]ZZ	Resect/Facial Muscle, [Opn, Perc Endo]
ØKT2[Ø,4]ZZ	Resect/Neck Muscle, Rt, [Opn, Perc Endo]
ØKT3[Ø,4]ZZ	Resect/Neck Muscle, Lt, [Opn, Perc Endo]
ØKT4[Ø,4]ZZ	Resect/Tongue, Palate, Pharynx Muscle, [Opn, Perc Endo]
ØKT5[Ø,4]ZZ	Resect/Shldr Muscle, Rt, [Opn, Perc Endo]
ØKT6[Ø,4]ZZ	Resect/Shldr Muscle, Lt, [Opn, Perc Endo]
ØKT7[Ø,4]ZZ	Resect/Upr Arm Muscle, Rt, [Opn, Perc Endo]
ØKT8[Ø,4]ZZ	Resect/Upr Arm Muscle, Lt, [Opn, Perc Endo]
ØKT9[Ø,4]ZZ	Resect/Lwr Arm and Wrist Muscle, Rt, [Opn, Perc Endo]
ØKTB[Ø,4]ZZ	Resect/Lwr Arm and Wrist Muscle, Lt, [Opn, Perc Endo]
ØKTF[Ø,4]ZZ	Resect/Trunk Muscle, Rt, [Opn, Perc Endo]
ØKTG[Ø,4]ZZ	Resect/Trunk Muscle, Lt, [Opn, Perc Endo]
ØKTH[Ø,4]ZZ	Resect/Thorax Muscle, Rt, [Opn, Perc Endo]
ØKTJ[Ø,4]ZZ	Resect/Thorax Muscle, Lt, [Opn, Perc Endo]
ØKTK[Ø,4]ZZ	Resect/Abd Muscle, Rt, [Opn, Perc Endo]
ØKTL[Ø,4]ZZ	Resect/Abd Muscle, Lt, [Opn, Perc Endo]
ØKTM[Ø,4]ZZ	Resect/Perineum Muscle, [Opn, Perc Endo]
ØKTN[Ø,4]ZZ	Resect/Hip Muscle, Rt, [Opn, Perc Endo]
ØKTP[Ø,4]ZZ	Resect/Hip Muscle, Lt, [Opn, Perc Endo]
ØKTQ[Ø,4]ZZ	Resect/Upr Leg Muscle, Rt, [Opn, Perc Endo]
ØKTR[Ø,4]ZZ	Resect/Upr Leg Muscle, Lt, [Opn, Perc Endo]
ØKTS[Ø,4]ZZ	Resect/Lwr Leg Muscle, Rt, [Opn, Perc Endo]
ØKTT[Ø,4]ZZ	Resect/Lwr Leg Muscle, Lt, [Opn, Perc Endo]
ØKTV[Ø,4]ZZ	Resect/Foot Muscle, Rt, [Opn, Perc Endo]
ØKTW[Ø,4]ZZ	Resect/Foot Muscle, Lt, [Opn, Perc Endo]
ØKUØ[Ø,4][7,J,K]Z	Supl/Head Muscle, [Opn, Perc Endo], [Auto Tissue Sub, Synth Sub, Nonauto Tissue Sub], NQ
ØKU1[Ø,4][7,J,K]Z	Supl/Facial Muscle, [Opn, Perc Endo], [Auto Tissue Sub, Synth Sub, Nonauto Tissue Sub], NQ
ØKU2[Ø,4][7,J,K]Z	Supl/Neck Muscle, Rt, [Opn, Perc Endo], [Auto Tissue Sub, Synth Sub, Nonauto Tissue Sub], NQ
ØKU3[Ø,4][7,J,K]Z	Supl/Neck Muscle, Lt, [Opn, Perc Endo], [Auto Tissue Sub, Synth Sub, Nonauto Tissue Sub], NQ
ØKU4[Ø,4][7,J,K]Z	Supl/Tongue, Palate, Pharynx Muscle, [Opn, Perc Endo], [Auto Tissue Sub, Synth Sub, Nonauto Tissue Sub], NQ
ØKU5[Ø,4][7,J,K]Z	Supl/Shldr Muscle, Rt, [Opn, Perc Endo], [Auto Tissue Sub, Synth Sub, Nonauto Tissue Sub], NQ
ØKU6[Ø,4][7,J,K]Z	Supl/Shldr Muscle, Lt, [Opn, Perc Endo], [Auto Tissue Sub, Synth Sub, Nonauto Tissue Sub], NQ
ØKU7[Ø,4][7,J,K]Z	Supl/Upr Arm Muscle, Rt, [Opn, Perc Endo], [Auto Tissue Sub, Synth Sub, Nonauto Tissue Sub], NQ
ØKU8[Ø,4][7,J,K]Z	Supl/Upr Arm Muscle, Lt, [Opn, Perc Endo], [Auto Tissue Sub, Synth Sub, Nonauto Tissue Sub], NQ
ØKU9[Ø,4][7,J,K]Z	Supl/Lwr Arm and Wrist Muscle, Rt, [Opn, Perc Endo], [Auto Tissue Sub, Synth Sub, Nonauto Tissue Sub], NQ
ØKUB[Ø,4][7,J,K]Z	Supl/Lwr Arm and Wrist Muscle, Lt, [Opn, Perc Endo], [Auto Tissue Sub, Synth Sub, Nonauto Tissue Sub], NQ
ØKUC[Ø,4][7,J,K]Z	Supl/Hand Muscle, Rt, [Opn, Perc Endo], [Auto Tissue Sub, Synth Sub, Nonauto Tissue Sub], NQ
ØKUD[Ø,4][7,J,K]Z	Supl/Hand Muscle, Lt, [Opn, Perc Endo], [Auto Tissue Sub, Synth Sub, Nonauto Tissue Sub], NQ
ØKUF[Ø,4][7,J,K]Z	Supl/Trunk Muscle, Rt, [Opn, Perc Endo], [Auto Tissue Sub, Synth Sub, Nonauto Tissue Sub], NQ
ØKUG[Ø,4][7,J,K]Z	Supl/Trunk Muscle, Lt, [Opn, Perc Endo], [Auto Tissue Sub, Synth Sub, Nonauto Tissue Sub], NQ
ØKUH[Ø,4][7,J,K]Z	Supl/Thorax Muscle, Rt, [Opn, Perc Endo], [Auto Tissue Sub, Synth Sub, Nonauto Tissue Sub], NQ
ØKUJ[Ø,4][7,J,K]Z	Supl/Thorax Muscle, Lt, [Opn, Perc Endo], [Auto Tissue Sub, Synth Sub, Nonauto Tissue Sub], NQ
ØKUK[Ø,4][7,J,K]Z	Supl/Abd Muscle, Rt, [Opn, Perc Endo], [Auto Tissue Sub, Synth Sub, Nonauto Tissue Sub], NQ
ØKUL[Ø,4][7,J,K]Z	Supl/Abd Muscle, Lt, [Opn, Perc Endo], [Auto Tissue Sub, Synth Sub, Nonauto Tissue Sub], NQ
ØKUM[Ø,4][7,J,K]Z	Supl/Perineum Muscle, [Opn, Perc Endo], [Auto Tissue Sub, Synth Sub, Nonauto Tissue Sub], NQ
ØKUN[Ø,4][7,J,K]Z	Supl/Hip Muscle, Rt, [Opn, Perc Endo], [Auto Tissue Sub, Synth Sub, Nonauto Tissue Sub], NQ
ØKUP[Ø,4][7,J,K]Z	Supl/Hip Muscle, Lt, [Opn, Perc Endo], [Auto Tissue Sub, Synth Sub, Nonauto Tissue Sub], NQ
ØKUQ[Ø,4][7,J,K]Z	Supl/Upr Leg Muscle, Rt, [Opn, Perc Endo], [Auto Tissue Sub, Synth Sub, Nonauto Tissue Sub], NQ
ØKUR[Ø,4][7,J,K]Z	Supl/Upr Leg Muscle, Lt, [Opn, Perc Endo], [Auto Tissue Sub, Synth Sub, Nonauto Tissue Sub], NQ
ØKUS[Ø,4][7,J,K]Z	Supl/Lwr Leg Muscle, Rt, [Opn, Perc Endo], [Auto Tissue Sub, Synth Sub, Nonauto Tissue Sub], NQ
ØKUT[Ø,4][7,J,K]Z	Supl/Lwr Leg Muscle, Lt, [Opn, Perc Endo], [Auto Tissue Sub, Synth Sub, Nonauto Tissue Sub], NQ
ØKUV[Ø,4][7,J,K]Z	Supl/Foot Muscle, Rt, [Opn, Perc Endo], [Auto Tissue Sub, Synth Sub, Nonauto Tissue Sub], NQ
ØKUW[Ø,4][7,J,K]Z	Supl/Foot Muscle, Lt, [Opn, Perc Endo], [Auto Tissue Sub, Synth Sub, Nonauto Tissue Sub], NQ
ØKWX[Ø,3,4][Ø,7,J,K,M]Z	Rev/Upr Muscle, [Opn, Perc, Perc Endo], [Drain Dev, Auto Tissue Sub, Synth Sub, Nonauto Tissue Sub, Stimulator Lead], NQ
ØKWY[Ø,3,4][Ø,7,J,K,M]Z	Rev/Lwr Muscle, [Opn, Perc, Perc Endo], [Drain Dev, Auto Tissue Sub, Synth Sub, Nonauto Tissue Sub, Stimulator Lead], NQ
ØL57[Ø,3,4]ZZ	Destr/Hand Tndn, Rt, [Opn, Perc, Perc Endo]
ØL58[Ø,3,4]ZZ	Destr/Hand Tndn, Lt, [Opn, Perc, Perc Endo]
ØL9ØØZX	Drain of Head and Neck Tndn, Opn Appr, Diagnostic
ØL91ØZX	Drain of Rt Shldr Tndn, Opn Appr, Diagnostic
ØL92ØZX	Drain of Lt Shldr Tndn, Opn Appr, Diagnostic
ØL93ØZX	Drain of Rt Upr Arm Tndn, Opn Appr, Diagn
ØL94ØZX	Drain of Lt Upr Arm Tndn, Opn Appr, Diagnostic
ØL95ØZX	Drain of Rt Low Arm & Wrist Tndn, Opn Appr, Diagn
ØL96ØZX	Drain of Lt Low Arm & Wrist Tndn, Opn Appr, Diagn
ØL97ØZX	Drain of Rt Hand Tndn, Opn Appr, Diagnostic
ØL98ØZX	Drain of Lt Hand Tndn, Opn Appr, Diagnostic
ØL99ØZX	Drain of Rt Trunk Tndn, Opn Appr, Diagnostic
ØL9BØZX	Drain of Lt Trunk Tndn, Opn Appr, Diagnostic
ØL9CØZX	Drain of Rt Thorax Tndn, Opn Appr, Diagnostic
ØL9DØZX	Drain of Lt Thorax Tndn, Opn Appr, Diagnostic
ØL9FØZX	Drain of Rt Abd Tndn, Opn Appr, Diagnostic
ØL9GØZX	Drain of Lt Abd Tndn, Opn Appr, Diagnostic
ØL9HØZX	Drain of Perineum Tndn, Opn Appr, Diagnostic
ØL9JØZX	Drain of Rt Hip Tndn, Opn Appr, Diagnostic
ØL9KØZX	Drain of Lt Hip Tndn, Opn Appr, Diagnostic
ØL9LØZX	Drain of Rt Upr Leg Tndn, Opn Appr, Diagn
ØL9MØZX	Drain of Lt Upr Leg Tndn, Opn Appr, Diagnostic
ØL9NØZX	Drain of Rt Lwr Leg Tndn, Opn Appr, Diagn
ØL9PØZX	Drain of Lt Lwr Leg Tndn, Opn Appr, Diagnostic
ØL9QØZX	Drain of Rt Knee Tndn, Opn Appr, Diagnostic
ØL9RØZX	Drain of Lt Knee Tndn, Opn Appr, Diagnostic
ØL9SØZX	Drain of Rt Ankle Tndn, Opn Appr, Diagnostic
ØL9TØZX	Drain of Lt Ankle Tndn, Opn Appr, Diagnostic
ØL9VØZX	Drain of Rt Foot Tndn, Opn Appr, Diagnostic
ØL9WØZX	Drain of Lt Foot Tndn, Opn Appr, Diagnostic
ØLBØØZX	Exc of Head and Neck Tndn, Opn Appr, Diagnostic
ØLB1ØZX	Exc of Rt Shldr Tndn, Opn Appr, Diagnostic
ØLB2ØZX	Exc of Lt Shldr Tndn, Opn Appr, Diagnostic
ØLB3ØZX	Exc of Rt Upr Arm Tndn, Opn Appr, Diagn
ØLB4ØZX	Exc of Lt Upr Arm Tndn, Opn Appr, Diagnostic
ØLB5ØZX	Exc of Rt Low Arm & Wrist Tndn, Opn Appr, Diagn
ØLB6ØZX	Exc of Lt Low Arm & Wrist Tndn, Opn Appr, Diagn
ØLB7ØZX	Exc of Rt Hand Tndn, Opn Appr, Diagnostic
ØLB8ØZX	Exc of Lt Hand Tndn, Opn Appr, Diagnostic
ØLB9ØZX	Exc of Rt Trunk Tndn, Opn Appr, Diagnostic

Surgical   **Medical**   **CC Indicator**   **MCC Indicator**   **Procedure Proxy**   **PDxMCC** **PDx acts as own MCC**   **PDxCC PDx acts as own CC**

© 2015 Optum360, LLC

ØLBBØZX	Exc of Lt Trunk Tndn, Opn Appr, Diagnostic	ØM99ØZX	Drain of Rt Up Extrem Bursa/Lig, Opn Appr, Diagn
ØLBCØZX	Exc of Rt Thorax Tndn, Opn Appr, Diagnostic	ØM9BØZX	Drain of Lt Up Extrem Bursa/Lig, Opn Appr, Diagn
ØLBDØZX	Exc of Lt Thorax Tndn, Opn Appr, Diagnostic	ØM9HØZX	Drain of Rt Abd Bursa/Lig, Opn Appr, Diagn
ØLBFØZX	Exc of Rt Abd Tndn, Opn Appr, Diagnostic	ØM9JØZX	Drain of Lt Abd Bursa/Lig, Opn Appr, Diagn
ØLBGØZX	Exc of Lt Abd Tndn, Opn Appr, Diagnostic	ØM9KØZX	Drain of Perineum Bursa/Lig, Opn Appr, Diagn
ØLBHØZX	Exc of Perineum Tndn, Opn Appr, Diagnostic	ØM9VØZX	Drain of Rt Low Extrem Bursa/Lig, Opn Appr, Diagn
ØLBJØZX	Exc of Rt Hip Tndn, Opn Appr, Diagnostic	ØM9WØZX	Drain of Lt Low Extrem Bursa/Lig, Opn Appr, Diagn
ØLBKØZX	Exc of Lt Hip Tndn, Opn Appr, Diagnostic	ØMB9ØZX	Exc of Rt Up Extrem Bursa/Lig, Opn Appr, Diagn
ØLBLØZX	Exc of Rt Upr Leg Tndn, Opn Appr, Diagn	ØMBHØZX	Exc of Rt Abd Bursa/Lig, Opn Appr, Diagn
ØLBMØZX	Exc of Lt Upr Leg Tndn, Opn Appr, Diagnostic	ØMBJØZX	Exc of Lt Abd Bursa/Lig, Opn Appr, Diagn
ØLBNØZX	Exc of Rt Lwr Leg Tndn, Opn Appr, Diagn	ØMBKØZX	Exc of Perineum Bursa/Lig, Opn Appr, Diagn
ØLBPØZX	Exc of Lt Lwr Leg Tndn, Opn Appr, Diagnostic	ØMBVØZX	Exc of Rt Low Extrem Bursa/Lig, Opn Appr, Diagn
ØLBQØZX	Exc of Rt Knee Tndn, Opn Appr, Diagnostic	ØMBWØZX	Exc of Lt Low Extrem Bursa/Lig, Opn Appr, Diagn
ØLBRØZX	Exc of Lt Knee Tndn, Opn Appr, Diagnostic	ØMN7[Ø,3,4,X]ZZ	Rls/Hand Bursa & Lgmt, Rt, [Opn, Perc, Perc Endo, Ext]
ØLBSØZX	Exc of Rt Ankle Tndn, Opn Appr, Diagnostic	ØMN8[Ø,3,4,X]ZZ	Rls/Hand Bursa & Lgmt, Lt, [Opn, Perc, Perc Endo, Ext]
ØLBSØZZ	Exc of Rt Ankle Tndn, Opn Appr	ØNNX[Ø,3,4]ZZ	Rls/Hyoid Bone, [Opn, Perc, Perc Endo]
ØLBTØZX	Exc of Lt Ankle Tndn, Opn Appr, Diagnostic	ØNQB[Ø,3,4,X]ZZ	Rpr/Nasal Bone, [Opn, Perc, Perc Endo, Ext]
ØLBTØZZ	Exc of Lt Ankle Tndn, Opn Appr	ØNRB[Ø,3,4][7,J,K]Z	Replace/Nasal Bone, [Opn, Perc, Perc Endo], [Auto Tissue Sub, Synth Sub, Nonauto Tissue Sub], NQ
ØLBVØZX	Exc of Rt Foot Tndn, Opn Appr, Diagnostic	ØNSBØ[4,Z]Z	Repos/Nasal Bone, Opn, [Int Fix Dev, No Dev], NQ
ØLBWØZX	Exc of Lt Foot Tndn, Opn Appr, Diagnostic	ØNUB[Ø,3,4][7,J,K]Z	Supl/Nasal Bone, [Opn, Perc, Perc Endo], [Auto Tissue Sub, Synth Sub, Nonauto Tissue Sub], NQ
ØLN7[Ø,3,4]ZZ	Rls/Hand Tndn, Rt, [Opn, Perc, Perc Endo]	ØNUT[Ø,3,4][7,J,K]Z	Supl/Mandible, Rt, [Opn, Perc, Perc Endo], [Auto Tissue Sub, Synth Sub, Nonauto Tissue Sub], NQ
ØLN8[Ø,3,4]ZZ	Rls/Hand Tndn, Lt, [Opn, Perc, Perc Endo]	ØNUV[Ø,3,4][7,J,K]Z	Supl/Mandible, Lt, [Opn, Perc, Perc Endo], [Auto Tissue Sub, Synth Sub, Nonauto Tissue Sub], NQ
ØLQ0[Ø,3,4]ZZ	Rpr/Head and Neck Tndn, [Opn, Perc, Perc Endo]	ØP90[Ø,3,4]ZX	Drain/Sternum, [Opn, Perc, Perc Endo]
ØLQ3[Ø,3,4]ZZ	Rpr/Upr Arm Tndn, Rt, [Opn, Perc, Perc Endo]	ØP91[Ø,3,4]ZX	Drain/Rib, Rt, [Opn, Perc, Perc Endo]
ØLQ4[Ø,3,4]ZZ	Rpr/Upr Arm Tndn, Lt, [Opn, Perc, Perc Endo]	ØP92[Ø,3,4]ZX	Drain/Rib, Lt, [Opn, Perc, Perc Endo]
ØLQ5[Ø,3,4]ZZ	Rpr/Lwr Arm and Wrist Tndn, Rt, [Opn, Perc, Perc Endo]	ØP95[Ø,3,4]ZX	Drain/Scapula, Rt, [Opn, Perc, Perc Endo]
ØLQ6[Ø,3,4]ZZ	Rpr/Lwr Arm and Wrist Tndn, Lt, [Opn, Perc, Perc Endo]	ØP96[Ø,3,4]ZX	Drain/Scapula, Lt, [Opn, Perc, Perc Endo]
ØLQ7[Ø,3,4]ZZ	Rpr/Hand Tndn, Rt, [Opn, Perc, Perc Endo]	ØP97[Ø,3,4]ZX	Drain/Glenoid Cavity, Rt, [Opn, Perc, Perc Endo]
ØLQ8[Ø,3,4]ZZ	Rpr/Hand Tndn, Lt, [Opn, Perc, Perc Endo]	ØP98[Ø,3,4]ZX	Drain/Glenoid Cavity, Lt, [Opn, Perc, Perc Endo]
ØLQ9[Ø,3,4]ZZ	Rpr/Trunk Tndn, Rt, [Opn, Perc, Perc Endo]	ØP99[Ø,3,4]ZX	Drain/Clavicle, Rt, [Opn, Perc, Perc Endo]
ØLQB[Ø,3,4]ZZ	Rpr/Trunk Tndn, Lt, [Opn, Perc, Perc Endo]	ØP9B[Ø,3,4]ZX	Drain/Clavicle, Lt, [Opn, Perc, Perc Endo]
ØLQC[Ø,3,4]ZZ	Rpr/Thorax Tndn, Rt, [Opn, Perc, Perc Endo]	ØP9C[Ø,3,4]ZX	Drain/Humeral Head, Rt, [Opn, Perc, Perc Endo]
ØLQD[Ø,3,4]ZZ	Rpr/Thorax Tndn, Lt, [Opn, Perc, Perc Endo]	ØP9D[Ø,3,4]ZX	Drain/Humeral Head, Lt, [Opn, Perc, Perc Endo]
ØLQF[Ø,3,4]ZZ	Rpr/Abd Tndn, Rt, [Opn, Perc, Perc Endo]	ØP9F[Ø,3,4]ZX	Drain/Humeral Shaft, Rt, [Opn, Perc, Perc Endo]
ØLQG[Ø,3,4]ZZ	Rpr/Abd Tndn, Lt, [Opn, Perc, Perc Endo]	ØP9G[Ø,3,4]ZX	Drain/Humeral Shaft, Lt, [Opn, Perc, Perc Endo]
ØLQH[Ø,3,4]ZZ	Rpr/Perineum Tndn, [Opn, Perc, Perc Endo]	ØP9H[Ø,3,4]ZX	Drain/Radius, Rt, [Opn, Perc, Perc Endo]
ØLQJ[Ø,3,4]ZZ	Rpr/Hip Tndn, Rt, [Opn, Perc, Perc Endo]	ØP9J[Ø,3,4]ZX	Drain/Radius, Lt, [Opn, Perc, Perc Endo]
ØLQK[Ø,3,4]ZZ	Rpr/Hip Tndn, Lt, [Opn, Perc, Perc Endo]	ØP9K[Ø,3,4]ZX	Drain/Ulna, Rt, [Opn, Perc, Perc Endo]
ØLQL[Ø,3,4]ZZ	Rpr/Upr Leg Tndn, Rt, [Opn, Perc, Perc Endo]	ØP9L[Ø,3,4]ZX	Drain/Ulna, Lt, [Opn, Perc, Perc Endo]
ØLQM[Ø,3,4]ZZ	Rpr/Upr Leg Tndn, Lt, [Opn, Perc, Perc Endo]	ØP9M[Ø,3,4]ZX	Drain/Carpal, Rt, [Opn, Perc, Perc Endo]
ØLQN[Ø,3,4]ZZ	Rpr/Lwr Leg Tndn, Rt, [Opn, Perc, Perc Endo]	ØP9N[Ø,3,4]ZX	Drain/Carpal, Lt, [Opn, Perc, Perc Endo]
ØLQP[Ø,3,4]ZZ	Rpr/Lwr Leg Tndn, Lt, [Opn, Perc, Perc Endo]	ØP9P[Ø,3,4]ZX	Drain/Metacarpal, Rt, [Opn, Perc, Perc Endo]
ØLQV[Ø,3,4]ZZ	Rpr/Foot Tndn, Rt, [Opn, Perc, Perc Endo]	ØP9Q[Ø,3,4]ZX	Drain/Metacarpal, Lt, [Opn, Perc, Perc Endo]
ØLQW[Ø,3,4]ZZ	Rpr/Foot Tndn, Lt, [Opn, Perc, Perc Endo]	ØP9R[Ø,3,4]ZX	Drain/Thumb Phalanx, Rt, [Opn, Perc, Perc Endo]
ØLR7[Ø,4][7,J,K]Z	Replace/Hand Tndn, Rt, [Opn, Perc Endo], [Auto Tissue Sub, Synth Sub, Nonauto Tissue Sub], NQ	ØP9S[Ø,3,4]ZX	Drain/Thumb Phalanx, Lt, [Opn, Perc, Perc Endo]
ØLR8[Ø,4][7,J,K]Z	Replace/Hand Tndn, Lt, [Opn, Perc Endo], [Auto Tissue Sub, Synth Sub, Nonauto Tissue Sub], NQ	ØP9T[Ø,3,4]ZX	Drain/Finger Phalanx, Rt, [Opn, Perc, Perc Endo]
		ØP9V[Ø,3,4]ZX	Drain/Finger Phalanx, Lt, [Opn, Perc, Perc Endo]
ØLSØ[Ø,4]ZZ	Repos/Head and Neck Tndn, [Opn, Perc Endo]	ØPB0[Ø,3,4]ZX	Exc/Sternum, [Opn, Perc, Perc Endo]
ØLS1[Ø,4]ZZ	Repos/Shldr Tndn, Rt, [Opn, Perc Endo]	ØPB1[Ø,3,4]ZX	Exc/Rib, Rt, [Opn, Perc, Perc Endo]
ØLS2[Ø,4]ZZ	Repos/Shldr Tndn, Lt, [Opn, Perc Endo]	ØPB2[Ø,3,4]ZX	Exc/Rib, Lt, [Opn, Perc, Perc Endo]
ØLS3[Ø,4]ZZ	Repos/Upr Arm Tndn, Rt, [Opn, Perc Endo]	ØPB5[Ø,3,4]ZX	Exc/Scapula, Rt, [Opn, Perc, Perc Endo]
ØLS4[Ø,4]ZZ	Repos/Upr Arm Tndn, Lt, [Opn, Perc Endo]	ØPB6[Ø,3,4]ZX	Exc/Scapula, Lt, [Opn, Perc, Perc Endo]
ØLS5[Ø,4]ZZ	Repos/Lwr Arm and Wrist Tndn, Rt, [Opn, Perc Endo]	ØPB7[Ø,3,4]ZX	Exc/Glenoid Cavity, Rt, [Opn, Perc, Perc Endo]
ØLS6[Ø,4]ZZ	Repos/Lwr Arm and Wrist Tndn, Lt, [Opn, Perc Endo]	ØPB8[Ø,3,4]ZX	Exc/Glenoid Cavity, Lt, [Opn, Perc, Perc Endo]
ØLS9[Ø,4]ZZ	Repos/Trunk Tndn, Rt, [Opn, Perc Endo]	ØPB9[Ø,3,4]ZX	Exc/Clavicle, Rt, [Opn, Perc, Perc Endo]
ØLSB[Ø,4]ZZ	Repos/Trunk Tndn, Lt, [Opn, Perc Endo]	ØPBB[Ø,3,4]ZX	Exc/Clavicle, Lt, [Opn, Perc, Perc Endo]
ØLSC[Ø,4]ZZ	Repos/Thorax Tndn, Rt, [Opn, Perc Endo]	ØPBC[Ø,3,4]ZX	Exc/Humeral Head, Rt, [Opn, Perc, Perc Endo]
ØLSD[Ø,4]ZZ	Repos/Thorax Tndn, Lt, [Opn, Perc Endo]	ØPBD[Ø,3,4]ZX	Exc/Humeral Head, Lt, [Opn, Perc, Perc Endo]
ØLSF[Ø,4]ZZ	Repos/Abd Tndn, Rt, [Opn, Perc Endo]	ØPBF[Ø,3,4]ZX	Exc/Humeral Shaft, Rt, [Opn, Perc, Perc Endo]
ØLSG[Ø,4]ZZ	Repos/Abd Tndn, Lt, [Opn, Perc Endo]	ØPBG[Ø,3,4]ZX	Exc/Humeral Shaft, Lt, [Opn, Perc, Perc Endo]
ØLSH[Ø,4]ZZ	Repos/Perineum Tndn, [Opn, Perc Endo]	ØPBH[Ø,3,4]ZX	Exc/Radius, Rt, [Opn, Perc, Perc Endo]
ØLSJ[Ø,4]ZZ	Repos/Hip Tndn, Rt, [Opn, Perc Endo]	ØPBJ[Ø,3,4]ZX	Exc/Radius, Lt, [Opn, Perc, Perc Endo]
ØLSK[Ø,4]ZZ	Repos/Hip Tndn, Lt, [Opn, Perc Endo]	ØPBK[Ø,3,4]ZX	Exc/Ulna, Rt, [Opn, Perc, Perc Endo]
ØLSL[Ø,4]ZZ	Repos/Upr Leg Tndn, Rt, [Opn, Perc Endo]	ØPBL[Ø,3,4]ZX	Exc/Ulna, Lt, [Opn, Perc, Perc Endo]
ØLSM[Ø,4]ZZ	Repos/Upr Leg Tndn, Lt, [Opn, Perc Endo]	ØPBM[Ø,3,4]ZX	Exc/Carpal, Rt, [Opn, Perc, Perc Endo]
ØLSN[Ø,4]ZZ	Repos/Lwr Leg Tndn, Rt, [Opn, Perc Endo]	ØPBN[Ø,3,4]ZX	Exc/Carpal, Lt, [Opn, Perc, Perc Endo]
ØLSP[Ø,4]ZZ	Repos/Lwr Leg Tndn, Lt, [Opn, Perc Endo]	ØPBP[Ø,3,4]ZX	Exc/Metacarpal, Rt, [Opn, Perc, Perc Endo]
ØLSQ[Ø,4]ZZ	Repos/Knee Tndn, Rt, [Opn, Perc Endo]	ØPBQ[Ø,3,4]ZX	Exc/Metacarpal, Lt, [Opn, Perc, Perc Endo]
ØLSR[Ø,4]ZZ	Repos/Knee Tndn, Lt, [Opn, Perc Endo]	ØPBR[Ø,3,4]ZX	Exc/Thumb Phalanx, Rt, [Opn, Perc, Perc Endo]
ØLSS[Ø,4]ZZ	Repos/Ankle Tndn, Rt, [Opn, Perc Endo]	ØPBS[Ø,3,4]ZX	Exc/Thumb Phalanx, Lt, [Opn, Perc, Perc Endo]
ØLST[Ø,4]ZZ	Repos/Ankle Tndn, Lt, [Opn, Perc Endo]	ØPBT[Ø,3,4]ZX	Exc/Finger Phalanx, Rt, [Opn, Perc, Perc Endo]
ØLSV[Ø,4]ZZ	Repos/Foot Tndn, Rt, [Opn, Perc Endo]	ØPBV[Ø,3,4]ZX	Exc/Finger Phalanx, Lt, [Opn, Perc, Perc Endo]
ØLSW[Ø,4]ZZ	Repos/Foot Tndn, Lt, [Opn, Perc Endo]	ØQ96[Ø,3,4]ZX	Drain/Upr Femur, Rt, [Opn, Perc, Perc Endo]
ØLU7[Ø,4][7,J,K]Z	Supl/Hand Tndn, Rt, [Opn, Perc Endo], [Auto Tissue Sub, Synth Sub, Nonauto Tissue Sub], NQ	ØQ97[Ø,3,4]ZX	Drain/Upr Femur, Lt, [Opn, Perc, Perc Endo]
ØLU8[Ø,4][7,J,K]Z	Supl/Hand Tndn, Lt, [Opn, Perc Endo], [Auto Tissue Sub, Synth Sub, Nonauto Tissue Sub], NQ	ØQ98[Ø,3,4]ZX	Drain/Femor Shaft, Rt, [Opn, Perc, Perc Endo]
ØM55[Ø,3,4]ZZ	Destr/Wrist Bursa & Lgmt, Rt, [Opn, Perc, Perc Endo]	ØQ99[Ø,3,4]ZX	Drain/Femor Shaft, Lt, [Opn, Perc, Perc Endo]
ØM56[Ø,3,4]ZZ	Destr/Wrist Bursa & Lgmt, Lt, [Opn, Perc, Perc Endo]		

Ⓣ **Transfer DRG**   ⓈⓅ **Special Payment**   * **Code Range**   6th and 7th Character of ZZ = No Device, No Qualifier ZX = No Device, Diagnostic

0Q9B[0,3,4]ZX	Drain/Lwr Femur, Rt, [Opn, Perc, Perc Endo]
0Q9C[0,3,4]ZX	Drain/Lwr Femur, Lt, [Opn, Perc, Perc Endo]
0Q9D[0,3,4]ZX	Drain/Patella, Rt, [Opn, Perc, Perc Endo]
0Q9F[0,3,4]ZX	Drain/Patella, Lt, [Opn, Perc, Perc Endo]
0Q9G[0,3,4]ZX	Drain/Tibia, Rt, [Opn, Perc, Perc Endo]
0Q9H[0,3,4]ZX	Drain/Tibia, Lt, [Opn, Perc, Perc Endo]
0Q9J[0,3,4]ZX	Drain/Fibula, Rt, [Opn, Perc, Perc Endo]
0Q9K[0,3,4]ZX	Drain/Fibula, Lt, [Opn, Perc, Perc Endo]
0Q9L[0,3,4]ZX	Drain/Tarsal, Rt, [Opn, Perc, Perc Endo]
0Q9M[0,3,4]ZX	Drain/Tarsal, Lt, [Opn, Perc, Perc Endo]
0Q9N[0,3,4]ZX	Drain/Metatarsal, Rt, [Opn, Perc, Perc Endo]
0Q9P[0,3,4]ZX	Drain/Metatarsal, Lt, [Opn, Perc, Perc Endo]
0Q9Q[0,3,4]ZX	Drain/Toe Phalanx, Rt, [Opn, Perc, Perc Endo]
0Q9R[0,3,4]ZX	Drain/Toe Phalanx, Lt, [Opn, Perc, Perc Endo]
0QB6[0,3,4]ZX	Exc/Upr Femur, Rt, [Opn, Perc, Perc Endo]
0QB7[0,3,4]ZX	Exc/Upr Femur, Lt, [Opn, Perc, Perc Endo]
0QB8[0,3,4]ZX	Exc/Femor Shaft, Rt, [Opn, Perc, Perc Endo]
0QB9[0,3,4]ZX	Exc/Femor Shaft, Lt, [Opn, Perc, Perc Endo]
0QBB[0,3,4]ZX	Exc/Lwr Femur, Rt, [Opn, Perc, Perc Endo]
0QBC[0,3,4]ZX	Exc/Lwr Femur, Lt, [Opn, Perc, Perc Endo]
0QBD[0,3,4]ZX	Exc/Patella, Rt, [Opn, Perc, Perc Endo]
0QBF[0,3,4]ZX	Exc/Patella, Lt, [Opn, Perc, Perc Endo]
0QBG[0,3,4]ZX	Exc/Tibia, Rt, [Opn, Perc, Perc Endo]
0QBH[0,3,4]ZX	Exc/Tibia, Lt, [Opn, Perc, Perc Endo]
0QBJ[0,3,4]ZX	Exc/Fibula, Rt, [Opn, Perc, Perc Endo]
0QBK[0,3,4]ZX	Exc/Fibula, Lt, [Opn, Perc, Perc Endo]
0QBL[0,3,4]ZX	Exc/Tarsal, Rt, [Opn, Perc, Perc Endo]
0QBM[0,3,4]ZX	Exc/Tarsal, Lt, [Opn, Perc, Perc Endo]
0QBN[0,3,4]ZX	Exc/Metatarsal, Rt, [Opn, Perc, Perc Endo]
0QBP[0,3,4]ZX	Exc/Metatarsal, Lt, [Opn, Perc, Perc Endo]
0QBQ[0,3,4]ZX	Exc/Toe Phalanx, Rt, [Opn, Perc, Perc Endo]
0QBR[0,3,4]ZX	Exc/Toe Phalanx, Lt, [Opn, Perc, Perc Endo]
0R5N[0,3,4]ZZ	Destr/Wrist Jt, Rt, [Opn, Perc, Perc Endo]
0R5P[0,3,4]ZZ	Destr/Wrist Jt, Lt, [Opn, Perc, Perc Endo]
0U5G[0,3,4,7,8,X]ZZ	Destr/Vagina, [Opn, Perc, Perc Endo, Via Natrl or Artfcl Opng, Via Natrl or Artfcl Opng Endo, Ext]
0U5L[0,X]ZZ	Destr/Vestibular Gland, [Opn, Ext]
0U5M[0,X]ZZ	Destr/Vulva, [Opn, Ext]
0U9C[0,3,4,7,8]ZX	Drain/Cervix, [Opn, Perc, Perc Endo, Via Natrl or Artfcl Opng, Via Natrl or Artfcl Opng Endo]
0U9G[0,3,4,7,8,X]ZX	Drain/Vagina, [Opn, Perc, Perc Endo, Via Natrl or Artfcl Opng, Via Natrl or Artfcl Opng Endo, Ext]
0U9J[0,X]ZX	Drain/Clitoris, [Opn, Ext]
0U9M[0,X]ZX	Drain/Vulva, [Opn, Ext]
0U9M[0,X][0,Z]Z	Drain/Vulva, [Opn, Ext], [Drain Dev, No Dev], NQ
0UBC[0,3,4,7,8]Z[X,Z]	Exc/Cervix, [Opn, Perc, Perc Endo, Via Natrl or Artfcl Opng, Via Natrl or Artfcl Opng Endo], No Dev, [Dx, NQ]
0UBG[0,3,4,7,8,X]Z[X,Z]	Exc/Vagina, [Opn, Perc, Perc Endo, Via Natrl or Artfcl Opng, Via Natrl or Artfcl Opng Endo, Ext], No Dev, [Dx, NQ]
0UBL[0,X]ZZ	Exc/Vestibular Gland, [Opn, Ext]
0UBM[0,X]ZZ	Exc/Vulva, [Opn, Ext]
0UCM0ZZ	Extir of Matter from Vulva, Opn Appr
0UJM0ZZ	Inspect of Vulva, Opn Appr
0UPM0[0,7,J,K]Z	Rmvl/Vulva, Opn, [Drain Dev, Auto Tissue Sub, Synth Sub, Nonauto Tissue Sub], NQ
0UQG[7,8,X]ZZ	Rpr/Vagina, [Via Natrl or Artfcl Opng, Via Natrl or Artfcl Opng Endo, Ext]
0UQM[0,X]ZZ	Rpr/Vulva, [Opn, Ext]
0UT0[0,4,7,8,F]ZZ	Resect/Ovary, Rt, [Opn, Perc Endo, Via Natrl or Artfcl Opng, Via Natrl or Artfcl Opng Endo, Via Natrl or Artfcl Opng w/ Perc Endo Assistance]
0UT1[0,4,7,8,F]ZZ	Resect/Ovary, Lt, [Opn, Perc Endo, Via Natrl or Artfcl Opng, Via Natrl or Artfcl Opng Endo, Via Natrl or Artfcl Opng w/ Perc Endo Assistance]
0UT2[0,4,7,8,F]ZZ	Resect/Ovaries, Bilat, [Opn, Perc Endo, Via Natrl or Artfcl Opng, Via Natrl or Artfcl Opng Endo, Via Natrl or Artfcl Opng w/ Perc Endo Assistance]
0UTL[0,X]ZZ	Resect/Vestibular Gland, [Opn, Ext]
0UTM[0,X]ZZ	Resect/Vulva, [Opn, Ext]
0UWM0[0,7,J,K]Z	Rev/Vulva, Opn, [Drain Dev, Auto Tissue Sub, Synth Sub, Nonauto Tissue Sub], NQ
0V5S[0,3,4,X]ZZ	Destr/Penis, [Opn, Perc, Perc Endo, Ext]
0V5T[0,3,4,X]ZZ	Destr/Prepuce, [Opn, Perc, Perc Endo, Ext]
0V9S[0,3,4,X]ZX	Drain/Penis, [Opn, Perc, Perc Endo, Ext]
0V9T[0,3,4,X]ZX	Drain/Prepuce, [Opn, Perc, Perc Endo, Ext]
0VBS[0,3,4,X]Z[X,Z]	Exc/Penis, [Opn, Perc, Perc Endo, Ext], No Dev, [Dx, NQ]
0VBT[0,3,4,X]Z[X,Z]	Exc/Prepuce, [Opn, Perc, Perc Endo, Ext], No Dev, [Dx, NQ]
0VQS[0,3,4]ZZ	Rpr/Penis, [Opn, Perc, Perc Endo]
0VQT[0,3,4,X]ZZ	Rpr/Prepuce, [Opn, Perc, Perc Endo, Ext]
0VUT[0,4,X][7,J,K]ZSupl/Prepuce, [Opn, Perc Endo, Ext], [Auto Tissue Sub, Synth Sub, Nonauto Tissue Sub], NQ
0W00[0,3,4][7,J,K,Z]Z	Alter/Head, [Opn, Perc, Perc Endo], [Auto Tissue Sub, Synth Sub, Nonauto Tissue Sub, No Dev], NQ
0W02[0,3,4][7,J,K,Z]Z	Alter/Face, [Opn, Perc, Perc Endo], [Auto Tissue Sub, Synth Sub, Nonauto Tissue Sub, No Dev], NQ
0W06[0,3,4][7,J,K,Z]Z	Alter/Neck, [Opn, Perc, Perc Endo], [Auto Tissue Sub, Synth Sub, Nonauto Tissue Sub, No Dev], NQ
0W08[0,3,4][7,J,K,Z]Z	Alter/Chest Wall, [Opn, Perc, Perc Endo], [Auto Tissue Sub, Synth Sub, Nonauto Tissue Sub, No Dev], NQ
0W0F[0,3,4][7,J,K,Z]Z	Alter/Abd Wall, [Opn, Perc, Perc Endo], [Auto Tissue Sub, Synth Sub, Nonauto Tissue Sub, No Dev], NQ
0W0K[0,3,4][7,J,K,Z]Z	Alter/Upr Back, [Opn, Perc, Perc Endo], [Auto Tissue Sub, Synth Sub, Nonauto Tissue Sub, No Dev], NQ
0W0L[0,3,4][7,J,K,Z]Z	Alter/Lwr Back, [Opn, Perc, Perc Endo], [Auto Tissue Sub, Synth Sub, Nonauto Tissue Sub, No Dev], NQ
0W0M[0,3,4][7,J,K,Z]Z	Alter/Perineum, Male, [Opn, Perc, Perc Endo], [Auto Tissue Sub, Synth Sub, Nonauto Tissue Sub, No Dev], NQ
0W38[0,3,4]ZZ	Control/Chest Wall, [Opn, Perc, Perc Endo]
0W3F[0,3,4]ZZ	Control/Abd Wall, [Opn, Perc, Perc Endo]
0W3K[0,3,4]ZZ	Control/Upr Back, [Opn, Perc, Perc Endo]
0W3L[0,3,4]ZZ	Control/Lwr Back, [Opn, Perc, Perc Endo]
0W92[0,3,4][0,Z]Z	Drain/Face, [Opn, Perc, Perc Endo], [Drain Dev, No Dev], NQ
0W93[0,3,4][0,Z]Z	Drain/Oral Cavity and Throat, [Opn, Perc, Perc Endo], [Drain Dev, No Dev], NQ
0W94[0,3,4][0,Z]Z	Drain/Upr Jaw, [Opn, Perc, Perc Endo], [Drain Dev, No Dev], NQ
0W95[0,3,4][0,Z]Z	Drain/Lwr Jaw, [Opn, Perc, Perc Endo], [Drain Dev, No Dev], NQ
0W96[0,3,4][0,Z]Z	Drain/Neck, [Opn, Perc, Perc Endo], [Drain Dev, No Dev], NQ
0W9F00Z	Drain of Abd Wall with Drain Dev, Opn Appr
0W9F0ZZ	Drain of Abd Wall, Opn Appr
0W9F[0,3,4]ZX	Drain/Abd Wall, [Opn, Perc, Perc Endo]
0W9H[0,3,4][0,Z]ZDrain/Retroperitoneum, [Opn, Perc, Perc Endo], [Drain Dev, No Dev], NQ
0W9N[0,3,4][0,Z]Z	Drain/Perineum, Female, [Opn, Perc, Perc Endo], [Drain Dev, No Dev], NQ
0WB6XZ2	Exc of Neck, Stoma, Ext Appr
0WB8[0,3,4,X]ZZ	Exc/Chest Wall, [Opn, Perc, Perc Endo, Ext]
0WBFXZ2	Exc of Abd Wall, Stoma, Ext Appr
0WBF[0,3,4,X]Z[X,Z]	Exc/Abd Wall, [Opn, Perc, Perc Endo, Ext], No Dev, [Dx, NQ]
0WBH[0,3,4]ZZ	Exc/Retroperitoneum, [Opn, Perc, Perc Endo]
0WBN[0,3,4]Z[X,Z]	Exc/Perineum, Female, [Opn, Perc, Perc Endo, Ext], No Dev, [Dx, NQ]
0WC3[0,3,4]ZZ	Extir/Oral Cavity and Throat, [Opn, Perc, Perc Endo]
0WCJ[3,4]ZZ	Extir/Pelvic Cavity, [Perc, Perc Endo]
0WCP[3,4]ZZ	Extir/Gastrointestinal Tract, [Perc, Perc Endo]
0WCR[3,4]ZZ	Extir/Genitourinary Tract, [Perc, Perc Endo]
0WF3[0,3,4]ZZ	Fragmn/Oral Cavity and Throat, [Opn, Perc, Perc Endo]
0WH3[0,3,4][3,Y]Z	Insert/Oral Cavity and Throat, [Opn, Perc, Perc Endo], [Inf Dev, Oth Dev], NQ
0WHN[0,3,4][3,Y]Z	Insert/Perineum, Female, [Opn, Perc, Perc Endo], [Inf Dev, Oth Dev], NQ
0WJ60ZZ	Inspect of Neck, Opn Appr
0WJF[0,4]ZZ	Inspect/Abd Wall, [Opn, Perc Endo]
0WJG[0,4]ZZ	Inspect/Peritoneal Cavity, [Opn, Perc Endo]
0WJH0ZZ	Inspect of Retroperitoneum, Opn Appr
0WJJ[0,4]ZZ	Inspect/Pelvic Cavity, [Opn, Perc Endo]
0WJP[0,4]ZZ	Inspect/Gastrointestinal Tract, [Opn, Perc Endo]
0WJR[0,4]ZZ	Inspect/Genitourinary Tract, [Opn, Perc Endo]
0WM20ZZ	Reattach of Face, Opn Appr
0WM40ZZ	Reattach of Upr Jaw, Opn Appr
0WM50ZZ	Reattach of Lwr Jaw, Opn Appr
0WM60ZZ	Reattach of Neck, Opn Appr
0WM80ZZ	Reattach of Chest Wall, Opn Appr
0WMF0ZZ	Reattach of Abd Wall, Opn Appr
0WMK0ZZ	Reattach of Upr Back, Opn Appr
0WML0ZZ	Reattach of Lwr Back, Opn Appr
0WMM0ZZ	Reattach of Male Perineum, Opn Appr
0WPN[0,3,4][0,1,3,7,J,K,Y]Z	Rmvl/Perineum, Female, [Opn, Perc, Perc Endo], [Drain Dev, Radioact Elmt, Inf Dev, Auto Tissue Sub, Synth Sub, Nonauto Tissue Sub, Oth Dev], NQ
0WQ0[0,3,4,X]ZZ	Rpr/Head, [Opn, Perc, Perc Endo, Ext]
0WQ2[0,3,4,X]ZZ	Rpr/Face, [Opn, Perc, Perc Endo, Ext]
0WQ4[0,3,4,X]ZZ	Rpr/Upr Jaw, [Opn, Perc, Perc Endo, Ext]
0WQ5[0,3,4,X]ZZ	Rpr/Lwr Jaw, [Opn, Perc, Perc Endo, Ext]
0WQ6XZ2	Repair Neck, Stoma, Ext Appr
0WQ6[0,3,4,X]ZZ	Rpr/Neck, [Opn, Perc, Perc Endo, Ext]
0WQ8[0,3,4,X]ZZ	Rpr/Chest Wall, [Opn, Perc, Perc Endo, Ext]
0WQF[3,4,X]ZZ	Rpr/Abd Wall, [Perc, Perc Endo, Ext]
0WQK[0,3,4,X]ZZ	Rpr/Upr Back, [Opn, Perc, Perc Endo, Ext]
0WQL[0,3,4,X]ZZ	Rpr/Lwr Back, [Opn, Perc, Perc Endo, Ext]

Surgical　　**Medical**　　**CC Indicator**　　**MCC Indicator**　　**Procedure Proxy**　　**PDxMCC PDx acts as own MCC**　　**PDxCC PDx acts as own CC**

ØWQM[Ø,3,4,X]ZZ Rpr/Perineum, Male, [Opn, Perc, Perc Endo, Ext]
ØWU0[Ø,4][J,K]Z Supl/Head, [Opn, Perc Endo], [Synth Sub, Nonauto Tissue Sub], NQ
ØWU2[Ø,4][7,J,K]Z Supl/Face, [Opn, Perc Endo], [Auto Tissue Sub, Synth Sub, Nonauto Tissue Sub], NQ
ØWU4[Ø,4]7Z Supl/Upr Jaw, [Opn, Perc Endo], Auto Tissue Sub, NQ
ØWU5[Ø,4]7Z Supl/Lwr Jaw, [Opn, Perc Endo], Auto Tissue Sub, NQ
ØWU6[Ø,4][J,K]Z Supl/Neck, [Opn, Perc Endo], [Synth Sub, Nonauto Tissue Sub], NQ
ØWUK[Ø,4][J,K]Z Supl/Upr Back, [Opn, Perc Endo], [Synth Sub, Nonauto Tissue Sub], NQ
ØWUL[Ø,4][J,K]Z Supl/Lwr Back, [Opn, Perc Endo], [Synth Sub, Nonauto Tissue Sub], NQ
ØWUM[Ø,4][J,K]Z Supl/Perineum, Male, [Opn, Perc Endo], [Synth Sub, Nonauto Tissue Sub], NQ
ØWWN[Ø,3,4][Ø,1,3,7,J,K,Y]ZRev/Perineum, Female, [Opn, Perc, Perc Endo], [Drain Dev, Radioact Elmt, Inf Dev, Auto Tissue Sub, Synth Sub, Nonauto Tissue Sub, Oth Dev], NQ
ØX02[Ø,3,4][7,J,K,Z]Z Alter/Shldr Rgn, Rt, [Opn, Perc, Perc Endo], [Auto Tissue Sub, Synth Sub, Nonauto Tissue Sub, No Dev], NQ
ØX03[Ø,3,4][7,J,K,Z]Z Alter/Shldr Rgn, Lt, [Opn, Perc, Perc Endo], [Auto Tissue Sub, Synth Sub, Nonauto Tissue Sub, No Dev], NQ
ØX04[Ø,3,4][7,J,K,Z]Z Alter/Axilla, Rt, [Opn, Perc, Perc Endo], [Auto Tissue Sub, Synth Sub, Nonauto Tissue Sub, No Dev], NQ
ØX05[Ø,3,4][7,J,K,Z]Z Alter/Axilla, Lt, [Opn, Perc, Perc Endo], [Auto Tissue Sub, Synth Sub, Nonauto Tissue Sub, No Dev], NQ
ØX06[Ø,3,4][7,J,K,Z]Z Alter/Upr Extr, Rt, [Opn, Perc, Perc Endo], [Auto Tissue Sub, Synth Sub, Nonauto Tissue Sub, No Dev], NQ
ØX07[Ø,3,4][7,J,K,Z]Z Alter/Upr Extr, Lt, [Opn, Perc, Perc Endo], [Auto Tissue Sub, Synth Sub, Nonauto Tissue Sub, No Dev], NQ
ØX08[Ø,3,4][7,J,K,Z]Z Alter/Upr Arm, Rt, [Opn, Perc, Perc Endo], [Auto Tissue Sub, Synth Sub, Nonauto Tissue Sub, No Dev], NQ
ØX09[Ø,3,4][7,J,K,Z]Z Alter/Upr Arm, Lt, [Opn, Perc, Perc Endo], [Auto Tissue Sub, Synth Sub, Nonauto Tissue Sub, No Dev], NQ
ØX0B[Ø,3,4][7,J,K,Z]Z Alter/Elbow Rgn, Rt, [Opn, Perc, Perc Endo], [Auto Tissue Sub, Synth Sub, Nonauto Tissue Sub, No Dev], NQ
ØX0C[Ø,3,4][7,J,K,Z]Z Alter/Elbow Rgn, Lt, [Opn, Perc, Perc Endo], [Auto Tissue Sub, Synth Sub, Nonauto Tissue Sub, No Dev], NQ
ØX0D[Ø,3,4][7,J,K,Z]Z Alter/Lwr Arm, Rt, [Opn, Perc, Perc Endo], [Auto Tissue Sub, Synth Sub, Nonauto Tissue Sub, No Dev], NQ
ØX0F[Ø,3,4][7,J,K,Z]Z Alter/Lwr Arm, Lt, [Opn, Perc, Perc Endo], [Auto Tissue Sub, Synth Sub, Nonauto Tissue Sub, No Dev], NQ
ØX0G[Ø,3,4][7,J,K,Z]Z Alter/Wrist Rgn, Rt, [Opn, Perc, Perc Endo], [Auto Tissue Sub, Synth Sub, Nonauto Tissue Sub, No Dev], NQ
ØX0H[Ø,3,4][7,J,K,Z]Z Alter/Wrist Rgn, Lt, [Opn, Perc, Perc Endo], [Auto Tissue Sub, Synth Sub, Nonauto Tissue Sub, No Dev], NQ
ØX32[Ø,3,4]ZZ Control/Shldr Rgn, Rt, [Opn, Perc, Perc Endo]
ØX33[Ø,3,4]ZZ Control/Shldr Rgn, Lt, [Opn, Perc, Perc Endo]
ØX34[Ø,3,4]ZZ Control/Axilla, Rt, [Opn, Perc, Perc Endo]
ØX35[Ø,3,4]ZZ Control/Axilla, Lt, [Opn, Perc, Perc Endo]
ØX36[Ø,3,4]ZZ Control/Upr Extr, Rt, [Opn, Perc, Perc Endo]
ØX37[Ø,3,4]ZZ Control/Upr Extr, Lt, [Opn, Perc, Perc Endo]
ØX38[Ø,3,4]ZZ Control/Upr Arm, Rt, [Opn, Perc, Perc Endo]
ØX39[Ø,3,4]ZZ Control/Upr Arm, Lt, [Opn, Perc, Perc Endo]
ØX3B[Ø,3,4]ZZ Control/Elbow Rgn, Rt, [Opn, Perc, Perc Endo]
ØX3C[Ø,3,4]ZZ Control/Elbow Rgn, Lt, [Opn, Perc, Perc Endo]
ØX3D[Ø,3,4]ZZ Control/Lwr Arm, Rt, [Opn, Perc, Perc Endo]
ØX3F[Ø,3,4]ZZ Control/Lwr Arm, Lt, [Opn, Perc, Perc Endo]
ØX3G[Ø,3,4]ZZ Control/Wrist Rgn, Rt, [Opn, Perc, Perc Endo]
ØX3H[Ø,3,4]ZZ Control/Wrist Rgn, Lt, [Opn, Perc, Perc Endo]
ØX3J[Ø,3,4]ZZ Control/Hand, Rt, [Opn, Perc, Perc Endo]
ØX3K[Ø,3,4]ZZ Control/Hand, Lt, [Opn, Perc, Perc Endo]
ØX600ZZ Detach at Rt Forequarter, Opn Appr
ØX610ZZ Detach at Lt Forequarter, Opn Appr
ØX620ZZ Detach at Rt Shldr Region, Opn Appr
ØX630ZZ Detach at Lt Shldr Region, Opn Appr
ØX680Z[1,2,3] Detach/Upr Arm, Rt, Opn, No Dev, [High, Mid, Low]
ØX690Z[1,2,3] Detach/Upr Arm, Lt, Opn, No Dev, [High, Mid, Low]
ØX6B0ZZ Detach at Rt Elbow Region, Opn Appr
ØX6C0ZZ Detach at Lt Elbow Region, Opn Appr
ØX6D0Z[1,2,3] Detach/Lwr Arm, Rt, Opn, No Dev, [High, Mid, Low]
ØX6F0Z[1,2,3] Detach/Lwr Arm, Lt, Opn, No Dev, [High, Mid, Low]
ØX6J0Z[Ø,4,5,6,7,8,9,B,C,D,F] Detach/Hand, Rt, Opn, No Dev, [Complete, Complete 1st Ray, Complete 2nd Ray, Complete 3rd Ray, Complete 4th Ray, Complete 5th Ray, Partial 1st Ray, Partial 2nd Ray, Partial 3rd Ray, Partial 4th Ray, Partial 5th Ray]
ØX6K0Z[Ø,4,5,6,7,8,9,B,C,D,F] Detach/Hand, Lt, Opn, No Dev, [Complete, Complete 1st Ray, Complete 2nd Ray, Complete 3rd Ray, Complete 4th Ray, Complete 5th Ray, Partial 1st Ray, Partial 2nd Ray, Partial 3rd Ray, Partial 4th Ray, Partial 5th Ray]

ØX6L0Z[Ø,1,2,3] Detach/Thumb, Rt, Opn, No Dev, [Complete, High, Mid, Low]
ØX6M0Z[Ø,1,2,3] Detach/Thumb, Lt, Opn, No Dev, [Complete, High, Mid, Low]
ØX6N0Z[Ø,1,2,3] Detach/Index Finger, Rt, Opn, No Dev, [Complete, High, Mid, Low]
ØX6P0Z[Ø,1,2,3] Detach/Index Finger, Lt, Opn, No Dev, [Complete, High, Mid, Low]
ØX6Q0Z[Ø,1,2,3] Detach/Mid Finger, Rt, Opn, No Dev, [Compl, High, Mid, Low]
ØX6R0Z[Ø,1,2,3] Detach/Mid Finger, Lt, Opn, No Dev, [Compl, High, Mid, Low]
ØX6S0Z[Ø,1,2,3] Detach/Ring Finger, Rt, Opn, No Dev, [Compl, High, Mid, Low]
ØX6T0Z[Ø,1,2,3] Detach/Ring Finger, Lt, Opn, No Dev, [Compl, High, Mid, Low]
ØX6V0Z[Ø,1,2,3] Detach/Little Finger, Rt, Opn, No Dev, [Compl, High, Mid, Low]
ØX6W0Z[Ø,1,2,3] Detach/Little Finger, Lt, Opn, No Dev, [Compl, High, Mid, Low]
ØXU2[Ø,4][J,K]Z Supl/Shldr Rgn, Rt, [Opn, Perc Endo], [Synth Sub, Nonauto Tissue Sub], NQ
ØXU3[Ø,4][J,K]Z Supl/Shldr Rgn, Lt, [Opn, Perc Endo], [Synth Sub, Nonauto Tissue Sub], NQ
ØXU4[Ø,4][J,K]Z Supl/Axilla, Rt, [Opn, Perc Endo], [Synth Sub, Nonauto Tissue Sub], NQ
ØXU5[Ø,4][J,K]Z Supl/Axilla, Lt, [Opn, Perc Endo], [Synth Sub, Nonauto Tissue Sub], NQ
ØXU6[Ø,4][J,K]Z Supl/Upr Extr, Rt, [Opn, Perc Endo], [Synth Sub, Nonauto Tissue Sub], NQ
ØXU7[Ø,4][J,K]Z Supl/Upr Extr, Lt, [Opn, Perc Endo], [Synth Sub, Nonauto Tissue Sub], NQ
ØXU8[Ø,4][J,K]Z Supl/Upr Arm, Rt, [Opn, Perc Endo], [Synth Sub, Nonauto Tissue Sub], NQ
ØXU9[Ø,4][J,K]Z Supl/Upr Arm, Lt, [Opn, Perc Endo], [Synth Sub, Nonauto Tissue Sub], NQ
ØXUB[Ø,4][J,K]Z Supl/Elbow Rgn, Rt, [Opn, Perc Endo], [Synth Sub, Nonauto Tissue Sub], NQ
ØXUC[Ø,4][J,K]Z Supl/Elbow Rgn, Lt, [Opn, Perc Endo], [Synth Sub, Nonauto Tissue Sub], NQ
ØXUD[Ø,4][J,K]Z Supl/Lwr Arm, Rt, [Opn, Perc Endo], [Synth Sub, Nonauto Tissue Sub], NQ
ØXUF[Ø,4][J,K]Z Supl/Lwr Arm, Lt, [Opn, Perc Endo], [Synth Sub, Nonauto Tissue Sub], NQ
ØXUG[Ø,4][J,K]Z Supl/Wrist Rgn, Rt, [Opn, Perc Endo], [Synth Sub, Nonauto Tissue Sub], NQ
ØXUH[Ø,4][J,K]Z Supl/Wrist Rgn, Lt, [Opn, Perc Endo], [Synth Sub, Nonauto Tissue Sub], NQ
ØXUJ[Ø,4][J,K]Z Supl/Hand, Rt, [Opn, Perc Endo], [Synth Sub, Nonauto Tissue Sub], NQ
ØXUK[Ø,4][J,K]Z Supl/Hand, Lt, [Opn, Perc Endo], [Synth Sub, Nonauto Tissue Sub], NQ
ØXUL[Ø,4][J,K]Z Supl/Thumb, Rt, [Opn, Perc Endo], [Synth Sub, Nonauto Tissue Sub], NQ
ØXUM[Ø,4][J,K]Z Supl/Thumb, Lt, [Opn, Perc Endo], [Synth Sub, Nonauto Tissue Sub], NQ
ØXUN[Ø,4][J,K]Z Supl/Index Finger, Rt, [Opn, Perc Endo], [Synth Sub, Nonauto Tissue Sub], NQ
ØXUP[Ø,4][J,K]Z Supl/Index Finger, Lt, [Opn, Perc Endo], [Synth Sub, Nonauto Tissue Sub], NQ
ØXUQ[Ø,4][J,K]Z Supl/Mid Finger, Rt, [Opn, Perc Endo], [Synth Sub, Nonauto Tissue Sub], NQ
ØXUR[Ø,4][J,K]Z Supl/Mid Finger, Lt, [Opn, Perc Endo], [Synth Sub, Nonauto Tissue Sub], NQ
ØXUS[Ø,4][J,K]Z Supl/Ring Finger, Rt, [Opn, Perc Endo], [Synth Sub, Nonauto Tissue Sub], NQ
ØXUT[Ø,4][J,K]Z Supl/Ring Finger, Lt, [Opn, Perc Endo], [Synth Sub, Nonauto Tissue Sub], NQ
ØXUV[Ø,4][J,K]Z Supl/Little Finger, Rt, [Opn, Perc Endo], [Synth Sub, Nonauto Tissue Sub], NQ
ØXUW[Ø,4][J,K]Z Supl/Little Finger, Lt, [Opn, Perc Endo], [Synth Sub, Nonauto Tissue Sub], NQ
ØY00[Ø,3,4][7,J,K,Z]Z Alter/Buttock, Rt, [Opn, Perc, Perc Endo], [Auto Tissue Sub, Synth Sub, Nonauto Tissue Sub, No Dev], NQ
ØY01[Ø,3,4][7,J,K,Z]Z Alter/Buttock, Lt, [Opn, Perc, Perc Endo], [Auto Tissue Sub, Synth Sub, Nonauto Tissue Sub, No Dev], NQ
ØY09[Ø,3,4][7,J,K,Z]Z Alter/Lwr Extr, Rt, [Opn, Perc, Perc Endo], [Auto Tissue Sub, Synth Sub, Nonauto Tissue Sub, No Dev], NQ
ØY0B[Ø,3,4][7,J,K,Z]Z Alter/Lwr Extr, Lt, [Opn, Perc, Perc Endo], [Auto Tissue Sub, Synth Sub, Nonauto Tissue Sub, No Dev], NQ
ØY0C[Ø,3,4][7,J,K,Z]Z Alter/Upr Leg, Rt, [Opn, Perc, Perc Endo], [Auto Tissue Sub, Synth Sub, Nonauto Tissue Sub, No Dev], NQ
ØY0D[Ø,3,4][7,J,K,Z]Z Alter/Upr Leg, Lt, [Opn, Perc, Perc Endo], [Auto Tissue Sub, Synth Sub, Nonauto Tissue Sub, No Dev], NQ
ØY0F[Ø,3,4][7,J,K,Z]Z Alter/Knee Rgn, Rt, [Opn, Perc, Perc Endo], [Auto Tissue Sub, Synth Sub, Nonauto Tissue Sub, No Dev], NQ
ØY0G[Ø,3,4][7,J,K,Z]Z Alter/Knee Rgn, Lt, [Opn, Perc, Perc Endo], [Auto Tissue Sub, Synth Sub, Nonauto Tissue Sub, No Dev], NQ

T Transfer DRG   SP Special Payment   * Code Range   6th and 7th Character of ZZ = No Device, No Qualifier ZX = No Device, Diagnostic

218   MS-DRG Version 33.0   © 2015 Optum360, LLC

0Y0H[0,3,4][7,J,K,Z]Z	Alter/Lwr Leg, Rt, [Opn, Perc, Perc Endo], [Auto Tissue Sub, Synth Sub, Nonauto Tissue Sub, No Dev], NQ
0Y0J[0,3,4][7,J,K,Z]Z	Alter/Lwr Leg, Lt, [Opn, Perc, Perc Endo], [Auto Tissue Sub, Synth Sub, Nonauto Tissue Sub, No Dev], NQ
0Y0K[0,3,4][7,J,K,Z]Z	Alter/Ankle Rgn, Rt, [Opn, Perc, Perc Endo], [Auto Tissue Sub, Synth Sub, Nonauto Tissue Sub, No Dev], NQ
0Y0L[0,3,4][7,J,K,Z]Z	Alter/Ankle Rgn, Lt, [Opn, Perc, Perc Endo], [Auto Tissue Sub, Synth Sub, Nonauto Tissue Sub, No Dev], NQ
0Y30[0,3,4]ZZ	Control/Buttock, Rt, [Opn, Perc, Perc Endo]
0Y31[0,3,4]ZZ	Control/Buttock, Lt, [Opn, Perc, Perc Endo]
0Y35[0,3,4]ZZ	Control/Inguinal Rgn, Rt, [Opn, Perc, Perc Endo]
0Y36[0,3,4]ZZ	Control/Inguinal Rgn, Lt, [Opn, Perc, Perc Endo]
0Y37[0,3,4]ZZ	Control/Femor Rgn, Rt, [Opn, Perc, Perc Endo]
0Y38[0,3,4]ZZ	Control/Femor Rgn, Lt, [Opn, Perc, Perc Endo]
0Y39[0,3,4]ZZ	Control/Lwr Extr, Rt, [Opn, Perc, Perc Endo]
0Y3B[0,3,4]ZZ	Control/Lwr Extr, Lt, [Opn, Perc, Perc Endo]
0Y3C[0,3,4]ZZ	Control/Upr Leg, Rt, [Opn, Perc, Perc Endo]
0Y3D[0,3,4]ZZ	Control/Upr Leg, Lt, [Opn, Perc, Perc Endo]
0Y3F[0,3,4]ZZ	Control/Knee Rgn, Rt, [Opn, Perc, Perc Endo]
0Y3G[0,3,4]ZZ	Control/Knee Rgn, Lt, [Opn, Perc, Perc Endo]
0Y3H[0,3,4]ZZ	Control/Lwr Leg, Rt, [Opn, Perc, Perc Endo]
0Y3J[0,3,4]ZZ	Control/Lwr Leg, Lt, [Opn, Perc, Perc Endo]
0Y3K[0,3,4]ZZ	Control/Ankle Rgn, Rt, [Opn, Perc, Perc Endo]
0Y3L[0,3,4]ZZ	Control/Ankle Rgn, Lt, [Opn, Perc, Perc Endo]
0Y3M[0,3,4]ZZ	Control/Foot, Rt, [Opn, Perc, Perc Endo]
0Y3N[0,3,4]ZZ	Control/Foot, Lt, [Opn, Perc, Perc Endo]
0Y620ZZ	Detach at Rt Hindquarter, Opn Appr
0Y630ZZ	Detach at Lt Hindquarter, Opn Appr
0Y640ZZ	Detach at Bilat Hindquarter, Opn Appr
0Y670ZZ	Detach at Rt Femor Region, Opn Appr
0Y680ZZ	Detach at Lt Femor Region, Opn Appr
0Y6C0Z[1,2,3]	Detach/Upr Leg, Rt, Opn, No Dev, [High, Mid, Low]
0Y6D0Z[1,2,3]	Detach/Upr Leg, Lt, Opn, No Dev, [High, Mid, Low]
0Y6F0ZZ	Detach at Rt Knee Region, Opn Appr
0Y6G0ZZ	Detach at Lt Knee Region, Opn Appr
0Y6H0Z[1,2,3]	Detach/Lwr Leg, Rt, Opn, No Dev, [High, Mid, Low]
0Y6J0Z[1,2,3]	Detach/Lwr Leg, Lt, Opn, No Dev, [High, Mid, Low]
0Y6M0Z[0,4,5,6,7,8,9,B,C,D,F]	Detach/Foot, Rt, Opn, No Dev, [Complete, Complete 1st Ray, Complete 2nd Ray, Complete 3rd Ray, Complete 4th Ray, Complete 5th Ray, Partial 1st Ray, Partial 2nd Ray, Partial 3rd Ray, Partial 4th Ray, Partial 5th Ray]
0Y6N0Z[0,4,5,6,7,8,9,B,C,D,F]	Detach/Foot, Lt, Opn, No Dev, [Complete, Complete 1st Ray, Complete 2nd Ray, Complete 3rd Ray, Complete 4th Ray, Complete 5th Ray, Partial 1st Ray, Partial 2nd Ray, Partial 3rd Ray, Partial 4th Ray, Partial 5th Ray]
0Y6P0Z[0,1,2,3]	Detach/1st Toe, Rt, Opn, No Dev, [Complete, High, Mid, Low]
0Y6Q0Z[0,1,2,3]	Detach/1st Toe, Lt, Opn, No Dev, [Complete, High, Mid, Low]
0Y6R0Z[0,1,2,3]	Detach/2nd Toe, Rt, Opn, No Dev, [Complete, High, Mid, Low]
0Y6S0Z[0,1,2,3]	Detach/2nd Toe, Lt, Opn, No Dev, [Complete, High, Mid, Low]
0Y6T0Z[0,1,2,3]	Detach/3rd Toe, Rt, Opn, No Dev, [Complete, High, Mid, Low]
0Y6U0Z[0,1,2,3]	Detach/3rd Toe, Lt, Opn, No Dev, [Complete, High, Mid, Low]
0Y6V0Z[0,1,2,3]	Detach/4th Toe, Rt, Opn, No Dev, [Complete, High, Mid, Low]
0Y6W0Z[0,1,2,3]	Detach/4th Toe, Lt, Opn, No Dev, [Complete, High, Mid, Low]
0Y6X0Z[0,1,2,3]	Detach/5th Toe, Rt, Opn, No Dev, [Complete, High, Mid, Low]
0Y6Y0Z[0,1,2,3]	Detach/5th Toe, Lt, Opn, No Dev, [Complete, High, Mid, Low]
0Y95[0,3,4][0,Z]Z	Drain/Inguinal Rgn, Rt, [Opn, Perc, Perc Endo], [Drain Dev, No Dev], NQ
0Y96[0,3,4][0,Z]Z	Drain/Inguinal Rgn, Lt, [Opn, Perc, Perc Endo], [Drain Dev, No Dev], NQ
0YB5[0,3,4]ZZ	Exc/Inguinal Rgn, Rt, [Opn, Perc, Perc Endo]
0YB6[0,3,4]ZZ	Exc/Inguinal Rgn, Lt, [Opn, Perc, Perc Endo]
0YB7[0,3,4]ZZ	Exc/Femor Rgn, Rt, [Opn, Perc, Perc Endo]
0YB8[0,3,4]ZZ	Exc/Femor Rgn, Lt, [Opn, Perc, Perc Endo]
0YJ50ZZ	Inspect of Rt Inguinal Region, Opn Appr
0YJ60ZZ	Inspect of Lt Inguinal Region, Opn Appr
0YJ70ZZ	Inspect of Rt Femor Region, Opn Appr
0YJA0ZZ	Inspect of Bilat Inguinal Region, Opn Appr
0YM00ZZ	Reattach of Rt Buttock, Opn Appr
0YM10ZZ	Reattach of Lt Buttock, Opn Appr
0YU0[0,4][7,J,K]Z	Supl/Buttock, Rt, [Opn, Perc Endo], [Auto Tissue Sub, Synth Sub, Nonauto Tissue Sub], NQ
0YU1[0,4][7,J,K]Z	Supl/Buttock, Lt, [Opn, Perc Endo], [Auto Tissue Sub, Synth Sub, Nonauto Tissue Sub], NQ
0YU9[0,4][7,J,K]Z	Supl/Lwr Extr, Rt, [Opn, Perc Endo], [Auto Tissue Sub, Synth Sub, Nonauto Tissue Sub], NQ
0YUB[0,4][7,J,K]Z	Supl/Lwr Extr, Lt, [Opn, Perc Endo], [Auto Tissue Sub, Synth Sub, Nonauto Tissue Sub], NQ
0YUC[0,4][7,J,K]Z	Supl/Upr Leg, Rt, [Opn, Perc Endo], [Auto Tissue Sub, Synth Sub, Nonauto Tissue Sub], NQ
0YUD[0,4][7,J,K]Z	Supl/Upr Leg, Lt, [Opn, Perc Endo], [Auto Tissue Sub, Synth Sub, Nonauto Tissue Sub], NQ
0YUF[0,4][7,J,K]Z	Supl/Knee Rgn, Rt, [Opn, Perc Endo], [Auto Tissue Sub, Synth Sub, Nonauto Tissue Sub], NQ
0YUG[0,4][7,J,K]Z	Supl/Knee Rgn, Lt, [Opn, Perc Endo], [Auto Tissue Sub, Synth Sub, Nonauto Tissue Sub], NQ
0YUH[0,4][7,J,K]Z	Supl/Lwr Leg, Rt, [Opn, Perc Endo], [Auto Tissue Sub, Synth Sub, Nonauto Tissue Sub], NQ
0YUJ[0,4][7,J,K]Z	Supl/Lwr Leg, Lt, [Opn, Perc Endo], [Auto Tissue Sub, Synth Sub, Nonauto Tissue Sub], NQ
0YUK[0,4][7,J,K]Z	Supl/Ankle Rgn, Rt, [Opn, Perc Endo], [Auto Tissue Sub, Synth Sub, Nonauto Tissue Sub], NQ
0YUL[0,4][7,J,K]Z	Supl/Ankle Rgn, Lt, [Opn, Perc Endo], [Auto Tissue Sub, Synth Sub, Nonauto Tissue Sub], NQ
0YUM[0,4][7,J,K]Z	Supl/Foot, Rt, [Opn, Perc Endo], [Auto Tissue Sub, Synth Sub, Nonauto Tissue Sub], NQ
0YUN[0,4][7,J,K]Z	Supl/Foot, Lt, [Opn, Perc Endo], [Auto Tissue Sub, Synth Sub, Nonauto Tissue Sub], NQ
0YUP[0,4][7,J,K]Z	Supl/1st Toe, Rt, [Opn, Perc Endo], [Auto Tissue Sub, Synth Sub, Nonauto Tissue Sub], NQ
0YUQ[0,4][7,J,K]Z	Supl/1st Toe, Lt, [Opn, Perc Endo], [Auto Tissue Sub, Synth Sub, Nonauto Tissue Sub], NQ
0YUR[0,4][7,J,K]Z	Supl/2nd Toe, Rt, [Opn, Perc Endo], [Auto Tissue Sub, Synth Sub, Nonauto Tissue Sub], NQ
0YUS[0,4][7,J,K]Z	Supl/2nd Toe, Lt, [Opn, Perc Endo], [Auto Tissue Sub, Synth Sub, Nonauto Tissue Sub], NQ
0YUT[0,4][7,J,K]Z	Supl/3rd Toe, Rt, [Opn, Perc Endo], [Auto Tissue Sub, Synth Sub, Nonauto Tissue Sub], NQ
0YUU[0,4][7,J,K]Z	Supl/3rd Toe, Lt, [Opn, Perc Endo], [Auto Tissue Sub, Synth Sub, Nonauto Tissue Sub], NQ
0YUV[0,4][7,J,K]Z	Supl/4th Toe, Rt, [Opn, Perc Endo], [Auto Tissue Sub, Synth Sub, Nonauto Tissue Sub], NQ
0YUW[0,4][7,J,K]Z	Supl/4th Toe, Lt, [Opn, Perc Endo], [Auto Tissue Sub, Synth Sub, Nonauto Tissue Sub], NQ
0YUX[0,4][7,J,K]Z	Supl/5th Toe, Rt, [Opn, Perc Endo], [Auto Tissue Sub, Synth Sub, Nonauto Tissue Sub], NQ
0YUY[0,4][7,J,K]Z	Supl/5th Toe, Lt, [Opn, Perc Endo], [Auto Tissue Sub, Synth Sub, Nonauto Tissue Sub], NQ
4A06*	Measurement/Lymphatic
4A16*	Monitoring/Lymphatic

OR

Nonoperating Room Procedures

0H50XZ[D,Z]	Destr/Skin, Scalp, Ext, No Dev, [Multi, NQ]
0H51XZ[D,Z]	Destr/Skin, Face, Ext, No Dev, [Multi, NQ]
0H54XZ[D,Z]	Destr/Skin, Neck, Ext, No Dev, [Multi, NQ]
0H55XZ[D,Z]	Destr/Skin, Chest, Ext, No Dev, [Multi, NQ]
0H56XZ[D,Z]	Destr/Skin, Back, Ext, No Dev, [Multi, NQ]
0H57XZ[D,Z]	Destr/Skin, Abd, Ext, No Dev, [Multi, NQ]
0H58XZ[D,Z]	Destr/Skin, Buttock, Ext, No Dev, [Multi, NQ]
0H59XZ[D,Z]	Destr/Skin, Perineum, Ext, No Dev, [Multi, NQ]
0H5AXZ[D,Z]	Destr/Skin, Genitalia, Ext, No Dev, [Multi, NQ]
0H5BXZ[D,Z]	Destr/Skin, Rt Upr Arm, Ext, No Dev, [Multi, NQ]
0H5CXZ[D,Z]	Destr/Skin, Lt Upr Arm, Ext, No Dev, [Multi, NQ]
0H5DXZ[D,Z]	Destr/Skin, Rt Lwr Arm, Ext, No Dev, [Multi, NQ]
0H5EXZ[D,Z]	Destr/Skin, Lt Lwr Arm, Ext, No Dev, [Multi, NQ]
0H5FXZ[D,Z]	Destr/Skin, Rt Hand, Ext, No Dev, [Multi, NQ]
0H5GXZ[D,Z]	Destr/Skin, Lt Hand, Ext, No Dev, [Multi, NQ]
0H5HXZ[D,Z]	Destr/Skin, Rt Upr Leg, Ext, No Dev, [Multi, NQ]
0H5JXZ[D,Z]	Destr/Skin, Lt Upr Leg, Ext, No Dev, [Multi, NQ]
0H5KXZ[D,Z]	Destr/Skin, Rt Lwr Leg, Ext, No Dev, [Multi, NQ]
0H5LXZ[D,Z]	Destr/Skin, Lt Lwr Leg, Ext, No Dev, [Multi, NQ]
0H5MXZ[D,Z]	Destr/Skin, Rt Foot, Ext, No Dev, [Multi, NQ]
0H5NXZ[D,Z]	Destr/Skin, Lt Foot, Ext, No Dev, [Multi, NQ]
0H5QXZZ	Destr of Finger Nail, Ext Appr
0H5RXZZ	Destr of Toe Nail, Ext Appr
0HB9XZZ	Exc of Perineum Skin, Ext Appr
0J50[0,3]ZZ	Destr/SQ Tissue & Fascia, Scalp, [Opn, Perc]
0J51[0,3]ZZ	Destr/SQ Tissue & Fascia, Face, [Opn, Perc]
0J54[0,3]ZZ	Destr/SQ Tissue & Fascia, Ant Neck, [Opn, Perc]
0J55[0,3]ZZ	Destr/SQ Tissue & Fascia, Post Neck, [Opn, Perc]
0J56[0,3]ZZ	Destr/SQ Tissue & Fascia, Chest, [Opn, Perc]
0J57[0,3]ZZ	Destr/SQ Tissue & Fascia, Back, [Opn, Perc]
0J58[0,3]ZZ	Destr/SQ Tissue & Fascia, Abd, [Opn, Perc]
0J59[0,3]ZZ	Destr/SQ Tissue & Fascia, Buttock, [Opn, Perc]
0J5B[0,3]ZZ	Destr/SQ Tissue & Fascia, Perineum, [Opn, Perc]
0J5C[0,3]ZZ	Destr/SQ Tissue & Fascia, Genitalia, [Opn, Perc]
0J5D[0,3]ZZ	Destr/SQ Tissue & Fascia, Rt Upr Arm, [Opn, Perc]
0J5F[0,3]ZZ	Destr/SQ Tissue & Fascia, Lt Upr Arm, [Opn, Perc]
0J5G[0,3]ZZ	Destr/SQ Tissue & Fascia, Rt Lwr Arm, [Opn, Perc]

Surgical   **Medical**   **CC Indicator**   **MCC Indicator**   **Procedure Proxy**   PDxMCC **PDx acts as own MCC**   PDxCC **PDx acts as own CC**

MDC 9: Diseases And Disorders Of The Skin, Subcutaneous Tissue And Breast—SURGICAL

ØJ5H[Ø,3]ZZ Destr/SQ Tissue & Fascia, Lt Lwr Arm, [Opn, Perc]
ØJ5J[Ø,3]ZZ Destr/SQ Tissue & Fascia, Rt Hand, [Opn, Perc]
ØJ5K[Ø,3]ZZ Destr/SQ Tissue & Fascia, Lt Hand, [Opn, Perc]
ØJ5L[Ø,3]ZZ Destr/SQ Tissue & Fascia, Rt Upr Leg, [Opn, Perc]
ØJ5M[Ø,3]ZZ Destr/SQ Tissue & Fascia, Lt Upr Leg, [Opn, Perc]
ØJ5N[Ø,3]ZZ Destr/SQ Tissue & Fascia, Rt Lwr Leg, [Opn, Perc]
ØJ5P[Ø,3]ZZ Destr/SQ Tissue & Fascia, Lt Lwr Leg, [Opn, Perc]
ØJ5Q[Ø,3]ZZ Destr/SQ Tissue & Fascia, Rt Foot, [Opn, Perc]
ØJ5R[Ø,3]ZZ Destr/SQ Tissue & Fascia, Lt Foot, [Opn, Perc]
ØJH6[Ø,3][2,H,W,X]Z Insert/SQ Tissue & Fascia, Chest, [Opn, Perc], [Monitoring Dev, Contraceptive Dev, Reservoir, Vascular Access Dev], NQ
ØJH8[Ø,3][2,H,W,X]Z Insert/SQ Tissue & Fascia, Abd, [Opn, Perc], [Monitoring Dev, Contraceptive Dev, Reservoir, Vascular Access Dev], NQ
ØJHD[Ø,3][W,X]Z Insert/SQ Tissue & Fascia, Rt Upr Arm, [Opn, Perc], [Reservoir, Vascular Access Dev], NQ
ØJHF[Ø,3][W,X]Z Insert/SQ Tissue & Fascia, Lt Upr Arm, [Opn, Perc], [Reservoir, Vascular Access Dev], NQ
ØJHG[Ø,3][W,X]Z Insert/SQ Tissue & Fascia, Rt Lwr Arm, [Opn, Perc], [Reservoir, Vascular Access Dev], NQ
ØJHH[Ø,3][W,X]Z Insert/SQ Tissue & Fascia, Lt Lwr Arm, [Opn, Perc], [Reservoir, Vascular Access Dev], NQ
ØJHL[Ø,3][W,X]Z Insert/SQ Tissue & Fascia, Rt Upr Leg, [Opn, Perc], [Reservoir, Vascular Access Dev], NQ
ØJHM[Ø,3][W,X]Z Insert/SQ Tissue & Fascia, Lt Upr Leg, [Opn, Perc], [Reservoir, Vascular Access Dev], NQ
ØJHN3HZ Insert Contracept Dev in Rt Low Leg SQ/Fascia, Perc
ØJHN[Ø,3][W,X]Z Insert/SQ Tissue & Fascia, Rt Lwr Leg, [Opn, Perc], [Reservoir, Vascular Access Dev], NQ
ØJHP[Ø,3][H,W,X]Z Insert/SQ Tissue & Fascia, Lt Lwr Leg, [Opn, Perc], [Contraceptive Dev, Reservoir, Vascular Access Dev], NQ
ØJWS[Ø,3][Ø,3,7,J,K,N]Z Rev/SQ Tissue & Fascia, Head and Neck, [Opn, Perc], [Drain Dev, Inf Dev, Auto Tissue Sub, Synth Sub, Nonauto Tissue Sub, Tissue Expander], NQ
ØJWT[Ø,3][Ø,2,3,7,H,J,K,N,V,W,X]Z Rev/SQ Tissue & Fascia, Trunk, [Opn, Perc], [Drain Dev, Monitoring Dev, Inf Dev, Auto Tissue Sub, Contraceptive Dev, Synth Sub, Nonauto Tissue Sub, Tissue Expander, Inf Pump, Reservoir, Vascular Access Dev], NQ
ØJWV[Ø,3][Ø,3,7,H,J,K,N,V,W,X]Z Rev/SQ Tissue & Fascia, Upr Extr, [Opn, Perc], [Drain Dev, Inf Dev, Auto Tissue Sub, Contraceptive Dev, Synth Sub, Nonauto Tissue Sub, Tissue Expander, Inf Pump, Reservoir, Vascular Access Dev], NQ
ØJWW[Ø,3][Ø,3,7,H,J,K,N,V,W,X]Z Rev/SQ Tissue & Fascia, Lwr Extr, [Opn, Perc], [Drain Dev, Inf Dev, Auto Tissue Sub, Contraceptive Dev, Synth Sub, Nonauto Tissue Sub, Tissue Expander, Inf Pump, Reservoir, Vascular Access Dev], NQ
ØWHØ[Ø,3,4][3,Y]Z Insert/Head, [Opn, Perc, Perc Endo], [Inf Dev, Oth Dev], NQ
ØWH2[Ø,3,4][3,Y]Z Insert/Face, [Opn, Perc, Perc Endo], [Inf Dev, Oth Dev], NQ
ØWH4[Ø,3,4][3,Y]Z Insert/Upr Jaw, [Opn, Perc, Perc Endo], [Inf Dev, Oth Dev], NQ
ØWH5[Ø,3,4][3,Y]Z Insert/Lwr Jaw, [Opn, Perc, Perc Endo], [Inf Dev, Oth Dev], NQ
ØWH6[Ø,3,4][3,Y]Z Insert/Neck, [Opn, Perc, Perc Endo], [Inf Dev, Oth Dev], NQ
ØWHK[Ø,3,4][3,Y]Z Insert/Upr Back, [Opn, Perc, Perc Endo], [Inf Dev, Oth Dev], NQ
ØWHL[Ø,3,4][3,Y]Z Insert/Lwr Back, [Opn, Perc, Perc Endo], [Inf Dev, Oth Dev], NQ
ØWHM[Ø,3,4][3,Y]Z Insert/Perineum, Male, [Opn, Perc, Perc Endo], [Inf Dev, Oth Dev], NQ
ØWJ00ZZ Inspect of Head, Opn Appr
ØWJ20ZZ Inspect of Face, Opn Appr
ØWJ40ZZ Inspect of Upr Jaw, Opn Appr
ØWJ50ZZ Inspect of Lwr Jaw, Opn Appr
ØWJK0ZZ Inspect of Upr Back, Opn Appr
ØWJL0ZZ Inspect of Lwr Back, Opn Appr
ØWJM[Ø,4]ZZ Inspect/Perineum, Male, [Opn, Perc Endo]
ØWWØ[Ø,3,4][Ø,1,3,7,J,K,Y]Z Rev/Head, [Opn, Perc, Perc Endo], [Drain Dev, Radioact Elmt, Inf Dev, Auto Tissue Sub, Synth Sub, Nonauto Tissue Sub, Oth Dev], NQ
ØWW2[Ø,3,4][Ø,1,3,7,J,K,Y]Z Rev/Face, [Opn, Perc, Perc Endo], [Drain Dev, Radioact Elmt, Inf Dev, Auto Tissue Sub, Synth Sub, Nonauto Tissue Sub, Oth Dev], NQ
ØWW4[Ø,3,4][Ø,1,3,7,J,K,Y]Z Rev/Upr Jaw, [Opn, Perc, Perc Endo], [Drain Dev, Radioact Elmt, Inf Dev, Auto Tissue Sub, Synth Sub, Nonauto Tissue Sub, Oth Dev], NQ
ØWW5[Ø,3,4][Ø,1,3,7,J,K,Y]Z Rev/Lwr Jaw, [Opn, Perc, Perc Endo], [Drain Dev, Radioact Elmt, Inf Dev, Auto Tissue Sub, Synth Sub, Nonauto Tissue Sub, Oth Dev], NQ
ØWW6[Ø,3,4][Ø,1,3,7,J,K,Y]Z Rev/Neck, [Opn, Perc, Perc Endo], [Drain Dev, Radioact Elmt, Inf Dev, Auto Tissue Sub, Synth Sub, Nonauto Tissue Sub, Oth Dev], NQ
ØWWK[Ø,3,4][Ø,1,3,7,J,K,Y]Z Rev/Upr Back, [Opn, Perc, Perc Endo], [Drain Dev, Radioact Elmt, Inf Dev, Auto Tissue Sub, Synth Sub, Nonauto Tissue Sub, Oth Dev], NQ

ØWWL[Ø,3,4][Ø,1,3,7,J,K,Y]Z Rev/Lwr Back, [Opn, Perc, Perc Endo], [Drain Dev, Radioact Elmt, Inf Dev, Auto Tissue Sub, Synth Sub, Nonauto Tissue Sub, Oth Dev], NQ
ØWWM[Ø,3,4][Ø,1,3,J,K,Y]Z Rev/Perineum, Male, [Opn, Perc, Perc Endo], [Drain Dev, Radioact Elmt, Inf Dev, Synth Sub, Oth Dev], NQ
ØXH2[Ø,3,4][3,Y]Z Insert/Shldr Rgn, Rt, [Opn, Perc, Perc Endo], [Inf Dev, Oth Dev], NQ
ØXH3[Ø,3,4][3,Y]Z Insert/Shldr Rgn, Lt, [Opn, Perc, Perc Endo], [Inf Dev, Oth Dev], NQ
ØXH4[Ø,3,4][3,Y]Z Insert/Axilla, Rt, [Opn, Perc, Perc Endo], [Inf Dev, Oth Dev], NQ
ØXH5[Ø,3,4][3,Y]Z Insert/Axilla, Lt, [Opn, Perc, Perc Endo], [Inf Dev, Oth Dev], NQ
ØXH6[Ø,3,4][3,Y]Z Insert/Upr Extr, Rt, [Opn, Perc, Perc Endo], [Inf Dev, Oth Dev], NQ
ØXH7[Ø,3,4][3,Y]Z Insert/Upr Extr, Lt, [Opn, Perc, Perc Endo], [Inf Dev, Oth Dev], NQ
ØXH8[Ø,3,4][3,Y]Z Insert/Upr Arm, Rt, [Opn, Perc, Perc Endo], [Inf Dev, Oth Dev], NQ
ØXH9[Ø,3,4][3,Y]Z Insert/Upr Arm, Lt, [Opn, Perc, Perc Endo], [Inf Dev, Oth Dev], NQ
ØXHB[Ø,3,4][3,Y]Z Insert/Elbow Rgn, Rt, [Opn, Perc, Perc Endo], [Inf Dev, Oth Dev], NQ
ØXHC[Ø,3,4][3,Y]Z Insert/Elbow Rgn, Lt, [Opn, Perc, Perc Endo], [Inf Dev, Oth Dev], NQ
ØXHD[Ø,3,4][3,Y]Z Insert/Lwr Arm, Rt, [Opn, Perc, Perc Endo], [Inf Dev, Oth Dev], NQ
ØXHF[Ø,3,4][3,Y]Z Insert/Lwr Arm, Lt, [Opn, Perc, Perc Endo], [Inf Dev, Oth Dev], NQ
ØXHG[Ø,3,4][3,Y]Z Insert/Wrist Rgn, Rt, [Opn, Perc, Perc Endo], [Inf Dev, Oth Dev], NQ
ØXHH[Ø,3,4][3,Y]Z Insert/Wrist Rgn, Lt, [Opn, Perc, Perc Endo], [Inf Dev, Oth Dev], NQ
ØXHJ[Ø,3,4][3,Y]Z Insert/Hand, Rt, [Opn, Perc, Perc Endo], [Inf Dev, Oth Dev], NQ
ØXHK[Ø,3,4][3,Y]Z Insert/Hand, Lt, [Opn, Perc, Perc Endo], [Inf Dev, Oth Dev], NQ
ØXJ20ZZ Inspect of Rt Shldr Region, Opn Appr
ØXJ30ZZ Inspect of Lt Shldr Region, Opn Appr
ØXJ40ZZ Inspect of Rt Axilla, Opn Appr
ØXJ50ZZ Inspect of Lt Axilla, Opn Appr
ØXJ60ZZ Inspect of Rt Upr Extr, Opn Appr
ØXJ70ZZ Inspect of Lt Upr Extr, Opn Appr
ØXJ80ZZ Inspect of Rt Upr Arm, Opn Appr
ØXJ90ZZ Inspect of Lt Upr Arm, Opn Appr
ØXJB0ZZ Inspect of Rt Elbow Region, Opn Appr
ØXJC0ZZ Inspect of Lt Elbow Region, Opn Appr
ØXJD0ZZ Inspect of Rt Lwr Arm, Opn Appr
ØXJF0ZZ Inspect of Lt Lwr Arm, Opn Appr
ØXJG0ZZ Inspect of Rt Wrist Region, Opn Appr
ØXJH0ZZ Inspect of Lt Wrist Region, Opn Appr
ØXJJ0ZZ Inspect of Rt Hand, Opn Appr
ØXJK0ZZ Inspect of Lt Hand, Opn Appr
ØXW6[Ø,3,4][Ø,3,7,J,K,Y]Z Rev/Upr Extr, Rt, [Opn, Perc, Perc Endo], [Drain Dev, Inf Dev, Auto Tissue Sub, Synth Sub, Nonauto Tissue Sub, Oth Dev], NQ
ØXW7[Ø,3,4][Ø,3,7,J,K,Y]Z Rev/Upr Extr, Lt, [Opn, Perc, Perc Endo], [Drain Dev, Inf Dev, Auto Tissue Sub, Synth Sub, Nonauto Tissue Sub, Oth Dev], NQ
ØYHØ[Ø,3,4][3,Y]Z Insert/Buttock, Rt, [Opn, Perc, Perc Endo], [Inf Dev, Oth Dev], NQ
ØYH1[Ø,3,4][3,Y]Z Insert/Buttock, Lt, [Opn, Perc, Perc Endo], [Inf Dev, Oth Dev], NQ
ØYH5[Ø,3,4][3,Y]Z Insert/Inguinal Rgn, Rt, [Opn, Perc, Perc Endo], [Inf Dev, Oth Dev], NQ
ØYH6[Ø,3,4][3,Y]Z Insert/Inguinal Rgn, Lt, [Opn, Perc, Perc Endo], [Inf Dev, Oth Dev], NQ
ØYH7[Ø,3,4][3,Y]Z Insert/Femor Rgn, Rt, [Opn, Perc, Perc Endo], [Inf Dev, Oth Dev], NQ
ØYH8[Ø,3,4][3,Y]Z Insert/Femor Rgn, Lt, [Opn, Perc, Perc Endo], [Inf Dev, Oth Dev], NQ
ØYH9[Ø,3,4][3,Y]Z Insert/Lwr Extr, Rt, [Opn, Perc, Perc Endo], [Inf Dev, Oth Dev], NQ
ØYHB[Ø,3,4][3,Y]Z Insert/Lwr Extr, Lt, [Opn, Perc, Perc Endo], [Inf Dev, Oth Dev], NQ
ØYHC[Ø,3,4][3,Y]Z Insert/Upr Leg, Rt, [Opn, Perc, Perc Endo], [Inf Dev, Oth Dev], NQ
ØYHD[Ø,3,4][3,Y]Z Insert/Upr Leg, Lt, [Opn, Perc, Perc Endo], [Inf Dev, Oth Dev], NQ
ØYHF[Ø,3,4][3,Y]Z Insert/Knee Rgn, Rt, [Opn, Perc, Perc Endo], [Inf Dev, Oth Dev], NQ
ØYHG[Ø,3,4][3,Y]Z Insert/Knee Rgn, Lt, [Opn, Perc, Perc Endo], [Inf Dev, Oth Dev], NQ
ØYHH[Ø,3,4][3,Y]Z Insert/Lwr Leg, Rt, [Opn, Perc, Perc Endo], [Inf Dev, Oth Dev], NQ
ØYHJ[Ø,3,4][3,Y]Z Insert/Lwr Leg, Lt, [Opn, Perc, Perc Endo], [Inf Dev, Oth Dev], NQ
ØYHK[Ø,3,4][3,Y]Z Insert/Ankle Rgn, Rt, [Opn, Perc, Perc Endo], [Inf Dev, Oth Dev], NQ
ØYHL[Ø,3,4][3,Y]Z Insert/Ankle Rgn, Lt, [Opn, Perc, Perc Endo], [Inf Dev, Oth Dev], NQ
ØYHM[Ø,3,4][3,Y]Z Insert/Foot, Rt, [Opn, Perc, Perc Endo], [Inf Dev, Oth Dev], NQ
ØYHN[Ø,3,4][3,Y]Z Insert/Foot, Lt, [Opn, Perc, Perc Endo], [Inf Dev, Oth Dev], NQ
ØYJ00ZZ Inspect of Rt Buttock, Opn Appr
ØYJ10ZZ Inspect of Lt Buttock, Opn Appr
ØYJ80ZZ Inspect of Lt Femor Region, Opn Appr
ØYJ90ZZ Inspect of Rt Lwr Extr, Opn Appr
ØYJB0ZZ Inspect of Lt Lwr Extr, Opn Appr

T Transfer DRG   SP Special Payment   * Code Range   6th and 7th Character of ZZ = No Device, No Qualifier ZX = No Device, Diagnostic

220   MS-DRG Version 33.0   © 2015 Optum360, LLC

0YJC0ZZ	Inspect of Rt Upr Leg, Opn Appr
0YJD0ZZ	Inspect of Lt Upr Leg, Opn Appr
0YJE0ZZ	Inspect of Bilat Femor Region, Opn Appr
0YJF0ZZ	Inspect of Rt Knee Region, Opn Appr
0YJG0ZZ	Inspect of Lt Knee Region, Opn Appr
0YJH0ZZ	Inspect of Rt Lwr Leg, Opn Appr
0YJJ0ZZ	Inspect of Lt Lwr Leg, Opn Appr
0YJK0ZZ	Inspect of Rt Ankle Region, Opn Appr
0YJL0ZZ	Inspect of Lt Ankle Region, Opn Appr
0YJM0ZZ	Inspect of Rt Foot, Opn Appr
0YJN0ZZ	Inspect of Lt Foot, Opn Appr
0YW9[0,3,4][0,3,7,J,K,Y]Z	Rev/Lwr Extr, Rt, [Opn, Perc, Perc Endo], [Drain Dev, Inf Dev, Auto Tissue Sub, Synth Sub, Nonauto Tissue Sub, Oth Dev], NQ
0YWB[0,3,4][0,3,7,J,K,Y]Z	Rev/Lwr Extr, Lt, [Opn, Perc, Perc Endo], [Drain Dev, Inf Dev, Auto Tissue Sub, Synth Sub, Nonauto Tissue Sub, Oth Dev], NQ

DRG 580 Other Skin, Subcutaneous Tissue and Breast Procedures with CC
GMLOS 4.0   AMLOS 5.3   RW 1.6155 [T]

Select operating room procedures or nonoperating room procedures listed under DRG 579

DRG 581 Other Skin, Subcutaneous Tissue and Breast Procedures without CC/MCC
GMLOS 2.2   AMLOS 2.8   RW 1.1834 [T]

Select operating room procedures or nonoperating room procedures listed under DRG 579

DRG 582 Mastectomy for Malignancy with CC/MCC
GMLOS 2.2   AMLOS 2.9   RW 1.3370

Principal or Secondary Diagnosis
C50.0[1,2][1,2,9]	Malig neoplasm of nipple and areola, [rt, lt, unsp] [female, male] breast
C50.1[1,2][1,2,9]	Malig neoplasm of central portion of [rt, lt, unsp] [female, male] breast
C50.2[1,2][1,2,9]	Malig neoplasm of upr-inner quadrant of [rt, lt, unsp] [female, male] breast
C50.3[1,2][1,2,9]	Malig neoplasm of lwr-inner quadrant of [rt, lt, unsp] [female, male] breast
C50.4[1,2][1,2,9]	Malig neoplasm of upr-outer quadrant of [rt, lt, unsp] [female, male] breast
C50.5[1,2][1,2,9]	Malig neoplasm of lwr-outer quadrant of [rt, lt, unsp] [female, male] breast
C50.6[1,2][1,2,9]	Malig neoplasm of axillary tail of [rt, lt, unsp] [female, male] breast
C50.8[1,2][1,2,9]	Malig neoplasm of overlapping sites of [rt, lt, unsp] [female, male] breast
C50.9[1,2][1,2,9]	Malig neoplasm of unsp site of [rt, lt, unsp] [female, male] breast
C79.2	Secondary malig neoplasm of skin
C79.81	Secondary malig neoplasm of breast
D05.[0,1,8,9][0,1,2]	[Lobular, Intraductal, Oth spec type of, Unsp type of] carcinoma in situ of [unsp, rt, lt] breast
D48.6[0,1,2]	Neoplasm of uncertain behav of [unsp, rt, lt] breast
AND

Operating Room Procedures
0H0V[0,3]JZ	Alter/Breast, Bilat, [Opn, Perc], Synth Sub, NQ
0HBT[0,3]ZZ	Exc/Breast, Rt, [Opn, Perc]
0HBU[0,3]ZZ	Exc/Breast, Lt, [Opn, Perc]
0HBV[0,3]ZZ	Exc/Breast, Bilat, [Opn, Perc]
0HRT07[5,6,7,8,9,Z]	Replace/Breast, Rt, Opn, Auto Tissue Sub, [Latissimus Dorsi Myocutaneous Flap, Transv Rectus Abdominis Myocutaneous Flap, Deep Inferior Epigastric Artery Perforator Flap, Superf Inferior Epigastric Artery Flap, Gluteal Artery Perforator Flap, NQ]
0HRT0JZ	Replace of Rt Breast with Synth Sub, Opn Appr
0HRT0KZ	Replace of Rt Breast with Nonaut Sub, Opn Appr
0HRT3JZ	Replace of Rt Breast with Synth Sub, Perc Appr
0HRU07[5,6,7,8,9,Z]	Replace/Breast, Lt, Opn, Auto Tissue Sub, [Latissimus Dorsi Myocutaneous Flap, Transv Rectus Abdominis Myocutaneous Flap, Deep Inferior Epigastric Artery Perforator Flap, Superf Inferior Epigastric Artery Flap, Gluteal Artery Perforator Flap, NQ]

0HRU0JZ	Replace of Lt Breast with Synth Sub, Opn Appr
0HRU0KZ	Replace of Lt Breast with Nonaut Sub, Opn Appr
0HRU3JZ	Replace of Lt Breast with Synth Sub, Perc Appr
0HRV07[5,6,7,8,9]	Replace/Breast, Bilat, Opn, Auto Tissue Sub, [Latissimus Dorsi Myocutaneous Flap, Transv Rectus Abdominis Myocutaneous Flap, Deep Inferior Epigastric Artery Perforator Flap, Superf Inferior Epigastric Artery Flap, Gluteal Artery Perforator Flap]
0HRV0JZ	Replace of Bi Breast with Synth Sub, Opn Appr
0HRV3JZ	Replace of Bi Breast with Synth Sub, Perc Appr
0HTT0ZZ	Resect of Rt Breast, Opn Appr
0HTU0ZZ	Resect of Lt Breast, Opn Appr
0HTV0ZZ	Resect of Bilat Breast, Opn Appr
0KXK[0,4]Z6	Transfer/Abd Muscle, Rt, [Opn, Perc Endo], No Dev, Transv Rectus Abdominis Myocutaneous Flap
0KXL[0,4]Z6	Transfer/Abd Muscle, Lt, [Opn, Perc Endo], No Dev, Transv Rectus Abdominis Myocutaneous Flap

OR
0HTT0ZZ	Resect of Rt Breast, Opn Appr
AND
| 07T50ZZ | Resect of Rt Axillary Lymphatic, Opn Appr |
OR
| 0HTU0ZZ | Resect of Lt Breast, Opn Appr |
AND
| 07T60ZZ | Resect of Lt Axillary Lymphatic, Opn Appr |
OR
| 0HTV0ZZ | Resect of Bilat Breast, Opn Appr |
AND

Both
| 07T50ZZ | Resect of Rt Axillary Lymphatic, Opn Appr |
| 07T60ZZ | Resect of Lt Axillary Lymphatic, Opn Appr |
OR
| 0HTT0ZZ | Resect of Rt Breast, Opn Appr |
AND

Both
| 07T50ZZ | Resect of Rt Axillary Lymphatic, Opn Appr |
| 0KTH0ZZ | Resect of Rt Thorax Muscle, Opn Appr |
OR
| 0HTU0ZZ | Resect of Lt Breast, Opn Appr |
AND

Both
| 07T60ZZ | Resect of Lt Axillary Lymphatic, Opn Appr |
| 0KTJ0ZZ | Resect of Lt Thorax Muscle, Opn Appr |
OR
| 0HTV0ZZ | Resect of Bilat Breast, Opn Appr |
AND

All of the following
07T50ZZ	Resect of Rt Axillary Lymphatic, Opn Appr
07T60ZZ	Resect of Lt Axillary Lymphatic, Opn Appr
0KTH0ZZ	Resect of Rt Thorax Muscle, Opn Appr
0KTJ0ZZ	Resect of Lt Thorax Muscle, Opn Appr
OR
| 0HTT0ZZ | Resect of Rt Breast, Opn Appr |
AND

All of the following
07T50ZZ	Resect of Rt Axillary Lymphatic, Opn Appr
07T70ZZ	Resect of Thorax Lymphatic, Opn Appr
07T80ZZ	Resect of Rt Int Mammary Lymphatic, Opn Appr
0KTH0ZZ	Resect of Rt Thorax Muscle, Opn Appr
OR
| 0HTU0ZZ | Resect of Lt Breast, Opn Appr |
AND

All of the following
07T60ZZ	Resect of Lt Axillary Lymphatic, Opn Appr
07T70ZZ	Resect of Thorax Lymphatic, Opn Appr
07T90ZZ	Resect of Lt Int Mammary Lymphatic, Opn Appr
0KTJ0ZZ	Resect of Lt Thorax Muscle, Opn Appr
OR
| 0HTV0ZZ | Resect of Bilat Breast, Opn Appr |
AND

All of the following
| 07T50ZZ | Resect of Rt Axillary Lymphatic, Opn Appr |

07T60ZZ	Resect of Lt Axillary Lymphatic, Opn Appr
07T70ZZ	Resect of Thorax Lymphatic, Opn Appr
07T80ZZ	Resect of Rt Int Mammary Lymphatic, Opn Appr
07T90ZZ	Resect of Lt Int Mammary Lymphatic, Opn Appr
0KTH0ZZ	Resect of Rt Thorax Muscle, Opn Appr
0KTJ0ZZ	Resect of Lt Thorax Muscle, Opn Appr

DRG 583   Mastectomy for Malignancy without CC/MCC

GMLOS 1.6   **AMLOS 1.9**   **RW 1.1856**

Select principal or secondary diagnosis AND operating room procedures or procedure combinations listed under DRG 582

DRG 584   Breast Biopsy, Local Excision and Other Breast Procedures with CC/MCC

GMLOS 3.7   **AMLOS 5.0**   **RW 1.6794**

Operating Room Procedures

0H0*	Skin and Breast, Alter
0H5T*	Destr/Breast, Rt
0H5U*	Destr/Breast, Lt
0H5V*	Destr/Breast, Bilat
0H5W*	Destr/Nipple, Rt
0H5X*	Destr/Nipple, Lt
0H9T0ZX	Drain of Rt Breast, Opn Appr, Diagnostic
0H9U0ZX	Drain of Lt Breast, Opn Appr, Diagnostic
0H9V0ZX	Drain of Bilat Breast, Opn Appr, Diagnostic
0H9W0ZX	Drain of Rt Nipple, Opn Appr, Diagnostic
0H9X0ZX	Drain of Lt Nipple, Opn Appr, Diagnostic
0HBT0ZX	Exc of Rt Breast, Opn Appr, Diagnostic
0HBT[0,3,7,8,X]ZZ	Exc/Breast, Rt, [Opn, Perc, Via Natrl or Artfcl Opng, Via Natrl or Artfcl Opng Endo, Ext]
0HBU0ZX	Exc of Lt Breast, Opn Appr, Diagnostic
0HBU[0,3,7,8,X]ZZ	Exc/Breast, Lt, [Opn, Perc, Via Natrl or Artfcl Opng, Via Natrl or Artfcl Opng Endo, Ext]
0HBV0ZX	Exc of Bilat Breast, Opn Appr, Diagnostic
0HBV[0,3,7,8,X]ZZ	Exc/Breast, Bilat, [Opn, Perc, Via Natrl or Artfcl Opng, Via Natrl or Artfcl Opng Endo, Ext]
0HBW0ZX	Exc of Rt Nipple, Opn Appr, Diagnostic
0HBW[0,3,7,8,X]ZZ	Exc/Nipple, Rt, [Opn, Perc, Via Natrl or Artfcl Opng, Via Natrl or Artfcl Opng Endo, Ext]
0HBX0ZX	Exc of Lt Nipple, Opn Appr, Diagnostic
0HBX[0,3,7,8,X]ZZ	Exc/Nipple, Lt, [Opn, Perc, Via Natrl or Artfcl Opng, Via Natrl or Artfcl Opng Endo, Ext]
0HBY0ZX	Exc of Supernumerary Breast, Opn Appr, Diagnostic
0HBY[0,3,7,8,X]ZZ	Exc/Supernumerary Breast, [Opn, Perc, Via Natrl or Artfcl Opng, Via Natrl or Artfcl Opng Endo, Ext]
0HHT[0,3,7,8]NZ	Insert/Breast, Rt, [Opn, Perc, Via Natrl or Artfcl Opng, Via Natrl or Artfcl Opng Endo], Tissue Expander, NQ
0HHU[0,3,7,8]NZ	Insert/Breast, Lt, [Opn, Perc, Via Natrl or Artfcl Opng, Via Natrl or Artfcl Opng Endo], Tissue Expander, NQ
0HHV[0,3,7,8]NZ	Insert/Breast, Bilat, [Opn, Perc, Via Natrl or Artfcl Opng, Via Natrl or Artfcl Opng Endo], Tissue Expander, NQ
0HHW[0,3,7,8]NZ	Insert/Nipple, Rt, [Opn, Perc, Via Natrl or Artfcl Opng, Via Natrl or Artfcl Opng Endo], Tissue Expander, NQ
0HHX[0,3,7,8]NZ	Insert/Nipple, Lt, [Opn, Perc, Via Natrl or Artfcl Opng, Via Natrl or Artfcl Opng Endo], Tissue Expander, NQ
0HMTXZZ	Reattach of Rt Breast, Ext Appr
0HMUXZZ	Reattach of Lt Breast, Ext Appr
0HMVXZZ	Reattach of Bilat Breast, Ext Appr
0HMWXZZ	Reattach of Rt Nipple, Ext Appr
0HMXXZZ	Reattach of Lt Nipple, Ext Appr
0HNT*	Rls/Breast, Rt
0HNU*	Rls/Breast, Lt
0HNV*	Rls/Breast, Bilat
0HNW*	Rls/Nipple, Rt
0HNX*	Rls/Nipple, Lt
0HPT[0,3][J,N]Z	Rmvl/Breast, Rt, [Opn, Perc], [Synth Sub, Tissue Expander], NQ
0HPU[0,3][J,N]Z	Rmvl/Breast, Lt, [Opn, Perc], [Synth Sub, Tissue Expander], NQ
0HQT[0,3,7,8]ZZ	Rpr/Breast, Rt, [Opn, Perc, Via Natrl or Artfcl Opng, Via Natrl or Artfcl Opng Endo]
0HQU[0,3,7,8]ZZ	Rpr/Breast, Lt, [Opn, Perc, Via Natrl or Artfcl Opng, Via Natrl or Artfcl Opng Endo]
0HQV[0,3,7,8]ZZ	Rpr/Breast, Bilat, [Opn, Perc, Via Natrl or Artfcl Opng, Via Natrl or Artfcl Opng Endo]
0HQW*	Repair/Nipple, Rt
0HQX*	Repair/Nipple, Lt
0HQY[0,3,7,8]ZZ	Rpr/Supernumerary Breast, [Opn, Perc, Via Natrl or Artfcl Opng, Via Natrl or Artfcl Opng Endo]

0HRT07[5,6,7,8,9,Z]	Replace/Breast, Rt, Opn, Auto Tissue Sub, [Latissimus Dorsi Myocutaneous Flap, Transv Rectus Abdominis Myocutaneous Flap, Deep Inferior Epigastric Artery Perforator Flap, Superf Inferior Epigastric Artery Flap, Gluteal Artery Perforator Flap, NQ]
0HRT0JZ	Replace of Rt Breast with Synth Sub, Opn Appr
0HRT0KZ	Replace of Rt Breast with Nonaut Sub, Opn Appr
0HRT3[7,J,K]Z	Replace/Breast, Rt, Perc, [Auto Tissue Sub, Synth Sub, Nonauto Tissue Sub], NQ
0HRTXJZ	Replace of Rt Breast with Synth Sub, Extern Appr
0HRU07[5,6,7,8,9,Z]	Replace/Breast, Lt, Opn, Auto Tissue Sub, [Latissimus Dorsi Myocutaneous Flap, Transv Rectus Abdominis Myocutaneous Flap, Deep Inferior Epigastric Artery Perforator Flap, Superf Inferior Epigastric Artery Flap, Gluteal Artery Perforator Flap, NQ]
0HRU0JZ	Replace of Lt Breast with Synth Sub, Opn Appr
0HRU0KZ	Replace of Lt Breast with Nonaut Sub, Opn Appr
0HRU3[7,J,K]Z	Replace/Breast, Lt, Perc, [Auto Tissue Sub, Synth Sub, Nonauto Tissue Sub], NQ
0HRUXJZ	Replace of Lt Breast with Synth Sub, Extern Appr
0HRV07[5,6,7,8,9,Z]	Replace/Breast, Bilat, Opn, Auto Tissue Sub, [Latissimus Dorsi Myocutaneous Flap, Transv Rectus Abdominis Myocutaneous Flap, Deep Inferior Epigastric Artery Perforator Flap, Superf Inferior Epigastric Artery Flap, Gluteal Artery Perforator Flap, NQ]
0HRV0JZ	Replace of Bi Breast with Synth Sub, Opn Appr
0HRV0KZ	Replace of Bi Breast with Nonaut Sub, Opn Appr
0HRV3[7,J,K]Z	Replace/Breast, Bilat, Perc, [Auto Tissue Sub, Synth Sub, Nonauto Tissue Sub], NQ
0HRVXJZ	Replace of Bi Breast with Synth Sub, Extern Appr
0HRW*	Replace/Nipple, Rt
0HRX*	Replace/Nipple, Lt
0HST0ZZ	Repos Rt Breast, Opn Appr
0HSU0ZZ	Repos Lt Breast, Opn Appr
0HSV0ZZ	Repos Bilat Breast, Opn Appr
0HSWXZZ	Repos Rt Nipple, Ext Appr
0HSXXZZ	Repos Lt Nipple, Ext Appr
0HTT0ZZ	Resect of Rt Breast, Opn Appr
0HTU0ZZ	Resect of Lt Breast, Opn Appr
0HTV0ZZ	Resect of Bilat Breast, Opn Appr
0HTWXZZ	Resect of Rt Nipple, Ext Appr
0HTXXZZ	Resect of Lt Nipple, Ext Appr
0HTY0ZZ	Resect of Supernumerary Breast, Opn Appr
0HU*	Skin and Breast, Supl
0HWT[0,3]JZ	Rev/Breast, Rt, [Opn, Perc], Synth Sub, NQ
0HWU[0,3]JZ	Rev/Breast, Lt, [Opn, Perc], Synth Sub, NQ
0KXK[0,4]Z6	Transfer/Abd Muscle, Rt, [Opn, Perc Endo], No Dev, Transv Rectus Abdominis Myocutaneous Flap
0KXL[0,4]Z6	Transfer/Abd Muscle, Lt, [Opn, Perc Endo], No Dev, Transv Rectus Abdominis Myocutaneous Flap
OR	
0HTT0ZZ	Resect of Rt Breast, Opn Appr
AND	
07T50ZZ	Resect of Rt Axillary Lymphatic, Opn Appr
OR	
0HTU0ZZ	Resect of Lt Breast, Opn Appr
AND	
07T60ZZ	Resect of Lt Axillary Lymphatic, Opn Appr
OR	
0HTV0ZZ	Resect of Bilat Breast, Opn Appr
AND	
Both	
07T50ZZ	Resect of Rt Axillary Lymphatic, Opn Appr
07T60ZZ	Resect of Lt Axillary Lymphatic, Opn Appr
OR	
0HTT0ZZ	Resect of Rt Breast, Opn Appr
AND	
Both	
07T50ZZ	Resect of Rt Axillary Lymphatic, Opn Appr
0KTH0ZZ	Resect of Rt Thorax Muscle, Opn Appr
OR	
0HTU0ZZ	Resect of Lt Breast, Opn Appr
AND	
Both	
07T60ZZ	Resect of Lt Axillary Lymphatic, Opn Appr
0KTJ0ZZ	Resect of Lt Thorax Muscle, Opn Appr
OR	
0HTV0ZZ	Resect of Bilat Breast, Opn Appr

T Transfer DRG	SP Special Payment	* Code Range	6th and 7th Character of ZZ = No Device, No Qualifier ZX = No Device, Diagnostic

AND

All of the following

07T50ZZ	Resect of Rt Axillary Lymphatic, Opn Appr
07T60ZZ	Resect of Lt Axillary Lymphatic, Opn Appr
0KTH0ZZ	Resect of Rt Thorax Muscle, Opn Appr
0KTJ0ZZ	Resect of Lt Thorax Muscle, Opn Appr

OR

0HTT0ZZ	Resect of Rt Breast, Opn Appr

AND

All of the following

07T50ZZ	Resect of Rt Axillary Lymphatic, Opn Appr
07T70ZZ	Resect of Thorax Lymphatic, Opn Appr
07T80ZZ	Resect of Rt Int Mammary Lymphatic, Opn Appr
0KTH0ZZ	Resect of Rt Thorax Muscle, Opn Appr

OR

0HTU0ZZ	Resect of Lt Breast, Opn Appr

AND

All of the following

07T60ZZ	Resect of Lt Axillary Lymphatic, Opn Appr
07T70ZZ	Resect of Thorax Lymphatic, Opn Appr
07T90ZZ	Resect of Lt Int Mammary Lymphatic, Opn Appr
0KTJ0ZZ	Resect of Lt Thorax Muscle, Opn Appr

OR

0HTV0ZZ	Resect of Bilat Breast, Opn Appr

AND

All of the following

07T50ZZ	Resect of Rt Axillary Lymphatic, Opn Appr
07T60ZZ	Resect of Lt Axillary Lymphatic, Opn Appr
07T70ZZ	Resect of Thorax Lymphatic, Opn Appr
07T80ZZ	Resect of Rt Int Mammary Lymphatic, Opn Appr
07T90ZZ	Resect of Lt Int Mammary Lymphatic, Opn Appr
0KTH0ZZ	Resect of Rt Thorax Muscle, Opn Appr
0KTJ0ZZ	Resect of Lt Thorax Muscle, Opn Appr

OR

0HRT37Z	Replace of Rt Breast with Autol Sub, Perc Appr
0HRU37Z	Replace of Lt Breast with Autol Sub, Perc Appr
0HRV37Z	Replace of Bi Breast with Autol Sub, Perc Appr

AND

0JD63ZZ	Extract of Chest SQ/Fascia, Perc Appr
0JD73ZZ	Extract of Back SQ/Fascia, Perc Appr
0JD83ZZ	Extract of Abd SQ/Fascia, Perc Appr
0JD93ZZ	Extract of Buttock SQ/Fascia, Perc Appr
0JDL3ZZ	Extract of Rt Up Leg SQ/Fascia, Perc Appr
0JDM3ZZ	Extract of Lt Up Leg SQ/Fascia, Perc Appr

OR

DBY0KZZ	Laser Interstitial Thermal Therapy of Trachea
DBY1KZZ	Laser Interstitial Thermal Therapy of Bronchus
DBY2KZZ	Laser Interstitial Thermal Therapy of Lung
DBY5KZZ	Laser Interstitial Thermal Therapy of Pleura
DBY6KZZ	Laser Interstitial Thermal Therapy of Mediastinum
DBY7KZZ	Laser Interstitial Thermal Therapy of Chest Wall
DBY8KZZ	Laser Interstitial Thermal Therapy of Diaphragm
DMY0KZZ	Laser Interstitial Thermal Therapy of Lt Breast
DMY1KZZ	Laser Interstitial Thermal Therapy of Rt Breast
DVY0KZZ	Laser Interstitial Thermal Therapy of Prostate

DRG 585   Breast Biopsy, Local Excision and Other Breast Procedures without CC/MCC

GMLOS 2.1   AMLOS 2.5   RW 1.5184

Select operating room procedures or procedure combinations listed under DRG 584

MEDICAL

DRG 592   Skin Ulcers with MCC

GMLOS 5.0   AMLOS 6.4   RW 1.4255   T

Principal Diagnosis

L89*	Pressure ulcer
L97*	Non-pressure chr ulcer of lwr limb, NEC
L98.4*	Non-pressure chr ulcer of skin, NEC

DRG 593   Skin Ulcers with CC

GMLOS 4.2   AMLOS 5.1   RW 1.0198   T

Select principal diagnosis listed under DRG 592

DRG 594   Skin Ulcers without CC/MCC

GMLOS 3.1   AMLOS 3.7   RW 0.7049   T

Select principal diagnosis listed under DRG 592

DRG 595   Major Skin Disorders with MCC

GMLOS 5.4   AMLOS 7.3   RW 1.8480

Principal Diagnosis

B02.9	Zoster w/o comp
C43.0	Malig melanoma of lip
C43.2*	Malig melanoma of ear and ext auricular canal
C43.3*	Malig melanoma of oth and unsp parts of face
C43.4	Malig melanoma of scalp and neck
C43.5*	Malig melanoma of trunk
C43.6*	Malig melanoma of upr limb, incl* shldr
C43.7*	Malig melanoma of lwr limb, incl* hip
C43.8	Malig melanoma of overlapping sites of skin
C43.9	Malig melanoma of skin, unsp
C4A*	Merkel cell carcinoma
D03.0	Melanoma in situ of lip
D03.2*	Melanoma in situ of ear and ext auricular canal
D03.3*	Melanoma in situ of oth and unsp parts of face
D03.4	Melanoma in situ of scalp and neck
D03.5*	Melanoma in situ of trunk
D03.6*	Melanoma in situ of upr limb, incl* shldr
D03.7*	Melanoma in situ of lwr limb, incl* hip
D03.8	Melanoma in situ of oth sites
D03.9	Melanoma in situ, unsp
L00	Staphylococcal scalded skin synd
L10*	Pemphigus
L12.0	Bullous pemphigoid
L12.1	Cicatricial pemphigoid
L12.3*	Acquired epidermolysis bullosa
L12.8	Oth pemphigoid
L12.9	Pemphigoid, unsp
L13.8	Oth spec bullous d/o
L13.9	Bullous d/o, unsp
L14	Bullous d/o in dz classified elsw
L40.0	Psoriasis vulgaris
L40.2	Acrodermatitis continua
L40.3	Pustulosis palmaris et plantaris
L40.4	Guttate psoriasis
L40.8	Oth psoriasis
L40.9	Psoriasis, unsp
L41*	Parapsoriasis
L51*	Erythema multiforme
L52	Erythema nodosum
L53.0	Txc erythema
L53.1	Erythema annulare centrifugum
L53.2	Erythema marginatum
L53.3	Oth chr figurate erythema
L93*	Lupus erythematosus
L94.5	Poikiloderma vasculare atrophicans

DRG 596   Major Skin Disorders without MCC

GMLOS 3.6   AMLOS 4.4   RW 0.9375

Select principal diagnosis listed under DRG 595

DRG 597   Malignant Breast Disorders with MCC

GMLOS 5.3   AMLOS 7.0   RW 1.7397

Principal Diagnosis

C50*	Malig neoplasm of breast
C79.2	Secondary malig neoplasm of skin
C79.81	Secondary malig neoplasm of breast
D05*	Carcinoma in situ of breast
D48.6*	Neoplasm of uncertain behav of breast

Surgical	Medical	CC Indicator	MCC Indicator	Procedure Proxy	PDxMCC PDx acts as own MCC	PDxCC PDx acts as own CC

MDC 9: Diseases And Disorders Of The Skin, Subcutaneous Tissue And Breast—MEDICAL

DRG 598 Malignant Breast Disorders with CC
GMLOS 3.7   AMLOS 4.7   RW 1.0617

Select principal diagnosis listed under DRG 597

DRG 599 Malignant Breast Disorders without CC/MCC
GMLOS 2.3   AMLOS 3.0   RW 0.7211

Select principal diagnosis listed under DRG 597

DRG 600 Nonmalignant Breast Disorders with CC/MCC
GMLOS 3.7   AMLOS 4.6   RW 0.9843

Principal Diagnosis

D49.3	Neoplasm of unsp behav of breast
I97.2	Postmastectomy lymphedema synd
N60*	Benign mammary dysplasia
N61	Inflam d/o of breast
N62	Hypertrophy of breast
N63	Unsp lump in breast
N64*	Oth d/o of breast
N65*	Deformity and disproportion of reconstructed breast
Q83*	Congenital malformations of breast
R92*	Abnormal and inconclusive findings on dx imaging of breast
T85.41XA	Breakdown of breast prosthesis and implant, init
T85.42XA	Displac of breast prosthesis and implant, init enc
T85.43XA	Leakage of breast prosthesis and implant, init enc
T85.44XA	Capsular contracture of breast implant, init enc
T85.49XA	Mech compl of breast prosthesis and implant, init enc
Z40.01	Enc for prophylactic rmvl of breast

DRG 601 Nonmalignant Breast Disorders without CC/MCC
GMLOS 2.8   AMLOS 3.3   RW 0.6799

Select principal diagnosis listed under DRG 600

DRG 602 Cellulitis with MCC
GMLOS 4.9   AMLOS 6.1   RW 1.4371   ⊤

Principal Diagnosis

A46	Erysipelas
B78.1	Cutaneous strongyloidiasis
E83.2	D/o of zinc metabolism
I89.1	Lymphangitis
L01*	Impetigo
L02*	Cutaneous abscess, furuncle and carbuncle
L03*	Cellulitis and acute lymphangitis
L05*	Pilonidal cyst and sinus
L08.0	Pyoderma
L08.8*	Oth local infections of the skin and SQ tissue
L08.9	Local infxn of the skin and SQ tissue, unsp
L88	Pyoderma gangrenosum
L92.8	Oth granulomatous d/o of the skin, SQ
L98.0	Pyogenic granuloma
L98.3	Eosinophilic cellulitis [Wells]

DRG 603 Cellulitis without MCC
GMLOS 3.5   AMLOS 4.1   RW 0.8429   ⊤

Select principal diagnosis listed under DRG 602

DRG 604 Trauma to the Skin, Subcutaneous Tissue and Breast with MCC
GMLOS 3.9   AMLOS 5.1   RW 1.3527

Principal Diagnosis

S00.00X[A,S]	Unsp superf inj of scalp, [init enc, seq]
S00.01X[A,S]	Abrasion of scalp, [init enc, seq]
S00.02XS	Blister (nonthermal) of scalp, seq
S00.03X[A,S]	Contsn of scalp, [init enc, seq]
S00.04X[A,S]	Ext constriction of part of scalp, [init enc, seq]
S00.05X[A,S]	Superf FB of scalp, [init enc, seq]
S00.06XS	Insect bite (nonvenomous) of scalp, seq
S00.07X[A,S]	Oth superf bite of scalp, [init enc, seq]
S00.1[0,1,2]XS	Contsn of [unsp, rt, lt] eyelid and periocular area, seq
S00.20[1,2,9]S	Unsp superf inj of [rt, lt, unsp] eyelid and periocular area, seq
S00.21[1,2,9]S	Abrasion of [rt, lt, unsp] eyelid and periocular area, seq

S00.22[1,2,9]S	Blister (nonthermal) of [rt, lt, unsp] eyelid and periocular area, seq
S00.24[1,2,9]S	Ext constriction of [rt, lt, unsp] eyelid and periocular area, seq
S00.25[1,2,9]S	Superf FB of [rt, lt, unsp] eyelid and periocular area, seq
S00.26[1,2,9]S	Insect bite (nonvenomous) of [rt, lt, unsp] eyelid and periocular area, seq
S00.27[1,2,9]S	Oth superf bite of [rt, lt, unsp] eyelid and periocular area, seq
S00.32XS	Blister (nonthermal) of nose, seq
S00.35X[A,S]	Superf FB of nose, [init enc, seq]
S00.36XS	Insect bite (nonvenomous) of nose, seq
S00.37X[A,S]	Oth superf bite of nose, [init enc, seq]
S00.3[0,1]X[A,S]	[Unsp superf inj, abrasion] of nose, [init enc, seq]
S00.3[3,4]X[A,S]	[Contsn, Ext constriction] of nose, [init enc, seq]
S00.40[1,2,9][A,S]	Unsp superf inj of [rt, lt, unsp] ear, [init enc, seq]
S00.41[1,2,9][A,S]	Abrasion of [rt, lt, unsp] ear, [init enc, seq]
S00.42[1,2,9]S	Blister (nonthermal) of [rt, lt, unsp] ear, seq
S00.43[1,2,9][A,S]	Contsn of [rt, lt, unsp] ear, [init enc, seq]
S00.44[1,2,9][A,S]	Ext constriction of [rt, lt, unsp] ear, [init enc, seq]
S00.45[1,2,9][A,S]	Superf FB of [rt, lt, unsp] ear, [init enc, seq]
S00.46[1,2,9]S	Insect bite (nonvenomous) of [rt, lt, unsp] ear, seq
S00.47[1,2,9][A,S]	Oth superf bite of [rt, lt, unsp] ear, [init enc, seq]
S00.50[1,2][A,S]	Unsp superf inj of [lip, oral cavity], [init enc, seq]
S00.51[1,2][A,S]	Abrasion of [lip, oral cavity], [init enc, seq]
S00.52[1,2]S	Blister (nonthermal) of [lip, oral cavity], seq
S00.53[1,2][A,S]	Contsn of [lip, oral cavity], [init enc, seq]
S00.54[1,2][A,S]	Ext constriction of [lip, oral cavity], [init enc, seq]
S00.55[1,2][A,S]	Superf FB of [lip, oral cavity], [init enc, seq]
S00.56[1,2]S	Insect bite (nonvenomous) of [lip, oral cavity], seq
S00.57[1,2][A,S]	Oth superf bite of [lip, oral cavity], [init enc, seq]
S00.82XS	Blister (nonthermal) of oth part of head, seq
S00.85X[A,S]	Superf FB of oth part of head, [init enc, seq]
S00.86XS	Insect bite (nonvenomous) of oth part of head, seq
S00.87X[A,S]	Oth superf bite of oth part of head, [init enc, seq]
S00.8[0,1]X[A,S]	[Unsp superf inj, abrasion] of oth part of head, [init enc, seq]
S00.8[3,4]X[A,S]	[Contsn, ext constriction] of oth part of head, [init enc, seq]
S00.92XS	Blister (nonthermal) of unsp part of head, seq
S00.95X[A,S]	Superf FB of unsp part of head, [init enc, seq]
S00.96XS	Insect bite (nonvenomous) of unsp part of head, seq
S00.97X[A,S]	Oth superf bite of unsp part of head, [init enc, seq]
S00.9[0,1]X[A,S]	[Unsp superf inj, abrasion] of unsp part of head, [init enc, seq]
S00.9[3,4]X[A,S]	[Contsn, ext constriction] of unsp part of head, [init enc, seq]
S01.00X[A,S]	Unsp opn wnd of scalp, [init enc, seq]
S01.05X[A,S]	Opn bite of scalp, [init enc, seq]
S01.0[1,2]X[A,S]	Lac [w/o, w/] FB of scalp, [init enc, seq]
S01.0[3,4]X[A,S]	Punc wnd [w/o, w/] FB of scalp, [init enc, seq]
S01.10[1,2,9]S	Unsp opn wnd of [rt, lt, unsp] eyelid and periocular area, seq
S01.15[1,2,9]S	Opn bite of [rt, lt, unsp] eyelid and periocular area, seq
S01.1[1,2][1,2,9]S	Lac [w/o, w/] FB of [rt, lt, unsp] eyelid and periocular area, seq
S01.1[3,4][1,2,9]S	Punc wnd [w/o, w/] FB of [rt, lt, unsp] eyelid and periocular area, seq
S01.20XS	Unsp opn wnd of nose, [init enc, seq]
S01.25XS	Opn bite of nose, seq
S01.2[1,2,3,4]XS	[Lac w/o, Lac w/, Punc wnd w/o, Punc wnd w/] FB of nose, seq
S01.30[1,2,9]S	Unsp opn wnd of [rt, lt, unsp] ear, seq
S01.35[1,2,9]S	Opn bite of [rt, lt, unsp] ear, seq
S01.3[1,2][1,2,9]S	Lac [w/o, w/] FB of [rt, lt, unsp] ear, seq
S01.3[3,4][1,2,9]S	Punc wnd [w/o, w/] FB of [rt, lt, unsp] ear, seq
S01.40[1,2,9][A,S]	Unsp opn wnd of [rt, lt, unsp] cheek and temporomandibular area, [init enc, seq]
S01.45[1,2,9][A,S]	Opn bite of [rt, lt, unsp] cheek and temporomandibular area, [init enc, seq]
S01.4[1,2][1,2,9][A,S]	Lac [w/o, w/] FB of [rt, lt, unsp] cheek and temporomandibular area, [init enc, seq]
S01.4[3,4][1,2,9][A,S]	Punc wnd [w/o, w/] FB of [rt, lt, unsp] cheek and temporomandibular area, [init enc, seq]
S01.50[1,2]S	Unsp opn wnd of [lip, oral cavity], seq
S01.55[1,2]S	Opn bite of [lip, oral cavity], seq
S01.5[1,2][1,2]S	Lac [w/o, w/] FB of [lip, oral cavity], seq
S01.5[3,4][1,2]S	Punc wnd [w/o, w/] FB of [lip, oral cavity], seq
S01.80X[A,S]	Unsp opn wnd of oth part of head, [init enc, seq]
S01.85X[A,S]	Opn bite of oth part of head, [init enc, seq]
S01.8[1,2]X[A,S]	Lac [w/o, w/] FB of oth part of head, [init enc, seq]
S01.8[3,4]X[A,S]	Punc wnd [w/o, w/] FB of oth part of head, [init enc, seq]
S01.90X[A,S]	Unsp opn wnd of unsp part of head, [init enc, seq]
S01.95X[A,S]	Opn bite of unsp part of head, [init enc, seq]
S01.9[1,2]X[A,S]	Lac [w/o, w/] FB of unsp part of head, [init enc, seq]
S01.9[3,4]X[A,S]	Punc wnd [w/o, w/] FB of unsp part of head, [init enc, seq]
S03.2XXS	Disloc of tooth, seq
S05.0[0,1,2]XS	Inj of conjunctiva and corneal abrasion w/o FB, [unsp, rt, lt] eye, seq

---

⊤ Transfer DRG   ℠ᴾ Special Payment   * Code Range   **6th and 7th Character of ZZ = No Device, No Qualifier ZX = No Device, Diagnostic**

S05.1[0,1,2]XS	Contsn of eyeball and orbital tissues, [unsp, rt, lt] eye, seq
S05.4[0,1,2]XS	Penetrating wnd of orbit w/ or w/o FB, [unsp, rt, lt] eye, seq
S05.[2,3][0,1,2]XS	Ocular lac and rupture [w/, w/o] prolapse or loss of intraocular tissue, [unsp, rt, lt] eye, seq
S05.[5,6][0,1,2]XS	Penetrating wnd [w/, w/o] FB of [unsp, rt, lt] eyeball, seq
S07.9XXS	Crushing inj of head, part unsp, seq
S07.[0,1,8]XXS	Crushing inj of [face, skull, oth parts of head], seq
S08.0XX[A,S]	Avulsion of scalp, [init enc, seq]
S08.1[1,2][1,2,9]S	[Complete, partial] traum amp of [rt, lt, unsp] ear, seq
S08.81[1,2]S	[Complete, partial] traum amp of nose, seq
S08.89X[A,S]	Traum amp of oth parts of head, [init enc, seq]
S09.12X[A,S]	Lac of muscle and tndn of head, [init enc, seq]
S09.2[1,2]XS	Traum rupture of [rt, lt] ear drum, seq
S09.31[1,2,3,9]S	Primary blast inj of [rt, lt, bilat, unsp] ear, seq
S10.0XX[A,S]	Contsn of throat, [init enc, seq]
S10.12XS	Blister (nonthermal) of throat, seq
S10.14X[A,S]	Ext constriction of part of throat, [init enc, seq]
S10.15X[A,S]	Superf FB of throat, [init enc, seq]
S10.16XS	Insect bite (nonvenomous) of throat, seq
S10.17X[A,S]	Oth superf bite of throat, [init enc, seq]
S10.1[0,1]X[A,S]	[Unsp superf injuries, abrasion] of throat, [init enc, seq]
S10.82XS	Blister (nonthermal) of oth part of neck, seq
S10.86XS	Insect bite of oth spec part of neck, seq
S10.8[0,1]X[A,S]	[Unsp superf inj, abrasion] of oth spec part of neck, [init enc, seq]
S10.8[3,4]X[A,S]	[Contsn, ext constriction] of oth spec part of neck, [init enc, seq]
S10.8[5,7]X[A,S]	[Superf FB, oth superf bite] of oth spec part of neck, [init enc, seq]
S10.92XS	Blister (nonthermal) of unsp part of neck, seq
S10.96XS	Insect bite of unsp part of neck, seq
S10.9[0,1]X[A,S]	[Unsp superf inj, abrasion] of unsp part of neck, [init enc, seq]
S10.9[3,4]X[A,S]	[Contsn, ext constriction] of unsp part of neck, [init enc, seq]
S10.9[5,7]X[A,S]	[Superf FB, oth superf bite] of unsp part of neck, [init enc, seq]
S11.015S	Opn bite of larynx, seq
S11.019S	Unsp opn wnd of larynx, seq
S11.01[1,2,3,4]S	[Lac, punc wnd] [w/o, w/] FB of larynx, seq
S11.025S	Opn bite of trachea, seq
S11.029S	Unsp opn wnd of trachea, seq
S11.02[1,2,3,4]S	[Lac, punc wnd] [w/o, w/] FB of trachea, seq
S11.035S	Opn bite of vocal cord, seq
S11.039S	Unsp opn wnd of vocal cord, seq
S11.03[1,2,3,4]S	[Lac, punc wnd] [w/o, w/] FB of vocal cord, seq
S11.10XS	Unsp opn wnd of thyroid gland, seq
S11.15XS	Opn bite of thyroid gland, seq
S11.1[1,2,3,4]XS	[Lac, punc wnd] [w/o, w/] FB of thyroid gland, seq
S11.20XS	Unsp opn wnd of pharynx and cervical esophagus, seq
S11.25XS	Opn bite of pharynx and cervical esophagus, seq
S11.2[1,2,3,4]XS	[Lac, punc wnd] [w/o, w/] FB of pharynx and cervical esophagus, seq
S11.80X[A,S]	Unsp opn wnd of oth spec part of neck, [init enc, seq]
S11.85X[A,S]	Opn bite of oth spec part of neck, [init enc, seq]
S11.89X[A,S]	Oth opn wnd of oth spec part of neck, [init enc, seq]
S11.8[1,2]X[A,S]	Lac [w/o, w/] FB of oth spec part of neck, [init enc, seq]
S11.8[3,4]X[A,S]	Punc wnd [w/o, w/] FB of oth spec part of neck, [init enc, seq]
S11.90X[A,S]	Unsp opn wnd of unsp part of neck, [init enc, seq]
S11.95X[A,S]	Opn bite of unsp part of neck, [init enc, seq]
S11.9[1,2]X[A,S]	Lac [w/o, w/] FB of unsp part of neck, [init enc, seq]
S11.9[3,4]X[A,S]	Punc wnd [w/o, w/] FB of unsp part of neck, [init enc, seq]
S16.2XX[A,S]	Lac of muscle, fascia and tndn at neck lvl, [init enc, seq]
S17.0XXS	Crushing inj of larynx and trachea, seq
S17.8XXS	Crushing inj of oth spec parts of neck, seq
S17.9XXS	Crushing inj of neck, part unsp, seq
S20.0[0,1,2]X[A,S]	Contsn of [unsp, rt, lt] breast, [init enc, seq]
S20.10[1,2,9][A,S]	Unsp superf injuries of breast, [rt, lt, unsp] breast, [init enc, seq]
S20.11[1,2,9][A,S]	Abrasion of breast, [rt, lt, unsp] breast, [init enc, seq]
S20.12[1,2,9]S	Blister (nonthermal) of breast, [rt, lt, unsp] breast, seq
S20.14[1,2,9][A,S]	Ext constriction of part of breast, [rt, lt, unsp] breast, [init enc, seq]
S20.15[1,2,9][A,S]	Superf FB of breast, [rt, lt, unsp] breast, [init enc, seq]
S20.16[1,2,9]S	Insect bite (nonvenomous) of breast, [rt, lt, unsp] breast, seq
S20.17[1,2,9][A,S]	Oth superf bite of breast, [rt, lt, unsp] breast, [init enc, seq]
S20.2X[A,S]	Contsn of thorax, unsp, [init enc, seq]
S20.21[1,2,9][A,S]	Contsn of [rt, lt, unsp] front wall of thorax, [init enc, seq]
S20.22[1,2,9][A,S]	Contsn of [rt, lt, unsp] back wall of thorax, [init enc, seq]
S20.30[1,2,9][A,S]	Unsp superf injuries of [rt, lt, unsp] front wall of thorax, [init enc, seq]
S20.31[1,2,9][A,S]	Abrasion of [rt, lt, unsp] front wall of thorax, [init enc, seq]
S20.32[1,2,9]S	Blister (nonthermal) of [rt, lt, unsp] front wall of thorax, seq

S20.34[1,2,9][A,S]	Ext constriction of [rt, lt, unsp] front wall of thorax, [init enc, seq]
S20.35[1,2,9][A,S]	Superf FB of [rt, lt, unsp] front wall of thorax, [init enc, seq]
S20.36[1,2,9]S	Insect bite (nonvenomous) of [rt, lt, unsp] front wall of thorax, seq
S20.37[1,2,9][A,S]	Oth superf bite of [rt, lt, unsp] front wall of thorax, [init enc, seq]
S20.40[1,2,9][A,S]	Unsp superf injuries of [rt, lt, unsp] back wall of thorax, [init enc, seq]
S20.41[1,2,9][A,S]	Abrasion of [rt, lt, unsp] back wall of thorax, [init enc, seq]
S20.42[1,2,9]S	Blister (nonthermal) of [rt, lt, unsp] back wall of thorax, seq
S20.44[1,2,9][A,S]	Ext constriction of [rt, lt, unsp] back wall of thorax, [init enc, seq]
S20.45[1,2,9][A,S]	Superf FB of [rt, lt, unsp] back wall of thorax, [init enc, seq]
S20.46[1,2,9]S	Insect bite (nonvenomous) of [rt, lt, unsp] back wall of thorax, seq
S20.47[1,2,9][A,S]	Oth superf bite of [rt, lt, unsp] back wall of thorax, [init enc, seq]
S20.92XS	Blister (nonthermal) of unsp parts of thorax, seq
S20.94X[A,S]	Ext constriction of unsp parts of thorax, [init enc, seq]
S20.95X[A,S]	Superf FB of unsp parts of thorax, [init enc, seq]
S20.96XS	Insect bite (nonvenomous) of unsp parts of thorax, seq
S20.97X[A,S]	Oth superf bite of unsp parts of thorax, [init enc, seq]
S20.9[0,1]X[A,S]	[Unsp superf inj, abrasion] of unsp parts of thorax, [init enc, seq]
S21.00[1,2,9][A,S]	Unsp opn wnd of [rt, lt, unsp] breast, [init enc, seq]
S21.01[1,2,9][A,S]	Lac w/o FB of [rt, lt, unsp] breast, [init enc, seq]
S21.02[1,2,9][A,S]	Lac w/ FB of [rt, lt, unsp] breast, [init enc, seq]
S21.03[1,2,9][A,S]	Punc wnd w/o FB of [rt, lt, unsp] breast, [init enc, seq]
S21.04[1,2,9][A,S]	Punc wnd w/ FB of [rt, lt, unsp] breast, [init enc, seq]
S21.05[1,2,9][A,S]	Opn bite of [rt, lt, unsp] breast, [init enc, seq]
S21.10[1,2,9][A,S]	Unsp opn wnd of [rt, lt, unsp] front wall of thorax w/o penetration into thoracic cavity, [init enc, seq]
S21.11[1,2,9][A,S]	Lac w/o FB of [rt, lt, unsp] front wall of thorax w/o penetration into thoracic cavity, [init enc, seq]
S21.12[1,2,9]S	Lac w/ FB of [rt, lt, unsp] front wall of thorax w/o penetration into thoracic cavity, seq
S21.13[1,2,9][A,S]	Punc wnd w/o FB of [rt, lt, unsp] front wall of thorax w/o penetration into thoracic cavity, [init enc, seq]
S21.14[1,2,9]S	Punc wnd w/ FB of [rt, lt, unsp] front wall of thorax w/o penetration into thoracic cavity, seq
S21.15[1,2,9][A,S]	Opn bite of [rt, lt, unsp] front wall of thorax w/o penetration into thoracic cavity, [init enc, seq]
S21.20[1,2,9][A,S]	Unsp opn wnd of [rt, lt, unsp] back wall of thorax w/o penetration into thoracic cavity, [init enc, seq]
S21.21[1,2,9][A,S]	Lac w/o FB of [rt, lt, unsp] back wall of thorax w/o penetration into thoracic cavity, [init enc, seq]
S21.22[1,2,9][A,S]	Lac w/ FB of [rt, lt, unsp] back wall of thorax w/o penetration into thoracic cavity, [init enc, seq]
S21.23[1,2,9][A,S]	Punc wnd w/o FB of [rt, lt, unsp] back wall of thorax w/o penetration into thoracic cavity, [init enc, seq]
S21.24[1,2,9][A,S]	Punc wnd w/ FB of [rt, lt, unsp] back wall of thorax w/o penetration into thoracic cavity, [init enc, seq]
S21.25[1,2,9][A,S]	Opn bite of [rt, lt, unsp] back wall of thorax w/o penetration into thoracic cavity, [init enc, seq]
S21.30[1,2,9]S	Unsp opn wnd of [rt, lt, unsp] front wall of thorax w/ penetration into thoracic cavity, seq
S21.35[1,2,9]S	Opn bite of [rt, lt, unsp] front wall of thorax w/ penetration into thoracic cavity, seq
S21.3[1,2][1,2,9]S	Lac [w/o, w/] FB of [rt, lt, unsp] front wall of thorax w/ penetration into thoracic cavity, seq
S21.3[3,4][1,2,9]S	Punc wnd [w/o, w/] FB of [rt, lt, unsp] front wall of thorax w/ penetration into thoracic cavity, seq
S21.40[1,2,9]S	Unsp opn wnd of [rt, lt, unsp] back wall of thorax w/ penetration into thoracic cavity, seq
S21.45[1,2,9]S	Opn bite of [rt, lt, unsp] back wall of thorax w/ penetration into thoracic cavity, seq
S21.4[1,2][1,2,9]S	Lac [w/o, w/] FB of [rt, lt, unsp] back wall of thorax w/ penetration into thoracic cavity, seq
S21.4[3,4][1,2,9]S	Punc wnd [w/o, w/] FB of [rt, lt, unsp] back wall of thorax w/ penetration into thoracic cavity, seq
S21.90X[A,S]	Unsp opn wnd of unsp part of thorax, [init enc, seq]
S21.91X[A,S]	Lac w/o FB of unsp part of thorax, [init enc, seq]
S21.92XS	Lac with FB of unsp part of thorax, seq
S21.93X[A,S]	Punc wnd w/o FB of unsp part of thorax, [init enc, seq]
S21.94XS	Punc w FB of unsp part of thorax, seq
S21.95X[A,S]	Opn bite of unsp part of thorax, [init enc, seq]
S28.0XXS	Crushed chest, seq
S28.1XX[A,S]	Traum amp (partial) of part of thorax, except breast, [init enc, seq]

Surgical   **Medical**   **CC Indicator**   **MCC Indicator**   **Procedure Proxy**   🔲PDx MCC **PDx acts as own MCC**   🔲PDx CC **PDx acts as own CC**

S28.21[1,2,9][A,S]	Complete traum amp of [rt, lt, unsp] breast, [init enc, seq]
S28.22[1,2,9][A,S]	Partial traum amp of [rt, lt, unsp] breast, [init enc, seq]
S29.02[1,2,9][A,S]	Lac of muscle and tndn of [front, back, unsp] wall of thorax, [init enc, seq]
S30.0XX[A,S]	Contsn of lwr back and pelvis, [init enc, seq]
S30.1XX[A,S]	Contsn of abd wall, [init enc, seq]
S30.20[1,2]S	Contsn of unsp ext genital organ, [male, female], seq
S30.21XS	Contsn of penis, seq
S30.22XS	Contsn of scrotum and testes, seq
S30.23XS	Contsn of vagina and vulva, seq
S30.3XX[A,S]	Contsn of anus, [init enc, seq]
S30.810[A,S]	Abrasion of lwr back and pelvis, [init enc, seq]
S30.811[A,S]	Abrasion of abd wall, [init enc, seq]
S30.814[A,S]	Abrasion of vagina and vulva, [init enc, seq]
S30.817[A,S]	Abrasion of anus, [init enc, seq]
S30.81[2,3][A,S]	Abrasion of [penis, scrotum and testes], [init enc, seq]
S30.81[5,6][A,S]	Abrasion of unsp ext genital organs, [male, female], [init enc, seq]
S30.820S	Blister (nonthermal) of lwr back and pelvis, seq
S30.821S	Blister (nonthermal) of abd wall, seq
S30.824S	Blister (nonthermal) of vagina and vulva, seq
S30.827S	Blister (nonthermal) of anus, seq
S30.82[2,3]S	Blister (nonthermal) of [penis, scrotum and testes], seq
S30.82[5,6]S	Blister (nonthermal) of unsp ext genital organs, [male, female], seq
S30.840[A,S]	Ext constriction of lwr back and pelvis, [init enc, seq]
S30.841[A,S]	Ext constriction of abd wall, [init enc, seq]
S30.844[A,S]	Ext constriction of vagina and vulva, [init enc, seq]
S30.84[2,3][A,S]	Ext constriction of [penis, scrotum and testes], [init enc, seq]
S30.84[5,6][A,S]	Ext constriction of unsp ext genital organs, [male, female], [init enc, seq]
S30.850[A,S]	Superf FB of lwr back and pelvis, [init enc, seq]
S30.851[A,S]	Superf FB of abd wall, [init enc, seq]
S30.854[A,S]	Superf FB of vagina and vulva, [init enc, seq]
S30.857[A,S]	Superf FB of anus, [init enc, seq]
S30.85[2,3][A,S]	Superf FB of [penis, scrotum and testes], [init enc, seq]
S30.85[5,6][A,S]	Superf FB of unsp ext genital organs, [male, female], [init enc, seq]
S30.860S	Insect bite (nonvenomous) of lwr back and pelvis, seq
S30.861S	Insect bite (nonvenomous) of abd wall, seq
S30.864S	Insect bite (nonvenomous) of vagina and vulva, seq
S30.867S	Insect bite (nonvenomous) of anus, seq
S30.86[2,3]S	Insect bite (nonvenomous) of [penis, scrotum and testes], seq
S30.86[5,6]S	Insect bite (nonvenomous) of unsp ext genital organs, [male, female], seq
S30.870[A,S]	Oth superf bite of lwr back and pelvis, [init enc, seq]
S30.871[A,S]	Oth superf bite of abd wall, [init enc, seq]
S30.874[A,S]	Oth superf bite of vagina and vulva, [init enc, seq]
S30.877[A,S]	Oth superf bite of anus, [init enc, seq]
S30.87[2,3][A,S]	Oth superf bite of [penis, scrotum and testes], [init enc, seq]
S30.87[5,6][A,S]	Oth superf bite of unsp ext genital organs, [male, female], [init enc, seq]
S30.91X[A,S]	Unsp superf inj of lwr back and pelvis, [init enc, seq]
S30.92X[A,S]	Unsp superf inj of abd wall, [init enc, seq]
S30.95X[A,S]	Unsp superf inj of vagina and vulva, [init enc, seq]
S30.98X[A,S]	Unsp superf inj of anus, [init enc, seq]
S30.9[3,4]X[A,S]	Unsp superf inj of [penis, scrotum and testes], [init enc, seq]
S30.9[6,7]X[A,S]	Unsp superf inj of unsp ext genital organs, [male, female], [init enc, seq]
S31.000[A,S]	Unsp opn wnd of lwr back and pelvis w/o penetration into retroperitoneum, [init enc, seq]
S31.001S	Unsp opn wnd low back and pelvis w penet retroperiton, seq
S31.010[A,S]	Lac w/o FB of lwr back and pelvis w/o penetration into retroperitoneum, [init enc, seq]
S31.011S	Lac w/o fb of low back and pelvis w penet retroperiton, seq
S31.020[A,S]	Lac w/ FB of lwr back and pelvis w/o penetration into retroperitoneum, [init enc, seq]
S31.021S	Lac w fb of low back and pelvis w penet retroperiton, seq
S31.030[A,S]	Punc wnd w/o FB of lwr back and pelvis w/o penetration into retroperitoneum, [init enc, seq]
S31.031S	Punc w/o fb of low back and pelv w penet retroperiton, seq
S31.040[A,S]	Punc wnd w/ FB of lwr back and pelvis w/o penetration into retroperitoneum, [init enc, seq]
S31.041S	Punc w fb of low back and pelvis w penet retroperiton, seq
S31.050[A,S]	Opn bite of lwr back and pelvis w/o penetration into retroperitoneum, [init enc, seq]
S31.051S	Opn bite of low back and pelvis w penet retroperiton, seq
S31.102[A,S]	Unsp opn wnd of abd wall, epigastric rgn w/o penetration into peritoneal cavity, [init enc, seq]
S31.105[A,S]	Unsp opn wnd of abd wall, periumbilic rgn w/o penetration into peritoneal cavity, [init enc, seq]
S31.109[A,S]	Unsp opn wnd of abd wall, unsp quadrant w/o penetration into peritoneal cavity, [init enc, seq]
S31.10[0,1][A,S]	Unsp opn wnd of abd wall, [rt, lt] upr quadrant w/o penetration into peritoneal cavity, [init enc, seq]
S31.10[3,4][A,S]	Unsp opn wnd of abd wall, [rt, lt] lwr quadrant w/o penetration into peritoneal cavity, [init enc, seq]
S31.112[A,S]	Lac w/o FB of abd wall, epigastric rgn w/o penetration into peritoneal cavity, [init enc, seq]
S31.115[A,S]	Lac w/o FB of abd wall, periumbilic rgn w/o penetration into peritoneal cavity, [init enc, seq]
S31.119[A,S]	Lac w/o FB of abd wall, unsp quadrant w/o penetration into peritoneal cavity, [init enc, seq]
S31.11[0,1][A,S]	Lac w/o FB of abd wall, [rt, lt] upr quadrant w/o penetration into peritoneal cavity, [init enc, seq]
S31.11[3,4][A,S]	Lac w/o FB of abd wall, [rt, lt] lwr quadrant w/o penetration into peritoneal cavity, [init enc, seq]
S31.122S	Lacerat abd wall w fb, epigst rgn w/o penet perit cav, seq
S31.125S	Lacerat abd wall w fb, periumb rgn w/o penet perit cav, seq
S31.129S	Lacerat abd wall w fb, unsp q w/o penet perit cav, seq
S31.12[0,1]S	Lac of abd wall w/ FB, [rt, lt] upr quadrant w/o penetration into peritoneal cavity, seq
S31.12[3,4]S	Lac of abd wall w/ FB, [rt, lt] lwr quadrant w/o penetration into peritoneal cavity, seq
S31.132[A,S]	Punc wnd of abd wall w/o FB, epigastric rgn w/o penetration into peritoneal cavity, [init enc, seq]
S31.135[A,S]	Punc wnd of abd wall w/o FB, periumbilic rgn w/o penetration into peritoneal cavity, [init enc, seq]
S31.139[A,S]	Punc wnd of abd wall w/o FB, unsp quadrant w/o penetration into peritoneal cavity, [init enc, seq]
S31.13[0,1][A,S]	Punc wnd of abd wall w/o FB, [rt, lt] upr quadrant w/o penetration into peritoneal cavity, [init enc, seq]
S31.13[3,4][A,S]	Punc wnd of abd wall w/o FB, [rt, lt] lwr quadrant w/o penetration into peritoneal cavity, [init enc, seq]
S31.142S	Punc of abd wall w fb, epigst rgn w/o penet perit cav, seq
S31.145S	Punc of abd wl w fb, periumb rgn w/o penet perit cav, seq
S31.149S	Punc of abd wall w fb, unsp q w/o penet perit cav, seq
S31.14[0,1]S	Punc wnd of abd wall w/ FB, [rt, lt] upr quadrant w/o penetration into peritoneal cavity, seq
S31.14[3,4]S	Punc wnd of abd wall w/ FB, [rt, lt] lwr quadrant w/o penetration into peritoneal cavity, seq
S31.152[A,S]	Opn bite of abd wall, epigastric rgn w/o penetration into peritoneal cavity, [init enc, seq]
S31.155[A,S]	Opn bite of abd wall, periumbilic rgn w/o penetration into peritoneal cavity, [init enc, seq]
S31.159[A,S]	Opn bite of abd wall, unsp quadrant w/o penetration into peritoneal cavity, [init enc, seq]
S31.15[0,1][A,S]	Opn bite of abd wall, [rt, lt] upr quadrant w/o penetration into peritoneal cavity, [init enc, seq]
S31.15[3,4][A,S]	Opn bite of abd wall, [rt, lt] lwr quadrant w/o penetration into peritoneal cavity, [init enc, seq]
S31.25XS	Opn bite of penis, seq
S31.2[1,2]XS	Lac [w/o, w/] FB of penis, seq
S31.2[3,4]XS	Punc wnd [w/o, w/] FB of penis, seq
S31.35XS	Opn bite of scrotum and testes, seq
S31.3[1,2,3,4]XS	[Lac, punc wnd] [w/o, w/] FB of scrotum and testes, seq
S31.40XS	Unsp opn wnd of vagina and vulva, seq
S31.45XS	Opn bite of vagina and vulva, seq
S31.4[1,2]XS	Lac [w/o, w/] FB of vagina and vulva, seq
S31.4[3,4]XS	Punc wnd [w/o, w/] FB of vagina and vulva, seq
S31.602S	Unsp opn wnd abd wall, epigst rgn w penet perit cav, seq
S31.605S	Unsp opn wnd abd wall, periumb rgn w penet perit cav, seq
S31.609S	Unsp opn wnd abd wall, unsp q w penet perit cav, seq
S31.60[0,1,3,4]S	Unsp opn wnd of abd wall, [rt, lt] [upr, lwr] quadrant w/ penetration into peritoneal cavity, seq
S31.612S	Lac w/o fb of abd wall, epigst rgn w penet perit cav, seq
S31.615S	Lac w/o fb of abd wall, periumb rgn w penet perit cav, seq
S31.619S	Lac w/o fb of abd wall, unsp q w penet perit cav, seq
S31.61[0,1,3,4]S	Lac w/o FB of abd wall, [rt, lt] [upr, lwr] quadrant w/ penetration into peritoneal cavity, seq
S31.622S	Lac w fb of abd wall, epigst rgn w penet perit cav, seq
S31.625S	Lac w fb of abd wall, periumb rgn w penet perit cav, seq
S31.629S	Lac w fb of abd wall, unsp q w penet perit cav, seq
S31.62[0,1,3,4]S	Lac w/ FB of abd wall, [rt, lt] [upr, lwr] quadrant w/ penetration into peritoneal cavity, seq
S31.632S	Punc w/o fb of abd wall, epigst rgn w penet perit cav, seq
S31.635S	Punc w/o fb of abd wl, periumb rgn w penet perit cav, seq
S31.639S	Punc w/o fb of abd wall, unsp q w penet perit cav, seq

---

Ⓣ **Transfer DRG**   ⓢⓟ **Special Payment**   * **Code Range**   **6th and 7th Character of ZZ = No Device, No Qualifier ZX = No Device, Diagnostic**

S31.63[0,1,3,4]S	Punc wnd w/o FB of abd wall, [rt, lt] [upr, lwr] quadrant w/ penetration into peritoneal cavity, seq
S31.642S	Punc w fb of abd wall, epigst rgn w penet perit cav, seq
S31.645S	Punc w fb of abd wall, periumb rgn w penet perit cav, seq
S31.649S	Punc w fb of abd wall, unsp q w penet perit cav, seq
S31.64[0,1,3,4]S	Punc wnd w/ FB of abd wall, [rt, lt] [upr, lwr] quadrant w/ penetration into peritoneal cavity, seq
S31.652S	Opn bite of abd wall, epigst rgn w penet perit cav, seq
S31.655S	Opn bite of abd wall, periumb rgn w penet perit cav, seq
S31.659S	Opn bite of abd wall, unsp q w penet perit cav, seq
S31.65[0,1,3,4]S	Opn bite of abd wall, [rt, lt] [upr, lwr] quadrant w/ penetration into peritoneal cavity, seq
S31.805[A,S]	Opn bite of unsp buttock, [init enc, seq]
S31.809[A,S]	Unsp opn wnd of unsp buttock, [init enc, seq]
S31.80[1,2][A,S]	Lac [w/o, w/] FB of unsp buttock, [init enc, seq]
S31.80[3,4][A,S]	Punc wnd [w/o, w/] FB of unsp buttock, [init enc, seq]
S31.815[A,S]	Opn bite of rt buttock, [init enc, seq]
S31.819[A,S]	Unsp opn wnd of rt buttock, [init enc, seq]
S31.81[1,2][A,S]	Lac [w/o, w/] FB of rt buttock, [init enc, seq]
S31.81[3,4][A,S]	Punc wnd [w/o, w/] FB of rt buttock, [init enc, seq]
S31.825[A,S]	Opn bite of lt buttock, [init enc, seq]
S31.829[A,S]	Unsp opn wnd of lt buttock, [init enc, seq]
S31.82[1,2][A,S]	Lac [w/o, w/] FB of lt buttock, [init enc, seq]
S31.82[3,4][A,S]	Punc wnd [w/o, w/] FB of lt buttock, [init enc, seq]
S31.831[A,S]	Lac w/o FB of anus, [init enc, seq]
S31.832S	Lac with FB of anus, seq
S31.833[A,S]	Punc wnd w/o FB of anus, [init enc, seq]
S31.834S	Punc wnd with FB of anus, seq
S31.835[A,S]	Opn bite of anus, [init enc, seq]
S31.839[A,S]	Unsp opn wnd of anus, [init enc, seq]
S31.[2,3]0XS	Unsp opn wnd of [penis, scrotum and testes], seq
S38.00[1,2]S	Crushing inj of unsp ext genital organs, [male, female], seq
S38.03XS	Crushing inj of vulva, seq
S38.0[1,2]XS	Crushing inj of [penis, scrotum and testes], seq
S38.1XXS	Crushing inj of abd, lwr back, and pelvis, seq
S38.21[1,2]S	[Complete, partial] traum amp of female ext genital organs, seq
S38.2[2,3][1,2]S	[Complete, partial] traum amp of [penis, scrotum and testes], seq
S38.3XX[A,S]	Transection (partial) of abd, [init enc, seq]
S39.023[A,S]	Lac of muscle, fascia and tndn of pelvis, [init enc, seq]
S39.02[1,2][A,S]	Lac of muscle, fascia and tndn of [abd, lwr back], [init enc, seq]
S40.01[1,2,9][A,S]	Contsn of [rt, lt, unsp] shldr, [init enc, seq]
S40.02[1,2,9][A,S]	Contsn of [rt, lt, unsp] upr arm, [init enc, seq]
S40.21[1,2,9][A,S]	Abrasion of [rt, lt, unsp] shldr, [init enc, seq]
S40.22[1,2,9][A,S]	Blister (nonthermal) of [rt, lt, unsp] shldr, [init enc, seq]
S40.24[1,2,9][A,S]	Ext constriction of [rt, lt, unsp] shldr, [init enc, seq]
S40.25[1,2,9][A,S]	Superf FB of [rt, lt, unsp] shldr, [init enc, seq]
S40.26[1,2,9]S	Insect bite (nonvenomous) of [rt, lt, unsp] shldr, seq
S40.27[1,2,9][A,S]	Oth superf bite of [rt, lt, unsp] shldr, [init enc, seq]
S40.81[1,2,9][A,S]	Abrasion of [rt, lt, unsp] upr arm, [init enc, seq]
S40.82[1,2,9][A,S]	Blister (nonthermal) of [rt, lt, unsp] upr arm, [init enc, seq]
S40.84[1,2,9][A,S]	Ext constriction of [rt, lt, unsp] upr arm, [init enc, seq]
S40.85[1,2,9][A,S]	Superf FB of [rt, lt, unsp] upr arm, [init enc, seq]
S40.86[1,2,9]S	Insect bite (nonvenomous) of [rt, lt, unsp] upr arm, seq
S40.87[1,2,9][A,S]	Oth superf bite of [rt, lt, unsp] upr arm, [init enc, seq]
S40.91[1,2,9][A,S]	Unsp superf inj of [rt, lt, unsp] shldr, [init enc, seq]
S40.92[1,2,9][A,S]	Unsp superf inj of [rt, lt, unsp] upr arm, [init enc, seq]
S41.00[1,2,9][A,S]	Unsp opn wnd of [rt, lt, unsp] shldr, [init enc, seq]
S41.01[1,2,9][A,S]	Lac w/o FB of [rt, lt, unsp] shldr, [init enc, seq]
S41.02[1,2,9]S	Lac w/ FB of [rt, lt, unsp] shldr, seq
S41.03[1,2,9][A,S]	Punc wnd w/o FB of [rt, lt, unsp] shldr, [init enc, seq]
S41.04[1,2,9]S	Punc wnd w/ FB of [rt, lt, unsp] shldr, seq
S41.05[1,2,9][A,S]	Opn bite of [rt, lt, unsp] shldr, [init enc, seq]
S41.10[1,2,9][A,S]	Unsp opn wnd of [rt, lt, unsp] upr arm, [init enc, seq]
S41.11[1,2,9][A,S]	Lac w/o FB of [rt, lt, unsp] upr arm, [init enc, seq]
S41.12[1,2,9]S	Lac w/ FB of [rt, lt, unsp] upr arm, seq
S41.13[1,2,9][A,S]	Punc wnd w/o FB of [rt, lt, unsp] upr arm, [init enc, seq]
S41.14[1,2,9]S	Punc wnd w/ FB of [rt, lt, unsp] upr arm, seq
S41.15[1,2,9][A,S]	Opn bite of [rt, lt, unsp] upr arm, [init enc, seq]
S46.02[1,2,9]S	Lac of muscle(s) and tndn(s) of the rotator cuff of [rt, lt, unsp] shldr, seq
S46.32[1,2,9]S	Lac of muscle, fascia and tndn of triceps, [rt, lt, unsp] arm, seq
S46.[1,2]2[1,2,9]S	Lac of muscle, fascia and tndn of [long head, oth parts] of biceps, [rt, lt, unsp] arm, seq
S46.[8,9]2[1,2,9]S	Lac of [oth, unsp] muscles, fascia and tndns at shldr and upr arm lvl, [rt, lt, unsp] arm, seq
S47.[1,2,9]XXS	Crushing inj of [rt, lt, unsp] shldr and upr arm, seq
S50.0[0,1,2]X[A,S]	Contsn of [unsp, rt, lt] elbow, [init enc, seq]
S50.1[0,1,2]X[A,S]	Contsn of [unsp, rt, lt] forearm, [init enc, seq]

S50.31[1,2,9][A,S]	Abrasion of [rt, lt, unsp] elbow, [init enc, seq]
S50.32[1,2,9]S	Blister (nonthermal) of [rt, lt, unsp] elbow, seq
S50.34[1,2,9][A,S]	Ext constriction of [rt, lt, unsp] elbow, [init enc, seq]
S50.35[1,2,9][A,S]	Superf FB of [rt, lt, unsp] elbow, [init enc, seq]
S50.36[1,2,9]S	Insect bite (nonvenomous) of [rt, lt, unsp] elbow, seq
S50.37[1,2,9][A,S]	Oth superf bite of [rt, lt, unsp] elbow, [init enc, seq]
S50.81[1,2,9][A,S]	Abrasion of [rt, lt, unsp] forearm, [init enc, seq]
S50.82[1,2,9]S	Blister (nonthermal) of [rt, lt, unsp] forearm, seq
S50.84[1,2,9][A,S]	Ext constriction of [rt, lt, unsp] forearm, [init enc, seq]
S50.85[1,2,9][A,S]	Superf FB of [rt, lt, unsp] forearm, [init enc, seq]
S50.86[1,2,9]S	Insect bite (nonvenomous) of [rt, lt, unsp] forearm, seq
S50.87[1,2,9][A,S]	Oth superf bite of [rt, lt, unsp] forearm, [init enc, seq]
S50.90[1,2,9][A,S]	Unsp superf inj of [rt, lt, unsp] elbow, [init enc, seq]
S50.91[1,2,9][A,S]	Unsp superf inj of [rt, lt, unsp] forearm, [init enc, seq]
S51.00[1,2,9][A,S]	Unsp opn wnd of [rt, lt, unsp] elbow, [init enc, seq]
S51.01[1,2,9][A,S]	Lac w/o FB of [rt, lt, unsp] elbow, [init enc, seq]
S51.02[1,2,9]S	Lac w/ FB of [rt, lt, unsp] elbow, seq
S51.03[1,2,9][A,S]	Punc wnd w/o FB of [rt, lt, unsp] elbow, [init enc, seq]
S51.04[1,2,9]S	Punc wnd w/ FB of [rt, lt, unsp] elbow, seq
S51.05[1,2,9][A,S]	Opn bite, [rt, lt, unsp] elbow, [init enc, seq]
S51.80[1,2,9][A,S]	Unsp opn wnd of [rt, lt, unsp] forearm, [init enc, seq]
S51.81[1,2,9][A,S]	Lac w/o FB of [rt, lt, unsp] forearm, [init enc, seq]
S51.82[1,2,9]S	Lac w/ FB of [rt, lt, unsp] forearm, seq
S51.83[1,2,9][A,S]	Punc wnd w/o FB of [rt, lt, unsp] forearm, [init enc, seq]
S51.84[1,2,9]S	Punc wnd w/ FB of [rt, lt, unsp] forearm, seq
S51.85[1,2,9][A,S]	Opn bite of [rt, lt, unsp] forearm, [init enc, seq]
S56.02[1,2,9]S	Lac of flexor muscle, fascia and tndn of [rt, lt, unsp] thumb at forearm lvl, seq
S56.129S	Lacerat flexor musc/fasc/tend unsp finger at forearm lv, seq
S56.12[1,2]S	Lac of flexor muscle, fascia and tndn of [rt, lt] index finger at forearm lvl, seq
S56.12[3,4]S	Lac of flexor muscle, fascia and tndn of [rt, lt] mid finger at forearm lvl, seq
S56.12[5,6]S	Lac of flexor muscle, fascia and tndn of [rt, lt] ring finger at forearm lvl, seq
S56.12[7,8]S	Lac of flexor muscle, fascia and tndn of [rt, lt] little finger at forearm lvl, seq
S56.22[1,2,9]S	Lac of oth flexor muscle, fascia and tndn at forearm lvl, [rt, lt, unsp] arm, seq
S56.32[1,2,9]S	Lac of extensor or abductor muscles, fascia and tndns of [rt, lt, unsp] thumb at forearm lvl, seq
S56.429S	Lacerat extn musc/fasc/tend unsp finger at forearm lv, seq
S56.42[1,2]S	Lac of extensor muscle, fascia and tndn of [rt, lt] index finger at forearm lvl, seq
S56.42[3,4]S	Lac of extensor muscle, fascia and tndn of [rt, lt] mid finger at forearm lvl, seq
S56.42[5,6]S	Lac of extensor muscle, fascia and tndn of [rt, lt] ring finger at forearm lvl, seq
S56.42[7,8]S	Lac of extensor muscle, fascia and tndn of [rt, lt] little finger at forearm lvl, seq
S56.52[1,2,9]S	Lac of oth extensor muscle, fascia and tndn at forearm lvl, [rt, lt, unsp] arm, seq
S56.[8,9]2[1,2,9]S	Lac of [oth, unsp] muscles, fascia and tndns at forearm lvl, [rt, lt, unsp] arm, seq
S57.0[0,1,2]XS	Crushing inj of [unsp, rt, lt] elbow, seq
S57.8[0,1,2]XS	Crushing inj of [unsp, rt, lt] forearm, seq
S60.00X[A,S]	Contsn of unsp finger w/o damage to nail, [init enc, seq]
S60.01[1,2,9][A,S]	Contsn of [rt, lt, unsp] thumb w/o damage to nail, [init enc, seq]
S60.02[1,2,9][A,S]	Contsn of [rt, lt, unsp] index finger w/o damage to nail, [init enc, seq]
S60.03[1,2,9][A,S]	Contsn of [rt, lt, unsp] mid finger w/o damage to nail, [init enc, seq]
S60.04[1,2,9][A,S]	Contsn of [rt, lt, unsp] ring finger w/o damage to nail, [init enc, seq]
S60.05[1,2,9][A,S]	Contsn of [rt, lt, unsp] little finger w/o damage to nail, [init enc, seq]
S60.10X[A,S]	Contsn of unsp finger w/ damage to nail, [init enc, seq]
S60.11[1,2,9][A,S]	Contsn of [rt, lt, unsp] thumb w/ damage to nail, [init enc, seq]
S60.12[1,2,9][A,S]	Contsn of [rt, lt, unsp] index finger w/ damage to nail, [init enc, seq]
S60.13[1,2,9][A,S]	Contsn of [rt, lt, unsp] mid finger w/ damage to nail, [init enc, seq]
S60.14[1,2,9][A,S]	Contsn of [rt, lt, unsp] ring finger w/ damage to nail, [init enc, seq]
S60.15[1,2,9][A,S]	Contsn of [rt, lt, unsp] little finger w/ damage to nail, [init enc, seq]
S60.21[1,2,9][A,S]	Contsn of [rt, lt, unsp] wrist, [init enc, seq]
S60.22[1,2,9][A,S]	Contsn of [rt, lt, unsp] hand, [init enc, seq]
S60.31[1,2,9][A,S]	Abrasion of [rt, lt, unsp] thumb, [init enc, seq]

Surgical   **Medical**   **CC Indicator**   **MCC Indicator**   **Procedure Proxy**   PDxMCC **PDx acts as own MCC**   PDxCC **PDx acts as own CC**

© 2015 Optum360, LLC   MS-DRG Version 33.0   **227**

MDC 9: Diseases And Disorders Of The Skin, Subcutaneous Tissue And Breast—MEDICAL

S60.32[1,2,9]S   Blister (nonthermal) of [rt, lt, unsp] thumb, seq
S60.34[1,2,9][A,S] Ext constriction of [rt, lt, unsp] thumb, [init enc, seq]
S60.35[1,2,9][A,S] Superf FB of [rt, lt, unsp] thumb, [init enc, seq]
S60.36[1,2,9]S   Insect bite (nonvenomous) of [rt, lt, unsp] thumb, seq
S60.37[1,2,9][A,S] Oth superf bite of [rt, lt, unsp] thumb, [init enc, seq]
S60.39[1,2,9][A,S] Oth superf injuries of [rt, lt, unsp] thumb, [init enc, seq]
S60.41[0,1][A,S] Abrasion of [rt, lt] index finger, [init enc, seq]
S60.41[2,3][A,S] Abrasion of [rt, lt] mid finger, [init enc, seq]
S60.41[4,5][A,S] Abrasion of [rt, lt] ring finger, [init enc, seq]
S60.41[6,7][A,S] Abrasion of [rt, lt] little finger, [init enc, seq]
S60.41[8,9][A,S] Abrasion of [oth, unsp] finger, [init enc, seq]
S60.42[0,1]S   Blister (nonthermal) of [rt, lt] index finger, seq
S60.42[2,3]S   Blister (nonthermal) of [rt, lt] mid finger, seq
S60.42[4,5]S   Blister (nonthermal) of [rt, lt] ring finger, seq
S60.42[6,7]S   Blister (nonthermal) of [rt, lt] little finger, seq
S60.42[8,9]S   Blister (nonthermal) of [oth, unsp] finger, seq
S60.44[0,1][A,S] Ext constriction of [rt, lt] index finger, [init enc, seq]
S60.44[2,3][A,S] Ext constriction of [rt, lt] mid finger, [init enc, seq]
S60.44[4,5][A,S] Ext constriction of [rt, lt] ring finger, [init enc, seq]
S60.44[6,7][A,S] Ext constriction of [rt, lt] little finger, [init enc, seq]
S60.44[8,9][A,S] Ext constriction of [oth, unsp] finger, [init enc, seq]
S60.45[0,1][A,S] Superf FB of [rt, lt] index finger, [init enc, seq]
S60.45[2,3][A,S] Superf FB of [rt, lt] mid finger, [init enc, seq]
S60.45[4,5][A,S] Superf FB of [rt, lt] ring finger, [init enc, seq]
S60.45[6,7][A,S] Superf FB of [rt, lt] little finger, [init enc, seq]
S60.45[8,9][A,S] Superf FB of [oth, unsp] finger, [init enc, seq]
S60.46[0,1]S   Insect bite (nonvenomous) of [rt, lt] index finger, seq
S60.46[2,3]S   Insect bite (nonvenomous) of [rt, lt] mid finger, seq
S60.46[4,5]S   Insect bite (nonvenomous) of [rt, lt] ring finger, seq
S60.46[6,7]S   Insect bite (nonvenomous) of [rt, lt] little finger, seq
S60.46[8,9]S   Insect bite (nonvenomous) of [oth, unsp] finger, seq
S60.47[0,1][A,S] Oth superf bite of [rt, lt] index finger, [init enc, seq]
S60.47[2,3][A,S] Oth superf bite of [rt, lt] mid finger, [init enc, seq]
S60.47[4,5][A,S] Oth superf bite of [rt, lt] ring finger, [init enc, seq]
S60.47[6,7][A,S] Oth superf bite of [rt, lt] little finger, [init enc, seq]
S60.47[8,9][A,S] Oth superf bite of [oth, unsp] finger, [init enc, seq]
S60.51[1,2,9][A,S] Abrasion of [rt, lt, unsp] hand, [init enc, seq]
S60.52[1,2,9]S   Blister (nonthermal) of [rt, lt, unsp] hand, seq
S60.54[1,2,9][A,S] Ext constriction of [rt, lt, unsp] hand, [init enc, seq]
S60.55[1,2,9][A,S] Superf FB of [rt, lt, unsp] hand, [init enc, seq]
S60.56[1,2,9]S   Insect bite (nonvenomous) of [rt, lt, unsp] hand, seq
S60.57[1,2,9]S   Oth superf bite of hand of [rt, lt, unsp] hand, [init enc, seq]
S60.81[1,2,9][A,S] Abrasion of [rt, lt, unsp] wrist, [init enc, seq]
S60.82[1,2,9]S   Blister (nonthermal) of [rt, lt, unsp] wrist, seq
S60.84[1,2,9][A,S] Ext constriction of [rt, lt, unsp] wrist, [init enc, seq]
S60.85[1,2,9][A,S] Superf FB of [rt, lt, unsp] wrist, [init enc, seq]
S60.86[1,2,9]S   Insect bite (nonvenomous) of [rt, lt, unsp] wrist, seq
S60.87[1,2,9][A,S] Oth superf bite of [rt, lt, unsp] wrist, [init enc, seq]
S60.91[1,2,9][A,S] Unsp superf inj of [rt, lt, unsp] wrist, [init enc, seq]
S60.92[1,2,9][A,S] Unsp superf inj of [rt, lt, unsp] hand, [init enc, seq]
S60.93[1,2,9][A,S] Unsp superf inj of [rt, lt, unsp] thumb, [init enc, seq]
S60.94[0,1][A,S] Unsp superf inj of [rt, lt] index finger, [init enc, seq]
S60.94[2,3][A,S] Unsp superf inj of [rt, lt] mid finger, [init enc, seq]
S60.94[4,5][A,S] Unsp superf inj of [rt, lt] ring finger, [init enc, seq]
S60.94[6,7][A,S] Unsp superf inj of [rt, lt] little finger, [init enc, seq]
S60.94[8,9][A,S] Unsp superf inj of [oth, unsp] finger, [init enc, seq]
S61.00[1,2,9][A,S] Unsp opn wnd of [rt, lt, unsp] thumb w/o damage to nail, [init enc, seq]
S61.01[1,2,9][A,S] Lac w/o FB of [rt, lt, unsp] thumb w/o damage to nail, [init enc, seq]
S61.02[1,2,9]S   Lac w/ FB of [rt, lt, unsp] thumb w/o damage to nail, seq
S61.03[1,2,9][A,S] Punc wnd w/o FB of [rt, lt, unsp] thumb w/o damage to nail, [init enc, seq]
S61.04[1,2,9]S   Punc wnd w/ FB of [rt, lt, unsp] thumb w/o damage to nail, seq
S61.05[1,2,9][A,S] Opn bite of [rt, lt, unsp] thumb w/o damage to nail, [init enc, seq]
S61.10[1,2,9][A,S] Unsp opn wnd of [rt, lt, unsp] thumb w/ damage to nail, [init enc, seq]
S61.11[1,2,9][A,S] Lac w/o FB of [rt, lt, unsp] thumb w/ damage to nail, [init enc, seq]
S61.12[1,2,9]S   Lac w/ FB of [rt, lt, unsp] thumb w/ damage to nail, seq
S61.13[1,2,9][A,S] Punc wnd w/o FB of [rt, lt, unsp] thumb w/ damage to nail, [init enc, seq]
S61.14[1,2,9]S   Punc wnd w/ FB of [rt, lt, unsp] thumb w/ damage to nail, seq
S61.15[1,2,9][A,S] Opn bite of [rt, lt, unsp] thumb w/ damage to nail, [init enc, seq]
S61.20[0,1][A,S] Unsp opn wnd of [rt, lt] index finger w/o damage to nail, [init enc, seq]

S61.20[2,3][A,S] Unsp opn wnd of [rt, lt] mid finger w/o damage to nail, [init enc, seq]
S61.20[4,5][A,S] Unsp opn wnd of [rt, lt] ring finger w/o damage to nail, [init enc, seq]
S61.20[6,7][A,S] Unsp opn wnd of [rt, lt] little finger w/o damage to nail, [init enc, seq]
S61.20[8,9][A,S] Unsp opn wnd of [oth, unsp] finger w/o damage to nail, [init enc, seq]
S61.21[0,1][A,S] Lac w/o FB of [rt, lt] index finger w/o damage to nail, [init enc, seq]
S61.21[2,3][A,S] Lac w/o FB of [rt, lt] mid finger w/o damage to nail, [init enc, seq]
S61.21[4,5][A,S] Lac w/o FB of [rt, lt] ring finger w/o damage to nail, [init enc, seq]
S61.21[6,7][A,S] Lac w/o FB of [rt, lt] little finger w/o damage to nail, [init enc, seq]
S61.21[8,9][A,S] Lac w/o FB of [oth, unsp] finger w/o damage to nail, [init enc, seq]
S61.22[0,1]S   Lac w/ FB of [rt, lt] index finger w/o damage to nail, seq
S61.22[2,3]S   Lac w/ FB of [rt, lt] mid finger w/o damage to nail, seq
S61.22[4,5]S   Lac w/ FB of [rt, lt] ring finger w/o damage to nail, seq
S61.22[6,7]S   Lac w/ FB of [rt, lt] little finger w/o damage to nail, seq
S61.22[8,9]S   Lac w/ FB of [oth, unsp] finger w/o damage to nail, seq
S61.23[0,1][A,S] Punc wnd w/o FB of [rt, lt] index finger w/o damage to nail, [init enc, seq]
S61.23[2,3][A,S] Punc wnd w/o FB of [rt, lt] mid finger w/o damage to nail, [init enc, seq]
S61.23[4,5][A,S] Punc wnd w/o FB of [rt, lt] ring finger w/o damage to nail, [init enc, seq]
S61.23[6,7][A,S] Punc wnd w/o FB of [rt, lt] little finger w/o damage to nail, [init enc, seq]
S61.23[8,9][A,S] Punc wnd w/o FB of [oth, unsp] finger w/o damage to nail, [init enc, seq]
S61.24[0,1]S   Punc wnd w/ FB of [rt, lt] index finger w/o damage to nail, seq
S61.24[2,3]S   Punc wnd w/ FB of [rt, lt] mid finger w/o damage to nail, seq
S61.24[4,5]S   Punc wnd w/ FB of [rt, lt] ring finger w/o damage to nail, seq
S61.24[6,7]S   Punc wnd w/ FB of [rt, lt] little finger w/o damage to nail, seq
S61.24[8,9]S   Punc wnd w/ FB of [oth, unsp] finger w/o damage to nail, seq
S61.25[0,1][A,S] Opn bite of [rt, lt] index finger w/o damage to nail, [init enc, seq]
S61.25[2,3][A,S] Opn bite of [rt, lt] mid finger w/o damage to nail, [init enc, seq]
S61.25[4,5][A,S] Opn bite of [rt, lt] ring finger w/o damage to nail, [init enc, seq]
S61.25[6,7][A,S] Opn bite of [rt, lt] little finger w/o damage to nail, [init enc, seq]
S61.25[8,9][A,S] Opn bite of [oth, unsp] finger w/o damage to nail, [init enc, seq]
S61.30[0,1][A,S] Unsp opn wnd of [rt, lt] index finger w/ damage to nail, [init enc, seq]
S61.30[2,3][A,S] Unsp opn wnd of [rt, lt] mid finger w/ damage to nail, [init enc, seq]
S61.30[4,5][A,S] Unsp opn wnd of [rt, lt] ring finger w/ damage to nail, [init enc, seq]
S61.30[6,7][A,S] Unsp opn wnd of [rt, lt] little finger w/ damage to nail, [init enc, seq]
S61.30[8,9][A,S] Unsp opn wnd of [oth, unsp] finger w/ damage to nail, [init enc, seq]
S61.31[0,1][A,S] Lac w/o FB of [rt, lt] index finger w/ damage to nail, [init enc, seq]
S61.31[2,3][A,S] Lac w/o FB of [rt, lt] mid finger w/ damage to nail, [init enc, seq]
S61.31[4,5][A,S] Lac w/o FB of [rt, lt] ring finger w/ damage to nail, [init enc, seq]
S61.31[6,7][A,S] Lac w/o FB of [rt, lt] little finger w/ damage to nail, [init enc, seq]
S61.31[8,9][A,S] Lac w/o FB of [oth, unsp] finger w/ damage to nail, [init enc, seq]
S61.32[0,1]S   Lac w/ FB of [rt, lt] index finger w/ damage to nail, seq
S61.32[2,3]S   Lac w/ FB of [rt, lt] mid finger w/ damage to nail, seq
S61.32[4,5]S   Lac w/ FB of [rt, lt] ring finger w/ damage to nail, seq
S61.32[6,7]S   Lac w/ FB of [rt, lt] little finger w/ damage to nail, seq
S61.32[8,9]S   Lac w/ FB of [oth, unsp] finger w/ damage to nail, seq
S61.33[0,1][A,S] Punc wnd w/o FB of [rt, lt] index finger w/ damage to nail, [init enc, seq]
S61.33[2,3][A,S] Punc wnd w/o FB of [rt, lt] mid finger w/ damage to nail, [init enc, seq]
S61.33[4,5][A,S] Punc wnd w/o FB of [rt, lt] ring finger w/ damage to nail, [init enc, seq]

T **Transfer DRG**   **SP** **Special Payment**   * **Code Range**   **6th and 7th Character of ZZ = No Device, No Qualifier ZX = No Device, Diagnostic**

228   MS-DRG Version 33.0   © 2015 Optum360, LLC

Code	Description
S61.33[6,7][A,S]	Punc wnd w/o FB of [rt, lt] little finger w/ damage to nail, [init enc, seq]
S61.33[8,9][A,S]	Punc wnd w/o FB of [oth, unsp] finger w/ damage to nail, [init enc, seq]
S61.34[0,1]S	Punc wnd w/ FB of [rt, lt] index finger w/ damage to nail, seq
S61.34[2,3]S	Punc wnd w/ FB of [rt, lt] mid finger w/ damage to nail, seq
S61.34[4,5]S	Punc wnd w/ FB of [rt, lt] ring finger w/ damage to nail, seq
S61.34[6,7]S	Punc wnd w/ FB of [rt, lt] little finger w/ damage to nail, seq
S61.34[8,9]S	Punc wnd w/ FB of [oth, unsp] finger w/ damage to nail, seq
S61.35[0,1][A,S]	Opn bite of [rt, lt] index finger w/ damage to nail, [init enc, seq]
S61.35[2,3][A,S]	Opn bite of [rt, lt] mid finger w/ damage to nail, [init enc, seq]
S61.35[4,5][A,S]	Opn bite of [rt, lt] ring finger w/ damage to nail, [init enc, seq]
S61.35[6,7][A,S]	Opn bite of [rt, lt] little finger w/ damage to nail, [init enc, seq]
S61.35[8,9][A,S]	Opn bite of [oth, unsp] finger w/ damage to nail, [init enc, seq]
S61.40[1,2,9][A,S]	Unsp opn wnd of [rt, lt, unsp] hand, [init enc, seq]
S61.41[1,2,9][A,S]	Lac w/o FB of [rt, lt, unsp] hand, [init enc, seq]
S61.42[1,2,9]S	Lac w/ FB of [rt, lt, unsp] hand, seq
S61.43[1,2,9][A,S]	Punc wnd w/o FB of [rt, lt, unsp] hand, [init enc, seq]
S61.44[1,2,9]S	Punc wnd w/ FB of [rt, lt, unsp] hand, seq
S61.45[1,2,9][A,S]	Opn bite of [rt, lt, unsp] hand, [init enc, seq]
S61.50[1,2,9][A,S]	Unsp opn wnd of [rt, lt, unsp] wrist, [init enc, seq]
S61.51[1,2,9][A,S]	Lac w/o FB of [rt, lt, unsp] wrist, [init enc, seq]
S61.52[1,2,9]S	Lac w/ FB of [rt, lt, unsp] wrist, seq
S61.53[1,2,9][A,S]	Punc wnd w/o FB of [rt, lt, unsp] wrist, [init enc, seq]
S61.54[1,2,9]S	Punc wnd w/ FB of [rt, lt, unsp] wrist, seq
S61.55[1,2,9][A,S]	Opn bite of [rt, lt, unsp] wrist, [init enc, seq]
S66.02[1,2,9]S	Lac of long flexor muscle, fascia and tndn of [rt, lt, unsp] thumb at wrist and hand lvl, seq
S66.12[0,1]S	Lac of flexor muscle, fascia and tndn of [rt, lt] index finger at wrist and hand lvl, seq
S66.12[2,3]S	Lac of flexor muscle, fascia and tndn of [rt, lt] mid finger at wrist and hand lvl, seq
S66.12[4,5]S	Lac of flexor muscle, fascia and tndn of [rt, lt] ring finger at wrist and hand lvl, seq
S66.12[6,7]S	Lac of flexor muscle, fascia and tndn of [rt, lt] little finger at wrist and hand lvl, seq
S66.12[8,9]S	Lac of flexor muscle, fascia and tndn of [oth, unsp] finger at wrist and hand lvl, seq
S66.22[1,2,9]S	Lac of extensor muscle, fascia and tndn of [rt, lt, unsp] thumb at wrist and hand lvl, seq
S66.32[0,1]S	Lac of extensor muscle, fascia and tndn of [rt, lt] index finger at wrist and hand lvl, seq
S66.32[2,3]S	Lac of extensor muscle, fascia and tndn of [rt, lt] mid finger at wrist and hand lvl, seq
S66.32[4,5]S	Lac of extensor muscle, fascia and tndn of [rt, lt] ring finger at wrist and hand lvl, seq
S66.32[6,7]S	Lac of extensor muscle, fascia and tndn of [rt, lt] little finger at wrist and hand lvl, seq
S66.32[8,9]S	Lac of extensor muscle, fascia and tndn of [oth, unsp] finger at wrist and hand lvl, seq
S66.42[1,2,9]S	Lac of intrinsic muscle, fascia and tndn of [rt, lt, unsp] thumb at wrist and hand lvl, seq
S66.52[0,1]S	Lac of intrinsic muscle, fascia and tndn of [rt, lt] index finger at wrist and hand lvl, seq
S66.52[2,3]S	Lac of intrinsic muscle, fascia and tndn of [rt, lt] mid finger at wrist and hand lvl, seq
S66.52[4,5]S	Lac of intrinsic muscle, fascia and tndn of [rt, lt] ring finger at wrist and hand lvl, seq
S66.52[6,7]S	Lac of intrinsic muscle, fascia and tndn of [rt, lt] little finger at wrist and hand lvl, seq
S66.52[8,9]S	Lac of intrinsic muscle, fascia and tndn of [oth, unsp] finger at wrist and hand lvl, seq
S66.82[1,2,9]S	Lac of oth spec muscles, fascia and tndns at wrist and hand lvl, [rt, lt, unsp] hand, seq
S66.92[1,2,9]S	Lac of unsp muscle, fascia and tndn at wrist and hand lvl, [rt, lt, unsp] hand, seq
S67.0[0,1,2]XS	Crushing inj of [unsp, rt, lt] thumb, seq
S67.10XS	Crushing inj of unsp finger(s), seq
S67.198S	Crushing inj of oth finger, seq
S67.19[0,1]S	Crushing inj of [rt, lt] index finger, seq
S67.19[2,3]S	Crushing inj of [rt, lt] mid finger, seq
S67.19[4,5]S	Crushing inj of [rt, lt] ring finger, seq
S67.19[6,7]S	Crushing inj of [rt, lt] little finger, seq
S67.2[0,1,2]XS	Crushing inj of [unsp, rt, lt] hand, seq
S67.3[0,1,2]XS	Crushing inj of [unsp, rt, lt] wrist, seq
S67.4[0,1,2]XS	Crushing inj of [unsp, rt, lt] wrist and hand, seq
S67.9[0,1,2]XS	Crushing inj of [unsp, rt, lt] part(s) of unsp wrist, hand and fingers, seq
S70.0[0,1,2]X[A,S]	Contsn of [unsp, rt, lt] hip, [init enc, seq]
S70.1[0,1,2]X[A,S]	Contsn of [unsp, rt, lt] thigh, [init enc, tseq]
S70.21[1,2,9][A,S]	Abrasion, [rt, lt, unsp] hip, [init enc, seq]
S70.22[1,2,9]S	Blister (nonthermal), [rt, lt, unsp] hip, seq
S70.24[1,2,9][A,S]	Ext constriction, [rt, lt, unsp] hip, [init enc, seq]
S70.25[1,2,9][A,S]	Superf FB, [rt, lt, unsp] hip, [init enc, seq]
S70.26[1,2,9]S	Insect bite (nonvenomous), [rt, lt, unsp] hip, seq
S70.27[1,2,9][A,S]	Oth superf bite of hip, [rt, lt, unsp] [init enc, seq]
S70.31[1,2,9][A,S]	Abrasion, [rt, lt, unsp] thigh, [init enc, seq]
S70.32[1,2,9]S	Blister (nonthermal), [rt, lt, unsp] thigh, seq
S70.34[1,2,9][A,S]	Ext constriction, [rt, lt, unsp] thigh, [init enc, seq]
S70.35[1,2,9][A,S]	Superf FB, [rt, lt, unsp] thigh, [init enc, seq]
S70.36[1,2,9]S	Insect bite (nonvenomous), [rt, lt, unsp] thigh, seq
S70.37[1,2,9][A,S]	Oth superf bite of [rt, lt, unsp] thigh, [init enc, seq]
S70.91[1,2,9][A,S]	Unsp superf inj of [rt, lt, unsp] hip, [init enc, seq]
S70.92[1,2,9][A,S]	Unsp superf inj of [rt, lt, unsp] thigh, [init enc, seq]
S71.00[1,2,9][A,S]	Unsp opn wnd, [rt, lt, unsp] hip, [init enc, seq]
S71.01[1,2,9][A,S]	Lac w/o FB, [rt, lt, unsp] hip, [init enc, seq]
S71.02[1,2,9]S	Lac w/ FB, [rt, lt, unsp] hip, seq
S71.03[1,2,9][A,S]	Punc wnd w/o FB, [rt, lt, unsp] hip, [init enc, seq]
S71.04[1,2,9]S	Punc wnd w/ FB, [rt, lt, unsp] hip, seq
S71.05[1,2,9][A,S]	Opn bite, [rt, lt, unsp] hip, [init enc, seq]
S71.10[1,2,9][A,S]	Unsp opn wnd, [rt, lt, unsp] thigh, [init enc, seq]
S71.11[1,2,9][A,S]	Lac w/o FB, [rt, lt, unsp] thigh, [init enc, seq]
S71.12[1,2,9]S	Lac w/ FB, [rt, lt, unsp] thigh, seq
S71.13[1,2,9][A,S]	Punc wnd w/o FB, [rt, lt, unsp] thigh, [init enc, seq]
S71.14[1,2,9]S	Punc wnd w/ FB, [rt, lt, unsp] thigh, seq
S71.15[1,2,9][A,S]	Opn bite, [rt, lt, unsp] thigh, [init enc, seq]
S76.02[1,2,9]S	Lac of muscle, fascia and tndn of [rt, lt, unsp] hip, seq
S76.12[1,2,9]S	Lac of [rt, lt, unsp] quadriceps muscle, fascia and tndn, seq
S76.22[1,2,9]S	Lac of adductor muscle, fascia and tndn of [rt, lt, unsp] thigh, seq
S76.32[1,2,9]S	Lac of muscle, fascia and tndn of the post muscle group at thigh lvl, [rt, lt, unsp] thigh, seq
S76.82[1,2,9]S	Lac of oth spec muscles, fascia and tndns at thigh lvl, [rt, lt, unsp] thigh, seq
S76.92[1,2,9]S	Lac of unsp muscles, fascia and tndns at thigh lvl, [rt, lt, unsp] thigh, seq
S77.0[0,1,2]XS	Crushing inj of [unsp, rt, lt] hip, seq
S77.1[0,1,2]XS	Crushing inj of [unsp, rt, lt] thigh, seq
S77.2[0,1,2]XS	Crushing inj of [unsp, rt, lt] hip w/ thigh, seq
S80.0[0,1,2]X[A,S]	Contsn of [unsp, rt, lt] knee, [init enc, seq]
S80.1[0,1,2]X[A,S]	Contsn of [unsp, rt, lt] lwr leg, [init enc, seq]
S80.21[1,2,9][A,S]	Abrasion, [rt, lt, unsp] knee, [init enc, seq]
S80.22[1,2,9]S	Blister (nonthermal), [rt, lt, unsp] knee, seq
S80.24[1,2,9][A,S]	Ext constriction, [rt, lt, unsp] knee, [init enc, seq]
S80.25[1,2,9][A,S]	Superf FB, [rt, lt, unsp] knee, [init enc, seq]
S80.26[1,2,9]S	Insect bite (nonvenomous), [rt, lt, unsp] knee, seq
S80.27[1,2,9][A,S]	Oth superf bite of [rt, lt, unsp] knee, [init enc, seq]
S80.81[1,2,9][A,S]	Abrasion, [rt, lt, unsp] lwr leg, [init enc, seq]
S80.82[1,2,9]S	Blister (nonthermal), [rt, lt, unsp] lwr leg, seq
S80.84[1,2,9][A,S]	Ext constriction, [rt, lt, unsp] lwr leg, [init enc, seq]
S80.85[1,2,9][A,S]	Superf FB, [rt, lt, unsp] lwr leg, [init enc, seq]
S80.86[1,2,9]S	Insect bite (nonvenomous), [rt, lt, unsp] lwr leg, seq
S80.87[1,2,9][A,S]	Oth superf bite, [rt, lt, unsp] lwr leg, [init enc, seq]
S80.91[1,2,9][A,S]	Unsp superf inj of [rt, lt, unsp] knee, [init enc, seq]
S80.92[1,2,9][A,S]	Unsp superf inj of [rt, lt, unsp] lwr leg, [init enc, seq]
S81.00[1,2,9][A,S]	Unsp opn wnd, [rt, lt, unsp] knee, [init enc, seq]
S81.01[1,2,9][A,S]	Lac w/o FB, [rt, lt, unsp] knee, [init enc, seq]
S81.02[1,2,9]S	Lac w/ FB, [rt, lt, unsp] knee, seq
S81.03[1,2,9][A,S]	Punc wnd w/o FB, [rt, lt, unsp] knee, [init enc, seq]
S81.04[1,2,9]S	Punc wnd w/ FB, [rt, lt, unsp] knee, seq
S81.05[1,2,9][A,S]	Opn bite, [rt, lt, unsp] knee, [init enc, seq]
S81.80[1,2,9][A,S]	Unsp opn wnd, [rt, lt, unsp] lwr leg, [init enc, seq]
S81.81[1,2,9][A,S]	Lac w/o FB, [rt, lt, unsp] lwr leg, [init enc, seq]
S81.82[1,2,9]S	Lac w/ FB, [rt, lt, unsp] lwr leg, seq
S81.83[1,2,9][A,S]	Punc wnd w/o FB, [rt, lt, unsp] lwr leg, [init enc, seq]
S81.84[1,2,9]S	Punc wnd w/ FB, [rt, lt, unsp] lwr leg, seq
S81.85[1,2,9][A,S]	Opn bite, [rt, lt, unsp] lwr leg, [init enc, seq]
S86.02[1,2,9]S	Lac of [rt, lt, unsp] Achilles tndn, seq
S86.12[1,2,9]S	Lac of oth muscle(s) and tndn(s) of post muscle group at lwr leg lvl, [rt, lt, unsp] leg, seq
S86.22[1,2,9]S	Lac of muscle(s) and tndn(s) of ant muscle group at lwr leg lvl, [rt, lt, unsp] leg, seq
S86.32[1,2,9]S	Lac of muscle(s) and tndn(s) of peroneal muscle group at lwr leg lvl, [rt, lt, unsp] leg, seq
S86.[8,9]2[1,2,9]S	Lac of [oth, unsp] muscle(s) and tndn(s) at lwr leg lvl, [rt, lt, unsp] leg, seq
S87.0[0,1,2]XS	Crushing inj of [unsp, rt, lt] knee, seq
S87.8[0,1,2]XS	Crushing inj of [unsp, rt, lt] lwr leg, seq
S90.0[0,1,2]X[A,S]	Contsn of [unsp, rt, lt] ankle, [init enc, seq]

Surgical   **Medical**   CC Indicator   MCC Indicator   **Procedure Proxy**   PDxMCC **PDx acts as own MCC**   PDxCC **PDx acts as own CC**

Code	Description
S90.11[1,2,9][A,S]	Contsn of [rt, lt, unsp] great toe w/o damage to nail, [init enc, seq]
S90.12[1,2,9][A,S]	Contsn of [rt, lt, unsp] lesser toe(s) w/o damage to nail, [init enc, seq]
S90.21[1,2,9][A,S]	Contsn of [rt, lt, unsp] great toe w/ damage to nail, [init enc, seq]
S90.22[1,2,9][A,S]	Contsn of [rt, lt, unsp] lesser toe(s) w/ damage to nail, [init enc, seq]
S90.3[0,1,2]X[A,S]	Contsn of [unsp, rt, lt] foot, [init enc, seq]
S90.41[1,2,3][A,S]	Abrasion, [rt, lt, unsp] great toe, [init enc, seq]
S90.41[4,5,6][A,S]	Abrasion, [rt, lt, unsp] lesser toe(s), [init enc, seq]
S90.42[1,2,3]S	Blister (nonthermal), [rt, lt, unsp] great toe, seq
S90.42[4,5,6]S	Blister (nonthermal), [rt, lt, unsp] lesser toe(s), seq
S90.44[1,2,3][A,S]	Ext constriction, [rt, lt, unsp] great toe, [init enc, seq]
S90.44[4,5,6][A,S]	Ext constriction, [rt, lt, unsp] lesser toe(s), [init enc, seq]
S90.45[1,2,3][A,S]	Superf FB, [rt, lt, unsp] great toe, [init enc, seq]
S90.45[4,5,6][A,S]	Superf FB, [rt, lt, unsp] lesser toe(s), [init enc, seq]
S90.46[1,2,3]S	Insect bite (nonvenomous), [rt, lt, unsp] great toe, seq
S90.46[4,5,6]S	Insect bite (nonvenomous), [rt, lt, unsp] lesser toe(s), seq
S90.47[1,2,3][A,S]	Oth superf bite of [rt, lt, unsp] great toe, [init enc, seq]
S90.47[4,5,6][A,S]	Oth superf bite of [rt, lt, unsp] lesser toe(s), [init enc, seq]
S90.51[1,2,9][A,S]	Abrasion, [rt, lt, unsp] ankle, [init enc, seq]
S90.52[1,2,9]S	Blister (nonthermal), [rt, lt, unsp] ankle, seq
S90.54[1,2,9][A,S]	Ext constriction, [rt, lt, unsp] ankle, [init enc, seq]
S90.55[1,2,9][A,S]	Superf FB, [rt, lt, unsp] ankle, [init enc, seq]
S90.56[1,2,9]S	Insect bite (nonvenomous), [rt, lt, unsp] ankle, seq
S90.57[1,2,9][A,S]	Oth superf bite of ankle, [rt, lt, unsp] ankle, [init enc, seq]
S90.81[1,2,9][A,S]	Abrasion, [rt, lt, unsp] foot, [init enc, seq]
S90.82[1,2,9]S	Blister (nonthermal), [rt, lt, unsp] foot, seq
S90.84[1,2,9][A,S]	Ext constriction, [rt, lt, unsp] foot, [init enc, seq]
S90.85[1,2,9][A,S]	Superf FB, [rt, lt, unsp] foot, [init enc, seq]
S90.86[1,2,9]S	Insect bite (nonvenomous), [rt, lt, unsp] foot, seq
S90.87[1,2,9][A,S]	Oth superf bite of [rt, lt, unsp] foot, [init enc, seq]
S90.91[1,2,9][A,S]	Unsp superf inj of [rt, lt, unsp] ankle, [init enc, seq]
S90.92[1,2,9][A,S]	Unsp superf inj of [rt, lt, unsp] foot, [init enc, seq]
S90.93[1,2,3][A,S]	Unsp superf inj of [rt, lt, unsp] great toe, [init enc, seq]
S90.93[4,5,6][A,S]	Unsp superf inj of [rt, lt, unsp] lesser toe(s), [init enc, seq]
S91.00[1,2,9][A,S]	Unsp opn wnd, [rt, lt, unsp] ankle, [init enc, seq]
S91.01[1,2,9][A,S]	Lac w/o FB, [rt, lt, unsp] ankle, [init enc, seq]
S91.02[1,2,9]S	Lac w/ FB, [rt, lt, unsp] ankle, seq
S91.03[1,2,9][A,S]	Punc wnd w/o FB, [rt, lt, unsp] ankle, [init enc, seq]
S91.04[1,2,9]S	Punc wnd w/ FB, [rt, lt, unsp] ankle, seq
S91.05[1,2,9][A,S]	Opn bite, [rt, lt, unsp] ankle, [init enc, seq]
S91.109[A,S]	Unsp opn wnd of unsp toe(s) w/o damage to nail, [init enc, seq]
S91.10[1,2,3][A,S]	Unsp opn wnd of [rt, lt, unsp] great toe w/o damage to nail, [init enc, seq]
S91.10[4,5,6][A,S]	Unsp opn wnd of [rt, lt, unsp] lesser toe(s) w/o damage to nail, [init enc, seq]
S91.119[A,S]	Lac w/o FB of unsp toe w/o damage to nail, [init enc, seq]
S91.11[1,2,3][A,S]	Lac w/o FB of [rt, lt, unsp] great toe w/o damage to nail, [init enc, seq]
S91.11[4,5,6][A,S]	Lac w/o FB of [rt, lt, unsp] lesser toe(s) w/o damage to nail, [init enc, seq]
S91.129S	Lac w fb of unsp toe(s) w/o damage to nail, seq
S91.12[1,2,3]S	Lac w/ FB of [rt, lt, unsp] great toe w/o damage to nail, seq
S91.12[4,5,6]S	Lac w/ FB of [rt, lt, unsp] lesser toe(s) w/o damage to nail, seq
S91.139[A,S]	Punc wnd w/o FB of unsp toe(s) w/o damage to nail, [init enc, seq]
S91.13[1,2,3][A,S]	Punc wnd w/o FB of [rt, lt, unsp] great toe w/o damage to nail, [init enc, seq]
S91.13[4,5,6][A,S]	Punc wnd w/o FB of [rt, lt, unsp] lesser toe(s) w/o damage to nail, [init enc, seq]
S91.149S	Punc w fb of unsp toe(s) w/o damage to nail, seq
S91.14[1,2,3]S	Punc wnd w/ FB of [rt, lt, unsp] great toe w/o damage to nail, seq
S91.14[4,5,6]S	Punc wnd w/ FB of [rt, lt, unsp] lesser toe(s) w/o damage to nail, seq
S91.159[A,S]	Opn bite of unsp toe(s) w/o damage to nail, [init enc, seq]
S91.15[1,2,3][A,S]	Opn bite of [rt, lt, unsp] great toe w/o damage to nail, [init enc, seq]
S91.15[4,5,6][A,S]	Opn bite of [rt, lt, unsp] lesser toe(s) w/o damage to nail, [init enc, seq]
S91.209[A,S]	Unsp opn wnd of unsp toe(s) w/ damage to nail, [init enc, seq]
S91.20[1,2,3][A,S]	Unsp opn wnd of [rt, lt, unsp] great toe w/ damage to nail, [init enc, seq]
S91.20[4,5,6][A,S]	Unsp opn wnd of [rt, lt, unsp] lesser toe(s) w/ damage to nail, [init enc, seq]
S91.219[A,S]	Lac w/o FB of unsp toe(s) w/ damage to nail, [init enc, seq]
S91.21[1,2,3][A,S]	Lac w/o FB of [rt, lt, unsp] great toe w/ damage to nail, [init enc, seq]
S91.21[4,5,6][A,S]	Lac w/o FB of [rt, lt, unsp] lesser toe(s) w/ damage to nail, [init enc, seq]
S91.229S	Lac w fb of unsp toe(s) w damage to nail, seq
S91.22[1,2,3]S	Lac w/ FB of [rt, lt, unsp] great toe w/ damage to nail, seq
S91.22[4,5,6]S	Lac w/ FB of [rt, lt, unsp] lesser toe(s) w/ damage to nail, seq
S91.239[A,S]	Punc wnd w/o FB of unsp toe(s) w/ damage to nail, [init enc, seq]
S91.23[1,2,3][A,S]	Punc wnd w/o FB of [rt, lt, unsp] great toe w/ damage to nail, [init enc, seq]
S91.23[4,5,6][A,S]	Punc wnd w/o FB of [rt, lt, unsp] lesser toe(s) w/ damage to nail, [init enc, seq]
S91.249S	Punc w fb of unsp toe(s) w damage to nail, seq
S91.24[1,2,3]S	Punc wnd w/ FB of [rt, lt, unsp] great toe w/ damage to nail, seq
S91.24[4,5,6]S	Punc wnd w/ FB of [rt, lt, unsp] lesser toe(s) w/ damage to nail, seq
S91.259[A,S]	Opn bite of unsp toe(s) w/ damage to nail, [init enc, seq]
S91.25[1,2,3][A,S]	Opn bite of [rt, lt, unsp] great toe w/ damage to nail, [init enc, seq]
S91.25[4,5,6][A,S]	Opn bite of [rt, lt, unsp] lesser toe(s) w/ damage to nail, [init enc, seq]
S91.30[1,2,9][A,S]	Unsp opn wnd, [rt, lt, unsp] foot, [init enc, seq]
S91.31[1,2,9][A,S]	Lac w/o FB, [rt, lt, unsp] foot, [init enc, seq]
S91.32[1,2,9]S	Lac w/ FB, [rt, lt, unsp] foot, seq
S91.33[1,2,9][A,S]	Punc wnd w/o FB, [rt, lt, unsp] foot, [init enc, seq]
S91.34[1,2,9]S	Punc wnd w/ FB, [rt, lt, unsp] foot, seq
S91.35[1,2,9][A,S]	Opn bite, [rt, lt, unsp] foot, [init enc, seq]
S96.02[1,2,9]S	Lac of muscle and tndn of long flexor muscle of toe at ankle and foot lvl, [rt, lt, unsp] foot, seq
S96.12[1,2,9]S	Lac of muscle and tndn of long extensor muscle of toe at ankle and foot lvl, [rt, lt, unsp] foot, seq
S96.22[1,2,9]S	Lac of intrinsic muscle and tndn at ankle and foot lvl, [rt, lt, unsp] foot, seq
S96.82[1,2,9]S	Lac of oth spec muscles and tndns at ankle and foot lvl, [rt, lt, unsp] foot, seq
S96.92[1,2,9]S	Lac of unsp muscle and tndn at ankle and foot lvl, [rt, lt, unsp] foot, seq
S97.0[0,1,2]XS	Crushing inj of [unsp, rt, lt] ankle, seq
S97.10[1,2,9]S	Crushing inj of unsp [rt, lt, unsp] toe(s), seq
S97.11[1,2,9]S	Crushing inj of [rt, lt, unsp] great toe, seq
S97.12[1,2,9]S	Crushing inj of [rt, lt, unsp] lesser toe(s), seq
S97.8[0,1,2]XS	Crushing inj of [unsp, rt, lt] foot, seq
T07	Unsp multi injuries
T14.8	Oth inj of unsp body region
T20.00XS	Burn unsp degree of head, face, and neck, unsp site, seq
T20.01[1,2,9]S	Burn of unsp degree of [rt, lt, unsp] ear [any part, except ear drum], seq
T20.09XS	Burn of unsp deg mult sites of head, face, and neck, seq
T20.0[2,3,4]XS	Burn of unsp degree of [lip(s), chin, nose (septum)], seq
T20.0[5,6,7]XS	Burn of unsp degree of [scalp [any part], forehead and cheek, neck], seq
T20.10XS	Burn first degree of head, face, and neck, unsp site, seq
T20.11[1,2,9]S	Burn of 1st degree of [rt, lt, unsp] ear [any part, except ear drum], seq
T20.19XS	Burn first deg mult sites of head, face, and neck, seq
T20.1[2,3,4]XS	Burn of 1st degree of [lip(s), chin, nose (septum)], seq
T20.1[5,6,7]XS	Burn of 1st degree of [scalp [any part], forehead and cheek, neck], seq
T20.20XS	Burn 2nd degree of head, face, and neck, unsp site, seq
T20.21[1,2,9]S	Burn of 2nd degree of [rt, lt, unsp] ear [any part, except ear drum], seq
T20.29XS	Burn of 2nd deg mul sites of head, face, and neck, seq
T20.2[2,3,4]XS	Burn of 2nd degree of [lip(s), chin, nose (septum)], seq
T20.2[5,6,7]XS	Burn of 2nd degree of [scalp [any part], forehead and cheek, neck], seq
T20.30XS	Burn 3rd degree of head, face, and neck, unsp site, seq
T20.31[1,2,9]S	Burn of 3rd degree of [rt, lt, unsp] ear (any part, except ear drum), seq
T20.39XS	Burn of 3rd deg mu sites of head, face, and neck, seq
T20.3[2,3,4]XS	Burn of 3rd degree of [lip(s), chin, nose (septum)], seq
T20.3[5,6,7]XS	Burn of 3rd degree of [scalp [any part], forehead and cheek, neck], seq
T20.40XS	Corrosion unsp degree of head, face, and neck, unsp site, seq
T20.41[1,2,9]S	Corrosion of unsp degree of [rt, lt, unsp] ear [any part, except ear drum], seq
T20.49XS	Corrosion unsp deg mult sites of head, face, and neck, seq
T20.4[2,3,4]XS	Corrosion of unsp degree of [lip(s), chin, nose (septum)], seq
T20.4[5,6,7]XS	Corrosion of unsp degree of [scalp [any part], forehead and cheek, neck], seq
T20.50XS	Corrosion first degree of head, face, and neck, unsp site, seq

[T] **Transfer DRG**   [SP] **Special Payment**   * **Code Range**   **6th and 7th Character of ZZ = No Device, No Qualifier ZX = No Device, Diagnostic**

230   MS-DRG Version 33.0   © 2015 Optum360, LLC

T20.51[1,2,9]S	Corrosion of 1st degree of [rt, lt, unsp] ear [any part, except ear drum], seq
T20.59XS	Corrosion first deg mult sites of head, face, and neck, seq
T20.5[2,3,4]XS	Corrosion of 1st degree of [lip(s), chin, nose (septum)], seq
T20.5[5,6,7]XS	Corrosion of 1st degree of [scalp [any part], cheek, neck], seq
T20.60XS	Corrosion 2nd deg of head, face, and neck, unsp site, seq
T20.61[1,2,9]S	Corrosion of 2nd degree of [rt, lt, unsp] ear [any part, except ear drum], seq
T20.69XS	Corrosion 2nd deg mul sites of head, face, and neck, seq
T20.6[2,3,4]XS	Corrosion of 2nd degree of [lip(s), chin, nose (septum)], seq
T20.6[5,6,7]XS	Corrosion of 2nd degree of [scalp [any part], forehead and cheek, neck], seq
T20.70XS	Corrosion 3rd degree of head, face, and neck, unsp site, seq
T20.71[1,2,9]S	Corrosion of 3rd degree of [rt, lt, unsp] ear [any part, except ear drum], seq
T20.79XS	Corrosion 3rd deg mu sites of head, face, and neck, seq
T20.7[2,3,4]XS	Corrosion of 3rd degree of [lip(s), chin, nose (septum)], seq
T20.7[5,6,7]XS	Corrosion of 3rd degree of [scalp [any part], forehead and cheek, neck], seq
T21.00XS	Burn of unsp degree of trunk, unsp site, seq
T21.09XS	Burn of unsp degree of oth site of trunk, seq
T21.0[1,2]XS	Burn of unsp degree of [chest, abd] wall, seq
T21.0[3,4,5]XS	Burn of unsp degree of [upr back, lwr back, buttock], seq
T21.0[6,7]XS	Burn of unsp degree of [male, female] genital rgn, seq
T21.10XS	Burn of first degree of trunk, unsp site, seq
T21.19XS	Burn of first degree of oth site of trunk, seq
T21.1[1,2]XS	Burn of 1st degree of [chest, abd] wall, seq
T21.1[3,4,5]XS	Burn of 1st degree of [upr back, lwr back, buttock], seq
T21.1[6,7]XS	Burn of 1st degree of [male, female] genital rgn, seq
T21.20XS	Burn of 2nd degree of trunk, unsp site, seq
T21.29XS	Burn of 2nd degree of oth site of trunk, seq
T21.2[1,2]XS	Burn of 2nd degree of [chest, abd] wall, seq
T21.2[3,4,5]XS	Burn of 2nd degree of [upr back, lwr back, buttock], seq
T21.2[6,7]XS	Burn of 2nd degree of [male, female] genital rgn, seq
T21.30XS	Burn of 3rd degree of trunk, unsp site, seq
T21.39XS	Burn of 3rd degree of oth site of trunk, seq
T21.3[1,2]XS	Burn of 3rd degree of [chest, abd] wall, seq
T21.3[3,4,5]XS	Burn of 3rd degree of [upr back, lwr back, buttock], seq
T21.3[6,7]XS	Burn of 3rd degree of [male, female] genital rgn, seq
T21.40XS	Corrosion of unsp degree of trunk, unsp site, seq
T21.49XS	Corrosion of unsp degree of oth site of trunk, seq
T21.4[1,2]XS	Corrosion of unsp degree of [chest, abd] wall, seq
T21.4[3,4,5]XS	Corrosion of unsp degree of [upr back, lwr back, buttock], seq
T21.4[6,7]XS	Corrosion of unsp degree of [male, female] genital rgn, seq
T21.50XS	Corrosion of first degree of trunk, unsp site, seq
T21.59XS	Corrosion of first degree of oth site of trunk, seq
T21.5[1,2]XS	Corrosion of 1st degree of [chest, abd] wall, seq
T21.5[3,4,5]XS	Corrosion of 1st degree of [upr back, lwr back, buttock], seq
T21.5[6,7]XS	Corrosion of 1st degree of [male, female] genital rgn, seq
T21.60XS	Corrosion of 2nd degree of trunk, unsp site, seq
T21.69XS	Corrosion of 2nd degree of oth site of trunk, seq
T21.6[1,2]XS	Corrosion of 2nd degree of [chest, abd] wall, seq
T21.6[3,4,5]XS	Corrosion of 2nd degree of [upr back, lwr back, buttock], seq
T21.6[6,7]XS	Corrosion of 2nd degree of [male, female] genital rgn, seq
T21.70XS	Corrosion of 3rd degree of trunk, unsp site, seq
T21.79XS	Corrosion of 3rd degree of oth site of trunk, seq
T21.7[1,2]XS	Corrosion of 3rd degree of [chest, abd] wall, seq
T21.7[3,4,5]XS	Corrosion of 3rd degree of [upr back, lwr back, buttock], seq
T21.7[6,7]XS	Corrosion of 3rd degree of [male, female] genital rgn, seq
T22.00XS	Burn unsp deg of shldr/up lmb, ex wrs/hnd, unsp site, seq
T22.01[1,2,9]S	Burn of unsp degree of [rt, lt, unsp] forearm, seq
T22.02[1,2,9]S	Burn of unsp degree of [rt, lt, unsp] elbow, seq
T22.03[1,2,9]S	Burn of unsp degree of [rt, lt, unsp] upr arm, seq
T22.04[1,2,9]S	Burn of unsp degree of [rt, lt, unsp] axilla, seq
T22.05[1,2,9]S	Burn of unsp degree of [rt, lt, unsp] shldr, seq
T22.06[1,2,9]S	Burn of unsp degree of [rt, lt, unsp] scapular rgn, seq
T22.09[1,2,9]S	Burn of unsp degree of multi sites of [rt, lt, unsp] shldr and upr limb, except wrist and hand, seq
T22.10XS	Burn first deg of shldr/up lmb, ex wrs/hnd, unsp site, seq
T22.11[1,2,9]S	Burn of 1st degree of [rt, lt, unsp] forearm, seq
T22.12[1,2,9]S	Burn of 1st degree of [rt, lt, unsp] elbow, seq
T22.13[1,2,9]S	Burn of 1st degree of [rt, lt, unsp] upr arm, seq
T22.14[1,2,9]S	Burn of 1st degree of [rt, lt, unsp] axilla, seq
T22.15[1,2,9]S	Burn of 1st degree of [rt, lt, unsp] shldr, seq
T22.16[1,2,9]S	Burn of 1st degree of [rt, lt, unsp] scapular rgn, seq
T22.19[1,2,9]S	Burn of 1st degree of multi sites of [rt, lt, unsp] shldr and upr limb, except wrist and hand, seq
T22.20XS	Burn 2nd deg of shldr/up lmb, ex wrs/hnd, unsp site, seq
T22.21[1,2,9]S	Burn of 2nd degree of [rt, lt, unsp] forearm, seq
T22.22[1,2,9]S	Burn of 2nd degree of [rt, lt, unsp] elbow, seq
T22.23[1,2,9]S	Burn of 2nd degree of [rt, lt, unsp] upr arm, seq
T22.24[1,2,9]S	Burn of 2nd degree of [rt, lt, unsp] axilla, seq
T22.25[1,2,9]S	Burn of 2nd degree of [rt, lt, unsp] shldr, seq
T22.26[1,2,9]S	Burn of 2nd degree of [rt, lt, unsp] scapular rgn, seq
T22.29[1,2,9]S	Burn of 2nd degree of multi sites of [rt, lt, unsp] shldr and upr limb, except wrist and hand, seq
T22.30XS	Burn 3rd deg of shldr/up lmb, ex wrs/hnd, unsp site, seq
T22.31[1,2,9]S	Burn of 3rd degree of [rt, lt, unsp] forearm, seq
T22.32[1,2,9]S	Burn of 3rd degree of [rt, lt, unsp] elbow, seq
T22.33[1,2,9]S	Burn of 3rd degree of [rt, lt, unsp] upr arm, seq
T22.34[1,2,9]S	Burn of 3rd degree of [rt, lt, unsp] axilla, seq
T22.35[1,2,9]S	Burn of 3rd degree of [rt, lt, unsp] shldr, seq
T22.36[1,2,9]S	Burn of 3rd degree of [rt, lt, unsp] scapular rgn, seq
T22.39[1,2,9]S	Burn of 3rd degree of multi sites of [rt, lt, unsp] shldr and upr limb, except wrist and hand, seq
T22.40XS	Corrosion unsp deg of shldr/up lmb, ex wrs/hnd, unsp site, seq
T22.41[1,2,9]S	Corrosion of unsp degree of [rt, lt, unsp] forearm, seq
T22.42[1,2,9]S	Corrosion of unsp degree of [rt, lt, unsp] elbow, seq
T22.43[1,2,9]S	Corrosion of unsp degree of [rt, lt, unsp] upr arm, seq
T22.44[1,2,9]S	Corrosion of unsp degree of [rt, lt, unsp] axilla, seq
T22.45[1,2,9]S	Corrosion of unsp degree of [rt, lt, unsp] shldr, seq
T22.46[1,2,9]S	Corrosion of unsp degree of [rt, lt, unsp] scapular rgn, seq
T22.49[1,2,9]S	Corrosion of unsp degree of multi sites of [rt, lt, unsp] shldr and upr limb, except wrist and hand, seq
T22.50XS	Corrosion first deg of shldr/up lmb, ex wrs/hnd unsp site, seq
T22.51[1,2,9]S	Corrosion of 1st degree of [rt, lt, unsp] forearm, seq
T22.52[1,2,9]S	Corrosion of 1st degree of [rt, lt, unsp] elbow, seq
T22.53[1,2,9]S	Corrosion of 1st degree of [rt, lt, unsp] upr arm, seq
T22.54[1,2,9]S	Corrosion of 1st degree of [rt, lt, unsp] axilla, seq
T22.55[1,2,9]S	Corrosion of 1st degree of [rt, lt, unsp] shldr, seq
T22.56[1,2,9]S	Corrosion of 1st degree of [rt, lt, unsp] scapular rgn, seq
T22.59[1,2,9]S	Corrosion of 1st degree of multi sites of [rt, lt, unsp] shldr and upr limb, except wrist and hand, seq
T22.60XS	Corrosion 2nd deg of shldr/up lmb, ex wrs/hnd, unsp site, seq
T22.61[1,2,9]S	Corrosion of 2nd degree of [rt, lt, unsp] forearm, seq
T22.62[1,2,9]S	Corrosion of 2nd degree of [rt, lt, unsp] elbow, seq
T22.63[1,2,9]S	Corrosion of 2nd degree of [rt, lt, unsp] upr arm, seq
T22.64[1,2,9]S	Corrosion of 2nd degree of [rt, lt, unsp] axilla, seq
T22.65[1,2,9]S	Corrosion of 2nd degree of [rt, lt, unsp] shldr, seq
T22.66[1,2,9]S	Corrosion of 2nd degree of [rt, lt, unsp] scapular rgn, seq
T22.69[1,2,9]S	Corrosion of 2nd degree of multi sites of [rt, lt, unsp] shldr and upr limb, except wrist and hand, seq
T22.70XS	Corrosion 3rd deg of shldr/up lmb, ex wrs/hnd, unsp site, seq
T22.71[1,2,9]S	Corrosion of 3rd degree of [rt, lt, unsp] forearm, seq
T22.72[1,2,9]S	Corrosion of 3rd degree of [rt, lt, unsp] elbow, seq
T22.73[1,2,9]S	Corrosion of 3rd degree of [rt, lt, unsp] upr arm, seq
T22.74[1,2,9]S	Corrosion of 3rd degree of [rt, lt, unsp] axilla, seq
T22.75[1,2,9]S	Corrosion of 3rd degree of [rt, lt, unsp] shldr, seq
T22.76[1,2,9]S	Corrosion of 3rd degree of [rt, lt, unsp] scapular rgn, seq
T22.79[1,2,9]S	Corrosion of 3rd degree of multi sites of [rt, lt, unsp] shldr and upr limb, except wrist and hand, seq
T23.00[1,2,9]S	Burn of unsp degree of [rt, lt, unsp] hand, unsp site, seq
T23.01[1,2,9]S	Burn of unsp degree of [rt, lt, unsp] thumb (nail), seq
T23.02[1,2,9]S	Burn of unsp degree of single [rt, lt, unsp] finger (nail) except thumb, seq
T23.03[1,2,9]S	Burn of unsp degree of multi [rt, lt, unsp] fingers (nail), not incl* thumb, seq
T23.04[1,2,9]S	Burn of unsp degree of multi [rt, lt, unsp] fingers (nail), incl* thumb, seq
T23.05[1,2,9]S	Burn of unsp degree of [rt, lt, unsp] palm, seq
T23.06[1,2,9]S	Burn of unsp degree of back of [rt, lt, unsp] hand, seq
T23.07[1,2,9]S	Burn of unsp degree of [rt, lt, unsp] wrist, seq
T23.09[1,2,9]S	Burn of unsp degree of multi sites of [rt, lt, unsp] wrist and hand, seq
T23.10[1,2,9]S	Burn of 1st degree of [rt, lt, unsp] hand, unsp site, seq
T23.11[1,2,9]S	Burn of 1st degree of [rt, lt, unsp] thumb (nail), seq
T23.12[1,2,9]S	Burn of 1st degree of single [rt, lt, unsp] finger (nail) except thumb, seq
T23.13[1,2,9]S	Burn of 1st degree of multi [rt, lt, unsp] fingers (nail), not incl* thumb, seq
T23.14[1,2,9]S	Burn of 1st degree of multi [rt, lt, unsp] fingers (nail), incl* thumb, seq
T23.15[1,2,9]S	Burn of 1st degree of [rt, lt, unsp] palm, seq
T23.16[1,2,9]S	Burn of 1st degree of back of [rt, lt, unsp] hand, seq
T23.17[1,2,9]S	Burn of 1st degree of [rt, lt, unsp] wrist, seq
T23.19[1,2,9]S	Burn of 1st degree of multi sites of [rt, lt, unsp] wrist and hand, seq
T23.20[1,2,9]S	Burn of 2nd degree of [rt, lt, unsp] hand, unsp site, seq
T23.21[1,2,9]S	Burn of 2nd degree of [rt, lt, unsp] thumb (nail), seq

---

Surgical   **Medical**   **CC Indicator**   **MCC Indicator**   **Procedure Proxy**   **PDxMCC** **PDx acts as own MCC**   **PDxCC PDx acts as own CC**

Code	Description
T23.22[1,2,9]S	Burn of 2nd degree of single [rt, lt, unsp] finger (nail) except thumb, seq
T23.23[1,2,9]S	Burn of 2nd degree of multi [rt, lt, unsp] fingers (nail), not incl* thumb, seq
T23.24[1,2,9]S	Burn of 2nd degree of multi [rt, lt, unsp] fingers (nail), incl* thumb, seq
T23.25[1,2,9]S	Burn of 2nd degree of [rt, lt, unsp] palm, seq
T23.26[1,2,9]S	Burn of 2nd degree of back of [rt, lt, unsp] hand, seq
T23.27[1,2,9]S	Burn of 2nd degree of [rt, lt, unsp] wrist, seq
T23.29[1,2,9]S	Burn of 2nd degree of multi sites of [rt, lt, unsp] wrist and hand, seq
T23.30[1,2,9]S	Burn of 3rd degree of [rt, lt, unsp] hand, unsp site, seq
T23.31[1,2,9]S	Burn of 3rd degree of [rt, lt, unsp] thumb (nail), seq
T23.32[1,2,9]S	Burn of 3rd degree of single [rt, lt, unsp] finger (nail) except thumb, seq
T23.33[1,2,9]S	Burn of 3rd degree of multi [rt, lt, unsp] fingers (nail), not incl* thumb, seq
T23.34[1,2,9]S	Burn of 3rd degree of multi [rt, lt, unsp] fingers (nail), incl* thumb, seq
T23.35[1,2,9]S	Burn of 3rd degree of [rt, lt, unsp] palm, seq
T23.36[1,2,9]S	Burn of 3rd degree of back of [rt, lt, unsp] hand, seq
T23.37[1,2,9]S	Burn of 3rd degree of [rt, lt, unsp] wrist, seq
T23.39[1,2,9]S	Burn of 3rd degree of multi sites of [rt, lt, unsp] wrist and hand, seq
T23.40[1,2,9]S	Corrosion of unsp degree of [rt, lt, unsp] hand, unsp site, seq
T23.41[1,2,9]S	Corrosion of unsp degree of [rt, lt, unsp] thumb (nail), seq
T23.42[1,2,9]S	Corrosion of unsp degree of single [rt, lt, unsp] finger (nail) except thumb, seq
T23.43[1,2,9]S	Corrosion of unsp degree of multi [rt, lt, unsp] fingers (nail), not incl* thumb, seq
T23.44[1,2,9]S	Corrosion of unsp degree of multi [rt, lt, unsp] fingers (nail), incl* thumb, seq
T23.45[1,2,9]S	Corrosion of unsp degree of [rt, lt, unsp] palm, seq
T23.46[1,2,9]S	Corrosion of unsp degree of back of [rt, lt, unsp] hand, seq
T23.47[1,2,9]S	Corrosion of unsp degree of [rt, lt, unsp] wrist, seq
T23.49[1,2,9]S	Corrosion of unsp degree of multi sites of [rt, lt, unsp] wrist and hand, seq
T23.50[1,2,9]S	Corrosion of 1st degree of [rt, lt, unsp] hand, unsp site, seq
T23.51[1,2,9]S	Corrosion of 1st degree of [rt, lt, unsp] thumb (nail), seq
T23.52[1,2,9]S	Corrosion of 1st degree of single [rt, lt, unsp] finger (nail) except thumb, seq
T23.53[1,2,9]S	Corrosion of 1st degree of multi [rt, lt, unsp] fingers (nail), not incl* thumb, seq
T23.54[1,2,9]S	Corrosion of 1st degree of multi [rt, lt, unsp] fingers (nail), incl* thumb, seq
T23.55[1,2,9]S	Corrosion of 1st degree of [rt, lt, unsp] palm, seq
T23.56[1,2,9]S	Corrosion of 1st degree of back of [rt, lt, unsp] hand, seq
T23.57[1,2,9]S	Corrosion of 1st degree of [rt, lt, unsp] wrist, seq
T23.59[1,2,9]S	Corrosion of 1st degree of multi sites of [rt, lt, unsp] wrist and hand, seq
T23.60[1,2,9]S	Corrosion of 2nd degree of [rt, lt, unsp] hand, unsp site, seq
T23.61[1,2,9]S	Corrosion of 2nd degree of [rt, lt, unsp] thumb (nail), seq
T23.62[1,2,9]S	Corrosion of 2nd degree of single [rt, lt, unsp] finger (nail) except thumb, seq
T23.63[1,2,9]S	Corrosion of 2nd degree of multi [rt, lt, unsp] fingers (nail), not incl* thumb, seq
T23.64[1,2,9]S	Corrosion of 2nd degree of multi [rt, lt, unsp] fingers (nail), incl* thumb, seq
T23.65[1,2,9]S	Corrosion of 2nd degree of [rt, lt, unsp] palm, seq
T23.66[1,2,9]S	Corrosion of 2nd degree back of [rt, lt, unsp] hand, seq
T23.67[1,2,9]S	Corrosion of 2nd degree of [rt, lt, unsp] wrist, seq
T23.69[1,2,9]S	Corrosion of 2nd degree of multi sites of [rt, lt, unsp] wrist and hand, seq
T23.70[1,2,9]S	Corrosion of 3rd degree of [rt, lt, unsp] hand, unsp site, seq
T23.71[1,2,9]S	Corrosion of 3rd degree of [rt, lt, unsp] thumb (nail), seq
T23.72[1,2,9]S	Corrosion of 3rd degree of single [rt, lt, unsp] finger (nail) except thumb, seq
T23.73[1,2,9]S	Corrosion of 3rd degree of multi [rt, lt, unsp] fingers (nail), not incl* thumb, seq
T23.74[1,2,9]S	Corrosion of 3rd degree of multi [rt, lt, unsp] fingers (nail), incl* thumb, seq
T23.75[1,2,9]S	Corrosion of 3rd degree of [rt, lt, unsp] palm, seq
T23.76[1,2,9]S	Corrosion of 3rd degree of back of [rt, lt, unsp] hand, seq
T23.77[1,2,9]S	Corrosion of 3rd degree of [rt, lt, unsp] wrist, seq
T23.79[1,2,9]S	Corrosion of 3rd degree of multi sites of [rt, lt, unsp] wrist and hand, seq
T24.00[1,2,9]S	Burn of unsp degree of unsp site of [rt, lt, unsp] lwr limb, except ankle and foot, seq
T24.01[1,2,9]S	Burn of unsp degree of [rt, lt, unsp] thigh, seq
T24.02[1,2,9]S	Burn of unsp degree of [rt, lt, unsp] knee, seq
T24.03[1,2,9]S	Burn of unsp degree of [rt, lt, unsp] lwr leg, seq
T24.09[1,2,9]S	Burn of unsp degree of multi sites of [rt, lt, unsp] lwr limb, except ankle and foot, seq
T24.10[1,2,9]S	Burn of 1st degree of unsp site of [rt, lt, unsp] lwr limb, except ankle and foot, seq
T24.11[1,2,9]S	Burn of 1st degree of [rt, lt, unsp] thigh, seq
T24.12[1,2,9]S	Burn of 1st degree of [rt, lt, unsp] knee, seq
T24.13[1,2,9]S	Burn of 1st degree of [rt, lt, unsp] lwr leg, seq
T24.19[1,2,9]S	Burn of 1st degree of multi sites of [rt, lt, unsp] lwr limb, except ankle and foot, seq
T24.20[1,2,9]S	Burn of 2nd degree of unsp site of [rt, lt, unsp] lwr limb, except ankle and foot, seq
T24.21[1,2,9]S	Burn of 2nd degree of [rt, lt, unsp] thigh, seq
T24.22[1,2,9]S	Burn of 2nd degree of [rt, lt, unsp] knee, seq
T24.23[1,2,9]S	Burn of 2nd degree of [rt, lt, unsp] lwr leg, seq
T24.29[1,2,9]S	Burn of 2nd degree of multi sites of [rt, lt, unsp] lwr limb, except ankle and foot, seq
T24.30[1,2,9]S	Burn of 3rd degree of unsp site of [rt, lt, unsp] lwr limb, except ankle and foot, seq
T24.31[1,2,9]S	Burn of 3rd degree of [rt, lt, unsp] thigh, seq
T24.32[1,2,9]S	Burn of 3rd degree of [rt, lt, unsp] knee, seq
T24.33[1,2,9]S	Burn of 3rd degree of [rt, lt, unsp] lwr leg, seq
T24.39[1,2,9]S	Burn of 3rd degree of multi sites of [rt, lt, unsp] lwr limb, except ankle and foot, seq
T24.40[1,2,9]S	Corrosion of unsp degree of unsp site of [rt, lt, unsp] lwr limb, except ankle and foot, seq
T24.41[1,2,9]S	Corrosion of unsp degree of [rt, lt, unsp] thigh, seq
T24.42[1,2,9]S	Corrosion of unsp degree of [rt, lt, unsp] knee, seq
T24.43[1,2,9]S	Corrosion of unsp degree of [rt, lt, unsp] lwr leg, seq
T24.49[1,2,9]S	Corrosion of unsp degree of multi sites of [rt, lt, unsp] lwr limb, except ankle and foot, seq
T24.50[1,2,9]S	Corrosion of 1st degree of unsp site of [rt, lt, unsp] lwr limb, except ankle and foot, seq
T24.51[1,2,9]S	Corrosion of 1st degree of [rt, lt, unsp] thigh, seq
T24.52[1,2,9]S	Corrosion of 1st degree of [rt, lt, unsp] knee, seq
T24.53[1,2,9]S	Corrosion of 1st degree of [rt, lt, unsp] lwr leg, seq
T24.59[1,2,9]S	Corrosion of 1st degree of multi sites of [rt, lt, unsp] lwr limb, except ankle and foot, seq
T24.60[1,2,9]S	Corrosion of 2nd degree of unsp site of [rt, lt, unsp] lwr limb, except ankle and foot, seq
T24.61[1,2,9]S	Corrosion of 2nd degree of [rt, lt, unsp] thigh, seq
T24.62[1,2,9]S	Corrosion of 2nd degree of [rt, lt, unsp] knee, seq
T24.63[1,2,9]S	Corrosion of 2nd degree of [rt, lt, unsp] lwr leg, seq
T24.69[1,2,9]S	Corrosion of 2nd degree of multi sites of [rt, lt, unsp] lwr limb, except ankle and foot, seq
T24.70[1,2,9]S	Corrosion of 3rd degree of unsp site of [rt, lt, unsp] lwr limb, except ankle and foot, seq
T24.71[1,2,9]S	Corrosion of 3rd degree of [rt, lt, unsp] thigh, seq
T24.72[1,2,9]S	Corrosion of 3rd degree of [rt, lt, unsp] knee, seq
T24.73[1,2,9]S	Corrosion of 3rd degree of [rt, lt, unsp] lwr leg, seq
T24.79[1,2,9]S	Corrosion of 3rd degree of multi sites of [rt, lt, unsp] lwr limb, except ankle and foot, seq
T25.01[1,2,9]S	Burn of unsp degree of [rt, lt, unsp] ankle, seq
T25.02[1,2,9]S	Burn of unsp degree of [rt, lt, unsp] foot, seq
T25.03[1,2,9]S	Burn of unsp degree of [rt, lt, unsp] toe(s) (nail), seq
T25.09[1,2,9]S	Burn of unsp degree of multi sites of [rt, lt, unsp] ankle and foot, seq
T25.11[1,2,9]S	Burn of 1st degree of [rt, lt, unsp] ankle, seq
T25.12[1,2,9]S	Burn of 1st degree of [rt, lt, unsp] foot, seq
T25.13[1,2,9]S	Burn of 1st degree of [rt, lt, unsp] toe(s) (nail), seq
T25.19[1,2,9]S	Burn of 1st degree of multi sites of [rt, lt, unsp] ankle & foot, seq
T25.21[1,2,9]S	Burn of 2nd degree of [rt, lt, unsp] ankle, seq
T25.22[1,2,9]S	Burn of 2nd degree of [rt, lt, unsp] foot, seq
T25.23[1,2,9]S	Burn of 2nd degree of [rt, lt, unsp] toe(s) (nail), seq
T25.29[1,2,9]S	Burn of 2nd degree of multi sites of [rt, lt, unsp] ankle and foot, seq
T25.31[1,2,9]S	Burn of 3rd degree of [rt, lt, unsp] ankle, seq
T25.32[1,2,9]S	Burn of 3rd degree of [rt, lt, unsp] foot, seq
T25.33[1,2,9]S	Burn of 3rd degree of [rt, lt, unsp] toe(s) (nail), seq
T25.39[1,2,9]S	Burn of 3rd degree of multi sites of [rt, lt, unsp] ankle & foot, seq
T25.41[1,2,9]S	Corrosion of unsp degree of [rt, lt, unsp] ankle, seq
T25.42[1,2,9]S	Corrosion of unsp degree of [rt, lt, unsp] foot, seq
T25.43[1,2,9]S	Corrosion of unsp degree of [rt, lt, unsp] toe(s) (nail), seq
T25.49[1,2,9]S	Corrosion of unsp degree of multi sites of [rt, lt, unsp] ankle and foot, seq
T25.51[1,2,9]S	Corrosion of 1st degree of [rt, lt, unsp] ankle, seq
T25.52[1,2,9]S	Corrosion of 1st degree of [rt, lt, unsp] foot, seq
T25.53[1,2,9]S	Corrosion of 1st degree of [rt, lt, unsp] toe(s) (nail), seq

T Transfer DRG   SP Special Payment   * Code Range   6th and 7th Character of ZZ = No Device, No Qualifier ZX = No Device, Diagnostic

232   MS-DRG Version 33.0   © 2015 Optum360, LLC

T25.59[1,2,9]S	Corrosion of 1st degree of multi sites of [rt, lt, unsp] ankle and foot, seq
T25.61[1,2,9]S	Corrosion of 2nd degree of [rt, lt, unsp] ankle, seq
T25.62[1,2,9]S	Corrosion of 2nd degree of [rt, lt, unsp] foot, seq
T25.63[1,2,9]S	Corrosion of 2nd degree of [rt, lt, unsp] toe(s) (nail), seq
T25.69[1,2,9]S	Corrosion of 2nd degree of [rt, lt, unsp] ankle and foot, seq
T25.71[1,2,9]S	Corrosion of 3rd degree of [rt, lt, unsp] ankle, seq
T25.72[1,2,9]S	Corrosion of 3rd degree of [rt, lt, unsp] foot, seq
T25.73[1,2,9]S	Corrosion of 3rd degree of [rt, lt, unsp] toe(s) (nail), seq
T25.79[1,2,9]S	Corrosion of 3rd degree of multi sites of [rt, lt, unsp] ankle and foot, seq
T26.0[0,1,2]XS	Burn of [unsp, rt, lt] eyelid and periocular area, seq
T26.1[0,1,2]XS	Burn of cornea and conjunctival sac, [unsp, rt, lt] eye, seq
T26.2[0,1,2]XS	Burn w/ resulting rupture and destr of [unsp, rt, lt] eyeball, seq
T26.3[0,1,2]XS	Burns of oth spec parts of [unsp, rt, lt] eye and adnexa, seq
T26.4[0,1,2]XS	Burn of [unsp, rt, lt] eye and adnexa, part unsp, seq
T26.5[0,1,2]XS	Corrosion of [unsp, rt, lt] eyelid and periocular area, seq
T26.6[0,1,2]XS	Corrosion of cornea and conjunctival sac, [unsp, rt, lt] eye, seq
T26.7[0,1,2]XS	Corrosion w/ resulting rupture and destr of [unsp, rt, lt] eyeball, seq
T26.8[0,1,2]XS	Corrosion of oth spec parts of [unsp, rt, lt] eye and adnexa, seq
T26.9[0,1,2]XS	Corrosion of [unsp, rt, lt] eye and adnexa, part unsp, seq
T27.0XXS	Burn of larynx and trachea, seq
T27.1XXS	Burn involving larynx and trachea with lung, seq
T27.4XXS	Corrosion of larynx and trachea, seq
T27.5XXS	Corrosion involving larynx and trachea with lung, seq
T27.[2,3]XXS	Burn of [oth, unsp] parts of respiratory tract, seq
T27.[6,7]XXS	Corrosion of [oth, unsp] parts of respiratory tract, seq
T28.0XXS	Burn of mouth and pharynx, seq
T28.1XXS	Burn of esophagus, seq
T28.2XXS	Burn of oth parts of alimentary tract, seq
T28.3XXS	Burn of int genitourinary organs, seq
T28.40XS	Burn of unsp int organ, seq
T28.41[1,2,9]S	Burn of [rt, lt, unsp] ear drum, seq
T28.49XS	Burn of oth int organ, seq
T28.5XXS	Corrosion of mouth and pharynx, seq
T28.6XXS	Corrosion of esophagus, seq
T28.7XXS	Corrosion of oth parts of alimentary tract, seq
T28.8XXS	Corrosion of int genitourinary organs, seq
T28.90XS	Corrosions of unsp int organs, seq
T28.91[1,2,9]S	Corrosions of [rt, lt, unsp] ear drum, seq
T28.99XS	Corrosions of oth int organs, seq

DRG 605 Trauma to the Skin, Subcutaneous Tissue & Breast without MCC

GMLOS 2.6	AMLOS 3.2	RW 0.8019

Select principal diagnosis listed under DRG 604

DRG 606 Minor Skin Disorders with MCC

GMLOS 4.3 •	AMLOS 5.9	RW 1.3708

Principal diagnosis

A06.7	Cutaneous amebiasis
A18.4	Tuberculosis of skin and SQ tissue
A22.0	Cutaneous anthrax
A31.1	Cutaneous mycobacterial infxn
A36.3	Cutaneous diphtheria
A42.2	Cervicofacial actinomycosis
A43.1	Cutaneous nocardiosis
A51.3*	Secondary syphilis of skin and mucous membranes
A63.0	Anogenital (venereal) warts
A66.[0,1,2,3,4]	[Init lesions of, Multi papillomata and wet crab, Oth early skin lesions of, Hyperkeratosis of, Gummata and ulcers of] yaws
A67.[0,1,3]	[Primary, Intermediate, Mixed] lesions of pinta
B00.0	Eczema herpeticum
B00.9	Herpesviral infxn, unsp
B07*	Viral warts
B08.02	Orf virus dz
B08.03	Pseudocowpox [milker's node]
B08.1	Molluscum contagiosum
B10.8*	Oth human herpesvirus infxn
B35*	Dermatophytosis
B36*	Oth superf mycoses
B37.2	Candidiasis of skin and nail
B38.3	Cutaneous coccidioidomycosis
B38.81	Prostatic coccidioidomycosis
B47.9	Mycetoma, unsp
B55.[1,2]	[Cutaneous, Mucocutaneous] leishmaniasis

B65.3	Cercarial dermatitis
B83.4	Int hirudiniasis
B85*	Pediculosis and phthiriasis
B86	Scabies
B87*	Myiasis
B88*	Oth infestations
C44.0[0,1,2,9]	[Unsp malig neoplasm, Basal cell carcinoma, Squamous cell carcinoma, Oth spec malig neoplasm] of skin of lip
C44.2[0,1,2,9][1,2,9]	[Unsp malig neoplasm, Basal cell carcinoma, Squamous cell ca, Oth spec malig neoplasm] of skin of [unsp, rt, lt] ear and ext auricular canal
C44.3*	Oth and unsp malig neoplasm skin/ and unsp parts of face
C44.4[0,1,2,9]	[Unsp malig neoplasm, Basal cell carcinoma, Squamous cell ca, Oth spec malig neoplasm] of skin of scalp and neck
C44.5[0,1,2,9][0,1,9]	[Unsp malig neoplasm, Basal cell carcinoma, Squamous cell ca, Oth spec malig neoplasm] of [anal skin, skin of breast, skin of oth part of trunk]
C44.6[0,1,2,9][1,2,9]	[Unsp malig neoplasm, Basal cell carcinoma, Squamous cell ca, Oth spec malig neoplasm] of skin of [unsp, rt, lt] upr limb, incl* shldr
C44.7[0,1,2,9][1,2,9]	[Unsp malig neoplasm, Basal cell carcinoma, Squamous cell ca, Oth spec malig neoplasm] of skin of [unsp, rt, lt] lwr limb, incl* hip
C44.8[0,1,2,9]	[Unsp malig neoplasm, Basal cell carcinoma, Squamous cell ca, Oth spec malig neoplasm] of overlapping sites of skin
C44.9[0,1,2,9]	[Unsp malig neoplasm, Basal cell carcinoma, Squamous cell ca, Oth spec malig neoplasm] of skin, unsp
C46.[0,1,7,9]	Kaposi's sarcoma of [skin, soft tissue, oth sites, unsp]
D04.0	Carcinoma in situ of skin of lip
D04.2*	Carcinoma in situ skin of ear and ext auricular canal
D04.3*	Carcinoma in situ of skin of oth and unsp parts of face
D04.4	Carcinoma in situ of skin of scalp and neck
D04.5	Carcinoma in situ of skin of trunk
D04.6*	Carcinoma in situ of skin of upr limb, incl* shldr
D04.7*	Carcinoma in situ of skin of lwr limb, incl* hip
D04.8	Carcinoma in situ of skin of oth sites
D04.9	Carcinoma in situ of skin, unsp
D17.0	Ben lipomatous neoplm of skin, SQ of head, face and neck
D17.1	Benign lipomatous neoplasm of skin, SQ of trunk
D17.2*	Benign lipomatous neoplasm of skin, SQ of limb
D17.3*	Benign lipomatous neoplasm of skin, SQ of and unsp sites
D17.72	Benign lipomatous neoplasm of oth genitourinary organ
D17.79	Benign lipomatous neoplasm of oth sites
D17.9	Benign lipomatous neoplasm, unsp
D18.01	Hemangioma of skin and SQ tissue
D22.0	Melanocytic nevi of lip
D22.2*	Melanocytic nevi of ear and ext auricular canal
D22.3*	Melanocytic nevi of oth and unsp parts of face
D22.4	Melanocytic nevi of scalp and neck
D22.5	Melanocytic nevi of trunk
D22.6*	Melanocytic nevi of upr limb, incl* shldr
D22.7*	Melanocytic nevi of lwr limb, incl* hip
D22.9	Melanocytic nevi, unsp
D23.0	Oth benign neoplasm of skin of lip
D23.2*	Oth benign neoplasm skin/ ear and ext auricular canal
D23.3*	Oth benign neoplasm of skin of oth and unsp parts of face
D23.4	Oth benign neoplasm of skin of scalp and neck
D23.5	Oth benign neoplasm of skin of trunk
D23.6*	Oth benign neoplasm skin/ upr limb, incl* shldr
D23.7*	Oth benign neoplasm of skin of lwr limb, incl* hip
D23.9	Oth benign neoplasm of skin, unsp
D24*	Benign neoplasm of breast
D48.5	Neoplasm of uncertain behav of skin
H02.6*	Xanthelasma of eyelid
I78.1	Nevus, non-neoplastic
I89.0	Lymphedema, NEC
L08.1	Erythrasma
L11*	Oth acantholytic d/o
L12.2	Chr bullous dz of childhood
L13.0	Dermatitis herpetiformis
L13.1	Subcorneal pustular dermatitis
L20*	Atopic dermatitis
L21*	Seborrheic dermatitis
L22	Diaper dermatitis
L23*	Allergic contact dermatitis
L24*	Irritant contact dermatitis
L25*	Unsp contact dermatitis
L26	Exfoliative dermatitis
L27*	Dermatitis d/t substances taken internally
L28*	Lichen simplex chronicus and prurigo

Surgical   **Medical**   **CC Indicator**   **MCC Indicator**   **Procedure Proxy**   **PDxMCC** PDx acts as own MCC   **PDxCC** PDx acts as own CC

© 2015 Optum360, LLC   MS-DRG Version 33.0   233

L29.0	Pruritus ani
L29.8	Oth pruritus
L29.9	Pruritus, unsp
L30*	Oth and unsp dermatitis
L40.1	Generalized pustular psoriasis
L42	Pityriasis rosea
L43*	Lichen planus
L44.0	Pityriasis rubra pilaris
L44.8	Oth spec papulosquamous d/o
L44.9	Papulosquamous d/o, unsp
L44.[1,2,3]	Lichen [nitidus, striatus, ruber moniliformis]
L45	Papulosquamous d/o in dz classified elsw
L49*	Exfoliatn d/t erythemat cond accord extent body involv
L50*	Urticaria
L53.8	Oth spec erythematous conditions
L53.9	Erythematous condition, unsp
L54	Erythema in dz classified elsw
L55*	Sunburn
L56*	Oth acute skin changes d/t ultraviolet radiation
L57*	Skin changes d/t chr expsr to nonionizing radiation
L58*	Radiodermatitis
L59*	Oth d/o of skin, SQ related to radiation
L60*	Nail d/o
L62	Nail d/o in dz classified elsw
L63*	Alopecia areata
L64*	Androgenic alopecia
L65*	Oth nonscarring hair loss
L66*	Cicatricial alopecia [scarring hair loss]
L67*	Hair color and hair shaft abnormalities
L68*	Hypertrichosis
L70*	Acne
L71*	Rosacea
L72*	Follicular cysts of skin and SQ tissue
L73*	Oth follicular d/o
L74*	Eccrine sweat d/o
L75*	Apocrine sweat d/o
L80	Vitiligo
L81*	Oth d/o of pigmentation
L82*	Seborrheic keratosis
L83	Acanthosis nigricans
L84	Corns and callosities
L85*	Oth epidermal thickening
L86	Keratoderma in dz classified elsw
L87*	Transepidermal elimination d/o
L90*	Atrophic d/o of skin
L91*	Hypertrophic d/o of skin
L92.0	Granuloma annulare
L92.1	Necrobiosis lipoidica, NEC
L92.2	Granuloma faciale [eosinophilic granuloma of skin]
L92.3	FB granuloma of the skin and SQ tissue
L92.9	Granulomatous d/o of the skin, SQ, unsp
L94.0	Localized scleroderma [morphea]
L94.1	Linear scleroderma
L94.2	Calcinosis cutis
L94.3	Sclerodactyly
L94.4	Gottron's papules
L94.8	Oth spec localized connective tissue d/o
L94.9	Localized connective tissue d/o, unsp
L95*	Vasculitis limited to skin, NEC
L98.1	Factitial dermatitis
L98.2	Febrile neutrophilic dermatosis [Sweet]
L98.5	Mucinosis of the skin
L98.[6,8,9]	[Oth infiltrative, Oth spec, Unsp] d/os of the skin and SQ tissue
L99	Oth d/o of skin, SQ in dz classd elsw
M35.6	Relapsing panniculitis [Weber-Christian]
M54.0[0,1,2]	Panniculitis affecting rgns of neck and back, [unsp, occipito-atlanto-axial, cervical] rgn
M79.3	Panniculitis, unsp
M79.4	Hypertrophy of (infrapatellar) fat pad
N80.6	Endometriosis in cutaneous scar
Q18.3	Webbing of neck
Q18.9	Congenital malformation of face and neck, unsp
Q80*	Congenital ichthyosis
Q81*	Epidermolysis bullosa
Q82*	Oth congenital malformations of skin
Q84*	Oth congenital malformations of integument
R21	Rash and oth nonspecific skin eruption
R22.0	Localized swelling, mass and lump, head
R22.1	Localized swelling, mass and lump, neck
R22.3*	Localized swelling, mass and lump, upr limb

R22.4*	Localized swelling, mass and lump, lwr limb
R22.9	Localized swelling, mass and lump, unsp
R23.4	Changes in skin texture
R23.8	Oth skin changes
R23.9	Unsp skin changes
R61	Generalized hyperhidrosis
R90.0	Intcrn space-occupying lesion found on dx imaging of cnsl
S00.0[2,6]XA	[Blister (nonthermal), Insect bite (nonvenomous)] of scalp, init enc
S00.3[2,6]XA	[Blister (nonthermal), Insect bite (nonvenomous)] of nose, init enc
S00.4[2,6][1,2,9]A	[Blister (nonthermal), Insect bite (nonvenomous)] of [rt, lt, unsp] ear, init enc
S00.5[2,6][1,2]A	[Blister (nonthermal), Insect bite (nonvenomous)] of [lip, oral cavity], init enc
S00.[8,9][2,6]XA	[Blister (nonthermal), Insect bite (nonvenomous)] of [oth, unsp] part of head, init enc
S10.1[2,6]XA	[Blister (nonthermal), Insect bite (nonvenomous)] of throat, init enc
S10.8[2,6]XA	[Blister (nonthermal), Insect bite (nonvenomous)] of oth spec part of neck, init enc
S10.9[2,6]XA	[Blister (nonthermal), Insect bite (nonvenomous)] of unsp part of neck, init enc
S20.1[2,6][1,2,9]A	[Blister (nonthermal), Insect bite (nonvenomous)] of breast, [rt, lt, unsp] breast, init enc
S20.3[2,6][1,2,9]A	[Blister (nonthermal), Insect bite (nonvenomous)] of [rt, lt, unsp] front wall of thorax, init enc
S20.4[2,6][1,2,9]A	[Blister (nonthermal), Insect bite (nonvenomous)] of [rt, lt, unsp] back wall of thorax, init enc
S20.9[2,6]XA	[Blister (nonthermal), Insect bite (nonvenomous)] of unsp parts of thorax, init enc
S30.8[2,6][0,1,2,3,4,5,6,7]A	[Blister (nonthermal), Insect bite (nonvenomous)] of [lwr back and pelvis, abd wall, penis, scrotum and testes, vagina and vulva, unsp ext genital organs, male, unsp ext genital organs, female, anus], init enc
S40.26[1,2,9]A	Insect bite (nonvenomous) of [rt, lt, unsp] shldr, init enc
S40.86[1,2,9]A	Insect bite (nonvenomous) of [rt, lt, unsp] upr arm, init enc
S50.3[2,6][1,2,9]A	[Blister (nonthermal), Insect bite (nonvenomous)] of [rt, lt, unsp] elbow, init enc
S50.8[2,6][1,2,9]A	[Blister (nonthermal), Insect bite (nonvenomous)] of [rt, lt, unsp] forearm, init enc
S60.3[2,6][1,2,9]A	[Blister (nonthermal), Insect bite (nonvenomous)] of [rt, lt, unsp] thumb, init enc
S60.4[2,6][0,1,2,3,4,5,6,7,8,9]A	[Blister (nonthermal), Insect bite (nonvenomous)] of [rt index, lt index, rt mid, lt mid, rt ring, lt ring, rt little, lt little] finger, init enc
S60.5[2,6][1,2,9]A	[Blister (nonthermal), Insect bite (nonvenomous)] of [rt, lt, unsp] hand, init enc
S60.8[2,6][1,2,9]A	[Blister (nonthermal), Insect bite (nonvenomous)] of [rt, lt, unsp] wrist, init enc
S70.2[2,6][1,2,9]A	[Blister (nonthermal), Insect bite (nonvenomous)] of [rt, lt, unsp] hip, init enc
S70.3[2,6][1,2,9]A	[Blister (nonthermal), Insect bite (nonvenomous)] of [rt, lt, unsp] thigh, init enc
S80.2[2,6][1,2,9]A	[Blister (nonthermal), Insect bite (nonvenomous)] of [rt, lt, unsp] knee, init enc
S80.8[2,6][1,2,9]A	[Blister (nonthermal), Insect bite (nonvenomous)] of [rt, lt, unsp] lwr leg, init enc
S90.4[2,6][1,2,3]A	[Blister (nonthermal), Insect bite (nonvenomous)] of [rt, lt, unsp] great toe, init enc
S90.4[2,6][4,5,6]A	[Blister (nonthermal), Insect bite (nonvenomous)] of [rt, lt, unsp] lesser toe(s), init enc
S90.5[2,6][1,2,9]A	[Blister (nonthermal), Insect bite (nonvenomous)] of [rt, lt, unsp] ankle, init enc
S90.8[2,6][1,2,9]A	[Blister (nonthermal), Insect bite (nonvenomous)] of [rt, lt, unsp] foot, init enc
Z41.1	Enc for cosmetic surgery
Z42*	Enc for plast/recnst surg fol med proc or healed inj
Z52.1*	Skin donor
Z94.5	Skin transplant status

DRG 607   **Minor Skin Disorders without MCC**

GMLOS 2.8	AMLOS 3.6	RW 0.7258

Select principal diagnosis listed under DRG 606

T **Transfer DRG**   SP **Special Payment**   * **Code Range**   **6th and 7th Character of ZZ = No Device, No Qualifier ZX = No Device, Diagnostic**

MDC 10
Endocrine, Nutritional And Metabolic Diseases And Disorders

SURGICAL

DRG 614   Adrenal and Pituitary Procedures with CC/MCC
GMLOS 3.9   AMLOS 5.4   RW 2.3916

Operating Room Procedures

018M*	Div/Abd Sympathetic Nerve
06L9[0,3,4]ZZ	Occlsn/Renal Vein, Rt, [Opn, Perc, Perc Endo]
06LB[0,3,4]ZZ	Occlsn/Renal Vein, Lt, [Opn, Perc, Perc Endo]
07JM3ZZ	Inspect of Thymus, Perc Appr
0G50*	Destr/Pituitary Gland
0G51*	Destr/Pineal Body
0G52*	Destr/Adrenal Gland, Lt
0G53*	Destr/Adrenal Gland, Rt
0G54*	Destr/Adrenal Glands, Bilat
0G80*	Div/Pituitary Gland
0G90*	Drain/Pituitary Gland
0G91*	Drain/Pineal Body
0G920ZX	Drain of Lt Adrenal Gland, Opn Appr, Diagnostic
0G92[0,3,4][0,Z]Z	Drain/Lt Adrenal Gland, [Opn, Perc, Perc Endo], [Drain Dev, No Dev], NQ
0G930ZX	Drain of Rt Adrenal Gland, Opn Appr, Diagnostic
0G93[0,3,4][0,Z]Z	Drain/Rt Adrenal Gland, [Opn, Perc, Perc Endo], [Drain Dev, No Dev], NQ
0G940ZX	Drain of Bilat Adrenal Glands, Opn Appr, Diagn
0G94[0,3,4][0,Z]Z	Drain/Bilat Adrenal Glands, [Opn, Perc, Perc Endo], [Drain Dev, No Dev], NQ
0GB0*	Exc/Pituitary Gland
0GB1*	Exc/Pineal Body
0GB20ZX	Exc of Lt Adrenal Gland, Opn Appr, Diagnostic
0GB2[0,3,4]ZZ	Exc/Lt Adrenal Gland, [Opn, Perc, Perc Endo]
0GB30ZX	Exc of Rt Adrenal Gland, Opn Appr, Diagnostic
0GB3[0,3,4]ZZ	Exc/Rt Adrenal Gland, [Opn, Perc, Perc Endo]
0GB40ZX	Exc of Bilat Adrenal Glands, Opn Appr, Diagn
0GB4[0,3,4]ZZ	Exc/Bilat Adrenal Glands, [Opn, Perc, Perc Endo]
0GC0*	Extir/Pituitary Gland
0GC1*	Extir/Pineal Body
0GC2*	Extir/Adrenal Gland, Lt
0GC3*	Extir/Adrenal Gland, Rt
0GC4*	Extir/Adrenal Glands, Bilat
0GJ0*	Inspect/Pituitary Gland
0GJ1*	Inspect/Pineal Body
0GJ5*	Inspect/Adrenal Gland
0GM2*	Reattach/Adrenal Gland, Lt
0GM3*	Reattach/Adrenal Gland, Rt
0GN0*	Rls/Pituitary Gland
0GN1*	Rls/Pineal Body
0GN2*	Rls/Adrenal Gland, Lt
0GN3*	Rls/Adrenal Gland, Rt
0GN4*	Rls/Adrenal Glands, Bilat
0GP0[0,3,4]0Z	Rmvl/Pituitary Gland, [Opn, Perc, Perc Endo], Drain Dev, NQ
0GP1[0,3,4]0Z	Rmvl/Pineal Body, [Opn, Perc, Perc Endo], Drain Dev, NQ
0GP5[0,3,4]0Z	Rmvl/Adrenal Gland, [Opn, Perc, Perc Endo], Drain Dev, NQ
0GQ0*	Repair/Pituitary Gland
0GQ1*	Repair/Pineal Body
0GQ2*	Repair/Adrenal Gland, Lt
0GQ3*	Repair/Adrenal Gland, Rt
0GQ4*	Repair/Adrenal Glands, Bilat
0GS2*	Repos/Adrenal Gland, Lt
0GS3*	Repos/Adrenal Gland, Rt
0GT0*	Resect/Pituitary Gland
0GT1*	Resect/Pineal Body
0GT2*	Resect/Adrenal Gland, Lt
0GT3*	Resect/Adrenal Gland, Rt
0GT4*	Resect/Adrenal Glands, Bilat
0GW0[0,3,4]0Z	Rev/Pituitary Gland, [Opn, Perc, Perc Endo], Drain Dev, NQ
0GW1[0,3,4]0Z	Rev/Pineal Body, [Opn, Perc, Perc Endo], Drain Dev, NQ
0GW5[0,3,4]0Z	Rev/Adrenal Gland, [Opn, Perc, Perc Endo], Drain Dev, NQ

DRG 615   Adrenal and Pituitary Procedures without CC/MCC
GMLOS 2.1   AMLOS 2.5   RW 1.4254

Select operating room procedures listed under DRG 614

DRG 616   Amputation of Lower Limb for Endocrine, Nutritional, and Metabolic Disorders with MCC
GMLOS 10.3   AMLOS 12.6   RW 4.0054   [T]

Operating Room Procedures

0Y6C*	Detach/Upr Leg, Rt
0Y6D*	Detach/Upr Leg, Lt
0Y6F0ZZ	Detach at Rt Knee Region, Opn Appr
0Y6G0ZZ	Detach at Lt Knee Region, Opn Appr
0Y6H*	Detach/Lwr Leg, Rt
0Y6J*	Detach/Lwr Leg, Lt
0Y6M*	Detach/Foot, Rt
0Y6N*	Detach/Foot, Lt
0Y6P*	Detach/1st Toe, Rt
0Y6Q*	Detach/1st Toe, Lt
0Y6R*	Detach/2nd Toe, Rt
0Y6S*	Detach/2nd Toe, Lt
0Y6T*	Detach/3rd Toe, Rt
0Y6U*	Detach/3rd Toe, Lt
0Y6V*	Detach/4th Toe, Rt
0Y6W*	Detach/4th Toe, Lt
0Y6X*	Detach/5th Toe, Rt
0Y6Y*	Detach/5th Toe, Lt

DRG 617   Amputation of Lower Limb for Endocrine, Nutritional, and Metabolic Disorders with CC
GMLOS 6.0   AMLOS 7.2   RW 2.0064   [T]

Select operating room procedures listed under DRG 616

DRG 618   Amputation of Lower Limb for Endocrine, Nutritional, and Metabolic Disorders without CC/MCC
GMLOS 4.3   AMLOS 5.0   RW 1.1804   [T]

Select operating room procedures listed under DRG 616

DRG 619   O.R. Procedures for Obesity with MCC
GMLOS 3.8   AMLOS 5.7   RW 2.9418

Operating Room Procedures

0D16[0,4,8][7,J,K,Z][9,A,B,L]	Bypass/Stomach, [Opn, Perc Endo, Via Natrl or Artfcl Opng Endo], [Auto Tissue Sub, Synth Sub, Nonauto Tissue Sub, No Dev], [Duodenum, Jejunum, Ileum, Transv Colon]
0D19[0,4,8][7,J,K,Z][9,A,B]	Bypass/Duodenum, [Opn, Perc Endo, Via Natrl or Artfcl Opng Endo], [Auto Tissue Sub, Synth Sub, Nonauto Tissue Sub, No Dev], [Duodenum, Jejunum, Ileum]
0D1A8ZH	Bypass Jejunum to Cecum, Endo
0D1A[0,4,8][7,J,K,Z][A,B]	Bypass/Jejunum, [Opn, Perc Endo, Via Natrl or Artfcl Opng Endo], [Auto Tissue Sub, Synth Sub, Nonauto Tissue Sub, No Dev], [Jejunum, Ileum]
0D1B8ZH	Bypass Ileum to Cecum, Endo
0D1B[0,4,8][7,J,K,Z]B	Bypass/Ileum, [Opn, Perc Endo, Via Natrl or Artfcl Opng Endo], [Auto Tissue Sub, Synth Sub, Nonauto Tissue Sub, No Dev], Ileum
0D76*	Dilation/Stomach
0DB6[0,3,4,7,8]Z3	Exc/Stomach, [Opn, Perc, Perc Endo, Via Natrl or Artfcl Opng, Via Natrl or Artfcl Opng Endo], No Dev, Vertical
0DB6[0,3,7]ZZ	Exc/Stomach, [Opn, Perc, Via Natrl or Artfcl Opng]
0DF6[0,3,4,7,8]ZZ	Fragmn/Stomach, [Opn, Perc, Perc Endo, Via Natrl or Artfcl Opng, Via Natrl or Artfcl Opng Endo]
0DH6[0,3,4,7,8]DZ	Insert/Stomach, [Opn, Perc, Perc Endo, Via Natrl or Artfcl Opng, Via Natrl or Artfcl Opng Endo], Intralum Dev, NQ
0DL6*	Occlsn/Stomach
0DL7*	Occlsn/Stomach, Pylorus
0DM6*	Reattach/Stomach
0DN6*	Rls/Stomach
0DP64[3,C]Z	Rmvl/Stomach, Perc Endo, [Inf Dev, Extralum Dev], NQ

MDC 10: Endocrine, Nutritional And Metabolic Diseases And Disorders—SURGICAL

0DQ6*	Repair/Stomach
0DU6*	Supl/Stomach
0DV6[0,3,4][C,D,Z]Z	Restrict/Stomach, [Opn, Perc, Perc Endo], [Extralum Dev, Intralum Dev, No Dev], NQ
0DV6[7,8]ZZ	Restrict/Stomach, [Via Natrl or Artfcl Opng, Via Natrl or Artfcl Opng Endo]
0DW04UZ	Revise of Feeding Dev in Up Intest Tract, Perc Endo Appr
0DW64[3,C]Z	Rev/Stomach, Perc Endo, [Inf Dev, Extralum Dev], NQ
0DY6*	Transplantation/Stomach
0HBT[0,3]ZZ	Exc/Breast, Rt, [Opn, Perc]
0HBU[0,3]ZZ	Exc/Breast, Lt, [Opn, Perc]
0HBV[0,3]ZZ	Exc/Breast, Bilat, [Opn, Perc]
0HM7XZZ	Reattach of Abd Skin, Ext Appr
0HM9XZZ	Reattach of Perineum Skin, Ext Appr
0J04*	Alter/SQ Tissue & Fascia, Ant Neck
0J05*	Alter/SQ Tissue & Fascia, Posterior Neck
0J06*	Alter/SQ Tissue & Fascia, Chest
0J07*	Alter/SQ Tissue & Fascia, Back
0J08*	Alter/SQ Tissue & Fascia, Abd
0J09*	Alter/SQ Tissue & Fascia, Buttock
0J0D*	Alter/SQ Tissue & Fascia, Rt Upr Arm
0J0F*	Alter/SQ Tissue & Fascia, Lt Upr Arm
0J0G*	Alter/SQ Tissue & Fascia, Rt Lwr Arm
0J0H*	Alter/SQ Tissue & Fascia, Lt Lwr Arm
0J0L*	Alter/SQ Tissue & Fascia, Rt Upr Leg
0J0M*	Alter/SQ Tissue & Fascia, Lt Upr Leg
0J0N*	Alter/SQ Tissue & Fascia, Rt Lwr Leg
0J0P*	Alter/SQ Tissue & Fascia, Lt Lwr Leg
0JR037Z	Replace of Scalp SQ/Fascia with Autol Sub, Perc Appr
0JR137Z	Replace of Face SQ/Fascia with Autol Sub, Perc Appr
0JR437Z	Replace Ant Neck SQ/Fascia w Autol Sub, Perc
0JR537Z	Replace Post Neck SQ/Fascia w Autol Sub, Perc
0JR637Z	Replace of Chest SQ/Fascia with Autol Sub, Perc Appr
0JR737Z	Replace of Back SQ/Fascia with Autol Sub, Perc Appr
0JR837Z	Replace of Abd SQ/Fascia with Autol Sub, Perc Appr
0JR937Z	Replace Buttock SQ/Fascia w Autol Sub, Perc
0JRB37Z	Replace Perineum SQ/Fascia w Autol Sub, Perc
0JRC37Z	Replace of Pelvic SQ/Fascia with Autol Sub, Perc Appr
0JRD37Z	Replace Rt Up Arm SQ/Fascia w Autol Sub, Perc
0JRF37Z	Replace Lt Up Arm SQ/Fascia w Autol Sub, Perc
0JRG37Z	Replace Rt Low Arm SQ/Fascia w Autol Sub, Perc
0JRH37Z	Replace Lt Low Arm SQ/Fascia w Autol Sub, Perc
0JRJ37Z	Replace of Rt Hand SQ/Fascia with Autol Sub, Perc Appr
0JRK37Z	Replace of Lt Hand SQ/Fascia with Autol Sub, Perc Appr
0JRL37Z	Replace Rt Up Leg SQ/Fascia w Autol Sub, Perc
0JRM37Z	Replace Lt Up Leg SQ/Fascia w Autol Sub, Perc
0JRN37Z	Replace Rt Low Leg SQ/Fascia w Autol Sub, Perc
0JRP37Z	Replace Lt Low Leg SQ/Fascia w Autol Sub, Perc
0JRQ37Z	Replace of Rt Foot SQ/Fascia with Autol Sub, Perc Appr
0JRR37Z	Replace of Lt Foot SQ/Fascia with Autol Sub, Perc Appr
0W0F*	Alter/Abd Wall
3E0G3GC	Introduction of Oth Therap Subst into Up GI, Perc Appr

DRG 620 O.R. Procedures for Obesity with CC
GMLOS 2.5   **AMLOS** 3.0   **RW** 1.8407

Select operating room procedures listed under DRG 619

DRG 621 O.R. Procedures for Obesity without CC/MCC
GMLOS 1.8   **AMLOS** 1.9   **RW** 1.5484

Select operating room procedures listed under DRG 619

DRG 622 Skin Grafts and Wound Debridement for Endocrine, Nutritional and Metabolic Disorders with MCC
GMLOS 8.6   **AMLOS** 11.5   **RW** 3.5239   ⊤

Operating Room Procedures

0H80XZZ	Div of Scalp Skin, Ext Appr
0H81XZZ	Div of Face Skin, Ext Appr
0H84XZZ	Div of Neck Skin, Ext Appr
0H85XZZ	Div of Chest Skin, Ext Appr
0H86XZZ	Div of Back Skin, Ext Appr
0H87XZZ	Div of Abd Skin, Ext Appr
0H88XZZ	Div of Buttock Skin, Ext Appr
0H8AXZZ	Div of Genitalia Skin, Ext Appr
0H8BXZZ	Div of Rt Upr Arm Skin, Ext Appr
0H8CXZZ	Div of Lt Upr Arm Skin, Ext Appr
0H8DXZZ	Div of Rt Lwr Arm Skin, Ext Appr

0H8EXZZ	Div of Lt Lwr Arm Skin, Ext Appr
0H8FXZZ	Div of Rt Hand Skin, Ext Appr
0H8GXZZ	Div of Lt Hand Skin, Ext Appr
0H8HXZZ	Div of Rt Upr Leg Skin, Ext Appr
0H8JXZZ	Div of Lt Upr Leg Skin, Ext Appr
0H8KXZZ	Div of Rt Lwr Leg Skin, Ext Appr
0H8LXZZ	Div of Lt Lwr Leg Skin, Ext Appr
0H8MXZZ	Div of Rt Foot Skin, Ext Appr
0H8NXZZ	Div of Lt Foot Skin, Ext Appr
0HB0XZZ	Exc of Scalp Skin, Ext Appr
0HB1XZZ	Exc of Face Skin, Ext Appr
0HB4XZZ	Exc of Neck Skin, Ext Appr
0HB5XZZ	Exc of Chest Skin, Ext Appr
0HB6XZZ	Exc of Back Skin, Ext Appr
0HB7XZZ	Exc of Abd Skin, Ext Appr
0HB8XZZ	Exc of Buttock Skin, Ext Appr
0HBAXZZ	Exc of Genitalia Skin, Ext Appr
0HBBXZZ	Exc of Rt Upr Arm Skin, Ext Appr
0HBCXZZ	Exc of Lt Upr Arm Skin, Ext Appr
0HBDXZZ	Exc of Rt Lwr Arm Skin, Ext Appr
0HBEXZZ	Exc of Lt Lwr Arm Skin, Ext Appr
0HBFXZZ	Exc of Rt Hand Skin, Ext Appr
0HBGXZZ	Exc of Lt Hand Skin, Ext Appr
0HBHXZZ	Exc of Rt Upr Leg Skin, Ext Appr
0HBJXZZ	Exc of Lt Upr Leg Skin, Ext Appr
0HBKXZZ	Exc of Rt Lwr Leg Skin, Ext Appr
0HBLXZZ	Exc of Lt Lwr Leg Skin, Ext Appr
0HBMXZZ	Exc of Rt Foot Skin, Ext Appr
0HBNXZZ	Exc of Lt Foot Skin, Ext Appr
0HR0XJZ	Replace of Scalp Skin with Synth Sub, Extern Appr
0HR0X[7,J,K][3,4]	Replace/Skin, Scalp, Ext, [Auto Tissue Sub, Synth Sub, Nonauto Tissue Sub], [Full Thickness, Partial Thickness]
0HR1XJZ	Replace of Face Skin with Synth Sub, Extern Appr
0HR1X[7,J,K][3,4]	Replace/Skin, Face, Ext, [Auto Tissue Sub, Synth Sub, Nonauto Tissue Sub], [Full Thickness, Partial Thickness]
0HR4XJZ	Replace of Neck Skin with Synth Sub, Extern Appr
0HR4X[7,J,K][3,4]	Replace/Skin, Neck, Ext, [Auto Tissue Sub, Synth Sub, Nonauto Tissue Sub], [Full Thickness, Partial Thickness]
0HR5XJZ	Replace of Chest Skin with Synth Sub, Extern Appr
0HR5X[7,J,K][3,4]	Replace/Skin, Chest, Ext, [Auto Tissue Sub, Synth Sub, Nonauto Tissue Sub], [Full Thickness, Partial Thickness]
0HR6XJZ	Replace of Back Skin with Synth Sub, Extern Appr
0HR6X[7,J,K][3,4]	Replace/Skin, Back, Ext, [Auto Tissue Sub, Synth Sub, Nonauto Tissue Sub], [Full Thickness, Partial Thickness]
0HR7XJZ	Replace of Abd Skin with Synth Sub, Extern Appr
0HR7X[7,J,K][3,4]	Replace/Skin, Abd, Ext, [Auto Tissue Sub, Synth Sub, Nonauto Tissue Sub], [Full Thickness, Partial Thickness]
0HR8XJZ	Replace of Buttock Skin with Synth Sub, Extern Appr
0HR8X[7,J,K][3,4]	Replace/Skin, Buttock, Ext, [Auto Tissue Sub, Synth Sub, Nonauto Tissue Sub], [Full Thickness, Partial Thickness]
0HRAXJZ	Replace of Genitalia Skin with Synth Sub, Extern Appr
0HRAX[7,J][3,4]	Replace/Skin, Genitalia, Ext, [Auto Tissue Sub, Synth Sub], [Full Thickness, Partial Thickness]
0HRBXJZ	Replace of Rt Up Arm Skin with Synth Sub, Extern Appr
0HRBX[7,J][3,4]	Replace/Skin, Rt Upr Arm, Ext, [Auto Tissue Sub, Synth Sub], [Full Thickness, Partial Thickness]
0HRCXJZ	Replace of Lt Up Arm Skin with Synth Sub, Extern Appr
0HRCX[7,J][3,4]	Replace/Skin, Lt Upr Arm, Ext, [Auto Tissue Sub, Synth Sub], [Full Thickness, Partial Thickness]
0HRDXJZ	Replace of Rt Low Arm Skin with Synth Sub, Extern Appr
0HRDX[7,J][3,4]	Replace/Skin, Rt Lwr Arm, Ext, [Auto Tissue Sub, Synth Sub], [Full Thickness, Partial Thickness]
0HREXJZ	Replace of Lt Low Arm Skin with Synth Sub, Extern Appr
0HREX[7,J][3,4]	Replace/Skin, Lt Lwr Arm, Ext, [Auto Tissue Sub, Synth Sub], [Full Thickness, Partial Thickness]
0HRFXJ[3,4,Z]	Replace/Skin, Rt Hand, Ext, Synth Sub, [Full Thickness, Partial Thickness, NQ]
0HRGXJ[3,4,Z]	Replace/Skin, Lt Hand, Ext, Synth Sub, [Full Thickness, Partial Thickness, NQ]
0HRHXJZ	Replace of Rt Up Leg Skin with Synth Sub, Extern Appr
0HRHX[7,J][3,4]	Replace/Skin, Rt Upr Leg, Ext, [Auto Tissue Sub, Synth Sub], [Full Thickness, Partial Thickness]
0HRJXJZ	Replace of Lt Up Leg Skin with Synth Sub, Extern Appr
0HRJX[7,J][3,4]	Replace/Skin, Lt Upr Leg, Ext, [Auto Tissue Sub, Synth Sub], [Full Thickness, Partial Thickness]
0HRKXJZ	Replace of Rt Low Leg Skin with Synth Sub, Extern Appr
0HRKX[7,J][3,4]	Replace/Skin, Rt Lwr Leg, Ext, [Auto Tissue Sub, Synth Sub], [Full Thickness, Partial Thickness]
0HRLXJZ	Replace of Lt Low Leg Skin with Synth Sub, Extern Appr

⊤ Transfer DRG   SP Special Payment   * Code Range   6th and 7th Character of ZZ = No Device, No Qualifier ZX = No Device, Diagnostic

236   MS-DRG Version 33.0   © 2015 Optum360, LLC

ØHRLX[7,J][3,4]	Replace/Skin, Lt Lwr Leg, Ext, [Auto Tissue Sub, Synth Sub], [Full Thickness, Partial Thickness]
ØHRMXJZ	Replace of Rt Foot Skin with Synth Sub, Extern Appr
ØHRMX[7,J][3,4]	Replace/Skin, Rt Foot, Ext, [Auto Tissue Sub, Synth Sub], [Full Thickness, Partial Thickness]
ØHRNXJZ	Replace of Lt Foot Skin with Synth Sub, Extern Appr
ØHRNX[7,J][3,4]	Replace/Skin, Lt Foot, Ext, [Auto Tissue Sub, Synth Sub], [Full Thickness, Partial Thickness]
ØHXØXZZ	Transfer Scalp Skin, Ext Appr
ØHX1XZZ	Transfer Face Skin, Ext Appr
ØHX4XZZ	Transfer Neck Skin, Ext Appr
ØHX5XZZ	Transfer Chest Skin, Ext Appr
ØHX6XZZ	Transfer Back Skin, Ext Appr
ØHX7XZZ	Transfer Abd Skin, Ext Appr
ØHX8XZZ	Transfer Buttock Skin, Ext Appr
ØHX9XZZ	Transfer Perineum Skin, Ext Appr
ØHXAXZZ	Transfer Genitalia Skin, Ext Appr
ØHXBXZZ	Transfer Rt Upr Arm Skin, Ext Appr
ØHXCXZZ	Transfer Lt Upr Arm Skin, Ext Appr
ØHXDXZZ	Transfer Rt Lwr Arm Skin, Ext Appr
ØHXEXZZ	Transfer Lt Lwr Arm Skin, Ext Appr
ØHXFXZZ	Transfer Rt Hand Skin, Ext Appr
ØHXGXZZ	Transfer Lt Hand Skin, Ext Appr
ØHXHXZZ	Transfer Rt Upr Leg Skin, Ext Appr
ØHXJXZZ	Transfer Lt Upr Leg Skin, Ext Appr
ØHXKXZZ	Transfer Rt Lwr Leg Skin, Ext Appr
ØHXLXZZ	Transfer Lt Lwr Leg Skin, Ext Appr
ØHXMXZZ	Transfer Rt Foot Skin, Ext Appr
ØHXNXZZ	Transfer Lt Foot Skin, Ext Appr
ØJBØØZZ	Exc of Scalp SQ/Fascia, Opn Appr
ØJB1ØZZ	Exc of Face SQ/Fascia, Opn Appr
ØJB4ØZZ	Exc of Ant Neck SQ/Fascia, Opn Appr
ØJB5ØZZ	Exc of Post Neck SQ/Fascia, Opn Appr
ØJB6ØZZ	Exc of Chest SQ/Fascia, Opn Appr
ØJB7ØZZ	Exc of Back SQ/Fascia, Opn Appr
ØJB8ØZZ	Exc of Abd SQ/Fascia, Opn Appr
ØJB9ØZZ	Exc of Buttock SQ/Fascia, Opn Appr
ØJBBØZZ	Exc of Perineum SQ/Fascia, Opn Appr
ØJBCØZZ	Exc of Pelvic SQ/Fascia, Opn Appr
ØJBDØZZ	Exc of Rt Up Arm SQ/Fascia, Opn Appr
ØJBFØZZ	Exc of Lt Up Arm SQ/Fascia, Opn Appr
ØJBGØZZ	Exc of Rt Low Arm SQ/Fascia, Opn Appr
ØJBHØZZ	Exc of Lt Low Arm SQ/Fascia, Opn Appr
ØJBLØZZ	Exc of Rt Up Leg SQ/Fascia, Opn Appr
ØJBMØZZ	Exc of Lt Up Leg SQ/Fascia, Opn Appr
ØJBNØZZ	Exc of Rt Low Leg SQ/Fascia, Opn Appr
ØJBPØZZ	Exc of Lt Low Leg SQ/Fascia, Opn Appr
ØJBQØZZ	Exc of Rt Foot SQ/Fascia, Opn Appr
ØJBRØZZ	Exc of Lt Foot SQ/Fascia, Opn Appr
ØJHØ*	Insert/SQ Tissue & Fascia, Scalp
ØJH1*	Insert/SQ Tissue & Fascia, Face
ØJH4*	Insert/SQ Tissue & Fascia, Ant Neck
ØJH5*	Insert/SQ Tissue & Fascia, Posterior Neck
ØJH6[Ø,3]NZ	Insert/SQ Tissue & Fascia, Chest, [Opn, Perc], Tissue Expander, NQ
ØJH7[Ø,3]NZ	Insert/SQ Tissue & Fascia, Back, [Opn, Perc], Tissue Expander, NQ
ØJH8[Ø,3]NZ	Insert/SQ Tissue & Fascia, Abd, [Opn, Perc], Tissue Expander, NQ
ØJH9*	Insert/SQ Tissue & Fascia, Buttock
ØJHB*	Insert/SQ Tissue & Fascia, Perineum
ØJHC*	Insert/SQ Tissue & Fascia, Pelvic Region
ØJHD[Ø,3]NZ	Insert/SQ Tissue & Fascia, Rt Upr Arm, [Opn, Perc], Tissue Expander, NQ
ØJHF[Ø,3]NZ	Insert/SQ Tissue & Fascia, Lt Upr Arm, [Opn, Perc], Tissue Expander, NQ
ØJHG[Ø,3]NZ	Insert/SQ Tissue & Fascia, Rt Lwr Arm, [Opn, Perc], Tissue Expander, NQ
ØJHH[Ø,3]NZ	Insert/SQ Tissue & Fascia, Lt Lwr Arm, [Opn, Perc], Tissue Expander, NQ
ØJHJ*	Insert/SQ Tissue & Fascia, Rt Hand
ØJHK*	Insert/SQ Tissue & Fascia, Lt Hand
ØJHL[Ø,3]NZ	Insert/SQ Tissue & Fascia, Rt Upr Leg, [Opn, Perc], Tissue Expander, NQ
ØJHM[Ø,3]NZ	Insert/SQ Tissue & Fascia, Lt Upr Leg, [Opn, Perc], Tissue Expander, NQ
ØJHN[Ø,3]NZ	Insert/SQ Tissue & Fascia, Rt Lwr Leg, [Opn, Perc], Tissue Expander, NQ
ØJHP[Ø,3]NZ	Insert/SQ Tissue & Fascia, Lt Lwr Leg, [Opn, Perc], Tissue Expander, NQ
ØJHQ*	Insert/SQ Tissue & Fascia, Rt Foot
ØJHR*	Insert/SQ Tissue & Fascia, Lt Foot
ØJXØ[Ø,3]Z[B,C]	Transfer/SQ Tissue & Fascia, Scalp, [Opn, Perc], No Dev, [Skin and SQ Tissue, Skin, SQ Tissue & Fascia]
ØJX1[Ø,3]Z[B,C]	Transfer/SQ Tissue & Fascia, Face, [Opn, Perc], No Dev, [Skin and SQ Tissue, Skin, SQ Tissue & Fascia]
ØJX4[Ø,3]Z[B,C]	Transfer/SQ Tissue & Fascia, Ant Neck, [Opn, Perc], No Dev, [Skin and SQ Tissue, Skin, SQ Tissue & Fascia]
ØJX5[Ø,3]Z[B,C]	Transfer/SQ Tissue & Fascia, Post Neck, [Opn, Perc], No Dev, [Skin and SQ Tissue, Skin, SQ Tissue & Fascia]
ØJX6[Ø,3]Z[B,C]	Transfer/SQ Tissue & Fascia, Chest, [Opn, Perc], No Dev, [Skin and SQ Tissue, Skin, SQ Tissue & Fascia]
ØJX7[Ø,3]Z[B,C]	Transfer/SQ Tissue & Fascia, Back, [Opn, Perc], No Dev, [Skin and SQ Tissue, Skin, SQ Tissue & Fascia]
ØJX8[Ø,3]Z[B,C]	Transfer/SQ Tissue & Fascia, Abd, [Opn, Perc], No Dev, [Skin and SQ Tissue, Skin, SQ Tissue & Fascia]
ØJX9[Ø,3]Z[B,C]	Transfer/SQ Tissue & Fascia, Buttock, [Opn, Perc], No Dev, [Skin and SQ Tissue, Skin, SQ Tissue & Fascia]
ØJXB[Ø,3]Z[B,C]	Transfer/SQ Tissue & Fascia, Perineum, [Opn, Perc], No Dev, [Skin and SQ Tissue, Skin, SQ Tissue & Fascia]
ØJXC[Ø,3]Z[B,C]	Transfer/SQ Tissue & Fascia, Genitalia, [Opn, Perc], No Dev, [Skin and SQ Tissue, Skin, SQ Tissue & Fascia]
ØJXD[Ø,3]Z[B,C]	Transfer/SQ Tissue & Fascia, Rt Upr Arm, [Opn, Perc], No Dev, [Skin and SQ Tissue, Skin, SQ Tissue & Fascia]
ØJXF[Ø,3]Z[B,C]	Transfer/SQ Tissue & Fascia, Lt Upr Arm, [Opn, Perc], No Dev, [Skin and SQ Tissue, Skin, SQ Tissue & Fascia]
ØJXG[Ø,3]Z[B,C]	Transfer/SQ Tissue & Fascia, Rt Lwr Arm, [Opn, Perc], No Dev, [Skin and SQ Tissue, Skin, SQ Tissue & Fascia]
ØJXH[Ø,3]Z[B,C]	Transfer/SQ Tissue & Fascia, Lt Lwr Arm, [Opn, Perc], No Dev, [Skin and SQ Tissue, Skin, SQ Tissue & Fascia]
ØJXL[Ø,3]Z[B,C]	Transfer/SQ Tissue & Fascia, Rt Upr Leg, [Opn, Perc], No Dev, [Skin and SQ Tissue, Skin, SQ Tissue & Fascia]
ØJXM[Ø,3]Z[B,C]	Transfer/SQ Tissue & Fascia, Lt Upr Leg, [Opn, Perc], No Dev, [Skin and SQ Tissue, Skin, SQ Tissue & Fascia]
ØJXN[Ø,3]Z[B,C]	Transfer/SQ Tissue & Fascia, Rt Lwr Leg, [Opn, Perc], No Dev, [Skin and SQ Tissue, Skin, SQ Tissue & Fascia]
ØJXP[Ø,3]Z[B,C]	Transfer/SQ Tissue & Fascia, Lt Lwr Leg, [Opn, Perc], No Dev, [Skin and SQ Tissue, Skin, SQ Tissue & Fascia]
ØJXQ[Ø,3]Z[B,C]	Transfer/SQ Tissue & Fascia, Rt Foot, [Opn, Perc], No Dev, [Skin and SQ Tissue, Skin, SQ Tissue & Fascia]
ØJXR[Ø,3]Z[B,C]	Transfer/SQ Tissue & Fascia, Lt Foot, [Opn, Perc], No Dev, [Skin and SQ Tissue, Skin, SQ Tissue & Fascia]

DRG 623 **Skin Grafts and Wound Debridement for Endocrine, Nutritional and Metabolic Disorders with CC**

GMLOS 5.6	AMLOS 6.8	RW 1.8623

Select operating room procedures listed under DRG 622

DRG 624 **Skin Grafts and Wound Debridement for Endocrine, Nutritional and Metabolic Disorders without CC/MCC**

GMLOS 3.7	AMLOS 4.5	RW 1.1292

Select operating room procedures listed under DRG 622

DRG 625 **Thyroid, Parathyroid and Thyroglossal Procedures with MCC**

GMLOS 4.9	AMLOS 7.5	RW 2.6133

Operating Room Procedures

Ø3LU*	Occlsn/Thyroid Artery, Rt
Ø3LV*	Occlsn/Thyroid Artery, Lt
ØCB7[Ø,3,X]ZZ	Exc/Tongue, [Opn, Perc, Ext]
ØG5G*	Destr/Thyroid Gland Lobe, Lt
ØG5H*	Destr/Thyroid Gland Lobe, Rt
ØG5K*	Destr/Thyroid Gland
ØG5L*	Destr/Superior Parathyroid Gland, Rt
ØG5M*	Destr/Superior Parathyroid Gland, Lt
ØG5N*	Destr/Inferior Parathyroid Gland, Rt
ØG5P*	Destr/Inferior Parathyroid Gland, Lt
ØG5Q*	Destr/Parathyroid Glands, Multi
ØG5R*	Destr/Parathyroid Gland
ØG8J*	Div/Thyroid Gland Isthmus
ØG9GØØZ	Drain of Lt Thyroid Lobe with Drain Dev, Opn Appr
ØG9GØZ[X,Z]	Drain/Thyroid Gland Lobe, Lt, Opn, No Dev, [Dx, NQ]
ØG9HØØZ	Drain of Rt Thyroid Lobe with Drain Dev, Opn Appr
ØG9HØZ[X,Z]	Drain/Thyroid Gland Lobe, Rt, Opn, No Dev, [Dx, NQ]
ØG9KØØZ	Drain of Thyroid Gland with Drain Dev, Opn Appr
ØG9KØZ[X,Z]	Drain/Thyroid Gland Lobe, Opn, No Dev, [Dx, NQ]

Surgical   **Medical**   **CC Indicator**   **MCC Indicator**   **Procedure Proxy**   PDxMCC PDx acts as own MCC   PDxCC PDx acts as own CC

© 2015 Optum360, LLC

MS-DRG Version 33.0

237

0G9L0[0,Z]Z	Drain/Superior Parathyroid Gland, Rt, Opn, [Drain Dev, No Dev], NQ
0G9L[0,3,4]ZX	Drain/Superior Parathyroid Gland, Rt, [Opn, Perc, Perc Endo]
0G9M0[0,Z]Z	Drain/Superior Parathyroid Gland, Lt, Opn, [Drain Dev, No Dev], NQ
0G9M[0,3,4]ZX	Drain/Superior Parathyroid Gland, Lt, [Opn, Perc, Perc Endo]
0G9N0[0,Z]Z	Drain/Inferior Parathyroid Gland, Rt, Opn, [Drain Dev, No Dev], NQ
0G9N[0,3,4]ZX	Drain/Inferior Parathyroid Gland, Rt, [Opn, Perc, Perc Endo]
0G9P0[0,Z]Z	Drain/Inferior Parathyroid Gland, Lt, Opn, [Drain Dev, No Dev], NQ
0G9P[0,3,4]ZX	Drain/Inferior Parathyroid Gland, Lt, [Opn, Perc, Perc Endo]
0G9Q0[0,Z]Z	Drain/Parathyroid Glands, Multi, Opn, [Drain Dev, No Dev], NQ
0G9Q[0,3,4]ZX	Drain/Parathyroid Glands, Multi, [Opn, Perc, Perc Endo]
0G9R0[0,Z]Z	Drain/Parathyroid Gland, Opn, [Drain Dev, No Dev], NQ
0G9R[0,3,4]ZX	Drain/Parathyroid Gland, [Opn, Perc, Perc Endo]
0GBG0ZX	Exc of Lt Thyroid Gland Lobe, Opn Appr, Diagn
0GBG[0,3,4]ZZ	Exc/Thyroid Gland Lobe, Lt, [Opn, Perc, Perc Endo]
0GBH0ZX	Exc of Rt Thyroid Gland Lobe, Opn Appr, Diagn
0GBH[0,3,4]ZZ	Exc/Thyroid Gland Lobe, Rt, [Opn, Perc, Perc Endo]
0GBL*	Exc/Superior Parathyroid Gland, Rt
0GBM*	Exc/Superior Parathyroid Gland, Lt
0GBN*	Exc/Inferior Parathyroid Gland, Rt
0GBP*	Exc/Inferior Parathyroid Gland, Lt
0GBQ*	Exc/Parathyroid Glands, Multi
0GBR*	Exc/Parathyroid Gland
0GCG*	Extir/Thyroid Gland Lobe, Lt
0GCH*	Extir/Thyroid Gland Lobe, Rt
0GCK*	Extir/Thyroid Gland
0GCL*	Extir/Superior Parathyroid Gland, Rt
0GCM*	Extir/Superior Parathyroid Gland, Lt
0GCN*	Extir/Inferior Parathyroid Gland, Rt
0GCP*	Extir/Inferior Parathyroid Gland, Lt
0GCQ*	Extir/Parathyroid Glands, Multi
0GCR*	Extir/Parathyroid Gland
0GH*	Endocrine Sys, Insert
0GJK*	Inspect/Thyroid Gland
0GJR*	Inspect/Parathyroid Gland
0GJS*	Inspect/Endocrine Gland
0GMG*	Reattach/Thyroid Gland Lobe, Lt
0GMH*	Reattach/Thyroid Gland Lobe, Rt
0GML*	Reattach/Superior Parathyroid Gland, Rt
0GMM*	Reattach/Superior Parathyroid Gland, Lt
0GMN*	Reattach/Inferior Parathyroid Gland, Rt
0GMP*	Reattach/Inferior Parathyroid Gland, Lt
0GMQ*	Reattach/Parathyroid Glands, Multi
0GMR*	Reattach/Parathyroid Gland
0GNG*	Rls/Thyroid Gland Lobe, Lt
0GNH*	Rls/Thyroid Gland Lobe, Rt
0GNK*	Rls/Thyroid Gland
0GNL*	Rls/Superior Parathyroid Gland, Rt
0GNM*	Rls/Superior Parathyroid Gland, Lt
0GNN*	Rls/Inferior Parathyroid Gland, Rt
0GNP*	Rls/Inferior Parathyroid Gland, Lt
0GNQ*	Rls/Parathyroid Glands, Multi
0GNR*	Rls/Parathyroid Gland
0GPK[0,3,4]0Z	Rmvl/Thyroid Gland, [Opn, Perc, Perc Endo], Drain Dev, NQ
0GPR[0,3,4]0Z	Rmvl/Parathyroid Gland, [Opn, Perc, Perc Endo], Drain Dev, NQ
0GQG*	Repair/Thyroid Gland Lobe, Lt
0GQH*	Repair/Thyroid Gland Lobe, Rt
0GQJ*	Repair/Thyroid Gland Isthmus
0GQK*	Repair/Thyroid Gland
0GQL*	Repair/Superior Parathyroid Gland, Rt
0GQM*	Repair/Superior Parathyroid Gland, Lt
0GQN*	Repair/Inferior Parathyroid Gland, Rt
0GQP*	Repair/Inferior Parathyroid Gland, Lt
0GQQ*	Repair/Parathyroid Glands, Multi
0GQR*	Repair/Parathyroid Gland
0GSG*	Repos/Thyroid Gland Lobe, Lt
0GSH*	Repos/Thyroid Gland Lobe, Rt
0GSL*	Repos/Superior Parathyroid Gland, Rt
0GSM*	Repos/Superior Parathyroid Gland, Lt
0GSN*	Repos/Inferior Parathyroid Gland, Rt
0GSP*	Repos/Inferior Parathyroid Gland, Lt
0GSQ*	Repos/Parathyroid Glands, Multi
0GSR*	Repos/Parathyroid Gland
0GTG*	Resect/Thyroid Gland Lobe, Lt
0GTH*	Resect/Thyroid Gland Lobe, Rt
0GTK*	Resect/Thyroid Gland
0GTL*	Resect/Superior Parathyroid Gland, Rt

0GTM*	Resect/Superior Parathyroid Gland, Lt
0GTN*	Resect/Inferior Parathyroid Gland, Rt
0GTP*	Resect/Inferior Parathyroid Gland, Lt
0GTQ*	Resect/Parathyroid Glands, Multi
0GTR*	Resect/Parathyroid Gland
0GWK[0,3,4]0Z	Rev/Thyroid Gland, [Opn, Perc, Perc Endo], Drain Dev, NQ
0GWR[0,3,4]0Z	Rev/Parathyroid Gland, [Opn, Perc, Perc Endo], Drain Dev, NQ
0W96[0,3,4][0,Z]Z	Drain/Neck, [Opn, Perc, Perc Endo], [Drain Dev, No Dev], NQ
0WJ6[0,3,4]ZZ	Inspect/Neck, [Opn, Perc, Perc Endo]
DGY[0,1,4,5]KZZ	Laser Interstitial Thermal Therapy of [Pituitary Gland, Pineal Body, Parathyroid Glands, Thyroid]

DRG 626   Thyroid, Parathyroid and Thyroglossal Procedures with CC

GMLOS 2.2	AMLOS 3.2	RW 1.3936

Select operating room procedures listed under DRG 625

DRG 627   Thyroid, Parathyroid and Thyroglossal Procedures without CC/MCC

GMLOS 1.3	AMLOS 1.5	RW 0.9108

Select operating room procedures listed under DRG 625

DRG 628   Other Endocrine, Nutritional and Metabolic O.R. Procedures with MCC

GMLOS 7.0	AMLOS 9.8	RW 3.4413	[T]

Operating Room Procedures

02HV[0,3,4][2,D]Z	Insert/Superior Vena Cava, [Opn, Perc, Perc Endo], [Monitoring Dev, Intralum Dev], NQ
02LV*	Occlsn/Superior Vena Cava
02VV*	Restrict/Superior Vena Cava
03130ZD	Bypass Rt Subclavian Artery to Up Arm Vein, Opn Appr
03140ZD	Bypass Lt Subclavian Artery to Up Arm Vein, Opn Appr
03150ZD	Bypass Rt Axillary Artery to Up Arm Vein, Opn Appr
03150[9,A,J,K,Z]0	Bypass/Axillary Artery, Rt, Opn, [Auto Venous Tissue, Auto Arterial Tissue, Synth Sub, Nonauto Tissue Sub, No Dev], Upr Arm Artery, Rt
03160ZD	Bypass Lt Axillary Artery to Upr Arm Vein, Opn Appr
03160[9,A,J,K,Z]1	Bypass/Axillary Artery, Lt, Opn, [Auto Venous Tissue, Auto Arterial Tissue, Synth Sub, Nonauto Tissue Sub, No Dev], Upr Arm Artery, Lt
03170[9,A,J,K,Z][D,F]	Bypass/Brachial Artery, Rt, Opn, [Auto Venous Tissue, Auto Arterial Tissue, Synth Sub, Nonauto Tissue Sub, No Dev], [Upr Arm Vein, Lwr Arm Vein]
03180[9,A,J,K,Z][D,F]	Bypass/Brachial Artery, Lt, Opn, [Auto Venous Tissue, Auto Arterial Tissue, Synth Sub, Nonauto Tissue Sub, No Dev], [Upr Arm Vein, Lwr Arm Vein]
03190[9,A,J,K,Z]F	Bypass/Ulnar Artery, Rt, Opn, [Auto Venous Tissue, Auto Arterial Tissue, Synth Sub, Nonauto Tissue Sub, No Dev], Lwr Arm Vein
031A0[9,A,J,K,Z]F	Bypass/Ulnar Artery, Lt, Opn, [Auto Venous Tissue, Auto Arterial Tissue, Synth Sub, Nonauto Tissue Sub, No Dev], Lwr Arm Vein
031B0[9,A,J,K,Z]F	Bypass/Radial Artery, Rt, Opn, [Auto Venous Tissue, Auto Arterial Tissue, Synth Sub, Nonauto Tissue Sub, No Dev], Lwr Arm Vein
031C0[9,A,J,K,Z]F	Bypass/Radial Artery, Lt, Opn, [Auto Venous Tissue, Auto Arterial Tissue, Synth Sub, Nonauto Tissue Sub, No Dev], Lwr Arm Vein
031H0[9,A,J,K,Z]J	Bypass/Common Carotid Artery, Rt, Opn, [Auto Venous Tissue, Auto Arterial Tissue, Synth Sub, Nonauto Tissue Sub, No Dev], Extracranial Artery, Rt
031J0[9,A,J,K,Z]K	Bypass/Common Carotid Artery, Lt, Opn, [Auto Venous Tissue, Auto Arterial Tissue, Synth Sub, Nonauto Tissue Sub, No Dev], Extracranial Artery, Lt
031K0[9,A,J,K,Z]J	Bypass/Int Carotid Artery, Rt, Opn, [Auto Venous Tissue, Auto Arterial Tissue, Synth Sub, Nonauto Tissue Sub, No Dev], Extracranial Artery, Rt
031L0[9,A,J,K,Z]K	Bypass/Int Carotid Artery, Lt, Opn, [Auto Venous Tissue, Auto Arterial Tissue, Synth Sub, Nonauto Tissue Sub, No Dev], Extracranial Artery, Lt
031M0[9,A,J,K,Z]J	Bypass/Ext Carotid Artery, Rt, Opn, [Auto Venous Tissue, Auto Arterial Tissue, Synth Sub, Nonauto Tissue Sub, No Dev], Extracranial Artery, Rt
031N0[9,A,J,K,Z]K	Bypass/Ext Carotid Artery, Lt, Opn, [Auto Venous Tissue, Auto Arterial Tissue, Synth Sub, Nonauto Tissue Sub, No Dev], Extracranial Artery, Lt

---

[T] **Transfer DRG**   [SP] **Special Payment**   * Code Range   6th and 7th Character of ZZ = No Device, No Qualifier ZX = No Device, Diagnostic

0355*	Destr/Axillary Artery, Rt
0356*	Destr/Axillary Artery, Lt
0357*	Destr/Brachial Artery, Rt
0358*	Destr/Brachial Artery, Lt
0359*	Destr/Ulnar Artery, Rt
035A*	Destr/Ulnar Artery, Lt
035B*	Destr/Radial Artery, Rt
035C*	Destr/Radial Artery, Lt
035D*	Destr/Hand Artery, Rt
035F*	Destr/Hand Artery, Lt
035Y*	Destr/Upr Artery
03733[4,D,Z]Z	Dilation/Subclavian Artery, Rt, Perc, [Drug-eluting Intralum Dev, Intralum Dev, No Dev], NQ
03743[4,D,Z]Z	Dilation/Subclavian Artery, Lt, Perc, [Drug-eluting Intralum Dev, Intralum Dev, No Dev], NQ
03773[4,D,Z]Z	Dilation/Brachial Artery, Rt, Perc, [Drug-eluting Intralum Dev, Intralum Dev, No Dev], NQ
03783[4,D,Z]Z	Dilation/Brachial Artery, Lt, Perc, [Drug-eluting Intralum Dev, Intralum Dev, No Dev], NQ
03793[4,D,Z]Z	Dilation/Ulnar Artery, Rt, Perc, [Drug-eluting Intralum Dev, Intralum Dev, No Dev], NQ
037A3[4,D,Z]Z	Dilation/Ulnar Artery, Lt, Perc, [Drug-eluting Intralum Dev, Intralum Dev, No Dev], NQ
037Y3[4,D,Z]Z	Dilation/Upr Artery, Perc, [Drug-eluting Intralum Dev, Intralum Dev, No Dev], NQ
039S[0,3,4]ZX	Drain/Temporal Artery, Rt, [Opn, Perc, Perc Endo]
039T[0,3,4]ZX	Drain/Temporal Artery, Lt, [Opn, Perc, Perc Endo]
03B5[0,3,4]ZZ	Exc/Axillary Artery, Rt, [Opn, Perc, Perc Endo]
03B6[0,3,4]ZZ	Exc/Axillary Artery, Lt, [Opn, Perc, Perc Endo]
03B7[0,3,4]ZZ	Exc/Brachial Artery, Rt, [Opn, Perc, Perc Endo]
03B8[0,3,4]ZZ	Exc/Brachial Artery, Lt, [Opn, Perc, Perc Endo]
03B9[0,3,4]ZZ	Exc/Ulnar Artery, Rt, [Opn, Perc, Perc Endo]
03BA[0,3,4]ZZ	Exc/Ulnar Artery, Lt, [Opn, Perc, Perc Endo]
03BB[0,3,4]ZZ	Exc/Radial Artery, Rt, [Opn, Perc, Perc Endo]
03BC[0,3,4]ZZ	Exc/Radial Artery, Lt, [Opn, Perc, Perc Endo]
03BD[0,3,4]ZZ	Exc/Hand Artery, Rt, [Opn, Perc, Perc Endo]
03BF[0,3,4]ZZ	Exc/Hand Artery, Lt, [Opn, Perc, Perc Endo]
03BS[0,3,4]ZX	Exc/Temporal Artery, Rt, [Opn, Perc, Perc Endo]
03BT[0,3,4]ZX	Exc/Temporal Artery, Lt, [Opn, Perc, Perc Endo]
03BY[0,3,4]ZZ	Exc/Upr Artery, [Opn, Perc, Perc Endo]
03C5*	Extir/Axillary Artery, Rt
03C6*	Extir/Axillary Artery, Lt
03C7*	Extir/Brachial Artery, Rt
03C8*	Extir/Brachial Artery, Lt
03C9*	Extir/Ulnar Artery, Rt
03CA*	Extir/Ulnar Artery, Lt
03CB*	Extir/Radial Artery, Rt
03CC*	Extir/Radial Artery, Lt
03CD*	Extir/Hand Artery, Rt
03CF*	Extir/Hand Artery, Lt
03CH0ZZ	Extir of Matter from Rt Com Carotid, Opn Appr
03CJ0ZZ	Extir of Matter from Lt Com Carotid, Opn Appr
03CK0ZZ	Extir of Matter from Rt Int Carotid, Opn Appr
03CL0ZZ	Extir of Matter from Lt Int Carotid, Opn Appr
03CM0ZZ	Extir of Matter from Rt Ext Carotid, Opn Appr
03CN0ZZ	Extir of Matter from Lt Ext Carotid, Opn Appr
03CP0ZZ	Extir of Matter from Rt Verteb Art, Opn Appr
03CQ0ZZ	Extir of Matter from Lt Verteb Art, Opn Appr
03CR0ZZ	Extir of Matter from Face Artery, Opn Appr
03CS0ZZ	Extir of Matter from Rt Temporal Art, Opn Appr
03CT0ZZ	Extir of Matter from Lt Temporal Art, Opn Appr
03CU0ZZ	Extir of Matter from Rt Thyroid Art, Opn Appr
03CV0ZZ	Extir of Matter from Lt Thyroid Art, Opn Appr
03CY*	Extir/Upr Artery
03L5[0,3,4][C,Z]Z	Occlsn/Axillary Artery, Rt, [Opn, Perc, Perc Endo], [Extralum Dev, No Dev], NQ
03L6[0,3,4][C,Z]Z	Occlsn/Axillary Artery, Lt, [Opn, Perc, Perc Endo], [Extralum Dev, No Dev], NQ
03L7[0,3,4][C,Z]Z	Occlsn/Brachial Artery, Rt, [Opn, Perc, Perc Endo], [Extralum Dev, No Dev], NQ
03L8[0,3,4][C,Z]Z	Occlsn/Brachial Artery, Lt, [Opn, Perc, Perc Endo], [Extralum Dev, No Dev], NQ
03L9[0,3,4][C,Z]Z	Occlsn/Ulnar Artery, Rt, [Opn, Perc, Perc Endo], [Extralum Dev, No Dev], NQ
03LA[0,3,4][C,Z]Z	Occlsn/Ulnar Artery, Lt, [Opn, Perc, Perc Endo], [Extralum Dev, No Dev], NQ
03LB[0,3,4][C,Z]Z	Occlsn/Radial Artery, Rt, [Opn, Perc, Perc Endo], [Extralum Dev, No Dev], NQ
03LC[0,3,4][C,Z]Z	Occlsn/Radial Artery, Lt, [Opn, Perc, Perc Endo], [Extralum Dev, No Dev], NQ

03LD[0,3,4][C,Z]Z	Occlsn/Hand Artery, Rt, [Opn, Perc, Perc Endo], [Extralum Dev, No Dev], NQ
03LF[0,3,4][C,Z]Z	Occlsn/Hand Artery, Lt, [Opn, Perc, Perc Endo], [Extralum Dev, No Dev], NQ
03Q5*	Repair/Axillary Artery, Rt
03Q6*	Repair/Axillary Artery, Lt
03Q7*	Repair/Brachial Artery, Rt
03Q8*	Repair/Brachial Artery, Lt
03Q9*	Repair/Ulnar Artery, Rt
03QA*	Repair/Ulnar Artery, Lt
03QB*	Repair/Radial Artery, Rt
03QC*	Repair/Radial Artery, Lt
03QD*	Repair/Hand Artery, Rt
03QF*	Repair/Hand Artery, Lt
03QY*	Repair/Upr Artery
041K[0,4][9,A,J,K,Z][H,J,K,L]	Bypass/Femor Artery, Rt, [Opn, Perc Endo], [Auto Venous Tissue, Auto Arterial Tissue, Synth Sub, Nonauto Tissue Sub, No Dev], [Femor Artery, Rt, Femor Artery, Lt, Femor Arteries, Bilat, Popliteal Artery]
041L[0,4][9,A,J,K,Z][H,J,K,L]	Bypass/Femor Artery, Lt, [Opn, Perc Endo], [Auto Venous Tissue, Auto Arterial Tissue, Synth Sub, Nonauto Tissue Sub, No Dev], [Femor Artery, Rt, Femor Artery, Lt, Femor Arteries, Bilat, Popliteal Artery]
045K*	Destr/Femor Artery, Rt
045L*	Destr/Femor Artery, Lt
045M*	Destr/Popliteal Artery, Rt
045N*	Destr/Popliteal Artery, Lt
045P*	Destr/Ant Tibial Artery, Rt
045Q*	Destr/Ant Tibial Artery, Lt
045R*	Destr/Posterior Tibial Artery, Rt
045S*	Destr/Posterior Tibial Artery, Lt
045T*	Destr/Peroneal Artery, Rt
045U*	Destr/Peroneal Artery, Lt
045V*	Destr/Foot Artery, Rt
045W*	Destr/Foot Artery, Lt
045Y*	Destr/Lwr Artery
04703[4,D,Z]Z	Dilation/Abd Aorta, Perc, [Drug-eluting Intralum Dev, Intralum Dev, No Dev], NQ
04713[4,D,Z]Z	Dilation/Celiac Artery, Perc, [Drug-eluting Intralum Dev, Intralum Dev, No Dev], NQ
04723[4,D,Z]Z	Dilation/Gastric Artery, Perc, [Drug-eluting Intralum Dev, Intralum Dev, No Dev], NQ
04733[4,D,Z]Z	Dilation/Hepatic Artery, Perc, [Drug-eluting Intralum Dev, Intralum Dev, No Dev], NQ
04743[4,D,Z]Z	Dilation/Splenic Artery, Perc, [Drug-eluting Intralum Dev, Intralum Dev, No Dev], NQ
04753[4,D,Z]Z	Dilation/Superior Mesenteric Artery, Perc, [Drug-eluting Intralum Dev, Intralum Dev, No Dev], NQ
04763[4,D,Z]Z	Dilation/Colic Artery, Rt, Perc, [Drug-eluting Intralum Dev, Intralum Dev, No Dev], NQ
04773[4,D,Z]Z	Dilation/Colic Artery, Lt, Perc, [Drug-eluting Intralum Dev, Intralum Dev, No Dev], NQ
04783[4,D,Z]Z	Dilation/Colic Artery, Mid, Perc, [Drug-eluting Intralum Dev, Intralum Dev, No Dev], NQ
04793[4,D,Z]Z	Dilation/Renal Artery, Rt, Perc, [Drug-eluting Intralum Dev, Intralum Dev, No Dev], NQ
047A3[4,D,Z]Z	Dilation/Renal Artery, Lt, Perc, [Drug-eluting Intralum Dev, Intralum Dev, No Dev], NQ
047B3[4,D,Z]Z	Dilation/Inferior Mesenteric Artery, Perc, [Drug-eluting Intralum Dev, Intralum Dev, No Dev], NQ
047C3[4,D,Z]Z	Dilation/Common Iliac Artery, Rt, Perc, [Drug-eluting Intralum Dev, Intralum Dev, No Dev], NQ
047D3[4,D,Z]Z	Dilation/Common Iliac Artery, Lt, Perc, [Drug-eluting Intralum Dev, Intralum Dev, No Dev], NQ
047E3[4,D,Z]Z	Dilation/Int Iliac Artery, Rt, Perc, [Drug-eluting Intralum Dev, Intralum Dev, No Dev], NQ
047F3[4,D,Z]Z	Dilation/Int Iliac Artery, Lt, Perc, [Drug-eluting Intralum Dev, Intralum Dev, No Dev], NQ
047H3[4,D,Z]Z	Dilation/Ext Iliac Artery, Rt, Perc, [Drug-eluting Intralum Dev, Intralum Dev, No Dev], NQ
047J3[4,D,Z]Z	Dilation/Ext Iliac Artery, Lt, Perc, [Drug-eluting Intralum Dev, Intralum Dev, No Dev], NQ
047K041	Dilation Rt Fem Art w Drug-elut Intralum, Drug Blln, Opn
047K0D1	Dilation Rt Fem Art w Intralum Dev, Drug Blln, Opn
047K0Z1	Dilation of Rt Fem Art using Drug Blln, Opn Appr
047K341	Dilation Rt Fem Art w Drug-elut Intralum, Drug Blln, Perc
047K3D1	Dilation Rt Fem Art w Intralum Dev, Drug Blln, Perc
047K3Z1	Dilation of Rt Fem Art using Drug Blln, Perc Appr
047K3[4,D,Z]Z	Dilation/Femor Artery, Rt, Perc, [Drug-eluting Intralum Dev, Intralum Dev, No Dev], NQ

Surgical   **Medical**   **CC Indicator**   **MCC Indicator**   **Procedure Proxy**   **PDxMCC PDx acts as own MCC**   **PDxCC PDx acts as own CC**

© 2015 Optum360, LLC   MS-DRG Version 33.0   **239**

MDC 10: Endocrine, Nutritional And Metabolic Diseases And Disorders—SURGICAL

047K441	Dilation Rt Fem Art w Drug-elut Intralum, Drug Blln, Perc Endo	04QW*	Repair/Foot Artery, Lt
047K4D1	Dilation Rt Fem Art w Intralum Dev, Drug Blln, Perc Endo	04QY*	Repair/Lwr Artery
047K4Z1	Dilation of Rt Fem Art using Drug Blln, Perc Endo Appr	04RK*	Replace/Femor Artery, Rt
047L041	Dilation Lt Fem Art w Drug-elut Intralum, Drug Blln, Opn	04RL*	Replace/Femor Artery, Lt
047L0D1	Dilation Lt Fem Art w Intralum Dev, Drug Blln, Opn	04RM*	Replace/Popliteal Artery, Rt
047L0Z1	Dilation of Lt Fem Art using Drug Blln, Opn Appr	04RN*	Replace/Popliteal Artery, Lt
047L341	Dilation Lt Fem Art w Drug-elut Intralum, Drug Blln, Perc	04RP*	Replace/Ant Tibial Artery, Rt
047L3D1	Dilation Lt Fem Art w Intralum Dev, Drug Blln, Perc	04RQ*	Replace/Ant Tibial Artery, Lt
047L3Z1	Dilation of Lt Fem Art using Drug Blln, Perc Appr	04RR*	Replace/Posterior Tibial Artery, Rt
047L3[4,D,Z]Z	Dilation/Femor Artery, Lt, Perc, [Drug-eluting Intralum Dev, Intralum Dev, No Dev], NQ	04RS*	Replace/Posterior Tibial Artery, Lt
		04RT*	Replace/Peroneal Artery, Rt
047L441	Dilation Lt Fem Art w Drug-elut Intralum, Drug Blln, Perc Endo	04RU*	Replace/Peroneal Artery, Lt
047L4D1	Dilation Lt Fem Art w Intralum Dev, Drug Blln, Perc Endo	04RV*	Replace/Foot Artery, Rt
047L4Z1	Dilation of Lt Fem Art using Drug Blln, Perc Endo Appr	04RW*	Replace/Foot Artery, Lt
047M041	Dilation Rt Popl Art w Drug-elut Intralum, Drug Blln, Opn	04RY*	Replace/Lwr Artery
047M0D1	Dilation Rt Popl Art w Intralum Dev, Drug Blln, Opn	04S0*	Repos/Abd Aorta
047M0Z1	Dilation of Rt Popl Art using Drug Blln, Opn Appr	04S1*	Repos/Celiac Artery
047M341	Dilation Rt Popl Art w Drug-elut Intralum, Drug Blln, Perc	04S2*	Repos/Gastric Artery
047M3D1	Dilation Rt Popl Art w Intralum Dev, Drug Blln, Perc	04S3*	Repos/Hepatic Artery
047M3Z1	Dilation of Rt Popl Art using Drug Blln, Perc Appr	04S4*	Repos/Splenic Artery
047M441	Dilation Rt Popl Art w Drug-elut Intralum, Drug Blln, Perc Endo	04S5*	Repos/Superior Mesenteric Artery
047M4D1	Dilation Rt Popl Art w Intralum Dev, Drug Blln, Perc Endo	04S6*	Repos/Colic Artery, Rt
047M4Z1	Dilation of Rt Popl Art using Drug Blln, Perc Endo Appr	04S7*	Repos/Colic Artery, Lt
047N041	Dilation Lt Popl Art w Drug-elut Intralum, Drug Blln, Opn	04S8*	Repos/Colic Artery, Mid
047N0D1	Dilation Lt Popl Art w Intralum Dev, Drug Blln, Opn	04SB*	Repos/Inferior Mesenteric Artery
047N0Z1	Dilation of Lt Popl Art using Drug Blln, Opn Appr	04WY[0,3,4][0,2,3,C,D]Z	Rev/Lwr Artery, [Opn, Perc, Perc Endo], [Drain Dev, Monitoring Dev, Inf Dev, Extralum Dev, Intralum Dev], NQ
047N341	Dilation Lt Popl Art w Drug-elut Intralum, Drug Blln, Perc		
047N3D1	Dilation Lt Popl Art w Intralum Dev, Drug Blln, Perc	0557*	Destr/Axillary Vein, Rt
047N3Z1	Dilation of Lt Popl Art using Drug Blln, Perc Appr	0558*	Destr/Axillary Vein, Lt
047N441	Dilation Lt Popl Art w Drug-elut Intralum, Drug Blln, Perc Endo	0559*	Destr/Brachial Vein, Rt
047N4D1	Dilation Lt Popl Art w Intralum Dev, Drug Blln, Perc Endo	055A*	Destr/Brachial Vein, Lt
047N4Z1	Dilation of Lt Popl Art using Drug Blln, Perc Endo Appr	055B*	Destr/Basilic Vein, Rt
047Y3[4,D,Z]Z	Dilation/Lwr Artery, Perc, [Drug-eluting Intralum Dev, Intralum Dev, No Dev], NQ	055C*	Destr/Basilic Vein, Lt
		055D*	Destr/Cephalic Vein, Rt
04BK[0,3,4]ZZ	Exc/Femor Artery, Rt, [Opn, Perc, Perc Endo]	055F*	Destr/Cephalic Vein, Lt
04BL[0,3,4]ZZ	Exc/Femor Artery, Lt, [Opn, Perc, Perc Endo]	055G*	Destr/Hand Vein, Rt
04BM[0,3,4]ZZ	Exc/Popliteal Artery, Rt, [Opn, Perc, Perc Endo]	055H*	Destr/Hand Vein, Lt
04BN[0,3,4]ZZ	Exc/Popliteal Artery, Lt, [Opn, Perc, Perc Endo]	055Y*	Destr/Upr Vein
04BP[0,3,4]ZZ	Exc/Ant Tibial Artery, Rt, [Opn, Perc, Perc Endo]	05793[D,Z]Z	Dilation/Brachial Vein, Rt, Perc, [Intralum Dev, No Dev], NQ
04BQ[0,3,4]ZZ	Exc/Ant Tibial Artery, Lt, [Opn, Perc, Perc Endo]	057A3[D,Z]Z	Dilation/Brachial Vein, Lt, Perc, [Intralum Dev, No Dev], NQ
04BR[0,3,4]ZZ	Exc/Post Tibial Artery, Rt, [Opn, Perc, Perc Endo]	057B3[D,Z]Z	Dilation/Basilic Vein, Rt, Perc, [Intralum Dev, No Dev], NQ
04BS[0,3,4]ZZ	Exc/Post Tibial Artery, Lt, [Opn, Perc, Perc Endo]	057C3[D,Z]Z	Dilation/Basilic Vein, Lt, Perc, [Intralum Dev, No Dev], NQ
04BT[0,3,4]ZZ	Exc/Peroneal Artery, Rt, [Opn, Perc, Perc Endo]	057D3[D,Z]Z	Dilation/Cephalic Vein, Rt, Perc, [Intralum Dev, No Dev], NQ
04BU[0,3,4]ZZ	Exc/Peroneal Artery, Lt, [Opn, Perc, Perc Endo]	057F3[D,Z]Z	Dilation/Cephalic Vein, Lt, Perc, [Intralum Dev, No Dev], NQ
04BV[0,3,4]ZZ	Exc/Foot Artery, Rt, [Opn, Perc, Perc Endo]	05B7[0,3,4]ZZ	Exc/Axillary Vein, Rt, [Opn, Perc, Perc Endo]
04BW[0,3,4]ZZ	Exc/Foot Artery, Lt, [Opn, Perc, Perc Endo]	05B8[0,3,4]ZZ	Exc/Axillary Vein, Lt, [Opn, Perc, Perc Endo]
04BY[0,3,4]ZZ	Exc/Lwr Artery, [Opn, Perc, Perc Endo]	05B9[0,3,4]ZZ	Exc/Brachial Vein, Rt, [Opn, Perc, Perc Endo]
04CK*	Extir/Femor Artery, Rt	05BA[0,3,4]ZZ	Exc/Brachial Vein, Lt, [Opn, Perc, Perc Endo]
04CL*	Extir/Femor Artery, Lt	05BB[0,3,4]ZZ	Exc/Basilic Vein, Rt, [Opn, Perc, Perc Endo]
04CM*	Extir/Popliteal Artery, Rt	05BC[0,3,4]ZZ	Exc/Basilic Vein, Lt, [Opn, Perc, Perc Endo]
04CN*	Extir/Popliteal Artery, Lt	05BD[0,3,4]ZZ	Exc/Cephalic Vein, Rt, [Opn, Perc, Perc Endo]
04CP*	Extir/Ant Tibial Artery, Rt	05BF[0,3,4]ZZ	Exc/Cephalic Vein, Lt, [Opn, Perc, Perc Endo]
04CQ*	Extir/Ant Tibial Artery, Lt	05BG[0,3,4]ZZ	Exc/Hand Vein, Rt, [Opn, Perc, Perc Endo]
04CR*	Extir/Posterior Tibial Artery, Rt	05BH[0,3,4]ZZ	Exc/Hand Vein, Lt, [Opn, Perc, Perc Endo]
04CS*	Extir/Posterior Tibial Artery, Lt	05BY[0,3,4]ZZ	Exc/Upr Vein, [Opn, Perc, Perc Endo]
04CT*	Extir/Peroneal Artery, Rt	05C7*	Extir/Axillary Vein, Rt
04CU*	Extir/Peroneal Artery, Lt	05C8*	Extir/Axillary Vein, Lt
04CV*	Extir/Foot Artery, Rt	05C9*	Extir/Brachial Vein, Rt
04CW*	Extir/Foot Artery, Lt	05CA*	Extir/Brachial Vein, Lt
04CY*	Extir/Lwr Artery	05CB*	Extir/Basilic Vein, Rt
04HY[0,3,4]2Z	Insert/Lwr Artery, [Opn, Perc, Perc Endo], Monitoring Dev, NQ	05CC*	Extir/Basilic Vein, Lt
04PY[0,3,4][0,2,3,C,D]Z	Rmvl/Lwr Artery, [Opn, Perc, Perc Endo], [Drain Dev, Monitoring Dev, Inf Dev, Extralum Dev, Intralum Dev], NQ	05CD*	Extir/Cephalic Vein, Rt
		05CF*	Extir/Cephalic Vein, Lt
04QC*	Repair/Common Iliac Artery, Rt	05CG*	Extir/Hand Vein, Rt
04QD*	Repair/Common Iliac Artery, Lt	05CH*	Extir/Hand Vein, Lt
04QE*	Repair/Int Iliac Artery, Rt	05CM*	Extir/Int Jugular Vein, Rt
04QF*	Repair/Int Iliac Artery, Lt	05CN*	Extir/Int Jugular Vein, Lt
04QH*	Repair/Ext Iliac Artery, Rt	05CP*	Extir/Ext Jugular Vein, Rt
04QJ*	Repair/Ext Iliac Artery, Lt	05CQ*	Extir/Ext Jugular Vein, Lt
04QK*	Repair/Femor Artery, Rt	05CR*	Extir/Vert Vein, Rt
04QL*	Repair/Femor Artery, Lt	05CS*	Extir/Vert Vein, Lt
04QM*	Repair/Popliteal Artery, Rt	05CT*	Extir/Face Vein, Rt
04QN*	Repair/Popliteal Artery, Lt	05CV*	Extir/Face Vein, Lt
04QP*	Repair/Ant Tibial Artery, Rt	05CY*	Extir/Upr Vein
04QQ*	Repair/Ant Tibial Artery, Lt	05HY[0,3,4]2Z	Insert/Upr Vein, [Opn, Perc, Perc Endo], Monitoring Dev, NQ
04QR*	Repair/Posterior Tibial Artery, Rt	05L7[0,3,4][C,Z]Z	Occlsn/Axillary Vein, Rt, [Opn, Perc, Perc Endo], [Extralum Dev, No Dev], NQ
04QS*	Repair/Posterior Tibial Artery, Lt		
04QT*	Repair/Peroneal Artery, Rt	05L8[0,3,4][C,Z]Z	Occlsn/Axillary Vein, Lt, [Opn, Perc, Perc Endo], [Extralum Dev, No Dev], NQ
04QU*	Repair/Peroneal Artery, Lt		
04QV*	Repair/Foot Artery, Rt		

Ⓣ **Transfer DRG**   ⓢⓟ **Special Payment**   * **Code Range**   **6th and 7th Character of ZZ = No Device, No Qualifier ZX = No Device, Diagnostic**

Ø5L9[Ø,3,4][C,Z]Z	Occlsn/Brachial Vein, Rt, [Opn, Perc, Perc Endo], [Extralum Dev, No Dev], NQ
Ø5LA[Ø,3,4][C,Z]Z	Occlsn/Brachial Vein, Lt, [Opn, Perc, Perc Endo], [Extralum Dev, No Dev], NQ
Ø5LB[Ø,3,4][C,Z]Z	Occlsn/Basilic Vein, Rt, [Opn, Perc, Perc Endo], [Extralum Dev, No Dev], NQ
Ø5LC[Ø,3,4][C,Z]Z	Occlsn/Basilic Vein, Lt, [Opn, Perc, Perc Endo], [Extralum Dev, No Dev], NQ
Ø5LD[Ø,3,4][C,Z]Z	Occlsn/Cephalic Vein, Rt, [Opn, Perc, Perc Endo], [Extralum Dev, No Dev], NQ
Ø5LF[Ø,3,4][C,Z]Z	Occlsn/Cephalic Vein, Lt, [Opn, Perc, Perc Endo], [Extralum Dev, No Dev], NQ
Ø5LG[Ø,3,4][C,Z]Z	Occlsn/Hand Vein, Rt, [Opn, Perc, Perc Endo], [Extralum Dev, No Dev], NQ
Ø5LH[Ø,3,4][C,Z]Z	Occlsn/Hand Vein, Lt, [Opn, Perc, Perc Endo], [Extralum Dev, No Dev], NQ
Ø5QY*	Repair/Upr Vein
Ø67Ø3[D,Z]Z	Dilation/Inferior Vena Cava, Perc, [Intralum Dev, No Dev], NQ
Ø693[Ø,3,4][Ø,Z]Z	Drain/Esophageal Vein, [Opn, Perc, Perc Endo], [Drain Dev, No Dev], NQ
Ø6BY[Ø,3,4]ZZ	Exc/Lwr Vein, [Opn, Perc, Perc Endo]
Ø6C3*	Extir/Esophageal Vein
Ø6CY*	Extir/Lwr Vein
Ø6HØ[Ø,3,4]DZ	Insert/Inferior Vena Cava, [Opn, Perc, Perc Endo], Intralum Dev, NQ
Ø6LØ*	Occlsn/Inferior Vena Cava
Ø6QY*	Repair/Lwr Vein
Ø6SØ*	Repos/Inferior Vena Cava
Ø6S1*	Repos/Splenic Vein
Ø6S2*	Repos/Gastric Vein
Ø6S3*	Repos/Esophageal Vein
Ø6S4*	Repos/Hepatic Vein
Ø6S5*	Repos/Superior Mesenteric Vein
Ø6S6*	Repos/Inferior Mesenteric Vein
Ø6S7*	Repos/Colic Vein
Ø6S8*	Repos/Portal Vein
Ø6VØ*	Restrict/Inferior Vena Cava
Ø75M*	Destr/Thymus
Ø79Ø[Ø,3,4]ZX	Drain/Lymphatic, Head, [Opn, Perc, Perc Endo]
Ø791[Ø,3,4]ZX	Drain/Lymphatic, Rt Neck, [Opn, Perc, Perc Endo]
Ø792[Ø,3,4]ZX	Drain/Lymphatic, Lt Neck, [Opn, Perc, Perc Endo]
Ø793[Ø,3,4]ZX	Drain/Lymphatic, Rt Upr Extr, [Opn, Perc, Perc Endo]
Ø794[Ø,3,4]ZX	Drain/Lymphatic, Lt Upr Extr, [Opn, Perc, Perc Endo]
Ø795[Ø,3,4]ZX	Drain/Lymphatic, Rt Axillary, [Opn, Perc, Perc Endo]
Ø796[Ø,3,4]ZX	Drain/Lymphatic, Lt Axillary, [Opn, Perc, Perc Endo]
Ø797[Ø,3,4]ZX	Drain/Lymphatic, Thorax, [Opn, Perc, Perc Endo]
Ø798[Ø,3,4]ZX	Drain/Lymphatic, Int Mammary, Rt, [Opn, Perc, Perc Endo]
Ø799[Ø,3,4]ZX	Drain/Lymphatic, Int Mammary, Lt, [Opn, Perc, Perc Endo]
Ø79B[Ø,3,4]ZX	Drain/Lymphatic, Mesenteric, [Opn, Perc, Perc Endo]
Ø79C[Ø,3,4]ZX	Drain/Lymphatic, Pelvis, [Opn, Perc, Perc Endo]
Ø79D[Ø,3,4]ZX	Drain/Lymphatic, Aortic, [Opn, Perc, Perc Endo]
Ø79F[Ø,3,4]ZX	Drain/Lymphatic, Rt Lwr Extr, [Opn, Perc, Perc Endo]
Ø79G[Ø,3,4]ZX	Drain/Lymphatic, Lt Lwr Extr, [Opn, Perc, Perc Endo]
Ø79H[Ø,3,4]ZX	Drain/Lymphatic, Rt Inguinal, [Opn, Perc, Perc Endo]
Ø79J[Ø,3,4]ZX	Drain/Lymphatic, Lt Inguinal, [Opn, Perc, Perc Endo]
Ø79K[Ø,3,4]ZX	Drain/Thoracic Duct, [Opn, Perc, Perc Endo]
Ø79L[Ø,3,4]ZX	Drain/Cisterna Chyli, [Opn, Perc, Perc Endo]
Ø79M*	Drain/Thymus
Ø7BØ[Ø,3,4]ZX	Exc/Lymphatic, Head, [Opn, Perc, Perc Endo]
Ø7B1*	Exc/Lymphatic, Rt Neck
Ø7B2*	Exc/Lymphatic, Lt Neck
Ø7B3[Ø,3,4]ZX	Exc/Lymphatic, Rt Upr Extr, [Opn, Perc, Perc Endo]
Ø7B3[Ø,4]ZZ	Exc/Lymphatic, Rt Upr Extr, [Opn, Perc Endo]
Ø7B4[Ø,3,4]ZX	Exc/Lymphatic, Lt Upr Extr, [Opn, Perc, Perc Endo]
Ø7B4[Ø,4]ZZ	Exc/Lymphatic, Lt Upr Extr, [Opn, Perc Endo]
Ø7B5[Ø,3,4]ZX	Exc/Lymphatic, Rt Axillary, [Opn, Perc, Perc Endo]
Ø7B6[Ø,3,4]ZX	Exc/Lymphatic, Lt Axillary, [Opn, Perc, Perc Endo]
Ø7B7[Ø,3,4]ZX	Exc/Lymphatic, Thorax, [Opn, Perc, Perc Endo]
Ø7B7[Ø,4]ZZ	Exc/Lymphatic, Thorax, [Opn, Perc Endo]
Ø7B8[Ø,3,4]ZX	Exc/Lymphatic, Int Mammary, Rt, [Opn, Perc, Perc Endo]
Ø7B9[Ø,3,4]ZX	Exc/Lymphatic, Int Mammary, Lt, [Opn, Perc, Perc Endo]
Ø7BB[Ø,3,4]ZX	Exc/Lymphatic, Mesenteric, [Opn, Perc, Perc Endo]
Ø7BB[Ø,4]ZZ	Exc/Lymphatic, Mesenteric, [Opn, Perc Endo]
Ø7BC[Ø,3,4]ZX	Exc/Lymphatic, Pelvis, [Opn, Perc, Perc Endo]
Ø7BD[Ø,3,4]ZX	Exc/Lymphatic, Aortic, [Opn, Perc, Perc Endo]
Ø7BF[Ø,3,4]ZX	Exc/Lymphatic, Rt Lwr Extr, [Opn, Perc, Perc Endo]
Ø7BF[Ø,4]ZZ	Exc/Lymphatic, Rt Lwr Extr, [Opn, Perc Endo]
Ø7BG[Ø,3,4]ZX	Exc/Lymphatic, Lt Lwr Extr, [Opn, Perc, Perc Endo]
Ø7BG[Ø,4]ZZ	Exc/Lymphatic, Lt Lwr Extr, [Opn, Perc Endo]
Ø7BH[Ø,3,4]ZX	Exc/Lymphatic, Rt Inguinal, [Opn, Perc, Perc Endo]

Ø7BJ[Ø,3,4]ZX	Exc/Lymphatic, Lt Inguinal, [Opn, Perc, Perc Endo]
Ø7BK[Ø,3,4]ZX	Exc/Thoracic Duct, [Opn, Perc, Perc Endo]
Ø7BL[Ø,3,4]ZX	Exc/Cisterna Chyli, [Opn, Perc, Perc Endo]
Ø7BM*	Exc/Thymus
Ø7CM*	Extir/Thymus
Ø7JM[Ø,4]ZZ	Inspect/Thymus, [Opn, Perc Endo]
Ø7JPØZZ	Inspect of Spleen, Opn Appr
Ø7NM*	Rls/Thymus
Ø7PM[Ø,3,4][Ø,3]Z	Rmvl/Thymus, [Opn, Perc, Perc Endo], [Drain Dev, Inf Dev], NQ
Ø7QM*	Repair/Thymus
Ø7SMØZZ	Repos Thymus, Opn Appr
Ø7T1*	Resect/Lymphatic, Rt Neck
Ø7T2*	Resect/Lymphatic, Lt Neck
Ø7TC*	Resect/Lymphatic, Pelvis
Ø7TD*	Resect/Lymphatic, Aortic
Ø7TM*	Resect/Thymus
Ø7WM[Ø,3,4][Ø,3]Z	Rev/Thymus, [Opn, Perc, Perc Endo], [Drain Dev, Inf Dev], NQ
Ø7YM*	Transplantation/Thymus
Ø8123Z4	Bypass Rt Ant Chamber to Sclera, Perc Appr
Ø8133Z4	Bypass Lt Ant Chamber to Sclera, Perc Appr
Ø85C3ZZ	Destr of Rt Iris, Perc Appr
Ø85D3ZZ	Destr of Lt Iris, Perc Appr
Ø8943[Ø,Z]Z	Drain/Vitreous, Rt, Perc, [Drain Dev, No Dev], NQ
Ø8953[Ø,Z]Z	Drain/Vitreous, Lt, Perc, [Drain Dev, No Dev], NQ
Ø8BN[Ø,3,X]ZZ	Exc/Upr Eyelid, Rt, [Opn, Perc, Ext]
Ø8BP[Ø,3,X]ZZ	Exc/Upr Eyelid, Lt, [Opn, Perc, Ext]
Ø8BQ[Ø,3,X]ZZ	Exc/Lwr Eyelid, Rt, [Opn, Perc, Ext]
Ø8BR[Ø,3,X]ZZ	Exc/Lwr Eyelid, Lt, [Opn, Perc, Ext]
Ø8DJ3ZZ	Extract of Rt Lens, Perc Appr
Ø8DK3ZZ	Extract of Lt Lens, Perc Appr
Ø8PØ3JZ	Rmvl of Synth Sub from Rt Eye, Perc Appr
Ø8P13JZ	Rmvl of Synth Sub from Lt Eye, Perc Appr
Ø8QC3ZZ	Repair Rt Iris, Perc Appr
Ø8QD3ZZ	Repair Lt Iris, Perc Appr
Ø8QE3ZZ	Repair Rt Retina, Perc Appr
Ø8QF3ZZ	Repair Lt Retina, Perc Appr
Ø8RØØKZ	Replace of Rt Eye with Nonaut Sub, Opn Appr
Ø8RØ3JZ	Replace of Rt Eye with Synth Sub, Perc Appr
Ø8R1ØKZ	Replace of Lt Eye with Nonaut Sub, Opn Appr
Ø8R13JZ	Replace of Lt Eye with Synth Sub, Perc Appr
Ø8R4*	Replace/Vitreous, Rt
Ø8R5*	Replace/Vitreous, Lt
Ø8RN[Ø,3,X]JZ	Replace/Upr Eyelid, Rt, [Opn, Perc, Ext], Synth Sub, NQ
Ø8RP[Ø,3,X]JZ	Replace/Upr Eyelid, Lt, [Opn, Perc, Ext], Synth Sub, NQ
Ø8RQ[Ø,3,X]JZ	Replace/Lwr Eyelid, Rt, [Opn, Perc, Ext], Synth Sub, NQ
Ø8RR[Ø,3,X]JZ	Replace/Lwr Eyelid, Lt, [Opn, Perc, Ext], Synth Sub, NQ
Ø8SN*	Repos/Upr Eyelid, Rt
Ø8SP*	Repos/Upr Eyelid, Lt
Ø8SQ*	Repos/Lwr Eyelid, Rt
Ø8SR*	Repos/Lwr Eyelid, Lt
Ø8UØ*	Supl/Eye, Rt
Ø8U1*	Supl/Eye, Lt
Ø8UN[Ø,3,X]JZ	Supl/Upr Eyelid, Rt, [Opn, Perc, Ext], Synth Sub, NQ
Ø8UP[Ø,3,X]JZ	Supl/Upr Eyelid, Lt, [Opn, Perc, Ext], Synth Sub, NQ
Ø8UQ[Ø,3,X]JZ	Supl/Lwr Eyelid, Rt, [Opn, Perc, Ext], Synth Sub, NQ
Ø8UR[Ø,3,X]JZ	Supl/Lwr Eyelid, Lt, [Opn, Perc, Ext], Synth Sub, NQ
ØD19[Ø,4,8][7,J,K,Z]L	Bypass/Duodenum, [Opn, Perc Endo, Via Natrl or Artfcl Opng Endo], [Auto Tissue Sub, Synth Sub, Nonauto Tissue Sub, No Dev], Transv Colon
ØD1A[Ø,4,8][7,J,K,Z][K,L,M,N]	Bypass/Jejunum, [Opn, Perc Endo, Via Natrl or Artfcl Opng Endo], [Auto Tissue Sub, Synth Sub, Nonauto Tissue Sub, No Dev], [Ascending Colon, Transv Colon, Descending Colon, Sigmoid Colon]
ØD1A[Ø,4,8][7,J,K]H	Bypass/Jejunum, [Opn, Perc Endo, Via Natrl or Artfcl Opng Endo], [Auto Tissue Sub, Synth Sub, Nonauto Tissue Sub], Cecum
ØD1A[Ø,4]ZH	Bypass/Jejunum, [Opn, Perc Endo], No Dev, Cecum
ØD1B[Ø,4,8][7,J,K,Z][K,L,M,N]	Bypass/Ileum, [Opn, Perc Endo, Via Natrl or Artfcl Opng Endo], [Auto Tissue Sub, Synth Sub, Nonauto Tissue Sub, No Dev], [Ascending Colon, Transv Colon, Descending Colon, Sigmoid Colon]
ØD1B[Ø,4,8][7,J,K]H	Bypass/Ileum, [Opn, Perc Endo, Via Natrl or Artfcl Opng Endo], [Auto Tissue Sub, Synth Sub, Nonauto Tissue Sub], Cecum
ØD1B[Ø,4]ZH	Bypass/Ileum, [Opn, Perc Endo], No Dev, Cecum
ØD1H8[7,J,K,Z][H,K,L,M,N]	Bypass/Cecum, Via Natrl or Artfcl Opng Endo, [Auto Tissue Sub, Synth Sub, Nonauto Tissue Sub, No Dev], [Cecum, Ascending Colon, Transv Colon, Descending Colon, Sigmoid Colon]

Surgical	Medical	CC Indicator	MCC Indicator	Procedure Proxy	PDx MCC PDx acts as own MCC	PDx CC PDx acts as own CC

MDC 10: Endocrine, Nutritional And Metabolic Diseases And Disorders—SURGICAL

0D1H[0,4][7,J,K,Z][H,K,L,M,N,P] Bypass/Cecum, [Opn, Perc Endo], [Auto Tissue Sub, Synth Sub, Nonauto Tissue Sub, No Dev], [Cecum, Ascending Colon, Transv Colon, Descending Colon, Sigmoid Colon, Rectum]

0D1K[0,4,8][7,J,K,Z][K,L,M,N,P] Bypass/Ascending Colon, [Opn, Perc Endo, Via Natrl or Artfcl Opng Endo], [Auto Tissue Sub, Synth Sub, Nonauto Tissue Sub, No Dev], [Ascending Colon, Transv Colon, Descending Colon, Sigmoid Colon, Rectum]

0D1L[0,4,8][7,J,K,Z][L,M,N,P] Bypass/Transv Colon, [Opn, Perc Endo, Via Natrl or Artfcl Opng Endo], [Auto Tissue Sub, Synth Sub, Nonauto Tissue Sub, No Dev], [Transv Colon, Descending Colon, Sigmoid Colon, Rectum]

0D1M[0,4,8][7,J,K,Z][M,N,P] Bypass/Descending Colon, [Opn, Perc Endo, Via Natrl or Artfcl Opng Endo], [Auto Tissue Sub, Synth Sub, Nonauto Tissue Sub, No Dev], [Descending Colon, Sigmoid Colon, Rectum]

0D1N[0,4,8][7,J,K,Z][N,P] Bypass/Sigmoid Colon, [Opn, Perc Endo, Via Natrl or Artfcl Opng Endo], [Auto Tissue Sub, Synth Sub, Nonauto Tissue Sub, No Dev], [Sigmoid Colon, Rectum]

0D5S* Destr/Greater Omentum
0D5T* Destr/Lesser Omentum
0D5V* Destr/Mesentery
0D5W* Destr/Peritoneum
0DB7[0,3,7]ZZ Exc/Stomach, Pylorus, [Opn, Perc, Via Natrl or Artfcl Opng]
0DB8[0,4]ZZ Exc/Sm Intestine, [Opn, Perc Endo]
0DBE[0,3,7]ZZ Exc/Lg Intestine, [Opn, Perc, Via Natrl or Artfcl Opng]
0DBF[0,3,7]ZZ Exc/Lg Intestine, Rt, [Opn, Perc, Via Natrl or Artfcl Opng]
0DBG[0,3,7]ZZ Exc/Lg Intestine, Lt, [Opn, Perc, Via Natrl or Artfcl Opng]
0DBH[0,3,7]ZZ Exc/Cecum, [Opn, Perc, Via Natrl or Artfcl Opng]
0DBK[0,3,7]ZZ Exc/Ascending Colon, [Opn, Perc, Via Natrl or Artfcl Opng]
0DBL[0,3,7]ZZ Exc/Transv Colon, [Opn, Perc, Via Natrl or Artfcl Opng]
0DBM[0,3,7]ZZ Exc/Descending Colon, [Opn, Perc, Via Natrl or Artfcl Opng]
0DBN[0,3,7]ZZ Exc/Sigmoid Colon, [Opn, Perc, Via Natrl or Artfcl Opng]
0DBS[0,3,4]ZZ Exc/Greater Omentum, [Opn, Perc, Perc Endo]
0DBT[0,3,4]ZZ Exc/Lesser Omentum, [Opn, Perc, Perc Endo]
0DBV[0,3,4]ZZ Exc/Mesentery, [Opn, Perc, Perc Endo]
0DBW[0,3,4]ZZ Exc/Peritoneum, [Opn, Perc, Perc Endo]
0DJ00ZZ Inspect of Upr Intestinal Tract, Opn Appr
0DJ60ZZ Inspect of Stomach, Opn Appr
0DJD0ZZ Inspect of Lwr Intestinal Tract, Opn Appr
0DJU0ZZ Inspect of Omentum, Opn Appr
0DJV0ZZ Inspect of Mesentery, Opn Appr
0DJW0ZZ Inspect of Peritoneum, Opn Appr
0DN8[0,3]ZZ Rls/Sm Intestine, [Opn, Perc]
0DN9[0,3]ZZ Rls/Duodenum, [Opn, Perc]
0DNA[0,3]ZZ Rls/Jejunum, [Opn, Perc]
0DNB[0,3]ZZ Rls/Ileum, [Opn, Perc]
0DNC[0,3]ZZ Rls/Ileocecal Valve, [Opn, Perc]
0DNE[0,3]ZZ Rls/Lg Intestine, [Opn, Perc]
0DNF[0,3]ZZ Rls/Lg Intestine, Rt, [Opn, Perc]
0DNG[0,3]ZZ Rls/Lg Intestine, Lt, [Opn, Perc]
0DNH[0,3]ZZ Rls/Cecum, [Opn, Perc]
0DNJ[0,3]ZZ Rls/Appendix, [Opn, Perc]
0DNK[0,3]ZZ Rls/Ascending Colon, [Opn, Perc]
0DNL[0,3]ZZ Rls/Transv Colon, [Opn, Perc]
0DNM[0,3]ZZ Rls/Descending Colon, [Opn, Perc]
0DNN[0,3]ZZ Rls/Sigmoid Colon, [Opn, Perc]
0DNS[0,3]ZZ Rls/Greater Omentum, [Opn, Perc]
0DNT[0,3]ZZ Rls/Lesser Omentum, [Opn, Perc]
0DNV[0,3]ZZ Rls/Mesentery, [Opn, Perc]
0DNW[0,3]ZZ Rls/Peritoneum, [Opn, Perc]
0DS6[7,8]ZZ Repos/Stomach, [Via Natrl or Artfcl Opng, Via Natrl or Artfcl Opng Endo]
0DT9* Resect/Duodenum
0DTA* Resect/Jejunum
0DTB* Resect/Ileum
0DTC* Resect/Ileocecal Valve
0DTG* Resect/Large Intestine, Lt
0DTS* Resect/Greater Omentum
0DTT* Resect/Lesser Omentum
0F5D[0,3,7]ZZ Destr/Pancreatic Duct, [Opn, Perc, Via Natrl or Artfcl Opng]
0F5F[0,3,7]ZZ Destr/Pancreatic Duct, Accessory, [Opn, Perc, Via Natrl or Artfcl Opng]
0F5G[0,3]ZZ Destr/Pancreas, [Opn, Perc]
0F900ZX Drain of Liver, Opn Appr, Diagnostic
0F910ZX Drain of Rt Lobe Liver, Opn Appr, Diagnostic
0F920ZX Drain of Lt Lobe Liver, Opn Appr, Diagnostic
0F9F0ZX Drain of Accessory Pancreatic Duct, Opn Appr, Diagn
0F9G0ZX Drain of Pancreas, Opn Appr, Diagnostic
0FB00ZX Exc of Liver, Opn Appr, Diagnostic

0FB10ZX Exc of Rt Lobe Liver, Opn Appr, Diagnostic
0FB20ZX Exc of Lt Lobe Liver, Opn Appr, Diagnostic
0FBD0ZX Exc of Pancreatic Duct, Opn Appr, Diagnostic
0FBD[0,3,7]ZZ Exc/Pancreatic Duct, [Opn, Perc, Via Natrl or Artfcl Opng]
0FBF0ZX Exc of Accessory Pancreatic Duct, Opn Appr, Diagn
0FBF[0,3,7]ZZ Exc/Pancreatic Duct, Accessory, [Opn, Perc, Via Natrl or Artfcl Opng]
0FBG0ZX Exc of Pancreas, Opn Appr, Diagnostic
0FBG[0,3,4]ZZ Exc/Pancreas, [Opn, Perc, Perc Endo]
0FJ00ZZ Inspect of Liver, Opn Appr
0FJD[0,3,7,8]ZZ Inspect/Pancreatic Duct, [Opn, Perc, Via Natrl or Artfcl Opng, Via Natrl or Artfcl Opng Endo]
0FJG[0,3]ZZ Inspect/Pancreas, [Opn, Perc]
0FN0[0,3]ZZ Rls/Liver, [Opn, Perc]
0FN1[0,3]ZZ Rls/Liver, Rt Lobe, [Opn, Perc]
0FN2[0,3]ZZ Rls/Liver, Lt Lobe, [Opn, Perc]
0FN4[0,3]ZZ Rls/Gallbladder, [Opn, Perc]
0FN5[0,3,7,8]ZZ Rls/Hepatic Duct, Rt, [Opn, Perc, Via Natrl or Artfcl Opng, Via Natrl or Artfcl Opng Endo]
0FN6[0,3,7,8]ZZ Rls/Hepatic Duct, Lt, [Opn, Perc, Via Natrl or Artfcl Opng, Via Natrl or Artfcl Opng Endo]
0FN8[0,3,7,8]ZZ Rls/Cystic Duct, [Opn, Perc, Via Natrl or Artfcl Opng, Via Natrl or Artfcl Opng Endo]
0FN9[0,3,7,8]ZZ Rls/Common Bile Duct, [Opn, Perc, Via Natrl or Artfcl Opng, Via Natrl or Artfcl Opng Endo]
0FNC[0,3,7,8]ZZ Rls/Ampulla of Vater, [Opn, Perc, Via Natrl or Artfcl Opng, Via Natrl or Artfcl Opng Endo]
0FND[0,3,7,8]ZZ Rls/Pancreatic Duct, [Opn, Perc, Via Natrl or Artfcl Opng, Via Natrl or Artfcl Opng Endo]
0FNF[0,3,7,8]ZZ Rls/Pancreatic Duct, Accessory, [Opn, Perc, Via Natrl or Artfcl Opng, Via Natrl or Artfcl Opng Endo]
0FNG[0,3]ZZ Rls/Pancreas, [Opn, Perc]
0FTD[0,7]ZZ Resect/Pancreatic Duct, [Opn, Via Natrl or Artfcl Opng]
0FTF[0,7]ZZ Resect/Pancreatic Duct, Accessory, [Opn, Via Natrl or Artfcl Opng]
0FYG* Transplantation/Pancreas
0H9T0ZX Drain of Rt Breast, Opn Appr, Diagnostic
0H9U0ZX Drain of Lt Breast, Opn Appr, Diagnostic
0H9V0ZX Drain of Bilat Breast, Opn Appr, Diagnostic
0H9W0ZX Drain of Rt Nipple, Opn Appr, Diagnostic
0H9X0ZX Drain of Lt Nipple, Opn Appr, Diagnostic
0HBT0ZX Exc of Rt Breast, Opn Appr, Diagnostic
0HBT[7,8,X]ZZ Exc of Rt Breast, [Via Natrl or Artfcl Opng, Via Natrl or Artfcl Opng Endo, Ext Appr]
0HBU0ZX Exc of Lt Breast, Opn Appr, Diagnostic
0HBU[7,8,X]ZZ Exc of Lt Breast, [Via Natrl or Artfcl Opng, Via Natrl or Artfcl Opng Endo, Ext Appr]
0HBV0ZX Exc of Bilat Breast, Opn Appr, Diagnostic
0HBV[7,8,X]ZZ Exc of Bilat Breast, [Via Natrl or Artfcl Opng, Via Natrl or Artfcl Opng Endo, Ext Appr]
0HBW0ZX Exc of Rt Nipple, Opn Appr, Diagnostic
0HBX0ZX Exc of Lt Nipple, Opn Appr, Diagnostic
0HBY0ZX Exc of Supernumerary Breast, Opn Appr, Diagnostic
0JH6[0,3]VZ Insert/SQ Tissue & Fascia, Chest, [Opn, Perc], Inf Pump, NQ
0JH7[0,3]VZ Insert/SQ Tissue & Fascia, Back, [Opn, Perc], Inf Pump, NQ
0JH8[0,3]VZ Insert/SQ Tissue & Fascia, Abd, [Opn, Perc], Inf Pump, NQ
0JHT[0,3]VZ Insert/SQ Tissue & Fascia, Trunk, [Opn, Perc], Inf Pump, NQ
0JQB* Repair/SQ Tissue & Fascia, Perineum
0JQD* Repair/SQ Tissue & Fascia, Rt Upr Arm
0JQF* Repair/SQ Tissue & Fascia, Lt Upr Arm
0JQG* Repair/SQ Tissue & Fascia, Rt Lwr Arm
0JQH* Repair/SQ Tissue & Fascia, Lt Lwr Arm
0JQL* Repair/SQ Tissue & Fascia, Rt Upr Leg
0JQM* Repair/SQ Tissue & Fascia, Lt Upr Leg
0JQN* Repair/SQ Tissue & Fascia, Rt Lwr Leg
0JQP* Repair/SQ Tissue & Fascia, Lt Lwr Leg
0JQQ* Repair/SQ Tissue & Fascia, Rt Foot
0JQR* Repair/SQ Tissue & Fascia, Lt Foot
0KQ5* Repair/Shldr Muscle, Rt
0KQ6* Repair/Shldr Muscle, Lt
0KQ7* Repair/Upr Arm Muscle, Rt
0KQ8* Repair/Upr Arm Muscle, Lt
0KQ9* Repair/Lwr Arm and Wrist Muscle, Rt
0KQB* Repair/Lwr Arm and Wrist Muscle, Lt
0KQN* Repair/Hip Muscle, Rt
0KQP* Repair/Hip Muscle, Lt
0KQS* Repair/Lwr Leg Muscle, Rt
0KQT* Repair/Lwr Leg Muscle, Lt
0KQV* Repair/Foot Muscle, Rt
0KQW* Repair/Foot Muscle, Lt

T Transfer DRG   SP Special Payment   * Code Range   6th and 7th Character of ZZ = No Device, No Qualifier ZX = No Device, Diagnostic

ØKSØ*	Repos/Head Muscle
ØKS1*	Repos/Facial Muscle
ØKS2*	Repos/Neck Muscle, Rt
ØKS3*	Repos/Neck Muscle, Lt
ØKS4*	Repos/Tongue, Palate, Pharynx Muscle
ØKS5*	Repos/Shldr Muscle, Rt
ØKS6*	Repos/Shldr Muscle, Lt
ØKS7*	Repos/Upr Arm Muscle, Rt
ØKS8*	Repos/Upr Arm Muscle, Lt
ØKS9*	Repos/Lwr Arm and Wrist Muscle, Rt
ØKSB*	Repos/Lwr Arm and Wrist Muscle, Lt
ØKSF*	Repos/Trunk Muscle, Rt
ØKSG*	Repos/Trunk Muscle, Lt
ØKSH*	Repos/Thorax Muscle, Rt
ØKSJ*	Repos/Thorax Muscle, Lt
ØKSK*	Repos/Abd Muscle, Rt
ØKSL*	Repos/Abd Muscle, Lt
ØKSM*	Repos/Perineum Muscle
ØKSN*	Repos/Hip Muscle, Rt
ØKSP*	Repos/Hip Muscle, Lt
ØKSQ*	Repos/Upr Leg Muscle, Rt
ØKSR*	Repos/Upr Leg Muscle, Lt
ØKSS*	Repos/Lwr Leg Muscle, Rt
ØKST*	Repos/Lwr Leg Muscle, Lt
ØKSV*	Repos/Foot Muscle, Rt
ØKSW*	Repos/Foot Muscle, Lt
ØL5*	Tndns, Destr
ØL8Ø*	Div/Head and Neck Tndn
ØL81*	Div/Shldr Tndn, Rt
ØL82*	Div/Shldr Tndn, Lt
ØL83*	Div/Upr Arm Tndn, Rt
ØL84*	Div/Upr Arm Tndn, Lt
ØL85*	Div/Lwr Arm and Wrist Tndn, Rt
ØL86*	Div/Lwr Arm and Wrist Tndn, Lt
ØL89*	Div/Trunk Tndn, Rt
ØL8B*	Div/Trunk Tndn, Lt
ØL8C*	Div/Thorax Tndn, Rt
ØL8D*	Div/Thorax Tndn, Lt
ØL8F*	Div/Abd Tndn, Rt
ØL8G*	Div/Abd Tndn, Lt
ØL8H*	Div/Perineum Tndn
ØL8L*	Div/Upr Leg Tndn, Rt
ØL8M*	Div/Upr Leg Tndn, Lt
ØL8Q*	Div/Knee Tndn, Rt
ØL8R*	Div/Knee Tndn, Lt
ØL8S*	Div/Ankle Tndn, Rt
ØL8T*	Div/Ankle Tndn, Lt
ØL8V*	Div/Foot Tndn, Rt
ØL8W*	Div/Foot Tndn, Lt
ØLB7[Ø,3,4]ZZ	Exc/Hand Tndn, Rt, [Opn, Perc, Perc Endo]
ØLB8[Ø,3,4]ZZ	Exc/Hand Tndn, Lt, [Opn, Perc, Perc Endo]
ØLT7*	Resect/Hand Tndn, Rt
ØLT8*	Resect/Hand Tndn, Lt
ØLXØ*	Transfer/Head and Neck Tndn
ØLX1*	Transfer/Shldr Tndn, Rt
ØLX2*	Transfer/Shldr Tndn, Lt
ØLX3*	Transfer/Upr Arm Tndn, Rt
ØLX4*	Transfer/Upr Arm Tndn, Lt
ØLX5*	Transfer/Lwr Arm and Wrist Tndn, Rt
ØLX6*	Transfer/Lwr Arm and Wrist Tndn, Lt
ØLX9*	Transfer/Trunk Tndn, Rt
ØLXB*	Transfer/Trunk Tndn, Lt
ØLXC*	Transfer/Thorax Tndn, Rt
ØLXD*	Transfer/Thorax Tndn, Lt
ØLXF*	Transfer/Abd Tndn, Rt
ØLXG*	Transfer/Abd Tndn, Lt
ØLXH*	Transfer/Perineum Tndn
ØLXJ*	Transfer/Hip Tndn, Rt
ØLXK*	Transfer/Hip Tndn, Lt
ØLXL*	Transfer/Upr Leg Tndn, Rt
ØLXM*	Transfer/Upr Leg Tndn, Lt
ØLXN*	Transfer/Lwr Leg Tndn, Rt
ØLXP*	Transfer/Lwr Leg Tndn, Lt
ØLXQ*	Transfer/Knee Tndn, Rt
ØLXR*	Transfer/Knee Tndn, Lt
ØLXS*	Transfer/Ankle Tndn, Rt
ØLXT*	Transfer/Ankle Tndn, Lt
ØLXV*	Transfer/Foot Tndn, Rt
ØLXW*	Transfer/Foot Tndn, Lt
ØM53*	Destr/Elbow Bursa & Lgmt, Rt
ØM54*	Destr/Elbow Bursa & Lgmt, Lt
ØM5S*	Destr/Foot Bursa & Lgmt, Rt
ØM5T*	Destr/Foot Bursa & Lgmt, Lt
ØM934ZZ	Drain of Rt Elbow Bursa/Lig, Perc Endo Appr
ØM944ZZ	Drain of Lt Elbow Bursa/Lig, Perc Endo Appr
ØM9N[3,4]ØZ	Drain/Knee Bursa & Lgmt, Rt, [Perc, Perc Endo], Drain Dev, NQ
ØM9P[3,4]ØZ	Drain/Knee Bursa & Lgmt, Lt, [Perc, Perc Endo], Drain Dev, NQ
ØN9Ø[Ø,3,4]ZX	Drain/Skull, [Opn, Perc, Perc Endo]
ØN91[Ø,3,4]ZX	Drain/Frontal Bone, Rt, [Opn, Perc, Perc Endo]
ØN92[Ø,3,4]ZX	Drain/Frontal Bone, Lt, [Opn, Perc, Perc Endo]
ØN93[Ø,3,4]ZX	Drain/Parietal Bone, Rt, [Opn, Perc, Perc Endo]
ØN94[Ø,3,4]ZX	Drain/Parietal Bone, Lt, [Opn, Perc, Perc Endo]
ØN95[Ø,3,4]ZX	Drain/Temporal Bone, Rt, [Opn, Perc, Perc Endo]
ØN96[Ø,3,4]ZX	Drain/Temporal Bone, Lt, [Opn, Perc, Perc Endo]
ØN97[Ø,3,4]ZX	Drain/Occipital Bone, Rt, [Opn, Perc, Perc Endo]
ØN98[Ø,3,4]ZX	Drain/Occipital Bone, Lt, [Opn, Perc, Perc Endo]
ØNBØ[Ø,3,4]ZX	Exc/Skull, [Opn, Perc, Perc Endo]
ØNB1[Ø,3,4]ZX	Exc/Frontal Bone, Rt, [Opn, Perc, Perc Endo]
ØNB2[Ø,3,4]ZX	Exc/Frontal Bone, Lt, [Opn, Perc, Perc Endo]
ØNB3[Ø,3,4]ZX	Exc/Parietal Bone, Rt, [Opn, Perc, Perc Endo]
ØNB4[Ø,3,4]ZX	Exc/Parietal Bone, Lt, [Opn, Perc, Perc Endo]
ØNB5[Ø,3,4]ZX	Exc/Temporal Bone, Rt, [Opn, Perc, Perc Endo]
ØNB6[Ø,3,4]ZX	Exc/Temporal Bone, Lt, [Opn, Perc, Perc Endo]
ØNB7[Ø,3,4]ZX	Exc/Occipital Bone, Rt, [Opn, Perc, Perc Endo]
ØNB8[Ø,3,4]ZX	Exc/Occipital Bone, Lt, [Opn, Perc, Perc Endo]
ØP5Ø*	Destr/Sternum
ØP51*	Destr/Rib, Rt
ØP52*	Destr/Rib, Lt
ØP55*	Destr/Scapula, Rt
ØP56*	Destr/Scapula, Lt
ØP57*	Destr/Glenoid Cavity, Rt
ØP58*	Destr/Glenoid Cavity, Lt
ØP59*	Destr/Clavicle, Rt
ØP5B*	Destr/Clavicle, Lt
ØP9Ø[Ø,3,4]ZX	Drain/Sternum, [Opn, Perc, Perc Endo]
ØP91[Ø,3,4]ZX	Drain/Rib, Rt, [Opn, Perc, Perc Endo]
ØP92[Ø,3,4]ZX	Drain/Rib, Lt, [Opn, Perc, Perc Endo]
ØP95[Ø,3,4]ZX	Drain/Scapula, Rt, [Opn, Perc, Perc Endo]
ØP96[Ø,3,4]ZX	Drain/Scapula, Lt, [Opn, Perc, Perc Endo]
ØP97[Ø,3,4]ZX	Drain/Glenoid Cavity, Rt, [Opn, Perc, Perc Endo]
ØP98[Ø,3,4]ZX	Drain/Glenoid Cavity, Lt, [Opn, Perc, Perc Endo]
ØP99[Ø,3,4]ZX	Drain/Clavicle, Rt, [Opn, Perc, Perc Endo]
ØP9B[Ø,3,4]ZX	Drain/Clavicle, Lt, [Opn, Perc, Perc Endo]
ØP9C[Ø,3,4]ZX	Drain/Humeral Head, Rt, [Opn, Perc, Perc Endo]
ØP9D[Ø,3,4]ZX	Drain/Humeral Head, Lt, [Opn, Perc, Perc Endo]
ØP9F[Ø,3,4]ZX	Drain/Humeral Shaft, Rt, [Opn, Perc, Perc Endo]
ØP9G[Ø,3,4]ZX	Drain/Humeral Shaft, Lt, [Opn, Perc, Perc Endo]
ØP9H[Ø,3,4]ZX	Drain/Radius, Rt, [Opn, Perc, Perc Endo]
ØP9J[Ø,3,4]ZX	Drain/Radius, Lt, [Opn, Perc, Perc Endo]
ØP9K[Ø,3,4]ZX	Drain/Ulna, Rt, [Opn, Perc, Perc Endo]
ØP9L[Ø,3,4]ZX	Drain/Ulna, Lt, [Opn, Perc, Perc Endo]
ØP9M[Ø,3,4]ZX	Drain/Carpal, Rt, [Opn, Perc, Perc Endo]
ØP9N[Ø,3,4]ZX	Drain/Carpal, Lt, [Opn, Perc, Perc Endo]
ØP9P[Ø,3,4]ZX	Drain/Metacarpal, Rt, [Opn, Perc, Perc Endo]
ØP9Q[Ø,3,4]ZX	Drain/Metacarpal, Lt, [Opn, Perc, Perc Endo]
ØPBØ[Ø,3,4]ZX	Exc/Sternum, [Opn, Perc, Perc Endo]
ØPB1[Ø,3,4]ZX	Exc/Rib, Rt, [Opn, Perc, Perc Endo]
ØPB2[Ø,3,4]ZX	Exc/Rib, Lt, [Opn, Perc, Perc Endo]
ØPB3[Ø,3,4]ZZ	Exc/Cervical Vertebra, [Opn, Perc, Perc Endo]
ØPB4[Ø,3,4]ZZ	Exc/Thoracic Vertebra, [Opn, Perc, Perc Endo]
ØPB5[Ø,3,4]ZX	Exc/Scapula, Rt, [Opn, Perc, Perc Endo]
ØPB6[Ø,3,4]ZX	Exc/Scapula, Lt, [Opn, Perc, Perc Endo]
ØPB7[Ø,3,4]ZX	Exc/Glenoid Cavity, Rt, [Opn, Perc, Perc Endo]
ØPB8[Ø,3,4]ZX	Exc/Glenoid Cavity, Lt, [Opn, Perc, Perc Endo]
ØPB9[Ø,3,4]ZX	Exc/Clavicle, Rt, [Opn, Perc, Perc Endo]
ØPBB[Ø,3,4]ZX	Exc/Clavicle, Lt, [Opn, Perc, Perc Endo]
ØPBC[Ø,3,4]ZX	Exc/Humeral Head, Rt, [Opn, Perc, Perc Endo]
ØPBD[Ø,3,4]ZX	Exc/Humeral Head, Lt, [Opn, Perc, Perc Endo]
ØPBF[Ø,3,4]ZX	Exc/Humeral Shaft, Rt, [Opn, Perc, Perc Endo]
ØPBG[Ø,3,4]ZX	Exc/Humeral Shaft, Lt, [Opn, Perc, Perc Endo]
ØPBH[Ø,3,4]ZX	Exc/Radius, Rt, [Opn, Perc, Perc Endo]
ØPBJ[Ø,3,4]ZX	Exc/Radius, Lt, [Opn, Perc, Perc Endo]
ØPBK[Ø,3,4]ZX	Exc/Ulna, Rt, [Opn, Perc, Perc Endo]
ØPBL[Ø,3,4]ZX	Exc/Ulna, Lt, [Opn, Perc, Perc Endo]
ØPBM[Ø,3,4]ZX	Exc/Carpal, Rt, [Opn, Perc, Perc Endo]
ØPBN[Ø,3,4]ZX	Exc/Carpal, Lt, [Opn, Perc, Perc Endo]
ØPBP[Ø,3,4]ZX	Exc/Metacarpal, Rt, [Opn, Perc, Perc Endo]
ØPBQ[Ø,3,4]ZX	Exc/Metacarpal, Lt, [Opn, Perc, Perc Endo]
ØPBR[Ø,3,4]ZZ	Exc/Thumb Phalanx, Rt, [Opn, Perc, Perc Endo]
ØPBS[Ø,3,4]ZZ	Exc/Thumb Phalanx, Lt, [Opn, Perc, Perc Endo]

MDC 10: Endocrine, Nutritional And Metabolic Diseases And Disorders—SURGICAL

Surgical   Medical   CC Indicator   MCC Indicator   Procedure Proxy   PDxMCC PDx acts as own MCC   PDxCC PDx acts as own CC

0PBT[0,3,4]ZZ	Exc/Finger Phalanx, Rt, [Opn, Perc, Perc Endo]
0PBV[0,3,4]ZZ	Exc/Finger Phalanx, Lt, [Opn, Perc, Perc Endo]
0Q5L*	Destr/Tarsal, Rt
0Q5M*	Destr/Tarsal, Lt
0Q5N*	Destr/Metatarsal, Rt
0Q5P*	Destr/Metatarsal, Lt
0Q8G*	Div/Tibia, Rt
0Q8H*	Div/Tibia, Lt
0Q8J*	Div/Fibula, Rt
0Q8K*	Div/Fibula, Lt
0Q8L*	Div/Tarsal, Rt
0Q8M*	Div/Tarsal, Lt
0Q8N*	Div/Metatarsal, Rt
0Q8P*	Div/Metatarsal, Lt
0Q90[0,3,4]ZX	Drain/Lumbar Vertebra, [Opn, Perc, Perc Endo]
0Q91[0,3,4]ZX	Drain/Sacrum, [Opn, Perc, Perc Endo]
0Q92[0,3,4]ZX	Drain/Pelvic Bone, Rt, [Opn, Perc, Perc Endo]
0Q93[0,3,4]ZX	Drain/Pelvic Bone, Lt, [Opn, Perc, Perc Endo]
0Q94[0,3,4]ZX	Drain/Acetab, Rt, [Opn, Perc, Perc Endo]
0Q95[0,3,4]ZX	Drain/Acetab, Lt, [Opn, Perc, Perc Endo]
0Q96[0,3,4]ZX	Drain/Upr Femur, Rt, [Opn, Perc, Perc Endo]
0Q97[0,3,4]ZX	Drain/Upr Femur, Lt, [Opn, Perc, Perc Endo]
0Q98[0,3,4]ZX	Drain/Femor Shaft, Rt, [Opn, Perc, Perc Endo]
0Q99[0,3,4]ZX	Drain/Femor Shaft, Lt, [Opn, Perc, Perc Endo]
0Q9B[0,3,4]ZX	Drain/Lwr Femur, Rt, [Opn, Perc, Perc Endo]
0Q9C[0,3,4]ZX	Drain/Lwr Femur, Lt, [Opn, Perc, Perc Endo]
0Q9D[0,3,4]ZX	Drain/Patella, Rt, [Opn, Perc, Perc Endo]
0Q9F[0,3,4]ZX	Drain/Patella, Lt, [Opn, Perc, Perc Endo]
0Q9G[0,3,4]ZX	Drain/Tibia, Rt, [Opn, Perc, Perc Endo]
0Q9H[0,3,4]ZX	Drain/Tibia, Lt, [Opn, Perc, Perc Endo]
0Q9J[0,3,4]ZX	Drain/Fibula, Rt, [Opn, Perc, Perc Endo]
0Q9K[0,3,4]ZX	Drain/Fibula, Lt, [Opn, Perc, Perc Endo]
0Q9L[0,3,4]ZX	Drain/Tarsal, Rt, [Opn, Perc, Perc Endo]
0Q9M[0,3,4]ZX	Drain/Tarsal, Lt, [Opn, Perc, Perc Endo]
0Q9N[0,3,4]ZX	Drain/Metatarsal, Rt, [Opn, Perc, Perc Endo]
0Q9P[0,3,4]ZX	Drain/Metatarsal, Lt, [Opn, Perc, Perc Endo]
0Q9S[0,3,4]ZX	Drain/Coccyx, [Opn, Perc, Perc Endo]
0QB0*	Exc/Lumbar Vertebra
0QB1*	Exc/Sacrum
0QB2*	Exc/Pelvic Bone, Rt
0QB3*	Exc/Pelvic Bone, Lt
0QB4*	Exc/Acetabulum, Rt
0QB5*	Exc/Acetabulum, Lt
0QB6[0,3,4]ZX	Exc/Upr Femur, Rt, [Opn, Perc, Perc Endo]
0QB7[0,3,4]ZX	Exc/Upr Femur, Lt, [Opn, Perc, Perc Endo]
0QB8[0,3,4]ZX	Exc/Femor Shaft, Rt, [Opn, Perc, Perc Endo]
0QB9[0,3,4]ZX	Exc/Femor Shaft, Lt, [Opn, Perc, Perc Endo]
0QBB[0,3,4]ZX	Exc/Lwr Femur, Rt, [Opn, Perc, Perc Endo]
0QBC[0,3,4]ZX	Exc/Lwr Femur, Lt, [Opn, Perc, Perc Endo]
0QBD[0,3,4]ZX	Exc/Patella, Rt, [Opn, Perc, Perc Endo]
0QBF[0,3,4]ZX	Exc/Patella, Lt, [Opn, Perc, Perc Endo]
0QBG[0,3,4]ZX	Exc/Tibia, Rt, [Opn, Perc, Perc Endo]
0QBH[0,3,4]ZX	Exc/Tibia, Lt, [Opn, Perc, Perc Endo]
0QBJ[0,3,4]ZX	Exc/Fibula, Rt, [Opn, Perc, Perc Endo]
0QBK[0,3,4]ZX	Exc/Fibula, Lt, [Opn, Perc, Perc Endo]
0QBL*	Exc/Tarsal, Rt
0QBM*	Exc/Tarsal, Lt
0QBN*	Exc/Metatarsal, Rt
0QBP*	Exc/Metatarsal, Lt
0QBQ[0,3,4]ZZ	Exc/Toe Phalanx, Rt, [Opn, Perc, Perc Endo]
0QBR[0,3,4]ZZ	Exc/Toe Phalanx, Lt, [Opn, Perc, Perc Endo]
0QBS*	Exc/Coccyx
0QP6[0,3,4][4,5,7,J,K]ZRmvl/Upr Femur, Rt, [Opn, Perc, Perc Endo], [Int Fix Dev, Ext Fix Dev, Auto Tissue Sub, Synth Sub, Nonauto Tissue Sub], NQ
0QP7[0,3,4][4,5,7,J,K]ZRmvl/Upr Femur, Lt, [Opn, Perc, Perc Endo], [Int Fix Dev, Ext Fix Dev, Auto Tissue Sub, Synth Sub, Nonauto Tissue Sub], NQ
0QP8[0,3,4][4,5,7,J,K]ZRmvl/Femor Shaft, Rt, [Opn, Perc, Perc Endo], [Int Fix Dev, Ext Fix Dev, Auto Tissue Sub, Synth Sub, Nonauto Tissue Sub], NQ
0QP9[0,3,4][4,5,7,J,K]ZRmvl/Femor Shaft, Lt, [Opn, Perc, Perc Endo], [Int Fix Dev, Ext Fix Dev, Auto Tissue Sub, Synth Sub, Nonauto Tissue Sub], NQ
0QPB[0,3,4][4,5,7,J,K]ZRmvl/Lwr Femur, Rt, [Opn, Perc, Perc Endo], [Int Fix Dev, Ext Fix Dev, Auto Tissue Sub, Synth Sub, Nonauto Tissue Sub], NQ
0QPC[0,3,4][4,5,7,J,K]ZRmvl/Lwr Femur, Lt, [Opn, Perc, Perc Endo], [Int Fix Dev, Ext Fix Dev, Auto Tissue Sub, Synth Sub, Nonauto Tissue Sub], NQ

0QS60[4,6]Z	Repos/Upr Femur, Rt, Opn, [Int Fix Dev, Intramedullary Fix Dev], NQ
0QS70[4,6]Z	Repos/Upr Femur, Lt, Opn, [Int Fix Dev, Intramedullary Int Fix Dev], NQ
0QS80[4,6]Z	Repos/Femor Shaft, Rt, Opn, [Int Fix Dev, Intramedullary Int Fix Dev], NQ
0QS90[4,6]Z	Repos/Femor Shaft, Lt, Opn, [Int Fix Dev, Intramedullary Int Fix Dev], NQ
0QSB0[4,6]Z	Repos/Lwr Femur, Rt, Opn, [Int Fix Dev, Intramedullary Int Fix Dev], NQ
0QSC0[4,6]Z	Repos/Lwr Femur, Lt, Opn, [Int Fix Dev, Intramedullary Int Fix Dev], NQ
0QT40ZZ	Resect of Rt Acetabulum, Opn Appr
0QT50ZZ	Resect of Lt Acetabulum, Opn Appr
0R5L*	Destr/Elbow Jt, Rt
0R5M*	Destr/Elbow Jt, Lt
0R9L0[0,Z]Z	Drain/Elbow Jt, Rt, Opn, [Drain Dev, No Dev], NQ
0R9M0[0,Z]Z	Drain/Elbow Jt, Lt, Opn, [Drain Dev, No Dev], NQ
0RCL*	Extir/Elbow Jt, Rt
0RCM*	Extir/Elbow Jt, Lt
0S5H*	Destr/Tarsal Jt, Rt
0S5J*	Destr/Tarsal Jt, Lt
0S5K*	Destr/Metatarsal-Tarsal Jt, Rt
0S5L*	Destr/Metatarsal-Tarsal Jt, Lt
0S5M*	Destr/Metatarsal-Phalangeal Jt, Rt
0S5N*	Destr/Metatarsal-Phalangeal Jt, Lt
0S5P*	Destr/Toe Phalangeal Jt, Rt
0S5Q*	Destr/Toe Phalangeal Jt, Lt
0S9C0[0,Z]Z	Drain/Knee Jt, Rt, Opn, [Drain Dev, No Dev], NQ
0S9D0[0,Z]Z	Drain/Knee Jt, Lt, Opn, [Drain Dev, No Dev], NQ
0SBC[0,3,4]ZZ	Exc/Knee Jt, Rt, [Opn, Perc, Perc Endo]
0SBD[0,3,4]ZZ	Exc/Knee Jt, Lt, [Opn, Perc, Perc Endo]
0SCC*	Extir/Knee Jt, Rt
0SCD*	Extir/Knee Jt, Lt
0SGF*	Fusion/Ankle Jt, Rt
0SGG*	Fusion/Ankle Jt, Lt
0SJC4ZZ	Inspect of Rt Knee Jt, Perc Endo Appr
0SJD4ZZ	Inspect of Lt Knee Jt, Perc Endo Appr
0SRA*	Replace/Hip Jt, Acetabular Surface, Rt
0SRE*	Replace/Hip Jt, Acetabular Surface, Lt
0SRR*	Replace/Hip Jt, Femor Surface, Rt
0SRS*	Replace/Hip Jt, Femor Surface, Lt
0STH0ZZ	Resect of Rt Tarsal Jt, Opn Appr
0STJ0ZZ	Resect of Lt Tarsal Jt, Opn Appr
0STK0ZZ	Resect of Rt Metatarsal-Tarsal Jt, Opn Appr
0STL0ZZ	Resect of Lt Metatarsal-Tarsal Jt, Opn Appr
0STM0ZZ	Resect of Rt Metatarsophal Jt, Opn Appr
0STN0ZZ	Resect of Lt Metatarsal-Phalangeal Jt, Opn Appr
0STP0ZZ	Resect of Rt Toe Phalangeal Jt, Opn Appr
0STQ0ZZ	Resect of Lt Toe Phalangeal Jt, Opn Appr
0SUA0BZ	Supl Rt Hip Jt, Acetab with Resurf Dev, Opn Appr
0SUE0BZ	Supl Lt Hip Jt, Acetab with Resurf Dev, Opn Appr
0SUR0BZ	Supl Rt Hip Jt, Femor with Resurf Dev, Opn Appr
0SUS0BZ	Supl Lt Hip Jt, Femor with Resurf Dev, Opn Appr
0SW9[0,3,4]JZ	Rev/Hip Jt, Rt, [Opn, Perc, Perc Endo], Synth Sub, NQ
0SWB[0,3,4]JZ	Rev/Hip Jt, Lt, [Opn, Perc, Perc Endo], Synth Sub, NQ
0UB0[0,3,4,7,8]ZZ Exc/Ovary, Rt, [Opn, Perc, Perc Endo, Via Natrl or Artfcl Opng, Via Natrl or Artfcl Opng Endo]
0UB1[0,3,4,7,8]ZZ Exc/Ovary, Lt, [Opn, Perc, Perc Endo, Via Natrl or Artfcl Opng, Via Natrl or Artfcl Opng Endo]
0UB2[0,3,4,7,8]ZZ Exc/Ovaries, Bilat, [Opn, Perc, Perc Endo, Via Natrl or Artfcl Opng, Via Natrl or Artfcl Opng Endo]
0VR*	Male Reproductive Sys, Replace
0W30*	Control/Head
0W31*	Control/Cranial Cavity
0W32*	Control/Face
0W33*	Control/Oral Cavity and Throat
0W34*	Control/Upr Jaw
0W35*	Control/Lwr Jaw
0W36*	Control/Neck
0W39*	Control/Pleural Cavity, Rt
0W3B*	Control/Pleural Cavity, Lt
0W3C*	Control/Mediastinum
0W3K*	Control/Upr Back
0W3L*	Control/Lwr Back
0W3Q[3,4,7]ZZ	Control/Respiratory Tract, [Perc, Perc Endo, Via Natrl or Artfcl Opng]
0W9C0ZX	Drain of Mediastinum, Opn Appr, Diagnostic
0WB8[0,3,4,X]ZZ	Exc/Chest Wall, [Opn, Perc, Perc Endo, Ext]
0WBC0ZX	Exc of Mediastinum, Opn Appr, Diagnostic

T Transfer DRG   SP Special Payment   * Code Range   6th and 7th Character of ZZ = No Device, No Qualifier ZX = No Device, Diagnostic

ØWBC[Ø,3,4]ZZ   Exc/Mediastinum, [Opn, Perc, Perc Endo]
ØWBFXZ2   Exc of Abd Wall, Stoma, Ext Appr
ØWBF[Ø,3,4,X]ZZ   Exc/Abd Wall, [Opn, Perc, Perc Endo, Ext]
ØWH6[Ø,3,4]1Z   Insert/Neck, [Opn, Perc, Perc Endo], Radioact Elmt, NQ
ØWHG[Ø,3,4]1Z   Insert/Peritoneal Cavity, [Opn, Perc, Perc Endo], Radioact Elmt, NQ
ØWHH[Ø,3,4]1Z   Insert/Retroperitoneum, [Opn, Perc, Perc Endo], Radioact Elmt, NQ
ØWJGØZZ   Inspect of Peritoneal Cavity, Opn Appr
ØWJJØZZ   Inspect of Pelvic Cavity, Opn Appr
ØWJPØZZ   Inspect of Gastrointestinal Tract, Opn Appr
ØWJRØZZ   Inspect of Genitourinary Tract, Opn Appr
ØYB5[Ø,3,4]ZZ   Exc/Inguinal Rgn, Rt, [Opn, Perc, Perc Endo]
ØYB6[Ø,3,4]ZZ   Exc/Inguinal Rgn, Lt, [Opn, Perc, Perc Endo]
ØYB7[Ø,3,4]ZZ   Exc/Femor Rgn, Rt, [Opn, Perc, Perc Endo]
ØYB8[Ø,3,4]ZZ   Exc/Femor Rgn, Lt, [Opn, Perc, Perc Endo]
3EØCXSF   Introduction of Oth Gas into Eye, Ext Appr

OR

ØSR90[1,2,3,4,J][9,A,Z] Replace/Hip Jt, Rt, Opn, [Synth Sub, Metal, Synth Sub, Metal on Polyethylene, Synth Sub, Ceramic, Synth Sub, Ceramic on Polyethylene, Synth Sub], [Cemented, Uncemented, NQ]

     AND

ØSP9Ø8Z   Rmvl of Spacer from Rt Hip Jt, Opn Appr
ØSP9Ø9Z   Rmvl of Liner from Rt Hip Jt, Opn Appr
ØSP9ØBZ   Rmvl of Resurfacing Device from Rt Hip Jt, Opn Appr
ØSP9ØJZ   Rmvl of Synth Sub from Rt Hip Jt, Opn Appr
ØSP948Z   Rmvl of Spacer from Rt Hip Jt, Perc Endo Appr
ØSP94JZ   Rmvl of Synth Sub from Rt Hip Jt, Perc Endo Appr

OR

ØSRAØ[Ø,1,3,J][9,A,Z] Replace/Hip Jt, Acetabular Surface, Rt, Opn, [Synth Sub, Polyethylene, Synth Sub, Metal, Synth Sub, Ceramic, Synth Sub], [Cemented, Uncemented, NQ]

     AND

ØSP9Ø8Z   Rmvl of Spacer from Rt Hip Jt, Opn Appr
ØSP9Ø9Z   Rmvl of Liner from Rt Hip Jt, Opn Appr
ØSP9ØBZ   Rmvl of Resurfacing Device from Rt Hip Jt, Opn Appr
ØSP9ØJZ   Rmvl of Synth Sub from Rt Hip Jt, Opn Appr
ØSP948Z   Rmvl of Spacer from Rt Hip Jt, Perc Endo Appr
ØSP94JZ   Rmvl of Synth Sub from Rt Hip Jt, Perc Endo Appr

OR

ØSRRØ[1,3,J][9,A,Z] Replace/Hip Jt, Femor Surface, Rt, Opn, [Synth Sub, Metal, Synth Sub, Ceramic, Synth Sub], [Cemented, Uncemented, NQ]

     AND

ØSP9Ø8Z   Rmvl of Spacer from Rt Hip Jt, Opn Appr
ØSP9Ø9Z   Rmvl of Liner from Rt Hip Jt, Opn Appr
ØSP9ØBZ   Rmvl of Resurfacing Device from Rt Hip Jt, Opn Appr
ØSP9ØJZ   Rmvl of Synth Sub from Rt Hip Jt, Opn Appr
ØSP948Z   Rmvl of Spacer from Rt Hip Jt, Perc Endo Appr
ØSP94JZ   Rmvl of Synth Sub from Rt Hip Jt, Perc Endo Appr

OR

ØSU9Ø9Z   Supl Rt Hip Jt with Liner, Opn Appr
ØSUAØ9Z   Supl Rt Hip Jt, Acetab with Liner, Opn Appr
ØSURØ9Z   Supl Rt Hip Jt, Femor with Liner, Opn Appr

     AND

ØSP9Ø8Z   Rmvl of Spacer from Rt Hip Jt, Opn Appr
ØSP9Ø9Z   Rmvl of Liner from Rt Hip Jt, Opn Appr
ØSP9ØBZ   Rmvl of Resurfacing Device from Rt Hip Jt, Opn Appr
ØSP948Z   Rmvl of Spacer from Rt Hip Jt, Perc Endo Appr
ØSP94JZ   Rmvl of Synth Sub from Rt Hip Jt, Perc Endo Appr

OR

ØSRBØ[1,2,3,4,J][9,A,Z] Replace/Hip Jt, Lt, Opn, [Synth Sub, Metal, Synth Sub, Metal on Polyethylene, Synth Sub, Ceramic, Synth Sub, Ceramic on Polyethylene, Synth Sub], [Cemented, Uncemented, NQ]

     AND

ØSPBØ8Z   Rmvl of Spacer from Lt Hip Jt, Opn Appr
ØSPBØ9Z   Rmvl of Liner from Lt Hip Jt, Opn Appr
ØSPBØBZ   Rmvl of Resurfacing Device from Lt Hip Jt, Opn Appr
ØSPBØJZ   Rmvl of Synth Sub from Lt Hip Jt, Opn Appr
ØSPB48Z   Rmvl of Spacer from Lt Hip Jt, Perc Endo Appr
ØSPB4JZ   Rmvl of Synth Sub from Lt Hip Jt, Perc Endo Appr

OR

ØSREØ[Ø,1,3,J][9,A,Z] Replace/Hip Jt, Acetabular Surface, Lt, Opn, [Synth Sub, Polyethylene, Synth Sub, Metal, Synth Sub, Ceramic, Synth Sub], [Cemented, Uncemented, NQ]

     AND

ØSPBØ8Z   Rmvl of Spacer from Lt Hip Jt, Opn Appr
ØSPBØ9Z   Rmvl of Liner from Lt Hip Jt, Opn Appr
ØSPBØBZ   Rmvl of Resurfacing Device from Lt Hip Jt, Opn Appr
ØSPBØJZ   Rmvl of Synth Sub from Lt Hip Jt, Opn Appr
ØSPB48Z   Rmvl of Spacer from Lt Hip Jt, Perc Endo Appr
ØSPB4JZ   Rmvl of Synth Sub from Lt Hip Jt, Perc Endo Appr

ØSRSØ[1,3,J][9,A,Z] Replace/Hip Jt, Femor Surface, Lt, Opn, [Synth Sub, Metal, Synth Sub, Ceramic, Synth Sub], [Cemented, Uncemented, NQ]

     AND

ØSPBØ8Z   Rmvl of Spacer from Lt Hip Jt, Opn Appr
ØSPBØ9Z   Rmvl of Liner from Lt Hip Jt, Opn Appr
ØSPBØBZ   Rmvl of Resurfacing Device from Lt Hip Jt, Opn Appr
ØSPBØJZ   Rmvl of Synth Sub from Lt Hip Jt, Opn Appr
ØSPB48Z   Rmvl of Spacer from Lt Hip Jt, Perc Endo Appr
ØSPB4JZ   Rmvl of Synth Sub from Lt Hip Jt, Perc Endo Appr

OR

ØSUBØ9Z   Supl Lt Hip Jt with Liner, Opn Appr
ØSUEØ9Z   Supl Lt Hip Jt, Acetab with Liner, Opn Appr
ØSUSØ9Z   Supl Lt Hip Jt, Femor with Liner, Opn Appr

     AND

ØSPBØ8Z   Rmvl of Spacer from Lt Hip Jt, Opn Appr
ØSPBØ9Z   Rmvl of Liner from Lt Hip Jt, Opn Appr
ØSPBØBZ   Rmvl of Resurfacing Device from Lt Hip Jt, Opn Appr
ØSPB48Z   Rmvl of Spacer from Lt Hip Jt, Perc Endo Appr
ØSPB4JZ   Rmvl of Synth Sub from Lt Hip Jt, Perc Endo Appr

OR

ØSRCØJ[9,A,Z]   Replace/Knee Jt, Rt, Opn, Synth Sub, [Cemented, Uncemented, NQ]

     AND

ØSPCØ9Z   Rmvl of Liner from Rt Knee Jt, Opn Appr

OR

ØSRTØJ[9,A,Z]   Replace/Knee Jt, Femor Surface, Rt, Opn, Synth Sub, [Cemented, Uncemented, NQ]

     AND

ØSPCØ9Z   Rmvl of Liner from Rt Knee Jt, Opn Appr

OR

ØSRVØJ[9,A,Z]   Replace/Knee Jt, Tibial Surface, Rt, Opn, Synth Sub, [Cemented, Uncemented, NQ]

     AND

ØSPCØ9Z   Rmvl of Liner from Rt Knee Jt, Opn Appr

OR

ØSRTØJ9   Replace Rt Knee Jt, Femor w Synth Sub, Cement, Opn
ØSRTØJA   Replace Rt Knee Jt, Femor w Synth Sub, Uncement, Opn

     AND

ØSPCØJZ   Rmvl of Synth Sub from Rt Knee Jt, Opn Appr
ØSPC4JZ   Rmvl of Synth Sub from Rt Knee Jt, Perc Endo Appr

OR

ØSRVØJ9   Replace Rt Knee Jt, Tibial w Synth Sub, Cement, Opn
ØSRVØJA   Replace Rt Knee Jt, Tibial w Synth Sub, Uncement, Opn

     AND

ØSPCØJZ   Rmvl of Synth Sub from Rt Knee Jt, Opn Appr
ØSPC4JZ   Rmvl of Synth Sub from Rt Knee Jt, Perc Endo Appr

OR

ØSRDØJ[9,A,Z]   Replace/Knee Jt, Lt, Opn, Synth Sub, [Cemented, Uncemented, NQ]

     AND

ØSPDØ9Z   Rmvl of Liner from Lt Knee Jt, Opn Appr

OR

ØSRUØJ[9,A,Z]   Replace/Knee Jt, Femor Surface, Lt, Opn, Synth Sub, [Cemented, Uncemented, NQ]

     AND

ØSPDØ9Z   Rmvl of Liner from Lt Knee Jt, Opn Appr

OR

ØSRUØJ9   Replace Lt Knee Jt, Femor w Synth Sub, Cement, Opn
ØSRUØJA   Replace Lt Knee Jt, Femor w Synth Sub, Uncement, Opn

     AND

ØSPDØJZ   Rmvl of Synth Sub from Lt Knee Jt, Opn Appr
ØSPD4JZ   Rmvl of Synth Sub from Lt Knee Jt, Perc Endo Appr

OR

ØSRWØJ[9,A,Z]   Replace/Knee Jt, Tibial Surface, Lt, Opn, Synth Sub, [Cemented, Uncemented, NQ]

     AND

ØSPDØ9Z   Rmvl of Liner from Lt Knee Jt, Opn Appr

| ØSPDØJZ | Rmvl of Synth Sub from Lt Knee Jt, Opn Appr |
| ØSPD4JZ | Rmvl of Synth Sub from Lt Knee Jt, Perc Endo Appr |

OR

Nonoperating Room Procedures

D02*	Radiation Therapy, Central Periph Nerv Sys, Stereo Radiosurg
D72*	Radiation Therapy, Lymph & Hemat Sys, Stereo Radiosurg
D82*	Radiation Therapy, Eye, Stereotactic Radiosurgery
D92*	Radiation Therapy, ENT & Mouth, Stereo Radiosurg
DB2*	Radiation Therapy, Resp Sys, Stereo Radiosurg
DD2*	Radiation Therapy, GI Sys, Stereo Radiosurg
DF2*	Radiation Therapy, Hepatobil Pancreas, Stereo Radiosurg
DG2*	Radiation Therapy, Endocrine Sys, Stereo Radiosurg
DM2*	Radiation Therapy, Breast, Stereotactic Radiosurgery
DT2*	Radiation Therapy, Urinary Sys, Stereotactic Radiosurgery
DU2*	Radiation Therapy, Fem Reprod Sys, Stereo Radiosurg
DV2*	Radiation Therapy, Male Reprod Sys, Stereo Radiosurg
DW2*	Radiation Therapy, Anatomical Regions, Stereo Radiosurg

DRG 629   Other Endocrine, Nutritional and Metabolic O.R. Procedures with CC

| GMLOS 6.1 | AMLOS 7.2 | RW 2.1952 | T |

Select operating room procedures OR procedure combinations OR nonoperating room procedures listed under DRG 628

DRG 630   Other Endocrine, Nutritional and Metabolic O.R. Procedures without CC/MCC

| GMLOS 3.0 | AMLOS 3.9 | RW 1.3601 | T |

Select operating room procedures OR procedure combinations OR nonoperating room procedures listed under DRG 628

MEDICAL

DRG 637   Diabetes with MCC

| GMLOS 4.1 | AMLOS 5.3 | RW 1.3823 | T |

Principal Diagnosis

E08.0*	Diabetes d/t underlying condition w hyperosmolarity
E08.1*	Diabetes mellitus d/t underlying condition w ketoacidosis
E08.618	Diabetes d/t underlying condition w oth diabetic arthrop
E08.62*	Diabetes d/t underlying condition w skin comp
E08.63*	Diabetes d/t underlying condition w oral comp
E08.64*	Diabetes mellitus d/t underlying condition w hypoglycemia
E08.65	Diabetes d/t underlying condition w hyperglycemia
E08.69	Diabetes d/t underlying condition w oth comp
E08.8	Diabetes d/t underlying condition w unsp comp
E08.9	Diabetes d/t underlying condition w/o comp
E09.0*	Drug or chemical induced diabetes mellitus w hyperosmolarity
E09.1*	Drug or chemical induced diabetes mellitus with ketoacidosis
E09.618	Drug/chem diabetes mellitus w oth diabetic arthropathy
E09.62*	Drug/chem diabetes mellitus w skin comp
E09.63*	Drug/chem diabetes mellitus w oral comp
E09.64*	Drug or chemical induced diabetes mellitus with hypoglycemia
E09.65	Drug or chemical induced diabetes mellitus w hyperglycemia
E09.69	Drug/chem diabetes mellitus w oth comp
E09.8	Drug/chem diabetes mellitus w unsp comp
E09.9	Drug or chemical induced diabetes mellitus w/o comp
E10.1*	Type 1 diabetes mellitus with ketoacidosis
E10.618	Type 1 diabetes mellitus with oth diabetic arthropathy
E10.62*	Type 1 diabetes mellitus with skin comp
E10.63*	Type 1 diabetes mellitus with oral comp
E10.64*	Type 1 diabetes mellitus with hypoglycemia
E10.65	Type 1 diabetes mellitus with hyperglycemia
E10.69	Type 1 diabetes mellitus with oth spec comp
E10.8	Type 1 diabetes mellitus with unsp comp
E10.9	Type 1 diabetes mellitus w/o comp
E11.0*	Type 2 diabetes mellitus with hyperosmolarity
E11.618	Type 2 diabetes mellitus with oth diabetic arthropathy
E11.62*	Type 2 diabetes mellitus with skin comp
E11.63*	Type 2 diabetes mellitus with oral comp
E11.64*	Type 2 diabetes mellitus with hypoglycemia
E11.65	Type 2 diabetes mellitus with hyperglycemia
E11.69	Type 2 diabetes mellitus with oth spec comp
E11.8	Type 2 diabetes mellitus with unsp comp
E11.9	Type 2 diabetes mellitus w/o comp
E13.0*	Oth spec diabetes mellitus with hyperosmolarity
E13.1*	Oth spec diabetes mellitus with ketoacidosis
E13.618	Oth diabetes mellitus with oth diabetic arthropathy
E13.62*	Oth spec diabetes mellitus with skin comp
E13.63*	Oth spec diabetes mellitus with oral comp
E13.64*	Oth spec diabetes mellitus with hypoglycemia
E13.65	Oth spec diabetes mellitus with hyperglycemia
E13.69	Oth diabetes mellitus with oth spec comp
E13.8	Oth diabetes mellitus with unsp comp
E13.9	Oth spec diabetes mellitus w/o comp
R81	Glycosuria

DRG 638   Diabetes with CC

| GMLOS 3.0 | AMLOS 3.7 | RW 0.8463 | T |

Select principal diagnosis listed under DRG 637

DRG 639   Diabetes without CC/MCC

| GMLOS 2.2 | AMLOS 2.6 | RW 0.6007 | T |

Select principal diagnosis listed under DRG 637

DRG 640   Miscellaneous Disorders of Nutrition, Metabolism, and Fluids and Electrolytes with MCC

| GMLOS 3.3 | AMLOS 4.5 | RW 1.1318 | T |

Principal Diagnosis

D81.81[8,9]	[Oth, Unsp] biotin-dependent carboxylase deficiency
E15	Nondiabetic hypoglycemic coma
E16.2	Hypoglycemia, unsp
E20.1	Pseudohypoparathyroidism
E40	Kwashiorkor
E41	Nutritional marasmus
E42	Marasmic kwashiorkor
E43	Unsp severe protein-calorie malnut
E44*	Protein-calorie malnut of mod and mild degree
E45	Retarded development following protein-calorie malnut
E46	Unsp protein-calorie malnut
E50.8	Oth manifestations of vitamin A deficiency
E50.9	Vitamin A deficiency, unsp
E51*	Thiamine deficiency
E52	Niacin deficiency [pellagra]
E53*	Deficiency of oth B group vitamins
E54	Ascorbic acid deficiency
E55.9	Vitamin D deficiency, unsp
E56*	Oth vitamin deficiencies
E58	Dietary calcium deficiency
E59	Dietary selenium deficiency
E60	Dietary zinc deficiency
E61*	Deficiency of oth nutrient elements
E63*	Oth nutritional deficiencies
E64.0	Sequelae of protein-calorie malnut
E64.1	Sequelae of vitamin A deficiency
E64.2	Sequelae of vitamin C deficiency
E64.8	Sequelae of oth nutritional deficiencies
E64.9	Sequelae of unsp nutritional deficiency
E65	Localized adiposity
E66.0*	Obesity d/t excess calories
E66.1	Drug-induced obesity
E66.3	Overweight
E66.8	Oth obesity
E66.9	Obesity, unsp
E67*	Oth hyperalimentation
E68	Sequelae of hyperalimentation
E83.4*	D/o of magnesium metabolism
E83.5*	D/o of calcium metabolism
E83.81	Hungry bone synd
E84.8	Cystic fibrosis with oth manifestations
E84.9	Cystic fibrosis, unsp
E86*	Volume depletion
E87*	Oth d/o of fluid, electrolyte and acid-base balance
E89.1	Postprocedural hypoinsulinemia
P92.6	Failure to thrive in newborn
R29.0	Tetany
R62*	Lack of expected normal physiol dev in childhood and adults
R63*	Symptoms and signs concerning food and fluid intake

T **Transfer DRG**   SP **Special Payment**   * **Code Range**   **6th and 7th Character of ZZ = No Device, No Qualifier ZX = No Device, Diagnostic**

R73*	Elevated bld glucose lvl
R82.4	Acetonuria
Z68.4*	Body mass index (BMI) 40 or greater, adult

DRG 641 Miscellaneous Disorders of Nutrition, Metabolism, and Fluids and Electrolytes without MCC
GMLOS 2.7   AMLOS 3.3   RW 0.7221   T

Select principal diagnosis listed under DRG 640

DRG 642 Inborn and Other Disorders of Metabolism
GMLOS 3.4   AMLOS 4.5   RW 1.2246

Principal Diagnosis

C96.5	Multifocal and unisystemic Langerhans-cell histiocytosis
C96.6	Unifocal Langerhans-cell histiocytosis
D81.3	Adenosine deaminase [ADA] deficiency
D81.5	Purine nucleoside phosphorylase [PNP] deficiency
D81.810	Biotinidase deficiency
D84.1	Defects in the complement sys
E70*	D/o of aromatic amino-acid metabolism
E71*	D/o of branched-chain amino-acid metab & fatty-acid metab
E72*	Oth d/o of amino-acid metabolism
E74.0*	Glycogen storage dz
E74.2*	D/o of galactose metabolism
E74.4	D/o of pyruvate metabolism and gluconeogenesis
E74.8	Oth spec d/o of carbohydrate metabolism
E74.9	D/o of carbohydrate metabolism, unsp
E75.24*	Niemann-Pick dz
E75.2[1,2]	[Fabry (-Anderson), Gaucher] dz
E75.3	Sphingolipidosis, unsp
E75.5	Oth lipid storage d/o
E75.6	Lipid storage d/o, unsp
E76*	D/o of glycosaminoglycan metabolism
E77*	D/o of glycoprotein metabolism
E78.0	Pure hypercholesterolemia
E78.1	Pure hyperglyceridemia
E78.2	Mixed hyperlipidemia
E78.3	Hyperchylomicronemia
E78.4	Oth hyperlipidemia
E78.5	Hyperlipidemia, unsp
E78.6	Lipoprotein deficiency
E78.7[0,9]	[Unsp, Oth] d/o of bile acid and cholesterol metabolism
E78.8*	Oth d/o of lipoprotein metabolism
E78.9	D/o of lipoprotein metabolism, unsp
E79.1	Lesch-Nyhan synd
E79.2	Myoadenylate deaminase deficiency
E79.8	Oth d/o of purine and pyrimidine metabolism
E79.9	D/o of purine and pyrimidine metabolism, unsp
E80.0	Hereditary erythropoietic porphyria
E80.1	Porphyria cutanea tarda
E80.2*	Oth and unsp porphyria
E80.3	Defects of catalase and peroxidase
E83.0*	D/o of copper metabolism
E83.1*	D/o of iron metabolism
E83.3*	D/o of phosphorus metabolism and phosphatases
E83.89	Oth d/o of mineral metabolism
E83.9	D/o of mineral metabolism, unsp
E88.01	Alpha-1-antitrypsin deficiency
E88.1	Lipodystrophy, NEC
E88.2	Lipomatosis, NEC
E88.4*	Mitochondrial metabolism d/o
E88.8*	Oth spec metabolic d/o
E88.9	Metabolic d/o, unsp
H49.81*	Kearns-Sayre synd

DRG 643 Endocrine Disorders with MCC
GMLOS 5.3   AMLOS 6.7   RW 1.6249   T

Principal Diagnosis

A18.7	Tuberculosis of adrenal glands
A18.81	Tuberculosis of thyroid gland
B67.31	Echinococcus granulosus infxn, thyroid gland
C73	Malig neoplasm of thyroid gland
C74*	Malig neoplasm of adrenal gland
C75.0	Malig neoplasm of parathyroid gland
C75.1	Malig neoplasm of pituitary gland
C75.2	Malig neoplasm of craniopharyngeal duct

C75.8	Malig neoplasm with pluriglandular involvement, unsp
C75.9	Malig neoplasm of endocrine gland, unsp
C79.7*	Secondary malig neoplasm of adrenal gland
D13.7	Benign neoplasm of endocrine pancreas
D34	Benign neoplasm of thyroid gland
D35.0*	Benign neoplasm of adrenal gland
D35.1	Benign neoplasm of parathyroid gland
D35.2	Benign neoplasm of pituitary gland
D35.3	Benign neoplasm of craniopharyngeal duct
D35.7	Benign neoplasm of oth spec endocrine glands
D35.9	Benign neoplasm of endocrine gland, unsp
D44.0	Neoplasm of uncertain behav of thyroid gland
D44.1*	Neoplasm of uncertain behav of adrenal gland
D44.2	Neoplasm of uncertain behav of parathyroid gland
D44.3	Neoplasm of uncertain behav of pituitary gland
D44.4	Neoplasm of uncertain behav of craniopharyngeal duct
D44.9	Neoplasm of uncertain behav of unsp endocrine gland
D49.7	Neoplm of unsp behav of endo glands and oth prt nervous sys
E00*	Congenital iodine-deficiency synd
E01*	Iodine-deficiency related thyroid d/o and allied cond
E02	Subclinical iodine-deficiency hypothyroidism
E03.0	Congenital hypothyroidism with diffuse goiter
E03.1	Congenital hypothyroidism w/o goiter
E03.2	Hypothyroidism d/t meds and oth exogenous substances
E03.3	Postinfectious hypothyroidism
E03.4	Atrophy of thyroid (acquired)
E03.8	Oth spec hypothyroidism
E03.9	Hypothyroidism, unsp
E04*	Oth nontoxic goiter
E05*	Thyrotoxicosis [hyperthyroidism]
E06*	Thyroiditis
E07.0	Hypersecretion of calcitonin
E07.1	Dyshormogenetic goiter
E07.89	Oth spec d/o of thyroid
E07.9	D/o of thyroid, unsp
E16.0	Drug-induced hypoglycemia w/o coma
E16.1	Oth hypoglycemia
E16.3	Increased secretion of glucagon
E16.8	Oth spec d/o of pancreatic int secretion
E16.9	D/o of pancreatic int secretion, unsp
E20.0	Idiopathic hypoparathyroidism
E20.8	Oth hypoparathyroidism
E20.9	Hypoparathyroidism, unsp
E21*	Hyperparathyroidism and oth d/o of parathyroid gland
E22*	Hyperfunction of pituitary gland
E23*	Hypofunction and oth d/o of the pituitary gland
E24*	Cushing's synd
E25*	Adrenogenital d/o
E26*	Hyperaldosteronism
E27*	Oth d/o of adrenal gland
E29*	Testicular dysfunction
E30*	D/o of puberty, NEC
E31*	Polyglandular dysfunction
E34*	Oth endocrine d/o
E35	D/o of endocrine glands in dz classd elsw
E89.0	Postprocedural hypothyroidism
E89.2	Postprocedural hypoparathyroidism
E89.3	Postprocedural hypopituitarism
E89.5	Postprocedural testicular hypofunction
E89.6	Postprocedural adrenocortical (-medullary) hypofunction
Q89.1	Congenital malformations of adrenal gland
Q89.2	Congenital malformations of oth endocrine glands
R94.6	Abnormal results of thyroid function studies
R94.7	Abnormal results of oth endocrine function studies
S11.1[0,1,2,3,4,5]XA	[Unsp opn wnd, Lac w/o FB, Lac w/ FB, Punc wnd w/o FB, Punc wnd w/ FB, Opn bite] of thyroid gland, init enc
S37.81[2,3,8,9]A	[Contsn, Lac, Oth inj, Unsp inj] of adrenal gland, init enc

DRG 644 Endocrine Disorders with CC
GMLOS 3.7   AMLOS 4.6   RW 1.0123   T

Select principal diagnosis listed under DRG 643

DRG 645 Endocrine Disorders without CC/MCC
GMLOS 2.8   AMLOS 3.4   RW 0.7255   T

Select principal diagnosis listed under DRG 643

Surgical   **Medical**   **CC Indicator**   **MCC Indicator**   **Procedure Proxy**   PDxMCC **PDx acts as own MCC**   PDxCC **PDx acts as own CC**

MDC 11
Diseases And Disorders Of The Kidney And Urinary Tract

SURGICAL

DRG 652   Kidney Transplant
GMLOS 5.5   **AMLOS 6.5**   **RW 3.1540**

Operating Room Procedures

0TY*	Urinary Sys, Transplantation

DRG 653   Major Bladder Procedures with MCC
GMLOS 11.9   **AMLOS 14.8**   **RW 6.0456**   T

Operating Room Procedures

0JUC*	Supl/SQ Tissue & Fascia, Pelvic Region
0T1B0Z[9,C]	Bypass/Bladder, Opn, No Dev, [Colocutaneous, Ileocutaneous]
0T1B0[7,J,K][9,C,D]	Bypass/Bladder, Opn, [Auto Tissue Sub, Synth Sub, Nonauto Tissue Sub], [Colocutaneous, Ileocutaneous, Cutaneous]
0T1B3JD	Bypass Bladder to Cutaneous with Synth Sub, Perc Appr
0T1B4Z[9,C]	Bypass/Bladder, Perc Endo, No Dev, [Colocutaneous, Ileocutaneous]
0T1B4[7,J,K][9,C,D]	Bypass/Bladder, Perc Endo, [Auto Tissue Sub, Synth Sub, Nonauto Tissue Sub], [Colocutaneous, Ileocutaneous, Cutaneous]
0T7B*	Dilation/Bladder
0TBB[0,3,4]ZZ	Exc/Bladder, [Opn, Perc, Perc Endo]
0TBC[0,3,4]ZZ	Exc/Bladder Neck, [Opn, Perc, Perc Endo]
0TMB*	Reattach/Bladder
0TMC*	Reattach/Bladder Neck
0TQB*	Repair/Bladder
0TRB*	Replace/Bladder
0TRC*	Replace/Bladder Neck
0TSB*	Repos/Bladder
0TTB*	Resect/Bladder
0TTC*	Resect/Bladder Neck
0TUB*	Supl/Bladder
0TVB*	Restrict/Bladder
0TVC*	Restrict/Bladder Neck

DRG 654   Major Bladder Procedures with CC
GMLOS 7.2   **AMLOS 8.2**   **RW 3.0267**   T

Select operating room procedures listed under DRG 653

DRG 655   Major Bladder Procedures without CC/MCC
GMLOS 4.8   **AMLOS 5.4**   **RW 2.2796**   T

Select operating room procedures listed under DRG 653

DRG 656   Kidney and Ureter Procedures for Neoplasm with MCC
GMLOS 6.8   **AMLOS 8.8**   **RW 3.4617**

Principal Diagnosis

C64*	Malig neoplasm of kidney, except renal pelvis
C65*	Malig neoplasm of renal pelvis
C66*	Malig neoplasm of ureter
C67*	Malig neoplasm of bladder
C68*	Malig neoplasm of oth and unsp urinary organs
C79.0*	Secondary malig neoplasm of kidney and renal pelvis
C79.1*	Sec malig neoplm of bladder and oth and unsp urinary organs
C7A.093	Malig carcinoid tumor of the kidney
D09.0	Carcinoma in situ of bladder
D09.1*	Carcinoma in situ of oth and unsp urinary organs
D30*	Benign neoplasm of urinary organs
D3A.093	Benign carcinoid tumor of the kidney
D41*	Neoplasm of uncertain behav of urinary organs
D49.4	Neoplasm of unsp behav of bladder
D49.5	Neoplasm of unsp behav of oth genitourinary organs

AND

Operating Room Procedures

04100J[1,2,3,4,5]	Bypass/Abd Aorta, Opn, Synth Sub, [Celiac Artery, Mesenteric Artery, Rt Renal Artery, Lt Renal Artery, Bilat Renal Artery]
04100K[3,4,5]	Bypass/Abd Aorta, Opn, Nonauto Tissue Sub, [Rt Renal Artery, Lt Renal Artery, Bilat Renal Artery]
04100Z[1,2,3,4,5]	Bypass/Abd Aorta, Opn, No Dev, [Celiac Artery, Mesenteric Artery, Rt Renal Artery, Lt Renal Artery, Bilat Renal Artery]
04100[9,A][3,4,5]	Bypass/Abd Aorta, Opn, [Auto Venous Tissue, Auto Arterial Tissue], [Rt Renal Artery, Lt Renal Artery, Bilat Renal Artery]
04104[9,A,J,K,Z][3,4,5]	Bypass/Abd Aorta, Perc Endo, [Auto Venous Tissue, Auto Arterial Tissue, Synth Sub, Nonauto Tissue Sub, No Dev], [Rt Renal Artery, Lt Renal Artery, Bilat Renal Artery]
041C[0,4][J,Z][3,4,5]	Bypass/Common Iliac Artery, Rt, [Opn, Perc Endo], [Synth Sub, No Dev], [Renal Artery, Rt, Renal Artery, Lt, Renal Artery, Bilat]
041D[0,4][J,Z][3,4,5]	Bypass/Common Iliac Artery, Lt, [Opn, Perc Endo], [Synth Sub, No Dev], [Renal Artery, Rt, Renal Artery, Lt, Renal Artery, Bilat]
04S9*	Repos/Renal Artery, Rt
04SA*	Repos/Renal Artery, Lt
06S9*	Repos/Renal Vein, Rt
06SB*	Repos/Renal Vein, Lt
07T8*	Resect/Lymphatic, Int Mammary, Rt
07T9*	Resect/Lymphatic, Int Mammary, Lt
07TC*	Resect/Lymphatic, Pelvis
07TD*	Resect/Lymphatic, Aortic
07TH*	Resect/Lymphatic, Rt Inguinal
07TJ*	Resect/Lymphatic, Lt Inguinal
0T13*	Bypass/Kidney Pelvis, Rt
0T14*	Bypass/Kidney Pelvis, Lt
0T16*	Bypass/Ureter, Rt
0T17*	Bypass/Ureter, Lt
0T18*	Bypass/Ureters, Bilat
0T50*	Destr/Kidney, Rt
0T51*	Destr/Kidney, Lt
0T53*	Destr/Kidney Pelvis, Rt
0T54*	Destr/Kidney Pelvis, Lt
0T56*	Destr/Ureter, Rt
0T57*	Destr/Ureter, Lt
0T73*	Dilation/Kidney Pelvis, Rt
0T74*	Dilation/Kidney Pelvis, Lt
0T76[0,3,4,7,8]ZZ	Dilation/Ureter, Rt, [Opn, Perc, Perc Endo, Via Natrl or Artfcl Opng, Via Natrl or Artfcl Opng Endo]
0T77[0,3,4,7,8]ZZ	Dilation/Ureter, Lt, [Opn, Perc, Perc Endo, Via Natrl or Artfcl Opng, Via Natrl or Artfcl Opng Endo]
0T78[0,3,4]ZZ	Dilation/Ureters, Bilat, [Opn, Perc, Perc Endo]
0T82*	Div/Kidneys, Bilat
0T900ZX	Drain of Rt Kidney, Opn Appr, Diagnostic
0T90[0,3,4,7,8]0Z	Drain of Rt Kidney w/ Drain Dev, [Opn, Perc, Perc Endo, Via Natrl or Artfcl Opng, Via Natrl or Artfcl Opng Endo]
0T90[0,7,8]ZZ	Drain of Rt Kidney w/ No Dev, [Opn, Via Natrl or Artfcl Opng, Via Natrl or Artfcl Opng Endo]
0T910ZX	Drain of Lt Kidney, Opn Appr, Diagnostic
0T91[0,3,4,7,8]0Z	Drain of Lt Kidney w/ Drain Dev, [Opn, Perc, Perc Endo, Via Natrl or Artfcl Opng, Via Natrl or Artfcl Opng Endo]
0T91[0,7,8]ZZ	Drain of Lt Kidney w/ No Dev, [Opn, Via Natrl or Artfcl Opng, Via Natrl or Artfcl Opng Endo]
0T930ZX	Drain of Rt Kidney Pelvis, Opn Appr, Diagnostic
0T93[0,3,4,7,8]0Z	Drain of Rt Kidney Pelvis w/ Drain Dev, [Opn, Perc, Perc Endo, Via Natrl or Artfcl Opng, Via Natrl or Artfcl Opng Endo]
0T93[0,7,8]ZZ	Drain of Rt Kidney Pelvis w/ No Dev, [Opn, Via Natrl or Artfcl Opng, Via Natrl or Artfcl Opng Endo]
0T940ZX	Drain of Lt Kidney Pelvis, Opn Appr, Diagnostic
0T94[0,3,4,7,8]0Z	Drain of Lt Kidney Pelvis w/ Drain Dev, [Opn, Perc, Perc Endo, Via Natrl or Artfcl Opng, Via Natrl or Artfcl Opng Endo]
0T94[0,7,8]ZZ	Drain of Lt Kidney Pelvis w/ No Dev, [Opn, Via Natrl or Artfcl Opng, Via Natrl or Artfcl Opng Endo]
0T960ZX	Drain of Rt Ureter, Opn Appr, Diagnostic
0T96[0,3,4,7,8]ZZ	Drain/Ureter, Rt, [Opn, Perc, Perc Endo, Via Natrl or Artfcl Opng, Via Natrl or Artfcl Opng Endo]
0T970ZX	Drain of Lt Ureter, Opn Appr, Diagnostic
0T97[0,3,4,7,8]ZZ	Drain/Ureter, Lt, [Opn, Perc, Perc Endo, Via Natrl or Artfcl Opng, Via Natrl or Artfcl Opng Endo]
0T980ZX	Drain of Bilat Ureters, Opn Appr, Diagnostic
0T98[0,3,4,7,8]ZZ	Drain/Ureters, Bilat, [Opn, Perc, Perc Endo, Via Natrl or Artfcl Opng, Via Natrl or Artfcl Opng Endo]
0TB00ZX	Exc of Rt Kidney, Opn Appr, Diagnostic

T **Transfer DRG**   SP **Special Payment**   * **Code Range**   **6th and 7th Character of ZZ = No Device, No Qualifier ZX = No Device, Diagnostic**

ØTBØ[Ø,3,4,7,8]ZZ	Exc of Rt Kidney, [Opn, Perc, Perc Endo, Via Natrl or Artfcl Opng, Via Natrl or Artfcl Opng Endo]
ØTB1ØZX	Exc of Lt Kidney, Opn Appr, Diagnostic
ØTB1[Ø,3,4,7,8]ZZ	Exc of Lt Kidney, [Opn, Perc, Perc Endo, Via Natrl or Artfcl Opng, Via Natrl or Artfcl Opng Endo]
ØTB3ØZX	Exc of Rt Kidney Pelvis, Opn Appr, Diagnostic
ØTB3[Ø,3,4,7,8]ZZ	Exc of Rt Kidney Pelvis, [Opn, Perc, Perc Endo, Via Natrl or Artfcl Opng, Via Natrl or Artfcl Opng Endo]
ØTB4ØZX	Exc of Lt Kidney Pelvis, Opn Appr, Diagnostic
ØTB4[Ø,3,4,7,8]ZZ	Exc of Lt Kidney Pelvis, [Opn, Perc, Perc Endo, Via Natrl or Artfcl Opng, Via Natrl or Artfcl Opng Endo]
ØTB6ØZX	Exc of Rt Ureter, Opn Appr, Diagnostic
ØTB6[Ø,3,4,7,8]ZZ	Exc/Ureter, Rt, [Opn, Perc, Perc Endo, Via Natrl or Artfcl Opng, Via Natrl or Artfcl Opng Endo]
ØTB7ØZX	Exc of Lt Ureter, Opn Appr, Diagnostic
ØTB7[Ø,3,4,7,8]ZZ	Exc/Ureter, Lt, [Opn, Perc, Perc Endo, Via Natrl or Artfcl Opng, Via Natrl or Artfcl Opng Endo]
ØTCØ*	Extir/Kidney, Rt
ØTC1*	Extir/Kidney, Lt
ØTC3[Ø,3,4]ZZ	Extir/Kidney Pelvis, Rt, [Opn, Perc, Perc Endo]
ØTC4[Ø,3,4]ZZ	Extir/Kidney Pelvis, Lt, [Opn, Perc, Perc Endo]
ØTC6[Ø,3,4]ZZ	Extir/Ureter, Rt, [Opn, Perc, Perc Endo]
ØTC7[Ø,3,4]ZZ	Extir/Ureter, Lt, [Opn, Perc, Perc Endo]
ØTDØ*	Extract/Kidney, Rt
ØTD1*	Extract/Kidney, Lt
ØTF3[3,4]ZZ	Fragmn/Kidney Pelvis, Rt, [Perc, Perc Endo]
ØTF4[3,4]ZZ	Fragmn/Kidney Pelvis, Lt, [Perc, Perc Endo]
ØTH5[Ø,3,4,7,8]2Z	Insert/Kidney, [Opn, Perc, Perc Endo, Via Natrl or Artfcl Opng, Via Natrl or Artfcl Opng Endo], Monitoring Dev, NQ
ØTH9[Ø,3,4,7,8][2,M]Z	Insert/Ureter, [Opn, Perc, Perc Endo, Via Natrl or Artfcl Opng, Via Natrl or Artfcl Opng Endo], [Monitoring Dev, Stimulator Lead], NQ
ØTJ5[Ø,3,7]ZZ	Inspect/Kidney, [Opn, Perc, Via Natrl or Artfcl Opng]
ØTJ9[Ø,3,7]ZZ	Inspect/Ureter, [Opn, Perc, Via Natrl or Artfcl Opng]
ØTL3*	Occlsn/Kidney Pelvis, Rt
ØTL4*	Occlsn/Kidney Pelvis, Lt
ØTL6*	Occlsn/Ureter, Rt
ØTL7*	Occlsn/Ureter, Lt
ØTMØ*	Reattach/Kidney, Rt
ØTM1*	Reattach/Kidney, Lt
ØTM2*	Reattach/Kidneys, Bilat
ØTM3*	Reattach/Kidney Pelvis, Rt
ØTM4*	Reattach/Kidney Pelvis, Lt
ØTM6*	Reattach/Ureter, Rt
ØTM7*	Reattach/Ureter, Lt
ØTM8*	Reattach/Ureters, Bilat
ØTNØ*	Rls/Kidney, Rt
ØTN1*	Rls/Kidney, Lt
ØTN3*	Rls/Kidney Pelvis, Rt
ØTN4*	Rls/Kidney Pelvis, Lt
ØTN6*	Rls/Ureter, Rt
ØTN7*	Rls/Ureter, Lt
ØTP5[Ø,3,4,7,8][Ø,2,3,7,C,D,J,K]Z	Rmvl/Kidney, [Opn, Perc, Perc Endo, Via Natrl or Artfcl Opng, Via Natrl or Artfcl Opng Endo], [Drain Dev, Monitoring Dev, Inf Dev, Auto Tissue Sub, Extralum Dev, Intralum Dev, Synth Sub, Nonauto Tissue Sub], NQ
ØTP9XMZ	Rmvl of Stimulator Lead from Ureter, Ext Appr
ØTP9[Ø,3,4,7,8][Ø,2,3,7,C,D,J,K,M]Z	Rmvl/Ureter, [Opn, Perc, Perc Endo, Via Natrl or Artfcl Opng, Via Natrl or Artfcl Opng Endo], [Drain Dev, Monitoring Dev, Inf Dev, Auto Tissue Sub, Extralum Dev, Intralum Dev, Synth Sub, Nonauto Tissue Sub, Stimulator Lead], NQ
ØTQØ*	Repair/Kidney, Rt
ØTQ1*	Repair/Kidney, Lt
ØTQ3*	Repair/Kidney Pelvis, Rt
ØTQ4*	Repair/Kidney Pelvis, Lt
ØTQ6*	Repair/Ureter, Rt
ØTQ7*	Repair/Ureter, Lt
ØTR3*	Replace/Kidney Pelvis, Rt
ØTR4*	Replace/Kidney Pelvis, Lt
ØTR6*	Replace/Ureter, Rt
ØTR7*	Replace/Ureter, Lt
ØTSØ*	Repos/Kidney, Rt
ØTS1*	Repos/Kidney, Lt
ØTS2*	Repos/Kidneys, Bilat
ØTS3*	Repos/Kidney Pelvis, Rt
ØTS4*	Repos/Kidney Pelvis, Lt
ØTS6*	Repos/Ureter, Rt
ØTS7*	Repos/Ureter, Lt
ØTS8*	Repos/Ureters, Bilat

ØTTØ*	Resect/Kidney, Rt
ØTT1*	Resect/Kidney, Lt
ØTT2*	Resect/Kidneys, Bilat
ØTT3*	Resect/Kidney Pelvis, Rt
ØTT4*	Resect/Kidney Pelvis, Lt
ØTT6*	Resect/Ureter, Rt
ØTT7*	Resect/Ureter, Lt
ØTU3*	Supl/Kidney Pelvis, Rt
ØTU4*	Supl/Kidney Pelvis, Lt
ØTU6*	Supl/Ureter, Rt
ØTU7*	Supl/Ureter, Lt
ØTV3*	Restrict/Kidney Pelvis, Rt
ØTV4*	Restrict/Kidney Pelvis, Lt
ØTV6*	Restrict/Ureter, Rt
ØTV7*	Restrict/Ureter, Lt
ØTW5[Ø,3,4,7,8][Ø,2,3,7,C,D,J,K]Z	Rev/Kidney, [Opn, Perc, Perc Endo, Via Natrl or Artfcl Opng, Via Natrl or Artfcl Opng Endo], [Drain Dev, Monitoring Dev, Inf Dev, Auto Tissue Sub, Extralum Dev, Intralum Dev, Synth Sub, Nonauto Tissue Sub], NQ
ØTW9[Ø,3,4,7,8][Ø,2,3,7,C,D,J,K,M]Z	Rev/Ureter, [Opn, Perc, Perc Endo, Via Natrl or Artfcl Opng, Via Natrl or Artfcl Opng Endo], [Drain Dev, Monitoring Dev, Inf Dev, Auto Tissue Sub, Extralum Dev, Intralum Dev, Synth Sub, Nonauto Tissue Sub, Stimulator Lead], NQ
ØWBH[Ø,3,4]ZZ	Exc/Retroperitoneum, [Opn, Perc, Perc Endo]
ØWQF[Ø,3,4]ZZ	Rpr/Abd Wall, [Opn, Perc, Perc Endo]

DRG 657 **Kidney and Ureter Procedures for Neoplasm with CC**
GMLOS 4.2   AMLOS 5.Ø   RW 2.ØØ91

Select principal diagnosis AND operating room procedures listed under DRG 656

DRG 658 **Kidney and Ureter Procedures for Neoplasm without CC/MCC**
GMLOS 2.6   AMLOS 3.Ø   RW 1.5337

Select principal diagnosis AND operating room procedures listed under DRG 656

DRG 659 **Kidney and Ureter Procedures for Non-neoplasm with MCC**
GMLOS 7.5   AMLOS 1Ø.1   RW 3.4848   T

Select only operating room procedures listed under DRG 656

DRG 660 **Kidney and Ureter Procedures for Non-neoplasm with CC**
GMLOS 4.1   AMLOS 5.5   RW 1.9Ø3Ø   T

Select only operating room procedures listed under DRG 656

DRG 661 **Kidney and Ureter Procedures for Non-neoplasm without CC/MCC**
GMLOS 2.3   AMLOS 2.7   RW 1.3981   T

Select only operating room procedures listed under DRG 656

DRG 662 **Minor Bladder Procedures with MCC**
GMLOS 7.6   AMLOS 1Ø.Ø   RW 2.8897

Operating Room Procedures

ØJQC*	Repair/SQ Tissue & Fascia, Pelvic Region
ØT1B[Ø,4]ZD	Bypass/Bladder, [Opn, Perc Endo], No Dev, Cutaneous
ØT5B[Ø,3,4]ZZ	Destr/Bladder, [Opn, Perc, Perc Endo]
ØT5C[Ø,3,4]ZZ	Destr/Bladder Neck, [Opn, Perc, Perc Endo]
ØT8C*	Div/Bladder Neck
ØT9BØZX	Drain of Bladder, Opn Appr, Diagnostic
ØT9B[Ø,Z]Z	Drain/Bladder, Opn, [Drain Dev, No Dev], NQ
ØT9CØZX	Drain of Bladder Neck, Opn Appr, Diagnostic
ØT9C[Ø,Z]Z	Drain/Bladder Neck, Opn, [Drain Dev, No Dev], NQ
ØTBBØZX	Exc of Bladder, Opn Appr, Diagnostic
ØTBCØZX	Exc of Bladder Neck, Opn Appr, Diagnostic
ØTCB[Ø,3,4]ZZ	Extir/Bladder, [Opn, Perc, Perc Endo]
ØTCC[Ø,3,4]ZZ	Extir/Bladder Neck, [Opn, Perc, Perc Endo]
ØTHB[Ø,3,4,7,8][2,L,M]Z	Insert/Bladder, [Opn, Perc, Perc Endo, Via Natrl or Artfcl Opng, Via Natrl or Artfcl Opng Endo], [Monitoring Dev, Artfcl Sphincter, Stimulator Lead], NQ
ØTHC*	Insert/Bladder Neck
ØTHD[Ø,3,4,7,8,X]LZ	Insert/Urethra, [Opn, Perc, Perc Endo, Via Natrl or Artfcl Opng, Via Natrl or Artfcl Opng Endo, Ext], Artfcl Sphincter, NQ

Surgical	Medical	CC Indicator	MCC Indicator	Procedure Proxy	PDxMCC PDx acts as own MCC	PDxCC PDx acts as own CC

ØTJB[Ø,3,4,7]ZZ   Inspect/Bladder, [Opn, Perc, Perc Endo, Via Natrl or Artfcl Opng]
ØTLB*   Occlsn/Bladder
ØTLC*   Occlsn/Bladder Neck
ØTNB[Ø,3,4]ZZ   Rls/Bladder, [Opn, Perc, Perc Endo]
ØTNC[Ø,3,4]ZZ   Rls/Bladder Neck, [Opn, Perc, Perc Endo]
ØTPBXMZ   Rmvl of Stimulator Lead from Bladder, Ext Appr
ØTPB[Ø,3,4,7,8][Ø,2,3,7,C,D,J,K,L,M]Z Rmvl/Bladder, [Opn, Perc, Perc Endo, Via Natrl or Artfcl Opng, Via Natrl or Artfcl Opng Endo], [Drain Dev, Monitoring Dev, Inf Dev, Auto Tissue Sub, Extralum Dev, Intralum Dev, Synth Sub, Nonauto Tissue Sub, Artfcl Sphincter, Stimulator Lead], NQ
ØTQD[Ø,3,4]ZZ   Rpr/Urethra, [Opn, Perc, Perc Endo]
ØTSC*   Repos/Bladder Neck
ØTSD*   Repos/Urethra
ØTUC*   Supl/Bladder Neck
ØTWB[Ø,3,4,7,8][Ø,2,3,7,C,D,J,K,L,M]Z Rev/Bladder, [Opn, Perc, Perc Endo, Via Natrl or Artfcl Opng, Via Natrl or Artfcl Opng Endo], [Drain Dev, Monitoring Dev, Inf Dev, Auto Tissue Sub, Extralum Dev, Intralum Dev, Synth Sub, Nonauto Tissue Sub, Artfcl Sphincter, Stimulator Lead], NQ
ØUSG*   Repos/Vagina
ØW3R*   Control/Genitourinary Tract
ØWQFXZ[2,Z]   Rpr/Abd Wall, Ext, No Dev, [Stoma, NQ]
OR
ØTQB[Ø,3,4]ZZ   Rpr/Bladder, [Opn, Perc, Perc Endo]
                  AND
ØWQFXZ[2,Z]   Rpr/Abd Wall, Ext, No Dev, [Stoma, NQ]

DRG 663 — Minor Bladder Procedures with CC
GMLOS 4.1   AMLOS 5.4   RW 1.6652

Select operating room procedures or procedure combination listed under DRG 662

DRG 664 — Minor Bladder Procedures without CC/MCC
GMLOS 2.Ø   AMLOS 2.5   RW 1.2987

Select operating room procedures or procedure combination listed under DRG 662

DRG 665 — Prostatectomy with MCC
GMLOS 8.9   AMLOS 11.2   RW 3.1132

Operating Room Procedures
ØV5Ø*   Destr/Prostate
ØVBØ[7,8]ZZ   Exc/Prostate, [Via Natrl or Artfcl Opng, Via Natrl or Artfcl Opng Endo]
ØVTØ*   Resect/Prostate
OR
ØVTØ*   Resect/Prostate
                  AND
ØVT3*   Resect/Seminal Vesicles, Bilat

DRG 666 — Prostatectomy with CC
GMLOS 4.6   AMLOS 6.3   RW 1.7878

Select operating room procedures or procedure combination listed under DRG 665

DRG 667 — Prostatectomy without CC/MCC
GMLOS 2.3   AMLOS 3.Ø   RW Ø.9964

Select operating room procedures or procedure combination listed under DRG 665

DRG 668 — Transurethral Procedures with MCC
GMLOS 6.3   AMLOS 8.4   RW 2.4521

Operating Room Procedures
ØT5B[7,8]ZZ   Destr/Bladder, [Via Natrl or Artfcl Opng, Via Natrl or Artfcl Opng Endo]
ØT5C[7,8]ZZ   Destr/Bladder Neck, [Via Natrl or Artfcl Opng, Via Natrl or Artfcl Opng Endo]
ØT9B[3,4,7,8]ZX   Drain/Bladder, [Perc, Perc Endo, Via Natrl or Artfcl Opng, Via Natrl or Artfcl Opng Endo]

ØT9C[3,4,7,8]ZX   Drain/Bladder Neck, [Perc, Perc Endo, Via Natrl or Artfcl Opng Endo]
ØTBB[3,4,7,8]ZX   Exc/Bladder, [Perc, Perc Endo, Via Natrl or Artfcl Opng, Via Natrl or Artfcl Opng Endo]
ØTBB[7,8]ZZ   Exc/Bladder, [Via Natrl or Artfcl Opng, Via Natrl or Artfcl Opng Endo]
ØTBC[3,4,7,8]ZX   Exc/Bladder Neck, [Perc, Perc Endo, Via Natrl or Artfcl Opng, Via Natrl or Artfcl Opng Endo]
ØTBC[7,8]ZZ   Exc/Bladder Neck, [Via Natrl or Artfcl Opng, Via Natrl or Artfcl Opng Endo]
ØTC3[7,8]ZZ   Extir/Kidney Pelvis, Rt, [Via Natrl or Artfcl Opng, Via Natrl or Artfcl Opng Endo]
ØTC4[7,8]ZZ   Extir/Kidney Pelvis, Lt, [Via Natrl or Artfcl Opng, Via Natrl or Artfcl Opng Endo]
ØTC6[7,8]ZZ   Extir/Ureter, Rt, [Via Natrl or Artfcl Opng, Via Natrl or Artfcl Opng Endo]
ØTC7[7,8]ZZ   Extir/Ureter, Lt, [Via Natrl or Artfcl Opng, Via Natrl or Artfcl Opng Endo]
ØTNB[7,8]ZZ   Rls/Bladder, [Via Natrl or Artfcl Opng, Via Natrl or Artfcl Opng Endo]
ØTNC[7,8]ZZ   Rls/Bladder Neck, [Via Natrl or Artfcl Opng, Via Natrl or Artfcl Opng Endo]
ØV9ØØZX   Drain of Prostate, Opn Appr, Diagnostic
ØVBØØZX   Exc of Prostate, Opn Appr, Diagnostic

DRG 669 — Transurethral Procedures with CC
GMLOS 3.1   AMLOS 4.1   RW 1.3111

Select operating room procedures listed under DRG 668

DRG 670 — Transurethral Procedures without CC/MCC
GMLOS 2.1   AMLOS 2.6   RW Ø.92Ø7

Select operating room procedures listed under DRG 668

DRG 671 — Urethral Procedures with CC/MCC
GMLOS 4.1   AMLOS 5.4   RW 1.57Ø5

Operating Room Procedures
ØT7D[Ø,3,4]ZZ   Dilation/Urethra, [Opn, Perc, Perc Endo]
ØT9D[Ø,3,4,7,8,X][Ø,Z]Z Drain/Urethra, [Opn, Perc, Perc Endo, Via Natrl or Artfcl Opng, Via Natrl or Artfcl Opng Endo, Ext], [Drain Dev, No Dev], NQ
ØTBD[Ø,3,4,7,8,X]ZZ Exc/Urethra, [Opn, Perc, Perc Endo, Via Natrl or Artfcl Opng, Via Natrl or Artfcl Opng Endo, Ext]
ØTCD[Ø,3,4]ZZ   Extir/Urethra, [Opn, Perc, Perc Endo]
ØTHD[Ø,3,4,7,8,X]2 ZInsert/Urethra, [Opn, Perc, Perc Endo, Via Natrl or Artfcl Opng, Via Natrl or Artfcl Opng Endo, Ext], Monitoring Dev, NQ
ØTJDØZZ   Inspect of Urethra, Opn Appr
ØTLD*   Occlsn/Urethra
ØTMD*   Reattach/Urethra
ØTND*   Rls/Urethra
ØTPDXLZ   Rmvl of Artif Sphincter from Urethra, Extern Appr
ØTPD[Ø,3,4,7,8][Ø,2,3,7,C,D,J,K,L]Z Rmvl/Urethra, [Opn, Perc, Perc Endo, Via Natrl or Artfcl Opng, Via Natrl or Artfcl Opng Endo], [Drain Dev, Monitoring Dev, Inf Dev, Auto Tissue Sub, Extralum Dev, Intralum Dev, Synth Sub, Nonauto Tissue Sub, Artfcl Sphincter], NQ
ØTQD[7,8,X]ZZ   Rpr/Urethra, [Via Natrl or Artfcl Opng, Via Natrl or Artfcl Opng Endo, Ext]
ØTRD*   Replace/Urethra
ØTUD*   Supl/Urethra
ØTVD*   Restrict/Urethra
ØTWD[Ø,3,4,7,8][Ø,2,3,7,C,D,J,K,L]Z Rev/Urethra, [Opn, Perc, Perc Endo, Via Natrl or Artfcl Opng, Via Natrl or Artfcl Opng Endo], [Drain Dev, Monitoring Dev, Inf Dev, Auto Tissue Sub, Extralum Dev, Intralum Dev, Synth Sub, Nonauto Tissue Sub, Artfcl Sphincter], NQ

T Transfer DRG   SP Special Payment   * Code Range   6th and 7th Character of ZZ = No Device, No Qualifier ZX = No Device, Diagnostic

DRG 672   Urethral Procedures without CC/MCC
    GMLOS 1.9   AMLOS 2.4   RW 0.8742

Select operating room procedures listed under DRG 671

DRG 673   Other Kidney and Urinary Tract Procedures with MCC
    GMLOS 7.3   AMLOS 10.3   RW 3.3559

Operating Room Procedures

00HE[0,3,4]MZ	Insert/Cranial Nerve, [Opn, Perc, Perc Endo], Neurostimulator Lead, NQ
00HU[0,3,4]MZ	Insert/Spinal Canal, [Opn, Perc, Perc Endo], Neurostimulator Lead, NQ
00HV[0,3,4]MZ	Insert/Spinal Cord, [Opn, Perc, Perc Endo], Neurostimulator Lead, NQ
00PU[0,3,4]MZ	Rmvl/Spinal Canal, [Opn, Perc, Perc Endo], Neurostimulator Lead, NQ
00PV[0,3,4]MZ	Rmvl/Spinal Cord, [Opn, Perc, Perc Endo], Neurostimulator Lead, NQ
01HY[0,3,4]MZ	Insert/Peripheral Nerve, [Opn, Perc, Perc Endo], Neurostimulator Lead, NQ
02HV[0,3,4][2,D]Z	Insert/Superior Vena Cava, [Opn, Perc, Perc Endo], [Monitoring Dev, Intralum Dev], NQ
02JA0ZZ	Inspect of Heart, Opn Appr
02JY0ZZ	Inspect of Great Vessel, Opn Appr
02LV*	Occlsn/Superior Vena Cava
02UW[3,4]JZ	Supl/Thoracic Aorta, [Perc, Perc Endo], Synth Sub, NQ
02VV*	Restrict/Superior Vena Cava
02VW[0,3,4]DZ	Restrict/Thoracic Aorta, [Opn, Perc, Perc Endo], Intralum Dev, NQ
03130ZD	Bypass Rt Subclavian Artery to Up Arm Vein, Opn Appr
03140ZD	Bypass Lt Subclavian Artery to Up Arm Vein, Opn Appr
03150ZD	Bypass Rt Axillary Artery to Up Arm Vein, Opn Appr
03160ZD	Bypass Lt Axillary Artery to Upr Arm Vein, Opn Appr
03170[9,A,J,K,Z][D,F]	Bypass/Brachial Artery, Rt, Opn, [Auto Venous Tissue, Auto Arterial Tissue, Synth Sub, Nonauto Tissue Sub, No Dev], [Upr Arm Vein, Lwr Arm Vein]
03180[9,A,J,K,Z][D,F]	Bypass/Brachial Artery, Lt, Opn, [Auto Venous Tissue, Auto Arterial Tissue, Synth Sub, Nonauto Tissue Sub, No Dev], [Upr Arm Vein, Lwr Arm Vein]
03190[9,A,J,K,Z]F	Bypass/Ulnar Artery, Rt, Opn, [Auto Venous Tissue, Auto Arterial Tissue, Synth Sub, Nonauto Tissue Sub, No Dev], Lwr Arm Vein
031A0[9,A,J,K,Z]F	Bypass/Ulnar Artery, Lt, Opn, [Auto Venous Tissue, Auto Arterial Tissue, Synth Sub, Nonauto Tissue Sub, No Dev], Lwr Arm Vein
031B0[9,A,J,K,Z]F	Bypass/Radial Artery, Rt, Opn, [Auto Venous Tissue, Auto Arterial Tissue, Synth Sub, Nonauto Tissue Sub, No Dev], Lwr Arm Vein
031C0[9,A,J,K,Z]F	Bypass/Radial Artery, Lt, Opn, [Auto Venous Tissue, Auto Arterial Tissue, Synth Sub, Nonauto Tissue Sub, No Dev], Lwr Arm Vein
03733[4,D,Z]Z	Dilation/Subclavian Artery, Rt, Perc, [Drug-eluting Intralum Dev, Intralum Dev, No Dev], NQ
03743[4,D,Z]Z	Dilation/Subclavian Artery, Lt, Perc, [Drug-eluting Intralum Dev, Intralum Dev, No Dev], NQ
03773[4,D,Z]Z	Dilation/Brachial Artery, Rt, Perc, [Drug-eluting Intralum Dev, Intralum Dev, No Dev], NQ
03783[4,D,Z]Z	Dilation/Brachial Artery, Lt, Perc, [Drug-eluting Intralum Dev, Intralum Dev, No Dev], NQ
03793[4,D,Z]Z	Dilation/Ulnar Artery, Rt, Perc, [Drug-eluting Intralum Dev, Intralum Dev, No Dev], NQ
037A3[4,D,Z]Z	Dilation/Ulnar Artery, Lt, Perc, [Drug-eluting Intralum Dev, Intralum Dev, No Dev], NQ
037Y3[4,D,Z]Z	Dilation/Upr Artery, Perc, [Drug-eluting Intralum Dev, Intralum Dev, No Dev], NQ
039S[0,3,4]ZX	Drain/Temporal Artery, Rt, [Opn, Perc, Perc Endo]
039T[0,3,4]ZX	Drain/Temporal Artery, Lt, [Opn, Perc, Perc Endo]
03BS[0,3,4]ZX	Exc/Temporal Artery, Rt, [Opn, Perc, Perc Endo]
03BT[0,3,4]ZX	Exc/Temporal Artery, Lt, [Opn, Perc, Perc Endo]
03CY*	Extir/Upr Artery
03LG[0,3,4][B,D]Z	Occlsn/Intracranial Artery, [Opn, Perc, Perc Endo], [Bioactive Intralum Dev, Intralum Dev], NQ
03LH[0,3,4][B,D]Z	Occlsn/Common Carotid Artery, Rt, [Opn, Perc, Perc Endo], [Bioactive Intralum Dev, Intralum Dev], NQ
03LJ[0,3,4][B,D]Z	Occlsn/Common Carotid Artery, Lt, [Opn, Perc, Perc Endo], [Bioactive Intralum Dev, Intralum Dev], NQ
03LK[0,3,4][B,D]Z	Occlsn/Int Carotid Artery, Rt, [Opn, Perc, Perc Endo], [Bioactive Intralum Dev, Intralum Dev], NQ
03LL[0,3,4][B,D]Z	Occlsn/Int Carotid Artery, Lt, [Opn, Perc, Perc Endo], [Bioactive Intralum Dev, Intralum Dev], NQ
03LM[0,3,4][B,D]Z	Occlsn/Ext Carotid Artery, Rt, [Opn, Perc, Perc Endo], [Bioactive Intralum Dev, Intralum Dev], NQ
03LN[0,3,4][B,D]Z	Occlsn/Ext Carotid Artery, Lt, [Opn, Perc, Perc Endo], [Bioactive Intralum Dev, Intralum Dev], NQ
03LP[0,3,4][B,D]Z	Occlsn/Vert Artery, Rt, [Opn, Perc, Perc Endo], [Bioactive Intralum Dev, Intralum Dev], NQ
03LQ[0,3,4][B,D]Z	Occlsn/Vert Artery, Lt, [Opn, Perc, Perc Endo], [Bioactive Intralum Dev, Intralum Dev], NQ
03LR[0,3,4]DZ	Occlsn/Face Artery, [Opn, Perc, Perc Endo], Intralum Dev, NQ
03LS[0,3,4]DZ	Occlsn/Temporal Artery, Rt, [Opn, Perc, Perc Endo], Intralum Dev, NQ
03LT[0,3,4]DZ	Occlsn/Temporal Artery, Lt, [Opn, Perc, Perc Endo], Intralum Dev, NQ
03PY[0,3,4][7,J,K]Z	Rmvl/Upr Artery, [Opn, Perc, Perc Endo], [Auto Tissue Sub, Synth Sub, Nonauto Tissue Sub], NQ
03QY*	Repair/Upr Artery
03VG[0,3,4][B,D]Z	Restrict/Intracranial Artery, [Opn, Perc, Perc Endo], [Bioactive Intralum Dev, Intralum Dev], NQ
03VH[0,3,4][B,D]Z	Restrict/Common Carotid Artery, Rt, [Opn, Perc, Perc Endo], [Bioactive Intralum Dev, Intralum Dev], NQ
03VJ[0,3,4][B,D]Z	Restrict/Common Carotid Artery, Lt, [Opn, Perc, Perc Endo], [Bioactive Intralum Dev, Intralum Dev], NQ
03VK[0,3,4][B,D]Z	Restrict/Int Carotid Artery, Rt, [Opn, Perc, Perc Endo], [Bioactive Intralum Dev, Intralum Dev], NQ
03VL[0,3,4][B,D]Z	Restrict/Int Carotid Artery, Lt, [Opn, Perc, Perc Endo], [Bioactive Intralum Dev, Intralum Dev], NQ
03VM[0,3,4][B,D]Z	Restrict/Ext Carotid Artery, Rt, [Opn, Perc, Perc Endo], [Bioactive Intralum Dev, Intralum Dev], NQ
03VN[0,3,4][B,D]Z	Restrict/Ext Carotid Artery, Lt, [Opn, Perc, Perc Endo], [Bioactive Intralum Dev, Intralum Dev], NQ
03VP[0,3,4][B,D]Z	Restrict/Vert Artery, Rt, [Opn, Perc, Perc Endo], [Bioactive Intralum Dev, Intralum Dev], NQ
03VQ[0,3,4][B,D]Z	Restrict/Vert Artery, Lt, [Opn, Perc, Perc Endo], [Bioactive Intralum Dev, Intralum Dev], NQ
03VR[0,3,4]DZ	Restrict/Face Artery, [Opn, Perc, Perc Endo], Intralum Dev, NQ
03VS[0,3,4]DZ	Restrict/Temporal Artery, Rt, [Opn, Perc, Perc Endo], Intralum Dev, NQ
03VT[0,3,4]DZ	Restrict/Temporal Artery, Lt, [Opn, Perc, Perc Endo], Intralum Dev, NQ
03VU[0,3,4]DZ	Restrict/Thyroid Artery, Rt, [Opn, Perc, Perc Endo], Intralum Dev, NQ
03VV[0,3,4]DZ	Restrict/Thyroid Artery, Lt, [Opn, Perc, Perc Endo], Intralum Dev, NQ
03WY[0,3,4]JZ	Rev/Upr Artery, [Opn, Perc, Perc Endo], Synth Sub, NQ
0459*	Destr/Renal Artery, Rt
045A*	Destr/Renal Artery, Lt
04703[4,D,Z]Z	Dilation/Abd Aorta, Perc, [Drug-eluting Intralum Dev, Intralum Dev, No Dev], NQ
04713[4,D,Z]Z	Dilation/Celiac Artery, Perc, [Drug-eluting Intralum Dev, Intralum Dev, No Dev], NQ
04723[4,D,Z]Z	Dilation/Gastric Artery, Perc, [Drug-eluting Intralum Dev, Intralum Dev, No Dev], NQ
04733[4,D,Z]Z	Dilation/Hepatic Artery, Perc, [Drug-eluting Intralum Dev, Intralum Dev, No Dev], NQ
04743[4,D,Z]Z	Dilation/Splenic Artery, Perc, [Drug-eluting Intralum Dev, Intralum Dev, No Dev], NQ
04753[4,D,Z]Z	Dilation/Superior Mesenteric Artery, Perc, [Drug-eluting Intralum Dev, Intralum Dev, No Dev], NQ
04763[4,D,Z]Z	Dilation/Colic Artery, Rt, Perc, [Drug-eluting Intralum Dev, Intralum Dev, No Dev], NQ
04773[4,D,Z]Z	Dilation/Colic Artery, Lt, Perc, [Drug-eluting Intralum Dev, Intralum Dev, No Dev], NQ
04783[4,D,Z]Z	Dilation/Colic Artery, Mid, Perc, [Drug-eluting Intralum Dev, Intralum Dev, No Dev], NQ
04793[4,D,Z]Z	Dilation/Renal Artery, Rt, Perc, [Drug-eluting Intralum Dev, Intralum Dev, No Dev], NQ
047A3[4,D,Z]Z	Dilation/Renal Artery, Lt, Perc, [Drug-eluting Intralum Dev, Intralum Dev, No Dev], NQ
047B3[4,D,Z]Z	Dilation/Inferior Mesenteric Artery, Perc, [Drug-eluting Intralum Dev, Intralum Dev, No Dev], NQ
047C3[4,D,Z]Z	Dilation/Common Iliac Artery, Rt, Perc, [Drug-eluting Intralum Dev, Intralum Dev, No Dev], NQ
047D3[4,D,Z]Z	Dilation/Common Iliac Artery, Lt, Perc, [Drug-eluting Intralum Dev, Intralum Dev, No Dev], NQ
047E3[4,D,Z]Z	Dilation/Int Iliac Artery, Rt, Perc, [Drug-eluting Intralum Dev, Intralum Dev, No Dev], NQ
047F3[4,D,Z]Z	Dilation/Int Iliac Artery, Lt, Perc, [Drug-eluting Intralum Dev, Intralum Dev, No Dev], NQ

Surgical   **Medical**   **CC Indicator**   **MCC Indicator**   **Procedure Proxy**   **PDxMCC** PDx acts as own MCC   **PDxCC** PDx acts as own CC

Code	Description
047H3[4,D,Z]Z	Dilation/Ext Iliac Artery, Rt, Perc, [Drug-eluting Intralum Dev, Intralum Dev, No Dev], NQ
047J3[4,D,Z]Z	Dilation/Ext Iliac Artery, Lt, Perc, [Drug-eluting Intralum Dev, Intralum Dev, No Dev], NQ
047K041	Dilation Rt Fem Art w Drug-elut Intralum, Drug Blln, Opn
047K0D1	Dilation Rt Fem Art w Intralum Dev, Drug Blln, Opn
047K0Z1	Dilation of Rt Fem Art using Drug Blln, Opn Appr
047K341	Dilation Rt Fem Art w Drug-elut Intralum, Drug Blln, Perc
047K3D1	Dilation Rt Fem Art w Intralum Dev, Drug Blln, Perc
047K3Z1	Dilation of Rt Fem Art using Drug Blln, Perc Appr
047K3[4,D,Z]Z	Dilation/Femor Artery, Rt, Perc, [Drug-eluting Intralum Dev, Intralum Dev, No Dev], NQ
047K441	Dilation Rt Fem Art w Drug-elut Intralum, Drug Blln, Perc Endo
047K4D1	Dilation Rt Fem Art w Intralum Dev, Drug Blln, Perc Endo
047K4Z1	Dilation of Rt Fem Art using Drug Blln, Perc Endo Appr
047L041	Dilation Lt Fem Art w Drug-elut Intralum, Drug Blln, Opn
047L0D1	Dilation Lt Fem Art w Intralum Dev, Drug Blln, Opn
047L0Z1	Dilation of Lt Fem Art using Drug Blln, Opn Appr
047L341	Dilation Lt Fem Art w Drug-elut Intralum, Drug Blln, Perc
047L3D1	Dilation Lt Fem Art w Intralum Dev, Drug Blln, Perc
047L3Z1	Dilation of Lt Fem Art using Drug Blln, Perc Appr
047L3[4,D,Z]Z	Dilation/Femor Artery, Lt, Perc, [Drug-eluting Intralum Dev, Intralum Dev, No Dev], NQ
047L441	Dilation Lt Fem Art w Drug-elut Intralum, Drug Blln, Perc Endo
047L4D1	Dilation Lt Fem Art w Intralum Dev, Drug Blln, Perc Endo
047L4Z1	Dilation of Lt Fem Art using Drug Blln, Perc Endo Appr
047M041	Dilation Rt Popl Art w Drug-elut Intralum, Drug Blln, Opn
047M0D1	Dilation Rt Popl Art w Intralum Dev, Drug Blln, Opn
047M0Z1	Dilation of Rt Popl Art using Drug Blln, Opn Appr
047M341	Dilation Rt Popl Art w Drug-elut Intralum, Drug Blln, Perc
047M3D1	Dilation Rt Popl Art w Intralum Dev, Drug Blln, Perc
047M3Z1	Dilation of Rt Popl Art using Drug Blln, Perc Appr
047M441	Dilation Rt Popl Art w Drug-elut Intralum, Drug Blln, Perc Endo
047M4D1	Dilation Rt Popl Art w Intralum Dev, Drug Blln, Perc Endo
047M4Z1	Dilation of Rt Popl Art using Drug Blln, Perc Endo Appr
047N041	Dilation Lt Popl Art w Drug-elut Intralum, Drug Blln, Opn
047N0D1	Dilation Lt Popl Art w Intralum Dev, Drug Blln, Opn
047N0Z1	Dilation of Lt Popl Art using Drug Blln, Opn Appr
047N341	Dilation Lt Popl Art w Drug-elut Intralum, Drug Blln, Perc
047N3D1	Dilation Lt Popl Art w Intralum Dev, Drug Blln, Perc
047N3Z1	Dilation of Lt Popl Art using Drug Blln, Perc Appr
047N441	Dilation Lt Popl Art w Drug-elut Intralum, Drug Blln, Perc Endo
047N4D1	Dilation Lt Popl Art w Intralum Dev, Drug Blln, Perc Endo
047N4Z1	Dilation of Lt Popl Art using Drug Blln, Perc Endo Appr
047Y3[4,D,Z]Z	Dilation/Lwr Artery, Perc, [Drug-eluting Intralum Dev, Intralum Dev, No Dev], NQ
04C1*	Extir/Celiac Artery
04C2*	Extir/Gastric Artery
04C3*	Extir/Hepatic Artery
04C4*	Extir/Splenic Artery
04C5*	Extir/Superior Mesenteric Artery
04C6*	Extir/Colic Artery, Rt
04C7*	Extir/Colic Artery, Lt
04C8*	Extir/Colic Artery, Mid
04C9*	Extir/Renal Artery, Rt
04CA*	Extir/Renal Artery, Lt
04CB*	Extir/Inferior Mesenteric Artery
04CC*	Extir/Common Iliac Artery, Rt
04CD*	Extir/Common Iliac Artery, Lt
04CE*	Extir/Int Iliac Artery, Rt
04CF*	Extir/Int Iliac Artery, Lt
04CH*	Extir/Ext Iliac Artery, Rt
04CJ*	Extir/Ext Iliac Artery, Lt
04CY*	Extir/Lwr Artery
04L9*	Occlsn/Renal Artery, Rt
04LA*	Occlsn/Renal Artery, Lt
04QY*	Repair/Lwr Artery
04R9*	Replace/Renal Artery, Rt
04RA*	Replace/Renal Artery, Lt
04S0*	Repos/Abd Aorta
04S1*	Repos/Celiac Artery
04S2*	Repos/Gastric Artery
04S3*	Repos/Hepatic Artery
04S4*	Repos/Splenic Artery
04S5*	Repos/Superior Mesenteric Artery
04S6*	Repos/Colic Artery, Rt
04S7*	Repos/Colic Artery, Lt
04S8*	Repos/Colic Artery, Mid
04SB*	Repos/Inferior Mesenteric Artery
04U0[3,4]JZ	Supl/Abd Aorta, [Perc, Perc Endo], Synth Sub, NQ
04U9[0,3,4][7,J]Z	Supl/Renal Artery, Rt, [Opn, Perc, Perc Endo], [Auto Tissue Sub, Synth Sub], NQ
04UA[0,3,4][7,J]Z	Supl/Renal Artery, Lt, [Opn, Perc, Perc Endo], [Auto Tissue Sub, Synth Sub], NQ
04V0[0,3,4][D,Z]Z	Restrict/Abd Aorta, [Opn, Perc, Perc Endo], [Intralum Dev, No Dev], NQ
04V1[0,3,4]ZZ	Restrict/Celiac Artery, [Opn, Perc, Perc Endo]
04V2[0,3,4]ZZ	Restrict/Gastric Artery, [Opn, Perc, Perc Endo]
04V3[0,3,4]ZZ	Restrict/Hepatic Artery, [Opn, Perc, Perc Endo]
04V4[0,3,4]ZZ	Restrict/Splenic Artery, [Opn, Perc, Perc Endo]
04V5[0,3,4]ZZ	Restrict/Superior Mesenteric Artery, [Opn, Perc, Perc Endo]
04V6[0,3,4]ZZ	Restrict/Colic Artery, Rt, [Opn, Perc, Perc Endo]
04V7[0,3,4]ZZ	Restrict/Colic Artery, Lt, [Opn, Perc, Perc Endo]
04V8[0,3,4]ZZ	Restrict/Colic Artery, Mid, [Opn, Perc, Perc Endo]
04V9[0,3,4][D,Z]Z	Restrict/Renal Artery, Rt, [Opn, Perc, Perc Endo], [Intralum Dev, No Dev], NQ
04VA[0,3,4][D,Z]Z	Restrict/Renal Artery, Lt, [Opn, Perc, Perc Endo], [Intralum Dev, No Dev], NQ
04VB[0,3,4]ZZ	Restrict/Inferior Mesenteric Artery, [Opn, Perc, Perc Endo]
05793[D,Z]Z	Dilation/Brachial Vein, Rt, Perc, [Intralum Dev, No Dev], NQ
057A3[D,Z]Z	Dilation/Brachial Vein, Lt, Perc, [Intralum Dev, No Dev], NQ
057B3[D,Z]Z	Dilation/Basilic Vein, Rt, Perc, [Intralum Dev, No Dev], NQ
057C3[D,Z]Z	Dilation/Basilic Vein, Lt, Perc, [Intralum Dev, No Dev], NQ
057D3[D,Z]Z	Dilation/Cephalic Vein, Rt, Perc, [Intralum Dev, No Dev], NQ
057F3[D,Z]Z	Dilation/Cephalic Vein, Lt, Perc, [Intralum Dev, No Dev], NQ
05CY*	Extir/Upr Vein
05QY*	Repair/Upr Vein
06703[D,Z]Z	Dilation/Inferior Vena Cava, Perc, [Intralum Dev, No Dev], NQ
06C9*	Extir/Renal Vein, Rt
06CB*	Extir/Renal Vein, Lt
06CY*	Extir/Lwr Vein
06H0[0,3,4]DZ	Insert/Inferior Vena Cava, [Opn, Perc, Perc Endo], Intralum Dev, NQ
06L0*	Occlsn/Inferior Vena Cava
06L9[0,3,4][C,Z]Z	Occlsn/Renal Vein, Rt, [Opn, Perc, Perc Endo], [Extralum Dev, No Dev], NQ
06LB[0,3,4][C,Z]Z	Occlsn/Renal Vein, Lt, [Opn, Perc, Perc Endo], [Extralum Dev, No Dev], NQ
06QY*	Repair/Lwr Vein
06S0*	Repos/Inferior Vena Cava
06S1*	Repos/Splenic Vein
06S2*	Repos/Gastric Vein
06S3*	Repos/Esophageal Vein
06S4*	Repos/Hepatic Vein
06S5*	Repos/Superior Mesenteric Vein
06S6*	Repos/Inferior Mesenteric Vein
06S7*	Repos/Colic Vein
06S8*	Repos/Portal Vein
06U9[0,3,4][7,J]Z	Supl/Renal Vein, Rt, [Opn, Perc, Perc Endo], [Auto Tissue Sub, Synth Sub], NQ
06UB[0,3,4][7,J]Z	Supl/Renal Vein, Lt, [Opn, Perc, Perc Endo], [Auto Tissue Sub, Synth Sub], NQ
06V0*	Restrict/Inferior Vena Cava
06V1[0,3,4]ZZ	Restrict/Splenic Vein, [Opn, Perc, Perc Endo]
06V2[0,3,4]ZZ	Restrict/Gastric Vein, [Opn, Perc, Perc Endo]
06V3[0,3,4]ZZ	Restrict/Esophageal Vein, [Opn, Perc, Perc Endo]
06V4[0,3,4]ZZ	Restrict/Hepatic Vein, [Opn, Perc, Perc Endo]
06V5[0,3,4]ZZ	Restrict/Superior Mesenteric Vein, [Opn, Perc, Perc Endo]
06V6[0,3,4]ZZ	Restrict/Inferior Mesenteric Vein, [Opn, Perc, Perc Endo]
06V7[0,3,4]ZZ	Restrict/Colic Vein, [Opn, Perc, Perc Endo]
06V8[0,3,4]ZZ	Restrict/Portal Vein, [Opn, Perc, Perc Endo]
06V9[0,3,4][D,Z]Z	Restrict/Renal Vein, Rt, [Opn, Perc, Perc Endo], [Intralum Dev, No Dev], NQ
06VB[0,3,4][D,Z]Z	Restrict/Renal Vein, Lt, [Opn, Perc, Perc Endo], [Intralum Dev, No Dev], NQ
079C[0,3,4]ZX	Drain/Lymphatic, Pelvis, [Opn, Perc, Perc Endo]
079D[0,3,4]ZX	Drain/Lymphatic, Aortic, [Opn, Perc, Perc Endo]
079L[0,3,4]ZX	Drain/Cisterna Chyli, [Opn, Perc, Perc Endo]
07BC[0,3,4]ZX	Exc/Lymphatic, Pelvis, [Opn, Perc, Perc Endo]
07BD[0,3,4]ZX	Exc/Lymphatic, Aortic, [Opn, Perc, Perc Endo]
07BH[0,3,4]ZZ	Exc/Lymphatic, Rt Inguinal, [Opn, Perc, Perc Endo]
07BJ[0,3,4]ZZ	Exc/Lymphatic, Lt Inguinal, [Opn, Perc, Perc Endo]
07BL[0,3,4]ZX	Exc/Cisterna Chyli, [Opn, Perc, Perc Endo]
07JP0ZZ	Inspect of Spleen, Opn Appr
07T0*	Resect/Lymphatic, Head
07T3*	Resect/Lymphatic, Rt Upr Extr
07T4*	Resect/Lymphatic, Lt Upr Extr
07T7*	Resect/Lymphatic, Thorax
07TB*	Resect/Lymphatic, Mesenteric
07TF*	Resect/Lymphatic, Rt Lwr Extr

T Transfer DRG **SP** Special Payment * Code Range **6th and 7th Character of ZZ = No Device, No Qualifier ZX = No Device, Diagnostic**

Code	Description
07TG*	Resect/Lymphatic, Lt Lwr Extr
0B9C0ZX	Drain of Rt Upr Lung Lobe, Opn Appr, Diagnostic
0B9D0ZX	Drain of Rt Mid Lung Lobe, Opn Appr, Diagn
0B9F0ZX	Drain of Rt Lwr Lung Lobe, Opn Appr, Diagnostic
0B9G0ZX	Drain of Lt Upr Lung Lobe, Opn Appr, Diagnostic
0B9H0ZX	Drain of Lung Lingula, Opn Appr, Diagnostic
0B9J0ZX	Drain of Lt Lwr Lung Lobe, Opn Appr, Diagnostic
0B9K0ZX	Drain of Rt Lung, Opn Appr, Diagnostic
0B9L0ZX	Drain of Lt Lung, Opn Appr, Diagnostic
0B9M0ZX	Drain of Bilat Lungs, Opn Appr, Diagnostic
0BBC[0,4]ZX	Exc/Upr Lung Lobe, Rt, [Opn, Perc Endo]
0BBD[0,4]ZX	Exc/Mid Lung Lobe, Rt, [Opn, Perc Endo]
0BBF[0,4]ZX	Exc/Lwr Lung Lobe, Rt, [Opn, Perc Endo]
0BBG[0,4]ZX	Exc/Upr Lung Lobe, Lt, [Opn, Perc Endo]
0BBH[0,4]ZX	Exc/Lung Lingula, [Opn, Perc Endo]
0BBJ[0,4]ZX	Exc/Lwr Lung Lobe, Lt, [Opn, Perc Endo]
0BBK[0,4]ZX	Exc/Lung, Rt, [Opn, Perc Endo]
0BBL[0,4]ZX	Exc/Lung, Lt, [Opn, Perc Endo]
0BBM0ZX	Exc of Bilat Lungs, Opn Appr, Diagnostic
0DCS*	Extir/Greater Omentum
0DCT*	Extir/Lesser Omentum
0DCV*	Extir/Mesentery
0DCW*	Extir/Peritoneum
0DH6[0,3,4]MZ	Insert/Stomach, [Opn, Perc, Perc Endo], Stimulator Lead, NQ
0DJ00ZZ	Inspect of Upr Intestinal Tract, Opn Appr
0DJ60ZZ	Inspect of Stomach, Opn Appr
0DJD0ZZ	Inspect of Lwr Intestinal Tract, Opn Appr
0DJU[0,4]ZZ	Inspect/Omentum, [Opn, Perc Endo]
0DJV[0,4]ZZ	Inspect/Mesentery, [Opn, Perc Endo]
0DJW[0,4]ZZ	Inspect/Peritoneum, [Opn, Perc Endo]
0DN8[0,3,4]ZZ	Rls/Sm Intestine, [Opn, Perc, Perc Endo]
0DN9[0,3,4]ZZ	Rls/Duodenum, [Opn, Perc, Perc Endo]
0DNA[0,3,4]ZZ	Rls/Jejunum, [Opn, Perc, Perc Endo]
0DNB[0,3,4]ZZ	Rls/Ileum, [Opn, Perc, Perc Endo]
0DNC[0,3,4]ZZ	Rls/Ileocecal Valve, [Opn, Perc, Perc Endo]
0DNE[0,3,4]ZZ	Rls/Lg Intestine, [Opn, Perc, Perc Endo]
0DNF[0,3,4]ZZ	Rls/Lg Intestine, Rt, [Opn, Perc, Perc Endo]
0DNG[0,3,4]ZZ	Rls/Lg Intestine, Lt, [Opn, Perc, Perc Endo]
0DNH[0,3,4]ZZ	Rls/Cecum, [Opn, Perc, Perc Endo]
0DNJ[0,3,4]ZZ	Rls/Appendix, [Opn, Perc, Perc Endo]
0DNK[0,3,4]ZZ	Rls/Ascending Colon, [Opn, Perc, Perc Endo]
0DNL[0,3,4]ZZ	Rls/Transv Colon, [Opn, Perc, Perc Endo]
0DNM[0,3,4]ZZ	Rls/Descending Colon, [Opn, Perc, Perc Endo]
0DNN[0,3,4]ZZ	Rls/Sigmoid Colon, [Opn, Perc, Perc Endo]
0DNS*	Rls/Greater Omentum
0DNT*	Rls/Lesser Omentum
0DNV*	Rls/Mesentery
0DNW*	Rls/Peritoneum
0DWW[0,3,4]JZ	Rev/Peritoneum, [Opn, Perc, Perc Endo], Synth Sub, NQ
0F900ZX	Drain of Liver, Opn Appr, Diagnostic
0F910ZX	Drain of Rt Lobe Liver, Opn Appr, Diagnostic
0F920ZX	Drain of Lt Lobe Liver, Opn Appr, Diagnostic
0FB0[0,4]ZX	Exc/Liver, [Opn, Perc Endo]
0FB1[0,4]ZX	Exc/Liver, Rt Lobe, [Opn, Perc Endo]
0FB2[0,4]ZX	Exc/Liver, Lt Lobe, [Opn, Perc Endo]
0FJ0[0,3,4]ZZ	Inspect/Liver, [Opn, Perc, Perc Endo]
0FJ44ZZ	Inspect of Gallbladder, Perc Endo Appr
0FJD4ZZ	Inspect of Pancreatic Duct, Perc Endo Appr
0FJG4ZZ	Inspect of Pancreas, Perc Endo Appr
0FN*	Hepatobiliary Sys and Pancreas, Rls
0G5L*	Destr/Superior Parathyroid Gland, Rt
0G5M*	Destr/Superior Parathyroid Gland, Lt
0G5N*	Destr/Inferior Parathyroid Gland, Rt
0G5P*	Destr/Inferior Parathyroid Gland, Lt
0G5Q*	Destr/Parathyroid Glands, Multi
0G5R*	Destr/Parathyroid Gland
0GBL[0,3,4]ZZ	Exc/Superior Parathyroid Gland, Rt, [Opn, Perc, Perc Endo]
0GBM[0,3,4]ZZ	Exc/Superior Parathyroid Gland, Lt, [Opn, Perc, Perc Endo]
0GBN[0,3,4]ZZ	Exc/Inferior Parathyroid Gland, Rt, [Opn, Perc, Perc Endo]
0GBP[0,3,4]ZZ	Exc/Inferior Parathyroid Gland, Lt, [Opn, Perc, Perc Endo]
0GBQ[0,3,4]ZZ	Exc/Parathyroid Glands, Multi, [Opn, Perc, Perc Endo]
0GBR[0,3,4]ZZ	Exc/Parathyroid Gland, [Opn, Perc, Perc Endo]
0GTL*	Resect/Superior Parathyroid Gland, Rt
0GTM*	Resect/Superior Parathyroid Gland, Lt
0GTN*	Resect/Inferior Parathyroid Gland, Rt
0GTP*	Resect/Inferior Parathyroid Gland, Lt
0GTQ*	Resect/Parathyroid Glands, Multi
0GTR*	Resect/Parathyroid Gland

Code	Description
0HB[0,1,4,5,6,7,8,A,B,C,D,E,F,G,H,J,K,L,M,N]XZZ	Exc of [Scalp, Face, Neck, Chest, Back, Abd, Buttock, Genitalia, Rt Upr Arm, Lt Upr Arm, Rt Lwr Arm, Lt Lwr Arm, Rt Hand, Lt Hand, Rt Upr Leg, Lt Upr Leg, Rt Lwr Leg, Lt Lwr Leg, Rt Foot, Lt Foot], Skin, Ext Appr
0JB[0,1,4,5,6,7,8,9,B,C,D,F,G,H,L,M,N,P,Q,R]0ZZ	Exc of [Scalp, Face, Ant Neck, Post Neck, Chest, Back, Abd, Buttock, Perineum, Pelvic Rgn, [Rt, Lt] Upr Arm, [Rt, Lt] Lwr Arm, [Rt, Lt] Upr Leg, [Rt, Lt] Lwr Leg, [Rt, Lt] Foot], SQ Tissue & Fascia, Opn Appr
0JH6[0,3]VZ	Insert/SQ Tissue & Fascia, Chest, [Opn, Perc], Inf Pump, NQ
0JH7[0,3]VZ	Insert/SQ Tissue & Fascia, Back, [Opn, Perc], Inf Pump, NQ
0JH8[0,3]VZ	Insert/SQ Tissue & Fascia, Abd, [Opn, Perc], Inf Pump, NQ
0JHT[0,3]VZ	Insert/SQ Tissue & Fascia, Trunk, [Opn, Perc], Inf Pump, NQ
0P90[0,3,4]ZZ	Drain/Sternum, [Opn, Perc, Perc Endo]
0P91[0,3,4]ZX	Drain/Rib, Rt, [Opn, Perc, Perc Endo]
0P92[0,3,4]ZX	Drain/Rib, Lt, [Opn, Perc, Perc Endo]
0P95[0,3,4]ZX	Drain/Scapula, Rt, [Opn, Perc, Perc Endo]
0P96[0,3,4]ZX	Drain/Scapula, Lt, [Opn, Perc, Perc Endo]
0P97[0,3,4]ZX	Drain/Glenoid Cavity, Rt, [Opn, Perc, Perc Endo]
0P98[0,3,4]ZX	Drain/Glenoid Cavity, Lt, [Opn, Perc, Perc Endo]
0P99[0,3,4]ZX	Drain/Clavicle, Rt, [Opn, Perc, Perc Endo]
0P9B[0,3,4]ZX	Drain/Clavicle, Lt, [Opn, Perc, Perc Endo]
0P9C[0,3,4]ZX	Drain/Humeral Head, Rt, [Opn, Perc, Perc Endo]
0P9D[0,3,4]ZX	Drain/Humeral Head, Lt, [Opn, Perc, Perc Endo]
0P9F[0,3,4]ZX	Drain/Humeral Shaft, Rt, [Opn, Perc, Perc Endo]
0P9G[0,3,4]ZX	Drain/Humeral Shaft, Lt, [Opn, Perc, Perc Endo]
0P9H[0,3,4]ZX	Drain/Radius, Rt, [Opn, Perc, Perc Endo]
0P9J[0,3,4]ZX	Drain/Radius, Lt, [Opn, Perc, Perc Endo]
0P9K[0,3,4]ZX	Drain/Ulna, Rt, [Opn, Perc, Perc Endo]
0P9L[0,3,4]ZX	Drain/Ulna, Lt, [Opn, Perc, Perc Endo]
0P9M[0,3,4]ZX	Drain/Carpal, Rt, [Opn, Perc, Perc Endo]
0P9N[0,3,4]ZX	Drain/Carpal, Lt, [Opn, Perc, Perc Endo]
0P9P[0,3,4]ZX	Drain/Metacarpal, Rt, [Opn, Perc, Perc Endo]
0P9Q[0,3,4]ZX	Drain/Metacarpal, Lt, [Opn, Perc, Perc Endo]
0PB0[0,3,4]ZX	Exc/Sternum, [Opn, Perc, Perc Endo]
0PB1[0,3,4]ZX	Exc/Rib, Rt, [Opn, Perc, Perc Endo]
0PB2[0,3,4]ZX	Exc/Rib, Lt, [Opn, Perc, Perc Endo]
0PB5[0,3,4]ZX	Exc/Scapula, Rt, [Opn, Perc, Perc Endo]
0PB6[0,3,4]ZX	Exc/Scapula, Lt, [Opn, Perc, Perc Endo]
0PB7[0,3,4]ZX	Exc/Glenoid Cavity, Rt, [Opn, Perc, Perc Endo]
0PB8[0,3,4]ZX	Exc/Glenoid Cavity, Lt, [Opn, Perc, Perc Endo]
0PB9[0,3,4]ZX	Exc/Clavicle, Rt, [Opn, Perc, Perc Endo]
0PBB[0,3,4]ZX	Exc/Clavicle, Lt, [Opn, Perc, Perc Endo]
0PBC[0,3,4]ZX	Exc/Humeral Head, Rt, [Opn, Perc, Perc Endo]
0PBD[0,3,4]ZX	Exc/Humeral Head, Lt, [Opn, Perc, Perc Endo]
0PBF[0,3,4]ZX	Exc/Humeral Shaft, Rt, [Opn, Perc, Perc Endo]
0PBG[0,3,4]ZX	Exc/Humeral Shaft, Lt, [Opn, Perc, Perc Endo]
0PBH[0,3,4]ZX	Exc/Radius, Rt, [Opn, Perc, Perc Endo]
0PBJ[0,3,4]ZX	Exc/Radius, Lt, [Opn, Perc, Perc Endo]
0PBK[0,3,4]ZX	Exc/Ulna, Rt, [Opn, Perc, Perc Endo]
0PBL[0,3,4]ZX	Exc/Ulna, Lt, [Opn, Perc, Perc Endo]
0PBM[0,3,4]ZX	Exc/Carpal, Rt, [Opn, Perc, Perc Endo]
0PBN[0,3,4]ZX	Exc/Carpal, Lt, [Opn, Perc, Perc Endo]
0PBP[0,3,4]ZX	Exc/Metacarpal, Rt, [Opn, Perc, Perc Endo]
0PBQ[0,3,4]ZX	Exc/Metacarpal, Lt, [Opn, Perc, Perc Endo]
0Q90[0,3,4]ZX	Drain/Lumbar Vertebra, [Opn, Perc, Perc Endo]
0Q91[0,3,4]ZX	Drain/Sacrum, [Opn, Perc, Perc Endo]
0Q92[0,3,4]ZX	Drain/Pelvic Bone, Rt, [Opn, Perc, Perc Endo]
0Q93[0,3,4]ZX	Drain/Pelvic Bone, Lt, [Opn, Perc, Perc Endo]
0Q94[0,3,4]ZX	Drain/Acetab, Rt, [Opn, Perc, Perc Endo]
0Q95[0,3,4]ZX	Drain/Acetab, Lt, [Opn, Perc, Perc Endo]
0Q96[0,3,4]ZX	Drain/Upr Femur, Rt, [Opn, Perc, Perc Endo]
0Q97[0,3,4]ZX	Drain/Upr Femur, Lt, [Opn, Perc, Perc Endo]
0Q98[0,3,4]ZX	Drain/Femor Shaft, Rt, [Opn, Perc, Perc Endo]
0Q99[0,3,4]ZX	Drain/Femor Shaft, Lt, [Opn, Perc, Perc Endo]
0Q9B[0,3,4]ZX	Drain/Lwr Femur, Rt, [Opn, Perc, Perc Endo]
0Q9C[0,3,4]ZX	Drain/Lwr Femur, Lt, [Opn, Perc, Perc Endo]
0Q9D[0,3,4]ZX	Drain/Patella, Rt, [Opn, Perc, Perc Endo]
0Q9F[0,3,4]ZX	Drain/Patella, Lt, [Opn, Perc, Perc Endo]
0Q9G[0,3,4]ZX	Drain/Tibia, Rt, [Opn, Perc, Perc Endo]
0Q9H[0,3,4]ZX	Drain/Tibia, Lt, [Opn, Perc, Perc Endo]
0Q9J[0,3,4]ZX	Drain/Fibula, Rt, [Opn, Perc, Perc Endo]
0Q9K[0,3,4]ZX	Drain/Fibula, Lt, [Opn, Perc, Perc Endo]
0Q9L[0,3,4]ZX	Drain/Tarsal, Rt, [Opn, Perc, Perc Endo]
0Q9M[0,3,4]ZX	Drain/Tarsal, Lt, [Opn, Perc, Perc Endo]
0Q9N[0,3,4]ZX	Drain/Metatarsal, Rt, [Opn, Perc, Perc Endo]
0Q9P[0,3,4]ZX	Drain/Metatarsal, Lt, [Opn, Perc, Perc Endo]
0Q9S[0,3,4]ZX	Drain/Coccyx, [Opn, Perc, Perc Endo]
0QB0[0,3,4]ZX	Exc/Lumbar Vertebra, [Opn, Perc, Perc Endo]
0QB1[0,3,4]ZX	Exc/Sacrum, [Opn, Perc, Perc Endo]
0QB2[0,3,4]ZX	Exc/Pelvic Bone, Rt, [Opn, Perc, Perc Endo]

Surgical   **Medical**   **CC Indicator**   **MCC Indicator**   **Procedure Proxy**   PDx MCC **PDx acts as own MCC**   PDx CC **PDx acts as own CC**

MS-DRG Version 33.0

MDC 11: Diseases And Disorders Of The Kidney And Urinary Tract—MEDICAL

0QB3[0,3,4]ZX   Exc/Pelvic Bone, Lt, [Opn, Perc, Perc Endo]
0QB4[0,3,4]ZX   Exc/Acetab, Rt, [Opn, Perc, Perc Endo]
0QB5[0,3,4]ZX   Exc/Acetab, Lt, [Opn, Perc, Perc Endo]
0QB6[0,3,4]ZX   Exc/Upr Femur, Rt, [Opn, Perc, Perc Endo]
0QB7[0,3,4]ZX   Exc/Upr Femur, Lt, [Opn, Perc, Perc Endo]
0QB8[0,3,4]ZX   Exc/Femor Shaft, Rt, [Opn, Perc, Perc Endo]
0QB9[0,3,4]ZX   Exc/Femor Shaft, Lt, [Opn, Perc, Perc Endo]
0QBB[0,3,4]ZX   Exc/Lwr Femur, Rt, [Opn, Perc, Perc Endo]
0QBC[0,3,4]ZX   Exc/Lwr Femur, Lt, [Opn, Perc, Perc Endo]
0QBD[0,3,4]ZX   Exc/Patella, Rt, [Opn, Perc, Perc Endo]
0QBF[0,3,4]ZX   Exc/Patella, Lt, [Opn, Perc, Perc Endo]
0QBG[0,3,4]ZX   Exc/Tibia, Rt, [Opn, Perc, Perc Endo]
0QBH[0,3,4]ZX   Exc/Tibia, Lt, [Opn, Perc, Perc Endo]
0QBJ[0,3,4]ZX   Exc/Fibula, Rt, [Opn, Perc, Perc Endo]
0QBK[0,3,4]ZX   Exc/Fibula, Lt, [Opn, Perc, Perc Endo]
0QBL[0,3,4]ZX   Exc/Tarsal, Rt, [Opn, Perc, Perc Endo]
0QBM[0,3,4]ZX   Exc/Tarsal, Lt, [Opn, Perc, Perc Endo]
0QBN[0,3,4]ZX   Exc/Metatarsal, Rt, [Opn, Perc, Perc Endo]
0QBP[0,3,4]ZX   Exc/Metatarsal, Lt, [Opn, Perc, Perc Endo]
0QBS[0,3,4]ZX   Exc/Coccyx, [Opn, Perc, Perc Endo]
0VPS[0,3,4,7,8]JZ   Rmvl/Penis, [Opn, Perc, Perc Endo, Via Natrl or Artfcl Opng, Via Natrl or Artfcl Opng Endo], Synth Sub, NQ
0VUS[0,4]JZ   Supl/Penis, [Opn, Perc Endo], Synth Sub, NQ
0W1G[0,3,4]J4   Bypass/Peritoneal Cavity, [Opn, Perc, Perc Endo], Synth Sub, Cutaneous
0W3F*   Control/Abd Wall
0W3G[3,4]ZZ   Control/Peritoneal Cavity, [Perc, Perc Endo]
0W3H*   Control/Retroperitoneum
0W3J*   Control/Pelvic Cavity
0W3P[0,3,4]ZZ   Control/Gastrointestinal Tract, [Opn, Perc, Perc Endo]
0W9F0[0,Z]Z   Drain/Abd Wall, Opn, [Drain Dev, No Dev], NQ
0W9G0[0,Z]Z   Drain/Peritoneal Cavity, Opn, [Drain Dev, No Dev], NQ
0W9H[0,3,4][0,Z]Z   Drain/Retroperitoneum, [Opn, Perc, Perc Endo], [Drain Dev, No Dev], NQ
0W9J[0,4][0,Z]Z   Drain/Pelvic Cavity, [Opn, Perc Endo], [Drain Dev, No Dev], NQ
0WCG[0,3,4]ZZ   Extir/Peritoneal Cavity, [Opn, Perc, Perc Endo]
0WCJ[0,3,4]ZZ   Extir/Pelvic Cavity, [Opn, Perc, Perc Endo]
0WCP[0,3,4]ZZ   Extir/Gastrointestinal Tract, [Opn, Perc, Perc Endo]
0WCR[0,3,4]ZZ   Extir/Genitourinary Tract, [Opn, Perc, Perc Endo]
0WHH[0,3,4]1Z   Insert/Retroperitoneum, [Opn, Perc, Perc Endo], Radioact Elmt, NQ
0WHR[0,3,4,7,8]1Z   Insert/Genitourinary Tract, [Opn, Perc, Perc Endo, Via Natrl or Artfcl Opng, Via Natrl or Artfcl Opng Endo], Radioact Elmt, NQ
0WJ90ZZ   Inspect of Rt Pleural Cavity, Opn Appr
0WJB0ZZ   Inspect of Lt Pleural Cavity, Opn Appr
0WJC0ZZ   Inspect of Mediastinum, Opn Appr
0WJF[0,4]ZZ   Inspect/Abd Wall, [Opn, Perc Endo]
0WJG[0,4]ZZ   Inspect/Peritoneal Cavity, [Opn, Perc Endo]
0WJH0ZZ   Inspect of Retroperitoneum, Opn Appr
0WJJ[0,4]ZZ   Inspect/Pelvic Cavity, [Opn, Perc Endo]
0WJP[0,4]ZZ   Inspect/Gastrointestinal Tract, [Opn, Perc Endo]
0WJQ0ZZ   Inspect of Respiratory Tract, Opn Appr
0WJR[0,4]ZZ   Inspect/Genitourinary Tract, [Opn, Perc Endo]
0Y35*   Control/Inguinal Region, Rt
0Y36*   Control/Inguinal Region, Lt
0Y95[0,3,4][0,Z]Z   Drain/Inguinal Rgn, Rt, [Opn, Perc, Perc Endo], [Drain Dev, No Dev], NQ
0Y96[0,3,4][0,Z]Z   Drain/Inguinal Rgn, Lt, [Opn, Perc, Perc Endo], [Drain Dev, No Dev], NQ
0YJ50ZZ   Inspect of Rt Inguinal Region, Opn Appr
0YJ60ZZ   Inspect of Lt Inguinal Region, Opn Appr
0YJ70ZZ   Inspect of Rt Femor Region, Opn Appr
0YJA0ZZ   Inspect of Bilat Inguinal Region, Opn Appr
OR

Principal Diagnosis

E88.3   Tumor lysis synd
I12*   Hypertensive chr kidney dz
I13.11   Hyp hrt and chr kdny dis w/o hrt fail, w stg 5 chr kdny/ESRD
N17*   Acute kidney failure
N18*   Chr kidney dz (CKD)
N19   Unsp kidney failure
R34   Anuria and oliguria
T79.5XXA   Traum anuria, init enc
AND

Nonoperating Room Procedures

0JH6[0,3][W,X]Z   Insert/SQ Tissue & Fascia, Chest, [Opn, Perc], [Reservoir, Vascular Access Dev], NQ

0JH8[0,3][W,X]Z   Insert/SQ Tissue & Fascia, Abd, [Opn, Perc], [Reservoir, Vascular Access Dev], NQ
0JHD[0,3][W,X]Z   Insert/SQ Tissue & Fascia, Rt Upr Arm, [Opn, Perc], [Reservoir, Vascular Access Dev], NQ
0JHF[0,3][W,X]Z   Insert/SQ Tissue & Fascia, Lt Upr Arm, [Opn, Perc], [Reservoir, Vascular Access Dev], NQ
0JHG[0,3][W,X]Z   Insert/SQ Tissue & Fascia, Rt Lwr Arm, [Opn, Perc], [Reservoir, Vascular Access Dev], NQ
0JHH[0,3][W,X]Z   Insert/SQ Tissue & Fascia, Lt Lwr Arm, [Opn, Perc], [Reservoir, Vascular Access Dev], NQ
0JHL[0,3][W,X]Z   Insert/SQ Tissue & Fascia, Rt Upr Leg, [Opn, Perc], [Reservoir, Vascular Access Dev], NQ
0JHM[0,3][W,X]Z   Insert/SQ Tissue & Fascia, Lt Upr Leg, [Opn, Perc], [Reservoir, Vascular Access Dev], NQ
0JHN[0,3][W,X]Z   Insert/SQ Tissue & Fascia, Rt Lwr Leg, [Opn, Perc], [Reservoir, Vascular Access Dev], NQ
0JHP[0,3][W,X]Z   Insert/SQ Tissue & Fascia, Lt Lwr Leg, [Opn, Perc], [Reservoir, Vascular Access Dev], NQ
OR

Principal Diagnosis

E10.2*   Type 1 diabetes mellitus with kidney comp
AND

Nonoperating Room Procedures

3E03[0,3]U[0,1]   Introduction/Peripheral Vein, [Opn, Perc], Pancreatic Islet Cells, [Auto, Nonauto]
3E0J[3,7,8]U[0,1]   Introduction/Biliary and Pancreatic Tract, [Perc, Via Natrl or Artfcl Opng, Via Natrl or Artfcl Opng Endo], Pancreatic Islet Cells, [Auto, Nonauto]

DRG 674   Other Kidney and Urinary Tract Procedures with CC
GMLOS 5.4   AMLOS 7.1   RW 2.3148

Select operating room procedures OR principal diagnosis and nonoperating room procedures listed under DRG 673

DRG 675   Other Kidney and Urinary Tract Procedures without CC/MCC
GMLOS 2.4   AMLOS 3.2   RW 1.5595

Select operating room procedures OR principal diagnosis and nonoperating room procedures listed under DRG 673

MEDICAL

DRG 682   Renal Failure with MCC
GMLOS 4.6   AMLOS 6.0   RW 1.5085   [T]

Principal Diagnosis

E88.3   Tumor lysis synd
I12*   Hypertensive chr kidney dz
I13.11   Hyp hrt and chr kdny dis w/o hrt fail, w stg 5 chr kdny/ESRD
N17*   Acute kidney failure
N18*   Chr kidney dz (CKD)
N19   Unsp kidney failure
R34   Anuria and oliguria
T79.5XXA   Traum anuria, init enc

DRG 683   Renal Failure with CC
GMLOS 3.5   AMLOS 4.3   RW 0.9406   [T]

Select principal diagnosis listed under DRG 682

DRG 684   Renal Failure without CC/MCC
GMLOS 2.5   AMLOS 2.9   RW 0.6272   [T]

Select principal diagnosis listed under DRG 682

DRG 685   Admit for Renal Dialysis
GMLOS 2.9   AMLOS 3.8   RW 1.0369

Principal Diagnosis

Z49*   Enc for care involving renal dialysis

[T] **Transfer DRG**   [SP] **Special Payment**   * **Code Range**   **6th and 7th Character of ZZ = No Device, No Qualifier ZX = No Device, Diagnostic**

DRG 686   Kidney and Urinary Tract Neoplasms with MCC
      GMLOS 5.3   AMLOS 7.0   RW 1.6670

Principal Diagnosis

C64*	Malig neoplasm of kidney, except renal pelvis
C65*	Malig neoplasm of renal pelvis
C66*	Malig neoplasm of ureter
C67*	Malig neoplasm of bladder
C68*	Malig neoplasm of oth and unsp urinary organs
C79.0*	Secondary malig neoplasm of kidney and renal pelvis
C79.1*	Sec malig neoplm of bladder and oth and unsp urinary organs
C7A.093	Malig carcinoid tumor of the kidney
D09.0	Carcinoma in situ of bladder
D09.1*	Carcinoma in situ of oth and unsp urinary organs
D30*	Benign neoplasm of urinary organs
D3A.093	Benign carcinoid tumor of the kidney
D41*	Neoplasm of uncertain behav of urinary organs
D49.4	Neoplasm of unsp behav of bladder
D49.5	Neoplasm of unsp behav of oth genitourinary organs

DRG 687   Kidney and Urinary Tract Neoplasms with CC
      GMLOS 3.5   AMLOS 4.4   RW 1.0161

Select principal diagnosis listed under DRG 686

DRG 688   Kidney and Urinary Tract Neoplasms without CC/MCC
      GMLOS 2.2   AMLOS 2.8   RW 0.6607

Select principal diagnosis listed under DRG 686

DRG 689   Kidney and Urinary Tract Infections with MCC
      GMLOS 4.0   AMLOS 5.0   RW 1.0821   T

Principal Diagnosis

A18.1[0,1,2,3]	Tuberculosis of [genitourinary sys unsp, kidney and ureter, bladder, oth urinary organs]
A36.85	Diphtheritic cystitis
A52.75	Syphilis of kidney and ureter
A54.01	Gonococcal cystitis and urethritis, unsp
A56.1*	Chlamydial infxn of pelviperitoneum and oth GU organs
A98.5	Hemorrhagic fever with renal synd
B65.0	Schistosomiasis d/t Schistosoma haematobium
B90.1	Sequelae of genitourinary tuberculosis
N10	Acute tubulo-interstitial nephritis
N11.0	Nonobstructive reflux-associated chr pyelonephritis
N11.8	Oth chr tubulo-interstitial nephritis
N11.9	Chr tubulo-interstitial nephritis, unsp
N12	Tubulo-interstitial nephritis, not spcf as acute or chr
N13.5	Crossing vessel and stricture of ureter w/o hydronephrosis
N13.6	Pyonephrosis
N15.1	Renal and perinephric abscess
N28.8[4,5,6]	[Pyelitis, Pyeloureteritis, Ureteritis] cystica
N30.0*	Acute cystitis
N30.1*	Interstitial cystitis (chr)
N30.2*	Oth chr cystitis
N30.3*	Trigonitis
N30.8*	Oth cystitis
N30.9*	Cystitis, unsp
N34.0	Urethral abscess
N34.2	Oth urethritis
N34.3	Urethral synd, unsp
N39.0	Urinary tract infxn, site not spec

DRG 690   Kidney and Urinary Tract Infections without MCC
      GMLOS 3.1   AMLOS 3.7   RW 0.7828   T

Select principal diagnosis listed under DRG 689

DRG 691   Urinary Stones with ESW Lithotripsy with CC/MCC
      GMLOS 2.8   AMLOS 3.7   RW 1.5470

Principal Diagnosis

N11.1	Chr obstructive pyelonephritis	PDxCC
N13.1	Hydronephrosis w ureteral stricture, NEC	PDxCC
N13.2	Hydronephrosis with renal and ureteral calculous obstruction	PDxCC
N13.3*	Oth and unsp hydronephrosis	
N13.4	Hydroureter	

N13.8	Oth obstructive and reflux uropathy
N20*	Calculus of kidney and ureter
N21*	Calculus of lwr urinary tract
N22	Calculus of urinary tract in dz classified elsw
N23	Unsp renal colic

AND

Nonoperating Room Procedure

0TF3XZZ	Fragmn in Rt Kidney Pelvis, Ext Appr
0TF4XZZ	Fragmn in Lt Kidney Pelvis, Ext Appr
0TF6XZZ	Fragmn in Rt Ureter, Ext Appr
0TF7XZZ	Fragmn in Lt Ureter, Ext Appr
0TFBXZZ	Fragmn in Bladder, Ext Appr
0TFCXZZ	Fragmn in Bladder Neck, Ext Appr
0WFRXZZ	Fragmn in Genitourinary Tract, Ext Appr

DRG 692   Urinary Stones with ESW Lithotripsy without CC/MCC
      GMLOS 1.9   AMLOS 2.3   RW 1.2566

Select principal diagnosis AND nonoperating room procedure listed under DRG 691

DRG 693   Urinary Stones without ESW Lithotripsy with MCC
      GMLOS 3.8   AMLOS 4.9   RW 1.3323

Select only principal diagnosis listed under DRG 691

DRG 694   Urinary Stones without ESW Lithotripsy without MCC
      GMLOS 2.0   AMLOS 2.5   RW 0.7294

Select only principal diagnosis listed under DRG 691

DRG 695   Kidney and Urinary Tract Signs and Symptoms with MCC
      GMLOS 4.1   AMLOS 5.2   RW 1.2494

Principal Diagnosis

N39.3	Stress incontinence (female) (male)
N39.4*	Oth spec urinary incontinence
R30*	Pain associated with micturition
R31*	Hematuria
R32	Unsp urinary incontinence
R33*	Retention of urine
R35*	Polyuria
R36.0	Urethral discharge w/o bld
R36.9	Urethral discharge, unsp
R39*	Oth and unsp symptoms and signs involving the GU sys
R80.0	Isolated proteinuria
R80.1	Persistent proteinuria, unsp
R80.3	Bence Jones proteinuria
R80.8	Oth proteinuria
R80.9	Proteinuria, unsp
R82.0	Chyluria
R82.3	Hemoglobinuria
R82.5	Elevated urine levels of drug/meds/biol subst
R82.6	Abnormal urine levels of substances chiefly nonmed source
R82.7	Abnormal findings on microbiological exam of urine
R82.8	Abnormal findings on cytolog and histolog exam of urine
R82.9*	Oth and unsp abnormal findings in urine
R93.4	Abnormal findings on diagnostic imaging of urinary organs
R94.4	Abnormal results of kidney function studies
R94.8	Abnormal results of function studies of organs and systems

DRG 696   Kidney and Urinary Tract Signs and Symptoms without MCC
      GMLOS 2.6   AMLOS 3.2   RW 0.6934

Select principal diagnosis listed under DRG 695

DRG 697   Urethral Stricture
      GMLOS 2.8   AMLOS 3.6   RW 0.9417

Principal Diagnosis

N35*	Urethral stricture
N37	Urethral d/o in dz classified elsw
N99.1*	Postprocedural urethral stricture

MDC 11: Diseases And Disorders Of The Kidney And Urinary Tract—MEDICAL

Surgical	Medical	CC Indicator	MCC Indicator	Procedure Proxy	PDxMCC PDx acts as own MCC	PDxCC PDx acts as own CC

DRG 698   Other Kidney and Urinary Tract Diagnoses with MCC

    GMLOS 5.0   AMLOS 6.3   RW 1.5524   [T]

Principal Diagnosis

E08.2*	Diabetes d/t underlying condition w kidney comp
E09.2*	Drug/chem diabetes mellitus w kidney comp
E10.2*	Type 1 diabetes mellitus with kidney comp
E11.2*	Type 2 diabetes mellitus with kidney comp
E13.2*	Oth spec diabetes mellitus with kidney comp
I70.1	Atherosclerosis of renal artery
I72.2	Aneurysm of renal artery
I75.81	Atheroembolism of kidney
I77.73	Dissection of renal artery
I82.3	Embolism and thrombosis of renal vein
M10.3*	Gout d/t renal impairment
N00*	Acute nephritic synd
N01*	Rapidly progressive nephritic synd
N02*	Recurrent and persistent hematuria
N03*	Chr nephritic synd
N04*	Nephrotic synd
N05*	Unsp nephritic synd
N06*	Isolated proteinuria with spec morphological lesion
N07*	Hereditary nephropathy, NEC
N08	Glomerular d/o in dz classified elsw
N13.7*	Vesicoureteral-reflux
N13.9	Obstructive and reflux uropathy, unsp
N14*	Drug- & heavy-metal-induced tubulo-interstitial & tublr cond
N15.0	Balkan nephropathy
N15.8	Oth spec renal tubulo-interstitial dz
N15.9	Renal tubulo-interstitial dz, unsp
N16	Renal tubulo-interstitial dz in dz classd elsw
N25*	D/o resulting from impaired renal tubular function
N26.1	Atrophy of kidney (terminal)
N26.9	Renal sclerosis, unsp
N27*	Sm kidney of unknown cause
N28.0	Ischemia and infarction of kidney
N28.1	Cyst of kidney, acquired
N28.81	Hypertrophy of kidney
N28.82	Megaloureter
N28.83	Nephroptosis
N28.89	Oth spec d/o of kidney and ureter
N28.9	D/o of kidney and ureter, unsp
N29	Oth d/o of kidney and ureter in dz classd elsw
N30.4*	Irradiation cystitis
N31*	Neuromuscular dysfunction of bladder, NEC
N32*	Oth d/o of bladder
N33	Bladder d/o in dz classified elsw
N36*	Oth d/o of urethra
N39.8	Oth spec d/o of urinary sys
N39.9	D/o of urinary sys, unsp
N99.0	Postprocedural (acute) (chr) kidney failure
N99.5*	Comp of stoma of urinary tract
N99.8[1,9]	Oth [intraoperative, postprocedural] comps (and d/os) of genitourinary sys
Q60*	Renal agenesis and oth reduction defects of kidney
Q61*	Cystic kidney dz
Q62*	Congen defects of renal pelvis and congen malform of ureter
Q63*	Oth congenital malformations of kidney
Q64.1*	Exstrophy of urinary bladder
Q64.2	Congenital posterior urethral valves
Q64.3*	Oth atresia and stenosis of urethra and bladder neck
Q64.4	Malformation of urachus
Q64.5	Congenital absence of bladder and urethra
Q64.6	Congenital diverticulum of bladder
Q64.7*	Oth and unsp congenital malformations of bladder and urethra
Q64.8	Oth spec congenital malformations of urinary sys
Q64.9	Congenital malformation of urinary sys, unsp
R80.2	Orthostatic proteinuria, unsp
S31.0[0,1,2,3,4,5]1A	[Unsp opn wnd, Lac w/o FB, Lac w/ FB, Punc wnd w/o FB, Punc wnd w/ FB, Opn bite] of lwr back and pelvis w/ penetration into retroperitoneum, init enc
S37.00[1,2,9]A	Unsp inj of [rt, lt, unsp] kidney, init enc
S37.01[1,2,9]A	Unsp inj of [rt, lt, unsp] kidney, init enc
S37.02[1,2,9]A	Minor contsn of [rt, lt, unsp] kidney, init enc
S37.03[1,2,9]A	Lac of [rt, lt, unsp] kidney, unsp degree, init enc
S37.04[1,2,9]A	Minor lac of [rt,lt, unsp] kidney, init enc
S37.05[1,2,9]A	Mod lac of [rt, lt, unsp] kidney, init enc
S37.06[1,2,9]A	Major lac of [rt, lt, unsp] kidney, init enc
S37.09[1,2,9]A	Oth inj of [rt, lt, unsp] kidney, init enc

S37.1[0,2,3,9]XA	[Unsp inj, Contsn, Lac, Oth inj] of ureter, init enc
S37.2[0,2,3,9]XA	[Unsp inj, Contsn, Lac, Oth inj] of bladder, init enc
S37.3[0,2,3,9]XA	[Unsp inj, Contsn, Lac, Oth inj] of urethra, init enc
T19.0XXA	FB in urethra, init enc
T19.1XXA	FB in bladder, init enc
T19.8XXA	FB in oth prt genitourinary tract, init enc
T19.9XXA	FB in genitourinary tract, part unsp, init enc
T81.711A	Comp of renal artery following a procedure, NEC, init
T83.0[1,2,3,9][0,8]A	[Breakdown (mech), Displac, Leakage, Oth mech comp] of [cystostomy, oth indwelling urethral] catheter, init enc
T83.1[1,2,9][0,1,2,8] A	[Breakdown (mech), Displac, Oth mech comp] of [urinary electronic stimulator, urinary sphincter implant, urinary stent, oth urinary devs], init enc
T83.2[1,2,3,9]XA	[Breakdown (mech), Displac, Leakage, Oth mech comp] of graft of urinary organ, init enc
T83.4[1,2,9][0,8]A	[Breakdown (mech), Displac, Oth mech comp] of [penile (implanted) prosthesis, oth prosthetic devs, implants and grafts of genital tract], init enc
T83.5[1,9]XA	Infxn and inflam reaction d/t [indwelling urinary catheter, prosthetic dev, implant and graft in urinary sys], init enc
T83.6XXA	Infect/inflm react d/t prosth dev/grft in genitl trct, init
T83.7[1,2]8A	[Erosion, Exposure] of oth implanted mesh and oth prosthetic materials to surrounding organ or tissue, init enc
T83.8[1,2,3,4,5,6,9]XA	[Embolism, Fibrosis, Hemor, Pain, Stenosis, Thrombosis, Oth spec comp] of genitourinary prosthetic devs, implants and grafts, init enc
T83.9XXA	Unsp comp of genitourinary prosth dev/grft, init
T86.1*	Comp of kidney transplant
Z43.5	Enc for attention to cystostomy
Z43.6	Enc for attn to oth artif openings of urinary tract
Z46.6	Enc for fitting and adjustment of urinary device
Z52.4	Kidney donor
Z90.6	Acquired absence of oth parts of urinary tract
Z94.0	Kidney transplant status
Z96.0	Presence of urogenital implants

DRG 699   Other Kidney and Urinary Tract Diagnoses with CC

    GMLOS 3.5   AMLOS 4.4   RW 1.0246   [T]

Select principal diagnosis listed under DRG 698

DRG 700   Other Kidney and Urinary Tract Diagnoses without CC/MCC

    GMLOS 2.6   AMLOS 3.2   RW 0.7163   [T]

Select principal diagnosis listed under DRG 698

[T] **Transfer DRG**   [SP] **Special Payment**   * **Code Range**   **6th and 7th Character of ZZ = No Device, No Qualifier ZX = No Device, Diagnostic**

MDC 12
Diseases And Disorders Of The Male Reproductive System

SURGICAL

DRG 707   Major Male Pelvic Procedures with CC/MCC
GMLOS 2.8   AMLOS 3.8   RW 1.7753

Operating Room Procedures

07JP0ZZ	Inspect of Spleen, Opn Appr
07T8*	Resect/Lymphatic, Int Mammary, Rt
07T9*	Resect/Lymphatic, Int Mammary, Lt
07TC*	Resect/Lymphatic, Pelvis
07TD*	Resect/Lymphatic, Aortic
07TH*	Resect/Lymphatic, Rt Inguinal
07TJ*	Resect/Lymphatic, Lt Inguinal
0DBP[0,4]ZZ	Exc/Rectum, [Opn, Perc Endo]
0DJ00ZZ	Inspect of Upr Intestinal Tract, Opn Appr
0DJ60ZZ	Inspect of Stomach, Opn Appr
0DJD0ZZ	Inspect of Lwr Intestinal Tract, Opn Appr
0DJU0ZZ	Inspect of Omentum, Opn Appr
0DJV0ZZ	Inspect of Mesentery, Opn Appr
0DJW0ZZ	Inspect of Peritoneum, Opn Appr
0FJ00ZZ	Inspect of Liver, Opn Appr
0TBB[0,3,4]ZZ	Exc/Bladder, [Opn, Perc, Perc Endo]
0TBC[0,3,4]ZZ	Exc/Bladder Neck, [Opn, Perc, Perc Endo]
0TTB*	Resect/Bladder
0TTC*	Resect/Bladder Neck
0V50[0,3,4]ZZ	Destr/Prostate, [Opn, Perc, Perc Endo]
0VT0[0,4]ZZ	Resect/Prostate, [Opn, Perc Endo]
0WBH[0,3,4]ZZ	Exc/Retroperitoneum, [Opn, Perc, Perc Endo]
0WJG0ZZ	Inspect of Peritoneal Cavity, Opn Appr
0WJJ0ZZ	Inspect of Pelvic Cavity, Opn Appr
0WJP0ZZ	Inspect of Gastrointestinal Tract, Opn Appr
0WJR0ZZ	Inspect of Genitourinary Tract, Opn Appr

OR

0VT0*	Resect/Prostate

AND

0VT3*	Resect/Seminal Vesicles, Bilat

DRG 708   Major Male Pelvic Procedures without CC/MCC
GMLOS 1.4   AMLOS 1.6   RW 1.3146

Select operating room procedures or procedure combination listed under DRG 707

DRG 709   Penis Procedures with CC/MCC
GMLOS 4.0   AMLOS 5.9   RW 1.9721

Operating Room Procedures

0TMD*	Reattach/Urethra
0TND*	Rls/Urethra
0TQD*	Repair/Urethra
0TRD*	Replace/Urethra
0TSD*	Repos/Urethra
0TUD*	Supl/Urethra
0TVD*	Restrict/Urethra
0V5S*	Destr/Penis
0V5T*	Destr/Prepuce
0V9S*	Drain/Penis
0V9T*	Drain/Prepuce
0VBS*	Exc/Penis
0VBT*	Exc/Prepuce
0VCS[0,3,4]ZZ	Extir/Penis, [Opn, Perc, Perc Endo]
0VCT*	Extir/Prepuce
0VMSXZZ	Reattach of Penis, Ext Appr
0VNS*	Rls/Penis
0VPS[0,3,4,7,8][0,3,7,J,K]Z	Rmvl/Penis, [Opn, Perc, Perc Endo, Via Natrl or Artfcl Opng, Via Natrl or Artfcl Opng Endo], [Drain Dev, Inf Dev, Auto Tissue Sub, Synth Sub, Nonauto Tissue Sub], NQ
0VQS*	Repair/Penis
0VQT*	Repair/Prepuce
0VTS*	Resect/Penis

0VUS[0,4][7,J,K]Z	Supl/Penis, [Opn, Perc Endo], [Auto Tissue Sub, Synth Sub, Nonauto Tissue Sub], NQ
0VUT[0,4,X][7,J,K]Z	Supl/Prepuce, [Opn, Perc Endo, Ext], [Auto Tissue Sub, Synth Sub, Nonauto Tissue Sub], NQ
0VWS[0,3,4,7,8][0,3,7,J,K]Z	Rev/Penis, [Opn, Perc, Perc Endo, Via Natrl or Artfcl Opng, Via Natrl or Artfcl Opng Endo], [Drain Dev, Inf Dev, Auto Tissue Sub, Synth Sub, Nonauto Tissue Sub], NQ
0W4M*	Creation/Perineum, Male
0WPMX7Z	Rmvl of Autol Sub from Male Perineum, Extern Appr
0WPMXJZ	Rmvl of Synth Sub from Male Perineum, Extern Appr
0WPMXKZ	Rmvl of Nonaut Sub from Male Perineum, Extern Appr
0WPM[0,3,4][7,K]Z	Rmvl of [Auto Tissue Sub, Nonauto Tissue Sub] from Male Perineum, [Opn, Perc, Perc Endo, Ext]
0WUM[0,4]7Z	Supl/Perineum, Male, [Opn, Perc Endo], Auto Tissue Sub, NQ
0WWM[0,3,4][7,K]Z	Rev/Perineum, Male, [Opn, Perc, Perc Endo], [Auto Tissue Sub, Nonauto Tissue Sub], NQ
3E1N*	Irrigation/Male Reproductive

DRG 710   Penis Procedures without CC/MCC
GMLOS 1.8   AMLOS 2.4   RW 1.4170

Select operating room procedures listed under DRG 709

DRG 711   Testes Procedures with CC/MCC
GMLOS 5.2   AMLOS 7.3   RW 1.9959

Operating Room Procedures

0V1*	Male Reproductive Sys, Bypass
0V56*	Destr/Tunica Vaginalis, Rt
0V57*	Destr/Tunica Vaginalis, Lt
0V59*	Destr/Testis, Rt
0V5B*	Destr/Testis, Lt
0V5C*	Destr/Testes, Bilat
0V5F*	Destr/Spermatic Cord, Rt
0V5G*	Destr/Spermatic Cord, Lt
0V5H*	Destr/Spermatic Cords, Bilat
0V5J*	Destr/Epididymis, Rt
0V5K*	Destr/Epididymis, Lt
0V5L*	Destr/Epididymis, Bilat
0V7*	Male Reproductive Sys, Dilation
0V990ZX	Drain of Rt Testis, Opn Appr, Diagnostic
0V990[0,Z]Z	Drain/Testis, Rt, Opn, [Drain Dev, No Dev], NQ
0V9B0ZX	Drain of Lt Testis, Opn Appr, Diagnostic
0V9B0[0,Z]Z	Drain/Testis, Lt, Opn, [Drain Dev, No Dev], NQ
0V9C0ZX	Drain of Bilat Testes, Opn Appr, Diagnostic
0V9C0[0,Z]Z	Drain/Testes, Bilat, Opn, [Drain Dev, No Dev], NQ
0V9J[0,3,4][0,Z]Z	Drain/Epididymis, Rt, [Opn, Perc, Perc Endo], [Drain Dev, No Dev], NQ
0V9K[0,3,4][0,Z]Z	Drain/Epididymis, Lt, [Opn, Perc, Perc Endo], [Drain Dev, No Dev], NQ
0V9L[0,3,4][0,Z]Z	Drain/Epididymis, Bilat, [Opn, Perc, Perc Endo], [Drain Dev, No Dev], NQ
0VB6[0,3,4]ZZ	Exc/Tunica Vaginalis, Rt, [Opn, Perc, Perc Endo]
0VB7[0,3,4]ZZ	Exc/Tunica Vaginalis, Lt, [Opn, Perc, Perc Endo]
0VB90ZX	Exc of Rt Testis, Opn Appr, Diagnostic
0VB9[0,3,4]ZZ	Exc of Rt Testis, [Opn, Perc, Perc Endo]
0VBB0ZX	Exc of Lt Testis, Opn Appr, Diagnostic
0VBB[0,3,4]ZZ	Exc of Lt Testis, [Opn, Perc, Perc Endo]
0VBC0ZX	Exc of Bilat Testes, Opn Appr, Diagnostic
0VBC[0,3,4]ZZ	Exc of Bilat Testes, [Opn, Perc, Perc Endo]
0VBF[0,3,4]ZZ	Exc/Spermatic Cord, Rt, [Opn, Perc, Perc Endo]
0VBG[0,3,4]ZZ	Exc/Spermatic Cord, Lt, [Opn, Perc, Perc Endo]
0VBH[0,3,4]ZZ	Exc/Spermatic Cords, Bilat, [Opn, Perc, Perc Endo]
0VBJ[0,3,4]ZZ	Exc/Epididymis, Rt, [Opn, Perc, Perc Endo]
0VBK[0,3,4]ZZ	Exc/Epididymis, Lt, [Opn, Perc, Perc Endo]
0VBL[0,3,4]ZZ	Exc/Epididymis, Bilat, [Opn, Perc, Perc Endo]
0VC9*	Extir/Testis, Rt
0VCB*	Extir/Testis, Lt
0VCC*	Extir/Testes, Bilat
0VCF*	Extir/Spermatic Cord, Rt
0VCG*	Extir/Spermatic Cord, Lt
0VCH*	Extir/Spermatic Cords, Bilat
0VCJ*	Extir/Epididymis, Rt
0VCK*	Extir/Epididymis, Lt

Surgical	Medical	CC Indicator	MCC Indicator	Procedure Proxy	**PDx MCC** PDx acts as own MCC	**PDx CC** PDx acts as own CC

© 2015 Optum360, LLC   MS-DRG Version 33.0   **257**

Code	Description
ØVCL*	Extir/Epididymis, Bilat
ØVJD[Ø,3,4]ZZ	Inspect/Testis, [Opn, Perc, Perc Endo]
ØVJM[Ø,3,4]ZZ	Inspect/Epididymis and Spermatic Cord, [Opn, Perc, Perc Endo]
ØVJR[Ø,3,4]ZZ	Inspect/Vas Deferens, [Opn, Perc, Perc Endo]
ØVLN[Ø,3,4]DZ	Occlsn/Vas Deferens, Rt, [Opn, Perc, Perc Endo], Intralum Dev, NQ
ØVLP[Ø,3,4]DZ	Occlsn/Vas Deferens, Lt, [Opn, Perc, Perc Endo], Intralum Dev, NQ
ØVLQ[Ø,3,4]DZ	Occlsn/Vas Deferens, Bilat, [Opn, Perc, Perc Endo], Intralum Dev, NQ
ØVM5XZZ	Reattach of Scrotum, Ext Appr
ØVM6*	Reattach/Tunica Vaginalis, Rt
ØVM7*	Reattach/Tunica Vaginalis, Lt
ØVM9*	Reattach/Testis, Rt
ØVMB*	Reattach/Testis, Lt
ØVMC*	Reattach/Testes, Bilat
ØVMF*	Reattach/Spermatic Cord, Rt
ØVMG*	Reattach/Spermatic Cord, Lt
ØVMH*	Reattach/Spermatic Cords, Bilat
ØVN5*	Rls/Scrotum
ØVN6*	Rls/Tunica Vaginalis, Rt
ØVN7*	Rls/Tunica Vaginalis, Lt
ØVNF*	Rls/Spermatic Cord, Rt
ØVNG*	Rls/Spermatic Cord, Lt
ØVNH*	Rls/Spermatic Cords, Bilat
ØVNJ*	Rls/Epididymis, Rt
ØVNK*	Rls/Epididymis, Lt
ØVNL*	Rls/Epididymis, Bilat
ØVNN*	Rls/Vas Deferens, Rt
ØVNP*	Rls/Vas Deferens, Lt
ØVNQ*	Rls/Vas Deferens, Bilat
ØVPD[Ø,3,4,7,8][Ø,3,7,J,K]Z	Rmvl/Testis, [Opn, Perc, Perc Endo, Via Natrl or Artfcl Opng, Via Natrl or Artfcl Opng Endo], [Drain Dev, Inf Dev, Auto Tissue Sub, Synth Sub, Nonauto Tissue Sub], NQ
ØVPM[Ø,3,4,7,8][Ø,3,7,C,J,K]Z	Rmvl/Epididymis and Spermatic Cord, [Opn, Perc, Perc Endo, Via Natrl or Artfcl Opng, Via Natrl or Artfcl Opng Endo], [Drain Dev, Inf Dev, Auto Tissue Sub, Extralum Dev, Synth Sub, Nonauto Tissue Sub], NQ
ØVPR[Ø,3,4,7,8]DZ	Rmvl/Vas Deferens, [Opn, Perc, Perc Endo, Via Natrl or Artfcl Opng, Via Natrl or Artfcl Opng Endo], Intralum Dev, NQ
ØVQ9*	Repair/Testis, Rt
ØVQB*	Repair/Testis, Lt
ØVQC*	Repair/Testes, Bilat
ØVQF*	Repair/Spermatic Cord, Rt
ØVQG*	Repair/Spermatic Cord, Lt
ØVQH*	Repair/Spermatic Cords, Bilat
ØVQJ*	Repair/Epididymis, Rt
ØVQK*	Repair/Epididymis, Lt
ØVQL*	Repair/Epididymis, Bilat
ØVQN*	Repair/Vas Deferens, Rt
ØVQP*	Repair/Vas Deferens, Lt
ØVQQ*	Repair/Vas Deferens, Bilat
ØVR*	Male Reproductive Sys, Replace
ØVS*	Male Reproductive Sys, Repos
ØVT6*	Resect/Tunica Vaginalis, Rt
ØVT7*	Resect/Tunica Vaginalis, Lt
ØVT9*	Resect/Testis, Rt
ØVTB*	Resect/Testis, Lt
ØVTC*	Resect/Testes, Bilat
ØVTF*	Resect/Spermatic Cord, Rt
ØVTG*	Resect/Spermatic Cord, Lt
ØVTH*	Resect/Spermatic Cords, Bilat
ØVTJ*	Resect/Epididymis, Rt
ØVTK*	Resect/Epididymis, Lt
ØVTL*	Resect/Epididymis, Bilat
ØVU5*	Supl/Scrotum
ØVU6*	Supl/Tunica Vaginalis, Rt
ØVU7*	Supl/Tunica Vaginalis, Lt
ØVU9*	Supl/Testis, Rt
ØVUB*	Supl/Testis, Lt
ØVUC*	Supl/Testes, Bilat
ØVUF*	Supl/Spermatic Cord, Rt
ØVUG*	Supl/Spermatic Cord, Lt
ØVUH*	Supl/Spermatic Cords, Bilat
ØVUJ*	Supl/Epididymis, Rt
ØVUK*	Supl/Epididymis, Lt
ØVUL*	Supl/Epididymis, Bilat
ØVUN*	Supl/Vas Deferens, Rt
ØVUP*	Supl/Vas Deferens, Lt

Code	Description
ØVUQ*	Supl/Vas Deferens, Bilat
ØVWD[Ø,3,4,7,8][Ø,3,7,J,K]Z	Rev/Testis, [Opn, Perc, Perc Endo, Via Natrl or Artfcl Opng, Via Natrl or Artfcl Opng Endo], [Drain Dev, Inf Dev, Auto Tissue Sub, Synth Sub, Nonauto Tissue Sub], NQ
ØVWM[Ø,3,4,7,8][Ø,3,7,C,J,K]Z	Rev/Epididymis and Spermatic Cord, [Opn, Perc, Perc Endo, Via Natrl or Artfcl Opng, Via Natrl or Artfcl Opng Endo], [Drain Dev, Inf Dev, Auto Tissue Sub, Extralum Dev, Synth Sub, Nonauto Tissue Sub], NQ

DRG 712   Testes Procedures without CC/MCC
GMLOS 2.3   AMLOS 3.0   RW 0.9475

Select operating room procedures listed under DRG 711

DRG 713   Transurethral Prostatectomy with CC/MCC
GMLOS 3.4   AMLOS 4.7   RW 1.5077

Operating Room Procedures

Code	Description
ØV5Ø[7,8]ZZ	Destr/Prostate, [Via Natrl or Artfcl Opng, Via Natrl or Artfcl Opng Endo]
ØVBØ[7,8]ZZ	Exc/Prostate, [Via Natrl or Artfcl Opng, Via Natrl or Artfcl Opng Endo]
ØVTØ[7,8]ZZ	Resect/Prostate, [Via Natrl or Artfcl Opng, Via Natrl or Artfcl Opng Endo]

DRG 714   Transurethral Prostatectomy without CC/MCC
GMLOS 1.7   AMLOS 2.0   RW 0.8072

Select operating room procedures listed under DRG 713

DRG 715   Other Male Reproductive System O.R. Procedures for Malignancy with CC/MCC
GMLOS 5.2   AMLOS 7.0   RW 1.8793

Principal Diagnosis

Code	Description
C60*	Malig neoplasm of penis
C61	Malig neoplasm of prostate
C62*	Malig neoplasm of testis
C63*	Malig neoplasm of oth and unsp male genital organs
C76.3	Malig neoplasm of pelvis
C79.82	Secondary malig neoplasm of genital organs
D07.4	Carcinoma in situ of penis
D07.5	Carcinoma in situ of prostate
D07.6*	Carcinoma in situ of oth and unsp male genital organs
D40*	Neoplasm of uncertain behav of male genital organs
	AND

Operating Room Procedures

Code	Description
00HE[0,3,4]MZ	Insert/Cranial Nerve, [Opn, Perc, Perc Endo], Neurostimulator Lead, NQ
00HU[0,3,4]MZ	Insert/Spinal Canal, [Opn, Perc, Perc Endo], Neurostimulator Lead, NQ
00HV[0,3,4]MZ	Insert/Spinal Cord, [Opn, Perc, Perc Endo], Neurostimulator Lead, NQ
00PE[0,3,4,X]MZ	Rmvl/Cranial Nerve, [Opn, Perc, Perc Endo, Ext], Neurostimulator Lead, NQ
00PU[0,3,4]MZ	Rmvl/Spinal Canal, [Opn, Perc, Perc Endo], Neurostimulator Lead, NQ
00PV[0,3,4]MZ	Rmvl/Spinal Cord, [Opn, Perc, Perc Endo], Neurostimulator Lead, NQ
01HY[0,3,4]MZ	Insert/Peripheral Nerve, [Opn, Perc, Perc Endo], Neurostimulator Lead, NQ
01PY[0,3,4,X]MZ	Rmvl/Peripheral Nerve, [Opn, Perc, Perc Endo, Ext], Neurostimulator Lead, NQ
02HV[0,3,4][2,D]Z	Insert/Superior Vena Cava, [Opn, Perc, Perc Endo], [Monitoring Dev, Intralum Dev], NQ
02LV*	Occlsn/Superior Vena Cava
02VV*	Restrict/Superior Vena Cava
06H0[0,3,4]DZ	Insert/Inferior Vena Cava, [Opn, Perc, Perc Endo], Intralum Dev, NQ
06L0*	Occlsn/Inferior Vena Cava
06V0*	Restrict/Inferior Vena Cava
079C[0,3,4]ZX	Drain/Lymphatic, Pelvis, [Opn, Perc, Perc Endo]
079H[0,3,4]ZX	Drain/Lymphatic, Rt Inguinal, [Opn, Perc, Perc Endo]
079J[0,3,4]ZX	Drain/Lymphatic, Lt Inguinal, [Opn, Perc, Perc Endo]
07BC[0,3,4]ZX	Exc/Lymphatic, Pelvis, [Opn, Perc, Perc Endo]
07BH*	Exc/Lymphatic, Rt Inguinal
07BJ*	Exc/Lymphatic, Lt Inguinal

Ⓣ Transfer DRG   Ⓢᴾ Special Payment   * Code Range   6th and 7th Character of ZZ = No Device, No Qualifier   ZX = No Device, Diagnostic

258   MS-DRG Version 33.0   © 2015 Optum360, LLC

Ø7TØ*	Resect/Lymphatic, Head
Ø7T3*	Resect/Lymphatic, Rt Upr Extr
Ø7T4*	Resect/Lymphatic, Lt Upr Extr
Ø7T7*	Resect/Lymphatic, Thorax
Ø7TB*	Resect/Lymphatic, Mesenteric
Ø7TF*	Resect/Lymphatic, Rt Lwr Extr
Ø7TG*	Resect/Lymphatic, Lt Lwr Extr
ØDH6[Ø,3,4]MZ	Insert/Stomach, [Opn, Perc, Perc Endo], Stimulator Lead, NQ
ØDP6[Ø,3,4]MZ	Rmvl/Stomach, [Opn, Perc, Perc Endo], Stimulator Lead, NQ
ØDPR*	Rmvl/Anal Sphincter
ØF9[Ø,1,2]ØZX	Drain of [Liver, Rt Lobe Liver, Lt Lobe Liver], Opn Appr, Dx
ØFB[Ø,1,2]ØZX	Exc of [Liver, Rt Lobe Liver, Lt Lobe Liver], Opn Appr, Dx
ØHB[Ø,1,4,5,6,7,8,A,B,C,D,E,F,G,H,J,K,L,M,N]XZZ	Exc of [Scalp, Face, Neck, Chest, Back, Abd, Buttock, Genitalia, Rt Upr Arm, Lt Upr Arm, Rt Lwr Arm, Lt Lwr Arm, Rt Hand, Lt Hand, Rt Upr Leg, Lt Upr Leg, Rt Lwr Leg, Lt Lwr Leg, Rt Foot, Lt Foot], Skin, Ext Appr
ØJB[Ø,1,4,5,6,7,8,9,B,C,D,F,G,H,L,M,N,P,Q,R]ØZZ	Exc of [Scalp, Face, Ant Neck, Post Neck, Chest, Back, Abd, Buttock, Perineum, Pelvic Rgn, [Rt, Lt] Upr Arm, [Rt, Lt] Lwr Arm, [Rt, Lt] Upr Leg, [Rt, Lt] Lwr Leg, [Rt, Lt] Foot], SQ Tissue & Fascia, Opn Appr
ØJH6[Ø,3]VZ	Insert/SQ Tissue & Fascia, Chest, [Opn, Perc], Inf Pump, NQ
ØJH7[Ø,3]VZ	Insert/SQ Tissue & Fascia, Back, [Opn, Perc], Inf Pump, NQ
ØJH8[Ø,3]VZ	Insert/SQ Tissue & Fascia, Abd, [Opn, Perc], Inf Pump, NQ
ØJHT[Ø,3]VZ	Insert/SQ Tissue & Fascia, Trunk, [Opn, Perc], Inf Pump, NQ
ØP9Ø[Ø,3,4]ZX	Drain/Sternum, [Opn, Perc, Perc Endo]
ØP91[Ø,3,4]ZX	Drain/Rib, Rt, [Opn, Perc, Perc Endo]
ØP92[Ø,3,4]ZX	Drain/Rib, Lt, [Opn, Perc, Perc Endo]
ØP95[Ø,3,4]ZX	Drain/Scapula, Rt, [Opn, Perc, Perc Endo]
ØP96[Ø,3,4]ZX	Drain/Scapula, Lt, [Opn, Perc, Perc Endo]
ØP97[Ø,3,4]ZX	Drain/Glenoid Cavity, Rt, [Opn, Perc, Perc Endo]
ØP98[Ø,3,4]ZX	Drain/Glenoid Cavity, Lt, [Opn, Perc, Perc Endo]
ØP99[Ø,3,4]ZX	Drain/Clavicle, Rt, [Opn, Perc, Perc Endo]
ØP9B[Ø,3,4]ZX	Drain/Clavicle, Lt, [Opn, Perc, Perc Endo]
ØP9C[Ø,3,4]ZX	Drain/Humeral Head, Rt, [Opn, Perc, Perc Endo]
ØP9D[Ø,3,4]ZX	Drain/Humeral Head, Lt, [Opn, Perc, Perc Endo]
ØP9F[Ø,3,4]ZX	Drain/Humeral Shaft, Rt, [Opn, Perc, Perc Endo]
ØP9G[Ø,3,4]ZX	Drain/Humeral Shaft, Lt, [Opn, Perc, Perc Endo]
ØP9H[Ø,3,4]ZX	Drain/Radius, Rt, [Opn, Perc, Perc Endo]
ØP9J[Ø,3,4]ZX	Drain/Radius, Lt, [Opn, Perc, Perc Endo]
ØP9K[Ø,3,4]ZX	Drain/Ulna, Rt, [Opn, Perc, Perc Endo]
ØP9L[Ø,3,4]ZX	Drain/Ulna, Lt, [Opn, Perc, Perc Endo]
ØP9M[Ø,3,4]ZX	Drain/Carpal, Rt, [Opn, Perc, Perc Endo]
ØP9N[Ø,3,4]ZX	Drain/Carpal, Lt, [Opn, Perc, Perc Endo]
ØP9P[Ø,3,4]ZX	Drain/Metacarpal, Rt, [Opn, Perc, Perc Endo]
ØP9Q[Ø,3,4]ZX	Drain/Metacarpal, Lt, [Opn, Perc, Perc Endo]
ØPBØ[Ø,3,4]ZX	Exc/Sternum, [Opn, Perc, Perc Endo]
ØPB1[Ø,3,4]ZX	Exc/Rib, Rt, [Opn, Perc, Perc Endo]
ØPB2[Ø,3,4]ZX	Exc/Rib, Lt, [Opn, Perc, Perc Endo]
ØPB5[Ø,3,4]ZX	Exc/Scapula, Rt, [Opn, Perc, Perc Endo]
ØPB6[Ø,3,4]ZX	Exc/Scapula, Lt, [Opn, Perc, Perc Endo]
ØPB7[Ø,3,4]ZX	Exc/Glenoid Cavity, Rt, [Opn, Perc, Perc Endo]
ØPB8[Ø,3,4]ZX	Exc/Glenoid Cavity, Lt, [Opn, Perc, Perc Endo]
ØPB9[Ø,3,4]ZX	Exc/Clavicle, Rt, [Opn, Perc, Perc Endo]
ØPBB[Ø,3,4]ZX	Exc/Clavicle, Lt, [Opn, Perc, Perc Endo]
ØPBC[Ø,3,4]ZX	Exc/Humeral Head, Rt, [Opn, Perc, Perc Endo]
ØPBD[Ø,3,4]ZX	Exc/Humeral Head, Lt, [Opn, Perc, Perc Endo]
ØPBF[Ø,3,4]ZX	Exc/Humeral Shaft, Rt, [Opn, Perc, Perc Endo]
ØPBG[Ø,3,4]ZX	Exc/Humeral Shaft, Lt, [Opn, Perc, Perc Endo]
ØPBH[Ø,3,4]ZX	Exc/Radius, Rt, [Opn, Perc, Perc Endo]
ØPBJ[Ø,3,4]ZX	Exc/Radius, Lt, [Opn, Perc, Perc Endo]
ØPBK[Ø,3,4]ZX	Exc/Ulna, Rt, [Opn, Perc, Perc Endo]
ØPBL[Ø,3,4]ZX	Exc/Ulna, Lt, [Opn, Perc, Perc Endo]
ØPBM[Ø,3,4]ZX	Exc/Carpal, Rt, [Opn, Perc, Perc Endo]
ØPBN[Ø,3,4]ZX	Exc/Carpal, Lt, [Opn, Perc, Perc Endo]
ØPBP[Ø,3,4]ZX	Exc/Metacarpal, Rt, [Opn, Perc, Perc Endo]
ØPBQ[Ø,3,4]ZX	Exc/Metacarpal, Lt, [Opn, Perc, Perc Endo]
ØQ9Ø[Ø,3,4]ZX	Drain/Lumbar Vertebra, [Opn, Perc, Perc Endo]
ØQ91[Ø,3,4]ZX	Drain/Sacrum, [Opn, Perc, Perc Endo]
ØQ92[Ø,3,4]ZX	Drain/Pelvic Bone, Rt, [Opn, Perc, Perc Endo]
ØQ93[Ø,3,4]ZX	Drain/Pelvic Bone, Lt, [Opn, Perc, Perc Endo]
ØQ94[Ø,3,4]ZX	Drain/Acetab, Rt, [Opn, Perc, Perc Endo]
ØQ95[Ø,3,4]ZX	Drain/Acetab, Lt, [Opn, Perc, Perc Endo]
ØQ96[Ø,3,4]ZX	Drain/Upr Femur, Rt, [Opn, Perc, Perc Endo]
ØQ97[Ø,3,4]ZX	Drain/Upr Femur, Lt, [Opn, Perc, Perc Endo]
ØQ98[Ø,3,4]ZX	Drain/Femor Shaft, Rt, [Opn, Perc, Perc Endo]
ØQ99[Ø,3,4]ZX	Drain/Femor Shaft, Lt, [Opn, Perc, Perc Endo]
ØQ9B[Ø,3,4]ZX	Drain/Lwr Femur, Rt, [Opn, Perc, Perc Endo]
ØQ9C[Ø,3,4]ZX	Drain/Lwr Femur, Lt, [Opn, Perc, Perc Endo]
ØQ9D[Ø,3,4]ZX	Drain/Patella, Rt, [Opn, Perc, Perc Endo]
ØQ9F[Ø,3,4]ZX	Drain/Patella, Lt, [Opn, Perc, Perc Endo]
ØQ9G[Ø,3,4]ZX	Drain/Tibia, Rt, [Opn, Perc, Perc Endo]
ØQ9H[Ø,3,4]ZX	Drain/Tibia, Lt, [Opn, Perc, Perc Endo]
ØQ9J[Ø,3,4]ZX	Drain/Fibula, Rt, [Opn, Perc, Perc Endo]
ØQ9K[Ø,3,4]ZX	Drain/Fibula, Lt, [Opn, Perc, Perc Endo]
ØQ9L[Ø,3,4]ZX	Drain/Tarsal, Rt, [Opn, Perc, Perc Endo]
ØQ9M[Ø,3,4]ZX	Drain/Tarsal, Lt, [Opn, Perc, Perc Endo]
ØQ9N[Ø,3,4]ZX	Drain/Metatarsal, Rt, [Opn, Perc, Perc Endo]
ØQ9P[Ø,3,4]ZX	Drain/Metatarsal, Lt, [Opn, Perc, Perc Endo]
ØQ9S[Ø,3,4]ZX	Drain/Coccyx, [Opn, Perc, Perc Endo]
ØQBØ[Ø,3,4]ZX	Exc/Lumbar Vertebra, [Opn, Perc, Perc Endo]
ØQB1[Ø,3,4]ZX	Exc/Sacrum, [Opn, Perc, Perc Endo]
ØQB2[Ø,3,4]ZX	Exc/Pelvic Bone, Rt, [Opn, Perc, Perc Endo]
ØQB3[Ø,3,4]ZX	Exc/Pelvic Bone, Lt, [Opn, Perc, Perc Endo]
ØQB4[Ø,3,4]ZX	Exc/Acetab, Rt, [Opn, Perc, Perc Endo]
ØQB5[Ø,3,4]ZX	Exc/Acetab, Lt, [Opn, Perc, Perc Endo]
ØQB6[Ø,3,4]ZX	Exc/Upr Femur, Rt, [Opn, Perc, Perc Endo]
ØQB7[Ø,3,4]ZX	Exc/Upr Femur, Lt, [Opn, Perc, Perc Endo]
ØQB8[Ø,3,4]ZX	Exc/Femor Shaft, Rt, [Opn, Perc, Perc Endo]
ØQB9[Ø,3,4]ZX	Exc/Femor Shaft, Lt, [Opn, Perc, Perc Endo]
ØQBB[Ø,3,4]ZX	Exc/Lwr Femur, Rt, [Opn, Perc, Perc Endo]
ØQBC[Ø,3,4]ZX	Exc/Lwr Femur, Lt, [Opn, Perc, Perc Endo]
ØQBD[Ø,3,4]ZX	Exc/Patella, Rt, [Opn, Perc, Perc Endo]
ØQBF[Ø,3,4]ZX	Exc/Patella, Lt, [Opn, Perc, Perc Endo]
ØQBG[Ø,3,4]ZX	Exc/Tibia, Rt, [Opn, Perc, Perc Endo]
ØQBH[Ø,3,4]ZX	Exc/Tibia, Lt, [Opn, Perc, Perc Endo]
ØQBJ[Ø,3,4]ZX	Exc/Fibula, Rt, [Opn, Perc, Perc Endo]
ØQBK[Ø,3,4]ZX	Exc/Fibula, Lt, [Opn, Perc, Perc Endo]
ØQBL[Ø,3,4]ZX	Exc/Tarsal, Rt, [Opn, Perc, Perc Endo]
ØQBM[Ø,3,4]ZX	Exc/Tarsal, Lt, [Opn, Perc, Perc Endo]
ØQBN[Ø,3,4]ZX	Exc/Metatarsal, Rt, [Opn, Perc, Perc Endo]
ØQBP[Ø,3,4]ZX	Exc/Metatarsal, Lt, [Opn, Perc, Perc Endo]
ØQBS[Ø,3,4]ZX	Exc/Coccyx, [Opn, Perc, Perc Endo]
ØT13[Ø,4][7,J,K,Z]B	Bypass/Kidney Pelvis, Rt, [Opn, Perc Endo], [Auto Tissue Sub, Synth Sub, Nonauto Tissue Sub, No Dev], Bladder
ØT14[Ø,4][7,J,K,Z]B	Bypass/Kidney Pelvis, Lt, [Opn, Perc Endo], [Auto Tissue Sub, Synth Sub, Nonauto Tissue Sub, No Dev], Bladder
ØT163JD	Bypass Rt Ureter to Cutan with Synth Sub, Perc Appr
ØT16[Ø,4][7,J,K,Z][6,7,8,9,A,C,D]	Bypass/Ureter, Rt, [Opn, Perc Endo], [Auto Tissue Sub, Synth Sub, Nonauto Tissue Sub, No Dev], [Ureter, Rt, Ureter, Lt, Colon, Colocutaneous, Ileum, Ileocutaneous, Cutaneous]
ØT173JD	Bypass Lt Ureter to Cutan with Synth Sub, Perc Appr
ØT17[Ø,4][7,J,K,Z][6,7,8,9,A,C,D]	Bypass/Ureter, Lt, [Opn, Perc Endo], [Auto Tissue Sub, Synth Sub, Nonauto Tissue Sub, No Dev], [Ureter, Rt, Ureter, Lt, Colon, Colocutaneous, Ileum, Ileocutaneous, Cutaneous]
ØT183JD	Bypass Bi Ureter to Cutan with Synth Sub, Perc Appr
ØT18[Ø,4][7,J,K,Z][6,7,8,9,A,C,D]	Bypass/Ureters, Bilat, [Opn, Perc Endo], [Auto Tissue Sub, Synth Sub, Nonauto Tissue Sub, No Dev], [Ureter, Rt, Ureter, Lt, Colon, Colocutaneous, Ileum, Ileocutaneous, Cutaneous]
ØT1B*	Bypass/Bladder
ØT56*	Destr/Ureter, Rt
ØT57*	Destr/Ureter, Lt
ØT5B*	Destr/Bladder
ØT5C*	Destr/Bladder Neck
ØT7D[Ø,3,4]ZZ	Dilation/Urethra, [Opn, Perc, Perc Endo]
ØT93ØZZ	Drain of Rt Kidney Pelvis, Opn Appr
ØT93[Ø,3,4]ØZ	Drain/Kidney Pelvis, Rt, [Opn, Perc, Perc Endo], Drain Dev, NQ
ØT94ØZZ	Drain of Lt Kidney Pelvis, Opn Appr
ØT94[Ø,3,4]ØZ	Drain/Kidney Pelvis, Lt, [Opn, Perc, Perc Endo], Drain Dev, NQ
ØT9BØØZ	Drain of Bladder with Drain Device, Opn Appr
ØT9B[Ø,3,4,7,8]ZX	Drain/Bladder, [Opn, Perc, Perc Endo, Via Natrl or Artfcl Opng, Via Natrl or Artfcl Opng Endo]
ØT9C[Ø,3,4,7,8]ZX	Drain/Bladder Neck, [Opn, Perc, Perc Endo, Via Natrl or Artfcl Opng, Via Natrl or Artfcl Opng Endo]
ØTBØ[Ø,3,4]ZZ	Exc/Kidney, Rt, [Opn, Perc, Perc Endo]
ØTB1[Ø,3,4]ZZ	Exc/Kidney, Lt, [Opn, Perc, Perc Endo]
ØTB3[Ø,3,4]ZZ	Exc/Kidney Pelvis, Rt, [Opn, Perc, Perc Endo]
ØTB4[Ø,3,4]ZZ	Exc/Kidney Pelvis, Lt, [Opn, Perc, Perc Endo]
ØTB6[Ø,3,4,7,8]ZZ	Exc/Ureter, Rt, [Opn, Perc, Perc Endo, Via Natrl or Artfcl Opng, Via Natrl or Artfcl Opng Endo]
ØTB7[Ø,3,4,7,8]ZZ	Exc/Ureter, Lt, [Opn, Perc, Perc Endo, Via Natrl or Artfcl Opng, Via Natrl or Artfcl Opng Endo]
ØTBB[Ø,3,4,7,8]ZX	Exc/Bladder, [Opn, Perc, Perc Endo, Via Natrl or Artfcl Opng, Via Natrl or Artfcl Opng Endo]
ØTBB[7,8]ZZ	Exc/Bladder, [Via Natrl or Artfcl Opng, Via Natrl or Artfcl Opng Endo]
ØTBC[Ø,3,4,7,8]ZX	Exc/Bladder Neck, [Opn, Perc, Perc Endo, Via Natrl or Artfcl Opng, Via Natrl or Artfcl Opng Endo]

MDC 12: Diseases And Disorders Of The Male Reproductive System—MEDICAL

ØTBC[7,8]ZZ	Exc/Bladder Neck, [Via Natrl or Artfcl Opng, Via Natrl or Artfcl Opng Endo]
ØTJB[3,4,7]ZZ	Inspect/Bladder, [Perc, Perc Endo, Via Natrl or Artfcl Opng]
ØTLD*	Occlsn/Urethra
ØTNØ*	Rls/Kidney, Rt
ØTN1*	Rls/Kidney, Lt
ØTN3*	Rls/Kidney Pelvis, Rt
ØTN4*	Rls/Kidney Pelvis, Lt
ØTN6[Ø,3,4]ZZ	Rls/Ureter, Rt, [Opn, Perc, Perc Endo]
ØTN7[Ø,3,4]ZZ	Rls/Ureter, Lt, [Opn, Perc, Perc Endo]
ØTNB[3,4]ZZ	Rls/Bladder, [Perc, Perc Endo]
ØTNC[3,4]ZZ	Rls/Bladder Neck, [Perc, Perc Endo]
ØTPD[Ø,3,4,7,8,X]LZ	Rmvl/Urethra, [Opn, Perc, Perc Endo, Via Natrl or Artfcl Opng, Via Natrl or Artfcl Opng Endo, Ext], Artfcl Sphincter, NQ
ØTQØ*	Repair/Kidney, Rt
ØTQ1*	Repair/Kidney, Lt
ØTQ7*	Repair/Ureter, Lt
ØTQB*	Repair/Bladder
ØTWD[Ø,3,4,7,8]LZ	Rev/Urethra, [Opn, Perc, Perc Endo, Via Natrl or Artfcl Opng, Via Natrl or Artfcl Opng Endo], Artfcl Sphincter, NQ
ØV51*	Destr/Seminal Vesicle, Rt
ØV52*	Destr/Seminal Vesicle, Lt
ØV53*	Destr/Seminal Vesicles, Bilat
ØV900ZX	Drain of Prostate, Opn Appr, Diagnostic
ØV90[Ø,7,8][Ø,Z]Z	Drain/Prostate, [Opn, Via Natrl or Artfcl Opng, Via Natrl or Artfcl Opng Endo], [Drain Dev, No Dev], NQ
ØV910ZX	Drain of Rt Seminal Vesicle, Opn Appr, Diagnostic
ØV910[Ø,Z]Z	Drain/Seminal Vesicle, Rt, Opn, [Drain Dev, No Dev], NQ
ØV920ZX	Drain of Lt Seminal Vesicle, Opn Appr, Diagnostic
ØV920[Ø,Z]Z	Drain/Seminal Vesicle, Lt, Opn, [Drain Dev, No Dev], NQ
ØV930ZX	Drain of Bilat Seminal Vesicles, Opn Appr, Diagn
ØV930[Ø,Z]Z	Drain/Seminal Vesicles, Bilat, Opn, [Drain Dev, No Dev], NQ
ØVB00ZX	Exc of Prostate, Opn Appr, Diagnostic
ØVB0[Ø,3,4]ZZ	Exc/Prostate, [Opn, Perc, Perc Endo]
ØVB10ZX	Exc of Rt Seminal Vesicle, Opn Appr, Diagnostic
ØVB1[Ø,3,4]ZZ	Exc/Seminal Vesicle, Rt, [Opn, Perc, Perc Endo]
ØVB20ZX	Exc of Lt Seminal Vesicle, Opn Appr, Diagnostic
ØVB2[Ø,3,4]ZZ	Exc/Seminal Vesicle, Lt, [Opn, Perc, Perc Endo]
ØVB30ZX	Exc of Bilat Seminal Vesicles, Opn Appr, Diagn
ØVB3[Ø,3,4]ZZ	Exc/Seminal Vesicles, Bilat, [Opn, Perc, Perc Endo]
ØVCØ*	Extir/Prostate
ØVC1*	Extir/Seminal Vesicle, Rt
ØVC2*	Extir/Seminal Vesicle, Lt
ØVC3*	Extir/Seminal Vesicles, Bilat
ØVHØ*	Insert/Prostate
ØVJ4[Ø,3,4]ZZ	Inspect/Prostate and Seminal Vesicles, [Opn, Perc, Perc Endo]
ØVNØ*	Rls/Prostate
ØVN1*	Rls/Seminal Vesicle, Rt
ØVN2*	Rls/Seminal Vesicle, Lt
ØVN3*	Rls/Seminal Vesicles, Bilat
ØVP4[Ø,3,4,7,8][Ø,1,3,7,J,K]Z	Rmvl/Prostate and Seminal Vesicles, [Opn, Perc, Perc Endo, Via Natrl or Artfcl Opng, Via Natrl or Artfcl Opng Endo], [Drain Dev, Radioact Elmt, Inf Dev, Auto Tissue Sub, Synth Sub, Nonauto Tissue Sub], NQ
ØVQØ*	Repair/Prostate
ØVQ1*	Repair/Seminal Vesicle, Rt
ØVQ2*	Repair/Seminal Vesicle, Lt
ØVQ3*	Repair/Seminal Vesicles, Bilat
ØVT1*	Resect/Seminal Vesicle, Rt
ØVT2*	Resect/Seminal Vesicle, Lt
ØVT3*	Resect/Seminal Vesicles, Bilat
ØVU1*	Supl/Seminal Vesicle, Rt
ØVU2*	Supl/Seminal Vesicle, Lt
ØVU3*	Supl/Seminal Vesicles, Bilat
ØVW4[Ø,3,4,7,8][Ø,3,7,J,K]Z	Rev/Prostate and Seminal Vesicles, [Opn, Perc, Perc Endo, Via Natrl or Artfcl Opng, Via Natrl or Artfcl Opng Endo], [Drain Dev, Inf Dev, Auto Tissue Sub, Synth Sub, Nonauto Tissue Sub], NQ
ØW3M*	Control/Perineum, Male
ØW3R*	Control/Genitourinary Tract
ØWHJ[Ø,3,4]1Z	Insert/Pelvic Cavity, [Opn, Perc, Perc Endo], Radioact Elmt, NQ
ØWHM[Ø,3,4]1Z	Insert/Perineum, Male, [Opn, Perc, Perc Endo], Radioact Elmt, NQ
ØWHR[Ø,3,4,7,8]1Z	Insert/Genitourinary Tract, [Opn, Perc, Perc Endo, Via Natrl or Artfcl Opng, Via Natrl or Artfcl Opng Endo], Radioact Elmt, NQ
ØWQFXZ2	Repair Abd Wall, Stoma, Ext Appr
ØWQF[Ø,3,4,X]ZZ	Rpr/Abd Wall, [Opn, Perc, Perc Endo, Ext]
DØY6KZZ	Laser Interstitial Thermal Therapy of Spinal Cord
DØY7KZZ	Laser Interstitial Thermal Therapy of Peripheral Nerve
DBYØKZZ	Laser Interstitial Thermal Therapy of Trachea
DBY1KZZ	Laser Interstitial Thermal Therapy of Bronchus
DBY2KZZ	Laser Interstitial Thermal Therapy of Lung
DBY5KZZ	Laser Interstitial Thermal Therapy of Pleura
DBY6KZZ	Laser Interstitial Thermal Therapy of Mediastinum
DBY7KZZ	Laser Interstitial Thermal Therapy of Chest Wall
DBY8KZZ	Laser Interstitial Thermal Therapy of Diaphragm
DDY[Ø,1,2,3,4,5,7,8]KZZ	Laser Interstitital Thermal Therapy of [Esophagus, Stomach, Duodenum, Jejunum, Ileum, Colon, Rectum, Anus]
DFY[1,2,3]KZZ	Laser Interstitial Thermal Therapy of [Gallbladder, Bile Ducts, Pancreas]
DGY2KZZ	Laser Interstitial Thermal Therapy of Adrenal Glands
DMYØKZZ	Laser Interstitial Thermal Therapy of Lt Breast
DMY1KZZ	Laser Interstitial Thermal Therapy of Rt Breast
DVYØKZZ	Laser Interstitial Thermal Therapy of Prostate

DRG 716   Other Male Reproductive System O.R. Procedures for Malignancy without CC/MCC

GMLOS 1.6   AMLOS 2.Ø   RW 1.15Ø8

Select principal diagnosis AND operating room procedures listed under DRG 715

DRG 717   Other Male Reproductive System O.R. Procedures Except Malignancy with CC/MCC

GMLOS 4.7   AMLOS 6.3   RW 1.7645

Select only operating room procedures listed under DRG 715

DRG 718   Other Male Reproductive System O.R. Procedures Except Malignancy without CC/MCC

GMLOS 2.1   AMLOS 2.5   RW Ø.9Ø69

Select only operating room procedures listed under DRG 715

MEDICAL

DRG 722   Malignancy, Male Reproductive System with MCC

GMLOS 5.5   AMLOS 7.3   RW 1.737Ø

Principal Diagnosis

C6Ø*	Malig neoplasm of penis
C61	Malig neoplasm of prostate
C62*	Malig neoplasm of testis
C63*	Malig neoplasm of oth and unsp male genital organs
C76.3	Malig neoplasm of pelvis
C79.82	Secondary malig neoplasm of genital organs
DØ7.4	Carcinoma in situ of penis
DØ7.5	Carcinoma in situ of prostate
DØ7.6*	Carcinoma in situ of oth and unsp male genital organs
D4Ø*	Neoplasm of uncertain behav of male genital organs

DRG 723   Malignancy, Male Reproductive System with CC

GMLOS 3.8   AMLOS 4.8   RW 1.Ø979

Select principal diagnosis listed under DRG 722

DRG 724   Malignancy, Male Reproductive System without CC/MCC

GMLOS 2.Ø   AMLOS 2.9   RW Ø.6545

Select principal diagnosis listed under DRG 722

DRG 725   Benign Prostatic Hypertrophy with MCC

GMLOS 4.5   AMLOS 5.8   RW 1.3198

Principal Diagnosis

N4Ø*	Enlarged prostate
N42.83	Cyst of prostate

Ⓣ **Transfer DRG**   ⒮ᴾ **Special Payment**   * **Code Range**   6th and 7th Character of ZZ = No Device, No Qualifier ZX = No Device, Diagnostic

DRG 726   Benign Prostatic Hypertrophy without MCC
GMLOS 2.7   AMLOS 3.3   RW 0.7406

Select principal diagnosis listed under DRG 725

DRG 727   Inflammation of the Male Reproductive System with MCC
GMLOS 4.9   AMLOS 6.2   RW 1.4461

Principal Diagnosis

A18.1[4,5]	Tuberculosis of [prostate, oth male genital organs]
A51.0	Primary genital syphilis
A54.0[0,9]	Gonococcal infxn of lwr genitourinary tract [unsp, oth]
A54.1	Gonocl infxn of lwr GU tract w periureth and acc glnd abcs
A54.2[1,2,3,9]	Gonococcal [infxn of kidney and ureter, prostatitis, infxn of oth male genital organs, oth genitourinary infxns]
A55	Chlamydial lymphogranuloma (venereum)
A56.0[0,1,9]	Chlamydial [infxn of lwr genitourinary tract unsp, cystitis and urethritis, oth infxn of lwr genitourinary tract]
A56.2	Chlamydial infxn of genitourinary tract, unsp
A56.8	Sexually transmitted chlamydial infxn of oth sites
A57	Chancroid
A58	Granuloma inguinale
A59.0[0,2,3,9]	Trichomoniasis [urogenital unsp, prostatitis, cystitis and urethritis, Oth urogenital]
A60.0[0,1,2,9]	Herpesviral infxn of [urogenital sys unsp, penis, oth male genital organs, oth urogenital tract]
A60.1	Herpesviral infxn of perianal skin and rectum
A60.9	Anogenital herpesviral infxn, unsp
A63.8	Oth spec predominantly sexually transmitted dz
A64	Unsp sexually transmitted dz
B26.0	Mumps orchitis
B37.4*	Candidiasis of oth urogenital sites
N34.1	Nonspecific urethritis
N41*	Inflam dz of prostate
N43.1	Infected hydrocele
N45*	Orchitis and epididymitis
N47*	D/o of prepuce
N48.1	Balanitis
N48.2*	Oth inflam d/o of penis
N49*	Inflam d/o of male genital organs, NEC
Z41.2	Enc for routine and ritual male circumcision

DRG 728   Inflammation of the Male Reproductive System without MCC
GMLOS 3.1   AMLOS 3.8   RW 0.7838

Select principal diagnosis listed under DRG 727

DRG 729   Other Male Reproductive System Diagnoses with CC/MCC
GMLOS 3.5   AMLOS 4.6   RW 1.1169

Principal Diagnosis

D17.6	Benign lipomatous neoplasm of spermatic cord
D29*	Benign neoplasm of male genital organs
I86.1	Scrotal varices
I86.2	Pelvic varices
L29.1	Pruritus scroti
L29.3	Anogenital pruritus, unsp
N42.0	Calculus of prostate
N42.1	Congestion and hemor of prostate
N42.3	Dysplasia of prostate
N42.81	Prostatodynia synd
N42.82	Prostatosis synd
N42.89	Oth spec d/o of prostate
N42.9	D/o of prostate, unsp
N43.0	Encysted hydrocele
N43.2	Oth hydrocele
N43.3	Hydrocele, unsp
N43.4*	Spermatocele of epididymis
N44*	Noninflammatory d/o of testis
N46*	Male infertility
N48.0	Leukoplakia of penis
N48.3*	Priapism
N48.5	Ulcer of penis
N48.6	Induration penis plastica
N48.8*	Oth spec d/o of penis
N48.9	D/o of penis, unsp
N50*	Oth and unsp d/o of male genital organs
N51	D/o of male genital organs in dz classd elsw
N52*	Male erectile dysfunction

N53*	Oth male sexual dysfunction
Q53*	Undescended and ectopic testicle
Q54*	Hypospadias
Q55*	Oth congenital malformations of male genital organs
Q56.0	Hermaphroditism, NEC
Q56.1	Male pseudohermaphroditism, NEC
Q56.3	Pseudohermaphroditism, unsp
Q56.4	Indeterminate sex, unsp
Q64.0	Epispadias
Q98*	Oth sex chromosome abnormalities, male phenotype, NEC
Q99.0	Chimera 46, XX/46, XY
Q99.1	46, XX true hermaphrodite
Q99.8	Oth spec chromosome abnormalities
R36.1	Hematospermia
R86*	Abnormal findings in specimens from male genital organs
S30.201A	Contsn of unsp ext genital organ, male, init enc
S30.21XA	Contsn of penis, init enc
S30.22XA	Contsn of scrotum and testes, init enc
S31.2[0,1,2,3,4,5]XA	[Unsp opn wnd, Lac w/o FB, Lac w/ FB, Punc wnd w/o FB, Punc wnd w/ FB, Opn bite], of penis, init enc
S31.3[0,1,2,3,4,5]XA	[Unsp opn wnd, Lac w/o FB, Lac w/ FB, Punc wnd w/o FB, Punc wnd w/ FB, Opn bite], of scrotum and testes, init enc
S31.5[0,1,2,3,4,5]1A	[Unsp opn wnd, Lac w/o FB, Lac w/ FB, Punc wnd w/o FB, Punc wnd w/ FB, Opn bite], of unsp ext genital organs, male, init enc
S31.5[0,1,2,3,4,5]1S	[Unsp opn wnd, Lac w/o FB, Lac w/ FB, Punc wnd w/o FB, Punc wnd w/ FB, Opn bite], of unsp ext genital organs, male, seqe
S37.1[0,2,3,9]XS	[Unsp inj, Contsn, Lac, Oth inj] of ureter, seq
S37.2[0,2,3,9]XS	[Unsp inj, Contsn, Lac, Oth inj] of bladder, seq
S37.3[0,2,3,9]XS	[Unsp inj, Contsn, Lac, Oth inj] of urethra, seq
S37.81[2,3,8,9]S	[Contsn, Lac, Oth inj, Unsp inj] of adrenal gland, seq
S37.82[2,3,8,9]A	[Contsn, Lac, Oth inj, Unsp inj] of prostate, init enc
S37.82[2,3,8,9]S	[Contsn, Lac, Oth inj, Unsp inj] of prostate, seq
S37.89[2,3,8,9]A	[Contsn, Lac, Oth inj, Unsp inj] of oth urinary and pelvic organ, init enc
S37.89[2,3,8,9]S	[Contsn, Lac, Oth inj, Unsp inj] of oth urinary and pelvic organ, seq
S37.9[0,2,3,9]XA	[Unsp inj, Contsn, Lac, Oth inj] of unsp urinary and pelvic organ, init enc
S37.9[0,2,3,9]XS	[Unsp inj, Contsn, Lac, Oth inj] of unsp urinary and pelvic organ, seq
S38.001A	Crushing inj of unsp ext genital organs, male, init
S38.01XA	Crushing inj of penis, init enc
S38.02XA	Crushing inj of scrotum and testis, init enc
S38.22[1,2]A	[Complete, Partial] traum amp of penis, init enc
S38.23[1,2]A	[Complete, Partial] traum amp of scrotum and testis, init enc
T19.4XXA	FB in penis, init enc
Z30.2	Enc for sterilization
Z31.0	Enc for reversal of previous sterilization
Z90.79	Acquired absence of other genital organ(s)

DRG 730   Other Male Reproductive System Diagnoses without CC/MCC
GMLOS 2.3   AMLOS 2.9   RW 0.6036

Select principal diagnosis listed under DRG 729

Surgical   Medical   CC Indicator   MCC Indicator   Procedure Proxy   **PDxMCC** PDx acts as own MCC   **PDxCC** PDx acts as own CC

MDC 13
Diseases And Disorders Of The Female Reproductive System

SURGICAL

DRG 734 Pelvic Evisceration, Radical Hysterectomy and Radical Vulvectomy with CC/MCC

GMLOS 4.5 AMLOS 6.4 RW 2.5255

Operating Room Procedures

Ø7TØ*	Resect/Lymphatic, Head
Ø7T3*	Resect/Lymphatic, Rt Upr Extr
Ø7T4*	Resect/Lymphatic, Lt Upr Extr
Ø7T7*	Resect/Lymphatic, Thorax
Ø7T8*	Resect/Lymphatic, Int Mammary, Rt
Ø7T9*	Resect/Lymphatic, Int Mammary, Lt
Ø7TB*	Resect/Lymphatic, Mesenteric
Ø7TC*	Resect/Lymphatic, Pelvis
Ø7TD*	Resect/Lymphatic, Aortic
Ø7TF*	Resect/Lymphatic, Rt Lwr Extr
Ø7TG*	Resect/Lymphatic, Lt Lwr Extr
Ø7TH*	Resect/Lymphatic, Rt Inguinal
Ø7TJ*	Resect/Lymphatic, Lt Inguinal

OR

ØUT94ZZ Resect of Uterus, Perc Endo Appr

AND

Both

ØUT44ZZ	Resect of Uterine Support Struct, Perc Endo Appr
ØUTC4ZZ	Resect of Cervix, Perc Endo Appr

OR

ØUT9ØZZ Resect of Uterus, Opn Appr

AND

Both

ØUT4ØZZ	Resect of Uterine Supporting Structure, Opn Appr
ØUTCØZZ	Resect of Cervix, Opn Appr

OR

ØUT9ØZZ Resect of Uterus, Opn Appr

AND

All of the following

ØTTBØZZ	Resect of Bladder, Opn Appr
ØTTDØZZ	Resect of Urethra, Opn Appr
ØUT2ØZZ	Resect of Bilat Ovaries, Opn Appr
ØUT7ØZZ	Resect of Bilat Fallopian Tubes, Opn Appr
ØUT9ØZZ	Resect of Uterus, Opn Appr
ØUTCØZZ	Resect of Cervix, Opn Appr
ØUTGØZZ	Resect of Vagina, Opn Appr

OR

ØUTM* Resect/Vulva

AND

Ø7BH[Ø,4]ZZ	Exc/Lymphatic, Rt Inguinal, [Opn, Perc Endo]
Ø7BJ[Ø,4]ZZ	Exc/Lymphatic, Lt Inguinal, [Opn, Perc Endo]

OR

ØUT9FZZ Resect of Uterus, Via Opng w Perc Endo

AND

Both

ØUT44ZZ	Resect of Uterine Support Struct, Perc Endo Appr
ØUTC4ZZ	Resect of Cervix, Perc Endo Appr

OR

ØUT9[7,8]ZZ Resect/Uterus, [Via Natrl or Artfcl Opng, Via Natrl or Artfcl Opng Endo]

AND

ØUT4[7,8]ZZ Resect/Uterine Supporting Structure, [Via Natrl or Artfcl Opng, Via Natrl or Artfcl Opng Endo]

AND

ØUTC[7,8]ZZ Resect/Cervix, [Via Natrl or Artfcl Opng, Via Natrl or Artfcl Opng Endo]

DRG 735 Pelvic Evisceration, Radical Hysterectomy and Radical Vulvectomy without CC/MCC

GMLOS 1.8 AMLOS 2.2 RW 1.22Ø7

Select operating room procedures or procedure combinations listed under DRG 734

DRG 736 Uterine and Adnexa Procedures for Ovarian or Adnexal Malignancy with MCC

GMLOS 9.9 AMLOS 12.3 RW 4.3286

Principal Diagnosis

C56*	Malig neoplasm of ovary
C57.Ø*	Malig neoplasm of fallopian tube
C57.1*	Malig neoplasm of broad lgmt
C57.2*	Malig neoplasm of round lgmt
C57.3	Malig neoplasm of parametrium
C57.4	Malig neoplasm of uterine adnexa, unsp
C79.6*	Secondary malig neoplasm of ovary
D39.1*	Neoplasm of uncertain behav of ovary

AND

Operating Room Procedures

Ø15P*	Destr/Sacral Sympathetic Nerve
ØU1*	Female Reproductive Sys, Bypass
ØU5Ø*	Destr/Ovary, Rt
ØU51*	Destr/Ovary, Lt
ØU52*	Destr/Ovaries, Bilat
ØU54*	Destr/Uterine Supporting Structure
ØU55*	Destr/Fallopian Tube, Rt
ØU56*	Destr/Fallopian Tube, Lt
ØU59*	Destr/Uterus
ØU5B*	Destr/Endometrium
ØU75*	Dilation/Fallopian Tube, Rt
ØU76*	Dilation/Fallopian Tube, Lt
ØU77*	Dilation/Fallopian Tubes, Bilat
ØU79*	Dilation/Uterus
ØU8Ø*	Div/Ovary, Rt
ØU81*	Div/Ovary, Lt
ØU82*	Div/Ovaries, Bilat
ØU9Ø*	Drain/Ovary, Rt
ØU91*	Drain/Ovary, Lt
ØU92*	Drain/Ovaries, Bilat
ØU94ØZX	Drain of Uterine Support Struct, Opn Appr, Diagn
ØU95ØZZ	Drain of Rt Fallopian Tube, Opn Appr
ØU95[Ø,3,4,7,8]ØZ	Drain/Fallopian Tube, Rt, [Opn, Perc, Perc Endo, Via Natrl or Artfcl Opng, Via Natrl or Artfcl Opng Endo], Drain Dev, NQ
ØU95[Ø,3,4,7,8]ZX	Drain/Fallopian Tube, Rt, [Opn, Perc, Perc Endo, Via Natrl or Artfcl Opng, Via Natrl or Artfcl Opng Endo]
ØU96ØZZ	Drain of Lt Fallopian Tube, Opn Appr
ØU96[Ø,3,4,7,8]ØZ	Drain/Fallopian Tube, Lt, [Opn, Perc, Perc Endo, Via Natrl or Artfcl Opng, Via Natrl or Artfcl Opng Endo], Drain Dev, NQ
ØU96[Ø,3,4,7,8]ZX	Drain/Fallopian Tube, Lt, [Opn, Perc, Perc Endo, Via Natrl or Artfcl Opng, Via Natrl or Artfcl Opng Endo]
ØU97ØZZ	Drain of Bilat Fallopian Tubes, Opn Appr
ØU97[Ø,3,4,7,8]ØZ	Drain/Fallopian Tubes, Bilat, [Opn, Perc, Perc Endo, Via Natrl or Artfcl Opng, Via Natrl or Artfcl Opng Endo], Drain Dev, NQ
ØU97[Ø,3,4,7,8]ZX	Drain/Fallopian Tubes, Bilat, [Opn, Perc, Perc Endo, Via Natrl or Artfcl Opng, Via Natrl or Artfcl Opng Endo]
ØU99ØZX	Drain of Uterus, Opn Appr, Diagnostic
ØU99[Ø,3,4,7,8][Ø,Z]Z	Drain/Uterus, [Opn, Perc, Perc Endo, Via Natrl or Artfcl Opng, Via Natrl or Artfcl Opng Endo], [Drain Dev, No Dev], NQ
ØUBØ*	Exc/Ovary, Rt
ØUB1*	Exc/Ovary, Lt
ØUB2*	Exc/Ovaries, Bilat
ØUB4ØZX	Exc of Uterine Support Struct, Opn Appr, Diagn
ØUB4[Ø,3,4,7,8]ZZ	Exc/Uterine Supporting Structure, [Opn, Perc, Perc Endo, Via Natrl or Artfcl Opng, Via Natrl or Artfcl Opng Endo]
ØUB5*	Exc/Fallopian Tube, Rt
ØUB6*	Exc/Fallopian Tube, Lt
ØUB7[Ø,3,4,7,8]ZX	Exc/Fallopian Tubes, Bilat, [Opn, Perc, Perc Endo, Via Natrl or Artfcl Opng, Via Natrl or Artfcl Opng Endo]
ØUB9ØZX	Exc of Uterus, Opn Appr, Diagnostic

0UB9[0,3,4,7,8]ZZ	Exc/Uterus, [Opn, Perc, Perc Endo, Via Natrl or Artfcl Opng, Via Natrl or Artfcl Opng Endo]
0UC0*	Extir/Ovary, Rt
0UC1*	Extir/Ovary, Lt
0UC2*	Extir/Ovaries, Bilat
0UC5*	Extir/Fallopian Tube, Rt
0UC6*	Extir/Fallopian Tube, Lt
0UC7*	Extir/Fallopian Tubes, Bilat
0UC9[0,3,4]ZZ	Extir/Uterus, [Opn, Perc, Perc Endo]
0UDN*	Extract/Ova
0UF5[0,3,4,7,8]ZZ	Fragmn/Fallopian Tube, Rt, [Opn, Perc, Perc Endo, Via Natrl or Artfcl Opng, Via Natrl or Artfcl Opng Endo]
0UF6[0,3,4,7,8]ZZ	Fragmn/Fallopian Tube, Lt, [Opn, Perc, Perc Endo, Via Natrl or Artfcl Opng, Via Natrl or Artfcl Opng Endo]
0UF7[0,3,4,7,8]ZZ	Fragmn/Fallopian Tubes, Bilat, [Opn, Perc, Perc Endo, Via Natrl or Artfcl Opng, Via Natrl or Artfcl Opng Endo]
0UJ3[0,3,4]ZZ	Inspect/Ovary, [Opn, Perc, Perc Endo]
0UJ8[0,3,4,7,8]ZZ	Inspect/Fallopian Tube, [Opn, Perc, Perc Endo, Via Natrl or Artfcl Opng, Via Natrl or Artfcl Opng Endo]
0UJD[0,3,4]ZZ	Inspect/Uterus and Cervix, [Opn, Perc, Perc Endo]
0UL5*	Occlsn/Fallopian Tube, Rt
0UL6*	Occlsn/Fallopian Tube, Lt
0UM0*	Reattach/Ovary, Rt
0UM1*	Reattach/Ovary, Lt
0UM2*	Reattach/Ovaries, Bilat
0UM5*	Reattach/Fallopian Tube, Rt
0UM6*	Reattach/Fallopian Tube, Lt
0UM7*	Reattach/Fallopian Tubes, Bilat
0UN0*	Rls/Ovary, Rt
0UN1*	Rls/Ovary, Lt
0UN2*	Rls/Ovaries, Bilat
0UN5*	Rls/Fallopian Tube, Rt
0UN6*	Rls/Fallopian Tube, Lt
0UN7*	Rls/Fallopian Tubes, Bilat
0UP3[0,3,4][0,3]Z	Rmvl/Ovary, [Opn, Perc, Perc Endo], [Drain Dev, Inf Dev], NQ
0UP8[0,3,4,7,8][0,3,7,C,D,J,K]Z	Rmvl/Fallopian Tube, [Opn, Perc, Perc Endo, Via Natrl or Artfcl Opng, Via Natrl or Artfcl Opng Endo], [Drain Dev, Inf Dev, Auto Tissue Sub, Extralum Dev, Intralum Dev, Synth Sub, Nonauto Tissue Sub], NQ
0UPD[0,3,4,7,8][0,1,3,7,D,J,K]Z	Rmvl/Uterus and Cervix, [Opn, Perc, Perc Endo, Via Natrl or Artfcl Opng, Via Natrl or Artfcl Opng Endo], [Drain Dev, Radioact Elmt, Inf Dev, Auto Tissue Sub, Intralum Sub, Synth Sub, Nonauto Tissue Sub], NQ
0UPD[0,3,4]HZ	Rmvl/Uterus and Cervix, [Opn, Perc, Perc Endo], Contraceptive Dev, NQ
0UQ0*	Repair/Ovary, Rt
0UQ1*	Repair/Ovary, Lt
0UQ2*	Repair/Ovaries, Bilat
0UQ5*	Repair/Fallopian Tube, Rt
0UQ6*	Repair/Fallopian Tube, Lt
0UQ7*	Repair/Fallopian Tubes, Bilat
0UQ9*	Repair/Uterus
0US0*	Repos/Ovary, Rt
0US1*	Repos/Ovary, Lt
0US2*	Repos/Ovaries, Bilat
0US5*	Repos/Fallopian Tube, Rt
0US6*	Repos/Fallopian Tube, Lt
0US7*	Repos/Fallopian Tubes, Bilat
0USC*	Repos/Cervix
0UT0*	Resect/Ovary, Rt
0UT1*	Resect/Ovary, Lt
0UT2*	Resect/Ovaries, Bilat
0UT5*	Resect/Fallopian Tube, Rt
0UT6*	Resect/Fallopian Tube, Lt
0UT7*	Resect/Fallopian Tubes, Bilat
0UT9*	Resect/Uterus
0UU5*	Supl/Fallopian Tube, Rt
0UU6*	Supl/Fallopian Tube, Lt
0UU7*	Supl/Fallopian Tubes, Bilat
0UW3[0,3,4][0,3]Z	Rev/Ovary, [Opn, Perc, Perc Endo], [Drain Dev, Inf Dev], NQ
0UW8[0,3,4,7,8][0,3,7,C,D,J,K]Z	Rev/Fallopian Tube, [Opn, Perc, Perc Endo, Via Natrl or Artfcl Opng, Via Natrl or Artfcl Opng Endo], [Drain Dev, Inf Dev, Auto Tissue Sub, Extralum Dev, Intralum Dev, Synth Sub, Nonauto Tissue Sub], NQ
0UWD[0,3,4,7,8][0,1,3,7,D,H,J,K]Z	Rev/Uterus and Cervix, [Opn, Perc, Perc Endo, Via Natrl or Artfcl Opng, Via Natrl or Artfcl Opng Endo], [Drain Dev, Radioact Elmt, Inf Dev, Auto Tissue Sub, Contraceptive Dev, Synth Sub, Nonauto Tissue Sub], NQ
0UY*	Female Reproductive Sys, Transplantation
10D2*	Extract/Products of Conception, Ectopic

10T*	Obstetrics, Preg, Resect

DRG 737 Uterine and Adnexa Procedures for Ovarian or Adnexal Malignancy with CC

GMLOS 5.1   AMLOS 5.9   RW 2.0037

Select principal diagnosis AND operating room procedures listed under DRG 736

DRG 738 Uterine and Adnexa Procedures for Ovarian or Adnexal Malignancy without CC/MCC

GMLOS 3.0   AMLOS 3.4   RW 1.3498

Select principal diagnosis AND operating room procedures listed under DRG 736

DRG 739 Uterine, Adnexa Procedures for Nonovarian/Adnexal Malignancy with MCC

GMLOS 6.6   AMLOS 9.0   RW 3.4082

Principal Diagnosis

C51*	Malig neoplasm of vulva
C52	Malig neoplasm of vagina
C53*	Malig neoplasm of cervix uteri
C54*	Malig neoplasm of corpus uteri
C55	Malig neoplasm of uterus, part unsp
C57.7	Malig neoplasm of oth spec female genital organs
C57.8	Malig neoplasm of ovrlp sites of female genital organs
C57.9	Malig neoplasm of female genital organ, unsp
C58	Malig neoplasm of placenta
C76.3	Malig neoplasm of pelvis
C79.82	Secondary malig neoplasm of genital organs
D06*	Carcinoma in situ of cervix uteri
D07.0	Carcinoma in situ of endometrium
D07.1	Carcinoma in situ of vulva
D07.2	Carcinoma in situ of vagina
D07.3*	Carcinoma in situ of oth and unsp female genital organs
D39.0	Neoplasm of uncertain behav of uterus
D39.2	Neoplasm of uncertain behav of placenta
D39.8	Neoplasm of uncertain behav of oth female genital organs
D39.9	Neoplasm of uncertain behav of female genital organ, unsp

AND

Operating Room Procedures

015P*	Destr/Sacral Sympathetic Nerve
0U1*	Female Reproductive Sys, Bypass
0U50*	Destr/Ovary, Rt
0U51*	Destr/Ovary, Lt
0U52*	Destr/Ovaries, Bilat
0U54*	Destr/Uterine Supporting Structure
0U55*	Destr/Fallopian Tube, Rt
0U56*	Destr/Fallopian Tube, Lt
0U59*	Destr/Uterus
0U5B*	Destr/Endometrium
0U75*	Dilation/Fallopian Tube, Rt
0U76*	Dilation/Fallopian Tube, Lt
0U77*	Dilation/Fallopian Tubes, Bilat
0U79*	Dilation/Uterus
0U80*	Div/Ovary, Rt
0U81*	Div/Ovary, Lt
0U82*	Div/Ovaries, Bilat
0U90*	Drain/Ovary, Rt
0U91*	Drain/Ovary, Lt
0U92*	Drain/Ovaries, Bilat
0U940ZX	Drain of Uterine Support Struct, Opn Appr, Diagn
0U950ZZ	Drain of Rt Fallopian Tube, Opn Appr
0U95[0,3,4,7,8]0Z	Drain/Fallopian Tube, Rt, [Opn, Perc, Perc Endo, Via Natrl or Artfcl Opng, Via Natrl or Artfcl Opng Endo], Drain Dev, NQ
0U95[0,3,4,7,8]ZX	Drain/Fallopian Tube, Rt, [Opn, Perc, Perc Endo, Via Natrl or Artfcl Opng, Via Natrl or Artfcl Opng Endo]
0U960ZZ	Drain of Lt Fallopian Tube, Opn Appr
0U96[0,3,4,7,8]0Z	Drain/Fallopian Tube, Lt, [Opn, Perc, Perc Endo, Via Natrl or Artfcl Opng, Via Natrl or Artfcl Opng Endo], Drain Dev, NQ
0U96[0,3,4,7,8]ZX	Drain/Fallopian Tube, Lt, [Opn, Perc, Perc Endo, Via Natrl or Artfcl Opng, Via Natrl or Artfcl Opng Endo]
0U970ZZ	Drain of Bilat Fallopian Tubes, Opn Appr
0U97[0,3,4,7,8]0Z	Drain/Fallopian Tubes, Bilat, [Opn, Perc, Perc Endo, Via Natrl or Artfcl Opng, Via Natrl or Artfcl Opng Endo], Drain Dev, NQ

MDC 13: Diseases And Disorders Of The Female Reproductive System—SURGICAL

Surgical   **Medical**   **CC Indicator**   **MCC Indicator**   **Procedure Proxy**   PDxMCC **PDx acts as own MCC**   PDxCC **PDx acts as own CC**

Code	Description
0U97[0,3,4,7,8]ZX	Drain/Fallopian Tubes, Bilat, [Opn, Perc, Perc Endo, Via Natrl or Artfcl Opng, Via Natrl or Artfcl Opng Endo]
0U990ZX	Drain of Uterus, Opn Appr, Diagnostic
0U99[0,3,4,7,8][0,Z]Z	Drain/Uterus, [Opn, Perc, Perc Endo, Via Natrl or Artfcl Opng, Via Natrl or Artfcl Opng Endo], [Drain Dev, No Dev], NQ
0UB0*	Exc/Ovary, Rt
0UB1*	Exc/Ovary, Lt
0UB2*	Exc/Ovaries, Bilat
0UB40ZX	Exc of Uterine Support Struct, Opn Appr, Diagn
0UB4[0,3,4,7,8]ZX	Exc/Uterine Supporting Structure, [Opn, Perc, Perc Endo, Via Natrl or Artfcl Opng, Via Natrl or Artfcl Opng Endo]
0UB5*	Exc/Fallopian Tube, Rt
0UB6*	Exc/Fallopian Tube, Lt
0UB7[0,3,4,7,8]ZX	Exc/Fallopian Tubes, Bilat, [Opn, Perc, Perc Endo, Via Natrl or Artfcl Opng, Via Natrl or Artfcl Opng Endo]
0UB90ZX	Exc of Uterus, Opn Appr, Diagnostic
0UB9[0,3,4,7,8]ZZ	Exc/Uterus, [Opn, Perc, Perc Endo, Via Natrl or Artfcl Opng, Via Natrl or Artfcl Opng Endo]
0UC0*	Extir/Ovary, Rt
0UC1*	Extir/Ovary, Lt
0UC2*	Extir/Ovaries, Bilat
0UC5*	Extir/Fallopian Tube, Rt
0UC6*	Extir/Fallopian Tube, Lt
0UC7*	Extir/Fallopian Tubes, Bilat
0UC9[0,3,4]ZZ	Extir/Uterus, [Opn, Perc, Perc Endo]
0UDN*	Extract/Ova
0UF5[0,3,4,7,8]ZZ	Fragmn/Fallopian Tube, Rt, [Opn, Perc, Perc Endo, Via Natrl or Artfcl Opng, Via Natrl or Artfcl Opng Endo]
0UF6[0,3,4,7,8]ZZ	Fragmn/Fallopian Tube, Lt, [Opn, Perc, Perc Endo, Via Natrl or Artfcl Opng, Via Natrl or Artfcl Opng Endo]
0UF7[0,3,4,7,8]ZZ	Fragmn/Fallopian Tubes, Bilat, [Opn, Perc, Perc Endo, Via Natrl or Artfcl Opng, Via Natrl or Artfcl Opng Endo]
0UJ3[0,3,4]ZZ	Inspect/Ovary, [Opn, Perc, Perc Endo]
0UJ8[0,3,4,7,8]ZZ	Inspect/Fallopian Tube, [Opn, Perc, Perc Endo, Via Natrl or Artfcl Opng, Via Natrl or Artfcl Opng Endo]
0UJD[0,3,4]ZZ	Inspect/Uterus and Cervix, [Opn, Perc, Perc Endo]
0UL5*	Occlsn/Fallopian Tube, Rt
0UL6*	Occlsn/Fallopian Tube, Lt
0UM0*	Reattach/Ovary, Rt
0UM1*	Reattach/Ovary, Lt
0UM2*	Reattach/Ovaries, Bilat
0UM5*	Reattach/Fallopian Tube, Rt
0UM6*	Reattach/Fallopian Tube, Lt
0UM7*	Reattach/Fallopian Tubes, Bilat
0UN0*	Rls/Ovary, Rt
0UN1*	Rls/Ovary, Lt
0UN2*	Rls/Ovaries, Bilat
0UN5*	Rls/Fallopian Tube, Rt
0UN6*	Rls/Fallopian Tube, Lt
0UN7*	Rls/Fallopian Tubes, Bilat
0UP3[0,3,4][0,3]Z	Rmvl/Ovary, [Opn, Perc, Perc Endo], [Drain Dev, Inf Dev], NQ
0UP8[0,3,4,7,8][0,3,7,C,D,J,K]Z	Rmvl/Fallopian Tube, [Opn, Perc, Perc Endo, Via Natrl or Artfcl Opng, Via Natrl or Artfcl Opng Endo], [Drain Dev, Inf Dev, Auto Tissue Sub, Extralum Dev, Intralum Dev, Synth Sub, Nonauto Tissue Sub], NQ
0UPD[0,3,4,7,8][0,1,3,7,D,J,K]Z	Rmvl/Uterus and Cervix, [Opn, Perc, Perc Endo, Via Natrl or Artfcl Opng, Via Natrl or Artfcl Opng Endo], [Drain Dev, Radioact Elmt, Inf Dev, Auto Tissue Sub, Intralum Dev, Synth Sub, Nonauto Tissue Sub], NQ
0UPD[0,3,4]HZ	Rmvl/Uterus and Cervix, [Opn, Perc, Perc Endo], Contraceptive Dev, NQ
0UQ0*	Repair/Ovary, Rt
0UQ1*	Repair/Ovary, Lt
0UQ2*	Repair/Ovaries, Bilat
0UQ5*	Repair/Fallopian Tube, Rt
0UQ6*	Repair/Fallopian Tube, Lt
0UQ7*	Repair/Fallopian Tubes, Bilat
0UQ9*	Repair/Uterus
0US0*	Repos/Ovary, Rt
0US1*	Repos/Ovary, Lt
0US2*	Repos/Ovaries, Bilat
0US5*	Repos/Fallopian Tube, Rt
0US6*	Repos/Fallopian Tube, Lt
0US7*	Repos/Fallopian Tubes, Bilat
0USC*	Repos/Cervix
0UT0*	Resect/Ovary, Rt
0UT1*	Resect/Ovary, Lt
0UT2*	Resect/Ovaries, Bilat
0UT5*	Resect/Fallopian Tube, Rt
0UT6*	Resect/Fallopian Tube, Lt
0UT7*	Resect/Fallopian Tubes, Bilat
0UT9*	Resect/Uterus
0UU5*	Supl/Fallopian Tube, Rt
0UU6*	Supl/Fallopian Tube, Lt
0UU7*	Supl/Fallopian Tubes, Bilat
0UW3[0,3,4][0,3]Z	Rev/Ovary, [Opn, Perc, Perc Endo], [Drain Dev, Inf Dev], NQ
0UW8[0,3,4,7,8][0,3,7,C,D,J,K]Z	Rev/Fallopian Tube, [Opn, Perc, Perc Endo, Via Natrl or Artfcl Opng, Via Natrl or Artfcl Opng Endo], [Drain Dev, Inf Dev, Auto Tissue Sub, Extralum Dev, Intralum Dev, Synth Sub, Nonauto Tissue Sub], NQ
0UWD[0,3,4,7,8][0,1,3,7,D,H,J,K]Z	Rev/Uterus and Cervix, [Opn, Perc, Perc Endo, Via Natrl or Artfcl Opng, Via Natrl or Artfcl Opng Endo], [Drain Dev, Radioact Elmt, Inf Dev, Auto Tissue Sub, Intralum Dev, Contraceptive Dev, Synth Sub, Nonauto Tissue Sub], NQ
0UY*	Female Reproductive Sys, Transplantation
10D2*	Extract/Products of Conception, Ectopic
10T*	Obstetrics, Preg, Resect

DRG 740 Uterine, Adnexa Procedures for Nonovarian/Adnexal Malignancy with CC

GMLOS 3.3 **AMLOS 4.2** **RW 1.6920**

Select principal diagnosis AND operating room procedures listed under DRG 739

DRG 741 Uterine, Adnexa Procedures for Nonovarian/Adnexal Malignancy without CC/MCC

GMLOS 1.8 **AMLOS 2.2** **RW 1.1973**

Select principal diagnosis AND operating room procedures listed under DRG 739

DRG 742 Uterine and Adnexa Procedures for Nonmalignancy with CC/MCC

GMLOS 3.0 **AMLOS 4.0** **RW 1.5586**

Principal Diagnosis

Code	Description
A18.1[6,7,8]	Tuberculosis [of cervix, female pelvic inflam dz, of oth female genital organs]
A51.0	Primary genital syphilis
A54.0[0,2,3,9]	Gonococcal [infxn of lwr genitourinary tract unsp, vulvovaginitis unsp, cervicitis unsp, infxn of lwr genitourinary tract oth]
A54.1	Gonocl infxn of lwr GU tract w periureth and acc glnd abcs
A54.2[1,4,9]	Gonococcal [infxn of kidney and ureter, female pelvic inflam dz, oth genitourinary infxns]
A55	Chlamydial lymphogranuloma (venereum)
A56.0*	Chlamydial infxn of lwr genitourinary tract
A56.2	Chlamydial infxn of genitourinary tract, unsp
A56.8	Sexually transmitted chlamydial infxn of oth sites
A57	Chancroid
A58	Granuloma inguinale
A59.0[0,1,3,9]	Trichomoniasis [urogenital unsp, vulvovaginitis, cystitis and urethritis, oth urogenital]
A60.0[0,3,4,9]	Herpesviral [infxn of urogenital sys unsp, cervicitis, vulvovaginitis, infxn of oth urogenital tract]
A60.1	Herpesviral infxn of perianal skin and rectum
A60.9	Anogenital herpesviral infxn, unsp
A63.8	Oth spec predominantly sexually transmitted dz
A64	Unsp sexually transmitted dz
B37.3	Candidiasis of vulva and vagina
B37.41	Candidal cystitis and urethritis
B37.49	Oth urogenital candidiasis
D25*	Leiomyoma of uterus
D26*	Oth benign neoplasms of uterus
D27*	Benign neoplasm of ovary
D28*	Benign neoplasm of oth and unsp female genital organs
E28*	Ovarian dysfunction
E89.4*	Postprocedural ovarian failure
F52.5	Vaginismus not d/t a substance or known physiol condition
I86.2	Pelvic varices
I86.3	Vulval varices
L29.2	Pruritus vulvae
L29.3	Anogenital pruritus, unsp
N34.1	Nonspecific urethritis
N39.3	Stress incontinence (female) (male)
N70*	Salpingitis and oophoritis
N71*	Inflam dz of uterus, except cervix

T Transfer DRG SP Special Payment * Code Range 6th and 7th Character of ZZ = No Device, No Qualifier ZX = No Device, Diagnostic

264 MS-DRG Version 33.0 © 2015 Optum360, LLC

N72	Inflam dz of cervix uteri
N73*	Oth female pelvic inflam dz
N74	Female pelvic inflam d/o in dz classd elsw
N75*	Dz of Bartholin's gland
N76*	Oth inflam of vagina and vulva
N77*	Vulvovaginal ulceration and inflam in dz classd elsw
N80.0	Endometriosis of uterus
N80.1	Endometriosis of ovary
N80.2	Endometriosis of fallopian tube
N80.3	Endometriosis of pelvic peritoneum
N80.4	Endometriosis of rectovaginal septum and vagina
N80.8	Oth endometriosis
N80.9	Endometriosis, unsp
N81*	Female genital prolapse
N82.0	Vesicovaginal fistula
N82.1	Oth female urinary-genital tract fistulae
N82.5	Female genital tract-skin fistulae
N82.8	Oth female genital tract fistulae
N82.9	Female genital tract fistula, unsp
N83*	Noninflammatory d/o of ovary, fallop and broad lgmt
N84*	Polyp of female genital tract
N85*	Oth noninflammatory d/o of uterus, except cervix
N86	Erosion and ectropion of cervix uteri
N87*	Dysplasia of cervix uteri
N88*	Oth noninflammatory d/o of cervix uteri
N89*	Oth noninflammatory d/o of vagina
N90*	Oth noninflammatory d/o of vulva and perineum
N91*	Absent, scanty and rare menstruation
N92*	Excessive, frequent and irregular menstruation
N93*	Oth abnormal uterine and vaginal bleeding
N94*	Pain and oth cond assoc w fem gntl org and menstrual cycle
N95*	Menopausal and oth perimenopausal d/o
N96	Recurrent preg loss
N97*	Female infertility
N99.2	Postprocedural adhesions of vagina
N99.3	Prolapse of vaginal vault after hysterectomy
N99.83	Residual ovary synd
Q50*	Congen malform of ovaries, fallopian tubes & broad lgmt
Q51*	Congenital malformations of uterus and cervix
Q52*	Oth congenital malformations of female genitalia
Q56.0	Hermaphroditism, NEC
Q56.2	Female pseudohermaphroditism, NEC
Q56.3	Pseudohermaphroditism, unsp
Q56.4	Indeterminate sex, unsp
Q96*	Turner's synd
Q97*	Oth sex chromosome abnormalities, female phenotype, NEC
Q98.5	Karyotype 47, XYY
Q99.0	Chimera 46, XX/46, XY
Q99.1	46, XX true hermaphrodite
Q99.8	Oth spec chromosome abnormalities
R87.61[0,1,2,3,4,5,6]	[Atyp Sq Cells Undet Significance (Asc-us),atyp Sq Cells Cannot Exclude Hi G Sq Intraepithelial Les (Asc-h),l G Sq Intraepithelial Les (Lgsil),hi G Sq Intraepithelial Les (Hgsil),cytol Evidence Mal,unsatisfactory Cytol,satisfactory C Smer But Lacking Transformation Zone] Smer C
R87.628	Oth abnormal cytological findings on specimens from vagina
R87.62[0,1,2,3,4,5]	[Atyp Sq Cells Undet Significance (Asc-us),atyp Sq Cells Cannot Exclude Hi G Sq Intraepithelial Les (Asc-h),l G Sq Intraepithelial Les (Lgsil),hi G Sq Intraepithelial Les (Hgsil),cytol Evidence Mal,unsatisfactory Cytol] Smer Vag
R87.81[0,1]	Cervical [high, low] risk human papillomavirus (HPV) DNA test positive
R87.82[0,1]	Vaginal [high, low] risk human papillomavirus (HPV) DNA test positive
S30.2[02,3X]A	Contsn of [unsp ext genital organ female, vagina and vulva] init enc
S31.4[0,1,2,3,4,5]XA	[Unsp opn wnd, Lac w/o FB, Lac w/ FB, Punc wnd w/o FB, Punc wnd w/ FB, Opn bite] of vagina and vulva, init enc
S31.5[0,1,2,3,4,5]2A	[Unsp opn wnd, Lac w/o FB, Lac w/ FB, Punc wnd w/o FB, Punc wnd w/ FB, Opn bite] of unsp ext genital organs, female, init enc
S31.5[0,1,2,3,4,5]2S	[Unsp opn wnd, Lac w/o FB, Lac w/ FB, Punc wnd w/o FB, Punc wnd w/ FB, Opn bite] of unsp ext genital organs, female, seq
S37.1[0,2,3,9]XS	[Unsp inj, Contsn, Lac, Oth inj] of ureter, seq
S37.2[0,2,3,9]XS	[Unsp inj, Contsn, Lac, Oth inj] of bladder, seq
S37.3[0,2,3,9]XS	[Unsp inj, Contsn, Lac, Oth inj] of urethra, seq
S37.40[1,2,9]A	Unsp inj of ovary, [unilat, bilat, unsp], init enc
S37.40[1,2,9]S	Unsp inj of ovary, [unilat, bilat, unsp], seq
S37.42[1,2,9]A	Contsn of ovary, [unilat, bilat, unsp], init enc

S37.42[1,2,9]S	Contsn of ovary, [unilat, bilat, unsp], seq
S37.43[1,2,9]A	Lac of ovary, [unilat, bilat, unsp], init enc
S37.43[1,2,9]S	Lac of ovary, [unilat, bilat, unsp], seq
S37.49[1,2,9]A	Oth inj of ovary, [unilat, bilat, unsp], init enc
S37.49[1,2,9]S	Oth inj of ovary, [unilat, bilat, unsp], seq
S37.50[1,2,9]A	Unsp inj of fallopian tube, [unilat, bilat, unsp], init enc
S37.50[1,2,9]S	Unsp inj of fallopian tube, [unilat, bilat, unsp], seq
S37.51[1,2,9]A	Primary blast inj of fallopian tube, [unilat, bilat, unsp], init enc
S37.51[1,2,9]S	Primary blast inj of fallopian tube, [unilat, bilat, unsp], seq
S37.52[1,2,9]A	Contsn of fallopian tube, [unilat, bilat, unsp], init enc
S37.52[1,2,9]S	Contsn of fallopian tube, [unilat, bilat, unsp], seq
S37.53[1,2,9]A	Lac of fallopian tube, [unilat, bilat, unsp], init enc
S37.53[1,2,9]S	Lac of fallopian tube, [unilat, bilat, unsp], seq
S37.59[1,2,9]A	Oth inj of fallopian tube, [unilat, bilat, unsp], init enc
S37.59[1,2,9]S	Oth inj of fallopian tube, [unilat, bilat, unsp], seq
S37.6[0,2,3,9]XA	[Unsp inj, Contsn, Lac, Oth Inj] of uterus, init enc
S37.6[0,2,3,9]XS	[Unsp inj, Contsn, Lac, Oth Inj] of uterus, seq
S37.81[2,3,8,9]S	[Contsn, Lac, Oth inj, Unsp inj] of adrenal gland, seq
S37.89[2,3,8,9]A	[Contsn, Lac, Oth inj, Unsp inj] of oth urinary and pelvic organ, init enc
S37.89[2,3,8,9]S	[Contsn, Lac, Oth inj, Unsp inj] of oth urinary and pelvic organ, seq
S37.9[0,2,3,9]XA	[Unsp inj, Contsn, Lac, Oth inj] of unsp urinary and pelvic organ, init enc
S37.9[0,2,3,9]XS	[Unsp inj, Contsn, Lac, Oth inj] of unsp urinary and pelvic organ, seq
S38.0[02,3X]A	Crushing inj of [unsp ext genital organs female, vulva] init enc
S38.21[1,2]A	[Complete, Partial] traum amp of female ext genital organs, init enc
T19.2XXA	FB in vulva and vagina, init enc
T19.3XXA	FB in uterus, init enc
T83.3[1,2,9]XA	[Breakdown (mech), Displac, Oth mech comp] of intrauterine contraceptive dev, init enc
T83.7[1,2]1A	[Erosion, Exposure] of implanted vaginal mesh and oth prosthetic materials to surrounding organ or tissue, init enc
Z30.2	Enc for sterilization
Z31.0	Enc for reversal of previous sterilization
Z40.02	Enc for prophylactic rmvl of ovary
Z43.7	Enc for attention to artfcl vagina
Z64.1	Problems related to multiparity
Z90.7*	Acquired absence of genital organ(s)

AND

Operating Room Procedures

015P*	Destr/Sacral Sympathetic Nerve
0U1*	Female Reproductive Sys, Bypass
0U50*	Destr/Ovary, Rt
0U51*	Destr/Ovary, Lt
0U52*	Destr/Ovaries, Bilat
0U54*	Destr/Uterine Supporting Structure
0U55*	Destr/Fallopian Tube, Rt
0U56*	Destr/Fallopian Tube, Lt
0U59*	Destr/Uterus
0U5B*	Destr/Endometrium
0U75*	Dilation/Fallopian Tube, Rt
0U76*	Dilation/Fallopian Tube, Lt
0U77*	Dilation/Fallopian Tubes, Bilat
0U79*	Dilation/Uterus
0U80*	Div/Ovary, Rt
0U81*	Div/Ovary, Lt
0U82*	Div/Ovaries, Bilat
0U90*	Drain/Ovary, Rt
0U91*	Drain/Ovary, Lt
0U92*	Drain/Ovaries, Bilat
0U940ZX	Drain of Uterine Support Struct, Opn Appr, Diagn
0U950ZZ	Drain of Rt Fallopian Tube, Opn Appr
0U95[0,3,4,7,8]0Z	Drain/Fallopian Tube, Rt, [Opn, Perc, Perc Endo, Via Natrl or Artfcl Opng, Via Natrl or Artfcl Opng Endo], Drain Dev, NQ
0U95[0,3,4,7,8]ZX	Drain/Fallopian Tube, Rt, [Opn, Perc, Perc Endo, Via Natrl or Artfcl Opng, Via Natrl or Artfcl Opng Endo]
0U960ZZ	Drain of Lt Fallopian Tube, Opn Appr
0U96[0,3,4,7,8]0Z	Drain/Fallopian Tube, Lt, [Opn, Perc, Perc Endo, Via Natrl or Artfcl Opng, Via Natrl or Artfcl Opng Endo], Drain Dev, NQ
0U96[0,3,4,7,8]ZX	Drain/Fallopian Tube, Lt, [Opn, Perc, Perc Endo, Via Natrl or Artfcl Opng, Via Natrl or Artfcl Opng Endo]
0U970ZZ	Drain of Bilat Fallopian Tubes, Opn Appr
0U97[0,3,4,7,8]0Z	Drain/Fallopian Tubes, Bilat, [Opn, Perc, Perc Endo, Via Natrl or Artfcl Opng, Via Natrl or Artfcl Opng Endo], Drain Dev, NQ
0U97[0,3,4,7,8]ZX	Drain/Fallopian Tubes, Bilat, [Opn, Perc, Perc Endo, Via Natrl or Artfcl Opng, Via Natrl or Artfcl Opng Endo]

MDC 13: Diseases And Disorders Of The Female Reproductive System—SURGICAL

Surgical   **Medical**   **CC Indicator**   **MCC Indicator**   **Procedure Proxy**   PDxMCC **PDx acts as own MCC**   PDxCC **PDx acts as own CC**

ØU99ØZX	Drain of Uterus, Opn Appr, Diagnostic
ØU99[Ø,3,4,7,8][Ø,Z]Z	Drain/Uterus, [Opn, Perc, Perc Endo, Via Natrl or Artfcl Opng, Via Natrl or Artfcl Opng Endo], [Drain Dev, No Dev], NQ
ØUBØ*	Exc/Ovary, Rt
ØUB1*	Exc/Ovary, Lt
ØUB2*	Exc/Ovaries, Bilat
ØUB4ØZX	Exc of Uterine Support Struct, Opn Appr, Diagn
ØUB4[Ø,3,4,7,8]ZZ	Exc/Uterine Supporting Structure, [Opn, Perc, Perc Endo, Via Natrl or Artfcl Opng, Via Natrl or Artfcl Opng Endo]
ØUB5*	Exc/Fallopian Tube, Rt
ØUB6*	Exc/Fallopian Tube, Lt
ØUB7[Ø,3,4,7,8]ZX	Exc/Fallopian Tubes, Bilat, [Opn, Perc, Perc Endo, Via Natrl or Artfcl Opng, Via Natrl or Artfcl Opng Endo]
ØUB9ØZX	Exc of Uterus, Opn Appr, Diagnostic
ØUB9[Ø,3,4,7,8]ZZ	Exc/Uterus, [Opn, Perc, Perc Endo, Via Natrl or Artfcl Opng, Via Natrl or Artfcl Opng Endo]
ØUCØ*	Extir/Ovary, Rt
ØUC1*	Extir/Ovary, Lt
ØUC2*	Extir/Ovaries, Bilat
ØUC5*	Extir/Fallopian Tube, Rt
ØUC6*	Extir/Fallopian Tube, Lt
ØUC7*	Extir/Fallopian Tubes, Bilat
ØUC9[Ø,3,4]ZZ	Extir/Uterus, [Opn, Perc, Perc Endo]
ØUDN*	Extract/Ova
ØUF5[Ø,3,4,7,8]ZZ	Fragmn/Fallopian Tube, Rt, [Opn, Perc, Perc Endo, Via Natrl or Artfcl Opng, Via Natrl or Artfcl Opng Endo]
ØUF6[Ø,3,4,7,8]ZZ	Fragmn/Fallopian Tube, Lt, [Opn, Perc, Perc Endo, Via Natrl or Artfcl Opng, Via Natrl or Artfcl Opng Endo]
ØUF7[Ø,3,4,7,8]ZZ	Fragmn/Fallopian Tubes, Bilat, [Opn, Perc, Perc Endo, Via Natrl or Artfcl Opng, Via Natrl or Artfcl Opng Endo]
ØUJ3[Ø,3,4]ZZ	Inspect/Ovary, [Opn, Perc, Perc Endo]
ØUJ8[Ø,3,4,7,8]ZZ	Inspect/Fallopian Tube, [Opn, Perc, Perc Endo, Via Natrl or Artfcl Opng, Via Natrl or Artfcl Opng Endo]
ØUJD[Ø,3,4]ZZ	Inspect/Uterus and Cervix, [Opn, Perc, Perc Endo]
ØUL5*	Occlsn/Fallopian Tube, Rt
ØUL6*	Occlsn/Fallopian Tube, Lt
ØUMØ*	Reattach/Ovary, Rt
ØUM1*	Reattach/Ovary, Lt
ØUM2*	Reattach/Ovaries, Bilat
ØUM5*	Reattach/Fallopian Tube, Rt
ØUM6*	Reattach/Fallopian Tube, Lt
ØUM7*	Reattach/Fallopian Tubes, Bilat
ØUNØ*	Rls/Ovary, Rt
ØUN1*	Rls/Ovary, Lt
ØUN2*	Rls/Ovaries, Bilat
ØUN5*	Rls/Fallopian Tube, Rt
ØUN6*	Rls/Fallopian Tube, Lt
ØUN7*	Rls/Fallopian Tubes, Bilat
ØUP3[Ø,3,4][Ø,3]Z	Rmvl/Ovary, [Opn, Perc, Perc Endo], [Drain Dev, Inf Dev], NQ
ØUP8[Ø,3,4,7,8][Ø,3,7,C,D,J,K]Z	Rmvl/Fallopian Tube, [Opn, Perc, Perc Endo, Via Natrl or Artfcl Opng, Via Natrl or Artfcl Opng Endo], [Drain Dev, Inf Dev, Auto Tissue Sub, Extralum Dev, Intralum Dev, Synth Sub, Nonauto Tissue Sub], NQ
ØUPD[Ø,3,4,7,8][Ø,1,3,7,D,J,K]Z	Rmvl/Uterus and Cervix, [Opn, Perc, Perc Endo, Via Natrl or Artfcl Opng, Via Natrl or Artfcl Opng Endo], [Drain Dev, Radioact Elmt, Inf Dev, Auto Tissue Sub, Intralum Dev, Synth Sub, Nonauto Tissue Sub], NQ
ØUPD[Ø,3,4]HZ	Rmvl/Uterus and Cervix, [Opn, Perc, Perc Endo], Contraceptive Dev, NQ
ØUQØ*	Repair/Ovary, Rt
ØUQ1*	Repair/Ovary, Lt
ØUQ2*	Repair/Ovaries, Bilat
ØUQ5*	Repair/Fallopian Tube, Rt
ØUQ6*	Repair/Fallopian Tube, Lt
ØUQ7*	Repair/Fallopian Tubes, Bilat
ØUQ9*	Repair/Uterus
ØUSØ*	Repos/Ovary, Rt
ØUS1*	Repos/Ovary, Lt
ØUS2*	Repos/Ovaries, Bilat
ØUS5*	Repos/Fallopian Tube, Rt
ØUS6*	Repos/Fallopian Tube, Lt
ØUS7*	Repos/Fallopian Tubes, Bilat
ØUSC*	Repos/Cervix
ØUTØ*	Resect/Ovary, Rt
ØUT1*	Resect/Ovary, Lt
ØUT2*	Resect/Ovaries, Bilat
ØUT5*	Resect/Fallopian Tube, Rt
ØUT6*	Resect/Fallopian Tube, Lt
ØUT7*	Resect/Fallopian Tubes, Bilat
ØUT9*	Resect/Uterus

ØUU5*	Supl/Fallopian Tube, Rt
ØUU6*	Supl/Fallopian Tube, Lt
ØUU7*	Supl/Fallopian Tubes, Bilat
ØUW3[Ø,3,4][Ø,3]Z	Rev/Ovary, [Opn, Perc, Perc Endo], [Drain Dev, Inf Dev], NQ
ØUW8[Ø,3,4,7,8][Ø,3,7,C,D,J,K]Z	Rev/Fallopian Tube, [Opn, Perc, Perc Endo, Via Natrl or Artfcl Opng, Via Natrl or Artfcl Opng Endo], [Drain Dev, Inf Dev, Auto Tissue Sub, Extralum Dev, Intralum Dev, Synth Sub, Nonauto Tissue Sub], NQ
ØUWD[Ø,3,4,7,8][Ø,1,3,7,D,H,J,K]Z	Rev/Uterus and Cervix, [Opn, Perc, Perc Endo, Via Natrl or Artfcl Opng, Via Natrl or Artfcl Opng Endo], [Drain Dev, Radioact Elmt, Inf Dev, Auto Tissue Sub, Intralum Dev, Contraceptive Dev, Synth Sub, Nonauto Tissue Sub], NQ
ØUY*	Female Reproductive Sys, Transplantation
10D2*	Extract/Products of Conception, Ectopic
10T*	Obstetrics, Preg, Resect

DRG 743 Uterine and Adnexa Procedures for Nonmalignancy without CC/MCC

GMLOS 1.8   AMLOS 2.0   RW 1.0090

Select principal diagnosis AND operating room procedures listed under DRG 742

DRG 744 D&C, Conization, Laparoscopy and Tubal Interruption with CC/MCC

GMLOS 4.1   AMLOS 5.8   RW 1.6851

Operating Room Procedures

ØDJU4ZZ	Inspect of Omentum, Perc Endo Appr
ØDJV4ZZ	Inspect of Mesentery, Perc Endo Appr
ØDJW4ZZ	Inspect of Peritoneum, Perc Endo Appr
ØFJ04ZZ	Inspect of Liver, Perc Endo Appr
ØFJ44ZZ	Inspect of Gallbladder, Perc Endo Appr
ØFJD4ZZ	Inspect of Pancreatic Duct, Perc Endo Appr
ØFJG4ZZ	Inspect of Pancreas, Perc Endo Appr
ØU57*	Destr/Fallopian Tubes, Bilat
ØU94[3,4]ZX	Drain/Uterine Supporting Structure, [Perc, Perc Endo]
ØU99[3,4,7,8]ZX	Drain/Uterus, [Perc, Perc Endo, Via Natrl or Artfcl Opng, Via Natrl or Artfcl Opng Endo]
ØU9C[Ø,3,4,7,8]ZX	Drain/Cervix, [Opn, Perc, Perc Endo, Via Natrl or Artfcl Opng, Via Natrl or Artfcl Opng Endo]
ØUB4[3,4,7,8]ZX	Exc/Uterine Supporting Structure, [Perc, Perc Endo, Via Natrl or Artfcl Opng, Via Natrl or Artfcl Opng Endo]
ØUB7[Ø,3,4,7,8]ZZ	Exc/Fallopian Tubes, Bilat, [Opn, Perc, Perc Endo, Via Natrl or Artfcl Opng, Via Natrl or Artfcl Opng Endo]
ØUB9[3,4,7,8]ZX	Exc/Uterus, [Perc, Perc Endo, Via Natrl or Artfcl Opng, Via Natrl or Artfcl Opng Endo]
ØUBC[Ø,3,4,7,8]ZX	Exc/Cervix, [Opn, Perc, Perc Endo, Via Natrl or Artfcl Opng, Via Natrl or Artfcl Opng Endo]
ØUDB*	Extract/Endometrium
ØUHC[Ø,3,4,7,8]1Z	Insert/Cervix, [Opn, Perc, Perc Endo, Via Natrl or Artfcl Opng, Via Natrl or Artfcl Opng Endo], Radioact Elmt, NQ
ØUHG[Ø,3,4,7,8,X]1Z	Insert/Vagina, [Opn, Perc, Perc Endo, Via Natrl or Artfcl Opng, Via Natrl or Artfcl Opng Endo, Ext], Radioact Elmt, NQ
ØUL7*	Occlsn/Fallopian Tubes, Bilat
ØUN9*	Rls/Uterus
ØWHJ[Ø,3,4]1Z	Insert/Pelvic Cavity, [Opn, Perc, Perc Endo], Radioact Elmt, NQ
ØWHN[Ø,3,4]1Z	Insert/Perineum, Female, [Opn, Perc, Perc Endo], Radioact Elmt, NQ
ØWHR[Ø,3,4,7,8]1Z	Insert/Genitourinary Tract, [Opn, Perc, Perc Endo, Via Natrl or Artfcl Opng, Via Natrl or Artfcl Opng Endo], Radioact Elmt, NQ
ØWJF4ZZ	Inspect of Abd Wall, Perc Endo Appr
ØWJG4ZZ	Inspect of Peritoneal Cavity, Perc Endo Appr
ØWJJ4ZZ	Inspect of Pelvic Cavity, Perc Endo Appr
ØWJP4ZZ	Inspect of Gastrointestinal Tract, Perc Endo Appr
ØWJR4ZZ	Inspect of Genitourinary Tract, Perc Endo Appr

DRG 745 D&C, Conization, Laparoscopy and Tubal Interruption without CC/MCC

GMLOS 2.0   AMLOS 2.4   RW 0.9719

Select operating room procedures listed under DRG 744

DRG 746 Vagina, Cervix and Vulva Procedures with CC/MCC

GMLOS 3.3   AMLOS 4.8   RW 1.4628

Operating Room Procedures

ØH89XZZ	Div of Perineum Skin, Ext Appr

Ⓣ **Transfer DRG**   SP **Special Payment**   * **Code Range**   **6th and 7th Character of ZZ = No Device, No Qualifier ZX = No Device, Diagnostic**

MS-DRG Version 33.0   © 2015 Optum360, LLC

0H99X[0,Z]Z	Drain/Skin, Perineum, Ext, [Drain Dev, No Dev], NQ
0HQ9XZZ	Repair Perineum Skin, Ext Appr
0HR9*	Replace/Skin, Perineum
0T1B[0,4]ZD	Bypass/Bladder, [Opn, Perc Endo], No Dev, Cutaneous
0T9B00Z	Drain of Bladder with Drain Device, Opn Appr
0U5C*	Destr/Cervix
0U5F*	Destr/Cul-de-sac
0U5G*	Destr/Vagina
0U5J*	Destr/Clitoris
0U5K*	Destr/Hymen
0U5L*	Destr/Vestibular Gland
0U5M*	Destr/Vulva
0U7G[0,3,4][D,Z]Z	Dilation/Vagina, [Opn, Perc, Perc Endo], [Intralum Dev, No Dev], NQ
0U9C[0,3,4,7,8][0,Z]Z	Drain/Cervix, [Opn, Perc, Perc Endo, Via Natrl or Artfcl Opng, Via Natrl or Artfcl Opng Endo], [Drain Dev, No Dev], NQ
0U9F[0,3,4,7,8]ZX	Drain/Cul-de-sac, [Opn, Perc, Perc Endo, Via Natrl or Artfcl Opng, Via Natrl or Artfcl Opng Endo]
0U9G*	Drain/Vagina
0U9J*	Drain/Clitoris
0U9K[0,3,4,7,8,X]ZX	Drain/Hymen, [Opn, Perc, Perc Endo, Via Natrl or Artfcl Opng, Via Natrl or Artfcl Opng Endo, Ext]
0U9L[0,X]ZX	Drain/Vestibular Gland, [Opn, Ext]
0U9M*	Drain/Vulva
0UBC[0,3,4,7,8]ZZ	Exc/Cervix, [Opn, Perc, Perc Endo, Via Natrl or Artfcl Opng, Via Natrl or Artfcl Opng Endo]
0UBF*	Exc/Cul-de-sac
0UBG*	Exc/Vagina
0UBJ*	Exc/Clitoris
0UBK*	Exc/Hymen
0UBL*	Exc/Vestibular Gland
0UBM0ZX	Exc of Vulva, Opn Appr, Diagnostic
0UBM0ZZ	Exc of Vulva, Opn Appr
0UBMXZX	Exc of Vulva, Ext Appr, Diagnostic
0UCC*	Extir/Cervix
0UCG[0,3,4]ZZ	Extir/Vagina, [Opn, Perc, Perc Endo]
0UCJ*	Extir/Clitoris
0UCL*	Extir/Vestibular Gland
0UCM0ZZ	Extir of Matter from Vulva, Opn Appr
0UHH*	Insert/Vagina and Cul-de-sac
0UJH[0,3,4,7]ZZ	Inspect/Vagina and Cul-de-sac, [Opn, Perc, Perc Endo, Via Natrl or Artfcl Opng]
0UJM0ZZ	Inspect of Vulva, Opn Appr
0ULF*	Occlsn/Cul-de-sac
0UMF*	Reattach/Cul-de-sac
0UMG*	Reattach/Vagina
0UMJXZZ	Reattach of Clitoris, Ext Appr
0UMK*	Reattach/Hymen
0UMMXZZ	Reattach of Vulva, Ext Appr
0UNF*	Rls/Cul-de-sac
0UNG*	Rls/Vagina
0UNJ*	Rls/Clitoris
0UNK*	Rls/Hymen
0UNL*	Rls/Vestibular Gland
0UNM*	Rls/Vulva
0UPD0CZ	Rmvl of Extralum Dev from Uterus & Cervix, Opn Appr
0UPH[0,3,4,7,8][0,1,3,7,D,J,K]Z	Rmvl/Vagina and Cul-de-sac, [Opn, Perc, Perc Endo, Via Natrl or Artfcl Opng, Via Natrl or Artfcl Opng Endo], [Drain Dev, Radioact Elmt, Inf Dev, Auto Tissue Sub, Intralum Dev, Synth Sub, Nonauto Tissue Sub], NQ
0UPM0[0,7,J,K]Z	Rmvl/Vulva, Opn, [Drain Dev, Auto Tissue Sub, Synth Sub, Nonauto Tissue Sub], NQ
0UQC*	Repair/Cervix
0UQF*	Repair/Cul-de-sac
0UQG[0,3,4]ZZ	Rpr/Vagina, [Opn, Perc, Perc Endo]
0UQJ*	Repair/Clitoris
0UQK*	Repair/Hymen
0UQL*	Repair/Vestibular Gland
0UQM*	Repair/Vulva
0USF*	Repos/Cul-de-sac
0UTC*	Resect/Cervix
0UTF*	Resect/Cul-de-sac
0UTJ*	Resect/Clitoris
0UTK*	Resect/Hymen
0UTL*	Resect/Vestibular Gland
0UTM*	Resect/Vulva
0UUF*	Supl/Cul-de-sac
0UUJ*	Supl/Clitoris
0UUM*	Supl/Vulva
0UV*	Female Reproductive Sys, Restrict

0UWD[0,3,4,7,8]CZ	Rev/Uterus and Cervix, [Opn, Perc, Perc Endo, Via Natrl or Artfcl Opng, Via Natrl or Artfcl Opng Endo], Extralum Dev, NQ
0UWH[0,3,4,7,8][0,1,3,7,D,J,K]Z	Rev/Vagina and Cul-de-sac, [Opn, Perc, Perc Endo, Via Natrl or Artfcl Opng, Via Natrl or Artfcl Opng Endo], [Drain Dev, Radioact Elmt, Inf Dev, Auto Tissue Sub, Intralum Dev, Synth Sub, Nonauto Tissue Sub], NQ
0UWM0[0,7,J,K]Z	Rev/Vulva, Opn, [Drain Dev, Auto Tissue Sub, Synth Sub, Nonauto Tissue Sub], NQ
0W0N*	Alter/Perineum, Female
0W9N[0,3,4][0,Z]Z	Drain/Perineum, Female, [Opn, Perc, Perc Endo], [Drain Dev, No Dev], NQ
0WBN*	Exc/Perineum, Female
0WHN[0,3,4][3,Y]Z	Insert/Perineum, Female, [Opn, Perc, Perc Endo], [Inf Dev, Oth Dev], NQ
0WMN0ZZ	Reattach of Female Perineum, Opn Appr
0WPN[0,3,4][0,1,3,7,J,K,Y]Z	Rmvl/Perineum, Female, [Opn, Perc, Perc Endo], [Drain Dev, Radioact Elmt, Inf Dev, Auto Tissue Sub, Synth Sub, Nonauto Tissue Sub, Oth Dev], NQ
0WQN[0,3,4]ZZ	Rpr/Perineum, Female, [Opn, Perc, Perc Endo]
0WUN*	Supl/Perineum, Female
0WWN[0,3,4][0,1,3,7,J,K,Y]Z	Rev/Perineum, Female, [Opn, Perc, Perc Endo], [Drain Dev, Radioact Elmt, Inf Dev, Auto Tissue Sub, Synth Sub, Nonauto Tissue Sub, Oth Dev], NQ

DRG 747 Vagina, Cervix and Vulva Procedures without CC/MCC

GMLOS 1.6	AMLOS 1.9	RW 0.9099

Select operating room procedures listed under DRG 746

DRG 748 Female Reproductive System Reconstructive Procedures

GMLOS 1.6	AMLOS 2.0	RW 1.1241

Operating Room Procedures

0JQC*	Repair/SQ Tissue & Fascia, Pelvic Region
0JUC*	Supl/SQ Tissue & Fascia, Pelvic Region
0TSC*	Repos/Bladder Neck
0TSD*	Repos/Urethra
0TUC*	Supl/Bladder Neck
0TVC*	Restrict/Bladder Neck
0U7K*	Dilation/Hymen
0U84*	Div/Uterine Supporting Structure
0U94[0,3,4][0,Z]Z	Drain/Uterine Supporting Structure, [Opn, Perc, Perc Endo], [Drain Dev, No Dev], NQ
0UC4*	Extir/Uterine Supporting Structure
0ULG*	Occlsn/Vagina
0UM4*	Reattach/Uterine Supporting Structure
0UN4*	Rls/Uterine Supporting Structure
0UQ4*	Repair/Uterine Supporting Structure
0US4*	Repos/Uterine Supporting Structure
0US9[0,4]ZZ	Repos/Uterus, [Opn, Perc Endo]
0USG*	Repos/Vagina
0UT4*	Resect/Uterine Supporting Structure
0UTG*	Resect/Vagina
0UU4*	Supl/Uterine Supporting Structure
0UUG*	Supl/Vagina
0W4N*	Creation/Perineum, Female

DRG 749 Other Female Reproductive System O.R. Procedures with CC/MCC

GMLOS 6.1	AMLOS 8.5	RW 2.6452

Operating Room Procedures

00HE[0,3,4]MZ	Insert/Cranial Nerve, [Opn, Perc, Perc Endo], Neurostimulator Lead, NQ
00HU[0,3,4]MZ	Insert/Spinal Canal, [Opn, Perc, Perc Endo], Neurostimulator Lead, NQ
00HV[0,3,4]MZ	Insert/Spinal Cord, [Opn, Perc, Perc Endo], Neurostimulator Lead, NQ
00PE[0,3,4,X]MZ	Rmvl/Cranial Nerve, [Opn, Perc, Perc Endo, Ext], Neurostimulator Lead, NQ
00PU[0,3,4]MZ	Rmvl/Spinal Canal, [Opn, Perc, Perc Endo], Neurostimulator Lead, NQ
00PV[0,3,4]MZ	Rmvl/Spinal Cord, [Opn, Perc, Perc Endo], Neurostimulator Lead, NQ
01BP[0,3,4]ZZ	Exc/Sacral Sympathetic Nerve, [Opn, Perc, Perc Endo]
01DP*	Extract/Sacral Sympathetic Nerve
01HY[0,3,4]MZ	Insert/Peripheral Nerve, [Opn, Perc, Perc Endo], Neurostimulator Lead, NQ

MDC 13: Diseases And Disorders Of The Female Reproductive System—SURGICAL

Surgical	Medical	CC Indicator	MCC Indicator	Procedure Proxy	PDx MCC PDx acts as own MCC	PDx CC PDx acts as own CC

01PY[0,3,4,X]MZ	Rmvl/Peripheral Nerve, [Opn, Perc, Perc Endo, Ext], Neurostimulator Lead, NQ
02HV[0,3,4][2,D]Z	Insert/Superior Vena Cava, [Opn, Perc, Perc Endo], [Monitoring Dev, Intralum Dev], NQ
02LV*	Occlsn/Superior Vena Cava
02VV*	Restrict/Superior Vena Cava
04LE[0,3,4][C,D,Z]T	Occlsn/Int Iliac Artery, Rt, [Opn, Perc, Perc Endo], [Extralum Dev, Intralum Dev, No Dev], Uterine Artery, Rt
04LF[0,3,4][C,D,Z]U	Occlsn/Int Iliac Artery, Lt, [Opn, Perc, Perc Endo], [Extralum Dev, Intralum Dev, No Dev], Uterine Artery, Lt
06H0[0,3,4]DZ	Insert/Inferior Vena Cava, [Opn, Perc, Perc Endo], Intralum Dev, NQ
06L0*	Occlsn/Inferior Vena Cava
06V0*	Restrict/Inferior Vena Cava
079C[0,3,4]ZX	Drain/Lymphatic, Pelvis, [Opn, Perc, Perc Endo]
079H[0,3,4]ZX	Drain/Lymphatic, Rt Inguinal, [Opn, Perc, Perc Endo]
079J[0,3,4]ZX	Drain/Lymphatic, Lt Inguinal, [Opn, Perc, Perc Endo]
07BC[0,3,4]ZX	Exc/Lymphatic, Pelvis, [Opn, Perc, Perc Endo]
07BH*	Exc/Lymphatic, Rt Inguinal
07BJ*	Exc/Lymphatic, Lt Inguinal
07JP0ZZ	Inspect of Spleen, Opn Appr
0D5S*	Destr/Greater Omentum
0D5T*	Destr/Lesser Omentum
0D5V*	Destr/Mesentery
0D5W*	Destr/Peritoneum
0D9S[0,3,4]ZX	Drain/Greater Omentum, [Opn, Perc, Perc Endo]
0D9T[0,3,4]ZX	Drain/Lesser Omentum, [Opn, Perc, Perc Endo]
0D9V[0,3,4]ZX	Drain/Mesentery, [Opn, Perc, Perc Endo]
0D9W[0,3,4]ZX	Drain/Peritoneum, [Opn, Perc, Perc Endo]
0DBS0ZX	Exc of Greater Omentum, Opn Appr, Diagnostic
0DBS[0,3,4]ZZ	Exc/Greater Omentum, [Opn, Perc, Perc Endo]
0DBT0ZX	Exc of Lesser Omentum, Opn Appr, Diagnostic
0DBT[0,3,4]ZZ	Exc/Lesser Omentum, [Opn, Perc, Perc Endo]
0DBV0ZX	Exc of Mesentery, Opn Appr, Diagnostic
0DBV[0,3,4]ZZ	Exc/Mesentery, [Opn, Perc, Perc Endo]
0DBW0ZX	Exc of Peritoneum, Opn Appr, Diagnostic
0DBW[0,3,4]ZZ	Exc/Peritoneum, [Opn, Perc, Perc Endo]
0DH6[0,3,4]MZ	Insert/Stomach, [Opn, Perc, Perc Endo], Stimulator Lead, NQ
0DJ00ZZ	Inspect of Upr Intestinal Tract, Opn Appr
0DJ60ZZ	Inspect of Stomach, Opn Appr
0DJD0ZZ	Inspect of Lwr Intestinal Tract, Opn Appr
0DJU[0,3]ZZ	Inspect/Omentum, [Opn, Perc]
0DJV[0,3]ZZ	Inspect/Mesentery, [Opn, Perc]
0DJW[0,3]ZZ	Inspect/Peritoneum, [Opn, Perc]
0DN8[0,3,4]ZZ	Rls/Sm Intestine, [Opn, Perc, Perc Endo]
0DN9[0,3,4]ZZ	Rls/Duodenum, [Opn, Perc, Perc Endo]
0DNA[0,3,4]ZZ	Rls/Jejunum, [Opn, Perc, Perc Endo]
0DNB[0,3,4]ZZ	Rls/Ileum, [Opn, Perc, Perc Endo]
0DNC[0,3,4]ZZ	Rls/Ileocecal Valve, [Opn, Perc, Perc Endo]
0DNE[0,3,4]ZZ	Rls/Lg Intestine, [Opn, Perc, Perc Endo]
0DNF[0,3,4]ZZ	Rls/Lg Intestine, Rt, [Opn, Perc, Perc Endo]
0DNG[0,3,4]ZZ	Rls/Lg Intestine, Lt, [Opn, Perc, Perc Endo]
0DNH[0,3,4]ZZ	Rls/Cecum, [Opn, Perc, Perc Endo]
0DNJ[0,3,4]ZZ	Rls/Appendix, [Opn, Perc, Perc Endo]
0DNK[0,3,4]ZZ	Rls/Ascending Colon, [Opn, Perc, Perc Endo]
0DNL[0,3,4]ZZ	Rls/Transv Colon, [Opn, Perc, Perc Endo]
0DNM[0,3,4]ZZ	Rls/Descending Colon, [Opn, Perc, Perc Endo]
0DNN[0,3,4]ZZ	Rls/Sigmoid Colon, [Opn, Perc, Perc Endo]
0DNS*	Rls/Greater Omentum
0DNT*	Rls/Lesser Omentum
0DNV*	Rls/Mesentery
0DNW*	Rls/Peritoneum
0DP6[0,3,4]MZ	Rmvl/Stomach, [Opn, Perc, Perc Endo], Stimulator Lead, NQ
0DPR*	Rmvl/Anal Sphincter
0DTJ*	Resect/Appendix
0DTS*	Resect/Greater Omentum
0DTT*	Resect/Lesser Omentum
0F900ZX	Drain of Liver, Opn Appr, Diagnostic
0F910ZX	Drain of Rt Lobe Liver, Opn Appr, Diagnostic
0F920ZX	Drain of Lt Lobe Liver, Opn Appr, Diagnostic
0FB00ZX	Exc of Liver, Opn Appr, Diagnostic
0FB10ZX	Exc of Rt Lobe Liver, Opn Appr, Diagnostic
0FB20ZX	Exc of Lt Lobe Liver, Opn Appr, Diagnostic
0FJ00ZZ	Inspect of Liver, Opn Appr
0FN0*	Rls/Liver
0FN1*	Rls/Liver, Rt Lobe
0FN2*	Rls/Liver, Lt Lobe
0FN4*	Rls/Gallbladder
0FN5*	Rls/Hepatic Duct, Rt
0FN6*	Rls/Hepatic Duct, Lt

0FN8*	Rls/Cystic Duct
0FN9*	Rls/Common Bile Duct
0FNC*	Rls/Ampulla of Vater
0FND*	Rls/Pancreatic Duct
0FNF*	Rls/Pancreatic Duct, Accessory
0FNG*	Rls/Pancreas
0HB[0,1,4,5,6,7,8,A,B,C,D,E,F,G,H,J,K,L,M,N]XZZ	Exc of [Scalp, Face, Neck, Chest, Back, Abd, Buttock, Genitalia, Rt Upr Arm, Lt Upr Arm, Rt Lwr Arm, Lt Lwr Arm, Rt Hand, Lt Hand, Rt Upr Leg, Lt Upr Leg, Rt Lwr Leg, Lt Lwr Leg, Rt Foot, Lt Foot], Skin, Ext Appr
0JB[0,1,4,5,6,7,8,9,B,C,D,F,G,H,L,M,N,P,Q,R]0ZZ	Exc of [Scalp, Face, Ant Neck, Post Neck, Chest, Back, Abd, Buttock, Perineum, Pelvic Rgn, [Rt, Lt] Upr Arm, [Rt, Lt] Lwr Arm, [Rt, Lt] Upr Leg, [Rt, Lt] Lwr Leg, [Rt, Lt] Foot], SQ Tissue & Fascia, Opn Appr
0JH6[0,3]VZ	Insert/SQ Tissue & Fascia, Chest, [Opn, Perc], Inf Pump, NQ
0JH7[0,3]VZ	Insert/SQ Tissue & Fascia, Back, [Opn, Perc], Inf Pump, NQ
0JH8[0,3]VZ	Insert/SQ Tissue & Fascia, Abd, [Opn, Perc], Inf Pump, NQ
0JHT[0,3]VZ	Insert/SQ Tissue & Fascia, Trunk, [Opn, Perc], Inf Pump, NQ
0T13[0,4][7,J,K,Z]B	Bypass/Kidney Pelvis, Rt, [Opn, Perc Endo], [Auto Tissue Sub, Synth Sub, Nonauto Tissue Sub, No Dev], Bladder
0T14[0,4][7,J,K,Z]B	Bypass/Kidney Pelvis, Lt, [Opn, Perc Endo], [Auto Tissue Sub, Synth Sub, Nonauto Tissue Sub, No Dev], Bladder
0T163JD	Bypass Rt Ureter to Cutan with Synth Sub, Perc Appr
0T16[0,4][7,J,K,Z][6,7,8,9,A,C,D]	Bypass/Ureter, Rt, [Opn, Perc Endo], [Auto Tissue Sub, Synth Sub, Nonauto Tissue Sub, No Dev], [Ureter, Rt, Ureter, Lt, Colon, Colocutaneous, Ileum, Ileocutaneous, Cutaneous]
0T173JD	Bypass Lt Ureter to Cutan with Synth Sub, Perc Appr
0T17[0,4][7,J,K,Z][6,7,8,9,A,C,D]	Bypass/Ureter, Lt, [Opn, Perc Endo], [Auto Tissue Sub, Synth Sub, Nonauto Tissue Sub, No Dev], [Ureter, Rt, Ureter, Lt, Colon, Colocutaneous, Ileum, Ileocutaneous, Cutaneous]
0T183JD	Bypass Bi Ureter to Cutan with Synth Sub, Perc Appr
0T18[0,4][7,J,K,Z][6,7,8,9,A,C,D]	Bypass/Ureters, Bilat, [Opn, Perc Endo], [Auto Tissue Sub, Synth Sub, Nonauto Tissue Sub, No Dev], [Ureter, Rt, Ureter, Lt, Colon, Colocutaneous, Ileum, Ileocutaneous, Cutaneous]
0T56*	Destr/Ureter, Rt
0T57*	Destr/Ureter, Lt
0T5B[0,3,4]ZZ	Destr/Bladder, [Opn, Perc, Perc Endo]
0T5C[0,3,4]ZZ	Destr/Bladder Neck, [Opn, Perc, Perc Endo]
0T7B*	Dilation/Bladder
0T930ZZ	Drain of Rt Kidney Pelvis, Opn Appr
0T93[0,3,4]0Z	Drain/Kidney Pelvis, Rt, [Opn, Perc, Perc Endo], Drain Dev, NQ
0T940ZZ	Drain of Lt Kidney Pelvis, Opn Appr
0T94[0,3,4]0Z	Drain/Kidney Pelvis, Lt, [Opn, Perc, Perc Endo], Drain Dev, NQ
0T9B[0,3,4,7,8]ZX	Drain/Bladder, [Opn, Perc, Perc Endo, Via Natrl or Artfcl Opng, Via Natrl or Artfcl Opng Endo]
0T9C[0,3,4,7,8]ZX	Drain/Bladder Neck, [Opn, Perc, Perc Endo, Via Natrl or Artfcl Opng, Via Natrl or Artfcl Opng Endo]
0TB6[0,3,4,7,8]ZX	Exc/Ureter, Rt, [Opn, Perc, Perc Endo, Via Natrl or Artfcl Opng, Via Natrl or Artfcl Opng Endo]
0TB7[0,3,4,7,8]ZX	Exc/Ureter, Lt, [Opn, Perc, Perc Endo, Via Natrl or Artfcl Opng, Via Natrl or Artfcl Opng Endo]
0TBB[0,3,4,7,8]ZX	Exc/Bladder, [Opn, Perc, Perc Endo, Via Natrl or Artfcl Opng, Via Natrl or Artfcl Opng Endo]
0TBB[0,3,4]ZZ	Exc/Bladder, [Opn, Perc, Perc Endo]
0TBC[0,3,4,7,8]ZX	Exc/Bladder Neck, [Opn, Perc, Perc Endo, Via Natrl or Artfcl Opng, Via Natrl or Artfcl Opng Endo]
0TBC[0,3,4]ZZ	Exc/Bladder Neck, [Opn, Perc, Perc Endo]
0TJD0ZZ	Inspect of Urethra, Opn Appr
0TLD*	Occlsn/Urethra
0TMB*	Reattach/Bladder
0TMC*	Reattach/Bladder Neck
0TMD*	Reattach/Urethra
0TN0*	Rls/Kidney, Rt
0TN1*	Rls/Kidney, Lt
0TN3*	Rls/Kidney Pelvis, Rt
0TN4*	Rls/Kidney Pelvis, Lt
0TN6[0,3,4]ZZ	Rls/Ureter, Rt, [Opn, Perc, Perc Endo]
0TN7[0,3,4]ZZ	Rls/Ureter, Lt, [Opn, Perc, Perc Endo]
0TNB[3,4]ZZ	Rls/Bladder, [Perc, Perc Endo]
0TNC[3,4]ZZ	Rls/Bladder Neck, [Perc, Perc Endo]
0TND*	Rls/Urethra
0TPD[0,3,4,7,8,X]LZ	Rmvl/Urethra, [Opn, Perc, Perc Endo, Via Natrl or Artfcl Opng, Via Natrl or Artfcl Opng Endo, Ext], Artfcl Sphincter, NQ
0TQ7*	Repair/Ureter, Lt
0TQB*	Repair/Bladder
0TTB*	Resect/Bladder
0TTC*	Resect/Bladder Neck

T Transfer DRG   SP Special Payment   * Code Range   6th and 7th Character of ZZ = No Device, No Qualifier   ZX = No Device, Diagnostic

ØTVB*	Restrict/Bladder
ØTVD*	Restrict/Urethra
ØTWD[Ø,3,4,7,8]LZ	Rev/Urethra, [Opn, Perc, Perc Endo, Via Natrl or Artfcl Opng, Via Natrl or Artfcl Opng Endo], Artfcl Sphincter, NQ
ØU9F[Ø,7,8][Ø,Z]Z	Drain/Cul-de-sac, [Opn, Via Natrl or Artfcl Opng, Via Natrl or Artfcl Opng Endo], [Drain Dev, No Dev], NQ
ØUCB*	Extir/Endometrium
ØUCF*	Extir/Cul-de-sac
ØUF9[Ø,3,4,7,8]ZZ	Fragmn/Uterus, [Opn, Perc, Perc Endo, Via Natrl or Artfcl Opng, Via Natrl or Artfcl Opng Endo]
ØUM9*	Reattach/Uterus
ØUMC*	Reattach/Cervix
ØUNC*	Rls/Cervix
ØUUK*	Supl/Hymen
ØW1J[Ø,4]J[9,B,G,J]	Bypass/Pelvic Cavity, [Opn, Perc Endo], Synth Sub, [Pleural Cavity, Rt, Pleural Cavity, Lt, Peritoneal Cavity, Pelvic Cavity]
ØW3HØZZ	Control Bleeding in Retroperitoneum, Opn Appr
ØW3N*	Control/Perineum, Female
ØW3PØZZ	Control Bleeding in Gastrointestinal Tract, Opn Appr
ØW3R*	Control/Genitourinary Tract
ØW9GØ[Ø,Z]Z	Drain/Peritoneal Cavity, Opn, [Drain Dev, No Dev], NQ
ØW9G[Ø,3,4]ZX	Drain/Peritoneal Cavity, [Opn, Perc, Perc Endo]
ØW9H[Ø,3,4]ZX	Drain/Retroperitoneum, [Opn, Perc, Perc Endo]
ØW9J[Ø,3,4]ZX	Drain/Pelvic Cavity, [Opn, Perc, Perc Endo]
ØWBHØZX	Exc of Retroperitoneum, Opn Appr, Diagnostic
ØWBH[Ø,3,4]ZZ	Exc/Retroperitoneum, [Opn, Perc, Perc Endo]
ØWJF3ZZ	Inspect of Abd Wall, Perc Appr
ØWJG[Ø,3]ZZ	Inspect/Peritoneal Cavity, [Opn, Perc]
ØWJH[3,4]ZZ	Inspect/Retroperitoneum, [Perc, Perc Endo]
ØWJJ[Ø,3]ZZ	Inspect/Pelvic Cavity, [Opn, Perc]
ØWJN[Ø,3,4]ZZ	Inspect/Perineum, Female, [Opn, Perc, Perc Endo]
ØWJP[Ø,3,7,8]ZZ	Inspect/Gastrointestinal Tract, [Opn, Perc, Via Natrl or Artfcl Opng, Via Natrl or Artfcl Opng Endo]
ØWJR[Ø,3,7,8]ZZ	Inspect/Genitourinary Tract, [Opn, Perc, Via Natrl or Artfcl Opng, Via Natrl or Artfcl Opng Endo]
ØWQF*	Repair/Abd Wall
ØY95[Ø,3,4]ZX	Drain/Inguinal Rgn, Rt, [Opn, Perc, Perc Endo]
ØY96[Ø,3,4]ZX	Drain/Inguinal Rgn, Lt, [Opn, Perc, Perc Endo]
ØYB5[Ø,3,4]ZX	Exc/Inguinal Rgn, Rt, [Opn, Perc, Perc Endo]
ØYB6[Ø,3,4]ZX	Exc/Inguinal Rgn, Lt, [Opn, Perc, Perc Endo]
ØYB7[Ø,3,4]ZX	Exc/Femor Rgn, Rt, [Opn, Perc, Perc Endo]
ØYB8[Ø,3,4]ZX	Exc/Femor Rgn, Lt, [Opn, Perc, Perc Endo]
ØYJ5[3,4]ZZ	Inspect/Inguinal Rgn, Rt, [Perc, Perc Endo]
ØYJ6[3,4]ZZ	Inspect/Inguinal Rgn, Lt, [Perc, Perc Endo]
ØYJ7[3,4]ZZ	Inspect/Femor Rgn, Rt, [Perc, Perc Endo]
ØYJ8[3,4]ZZ	Inspect/Femor Rgn, Lt, [Perc, Perc Endo]
ØYJA[3,4]ZZ	Inspect/Inguinal Rgn, Bilat, [Perc, Perc Endo]
ØYJE[3,4]ZZ	Inspect/Femor Rgn, Bilat, [Perc, Perc Endo]
1ØS2*	Repos/Products of Conception, Ectopic
3EØP3QØ	Introduce Autol Fertilized Ovum in Fem Reprod, Perc
3EØP3Q1	Introduce Nonaut Fertilized Ovum in Fem Reprod, Perc
3EØP73Z	Introduction of Anti-inflam into Fem Reprod, Via Opng
3EØP7QØ	Introduce Autol Fertilized Ovum in Fem Reprod, Via Opng
3EØP7Q1	Introduce Nonaut Fertilized Ovum in Fem Reprod, Via Opng

DRG 750 Other Female Reproductive System O.R. Procedures without CC/MCC
GMLOS 2.4 AMLOS 3.1 RW 1.3346

Select operating room procedures listed under DRG 749

MEDICAL

DRG 754 Malignancy, Female Reproductive System with MCC
GMLOS 5.8 AMLOS 7.9 RW 1.92Ø4

Principal Diagnosis

C51*	Malig neoplasm of vulva
C52	Malig neoplasm of vagina
C53*	Malig neoplasm of cervix uteri
C54*	Malig neoplasm of corpus uteri
C55	Malig neoplasm of uterus, part unsp
C56*	Malig neoplasm of ovary
C57*	Malig neoplasm of oth and unsp female genital organs
C58	Malig neoplasm of placenta
C76.3	Malig neoplasm of pelvis
C79.6*	Secondary malig neoplasm of ovary
C79.82	Secondary malig neoplasm of genital organs
DØ6*	Carcinoma in situ of cervix uteri
DØ7.Ø	Carcinoma in situ of endometrium
DØ7.1	Carcinoma in situ of vulva
DØ7.2	Carcinoma in situ of vagina
DØ7.3*	Carcinoma in situ of oth and unsp female genital organs
D39*	Neoplasm of uncertain behav of female genital organs

DRG 755 Malignancy, Female Reproductive System with CC
GMLOS 3.7 AMLOS 4.9 RW 1.1325

Select principal diagnosis listed under DRG 754

DRG 756 Malignancy, Female Reproductive System without CC/MCC
GMLOS 2.2 AMLOS 2.8 RW Ø.59Ø8

Select principal diagnosis listed under DRG 754

DRG 757 Infections, Female Reproductive System with MCC
GMLOS 5.2 AMLOS 6.4 RW 1.3717

Principal Diagnosis

A18.1[6,7,8]	Tuberculosis [of cervix, female pelvic inflam dz, of oth female genital organs]
A51.Ø	Primary genital syphilis
A54.Ø[Ø,2,3,9]	Gonococcal [infxn of lwr genitourinary tract unsp, vulvovaginitis unsp, cervicitis unsp, infxn of lwr genitourinary tract oth]
A54.1	Gonocl infxn of lwr GU tract w periureth and acc glnd abcs
A54.2[1,4,9]	Gonococcal [infxn of kidney and ureter, female pelvic inflam dz, oth genitourinary infxns]
A55	Chlamydial lymphogranuloma (venereum)
A56.Ø*	Chlamydial infxn of lwr genitourinary tract
A56.2	Chlamydial infxn of genitourinary tract, unsp
A56.8	Sexually transmitted chlamydial infxn of oth sites
A57	Chancroid
A58	Granuloma inguinale
A59.Ø[Ø,1,3,9]	Trichomoniasis [urogenital unsp, vulvovaginitis, cystitis and urethritis, oth urogenital]
A6Ø.Ø[Ø,3,4,9]	Herpesviral [infxn of urogenital sys unsp, cervicitis, vulvovaginitis, infxn of oth urogenital tract]
A6Ø.1	Herpesviral infxn of perianal skin and rectum
A6Ø.9	Anogenital herpesviral infxn, unsp
A63.8	Oth spec predominantly sexually transmitted dz
A64	Unsp sexually transmitted dz
B37.3	Candidiasis of vulva and vagina
B37.41	Candidal cystitis and urethritis
B37.49	Oth urogenital candidiasis
L29.2	Pruritus vulvae
L29.3	Anogenital pruritus, unsp
N34.1	Nonspecific urethritis
N7Ø*	Salpingitis and oophoritis
N71*	Inflam dz of uterus, except cervix
N72	Inflam dz of cervix uteri
N73.Ø	Acute parametritis and pelvic cellulitis
N73.1	Chr parametritis and pelvic cellulitis
N73.2	Unsp parametritis and pelvic cellulitis
N73.3	Female acute pelvic peritonitis
N73.4	Female chr pelvic peritonitis
N73.5	Female pelvic peritonitis, unsp
N73.8	Oth spec female pelvic inflam dz
N73.9	Female pelvic inflam dz, unsp
N74	Female pelvic inflam d/o in dz classd elsw
N75.1	Abscess of Bartholin's gland
N75.9	Dz of Bartholin's gland, unsp
N76.Ø	Acute vaginitis
N76.1	Subacute and chr vaginitis
N76.2	Acute vulvitis
N76.3	Subacute and chr vulvitis
N76.4	Abscess of vulva
N76.5	Ulceration of vagina
N76.8*	Oth spec inflam of vagina and vulva
N77.1	Vaginitis, vulvitis and vulvovaginitis in dis classd elsw
N94.81Ø	Vulvar vestibulitis

MDC 13: Diseases And Disorders Of The Female Reproductive System—MEDICAL

MDC 13: Diseases And Disorders Of The Female Reproductive System—MEDICAL

DRG 758 **Infections, Female Reproductive System with CC**

GMLOS 4.1 AMLOS 5.0 RW 1.0090

Select principal diagnosis listed under DRG 757

DRG 759 **Infections, Female Reproductive System without CC/MCC**

GMLOS 3.2 AMLOS 3.8 RW 0.7595

Select principal diagnosis listed under DRG 757

DRG 760 **Menstrual and Other Female Reproductive System Disorders with CC/MCC**

GMLOS 2.8 AMLOS 3.6 RW 0.8524

Principal Diagnosis

D25*	Leiomyoma of uterus
D26*	Oth benign neoplasms of uterus
D27*	Benign neoplasm of ovary
D28*	Benign neoplasm of oth and unsp female genital organs
E28*	Ovarian dysfunction
E89.4*	Postprocedural ovarian failure
F52.5	Vaginismus not d/t a substance or known physiol condition
I86.2	Pelvic varices
I86.3	Vulval varices
N39.3	Stress incontinence (female) (male)
N73.6	Female pelvic peritoneal adhesions (postinfective)
N75.0	Cyst of Bartholin's gland
N75.8	Oth dz of Bartholin's gland
N76.6	Ulceration of vulva
N77.0	Ulceration of vulva in dz classified elsw
N80.8	Oth endometriosis
N80.9	Endometriosis, unsp
N80.[0,1,2,3,4]	Endometriosis of [uterus, ovary, fallopian tube, pelvic peritoneum, rectovaginal septum and vagina]
N81*	Female genital prolapse
N82.0	Vesicovaginal fistula
N82.1	Oth female urinary-genital tract fistulae
N82.5	Female genital tract-skin fistulae
N82.8	Oth female genital tract fistulae
N82.9	Female genital tract fistula, unsp
N83*	Noninflammatory d/o of ovary, fallop and broad lgmt
N84*	Polyp of female genital tract
N85*	Oth noninflammatory d/o of uterus, except cervix
N86	Erosion and ectropion of cervix uteri
N87*	Dysplasia of cervix uteri
N88*	Oth noninflammatory d/o of cervix uteri
N89*	Oth noninflammatory d/o of vagina
N90*	Oth noninflammatory d/o of vulva and perineum
N91*	Absent, scanty and rare menstruation
N92*	Excessive, frequent and irregular menstruation
N93*	Oth abnormal uterine and vaginal bleeding
N94.0	Mittelschmerz
N94.1	Dyspareunia
N94.2	Vaginismus
N94.3	Premenstrual tension synd
N94.4	Primary dysmenorrhea
N94.5	Secondary dysmenorrhea
N94.6	Dysmenorrhea, unsp
N94.81[8,9]	[Oth, unsp] vulvodynia
N94.89	Oth cond assoc w female genital organs and menstrual cycle
N94.9	Unsp cond assoc w female genital organs and menstrual cycle
N95*	Menopausal and oth perimenopausal d/o
N96	Recurrent preg loss
N97*	Female infertility
N99.2	Postprocedural adhesions of vagina
N99.3	Prolapse of vaginal vault after hysterectomy
N99.83	Residual ovary synd
Q50*	Congen malform of ovaries, fallopian tubes & broad lgmt
Q51*	Congenital malformations of uterus and cervix
Q52*	Oth congenital malformations of female genitalia
Q56.0	Hermaphroditism, NEC
Q56.2	Female pseudohermaphroditism, NEC
Q56.3	Pseudohermaphroditism, unsp
Q56.4	Indeterminate sex, unsp
Q96*	Turner's synd
Q97*	Oth sex chromosome abnormalities, female phenotype, NEC
Q98.5	Karyotype 47, XYY
Q99.0	Chimera 46, XX/46, XY
Q99.1	46, XX true hermaphrodite
Q99.8	Oth spec chromosome abnormalities
R87.61[0,1,2,3,4,5,6]	[Atyp Sq Cells Undet Significance (Asc-us),atyp Sq Cells Cannot Exclude Hi G Sq Intraepithelial Les (Asc-h),l G Sq Intraepithelial Les (Lgsil),hi G Sq Intraepithelial Les (Hgsil),cytol Evidence Mal,unsatisfactory Cytol,satisfactory C Smer But Lacking Transformation Zone] Smer C
R87.628	Oth abnormal cytological findings on specimens from vagina
R87.62[0,1,2,3,4,5]	[Atyp Sq Cells Undet Significance (Asc-us),atyp Sq Cells Cannot Exclude Hi G Sq Intraepithelial Les (Asc-h),l G Sq Intraepithelial Les (Lgsil),hi G Sq Intraepithelial Les (Hgsil),cytol Evidence Mal,unsatisfactory Cytol] Smer Vag
R87.81[0,1]	Cervical [high, low] risk human papillomavirus (HPV) DNA test positive
R87.82[0,1]	Vaginal [high, low] risk human papillomavirus (HPV) DNA test positive
S30.2[02,3X]A	Contsn of [unsp ext genital organ female, vagina and vulva] init enc
S31.4[0,1,2,3,4,5]XA	[Unsp opn wnd, Lac w/o FB, Lac w/ FB, Punc wnd w/o FB, Punc wnd w/ FB, Opn bite] of vagina and vulva, init enc
S31.5[0,1,2,3,4,5]2A	[Unsp opn wnd, Lac w/o FB, Lac w/ FB, Punc wnd w/o FB, Punc wnd w/ FB, Opn bite] of unsp ext genital organs, female, init enc
S31.5[0,1,2,3,4,5]2S	[Unsp opn wnd, Lac w/o FB, Lac w/ FB, Punc wnd w/o FB, Punc wnd w/ FB, Opn bite] of unsp ext genital organs, female, seq
S37.1[0,2,3,9]XS	[Unsp inj, Contsn, Lac, Oth inj] of ureter, seq
S37.2[0,2,3,9]XS	[Unsp inj, Contsn, Lac, Oth inj] of bladder, seq
S37.3[0,2,3,9]XS	[Unsp inj, Contsn, Lac, Oth inj] of urethra, seq
S37.40[1,2,9]A	Unsp inj of ovary, [unilat, bilat, unsp], init enc
S37.40[1,2,9]S	Unsp inj of ovary, [unilat, bilat, unsp], seq
S37.42[1,2,9]A	Contsn of ovary, [unilat, bilat, unsp], init enc
S37.42[1,2,9]S	Contsn of ovary, [unilat, bilat, unsp], seq
S37.43[1,2,9]A	Lac of ovary, [unilat, bilat, unsp], init enc
S37.43[1,2,9]S	Lac of ovary, [unilat, bilat, unsp], seq
S37.49[1,2,9]A	Oth inj of ovary, [unilat, bilat, unsp], init enc
S37.49[1,2,9]S	Oth inj of ovary, [unilat, bilat, unsp], seq
S37.50[1,2,9]A	Unsp inj of fallopian tube, [unilat, bilat, unsp], init enc
S37.50[1,2,9]S	Unsp inj of fallopian tube, [unilat, bilat, unsp], seq
S37.51[1,2,9]A	Primary blast inj of fallopian tube, [unilat, bilat, unsp], init enc
S37.51[1,2,9]S	Primary blast inj of fallopian tube, [unilat, bilat, unsp], seq
S37.52[1,2,9]A	Contsn of fallopian tube, [unilat, bilat, unsp], init enc
S37.52[1,2,9]S	Contsn of fallopian tube, [unilat, bilat, unsp], seq
S37.53[1,2,9]A	Lac of fallopian tube, [unilat, bilat, unsp], init enc
S37.53[1,2,9]S	Lac of fallopian tube, [unilat, bilat, unsp], seq
S37.59[1,2,9]A	Oth inj of fallopian tube, [unilat, bilat, unsp], init enc
S37.59[1,2,9]S	Oth inj of fallopian tube, [unilat, bilat, unsp], seq
S37.6[0,2,3,9]XA	[Unsp inj, Contsn, Lac, Oth Inj] of uterus, init enc
S37.6[0,2,3,9]XS	[Unsp inj, Contsn, Lac, Oth Inj] of uterus, seq
S37.81[2,3,8,9]S	[Contsn, Lac, Oth inj, Unsp inj] of adrenal gland, seq
S37.89[2,3,8,9]A	[Contsn, Lac, Oth inj, Unsp inj] of oth urinary and pelvic organ, init enc
S37.89[2,3,8,9]S	[Contsn, Lac, Oth inj, Unsp inj] of oth urinary and pelvic organ, seq
S37.9[0,2,3,9]XA	[Unsp inj, Contsn, Lac, Oth inj] of unsp urinary and pelvic organ, init enc
S37.9[0,2,3,9]XS	[Unsp inj, Contsn, Lac, Oth inj] of unsp urinary and pelvic organ, seq
S38.0[02,3X]A	Crushing inj of [unsp ext genital organs female, vulva] init enc
S38.21[1,2]A	[Complete, Partial] traum amp of female ext genital organs, init enc
T19.2XXA	FB in vulva and vagina, init enc
T19.3XXA	FB in uterus, init enc
T83.3[1,2,9]XA	[Breakdown (mech), Displac, Oth mech comp] of intrauterine contraceptive dev, init enc
T83.7[1,2]1A	[Erosion, Exposure] of implanted vaginal mesh and oth prosthetic materials to surrounding organ or tissue, init enc
Z30.2	Enc for sterilization
Z31.0	Enc for reversal of previous sterilization
Z40.02	Enc for prophylactic rmvl of ovary
Z43.7	Enc for attention to artfcl vagina
Z64.1	Problems related to multiparity
Z90.7*	Acquired absence of genital organ(s)

DRG 761 **Menstrual and Other Female Reproductive System Disorders without CC/MCC**

GMLOS 1.9 AMLOS 2.2 RW 0.5355

Select principal diagnosis listed under DRG 760

Ⓣ **Transfer DRG** ˢᴾ **Special Payment** * **Code Range** **6th and 7th Character of ZZ = No Device, No Qualifier ZX = No Device, Diagnostic**

SURGICAL

DRG 765   Cesarean Section with CC/MCC
     GMLOS 3.7   AMLOS 4.7   RW 1.1442

Operating Room Procedures

10D00Z[0,1,2]   Extract/Products of Conception, Opn, No Dev, [Classical, Low Cervical, Extraperitoneal]

DRG 766   Cesarean Section without CC/MCC
     GMLOS 2.8   AMLOS 3.0   RW 0.7807

Select operating room procedures listed under DRG 765

DRG 767   Vaginal Delivery with Sterilization and/or D&C
     GMLOS 2.7   AMLOS 3.8   RW 1.2965

Delivery Procedure

0DQP7ZZ   Repair Rectum, Via Natrl or Artfcl Opng
10A07Z6   Abortion of Products of Conception, Vacuum, Via Opng
10D07Z[3,4,5,6,7,8] Extract/Products of Conception, Via Natrl or Artfcl Opng, No Dev, [Low Forceps, Mid Forceps, High Forceps, Vacuum, Int Version, Oth]
10E0XZZ   Delivery of Products of Conception, Ext Appr
10S07ZZ   Repos Products of Conception, Via Opng
AND

Operating Room Procedures

0U57[0,3,4,7,8]ZZ Destr/Fallopian Tubes, Bilat, [Opn, Perc, Perc Endo, Via Natrl or Artfcl Opng, Via Natrl or Artfcl Opng Endo]
0UB5[0,3,4,7,8]ZZ Exc/Fallopian Tube, Rt, [Opn, Perc, Perc Endo, Via Natrl or Artfcl Opng, Via Natrl or Artfcl Opng Endo]
0UB6[0,3,4,7,8]ZZ Exc/Fallopian Tube, Lt, [Opn, Perc, Perc Endo, Via Natrl or Artfcl Opng, Via Natrl or Artfcl Opng Endo]
0UB7[0,3,4,7,8]ZZ Exc/Fallopian Tubes, Bilat, [Opn, Perc, Perc Endo, Via Natrl or Artfcl Opng, Via Natrl or Artfcl Opng Endo]
0UDB[7,8]Z[X,Z] Extract/Endometrium, [Via Natrl or Artfcl Opng, Via Natrl or Artfcl Opng Endo], No Dev, [Dx, NQ]
0UL5[0,3,4,7,8][D,Z]Z Occlsn/Fallopian Tube, Rt, [Opn, Perc, Perc Endo, Via Natrl or Artfcl Opng, Via Natrl or Artfcl Opng Endo], [Intralum Dev, No Dev], NQ
0UL5[0,3,4]CZ   Occlsn/Fallopian Tube, Rt, [Opn, Perc, Perc Endo], Extralum Dev, NQ
0UL6[0,3,4,7,8][D,Z]Z Occlsn/Fallopian Tube, Lt, [Opn, Perc, Perc Endo, Via Natrl or Artfcl Opng, Via Natrl or Artfcl Opng Endo], [Intralum Dev, No Dev], NQ
0UL6[0,3,4]CZ   Occlsn/Fallopian Tube, Lt, [Opn, Perc, Perc Endo], Extralum Dev, NQ
0UL7[0,3,4,7,8][D,Z]Z Occlsn/Fallopian Tubes, Bilat, [Opn, Perc, Perc Endo, Via Natrl or Artfcl Opng, Via Natrl or Artfcl Opng Endo], [Intralum Dev, No Dev], NQ
0UL7[0,3,4]CZ   Occlsn/Fallopian Tubes, Bilat, [Opn, Perc, Perc Endo], Extralum Dev, NQ
0UT5[0,4,7,8,F]ZZ Resect/Fallopian Tube, Rt, [Opn, Perc Endo, Via Natrl or Artfcl Opng, Via Natrl or Artfcl Opng Endo, Via Natrl or Artfcl Opng w/ Perc Endo Assistance]
0UT6[0,4,7,8,F]ZZ Resect/Fallopian Tube, Lt, [Opn, Perc Endo, Via Natrl or Artfcl Opng, Via Natrl or Artfcl Opng Endo, Via Natrl or Artfcl Opng w/ Perc Endo Assistance]
0UT7[0,4,7,8,F]ZZ Resect/Fallopian Tubes, Bilat, [Opn, Perc Endo, Via Natrl or Artfcl Opng, Via Natrl or Artfcl Opng Endo, Via Natrl or Artfcl Opng w/ Perc Endo Assistance]
10D1[7,8]ZZ   Extract/Products of Conception, Retained, [Via Natrl or Artfcl Opng, Via Natrl or Artfcl Opng Endo]

DRG 768   Vaginal Delivery with O.R. Procedure Except Sterilization and/or D&C
     GMLOS 3.6   AMLOS 4.3   RW 1.2618

Delivery Procedures

0DQP7ZZ   Repair Rectum, Via Natrl or Artfcl Opng

10A07Z6   Abortion of Products of Conception, Vacuum, Via Opng
10D07Z[3,4,5,6,7,8] Extract/Products of Conception, Via Natrl or Artfcl Opng, No Dev, [Low Forceps, Mid Forceps, High Forceps, Vacuum, Int Version, Oth]
10E0XZZ   Delivery of Products of Conception, Ext Appr
10S07ZZ   Repos Products of Conception, Via Opng
AND

Operating Room Procedures

02HV02Z   Insert of Monitor Dev into Sup Vena Cava, Opn Appr
02HV[0,3,4]DZ Insert/Superior Vena Cava, [Opn, Perc, Perc Endo], Intralum Dev, NQ
02HV[3,4]2Z Insert/Superior Vena Cava, [Perc, Perc Endo], Monitoring Dev, NQ
02LV*   Occlsn/Superior Vena Cava
02VV*   Restrict/Superior Vena Cava
05HY[0,3,4]DZ Insert/Upr Vein, [Opn, Perc, Perc Endo], Intralum Dev, NQ
06BY[0,3,4]ZC Exc/Lwr Vein, [Opn, Perc, Perc Endo], No Dev, Hemorrhoidal Plexus
06H0[0,3,4]DZ Insert/Inferior Vena Cava, [Opn, Perc, Perc Endo], Intralum Dev, NQ
06HC[0,3,4]DZ Insert/Common Iliac Vein, Rt, [Opn, Perc, Perc Endo], Intralum Dev, NQ
06HD[0,3,4]DZ Insert/Common Iliac Vein, Lt, [Opn, Perc, Perc Endo], Intralum Dev, NQ
06HF[0,3,4]DZ Insert/Ext Iliac Vein, Rt, [Opn, Perc, Perc Endo], Intralum Dev, NQ
06HG[0,3,4]DZ Insert/Ext Iliac Vein, Lt, [Opn, Perc, Perc Endo], Intralum Dev, NQ
06HH[0,3,4]DZ Insert/Hypogastric Vein, Rt, [Opn, Perc, Perc Endo], Intralum Dev, NQ
06HJ[0,3,4]DZ Insert/Hypogastric Vein, Lt, [Opn, Perc, Perc Endo], Intralum Dev, NQ
06HY[0,3,4]DZ Insert/Lwr Vein, [Opn, Perc, Perc Endo], Intralum Dev, NQ
06L0*   Occlsn/Inferior Vena Cava
06V0*   Restrict/Inferior Vena Cava
07BH[0,3,4]ZZ Exc/Lymphatic, Rt Inguinal, [Opn, Perc, Perc Endo]
07BJ[0,3,4]ZZ Exc/Lymphatic, Lt Inguinal, [Opn, Perc, Perc Endo]
07JP0ZZ   Inspect of Spleen, Opn Appr
0DFP[0,3,4,7,8]ZZ Fragmn/Rectum, [Opn, Perc, Perc Endo, Via Natrl or Artfcl Opng, Via Natrl or Artfcl Opng Endo]
0DJ00ZZ   Inspect of Upr Intestinal Tract, Opn Appr
0DJ60ZZ   Inspect of Stomach, Opn Appr
0DJD0ZZ   Inspect of Lwr Intestinal Tract, Opn Appr
0DJU[0,4]ZZ Inspect/Omentum, [Opn, Perc Endo]
0DJV[0,4]ZZ Inspect/Mesentery, [Opn, Perc Endo]
0DJW[0,4]ZZ Inspect/Peritoneum, [Opn, Perc Endo]
0DUP*   Supl/Rectum
0DVP*   Restrict/Rectum
0FJ0[0,4]ZZ Inspect/Liver, [Opn, Perc Endo]
0FJ44ZZ   Inspect of Gallbladder, Perc Endo Appr
0FJD4ZZ   Inspect of Pancreatic Duct, Perc Endo Appr
0FJG4ZZ   Inspect of Pancreas, Perc Endo Appr
0Q82*   Div/Pelvic Bone, Rt
0Q83*   Div/Pelvic Bone, Lt
0U5C*   Destr/Cervix
0U5F*   Destr/Cul-de-sac
0U5L*   Destr/Vestibular Gland
0U79*   Dilation/Uterus
0U99[0,3,4,7,8][0,Z]Z Drain/Uterus, [Opn, Perc, Perc Endo, Via Natrl or Artfcl Opng, Via Natrl or Artfcl Opng Endo], [Drain Dev, No Dev], NQ
0U9C*   Drain/Cervix
0U9F[0,3,4,7,8]ZX Drain/Cul-de-sac, [Opn, Perc, Perc Endo, Via Natrl or Artfcl Opng, Via Natrl or Artfcl Opng Endo]
0U9F[0,7,8]0Z Drain/Cul-de-sac, [Opn, Via Natrl or Artfcl Opng, Via Natrl or Artfcl Opng Endo], Drain Dev, NQ
0U9F[0,7,8]ZZ Drain/Cul-de-sac, [Opn, Via Natrl or Artfcl Opng, Via Natrl or Artfcl Opng Endo]
0U9K[0,3,4,7,8,X]ZX Drain/Hymen, [Opn, Perc, Perc Endo, Via Natrl or Artfcl Opng, Via Natrl or Artfcl Opng Endo, Ext]
0U9L[0,X]ZX Drain/Vestibular Gland, [Opn, Ext]
0UBC*   Exc/Cervix
0UBF*   Exc/Cul-de-sac
0UBK[0,3,4,7,8,X]ZX Exc/Hymen, [Opn, Perc, Perc Endo, Via Natrl or Artfcl Opng, Via Natrl or Artfcl Opng Endo, Ext]

Surgical   Medical   CC Indicator   MCC Indicator   Procedure Proxy   **PDx MCC** PDx acts as own MCC   **PDx CC** PDx acts as own CC

MDC 14: Pregnancy, Childbirth And The Puerperium—SURGICAL

0UBL*	Exc/Vestibular Gland
0UC9[0,3,4]ZZ	Extir/Uterus, [Opn, Perc, Perc Endo]
0UCF*	Extir/Cul-de-sac
0UCL*	Extir/Vestibular Gland
0UJH[0,3,4,7]ZZ	Inspect/Vagina and Cul-de-sac, [Opn, Perc, Perc Endo, Via Natrl or Artfcl Opng]
0UNL*	Rls/Vestibular Gland
0UPD0CZ	Rmvl of Extralum Dev from Uterus & Cervix, Opn Appr
0UPD[0,3,4,7,8][0,1,3,7,D,J,K]Z	Rmvl/Uterus and Cervix, [Opn, Perc, Perc Endo, Via Natrl or Artfcl Opng, Via Natrl or Artfcl Opng Endo], [Drain Dev, Radioact Elmt, Inf Dev, Auto Tissue Sub, Intralum Dev, Synth Sub, Nonauto Tissue Sub], NQ
0UPD[0,3,4]HZ	Rmvl/Uterus and Cervix, [Opn, Perc, Perc Endo], Contraceptive Dev, NQ
0UQ9*	Repair/Uterus
0UQL*	Repair/Vestibular Gland
0US9[0,4]ZZ	Repos/Uterus, [Opn, Perc Endo]
0USC*	Repos/Cervix
0UT9*	Resect/Uterus
0UTL*	Resect/Vestibular Gland
0UWD[0,3,4,7,8][0,1,3,7,C,D,H,J,K]Z	Rev/Uterus and Cervix, [Opn, Perc, Perc Endo, Via Natrl or Artfcl Opng, Via Natrl or Artfcl Opng Endo], [Drain Dev, Radioact Elmt, Inf Dev, Auto Tissue Sub, Extralum Dev, Intralum Dev, Contraceptive Dev, Synth Sub, Nonauto Tissue Sub], NQ
0W3N*	Control/Perineum, Female
0W3R*	Control/Genitourinary Tract
0WJF4ZZ	Inspect of Abd Wall, Perc Endo Appr
0WJG[0,4]ZZ	Inspect/Peritoneal Cavity, [Opn, Perc Endo]
0WJJ[0,4]ZZ	Inspect/Pelvic Cavity, [Opn, Perc Endo]
0WJP[0,4]ZZ	Inspect/Gastrointestinal Tract, [Opn, Perc Endo]
0WJR[0,4]ZZ	Inspect/Genitourinary Tract, [Opn, Perc Endo]
10H00[3,Y]Z	Insert/Products of Conception, Opn, [Monitoring Electrode, Oth Dev], NQ
10P*	Obstetrics, Preg, Rmvl
10T*	Obstetrics, Preg, Resect

DRG 769   Postpartum and Postabortion Diagnoses with O.R. Procedure

GMLOS 4.4   AMLOS 6.5   RW 2.1737

Select any operating room procedure except for the following

0DQP7ZZ	Repair Rectum, Via Natrl or Artfcl Opng
0DQQXZZ	Repair Anus, Ext Appr
0HQ9XZZ	Repair Perineum Skin, Ext Appr
0JQB0ZZ	Repair Perineum SQ/Fascia, Opn Appr
0TQB[0,3,4,7,8]ZZ	Rpr/Bladder, [Opn, Perc, Perc Endo, Via Natrl or Artfcl Opng, Via Natrl or Artfcl Opng Endo]
0TQD[0,3,4,7,8]ZZ	Rpr Urethra, [Opn, Perc, Perc Endo, Via Natrl or Artfcl Opng, Via Natrl or Artfcl Opng Endo]
0UQG[0,3,4,7,8,X]ZZ	Rpr/Vagina, [Opn, Perc, Perc Endo, Via Natrl or Artfcl Opng, Via Natrl or Artfcl Opng Endo, Ext]
0UQM[0,X]ZZ	Rpr/Vulva, [Opn, Ext]

AND

Principal Diagnosis

A34	Obstetrical tetanus
O08*	Comp following ectopic and molar preg
O10.[0,1,2,3,4,9]3	Pre-existing [essential hypertension, hypertensive heart dz, hypertensive chr kidney dz, hypertensive heart and chr kidney dz, 2ndary hypertension] compl the puerperium
O15.2	Eclampsia in the puerperium
O24.03	Pre-existing diabetes mellitus, type 1, in the puerperium
O24.13	Pre-existing diabetes mellitus, type 2, in the puerperium
O24.33	Unsp pre-existing diabetes mellitus in the puerperium
O24.43[0,4,9]	Gestational diabetes mellitus in the puerperium, [diet, insulin, unsp] controlled
O24.83	Oth pre-existing diabetes mellitus in the puerperium
O24.93	Unsp diabetes mellitus in the puerperium
O25.3	Malnut in the puerperium
O26.63	Liver and biliary tract d/o in the puerperium
O26.73	Sublux of symphysis (pubis) in the puerperium
O43.21[1,2,3]	Placenta accreta, [frist, 2nd, 3rd] trmstr
O43.22[1,2,3]	Placenta increta, [1st, 2nd, 3rd] trmstr
O43.23[1,2,3]	Placenta precreta, [1st, 2nd, 3rd] trmstr
O70*	Perineal lac during delivery
O71.2	Postpartum inversion of uterus
O71.3	Obstetric lac of cervix
O71.4	Obstetric high vaginal lac alone
O71.5	Oth obstetric inj to pelvic organs
O71.6	Obstetric damage to pelvic jts and lgmt

O71.7	Obstetric hematoma of pelvis
O71.82	Oth spec trauma to perineum and vulva
O71.89	Oth spec obstetric trauma
O71.9	Obstetric trauma, unsp
O72.2	Delayed and secondary postpartum hemor
O72.3	Postpartum coagulation defects
O73*	Retained placenta and membranes, w/o hemor
O75.0	Maternal distress during labor and delivery
O85	Puerperal sepsis
O86*	Oth puerperal infections
O87*	Venous comp and hemorrhoids in the puerperium
O88.[0,1,2,3,8]3	[Air, Amniotic fluid, Thrombo-, Pyemic and septic, Oth] embolism in the puerperium
O89*	Comp of anesthesia during the puerperium
O90.0	Disruption of cesarean delivery wnd
O90.1	Disruption of perineal obstetric wnd
O90.3	Peripartum cardiomyopathy
O90.4	Postpartum acute kidney failure
O90.5	Postpartum thyroiditis
O90.6	Postpartum mood disturbance
O90.8*	Oth comp of the puerperium, NEC
O90.9	Comp of the puerperium, unsp
O91.0[2,3]	Infxn of nipple associated w/ [the puerperium, lactation]
O91.1[2,3]	Abscess of breast associated w/ [the puerperium, lactation]
O91.2[2,3]	Nonpurulent mastitis associated w/ [the puerperium, lactation]
O92.0[2,3]	Retracted nipple associated w/ [the puerperium, lactation]
O92.1[2,3]	Cracked nipple assoicated w/ [the puerperium, lactation]
O92.2*	Oth and unsp d/o of breast assoc w preg and the puerp
O92.3	Agalactia
O92.4	Hypogalactia
O92.5	Suppressed lactation
O92.6	Galactorrhea
O92.7*	Oth and unsp d/o of lactation
O98.[0,1,2,3,4,5,6,7,8,9]3	[Tuberculosis, Syphilis, Gonorrhea, Oth infxns w/ a predominantly sexual mode of transmission, Viral hepatitis, Oth viral dzs, Protozoal dzs, Human immunodef virus (HIV) dz, Oth maternal infectious and parasitic dzs, Unsp maternal infectious and parasitic dz] compl the puerperium
O99.215	Obesity compl the puerperium
O99.285	Endocrine, nutritional and metabolic dz comp the puerp
O99.355	Dz of the nervous sys compl the puerperium
O99.3[1,2,3,4]5	[Alcohol use, Drug use, Smoking (tobacco), Oth mental d/os] compl the puerperium
O99.8[1,2,3,4]5	[Abnormal glucose, Streptococcus B carrier state, Oth infxn carrier state, Bariatric surgery status] compl the puerperium
O99.[0,1]3	[Anemia, Oth dzs of the bld and bld-forming organs and certain d/os involving the immune mech] compl the puerperium
O99.[4,5,6,7]3	Dz of the [circulatory, respiratory, digestive, skin and SQ tissue] sys compl the puerperium
O9A.13	Malig neoplasm compl the puerperium
O9A.23	Inj/poisn/oth conseq of ext causes comp the puerperium
O9A.[3,4,5]3	[Physical, Sexual, Psychological] abuse compl the puerperium
Z39.0	Enc for care and exam of mother immediately after del

DRG 770   Abortion with D&C, Aspiration Curettage or Hysterotomy

GMLOS 1.9   AMLOS 2.4   RW 0.8272

Principal Diagnosis

O02.1	Missed abortion
O03*	Spontaneous abortion
O04*	Comp following (induced) termination of preg
O07*	Failed attempted termination of preg
Z33.2	Enc for elective termination of preg
Z64.0	Problems related to unwanted preg

AND

Operating Room Procedures

0UDB*	Extract/Endometrium
10A0[0,3,4,7,8]ZZ	Abortion/Products of Conception, [Opn, Perc, Perc Endo, Via Natrl or Artfcl Opng, Via Natrl or Artfcl Opng Endo]
10D1*	Extract/Products of Conception, Retained

T Transfer DRG   SP Special Payment   * Code Range   **6th and 7th Character of ZZ = No Device, No Qualifier ZX = No Device, Diagnostic**

MEDICAL

DRG 774 Vaginal Delivery with Complicating Diagnoses
GMLOS 2.6   AMLOS 3.1   RW 0.7509

Principal Diagnosis

O10.[0,1,2,3,4,9]2	Pre-existing [essential hypertension, hypertensive heart dz, hypertensive chr kidney dz, hypertensive heart and chr kidney dz, 2ndary hypertension] compl childbirth
O15.1	Eclampsia in labor
O24.42[0,4,9]	Gestational diabetes mellitus in childbirth, [diet, insulin, unsp] controlled
O24.82	Oth pre-existing diabetes mellitus in childbirth
O24.92	Unsp diabetes mellitus in childbirth
O24.[0,1,3]2	Pre-existing diabetes mellitus, [type 1, type 2, type unsp], in childbirth
O25.2	Malnut in childbirth
O26.62	Liver and biliary tract d/o in childbirth
O26.72	Sublux of symphysis (pubis) in childbirth
O60.14X[0,1,2,3,4,5,9]	Preterm labor 3rd trmstr w/ preterm delivery, 3rd trmstr, fetus [N/A or unsp, 1, 2, 3, 4, 5, oth]
O60.1[2,3]X[0,1,2,3,4,5,9]	Preterm labor 2nd trmstr w/ preterm delivery [2nd, 3rd] trmstr, fetus [N/A or unsp, 1, 2, 3, 4, 5, oth]
O60.2[2,3]X[0,1,2,3,4,5,9]	Term delivery w/ preterm labor [2nd, 3rd] trmstr, fetus [N/A or unsp, 1, 2, 3, 4, 5, oth]
O64*	Obstructed labor d/t malposition and malpresent of fetus
O65*	Obstructed labor d/t maternal pelvic abnormality
O66.41	Failed attempt vaginal birth after previous cesarean del
O66.5	Attempted application of vacuum extractor and forceps
O66.6	Obstructed labor d/t oth multi fetuses
O66.8	Oth spec obstructed labor
O66.9	Obstructed labor, unsp
O66.[0,1,2,3]	Obstructed labor d/t [shldr dystocia, locked twins, unusually lg fetus, oth abnormalities of fetus]
O67*	Labor and delivery comp by intrapartum hemor, NEC
O68	Labor and delivery comp by abnlt of fetal acid-base balance
O69.0*	Labor and delivery complicated by prolapse of cord
O69.1*	Labor and delivery comp by cord around neck, w compression
O69.2*	Labor and delivery comp by oth cord entangle, w compression
O69.3*	Labor and delivery complicated by short cord
O69.4*	Labor and delivery complicated by vasa previa
O69.5*	Labor and delivery complicated by vascular lesion of cord
O69.8[1,2,9]X[1,2,3,4,5,9]	Labor and delivery comp by [cord around neck w/o compression, oth cord entanglement w/o compression, oth cord comp], fetus [1, 2, 3, 4, 5, oth]
O69.9*	Labor and delivery complicated by cord comp, unsp
O71.00	Rupture of uterus before onset of labor, unsp trmstr
O71.1	Rupture of uterus during labor
O71.81	Lac of uterus, NEC
O72.0	Third-stage hemor
O72.1	Oth immediate postpartum hemor
O74*	Comp of anesthesia during labor and delivery
O75.1	Shock during or following labor and delivery
O75.4	Oth comp of obstetric surgery and procedures
O75.5	Delayed delivery after artfcl rupture of membranes
O75.81	Maternal exhaustion compl labor and delivery
O75.82	Onset labor 37-39 weeks, w del by (planned) cesarean section
O77*	Oth fetal stress compl labor and delivery
O80	Enc for full-term uncomplicated delivery
O82	Enc for cesarean delivery w/o indication
O88.[0,1,2,3,8]2	[Air, Amniotic fluid, Thrombo-, Pyemic and septic, Oth] embolism in childbirth
O98.[0,1,2,3,4,5,6,7,8,9]2	[Tuberculosis, Syphilis, Gonorrhea, Oth infxns w/ a predominantly sexual mode of transmission, Viral hepatitis, Oth viral dzs, Protozoal dzs, Human immunodef virus (HIV) dz, Oth maternal infectious and parasitic dzs, Unsp maternal infectious and parasitic dz] compl childbirth
O99.2[1,8]4	[Obesity, Endocrine nutritional and metabolic dzs] compl childbirth
O99.354	Dz of the nervous sys compl childbirth
O99.3[1,2,3,4]4	[Alcohol use, Drug use, Smoking (tobacco), Oth mental d/os] compl childbirth
O99.8[1,2,3,4]4	[Abnormal glucose, Streptococcus B carrier state, Oth infxn carrier state, Bariatric surgery status] compl childbirth
O99.[0,1]2	[Anemia, Oth dzs of the bld and bld-forming organs and certain d/os involving the immune mech] compl childbirth
O99.[4,5,6,7]2	Dz of the [circulatory, respiratory, digestive, skin and SQ tissue] sys compl childbirth
O9A.12	Malig neoplasm compl childbirth
O9A.22	Inj/poisn/oth conseq of ext causes comp childbirth
O9A.[3,4,5]2	[Physical, Sexual, Psychological] abuse compl childbirth

OR

Delivery Procedure

0DQP7ZZ	Repair Rectum, Via Natrl or Artfcl Opng
10A07Z6	Abortion of Products of Conception, Vacuum, Via Opng
10D07Z[3,4,5,6,7,8]	Extract/Products of Conception, Via Natrl or Artfcl Opng, No Dev, [Low Forceps, Mid Forceps, High Forceps, Vacuum, Int Version, Oth]
10E0XZZ	Delivery of Products of Conception, Ext Appr
10S07ZZ	Repos Products of Conception, Via Opng

OR

Delivery outcome secondary diagnosis

Z37*	Outcome of delivery

AND

Complicating principal or secondary diagnosis

O10.01[1,2,3]	Pre-existing essential hypertension compl preg, [1st, 2nd, 3rd] trmstr
O10.02	Pre-existing essential hypertension compl childbirth
O10.03	Pre-existing essential hypertension comp the puerperium
O10.11[1,2,3]	Pre-existing hypertensive heart dz compl preg, [1st, 2nd, 3rd] trmstr
O10.12	Pre-existing hypertensive heart dz comp childbirth
O10.13	Pre-existing hypertensive heart dz comp the puerperium
O10.21[1,2,3]	Pre-existing hypertensive chr kidney dz compl preg, [1st, 2nd, 3rd] trmstr
O10.22	Pre-existing hyp chr kidney dz comp childbirth
O10.31[1,2,3]	Pre-existing hypertensive heart and chr kidney dz compl preg, [1st, 2nd, thrid] trmstr
O10.32	Pre-exist hyp heart and chr kidney dz comp chldbrth
O10.41[1,2,3]	Pre-existing 2ndary hypertension compl preg, [1st, 2nd, 3rd] trmstr
O10.42	Pre-existing secondary hypertension compl childbirth
O10.43	Pre-existing secondary hypertension comp the puerperium
O10.91[1,2,3]	Unsp pre-existing hypertension compl preg, [1st, 2nd, 3rd] trmstr
O10.92	Unsp pre-existing hypertension compl childbirth
O11.[1,2,3]	Pre-existing hypertension w/ pre-eclampsia, [1st, 2nd, 3rd] trmstr
O14.[0,1,2,9][2,3]	[Mild to mod pre-eclampsia, Severe pre-eclampsia, HELLP synd, Unsp pre-eclampsia], [2nd, 3rd] trmstr
O15.0[2,3]	Eclampsia in preg, [2nd, 3rd] trmstr
O15.1	Eclampsia in labor
O15.2	Eclampsia in the puerperium
O16*	Unsp maternal hypertension
O22.3[1,2,3]	Deep phlebothrombosis in preg, [1st, 2nd, 3rd] trmstr
O22.5[1,2,3]	Cerebral venous thrombosis in preg, [1st, 2nd, 3rd] trmstr
O24.01[1,2,3]	Pre-existing diabetes mellitus, type 1, in preg, [1st, 2nd, 3rd] trmstr
O24.02	Pre-existing diabetes mellitus, type 1, in childbirth
O24.11[1,2,3]	Pre-existing diabetes mellitus, type 2, in preg, [1st, 2nd, 3rd] trmstr
O24.12	Pre-existing diabetes mellitus, type 2, in childbirth
O24.31[1,2,3]	Unsp pre-existing diabetes mellitus in preg, [1st, 2nd, 3rd] trmstr
O24.32	Unsp pre-existing diabetes mellitus in childbirth
O24.81[1,2,3]	Oth pre-existing diabetes mellitus in preg, [1st, 2nd, 3rd] trmstr
O24.82	Oth pre-existing diabetes mellitus in childbirth
O24.91[1,2,3]	Unsp diabetes mellitus in preg, [1st, 2nd, 3rd] trmstr
O24.92	Unsp diabetes mellitus in childbirth
O24.93	Unsp diabetes mellitus in the puerperium
O43.21[1,2,3]	Placenta accreta, [frist, 2nd, 3rd] trmstr
O43.22[1,2,3]	Placenta increta, [1st, 2nd, 3rd] trmstr
O43.23[1,2,3]	Placenta precreta, [1st, 2nd, 3rd] trmstr
O44.[0,1][1,2,3]	Placenta previa [spec as w/o hemor, w/ hemor], [1st, 2nd, 3rd] trmstr
O45.0[0,1,2,9][1,2,3]	Premature separation of placenta w/ [coagulation defect unsp, afibrinogenemia, disseminated intravascular coagulation, oth coagulation defect], [1st, 2nd, 3rd] trmstr
O45.8X[1,2,3]	Oth premature separation of placenta, [1st, 2nd, 3rd] trmstr
O45.9[1,2,3]	Premature separation of placenta, unsp, [1st, 2nd 3rd] trmstr

---

Surgical	Medical	CC Indicator	MCC Indicator	Procedure Proxy	PDxMCC PDx acts as own MCC	PDxCC PDx acts as own CC

MDC 14: Pregnancy, Childbirth And The Puerperium—MEDICAL

O46.0[0,1,2,9][1,2,3]	Antepartum hemor w/ [coagulation defect unsp, afibrinogenemia, disseminated intravascular coagulation, oth coagulation defect], [1st, 2nd, 3rd] trmstr
O46.8X[1,2,3]	Oth antepartum hemor, [1st, 2nd, 3rd] trmstr
O46.9[1,2,3]	Antepartum hemor, unsp, [1st, 2nd, 3rd] trmstr
O67*	Labor and delivery comp by intrapartum hemor, NEC
O72.0	Third-stage hemor
O72.1	Oth immediate postpartum hemor
O72.2	Delayed and secondary postpartum hemor
O73*	Retained placenta and membranes, w/o hemor
O74*	Comp of anesthesia during labor and delivery
O75.1	Shock during or following labor and delivery
O75.2	Pyrexia during labor, NEC
O75.3	Oth infxn during labor
O75.4	Oth comp of obstetric surgery and procedures
O85	Puerperal sepsis
O86.0	infxn of obstetric surgical wnd
O86.12	Endometritis following delivery
O86.4	Pyrexia of unknown origin following delivery
O86.8*	Oth spec puerperal infections
O87.1	Deep phlebothrombosis in the puerperium
O87.3	Cerebral venous thrombosis in the puerperium
O88.01[1,2,3]	Air embolism in preg, [1st, 2nd, 3rd] trmstr
O88.02	Air embolism in childbirth
O88.03	Air embolism in the puerperium
O88.11[1,2,3]	Amniotic fluid embolism in preg, [1st, 2nd, 3rd] trmstr
O88.12	Amniotic fluid embolism in childbirth
O88.13	Amniotic fluid embolism in the puerperium
O88.21[1,2,3]	Thromboembolism in preg, [1st, 2nd, 3rd] trmstr
O88.22	Thromboembolism in childbirth
O88.23	Thromboembolism in the puerperium
O88.31[1,2,3]	Pyemic and septic embolism in preg, [1st, 2nd, 3rd] trmstr
O88.32	Pyemic and septic embolism in childbirth
O88.33	Pyemic and septic embolism in the puerperium
O88.81[1,2,3]	Oth embolism in preg, [1st, 2nd, 3rd] trmstr
O88.82	Oth embolism in childbirth
O88.83	Oth embolism in the puerperium
O89.09	Oth pulmn comp of anesthesia during the puerperium
O89.8	Oth comp of anesthesia during the puerperium
O90.0	Disruption of cesarean delivery wnd
O90.1	Disruption of perineal obstetric wnd
O90.2	Hematoma of obstetric wnd
O90.3	Peripartum cardiomyopathy
O90.89	Oth comp of the puerperium, NEC
O91.01[1,2,3]	Infxn of nipple associated w/ preg, [1st, 2nd, 3rd] trmstr
O91.02	infxn of nipple associated with the puerperium
O91.11[1,2,3]	Abscess of breast associated w/ preg, [1st, 2nd, 3rd] trmstr
O91.12	Abscess of breast associated with the puerperium
O91.21[1,2,3]	Nonpurulent mastitis associated w/ preg, [1st, 2nd, 3rd] trmstr
O91.22	Nonpurulent mastitis associated with the puerperium
O98.01[1,2,3]	Tuberculosis compl preg, [1st, 2nd, 3rd] trmstr
O98.02	Tuberculosis compl childbirth
O98.03	Tuberculosis compl the puerperium
O98.11[1,2,3]	Syphilis compl preg, [1st, 2nd, 3rd] trmstr
O98.12	Syphilis compl childbirth
O98.13	Syphilis compl the puerperium
O98.21[1,2,3]	Gonorrhea compl preg, [1st, 2nd, 3rd] trmstr
O98.22	Gonorrhea compl childbirth
O98.23	Gonorrhea compl the puerperium
O98.31[1,2,3]	Oth infxns w/ a predominantly sexual mode of transmission compl preg, [1st, 2nd, 3rd] trmstr
O98.32	Oth infections w sexl mode of transmiss comp childbirth
O98.33	Oth infections w sexl mode of transmiss comp the puerperium
O98.41[1,2,3]	Viral hepatitis compl preg, [1st, 2nd, 3rd] trmstr
O98.42	Viral hepatitis compl childbirth
O98.43	Viral hepatitis compl the puerperium
O98.51[1,2,3]	Oth viral dzs compl preg, [1st, 2nd, 3rd] trmstr
O98.52	Oth viral dz compl childbirth
O98.53	Oth viral dz compl the puerperium
O98.61[1,2,3]	Protozoal dzs compl preg, [1st, 2nd, 3rd] trmstr
O98.62	Protozoal dz compl childbirth
O98.63	Protozoal dz compl the puerperium
O98.71[1,2,3]	Human immunodef virus (HIV) dz compl preg, [1st, 2nd, 3rd] trmstr
O98.72	Human immunodef virus dz compl childbirth
O98.81[1,2,3]	Oth maternal infectious and parasitic dzs compl preg, [1st, 2nd, 3rd] trmstr
O98.82	Oth maternal infec/parastc dz compl childbirth
O98.83	Oth maternal infec/parastc dz comp the puerperium

O98.91[1,2,3]	Unsp maternal infectious and parasitic dz compl preg, [1st, 2nd, 3rd] trmstr
O98.92	Unsp maternal infec/parastc dz compl childbirth
O98.93	Unsp maternal infec/parastc dz comp the puerperium
O99.41[1,2,3]	Dz of the circulatory sys compl preg, [1st, 2nd, 3rd] trmstr
O99.42	Dz of the circulatory sys compl childbirth
O99.43	Dz of the circ sys compl the puerperium
O99.83[0,4,5]	Oth infxn carrier state compl [preg, childbirth, the puerperium]

OR

Secondary diagnosis

O72.3	Postpartum coagulation defects

AND

Only the following extensive operating room procedures

0DQP0ZZ	Repair Rectum, Opn Appr
0DQP3ZZ	Repair Rectum, Perc Appr
0DQP4ZZ	Repair Rectum, Perc Endo Appr
0DQP7ZZ	Repair Rectum, Via Natrl or Artfcl Opng
0DQP8ZZ	Repair Rectum, Via Natrl or Artfcl Opng Endo
0TQB0ZZ	Repair Bladder, Opn Appr
0TQB3ZZ	Repair Bladder, Perc Appr
0TQB4ZZ	Repair Bladder, Perc Endo Appr
0TQB7ZZ	Repair Bladder, Via Natrl or Artfcl Opng
0TQB8ZZ	Repair Bladder, Via Natrl or Artfcl Opng Endo
0TQD0ZZ	Repair Urethra, Opn Appr
0TQD3ZZ	Repair Urethra, Perc Appr
0TQD4ZZ	Repair Urethra, Perc Endo Appr
0TQD7ZZ	Repair Urethra, Via Natrl or Artfcl Opng
0TQD8ZZ	Repair Urethra, Via Natrl or Artfcl Opng Endo
0TQDXZZ	Repair Urethra, Ext Appr
0U7G0DZ	Dilation of Vagina with Intralum Device, Opn Appr
0U7G0ZZ	Dilation of Vagina, Opn Appr
0U7G3DZ	Dilation of Vagina with Intralum Device, Perc Appr
0U7G3ZZ	Dilation of Vagina, Perc Appr
0U7G4DZ	Dilation of Vagina with Intralum Dev, Perc Endo Appr
0U7G4ZZ	Dilation of Vagina, Perc Endo Appr
0UBMXZZ	Exc of Vulva, Ext Appr
0UMG0ZZ	Reattach of Vagina, Opn Appr
0UMG4ZZ	Reattach of Vagina, Perc Endo Appr
0UNG0ZZ	Rls Vagina, Opn Appr
0UNG3ZZ	Rls Vagina, Perc Appr
0UNG4ZZ	Rls Vagina, Perc Endo Appr
0UNG7ZZ	Rls Vagina, Via Natrl or Artfcl Opng
0UNG8ZZ	Rls Vagina, Via Natrl or Artfcl Opng Endo
0UNGXZZ	Rls Vagina, Ext Appr
0UNM0ZZ	Rls Vulva, Opn Appr
0UNMXZZ	Rls Vulva, Ext Appr
0UQC0ZZ	Repair Cervix, Opn Appr
0UQC3ZZ	Repair Cervix, Perc Appr
0UQC4ZZ	Repair Cervix, Perc Endo Appr
0UQC7ZZ	Repair Cervix, Via Natrl or Artfcl Opng
0UQC8ZZ	Repair Cervix, Via Natrl or Artfcl Opng Endo
0UVC0CZ	Restrict of Cervix with Extralum Dev, Opn Appr
0UVC0DZ	Restrict of Cervix with Intralum Dev, Opn Appr
0UVC0ZZ	Restrict of Cervix, Opn Appr
0UVC3CZ	Restrict of Cervix with Extralum Dev, Perc Appr
0UVC3DZ	Restrict of Cervix with Intralum Dev, Perc Appr
0UVC3ZZ	Restrict of Cervix, Perc Appr
0UVC4CZ	Restrict of Cervix with Extralum Dev, Perc Endo Appr
0UVC4DZ	Restrict of Cervix with Intralum Dev, Perc Endo Appr
0UVC4ZZ	Restrict of Cervix, Perc Endo Appr
0UVC7DZ	Restrict of Cervix with Intralum Device, Via Opng
0UVC7ZZ	Restrict of Cervix, Via Natrl or Artfcl Opng
0UVC8DZ	Restrict of Cervix with Intralum Device, Endo
0UVC8ZZ	Restrict of Cervix, Endo

OR

Only the following non-extensive operating room procedures

0D8R*	Div/Anal Sphincter
0D9R[0,3,4][0,Z]Z	Drain/Anal Sphincter, [Opn, Perc, Perc Endo], [Drain Dev, No Dev], NQ
0DCR*	Extir/Anal Sphincter
0H89XZZ	Div of Perineum Skin, Ext Appr
0H99X[0,Z]Z	Drain/Skin, Perineum, Ext, [Drain Dev, No Dev], NQ
0HQ9XZZ	Repair Perineum Skin, Ext Appr
0HR9*	Replace/Skin, Perineum
0U5G*	Destr/Vagina
0U5K*	Destr/Hymen

T Transfer DRG	SP Special Payment	* Code Range	6th and 7th Character of ZZ = No Device, No Qualifier ZX = No Device, Diagnostic

ØU5M*	Destr/Vulva
ØU9G*	Drain/Vagina
ØU9J[Ø,X]ZX	Drain/Clitoris, [Opn, Ext]
ØU9M*	Drain/Vulva
ØUBG*	Exc/Vagina
ØUBK[Ø,3,4,7,8,X]ZZ	Exc/Hymen, [Opn, Perc, Perc Endo, Via Natrl or Artfcl Opng, Via Natrl or Artfcl Opng Endo, Ext]
ØUBM[Ø,X]ZX	Exc/Vulva, [Opn, Ext]
ØUCG[Ø,3,4]ZZ	Extir/Vagina, [Opn, Perc, Perc Endo]
ØUCMØZZ	Extir of Matter from Vulva, Opn Appr
ØUHH*	Insert/Vagina and Cul-de-sac
ØUJMØZZ	Inspect of Vulva, Opn Appr
ØUMMXZZ	Reattach of Vulva, Ext Appr
ØUPH[Ø,3,4,7,8][Ø,1,3,7,D,J,K]Z	Rmvl/Vagina and Cul-de-sac, [Opn, Perc, Perc Endo, Via Natrl or Artfcl Opng, Via Natrl or Artfcl Opng Endo], [Drain Dev, Radioact Elmt, Inf Dev, Auto Tissue Sub, Intralum Dev, Synth Sub, Nonauto Tissue Sub], NQ
ØUPMØ[Ø,7,J,K]Z	Rmvl/Vulva, Opn, [Drain Dev, Auto Tissue Sub, Synth Sub, Nonauto Tissue Sub], NQ
ØUTK*	Resect/Hymen
ØUUM*	Supl/Vulva
ØUWH[Ø,3,4,7,8][Ø,1,3,7,D,J,K]Z	Rev/Vagina and Cul-de-sac, [Opn, Perc, Perc Endo, Via Natrl or Artfcl Opng, Via Natrl or Artfcl Opng Endo], [Drain Dev, Radioact Elmt, Inf Dev, Auto Tissue Sub, Intralum Dev, Synth Sub, Nonauto Tissue Sub], NQ
ØUWMØ[Ø,7,J,K]Z	Rev/Vulva, Opn, [Drain Dev, Auto Tissue Sub, Synth Sub, Nonauto Tissue Sub], NQ
ØWØN*	Alter/Perineum, Female
ØW9N[Ø,3,4][Ø,Z]Z	Drain/Perineum, Female, [Opn, Perc, Perc Endo], [Drain Dev, No Dev], NQ
ØWBN*	Exc/Perineum, Female
ØWHN[Ø,3,4][3,Y]Z	Insert/Perineum, Female, [Opn, Perc, Perc Endo], [Inf Dev, Oth Dev], NQ
ØWMNØZZ	Reattach of Female Perineum, Opn Appr
ØWPN[Ø,3,4][Ø,1,3,7,J,K,Y]Z	Rmvl/Perineum, Female, [Opn, Perc, Perc Endo], [Drain Dev, Radioact Elmt, Inf Dev, Auto Tissue Sub, Synth Sub, Nonauto Tissue Sub, Oth Dev], NQ
ØWQN[Ø,3,4]ZZ	Rpr/Perineum, Female, [Opn, Perc, Perc Endo]
ØWUN*	Supl/Perineum, Female
ØWWN[Ø,3,4][Ø,1,3,7,J,K,Y]Z	Rev/Perineum, Female, [Opn, Perc, Perc Endo], [Drain Dev, Radioact Elmt, Inf Dev, Auto Tissue Sub, Synth Sub, Nonauto Tissue Sub, Oth Dev], NQ

OR

No operating room procedures

DRG 775 **Vaginal Delivery without Complicating Diagnoses**
GMLOS 2.1   AMLOS 2.3   RW Ø.5865

Principal or secondary diagnosis

O24.42[Ø,4,9]	Gestational diabetes mellitus in childbirth, [diet, insulin, unsp] controlled
O25.2	Malnut in childbirth
O26.62	Liver and biliary tract d/o in childbirth
O26.72	Sublux of symphysis (pubis) in childbirth
O6Ø.14X[Ø,1,2,3,4,5,9]	Preterm labor 3rd trmstr w/ preterm delivery, 3rd trmstr, fetus [N/A or unsp, 1, 2, 3, 4, 5, oth]
O6Ø.1[2,3]X[Ø,1,2,3,4,5,9]	Preterm labor 2nd trmstr w/ preterm delivery [2nd, 3rd] trmstr, fetus [N/A or unsp, 1, 2, 3, 4, 5, oth]
O6Ø.2[2,3]X[Ø,1,2,3,4,5,9]	Term delivery w/ preterm labor [2nd, 3rd] trmstr, fetus [N/A or unsp, 1, 2, 3, 4, 5, oth]
O64*	Obstructed labor d/t malposition and malpresent of fetus
O65*	Obstructed labor d/t maternal pelvic abnormality
O66.41	Failed attempt vaginal birth after previous cesarean del
O66.5	Attempted application of vacuum extractor and forceps
O66.6	Obstructed labor d/t oth multi fetuses
O66.8	Oth spec obstructed labor
O66.9	Obstructed labor, unsp
O66.[Ø,1,2,3]	Obstructed labor d/t [shldr dystocia, locked twins, unusually lg fetus, oth abnormalities of fetus]
O68	Labor and delivery comp by abnlt of fetal acid-base balance
O69.Ø*	Labor and delivery complicated by prolapse of cord
O69.1*	Labor and delivery comp by cord around neck, w compression
O69.2*	Labor and delivery comp by oth cord entangle, w compression
O69.3*	Labor and delivery complicated by short cord
O69.4*	Labor and delivery complicated by vasa previa
O69.5*	Labor and delivery complicated by vascular lesion of cord
O69.8[1,2,9]X[1,2,3,4,5,9]	Labor and delivery comp by [cord around neck w/o compression, oth cord entanglement w/o compression, oth cord comp], fetus [1, 2, 3, 4, 5, oth]
O69.9*	Labor and delivery complicated by cord comp, unsp
O71.ØØ	Rupture of uterus before onset of labor, unsp trmstr
O71.1	Rupture of uterus during labor
O71.81	Lac of uterus, NEC
O75.5	Delayed delivery after artfcl rupture of membranes
O75.81	Maternal exhaustion compl labor and delivery
O75.82	Onset labor 37-39 weeks, w del by (planned) cesarean section
O77*	Oth fetal stress compl labor and delivery
O8Ø	Enc for full-term uncomplicated delivery
O82	Enc for cesarean delivery w/o indication
O99.2[1,8]4	[Obesity, Endocrine nutritional and metabolic dzs] compl childbirth
O99.354	Dz of the nervous sys compl childbirth
O99.3[1,2,3,4]4	[Alcohol use, Drug use, Smoking (tobacco), Oth mental d/os] compl childbirth
O99.52	Dz of the respiratory sys compl childbirth
O99.62	Dz of the digestive sys compl childbirth
O99.72	Dz of the skin, SQ compl childbirth
O99.814	Abnormal glucose compl childbirth
O99.824	Streptococcus B carrier state compl childbirth
O99.844	Bariatric surgery status compl childbirth
O99.[Ø,1]2	[Anemia, Oth dzs of the bld and bld-forming organs and certain d/os involving the immune mech] compl childbirth
O9A.12	Malig neoplasm compl childbirth
O9A.22	Inj/poisn/oth conseq of ext causes comp childbirth
O9A.[3,4,5]2	[Physical, Sexual, Psychological] abuse compl childbirth

OR

Delivery procedure

ØDQP7ZZ	Repair Rectum, Via Natrl or Artfcl Opng
1ØA07Z6	Abortion of Products of Conception, Vacuum, Via Opng
1ØD07Z[3,4,5,6,7,8]	Extract/Products of Conception, Via Natrl or Artfcl Opng, No Dev, [Low Forceps, Mid Forceps, High Forceps, Vacuum, Int Version, Oth]
1ØE0XZZ	Delivery of Products of Conception, Ext Appr
1ØS07ZZ	Repos Products of Conception, Via Opng

OR

Delivery outcome secondary diagnosis

Z37*	Outcome of delivery

DRG 776 **Postpartum and Postabortion Diagnoses without O.R. Procedure**
GMLOS 2.4   AMLOS 3.2   RW Ø.6766

Principal Diagnosis

A34	Obstetrical tetanus
O08*	Comp following ectopic and molar preg
O1Ø.Ø3	Pre-existing essential hypertension comp the puerperium
O1Ø.13	Pre-existing hypertensive heart dz comp the puerperium
O1Ø.23	Pre-existing hyp chr kidney dz comp the puerperium
O1Ø.33	Pre-exist hyp heart and chr kidney dz comp the puerp
O1Ø.43	Pre-existing secondary hypertension comp the puerperium
O1Ø.93	Unsp pre-existing hypertension compl the puerperium
O15.2	Eclampsia in the puerperium
O24.Ø3	Pre-existing diabetes mellitus, type 1, in the puerperium
O24.13	Pre-existing diabetes mellitus, type 2, in the puerperium
O24.33	Unsp pre-existing diabetes mellitus in the puerperium
O24.43[Ø,4,9]	Gestational diabetes mellitus in the puerperium, [diet, insulin, unsp] controlled
O24.83	Oth pre-existing diabetes mellitus in the puerperium
O24.93	Unsp diabetes mellitus in the puerperium
O25.3	Malnut in the puerperium
O26.63	Liver and biliary tract d/o in the puerperium
O26.73	Sublux of symphysis (pubis) in the puerperium
O43.21[1,2,3]	Placenta accreta, [frist, 2nd, 3rd] trmstr
O43.22[1,2,3]	Placenta increta, [1st, 2nd, 3rd] trmstr
O43.23[1,2,3]	Placenta percreta, [1st, 2nd, 3rd] trmstr
O7Ø*	Perineal lac during delivery
O71.2	Postpartum inversion of uterus
O71.3	Obstetric lac of cervix
O71.4	Obstetric high vaginal lac alone
O71.5	Oth obstetric inj to pelvic organs
O71.6	Obstetric damage to pelvic jts and lgmt
O71.7	Obstetric hematoma of pelvis
O71.82	Oth spec trauma to perineum and vulva

O71.89	Oth spec obstetric trauma
O71.9	Obstetric trauma, unsp
O72.2	Delayed and secondary postpartum hemor
O72.3	Postpartum coagulation defects
O73.0	Retained placenta w/o hemor
O73.1	Retained portions of placenta and membranes, w/o hemor
O75.0	Maternal distress during labor and delivery
O85	Puerperal sepsis
O86*	Oth puerperal infections
O87*	Venous comp and hemorrhoids in the puerperium
O88.03	Air embolism in the puerperium
O88.13	Amniotic fluid embolism in the puerperium
O88.23	Thromboembolism in the puerperium
O88.33	Pyemic and septic embolism in the puerperium
O88.83	Oth embolism in the puerperium
O89*	Comp of anesthesia during the puerperium
O90.0	Disruption of cesarean delivery wnd
O90.1	Disruption of perineal obstetric wnd
O90.3	Peripartum cardiomyopathy
O90.4	Postpartum acute kidney failure
O90.5	Postpartum thyroiditis
O90.6	Postpartum mood disturbance
O90.8*	Oth comp of the puerperium, NEC
O90.9	Comp of the puerperium, unsp
O91.0[2,3]	Infxn of nipple associated w/ [the puerperium, lactation]
O91.12	Abscess of breast associated with the puerperium
O91.13	Abscess of breast associated with lactation
O91.2[2,3]	Nonpurulent mastitis associated w/ [the puerperium, lactation]
O92.0[2,3]	Retracted nipple associated w/ [the puerperium, lactation]
O92.12	Cracked nipple associated with the puerperium
O92.13	Cracked nipple associated with lactation
O92.2*	Oth and unsp d/o of breast assoc w preg and the puerp
O92.3	Agalactia
O92.4	Hypogalactia
O92.5	Suppressed lactation
O92.6	Galactorrhea
O92.7*	Oth and unsp d/o of lactation
O98.03	Tuberculosis compl the puerperium
O98.13	Syphilis compl the puerperium
O98.23	Gonorrhea compl the puerperium
O98.33	Oth infections w sexl mode of transmiss comp the puerperium
O98.43	Viral hepatitis compl the puerperium
O98.53	Oth viral dz compl the puerperium
O98.63	Protozoal dz compl the puerperium
O98.73	Human immunodef virus dz compl the puerperium
O98.83	Oth maternal infec/parastc dz comp the puerperium
O98.93	Unsp maternal infec/parastc dz comp the puerperium
O99.03	Anemia compl the puerperium
O99.13	Oth dis of the bld/bld-form org/immun mechnsm comp the puerp
O99.215	Obesity compl the puerperium
O99.285	Endocrine, nutritional and metabolic dz comp the puerp
O99.315	Alcohol use compl the puerperium
O99.325	Drug use compl the puerperium
O99.335	Smoking (tobacco) compl the puerperium
O99.345	Oth mental d/o compl the puerperium
O99.355	Dz of the nervous sys compl the puerperium
O99.43	Dz of the circ sys compl the puerperium
O99.53	Dz of the resp sys compl the puerperium
O99.63	Dz of the digestive sys compl the puerperium
O99.73	Dz of the skin, SQ compl the puerperium
O99.815	Abnormal glucose compl the puerperium
O99.825	Streptococcus B carrier state compl the puerperium
O99.835	Oth infxn carrier state compl the puerperium
O99.845	Bariatric surgery status compl the puerperium
O9A.13	Malig neoplasm compl the puerperium
O9A.23	Inj/poisn/oth conseq of ext causes comp the puerperium
O9A.33	Physical abuse compl the puerperium
O9A.43	Sexual abuse compl the puerperium
O9A.53	Psychological abuse compl the puerperium
Z39.0	Enc for care and exam of mother immediately after del

DRG 777   Ectopic Pregnancy
      GMLOS 1.9   AMLOS 2.3   RW 0.9386

Principal Diagnosis

O00*	Ectopic preg

DRG 778   Threatened Abortion
      GMLOS 2.0   AMLOS 3.1   RW 0.5332

Principal Diagnosis

O20*	Hemor in early preg
O60.0*	Preterm labor w/o delivery

DRG 779   Abortion without D&C
      GMLOS 1.7   AMLOS 2.2   RW 0.6850

Principal Diagnosis

O02.1	Missed abortion
O03*	Spontaneous abortion
O04*	Comp following (induced) termination of preg
O07*	Failed attempted termination of preg
Z33.2	Enc for elective termination of preg
Z64.0	Problems related to unwanted preg

DRG 780   False Labor
      GMLOS 1.1   AMLOS 1.1   RW 0.2062

Principal Diagnosis

O47*	False labor

DRG 781   Other Antepartum Diagnoses with Medical Complications
      GMLOS 2.7   AMLOS 4.0   RW 0.8182

Principal Diagnosis

O10.01[1,2,3]	Pre-existing essential hypertension compl preg, [1st, 2nd, 3rd] trmstr
O10.11[1,2,3]	Pre-existing hypertensive heart dz compl preg, [1st, 2nd, 3rd] trmstr
O10.21[1,2,3]	Pre-existing hypertensive chr kidney dz compl preg, [1st, 2nd, 3rd] trmstr
O10.31[1,2,3]	Pre-existing hypertensive heart and chr kidney dz compl preg, [1st, 2nd, thrid] trmstr
O10.41[1,2,3]	Pre-existing 2ndary hypertension compl preg, [1st, 2nd, 3rd] trmstr
O10.91[1,2,3]	Unsp pre-existing hypertension compl preg, [1st, 2nd, 3rd] trmstr
O11*	Pre-existing hypertension with pre-eclampsia
O12*	Gestational edema and proteinuria w/o hypertension
O14.0[2,3]	Mild to mod pre-eclampsia, [2nd, 3rd] trmstr
O14.1*	Severe pre-eclampsia
O14.2*	HELLP synd
O14.9[2,3]	Unsp pre-eclampsia, [2nd, thrid] trmstr
O15.0*	Eclampsia in preg
O15.9	Eclampsia, unsp as to time period
O16.[1,2,3]	Unsp maternal hypertension, [1st, 2nd, 3rd] trmstr
O21*	Excessive vomiting in preg
O23*	Infections of genitourinary tract in preg
O24.01[1,2,3]	Pre-existing diabetes mellitus, type 1, in preg, [1st, 2nd, 3rd] trmstr
O24.11[1,2,3]	Pre-existing diabetes mellitus, type 2, in preg, [1st, 2nd, 3rd] trmstr
O24.31[1,2,3]	Unsp pre-existing diabetes mellitus in preg, [1st, 2nd, 3rd] trmstr
O24.41[0,4,9]	Gestational diabetes mellitus in preg, [diet, insulin, unsp] controlled
O24.81[1,2,3]	Oth pre-existing diabetes mellitus in preg, [1st, 2nd, 3rd] trmstr
O24.91[1,2,3]	Unsp diabetes mellitus in preg, [1st, 2nd, 3rd] trmstr
O25.1[1,2,3]	Malnut in preg, [1st, 2nd, 3rd] trmstr
O26.0[0,1,2,3]	Excessive weight gain in preg, [unsp, 1st, 2nd, 3rd] trmstr
O26.1*	Low weight gain in preg
O26.3*	Retained intrauterine contraceptive device in preg
O26.4*	Herpes gestationis
O26.61*	Liver and biliary tract d/o in preg
O26.71*	Sublux of symphysis (pubis) in preg
O26.81*	Preg related exhaustion and fatigue
O26.82[1,2,3]	Preg related peripheral neuritis, [1st,2nd, 3rd] trmstr
O26.83*	Preg related renal dz
O26.86	Pruritic urticarial papules and plaques of preg (PUPPP)
O26.89*	Oth spec preg related conditions
O26.9[1,2,3]	Preg related conditions, unsp, [1st, 2nd, 3rd] trmstr
O29*	Comp of anesthesia during preg
O33.0	Matern care for disproprtn d/t deformity of matern pelv bone
O45.0*	Premature separation of placenta with coagulation defect

Ⓣ **Transfer DRG**   ⓈⓅ **Special Payment**   * **Code Range**   **6th and 7th Character of ZZ = No Device, No Qualifier ZX = No Device, Diagnostic**

276   MS-DRG Version 33.0   © 2015 Optum360, LLC

O46.0*	Antepartum hemor with coagulation defect
O98.01[1,2,3]	Tuberculosis compl preg, [1st, 2nd, 3rd] trmstr
O98.11[1,2,3]	Syphilis compl preg, [1st, 2nd, 3rd] trmstr
O98.21[1,2,3]	Gonorrhea compl preg, [1st, 2nd, 3rd] trmstr
O98.31[1,2,3]	Oth infxns w/ a predominantly sexual mode of transmission compl preg, [1st, 2nd, 3rd] trmstr
O98.41[1,2,3]	Viral hepatitis compl preg, [1st, 2nd, 3rd] trmstr
O98.51[1,2,3]	Oth viral dzs compl preg, [1st, 2nd, 3rd] trmstr
O98.61[1,2,3]	Protozoal dzs compl preg, [1st, 2nd, 3rd] trmstr
O98.71[1,2,3]	Human immunodef virus (HIV) dz compl preg, [1st, 2nd, 3rd] trmstr
O98.81[1,2,3]	Oth maternal infectious and parasitic dzs compl preg, [1st, 2nd, 3rd] trmstr
O98.91[1,2,3]	Unsp maternal infectious and parasitic dz compl preg, [1st, 2nd, 3rd] trmstr
O99.01[1,2,3]	Anemia compl preg, [1st, 2nd, 3rd] trmstr
O99.28[1,2,3]	Endocrine, nutritional and metabolic dzs compl preg, [1st, 2nd, 3rd] trmstr
O99.31[1,2,3]	Alcohol use compl preg, [1st, 2nd, 3rd] trmstr
O99.32[1,2,3]	Drug use compl preg, [1st, 2nd, 3rd] trmstr
O99.34[1,2,3]	Oth mental d/os compl preg, [1st, 2nd, 3rd] trmstr
O99.350	Dz of the nervous sys comp preg, unsp trmstr
O99.35[1,2,3]	Dz of the nervous sys compl preg, [1st, 2nd, 3rd] trmstr
O99.41[1,2,3]	Dz of the circulatory sys compl preg, [1st, 2nd, 3rd] trmstr
O99.51[1,2,3]	Dz of the respiratory sys compl preg, [1st, 2nd, 3rd] trmstr
O99.61[1,2,3]	Dz of the digestive sys compl preg, [1st, 2nd, 3rd] trmstr
O99.71[1,2,3]	Dz of the skin and SQ tissue compl preg, [1st, 2nd, 3rd] trmstr
O99.810	Abnormal glucose compl preg
O99.820	Streptococcus B carrier state compl preg
O99.830	Oth infxn carrier state compl preg
O99.89	Oth dz and conditions compl preg/chldbrth
O9A.11[1,2,3]	Malig neoplasm compl preg, [1st, 2nd, 3rd] trmstr
O9A.21[1,2,3]	Inj, poison and certain oth consequences of ext causes compl preg, [1st, 2nd, 3rd] trmstr
O9A.31[1,2,3]	Physical abuse compl preg, [1st, 2nd, 3rd] trmstr
O9A.41[1,2,3]	Sexual abuse compl preg, [1st, 2nd, 3rd] trmstr
O9A.51[1,2,3]	Psychological abuse compl preg, [1st, 2nd, 3rd] trmstr

OR

Principal Diagnosis

O01*	Hydatidiform mole
O02.0	Blighted ovum and nonhydatidiform mole
O02.8*	Oth spec abnormal products of conception
O02.9	Abnormal product of conception, unsp
O09.4[1,2,3]	Supervision of preg w/ grand multiparity, [1st, 2nd, 3rd] trmstr
O10.91[1,2,3]	Unsp pre-existing hypertension compl preg, [1st, 2nd, 3rd] trmstr
O11.[1,2,3]	Pre-existing hypertension w/ pre-eclampsia, [1st, 2nd, 3rd] trmstr
O12.[0,1,2][1,2,3]	Gestational [edema, proteinuria, edema w/ proteinuria], [1st, 2nd, 3rd] trmstr
O13.[1,2,3]	Gestational (preg-induced) hypertension w/o significant proteinuria, [1st, 2nd, 3rd] trmstr
O14.2[2,3]	HELLP synd, [2nd, 3rd] trmstr
O14.9[2,3]	Unsp pre-eclampsia, [2nd, thrid] trmstr
O14.[0,1][2,3]	[Mild to mod, Severe] pre-eclampsia, [2nd, 3rd] trmstr
O15.0[2,3]	Eclampsia in preg, [2nd, 3rd] trmstr
O16.[1,2,3]	Unsp maternal hypertension, [1st, 2nd, 3rd] trmstr
O21*	Excessive vomiting in preg
O22.0[1,2,3]	Varicose veins of lwr extr in preg, [1st, 2nd, 3rd] trmstr
O22.1[1,2,3]	Genital varices in preg, [1st, 2nd, 3rd] trmstr
O22.2[1,2,3]	Superf thrombophlebitis in preg, [1st, 2nd, 3rd] trmstr
O22.3[1,2,3]	Deep phlebothrombosis in preg, [1st, 2nd, 3rd] trmstr
O22.4[1,2,3]	Hemorrhoids in preg, [1st, 2nd, 3rd] trmstr
O22.5[1,2,3]	Cerebral venous thrombosis in preg, [1st, 2nd, 3rd] trmstr
O22.8X[1,2,3]	Oth venous comps in preg, [1st, 2nd, 3rd] trmstr
O22.9[1,2,3]	Venous comp in preg, unsp, [1st, 2nd, 3rd] trmstr
O23.4[1,2,3]	Unsp infxn of urinary tract in preg, [1st, 2nd, 3rd] trmstr
O23.5[1,2,9][1,2,3]	[Infxns of cervix, Salpingo-oophoritis, Infxn of oth part of genital tract] in preg, [1st, 2nd, 3rd] trmstr
O23.9[1,2,3]	Unsp genitourinary tract infxn in preg, [1st, 2nd, 3rd] trmstr
O23.[0,1,2,3][1,2,3]	Infxns of [kidney, bladder, urethra, oth parts of urinary tract] in preg, [1st, 2nd, 3rd] trmstr
O24.31[1,2,3]	Unsp pre-existing diabetes mellitus in preg, [1st, 2nd, 3rd] trmstr
O24.41[0,4,9]	Gestational diabetes mellitus in preg, [diet, insulin, unsp] controlled
O24.81[1,2,3]	Oth pre-existing diabetes mellitus in preg, [1st, 2nd, 3rd] trmstr
O24.91[1,2,3]	Unsp diabetes mellitus in preg, [1st, 2nd, 3rd] trmstr
O24.[0,1]1[1,2,3]	Pre-existing diabetes mellitus, type [1, 2], in preg, [1st, 2nd, 3rd] trmstr
O25.1[1,2,3]	Malnut in preg, [1st, 2nd, 3rd] trmstr
O26.2[1,2,3]	Preg care for patient w/ recurrent preg loss, [1st, 2nd, 3rd] trmstr
O26.3[1,2,3]	Retained intrauterine contraceptive dev in preg, [1st, 2nd, 3rd] trmstr
O26.4[1,2,3]	Herpes gestationis, [1st, 2nd, 3rd] trmstr
O26.5[0,1,2,3]	Maternal hypotension synd, [unsp, 1st, 2nd, 3rd] trmstr
O26.61[1,2,3]	Liver and biliary tract d/os in preg, [1st, 2nd, 3rd] trmstr
O26.71[1,2,3]	Sublux of symphysis (pubis) in preg, [1st, 2nd, 3rd] trmstr
O26.81[1,2,3]	Preg related exhaustion and fatigue, [1st, 2nd, 3rd] trmstr
O26.82[1,2,3]	Preg related peripheral neuritis, [1st,2nd, 3rd] trmstr
O26.83[1,2,3]	Preg related renal dz, [1st, 2nd, 3rd] trmstr
O26.84[1,2,3]	Uterine size-date discrepancy, [1st, 2nd, 3rd] trmstr
O26.85[1,2,3]	Spotting compl preg, [1st, 2nd, 3rd] trmstr
O26.86	Pruritic urticarial papules and plaques of preg (PUPPP)
O26.87[2,3]	Cervical shortening, [2nd, 3rd] trmstr
O26.89[1,2,3]	Oth spec preg related conditions, [1st, 2nd, 3rd] trmstr
O26.9[1,2,3]	Preg related conditions, unsp, [1st, 2nd, 3rd] trmstr
O26.[0,1][1,2,3]	[Excessive, Low] weight gain in preg, [1st, 2nd, 3rd] trmstr
O28*	Abnormal findings on antenatal screening of mother
O29.01[1,2,3]	Aspiration pneumonitis d/t anesthesia during preg, [1st, 2nd, 3rd] trmstr
O29.02[1,2,3]	Pressure collapse of lung d/t anesthesia during preg, [1st, 2nd, 3rd] trmstr
O29.09[1,2,3]	Oth pulmn comps of anesthesia during preg, [1st, 2nd, 3rd] trmstr
O29.19[1,2,3]	Oth cardiac comps of anesthesia during preg, [1st, 2nd, 3rd] trmstr
O29.1[1,2][1,2,3]	Cardiac [arrest, failure] d/t anesthesia during preg, [1st, 2nd, 3rd] trmstr
O29.21[1,2,3]	Cerebral anoxia d/t anesthesia during preg, [1st, 2nd, 3rd] trmstr
O29.29[1,2,3]	Oth central nervous sys comps of anesthesia during preg, [1st, 2nd, 3rd] trmstr
O29.3X[1,2,3]	Txc reaction to local anesthesia during preg, [1st, 2nd, 3rd] trmstr
O29.4[1,2,3]	Spinal and epidural anesthesia induced headache during preg, [1st, 2nd, 3rd] trmstr
O29.5X[1,2,3]	Oth comps of spinal and epidural anesthesia during preg, [1st, 2nd, 3rd] trmstr
O29.6[1,2,3]	Failed or difficult intubation for anesthesia during preg, [1st, 2nd, 3rd] trmstr
O29.8X[1,2,3]	Oth comps of anesthesia during preg, [1st, 2nd, 3rd] trmstr
O29.9[1,2,3]	Unsp comp of anesthesia during preg, [1st, 2nd, 3rd] trmstr
O30.00[1,2,3]	Twin preg, unsp number of placenta and unsp number of amniotic sacs, [1st, 2nd, 3rd] trmstr
O30.01[1,2,3]	Twin preg, monochorionic/monoamniotic, [1st, 2nd, 3rd] trmstr
O30.02[1,2,3]	Conjoined twin preg, [1st, 2nd, 3rd] trmstr
O30.03[1,2,3]	Twin preg, monochorionic/diamniotic, [1st, 2nd, 3rd] trmstr
O30.04[1,2,3]	Twin preg, dichorionic/diamniotic, [1st, 2nd, 3rd] trmstr
O30.09[1,2,3]	Twin preg, unable to determine number of placenta and number of amniotic sacs, [1st, 2nd, 3rd] trmstr
O30.10[1,2,3]	Triplet preg, unsp number of placenta and unsp number of amniotic sacs, [1st, 2nd, 3rd] trmstr
O30.11[1,2,3]	Triplet preg w/ two or more monochorionic fetuses, [1st, 2nd, 3rd] trmstr
O30.12[1,2,3]	Triplet preg w/ two or more monoamniotic fetuses, [1st, 2nd, 3rd] trmstr
O30.19[1,2,3]	Triplet preg, unable to determine number of placenta and number of amniotic sacs, [1st, 2nd, 3rd] trmstr
O30.20[1,2,3]	Quadruplet preg, unsp number of placenta and unsp number of amniotic sacs, [1st, 2nd, 3rd] trmstr
O30.21[1,2,3]	Quadruplet preg w/ two or more monochorionic fetuses, [1st, 2nd, 3rd] trmstr
O30.22[1,2,3]	Quadruplet preg w/ two or more monoamniotic fetuses, [1st, 2nd, 3rd] trmstr
O30.29[1,2,3]	Quadruplet preg, unable to determine number of placenta and number of amniotic sacs, [1st, 2nd, 3rd] trmstr
O30.80[1,2,3]	Oth spec multi gestation, unsp number of placenta and unsp number of amniotic sacs, [1st, 2nd, 3rd] trmstr
O30.81[1,2,3]	Oth spec multi gestation w/ two or more monochorionic fetuses, [1st, 2nd, 3rd] trmstr
O30.82[1,2,3]	Oth spec multi gestation w/ two or more monoamniotic fetuses, [1st, 2nd, 3rd] trmstr
O30.89[1,2,3]	Oth spec multi gestation, unable to determine number of placenta and number of amniotic sacs, [1st, 2nd, 3rd] trmstr
O30.9[1,2,3]	Multi gestation, unsp, [1st, 2nd, 3rd] trmstr

Surgical   **Medical**   **CC Indicator**   **MCC Indicator**   **Procedure Proxy**   **PDx MCC** PDx acts as own MCC   **PDx CC** PDx acts as own CC

MDC 14: Pregnancy, Childbirth And The Puerperium—MEDICAL

MDC 14: Pregnancy, Childbirth And The Puerperium—MEDICAL

Code	Description
O31.0[0,1,2,3]X[0,1,2,3,4,5,9]	Papyraceous fetus, [unsp, 1st, 2nd, 3rd] trmstr, fetus [N/A or unsp, 1, 2, 3, 4, 5, oth]
O31.1[1,2,3]X[0,1,2,3,4,5,9]	Continuing preg after spontaneous abortion of one fetus or more, [1st, 2nd, 3rd] trmstr, fetus [N/A or unsp, 1, 2, 3, 4, 5, oth]
O31.2[1,2,3]X[0,1,2,3,4,5,9]	Continuing preg after intrauterine death of one fetus or more, [1st, 2nd, 3rd] trmstr, fetus [N/A or unsp, 1, 2, 3, 4, 5, oth]
O31.3[1,2,3]X[0,1,2,3,4,5,9]	Continuing preg after elective fetal reduction of one fetus or more, [1st, 2nd, 3rd] trmstr, fetus [N/A or unsp, 1, 2, 3, 4, 5, oth]
O31.8X[1,2,3][0,1,2,3,4,5,9]	Oth comps specific to multi gestation, [1st, 2nd, 3rd] trmstr, fetus [N/A or unsp, 1, 2, 3, 4, 5, oth]
O32*	Maternal care for malpresentation of fetus
O33.1	Matern care for disproprtn d/t generally contracted pelvis
O33.2	Matern care for disproprtn d/t inlet contrctn of pelvis
O33.3*	Matern care for disproprtn d/t outlet contrctn of pelvis
O33.4*	Matern care for disproprtn of mixed matern and fetal origin
O33.5*	Maternal care for disproportion d/t unusually large fetus
O33.6*	Maternal care for disproportion d/t hydrocephalic fetus
O33.7	Maternal care for disproportion d/t oth fetal deformities
O33.8	Maternal care for disproportion of oth origin
O33.9	Maternal care for disproportion, unsp
O34.2[1,9]	Maternal care d/t uterine scar from [previous cesarean delivery, oth previous surgery]
O34.5[1,2,3,9][1,2,3]	Maternal care for [incarceration, prolapse, retroversion, oth abnormalities] of gravid uterus, [1st, 2nd, 3rd] trmstr
O34.[0,1][1,2,3]	Maternal care for [congenital malformation of uterus, benign tumor of corpus uteri], [1st, 2nd, 3rd] trmstr
O34.[3,4][1,2,3]	Maternal care for [cervical incompetence, oth abnormalities of cervix], [1st, 2nd, 3rd] trmstr
O34.[6,7][1,2,3]	Maternal care for abnormality of [vagina, vulva and perineum], [1st, 2nd, 3rd] trmstr
O34.[8,9][1,2,3]	Maternal care for [oth, unsp] abnormalities of pelvic organs, [1st, 2nd, 3rd] trmstr
O35*	Maternal care for known or suspected fetal abnlt and damage
O36.0[1,9][1,2,3][0,1,2,3,4,5,9]	Maternal care for [anti-D (Rh) antibodies, oth rhesus isoimmunization], [1st, 2nd, 3rd] trmstr, fetus [N/A or unsp, 1, 2, 3, 4, 5, oth]
O36.1[1,9][1,2,3][0,1,2,3,4,5,9]	Maternal care for [anti-A (Rh) antibodies, oth isoimmunization], [1st, 2nd, 3rd] trmstr, fetus [N/A or unsp, 1, 2, 3, 4, 5, oth]
O36.2[1,2,3]X[0,1,2,3,4,5,9]	Maternal care for hydrops fetalis, [1st, 2nd, 3rd] trmstr, fetus [N/A or unsp, 1, 2, 3, 4, 5, oth]
O36.4XX[0,1,2,3,4,5,9]	Maternal care for intrauterine death, fetus [N/A or unsp, 1, 2, 3, 4, 5, oth]
O36.5[1,9][1,2,3][0,1,2,3,4,5,9]	Maternal care for [known or suspected placental insufficiency, oth known or suspected poor fetal growth], [1st, 2nd, 3rd] trmstr, fetus [N/A or unsp, 1, 2, 3, 4, 5, oth]
O36.6[1,2,3]X[0,1,2,3,4,5,9]	Maternal care for excessive fetal growth, [1st, 2nd, 3rd] trmstr, fetus [N/A or unsp, 1, 2, 3, 4, 5, oth]
O36.7[1,2,3]X[0,1,2,3,4,5,9]	Maternal care for viable fetus in abd preg, [1st, 2nd, 3rd] trmstr, fetus [N/A or unsp, 1, 2, 3, 4, 5, oth]
O36.81[2,3,9][0,1,2,3,4,5,9]	Decreased fetal movements [2nd, 3rd, unsp] trmstr, fetus [N/A or unsp, 1, 2, 3, 4, 5, oth]
O36.82[1,2,3][0,1,2,3,4,5,9]	Fetal anemia and thrombocytopnia, [1st, 2nd, 3rd] trmstr, fetus [N/A or unsp, 1, 2, 3, 4, 5, oth]
O36.89[1,2,3][0,1,2,3,4,5,9]	Maternal care for oth spec fetal problems, [1st, 2nd, 3rd] trmstr, fetus [N/A or unsp, 1, 2, 3, 4, 5, oth]
O36.9[1,2,3]X[0,1,2,3,4,5,9]	Maternal care for fetal problem, unsp [1st, 2nd, 3rd] trmstr, fetus [N/A or unsp, 1, 2, 3, 4, 5, oth]
O40.[1,2,3]XX[0,1,2,3,4,5,9]	Polyhydramnios, [1st, 2nd, 3rd] trmstr, fetus [N/A or unsp, 1, 2, 3, 4, 5, oth]
O41.0[1,2,3]X[0,1,2,3,4,5,9]	Oligohydramnios, [1st, 2nd, 3rd] trmstr, fetus [N/A or unsp, 1, 2, 3, 4, 5, oth]
O41.10[1,2,3,9][0,1,2,3,4,5,9]	Infxn of amniotic sac and membranes, unsp, [1st, 2nd, 3rd] trmstr, fetus [N/A or unsp, 1, 2, 3, 4, 5, oth]
O41.1[2,4][1,2,3,9][0,1,2,3,4,5,9]	[Chorioamnionitis, Placentitis], [1st, 2nd, 3rd, unsp] trmstr, fetus [N/A or unsp, 1, 2, 3, 4, 5, oth]
O41.8X[1,2,3][0,1,2,3,4,5,9]	Oth spec d/os of amniotic fluid and membranes, [1st, 2nd, 3rd] trmstr, fetus [N/A or unsp, 1, 2, 3, 4, 5, oth]
O41.9[1,2,3]X[0,1,2,3,4,5,9]	d/os of amniotic fluid and membranes, unsp, [1st, 2nd, 3rd] trmstr, fetus [N/A or unsp, 1, 2, 3, 4, 5, oth]
O42*	Premature rupture of membranes
O43.0[1,2][1,2,3]	[Fetomaternal, Fetus-to-fetus] placental transfusion synd, [1st, 2nd, 3rd] trmstr
O43.10[1,2,3]	Malformation of placenta, unsp, [1st, 2nd, 3rd] trmstr
O43.11[1,2,3]	Circumvallate placenta, [1st, 2nd, 3rd] trmstr
O43.19[1,2,3]	Oth malformation of placenta, [1st, 2nd, 3rd] trmstr
O43.81[1,2,3]	Placental infarction, [1st, 2nd, 3rd] trmstr
O43.89[1,2,3]	Oth placental d/os, [1st, 2nd, 3rd] trmstr
O43.9[1,2,3]	Unsp placental d/o, [1st, 2nd, 3rd] trmstr
O44.[0,1][1,2,3]	Placenta previa [spec as w/o hemor, w/ hemor], [1st, 2nd, 3rd] trmstr
O45.0[0,1,2,9][1,2,3]	Premature separation of placenta w/ [coagulation defect unsp, afibrinogenemia, disseminated intravascular coagulation, oth coagulation defect], [1st, 2nd, 3rd] trmstr
O45.8X[1,2,3]	Oth premature separation of placenta, [1st, 2nd, 3rd] trmstr
O45.9[1,2,3]	Premature separation of placenta, unsp, [1st, 2nd 3rd] trmstr
O46.0[0,1,2,9][1,2,3]	Antepartum hemor w/ [coagulation defect unsp, afibrinogenemia, disseminated intravascular coagulation, oth coagulation defect], [1st, 2nd, 3rd] trmstr
O46.8X[1,2,3]	Oth antepartum hemor, [1st, 2nd, 3rd] trmstr
O46.9[1,2,3]	Antepartum hemor, unsp, [1st, 2nd, 3rd] trmstr
O48*	Late preg
O60.10X[0,1,2,3,4,5,9]	Preterm labor w/ preterm delivery, unsp trmstr, fetus [N/A or unsp, 1, 2, 3, 4, 5, oth]
O60.20X[0,1,2,3,4,5,9]	Term delivery w/ preterm labor, unsp trmstr, fetus [N/A or unsp, 1, 2, 3, 4, 5, oth]
O61*	Failed induction of labor
O62*	Abnormalities of forces of labor
O63*	Long labor
O66.40	Failed trial of labor, unsp
O69.89X0	Labor and delivery complicated by oth cord comp, unsp
O69.8[1,2]X0	Labor and delivery comp by [cord around neck, oth cord entanglement], w/o compression, N/A or unsp
O71.0[2,3]	Rupture of uterus before onset of labor, [2nd, 3rd] trmstr
O75.2	Pyrexia during labor, NEC
O75.3	Oth infxn during labor
O75.89	Oth spec comp of labor and delivery
O75.9	Comp of labor and delivery, unsp
O76	Abnlt in fetal heart rate and rhythm comp labor and delivery
O88.[0,1,2,3,8]1[1,2,3]	[Air, Amniotic fluid, Thrombo-, Pyemic and septic, Oth] embolism in preg, [1st, 2nd, 3rd] trmstr
O91.01[1,2,3]	Infxn of nipple associated w/ preg, [1st, 2nd, 3rd] trmstr
O91.11[1,2,3]	Abscess of breast associated w/ preg, [1st, 2nd, 3rd] trmstr
O91.21[1,2,3]	Nonpurulent mastitis associated w/ preg, [1st, 2nd, 3rd] trmstr
O92.[0,1]1[1,2,3]	[Retracted, Cracked] nipple associated w/ preg, [1st, 2nd, 3rd] trmstr
O98.[0,1,2,3,4,5,6,7,8,9]1[1,2,3]	[Tuberculosis, Syphilis, Gonorrhea, Oth infxns w/ predominantly sexual mode of transmission, Viral hepatitis, Oth viral dzs, Protozoal dzs, Human immunodef virus (HIV) dz, Oth maternal infectious and parasitic dzs, Unsp maternal infectious and parasitic dzs] compl preg, [1st, 2nd, 3rd] trmstr
O99.01[1,2,3]	Anemia compl preg, [1st, 2nd, 3rd] trmstr
O99.11[1,2,3]	Oth dzs of the bld and bld-forming organs and certain d/os involving the immune mech compl preg, [1st, 2nd, 3rd] trmstr
O99.21[1,2,3]	Obesity compl preg, [1st, 2nd, 3rd] trmstr
O99.28[1,2,3]	Endocrine, nutritional and metabolic dzs compl preg, [1st, 2nd, 3rd] trmstr
O99.31[1,2,3]	Alcohol use compl preg, [1st, 2nd, 3rd] trmstr
O99.32[1,2,3]	Drug use compl preg, [1st, 2nd, 3rd] trmstr
O99.33[1,2,3]	Smoking (tobacco) compl preg, [1st, 2nd, 3rd] trmstr
O99.34[1,2,3]	Oth mental d/os compl preg, [1st, 2nd, 3rd] trmstr
O99.35[1,2,3]	Dz of the nervous sys compl preg, [1st, 2nd, 3rd] trmstr
O99.41[1,2,3]	Dz of the circulatory sys compl preg, [1st, 2nd, 3rd] trmstr
O99.51[1,2,3]	Dz of the respiratory sys compl preg, [1st, 2nd, 3rd] trmstr
O99.61[1,2,3]	Dz of the digestive sys compl preg, [1st, 2nd, 3rd] trmstr
O99.71[1,2,3]	Dz of the skin and SQ tissue compl preg, [1st, 2nd, 3rd] trmstr
O99.84[1,2,3]	Bariatric surgery status compl preg, [frist, 2nd, 3rd] trmstr
O99.89	Oth dz and conditions compl preg/chldbrth
O9A.11[1,2,3]	Malig neoplasm compl preg, [1st, 2nd, 3rd] trmstr
O9A.21[1,2,3]	Inj, poison and certain oth consequences of ext causes compl preg, [1st, 2nd, 3rd] trmstr
O9A.31[1,2,3]	Physical abuse compl preg, [1st, 2nd, 3rd] trmstr
O9A.41[1,2,3]	Sexual abuse compl preg, [1st, 2nd, 3rd] trmstr
O9A.51[1,2,3]	Psychological abuse compl preg, [1st, 2nd, 3rd] trmstr

AND

SECONDARY DIAGNOSIS

Code	Description
O10.011	Pre-existing essential hypertension comp preg, first trmstr
O10.012	Pre-existing essential hypertension comp preg, second trmstr
O10.013	Pre-existing essential hypertension comp preg, third trmstr
O10.111	Pre-exist hyp heart dz comp preg, first trmstr
O10.112	Pre-exist hyp heart dz comp preg, second trmstr
O10.113	Pre-exist hyp heart dz comp preg, third trmstr
O10.211	Pre-exist hyp chr kidney dz comp preg, first trmstr
O10.212	Pre-exist hyp chr kidney dz comp preg, second trmstr
O10.213	Pre-exist hyp chr kidney dz comp preg, third trmstr
O10.311	Pre-exist hyp heart and CKD comp preg, first trmstr
O10.312	Pre-exist hyp heart and CKD comp preg, second trmstr

T Transfer DRG   SP Special Payment   * Code Range   **6th and 7th Character of ZZ = No Device, No Qualifier ZX = No Device, Diagnostic**

O10.313	Pre-exist hyp heart and CKD comp preg, third trmstr
O10.411	Pre-existing secondary hypertension comp preg, first trmstr
O10.412	Pre-existing secondary hypertension comp preg, 2nd trmstr
O10.413	Pre-existing secondary hypertension comp preg, third trmstr
O10.911	Unsp pre-existing hypertension comp preg, first trmstr
O10.912	Unsp pre-existing hypertension comp preg, second trmstr
O10.913	Unsp pre-existing hypertension comp preg, third trmstr
O11.1	Pre-existing hypertension w pre-eclampsia, first trmstr
O11.2	Pre-existing hypertension w pre-eclampsia, second trmstr
O11.3	Pre-existing hypertension w pre-eclampsia, third trmstr
O11.9	Pre-existing hypertension with pre-eclampsia, unsp trmstr
O12.00	Gestational edema, unsp trmstr
O12.01	Gestational edema, first trmstr
O12.02	Gestational edema, second trmstr
O12.03	Gestational edema, third trmstr
O12.10	Gestational proteinuria, unsp trmstr
O12.11	Gestational proteinuria, first trmstr
O12.12	Gestational proteinuria, second trmstr
O12.13	Gestational proteinuria, third trmstr
O12.20	Gestational edema with proteinuria, unsp trmstr
O12.21	Gestational edema with proteinuria, first trmstr **PDxCC**
O12.22	Gestational edema with proteinuria, second trmstr **PDxCC**
O12.23	Gestational edema with proteinuria, third trmstr **PDxCC**
O14.02	Mild to mod pre-eclampsia, second trmstr
O14.03	Mild to mod pre-eclampsia, third trmstr
O14.10	Severe pre-eclampsia, unsp trmstr
O14.12	Severe pre-eclampsia, second trmstr
O14.13	Severe pre-eclampsia, third trmstr
O14.20	HELLP synd (HELLP), unsp trmstr
O14.22	HELLP synd (HELLP), second trmstr
O14.23	HELLP synd (HELLP), third trmstr
O14.92	Unsp pre-eclampsia, second trmstr
O14.93	Unsp pre-eclampsia, third trmstr
O15.00	Eclampsia in preg, unsp trmstr
O15.02	Eclampsia in preg, second trmstr
O15.03	Eclampsia in preg, third trmstr
O15.9	Eclampsia, unsp as to time period
O16.1	Unsp maternal hypertension, first trmstr
O16.2	Unsp maternal hypertension, second trmstr
O16.3	Unsp maternal hypertension, third trmstr
O21.0	Mild hyperemesis gravidarum
O21.1	Hyperemesis gravidarum with metabolic disturbance
O21.2	Late vomiting of preg
O21.8	Oth vomiting compl preg
O21.9	Vomiting of preg, unsp
O23.00	Infections of kidney in preg, unsp trmstr
O23.01	Infections of kidney in preg, first trmstr
O23.02	Infections of kidney in preg, second trmstr
O23.03	Infections of kidney in preg, third trmstr
O23.10	Infections of bladder in preg, unsp trmstr
O23.11	Infections of bladder in preg, first trmstr
O23.12	Infections of bladder in preg, second trmstr
O23.13	Infections of bladder in preg, third trmstr
O23.20	Infections of urethra in preg, unsp trmstr
O23.21	Infections of urethra in preg, first trmstr
O23.22	Infections of urethra in preg, second trmstr
O23.23	Infections of urethra in preg, third trmstr
O23.30	Infections of prt urinary tract in preg, unsp trmstr
O23.31	Infect of prt urinary tract in preg, first trmstr

DRG 782   Other Antepartum Diagnoses without Medical Complications
GMLOS 1.7 AMLOS 2.5 RW 0.5454

Principal Diagnosis

O01*	Hydatidiform mole
O02.0	Blighted ovum and nonhydatidiform mole
O02.8*	Oth specified abnormal products of conception
O02.9	Abnormal product of conception, unsp
O09.4[1,2,3]	Supervision of preg w grand multiparity, [1st, 2nd, 3rd] trmstr
O13.[1,2,3]	Gestational (preg-induced) hypertension without significant proteinuria, [1st, 2nd, 3rd] trmstr
O22.8X[1,2,3]	Oth venous comp in preg, [1st, 2nd, 3rd] trmstr
O22.9[1,2,3]	Venous complication in preg, unsp, [1st, 2nd, 3rd] trmstr
O22.[0,1,2,3,4,5][1,2,3]	[Varicose veins of lwr extremity, Genital varices, Superficial thrombophlebitis, Hemorrhoids, Cerebral venous thrombosis] in preg, [1st, 2nd, 3rd] trmstr
O26.2[1,2,3]	Preg care for patient w recurrent preg loss, [1st, 2nd, 3rd] trmstr
O26.5*	Maternal hypotension syndrome

O26.84[1,2,3]	Uterine size-date discrepancy, [1st, 2nd, 3rd] trmstr
O26.85[1,2,3]	Spotting comp preg, [1st, 2nd, 3rd] trmstr
O26.87[2,3]	Cervical shortening, [second, third] trmstr
O28*	Abnormal findings on antenatal screening of mother
O30.0[0,1,2,3,4,9][1,2,3]	Twin preg, [unsp number of placenta and unsp number of amniotic sacs, monoamniotic/monochorionic, conjoined twin preg, monochorionic/diamniotic, dichorionic/diamniotic, unable to determine number of placenta and amniotic sacs], [1st, 2nd, 3rd] trmstr
O30.1[0,1,2,9][1,2,3]	Triplet preg [unsp, two or more monochorionic fetuses, two or more monoamniotic fetuses, unable to determine the number of placenta and amniotic sacs], [1st, 2nd, 3rd] trmstr
O30.2[0,1,2,9][1,2,3]	Quadruplet preg [unsp, two or more monochorionic fetuses, two or more monoamniotic fetuses, unable to determine the number of placenta and amniotic sacs], [1st, 2nd, 3rd] trmstr
O30.8[0,1,2,9][1,2,3]	Oth specified multiple gestation, [unsp number of placenta and amniotic sacs, two or more monochorionic fetuses, two or more monoamniotic fetuses, unable to determine the number of placenta and amniotic sacs], [1st, 2nd, 3rd] trmstr
O30.9[1,2,3]	Multiple gestation, unsp, [1st, 2nd, 3rd] trmstr
O31.0*	Papyraceous fetus
O31.1[1,2,3]X[0,1,2,3,4,5,9]	Continuing preg after spontaneous abortion of one fetus or more, [1st, 2nd, 3rd] trmstr, fetus [N/A or unsp, 1, 2, 3, 4, 5, oth]
O31.2[1,2,3]X[0,1,2,3,4,5,9]	Continuing preg after intrauterine death of one fetus or more, [1st, 2nd, 3rd] trmstr, fetus [N/A or unsp, 1, 2, 3, 4, 5, oth]
O31.3[1,2,3]X[0,1,2,3,4,5,9]	Continuing preg after elective fetal reduction of one fetus or more, [1st, 2nd, 3rd] trmstr, fetus [N/A or unsp, 1, 2, 3, 4, 5, oth]
O31.8X[1,2,3][0,1,2,3,4,5,9]	Oth comp specific to multiple gestation, [1st, 2nd, 3rd] trmstr, fetus [N/A or unsp, 1, 2, 3, 4, 5, oth]
O32*	Maternal care for malpresentation of fetus
O33.1	Maternal care for disproportion d/t generally contracted pelvis
O33.2	Maternal care for disproportion d/t inlet contraction of pelvis
O33.3*	Maternal care for disproportion d/t outlet contraction of pelvis
O33.4*	Maternal care for disproportion of mixed maternal and fetal origin
O33.5*	Maternal care for disproportion d/t unusually large fetus
O33.6*	Maternal care for disproportion d/t hydrocephalic fetus
O33.7	Maternal care for disproportion d/t oth fetal deformities
O33.8	Maternal care for disproportion of oth origin
O33.9	Maternal care for disproportion, unsp
O34.2*	Maternal care d/t uterine scar from previous surgery
O34.5[1,2,3,9][1,2,3]	Maternal care for [incarceration, prolapse, retroversion, oth abnormalities] of gravid uterus, [1st, 2nd, 3rd] trmstr
O34.[0,1][1,2,3]	Maternal care for [congenital malformation of uterus, benign tumor of corpus uteri], [1st, 2nd, 3rd] trmstr
O34.[3,4][1,2,3]	Maternal care for [cervical incompetence, oth abnormalities of cervix], [1st, 2nd, 3rd] trmstr
O34.[6,7][1,2,3]	Maternal care for abnormality of [vagina, vulva and perineum], [1st, 2nd, 3rd] trmstr
O34.[8,9][1,2,3]	Maternal care for [oth, unsp] abnormalities of pelvic organs, [1st, 2nd, 3rd] trmstr
O35*	Maternal care for known or suspected fetal abnormality and damage
O36.0[1,9][1,2,3][0,1,2,3,4,5,9]	Maternal care for [anti-D (Rh) antibodies, oth rhesus isoimmunization], [1st, 2nd, 3rd] trmstr, fetus [N/A or unsp, 1, 2, 3, 4, 5, oth]
O36.1[1,9][1,2,3][0,1,2,3,4,5,9]	Maternal care for [anti-A (Rh) antibodies, oth isoimmunization], [1st, 2nd, 3rd] trmstr, fetus [N/A or unsp, 1, 2, 3, 4, 5, oth]
O36.2[1,2,3]X[0,1,2,3,4,5,9]	Maternal care for hydrops fetalis, [1st, 2nd, 3rd] trmstr, fetus [N/A or unsp, 1, 2, 3, 4, 5, oth]
O36.4*	Maternal care for intrauterine death
O36.5[1,9][1,2,3][0,1,2,3,4,5,9]	Maternal care for [known or suspected placental insufficiency, oth known or suspected poor fetal growth], [1st, 2nd, 3rd] trmstr, fetus [N/A or unsp, 1, 2, 3, 4, 5, oth]
O36.6[1,2,3]X[0,1,2,3,4,5,9]	Maternal care for excessive fetal growth, [1st, 2nd, 3rd] trmstr, fetus [N/A or unsp, 1, 2, 3, 4, 5, oth]
O36.7[1,2,3]X[0,1,2,3,4,5,9]	Maternal care for viable fetus in abdominal preg, [1st, 2nd, 3rd] trmstr, fetus [N/A or unsp, 1, 2, 3, 4, 5, oth]
O36.81[2,3,9][0,1,2,3,4,5,9]	Decreased fetal movements [second, third, unsp] trmstr, fetus [N/A or unsp, 1, 2, 3, 4, 5, oth]
O36.82[1,2,3][0,1,2,3,4,5,9]	Fetal anemia and thrombocytopenia, [1st, 2nd, 3rd] trmstr, fetus [N/A or unsp, 1, 2, 3, 4, 5, oth]

Surgical	**Medical**	**CC Indicator**	**MCC Indicator**	**Procedure Proxy**	**PDxMCC** PDx acts as own MCC	**PDxCC** PDx acts as own CC

MDC 14: Pregnancy, Childbirth And The Puerperium—MEDICAL

O36.89[1,2,3][0,1,2,3,4,5,9] Maternal care for oth specified fetal problems, [1st, 2nd, 3rd] trmstr, fetus [N/A or unsp, 1, 2, 3, 4, 5, oth]
O36.9[1,2,3]X[0,1,2,3,4,5,9] Maternal care for fetal problem, unsp [1st, 2nd, 3rd] trmstr, fetus [N/A or unsp, 1, 2, 3, 4, 5, oth]
O40.1* Polyhydramnios, first trmstr
O40.2* Polyhydramnios, second trmstr
O40.3* Polyhydramnios, third trmstr
O41.0[1,2,3]X[0,1,2,3,4,5,9] Oligohydramnios, [1st, 2nd, 3rd] trmstr, fetus [N/A or unsp, 1, 2, 3, 4, 5, oth]
O41.1* Infection of amniotic sac and membranes
O41.8X[1,2,3][0,1,2,3,4,5,9] Oth specified disorders of amniotic fluid and membranes, [1st, 2nd, 3rd] trmstr, fetus [N/A or unsp, 1, 2, 3, 4, 5, oth]
O41.9[1,2,3]X[0,1,2,3,4,5,9] Disorders of amniotic fluid and membranes, unsp, [1st, 2nd, 3rd] trmstr, fetus [N/A or unsp, 1, 2, 3, 4, 5, oth]
O42* Premature rupture of membranes
O43.0[1,2][1,2,3] [Fetomaternal, Fetus-to-fetus] placental transfusion syndrome, [1st, 2nd, 3rd] trmstr
O43.1[0,1,9][1,2,3] [Unsp malformation of, Circumvallate, Oth malformation of] placenta, [1st, 2nd, 3rd] trmstr
O43.8[1,9][1,2,3] [Placental infarction, Oth placental d/o], [1st, 2nd, 3rd] trmstr
O43.9[1,2,3] Unsp placental disorder, [1st, 2nd, 3rd] trmstr
O44.[0,1][1,2,3] Placenta previa [specified as without hemor, w hemor], [1st, 2nd, 3rd] trmstr
O45.8X[1,2,3] Oth premature separation of placenta, [1st, 2nd, 3rd] trmstr
O45.9[1,2,3] Premature separation of placenta, unsp, [1st, 2nd, 3rd] trmstr
O46.8X[1,2,3] Oth antepartum hemor, [1st, 2nd, 3rd] trmstr
O46.9[1,2,3] Antepartum hemor, unsp, [1st, 2nd, 3rd] trmstr
O48* Late preg
O60.10X[0,1,2,3,4,5,9] Preterm labor w preterm delivery, unsp trmstr, fetus [N/A or unsp, 1, 2, 3, 4, 5, oth]
O60.20X[0,1,2,3,4,5,9] Term delivery w preterm labor, unsp trmstr, fetus [N/A or unsp, 1, 2, 3, 4, 5, oth]
O61* Failed induction of labor
O62* Abnormalities of forces of labor
O63* Long labor
O66.40 Failed trial of labor, unsp
O69.8[1,2,9]X0 Labor and delivery compl by [cord around neck without compression, oth cord entanglement without compression, oth cord compl], N/A or unsp
O71.0[2,3] Rupture of uterus before onset of labor, [second, third] trmstr
O75.2 Pyrexia during labor, NEC
O75.3 Oth infection during labor
O75.89 Oth specified comp of labor and delivery
O75.9 Complication of labor and delivery, unsp
O76 Abnormality in fetal heart rate & rhythm comp labor & delivery
O88.[0,1,2,3,8]1[1,2,3] [Air, Amniotic fluid, Thrombo-, Pyemic and septic, Oth] embolism in preg, [1st, 2nd, 3rd] trmstr
O91.[0,1,2]1[1,2,3] [Infection of nipple, Abscess of breast, Nonpurulent mastitis] associated w preg, [1st, 2nd, 3rd] trmstr
O92.[0,1]1[1,2,3] [Retracted, Cracked] nipple associated w preg, [1st, 2nd, 3rd] trmstr
O99.11[1,2,3] Oth diseases of the blood and blood-forming organs and certain disorders involving the immune mechanism comp preg, [1st, 2nd, 3rd] trmstr
O99.21[1,2,3] Obesity comp preg, [1st, 2nd, 3rd] trmstr
O99.33[1,2,3] Smoking (tobacco) comp preg, [1st, 2nd, 3rd] trmstr
O99.84[1,2,3] Bariatric surgery status comp preg, [1st, 2nd, 3rd] trmstr

DRG 998 Principal Diagnosis Invalid as Discharge Diagnosis
GMLOS 0.0   AMLOS 0.0   RW 0.0000

Note: If there is no value in either the GMLOS or the ALMOS, the volume of cases is insufficient to determine meaningful computation of these statistics.

Principal Diagnosis

O09.0* Supervision of preg with history of infertility
O09.1* Suprvsn of preg w history of ectopic or molar preg
O09.2* Suprvsn of preg w poor reprodctv or obstetric history
O09.3* Supervision of preg with insufficient antenatal care
O09.40 Supervision of preg w grand multiparity, unsp trmstr
O09.5* Supervision of elderly primigravida and multigravida
O09.6* Supervision of young primigravida and multigravida
O09.7* Supervision of high risk preg d/t social problems
O09.8* Supervision of oth high risk pregnancies
O09.9* Supervision of high risk preg, unsp
O10.019 Pre-existing essential hypertension comp preg, unsp trmstr
O10.119 Pre-exist hyp heart dz comp preg, unsp trmstr

O10.219 Pre-exist hyp chr kidney dz comp preg, unsp trmstr
O10.319 Pre-exist hyp heart and CKD comp preg, unsp trmstr
O10.419 Pre-existing secondary hypertension comp preg, unsp trmstr
O10.919 Unsp pre-existing hypertension comp preg, unsp trmstr
O11.9 Pre-existing hypertension with pre-eclampsia, unsp trmstr
O12.00 Gestational edema, unsp trmstr
O12.10 Gestational proteinuria, unsp trmstr
O12.20 Gestational edema with proteinuria, unsp trmstr
O13.9 Gestational hypertension w/o signif proteinuria, unsp trmstr
O14.00 Mild to mod pre-eclampsia, unsp trmstr
O14.10 Severe pre-eclampsia, unsp trmstr
O14.20 HELLP synd (HELLP), unsp trmstr
O14.90 Unsp pre-eclampsia, unsp trmstr
O15.00 Eclampsia in preg, unsp trmstr
O15.9 Eclampsia, unsp as to time period
O16.9 Unsp maternal hypertension, unsp trmstr
O22.00 Varicose veins of low extrm in preg, unsp trmstr
O22.10 Genital varices in preg, unsp trmstr
O22.20 Superf thrombophlebitis in preg, unsp trmstr
O22.30 Deep phlebothrombosis in preg, unsp trmstr
O22.40 Hemorrhoids in preg, unsp trmstr
O22.50 Cerebral venous thrombosis in preg, unsp trmstr
O22.8X9 Oth venous comp in preg, unsp trmstr
O22.90 Venous comp in preg, unsp, unsp trmstr
O23.00 Infections of kidney in preg, unsp trmstr
O23.10 Infections of bladder in preg, unsp trmstr
O23.20 Infections of urethra in preg, unsp trmstr
O23.30 Infections of prt urinary tract in preg, unsp trmstr
O23.40 Unsp infxn of urinary tract in preg, unsp trmstr
O23.519 Infections of cervix in preg, unsp trmstr
O23.529 Salpingo-oophoritis in preg, unsp trmstr
O23.599 Infxn oth prt genital tract in preg, unsp trmstr
O23.90 Unsp GU tract infxn in preg, unsp trmstr
O24.019 Pre-existing diabetes, type 1, in preg, unsp trmstr
O24.119 Pre-existing diabetes, type 2, in preg, unsp trmstr
O24.319 Unsp pre-existing diabetes in preg, unsp trmstr
O24.819 Oth pre-existing diabetes in preg, unsp trmstr
O24.919 Unsp diabetes mellitus in preg, unsp trmstr
O25.10 Malnut in preg, unsp trmstr
O26.00 Excessive weight gain in preg, unsp trmstr
O26.10 Low weight gain in preg, unsp trmstr
O26.20 Preg care for patient w recurrent preg loss, unsp trmstr
O26.30 Retained uterin contracep dev in preg, unsp trmstr
O26.40 Herpes gestationis, unsp trmstr
O26.619 Liver and biliary tract d/o in preg, unsp trmstr
O26.719 Sublux of symphysis (pubis) in preg, unsp trmstr
O26.819 Preg related exhaustion and fatigue, unsp trmstr
O26.829 Preg related peripheral neuritis, unsp trmstr
O26.839 Preg related renal dz, unsp trmstr
O26.849 Uterine size-date discrepancy, unsp trmstr
O26.859 Spotting compl preg, unsp trmstr
O26.879 Cervical shortening, unsp trmstr
O26.899 Oth preg related conditions, unsp trmstr
O26.90 Preg related conditions, unsp, unsp trmstr
O29.019 Aspirat pneumonitis d/t anesth during preg, unsp trmstr
O29.029 Pressr collapse of lung d/t anesth during preg, unsp trmstr
O29.099 Oth pulmn comp of anesth during preg, unsp trmstr
O29.199 Oth cardiac comp of anesth during preg, unsp trmstr
O29.1[1,2]9 Cardiac [arrest, failure] d/t anesthesia druing preg, unsp trmstr
O29.219 Cerebral anoxia d/t anesth during preg, unsp trmstr
O29.299 Oth cnsl comp of anesthesia during preg, unsp trmstr
O29.3X9 Txc reaction to local anesth during preg, unsp trmstr
O29.40 Spinal and epidur anesth induce hdache during preg, unsp trmstr
O29.5X9 Oth comp of spinal and epidural anesth during preg, unsp trmstr
O29.60 Failed or difficult intubation for anesth dur preg, unsp trmstr
O29.8X9 Oth comp of anesthesia during preg, unsp trmstr
O29.90 Unsp comp of anesthesia during preg, unsp trmstr
O30.029 Conjoined twin preg, unsp trmstr
O30.0[0,1,3,4,9]9 Twin preg, [unsp number of placenta and unsp number of amniotic sacs, monochorionic/monoamniotic, monochorionic/diamniotic, dichorionic/diamniotic, unable to determine number of placenta and number of amniotic sacs], unsp trmstr
O30.1[0,1,2,9]9 Triplet preg, [unsp number of placenta and unsp number of amniotic sacs, two or more monochorionic fetuses, two or more monoamniotic fetuses, unable to determine the number of placenta and amniotic sacs], unsp trmstr

⊤ Transfer DRG   ⑤ᴾ Special Payment   * Code Range   6th and 7th Character of ZZ = No Device, No Qualifier ZX = No Device, Diagnostic

280   MS-DRG Version 33.0   © 2015 Optum360, LLC

O30.2[0,1,2,9]9	Quadruplet preg, [unsp number of placenta and unsp number of amniotic sacs, two or more monochorionic fetuses, two or more monoamniotic fetuses, unable to determine the number of placenta and amniotic sacs], unsp trmstr
O30.8[0,1,2,9]9	Oth spec multi gestation, [unsp, two or more monochorionic fetuses, two or more monoamniotic fetuses, unable to determine the number of placenta and amniotic sacs], unsp trmstr
O30.90	Multi gestation, unsp, unsp trmstr
O31.8X9[0,1,2,3,4,5,9]	Oth comps specific to multi gestation, unsp trmstr, fetus [N/A or unsp, 1, 2, 3, 4, 5, oth]
O31.[1,2,3]0X[0,1,2,3,4,5,9]	Continuing preg after [spontaneous abortion, intrauterine death, elective fetal reduction] of one fetus or more, unsp trmstr, fetus [N/A or unsp, 1, 2, 3, 4, 5, oth]
O34.00	Maternal care for unsp congen malform of uterus, unsp trmstr
O34.10	Maternal care for benign tumor of corpus uteri, unsp trmstr
O34.30	Maternal care for cervical incompetence, unsp trmstr
O34.40	Maternal care for oth abnlt of cervix, unsp trmstr
O34.519	Maternal care for incarceration of gravid uterus, unsp trmstr
O34.529	Maternal care for prolapse of gravid uterus, unsp trmstr
O34.539	Maternal care for retroversion of gravid uterus, unsp trmstr
O34.599	Maternal care for oth abnlt of gravid uterus, unsp trmstr
O34.60	Maternal care for abnormality of vagina, unsp trmstr
O34.70	Maternal care for abnlt of vulva and perineum, unsp trmstr
O34.80	Maternal care for oth abnlt of pelvic organs, unsp trmstr
O34.90	Maternal care for abnlt of pelvic organ, unsp, unsp trmstr
O36.0[1,9]9[0,1,2,3,4,5,9]	Maternal care for [anti-D (Rh) antibodies, oth isoimmunization], fetus [N/A or unsp, 1,2,3,4,5, oth]
O36.1[1,9]9[0,1,2,3,4,5,9]	Maternal care for [anti-A (Rh) antibodies, oth isoimmunization], unsp trmstr, fetus [N/A or unsp, 1, 2, 3, 4, oth]
O36.20X[0,1,2,3,4,5,9]	Maternal care for hydrops fetalis, unsp trmstr, fetus [N/A or unsp, 1, 2, 3, 4, oth]
O36.519[0,1,2,3,4,5,9]	Maternal care for known or suspected placental insufficiency, unsp trmstr, fetus [N/A or unsp, 1, 2, 3, 4, 5, oth]
O36.599[0,1,2,3,4,5,9]	Maternal care for oth known or suspected poor fetal growth, unsp trmstr, fetus [N/A or unsp, 1, 2, 3, 4, 5, oth]
O36.60X[0,1,2,3,4,5,9]	Maternal care for excessive fetal growth, unsp trmstr, fetus [N/A or unsp, 1, 2, 3, 4, 5, oth]
O36.70X[0,1,2,3,4,5,9]	Maternal care for viable fetus in abd preg, unsp trmstr, fetus [not appicable or unsp, 1, 2, 3, 4, 5, oth]
O36.80X0	Preg w inconclusive fetal viability, unsp
O36.80X1	Preg with inconclusive fetal viability, fetus 1
O36.80X2	Preg with inconclusive fetal viability, fetus 2
O36.80X3	Preg with inconclusive fetal viability, fetus 3
O36.80X4	Preg with inconclusive fetal viability, fetus 4
O36.80X5	Preg with inconclusive fetal viability, fetus 5
O36.80X9	Preg with inconclusive fetal viability, oth fetus
O36.829[0,1,2,3,4,5,9]	Maternal care for fetal anemia and thromboscytopnia, unsp trmstr, fetus [N/A or unsp, 1, 2, 3, 4, 5, oth]
O36.899[0,1,2,3,4,5,9]	Maternal care for oth spec fetal problems, unsp trmstr, fetus [N/A or unsp, 1, 2, 3, 4, 5, oth]
O36.90X[0,1,2,3,4,5,9]	Maternal care for fetal problem, unsp, unsp trmstr, fetus [N/A or unsp, 1, 2, 3, 4 5, oth]
O40.9*	Polyhydramnios, unsp trmstr
O41.00X[0,1,2,3,4,5,9]	Oligohydramnios, unsp trmstr, fetus [N/A or unsp, 1 2, 3, 4, 5, oth]
O41.8X9[0,1,2,3,4,5,9]	Oth spec d/os of amniotic fluid and membranes, unsp trmstr, fetus [N/A or unsp, 1, 2, 3, 4, 5, oth]
O41.90X[0,1,2,3,4,5,9]	D/o of amniotic fluid and membranes, unsp, unsp trmstr, fetus [N/A or unsp, 1, 2, 3, 4, 5, oth]
O43.019	Fetomaternal placental transfusion synd, unsp trmstr
O43.029	Fetus-to-fetus placental transfusion synd, unsp trmstr
O43.109	Malformation of placenta, unsp, unsp trmstr
O43.119	Circumvallate placenta, unsp trmstr
O43.121	Velamentous insert of umbilical cord, first trmstr
O43.122	Velamentous insert of umbilical cord, second trmstr
O43.123	Velamentous insert of umbilical cord, third trmstr
O43.129	Velamentous insert of umbilical cord, unsp trmstr
O43.199	Oth malformation of placenta, unsp trmstr
O43.2[1,2,3]9	Placenta [accreta, increta, percreta], unsp trmstr
O43.819	Placental infarction, unsp trmstr
O43.899	Oth placental d/o, unsp trmstr
O43.90	Unsp placental d/o, unsp trmstr
O44.00	Placenta previa spec as w/o hemor, unsp trmstr
O44.10	Placenta previa with hemor, unsp trmstr
O45.0[0,1,2,9]9	Premature separation of placenta w/ [coagulation defect unsp, afibrinogenemia, disseminated intravascular coagulation, oth coagulation defect], unsp trmstr
O45.8X9	Oth premature separation of placenta, unsp trmstr

O45.90	Premature separation of placenta, unsp, unsp trmstr
O46.0[0,1,2,9]9	Antepartum hemor w/ [coagulation defect unsp, afibrinogenemia, disseminated intrascular coagulation, ohter coagulation defect], unsp trmstr
O46.8X9	Oth antepartum hemor, unsp trmstr
O46.90	Antepartum hemor, unsp, unsp trmstr
O88.[0,1,2,3,8]19	[Air, Amniotic fluid, Thrombo-, Pyemic and septic, Oth] embolism, unsp trmstr
O91.[0,1,2]19	[Infxn of nipple, Abcess of breast, Nonpurulent mastitis] associated w/ preg, unsp trmstr
O92.019	Retracted nipple associated with preg, unsp trmstr
O92.119	Cracked nipple associated with preg, unsp trmstr
O94	Sequelae of comp of preg, chldbrth, and the puerperium
O98.[0,1,2,3,4,5,6,7,8,9]19	[Tuberculosis, Syphilis, Gonorrhea, Oth sexually transmitted dz, Viral hepatitis, Oth viral dzs, Protozoal dzs, HIV, Oth maternal infectious and parasitic dzs, Unsp maternal infectious and parasitic dzs] compl preg, childbirth and the puerperium, unsp trmstr
O99.019	Anemia compl preg, unsp trmstr
O99.119	Oth dis of bld/bld-form org/immun mechnsm comp preg,unsp trmstr
O99.210	Obesity compl preg, unsp trmstr
O99.280	Endo, nutritional and metab dz comp preg, unsp trmstr
O99.3[1,2,3,4,5]0	[Alcohol use, Drug use, Smoking (tobacco), Oth mental d/os, Dz of the nervous sys] compl preg, childbirth and puerperium, unsp trmstr
O99.419	Dz of the circ sys comp preg, unsp trmstr
O99.519	Dz of the resp sys comp preg, unsp trmstr
O99.619	Dz of the dgstv sys comp preg, unsp trmstr
O99.719	Dz of the skin, SQ comp preg, unsp trmstr
O99.840	Bariatric surgery status comp preg, unsp trmstr
O9A.119	Malig neoplasm compl preg, unsp trmstr
O9A.219	Inj/poisn/oth conseq of ext causes comp preg, unsp trmstr
O9A.319	Physical abuse compl preg, unsp trmstr
O9A.419	Sexual abuse compl preg, unsp trmstr
O9A.519	Psychological abuse compl preg, unsp trmstr

Surgical   **Medical**   **CC Indicator**   **MCC Indicator**   **Procedure Proxy**   **PDxMCC PDx acts as own MCC**   **PDxCC PDx acts as own CC**

MDC 15
Newborns And Other Neonates With Conditions Originating In The Perinatal Period

MEDICAL

DRG 789   **Neonates, Died or Transferred to Another Acute Care Facility**
  GMLOS 1.8   AMLOS 1.8   RW 1.5860

Discharge status of transfer to an acute care facility or expired

DRG 790   **Extreme Immaturity or Respiratory Distress Syndrome, Neonate**
  GMLOS 17.9   AMLOS 17.9   RW 5.2300

Principal or Secondary Diagnosis

P07.0[1,2,3]	Extremely low birth weight newborn, [< 500, 500-749, 750-999] grams
P07.2[1,2,3,4,5]	Extreme immaturity of newborn, gestational age [< 23, 23, 24, 25, 26] completed weeks
P22.0	Respiratory distress synd of newborn

DRG 791   **Prematurity with Major Problems**
  GMLOS 13.3   AMLOS 13.3   RW 3.5719

Principal or Secondary Diagnosis

P07.00	Extremely low birth weight newborn, unsp weight
P07.1*	Oth low birth weight newborn
P07.26	Extreme immaturity of NB, gestational age 27 compl weeks
P07.3*	Preterm [premature] newborn [oth]

AND

Principal or secondary diagnosis listed under DRG 793

DRG 792   **Prematurity without Major Problems**
  GMLOS 8.6   AMLOS 8.6   RW 2.1552

Principal or Secondary Diagnosis

P07.00	Extremely low birth weight newborn, unsp weight
P07.1*	Oth low birth weight newborn
P07.26	Extreme immaturity of NB, gestational age 27 compl weeks
P07.3*	Preterm [premature] newborn [oth]

DRG 793   **Full Term Neonate with Major Problems**
  GMLOS 4.7   AMLOS 4.7   RW 3.6692

Principal or secondary diagnosis

E84.11	Meconium ileus in cystic fibrosis
P03.4	Newborn (suspected to be) affected by Cesarean delivery
P05.1[1,2,3,4,5,6,7,8]	Newborn sm for gestational age, [< 500, 500-749, 750-999, 1000-1249, 1250-1499,1500-1749, 1750-1999, 2000-2499] grams
P05.2	Newborn affected by fetal malnut not light or sm for gestational age
P10*	Intracranial lac and hemor d/t birth inj
P11.0	Cerebral edema d/t birth inj
P11.2	Unsp brain damage d/t birth inj
P11.4	Birth inj to oth cranial nerves
P11.5	Birth inj to spine and spinal cord
P11.9	Birth inj to central nervous sys, unsp
P12.2	Epicranial subaponeurotic hemor d/t birth inj
P14.2	Phrenic nerve paralysis d/t birth inj
P14.8	Birth injuries to oth parts of peripheral nervous sys
P14.9	Birth inj to peripheral nervous sys, unsp
P23*	Congenital pneumonia
P24*	Neonatal aspiration
P25*	Interstit emphysema and rel cond origin in perinat period
P26*	Pulmn hemor originating in the perinatal period
P28.0	Primary atelectasis of newborn
P28.5	Respiratory failure of newborn
P29.3	Persistent fetal circulation
P29.81	Cardiac arrest of newborn
P35*	Congenital viral dz

P36*	Bacterial sepsis of newborn
P37.0	Congenital tuberculosis
P37.1	Congenital toxoplasmosis
P37.2	Neonatal (disseminated) listeriosis
P37.3	Congenital falciparum malaria
P37.4	Oth congenital malaria
P37.8	Oth spec congenital infectious and parasitic dz
P37.9	Congenital infectious or parasitic dz, unsp
P38*	Omphalitis of newborn
P39.0	Neonatal infective mastitis
P39.2	Intra-amniotic infxn affecting newborn, NEC
P39.3	Neonatal urinary tract infxn
P39.4	Neonatal skin infxn
P39.8	Oth spec infections specific to the perinatal period
P39.9	Infxn specific to the perinatal period, unsp
P50*	Newborn affected by intrauterine (fetal) bld loss
P52*	Intracranial nontraumatic hemor of newborn
P53	Hemorrhagic dz of newborn
P54.1	Neonatal melena
P54.2	Neonatal rectal hemor
P54.3	Oth neonatal gastrointestinal hemor
P54.4	Neonatal adrenal hemor
P55.8	Oth hemolytic dz of newborn
P55.9	Hemolytic dz of newborn, unsp
P56*	Hydrops fetalis d/t hemolytic dz
P57*	Kernicterus
P59.1	Inspissated bile synd
P59.2*	Neonatal jaundice from oth and unsp hepatocellular damage
P60	Disseminated intravascular coagulation of newborn
P61.0	Transient neonatal thrombocytopenia
P61.2	Anemia of prematurity
P61.6	Oth transient neonatal d/o of coagulation
P70.2	Neonatal diabetes mellitus
P70.3	Iatrogenic neonatal hypoglycemia
P70.4	Oth neonatal hypoglycemia
P71*	Transitory neonatal d/o of calcium and magnesium metab
P72.1	Transitory neonatal hyperthyroidism
P74.[0,1,2,3,4]	[Late metabolic acidosis, Dehydration, Disturbances of sodium balance, Disturbances of potassium balance, Oth transitory electrolyte disturbances] of newborn
P76.0	Meconium plug synd
P76.2	Intestinal obstruction d/t inspissated milk
P77*	Necrotizing enterocolitis of newborn
P78.0	Perinatal intestinal perforation
P83.2	Hydrops fetalis not d/t hemolytic dz
P90	Convulsions of newborn
P91.0	Neonatal cerebral ischemia
P91.1	Acquired periventricular cysts of newborn
P91.3	Neonatal cerebral irritability
P91.4	Neonatal cerebral depression
P91.5	Neonatal coma
P91.6[2,3]	[Mod, Severe] hypoxic ischemic encephalopathy (HIE)
P91.8	Oth spec disturbances of cerebral status of newborn
P91.9	Disturbance of cerebral status of newborn, unsp
P92.01	Bilious vomiting of newborn
P93*	Reactions and intoxications d/t drugs administered to NB
P94.0	Transient neonatal myasthenia gravis
P96.1	Neonatal w/drawal symp from matern use of drugs of addiction
P96.2	Withdrawal symptoms from therapeutic use of drugs in newborn

OR

Secondary diagnosis

A35	Oth tetanus
A39.1	Waterhouse-Friderichsen synd
A39.5*	Meningococcal heart dz
A39.82	Meningococcal retrobulbar neuritis
A39.8[3,4]	[Meningococcal, Postmeningococcal] arthritis
A40.9	Streptococcal sepsis, unsp
A41*	Oth sepsis
A42.7	Actinomycotic sepsis

T Transfer DRG   SP Special Payment   * Code Range   6th and 7th Character of ZZ = No Device, No Qualifier ZX = No Device, Diagnostic

A48.0	Gas gangrene
A48.1	Legionnaires' dz
A48.51	Infant botulism
A81.1	Subacute sclerosing panencephalitis
B00.0	Eczema herpeticum
B00.1	Herpesviral vesicular dermatitis
B00.2	Herpesviral gingivostomatitis and pharyngotonsillitis
B00.3	Herpesviral meningitis
B00.4	Herpesviral encephalitis
B00.5*	Herpesviral ocular dz
B00.7	Disseminated herpesviral dz
B00.81	Herpesviral hepatitis
B00.89	Oth herpesviral infxn
B01.0	Varicella meningitis
B01.11	Varicella encephalitis and encephalomyelitis
B01.2	Varicella pneumonia
B01.81	Varicella keratitis
B01.89	Oth varicella comp
B01.9	Varicella w/o comp
B02.0	Zoster encephalitis
B02.1	Zoster meningitis
B02.29	Oth postherpetic nervous sys involvement
B02.2[1,2,3]	Postherpetic [geniculate ganglionitis, trigeminal neuralgia, polyneuropathy]
B02.3*	Zoster ocular dz
B02.7	Disseminated zoster
B02.8	Zoster with oth comp
B02.9	Zoster w/o comp
B05.8*	Measles with oth comp
B05.[0,1,2,3,4]	Measles comp by [encephalitis, meningitis, pneumonia, otitis media, intestinal comps]
B06.0*	Rubella with neurological comp
B06.8*	Rubella with oth comp
B08.2*	Exanthema subitum [sixth dz]
B10.0*	Oth human herpesvirus encephalitis
B16*	Acute hepatitis B
B17*	Oth acute viral hepatitis
B18*	Chr viral hepatitis
B19.0	Unsp viral hepatitis with hepatic coma
B19.1*	Unsp viral hepatitis B
B19.9	Unsp viral hepatitis w/o hepatic coma
B25.2	Cytomegaloviral pancreatitis · PDx MCC
B26.8*	Mumps with oth comp
B26.[0,1,2,3]	Mumps [orchitis, meningitis, encephalitis, pancreatitis]
B37.1	Pulmn candidiasis
B37.5	Candidal meningitis
B37.6	Candidal endocarditis
B37.8[1,2,4]	Candidal [esophagitis, enteritis, otitis externa]
B38.4	Coccidioidomycosis meningitis
B38.7	Disseminated coccidioidomycosis
B38.89	Oth forms of coccidioidomycosis
B39.[0,1,2]	[Acute, Chr, Unsp] pulmn histoplasmosis capsulati
B40*	Blastomycosis
B41*	Paracoccidioidomycosis
B44.89	Oth forms of aspergillosis
B44.9	Aspergillosis, unsp
B44.[1,2,7]	[Oth pulmn, Tonsillar, Disseminated] aspergillosis
B45*	Cryptococcosis
B46*	Zygomycosis
B47.0	Eumycetoma
B48.2	Allescheriasis
B48.4	Penicillosis
B48.8	Oth spec mycoses
B58.0*	Toxoplasma oculopathy
B58.1	Toxoplasma hepatitis
B58.2	Toxoplasma meningoencephalitis
B58.3	Pulmn toxoplasmosis
B58.8*	Toxoplasmosis with oth organ involvement
B59	Pneumocystosis
B97.4	Respiratory syncytial virus causing dz classd elsw
D56.[0,1,2,5,8,9]	[Alpha, Beta, Delta-beta, Hemoglobin E-beta, Oth, Unsp] thalassemia
D57.4*	Sickle-cell thalassemia
D59.2	Drug-induced nonautoimmune hemolytic anemia
D59.3	Hemolytic-uremic synd
D59.4	Oth nonautoimmune hemolytic anemias
D59.5	Paroxysmal nocturnal hemoglobinuria [Marchiafava-Micheli]
D59.6	Hemoglobinuria d/t hemolysis from oth ext causes
D59.8	Oth acquired hemolytic anemias
D59.9	Acquired hemolytic anemia, unsp
D62	Acute posthemorrhagic anemia
D65	Disseminated intravascular coagulation
D69.5*	Secondary thrombocytopenia
D75.82	Heparin induced thrombocytopenia (HIT)
D78.1*	Accid punc & lac of the spleen during a procedure
E03.5	Myxedema coma
E15	Nondiabetic hypoglycemic coma
E20.[0,8,9]	[Idiopathic, Oth, Unsp] hypoparathyroidism
E23.2	Diabetes insipidus
E32.1	Abscess of thymus
E36.1*	Accid punc & lac of an endo sys org during a procedure
E41	Nutritional marasmus
E43	Unsp severe protein-calorie malnut
E44*	Protein-calorie malnut of mod and mild degree
E46	Unsp protein-calorie malnut
E64.0	Sequelae of protein-calorie malnut
E86*	Volume depletion
E87*	Oth d/o of fluid, electrolyte and acid-base balance
E88.3	Tumor lysis synd
E89.2	Postprocedural hypoparathyroidism
F11.[2,9]3	Opioid [dependence, use unsp] w/ w/drawal
F13.[2,9]3[0,1,2,9]	Sedative, hypnotic or anxiolytic [dependence, use unsp] w/ w/drawal [uncomp, delirium, perceptual disturbance, unsp]
F14.23	Cocaine dependence with withdrawal
F15.[2,9]3	Oth stimulant [dependence, use unsp] w/ w/drawal
F17.2[0,1,2,9]3	Nicotine dependence [unsp, cigarettes, chewing tobacco, oth tobacco product] w/ w/drawal
F19.[2,9]3[0,1,2,9]	Oth psychoactive substance [dependence, use unsp] w/ w/drawal [uncomp, delirium, perceptual disturbance, unsp]
G00*	Bacterial meningitis, NEC
G01	Meningitis in bacterial dz classified elsw
G02	Meningitis in oth infec/parastc dz classd elsw
G03.0	Nonpyogenic meningitis
G03.8	Meningitis d/t oth spec causes
G03.9	Meningitis, unsp
G04.2	Bacterial meningoencephalitis and meningomyelitis, NEC
G06*	Intracranial and intraspinal abscess and granuloma
G07	Intcrn & intraspinal abscs & granuloma in dis classd elsw
G90.1	Familial dysautonomia [Riley-Day]
G92	Txc encephalopathy
G93.1	Anoxic brain damage, NEC
G96.0	Cerebrospinal fluid leak
G96.11	Dural tear
G97.0	Cerebrospinal fluid leak from spinal punc
G97.1	Oth reaction to spinal and lumbar punc
G97.2	Intracranial hypotension following ventricular shunting
G97.4*	Accid punc & lac of a nervous sys org dur proc
G97.8*	Oth intraop and postproc comp and d/o of nervous sys
H47.1[0,1,2]	Papilledema [unsp, associated w/ increased intracranial pressure, associated w/ decreased ocular pressure]
H59.2*	Accid punc & lac of eye and adnexa during a procedure
H70.01[1,2,3,9]	Subperiosteal abscess of mastoid, [rt, lt, bilat, unsp] ear(s)
H70.81[1,2,3,9]	Postauricular fistula, [rt, lt, bilat, unsp] ear(s)
H95.3*	Accid punc & lac of ear/mastd during a procedure
I09.81	Rheumatic heart failure
I11.0	Hypertensive heart dz with heart failure
I13.0	Hyp hrt & chr kdny dis w hrt fail and stg 1-4/unsp chr kdny
I13.2	Hyp hrt & chr kdny dis w hrt fail and w stg 5 chr kdny/ESRD
I25.3	Aneurysm of heart
I26*	Pulmn embolism
I27.82	Chr pulmn embolism
I31.2	Hemopericardium, NEC
I32	Pericarditis in dz classified elsw
I33*	Acute and subacute endocarditis
I38	Endocarditis, valve unsp
I39	Endocarditis and heart valve d/o in dis classd elsw
I40.0	Infective myocarditis
I41	Myocarditis in dz classified elsw
I43	Cardiomyopathy in dz classified elsw
I44.2	Atrioventricular block, complete
I45.2	Bifascicular block
I45.3	Trifascicular block
I45.6	Pre-excitation synd
I45.89	Oth spec conduction d/o
I46*	Cardiac arrest
I47.0	Re-entry ventricular arrhythmia
I47.2	Ventricular tachycardia
I48*	Atrial fibrillation and flutter
I49.0[1,2]	Ventricular [fibrillation, flutter]
I50*	Heart failure

Surgical	**Medical**	**CC Indicator**	**MCC Indicator**	**Procedure Proxy**	PDx MCC PDx acts as own MCC	PDx CC PDx acts as own CC

MDC 15: Newborns And Other Neonates With Conditions Originating In The Perinatal Period—MEDICAL

I60*	Nontraumatic subarachnoid hemor
I61*	Nontraumatic intracerebral hemor
I62*	Oth and unsp nontraumatic intracranial hemor
I63*	Cerebral infarction
I66*	Occlsn and stenosis of cereb art, not rslt in cerebral infrc
I70.26[1,2,3,8,9]	Atherosclerosis of native arteries of extremities w/ gangrene, [rt leg, lt leg, bilat legs, oth extr, unsp extr]
I74*	Arterial embolism and thrombosis
I76	Septic arterial embolism
I80.1*	Phlebitis and thrombophlebitis of femor vein
I80.2*	Phlbts and thombophlb of and unsp deep vessels of low extrm
I80.3	Phlebitis and thrombophlebitis of lwr extremities, unsp
I82.22[0,1]	[Acute, Chr] embolism and thrombosis of inferior vena cava
I89.1	Lymphangitis
I96	Gangrene, NEC
I97.0	Postcardiotomy synd
I97.1*	Oth postprocedural cardiac functional disturbances
I97.5*	Accid punc & lac of a circ sys org dur proc
I97.7*	Intraoperative cardiac functional disturbances
I97.88	Oth intraoperative comp of the circ sys, NEC
I97.89	Oth postproc comp and d/o of the circ sys, NEC
J09.X[1,2]	flu d/t identified novel flu A virus w/ [pneumonia, oth respiratory manifestations]
J10.08	Flu d/t oth ident flu virus w oth pneumonia
J10.1	Flu d/t oth ident flu virus w oth resp manifest
J13	Pneumonia d/t Streptococcus pneumoniae
J14	Pneumonia d/t Hemophilus influenzae
J15*	Bacterial pneumonia, NEC
J16*	Pneumonia d/t oth infectious organisms, NEC
J18.9	Pneumonia, unsp organism
J18.[0,1,8]	[Broncho-, Lobar, Oth] pneumonia, unsp organism
J38.0*	Paralysis of vocal cords and larynx
J38.5	Laryngeal spasm
J39.0	Retropharyngeal and parapharyngeal abscess
J45.902	Unsp asthma with status asthmaticus
J45.[2,3]2	Mild [intermittent, persistent] asthma w/ status asthmaticus
J45.[4,5]2	[Mod, Severe] persistent asthma w/ status asthmaticus
J69.[0,8]	Pneumonitis d/t inhalation of [food and vomit, oth solids and liquids]
J70.0	Acute pulmn manifestations d/t radiation
J81.0	Acute pulmn edema
J84.83	Surfactant mutations of the lung
J84.84*	Oth interstitial lung dz of childhood
J85*	Abscess of lung and mediastinum
J86*	Pyothorax
J90	Pleural effusion, NEC
J91.8	Pleural effusion in oth conditions classified elsw
J94.0	Chylous effusion
J94.2	Hemothorax
J94.8	Oth spec pleural conditions
J95.1	Acute pulmn insufficiency following thoracic surgery
J95.2	Acute pulmn insufficiency following nonthoracic surgery
J95.3	Chr pulmn insufficiency following surgery
J95.4	Chemical pneumonitis d/t anesthesia
J95.5	Postprocedural subglottic stenosis
J95.7*	Accid punc & lac of a respiratory sys org dur proc
J95.851	Ventilator associated pneumonia
J95.859	Oth comp of respirator [ventilator]
J95.88	Oth intraoperative comp of respiratory sys, NEC
J95.89	Oth postproc comp and d/o of resp sys, NEC
J98.11	Atelectasis
J98.19	Oth pulmn collapse
J98.2	Interstitial emphysema
J98.5	Dz of mediastinum, NEC
K22.3	Perforation of esophagus
K31.0	Acute dilatation of stomach
K40.[0,1]0	Bilat inguinal hernia, w/ [obstruction w/o gangrene, gangrene], not spec as recurrent
K40.[3,4]0	Unilat inguinal hernia, w/ [obstruction w/o gangrene, gangrene], not spec as recurrent
K41.[0,1]0	Bilat femor hernia, w/ [obstruction w/o gangrene, gangrene], not spec as recurrent
K41.[3,4]0	Unilat femor hernia, w/ [obstruction w/o gangrene, gangrene], not spec as recurrent
K42.[0,1]	Umbilical hernia, w/ [obstruction w/o gangrene, gangrene], not spec as recurrent
K43.[0,1]	Incisional hernia, w/ [obstruction w/o gangrene, gangrene], not spec as recurrent

K43.[3,4]	Parastomal hernia, w/ [obstruction w/o gangrene, gangrene], not spec as recurrent
K43.[6,7]	Oth and unsp ventral hernia, w/ [obstruction w/o gangrene, gangrene], not spec as recurrent
K44.[0,1]	Diaphragmatic hernia, w/ [obstruction w/o gangrene, gangrene], not spec as recurrent
K45.[0,1]	Oth spec abd hernia, w/ [obstruction w/o gangrene, gangrene], not spec as recurrent
K46.[0,1]	Unsp abd hernia, w/ [obstruction w/o gangrene, gangrene], not spec as recurrent
K52.1	Txc gastroenteritis and colitis
K55.0	Acute vascular d/o of intestine
K56.0	Paralytic ileus
K56.1	Intussusception
K56.2	Volvulus
K56.4*	Oth impaction of intestine
K56.6*	Oth and unsp intestinal obstruction
K56.7	Ileus, unsp
K61*	Abscess of anal and rectal regions
K62.5	Hemor of anus and rectum
K63.1	Perforation of intestine (nontraumatic)
K65*	Peritonitis
K66.1	Hemoperitoneum
K67	D/o of peritoneum in infectious dz classd elsw
K68*	D/o of retroperitoneum
K71*	Txc liver dz
K72.0*	Acute and subacute hepatic failure
K72.9*	Hepatic failure, unsp
K75.0	Abscess of liver
K75.1	Phlebitis of portal vein
K75.2	Nonspecific reactive hepatitis
K75.3	Granulomatous hepatitis, NEC
K75.8*	Oth spec inflam liver dz
K75.9	Inflam liver dz, unsp
K76.2	Central hemorrhagic necrosis of liver
K76.3	Infarction of liver
K76.4	Peliosis hepatis
K76.7	Hepatorenal synd
K83.0	Cholangitis
K85*	Acute pancreatitis
K86.[2,3]	[Cyst, Pseudocyst] of pancreas
K91.2	Postsurgical malabsorption, NEC
K91.3	Postprocedural intestinal obstruction
K91.7*	Accid punc & lac of a digestive sys org dur proc
K91.81	Oth intraoperative comp of digestive sys
K91.82	Postprocedural hepatic failure
K91.83	Postprocedural hepatorenal synd
K91.850	Pouchitis
K91.858	Oth comp of intestinal pouch
K91.86	Retained cholelithiasis following cholecystectomy
K91.89	Oth postprocedural comp and d/o of dgstv sys
K92.0	Hematemesis
K92.1	Melena
K92.2	Gastrointestinal hemor, unsp
L02.21*	Cutaneous abscess of trunk
L02.31	Cutaneous abscess of buttock
L02.41*	Cutaneous abscess of limb
L02.51*	Cutaneous abscess of hand
L02.61*	Cutaneous abscess of foot
L02.81*	Cutaneous abscess of oth sites
L02.91	Cutaneous abscess, unsp
L02.[0,1]1	Cutaneous abscess of [face, neck]
L03.1*	Cellulitis and acute lymphangitis of oth parts of limb
L03.2*	Cellulitis and acute lymphangitis of face and neck
L03.3*	Cellulitis and acute lymphangitis of trunk
L03.8*	Cellulitis and acute lymphangitis of oth sites
L03.9*	Cellulitis and acute lymphangitis, unsp
L04*	Acute lymphadenitis
L27.0	Gen skin eruption d/t drugs and meds taken internally
L27.1	Localized skin eruption d/t drugs and meds taken internally
L50.0	Allergic urticaria
L53.0	Txc erythema
L53.1	Erythema annulare centrifugum
L53.2	Erythema marginatum
L53.3	Oth chr figurate erythema
L76.1*	Accid punc & lac of skin, SQ during a procedure
L98.3	Eosinophilic cellulitis [Wells]
M48.5[0,1,2,3,4,5,6,7,8]XA	Collapsed vertebra, NEC, [unsp, occipito-atlanto-axial, cervical, cervicothoracic, thoracic, thoracolumbar, lumbar, lumbosacral, sacral and sacrococcygeal] rgn, init enc for fx

Ⓣ **Transfer DRG**   🆂🅿 **Special Payment**   *** Code Range**   **6th and 7th Character of ZZ = No Device, No Qualifier ZX = No Device, Diagnostic**

M80.00XA	Age-rel osteopor w current path fx, unsp site, init
M80.01[1,2,9]A	Age-related osteoporosis w/ current path fx, [rt, lt, unsp] shldr, init enc for fx
M80.02[1,2,9]A	Age-related osteoporosis w/ current path fx, [rt, lt, unsp] humerus, init enc for fx
M80.03[1,2,9]A	Age-related osteoporosis w/ current path fx, [rt, lt, unsp] forearm, init enc for fx
M80.04[1,2,9]A	Age-related osteoporosis w/ current path fx, [rt, lt, unsp] hand, init enc for fx
M80.05[1,2,9]A	Age-related osteoporosis w/ current path fx, [rt, lt, unsp] femur, init enc for fx
M80.06[1,2,9]A	Age-related osteoporosis w/ current path fx, [rt, lt, unsp] lwr leg, init enc for fx
M80.07[1,2,9]A	Age-related osteoporosis w/ current path fx, [rt, lt, unsp] ankle and foot, init enc for fx
M80.08XA	Age-rel osteopor w current path fx, vertebra(e), init
M80.80XA	Oth osteopor w current path fx, unsp site, init
M80.81[1,2,9]A	Oth osteoporosis w/ current path fx, [rt, lt, unsp] shldr, init enc for fx
M80.82[1,2,9]A	Oth osteoporosis w/ current path fx, [rt, lt, unsp] humerus, init enc for fx
M80.83[1,2,9]A	Oth osteoporosis w/ current path fx, [rt, lt, unsp] forearm, init enc for fx
M80.84[1,2,9]A	Oth osteoporosis w/ current path fx, [rt, lt, unsp] hand, init enc for fx
M80.85[1,2,9]A	Oth osteoporosis w/ current path fx, [rt, lt, unsp] femur, init enc for fx
M80.86[1,2,9]A	Oth osteoporosis w/ current path fx, [rt, lt, unsp] lwr leg, init enc for fx
M80.87[1,2,9]A	Oth osteoporosis w/ current path fx, [rt, lt, unsp] ankle and foot, init enc for fx
M80.88XA	Oth osteopor w current path fx, vertebra(e), init
M84.40XA	Path fx, unsp site, init enc for fx
M84.41[1,2,9]A	Path fx, [rt, lt, unsp] shldr, init enc for fx
M84.42[1,2,9]A	Path fx, [rt, lt, unsp] humerus, init enc for fx
M84.43[1,2,3,4,9]A	Path fx, [rt ulna, lt ulna, rt radius, lt radius, unsp radius and ulna], init enc for fx
M84.44[1,2,3,4,5,6]A	Path fx, [rt hand, lt hand, unsp hand, rt finger(s), lt finger(s), unsp finger(s)], init enc for fx
M84.45[1,2,3,4,9]A	Path fx, [rt femur, lt femur, unsp femur, pelvis, unsp hip], init enc for fx
M84.46[1,2,3,4,9]A	Path fx, [rt tibia, lt tibia, rt fibula, lt fibula, unsp tibia & fibula], init enc for fx
M84.47[1,2,3,4,5,6,7,8,9]A	Path fx [rt ankle, lt ankle, unsp ankle, rt foot, lt foot, unsp foot, rt toe(s), lt toe(s), unsp toe(s)], init enc for fx
M84.48XA	Path fx, oth site, init enc for fx
M84.50XA	Path fx in neoplastic dz, unsp site, init
M84.51[1,2,9]A	Path fx in neoplastic dz, [rt, lt, unsp] shldr, init enc for fx
M84.52[1,2,9]A	Path fx in neoplastic dz, [rt, lt, unsp] humerus, init enc for fx
M84.53[1,2,3,4,9]A	Path fx in neoplastic dz, [rt ulna, lt ulna, rt radius, lt radius, unsp ulna and radius], init enc for fx
M84.54[1,2,9]A	Path fx in neoplastic dz, [rt, lt, unsp] hand, init enc for fx
M84.55[0,1,2,3,9]A	Path fx in neoplastic dz, [pelvis, rt femur, lt femur, unsp femur, unsp hip], init enc for fx
M84.56[1,2,3,4,9]A	Path fx in neoplastic dz, [rt tibia, lt tibia, rt fibula, lt fibula, unsp tibia & fibula], init enc for fx
M84.57[1,2,3,4,5,6]A	Path fx in neoplastic dz, [rt ankle, lt ankle, unsp ankle, rt foot, lt foot, unsp foot], init enc for fx
M84.58XA	Path fx in neoplastic dz, oth site, init
M84.60XA	Path fx in oth dz, unsp site, init for fx
M84.61[1,2,9]A	Path fx in oth dz, [rt, lt, unsp] shldr, init enc for fx
M84.62[1,2,9]A	Path fx in oth dz, [rt, lt, unsp] humerus, init enc for fx
M84.63[1,2,3,4,9]A	Path fx in oth dz, [rt ulna, lt ulna, rt radius, lt radius, unsp ulna and radius], init enc for fx
M84.64[1,2,9]A	Path fx in oth dz, [rt, lt, unsp] hand, init enc for fx
M84.65[0,1,2,3,9]A	Path fx in oth dz, [pelvis, rt femur, lt femur, unsp femur, hip NOS], init enc for fx
M84.66[1,2,3,4,9]A	Path fx in oth dz, [rt tibia, lt tibia, rt fibula, lt fibula, unsp tibia & fibula], init enc for fx
M84.67[1,2,3,4,5,6]A	Path fx in oth dz, [rt ankle, lt ankle, unsp ankle, rt foot, lt foot, unsp foot], init enc for fx
M84.68XA	Path fx in oth dz, oth site, init for fx
M96.82[0,1]	Accid punc and lac of a musculoskeletal structure during [a musculoskeletal sys, oth] procedure
N00*	Acute nephritic synd
N01*	Rapidly progressive nephritic synd
N10	Acute tubulo-interstitial nephritis
N11.9	Chr tubulo-interstitial nephritis, unsp
N12	Tubulo-interstitial nephritis, not spcf as acute or chr
N13.1	Hydronephrosis w ureteral stricture, NEC　　PDxCC

N13.2	Hydronephrosis with renal & ureteral calculous obstruction	PDxCC
N13.3*	Oth and unsp hydronephrosis	
N13.4	Hydroureter	
N13.6	Pyonephrosis	
N13.9	Obstructive and reflux uropathy, unsp	
N15.1	Renal and perinephric abscess	
N17*	Acute kidney failure	
N28.8[4,5,6]	[Pyelitis, Pyeloureteritis, Ureteritis] cystica	
N30.0*	Acute cystitis	
N30.8*	Oth cystitis	
N30.9*	Cystitis, unsp	
N31.2	Flaccid neuropathic bladder, NEC	
N32.0	Bladder-neck obstruction	
N32.1	Vesicointestinal fistula	
N32.2	Vesical fistula, NEC	
N34.0	Urethral abscess	
N39.0	Urinary tract infxn, site not spec	
N82.2	Fistula of vagina to sm intestine	
N82.3	Fistula of vagina to large intestine	
N82.4	Oth female intestinal-genital tract fistulae	
N82.8	Oth female genital tract fistulae	
N83.7	Hematoma of broad lgmt	
N98.0	infxn associated with artfcl insemination	
N99.0	Postprocedural (acute) (chr) kidney failure	
N99.5[2,3][0,1,2,8]	[Hemor, Infxn, Malfunction, Oth comp] of [oth ext, oth] stoma of urinary tract	
N99.7*	Accid punc & lac of a GU sys org dur proc	
N99.81	Oth intraoperative comp of genitourinary sys	
N99.89	Oth postprocedural comp and d/o of GU sys	
P91.2	Neonatal cerebral leukomalacia	
Q00*	Anencephaly and similar malformations	
Q01*	Encephalocele	
Q02	Microcephaly	
Q03*	Congenital hydrocephalus	
Q04*	Oth congenital malformations of brain	
Q05*	Spina bifida	
Q06*	Oth congenital malformations of spinal cord	
Q07*	Oth congenital malformations of nervous sys	
Q21.0	Ventricular septal defect	
Q79.2	Exomphalos	
Q79.3	Gastroschisis	
Q89.4	Conjoined twins	
R00.0	Tachycardia, unsp	
R09.2	Respiratory arrest	
R29.0	Tetany	
R31*	Hematuria	
R33*	Retention of urine	
R39.14	Feeling of incomplete bladder emptying	
R40.20	Unsp coma	
R40.21[1,2][0,1,2,3,4]	Coma scale, eyes opn, [never, to pain], [unsp time, in the field (EMT or ambulance), at arrival to emergency department, at hospital admission, 24 hrs or more after hospital admission]	
R40.22[1,2][0,1,2,3,4]	Coma scale, best verbal response, [none, incomprhensible words], [unsp time, in the field (EMT or ambulance), at arrival to emergency department, at hospital admission, 24 hrs or more after hospital admission]	
R40.23[1,2,4][0,1,2,3,4]	Coma scale, best motor response, [none, extension, flexion w/drawal], [unsp time, in the field (EMT or ambulance), at arrival to emergency department, at hospital admission, 24 hrs or more after hospital admission]	
R40.3	Persistent vegetative state	
R56.00	Simple febrile convulsions	
R56.9	Unsp convulsions	
R57.9	Shock, unsp	
R58	Hemor, NEC	
R78.81	Bacteremia	
R82.0	Chyluria	
S14.3XXA	Inj of brachial plexus, init enc	
S15.0[0,1,2,9][1,2,9]A	[Unsp inj, Minor lac, Major lac, Oth spec inj] of [rt, lt, unsp] carotid artery, init enc	
S15.2[0,1,2,9][1,2,9]A	[Unsp inj, Minor lac, Major lac, Oth spec inj] of [rt, lt, unsp] ext jugular vein, init enc	
S15.3[0,1,2,9][1,2,9]A	[Unsp inj, Minor lac, Major lac, Oth spec inj] of [rt, lt, unsp] int jugular vein, init enc	
S25.0[0,1,2,9]XA	[Unsp inj, Minor lac, Major lac, Oth spec inj] of thoracic aorta, init enc	
S25.1[0,1,2,9]A	[Unsp inj, Minor lac, Major lac, Oth spec inj] of [rt, lt, unsp] innominate or subclavian artery, init enc	

Surgical　　**Medical**　　**CC Indicator**　　**MCC Indicator**　　**Procedure Proxy**　　**PDxMCC PDx acts as own MCC**　　**PDxCC PDx acts as own CC**

MDC 15: Newborns And Other Neonates With Conditions Originating In The Perinatal Period—MEDICAL

MDC 15: Newborns And Other Neonates With Conditions Originating In The Perinatal Period—MEDICAL

S25.2[0,1,2,9]XA [Unsp inj, Minor lac, Major lac, Oth spec inj] of superior vena cava, init enc

S25.3[0,1,2,9][1,2,9]A [Unsp inj, Minor lac, Major lac, Oth spec inj] of [rt, lt, unsp] innominate or subclavian vein, init enc

S25.4[0,1,2,9][1,2,9]A [Unsp inj, Minor lac, Major lac, Oth spec inj] of [rt, lt, unsp] pulmn bld vessels, init enc

S27.[0,1,2]XXA Traum [pneumothorax, hemothorax, hemopneumothorax], init enc

S35.0[0,1,2,9]XA [Unsp inj, Minor lac, Major lac, Oth inj] of abd aorta, init enc

S35.1[0,1,2,9]XA [Unsp inj, Minor lac, Major lac, Oth inj] of inferior vena cava, init enc

S36.00XA Unsp inj of spleen, init enc

S36.02[0,1,9]A [Minor, Major, Unsp] contsn of spleen, init enc

S36.03[0,1,2,9]A [Superf (capsular), Mod, Major, Unsp] lac of spleen, init enc

S36.09XA Oth inj of spleen, init enc

S72.00[1,2,9][A,B,C] Fx of unsp part of neck of [rt, lt, unsp] femur, init enc for [clsd fx, opn fx type I or II, opn fx type IIIA, IIIB, or IIIC]

S72.01[1,2,9][A,B,C] Unsp intracapsular fx of [rt, lt, unsp] femur, init enc for [clsd fx, opn fx type I or II, opn fx type IIIA, IIIB, or IIIC]

S72.02[1,2,3][A,B,C] Disp fx of epiphysis (separation) (upr) of [rt, lt, unsp] femur, init enc for [clsd fx, opn fx type I or II or NOS, or opn fx type IIIA, IIIB, or IIIC]

S72.02[4,5,6][A,B,C] Nondisp fx of epiphysis (separation) (upr) of [rt, lt, unsp] femur, init enc for [clsd fx, opn fx type I or II or NOS, or opn fx type IIIA, IIIB, or IIIC]

S72.03[1,2,3][A,B,C] Disp midcervical fx of [rt, lt, unsp] femur, init enc for [clsd fx, opn fx type I or II or NOS, or opn fx type IIIA, IIIB, or IIIC]

S72.03[4,5,6][A,B,C] Nondisp midcervical fx of [rt, lt, unsp] femur, init enc for [clsd fx, opn fx type I or II or NOS, or opn fx type IIIA, IIIB, or IIIC]

S72.04[1,2,3][A,B,C] Disp fx of base of neck of [rt, lt, unsp] femur, init enc for opn fx type [I or II, IIIA IIIB or IIIC]

S72.04[4,5,6][A,B,C] Nondisp fx of base of neck of [rt, lt, unsp] femur, init enc for opn fx type [I or II, IIIA IIIB or IIIC]

S72.05[1,2,9][A,B,C] Unsp fx of head of [rt, lt, unsp] femur, init enc for [clsd fx, opn fx type I or II, opn fx type IIIA, IIIB, or IIIC]

S72.06[1,2,3][A,B,C] Disp articular fx of head of [rt, lt, unsp] femur, init enc for fx [clsd, opn fx type I or II or NOS, or opn fx type IIIA, IIIB, or IIIC]

S72.06[4,5,6][A,B,C] Nondisp articular fx of head of femur [rt, lt, unsp] init enc for fx [clsd, opn fx type I or II or NOS, or opn fx type IIIA, IIIB, or IIIC]

S72.09[1,2,9][A,B,C] Oth fx of head and neck of [rt, lt, unsp] femur, init enc for [clsd fx, opn fx type I or II, opn fx type IIIA, IIIB, or IIIC]

S72.10[1,2,9][A,B,C] Unsp trochanteric fx of [rt, lt, unsp] femur, init enc for [clsd fx, opn fx type I or II, opn fx type IIIA, IIIB, or IIIC]

S72.11[1,2,3][A,B,C] Disp fx of greater trochanter of [rt, lt, unsp] femur, init enc for fx [clsd, opn fx type I or II or NOS, or opn fx type IIIA, IIIB, or IIIC]

S72.11[4,5,6][A,B,C] Nondisp fx of greater trochanter of femur [rt, lt, unsp] init enc for fx [clsd, opn fx type I or II or NOS, or opn fx type IIIA, IIIB, or IIIC]

S72.12[1,2,3][A,B,C] Disp fx of lesser trochanter of [rt, lt, unsp] femur, init enc for [clsd fx, opn fx type I or II or NOS, or opn fx type IIIA, IIIB, or IIIC]

S72.12[4,5,6][A,B,C] Nondisp fx of lesser trochanter of [rt, lt, unsp] femur, init enc for [clsd fx, opn fx type I or II or NOS, or opn fx type IIIA, IIIB, or IIIC]

S72.13[1,2,3][A,B,C] Disp apophyseal fx of [rt, lt, unsp] femur, init enc for [clsd fx, opn fx type I or II or NOS, or opn fx type IIIA, IIIB, or IIIC]

S72.13[4,5,6][A,B,C] Nondisp apophyseal fx of [rt, lt, unsp] femur, init enc for [clsd fx, opn fx type I or II or NOS, or opn fx type IIIA, IIIB, or IIIC]

S72.14[1,2,3][A,B,C] Disp intertrochanteric fx of [rt, lt, unsp] femur, init enc for [clsd fx, opn fx type I or II or NOS, or opn fx type IIIA, IIIB, or IIIC]

S72.14[4,5,6][A,B,C] Nondisp intertrochanteric fx of [rt, lt, unsp] femur, init enc for [clsd fx, opn fx type I or II or NOS, or opn fx type IIIA, IIIB, or IIIC]

S72.2[1,2,3]X[A,B,C] Disp subtrochanteric fx of [rt, lt, unsp] femur, init enc for [clsd fractrure, opn fx type I or II or NOS, or opn fx type IIIA, IIIB, or IIIC]

S72.2[4,5,6]X[A,B,C] Nondisp subtrochanteric fx of [rt, lt, unsp] femur, init enc for [clsd fractrure, opn fx type I or II or NOS, or opn fx type IIIA, IIIB, or IIIC]

S72.30[1,2,9][A,B,C] Unsp fx of shaft of [rt, lt, unsp] femur, init enc for [clsd fx, opn fx type I or II, opn fx type IIIA, IIIB, or IIIC]

S72.32[1,2,3][A,B,C] Disp transv fx of shaft of [rt, lt, unsp] femur, init enc for [clsd fx, opn fx type I or II, opn fx type IIIA, IIIB, or IIIC]

S72.32[4,5,6][A,B,C] Nondisp transv fx of shaft of [rt, lt, unsp] femur, init enc for [clsd fx, opn fx type I or II, opn fx type IIIA, IIIB, or IIIC]

S72.33[1,2,3][A,B,C] Disp oblique fx of shaft of [rt, lt, unsp] femur, init enc for [clsd fx, opn fx type I or II , opn fx type IIIA, IIIB, or IIIC]

S72.33[4,5,6][A,B,C] Nondisp oblique fx of shaft of [rt, lt, unsp] femur, init enc for [clsd fx, opn fx type I or II, opn fx type IIIA, IIIB, or IIIC]

S72.34[1,2,3][A,B,C] Disp spiral fx of shaft of [rt, lt, unsp] femur, init enc for [clsd fx, opn fx type I or II, opn fx type IIIA, IIIB, or IIIC]

S72.34[4,5,6][A,B,C] Nondisp spiral fx of shaft of [rt, lt, unsp] femur, init enc for [clsd fx, opn fx type I or II, opn fx type IIIA, IIIB, or IIIC]

S72.35[1,2,3][A,B,C] Disp comm fx of shaft of [rt, lt, unsp] femur, init enc for [clsd fx, opn fx type I or II, opn fx type IIIA, IIIB, or IIIC]

S72.35[4,5,6][A,B,C] Nondisp comm fx of shaft of femur [rt, lt, unsp], init enc for [clsd fx, opn fx type I or II or NOS, opn fx type IIIA, IIIB, or IIIC]

S72.36[1,2,3][A,B,C] Disp seg fx of shaft of [rt, lt, unsp] femur, init enc for [clsd fx, opn fx type I or II, opn fx type IIIA, IIIB, or IIIC]

S72.36[4,5,6][A,B,C] Nondisp seg fx of shaft of [rt, lt, unsp] femur, init enc for [clsd fx, opn fx type I or II, opn fx type IIIA, IIIB, or IIIC]

S72.39[1,2,9][A,B,C] Oth fx of shaft of [rt, lt, unsp] femur, init enc for [clsd fx, opn fx type I or II, opn fx type IIIA, IIIB, or IIIC]

S72.8X[1,2,9][A,B,C] Oth fx of [rt, lt, unsp] femur, init enc for [clsd fx, opn fx type I or II, opn fx type IIIA, IIIB, or IIIC]

S72.9[0,1,2]X[A,B,C] Unsp fx of [unsp, rt lt] femur, init enc for [clsd fx, opn fx type I or II, opn fx type IIIA, IIIB, or IIIC]

S79.00[1,2,9]A Unsp physeal fx of upr end of [rt, lt, unsp] femur, init enc for clsd fx

S79.01[1,2,9]A Salter-Harris Type I physeal fx of upr end of [rt, lt, unsp] femur, init enc for clsd fx

S79.09[1,2,9]A Oth physeal fx of upr end of [rt, lt, unsp] femur, init enc for clsd fx

T36.0X5A Adverse effect of penicillins, init enc

T36.1X5A Adverse effect of cephalospor/oth beta-lactm antibiot, init

T36.2X5A Adverse effect of chloramphenicol group, init enc

T36.3X5A Adverse effect of macrolides, init enc

T36.4X5A Adverse effect of tetracyclines, init enc

T36.5X5A Adverse effect of aminoglycosides, init enc

T36.6X5A Adverse effect of rifampicins, init enc

T36.7X5A Adverse effect of antifungal antibiotics, sys used, init

T36.8X5A Adverse effect of oth systemic antibiotics, init enc

T36.95XA Adverse effect of unsp systemic antibiotic, init enc

T37.0X5A Adverse effect of sulfonamides, init enc

T37.1X5A Adverse effect of antimycobacterial drugs, init enc

T37.2X5A Advrs effect of antimalari/drugs acting on bld protzoa, init

T37.3X5A Adverse effect of oth antiprotozoal drugs, init enc

T37.4X5A Adverse effect of anthelminthics, init enc

T37.5X5A Adverse effect of antiviral drugs, init enc

T37.8X5A Adverse effect of systemic anti-infect/parasit, init

T37.95XA Advrs effect of unsp sys anti-infect and antiparasitic, init

T38.0X5A Adverse effect of glucocort/synth analog, init

T38.1X5A Adverse effect of thyroid hormones and substitutes, init

T38.2X5A Adverse effect of antithyroid drugs, init enc

T38.3X5A Adverse effect of insulin and oral hypoglycemic drugs, init

T38.4X5A Adverse effect of oral contraceptives, init enc

T38.5X5A Adverse effect of oth estrogens and progestogens, init

T38.6X5A Adverse effect of antigonadtr/antiestr/antiandrg, NEC, init

T38.7X5A Adverse effect of androgens and anabolic congeners, init

T38.8[0,1,9]5A Adverse effect of [unsp hormones and synth subs, ant pituitary [adenohypophyseal] hormones, oth hormones and synth subs], init enc

T38.9[0,9]5A Adverse effect of [unsp hormone antagonists, oth hormone antagonists], init enc

T39.0[1,9]5A Adverse effect of [aspirin, salicylates], init enc

T39.1X5A Adverse effect of 4-Aminophenol derivatives, init enc

T39.2X5A Adverse effect of pyrazolone derivatives, init enc

T39.3[1,9]5A Adverse effect of [propionic acid derivatives, oth nonsteroidal anti-inflam drugs (NSAID)], init enc

T39.4X5A Adverse effect of antirheumatics, NEC, init

T39.8X5A Adverse effect of nonopioid analges/antipyret, NEC, init

T39.95XA Adverse effect of unsp nonopi analgs/antipyr/antirheu, init

T40.0X5A Adverse effect of opium, init enc

T40.2X5A Adverse effect of oth opioids, init enc

T40.3X5A Adverse effect of methadone, init enc

T40.4X5A Adverse effect of oth synth narcotics, init enc

T40.5X5A Adverse effect of cocaine, init enc

T40.6[0,9]5A Adverse effect of [unsp, oth] narcotics, init enc

T40.7X5A Adverse effect of cannabis (derivatives), init enc

T40.9[0,9]5A Adverse effect of [unsp psychodysleptics (hallucinogens), oth psychodysleptics (hallucinogens)], init enc

T41.0X5A Adverse effect of inhaled anesthetics, init enc

T41.1X5A Adverse effect of intravenous anesthetics, init enc

T41.2[0,9]5A Adverse effect of [unsp general anesthetics, oth general anesthetics], init enc

---

[T] **Transfer DRG**   [SP] **Special Payment**   * **Code Range**   **6th and 7th Character of ZZ = No Device, No Qualifier ZX = No Device, Diagnostic**

MS-DRG Version 33.0   © 2015 Optum360, LLC

T41.3X5A	Adverse effect of local anesthetics, init enc
T41.45XA	Adverse effect of unsp anesthetic, init enc
T41.5X5A	Adverse effect of therapeutic gases, init enc
T42.0X5A	Adverse effect of hydantoin derivatives, init enc
T42.1X5A	Adverse effect of iminostilbenes, init enc
T42.2X5A	Adverse effect of succinimides and oxazolidinediones, init
T42.3X5A	Adverse effect of barbiturates, init enc
T42.4X5A	Adverse effect of benzodiazepines, init enc
T42.5X5A	Adverse effect of mixed antiepileptics, init enc
T42.6X5A	Adverse effect of antiepileptic and sed-hypntc drugs, init
T42.75XA	Adverse effect of unsp antieplptc and sed-hypntc drugs, init
T42.8X5A	Adverse effect of antiparkns drug/centr musc-tone depr, init
T43.0[1,2]5A	Adverse effect of [tricyclic, tetracyclic] antidepressants, init enc
T43.1X5A	Adverse effect of MAO inhib antidepressants, init
T43.205A	Adverse effect of unsp antidepressants, init enc
T43.2[1,2,9]5A	Adverse effect of [selective serotonin and norepinephrine reuptake inhibitors, selective serotonin reuptake inhibitors, oth antidepressants], init enc
T43.3X5A	Adverse effect of phenothiazine antipsychot/neurolept, init
T43.4X5A	Adverse effect of butyrophen/thiothixen neuroleptics, init
T43.5[0,9]5A	Adverse effect of [unsp, oth] antipsychotics and neuroleptics, init enc
T43.6[0,1,2,3,9]5A	Adverse effect of [unsp psychostimulants, caffeine, amphetamines, methylphenidate, oth psychostimulants], init enc
T43.8X5A	Adverse effect of oth psychotropic drugs, init enc
T43.95XA	Adverse effect of unsp psychotropic drug, init enc
T44.0X5A	Adverse effect of anticholinesterase agents, init enc
T44.1X5A	Adverse effect of oth parasympathomimetics, init enc
T44.2X5A	Adverse effect of ganglionic blocking drugs, init enc
T44.3X5A	Adverse effect of parasympatholytics and spasmolytics, init
T44.4X5A	Adverse effect of predom alpha-adrenocpt agonists, init
T44.5X5A	Adverse effect of predom beta-adrenocpt agonists, init
T44.6X5A	Adverse effect of alpha-adrenoreceptor antagonists, init
T44.7X5A	Adverse effect of beta-adrenoreceptor antagonists, init
T44.8X5A	Adverse effect of centr-acting/adren-neurn-block agnt, init
T44.9[0,9]5A	Adverse effect of [unsp, oth] drugs primarily affecting the autonomic nervous sys, init enc
T45.0X5A	Adverse effect of antiallergic and antiemetic drugs, init
T45.1X5A	Adverse effect of antineoplastic and immunosup drugs, init
T45.2X5A	Adverse effect of vitamins, init enc
T45.3X5A	Adverse effect of enzymes, init enc
T45.4X5A	Adverse effect of iron and its compounds, init enc
T45.5[1,2]5A	Adverse effect of [anticoagulants, antithrombotic drugs], init enc
T45.6[0,1,2,9]5A	Adverse effect of [unsp fibrinolysis-affecting, thrombolytic, hemostatic, oth fibrinolysis-affecting] drugs, init enc
T45.7X5A	Adverse effect of anticoag antag, vit K and oth coag, init
T45.8X5A	Adverse effect of prim systemic and hematolog agents, init
T45.95XA	Adverse effect of unsp prim sys and hematolog agent, init
T46.0X5A	Adverse effect of cardi-stim glycos/drug simlar act, init
T46.1X5A	Adverse effect of calcium-channel blockers, init enc
T46.2X5A	Adverse effect of oth antidysrhythmic drugs, init enc
T46.3X5A	Adverse effect of coronary vasodilators, init enc
T46.4X5A	Adverse effect of angiotens-convert-enzyme inhibitors, init
T46.5X5A	Adverse effect of oth antihypertensive drugs, init enc
T46.6X5A	Adverse effect of antihyperlip and antiarterio drugs, init
T46.7X5A	Adverse effect of peripheral vasodilators, init enc
T46.8X5A	Adverse effect of antivaric drugs, incl* scler agents, init
T46.9[0,9]5A	Adverse effect of [unsp, oth] agents primarily affecting the cardiovascular sys, init enc
T47.0X5A	Adverse effect of histamine H2-receptor blockers, init
T47.1X5A	Adverse effect of antacids and anti-gstrc-sec drugs, init
T47.2X5A	Adverse effect of stimulant laxatives, init enc
T47.3X5A	Adverse effect of saline and osmotic laxatives, init enc
T47.4X5A	Adverse effect of oth laxatives, init enc
T47.5X5A	Adverse effect of digestants, init enc
T47.6X5A	Adverse effect of antidiarrheal drugs, init enc
T47.7X5A	Adverse effect of emetics, init enc
T47.8X5A	Adverse effect of agents primarily affecting GI sys, init
T47.95XA	Adverse effect of unsp agents affected the GI sys, init
T48.0X5A	Adverse effect of oxytocic drugs, init enc
T48.1X5A	Adverse effect of skeletal muscle relaxants, init enc
T48.2[0,9]5A	Adverse effect of [unsp, oth] drugs acting on muscles, init enc
T48.3X5A	Adverse effect of antitussives, init enc
T48.4X5A	Adverse effect of expectorants, init enc
T48.5X5A	Adverse effect of oth anti-common-cold drugs, init enc
T48.6X5A	Adverse effect of antiasthmatics, init enc
T48.9[0,9]5A	Adverse effect of [unsp, oth] agents primarily acting on the respiratory sys, init enc
T49.0X5A	Adverse effect of local antifung/infect/inflamm drugs, init
T49.1X5A	Adverse effect of antipruritics, init enc
T49.2X5A	Adverse effect of local astringents/detergents, init
T49.3X5A	Adverse effect of emollients, demulcents and protect, init
T49.4X5A	Adverse effect of keratolyt/keratplst/hair trmt drug, init
T49.5X5A	Adverse effect of opth drugs and preparations, init
T49.6X5A	Adverse effect of otorhino drugs and preparations, init
T49.7X5A	Adverse effect of dental drugs, topically applied, init
T49.8X5A	Adverse effect of oth topical agents, init enc
T49.95XA	Adverse effect of unsp topical agent, init enc
T50.0X5A	Adverse effect of mineralocorticoids and their antag, init
T50.1X5A	Adverse effect of loop diuretics, init enc
T50.2X5A	Advrs eff of crbnc-anhydr inhibtr, benzo/oth diuretc, init
T50.3X5A	Adverse effect of electrolytic/caloric/wtr-bal agnt, init
T50.4X5A	Adverse effect of drugs affecting uric acid metabolism, init
T50.5X5A	Adverse effect of appetite depressants, init enc
T50.6X5A	Adverse effect of antidotes and chelating agents, init
T50.7X5A	Adverse effect of analeptics and opioid receptor antag, init
T50.8X5A	Adverse effect of diagnostic agents, init enc
T50.9[0,9]5A	Adverse effect of [unsp, oth] drugs, medicaments and biological substances, init enc
T50.A[1,2,9]5A	Adverse effect of [pertussis vaccine, incl* combinations w/ a pertussis component, mixed bacterial vaccines w/o a pertussis component, oth bacterial vaccines], init enc
T50.B[1,9]5A	Adverse effect of [smpox, oth viral] vaccines, init enc
T50.Z[1,9]5A	Adverse effect of [immunoglobulin, oth vaccines and biological substances], init enc
T78.41XA	Arthus phenomenon, init enc
T79.0XXA	Air embolism (traum), init enc
T79.1XXA	Fat embolism (traum), init enc
T79.2XXA	Traum secondary and recurrent hemor and seroma, init
T79.4XXA	Traum shock, init enc
T79.5XXA	Traum anuria, init enc
T79.7XXA	Traum SQ emphysema, init enc
T80.0XXA	Air embolism fol inf, transf and theraputc inject, init
T80.1XXA	Vascular comp fol infusn, transf and theraputc inject, init
T80.22XA	Acute infxn fol transf,infusn,inject bld/products, init
T80.29XA	Infxn fol oth inf, transfusion and theraputc inject, init
T80.30XA	ABO incompat react d/t transf of bld/bld prod, unsp, init
T80.31[0,1,9]A	ABO incompatibility w/ [acute, delayed, unsp] hemolytic transfusion reaction, init enc
T80.39XA	Oth ABO incompat react d/t transf of bld/bld prod, init
T80.40XA	Rh incompat react d/t transf of bld/bld prod, unsp, init
T80.41[0,1,9]A	Rh incompatibility w/ [acute, delayed, unsp] hemolytic transfusion reaction, init enc
T80.49XA	Oth Rh incompat reaction d/t transf of bld/bld prod, init
T80.5[1,2,9]XA	Anaphylactic reaction d/t [administration of bld and bld products, vaccination, oth serum], init enc
T80.6[1,2,9]XA	Oth serum reaction d/t [administration of bld and bld products, vaccination, oth serum], init enc
T80.81[0,8]A	Extravasation of [vesicant antineoplastic chemothapy, oth vesicant agent], init enc
T80.89XA	Oth comp fol inf, transfusion and theraputc inject, init
T80.90XA	Unsp comp following inf and therapeutic injection, init
T80.91[0,1,9]A	[Acute, Delayed, Unsp] hemolytic transfusion reaction, unsp incompatibility, init enc
T80.92XA	Unsp transfusion reaction, init enc
T80.A0XA	Non-ABO incompat react d/t transf of bld/bld prod,unsp, init
T80.A1[0,1,9]A	Non-ABO incompatibility w/ [acute, delayed, hemolytic] hemolytic transfusion reaction, init enc
T80.A9XA	Oth non-ABO incompat react d/t transf of bld/bld prod, init
T81.1[0,1,2,9]XA	Postprocedural [unsp, cardiogenic, septic, oth] shock, init enc
T81.4XXA	infxn following a procedure, init enc
T81.5[0,1,2,3,9][0,1,2,3,4,5,6,7,8,9]A	[Unsp comp, Adhesions, Obstruction, Perforation, Oth comps] d/t FB accidly lt in body following [surgical operation, inf or transfusion, kidney dialysis, injectionor immunization, endo exam, heart catheterization, aspiration punc or oth catheterization, rmvl of catheter or packing, oth procedure, unsp procedure], init enc
T81.6[0,1,9]XA	[Unsp acute reaction, Aseptic peritonitis, Oth acute reaction] d/t foreign substance accidably lt during a procedure, init enc
T81.71[0,1,8,9]A	Comp of [mesenteric, renal, oth, unsp] artery following a procedure, NEC, init enc
T81.72XA	Comp of vein following a procedure, NEC, init
T81.83XA	Persistent postprocedural fistula, init enc
T81.9XXA	Unsp comp of procedure, init enc
T88.0XXA	infxn following immunization, init enc
T88.2XXA	Shock d/t anesthesia, init enc
T88.59XA	Oth comp of anesthesia, init enc

Surgical   **Medical**   **CC Indicator**   **MCC Indicator**   **Procedure Proxy**   **PDxMCC PDx acts as own MCC**   **PDxCC PDx acts as own CC**

DRG 794   **Neonate with Other Significant Problems**

        GMLOS 3.4   AMLOS 3.4   RW 1.2987

Principal or secondary diagnosis of newborn or neonate with other significant problems, not assigned to DRGs 789 - 793, or 795

A33	Tetanus neonatorum
P00.0	Newborn affected by maternal hypertensive d/o
P00.1	Newborn affected by maternal renal and urinary tract dz
P00.3	Newborn affected by oth maternal circ and resp dz
P00.4	Newborn affected by maternal nutritional d/o
P00.5	Newborn (suspected to be) affected by maternal inj
P00.6	Newborn affected by surgical procedure on mother
P00.7	Newborn affected by oth medical procedures on mother, NEC
P00.81	Newborn affected by periodontal dz in mother
P00.9	Newborn affected by unsp maternal condition
P01*	Newborn affected by maternal comp of preg
P02.0	Newborn (suspected to be) affected by placenta previa
P02.1	Newborn affected by oth placental separation and hemor
P02.2*	Newborn affected by oth and unsp morpholog and function abnlt of placenta
P02.3	Newborn affected by placental transfusion syndromes
P02.7	Newborn (suspected to be) affected by chorioamnionitis
P02.8	Newborn affected by oth abnormalities of membranes
P02.9	Newborn affected by abnormality of membranes, unsp
P03.6	Newborn affected by abnormal uterine contractions
P03.8*	Newborn affected by oth comp of labor and delivery
P04*	Newborn affected by noxious substance transmitted via placenta or breast milk
P05.00	Newborn light for gestational age, unsp weight
P05.01	Newborn light for gestational age, < 500 grams
P05.02	Newborn light for gestational age, 500-749 grams
P05.03	Newborn light for gestational age, 750-999 grams
P05.04	Newborn light for gestational age, 1000-1249 grams
P05.05	Newborn light for gestational age, 1250-1499 grams
P05.06	Newborn light for gestational age, 1500-1749 grams
P05.07	Newborn light for gestational age, 1750-1999 grams
P05.10	Newborn sm for gestational age, unsp weight
P05.11	Newborn sm for gestational age, < 500 grams
P05.12	Newborn sm for gestational age, 500-749 grams
P05.13	Newborn sm for gestational age, 750-999 grams
P05.14	Newborn sm for gestational age, 1000-1249 grams
P05.15	Newborn sm for gestational age, 1250-1499 grams
P05.16	Newborn sm for gestational age, 1500-1749 grams
P05.17	Newborn sm for gestational age, 1750-1999 grams
P05.2	Newborn affected by fetal malnut not light or sm for gestational age
P05.9	Newborn affected by slow intrauterine growth, unsp
P11.1	Oth spec brain damage d/t birth inj
P11.3	Birth inj to facial nerve
P13*	Birth inj to skeleton
P14.0	Erb's paralysis d/t birth inj
P14.1	Klumpke's paralysis d/t birth inj
P14.3	Oth brachial plexus birth injuries
P15*	Oth birth injuries
P19*	Metabolic acidemia in newborn
P22.1	Transient tachypnea of newborn
P22.8	Oth respiratory distress of newborn
P22.9	Respiratory distress of newborn, unsp
P28.1*	Oth and unsp atelectasis of newborn
P28.2	Cyanotic attacks of newborn
P28.3	Primary sleep apnea of newborn
P28.4	Oth apnea of newborn
P28.8*	Oth spec respiratory conditions of newborn
P28.9	Respiratory condition of newborn, unsp
P29.0	Neonatal cardiac failure
P29.1*	Neonatal cardiac dysrhythmia
P29.2	Neonatal hypertension
P29.4	Transient myocardial ischemia in newborn
P29.89	Oth cardiovasc d/o originating in the perinatal period
P29.9	Cardiovasc d/o origin in the perinatal period, unsp
P37.5	Neonatal candidiasis
P39.1	Neonatal conjunctivitis and dacryocystitis
P51*	Umbilical hemor of newborn
P54.0	Neonatal hematemesis
P54.6	Neonatal vaginal hemor
P54.8	Oth spec neonatal hemorrhages
P54.9	Neonatal hemor, unsp
P55.0	Rh isoimmunization of newborn
P55.1	ABO isoimmunization of newborn
P58*	Neonatal jaundice d/t oth excessive hemolysis
P59.0	Neonatal jaundice associated with preterm delivery

P61.1	Polycythemia neonatorum
P61.3	Congenital anemia from fetal bld loss
P61.4	Oth congenital anemias, NEC
P61.5	Transient neonatal neutropenia
P61.8	Oth spec perinatal hematological d/o
P61.9	Perinatal hematological d/o, unsp
P70.0	Synd of infant of mother with gestational diabetes
P70.1	Synd of infant of a diabetic mother
P70.8	Oth transitory d/o of carbohydrate metab of newborn
P70.9	Transitory d/o of carbohydrate metab of newborn, unsp
P72.0	Neonatal goiter, NEC
P72.2	Oth transitory neonatal d/o of thyroid function, NEC
P72.8	Oth spec transitory neonatal endocrine d/o
P72.9	Transitory neonatal endocrine d/o, unsp
P74.5	Transitory tyrosinemia of newborn
P74.6	Transitory hyperammonemia of newborn
P74.8	Oth transitory metabolic disturbances of newborn
P74.9	Transitory metabolic disturbance of newborn, unsp
P76.1	Transitory ileus of newborn
P76.8	Oth spec intestinal obstruction of newborn
P76.9	Intestinal obstruction of newborn, unsp
P78.1	Oth neonatal peritonitis
P78.2	Neonatal hematemesis and melena d/t swallowed matern bld
P78.3	Noninfective neonatal diarrhea
P78.8*	Oth spec perinatal digestive sys d/o
P78.9	Perinatal digestive sys d/o, unsp
P80.0	Cold inj synd
P80.8	Oth hypothermia of newborn
P80.9	Hypothermia of newborn, unsp
P81*	Oth disturbances of temperature regulation of newborn
P83.0	Sclerema neonatorum
P83.3*	Oth and unsp edema specific to newborn
P83.4	Breast engorgement of newborn
P83.5	Congenital hydrocele
P83.9	Condition of the integument specific to newborn, unsp
P84	Oth problems with newborn
P91.60	Hypoxic ischemic encephalopathy [HIE], unsp
P91.61	Mild hypoxic ischemic encephalopathy [HIE]
P94.1	Congenital hypertonia
P94.2	Congenital hypotonia
P94.8	Oth d/o of muscle tone of newborn
P94.9	D/o of muscle tone of newborn, unsp
P95	Stillbirth
P96.0	Congenital renal failure
P96.3	Wide cranial sutures of newborn
P96.5	Comp to newborn d/t (fetal) intrauterine procedure
P96.81	Expsr to (environmental) tobacco smoke in the perinat period
P96.83	Meconium staining
P96.89	Oth conditions originating in the perinatal period
P96.9	Condition originating in the perinatal period, unsp
Q86*	Congen malform syndromes d/t known exogenous causes, NEC

DRG 795   **Normal Newborn**

        GMLOS 3.1   AMLOS 3.1   RW 0.1758

Principal Diagnosis

P00.3	Newborn affected by oth maternal circ and resp dz
P00.9	Newborn affected by unsp maternal condition
P02.4	Newborn (suspected to be) affected by prolapsed cord
P02.5	Newborn affected by oth compression of umbilical cord
P02.60	Newborn affected by unsp conditions of umbilical cord
P02.69	Newborn affected by oth conditions of umbilical cord
P03.0	Newborn affected by breech delivery and extract
P03.1	Newborn affected by oth malpresent, malpos & disproprtn dur labr & del
P03.2	Newborn (suspected to be) affected by forceps delivery
P03.3	Newborn affected by delivery by vacuum extractor
P03.5	Newborn (suspected to be) affected by precipitate delivery
P03.9	Newborn affected by comp of labor and delivery, unsp
P05.08	Newborn light for gestational age, 2000-2499 grams
P05.18	Newborn sm for gestational age, 2000-2499 grams
P07.20	Extreme immaturity of newborn, unsp weeks of gestation
P08.0	Exceptionally large newborn baby
P08.1	Oth heavy for gestational age newborn
P08.21	Post-term newborn
P08.22	Prolonged gestation of newborn
P12.0	Cephalhematoma d/t birth inj
P12.1	Chignon (from vacuum extract) d/t birth inj
P12.3	Bruising of scalp d/t birth inj

T Transfer DRG   **SP** Special Payment   * Code Range   6th and 7th Character of ZZ = No Device, No Qualifier ZX = No Device, Diagnostic

288   MS-DRG Version 33.0   © 2015 Optum360, LLC

P12.4	Inj of scalp of newborn d/t monitoring equipment
P12.81	Caput succedaneum
P12.89	Oth birth injuries to scalp
P12.9	Birth inj to scalp, unsp
P54.5	Neonatal cutaneous hemor
P59.3	Neonatal jaundice from breast milk inhibitor
P59.8	Neonatal jaundice from oth spec causes
P59.9	Neonatal jaundice, unsp
P83.1	Neonatal erythema toxicum
P83.6	Umbilical polyp of newborn
P83.8	Oth spec conditions of integument specific to newborn
P92.09	Oth vomiting of newborn
P92.1	Regurgitation and rumination of newborn
P92.2	Slow feeding of newborn
P92.3	Underfeeding of newborn
P92.4	Overfeeding of newborn
P92.5	Neonatal difficulty in feeding at breast
P92.8	Oth feeding problems of newborn
P92.9	Feeding problem of newborn, unsp
P96.82	Delayed separation of umbilical cord
Z38.00	Single liveborn infant, delivered vaginally
Z38.01	Single liveborn infant, delivered by cesarean
Z38.1	Single liveborn infant, born outside hospital
Z38.2	Single liveborn infant, unsp as to place of birth
Z38.30	Twin liveborn infant, delivered vaginally
Z38.31	Twin liveborn infant, delivered by cesarean
Z38.4	Twin liveborn infant, born outside hospital
Z38.5	Twin liveborn infant, unsp as to place of birth
Z38.61	Triplet liveborn infant, delivered vaginally
Z38.62	Triplet liveborn infant, delivered by cesarean
Z38.63	Quadruplet liveborn infant, delivered vaginally
Z38.64	Quadruplet liveborn infant, delivered by cesarean
Z38.65	Quintuplet liveborn infant, delivered vaginally
Z38.66	Quintuplet liveborn infant, delivered by cesarean
Z38.68	Oth multi liveborn infant, delivered vaginally
Z38.69	Oth multi liveborn infant, delivered by cesarean
Z38.7	Oth multi liveborn infant, born outside hospital
Z38.8	Oth multi liveborn infant, unsp as to place of birth

AND

No secondary diagnoses

OR

Only secondary diagnoses

J34.0	Abscess, furuncle and carbuncle of nose
J34.1	Cyst and mucocele of nose and nasal sinus
J34.81	Nasal mucositis (ulcerative)
J34.89	Oth spec d/o of nose and nasal sinuses
J34.9	Unsp d/o of nose and nasal sinuses
K00.6	Disturbances in tooth eruption
K01.0	Embedded teeth
K01.1	Impacted teeth
L08.9	Local infxn of the skin and SQ tissue, unsp
L22	Diaper dermatitis
L57.3	Poikiloderma of Civatte
L80	Vitiligo
L81.0	Postinflammatory hyperpigmentation
L81.1	Chloasma
L81.2	Freckles
L81.3	Cafe au lait spots
L81.4	Oth melanin hyperpigmentation
L81.5	Leukoderma, NEC
L81.6	Oth d/o of diminished melanin formation
L81.7	Pigmented purpuric dermatosis
L81.8	Oth spec d/o of pigmentation
L81.9	D/o of pigmentation, unsp
N47.0	Adherent prepuce, newborn
N47.1	Phimosis
N47.2	Paraphimosis
N47.3	Deficient foreskin
N47.4	Benign cyst of prepuce
N47.5	Adhesions of prepuce and glans penis
N47.7	Oth inflam dz of prepuce
N47.8	Oth d/o of prepuce
N89.8	Oth spec noninflammatory d/o of vagina
P00.2	Newborn affected by maternal infec/parastc dz
P00.89	Newborn affected by oth maternal conditions
Q17.0	Accessory auricle
Q53.00	Ectopic testis, unsp
Q53.01	Ectopic testis, unilat

Q53.02	Ectopic testes, bilat
Q53.10	Unsp undescended testicle, unilat
Q53.11	Abd testis, unilat
Q53.12	Ectopic perineal testis, unilat
Q53.20	Undescended testicle, unsp, bilat
Q53.21	Abd testis, bilat
Q53.22	Ectopic perineal testis, bilat
Q53.9	Undescended testicle, unsp
Q55.22	Retractile testis
Q66.50	Congenital pes planus, unsp foot
Q66.51	Congenital pes planus, rt foot
Q66.52	Congenital pes planus, lt foot
Q66.80	Congenital vertical talus deformity, unsp foot
Q66.81	Congenital vertical talus deformity, rt foot
Q66.82	Congenital vertical talus deformity, lt foot
Q81.0	Epidermolysis bullosa simplex
Q81.1	Epidermolysis bullosa letalis
Q81.2	Epidermolysis bullosa dystrophica
Q81.8	Oth epidermolysis bullosa
Q81.9	Epidermolysis bullosa, unsp
Q82.1	Xeroderma pigmentosum
Q82.2	Mastocytosis
Q82.3	Incontinentia pigmenti
Q82.8	Oth spec congenital malformations of skin
Q82.9	Congenital malformation of skin, unsp
R09.81	Nasal congestion
R87.618	Oth abnormal cytolog findings on specimens from cervix uteri
R87.619	Unsp abnormal cytolog findings in specmn from cervix uteri
R87.629	Unsp abnormal cytological findings in specimens from vagina
R89.7	Abnormal histolog findings in specimens from oth org/tiss
R94.120	Abnormal auditory function study
Z00.110	Health exam for newborn under 8 days old
Z00.111	Health exam for newborn 8 to 28 days old
Z00.121	Enc for routine child health exam w abnormal findings
Z00.129	Enc for routine child health exam w/o abnormal findings
Z01.10	Enc for exam of ears and hearing w/o abnormal findings
Z01.110	Enc for hearing exam following failed hear screening
Z01.118	Enc for exam of ears and hearing w oth abnormal findings
Z01.12	Enc for hearing conservation and tx
Z02.6	Enc for exam for insurance purposes
Z02.82	Enc for adoption services
Z02.89	Enc for oth administrative examinations
Z13.228	Enc for screening for oth metabolic d/o
Z20.09	Contact w and exposure to oth intestinal infectious dz
Z20.7	Cntct w & expsr to pediculosis, acariasis & oth infestations
Z20.810	Contact with and (suspected) exposure to anthrax
Z20.818	Contact w and exposure to oth bact communicable dz
Z20.89	Contact w and exposure to oth communicable dz
Z23	Enc for immunization
Z28.01	Immunization not crd out because of acute illness of patient
Z28.02	Immuniz not crd out bec chr illness or cond of patient
Z28.03	Immuniz not crd out bec immune compromised state of patient
Z28.04	Immuniz not crd out bec patient allergy to vaccine or cmpnt
Z28.09	Immunization not carried out because of oth contraindication
Z28.1	Immuniz not crd out because of patient belief/grp pressr
Z28.20	Immuniz not crd out bec patient decision for unsp reason
Z28.21	Immunization not carried out because of patient refusal
Z28.29	Immuniz not crd out bec patient decision for oth reason
Z28.81	Immuniz not crd out d/t patient having had the dz
Z28.82	Immunization not carried out because of caregiver refusal
Z28.89	Immunization not carried out for oth reason
Z28.9	Immunization not carried out for unsp reason
Z41.2	Enc for routine and ritual male circumcision
Z41.3	Enc for ear piercing
Z53.01	Proc/tx not carried out d/t patient smoking
Z53.09	Proc/tx not carried out because of contraindication
Z53.1	Proc/tx not crd out bec pt belief and group pressure
Z53.20	Proc/tx not crd out bec pt decision for unsp reasons
Z53.21	Proc/tx not crd out d/t pt lv bef seen by hlth care prov
Z53.29	Proc/tx not crd out bec pt decision for oth reasons
Z53.8	Procedure and tx not carried out for oth reasons
Z53.9	Procedure and tx not carried out, unsp reason
Z76.2	Enc for hlth suprvsn and care of healthy infant and child
Z81.8	Family history of oth mental and behavl d/o
Z82.0	Family history of epilepsy and oth dis of the nervous sys
Z82.49	Family hx of ischem heart dis and oth dis of the circ sys
Z83.1	Family history of oth infectious and parasitic dz
Z83.3	Family history of diabetes mellitus
Z83.49	Family history of endo, nutritional and metabolic dz

MDC 15: Newborns And Other Neonates With Conditions Originating In The Perinatal Period—MEDICAL

Surgical   **Medical**   **CC Indicator**   **MCC Indicator**   **Procedure Proxy**   **PDxMCC PDx acts as own MCC**   **PDxCC PDx acts as own CC**

MDC 16
Diseases And Disorders Of The Blood And Blood-Forming Organs And Immunological Disorders

SURGICAL

DRG 799   Splenectomy with MCC
GMLOS 9.2   AMLOS 11.6   RW 4.7569

Operating Room Procedures

075P*	Destr/Spleen
079P0ZX	Drain of Spleen, Opn Appr, Diagnostic
079P0[0,Z]Z	Drain/Spleen, Opn, [Drain Dev, No Dev], NQ
07BP0ZX	Exc of Spleen, Opn Appr, Diagnostic
07BP[0,3,4]ZZ	Exc/Spleen, [Opn, Perc, Perc Endo]
07CP0ZZ	Extir of Matter from Spleen, Opn Appr
07NP*	Rls/Spleen
07PP[0,3,4][0,3]Z	Rmvl/Spleen, [Opn, Perc, Perc Endo], [Drain Dev, Inf Dev], NQ
07QP*	Repair/Spleen
07SP0ZZ	Repos Spleen, Opn Appr
07TP*	Resect/Spleen
07WP[0,3,4][0,3]Z	Rev/Spleen, [Opn, Perc, Perc Endo], [Drain Dev, Inf Dev], NQ
07YP*	Transplantation/Spleen

DRG 800   Splenectomy with CC
GMLOS 5.3   AMLOS 6.8   RW 2.7364

Select operating room procedures listed under DRG 799

DRG 801   Splenectomy without CC/MCC
GMLOS 2.8   AMLOS 3.7   RW 1.7458

Select operating room procedures listed under DRG 799

DRG 802   Other O.R. Procedures of the Blood and Blood-Forming Organs with MCC
GMLOS 8.1   AMLOS 11.1   RW 3.3880

OPERATING ROOM PROCEDURES

02HV[0,3,4][2,D]Z	Insert/Superior Vena Cava, [Opn, Perc, Perc Endo], [Monitoring Dev, Intralum Dev], NQ
02J[A,Y]4ZZ	Inspect of [Heart, Great Vessel], Perc Endo Appr
02LV*	Occlsn/Superior Vena Cava
02VV*	Restrict/Superior Vena Cava
06H0[0,3,4]DZ	Insert/Inferior Vena Cava, [Opn, Perc, Perc Endo], Intralum Dev, NQ
06L0*	Occlsn/Inferior Vena Cava
06V0*	Restrict/Inferior Vena Cava
0750*	Destr/Lymphatic, Head
0751*	Destr/Lymphatic, Rt Neck
0752*	Destr/Lymphatic, Lt Neck
0753*	Destr/Lymphatic, Rt Upr Extr
0754*	Destr/Lymphatic, Lt Upr Extr
0755*	Destr/Lymphatic, Rt Axillary
0756*	Destr/Lymphatic, Lt Axillary
0757*	Destr/Lymphatic, Thorax
0758*	Destr/Lymphatic, Int Mammary, Rt
0759*	Destr/Lymphatic, Int Mammary, Lt
075B*	Destr/Lymphatic, Mesenteric
075C*	Destr/Lymphatic, Pelvis
075D*	Destr/Lymphatic, Aortic
075F*	Destr/Lymphatic, Rt Lwr Extr
075G*	Destr/Lymphatic, Lt Lwr Extr
075H*	Destr/Lymphatic, Rt Inguinal
075J*	Destr/Lymphatic, Lt Inguinal
075M*	Destr/Thymus
0790*	Drain/Lymphatic, Head
0791*	Drain/Lymphatic, Rt Neck
0792*	Drain/Lymphatic, Lt Neck
0793*	Drain/Lymphatic, Rt Upr Extr
0794*	Drain/Lymphatic, Lt Upr Extr
0795*	Drain/Lymphatic, Rt Axillary
0796*	Drain/Lymphatic, Lt Axillary
0797*	Drain/Lymphatic, Thorax
0798*	Drain/Lymphatic, Int Mammary, Rt
0799*	Drain/Lymphatic, Int Mammary, Lt
079B*	Drain/Lymphatic, Mesenteric
079C*	Drain/Lymphatic, Pelvis
079D*	Drain/Lymphatic, Aortic
079F*	Drain/Lymphatic, Rt Lwr Extr
079G*	Drain/Lymphatic, Lt Lwr Extr
079H*	Drain/Lymphatic, Rt Inguinal
079J*	Drain/Lymphatic, Lt Inguinal
079K[0,3,4]ZX	Drain/Thoracic Duct, [Opn, Perc, Perc Endo]
079L[0,3,4]ZX	Drain/Cisterna Chyli, [Opn, Perc, Perc Endo]
079M*	Drain/Thymus
07B0*	Exc/Lymphatic, Head
07B1*	Exc/Lymphatic, Rt Neck
07B2*	Exc/Lymphatic, Lt Neck
07B3*	Exc/Lymphatic, Rt Upr Extr
07B4*	Exc/Lymphatic, Lt Upr Extr
07B5*	Exc/Lymphatic, Rt Axillary
07B6*	Exc/Lymphatic, Lt Axillary
07B7*	Exc/Lymphatic, Thorax
07B8*	Exc/Lymphatic, Int Mammary, Rt
07B9*	Exc/Lymphatic, Int Mammary, Lt
07BB*	Exc/Lymphatic, Mesenteric
07BC*	Exc/Lymphatic, Pelvis
07BD*	Exc/Lymphatic, Aortic
07BF*	Exc/Lymphatic, Rt Lwr Extr
07BG*	Exc/Lymphatic, Lt Lwr Extr
07BH*	Exc/Lymphatic, Rt Inguinal
07BJ*	Exc/Lymphatic, Lt Inguinal
07BK[0,3,4]ZX	Exc/Thoracic Duct, [Opn, Perc, Perc Endo]
07BL[0,3,4]ZX	Exc/Cisterna Chyli, [Opn, Perc, Perc Endo]
07BM[0,3,4]Z[X,Z]	Exc/Thymus, [Opn, Perc, Perc Endo], No Dev, [Dx, NQ]
07C0[0,3,4]ZZ	Extir/Lymphatic, Head, [Opn, Perc, Perc Endo]
07C1[0,3,4]ZZ	Extir/Lymphatic, Rt Neck, [Opn, Perc, Perc Endo]
07C2[0,3,4]ZZ	Extir/Lymphatic, Lt Neck, [Opn, Perc, Perc Endo]
07C3[0,3,4]ZZ	Extir/Lymphatic, Rt Upr Extr, [Opn, Perc, Perc Endo]
07C4[0,3,4]ZZ	Extir/Lymphatic, Lt Upr Extr, [Opn, Perc, Perc Endo]
07C5[0,3,4]ZZ	Extir/Lymphatic, Rt Axillary, [Opn, Perc, Perc Endo]
07C6[0,3,4]ZZ	Extir/Lymphatic, Lt Axillary, [Opn, Perc, Perc Endo]
07C7[0,3,4]ZZ	Extir/Lymphatic, Thorax, [Opn, Perc, Perc Endo]
07C8[0,3,4]ZZ	Extir/Lymphatic, Int Mammary, Rt, [Opn, Perc, Perc Endo]
07C9[0,3,4]ZZ	Extir/Lymphatic, Int Mammary, Lt, [Opn, Perc, Perc Endo]
07CB[0,3,4]ZZ	Extir/Lymphatic, Mesenteric, [Opn, Perc, Perc Endo]
07CC[0,3,4]ZZ	Extir/Lymphatic, Pelvis, [Opn, Perc, Perc Endo]
07CD[0,3,4]ZZ	Extir/Lymphatic, Aortic, [Opn, Perc, Perc Endo]
07CF[0,3,4]ZZ	Extir/Lymphatic, Rt Lwr Extr, [Opn, Perc, Perc Endo]
07CG[0,3,4]ZZ	Extir/Lymphatic, Lt Lwr Extr, [Opn, Perc, Perc Endo]
07CH[0,3,4]ZZ	Extir/Lymphatic, Rt Inguinal, [Opn, Perc, Perc Endo]
07CJ[0,3,4]ZZ	Extir/Lymphatic, Lt Inguinal, [Opn, Perc, Perc Endo]
07CK[0,3,4]ZZ	Extir/Thoracic Duct, [Opn, Perc, Perc Endo]
07CL[0,3,4]ZZ	Extir/Cisterna Chyli, [Opn, Perc, Perc Endo]
07CM[0,3,4]ZZ	Extir/Thymus, [Opn, Perc, Perc Endo]
07JK[0,3,4]ZZ	Inspect/Thoracic Duct, [Opn, Perc, Perc Endo]
07JL[0,3,4]ZZ	Inspect/Cisterna Chyli, [Opn, Perc, Perc Endo]
07JM[0,4]ZZ	Inspect/Thymus, [Opn, Perc Endo]
07JN[0,3,4]ZZ	Inspect/Lymphatic, [Opn, Perc, Perc Endo]
07JP0ZZ	Inspect of Spleen, Opn Appr
07L0[0,3,4][C,D,Z]Z	Occlsn/Lymphatic, Head, [Opn, Perc, Perc Endo], [Extralum Dev, Intralum Dev, No Dev], NQ
07L1[0,3,4][C,D,Z]Z	Occlsn/Lymphatic, Rt Neck, [Opn, Perc, Perc Endo], [Extralum Dev, Intralum Dev, No Dev], NQ
07L2[0,3,4][C,D,Z]Z	Occlsn/Lymphatic, Lt Neck, [Opn, Perc, Perc Endo], [Extralum Dev, Intralum Dev, No Dev], NQ
07L3[0,3,4][C,D,Z]Z	Occlsn/Lymphatic, Rt Upr Extr, [Opn, Perc, Perc Endo], [Extralum Dev, Intralum Dev, No Dev], NQ
07L4[0,3,4][C,D,Z]Z	Occlsn/Lymphatic, Lt Upr Extr, [Opn, Perc, Perc Endo], [Extralum Dev, Intralum Dev, No Dev], NQ
07L5[0,3,4][C,D,Z]Z	Occlsn/Lymphatic, Rt Axillary, [Opn, Perc, Perc Endo], [Extralum Dev, Intralum Dev, No Dev], NQ
07L6[0,3,4][C,D,Z]Z	Occlsn/Lymphatic, Lt Axillary, [Opn, Perc, Perc Endo], [Extralum Dev, Intralum Dev, No Dev], NQ

Ⓣ **Transfer DRG**   ⓢⓟ **Special Payment**   * **Code Range**   **6th and 7th Character of ZZ = No Device, No QUALIFIER ZX = No Device, Diagnostic**

07L7[Ø,3,4][C,D,Z]Z Occlsn/Lymphatic, Thorax, [Opn, Perc, Perc Endo], [Extralum Dev, Intralum Dev, No Dev], NQ
07L8[Ø,3,4][C,D,Z]Z Occlsn/Lymphatic, Int Mammary, Rt, [Opn, Perc, Perc Endo], [Extralum Dev, Intralum Dev, No Dev], NQ
07L9[Ø,3,4][C,D,Z]Z Occlsn/Lymphatic, Int Mammary, Lt, [Opn, Perc, Perc Endo], [Extralum Dev, Intralum Dev, No Dev], NQ
07LB[Ø,3,4][C,D,Z]Z Occlsn/Lymphatic, Mesenteric, [Opn, Perc, Perc Endo], [Extralum Dev, Intralum Dev, No Dev], NQ
07LC[Ø,3,4][C,D,Z]Z Occlsn/Lymphatic, Pelvis, [Opn, Perc, Perc Endo], [Extralum Dev, Intralum Dev, No Dev], NQ
07LD[Ø,3,4][C,D,Z]Z Occlsn/Lymphatic, Aortic, [Opn, Perc, Perc Endo], [Extralum Dev, Intralum Dev, No Dev], NQ
07LF[Ø,3,4][C,D,Z]Z Occlsn/Lymphatic, Rt Lwr Extr, [Opn, Perc, Perc Endo], [Extralum Dev, Intralum Dev, No Dev], NQ
07LG[Ø,3,4][C,D,Z]Z Occlsn/Lymphatic, Lt Lwr Extr, [Opn, Perc, Perc Endo], [Extralum Dev, Intralum Dev, No Dev], NQ
07LH[Ø,3,4][C,D,Z]Z Occlsn/Lymphatic, Rt Inguinal, [Opn, Perc, Perc Endo], [Extralum Dev, Intralum Dev, No Dev], NQ
07LJ[Ø,3,4][C,D,Z]Z Occlsn/Lymphatic, Lt Inguinal, [Opn, Perc, Perc Endo], [Extralum Dev, Intralum Dev, No Dev], NQ
07NØ[Ø,3,4]ZZ Rls/Lymphatic, Head, [Opn, Perc, Perc Endo]
07N1[Ø,3,4]ZZ Rls/Lymphatic, Rt Neck, [Opn, Perc, Perc Endo]
07N2[Ø,3,4]ZZ Rls/Lymphatic, Lt Neck, [Opn, Perc, Perc Endo]
07N3[Ø,3,4]ZZ Rls/Lymphatic, Rt Upr Extr, [Opn, Perc, Perc Endo]
07N4[Ø,3,4]ZZ Rls/Lymphatic, Lt Upr Extr, [Opn, Perc, Perc Endo]
07N5[Ø,3,4]ZZ Rls/Lymphatic, Rt Axillary, [Opn, Perc, Perc Endo]
07N6[Ø,3,4]ZZ Rls/Lymphatic, Lt Axillary, [Opn, Perc, Perc Endo]
07N7[Ø,3,4]ZZ Rls/Lymphatic, Thorax, [Opn, Perc, Perc Endo]
07N8[Ø,3,4]ZZ Rls/Lymphatic, Int Mammary, Rt, [Opn, Perc, Perc Endo]
07N9[Ø,3,4]ZZ Rls/Lymphatic, Int Mammary, Lt, [Opn, Perc, Perc Endo]
07NB[Ø,3,4]ZZ Rls/Lymphatic, Mesenteric, [Opn, Perc, Perc Endo]
07NC[Ø,3,4]ZZ Rls/Lymphatic, Pelvis, [Opn, Perc, Perc Endo]
07ND[Ø,3,4]ZZ Rls/Lymphatic, Aortic, [Opn, Perc, Perc Endo]
07NF[Ø,3,4]ZZ Rls/Lymphatic, Rt Lwr Extr, [Opn, Perc, Perc Endo]
07NG[Ø,3,4]ZZ Rls/Lymphatic, Lt Lwr Extr, [Opn, Perc, Perc Endo]
07NH[Ø,3,4]ZZ Rls/Lymphatic, Rt Inguinal, [Opn, Perc, Perc Endo]
07NJ[Ø,3,4]ZZ Rls/Lymphatic, Lt Inguinal, [Opn, Perc, Perc Endo]
07NM[Ø,3,4]ZZ Rls/Thymus, [Opn, Perc, Perc Endo]
07PK[Ø,3,4][7,J,K]Z Rmvl/Thoracic Duct, [Opn, Perc, Perc Endo], [Auto Tissue Sub, Synth Sub, Nonauto Tissue Sub], NQ
07PL[Ø,3,4][7,J,K]Z Rmvl/Cisterna Chyli, [Opn, Perc, Perc Endo], [Auto Tissue Sub, Synth Sub, Nonauto Tissue Sub], NQ
07PM[Ø,3,4][Ø,3]Z Rmvl/Thymus, [Opn, Perc, Perc Endo], [Drain Dev, Inf Dev], NQ
07PN[Ø,3,4][Ø,3,7,C,D,J,K]Z Rmvl/Lymphatic, [Opn, Perc, Perc Endo], [Drain Dev, Inf Dev, Auto Tissue Sub, Extralum Dev, Intralum Dev, Synth Sub, Nonauto Tissue Sub], NQ
07QØ[Ø,3,4]ZZ Rpr/Lymphatic, Head, [Opn, Perc, Perc Endo]
07Q1[Ø,3,4]ZZ Rpr/Lymphatic, Rt Neck, [Opn, Perc, Perc Endo]
07Q2[Ø,3,4]ZZ Rpr/Lymphatic, Lt Neck, [Opn, Perc, Perc Endo]
07Q3[Ø,3,4]ZZ Rpr/Lymphatic, Rt Upr Extr, [Opn, Perc, Perc Endo]
07Q4[Ø,3,4]ZZ Rpr/Lymphatic, Lt Upr Extr, [Opn, Perc, Perc Endo]
07Q5[Ø,3,4]ZZ Rpr/Lymphatic, Rt Axillary, [Opn, Perc, Perc Endo]
07Q6[Ø,3,4]ZZ Rpr/Lymphatic, Lt Axillary, [Opn, Perc, Perc Endo]
07Q7[Ø,3,4]ZZ Rpr/Lymphatic, Thorax, [Opn, Perc, Perc Endo]
07Q8[Ø,3,4]ZZ Rpr/Lymphatic, Int Mammary, Rt, [Opn, Perc, Perc Endo]
07Q9[Ø,3,4]ZZ Rpr/Lymphatic, Int Mammary, Lt, [Opn, Perc, Perc Endo]
07QB[Ø,3,4]ZZ Rpr/Lymphatic, Mesenteric, [Opn, Perc, Perc Endo]
07QC[Ø,3,4]ZZ Rpr/Lymphatic, Pelvis, [Opn, Perc, Perc Endo]
07QD[Ø,3,4]ZZ Rpr/Lymphatic, Aortic, [Opn, Perc, Perc Endo]
07QF[Ø,3,4]ZZ Rpr/Lymphatic, Rt Lwr Extr, [Opn, Perc, Perc Endo]
07QG[Ø,3,4]ZZ Rpr/Lymphatic, Lt Lwr Extr, [Opn, Perc, Perc Endo]
07QH[Ø,3,4]ZZ Rpr/Lymphatic, Rt Inguinal, [Opn, Perc, Perc Endo]
07QJ[Ø,3,4]ZZ Rpr/Lymphatic, Lt Inguinal, [Opn, Perc, Perc Endo]
07QM[Ø,3,4]ZZ Rpr/Thymus, [Opn, Perc, Perc Endo]
07SMØZZ Repos Thymus, Opn Appr
07TØ[Ø,4]ZZ Resect/Lymphatic, Head, [Opn, Perc Endo]
07T1[Ø,4]ZZ Resect/Lymphatic, Rt Neck, [Opn, Perc Endo]
07T2[Ø,4]ZZ Resect/Lymphatic, Lt Neck, [Opn, Perc Endo]
07T3[Ø,4]ZZ Resect/Lymphatic, Rt Upr Extr, [Opn, Perc Endo]
07T4[Ø,4]ZZ Resect/Lymphatic, Lt Upr Extr, [Opn, Perc Endo]
07T5[Ø,4]ZZ Resect/Lymphatic, Rt Axillary, [Opn, Perc Endo]
07T6[Ø,4]ZZ Resect/Lymphatic, Lt Axillary, [Opn, Perc Endo]
07T7[Ø,4]ZZ Resect/Lymphatic, Thorax, [Opn, Perc Endo]
07T8[Ø,4]ZZ Resect/Lymphatic, Int Mammary, Rt, [Opn, Perc Endo]
07T9[Ø,4]ZZ Resect/Lymphatic, Int Mammary, Lt, [Opn, Perc Endo]
07TB[Ø,4]ZZ Resect/Lymphatic, Mesenteric, [Opn, Perc Endo]
07TC[Ø,4]ZZ Resect/Lymphatic, Pelvis, [Opn, Perc Endo]
07TD[Ø,4]ZZ Resect/Lymphatic, Aortic, [Opn, Perc Endo]
07TF[Ø,4]ZZ Resect/Lymphatic, Rt Lwr Extr, [Opn, Perc Endo]
07TG[Ø,4]ZZ Resect/Lymphatic, Lt Lwr Extr, [Opn, Perc Endo]

07TH[Ø,4]ZZ Resect/Lymphatic, Rt Inguinal, [Opn, Perc Endo]
07TJ[Ø,4]ZZ Resect/Lymphatic, Lt Inguinal, [Opn, Perc Endo]
07TM[Ø,4]ZZ Resect/Thymus, [Opn, Perc Endo]
07UØ[Ø,4][7,J,K]Z Supl/Lymphatic, Head, [Opn, Perc Endo] [Auto Tissue Sub, Synth Sub, Nonauto Tissue Sub], NQ
07U1[Ø,4][7,J,K]Z Supl/Lymphatic, Rt Neck, [Opn, Perc Endo], [Auto Tissue Sub, Synth Sub, Nonauto Tissue Sub], NQ
07U2[Ø,4][7,J,K]Z Supl/Lymphatic, Lt Neck, [Opn, Perc Endo], [Auto Tissue Sub, Synth Sub, Nonauto Tissue Sub], NQ
07U3[Ø,4][7,J,K]Z Supl/Lymphatic, Rt Upr Extr, [Opn, Perc Endo], [Auto Tissue Sub, Synth Sub, Nonauto Tissue Sub], NQ
07U4[Ø,4][7,J,K]Z Supl/Lymphatic, Lt Upr Extr, [Opn, Perc Endo], [Auto Tissue Sub, Synth Sub, Nonauto Tissue Sub], NQ
07U5[Ø,4][7,J,K]Z Supl/Lymphatic, Rt Axillary, [Opn, Perc Endo], [Auto Tissue Sub, Synth Sub, Nonauto Tissue Sub], NQ
07U6[Ø,4][7,J,K]Z Supl/Lymphatic, Lt Axillary, [Opn, Perc Endo], [Auto Tissue Sub, Synth Sub, Nonauto Tissue Sub], NQ
07U7[Ø,4][7,J,K]Z Supl/Lymphatic, Thorax, [Opn, Perc Endo], [Auto Tissue Sub, Synth Sub, Nonauto Tissue Sub], NQ
07U8[Ø,4][7,J,K]Z Supl/Lymphatic, Int Mammary, Rt, [Opn, Perc Endo], [Auto Tissue Sub, Synth Sub, Nonauto Tissue Sub], NQ
07U9[Ø,4][7,J,K]Z Supl/Lymphatic, Int Mammary, Lt, [Opn, Perc Endo], [Auto Tissue Sub, Synth Sub, Nonauto Tissue Sub], NQ
07UB[Ø,4][7,J,K]Z Supl/Lymphatic, Mesenteric, [Opn, Perc Endo], [Auto Tissue Sub, Synth Sub, Nonauto Tissue Sub], NQ
07UC[Ø,4][7,J,K]Z Supl/Lymphatic, Pelvis, [Opn, Perc Endo], [Auto Tissue Sub, Synth Sub, Nonauto Tissue Sub], NQ
07UD[Ø,4][7,J,K]Z Supl/Lymphatic, Aortic, [Opn, Perc Endo], [Auto Tissue Sub, Synth Sub, Nonauto Tissue Sub], NQ
07UF[Ø,4][7,J,K]Z Supl/Lymphatic, Rt Lwr Extr, [Opn, Perc Endo], [Auto Tissue Sub, Synth Sub, Nonauto Tissue Sub], NQ
07UG[Ø,4][7,J,K]Z Supl/Lymphatic, Lt Lwr Extr, [Opn, Perc Endo], [Auto Tissue Sub, Synth Sub, Nonauto Tissue Sub], NQ
07UH[Ø,4][7,J,K]Z Supl/Lymphatic, Rt Inguinal, [Opn, Perc Endo], [Auto Tissue Sub, Synth Sub, Nonauto Tissue Sub], NQ
07UJ[Ø,4][7,J,K]Z Supl/Lymphatic, Lt Inguinal, [Opn, Perc Endo], [Auto Tissue Sub, Synth Sub, Nonauto Tissue Sub], NQ
07VØ[Ø,3,4][C,D,Z]Z Restrict/Lymphatic, Head, [Opn, Perc, Perc Endo], [Extralum Dev, Intralum Dev, No Dev], NQ
07V1[Ø,3,4][C,D,Z]Z Restrict/Lymphatic, Rt Neck, [Opn, Perc, Perc Endo], [Extralum Dev, Intralum Dev, No Dev], NQ
07V2[Ø,3,4][C,D,Z]Z Restrict/Lymphatic, Lt Neck, [Opn, Perc, Perc Endo], [Extralum Dev, Intralum Dev, No Dev], NQ
07V3[Ø,3,4][C,D,Z]Z Restrict/Lymphatic, Rt Upr Extr, [Opn, Perc, Perc Endo], [Extralum Dev, Intralum Dev, No Dev], NQ
07V4[Ø,3,4][C,D,Z]Z Restrict/Lymphatic, Lt Upr Extr, [Opn, Perc, Perc Endo], [Extralum Dev, Intralum Dev, No Dev], NQ
07V5[Ø,3,4][C,D,Z]Z Restrict/Lymphatic, Rt Axillary, [Opn, Perc, Perc Endo], [Extralum Dev, Intralum Dev, No Dev], NQ
07V6[Ø,3,4][C,D,Z]Z Restrict/Lymphatic, Lt Axillary, [Opn, Perc, Perc Endo], [Extralum Dev, Intralum Dev, No Dev], NQ
07V7[Ø,3,4][C,D,Z]Z Restrict/Lymphatic, Thorax, [Opn, Perc, Perc Endo], [Extralum Dev, Intralum Dev, No Dev], NQ
07V8[Ø,3,4][C,D,Z]Z Restrict/Lymphatic, Int Mammary, Rt, [Opn, Perc, Perc Endo], [Extralum Dev, Intralum Dev, No Dev], NQ
07V9[Ø,3,4][C,D,Z]Z Restrict/Lymphatic, Int Mammary, Lt, [Opn, Perc, Perc Endo], [Extralum Dev, Intralum Dev, No Dev], NQ
07VB[Ø,3,4][C,D,Z]Z Restrict/Lymphatic, Mesenteric, [Opn, Perc, Perc Endo], [Extralum Dev, Intralum Dev, No Dev], NQ
07VC[Ø,3,4][C,D,Z]Z Restrict/Lymphatic, Pelvis, [Opn, Perc, Perc Endo], [Extralum Dev, Intralum Dev, No Dev], NQ
07VD[Ø,3,4][C,D,Z]Z Restrict/Lymphatic, Aortic, [Opn, Perc, Perc Endo], [Extralum Dev, Intralum Dev, No Dev], NQ
07VF[Ø,3,4][C,D,Z]Z Restrict/Lymphatic, Rt Lwr Extr, [Opn, Perc, Perc Endo], [Extralum Dev, Intralum Dev, No Dev], NQ
07VG[Ø,3,4][C,D,Z]Z Restrict/Lymphatic, Lt Lwr Extr, [Opn, Perc, Perc Endo], [Extralum Dev, Intralum Dev, No Dev], NQ
07VH[Ø,3,4][C,D,Z]Z Restrict/Lymphatic, Rt Inguinal, [Opn, Perc, Perc Endo], [Extralum Dev, Intralum Dev, No Dev], NQ
07VJ[Ø,3,4][C,D,Z]Z Restrict/Lymphatic, Lt Inguinal, [Opn, Perc, Perc Endo], [Extralum Dev, Intralum Dev, No Dev], NQ
07WK[Ø,3,4][7,J,K]Z Rev/Thoracic Duct, [Opn, Perc, Perc Endo], [Auto Tissue Sub, Synth Sub, Nonauto Tissue Sub], NQ
07WL[Ø,3,4][7,J,K]Z Rev/Cisterna Chyli, [Opn, Perc, Perc Endo], [Auto Tissue Sub, Synth Sub, Nonauto Tissue Sub], NQ
07WM[Ø,3,4][Ø,3]Z Rev/Thymus, [Opn, Perc, Perc Endo], [Drain Dev, Inf Dev], NQ
07WN[Ø,3,4][Ø,3,7,C,D,J,K]Z Rev/Lymphatic, [Opn, Perc, Perc Endo], [Drain Dev, Inf Dev, Auto Tissue Sub, Extralum Dev, Intralum Dev, Synth Sub, Nonauto Tissue Sub], NQ

Surgical   **Medical**   **CC Indicator**   **MCC Indicator**   **Procedure Proxy**   **PDxMCC** **PDx acts as own MCC**   **PDxCC** **PDx acts as own CC**

MS-DRG Version 33.0

Code	Description
07YMØZ[Ø,1,2]	Transplantation/Thymus, Opn, No Dev, [Allogeneic, Syngeneic, Zooplastic]
ØD9S[Ø,3,4]ZX	Drain/Greater Omentum, [Opn, Perc, Perc Endo]
ØD9T[Ø,3,4]ZX	Drain/Lesser Omentum, [Opn, Perc, Perc Endo]
ØD9V[Ø,3,4]ZX	Drain/Mesentery, [Opn, Perc, Perc Endo]
ØD9W[Ø,3,4]ZX	Drain/Peritoneum, [Opn, Perc, Perc Endo]
ØDBSØZX	Exc of Greater Omentum, Opn Appr, Diagnostic
ØDBTØZX	Exc of Lesser Omentum, Opn Appr, Diagnostic
ØDBVØZX	Exc of Mesentery, Opn Appr, Diagnostic
ØDBWØZX	Exc of Peritoneum, Opn Appr, Diagnostic
ØDJØØZZ	Inspect of Upr Intestinal Tract, Opn Appr
ØDJ6ØZZ	Inspect of Stomach, Opn Appr
ØDJDØZZ	Inspect of Lwr Intestinal Tract, Opn Appr
ØDJU[Ø,3,4]ZZ	Inspect/Omentum, [Opn, Perc, Perc Endo]
ØDJV[Ø,3,4]ZZ	Inspect/Mesentery, [Opn, Perc, Perc Endo]
ØDJW[Ø,3,4]ZZ	Inspect/Peritoneum, [Opn, Perc, Perc Endo]
ØF9ØØZX	Drain of Liver, Opn Appr, Diagnostic
ØF91ØZX	Drain of Rt Lobe Liver, Opn Appr, Diagnostic
ØF92ØZX	Drain of Lt Lobe Liver, Opn Appr, Diagnostic
ØFBØ[Ø,4]ZX	Exc/Liver, [Opn, Perc Endo]
ØFB1[Ø,4]ZX	Exc/Liver, Rt Lobe, [Opn, Perc Endo]
ØFB2[Ø,4]ZX	Exc/Liver, Lt Lobe, [Opn, Perc Endo]
ØFJØ[Ø,3,4]ZZ	Inspect/Liver, [Opn, Perc, Perc Endo]
ØFJ44ZZ	Inspect of Gallbladder, Perc Endo Appr
ØFJD4ZZ	Inspect of Pancreatic Duct, Perc Endo Appr
ØFJG4ZZ	Inspect of Pancreas, Perc Endo Appr
ØHBØXZZ	Exc of Scalp Skin, Ext Appr
ØHB1XZZ	Exc of Face Skin, Ext Appr
ØHB4XZZ	Exc of Neck Skin, Ext Appr
ØHB5XZZ	Exc of Chest Skin, Ext Appr
ØHB6XZZ	Exc of Back Skin, Ext Appr
ØHB7XZZ	Exc of Abd Skin, Ext Appr
ØHB8XZZ	Exc of Buttock Skin, Ext Appr
ØHBAXZZ	Exc of Genitalia Skin, Ext Appr
ØHBBXZZ	Exc of Rt Upr Arm Skin, Ext Appr
ØHBCXZZ	Exc of Lt Upr Arm Skin, Ext Appr
ØHBDXZZ	Exc of Rt Lwr Arm Skin, Ext Appr
ØHBEXZZ	Exc of Lt Lwr Arm Skin, Ext Appr
ØHBFXZZ	Exc of Rt Hand Skin, Ext Appr
ØHBGXZZ	Exc of Lt Hand Skin, Ext Appr
ØHBHXZZ	Exc of Rt Upr Leg Skin, Ext Appr
ØHBJXZZ	Exc of Lt Upr Leg Skin, Ext Appr
ØHBKXZZ	Exc of Rt Lwr Leg Skin, Ext Appr
ØHBLXZZ	Exc of Lt Lwr Leg Skin, Ext Appr
ØHBMXZZ	Exc of Rt Foot Skin, Ext Appr
ØHBNXZZ	Exc of Lt Foot Skin, Ext Appr
ØJBØØZZ	Exc of Scalp SQ/Fascia, Opn Appr
ØJB1ØZZ	Exc of Face SQ/Fascia, Opn Appr
ØJB4ØZZ	Exc of Ant Neck SQ/Fascia, Opn Appr
ØJB5ØZZ	Exc of Post Neck SQ/Fascia, Opn Appr
ØJB6ØZZ	Exc of Chest SQ/Fascia, Opn Appr
ØJB7ØZZ	Exc of Back SQ/Fascia, Opn Appr
ØJB8ØZZ	Exc of Abd SQ/Fascia, Opn Appr
ØJB9ØZZ	Exc of Buttock SQ/Fascia, Opn Appr
ØJBBØZZ	Exc of Perineum SQ/Fascia, Opn Appr
ØJBCØZZ	Exc of Pelvic SQ/Fascia, Opn Appr
ØJBDØZZ	Exc of Rt Up Arm SQ/Fascia, Opn Appr
ØJBFØZZ	Exc of Lt Up Arm SQ/Fascia, Opn Appr
ØJBGØZZ	Exc of Rt Low Arm SQ/Fascia, Opn Appr
ØJBHØZZ	Exc of Lt Low Arm SQ/Fascia, Opn Appr
ØJBLØZZ	Exc of Rt Up Leg SQ/Fascia, Opn Appr
ØJBMØZZ	Exc of Lt Up Leg SQ/Fascia, Opn Appr
ØJBNØZZ	Exc of Rt Low Leg SQ/Fascia, Opn Appr
ØJBPØZZ	Exc of Lt Low Leg SQ/Fascia, Opn Appr
ØJBQØZZ	Exc of Rt Foot SQ/Fascia, Opn Appr
ØJBRØZZ	Exc of Lt Foot SQ/Fascia, Opn Appr
ØJH6[Ø,3]VZ	Insert/SQ Tissue & Fascia, Chest, [Opn, Perc], Inf Pump, NQ
ØJH7[Ø,3]VZ	Insert/SQ Tissue & Fascia, Back, [Opn, Perc], Inf Pump, NQ
ØJH8[Ø,3]VZ	Insert/SQ Tissue & Fascia, Abd, [Opn, Perc], Inf Pump, NQ
ØJHT[Ø,3]VZ	Insert/SQ Tissue & Fascia, Trunk, [Opn, Perc], Inf Pump, NQ
ØK9ØØZX	Drain of Head Muscle, Opn Appr, Diagnostic
ØK91ØZX	Drain of Facial Muscle, Opn Appr, Diagnostic
ØK92ØZX	Drain of Rt Neck Muscle, Opn Appr, Diagnostic
ØK93ØZX	Drain of Lt Neck Muscle, Opn Appr, Diagnostic
ØK94ØZX	Drain of Tongue/Palate/Phar Muscle, Opn Appr, Diagn
ØK95ØZX	Drain of Rt Shldr Muscle, Opn Appr, Diagnostic
ØK96ØZX	Drain of Lt Shldr Muscle, Opn Appr, Diagnostic
ØK97ØZX	Drain of Rt Upr Arm Muscle, Opn Appr, Diagn
ØK98ØZX	Drain of Lt Upr Arm Muscle, Opn Appr, Diagnostic
ØK99ØZX	Drain of Rt Low Arm & Wrist Muscle, Opn Appr, Diagn
ØK9BØZX	Drain of Lt Low Arm & Wrist Muscle, Opn Appr, Diagn
ØK9CØZX	Drain of Rt Hand Muscle, Opn Appr, Diagnostic
ØK9DØZX	Drain of Lt Hand Muscle, Opn Appr, Diagnostic
ØK9FØZX	Drain of Rt Trunk Muscle, Opn Appr, Diagnostic
ØK9GØZX	Drain of Lt Trunk Muscle, Opn Appr, Diagnostic
ØK9HØZX	Drain of Rt Thorax Muscle, Opn Appr, Diagnostic
ØK9JØZX	Drain of Lt Thorax Muscle, Opn Appr, Diagnostic
ØK9KØZX	Drain of Rt Abd Muscle, Opn Appr, Diagnostic
ØK9LØZX	Drain of Lt Abd Muscle, Opn Appr, Diagnostic
ØK9MØZX	Drain of Perineum Muscle, Opn Appr, Diagnostic
ØK9NØZX	Drain of Rt Hip Muscle, Opn Appr, Diagnostic
ØK9PØZX	Drain of Lt Hip Muscle, Opn Appr, Diagnostic
ØK9QØZX	Drain of Rt Upr Leg Muscle, Opn Appr, Diagn
ØK9RØZX	Drain of Lt Upr Leg Muscle, Opn Appr, Diagn
ØK9SØZX	Drain of Rt Lwr Leg Muscle, Opn Appr, Diagn
ØK9TØZX	Drain of Lt Lwr Leg Muscle, Opn Appr, Diagnostic
ØK9VØZX	Drain of Rt Foot Muscle, Opn Appr, Diagnostic
ØK9WØZX	Drain of Lt Foot Muscle, Opn Appr, Diagnostic
ØKBØØZX	Exc of Head Muscle, Opn Appr, Diagnostic
ØKB1ØZX	Exc of Facial Muscle, Opn Appr, Diagnostic
ØKB2ØZX	Exc of Rt Neck Muscle, Opn Appr, Diagnostic
ØKB3ØZX	Exc of Lt Neck Muscle, Opn Appr, Diagnostic
ØKB4ØZX	Exc of Tongue/Palate/Phar Muscle, Opn Appr, Diagn
ØKB5ØZX	Exc of Rt Shldr Muscle, Opn Appr, Diagnostic
ØKB6ØZX	Exc of Lt Shldr Muscle, Opn Appr, Diagnostic
ØKB7ØZX	Exc of Rt Upr Arm Muscle, Opn Appr, Diagn
ØKB8ØZX	Exc of Lt Upr Arm Muscle, Opn Appr, Diagnostic
ØKB9ØZX	Exc of Rt Low Arm & Wrist Muscle, Opn Appr, Diagn
ØKBBØZX	Exc of Lt Low Arm & Wrist Muscle, Opn Appr, Diagn
ØKBCØZX	Exc of Rt Hand Muscle, Opn Appr, Diagnostic
ØKBDØZX	Exc of Lt Hand Muscle, Opn Appr, Diagnostic
ØKBFØZX	Exc of Rt Trunk Muscle, Opn Appr, Diagnostic
ØKBGØZX	Exc of Lt Trunk Muscle, Opn Appr, Diagnostic
ØKBHØZX	Exc of Rt Thorax Muscle, Opn Appr, Diagnostic
ØKBJØZX	Exc of Lt Thorax Muscle, Opn Appr, Diagnostic
ØKBKØZX	Exc of Rt Abd Muscle, Opn Appr, Diagnostic
ØKBLØZX	Exc of Lt Abd Muscle, Opn Appr, Diagnostic
ØKBMØZX	Exc of Perineum Muscle, Opn Appr, Diagnostic
ØKBNØZX	Exc of Rt Hip Muscle, Opn Appr, Diagnostic
ØKBPØZX	Exc of Lt Hip Muscle, Opn Appr, Diagnostic
ØKBQØZX	Exc of Rt Upr Leg Muscle, Opn Appr, Diagn
ØKBRØZX	Exc of Lt Upr Leg Muscle, Opn Appr, Diagnostic
ØKBSØZX	Exc of Rt Lwr Leg Muscle, Opn Appr, Diagn
ØKBTØZX	Exc of Lt Lwr Leg Muscle, Opn Appr, Diagnostic
ØKBVØZX	Exc of Rt Foot Muscle, Opn Appr, Diagnostic
ØKBWØZX	Exc of Lt Foot Muscle, Opn Appr, Diagnostic
ØP93[Ø,3,4]ZX	Drain/Cervical Vertebra, [Opn, Perc, Perc Endo]
ØP94[Ø,3,4]ZX	Drain/Thoracic Vertebra, [Opn, Perc, Perc Endo]
ØP9R[Ø,3,4]ZX	Drain/Thumb Phalanx, Rt, [Opn, Perc, Perc Endo]
ØP9S[Ø,3,4]ZX	Drain/Thumb Phalanx, Lt, [Opn, Perc, Perc Endo]
ØP9T[Ø,3,4]ZX	Drain/Finger Phalanx, Rt, [Opn, Perc, Perc Endo]
ØP9V[Ø,3,4]ZX	Drain/Finger Phalanx, Lt, [Opn, Perc, Perc Endo]
ØPB3[Ø,3,4]ZX	Exc/Cervical Vertebra, [Opn, Perc, Perc Endo]
ØPB4[Ø,3,4]ZX	Exc/Thoracic Vertebra, [Opn, Perc, Perc Endo]
ØPBR[Ø,3,4]ZX	Exc/Thumb Phalanx, Rt, [Opn, Perc, Perc Endo]
ØPBS[Ø,3,4]ZX	Exc/Thumb Phalanx, Lt, [Opn, Perc, Perc Endo]
ØPBT[Ø,3,4]ZX	Exc/Finger Phalanx, Rt, [Opn, Perc, Perc Endo]
ØPBV[Ø,3,4]ZX	Exc/Finger Phalanx, Lt, [Opn, Perc, Perc Endo]
ØQ9Ø[Ø,3,4]ZX	Drain/Lumbar Vertebra, [Opn, Perc, Perc Endo]
ØQ91[Ø,3,4]ZX	Drain/Sacrum, [Opn, Perc, Perc Endo]
ØQ92[Ø,3,4]ZX	Drain/Pelvic Bone, Rt, [Opn, Perc, Perc Endo]
ØQ93[Ø,3,4]ZX	Drain/Pelvic Bone, Lt, [Opn, Perc, Perc Endo]
ØQ94[Ø,3,4]ZX	Drain/Acetab, Rt, [Opn, Perc, Perc Endo]
ØQ95[Ø,3,4]ZX	Drain/Acetab, Lt, [Opn, Perc, Perc Endo]
ØQ9Q[Ø,3,4]ZX	Drain/Toe Phalanx, Rt, [Opn, Perc, Perc Endo]
ØQ9R[Ø,3,4]ZX	Drain/Toe Phalanx, Lt, [Opn, Perc, Perc Endo]
ØQ9S[Ø,3,4]ZX	Drain/Coccyx, [Opn, Perc, Perc Endo]
ØQBØ[Ø,3,4]ZX	Exc/Lumbar Vertebra, [Opn, Perc, Perc Endo]
ØQB1[Ø,3,4]ZX	Exc/Sacrum, [Opn, Perc, Perc Endo]
ØQB2[Ø,3,4]ZX	Exc/Pelvic Bone, Rt, [Opn, Perc, Perc Endo]
ØQB3[Ø,3,4]ZX	Exc/Pelvic Bone, Lt, [Opn, Perc, Perc Endo]
ØQB4[Ø,3,4]ZX	Exc/Acetab, Rt, [Opn, Perc, Perc Endo]
ØQB5[Ø,3,4]ZX	Exc/Acetab, Lt, [Opn, Perc, Perc Endo]
ØQBQ[Ø,3,4]ZX	Exc/Toe Phalanx, Rt, [Opn, Perc, Perc Endo]
ØQBR[Ø,3,4]ZX	Exc/Toe Phalanx, Lt, [Opn, Perc, Perc Endo]
ØQBS[Ø,3,4]ZX	Exc/Coccyx, [Opn, Perc, Perc Endo]
ØT9ØØZX	Drain of Rt Kidney, Opn Appr, Diagnostic
ØT91ØZX	Drain of Lt Kidney, Opn Appr, Diagnostic
ØT93ØZX	Drain of Rt Kidney Pelvis, Opn Appr, Diagnostic
ØT94ØZX	Drain of Lt Kidney Pelvis, Opn Appr, Diagnostic

T Transfer DRG   SP Special Payment   * Code Range   6th and 7th Character of ZZ = No Device, No Qualifier ZX = No Device, Diagnostic

MS-DRG Version 33.0

ØTBØØZX	Exc of Rt Kidney, Opn Appr, Diagnostic
ØTB1ØZX	Exc of Lt Kidney, Opn Appr, Diagnostic
ØTB3ØZX	Exc of Rt Kidney Pelvis, Opn Appr, Diagnostic
ØTB4ØZX	Exc of Lt Kidney Pelvis, Opn Appr, Diagnostic
ØTJ5[3,7]ZZ	Inspect/Kidney, [Perc, Via Natrl or Artfcl Opng]
ØW9CØZX	Drain of Mediastinum, Opn Appr, Diagnostic
ØW9GØØZ	Drain of Peritoneal Cavity with Drain Dev, Opn Appr
ØW9GØZZ	Drain of Peritoneal Cavity, Opn Appr
ØW9G[Ø,3,4]ZX	Drain/Peritoneal Cavity, [Opn, Perc, Perc Endo]
ØW9H[Ø,3,4]ZX	Drain/Retroperitoneum, [Opn, Perc, Perc Endo]
ØW9J[Ø,3,4]ZX	Drain/Pelvic Cavity, [Opn, Perc, Perc Endo]
ØWBCØZX	Exc of Mediastinum, Opn Appr, Diagnostic
ØWBHØZX	Exc of Retroperitoneum, Opn Appr, Diagnostic
ØWJC4ZZ	Inspect of Mediastinum, Perc Endo Appr
ØWJD4ZZ	Inspect of Pericardial Cavity, Perc Endo Appr
ØWJF[3,4]ZZ	Inspect/Abd Wall, [Perc, Perc Endo]
ØWJG[Ø,3,4]ZZ	Inspect/Peritoneal Cavity, [Opn, Perc, Perc Endo]
ØWJH[3,4]ZZ	Inspect/Retroperitoneum, [Perc, Perc Endo]
ØWJJ[Ø,3,4]ZZ	Inspect/Pelvic Cavity, [Opn, Perc, Perc Endo]
ØWJP[Ø,3,4,7,8]ZZ	Inspect/Gastrointestinal Tract, [Opn, Perc, Perc Endo, Via Natrl or Artfcl Opng, Via Natrl or Artfcl Opng Endo]
ØWJR[Ø,3,4,7,8]ZZ	Inspect/Genitourinary Tract, [Opn, Perc, Perc Endo, Via Natrl or Artfcl Opng, Via Natrl or Artfcl Opng Endo]
ØY95[Ø,3,4]ZX	Drain/Inguinal Rgn, Rt, [Opn, Perc, Perc Endo]
ØY96[Ø,3,4]ZX	Drain/Inguinal Rgn, Lt, [Opn, Perc, Perc Endo]
ØYB5[Ø,3,4]ZX	Exc/Inguinal Rgn, Rt, [Opn, Perc, Perc Endo]
ØYB6[Ø,3,4]ZX	Exc/Inguinal Rgn, Lt, [Opn, Perc, Perc Endo]
ØYB7[Ø,3,4]ZX	Exc/Femor Rgn, Rt, [Opn, Perc, Perc Endo]
ØYB8[Ø,3,4]ZX	Exc/Femor Rgn, Lt, [Opn, Perc, Perc Endo]
ØYJ5[3,4]ZZ	Inspect/Inguinal Rgn, Rt, [Perc, Perc Endo]
ØYJ6[3,4]ZZ	Inspect/Inguinal Rgn, Lt, [Perc, Perc Endo]
ØYJ7[3,4]ZZ	Inspect/Femor Rgn, Rt, [Perc, Perc Endo]
ØYJ8[3,4]ZZ	Inspect/Femor Rgn, Lt, [Perc, Perc Endo]
ØYJA[3,4]ZZ	Inspect/Inguinal Rgn, Bilat, [Perc, Perc Endo]
ØYJE[3,4]ZZ	Inspect/Femor Rgn, Bilat, [Perc, Perc Endo]
4AØ6[Ø,3][5,B]Z	Measurement/Lymphatic, [Opn, Perc], [Flow, Pressure], NQ
4A16[Ø,3][5,B]Z	Monitoring/Lymphatic, [Opn, Perc], [Flow, Pressure], NQ

DRG 803   Other O.R. Procedures of the Blood and Blood-Forming Organs with CC

GMLOS 4.7   AMLOS 6.Ø   RW 1.8719

Select operating room procedures listed under DRG 802

DRG 804   Other O.R. Procedures of the Blood and Blood-Forming Organs without CC/MCC

GMLOS 2.3   AMLOS 3.Ø   RW 1.1715

Select operating room procedures listed under DRG 802

MEDICAL

DRG 808   Major Hematologic/Immunologic Diagnoses Except Sickle Cell Crisis and Coagulation with MCC

GMLOS 6.Ø   AMLOS 8.Ø   RW 2.2346

Principal Diagnosis

D59.Ø	Drug-induced autoimmune hemolytic anemia
D59.1	Oth autoimmune hemolytic anemias
D59.2	Drug-induced nonautoimmune hemolytic anemia
D59.4	Oth nonautoimmune hemolytic anemias
D59.5	Paroxysmal nocturnal hemoglobinuria [Marchiafava-Micheli]
D59.6	Hemoglobinuria d/t hemolysis from oth ext causes
D59.8	Oth acquired hemolytic anemias
D59.9	Acquired hemolytic anemia, unsp
D6Ø.Ø	Chr acquired pure red cell aplasia
D6Ø.1	Transient acquired pure red cell aplasia
D6Ø.8	Oth acquired pure red cell aplasias
D6Ø.9	Acquired pure red cell aplasia, unsp
D61.Ø*	Constitutional aplastic anemia
D61.1	Drug-induced aplastic anemia
D61.2	Aplastic anemia d/t oth ext agents
D61.3	Idiopathic aplastic anemia
D61.81*	Pancytopenia
D61.89	Oth aplastic anemias and oth bone marrow failure synd
D61.9	Aplastic anemia, unsp

D7Ø.Ø	Congenital agranulocytosis
D7Ø.1	Agranulocytosis secondary to cancer chemotherapy
D7Ø.2	Oth drug-induced agranulocytosis
D7Ø.3	Neutropenia d/t infxn
D7Ø.4	Cyclic neutropenia
D7Ø.8	Oth neutropenia
D7Ø.9	Neutropenia, unsp
D71	Functional d/o of polymorphonuclear neutrophils
D72.Ø	Genetic anomalies of leukocytes
D8Ø.6	Antibody defic w near-norm immunoglob or w hyperimmunoglob
D8Ø.8	Oth immunodeficiencies with predominantly antibody defects
D8Ø.9	Immunodef w/ predominantly antibody defects, unsp
D81.Ø	Severe combined immunodef with reticular dysgenesis
D81.1	Severe combined immunodef w low T- and B-cell numbers
D81.2	Severe combined immunodef w low or normal B-cell numbers
D81.4	Nezelof's synd
D81.6	Major histocompatibility complex class I deficiency
D81.7	Major histocompatibility complex class II deficiency
D81.89	Oth combined immunodeficiencies
D81.9	Combined immunodef, unsp
D82.Ø	Wiskott-Aldrich synd
D82.1	Di George's synd
D89.81Ø	Acute graft-versus-host dz
D89.811	Chr graft-versus-host dz
D89.812	Acute on chr graft-versus-host dz
D89.813	Graft-versus-host dz, unsp
T86.Ø*	Comp of bone marrow transplant

DRG 809   Major Hematologic/Immunologic Diagnoses Except Sickle Cell Crisis and Coagulation with CC

GMLOS 3.8   AMLOS 4.7   RW 1.2235

Select principal diagnosis listed under DRG 808

DRG 810   Major Hematologic/Immunologic Diagnoses Except Sickle Cell Crisis and Coagulation without CC/MCC

GMLOS 2.7   AMLOS 3.3   RW Ø.8644

Select principal diagnosis listed under DRG 808

DRG 811   Red Blood Cell Disorders with MCC

GMLOS 3.7   AMLOS 4.9   RW 1.2992

Principal Diagnosis

D46*	Myelodysplastic syndromes
D5Ø*	Iron deficiency anemia
D51*	Vitamin B12 deficiency anemia
D52*	Folate deficiency anemia
D53*	Oth nutritional anemias
D55*	Anemia d/t enzyme d/o
D56*	Thalassemia
D57*	Sickle-cell d/o
D58*	Oth hereditary hemolytic anemias
D59.3	Hemolytic-uremic synd
D62	Acute posthemorrhagic anemia
D63*	Anemia in chr dz classified elsw
D64*	Oth anemias
D74*	Methemoglobinemia
R71*	Abnormality of red bld cells
T80.30XA	ABO incompat react d/t tranfs of bld/bld prod, unsp, init
T80.310A	ABO incompatibility w acute hemolytic transfs react, init
T80.311A	ABO incompatibility w delayed hemolytic transfs react, init
T80.319A	ABO incompatibility w hemolytic transfs react, unsp, init
T80.39XA	Oth ABO incompat react d/t tranfs of bld/bld prod, init
T80.40XA	Rh incompat react d/t tranfs of bld/bld prod, unsp, init
T80.410A	Rh incompatibility w acute hemolytic transfs react, init
T80.411A	Rh incompatibility w delayed hemolytic transfs react, init
T80.419A	Rh incompatibility w hemolytic transfs react, unsp, init
T80.49XA	Oth Rh incompat reaction d/t tranfs of bld/bld prod, init
T80.89XA	Oth comp fol inf, transfusion and theraputc inject, init
T80.910A	Acute hemolytic transfs react, unsp incompatibility, init
T80.911A	Delayed hemolytic transfs react, unsp incompatibility, init
T80.919A	Hemolytic transfs react, unsp incompat, unsp ac/delay, init
T80.92XA	Unsp transfusion reaction, init enc
T80.AØXA	Non-ABO incompat react d/t tranfs of bld/bld prod,unsp, init
T80.A1ØA	Non-ABO incompat w acute hemolytic transfs react, init

Surgical	**Medical**	**CC Indicator**	**MCC Indicator**	**Procedure Proxy**	**PDxMCC** PDx acts as own MCC	**PDxCC** PDx acts as own CC

T80.A11A	Non-ABO incompat w delayed hemolytic transfs react, init
T80.A19A	Non-ABO incompat w hemolytic transfs react, unsp, init
T80.A9XA	Oth non-ABO incompat react d/t transf of bld/bld prod, init

DRG 812 Red Blood Cell Disorders without MCC
GMLOS 2.8   AMLOS 3.5   RW 0.8572

Select principal diagnosis listed under DRG 811

DRG 813 Coagulation Disorders
GMLOS 3.7   AMLOS 5.1   RW 1.7350

Principal Diagnosis

D65	Disseminated intravascular coagulation
D66	Hereditary factor VIII deficiency
D67	Hereditary factor IX deficiency
D68.0	Von Willebrand's dz
D68.1	Hereditary factor XI deficiency
D68.2	Hereditary deficiency of oth clotting factors
D68.311	Acquired hemophilia
D68.318	Oth hemorrhagic d/o d/t intrns circ anticoag,antib,inhib
D68.32	Hemorrhagic d/o d/t extrinsic circulating anticoagulants
D68.4	Acquired coagulation factor deficiency
D68.8	Oth spec coagulation defects
D68.9	Coagulation defect, unsp
D69*	Purpura and oth hemorrhagic conditions
D75.82	Heparin induced thrombocytopenia (HIT)
R23.3	Spontaneous ecchymoses

DRG 814 Reticuloendothelial and Immunity Disorders with MCC
GMLOS 4.7   AMLOS 6.4   RW 1.6622

Principal Diagnosis

A18.2	Tuberculous peripheral lymphadenopathy
A18.85	Tuberculosis of spleen
A28.1	Cat-scratch dz
D15.0	Benign neoplasm of thymus
D18.1	Lymphangioma, any site
D36.0	Benign neoplasm of lymph nodes
D3A.091	Benign carcinoid tumor of the thymus
D47.2	Monoclonal gammopathy
D47.3	Essential (hemorrhagic) thrombocythemia
D47.4	Osteomyelofibrosis
D68.312	Antiphospholipid antibody with hemorrhagic d/o
D68.5*	Primary thrombophilia
D68.6*	Oth thrombophilia
D72.1	Eosinophilia
D72.8*	Oth spec d/o of white bld cells
D72.9	D/o of white bld cells, unsp
D73.0	Hyposplenism
D73.1	Hypersplenism
D73.2	Chr congestive splenomegaly
D73.3	Abscess of spleen
D73.4	Cyst of spleen
D73.5	Infarction of spleen
D73.8*	Oth dz of spleen
D73.9	Dz of spleen, unsp
D75.0	Familial erythrocytosis
D75.1	Secondary polycythemia
D75.89	Oth spec dz of bld and bld-forming organs
D75.9	Dz of bld and bld-forming organs, unsp
D76.1	Hemophagocytic lymphohistiocytosis
D76.2	Hemophagocytic synd, infxn-associated
D76.3	Oth histiocytosis syndromes
D77	Oth d/o of bld/bld-frm organs in dz classd elsw
D80.0	Hereditary hypogammaglobulinemia
D80.1	Nonfamilial hypogammaglobulinemia
D80.2	Selective deficiency of immunoglobulin A [IgA]
D80.3	Selective deficiency of immunoglobulin G [IgG] subclasses
D80.4	Selective deficiency of immunoglobulin M [IgM]
D80.5	Immunodef with increased immunoglobulin M [IgM]
D80.7	Transient hypogammaglobulinemia of infancy
D82.2	Immunodef with short-limbed stature
D82.3	Immunodef fol heredit defctv response to Epstein-Barr virus
D82.4	Hyperimmunoglobulin E [IgE] synd
D82.8	Immunodef associated with oth major defects
D82.9	Immunodef associated with major defect, unsp
D83.0	Com variab immunodef w predom abnlt of B-cell nums & function

D83.1	Com variab immunodef w predom immunoreg T-cell d/o
D83.2	Common variable immunodef w autoantibodies to B- or T-cells
D83.8	Oth common variable immunodeficiencies
D83.9	Common variable immunodef, unsp
D84.0	Lymphocyte function antigen-1 [LFA-1] defect
D84.8	Oth spec immunodeficiencies
D84.9	Immunodef, unsp
D89.0	Polyclonal hypergammaglobulinemia
D89.2	Hypergammaglobulinemia, unsp
D89.3	Immune reconstitution synd
D89.89	Oth disrd involving the immune mechanism, NEC
D89.9	D/o involving the immune mechanism, unsp
E32.0	Persistent hyperplasia of thymus
E32.1	Abscess of thymus
E32.8	Oth dz of thymus
E32.9	Dz of thymus, unsp
I88.1	Chr lymphadenitis, except mesenteric
I88.8	Oth nonspecific lymphadenitis
I88.9	Nonspecific lymphadenitis, unsp
I89.8	Oth noninfective d/o of lymphatic vessels and nodes
I89.9	Noninfective d/o of lymphatic vessels and nodes, unsp
L04.0	Acute lymphadenitis of face, head and neck
L04.1	Acute lymphadenitis of trunk
L04.2	Acute lymphadenitis of upr limb
L04.3	Acute lymphadenitis of lwr limb
L04.8	Acute lymphadenitis of oth sites
L04.9	Acute lymphadenitis, unsp
Q89.0*	Congenital absence and malformations of spleen
R16.1	Splenomegaly, NEC
R59.0	Localized enlarged lymph nodes
R59.1	Generalized enlarged lymph nodes
R59.9	Enlarged lymph nodes, unsp
R75	Inconclusive laboratory evidence of human immunodef virus
R76.0	Raised antibody titer
R76.8	Oth spec abnormal immunological findings in serum
R76.9	Abnormal immunological finding in serum, unsp
S36.00XA	Unsp inj of spleen, init enc
S36.020A	Minor contsn of spleen, init enc
S36.021A	Major contsn of spleen, init enc
S36.029A	Unsp contsn of spleen, init enc
S36.030A	Superf (capsular) lac of spleen, init enc
S36.031A	Mod lac of spleen, init enc
S36.032A	Major lac of spleen, init enc
S36.039A	Unsp lac of spleen, init enc
S36.09XA	Oth inj of spleen, init enc
Z94.81	Bone marrow transplant status
Z94.84	Stem cells transplant status

DRG 815 Reticuloendothelial and Immunity Disorders with CC
GMLOS 3.2   AMLOS 4.1   RW 0.9803

Select principal diagnosis listed under DRG 814

DRG 816 Reticuloendothelial and Immunity Disorders without CC/MCC
GMLOS 2.4   AMLOS 2.9   RW 0.6962

Select principal diagnosis listed under DRG 814

T Transfer DRG   SP Special Payment   * Code Range   6th and 7th Character of ZZ = No Device, No Qualifier ZX = No Device, Diagnostic

294   MS-DRG Version 33.0   © 2015 Optum360, LLC

MDC 17
Myeloproliferative Diseases And Disorders And Poorly Differentiated Neoplasms

SURGICAL

DRG 820	Lymphoma and Leukemia with Major O.R. Procedure with MCC
GMLOS 12.1	AMLOS 16.2	RW 5.9153

Principal Diagnosis

C26.1	Malig neoplasm of spleen
C46.3	Kaposi's sarcoma of lymph nodes
C77*	Secondary and unsp malig neoplasm of lymph nodes
C7B.Ø1	Secondary carcinoid tumors of distant lymph nodes
C81*	Hodgkin lymphoma
C82*	Follicular lymphoma
C83*	Non-follicular lymphoma
C84*	Mature T/NK-cell lymphomas
C85*	Oth and unsp types of non-Hodgkin lymphoma
C86*	Oth spec types of T/NK-cell lymphoma
C88*	Malig immunoproliferative dis and certain oth B-cell lymph
C90*	Multi myeloma and malig plasma cell neoplasms
C91*	Lymphoid leukemia
C92*	Myeloid leukemia
C93*	Monocytic leukemia
C94*	Oth leukemias of spec cell type
C95*	Leukemia of unsp cell type
C96.2	Malig mast cell tumor
C96.4	Sarcoma of dendritic cells (accessory cells)
C96.9	Malig neoplm of lymphoid, hematpoetc and rel tissue, unsp
C96.A	Histiocytic sarcoma
C96.Z	Oth malig neoplm of lymphoid, hematpoetc and related tissue
D45	Polycythemia vera
D47.Ø	Histiocytic and mast cell tumors of uncertain behav
D47.1	Chr myeloproliferative dz
D47.9	Neoplm of uncertain behav of lymphoid,hematpoetc & rel tiss,unsp
D47.Z9	Oth neoplm of uncertain behav of lymphoid, hematpoetc & rel tiss
D61.82	Myelophthisis
D75.81	Myelofibrosis
D89.1	Cryoglobulinemia

AND

Operating Room Procedures

001*	Central Nervous Sys, Bypass
0050[0,3,4]ZZ	Destr/Brain, [Opn, Perc, Perc Endo]
0051[0,3,4]ZZ	Destr/Cerebral Meninges, [Opn, Perc, Perc Endo]
0052[0,3,4]ZZ	Destr/Dura Mater, [Opn, Perc, Perc Endo]
0057[0,3,4]ZZ	Destr/Cerebral Hemisphere, [Opn, Perc, Perc Endo]
0058[0,3,4]ZZ	Destr/Basal Ganglia, [Opn, Perc, Perc Endo]
0059[0,3,4]ZZ	Destr/Thalamus, [Opn, Perc, Perc Endo]
005A[0,3,4]ZZ	Destr/Hypothalamus, [Opn, Perc, Perc Endo]
005B[0,3,4]ZZ	Destr/Pons, [Opn, Perc, Perc Endo]
005C[0,3,4]ZZ	Destr/Cerebellum, [Opn, Perc, Perc Endo]
005D[0,3,4]ZZ	Destr/Medulla Oblongata, [Opn, Perc, Perc Endo]
005T[0,3,4]ZZ	Destr/Spinal Meninges, [Opn, Perc, Perc Endo]
005W[0,3,4]ZZ	Destr/Cervical Spinal Cord, [Opn, Perc, Perc Endo]
005X[0,3,4]ZZ	Destr/Thoracic Spinal Cord, [Opn, Perc, Perc Endo]
005Y[0,3,4]ZZ	Destr/Lumbar Spinal Cord, [Opn, Perc, Perc Endo]
0080[0,3,4]ZZ	Div/Brain, [Opn, Perc, Perc Endo]
0087[0,3,4]ZZ	Div/Cerebral Hemisphere, [Opn, Perc, Perc Endo]
0088[0,3,4]ZZ	Div/Basal Ganglia, [Opn, Perc, Perc Endo]
008W[0,3,4]ZZ	Div/Cervical Spinal Cord, [Opn, Perc, Perc Endo]
008X[0,3,4]ZZ	Div/Thoracic Spinal Cord, [Opn, Perc, Perc Endo]
008Y[0,3,4]ZZ	Div/Lumbar Spinal Cord, [Opn, Perc, Perc Endo]
00900ZX	Drain of Brain, Opn Appr, Diagnostic
00910ZX	Drain of Cerebral Meninges, Opn Appr, Diagnostic
00910[0,Z]Z	Drain/Cerebral Meninges, Opn, [Drain Dev, No Dev], NQ
00920ZX	Drain of Dura Mater, Opn Appr, Diagnostic
00920[0,Z]Z	Drain/Dura Mater, Opn, [Drain Dev, No Dev], NQ
00930ZX	Drain of Epidural Space, Opn Appr, Diagnostic
00940ZX	Drain of Subdural Space, Opn Appr, Diagnostic
00940[0,Z]Z	Drain/Subdural Space, Opn, [Drain Dev, No Dev], NQ
00950ZX	Drain of Subarachnoid Space, Opn Appr, Diagnostic
00950[0,Z]Z	Drain/Subarachnoid Space, Opn, [Drain Dev, No Dev], NQ
00960ZX	Drain of Cerebral Ventricle, Opn Appr, Diagnostic
0096[0,3,4]0Z	Drain/Cerebral Ventricle, [Opn, Perc, Perc Endo], Drain Dev, NQ
00970ZX	Drain of Cerebral Hemisphere, Opn Appr, Diagnostic
00980ZX	Drain of Basal Ganglia, Opn Appr, Diagnostic
0098[0,3,4][0,Z]Z	Drain/Basal Ganglia, [Opn, Perc, Perc Endo], [Drain Dev, No Dev], NQ
00990ZX	Drain of Thalamus, Opn Appr, Diagnostic
0099[0,3,4][0,Z]Z	Drain/Thalamus, [Opn, Perc, Perc Endo], [Drain Dev, No Dev], NQ
009A0ZX	Drain of Hypothalamus, Opn Appr, Diagnostic
009A[0,3,4][0,Z]Z	Drain/Hypothalamus, [Opn, Perc, Perc Endo], [Drain Dev, No Dev], NQ
009B0ZX	Drain of Pons, Opn Appr, Diagnostic
009C0ZX	Drain of Cerebellum, Opn Appr, Diagnostic
009D0ZX	Drain of Medulla Oblongata, Opn Appr, Diagnostic
009T[0,3,4]ZX	Drain/Spinal Meninges, [Opn, Perc, Perc Endo]
009T[0,3,4][0,Z]Z	Drain/Spinal Meninges, [Opn, Perc, Perc Endo], [Drain Dev, No Dev], NQ
009U00Z	Drain of Spinal Canal with Drain Device, Opn Appr
009U0ZX	Drain of Spinal Canal, Opn Appr, Diagnostic
009U0ZZ	Drain of Spinal Canal, Opn Appr
009W[0,3,4]ZX	Drain/Cervical Spinal Cord, [Opn, Perc, Perc Endo]
009W[0,3,4][0,Z]Z	Drain/Cervical Spinal Cord, [Opn, Perc, Perc Endo], [Drain Dev, No Dev], NQ
009X[0,3,4]ZX	Drain/Thoracic Spinal Cord, [Opn, Perc, Perc Endo]
009X[0,3,4][0,Z]Z	Drain/Thoracic Spinal Cord, [Opn, Perc, Perc Endo], [Drain Dev, No Dev], NQ
009Y[0,3,4]ZX	Drain/Lumbar Spinal Cord, [Opn, Perc, Perc Endo]
009Y[0,3,4][0,Z]Z	Drain/Lumbar Spinal Cord, [Opn, Perc, Perc Endo], [Drain Dev, No Dev], NQ
00B00ZX	Exc of Brain, Opn Appr, Diagnostic
00B0[0,3,4]ZZ	Exc/Brain, [Opn, Perc, Perc Endo]
00B10ZX	Exc of Cerebral Meninges, Opn Appr, Diagnostic
00B1[0,3,4]ZZ	Exc/Cerebral Meninges, [Opn, Perc, Perc Endo]
00B20ZX	Exc of Dura Mater, Opn Appr, Diagnostic
00B2[0,3,4]ZZ	Exc/Dura Mater, [Opn, Perc, Perc Endo]
00B60ZX	Exc of Cerebral Ventricle, Opn Appr, Diagnostic
00B6[0,3,4]ZZ	Exc/Cerebral Ventricle, [Opn, Perc, Perc Endo]
00B70ZX	Exc of Cerebral Hemisphere, Opn Appr, Diagnostic
00B7[0,3,4]ZZ	Exc/Cerebral Hemisphere, [Opn, Perc, Perc Endo]
00B80ZX	Exc of Basal Ganglia, Opn Appr, Diagnostic
00B8[0,3,4]ZZ	Exc/Basal Ganglia, [Opn, Perc, Perc Endo]
00B90ZX	Exc of Thalamus, Opn Appr, Diagnostic
00B9[0,3,4]ZZ	Exc/Thalamus, [Opn, Perc, Perc Endo]
00BA0ZX	Exc of Hypothalamus, Opn Appr, Diagnostic
00BA[0,3,4]ZZ	Exc/Hypothalamus, [Opn, Perc, Perc Endo]
00BB0ZX	Exc of Pons, Opn Appr, Diagnostic
00BB[0,3,4]ZZ	Exc/Pons, [Opn, Perc, Perc Endo]
00BC0ZX	Exc of Cerebellum, Opn Appr, Diagnostic
00BC[0,3,4]ZZ	Exc/Cerebellum, [Opn, Perc, Perc Endo]
00BD0ZX	Exc of Medulla Oblongata, Opn Appr, Diagnostic
00BD[0,3,4]ZZ	Exc/Medulla Oblongata, [Opn, Perc, Perc Endo]
00BT[0,3,4]Z[X,Z]	Exc/Spinal Meninges, [Opn, Perc, Perc Endo], No Dev, [Dx, NQ]
00BW[0,3,4]Z[X,Z]	Exc/Cervical Spinal Cord, [Opn, Perc, Perc Endo], No Dev, [Dx, NQ]
00BX[0,3,4]Z[X,Z]	Exc/Thoracic Spinal Cord, [Opn, Perc, Perc Endo], No Dev, [Dx, NQ]
00BY[0,3,4]Z[X,Z]	Exc/Lumbar Spinal Cord, [Opn, Perc, Perc Endo], No Dev, [Dx, NQ]
00C1[0,3,4]ZZ	Extir/Cerebral Meninges, [Opn, Perc, Perc Endo]
00C2[0,3,4]ZZ	Extir/Dura Mater, [Opn, Perc, Perc Endo]
00C4[0,3,4]ZZ	Extir/Subdural Space, [Opn, Perc, Perc Endo]
00C5[0,3,4]ZZ	Extir/Subarachnoid Space, [Opn, Perc, Perc Endo]
00C8[0,3,4]ZZ	Extir/Basal Ganglia, [Opn, Perc, Perc Endo]
00C9[0,3,4]ZZ	Extir/Thalamus, [Opn, Perc, Perc Endo]
00CA[0,3,4]ZZ	Extir/Hypothalamus, [Opn, Perc, Perc Endo]
00D1[0,3,4]ZZ	Extract/Cerebral Meninges, [Opn, Perc, Perc Endo]
00D2[0,3,4]ZZ	Extract/Dura Mater, [Opn, Perc, Perc Endo]
00DT[0,3,4]ZZ	Extract/Spinal Meninges, [Opn, Perc, Perc Endo]

MDC 17: Myeloproliferative Diseases And Disorders And Poorly Differentiated Neoplasms—SURGICAL

Code	Description
00FU[0,3,4,X]ZZ	Fragmn/Spinal Canal, [Opn, Perc, Perc Endo, Ext]
00H033Z	Insert of Inf Device into Brain, Perc Appr
00H0[0,3,4]MZ	Insert/Brain, [Opn, Perc, Perc Endo], Neurostimulator Lead, NQ
00H6[0,3,4]MZ	Insert/Cerebral Ventricle, [Opn, Perc, Perc Endo], Neurostimulator Lead, NQ
00HU[0,3,4][2,M]Z	Insert/Spinal Canal, [Opn, Perc, Perc Endo], [Monitoring Dev, Neurostimulator Lead], NQ
00HV[0,3,4][2,M]Z	Insert/Spinal Cord, [Opn, Perc, Perc Endo], [Monitoring Dev, Neurostimulator Lead], NQ
00J0[0,3,4]ZZ	Inspect/Brain, [Opn, Perc, Perc Endo]
00JU[0,3,4]ZZ	Inspect/Spinal Canal, [Opn, Perc, Perc Endo]
00JV[0,3,4]ZZ	Inspect/Spinal Cord, [Opn, Perc, Perc Endo]
00K0[0,3,4]ZZ	Map/Brain, [Opn, Perc, Perc Endo]
00K7[0,3,4]ZZ	Map/Cerebral Hemisphere, [Opn, Perc, Perc Endo]
00K8[0,3,4]ZZ	Map/Basal Ganglia, [Opn, Perc, Perc Endo]
00K9[0,3,4]ZZ	Map/Thalamus, [Opn, Perc, Perc Endo]
00KA[0,3,4]ZZ	Map/Hypothalamus, [Opn, Perc, Perc Endo]
00KB[0,3,4]ZZ	Map/Pons, [Opn, Perc, Perc Endo]
00KC[0,3,4]ZZ	Map/Cerebellum, [Opn, Perc, Perc Endo]
00KD[0,3,4]ZZ	Map/Medulla Oblongata, [Opn, Perc, Perc Endo]
00N0[0,3,4]ZZ	Rls/Brain, [Opn, Perc, Perc Endo]
00N1[0,3,4]ZZ	Rls/Cerebral Meninges, [Opn, Perc, Perc Endo]
00N2[0,3,4]ZZ	Rls/Dura Mater, [Opn, Perc, Perc Endo]
00N7[0,3,4]ZZ	Rls/Cerebral Hemisphere, [Opn, Perc, Perc Endo]
00N9[0,3,4]ZZ	Rls/Thalamus, [Opn, Perc, Perc Endo]
00NA[0,3,4]ZZ	Rls/Hypothalamus, [Opn, Perc, Perc Endo]
00NT[0,3,4]ZZ	Rls/Spinal Meninges, [Opn, Perc, Perc Endo]
00NW[0,3,4]ZZ	Rls/Cervical Spinal Cord, [Opn, Perc, Perc Endo]
00NX[0,3,4]ZZ	Rls/Thoracic Spinal Cord, [Opn, Perc, Perc Endo]
00NY[0,3,4]ZZ	Rls/Lumbar Spinal Cord, [Opn, Perc, Perc Endo]
00P0[0,3,4]MZ	Rmvl/Brain, [Opn, Perc, Perc Endo], Neurostimulator Lead, NQ
00P6[0,3,4,X]MZ	Rmvl/Cerebral Ventricle, [Opn, Perc, Perc Endo, Ext], Neurostimulator Lead, NQ
00PU[0,3,4][0,2,3]Z	Rmvl/Spinal Canal, [Opn, Perc, Perc Endo], [Drain Dev, Monitoring Dev, Inf Dev], NQ
00PV[0,3,4][0,2,3,7,J,K]Z	Rmvl/Spinal Cord, [Opn, Perc, Perc Endo], [Drain Dev, Monitoring Dev, Inf Dev, Auto Tissue Sub, Synth Sub, Nonauto Tissue Sub], NQ
00Q9[0,3,4]ZZ	Rpr/Thalamus, [Opn, Perc, Perc Endo]
00QA[0,3,4]ZZ	Rpr/Hypothalamus, [Opn, Perc, Perc Endo]
00QT[0,3,4]ZZ	Rpr/Spinal Meninges, [Opn, Perc, Perc Endo]
00QW[0,3,4]ZZ	Rpr/Cervical Spinal Cord, [Opn, Perc, Perc Endo]
00QX[0,3,4]ZZ	Rpr/Thoracic Spinal Cord, [Opn, Perc, Perc Endo]
00QY[0,3,4]ZZ	Rpr/Lumbar Spinal Cord, [Opn, Perc, Perc Endo]
00SW[0,3,4]ZZ	Repos/Cervical Spinal Cord, [Opn, Perc, Perc Endo]
00SX[0,3,4]ZZ	Repos/Thoracic Spinal Cord, [Opn, Perc, Perc Endo]
00SY[0,3,4]ZZ	Repos/Lumbar Spinal Cord, [Opn, Perc, Perc Endo]
00T7[0,3,4]ZZ	Resect/Cerebral Hemisphere, [Opn, Perc, Perc Endo]
00UT[0,3,4][7,J,K]Z	Supl/Spinal Meninges, [Opn, Perc, Perc Endo], [Auto Tissue Sub, Synth Sub, Nonauto Tissue Sub]
00W6[0,3,4]JZ	Rev/Cerebral Ventricle, [Opn, Perc, Perc Endo], Synth Sub, NQ
00WU[0,3,4][0,2,3,J,M]Z	Rev/Spinal Canal, [Opn, Perc, Perc Endo], [Drain Dev, Monitoring Dev, Inf Dev, Synth Sub, Neurostimulator Lead], NQ
00WV[0,3,4][0,2,3,7,J,K,M]Z	Rev/Spinal Cord, [Opn, Perc, Perc Endo], [Drain Dev, Monitoring Dev, Inf Dev, Auto Tissue Sub, Synth Sub, Nonauto Tissue Sub, Neurostimulator Lead], NQ
0151[0,4]ZZ	Destr/Cervical Nerve, [Opn, Perc Endo]
0158[0,4]ZZ	Destr/Thoracic Nerve, [Opn, Perc Endo]
015B[0,4]ZZ	Destr/Lumbar Nerve, [Opn, Perc Endo]
015R[0,4]ZZ	Destr/Sacral Nerve, [Opn, Perc Endo]
0181[0,3,4]ZZ	Div/Cervical Nerve, [Opn, Perc, Perc Endo]
0188[0,3,4]ZZ	Div/Thoracic Nerve, [Opn, Perc, Perc Endo]
018B[0,3,4]ZZ	Div/Lumbar Nerve, [Opn, Perc, Perc Endo]
018R[0,3,4]ZZ	Div/Sacral Nerve, [Opn, Perc, Perc Endo]
025N[0,3,4]ZZ	Destr/Pericardium, [Opn, Perc, Perc Endo]
02BN[0,3,4]Z[X,Z]	Exc/Pericardium, [Opn, Perc, Perc Endo], No Dev, [Dx, NQ]
02CN[0,3,4]ZZ	Extir/Pericardium, [Opn, Perc, Perc Endo]
02HN[0,3,4][0,2]Z	Insert/Pericardium, [Opn, Perc, Perc Endo], [Monitoring Dev, Pressure Sensor, Monitoring Dev], NQ
02JA[0,4]ZZ	Inspect/Heart, [Opn, Perc Endo]
02JY[0,4]ZZ	Inspect/Great Vessel, [Opn, Perc Endo]
02NN[0,3,4]ZZ	Rls/Pericardium, [Opn, Perc, Perc Endo]
02QA0ZZ	Repair Heart, Opn Appr
02TN[0,3,4]ZZ	Resect/Pericardium, [Opn, Perc, Perc Endo]
03H0[0,3,4]DZ	Insert/Int Mammary Artery, Rt, [Opn, Perc, Perc Endo], Intralum Dev, NQ
03H1[0,3,4]DZ	Insert/Int Mammary Artery, Lt, [Opn, Perc, Perc Endo], Intralum Dev, NQ
03H2[0,3,4]DZ	Insert/Innominate Artery, [Opn, Perc, Perc Endo], Intralum Dev, NQ
03H3[0,3,4]DZ	Insert/Subclavian Artery, Rt, [Opn, Perc, Perc Endo], Intralum Dev, NQ
03H4[0,3,4]DZ	Insert/Subclavian Artery, Lt, [Opn, Perc, Perc Endo], Intralum Dev, NQ
03H5[0,3,4]DZ	Insert/Axillary Artery, Rt, [Opn, Perc, Perc Endo], Intralum Dev, NQ
03H6[0,3,4]DZ	Insert/Axillary Artery, Lt, [Opn, Perc, Perc Endo], Intralum Dev, NQ
03H7[0,3,4]DZ	Insert/Brachial Artery, Rt, [Opn, Perc, Perc Endo], Intralum Dev, NQ
03H8[0,3,4]DZ	Insert/Brachial Artery, Lt, [Opn, Perc, Perc Endo], Intralum Dev, NQ
03H9[0,3,4]DZ	Insert/Ulnar Artery, Rt, [Opn, Perc, Perc Endo], Intralum Dev, NQ
03HA[0,3,4]DZ	Insert/Ulnar Artery, Lt, [Opn, Perc, Perc Endo], Intralum Dev, NQ
03HB[0,3,4]DZ	Insert/Radial Artery, Rt, [Opn, Perc, Perc Endo], Intralum Dev, NQ
03HC[0,3,4]DZ	Insert/Radial Artery, Lt, [Opn, Perc, Perc Endo], Intralum Dev, NQ
03HD[0,3,4]DZ	Insert/Hand Artery, Rt, [Opn, Perc, Perc Endo], Intralum Dev, NQ
03HF[0,3,4]DZ	Insert/Hand Artery, Lt, [Opn, Perc, Perc Endo], Intralum Dev, NQ
03HG[0,3,4]DZ	Insert/Intracranial Artery, [Opn, Perc, Perc Endo], Intralum Dev, NQ
03HH[0,3,4]DZ	Insert/Common Carotid Artery, Rt, [Opn, Perc, Perc Endo], Intralum Dev, NQ
03HJ[0,3,4]DZ	Insert/Common Carotid Artery, Lt, [Opn, Perc, Perc Endo], Intralum Dev, NQ
03HK[0,3,4]DZ	Insert/Int Carotid Artery, Rt, [Opn, Perc, Perc Endo], Intralum Dev, NQ
03HL[0,3,4]DZ	Insert/Int Carotid Artery, Lt, [Opn, Perc, Perc Endo], Intralum Dev, NQ
03HM[0,3,4]DZ	Insert/Ext Carotid Artery, Rt, [Opn, Perc, Perc Endo], Intralum Dev, NQ
03HN[0,3,4]DZ	Insert/Ext Carotid Artery, Lt, [Opn, Perc, Perc Endo], Intralum Dev, NQ
03HP[0,3,4]DZ	Insert/Vert Artery, Rt, [Opn, Perc, Perc Endo], Intralum Dev, NQ
03HQ[0,3,4]DZ	Insert/Vert Artery, Lt, [Opn, Perc, Perc Endo], Intralum Dev, NQ
03HR[0,3,4]DZ	Insert/Face Artery, [Opn, Perc, Perc Endo], Intralum Dev, NQ
03HS[0,3,4]DZ	Insert/Temporal Artery, Rt, [Opn, Perc, Perc Endo], Intralum Dev, NQ
03HT[0,3,4]DZ	Insert/Temporal Artery, Lt, [Opn, Perc, Perc Endo], Intralum Dev, NQ
03HU[0,3,4]DZ	Insert/Thyroid Artery, Rt, [Opn, Perc, Perc Endo], Intralum Dev, NQ
03HV[0,3,4]DZ	Insert/Thyroid Artery, Lt, [Opn, Perc, Perc Endo], Intralum Dev, NQ
03HY[0,3,4]DZ	Insert/Upr Artery, [Opn, Perc, Perc Endo], Intralum Dev, NQ
04CK[0,3,4]ZZ	Extir/Femor Artery, Rt, [Opn, Perc, Perc Endo]
04CL[0,3,4]ZZ	Extir/Femor Artery, Lt, [Opn, Perc, Perc Endo]
04CM[0,3,4]ZZ	Extir/Popliteal Artery, Rt, [Opn, Perc, Perc Endo]
04CN[0,3,4]ZZ	Extir/Popliteal Artery, Lt, [Opn, Perc, Perc Endo]
04CP[0,3,4]ZZ	Extir/Ant Tibial Artery, Rt, [Opn, Perc, Perc Endo]
04CQ[0,3,4]ZZ	Extir/Ant Tibial Artery, Lt, [Opn, Perc, Perc Endo]
04CR[0,3,4]ZZ	Extir/Post Tibial Artery, Rt, [Opn, Perc, Perc Endo]
04CS[0,3,4]ZZ	Extir/Post Tibial Artery, Lt, [Opn, Perc, Perc Endo]
04CT[0,3,4]ZZ	Extir/Peroneal Artery, Rt, [Opn, Perc, Perc Endo]
04CU[0,3,4]ZZ	Extir/Peroneal Artery, Lt, [Opn, Perc, Perc Endo]
04CV[0,3,4]ZZ	Extir/Foot Artery, Rt, [Opn, Perc, Perc Endo]
04CW[0,3,4]ZZ	Extir/Foot Artery, Lt, [Opn, Perc, Perc Endo]
04CY[0,3,4]ZZ	Extir/Lwr Artery, [Opn, Perc, Perc Endo]
04H0[0,3,4]DZ	Insert/Abd Aorta, [Opn, Perc, Perc Endo], Intralum Dev, NQ
04H1[0,3,4]DZ	Insert/Celiac Artery, [Opn, Perc, Perc Endo], Intralum Dev, NQ
04H2[0,3,4]DZ	Insert/Gastric Artery, [Opn, Perc, Perc Endo], Intralum Dev, NQ
04H3[0,3,4]DZ	Insert/Hepatic Artery, [Opn, Perc, Perc Endo], Intralum Dev, NQ
04H4[0,3,4]DZ	Insert/Splenic Artery, [Opn, Perc, Perc Endo], Intralum Dev, NQ
04H5[0,3,4]DZ	Insert/Superior Mesenteric Artery, [Opn, Perc, Perc Endo], Intralum Dev, NQ
04H6[0,3,4]DZ	Insert/Colic Artery, Rt, [Opn, Perc, Perc Endo], Intralum Dev, NQ
04H7[0,3,4]DZ	Insert/Colic Artery, Lt, [Opn, Perc, Perc Endo], Intralum Dev, NQ
04H8[0,3,4]DZ	Insert/Colic Artery, Mid, [Opn, Perc, Perc Endo], Intralum Dev, NQ

T Transfer DRG   SP Special Payment   * Code Range   **6th and 7th Character of ZZ = No Device, No Qualifier ZX = No Device, Diagnostic**

296   MS-DRG Version 33.0   © 2015 Optum360, LLC

04H9[0,3,4]DZ Insert/Renal Artery, Rt, [Opn, Perc, Perc Endo], Intralum Dev, NQ
04HA[0,3,4]DZ Insert/Renal Artery, Lt, [Opn, Perc, Perc Endo], Intralum Dev, NQ
04HB[0,3,4]DZ Insert/Inferior Mesenteric Artery, [Opn, Perc, Perc Endo], Intralum Dev, NQ
04HC[0,3,4]DZ Insert/Common Iliac Artery, Rt, [Opn, Perc, Perc Endo], Intralum Dev, NQ
04HD[0,3,4]DZ Insert/Common Iliac Artery, Lt, [Opn, Perc, Perc Endo], Intralum Dev, NQ
04HE[0,3,4]DZ Insert/Int Iliac Artery, Rt, [Opn, Perc, Perc Endo], Intralum Dev, NQ
04HF[0,3,4]DZ Insert/Int Iliac Artery, Lt, [Opn, Perc, Perc Endo], Intralum Dev, NQ
04HH[0,3,4]DZ Insert/Ext Iliac Artery, Rt, [Opn, Perc, Perc Endo], Intralum Dev, NQ
04HJ[0,3,4]DZ Insert/Ext Iliac Artery, Lt, [Opn, Perc, Perc Endo], Intralum Dev, NQ
04HK[0,3,4]DZ Insert/Femor Artery, Rt, [Opn, Perc, Perc Endo], Intralum Dev, NQ
04HL[0,3,4]DZ Insert/Femor Artery, Lt, [Opn, Perc, Perc Endo], Intralum Dev, NQ
04HM[0,3,4]DZ Insert/Popliteal Artery, Rt, [Opn, Perc, Perc Endo], Intralum Dev, NQ
04HN[0,3,4]DZ Insert/Popliteal Artery, Lt, [Opn, Perc, Perc Endo], Intralum Dev, NQ
04HP[0,3,4]DZ Insert/Ant Tibial Artery, Rt, [Opn, Perc, Perc Endo], Intralum Dev, NQ
04HQ[0,3,4]DZ Insert/Ant Tibial Artery, Lt, [Opn, Perc, Perc Endo], Intralum Dev, NQ
04HR[0,3,4]DZ Insert/Post Tibial Artery, Rt, [Opn, Perc, Perc Endo], Intralum Dev, NQ
04HS[0,3,4]DZ Insert/Post Tibial Artery, Lt, [Opn, Perc, Perc Endo], Intralum Dev, NQ
04HT[0,3,4]DZ Insert/Peroneal Artery, Rt, [Opn, Perc, Perc Endo], Intralum Dev, NQ
04HU[0,3,4]DZ Insert/Peroneal Artery, Lt, [Opn, Perc, Perc Endo], Intralum Dev, NQ
04HV[0,3,4]DZ Insert/Foot Artery, Rt, [Opn, Perc, Perc Endo], Intralum Dev, NQ
04HW[0,3,4]DZ Insert/Foot Artery, Lt, [Opn, Perc, Perc Endo], Intralum Dev, NQ
04HY[0,3,4][2,D]Z Insert/Lwr Artery, [Opn, Perc, Perc Endo], [Monitoring Dev, Intralum Dev], NQ
04PY[0,3,4][0,2,3,C,D]ZRmvl/Lwr Artery, [Opn, Perc, Perc Endo], [Drain Dev, Monitoring Dev, Inf Dev, Extralum Dev, Intralum Dev], NQ
04WY[0,3,4][0,2,3,C,D]ZRev/Lwr Artery, [Opn, Perc, Perc Endo], [Drain Dev, Monitoring Dev, Inf Dev, Extralum Dev, Intralum Dev], NQ
05H0[0,3,4]DZ Insert/Azygos Vein, [Opn, Perc, Perc Endo], Intralum Dev, NQ
05H1[0,3,4]DZ Insert/Hemiazygos Vein, [Opn, Perc, Perc Endo], Intralum Dev, NQ
05H3[0,3,4]DZ Insert/Innominate Vein, Rt, [Opn, Perc, Perc Endo], Intralum Dev, NQ
05H4[0,3,4]DZ Insert/Innominate Vein, Lt, [Opn, Perc, Perc Endo], Intralum Dev, NQ
05H5[0,3,4]DZ Insert/Subclavian Vein, Rt, [Opn, Perc, Perc Endo], Intralum Dev, NQ
05H6[0,3,4]DZ Insert/Subclavian Vein, Lt, [Opn, Perc, Perc Endo], Intralum Dev, NQ
05H7[0,3,4]DZ Insert/Axillary Vein, Rt, [Opn, Perc, Perc Endo], Intralum Dev, NQ
05H8[0,3,4]DZ Insert/Axillary Vein, Lt, [Opn, Perc, Perc Endo], Intralum Dev, NQ
05H9[0,3,4]DZ Insert/Brachial Vein, Rt, [Opn, Perc, Perc Endo], Intralum Dev, NQ
05HA[0,3,4]DZ Insert/Brachial Vein, Lt, [Opn, Perc, Perc Endo], Intralum Dev, NQ
05HB[0,3,4]DZ Insert/Basilic Vein, Rt, [Opn, Perc, Perc Endo], Intralum Dev, NQ
05HC[0,3,4]DZ Insert/Basilic Vein, Lt, [Opn, Perc, Perc Endo], Intralum Dev, NQ
05HD[0,3,4]DZ Insert/Cephalic Vein, Rt, [Opn, Perc, Perc Endo], Intralum Dev, NQ
05HF[0,3,4]DZ Insert/Cephalic Vein, Lt, [Opn, Perc, Perc Endo], Intralum Dev, NQ
05HG[0,3,4]DZ Insert/Hand Vein, Rt, [Opn, Perc, Perc Endo], Intralum Dev, NQ
05HH[0,3,4]DZ Insert/Hand Vein, Lt, [Opn, Perc, Perc Endo], Intralum Dev, NQ
05HL[0,3,4]DZ Insert/Intracranial Vein, [Opn, Perc, Perc Endo], Intralum Dev, NQ
05HM[0,3,4]DZ Insert/Int Jugular Vein, Rt, [Opn, Perc, Perc Endo], Intralum Dev, NQ
05HN[0,3,4]DZ Insert/Int Jugular Vein, Lt, [Opn, Perc, Perc Endo], Intralum Dev, NQ

05HP[0,3,4]DZ Insert/Ext Jugular Vein, Rt, [Opn, Perc, Perc Endo], Intralum Dev, NQ
05HQ[0,3,4]DZ Insert/Ext Jugular Vein, Lt, [Opn, Perc, Perc Endo], Intralum Dev, NQ
05HR[0,3,4]DZ Insert/Vert Vein, Rt, [Opn, Perc, Perc Endo], Intralum Dev, NQ
05HS[0,3,4]DZ Insert/Vert Vein, Lt, [Opn, Perc, Perc Endo], Intralum Dev, NQ
05HT[0,3,4]DZ Insert/Face Vein, Rt, [Opn, Perc, Perc Endo], Intralum Dev, NQ
05HV[0,3,4]DZ Insert/Face Vein, Lt, [Opn, Perc, Perc Endo], Intralum Dev, NQ
05HY[0,3,4]DZ Insert/Upr Vein, [Opn, Perc, Perc Endo], Intralum Dev, NQ
06H1[0,3,4]DZ Insert/Splenic Vein, [Opn, Perc, Perc Endo], Intralum Dev, NQ
06H2[0,3,4]DZ Insert/Gastric Vein, [Opn, Perc, Perc Endo], Intralum Dev, NQ
06H3[0,3,4]DZ Insert/Esophageal Vein, [Opn, Perc, Perc Endo], Intralum Dev, NQ
06H4[0,3,4]DZ Insert/Hepatic Vein, [Opn, Perc, Perc Endo], Intralum Dev, NQ
06H5[0,3,4]DZ Insert/Superior Mesenteric Vein, [Opn, Perc, Perc Endo], Intralum Dev, NQ
06H6[0,3,4]DZ Insert/Inferior Mesenteric Vein, [Opn, Perc, Perc Endo], Intralum Dev, NQ
06H7[0,3,4]DZ Insert/Colic Vein, [Opn, Perc, Perc Endo], Intralum Dev, NQ
06H8[0,3,4]DZ Insert/Portal Vein, [Opn, Perc, Perc Endo], Intralum Dev, NQ
06H9[0,3,4]DZ Insert/Renal Vein, Rt, [Opn, Perc, Perc Endo], Intralum Dev, NQ
06HB[0,3,4]DZ Insert/Renal Vein, Lt, [Opn, Perc, Perc Endo], Intralum Dev, NQ
06HC[0,3,4]DZ Insert/Common Iliac Vein, Rt, [Opn, Perc, Perc Endo], Intralum Dev, NQ
06HD[0,3,4]DZ Insert/Common Iliac Vein, Lt, [Opn, Perc, Perc Endo], Intralum Dev, NQ
06HF[0,3,4]DZ Insert/Ext Iliac Vein, Rt, [Opn, Perc, Perc Endo], Intralum Dev, NQ
06HG[0,3,4]DZ Insert/Ext Iliac Vein, Lt, [Opn, Perc, Perc Endo], Intralum Dev, NQ
06HH[0,3,4]DZ Insert/Hypogastric Vein, Rt, [Opn, Perc, Perc Endo], Intralum Dev, NQ
06HJ[0,3,4]DZ Insert/Hypogastric Vein, Lt, [Opn, Perc, Perc Endo], Intralum Dev, NQ
06HM[0,3,4]DZ Insert/Femor Vein, Rt, [Opn, Perc, Perc Endo], Intralum Dev, NQ
06HN[0,3,4]DZ Insert/Femor Vein, Lt, [Opn, Perc, Perc Endo], Intralum Dev, NQ
06HP[0,3,4]DZ Insert/Greater Saphenous Vein, Rt, [Opn, Perc, Perc Endo], Intralum Dev, NQ
06HQ[0,3,4]DZ Insert/Greater Saphenous Vein, Lt, [Opn, Perc, Perc Endo], Intralum Dev, NQ
06HR[0,3,4]DZ Insert/Lesser Saphenous Vein, Rt, [Opn, Perc, Perc Endo], Intralum Dev, NQ
06HS[0,3,4]DZ Insert/Lesser Saphenous Vein, Lt, [Opn, Perc, Perc Endo], Intralum Dev, NQ
06HT[0,3,4]DZ Insert/Foot Vein, Rt, [Opn, Perc, Perc Endo], Intralum Dev, NQ
06HV[0,3,4]DZ Insert/Foot Vein, Lt, [Opn, Perc, Perc Endo], Intralum Dev, NQ
06HY[0,3,4]DZ Insert/Lwr Vein, [Opn, Perc, Perc Endo], Intralum Dev, NQ
0750[0,3,4]ZZ Destr/Lymphatic, Head, [Opn, Perc, Perc Endo]
0751[0,3,4]ZZ Destr/Lymphatic, Rt Neck, [Opn, Perc, Perc Endo]
0752[0,3,4]ZZ Destr/Lymphatic, Lt Neck, [Opn, Perc, Perc Endo]
0753[0,3,4]ZZ Destr/Lymphatic, Rt Upr Extr, [Opn, Perc, Perc Endo]
0754[0,3,4]ZZ Destr/Lymphatic, Lt Upr Extr, [Opn, Perc, Perc Endo]
0755[0,3,4]ZZ Destr/Lymphatic, Rt Axillary, [Opn, Perc, Perc Endo]
0756[0,3,4]ZZ Destr/Lymphatic, Lt Axillary, [Opn, Perc, Perc Endo]
0757[0,3,4]ZZ Destr/Lymphatic, Thorax, [Opn, Perc, Perc Endo]
0758[0,3,4]ZZ Destr/Lymphatic, Int Mammary, Rt, [Opn, Perc, Perc Endo]
0759[0,3,4]ZZ Destr/Lymphatic, Int Mammary, Lt, [Opn, Perc, Perc Endo]
075B[0,3,4]ZZ Destr/Lymphatic, Mesenteric, [Opn, Perc, Perc Endo]
075C[0,3,4]ZZ Destr/Lymphatic, Pelvis, [Opn, Perc, Perc Endo]
075D[0,3,4]ZZ Destr/Lymphatic, Aortic, [Opn, Perc, Perc Endo]
075F[0,3,4]ZZ Destr/Lymphatic, Rt Lwr Extr, [Opn, Perc, Perc Endo]
075G[0,3,4]ZZ Destr/Lymphatic, Lt Lwr Extr, [Opn, Perc, Perc Endo]
075H[0,3,4]ZZ Destr/Lymphatic, Rt Inguinal, [Opn, Perc, Perc Endo]
075J[0,3,4]ZZ Destr/Lymphatic, Lt Inguinal, [Opn, Perc, Perc Endo]
075M[0,3,4]ZZ Destr/Thymus, [Opn, Perc, Perc Endo]
075P[0,3,4]ZZ Destr/Spleen, [Opn, Perc, Perc Endo]
079M[0,3,4]ZX Drain/Thymus, [Opn, Perc, Perc Endo]
079M[0,3,4][0,Z]Z Drain/Thymus, [Opn, Perc, Perc Endo], [Drain Dev, No Dev], NQ
079P0ZX Drain of Spleen, Opn Appr, Diagnostic
079P0[0,Z]Z Drain/Spleen, Opn, [Drain Dev, No Dev], NQ
07B0[0,4]ZZ Exc/Lymphatic, Head, [Opn, Perc Endo]
07B3[0,4]ZZ Exc/Lymphatic, Rt Upr Extr, [Opn, Perc Endo]
07B4[0,4]ZZ Exc/Lymphatic, Lt Upr Extr, [Opn, Perc Endo]
07B7[0,4]ZZ Exc/Lymphatic, Thorax, [Opn, Perc Endo]
07BB[0,4]ZZ Exc/Lymphatic, Mesenteric, [Opn, Perc Endo]
07BF[0,4]ZZ Exc/Lymphatic, Rt Lwr Extr, [Opn, Perc Endo]
07BG[0,4]ZZ Exc/Lymphatic, Lt Lwr Extr, [Opn, Perc Endo]
07BM[0,3,4]Z[X,Z] Exc/Thymus, [Opn, Perc, Perc Endo], No Dev, [Dx, NQ]
07BP0ZX Exc of Spleen, Opn Appr, Diagnostic

| Surgical | Medical | CC Indicator | MCC Indicator | Procedure Proxy | PDx MCC PDx acts as own MCC | PDx CC PDx acts as own CC |

MDC 17: Myeloproliferative Diseases And Disorders And Poorly Differentiated Neoplasms—SURGICAL

07BP[0,3,4]ZZ	Exc/Spleen, [Opn, Perc, Perc Endo]
07CM[0,3,4]ZZ	Extir/Thymus, [Opn, Perc, Perc Endo]
07CP0ZZ	Extir of Matter from Spleen, Opn Appr
07JM[0,4]ZZ	Inspect/Thymus, [Opn, Perc Endo]
07JP0ZZ	Inspect of Spleen, Opn Appr
07L0[0,3,4][C,D,Z]Z	Occlsn/Lymphatic, Head, [Opn, Perc, Perc Endo], [Extralum Dev, Intralum Dev, No Dev], NQ
07L1[0,3,4][C,D,Z]Z	Occlsn/Lymphatic, Rt Neck, [Opn, Perc, Perc Endo], [Extralum Dev, Intralum Dev, No Dev], NQ
07L2[0,3,4][C,D,Z]Z	Occlsn/Lymphatic, Lt Neck, [Opn, Perc, Perc Endo], [Extralum Dev, Intralum Dev, No Dev], NQ
07L3[0,3,4][C,D,Z]Z	Occlsn/Lymphatic, Rt Upr Extr, [Opn, Perc, Perc Endo], [Extralum Dev, Intralum Dev, No Dev], NQ
07L4[0,3,4][C,D,Z]Z	Occlsn/Lymphatic, Lt Upr Extr, [Opn, Perc, Perc Endo], [Extralum Dev, Intralum Dev, No Dev], NQ
07L5[0,3,4][C,D,Z]Z	Occlsn/Lymphatic, Rt Axillary, [Opn, Perc, Perc Endo], [Extralum Dev, Intralum Dev, No Dev], NQ
07L6[0,3,4][C,D,Z]Z	Occlsn/Lymphatic, Lt Axillary, [Opn, Perc, Perc Endo], [Extralum Dev, Intralum Dev, No Dev], NQ
07L7[0,3,4][C,D,Z]Z	Occlsn/Lymphatic, Thorax, [Opn, Perc, Perc Endo], [Extralum Dev, Intralum Dev, No Dev], NQ
07L8[0,3,4][C,D,Z]Z	Occlsn/Lymphatic, Int Mammary, Rt, [Opn, Perc, Perc Endo], [Extralum Dev, Intralum Dev, No Dev], NQ
07L9[0,3,4][C,D,Z]Z	Occlsn/Lymphatic, Int Mammary, Lt, [Opn, Perc, Perc Endo], [Extralum Dev, Intralum Dev, No Dev], NQ
07LB[0,3,4][C,D,Z]Z	Occlsn/Lymphatic, Mesenteric, [Opn, Perc, Perc Endo], [Extralum Dev, Intralum Dev, No Dev], NQ
07LC[0,3,4][C,D,Z]Z	Occlsn/Lymphatic, Pelvis, [Opn, Perc, Perc Endo], [Extralum Dev, Intralum Dev, No Dev], NQ
07LD[0,3,4][C,D,Z]Z	Occlsn/Lymphatic, Aortic, [Opn, Perc, Perc Endo], [Extralum Dev, Intralum Dev, No Dev], NQ
07LF[0,3,4][C,D,Z]Z	Occlsn/Lymphatic, Rt Lwr Extr, [Opn, Perc, Perc Endo], [Extralum Dev, Intralum Dev, No Dev], NQ
07LG[0,3,4][C,D,Z]Z	Occlsn/Lymphatic, Lt Lwr Extr, [Opn, Perc, Perc Endo], [Extralum Dev, Intralum Dev, No Dev], NQ
07LH[0,3,4][C,D,Z]Z	Occlsn/Lymphatic, Rt Inguinal, [Opn, Perc, Perc Endo], [Extralum Dev, Intralum Dev, No Dev], NQ
07LJ[0,3,4][C,D,Z]Z	Occlsn/Lymphatic, Lt Inguinal, [Opn, Perc, Perc Endo], [Extralum Dev, Intralum Dev, No Dev], NQ
07N0[0,3,4]ZZ	Rls/Lymphatic, Head, [Opn, Perc, Perc Endo]
07N1[0,3,4]ZZ	Rls/Lymphatic, Rt Neck, [Opn, Perc, Perc Endo]
07N2[0,3,4]ZZ	Rls/Lymphatic, Lt Neck, [Opn, Perc, Perc Endo]
07N3[0,3,4]ZZ	Rls/Lymphatic, Rt Upr Extr, [Opn, Perc, Perc Endo]
07N4[0,3,4]ZZ	Rls/Lymphatic, Lt Upr Extr, [Opn, Perc, Perc Endo]
07N5[0,3,4]ZZ	Rls/Lymphatic, Rt Axillary, [Opn, Perc, Perc Endo]
07N6[0,3,4]ZZ	Rls/Lymphatic, Lt Axillary, [Opn, Perc, Perc Endo]
07N7[0,3,4]ZZ	Rls/Lymphatic, Thorax, [Opn, Perc, Perc Endo]
07N8[0,3,4]ZZ	Rls/Lymphatic, Int Mammary, Rt, [Opn, Perc, Perc Endo]
07N9[0,3,4]ZZ	Rls/Lymphatic, Int Mammary, Lt, [Opn, Perc, Perc Endo]
07NB[0,3,4]ZZ	Rls/Lymphatic, Mesenteric, [Opn, Perc, Perc Endo]
07NC[0,3,4]ZZ	Rls/Lymphatic, Pelvis, [Opn, Perc, Perc Endo]
07ND[0,3,4]ZZ	Rls/Lymphatic, Aortic, [Opn, Perc, Perc Endo]
07NF[0,3,4]ZZ	Rls/Lymphatic, Rt Lwr Extr, [Opn, Perc, Perc Endo]
07NG[0,3,4]ZZ	Rls/Lymphatic, Lt Lwr Extr, [Opn, Perc, Perc Endo]
07NH[0,3,4]ZZ	Rls/Lymphatic, Rt Inguinal, [Opn, Perc, Perc Endo]
07NJ[0,3,4]ZZ	Rls/Lymphatic, Lt Inguinal, [Opn, Perc, Perc Endo]
07NM[0,3,4]ZZ	Rls/Thymus, [Opn, Perc, Perc Endo]
07NP[0,3,4]ZZ	Rls/Spleen, [Opn, Perc, Perc Endo]
07PK[0,3,4][7,J,K]Z	Rmvl/Thoracic Duct, [Opn, Perc, Perc Endo], [Auto Tissue Sub, Synth Sub, Nonauto Tissue Sub], NQ
07PL[0,3,4][7,J,K]Z	Rmvl/Cisterna Chyli, [Opn, Perc, Perc Endo], [Auto Tissue Sub, Synth Sub, Nonauto Tissue Sub], NQ
07PM[0,3,4][0,3]Z	Rmvl/Thymus, [Opn, Perc, Perc Endo], [Drain Dev, Inf Dev], NQ
07PN[0,3,4][7,J,K]Z	Rmvl/Lymphatic, [Opn, Perc, Perc Endo], [Auto Tissue Sub, Synth Sub, Nonauto Tissue Sub], NQ
07PP[0,3,4][0,3]Z	Rmvl/Spleen, [Opn, Perc, Perc Endo], [Drain Dev, Inf Dev], NQ
07Q0[0,3,4]ZZ	Rpr/Lymphatic, Head, [Opn, Perc, Perc Endo]
07Q1[0,3,4]ZZ	Rpr/Lymphatic, Rt Neck, [Opn, Perc, Perc Endo]
07Q2[0,3,4]ZZ	Rpr/Lymphatic, Lt Neck, [Opn, Perc, Perc Endo]
07Q3[0,3,4]ZZ	Rpr/Lymphatic, Rt Upr Extr, [Opn, Perc, Perc Endo]
07Q4[0,3,4]ZZ	Rpr/Lymphatic, Lt Upr Extr, [Opn, Perc, Perc Endo]
07Q5[0,3,4]ZZ	Rpr/Lymphatic, Rt Axillary, [Opn, Perc, Perc Endo]
07Q6[0,3,4]ZZ	Rpr/Lymphatic, Lt Axillary, [Opn, Perc, Perc Endo]
07Q7[0,3,4]ZZ	Rpr/Lymphatic, Thorax, [Opn, Perc, Perc Endo]
07Q8[0,3,4]ZZ	Rpr/Lymphatic, Int Mammary, Rt, [Opn, Perc, Perc Endo]
07Q9[0,3,4]ZZ	Rpr/Lymphatic, Int Mammary, Lt, [Opn, Perc, Perc Endo]
07QB[0,3,4]ZZ	Rpr/Lymphatic, Mesenteric, [Opn, Perc, Perc Endo]
07QC[0,3,4]ZZ	Rpr/Lymphatic, Pelvis, [Opn, Perc, Perc Endo]
07QD[0,3,4]ZZ	Rpr/Lymphatic, Aortic, [Opn, Perc, Perc Endo]
07QF[0,3,4]ZZ	Rpr/Lymphatic, Rt Lwr Extr, [Opn, Perc, Perc Endo]
07QG[0,3,4]ZZ	Rpr/Lymphatic, Lt Lwr Extr, [Opn, Perc, Perc Endo]
07QH[0,3,4]ZZ	Rpr/Lymphatic, Rt Inguinal, [Opn, Perc, Perc Endo]
07QJ[0,3,4]ZZ	Rpr/Lymphatic, Lt Inguinal, [Opn, Perc, Perc Endo]
07QM[0,3,4]ZZ	Rpr/Thymus, [Opn, Perc, Perc Endo]
07QP[0,3,4]ZZ	Rpr/Spleen, [Opn, Perc, Perc Endo]
07SM0ZZ	Repos Thymus, Opn Appr
07SP0ZZ	Repos Spleen, Opn Appr
07T0[0,4]ZZ	Resect/Lymphatic, Head, [Opn, Perc Endo]
07T1[0,4]ZZ	Resect/Lymphatic, Rt Neck, [Opn, Perc Endo]
07T2[0,4]ZZ	Resect/Lymphatic, Lt Neck, [Opn, Perc Endo]
07T3[0,4]ZZ	Resect/Lymphatic, Rt Upr Extr, [Opn, Perc Endo]
07T4[0,4]ZZ	Resect/Lymphatic, Lt Upr Extr, [Opn, Perc Endo]
07T5[0,4]ZZ	Resect/Lymphatic, Rt Axillary, [Opn, Perc Endo]
07T6[0,4]ZZ	Resect/Lymphatic, Lt Axillary, [Opn, Perc Endo]
07T7[0,4]ZZ	Resect/Lymphatic, Thorax, [Opn, Perc Endo]
07T8[0,4]ZZ	Resect/Lymphatic, Int Mammary, Rt, [Opn, Perc Endo]
07T9[0,4]ZZ	Resect/Lymphatic, Int Mammary, Lt, [Opn, Perc Endo]
07TB[0,4]ZZ	Resect/Lymphatic, Mesenteric, [Opn, Perc Endo]
07TC[0,4]ZZ	Resect/Lymphatic, Pelvis, [Opn, Perc Endo]
07TD[0,4]ZZ	Resect/Lymphatic, Aortic, [Opn, Perc Endo]
07TF[0,4]ZZ	Resect/Lymphatic, Rt Lwr Extr, [Opn, Perc Endo]
07TG[0,4]ZZ	Resect/Lymphatic, Lt Lwr Extr, [Opn, Perc Endo]
07TH[0,4]ZZ	Resect/Lymphatic, Rt Inguinal, [Opn, Perc Endo]
07TJ[0,4]ZZ	Resect/Lymphatic, Lt Inguinal, [Opn, Perc Endo]
07TM[0,4]ZZ	Resect/Thymus, [Opn, Perc Endo]
07TP[0,4]ZZ	Resect/Spleen, [Opn, Perc Endo]
07U0[0,4][7,J,K]Z	Supl/Lymphatic, Head, [Opn, Perc Endo], [Auto Tissue Sub, Synth Sub, Nonauto Tissue Sub], NQ
07U1[0,4][7,J,K]Z	Supl/Lymphatic, Rt Neck, [Opn, Perc Endo], [Auto Tissue Sub, Synth Sub, Nonauto Tissue Sub], NQ
07U2[0,4][7,J,K]Z	Supl/Lymphatic, Lt Neck, [Opn, Perc Endo], [Auto Tissue Sub, Synth Sub, Nonauto Tissue Sub], NQ
07U3[0,4][7,J,K]Z	Supl/Lymphatic, Rt Upr Extr, [Opn, Perc Endo], [Auto Tissue Sub, Synth Sub, Nonauto Tissue Sub], NQ
07U4[0,4][7,J,K]Z	Supl/Lymphatic, Lt Upr Extr, [Opn, Perc Endo], [Auto Tissue Sub, Synth Sub, Nonauto Tissue Sub], NQ
07U5[0,4][7,J,K]Z	Supl/Lymphatic, Rt Axillary, [Opn, Perc Endo], [Auto Tissue Sub, Synth Sub, Nonauto Tissue Sub], NQ
07U6[0,4][7,J,K]Z	Supl/Lymphatic, Lt Axillary, [Opn, Perc Endo], [Auto Tissue Sub, Synth Sub, Nonauto Tissue Sub], NQ
07U7[0,4][7,J,K]Z	Supl/Lymphatic, Thorax, [Opn, Perc Endo], [Auto Tissue Sub, Synth Sub, Nonauto Tissue Sub], NQ
07U8[0,4][7,J,K]Z	Supl/Lymphatic, Int Mammary, Rt, [Opn, Perc Endo], [Auto Tissue Sub, Synth Sub, Nonauto Tissue Sub], NQ
07U9[0,4][7,J,K]Z	Supl/Lymphatic, Int Mammary, Lt, [Opn, Perc Endo], [Auto Tissue Sub, Synth Sub, Nonauto Tissue Sub], NQ
07UB[0,4][7,J,K]Z	Supl/Lymphatic, Mesenteric, [Opn, Perc Endo], [Auto Tissue Sub, Synth Sub, Nonauto Tissue Sub], NQ
07UC[0,4][7,J,K]Z	Supl/Lymphatic, Pelvis, [Opn, Perc Endo], [Auto Tissue Sub, Synth Sub, Nonauto Tissue Sub], NQ
07UD[0,4][7,J,K]Z	Supl/Lymphatic, Aortic, [Opn, Perc Endo], [Auto Tissue Sub, Synth Sub, Nonauto Tissue Sub], NQ
07UF[0,4][7,J,K]Z	Supl/Lymphatic, Rt Lwr Extr, [Opn, Perc Endo], [Auto Tissue Sub, Synth Sub, Nonauto Tissue Sub], NQ
07UG[0,4][7,J,K]Z	Supl/Lymphatic, Lt Lwr Extr, [Opn, Perc Endo], [Auto Tissue Sub, Synth Sub, Nonauto Tissue Sub], NQ
07UH[0,4][7,J,K]Z	Supl/Lymphatic, Rt Inguinal, [Opn, Perc Endo], [Auto Tissue Sub, Synth Sub, Nonauto Tissue Sub], NQ
07UJ[0,4][7,J,K]Z	Supl/Lymphatic, Lt Inguinal, [Opn, Perc Endo], [Auto Tissue Sub, Synth Sub, Nonauto Tissue Sub], NQ
07V0[0,3,4][C,D,Z]Z	Restrict/Lymphatic, Head, [Opn, Perc, Perc Endo], [Extralum Dev, Intralum Dev, No Dev], NQ
07V1[0,3,4][C,D,Z]Z	Restrict/Lymphatic, Rt Neck, [Opn, Perc, Perc Endo], [Extralum Dev, Intralum Dev, No Dev], NQ
07V2[0,3,4][C,D,Z]Z	Restrict/Lymphatic, Lt Neck, [Opn, Perc, Perc Endo], [Extralum Dev, Intralum Dev, No Dev], NQ
07V3[0,3,4][C,D,Z]Z	Restrict/Lymphatic, Rt Upr Extr, [Opn, Perc, Perc Endo], [Extralum Dev, Intralum Dev, No Dev], NQ
07V4[0,3,4][C,D,Z]Z	Restrict/Lymphatic, Lt Upr Extr, [Opn, Perc, Perc Endo], [Extralum Dev, Intralum Dev, No Dev], NQ
07V5[0,3,4][C,D,Z]Z	Restrict/Lymphatic, Rt Axillary, [Opn, Perc, Perc Endo], [Extralum Dev, Intralum Dev, No Dev], NQ
07V6[0,3,4][C,D,Z]Z	Restrict/Lymphatic, Lt Axillary, [Opn, Perc, Perc Endo], [Extralum Dev, Intralum Dev, No Dev], NQ
07V7[0,3,4][C,D,Z]Z	Restrict/Lymphatic, Thorax, [Opn, Perc, Perc Endo], [Extralum Dev, Intralum Dev, No Dev], NQ
07V8[0,3,4][C,D,Z]Z	Restrict/Lymphatic, Int Mammary, Rt, [Opn, Perc, Perc Endo], [Extralum Dev, Intralum Dev, No Dev], NQ
07V9[0,3,4][C,D,Z]Z	Restrict/Lymphatic, Int Mammary, Lt, [Opn, Perc, Perc Endo], [Extralum Dev, Intralum Dev, No Dev], NQ

T Transfer DRG   SP Special Payment   * Code Range   6th and 7th Character of ZZ = No Device, No Qualifier ZX = No Device, Diagnostic

MS-DRG Version 33.0

© 2015 Optum360, LLC

07VB[0,3,4][C,D,Z]Z Restrict/Lymphatic, Mesenteric, [Opn, Perc, Perc Endo], [Extralum Dev, Intralum Dev, No Dev], NQ

07VC[0,3,4][C,D,Z]Z Restrict/Lymphatic, Pelvis, [Opn, Perc, Perc Endo], [Extralum Dev, Intralum Dev, No Dev], NQ

07VD[0,3,4][C,D,Z]Z Restrict/Lymphatic, Aortic, [Opn, Perc, Perc Endo], [Extralum Dev, Intralum Dev, No Dev], NQ

07VF[0,3,4][C,D,Z]Z Restrict/Lymphatic, Rt Lwr Extr, [Opn, Perc, Perc Endo], [Extralum Dev, Intralum Dev, No Dev], NQ

07VG[0,3,4][C,D,Z]Z Restrict/Lymphatic, Lt Lwr Extr, [Opn, Perc, Perc Endo], [Extralum Dev, Intralum Dev, No Dev], NQ

07VH[0,3,4][C,D,Z]Z Restrict/Lymphatic, Rt Inguinal, [Opn, Perc, Perc Endo], [Extralum Dev, Intralum Dev, No Dev], NQ

07VJ[0,3,4][C,D,Z]Z Restrict/Lymphatic, Lt Inguinal, [Opn, Perc, Perc Endo], [Extralum Dev, Intralum Dev, No Dev], NQ

07WK[0,3,4][7,J,K]Z Rev/Thoracic Duct, [Opn, Perc, Perc Endo], [Auto Tissue Sub, Synth Sub, Nonauto Tissue Sub], NQ

07WL[0,3,4][7,J,K]Z Rev/Cisterna Chyli, [Opn, Perc, Perc Endo], [Auto Tissue Sub, Synth Sub, Nonauto Tissue Sub], NQ

07WM[0,3,4][0,3] Rev/Thymus, [Opn, Perc, Perc Endo], [Drain Dev, Inf Dev], NQ

07WN[0,3,4][7,J,K]ZRev/Lymphatic, [Opn, Perc, Perc Endo], [Auto Tissue Sub, Synth Sub, Nonauto Tissue Sub], NQ

07WP[0,3,4][0,3] Rev/Spleen, [Opn, Perc, Perc Endo], [Drain Dev, Inf Dev], NQ

07YM0Z[0,1,2] Transplantation/Thymus, Opn, No Dev, [Allogeneic, Syngeneic, Zooplastic]

07YP0Z[0,1,2] Transplantation/Spleen, Opn, No Dev, [Allogeneic, Syngeneic, Zooplastic]

0B5C[0,4]ZZ Destr/Upr Lung Lobe, Rt, [Opn, Perc Endo]

0B5D[0,4]ZZ Destr/Mid Lung Lobe, Rt, [Opn, Perc Endo]

0B5F[0,4]ZZ Destr/Lwr Lung Lobe, Rt, [Opn, Perc Endo]

0B5G[0,4]ZZ Destr/Upr Lung Lobe, Lt, [Opn, Perc Endo]

0B5H[0,4]ZZ Destr/Lung Lingula, [Opn, Perc Endo]

0B5J[0,4]ZZ Destr/Lwr Lung Lobe, Lt, [Opn, Perc Endo]

0B5K[0,4]ZZ Destr/Lung, Rt, [Opn, Perc Endo]

0B5L[0,4]ZZ Destr/Lung, Lt, [Opn, Perc Endo]

0B5M[0,4]ZZ Destr/Lungs, Bilat, [Opn, Perc Endo]

0B5N[0,3,4]ZZ Destr/Pleura, Rt, [Opn, Perc, Perc Endo]

0B5P[0,3,4]ZZ Destr/Pleura, Lt, [Opn, Perc, Perc Endo]

0B9C0ZX Drain of Rt Upr Lung Lobe, Opn Appr, Diagnostic

0B9D0ZX Drain of Rt Mid Lung Lobe, Opn Appr, Diagn

0B9F0ZX Drain of Rt Lwr Lung Lobe, Opn Appr, Diagnostic

0B9G0ZX Drain of Lt Upr Lung Lobe, Opn Appr, Diagnostic

0B9H0ZX Drain of Lung Lingula, Opn Appr, Diagnostic

0B9J0ZX Drain of Lt Lwr Lung Lobe, Opn Appr, Diagnostic

0B9K0ZX Drain of Rt Lung, Opn Appr, Diagnostic

0B9L0ZX Drain of Lt Lung, Opn Appr, Diagnostic

0B9M0ZX Drain of Bilat Lungs, Opn Appr, Diagnostic

0BBC0ZX Exc of Rt Upr Lung Lobe, Opn Appr, Diagnostic

0BBC[0,3,4,7]ZZ Exc/Upr Lung Lobe, Rt, [Opn, Perc, Perc Endo, Via Natrl or Artfcl Opng]

0BBD0ZX Exc of Rt Mid Lung Lobe, Opn Appr, Diagn

0BBD[0,3,4,7]ZZ Exc/Mid Lung Lobe, Rt, [Opn, Perc, Perc Endo, Via Natrl or Artfcl Opng]

0BBF0ZX Exc of Rt Lwr Lung Lobe, Opn Appr, Diagnostic

0BBF[0,3,4,7]ZZ Exc/Lwr Lung Lobe, Rt, [Opn, Perc, Perc Endo, Via Natrl or Artfcl Opng]

0BBG0ZX Exc of Lt Upr Lung Lobe, Opn Appr, Diagnostic

0BBG[0,3,4,7]ZZ Exc/Upr Lung Lobe, Lt, [Opn, Perc, Perc Endo, Via Natrl or Artfcl Opng]

0BBH0ZX Exc of Lung Lingula, Opn Appr, Diagnostic

0BBH[0,3,4,7]ZZ Exc/Lung Lingula, [Opn, Perc, Perc Endo, Via Natrl or Artfcl Opng]

0BBJ0ZX Exc of Lt Lwr Lung Lobe, Opn Appr, Diagnostic

0BBJ[0,3,4,7]ZZ Exc/Lwr Lung Lobe, Lt, [Opn, Perc, Perc Endo, Via Natrl or Artfcl Opng]

0BBK0ZX Exc of Rt Lung, Opn Appr, Diagnostic

0BBK[0,3,4,7]ZZ Exc/Lung, Rt, [Opn, Perc, Perc Endo, Via Natrl or Artfcl Opng]

0BBL0ZX Exc of Lt Lung, Opn Appr, Diagnostic

0BBL[0,3,4,7]ZZ Exc/Lung, Lt, [Opn, Perc, Perc Endo, Via Natrl or Artfcl Opng]

0BBM0ZX Exc of Bilat Lungs, Opn Appr, Diagnostic

0BBM[0,3,7]ZZ Exc/Lungs, Bilat, [Opn, Perc, Via Natrl or Artfcl Opng]

0BDN[0,3,4]Z[X,Z] Extract/Pleura, Rt, [Opn, Perc, Perc Endo], No Dev, [Dx, NQ]

0BDP[0,3,4]Z[X,Z] Extract/Pleura, Lt, [Opn, Perc, Perc Endo], No Dev, [Dx, NQ]

0BTH[0,4]ZZ Resect/Lung Lingula, [Opn, Perc Endo]

0D113J4 Bypass Up Esophag to Cutan with Synth Sub, Perc Appr

0D11[0,4,8][7,J,K,Z][4,6] Bypass/Esophagus, Upr, [Opn, Perc Endo, Via Natrl or Artfcl Opng Endo], [Auto Tissue Sub, Synth Sub, Nonauto Tissue Sub, No Dev], [Cutaneous, Stomach]

0D123J4 Bypass Mid Esophag to Cutan with Synth Sub, Perc Appr

0D12[0,4,8][7,J,K,Z][4,6] Bypass/Esophagus, Mid, [Opn, Perc Endo, Via Natrl or Artfcl Opng Endo], [Auto Tissue Sub, Synth Sub, Nonauto Tissue Sub, No Dev], [Cutaneous, Stomach]

0D133J4 Bypass Low Esophag to Cutan with Synth Sub, Perc Appr

0D13[0,4,8][7,J,K,Z][4,6] Bypass/Esophagus, Lwr, [Opn, Perc Endo, Via Natrl or Artfcl Opng Endo], [Auto Tissue Sub, Synth Sub, Nonauto Tissue Sub, No Dev], [Cutaneous, Stomach]

0D153J4 Bypass Esophagus to Cutaneous with Synth Sub, Perc Appr

0D15[0,4,8][7,J,K,Z][4,6,9,A,B] Bypass/Esophagus, [Opn, Perc Endo, Via Natrl or Artfcl Opng Endo], [Auto Tissue Sub, Synth Sub, Nonauto Tissue Sub, No Dev], [Cutaneous, Stomach, Duodenum, Jejunum, Ileum]

0D16[0,4,8][7,J,K,Z][9,A,B,L] Bypass/Stomach, [Opn, Perc Endo, Via Natrl or Artfcl Opng Endo], [Auto Tissue Sub, Synth Sub, Nonauto Tissue Sub, No Dev], [Duodenum, Jejunum, Ileum, Transv Colon]

0D193J4 Bypass Duodenum to Cutaneous with Synth Sub, Perc Appr

0D19[0,4,8][7,J,K,Z][4,9,A,B,L] Bypass/Duodenum, [Opn, Perc Endo, Via Natrl or Artfcl Opng Endo], [Auto Tissue Sub, Synth Sub, Nonauto Tissue Sub, No Dev], [Cutaneous, Duodenum, Jejunum, Ileum, Transv Colon]

0D1A3J4 Bypass Jejunum to Cutaneous with Synth Sub, Perc Appr

0D1A[0,4,8][7,J,K,Z][4,A,B,H,K,L,M,N,P,Q] Bypass/Jejunum, [Opn, Perc Endo, Via Natrl or Artfcl Opng Endo], [Auto Tissue Sub, Synth Sub, Nonauto Tissue Sub, No Dev], [Cutaneous, Jejunum, Ileum, Cecum, Ascending Colon, Transv Colon, Descending Colon, Sigmoid Colon, Rectum, Anus]

0D1B3J4 Bypass Ileum to Cutaneous with Synth Sub, Perc Appr

0D1B[0,4,8][7,J,K,Z][4,B,H,K,L,M,N,P,Q] Bypass/Ileum, [Opn, Perc Endo, Via Natrl or Artfcl Opng Endo], [Auto Tissue Sub, Synth Sub, Nonauto Tissue Sub, No Dev], [Cutaneous, Ileum, Cecum, Ascending Colon, Transv Colon, Descending Colon, Sigmoid Colon, Rectum, Anus]

0D1H3J4 Bypass Cecum to Cutaneous with Synth Sub, Perc Appr

0D1H8[7,J,K,Z]P Bypass/Cecum, Via Natrl or Artfcl Opng Endo, [Auto Tissue Sub, Synth Sub, Nonauto Tissue Sub, No Dev], Rectum

0D1H[0,4,8][7,J,K,Z]4 Bypass/Cecum, [Opn, Perc Endo, Via Natrl or Artfcl Opng Endo], [Auto Tissue Sub, Synth Sub, Nonauto Tissue Sub, No Dev], Cutaneous

0D1K3J4 Bypass Asc Colon to Cutan with Synth Sub, Perc Appr

0D1K[0,4,8][7,J,K,Z]4 Bypass/Ascending Colon, [Opn, Perc Endo, Via Natrl or Artfcl Opng Endo], [Auto Tissue Sub, Synth Sub, Nonauto Tissue Sub, No Dev], Cutaneous

0D1L3J4 Bypass Trans Colon to Cutan with Synth Sub, Perc Appr

0D1L[0,4,8][7,J,K,Z]4 Bypass/Transv Colon, [Opn, Perc Endo, Via Natrl or Artfcl Opng Endo], [Auto Tissue Sub, Synth Sub, Nonauto Tissue Sub, No Dev], Cutaneous

0D1M3J4 Bypass Descend Colon to Cutan with Synth Sub, Perc Appr

0D1M[0,4,8][7,J,K,Z]4 Bypass/Descending Colon, [Opn, Perc Endo, Via Natrl or Artfcl Opng Endo], [Auto Tissue Sub, Synth Sub, Nonauto Tissue Sub, No Dev], Cutaneous

0D1N3J4 Bypass Sigmoid Colon to Cutan with Synth Sub, Perc Appr

0D1N[0,4,8][7,J,K] 4Bypass/Sigmoid Colon, [Opn, Perc Endo, Via Natrl or Artfcl Opng Endo], [Auto Tissue Sub, Synth Sub, Nonauto Tissue Sub], Cutaneous

0D1N[4,8]Z4 Bypass/Sigmoid Colon, [Perc Endo, Via Natrl or Artfcl Opng Endo], No Dev, Cutaneous

0D51[0,3,7]ZZ Destr/Esophagus, Upr, [Opn, Perc, Via Natrl or Artfcl Opng]

0D52[0,3,7]ZZ Destr/Esophagus, Mid, [Opn, Perc, Via Natrl or Artfcl Opng]

0D53[0,3,7]ZZ Destr/Esophagus, Lwr, [Opn, Perc, Via Natrl or Artfcl Opng]

0D54[0,3,7]ZZ Destr/Esophagogastric Junction, [Opn, Perc, Via Natrl or Artfcl Opng]

0D55[0,3,7]ZZ Destr/Esophagus, [Opn, Perc, Via Natrl or Artfcl Opng]

0D58[0,3,4,7,8]ZZ Destr/Sm Intestine, [Opn, Perc, Perc Endo, Via Natrl or Artfcl Opng, Via Natrl or Artfcl Opng Endo]

0D59[0,3,7]ZZ Destr/Duodenum, [Opn, Perc, Via Natrl or Artfcl Opng]

0D5A[0,3,4,7,8]ZZ Destr/Jejunum, [Opn, Perc, Perc Endo, Via Natrl or Artfcl Opng, Via Natrl or Artfcl Opng Endo]

0D5B[0,3,4,7,8]ZZ Destr/Ileum, [Opn, Perc, Perc Endo, Via Natrl or Artfcl Opng, Via Natrl or Artfcl Opng Endo]

0D5C[0,3,4,7,8]ZZ Destr/Ileocecal Valve, [Opn, Perc, Perc Endo, Via Natrl or Artfcl Opng, Via Natrl or Artfcl Opng Endo]

0D5E[0,3,7]ZZ Destr/Lg Intestine, [Opn, Perc, Via Natrl or Artfcl Opng]

0D5F[0,3,7]ZZ Destr/Lg Intestine, Rt, [Opn, Perc, Via Natrl or Artfcl Opng]

0D5G[0,3,7]ZZ Destr/Lg Intestine, Lt, [Opn, Perc, Via Natrl or Artfcl Opng]

0D5H[0,3,7]ZZ Destr/Cecum, [Opn, Perc, Via Natrl or Artfcl Opng]

0D5K[0,3,7]ZZ Destr/Ascending Colon, [Opn, Perc, Via Natrl or Artfcl Opng]

0D5L[0,3,7]ZZ Destr/Transv Colon, [Opn, Perc, Via Natrl or Artfcl Opng]

0D5M[0,3,7]ZZ Destr/Descending Colon, [Opn, Perc, Via Natrl or Artfcl Opng]

0D5N[0,3,7]ZZ Destr/Sigmoid Colon, [Opn, Perc, Via Natrl or Artfcl Opng]

0D5S[0,3,4]ZZ Destr/Greater Omentum, [Opn, Perc, Perc Endo]

Surgical   **Medical**   **CC Indicator**   **MCC Indicator**   **Procedure Proxy**   PDxMCC **PDx acts as own MCC**   PDxCC **PDx acts as own CC**

MDC 17: Myeloproliferative Diseases And Disorders And Poorly Differentiated Neoplasms—SURGICAL

ØD5T[Ø,3,4]ZZ	Destr/Lesser Omentum, [Opn, Perc, Perc Endo]
ØD5V[Ø,3,4]ZZ	Destr/Mesentery, [Opn, Perc, Perc Endo]
ØD5W[Ø,3,4]ZZ	Destr/Peritoneum, [Opn, Perc, Perc Endo]
ØD71[Ø,3,4][D,Z]Z	Dilation/Esophagus, Upr, [Opn, Perc, Perc Endo], [Intralum Dev, No Dev], NQ
ØD72[Ø,3,4][D,Z]Z	Dilation/Esophagus, Mid, [Opn, Perc, Perc Endo], [Intralum Dev, No Dev], NQ
ØD73[Ø,3,4][D,Z]Z	Dilation/Esophagus, Lwr, [Opn, Perc, Perc Endo], [Intralum Dev, No Dev], NQ
ØD74[Ø,3,4][D,Z]Z	Dilation/Esophagogastric Junction, [Opn, Perc, Perc Endo], [Intralum Dev, No Dev], NQ
ØD75[Ø,3,4][D,Z]Z	Dilation/Esophagus, [Opn, Perc, Perc Endo], [Intralum Dev, No Dev], NQ
ØD84[Ø,3,4,7,8]ZZ	Div/Esophagogastric Junction, [Opn, Perc, Perc Endo, Via Natrl or Artfcl Opng, Via Natrl or Artfcl Opng Endo]
ØD91ØZX	Drain of Upr Esophagus, Opn Appr, Diagnostic
ØD92ØZX	Drain of Mid Esophagus, Opn Appr, Diagnostic
ØD93ØZX	Drain of Lwr Esophagus, Opn Appr, Diagnostic
ØD94ØZX	Drain of Esophagogastric Junction, Opn Appr, Diagn
ØD95ØZX	Drain of Esophagus, Opn Appr, Diagnostic
ØD98[Ø,3,4,7,8]ZZ	Drain/Sm Intestine, [Opn, Perc, Perc Endo, Via Natrl or Artfcl Opng, Via Natrl or Artfcl Opng Endo]
ØD98[Ø,3,4]ØZ	Drain/Sm Intestine, [Opn, Perc, Perc Endo], Drain Dev, NQ
ØD9A[Ø,3,4,7,8]ZZ	Drain/Jejunum, [Opn, Perc, Perc Endo, Via Natrl or Artfcl Opng, Via Natrl or Artfcl Opng Endo]
ØD9A[Ø,3,4]ØZ	Drain/Jejunum, [Opn, Perc, Perc Endo], Drain Dev, NQ
ØD9B[Ø,3,4,7,8]ZZ	Drain/Ileum, [Opn, Perc, Perc Endo, Via Natrl or Artfcl Opng, Via Natrl or Artfcl Opng Endo]
ØD9B[Ø,3,4]ØZ	Drain/Ileum, [Opn, Perc, Perc Endo], Drain Dev, NQ
ØD9C[Ø,3,4,7,8][Ø,Z]Z	Drain/Ileocecal Valve, [Opn, Perc, Perc Endo, Via Natrl or Artfcl Opng, Via Natrl or Artfcl Opng Endo], [Drain Dev, No Dev], NQ
ØDB1ØZX	Exc of Upr Esophagus, Opn Appr, Diagnostic
ØDB1[Ø,3,7]ZZ	Exc/Esophagus, Upr, [Opn, Perc, Via Natrl or Artfcl Opng]
ØDB2ØZX	Exc of Mid Esophagus, Opn Appr, Diagnostic
ØDB2[Ø,3,7]ZZ	Exc/Esophagus, Mid, [Opn, Perc, Via Natrl or Artfcl Opng]
ØDB3ØZX	Exc of Lwr Esophagus, Opn Appr, Diagnostic
ØDB3[Ø,3,7]ZZ	Exc/Esophagus, Lwr, [Opn, Perc, Via Natrl or Artfcl Opng]
ØDB4ØZX	Exc of Esophagogastric Junction, Opn Appr, Diagn
ØDB4[Ø,3,4,7]ZZ	Exc/Esophagogastric Junction, [Opn, Perc, Perc Endo, Via Natrl or Artfcl Opng]
ØDB5ØZX	Exc of Esophagus, Opn Appr, Diagnostic
ØDB5[Ø,3,7]ZZ	Exc/Esophagus, [Opn, Perc, Via Natrl or Artfcl Opng]
ØDB6[Ø,3,4,7,8]Z3	Exc/Stomach, [Opn, Perc, Perc Endo, Via Natrl or Artfcl Opng, Via Natrl or Artfcl Opng Endo], No Dev, Vertical
ØDB6[Ø,3,7]ZZ	Exc/Stomach, [Opn, Perc, Via Natrl or Artfcl Opng]
ØDB8[Ø,3,4,7,8]ZZ	Exc/Sm Intestine, [Opn, Perc, Perc Endo, Via Natrl or Artfcl Opng, Via Natrl or Artfcl Opng Endo]
ØDB9[Ø,3]ZZ	Exc/Duodenum, [Opn, Perc]
ØDBA7ZZ	Exc of Jejunum, Via Natrl or Artfcl Opng
ØDBB7ZZ	Exc of Ileum, Via Natrl or Artfcl Opng
ØDBC7ZZ	Exc of Ileocecal Valve, Via Opng
ØDBE[Ø,3,4]ZZ	Exc/Lg Intestine, [Opn, Perc, Perc Endo]
ØDBF[Ø,3,4]ZZ	Exc/Lg Intestine, Rt, [Opn, Perc, Perc Endo]
ØDBG[Ø,3,4]ZZ	Exc/Lg Intestine, Lt, [Opn, Perc, Perc Endo]
ØDBH[Ø,3,4]ZZ	Exc/Cecum, [Opn, Perc, Perc Endo]
ØDBK[Ø,3,4]ZZ	Exc/Ascending Colon, [Opn, Perc, Perc Endo]
ØDBL[Ø,3,4]ZZ	Exc/Transv Colon, [Opn, Perc, Perc Endo]
ØDBM[Ø,3,4]ZZ	Exc/Descending Colon, [Opn, Perc, Perc Endo]
ØDBN[Ø,3,4]ZZ	Exc/Sigmoid Colon, [Opn, Perc, Perc Endo]
ØDBP[Ø,4]ZZ	Exc/Rectum, [Opn, Perc Endo]
ØDBS[Ø,3,4]ZZ	Exc/Greater Omentum, [Opn, Perc, Perc Endo]
ØDBT[Ø,3,4]ZZ	Exc/Lesser Omentum, [Opn, Perc, Perc Endo]
ØDBV[Ø,3,4]ZZ	Exc/Mesentery, [Opn, Perc, Perc Endo]
ØDBW[Ø,3,4]ZZ	Exc/Peritoneum, [Opn, Perc, Perc Endo]
ØDC8[Ø,3,4]ZZ	Extir/Sm Intestine, [Opn, Perc, Perc Endo]
ØDCA[Ø,3,4]ZZ	Extir/Jejunum, [Opn, Perc, Perc Endo]
ØDCB[Ø,3,4]ZZ	Extir/Ileum, [Opn, Perc, Perc Endo]
ØDCC[Ø,3,4]ZZ	Extir/Ileocecal Valve, [Opn, Perc, Perc Endo]
ØDJØ[Ø,4]ZZ	Inspect/Upr Intestinal Tract, [Opn, Perc Endo]
ØDJ6[Ø,4]ZZ	Inspect/Stomach, [Opn, Perc Endo]
ØDJD[Ø,4]ZZ	Inspect/Lwr Intestinal Tract, [Opn, Perc Endo]
ØDJU[Ø,3]ZZ	Inspect/Omentum, [Opn, Perc]
ØDJV[Ø,3]ZZ	Inspect/Mesentery, [Opn, Perc]
ØDJW[Ø,3]ZZ	Inspect/Peritoneum, [Opn, Perc]
ØDQ5[Ø,3,4,7,8]ZZ	Rpr/Esophagus, [Opn, Perc, Perc Endo, Via Natrl or Artfcl Opng, Via Natrl or Artfcl Opng Endo]
ØDQ6[Ø,3,7,8]ZZ	Rpr/Stomach, [Opn, Perc, Via Natrl or Artfcl Opng, Via Natrl or Artfcl Opng Endo]
ØDQV[Ø,3,4]ZZ	Rpr/Mesentery, [Opn, Perc, Perc Endo]

ØDQW[Ø,3,4]ZZ	Rpr/Peritoneum, [Opn, Perc, Perc Endo]
ØDR5[Ø,4,7,8][7,J,K]Z	Replace/Esophagus, [Opn, Perc Endo, Via Natrl or Artfcl Opng, Via Natrl or Artfcl Opng Endo], [Auto Tissue Sub, Synth Sub, Nonauto Tissue Sub], NQ
ØDRS[Ø,4][7,J,K]Z	Replace/Greater Omentum, [Opn, Perc Endo], [Auto Tissue Sub, Synth Sub, Nonauto Tissue Sub], NQ
ØDRT[Ø,4][7,J,K]Z	Replace/Lesser Omentum, [Opn, Perc Endo], [Auto Tissue Sub, Synth Sub, Nonauto Tissue Sub], NQ
ØDRV[Ø,4][7,J,K]Z	Replace/Mesentery, [Opn, Perc Endo], [Auto Tissue Sub, Synth Sub, Nonauto Tissue Sub], NQ
ØDRW[Ø,4][7,J,K]Z	Replace/Peritoneum, [Opn, Perc Endo], [Auto Tissue Sub, Synth Sub, Nonauto Tissue Sub], NQ
ØDSB[Ø,4,7,8]ZZ	Repos/Ileum, [Opn, Perc Endo, Via Natrl or Artfcl Opng, Via Natrl or Artfcl Opng Endo]
ØDSH[Ø,4,7,8]ZZ	Repos/Cecum, [Opn, Perc Endo, Via Natrl or Artfcl Opng, Via Natrl or Artfcl Opng Endo]
ØDT1[Ø,4,7,8]ZZ	Resect/Esophagus, Upr, [Opn, Perc Endo, Via Natrl or Artfcl Opng, Via Natrl or Artfcl Opng Endo]
ØDT2[Ø,4,7,8]ZZ	Resect/Esophagus, Mid, [Opn, Perc Endo, Via Natrl or Artfcl Opng, Via Natrl or Artfcl Opng Endo]
ØDT3[Ø,4,7,8]ZZ	Resect/Esophagus, Lwr, [Opn, Perc Endo, Via Natrl or Artfcl Opng, Via Natrl or Artfcl Opng Endo]
ØDT4[Ø,4,7,8]ZZ	Resect/Esophagogastric Junction, [Opn, Perc Endo, Via Natrl or Artfcl Opng, Via Natrl or Artfcl Opng Endo]
ØDT5[Ø,4,7,8]ZZ	Resect/Esophagus, [Opn, Perc Endo, Via Natrl or Artfcl Opng, Via Natrl or Artfcl Opng Endo]
ØDT6[Ø,4,7,8]ZZ	Resect/Stomach, [Opn, Perc Endo, Via Natrl or Artfcl Opng, Via Natrl or Artfcl Opng Endo]
ØDT7[Ø,4,7,8]ZZ	Resect/Stomach, Pylorus, [Opn, Perc Endo, Via Natrl or Artfcl Opng, Via Natrl or Artfcl Opng Endo]
ØDT8[Ø,4,7,8]ZZ	Resect/Sm Intestine, [Opn, Perc Endo, Via Natrl or Artfcl Opng, Via Natrl or Artfcl Opng Endo]
ØDT9[Ø,4,7,8]ZZ	Resect/Duodenum, [Opn, Perc Endo, Via Natrl or Artfcl Opng, Via Natrl or Artfcl Opng Endo]
ØDTA[Ø,4,7,8]ZZ	Resect/Jejunum, [Opn, Perc Endo, Via Natrl or Artfcl Opng, Via Natrl or Artfcl Opng Endo]
ØDTB[Ø,4,7,8]ZZ	Resect/Ileum, [Opn, Perc Endo, Via Natrl or Artfcl Opng, Via Natrl or Artfcl Opng Endo]
ØDTC[Ø,4,7,8]ZZ	Resect/Ileocecal Valve, [Opn, Perc Endo, Via Natrl or Artfcl Opng, Via Natrl or Artfcl Opng Endo]
ØDTE[Ø,4,7,8]ZZ	Resect/Lg Intestine, [Opn, Perc Endo, Via Natrl or Artfcl Opng, Via Natrl or Artfcl Opng Endo]
ØDTF[Ø,4,7,8]ZZ	Resect/Lg Intestine, Rt, [Opn, Perc Endo, Via Natrl or Artfcl Opng, Via Natrl or Artfcl Opng Endo]
ØDTG[Ø,4,7,8]ZZ	Resect/Lg Intestine, Lt, [Opn, Perc Endo, Via Natrl or Artfcl Opng, Via Natrl or Artfcl Opng Endo]
ØDTK[Ø,4,7,8]ZZ	Resect/Ascending Colon, [Opn, Perc Endo, Via Natrl or Artfcl Opng, Via Natrl or Artfcl Opng Endo]
ØDTL[Ø,4,7,8]ZZ	Resect/Transv Colon, [Opn, Perc Endo, Via Natrl or Artfcl Opng, Via Natrl or Artfcl Opng Endo]
ØDTM[Ø,4,7,8]ZZ	Resect/Descending Colon, [Opn, Perc Endo, Via Natrl or Artfcl Opng, Via Natrl or Artfcl Opng Endo]
ØDTN[Ø,4,7,8]ZZ	Resect/Sigmoid Colon, [Opn, Perc Endo, Via Natrl or Artfcl Opng, Via Natrl or Artfcl Opng Endo]
ØDTP[Ø,4,7,8]ZZ	Resect/Rectum, [Opn, Perc Endo, Via Natrl or Artfcl Opng, Via Natrl or Artfcl Opng Endo]
ØDTS[Ø,4]ZZ	Resect/Greater Omentum, [Opn, Perc Endo]
ØDTT[Ø,4]ZZ	Resect/Lesser Omentum, [Opn, Perc Endo]
ØDU1[Ø,4,7,8][7,J,K]Z	Supl/Esophagus, Upr, [Opn, Perc Endo, Via Natrl or Artfcl Opng, Via Natrl or Artfcl Opng Endo], [Auto Tissue Sub, Synth Sub, Nonauto Tissue Sub], NQ
ØDU2[Ø,4,7,8][7,J,K]Z	Supl/Esophagus, Mid, [Opn, Perc Endo, Via Natrl or Artfcl Opng, Via Natrl or Artfcl Opng Endo], [Auto Tissue Sub, Synth Sub, Nonauto Tissue Sub], NQ
ØDU3[Ø,4,7,8][7,J,K]Z	Supl/Esophagus, Lwr, [Opn, Perc Endo, Via Natrl or Artfcl Opng, Via Natrl or Artfcl Opng Endo], [Auto Tissue Sub, Synth Sub, Nonauto Tissue Sub], NQ
ØDU5[Ø,4,7,8][7,J,K]Z	Supl/Esophagus, [Opn, Perc Endo, Via Natrl or Artfcl Opng, Via Natrl or Artfcl Opng Endo], [Auto Tissue Sub, Synth Sub, Nonauto Tissue Sub], NQ
ØDUS[Ø,4][7,J,K]Z	Supl/Greater Omentum, [Opn, Perc Endo], [Auto Tissue Sub, Synth Sub, Nonauto Tissue Sub], NQ
ØDUT[Ø,4][7,J,K]Z	Supl/Lesser Omentum, [Opn, Perc Endo], [Auto Tissue Sub, Synth Sub, Nonauto Tissue Sub], NQ
ØDUV[Ø,4][7,J,K]Z	Supl/Mesentery, [Opn, Perc Endo], [Auto Tissue Sub, Synth Sub, Nonauto Tissue Sub], NQ
ØDUW[Ø,4][7,J,K]Z	Supl/Peritoneum, [Opn, Perc Endo], [Auto Tissue Sub, Synth Sub, Nonauto Tissue Sub], NQ
ØDWØ4UZ	Revise of Feeding Dev in Up Intest Tract, Perc Endo Appr
ØDX6[Ø,4]Z5	Transfer/Stomach, [Opn, Perc Endo], No Dev, Esophagus

---

T **Transfer DRG**   SP **Special Payment**   * **Code Range**   **6th and 7th Character of ZZ = No Device, No Qualifier ZX = No Device, Diagnostic**

MS-DRG Version 33.0   © 2015 Optum360, LLC

0DX8[0,4]Z5	Transfer/Sm Intestine, [Opn, Perc Endo], No Dev, Esophagus
0DXE[0,4]Z5	Transfer/Lg Intestine, [Opn, Perc Endo], No Dev, Esophagus
0F14[0,4][D,Z][3,4,5,6,7,8,9,B]	Bypass/Gallbladder, [Opn, Perc Endo], [Intralum Dev, No Dev], [Duodenum, Stomach, Hepatic Duct, Rt, Hepatic Duct, Lt, Hepatic Duct, Caudate, Cystic Duct, Common Bile Duct, Sm Intestine]
0F15[0,4][D,Z][3,4,5,6,7,8,9,B]	Bypass/Hepatic Duct, Rt, [Opn, Perc Endo], [Intralum Dev, No Dev], [Duodenum, Stomach, Hepatic Duct, Rt, Hepatic Duct, Lt, Hepatic Duct, Caudate, Cystic Duct, Common Bile Duct, Sm Intestine]
0F16[0,4][D,Z][3,4,5,6,7,8,9,B]	Bypass/Hepatic Duct, Lt, [Opn, Perc Endo], [Intralum Dev, No Dev], [Duodenum, Stomach, Hepatic Duct, Rt, Hepatic Duct, Lt, Hepatic Duct, Caudate, Cystic Duct, Common Bile Duct, Sm Intestine]
0F18[0,4][D,Z][3,4,5,6,7,8,9,B]	Bypass/Cystic Duct, [Opn, Perc Endo], [Intralum Dev, No Dev], [Duodenum, Stomach, Hepatic Duct, Rt, Hepatic Duct, Lt, Hepatic Duct, Caudate, Cystic Duct, Common Bile Duct, Sm Intestine]
0F19[0,4][D,Z][3,4,5,6,7,8,9,B]	Bypass/Common Bile Duct, [Opn, Perc Endo], [Intralum Dev, No Dev], [Duodenum, Stomach, Hepatic Duct, Rt, Hepatic Duct, Lt, Hepatic Duct, Caudate, Cystic Duct, Common Bile Duct, Sm Intestine]
0F54[0,3,4]ZZ	Destr/Gallbladder, [Opn, Perc, Perc Endo]
0F7D[0,3,7]DZ	Dilation/Pancreatic Duct, [Opn, Perc, Via Natrl or Artfcl Opng], Intralum Dev, NQ
0F7F[0,3,7]DZ	Dilation/Pancreatic Duct, Accessory, [Opn, Perc, Via Natrl or Artfcl Opng], Intralum Dev, NQ
0F900ZX	Drain of Liver, Opn Appr, Diagnostic
0F910ZX	Drain of Rt Lobe Liver, Opn Appr, Diagnostic
0F920ZX	Drain of Lt Lobe Liver, Opn Appr, Diagnostic
0F9970Z	Drain of Common Bile Duct with Drain Dev, Via Opng
0F9F0ZX	Drain of Accessory Pancreatic Duct, Opn Appr, Diagn
0F9G0ZX	Drain of Pancreas, Opn Appr, Diagnostic
0FB0[0,4]ZX	Exc/Liver, [Opn, Perc Endo]
0FB1[0,4]ZX	Exc/Liver, Rt Lobe, [Opn, Perc Endo]
0FB2[0,4]ZX	Exc/Liver, Lt Lobe, [Opn, Perc Endo]
0FB4[0,3,4]ZZ	Exc/Gallbladder, [Opn, Perc, Perc Endo]
0FBD0ZX	Exc of Pancreatic Duct, Opn Appr, Diagnostic
0FBF0ZX	Exc of Accessory Pancreatic Duct, Opn Appr, Diagn
0FBG0ZX	Exc of Pancreas, Opn Appr, Diagnostic
0FC50ZZ	Extir of Matter from Rt Hepatic Duct, Opn Appr
0FC60ZZ	Extir of Matter from Lt Hepatic Duct, Opn Appr
0FC80ZZ	Extir of Matter from Cystic Duct, Opn Appr
0FC90ZZ	Extir of Matter from Common Bile Duct, Opn Appr
0FF5[0,3,4,7]ZZ	Fragmn/Hepatic Duct, Rt, [Opn, Perc, Perc Endo, Via Natrl or Artfcl Opng]
0FF6[0,3,4,7]ZZ	Fragmn/Hepatic Duct, Lt, [Opn, Perc, Perc Endo, Via Natrl or Artfcl Opng]
0FF8[0,3,4,7]ZZ	Fragmn/Cystic Duct, [Opn, Perc, Perc Endo, Via Natrl or Artfcl Opng]
0FF9[0,3,4,7]ZZ	Fragmn/Common Bile Duct, [Opn, Perc, Perc Endo, Via Natrl or Artfcl Opng]
0FFC[0,3,4,7]ZZ	Fragmn/Ampulla of Vater, [Opn, Perc, Perc Endo, Via Natrl or Artfcl Opng]
0FHB[0,3,7]DZ	Insert/Hepatobiliary Duct, [Opn, Perc, Via Natrl or Artfcl Opng], Intralum Dev, NQ
0FHD[0,3,7]DZ	Insert/Pancreatic Duct, [Opn, Perc, Via Natrl or Artfcl Opng], Intralum Dev, NQ
0FJ0[0,3]ZZ	Inspect/Liver, [Opn, Perc]
0FJD[0,3,7,8]ZZ	Inspect/Pancreatic Duct, [Opn, Perc, Via Natrl or Artfcl Opng, Via Natrl or Artfcl Opng Endo]
0FJG[0,3]ZZ	Inspect/Pancreas, [Opn, Perc]
0FL50[C,D,Z]Z	Occlsn/Hepatic Duct, Rt, Opn, [Extralum Dev, Intralum Dev, No Dev], NQ
0FL60[C,D,Z]Z	Occlsn/Hepatic Duct, Lt, Opn, [Extralum Dev, Intralum Dev, No Dev], NQ
0FL80[C,D,Z]Z	Occlsn/Cystic Duct, Opn, [Extralum Dev, Intralum Dev, No Dev], NQ
0FL90[C,D,Z]Z	Occlsn/Common Bile Duct, Opn, [Extralum Dev, Intralum Dev, No Dev], NQ
0FM40ZZ	Reattach of Gallbladder, Opn Appr
0FP4[0,3,4]DZ	Rmvl/Gallbladder, [Opn, Perc, Perc Endo], Intralum Dev, NQ
0FQ4[0,3,4]ZZ	Rpr/Gallbladder, [Opn, Perc, Perc Endo]
0FQ5[0,3,4,7,8]ZZ	Rpr/Hepatic Duct, Rt, [Opn, Perc, Perc Endo, Via Natrl or Artfcl Opng, Via Natrl or Artfcl Opng Endo]
0FQ6[0,3,4,7,8]ZZ	Rpr/Hepatic Duct, Lt, [Opn, Perc, Perc Endo, Via Natrl or Artfcl Opng, Via Natrl or Artfcl Opng Endo]
0FQ8[0,3,4,7,8]ZZ	Rpr/Cystic Duct, [Opn, Perc, Perc Endo, Via Natrl or Artfcl Opng, Via Natrl or Artfcl Opng Endo]
0FQ9[0,3,4,7,8]ZZ	Rpr/Common Bile Duct, [Opn, Perc, Perc Endo, Via Natrl or Artfcl Opng, Via Natrl or Artfcl Opng Endo]
0FR5[0,4]JZ	Replace/Hepatic Duct, Rt, [Opn, Perc Endo], Synth Sub, NQ
0FR6[0,4]JZ	Replace/Hepatic Duct, Lt, [Opn, Perc Endo], Synth Sub, NQ
0FR8[0,4]JZ	Replace/Cystic Duct, [Opn, Perc Endo], Synth Sub, NQ
0FR9[0,4]JZ	Replace/Common Bile Duct, [Opn, Perc Endo], Synth Sub, NQ
0FS4[0,4]ZZ	Repos/Gallbladder, [Opn, Perc Endo]
0FT4[0,4]ZZ	Resect/Gallbladder, [Opn, Perc Endo]
0FUD[3,4]7Z	Supl/Pancreatic Duct, [Perc, Perc Endo], Auto Tissue Sub, NQ
0FV50[C,D,Z]Z	Restrict/Hepatic Duct, Rt, Opn, [Extralum Dev, Intralum Dev, No Dev], NQ
0FV60[C,D,Z]Z	Restrict/Hepatic Duct, Lt, Opn, [Extralum Dev, Intralum Dev, No Dev], NQ
0FV80[C,D,Z]Z	Restrict/Cystic Duct, Opn, [Extralum Dev, Intralum Dev, No Dev], NQ
0FV90[C,D,Z]Z	Restrict/Common Bile Duct, Opn, [Extralum Dev, Intralum Dev, No Dev], NQ
0N50[0,3,4]ZZ	Destr/Skull, [Opn, Perc, Perc Endo]
0N51[0,3,4]ZZ	Destr/Frontal Bone, Rt, [Opn, Perc, Perc Endo]
0N52[0,3,4]ZZ	Destr/Frontal Bone, Lt, [Opn, Perc, Perc Endo]
0N53[0,3,4]ZZ	Destr/Parietal Bone, Rt, [Opn, Perc, Perc Endo]
0N54[0,3,4]ZZ	Destr/Parietal Bone, Lt, [Opn, Perc, Perc Endo]
0N55[0,3,4]ZZ	Destr/Temporal Bone, Rt, [Opn, Perc, Perc Endo]
0N56[0,3,4]ZZ	Destr/Temporal Bone, Lt, [Opn, Perc, Perc Endo]
0N57[0,3,4]ZZ	Destr/Occipital Bone, Rt, [Opn, Perc, Perc Endo]
0N58[0,3,4]ZZ	Destr/Occipital Bone, Lt, [Opn, Perc, Perc Endo]
0NB0[0,3,4]ZZ	Exc/Skull, [Opn, Perc, Perc Endo]
0NB1[0,3,4]ZZ	Exc/Frontal Bone, Rt, [Opn, Perc, Perc Endo]
0NB2[0,3,4]ZZ	Exc/Frontal Bone, Lt, [Opn, Perc, Perc Endo]
0NB3[0,3,4]ZZ	Exc/Parietal Bone, Rt, [Opn, Perc, Perc Endo]
0NB4[0,3,4]ZZ	Exc/Parietal Bone, Lt, [Opn, Perc, Perc Endo]
0NB5[0,3,4]ZZ	Exc/Temporal Bone, Rt, [Opn, Perc, Perc Endo]
0NB6[0,3,4]ZZ	Exc/Temporal Bone, Lt, [Opn, Perc, Perc Endo]
0NB7[0,3,4]ZZ	Exc/Occipital Bone, Rt, [Opn, Perc, Perc Endo]
0NB8[0,3,4]ZZ	Exc/Occipital Bone, Lt, [Opn, Perc, Perc Endo]
0NC1[0,3,4]ZZ	Extir/Frontal Bone, Rt, [Opn, Perc, Perc Endo]
0NC2[0,3,4]ZZ	Extir/Frontal Bone, Lt, [Opn, Perc, Perc Endo]
0NC3[0,3,4]ZZ	Extir/Parietal Bone, Rt, [Opn, Perc, Perc Endo]
0NC4[0,3,4]ZZ	Extir/Parietal Bone, Lt, [Opn, Perc, Perc Endo]
0NC5[0,3,4]ZZ	Extir/Temporal Bone, Rt, [Opn, Perc, Perc Endo]
0NC6[0,3,4]ZZ	Extir/Temporal Bone, Lt, [Opn, Perc, Perc Endo]
0NC7[0,3,4]ZZ	Extir/Occipital Bone, Rt, [Opn, Perc, Perc Endo]
0NC8[0,3,4]ZZ	Extir/Occipital Bone, Lt, [Opn, Perc, Perc Endo]
0NP0[0,3,4,X]MZ	Rmvl/Skull, [Opn, Perc, Perc Endo, Ext], Bone Growth Stimulator, NQ
0NQ0XZZ	Repair Skull, Ext Appr
0NT10ZZ	Resect of Rt Frontal Bone, Opn Appr
0NT20ZZ	Resect of Lt Frontal Bone, Opn Appr
0NT30ZZ	Resect of Rt Parietal Bone, Opn Appr
0NT40ZZ	Resect of Lt Parietal Bone, Opn Appr
0NT50ZZ	Resect of Rt Temporal Bone, Opn Appr
0NT60ZZ	Resect of Lt Temporal Bone, Opn Appr
0NT70ZZ	Resect of Rt Occipital Bone, Opn Appr
0NT80ZZ	Resect of Lt Occipital Bone, Opn Appr
0PS3XZZ	Repos Cervical Vertebra, Ext Appr
0PS3[0,3,4]4Z	Repos/Cervical Vertebra, [Opn, Perc, Perc Endo], Int Fix Dev, NQ
0PS3[0,4]ZZ	Repos/Cervical Vertebra, [Opn, Perc Endo]
0PS4XZZ	Repos Thoracic Vertebra, Ext Appr
0PS4[0,3,4]4Z	Repos/Thoracic Vertebra, [Opn, Perc, Perc Endo], Int Fix Dev, NQ
0PS4[0,4]ZZ	Repos/Thoracic Vertebra, [Opn, Perc Endo]
0QS0XZZ	Repos Lumbar Vertebra, Ext Appr
0QS0[0,3,4]4Z	Repos/Lumbar Vertebra, [Opn, Perc, Perc Endo], Int Fix Dev, NQ
0QS0[0,4]ZZ	Repos/Lumbar Vertebra, [Opn, Perc Endo]
0QS1XZZ	Repos Sacrum, Ext Appr
0QS1[0,3,4]4Z	Repos/Sacrum, [Opn, Perc, Perc Endo], Int Fix Dev, NQ
0QS1[0,4]ZZ	Repos/Sacrum, [Opn, Perc Endo]
0QSS[0,3,4,X]ZZ	Repos/Coccyx, [Opn, Perc, Perc Endo, Ext]
0QSS[0,3,4]4Z	Repos/Coccyx, [Opn, Perc, Perc Endo], Int Fix Dev, NQ
0RB0[0,3,4]ZZ	Exc/Occipital-cervical Jt, [Opn, Perc, Perc Endo]
0RB1[0,3,4]ZZ	Exc/Cervical Vert Jt, [Opn, Perc, Perc Endo]
0RB4[0,3,4]ZZ	Exc/Cervicothoracic Vert Jt, [Opn, Perc, Perc Endo]
0RB6[0,3,4]ZZ	Exc/Thoracic Vert Jt, [Opn, Perc, Perc Endo]
0RBA[0,3,4]ZZ	Exc/Thoracolumbar Vert Jt, [Opn, Perc, Perc Endo]
0RQ30ZZ	Repair Cervical Vert Disc, Opn Appr
0RQ90ZZ	Repair Thoracic Vert Disc, Opn Appr
0RQB0ZZ	Repair Thoracolumbar Vert Disc, Opn Appr

Surgical | **Medical** | **CC Indicator** | **MCC Indicator** | **Procedure Proxy** | **PDxMCC PDx acts as own MCC** | **PDxCC PDx acts as own CC**

ØRU3[Ø,3,4][7,J,K]Z	Supl/Cervical Vert Disc, [Opn, Perc, Perc Endo], [Auto Tissue Sub, Synth Sub, Nonauto Tissue Sub], NQ
ØRU9[Ø,3,4][7,J,K]Z	Supl/Thoracic Vert Disc, [Opn, Perc, Perc Endo], [Auto Tissue Sub, Synth Sub, Nonauto Tissue Sub], NQ
ØRUB[Ø,3,4][7,J,K]Z	Supl/Thoracolumbar Vert Disc, [Opn, Perc, Perc Endo], [Auto Tissue Sub, Synth Sub, Nonauto Tissue Sub], NQ
ØSBØ[Ø,3,4]ZZ	Exc/Lumbar Vert Jt, [Opn, Perc, Perc Endo]
ØSB3[Ø,3,4]ZZ	Exc/Lumbosacral Jt, [Opn, Perc, Perc Endo]
ØSB5[Ø,3,4]ZZ	Exc/Sacrococcygeal Jt, [Opn, Perc, Perc Endo]
ØSB6[Ø,3,4]ZZ	Exc/Coccygeal Jt, [Opn, Perc, Perc Endo]
ØSB7[Ø,3,4]ZZ	Exc/Sacroiliac Jt, Rt, [Opn, Perc, Perc Endo]
ØSB8[Ø,3,4]ZZ	Exc/Sacroiliac Jt, Lt, [Opn, Perc, Perc Endo]
ØSQ2ØZZ	Repair Lumbar Vert Disc, Opn Appr
ØSQ4ØZZ	Repair Lumbosacral Disc, Opn Appr
ØSU2[Ø,3,4][7,J,K]Z	Supl/Lumbar Vert Disc, [Opn, Perc, Perc Endo], [Auto Tissue Sub, Synth Sub, Nonauto Tissue Sub], NQ
ØSU4[Ø,3,4][7,J,K]Z	Supl/Lumbosacral Disc, [Opn, Perc, Perc Endo], [Auto Tissue Sub, Synth Sub, Nonauto Tissue Sub], NQ
ØT13[Ø,4][7,J,K,Z]B	Bypass/Kidney Pelvis, Rt, [Opn, Perc Endo], [Auto Tissue Sub, Synth Sub, Nonauto Tissue Sub, No Dev], Bladder
ØT14[Ø,4][7,J,K,Z]B	Bypass/Kidney Pelvis, Lt, [Opn, Perc Endo], [Auto Tissue Sub, Synth Sub, Nonauto Tissue Sub, No Dev], Bladder
ØT163JD	Bypass Rt Ureter to Cutan with Synth Sub, Perc Appr
ØT16[Ø,4][7,J,K,Z][6,7,8,9,A,C,D]	Bypass/Ureter, Rt, [Opn, Perc Endo], [Auto Tissue Sub, Synth Sub, Nonauto Tissue Sub, No Dev], [Ureter, Rt, Ureter, Lt, Colon, Colocutaneous, Ileum, Ileocutaneous, Cutaneous]
ØT173JD	Bypass Lt Ureter to Cutan with Synth Sub, Perc Appr
ØT17[Ø,4][7,J,K,Z][6,7,8,9,A,C,D]	Bypass/Ureter, Lt, [Opn, Perc Endo], [Auto Tissue Sub, Synth Sub, Nonauto Tissue Sub, No Dev], [Ureter, Rt, Ureter, Lt, Colon, Colocutaneous, Ileum, Ileocutaneous, Cutaneous]
ØT183JD	Bypass Bi Ureter to Cutan with Synth Sub, Perc Appr
ØT18[Ø,4][7,J,K,Z][6,7,8,9,A,C,D]	Bypass/Ureters, Bilat, [Opn, Perc Endo], [Auto Tissue Sub, Synth Sub, Nonauto Tissue Sub, No Dev], [Ureter, Rt, Ureter, Lt, Colon, Colocutaneous, Ileum, Ileocutaneous, Cutaneous]
ØT1B3JD	Bypass Bladder to Cutaneous with Synth Sub, Perc Appr
ØT1B[Ø,4][7,J,K,Z][9,C,D]	Bypass/Bladder, [Opn, Perc Endo], [Auto Tissue Sub, Synth Sub, Nonauto Tissue Sub, No Dev], [Colocutaneous, Ileocutaneous, Cutaneous]
ØT5B[Ø,3,4]ZZ	Destr/Bladder, [Opn, Perc, Perc Endo]
ØT5C[Ø,3,4]ZZ	Destr/Bladder Neck, [Opn, Perc, Perc Endo]
ØT9ØØZX	Drain of Rt Kidney, Opn Appr, Diagnostic
ØT91ØZX	Drain of Lt Kidney, Opn Appr, Diagnostic
ØT93ØZX	Drain of Rt Kidney Pelvis, Opn Appr, Diagnostic
ØT93ØZZ	Drain of Rt Kidney Pelvis, Opn Appr
ØT93[Ø,3,4]ØZ	Drain/Kidney Pelvis, Rt, [Opn, Perc, Perc Endo], Drain Dev, NQ
ØT94ØZX	Drain of Lt Kidney Pelvis, Opn Appr, Diagnostic
ØT94ØZZ	Drain of Lt Kidney Pelvis, Opn Appr
ØT94[Ø,3,4]ØZ	Drain/Kidney Pelvis, Lt, [Opn, Perc, Perc Endo], Drain Dev, NQ
ØT9BØØZ	Drain of Bladder with Drain Device, Opn Appr
ØT9BØZX	Drain of Bladder, Opn Appr, Diagnostic
ØT9CØZX	Drain of Bladder Neck, Opn Appr, Diagnostic
ØTBØØZX	Exc of Rt Kidney, Opn Appr, Diagnostic
ØTBØ[Ø,3,4]ZZ	Exc/Kidney, Rt, [Opn, Perc, Perc Endo]
ØTB1ØZX	Exc of Lt Kidney, Opn Appr, Diagnostic
ØTB1[Ø,3,4]ZZ	Exc/Kidney, Lt, [Opn, Perc, Perc Endo]
ØTB3ØZX	Exc of Rt Kidney Pelvis, Opn Appr, Diagnostic
ØTB3[Ø,3,4]ZZ	Exc/Kidney Pelvis, Rt, [Opn, Perc, Perc Endo]
ØTB4ØZX	Exc of Lt Kidney Pelvis, Opn Appr, Diagnostic
ØTB4[Ø,3,4]ZZ	Exc/Kidney Pelvis, Lt, [Opn, Perc, Perc Endo]
ØTBBØZX	Exc of Bladder, Opn Appr, Diagnostic
ØTBB[Ø,3,4]ZZ	Exc/Bladder, [Opn, Perc, Perc Endo]
ØTBCØZX	Exc of Bladder Neck, Opn Appr, Diagnostic
ØTBC[Ø,3,4]ZZ	Exc/Bladder Neck, [Opn, Perc, Perc Endo]
ØTJ5[3,7]ZZ	Inspect/Kidney, [Perc, Via Natrl or Artfcl Opng]
ØTJB[3,4,7]ZZ	Inspect/Bladder, [Perc, Perc Endo, Via Natrl or Artfcl Opng]
ØTNØ[Ø,3,4,7,8]ZZ	Rls/Kidney, Rt, [Opn, Perc, Perc Endo, Via Natrl or Artfcl Opng, Via Natrl or Artfcl Opng Endo]
ØTN1[Ø,3,4,7,8]ZZ	Rls/Kidney, Lt, [Opn, Perc, Perc Endo, Via Natrl or Artfcl Opng, Via Natrl or Artfcl Opng Endo]
ØTN3[Ø,3,4,7,8]ZZ	Rls/Kidney Pelvis, Rt, [Opn, Perc, Perc Endo, Via Natrl or Artfcl Opng, Via Natrl or Artfcl Opng Endo]
ØTN4[Ø,3,4,7,8]ZZ	Rls/Kidney Pelvis, Lt, [Opn, Perc, Perc Endo, Via Natrl or Artfcl Opng, Via Natrl or Artfcl Opng Endo]
ØTN6[Ø,3,4]ZZ	Rls/Ureter, Rt, [Opn, Perc, Perc Endo]
ØTN7[Ø,3,4]ZZ	Rls/Ureter, Lt, [Opn, Perc, Perc Endo]
ØTNB[3,4]ZZ	Rls/Bladder, [Perc, Perc Endo]
ØTNC[3,4]ZZ	Rls/Bladder Neck, [Perc, Perc Endo]

ØTQØ[Ø,3,4,7,8]ZZ	Rpr/Kidney, Rt, [Opn, Perc, Perc Endo, Via Natrl or Artfcl Opng, Via Natrl or Artfcl Opng Endo]
ØTQ1[Ø,3,4,7,8]ZZ	Rpr/Kidney, Lt, [Opn, Perc, Perc Endo, Via Natrl or Artfcl Opng, Via Natrl or Artfcl Opng Endo]
ØTQ7[Ø,3,4,7,8]ZZ	Rpr/Ureter, Lt, [Opn, Perc, Perc Endo, Via Natrl or Artfcl Opng, Via Natrl or Artfcl Opng Endo]
ØTQB[Ø,3,4,7,8]ZZ	Rpr/Bladder, [Opn, Perc, Perc Endo, Via Natrl or Artfcl Opng, Via Natrl or Artfcl Opng Endo]
ØTQD[Ø,3,4,7,8,X]ZZ	Rpr/Urethra, [Opn, Perc, Perc Endo, Via Natrl or Artfcl Opng, Via Natrl or Artfcl Opng Endo, Ext]
ØTTB[Ø,4,7,8]ZZ	Resect/Bladder, [Opn, Perc Endo, Via Natrl or Artfcl Opng, Via Natrl or Artfcl Opng Endo]
ØTTC[Ø,4,7,8]ZZ	Resect/Bladder Neck, [Opn, Perc Endo, Via Natrl or Artfcl Opng, Via Natrl or Artfcl Opng Endo]
ØUQG[Ø,3,4,7,8,X]ZZ	Rpr/Vagina, [Opn, Perc, Perc Endo, Via Natrl or Artfcl Opng, Via Natrl or Artfcl Opng Endo, Ext]
ØW11ØJ[9,B,G,J]	Bypass/Cranial Cavity, Opn, Synth Sub, [Pleural Cavity, Rt, Pleural Cavity, Lt, Peritoneal Cavity, Pelvic Cavity]
ØW1G[Ø,3,4]J4	Bypass/Peritoneal Cavity, [Opn, Perc, Perc Endo], Synth Sub, Cutaneous
ØW1G[Ø,4]JY	Bypass/Peritoneal Cavity, [Opn, Perc, Perc Endo], Synth Sub, Lwr Vein
ØW3Ø[Ø,3,4]ZZ	Control/Head, [Opn, Perc, Perc Endo]
ØW31[Ø,3,4]ZZ	Control/Cranial Cavity, [Opn, Perc, Perc Endo]
ØW32[Ø,3,4]ZZ	Control/Face, [Opn, Perc, Perc Endo]
ØW33*	Control/Oral Cavity and Throat
ØW34[Ø,3,4]ZZ	Control/Upr Jaw, [Opn, Perc, Perc Endo]
ØW35[Ø,3,4]ZZ	Control/Lwr Jaw, [Opn, Perc, Perc Endo]
ØW36[Ø,3,4]ZZ	Control/Neck, [Opn, Perc, Perc Endo]
ØW38[Ø,3,4]ZZ	Control/Chest Wall, [Opn, Perc, Perc Endo]
ØW39[Ø,3,4]ZZ	Control/Pleural Cavity, Rt, [Opn, Perc, Perc Endo]
ØW3B[Ø,3,4]ZZ	Control/Pleural Cavity, Lt, [Opn, Perc, Perc Endo]
ØW3D[Ø,3,4]ZZ	Control/Pericardial Cavity, [Opn, Perc, Perc Endo]
ØW3F[Ø,3,4]ZZ	Control/Abd Wall, [Opn, Perc, Perc Endo]
ØW3G[3,4]ZZ	Control/Peritoneal Cavity, [Perc, Perc Endo]
ØW3H[Ø,3,4]ZZ	Control/Retroperitoneum, [Opn, Perc, Perc Endo]
ØW3J[Ø,3,4]ZZ	Control/Pelvic Cavity, [Opn, Perc, Perc Endo]
ØW3K[Ø,3,4]ZZ	Control/Upr Back, [Opn, Perc, Perc Endo]
ØW3L[Ø,3,4]ZZ	Control/Lwr Back, [Opn, Perc, Perc Endo]
ØW3M[Ø,3,4]ZZ	Control/Perineum, Male, [Opn, Perc, Perc Endo]
ØW3N[Ø,3,4]ZZ	Control/Perineum, Female, [Opn, Perc, Perc Endo]
ØW3P[Ø,3,4]ZZ	Control/Gastrointestinal Tract, [Opn, Perc, Perc Endo]
ØW3Q[3,4,7,8]ZZ	Control/Respiratory Tract, [Perc, Perc Endo, Via Natrl or Artfcl Opng, Via Natrl or Artfcl Opng Endo]
ØW3R[Ø,3,4,7,8]ZZ	Control/Genitourinary Tract, [Opn, Perc, Perc Endo, Via Natrl or Artfcl Opng, Via Natrl or Artfcl Opng Endo]
ØW91ØZX	Drain of Cranial Cavity, Opn Appr, Diagnostic
ØW91Ø[Ø,Z]Z	Drain/Cranial Cavity, Opn, [Drain Dev, No Dev], NQ
ØW9CØZX	Drain of Mediastinum, Opn Appr, Diagnostic
ØW9DØZX	Drain of Pericardial Cavity, Opn Appr, Diagnostic
ØW9DØ[Ø,Z]Z	Drain/Pericardial Cavity, Opn, [Drain Dev, No Dev], NQ
ØW9FØØZ	Drain of Abd Wall with Drain Dev, Opn Appr
ØW9FØZZ	Drain of Abd Wall, Opn Appr
ØW9F[Ø,3,4]ZX	Drain/Abd Wall, [Opn, Perc, Perc Endo]
ØW9GØØZ	Drain of Peritoneal Cavity with Drain Dev, Opn Appr
ØW9GØZZ	Drain of Peritoneal Cavity, Opn Appr
ØW9G[Ø,3,4]ZX	Drain/Peritoneal Cavity, [Opn, Perc, Perc Endo]
ØW9H[Ø,3,4]ZX	Drain/Retroperitoneum, [Opn, Perc, Perc Endo]
ØW9H[Ø,3,4][Ø,Z]Z	Drain/Retroperitoneum, [Opn, Perc, Perc Endo], [Drain Dev, No Dev], NQ
ØW9J[Ø,3,4]ZX	Drain/Pelvic Cavity, [Opn, Perc, Perc Endo]
ØWB8[Ø,3,4,X]ZZ	Exc/Chest Wall, [Opn, Perc, Perc Endo, Ext]
ØWBCØZX	Exc of Mediastinum, Opn Appr, Diagnostic
ØWBC[Ø,3,4]ZZ	Exc/Mediastinum, [Opn, Perc, Perc Endo]
ØWBFXZ2	Exc of Abd Wall, Stoma, Ext Appr
ØWBF[Ø,3,4,X]Z[X,Z]	Exc/Abd Wall, [Opn, Perc, Perc Endo, Ext], No Dev, [Dx, NQ]
ØWBH[Ø,3,4]ZZ	Exc/Retroperitoneum, [Opn, Perc, Perc Endo]
ØWC1[Ø,3,4]ZZ	Extir/Cranial Cavity, [Opn, Perc, Perc Endo]
ØWCD[Ø,3,4]ZZ	Extir/Pericardial Cavity, [Opn, Perc, Perc Endo]
ØWCJ[Ø,3,4]ZZ	Extir/Pelvic Cavity, [Opn, Perc, Perc Endo]
ØWCP[Ø,3,4]ZZ	Extir/Gastrointestinal Tract, [Opn, Perc, Perc Endo]
ØWCR[Ø,3,4]ZZ	Extir/Genitourinary Tract, [Opn, Perc, Perc Endo]
ØWFG[Ø,3,4]ZZ	Fragmn/Peritoneal Cavity, [Opn, Perc, Perc Endo]
ØWHD[Ø,3,4][3,Y]Z	Insert/Pericardial Cavity, [Opn, Perc, Perc Endo], [Inf Dev, Oth Dev], NQ
ØWJ1[Ø,3,4]ZZ	Inspect/Cranial Cavity, [Opn, Perc, Perc Endo]
ØWJ9ØZZ	Inspect of Rt Pleural Cavity, Opn Appr
ØWJBØZZ	Inspect of Lt Pleural Cavity, Opn Appr
ØWJC[Ø,4]ZZ	Inspect/Mediastinum, [Opn, Perc, Perc Endo]
ØWJD4ZZ	Inspect of Pericardial Cavity, Perc Endo Appr

T Transfer DRG	SP Special Payment	* Code Range	6th and 7th Character of ZZ = No Device, No Qualifier ZX = No Device, Diagnostic

ØWJF[Ø,3]ZZ Inspect/Abd Wall, [Opn, Perc]
ØWJG[Ø,3]ZZ Inspect/Peritoneal Cavity, [Opn, Perc]
ØWJH[Ø,3,4]ZZ Inspect/Retroperitoneum, [Opn, Perc, Perc Endo]
ØWJJ[Ø,3]ZZ Inspect/Pelvic Cavity, [Opn, Perc]
ØWJP[Ø,3,7,8]ZZ Inspect/Gastrointestinal Tract, [Opn, Perc, Via Natrl or Artfcl Opng, Via Natrl or Artfcl Opng Endo]
ØWJQØZZ Inspect of Respiratory Tract, Opn Appr
ØWJR[Ø,3,7,8]ZZ Inspect/Genitourinary Tract, [Opn, Perc, Via Natrl or Artfcl Opng, Via Natrl or Artfcl Opng Endo]
ØWMFØZZ Reattach of Abd Wall, Opn Appr
ØWPD[Ø,3,4][Ø,1,3,Y]Z Rmvl/Pericardial Cavity, [Opn, Perc, Perc Endo], [Drain Dev, Radioact Elmt, Inf Dev, Oth Dev], NQ
ØWQ6XZ2 Repair Neck, Stoma, Ext Appr
ØWQFXZ2 Repair Abd Wall, Stoma, Ext Appr
ØWQF[Ø,3,4,X]ZZ Rpr/Abd Wall, [Opn, Perc, Perc Endo, Ext]
ØWWD[Ø,3,4][Ø,1,3,Y]ZR ev/Pericardial Cavity, [Opn, Perc, Perc Endo], [Drain Dev, Radioact Elmt, Inf Dev, Oth Dev], NQ
ØX32[Ø,3,4]ZZ Control/Shldr Rgn, Rt, [Opn, Perc, Perc Endo]
ØX33[Ø,3,4]ZZ Control/Shldr Rgn, Lt, [Opn, Perc, Perc Endo]
ØX34[Ø,3,4]ZZ Control/Axilla, Rt, [Opn, Perc, Perc Endo]
ØX35[Ø,3,4]ZZ Control/Axilla, Lt, [Opn, Perc, Perc Endo]
ØX36[Ø,3,4]ZZ Control/Upr Extr, Rt, [Opn, Perc, Perc Endo]
ØX37[Ø,3,4]ZZ Control/Upr Extr, Lt, [Opn, Perc, Perc Endo]
ØX38[Ø,3,4]ZZ Control/Upr Arm, Rt, [Opn, Perc, Perc Endo]
ØX39[Ø,3,4]ZZ Control/Upr Arm, Lt, [Opn, Perc, Perc Endo]
ØX3B[Ø,3,4]ZZ Control/Elbow Rgn, Rt, [Opn, Perc, Perc Endo]
ØX3C[Ø,3,4]ZZ Control/Elbow Rgn, Lt, [Opn, Perc, Perc Endo]
ØX3D[Ø,3,4]ZZ Control/Lwr Arm, Rt, [Opn, Perc, Perc Endo]
ØX3F[Ø,3,4]ZZ Control/Lwr Arm, Lt, [Opn, Perc, Perc Endo]
ØX3G[Ø,3,4]ZZ Control/Wrist Rgn, Rt, [Opn, Perc, Perc Endo]
ØX3H[Ø,3,4]ZZ Control/Wrist Rgn, Lt, [Opn, Perc, Perc Endo]
ØX3J[Ø,3,4]ZZ Control/Hand, Rt, [Opn, Perc, Perc Endo]
ØX3K[Ø,3,4]ZZ Control/Hand, Lt, [Opn, Perc, Perc Endo]
ØY30[Ø,3,4]ZZ Control/Buttock, Rt, [Opn, Perc, Perc Endo]
ØY31[Ø,3,4]ZZ Control/Buttock, Lt, [Opn, Perc, Perc Endo]
ØY35[Ø,3,4]ZZ Control/Inguinal Rgn, Rt, [Opn, Perc, Perc Endo]
ØY36[Ø,3,4]ZZ Control/Inguinal Rgn, Lt, [Opn, Perc, Perc Endo]
ØY37[Ø,3,4]ZZ Control/Femor Rgn, Rt, [Opn, Perc, Perc Endo]
ØY38[Ø,3,4]ZZ Control/Femor Rgn, Lt, [Opn, Perc, Perc Endo]
ØY39[Ø,3,4]ZZ Control/Lwr Extr, Rt, [Opn, Perc, Perc Endo]
ØY3B[Ø,3,4]ZZ Control/Lwr Extr, Lt, [Opn, Perc, Perc Endo]
ØY3C[Ø,3,4]ZZ Control/Upr Leg, Rt, [Opn, Perc, Perc Endo]
ØY3D[Ø,3,4]ZZ Control/Upr Leg, Lt, [Opn, Perc, Perc Endo]
ØY3F[Ø,3,4]ZZ Control/Knee Rgn, Rt, [Opn, Perc, Perc Endo]
ØY3G[Ø,3,4]ZZ Control/Knee Rgn, Lt, [Opn, Perc, Perc Endo]
ØY3H[Ø,3,4]ZZ Control/Lwr Leg, Rt, [Opn, Perc, Perc Endo]
ØY3J[Ø,3,4]ZZ Control/Lwr Leg, Lt, [Opn, Perc, Perc Endo]
ØY3K[Ø,3,4]ZZ Control/Ankle Rgn, Rt, [Opn, Perc, Perc Endo]
ØY3L[Ø,3,4]ZZ Control/Ankle Rgn, Lt, [Opn, Perc, Perc Endo]
ØY3M[Ø,3,4]ZZ Control/Foot, Rt, [Opn, Perc, Perc Endo]
ØY3N[Ø,3,4]ZZ Control/Foot, Lt, [Opn, Perc, Perc Endo]
ØY95[Ø,3,4]ZX Drain/Inguinal Rgn, Rt, [Opn, Perc, Perc Endo]
ØY95[Ø,3,4][Ø,Z]Z Drain/Inguinal Rgn, Rt, [Opn, Perc, Perc Endo], [Drain Dev, No Dev], NQ
ØY96[Ø,3,4]ZX Drain/Inguinal Rgn, Lt, [Opn, Perc, Perc Endo]
ØY96[Ø,3,4][Ø,Z]Z Drain/Inguinal Rgn, Lt, [Opn, Perc, Perc Endo], [Drain Dev, No Dev], NQ
ØYB5[Ø,3,4]Z[X,Z] Exc/Inguinal Rgn, Rt, [Opn, Perc, Perc Endo], No Dev, [Dx, NQ]
ØYB6[Ø,3,4]Z[X,Z] Exc/Inguinal Rgn, Lt, [Opn, Perc, Perc Endo], No Dev, [Dx, NQ]
ØYB7[Ø,3,4]Z[X,Z] Exc/Femor Rgn, Rt, [Opn, Perc, Perc Endo], No Dev, [Dx, NQ]
ØYB8[Ø,3,4]Z[X,Z] Exc/Femor Rgn, Lt, [Opn, Perc, Perc Endo], No Dev, [Dx, NQ]
ØYJ5[Ø,3,4]ZZ Inspect/Inguinal Rgn, Rt, [Opn, Perc, Perc Endo]
ØYJ6[Ø,3,4]ZZ Inspect/Inguinal Rgn, Lt, [Opn, Perc, Perc Endo]
ØYJ7[Ø,3,4]ZZ Inspect/Femor Rgn, Rt, [Opn, Perc, Perc Endo]
ØYJ8[3,4]ZZ Inspect/Femor Rgn, Lt, [Perc, Perc Endo]
ØYJA[Ø,3,4]ZZ Inspect/Inguinal Rgn, Bilat, [Opn, Perc, Perc Endo]
ØYJE[3,4]ZZ Inspect/Femor Rgn, Bilat, [Perc, Perc Endo]
DØY6KZZ Laser Interstitial Thermal Therapy of Spinal Cord
DØY7KZZ Laser Interstitial Thermal Therapy of Peripheral Nerve
DBYØKZZ Laser Interstitial Thermal Therapy of Trachea
DBY1KZZ Laser Interstitial Thermal Therapy of Bronchus
DBY2KZZ Laser Interstitial Thermal Therapy of Lung
DBY5KZZ Laser Interstitial Thermal Therapy of Pleura
DBY6KZZ Laser Interstitial Thermal Therapy of Mediastinum
DBY7KZZ Laser Interstitial Thermal Therapy of Chest Wall
DBY8KZZ Laser Interstitial Thermal Therapy of Diaphragm
DDY[Ø,1,2,3,4,5,7,8]KZZ Laser Interstitial Thermal Therapy of [Esophagus, Stomach, Duodenum, Jejunum, Ileum, Colon, Rectum, Anus]
DFY[1,2,3]KZZ Laser Interstitial Thermal Therapy of [Gallbladder, Bile Ducts, Pancreas]

DGYØKZZ Laser Interstitial Thermal Therapy of Pituitary Gland
DGY1KZZ Laser Interstitial Thermal Therapy of Pineal Body
DGY2KZZ Laser Interstitial Thermal Therapy of Adrenal Glands
DGY4KZZ Laser Interstitial Thermal Therapy of Parathyroid Glands
DGY5KZZ Laser Interstitial Thermal Therapy of Thyroid
DMYØKZZ Laser Interstitial Thermal Therapy of Lt Breast
DMY1KZZ Laser Interstitial Thermal Therapy of Rt Breast
DVYØKZZ Laser Interstitial Thermal Therapy of Prostate

DRG 821 Lymphoma and Leukemia with Major O.R. Procedure with CC

GMLOS 4.7 AMLOS 6.5 RW 2.3113

Select principal diagnosis AND operating room procedures listed under DRG 820

DRG 822 Lymphoma and Leukemia with Major O.R. Procedure without CC/MCC

GMLOS 2.1 AMLOS 2.7 RW 1.2851

Select principal diagnosis AND operating room procedures listed under DRG 820

DRG 823 Lymphoma and Nonacute Leukemia with Other O.R. Procedure with MCC

GMLOS 11.1 AMLOS 14.3 RW 4.4536

Principal Diagnosis

C26.1 Malig neoplasm of spleen
C46.3 Kaposi's sarcoma of lymph nodes
C77* Secondary and unsp malig neoplasm of lymph nodes
C7B.Ø1 Secondary carcinoid tumors of distant lymph nodes
C81* Hodgkin lymphoma
C82* Follicular lymphoma
C83* Non-follicular lymphoma
C84* Mature T/NK-cell lymphomas
C85* Oth and unsp types of non-Hodgkin lymphoma
C86* Oth spec types of T/NK-cell lymphoma
C88* Malig immunoproliferative dis and certain oth B-cell lymph
C90* Multi myeloma and malig plasma cell neoplasms
C91.1* Chr lymphocytic leukemia of B-cell type
C91.3* Prolymphocytic leukemia of B-cell type
C91.4* Hairy cell leukemia
C91.5* Adult T-cell lymphoma/leukemia (HTLV-1-associated)
C91.6* Prolymphocytic leukemia of T-cell type
C91.9* Lymphoid leukemia, unsp
C91.A* Mature B-cell leukemia Burkitt-type
C91.Z* Oth lymphoid leukemia
C92.1* Chr myeloid leukemia, BCR/ABL-positive
C92.2* Atypical chr myeloid leukemia, BCR/ABL-negative
C92.3* Myeloid sarcoma
C92.9* Myeloid leukemia, unsp
C92.Z* Oth myeloid leukemia
C93.1* Chr myelomonocytic leukemia
C93.3* Juvenile myelomonocytic leukemia
C93.9* Monocytic leukemia, unsp
C93.Z* Oth monocytic leukemia
C94.2* Acute megakaryoblastic leukemia
C94.3* Mast cell leukemia
C94.4* Acute panmyelosis with myelofibrosis
C94.6 Myelodysplastic dz, not classified
C94.8* Oth spec leukemias
C95.1* Chr leukemia of unsp cell type
C95.9* Leukemia, unsp
C96.2 Malig mast cell tumor
C96.4 Sarcoma of dendritic cells (accessory cells)
C96.9 Malig neoplm of lymphoid, hematpoetc and rel tissue, unsp
C96.A Histiocytic sarcoma
C96.Z Oth malig neoplm of lymphoid, hematpoetc and related tissue
D45 Polycythemia vera
D47.Ø Histiocytic and mast cell tumors of uncertain behav
D47.1 Chr myeloproliferative dz
D47.9 Neoplm of uncertain behav of lymphoid,hematpoetc & rel tiss,unsp
D47.Z9 Oth neoplm of uncertain behav of lymphoid, hematpoetc & rel tiss
D61.82 Myelophthisis
D75.81 Myelofibrosis

Surgical Medical CC Indicator MCC Indicator Procedure Proxy PDxMCC PDx acts as own MCC PDxCC PDx acts as own CC

© 2015 Optum360, LLC MS-DRG Version 33.0 303

| D89.1 | Cryoglobulinemia |

AND

Select any other operating room procedures not listed under DRG 820

OR

Nonoperating Room Procedures

D02*	Radiation Therapy, Central Periph Nerv Sys, Stereo Radiosurg
D72*	Radiation Therapy, Lymph & Hemat Sys, Stereo Radiosurg
D82*	Radiation Therapy, Eye, Stereotactic Radiosurgery
D92*	Radiation Therapy, ENT & Mouth, Stereo Radiosurg
DB2*	Radiation Therapy, Resp Sys, Stereo Radiosurg
DD2*	Radiation Therapy, GI Sys, Stereo Radiosurg
DF2*	Radiation Therapy, Hepatobil Pancreas, Stereo Radiosurg
DG2*	Radiation Therapy, Endocrine Sys, Stereo Radiosurg
DM2*	Radiation Therapy, Breast, Stereotactic Radiosurgery
DT2*	Radiation Therapy, Urinary Sys, Stereotactic Radiosurgery
DU2*	Radiation Therapy, Fem Reprod Sys, Stereo Radiosurg
DV2*	Radiation Therapy, Male Reprod Sys, Stereo Radiosurg
DW2*	Radiation Therapy, Anatomical Regions, Stereo Radiosurg

DRG 824 Lymphoma and Nonacute Leukemia with Other O.R. Procedure with CC

| GMLOS 6.0 | AMLOS 7.9 | RW 2.3467 |

Select principal diagnosis listed under DRG 823

Select any other operating room procedures not listed under DRG 820

OR

Select nonoperating room procedures listed under DRG 823

DRG 825 Lymphoma and Nonacute Leukemia with Other O.R. Procedure without CC/MCC

| GMLOS 2.9 | AMLOS 3.9 | RW 1.3967 |

Select principal diagnosis listed under DRG 823

Select any other operating room procedures not listed under DRG 820

OR

Select nonoperating room procedures listed under DRG 823

DRG 826 Myeloproliferative Disorders or Poorly Differentiated Neoplasms with Major O.R. Procedure with MCC

| GMLOS 10.8 | AMLOS 14.3 | RW 5.1814 |

Principal Diagnosis

C37	Malig neoplasm of thymus
C45.7	Mesothelioma of oth sites
C45.9	Mesothelioma, unsp
C48.0	Malig neoplasm of retroperitoneum
C76.4*	Malig neoplasm of upr limb
C76.5*	Malig neoplasm of lwr limb
C76.8	Malig neoplasm of oth spec ill-defined sites
C79.89	Secondary malig neoplasm of oth spec sites
C79.9	Secondary malig neoplasm of unsp site
C7A.00	Malig carcinoid tumor of unsp site
C7A.091	Malig carcinoid tumor of the thymus
C7A.098	Malig carcinoid tumors of oth sites
C7A.1	Malig poorly differentiated neuroendocrine tumors
C7A.8	Oth malig neuroendocrine tumors
C7B.00	Secondary carcinoid tumors, unsp site
C7B.09	Secondary carcinoid tumors of oth sites
C7B.1	Secondary Merkel cell carcinoma
C7B.8	Oth secondary neuroendocrine tumors
C80.0	Disseminated malig neoplasm, unsp
C80.1	Malig (primary) neoplasm, unsp
C80.2	Malig neoplasm associated with transplanted organ
C91.0*	Acute lymphoblastic leukemia [ALL]
C92.0*	Acute myeloblastic leukemia
C92.4*	Acute promyelocytic leukemia
C92.5*	Acute myelomonocytic leukemia
C92.6*	Acute myeloid leukemia with 11q23-abnormality
C92.A*	Acute myeloid leukemia with multilineage dysplasia
C93.0*	Acute monoblastic/monocytic leukemia
C94.0*	Acute erythroid leukemia
C95.0*	Acute leukemia of unsp cell type
C96.0	Multifocal and multisystemic Langerhans-cell histiocytosis
D09.3	Carcinoma in situ of thyroid and oth endocrine glands

D09.8	Carcinoma in situ of oth spec sites
D09.9	Carcinoma in situ, unsp
D19.7	Benign neoplasm of mesothelial tissue of oth sites
D19.9	Benign neoplasm of mesothelial tissue, unsp
D36.7	Benign neoplasm of oth spec sites
D36.9	Benign neoplasm, unsp site
D3A.00	Benign carcinoid tumor of unsp site
D3A.098	Benign carcinoid tumors of oth sites
D3A.8	Oth benign neuroendocrine tumors
D48.7	Neoplasm of uncertain behav of oth spec sites
D48.9	Neoplasm of uncertain behav, unsp
D49.8*	Neoplasm of unsp behav of oth spec sites
D49.9	Neoplasm of unsp behav of unsp site
E88.09	Oth d/o of plasma-protein metabolism, NEC
Q85.8	Oth phakomatoses, NEC
Q85.9	Phakomatosis, unsp
Z08	Enc for follow-up exam after tx for malig neoplasm
Z51.0	Enc for antineoplastic radiation therapy
Z51.1*	Enc for antineoplastic chemotherapy and immunotherapy
Z85*	Personal history of malig neoplasm
Z87.410	Personal history of cervical dysplasia

AND

Select operating room procedures listed under DRG 820

DRG 827 Myeloproliferative Disorders or Poorly Differentiated Neoplasms with Major O.R. Procedure with CC

| GMLOS 5.0 | AMLOS 6.5 | RW 2.3141 |

Select principal diagnosis listed under DRG 826 AND operating room procedures listed under DRG 820

DRG 828 Myeloproliferative Disorders or Poorly Differentiated Neoplasms with Major O.R. Procedure without CC/MCC

| GMLOS 2.8 | AMLOS 3.5 | RW 1.5139 |

Select principal diagnosis listed under DRG 826 AND operating room procedures listed under DRG 820

DRG 829 Myeloproliferative Disorders or Poorly Differentiated Neoplasms with Other O.R. Procedure with CC/MCC

| GMLOS 6.8 | AMLOS 10.2 | RW 3.3241 |

Select principal diagnosis listed under DRG 826

Select any other operating room procedures not listed under DRG 820

OR

Select nonoperating room procedures listed under DRG 823

DRG 830 Myeloproliferative Disorders or Poorly Differentiated Neoplasms with Other O.R. Procedure without CC/MCC

| GMLOS 2.6 | AMLOS 3.5 | RW 1.3670 |

Select principal diagnosis listed under DRG 826

Select any other operating room procedures not listed under DRG 820

OR

Select nonoperating room procedures listed under DRG 823

MEDICAL

DRG 834 Acute Leukemia without Major O.R. Procedure with MCC

| GMLOS 10.4 | AMLOS 17.2 | RW 5.5990 |

Principal Diagnosis

C91.0*	Acute lymphoblastic leukemia [ALL]
C92.0*	Acute myeloblastic leukemia
C92.4*	Acute promyelocytic leukemia
C92.5*	Acute myelomonocytic leukemia
C92.6*	Acute myeloid leukemia with 11q23-abnormality
C92.A*	Acute myeloid leukemia with multilineage dysplasia
C93.0*	Acute monoblastic/monocytic leukemia
C94.0*	Acute erythroid leukemia
C95.0*	Acute leukemia of unsp cell type

T Transfer DRG   SP Special Payment   * Code Range   6th and 7th Character of ZZ = No Device, No Qualifier ZX = No Device, Diagnostic

304   MS-DRG Version 33.0   © 2015 Optum360, LLC

DRG 835   Acute Leukemia without Major O.R. Procedure with CC
     GMLOS 4.9   AMLOS 7.7   RW 2.3024

Select principal diagnosis listed under DRG 834

DRG 836   Acute Leukemia without Major O.R. Procedure without CC/MCC
     GMLOS 2.9   AMLOS 4.0   RW 1.1381

Select principal diagnosis listed under DRG 834

DRG 837   Chemotherapy with Acute Leukemia as Secondary Diagnosis or with High Dose Chemotherapy Agent with MCC
     GMLOS 15.7   AMLOS 21.6   RW 6.1348

Principal Diagnosis

Z08	Enc for follow-up exam after tx for malig neoplasm
Z51.1*	Enc for antineoplastic chemotherapy and immunotherapy

AND

Secondary Diagnosis

C91.0*	Acute lymphoblastic leukemia [ALL]
C92.0*	Acute myeloblastic leukemia
C92.4*	Acute promyelocytic leukemia
C92.5*	Acute myelomonocytic leukemia
C92.6*	Acute myeloid leukemia with 11q23-abnormality
C92.A*	Acute myeloid leukemia with multilineage dysplasia
C93.0*	Acute monoblastic/monocytic leukemia
C94.0*	Acute erythroid leukemia
C95.0*	Acute leukemia of unsp cell type

OR

Nonoperating Room Procedure

3E03[0,3]02	Introduction/Peripheral Vein, [Opn, Perc], Antineoplastic, High-dose Interleukin-2
3E04[0,3]02	Introduction/Central Vein, [Opn, Perc], Antineoplastic, High-dose Interleukin-2
3E05[0,3]02	Introduction/Peripheral Artery, [Opn, Perc], Antineoplastic, High-dose Interleukin-2
3E06[0,3]02	Introduction/Central Artery, [Opn, Perc], Antineoplastic, High-dose Interleukin-2
3E0R302	Introduce of High dose IL-2 into Spinal Canal, Perc Appr
3E0S302	Introduce High dose IL-2 in Epidural Space, Perc

DRG 838   Chemotherapy with Acute Leukemia as Secondary Diagnosis with CC or High Dose Chemotherapy Agent
     GMLOS 7.0   AMLOS 9.8   RW 2.7707

Select principal and secondary diagnosis OR nonoperating room procedure listed under DRG 837

DRG 839   Chemotherapy with Acute Leukemia as Secondary Diagnosis without CC/MCC
     GMLOS 4.9   AMLOS 5.5   RW 1.3190

Select principal diagnosis AND secondary diagnosis listed under DRG 837

DRG 840   Lymphoma and Nonacute Leukemia with MCC
     GMLOS 7.6   AMLOS 10.4   RW 3.1449   ⊤

Principal Diagnosis

C26.1	Malig neoplasm of spleen
C46.3	Kaposi's sarcoma of lymph nodes
C77*	Secondary and unsp malig neoplasm of lymph nodes
C7B.01	Secondary carcinoid tumors of distant lymph nodes
C81*	Hodgkin lymphoma
C82*	Follicular lymphoma
C83*	Non-follicular lymphoma
C84*	Mature T/NK-cell lymphomas
C85*	Oth and unsp types of non-Hodgkin lymphoma
C86*	Oth spec types of T/NK-cell lymphoma
C88*	Malig immunoproliferative dis and certain oth B-cell lymph
C90*	Multi myeloma and malig plasma cell neoplasms
C91.1*	Chr lymphocytic leukemia of B-cell type
C91.3*	Prolymphocytic leukemia of B-cell type
C91.4*	Hairy cell leukemia
C91.5*	Adult T-cell lymphoma/leukemia (HTLV-1-associated)

C91.6*	Prolymphocytic leukemia of T-cell type
C91.9*	Lymphoid leukemia, unsp
C91.A*	Mature B-cell leukemia Burkitt-type
C91.Z*	Oth lymphoid leukemia
C92.1*	Chr myeloid leukemia, BCR/ABL-positive
C92.2*	Atypical chr myeloid leukemia, BCR/ABL-negative
C92.3*	Myeloid sarcoma
C92.9*	Myeloid leukemia, unsp
C92.Z*	Oth myeloid leukemia
C93.1*	Chr myelomonocytic leukemia
C93.3*	Juvenile myelomonocytic leukemia
C93.9*	Monocytic leukemia, unsp
C93.Z*	Oth monocytic leukemia
C94.2*	Acute megakaryoblastic leukemia
C94.3*	Mast cell leukemia
C94.4*	Acute panmyelosis with myelofibrosis
C94.6	Myelodysplastic dz, not classified
C94.8*	Oth spec leukemias
C95.1*	Chr leukemia of unsp cell type
C95.9*	Leukemia, unsp
C96.2	Malig mast cell tumor
C96.4	Sarcoma of dendritic cells (accessory cells)
C96.9	Malig neoplm of lymphoid, hematpoetc and rel tissue, unsp
C96.A	Histiocytic sarcoma
C96.Z	Oth malig neoplm of lymphoid, hematpoetc and related tissue
D45	Polycythemia vera
D47.0	Histiocytic and mast cell tumors of uncertain behav
D47.1	Chr myeloproliferative dz
D47.9	Neoplm of uncertain behav of lymphoid,hematpoetc & rel tiss,unsp
D47.Z9	Oth neoplm of uncertain behav of lymphoid, hematpoetc & rel tiss
D61.82	Myelophthisis
D75.81	Myelofibrosis
D89.1	Cryoglobulinemia

DRG 841   Lymphoma and Nonacute Leukemia with CC
     GMLOS 4.7   AMLOS 6.6   RW 1.6118   ⊤

Select principal diagnosis listed under DRG 840

DRG 842   Lymphoma and Nonacute Leukemia without CC/MCC
     GMLOS 3.1   AMLOS 4.0   RW 1.1167   ⊤

Select principal diagnosis listed under DRG 840

DRG 843   Other Myeloproliferative Disorders or Poorly Differentiated Neoplasm Diagnoses with MCC
     GMLOS 5.6   AMLOS 7.6   RW 1.8464

Principal Diagnosis

C37	Malig neoplasm of thymus
C45.7	Mesothelioma of oth sites
C45.9	Mesothelioma, unsp
C48.0	Malig neoplasm of retroperitoneum
C76.4*	Malig neoplasm of upr limb
C76.5*	Malig neoplasm of lwr limb
C76.8	Malig neoplasm of oth spec ill-defined sites
C79.89	Secondary malig neoplasm of oth spec sites
C79.9	Secondary malig neoplasm of unsp site
C7A.00	Malig carcinoid tumor of unsp site
C7A.091	Malig carcinoid tumor of the thymus
C7A.098	Malig carcinoid tumors of oth sites
C7A.1	Malig poorly differentiated neuroendocrine tumors
C7A.8	Oth malig neuroendocrine tumors
C7B.00	Secondary carcinoid tumors, unsp site
C7B.09	Secondary carcinoid tumors of oth sites
C7B.1	Secondary Merkel cell carcinoma
C7B.8	Oth secondary neuroendocrine tumors
C80.0	Disseminated malig neoplasm, unsp
C80.1	Malig (primary) neoplasm, unsp
C80.2	Malig neoplasm associated with transplanted organ
C96.0	Multifocal and multisystemic Langerhans-cell histiocytosis
D09.3	Carcinoma in situ of thyroid and oth endocrine glands
D09.8	Carcinoma in situ of oth spec sites
D09.9	Carcinoma in situ, unsp
D19.7	Benign neoplasm of mesothelial tissue of oth sites
D19.9	Benign neoplasm of mesothelial tissue, unsp

MDC 17: Myeloproliferative Diseases And Disorders And Poorly Differentiated Neoplasms—MEDICAL

Surgical	**Medical**	**CC Indicator**	**MCC Indicator**	**Procedure Proxy**	**PDxMCC** PDx acts as own MCC	**PDxCC** PDx acts as own CC

D36.7	Benign neoplasm of oth spec sites
D36.9	Benign neoplasm, unsp site
D3A.00	Benign carcinoid tumor of unsp site
D3A.098	Benign carcinoid tumors of oth sites
D3A.8	Oth benign neuroendocrine tumors
D48.7	Neoplasm of uncertain behav of oth spec sites
D48.9	Neoplasm of uncertain behav, unsp
D49.8*	Neoplasm of unsp behav of oth spec sites
D49.9	Neoplasm of unsp behav of unsp site
E88.09	Oth d/o of plasma-protein metabolism, NEC
Q85.8	Oth phakomatoses, NEC
Q85.9	Phakomatosis, unsp
Z85.0*	Personal history of malig neoplasm of digestive organs
Z85.1*	Personal history of malig neoplm of trachea, bronc and lung
Z85.2*	Prsnl history of malig neoplm of resp and intrathorac organs
Z85.3	Personal history of malig neoplasm of breast
Z85.4*	Personal history of malig neoplasm of genital organs
Z85.5*	Personal history of malig neoplasm of urinary tract
Z85.6	Personal history of leukemia
Z85.7*	Prsnl hx of malig neoplm of lymphoid, hematpoetc & rel tiss
Z85.8*	Personal history of malig neoplasms of organs and systems
Z85.9	Personal history of malig neoplasm, unsp
Z87.410	Personal history of cervical dysplasia

DRG 844 **Other Myeloproliferative Disorders or Poorly Differentiated Neoplasm Diagnoses with CC**

     GMLOS 4.0   AMLOS 5.1   RW 1.1233

Select principal diagnosis listed under DRG 843

DRG 845 **Other Myeloproliferative Disorders or Poorly Differentiated Neoplasm Diagnoses without CC/MCC**

     GMLOS 2.8   AMLOS 3.6   RW 0.8261

Select principal diagnosis listed under DRG 843

DRG 846 **Chemotherapy without Acute Leukemia as Secondary Diagnosis with MCC**

     GMLOS 5.9   AMLOS 8.0   RW 2.4618

Principal Diagnosis

Z08	Enc for follow-up exam after tx for malig neoplasm
Z51.1*	Enc for antineoplastic chemotherapy and immunotherapy

DRG 847 **Chemotherapy without Acute Leukemia as Secondary Diagnosis with CC**

     GMLOS 3.4   AMLOS 3.9   RW 1.1883

Select principal diagnosis listed under DRG 846

DRG 848 **Chemotherapy without Acute Leukemia as Secondary Diagnosis without CC/MCC**

     GMLOS 2.8   AMLOS 3.3   RW 0.9352

Select principal diagnosis listed under DRG 846

DRG 849 **Radiotherapy**

     GMLOS 4.9   AMLOS 6.5   RW 1.6745

Principal Diagnosis

Z51.0	Enc for antineoplastic radiation therapy

Ⓣ **Transfer DRG**   ⓈⓅ **Special Payment**   * **Code Range**   **6th and 7th Character of ZZ = No Device, No Qualifier ZX = No Device, Diagnostic**

306   MS-DRG Version 33.0   © 2015 Optum360, LLC

SURGICAL

DRG 853 Infectious and Parasitic Diseases with O.R. Procedure with MCC
GMLOS 10.7   **AMLOS 13.7**   **RW 5.1334**   T

Select any principal diagnosis from MDC 18 excluding

K68.11	Postprocedural retroperitoneal abscess
N98.0	Infxn associated with artfcl insemination
T80.22XA	Acute infxn fol tranfs,infusn,inject bld/products, init
T80.29XA	Infxn fol oth inf, transfusion and theraputc inject, init
T81.4XXA	Infxn following a procedure, init enc
T88.0XXA	Infxn following immunization, init enc

AND

Select any operating room procedures

DRG 854 Infectious and Parasitic Diseases with O.R. Procedure with CC
GMLOS 6.6   **AMLOS 7.9**   **RW 2.3804**   T

Select principal diagnosis AND operating room procedure under DRG 853

DRG 855 Infectious and Parasitic Diseases with O.R. Procedure without CC/MCC
GMLOS 3.5   **AMLOS 4.7**   **RW 1.5124**   T

Select principal diagnosis AND operating room procedure under DRG 853

DRG 856 Postoperative or Posttraumatic Infections with O.R. Procedure with MCC
GMLOS 9.8   **AMLOS 12.8**   **RW 4.6569**   T

Principal Diagnosis

K68.11	Postprocedural retroperitoneal abscess
N98.0	Infxn associated with artfcl insemination
T80.22XA	Acute infxn fol tranfs,infusn,inject bld/products, init
T80.29XA	Infxn fol oth inf, transfusion and theraputc inject, init
T81.4XXA	Infxn following a procedure, init enc
T88.0XXA	Infxn following immunization, init enc

AND

Select any operating room procedure

DRG 857 Postoperative or Posttraumatic Infections with O.R. Procedure with CC
GMLOS 5.6   **AMLOS 7.0**   **RW 2.0516**   T

Select principal diagnosis AND operating room procedure under DRG 856

DRG 858 Postoperative or Posttraumatic Infections with O.R. Procedure without CC/MCC
GMLOS 3.8   **AMLOS 4.5**   **RW 1.3300**   T

Select principal diagnosis AND operating room procedure under DRG 856

MEDICAL

DRG 862 Postoperative and Posttraumatic Infections with MCC
GMLOS 5.5   **AMLOS 7.1**   **RW 1.8550**   T

Principal Diagnosis

K68.11	Postprocedural retroperitoneal abscess
T81.4XXA	Infxn following a procedure, init enc

DRG 863 Postoperative and Posttraumatic Infections without MCC
GMLOS 3.7   **AMLOS 4.5**   **RW 1.0089**   T

Select principal diagnosis listed under DRG 862

DRG 864 Fever
GMLOS 2.8   **AMLOS 3.5**   **RW 0.8481**

Principal Diagnosis

R50*	Fever of oth and unknown origin

DRG 865 Viral Illness with MCC
GMLOS 4.2   **AMLOS 5.9**   **RW 1.5273**

Principal Diagnosis

A70	Chlamydia psittaci infections
A74.8*	Oth chlamydial dz
A74.9	Chlamydial infxn, unsp
A80.4	Acute nonparalytic poliomyelitis
A90	Dengue fever [classical dengue]
A91	Dengue hemorrhagic fever
A92.0	Chikungunya virus dz
A92.1	O'nyong-nyong fever
A92.3*	West Nile virus infxn
A92.4	Rift Valley fever
A92.8	Oth spec mosquito-borne viral fevers
A92.9	Mosquito-borne viral fever, unsp
A93*	Oth arthropod-borne viral fevers, NEC
A94	Unsp arthropod-borne viral fever
A95*	Yellow fever
A96*	Arenaviral hemorrhagic fever
A98.0	Crimean-Congo hemorrhagic fever
A98.1	Omsk hemorrhagic fever
A98.2	Kyasanur Forest dz
A98.3	Marburg virus dz
A98.4	Ebola virus dz
A98.8	Oth spec viral hemorrhagic fevers
A99	Unsp viral hemorrhagic fever
B00.89	Oth herpesviral infxn
B01.0	Varicella meningitis
B01.8*	Varicella with oth comp
B01.9	Varicella w/o comp
B02.7	Disseminated zoster
B02.8	Zoster with oth comp
B03	Smallpox
B04	Monkeypox
B05.1	Measles complicated by meningitis
B05.4	Measles with intestinal comp
B05.89	Oth measles comp
B05.9	Measles w/o comp
B06.81	Rubella pneumonia
B06.89	Oth rubella comp
B06.9	Rubella w/o comp
B08.010	Cowpox
B08.011	Vaccinia not from vaccine
B08.04	Paravaccinia, unsp
B08.09	Oth orthopoxvirus infections
B08.2*	Exanthema subitum [sixth dz]
B08.3	Erythema infectiosum [fifth dz]
B08.4	Enteroviral vesicular stomatitis with exanthem
B08.6*	Parapoxvirus infections
B08.7*	Yatapoxvirus infections
B08.8	Oth viral infections with skin and mucous membrane lesions
B09	Unsp viral infxn with skin and mucous membrane lesions
B25.8	Oth cytomegaloviral dz
B25.9	Cytomegaloviral dz, unsp
B26.89	Oth mumps comp
B26.8[2,3,5]	Mumps [myocarditis, nephritis, arthritis]
B26.9	Mumps w/o comp
B27*	Infectious mononucleosis
B33.1	Ross River dz
B33.24	Viral cardiomyopathy
B33.3	Retrovirus infections, NEC
B33.4	Hantavirus (cardio)-pulmn synd [HPS] [HCPS]

Surgical   **Medical**   **CC Indicator**   **MCC Indicator**   **Procedure Proxy**   PDxMCC **PDx acts as own MCC**   PDxCC **PDx acts as own CC**

© 2015 Optum360, LLC   MS-DRG Version 33.0   307

B33.8	Oth spec viral dz
B34*	Viral infxn of unsp site
B97*	Viral agents as the cause of dz classified elsw
J09.X[3,9]	flu d/t identified novel flu A virus w/ [gastrointestinal, oth] manifestations
J10.2	Flu d/t oth ident flu virus w GI manifest
J10.8*	Flu d/t oth ident flu virus w oth manifest
J11.2	Flu d/t unidentified flu virus w GI manifest
J11.8*	Flu d/t unidentified flu virus w oth manifest
L44.4	Infantile papular acrodermatitis [Gianotti-Crosti]
T88.1XXA	Oth comp following immunization, NEC, init
Z21	Asymptomatic human immunodef virus infxn status

DRG 866   Viral Illness without MCC

GMLOS 2.8   AMLOS 3.4   RW 0.7739

Select principal diagnosis listed under DRG 865

DRG 867   Other Infectious and Parasitic Diseases Diagnoses with MCC

GMLOS 6.7   AMLOS 9.0   RW 2.6068   [T]

Principal Diagnosis

A01*	Typhoid and paratyphoid fevers
A02.20	Localized salmonella infxn, unsp
A02.25	Salmonella pyelonephritis
A02.29	Salmonella with oth localized infxn
A02.8	Oth spec salmonella infections
A02.9	Salmonella infxn, unsp
A05.1	Botulism food poison
A06.3	Ameboma of intestine
A06.8*	Amebic infxn of oth sites
A06.9	Amebiasis, unsp
A17.9	Tuberculosis of nervous sys, unsp
A18.8[2,4,9]	Tuberculosis of [oth endocrine glands, heart, oth sites]
A19*	Miliary tuberculosis
A20.0	Bubonic plague
A20.1	Cellulocutaneous plague
A20.3	Plague meningitis
A20.8	Oth forms of plague
A20.9	Plague, unsp
A21.[0,1,7,8,9]	[Ulceroglandular, Oculoglandular, Generalized, Oth forms, Unsp] tularemia
A22.8	Oth forms of anthrax
A22.9	Anthrax, unsp
A23*	Brucellosis
A24*	Glanders and melioidosis
A25*	Rat-bite fevers
A26.0	Cutaneous erysipeloid
A26.8	Oth forms of erysipeloid
A26.9	Erysipeloid, unsp
A27.0	Leptospirosis icterohemorrhagica
A27.9	Leptospirosis, unsp
A28.0	Pasteurellosis
A28.2	Extraintestinal yersiniosis
A28.8	Oth zoonotic bacterial dz, NEC
A28.9	Zoonotic bacterial dz, unsp
A30*	Leprosy [Hansen's dz]
A31.2	Dissem mycobacterium avium-intracellulare complex (DMAC)
A31.8	Oth mycobacterial infections
A31.9	Mycobacterial infxn, unsp
A32.0	Cutaneous listeriosis
A32.1*	Listerial meningitis and meningoencephalitis
A32.8*	Oth forms of listeriosis
A32.9	Listeriosis, unsp
A35	Oth tetanus
A36.89	Oth diphtheritic comp
A36.8[2,3,4]	Diphtheritic [radiculomyelitis, polyneuritis, tubulo-interstitial nephropathy]
A36.9	Diphtheria, unsp
A38*	Scarlet fever
A42.8*	Oth forms of actinomycosis
A42.9	Actinomycosis, unsp
A43.8	Oth forms of nocardiosis
A43.9	Nocardiosis, unsp
A44*	Bartonellosis
A48.0	Gas gangrene
A48.2	Nonpneumonic Legionnaires' dz [Pontiac fever]
A48.3	Txc shock synd
A48.4	Brazilian purpuric fever

A48.5*	Oth spec botulism
A48.8	Oth spec bacterial dz
A49*	Bacterial infxn of unsp site
A50.0*	Early congenital syphilis, symptomatic
A50.1	Early congenital syphilis, latent
A50.2	Early congenital syphilis, unsp
A50.30	Late congenital syphilitic oculopathy, unsp
A50.32	Late congenital syphilitic chorioretinitis
A50.39	Oth late congenital syphilitic oculopathy
A50.44	Late congenital syphilitic optic nerve atrophy
A50.5*	Oth late congenital syphilis, symptomatic
A50.6	Late congenital syphilis, latent
A50.7	Late congenital syphilis, unsp
A50.9	Congenital syphilis, unsp
A51.2	Primary syphilis of oth sites
A51.42	Secondary syphilitic female pelvic dz
A51.44	Secondary syphilitic nephritis
A51.49	Oth secondary syphilitic conditions
A51.5	Early syphilis, latent
A51.9	Early syphilis, unsp
A52.73	Symptomatic late syphilis of oth respiratory organs
A52.76	Oth genitourinary symptomatic late syphilis
A52.79	Oth symptomatic late syphilis
A52.8	Late syphilis, latent
A52.9	Late syphilis, unsp
A53*	Oth and unsp syphilis
A54.82	Gonococcal brain abscess
A54.84	Gonococcal pneumonia
A54.89	Oth gonococcal infections
A54.9	Gonococcal infxn, unsp
A59.8	Trichomoniasis of oth sites
A59.9	Trichomoniasis, unsp
A65	Nonvenereal syphilis
A66.7	Oth manifestations of yaws
A66.8	Latent yaws
A66.9	Yaws, unsp
A67.2	Late lesions of pinta
A67.9	Pinta, unsp
A68*	Relapsing fevers
A69.2*	Lyme dz
A69.8	Oth spec spirochetal infections
A69.9	Spirochetal infxn, unsp
A75*	Typhus fever
A77*	Spotted fever [tick-borne rickettsioses]
A78	Q fever
A79*	Oth rickettsioses
B37.89	Oth sites of candidiasis
B37.9	Candidiasis, unsp
B38.7	Disseminated coccidioidomycosis
B38.89	Oth forms of coccidioidomycosis
B38.9	Coccidioidomycosis, unsp
B39.3	Disseminated histoplasmosis capsulati
B39.4	Histoplasmosis capsulati, unsp
B39.5	Histoplasmosis duboisii
B39.9	Histoplasmosis, unsp
B40*	Blastomycosis
B41*	Paracoccidioidomycosis
B42*	Sporotrichosis
B43*	Chromomycosis and pheomycotic abscess
B44.89	Oth forms of aspergillosis
B44.9	Aspergillosis, unsp
B44.[1,2,7]	[Oth pulmn, Tonsillar, Disseminated] aspergillosis
B45.[0,2,3,7,8,9]	[Pulmn, Cutaneous, Osseous, Disseminated, Oth forms of, Unsp] cryptococcosis
B46*	Zygomycosis
B47.0	Eumycetoma
B47.1	Actinomycetoma
B48*	Oth mycoses, NEC
B49	Unsp mycosis
B50*	Plasmodium falciparum malaria
B51*	Plasmodium vivax malaria
B52*	Plasmodium malariae malaria
B53*	Oth spec malaria
B54	Unsp malaria
B55.0	Visceral leishmaniasis
B55.9	Leishmaniasis, unsp
B56*	African trypanosomiasis
B57.1	Acute Chagas' dz w/o heart involvement
B57.3*	Chagas' dz (chr) with digestive sys involvement
B57.4*	Chagas' dz (chr) with nervous sys involvement

[T] **Transfer DRG**   [SP] **Special Payment**   * **Code Range**   **6th and 7th Character of ZZ = No Device, No Qualifier ZX = No Device, Diagnostic**

B57.5	Chagas' dz (chr) with oth organ involvement
B58.00	Toxoplasma oculopathy, unsp
B58.82	Toxoplasma myositis
B58.83	Toxoplasma tubulo-interstitial nephropathy
B58.89	Toxoplasmosis with oth organ involvement
B58.9	Toxoplasmosis, unsp
B60.0	Babesiosis
B60.10	Acanthamebiasis, unsp
B60.11	Meningoencephalitis d/t Acanthamoeba (culbertsoni)
B60.19	Oth acanthamebic dz
B60.2	Naegleriasis
B60.8	Oth spec protozoal dz
B64	Unsp protozoal dz
B65.2	Schistosomiasis d/t Schistosoma japonicum
B65.8	Oth schistosomiasis
B65.9	Schistosomiasis, unsp
B66.2	Dicroceliasis
B66.8	Oth spec fluke infections
B66.9	Fluke infxn, unsp
B67.2	Echinococcus granulosus infxn of bone
B67.32	Echinococcus granulosus infxn, multi sites
B67.39	Echinococcus granulosus infxn, oth sites
B67.4	Echinococcus granulosus infxn, unsp
B67.6*	Echinococcus multilocularis infxn, oth and multi sites
B67.7	Echinococcus multilocularis infxn, unsp
B67.90	Echinococcosis, unsp
B67.99	Oth echinococcosis
B72	Dracunculiasis
B73*	Onchocerciasis
B74*	Filariasis
B75	Trichinellosis
B81.4	Mixed intestinal helminthiases
B83.0	Visceral larva migrans
B83.1	Gnathostomiasis
B83.2	Angiostrongyliasis d/t Parastrongylus cantonensis
B83.3	Syngamiasis
B83.8	Oth spec helminthiases
B83.9	Helminthiasis, unsp
B89	Unsp parasitic dz
B90.8	Sequelae of tuberculosis of oth organs
B92	Sequelae of leprosy
B94.2	Sequelae of viral hepatitis
B94.8	Sequelae of oth infectious and parasitic dz
B94.9	Sequelae of unsp infectious and parasitic dz
B95*	Strep as the cause of dz classified elsw
B96*	Oth bacterial agents as the cause of dz classd elsw
B99*	Oth and unsp infectious dz
L94.6	Ainhum
N98.0	Infxn associated with artfcl insemination
R89.9	Unsp abnormal finding in specimens from oth org/tiss
T80.22XA	Acute infxn fol tranfs,infusn,inject bld/products, init
T80.29XA	Infxn fol oth inf, transfusion and theraputc inject, init
T88.0XXA	Infxn following immunization, init enc
Z16*	Resistance to antimicrobial drugs

DRG 868　Other Infectious and Parasitic Diseases Diagnoses with CC
GMLOS 3.8　　AMLOS 4.7　　RW 1.0292　　T

Select principal diagnosis listed under DRG 867

DRG 869　Other Infectious and Parasitic Diseases Diagnoses without CC/MCC
GMLOS 2.8　　AMLOS 3.4　　RW 0.7091　　T

Select principal diagnosis listed under DRG 867

▲DRG 870　Septicemia or Severe Sepsis with Mechanical Ventilation >96 Hours
GMLOS 12.6　　AMLOS 14.6　　RW 5.8782　　T

Principal Diagnosis

A02.1	Salmonella sepsis	
A20.7	Septicemic plague	
A22.7	Anthrax sepsis	PDx MCC
A26.7	Erysipelothrix sepsis	PDx MCC
A32.7	Listerial sepsis	PDx MCC
A39.1	Waterhouse-Friderichsen synd	
A39.2	Acute meningococcemia	

A39.3	Chr meningococcemia	
A39.4	Meningococcemia, unsp	
A39.89	Oth meningococcal infections	
A39.9	Meningococcal infxn, unsp	
A40*	Streptococcal sepsis	
A41*	Oth sepsis	
A42.7	Actinomycotic sepsis	
A54.86	Gonococcal sepsis	PDx MCC
B00.7	Disseminated herpesviral dz	
B37.7	Candidal sepsis	PDx MCC
R57.1	Hypovolemic shock	
R57.8	Oth shock	
R65*	Symp and signs specifically assoc w sys inflam and infxn	
R78.81	Bacteremia	

AND

Nonoperating Room Procedure

5A1955Z	Respiratory Ventilation, > 96 Consecutive Hrs

▲DRG 871　Septicemia or Severe Sepsis without Mechanical Ventilation >96 Hours with MCC
GMLOS 5.0　　AMLOS 6.5　　RW 1.7926　　T

Principal Diagnosis

A02.1	Salmonella sepsis	
A20.7	Septicemic plague	
A22.7	Anthrax sepsis	PDx MCC
A26.7	Erysipelothrix sepsis	PDx MCC
A32.7	Listerial sepsis	PDx MCC
A39.1	Waterhouse-Friderichsen synd	
A39.2	Acute meningococcemia	
A39.3	Chr meningococcemia	
A39.4	Meningococcemia, unsp	
A39.89	Oth meningococcal infections	
A39.9	Meningococcal infxn, unsp	
A40*	Streptococcal sepsis	
A41*	Oth sepsis	
A42.7	Actinomycotic sepsis	
A54.86	Gonococcal sepsis	PDx MCC
B00.7	Disseminated herpesviral dz	
B37.7	Candidal sepsis	PDx MCC
R57.1	Hypovolemic shock	
R57.8	Oth shock	
R65*	Symp and signs specifically assoc w sys inflam and infxn	
R78.81	Bacteremia	

▲DRG 872　Septicemia or Severe Sepsis without Mechanical Ventilation >96 Hours without MCC
GMLOS 3.9　　AMLOS 4.6　　RW 1.0427　　T

Select principal diagnosis listed under DRG 871

Surgical	Medical	CC Indicator	MCC Indicator	Procedure Proxy	PDxMCC PDx acts as own MCC	PDxCC PDx acts as own CC

SURGICAL

DRG 876 **O.R. Procedure with Principal Diagnoses of Mental Illness**
GMLOS 7.8   AMLOS 13.5   RW 3.0841

Select any operating room procedure

MEDICAL

DRG 880 **Acute Adjustment Reaction and Psychosocial Dysfunction**
GMLOS 2.4   AMLOS 3.3   RW 0.7227

Principal Diagnosis

F05	Delirium d/t known physiological condition
F41*	Oth anxiety d/o
F43.0	Acute stress reaction
F44.0	Dissociative amnesia
F44.1	Dissociative fugue
F44.2	Dissociative stupor
F44.4	Conversion d/o with motor symptom or deficit
F44.5	Conversion d/o with seizures or convulsions
F44.6	Conversion d/o with sensory symptom or deficit
F44.7	Conversion d/o with mixed symptom presentation
F44.9	Dissociative and conversion d/o, unsp
F48.9	Nonpsychotic mental d/o, unsp
F68.11	Factitious d/o w predom psych signs and symptoms
F68.13	Factitious d/o w comb psych and physcl signs and symptoms
F68.8	Oth spec d/o of adult personality and behav
F99	Mental d/o, not otherwise spec
R44.0	Auditory hallucinations
R44.2	Oth hallucinations
R44.3	Hallucinations, unsp
R45.0	Nervousness
R45.2	Unhappiness
R45.3	Demoralization and apathy
R45.4	Irritability and anger
R45.5	Hostility
R45.6	Violent behav
R45.7	State of emotional shock and stress, unsp
R45.851	Suicidal ideations
R45.89	Oth symptoms and signs involving emotional state
Z72.810	Child and adolescent antisocial behav
Z72.811	Adult antisocial behav

DRG 881 **Depressive Neuroses**
GMLOS 3.4   AMLOS 4.5   RW 0.6618

Principal Diagnosis

F32.9	Major depressive d/o, single episode, unsp
F34.1	Dysthymic d/o
F43.21	Adjustment d/o with depressed mood

DRG 882 **Neuroses Except Depressive**
GMLOS 3.3   AMLOS 4.5   RW 0.6924

Principal Diagnosis

F40*	Phobic anxiety d/o
F42	Obsessive-compulsive d/o
F43.1*	Post-traum stress d/o (PTSD)
F43.20	Adjustment d/o, unsp
F43.22	Adjustment d/o with anxiety
F43.23	Adjustment d/o with mixed anxiety and depressed mood
F43.24	Adjustment d/o with disturbance of conduct
F43.25	Adjustment d/o w mixed disturb of emotions & conduct
F43.29	Adjustment d/o with oth symptoms
F43.8	Oth reactions to severe stress
F43.9	Reaction to severe stress, unsp
F45*	Somatoform d/o
F48.1	Depersonalization-derealization synd

F48.8	Oth spec nonpsychotic mental d/o
F93.0	Separation anxiety d/o of childhood
F98.21	Rumination d/o of infancy
R45.87	Impulsiveness

DRG 883 **Disorders of Personality and Impulse Control**
GMLOS 4.6   AMLOS 8.0   RW 1.3737

Principal Diagnosis

F21	Schizotypal d/o
F34.0	Cyclothymic d/o
F44.81	Dissociative identity d/o
F50.0*	Anorexia nervosa
F60*	Specific personality d/o
F63.0	Path gambling
F63.2	Kleptomania
F63.8*	Oth impulse d/o
F68.1[0,2]	Factitious d/o, [unsp, w/ predominantly physical signs and symptoms]
F69	Unsp d/o of adult personality and behav
R45.86	Emotional lability

DRG 884 **Organic Disturbances and Mental Retardation** $\boxed{\text{T}}$
GMLOS 4.3   AMLOS 6.3   RW 1.1483

Principal Diagnosis

F01*	Vascular dementia
F02*	Dementia in oth dz classified elsw
F03*	Unsp dementia
F04	Amnestic d/o d/t known physiological condition
F06*	Oth mental d/o d/t known physiological condition
F07.0	Personality change d/t known physiological condition
F07.9	Unsp personality & behavrl d/o d/t known physiol cond
F09	Unsp mental d/o d/t known physiological condition
F53	Puerperal psychosis
F54	Psych & behavrl factors assoc w d/o or dis classd elsw
F63.3	Trichotillomania
F70	Mild intellectual disabilities
F71	Mod intellectual disabilities
F72	Severe intellectual disabilities
F73	Profound intellectual disabilities
F78	Oth intellectual disabilities
F79	Unsp intellectual disabilities
F84.0	Autistic d/o
F84.3	Oth childhood disintegrative d/o
Q90*	Down synd
Q91*	Trisomy 18 and Trisomy 13
Q93.3	Deletion of short arm of chromosome 4
Q93.4	Deletion of short arm of chromosome 5
Q93.5	Oth deletions of part of a chromosome
Q93.7	Deletions with oth complex rearrangements
Q93.8*	Oth deletions from the autosomes
Q93.9	Deletion from autosomes, unsp
Q99.2	Fragile X chromosome
R40.4	Transient alter of awareness
R41.81	Age-related cognitive decline
R41.841	Cognitive communication deficit
R41.843	Psychomotor deficit
R41.844	Frontal lobe and executive function deficit
R41.89	Oth symptoms and signs w cognitive functions & awareness
R45.1	Restlessness and agitation
R45.81	Low self-esteem
R45.82	Worries
R54	Age-related physical debility

DRG 885 **Psychoses**
GMLOS 5.6   AMLOS 7.7   RW 1.0575

Principal Diagnosis

F20*	Schizophrenia
F22	Delusional d/o
F23	Brief psychotic d/o
F24	Shared psychotic d/o

$\boxed{\text{T}}$ Transfer DRG $\boxed{\text{SP}}$ Special Payment   * Code Range   6th and 7th Character of ZZ = No Device, No Qualifier ZX = No Device, Diagnostic

F25*	Schizoaffective d/o
F28	Oth psych d/o not d/t a sub or known physiol cond
F29	Unsp psychosis not d/t a substance or known physiol cond
F30*	Manic episode
F31*	Bipolar d/o
F32.0	Major depressive d/o, single episode, mild
F32.1	Major depressive d/o, single episode, mod
F32.2	Major depressv d/o, single epsd, sev w/o psych features
F32.3	Major depressv d/o, single epsd, severe w psych features
F32.4	Major depressv d/o, single episode, in partial remis
F32.5	Major depressive d/o, single episode, in full remission
F32.8	Oth depressive episodes
F33*	Major depressive d/o, recurrent
F34.8	Oth persistent mood [affective] d/o
F34.9	Persistent mood [affective] d/o, unsp
F39	Unsp mood [affective] d/o
F84.5	Asperger's synd
F84.8	Oth pervasive developmental d/o
F84.9	Pervasive developmental d/o, unsp

G47.9	Sleep d/o, unsp
R37	Sexual dysfunction, unsp
R48.9	Unsp symbolic dysfunctions
Z87.890	Personal history of sex reassignment

DRG 886   Behavioral and Developmental Disorders

GMLOS 3.9   AMLOS 6.0   RW 0.8718

Principal Diagnosis

F63.1	Pyromania
F63.9	Impulse d/o, unsp
F80.0	Phonological d/o
F80.1	Expressive language d/o
F80.2	Mixed receptive-expressive language d/o
F80.4	Speech and language development delay d/t hearing loss
F80.89	Oth developmental d/o of speech and language
F80.9	Developmental d/o of speech and language, unsp
F81*	Specific developmental d/o of scholastic skills
F82	Specific developmental d/o of motor function
F88	Oth d/o of psychological development
F89	Unsp d/o of psychological development
F90*	Attention-deficit hyperactivity d/o
F91*	Conduct d/o
F93.8	Oth childhood emotional d/o
F93.9	Childhood emotional d/o, unsp
F94*	D/o social w onset specific to childhood and adolescence
F98.0	Enuresis not d/t a substance or known physiol condition
F98.1	Encopresis not d/t a substance or known physiol condition
F98.3	Pica of infancy and childhood
F98.8	Oth behav/emotn d/o w onset usly occur in chldhd and adol
F98.9	Unsp behav/emotn d/o w onst usly occur in chldhd and adol
H93.25	Central auditory processing d/o
R41.840	Attention and concentration deficit
R48.0	Dyslexia and alexia
R48.1	Agnosia
R48.2	Apraxia
R48.8	Oth symbolic dysfunctions

DRG 887   Other Mental Disorder Diagnoses

GMLOS 3.0   AMLOS 4.6   RW 0.9939

Principal Diagnosis

F44.89	Oth dissociative and conversion d/o
F50.2	Bulimia nervosa
F50.8	Oth eating d/o
F50.9	Eating d/o, unsp
F51*	Sleep d/o not d/t a substance or known physiol cond
F52.0	Hypoactive sexual desire d/o
F52.1	Sexual aversion d/o
F52.2*	Sexual arousal d/o
F52.3*	Orgasmic d/o
F52.4	Premature ejaculation
F52.6	Dyspareunia not d/t a substance or known physiol cond
F52.8	Oth sexual dysfnct not d/t a sub or known physiol cond
F52.9	Unsp sexual dysfnct not d/t a sub or known physiol cond
F59	Unsp behavrl synd assoc w physiol disturb and physcl factors
F64*	Gender identity d/o
F65*	Paraphilias
F66	Oth sexual d/o
F98.29	Oth feeding d/o of infancy and early childhood
F98.4	Stereotyped movement d/o
F98.5	Adult onset fluency d/o
G47.0*	Insomnia
G47.1*	Hypersomnia

Surgical   Medical   CC Indicator   MCC Indicator   Procedure Proxy   PDxMCC PDx acts as own MCC   PDxCC PDx acts as own CC

MEDICAL

DRG 894   **Alcohol/Drug Abuse or Dependence, Left Against Medical Advice**

GMLOS 2.1   AMLOS 3.1   RW 0.4859

Select principal diagnosis in MDC 20

AND

Discharge status of against medical advice (AMA)

DRG 895   **Alcohol/Drug Abuse or Dependence with Rehabilitation Therapy**

GMLOS 9.3   AMLOS 12.0   RW 1.2435

Select principal diagnosis in MDC 20

AND

Nonoperating Room Procedure

HZ30ZZZ	Indiv Counsel for Substance Abuse Tx, Cognitive
HZ31ZZZ	Indiv Counsel for Substance Abuse Tx, Behavioral
HZ32ZZZ	Indiv Counsel for Substance Abuse, Cognitive Behavioral
HZ33ZZZ	Individual Counseling for Substance Abuse Tx, 12-Step
HZ34ZZZ	Indiv Counsel for Substance Abuse Tx, Interpersonal
HZ35ZZZ	Indiv Counsel for Substance Abuse Tx, Vocational
HZ36ZZZ	Indiv Counsel for Substance Abuse Tx, Psychoeducation
HZ37ZZZ	Indiv Counsel for Substance Abuse, Motivational Enhance
HZ38ZZZ	Indiv Counsel for Substance Abuse Tx, Confrontational
HZ39ZZZ	Indiv Counsel for Substance Abuse Tx, Continuing Care
HZ3BZZZ	Indiv Counsel for Substance Abuse Tx, Spiritual
HZ40ZZZ	Group Counseling for Substance Abuse Tx, Cognitive
HZ41ZZZ	Group Counseling for Substance Abuse Tx, Behavioral
HZ42ZZZ	Group Counsel for Substance Abuse, Cognitive Behavioral
HZ43ZZZ	Group Counseling for Substance Abuse Tx, 12-Step
HZ44ZZZ	Group Counsel for Substance Abuse Tx, Interpersonal
HZ45ZZZ	Group Counseling for Substance Abuse Tx, Vocational
HZ46ZZZ	Group Counsel for Substance Abuse Tx, Psychoeducation
HZ47ZZZ	Group Counsel for Substance Abuse, Motivational Enhance
HZ48ZZZ	Group Counsel for Substance Abuse Tx, Confrontational
HZ49ZZZ	Group Counsel for Substance Abuse Tx, Continuing Care
HZ4BZZZ	Group Counseling for Substance Abuse Tx, Spiritual
HZ50ZZZ	Indiv Psychotherapy for Substance Abuse Tx, Cognitive
HZ51ZZZ	Indiv Psychotherapy for Substance Abuse, Behavioral
HZ52ZZZ	Indiv Psychotherapy for Substance Abuse, Cognitiv Behavioral
HZ53ZZZ	Indiv Psychotherapy for Substance Abuse Tx, 12 Step
HZ54ZZZ	Indiv Psychotherapy for Substance Abuse, Interpersonal
HZ55ZZZ	Indiv Psychotherapy for Substance Abuse, Interactive
HZ56ZZZ	Indiv Psychotherapy for Substance Abuse, Psychoeducation
HZ57ZZZ	Indiv Psychotherapy for Substance Abuse, Motivation Enhance
HZ58ZZZ	Indiv Psychotherapy for Substance Abuse, Confrontational
HZ59ZZZ	Indiv Psychotherapy for Substance Abuse Tx, Support
HZ5BZZZ	Indiv Psychotherapy for Substance Abuse, Psychoanalysis
HZ5CZZZ	Indiv Psychotherapy for Substance Abuse, Psychodynamic
HZ5DZZZ	Indiv Psychotherapy for Substance Abuse, Psychophys

DRG 896   **Alcohol/Drug Abuse or Dependence without Rehabilitation Therapy with MCC**

GMLOS 4.8   AMLOS 6.6   RW 1.5678   [T]

Select principal diagnosis in MDC 20

DRG 897   **Alcohol/Drug Abuse or Dependence without Rehabilitation Therapy without MCC**

GMLOS 3.3   AMLOS 4.1   RW 0.7231   [T]

Select principal diagnosis in MDC 20

[T] Transfer DRG   [SP] Special Payment   * Code Range   6th and 7th Character of ZZ = No Device, No Qualifier ZX = No Device, Diagnostic

312   MS-DRG Version 33.0   © 2015 Optum360, LLC

SURGICAL

DRG 901 **Wound Debridements for Injuries with MCC**
    GMLOS 9.2   AMLOS 13.3   RW 3.9370

Operating Room Procedures

ØHB[Ø,1,4,5,6,7,8,A]XZZ Exc [Scalp, Face, Neck, Chest, Back, Abd, Buttock, Genitalia] Skin, Ext
ØHB[B,C,D,E,F,G]XZZ Exc of Skin of [Rt Upr Arm, Lt Upr Arm, Rt Lwr Arm, Lt Lwr Arm, Rt Hand, Lt Hand], Ext
ØHB[H,J,K,L,M,N]XZZ Exc of Skin of [Rt Upr Leg, Lt Upr Leg, Rt Lwr Leg, Lt Lwr Leg, Rt Foot, Lt Foot], Ext
ØJB[Ø,1,4,5,6]ØZZ Exc of SQ Tissue & Fascia of [Scalp, Face, Ant Neck, Post Neck, Chest], Opn
ØJB[7,8,9,B,C]ØZZ Exc of SQ Tissue & Fascia of [Back, Abd, Buttock, Perineum, Pelvic Rgn], Opn
ØJB[D,F,G,H]ØZZ Exc of SQ Tissue & Fascia of [Rt Upr Arm, Lt Upr Arm, Rt Lwr Arm, Lt Lwr Arm], Opn
ØJB[L,M,N,P,Q,R]ØZZ Exc of SQ Tissue & Fascia of [Rt Upr Leg, Lt Upr Leg, Rt Lwr Leg, Lt Lwr Leg, Rt Foot, Lt Foot], Opn

DRG 902 **Wound Debridements for Injuries with CC**
    GMLOS 5.3   AMLOS 7.1   RW 1.8265

Select operating room procedures listed under DRG 901

DRG 903 **Wound Debridements for Injuries without CC/MCC**
    GMLOS 3.3   AMLOS 4.3   RW 1.1723

Select operating room procedures listed under DRG 901

DRG 904 **Skin Grafts for Injuries with CC/MCC**
    GMLOS 7.1   AMLOS 1Ø.4   RW 3.214Ø

Operating Room Procedures

ØH8ØXZZ   Div of Scalp Skin, Ext Appr
ØH81XZZ   Div of Face Skin, Ext Appr
ØH84XZZ   Div of Neck Skin, Ext Appr
ØH85XZZ   Div of Chest Skin, Ext Appr
ØH86XZZ   Div of Back Skin, Ext Appr
ØH87XZZ   Div of Abd Skin, Ext Appr
ØH88XZZ   Div of Buttock Skin, Ext Appr
ØH8AXZZ   Div of Genitalia Skin, Ext Appr
ØH8BXZZ   Div of Rt Upr Arm Skin, Ext Appr
ØH8CXZZ   Div of Lt Upr Arm Skin, Ext Appr
ØH8DXZZ   Div of Rt Lwr Arm Skin, Ext Appr
ØH8EXZZ   Div of Lt Lwr Arm Skin, Ext Appr
ØH8FXZZ   Div of Rt Hand Skin, Ext Appr
ØH8GXZZ   Div of Lt Hand Skin, Ext Appr
ØH8HXZZ   Div of Rt Upr Leg Skin, Ext Appr
ØH8JXZZ   Div of Lt Upr Leg Skin, Ext Appr
ØH8KXZZ   Div of Rt Lwr Leg Skin, Ext Appr
ØH8LXZZ   Div of Lt Lwr Leg Skin, Ext Appr
ØH8MXZZ   Div of Rt Foot Skin, Ext Appr
ØH8NXZZ   Div of Lt Foot Skin, Ext Appr
ØHRØXJZ   Replace of Scalp Skin with Synth Sub, Extern Appr
ØHRØX[7,J,K][3,4] Replace/Skin, Scalp, Ext, [Auto Tissue Sub, Synth Sub, Nonauto Tissue Sub], [Full Thickness, Partial Thickness]
ØHR1XJZ   Replace of Face Skin with Synth Sub, Extern Appr
ØHR1X[7,J,K][3,4] Replace/Skin, Face, Ext, [Auto Tissue Sub, Synth Sub, Nonauto Tissue Sub], [Full Thickness, Partial Thickness]
ØHR4XJZ   Replace of Neck Skin with Synth Sub, Extern Appr
ØHR4X[7,J,K][3,4] Replace/Skin, Neck, Ext, [Auto Tissue Sub, Synth Sub, Nonauto Tissue Sub], [Full Thickness, Partial Thickness]
ØHR5XJZ   Replace of Chest Skin with Synth Sub, Extern Appr
ØHR5X[7,J,K][3,4] Replace/Skin, Chest, Ext, [Auto Tissue Sub, Synth Sub, Nonauto Tissue Sub], [Full Thickness, Partial Thickness]
ØHR6XJZ   Replace of Back Skin with Synth Sub, Extern Appr
ØHR6X[7,J,K][3,4] Replace/Skin, Back, Ext, [Auto Tissue Sub, Synth Sub, Nonauto Tissue Sub], [Full Thickness, Partial Thickness]
ØHR7XJZ   Replace of Abd Skin with Synth Sub, Extern Appr

ØHR7X[7,J,K][3,4] Replace/Skin, Abd, Ext, [Auto Tissue Sub, Synth Sub, Nonauto Tissue Sub], [Full Thickness, Partial Thickness]
ØHR8XJZ   Replace of Buttock Skin with Synth Sub, Extern Appr
ØHR8X[7,J,K][3,4] Replace/Skin, Buttock, Ext, [Auto Tissue Sub, Synth Sub, Nonauto Tissue Sub], [Full Thickness, Partial Thickness]
ØHRAXJZ   Replace of Genitalia Skin with Synth Sub, Extern Appr
ØHRAX[7,J,K][3,4] Replace/Skin, Genitalia, Ext, [Auto Tissue Sub, Synth Sub, Nonauto Tissue Sub], [Full Thickness, Partial Thickness]
ØHRBXJZ   Replace of Rt Up Arm Skin with Synth Sub, Extern Appr
ØHRBX[7,J,K][3,4] Replace/Skin, Rt Upr Arm, Ext, [Auto Tissue Sub, Synth Sub, Nonauto Tissue Sub], [Full Thickness, Partial Thickness]
ØHRCXJZ   Replace of Lt Up Arm Skin with Synth Sub, Extern Appr
ØHRCX[7,J,K][3,4] Replace/Skin, Lt Upr Arm, Ext, [Auto Tissue Sub, Synth Sub, Nonauto Tissue Sub], [Full Thickness, Partial Thickness]
ØHRDXJZ   Replace of Rt Low Arm Skin with Synth Sub, Extern Appr
ØHRDX[7,J,K][3,4] Replace/Skin, Rt Lwr Arm, Ext, [Auto Tissue Sub, Synth Sub, Nonauto Tissue Sub], [Full Thickness, Partial Thickness]
ØHREXJZ   Replace of Lt Low Arm Skin with Synth Sub, Extern Appr
ØHREX[7,J,K][3,4] Replace/Skin, Lt Lwr Arm, Ext, [Auto Tissue Sub, Synth Sub, Nonauto Tissue Sub], [Full Thickness, Partial Thickness]
ØHRFXJZ   Replace of Rt Hand Skin with Synth Sub, Extern Appr
ØHRFX[J,K][3,4] Replace/Skin, Rt Hand, Ext, [Synth Sub, Nonauto Tissue Sub], [Full Thickness, Partial Thickness]
ØHRGXJZ   Replace of Lt Hand Skin with Synth Sub, Extern Appr
ØHRGX[J,K][3,4] Replace/Skin, Lt Hand, Ext, [Synth Sub, Nonauto Tissue Sub], [Full Thickness, Partial Thickness]
ØHRHXJZ   Replace of Rt Up Leg Skin with Synth Sub, Extern Appr
ØHRHX[7,J,K][3,4] Replace/Skin, Rt Upr Leg, Ext, [Auto Tissue Sub, Synth Sub, Nonauto Tissue Sub], [Full Thickness, Partial Thickness]
ØHRJXJZ   Replace of Lt Up Leg Skin with Synth Sub, Extern Appr
ØHRJX[7,J,K][3,4] Replace/Skin, Lt Upr Leg, Ext, [Auto Tissue Sub, Synth Sub, Nonauto Tissue Sub], [Full Thickness, Partial Thickness]
ØHRKXJZ   Replace of Rt Low Leg Skin with Synth Sub, Extern Appr
ØHRKX[7,J,K][3,4] Replace/Skin, Rt Lwr Leg, Ext, [Auto Tissue Sub, Synth Sub, Nonauto Tissue Sub], [Full Thickness, Partial Thickness]
ØHRLXJZ   Replace of Lt Low Leg Skin with Synth Sub, Extern Appr
ØHRLX[7,J,K][3,4] Replace/Skin, Lt Lwr Leg, Ext, [Auto Tissue Sub, Synth Sub, Nonauto Tissue Sub], [Full Thickness, Partial Thickness]
ØHRMXJZ   Replace of Rt Foot Skin with Synth Sub, Extern Appr
ØHRMX[7,J,K][3,4] Replace/Skin, Rt Foot, Ext, [Auto Tissue Sub, Synth Sub, Nonauto Tissue Sub], [Full Thickness, Partial Thickness]
ØHRNXJZ   Replace of Lt Foot Skin with Synth Sub, Extern Appr
ØHRNX[7,J,K][3,4] Replace/Skin, Lt Foot, Ext, [Auto Tissue Sub, Synth Sub, Nonauto Tissue Sub], [Full Thickness, Partial Thickness]
ØHRTX[7,K]Z   Replace/Breast, Rt, Ext, [Auto Tissue Sub, Nonauto Tissue Sub], NQ
ØHRUX[7,K]Z   Replace/Breast, Lt, Ext, [Auto Tissue Sub, Nonauto Tissue Sub], NQ
ØHRVX[7,K]Z   Replace/Breast, Bilat, Ext, [Auto Tissue Sub, Nonauto Tissue Sub], NQ
ØHXØXZZ   Transfer Scalp Skin, Ext Appr
ØHX1XZZ   Transfer Face Skin, Ext Appr
ØHX4XZZ   Transfer Neck Skin, Ext Appr
ØHX5XZZ   Transfer Chest Skin, Ext Appr
ØHX6XZZ   Transfer Back Skin, Ext Appr
ØHX7XZZ   Transfer Abd Skin, Ext Appr
ØHX8XZZ   Transfer Buttock Skin, Ext Appr
ØHX9XZZ   Transfer Perineum Skin, Ext Appr
ØHXAXZZ   Transfer Genitalia Skin, Ext Appr
ØHXBXZZ   Transfer Rt Upr Arm Skin, Ext Appr
ØHXCXZZ   Transfer Lt Upr Arm Skin, Ext Appr
ØHXDXZZ   Transfer Rt Lwr Arm Skin, Ext Appr
ØHXEXZZ   Transfer Lt Lwr Arm Skin, Ext Appr
ØHXFXZZ   Transfer Rt Hand Skin, Ext Appr
ØHXGXZZ   Transfer Lt Hand Skin, Ext Appr
ØHXHXZZ   Transfer Rt Upr Leg Skin, Ext Appr
ØHXJXZZ   Transfer Lt Upr Leg Skin, Ext Appr
ØHXKXZZ   Transfer Rt Lwr Leg Skin, Ext Appr
ØHXLXZZ   Transfer Lt Lwr Leg Skin, Ext Appr
ØHXMXZZ   Transfer Rt Foot Skin, Ext Appr
ØHXNXZZ   TransferLtFootSkin,ExtAppr
ØJHØ[Ø,3]NZ   Insert/SQ Tissue & Fascia, Scalp, [Opn, Perc], Tissue Expander, NQ
ØJH1[Ø,3]NZ   Insert/SQ Tissue & Fascia, Face, [Opn, Perc], Tissue Expander, NQ

Surgical   **Medical**   **CC Indicator**   **MCC Indicator**   **Procedure Proxy**   **PDxMCC PDx acts as own MCC**   **PDxCC PDx acts as own CC**

MDC 21: Injuries, Poisonings And Toxic Effects Of Drugs—SURGICAL

Code	Description
0JH4[0,3]NZ	Insert/SQ Tissue & Fascia, Ant Neck, [Opn, Perc], Tissue Expander, NQ
0JH5[0,3]NZ	Insert/SQ Tissue & Fascia, Post Neck, [Opn, Perc], Tissue Expander, NQ
0JH6[0,3]NZ	Insert/SQ Tissue & Fascia, Chest, [Opn, Perc], Tissue Expander, NQ
0JH7[0,3]NZ	Insert/SQ Tissue & Fascia, Back, [Opn, Perc], Tissue Expander, NQ
0JH8[0,3]NZ	Insert/SQ Tissue & Fascia, Abd, [Opn, Perc], Tissue Expander, NQ
0JH9[0,3]NZ	Insert/SQ Tissue & Fascia, Buttock, [Opn, Perc], Tissue Expander, NQ
0JHB[0,3]NZ	Insert/SQ Tissue & Fascia, Perineum, [Opn, Perc], Tissue Expander, NQ
0JHC[0,3]NZ	Insert/SQ Tissue & Fascia, Genitalia, [Opn, Perc], Tissue Expander, NQ
0JHD[0,3]NZ	Insert/SQ Tissue & Fascia, Rt Upr Arm, [Opn, Perc], Tissue Expander, NQ
0JHF[0,3]NZ	Insert/SQ Tissue & Fascia, Lt Upr Arm, [Opn, Perc], Tissue Expander, NQ
0JHG[0,3]NZ	Insert/SQ Tissue & Fascia, Rt Lwr Arm, [Opn, Perc], Tissue Expander, NQ
0JHH[0,3]NZ	Insert/SQ Tissue & Fascia, Lt Lwr Arm, [Opn, Perc], Tissue Expander, NQ
0JHJ[0,3]NZ	Insert/SQ Tissue & Fascia, Rt Hand, [Opn, Perc], Tissue Expander, NQ
0JHK[0,3]NZ	Insert/SQ Tissue & Fascia, Lt Hand, [Opn, Perc], Tissue Expander, NQ
0JHL[0,3]NZ	Insert/SQ Tissue & Fascia, Rt Upr Leg, [Opn, Perc], Tissue Expander, NQ
0JHM[0,3]NZ	Insert/SQ Tissue & Fascia, Lt Upr Leg, [Opn, Perc], Tissue Expander, NQ
0JHN[0,3]NZ	Insert/SQ Tissue & Fascia, Rt Lwr Leg, [Opn, Perc], Tissue Expander, NQ
0JHP[0,3]NZ	Insert/SQ Tissue & Fascia, Lt Lwr Leg, [Opn, Perc], Tissue Expander, NQ
0JHQ[0,3]NZ	Insert/SQ Tissue & Fascia, Rt Foot, [Opn, Perc], Tissue Expander, NQ
0JHR[0,3]NZ	Insert/SQ Tissue & Fascia, Lt Foot, [Opn, Perc], Tissue Expander, NQ
0JX0[0,3]Z[B,C]	Transfer/SQ Tissue & Fascia, Scalp, [Opn, Perc], No Dev, [Skin and SQ Tissue, Skin, SQ Tissue & Fascia]
0JX1[0,3]Z[B,C]	Transfer/SQ Tissue & Fascia, Face, [Opn, Perc], No Dev, [Skin and SQ Tissue, Skin, SQ Tissue & Fascia]
0JX4[0,3]Z[B,C]	Transfer/SQ Tissue & Fascia, Ant Neck, [Opn, Perc], No Dev, [Skin and SQ Tissue, Skin, SQ Tissue & Fascia]
0JX5[0,3]Z[B,C]	Transfer/SQ Tissue & Fascia, Post Neck, [Opn, Perc], No Dev, [Skin and SQ Tissue, Skin, SQ Tissue & Fascia]
0JX6[0,3]Z[B,C]	Transfer/SQ Tissue & Fascia, Chest, [Opn, Perc], No Dev, [Skin and SQ Tissue, Skin, SQ Tissue & Fascia]
0JX7[0,3]Z[B,C]	Transfer/SQ Tissue & Fascia, Back, [Opn, Perc], No Dev, [Skin and SQ Tissue, Skin, SQ Tissue & Fascia]
0JX8[0,3]Z[B,C]	Transfer/SQ Tissue & Fascia, Abd, [Opn, Perc], No Dev, [Skin and SQ Tissue, Skin, SQ Tissue & Fascia]
0JX9[0,3]Z[B,C]	Transfer/SQ Tissue & Fascia, Buttock, [Opn, Perc], No Dev, [Skin and SQ Tissue, Skin, SQ Tissue & Fascia]
0JXB[0,3]Z[B,C]	Transfer/SQ Tissue & Fascia, Perineum, [Opn, Perc], No Dev, [Skin and SQ Tissue, Skin, SQ Tissue & Fascia]
0JXC[0,3]Z[B,C]	Transfer/SQ Tissue & Fascia, Genitalia, [Opn, Perc], No Dev, [Skin and SQ Tissue, Skin, SQ Tissue & Fascia]
0JXD[0,3]Z[B,C]	Transfer/SQ Tissue & Fascia, Rt Upr Arm, [Opn, Perc], No Dev, [Skin and SQ Tissue, Skin, SQ Tissue & Fascia]
0JXF[0,3]Z[B,C]	Transfer/SQ Tissue & Fascia, Lt Upr Arm, [Opn, Perc], No Dev, [Skin and SQ Tissue, Skin, SQ Tissue & Fascia]
0JXG[0,3]Z[B,C]	Transfer/SQ Tissue & Fascia, Rt Lwr Arm, [Opn, Perc], No Dev, [Skin and SQ Tissue, Skin, SQ Tissue & Fascia]
0JXH[0,3]Z[B,C]	Transfer/SQ Tissue & Fascia, Lt Lwr Arm, [Opn, Perc], No Dev, [Skin and SQ Tissue, Skin, SQ Tissue & Fascia]
0JXL[0,3]Z[B,C]	Transfer/SQ Tissue & Fascia, Rt Upr Leg, [Opn, Perc], No Dev, [Skin and SQ Tissue, Skin, SQ Tissue & Fascia]
0JXM[0,3]Z[B,C]	Transfer/SQ Tissue & Fascia, Lt Upr Leg, [Opn, Perc], No Dev, [Skin and SQ Tissue, Skin, SQ Tissue & Fascia]
0JXN[0,3]Z[B,C]	Transfer/SQ Tissue & Fascia, Rt Lwr Leg, [Opn, Perc], No Dev, [Skin and SQ Tissue, Skin, SQ Tissue & Fascia]
0JXP[0,3]Z[B,C]	Transfer/SQ Tissue & Fascia, Lt Lwr Leg, [Opn, Perc], No Dev, [Skin and SQ Tissue, Skin, SQ Tissue & Fascia]
0JXQ[0,3]Z[B,C]	Transfer/SQ Tissue & Fascia, Rt Foot, [Opn, Perc], No Dev, [Skin and SQ Tissue, Skin, SQ Tissue & Fascia]
0JXR[0,3]Z[B,C]	Transfer/SQ Tissue & Fascia, Lt Foot, [Opn, Perc], No Dev, [Skin and SQ Tissue, Skin, SQ Tissue & Fascia]

DRG 905 **Skin Grafts for Injuries without CC/MCC**

GMLOS 3.6	AMLOS 4.7	RW 1.4233

Select operating room procedures listed under DRG 904

DRG 906 **Hand Procedures for Injuries**

GMLOS 2.8	AMLOS 4.4	RW 1.5670

Operating Room Procedures

Code	Description
01N5[0,3,4]ZZ	Rls/Median Nerve, [Opn, Perc, Perc Endo]
0HRFX7[3,4]	Replace/Skin, Rt Hand, Ext, Auto Tissue Sub, [Full Thickness, Partial Thickness]
0HRGX7[3,4]	Replace/Skin, Lt Hand, Ext, Auto Tissue Sub, [Full Thickness, Partial Thickness]
0J8J[0,3]ZZ	Div/SQ Tissue & Fascia, Rt Hand, [Opn, Perc]
0J8K[0,3]ZZ	Div/SQ Tissue & Fascia, Lt Hand, [Opn, Perc]
0J9J[0,3][0,Z]Z	Drain/SQ Tissue & Fascia, Rt Hand, [Opn, Perc], [Drain Dev, No Dev], NQ
0J9K[0,3][0,Z]Z	Drain/SQ Tissue & Fascia, Lt Hand, [Opn, Perc], [Drain Dev, No Dev], NQ
0JBJ[0,3]ZZ	Exc/SQ Tissue & Fascia, Rt Hand, [Opn, Perc]
0JBK[0,3]ZZ	Exc/SQ Tissue & Fascia, Lt Hand, [Opn, Perc]
0JDJ[0,3]ZZ	Extract/SQ Tissue & Fascia, Rt Hand, [Opn, Perc]
0JDK[0,3]ZZ	Extract/SQ Tissue & Fascia, Lt Hand, [Opn, Perc]
0JNJ[0,3]ZZ	Rls/SQ Tissue & Fascia, Rt Hand, [Opn, Perc]
0JNK[0,3]ZZ	Rls/SQ Tissue & Fascia, Lt Hand, [Opn, Perc]
0JQJ[0,3]ZZ	Rpr/SQ Tissue & Fascia, Rt Hand, [Opn, Perc]
0JQK[0,3]ZZ	Rpr/SQ Tissue & Fascia, Lt Hand, [Opn, Perc]
0JRJ07Z	Replace of Rt Hand SQ/Fascia with Autol Sub, Opn Appr
0JRJ[0,3][J,K]Z	Replace/SQ Tissue & Fascia, Rt Hand, [Opn, Perc], [Synth Sub, Nonauto Tissue Sub], NQ
0JRK07Z	Replace of Lt Hand SQ/Fascia with Autol Sub, Opn Appr
0JRK[0,3][J,K]Z	Replace/SQ Tissue & Fascia, Lt Hand, [Opn, Perc], [Synth Sub, Nonauto Tissue Sub], NQ
0JUJ[0,3][7,J,K]Z	Supl/SQ Tissue & Fascia, Rt Hand, [Opn, Perc], [Auto Tissue Sub, Synth Sub, Nonauto Tissue Sub], NQ
0JUK[0,3][7,J,K]Z	Supl/SQ Tissue & Fascia, Lt Hand, [Opn, Perc], [Auto Tissue Sub, Synth Sub, Nonauto Tissue Sub], NQ
0JXJ[0,3]Z[B,C]	Transfer/SQ Tissue & Fascia, Rt Hand, [Opn, Perc], No Dev, [Skin and SQ Tissue, Skin, SQ Tissue & Fascia]
0JXK[0,3]Z[B,C]	Transfer/SQ Tissue & Fascia, Lt Hand, [Opn, Perc], No Dev, [Skin and SQ Tissue, Skin, SQ Tissue & Fascia]
0K5C[0,3,4]ZZ	Destr/Hand Muscle, Rt, [Opn, Perc, Perc Endo]
0K5D[0,3,4]ZZ	Destr/Hand Muscle, Lt, [Opn, Perc, Perc Endo]
0K8C[0,3,4]ZZ	Div/Hand Muscle, Rt, [Opn, Perc, Perc Endo]
0K8D[0,3,4]ZZ	Div/Hand Muscle, Lt, [Opn, Perc, Perc Endo]
0K9C0ZZ	Drain of Rt Hand Muscle, Opn Appr
0K9C[0,3,4]0Z	Drain/Hand Muscle, Rt, [Opn, Perc, Perc Endo], Drain Dev, NQ
0K9D0ZZ	Drain of Lt Hand Muscle, Opn Appr
0K9D[0,3,4]0Z	Drain/Hand Muscle, Lt, [Opn, Perc, Perc Endo], Drain Dev, NQ
0KBC[0,3,4]ZZ	Exc/Hand Muscle, Rt, [Opn, Perc, Perc Endo]
0KBD[0,3,4]ZZ	Exc/Hand Muscle, Lt, [Opn, Perc, Perc Endo]
0KCC[0,3,4]ZZ	Extir/Hand Muscle, Rt, [Opn, Perc, Perc Endo]
0KCD[0,3,4]ZZ	Extir/Hand Muscle, Lt, [Opn, Perc, Perc Endo]
0KMC[0,4]ZZ	Reattach/Hand Muscle, Rt, [Opn, Perc Endo]
0KMD[0,4]ZZ	Reattach/Hand Muscle, Lt, [Opn, Perc Endo]
0KNC[0,3,4]ZZ	Rls/Hand Muscle, Rt, [Opn, Perc, Perc Endo]
0KND[0,3,4]ZZ	Rls/Hand Muscle, Lt, [Opn, Perc, Perc Endo]
0KQC[0,3,4]ZZ	Rpr/Hand Muscle, Rt, [Opn, Perc, Perc Endo]
0KQD[0,3,4]ZZ	Rpr/Hand Muscle, Lt, [Opn, Perc, Perc Endo]
0KSC[0,4]ZZ	Repos/Hand Muscle, Rt, [Opn, Perc Endo]
0KSD[0,4]ZZ	Repos/Hand Muscle, Lt, [Opn, Perc Endo]
0KTC[0,4]ZZ	Resect/Hand Muscle, Rt, [Opn, Perc Endo]
0KTD[0,4]ZZ	Resect/Hand Muscle, Lt, [Opn, Perc Endo]
0KUC[0,4][7,J,K]Z	Supl/Hand Muscle, Rt, [Opn, Perc Endo], [Auto Tissue Sub, Synth Sub, Nonauto Tissue Sub], NQ
0KUD[0,4][7,J,K]Z	Supl/Hand Muscle, Lt, [Opn, Perc Endo], [Auto Tissue Sub, Synth Sub, Nonauto Tissue Sub], NQ
0KXC[0,4]Z[0,1,2,Z]	Transfer/Hand Muscle, Rt, [Opn, Perc Endo], No Dev, [Skin, SQ Tissue, Skin and SQ Tissue, NQ]
0KXD[0,4]Z[0,1,2,Z]	Transfer/Hand Muscle, Lt, [Opn, Perc Endo], No Dev, [Skin, SQ Tissue, Skin and SQ Tissue, NQ]
0L57[0,3,4]ZZ	Destr/Hand Tndn, Rt, [Opn, Perc, Perc Endo]
0L58[0,3,4]ZZ	Destr/Hand Tndn, Lt, [Opn, Perc, Perc Endo]
0L87[0,3,4]ZZ	Div/Hand Tndn, Rt, [Opn, Perc, Perc Endo]
0L88[0,3,4]ZZ	Div/Hand Tndn, Lt, [Opn, Perc, Perc Endo]
0L970ZZ	Drain of Rt Hand Tndn, Opn Appr
0L97[0,3,4]0Z	Drain/Hand Tndn, Rt, [Opn, Perc, Perc Endo], Drain Dev, NQ
0L980ZZ	Drain of Lt Hand Tndn, Opn Appr
0L98[0,3,4]0Z	Drain/Hand Tndn, Lt, [Opn, Perc, Perc Endo], Drain Dev, NQ

T Transfer DRG   SP Special Payment   * Code Range   6th and 7th Character of ZZ = No Device, No Qualifier ZX = No Device, Diagnostic

Code	Description
0LB7[0,3,4]ZZ	Exc/Hand Tndn, Rt, [Opn, Perc, Perc Endo]
0LB8[0,3,4]ZZ	Exc/Hand Tndn, Lt, [Opn, Perc, Perc Endo]
0LC7[0,3,4]ZZ	Extir/Hand Tndn, Rt, [Opn, Perc, Perc Endo]
0LC8[0,3,4]ZZ	Extir/Hand Tndn, Lt, [Opn, Perc, Perc Endo]
0LJX[0,3,4]ZZ	Inspect/Upr Tndn, [Opn, Perc, Perc Endo]
0LM7[0,4]ZZ	Reattach/Hand Tndn, Rt, [Opn, Perc Endo]
0LM8[0,4]ZZ	Reattach/Hand Tndn, Lt, [Opn, Perc Endo]
0LN7[0,4]ZZ	Rls/Hand Tndn, Rt, [Opn, Perc Endo]
0LN8[0,4]ZZ	Rls/Hand Tndn, Lt, [Opn, Perc Endo]
0LQ7[0,3,4]ZZ	Rpr/Hand Tndn, Rt, [Opn, Perc, Perc Endo]
0LQ8[0,3,4]ZZ	Rpr/Hand Tndn, Lt, [Opn, Perc, Perc Endo]
0LR7[0,4][7,J,K]Z	Replace/Hand Tndn, Rt, [Opn, Perc Endo], [Auto Tissue Sub, Synth Sub, Nonauto Tissue Sub], NQ
0LR8[0,4][7,J,K]Z	Replace/Hand Tndn, Lt, [Opn, Perc Endo], [Auto Tissue Sub, Synth Sub, Nonauto Tissue Sub], NQ
0LS7[0,4]ZZ	Repos/Hand Tndn, Rt, [Opn, Perc Endo]
0LS8[0,4]ZZ	Repos/Hand Tndn, Lt, [Opn, Perc Endo]
0LT7[0,4]ZZ	Resect/Hand Tndn, Rt, [Opn, Perc Endo]
0LT8[0,4]ZZ	Resect/Hand Tndn, Lt, [Opn, Perc Endo]
0LU7[0,4][7,J,K]Z	Supl/Hand Tndn, Rt, [Opn, Perc Endo], [Auto Tissue Sub, Synth Sub, Nonauto Tissue Sub], NQ
0LU8[0,4][7,J,K]Z	Supl/Hand Tndn, Lt, [Opn, Perc Endo], [Auto Tissue Sub, Synth Sub, Nonauto Tissue Sub], NQ
0LX7[0,4]ZZ	Transfer/Hand Tndn, Rt, [Opn, Perc Endo]
0LX8[0,4]ZZ	Transfer/Hand Tndn, Lt, [Opn, Perc Endo]
0M55[0,3,4]ZZ	Destr/Wrist Bursa & Lgmt, Rt, [Opn, Perc, Perc Endo]
0M56[0,3,4]ZZ	Destr/Wrist Bursa & Lgmt, Lt, [Opn, Perc, Perc Endo]
0M57[0,3,4]ZZ	Destr/Hand Bursa & Lgmt, Rt, [Opn, Perc, Perc Endo]
0M58[0,3,4]ZZ	Destr/Hand Bursa & Lgmt, Lt, [Opn, Perc, Perc Endo]
0M87[0,3,4]ZZ	Div/Hand Bursa & Lgmt, Rt, [Opn, Perc, Perc Endo]
0M88[0,3,4]ZZ	Div/Hand Bursa & Lgmt, Lt, [Opn, Perc, Perc Endo]
0M950ZZ	Drain of Rt Wrist Bursa & Lgmt, Opn Appr
0M95[0,3,4]0Z	Drain/Wrist Bursa & Lgmt, Rt, [Opn, Perc, Perc Endo], Drain Dev, NQ
0M960ZZ	Drain of Lt Wrist Bursa & Lgmt, Opn Appr
0M96[0,3,4]0Z	Drain/Wrist Bursa & Lgmt, Lt, [Opn, Perc, Perc Endo], Drain Dev, NQ
0M97[0,Z]Z	Drain/Hand Bursa & Lgmt, Rt, Opn, [Drain Dev, No Dev], NQ
0M98[0,Z]Z	Drain/Hand Bursa & Lgmt, Lt, Opn, [Drain Dev, No Dev], NQ
0MB7[0,3,4]ZZ	Exc/Hand Bursa & Lgmt, Rt, [Opn, Perc, Perc Endo]
0MB8[0,3,4]ZZ	Exc/Hand Bursa & Lgmt, Lt, [Opn, Perc, Perc Endo]
0MC5[0,3,4]ZZ	Extir/Wrist Bursa & Lgmt, Rt, [Opn, Perc, Perc Endo]
0MC6[0,3,4]ZZ	Extir/Wrist Bursa & Lgmt, Lt, [Opn, Perc, Perc Endo]
0MC7[0,3,4]ZZ	Extir/Hand Bursa & Lgmt, Rt, [Opn, Perc, Perc Endo]
0MC8[0,3,4]ZZ	Extir/Hand Bursa & Lgmt, Lt, [Opn, Perc, Perc Endo]
0MD7[0,3,4]ZZ	Extract/Hand Bursa & Lgmt, Rt, [Opn, Perc, Perc Endo]
0MD8[0,3,4]ZZ	Extract/Hand Bursa & Lgmt, Lt, [Opn, Perc, Perc Endo]
0MN7[0,3,4,X]ZZ	Rls/Hand Bursa & Lgmt, Rt, [Opn, Perc, Perc Endo, Ext]
0MN8[0,3,4,X]ZZ	Rls/Hand Bursa & Lgmt, Lt, [Opn, Perc, Perc Endo, Ext]
0MT7[0,4]ZZ	Resect/Hand Bursa & Lgmt, Rt, [Opn, Perc Endo]
0MT8[0,4]ZZ	Resect/Hand Bursa & Lgmt, Lt, [Opn, Perc Endo]
0P5M[0,3,4]ZZ	Destr/Carpal, Rt, [Opn, Perc, Perc Endo]
0P5N[0,3,4]ZZ	Destr/Carpal, Lt, [Opn, Perc, Perc Endo]
0P5P[0,3,4]ZZ	Destr/Metacarpal, Rt, [Opn, Perc, Perc Endo]
0P5Q[0,3,4]ZZ	Destr/Metacarpal, Lt, [Opn, Perc, Perc Endo]
0P8M[0,3,4]ZZ	Div/Carpal, Rt, [Opn, Perc, Perc Endo]
0P8N[0,3,4]ZZ	Div/Carpal, Lt, [Opn, Perc, Perc Endo]
0P8P[0,3,4]ZZ	Div/Metacarpal, Rt, [Opn, Perc, Perc Endo]
0P8Q[0,3,4]ZZ	Div/Metacarpal, Lt, [Opn, Perc, Perc Endo]
0P9M[0,3,4]ZX	Drain/Carpal, Rt, [Opn, Perc, Perc Endo]
0P9N[0,3,4]ZX	Drain/Carpal, Lt, [Opn, Perc, Perc Endo]
0P9P[0,3,4]ZX	Drain/Metacarpal, Rt, [Opn, Perc, Perc Endo]
0P9Q[0,3,4]ZX	Drain/Metacarpal, Lt, [Opn, Perc, Perc Endo]
0PBM[0,3,4]Z[X,Z]	Exc/Carpal, Rt, [Opn, Perc, Perc Endo], No Dev, [Dx, NQ]
0PBN[0,3,4]Z[X,Z]	Exc/Carpal, Lt, [Opn, Perc, Perc Endo], No Dev, [Dx, NQ]
0PBP[0,3,4]Z[X,Z]	Exc/Metacarpal, Rt, [Opn, Perc, Perc Endo], No Dev, [Dx, NQ]
0PBQ[0,3,4]Z[X,Z]	Exc/Metacarpal, Lt, [Opn, Perc, Perc Endo], No Dev, [Dx, NQ]
0PCM[0,3,4]ZZ	Extir/Carpal, Rt, [Opn, Perc, Perc Endo]
0PCN[0,3,4]ZZ	Extir/Carpal, Lt, [Opn, Perc, Perc Endo]
0PCP[0,3,4]ZZ	Extir/Metacarpal, Rt, [Opn, Perc, Perc Endo]
0PCQ[0,3,4]ZZ	Extir/Metacarpal, Lt, [Opn, Perc, Perc Endo]
0PHM[0,3,4][4,5]Z	Insert/Carpal, Rt, [Opn, Perc, Perc Endo], [Int Fix Dev, Ext Fix Dev], NQ
0PHN[0,3,4][4,5]Z	Insert/Carpal, Lt, [Opn, Perc, Perc Endo], [Int Fix Dev, Ext Fix Dev], NQ
0PHP[0,3,4][4,5]Z	Insert/Metacarpal, Rt, [Opn, Perc, Perc Endo], [Int Fix Dev, Ext Fix Dev], NQ
0PHQ[0,3,4][4,5]Z	Insert/Metacarpal, Lt, [Opn, Perc, Perc Endo], [Int Fix Dev, Ext Fix Dev], NQ
0PNM[0,3,4]ZZ	Rls/Carpal, Rt, [Opn, Perc, Perc Endo]
0PNN[0,3,4]ZZ	Rls/Carpal, Lt, [Opn, Perc, Perc Endo]
0PNP[0,3,4]ZZ	Rls/Metacarpal, Rt, [Opn, Perc, Perc Endo]
0PNQ[0,3,4]ZZ	Rls/Metacarpal, Lt, [Opn, Perc, Perc Endo]
0PPM[0,3,4][4,5,7,J,K]Z	Rmvl/Carpal, Rt, [Opn, Perc, Perc Endo], [Int Fix Dev, Ext Fix Dev, Auto Tissue Sub, Synth Sub, Nonauto Tissue Sub], NQ
0PPN[0,3,4][4,5,7,J,K]Z	Rmvl/Carpal, Lt, [Opn, Perc, Perc Endo], [Int Fix Dev, Ext Fix Dev, Auto Tissue Sub, Synth Sub, Nonauto Tissue Sub], NQ
0PPP[0,3,4][4,5,7,J,K]Z	Rmvl/Metacarpal, Rt, [Opn, Perc, Perc Endo], [Int Fix Dev, Ext Fix Dev, Auto Tissue Sub, Synth Sub, Nonauto Tissue Sub], NQ
0PPQ[0,3,4][4,5,7,J,K]Z	Rmvl/Metacarpal, Lt, [Opn, Perc, Perc Endo], [Int Fix Dev, Ext Fix Dev, Auto Tissue Sub, Synth Sub, Nonauto Tissue Sub], NQ
0PQM[0,3,4,X]ZZ	Rpr/Carpal, Rt, [Opn, Perc, Perc Endo, Ext]
0PQN[0,3,4,X]ZZ	Rpr/Carpal, Lt, [Opn, Perc, Perc Endo, Ext]
0PQP[0,3,4,X]ZZ	Rpr/Metacarpal, Rt, [Opn, Perc, Perc Endo, Ext]
0PQQ[0,3,4,X]ZZ	Rpr/Metacarpal, Lt, [Opn, Perc, Perc Endo, Ext]
0PRM[0,3,4][7,J,K]Z	Replace/Carpal, Rt, [Opn, Perc, Perc Endo], [Auto Tissue Sub, Synth Sub, Nonauto Tissue Sub], NQ
0PRN[0,3,4][7,J,K]Z	Replace/Carpal, Lt, [Opn, Perc, Perc Endo], [Auto Tissue Sub, Synth Sub, Nonauto Tissue Sub], NQ
0PRP[0,3,4][7,J,K]Z	Replace/Metacarpal, Rt, [Opn, Perc, Perc Endo], [Auto Tissue Sub, Synth Sub, Nonauto Tissue Sub], NQ
0PRQ[0,3,4][7,J,K]Z	Replace/Metacarpal, Lt, [Opn, Perc, Perc Endo], [Auto Tissue Sub, Synth Sub, Nonauto Tissue Sub], NQ
0PSM0ZZ	Repos Rt Carpal, Opn Appr
0PSM[0,3,4][4,5]Z	Repos/Carpal, Rt, [Opn, Perc, Perc Endo], [Int Fix Dev, Ext Fix Dev], NQ
0PSN0ZZ	Repos Lt Carpal, Opn Appr
0PSN[0,3,4][4,5]Z	Repos/Carpal, Lt, [Opn, Perc, Perc Endo], [Int Fix Dev, Ext Fix Dev], NQ
0PSP0ZZ	Repos Rt Metacarpal, Opn Appr
0PSP[0,3,4][4,5]Z	Repos/Metacarpal, Rt, [Opn, Perc, Perc Endo], [Int Fix Dev, Ext Fix Dev], NQ
0PSQ0ZZ	Repos Lt Metacarpal, Opn Appr
0PSQ[0,3,4][4,5]Z	Repos/Metacarpal, Lt, [Opn, Perc, Perc Endo], [Int Fix Dev, Ext Fix Dev], NQ
0PSR0ZZ	Repos Rt Thumb Phalanx, Opn Appr
0PSR[0,3,4]4Z	Repos/Thumb Phalanx, Rt, [Opn, Perc, Perc Endo], Int Fix Dev, NQ
0PSS0ZZ	Repos Lt Thumb Phalanx, Opn Appr
0PSS[0,3,4]4Z	Repos/Thumb Phalanx, Lt, [Opn, Perc, Perc Endo], Int Fix Dev, NQ
0PST0ZZ	Repos Rt Finger Phalanx, Opn Appr
0PST[0,3,4]4Z	Repos/Finger Phalanx, Rt, [Opn, Perc, Perc Endo], Int Fix Dev, NQ
0PSV0ZZ	Repos Lt Finger Phalanx, Opn Appr
0PSV[0,3,4]4Z	Repos/Finger Phalanx, Lt, [Opn, Perc, Perc Endo], Int Fix Dev, NQ
0PTM0ZZ	Resect of Rt Carpal, Opn Appr
0PTN0ZZ	Resect of Lt Carpal, Opn Appr
0PTP0ZZ	Resect of Rt Metacarpal, Opn Appr
0PTQ0ZZ	Resect of Lt Metacarpal, Opn Appr
0PUM[0,3,4][7,J,K]Z	Supl/Carpal, Rt, [Opn, Perc, Perc Endo], [Auto Tissue Sub, Synth Sub, Nonauto Tissue Sub], NQ
0PUN[0,3,4][7,J,K]Z	Supl/Carpal, Lt, [Opn, Perc, Perc Endo], [Auto Tissue Sub, Synth Sub, Nonauto Tissue Sub], NQ
0PUP[0,3,4][7,J,K]Z	Supl/Metacarpal, Rt, [Opn, Perc, Perc Endo], [Auto Tissue Sub, Synth Sub, Nonauto Tissue Sub], NQ
0PUQ[0,3,4][7,J,K]Z	Supl/Metacarpal, Lt, [Opn, Perc, Perc Endo], [Auto Tissue Sub, Synth Sub, Nonauto Tissue Sub], NQ
0R5N[0,3,4]ZZ	Destr/Wrist Jt, Rt, [Opn, Perc, Perc Endo]
0R5P[0,3,4]ZZ	Destr/Wrist Jt, Lt, [Opn, Perc, Perc Endo]
0R5Q[0,3,4]ZZ	Destr/Carpal Jt, Rt, [Opn, Perc, Perc Endo]
0R5R[0,3,4]ZZ	Destr/Carpal Jt, Lt, [Opn, Perc, Perc Endo]
0R5S[0,3,4]ZZ	Destr/Metacarpocarpal Jt, Rt, [Opn, Perc, Perc Endo]
0R5T[0,3,4]ZZ	Destr/Metacarpocarpal Jt, Lt, [Opn, Perc, Perc Endo]
0R5U[0,3,4]ZZ	Destr/Metacarpophalangeal Jt, Rt, [Opn, Perc, Perc Endo]
0R5V[0,3,4]ZZ	Destr/Metacarpophalangeal Jt, Lt, [Opn, Perc, Perc Endo]
0R5W[0,3,4]ZZ	Destr/Finger Phalangeal Jt, Rt, [Opn, Perc, Perc Endo]
0R5X[0,3,4]ZZ	Destr/Finger Phalangeal Jt, Lt, [Opn, Perc, Perc Endo]
0R9N0[0,Z]Z	Drain/Wrist Jt, Rt, Opn, [Drain Dev, No Dev], NQ
0R9P0[0,Z]Z	Drain/Wrist Jt, Lt, Opn, [Drain Dev, No Dev], NQ
0R9Q0[0,Z]Z	Drain/Carpal Jt, Rt, Opn, [Drain Dev, No Dev], NQ
0R9R0[0,Z]Z	Drain/Carpal Jt, Lt, Opn, [Drain Dev, No Dev], NQ
0R9S0[0,Z]Z	Drain/Metacarpocarpal Jt, Rt, Opn, [Drain Dev, No Dev], NQ
0R9T0[0,Z]Z	Drain/Metacarpocarpal Jt, Lt, Opn, [Drain Dev, No Dev], NQ
0R9U0[0,Z]Z	Drain/Metacarpophalangeal Jt, Rt, Opn, [Drain Dev, No Dev], NQ

Surgical   **Medical**   **CC Indicator**   **MCC Indicator**   **Procedure Proxy**   PDxMCC **PDx acts as own MCC**   PDxCC **PDx acts as own CC**

© 2015 Optum360, LLC   MS-DRG Version 33.0   **315**

ØR9VØ[Ø,Z]Z	Drain/Metacarpophalangeal Jt, Lt, Opn, [Drain Dev, No Dev], NQ
ØR9WØ[Ø,Z]Z	Drain/Finger Phalangeal Jt, Rt, Opn, [Drain Dev, No Dev], NQ
ØR9XØ[Ø,Z]Z	Drain/Finger Phalangeal Jt, Lt, Opn, [Drain Dev, No Dev], NQ
ØRBN[Ø,3,4]ZZ	Exc/Wrist Jt, Rt, [Opn, Perc, Perc Endo]
ØRBP[Ø,3,4]ZZ	Exc/Wrist Jt, Lt, [Opn, Perc, Perc Endo]
ØRBQ[Ø,3,4]ZZ	Exc/Carpal Jt, Rt, [Opn, Perc, Perc Endo]
ØRBR[Ø,3,4]ZZ	Exc/Carpal Jt, Lt, [Opn, Perc, Perc Endo]
ØRBS[Ø,3,4]ZZ	Exc/Metacarpocarpal Jt, Rt, [Opn, Perc, Perc Endo]
ØRBT[Ø,3,4]ZZ	Exc/Metacarpocarpal Jt, Lt, [Opn, Perc, Perc Endo]
ØRBU[Ø,3,4]ZZ	Exc/Metacarpophalangeal Jt, Rt, [Opn, Perc, Perc Endo]
ØRBV[Ø,3,4]ZZ	Exc/Metacarpophalangeal Jt, Lt, [Opn, Perc, Perc Endo]
ØRBW[Ø,3,4]ZZ	Exc/Finger Phalangeal Jt, Rt, [Opn, Perc, Perc Endo]
ØRBX[Ø,3,4]ZZ	Exc/Finger Phalangeal Jt, Lt, [Opn, Perc, Perc Endo]
ØRCN[Ø,3,4]ZZ	Extir/Wrist Jt, Rt, [Opn, Perc, Perc Endo]
ØRCP[Ø,3,4]ZZ	Extir/Wrist Jt, Lt, [Opn, Perc, Perc Endo]
ØRCQ[Ø,3,4]ZZ	Extir/Carpal Jt, Rt, [Opn, Perc, Perc Endo]
ØRCR[Ø,3,4]ZZ	Extir/Carpal Jt, Lt, [Opn, Perc, Perc Endo]
ØRCS[Ø,3,4]ZZ	Extir/Metacarpocarpal Jt, Rt, [Opn, Perc, Perc Endo]
ØRCT[Ø,3,4]ZZ	Extir/Metacarpocarpal Jt, Lt, [Opn, Perc, Perc Endo]
ØRCU[Ø,3,4]ZZ	Extir/Metacarpophalangeal Jt, Rt, [Opn, Perc, Perc Endo]
ØRCV[Ø,3,4]ZZ	Extir/Metacarpophalangeal Jt, Lt, [Opn, Perc, Perc Endo]
ØRCW[Ø,3,4]ZZ	Extir/Finger Phalangeal Jt, Rt, [Opn, Perc, Perc Endo]
ØRCX[Ø,3,4]ZZ	Extir/Finger Phalangeal Jt, Lt, [Opn, Perc, Perc Endo]
Ørgn[Ø,3,4][4,5,7,J,K,Z]Z	Fusion/Wrist Jt, Rt, [Opn, Perc, Perc Endo], [Int Fix Dev, Ext Fix Dev, Auto Tissue Sub, Synth Sub, Nonauto Tissue Sub, No Dev], NQ
ØRGP[Ø,3,4][4,5,7,J,K,Z]Z	Fusion/Wrist Jt, Lt, [Opn, Perc, Perc Endo], [Int Fix Dev, Ext Fix Dev, Auto Tissue Sub, Synth Sub, Nonauto Tissue Sub, No Dev], NQ
ØRGQ[Ø,3,4][4,5,7,J,K,Z]Z	Fusion/Carpal Jt, Rt, [Opn, Perc, Perc Endo], [Int Fix Dev, Ext Fix Dev, Auto Tissue Sub, Synth Sub, Nonauto Tissue Sub, No Dev], NQ
ØRGR[Ø,3,4][4,5,7,J,K,Z]Z	Fusion/Carpal Jt, Lt, [Opn, Perc, Perc Endo], [Int Fix Dev, Ext Fix Dev, Auto Tissue Sub, Synth Sub, Nonauto Tissue Sub, No Dev], NQ
ØRGS[Ø,3,4][4,5,7,J,K,Z]Z	Fusion/Metacarpocarpal Jt, Rt, [Opn, Perc, Perc Endo], [Int Fix Dev, Ext Fix Dev, Auto Tissue Sub, Synth Sub, Nonauto Tissue Sub, No Dev], NQ
ØRGT[Ø,3,4][4,5,7,J,K,Z]Z	Fusion/Metacarpocarpal Jt, Lt, [Opn, Perc, Perc Endo], [Int Fix Dev, Ext Fix Dev, Auto Tissue Sub, Synth Sub, Nonauto Tissue Sub, No Dev], NQ
ØRGU[Ø,3,4][4,5,7,J,K,Z]Z	Fusion/Metacarpophalangeal Jt, Rt, [Opn, Perc, Perc Endo], [Int Fix Dev, Ext Fix Dev, Auto Tissue Sub, Synth Sub, Nonauto Tissue Sub, No Dev], NQ
ØRGV[Ø,3,4][4,5,7,J,K,Z]Z	Fusion/Metacarpophalangeal Jt, Lt, [Opn, Perc, Perc Endo], [Int Fix Dev, Ext Fix Dev, Auto Tissue Sub, Synth Sub, Nonauto Tissue Sub, No Dev], NQ
ØRGW[Ø,3,4][4,5,7,J,K,Z]Z	Fusion/Finger Phalangeal Jt, Rt, [Opn, Perc, Perc Endo], [Int Fix Dev, Ext Fix Dev, Auto Tissue Sub, Synth Sub, Nonauto Tissue Sub, No Dev], NQ
ØRGX[Ø,3,4][4,5,7,J,K,Z]Z	Fusion/Finger Phalangeal Jt, Lt, [Opn, Perc, Perc Endo], [Int Fix Dev, Ext Fix Dev, Auto Tissue Sub, Synth Sub, Nonauto Tissue Sub, No Dev], NQ
ØRHN[Ø,3,4][4,5]Z	Insert/Wrist Jt, Rt, [Opn, Perc, Perc Endo], [Int Fix Dev, Ext Fix Dev], NQ
ØRHP[Ø,3,4][4,5]Z	Insert/Wrist Jt, Lt, [Opn, Perc, Perc Endo], [Int Fix Dev, Ext Fix Dev], NQ
ØRHQ[Ø,3,4][4,5]Z	Insert/Carpal Jt, Rt, [Opn, Perc, Perc Endo], [Int Fix Dev, Ext Fix Dev], NQ
ØRHR[Ø,3,4][4,5]Z	Insert/Carpal Jt, Lt, [Opn, Perc, Perc Endo], [Int Fix Dev, Ext Fix Dev], NQ
ØRHS[Ø,3,4][4,5]Z	Insert/Metacarpocarpal Jt, Rt, [Opn, Perc, Perc Endo], [Int Fix Dev, Ext Fix Dev], NQ
ØRHT[Ø,3,4][4,5]Z	Insert/Metacarpocarpal Jt, Lt, [Opn, Perc, Perc Endo], [Int Fix Dev, Ext Fix Dev], NQ
ØRHU[Ø,3,4][4,5]Z	Insert/Metacarpophalangeal Jt, Rt, [Opn, Perc, Perc Endo], [Int Fix Dev, Ext Fix Dev], NQ
ØRHV[Ø,3,4][4,5]Z	Insert/Metacarpophalangeal Jt, Lt, [Opn, Perc, Perc Endo], [Int Fix Dev, Ext Fix Dev], NQ
ØRHW[Ø,3,4][4,5]Z	Insert/Finger Phalangeal Jt, Rt, [Opn, Perc, Perc Endo], [Int Fix Dev, Ext Fix Dev], NQ
ØRHX[Ø,3,4][4,5]Z	Insert/Finger Phalangeal Jt, Lt, [Opn, Perc, Perc Endo], [Int Fix Dev, Ext Fix Dev], NQ
ØRJNØZZ	Inspect of Rt Wrist Jt, Opn Appr
ØRJPØZZ	Inspect of Lt Wrist Jt, Opn Appr
ØRJQØZZ	Inspect of Rt Carpal Jt, Opn Appr
ØRJRØZZ	Inspect of Lt Carpal Jt, Opn Appr
ØRJSØZZ	Inspect of Rt Metacarpocarpal Jt, Opn Appr
ØRJTØZZ	Inspect of Lt Metacarpocarpal Jt, Opn Appr
ØRJUØZZ	Inspect of Rt Metacarpophalangeal Jt, Opn Appr
ØRJVØZZ	Inspect of Lt Metacarpophalangeal Jt, Opn Appr
ØRJWØZZ	Inspect of Rt Finger Phalangeal Jt, Opn Appr
ØRJXØZZ	Inspect of Lt Finger Phalangeal Jt, Opn Appr
ØRNN[Ø,3,4]ZZ	Rls/Wrist Jt, Rt, [Opn, Perc, Perc Endo]
ØRNP[Ø,3,4]ZZ	Rls/Wrist Jt, Lt, [Opn, Perc, Perc Endo]
ØRNQ[Ø,3,4]ZZ	Rls/Carpal Jt, Rt, [Opn, Perc, Perc Endo]
ØRNR[Ø,3,4]ZZ	Rls/Carpal Jt, Lt, [Opn, Perc, Perc Endo]
ØRNS[Ø,3,4]ZZ	Rls/Metacarpocarpal Jt, Rt, [Opn, Perc, Perc Endo]
ØRNT[Ø,3,4]ZZ	Rls/Metacarpocarpal Jt, Lt, [Opn, Perc, Perc Endo]
ØRNU[Ø,3,4]ZZ	Rls/Metacarpophalangeal Jt, Rt, [Opn, Perc, Perc Endo]
ØRNV[Ø,3,4]ZZ	Rls/Metacarpophalangeal Jt, Lt, [Opn, Perc, Perc Endo]
ØRNW[Ø,3,4]ZZ	Rls/Finger Phalangeal Jt, Rt, [Opn, Perc, Perc Endo]
ØRNX[Ø,3,4]ZZ	Rls/Finger Phalangeal Jt, Lt, [Opn, Perc, Perc Endo]
ØRPN[Ø,3,4][Ø,3,4,5,7,J,K]Z	Rmvl/Wrist Jt, Rt, [Opn, Perc, Perc Endo], [Drain Dev, Inf Dev, Int Fix Dev, Ext Fix Dev, Auto Tissue Sub, Synth Sub, Nonauto Tissue Sub], NQ
ØRPP[Ø,3,4][Ø,3,4,5,7,J,K]Z	Rmvl/Wrist Jt, Lt, [Opn, Perc, Perc Endo], [Drain Dev, Inf Dev, Int Fix Dev, Ext Fix Dev, Auto Tissue Sub, Synth Sub, Nonauto Tissue Sub], NQ
ØRPQ[Ø,3,4][Ø,3,4,5,7,J,K]Z	Rmvl/Carpal Jt, Rt, [Opn, Perc, Perc Endo], [Drain Dev, Inf Dev, Int Fix Dev, Ext Fix Dev, Auto Tissue Sub, Synth Sub, Nonauto Tissue Sub], NQ
ØRPR[Ø,3,4][Ø,3,4,5,7,J,K]Z	Rmvl/Carpal Jt, Lt, [Opn, Perc, Perc Endo], [Drain Dev, Inf Dev, Int Fix Dev, Ext Fix Dev, Auto Tissue Sub, Synth Sub, Nonauto Tissue Sub], NQ
ØRPS[Ø,3,4][Ø,3,4,5,7,J,K]Z	Rmvl/Metacarpocarpal Jt, Rt, [Opn, Perc, Perc Endo], [Drain Dev, Inf Dev, Int Fix Dev, Ext Fix Dev, Auto Tissue Sub, Synth Sub, Nonauto Tissue Sub], NQ
ØRPT[Ø,3,4][Ø,3,4,5,7,J,K]Z	Rmvl/Metacarpocarpal Jt, Lt, [Opn, Perc, Perc Endo], [Drain Dev, Inf Dev, Int Fix Dev, Ext Fix Dev, Auto Tissue Sub, Synth Sub, Nonauto Tissue Sub], NQ
ØRPU[Ø,3,4][Ø,3,4,5,7,J,K]Z	Rmvl/Metacarpophalangeal Jt, Rt, [Opn, Perc, Perc Endo], [Drain Dev, Inf Dev, Int Fix Dev, Ext Fix Dev, Auto Tissue Sub, Synth Sub, Nonauto Tissue Sub], NQ
ØRPV[Ø,3,4][Ø,3,4,5,7,J,K]Z	Rmvl/Metacarpophalangeal Jt, Lt, [Opn, Perc, Perc Endo], [Drain Dev, Inf Dev, Int Fix Dev, Ext Fix Dev, Auto Tissue Sub, Synth Sub, Nonauto Tissue Sub], NQ
ØRPW[Ø,3,4][Ø,3,4,5,7,J,K]Z	Rmvl/Finger Phalangeal Jt, Rt, [Opn, Perc, Perc Endo], [Drain Dev, Inf Dev, Int Fix Dev, Ext Fix Dev, Auto Tissue Sub, Synth Sub, Nonauto Tissue Sub], NQ
ØRPX[Ø,3,4][Ø,3,4,5,7,J,K]Z	Rmvl/Finger Phalangeal Jt, Lt, [Opn, Perc, Perc Endo], [Drain Dev, Inf Dev, Int Fix Dev, Ext Fix Dev, Auto Tissue Sub, Synth Sub, Nonauto Tissue Sub], NQ
ØRQN[Ø,3,4,X]ZZ	Rpr/Wrist Jt, Rt, [Opn, Perc, Perc Endo, Ext]
ØRQP[Ø,3,4,X]ZZ	Rpr/Wrist Jt, Lt, [Opn, Perc, Perc Endo, Ext]
ØRQQ[Ø,3,4,X]ZZ	Rpr/Carpal Jt, Rt, [Opn, Perc, Perc Endo, Ext]
ØRQR[Ø,3,4,X]ZZ	Rpr/Carpal Jt, Lt, [Opn, Perc, Perc Endo, Ext]
ØRQS[Ø,3,4,X]ZZ	Rpr/Metacarpocarpal Jt, Rt, [Opn, Perc, Perc Endo, Ext]
ØRQT[Ø,3,4,X]ZZ	Rpr/Metacarpocarpal Jt, Lt, [Opn, Perc, Perc Endo, Ext]
ØRQU[Ø,3,4,X]ZZ	Rpr/Metacarpophalangeal Jt, Rt, [Opn, Perc, Perc Endo, Ext]
ØRQV[Ø,3,4,X]ZZ	Rpr/Metacarpophalangeal Jt, Lt, [Opn, Perc, Perc Endo, Ext]
ØRQW[Ø,3,4,X]ZZ	Rpr/Finger Phalangeal Jt, Rt, [Opn, Perc, Perc Endo, Ext]
ØRQX[Ø,3,4,X]ZZ	Rpr/Finger Phalangeal Jt, Lt, [Opn, Perc, Perc Endo, Ext]
ØRRQØ[7,J,K]Z	Replace/Carpal Jt, Rt, Opn, [Auto Tissue Sub, Synth Sub, Nonauto Tissue Sub], NQ
ØRRRØ[7,J,K]Z	Replace/Carpal Jt, Lt, Opn, [Auto Tissue Sub, Synth Sub, Nonauto Tissue Sub], NQ
ØRRSØ[7,J,K]Z	Replace/Metacarpocarpal Jt, Rt, Opn, [Auto Tissue Sub, Synth Sub, Nonauto Tissue Sub], NQ
ØRRTØ[7,J,K]Z	Replace/Metacarpocarpal Jt, Lt, Opn, [Auto Tissue Sub, Synth Sub, Nonauto Tissue Sub], NQ
ØRRUØ[7,J,K]Z	Replace/Metacarpophalangeal Jt, Rt, Opn, [Auto Tissue Sub, Synth Sub, Nonauto Tissue Sub], NQ
ØRRVØ[7,J,K]Z	Replace/Metacarpophalangeal Jt, Lt, Opn, [Auto Tissue Sub, Synth Sub, Nonauto Tissue Sub], NQ
ØRRWØ[7,J,K]Z	Replace/Finger Phalangeal Jt, Rt, Opn, [Auto Tissue Sub, Synth Sub, Nonauto Tissue Sub], NQ
ØRRXØ[7,J,K]Z	Replace/Finger Phalangeal Jt, Lt, Opn, [Auto Tissue Sub, Synth Sub, Nonauto Tissue Sub], NQ
ØRSNØ[4,5,Z]Z	Repos/Wrist Jt, Rt, Opn, [Int Fix Dev, Ext Fix Dev, No Dev], NQ
ØRSPØ[4,5,Z]Z	Repos/Wrist Jt, Lt, Opn, [Int Fix Dev, Ext Fix Dev, No Dev], NQ
ØRSQØ[4,5,Z]Z	Repos/Carpal Jt, Rt, Opn, [Int Fix Dev, Ext Fix Dev, No Dev], NQ
ØRSRØ[4,5,Z]Z	Repos/Carpal Jt, Lt, Opn, [Int Fix Dev, Ext Fix Dev, No Dev], NQ
ØRSSØ[4,5,Z]Z	Repos/Metacarpocarpal Jt, Rt, Opn, [Int Fix Dev, Ext Fix Dev, No Dev], NQ
ØRSTØ[4,5,Z]Z	Repos/Metacarpocarpal Jt, Lt, Opn, [Int Fix Dev, Ext Fix Dev, No Dev], NQ
ØRSUØ[4,5,Z]Z	Repos/Metacarpophalangeal Jt, Rt, Opn, [Int Fix Dev, Ext Fix Dev, No Dev], NQ

T Transfer DRG   SP Special Payment   * Code Range   6th and 7th Character of ZZ = No Device, No Qualifier ZX = No Device, Diagnostic

316   MS-DRG Version 33.0   © 2015 Optum360, LLC

ØRSVØ[4,5,Z]Z	Repos/Metacarpophalangeal Jt, Lt, Opn, [Int Fix Dev, Ext Fix Dev, No Dev], NQ
ØRSWØ[4,5,Z]Z	Repos/Finger Phalangeal Jt, Rt, Opn, [Int Fix Dev, Ext Fix Dev, No Dev], NQ
ØRSXØ[4,5,Z]Z	Repos/Finger Phalangeal Jt, Lt, Opn, [Int Fix Dev, Ext Fix Dev, No Dev], NQ
ØRTNØZZ	Resect of Rt Wrist Jt, Opn Appr
ØRTPØZZ	Resect of Lt Wrist Jt, Opn Appr
ØRTQØZZ	Resect of Rt Carpal Jt, Opn Appr
ØRTRØZZ	Resect of Lt Carpal Jt, Opn Appr
ØRTSØZZ	Resect of Rt Metacarpocarpal Jt, Opn Appr
ØRTTØZZ	Resect of Lt Metacarpocarpal Jt, Opn Appr
ØRTUØZZ	Resect of Rt Metacarpophalangeal Jt, Opn Appr
ØRTVØZZ	Resect of Lt Metacarpophalangeal Jt, Opn Appr
ØRTWØZZ	Resect of Rt Finger Phalangeal Jt, Opn Appr
ØRTXØZZ	Resect of Lt Finger Phalangeal Jt, Opn Appr
ØRUN[Ø,3,4][7,J,K]Z	Supl/Wrist Jt, Rt, [Opn, Perc, Perc Endo], [Auto Tissue Sub, Synth Sub, Nonauto Tissue Sub], NQ
ØRUP[Ø,3,4][7,J,K]Z	Supl/Wrist Jt, Lt, [Opn, Perc, Perc Endo], [Auto Tissue Sub, Synth Sub, Nonauto Tissue Sub], NQ
ØRUQ[Ø,3,4][7,J,K]Z	Supl/Carpal Jt, Rt, [Opn, Perc, Perc Endo], [Auto Tissue Sub, Synth Sub, Nonauto Tissue Sub], NQ
ØRUR[Ø,3,4][7,J,K]Z	Supl/Carpal Jt, Lt, [Opn, Perc, Perc Endo], [Auto Tissue Sub, Synth Sub, Nonauto Tissue Sub], NQ
ØRUS[Ø,3,4][7,J,K]Z	Supl/Metacarpocarpal Jt, Rt, [Opn, Perc, Perc Endo], [Auto Tissue Sub, Synth Sub, Nonauto Tissue Sub], NQ
ØRUT[Ø,3,4][7,J,K]Z	Supl/Metacarpocarpal Jt, Lt, [Opn, Perc, Perc Endo], [Auto Tissue Sub, Synth Sub, Nonauto Tissue Sub], NQ
ØRUU[Ø,3,4][7,J,K]Z	Supl/Metacarpophalangeal Jt, Rt, [Opn, Perc, Perc Endo], [Auto Tissue Sub, Synth Sub, Nonauto Tissue Sub], NQ
ØRUV[Ø,3,4][7,J,K]Z	Supl/Metacarpophalangeal Jt, Lt, [Opn, Perc, Perc Endo], [Auto Tissue Sub, Synth Sub, Nonauto Tissue Sub], NQ
ØRUW[Ø,3,4][7,J,K]Z	Supl/Finger Phalangeal Jt, Rt, [Opn, Perc, Perc Endo], [Auto Tissue Sub, Synth Sub, Nonauto Tissue Sub], NQ
ØRUX[Ø,3,4][7,J,K]Z	Supl/Finger Phalangeal Jt, Lt, [Opn, Perc, Perc Endo], [Auto Tissue Sub, Synth Sub, Nonauto Tissue Sub], NQ
ØRWN[Ø,3,4][Ø,3,4,5,7,8,K]Z	Rev/Wrist Jt, Rt, [Opn, Perc, Perc Endo], [Drain Dev, Inf Dev, Int Fix Dev, Ext Fix Dev, Auto Tissue Sub, Spacer, Nonauto Tissue Sub], NQ
ØRWP[Ø,3,4][Ø,3,4,5,7,8,K]Z	Rev/Wrist Jt, Lt, [Opn, Perc, Perc Endo], [Drain Dev, Inf Dev, Int Fix Dev, Ext Fix Dev, Auto Tissue Sub, Spacer, Nonauto Tissue Sub], NQ
ØRWQ[Ø,3,4][Ø,3,4,5,7,8,K]Z	Rev/Carpal Jt, Rt, [Opn, Perc, Perc Endo], [Drain Dev, Inf Dev, Int Fix Dev, Ext Fix Dev, Auto Tissue Sub, Spacer, Nonauto Tissue Sub], NQ
ØRWR[Ø,3,4][Ø,3,4,5,7,8,K]Z	Rev/Carpal Jt, Lt, [Opn, Perc, Perc Endo], [Drain Dev, Inf Dev, Int Fix Dev, Ext Fix Dev, Auto Tissue Sub, Spacer, Nonauto Tissue Sub], NQ
ØRWS[Ø,3,4][Ø,3,4,5,7,8,K]Z	Rev/Metacarpocarpal Jt, Rt, [Opn, Perc, Perc Endo], [Drain Dev, Inf Dev, Int Fix Dev, Ext Fix Dev, Auto Tissue Sub, Spacer, Nonauto Tissue Sub], NQ
ØRWT[Ø,3,4][Ø,3,4,5,7,8,K]Z	Rev/Metacarpocarpal Jt, Lt, [Opn, Perc, Perc Endo], [Drain Dev, Inf Dev, Int Fix Dev, Ext Fix Dev, Auto Tissue Sub, Spacer, Nonauto Tissue Sub], NQ
ØRWU[Ø,3,4][Ø,3,4,5,7,8,K]Z	Rev/Metacarpophalangeal Jt, Rt, [Opn, Perc, Perc Endo], [Drain Dev, Inf Dev, Int Fix Dev, Ext Fix Dev, Auto Tissue Sub, Spacer, Nonauto Tissue Sub], NQ
ØRWV[Ø,3,4][Ø,3,4,5,7,8,K]Z	Rev/Metacarpophalangeal Jt, Lt, [Opn, Perc, Perc Endo], [Drain Dev, Inf Dev, Int Fix Dev, Ext Fix Dev, Auto Tissue Sub, Spacer, Nonauto Tissue Sub], NQ
ØRWW[Ø,3,4][Ø,3,4,5,7,8,K]Z	Rev/Finger Phalangeal Jt, Rt, [Opn, Perc, Perc Endo], [Drain Dev, Inf Dev, Int Fix Dev, Ext Fix Dev, Auto Tissue Sub, Spacer, Nonauto Tissue Sub], NQ
ØRWX[Ø,3,4][Ø,3,4,5,7,8,K]Z	Rev/Finger Phalangeal Jt, Lt, [Opn, Perc, Perc Endo], [Drain Dev, Inf Dev, Int Fix Dev, Ext Fix Dev, Auto Tissue Sub, Spacer, Nonauto Tissue Sub], NQ
ØX6LØZ[Ø,1,2,3]	Detach/Thumb, Rt, Opn, No Dev, [Complete, High, Mid, Low]
ØX6MØZ[Ø,1,2,3]	Detach/Thumb, Lt, Opn, No Dev, [Complete, High, Mid, Low]
ØX6NØZ[Ø,1,2,3]	Detach/Index Finger, Rt, Opn, No Dev, [Complete, High, Mid, Low]
ØX6PØZ[Ø,1,2,3]	Detach/Index Finger, Lt, Opn, No Dev, [Complete, High, Mid, Low]
ØX6QØZ[Ø,1,2,3]	Detach/Mid Finger, Rt, Opn, No Dev, [Complete, High, Mid, Low]
ØX6RØZ[Ø,1,2,3]	Detach/Mid Finger, Lt, Opn, No Dev, [Complete, High, Mid, Low]
ØX6SØZ[Ø,1,2,3]	Detach/Ring Finger, Rt, Opn, No Dev, [Complete, High, Mid, Low]
ØX6TØZ[Ø,1,2,3]	Detach/Ring Finger, Lt, Opn, No Dev, [Complete, High, Mid, Low]
ØX6VØZ[Ø,1,2,3]	Detach/Little Finger, Rt, Opn, No Dev, [Complete, High, Mid, Low]
ØX6WØZ[Ø,1,2,3]	Detach/Little Finger, Lt, Opn, No Dev, [Complete, High, Mid, Low]
ØXMLØZZ	Reattach of Rt Thumb, Opn Appr
ØXMMØZZ	Reattach of Lt Thumb, Opn Appr
ØXMNØZZ	Reattach of Rt Index Finger, Opn Appr
ØXMPØZZ	Reattach of Lt Index Finger, Opn Appr
ØXMQØZZ	Reattach of Rt Mid Finger, Opn Appr
ØXMRØZZ	Reattach of Lt Mid Finger, Opn Appr
ØXMSØZZ	Reattach of Rt Ring Finger, Opn Appr
ØXMTØZZ	Reattach of Lt Ring Finger, Opn Appr
ØXMVØZZ	Reattach of Rt Little Finger, Opn Appr
ØXMWØZZ	Reattach of Lt Little Finger, Opn Appr
ØXRL[Ø,4]7[N,P]	Replace/Thumb, Rt, [Opn, Perc Endo], Auto Tissue Sub, [Toe, Rt, Toe, Lt]
ØXRM[Ø,4]7[N,P]	Replace/Thumb, Lt, [Opn, Perc Endo], Auto Tissue Sub, [Toe, Rt, Toe, Lt]
ØXUJ[Ø,4]7Z	Supl/Hand, Rt, [Opn, Perc Endo], Auto Tissue Sub, NQ
ØXUK[Ø,4]7Z	Supl/Hand, Lt, [Opn, Perc Endo], Auto Tissue Sub, NQ
ØXUL[Ø,4]7Z	Supl/Thumb, Rt, [Opn, Perc Endo], Auto Tissue Sub, NQ
ØXUM[Ø,4]7Z	Supl/Thumb, Lt, [Opn, Perc Endo], Auto Tissue Sub, NQ
ØXUN[Ø,4]7Z	Supl/Index Finger, Rt, [Opn, Perc Endo], Auto Tissue Sub, NQ
ØXUP[Ø,4]7Z	Supl/Index Finger, Lt, [Opn, Perc Endo], Auto Tissue Sub, NQ
ØXUQ[Ø,4]7Z	Supl/Mid Finger, Rt, [Opn, Perc Endo], Auto Tissue Sub, NQ
ØXUR[Ø,4]7Z	Supl/Mid Finger, Lt, [Opn, Perc Endo], Auto Tissue Sub, NQ
ØXUS[Ø,4]7Z	Supl/Ring Finger, Rt, [Opn, Perc Endo], Auto Tissue Sub, NQ
ØXUT[Ø,4]7Z	Supl/Ring Finger, Lt, [Opn, Perc Endo], Auto Tissue Sub, NQ
ØXUV[Ø,4]7Z	Supl/Little Finger, Rt, [Opn, Perc Endo], Auto Tissue Sub, NQ
ØXUW[Ø,4]7Z	Supl/Little Finger, Lt, [Opn, Perc Endo], Auto Tissue Sub, NQ
ØXXNØZL	Transfer Rt Index Finger to Rt Thumb, Opn Appr
ØXXPØZM	Transfer Lt Index Finger to Lt Thumb, Opn Appr

DRG 907 **Other O.R. Procedures for Injuries with MCC**

GMLOS 7.5	AMLOS 10.3	RW 3.8073	[T]

Operating Room Procedures

ØØ16*	Bypass/Cerebral Ventricle
ØØ5Ø*	Destr/Brain
ØØ57*	Destr/Cerebral Hemisphere
ØØ59*	Destr/Thalamus
ØØ5A*	Destr/Hypothalamus
ØØ5B*	Destr/Pons
ØØ5C*	Destr/Cerebellum
ØØ5D*	Destr/Medulla Oblongata
ØØ8Ø*	Div/Brain
ØØ87*	Div/Cerebral Hemisphere
ØØ8F*	Div/Olfactory Nerve
ØØ8G*	Div/Optic Nerve
ØØ8H*	Div/Oculomotor Nerve
ØØ8J*	Div/Trochlear Nerve
ØØ8K*	Div/Trigeminal Nerve
ØØ8L*	Div/Abducens Nerve
ØØ8M*	Div/Facial Nerve
ØØ8N*	Div/Acoustic Nerve
ØØ8R*	Div/Accessory Nerve
ØØ8S*	Div/Hypoglossal Nerve
ØØ8W*	Div/Cervical Spinal Cord
ØØ8X*	Div/Thoracic Spinal Cord
ØØ8Y*	Div/Lumbar Spinal Cord
ØØ9Ø[Ø,3,4][Ø,Z]Z	Drain/Brain, [Opn, Perc, Perc Endo], [Drain Dev, No Dev], NQ
ØØ91Ø[Ø,Z]Z	Drain/Cerebral Meninges, Opn, [Drain Dev, No Dev], NQ
ØØ92Ø[Ø,Z]Z	Drain/Dura Mater, Opn, [Drain Dev, No Dev], NQ
ØØ93[Ø,3,4][Ø,Z]Z	Drain/Epidural Space, [Opn, Perc, Perc Endo], [Drain Dev, No Dev], NQ
ØØ94Ø[Ø,Z]Z	Drain/Subdural Space, Opn, [Drain Dev, No Dev], NQ
ØØ95Ø[Ø,Z]Z	Drain/Subarachnoid Space, Opn, [Drain Dev, No Dev], NQ
ØØ96ØZZ	Drain of Cerebral Ventricle, Opn Appr
ØØ96[Ø,3,4]ØZ	Drain/Cerebral Ventricle, [Opn, Perc, Perc Endo], Drain Dev, NQ
ØØ97[Ø,3,4][Ø,Z]Z	Drain/Cerebral Hemisphere, [Opn, Perc, Perc Endo], [Drain Dev, No Dev], NQ
ØØ99[Ø,3,4][Ø,Z]Z	Drain/Thalamus, [Opn, Perc, Perc Endo], [Drain Dev, No Dev], NQ
ØØ9A[Ø,3,4][Ø,Z]Z	Drain/Hypothalamus, [Opn, Perc, Perc Endo], [Drain Dev, No Dev], NQ
ØØ9B[Ø,3,4][Ø,Z]Z	Drain/Pons, [Opn, Perc, Perc Endo], [Drain Dev, No Dev], NQ
ØØ9C[Ø,3,4][Ø,Z]Z	Drain/Cerebellum, [Opn, Perc, Perc Endo], [Drain Dev, No Dev], NQ

MDC 21: Injuries, Poisonings And Toxic Effects Of Drugs—SURGICAL

Surgical	Medical	CC Indicator	MCC Indicator	Procedure Proxy	PDxMCC PDx acts as own MCC	PDxCC PDx acts as own CC

MDC 21: Injuries, Poisonings And Toxic Effects Of Drugs—SURGICAL

Code	Description
009D[0,3,4][0,Z]Z	Drain/Medulla Oblongata, [Opn, Perc, Perc Endo], [Drain Dev, No Dev], NQ
009F0ZX	Drain of Olfactory Nerve, Opn Appr, Diagnostic
009G0ZX	Drain of Optic Nerve, Opn Appr, Diagnostic
009H0ZX	Drain of Oculomotor Nerve, Opn Appr, Diagnostic
009J0ZX	Drain of Trochlear Nerve, Opn Appr, Diagnostic
009K0ZX	Drain of Trigeminal Nerve, Opn Appr, Diagnostic
009L0ZX	Drain of Abducens Nerve, Opn Appr, Diagnostic
009M0ZX	Drain of Facial Nerve, Opn Appr, Diagnostic
009N0ZX	Drain of Acoustic Nerve, Opn Appr, Diagnostic
009P0ZX	Drain of Glossopharyngeal Nerve, Opn Appr, Diagn
009Q0ZX	Drain of Vagus Nerve, Opn Appr, Diagnostic
009R0ZX	Drain of Accessory Nerve, Opn Appr, Diagnostic
009S0ZX	Drain of Hypoglossal Nerve, Opn Appr, Diagnostic
009T[0,3,4][0,Z]Z	Drain/Spinal Meninges, [Opn, Perc, Perc Endo], [Drain Dev, No Dev], NQ
009U0[0,Z]Z	Drain/Spinal Canal, Opn, [Drain Dev, No Dev], NQ
009W[0,3,4][0,Z]Z	Drain/Cervical Spinal Cord, [Opn, Perc, Perc Endo], [Drain Dev, No Dev], NQ
009X[0,3,4][0,Z]Z	Drain/Thoracic Spinal Cord, [Opn, Perc, Perc Endo], [Drain Dev, No Dev], NQ
009Y[0,3,4][0,Z]Z	Drain/Lumbar Spinal Cord, [Opn, Perc, Perc Endo], [Drain Dev, No Dev], NQ
00B0[0,3,4]ZZ	Exc/Brain, [Opn, Perc, Perc Endo]
00B6[0,3,4]ZZ	Exc/Cerebral Ventricle, [Opn, Perc, Perc Endo]
00B7[0,3,4]ZZ	Exc/Cerebral Hemisphere, [Opn, Perc, Perc Endo]
00B9[0,3,4]ZZ	Exc/Thalamus, [Opn, Perc, Perc Endo]
00BA[0,3,4]ZZ	Exc/Hypothalamus, [Opn, Perc, Perc Endo]
00BB[0,3,4]ZZ	Exc/Pons, [Opn, Perc, Perc Endo]
00BC[0,3,4]ZZ	Exc/Cerebellum, [Opn, Perc, Perc Endo]
00BD[0,3,4]ZZ	Exc/Medulla Oblongata, [Opn, Perc, Perc Endo]
00BF0ZX	Exc of Olfactory Nerve, Opn Appr, Diagnostic
00BF[0,3,4]ZZ	Exc/Olfactory Nerve, [Opn, Perc, Perc Endo]
00BG0ZX	Exc of Optic Nerve, Opn Appr, Diagnostic
00BG[0,3,4]ZZ	Exc/Optic Nerve, [Opn, Perc, Perc Endo]
00BH0ZX	Exc of Oculomotor Nerve, Opn Appr, Diagnostic
00BH[0,3,4]ZZ	Exc/Oculomotor Nerve, [Opn, Perc, Perc Endo]
00BJ0ZX	Exc of Trochlear Nerve, Opn Appr, Diagnostic
00BJ[0,3,4]ZZ	Exc/Trochlear Nerve, [Opn, Perc, Perc Endo]
00BK0ZX	Exc of Trigeminal Nerve, Opn Appr, Diagnostic
00BK[0,3,4]ZZ	Exc/Trigeminal Nerve, [Opn, Perc, Perc Endo]
00BL0ZX	Exc of Abducens Nerve, Opn Appr, Diagnostic
00BL[0,3,4]ZZ	Exc/Abducens Nerve, [Opn, Perc, Perc Endo]
00BM0ZX	Exc of Facial Nerve, Opn Appr, Diagnostic
00BM[0,3,4]ZZ	Exc/Facial Nerve, [Opn, Perc, Perc Endo]
00BN0ZX	Exc of Acoustic Nerve, Opn Appr, Diagnostic
00BN[3,4]ZZ	Exc/Acoustic Nerve, [Perc, Perc Endo]
00BP0ZX	Exc of Glossopharyngeal Nerve, Opn Appr, Diagn
00BP[0,3,4]ZZ	Exc/Glossopharyngeal Nerve, [Opn, Perc, Perc Endo]
00BQ0ZX	Exc of Vagus Nerve, Opn Appr, Diagnostic
00BQ[0,3,4]ZZ	Exc/Vagus Nerve, [Opn, Perc, Perc Endo]
00BR0ZX	Exc of Accessory Nerve, Opn Appr, Diagnostic
00BR[0,3,4]ZZ	Exc/Accessory Nerve, [Opn, Perc, Perc Endo]
00BS0ZX	Exc of Hypoglossal Nerve, Opn Appr, Diagnostic
00BS[0,3,4]ZZ	Exc/Hypoglossal Nerve, [Opn, Perc, Perc Endo]
00C0*	Extir/Brain
00C1*	Extir/Cerebral Meninges
00C2*	Extir/Dura Mater
00C3*	Extir/Epidural Space
00C4*	Extir/Subdural Space
00C5*	Extir/Subarachnoid Space
00C6*	Extir/Cerebral Ventricle
00C7*	Extir/Cerebral Hemisphere
00C9*	Extir/Thalamus
00CA*	Extir/Hypothalamus
00CB*	Extir/Pons
00CC*	Extir/Cerebellum
00CD*	Extir/Medulla Oblongata
00CT*	Extir/Spinal Meninges
00CW*	Extir/Cervical Spinal Cord
00CX*	Extir/Thoracic Spinal Cord
00CY*	Extir/Lumbar Spinal Cord
00DF*	Extract/Olfactory Nerve
00DG*	Extract/Optic Nerve
00DH*	Extract/Oculomotor Nerve
00DJ*	Extract/Trochlear Nerve
00DK*	Extract/Trigeminal Nerve
00DL*	Extract/Abducens Nerve
00DM*	Extract/Facial Nerve
00DN*	Extract/Acoustic Nerve
00DP*	Extract/Glossopharyngeal Nerve
00DQ*	Extract/Vagus Nerve
00DR*	Extract/Accessory Nerve
00DS*	Extract/Hypoglossal Nerve
00DT*	Extract/Spinal Meninges
00F3[0,3,4]ZZ	Fragmn/Epidural Space, [Opn, Perc, Perc Endo]
00F4[0,3,4]ZZ	Fragmn/Subdural Space, [Opn, Perc, Perc Endo]
00F5[0,3,4]ZZ	Fragmn/Subarachnoid Space, [Opn, Perc, Perc Endo]
00F6[0,3,4]ZZ	Fragmn/Cerebral Ventricle, [Opn, Perc, Perc Endo]
00FU*	Fragmn/Spinal Canal
00H0*	Insert/Brain
00H6*	Insert/Cerebral Ventricle
00HE[0,3,4]MZ	Insert/Cranial Nerve, [Opn, Perc, Perc Endo], Neurostimulator Lead, NQ
00HU[0,3,4][2,M]Z	Insert/Spinal Canal, [Opn, Perc, Perc Endo], [Monitoring Dev, Neurostimulator Lead], NQ
00HV[0,3,4][2,M]Z	Insert/Spinal Cord, [Opn, Perc, Perc Endo], [Monitoring Dev, Neurostimulator Lead], NQ
00J0*	Inspect/Brain
00JU0ZZ	Inspect of Spinal Canal, Opn Appr
00JV0ZZ	Inspect of Spinal Cord, Opn Appr
00K*	Central Nervous Sys, Map
00N*	Central Nervous Sys, Rls
00P0[0,3,4][0,2,3,7,J,K]Z	Rmvl/Brain, [Opn, Perc, Perc Endo], [Drain Dev, Monitoring Dev, Inf Dev, Auto Tissue Sub, Synth Sub, Nonauto Tissue Sub], NQ
00P6X2Z	Rmvl of Monitor Dev from Cereb Ventricle, Extern Appr
00P6[0,3,4][0,2,3,J]Z	Rmvl/Cerebral Ventricle, [Opn, Perc, Perc Endo], [Drain Dev, Monitoring Dev, Inf Dev, Synth Sub], NQ
00PE[0,3,4,X]MZ	Rmvl/Cranial Nerve, [Opn, Perc, Perc Endo, Ext], Neurostimulator Lead, NQ
00PU[0,3,4][0,2,3,J,M]Z	Rmvl/Spinal Canal, [Opn, Perc, Perc Endo], [Drain Dev, Monitoring Dev, Inf Dev, Synth Sub, Neurostimulator Lead], NQ
00PV[0,3,4][0,2,3,7,J,K,M]Z	Rmvl/Spinal Cord, [Opn, Perc, Perc Endo], [Drain Dev, Monitoring Dev, Inf Dev, Auto Tissue Sub, Synth Sub, Nonauto Tissue Sub, Neurostimulator Lead], NQ
00Q*	Central Nervous Sys, Repair
00SW*	Repos/Cervical Spinal Cord
00SX*	Repos/Thoracic Spinal Cord
00SY*	Repos/Lumbar Spinal Cord
00T*	Central Nervous Sys, Resect
00U*	Central Nervous Sys, Supl
00W00[0,2,3,7,M]Z	Rev/Brain, Opn, [Drain Dev, Monitoring Dev, Inf Dev, Auto Tissue Sub, Neurostimulator Lead], NQ
00W0[3,4][0,2,3,7,J,K,M]Z	Rev/Brain, [Perc, Perc Endo], [Drain Dev, Monitoring Dev, Inf Dev, Auto Tissue Sub, Synth Sub, Nonauto Tissue Sub, Neurostimulator Lead], NQ
00W6[0,3,4][0,2,3,J,M]Z	Rev/Cerebral Ventricle, [Opn, Perc, Perc Endo], [Drain Dev, Monitoring Dev, Inf Dev, Synth Sub, Neurostimulator Lead], NQ
00WU[0,3,4][0,2,3,J,M]Z	Rev/Spinal Canal, [Opn, Perc, Perc Endo], [Drain Dev, Monitoring Dev, Inf Dev, Synth Sub, Neurostimulator Lead], NQ
00WV[0,3,4][0,2,3,7,J,K,M]Z	Rev/Spinal Cord, [Opn, Perc, Perc Endo], [Drain Dev, Monitoring Dev, Inf Dev, Auto Tissue Sub, Synth Sub, Nonauto Tissue Sub, Neurostimulator Lead], NQ
00X*	Central Nervous Sys, Transfer
0151[0,4]ZZ	Destr/Cervical Nerve, [Opn, Perc Endo]
0158[0,4]ZZ	Destr/Thoracic Nerve, [Opn, Perc Endo]
015B[0,4]ZZ	Destr/Lumbar Nerve, [Opn, Perc Endo]
015R[0,4]ZZ	Destr/Sacral Nerve, [Opn, Perc Endo]
0180*	Div/Cervical Plexus
0181*	Div/Cervical Nerve
0182*	Div/Phrenic Nerve
0183*	Div/Brachial Plexus
0184*	Div/Ulnar Nerve
0185*	Div/Median Nerve
0186*	Div/Radial Nerve
0188*	Div/Thoracic Nerve
0189*	Div/Lumbar Plexus
018A*	Div/Lumbosacral Plexus
018B*	Div/Lumbar Nerve
018C*	Div/Pudendal Nerve
018D*	Div/Femor Nerve
018F*	Div/Sciatic Nerve
018G*	Div/Tibial Nerve
018H*	Div/Peroneal Nerve
018Q*	Div/Sacral Plexus
018R*	Div/Sacral Nerve

T Transfer DRG   SP Special Payment   * Code Range   6th and 7th Character of ZZ = No Device, No Qualifier ZX = No Device, Diagnostic

MS-DRG Version 33.0   © 2015 Optum360, LLC

01900ZX	Drain of Cervical Plexus, Opn Appr, Diagnostic
01910ZX	Drain of Cervical Nerve, Opn Appr, Diagnostic
01920ZX	Drain of Phrenic Nerve, Opn Appr, Diagnostic
01930ZX	Drain of Brachial Plexus, Opn Appr, Diagnostic
01940ZX	Drain of Ulnar Nerve, Opn Appr, Diagnostic
01950ZX	Drain of Median Nerve, Opn Appr, Diagnostic
01960ZX	Drain of Radial Nerve, Opn Appr, Diagnostic
01980ZX	Drain of Thoracic Nerve, Opn Appr, Diagnostic
01990ZX	Drain of Lumbar Plexus, Opn Appr, Diagnostic
019A0ZX	Drain of Lumbosacral Plexus, Opn Appr, Diagnostic
019B0ZX	Drain of Lumbar Nerve, Opn Appr, Diagnostic
019C0ZX	Drain of Pudendal Nerve, Opn Appr, Diagnostic
019D0ZX	Drain of Femor Nerve, Opn Appr, Diagnostic
019F0ZX	Drain of Sciatic Nerve, Opn Appr, Diagnostic
019G0ZX	Drain of Tibial Nerve, Opn Appr, Diagnostic
019H0ZX	Drain of Peroneal Nerve, Opn Appr, Diagnostic
019Q0ZX	Drain of Sacral Plexus, Opn Appr, Diagnostic
019R0ZX	Drain of Sacral Nerve, Opn Appr, Diagnostic
01B00ZX	Exc of Cervical Plexus, Opn Appr, Diagnostic
01B0[0,3,4]ZZ	Exc/Cervical Plexus, [Opn, Perc, Perc Endo]
01B10ZX	Exc of Cervical Nerve, Opn Appr, Diagnostic
01B1[0,3,4]ZZ	Exc/Cervical Nerve, [Opn, Perc, Perc Endo]
01B20ZX	Exc of Phrenic Nerve, Opn Appr, Diagnostic
01B2[0,3,4]ZZ	Exc/Phrenic Nerve, [Opn, Perc, Perc Endo]
01B30ZX	Exc of Brachial Plexus, Opn Appr, Diagnostic
01B3[0,3,4]ZZ	Exc/Brachial Plexus, [Opn, Perc, Perc Endo]
01B40ZX	Exc of Ulnar Nerve, Opn Appr, Diagnostic
01B4[0,3,4]ZZ	Exc/Ulnar Nerve, [Opn, Perc, Perc Endo]
01B50ZX	Exc of Median Nerve, Opn Appr, Diagnostic
01B5[0,3,4]ZZ	Exc/Median Nerve, [Opn, Perc, Perc Endo]
01B60ZX	Exc of Radial Nerve, Opn Appr, Diagnostic
01B6[0,3,4]ZZ	Exc/Radial Nerve, [Opn, Perc, Perc Endo]
01B80ZX	Exc of Thoracic Nerve, Opn Appr, Diagnostic
01B8[0,3,4]ZZ	Exc/Thoracic Nerve, [Opn, Perc, Perc Endo]
01B90ZX	Exc of Lumbar Plexus, Opn Appr, Diagnostic
01B9[0,3,4]ZZ	Exc/Lumbar Plexus, [Opn, Perc, Perc Endo]
01BA0ZX	Exc of Lumbosacral Plexus, Opn Appr, Diagnostic
01BA[0,3,4]ZZ	Exc/Lumbosacral Plexus, [Opn, Perc, Perc Endo]
01BB0ZX	Exc of Lumbar Nerve, Opn Appr, Diagnostic
01BB[0,3,4]ZZ	Exc/Lumbar Nerve, [Opn, Perc, Perc Endo]
01BC0ZX	Exc of Pudendal Nerve, Opn Appr, Diagnostic
01BC[0,3,4]ZZ	Exc/Pudendal Nerve, [Opn, Perc, Perc Endo]
01BD0ZX	Exc of Femor Nerve, Opn Appr, Diagnostic
01BD[0,3,4]ZZ	Exc/Femor Nerve, [Opn, Perc, Perc Endo]
01BF0ZX	Exc of Sciatic Nerve, Opn Appr, Diagnostic
01BF[0,3,4]ZZ	Exc/Sciatic Nerve, [Opn, Perc, Perc Endo]
01BG0ZX	Exc of Tibial Nerve, Opn Appr, Diagnostic
01BG[0,3,4]ZZ	Exc/Tibial Nerve, [Opn, Perc, Perc Endo]
01BH0ZX	Exc of Peroneal Nerve, Opn Appr, Diagnostic
01BH[0,3,4]ZZ	Exc/Peroneal Nerve, [Opn, Perc, Perc Endo]
01BQ0ZX	Exc of Sacral Plexus, Opn Appr, Diagnostic
01BQ[0,3,4]ZZ	Exc/Sacral Plexus, [Opn, Perc, Perc Endo]
01BR0ZX	Exc of Sacral Nerve, Opn Appr, Diagnostic
01BR[0,3,4]ZZ	Exc/Sacral Nerve, [Opn, Perc, Perc Endo]
01D0*	Extract/Cervical Plexus
01D1*	Extract/Cervical Nerve
01D2*	Extract/Phrenic Nerve
01D3*	Extract/Brachial Plexus
01D4*	Extract/Ulnar Nerve
01D5*	Extract/Median Nerve
01D6*	Extract/Radial Nerve
01D8*	Extract/Thoracic Nerve
01D9*	Extract/Lumbar Plexus
01DA*	Extract/Lumbosacral Plexus
01DB*	Extract/Lumbar Nerve
01DC*	Extract/Pudendal Nerve
01DD*	Extract/Femor Nerve
01DF*	Extract/Sciatic Nerve
01DG*	Extract/Tibial Nerve
01DH*	Extract/Peroneal Nerve
01DQ*	Extract/Sacral Plexus
01DR*	Extract/Sacral Nerve
01HY[0,3,4]MZ	Insert/Peripheral Nerve, [Opn, Perc, Perc Endo], Neurostimulator Lead, NQ
01N0*	Rls/Cervical Plexus
01N1*	Rls/Cervical Nerve
01N2*	Rls/Phrenic Nerve
01N3*	Rls/Brachial Plexus
01N4*	Rls/Ulnar Nerve
01N6*	Rls/Radial Nerve
01N8*	Rls/Thoracic Nerve
01N9*	Rls/Lumbar Plexus
01NA*	Rls/Lumbosacral Plexus
01NB*	Rls/Lumbar Nerve
01NC*	Rls/Pudendal Nerve
01ND*	Rls/Femor Nerve
01NF*	Rls/Sciatic Nerve
01NG*	Rls/Tibial Nerve
01NH*	Rls/Peroneal Nerve
01NQ*	Rls/Sacral Plexus
01NR*	Rls/Sacral Nerve
01PY[0,3,4,X]MZ	Rmvl/Peripheral Nerve, [Opn, Perc, Perc Endo, Ext], Neurostimulator Lead, NQ
01Q0*	Repair/Cervical Plexus
01Q1*	Repair/Cervical Nerve
01Q2*	Repair/Phrenic Nerve
01Q3*	Repair/Brachial Plexus
01Q4*	Repair/Ulnar Nerve
01Q5*	Repair/Median Nerve
01Q6*	Repair/Radial Nerve
01Q8*	Repair/Thoracic Nerve
01Q9*	Repair/Lumbar Plexus
01QA*	Repair/Lumbosacral Plexus
01QB*	Repair/Lumbar Nerve
01QC*	Repair/Pudendal Nerve
01QD*	Repair/Femor Nerve
01QF*	Repair/Sciatic Nerve
01QG*	Repair/Tibial Nerve
01QH*	Repair/Peroneal Nerve
01QQ*	Repair/Sacral Plexus
01QR*	Repair/Sacral Nerve
01U*	Peripheral Nervous Sys, Supl
0216[0,4]Z7	Bypass/Atrium, Rt, [Opn, Perc Endo], No Dev, Atrium, Lt
021W[0,4][9,A,J,K,Z][B,D]	Bypass/Thoracic Aorta, [Opn, Perc Endo], [Auto Venous Tissue, Auto Arterial Tissue, Synth Sub, Nonauto Tissue Sub, No Dev], [Subclavian, Carotid]
025N*	Destr/Pericardium
027K*	Dilation/Ventricle, Rt
027R[0,3,4][4,D,Z]T	Dilation/Pulmn Artery, Lt, [Opn, Perc, Perc Endo], [Drug-eluting Intralum Dev, Intralum Dev, No Dev], Ductus Arteriosus
02BN[0,3,4]ZZ	Exc/Pericardium, [Opn, Perc, Perc Endo]
02BP3ZZ	Exc of Pulmn Trunk, Perc Appr
02BQ3ZZ	Exc of Rt Pulmn Artery, Perc Appr
02BR3ZZ	Exc of Lt Pulmn Artery, Perc Appr
02BS3ZZ	Exc of Rt Pulmn Vein, Perc Appr
02BT3ZZ	Exc of Lt Pulmn Vein, Perc Appr
02BV3ZZ	Exc of Superior Vena Cava, Perc Appr
02BW[0,3,4]ZZ	Exc/Thoracic Aorta, [Opn, Perc, Perc Endo]
02CN*	Extir/Pericardium
02CP*	Extir/Pulmn Trunk
02CQ*	Extir/Pulmn Artery, Rt
02CR*	Extir/Pulmn Artery, Lt
02CS*	Extir/Pulmn Vein, Rt
02CT*	Extir/Pulmn Vein, Lt
02CV*	Extir/Superior Vena Cava
02CW*	Extir/Thoracic Aorta
02FN[0,3,4]ZZ	Fragmn/Pericardium, [Opn, Perc, Perc Endo]
02H602Z	Insert of Monitoring Device into Rt Atrium, Opn Appr
02H63[2,J,M]Z	Insert/Atrium, Rt, Perc, [Monitoring Dev, Cardiac Lead, Pacemaker, Cardiac Lead], NQ
02H642Z	Insert of Monitor Dev into Rt Atrium, Perc Endo Appr
02H702Z	Insert of Monitoring Device into Lt Atrium, Opn Appr
02H73[2,J,M]Z	Insert/Atrium, Lt, Perc, [Monitoring Dev, Cardiac Lead, Pacemaker, Cardiac Lead], NQ
02H742Z	Insert of Monitor Dev into Lt Atrium, Perc Endo Appr
02HK3JZ	Insert of Pacemaker Lead into Rt Ventricle, Perc Appr
02HL3JZ	Insert of Pacemaker Lead into Lt Ventricle, Perc Appr
02HL[0,3,4]2Z	Insert/Ventricle, Lt, [Opn, Perc, Perc Endo], Monitoring Dev, NQ
02HN[0,3,4][0,2,J,M]Z	Insert/Pericardium, [Opn, Perc, Perc Endo], [Monitoring Dev, Pressure Sensor, Monitoring Dev, Cardiac Lead, Pacemaker, Cardiac Lead], NQ
02HV[0,3,4][2,D]Z	Insert/Superior Vena Cava, [Opn, Perc, Perc Endo], [Monitoring Dev, Intralum Dev], NQ
02JA0ZZ	Inspect of Heart, Opn Appr
02JY0ZZ	Inspect of Great Vessel, Opn Appr
02LR[0,3,4][C,D,Z]T	Occlsn/Pulmn Artery, Lt, [Opn, Perc, Perc Endo], [Extralum Dev, Intralum Dev, No Dev], Ductus Arteriosus

---

Surgical   **Medical**   **CC Indicator**   **MCC Indicator**   **Procedure Proxy**   PDxMCC **PDx acts as own MCC**   PDxCC **PDx acts as own CC**

MDC 21: Injuries, Poisonings And Toxic Effects Of Drugs—SURGICAL

Code	Description
02LS[Ø,3,4][C,D,Z]Z	Occlsn/Pulmn Vein, Rt, [Opn, Perc, Perc Endo], [Extralum Dev, Intralum Dev, No Dev], NQ
02LT[Ø,3,4][C,D,Z]Z	Occlsn/Pulmn Vein, Lt, [Opn, Perc, Perc Endo], [Extralum Dev, Intralum Dev, No Dev], NQ
02LV[Ø,3,4][C,D,Z]Z	Occlsn/Superior Vena Cava, [Opn, Perc, Perc Endo], [Extralum Dev, Intralum Dev, No Dev], NQ
02N4*	Rls/Coronary Vein
02N8*	Rls/Conduction Mechanism
02NN*	Rls/Pericardium
02PA[Ø,3,4,X]MZ	Rmvl/Heart, [Opn, Perc, Perc Endo, Ext], Cardiac Lead, NQ
02Q6*	Repair/Atrium, Rt
02Q7*	Repair/Atrium, Lt
02Q8*	Repair/Conduction Mechanism
02QA*	Repair/Heart
02QK*	Repair/Ventricle, Rt
02QL*	Repair/Ventricle, Lt
02QN*	Repair/Pericardium
02QP*	Repair/Pulmn Trunk
02QQ*	Repair/Pulmn Artery, Rt
02QR*	Repair/Pulmn Artery, Lt
02QS*	Repair/Pulmn Vein, Rt
02QT*	Repair/Pulmn Vein, Lt
02QV*	Repair/Superior Vena Cava
02QW*	Repair/Thoracic Aorta
02R5*	Replace/Atrial Septum
02R6*	Replace/Atrium, Rt
02R7*	Replace/Atrium, Lt
02RK[Ø,4][8,J]Z	Replace/Ventricle, Rt, [Opn, Perc Endo], [Zooplastic Tissue, Synth Sub], NQ
02RL[Ø,4][8,J]Z	Replace/Ventricle, Lt, [Opn, Perc Endo], [Zooplastic Tissue, Synth Sub], NQ
02RM[Ø,4]8Z	Replace/Ventricular Septum, [Opn, Perc Endo], Zooplastic Tissue, NQ
02RN*	Replace/Pericardium
02RP*	Replace/Pulmn Trunk
02RQ*	Replace/Pulmn Artery, Rt
02RR*	Replace/Pulmn Artery, Lt
02RS*	Replace/Pulmn Vein, Rt
02RT*	Replace/Pulmn Vein, Lt
02RV*	Replace/Superior Vena Cava
02RW*	Replace/Thoracic Aorta
02S*	Heart and Great Vessels, Repos
02TN*	Resect/Pericardium
02U6Ø0JZ	Supl Rt Atrium with Synth Sub, Opn Appr
02U6[3,4][7,8,J,K]Z	Supl/Atrium, Rt, [Perc, Perc Endo], [Auto Tissue Sub, Zooplastic Tissue, Synth Sub, Nonauto Tissue Sub], NQ
02U70JZ	Supl Lt Atrium with Synth Sub, Opn Appr
02UA[Ø,3,4][7,8,K]Z	Supl/Heart, [Opn, Perc, Perc Endo], [Auto Tissue Sub, Zooplastic Tissue, Nonauto Tissue Sub], NQ
02UK[Ø,3,4][7,8,J]Z	Supl/Ventricle, Rt, [Opn, Perc, Perc Endo], [Auto Tissue Sub, Zooplastic Tissue, Synth Sub], NQ
02UL[Ø,3,4][7,8,J]Z	Supl/Ventricle, Lt, [Opn, Perc, Perc Endo], [Auto Tissue Sub, Zooplastic Tissue, Synth Sub], NQ
02UM08Z	Supl Ventricular Septum with Zooplastic, Opn Appr
02UN*	Supl/Pericardium
02UP*	Supl/Pulmn Trunk
02UQ*	Supl/Pulmn Artery, Rt
02UR*	Supl/Pulmn Artery, Lt
02US*	Supl/Pulmn Vein, Rt
02UT*	Supl/Pulmn Vein, Lt
02UV*	Supl/Superior Vena Cava
02UW*	Supl/Thoracic Aorta
02VA*	Restrict/Heart
02VP[Ø,3,4][D,Z]Z	Restrict/Pulmn Trunk, [Opn, Perc, Perc Endo], [Intralum Dev, No Dev], NQ
02VQ[Ø,3,4][D,Z]Z	Restrict/Pulmn Artery, Rt, [Opn, Perc, Perc Endo], [Intralum Dev, No Dev], NQ
02VR[Ø,3,4][D,Z][T,Z]	Restrict/Pulmn Artery, Lt, [Opn, Perc, Perc Endo], [Intralum Dev, No Dev], [Ductus Arteriosus, NQ]
02VS[Ø,3,4][D,Z]Z	Restrict/Pulmn Vein, Rt, [Opn, Perc, Perc Endo], [Intralum Dev, No Dev], NQ
02VT[Ø,3,4][D,Z]Z	Restrict/Pulmn Vein, Lt, [Opn, Perc, Perc Endo], [Intralum Dev, No Dev], NQ
02VV*	Restrict/Superior Vena Cava
02VW[Ø,3,4][D,Z]Z	Restrict/Thoracic Aorta, [Opn, Perc, Perc Endo], [Intralum Dev, No Dev], NQ
02WA[Ø,3,4][K,M]Z	Rev/Heart, [Opn, Perc, Perc Endo], [Nonauto Tissue Sub, Cardiac Lead], NQ
02WA[3,4]JZ	Rev/Heart, [Perc, Perc Endo], Synth Sub, NQ
0313ØZD	Bypass Rt Subclavian Artery to Up Arm Vein, Opn Appr
0314ØZD	Bypass Lt Subclavian Artery to Up Arm Vein, Opn Appr
0315ØZD	Bypass Rt Axillary Artery to Up Arm Vein, Opn Appr
0315Ø[9,A,J,K,Z]0	Bypass/Axillary Artery, Rt, Opn, [Auto Venous Tissue, Auto Arterial Tissue, Synth Sub, Nonauto Tissue Sub, No Dev], Upr Arm Artery, Rt
0316ØZD	Bypass Lt Axillary Artery to Upr Arm Vein, Opn Appr
0316Ø[9,A,J,K,Z]1	Bypass/Axillary Artery, Lt, Opn, [Auto Venous Tissue, Auto Arterial Tissue, Synth Sub, Nonauto Tissue Sub, No Dev], Upr Arm Artery, Lt
0317Ø[9,A,J,K,Z][D,F]	Bypass/Brachial Artery, Rt, Opn, [Auto Venous Tissue, Auto Arterial Tissue, Synth Sub, Nonauto Tissue Sub, No Dev], [Upr Arm Vein, Lwr Arm Vein]
0318Ø[9,A,J,K,Z][D,F]	Bypass/Brachial Artery, Lt, Opn, [Auto Venous Tissue, Auto Arterial Tissue, Synth Sub, Nonauto Tissue Sub, No Dev], [Upr Arm Vein, Lwr Arm Vein]
0319Ø[9,A,J,K,Z]F	Bypass/Ulnar Artery, Rt, Opn, [Auto Venous Tissue, Auto Arterial Tissue, Synth Sub, Nonauto Tissue Sub, No Dev], Lwr Arm Vein
031AØ[9,A,J,K,Z]F	Bypass/Ulnar Artery, Lt, Opn, [Auto Venous Tissue, Auto Arterial Tissue, Synth Sub, Nonauto Tissue Sub, No Dev], Lwr Arm Vein
031BØ[9,A,J,K,Z]F	Bypass/Radial Artery, Rt, Opn, [Auto Venous Tissue, Auto Arterial Tissue, Synth Sub, Nonauto Tissue Sub, No Dev], Lwr Arm Vein
031CØ[9,A,J,K,Z]F	Bypass/Radial Artery, Lt, Opn, [Auto Venous Tissue, Auto Arterial Tissue, Synth Sub, Nonauto Tissue Sub, No Dev], Lwr Arm Vein
031H*	Bypass/Common Carotid Artery, Rt
031J*	Bypass/Common Carotid Artery, Lt
031K*	Bypass/Int Carotid Artery, Rt
031L*	Bypass/Int Carotid Artery, Lt
031M*	Bypass/Ext Carotid Artery, Rt
031N*	Bypass/Ext Carotid Artery, Lt
031S*	Bypass/Temporal Artery, Rt
031T*	Bypass/Temporal Artery, Lt
0355*	Destr/Axillary Artery, Rt
0356*	Destr/Axillary Artery, Lt
0357*	Destr/Brachial Artery, Rt
0358*	Destr/Brachial Artery, Lt
0359*	Destr/Ulnar Artery, Rt
035A*	Destr/Ulnar Artery, Lt
035B*	Destr/Radial Artery, Rt
035C*	Destr/Radial Artery, Lt
035D*	Destr/Hand Artery, Rt
035F*	Destr/Hand Artery, Lt
035G*	Destr/Intracranial Artery
035H*	Destr/Common Carotid Artery, Rt
035J*	Destr/Common Carotid Artery, Lt
035K*	Destr/Int Carotid Artery, Rt
035L*	Destr/Int Carotid Artery, Lt
035M*	Destr/Ext Carotid Artery, Rt
035N*	Destr/Ext Carotid Artery, Lt
035P*	Destr/Vert Artery, Rt
035Q*	Destr/Vert Artery, Lt
035R*	Destr/Face Artery
035S*	Destr/Temporal Artery, Rt
035T*	Destr/Temporal Artery, Lt
035U*	Destr/Thyroid Artery, Rt
035V*	Destr/Thyroid Artery, Lt
035Y*	Destr/Upr Artery
03733[4,D,Z]Z	Dilation/Subclavian Artery, Rt, Perc, [Drug-eluting Intralum Dev, Intralum Dev, No Dev], NQ
03743[4,D,Z]Z	Dilation/Subclavian Artery, Lt, Perc, [Drug-eluting Intralum Dev, Intralum Dev, No Dev], NQ
03773[4,D,Z]Z	Dilation/Brachial Artery, Rt, Perc, [Drug-eluting Intralum Dev, Intralum Dev, No Dev], NQ
03783[4,D,Z]Z	Dilation/Brachial Artery, Lt, Perc, [Drug-eluting Intralum Dev, Intralum Dev, No Dev], NQ
03793[4,D,Z]Z	Dilation/Ulnar Artery, Rt, Perc, [Drug-eluting Intralum Dev, Intralum Dev, No Dev], NQ
037A3[4,D,Z]Z	Dilation/Ulnar Artery, Lt, Perc, [Drug-eluting Intralum Dev, Intralum Dev, No Dev], NQ
037G[3,4][4,D,Z]Z	Dilation/Intracranial Artery, [Perc, Perc Endo], [Drug-eluting Intralum Dev, Intralum Dev, No Dev], NQ
037H[3,4][4,D,Z]Z	Dilation/Common Carotid Artery, Rt, [Perc, Perc Endo], [Drug-eluting Intralum Dev, Intralum Dev, No Dev], NQ
037J[3,4][4,D,Z]Z	Dilation/Common Carotid Artery, Lt, [Perc, Perc Endo], [Drug-eluting Intralum Dev, Intralum Dev, No Dev], NQ
037K[3,4][4,D,Z]Z	Dilation/Int Carotid Artery, Rt, [Perc, Perc Endo], [Drug-eluting Intralum Dev, Intralum Dev, No Dev], NQ

T Transfer DRG   SP Special Payment   * Code Range   6th and 7th Character of ZZ = No Device, No Qualifier ZX = No Device, Diagnostic

MS-DRG Version 33.0

037L[3,4][4,D,Z]Z	Dilation/Int Carotid Artery, Lt, [Perc, Perc Endo], [Drug-eluting Intralum Dev, Intralum Dev, No Dev], NQ
037M[3,4][4,D,Z]Z	Dilation/Ext Carotid Artery, Rt, [Perc, Perc Endo], [Drug-eluting Intralum Dev, Intralum Dev, No Dev], NQ
037N[3,4][4,D,Z]Z	Dilation/Ext Carotid Artery, Lt, [Perc, Perc Endo], [Drug-eluting Intralum Dev, Intralum Dev, No Dev], NQ
037P[3,4][4,D,Z]Z	Dilation/Vert Artery, Rt, [Perc, Perc Endo], [Drug-eluting Intralum Dev, Intralum Dev, No Dev], NQ
037Q[3,4][4,D,Z]Z	Dilation/Vert Artery, Lt, [Perc, Perc Endo], [Drug-eluting Intralum Dev, Intralum Dev, No Dev], NQ
037Y3[4,D,Z]Z	Dilation/Upr Artery, Perc, [Drug-eluting Intralum Dev, Intralum Dev, No Dev], NQ
03B03ZZ	Exc of Rt Int Mammary Artery, Perc Appr
03B13ZZ	Exc of Lt Int Mammary Artery, Perc Appr
03B23ZZ	Exc of Innominate Artery, Perc Appr
03B33ZZ	Exc of Rt Subclavian Artery, Perc Appr
03B43ZZ	Exc of Lt Subclavian Artery, Perc Appr
03B5[0,3,4]ZZ	Exc/Axillary Artery, Rt, [Opn, Perc, Perc Endo]
03B6[0,3,4]ZZ	Exc/Axillary Artery, Lt, [Opn, Perc, Perc Endo]
03B7[0,3,4]ZZ	Exc/Brachial Artery, Rt, [Opn, Perc, Perc Endo]
03B8[0,3,4]ZZ	Exc/Brachial Artery, Lt, [Opn, Perc, Perc Endo]
03B9[0,3,4]ZZ	Exc/Ulnar Artery, Rt, [Opn, Perc, Perc Endo]
03BA[0,3,4]ZZ	Exc/Ulnar Artery, Lt, [Opn, Perc, Perc Endo]
03BB[0,3,4]ZZ	Exc/Radial Artery, Rt, [Opn, Perc, Perc Endo]
03BC[0,3,4]ZZ	Exc/Radial Artery, Lt, [Opn, Perc, Perc Endo]
03BD[0,3,4]ZZ	Exc/Hand Artery, Rt, [Opn, Perc, Perc Endo]
03BF[0,3,4]ZZ	Exc/Hand Artery, Lt, [Opn, Perc, Perc Endo]
03BG[0,3,4]ZZ	Exc/Intracranial Artery, [Opn, Perc, Perc Endo]
03BH[0,3,4]ZZ	Exc/Common Carotid Artery, Rt, [Opn, Perc, Perc Endo]
03BJ[0,3,4]ZZ	Exc/Common Carotid Artery, Lt, [Opn, Perc, Perc Endo]
03BK[0,3,4]ZZ	Exc/Int Carotid Artery, Rt, [Opn, Perc, Perc Endo]
03BL[0,3,4]ZZ	Exc/Int Carotid Artery, Lt, [Opn, Perc, Perc Endo]
03BM[0,3,4]ZZ	Exc/Ext Carotid Artery, Rt, [Opn, Perc, Perc Endo]
03BN[0,3,4]ZZ	Exc/Ext Carotid Artery, Lt, [Opn, Perc, Perc Endo]
03BP[0,3,4]ZZ	Exc/Vert Artery, Rt, [Opn, Perc, Perc Endo]
03BQ[0,3,4]ZZ	Exc/Vert Artery, Lt, [Opn, Perc, Perc Endo]
03BR[0,3,4]ZZ	Exc/Face Artery, [Opn, Perc, Perc Endo]
03BS[0,3,4]ZZ	Exc/Temporal Artery, Rt, [Opn, Perc, Perc Endo]
03BT[0,3,4]ZZ	Exc/Temporal Artery, Lt, [Opn, Perc, Perc Endo]
03BU[0,3,4]ZZ	Exc/Thyroid Artery, Rt, [Opn, Perc, Perc Endo]
03BV[0,3,4]ZZ	Exc/Thyroid Artery, Lt, [Opn, Perc, Perc Endo]
03BY[0,3,4]ZZ	Exc/Upr Artery, [Opn, Perc, Perc Endo]
03C*	Upr Arteries, Extir
03H0[0,3,4]DZ	Insert/Int Mammary Artery, Rt, [Opn, Perc, Perc Endo], Intralum Dev, NQ
03H1[0,3,4]DZ	Insert/Int Mammary Artery, Lt, [Opn, Perc, Perc Endo], Intralum Dev, NQ
03H2[0,3,4]DZ	Insert/Innominate Artery, [Opn, Perc, Perc Endo], Intralum Dev, NQ
03H3[0,3,4]DZ	Insert/Subclavian Artery, Rt, [Opn, Perc, Perc Endo], Intralum Dev, NQ
03H4[0,3,4]DZ	Insert/Subclavian Artery, Lt, [Opn, Perc, Perc Endo], Intralum Dev, NQ
03H5[0,3,4]DZ	Insert/Axillary Artery, Rt, [Opn, Perc, Perc Endo], Intralum Dev, NQ
03H6[0,3,4]DZ	Insert/Axillary Artery, Lt, [Opn, Perc, Perc Endo], Intralum Dev, NQ
03H7[0,3,4]DZ	Insert/Brachial Artery, Rt, [Opn, Perc, Perc Endo], Intralum Dev, NQ
03H8[0,3,4]DZ	Insert/Brachial Artery, Lt, [Opn, Perc, Perc Endo], Intralum Dev, NQ
03H9[0,3,4]DZ	Insert/Ulnar Artery, Rt, [Opn, Perc, Perc Endo], Intralum Dev, NQ
03HA[0,3,4]DZ	Insert/Ulnar Artery, Lt, [Opn, Perc, Perc Endo], Intralum Dev, NQ
03HB[0,3,4]DZ	Insert/Radial Artery, Rt, [Opn, Perc, Perc Endo], Intralum Dev, NQ
03HC[0,3,4]DZ	Insert/Radial Artery, Lt, [Opn, Perc, Perc Endo], Intralum Dev, NQ
03HD[0,3,4]DZ	Insert/Hand Artery, Rt, [Opn, Perc, Perc Endo], Intralum Dev, NQ
03HF[0,3,4]DZ	Insert/Hand Artery, Lt, [Opn, Perc, Perc Endo], Intralum Dev, NQ
03HG[0,3,4]DZ	Insert/Intracranial Artery, [Opn, Perc, Perc Endo], Intralum Dev, NQ
03HH[0,3,4]DZ	Insert/Common Carotid Artery, Rt, [Opn, Perc, Perc Endo], Intralum Dev, NQ
03HJ[0,3,4]DZ	Insert/Common Carotid Artery, Lt, [Opn, Perc, Perc Endo], Intralum Dev, NQ
03HK[0,3,4]DZ	Insert/Int Carotid Artery, Rt, [Opn, Perc, Perc Endo], Intralum Dev, NQ
03HL[0,3,4]DZ	Insert/Int Carotid Artery, Lt, [Opn, Perc, Perc Endo], Intralum Dev, NQ
03HM[0,3,4]DZ	Insert/Ext Carotid Artery, Rt, [Opn, Perc, Perc Endo], Intralum Dev, NQ
03HN[0,3,4]DZ	Insert/Ext Carotid Artery, Lt, [Opn, Perc, Perc Endo], Intralum Dev, NQ
03HP[0,3,4]DZ	Insert/Vert Artery, Rt, [Opn, Perc, Perc Endo], Intralum Dev, NQ
03HQ[0,3,4]DZ	Insert/Vert Artery, Lt, [Opn, Perc, Perc Endo], Intralum Dev, NQ
03HR[0,3,4]DZ	Insert/Face Artery, [Opn, Perc, Perc Endo], Intralum Dev, NQ
03HS[0,3,4]DZ	Insert/Temporal Artery, Rt, [Opn, Perc, Perc Endo], Intralum Dev, NQ
03HT[0,3,4]DZ	Insert/Temporal Artery, Lt, [Opn, Perc, Perc Endo], Intralum Dev, NQ
03HU[0,3,4]DZ	Insert/Thyroid Artery, Rt, [Opn, Perc, Perc Endo], Intralum Dev, NQ
03HV[0,3,4]DZ	Insert/Thyroid Artery, Lt, [Opn, Perc, Perc Endo], Intralum Dev, NQ
03HY[0,3,4]DZ	Insert/Upr Artery, [Opn, Perc, Perc Endo], Intralum Dev, NQ
03L0*	Occlsn/Int Mammary Artery, Rt
03L1*	Occlsn/Int Mammary Artery, Lt
03L2*	Occlsn/Innominate Artery
03L3*	Occlsn/Subclavian Artery, Rt
03L4*	Occlsn/Subclavian Artery, Lt
03L5*	Occlsn/Axillary Artery, Rt
03L6*	Occlsn/Axillary Artery, Lt
03L7*	Occlsn/Brachial Artery, Rt
03L8*	Occlsn/Brachial Artery, Lt
03L9*	Occlsn/Ulnar Artery, Rt
03LA*	Occlsn/Ulnar Artery, Lt
03LB*	Occlsn/Radial Artery, Rt
03LC*	Occlsn/Radial Artery, Lt
03LD*	Occlsn/Hand Artery, Rt
03LF*	Occlsn/Hand Artery, Lt
03LG*	Occlsn/Intracranial Artery
03LH*	Occlsn/Common Carotid Artery, Rt
03LJ*	Occlsn/Common Carotid Artery, Lt
03LK[0,3,4][B,D]Z	Occlsn/Int Carotid Artery, Rt, [Opn, Perc, Perc Endo], [Bioactive Intralum Dev, Intralum Dev], NQ
03LL[0,3,4][B,D]Z	Occlsn/Int Carotid Artery, Lt, [Opn, Perc, Perc Endo], [Bioactive Intralum Dev, Intralum Dev], NQ
03LM*	Occlsn/Ext Carotid Artery, Rt
03LN*	Occlsn/Ext Carotid Artery, Lt
03LP*	Occlsn/Vert Artery, Rt
03LQ*	Occlsn/Vert Artery, Lt
03LR*	Occlsn/Face Artery
03LS*	Occlsn/Temporal Artery, Rt
03LT*	Occlsn/Temporal Artery, Lt
03LU*	Occlsn/Thyroid Artery, Rt
03LV*	Occlsn/Thyroid Artery, Lt
03LY*	Occlsn/Upr Artery
03PY[0,3,4][7,J,K]Z	Rmvl/Upr Artery, [Opn, Perc, Perc Endo], [Auto Tissue Sub, Synth Sub, Nonauto Tissue Sub], NQ
03Q*	Upr Arteries, Repair
03R0*	Replace/Int Mammary Artery, Rt
03R1*	Replace/Int Mammary Artery, Lt
03R2*	Replace/Innominate Artery
03R3*	Replace/Subclavian Artery, Rt
03R4*	Replace/Subclavian Artery, Lt
03R5*	Replace/Axillary Artery, Rt
03R6*	Replace/Axillary Artery, Lt
03R7*	Replace/Brachial Artery, Rt
03R8*	Replace/Brachial Artery, Lt
03R9*	Replace/Ulnar Artery, Rt
03RA*	Replace/Ulnar Artery, Lt
03RB*	Replace/Radial Artery, Rt
03RC*	Replace/Radial Artery, Lt
03RD*	Replace/Hand Artery, Rt
03RF*	Replace/Hand Artery, Lt
03RG*	Replace/Intracranial Artery
03RY*	Replace/Upr Artery
03S*	Upr Arteries, Repos
03U0[0,3,4][7,J]Z	Supl/Int Mammary Artery, Rt, [Opn, Perc, Perc Endo], [Auto Tissue Sub, Synth Sub], NQ
03U1[0,3,4][7,J]Z	Supl/Int Mammary Artery, Lt, [Opn, Perc, Perc Endo], [Auto Tissue Sub, Synth Sub], NQ
03U2[0,3,4][7,J]Z	Supl/Innominate Artery, [Opn, Perc, Perc Endo], [Auto Tissue Sub, Synth Sub], NQ

Surgical   **Medical**   **CC Indicator**   **MCC Indicator**   **Procedure Proxy**   PDxMCC **PDx acts as own MCC**   PDxCC **PDx acts as own CC**

03U3[0,3,4][7,J]Z Supl/Subclavian Artery, Rt, [Opn, Perc, Perc Endo], [Auto Tissue Sub, Synth Sub], NQ

03U4[0,3,4][7,J]Z Supl/Subclavian Artery, Lt, [Opn, Perc, Perc Endo], [Auto Tissue Sub, Synth Sub], NQ

03U5[0,3,4][7,J]Z Supl/Axillary Artery, Rt, [Opn, Perc, Perc Endo], [Auto Tissue Sub, Synth Sub], NQ

03U6[0,3,4][7,J]Z Supl/Axillary Artery, Lt, [Opn, Perc, Perc Endo], [Auto Tissue Sub, Synth Sub], NQ

03U7[0,3,4][7,J]Z Supl/Brachial Artery, Rt, [Opn, Perc, Perc Endo], [Auto Tissue Sub, Synth Sub], NQ

03U8[0,3,4][7,J]Z Supl/Brachial Artery, Lt, [Opn, Perc, Perc Endo], [Auto Tissue Sub, Synth Sub], NQ

03U9[0,3,4][7,J]Z Supl/Ulnar Artery, Rt, [Opn, Perc, Perc Endo], [Auto Tissue Sub, Synth Sub], NQ

03UA[0,3,4][7,J]Z Supl/Ulnar Artery, Lt, [Opn, Perc, Perc Endo], [Auto Tissue Sub, Synth Sub], NQ

03UB[0,3,4][7,J]Z Supl/Radial Artery, Rt, [Opn, Perc, Perc Endo], [Auto Tissue Sub, Synth Sub], NQ

03UC[0,3,4][7,J]Z Supl/Radial Artery, Lt, [Opn, Perc, Perc Endo], [Auto Tissue Sub, Synth Sub], NQ

03UD[0,3,4][7,J]Z Supl/Hand Artery, Rt, [Opn, Perc, Perc Endo], [Auto Tissue Sub, Synth Sub], NQ

03UF[0,3,4][7,J]Z Supl/Hand Artery, Lt, [Opn, Perc, Perc Endo], [Auto Tissue Sub, Synth Sub], NQ

03UG[0,3,4][7,J]Z Supl/Intracranial Artery, [Opn, Perc, Perc Endo], [Auto Tissue Sub, Synth Sub], NQ

03UH[0,3,4][7,J]Z Supl/Common Carotid Artery, Rt, [Opn, Perc, Perc Endo], [Auto Tissue Sub, Synth Sub], NQ

03UJ[0,3,4][7,J]Z Supl/Common Carotid Artery, Lt, [Opn, Perc, Perc Endo], [Auto Tissue Sub, Synth Sub], NQ

03UK[0,3,4][7,J]Z Supl/Int Carotid Artery, Rt, [Opn, Perc, Perc Endo], [Auto Tissue Sub, Synth Sub], NQ

03UL[0,3,4][7,J]Z Supl/Int Carotid Artery, Lt, [Opn, Perc, Perc Endo], [Auto Tissue Sub, Synth Sub], NQ

03UM[0,3,4][7,J]Z Supl/Ext Carotid Artery, Rt, [Opn, Perc, Perc Endo], [Auto Tissue Sub, Synth Sub], NQ

03UN[0,3,4][7,J]Z Supl/Ext Carotid Artery, Lt, [Opn, Perc, Perc Endo], [Auto Tissue Sub, Synth Sub], NQ

03UP[0,3,4][7,J]Z Supl/Vert Artery, Rt, [Opn, Perc, Perc Endo], [Auto Tissue Sub, Synth Sub], NQ

03UQ[0,3,4][7,J]Z Supl/Vert Artery, Lt, [Opn, Perc, Perc Endo], [Auto Tissue Sub, Synth Sub], NQ

03UR[0,3,4][7,J]Z Supl/Face Artery, [Opn, Perc, Perc Endo], [Auto Tissue Sub, Synth Sub], NQ

03US[0,3,4][7,J]Z Supl/Temporal Artery, Rt, [Opn, Perc, Perc Endo], [Auto Tissue Sub, Synth Sub], NQ

03UT[0,3,4][7,J]Z Supl/Temporal Artery, Lt, [Opn, Perc, Perc Endo], [Auto Tissue Sub, Synth Sub], NQ

03UU[0,3,4][7,J]Z Supl/Thyroid Artery, Rt, [Opn, Perc, Perc Endo], [Auto Tissue Sub, Synth Sub], NQ

03UV[0,3,4][7,J]Z Supl/Thyroid Artery, Lt, [Opn, Perc, Perc Endo], [Auto Tissue Sub, Synth Sub], NQ

03UY[0,3,4][7,J]Z Supl/Upr Artery, [Opn, Perc, Perc Endo], [Auto Tissue Sub, Synth Sub], NQ

03V0[0,3,4][D,Z]Z Restrict/Int Mammary Artery, Rt, [Opn, Perc, Perc Endo], [Intralum Dev, No Dev], NQ

03V1[0,3,4][D,Z]Z Restrict/Int Mammary Artery, Lt, [Opn, Perc, Perc Endo], [Intralum Dev, No Dev], NQ

03V2[0,3,4][D,Z]Z Restrict/Innominate Artery, [Opn, Perc, Perc Endo], [Intralum Dev, No Dev], NQ

03V3[0,3,4][D,Z]Z Restrict/Subclavian Artery, Rt, [Opn, Perc, Perc Endo], [Intralum Dev, No Dev], NQ

03V4[0,3,4][D,Z]Z Restrict/Subclavian Artery, Lt, [Opn, Perc, Perc Endo], [Intralum Dev, No Dev], NQ

03V5[0,3,4][D,Z]Z Restrict/Axillary Artery, Rt, [Opn, Perc, Perc Endo], [Intralum Dev, No Dev], NQ

03V6[0,3,4][D,Z]Z Restrict/Axillary Artery, Lt, [Opn, Perc, Perc Endo], [Intralum Dev, No Dev], NQ

03V7[0,3,4][D,Z]Z Restrict/Brachial Artery, Rt, [Opn, Perc, Perc Endo], [Intralum Dev, No Dev], NQ

03V8[0,3,4][D,Z]Z Restrict/Brachial Artery, Lt, [Opn, Perc, Perc Endo], [Intralum Dev, No Dev], NQ

03V9[0,3,4][D,Z]Z Restrict/Ulnar Artery, Rt, [Opn, Perc, Perc Endo], [Intralum Dev, No Dev], NQ

03VA[0,3,4][D,Z]Z Restrict/Ulnar Artery, Lt, [Opn, Perc, Perc Endo], [Intralum Dev, No Dev], NQ

03VB[0,3,4][D,Z]Z Restrict/Radial Artery, Rt, [Opn, Perc, Perc Endo], [Intralum Dev, No Dev], NQ

03VC[0,3,4][D,Z]Z Restrict/Radial Artery, Lt, [Opn, Perc, Perc Endo], [Intralum Dev, No Dev], NQ

03VD[0,3,4][D,Z]Z Restrict/Hand Artery, Rt, [Opn, Perc, Perc Endo], [Intralum Dev, No Dev], NQ

03VF[0,3,4][D,Z]Z Restrict/Hand Artery, Lt, [Opn, Perc, Perc Endo], [Intralum Dev, No Dev], NQ

03VG[0,3,4][B,D,Z]Z Restrict/Intracranial Artery, [Opn, Perc, Perc Endo], [Bioactive Intralum Dev, Intralum Dev, No Dev], NQ

03VH[0,3,4][B,D,Z]Z Restrict/Common Carotid Artery, Rt, [Opn, Perc, Perc Endo], [Bioactive Intralum Dev, Intralum Dev, No Dev], NQ

03VJ[0,3,4][B,D,Z]Z Restrict/Common Carotid Artery, Lt, [Opn, Perc, Perc Endo], [Bioactive Intralum Dev, Intralum Dev, No Dev], NQ

03VK[0,3,4][B,D,Z]Z Restrict/Int Carotid Artery, Rt, [Opn, Perc, Perc Endo], [Bioactive Intralum Dev, Intralum Dev, No Dev], NQ

03VL[0,3,4][B,D,Z]Z Restrict/Int Carotid Artery, Lt, [Opn, Perc, Perc Endo], [Bioactive Intralum Dev, Intralum Dev, No Dev], NQ

03VM[0,3,4][B,D,Z]Z Restrict/Ext Carotid Artery, Rt, [Opn, Perc, Perc Endo], [Bioactive Intralum Dev, Intralum Dev, No Dev], NQ

03VN[0,3,4][B,D,Z]Z Restrict/Ext Carotid Artery, Lt, [Opn, Perc, Perc Endo], [Bioactive Intralum Dev, Intralum Dev, No Dev], NQ

03VP[0,3,4][B,D,Z]Z Restrict/Vert Artery, Rt, [Opn, Perc, Perc Endo], [Bioactive Intralum Dev, Intralum Dev, No Dev], NQ

03VQ[0,3,4][B,D,Z]Z Restrict/Vert Artery, Lt, [Opn, Perc, Perc Endo], [Bioactive Intralum Dev, Intralum Dev, No Dev], NQ

03VR[0,3,4][D,Z]Z Restrict/Face Artery, [Opn, Perc, Perc Endo], [Intralum Dev, No Dev], NQ

03VS[0,3,4][D,Z]Z Restrict/Temporal Artery, Rt, [Opn, Perc, Perc Endo], [Intralum Dev, No Dev], NQ

03VT[0,3,4][D,Z]Z Restrict/Temporal Artery, Lt, [Opn, Perc, Perc Endo], [Intralum Dev, No Dev], NQ

03VU[0,3,4][D,Z]Z Restrict/Thyroid Artery, Rt, [Opn, Perc, Perc Endo], [Intralum Dev, No Dev], NQ

03VV[0,3,4][D,Z]Z Restrict/Thyroid Artery, Lt, [Opn, Perc, Perc Endo], [Intralum Dev, No Dev], NQ

03VY[0,3,4][D,Z]Z Restrict/Upr Artery, [Opn, Perc, Perc Endo], [Intralum Dev, No Dev], NQ

0410[0,4][9,A,J,K,Z][3,4,5] Bypass/Abd Aorta, [Opn, Perc Endo], [Auto Venous Tissue, Auto Arterial Tissue, Synth Sub, Nonauto Tissue Sub, No Dev], [Renal Artery, Rt, Renal Artery, Lt, Renal Artery, Bilat]

0410[0,4][9,A,J,K,Z][6,7,8,9,B,C,D,F,G,H,J,K,Q,R] Bypass/Abd Aorta, [Opn, Perc Endo], [Auto Venous Tissue, Auto Arterial Tissue, Synth Sub, Nonauto Tissue Sub, No Dev], [Common Iliac Artery, Rt, Common Iliac Artery, Lt, Common Iliac Arteries, Bilat, Int Iliac Artery, Rt, Int Iliac Artery, Lt, Int Iliac Arteries, Bilat, Ext Iliac Artery, Rt, Ext Iliac Artery, Lt, Ext Iliac Arteries, Bilat, Femor Artery, Rt, Femor Artery, Lt, Femor Arteries, Bilat, Lwr Extr Artery, Lwr Artery]

041C[0,4][9,A,J,K,Z][H,J,K] Bypass/Common Iliac Artery, Rt, [Opn, Perc Endo], [Auto Venous Tissue, Auto Arterial Tissue, Synth Sub, Nonauto Tissue Sub, No Dev], [Femor Artery, Rt, Femor Artery, Lt, Femor Arteries, Bilat]

041D[0,4][9,A,J,K,Z][H,J,K] Bypass/Common Iliac Artery, Lt, [Opn, Perc Endo], [Auto Venous Tissue, Auto Arterial Tissue, Synth Sub, Nonauto Tissue Sub, No Dev], [Femor Artery, Rt, Femor Artery, Lt, Femor Arteries, Bilat]

041E[0,4][9,A,J,K,Z][H,J,K] Bypass/Int Iliac Artery, Rt, [Opn, Perc Endo], [Auto Venous Tissue, Auto Arterial Tissue, Synth Sub, Nonauto Tissue Sub, No Dev], [Femor Artery, Rt, Femor Artery, Lt, Femor Arteries, Bilat]

041F[0,4][9,A,J,K,Z][H,J,K] Bypass/Int Iliac Artery, Lt, [Opn, Perc Endo], [Auto Venous Tissue, Auto Arterial Tissue, Synth Sub, Nonauto Tissue Sub, No Dev], [Femor Artery, Rt, Femor Artery, Lt, Femor Arteries, Bilat]

041H[0,4][9,A,J,K,Z][H,J,K] Bypass/Ext Iliac Artery, Rt, [Opn, Perc Endo], [Auto Venous Tissue, Auto Arterial Tissue, Synth Sub, Nonauto Tissue Sub, No Dev], [Femor Artery, Rt, Femor Artery, Lt, Femor Arteries, Bilat]

041J[0,4][9,A,J,K,Z][H,J,K] Bypass/Ext Iliac Artery, Lt, [Opn, Perc Endo], [Auto Venous Tissue, Auto Arterial Tissue, Synth Sub, Nonauto Tissue Sub, No Dev], [Femor Artery, Rt, Femor Artery, Lt, Femor Arteries, Bilat]

041K[0,4][9,A,J,K,Z][H,J,K,L] Bypass/Femor Artery, Rt, [Opn, Perc Endo], [Auto Venous Tissue, Auto Arterial Tissue, Synth Sub, Nonauto Tissue Sub, No Dev], [Femor Artery, Rt, Femor Artery, Lt, Femor Arteries, Bilat, Popliteal Artery]

041L[0,4][9,A,J,K,Z][H,J,K,L] Bypass/Femor Artery, Lt, [Opn, Perc Endo], [Auto Venous Tissue, Auto Arterial Tissue, Synth Sub, Nonauto Tissue Sub, No Dev], [Femor Artery, Rt, Femor Artery, Lt, Femor Arteries, Bilat, Popliteal Artery]

0450* Destr/Abd Aorta

045K* Destr/Femor Artery, Rt

045L* Destr/Femor Artery, Lt

T Transfer DRG   SP Special Payment   * Code Range   6th and 7th Character of ZZ = No Device, No Qualifier ZX = No Device, Diagnostic

045M*	Destr/Popliteal Artery, Rt
045N*	Destr/Popliteal Artery, Lt
045P*	Destr/Ant Tibial Artery, Rt
045Q*	Destr/Ant Tibial Artery, Lt
045R*	Destr/Posterior Tibial Artery, Rt
045S*	Destr/Posterior Tibial Artery, Lt
045T*	Destr/Peroneal Artery, Rt
045U*	Destr/Peroneal Artery, Lt
045V*	Destr/Foot Artery, Rt
045W*	Destr/Foot Artery, Lt
045Y*	Destr/Lwr Artery
04703[4,D,Z]Z	Dilation/Abd Aorta, Perc, [Drug-eluting Intralum Dev, Intralum Dev, No Dev], NQ
04713[4,D,Z]Z	Dilation/Celiac Artery, Perc, [Drug-eluting Intralum Dev, Intralum Dev, No Dev], NQ
04723[4,D,Z]Z	Dilation/Gastric Artery, Perc, [Drug-eluting Intralum Dev, Intralum Dev, No Dev], NQ
04733[4,D,Z]Z	Dilation/Hepatic Artery, Perc, [Drug-eluting Intralum Dev, Intralum Dev, No Dev], NQ
04743[4,D,Z]Z	Dilation/Splenic Artery, Perc, [Drug-eluting Intralum Dev, Intralum Dev, No Dev], NQ
04753[4,D,Z]Z	Dilation/Superior Mesenteric Artery, Perc, [Drug-eluting Intralum Dev, Intralum Dev, No Dev], NQ
04763[4,D,Z]Z	Dilation/Colic Artery, Rt, Perc, [Drug-eluting Intralum Dev, Intralum Dev, No Dev], NQ
04773[4,D,Z]Z	Dilation/Colic Artery, Lt, Perc, [Drug-eluting Intralum Dev, Intralum Dev, No Dev], NQ
04783[4,D,Z]Z	Dilation/Colic Artery, Mid, Perc, [Drug-eluting Intralum Dev, Intralum Dev, No Dev], NQ
04793[4,D,Z]Z	Dilation/Renal Artery, Rt, Perc, [Drug-eluting Intralum Dev, Intralum Dev, No Dev], NQ
047A3[4,D,Z]Z	Dilation/Renal Artery, Lt, Perc, [Drug-eluting Intralum Dev, Intralum Dev, No Dev], NQ
047B3[4,D,Z]Z	Dilation/Inferior Mesenteric Artery, Perc, [Drug-eluting Intralum Dev, Intralum Dev, No Dev], NQ
047C3[4,D,Z]Z	Dilation/Common Iliac Artery, Rt, Perc, [Drug-eluting Intralum Dev, Intralum Dev, No Dev], NQ
047D3[4,D,Z]Z	Dilation/Common Iliac Artery, Lt, Perc, [Drug-eluting Intralum Dev, Intralum Dev, No Dev], NQ
047E3[4,D,Z]Z	Dilation/Int Iliac Artery, Rt, Perc, [Drug-eluting Intralum Dev, Intralum Dev, No Dev], NQ
047F3[4,D,Z]Z	Dilation/Int Iliac Artery, Lt, Perc, [Drug-eluting Intralum Dev, Intralum Dev, No Dev], NQ
047H3[4,D,Z]Z	Dilation/Ext Iliac Artery, Rt, Perc, [Drug-eluting Intralum Dev, Intralum Dev, No Dev], NQ
047J3[4,D,Z]Z	Dilation/Ext Iliac Artery, Lt, Perc, [Drug-eluting Intralum Dev, Intralum Dev, No Dev], NQ
047K041	Dilation Rt Fem Art w Drug-elut Intralum, Drug Blln, Opn
047K0D1	Dilation Rt Fem Art w Intralum Dev, Drug Blln, Opn
047K0Z1	Dilation of Rt Fem Art using Drug Blln, Opn Appr
047K341	Dilation Rt Fem Art w Drug-elut Intralum, Drug Blln, Perc
047K3D1	Dilation Rt Fem Art w Intralum Dev, Drug Blln, Perc
047K3Z1	Dilation of Rt Fem Art using Drug Blln, Perc Appr
047K3[4,D,Z]Z	Dilation/Femor Artery, Rt, Perc, [Drug-eluting Intralum Dev, Intralum Dev, No Dev], NQ
047K441	Dilation Rt Fem Art w Drug-elut Intralum, Drug Blln, Perc Endo
047K4D1	Dilation Rt Fem Art w Intralum Dev, Drug Blln, Perc Endo
047K4Z1	Dilation of Rt Fem Art using Drug Blln, Perc Endo Appr
047L041	Dilation Lt Fem Art w Drug-elut Intralum, Drug Blln, Opn
047L0D1	Dilation Lt Fem Art w Intralum Dev, Drug Blln, Opn
047L0Z1	Dilation of Lt Fem Art using Drug Blln, Opn Appr
047L341	Dilation Lt Fem Art w Drug-elut Intralum, Drug Blln, Perc
047L3D1	Dilation Lt Fem Art w Intralum Dev, Drug Blln, Perc
047L3Z1	Dilation of Lt Fem Art using Drug Blln, Perc Appr
047L3[4,D,Z]Z	Dilation/Femor Artery, Lt, Perc, [Drug-eluting Intralum Dev, Intralum Dev, No Dev], NQ
047L441	Dilation Lt Fem Art w Drug-elut Intralum, Drug Blln, Perc Endo
047L4D1	Dilation Lt Fem Art w Intralum Dev, Drug Blln, Perc Endo
047L4Z1	Dilation of Lt Fem Art using Drug Blln, Perc Endo Appr
047M041	Dilation Rt Popl Art w Drug-elut Intralum, Drug Blln, Opn
047M0D1	Dilation Rt Popl Art w Intralum Dev, Drug Blln, Opn
047M0Z1	Dilation of Rt Popl Art using Drug Blln, Opn Appr
047M341	Dilation Rt Popl Art w Drug-elut Intralum, Drug Blln, Perc
047M3D1	Dilation Rt Popl Art w Intralum Dev, Drug Blln, Perc
047M3Z1	Dilation of Rt Popl Art using Drug Blln, Perc Appr
047M441	Dilation Rt Popl Art w Drug-elut Intralum, Drug Blln, Perc Endo
047M4D1	Dilation Rt Popl Art w Intralum Dev, Drug Blln, Perc Endo
047M4Z1	Dilation of Rt Popl Art using Drug Blln, Perc Endo Appr
047N041	Dilation Lt Popl Art w Drug-elut Intralum, Drug Blln, Opn
047N0D1	Dilation Lt Popl Art w Intralum Dev, Drug Blln, Opn
047N0Z1	Dilation of Lt Popl Art using Drug Blln, Opn Appr
047N341	Dilation Lt Popl Art w Drug-elut Intralum, Drug Blln, Perc
047N3D1	Dilation Lt Popl Art w Intralum Dev, Drug Blln, Perc
047N3Z1	Dilation of Lt Popl Art using Drug Blln, Perc Appr
047N441	Dilation Lt Popl Art w Drug-elut Intralum, Drug Blln, Perc Endo
047N4D1	Dilation Lt Popl Art w Intralum Dev, Drug Blln, Perc Endo
047N4Z1	Dilation of Lt Popl Art using Drug Blln, Perc Endo Appr
047Y3[4,D,Z]Z	Dilation/Lwr Artery, Perc, [Drug-eluting Intralum Dev, Intralum Dev, No Dev], NQ
04B0[0,3,4]ZZ	Exc/Abd Aorta, [Opn, Perc, Perc Endo]
04BK[0,3,4]ZZ	Exc/Femor Artery, Rt, [Opn, Perc, Perc Endo]
04BL[0,3,4]ZZ	Exc/Femor Artery, Lt, [Opn, Perc, Perc Endo]
04BM[0,3,4]ZZ	Exc/Popliteal Artery, Rt, [Opn, Perc, Perc Endo]
04BN[0,3,4]ZZ	Exc/Popliteal Artery, Lt, [Opn, Perc, Perc Endo]
04BP[0,3,4]ZZ	Exc/Ant Tibial Artery, Rt, [Opn, Perc, Perc Endo]
04BQ[0,3,4]ZZ	Exc/Ant Tibial Artery, Lt, [Opn, Perc, Perc Endo]
04BR[0,3,4]ZZ	Exc/Post Tibial Artery, Rt, [Opn, Perc, Perc Endo]
04BS[0,3,4]ZZ	Exc/Post Tibial Artery, Lt, [Opn, Perc, Perc Endo]
04BT[0,3,4]ZZ	Exc/Peroneal Artery, Rt, [Opn, Perc, Perc Endo]
04BU[0,3,4]ZZ	Exc/Peroneal Artery, Lt, [Opn, Perc, Perc Endo]
04BV[0,3,4]ZZ	Exc/Foot Artery, Rt, [Opn, Perc, Perc Endo]
04BW[0,3,4]ZZ	Exc/Foot Artery, Lt, [Opn, Perc, Perc Endo]
04BY[0,3,4]ZZ	Exc/Lwr Artery, [Opn, Perc, Perc Endo]
04C*	Lwr Arteries, Extir
04H0[0,3,4]DZ	Insert/Abd Aorta, [Opn, Perc, Perc Endo], Intralum Dev, NQ
04H1[0,3,4]DZ	Insert/Celiac Artery, [Opn, Perc, Perc Endo], Intralum Dev, NQ
04H2[0,3,4]DZ	Insert/Gastric Artery, [Opn, Perc, Perc Endo], Intralum Dev, NQ
04H3[0,3,4]DZ	Insert/Hepatic Artery, [Opn, Perc, Perc Endo], Intralum Dev, NQ
04H4[0,3,4]DZ	Insert/Splenic Artery, [Opn, Perc, Perc Endo], Intralum Dev, NQ
04H5[0,3,4]DZ	Insert/Superior Mesenteric Artery, [Opn, Perc, Perc Endo], Intralum Dev, NQ
04H6[0,3,4]DZ	Insert/Colic Artery, Rt, [Opn, Perc, Perc Endo], Intralum Dev, NQ
04H7[0,3,4]DZ	Insert/Colic Artery, Lt, [Opn, Perc, Perc Endo], Intralum Dev, NQ
04H8[0,3,4]DZ	Insert/Colic Artery, Mid, [Opn, Perc, Perc Endo], Intralum Dev, NQ
04H9[0,3,4]DZ	Insert/Renal Artery, Rt, [Opn, Perc, Perc Endo], Intralum Dev, NQ
04HA[0,3,4]DZ	Insert/Renal Artery, Lt, [Opn, Perc, Perc Endo], Intralum Dev, NQ
04HB[0,3,4]DZ	Insert/Inferior Mesenteric Artery, [Opn, Perc, Perc Endo], Intralum Dev, NQ
04HC[0,3,4]DZ	Insert/Common Iliac Artery, Rt, [Opn, Perc, Perc Endo], Intralum Dev, NQ
04HD[0,3,4]DZ	Insert/Common Iliac Artery, Lt, [Opn, Perc, Perc Endo], Intralum Dev, NQ
04HE[0,3,4]DZ	Insert/Int Iliac Artery, Rt, [Opn, Perc, Perc Endo], Intralum Dev, NQ
04HF[0,3,4]DZ	Insert/Int Iliac Artery, Lt, [Opn, Perc, Perc Endo], Intralum Dev, NQ
04HH[0,3,4]DZ	Insert/Ext Iliac Artery, Rt, [Opn, Perc, Perc Endo], Intralum Dev, NQ
04HJ[0,3,4]DZ	Insert/Ext Iliac Artery, Lt, [Opn, Perc, Perc Endo], Intralum Dev, NQ
04HK[0,3,4]DZ	Insert/Femor Artery, Rt, [Opn, Perc, Perc Endo], Intralum Dev, NQ
04HL[0,3,4]DZ	Insert/Femor Artery, Lt, [Opn, Perc, Perc Endo], Intralum Dev, NQ
04HM[0,3,4]DZ	Insert/Popliteal Artery, Rt, [Opn, Perc, Perc Endo], Intralum Dev, NQ
04HN[0,3,4]DZ	Insert/Popliteal Artery, Lt, [Opn, Perc, Perc Endo], Intralum Dev, NQ
04HP[0,3,4]DZ	Insert/Ant Tibial Artery, Rt, [Opn, Perc, Perc Endo], Intralum Dev, NQ
04HQ[0,3,4]DZ	Insert/Ant Tibial Artery, Lt, [Opn, Perc, Perc Endo], Intralum Dev, NQ
04HR[0,3,4]DZ	Insert/Post Tibial Artery, Rt, [Opn, Perc, Perc Endo], Intralum Dev, NQ
04HS[0,3,4]DZ	Insert/Post Tibial Artery, Lt, [Opn, Perc, Perc Endo], Intralum Dev, NQ
04HT[0,3,4]DZ	Insert/Peroneal Artery, Rt, [Opn, Perc, Perc Endo], Intralum Dev, NQ
04HU[0,3,4]DZ	Insert/Peroneal Artery, Lt, [Opn, Perc, Perc Endo], Intralum Dev, NQ
04HV[0,3,4]DZ	Insert/Foot Artery, Rt, [Opn, Perc, Perc Endo], Intralum Dev, NQ
04HW[0,3,4]DZ	Insert/Foot Artery, Lt, [Opn, Perc, Perc Endo], Intralum Dev, NQ

MDC 21: Injuries, Poisonings And Toxic Effects Of Drugs—SURGICAL

Surgical **Medical** **CC Indicator** **MCC Indicator** **Procedure Proxy** [PDxMCC] **PDx acts as own MCC** [PDxCC] **PDx acts as own CC**

Code	Description
04HY[Ø,3,4][2,D]Z	Insert/Lwr Artery, [Opn, Perc, Perc Endo], [Monitoring Dev, Intralum Dev], NQ
04LØ*	Occlsn/Abd Aorta
04L1*	Occlsn/Celiac Artery
04L2[Ø,3,4][C,Z]Z	Occlsn/Gastric Artery, [Opn, Perc, Perc Endo], [Extralum Dev, No Dev], NQ
04L2[Ø,4]DZ	Occlsn/Gastric Artery, [Opn, Perc Endo], Intralum Dev, NQ
04L3*	Occlsn/Hepatic Artery
04L4*	Occlsn/Splenic Artery
04L5*	Occlsn/Superior Mesenteric Artery
04L6*	Occlsn/Colic Artery, Rt
04L7*	Occlsn/Colic Artery, Lt
04L8*	Occlsn/Colic Artery, Mid
04L9*	Occlsn/Renal Artery, Rt
04LA*	Occlsn/Renal Artery, Lt
04LB*	Occlsn/Inferior Mesenteric Artery
04LC*	Occlsn/Common Iliac Artery, Rt
04LD*	Occlsn/Common Iliac Artery, Lt
04LE[Ø,3,4][C,D,Z]Z	Occlsn/Int Iliac Artery, Rt, [Opn, Perc, Perc Endo], [Extralum Dev, Intralum Dev, No Dev], NQ
04LF[Ø,3,4][C,D,Z]Z	Occlsn/Int Iliac Artery, Lt, [Opn, Perc, Perc Endo], [Extralum Dev, Intralum Dev, No Dev], NQ
04LH*	Occlsn/Ext Iliac Artery, Rt
04LJ*	Occlsn/Ext Iliac Artery, Lt
04LK*	Occlsn/Femor Artery, Rt
04LL*	Occlsn/Femor Artery, Lt
04LM*	Occlsn/Popliteal Artery, Rt
04LN*	Occlsn/Popliteal Artery, Lt
04LP*	Occlsn/Ant Tibial Artery, Rt
04LQ*	Occlsn/Ant Tibial Artery, Lt
04LR*	Occlsn/Posterior Tibial Artery, Rt
04LS*	Occlsn/Posterior Tibial Artery, Lt
04LT*	Occlsn/Peroneal Artery, Rt
04LU*	Occlsn/Peroneal Artery, Lt
04LV*	Occlsn/Foot Artery, Rt
04LW*	Occlsn/Foot Artery, Lt
04LY*	Occlsn/Lwr Artery
04PY[Ø,3,4][Ø,2,3,C,D]Z	Rmvl/Lwr Artery, [Opn, Perc, Perc Endo], [Drain Dev, Monitoring Dev, Inf Dev, Extralum Dev, Intralum Dev], NQ
04Q*	Lwr Arteries, Repair
04RØ*	Replace/Abd Aorta
04R1*	Replace/Celiac Artery
04R2*	Replace/Gastric Artery
04R3*	Replace/Hepatic Artery
04R4*	Replace/Splenic Artery
04R5*	Replace/Superior Mesenteric Artery
04R6*	Replace/Colic Artery, Rt
04R7*	Replace/Colic Artery, Lt
04R8*	Replace/Colic Artery, Mid
04RB*	Replace/Inferior Mesenteric Artery
04RC*	Replace/Common Iliac Artery, Rt
04RD*	Replace/Common Iliac Artery, Lt
04RE*	Replace/Int Iliac Artery, Rt
04RF*	Replace/Int Iliac Artery, Lt
04RH*	Replace/Ext Iliac Artery, Rt
04RJ*	Replace/Ext Iliac Artery, Lt
04RK*	Replace/Femor Artery, Rt
04RL*	Replace/Femor Artery, Lt
04RM*	Replace/Popliteal Artery, Rt
04RN*	Replace/Popliteal Artery, Lt
04RP*	Replace/Ant Tibial Artery, Rt
04RQ*	Replace/Ant Tibial Artery, Lt
04RR*	Replace/Posterior Tibial Artery, Rt
04RS*	Replace/Posterior Tibial Artery, Lt
04RT*	Replace/Peroneal Artery, Rt
04RU*	Replace/Peroneal Artery, Lt
04RV*	Replace/Foot Artery, Rt
04RW*	Replace/Foot Artery, Lt
04RY*	Replace/Lwr Artery
04SØ*	Repos/Abd Aorta
04S1*	Repos/Celiac Artery
04S2*	Repos/Gastric Artery
04S3*	Repos/Hepatic Artery
04S4*	Repos/Splenic Artery
04S5*	Repos/Superior Mesenteric Artery
04S6*	Repos/Colic Artery, Rt
04S7*	Repos/Colic Artery, Lt
04S8*	Repos/Colic Artery, Mid
04SB*	Repos/Inferior Mesenteric Artery
04SC*	Repos/Common Iliac Artery, Rt
04SD*	Repos/Common Iliac Artery, Lt
04SE*	Repos/Int Iliac Artery, Rt
04SF*	Repos/Int Iliac Artery, Lt
04SH*	Repos/Ext Iliac Artery, Rt
04SJ*	Repos/Ext Iliac Artery, Lt
04SK*	Repos/Femor Artery, Rt
04SL*	Repos/Femor Artery, Lt
04SM*	Repos/Popliteal Artery, Rt
04SN*	Repos/Popliteal Artery, Lt
04SP*	Repos/Ant Tibial Artery, Rt
04SQ*	Repos/Ant Tibial Artery, Lt
04SR*	Repos/Posterior Tibial Artery, Rt
04SS*	Repos/Posterior Tibial Artery, Lt
04ST*	Repos/Peroneal Artery, Rt
04SU*	Repos/Peroneal Artery, Lt
04SV*	Repos/Foot Artery, Rt
04SW*	Repos/Foot Artery, Lt
04SY*	Repos/Lwr Artery
04U0[Ø,3,4][7,J]Z	Supl/Abd Aorta, [Opn, Perc, Perc Endo], [Auto Tissue Sub, Synth Sub], NQ
04U1[Ø,3,4][7,J]Z	Supl/Celiac Artery, [Opn, Perc, Perc Endo], [Auto Tissue Sub, Synth Sub], NQ
04U2[Ø,3,4][7,J]Z	Supl/Gastric Artery, [Opn, Perc, Perc Endo], [Auto Tissue Sub, Synth Sub], NQ
04U3[Ø,3,4][7,J]Z	Supl/Hepatic Artery, [Opn, Perc, Perc Endo], [Auto Tissue Sub, Synth Sub], NQ
04U4[Ø,3,4][7,J]Z	Supl/Splenic Artery, [Opn, Perc, Perc Endo], [Auto Tissue Sub, Synth Sub], NQ
04U5[Ø,3,4][7,J]Z	Supl/Superior Mesenteric Artery, [Opn, Perc, Perc Endo], [Auto Tissue Sub, Synth Sub], NQ
04U6[Ø,3,4][7,J]Z	Supl/Colic Artery, Rt, [Opn, Perc, Perc Endo], [Auto Tissue Sub, Synth Sub], NQ
04U7[Ø,3,4][7,J]Z	Supl/Colic Artery, Lt, [Opn, Perc, Perc Endo], [Auto Tissue Sub, Synth Sub], NQ
04U8[Ø,3,4][7,J]Z	Supl/Colic Artery, Mid, [Opn, Perc, Perc Endo], [Auto Tissue Sub, Synth Sub], NQ
04U9[Ø,3,4][7,J]Z	Supl/Renal Artery, Rt, [Opn, Perc, Perc Endo], [Auto Tissue Sub, Synth Sub], NQ
04UA[Ø,3,4][7,J]Z	Supl/Renal Artery, Lt, [Opn, Perc, Perc Endo], [Auto Tissue Sub, Synth Sub], NQ
04UB[Ø,3,4][7,J]Z	Supl/Inferior Mesenteric Artery, [Opn, Perc, Perc Endo], [Auto Tissue Sub, Synth Sub], NQ
04UC[Ø,3,4][7,J]Z	Supl/Common Iliac Artery, Rt, [Opn, Perc, Perc Endo], [Auto Tissue Sub, Synth Sub], NQ
04UD[Ø,3,4][7,J]Z	Supl/Common Iliac Artery, Lt, [Opn, Perc, Perc Endo], [Auto Tissue Sub, Synth Sub], NQ
04UE[Ø,3,4][7,J]Z	Supl/Int Iliac Artery, Rt, [Opn, Perc, Perc Endo], [Auto Tissue Sub, Synth Sub], NQ
04UF[Ø,3,4][7,J]Z	Supl/Int Iliac Artery, Lt, [Opn, Perc, Perc Endo], [Auto Tissue Sub, Synth Sub], NQ
04UH[Ø,3,4][7,J]Z	Supl/Ext Iliac Artery, Rt, [Opn, Perc, Perc Endo], [Auto Tissue Sub, Synth Sub], NQ
04UJ[Ø,3,4][7,J]Z	Supl/Ext Iliac Artery, Lt, [Opn, Perc, Perc Endo], [Auto Tissue Sub, Synth Sub], NQ
04UK[Ø,3,4][7,J]Z	Supl/Femor Artery, Rt, [Opn, Perc, Perc Endo], [Auto Tissue Sub, Synth Sub], NQ
04UL[Ø,3,4][7,J]Z	Supl/Femor Artery, Lt, [Opn, Perc, Perc Endo], [Auto Tissue Sub, Synth Sub], NQ
04UM[Ø,3,4][7,J]Z	Supl/Popliteal Artery, Rt, [Opn, Perc, Perc Endo], [Auto Tissue Sub, Synth Sub], NQ
04UN[Ø,3,4][7,J]Z	Supl/Popliteal Artery, Lt, [Opn, Perc, Perc Endo], [Auto Tissue Sub, Synth Sub], NQ
04UP[Ø,3,4][7,J]Z	Supl/Ant Tibial Artery, Rt, [Opn, Perc, Perc Endo], [Auto Tissue Sub, Synth Sub], NQ
04UQ[Ø,3,4][7,J]Z	Supl/Ant Tibial Artery, Lt, [Opn, Perc, Perc Endo], [Auto Tissue Sub, Synth Sub], NQ
04UR[Ø,3,4][7,J]Z	Supl/Post Tibial Artery, Rt, [Opn, Perc, Perc Endo], [Auto Tissue Sub, Synth Sub], NQ
04US[Ø,3,4][7,J]Z	Supl/Post Tibial Artery, Lt, [Opn, Perc, Perc Endo], [Auto Tissue Sub, Synth Sub], NQ
04UT[Ø,3,4][7,J]Z	Supl/Peroneal Artery, Rt, [Opn, Perc, Perc Endo], [Auto Tissue Sub, Synth Sub], NQ
04UU[Ø,3,4][7,J]Z	Supl/Peroneal Artery, Lt, [Opn, Perc, Perc Endo], [Auto Tissue Sub, Synth Sub], NQ
04UV[Ø,3,4][7,J]Z	Supl/Foot Artery, Rt, [Opn, Perc, Perc Endo], [Auto Tissue Sub, Synth Sub], NQ
04UW[Ø,3,4][7,J]Z	Supl/Foot Artery, Lt, [Opn, Perc, Perc Endo], [Auto Tissue Sub, Synth Sub], NQ
04UY[Ø,3,4][7,J]Z	Supl/Lwr Artery, [Opn, Perc, Perc Endo], [Auto Tissue Sub, Synth Sub], NQ

Ⓣ **Transfer DRG**　　Ⓢ **Special Payment**　　* **Code Range**　　**6th and 7th Character of ZZ = No Device, No Qualifier ZX = No Device, Diagnostic**

04V0[0,3,4]DJ	Restrict/Abd Aorta, [Opn, Perc, Perc Endo], Intralum Dev, Temporary
04V0[0,3,4][D,Z]Z	Restrict/Abd Aorta, [Opn, Perc, Perc Endo], [Intralum Dev, No Dev], NQ
04V1[0,3,4][D,Z]Z	Restrict/Celiac Artery, [Opn, Perc, Perc Endo], [Intralum Dev, No Dev], NQ
04V2[0,3,4][D,Z]Z	Restrict/Gastric Artery, [Opn, Perc, Perc Endo], [Intralum Dev, No Dev], NQ
04V3[0,3,4][D,Z]Z	Restrict/Hepatic Artery, [Opn, Perc, Perc Endo], [Intralum Dev, No Dev], NQ
04V4[0,3,4][D,Z]Z	Restrict/Splenic Artery, [Opn, Perc, Perc Endo], [Intralum Dev, No Dev], NQ
04V5[0,3,4][D,Z]Z	Restrict/Superior Mesenteric Artery, [Opn, Perc, Perc Endo], [Intralum Dev, No Dev], NQ
04V6[0,3,4][D,Z]Z	Restrict/Colic Artery, Rt, [Opn, Perc, Perc Endo], [Intralum Dev, No Dev], NQ
04V7[0,3,4][D,Z]Z	Restrict/Colic Artery, Lt, [Opn, Perc, Perc Endo], [Intralum Dev, No Dev], NQ
04V8[0,3,4][D,Z]Z	Restrict/Colic Artery, Mid, [Opn, Perc, Perc Endo], [Intralum Dev, No Dev], NQ
04V9[0,3,4][D,Z]Z	Restrict/Renal Artery, Rt, [Opn, Perc, Perc Endo], [Intralum Dev, No Dev], NQ
04VA[0,3,4][D,Z]Z	Restrict/Renal Artery, Lt, [Opn, Perc, Perc Endo], [Intralum Dev, No Dev], NQ
04VB[0,3,4][D,Z]Z	Restrict/Inferior Mesenteric Artery, [Opn, Perc, Perc Endo], [Intralum Dev, No Dev], NQ
04VC[0,3,4][D,Z]Z	Restrict/Common Iliac Artery, Rt, [Opn, Perc, Perc Endo], [Intralum Dev, No Dev], NQ
04VD[0,3,4][D,Z]Z	Restrict/Common Iliac Artery, Lt, [Opn, Perc, Perc Endo], [Intralum Dev, No Dev], NQ
04VE[0,3,4][D,Z]Z	Restrict/Int Iliac Artery, Rt, [Opn, Perc, Perc Endo], [Intralum Dev, No Dev], NQ
04VF[0,3,4][D,Z]Z	Restrict/Int Iliac Artery, Lt, [Opn, Perc, Perc Endo], [Intralum Dev, No Dev], NQ
04VH[0,3,4][D,Z]Z	Restrict/Ext Iliac Artery, Rt, [Opn, Perc, Perc Endo], [Intralum Dev, No Dev], NQ
04VJ[0,3,4][D,Z]Z	Restrict/Ext Iliac Artery, Lt, [Opn, Perc, Perc Endo], [Intralum Dev, No Dev], NQ
04VK[0,3,4][D,Z]Z	Restrict/Femor Artery, Rt, [Opn, Perc, Perc Endo], [Intralum Dev, No Dev], NQ
04VL[0,3,4][D,Z]Z	Restrict/Femor Artery, Lt, [Opn, Perc, Perc Endo], [Intralum Dev, No Dev], NQ
04VM[0,3,4][D,Z]Z	Restrict/Popliteal Artery, Rt, [Opn, Perc, Perc Endo], [Intralum Dev, No Dev], NQ
04VN[0,3,4][D,Z]Z	Restrict/Popliteal Artery, Lt, [Opn, Perc, Perc Endo], [Intralum Dev, No Dev], NQ
04VP[0,3,4][D,Z]Z	Restrict/Ant Tibial Artery, Rt, [Opn, Perc, Perc Endo], [Intralum Dev, No Dev], NQ
04VQ[0,3,4][D,Z]Z	Restrict/Ant Tibial Artery, Lt, [Opn, Perc, Perc Endo], [Intralum Dev, No Dev], NQ
04VR[0,3,4][D,Z]Z	Restrict/Post Tibial Artery, Rt, [Opn, Perc, Perc Endo], [Intralum Dev, No Dev], NQ
04VS[0,3,4][D,Z]Z	Restrict/Post Tibial Artery, Lt, [Opn, Perc, Perc Endo], [Intralum Dev, No Dev], NQ
04VT[0,3,4][D,Z]Z	Restrict/Peroneal Artery, Rt, [Opn, Perc, Perc Endo], [Intralum Dev, No Dev], NQ
04VU[0,3,4][D,Z]Z	Restrict/Peroneal Artery, Lt, [Opn, Perc, Perc Endo], [Intralum Dev, No Dev], NQ
04VV[0,3,4][D,Z]Z	Restrict/Foot Artery, Rt, [Opn, Perc, Perc Endo], [Intralum Dev, No Dev], NQ
04VW[0,3,4][D,Z]Z	Restrict/Foot Artery, Lt, [Opn, Perc, Perc Endo], [Intralum Dev, No Dev], NQ
04VY[0,3,4][D,Z]Z	Restrict/Lwr Artery, [Opn, Perc, Perc Endo], [Intralum Dev, No Dev], NQ
04WY[0,3,4][0,2,3,C,D]Z	Rev/Lwr Artery, [Opn, Perc, Perc Endo], [Drain Dev, Monitoring Dev, Inf Dev, Extralum Dev, Intralum Dev], NQ
0510*	Bypass/Azygos Vein
0511*	Bypass/Hemiazygos Vein
0513*	Bypass/Innominate Vein, Rt
0514*	Bypass/Innominate Vein, Lt
0515*	Bypass/Subclavian Vein, Rt
0516*	Bypass/Subclavian Vein, Lt
0557*	Destr/Axillary Vein, Rt
0558*	Destr/Axillary Vein, Lt
0559*	Destr/Brachial Vein, Rt
055A*	Destr/Brachial Vein, Lt
055B*	Destr/Basilic Vein, Rt
055C*	Destr/Basilic Vein, Lt
055D*	Destr/Cephalic Vein, Rt
055F*	Destr/Cephalic Vein, Lt
055G*	Destr/Hand Vein, Rt
055H*	Destr/Hand Vein, Lt
055L*	Destr/Intracranial Vein
055M*	Destr/Int Jugular Vein, Rt
055N*	Destr/Int Jugular Vein, Lt
055P*	Destr/Ext Jugular Vein, Rt
055Q*	Destr/Ext Jugular Vein, Lt
055R*	Destr/Vert Vein, Rt
055S*	Destr/Vert Vein, Lt
055T*	Destr/Face Vein, Rt
055V*	Destr/Face Vein, Lt
055Y*	Destr/Upr Vein
05793[D,Z]Z	Dilation/Brachial Vein, Rt, Perc, [Intralum Dev, No Dev], NQ
057A3[D,Z]Z	Dilation/Brachial Vein, Lt, Perc, [Intralum Dev, No Dev], NQ
057B3[D,Z]Z	Dilation/Basilic Vein, Rt, Perc, [Intralum Dev, No Dev], NQ
057C3[D,Z]Z	Dilation/Basilic Vein, Lt, Perc, [Intralum Dev, No Dev], NQ
057D3[D,Z]Z	Dilation/Cephalic Vein, Rt, Perc, [Intralum Dev, No Dev], NQ
057F3[D,Z]Z	Dilation/Cephalic Vein, Lt, Perc, [Intralum Dev, No Dev], NQ
057L[3,4]DZ	Dilation/Intracranial Vein, [Perc, Perc Endo], Intralum Dev, NQ
057M[3,4]DZ	Dilation/Int Jugular Vein, Rt, [Perc, Perc Endo], Intralum Dev, NQ
057N[3,4]DZ	Dilation/Int Jugular Vein, Lt, [Perc, Perc Endo], Intralum Dev, NQ
057P[3,4]DZ	Dilation/Ext Jugular Vein, Rt, [Perc, Perc Endo], Intralum Dev, NQ
057Q[3,4]DZ	Dilation/Ext Jugular Vein, Lt, [Perc, Perc Endo], Intralum Dev, NQ
057R[3,4]DZ	Dilation/Vert Vein, Rt, [Perc, Perc Endo], Intralum Dev, NQ
057S[3,4]DZ	Dilation/Vert Vein, Lt, [Perc, Perc Endo], Intralum Dev, NQ
057T[3,4]DZ	Dilation/Face Vein, Rt, [Perc, Perc Endo], Intralum Dev, NQ
05B7[0,3,4]ZZ	Exc/Axillary Vein, Rt, [Opn, Perc, Perc Endo]
05B8[0,3,4]ZZ	Exc/Axillary Vein, Lt, [Opn, Perc, Perc Endo]
05B9[0,3,4]ZZ	Exc/Brachial Vein, Rt, [Opn, Perc, Perc Endo]
05BA[0,3,4]ZZ	Exc/Brachial Vein, Lt, [Opn, Perc, Perc Endo]
05BB[0,3,4]ZZ	Exc/Basilic Vein, Rt, [Opn, Perc, Perc Endo]
05BC[0,3,4]ZZ	Exc/Basilic Vein, Lt, [Opn, Perc, Perc Endo]
05BD[0,3,4]ZZ	Exc/Cephalic Vein, Rt, [Opn, Perc, Perc Endo]
05BF[0,3,4]ZZ	Exc/Cephalic Vein, Lt, [Opn, Perc, Perc Endo]
05BG[0,3,4]ZZ	Exc/Hand Vein, Rt, [Opn, Perc, Perc Endo]
05BH[0,3,4]ZZ	Exc/Hand Vein, Lt, [Opn, Perc, Perc Endo]
05BL[0,3,4]ZZ	Exc/Intracranial Vein, [Opn, Perc, Perc Endo]
05BM[0,3,4]ZZ	Exc/Int Jugular Vein, Rt, [Opn, Perc, Perc Endo]
05BN[0,3,4]ZZ	Exc/Int Jugular Vein, Lt, [Opn, Perc, Perc Endo]
05BP[0,3,4]ZZ	Exc/Ext Jugular Vein, Rt, [Opn, Perc, Perc Endo]
05BQ[0,3,4]ZZ	Exc/Ext Jugular Vein, Lt, [Opn, Perc, Perc Endo]
05BR[0,3,4]ZZ	Exc/Vert Vein, Rt, [Opn, Perc, Perc Endo]
05BS[0,3,4]ZZ	Exc/Vert Vein, Lt, [Opn, Perc, Perc Endo]
05BT[0,3,4]ZZ	Exc/Face Vein, Rt, [Opn, Perc, Perc Endo]
05BV[0,3,4]ZZ	Exc/Face Vein, Lt, [Opn, Perc, Perc Endo]
05BY[0,3,4]ZZ	Exc/Upr Vein, [Opn, Perc, Perc Endo]
05C7*	Extir/Axillary Vein, Rt
05C8*	Extir/Axillary Vein, Lt
05C9*	Extir/Brachial Vein, Rt
05CA*	Extir/Brachial Vein, Lt
05CB*	Extir/Basilic Vein, Rt
05CC*	Extir/Basilic Vein, Lt
05CD*	Extir/Cephalic Vein, Rt
05CF*	Extir/Cephalic Vein, Lt
05CG*	Extir/Hand Vein, Rt
05CH*	Extir/Hand Vein, Lt
05CL*	Extir/Intracranial Vein
05CM*	Extir/Int Jugular Vein, Rt
05CN*	Extir/Int Jugular Vein, Lt
05CP*	Extir/Ext Jugular Vein, Rt
05CQ*	Extir/Ext Jugular Vein, Lt
05CR*	Extir/Vert Vein, Rt
05CS*	Extir/Vert Vein, Lt
05CT*	Extir/Face Vein, Rt
05CV*	Extir/Face Vein, Lt
05CY*	Extir/Upr Vein
05H0[0,3,4]DZ	Insert/Azygos Vein, [Opn, Perc, Perc Endo], Intralum Dev, NQ
05H1[0,3,4]DZ	Insert/Hemiazygos Vein, [Opn, Perc, Perc Endo], Intralum Dev, NQ
05H3[0,3,4]DZ	Insert/Innominate Vein, Rt, [Opn, Perc, Perc Endo], Intralum Dev, NQ
05H4[0,3,4]DZ	Insert/Innominate Vein, Lt, [Opn, Perc, Perc Endo], Intralum Dev, NQ
05H5[0,3,4]DZ	Insert/Subclavian Vein, Rt, [Opn, Perc, Perc Endo], Intralum Dev, NQ

Surgical   **Medical**   **CC Indicator**   **MCC Indicator**   **Procedure Proxy**   PDxMCC **PDx acts as own MCC**   PDxCC **PDx acts as own CC**

MDC 21: Injuries, Poisonings And Toxic Effects Of Drugs—SURGICAL

05H6[0,3,4]DZ	Insert/Subclavian Vein, Lt, [Opn, Perc, Perc Endo], Intralum Dev, NQ
05H7[0,3,4]DZ	Insert/Axillary Vein, Rt [Opn, Perc, Perc Endo], Intralum Dev, NQ
05H8[0,3,4]DZ	Insert/Axillary Vein, Lt, [Opn, Perc, Perc Endo], Intralum Dev, NQ
05H9[0,3,4]DZ	Insert/Brachial Vein, Rt, [Opn, Perc, Perc Endo], Intralum Dev, NQ
05HA[0,3,4]DZ	Insert/Brachial Vein, Lt, [Opn, Perc, Perc Endo], Intralum Dev, NQ
05HB[0,3,4]DZ	Insert/Basilic Vein, Rt, [Opn, Perc, Perc Endo], Intralum Dev, NQ
05HC[0,3,4]DZ	Insert/Basilic Vein, Lt, [Opn, Perc, Perc Endo], Intralum Dev, NQ
05HD[0,3,4]DZ	Insert/Cephalic Vein, Rt, [Opn, Perc, Perc Endo], Intralum Dev, NQ
05HF[0,3,4]DZ	Insert/Cephalic Vein, Lt, [Opn, Perc, Perc Endo], Intralum Dev, NQ
05HG[0,3,4]DZ	Insert/Hand Vein, Rt, [Opn, Perc, Perc Endo], Intralum Dev, NQ
05HH[0,3,4]DZ	Insert/Hand Vein, Lt, [Opn, Perc, Perc Endo], Intralum Dev, NQ
05HL[0,3,4]DZ	Insert/Intracranial Vein, [Opn, Perc, Perc Endo], Intralum Dev, NQ
05HM[0,3,4]DZ	Insert/Int Jugular Vein, Rt, [Opn, Perc, Perc Endo], Intralum Dev, NQ
05HN[0,3,4]DZ	Insert/Int Jugular Vein, Lt, [Opn, Perc, Perc Endo], Intralum Dev, NQ
05HP[0,3,4]DZ	Insert/Ext Jugular Vein, Rt, [Opn, Perc, Perc Endo], Intralum Dev, NQ
05HQ[0,3,4]DZ	Insert/Ext Jugular Vein, Lt, [Opn, Perc, Perc Endo], Intralum Dev, NQ
05HR[0,3,4]DZ	Insert/Vert Vein, Rt, [Opn, Perc, Perc Endo], Intralum Dev, NQ
05HS[0,3,4]DZ	Insert/Vert Vein, Lt, [Opn, Perc, Perc Endo], Intralum Dev, NQ
05HT[0,3,4]DZ	Insert/Face Vein, Rt, [Opn, Perc, Perc Endo], Intralum Dev, NQ
05HV[0,3,4]DZ	Insert/Face Vein, Lt, [Opn, Perc, Perc Endo], Intralum Dev, NQ
05HY[0,3,4][2,D]Z	Insert/Upr Vein, [Opn, Perc, Perc Endo], [Monitoring Dev, Intralum Dev], NQ
05L*	Upr Veins, Occlsn
05Q*	Upr Veins, Repair
05R0*	Replace/Azygos Vein
05R1*	Replace/Hemiazygos Vein
05R3*	Replace/Innominate Vein, Rt
05R4*	Replace/Innominate Vein, Lt
05R5*	Replace/Subclavian Vein, Rt
05R6*	Replace/Subclavian Vein, Lt
05R7*	Replace/Axillary Vein, Rt
05R8*	Replace/Axillary Vein, Lt
05R9*	Replace/Brachial Vein, Rt
05RA*	Replace/Brachial Vein, Lt
05RB*	Replace/Basilic Vein, Rt
05RC*	Replace/Basilic Vein, Lt
05RD*	Replace/Cephalic Vein, Rt
05RF*	Replace/Cephalic Vein, Lt
05RG*	Replace/Hand Vein, Rt
05RH*	Replace/Hand Vein, Lt
05RL*	Replace/Intracranial Vein
05RY*	Replace/Upr Vein
05S*	Upr Veins, Repos
05U0[0,3,4][7,J]Z	Supl/Azygos Vein, [Opn, Perc, Perc Endo], [Auto Tissue Sub, Synth Sub], NQ
05U1[0,3,4][7,J]Z	Supl/Hemiazygos Vein, [Opn, Perc, Perc Endo], [Auto Tissue Sub, Synth Sub], NQ
05U3[0,3,4][7,J]Z	Supl/Innominate Vein, Rt, [Opn, Perc, Perc Endo], [Auto Tissue Sub, Synth Sub], NQ
05U4[0,3,4][7,J]Z	Supl/Innominate Vein, Lt, [Opn, Perc, Perc Endo], [Auto Tissue Sub, Synth Sub], NQ
05U5[0,3,4][7,J]Z	Supl/Subclavian Vein, Rt, [Opn, Perc, Perc Endo], [Auto Tissue Sub, Synth Sub], NQ
05U6[0,3,4][7,J]Z	Supl/Subclavian Vein, Lt, [Opn, Perc, Perc Endo], [Auto Tissue Sub, Synth Sub], NQ
05U7[0,3,4][7,J]Z	Supl/Axillary Vein, Rt, [Opn, Perc, Perc Endo], [Auto Tissue Sub, Synth Sub], NQ
05U8[0,3,4][7,J]Z	Supl/Axillary Vein, Lt, [Opn, Perc, Perc Endo], [Auto Tissue Sub, Synth Sub], NQ
05U9[0,3,4][7,J]Z	Supl/Brachial Vein, Rt, [Opn, Perc, Perc Endo], [Auto Tissue Sub, Synth Sub], NQ
05UA[0,3,4][7,J]Z	Supl/Brachial Vein, Lt, [Opn, Perc, Perc Endo], [Auto Tissue Sub, Synth Sub], NQ
05UB[0,3,4][7,J]Z	Supl/Basilic Vein, Rt, [Opn, Perc, Perc Endo], [Auto Tissue Sub, Synth Sub], NQ
05UC[0,3,4][7,J]Z	Supl/Basilic Vein, Lt, [Opn, Perc, Perc Endo], [Auto Tissue Sub, Synth Sub], NQ
05UD[0,3,4][7,J]Z	Supl/Cephalic Vein, Rt, [Opn, Perc, Perc Endo], [Auto Tissue Sub, Synth Sub], NQ
05UF[0,3,4][7,J]Z	Supl/Cephalic Vein, Lt, [Opn, Perc, Perc Endo], [Auto Tissue Sub, Synth Sub], NQ
05UG[0,3,4][7,J]Z	Supl/Hand Vein, Rt, [Opn, Perc, Perc Endo], [Auto Tissue Sub, Synth Sub], NQ
05UH[0,3,4][7,J]Z	Supl/Hand Vein, Lt, [Opn, Perc, Perc Endo], [Auto Tissue Sub, Synth Sub], NQ
05UL[0,3,4][7,J]Z	Supl/Intracranial Vein, [Opn, Perc, Perc Endo], [Auto Tissue Sub, Synth Sub], NQ
05UM[0,3,4][7,J]Z	Supl/Int Jugular Vein, Rt, [Opn, Perc, Perc Endo], [Auto Tissue Sub, Synth Sub], NQ
05UN[0,3,4][7,J]Z	Supl/Int Jugular Vein, Lt, [Opn, Perc, Perc Endo], [Auto Tissue Sub, Synth Sub], NQ
05UP[0,3,4][7,J]Z	Supl/Ext Jugular Vein, Rt, [Opn, Perc, Perc Endo], [Auto Tissue Sub, Synth Sub], NQ
05UQ[0,3,4][7,J]Z	Supl/Ext Jugular Vein, Lt, [Opn, Perc, Perc Endo], [Auto Tissue Sub, Synth Sub], NQ
05UR[0,3,4][7,J]Z	Supl/Vert Vein, Rt, [Opn, Perc, Perc Endo], [Auto Tissue Sub, Synth Sub], NQ
05US[0,3,4][7,J]Z	Supl/Vert Vein, Lt, [Opn, Perc, Perc Endo], [Auto Tissue Sub, Synth Sub], NQ
05UT[0,3,4][7,J]Z	Supl/Face Vein, Rt, [Opn, Perc, Perc Endo], [Auto Tissue Sub, Synth Sub], NQ
05UV[0,3,4][7,J]Z	Supl/Face Vein, Lt, [Opn, Perc, Perc Endo], [Auto Tissue Sub, Synth Sub], NQ
05UY[0,3,4][7,J]Z	Supl/Upr Vein, [Opn, Perc, Perc Endo], [Auto Tissue Sub, Synth Sub], NQ
05V0[0,3,4][D,Z]Z	Restrict/Azygos Vein, [Opn, Perc, Perc Endo], [Intralum Dev, No Dev], NQ
05V1[0,3,4][D,Z]Z	Restrict/Hemiazygos Vein, [Opn, Perc, Perc Endo], [Intralum Dev, No Dev], NQ
05V3[0,3,4][D,Z]Z	Restrict/Innominate Vein, Rt, [Opn, Perc, Perc Endo], [Intralum Dev, No Dev], NQ
05V4[0,3,4][D,Z]Z	Restrict/Innominate Vein, Lt, [Opn, Perc, Perc Endo], [Intralum Dev, No Dev], NQ
05V5[0,3,4][D,Z]Z	Restrict/Subclavian Vein, Rt, [Opn, Perc, Perc Endo], [Intralum Dev, No Dev], NQ
05V6[0,3,4][D,Z]Z	Restrict/Subclavian Vein, Lt, [Opn, Perc, Perc Endo], [Intralum Dev, No Dev], NQ
05V7[0,3,4][D,Z]Z	Restrict/Axillary Vein, Rt, [Opn, Perc, Perc Endo], [Intralum Dev, No Dev], NQ
05V8[0,3,4][D,Z]Z	Restrict/Axillary Vein, Lt, [Opn, Perc, Perc Endo], [Intralum Dev, No Dev], NQ
05V9[0,3,4][D,Z]Z	Restrict/Brachial Vein, Rt, [Opn, Perc, Perc Endo], [Intralum Dev, No Dev], NQ
05VA[0,3,4][D,Z]Z	Restrict/Brachial Vein, Lt, [Opn, Perc, Perc Endo], [Intralum Dev, No Dev], NQ
05VB[0,3,4][D,Z]Z	Restrict/Basilic Vein, Rt, [Opn, Perc, Perc Endo], [Intralum Dev, No Dev], NQ
05VC[0,3,4][D,Z]Z	Restrict/Basilic Vein, Lt, [Opn, Perc, Perc Endo], [Intralum Dev, No Dev], NQ
05VD[0,3,4][D,Z]Z	Restrict/Cephalic Vein, Rt, [Opn, Perc, Perc Endo], [Intralum Dev, No Dev], NQ
05VF[0,3,4][D,Z]Z	Restrict/Cephalic Vein, Lt, [Opn, Perc, Perc Endo], [Intralum Dev, No Dev], NQ
05VG[0,3,4][D,Z]Z	Restrict/Hand Vein, Rt, [Opn, Perc, Perc Endo], [Intralum Dev, No Dev], NQ
05VH[0,3,4][D,Z]Z	Restrict/Hand Vein, Lt, [Opn, Perc, Perc Endo], [Intralum Dev, No Dev], NQ
05VL[0,3,4][D,Z]Z	Restrict/Intracranial Vein, [Opn, Perc, Perc Endo], [Intralum Dev, No Dev], NQ
05VM[0,3,4][D,Z]Z	Restrict/Int Jugular Vein, Rt, [Opn, Perc, Perc Endo], [Intralum Dev, No Dev], NQ
05VN[0,3,4][D,Z]Z	Restrict/Int Jugular Vein, Lt, [Opn, Perc, Perc Endo], [Intralum Dev, No Dev], NQ
05VP[0,3,4][D,Z]Z	Restrict/Ext Jugular Vein, Rt, [Opn, Perc, Perc Endo], [Intralum Dev, No Dev], NQ
05VQ[0,3,4][D,Z]Z	Restrict/Ext Jugular Vein, Lt, [Opn, Perc, Perc Endo], [Intralum Dev, No Dev], NQ
05VR[0,3,4][D,Z]Z	Restrict/Vert Vein, Rt, [Opn, Perc, Perc Endo], [Intralum Dev, No Dev], NQ
05VS[0,3,4][D,Z]Z	Restrict/Vert Vein, Lt, [Opn, Perc, Perc Endo], [Intralum Dev, No Dev], NQ
05VT[0,3,4][D,Z]Z	Restrict/Face Vein, Rt, [Opn, Perc, Perc Endo], [Intralum Dev, No Dev], NQ
05VV[0,3,4][D,Z]Z	Restrict/Face Vein, Lt, [Opn, Perc, Perc Endo], [Intralum Dev, No Dev], NQ
05VY[0,3,4][D,Z]Z	Restrict/Upr Vein, [Opn, Perc, Perc Endo], [Intralum Dev, No Dev], NQ

Ⓣ **Transfer DRG**   ⓈⓅ **Special Payment**   *** Code Range**   **6th and 7th Character of ZZ = No Device, No Qualifier ZX = No Device, Diagnostic**

MS-DRG Version 33.0

© 2015 Optum360, LLC

0653*	Destr/Esophageal Vein
065M*	Destr/Femor Vein, Rt
065N*	Destr/Femor Vein, Lt
065P*	Destr/Greater Saphenous Vein, Rt
065Q*	Destr/Greater Saphenous Vein, Lt
065R*	Destr/Lesser Saphenous Vein, Rt
065S*	Destr/Lesser Saphenous Vein, Lt
065T*	Destr/Foot Vein, Rt
065V*	Destr/Foot Vein, Lt
065Y[0,3,4]ZZ	Destr/Lwr Vein, [Opn, Perc, Perc Endo]
0670[D,Z]Z	Dilation/Inferior Vena Cava, Perc, [Intralum Dev, No Dev], NQ
0693[0,3,4][0,Z]Z	Drain/Esophageal Vein, [Opn, Perc, Perc Endo], [Drain Dev, No Dev], NQ
06B3[0,3,4]ZZ	Exc/Esophageal Vein, [Opn, Perc, Perc Endo]
06BM[0,3,4]ZZ	Exc/Femor Vein, Rt, [Opn, Perc, Perc Endo]
06BN[0,3,4]ZZ	Exc/Femor Vein, Lt, [Opn, Perc, Perc Endo]
06BP[0,3,4]ZZ	Exc/Greater Saphenous Vein, Rt, [Opn, Perc, Perc Endo]
06BQ[0,3,4]ZZ	Exc/Greater Saphenous Vein, Lt, [Opn, Perc, Perc Endo]
06BR[0,3,4]ZZ	Exc/Lesser Saphenous Vein, Rt, [Opn, Perc, Perc Endo]
06BS[0,3,4]ZZ	Exc/Lesser Saphenous Vein, Lt, [Opn, Perc, Perc Endo]
06BT[0,3,4]ZZ	Exc/Foot Vein, Rt, [Opn, Perc, Perc Endo]
06BV[0,3,4]ZZ	Exc/Foot Vein, Lt, [Opn, Perc, Perc Endo]
06BY[0,3,4]ZZ	Exc/Lwr Vein, [Opn, Perc, Perc Endo]
06C3*	Extir/Esophageal Vein
06CM*	Extir/Femor Vein, Rt
06CN*	Extir/Femor Vein, Lt
06CP*	Extir/Greater Saphenous Vein, Rt
06CQ*	Extir/Greater Saphenous Vein, Lt
06CR*	Extir/Lesser Saphenous Vein, Rt
06CS*	Extir/Lesser Saphenous Vein, Lt
06CT*	Extir/Foot Vein, Rt
06CV*	Extir/Foot Vein, Lt
06CY*	Extir/Lwr Vein
06H0[0,3,4]DZ	Insert/Inferior Vena Cava, [Opn, Perc, Perc Endo], Intralum Dev, NQ
06H1[0,3,4]DZ	Insert/Splenic Vein, [Opn, Perc, Perc Endo], Intralum Dev, NQ
06H2[0,3,4]DZ	Insert/Gastric Vein, [Opn, Perc, Perc Endo], Intralum Dev, NQ
06H3[0,3,4]DZ	Insert/Esophageal Vein, [Opn, Perc, Perc Endo], Intralum Dev, NQ
06H4[0,3,4]DZ	Insert/Hepatic Vein, [Opn, Perc, Perc Endo], Intralum Dev, NQ
06H5[0,3,4]DZ	Insert/Superior Mesenteric Vein, [Opn, Perc, Perc Endo], Intralum Dev, NQ
06H6[0,3,4]DZ	Insert/Inferior Mesenteric Vein, [Opn, Perc, Perc Endo], Intralum Dev, NQ
06H7[0,3,4]DZ	Insert/Colic Vein, [Opn, Perc, Perc Endo], Intralum Dev, NQ
06H8[0,3,4]DZ	Insert/Portal Vein, [Opn, Perc, Perc Endo], Intralum Dev, NQ
06H9[0,3,4]DZ	Insert/Renal Vein, Rt, [Opn, Perc, Perc Endo], Intralum Dev, NQ
06HB[0,3,4]DZ	Insert/Renal Vein, Lt, [Opn, Perc, Perc Endo], Intralum Dev, NQ
06HC[0,3,4]DZ	Insert/Common Iliac Vein, Rt, [Opn, Perc, Perc Endo], Intralum Dev, NQ
06HD[0,3,4]DZ	Insert/Common Iliac Vein, Lt, [Opn, Perc, Perc Endo], Intralum Dev, NQ
06HF[0,3,4]DZ	Insert/Ext Iliac Vein, Rt, [Opn, Perc, Perc Endo], Intralum Dev, NQ
06HG[0,3,4]DZ	Insert/Ext Iliac Vein, Lt, [Opn, Perc, Perc Endo], Intralum Dev, NQ
06HH[0,3,4]DZ	Insert/Hypogastric Vein, Rt, [Opn, Perc, Perc Endo], Intralum Dev, NQ
06HJ[0,3,4]DZ	Insert/Hypogastric Vein, Lt, [Opn, Perc, Perc Endo], Intralum Dev, NQ
06HM[0,3,4]DZ	Insert/Femor Vein, Rt, [Opn, Perc, Perc Endo], Intralum Dev, NQ
06HN[0,3,4]DZ	Insert/Femor Vein, Lt, [Opn, Perc, Perc Endo], Intralum Dev, NQ
06HP[0,3,4]DZ	Insert/Greater Saphenous Vein, Rt, [Opn, Perc, Perc Endo], Intralum Dev, NQ
06HQ[0,3,4]DZ	Insert/Greater Saphenous Vein, Lt, [Opn, Perc, Perc Endo], Intralum Dev, NQ
06HR[0,3,4]DZ	Insert/Lesser Saphenous Vein, Rt, [Opn, Perc, Perc Endo], Intralum Dev, NQ
06HS[0,3,4]DZ	Insert/Lesser Saphenous Vein, Lt, [Opn, Perc, Perc Endo], Intralum Dev, NQ
06HT[0,3,4]DZ	Insert/Foot Vein, Rt, [Opn, Perc, Perc Endo], Intralum Dev, NQ
06HV[0,3,4]DZ	Insert/Foot Vein, Lt, [Opn, Perc, Perc Endo], Intralum Dev, NQ
06HY[0,3,4][2,D]Z	Insert/Lwr Vein, [Opn, Perc, Perc Endo], [Monitoring Dev, Intralum Dev], NQ
06L0*	Occlsn/Inferior Vena Cava
06L1*	Occlsn/Splenic Vein
06L2*	Occlsn/Gastric Vein
06L3*	Occlsn/Esophageal Vein
06L4*	Occlsn/Hepatic Vein
06L5*	Occlsn/Superior Mesenteric Vein
06L6*	Occlsn/Inferior Mesenteric Vein
06L7*	Occlsn/Colic Vein
06L8*	Occlsn/Portal Vein
06L9*	Occlsn/Renal Vein, Rt
06LB*	Occlsn/Renal Vein, Lt
06LC*	Occlsn/Common Iliac Vein, Rt
06LD*	Occlsn/Common Iliac Vein, Lt
06LF*	Occlsn/Ext Iliac Vein, Rt
06LG*	Occlsn/Ext Iliac Vein, Lt
06LH*	Occlsn/Hypogastric Vein, Rt
06LJ*	Occlsn/Hypogastric Vein, Lt
06LM*	Occlsn/Femor Vein, Rt
06LN*	Occlsn/Femor Vein, Lt
06LP*	Occlsn/Greater Saphenous Vein, Rt
06LQ*	Occlsn/Greater Saphenous Vein, Lt
06LR*	Occlsn/Lesser Saphenous Vein, Rt
06LS*	Occlsn/Lesser Saphenous Vein, Lt
06LT*	Occlsn/Foot Vein, Rt
06LV*	Occlsn/Foot Vein, Lt
06LY[0,3,4][C,D,Z]Z	Occlsn/Lwr Vein, [Opn, Perc, Perc Endo], [Extralum Dev, Intralum Dev, No Dev], NQ
06PY[0,3,4][0,2,3,C,D]Z	Rmvl/Lwr Vein, [Opn, Perc, Perc Endo], [Drain Dev, Monitoring Dev, Inf Dev, Extralum Dev, Intralum Dev], NQ
06Q*	Lwr Veins, Repair
06RM*	Replace/Femor Vein, Rt
06RN*	Replace/Femor Vein, Lt
06RP*	Replace/Greater Saphenous Vein, Rt
06RQ*	Replace/Greater Saphenous Vein, Lt
06RR*	Replace/Lesser Saphenous Vein, Rt
06RS*	Replace/Lesser Saphenous Vein, Lt
06RT*	Replace/Foot Vein, Rt
06RV*	Replace/Foot Vein, Lt
06RY*	Replace/Lwr Vein
06S0*	Repos/Inferior Vena Cava
06S1*	Repos/Splenic Vein
06S2*	Repos/Gastric Vein
06S3*	Repos/Esophageal Vein
06S4*	Repos/Hepatic Vein
06S5*	Repos/Superior Mesenteric Vein
06S6*	Repos/Inferior Mesenteric Vein
06S7*	Repos/Colic Vein
06S8*	Repos/Portal Vein
06SC*	Repos/Common Iliac Vein, Rt
06SD*	Repos/Common Iliac Vein, Lt
06SF*	Repos/Ext Iliac Vein, Rt
06SG*	Repos/Ext Iliac Vein, Lt
06SH*	Repos/Hypogastric Vein, Rt
06SJ*	Repos/Hypogastric Vein, Lt
06SM*	Repos/Femor Vein, Rt
06SN*	Repos/Femor Vein, Lt
06SP*	Repos/Greater Saphenous Vein, Rt
06SQ*	Repos/Greater Saphenous Vein, Lt
06SR*	Repos/Lesser Saphenous Vein, Rt
06SS*	Repos/Lesser Saphenous Vein, Lt
06ST*	Repos/Foot Vein, Rt
06SV*	Repos/Foot Vein, Lt
06SY*	Repos/Lwr Vein
06U0[0,3,4][7,J]Z	Supl/Inferior Vena Cava, [Opn, Perc, Perc Endo], [Auto Tissue Sub, Synth Sub], NQ
06U1[0,3,4][7,J]Z	Supl/Splenic Vein, [Opn, Perc, Perc Endo], [Auto Tissue Sub, Synth Sub], NQ
06U2[0,3,4][7,J]Z	Supl/Gastric Vein, [Opn, Perc, Perc Endo], [Auto Tissue Sub, Synth Sub], NQ
06U3[0,3,4][7,J]Z	Supl/Esophageal Vein, [Opn, Perc, Perc Endo], [Auto Tissue Sub, Synth Sub], NQ
06U4[0,3,4][7,J]Z	Supl/Hepatic Vein, [Opn, Perc, Perc Endo], [Auto Tissue Sub, Synth Sub], NQ
06U5[0,3,4][7,J]Z	Supl/Superior Mesenteric Vein, [Opn, Perc, Perc Endo], [Auto Tissue Sub, Synth Sub], NQ
06U6[0,3,4][7,J]Z	Supl/Inferior Mesenteric Vein, [Opn, Perc, Perc Endo], [Auto Tissue Sub, Synth Sub], NQ
06U7[0,3,4][7,J]Z	Supl/Colic Vein, [Opn, Perc, Perc Endo], [Auto Tissue Sub, Synth Sub], NQ
06U8[0,3,4][7,J]Z	Supl/Portal Vein, [Opn, Perc, Perc Endo], [Auto Tissue Sub, Synth Sub], NQ
06U9[0,3,4][7,J]Z	Supl/Renal Vein, Rt, [Opn, Perc, Perc Endo], [Auto Tissue Sub, Synth Sub], NQ
06UB[0,3,4][7,J]Z	Supl/Renal Vein, Lt, [Opn, Perc, Perc Endo], [Auto Tissue Sub, Synth Sub], NQ

MDC 21: Injuries, Poisonings And Toxic Effects Of Drugs—SURGICAL

Surgical   Medical   CC Indicator   MCC Indicator   Procedure Proxy   PDxMCC PDx acts as own MCC   PDxCC PDx acts as own CC

MDC 21: Injuries, Poisonings And Toxic Effects Of Drugs—SURGICAL

Code	Description
06UC[0,3,4][7,J]Z	Supl/Common Iliac Vein, Rt, [Opn, Perc, Perc Endo], [Auto Tissue Sub, Synth Sub], NQ
06UD[0,3,4][7,J]Z	Supl/Common Iliac Vein, Lt, [Opn, Perc, Perc Endo], [Auto Tissue Sub, Synth Sub], NQ
06UF[0,3,4][7,J]Z	Supl/Ext Iliac Vein, Rt, [Opn, Perc, Perc Endo], [Auto Tissue Sub, Synth Sub], NQ
06UG[0,3,4][7,J]Z	Supl/Ext Iliac Vein, Lt, [Opn, Perc, Perc Endo], [Auto Tissue Sub, Synth Sub], NQ
06UH[0,3,4][7,J]Z	Supl/Hypogastric Vein, Rt, [Opn, Perc, Perc Endo], [Auto Tissue Sub, Synth Sub], NQ
06UJ[0,3,4][7,J]Z	Supl/Hypogastric Vein, Lt, [Opn, Perc, Perc Endo], [Auto Tissue Sub, Synth Sub], NQ
06UM[0,3,4][7,J]Z	Supl/Femor Vein, Rt, [Opn, Perc, Perc Endo], [Auto Tissue Sub, Synth Sub], NQ
06UN[0,3,4][7,J]Z	Supl/Femor Vein, Lt, [Opn, Perc, Perc Endo], [Auto Tissue Sub, Synth Sub], NQ
06UP[0,3,4][7,J]Z	Supl/Greater Saphenous Vein, Rt, [Opn, Perc, Perc Endo], [Auto Tissue Sub, Synth Sub], NQ
06UQ[0,3,4][7,J]Z	Supl/Greater Saphenous Vein, Lt, [Opn, Perc, Perc Endo], [Auto Tissue Sub, Synth Sub], NQ
06UR[0,3,4][7,J]Z	Supl/Lesser Saphenous Vein, Rt, [Opn, Perc, Perc Endo], [Auto Tissue Sub, Synth Sub], NQ
06US[0,3,4][7,J]Z	Supl/Lesser Saphenous Vein, Lt, [Opn, Perc, Perc Endo], [Auto Tissue Sub, Synth Sub], NQ
06UT[0,3,4][7,J]Z	Supl/Foot Vein, Rt, [Opn, Perc, Perc Endo], [Auto Tissue Sub, Synth Sub], NQ
06UV[0,3,4][7,J]Z	Supl/Foot Vein, Lt, [Opn, Perc, Perc Endo], [Auto Tissue Sub, Synth Sub], NQ
06UY[0,3,4][7,J]Z	Supl/Lwr Vein, [Opn, Perc, Perc Endo], [Auto Tissue Sub, Synth Sub], NQ
06V0*	Restrict/Inferior Vena Cava
06V1[0,3,4][D,Z]Z	Restrict/Splenic Vein, [Opn, Perc, Perc Endo], [Intralum Dev, No Dev], NQ
06V2[0,3,4][D,Z]Z	Restrict/Gastric Vein, [Opn, Perc, Perc Endo], [Intralum Dev, No Dev], NQ
06V3[0,3,4][D,Z]Z	Restrict/Esophageal Vein, [Opn, Perc, Perc Endo], [Intralum Dev, No Dev], NQ
06V4[0,3,4][D,Z]Z	Restrict/Hepatic Vein, [Opn, Perc, Perc Endo], [Intralum Dev, No Dev], NQ
06V5[0,3,4][D,Z]Z	Restrict/Superior Mesenteric Vein, [Opn, Perc, Perc Endo], [Intralum Dev, No Dev], NQ
06V6[0,3,4][D,Z]Z	Restrict/Inferior Mesenteric Vein, [Opn, Perc, Perc Endo], [Intralum Dev, No Dev], NQ
06V7[0,3,4][D,Z]Z	Restrict/Colic Vein, [Opn, Perc, Perc Endo], [Intralum Dev, No Dev], NQ
06V8[0,3,4][D,Z]Z	Restrict/Portal Vein, [Opn, Perc, Perc Endo], [Intralum Dev, No Dev], NQ
06V9[0,3,4][D,Z]Z	Restrict/Renal Vein, Rt, [Opn, Perc, Perc Endo], [Intralum Dev, No Dev], NQ
06VB[0,3,4][D,Z]Z	Restrict/Renal Vein, Lt, [Opn, Perc, Perc Endo], [Intralum Dev, No Dev], NQ
06VC[0,3,4][D,Z]Z	Restrict/Common Iliac Vein, Rt, [Opn, Perc, Perc Endo], [Intralum Dev, No Dev], NQ
06VD[0,3,4][D,Z]Z	Restrict/Common Iliac Vein, Lt, [Opn, Perc, Perc Endo], [Intralum Dev, No Dev], NQ
06VF[0,3,4][D,Z]Z	Restrict/Ext Iliac Vein, Rt, [Opn, Perc, Perc Endo], [Intralum Dev, No Dev], NQ
06VG[0,3,4][D,Z]Z	Restrict/Ext Iliac Vein, Lt, [Opn, Perc, Perc Endo], [Intralum Dev, No Dev], NQ
06VH[0,3,4][D,Z]Z	Restrict/Hypogastric Vein, Rt, [Opn, Perc, Perc Endo], [Intralum Dev, No Dev], NQ
06VJ[0,3,4][D,Z]Z	Restrict/Hypogastric Vein, Lt, [Opn, Perc, Perc Endo], [Intralum Dev, No Dev], NQ
06VM[0,3,4][D,Z]Z	Restrict/Femor Vein, Rt, [Opn, Perc, Perc Endo], [Intralum Dev, No Dev], NQ
06VN[0,3,4][D,Z]Z	Restrict/Femor Vein, Lt, [Opn, Perc, Perc Endo], [Intralum Dev, No Dev], NQ
06VP[0,3,4][D,Z]Z	Restrict/Greater Saphenous Vein, Rt, [Opn, Perc, Perc Endo], [Intralum Dev, No Dev], NQ
06VQ[0,3,4][D,Z]Z	Restrict/Greater Saphenous Vein, Lt, [Opn, Perc, Perc Endo], [Intralum Dev, No Dev], NQ
06VR[0,3,4][D,Z]Z	Restrict/Lesser Saphenous Vein, Rt, [Opn, Perc, Perc Endo], [Intralum Dev, No Dev], NQ
06VS[0,3,4][D,Z]Z	Restrict/Lesser Saphenous Vein, Lt, [Opn, Perc, Perc Endo], [Intralum Dev, No Dev], NQ
06VT[0,3,4][D,Z]Z	Restrict/Foot Vein, Rt, [Opn, Perc, Perc Endo], [Intralum Dev, No Dev], NQ
06VV[0,3,4][D,Z]Z	Restrict/Foot Vein, Lt, [Opn, Perc, Perc Endo], [Intralum Dev, No Dev], NQ
06VY[0,3,4][D,Z]Z	Restrict/Lwr Vein, [Opn, Perc, Perc Endo], [Intralum Dev, No Dev], NQ
06WY[0,3,4][0,2,3,C,D]Z	Rev/Lwr Vein, [Opn, Perc, Perc Endo], [Drain Dev, Monitoring Dev, Inf Dev, Extralum Dev, Intralum Dev], NQ
0750*	Destr/Lymphatic, Head
0751*	Destr/Lymphatic, Rt Neck
0752*	Destr/Lymphatic, Lt Neck
0753*	Destr/Lymphatic, Rt Upr Extr
0754*	Destr/Lymphatic, Lt Upr Extr
0755*	Destr/Lymphatic, Rt Axillary
0756*	Destr/Lymphatic, Lt Axillary
0757*	Destr/Lymphatic, Thorax
0758*	Destr/Lymphatic, Int Mammary, Rt
0759*	Destr/Lymphatic, Int Mammary, Lt
075B*	Destr/Lymphatic, Mesenteric
075C*	Destr/Lymphatic, Pelvis
075D*	Destr/Lymphatic, Aortic
075F*	Destr/Lymphatic, Rt Lwr Extr
075G*	Destr/Lymphatic, Lt Lwr Extr
075H*	Destr/Lymphatic, Rt Inguinal
075J*	Destr/Lymphatic, Lt Inguinal
075M*	Destr/Thymus
075P*	Destr/Spleen
079K[0,3,4][0,Z]Z	Drain/Thoracic Duct, [Opn, Perc, Perc Endo], [Drain Dev, No Dev], NQ
079L[0,3,4][0,Z]Z	Drain/Cisterna Chyli, [Opn, Perc, Perc Endo], [Drain Dev, No Dev], NQ
079M[0,3,4][0,Z]Z	Drain/Thymus, [Opn, Perc, Perc Endo], [Drain Dev, No Dev], NQ
079P0[0,Z]Z	Drain/Spleen, Opn, [Drain Dev, No Dev], NQ
07BM[0,3,4]ZZ	Exc/Thymus, [Opn, Perc, Perc Endo]
07BP[0,3,4]ZZ	Exc/Spleen, [Opn, Perc, Perc Endo]
07CM*	Extir/Thymus
07CP0ZZ	Extir of Matter from Spleen, Opn Appr
07JM[0,4]ZZ	Inspect/Thymus, [Opn, Perc Endo]
07JP0ZZ	Inspect of Spleen, Opn Appr
07L*	Lymphatic and Hemic Systems, Occlsn
07N0*	Rls/Lymphatic, Head
07N1*	Rls/Lymphatic, Rt Neck
07N2*	Rls/Lymphatic, Lt Neck
07N3*	Rls/Lymphatic, Rt Upr Extr
07N4*	Rls/Lymphatic, Lt Upr Extr
07N5*	Rls/Lymphatic, Rt Axillary
07N6*	Rls/Lymphatic, Lt Axillary
07N7*	Rls/Lymphatic, Thorax
07N8*	Rls/Lymphatic, Int Mammary, Rt
07N9*	Rls/Lymphatic, Int Mammary, Lt
07NB*	Rls/Lymphatic, Mesenteric
07NC*	Rls/Lymphatic, Pelvis
07ND*	Rls/Lymphatic, Aortic
07NF*	Rls/Lymphatic, Rt Lwr Extr
07NG*	Rls/Lymphatic, Lt Lwr Extr
07NH*	Rls/Lymphatic, Rt Inguinal
07NJ*	Rls/Lymphatic, Lt Inguinal
07NM*	Rls/Thymus
07NP*	Rls/Spleen
07PK[0,3,4][7,J,K]Z	Rmvl/Thoracic Duct, [Opn, Perc, Perc Endo], [Auto Tissue Sub, Synth Sub, Nonauto Tissue Sub], NQ
07PL[0,3,4][7,J,K]Z	Rmvl/Cisterna Chyli, [Opn, Perc, Perc Endo], [Auto Tissue Sub, Synth Sub, Nonauto Tissue Sub], NQ
07PM[0,3,4][0,3]Z	Rmvl/Thymus, [Opn, Perc, Perc Endo], [Drain Dev, Inf Dev], NQ
07PN[0,3,4][7,J,K]Z	Rmvl/Lymphatic, [Opn, Perc, Perc Endo], [Auto Tissue Sub, Synth Sub, Nonauto Tissue Sub], NQ
07PP[0,3,4][0,3]Z	Rmvl/Spleen, [Opn, Perc, Perc Endo], [Drain Dev, Inf Dev], NQ
07Q0*	Repair/Lymphatic, Head
07Q1*	Repair/Lymphatic, Rt Neck
07Q2*	Repair/Lymphatic, Lt Neck
07Q3*	Repair/Lymphatic, Rt Upr Extr
07Q4*	Repair/Lymphatic, Lt Upr Extr
07Q5*	Repair/Lymphatic, Rt Axillary
07Q6*	Repair/Lymphatic, Lt Axillary
07Q7*	Repair/Lymphatic, Thorax
07Q8*	Repair/Lymphatic, Int Mammary, Rt
07Q9*	Repair/Lymphatic, Int Mammary, Lt
07QB*	Repair/Lymphatic, Mesenteric
07QC*	Repair/Lymphatic, Pelvis
07QD*	Repair/Lymphatic, Aortic
07QF*	Repair/Lymphatic, Rt Lwr Extr
07QG*	Repair/Lymphatic, Lt Lwr Extr
07QH*	Repair/Lymphatic, Rt Inguinal
07QJ*	Repair/Lymphatic, Lt Inguinal

T Transfer DRG   SP Special Payment   * Code Range   6th and 7th Character of ZZ = No Device, No Qualifier ZX = No Device, Diagnostic

07QK*	Repair/Thoracic Duct		0893*	Drain/Ant Chamber, Lt
07QM*	Repair/Thymus		08943[0,Z]Z	Drain/Vitreous, Rt, Perc, [Drain Dev, No Dev], NQ
07QP*	Repair/Spleen		08953[0,Z]Z	Drain/Vitreous, Lt, Perc, [Drain Dev, No Dev], NQ
07S*	Lymphatic and Hemic Systems, Repos		0896*	Drain/Sclera, Rt
07TM*	Resect/Thymus		0897*	Drain/Sclera, Lt
07TP*	Resect/Spleen		0898*	Drain/Cornea, Rt
07U0*	Supl/Lymphatic, Head		0899*	Drain/Cornea, Lt
07U1*	Supl/Lymphatic, Rt Neck		089A[0,3][0,Z]Z	Drain/Choroid, Rt, [Opn, Perc], [Drain Dev, No Dev], NQ
07U2*	Supl/Lymphatic, Lt Neck		089B[0,3][0,Z]Z	Drain/Choroid, Lt, [Opn, Perc], [Drain Dev, No Dev], NQ
07U3*	Supl/Lymphatic, Rt Upr Extr		089C*	Drain/Iris, Rt
07U4*	Supl/Lymphatic, Lt Upr Extr		089D*	Drain/Iris, Lt
07U5*	Supl/Lymphatic, Rt Axillary		089E3[0,Z]Z	Drain/Retina, Rt, Perc, [Drain Dev, No Dev], NQ
07U6*	Supl/Lymphatic, Lt Axillary		089F3[0,Z]Z	Drain/Retina, Lt, Perc, [Drain Dev, No Dev], NQ
07U7*	Supl/Lymphatic, Thorax		089G3[0,Z]Z	Drain/Retinal Vessel, Rt, Perc, [Drain Dev, No Dev], NQ
07U8*	Supl/Lymphatic, Int Mammary, Rt		089H3[0,Z]Z	Drain/Retinal Vessel, Lt, Perc, [Drain Dev, No Dev], NQ
07U9*	Supl/Lymphatic, Int Mammary, Lt		089J*	Drain/Lens, Rt
07UB*	Supl/Lymphatic, Mesenteric		089K*	Drain/Lens, Lt
07UC*	Supl/Lymphatic, Pelvis		089L[0,3][0,Z]Z	Drain/Extraocular Muscle, Rt, [Opn, Perc], [Drain Dev, No Dev], NQ
07UD*	Supl/Lymphatic, Aortic			
07UF*	Supl/Lymphatic, Rt Lwr Extr		089M[0,3][0,Z]Z	Drain/Extraocular Muscle, Lt, [Opn, Perc], [Drain Dev, No Dev], NQ
07UG*	Supl/Lymphatic, Lt Lwr Extr			
07UH*	Supl/Lymphatic, Rt Inguinal		089N[0,3,X]ZX	Drain/Upr Eyelid, Rt, [Opn, Perc, Ext]
07UJ*	Supl/Lymphatic, Lt Inguinal		089P[0,3,X]ZX	Drain/Upr Eyelid, Lt, [Opn, Perc, Ext]
07V0*	Restrict/Lymphatic, Head		089Q[0,3,X]ZX	Drain/Lwr Eyelid, Rt, [Opn, Perc, Ext]
07V1*	Restrict/Lymphatic, Rt Neck		089R[0,3,X]ZX	Drain/Lwr Eyelid, Lt, [Opn, Perc, Ext]
07V2*	Restrict/Lymphatic, Lt Neck		089V[0,3]ZX	Drain/Lacrimal Gland, Rt, [Opn, Perc]
07V3*	Restrict/Lymphatic, Rt Upr Extr		089W[0,3]ZX	Drain/Lacrimal Gland, Lt, [Opn, Perc]
07V4*	Restrict/Lymphatic, Lt Upr Extr		089X[7,8][0,Z]Z	Drain/Lacrimal Duct, Rt, [Via Natrl or Artfcl Opng, Via Natrl or Artfcl Opng Endo], [Drain Dev, No Dev], NQ
07V5*	Restrict/Lymphatic, Rt Axillary			
07V6*	Restrict/Lymphatic, Lt Axillary		089Y[7,8][0,Z]Z	Drain/Lacrimal Duct, Lt, [Via Natrl or Artfcl Opng, Via Natrl or Artfcl Opng Endo], [Drain Dev, No Dev], NQ
07V7*	Restrict/Lymphatic, Thorax			
07V8*	Restrict/Lymphatic, Int Mammary, Rt		08B0[0,3,X]ZZ	Exc/Eye, Rt, [Opn, Perc, Ext]
07V9*	Restrict/Lymphatic, Int Mammary, Lt		08B1[0,3,X]ZZ	Exc/Eye, Lt, [Opn, Perc, Ext]
07VB*	Restrict/Lymphatic, Mesenteric		08B43ZZ	Exc of Rt Vitreous, Perc Appr
07VC*	Restrict/Lymphatic, Pelvis		08B53ZZ	Exc of Lt Vitreous, Perc Appr
07VD*	Restrict/Lymphatic, Aortic		08B6*	Exc/Sclera, Rt
07VF*	Restrict/Lymphatic, Rt Lwr Extr		08B7*	Exc/Sclera, Lt
07VG*	Restrict/Lymphatic, Lt Lwr Extr		08B8*	Exc/Cornea, Rt
07VH*	Restrict/Lymphatic, Rt Inguinal		08B9*	Exc/Cornea, Lt
07VJ*	Restrict/Lymphatic, Lt Inguinal		08BA[0,3]ZZ	Exc/Choroid, Rt, [Opn, Perc]
07WK[0,3,4][7,J,K]Z	Rev/Thoracic Duct, [Opn, Perc, Perc Endo], [Auto Tissue Sub, Synth Sub, Nonauto Tissue Sub], NQ		08BB[0,3]ZZ	Exc/Choroid, Lt, [Opn, Perc]
			08BC*	Exc/Iris, Rt
07WL[0,3,4][7,J,K]Z	Rev/Cisterna Chyli, [Opn, Perc, Perc Endo], [Auto Tissue Sub, Synth Sub, Nonauto Tissue Sub], NQ		08BD*	Exc/Iris, Lt
			08BJ3ZX	Exc of Rt Lens, Perc Appr, Diagnostic
07WM[0,3,4][0,3]Z	Rev/Thymus, [Opn, Perc, Perc Endo], [Drain Dev, Inf Dev], NQ		08BK3ZX	Exc of Lt Lens, Perc Appr, Diagnostic
			08BN*	Exc/Upr Eyelid, Rt
07WN[0,3,4][7,J,K]Z	Rev/Lymphatic, [Opn, Perc, Perc Endo], [Auto Tissue Sub, Synth Sub, Nonauto Tissue Sub], NQ		08BP*	Exc/Upr Eyelid, Lt
			08BQ*	Exc/Lwr Eyelid, Rt
07WP[0,3,4][0,3]Z	Rev/Spleen, [Opn, Perc, Perc Endo], [Drain Dev, Inf Dev], NQ		08BR*	Exc/Lwr Eyelid, Lt
081*	Eye, Bypass		08BSXZZ	Exc of Rt Conjunctiva, Ext Appr
08523ZZ	Destr of Rt Ant Chamber, Perc Appr		08BTXZZ	Exc of Lt Conjunctiva, Ext Appr
08533ZZ	Destr of Lt Ant Chamber, Perc Appr		08BV*	Exc/Lacrimal Gland, Rt
08543ZZ	Destr of Rt Vitreous, Perc Appr		08BW*	Exc/Lacrimal Gland, Lt
08553ZZ	Destr of Lt Vitreous, Perc Appr		08BX[0,3,7,8]ZZ	Exc/Lacrimal Duct, Rt, [Opn, Perc, Via Natrl or Artfcl Opng, Via Natrl or Artfcl Opng Endo]
0856XZZ	Destr of Rt Sclera, Ext Appr			
0857XZZ	Destr of Lt Sclera, Ext Appr		08BY[0,3,7,8]ZZ	Exc/Lacrimal Duct, Lt, [Opn, Perc, Via Natrl or Artfcl Opng, Via Natrl or Artfcl Opng Endo]
0858XZZ	Destr of Rt Cornea, Ext Appr			
0859XZZ	Destr of Lt Cornea, Ext Appr		08C0XZZ	Extir of Matter from Rt Eye, Ext Appr
085A*	Destr/Choroid, Rt		08C1XZZ	Extir of Matter from Lt Eye, Ext Appr
085B*	Destr/Choroid, Lt		08C23ZZ	Extir of Matter from Rt Ant Chamber, Perc Appr
085C3ZZ	Destr of Rt Iris, Perc Appr		08C33ZZ	Extir of Matter from Lt Ant Chamber, Perc Appr
085D3ZZ	Destr of Lt Iris, Perc Appr		08C4*	Extir/Vitreous, Rt
085G3ZZ	Destr of Rt Retinal Vessel, Perc Appr		08C5*	Extir/Vitreous, Lt
085H3ZZ	Destr of Lt Retinal Vessel, Perc Appr		08C8XZZ	Extir of Matter from Rt Cornea, Ext Appr
085L*	Destr/Extraocular Muscle, Rt		08C9XZZ	Extir of Matter from Lt Cornea, Ext Appr
085M*	Destr/Extraocular Muscle, Lt		08CA*	Extir/Choroid, Rt
085N*	Destr/Upr Eyelid, Rt		08CB*	Extir/Choroid, Lt
085P*	Destr/Upr Eyelid, Lt		08CC*	Extir/Iris, Rt
085Q*	Destr/Lwr Eyelid, Rt		08CD*	Extir/Iris, Lt
085R*	Destr/Lwr Eyelid, Lt		08CE*	Extir/Retina, Rt
085SXZZ	Destr of Rt Conjunctiva, Ext Appr		08CF*	Extir/Retina, Lt
085TXZZ	Destr of Lt Conjunctiva, Ext Appr		08CG*	Extir/Retinal Vessel, Rt
085V*	Destr/Lacrimal Gland, Rt		08CH*	Extir/Retinal Vessel, Lt
085W*	Destr/Lacrimal Gland, Lt		08CJ*	Extir/Lens, Rt
085X*	Destr/Lacrimal Duct, Rt		08CK*	Extir/Lens, Lt
085Y*	Destr/Lacrimal Duct, Lt		08CL*	Extir/Extraocular Muscle, Rt
087X[0,3,7,8]DZ	Dilation/Lacrimal Duct, Rt, [Opn, Perc, Via Natrl or Artfcl Opng, Via Natrl or Artfcl Opng Endo], Intralum Dev, NQ		08CM*	Extir/Extraocular Muscle, Lt
			08CSXZZ	Extir of Matter from Rt Conjunctiva, Extern Appr
087Y[0,3,7,8]DZ	Dilation/Lacrimal Duct, Lt, [Opn, Perc, Via Natrl or Artfcl Opng, Via Natrl or Artfcl Opng Endo], Intralum Dev, NQ		08CTXZZ	Extir of Matter from Lt Conjunctiva, Extern Appr
			08CV[3,X]ZZ	Extir/Lacrimal Gland, Rt, [Perc, Ext]
0892*	Drain/Ant Chamber, Rt			

Surgical	**Medical**	**CC Indicator**	**MCC Indicator**	**Procedure Proxy**	**PDxMCC** PDx acts as own MCC	**PDxCC** PDx acts as own CC

08CW[3,X]ZZ	Extir/Lacrimal Gland, Lt, [Perc, Ext]
08F43ZZ	Fragmn in Rt Vitreous, Perc Appr
08F53ZZ	Fragmn in Lt Vitreous, Perc Appr
08H0[3,X]1Z	Insert/Eye, Rt, [Perc, Ext], Radioact Elmt, NQ
08H1[3,X]1Z	Insert/Eye, Lt, [Perc, Ext], Radioact Elmt, NQ
08H[0,1]05Z	Insert/Eye, [Rt, Lt], Opn, Epiretinal Visual Prosthesis, NQ
08J0XZZ	Inspect of Rt Eye, Ext Appr
08J1XZZ	Inspect of Lt Eye, Ext Appr
08L*	Eye, Occlsn
08M*	Eye, Reattach
08N23ZZ	Rls Rt Ant Chamber, Perc Appr
08N33ZZ	Rls Lt Ant Chamber, Perc Appr
08N43ZZ	Rls Rt Vitreous, Perc Appr
08N53ZZ	Rls Lt Vitreous, Perc Appr
08N6XZZ	Rls Rt Sclera, Ext Appr
08N7XZZ	Rls Lt Sclera, Ext Appr
08N8XZZ	Rls Rt Cornea, Ext Appr
08N9XZZ	Rls Lt Cornea, Ext Appr
08NA*	Rls/Choroid, Rt
08NB*	Rls/Choroid, Lt
08NC3ZZ	Rls Rt Iris, Perc Appr
08ND3ZZ	Rls Lt Iris, Perc Appr
08NE3ZZ	Rls Rt Retina, Perc Appr
08NF3ZZ	Rls Lt Retina, Perc Appr
08NG3ZZ	Rls Rt Retinal Vessel, Perc Appr
08NH3ZZ	Rls Lt Retinal Vessel, Perc Appr
08NJ3ZZ	Rls Rt Lens, Perc Appr
08NK3ZZ	Rls Lt Lens, Perc Appr
08NL*	Rls/Extraocular Muscle, Rt
08NM*	Rls/Extraocular Muscle, Lt
08NN*	Rls/Upr Eyelid, Rt
08NP*	Rls/Upr Eyelid, Lt
08NQ*	Rls/Lwr Eyelid, Rt
08NR*	Rls/Lwr Eyelid, Lt
08NV*	Rls/Lacrimal Gland, Rt
08NW*	Rls/Lacrimal Gland, Lt
08NX*	Rls/Lacrimal Duct, Rt
08NY*	Rls/Lacrimal Duct, Lt
08P003Z	Rmvl of Inf Device from Rt Eye, Opn Appr
08P0[0,3,X]JZ	Rmvl/Eye, Rt, [Opn, Perc, Ext], Synth Sub, NQ
08P103Z	Rmvl of Inf Device from Lt Eye, Opn Appr
08P1[0,3,X]JZ	Rmvl/Eye, Lt, [Opn, Perc, Ext], Synth Sub, NQ
08PJ3JZ	Rmvl of Synth Sub from Rt Lens, Perc Appr
08PK3JZ	Rmvl of Synth Sub from Lt Lens, Perc Appr
08PL[0,3]0Z	Rmvl/Extraocular Muscle, Rt, [Opn, Perc], Drain Dev, NQ
08PM[0,3]0Z	Rmvl/Extraocular Muscle, Lt, [Opn, Perc], Drain Dev, NQ
08Q0XZZ	Repair Rt Eye, Ext Appr
08Q1XZZ	Repair Lt Eye, Ext Appr
08Q23ZZ	Repair Rt Ant Chamber, Perc Appr
08Q33ZZ	Repair Lt Ant Chamber, Perc Appr
08Q43ZZ	Repair Rt Vitreous, Perc Appr
08Q53ZZ	Repair Lt Vitreous, Perc Appr
08Q6XZZ	Repair Rt Sclera, Ext Appr
08Q7XZZ	Repair Lt Sclera, Ext Appr
08Q8XZZ	Repair Rt Cornea, Ext Appr
08Q9XZZ	Repair Lt Cornea, Ext Appr
08QA*	Repair/Choroid, Rt
08QB*	Repair/Choroid, Lt
08QC3ZZ	Repair Rt Iris, Perc Appr
08QD3ZZ	Repair Lt Iris, Perc Appr
08QE3ZZ	Repair Rt Retina, Perc Appr
08QF3ZZ	Repair Lt Retina, Perc Appr
08QG3ZZ	Repair Rt Retinal Vessel, Perc Appr
08QH3ZZ	Repair Lt Retinal Vessel, Perc Appr
08QJ3ZZ	Repair Rt Lens, Perc Appr
08QK3ZZ	Repair Lt Lens, Perc Appr
08QL*	Repair/Extraocular Muscle, Rt
08QM*	Repair/Extraocular Muscle, Lt
08QSXZZ	Repair Rt Conjunctiva, Ext Appr
08QTXZZ	Repair Lt Conjunctiva, Ext Appr
08QV*	Repair/Lacrimal Gland, Rt
08QW*	Repair/Lacrimal Gland, Lt
08QX*	Repair/Lacrimal Duct, Rt
08QY*	Repair/Lacrimal Duct, Lt
08R*	Eye, Replace
08SC3ZZ	Repos Rt Iris, Perc Appr
08SD3ZZ	Repos Lt Iris, Perc Appr
08SG3ZZ	Repos Rt Retinal Vessel, Perc Appr
08SH3ZZ	Repos Lt Retinal Vessel, Perc Appr
08SJ3ZZ	Repos Rt Lens, Perc Appr

08SK3ZZ	Repos Lt Lens, Perc Appr
08SN*	Repos/Upr Eyelid, Rt
08SP*	Repos/Upr Eyelid, Lt
08SQ*	Repos/Lwr Eyelid, Rt
08SR*	Repos/Lwr Eyelid, Lt
08SV*	Repos/Lacrimal Gland, Rt
08SW*	Repos/Lacrimal Gland, Lt
08SX*	Repos/Lacrimal Duct, Rt
08SY*	Repos/Lacrimal Duct, Lt
08T0XZZ	Resect of Rt Eye, Ext Appr
08T1XZZ	Resect of Lt Eye, Ext Appr
08T43ZZ	Resect of Rt Vitreous, Perc Appr
08T53ZZ	Resect of Lt Vitreous, Perc Appr
08T8XZZ	Resect of Rt Cornea, Ext Appr
08T9XZZ	Resect of Lt Cornea, Ext Appr
08TC3ZZ	Resect of Rt Iris, Perc Appr
08TD3ZZ	Resect of Lt Iris, Perc Appr
08TJ3ZZ	Resect of Rt Lens, Perc Appr
08TK3ZZ	Resect of Lt Lens, Perc Appr
08TN*	Resect/Upr Eyelid, Rt
08TP*	Resect/Upr Eyelid, Lt
08TQ*	Resect/Lwr Eyelid, Rt
08TR*	Resect/Lwr Eyelid, Lt
08TV*	Resect/Lacrimal Gland, Rt
08TW*	Resect/Lacrimal Gland, Lt
08TX*	Resect/Lacrimal Duct, Rt
08TY*	Resect/Lacrimal Duct, Lt
08U0*	Supl/Eye, Rt
08U1*	Supl/Eye, Lt
08U8*	Supl/Cornea, Rt
08U9*	Supl/Cornea, Lt
08UC*	Supl/Iris, Rt
08UD*	Supl/Iris, Lt
08UE[0,3]JZ	Supl/Retina, Rt, [Opn, Perc], Synth Sub, NQ
08UF[0,3]JZ	Supl/Retina, Lt, [Opn, Perc], Synth Sub, NQ
08UG*	Supl/Retinal Vessel, Rt
08UH*	Supl/Retinal Vessel, Lt
08UL*	Supl/Extraocular Muscle, Rt
08UM*	Supl/Extraocular Muscle, Lt
08UN*	Supl/Upr Eyelid, Rt
08UP*	Supl/Upr Eyelid, Lt
08UQ*	Supl/Lwr Eyelid, Rt
08UR*	Supl/Lwr Eyelid, Lt
08UX*	Supl/Lacrimal Duct, Rt
08UY*	Supl/Lacrimal Duct, Lt
08V*	Eye, Restrict
08W0[0,3]JZ	Rev/Eye, Rt, [Opn, Perc], Synth Sub, NQ
08W1[0,3]JZ	Rev/Eye, Lt, [Opn, Perc], Synth Sub, NQ
08WJ3JZ	Rev of Synth Sub in Rt Lens, Perc Appr
08WK3JZ	Rev of Synth Sub in Lt Lens, Perc Appr
08WL[0,3]0Z	Rev/Extraocular Muscle, Rt, [Opn, Perc], Drain Dev, NQ
08WM[0,3]0Z	Rev/Extraocular Muscle, Lt, [Opn, Perc], Drain Dev, NQ
090*	Ear, Nose, Sinus, Alter
098L*	Div/Nasal Turbinate
099N[0,3,4,7,8][0,Z]Z	Drain/Nasopharynx, [Opn, Perc, Perc Endo, Via Natrl or Artfcl Opng, Via Natrl or Artfcl Opng Endo], [Drain Dev, No Dev], NQ
09BL[0,3,4,7,8]ZZ	Exc/Nasal Turbinate, [Opn, Perc, Perc Endo, Via Natrl or Artfcl Opng, Via Natrl or Artfcl Opng Endo]
09BM[0,3,4]ZZ	Exc/Nasal Septum, [Opn, Perc, Perc Endo]
09CN*	Extir/Nasopharynx
09DL*	Extract/Nasal Turbinate
09DM*	Extract/Nasal Septum
09M*	Ear, Nose, Sinus, Reattach
09N0*	Rls/Ext Ear, Rt
09N1*	Rls/Ext Ear, Lt
09N3*	Rls/Ext Auditory Canal, Rt
09N4*	Rls/Ext Auditory Canal, Lt
09Q0[0,3,4]ZZ	Rpr/Ext Ear, Rt, [Opn, Perc, Perc Endo]
09Q1[0,3,4]ZZ	Rpr/Ext Ear, Lt, [Opn, Perc, Perc Endo]
09Q2[0,3,4]ZZ	Rpr/Ext Ear, Bilat, [Opn, Perc, Perc Endo]
09Q3[0,3,4,7,8]ZZ	Rpr/Ext Auditory Canal, Rt, [Opn, Perc, Perc Endo, Via Natrl or Artfcl Opng, Via Natrl or Artfcl Opng Endo]
09Q4[0,3,4,7,8]ZZ	Rpr/Ext Auditory Canal, Lt, [Opn, Perc, Perc Endo, Via Natrl or Artfcl Opng, Via Natrl or Artfcl Opng Endo]
09QK*	Repair/Nose
09QL*	Repair/Nasal Turbinate
09QM*	Repair/Nasal Septum
09QN*	Repair/Nasopharynx
09R0*	Replace/Ext Ear, Rt

MDC 21: Injuries, Poisonings And Toxic Effects Of Drugs—SURGICAL

T Transfer DRG   SP Special Payment   * Code Range   6th and 7th Character of ZZ = No Device, No Qualifier ZX = No Device, Diagnostic

Ø9R1*	Replace/Ext Ear, Lt
Ø9R2*	Replace/Ext Ear, Bilat
Ø9RK*	Replace/Nose
Ø9RL*	Replace/Nasal Turbinate
Ø9RM*	Replace/Nasal Septum
Ø9RN*	Replace/Nasopharynx
Ø9SØ*	Repos/Ext Ear, Rt
Ø9S1*	Repos/Ext Ear, Lt
Ø9S2*	Repos/Ext Ear, Bilat
Ø9SK*	Repos/Nose
Ø9SL*	Repos/Nasal Turbinate
Ø9SM*	Repos/Nasal Septum
Ø9TØ*	Resect/Ext Ear, Rt
Ø9T1*	Resect/Ext Ear, Lt
Ø9TK*	Resect/Nose
Ø9TL*	Resect/Nasal Turbinate
Ø9TM*	Resect/Nasal Septum
Ø9UØ*	Supl/Ext Ear, Rt
Ø9U1*	Supl/Ext Ear, Lt
Ø9U2*	Supl/Ext Ear, Bilat
Ø9UK*	Supl/Nose
Ø9UL*	Supl/Nasal Turbinate
Ø9UM*	Supl/Nasal Septum
Ø9UN*	Supl/Nasopharynx
ØB5K[Ø,7]ZZ	Destr/Lung, Rt, [Opn, Via Natrl or Artfcl Opng]
ØB5L[Ø,7]ZZ	Destr/Lung, Lt, [Opn, Via Natrl or Artfcl Opng]
ØB5M[Ø,7]ZZ	Destr/Lungs, Bilat, [Opn, Via Natrl or Artfcl Opng]
ØB5N*	Destr/Pleura, Rt
ØB5P*	Destr/Pleura, Lt
ØB71*	Dilation/Trachea
ØB72*	Dilation/Carina
ØB9CØ[Ø,Z]Z	Drain/Upr Lung Lobe, Rt, Opn, [Drain Dev, No Dev], NQ
ØB9DØ[Ø,Z]Z	Drain/Mid Lung Lobe, Rt, Opn, [Drain Dev, No Dev], NQ
ØB9FØ[Ø,Z]Z	Drain/Lwr Lung Lobe, Rt, Opn, [Drain Dev, No Dev], NQ
ØB9GØ[Ø,Z]Z	Drain/Upr Lung Lobe, Lt, Opn, [Drain Dev, No Dev], NQ
ØB9HØ[Ø,Z]Z	Drain/Lung Lingula, Opn, [Drain Dev, No Dev], NQ
ØB9JØ[Ø,Z]Z	Drain/Lwr Lung Lobe, Lt, Opn, [Drain Dev, No Dev], NQ
ØB9KØ[Ø,Z]Z	Drain/Lung, Rt, Opn, [Drain Dev, No Dev], NQ
ØB9LØ[Ø,Z]Z	Drain/Lung, Lt, Opn, [Drain Dev, No Dev], NQ
ØB9MØ[Ø,Z]Z	Drain/Lungs, Bilat, Opn, [Drain Dev, No Dev], NQ
ØBBC4ZZ	Exc of Rt Upr Lung Lobe, Perc Endo Appr
ØBBD4ZZ	Exc of Rt Mid Lung Lobe, Perc Endo Appr
ØBBF4ZZ	Exc of Rt Lwr Lung Lobe, Perc Endo Appr
ØBBG4ZZ	Exc of Lt Upr Lung Lobe, Perc Endo Appr
ØBBH4ZZ	Exc of Lung Lingula, Perc Endo Appr
ØBBJ4ZZ	Exc of Lt Lwr Lung Lobe, Perc Endo Appr
ØBBK4ZZ	Exc of Rt Lung, Perc Endo Appr
ØBBL4ZZ	Exc of Lt Lung, Perc Endo Appr
ØBBM[Ø,3,7]ZZ	Exc/Lungs, Bilat, [Opn, Perc, Via Natrl or Artfcl Opng]
ØBBN[Ø,3,4]ZZ	Exc/Pleura, Rt, [Opn, Perc, Perc Endo]
ØBBP[Ø,3,4]ZZ	Exc/Pleura, Lt, [Opn, Perc, Perc Endo]
ØBCC*	Extir/Upr Lung Lobe, Rt
ØBCD*	Extir/Mid Lung Lobe, Rt
ØBCF*	Extir/Lwr Lung Lobe, Rt
ØBCG*	Extir/Upr Lung Lobe, Lt
ØBCH*	Extir/Lung Lingula
ØBCJ*	Extir/Lwr Lung Lobe, Lt
ØBCK*	Extir/Lung, Rt
ØBCL*	Extir/Lung, Lt
ØBCM*	Extir/Lungs, Bilat
ØBD*	Respiratory Sys, Extract
ØBF1[Ø,3,4,7,8]ZZ	Fragmn/Trachea, [Opn, Perc, Perc Endo, Via Natrl or Artfcl Opng, Via Natrl or Artfcl Opng Endo]
ØBF2[Ø,3,4,7,8]ZZ	Fragmn/Carina, [Opn, Perc, Perc Endo, Via Natrl or Artfcl Opng, Via Natrl or Artfcl Opng Endo]
ØBHØ[Ø,3,4,7,8]1Z	Insert/Tracheobronchial Tree, [Opn, Perc, Perc Endo, Via Natrl or Artfcl Opng, Via Natrl or Artfcl Opng Endo], Radioact Elmt, NQ
ØBHK*	Insert/Lung, Rt
ØBHL*	Insert/Lung, Lt
ØBHR[Ø,3,4]MZ	Insert/Diaphragm, Rt, [Opn, Perc, Perc Endo], Diaphragmatic Pacemaker Lead, NQ
ØBHS[Ø,3,4]MZ	Insert/Diaphragm, Lt, [Opn, Perc, Perc Endo], Diaphragmatic Pacemaker Lead, NQ
ØBJØ4ZZ	Inspect of Tracheobronchial Tree, Perc Endo Appr
ØBJK4ZZ	Inspect of Rt Lung, Perc Endo Appr
ØBJL4ZZ	Inspect of Lt Lung, Perc Endo Appr
ØBL1*	Occlsn/Trachea
ØBL2*	Occlsn/Carina
ØBM1ØZZ	Reattach of Trachea, Opn Appr

ØBM2ØZZ	Reattach of Carina, Opn Appr
ØBN1*	Rls/Trachea
ØBN2*	Rls/Carina
ØBNN*	Rls/Pleura, Rt
ØBNP*	Rls/Pleura, Lt
ØBPK[Ø,3,4,7,8][Ø,1,2,3]Z	Rmvl/Lung, Rt, [Opn, Perc, Perc Endo, Via Natrl or Artfcl Opng, Via Natrl or Artfcl Opng Endo], [Drain Dev, Radioact Elmt, Monitoring Dev, Inf Dev], NQ
ØBPL[Ø,3,4,7,8][Ø,1,2,3]Z	Rmvl/Lung, Lt, [Opn, Perc, Perc Endo, Via Natrl or Artfcl Opng, Via Natrl or Artfcl Opng Endo], [Drain Dev, Radioact Elmt, Monitoring Dev, Inf Dev], NQ
ØBQ1*	Repair/Trachea
ØBQ2*	Repair/Carina
ØBQ3*	Repair/Main Bronchus, Rt
ØBQ4*	Repair/Upr Lobe Bronchus, Rt
ØBQ5*	Repair/Mid Lobe Bronchus, Rt
ØBQ6*	Repair/Lwr Lobe Bronchus, Rt
ØBQ7*	Repair/Main Bronchus, Lt
ØBQ8*	Repair/Upr Lobe Bronchus, Lt
ØBQ9*	Repair/Lingula Bronchus
ØBQB*	Repair/Lwr Lobe Bronchus, Lt
ØBQK*	Repair/Lung, Rt
ØBQL*	Repair/Lung, Lt
ØBQM*	Repair/Lungs, Bilat
ØBQN*	Repair/Pleura, Rt
ØBQP*	Repair/Pleura, Lt
ØBQR*	Repair/Diaphragm, Rt
ØBQS*	Repair/Diaphragm, Lt
ØBS1ØZZ	Repos Trachea, Opn Appr
ØBS2ØZZ	Repos Carina, Opn Appr
ØBT*	Respiratory Sys, Resect
ØBU1*	Supl/Trachea
ØBU2*	Supl/Carina
ØBUR*	Supl/Diaphragm, Rt
ØBUS*	Supl/Diaphragm, Lt
ØBV1*	Restrict/Trachea
ØBV2*	Restrict/Carina
ØBW1[Ø,3,4]FZ	Rev/Trachea, [Opn, Perc, Perc Endo], Tracheostomy Dev, NQ
ØBWK[Ø,3,4,7,8][Ø,2,3]Z	Rev/Lung, Rt, [Opn, Perc, Perc Endo, Via Natrl or Artfcl Opng, Via Natrl or Artfcl Opng Endo], [Drain Dev, Monitoring Dev, Inf Dev], NQ
ØBWL[Ø,3,4,7,8][Ø,2,3]Z	Rev/Lung, Lt, [Opn, Perc, Perc Endo, Via Natrl or Artfcl Opng, Via Natrl or Artfcl Opng Endo], [Drain Dev, Monitoring Dev, Inf Dev], NQ
ØCØ*	Mouth and Throat, Alter
ØC53*	Destr/Soft Palate
ØC54*	Destr/Buccal Mucosa
ØC5R*	Destr/Epiglottis
ØC9Ø[Ø,3,X][Ø,Z]Z	Drain/Upr Lip, [Opn, Perc, Ext], [Drain Dev, No Dev], NQ
ØC91[Ø,3,X][Ø,Z]Z	Drain/Lwr Lip, [Opn, Perc, Ext], [Drain Dev, No Dev], NQ
ØC94[Ø,3,X][Ø,Z]Z	Drain/Buccal Mucosa, [Opn, Perc, Ext], [Drain Dev, No Dev], NQ
ØC9M[Ø,3,4,7,8][Ø,Z]Z	Drain/Pharynx, [Opn, Perc, Perc Endo, Via Natrl or Artfcl Opng, Via Natrl or Artfcl Opng Endo], [Drain Dev, No Dev], NQ
ØCB3[Ø,3,X]ZZ	Exc/Soft Palate, [Opn, Perc, Ext]
ØCB4[Ø,3,X]ZZ	Exc/Buccal Mucosa, [Opn, Perc, Ext]
ØCBR[Ø,3,4,7,8]ZZ	Exc/Epiglottis, [Opn, Perc, Perc Endo, Via Natrl or Artfcl Opng, Via Natrl or Artfcl Opng Endo]
ØCBS[Ø,3,4,7,8]ZZ	Exc/Larynx, [Opn, Perc, Perc Endo, Via Natrl or Artfcl Opng, Via Natrl or Artfcl Opng Endo]
ØCBT[Ø,3,4,7,8]ZZ	Exc/Vocal Cord, Rt, [Opn, Perc, Perc Endo, Via Natrl or Artfcl Opng, Via Natrl or Artfcl Opng Endo]
ØCBV[Ø,3,4,7,8]ZZ	Exc/Vocal Cord, Lt, [Opn, Perc, Perc Endo, Via Natrl or Artfcl Opng, Via Natrl or Artfcl Opng Endo]
ØCCØ[Ø,3]ZZ	Extir/Upr Lip, [Opn, Perc]
ØCC1[Ø,3]ZZ	Extir/Lwr Lip, [Opn, Perc]
ØCC4[Ø,3]ZZ	Extir/Buccal Mucosa, [Opn, Perc]
ØCCM[Ø,3,4]ZZ	Extir/Pharynx, [Opn, Perc, Perc Endo]
ØCCP[Ø,3]ZZ	Extir/Tonsils, [Opn, Perc]
ØCCQ[Ø,3]ZZ	Extir/Adenoids, [Opn, Perc]
ØCH7*	Insert/Tongue
ØCMØØZZ	Reattach of Upr Lip, Opn Appr
ØCM1ØZZ	Reattach of Lwr Lip, Opn Appr
ØCM3ØZZ	Reattach of Soft Palate, Opn Appr
ØCM7ØZZ	Reattach of Tongue, Opn Appr
ØCN2*	Rls/Hard Palate
ØCN3*	Rls/Soft Palate
ØCN4*	Rls/Buccal Mucosa
ØCN8*	Rls/Parotid Gland, Rt
ØCN9*	Rls/Parotid Gland, Lt
ØCNB*	Rls/Parotid Duct, Rt

MDC 21: Injuries, Poisonings And Toxic Effects Of Drugs—SURGICAL

Surgical	**Medical**	**CC Indicator**	**MCC Indicator**	**Procedure Proxy**	**PDx MCC** PDx acts as own MCC	**PDx CC** PDx acts as own CC

MDC 21: Injuries, Poisonings And Toxic Effects Of Drugs—SURGICAL

ØCNC*	Rls/Parotid Duct, Lt
ØCND*	Rls/Sublingual Gland, Rt
ØCNF*	Rls/Sublingual Gland, Lt
ØCNG*	Rls/Submaxillary Gland, Rt
ØCNH*	Rls/Submaxillary Gland, Lt
ØCNJ*	Rls/Minor Salivary Gland
ØCNR*	Rls/Epiglottis
ØCNS*	Rls/Larynx
ØCNT*	Rls/Vocal Cord, Rt
ØCNV*	Rls/Vocal Cord, Lt
ØCPY7[1,7,J,K]Z	Rmvl/Mouth and Throat, Via Natrl or Artfcl Opng, [Radioact Elmt, Auto Tissue Sub, Synth Sub, Nonauto Tissue Sub], NQ
ØCPY8[1,7,J,K]Z	Rmvl/Mouth and Throat, Via Natrl or Artfcl Opng Endo, [Radioact Elmt, Auto Tissue Sub, Synth Sub, Nonauto Tissue Sub], NQ
ØCPY[Ø,3][Ø,1,7,D,J,K]Z	Rmvl/Mouth and Throat, [Opn, Perc], [Drain Dev, Radioact Elmt, Auto Tissue Sub, Intralum Dev, Synth Sub, Nonauto Tissue Sub], NQ
ØCQØ[Ø,3]ZZ	Rpr/Upr Lip, [Opn, Perc]
ØCQ1[Ø,3]ZZ	Rpr/Lwr Lip, [Opn, Perc]
ØCQ2*	Repair/Hard Palate
ØCQ3*	Repair/Soft Palate
ØCQ4*	Repair/Buccal Mucosa
ØCQ8*	Repair/Parotid Gland, Rt
ØCQ9*	Repair/Parotid Gland, Lt
ØCQB*	Repair/Parotid Duct, Rt
ØCQC*	Repair/Parotid Duct, Lt
ØCQD*	Repair/Sublingual Gland, Rt
ØCQF*	Repair/Sublingual Gland, Lt
ØCQG*	Repair/Submaxillary Gland, Rt
ØCQH*	Repair/Submaxillary Gland, Lt
ØCQJ*	Repair/Minor Salivary Gland
ØCQM*	Repair/Pharynx
ØCQR*	Repair/Epiglottis
ØCQS*	Repair/Larynx
ØCQT*	Repair/Vocal Cord, Rt
ØCQV*	Repair/Vocal Cord, Lt
ØCRØ*	Replace/Upr Lip
ØCR1*	Replace/Lwr Lip
ØCR4*	Replace/Buccal Mucosa
ØCR5*	Replace/Upr Gingiva
ØCR6*	Replace/Lwr Gingiva
ØCR7*	Replace/Tongue
ØCRB*	Replace/Parotid Duct, Rt
ØCRC*	Replace/Parotid Duct, Lt
ØCRM*	Replace/Pharynx
ØCRR*	Replace/Epiglottis
ØCRS*	Replace/Larynx
ØCRT[Ø,7,8][7,K]Z	Replace/Vocal Cord, Rt, [Opn, Via Natrl or Artfcl Opng, Via Natrl or Artfcl Opng Endo], [Auto Tissue Sub, Nonauto Tissue Sub], NQ
ØCRV8[J,K]Z	Replace/Vocal Cord, Lt, Via Natrl or Artfcl Opng Endo, [Synth Sub, Nonauto Tissue Sub], NQ
ØCRV[Ø,7][7,K]Z	Replace/Vocal Cord, Lt, [Opn, Via Natrl or Artfcl Opng], [Auto Tissue Sub, Nonauto Tissue Sub], NQ
ØCSØ*	Repos/Upr Lip
ØCS1*	Repos/Lwr Lip
ØCS7*	Repos/Tongue
ØCSB*	Repos/Parotid Duct, Rt
ØCSC*	Repos/Parotid Duct, Lt
ØCSR*	Repos/Epiglottis
ØCST*	Repos/Vocal Cord, Rt
ØCSV*	Repos/Vocal Cord, Lt
ØCTØ*	Resect/Upr Lip
ØCT1*	Resect/Lwr Lip
ØCT3*	Resect/Soft Palate
ØCTR*	Resect/Epiglottis
ØCTT*	Resect/Vocal Cord, Rt
ØCTV*	Resect/Vocal Cord, Lt
ØCUØ*	Supl/Upr Lip
ØCU1*	Supl/Lwr Lip
ØCU4*	Supl/Buccal Mucosa
ØCU5*	Supl/Upr Gingiva
ØCU6*	Supl/Lwr Gingiva
ØCU7*	Supl/Tongue
ØCUM*	Supl/Pharynx
ØCUR*	Supl/Epiglottis
ØCUS*	Supl/Larynx
ØCUT*	Supl/Vocal Cord, Rt
ØCUV*	Supl/Vocal Cord, Lt

ØCVB[7,8][D,Z]Z	Restrict/Parotid Duct, Rt, [Via Natrl or Artfcl Opng, Via Natrl or Artfcl Opng Endo], [Intralum Dev, No Dev], NQ
ØCVC[7,8][D,Z]Z	Restrict/Parotid Duct, Lt, [Via Natrl or Artfcl Opng, Via Natrl or Artfcl Opng Endo], [Intralum Dev, No Dev], NQ
ØCWY[Ø,3,7,8][Ø,1,D,J,K]Z	Rev/Mouth and Throat, [Opn, Perc, Via Natrl or Artfcl Opng, Via Natrl or Artfcl Opng Endo], [Drain Dev, Radioact Elmt, Intralum Dev, Synth Sub, Nonauto Tissue Sub], NQ
ØCWY[3,7,8]7Z	Rev/Mouth and Throat, [Perc, Via Natrl or Artfcl Opng, Via Natrl or Artfcl Opng Endo], Auto Tissue Sub, NQ
ØCX*	Mouth and Throat, Transfer
ØD113J4	Bypass Up Esophag to Cutan with Synth Sub, Perc Appr
ØD11[Ø,4,8][7,J,K,Z][4,6]	Bypass/Esophagus, Upr, [Opn, Perc Endo, Via Natrl or Artfcl Opng Endo], [Auto Tissue Sub, Synth Sub, Nonauto Tissue Sub, No Dev], [Cutaneous, Stomach]
ØD123J4	Bypass Mid Esophag to Cutan with Synth Sub, Perc Appr
ØD12[Ø,4,8][7,J,K,Z][4,6]	Bypass/Esophagus, Mid, [Opn, Perc Endo, Via Natrl or Artfcl Opng Endo], [Auto Tissue Sub, Synth Sub, Nonauto Tissue Sub, No Dev], [Cutaneous, Stomach]
ØD133J4	Bypass Low Esophag to Cutan with Synth Sub, Perc Appr
ØD13[Ø,4,8][7,J,K,Z][4,6]	Bypass/Esophagus, Lwr, [Opn, Perc Endo, Via Natrl or Artfcl Opng Endo], [Auto Tissue Sub, Synth Sub, Nonauto Tissue Sub, No Dev], [Cutaneous, Stomach]
ØD15*	Bypass/Esophagus
ØD19*	Bypass/Duodenum
ØD1A*	Bypass/Jejunum
ØD1B*	Bypass/Ileum
ØD1H*	Bypass/Cecum
ØD1K*	Bypass/Ascending Colon
ØD1L*	Bypass/Transv Colon
ØD1M*	Bypass/Descending Colon
ØD1N3J4	Bypass Sigmoid Colon to Cutan with Synth Sub, Perc Appr
ØD1N[Ø,4,8][7,J,K,Z][N,P]	Bypass/Sigmoid Colon, [Opn, Perc Endo, Via Natrl or Artfcl Opng Endo], [Auto Tissue Sub, Synth Sub, Nonauto Tissue Sub, No Dev], [Sigmoid Colon, Rectum]
ØD1N[Ø,4,8][7,J,K]4	Bypass/Sigmoid Colon, [Opn, Perc Endo, Via Natrl or Artfcl Opng Endo], [Auto Tissue Sub, Synth Sub, Nonauto Tissue Sub], Cutaneous
ØD1N[4,8]Z4	Bypass/Sigmoid Colon, [Perc Endo, Via Natrl or Artfcl Opng Endo], No Dev, Cutaneous
ØD71[Ø,3,4][D,Z]Z	Dilation/Esophagus, Upr, [Opn, Perc, Perc Endo], [Intralum Dev, No Dev], NQ
ØD72[Ø,3,4][D,Z]Z	Dilation/Esophagus, Mid, [Opn, Perc, Perc Endo], [Intralum Dev, No Dev], NQ
ØD73[Ø,3,4][D,Z]Z	Dilation/Esophagus, Lwr, [Opn, Perc, Perc Endo], [Intralum Dev, No Dev], NQ
ØD74[Ø,3,4][D,Z]Z	Dilation/Esophagogastric Junction, [Opn, Perc, Perc Endo], [Intralum Dev, No Dev], NQ
ØD75[Ø,3,4][D,Z]Z	Dilation/Esophagus, [Opn, Perc, Perc Endo], [Intralum Dev, No Dev], NQ
ØD76*	Dilation/Stomach
ØD7Q[Ø,3,4][D,Z]Z	Dilation/Anus, [Opn, Perc, Perc Endo], [Intralum Dev, No Dev], NQ
ØD84*	Div/Esophagogastric Junction
ØD91[Ø,3,4,7,8][Ø,Z]Z	Drain/Esophagus, Upr, [Opn, Perc, Perc Endo, Via Natrl or Artfcl Opng, Via Natrl or Artfcl Opng Endo], [Drain Dev, No Dev], NQ
ØD92[Ø,3,4,7,8][Ø,Z]Z	Drain/Esophagus, Mid, [Opn, Perc, Perc Endo, Via Natrl or Artfcl Opng, Via Natrl or Artfcl Opng Endo], [Drain Dev, No Dev], NQ
ØD93[Ø,3,4,7,8][Ø,Z]Z	Drain/Esophagus, Lwr, [Opn, Perc, Perc Endo, Via Natrl or Artfcl Opng, Via Natrl or Artfcl Opng Endo], [Drain Dev, No Dev], NQ
ØD94[Ø,3,4,7,8][Ø,Z]Z	Drain/Esophagogastric Junction, [Opn, Perc, Perc Endo, Via Natrl or Artfcl Opng, Via Natrl or Artfcl Opng Endo], [Drain Dev, No Dev], NQ
ØD95[Ø,3,4,7,8][Ø,Z]Z	Drain/Esophagus, [Opn, Perc, Perc Endo, Via Natrl or Artfcl Opng, Via Natrl or Artfcl Opng Endo], [Drain Dev, No Dev], NQ
ØD96[Ø,3,4,7,8]ZZ	Drain/Stomach, [Opn, Perc, Perc Endo, Via Natrl or Artfcl Opng, Via Natrl or Artfcl Opng Endo]
ØD96[Ø,3,4]ØZ	Drain/Stomach, [Opn, Perc, Perc Endo], Drain Dev, NQ
ØD98[Ø,3,4,7,8]ZZ	Drain/Sm Intestine, [Opn, Perc, Perc Endo, Via Natrl or Artfcl Opng, Via Natrl or Artfcl Opng Endo]
ØD98[Ø,3,4]ØZ	Drain/Sm Intestine, [Opn, Perc, Perc Endo], Drain Dev, NQ
ØD99[Ø,3,4,7,8]ZZ	Drain/Duodenum, [Opn, Perc, Perc Endo, Via Natrl or Artfcl Opng, Via Natrl or Artfcl Opng Endo]
ØD99[Ø,3,4]ØZ	Drain/Duodenum, [Opn, Perc, Perc Endo], Drain Dev, NQ
ØD9A[Ø,3,4,7,8]ZZ	Drain/Jejunum, [Opn, Perc, Perc Endo, Via Natrl or Artfcl Opng, Via Natrl or Artfcl Opng Endo]
ØD9A[Ø,3,4]ØZ	Drain/Jejunum, [Opn, Perc, Perc Endo], Drain Dev, NQ

T **Transfer DRG**   SP **Special Payment**   * **Code Range**   **6th and 7th Character of ZZ = No Device, No Qualifier ZX = No Device, Diagnostic**

MS-DRG Version 33.0

© 2015 Optum360, LLC

ØD9B[Ø,3,4,7,8]ZZ Drain/Ileum, [Opn, Perc, Perc Endo, Via Natrl or Artfcl Opng, Via Natrl or Artfcl Opng Endo]
ØD9B[Ø,3,4]ØZ Drain/Ileum, [Opn, Perc, Perc Endo], Drain Dev, NQ
ØD9C[Ø,3,4,7,8][Ø,Z]Z Drain/Ileocecal Valve, [Opn, Perc, Perc Endo, Via Natrl or Artfcl Opng, Via Natrl or Artfcl Opng Endo], [Drain Dev, No Dev], NQ
ØD9E[Ø,3,4,7,8]ZZ Drain/Lg Intestine, [Opn, Perc, Perc Endo, Via Natrl or Artfcl Opng, Via Natrl or Artfcl Opng Endo]
ØD9E[Ø,3,4]ØZ Drain/Lg Intestine, [Opn, Perc, Perc Endo], Drain Dev, NQ
ØD9F[Ø,3,4,7,8]ZZ Drain/Lg Intestine, Rt, [Opn, Perc, Perc Endo, Via Natrl or Artfcl Opng, Via Natrl or Artfcl Opng Endo]
ØD9F[Ø,3,4]ØZ Drain/Lg Intestine, Rt, [Opn, Perc, Perc Endo], Drain Dev, NQ
ØD9G[Ø,3,4,7,8]ZZ Drain/Lg Intestine, Lt, [Opn, Perc, Perc Endo, Via Natrl or Artfcl Opng, Via Natrl or Artfcl Opng Endo]
ØD9G[Ø,3,4]ØZ Drain/Lg Intestine, Lt, [Opn, Perc, Perc Endo], Drain Dev, NQ
ØD9H[Ø,3,4,7,8]ZZ Drain/Cecum, [Opn, Perc, Perc Endo, Via Natrl or Artfcl Opng, Via Natrl or Artfcl Opng Endo]
ØD9H[Ø,3,4]ØZ Drain/Cecum, [Opn, Perc, Perc Endo], Drain Dev, NQ
ØD9K[Ø,3,4,7,8]ZZ Drain/Ascending Colon, [Opn, Perc, Perc Endo, Via Natrl or Artfcl Opng, Via Natrl or Artfcl Opng Endo]
ØD9K[Ø,3,4]ØZ Drain/Ascending Colon, [Opn, Perc, Perc Endo], Drain Dev, NQ
ØD9L[Ø,3,4,7,8]ZZ Drain/Transv Colon, [Opn, Perc, Perc Endo, Via Natrl or Artfcl Opng, Via Natrl or Artfcl Opng Endo]
ØD9L[Ø,3,4]ØZ Drain/Transv Colon, [Opn, Perc, Perc Endo], Drain Dev, NQ
ØD9M[Ø,3,4,7,8]ZZ Drain/Descending Colon, [Opn, Perc, Perc Endo, Via Natrl or Artfcl Opng, Via Natrl or Artfcl Opng Endo]
ØD9M[Ø,3,4]ØZ Drain/Descending Colon, [Opn, Perc, Perc Endo], Drain Dev, NQ
ØD9N[Ø,3,4,7,8]ZZ Drain/Sigmoid Colon, [Opn, Perc, Perc Endo, Via Natrl or Artfcl Opng, Via Natrl or Artfcl Opng Endo]
ØD9N[Ø,3,4]ØZ Drain/Sigmoid Colon, [Opn, Perc, Perc Endo], Drain Dev, NQ
ØD9P[Ø,3,4,7,8]ZZ Drain/Rectum, [Opn, Perc, Perc Endo, Via Natrl or Artfcl Opng, Via Natrl or Artfcl Opng Endo]
ØD9P[Ø,3,4]ØZ Drain/Rectum, [Opn, Perc, Perc Endo], Drain Dev, NQ
ØD9SØ[Ø,Z]Z Drain/Greater Omentum, Opn, [Drain Dev, No Dev], NQ
ØD9TØ[Ø,Z]Z Drain/Lesser Omentum, Opn, [Drain Dev, No Dev], NQ
ØD9VØ[Ø,Z]Z Drain/Mesentery, Opn, [Drain Dev, No Dev], NQ
ØD9WØ[Ø,Z]Z Drain/Peritoneum, Opn, [Drain Dev, No Dev], NQ
ØDB1[Ø,3,7]ZZ Exc/Esophagus, Upr, [Opn, Perc, Via Natrl or Artfcl Opng]
ØDB2[Ø,3,7]ZZ Exc/Esophagus, Mid, [Opn, Perc, Via Natrl or Artfcl Opng]
ØDB3[Ø,3,7]ZZ Exc/Esophagus, Lwr, [Opn, Perc, Via Natrl or Artfcl Opng]
ØDB4[Ø,3,4,7]ZZ Exc/Esophagogastric Junction, [Opn, Perc, Perc Endo, Via Natrl or Artfcl Opng]
ØDB5[Ø,3,7]ZZ Exc/Esophagus, [Opn, Perc, Via Natrl or Artfcl Opng]
ØDB6[Ø,3,4,7,8]Z3 Exc/Stomach, [Opn, Perc, Perc Endo, Via Natrl or Artfcl Opng, Via Natrl or Artfcl Opng Endo], No Dev, Vertical
ØDB6[Ø,3,7]ZZ Exc/Stomach, [Opn, Perc, Via Natrl or Artfcl Opng]
ØDB8[Ø,4,7]ZZ Exc/Sm Intestine, [Opn, Perc Endo, Via Natrl or Artfcl Opng]
ØDB97ZZ Exc of Duodenum, Via Natrl or Artfcl Opng
ØDBA7ZZ Exc of Jejunum, Via Natrl or Artfcl Opng
ØDBB7ZZ Exc of Ileum, Via Natrl or Artfcl Opng
ØDBE[Ø,3,4]ZZ Exc/Lg Intestine, [Opn, Perc, Perc Endo]
ØDBF[Ø,3,4]ZZ Exc/Lg Intestine, Rt, [Opn, Perc, Perc Endo]
ØDBG[Ø,3,4]ZZ Exc/Lg Intestine, Lt, [Opn, Perc, Perc Endo]
ØDBH[Ø,3,4]ZZ Exc/Cecum, [Opn, Perc, Perc Endo]
ØDBK[Ø,3,4]ZZ Exc/Ascending Colon, [Opn, Perc, Perc Endo]
ØDBL[Ø,3,4]ZZ Exc/Transv Colon, [Opn, Perc, Perc Endo]
ØDBM[Ø,3,4]ZZ Exc/Descending Colon, [Opn, Perc, Perc Endo]
ØDBN[Ø,3,4]ZZ Exc/Sigmoid Colon, [Opn, Perc, Perc Endo]
ØDBP[Ø,3,4,7]ZZ Exc/Rectum, [Opn, Perc, Perc Endo, Via Natrl or Artfcl Opng]
ØDBQ[Ø,3,4]ZZ Exc/Anus, [Opn, Perc, Perc Endo]
ØDC1[Ø,3,4]ZZ Extir/Esophagus, Upr, [Opn, Perc, Perc Endo]
ØDC2[Ø,3,4]ZZ Extir/Esophagus, Mid, [Opn, Perc, Perc Endo]
ØDC3[Ø,3,4]ZZ Extir/Esophagus, Lwr, [Opn, Perc, Perc Endo]
ØDC4[Ø,3,4]ZZ Extir/Esophagogastric Junction, [Opn, Perc, Perc Endo]
ØDC5[Ø,3,4]ZZ Extir/Esophagus, [Opn, Perc, Perc Endo]
ØDC6[Ø,3,4]ZZ Extir/Stomach, [Opn, Perc, Perc Endo]
ØDC8[Ø,3,4]ZZ Extir/Sm Intestine, [Opn, Perc, Perc Endo]
ØDC9[Ø,3,4]ZZ Extir/Duodenum, [Opn, Perc, Perc Endo]
ØDCA[Ø,3,4]ZZ Extir/Jejunum, [Opn, Perc, Perc Endo]
ØDCB[Ø,3,4]ZZ Extir/Ileum, [Opn, Perc, Perc Endo]
ØDCC[Ø,3,4]ZZ Extir/Ileocecal Valve, [Opn, Perc, Perc Endo]
ØDCE[Ø,3,4]ZZ Extir/Lg Intestine, [Opn, Perc, Perc Endo]
ØDCF[Ø,3,4]ZZ Extir/Lg Intestine, Rt, [Opn, Perc, Perc Endo]
ØDCG[Ø,3,4]ZZ Extir/Lg Intestine, Lt, [Opn, Perc, Perc Endo]
ØDCH[Ø,3,4]ZZ Extir/Cecum, [Opn, Perc, Perc Endo]
ØDCK[Ø,3,4]ZZ Extir/Ascending Colon, [Opn, Perc, Perc Endo]
ØDCL[Ø,3,4]ZZ Extir/Transv Colon, [Opn, Perc, Perc Endo]
ØDCM[Ø,3,4]ZZ Extir/Descending Colon, [Opn, Perc, Perc Endo]
ØDCN[Ø,3,4]ZZ Extir/Sigmoid Colon, [Opn, Perc, Perc Endo]

ØDCP[Ø,3,4]ZZ Extir/Rectum, [Opn, Perc, Perc Endo]
ØDCS* Extir/Greater Omentum
ØDCT* Extir/Lesser Omentum
ØDCV* Extir/Mesentery
ØDCW* Extir/Peritoneum
ØDF5[Ø,3,4,7,8]ZZ Fragmn/Esophagus, [Opn, Perc, Perc Endo, Via Natrl or Artfcl Opng, Via Natrl or Artfcl Opng Endo]
ØDF6[Ø,3,4,7,8]ZZ Fragmn/Stomach, [Opn, Perc, Perc Endo, Via Natrl or Artfcl Opng, Via Natrl or Artfcl Opng Endo]
ØDF8[Ø,3,4,7,8]ZZ Fragmn/Sm Intestine, [Opn, Perc, Perc Endo, Via Natrl or Artfcl Opng, Via Natrl or Artfcl Opng Endo]
ØDF9[Ø,3,4,7,8]ZZ Fragmn/Duodenum, [Opn, Perc, Perc Endo, Via Natrl or Artfcl Opng, Via Natrl or Artfcl Opng Endo]
ØDFA[Ø,3,4,7,8]ZZ Fragmn/Jejunum, [Opn, Perc, Perc Endo, Via Natrl or Artfcl Opng, Via Natrl or Artfcl Opng Endo]
ØDFB[Ø,3,4,7,8]ZZ Fragmn/Ileum, [Opn, Perc, Perc Endo, Via Natrl or Artfcl Opng, Via Natrl or Artfcl Opng Endo]
ØDFE[Ø,3,4,7,8]ZZ Fragmn/Lg Intestine, [Opn, Perc, Perc Endo, Via Natrl or Artfcl Opng, Via Natrl or Artfcl Opng Endo]
ØDFF[Ø,3,4,7,8]ZZ Fragmn/Lg Intestine, Rt, [Opn, Perc, Perc Endo, Via Natrl or Artfcl Opng, Via Natrl or Artfcl Opng Endo]
ØDFG[Ø,3,4,7,8]ZZ Fragmn/Lg Intestine, Lt, [Opn, Perc, Perc Endo, Via Natrl or Artfcl Opng, Via Natrl or Artfcl Opng Endo]
ØDFH[Ø,3,4,7,8]ZZ Fragmn/Cecum, [Opn, Perc, Perc Endo, Via Natrl or Artfcl Opng, Via Natrl or Artfcl Opng Endo]
ØDFK[Ø,3,4,7,8]ZZ Fragmn/Ascending Colon, [Opn, Perc, Perc Endo, Via Natrl or Artfcl Opng, Via Natrl or Artfcl Opng Endo]
ØDFL[Ø,3,4,7,8]ZZ Fragmn/Transv Colon, [Opn, Perc, Perc Endo, Via Natrl or Artfcl Opng, Via Natrl or Artfcl Opng Endo]
ØDFM[Ø,3,4,7,8]ZZ Fragmn/Descending Colon, [Opn, Perc, Perc Endo, Via Natrl or Artfcl Opng, Via Natrl or Artfcl Opng Endo]
ØDFN[Ø,3,4,7,8]ZZ Fragmn/Sigmoid Colon, [Opn, Perc, Perc Endo, Via Natrl or Artfcl Opng, Via Natrl or Artfcl Opng Endo]
ØDFP[Ø,3,4,7,8]ZZ Fragmn/Rectum, [Opn, Perc, Perc Endo, Via Natrl or Artfcl Opng, Via Natrl or Artfcl Opng Endo]
ØDFQ[Ø,3,4,7,8]ZZ Fragmn/Anus, [Opn, Perc, Perc Endo, Via Natrl or Artfcl Opng, Via Natrl or Artfcl Opng Endo]
ØDH5[Ø,3,4,7,8][1,2,3]Z Insert/Esophagus, [Opn, Perc, Perc Endo, Via Natrl or Artfcl Opng, Via Natrl or Artfcl Opng Endo], [Radioact Elmt, Monitoring Dev, Inf Dev], NQ
ØDH6ØUZ Insert of Feeding Device into Stomach, Opn Appr
ØDH6[Ø,3,4,7,8][2,3,D]Z Insert/Stomach, [Opn, Perc, Perc Endo, Via Natrl or Artfcl Opng, Via Natrl or Artfcl Opng Endo], [Monitoring Dev, Inf Dev, Intralum Dev], NQ
ØDH6[Ø,3,4]MZ Insert/Stomach, [Opn, Perc, Perc Endo], Stimulator Lead, NQ
ØDH8[Ø,3,4,7,8][2,3]Z Insert/Sm Intestine, [Opn, Perc, Perc Endo, Via Natrl or Artfcl Opng, Via Natrl or Artfcl Opng Endo], [Monitoring Dev, Inf Dev], NQ
ØDH9[Ø,3,4,7,8][2,3]Z Insert/Duodenum, [Opn, Perc, Perc Endo, Via Natrl or Artfcl Opng, Via Natrl or Artfcl Opng Endo], [Monitoring Dev, Inf Dev], NQ
ØDHA[Ø,3,4,7,8][2,3]Z Insert/Jejunum, [Opn, Perc, Perc Endo, Via Natrl or Artfcl Opng, Via Natrl or Artfcl Opng Endo], [Monitoring Dev, Inf Dev], NQ
ØDHB[Ø,3,4,7,8][2,3]Z Insert/Ileum, [Opn, Perc, Perc Endo, Via Natrl or Artfcl Opng, Via Natrl or Artfcl Opng Endo], [Monitoring Dev, Inf Dev], NQ
ØDHP[Ø,3,4,7,8]1Z Insert/Rectum, [Opn, Perc, Perc Endo, Via Natrl or Artfcl Opng, Via Natrl or Artfcl Opng Endo], Radioact Elmt, NQ
ØDHQ* Insert/Anus
ØDJØ[Ø,4]ZZ Inspect/Upr Intestinal Tract, [Opn, Perc Endo]
ØDJ6[Ø,4]ZZ Inspect/Stomach, [Opn, Perc Endo]
ØDJD[Ø,4]ZZ Inspect/Lwr Intestinal Tract, [Opn, Perc Endo]
ØDJU[Ø,3,4]ZZ Inspect/Omentum, [Opn, Perc, Perc Endo]
ØDJV[Ø,3,4]ZZ Inspect/Mesentery, [Opn, Perc, Perc Endo]
ØDJW[Ø,3,4]ZZ Inspect/Peritoneum, [Opn, Perc, Perc Endo]
ØDL6* Occlsn/Stomach
ØDL7* Occlsn/Stomach, Pylorus
ØDLQ* Occlsn/Anus
ØDM* Gastrointestinal Sys, Reattach
ØDN1* Rls/Esophagus, Upr
ØDN2* Rls/Esophagus, Mid
ØDN3* Rls/Esophagus, Lwr
ØDN4* Rls/Esophagogastric Junction
ØDN5* Rls/Esophagus
ØDN6* Rls/Stomach
ØDN8[Ø,3,4]ZZ Rls/Sm Intestine, [Opn, Perc, Perc Endo]
ØDN9[Ø,3,4]ZZ Rls/Duodenum, [Opn, Perc, Perc Endo]
ØDNA[Ø,3,4]ZZ Rls/Jejunum, [Opn, Perc, Perc Endo]
ØDNB[Ø,3,4]ZZ Rls/Ileum, [Opn, Perc, Perc Endo]

Surgical **Medical** **CC Indicator** **MCC Indicator** **Procedure Proxy** PDxMCC **PDx acts as own MCC** PDxCC **PDx acts as own CC**

MDC 21: Injuries, Poisonings And Toxic Effects Of Drugs—SURGICAL

ØDNC*	Rls/Ileocecal Valve
ØDNE[Ø,3,4]ZZ	Rls/Lg Intestine, [Opn, Perc, Perc Endo]
ØDNF[Ø,3,4]ZZ	Rls/Lg Intestine, Rt, [Opn, Perc, Perc Endo]
ØDNG[Ø,3,4]ZZ	Rls/Lg Intestine, Lt, [Opn, Perc, Perc Endo]
ØDNH[Ø,3,4]ZZ	Rls/Cecum, [Opn, Perc, Perc Endo]
ØDNJ[Ø,3,4]ZZ	Rls/Appendix, [Opn, Perc, Perc Endo]
ØDNK[Ø,3,4]ZZ	Rls/Ascending Colon, [Opn, Perc, Perc Endo]
ØDNL[Ø,3,4]ZZ	Rls/Transv Colon, [Opn, Perc, Perc Endo]
ØDNM[Ø,3,4]ZZ	Rls/Descending Colon, [Opn, Perc, Perc Endo]
ØDNN[Ø,3,4]ZZ	Rls/Sigmoid Colon, [Opn, Perc, Perc Endo]
ØDNP*	Rls/Rectum
ØDNR*	Rls/Anal Sphincter
ØDNS*	Rls/Greater Omentum
ØDNT*	Rls/Lesser Omentum
ØDNV*	Rls/Mesentery
ØDNW*	Rls/Peritoneum
ØDPØ[Ø,3,4,7,8][Ø,2,3,7,C,D,J,K,U]Z	Rmvl/Upr Intestinal Tract, [Opn, Perc, Perc Endo, Via Natrl or Artfcl Opng, Via Natrl or Artfcl Opng Endo], [Drain Dev, Monitoring Dev, Inf Dev, Auto Tissue Sub, Extralum Dev, Intralum Dev, Synth Sub, Nonauto Tissue Sub, Feeding Dev], NQ
ØDP57DZ	Rmvl of Intralum Device from Esophagus, Via Opng
ØDP58DZ	Rmvl of Intralum Device from Esophagus, Endo
ØDP5[Ø,3,4][1,2,3,U]Z	Rmvl/Esophagus, [Opn, Perc, Perc Endo], [Radioact Elmt, Monitoring Dev, Inf Dev, Feeding Dev], NQ
ØDP64[Ø,2,7,D,J,K,M,U]Z	Rmvl/Stomach, Perc Endo, [Drain Dev, Monitoring Dev, Auto Tissue Sub, Intralum Dev, Synth Sub, Nonauto Tissue Sub, Stimulator Lead, Feeding Dev], NQ
ØDP67[Ø,2,3,7,C,J,K,U]Z	Rmvl/Stomach, Via Natrl or Artfcl Opng, [Drain Dev, Monitoring Dev, Inf Dev, Auto Tissue Sub, Extralum Dev, Synth Sub, Nonauto Tissue Sub, Feeding Dev], NQ
ØDP68[Ø,2,3,7,C,J,K,U]Z	Rmvl/Stomach, Via Natrl or Artfcl Opng Endo, [Drain Dev, Monitoring Dev, Inf Dev, Auto Tissue Sub, Extralum Dev, Synth Sub, Nonauto Tissue Sub, Feeding Dev], NQ
ØDP6[Ø,3][Ø,2,3,7,C,D,J,K,M,U]Z	Rmvl/Stomach, [Opn, Perc], [Drain Dev, Monitoring Dev, Inf Dev, Auto Tissue Sub, Extralum Dev, Intralum Dev, Synth Sub, Nonauto Tissue Sub, Stimulator Lead, Feeding Dev], NQ
ØDPD[Ø,3,4,7,8][Ø,2,3,7,C,D,J,K,U]Z	Rmvl/Lwr Intestinal Tract, [Opn, Perc, Perc Endo, Via Natrl or Artfcl Opng, Via Natrl or Artfcl Opng Endo], [Drain Dev, Monitoring Dev, Inf Dev, Auto Tissue Sub, Extralum Dev, Intralum Dev, Synth Sub, Nonauto Tissue Sub, Feeding Dev], NQ
ØDPP[Ø,3,4]1Z	Rmvl/Rectum, [Opn, Perc, Perc Endo], Radioact Elmt, NQ
ØDPQ*	Rmvl/Anus
ØDPR*	Rmvl/Anal Sphincter
ØDQ1*	Repair/Esophagus, Upr
ØDQ2*	Repair/Esophagus, Mid
ØDQ3*	Repair/Esophagus, Lwr
ØDQ4*	Repair/Esophagogastric Junction
ØDQ5*	Repair/Esophagus
ØDQ6*	Repair/Stomach
ØDQ8*	Repair/Sm Intestine
ØDQ9*	Repair/Duodenum
ØDQA*	Repair/Jejunum
ØDQB*	Repair/Ileum
ØDQC*	Repair/Ileocecal Valve
ØDQE*	Repair/Large Intestine
ØDQF[3,4,7,8]ZZ	Rpr/Lg Intestine, Rt, [Perc, Perc Endo, Via Natrl or Artfcl Opng, Via Natrl or Artfcl Opng Endo]
ØDQG[3,4,7,8]ZZ	Rpr/Lg Intestine, Lt, [Perc, Perc Endo, Via Natrl or Artfcl Opng, Via Natrl or Artfcl Opng Endo]
ØDQH*	Repair/Cecum
ØDQJ*	Repair/Appendix
ØDQK*	Repair/Ascending Colon
ØDQL[3,4,7,8]ZZ	Rpr/Transv Colon, [Perc, Perc Endo, Via Natrl or Artfcl Opng, Via Natrl or Artfcl Opng Endo]
ØDQM[3,4,7,8]ZZ	Rpr/Descending Colon, [Perc, Perc Endo, Via Natrl or Artfcl Opng, Via Natrl or Artfcl Opng Endo]
ØDQN*	Repair/Sigmoid Colon
ØDQP*	Repair/Rectum
ØDQQ*	Repair/Anus
ØDQR*	Repair/Anal Sphincter
ØDQV*	Repair/Mesentery
ØDQW*	Repair/Peritoneum
ØDR*	Gastrointestinal Sys, Replace
ØDS5*	Repos/Esophagus
ØDS60ZZ	Repos Stomach, Opn Appr
ØDS64ZZ	Repos Stomach, Perc Endo Appr
ØDS67ZZ	Repos Stomach, Via Natrl or Artfcl Opng
ØDS68ZZ	Repos Stomach, Endo
ØDSB[Ø,4,7,8]ZZ	Repos/Ileum, [Opn, Perc Endo, Via Natrl or Artfcl Opng, Via Natrl or Artfcl Opng Endo]
ØDSH[Ø,4,7,8]ZZ	Repos/Cecum, [Opn, Perc Endo, Via Natrl or Artfcl Opng, Via Natrl or Artfcl Opng Endo]
ØDSP[Ø,4,7,8]ZZ	Repos/Rectum, [Opn, Perc Endo, Via Natrl or Artfcl Opng, Via Natrl or Artfcl Opng Endo]
ØDT1*	Resect/Esophagus, Upr
ØDT2*	Resect/Esophagus, Mid
ØDT3*	Resect/Esophagus, Lwr
ØDT4*	Resect/Esophagogastric Junction
ØDT5*	Resect/Esophagus
ØDT6*	Resect/Stomach
ØDT7*	Resect/Stomach, Pylorus
ØDT8*	Resect/Sm Intestine
ØDT9*	Resect/Duodenum
ØDTA*	Resect/Jejunum
ØDTB*	Resect/Ileum
ØDTC*	Resect/Ileocecal Valve
ØDTE*	Resect/Large Intestine
ØDTF*	Resect/Large Intestine, Rt
ØDTG*	Resect/Large Intestine, Lt
ØDTH*	Resect/Cecum
ØDTJ*	Resect/Appendix
ØDTK*	Resect/Ascending Colon
ØDTL*	Resect/Transv Colon
ØDTM*	Resect/Descending Colon
ØDTN*	Resect/Sigmoid Colon
ØDTP[Ø,4]ZZ	Resect/Rectum, [Opn, Perc Endo]
ØDU1*	Supl/Esophagus, Upr
ØDU2*	Supl/Esophagus, Mid
ØDU3*	Supl/Esophagus, Lwr
ØDU4*	Supl/Esophagogastric Junction
ØDU5*	Supl/Esophagus
ØDU6*	Supl/Stomach
ØDU8*	Supl/Sm Intestine
ØDU9*	Supl/Duodenum
ØDUA*	Supl/Jejunum
ØDUB*	Supl/Ileum
ØDUC*	Supl/Ileocecal Valve
ØDUE*	Supl/Large Intestine
ØDUF*	Supl/Large Intestine, Rt
ØDUG*	Supl/Large Intestine, Lt
ØDUH*	Supl/Cecum
ØDUK*	Supl/Ascending Colon
ØDUL*	Supl/Transv Colon
ØDUM*	Supl/Descending Colon
ØDUN*	Supl/Sigmoid Colon
ØDUP*	Supl/Rectum
ØDUQ*	Supl/Anus
ØDUR*	Supl/Anal Sphincter
ØDUS*	Supl/Greater Omentum
ØDUT*	Supl/Lesser Omentum
ØDUV*	Supl/Mesentery
ØDUW*	Supl/Peritoneum
ØDV1*	Restrict/Esophagus, Upr
ØDV2*	Restrict/Esophagus, Mid
ØDV3*	Restrict/Esophagus, Lwr
ØDV4*	Restrict/Esophagogastric Junction
ØDV5*	Restrict/Esophagus
ØDV67ZZ	Restrict of Stomach, Via Natrl or Artfcl Opng
ØDV68ZZ	Restrict of Stomach, Endo
ØDV6[Ø,3,4][C,D,Z]Z	Restrict/Stomach, [Opn, Perc, Perc Endo], [Extralum Dev, Intralum Dev, No Dev], NQ
ØDV8*	Restrict/Sm Intestine
ØDV9*	Restrict/Duodenum
ØDVA*	Restrict/Jejunum
ØDVB*	Restrict/Ileum
ØDVC*	Restrict/Ileocecal Valve
ØDVE*	Restrict/Large Intestine
ØDVF*	Restrict/Large Intestine, Rt
ØDVG*	Restrict/Large Intestine, Lt
ØDVH*	Restrict/Cecum
ØDVK*	Restrict/Ascending Colon
ØDVL*	Restrict/Transv Colon
ØDVM*	Restrict/Descending Colon
ØDVN*	Restrict/Sigmoid Colon
ØDVP*	Restrict/Rectum

T **Transfer DRG**   SP **Special Payment**   * **Code Range**   **6th and 7th Character of ZZ = No Device, No Qualifier ZX = No Device, Diagnostic**

0DW0[0,3,4,7,8][0,2,3,7,C,D,J,K]Z Rev/Upr Intestinal Tract, [Opn, Perc, Perc Endo, Via Natrl or Artfcl Opng, Via Natrl or Artfcl Opng Endo], [Drain Dev, Monitoring Dev, Inf Dev, Auto Tissue Sub, Extralum Dev, Intralum Dev, Synth Sub, Nonauto Tissue Sub], NQ

0DW0[0,3,7,8]UZ Rev/Upr Intestinal Tract, [Opn, Perc, Via Natrl or Artfcl Opng, Via Natrl or Artfcl Opng Endo], Feeding Dev, NQ

0DW5[7,8]DZ Rev/Esophagus, [Via Natrl or Artfcl Opng, Via Natrl or Artfcl Opng Endo], Intralum Dev, NQ

0DW64[0,2,7,D,J,K,M,U]Z Rev/Stomach, Perc Endo, [Drain Dev, Monitoring Dev, Auto Tissue Sub, Intralum Dev, Synth Sub, Nonauto Tissue Sub, Stimulator Lead, Feeding Dev], NQ

0DW6[0,3,7,8][0,2,3,7,C,D,J,K,U]Z Rev/Stomach, [Opn, Perc, Via Natrl or Artfcl Opng, Via Natrl or Artfcl Opng Endo], [Drain Dev, Monitoring Dev, Inf Dev, Auto Tissue Sub, Extralum Dev, Intralum Dev, Synth Sub, Nonauto Tissue Sub, Feeding Dev], NQ

0DW6[0,3]MZ Rev/Stomach, [Opn, Perc], Stimulator Lead, NQ

0DW8* Rev/Sm Intestine

0DWD[0,3,4,7,8][0,2,3,7,C,D,J,K,U]Z Rev/Lwr Intestinal Tract, [Opn, Perc, Perc Endo, Via Natrl or Artfcl Opng, Via Natrl or Artfcl Opng Endo], [Drain Dev, Monitoring Dev, Inf Dev, Auto Tissue Sub, Extralum Dev, Intralum Dev, Synth Sub, Nonauto Tissue Sub, Feeding Dev], NQ

0DWE* Rev/Large Intestine

0DWQ* Rev/Anus

0DWW[0,3,4]JZ Rev/Peritoneum, [Opn, Perc, Perc Endo], Synth Sub, NQ

0DX* Gastrointestinal Sys, Transfer

0DY6* Transplantation/Stomach

0F1* Hepatobiliary Sys and Pancreas, Bypass

0F54* Destr/Gallbladder

0F750DZ Dilation of Rt Hepatic Duct with Intralum Dev, Opn Appr

0F75[0,7]ZZ Dilation/Hepatic Duct, Rt, [Opn, Via Natrl or Artfcl Opng]

0F760DZ Dilation of Lt Hepatic Duct with Intralum Dev, Opn Appr

0F76[0,7]ZZ Dilation/Hepatic Duct, Lt, [Opn, Via Natrl or Artfcl Opng]

0F780DZ Dilation of Cystic Duct with Intralum Dev, Opn Appr

0F78[0,7]ZZ Dilation/Cystic Duct, [Opn, Via Natrl or Artfcl Opng]

0F790DZ Dilation of Com Bile Duct with Intralum Dev, Opn Appr

0F79[0,7]ZZ Dilation/Common Bile Duct, [Opn, Via Natrl or Artfcl Opng]

0F7C[0,3,4,7][D,Z]Z Dilation/Ampulla of Vater, [Opn, Perc, Perc Endo, Via Natrl or Artfcl Opng], [Intralum Dev, No Dev], NQ

0F7D[0,3,7][D,Z]Z Dilation/Pancreatic Duct, [Opn, Perc, Via Natrl or Artfcl Opng], [Intralum Dev, No Dev], NQ

0F7F[0,3,7][D,Z]Z Dilation/Pancreatic Duct, Accessory, [Opn, Perc, Via Natrl or Artfcl Opng], [Intralum Dev, No Dev], NQ

0F8G[0,3]ZZ Div/Pancreas, [Opn, Perc]

0F900ZX Drain of Liver, Opn Appr, Diagnostic

0F900[0,Z]Z Drain/Liver, Opn, [Drain Dev, No Dev], NQ

0F910ZX Drain of Rt Lobe Liver, Opn Appr, Diagnostic

0F910[0,Z]Z Drain/Liver, Rt Lobe, Opn, [Drain Dev, No Dev], NQ

0F920ZX Drain of Lt Lobe Liver, Opn Appr, Diagnostic

0F920[0,Z]Z Drain/Liver, Lt Lobe, Opn, [Drain Dev, No Dev], NQ

0F95[0,3,4,7,8][0,Z]Z Drain/Hepatic Duct, Rt, [Opn, Perc, Perc Endo, Via Natrl or Artfcl Opng, Via Natrl or Artfcl Opng Endo], [Drain Dev, No Dev], NQ

0F96[0,3,4,7,8][0,Z]Z Drain/Hepatic Duct, Lt, [Opn, Perc, Perc Endo, Via Natrl or Artfcl Opng, Via Natrl or Artfcl Opng Endo], [Drain Dev, No Dev], NQ

0F98[0,3,4,7,8][0,Z]Z Drain/Cystic Duct, [Opn, Perc, Perc Endo, Via Natrl or Artfcl Opng, Via Natrl or Artfcl Opng Endo], [Drain Dev, No Dev], NQ

0F9970Z Drain of Common Bile Duct with Drain Dev, Via Opng

0F9C[0,3,7][0,Z]Z Drain/Ampulla of Vater, [Opn, Perc, Via Natrl or Artfcl Opng], [Drain Dev, No Dev], NQ

0F9F0ZX Drain of Accessory Pancreatic Duct, Opn Appr, Diagn

0F9G0ZX Drain of Pancreas, Opn Appr, Diagnostic

0FB0[0,3,4]ZZ Exc/Liver, [Opn, Perc, Perc Endo]

0FB0[0,4]ZX Exc/Liver, [Opn, Perc Endo]

0FB1[0,3,4]ZZ Exc/Liver, Rt Lobe, [Opn, Perc, Perc Endo]

0FB1[0,4]ZX Exc/Liver, Rt Lobe, [Opn, Perc Endo]

0FB2[0,3,4]ZZ Exc/Liver, Lt Lobe, [Opn, Perc, Perc Endo]

0FB2[0,4]ZX Exc/Liver, Lt Lobe, [Opn, Perc Endo]

0FB4[0,3,4]ZZ Exc/Gallbladder, [Opn, Perc, Perc Endo]

0FB8[0,3,7]ZZ Exc/Cystic Duct, [Opn, Perc, Via Natrl or Artfcl Opng]

0FBD0ZX Exc of Pancreatic Duct, Opn Appr, Diagnostic

0FBF0ZX Exc of Accessory Pancreatic Duct, Opn Appr, Diagn

0FBG0ZX Exc of Pancreas, Opn Appr, Diagnostic

0FBG[0,3,4]ZZ Exc/Pancreas, [Opn, Perc, Perc Endo]

0FC0* Extir/Liver

0FC1* Extir/Liver, Rt Lobe

0FC2* Extir/Liver, Lt Lobe

0FC90ZZ Extir of Matter from Common Bile Duct, Opn Appr

0FCC[0,3,7]ZZ Extir/Ampulla of Vater, [Opn, Perc, Via Natrl or Artfcl Opng]

0FH0[0,3,4]2Z Insert/Liver, [Opn, Perc, Perc Endo], Monitoring Dev, NQ

0FH1[0,3,4]2Z Insert/Liver, Rt Lobe, [Opn, Perc, Perc Endo], Monitoring Dev, NQ

0FH2[0,3,4]2Z Insert/Liver, Lt Lobe, [Opn, Perc, Perc Endo], Monitoring Dev, NQ

0FHB[0,3,4,7,8][1,2]Z Insert/Hepatobiliary Duct, [Opn, Perc, Perc Endo, Via Natrl or Artfcl Opng, Via Natrl or Artfcl Opng Endo], [Radioact Elmt, Monitoring Dev], NQ

0FHB[0,3,7]DZ Insert/Hepatobiliary Duct, [Opn, Perc, Via Natrl or Artfcl Opng], Intralum Dev, NQ

0FHD[0,3,4,7,8]1Z Insert/Pancreatic Duct, [Opn, Perc, Perc Endo, Via Natrl or Artfcl Opng, Via Natrl or Artfcl Opng Endo], Radioact Elmt, NQ

0FHD[0,3,7]DZ Insert/Pancreatic Duct, [Opn, Perc, Via Natrl or Artfcl Opng], Intralum Dev, NQ

0FJ0[0,3,4]ZZ Inspect/Liver, [Opn, Perc, Perc Endo]

0FJ44ZZ Inspect of Gallbladder, Perc Endo Appr

0FJD* Inspect/Pancreatic Duct

0FJG[0,3,4]ZZ Inspect/Pancreas, [Opn, Perc, Perc Endo]

0FL50[C,D,Z]Z Occlsn/Hepatic Duct, Rt, Opn, [Extralum Dev, Intralum Dev, No Dev], NQ

0FL60[C,D,Z]Z Occlsn/Hepatic Duct, Lt, Opn, [Extralum Dev, Intralum Dev, No Dev], NQ

0FL80[C,D,Z]Z Occlsn/Cystic Duct, Opn, [Extralum Dev, Intralum Dev, No Dev], NQ

0FL90[C,D,Z]Z Occlsn/Common Bile Duct, Opn, [Extralum Dev, Intralum Dev, No Dev], NQ

0FLC* Occlsn/Ampulla of Vater

0FLD* Occlsn/Pancreatic Duct

0FLF* Occlsn/Pancreatic Duct, Accessory

0FM0* Reattach/Liver

0FM1* Reattach/Liver, Rt Lobe

0FM2* Reattach/Liver, Lt Lobe

0FM40ZZ Reattach of Gallbladder, Opn Appr

0FM50ZZ Reattach of Rt Hepatic Duct, Opn Appr

0FM60ZZ Reattach of Lt Hepatic Duct, Opn Appr

0FM80ZZ Reattach of Cystic Duct, Opn Appr

0FM90ZZ Reattach of Common Bile Duct, Opn Appr

0FMC* Reattach/Ampulla of Vater

0FMD* Reattach/Pancreatic Duct

0FMF* Reattach/Pancreatic Duct, Accessory

0FMG* Reattach/Pancreas

0FN* Hepatobiliary Sys and Pancreas, Rls

0FP0[0,3,4][0,2,3]Z Rmvl/Liver, [Opn, Perc, Perc Endo], [Drain Dev, Monitoring Dev, Inf Dev], NQ

0FP4[0,3,4]DZ Rmvl/Gallbladder, [Opn, Perc, Perc Endo], Intralum Dev, NQ

0FPB[0,3,4,7,8][0,1,2,3,7,C,D,J,K]Z Rmvl/Hepatobiliary Duct, [Opn, Perc, Perc Endo, Via Natrl or Artfcl Opng, Via Natrl or Artfcl Opng Endo], [Drain Dev, Radioact Elmt, Monitoring Dev, Inf Dev, Auto Tissue Sub, Extralum Dev, Intralum Dev, Synth Sub, Nonauto Tissue Sub], NQ

0FQ* Hepatobiliary Sys and Pancreas, Repair

0FR* Hepatobiliary Sys and Pancreas, Replace

0FS0* Repos/Liver

0FS4* Repos/Gallbladder

0FS5* Repos/Hepatic Duct, Rt

0FS6* Repos/Hepatic Duct, Lt

0FS8* Repos/Cystic Duct

0FS9* Repos/Common Bile Duct

0FSC* Repos/Ampulla of Vater

0FSD* Repos/Pancreatic Duct

0FSF* Repos/Pancreatic Duct, Accessory

0FT0* Resect/Liver

0FT1* Resect/Liver, Rt Lobe

0FT2* Resect/Liver, Lt Lobe

0FT4* Resect/Gallbladder

0FTG* Resect/Pancreas

0FU* Hepatobiliary Sys and Pancreas, Supl

0FV50[C,D,Z]Z Restrict/Hepatic Duct, Rt, Opn, [Extralum Dev, Intralum Dev, No Dev], NQ

0FV60[C,D,Z]Z Restrict/Hepatic Duct, Lt, Opn, [Extralum Dev, Intralum Dev, No Dev], NQ

0FV80[C,D,Z]Z Restrict/Cystic Duct, Opn, [Extralum Dev, Intralum Dev, No Dev], NQ

0FV90[C,D,Z]Z Restrict/Common Bile Duct, Opn, [Extralum Dev, Intralum Dev, No Dev], NQ

0FVC* Restrict/Ampulla of Vater

0FVD* Restrict/Pancreatic Duct

0FVF* Restrict/Pancreatic Duct, Accessory

0FW0[0,3,4][0,2,3]ZRev/Liver, [Opn, Perc, Perc Endo], [Drain Dev, Monitoring Dev, Inf Dev], NQ

Surgical **Medical** **CC Indicator** **MCC Indicator** **Procedure Proxy** **PDxMCC PDx acts as own MCC** **PDxCC PDx acts as own CC**

ØFWB[Ø,3,4,7,8][Ø,2,3,7,C,D,J,K]Z	Rev/Hepatobiliary Duct, [Opn, Perc, Perc Endo, Via Natrl or Artfcl Opng, Via Natrl or Artfcl Opng Endo], [Drain Dev, Monitoring Dev, Inf Dev, Auto Tissue Sub, Extralum Dev, Intralum Dev, Synth Sub, Nonauto Sub], NQ
ØG9GØ[Ø,Z]Z	Drain/Thyroid Gland Lobe, Lt, Opn, [Drain Dev, No Dev], NQ
ØG9HØ[Ø,Z]Z	Drain/Thyroid Gland Lobe, Rt, Opn, [Drain Dev, No Dev], NQ
ØG9KØ[Ø,Z]Z	Drain/Thyroid Gland, Opn, [Drain Dev, No Dev], NQ
ØG9LØ[Ø,Z]Z	Drain/Superior Parathyroid Gland, Rt, Opn, [Drain Dev, No Dev], NQ
ØG9MØ[Ø,Z]Z	Drain/Superior Parathyroid Gland, Lt, Opn, [Drain Dev, No Dev], NQ
ØG9NØ[Ø,Z]Z	Drain/Inferior Parathyroid Gland, Rt, Opn, [Drain Dev, No Dev], NQ
ØG9PØ[Ø,Z]Z	Drain/Inferior Parathyroid Gland, Lt, Opn, [Drain Dev, No Dev], NQ
ØG9QØ[Ø,Z]Z	Drain/Parathyroid Glands, Multi, Opn, [Drain Dev, No Dev], NQ
ØG9RØ[Ø,Z]Z	Drain/Parathyroid Gland, Opn, [Drain Dev, No Dev], NQ
ØGCG*	Extir/Thyroid Gland Lobe, Lt
ØGCH*	Extir/Thyroid Gland Lobe, Rt
ØGCK*	Extir/Thyroid Gland
ØGCL*	Extir/Superior Parathyroid Gland, Rt
ØGCM*	Extir/Superior Parathyroid Gland, Lt
ØGCN*	Extir/Inferior Parathyroid Gland, Rt
ØGCP*	Extir/Inferior Parathyroid Gland, Lt
ØGCQ*	Extir/Parathyroid Glands, Multi
ØGCR*	Extir/Parathyroid Gland
ØGH*	Endocrine Sys, Insert
ØGJKØZZ	Inspect of Thyroid Gland, Opn Appr
ØGJRØZZ	Inspect of Parathyroid Gland, Opn Appr
ØGJSØZZ	Inspect of Endocrine Gland, Opn Appr
ØGM2*	Reattach/Adrenal Gland, Lt
ØGM3*	Reattach/Adrenal Gland, Rt
ØGN2*	Rls/Adrenal Gland, Lt
ØGN3*	Rls/Adrenal Gland, Rt
ØGN4*	Rls/Adrenal Glands, Bilat
ØGPK[Ø,3,4]ØZ	Rmvl/Adrenal Gland, [Opn, Perc, Perc Endo], Drain Dev, NQ
ØGPR[Ø,3,4]ØZ	Rmvl/Parathyroid Gland, [Opn, Perc, Perc Endo], Drain Dev, NQ
ØGQ2*	Repair/Adrenal Gland, Lt
ØGQ3*	Repair/Adrenal Gland, Rt
ØGQ4*	Repair/Adrenal Glands, Bilat
ØGQG*	Repair/Thyroid Gland Lobe, Lt
ØGQH*	Repair/Thyroid Gland Lobe, Rt
ØGQJ*	Repair/Thyroid Gland Isthmus
ØGQK*	Repair/Thyroid Gland
ØGS2*	Repos/Adrenal Gland, Lt
ØGS3*	Repos/Adrenal Gland, Rt
ØGWK[Ø,3,4]ØZ	Rev/Thyroid Gland, [Opn, Perc, Perc Endo], Drain Dev, NQ
ØGWR[Ø,3,4]ØZ	Rev/Parathyroid Gland, [Opn, Perc, Perc Endo], Drain Dev, NQ
ØHØT37Z	Alter of Rt Breast with Autol Sub, Perc Appr
ØHØTX[7,J,K]Z	Alter/Breast, Rt, Ext, [Auto Tissue Sub, Synth Sub, Nonauto Tissue Sub], NQ
ØHØT[Ø,3]7Z	Alter of Rt Breast w/ Auto Tissue Sub, [Opn, Perc] Appr
ØHØU37Z	Alter of Lt Breast with Autol Sub, Perc Appr
ØHØUX[7,J,K]Z	Alter/Breast, Lt, Ext, [Auto Tissue Sub, Synth Sub, Nonauto Tissue Sub], NQ
ØHØU[Ø,3]7Z	Alter of Lt Breast w/ Auto Tissue Sub, [Opn, Perc] Appr
ØHØV[Ø,3,X][7,J,K]Z	Alter/Breast, Bilat, [Opn, Perc, Ext], [Auto Tissue Sub, Synth Sub, Nonauto Tissue Sub], NQ
ØH5T*	Destr/Breast, Rt
ØH5U*	Destr/Breast, Lt
ØH5V*	Destr/Breast, Bilat
ØH5W*	Destr/Nipple, Rt
ØH5X*	Destr/Nipple, Lt
ØH89XZZ	Div of Perineum Skin, Ext Appr
ØH9TØZX	Drain of Rt Breast, Opn Appr, Diagnostic
ØH9UØZX	Drain of Lt Breast, Opn Appr, Diagnostic
ØH9VØZX	Drain of Bilat Breast, Opn Appr, Diagnostic
ØH9WØZX	Drain of Rt Nipple, Opn Appr, Diagnostic
ØH9XØZX	Drain of Lt Nipple, Opn Appr, Diagnostic
ØHBTØZX	Exc of Rt Breast, Opn Appr, Diagnostic
ØHBT[Ø,3,7,8,X]ZZ	Exc/Breast, Rt, [Opn, Perc, Via Natrl or Artfcl Opng, Via Natrl or Artfcl Opng Endo, Ext]
ØHBUØZX	Exc of Lt Breast, Opn Appr, Diagnostic
ØHBU[Ø,3,7,8,X]ZZ	Exc/Breast, Lt, [Opn, Perc, Via Natrl or Artfcl Opng, Via Natrl or Artfcl Opng Endo, Ext]
ØHBVØZX	Exc of Bilat Breast, Opn Appr, Diagnostic
ØHBV[Ø,3,7,8,X]ZZ	Exc/Breast, Bilat, [Opn, Perc, Via Natrl or Artfcl Opng, Via Natrl or Artfcl Opng Endo, Ext]
ØHBWØZX	Exc of Rt Nipple, Opn Appr, Diagnostic
ØHBW[Ø,3,7,8,X]ZZ	Exc/Nipple, Rt, [Opn, Perc, Via Natrl or Artfcl Opng, Via Natrl or Artfcl Opng Endo, Ext]
ØHBXØZX	Exc of Lt Nipple, Opn Appr, Diagnostic
ØHBX[Ø,3,7,8,X]ZZ	Exc/Nipple, Lt, [Opn, Perc, Via Natrl or Artfcl Opng, Via Natrl or Artfcl Opng Endo, Ext]
ØHBYØZX	Exc of Supernumerary Breast, Opn Appr, Diagnostic
ØHBY[Ø,3,7,8,X]ZZ	Exc/Supernumerary Breast, [Opn, Perc, Via Natrl or Artfcl Opng, Via Natrl or Artfcl Opng Endo, Ext]
ØHH*	Skin and Breast, Insert
ØHM1XZZ	Reattach of Face Skin, Ext Appr
ØHM2XZZ	Reattach of Rt Ear Skin, Ext Appr
ØHM3XZZ	Reattach of Lt Ear Skin, Ext Appr
ØHM4XZZ	Reattach of Neck Skin, Ext Appr
ØHM5XZZ	Reattach of Chest Skin, Ext Appr
ØHM6XZZ	Reattach of Back Skin, Ext Appr
ØHM7XZZ	Reattach of Abd Skin, Ext Appr
ØHM8XZZ	Reattach of Buttock Skin, Ext Appr
ØHM9XZZ	Reattach of Perineum Skin, Ext Appr
ØHMAXZZ	Reattach of Genitalia Skin, Ext Appr
ØHMBXZZ	Reattach of Rt Upr Arm Skin, Ext Appr
ØHMCXZZ	Reattach of Lt Upr Arm Skin, Ext Appr
ØHMDXZZ	Reattach of Rt Lwr Arm Skin, Ext Appr
ØHMEXZZ	Reattach of Lt Lwr Arm Skin, Ext Appr
ØHMFXZZ	Reattach of Rt Hand Skin, Ext Appr
ØHMGXZZ	Reattach of Lt Hand Skin, Ext Appr
ØHMHXZZ	Reattach of Rt Upr Leg Skin, Ext Appr
ØHMJXZZ	Reattach of Lt Upr Leg Skin, Ext Appr
ØHMKXZZ	Reattach of Rt Lwr Leg Skin, Ext Appr
ØHMLXZZ	Reattach of Lt Lwr Leg Skin, Ext Appr
ØHMMXZZ	Reattach of Rt Foot Skin, Ext Appr
ØHMNXZZ	Reattach of Lt Foot Skin, Ext Appr
ØHMWXZZ	Reattach of Rt Nipple, Ext Appr
ØHMXXZZ	Reattach of Lt Nipple, Ext Appr
ØHNØXZZ	Rls Scalp Skin, Ext Appr
ØHN1XZZ	Rls Face Skin, Ext Appr
ØHN2XZZ	Rls Rt Ear Skin, Ext Appr
ØHN3XZZ	Rls Lt Ear Skin, Ext Appr
ØHN4XZZ	Rls Neck Skin, Ext Appr
ØHN5XZZ	Rls Chest Skin, Ext Appr
ØHN6XZZ	Rls Back Skin, Ext Appr
ØHN7XZZ	Rls Abd Skin, Ext Appr
ØHN8XZZ	Rls Buttock Skin, Ext Appr
ØHN9XZZ	Rls Perineum Skin, Ext Appr
ØHNAXZZ	Rls Genitalia Skin, Ext Appr
ØHNBXZZ	Rls Rt Upr Arm Skin, Ext Appr
ØHNCXZZ	Rls Lt Upr Arm Skin, Ext Appr
ØHNDXZZ	Rls Rt Lwr Arm Skin, Ext Appr
ØHNEXZZ	Rls Lt Lwr Arm Skin, Ext Appr
ØHNFXZZ	Rls Rt Hand Skin, Ext Appr
ØHNGXZZ	Rls Lt Hand Skin, Ext Appr
ØHNHXZZ	Rls Rt Upr Leg Skin, Ext Appr
ØHNJXZZ	Rls Lt Upr Leg Skin, Ext Appr
ØHNKXZZ	Rls Rt Lwr Leg Skin, Ext Appr
ØHNLXZZ	Rls Lt Lwr Leg Skin, Ext Appr
ØHNLXZZ	Rls Lt Lwr Leg Skin, Ext Appr
ØHNMXZZ	Rls Rt Foot Skin, Ext Appr
ØHNMXZZ	Rls Rt Foot Skin, Ext Appr
ØHNNXZZ	Rls Lt Foot Skin, Ext Appr
ØHNNXZZ	Rls Lt Foot Skin, Ext Appr
ØHNQXZZ	Rls Finger Nail, Ext Appr
ØHNQXZZ	Rls Finger Nail, Ext Appr
ØHNRXZZ	Rls Toe Nail, Ext Appr
ØHNRXZZ	Rls Toe Nail, Ext Appr
ØHPT[Ø,3][J,N]Z	Rmvl/Breast, Rt, [Opn, Perc], [Synth Sub, Tissue Expander], NQ
ØHPU[Ø,3][J,N]Z	Rmvl/Breast, Lt, [Opn, Perc], [Synth Sub, Tissue Expander], NQ
ØHQQXZZ	Repair Finger Nail, Ext Appr
ØHQRXZZ	Repair Toe Nail, Ext Appr
ØHQT[Ø,3,7,8]ZZ	Rpr/Breast, Rt, [Opn, Perc, Via Natrl or Artfcl Opng Endo]
ØHQU[Ø,3,7,8]ZZ	Rpr/Breast, Lt, [Opn, Perc, Via Natrl or Artfcl Opng, Via Natrl or Artfcl Opng Endo]
ØHQW*	Repair/Nipple, Rt
ØHQX*	Repair/Nipple, Lt
ØHR2*	Replace/Skin, Rt Ear
ØHR3*	Replace/Skin, Lt Ear
ØHR9*	Replace/Skin, Perineum
ØHR9X[7,J,K][3,4]	Replace/Skin, Perineum, Ext, [Auto Tissue Sub, Synth Sub, Nonauto Tissue Sub], [Full Thickness, Partial Thickness]
ØHRQ*	Replace/Finger Nail

Ⓣ **Transfer DRG**   ⓈⓅ **Special Payment**   *** Code Range**   **6th and 7th Character of ZZ = No Device, No Qualifier ZX = No Device, Diagnostic**

Code	Description
ØHRQX[7,J,K]Z	Replace/Finger Nail, Ext, [Auto Tissue Sub, Synth Sub, Nonauto Tissue Sub], NQ
ØHRR*	Replace/Toe Nail
ØHRRX[7,J,K]Z	Replace/Toe Nail, Ext, [Auto Tissue Sub, Synth Sub, Nonauto Tissue Sub], NQ
ØHRSX[J,K]Z	Replace/Hair, Ext, [Synth Sub, Nonauto Tissue Sub], NQ
ØHRT07[5,6,7,8,9,Z]	Replace/Breast, Rt, Opn, Auto Tissue Sub, [Latissimus Dorsi Myocutaneous Flap, Transv Rectus Abdominis Myocutaneous Flap, Deep Inferior Epigastric Artery Perforator Flap, Superf Inferior Epigastric Artery Flap, Gluteal Artery Perforator Flap, NQ]
ØHRT0JZ	Replace of Rt Breast with Synth Sub, Opn Appr
ØHRT0KZ	Replace of Rt Breast with Nonaut Sub, Opn Appr
ØHRT3JZ	Replace of Rt Breast with Synth Sub, Perc Appr
ØHRU07[5,6,7,8,9,Z]	Replace/Breast, Lt, Opn, Auto Tissue Sub, [Latissimus Dorsi Myocutaneous Flap, Transv Rectus Abdominis Myocutaneous Flap, Deep Inferior Epigastric Artery Perforator Flap, Superf Inferior Epigastric Artery Flap, Gluteal Artery Perforator Flap, NQ]
ØHRU0JZ	Replace of Lt Breast with Synth Sub, Opn Appr
ØHRU0KZ	Replace of Lt Breast with Nonaut Sub, Opn Appr
ØHRU3JZ	Replace of Lt Breast with Synth Sub, Perc Appr
ØHRV07[5,6,7,8,9]	Replace/Breast, Bilat, Opn, Auto Tissue Sub, [Latissimus Dorsi Myocutaneous Flap, Transv Rectus Abdominis Myocutaneous Flap, Deep Inferior Epigastric Artery Perforator Flap, Superf Inferior Epigastric Artery Flap, Gluteal Artery Perforator Flap]
ØHRV0JZ	Replace of Bi Breast with Synth Sub, Opn Appr
ØHRV3JZ	Replace of Bi Breast with Synth Sub, Perc Appr
ØHRW*	Replace/Nipple, Rt
ØHRX*	Replace/Nipple, Lt
ØHST0ZZ	Repos Rt Breast, Opn Appr
ØHSU0ZZ	Repos Lt Breast, Opn Appr
ØHSV0ZZ	Repos Bilat Breast, Opn Appr
ØHSWXZZ	Repos Rt Nipple, Ext Appr
ØHSXXZZ	Repos Lt Nipple, Ext Appr
ØHTT0ZZ	Resect of Rt Breast, Opn Appr
ØHTU0ZZ	Resect of Lt Breast, Opn Appr
ØHTV0ZZ	Resect of Bilat Breast, Opn Appr
ØHTWXZZ	Resect of Rt Nipple, Ext Appr
ØHTXXZZ	Resect of Lt Nipple, Ext Appr
ØHTY0ZZ	Resect of Supernumerary Breast, Opn Appr
ØHUW*	Supl/Nipple, Rt
ØHUX*	Supl/Nipple, Lt
ØHWT[0,3]JZ	Rev/Breast, Rt, [Opn, Perc], Synth Sub, NQ
ØHWU[0,3]JZ	Rev/Breast, Lt, [Opn, Perc], Synth Sub, NQ
ØHX2XZZ	Transfer Rt Ear Skin, Ext Appr
ØHX3XZZ	Transfer Lt Ear Skin, Ext Appr
ØJ0*	SQ Tissue & Fascia, Alter
ØJ80*	Div/SQ Tissue & Fascia, Scalp
ØJ81*	Div/SQ Tissue & Fascia, Face
ØJ84*	Div/SQ Tissue & Fascia, Ant Neck
ØJ85*	Div/SQ Tissue & Fascia, Posterior Neck
ØJ86*	Div/SQ Tissue & Fascia, Chest
ØJ87*	Div/SQ Tissue & Fascia, Back
ØJ88*	Div/SQ Tissue & Fascia, Abd
ØJ89*	Div/SQ Tissue & Fascia, Buttock
ØJ8B*	Div/SQ Tissue & Fascia, Perineum
ØJ8C*	Div/SQ Tissue & Fascia, Pelvic Region
ØJ8D*	Div/SQ Tissue & Fascia, Rt Upr Arm
ØJ8F*	Div/SQ Tissue & Fascia, Lt Upr Arm
ØJ8G*	Div/SQ Tissue & Fascia, Rt Lwr Arm
ØJ8H*	Div/SQ Tissue & Fascia, Lt Lwr Arm
ØJ8L*	Div/SQ Tissue & Fascia, Rt Upr Leg
ØJ8M*	Div/SQ Tissue & Fascia, Lt Upr Leg
ØJ8N*	Div/SQ Tissue & Fascia, Rt Lwr Leg
ØJ8P*	Div/SQ Tissue & Fascia, Lt Lwr Leg
ØJ8Q*	Div/SQ Tissue & Fascia, Rt Foot
ØJ8R*	Div/SQ Tissue & Fascia, Lt Foot
ØJ8S*	Div/SQ Tissue & Fascia, Head and Neck
ØJ8T*	Div/SQ Tissue & Fascia, Trunk
ØJ8V*	Div/SQ Tissue & Fascia, Upr Extr
ØJ8W*	Div/SQ Tissue & Fascia, Lwr Extr
ØJ900ZZ	Drain of Scalp SQ/Fascia, Opn Appr
ØJ910ZZ	Drain of Face SQ/Fascia, Opn Appr
ØJ91[0,3]0Z	Drain/SQ Tissue & Fascia, Face, [Opn, Perc], Drain Dev, NQ
ØJ940ZZ	Drain of Ant Neck SQ/Fascia, Opn Appr
ØJ950ZZ	Drain of Post Neck SQ/Fascia, Opn Appr
ØJ960ZZ	Drain of Chest SQ/Fascia, Opn Appr
ØJ970ZZ	Drain of Back SQ/Fascia, Opn Appr
ØJ980ZZ	Drain of Abd SQ/Fascia, Opn Appr
ØJ990ZZ	Drain of Buttock SQ/Fascia, Opn Appr
ØJ9B0ZZ	Drain of Perineum SQ/Fascia, Opn Appr
ØJ9C0ZZ	Drain of Pelvic SQ/Fascia, Opn Appr
ØJ9D0ZZ	Drain of Rt Up Arm SQ/Fascia, Opn Appr
ØJ9F0ZZ	Drain of Lt Up Arm SQ/Fascia, Opn Appr
ØJ9G0ZZ	Drain of Rt Low Arm SQ/Fascia, Opn Appr
ØJ9H0ZZ	Drain of Lt Low Arm SQ/Fascia, Opn Appr
ØJ9L0ZZ	Drain of Rt Up Leg SQ/Fascia, Opn Appr
ØJ9M0ZZ	Drain of Lt Up Leg SQ/Fascia, Opn Appr
ØJ9N0ZZ	Drain of Rt Low Leg SQ/Fascia, Opn Appr
ØJ9P0ZZ	Drain of Lt Low Leg SQ/Fascia, Opn Appr
ØJ9Q0ZZ	Drain of Rt Foot SQ/Fascia, Opn Appr
ØJ9R0ZZ	Drain of Lt Foot SQ/Fascia, Opn Appr
ØJD0*	Extract/SQ Tissue & Fascia, Scalp
ØJD1*	Extract/SQ Tissue & Fascia, Face
ØJD4*	Extract/SQ Tissue & Fascia, Ant Neck
ØJD5*	Extract/SQ Tissue & Fascia, Posterior Neck
ØJD6*	Extract/SQ Tissue & Fascia, Chest
ØJD7*	Extract/SQ Tissue & Fascia, Back
ØJD8*	Extract/SQ Tissue & Fascia, Abd
ØJD9*	Extract/SQ Tissue & Fascia, Buttock
ØJDB*	Extract/SQ Tissue & Fascia, Perineum
ØJDC*	Extract/SQ Tissue & Fascia, Pelvic Region
ØJDD*	Extract/SQ Tissue & Fascia, Rt Upr Arm
ØJDF*	Extract/SQ Tissue & Fascia, Lt Upr Arm
ØJDG*	Extract/SQ Tissue & Fascia, Rt Lwr Arm
ØJDH*	Extract/SQ Tissue & Fascia, Lt Lwr Arm
ØJDL*	Extract/SQ Tissue & Fascia, Rt Upr Leg
ØJDM*	Extract/SQ Tissue & Fascia, Lt Upr Leg
ØJDN*	Extract/SQ Tissue & Fascia, Rt Lwr Leg
ØJDP*	Extract/SQ Tissue & Fascia, Lt Lwr Leg
ØJDQ*	Extract/SQ Tissue & Fascia, Rt Foot
ØJDR*	Extract/SQ Tissue & Fascia, Lt Foot
ØJH6[0,3][P,V]Z	Insert/SQ Tissue & Fascia, Chest, [Opn, Perc], [Cardiac Rhythm Related Dev, Inf Pump], NQ
ØJH7[0,3]VZ	Insert/SQ Tissue & Fascia, Back, [Opn, Perc], Inf Pump, NQ
ØJH8[0,3][P,V]Z	Insert/SQ Tissue & Fascia, Abd, [Opn, Perc], [Cardiac Rhythm Related Dev, Inf Pump], NQ
ØJHS[0,3]1Z	Insert/SQ Tissue & Fascia, Head and Neck, [Opn, Perc], Radioact Elmt, NQ
ØJHT[0,3][1,V]Z	Insert/SQ Tissue & Fascia, Trunk, [Opn, Perc], [Radioact Elmt, Inf Pump], NQ
ØJHV[0,3]1Z	Insert/SQ Tissue & Fascia, Upr Extr, [Opn, Perc], Radioact Elmt, NQ
ØJHW[0,3]1Z	Insert/SQ Tissue & Fascia, Lwr Extr, [Opn, Perc], Radioact Elmt, NQ
ØJPT[0,3]PZ	Rmvl/SQ Tissue & Fascia, Trunk, [Opn, Perc], Cardiac Rhythm Related Dev, NQ
ØJQ0*	Repair/SQ Tissue & Fascia, Scalp
ØJQ1*	Repair/SQ Tissue & Fascia, Face
ØJQ4*	Repair/SQ Tissue & Fascia, Ant Neck
ØJQ5*	Repair/SQ Tissue & Fascia, Posterior Neck
ØJQ6*	Repair/SQ Tissue & Fascia, Chest
ØJQ7*	Repair/SQ Tissue & Fascia, Back
ØJQ8*	Repair/SQ Tissue & Fascia, Abd
ØJQ9*	Repair/SQ Tissue & Fascia, Buttock
ØJQB*	Repair/SQ Tissue & Fascia, Perineum
ØJQC*	Repair/SQ Tissue & Fascia, Pelvic Region
ØJQD*	Repair/SQ Tissue & Fascia, Rt Upr Arm
ØJQF*	Repair/SQ Tissue & Fascia, Lt Upr Arm
ØJQG*	Repair/SQ Tissue & Fascia, Rt Lwr Arm
ØJQH*	Repair/SQ Tissue & Fascia, Lt Lwr Arm
ØJQL*	Repair/SQ Tissue & Fascia, Rt Upr Leg
ØJQM*	Repair/SQ Tissue & Fascia, Lt Upr Leg
ØJQN*	Repair/SQ Tissue & Fascia, Rt Lwr Leg
ØJQP*	Repair/SQ Tissue & Fascia, Lt Lwr Leg
ØJQQ*	Repair/SQ Tissue & Fascia, Rt Foot
ØJQR*	Repair/SQ Tissue & Fascia, Lt Foot
ØJR0*	Replace/SQ Tissue & Fascia, Scalp
ØJR1*	Replace/SQ Tissue & Fascia, Face
ØJR4*	Replace/SQ Tissue & Fascia, Ant Neck
ØJR5*	Replace/SQ Tissue & Fascia, Posterior Neck
ØJR6*	Replace/SQ Tissue & Fascia, Chest
ØJR7*	Replace/SQ Tissue & Fascia, Back
ØJR8*	Replace/SQ Tissue & Fascia, Abd
ØJR9*	Replace/SQ Tissue & Fascia, Buttock
ØJRB*	Replace/SQ Tissue & Fascia, Perineum
ØJRC*	Replace/SQ Tissue & Fascia, Pelvic Region
ØJRD*	Replace/SQ Tissue & Fascia, Rt Upr Arm
ØJRF*	Replace/SQ Tissue & Fascia, Lt Upr Arm

Surgical **Medical** **CC Indicator** **MCC Indicator** **Procedure Proxy** PDxMCC **PDx acts as own MCC** PDxCC **PDx acts as own CC**

MDC 21: Injuries, Poisonings And Toxic Effects Of Drugs—SURGICAL

Code	Description
0JRG*	Replace/SQ Tissue & Fascia, Rt Lwr Arm
0JRH*	Replace/SQ Tissue & Fascia, Lt Lwr Arm
0JRJ37Z	Replace of Rt Hand SQ/Fascia with Autol Sub, Perc Appr
0JRK37Z	Replace of Lt Hand SQ/Fascia with Autol Sub, Perc Appr
0JRL*	Replace/SQ Tissue & Fascia, Rt Upr Leg
0JRM*	Replace/SQ Tissue & Fascia, Lt Upr Leg
0JRN*	Replace/SQ Tissue & Fascia, Rt Lwr Leg
0JRP*	Replace/SQ Tissue & Fascia, Lt Lwr Leg
0JRQ*	Replace/SQ Tissue & Fascia, Rt Foot
0JRR*	Replace/SQ Tissue & Fascia, Lt Foot
0JU0*	Supl/SQ Tissue & Fascia, Scalp
0JU1*	Supl/SQ Tissue & Fascia, Face
0JU4*	Supl/SQ Tissue & Fascia, Ant Neck
0JU5*	Supl/SQ Tissue & Fascia, Posterior Neck
0JU6*	Supl/SQ Tissue & Fascia, Chest
0JU7*	Supl/SQ Tissue & Fascia, Back
0JU8*	Supl/SQ Tissue & Fascia, Abd
0JU9*	Supl/SQ Tissue & Fascia, Buttock
0JUB*	Supl/SQ Tissue & Fascia, Perineum
0JUC*	Supl/SQ Tissue & Fascia, Pelvic Region
0JUD*	Supl/SQ Tissue & Fascia, Rt Upr Arm
0JUF*	Supl/SQ Tissue & Fascia, Lt Upr Arm
0JUG*	Supl/SQ Tissue & Fascia, Rt Lwr Arm
0JUH*	Supl/SQ Tissue & Fascia, Lt Lwr Arm
0JUL*	Supl/SQ Tissue & Fascia, Rt Upr Leg
0JUM*	Supl/SQ Tissue & Fascia, Lt Upr Leg
0JUN*	Supl/SQ Tissue & Fascia, Rt Lwr Leg
0JUP*	Supl/SQ Tissue & Fascia, Lt Lwr Leg
0JUQ*	Supl/SQ Tissue & Fascia, Rt Foot
0JUR*	Supl/SQ Tissue & Fascia, Lt Foot
0JWT[0,3]PZ	Rev/SQ Tissue & Fascia, Trunk, [Opn, Perc], Cardiac Rhythm Related Dev, NQ
0JX0[0,3]ZZ	Transfer/SQ Tissue & Fascia, Scalp, [Opn, Perc]
0JX1[0,3]ZZ	Transfer/SQ Tissue & Fascia, Face, [Opn, Perc]
0JX4[0,3]ZZ	Transfer/SQ Tissue & Fascia, Ant Neck, [Opn, Perc]
0JX5[0,3]ZZ	Transfer/SQ Tissue & Fascia, Post Neck, [Opn, Perc]
0JX6[0,3]ZZ	Transfer/SQ Tissue & Fascia, Chest, [Opn, Perc]
0JX7[0,3]ZZ	Transfer/SQ Tissue & Fascia, Back, [Opn, Perc]
0JX8[0,3]ZZ	Transfer/SQ Tissue & Fascia, Abd, [Opn, Perc]
0JX9[0,3]ZZ	Transfer/SQ Tissue & Fascia, Buttock, [Opn, Perc]
0JXB[0,3]ZZ	Transfer/SQ Tissue & Fascia, Perineum, [Opn, Perc]
0JXC[0,3]ZZ	Transfer/SQ Tissue & Fascia, Genitalia, [Opn, Perc]
0JXD[0,3]ZZ	Transfer/SQ Tissue & Fascia, Rt Upr Arm, [Opn, Perc]
0JXF[0,3]ZZ	Transfer/SQ Tissue & Fascia, Lt Upr Arm, [Opn, Perc]
0JXG[0,3]ZZ	Transfer/SQ Tissue & Fascia, Rt Lwr Arm, [Opn, Perc]
0JXH[0,3]ZZ	Transfer/SQ Tissue & Fascia, Lt Lwr Arm, [Opn, Perc]
0JXJ[0,3]ZZ	Transfer/SQ Tissue & Fascia, Rt Hand, [Opn, Perc]
0JXK[0,3]ZZ	Transfer/SQ Tissue & Fascia, Lt Hand, [Opn, Perc]
0JXL[0,3]ZZ	Transfer/SQ Tissue & Fascia, Rt Upr Leg, [Opn, Perc]
0JXM[0,3]ZZ	Transfer/SQ Tissue & Fascia, Lt Upr Leg, [Opn, Perc]
0JXN[0,3]ZZ	Transfer/SQ Tissue & Fascia, Rt Lwr Leg, [Opn, Perc]
0JXP[0,3]ZZ	Transfer/SQ Tissue & Fascia, Lt Lwr Leg, [Opn, Perc]
0JXQ[0,3]ZZ	Transfer/SQ Tissue & Fascia, Rt Foot, [Opn, Perc]
0JXR[0,3]ZZ	Transfer/SQ Tissue & Fascia, Lt Foot, [Opn, Perc]
0K50*	Destr/Head Muscle
0K51*	Destr/Facial Muscle
0K52*	Destr/Neck Muscle, Rt
0K53*	Destr/Neck Muscle, Lt
0K54*	Destr/Tongue, Palate, Pharynx Muscle
0K55*	Destr/Shldr Muscle, Rt
0K56*	Destr/Shldr Muscle, Lt
0K57*	Destr/Upr Arm Muscle, Rt
0K58*	Destr/Upr Arm Muscle, Lt
0K59*	Destr/Lwr Arm and Wrist Muscle, Rt
0K5B*	Destr/Lwr Arm and Wrist Muscle, Lt
0K5F*	Destr/Trunk Muscle, Rt
0K5G*	Destr/Trunk Muscle, Lt
0K5H*	Destr/Thorax Muscle, Rt
0K5J*	Destr/Thorax Muscle, Lt
0K5K*	Destr/Abd Muscle, Rt
0K5L*	Destr/Abd Muscle, Lt
0K5M*	Destr/Perineum Muscle
0K5N*	Destr/Hip Muscle, Rt
0K5P*	Destr/Hip Muscle, Lt
0K5Q*	Destr/Upr Leg Muscle, Rt
0K5R*	Destr/Upr Leg Muscle, Lt
0K5S*	Destr/Lwr Leg Muscle, Rt
0K5T*	Destr/Lwr Leg Muscle, Lt
0K5V*	Destr/Foot Muscle, Rt
0K5W*	Destr/Foot Muscle, Lt
0K80*	Div/Head Muscle
0K81*	Div/Facial Muscle
0K82*	Div/Neck Muscle, Rt
0K83*	Div/Neck Muscle, Lt
0K85*	Div/Shldr Muscle, Rt
0K86*	Div/Shldr Muscle, Lt
0K87*	Div/Upr Arm Muscle, Rt
0K88*	Div/Upr Arm Muscle, Lt
0K89*	Div/Lwr Arm and Wrist Muscle, Rt
0K8B*	Div/Lwr Arm and Wrist Muscle, Lt
0K8F*	Div/Trunk Muscle, Rt
0K8G*	Div/Trunk Muscle, Lt
0K8H*	Div/Thorax Muscle, Rt
0K8J*	Div/Thorax Muscle, Lt
0K8K*	Div/Abd Muscle, Rt
0K8L*	Div/Abd Muscle, Lt
0K8M*	Div/Perineum Muscle
0K8N*	Div/Hip Muscle, Rt
0K8P*	Div/Hip Muscle, Lt
0K8Q*	Div/Upr Leg Muscle, Rt
0K8R*	Div/Upr Leg Muscle, Lt
0K8S*	Div/Lwr Leg Muscle, Rt
0K8T*	Div/Lwr Leg Muscle, Lt
0K8V*	Div/Foot Muscle, Rt
0K8W*	Div/Foot Muscle, Lt
0K90[0,3,4]0Z	Drain/Head Muscle, [Opn, Perc, Perc Endo], Drain Dev, NQ
0K90[0,4]ZZ	Drain/Head Muscle, [Opn, Perc Endo]
0K91[0,3,4]0Z	Drain/Facial Muscle, [Opn, Perc, Perc Endo], Drain Dev, NQ
0K91[0,4]ZZ	Drain/Facial Muscle, [Opn, Perc Endo]
0K92[0,3,4]0Z	Drain/Neck Muscle, Rt, [Opn, Perc, Perc Endo], Drain Dev, NQ
0K92[0,4]ZZ	Drain/Neck Muscle, Rt, [Opn, Perc Endo]
0K93[0,3,4]0Z	Drain/Neck Muscle, Lt, [Opn, Perc, Perc Endo], Drain Dev, NQ
0K93[0,4]ZZ	Drain/Neck Muscle, Lt, [Opn, Perc Endo]
0K94[0,3,4]0Z	Drain/Tongue, Palate, Pharynx Muscle, [Opn, Perc, Perc Endo], Drain Dev, NQ
0K94[0,4]ZZ	Drain/Tongue, Palate, Pharynx Muscle, [Opn, Perc Endo]
0K95[0,3,4]0Z	Drain/Shldr Muscle, Rt, [Opn, Perc, Perc Endo], Drain Dev, NQ
0K95[0,4]ZZ	Drain/Shldr Muscle, Rt, [Opn, Perc Endo]
0K96[0,3,4]0Z	Drain/Shldr Muscle, Lt, [Opn, Perc, Perc Endo], Drain Dev, NQ
0K96[0,4]ZZ	Drain/Shldr Muscle, Lt, [Opn, Perc Endo]
0K97[0,3,4]0Z	Drain/Upr Arm Muscle, Rt, [Opn, Perc, Perc Endo], Drain Dev, NQ
0K97[0,4]ZZ	Drain/Upr Arm Muscle, Rt, [Opn, Perc Endo]
0K98[0,3,4]0Z	Drain/Upr Arm Muscle, Lt, [Opn, Perc, Perc Endo], Drain Dev, NQ
0K98[0,4]ZZ	Drain/Upr Arm Muscle, Lt, [Opn, Perc Endo]
0K99[0,3,4]0Z	Drain/Lwr Arm and Wrist Muscle, Rt, [Opn, Perc, Perc Endo], Drain Dev, NQ
0K99[0,4]ZZ	Drain/Lwr Arm and Wrist Muscle, Rt, [Opn, Perc Endo]
0K9B[0,3,4]0Z	Drain/Lwr Arm and Wrist Muscle, Lt, [Opn, Perc, Perc Endo], Drain Dev, NQ
0K9B[0,4]ZZ	Drain/Lwr Arm and Wrist Muscle, Lt, [Opn, Perc Endo]
0K9F[0,3,4]0Z	Drain/Trunk Muscle, Rt, [Opn, Perc, Perc Endo], Drain Dev, NQ
0K9F[0,4]ZZ	Drain/Trunk Muscle, Rt, [Opn, Perc Endo]
0K9G[0,3,4]0Z	Drain/Trunk Muscle, Lt, [Opn, Perc, Perc Endo], Drain Dev, NQ
0K9G[0,4]ZZ	Drain/Trunk Muscle, Lt, [Opn, Perc Endo]
0K9H[0,3,4]0Z	Drain/Thorax Muscle, Rt, [Opn, Perc, Perc Endo], Drain Dev, NQ
0K9H[0,4]ZZ	Drain/Thorax Muscle, Rt, [Opn, Perc Endo]
0K9J[0,3,4]0Z	Drain/Thorax Muscle, Lt, [Opn, Perc, Perc Endo], Drain Dev, NQ
0K9J[0,4]ZZ	Drain/Thorax Muscle, Lt, [Opn, Perc Endo]
0K9K[0,3,4]0Z	Drain/Abd Muscle, Rt, [Opn, Perc, Perc Endo], Drain Dev, NQ
0K9K[0,4]ZZ	Drain/Abd Muscle, Rt, [Opn, Perc Endo]
0K9L[0,3,4]0Z	Drain/Abd Muscle, Lt, [Opn, Perc, Perc Endo], Drain Dev, NQ
0K9L[0,4]ZZ	Drain/Abd Muscle, Lt, [Opn, Perc Endo]
0K9M[0,3,4]0Z	Drain/Perineum Muscle, [Opn, Perc, Perc Endo], Drain Dev, NQ
0K9M[0,4]ZZ	Drain/Perineum Muscle, [Opn, Perc Endo]
0K9N[0,3,4]0Z	Drain/Hip Muscle, Rt, [Opn, Perc, Perc Endo], Drain Dev, NQ
0K9N[0,4]ZZ	Drain/Hip Muscle, Rt, [Opn, Perc Endo]
0K9P[0,3,4]0Z	Drain/Hip Muscle, Lt, [Opn, Perc, Perc Endo], Drain Dev, NQ
0K9P[0,4]ZZ	Drain/Hip Muscle, Lt, [Opn, Perc Endo]
0K9Q[0,3,4]0Z	Drain/Upr Leg Muscle, Rt, [Opn, Perc, Perc Endo], Drain Dev, NQ
0K9Q[0,4]ZZ	Drain/Upr Leg Muscle, Rt, [Opn, Perc Endo]
0K9R[0,3,4]0Z	Drain/Upr Leg Muscle, Lt, [Opn, Perc, Perc Endo], Drain Dev, NQ
0K9R[0,4]ZZ	Drain/Upr Leg Muscle, Lt, [Opn, Perc Endo]
0K9S[0,3,4]0Z	Drain/Lwr Leg Muscle, Rt, [Opn, Perc, Perc Endo], Drain Dev, NQ
0K9S[0,4]ZZ	Drain/Lwr Leg Muscle, Rt, [Opn, Perc Endo]

T Transfer DRG　　　SP Special Payment　　　* Code Range　　　6th and 7th Character of ZZ = No Device, No Qualifier ZX = No Device, Diagnostic

0K9T[0,3,4]0Z Drain/Lwr Leg Muscle, Lt, [Opn, Perc, Perc Endo], Drain Dev, NQ
0K9T[0,4]ZZ Drain/Lwr Leg Muscle, Lt, [Opn, Perc Endo]
0K9V[0,3,4]0Z Drain/Foot Muscle, Rt, [Opn, Perc, Perc Endo], Drain Dev, NQ
0K9V[0,4]ZZ Drain/Foot Muscle, Rt, [Opn, Perc Endo]
0K9W[0,3,4]0Z Drain/Foot Muscle, Lt, [Opn, Perc, Perc Endo], Drain Dev, NQ
0K9W[0,4]ZZ Drain/Foot Muscle, Lt, [Opn, Perc Endo]
0KB0[0,3,4]ZZ Exc/Head Muscle, [Opn, Perc, Perc Endo]
0KB1[0,3,4]ZZ Exc/Facial Muscle, [Opn, Perc, Perc Endo]
0KB2[0,3,4]ZZ Exc/Neck Muscle, Rt, [Opn, Perc, Perc Endo]
0KB3[0,3,4]ZZ Exc/Neck Muscle, Lt, [Opn, Perc, Perc Endo]
0KB4[0,3,4]ZZ Exc/Tongue, Palate, Pharynx Muscle, [Opn, Perc, Perc Endo]
0KB5[0,3,4]ZZ Exc/Shldr Muscle, Rt, [Opn, Perc, Perc Endo]
0KB6[0,3,4]ZZ Exc/Shldr Muscle, Lt, [Opn, Perc, Perc Endo]
0KB7[0,3,4]ZZ Exc/Upr Arm Muscle, Rt, [Opn, Perc, Perc Endo]
0KB8[0,3,4]ZZ Exc/Upr Arm Muscle, Lt, [Opn, Perc, Perc Endo]
0KB9[0,3,4]ZZ Exc/Lwr Arm and Wrist Muscle, Rt, [Opn, Perc, Perc Endo]
0KBB[0,3,4]ZZ Exc/Lwr Arm and Wrist Muscle, Lt, [Opn, Perc, Perc Endo]
0KBF[0,3,4]ZZ Exc/Trunk Muscle, Rt, [Opn, Perc, Perc Endo]
0KBG[0,3,4]ZZ Exc/Trunk Muscle, Lt, [Opn, Perc, Perc Endo]
0KBH[0,3,4]ZZ Exc/Thorax Muscle, Rt, [Opn, Perc, Perc Endo]
0KBJ[0,3,4]ZZ Exc/Thorax Muscle, Lt, [Opn, Perc, Perc Endo]
0KBK[0,3,4]ZZ Exc/Abd Muscle, Rt, [Opn, Perc, Perc Endo]
0KBL[0,3,4]ZZ Exc/Abd Muscle, Lt, [Opn, Perc, Perc Endo]
0KBM[0,3,4]ZZ Exc/Perineum Muscle, [Opn, Perc, Perc Endo]
0KBN[0,3,4]ZZ Exc/Hip Muscle, Rt, [Opn, Perc, Perc Endo]
0KBP[0,3,4]ZZ Exc/Hip Muscle, Lt, [Opn, Perc, Perc Endo]
0KBQ[0,3,4]ZZ Exc/Upr Leg Muscle, Rt, [Opn, Perc, Perc Endo]
0KBR[0,3,4]ZZ Exc/Upr Leg Muscle, Lt, [Opn, Perc, Perc Endo]
0KBS[0,3,4]ZZ Exc/Lwr Leg Muscle, Rt, [Opn, Perc, Perc Endo]
0KBT[0,3,4]ZZ Exc/Lwr Leg Muscle, Lt, [Opn, Perc, Perc Endo]
0KBV[0,3,4]ZZ Exc/Foot Muscle, Rt, [Opn, Perc, Perc Endo]
0KBW[0,3,4]ZZ Exc/Foot Muscle, Lt, [Opn, Perc, Perc Endo]
0KC0* Extir/Head Muscle
0KC1* Extir/Facial Muscle
0KC2* Extir/Neck Muscle, Rt
0KC3* Extir/Neck Muscle, Lt
0KC4* Extir/Tongue, Palate, Pharynx Muscle
0KC5* Extir/Shldr Muscle, Rt
0KC6* Extir/Shldr Muscle, Lt
0KC7* Extir/Upr Arm Muscle, Rt
0KC8* Extir/Upr Arm Muscle, Lt
0KC9* Extir/Lwr Arm and Wrist Muscle, Rt
0KCB* Extir/Lwr Arm and Wrist Muscle, Lt
0KCF* Extir/Trunk Muscle, Rt
0KCG* Extir/Trunk Muscle, Lt
0KCH* Extir/Thorax Muscle, Rt
0KCJ* Extir/Thorax Muscle, Lt
0KCK* Extir/Abd Muscle, Rt
0KCL* Extir/Abd Muscle, Lt
0KCM* Extir/Perineum Muscle
0KCN* Extir/Hip Muscle, Rt
0KCP* Extir/Hip Muscle, Lt
0KCQ* Extir/Upr Leg Muscle, Rt
0KCR* Extir/Upr Leg Muscle, Lt
0KCS* Extir/Lwr Leg Muscle, Rt
0KCT* Extir/Lwr Leg Muscle, Lt
0KCV* Extir/Foot Muscle, Rt
0KCW* Extir/Foot Muscle, Lt
0KH* Muscles, Insert
0KM0* Reattach/Head Muscle
0KM1* Reattach/Facial Muscle
0KM2* Reattach/Neck Muscle, Rt
0KM3* Reattach/Neck Muscle, Lt
0KM4* Reattach/Tongue, Palate, Pharynx Muscle
0KM5* Reattach/Shldr Muscle, Rt
0KM6* Reattach/Shldr Muscle, Lt
0KM7* Reattach/Upr Arm Muscle, Rt
0KM8* Reattach/Upr Arm Muscle, Lt
0KM9* Reattach/Lwr Arm and Wrist Muscle, Rt
0KMB* Reattach/Lwr Arm and Wrist Muscle, Lt
0KMF* Reattach/Trunk Muscle, Rt
0KMG* Reattach/Trunk Muscle, Lt
0KMH* Reattach/Thorax Muscle, Rt
0KMJ* Reattach/Thorax Muscle, Lt
0KMK* Reattach/Abd Muscle, Rt
0KML* Reattach/Abd Muscle, Lt
0KMM* Reattach/Perineum Muscle
0KMN* Reattach/Hip Muscle, Rt
0KMP* Reattach/Hip Muscle, Lt

0KMQ* Reattach/Upr Leg Muscle, Rt
0KMR* Reattach/Upr Leg Muscle, Lt
0KMS* Reattach/Lwr Leg Muscle, Rt
0KMT* Reattach/Lwr Leg Muscle, Lt
0KMV* Reattach/Foot Muscle, Rt
0KMW* Reattach/Foot Muscle, Lt
0KPX[0,3,4][0,7,J,K,M]Z Rmvl/Upr Muscle, [Opn, Perc, Perc Endo], [Drain Dev, Auto Tissue Sub, Synth Sub, Nonauto Tissue Sub, Stimulator Lead], NQ
0KPY[0,3,4][0,7,J,K,M]Z Rmvl/Lwr Muscle, [Opn, Perc, Perc Endo], [Drain Dev, Auto Tissue Sub, Synth Sub, Nonauto Tissue Sub, Stimulator Lead], NQ
0KQ0* Repair/Head Muscle
0KQ1* Repair/Facial Muscle
0KQ2* Repair/Neck Muscle, Rt
0KQ3* Repair/Neck Muscle, Lt
0KQ4* Repair/Tongue, Palate, Pharynx Muscle
0KQ5* Repair/Shldr Muscle, Rt
0KQ6* Repair/Shldr Muscle, Lt
0KQ7* Repair/Upr Arm Muscle, Rt
0KQ8* Repair/Upr Arm Muscle, Lt
0KQ9* Repair/Lwr Arm and Wrist Muscle, Rt
0KQB* Repair/Lwr Arm and Wrist Muscle, Lt
0KQF* Repair/Trunk Muscle, Rt
0KQG* Repair/Trunk Muscle, Lt
0KQH* Repair/Thorax Muscle, Rt
0KQJ* Repair/Thorax Muscle, Lt
0KQK* Repair/Abd Muscle, Rt
0KQL* Repair/Abd Muscle, Lt
0KQM* Repair/Perineum Muscle
0KQN* Repair/Hip Muscle, Rt
0KQP* Repair/Hip Muscle, Lt
0KQQ* Repair/Upr Leg Muscle, Rt
0KQR* Repair/Upr Leg Muscle, Lt
0KQS* Repair/Lwr Leg Muscle, Rt
0KQT* Repair/Lwr Leg Muscle, Lt
0KQV* Repair/Foot Muscle, Rt
0KQW* Repair/Foot Muscle, Lt
0KS0* Repos/Head Muscle
0KS1* Repos/Facial Muscle
0KS2* Repos/Neck Muscle, Rt
0KS3* Repos/Neck Muscle, Lt
0KS4* Repos/Tongue, Palate, Pharynx Muscle
0KS5* Repos/Shldr Muscle, Rt
0KS6* Repos/Shldr Muscle, Lt
0KS7* Repos/Upr Arm Muscle, Rt
0KS8* Repos/Upr Arm Muscle, Lt
0KS9* Repos/Lwr Arm and Wrist Muscle, Rt
0KSB* Repos/Lwr Arm and Wrist Muscle, Lt
0KSF* Repos/Trunk Muscle, Rt
0KSG* Repos/Trunk Muscle, Lt
0KSH* Repos/Thorax Muscle, Rt
0KSJ* Repos/Thorax Muscle, Lt
0KSK* Repos/Abd Muscle, Rt
0KSL* Repos/Abd Muscle, Lt
0KSM* Repos/Perineum Muscle
0KSN* Repos/Hip Muscle, Rt
0KSP* Repos/Hip Muscle, Lt
0KSQ* Repos/Upr Leg Muscle, Rt
0KSR* Repos/Upr Leg Muscle, Lt
0KSS* Repos/Lwr Leg Muscle, Rt
0KST* Repos/Lwr Leg Muscle, Lt
0KSV* Repos/Foot Muscle, Rt
0KSW* Repos/Foot Muscle, Lt
0KT0* Resect/Head Muscle
0KT1* Resect/Facial Muscle
0KT2* Resect/Neck Muscle, Rt
0KT3* Resect/Neck Muscle, Lt
0KT4* Resect/Tongue, Palate, Pharynx Muscle
0KT5* Resect/Shldr Muscle, Rt
0KT6* Resect/Shldr Muscle, Lt
0KT7* Resect/Upr Arm Muscle, Rt
0KT8* Resect/Upr Arm Muscle, Lt
0KT9* Resect/Lwr Arm and Wrist Muscle, Rt
0KTB* Resect/Lwr Arm and Wrist Muscle, Lt
0KTF* Resect/Trunk Muscle, Rt
0KTG* Resect/Trunk Muscle, Lt
0KTH* Resect/Thorax Muscle, Rt
0KTJ* Resect/Thorax Muscle, Lt
0KTK* Resect/Abd Muscle, Rt

MDC 21: Injuries, Poisonings And Toxic Effects Of Drugs—SURGICAL

Surgical   **Medical**   **CC Indicator**   **MCC Indicator**   **Procedure Proxy**   PDxMCC **PDx acts as own MCC**   PDxCC **PDx acts as own CC**

ØKTL*	Resect/Abd Muscle, Lt
ØKTM*	Resect/Perineum Muscle
ØKTN*	Resect/Hip Muscle, Rt
ØKTP*	Resect/Hip Muscle, Lt
ØKTQ*	Resect/Upr Leg Muscle, Rt
ØKTR*	Resect/Upr Leg Muscle, Lt
ØKTS*	Resect/Lwr Leg Muscle, Rt
ØKTT*	Resect/Lwr Leg Muscle, Lt
ØKTV*	Resect/Foot Muscle, Rt
ØKTW*	Resect/Foot Muscle, Lt
ØKUØ*	Supl/Head Muscle
ØKU1*	Supl/Facial Muscle
ØKU2*	Supl/Neck Muscle, Rt
ØKU3*	Supl/Neck Muscle, Lt
ØKU4*	Supl/Tongue, Palate, Pharynx Muscle
ØKU5*	Supl/Shldr Muscle, Rt
ØKU6*	Supl/Shldr Muscle, Lt
ØKU7*	Supl/Upr Arm Muscle, Rt
ØKU8*	Supl/Upr Arm Muscle, Lt
ØKU9*	Supl/Lwr Arm and Wrist Muscle, Rt
ØKUB*	Supl/Lwr Arm and Wrist Muscle, Lt
ØKUF*	Supl/Trunk Muscle, Rt
ØKUG*	Supl/Trunk Muscle, Lt
ØKUH*	Supl/Thorax Muscle, Rt
ØKUJ*	Supl/Thorax Muscle, Lt
ØKUK*	Supl/Abd Muscle, Rt
ØKUL*	Supl/Abd Muscle, Lt
ØKUM*	Supl/Perineum Muscle
ØKUN*	Supl/Hip Muscle, Rt
ØKUP*	Supl/Hip Muscle, Lt
ØKUQ*	Supl/Upr Leg Muscle, Rt
ØKUR*	Supl/Upr Leg Muscle, Lt
ØKUS*	Supl/Lwr Leg Muscle, Rt
ØKUT*	Supl/Lwr Leg Muscle, Lt
ØKUV*	Supl/Foot Muscle, Rt
ØKUW*	Supl/Foot Muscle, Lt
ØKWX[Ø,3,4][Ø,7,J,K,M]Z	Rev/Upr Muscle, [Opn, Perc, Perc Endo], [Drain Dev, Auto Tissue Sub, Synth Sub, Nonauto Tissue Sub, Stimulator Lead], NQ
ØKWY[Ø,3,4][Ø,7,J,K,M]Z	Rev/Lwr Muscle, [Opn, Perc, Perc Endo], [Drain Dev, Auto Tissue Sub, Synth Sub, Nonauto Tissue Sub, Stimulator Lead], NQ
ØKXH[Ø,4]ZZ	Transfer/Thorax Muscle, Rt, [Opn, Perc Endo]
ØKXJ[Ø,4]ZZ	Transfer/Thorax Muscle, Lt, [Opn, Perc Endo]
ØKXK[Ø,4]Z6	Transfer/Abd Muscle, Rt, [Opn, Perc Endo], No Dev, Transv Rectus Abdominis Myocutaneous Flap
ØKXL[Ø,4]Z6	Transfer/Abd Muscle, Lt, [Opn, Perc Endo], No Dev, Transv Rectus Abdominis Myocutaneous Flap
ØL5Ø*	Destr/Head and Neck Tndn
ØL51*	Destr/Shldr Tndn, Rt
ØL52*	Destr/Shldr Tndn, Lt
ØL53*	Destr/Upr Arm Tndn, Rt
ØL54*	Destr/Upr Arm Tndn, Lt
ØL55*	Destr/Lwr Arm and Wrist Tndn, Rt
ØL56*	Destr/Lwr Arm and Wrist Tndn, Lt
ØL59*	Destr/Trunk Tndn, Rt
ØL5B*	Destr/Trunk Tndn, Lt
ØL5C*	Destr/Thorax Tndn, Rt
ØL5D*	Destr/Thorax Tndn, Lt
ØL5F*	Destr/Abd Tndn, Rt
ØL5G*	Destr/Abd Tndn, Lt
ØL5H*	Destr/Perineum Tndn
ØL5J*	Destr/Hip Tndn, Rt
ØL5K*	Destr/Hip Tndn, Lt
ØL5L*	Destr/Upr Leg Tndn, Rt
ØL5M*	Destr/Upr Leg Tndn, Lt
ØL5N*	Destr/Lwr Leg Tndn, Rt
ØL5P*	Destr/Lwr Leg Tndn, Lt
ØL5Q*	Destr/Knee Tndn, Rt
ØL5R*	Destr/Knee Tndn, Lt
ØL5S*	Destr/Ankle Tndn, Rt
ØL5T*	Destr/Ankle Tndn, Lt
ØL5V*	Destr/Foot Tndn, Rt
ØL5W*	Destr/Foot Tndn, Lt
ØL8Ø*	Div/Head and Neck Tndn
ØL81*	Div/Shldr Tndn, Rt
ØL82*	Div/Shldr Tndn, Lt
ØL83*	Div/Upr Arm Tndn, Rt
ØL84*	Div/Upr Arm Tndn, Lt
ØL85*	Div/Lwr Arm and Wrist Tndn, Rt

ØL86*	Div/Lwr Arm and Wrist Tndn, Lt
ØL89*	Div/Trunk Tndn, Rt
ØL8B*	Div/Trunk Tndn, Lt
ØL8C*	Div/Thorax Tndn, Rt
ØL8D*	Div/Thorax Tndn, Lt
ØL8F*	Div/Abd Tndn, Rt
ØL8G*	Div/Abd Tndn, Lt
ØL8H*	Div/Perineum Tndn
ØL8J*	Div/Hip Tndn, Rt
ØL8K*	Div/Hip Tndn, Lt
ØL8L*	Div/Upr Leg Tndn, Rt
ØL8M*	Div/Upr Leg Tndn, Lt
ØL8N*	Div/Lwr Leg Tndn, Rt
ØL8P*	Div/Lwr Leg Tndn, Lt
ØL8Q*	Div/Knee Tndn, Rt
ØL8R*	Div/Knee Tndn, Lt
ØL8S*	Div/Ankle Tndn, Rt
ØL8T*	Div/Ankle Tndn, Lt
ØL8V*	Div/Foot Tndn, Rt
ØL8W*	Div/Foot Tndn, Lt
ØL9Ø[Ø,3,4][Ø,Z]Z	Drain/Head and Neck Tndn, [Opn, Perc, Perc Endo], [Drain Dev, No Dev], NQ
ØL91[Ø,3,4][Ø,Z]Z	Drain/Shldr Tndn, Rt, [Opn, Perc, Perc Endo], [Drain Dev, No Dev], NQ
ØL92[Ø,3,4][Ø,Z]Z	Drain/Shldr Tndn, Lt, [Opn, Perc, Perc Endo], [Drain Dev, No Dev], NQ
ØL93[Ø,3,4][Ø,Z]Z	Drain/Upr Arm Tndn, Rt, [Opn, Perc, Perc Endo], [Drain Dev, No Dev], NQ
ØL94[Ø,3,4][Ø,Z]Z	Drain/Upr Arm Tndn, Lt, [Opn, Perc, Perc Endo], [Drain Dev, No Dev], NQ
ØL95[Ø,3,4][Ø,Z]Z	Drain/Lwr Arm and Wrist Tndn, Rt, [Opn, Perc, Perc Endo], [Drain Dev, No Dev], NQ
ØL96[Ø,3,4][Ø,Z]Z	Drain/Lwr Arm and Wrist Tndn, Lt, [Opn, Perc, Perc Endo], [Drain Dev, No Dev], NQ
ØL99[Ø,3,4][Ø,Z]Z	Drain/Trunk Tndn, Rt, [Opn, Perc, Perc Endo], [Drain Dev, No Dev], NQ
ØL9B[Ø,3,4][Ø,Z]Z	Drain/Trunk Tndn, Lt, [Opn, Perc, Perc Endo], [Drain Dev, No Dev], NQ
ØL9C[Ø,3,4][Ø,Z]Z	Drain/Thorax Tndn, Rt, [Opn, Perc, Perc Endo], [Drain Dev, No Dev], NQ
ØL9D[Ø,3,4][Ø,Z]Z	Drain/Thorax Tndn, Lt, [Opn, Perc, Perc Endo], [Drain Dev, No Dev], NQ
ØL9F[Ø,3,4][Ø,Z]Z	Drain/Abd Tndn, Rt, [Opn, Perc, Perc Endo], [Drain Dev, No Dev], NQ
ØL9G[Ø,3,4][Ø,Z]Z	Drain/Abd Tndn, Lt, [Opn, Perc, Perc Endo], [Drain Dev, No Dev], NQ
ØL9H[Ø,3,4][Ø,Z]Z	Drain/Perineum Tndn, [Opn, Perc, Perc Endo], [Drain Dev, No Dev], NQ
ØL9J[Ø,3,4][Ø,Z]Z	Drain/Hip Tndn, Rt, [Opn, Perc, Perc Endo], [Drain Dev, No Dev], NQ
ØL9K[Ø,3,4][Ø,Z]Z	Drain/Hip Tndn, Lt, [Opn, Perc, Perc Endo], [Drain Dev, No Dev], NQ
ØL9L[Ø,3,4][Ø,Z]Z	Drain/Upr Leg Tndn, Rt, [Opn, Perc, Perc Endo], [Drain Dev, No Dev], NQ
ØL9M[Ø,3,4][Ø,Z]Z	Drain/Upr Leg Tndn, Lt, [Opn, Perc, Perc Endo], [Drain Dev, No Dev], NQ
ØL9N[Ø,3,4][Ø,Z]Z	Drain/Lwr Leg Tndn, Rt, [Opn, Perc, Perc Endo], [Drain Dev, No Dev], NQ
ØL9P[Ø,3,4][Ø,Z]Z	Drain/Lwr Leg Tndn, Lt, [Opn, Perc, Perc Endo], [Drain Dev, No Dev], NQ
ØL9Q[Ø,3,4][Ø,Z]Z	Drain/Knee Tndn, Rt, [Opn, Perc, Perc Endo], [Drain Dev, No Dev], NQ
ØL9R[Ø,3,4][Ø,Z]Z	Drain/Knee Tndn, Lt, [Opn, Perc, Perc Endo], [Drain Dev, No Dev], NQ
ØL9S[Ø,3,4][Ø,Z]Z	Drain/Ankle Tndn, Rt, [Opn, Perc, Perc Endo], [Drain Dev, No Dev], NQ
ØL9T[Ø,3,4][Ø,Z]Z	Drain/Ankle Tndn, Lt, [Opn, Perc, Perc Endo], [Drain Dev, No Dev], NQ
ØL9V[Ø,3,4][Ø,Z]Z	Drain/Foot Tndn, Rt, [Opn, Perc, Perc Endo], [Drain Dev, No Dev], NQ
ØL9W[Ø,3,4][Ø,Z]Z	Drain/Foot Tndn, Lt, [Opn, Perc, Perc Endo], [Drain Dev, No Dev], NQ
ØLBØ[Ø,3,4]ZZ	Exc/Head and Neck Tndn, [Opn, Perc, Perc Endo]
ØLB1[Ø,3,4]ZZ	Exc/Shldr Tndn, Rt, [Opn, Perc, Perc Endo]
ØLB2[Ø,3,4]ZZ	Exc/Shldr Tndn, Lt, [Opn, Perc, Perc Endo]
ØLB3[Ø,3,4]ZZ	Exc/Upr Arm Tndn, Rt, [Opn, Perc, Perc Endo]
ØLB4[Ø,3,4]ZZ	Exc/Upr Arm Tndn, Lt, [Opn, Perc, Perc Endo]
ØLB5[Ø,3,4]ZZ	Exc/Lwr Arm and Wrist Tndn, Rt, [Opn, Perc, Perc Endo]
ØLB6[Ø,3,4]ZZ	Exc/Lwr Arm and Wrist Tndn, Lt, [Opn, Perc, Perc Endo]
ØLB9[Ø,3,4]ZZ	Exc/Trunk Tndn, Rt, [Opn, Perc, Perc Endo]

Ⓣ **Transfer DRG**   🆂🅿 **Special Payment**   * **Code Range**   **6th and 7th Character of ZZ = No Device, No Qualifier ZX = No Device, Diagnostic**

MS-DRG Version 33.0

ØLBB[Ø,3,4]ZZ	Exc/Trunk Tndn, Lt, [Opn, Perc, Perc Endo]
ØLBC[Ø,3,4]ZZ	Exc/Thorax Tndn, Rt, [Opn, Perc, Perc Endo]
ØLBD[Ø,3,4]ZZ	Exc/Thorax Tndn, Lt, [Opn, Perc, Perc Endo]
ØLBF[Ø,3,4]ZZ	Exc/Abd Tndn, Rt, [Opn, Perc, Perc Endo]
ØLBG[Ø,3,4]ZZ	Exc/Abd Tndn, Lt, [Opn, Perc, Perc Endo]
ØLBH[Ø,3,4]ZZ	Exc/Perineum Tndn, [Opn, Perc, Perc Endo]
ØLBJ[Ø,3,4]ZZ	Exc/Hip Tndn, Rt, [Opn, Perc, Perc Endo]
ØLBK[Ø,3,4]ZZ	Exc/Hip Tndn, Lt, [Opn, Perc, Perc Endo]
ØLBL[Ø,3,4]ZZ	Exc/Upr Leg Tndn, Rt, [Opn, Perc, Perc Endo]
ØLBM[Ø,3,4]ZZ	Exc/Upr Leg Tndn, Lt, [Opn, Perc, Perc Endo]
ØLBN[Ø,3,4]ZZ	Exc/Lwr Leg Tndn, Rt, [Opn, Perc, Perc Endo]
ØLBP[Ø,3,4]ZZ	Exc/Lwr Leg Tndn, Lt, [Opn, Perc, Perc Endo]
ØLBQ[Ø,3,4]ZZ	Exc/Knee Tndn, Rt, [Opn, Perc, Perc Endo]
ØLBR[Ø,3,4]ZZ	Exc/Knee Tndn, Lt, [Opn, Perc, Perc Endo]
ØLBS[Ø,3,4]ZZ	Exc/Ankle Tndn, Rt, [Opn, Perc, Perc Endo]
ØLBT[Ø,3,4]ZZ	Exc/Ankle Tndn, Lt, [Opn, Perc, Perc Endo]
ØLBV[Ø,3,4]ZZ	Exc/Foot Tndn, Rt, [Opn, Perc, Perc Endo]
ØLBW[Ø,3,4]ZZ	Exc/Foot Tndn, Lt, [Opn, Perc, Perc Endo]
ØLCØ*	Extir/Head and Neck Tndn
ØLC1*	Extir/Shldr Tndn, Rt
ØLC2*	Extir/Shldr Tndn, Lt
ØLC3*	Extir/Upr Arm Tndn, Rt
ØLC4*	Extir/Upr Arm Tndn, Lt
ØLC5*	Extir/Lwr Arm and Wrist Tndn, Rt
ØLC6*	Extir/Lwr Arm and Wrist Tndn, Lt
ØLC9*	Extir/Trunk Tndn, Rt
ØLCB*	Extir/Trunk Tndn, Lt
ØLCC*	Extir/Thorax Tndn, Rt
ØLCD*	Extir/Thorax Tndn, Lt
ØLCF*	Extir/Abd Tndn, Rt
ØLCG*	Extir/Abd Tndn, Lt
ØLCH*	Extir/Perineum Tndn
ØLCJ*	Extir/Hip Tndn, Rt
ØLCK*	Extir/Hip Tndn, Lt
ØLCL*	Extir/Upr Leg Tndn, Rt
ØLCM*	Extir/Upr Leg Tndn, Lt
ØLCN*	Extir/Lwr Leg Tndn, Rt
ØLCP*	Extir/Lwr Leg Tndn, Lt
ØLCQ*	Extir/Knee Tndn, Rt
ØLCR*	Extir/Knee Tndn, Lt
ØLCS*	Extir/Ankle Tndn, Rt
ØLCT*	Extir/Ankle Tndn, Lt
ØLCV*	Extir/Foot Tndn, Rt
ØLCW*	Extir/Foot Tndn, Lt
ØLMØ*	Reattach/Head and Neck Tndn
ØLM1*	Reattach/Shldr Tndn, Rt
ØLM2*	Reattach/Shldr Tndn, Lt
ØLM3*	Reattach/Upr Arm Tndn, Rt
ØLM4*	Reattach/Upr Arm Tndn, Lt
ØLM5*	Reattach/Lwr Arm and Wrist Tndn, Rt
ØLM6*	Reattach/Lwr Arm and Wrist Tndn, Lt
ØLM9*	Reattach/Trunk Tndn, Rt
ØLMB*	Reattach/Trunk Tndn, Lt
ØLMC*	Reattach/Thorax Tndn, Rt
ØLMD*	Reattach/Thorax Tndn, Lt
ØLMF*	Reattach/Abd Tndn, Rt
ØLMG*	Reattach/Abd Tndn, Lt
ØLMH*	Reattach/Perineum Tndn
ØLMJ*	Reattach/Hip Tndn, Rt
ØLMK*	Reattach/Hip Tndn, Lt
ØLML*	Reattach/Upr Leg Tndn, Rt
ØLMM*	Reattach/Upr Leg Tndn, Lt
ØLMN*	Reattach/Lwr Leg Tndn, Rt
ØLMP*	Reattach/Lwr Leg Tndn, Lt
ØLMQ*	Reattach/Knee Tndn, Rt
ØLMR*	Reattach/Knee Tndn, Lt
ØLMS*	Reattach/Ankle Tndn, Rt
ØLMT*	Reattach/Ankle Tndn, Lt
ØLMV*	Reattach/Foot Tndn, Rt
ØLMW*	Reattach/Foot Tndn, Lt
ØLPX[Ø,3,4][Ø,7,J,K]Z	Rmvl/Upr Tndn, [Opn, Perc, Perc Endo], [Drain Dev, Auto Tissue Sub, Synth Sub, Nonauto Tissue Sub], NQ
ØLPY[Ø,3,4][Ø,7,J,K]Z	Rmvl/Lwr Tndn, [Opn, Perc, Perc Endo], [Drain Dev, Auto Tissue Sub, Synth Sub, Nonauto Tissue Sub], NQ
ØLQØ*	Repair/Head and Neck Tndn
ØLQ1*	Repair/Shldr Tndn, Rt
ØLQ2*	Repair/Shldr Tndn, Lt
ØLQ3*	Repair/Upr Arm Tndn, Rt
ØLQ4*	Repair/Upr Arm Tndn, Lt
ØLQ5*	Repair/Lwr Arm and Wrist Tndn, Rt

ØLQ6*	Repair/Lwr Arm and Wrist Tndn, Lt
ØLQ9*	Repair/Trunk Tndn, Rt
ØLQB*	Repair/Trunk Tndn, Lt
ØLQC*	Repair/Thorax Tndn, Rt
ØLQD*	Repair/Thorax Tndn, Lt
ØLQF*	Repair/Abd Tndn, Rt
ØLQG*	Repair/Abd Tndn, Lt
ØLQH*	Repair/Perineum Tndn
ØLQJ*	Repair/Hip Tndn, Rt
ØLQK*	Repair/Hip Tndn, Lt
ØLQL*	Repair/Upr Leg Tndn, Rt
ØLQM*	Repair/Upr Leg Tndn, Lt
ØLQN*	Repair/Lwr Leg Tndn, Rt
ØLQP*	Repair/Lwr Leg Tndn, Lt
ØLQQ*	Repair/Knee Tndn, Rt
ØLQR*	Repair/Knee Tndn, Lt
ØLQS*	Repair/Ankle Tndn, Rt
ØLQT*	Repair/Ankle Tndn, Lt
ØLQV*	Repair/Foot Tndn, Rt
ØLQW*	Repair/Foot Tndn, Lt
ØLRØ*	Replace/Head and Neck Tndn
ØLR1*	Replace/Shldr Tndn, Rt
ØLR2*	Replace/Shldr Tndn, Lt
ØLR3*	Replace/Upr Arm Tndn, Rt
ØLR4*	Replace/Upr Arm Tndn, Lt
ØLR5*	Replace/Lwr Arm and Wrist Tndn, Rt
ØLR6*	Replace/Lwr Arm and Wrist Tndn, Lt
ØLR9*	Replace/Trunk Tndn, Rt
ØLRB*	Replace/Trunk Tndn, Lt
ØLRC*	Replace/Thorax Tndn, Rt
ØLRD*	Replace/Thorax Tndn, Lt
ØLRF*	Replace/Abd Tndn, Rt
ØLRG*	Replace/Abd Tndn, Lt
ØLRH*	Replace/Perineum Tndn
ØLRJ*	Replace/Hip Tndn, Rt
ØLRK*	Replace/Hip Tndn, Lt
ØLRL*	Replace/Upr Leg Tndn, Rt
ØLRM*	Replace/Upr Leg Tndn, Lt
ØLRN*	Replace/Lwr Leg Tndn, Rt
ØLRP*	Replace/Lwr Leg Tndn, Lt
ØLRQ*	Replace/Knee Tndn, Rt
ØLRR*	Replace/Knee Tndn, Lt
ØLRS*	Replace/Ankle Tndn, Rt
ØLRT*	Replace/Ankle Tndn, Lt
ØLRV*	Replace/Foot Tndn, Rt
ØLRW*	Replace/Foot Tndn, Lt
ØLSØ*	Repos/Head and Neck Tndn
ØLS1*	Repos/Shldr Tndn, Rt
ØLS2*	Repos/Shldr Tndn, Lt
ØLS3*	Repos/Upr Arm Tndn, Rt
ØLS4*	Repos/Upr Arm Tndn, Lt
ØLS5*	Repos/Lwr Arm and Wrist Tndn, Rt
ØLS6*	Repos/Lwr Arm and Wrist Tndn, Lt
ØLS9*	Repos/Trunk Tndn, Rt
ØLSB*	Repos/Trunk Tndn, Lt
ØLSC*	Repos/Thorax Tndn, Rt
ØLSD*	Repos/Thorax Tndn, Lt
ØLSF*	Repos/Abd Tndn, Rt
ØLSG*	Repos/Abd Tndn, Lt
ØLSH*	Repos/Perineum Tndn
ØLSJ*	Repos/Hip Tndn, Rt
ØLSK*	Repos/Hip Tndn, Lt
ØLSL*	Repos/Upr Leg Tndn, Rt
ØLSM*	Repos/Upr Leg Tndn, Lt
ØLSN*	Repos/Lwr Leg Tndn, Rt
ØLSP*	Repos/Lwr Leg Tndn, Lt
ØLSQ*	Repos/Knee Tndn, Rt
ØLSR*	Repos/Knee Tndn, Lt
ØLSS*	Repos/Ankle Tndn, Rt
ØLST*	Repos/Ankle Tndn, Lt
ØLSV*	Repos/Foot Tndn, Rt
ØLSW*	Repos/Foot Tndn, Lt
ØLTØ*	Resect/Head and Neck Tndn
ØLT1*	Resect/Shldr Tndn, Rt
ØLT2*	Resect/Shldr Tndn, Lt
ØLT3*	Resect/Upr Arm Tndn, Rt
ØLT4*	Resect/Upr Arm Tndn, Lt
ØLT5*	Resect/Lwr Arm and Wrist Tndn, Rt
ØLT6*	Resect/Lwr Arm and Wrist Tndn, Lt
ØLT9*	Resect/Trunk Tndn, Rt

MDC 21: Injuries, Poisonings And Toxic Effects Of Drugs—SURGICAL

Surgical   **Medical**   **CC Indicator**   **MCC Indicator**   **Procedure Proxy**   **PDxMCC** **PDx acts as own MCC**   **PDxCC** **PDx acts as own CC**

MS-DRG Version 33.0

Code	Description
ØLTB*	Resect/Trunk Tndn, Lt
ØLTC*	Resect/Thorax Tndn, Rt
ØLTD*	Resect/Thorax Tndn, Lt
ØLTF*	Resect/Abd Tndn, Rt
ØLTG*	Resect/Abd Tndn, Lt
ØLTH*	Resect/Perineum Tndn
ØLTJ*	Resect/Hip Tndn, Rt
ØLTK*	Resect/Hip Tndn, Lt
ØLTL*	Resect/Upr Leg Tndn, Rt
ØLTM*	Resect/Upr Leg Tndn, Lt
ØLTN*	Resect/Lwr Leg Tndn, Rt
ØLTP*	Resect/Lwr Leg Tndn, Lt
ØLTQ*	Resect/Knee Tndn, Rt
ØLTR*	Resect/Knee Tndn, Lt
ØLTS*	Resect/Ankle Tndn, Rt
ØLTT*	Resect/Ankle Tndn, Lt
ØLTV*	Resect/Foot Tndn, Rt
ØLTW*	Resect/Foot Tndn, Lt
ØLUØ*	Supl/Head and Neck Tndn
ØLU1*	Supl/Shldr Tndn, Rt
ØLU2*	Supl/Shldr Tndn, Lt
ØLU3*	Supl/Upr Arm Tndn, Rt
ØLU4*	Supl/Upr Arm Tndn, Lt
ØLU5*	Supl/Lwr Arm and Wrist Tndn, Rt
ØLU6*	Supl/Lwr Arm and Wrist Tndn, Lt
ØLU9*	Supl/Trunk Tndn, Rt
ØLUB*	Supl/Trunk Tndn, Lt
ØLUC*	Supl/Thorax Tndn, Rt
ØLUD*	Supl/Thorax Tndn, Lt
ØLUF*	Supl/Abd Tndn, Rt
ØLUG*	Supl/Abd Tndn, Lt
ØLUH*	Supl/Perineum Tndn
ØLUJ*	Supl/Hip Tndn, Rt
ØLUK*	Supl/Hip Tndn, Lt
ØLUL*	Supl/Upr Leg Tndn, Rt
ØLUM*	Supl/Upr Leg Tndn, Lt
ØLUN*	Supl/Lwr Leg Tndn, Rt
ØLUP*	Supl/Lwr Leg Tndn, Lt
ØLUQ*	Supl/Knee Tndn, Rt
ØLUR*	Supl/Knee Tndn, Lt
ØLUS*	Supl/Ankle Tndn, Rt
ØLUT*	Supl/Ankle Tndn, Lt
ØLUV*	Supl/Foot Tndn, Rt
ØLUW*	Supl/Foot Tndn, Lt
ØLWX[Ø,3,4][Ø,7,J,K]Z	Rev/Upr Tndn, [Opn, Perc, Perc Endo], [Drain Dev, Auto Tissue Sub, Synth Sub, Nonauto Tissue Sub], NQ
ØLWY[Ø,3,4][Ø,7,J,K]Z	Rev/Lwr Tndn, [Opn, Perc, Perc Endo], [Drain Dev, Auto Tissue Sub, Synth Sub, Nonauto Tissue Sub], NQ
ØLXØ*	Transfer/Head and Neck Tndn
ØLX1*	Transfer/Shldr Tndn, Rt
ØLX2*	Transfer/Shldr Tndn, Lt
ØLX3*	Transfer/Upr Arm Tndn, Rt
ØLX4*	Transfer/Upr Arm Tndn, Lt
ØLX5*	Transfer/Lwr Arm and Wrist Tndn, Rt
ØLX6*	Transfer/Lwr Arm and Wrist Tndn, Lt
ØLX9*	Transfer/Trunk Tndn, Rt
ØLXB*	Transfer/Trunk Tndn, Lt
ØLXC*	Transfer/Thorax Tndn, Rt
ØLXD*	Transfer/Thorax Tndn, Lt
ØLXF*	Transfer/Abd Tndn, Rt
ØLXG*	Transfer/Abd Tndn, Lt
ØLXH*	Transfer/Perineum Tndn
ØLXJ*	Transfer/Hip Tndn, Rt
ØLXK*	Transfer/Hip Tndn, Lt
ØLXL*	Transfer/Upr Leg Tndn, Rt
ØLXM*	Transfer/Upr Leg Tndn, Lt
ØLXN*	Transfer/Lwr Leg Tndn, Rt
ØLXP*	Transfer/Lwr Leg Tndn, Lt
ØLXQ*	Transfer/Knee Tndn, Rt
ØLXR*	Transfer/Knee Tndn, Lt
ØLXS*	Transfer/Ankle Tndn, Rt
ØLXT*	Transfer/Ankle Tndn, Lt
ØLXV*	Transfer/Foot Tndn, Rt
ØLXW*	Transfer/Foot Tndn, Lt
ØM50*	Destr/Head and Neck Bursa & Lgmt
ØM51*	Destr/Shldr Bursa & Lgmt, Rt
ØM52*	Destr/Shldr Bursa & Lgmt, Lt
ØM53*	Destr/Elbow Bursa & Lgmt, Rt
ØM54*	Destr/Elbow Bursa & Lgmt, Lt
ØM59*	Destr/Upr Extr Bursa & Lgmt, Rt

Code	Description
ØM5B*	Destr/Upr Extr Bursa & Lgmt, Lt
ØM5C*	Destr/Trunk Bursa & Lgmt, Rt
ØM5D*	Destr/Trunk Bursa & Lgmt, Lt
ØM5F*	Destr/Thorax Bursa & Lgmt, Rt
ØM5G*	Destr/Thorax Bursa & Lgmt, Lt
ØM5H*	Destr/Abd Bursa & Lgmt, Rt
ØM5J*	Destr/Abd Bursa & Lgmt, Lt
ØM5K*	Destr/Perineum Bursa & Lgmt
ØM5L*	Destr/Hip Bursa & Lgmt, Rt
ØM5M*	Destr/Hip Bursa & Lgmt, Lt
ØM5N*	Destr/Knee Bursa & Lgmt, Rt
ØM5P*	Destr/Knee Bursa & Lgmt, Lt
ØM5Q*	Destr/Ankle Bursa & Lgmt, Rt
ØM5R*	Destr/Ankle Bursa & Lgmt, Lt
ØM5S*	Destr/Foot Bursa & Lgmt, Rt
ØM5T*	Destr/Foot Bursa & Lgmt, Lt
ØM80*	Div/Head and Neck Bursa & Lgmt
ØM81*	Div/Shldr Bursa & Lgmt, Rt
ØM82*	Div/Shldr Bursa & Lgmt, Lt
ØM83*	Div/Elbow Bursa & Lgmt, Rt
ØM84*	Div/Elbow Bursa & Lgmt, Lt
ØM89*	Div/Upr Extr Bursa & Lgmt, Rt
ØM8B*	Div/Upr Extr Bursa & Lgmt, Lt
ØM8C*	Div/Trunk Bursa & Lgmt, Rt
ØM8D*	Div/Trunk Bursa & Lgmt, Lt
ØM8F*	Div/Thorax Bursa & Lgmt, Rt
ØM8G*	Div/Thorax Bursa & Lgmt, Lt
ØM8H*	Div/Abd Bursa & Lgmt, Rt
ØM8J*	Div/Abd Bursa & Lgmt, Lt
ØM8K*	Div/Perineum Bursa & Lgmt
ØM8L*	Div/Hip Bursa & Lgmt, Rt
ØM8M*	Div/Hip Bursa & Lgmt, Lt
ØM8N*	Div/Knee Bursa & Lgmt, Rt
ØM8P*	Div/Knee Bursa & Lgmt, Lt
ØM8Q*	Div/Ankle Bursa & Lgmt, Rt
ØM8R*	Div/Ankle Bursa & Lgmt, Lt
ØM8S*	Div/Foot Bursa & Lgmt, Rt
ØM8T*	Div/Foot Bursa & Lgmt, Lt
ØM8V*	Div/Lwr Extr Bursa & Lgmt, Rt
ØM8W*	Div/Lwr Extr Bursa & Lgmt, Lt
ØM90Ø[Ø,Z]Z	Drain/Head and Neck Bursa & Lgmt, Opn, [Drain Dev, No Dev], NQ
ØM91ØØZ	Drain of Rt Shldr Bursa/Lig with Drain Dev, Opn Appr
ØM91[Ø,4]ZZ	Drain/Shldr Bursa & Lgmt, Rt, [Opn, Perc Endo]
ØM92ØØZ	Drain of Lt Shldr Bursa/Lig with Drain Dev, Opn Appr
ØM92[Ø,4]ZZ	Drain/Shldr Bursa & Lgmt, Lt, [Opn, Perc Endo]
ØM93ØØZ	Drain of Rt Elbow Bursa/Lig with Drain Dev, Opn Appr
ØM93[Ø,4]ZZ	Drain/Elbow Bursa & Lgmt, Rt, [Opn, Perc Endo]
ØM94ØØZ	Drain of Lt Elbow Bursa/Lig with Drain Dev, Opn Appr
ØM94[Ø,4]ZZ	Drain/Elbow Bursa & Lgmt, Lt, [Opn, Perc Endo]
ØM99Ø[Ø,Z]Z	Drain/Upr Extr Bursa & Lgmt, Rt, Opn, [Drain Dev, No Dev], NQ
ØM9BØ[Ø,Z]Z	Drain/Upr Extr Bursa & Lgmt, Lt, Opn, [Drain Dev, No Dev], NQ
ØM9CØ[Ø,Z]Z	Drain/Trunk Bursa & Lgmt, Rt, Opn, [Drain Dev, No Dev], NQ
ØM9DØ[Ø,Z]Z	Drain/Trunk Bursa & Lgmt, Lt, Opn, [Drain Dev, No Dev], NQ
ØM9FØ[Ø,Z]Z	Drain/Thorax Bursa & Lgmt, Rt, Opn, [Drain Dev, No Dev], NQ
ØM9GØ[Ø,Z]Z	Drain/Thorax Bursa & Lgmt, Lt, Opn, [Drain Dev, No Dev], NQ
ØM9HØ[Ø,Z]Z	Drain/Abd Bursa & Lgmt, Rt, Opn, [Drain Dev, No Dev], NQ
ØM9JØ[Ø,Z]Z	Drain/Abd Bursa & Lgmt, Lt, Opn, [Drain Dev, No Dev], NQ
ØM9KØ[Ø,Z]Z	Drain/Perineum Bursa & Lgmt, Opn, [Drain Dev, No Dev], NQ
ØM9LØØZ	Drain of Rt Hip Bursa/Lig with Drain Dev, Opn Appr
ØM9L[Ø,4]ZZ	Drain/Hip Bursa & Lgmt, Rt, [Opn, Perc Endo]
ØM9MØØZ	Drain of Lt Hip Bursa/Lig with Drain Dev, Opn Appr
ØM9M[Ø,4]ZZ	Drain/Hip Bursa & Lgmt, Lt, [Opn, Perc Endo]
ØM9NØZZ	Drain of Rt Knee Bursa & Lgmt, Opn Appr
ØM9N[Ø,3,4]ØZ	Drain/Knee Bursa & Lgmt, Rt, [Opn, Perc, Perc Endo], Drain Dev, NQ
ØM9PØZZ	Drain of Lt Knee Bursa & Lgmt, Opn Appr
ØM9P[Ø,3,4]ØZ	Drain/Knee Bursa & Lgmt, Lt, [Opn, Perc, Perc Endo], Drain Dev, NQ
ØM9QØZZ	Drain of Rt Ankle Bursa & Lgmt, Opn Appr
ØM9Q[Ø,3,4]ØZ	Drain/Ankle Bursa & Lgmt, Rt, [Opn, Perc, Perc Endo], Drain Dev, NQ
ØM9RØZZ	Drain of Lt Ankle Bursa & Lgmt, Opn Appr
ØM9R[Ø,3,4]ØZ	Drain/Ankle Bursa & Lgmt, Lt, [Opn, Perc, Perc Endo], Drain Dev, NQ
ØM9SØZZ	Drain of Rt Foot Bursa & Lgmt, Opn Appr
ØM9S[Ø,3,4]ØZ	Drain/Foot Bursa & Lgmt, Rt, [Opn, Perc, Perc Endo], Drain Dev, NQ
ØM9TØZZ	Drain of Lt Foot Bursa & Lgmt, Opn Appr

T **Transfer DRG**　　SP **Special Payment**　　* **Code Range**　　**6th and 7th Character of ZZ = No Device, No Qualifier ZX = No Device, Diagnostic**

Code	Description
ØM9T[Ø,3,4]ØZ	Drain/Foot Bursa & Lgmt, Lt, [Opn, Perc, Perc Endo], Drain Dev, NQ
ØM9VØ[Ø,Z]Z	Drain/Lwr Extr Bursa & Lgmt, Rt, Opn, [Drain Dev, No Dev], NQ
ØM9WØ[Ø,Z]Z	Drain/Lwr Extr Bursa & Lgmt, Lt, Opn, [Drain Dev, No Dev], NQ
ØMBØ[Ø,3,4]ZZ	Exc/Head and Neck Bursa & Lgmt, [Opn, Perc, Perc Endo]
ØMB1[Ø,3,4]ZZ	Exc/Shldr Bursa & Lgmt, Rt, [Opn, Perc, Perc Endo]
ØMB2[Ø,3,4]ZZ	Exc/Shldr Bursa & Lgmt, Lt, [Opn, Perc, Perc Endo]
ØMB3[Ø,3,4]ZZ	Exc/Elbow Bursa & Lgmt, Rt, [Opn, Perc, Perc Endo]
ØMB4[Ø,3,4]ZZ	Exc/Elbow Bursa & Lgmt, Lt, [Opn, Perc, Perc Endo]
ØMB5[Ø,3,4]ZZ	Exc/Wrist Bursa & Lgmt, Rt, [Opn, Perc, Perc Endo]
ØMB6[Ø,3,4]ZZ	Exc/Wrist Bursa & Lgmt, Lt, [Opn, Perc, Perc Endo]
ØMB9[Ø,3,4]ZZ	Exc/Upr Extr Bursa & Lgmt, Rt, [Opn, Perc, Perc Endo]
ØMBB[Ø,3,4]ZZ	Exc/Upr Extr Bursa & Lgmt, Lt, [Opn, Perc, Perc Endo]
ØMBC[Ø,3,4]ZZ	Exc/Trunk Bursa & Lgmt, Rt, [Opn, Perc, Perc Endo]
ØMBD[Ø,3,4]ZZ	Exc/Trunk Bursa & Lgmt, Lt, [Opn, Perc, Perc Endo]
ØMBF[Ø,3,4]ZZ	Exc/Thorax Bursa & Lgmt, Rt, [Opn, Perc, Perc Endo]
ØMBG[Ø,3,4]ZZ	Exc/Thorax Bursa & Lgmt, Lt, [Opn, Perc, Perc Endo]
ØMBH[Ø,3,4]ZZ	Exc/Abd Bursa & Lgmt, Rt, [Opn, Perc, Perc Endo]
ØMBJ[Ø,3,4]ZZ	Exc/Abd Bursa & Lgmt, Lt, [Opn, Perc, Perc Endo]
ØMBK[Ø,3,4]ZZ	Exc/Perineum Bursa & Lgmt, [Opn, Perc, Perc Endo]
ØMBL[Ø,3,4]ZZ	Exc/Hip Bursa & Lgmt, Rt, [Opn, Perc, Perc Endo]
ØMBM[Ø,3,4]ZZ	Exc/Hip Bursa & Lgmt, Lt, [Opn, Perc, Perc Endo]
ØMBN[Ø,3,4]ZZ	Exc/Knee Bursa & Lgmt, Rt, [Opn, Perc, Perc Endo]
ØMBP[Ø,3,4]ZZ	Exc/Knee Bursa & Lgmt, Lt, [Opn, Perc, Perc Endo]
ØMBQ[Ø,3,4]ZZ	Exc/Ankle Bursa & Lgmt, Rt, [Opn, Perc, Perc Endo]
ØMBR[Ø,3,4]ZZ	Exc/Ankle Bursa & Lgmt, Lt, [Opn, Perc, Perc Endo]
ØMBS[Ø,3,4]ZZ	Exc/Foot Bursa & Lgmt, Rt, [Opn, Perc, Perc Endo]
ØMBT[Ø,3,4]ZZ	Exc/Foot Bursa & Lgmt, Lt, [Opn, Perc, Perc Endo]
ØMBV[Ø,3,4]ZZ	Exc/Lwr Extr Bursa & Lgmt, Rt, [Opn, Perc, Perc Endo]
ØMBW[Ø,3,4]ZZ	Exc/Lwr Extr Bursa & Lgmt, Lt, [Opn, Perc, Perc Endo]
ØMCØ*	Extir/Head and Neck Bursa & Lgmt
ØMC1*	Extir/Shldr Bursa & Lgmt, Rt
ØMC2*	Extir/Shldr Bursa & Lgmt, Lt
ØMC3*	Extir/Elbow Bursa & Lgmt, Rt
ØMC4*	Extir/Elbow Bursa & Lgmt, Lt
ØMC9*	Extir/Upr Extr Bursa & Lgmt, Rt
ØMCB*	Extir/Upr Extr Bursa & Lgmt, Lt
ØMCC*	Extir/Trunk Bursa & Lgmt, Rt
ØMCD*	Extir/Trunk Bursa & Lgmt, Lt
ØMCF*	Extir/Thorax Bursa & Lgmt, Rt
ØMCG*	Extir/Thorax Bursa & Lgmt, Lt
ØMCH*	Extir/Abd Bursa & Lgmt, Rt
ØMCJ*	Extir/Abd Bursa & Lgmt, Lt
ØMCK*	Extir/Perineum Bursa & Lgmt
ØMCL*	Extir/Hip Bursa & Lgmt, Rt
ØMCM*	Extir/Hip Bursa & Lgmt, Lt
ØMCN*	Extir/Knee Bursa & Lgmt, Rt
ØMCP*	Extir/Knee Bursa & Lgmt, Lt
ØMCQ*	Extir/Ankle Bursa & Lgmt, Rt
ØMCR*	Extir/Ankle Bursa & Lgmt, Lt
ØMCS*	Extir/Foot Bursa & Lgmt, Rt
ØMCT*	Extir/Foot Bursa & Lgmt, Lt
ØMCV*	Extir/Lwr Extr Bursa & Lgmt, Rt
ØMCW*	Extir/Lwr Extr Bursa & Lgmt, Lt
ØMDØ*	Extract/Head and Neck Bursa & Lgmt
ØMD1*	Extract/Shldr Bursa & Lgmt, Rt
ØMD2*	Extract/Shldr Bursa & Lgmt, Lt
ØMD3*	Extract/Elbow Bursa & Lgmt, Rt
ØMD4*	Extract/Elbow Bursa & Lgmt, Lt
ØMD5*	Extract/Wrist Bursa & Lgmt, Rt
ØMD6*	Extract/Wrist Bursa & Lgmt, Lt
ØMD9*	Extract/Upr Extr Bursa & Lgmt, Rt
ØMDB*	Extract/Upr Extr Bursa & Lgmt, Lt
ØMDC*	Extract/Trunk Bursa & Lgmt, Rt
ØMDD*	Extract/Trunk Bursa & Lgmt, Lt
ØMDF*	Extract/Thorax Bursa & Lgmt, Rt
ØMDG*	Extract/Thorax Bursa & Lgmt, Lt
ØMDH*	Extract/Abd Bursa & Lgmt, Rt
ØMDJ*	Extract/Abd Bursa & Lgmt, Lt
ØMDK*	Extract/Perineum Bursa & Lgmt
ØMDL*	Extract/Hip Bursa & Lgmt, Rt
ØMDM*	Extract/Hip Bursa & Lgmt, Lt
ØMDN*	Extract/Knee Bursa & Lgmt, Rt
ØMDP*	Extract/Knee Bursa & Lgmt, Lt
ØMDQ*	Extract/Ankle Bursa & Lgmt, Rt
ØMDR*	Extract/Ankle Bursa & Lgmt, Lt
ØMDS*	Extract/Foot Bursa & Lgmt, Rt
ØMDT*	Extract/Foot Bursa & Lgmt, Lt
ØMDV*	Extract/Lwr Extr Bursa & Lgmt, Rt
ØMDW*	Extract/Lwr Extr Bursa & Lgmt, Lt
ØMPX[Ø,3,4][7,K]Z	Rmvl/Upr Bursa & Lgmt, [Opn, Perc, Perc Endo], [Auto Tissue Sub, Nonauto Tissue Sub], NQ
ØMPY[Ø,3,4][7,K]Z	Rmvl/Lwr Bursa & Lgmt, [Opn, Perc, Perc Endo], [Auto Tissue Sub, Nonauto Tissue Sub], NQ
ØMQ1*	Repair/Shldr Bursa & Lgmt, Rt
ØMQ2*	Repair/Shldr Bursa & Lgmt, Lt
ØMQ3*	Repair/Elbow Bursa & Lgmt, Rt
ØMQ4*	Repair/Elbow Bursa & Lgmt, Lt
ØMQ5*	Repair/Wrist Bursa & Lgmt, Rt
ØMQ6*	Repair/Wrist Bursa & Lgmt, Lt
ØMQ7*	Repair/Hand Bursa & Lgmt, Rt
ØMQ8*	Repair/Hand Bursa & Lgmt, Lt
ØMQN*	Repair/Knee Bursa & Lgmt, Rt
ØMQP*	Repair/Knee Bursa & Lgmt, Lt
ØMQQ*	Repair/Ankle Bursa & Lgmt, Rt
ØMQR*	Repair/Ankle Bursa & Lgmt, Lt
ØMQS*	Repair/Foot Bursa & Lgmt, Rt
ØMQT*	Repair/Foot Bursa & Lgmt, Lt
ØMTØ*	Resect/Head and Neck Bursa & Lgmt
ØMT1*	Resect/Shldr Bursa & Lgmt, Rt
ØMT2*	Resect/Shldr Bursa & Lgmt, Lt
ØMT3*	Resect/Elbow Bursa & Lgmt, Rt
ØMT4*	Resect/Elbow Bursa & Lgmt, Lt
ØMT5*	Resect/Wrist Bursa & Lgmt, Rt
ØMT6*	Resect/Wrist Bursa & Lgmt, Lt
ØMT9*	Resect/Upr Extr Bursa & Lgmt, Rt
ØMTB*	Resect/Upr Extr Bursa & Lgmt, Lt
ØMTC*	Resect/Trunk Bursa & Lgmt, Rt
ØMTD*	Resect/Trunk Bursa & Lgmt, Lt
ØMTF*	Resect/Thorax Bursa & Lgmt, Rt
ØMTG*	Resect/Thorax Bursa & Lgmt, Lt
ØMTH*	Resect/Abd Bursa & Lgmt, Rt
ØMTJ*	Resect/Abd Bursa & Lgmt, Lt
ØMTK*	Resect/Perineum Bursa & Lgmt
ØMTL*	Resect/Hip Bursa & Lgmt, Rt
ØMTM*	Resect/Hip Bursa & Lgmt, Lt
ØMTN*	Resect/Knee Bursa & Lgmt, Rt
ØMTP*	Resect/Knee Bursa & Lgmt, Lt
ØMTQ*	Resect/Ankle Bursa & Lgmt, Rt
ØMTR*	Resect/Ankle Bursa & Lgmt, Lt
ØMTS*	Resect/Foot Bursa & Lgmt, Rt
ØMTT*	Resect/Foot Bursa & Lgmt, Lt
ØMTV*	Resect/Lwr Extr Bursa & Lgmt, Rt
ØMTW*	Resect/Lwr Extr Bursa & Lgmt, Lt
ØMWX[Ø,3,4][Ø,7,J,K]Z	Rev/Upr Bursa & Lgmt, [Opn, Perc, Perc Endo], [Drain Dev, Auto Tissue Sub, Synth Sub, Nonauto Tissue Sub], NQ
ØMWY[Ø,3,4][Ø,7,J,K]Z	Rev/Lwr Bursa & Lgmt, [Opn, Perc, Perc Endo], [Drain Dev, Auto Tissue Sub, Synth Sub, Nonauto Tissue Sub], NQ
ØN5*	Head and Facial Bones, Destr
ØN8P*	Div/Orbit, Rt
ØN8Q*	Div/Orbit, Lt
ØN9P[Ø,3,4]ØZ	Drain/Orbit, Rt, [Opn, Perc, Perc Endo], Drain Dev, NQ
ØN9P[Ø,4]ZZ	Drain/Orbit, Rt, [Opn, Perc Endo]
ØN9Q[Ø,3,4]ØZ	Drain/Orbit, Lt, [Opn, Perc, Perc Endo], Drain Dev, NQ
ØN9Q[Ø,4]ZZ	Drain/Orbit, Lt, [Opn, Perc Endo]
ØNBØ[Ø,3,4]ZZ	Exc/Skull, [Opn, Perc, Perc Endo]
ØNB1[Ø,3,4]ZZ	Exc/Frontal Bone, Rt, [Opn, Perc, Perc Endo]
ØNB2[Ø,3,4]ZZ	Exc/Frontal Bone, Lt, [Opn, Perc, Perc Endo]
ØNB3[Ø,3,4]ZZ	Exc/Parietal Bone, Rt, [Opn, Perc, Perc Endo]
ØNB4[Ø,3,4]ZZ	Exc/Parietal Bone, Lt, [Opn, Perc, Perc Endo]
ØNB5[Ø,3,4]ZZ	Exc/Temporal Bone, Rt, [Opn, Perc, Perc Endo]
ØNB6[Ø,3,4]ZZ	Exc/Temporal Bone, Lt, [Opn, Perc, Perc Endo]
ØNB7[Ø,3,4]ZZ	Exc/Occipital Bone, Rt, [Opn, Perc, Perc Endo]
ØNB8[Ø,3,4]ZZ	Exc/Occipital Bone, Lt, [Opn, Perc, Perc Endo]
ØNBB[Ø,3,4]ZZ	Exc/Nasal Bone, [Opn, Perc, Perc Endo]
ØNBC[Ø,3,4]ZZ	Exc/Sphenoid Bone, Rt, [Opn, Perc, Perc Endo]
ØNBD[Ø,3,4]ZZ	Exc/Sphenoid Bone, Lt, [Opn, Perc, Perc Endo]
ØNBF[Ø,3,4]ZZ	Exc/Ethmoid Bone, Rt, [Opn, Perc, Perc Endo]
ØNBG[Ø,3,4]ZZ	Exc/Ethmoid Bone, Lt, [Opn, Perc, Perc Endo]
ØNBH[Ø,3,4]ZZ	Exc/Lacrimal Bone, Rt, [Opn, Perc, Perc Endo]
ØNBJ[Ø,3,4]ZZ	Exc/Lacrimal Bone, Lt, [Opn, Perc, Perc Endo]
ØNBK[Ø,3,4]ZZ	Exc/Palatine Bone, Rt, [Opn, Perc, Perc Endo]
ØNBL[Ø,3,4]ZZ	Exc/Palatine Bone, Lt, [Opn, Perc, Perc Endo]
ØNBM[Ø,3,4]ZZ	Exc/Zygomatic Bone, Rt, [Opn, Perc, Perc Endo]
ØNBN[Ø,3,4]ZZ	Exc/Zygomatic Bone, Lt, [Opn, Perc, Perc Endo]
ØNBP[Ø,3,4]ZZ	Exc/Orbit, Rt, [Opn, Perc, Perc Endo]
ØNBQ[Ø,3,4]ZZ	Exc/Orbit, Lt, [Opn, Perc, Perc Endo]
ØNBR[Ø,3,4]ZZ	Exc/Maxilla, Rt, [Opn, Perc, Perc Endo]
ØNBS[Ø,3,4]ZZ	Exc/Maxilla, Lt, [Opn, Perc, Perc Endo]
ØNBT[Ø,3,4]ZZ	Exc/Mandible, Rt, [Opn, Perc, Perc Endo]

Surgical   **Medical**   **CC Indicator**   **MCC Indicator**   **Procedure Proxy**   PDxMCC **PDx acts as own MCC**   PDxCC **PDx acts as own CC**

MDC 21: Injuries, Poisonings And Toxic Effects Of Drugs—SURGICAL

ØNBV[Ø,3,4]ZZ	Exc/Mandible, Lt, [Opn, Perc, Perc Endo]
ØNBX[Ø,3,4]ZZ	Exc/Hyoid Bone, [Opn, Perc, Perc Endo]
ØNC1*	Extir/Frontal Bone, Rt
ØNC2*	Extir/Frontal Bone, Lt
ØNC3*	Extir/Parietal Bone, Rt
ØNC4*	Extir/Parietal Bone, Lt
ØNC5*	Extir/Temporal Bone, Rt
ØNC6*	Extir/Temporal Bone, Lt
ØNC7*	Extir/Occipital Bone, Rt
ØNC8*	Extir/Occipital Bone, Lt
ØNHØ[Ø,3,4]4Z	Insert/Skull, [Opn, Perc, Perc Endo], Int Fix Dev, NQ
ØNH1*	Insert/Frontal Bone, Rt
ØNH2*	Insert/Frontal Bone, Lt
ØNH3*	Insert/Parietal Bone, Rt
ØNH4*	Insert/Parietal Bone, Lt
ØNH5[Ø,3,4]4Z	Insert/Temporal Bone, Rt, [Opn, Perc, Perc Endo], Int Fix Dev, NQ
ØNH6[Ø,3,4]4Z	Insert/Temporal Bone, Lt, [Opn, Perc, Perc Endo], Int Fix Dev, NQ
ØNH7*	Insert/Occipital Bone, Rt
ØNH8*	Insert/Occipital Bone, Lt
ØNJØ[Ø,3,4]ZZ	Inspect/Skull, [Opn, Perc, Perc Endo]
ØNJB[Ø,3,4]ZZ	Inspect/Nasal Bone, [Opn, Perc, Perc Endo]
ØNJW[Ø,3,4]ZZ	Inspect/Facial Bone, [Opn, Perc, Perc Endo]
ØNN1*	Rls/Frontal Bone, Rt
ØNN2*	Rls/Frontal Bone, Lt
ØNN3*	Rls/Parietal Bone, Rt
ØNN4*	Rls/Parietal Bone, Lt
ØNN5*	Rls/Temporal Bone, Rt
ØNN6*	Rls/Temporal Bone, Lt
ØNN7*	Rls/Occipital Bone, Rt
ØNN8*	Rls/Occipital Bone, Lt
ØNNC*	Rls/Sphenoid Bone, Rt
ØNND*	Rls/Sphenoid Bone, Lt
ØNNF*	Rls/Ethmoid Bone, Rt
ØNNG*	Rls/Ethmoid Bone, Lt
ØNNH*	Rls/Lacrimal Bone, Rt
ØNNJ*	Rls/Lacrimal Bone, Lt
ØNNK*	Rls/Palatine Bone, Rt
ØNNL*	Rls/Palatine Bone, Lt
ØNNM*	Rls/Zygomatic Bone, Rt
ØNNN*	Rls/Zygomatic Bone, Lt
ØNNP*	Rls/Orbit, Rt
ØNNQ*	Rls/Orbit, Lt
ØNNR*	Rls/Maxilla, Rt
ØNNS*	Rls/Maxilla, Lt
ØNNT*	Rls/Mandible, Rt
ØNNV*	Rls/Mandible, Lt
ØNNX*	Rls/Hyoid Bone
ØNPØ[Ø,3,4]JZ	Rmvl/Skull, [Opn, Perc, Perc Endo], Synth Sub, NQ
ØNPW[Ø,3,4,X]4Z	Rmvl/Facial Bone, [Opn, Perc, Perc Endo, Ext], Int Fix Dev, NQ
ØNPW[Ø,3,4]JZ	Rmvl/Facial Bone, [Opn, Perc, Perc Endo], Synth Sub, NQ
ØNQ*	Head and Facial Bones, Repair
ØNRØ*	Replace/Skull
ØNR1[Ø,3,4]JZ	Replace/Frontal Bone, Rt, [Opn, Perc, Perc Endo], Synth Sub, NQ
ØNR2[Ø,3,4]JZ	Replace/Frontal Bone, Lt, [Opn, Perc, Perc Endo], Synth Sub, NQ
ØNR3[Ø,3,4]JZ	Replace/Parietal Bone, Rt, [Opn, Perc, Perc Endo], Synth Sub, NQ
ØNR4[Ø,3,4]JZ	Replace/Parietal Bone, Lt, [Opn, Perc, Perc Endo], Synth Sub, NQ
ØNR5[Ø,3,4]JZ	Replace/Temporal Bone, Rt, [Opn, Perc, Perc Endo], Synth Sub, NQ
ØNR6[Ø,3,4]JZ	Replace/Temporal Bone, Lt, [Opn, Perc, Perc Endo], Synth Sub, NQ
ØNR7[Ø,3,4]JZ	Replace/Occipital Bone, Rt, [Opn, Perc, Perc Endo], Synth Sub, NQ
ØNR8[Ø,3,4]JZ	Replace/Occipital Bone, Lt, [Opn, Perc, Perc Endo], Synth Sub, NQ
ØNRB*	Replace/Nasal Bone
ØNRC[Ø,3,4]JZ	Replace/Sphenoid Bone, Rt, [Opn, Perc, Perc Endo], Synth Sub, NQ
ØNRD[Ø,3,4]JZ	Replace/Sphenoid Bone, Lt, [Opn, Perc, Perc Endo], Synth Sub, NQ
ØNRF[Ø,3,4]JZ	Replace/Ethmoid Bone, Rt, [Opn, Perc, Perc Endo], Synth Sub, NQ
ØNRG[Ø,3,4]JZ	Replace/Ethmoid Bone, Lt, [Opn, Perc, Perc Endo], Synth Sub, NQ
ØNRH[Ø,3,4]JZ	Replace/Lacrimal Bone, Rt, [Opn, Perc, Perc Endo], Synth Sub, NQ
ØNRJ[Ø,3,4]JZ	Replace/Lacrimal Bone, Lt, [Opn, Perc, Perc Endo], Synth Sub, NQ
ØNRK[Ø,3,4]JZ	Replace/Palatine Bone, Rt, [Opn, Perc, Perc Endo], Synth Sub, NQ
ØNRL[Ø,3,4]JZ	Replace/Palatine Bone, Lt, [Opn, Perc, Perc Endo], Synth Sub, NQ
ØNRM[Ø,3,4]JZ	Replace/Zygomatic Bone, Rt, [Opn, Perc, Perc Endo], Synth Sub, NQ
ØNRN[Ø,3,4]JZ	Replace/Zygomatic Bone, Lt, [Opn, Perc, Perc Endo], Synth Sub, NQ
ØNRP[Ø,3,4][7,J]Z	Replace/Orbit, Rt, [Opn, Perc, Perc Endo], [Auto Tissue Sub, Synth Sub], NQ
ØNRQ[Ø,3,4][7,J]Z	Replace/Orbit, Lt, [Opn, Perc, Perc Endo], [Auto Tissue Sub, Synth Sub], NQ
ØNRR*	Replace/Maxilla, Rt
ØNRS*	Replace/Maxilla, Lt
ØNRT*	Replace/Mandible, Rt
ØNRV*	Replace/Mandible, Lt
ØNRX[Ø,3,4]JZ	Replace/Hyoid Bone, [Opn, Perc, Perc Endo], Synth Sub, NQ
ØNSØ*	Repos/Skull
ØNS1*	Repos/Frontal Bone, Rt
ØNS2*	Repos/Frontal Bone, Lt
ØNS3*	Repos/Parietal Bone, Rt
ØNS4*	Repos/Parietal Bone, Lt
ØNS5*	Repos/Temporal Bone, Rt
ØNS6*	Repos/Temporal Bone, Lt
ØNS7*	Repos/Occipital Bone, Rt
ØNS8*	Repos/Occipital Bone, Lt
ØNSBØ[4,Z]Z	Repos/Nasal Bone, Opn, [Int Fix Dev, No Dev], NQ
ØNSCØ[4,Z]Z	Repos/Sphenoid Bone, Rt, Opn, [Int Fix Dev, No Dev], NQ
ØNSDØ[4,Z]Z	Repos/Sphenoid Bone, Lt, Opn, [Int Fix Dev, No Dev], NQ
ØNSFØ[4,Z]Z	Repos/Ethmoid Bone, Rt, Opn, [Int Fix Dev, No Dev], NQ
ØNSGØ[4,Z]Z	Repos/Ethmoid Bone, Lt, Opn, [Int Fix Dev, No Dev], NQ
ØNSHØ[4,Z]Z	Repos/Lacrimal Bone, Rt, Opn, [Int Fix Dev, No Dev], NQ
ØNSJØ[4,Z]Z	Repos/Lacrimal Bone, Lt, Opn, [Int Fix Dev, No Dev], NQ
ØNSKØ[4,Z]Z	Repos/Palatine Bone, Rt, Opn, [Int Fix Dev, No Dev], NQ
ØNSLØ[4,Z]Z	Repos/Palatine Bone, Lt, Opn, [Int Fix Dev, No Dev], NQ
ØNSMØ[4,Z]Z	Repos/Zygomatic Bone, Rt, Opn, [Int Fix Dev, No Dev], NQ
ØNSNØ[4,Z]Z	Repos/Zygomatic Bone, Lt, Opn, [Int Fix Dev, No Dev], NQ
ØNSPØ[4,Z]Z	Repos/Orbit, Rt, Opn, [Int Fix Dev, No Dev], NQ
ØNSQØ[4,Z]Z	Repos/Orbit, Lt, Opn, [Int Fix Dev, No Dev], NQ
ØNSRØ[4,5,Z]Z	Repos/Maxilla, Rt, Opn, [Int Fix Dev, Ext Fix Dev, No Dev], NQ
ØNSSØ[4,5,Z]Z	Repos/Maxilla, Lt, Opn, [Int Fix Dev, Ext Fix Dev, No Dev], NQ
ØNSTØ[4,5,Z]Z	Repos/Mandible, Rt, Opn, [Int Fix Dev, Ext Fix Dev, No Dev], NQ
ØNSVØ[4,5,Z]Z	Repos/Mandible, Lt, Opn, [Int Fix Dev, Ext Fix Dev, No Dev], NQ
ØNSXØ[4,Z]Z	Repos/Hyoid Bone, Opn, [Int Fix Dev, No Dev], NQ
ØNT*	Head and Facial Bones, Resect
ØNUØ[Ø,3,4]JZ	Supl/Skull, [Opn, Perc, Perc Endo], Synth Sub, NQ
ØNU1[Ø,3,4]JZ	Supl/Frontal Bone, Rt, [Opn, Perc, Perc Endo], Synth Sub, NQ
ØNU2[Ø,3,4]JZ	Supl/Frontal Bone, Lt, [Opn, Perc, Perc Endo], Synth Sub, NQ
ØNU3[Ø,3,4]JZ	Supl/Parietal Bone, Rt, [Opn, Perc, Perc Endo], Synth Sub, NQ
ØNU4[Ø,3,4]JZ	Supl/Parietal Bone, Lt, [Opn, Perc, Perc Endo], Synth Sub, NQ
ØNU5[Ø,3,4]JZ	Supl/Temporal Bone, Rt, [Opn, Perc, Perc Endo], Synth Sub, NQ
ØNU6[Ø,3,4]JZ	Supl/Temporal Bone, Lt, [Opn, Perc, Perc Endo], Synth Sub, NQ
ØNU7[Ø,3,4]JZ	Supl/Occipital Bone, Rt, [Opn, Perc, Perc Endo], Synth Sub, NQ
ØNU8[Ø,3,4]JZ	Supl/Occipital Bone, Lt, [Opn, Perc, Perc Endo], Synth Sub, NQ
ØNUB*	Supl/Nasal Bone
ØNUC[Ø,3,4]JZ	Supl/Sphenoid Bone, Rt, [Opn, Perc, Perc Endo], Synth Sub, NQ
ØNUD[Ø,3,4]JZ	Supl/Sphenoid Bone, Lt, [Opn, Perc, Perc Endo], Synth Sub, NQ
ØNUF[Ø,3,4]JZ	Supl/Ethmoid Bone, Rt, [Opn, Perc, Perc Endo], Synth Sub, NQ
ØNUG[Ø,3,4]JZ	Supl/Ethmoid Bone, Lt, [Opn, Perc, Perc Endo], Synth Sub, NQ
ØNUH[Ø,3,4]JZ	Supl/Lacrimal Bone, Rt, [Opn, Perc, Perc Endo], Synth Sub, NQ
ØNUJ[Ø,3,4]JZ	Supl/Lacrimal Bone, Lt, [Opn, Perc, Perc Endo], Synth Sub, NQ
ØNUK[Ø,3,4]JZ	Supl/Palatine Bone, Rt, [Opn, Perc, Perc Endo], Synth Sub, NQ
ØNUL[Ø,3,4]JZ	Supl/Palatine Bone, Lt, [Opn, Perc, Perc Endo], Synth Sub, NQ
ØNUM[Ø,3,4]JZ	Supl/Zygomatic Bone, Rt, [Opn, Perc, Perc Endo], Synth Sub, NQ
ØNUN[Ø,3,4]JZ	Supl/Zygomatic Bone, Lt, [Opn, Perc, Perc Endo], Synth Sub, NQ
ØNUP[Ø,3,4]JZ	Supl/Orbit, Rt, [Opn, Perc, Perc Endo], Synth Sub, NQ
ØNUQ[Ø,3,4]JZ	Supl/Orbit, Lt, [Opn, Perc, Perc Endo], Synth Sub, NQ
ØNUR*	Supl/Maxilla, Rt
ØNUS*	Supl/Maxilla, Lt
ØNUT*	Supl/Mandible, Rt
ØNUV*	Supl/Mandible, Lt
ØNUX[Ø,3,4]JZ	Supl/Hyoid Bone, [Opn, Perc, Perc Endo], Synth Sub, NQ
ØP5Ø*	Destr/Sternum

T Transfer DRG   SP Special Payment   * Code Range   6th and 7th Character of ZZ = No Device, No Qualifier ZX = No Device, Diagnostic

344   MS-DRG Version 33.0   © 2015 Optum360, LLC

0P51*	Destr/Rib, Rt
0P52*	Destr/Rib, Lt
0P53*	Destr/Cervical Vertebra
0P54*	Destr/Thoracic Vertebra
0P55*	Destr/Scapula, Rt
0P56*	Destr/Scapula, Lt
0P57*	Destr/Glenoid Cavity, Rt
0P58*	Destr/Glenoid Cavity, Lt
0P59*	Destr/Clavicle, Rt
0P5B*	Destr/Clavicle, Lt
0P5C*	Destr/Humeral Head, Rt
0P5D*	Destr/Humeral Head, Lt
0P5F*	Destr/Humeral Shaft, Rt
0P5G*	Destr/Humeral Shaft, Lt
0P5H*	Destr/Radius, Rt
0P5J*	Destr/Radius, Lt
0P5K*	Destr/Ulna, Rt
0P5L*	Destr/Ulna, Lt
0P5R*	Destr/Thumb Phalanx, Rt
0P5S*	Destr/Thumb Phalanx, Lt
0P5T*	Destr/Finger Phalanx, Rt
0P5V*	Destr/Finger Phalanx, Lt
0P80*	Div/Sternum
0P81*	Div/Rib, Rt
0P82*	Div/Rib, Lt
0P83*	Div/Cervical Vertebra
0P84*	Div/Thoracic Vertebra
0P85*	Div/Scapula, Rt
0P86*	Div/Scapula, Lt
0P87*	Div/Glenoid Cavity, Rt
0P88*	Div/Glenoid Cavity, Lt
0P89*	Div/Clavicle, Rt
0P8B*	Div/Clavicle, Lt
0P8C*	Div/Humeral Head, Rt
0P8D*	Div/Humeral Head, Lt
0P8F*	Div/Humeral Shaft, Rt
0P8G*	Div/Humeral Shaft, Lt
0P8H*	Div/Radius, Rt
0P8J*	Div/Radius, Lt
0P8K*	Div/Ulna, Rt
0P8L*	Div/Ulna, Lt
0P8R*	Div/Thumb Phalanx, Rt
0P8S*	Div/Thumb Phalanx, Lt
0P8T*	Div/Finger Phalanx, Rt
0P8V*	Div/Finger Phalanx, Lt
0PB0[0,3,4]ZZ	Exc/Sternum, [Opn, Perc, Perc Endo]
0PB1[0,3,4]ZZ	Exc/Rib, Rt, [Opn, Perc, Perc Endo]
0PB2[0,3,4]ZZ	Exc/Rib, Lt, [Opn, Perc, Perc Endo]
0PB3[0,3,4]ZZ	Exc/Cervical Vertebra, [Opn, Perc, Perc Endo]
0PB4[0,3,4]ZZ	Exc/Thoracic Vertebra, [Opn, Perc, Perc Endo]
0PB5[0,3,4]ZZ	Exc/Scapula, Rt, [Opn, Perc, Perc Endo]
0PB6[0,3,4]ZZ	Exc/Scapula, Lt, [Opn, Perc, Perc Endo]
0PB7[0,3,4]ZZ	Exc/Glenoid Cavity, Rt, [Opn, Perc, Perc Endo]
0PB8[0,3,4]ZZ	Exc/Glenoid Cavity, Lt, [Opn, Perc, Perc Endo]
0PB9[0,3,4]ZZ	Exc/Clavicle, Rt, [Opn, Perc, Perc Endo]
0PBB[0,3,4]ZZ	Exc/Clavicle, Lt, [Opn, Perc, Perc Endo]
0PBC[0,3,4]ZZ	Exc/Humeral Head, Rt, [Opn, Perc, Perc Endo]
0PBD[0,3,4]ZZ	Exc/Humeral Head, Lt, [Opn, Perc, Perc Endo]
0PBF[0,3,4]ZZ	Exc/Humeral Shaft, Rt, [Opn, Perc, Perc Endo]
0PBG[0,3,4]ZZ	Exc/Humeral Shaft, Lt, [Opn, Perc, Perc Endo]
0PBH[0,3,4]ZZ	Exc/Radius, Rt, [Opn, Perc, Perc Endo]
0PBJ[0,3,4]ZZ	Exc/Radius, Lt, [Opn, Perc, Perc Endo]
0PBK[0,3,4]ZZ	Exc/Ulna, Rt, [Opn, Perc, Perc Endo]
0PBL[0,3,4]ZZ	Exc/Ulna, Lt, [Opn, Perc, Perc Endo]
0PBR[0,3,4]ZZ	Exc/Thumb Phalanx, Rt, [Opn, Perc, Perc Endo]
0PBS[0,3,4]ZZ	Exc/Thumb Phalanx, Lt, [Opn, Perc, Perc Endo]
0PBT[0,3,4]ZZ	Exc/Finger Phalanx, Rt, [Opn, Perc, Perc Endo]
0PBV[0,3,4]ZZ	Exc/Finger Phalanx, Lt, [Opn, Perc, Perc Endo]
0PC0*	Extir/Sternum
0PC1*	Extir/Rib, Rt
0PC2*	Extir/Rib, Lt
0PC3*	Extir/Cervical Vertebra
0PC4*	Extir/Thoracic Vertebra
0PC5*	Extir/Scapula, Rt
0PC6*	Extir/Scapula, Lt
0PC7*	Extir/Glenoid Cavity, Rt
0PC8*	Extir/Glenoid Cavity, Lt
0PC9*	Extir/Clavicle, Rt
0PCB*	Extir/Clavicle, Lt
0PCC*	Extir/Humeral Head, Rt

0PCD*	Extir/Humeral Head, Lt
0PCF*	Extir/Humeral Shaft, Rt
0PCG*	Extir/Humeral Shaft, Lt
0PCH*	Extir/Radius, Rt
0PCJ*	Extir/Radius, Lt
0PCK*	Extir/Ulna, Rt
0PCL*	Extir/Ulna, Lt
0PCR*	Extir/Thumb Phalanx, Rt
0PCS*	Extir/Thumb Phalanx, Lt
0PCT*	Extir/Finger Phalanx, Rt
0PCV*	Extir/Finger Phalanx, Lt
0PH0*	Insert/Sternum
0PH1*	Insert/Rib, Rt
0PH2*	Insert/Rib, Lt
0PH3*	Insert/Cervical Vertebra
0PH4*	Insert/Thoracic Vertebra
0PH5*	Insert/Scapula, Rt
0PH6*	Insert/Scapula, Lt
0PH7*	Insert/Glenoid Cavity, Rt
0PH8*	Insert/Glenoid Cavity, Lt
0PH9*	Insert/Clavicle, Rt
0PHB*	Insert/Clavicle, Lt
0PHC[0,3,4][4,5,6,B,C,D]Z	Insert/Humeral Head, Rt, [Opn, Perc, Perc Endo], [Int Fix Dev, Ext Fix Dev, Int Fix Dev, Intramedullary Int Fix Dev, Ext Fix Dev, Monop, Ext Fix Dev, Ring, Ext Fix Dev, Hybrid], NQ
0PHD[0,3,4][4,5,6,B,C,D]Z	Insert/Humeral Head, Lt, [Opn, Perc, Perc Endo], [Int Fix Dev, Ext Fix Dev, Int Fix Dev, Intramedullary Int Fix Dev, Ext Fix Dev, Monop, Ext Fix Dev, Ring, Ext Fix Dev, Hybrid], NQ
0PHF[0,3,4][4,5,6,B,C,D]Z	Insert/Humeral Shaft, Rt, [Opn, Perc, Perc Endo], [Int Fix Dev, Ext Fix Dev, Int Fix Dev, Intramedullary Int Fix Dev, Ext Fix Dev, Monop, Ext Fix Dev, Ring, Ext Fix Dev, Hybrid], NQ
0PHG[0,3,4][4,5,6,B,C,D]Z	Insert/Humeral Shaft, Lt, [Opn, Perc, Perc Endo], [Int Fix Dev, Ext Fix Dev, Int Fix Dev, Intramedullary Int Fix Dev, Ext Fix Dev, Monop, Ext Fix Dev, Ring, Ext Fix Dev, Hybrid], NQ
0PHH[0,3,4][4,5,6,B,C,D]Z	Insert/Radius, Rt, [Opn, Perc, Perc Endo], [Int Fix Dev, Ext Fix Dev, Int Fix Dev, Intramedullary Int Fix Dev, Ext Fix Dev, Monop, Ext Fix Dev, Ring, Ext Fix Dev, Hybrid], NQ
0PHJ[0,3,4][4,5,6,B,C,D]Z	Insert/Radius, Lt, [Opn, Perc, Perc Endo], [Int Fix Dev, Ext Fix Dev, Int Fix Dev, Intramedullary Int Fix Dev, Ext Fix Dev, Monop, Ext Fix Dev, Ring, Ext Fix Dev, Hybrid], NQ
0PHK[0,3,4][4,5,6,B,C,D]Z	Insert/Ulna, Rt, [Opn, Perc, Perc Endo], [Int Fix Dev, Ext Fix Dev, Int Fix Dev, Intramedullary Int Fix Dev, Ext Fix Dev, Monop, Ext Fix Dev, Ring, Ext Fix Dev, Hybrid], NQ
0PHL[0,3,4][4,5,6,B,C,D]Z	Insert/Ulna, Lt, [Opn, Perc, Perc Endo], [Int Fix Dev, Ext Fix Dev, Int Fix Dev, Intramedullary Int Fix Dev, Ext Fix Dev, Monop, Ext Fix Dev, Ring, Ext Fix Dev, Hybrid], NQ
0PHR*	Insert/Thumb Phalanx, Rt
0PHS*	Insert/Thumb Phalanx, Lt
0PHT*	Insert/Finger Phalanx, Rt
0PHV*	Insert/Finger Phalanx, Lt
0PHY*	Insert/Upr Bone
0PN0*	Rls/Sternum
0PN1*	Rls/Rib, Rt
0PN2*	Rls/Rib, Lt
0PN5*	Rls/Scapula, Rt
0PN6*	Rls/Scapula, Lt
0PN7*	Rls/Glenoid Cavity, Rt
0PN8*	Rls/Glenoid Cavity, Lt
0PN9*	Rls/Clavicle, Rt
0PNB*	Rls/Clavicle, Lt
0PNC*	Rls/Humeral Head, Rt
0PND*	Rls/Humeral Head, Lt
0PNF*	Rls/Humeral Shaft, Rt
0PNG*	Rls/Humeral Shaft, Lt
0PNH*	Rls/Radius, Rt
0PNJ*	Rls/Radius, Lt
0PNK*	Rls/Ulna, Rt
0PNL*	Rls/Ulna, Lt
0PP0[0,3,4][4,7,J,K]Z	Rmvl/Sternum, [Opn, Perc, Perc Endo], [Int Fix Dev, Auto Tissue Sub, Synth Sub, Nonauto Tissue Sub], NQ
0PP1[0,3,4][4,7,J,K]Z	Rmvl/Rib, Rt, [Opn, Perc, Perc Endo], [Int Fix Dev, Auto Tissue Sub, Synth Sub, Nonauto Tissue Sub], NQ
0PP2[0,3,4][4,7,J,K]Z	Rmvl/Rib, Lt, [Opn, Perc, Perc Endo], [Int Fix Dev, Auto Tissue Sub, Synth Sub, Nonauto Tissue Sub], NQ
0PP3[0,3,4][4,7,J,K]Z	Rmvl/Cervical Vertebra, [Opn, Perc, Perc Endo], [Int Fix Dev, Auto Tissue Sub, Synth Sub, Nonauto Tissue Sub], NQ
0PP4[0,3,4][4,7,J,K]Z	Rmvl/Thoracic Vertebra, [Opn, Perc, Perc Endo], [Int Fix Dev, Auto Tissue Sub, Synth Sub, Nonauto Tissue Sub], NQ
0PP5[0,3,4][4,7,J,K]Z	Rmvl/Scapula, Rt, [Opn, Perc, Perc Endo], [Int Fix Dev, Auto Tissue Sub, Synth Sub, Nonauto Tissue Sub], NQ

Surgical   **Medical**   **CC Indicator**   **MCC Indicator**   **Procedure Proxy**   PDxMCC **PDx acts as own MCC**   PDxCC **PDx acts as own CC**

ØPP6[Ø,3,4][4,7,J,K]Z Rmvl/Scapula, Lt, [Opn, Perc, Perc Endo], [Int Fix Dev, Auto Tissue Sub, Synth Sub, Nonauto Tissue Sub], NQ
ØPP7[Ø,3,4][4,7,J,K]Z Rmvl/Glenoid Cavity, Rt, [Opn, Perc, Perc Endo], [Int Fix Dev, Auto Tissue Sub, Synth Sub, Nonauto Tissue Sub], NQ
ØPP8[Ø,3,4][4,7,J,K]Z Rmvl/Glenoid Cavity, Lt, [Opn, Perc, Perc Endo], [Int Fix Dev, Auto Tissue Sub, Synth Sub, Nonauto Tissue Sub], NQ
ØPP9[Ø,3,4][4,7,J,K]Z Rmvl/Clavicle, Rt, [Opn, Perc, Perc Endo], [Int Fix Dev, Auto Tissue Sub, Synth Sub, Nonauto Tissue Sub], NQ
ØPPB[Ø,3,4][4,7,J,K]Z Rmvl/Clavicle, Lt, [Opn, Perc, Perc Endo], [Int Fix Dev, Auto Tissue Sub, Synth Sub, Nonauto Tissue Sub], NQ
ØPPC[Ø,3,4][4,5,7,J,K]Z Rmvl/Humeral Head, Rt, [Opn, Perc, Perc Endo], [Int Fix Dev, Ext Fix Dev, Auto Tissue Sub, Synth Sub, Nonauto Tissue Sub], NQ
ØPPD[Ø,3,4][4,5,7,J,K]Z Rmvl/Humeral Head, Lt, [Opn, Perc, Perc Endo], [Int Fix Dev, Ext Fix Dev, Auto Tissue Sub, Synth Sub, Nonauto Tissue Sub], NQ
ØPPF[Ø,3,4][4,5,7,J,K]Z Rmvl/Humeral Shaft, Rt, [Opn, Perc, Perc Endo], [Int Fix Dev, Ext Fix Dev, Auto Tissue Sub, Synth Sub, Nonauto Tissue Sub], NQ
ØPPG[Ø,3,4][4,5,7,J,K]Z Rmvl/Humeral Shaft, Lt, [Opn, Perc, Perc Endo], [Int Fix Dev, Ext Fix Dev, Auto Tissue Sub, Synth Sub, Nonauto Tissue Sub], NQ
ØPPH[Ø,3,4][4,5,7,J,K]Z Rmvl/Radius, Rt, [Opn, Perc, Perc Endo], [Int Fix Dev, Ext Fix Dev, Auto Tissue Sub, Synth Sub, Nonauto Tissue Sub], NQ
ØPPJ[Ø,3,4][4,5,7,J,K]Z Rmvl/Radius, Lt, [Opn, Perc, Perc Endo], [Int Fix Dev, Ext Fix Dev, Auto Tissue Sub, Synth Sub, Nonauto Tissue Sub], NQ
ØPPK[Ø,3,4][4,5,7,J,K]Z Rmvl/Ulna, Rt, [Opn, Perc, Perc Endo], [Int Fix Dev, Ext Fix Dev, Auto Tissue Sub, Synth Sub, Nonauto Tissue Sub], NQ
ØPPL[Ø,3,4][4,5,7,J,K]Z Rmvl/Ulna, Lt, [Opn, Perc, Perc Endo], [Int Fix Dev, Ext Fix Dev, Auto Tissue Sub, Synth Sub, Nonauto Tissue Sub], NQ
ØPPR[Ø,3,4][4,5,7,J,K]Z Rmvl/Thumb Phalanx, Rt, [Opn, Perc, Perc Endo], [Int Fix Dev, Ext Fix Dev, Auto Tissue Sub, Synth Sub, Nonauto Tissue Sub], NQ
ØPPS[Ø,3,4][4,5,7,J,K]Z Rmvl/Thumb Phalanx, Lt, [Opn, Perc, Perc Endo], [Int Fix Dev, Ext Fix Dev, Auto Tissue Sub, Synth Sub, Nonauto Tissue Sub], NQ
ØPPT[Ø,3,4][4,5,7,J,K]Z Rmvl/Finger Phalanx, Rt, [Opn, Perc, Perc Endo], [Int Fix Dev, Ext Fix Dev, Auto Tissue Sub, Synth Sub, Nonauto Tissue Sub], NQ
ØPPV[Ø,3,4][4,5,7,J,K]Z Rmvl/Finger Phalanx, Lt, [Opn, Perc, Perc Endo], [Int Fix Dev, Ext Fix Dev, Auto Tissue Sub, Synth Sub, Nonauto Tissue Sub], NQ
ØPPY[Ø,3,4]MZ Rmvl/Upr Bone, [Opn, Perc, Perc Endo], Bone Growth Stimulator, NQ
ØPQØ* Repair/Sternum
ØPQ1* Repair/Rib, Rt
ØPQ2* Repair/Rib, Lt
ØPQ5* Repair/Scapula, Rt
ØPQ6* Repair/Scapula, Lt
ØPQ7* Repair/Glenoid Cavity, Rt
ØPQ8* Repair/Glenoid Cavity, Lt
ØPQ9* Repair/Clavicle, Rt
ØPQB* Repair/Clavicle, Lt
ØPQC* Repair/Humeral Head, Rt
ØPQD* Repair/Humeral Head, Lt
ØPQF* Repair/Humeral Shaft, Rt
ØPQG* Repair/Humeral Shaft, Lt
ØPQH* Repair/Radius, Rt
ØPQJ* Repair/Radius, Lt
ØPQK* Repair/Ulna, Rt
ØPQL* Repair/Ulna, Lt
ØPRØ[Ø,3,4]JZ Replace/Sternum, [Opn, Perc, Perc Endo], Synth Sub, NQ
ØPR1[Ø,3,4]JZ Replace/Rib, Rt, [Opn, Perc, Perc Endo], Synth Sub, NQ
ØPR2[Ø,3,4]JZ Replace/Rib, Lt, [Opn, Perc, Perc Endo], Synth Sub, NQ
ØPR5[Ø,3,4]JZ Replace/Scapula, Rt, [Opn, Perc, Perc Endo], Synth Sub, NQ
ØPR6[Ø,3,4]JZ Replace/Scapula, Lt, [Opn, Perc, Perc Endo], Synth Sub, NQ
ØPR7[Ø,3,4]JZ Replace/Glenoid Cavity, Rt, [Opn, Perc, Perc Endo], Synth Sub, NQ
ØPR8[Ø,3,4]JZ Replace/Glenoid Cavity, Lt, [Opn, Perc, Perc Endo], Synth Sub, NQ
ØPR9[Ø,3,4]JZ Replace/Clavicle, Rt, [Opn, Perc, Perc Endo], Synth Sub, NQ
ØPRB[Ø,3,4]JZ Replace/Clavicle, Lt, [Opn, Perc, Perc Endo], Synth Sub, NQ
ØPRC[Ø,3,4][7,K]Z Replace/Humeral Head, Rt, [Opn, Perc, Perc Endo], [Auto Tissue Sub, Nonauto Tissue Sub], NQ
ØPRC[3,4]JZ Replace/Humeral Head, Rt, [Perc, Perc Endo], Synth Sub, NQ
ØPRD[Ø,3,4][7,K]Z Replace/Humeral Head, Lt, [Opn, Perc, Perc Endo], [Auto Tissue Sub, Nonauto Tissue Sub], NQ
ØPRD[3,4]JZ Replace/Humeral Head, Lt, [Perc, Perc Endo], Synth Sub, NQ
ØPRF* Replace/Humeral Shaft, Rt
ØPRG* Replace/Humeral Shaft, Lt

ØPRH* Replace/Radius, Rt
ØPRJ* Replace/Radius, Lt
ØPRK* Replace/Ulna, Rt
ØPRL* Replace/Ulna, Lt
ØPSØØZZ Repos Sternum, Opn Appr
ØPSØ[Ø,3,4][Ø,4]Z Repos/Sternum, [Opn, Perc, Perc Endo], [Int Fix Dev, Rigid Plate, Int Fix Dev], NQ
ØPS1ØZZ Repos Rt Rib, Opn Appr
ØPS1[Ø,3,4]4Z Repos/Rib, Rt, [Opn, Perc, Perc Endo], Int Fix Dev, NQ
ØPS2ØZZ Repos Lt Rib, Opn Appr
ØPS2[Ø,3,4]4Z Repos/Rib, Lt, [Opn, Perc, Perc Endo], Int Fix Dev, NQ
ØPS3XZZ Repos Cervical Vertebra, Ext Appr
ØPS3[Ø,3,4]4Z Repos/Cervical Vertebra, [Opn, Perc, Perc Endo], Int Fix Dev, NQ
ØPS3[Ø,4]ZZ Repos/Cervical Vertebra, [Opn, Perc Endo]
ØPS4XZZ Repos Thoracic Vertebra, Ext Appr
ØPS4[Ø,3,4]4Z Repos/Thoracic Vertebra, [Opn, Perc, Perc Endo], Int Fix Dev, NQ
ØPS4[Ø,4]ZZ Repos/Thoracic Vertebra, [Opn, Perc Endo]
ØPS5ØZZ Repos Rt Scapula, Opn Appr
ØPS5[Ø,3,4]4Z Repos/Scapula, Rt, [Opn, Perc, Perc Endo], Int Fix Dev, NQ
ØPS6ØZZ Repos Lt Scapula, Opn Appr
ØPS6[Ø,3,4]4Z Repos/Scapula, Lt, [Opn, Perc, Perc Endo], Int Fix Dev, NQ
ØPS7ØZZ Repos Rt Glenoid Cavity, Opn Appr
ØPS7[Ø,3,4]4Z Repos/Glenoid Cavity, Rt, [Opn, Perc, Perc Endo], Int Fix Dev, NQ
ØPS8ØZZ Repos Lt Glenoid Cavity, Opn Appr
ØPS8[Ø,3,4]4Z Repos/Glenoid Cavity, Lt, [Opn, Perc, Perc Endo], Int Fix Dev, NQ
ØPS9ØZZ Repos Rt Clavicle, Opn Appr
ØPS9[Ø,3,4]4Z Repos/Clavicle, Rt, [Opn, Perc, Perc Endo], Int Fix Dev, NQ
ØPSBØZZ Repos Lt Clavicle, Opn Appr
ØPSB[Ø,3,4]4Z Repos/Clavicle, Lt, [Opn, Perc, Perc Endo], Int Fix Dev, NQ
ØPSCØZZ Repos Rt Humeral Head, Opn Appr
ØPSC[Ø,3,4][4,5,6,B,C,D]Z Repos/Humeral Head, Rt, [Opn, Perc, Perc Endo], [Int Fix Dev, Ext Fix Dev, Int Fix Dev, Intramedullary Int Fix Dev, Ext Fix Dev, Monop, Ext Fix Dev, Ring, Ext Fix Dev, Hybrid], NQ
ØPSDØZZ Repos Lt Humeral Head, Opn Appr
ØPSD[Ø,3,4][4,5,6,B,C,D]Z Repos/Humeral Head, Lt, [Opn, Perc, Perc Endo], [Int Fix Dev, Ext Fix Dev, Int Fix Dev, Intramedullary Int Fix Dev, Ext Fix Dev, Monop, Ext Fix Dev, Ring, Ext Fix Dev, Hybrid], NQ
ØPSFØZZ Repos Rt Humeral Shaft, Opn Appr
ØPSF[Ø,3,4][4,5,6,B,C,D]Z Repos/Humeral Shaft, Rt, [Opn, Perc, Perc Endo], [Int Fix Dev, Ext Fix Dev, Int Fix Dev, Intramedullary Int Fix Dev, Ext Fix Dev, Monop, Ext Fix Dev, Ring, Ext Fix Dev, Hybrid], NQ
ØPSGØZZ Repos Lt Humeral Shaft, Opn Appr
ØPSG[Ø,3,4][4,5,6,B,C,D]Z Repos/Humeral Shaft, Lt, [Opn, Perc, Perc Endo], [Int Fix Dev, Ext Fix Dev, Int Fix Dev, Intramedullary Int Fix Dev, Ext Fix Dev, Monop, Ext Fix Dev, Ring, Ext Fix Dev, Hybrid], NQ
ØPSHØZZ Repos Rt Radius, Opn Appr
ØPSH[Ø,3,4][4,5,6,B,C,D]Z Repos/Radius, Rt, [Opn, Perc, Perc Endo], [Int Fix Dev, Ext Fix Dev, Int Fix Dev, Intramedullary Int Fix Dev, Ext Fix Dev, Monop, Ext Fix Dev, Ring, Ext Fix Dev, Hybrid], NQ
ØPSJØZZ Repos Lt Radius, Opn Appr
ØPSJ[Ø,3,4][4,5,6,B,C,D]Z Repos/Radius, Lt, [Opn, Perc, Perc Endo], [Int Fix Dev, Ext Fix Dev, Int Fix Dev, Intramedullary Int Fix Dev, Ext Fix Dev, Monop, Ext Fix Dev, Ring, Ext Fix Dev, Hybrid], NQ
ØPSKØZZ Repos Rt Ulna, Opn Appr
ØPSK[Ø,3,4][4,5,6,B,C,D]Z Repos/Ulna, Rt, [Opn, Perc, Perc Endo], [Int Fix Dev, Ext Fix Dev, Int Fix Dev, Intramedullary Int Fix Dev, Ext Fix Dev, Monop, Ext Fix Dev, Ring, Ext Fix Dev, Hybrid], NQ
ØPSLØZZ Repos Lt Ulna, Opn Appr
ØPSL[Ø,3,4][4,5,6,B,C,D]Z Repos/Ulna, Lt, [Opn, Perc, Perc Endo], [Int Fix Dev, Ext Fix Dev, Int Fix Dev, Intramedullary Int Fix Dev, Ext Fix Dev, Monop, Ext Fix Dev, Ring, Ext Fix Dev, Hybrid], NQ
ØPSR[Ø,3,4]5Z Repos/Thumb Phalanx, Rt, [Opn, Perc, Perc Endo], Ext Fix Dev, NQ
ØPSS[Ø,3,4]5Z Repos/Thumb Phalanx, Lt, [Opn, Perc, Perc Endo], Ext Fix Dev, NQ
ØPST[Ø,3,4]5Z Repos/Finger Phalanx, Rt, [Opn, Perc, Perc Endo], Ext Fix Dev, NQ
ØPSV[Ø,3,4]5Z Repos/Finger Phalanx, Lt, [Opn, Perc, Perc Endo], Ext Fix Dev, NQ
ØPTØØZZ Resect of Sternum, Opn Appr
ØPT1ØZZ Resect of Rt Rib, Opn Appr
ØPT2ØZZ Resect of Lt Rib, Opn Appr
ØPT5ØZZ Resect of Rt Scapula, Opn Appr
ØPT6ØZZ Resect of Lt Scapula, Opn Appr
ØPT7ØZZ Resect of Rt Glenoid Cavity, Opn Appr
ØPT8ØZZ Resect of Lt Glenoid Cavity, Opn Appr

T Transfer DRG   SP Special Payment   * Code Range   6th and 7th Character of ZZ = No Device, No Qualifier ZX = No Device, Diagnostic

Code	Description
ØPT9ØZZ	Resect of Rt Clavicle, Opn Appr
ØPTBØZZ	Resect of Lt Clavicle, Opn Appr
ØPTCØZZ	Resect of Rt Humeral Head, Opn Appr
ØPTDØZZ	Resect of Lt Humeral Head, Opn Appr
ØPTFØZZ	Resect of Rt Humeral Shaft, Opn Appr
ØPTGØZZ	Resect of Lt Humeral Shaft, Opn Appr
ØPTHØZZ	Resect of Rt Radius, Opn Appr
ØPTJØZZ	Resect of Lt Radius, Opn Appr
ØPTKØZZ	Resect of Rt Ulna, Opn Appr
ØPTLØZZ	Resect of Lt Ulna, Opn Appr
ØPTRØZZ	Resect of Rt Thumb Phalanx, Opn Appr
ØPTSØZZ	Resect of Lt Thumb Phalanx, Opn Appr
ØPTTØZZ	Resect of Rt Finger Phalanx, Opn Appr
ØPTVØZZ	Resect of Lt Finger Phalanx, Opn Appr
ØPUØ[Ø,3,4]JZ	Supl/Sternum, [Opn, Perc, Perc Endo], Synth Sub, NQ
ØPU1[Ø,3,4]JZ	Supl/Rib, Rt, [Opn, Perc, Perc Endo], Synth Sub, NQ
ØPU2[Ø,3,4]JZ	Supl/Rib, Lt, [Opn, Perc, Perc Endo], Synth Sub, NQ
ØPU3[Ø,3,4]JZ	Supl/Cervical Vertebra, [Opn, Perc, Perc Endo], Synth Sub, NQ
ØPU4[Ø,3,4]JZ	Supl/Thoracic Vertebra, [Opn, Perc, Perc Endo], Synth Sub, NQ
ØPU5[Ø,3,4]JZ	Supl/Scapula, Rt, [Opn, Perc, Perc Endo], Synth Sub, NQ
ØPU6[Ø,3,4]JZ	Supl/Scapula, Lt, [Opn, Perc, Perc Endo], Synth Sub, NQ
ØPU7[Ø,3,4]JZ	Supl/Glenoid Cavity, Rt, [Opn, Perc, Perc Endo], Synth Sub, NQ
ØPU8[Ø,3,4]JZ	Supl/Glenoid Cavity, Lt, [Opn, Perc, Perc Endo], Synth Sub, NQ
ØPU9[Ø,3,4]JZ	Supl/Clavicle, Rt, [Opn, Perc, Perc Endo], Synth Sub, NQ
ØPUB[Ø,3,4]JZ	Supl/Clavicle, Lt, [Opn, Perc, Perc Endo], Synth Sub, NQ
ØPUC*	Supl/Humeral Head, Rt
ØPUD*	Supl/Humeral Head, Lt
ØPUF*	Supl/Humeral Shaft, Rt
ØPUG*	Supl/Humeral Shaft, Lt
ØPUH*	Supl/Radius, Rt
ØPUJ*	Supl/Radius, Lt
ØPUK*	Supl/Ulna, Rt
ØPUL*	Supl/Ulna, Lt
ØQ5*	Lwr Bones, Destr
ØQ8*	Lwr Bones, Div
ØQ9D[Ø,3,4][Ø,Z]Z	Drain/Patella, Rt, [Opn, Perc, Perc Endo], [Drain Dev, No Dev], NQ
ØQ9F[Ø,3,4][Ø,Z]Z	Drain/Patella, Lt, [Opn, Perc, Perc Endo], [Drain Dev, No Dev], NQ
ØQBØ[Ø,3,4]ZZ	Exc/Lumbar Vertebra, [Opn, Perc, Perc Endo]
ØQB1[Ø,3,4]ZZ	Exc/Sacrum, [Opn, Perc, Perc Endo]
ØQB2[Ø,3,4]ZZ	Exc/Pelvic Bone, Rt, [Opn, Perc, Perc Endo]
ØQB3[Ø,3,4]ZZ	Exc/Pelvic Bone, Lt, [Opn, Perc, Perc Endo]
ØQB4[Ø,3,4]ZZ	Exc/Acetab, Rt, [Opn, Perc, Perc Endo]
ØQB5[Ø,3,4]ZZ	Exc/Acetab, Lt, [Opn, Perc, Perc Endo]
ØQB6[Ø,3,4]ZZ	Exc/Upr Femur, Rt, [Opn, Perc, Perc Endo]
ØQB7[Ø,3,4]ZZ	Exc/Upr Femur, Lt, [Opn, Perc, Perc Endo]
ØQB8[Ø,3,4]ZZ	Exc/Femor Shaft, Rt, [Opn, Perc, Perc Endo]
ØQB9[Ø,3,4]ZZ	Exc/Femor Shaft, Lt, [Opn, Perc, Perc Endo]
ØQBB[Ø,3,4]ZZ	Exc/Lwr Femur, Rt, [Opn, Perc, Perc Endo]
ØQBC[Ø,3,4]ZZ	Exc/Lwr Femur, Lt, [Opn, Perc, Perc Endo]
ØQBD[Ø,3,4]ZZ	Exc/Patella, Rt, [Opn, Perc, Perc Endo]
ØQBF[Ø,3,4]ZZ	Exc/Patella, Lt, [Opn, Perc, Perc Endo]
ØQBG[Ø,3,4]ZZ	Exc/Tibia, Rt, [Opn, Perc, Perc Endo]
ØQBH[Ø,3,4]ZZ	Exc/Tibia, Lt, [Opn, Perc, Perc Endo]
ØQBJ[Ø,3,4]ZZ	Exc/Fibula, Rt, [Opn, Perc, Perc Endo]
ØQBK[Ø,3,4]ZZ	Exc/Fibula, Lt, [Opn, Perc, Perc Endo]
ØQBL[Ø,3,4]ZZ	Exc/Tarsal, Rt, [Opn, Perc, Perc Endo]
ØQBM[Ø,3,4]ZZ	Exc/Tarsal, Lt, [Opn, Perc, Perc Endo]
ØQBN[Ø,3,4]ZZ	Exc/Metatarsal, Rt, [Opn, Perc, Perc Endo]
ØQBP[Ø,3,4]ZZ	Exc/Metatarsal, Lt, [Opn, Perc, Perc Endo]
ØQBQ[Ø,3,4]ZZ	Exc/Toe Phalanx, Rt, [Opn, Perc, Perc Endo]
ØQBR[Ø,3,4]ZZ	Exc/Toe Phalanx, Lt, [Opn, Perc, Perc Endo]
ØQBS[Ø,3,4]ZZ	Exc/Coccyx, [Opn, Perc, Perc Endo]
ØQC*	Lwr Bones, Extir
ØQHØ*	Insert/Lumbar Vertebra
ØQH1*	Insert/Sacrum
ØQH2*	Insert/Pelvic Bone, Rt
ØQH3*	Insert/Pelvic Bone, Lt
ØQH4*	Insert/Acetabulum, Rt
ØQH5*	Insert/Acetabulum, Lt
ØQH6[Ø,3,4][4,5,6,B,C,D]Z	Insert/Upr Femur, Rt, [Opn, Perc, Perc Endo], [Int Fix Dev, Ext Fix Dev, Int Fix Dev, Intramedullary Int Fix Dev, Ext Fix Dev, Monop, Ext Fix Dev, Ring, Ext Fix Dev, Hybrid], NQ
ØQH7[Ø,3,4][4,5,6,B,C,D]Z	Insert/Upr Femur, Lt, [Opn, Perc, Perc Endo], [Int Fix Dev, Ext Fix Dev, Int Fix Dev, Intramedullary Int Fix Dev, Ext Fix Dev, Monop, Ext Fix Dev, Ring, Ext Fix Dev, Hybrid], NQ
ØQH8[Ø,3,4][4,5,6,B,C,D]Z	Insert/Femor Shaft, Rt, [Opn, Perc, Perc Endo], [Int Fix Dev, Ext Fix Dev, Int Fix Dev, Intramedullary Int Fix Dev, Ext Fix Dev, Monop, Ext Fix Dev, Ring, Ext Fix Dev, Hybrid], NQ
ØQH9[Ø,3,4][4,5,6,B,C,D]Z	Insert/Femor Shaft, Lt, [Opn, Perc, Perc Endo], [Int Fix Dev, Ext Fix Dev, Int Fix Dev, Intramedullary Int Fix Dev, Ext Fix Dev, Monop, Ext Fix Dev, Ring, Ext Fix Dev, Hybrid], NQ
ØQHB[Ø,3,4][4,5,6,B,C,D]Z	Insert/Lwr Femur, Rt, [Opn, Perc, Perc Endo], [Int Fix Dev, Ext Fix Dev, Int Fix Dev, Intramedullary Int Fix Dev, Ext Fix Dev, Monop, Ext Fix Dev, Ring, Ext Fix Dev, Hybrid], NQ
ØQHC[Ø,3,4][4,5,6,B,C,D]Z	Insert/Lwr Femur, Lt, [Opn, Perc, Perc Endo], [Int Fix Dev, Ext Fix Dev, Int Fix Dev, Intramedullary Int Fix Dev, Ext Fix Dev, Monop, Ext Fix Dev, Ring, Ext Fix Dev, Hybrid], NQ
ØQHD*	Insert/Patella, Rt
ØQHF*	Insert/Patella, Lt
ØQHG[Ø,3,4][4,5,6,B,C,D]Z	Insert/Tibia, Rt, [Opn, Perc, Perc Endo], [Int Fix Dev, Ext Fix Dev, Int Fix Dev, Intramedullary Int Fix Dev, Ext Fix Dev, Monop, Ext Fix Dev, Ring, Ext Fix Dev, Hybrid], NQ
ØQHH[Ø,3,4][4,5,6,B,C,D]Z	Insert/Tibia, Lt, [Opn, Perc, Perc Endo], [Int Fix Dev, Ext Fix Dev, Int Fix Dev, Intramedullary Int Fix Dev, Ext Fix Dev, Monop, Ext Fix Dev, Ring, Ext Fix Dev, Hybrid], NQ
ØQHJ[Ø,3,4][4,5,6,B,C,D]Z	Insert/Fibula, Rt, [Opn, Perc, Perc Endo], [Int Fix Dev, Ext Fix Dev, Int Fix Dev, Intramedullary Int Fix Dev, Ext Fix Dev, Monop, Ext Fix Dev, Ring, Ext Fix Dev, Hybrid], NQ
ØQHK[Ø,3,4][4,5,6,B,C,D]Z	Insert/Fibula, Lt, [Opn, Perc, Perc Endo], [Int Fix Dev, Ext Fix Dev, Int Fix Dev, Intramedullary Int Fix Dev, Ext Fix Dev, Monop, Ext Fix Dev, Ring, Ext Fix Dev, Hybrid], NQ
ØQHL*	Insert/Tarsal, Rt
ØQHM*	Insert/Tarsal, Lt
ØQHN*	Insert/Metatarsal, Rt
ØQHP*	Insert/Metatarsal, Lt
ØQHQ*	Insert/Toe Phalanx, Rt
ØQHR*	Insert/Toe Phalanx, Lt
ØQHS*	Insert/Coccyx
ØQHY*	Insert/Lwr Bone
ØQN6*	Rls/Upr Femur, Rt
ØQN7*	Rls/Upr Femur, Lt
ØQN8*	Rls/Femor Shaft, Rt
ØQN9*	Rls/Femor Shaft, Lt
ØQNB*	Rls/Lwr Femur, Rt
ØQNC*	Rls/Lwr Femur, Lt
ØQND*	Rls/Patella, Rt
ØQNF*	Rls/Patella, Lt
ØQNG*	Rls/Tibia, Rt
ØQNH*	Rls/Tibia, Lt
ØQNJ*	Rls/Fibula, Rt
ØQNK*	Rls/Fibula, Lt
ØQNL*	Rls/Tarsal, Rt
ØQNM*	Rls/Tarsal, Lt
ØQNN*	Rls/Metatarsal, Rt
ØQNP*	Rls/Metatarsal, Lt
ØQPØ[Ø,3,4][4,7,J,K]Z	Rmvl/Lumbar Vertebra, [Opn, Perc, Perc Endo], [Int Fix Dev, Auto Tissue Sub, Synth Sub, Nonauto Tissue Sub], NQ
ØQP1[Ø,3,4][4,7,J,K]Z	Rmvl/Sacrum, [Opn, Perc, Perc Endo], [Int Fix Dev, Auto Tissue Sub, Synth Sub, Nonauto Tissue Sub], NQ
ØQP2[Ø,3,4][4,5,7,J,K]Z	Rmvl/Pelvic Bone, Rt, [Opn, Perc, Perc Endo], [Int Fix Dev, Ext Fix Dev, Auto Tissue Sub, Synth Sub, Nonauto Tissue Sub], NQ
ØQP3[Ø,3,4][4,5,7,J,K]Z	Rmvl/Pelvic Bone, Lt, [Opn, Perc, Perc Endo], [Int Fix Dev, Ext Fix Dev, Auto Tissue Sub, Synth Sub, Nonauto Tissue Sub], NQ
ØQP4[Ø,3,4][4,7,J,K]Z	Rmvl/Acetab, Rt, [Opn, Perc, Perc Endo], [Int Fix Dev, Auto Tissue Sub, Synth Sub, Nonauto Tissue Sub], NQ
ØQP5[Ø,3,4][4,7,J,K]Z	Rmvl/Acetab, Lt, [Opn, Perc, Perc Endo], [Int Fix Dev, Auto Tissue Sub, Synth Sub, Nonauto Tissue Sub], NQ
ØQP6[Ø,3,4][4,5,7,J,K]Z	Rmvl/Upr Femur, Rt, [Opn, Perc, Perc Endo], [Int Fix Dev, Ext Fix Dev, Auto Tissue Sub, Synth Sub, Nonauto Tissue Sub], NQ
ØQP7[Ø,3,4][4,5,7,J,K]Z	Rmvl/Upr Femur, Lt, [Opn, Perc, Perc Endo], [Int Fix Dev, Ext Fix Dev, Auto Tissue Sub, Synth Sub, Nonauto Tissue Sub], NQ
ØQP8[Ø,3,4][4,5,7,J,K]Z	Rmvl/Femor Shaft, Rt, [Opn, Perc, Perc Endo], [Int Fix Dev, Ext Fix Dev, Auto Tissue Sub, Synth Sub, Nonauto Tissue Sub], NQ
ØQP9[Ø,3,4][4,5,7,J,K]Z	Rmvl/Femor Shaft, Lt, [Opn, Perc, Perc Endo], [Int Fix Dev, Ext Fix Dev, Auto Tissue Sub, Synth Sub, Nonauto Tissue Sub], NQ
ØQPB[Ø,3,4][4,5,7,J,K]Z	Rmvl/Lwr Femur, Rt, [Opn, Perc, Perc Endo], [Int Fix Dev, Ext Fix Dev, Auto Tissue Sub, Synth Sub, Nonauto Tissue Sub], NQ
ØQPC[Ø,3,4][4,5,7,J,K]Z	Rmvl/Lwr Femur, Lt, [Opn, Perc, Perc Endo], [Int Fix Dev, Ext Fix Dev, Auto Tissue Sub, Synth Sub, Nonauto Tissue Sub], NQ

MDC 21: Injuries, Poisonings And Toxic Effects Of Drugs—SURGICAL

Surgical   **Medical**   **CC Indicator**   **MCC Indicator**   **Procedure Proxy**   **PDxMCC** PDx acts as own MCC   **PDxCC** PDx acts as own CC

0QPD[0,3,4][4,5,7,J,K]Z Rmvl/Patella, Rt, [Opn, Perc, Perc Endo], [Int Fix Dev, Ext Fix Dev, Auto Tissue Sub, Synth Sub, Nonauto Tissue Sub], NQ

0QPF[0,3,4][4,5,7,J,K]Z Rmvl/Patella, Lt, [Opn, Perc, Perc Endo], [Int Fix Dev, Ext Fix Dev, Auto Tissue Sub, Synth Sub, Nonauto Tissue Sub], NQ

0QPG[0,3,4][4,5,7,J,K]Z Rmvl/Tibia, Rt, [Opn, Perc, Perc Endo], [Int Fix Dev, Ext Fix Dev, Auto Tissue Sub, Synth Sub, Nonauto Tissue Sub], NQ

0QPH[0,3,4][4,5,7,J,K]Z Rmvl/Tibia, Lt, [Opn, Perc, Perc Endo], [Int Fix Dev, Ext Fix Dev, Auto Tissue Sub, Synth Sub, Nonauto Tissue Sub], NQ

0QPJ[0,3,4][4,5,7,J,K]Z Rmvl/Fibula, Rt, [Opn, Perc, Perc Endo], [Int Fix Dev, Ext Fix Dev, Auto Tissue Sub, Synth Sub, Nonauto Tissue Sub], NQ

0QPK[0,3,4][4,5,7,J,K]Z Rmvl/Fibula, Lt, [Opn, Perc, Perc Endo], [Int Fix Dev, Ext Fix Dev, Auto Tissue Sub, Synth Sub, Nonauto Tissue Sub], NQ

0QPL[0,3,4][4,5,7,J,K]Z Rmvl/Tarsal, Rt, [Opn, Perc, Perc Endo], [Int Fix Dev, Ext Fix Dev, Auto Tissue Sub, Synth Sub, Nonauto Tissue Sub], NQ

0QPM[0,3,4][4,5,7,J,K]Z Rmvl/Tarsal, Lt, [Opn, Perc, Perc Endo], [Int Fix Dev, Ext Fix Dev, Auto Tissue Sub, Synth Sub, Nonauto Tissue Sub], NQ

0QPN[0,3,4][4,5,7,J,K]Z Rmvl/Metatarsal, Rt, [Opn, Perc, Perc Endo], [Int Fix Dev, Ext Fix Dev, Auto Tissue Sub, Synth Sub, Nonauto Tissue Sub], NQ

0QPP[0,3,4][4,5,7,J,K]Z Rmvl/Metatarsal, Lt, [Opn, Perc, Perc Endo], [Int Fix Dev, Ext Fix Dev, Auto Tissue Sub, Synth Sub, Nonauto Tissue Sub], NQ

0QPQ[0,3,4][4,5,7,J,K]Z Rmvl/Toe Phalanx, Rt, [Opn, Perc, Perc Endo], [Int Fix Dev, Ext Fix Dev, Auto Tissue Sub, Synth Sub, Nonauto Tissue Sub], NQ

0QPR[0,3,4][4,5,7,J,K]Z Rmvl/Toe Phalanx, Lt, [Opn, Perc, Perc Endo], [Int Fix Dev, Ext Fix Dev, Auto Tissue Sub, Synth Sub, Nonauto Tissue Sub], NQ

0QPS[0,3,4][4,7,J,K]Z Rmvl/Coccyx, [Opn, Perc, Perc Endo], [Int Fix Dev, Auto Tissue Sub, Synth Sub, Nonauto Tissue Sub], NQ

0QPY[0,3,4]MZ Rmvl/Lwr Bone, [Opn, Perc, Perc Endo], Bone Growth Stimulator, NQ

0QQ6* Repair/Upr Femur, Rt
0QQ7* Repair/Upr Femur, Lt
0QQ8* Repair/Femor Shaft, Rt
0QQ9* Repair/Femor Shaft, Lt
0QQB* Repair/Lwr Femur, Rt
0QQC* Repair/Lwr Femur, Lt
0QQD[0,4,X]ZZ Rpr/Patella, Rt, [Opn, Perc Endo, Ext]
0QQF[0,4,X]ZZ Rpr/Patella, Lt, [Opn, Perc Endo, Ext]
0QQG* Repair/Tibia, Rt
0QQH* Repair/Tibia, Lt
0QQJ* Repair/Fibula, Rt
0QQK* Repair/Fibula, Lt
0QQL* Repair/Tarsal, Rt
0QQM* Repair/Tarsal, Lt
0QQN* Repair/Metatarsal, Rt
0QQP* Repair/Metatarsal, Lt
0QQQ* Repair/Toe Phalanx, Rt
0QQR* Repair/Toe Phalanx, Lt
0QR4[0,3,4]JZ Replace/Acetab, Rt, [Opn, Perc, Perc Endo], Synth Sub, NQ
0QR5[0,3,4]JZ Replace/Acetab, Lt, [Opn, Perc, Perc Endo], Synth Sub, NQ
0QR6* Replace/Upr Femur, Rt
0QR7* Replace/Upr Femur, Lt
0QR8* Replace/Femor Shaft, Rt
0QR9* Replace/Femor Shaft, Lt
0QRB* Replace/Lwr Femur, Rt
0QRC* Replace/Lwr Femur, Lt
0QRD* Replace/Patella, Rt
0QRF* Replace/Patella, Lt
0QRG* Replace/Tibia, Rt
0QRH* Replace/Tibia, Lt
0QRJ* Replace/Fibula, Rt
0QRK* Replace/Fibula, Lt
0QRL* Replace/Tarsal, Rt
0QRM* Replace/Tarsal, Lt
0QRN* Replace/Metatarsal, Rt
0QRP* Replace/Metatarsal, Lt
0QS0XZZ Repos Lumbar Vertebra, Ext Appr
0QS0[0,3,4]4Z Repos/Lumbar Vertebra, [Opn, Perc, Perc Endo], Int Fix Dev, NQ
0QS0[0,4]ZZ Repos/Lumbar Vertebra, [Opn, Perc Endo]
0QS1XZZ Repos Sacrum, Ext Appr
0QS1[0,3,4]4Z Repos/Sacrum, [Opn, Perc, Perc Endo], Int Fix Dev, NQ
0QS1[0,4]ZZ Repos/Sacrum, [Opn, Perc Endo]
0QS20ZZ Repos Rt Pelvic Bone, Opn Appr
0QS2[0,3,4][4,5]Z Repos/Pelvic Bone, Rt, [Opn, Perc, Perc Endo], [Int Fix Dev, Ext Fix Dev], NQ
0QS30ZZ Repos Lt Pelvic Bone, Opn Appr

0QS3[0,3,4][4,5]Z Repos/Pelvic Bone, Lt, [Opn, Perc, Perc Endo], [Int Fix Dev, Ext Fix Dev], NQ
0QS40ZZ Repos Rt Acetabulum, Opn Appr
0QS4[0,3,4]4Z Repos/Acetab, Rt, [Opn, Perc, Perc Endo], Int Fix Dev, NQ
0QS50ZZ Repos Lt Acetabulum, Opn Appr
0QS5[0,3,4]4Z Repos/Acetab, Lt, [Opn, Perc, Perc Endo], Int Fix Dev, NQ
0QS60ZZ Repos Rt Upr Femur, Opn Appr
0QS6[0,3,4][4,5,6,B,C,D]Z Repos/Upr Femur, Rt, [Opn, Perc, Perc Endo], [Int Fix Dev, Ext Fix Dev, Intramedullary Int Fix Dev, Ext Fix Dev, Monop, Ext Fix Dev, Ring, Ext Fix Dev, Hybrid], NQ
0QS70ZZ Repos Lt Upr Femur, Opn Appr
0QS7[0,3,4][4,5,6,B,C,D]Z Repos/Upr Femur, Lt, [Opn, Perc, Perc Endo], [Int Fix Dev, Ext Fix Dev, Int Fix Dev, Intramedullary Int Fix Dev, Ext Fix Dev, Monop, Ext Fix Dev, Ring, Ext Fix Dev, Hybrid], NQ
0QS80ZZ Repos Rt Femor Shaft, Opn Appr
0QS8[0,3,4][4,5,6,B,C,D]Z Repos/Femor Shaft, Rt, [Opn, Perc, Perc Endo], [Int Fix Dev, Ext Fix Dev, Int Fix Dev, Intramedullary Int Fix Dev, Ext Fix Dev, Monop, Ext Fix Dev, Ring, Ext Fix Dev, Hybrid], NQ
0QS90ZZ Repos Lt Femor Shaft, Opn Appr
0QS9[0,3,4][4,5,6,B,C,D]Z Repos/Femor Shaft, Lt, [Opn, Perc, Perc Endo], [Int Fix Dev, Ext Fix Dev, Int Fix Dev, Intramedullary Int Fix Dev, Ext Fix Dev, Monop, Ext Fix Dev, Ring, Ext Fix Dev, Hybrid], NQ
0QSB0ZZ Repos Rt Lwr Femur, Opn Appr
0QSB[0,3,4][4,5,6,B,C,D]Z Repos/Lwr Femur, Rt, [Opn, Perc, Perc Endo], [Int Fix Dev, Ext Fix Dev, Int Fix Dev, Intramedullary Int Fix Dev, Ext Fix Dev, Monop, Ext Fix Dev, Ring, Ext Fix Dev, Hybrid], NQ
0QSC0ZZ Repos Lt Lwr Femur, Opn Appr
0QSC[0,3,4][4,5,6,B,C,D]Z Repos/Lwr Femur, Lt, [Opn, Perc, Perc Endo], [Int Fix Dev, Ext Fix Dev, Int Fix Dev, Intramedullary Int Fix Dev, Ext Fix Dev, Monop, Ext Fix Dev, Ring, Ext Fix Dev, Hybrid], NQ
0QSD0ZZ Repos Rt Patella, Opn Appr
0QSD[0,3,4][4,5]Z Repos/Patella, Rt, [Opn, Perc, Perc Endo], [Int Fix Dev, Ext Fix Dev], NQ
0QSF0ZZ Repos Lt Patella, Opn Appr
0QSF[0,3,4][4,5]Z Repos/Patella, Lt, [Opn, Perc, Perc Endo], [Int Fix Dev, Ext Fix Dev], NQ
0QSG0ZZ Repos Rt Tibia, Opn Appr
0QSG[0,3,4][4,5,6,B,C,D]Z Repos/Tibia, Rt, [Opn, Perc, Perc Endo], [Int Fix Dev, Ext Fix Dev, Int Fix Dev, Intramedullary Int Fix Dev, Ext Fix Dev, Monop, Ext Fix Dev, Ring, Ext Fix Dev, Hybrid], NQ
0QSH0ZZ Repos Lt Tibia, Opn Appr
0QSH[0,3,4][4,5,6,B,C,D]Z Repos/Tibia, Lt, [Opn, Perc, Perc Endo], [Int Fix Dev, Ext Fix Dev, Int Fix Dev, Intramedullary Int Fix Dev, Ext Fix Dev, Monop, Ext Fix Dev, Ring, Ext Fix Dev, Hybrid], NQ
0QSJ0ZZ Repos Rt Fibula, Opn Appr
0QSJ[0,3,4][4,5,6,B,C,D]Z Repos/Fibula, Rt, [Opn, Perc, Perc Endo], [Int Fix Dev, Ext Fix Dev, Int Fix Dev, Intramedullary Int Fix Dev, Ext Fix Dev, Monop, Ext Fix Dev, Ring, Ext Fix Dev, Hybrid], NQ
0QSK0ZZ Repos Lt Fibula, Opn Appr
0QSK[0,3,4][4,5,6,B,C,D]Z Repos/Fibula, Lt, [Opn, Perc, Perc Endo], [Int Fix Dev, Ext Fix Dev, Int Fix Dev, Intramedullary Int Fix Dev, Ext Fix Dev, Monop, Ext Fix Dev, Ring, Ext Fix Dev, Hybrid], NQ
0QSL0ZZ Repos Rt Tarsal, Opn Appr
0QSL[0,3,4][4,5]Z Repos/Tarsal, Rt, [Opn, Perc, Perc Endo], [Int Fix Dev, Ext Fix Dev], NQ
0QSM0ZZ Repos Lt Tarsal, Opn Appr
0QSM[0,3,4][4,5]Z Repos/Tarsal, Lt, [Opn, Perc, Perc Endo], [Int Fix Dev, Ext Fix Dev], NQ
0QSN0ZZ Repos Rt Metatarsal, Opn Appr
0QSN[0,3,4][4,5]Z Repos/Metatarsal, Rt, [Opn, Perc, Perc Endo], [Int Fix Dev, Ext Fix Dev], NQ
0QSP0ZZ Repos Lt Metatarsal, Opn Appr
0QSP[0,3,4][4,5]Z Repos/Metatarsal, Lt, [Opn, Perc, Perc Endo], [Int Fix Dev, Ext Fix Dev], NQ
0QSQ0ZZ Repos Rt Toe Phalanx, Opn Appr
0QSQ[0,3,4][4,5]Z Repos/Toe Phalanx, Rt, [Opn, Perc, Perc Endo], [Int Fix Dev, Ext Fix Dev], NQ
0QSR0ZZ Repos Lt Toe Phalanx, Opn Appr
0QSR[0,3,4][4,5]Z Repos/Toe Phalanx, Lt, [Opn, Perc, Perc Endo], [Int Fix Dev, Ext Fix Dev], NQ
0QSS* Repos/Coccyx
0QT* Lwr Bones, Resect
0QU0[0,3,4]JZ Supl/Lumbar Vertebra, [Opn, Perc, Perc Endo], Synth Sub, NQ
0QU1[0,3,4]JZ Supl/Sacrum, [Opn, Perc, Perc Endo], Synth Sub, NQ
0QU4[0,3,4]JZ Supl/Acetab, Rt, [Opn, Perc, Perc Endo], Synth Sub, NQ
0QU5[0,3,4]JZ Supl/Acetab, Lt, [Opn, Perc, Perc Endo], Synth Sub, NQ
0QU6* Supl/Upr Femur, Rt
0QU7* Supl/Upr Femur, Lt
0QU8* Supl/Femor Shaft, Rt
0QU9* Supl/Femor Shaft, Lt

T Transfer DRG   SP Special Payment   * Code Range   6th and 7th Character of ZZ = No Device, No Qualifier ZX = No Device, Diagnostic

348   MS-DRG Version 33.0   © 2015 Optum360, LLC

ØQUB*	Supl/Lwr Femur, Rt
ØQUC*	Supl/Lwr Femur, Lt
ØQUD*	Supl/Patella, Rt
ØQUF*	Supl/Patella, Lt
ØQUG*	Supl/Tibia, Rt
ØQUH*	Supl/Tibia, Lt
ØQUJ*	Supl/Fibula, Rt
ØQUK*	Supl/Fibula, Lt
ØQUL*	Supl/Tarsal, Rt
ØQUM*	Supl/Tarsal, Lt
ØQUN*	Supl/Metatarsal, Rt
ØQUP*	Supl/Metatarsal, Lt
ØQWD[Ø,3,4][4,5,7,J,K]Z	Rev/Patella, Rt, [Opn, Perc, Perc Endo], [Int Fix Dev, Ext Fix Dev, Auto Tissue Sub, Synth Sub, Nonauto Tissue Sub], NQ
ØQWF[Ø,3,4][4,5,7,J,K]Z	Rev/Patella, Lt, [Opn, Perc, Perc Endo], [Int Fix Dev, Ext Fix Dev, Auto Tissue Sub, Synth Sub, Nonauto Tissue Sub], NQ
ØR5Ø*	Destr/Occipital-cervical Jt
ØR51*	Destr/Cervical Vert Jt
ØR53ØZZ	Destr of Cervical Vert Disc, Opn Appr
ØR54*	Destr/Cervicothoracic Vert Jt
ØR55ØZZ	Destr of Cervicothoracic Vert Disc, Opn Appr
ØR56*	Destr/Thoracic Vert Jt
ØR59ØZZ	Destr of Thoracic Vert Disc, Opn Appr
ØR5A*	Destr/Thoracolumbar Vert Jt
ØR5BØZZ	Destr of Thoracolumbar Vert Disc, Opn Appr
ØR5C*	Destr/Temporomandibular Jt, Rt
ØR5D*	Destr/Temporomandibular Jt, Lt
ØR5E*	Destr/Sternoclavicular Jt, Rt
ØR5F*	Destr/Sternoclavicular Jt, Lt
ØR5G*	Destr/Acromioclavicular Jt, Rt
ØR5H*	Destr/Acromioclavicular Jt, Lt
ØR5J*	Destr/Shldr Jt, Rt
ØR5K*	Destr/Shldr Jt, Lt
ØR5L*	Destr/Elbow Jt, Rt
ØR5M*	Destr/Elbow Jt, Lt
ØR9EØ[Ø,Z]Z	Drain/Sternoclavicular Jt, Rt, Opn, [Drain Dev, No Dev], NQ
ØR9FØ[Ø,Z]Z	Drain/Sternoclavicular Jt, Lt, Opn, [Drain Dev, No Dev], NQ
ØR9GØ[Ø,Z]Z	Drain/Acromioclavicular Jt, Rt, Opn, [Drain Dev, No Dev], NQ
ØR9HØ[Ø,Z]Z	Drain/Acromioclavicular Jt, Lt, Opn, [Drain Dev, No Dev], NQ
ØR9JØ[Ø,Z]Z	Drain/Shldr Jt, Rt, Opn, [Drain Dev, No Dev], NQ
ØR9KØ[Ø,Z]Z	Drain/Shldr Jt, Lt, Opn, [Drain Dev, No Dev], NQ
ØR9LØ[Ø,Z]Z	Drain/Elbow Jt, Rt, Opn, [Drain Dev, No Dev], NQ
ØR9MØ[Ø,Z]Z	Drain/Elbow Jt, Lt, Opn, [Drain Dev, No Dev], NQ
ØRBØ[Ø,3,4]ZZ	Exc/Occipital-cervical Jt, [Opn, Perc, Perc Endo]
ØRB1[Ø,3,4]ZZ	Exc/Cervical Vert Jt, [Opn, Perc, Perc Endo]
ØRB3[Ø,3,4]ZZ	Exc/Cervical Vert Disc, [Opn, Perc, Perc Endo]
ØRB4[Ø,3,4]ZZ	Exc/Cervicothoracic Vert Jt, [Opn, Perc, Perc Endo]
ØRB5[Ø,3,4]ZZ	Exc/Cervicothoracic Vert Disc, [Opn, Perc, Perc Endo]
ØRB6[Ø,3,4]ZZ	Exc/Thoracic Vert Jt, [Opn, Perc, Perc Endo]
ØRB9[Ø,3,4]ZZ	Exc/Thoracic Vert Disc, [Opn, Perc, Perc Endo]
ØRBA[Ø,3,4]ZZ	Exc/Thoracolumbar Vert Jt, [Opn, Perc, Perc Endo]
ØRBB[Ø,3,4]ZZ	Exc/Thoracolumbar Vert Disc, [Opn, Perc, Perc Endo]
ØRBC[Ø,3,4]ZZ	Exc/Temporomandibular Jt, Rt, [Opn, Perc, Perc Endo]
ØRBD[Ø,3,4]ZZ	Exc/Temporomandibular Jt, Lt, [Opn, Perc, Perc Endo]
ØRBE[Ø,3,4]ZZ	Exc/Sternoclavicular Jt, Rt, [Opn, Perc, Perc Endo]
ØRBF[Ø,3,4]ZZ	Exc/Sternoclavicular Jt, Lt, [Opn, Perc, Perc Endo]
ØRBG[Ø,3,4]ZZ	Exc/Acromioclavicular Jt, Rt, [Opn, Perc, Perc Endo]
ØRBH[Ø,3,4]ZZ	Exc/Acromioclavicular Jt, Lt, [Opn, Perc, Perc Endo]
ØRBJ[Ø,3,4]ZZ	Exc/Shldr Jt, Rt, [Opn, Perc, Perc Endo]
ØRBK[Ø,3,4]ZZ	Exc/Shldr Jt, Lt, [Opn, Perc, Perc Endo]
ØRBL[Ø,3,4]ZZ	Exc/Elbow Jt, Rt, [Opn, Perc, Perc Endo]
ØRBM[Ø,3,4]ZZ	Exc/Elbow Jt, Lt, [Opn, Perc, Perc Endo]
ØRCC*	Extir/Temporomandibular Jt, Rt
ØRCD*	Extir/Temporomandibular Jt, Lt
ØRCE*	Extir/Sternoclavicular Jt, Rt
ØRCF*	Extir/Sternoclavicular Jt, Lt
ØRCG*	Extir/Acromioclavicular Jt, Rt
ØRCH*	Extir/Acromioclavicular Jt, Lt
ØRCJ*	Extir/Shldr Jt, Rt
ØRCK*	Extir/Shldr Jt, Lt
ØRCL*	Extir/Elbow Jt, Rt
ØRCM*	Extir/Elbow Jt, Lt
ØRGØ*	Fusion/Occipital-cervical Jt
ØRG1*	Fusion/Cervical Vert Jt
ØRG2*	Fusion/Cervical Vert Jts, 2 or more
ØRG4*	Fusion/Cervicothoracic Vert Jt
ØRG6*	Fusion/Thoracic Vert Jt
ØRG7*	Fusion/Thoracic Vert Jts, 2 to 7
ØRG8*	Fusion/Thoracic Vert Jts, 8 or more
ØRGA*	Fusion/Thoracolumbar Vert Jt
ØRGC*	Fusion/Temporomandibular Jt, Rt
ØRGD*	Fusion/Temporomandibular Jt, Lt
ØRGL*	Fusion/Elbow Jt, Rt
ØRGM*	Fusion/Elbow Jt, Lt
ØRHØ[Ø,3,4][B,C,D]Z	Insert/Occipital-cervical Jt, [Opn, Perc, Perc Endo], [Spinal Stabliz Dev, Interspinous Process, Spinal Stabliz Dev, Pedicle-Based, Spinal Stabliz Dev, Facet Replace], NQ
ØRH1[Ø,3,4][B,C,D]Z	Insert/Cervical Vert Jt, [Opn, Perc, Perc Endo], [Spinal Stabliz Dev, Interspinous Process, Spinal Stabliz Dev, Pedicle-Based, Spinal Stabliz Dev, Facet Replace], NQ
ØRH4[Ø,3,4][B,C,D]Z	Insert/Cervicothoracic Vert Jt, [Opn, Perc, Perc Endo], [Spinal Stabliz Dev, Interspinous Process, Spinal Stabliz Dev, Pedicle-Based, Spinal Stabliz Dev, Facet Replace], NQ
ØRH6[Ø,3,4][B,C,D]Z	Insert/Thoracic Vert Jt, [Opn, Perc, Perc Endo], [Spinal Stabliz Dev, Interspinous Process, Spinal Stabliz Dev, Pedicle-Based, Spinal Stabliz Dev, Facet Replace], NQ
ØRHA[Ø,3,4][B,C,D]Z	Insert/Thoracolumbar Vert Jt, [Opn, Perc, Perc Endo], [Spinal Stabliz Dev, Interspinous Process, Spinal Stabliz Dev, Pedicle-Based, Spinal Stabliz Dev, Facet Replace], NQ
ØRHE[Ø,3,4]4Z	Insert/Sternoclavicular Jt, Rt, [Opn, Perc, Perc Endo], Int Fix Dev, NQ
ØRHF[Ø,3,4]4Z	Insert/Sternoclavicular Jt, Lt, [Opn, Perc, Perc Endo], Int Fix Dev, NQ
ØRHG[Ø,3,4]4Z	Insert/Acromioclavicular Jt, Rt, [Opn, Perc, Perc Endo], Int Fix Dev, NQ
ØRHH[Ø,3,4]4Z	Insert/Acromioclavicular Jt, Lt, [Opn, Perc, Perc Endo], Int Fix Dev, NQ
ØRHJ[Ø,3,4]Z	Insert/Shldr Jt, Rt, [Opn, Perc, Perc Endo], Int Fix Dev, NQ
ØRHK[Ø,3,4]Z	Insert/Shldr Jt, Lt, [Opn, Perc, Perc Endo], Int Fix Dev, NQ
ØRHL[Ø,3,4][4,5]Z	Insert/Elbow Jt, Rt, [Opn, Perc, Perc Endo], [Int Fix Dev, Ext Fix Dev], NQ
ØRHM[Ø,3,4][4,5]Z	Insert/Elbow Jt, Lt, [Opn, Perc, Perc Endo], [Int Fix Dev, Ext Fix Dev], NQ
ØRJØ4ZZ	Inspect of Occipital-cervical Jt, Perc Endo Appr
ØRJ14ZZ	Inspect of Cervical Vert Jt, Perc Endo Appr
ØRJ34ZZ	Inspect of Cervical Vert Disc, Perc Endo Appr
ØRJ44ZZ	Inspect of C-thor Jt, Perc Endo Appr
ØRJ54ZZ	Inspect of C-thor Disc, Perc Endo Appr
ØRJ64ZZ	Inspect of Thoracic Vert Jt, Perc Endo Appr
ØRJ94ZZ	Inspect of Thoracic Vert Disc, Perc Endo Appr
ØRJA4ZZ	Inspect of T-lum Jt, Perc Endo Appr
ØRJB4ZZ	Inspect of T-lum Disc, Perc Endo Appr
ØRJC[Ø,3,4]ZZ	Inspect/Temporomandibular Jt, Rt, [Opn, Perc, Perc Endo]
ØRJD[Ø,3,4]ZZ	Inspect/Temporomandibular Jt, Lt, [Opn, Perc, Perc Endo]
ØRJE[Ø,4]ZZ	Inspect/Sternoclavicular Jt, Rt, [Opn, Perc Endo]
ØRJF[Ø,4]ZZ	Inspect/Sternoclavicular Jt, Lt, [Opn, Perc Endo]
ØRJG[Ø,4]ZZ	Inspect/Acromioclavicular Jt, Rt, [Opn, Perc Endo]
ØRJH[Ø,4]ZZ	Inspect/Acromioclavicular Jt, Lt, [Opn, Perc Endo]
ØRJJ[Ø,4]ZZ	Inspect/Shldr Jt, Rt, [Opn, Perc Endo]
ØRJK[Ø,4]ZZ	Inspect/Shldr Jt, Lt, [Opn, Perc Endo]
ØRJL[Ø,4]ZZ	Inspect/Elbow Jt, Rt, [Opn, Perc Endo]
ØRJM[Ø,4]ZZ	Inspect/Elbow Jt, Lt, [Opn, Perc Endo]
ØRJN4ZZ	Inspect of Rt Wrist Jt, Perc Endo Appr
ØRJP4ZZ	Inspect of Lt Wrist Jt, Perc Endo Appr
ØRJQ4ZZ	Inspect of Rt Carpal Jt, Perc Endo Appr
ØRJR4ZZ	Inspect of Lt Carpal Jt, Perc Endo Appr
ØRJS4ZZ	Inspect of Rt Metacarpocarp Jt, Perc Endo Appr
ØRJT4ZZ	Inspect of Lt Metacarpocarpal Jt, Perc Endo Appr
ØRJU4ZZ	Inspect of Rt Metacarpophal Jt, Perc Endo Appr
ØRJV4ZZ	Inspect of Lt Metacarpophal Jt, Perc Endo Appr
ØRJW4ZZ	Inspect of Rt Finger Phalanx Jt, Perc Endo Appr
ØRJX4ZZ	Inspect of Lt Finger Phalanx Jt, Perc Endo Appr
ØRNØ[Ø,3,4]ZZ	Rls/Occipital-cervical Jt, [Opn, Perc, Perc Endo]
ØRN1[Ø,3,4]ZZ	Rls/Cervical Vert Jt, [Opn, Perc, Perc Endo]
ØRN3[Ø,3,4]ZZ	Rls/Cervical Vert Disc, [Opn, Perc, Perc Endo]
ØRN4[Ø,3,4]ZZ	Rls/Cervicothoracic Vert Jt, [Opn, Perc, Perc Endo]
ØRN5[Ø,3,4]ZZ	Rls/Cervicothoracic Vert Disc, [Opn, Perc, Perc Endo]
ØRN6[Ø,3,4]ZZ	Rls/Thoracic Vert Jt, [Opn, Perc, Perc Endo]
ØRN9[Ø,3,4]ZZ	Rls/Thoracic Vert Disc, [Opn, Perc, Perc Endo]
ØRNA[Ø,3,4]ZZ	Rls/Thoracolumbar Vert Jt, [Opn, Perc, Perc Endo]
ØRNB[Ø,3,4]ZZ	Rls/Thoracolumbar Vert Disc, [Opn, Perc, Perc Endo]
ØRNC[Ø,3,4]ZZ	Rls/Temporomandibular Jt, Rt, [Opn, Perc, Perc Endo]
ØRND[Ø,3,4]ZZ	Rls/Temporomandibular Jt, Lt, [Opn, Perc, Perc Endo]
ØRNE[Ø,3,4]ZZ	Rls/Sternoclavicular Jt, Rt, [Opn, Perc, Perc Endo]
ØRNF[Ø,3,4]ZZ	Rls/Sternoclavicular Jt, Lt, [Opn, Perc, Perc Endo]
ØRNG[Ø,3,4]ZZ	Rls/Acromioclavicular Jt, Rt, [Opn, Perc, Perc Endo]
ØRNH[Ø,3,4]ZZ	Rls/Acromioclavicular Jt, Lt, [Opn, Perc, Perc Endo]
ØRNJ[Ø,3,4]ZZ	Rls/Shldr Jt, Rt, [Opn, Perc, Perc Endo]
ØRNK[Ø,3,4]ZZ	Rls/Shldr Jt, Lt, [Opn, Perc, Perc Endo]
ØRNL[Ø,3,4]ZZ	Rls/Elbow Jt, Rt, [Opn, Perc, Perc Endo]

Surgical **Medical** **CC Indicator** **MCC Indicator** **Procedure Proxy** PDxMCC PDx acts as own MCC PDxCC PDx acts as own CC

MDC 21: Injuries, Poisonings And Toxic Effects Of Drugs—SURGICAL

Code	Description
ØRNM[Ø,3,4]ZZ	Rls/Elbow Jt, Lt, [Opn, Perc, Perc Endo]
ØRPØ[Ø,3,4]JZ	Rmvl/Occipital-cervical Jt, [Opn, Perc, Perc Endo], Synth Sub, NQ
ØRP1[Ø,3,4]JZ	Rmvl/Cervical Vert Jt, [Opn, Perc, Perc Endo], Synth Sub, NQ
ØRP3[Ø,3,4]JZ	Rmvl/Cervical Vert Disc, [Opn, Perc, Perc Endo], Synth Sub, NQ
ØRP4[Ø,3,4]JZ	Rmvl/Cervicothoracic Vert Jt, [Opn, Perc, Perc Endo], Synth Sub, NQ
ØRP5[Ø,3,4]JZ	Rmvl/Cervicothoracic Vert Disc, [Opn, Perc, Perc Endo], Synth Sub, NQ
ØRP6[Ø,3,4]JZ	Rmvl/Thoracic Vert Jt, [Opn, Perc, Perc Endo], Synth Sub, NQ
ØRP9[Ø,3,4]JZ	Rmvl/Thoracic Vert Disc, [Opn, Perc, Perc Endo], Synth Sub, NQ
ØRPA[Ø,3,4]JZ	Rmvl/Thoracolumbar Vert Jt, [Opn, Perc, Perc Endo], Synth Sub, NQ
ØRPB[Ø,3,4]JZ	Rmvl/Thoracolumbar Vert Disc, [Opn, Perc, Perc Endo], Synth Sub, NQ
ØRPC[Ø,3,4,X]4Z	Rmvl/Temporomandibular Jt, Rt, [Opn, Perc, Perc Endo, Ext], Int Fix Dev, NQ
ØRPD[Ø,3,4,X]4Z	Rmvl/Temporomandibular Jt, Lt, [Opn, Perc, Perc Endo, Ext], Int Fix Dev, NQ
ØRPE[Ø,3,4][Ø,3,4,7,J,K]Z	Rmvl/Sternoclavicular Jt, Rt, [Opn, Perc, Perc Endo], [Drain Dev, Inf Dev, Int Fix Dev, Auto Tissue Sub, Synth Sub, Nonauto Tissue Sub], NQ
ØRPF[Ø,3,4][Ø,3,4,7,J,K]Z	Rmvl/Sternoclavicular Jt, Lt, [Opn, Perc, Perc Endo], [Drain Dev, Inf Dev, Int Fix Dev, Auto Tissue Sub, Synth Sub, Nonauto Tissue Sub], NQ
ØRPG[Ø,3,4][Ø,3,4,7,J,K]Z	Rmvl/Acromioclavicular Jt, Rt, [Opn, Perc, Perc Endo], [Drain Dev, Inf Dev, Int Fix Dev, Auto Tissue Sub, Synth Sub, Nonauto Tissue Sub], NQ
ØRPH[Ø,3,4][Ø,3,4,7,J,K]Z	Rmvl/Acromioclavicular Jt, Lt, [Opn, Perc, Perc Endo], [Drain Dev, Inf Dev, Int Fix Dev, Auto Tissue Sub, Synth Sub, Nonauto Tissue Sub], NQ
ØRPJ[Ø,3,4][Ø,3,4,7,J,K]Z	Rmvl/Shldr Jt, Rt, [Opn, Perc, Perc Endo], [Drain Dev, Inf Dev, Int Fix Dev, Auto Tissue Sub, Synth Sub, Nonauto Tissue Sub], NQ
ØRPK[Ø,3,4][Ø,3,4,7,J,K]Z	Rmvl/Shldr Jt, Lt, [Opn, Perc, Perc Endo], [Drain Dev, Inf Dev, Int Fix Dev, Auto Tissue Sub, Synth Sub, Nonauto Tissue Sub], NQ
ØRPL[Ø,3,4][Ø,3,4,5,7,J,K]Z	Rmvl/Elbow Jt, Rt, [Opn, Perc, Perc Endo], [Drain Dev, Inf Dev, Int Fix Dev, Ext Fix Dev, Auto Tissue Sub, Synth Sub, Nonauto Tissue Sub], NQ
ØRPM[Ø,3,4][Ø,3,4,5,7,J,K]Z	Rmvl/Elbow Jt, Lt, [Opn, Perc, Perc Endo], [Drain Dev, Inf Dev, Int Fix Dev, Ext Fix Dev, Auto Tissue Sub, Synth Sub, Nonauto Tissue Sub], NQ
ØRQ3ØZZ	Repair Cervical Vert Disc, Opn Appr
ØRQ9ØZZ	Repair Thoracic Vert Disc, Opn Appr
ØRQBØZZ	Repair Thoracolumbar Vert Disc, Opn Appr
ØRQC[Ø,3,4]ZZ	Rpr/Temporomandibular Jt, Rt, [Opn, Perc, Perc Endo]
ØRQD[Ø,3,4]ZZ	Rpr/Temporomandibular Jt, Lt, [Opn, Perc, Perc Endo]
ØRQE*	Repair/Sternoclavicular Jt, Rt
ØRQF*	Repair/Sternoclavicular Jt, Lt
ØRQG*	Repair/Acromioclavicular Jt, Rt
ØRQH*	Repair/Acromioclavicular Jt, Lt
ØRQJ*	Repair/Shldr Jt, Rt
ØRQK*	Repair/Shldr Jt, Lt
ØRQL*	Repair/Elbow Jt, Rt
ØRQM*	Repair/Elbow Jt, Lt
ØRR3ØJZ	Replace of Cerv Disc with Synth Sub, Opn Appr
ØRR5ØJZ	Replace of C-thor Disc with Synth Sub, Opn Appr
ØRR9ØJZ	Replace of Thor Disc with Synth Sub, Opn Appr
ØRRBØJZ	Replace of T-lum Disc with Synth Sub, Opn Appr
ØRRC*	Replace/Temporomandibular Jt, Rt
ØRRD*	Replace/Temporomandibular Jt, Lt
ØRRE*	Replace/Sternoclavicular Jt, Rt
ØRRF*	Replace/Sternoclavicular Jt, Lt
ØRRG*	Replace/Acromioclavicular Jt, Rt
ØRRH*	Replace/Acromioclavicular Jt, Lt
ØRRJ*	Replace/Shldr Jt, Rt
ØRRK*	Replace/Shldr Jt, Lt
ØRRL*	Replace/Elbow Jt, Rt
ØRRM*	Replace/Elbow Jt, Lt
ØRRN*	Replace/Wrist Jt, Rt
ØRRP*	Replace/Wrist Jt, Lt
ØRS0Ø[4,Z]Z	Repos/Occipital-cervical Jt, Opn, [Int Fix Dev, No Dev], NQ
ØRS1Ø[4,Z]Z	Repos/Cervical Vert Jt, Opn, [Int Fix Dev, No Dev], NQ
ØRS4Ø[4,Z]Z	Repos/Cervicothoracic Vert Jt, Opn, [Int Fix Dev, No Dev], NQ
ØRS6Ø[4,Z]Z	Repos/Thoracic Vert Jt, Opn, [Int Fix Dev, No Dev], NQ
ØRSAØ[4,Z]Z	Repos/Thoracolumbar Vert Jt, Opn, [Int Fix Dev, No Dev], NQ
ØRSCØ[4,Z]Z	Repos/Temporomandibular Jt, Rt, Opn, [Int Fix Dev, No Dev], NQ
ØRSDØ[4,Z]Z	Repos/Temporomandibular Jt, Lt, Opn, [Int Fix Dev, No Dev], NQ
ØRSEØ[4,Z]Z	Repos/Sternoclavicular Jt, Rt, Opn, [Int Fix Dev, No Dev], NQ
ØRSFØ[4,Z]Z	Repos/Sternoclavicular Jt, Lt, Opn, [Int Fix Dev, No Dev], NQ
ØRSGØ[4,Z]Z	Repos/Acromioclavicular Jt, Rt, Opn, [Int Fix Dev, No Dev], NQ
ØRSHØ[4,Z]Z	Repos/Acromioclavicular Jt, Lt, Opn, [Int Fix Dev, No Dev], NQ
ØRSJ[4,Z]Z	Repos/Shldr Jt, Rt, Opn, [Int Fix Dev, No Dev], NQ
ØRSK[4,Z]Z	Repos/Shldr Jt, Lt, Opn, [Int Fix Dev, No Dev], NQ
ØRSLØ[4,5,Z]Z	Repos/Elbow Jt, Rt, Opn, [Int Fix Dev, Ext Fix Dev, No Dev], NQ
ØRSMØ[4,5,Z]Z	Repos/Elbow Jt, Lt, Opn, [Int Fix Dev, Ext Fix Dev, No Dev], NQ
ØRT3ØZZ	Resect of Cervical Vert Disc, Opn Appr
ØRT4ØZZ	Resect of Cervicothoracic Vert Jt, Opn Appr
ØRT5ØZZ	Resect of Cervicothoracic Vert Disc, Opn Appr
ØRT9ØZZ	Resect of Thoracic Vert Disc, Opn Appr
ØRTBØZZ	Resect of Thoracolumbar Vert Disc, Opn Appr
ØRTCØZZ	Resect of Rt Temporomandibular Jt, Opn Appr
ØRTDØZZ	Resect of Lt Temporomandibular Jt, Opn Appr
ØRTEØZZ	Resect of Rt Sternoclavicular Jt, Opn Appr
ØRTFØZZ	Resect of Lt Sternoclavicular Jt, Opn Appr
ØRTGØZZ	Resect of Rt Acromioclavicular Jt, Opn Appr
ØRTHØZZ	Resect of Lt Acromioclavicular Jt, Opn Appr
ØRTJØZZ	Resect of Rt Shldr Jt, Opn Appr
ØRTKØZZ	Resect of Lt Shldr Jt, Opn Appr
ØRTLØZZ	Resect of Rt Elbow Jt, Opn Appr
ØRTMØZZ	Resect of Lt Elbow Jt, Opn Appr
ØRUØ[Ø,3,4]JZ	Supl/Occipital-cervical Jt, [Opn, Perc, Perc Endo], Synth Sub, NQ
ØRU1[Ø,3,4]JZ	Supl/Cervical Vert Jt, [Opn, Perc, Perc Endo], Synth Sub, NQ
ØRU3*	Supl/Cervical Vert Disc
ØRU4[Ø,3,4]JZ	Supl/Cervicothoracic Vert Jt, [Opn, Perc, Perc Endo], Synth Sub, NQ
ØRU5[Ø,3,4]JZ	Supl/Cervicothoracic Vert Disc, [Opn, Perc, Perc Endo], Synth Sub, NQ
ØRU6[Ø,3,4]JZ	Supl/Thoracic Vert Jt, [Opn, Perc, Perc Endo], Synth Sub, NQ
ØRU9*	Supl/Thoracic Vert Disc
ØRUA[Ø,3,4]JZ	Supl/Thoracolumbar Vert Jt, [Opn, Perc, Perc Endo], Synth Sub, NQ
ØRUB*	Supl/Thoracolumbar Vert Disc
ØRUC*	Supl/Temporomandibular Jt, Rt
ØRUD*	Supl/Temporomandibular Jt, Lt
ØRUE*	Supl/Sternoclavicular Jt, Rt
ØRUF*	Supl/Sternoclavicular Jt, Lt
ØRUG*	Supl/Acromioclavicular Jt, Rt
ØRUH*	Supl/Acromioclavicular Jt, Lt
ØRUJ*	Supl/Shldr Jt, Rt
ØRUK*	Supl/Shldr Jt, Lt
ØRUL*	Supl/Elbow Jt, Rt
ØRUM*	Supl/Elbow Jt, Lt
ØRWØ[Ø,3,4][4,J]Z	Rev/Occipital-cervical Jt, [Opn, Perc, Perc Endo], [Int Fix Dev, Synth Sub], NQ
ØRW1[Ø,3,4][4,J]Z	Rev/Cervical Vert Jt, [Opn, Perc, Perc Endo], [Int Fix Dev, Synth Sub], NQ
ØRW3[Ø,3,4]JZ	Rev/Cervical Vert Disc, [Opn, Perc, Perc Endo], Synth Sub, NQ
ØRW4[Ø,3,4][4,J]Z	Rev/Cervicothoracic Vert Jt, [Opn, Perc, Perc Endo], [Int Fix Dev, Synth Sub], NQ
ØRW5[Ø,3,4]JZ	Rev/Cervicothoracic Vert Disc, [Opn, Perc, Perc Endo], Synth Sub, NQ
ØRW6[Ø,3,4][4,J]Z	Rev/Thoracic Vert Jt, [Opn, Perc, Perc Endo], [Int Fix Dev, Synth Sub], NQ
ØRW9[Ø,3,4]JZ	Rev/Thoracic Vert Disc, [Opn, Perc, Perc Endo], Synth Sub, NQ
ØRWA[Ø,3,4][4,J]Z	Rev/Thoracolumbar Vert Jt, [Opn, Perc, Perc Endo], [Int Fix Dev, Synth Sub], NQ
ØRWB[Ø,3,4]JZ	Rev/Thoracolumbar Vert Disc, [Opn, Perc, Perc Endo], Synth Sub, NQ
ØRWE[Ø,3,4][Ø,3,4,7,8,J,K]Z	Rev/Sternoclavicular Jt, Rt, [Opn, Perc, Perc Endo], [Drain Dev, Inf Dev, Int Fix Dev, Auto Tissue Sub, Spacer, Synth Sub, Nonauto Tissue Sub], NQ
ØRWF[Ø,3,4][Ø,3,4,7,8,J,K]Z	Rev/Sternoclavicular Jt, Lt, [Opn, Perc, Perc Endo], [Drain Dev, Inf Dev, Int Fix Dev, Auto Tissue Sub, Spacer, Synth Sub, Nonauto Tissue Sub], NQ
ØRWG[Ø,3,4][Ø,3,4,7,8,J,K]Z	Rev/Acromioclavicular Jt, Rt, [Opn, Perc, Perc Endo], [Drain Dev, Inf Dev, Int Fix Dev, Auto Tissue Sub, Spacer, Synth Sub, Nonauto Tissue Sub], NQ
ØRWH[Ø,3,4][Ø,3,4,7,8,J,K]Z	Rev/Acromioclavicular Jt, Lt, [Opn, Perc, Perc Endo], [Drain Dev, Inf Dev, Int Fix Dev, Auto Tissue Sub, Spacer, Synth Sub, Nonauto Tissue Sub], NQ
ØRWJ[Ø,3,4][Ø,3,4,7,8,J,K]Z	Rev/Shldr Jt, Rt, [Opn, Perc, Perc Endo], [Drain Dev, Inf Dev, Int Fix Dev, Auto Tissue Sub, Spacer, Synth Sub, Nonauto Tissue Sub], NQ

T Transfer DRG   SP Special Payment   * Code Range   6th and 7th Character of ZZ = No Device, No Qualifier ZX = No Device, Diagnostic

ØRWK[Ø,3,4][Ø,3,4,7,8,J,K]Z Rev/Shldr Jt, Lt, [Opn, Perc, Perc Endo], [Drain Dev, Inf Dev, Int Fix Dev, Auto Tissue Sub, Spacer, Synth Sub, Nonauto Tissue Sub], NQ

ØRWL[Ø,3,4][Ø,3,4,5,7,8,J,K]Z Rev/Elbow Jt, Rt, [Opn, Perc, Perc Endo], [Drain Dev, Inf Dev, Int Fix Dev, Ext Fix Dev, Auto Tissue Sub, Spacer, Synth Sub, Nonauto Tissue Sub], NQ

ØRWM[Ø,3,4][Ø,3,4,5,7,8,J,K]Z Rev/Elbow Jt, Lt, [Opn, Perc, Perc Endo], [Drain Dev, Inf Dev, Int Fix Dev, Ext Fix Dev, Auto Tissue Sub, Spacer, Synth Sub, Nonauto Tissue Sub], NQ

ØRWN[Ø,3,4]JZ Rev/Wrist Jt, Rt, [Opn, Perc, Perc Endo], Synth Sub, NQ
ØRWP[Ø,3,4]JZ Rev/Wrist Jt, Lt, [Opn, Perc, Perc Endo], Synth Sub, NQ
ØRWQ[Ø,3,4]JZ Rev/Carpal Jt, Rt, [Opn, Perc, Perc Endo], Synth Sub, NQ
ØRWR[Ø,3,4]JZ Rev/Carpal Jt, Lt, [Opn, Perc, Perc Endo], Synth Sub, NQ
ØRWS[Ø,3,4]JZ Rev/Metacarpocarpal Jt, Rt, [Opn, Perc, Perc Endo], Synth Sub, NQ
ØRWT[Ø,3,4]JZ Rev/Metacarpocarpal Jt, Lt, [Opn, Perc, Perc Endo], Synth Sub, NQ
ØRWU[Ø,3,4]JZ Rev/Metacarpophalangeal Jt, Rt, [Opn, Perc, Perc Endo], Synth Sub, NQ
ØRWV[Ø,3,4]JZ Rev/Metacarpophalangeal Jt, Lt, [Opn, Perc, Perc Endo], Synth Sub, NQ
ØRWW[Ø,3,4]JZ Rev/Finger Phalangeal Jt, Rt, [Opn, Perc, Perc Endo], Synth Sub, NQ
ØRWX[Ø,3,4]JZ Rev/Finger Phalangeal Jt, Lt, [Opn, Perc, Perc Endo], Synth Sub, NQ
ØS5* Lwr Jts, Destr
ØS99Ø[Ø,Z]Z Drain/Hip Jt, Rt, Opn, [Drain Dev, No Dev], NQ
ØS9BØ[Ø,Z]Z Drain/Hip Jt, Lt, Opn, [Drain Dev, No Dev], NQ
ØS9CØ[Ø,Z]Z Drain/Knee Jt, Rt, Opn, [Drain Dev, No Dev], NQ
ØS9DØ[Ø,Z]Z Drain/Knee Jt, Lt, Opn, [Drain Dev, No Dev], NQ
ØS9FØ[Ø,Z]Z Drain/Ankle Jt, Rt, Opn, [Drain Dev, No Dev], NQ
ØS9GØ[Ø,Z]Z Drain/Ankle Jt, Lt, Opn, [Drain Dev, No Dev], NQ
ØS9HØ[Ø,Z]Z Drain/Tarsal Jt, Rt, Opn, [Drain Dev, No Dev], NQ
ØS9JØ[Ø,Z]Z Drain/Tarsal Jt, Lt, Opn, [Drain Dev, No Dev], NQ
ØS9KØ[Ø,Z]Z Drain/Metatarsal-Tarsal Jt, Rt, Opn, [Drain Dev, No Dev], NQ
ØS9LØ[Ø,Z]Z Drain/Metatarsal-Tarsal Jt, Lt, Opn, [Drain Dev, No Dev], NQ
ØS9MØ[Ø,Z]Z Drain/Metatarsal-Phalangeal Jt, Rt, Opn, [Drain Dev, No Dev], NQ
ØS9NØ[Ø,Z]Z Drain/Metatarsal-Phalangeal Jt, Lt, Opn, [Drain Dev, No Dev], NQ
ØS9PØ[Ø,Z]Z Drain/Toe Phalangeal Jt, Rt, Opn, [Drain Dev, No Dev], NQ
ØS9QØ[Ø,Z]Z Drain/Toe Phalangeal Jt, Lt, Opn, [Drain Dev, No Dev], NQ
ØSBØ[Ø,3,4]ZZ Exc/Lumbar Vert Jt, [Opn, Perc, Perc Endo]
ØSB2[Ø,3,4]ZZ Exc/Lumbar Vert Disc, [Opn, Perc, Perc Endo]
ØSB3[Ø,3,4]ZZ Exc/Lumbosacral Jt, [Opn, Perc, Perc Endo]
ØSB4[Ø,3,4]ZZ Exc/Lumbosacral Disc, [Opn, Perc, Perc Endo]
ØSB5[Ø,3,4]ZZ Exc/Sacrococcygeal Jt, [Opn, Perc, Perc Endo]
ØSB6[Ø,3,4]ZZ Exc/Coccygeal Jt, [Opn, Perc, Perc Endo]
ØSB7[Ø,3,4]ZZ Exc/Sacroiliac Jt, Rt, [Opn, Perc, Perc Endo]
ØSB8[Ø,3,4]ZZ Exc/Sacroiliac Jt, Lt, [Opn, Perc, Perc Endo]
ØSB9[Ø,3,4]ZZ Exc/Hip Jt, Rt, [Opn, Perc, Perc Endo]
ØSBB[Ø,3,4]ZZ Exc/Hip Jt, Lt, [Opn, Perc, Perc Endo]
ØSBC[Ø,3,4]ZZ Exc/Knee Jt, Rt, [Opn, Perc, Perc Endo]
ØSBD[Ø,3,4]ZZ Exc/Knee Jt, Lt, [Opn, Perc, Perc Endo]
ØSBF[Ø,3,4]ZZ Exc/Ankle Jt, Rt, [Opn, Perc, Perc Endo]
ØSBG[Ø,3,4]ZZ Exc/Ankle Jt, Lt, [Opn, Perc, Perc Endo]
ØSBH[Ø,3,4]ZZ Exc/Tarsal Jt, Rt, [Opn, Perc, Perc Endo]
ØSBJ[Ø,3,4]ZZ Exc/Tarsal Jt, Lt, [Opn, Perc, Perc Endo]
ØSBK[Ø,3,4]ZZ Exc/Metatarsal-Tarsal Jt, Rt, [Opn, Perc, Perc Endo]
ØSBL[Ø,3,4]ZZ Exc/Metatarsal-Tarsal Jt, Lt, [Opn, Perc, Perc Endo]
ØSBM[Ø,3,4]ZZ Exc/Metatarsal-Phalangeal Jt, Rt, [Opn, Perc, Perc Endo]
ØSBN[Ø,3,4]ZZ Exc/Metatarsal-Phalangeal Jt, Lt, [Opn, Perc, Perc Endo]
ØSBP[Ø,3,4]ZZ Exc/Toe Phalangeal Jt, Rt, [Opn, Perc, Perc Endo]
ØSBQ[Ø,3,4]ZZ Exc/Toe Phalangeal Jt, Lt, [Opn, Perc, Perc Endo]
ØSC9* Extir/Hip Jt, Rt
ØSCB* Extir/Hip Jt, Lt
ØSCC* Extir/Knee Jt, Rt
ØSCD* Extir/Knee Jt, Lt
ØSCF* Extir/Ankle Jt, Rt
ØSCG* Extir/Ankle Jt, Lt
ØSCH* Extir/Tarsal Jt, Rt
ØSCJ* Extir/Tarsal Jt, Lt
ØSCK* Extir/Metatarsal-Tarsal Jt, Rt
ØSCL* Extir/Metatarsal-Tarsal Jt, Lt
ØSCM* Extir/Metatarsal-Phalangeal Jt, Rt
ØSCN* Extir/Metatarsal-Phalangeal Jt, Lt
ØSCP* Extir/Toe Phalangeal Jt, Rt
ØSCQ* Extir/Toe Phalangeal Jt, Lt
ØSGØ* Fusion/Lumbar Vert Jt
ØSG1* Fusion/Lumbar Vert Jts, 2 or more

ØSG3* Fusion/Lumbosacral Jt
ØSG5* Fusion/Sacrococcygeal Jt
ØSG6* Fusion/Coccygeal Jt
ØSG7* Fusion/Sacroiliac Jt, Rt
ØSG8* Fusion/Sacroiliac Jt, Lt
ØSG9* Fusion/Hip Jt, Rt
ØSGB* Fusion/Hip Jt, Lt
ØSGC* Fusion/Knee Jt, Rt
ØSGD* Fusion/Knee Jt, Lt
ØSGF* Fusion/Ankle Jt, Rt
ØSGG* Fusion/Ankle Jt, Lt
ØSGH* Fusion/Tarsal Jt, Rt
ØSGJ* Fusion/Tarsal Jt, Lt
ØSGK* Fusion/Metatarsal-Tarsal Jt, Rt
ØSGL* Fusion/Metatarsal-Tarsal Jt, Lt
ØSGM* Fusion/Metatarsal-Phalangeal Jt, Rt
ØSGN* Fusion/Metatarsal-Phalangeal Jt, Lt
ØSHØ[Ø,3,4][B,C,D]Z Insert/Lumbar Vert Jt, [Opn, Perc, Perc Endo], [Spinal Stabliz Dev, Interspinous Process, Spinal Stabliz Dev, Pedicle-Based, Spinal Stabliz Dev, Facet Replace], NQ
ØSH3[Ø,3,4][B,C,D]Z Insert/Lumbosacral Jt, [Opn, Perc, Perc Endo], [Spinal Stabliz Dev, Interspinous Process, Spinal Stabliz Dev, Pedicle-Based, Spinal Stabliz Dev, Facet Replace], NQ
ØSH9[Ø,3,4][4,5]Z Insert/Hip Jt, Rt, [Opn, Perc, Perc Endo], [Int Fix Dev, Ext Fix Dev], NQ
ØSHB[Ø,3,4][4,5]Z Insert/Hip Jt, Lt, [Opn, Perc, Perc Endo], [Int Fix Dev, Ext Fix Dev], NQ
ØSHC[Ø,3,4][4,5]Z Insert/Knee Jt, Rt, [Opn, Perc, Perc Endo], [Int Fix Dev, Ext Fix Dev], NQ
ØSHD[Ø,3,4][4,5]Z Insert/Knee Jt, Lt, [Opn, Perc, Perc Endo], [Int Fix Dev, Ext Fix Dev], NQ
ØSHF[Ø,3,4][4,5]Z Insert/Ankle Jt, Rt, [Opn, Perc, Perc Endo], [Int Fix Dev, Ext Fix Dev], NQ
ØSHG[Ø,3,4][4,5]Z Insert/Ankle Jt, Lt, [Opn, Perc, Perc Endo], [Int Fix Dev, Ext Fix Dev], NQ
ØSHH[Ø,3,4][4,5]Z Insert/Tarsal Jt, Rt, [Opn, Perc, Perc Endo], [Int Fix Dev, Ext Fix Dev], NQ
ØSHJ[Ø,3,4][4,5]Z Insert/Tarsal Jt, Lt, [Opn, Perc, Perc Endo], [Int Fix Dev, Ext Fix Dev], NQ
ØSHK[Ø,3,4][4,5]Z Insert/Metatarsal-Tarsal Jt, Rt, [Opn, Perc, Perc Endo], [Int Fix Dev, Ext Fix Dev], NQ
ØSHL[Ø,3,4][4,5]Z Insert/Metatarsal-Tarsal Jt, Lt, [Opn, Perc, Perc Endo], [Int Fix Dev, Ext Fix Dev], NQ
ØSHM[Ø,3,4][4,5]Z Insert/Metatarsal-Phalangeal Jt, Rt, [Opn, Perc, Perc Endo], [Int Fix Dev, Ext Fix Dev], NQ
ØSHN[Ø,3,4][4,5]Z Insert/Metatarsal-Phalangeal Jt, Lt, [Opn, Perc, Perc Endo], [Int Fix Dev, Ext Fix Dev], NQ
ØSHP[Ø,3,4][4,5]Z Insert/Toe Phalangeal Jt, Rt, [Opn, Perc, Perc Endo], [Int Fix Dev, Ext Fix Dev], NQ
ØSHQ[Ø,3,4][4,5]Z Insert/Toe Phalangeal Jt, Lt, [Opn, Perc, Perc Endo], [Int Fix Dev, Ext Fix Dev], NQ
ØSJØ4ZZ Inspect of Lumbar Vert Jt, Perc Endo Appr
ØSJ34ZZ Inspect of Lumbosacral Jt, Perc Endo Appr
ØSJ54ZZ Inspect of Sacrococcygeal Jt, Perc Endo Appr
ØSJ64ZZ Inspect of Coccygeal Jt, Perc Endo Appr
ØSJ74ZZ Inspect of Rt Sacroiliac Jt, Perc Endo Appr
ØSJ84ZZ Inspect of Lt Sacroiliac Jt, Perc Endo Appr
ØSJ9[Ø,4]ZZ Inspect/Hip Jt, Rt, [Opn, Perc Endo]
ØSJB[Ø,4]ZZ Inspect/Hip Jt, Lt, [Opn, Perc Endo]
ØSJC[Ø,4]ZZ Inspect/Knee Jt, Rt, [Opn, Perc Endo]
ØSJD[Ø,4]ZZ Inspect/Knee Jt, Lt, [Opn, Perc Endo]
ØSJF[Ø,4]ZZ Inspect/Ankle Jt, Rt, [Opn, Perc Endo]
ØSJG[Ø,4]ZZ Inspect/Ankle Jt, Lt, [Opn, Perc Endo]
ØSJH[Ø,4]ZZ Inspect/Tarsal Jt, Rt, [Opn, Perc Endo]
ØSJJ[Ø,4]ZZ Inspect/Tarsal Jt, Lt, [Opn, Perc Endo]
ØSJK[Ø,4]ZZ Inspect/Metatarsal-Tarsal Jt, Rt, [Opn, Perc Endo]
ØSJL[Ø,4]ZZ Inspect/Metatarsal-Tarsal Jt, Lt, [Opn, Perc Endo]
ØSJM[Ø,4]ZZ Inspect/Metatarsal-Phalangeal Jt, Rt, [Opn, Perc Endo]
ØSJN[Ø,4]ZZ Inspect/Metatarsal-Phalangeal Jt, Lt, [Opn, Perc Endo]
ØSJP[Ø,4]ZZ Inspect/Toe Phalangeal Jt, Rt, [Opn, Perc Endo]
ØSJQ[Ø,4]ZZ Inspect/Toe Phalangeal Jt, Lt, [Opn, Perc Endo]
ØSNØ[Ø,3,4]ZZ Rls/Lumbar Vert Jt, [Opn, Perc, Perc Endo]
ØSN2[Ø,3,4]ZZ Rls/Lumbar Vert Disc, [Opn, Perc, Perc Endo]
ØSN3[Ø,3,4]ZZ Rls/Lumbosacral Jt, [Opn, Perc, Perc Endo]
ØSN4[Ø,3,4]ZZ Rls/Lumbosacral Disc, [Opn, Perc, Perc Endo]
ØSN5[Ø,3,4]ZZ Rls/Sacrococcygeal Jt, [Opn, Perc, Perc Endo]
ØSN6[Ø,3,4]ZZ Rls/Coccygeal Jt, [Opn, Perc, Perc Endo]
ØSN7[Ø,3,4]ZZ Rls/Sacroiliac Jt, Rt, [Opn, Perc, Perc Endo]
ØSN8[Ø,3,4]ZZ Rls/Sacroiliac Jt, Lt, [Opn, Perc, Perc Endo]
ØSN9[Ø,3,4]ZZ Rls/Hip Jt, Rt, [Opn, Perc, Perc Endo]

MDC 21: Injuries, Poisonings And Toxic Effects Of Drugs—SURGICAL

Surgical **Medical** **CC Indicator** **MCC Indicator** **Procedure Proxy** PDxMCC **PDx acts as own MCC** PDxCC **PDx acts as own CC**

MDC 21: Injuries, Poisonings And Toxic Effects Of Drugs—SURGICAL

0SNB[0,3,4]ZZ	Rls/Hip Jt, Lt, [Opn, Perc, Perc Endo]
0SNC[0,3,4]ZZ	Rls/Knee Jt, Rt, [Opn, Perc, Perc Endo]
0SND[0,3,4]ZZ	Rls/Knee Jt, Lt, [Opn, Perc, Perc Endo]
0SNF[0,3,4]ZZ	Rls/Ankle Jt, Rt, [Opn, Perc, Perc Endo]
0SNG[0,3,4]ZZ	Rls/Ankle Jt, Lt, [Opn, Perc, Perc Endo]
0SNH[0,3,4]ZZ	Rls/Tarsal Jt, Rt, [Opn, Perc, Perc Endo]
0SNJ[0,3,4]ZZ	Rls/Tarsal Jt, Lt, [Opn, Perc, Perc Endo]
0SNK[0,3,4]ZZ	Rls/Metatarsal-Tarsal Jt, Rt, [Opn, Perc, Perc Endo]
0SNL[0,3,4]ZZ	Rls/Metatarsal-Tarsal Jt, Lt, [Opn, Perc, Perc Endo]
0SNM[0,3,4]ZZ	Rls/Metatarsal-Phalangeal Jt, Rt, [Opn, Perc, Perc Endo]
0SNN[0,3,4]ZZ	Rls/Metatarsal-Phalangeal Jt, Lt, [Opn, Perc, Perc Endo]
0SNP[0,3,4]ZZ	Rls/Toe Phalangeal Jt, Rt, [Opn, Perc, Perc Endo]
0SNQ[0,3,4]ZZ	Rls/Toe Phalangeal Jt, Lt, [Opn, Perc, Perc Endo]
0SP0[0,3,4]JZ	Rmvl/Lumbar Vert Jt, [Opn, Perc, Perc Endo], Synth Sub, NQ
0SP2[0,3,4]JZ	Rmvl/Lumbar Vert Disc, [Opn, Perc, Perc Endo], Synth Sub, NQ
0SP3[0,3,4]JZ	Rmvl/Lumbosacral Jt, [Opn, Perc, Perc Endo], Synth Sub, NQ
0SP4[0,3,4]JZ	Rmvl/Lumbosacral Disc, [Opn, Perc, Perc Endo], Synth Sub, NQ
0SP5[0,3,4]JZ	Rmvl/Sacrococcygeal Jt, [Opn, Perc, Perc Endo], Synth Sub, NQ
0SP6[0,3,4]JZ	Rmvl/Coccygeal Jt, [Opn, Perc, Perc Endo], Synth Sub, NQ
0SP7[0,3,4]JZ	Rmvl/Sacroiliac Jt, Rt, [Opn, Perc, Perc Endo], Synth Sub, NQ
0SP8[0,3,4]JZ	Rmvl/Sacroiliac Jt, Lt, [Opn, Perc, Perc Endo], Synth Sub, NQ
0SP90[0,3,4,5,7,9,B,J,K]Z	Rmvl/Hip Jt, Rt, Opn, [Drain Dev, Inf Dev, Int Fix Dev, Ext Fix Dev, Auto Tissue Sub, Liner, Resurfacing Dev, Synth Sub, Nonauto Tissue Sub], NQ
0SP93[0,3,4,5,7,J,K]Z	Rmvl/Hip Jt, Rt, Perc, [Drain Dev, Inf Dev, Int Fix Dev, Ext Fix Dev, Auto Tissue Sub, Synth Sub, Nonauto Tissue Sub], NQ
0SP94[0,3,4,5,7,J,K]Z	Rmvl/Hip Jt, Rt, Perc Endo, [Drain Dev, Inf Dev, Int Fix Dev, Ext Fix Dev, Auto Tissue Sub, Synth Sub, Nonauto Tissue Sub], NQ
0SPB0[0,3,4,5,7,9,B,J,K]Z	Rmvl/Hip Jt, Lt, Opn, [Drain Dev, Inf Dev, Int Fix Dev, Ext Fix Dev, Auto Tissue Sub, Liner, Resurfacing Dev, Synth Sub, Nonauto Tissue Sub], NQ
0SPB3[0,3,4,5,7,J,K]Z	Rmvl/Hip Jt, Lt, Perc, [Drain Dev, Inf Dev, Int Fix Dev, Ext Fix Dev, Auto Tissue Sub, Synth Sub, Nonauto Tissue Sub], NQ
0SPB4[0,3,4,5,7,J,K]Z	Rmvl/Hip Jt, Lt, Perc Endo, [Drain Dev, Inf Dev, Int Fix Dev, Ext Fix Dev, Auto Tissue Sub, Synth Sub, Nonauto Tissue Sub], NQ
0SPC09Z	Rmvl of Liner from Rt Knee Jt, Opn Appr
0SPC[0,3,4][0,3,4,5,7,J,K]Z	Rmvl/Knee Jt, Rt, [Opn, Perc, Perc Endo], [Drain Dev, Inf Dev, Int Fix Dev, Ext Fix Dev, Auto Tissue Sub, Synth Sub, Nonauto Tissue Sub], NQ
0SPD09Z	Rmvl of Liner from Lt Knee Jt, Opn Appr
0SPD[0,3,4][0,3,4,5,7,J,K]Z	Rmvl/Knee Jt, Lt, [Opn, Perc, Perc Endo], [Drain Dev, Inf Dev, Int Fix Dev, Ext Fix Dev, Auto Tissue Sub, Synth Sub, Nonauto Tissue Sub], NQ
0SPF[0,3,4][0,3,4,5,7,J,K]Z	Rmvl/Ankle Jt, Rt, [Opn, Perc, Perc Endo], [Drain Dev, Inf Dev, Int Fix Dev, Ext Fix Dev, Auto Tissue Sub, Synth Sub, Nonauto Tissue Sub], NQ
0SPG[0,3,4][0,3,4,5,7,J,K]Z	Rmvl/Ankle Jt, Lt, [Opn, Perc, Perc Endo], [Drain Dev, Inf Dev, Int Fix Dev, Ext Fix Dev, Auto Tissue Sub, Synth Sub, Nonauto Tissue Sub], NQ
0SPH[0,3,4][0,3,4,5,7,J,K]Z	Rmvl/Tarsal Jt, Rt, [Opn, Perc, Perc Endo], [Drain Dev, Inf Dev, Int Fix Dev, Ext Fix Dev, Auto Tissue Sub, Synth Sub, Nonauto Tissue Sub], NQ
0SPJ[0,3,4][0,3,4,5,7,J,K]Z	Rmvl/Tarsal Jt, Lt, [Opn, Perc, Perc Endo], [Drain Dev, Inf Dev, Int Fix Dev, Ext Fix Dev, Auto Tissue Sub, Synth Sub, Nonauto Tissue Sub], NQ
0SPK[0,3,4][0,3,4,5,7,J,K]Z	Rmvl/Metatarsal-Tarsal Jt, Rt, [Opn, Perc, Perc Endo], [Drain Dev, Inf Dev, Int Fix Dev, Ext Fix Dev, Auto Tissue Sub, Synth Sub, Nonauto Tissue Sub], NQ
0SPL[0,3,4][0,3,4,5,7,J,K]Z	Rmvl/Metatarsal-Tarsal Jt, Lt, [Opn, Perc, Perc Endo], [Drain Dev, Inf Dev, Int Fix Dev, Ext Fix Dev, Auto Tissue Sub, Synth Sub, Nonauto Tissue Sub], NQ
0SPM[0,3,4][0,3,4,5,7,J,K]Z	Rmvl/Metatarsal-Phalangeal Jt, Rt, [Opn, Perc, Perc Endo], [Drain Dev, Inf Dev, Int Fix Dev, Ext Fix Dev, Auto Tissue Sub, Synth Sub, Nonauto Tissue Sub], NQ
0SPN[0,3,4][0,3,4,5,7,J,K]Z	Rmvl/Metatarsal-Phalangeal Jt, Lt, [Opn, Perc, Perc Endo], [Drain Dev, Inf Dev, Int Fix Dev, Ext Fix Dev, Auto Tissue Sub, Synth Sub, Nonauto Tissue Sub], NQ
0SPP[0,3,4][0,3,4,5,7,J,K]Z	Rmvl/Toe Phalangeal Jt, Rt, [Opn, Perc, Perc Endo], [Drain Dev, Inf Dev, Int Fix Dev, Ext Fix Dev, Auto Tissue Sub, Synth Sub, Nonauto Tissue Sub], NQ
0SPQ[0,3,4][0,3,4,5,7,J,K]Z	Rmvl/Toe Phalangeal Jt, Lt, [Opn, Perc, Perc Endo], [Drain Dev, Inf Dev, Int Fix Dev, Ext Fix Dev, Auto Tissue Sub, Synth Sub, Nonauto Tissue Sub], NQ
0SQ20ZZ	Repair Lumbar Vert Disc, Opn Appr
0SQ40ZZ	Repair Lumbosacral Disc, Opn Appr
0SQ9*	Repair/Hip Jt, Rt
0SQB*	Repair/Hip Jt, Lt
0SQC*	Repair/Knee Jt, Rt
0SQD*	Repair/Knee Jt, Lt
0SQF*	Repair/Ankle Jt, Rt
0SQG*	Repair/Ankle Jt, Lt
0SR20JZ	Replace of Lum Disc with Synth Sub, Opn Appr
0SR40JZ	Replace of Lumsac Disc with Synth Sub, Opn Appr
0SR9*	Replace/Hip Jt, Rt
0SRA*	Replace/Hip Jt, Acetabular Surface, Rt
0SRB*	Replace/Hip Jt, Lt
0SRC*	Replace/Knee Jt, Rt
0SRD*	Replace/Knee Jt, Lt
0SRE*	Replace/Hip Jt, Acetabular Surface, Lt
0SRF*	Replace/Ankle Jt, Rt
0SRG*	Replace/Ankle Jt, Lt
0SRH*	Replace/Tarsal Jt, Rt
0SRJ*	Replace/Tarsal Jt, Lt
0SRK*	Replace/Metatarsal-Tarsal Jt, Rt
0SRL*	Replace/Metatarsal-Tarsal Jt, Lt
0SRM*	Replace/Metatarsal-Phalangeal Jt, Rt
0SRN*	Replace/Metatarsal-Phalangeal Jt, Lt
0SRP*	Replace/Toe Phalangeal Jt, Rt
0SRQ*	Replace/Toe Phalangeal Jt, Lt
0SRR*	Replace/Hip Jt, Femor Surface, Rt
0SRS*	Replace/Hip Jt, Femor Surface, Lt
0SRT*	Replace/Knee Jt, Femor Surface, Rt
0SRU*	Replace/Knee Jt, Femor Surface, Lt
0SRV*	Replace/Knee Jt, Tibial Surface, Rt
0SRW*	Replace/Knee Jt, Tibial Surface, Lt
0SS00[4,Z]Z	Repos/Lumbar Vert Jt, Opn, [Int Fix Dev, No Dev], NQ
0SS30[4,Z]Z	Repos/Lumbosacral Jt, Opn, [Int Fix Dev, No Dev], NQ
0SS50[4,Z]Z	Repos/Sacrococcygeal Jt, Opn, [Int Fix Dev, No Dev], NQ
0SS60[4,Z]Z	Repos/Coccygeal Jt, Opn, [Int Fix Dev, No Dev], NQ
0SS70[4,Z]Z	Repos/Sacroiliac Jt, Rt, Opn, [Int Fix Dev, No Dev], NQ
0SS80[4,Z]Z	Repos/Sacroiliac Jt, Lt, Opn, [Int Fix Dev, No Dev], NQ
0SS90[4,5,Z]Z	Repos/Hip Jt, Rt, Opn, [Int Fix Dev, Ext Fix Dev, No Dev], NQ
0SSB0[4,5,Z]Z	Repos/Hip Jt, Lt, Opn, [Int Fix Dev, Ext Fix Dev, No Dev], NQ
0SSC0[4,5,Z]Z	Repos/Knee Jt, Rt, Opn, [Int Fix Dev, Ext Fix Dev, No Dev], NQ
0SSD0[4,5,Z]Z	Repos/Knee Jt, Lt, Opn, [Int Fix Dev, Ext Fix Dev, No Dev], NQ
0SSF0[4,5,Z]Z	Repos/Ankle Jt, Rt, Opn, [Int Fix Dev, Ext Fix Dev, No Dev], NQ
0SSG0[4,5,Z]Z	Repos/Ankle Jt, Lt, Opn, [Int Fix Dev, Ext Fix Dev, No Dev], NQ
0SSH0[4,5,Z]Z	Repos/Tarsal Jt, Rt, Opn, [Int Fix Dev, Ext Fix Dev, No Dev], NQ
0SSJ0[4,5,Z]Z	Repos/Tarsal Jt, Lt, Opn, [Int Fix Dev, Ext Fix Dev, No Dev], NQ
0SSK0[4,5,Z]Z	Repos/Metatarsal-Tarsal Jt, Rt, Opn, [Int Fix Dev, Ext Fix Dev, No Dev], NQ
0SSL0[4,5,Z]Z	Repos/Metatarsal-Tarsal Jt, Lt, Opn, [Int Fix Dev, Ext Fix Dev, No Dev], NQ
0SSM0[4,5,Z]Z	Repos/Metatarsal-Phalangeal Jt, Rt, Opn, [Int Fix Dev, Ext Fix Dev, No Dev], NQ
0SSN0[4,5,Z]Z	Repos/Metatarsal-Phalangeal Jt, Lt, Opn, [Int Fix Dev, Ext Fix Dev, No Dev], NQ
0SSP0[4,5,Z]Z	Repos/Toe Phalangeal Jt, Rt, Opn, [Int Fix Dev, Ext Fix Dev, No Dev], NQ
0SSQ0[4,5,Z]Z	Repos/Toe Phalangeal Jt, Lt, Opn, [Int Fix Dev, Ext Fix Dev, No Dev], NQ
0ST*	Lwr Jts, Resect
0SU0[0,3,4]JZ	Supl/Lumbar Vert Jt, [Opn, Perc, Perc Endo], Synth Sub, NQ
0SU2*	Supl/Lumbar Vert Disc
0SU3[0,3,4]JZ	Supl/Lumbosacral Jt, [Opn, Perc, Perc Endo], Synth Sub, NQ
0SU4*	Supl/Lumbosacral Disc
0SU5[0,3,4]JZ	Supl/Sacrococcygeal Jt, [Opn, Perc, Perc Endo], Synth Sub, NQ
0SU6[0,3,4]JZ	Supl/Coccygeal Jt, [Opn, Perc, Perc Endo], Synth Sub, NQ
0SU90BZ	Supl Rt Hip Jt with Resurf Dev, Opn Appr
0SUA0BZ	Supl Rt Hip Jt, Acetab with Resurf Dev, Opn Appr
0SUB0BZ	Supl Lt Hip Jt with Resurf Dev, Opn Appr
0SUE0BZ	Supl Lt Hip Jt, Acetab with Resurf Dev, Opn Appr
0SUH[0,3,4]JZ	Supl/Tarsal Jt, Rt, [Opn, Perc, Perc Endo], Synth Sub, NQ
0SUJ[0,3,4]JZ	Supl/Tarsal Jt, Lt, [Opn, Perc, Perc Endo], Synth Sub, NQ
0SUR*	Supl/Hip Jt, Femor Surface, Rt
0SUS*	Supl/Hip Jt, Femor Surface, Lt
0SUV09Z	Supl Rt Knee Jt, Tibial with Liner, Opn Appr
0SUW09Z	Supl Lt Knee Jt, Tibial with Liner, Opn Appr
0SW0[0,3,4][4,J]Z	Rev/Lumbar Vert Jt, [Opn, Perc, Perc Endo], [Int Fix Dev, Synth Sub], NQ
0SW2[0,3,4]JZ	Rev/Lumbar Vert Disc, [Opn, Perc, Perc Endo], Synth Sub, NQ
0SW3[0,3,4][4,J]Z	Rev/Lumbosacral Jt, [Opn, Perc, Perc Endo], [Int Fix Dev, Synth Sub], NQ
0SW4[0,3,4]JZ	Rev/Lumbosacral Disc, [Opn, Perc, Perc Endo], Synth Sub, NQ
0SW90[0,3,4,5,7,8,9,B,J,K]Z	Rev/Hip Jt, Rt, Opn, [Drain Dev, Inf Dev, Int Fix Dev, Ext Fix Dev, Auto Tissue Sub, Spacer, Liner, Resurfacing Dev, Synth Sub, Nonauto Tissue Sub], NQ

T Transfer DRG   SP Special Payment   * Code Range   6th and 7th Character of ZZ = No Device, No Qualifier ZX = No Device, Diagnostic

MS-DRG Version 33.0

© 2015 Optum360, LLC

0SW93[0,3,4,5,7,8,J,K]Z	Rev/Hip Jt, Rt, Perc, [Drain Dev, Inf Dev, Int Fix Dev, Ext Fix Dev, Auto Tissue Sub, Spacer, Synth Sub, Nonauto Tissue Sub], NQ
0SW94[0,3,4,5,7,8,J,K]Z	Rev/Hip Jt, Rt, Perc Endo, [Drain Dev, Inf Dev, Int Fix Dev, Ext Fix Dev, Auto Tissue Sub, Spacer, Synth Sub, Nonauto Tissue Sub], NQ
0SWB0[0,3,4,5,7,8,9,B,J,K]Z	Rev/Hip Jt, Lt, Opn, [Drain Dev, Inf Dev, Int Fix Dev, Ext Fix Dev, Auto Tissue Sub, Spacer, Liner, Resurfacing Dev, Synth Sub, Nonauto Tissue Sub], NQ
0SWB3[0,3,4,5,7,8,J,K]Z	Rev/Hip Jt, Lt, Perc, [Drain Dev, Inf Dev, Int Fix Dev, Ext Fix Dev, Auto Tissue Sub, Spacer, Synth Sub, Nonauto Tissue Sub], NQ
0SWB4[0,3,4,5,7,8,J,K]Z	Rev/Hip Jt, Lt, Perc Endo, [Drain Dev, Inf Dev, Int Fix Dev, Ext Fix Dev, Auto Tissue Sub, Spacer, Synth Sub, Nonauto Tissue Sub], NQ
0SWC09Z	Rev of Liner in Rt Knee Jt, Opn Appr
0SWC[0,3,4][0,3,4,5,7,8,J,K]Z	Rev/Knee Jt, Rt, [Opn, Perc, Perc Endo], [Drain Dev, Inf Dev, Int Fix Dev, Ext Fix Dev, Auto Tissue Sub, Spacer, Synth Sub, Nonauto Tissue Sub], NQ
0SWD09Z	Rev of Liner in Lt Knee Jt, Opn Appr
0SWD[0,3,4][0,3,4,5,7,8,J,K]Z	Rev/Knee Jt, Lt, [Opn, Perc, Perc Endo], [Drain Dev, Inf Dev, Int Fix Dev, Ext Fix Dev, Auto Tissue Sub, Spacer, Synth Sub, Nonauto Tissue Sub], NQ
0SWF[0,3,4][0,3,4,5,7,8,J,K]Z	Rev/Ankle Jt, Rt, [Opn, Perc, Perc Endo], [Drain Dev, Inf Dev, Int Fix Dev, Ext Fix Dev, Auto Tissue Sub, Spacer, Synth Sub, Nonauto Tissue Sub], NQ
0SWG[0,3,4][0,3,4,5,7,8,J,K]Z	Rev/Ankle Jt, Lt, [Opn, Perc, Perc Endo], [Drain Dev, Inf Dev, Int Fix Dev, Ext Fix Dev, Auto Tissue Sub, Spacer, Synth Sub, Nonauto Tissue Sub], NQ
0SWH[0,3,4][0,3,4,5,7,8,J,K]Z	Rev/Tarsal Jt, Rt, [Opn, Perc, Perc Endo], [Drain Dev, Inf Dev, Int Fix Dev, Ext Fix Dev, Auto Tissue Sub, Spacer, Synth Sub, Nonauto Tissue Sub], NQ
0SWJ[0,3,4][0,3,4,5,7,8,J,K]Z	Rev/Tarsal Jt, Lt, [Opn, Perc, Perc Endo], [Drain Dev, Inf Dev, Int Fix Dev, Ext Fix Dev, Auto Tissue Sub, Spacer, Synth Sub, Nonauto Tissue Sub], NQ
0SWK[0,3,4][0,3,4,5,7,8,J,K]Z	Rev/Metatarsal-Tarsal Jt, Rt, [Opn, Perc, Perc Endo], [Drain Dev, Inf Dev, Int Fix Dev, Ext Fix Dev, Auto Tissue Sub, Spacer, Synth Sub, Nonauto Tissue Sub], NQ
0SWL[0,3,4][0,3,4,5,7,8,J,K]Z	Rev/Metatarsal-Tarsal Jt, Lt, [Opn, Perc, Perc Endo], [Drain Dev, Inf Dev, Int Fix Dev, Ext Fix Dev, Auto Tissue Sub, Spacer, Synth Sub, Nonauto Tissue Sub], NQ
0SWM[0,3,4][0,3,4,5,7,8,J,K]Z	Rev/Metatarsal-Phalangeal Jt, Rt, [Opn, Perc, Perc Endo], [Drain Dev, Inf Dev, Int Fix Dev, Ext Fix Dev, Auto Tissue Sub, Spacer, Synth Sub, Nonauto Tissue Sub], NQ
0SWN[0,3,4][0,3,4,5,7,8,J,K]Z	Rev/Metatarsal-Phalangeal Jt, Lt, [Opn, Perc, Perc Endo], [Drain Dev, Inf Dev, Int Fix Dev, Ext Fix Dev, Auto Tissue Sub, Spacer, Synth Sub, Nonauto Tissue Sub], NQ
0SWP[0,3,4][0,3,4,5,7,8,J,K]Z	Rev/Toe Phalangeal Jt, Rt, [Opn, Perc, Perc Endo], [Drain Dev, Inf Dev, Int Fix Dev, Ext Fix Dev, Auto Tissue Sub, Spacer, Synth Sub, Nonauto Tissue Sub], NQ
0SWQ[0,3,4][0,3,4,5,7,8,J,K]Z	Rev/Toe Phalangeal Jt, Lt, [Opn, Perc, Perc Endo], [Drain Dev, Inf Dev, Int Fix Dev, Ext Fix Dev, Auto Tissue Sub, Spacer, Synth Sub, Nonauto Tissue Sub], NQ
0T13[0,4][7,J,K,Z]B	Bypass/Kidney Pelvis, Rt, [Opn, Perc Endo], [Auto Tissue Sub, Synth Sub, Nonauto Tissue Sub, No Dev], Bladder
0T14[0,4][7,J,K,Z]B	Bypass/Kidney Pelvis, Lt, [Opn, Perc Endo], [Auto Tissue Sub, Synth Sub, Nonauto Tissue Sub, No Dev], Bladder
0T16*	Bypass/Ureter, Rt
0T17*	Bypass/Ureter, Lt
0T18*	Bypass/Ureters, Bilat
0T1B[0,4]ZD	Bypass/Bladder, [Opn, Perc Endo], No Dev, Cutaneous
0T56*	Destr/Ureter, Rt
0T57*	Destr/Ureter, Lt
0T76[0,3,4,7,8]ZZ	Dilation/Ureter, Rt, [Opn, Perc, Perc Endo, Via Natrl or Artfcl Opng, Via Natrl or Artfcl Opng Endo]
0T77[0,3,4,7,8]ZZ	Dilation/Ureter, Lt, [Opn, Perc, Perc Endo, Via Natrl or Artfcl Opng, Via Natrl or Artfcl Opng Endo]
0T78[0,3,4]ZZ	Dilation/Ureters, Bilat, [Opn, Perc, Perc Endo]
0T7B*	Dilation/Bladder
0T7D[0,3,4]ZZ	Dilation/Urethra, [Opn, Perc, Perc Endo]
0T900ZX	Drain of Rt Kidney, Opn Appr, Diagnostic
0T90[0,3,4,7,8]0Z	Drain of Rt Kidney w/ Drain Dev, [Opn, Perc, Perc Endo, Via Natrl or Artfcl Opng, Via Natrl or Artfcl Opng Endo]
0T90[0,7,8]ZZ	Drain of Rt Kidney w/ No Dev, [Opn, Via Natrl or Artfcl Opng, Via Natrl or Artfcl Opng Endo]
0T910ZX	Drain of Lt Kidney, Opn Appr, Diagnostic
0T91[0,3,4,7,8]0Z	Drain of Lt Kidney w/ Drain Dev, [Opn, Perc, Perc Endo, Via Natrl or Artfcl Opng, Via Natrl or Artfcl Opng Endo]
0T91[0,7,8]ZZ	Drain of Lt Kidney w/ No Dev, [Opn, Via Natrl or Artfcl Opng, Via Natrl or Artfcl Opng Endo]
0T930ZX	Drain of Rt Kidney Pelvis, Opn Appr, Diagnostic
0T93[0,3,4,7,8]0Z	Drain of Rt Kidney Pelvis w/ Drain Dev, [Opn, Perc, Perc Endo, Via Natrl or Artfcl Opng, Via Natrl or Artfcl Opng Endo]
0T93[0,7,8]ZZ	Drain of Rt Kidney Pelvis w/ No Dev, [Opn, Via Natrl or Artfcl Opng, Via Natrl or Artfcl Opng Endo]
0T940ZX	Drain of Lt Kidney Pelvis, Opn Appr, Diagnostic
0T94[0,3,4,7,8]0Z	Drain of Lt Kidney Pelvis w/ Drain Dev, [Opn, Perc, Perc Endo, Via Natrl or Artfcl Opng, Via Natrl or Artfcl Opng Endo]
0T94[0,7,8]ZZ	Drain of Lt Kidney Pelvis w/ No Dev, [Opn, Via Natrl or Artfcl Opng, Via Natrl or Artfcl Opng Endo]
0T9B0[0,Z]Z	Drain/Bladder, Opn, [Drain Dev, No Dev], NQ
0T9C0[0,Z]Z	Drain/Bladder Neck, Opn, [Drain Dev, No Dev], NQ
0T9D[0,3,4]0Z	Drain/Urethra, [Opn, Perc, Perc Endo], Drain Dev, NQ
0TB00ZX	Exc of Rt Kidney, Opn Appr, Diagnostic
0TB0[0,3,4,7,8]ZZ	Exc of Rt Kidney, [Opn, Perc, Perc Endo, Via Natrl or Artfcl Opng, Via Natrl or Artfcl Opng Endo]
0TB10ZX	Exc of Lt Kidney, Opn Appr, Diagnostic
0TB1[0,3,4,7,8]ZZ	Exc of Lt Kidney, [Opn, Perc, Perc Endo, Via Natrl or Artfcl Opng, Via Natrl or Artfcl Opng Endo]
0TB30ZX	Exc of Rt Kidney Pelvis, Opn Appr, Diagnostic
0TB3[0,3,4,7,8]ZZ	Exc of Rt Kidney Pelvis, [Opn, Perc, Perc Endo, Via Natrl or Artfcl Opng, Via Natrl or Artfcl Opng Endo]
0TB40ZX	Exc of Lt Kidney Pelvis, Opn Appr, Diagnostic
0TB4[0,3,4,7,8]ZZ	Exc of Lt Kidney Pelvis, [Opn, Perc, Perc Endo, Via Natrl or Artfcl Opng, Via Natrl or Artfcl Opng Endo]
0TB6[0,3,4,7,8]ZZ	Exc/Ureter, Rt, [Opn, Perc, Perc Endo, Via Natrl or Artfcl Opng, Via Natrl or Artfcl Opng Endo]
0TB7[0,3,4,7,8]ZZ	Exc/Ureter, Lt, [Opn, Perc, Perc Endo, Via Natrl or Artfcl Opng, Via Natrl or Artfcl Opng Endo]
0TBB[0,3,4]ZZ	Exc/Bladder, [Opn, Perc, Perc Endo]
0TBC[0,3,4]ZZ	Exc/Bladder Neck, [Opn, Perc, Perc Endo]
0TC0*	Extir/Kidney, Rt
0TC1*	Extir/Kidney, Lt
0TC3*	Extir/Kidney Pelvis, Rt
0TC4*	Extir/Kidney Pelvis, Lt
0TC6[7,8]ZZ	Extir/Ureter, Rt, [Via Natrl or Artfcl Opng, Via Natrl or Artfcl Opng Endo]
0TC7[7,8]ZZ	Extir/Ureter, Lt, [Via Natrl or Artfcl Opng, Via Natrl or Artfcl Opng Endo]
0TCB[0,3,4]ZZ	Extir/Bladder, [Opn, Perc, Perc Endo]
0TCC[0,3,4]ZZ	Extir/Bladder Neck, [Opn, Perc, Perc Endo]
0TCD[0,3,4]ZZ	Extir/Urethra, [Opn, Perc, Perc Endo]
0TF3[3,4]ZZ	Fragmn/Kidney Pelvis, Rt, [Perc, Perc Endo]
0TF4[3,4]ZZ	Fragmn/Kidney Pelvis, Lt, [Perc, Perc Endo]
0TH5[0,3,4,7,8]2Z	Insert/Kidney, [Opn, Perc, Perc Endo, Via Natrl or Artfcl Opng, Via Natrl or Artfcl Opng Endo], Monitoring Dev, NQ
0THB[0,3,4,7,8][2,L]Z	Insert/Bladder, [Opn, Perc, Perc Endo, Via Natrl or Artfcl Opng, Via Natrl or Artfcl Opng Endo], [Monitoring Dev, Artfcl Sphincter], NQ
0THC*	Insert/Bladder Neck
0THD[0,3,4,7,8,X][2,L]Z	Insert/Urethra, [Opn, Perc, Perc Endo, Via Natrl or Artfcl Opng, Via Natrl or Artfcl Opng Endo, Ext], [Monitoring Dev, Artfcl Sphincter], NQ
0TJ5[0,3,7]ZZ	Inspect/Kidney, [Opn, Perc, Via Natrl or Artfcl Opng]
0TJB[0,3,4,7]ZZ	Inspect/Bladder, [Opn, Perc, Perc Endo, Via Natrl or Artfcl Opng]
0TJD0ZZ	Inspect of Urethra, Opn Appr
0TL3*	Occlsn/Kidney Pelvis, Rt
0TL4*	Occlsn/Kidney Pelvis, Lt
0TL6*	Occlsn/Ureter, Rt
0TL7*	Occlsn/Ureter, Lt
0TLB*	Occlsn/Bladder
0TLC*	Occlsn/Bladder Neck
0TM6*	Reattach/Ureter, Rt
0TM7*	Reattach/Ureter, Lt
0TM8*	Reattach/Ureters, Bilat
0TMB*	Reattach/Bladder
0TMC*	Reattach/Bladder Neck
0TMD*	Reattach/Urethra
0TN0*	Rls/Kidney, Rt
0TN1*	Rls/Kidney, Lt
0TN3*	Rls/Kidney Pelvis, Rt
0TN4*	Rls/Kidney Pelvis, Lt
0TN6*	Rls/Ureter, Rt
0TN7*	Rls/Ureter, Lt
0TNB[0,3,4]ZZ	Rls/Bladder, [Opn, Perc, Perc Endo]
0TNC[0,3,4]ZZ	Rls/Bladder Neck, [Opn, Perc, Perc Endo]
0TND*	Rls/Urethra

Surgical   **Medical**   **CC Indicator**   **MCC Indicator**   **Procedure Proxy**   PDxMCC **PDx acts as own MCC**   PDxCC **PDx acts as own CC**

MDC 21: Injuries, Poisonings And Toxic Effects Of Drugs—SURGICAL

MDC 21: Injuries, Poisonings And Toxic Effects Of Drugs—SURGICAL

ØTP5[Ø,3,4,7,8][Ø,2,3,7,C,D,J,K]Z Rmvl/Kidney, [Opn, Perc, Perc Endo, Via Natrl or Artfcl Opng, Via Natrl or Artfcl Opng Endo], [Drain Dev, Monitoring Dev, Inf Dev, Auto Tissue Sub, Extralum Dev, Intralum Dev, Synth Sub, Nonauto Tissue Sub], NQ

ØTPB[Ø,3,4,7,8][Ø,2,3,7,C,D,J,K,L]Z Rmvl/Bladder, [Opn, Perc, Perc Endo, Via Natrl or Artfcl Opng, Via Natrl or Artfcl Opng Endo], [Drain Dev, Monitoring Dev, Inf Dev, Auto Tissue Sub, Extralum Dev, Intralum Dev, Synth Sub, Nonauto Tissue Sub, Artfcl Sphincter], NQ

ØTPD[Ø,3,4,7,8][Ø,2,3,7,C,D,J,K]Z Rmvl/Urethra, [Opn, Perc, Perc Endo, Via Natrl or Artfcl Opng, Via Natrl or Artfcl Opng Endo], [Drain Dev, Monitoring Dev, Inf Dev, Auto Tissue Sub, Extralum Dev, Intralum Dev, Synth Sub, Nonauto Tissue Sub], NQ

ØTQ3* Repair/Kidney Pelvis, Rt
ØTQ4* Repair/Kidney Pelvis, Lt
ØTQ6* Repair/Ureter, Rt
ØTQ7* Repair/Ureter, Lt
ØTQB* Repair/Bladder
ØTQD* Repair/Urethra
ØTR6* Replace/Ureter, Rt
ØTR7* Replace/Ureter, Lt
ØTRB* Replace/Bladder
ØTRC* Replace/Bladder Neck
ØTRD* Replace/Urethra
ØTSØ* Repos/Kidney, Rt
ØTS1* Repos/Kidney, Lt
ØTS2* Repos/Kidneys, Bilat
ØTTØ* Resect/Kidney, Rt
ØTT1* Resect/Kidney, Lt
ØTT2* Resect/Kidneys, Bilat
ØTT3* Resect/Kidney Pelvis, Rt
ØTT4* Resect/Kidney Pelvis, Lt
ØTT6* Resect/Ureter, Rt
ØTT7* Resect/Ureter, Lt
ØTTB* Resect/Bladder
ØTTC* Resect/Bladder Neck
ØTU6* Supl/Ureter, Rt
ØTU7* Supl/Ureter, Lt
ØTUB* Supl/Bladder
ØTUD* Supl/Urethra
ØTV6* Restrict/Ureter, Rt
ØTV7* Restrict/Ureter, Lt
ØTVB* Restrict/Bladder
ØTVD* Restrict/Urethra

ØTW5[Ø,3,4,7,8][Ø,2,3,7,C,D,J,K]Z Rev/Kidney, [Opn, Perc, Perc Endo, Via Natrl or Artfcl Opng, Via Natrl or Artfcl Opng Endo], [Drain Dev, Monitoring Dev, Inf Dev, Auto Tissue Sub, Extralum Dev, Intralum Dev, Synth Sub, Nonauto Tissue Sub], NQ

ØTWB[Ø,3,4,7,8][Ø,2,3,7,C,D,J,K,L,M]Z Rev/Bladder, [Opn, Perc, Perc Endo, Via Natrl or Artfcl Opng, Via Natrl or Artfcl Opng Endo], [Drain Dev, Monitoring Dev, Inf Dev, Auto Tissue Sub, Extralum Dev, Intralum Dev, Synth Sub, Nonauto Tissue Sub, Artfcl Sphincter, Stimulator Lead], NQ

ØTWD[Ø,3,4,7,8][Ø,2,3,7,C,D,J,K]Z Rev/Urethra, [Opn, Perc, Perc Endo, Via Natrl or Artfcl Opng, Via Natrl or Artfcl Opng Endo], [Drain Dev, Monitoring Dev, Inf Dev, Auto Tissue Sub, Extralum Dev, Intralum Dev, Synth Sub, Nonauto Tissue Sub], NQ

ØU79* Dilation/Uterus
ØU7G[Ø,3,4][D,Z]Z Dilation/Vagina, [Opn, Perc, Perc Endo], [Intralum Dev, No Dev], NQ
ØU7K* Dilation/Hymen
ØU99[Ø,3,4,7,8][Ø,Z]ZDrain/Uterus, [Opn, Perc, Perc Endo, Via Natrl or Artfcl Opng, Via Natrl or Artfcl Opng Endo], [Drain Dev, No Dev], NQ
ØUC9[Ø,3,4]ZZ Extir/Uterus, [Opn, Perc, Perc Endo]
ØUCC* Extir/Cervix
ØUF5[Ø,3,4,7,8]ZZ Fragmn/Fallopian Tube, Rt, [Opn, Perc, Perc Endo, Via Natrl or Artfcl Opng, Via Natrl or Artfcl Opng Endo]
ØUF6[Ø,3,4,7,8]ZZ Fragmn/Fallopian Tube, Lt, [Opn, Perc, Perc Endo, Via Natrl or Artfcl Opng, Via Natrl or Artfcl Opng Endo]
ØUF7[Ø,3,4,7,8]ZZ Fragmn/Fallopian Tubes, Bilat, [Opn, Perc, Perc Endo, Via Natrl or Artfcl Opng, Via Natrl or Artfcl Opng Endo]
ØUHC[Ø,3,4,7,8]1Z Insert/Cervix, [Opn, Perc, Perc Endo, Via Natrl or Artfcl Opng, Via Natrl or Artfcl Opng Endo], Radioact Elmt, NQ
ØUHG[Ø,3,4,7,8,X]1Z Insert/Vagina, [Opn, Perc, Perc Endo, Via Natrl or Artfcl Opng, Via Natrl or Artfcl Opng Endo, Ext], Radioact Elmt, NQ
ØUMØ* Reattach/Ovary, Rt
ØUM1* Reattach/Ovary, Lt
ØUM2* Reattach/Ovaries, Bilat
ØUM4* Reattach/Uterine Supporting Structure
ØUM5* Reattach/Fallopian Tube, Rt

ØUM6* Reattach/Fallopian Tube, Lt
ØUM7* Reattach/Fallopian Tubes, Bilat
ØUMG* Reattach/Vagina
ØUMMXZZ Reattach of Vulva, Ext Appr
ØUNØ* Rls/Ovary, Rt
ØUN1* Rls/Ovary, Lt
ØUN2* Rls/Ovaries, Bilat
ØUN4* Rls/Uterine Supporting Structure
ØUN5* Rls/Fallopian Tube, Rt
ØUN6* Rls/Fallopian Tube, Lt
ØUN7* Rls/Fallopian Tubes, Bilat
ØUNG* Rls/Vagina
ØUNM* Rls/Vulva

ØUPD[Ø,3,4,7,8][Ø,1,3,7,D,J,K]Z Rmvl/Uterus and Cervix, [Opn, Perc, Perc Endo, Via Natrl or Artfcl Opng, Via Natrl or Artfcl Opng Endo], [Drain Dev, Radioact Elmt, Inf Dev, Auto Tissue Sub, Intralum Dev, Synth Sub, Nonauto Tissue Sub], NQ

ØUPD[Ø,3,4]HZ Rmvl/Uterus and Cervix, [Opn, Perc, Perc Endo], Contraceptive Dev, NQ

ØUQØ* Repair/Ovary, Rt
ØUQ1* Repair/Ovary, Lt
ØUQ2* Repair/Ovaries, Bilat
ØUQ4* Repair/Uterine Supporting Structure
ØUQ5* Repair/Fallopian Tube, Rt
ØUQ6* Repair/Fallopian Tube, Lt
ØUQ7* Repair/Fallopian Tubes, Bilat
ØUQ9* Repair/Uterus
ØUQC* Repair/Cervix
ØUQG* Repair/Vagina
ØUQM* Repair/Vulva
ØUSØ* Repos/Ovary, Rt
ØUS1* Repos/Ovary, Lt
ØUS2* Repos/Ovaries, Bilat
ØUS4* Repos/Uterine Supporting Structure
ØUS5* Repos/Fallopian Tube, Rt
ØUS6* Repos/Fallopian Tube, Lt
ØUS7* Repos/Fallopian Tubes, Bilat
ØUSC* Repos/Cervix
ØUU4* Supl/Uterine Supporting Structure

ØUU5[Ø,4,7,8][7,K]Z Supl/Fallopian Tube, Rt, [Opn, Perc Endo, Via Natrl Opng, Via Natrl or Artfcl Opng Endo], [Auto Tissue Sub, Nonauto Tissue Sub], NQ

ØUU6[Ø,4,7,8][7,K]Z Supl/Fallopian Tube, Lt, [Opn, Perc Endo, Via Natrl or Artfcl Opng, Via Natrl or Artfcl Opng Endo], [Auto Tissue Sub, Nonauto Tissue Sub], NQ

ØUU7[Ø,4,7,8][7,K]Z Supl/Fallopian Tubes, Bilat, [Opn, Perc Endo, Via Natrl or Artfcl Opng, Via Natrl or Artfcl Opng Endo], [Auto Tissue Sub, Nonauto Tissue Sub], NQ

ØUUG* Supl/Vagina
ØUUM* Supl/Vulva
ØUV* Female Reproductive Sys, Restrict

ØUWD[Ø,3,4,7,8][Ø,1,3,7,D,H,J,K]Z Rev/Uterus and Cervix, [Opn, Perc, Perc Endo, Via Natrl or Artfcl Opng, Via Natrl or Artfcl Opng Endo], [Drain Dev, Radioact Elmt, Inf Dev, Auto Tissue Sub, Intralum Dev, Contraceptive Dev, Synth Sub, Nonauto Tissue Sub], NQ

ØV7* Male Reproductive Sys, Dilation
ØV99Ø[Ø,Z]Z Drain/Testis, Rt, Opn, [Drain Dev, No Dev], NQ
ØV9BØ[Ø,Z]Z Drain/Testis, Lt, Opn, [Drain Dev, No Dev], NQ
ØV9CØ[Ø,Z]Z Drain/Testes, Bilat, Opn, [Drain Dev, No Dev], NQ
ØVC9* Extir/Testis, Rt
ØVCB* Extir/Testis, Lt
ØVCC* Extir/Testes, Bilat
ØVHØ* Insert/Prostate
ØVLN[Ø,3,4]DZ Occlsn/Vas Deferens, Rt, [Opn, Perc, Perc Endo], Intralum Dev, NQ
ØVLP[Ø,3,4]DZ Occlsn/Vas Deferens, Lt, [Opn, Perc, Perc Endo], Intralum Dev, NQ
ØVLQ[Ø,3,4]DZ Occlsn/Vas Deferens, Bilat, [Opn, Perc, Perc Endo], Intralum Dev, NQ
ØVM* Male Reproductive Sys, Reattach
ØVNØ* Rls/Prostate
ØVN5* Rls/Scrotum
ØVN6* Rls/Tunica Vaginalis, Rt
ØVN7* Rls/Tunica Vaginalis, Lt
ØVNF* Rls/Spermatic Cord, Rt
ØVNG* Rls/Spermatic Cord, Lt
ØVNH* Rls/Spermatic Cords, Bilat
ØVNJ* Rls/Epididymis, Rt
ØVNK* Rls/Epididymis, Lt
ØVNL* Rls/Epididymis, Bilat

T Transfer DRG   SP Special Payment   * Code Range   6th and 7th Character of ZZ = No Device, No Qualifier ZX = No Device, Diagnostic

Code	Description
ØVNN*	Rls/Vas Deferens, Rt
ØVNP*	Rls/Vas Deferens, Lt
ØVNQ*	Rls/Vas Deferens, Bilat
ØVPD[Ø,3,4,7,8][Ø,3,7,J,K]Z	Rmvl/Testis, [Opn, Perc, Perc Endo, Via Natrl or Artfcl Opng, Via Natrl or Artfcl Opng Endo], [Drain Dev, Inf Dev, Auto Tissue Sub, Synth Sub, Nonauto Tissue Sub], NQ
ØVQØ*	Repair/Prostate
ØVQ9*	Repair/Testis, Rt
ØVQB*	Repair/Testis, Lt
ØVQC*	Repair/Testes, Bilat
ØVQF*	Repair/Spermatic Cord, Rt
ØVQG*	Repair/Spermatic Cord, Lt
ØVQH*	Repair/Spermatic Cords, Bilat
ØVQJ*	Repair/Epididymis, Rt
ØVQK*	Repair/Epididymis, Lt
ØVQL*	Repair/Epididymis, Bilat
ØVQN*	Repair/Vas Deferens, Rt
ØVQP*	Repair/Vas Deferens, Lt
ØVQQ*	Repair/Vas Deferens, Bilat
ØVQS*	Repair/Penis
ØVQT*	Repair/Prepuce
ØVSF*	Repos/Spermatic Cord, Rt
ØVSG*	Repos/Spermatic Cord, Lt
ØVSH*	Repos/Spermatic Cords, Bilat
ØVT9*	Resect/Testis, Rt
ØVTB*	Resect/Testis, Lt
ØVTC*	Resect/Testes, Bilat
ØVU5*	Supl/Scrotum
ØVU6*	Supl/Tunica Vaginalis, Rt
ØVU7*	Supl/Tunica Vaginalis, Lt
ØVU9*	Supl/Testis, Rt
ØVUB*	Supl/Testis, Lt
ØVUC*	Supl/Testes, Bilat
ØVUF*	Supl/Spermatic Cord, Rt
ØVUG*	Supl/Spermatic Cord, Lt
ØVUH*	Supl/Spermatic Cords, Bilat
ØVUJ*	Supl/Epididymis, Rt
ØVUK*	Supl/Epididymis, Lt
ØVUL*	Supl/Epididymis, Bilat
ØVUN*	Supl/Vas Deferens, Rt
ØVUP*	Supl/Vas Deferens, Lt
ØVUQ*	Supl/Vas Deferens, Bilat
ØVUS[Ø,4][7,K]Z	Supl/Penis, [Opn, Perc Endo], [Auto Tissue Sub, Nonauto Tissue Sub], NQ
ØVUT*	Supl/Prepuce
ØVWD[Ø,3,4,7,8][Ø,3,7,J,K]Z	Rev/Testis, [Opn, Perc, Perc Endo, Via Natrl or Artfcl Opng, Via Natrl or Artfcl Opng Endo], [Drain Dev, Inf Dev, Auto Tissue Sub, Synth Sub, Nonauto Tissue Sub], NQ
ØWØ*	Anatomical Regions, General, Alter
ØW11*	Bypass/Cranial Cavity
ØW19[Ø,4]J[9,B,J]	Bypass/Pleural Cavity, Rt, [Opn, Perc Endo], Synth Sub, [Pleural Cavity, Rt, Pleural Cavity, Lt, Pelvic Cavity]
ØW1B[Ø,4]J[9,B,J]	Bypass/Pleural Cavity, Lt, [Opn, Perc Endo], Synth Sub, [Pleural Cavity, Rt, Pleural Cavity, Lt, Pelvic Cavity]
ØW1G[Ø,3,4]J4	Bypass/Peritoneal Cavity, [Opn, Perc, Perc Endo], Synth Sub, Cutaneous
ØW3Ø*	Control/Head
ØW31*	Control/Cranial Cavity
ØW32*	Control/Face
ØW33*	Control/Oral Cavity and Throat
ØW34*	Control/Upr Jaw
ØW35*	Control/Lwr Jaw
ØW36*	Control/Neck
ØW38*	Control/Chest Wall
ØW39*	Control/Pleural Cavity, Rt
ØW3B*	Control/Pleural Cavity, Lt
ØW3C*	Control/Mediastinum
ØW3D*	Control/Pericardial Cavity
ØW3F*	Control/Abd Wall
ØW3G[3,4]ZZ	Control/Peritoneal Cavity, [Perc, Perc Endo]
ØW3H*	Control/Retroperitoneum
ØW3J*	Control/Pelvic Cavity
ØW3K*	Control/Upr Back
ØW3L*	Control/Lwr Back
ØW3M*	Control/Perineum, Male
ØW3N*	Control/Perineum, Female
ØW3P[Ø,3,4,7]ZZ	Control/Gastrointestinal Tract, [Opn, Perc, Perc Endo, Via Natrl or Artfcl Opng]
ØW3Q*	Control/Respiratory Tract
ØW3R*	Control/Genitourinary Tract
ØW91Ø[Ø,Z]Z	Drain/Cranial Cavity, Opn, [Drain Dev, No Dev], NQ
ØW92[Ø,3,4][Ø,Z]Z	Drain/Face, [Opn, Perc, Perc Endo], [Drain Dev, No Dev], NQ
ØW93[Ø,3,4][Ø,Z]Z	Drain/Oral Cavity and Throat, [Opn, Perc, Perc Endo], [Drain Dev, No Dev], NQ
ØW94[Ø,3,4][Ø,Z]Z	Drain/Upr Jaw, [Opn, Perc, Perc Endo], [Drain Dev, No Dev], NQ
ØW95[Ø,3,4][Ø,Z]Z	Drain/Lwr Jaw, [Opn, Perc, Perc Endo], [Drain Dev, No Dev], NQ
ØW96[Ø,3,4][Ø,Z]Z	Drain/Neck, [Opn, Perc, Perc Endo], [Drain Dev, No Dev], NQ
ØW9C[Ø,3,4][Ø,Z]Z	Drain/Mediastinum, [Opn, Perc, Perc Endo], [Drain Dev, No Dev], NQ
ØW9DØZX	Drain of Pericardial Cavity, Opn Appr, Diagnostic
ØW9DØ[Ø,Z]Z	Drain/Pericardial Cavity, Opn, [Drain Dev, No Dev], NQ
ØW9FØØZ	Drain of Abd Wall with Drain Dev, Opn Appr
ØW9FØZZ	Drain of Abd Wall, Opn Appr
ØW9F[Ø,3,4]ZX	Drain/Abd Wall, [Opn, Perc, Perc Endo]
ØW9GØØZ	Drain of Peritoneal Cavity with Drain Dev, Opn Appr
ØW9GØZZ	Drain of Peritoneal Cavity, Opn Appr
ØW9G[Ø,3,4]ZX	Drain/Peritoneal Cavity, [Opn, Perc, Perc Endo]
ØW9H*	Drain/Retroperitoneum
ØW9J[Ø,3,4]ZX	Drain/Pelvic Cavity, [Opn, Perc, Perc Endo]
ØW9J[Ø,4]ØZ	Drain/Pelvic Cavity, [Opn, Perc Endo], Drain Dev, NQ
ØW9J[Ø,4]ZZ	Drain/Pelvic Cavity, [Opn, Perc Endo]
ØWBØ[Ø,3,4,X]ZZ	Exc/Head, [Opn, Perc, Perc Endo, Ext]
ØWB2[Ø,3,4,X]ZZ	Exc/Face, [Opn, Perc, Perc Endo, Ext]
ØWB4[Ø,3,4,X]ZZ	Exc/Upr Jaw, [Opn, Perc, Perc Endo, Ext]
ØWB5[Ø,3,4,X]ZZ	Exc/Lwr Jaw, [Opn, Perc, Perc Endo, Ext]
ØWB6XZ2	Exc of Neck, Stoma, Ext Appr
ØWB6[Ø,3,4,X]ZZ	Exc/Neck, [Opn, Perc, Perc Endo, Ext]
ØWBF[Ø,3,4,X]ZX	Exc/Abd Wall, [Opn, Perc, Perc Endo, Ext]
ØWBK[Ø,3,4,X]ZZ	Exc/Upr Back, [Opn, Perc, Perc Endo, Ext]
ØWBL[Ø,3,4,X]ZZ	Exc/Lwr Back, [Opn, Perc, Perc Endo, Ext]
ØWBM[Ø,3,4,X]ZZ	Exc/Perineum, Male, [Opn, Perc, Perc Endo, Ext]
ØWC1[Ø,3,4]ZZ	Extir/Cranial Cavity, [Opn, Perc, Perc Endo]
ØWC3[Ø,3,4]ZZ	Extir/Oral Cavity and Throat, [Opn, Perc, Perc Endo]
ØWCC[Ø,3,4]ZZ	Extir/Mediastinum, [Opn, Perc, Perc Endo]
ØWCD[Ø,3,4]ZZ	Extir/Pericardial Cavity, [Opn, Perc, Perc Endo]
ØWCG[Ø,3,4]ZZ	Extir/Peritoneal Cavity, [Opn, Perc, Perc Endo]
ØWCJ[Ø,3,4]ZZ	Extir/Pelvic Cavity, [Opn, Perc, Perc Endo]
ØWCP[Ø,3,4]ZZ	Extir/Gastrointestinal Tract, [Opn, Perc, Perc Endo]
ØWCQ[7,8]ZZ	Extir/Respiratory Tract, [Via Natrl or Artfcl Opng, Via Natrl or Artfcl Opng Endo]
ØWCR[Ø,3,4]ZZ	Extir/Genitourinary Tract, [Opn, Perc, Perc Endo]
ØWF1[Ø,3,4]ZZ	Fragmn/Cranial Cavity, [Opn, Perc, Perc Endo]
ØWF3[Ø,3,4]ZZ	Fragmn/Oral Cavity and Throat, [Opn, Perc, Perc Endo]
ØWF9[Ø,3,4]ZZ	Fragmn/Pleural Cavity, Rt, [Opn, Perc, Perc Endo]
ØWFB[Ø,3,4]ZZ	Fragmn/Pleural Cavity, Lt, [Opn, Perc, Perc Endo]
ØWFC[Ø,3,4]ZZ	Fragmn/Mediastinum, [Opn, Perc, Perc Endo]
ØWFD*	Fragmn/Pericardial Cavity
ØWFG[Ø,3,4]ZZ	Fragmn/Peritoneal Cavity, [Opn, Perc, Perc Endo]
ØWFQ[Ø,3,4,7,8]ZZ	Fragmn/Respiratory Tract, [Opn, Perc, Perc Endo, Via Natrl or Artfcl Opng, Via Natrl or Artfcl Opng Endo]
ØWHØ[Ø,3,4]1Z	Insert/Head, [Opn, Perc, Perc Endo], Radioact Elmt, NQ
ØWH1[Ø,3,4]1Z	Insert/Cranial Cavity, [Opn, Perc, Perc Endo], Radioact Elmt, NQ
ØWH2[Ø,3,4]1Z	Insert/Face, [Opn, Perc, Perc Endo], Radioact Elmt, NQ
ØWH3*	Insert/Oral Cavity and Throat
ØWH4[Ø,3,4]1Z	Insert/Upr Jaw, [Opn, Perc, Perc Endo], Radioact Elmt, NQ
ØWH5[Ø,3,4]1Z	Insert/Lwr Jaw, [Opn, Perc, Perc Endo], Radioact Elmt, NQ
ØWH6[Ø,3,4]1Z	Insert/Neck, [Opn, Perc, Perc Endo], Radioact Elmt, NQ
ØWH8[Ø,3,4]1Z	Insert/Chest Wall, [Opn, Perc, Perc Endo], Radioact Elmt, NQ
ØWH9[Ø,3,4]1Z	Insert/Pleural Cavity, Rt, [Opn, Perc, Perc Endo], Radioact Elmt, NQ
ØWHB[Ø,3,4]1Z	Insert/Pleural Cavity, Lt, [Opn, Perc, Perc Endo], Radioact Elmt, NQ
ØWHC*	Insert/Mediastinum
ØWHD*	Insert/Pericardial Cavity
ØWHF*	Insert/Abd Wall
ØWHG[Ø,3,4]1Z	Insert/Peritoneal Cavity, [Opn, Perc, Perc Endo], Radioact Elmt, NQ
ØWHH[Ø,3,4]1Z	Insert/Retroperitoneum, [Opn, Perc, Perc Endo], Radioact Elmt, NQ
ØWHJ[Ø,3,4]1Z	Insert/Pelvic Cavity, [Opn, Perc, Perc Endo], Radioact Elmt, NQ
ØWHK[Ø,3,4]1Z	Insert/Upr Back, [Opn, Perc, Perc Endo], Radioact Elmt, NQ
ØWHL[Ø,3,4]1Z	Insert/Lwr Back, [Opn, Perc, Perc Endo], Radioact Elmt, NQ
ØWHM[Ø,3,4]1Z	Insert/Perineum, Male, [Opn, Perc, Perc Endo], Radioact Elmt, NQ
ØWHN[Ø,3,4]1Z	Insert/Perineum, Female, [Opn, Perc, Perc Endo], Radioact Elmt, NQ
ØWHP[Ø,3,4,7,8]1Z	Insert/Gastrointestinal Tract, [Opn, Perc, Perc Endo, Via Natrl or Artfcl Opng, Via Natrl or Artfcl Opng Endo], Radioact Elmt, NQ

Surgical   **Medical**   **CC Indicator**   **MCC Indicator**   **Procedure Proxy**   **PDxMCC** **PDx acts as own MCC**   **PDxCC** **PDx acts as own CC**

© 2015 Optum360, LLC   MS-DRG Version 33.0   **355**

MDC 21: Injuries, Poisonings And Toxic Effects Of Drugs—SURGICAL

MDC 21: Injuries, Poisonings And Toxic Effects Of Drugs—SURGICAL

Code	Description
0WHQ[0,3,4,7,8]1Z	Insert/Respiratory Tract, [Opn, Perc, Perc Endo, Via Natrl or Artfcl Opng, Via Natrl or Artfcl Opng Endo], Radioact Elmt, NQ
0WHQ[3,4]3Z	Insert/Respiratory Tract, [Perc, Perc Endo], Inf Dev, NQ
0WHQ[3,4]YZ	Insert/Respiratory Tract, [Perc, Perc Endo], Oth Dev, NQ
0WHR[0,3,4,7,8]1Z	Insert/Genitourinary Tract, [Opn, Perc, Perc Endo, Via Natrl or Artfcl Opng, Via Natrl or Artfcl Opng Endo], Radioact Elmt, NQ
0WJ1*	Inspect/Cranial Cavity
0WJ6[0,3,4]ZZ	Inspect/Neck, [Opn, Perc, Perc Endo]
0WJ9[0,4]ZZ	Inspect/Pleural Cavity, Rt, [Opn, Perc Endo]
0WJB[0,4]ZZ	Inspect/Pleural Cavity, Lt, [Opn, Perc Endo]
0WJC0ZZ	Inspect of Mediastinum, Opn Appr
0WJF[0,3,4]ZZ	Inspect/Abd Wall, [Opn, Perc, Perc Endo]
0WJG*	Inspect/Peritoneal Cavity
0WJH*	Inspect/Retroperitoneum
0WJJ*	Inspect/Pelvic Cavity
0WJP*	Inspect/Gastrointestinal Tract
0WJQ[0,4]ZZ	Inspect/Respiratory Tract, [Opn, Perc Endo]
0WJR*	Inspect/Genitourinary Tract
0WM*	Anatomical Regions, General, Reattach
0WPC[0,3,4][0,1,3,7,J,K,Y]Z	Rmvl/Mediastinum, [Opn, Perc, Perc Endo], [Drain Dev, Radioact Elmt, Inf Dev, Auto Tissue Sub, Synth Sub, Nonauto Tissue Sub, Oth Dev], NQ
0WPD[0,3,4][0,1,3,Y]Z	Rmvl/Pericardial Cavity, [Opn, Perc, Perc Endo], [Drain Dev, Radioact Elmt, Inf Dev, Oth Dev], NQ
0WPF[0,3,4][0,1,3,7,J,K,Y]Z	Rmvl/Abd Wall, [Opn, Perc, Perc Endo], [Drain Dev, Radioact Elmt, Inf Dev, Auto Tissue Sub, Synth Sub, Nonauto Tissue Sub, Oth Dev], NQ
0WPQ81Z	Rmvl of Radioact Elmt from Respiratory Tract, Endo
0WPQ[3,4,7][1,3,Y]Z	Rmvl/Respiratory Tract, [Perc, Perc Endo, Via Natrl or Artfcl Opng], [Radioact Elmt, Inf Dev, Oth Dev], NQ
0WQ0*	Repair/Head
0WQ2*	Repair/Face
0WQ4*	Repair/Upr Jaw
0WQ5*	Repair/Lwr Jaw
0WQ6*	Repair/Neck
0WQ8*	Repair/Chest Wall
0WQC*	Repair/Mediastinum
0WQF*	Repair/Abd Wall
0WQK*	Repair/Upr Back
0WQL*	Repair/Lwr Back
0WQM*	Repair/Perineum, Male
0WQN[0,3,4]ZZ	Rpr/Perineum, Female, [Opn, Perc, Perc Endo]
0WU0[0,4][J,K]Z	Supl/Head, [Opn, Perc Endo], [Synth Sub, Nonauto Tissue Sub], NQ
0WU2*	Supl/Face
0WU4*	Supl/Upr Jaw
0WU5*	Supl/Lwr Jaw
0WU6[0,4][J,K]Z	Supl/Neck, [Opn, Perc Endo], [Synth Sub, Nonauto Tissue Sub], NQ
0WUC*	Supl/Mediastinum
0WUF*	Supl/Abd Wall
0WUK[0,4][J,K]Z	Supl/Upr Back, [Opn, Perc Endo], [Synth Sub, Nonauto Tissue Sub], NQ
0WUL[0,4][J,K]Z	Supl/Lwr Back, [Opn, Perc Endo], [Synth Sub, Nonauto Tissue Sub], NQ
0WUM[0,4][J,K]Z	Supl/Perineum, Male, [Opn, Perc Endo], [Synth Sub, Nonauto Tissue Sub], NQ
0WUN*	Supl/Perineum, Female
0WWC[0,3,4][0,1,3,7,J,K,Y]Z	Rev/Mediastinum, [Opn, Perc, Perc Endo], [Drain Dev, Radioact Elmt, Inf Dev, Auto Tissue Sub, Synth Sub, Nonauto Tissue Sub, Oth Dev], NQ
0WWD[0,3,4][0,1,3,Y]Z	Rev/Pericardial Cavity, [Opn, Perc, Perc Endo], [Drain Dev, Radioact Elmt, Inf Dev, Oth Dev], NQ
0WWF[0,3,4][0,1,3,7,J,K,Y]Z	Rev/Abd Wall, [Opn, Perc, Perc Endo], [Drain Dev, Radioact Elmt, Inf Dev, Auto Tissue Sub, Synth Sub, Nonauto Tissue Sub, Oth Dev], NQ
0WWQ[3,4,7,8][1,3,Y]Z	Rev/Respiratory Tract, [Perc, Perc Endo, Via Natrl or Artfcl Opng, Via Natrl or Artfcl Opng Endo], [Radioact Elmt, Inf Dev, Oth Dev], NQ
0X0*	Anatomical Regions, Upr Extremities, Alter
0X3*	Anatomical Regions, Upr Extremities, Control
0X600ZZ	Detach at Rt Forequarter, Opn Appr
0X610ZZ	Detach at Lt Forequarter, Opn Appr
0X620ZZ	Detach at Rt Shldr Region, Opn Appr
0X630ZZ	Detach at Lt Shldr Region, Opn Appr
0X68*	Detach/Upr Arm, Rt
0X69*	Detach/Upr Arm, Lt
0X6B0ZZ	Detach at Rt Elbow Region, Opn Appr
0X6C0ZZ	Detach at Lt Elbow Region, Opn Appr
0X6D*	Detach/Lwr Arm, Rt
0X6F*	Detach/Lwr Arm, Lt
0X6J*	Detach/Hand, Rt
0X6K*	Detach/Hand, Lt
0XB2[0,3,4]ZZ	Exc/Shldr Rgn, Rt, [Opn, Perc, Perc Endo]
0XB3[0,3,4]ZZ	Exc/Shldr Rgn, Lt, [Opn, Perc, Perc Endo]
0XB4[0,3,4]ZZ	Exc/Axilla, Rt, [Opn, Perc, Perc Endo]
0XB5[0,3,4]ZZ	Exc/Axilla, Lt, [Opn, Perc, Perc Endo]
0XB6[0,3,4]ZZ	Exc/Upr Extr, Rt, [Opn, Perc, Perc Endo]
0XB7[0,3,4]ZZ	Exc/Upr Extr, Lt, [Opn, Perc, Perc Endo]
0XB8[0,3,4]ZZ	Exc/Upr Arm, Rt, [Opn, Perc, Perc Endo]
0XB9[0,3,4]ZZ	Exc/Upr Arm, Lt, [Opn, Perc, Perc Endo]
0XBB[0,3,4]ZZ	Exc/Elbow Rgn, Rt, [Opn, Perc, Perc Endo]
0XBC[0,3,4]ZZ	Exc/Elbow Rgn, Lt, [Opn, Perc, Perc Endo]
0XBD[0,3,4]ZZ	Exc/Lwr Arm, Rt, [Opn, Perc, Perc Endo]
0XBF[0,3,4]ZZ	Exc/Lwr Arm, Lt, [Opn, Perc, Perc Endo]
0XBG[0,3,4]ZZ	Exc/Wrist Rgn, Rt, [Opn, Perc, Perc Endo]
0XBH[0,3,4]ZZ	Exc/Wrist Rgn, Lt, [Opn, Perc, Perc Endo]
0XBJ[0,3,4]ZZ	Exc/Hand, Rt, [Opn, Perc, Perc Endo]
0XBK[0,3,4]ZZ	Exc/Hand, Lt, [Opn, Perc, Perc Endo]
0XH2[0,3,4]1Z	Insert/Shldr Rgn, Rt, [Opn, Perc, Perc Endo], Radioact Elmt, NQ
0XH3[0,3,4]1Z	Insert/Shldr Rgn, Lt, [Opn, Perc, Perc Endo], Radioact Elmt, NQ
0XH4[0,3,4]1Z	Insert/Axilla, Rt, [Opn, Perc, Perc Endo], Radioact Elmt, NQ
0XH5[0,3,4]1Z	Insert/Axilla, Lt, [Opn, Perc, Perc Endo], Radioact Elmt, NQ
0XH6[0,3,4]1Z	Insert/Upr Extr, Rt, [Opn, Perc, Perc Endo], Radioact Elmt, NQ
0XH7[0,3,4]1Z	Insert/Upr Extr, Lt, [Opn, Perc, Perc Endo], Radioact Elmt, NQ
0XH8[0,3,4]1Z	Insert/Upr Arm, Rt, [Opn, Perc, Perc Endo], Radioact Elmt, NQ
0XH9[0,3,4]1Z	Insert/Upr Arm, Lt, [Opn, Perc, Perc Endo], Radioact Elmt, NQ
0XHB[0,3,4]1Z	Insert/Elbow Rgn, Rt, [Opn, Perc, Perc Endo], Radioact Elmt, NQ
0XHC[0,3,4]1Z	Insert/Elbow Rgn, Lt, [Opn, Perc, Perc Endo], Radioact Elmt, NQ
0XHD[0,3,4]1Z	Insert/Lwr Arm, Rt, [Opn, Perc, Perc Endo], Radioact Elmt, NQ
0XHF[0,3,4]1Z	Insert/Lwr Arm, Lt, [Opn, Perc, Perc Endo], Radioact Elmt, NQ
0XHG[0,3,4]1Z	Insert/Wrist Rgn, Rt, [Opn, Perc, Perc Endo], Radioact Elmt, NQ
0XHH[0,3,4]1Z	Insert/Wrist Rgn, Lt, [Opn, Perc, Perc Endo], Radioact Elmt, NQ
0XHJ[0,3,4]1Z	Insert/Hand, Rt, [Opn, Perc, Perc Endo], Radioact Elmt, NQ
0XHK[0,3,4]1Z	Insert/Hand, Lt, [Opn, Perc, Perc Endo], Radioact Elmt, NQ
0XM00ZZ	Reattach of Rt Forequarter, Opn Appr
0XM10ZZ	Reattach of Lt Forequarter, Opn Appr
0XM20ZZ	Reattach of Rt Shldr Region, Opn Appr
0XM30ZZ	Reattach of Lt Shldr Region, Opn Appr
0XM40ZZ	Reattach of Rt Axilla, Opn Appr
0XM50ZZ	Reattach of Lt Axilla, Opn Appr
0XM60ZZ	Reattach of Rt Upr Extr, Opn Appr
0XM70ZZ	Reattach of Lt Upr Extr, Opn Appr
0XM80ZZ	Reattach of Rt Upr Arm, Opn Appr
0XM90ZZ	Reattach of Lt Upr Arm, Opn Appr
0XMB0ZZ	Reattach of Rt Elbow Region, Opn Appr
0XMC0ZZ	Reattach of Lt Elbow Region, Opn Appr
0XMD0ZZ	Reattach of Rt Lwr Arm, Opn Appr
0XMF0ZZ	Reattach of Lt Lwr Arm, Opn Appr
0XMG0ZZ	Reattach of Rt Wrist Region, Opn Appr
0XMH0ZZ	Reattach of Lt Wrist Region, Opn Appr
0XMJ0ZZ	Reattach of Rt Hand, Opn Appr
0XMK0ZZ	Reattach of Lt Hand, Opn Appr
0XQ*	Anatomical Regions, Upr Extremities, Repair
0XU2[0,4][J,K]Z	Supl/Shldr Rgn, Rt, [Opn, Perc Endo], [Synth Sub, Nonauto Tissue Sub], NQ
0XU3[0,4][J,K]Z	Supl/Shldr Rgn, Lt, [Opn, Perc Endo], [Synth Sub, Nonauto Tissue Sub], NQ
0XU4[0,4][J,K]Z	Supl/Axilla, Rt, [Opn, Perc Endo], [Synth Sub, Nonauto Tissue Sub], NQ
0XU5[0,4][J,K]Z	Supl/Axilla, Lt, [Opn, Perc Endo], [Synth Sub, Nonauto Tissue Sub], NQ
0XU6[0,4][J,K]Z	Supl/Upr Extr, Rt, [Opn, Perc Endo], [Synth Sub, Nonauto Tissue Sub], NQ
0XU7[0,4][J,K]Z	Supl/Upr Extr, Lt, [Opn, Perc Endo], [Synth Sub, Nonauto Tissue Sub], NQ
0XU8[0,4][J,K]Z	Supl/Upr Arm, Rt, [Opn, Perc Endo], [Synth Sub, Nonauto Tissue Sub], NQ
0XU9[0,4][J,K]Z	Supl/Upr Arm, Lt, [Opn, Perc Endo], [Synth Sub, Nonauto Tissue Sub], NQ
0XUB[0,4][J,K]Z	Supl/Elbow Rgn, Rt, [Opn, Perc Endo], [Synth Sub, Nonauto Tissue Sub], NQ
0XUC[0,4][J,K]Z	Supl/Elbow Rgn, Lt, [Opn, Perc Endo], [Synth Sub, Nonauto Tissue Sub], NQ
0XUD[0,4][J,K]Z	Supl/Lwr Arm, Rt, [Opn, Perc Endo], [Synth Sub, Nonauto Tissue Sub], NQ
0XUF[0,4][J,K]Z	Supl/Lwr Arm, Lt, [Opn, Perc Endo], [Synth Sub, Nonauto Tissue Sub], NQ

Ⓣ **Transfer DRG**   ⓈⓅ **Special Payment**   * **Code Range**   **6th and 7th Character of ZZ = No Device, No Qualifier ZX = No Device, Diagnostic**

ØXUG[Ø,4][J,K]Z	Supl/Wrist Rgn, Rt, [Opn, Perc Endo], [Synth Sub, Nonauto Tissue Sub], NQ
ØXUH[Ø,4][J,K]Z	Supl/Wrist Rgn, Lt, [Opn, Perc Endo], [Synth Sub, Nonauto Tissue Sub], NQ
ØXUJ[Ø,4][J,K]Z	Supl/Hand, Rt, [Opn, Perc Endo], [Synth Sub, Nonauto Tissue Sub], NQ
ØXUK[Ø,4][J,K]Z	Supl/Hand, Lt, [Opn, Perc Endo], [Synth Sub, Nonauto Tissue Sub], NQ
ØXUL[Ø,4][J,K]Z	Supl/Thumb, Rt, [Opn, Perc Endo], [Synth Sub, Nonauto Tissue Sub], NQ
ØXUM[Ø,4][J,K]Z	Supl/Thumb, Lt, [Opn, Perc Endo], [Synth Sub, Nonauto Tissue Sub], NQ
ØXUN[Ø,4][J,K]Z	Supl/Index Finger, Rt, [Opn, Perc Endo], [Synth Sub, Nonauto Tissue Sub], NQ
ØXUP[Ø,4][J,K]Z	Supl/Index Finger, Lt, [Opn, Perc Endo], [Synth Sub, Nonauto Tissue Sub], NQ
ØXUQ[Ø,4][J,K]Z	Supl/Mid Finger, Rt, [Opn, Perc Endo], [Synth Sub, Nonauto Tissue Sub], NQ
ØXUR[Ø,4][J,K]Z	Supl/Mid Finger, Lt, [Opn, Perc Endo], [Synth Sub, Nonauto Tissue Sub], NQ
ØXUS[Ø,4][J,K]Z	Supl/Ring Finger, Rt, [Opn, Perc Endo], [Synth Sub, Nonauto Tissue Sub], NQ
ØXUT[Ø,4][J,K]Z	Supl/Ring Finger, Lt, [Opn, Perc Endo], [Synth Sub, Nonauto Tissue Sub], NQ
ØXUV[Ø,4][J,K]Z	Supl/Little Finger, Rt, [Opn, Perc Endo], [Synth Sub, Nonauto Tissue Sub], NQ
ØXUW[Ø,4][J,K]Z	Supl/Little Finger, Lt, [Opn, Perc Endo], [Synth Sub, Nonauto Tissue Sub], NQ
ØYØ*	Anatomical Regions, Lwr Extremities, Alter
ØY3*	Anatomical Regions, Lwr Extremities, Control
ØY6*	Anatomical Regions, Lwr Extremities, Detach
ØY95*	Drain/Inguinal Region, Rt
ØY96*	Drain/Inguinal Region, Lt
ØYBØ[Ø,3,4]ZZ	Exc/Buttock, Rt, [Opn, Perc, Perc Endo]
ØYB1[Ø,3,4]ZZ	Exc/Buttock, Lt, [Opn, Perc, Perc Endo]
ØYB5[Ø,3,4]ZX	Exc/Inguinal Rgn, Rt, [Opn, Perc, Perc Endo]
ØYB6[Ø,3,4]ZX	Exc/Inguinal Rgn, Lt, [Opn, Perc, Perc Endo]
ØYB7[Ø,3,4]ZX	Exc/Femor Rgn, Rt, [Opn, Perc, Perc Endo]
ØYB8[Ø,3,4]ZX	Exc/Femor Rgn, Lt, [Opn, Perc, Perc Endo]
ØYB9[Ø,3,4]ZZ	Exc/Lwr Extr, Rt, [Opn, Perc, Perc Endo]
ØYBB[Ø,3,4]ZZ	Exc/Lwr Extr, Lt, [Opn, Perc, Perc Endo]
ØYBC[Ø,3,4]ZZ	Exc/Upr Leg, Rt, [Opn, Perc, Perc Endo]
ØYBD[Ø,3,4]ZZ	Exc/Upr Leg, Lt, [Opn, Perc, Perc Endo]
ØYBF[Ø,3,4]ZZ	Exc/Knee Rgn, Rt, [Opn, Perc, Perc Endo]
ØYBG[Ø,3,4]ZZ	Exc/Knee Rgn, Lt, [Opn, Perc, Perc Endo]
ØYBH[Ø,3,4]ZZ	Exc/Lwr Leg, Rt, [Opn, Perc, Perc Endo]
ØYBJ[Ø,3,4]ZZ	Exc/Lwr Leg, Lt, [Opn, Perc, Perc Endo]
ØYBK[Ø,3,4]ZZ	Exc/Ankle Rgn, Rt, [Opn, Perc, Perc Endo]
ØYBL[Ø,3,4]ZZ	Exc/Ankle Rgn, Lt, [Opn, Perc, Perc Endo]
ØYBM[Ø,3,4]ZZ	Exc/Foot, Rt, [Opn, Perc, Perc Endo]
ØYBN[Ø,3,4]ZZ	Exc/Foot, Lt, [Opn, Perc, Perc Endo]
ØYHØ[Ø,3,4]1Z	Insert/Buttock, Rt, [Opn, Perc, Perc Endo], Radioact Elmt, NQ
ØYH1[Ø,3,4]1Z	Insert/Buttock, Lt, [Opn, Perc, Perc Endo], Radioact Elmt, NQ
ØYH5[Ø,3,4]1Z	Insert/Inguinal Rgn, Rt, [Opn, Perc, Perc Endo], Radioact Elmt, NQ
ØYH6[Ø,3,4]1Z	Insert/Inguinal Rgn, Lt, [Opn, Perc, Perc Endo], Radioact Elmt, NQ
ØYH7[Ø,3,4]1Z	Insert/Femor Rgn, Rt, [Opn, Perc, Perc Endo], Radioact Elmt, NQ
ØYH8[Ø,3,4]1Z	Insert/Femor Rgn, Lt, [Opn, Perc, Perc Endo], Radioact Elmt, NQ
ØYH9[Ø,3,4]1Z	Insert/Lwr Extr, Rt, [Opn, Perc, Perc Endo], Radioact Elmt, NQ
ØYHB[Ø,3,4]1Z	Insert/Lwr Extr, Lt, [Opn, Perc, Perc Endo], Radioact Elmt, NQ
ØYHC[Ø,3,4]1Z	Insert/Upr Leg, Rt, [Opn, Perc, Perc Endo], Radioact Elmt, NQ
ØYHD[Ø,3,4]1Z	Insert/Upr Leg, Lt, [Opn, Perc, Perc Endo], Radioact Elmt, NQ
ØYHF[Ø,3,4]1Z	Insert/Knee Rgn, Rt, [Opn, Perc, Perc Endo], Radioact Elmt, NQ
ØYHG[Ø,3,4]1Z	Insert/Knee Rgn, Lt, [Opn, Perc, Perc Endo], Radioact Elmt, NQ
ØYHH[Ø,3,4]1Z	Insert/Lwr Leg, Rt, [Opn, Perc, Perc Endo], Radioact Elmt, NQ
ØYHJ[Ø,3,4]1Z	Insert/Lwr Leg, Lt, [Opn, Perc, Perc Endo], Radioact Elmt, NQ
ØYHK[Ø,3,4]1Z	Insert/Ankle Rgn, Rt, [Opn, Perc, Perc Endo], Radioact Elmt, NQ
ØYHL[Ø,3,4]1Z	Insert/Ankle Rgn, Lt, [Opn, Perc, Perc Endo], Radioact Elmt, NQ
ØYHM[Ø,3,4]1Z	Insert/Foot, Rt, [Opn, Perc, Perc Endo], Radioact Elmt, NQ
ØYHN[Ø,3,4]1Z	Insert/Foot, Lt, [Opn, Perc, Perc Endo], Radioact Elmt, NQ
ØYJ5[Ø,3,4]ZZ	Inspect/Inguinal Rgn, Rt, [Opn, Perc, Perc Endo]
ØYJ6[Ø,3,4]ZZ	Inspect/Inguinal Rgn, Lt, [Opn, Perc, Perc Endo]
ØYJ7[Ø,3,4]ZZ	Inspect/Femor Rgn, Rt, [Opn, Perc, Perc Endo]
ØYJ8[3,4]ZZ	Inspect/Femor Rgn, Lt, [Perc, Perc Endo]
ØYJA[Ø,3,4]ZZ	Inspect/Inguinal Rgn, Bilat, [Opn, Perc, Perc Endo]
ØYJE[3,4]ZZ	Inspect/Femor Rgn, Bilat, [Perc, Perc Endo]
ØYM*	Anatomical Regions, Lwr Extremities, Reattach

ØYQØ*	Repair/Buttock, Rt
ØYQ1*	Repair/Buttock, Lt
ØYQ9*	Repair/Lwr Extr, Rt
ØYQB*	Repair/Lwr Extr, Lt
ØYQC*	Repair/Upr Leg, Rt
ØYQD*	Repair/Upr Leg, Lt
ØYQF*	Repair/Knee Region, Rt
ØYQG*	Repair/Knee Region, Lt
ØYQH*	Repair/Lwr Leg, Rt
ØYQJ*	Repair/Lwr Leg, Lt
ØYQK*	Repair/Ankle Region, Rt
ØYQL*	Repair/Ankle Region, Lt
ØYQM*	Repair/Foot, Rt
ØYQN*	Repair/Foot, Lt
ØYQP*	Repair/1st Toe, Rt
ØYQQ*	Repair/1st Toe, Lt
ØYQR*	Repair/2nd Toe, Rt
ØYQS*	Repair/2nd Toe, Lt
ØYQT*	Repair/3rd Toe, Rt
ØYQU*	Repair/3rd Toe, Lt
ØYQV*	Repair/4th Toe, Rt
ØYQW*	Repair/4th Toe, Lt
ØYQX*	Repair/5th Toe, Rt
ØYQY*	Repair/5th Toe, Lt
ØYUØ*	Supl/Buttock, Rt
ØYU1*	Supl/Buttock, Lt
ØYU9*	Supl/Lwr Extr, Rt
ØYUB*	Supl/Lwr Extr, Lt
ØYUC*	Supl/Upr Leg, Rt
ØYUD*	Supl/Upr Leg, Lt
ØYUF*	Supl/Knee Region, Rt
ØYUG*	Supl/Knee Region, Lt
ØYUH*	Supl/Lwr Leg, Rt
ØYUJ*	Supl/Lwr Leg, Lt
ØYUK*	Supl/Ankle Region, Rt
ØYUL*	Supl/Ankle Region, Lt
ØYUM*	Supl/Foot, Rt
ØYUN*	Supl/Foot, Lt
ØYUP*	Supl/1st Toe, Rt
ØYUQ*	Supl/1st Toe, Lt
ØYUR*	Supl/2nd Toe, Rt
ØYUS*	Supl/2nd Toe, Lt
ØYUT*	Supl/3rd Toe, Rt
ØYUU*	Supl/3rd Toe, Lt
ØYUV*	Supl/4th Toe, Rt
ØYUW*	Supl/4th Toe, Lt
ØYUX*	Supl/5th Toe, Rt
ØYUY*	Supl/5th Toe, Lt
3EØC3GC	Introduction of Oth Therap Subst into Eye, Perc Appr
3EØC[3,7,X]MZ	Introduction/Eye, [Perc, Via Natrl or Artfcl Opng, Ext], Pigment, NQ
3EØC[3,X]SF	Introduction/Eye, [Perc, Ext], Gas, Oth Gas
FØDZ8ZZ	Prosthesis Device Fitting
FØDZ9[E,F,U,Z]Z	Adaptive,Supportive or Protective Devs Dev Fitting using [Orthosis, Assistive, Adaptive, Supportive or Protective Equipment, Prosthesis, No Dev]

OR

Any of the following procedure combinations

02H4[Ø,4][J,M]Z	Insert/Coronary Vein, [Opn, Perc Endo], [Cardiac Lead, Pacemaker, Cardiac Lead], NQ
02H6[Ø,3,4]JZ	Insert/Atrium, Rt, [Opn, Perc, Perc Endo], Cardiac Lead, Pacemaker, NQ
02H6[Ø,4]MZ	Insert/Atrium, Rt, [Opn, Perc Endo], Cardiac Lead, NQ
02H7[Ø,3,4]JZ	Insert/Atrium, Lt, [Opn, Perc, Perc Endo], Cardiac Lead, Pacemaker, NQ
02H7[Ø,4]MZ	Insert/Atrium, Lt, [Opn, Perc Endo], Cardiac Lead, NQ
02HK[Ø,3,4][J,M]Z	Insert/Ventricle, Rt, [Opn, Perc, Perc Endo], [Cardiac Lead, Pacemaker, Cardiac Lead], NQ
02HL[Ø,3,4][J,M]Z	Insert/Ventricle, Lt, [Opn, Perc, Perc Endo], [Cardiac Lead, Pacemaker, Cardiac Lead], NQ
	AND
ØJH6[Ø,3][4,5,P]Z	Insert/SQ Tissue & Fascia, Chest, [Opn, Perc], [Pacemaker, Single Chamber, Single Chamber Rate Responsive, Cardiac Rhythm Related Dev], NQ
ØJH8[Ø,3][4,5,P]Z	Insert/SQ Tissue & Fascia, Abd, [Opn, Perc], [Pacemaker, Single Chamber, Pacemaker, Single Chamber Rate Responsive, Cardiac Rhythm Related Dev], NQ

Surgical   **Medical**   **CC Indicator**   **MCC Indicator**   **Procedure Proxy**   PDxMCC **PDx acts as own MCC**   PDxCC **PDx acts as own CC**

MDC 21: Injuries, Poisonings And Toxic Effects Of Drugs—SURGICAL

OR

02H4[0,4][J,M]Z	Insert/Coronary Vein, [Opn, Perc Endo], [Cardiac Lead, Pacemaker, Cardiac Lead], NQ
02H6[0,3,4]JZ	Insert/Atrium, Rt, [Opn, Perc, Perc Endo], Cardiac Lead, Pacemaker, NQ
02H6[0,4]MZ	Insert/Atrium, Rt, [Opn, Perc Endo], Cardiac Lead, NQ
02H7[0,3,4]JZ	Insert/Atrium, Lt, [Opn, Perc, Perc Endo], Cardiac Lead, Pacemaker, NQ
02H7[0,4]MZ	Insert/Atrium, Lt, [Opn, Perc Endo], Cardiac Lead, NQ
02HK[0,3,4][J,M]Z	Insert/Ventricle, Rt, [Opn, Perc, Perc Endo], [Cardiac Lead, Pacemaker, Cardiac Lead], NQ
02HL[0,3,4][J,M]Z	Insert/Ventricle, Lt, [Opn, Perc, Perc Endo], [Cardiac Lead, Pacemaker, Cardiac Lead], NQ

AND

0JH6[0,3][4,5,6]Z	Insert/SQ Tissue & Fascia, Chest, [Opn, Perc], [Pacemaker, Single Chamber, Pacemaker, Single Chamber Rate Responsive, Pacemaker, Dual Chamber], NQ
0JH8[0,3][4,5,6]Z	Insert/SQ Tissue & Fascia, Abd, [Opn, Perc], [Pacemaker, Single Chamber, Pacemaker, Single Chamber Rate Responsive, Pacemaker, Dual Chamber], NQ

AND

0JPT[0,3]PZ	Rmvl/SQ Tissue & Fascia, Trunk, [Opn, Perc], Cardiac Rhythm Related Dev, NQ

OR

02HK[3,4][J,M]Z	Insert/Ventricle, Rt, [Perc, Perc Endo], [Cardiac Lead, Pacemaker, Cardiac Lead], NQ
02HL[0,3,4][J,M]Z	Insert/Ventricle, Lt, [Opn, Perc, Perc Endo], [Cardiac Lead, Pacemaker, Cardiac Lead], NQ

AND

0JH6[0,3][4,5,6]Z	Insert/SQ Tissue & Fascia, Chest, [Opn, Perc], [Pacemaker, Single Chamber, Pacemaker, Single Chamber Rate Responsive, Pacemaker, Dual Chamber], NQ
0JH8[0,3][4,5,6]Z	Insert/SQ Tissue & Fascia, Abd, [Opn, Perc], [Pacemaker, Single Chamber, Pacemaker, Single Chamber Rate Responsive, Pacemaker, Dual Chamber], NQ

AND

0JPT[0,3]PZ	Rmvl/SQ Tissue & Fascia, Trunk, [Opn, Perc], Cardiac Rhythm Related Dev, NQ

OR

02HK3JZ	Insert of Pacemaker Lead into Rt Ventricle, Perc Appr
02HL3JZ	Insert of Pacemaker Lead into Lt Ventricle, Perc Appr

AND

0JH6[0,3][6,P]Z	Insert/SQ Tissue & Fascia, Chest, [Opn, Perc], [Pacemaker, Dual Chamber, Cardiac Rhythm Related Dev], NQ
0JH8[0,3][6,P]Z	Insert/SQ Tissue & Fascia, Abd, [Opn, Perc], [Pacemaker, Dual Chamber, Cardiac Rhythm Related Dev], NQ

OR

02H64MZ	Insert of Cardiac Lead into Rt Atrium, Perc Endo Appr
02H6[3,4]JZ	Insert/Atrium, Rt, [Perc, Perc Endo], Cardiac Lead, Pacemaker, NQ
02H7[0,3,4]JZ	Insert/Atrium, Lt, [Opn, Perc, Perc Endo], Cardiac Lead, Pacemaker, NQ
02H7[0,4]MZ	Insert/Atrium, Lt, [Opn, Perc Endo], Cardiac Lead, NQ
02HK[0,3,4][J,M]Z	Insert/Ventricle, Rt, [Opn, Perc, Perc Endo], [Cardiac Lead, Pacemaker, Cardiac Lead], NQ
02HL[0,3,4][J,M]Z	Insert/Ventricle, Lt, [Opn, Perc, Perc Endo], [Cardiac Lead, Pacemaker, Cardiac Lead], NQ

AND

0JH6[0,3][4,5,6]Z	Insert/SQ Tissue & Fascia, Chest, [Opn, Perc], [Pacemaker, Single Chamber, Pacemaker, Single Chamber Rate Responsive, Pacemaker, Dual Chamber], NQ
0JH8[0,3][4,5,6]Z	Insert/SQ Tissue & Fascia, Abd, [Opn, Perc], [Pacemaker, Single Chamber, Pacemaker, Single Chamber Rate Responsive, Pacemaker, Dual Chamber], NQ

AND

0JPT[0,3]PZ	Rmvl/SQ Tissue & Fascia, Trunk, [Opn, Perc], Cardiac Rhythm Related Dev, NQ

OR

02HN[0,3,4][J,M]Z	Insert/Pericardium, [Opn, Perc, Perc Endo], [Cardiac Lead, Pacemaker, Cardiac Lead], NQ

AND

0JH6[0,3][4,5,6,P]Z	Insert/SQ Tissue & Fascia, Chest, [Opn, Perc], [Pacemaker, Single Chamber, Pacemaker, Single Chamber Rate Responsive, Pacemaker, Dual Chamber, Cardiac Rhythm Related Dev], NQ
0JH8[0,3][4,5,6,P]Z	Insert/SQ Tissue & Fascia, Abd, [Opn, Perc], [Pacemaker, Single Chamber, Pacemaker, Single Chamber Rate Responsive, Pacemaker, Dual Chamber, Cardiac Rhythm Related Dev], NQ

OR

02HN[0,3,4][J,M]Z	Insert/Pericardium, [Opn, Perc, Perc Endo], [Cardiac Lead, Pacemaker, Cardiac Lead], NQ

AND

0JH6[0,3][4,5,6]Z	Insert/SQ Tissue & Fascia, Chest, [Opn, Perc], [Pacemaker, Single Chamber, Pacemaker, Single Chamber Rate Responsive, Pacemaker, Dual Chamber], NQ
0JH8[0,3][4,5,6]Z	Insert/SQ Tissue & Fascia, Abd, [Opn, Perc], [Pacemaker, Single Chamber, Pacemaker, Single Chamber Rate Responsive, Pacemaker, Dual Chamber], NQ

AND

0JPT[0,3]PZ	Rmvl/SQ Tissue & Fascia, Trunk, [Opn, Perc], Cardiac Rhythm Related Dev, NQ

OR

02H63MZ	Insert of Cardiac Lead into Rt Atrium, Perc Appr
02H73MZ	Insert of Cardiac Lead into Lt Atrium, Perc Appr

AND

0JH6[0,3]PZ	Insert/SQ Tissue & Fascia, Chest, [Opn, Perc], Cardiac Rhythm Related Dev, NQ
0JH8[0,3]PZ	Insert/SQ Tissue & Fascia, Abd, [Opn, Perc], Cardiac Rhythm Related Dev, NQ

OR

02H63MZ	Insert of Cardiac Lead into Rt Atrium, Perc Appr
02H73MZ	Insert of Cardiac Lead into Lt Atrium, Perc Appr

AND

0JH6[0,3][4,5,6]Z	Insert/SQ Tissue & Fascia, Chest, [Opn, Perc], [Pacemaker, Single Chamber, Pacemaker, Single Chamber Rate Responsive, Pacemaker, Dual Chamber], NQ
0JH8[0,3][4,5,6]Z	Insert/SQ Tissue & Fascia, Abd, [Opn, Perc], [Pacemaker, Single Chamber, Pacemaker, Single Chamber Rate Responsive, Pacemaker, Dual Chamber], NQ

AND

0JPT[0,3]PZ	Rmvl/SQ Tissue & Fascia, Trunk, [Opn, Perc], Cardiac Rhythm Related Dev, NQ

OR

02H63JZ	Insert of Pacemaker Lead into Rt Atrium, Perc Appr
02H73JZ	Insert of Pacemaker Lead into Lt Atrium, Perc Appr
02HK3JZ	Insert of Pacemaker Lead into Rt Ventricle, Perc Appr
02HL3JZ	Insert of Pacemaker Lead into Lt Ventricle, Perc Appr

AND

02PA[0,3,4,X]MZ	Rmvl/Heart, [Opn, Perc, Perc Endo, Ext], Cardiac Lead, NQ

AND

0JH6[0,3]PZ	Insert/SQ Tissue & Fascia, Chest, [Opn, Perc], Cardiac Rhythm Related Dev, NQ
0JH8[0,3]PZ	Insert/SQ Tissue & Fascia, Abd, [Opn, Perc], Cardiac Rhythm Related Dev, NQ

OR

02H63JZ	Insert of Pacemaker Lead into Rt Atrium, Perc Appr
02H73JZ	Insert of Pacemaker Lead into Lt Atrium, Perc Appr
02HK3JZ	Insert of Pacemaker Lead into Rt Ventricle, Perc Appr
02HL3JZ	Insert of Pacemaker Lead into Lt Ventricle, Perc Appr

AND

02PA[0,3,4,X]MZ	Rmvl/Heart, [Opn, Perc, Perc Endo, Ext], Cardiac Lead, NQ

AND

0JH6[0,3][4,5,6]Z	Insert/SQ Tissue & Fascia, Chest, [Opn, Perc], [Pacemaker, Single Chamber, Pacemaker, Single Chamber Rate Responsive, Pacemaker, Dual Chamber], NQ
0JH8[0,3][4,5,6]Z	Insert/SQ Tissue & Fascia, Abd, [Opn, Perc], [Pacemaker, Single Chamber, Pacemaker, Single Chamber Rate Responsive, Pacemaker, Dual Chamber], NQ

AND

0JPT[0,3]PZ	Rmvl/SQ Tissue & Fascia, Trunk, [Opn, Perc], Cardiac Rhythm Related Dev, NQ

DRG 908 **Other O.R. Procedures for Injuries with CC**

GMLOS 4.3	AMLOS 5.7	RW 1.9904	T

Select operating room procedures or procedure combinations listed under DRG 907

DRG 909 **Other O.R. Procedures for Injuries without CC/MCC**

GMLOS 2.6	AMLOS 3.3	RW 1.2992	T

Select operating room procedures or procedure combinations listed under DRG 907

T Transfer DRG   SP Special Payment   * Code Range   6th and 7th Character of ZZ = No Device, No Qualifier ZX = No Device, Diagnostic

358   MS-DRG Version 33.0   © 2015 Optum360, LLC

MEDICAL

DRG 913 Traumatic Injury with MCC
GMLOS 3.8   **AMLOS 5.1**   **RW 1.3561**

Principal Diagnosis

S05.7[Ø,1,2]XS   Avulsion of [unsp, rt, lt] eye, seq
S05.8X[1,2,9]S   Oth injuries of [rt, lt, unsp] eye and orbit, seq
S05.9[Ø,1,2]XS   Unsp inj of [unsp, rt, lt] eye and orbit, seq
S07.[Ø,1,8,9]XXA   Crushing inj of [face, skull, oth parts of head, head part unsp], init enc
S09.ØXXA   Inj of bld vessels of head, NEC, init
S09.10X[A,S]   Unsp inj of muscle and tndn of head, [init enc, seq]
S09.11XA   Strain of muscle and tndn of head, init enc
S09.19X[A,S]   Oth spec inj of muscle and tndn of head, [init enc, seq]
S09.20XS   Traum rupture of unsp ear drum, seq
S09.3[Ø,9][1,2,9]S   [Unsp, Oth spec] inj of [rt, lt, unsp] mid and inner ear, seq
S09.8XX[A,S]   Oth spec injuries of head, [init enc, seq]
S09.90X[A,S]   Unsp inj of head, [init enc, seq]
S09.91XS   Unsp inj of ear, seq
S09.9[2,3]X[A,S]   Unsp inj of [nose, face], [init enc, seq]
S15.Ø[Ø,1,2,9][1,2,9]A   [Unsp inj, Minor lac, Major lac, Oth spec inj] of [rt, lt, unsp] carotid artery, init enc
S15.1[Ø,1,2,9][1,2,9]A   [Unsp inj, Minor lac, Major lac, Oth spec inj] of [rt, lt, unsp] vert artery, init enc
S15.2[Ø,1,2,9][1,2,9]A   [Unsp inj, Minor lac, Major lac, Oth spec inj] of [rt, lt, unsp] ext jugular vein, init enc
S15.3[Ø,1,2,9][1,2,9]A   [Unsp inj, Minor lac, Major lac, Oth spec inj] of [rt, lt, unsp] int jugular vein, init enc
S15.[8,9]XXA   Inj of [oth spec, unsp] bld vessel(s) at neck lvl, init enc
S16.[8,9]XX[A,S]   [Oth spec, Unsp] inj of muscle, fascia and tndn at neck lvl, [init enc, seq]
S17.[Ø,8,9]XXA   Crushing inj of [larynx and trachea, oth spec parts of neck, unsp part of neck], init enc
S19.8[Ø,1,2,3,4,5,9]X[A,S]   Oth spec injuries of [unsp part of neck, larynx, cervical trachea, vocal cord, thyroid gland, pharynx and cervical esophagus, oth spec part of neck], [init enc, seq]
S19.9XX[A,S]   Unsp inj of neck, [init enc, seq]
S21.1[2,4][1,2,9]A   [Lac, Punc wnd] w/ FB of [rt, lt, unsp] front wall of thorax w/o penetration into thoracic cavity, init enc
S21.3Ø[1,2,9]A   Unsp opn wnd of [rt, lt, unsp] front wall of thorax w/ penetration into thoracic cavity, init enc
S21.35[1,2,9]A   Opn bite of [rt, lt, unsp] front wall of thorax w/ penetration into thoracic cavity, init enc
S21.3[1,2][1,2,9]A   Lac [w/o, w/] FB of [rt, lt, unsp] front wall of thorax w/ penetration into thoracic cavity, init enc
S21.3[3,4][1,2,9]A   Punc wnd [w/o, w/] FB of [rt, lt, unsp] front wall of thorax w/ penetration into thoracic cavity, init enc
S21.4Ø[1,2,9]A   Unsp opn wnd of [rt, lt, unsp] back wall of thorax w/ penetration into thoracic cavity, init enc
S21.45[1,2,9]A   Opn bite of [rt, lt, unsp] back wall of thorax w/ penetration into thoracic cavity, init enc
S21.4[1,2][1,2,9]A   Lac [w/o, w/] FB of [rt, lt, unsp] back wall of thorax w/ penetration into thoracic cavity, init enc
S21.4[3,4][1,2,9]A   Punc wnd [w/o, w/] FB of [rt, lt, unsp] back wall of thorax w/ penetration into thoracic cavity, init enc
S21.9[2,4]XA   [Lac, Punc wnd] w/ FB of unsp part of thorax, init enc
S25.Ø[Ø,1,2,9]XA   [Unsp inj, Minor lac, Major lac, Oth spec inj] of thoracic aorta, init enc
S25.1[Ø,1,2,9][1,2,9]A   [Unsp inj, Minor lac, Major lac, Oth spec inj] of [rt, lt, unsp] innominate or subclavian artery, init enc
S25.2[Ø,1,2,9]XA   [Unsp inj, Minor lac, Major lac, Oth spec inj] of superior vena cava, init enc
S25.3[Ø,1,2,9][1,2,9]A   [Unsp inj, Minor lac, Major lac, Oth spec inj] of [rt, lt, unsp] innominate or subclavian vein, init enc
S25.4[Ø,1,2,9][1,2,9]A   [Unsp inj, Minor lac, Major lac, Oth spec inj] of [rt, lt, unsp] pulmn bld vessels, init enc
S25.5[Ø,1,9][1,2,9]A   [Unsp inj, Lac, Oth spec inj] of intercostal bld vessels, [rt, lt, unsp] side, init enc
S25.8[Ø,1,9][1,2,9]A   [Unsp inj, Lac, Oth spec inj] of oth bld vessels of thorax, [rt, lt, unsp] side, init enc
S25.9[Ø,1,9]XA   [Unsp inj, Lac, Oth spec inj] of unsp bld vessel of thorax, init enc
S27.9XXA   Inj of unsp intrathoracic organ, init enc
S28.ØXXA   Crushed chest, init enc
S29.Ø[Ø,9][1,2,9][A,S]   [Unsp, Oth] inj of muscle and tndn of [front, back, unsp] wall of thorax, [init enc, seq]
S29.[8,9]XX[A,S]   [Oth spec injuries, Unsp inj] of thorax, [init enc, seq]

S31.1[2,4][Ø,1,2,3,4,5,9]A   [Lac, Punc wnd] of abd wall w/ FB, [rt upr quadrant, lt upr quadrant, epigastric rgn, rt lwr quadrant, lt lwr quadrant, periumbilic rgn, unsp quadrant], w/o penetration into peritoneal cavity, init enc
S31.83[2,4]A   [Lac, Punc wnd] w/ FB of anus, init enc
S35.Ø[Ø,1,2,9]XA   [Unsp inj, Minor lac, Major lac, Oth inj] of abd aorta, init enc
S35.1[Ø,1,2,9]XA   [Unsp inj, Minor lac, Major lac, Oth inj] of inferior vena cava, init enc
S35.2[1,2,3,9][1,2,8,9]A   [Minor lac, Major lac, Oth inj, Unsp inj] of [celiac, superior mesenteric, inferior mesenteric, branches of celiac and mesenteric] artery, init enc
S35.3[1,2,3,4][1,8,9]A   [Lac, Oth spec inj, Unsp inj] of [portal, splenic, superior mesenteric, inferior mesenteric] vein, init enc
S35.4[Ø,1,9][1,2,3,4,5,6]A   [Unsp inj, Lac, Oth spec inj] of [rt renal artery, lt renal artery, unsp renal artery, rt renal vein, lt renal vein, unsp renal vein], init enc
S35.5ØXA   Inj of unsp iliac bld vessel(s), init enc
S35.51[1,2,3,4,5,6]A   Inj of [rt iliac artery, lt iliac artery, unsp iliac artery, rt iliac vein, lt iliac vein, unsp iliac vein], init enc
S35.53[1,2,3,4,5,6]A   Inj of [rt uterine artery, lt uterine artery, unsp uterine artery, rt uterine vein, lt uterine vein, unsp uterine vein], init enc
S35.59XA   Inj of oth iliac bld vessels, init enc
S35.8X[1,8,9]A   [Lac, Oth spec, Unsp inj] of oth bld vessels at abd, lwr back and pelvis lvl, init enc
S35.9[Ø,1,9]XA   [Unsp inj, Lac, Oth spec inj] of unsp bld vessel at abd, lwr back and pelvis lvl, init enc
S36.89[2,3,8,9]A   [Contsn, Lac, Oth inj, Unsp inj] of oth intra-abd organs, init enc
S38.1XXA   Crushing inj of abd, lwr back, and pelvis, init
S39.Ø[Ø,9][1,2,3][A,S]   [Unsp, Oth] inj of muscle, fascia and tndn of [abd, lwr back, pelvis], [init enc, seq]
S39.84Ø[A,S]   Fx of corpus cavernosum penis, [init enc, seq]
S39.848[A,S]   Oth spec injuries of ext genitals, [init enc, seq]
S39.8[1,2,3]X[A,S]   Oth spec injuries of [abd, lwr back, pelvis], [init enc, seq]
S39.9[1,2,3,4]X[A,S]   Oth spec injuries of [abd, lwr back, pelvis, ext genitals], [init enc, seq]
S41.Ø[2,4][1,2,9]A   [Lac, Punc wnd] w/ FB of [rt, lt, unsp] shldr, init enc
S41.1[2,4][1,2,9]A   [Lac, Punc wnd] w/ FB of [rt, lt, unsp] upr arm, init enc
S45.Ø[Ø,1,9][1,2,9]A   [Unsp inj, Lac, Oth spec inj] of axillary artery, [rt, lt, unsp] side, init enc
S45.1[Ø,1,9][1,2,9]A   [Unsp inj, Lac, Oth spec inj] of brachial artery, [rt, lt, unsp] side, init enc
S45.2[Ø,1,9][1,2,9]A   [Unsp inj, Lac, Oth spec inj] of axillary or brachial vein, [rt, lt, unsp] side, init enc
S45.3[Ø,1,9][1,2,9]A   [Unsp inj, Lac, Oth spec inj] of superf vein at shldr and upr arm lvl, [rt, lt, unsp] arm, init enc
S45.8[Ø,1,9][1,2,9]A   [Unsp inj, Lac, Oth spec inj] of oth spec bld vessels at shldr and upr arm lvl, [rt, lt, unsp] arm, init enc
S45.9[Ø,1,9][1,2,9]A   [Unsp inj, Lac, Oth spec inj] of unsp bld vessel at shldr and upr arm lvl, [rt, lt, unsp] arm, init enc
S46.Ø[Ø,9][1,2,9][A,S]   [Unsp, Oth] inj of muscle(s) and tndn(s) of the rotator cuff of [rt, lt, unsp] shldr, [init enc, seq]
S46.1[Ø,9][1,2,9][A,S]   [Unsp, Oth] inj of muscle, fascia and tndn of long head of biceps, [rt, lt, unsp] arm, [init enc, seq]
S46.2[Ø,9][1,2,9][A,S]   [Unsp, Oth] inj of muscle, fascia and tndn of oth part of biceps, [rt, lt, unsp] arm, [init enc, seq]
S46.3[Ø,9][1,2,9][A,S]   [Unsp, Oth] inj of muscle, fascia and tndn of triceps, [rt, lt, unsp] arm, [init enc, seq]
S46.8[Ø,9][1,2,9][A,S]   [Unsp, Oth] inj of oth muscles, fascia and tndns at shldr and upr arm lvl, [rt, lt, unsp] arm, [init enc, seq]
S46.9[Ø,9][1,2,9][A,S]   [Unsp, Oth] inj of unsp muscles, fascia and tndns at shldr and upr arm lvl, [rt, lt, unsp] arm, [init enc, seq]
S47.[1,2,9]XXA   Crushing inj of [rt, lt, unsp] shldr and upr arm, init enc
S48.Ø[1,2][1,2,9]A   [Complete, Partial] traum amp at [rt, lt, unsp] shldr jt, init enc
S48.1[1,2][1,2,9]A   [Complete, Partial] traum amp at lvl between [rt, lt, unsp] shldr and elbow, init enc
S48.9[1,2][1,2,9]A   [Complete, Partial] traum amp of [rt, lt, unsp] shldr and upr arm, lvl unsp, init enc
S49.[8,9][Ø,1,2]X[A,S]   [Oth spec injuries, Unsp inj] of shldr and upr arm, [unsp, rt, lt] arm, [init enc, seq]
S51.Ø[2,4][1,2,9]A   [Lac, Punc wnd] w/ FB of [rt, lt, unsp] elbow, init enc
S51.8[2,4][1,2,9]A   [Lac, Punc wnd] w/ FB of [rt, lt, unsp] forearm, init enc
S55.Ø[Ø,1,9][1,2,9]A   [Unsp inj, Lac, Oth spec inj] of ulnar artery at forearm lvl, [rt, lt, unsp] arm, init enc
S55.1[Ø,1,9][1,2,9]A   [Unsp inj, Lac, Oth spec inj] of radial artery at forearm lvl, [rt, lt, unsp] arm, init enc
S55.2[Ø,1,9][1,2,9]A   [Unsp inj, Lac, Oth spec inj] of vein at forearm lvl, [rt, lt, unsp] arm, init enc
S55.8[Ø,1,9][1,2,9]A   [Unsp inj, Lac, Oth spec inj] of oth bld vessels at forearm lvl, [rt, lt, unsp] arm, init enc

---

Surgical   **Medical**   **CC Indicator**   **MCC Indicator**   **Procedure Proxy**   **PDxMCC PDx acts as own MCC**   **PDxCC PDx acts as own CC**

S55.9[0,1,9][1,2,9]A [Unsp inj, Lac, Oth spec inj] of unsp bld vessel at forearm lvl, [rt, lt, unsp] arm, init enc

S56.0[0,9][1,2,9][A,S] [Unsp, Oth] inj of flexor muscle, fascia and tndn of [rt, lt, unsp] thumb at forearm lvl, [init enc, seq]

S56.1[0,9][1,2,3,4,5,6,7,8,9][A,S] [Unsp, Oth] inj of flexor muscle, fascia and tndn of [rt index, lt index, rt mid, lt mid, rt ring, lt ring, rt little, lt little, unsp] finger at forearm lvl, [init enc, seq]

S56.2[0,9][1,2,9][A,S] [Unsp, Oth] inj of oth flexor muscle, fascia and tndn at forearm lvl, [rt, lt, unsp] arm, [init enc, seq]

S56.3[0,9][1,2,9][A,S] [Unsp, Oth] inj of extensor or abductor muscles, fascia and tndns of [rt, lt, unsp] thumb at forearm lvl, [init enc, seq]

S56.4[0,9][1,2,3,4,5,6,7,8,9][A,S] [Unsp, Oth] inj of extensor muscle, fascia and tndn of [rt index, lt index, rt mid, lt mid, rt ring, lt ring, rt little, lt little] finger at forearm lvl, [init enc, seq]

S56.5[0,9][1,2,9][A,S] [Unsp, Oth] inj of oth extensor muscle, fascia and tndn at forearm lvl, [rt, lt, unsp] arm, [init enc, seq]

S56.8[0,9][1,2,9][A,S] [Unsp, Oth] inj of oth muscles, fascia and tndns at forearm lvl, [rt, lt, unsp] arm, [init enc, seq]

S56.9[0,9][1,2,9][A,S] [Unsp, Oth] inj of unsp muscles, fascia and tndns at forearm lvl, [rt, lt, unsp] arm, [init enc, seq]

S57.00XA Crushing inj of unsp elbow, init enc
S57.01XA Crushing inj of rt elbow, init enc
S57.02XA Crushing inj of lt elbow, init enc
S57.80XA Crushing inj of unsp forearm, init enc
S57.81XA Crushing inj of rt forearm, init enc
S57.82XA Crushing inj of lt forearm, init enc

S58.0[1,2][1,2,9]A [Complete, Partial] traum amp at elbow lvl, [rt, lt, unsp] arm, init enc

S58.1[1,2][1,2,9]A [Complete, Partial] traum amp at lvl between elbow and wrist, [rt, lt, unsp] arm, init enc

S58.9[1,2][1,2,9]A [Complete, Partial] traum amp of [rt, lt, unsp] forearm, lvl unsp, init enc

S59.80[1,2,9][A,S] Oth spec injuries of [rt, lt, unsp] elbow, [init enc, seq]
S59.81[1,2,9][A,S] Oth spec injuries of [rt, lt, unsp] forearm, [init enc, seq]
S59.90[1,2,9][A,S] Unsp injuries of [rt, lt, unsp] elbow, [init enc, seq]
S59.91[1,2,9][A,S] Unsp injuries of [rt, lt, unsp] forearm, [init enc, seq]

S61.0[2,4][1,2,9]A [Lac, Punc wnd] w/ FB of [rt, lt, unsp] thumb w/o damage to nail, init enc

S61.1[2,4][1,2,9]A [Lac, Punc wnd] w/ FB of [rt, lt, unsp] thumb w/ damage to nail, init enc

S61.2[2,4][0,1,2,3,4,5,6,7,8,9]A [Lac, Punc wnd] w/ FB of [rt index, lt index, rt mid, lt mid, rt ring, lt ring, rt little, lt little, oth, unsp] finger w/o damage to nail, init enc

S61.3[2,4][0,1,2,3,4,5,6,7,8,9]A [Lac, Punc wnd] w/ FB of [rt index, lt index, rt mid, lt mid, rt ring, lt ring, rt little, lt little, oth, unsp] finger w/ damage to nail, init enc

S61.4[2,4][1,2,9]A [Lac, Punc wnd] w/ FB of [rt, lt, unsp] hand, init enc
S61.5[2,4][1,2,9]A [Lac, Punc wnd] w/ FB of [rt, lt, unsp] wrist, init enc

S65.0[0,1,9][1,2,9]A [Unsp inj, Lac, Oth spec inj] of ulnar artery at wrist and hand lvl of [rt, lt, unsp] arm, init enc

S65.1[0,1,9][1,2,9]A [Unsp inj, Lac, Oth spec inj] of radial artery at wrist and hand lvl of [rt, lt, unsp] arm, init enc

S65.2[0,1,9][1,2,9]A [Unsp inj, Lac, Oth spec inj] of superf palmar arch of [rt, lt, unsp] hand, init enc

S65.3[0,1,9][1,2,9]A [Unsp inj, Lac, Oth spec inj] of deep palmar arch of [rt, lt, unsp] hand, init enc

S65.4[0,1,9][1,2,9]A [Unsp inj, Lac, Oth spec inj] of bld vessel of [rt, lt, unsp] thumb, init enc

S65.5[0,1,9][0,1,2,3,4,5,6,7,8,9]A [Unsp inj, Lac, Oth spec inj] of bld vessel of [rt index, lt index, rt mid, lt mid, rt ring, lt ring, rt little, lt little, oth, unsp] finger, init enc

S65.8[0,1,9][1,2,9]A [Unsp inj, Lac, Oth spec inj] of oth bld vessels at wrist and hand lvl of [rt, lt, unsp] arm, init enc

S65.9[0,1,9][1,2,9]A [Unsp inj, Lac, Oth spec inj] of unsp bld vessels at wrist and hand lvl of [rt, lt, unsp] arm, init enc

S66.0[0,9][1,2,9][A,S] [Unsp, Oth spec] inj of long flexor muscle, fascia and tndn of [rt, lt, unsp] thumb at wrist and hand lvl, [init enc, seq]

S66.1[0,9][0,1,2,3,4,5,6,7,8,9][A,S] [Unsp, Oth spec] inj of flexor muscle, fascia and tndn of [rt index, lt index, rt mid, lt mid, rt ring, lt ring, rt little, lt little, oth, unsp] finger at wrist and hand lvl, [init enc, seq]

S66.2[0,9][1,2,9][A,S] [Unsp, Oth spec] inj of extensor muscle, fascia and tndn of [rt, lt, unsp] thumb at wrist and hand lvl, [init enc, seq]

S66.3[0,9][0,1,2,3,4,5,6,7,8,9][A,S] [Unsp, Oth spec] inj of extensor muscle, fascia and tndn of [rt index, lt index, rt mid, lt mid, rt ring, lt ring, rt little, lt little, oth, unsp] finger at wrist and hand lvl, [init enc, seq]

S66.4[0,9][1,2,9][A,S] [Unsp, Oth spec] inj of intrinsic muscle, fascia and tndn of [rt, lt, unsp] thumb at wrist and hand lvl, [init enc, seq]

S66.5[0,9][0,1,2,3,4,5,6,7,8,9][A,S] [Unsp, Oth spec] inj of intrinsic muscle, fascia and tndn of [rt index, lt index, rt mid, lt mid, rt ring, lt ring, rt little, lt little, oth, unsp] finger at wrist and hand lvl, [init enc, seq]

S66.8[0,9][1,2,9][A,S] [Unsp, Oth spec] inj of oth spec muscles, fascia and tndns at wrist and hand lvl, [rt, lt, unsp] hand, [init enc, seq]

S66.9[0,9][1,2,9][A,S] [Unsp, Oth spec] inj of unsp muscles, fascia and tndns at wrist and hand lvl, [rt, lt, unsp] hand, [init enc, seq]

S67.0[0,1,2]XA Crushing inj of [unsp, rt, lt] thumb, init enc
S67.10XA Crushing inj of unsp finger(s), init enc
S67.19[0,1,2,3,4,5,6,7,8]A Crushing inj of [rt index, lt index, rt ring, lt ring, rt mid, lt mid, rt little, lt little, oth] finger, init enc
S67.2[0,1,2]XA Crushing inj of [unsp, rt, lt] hand, init enc
S67.3[0,1,2]XA Crushing inj of [unsp, rt, lt] wrist, init enc
S67.4[0,1,2]XA Crushing inj of [unsp, rt, lt] wrist and hand, init enc
S67.9[0,1,2]XA Crushing inj of unsp parts of [unsp, rt, lt] hand and fingers, init enc

S68.0[1,2][1,2,9]A [Complete, Partial] traum metacarpophalangeal amp of [rt, lt, unsp] thumb, init enc

S68.1[1,2][0,1,2,3,4,5,6,7,8,9]A [Complete, Partial] traum metacarpophalangeal amp of [rt index, lt index, rt mid, lt mid, rt ring, lt ring, rt little, lt little, oth, unsp] finger, init enc

S68.4[1,2][1,2,9]A [Complete, Partial] traum amp of [rt, lt, unsp] hand at wrist lvl, init enc

S68.5[1,2][1,2,9]A [Complete, Partial] traum transphalangeal amp of [rt, lt, unsp] thumb, init enc

S68.6[1,2][0,1,2,3,4,5,6,7,8,9]A [Complete, Partial] traum transphalangeal amp of [rt index, lt index, rt mid, lt mid, rt ring, lt ring, rt little, lt little, oth, unsp] finger, init enc

S68.7[1,2][1,2,9]A [Complete, Partial] traum transmetacarpal amp of [rt, lt, unsp] hand, init enc

S69.[8,9][0,1,2]X[A,S] [Oth spec injuries, Unsp inj] of [unsp, rt, lt] wrist, hand and finger(s), [init enc, seq]

S71.0[2,4][1,2,9]A [Lac, Punc wnd] w/ FB, [rt, lt, unsp] hip, init enc
S71.1[2,4][1,2,9]A [Lac, Punc wnd] w/ FB, [rt, lt, unsp] thigh, init enc

S75.0[0,1,2,9][1,2,9]A [Unsp inj, Minor lac, Major lac, Oth spec inj] of femur artery, [rt, lt, unsp] leg, init enc

S75.1[0,1,2,9][1,2,9]A [Unsp inj, Minor lac, Major lac, Oth spec inj] of femur vein at hip & thigh lvl, [rt, lt, unsp] leg, init enc

S75.2[0,1,2,9][1,2,9]A [Unsp inj, Minor lac, Major lac, Oth spec inj] of greater saphenous vein at hip & thigh lvl, [rt, lt, unsp] leg, init enc

S75.8[0,1,9][1,2,9]A [Unsp inj, Lac, Oth spec inj] of oth bld vessels at hip & thigh lvl, [rt, lt, unsp] leg, init enc

S75.9[0,1,9][1,2,9]A [Unsp inj, Lac, Oth spec inj] of unsp bld vessel at hip & thigh lvl, [rt, lt, unsp] leg, init enc

S76.0[0,9][1,2,9][A,S] [Unsp, Oth spec] inj of muscle, fascia and tndn of [rt, lt, unsp] hip, [init enc, seq]

S76.1[0,9][1,2,9][A,S] [Unsp, Oth spec] inj of [rt, lt, unsp] quadriceps muscle, fascia and tndn, [init enc, seq]

S76.2[0,9][1,2,9][A,S] [Unsp, Oth spec] inj of adductor muscle, fascia and tndn of [rt, lt, unsp] thigh, [init enc, seq]

S76.3[0,9][1,2,9][A,S] [Unsp, Oth spec] inj of muscle, fascia and tndn of the post muscle group at thigh lvl, [rt, lt, unsp] thigh, [init enc, seq]

S76.8[0,9][1,2,9][A,S] [Unsp, Oth spec] inj of oth spec muscles, fascia and tndns at thigh lvl, [rt, lt, unsp] thigh, [init enc, seq]

S76.9[0,9][1,2,9][A,S] [Unsp, Oth spec] inj of unsp muscles, fascia and tndns at thigh lvl, [rt, lt, unsp] thigh, [init enc, seq]

S77.0[0,1,2]XA Crushing inj of [unsp, rt, lt] hip, intial enc
S77.1[0,1,2]XA Crushing inj of [unsp, rt, lt] thigh, intial enc
S77.2[0,1,2]XA Crushing inj of [unsp, rt, lt] hip w/ thigh, intial enc

S78.0[1,2][1,2,9]A [Complete, Partial] traum amp at [rt, lt, unsp] hip jt, init enc

S78.1[1,2][1,2,9]A [Complete, Partial] traum amp at lvl between [rt, lt, unsp] hip and knee, init enc

S78.9[1,2][1,2,9]A [Complete, Partial] traum amp of [rt, lt, unsp] hip & thigh, lvl unsp, init enc

S79.81[1,2,9][A,S] Oth spec injuries of [rt, lt, unsp] hip, [init enc, seq]
S79.82[1,2,9][A,S] Oth spec injuries of [rt, lt, unsp] thigh, [init enc, seq]
S79.91[1,2,9][A,S] Unsp injuries of [rt, lt, unsp] hip, [init enc, seq]
S79.92[1,2,9][A,S] Unsp injuries of [rt, lt, unsp] thigh, [init enc, seq]
S81.0[2,4][1,2,9]A [Lac, Punc wnd] w/ FB, [rt, lt, unsp] knee, init enc
S81.8[2,4][1,2,9]A [Lac, Punc wnd] w/ FB, [rt, lt, unsp] lwr leg, init enc

S85.0[0,1,9][1,2,9]A [Unsp inj, Lac, Oth spec inj] of popliteal artery, [rt, lt, unsp] leg, init enc

S85.1[0,1,2][1,2,9]A [Unsp inj, Lac, Oth spec inj] of unsp tibial artery, [rt, lt, unsp] leg, init enc

S85.1[3,4,5][1,2,9]A [Unsp inj, Lac, Oth spec inj] of ant tibial artery, [rt, lt, unsp] leg, init enc

S85.1[6,7,8][1,2,9]A [Unsp inj, Lac, Oth spec inj] of post tibial artery, [rt, lt, unsp] leg, init enc

---

⊤ Transfer DRG   SP Special Payment   * Code Range   6th and 7th Character of ZZ = No Device, No Qualifier ZX = No Device, Diagnostic

360   MS-DRG Version 33.0   © 2015 Optum360, LLC

S85.2[0,1,9][1,2,9]A [Unsp inj, Lac, Oth spec inj] of peroneal artery, [rt, lt, unsp] leg, init enc
S85.3[0,1,9][1,2,9]A [Unsp inj, Lac, Oth spec inj] of greater saphenous vein at lwr leg lvl, [rt, lt, unsp] leg, init enc
S85.4[0,1,9][1,2,9]A [Unsp inj, Lac, Oth spec inj] of lesser saphenous vein at lwr leg lvl, [rt, lt, unsp] leg, init enc
S85.5[0,1,9][1,2,9]A [Unsp inj, Lac, Oth spec inj] of popliteal vein, [rt, lt, unsp] leg, init enc
S85.8[0,1,9][1,2,9]A [Unsp inj, Lac, Oth spec inj] of oth bood vessels at lwr leg lvl, [rt, lt, unsp] leg, init enc
S85.9[0,1,9][1,2,9]A [Unsp inj, Lac, Oth spec inj] of unsp bood vessels at lwr leg lvl, [rt, lt, unsp] leg, init enc
S86.0[0,9][1,2,9][A,S] [Unsp, Oth spec] inj of [rt, lt, unsp] Achilles tndn, [init enc, seq]
S86.1[0,9][1,2,9][A,S] [Unsp, Oth spec] of oth muscle(s) and tndn(s) of post muscle group at lwr leg lvl, [rt, lt, unsp] leg, [init enc, seq]
S86.2[0,9][1,2,9][A,S] [Unsp, Oth spec] of oth muscle(s) and tndn(s) of ant muscle group at lwr leg lvl, [rt, lt, unsp] leg, [init enc, seq]
S86.3[0,9][1,2,9][A,S] [Unsp, Oth spec] of oth muscle(s) and tndn(s) of peroneal muscle group at lwr leg lvl, [rt, lt, unsp] leg, [init enc, seq]
S86.8[0,9][1,2,9][A,S] [Unsp, Oth spec] of oth muscle(s) and tndn(s) at lwr leg lvl, [rt, lt, unsp] leg, [init enc, seq]
S86.9[0,9][1,2,9][A,S] [Unsp, Oth spec] of unsp muscle(s) and tndn(s) at lwr leg lvl, [rt, lt, unsp] leg, [init enc, seq]
S87.0[0,1,2]XA Crushing inj of [unsp, rt, lt] knee, init enc
S87.8[0,1,2]XA Crushing inj of [unsp, rt, lt] lwr leg, init enc
S88.0[1,2][1,2,9]A [Complete, Partial] traum amp at knee lvl, [rt, lt, unsp] lwr leg, init enc
S88.1[1,2][1,2,9]A [Complete, Partial] traum amp at lvl between knee and ankle, [rt, lt, unsp] lwr leg, init enc
S88.9[1,2][1,2,9]A [Complete, Partial] traum amp of [rt, lt, unsp] lwr leg, lvl unsp, init enc
S89.[8,9][0,1,2]X[A,S] [Oth spec injuries, Unsp inj] of [unsp, rt, lt] lwr leg, [init enc, seq]
S91.0[2,4][1,2,9]A [Lac, Punc wnd] w/ FB, [rt, lt, unsp] ankle, init enc
S91.1[2,4][1,2,3,4,5,6,9]A [Lac, Punc wnd] w/ FB of [rt great, lt great, unsp great, rt lesser, lt lesser, unsp lesser, unsp] toe(s) w/o damage to nail, init enc
S91.2[2,4][1,2,3,4,5,6,9]A [Lac, Punc wnd] w/ FB of [rt great, lt great, unsp great, rt lesser, lt lesser, unsp lesser, unsp] toe(s) w/ damage to nail, init enc
S91.3[2,4][1,2,9]A [Lac, Punc wnd] w/ FB of [rt, lt, unsp] foot, init enc
S95.0[0,1,9][1,2,9]A [Unsp inj, Lac, Oth spec inj] of dorsal artery of [rt, lt, unsp] foot, init enc
S95.1[0,1,9][1,2,9]A [Unsp inj, Lac, Oth spec inj] of plantar artery of [rt, lt, unsp] foot, init enc
S95.2[0,1,9][1,2,9]A [Unsp inj, Lac, Oth spec inj] of dorsal vein of [rt, lt, unsp] foot, init enc
S95.8[0,1,9][1,2,9]A [Unsp inj, Lac, Oth spec inj] of oth bld vessels at ankle and foot lvl, [rt, lt, unsp] leg, init enc
S95.9[0,1,9][1,2,9]A [Unsp inj, Lac, Oth spec inj] of unsp bld vessel at ankle and foot lvl, [rt, lt, unsp] leg, init enc
S96.0[0,9][1,2,9][A,S] [Unsp, Oth] inj of muscle and tndn of long flexor muscle of toe at ankle and foot lvl, [rt, lt, unsp] foot, [init enc, seq]
S96.1[0,9][1,2,9][A,S] [Unsp, Oth] inj of muscle and tndn of long extensor muscle of toe at ankle and foot lvl, [rt, lt, unsp] foot, [init enc, seq]
S96.2[0,9][1,2,9][A,S] [Unsp, Oth] inj of intrinsic muscle and tndn at ankle and foot lvl, [rt, lt, unsp] foot, [init enc, seq]
S96.8[0,9][1,2,9][A,S] [Unsp, Oth] inj of oth spec muscles and tndns at ankle and foot lvl, [rt, lt, unsp] foot, [init enc, seq]
S96.9[0,9][1,2,9][A,S] [Unsp, Oth] inj of unsp muscle and tndn at ankle and foot lvl, [rt, lt, unsp] foot, [init enc, seq]
S97.0[0,1,2]XA Crushing inj of [unsp, rt, lt] ankle, init enc
S97.1[0,1,2][1,2,9]A Crushing inj of [unsp rt, unsp lt, unsp, rt great, lt great, unsp great, rt lesser, lt lesser, unsp lesser] toe(s), init enc
S97.8[0,1,2]XA Crushing inj of [unsp, rt, lt] foot, init enc
S98.0[1,2][1,2,9]A [Complete, Partial] traum amp of [rt, lt, unsp] foot at ankle lvl, init enc
S98.1[1,2][1,2,9]A [Complete, Partial] traum amp of [rt, lt, unsp] great toe, init enc
S98.1[3,4][1,2,9]A [Complete, Partial] traum amp of one [rt, lt, unsp] lesser toe, init enc
S98.2[1,2][1,2,9]A [Complete, Partial] traum amp of two or more [rt, lt, unsp] lesser toes, init enc
S98.3[1,2][1,2,9]A [Complete, Partial] traum amp of [rt, lt, unsp] midfoot, init enc
S98.9[1,2][1,2,9]A [Complete, Partial] traum amp of [rt, lt, unsp] foot, lvl unsp, init enc
S99.81[1,2,9][A,S] Oth spec injuries of [rt, lt, unsp] ankle, [init enc, seq]
S99.82[1,2,9][A,S] Oth spec injuries of [rt, lt, unsp] foot, [init enc, seq]
S99.91[1,2,9][A,S] Unsp inj of [rt, lt, unsp] ankle, [init enc, seq]

S99.92[1,2,9][A,S] Unsp inj of [rt, lt, unsp] foot, [init enc, seq]
T14.90 Inj, unsp
T14.91 Suicide attempt
T15.0[0,1,2]XS FB in cornea, [unsp, rt, lt] eye, seq
T15.1[0,1,2]XS FB in conjunctival sac, [unsp, rt, lt] eye, seq
T15.8[0,1,2]XS FB in oth and multi parts of ext eye, [unsp, rt, lt] eye, seq
T15.9[0,1,2]XS FB on ext eye, part unsp, [unsp, rt, lt] eye, seq
T16.[1,2,9]XXS FB in [rt, lt, unsp] ear, seq
T17.2[0,1,2,9][0,8]S [Unsp FB, Gastric contents, Food, Oth foreign object] in pharynx causing [asphyxiation, oth inj], seq
T17.3[0,1,2,9][0,8]S [Unsp FB, Gastric contents, Food, Oth foreign object] in larynx causing [asphyxiation, oth inj], seq
T17.4[0,1,2,9][0,8]S [Unsp FB, Gastric contents, Food, Oth foreign object] in trachea causing [asphyxiation, oth inj], seq
T17.5[0,1,2,9][0,8]S [Unsp FB, Gastric contents, Food, Oth foreign object] in bronchus causing [asphyxiation, oth inj], seq
T17.8[0,1,2,9][0,8]S [Unsp FB, Gastric contents, Food, Oth foreign object] in oth parts of respiratory tract causing [asphyxiation, oth inj], seq
T17.9[0,1,2,9][0,8]S [Unsp FB, Gastric contents, Food, Oth foreign object] in respiratory tract, part unsp causing [asphyxiation, oth inj], seq
T17.[0,1]XXS FB in [nasal sinus, nostril], seq
T18.0XXS FB in mouth, seq
T18.1[0,1,2,9][0,8]S [Unsp FB, Gastric contents, Food, Oth foreign object] in esophagus causing [compression of trachea, oth inj], seq
T18.[2,3,4,5,8,9]XXS FB in [stomach, sm intestine, colon, anus and rectum, oth parts of alimentary tract, alimentary tract part unsp], seq
T19.[0,1,2,3,4,8,9]XXS FB in [urethra, bladder, vulva and vagina, uterus, penis, oth parts of genitourinary tract, genitourinary tract part unsp], seq
T79.2XXS Traum secondary and recurrent hemor and seroma, seq
T79.4XXS Traum shock, seq
T79.5XXS Traum anuria, seq
T79.6XXS Traum ischemia of muscle, seq
T79.7XXS Traum SQ emphysema, seq
T79.A0XS Compartment synd, unsp, seq
T79.A1[1,2,9]S Traum compartment synd of [rt, lt, unsp] upr extr, seq
T79.A2[1,2,9]S Traum compartment synd of [rt, lt, unsp] lwr extr, seq
T79.A[3,9]XS Traum compartment synd of [abd, oth sites], seq
T79.[0,1]XXS [Air, Fat] embolism (traum), seq
T79.[8,9]XXS [Oth, Unsp] early comp of trauma, seq

DRG 914 **Traumatic Injury without MCC**
GMLOS 2.5   AMLOS 3.1   RW 0.7317

Select principal diagnosis listed under DRG 913

DRG 915 **Allergic Reactions with MCC**
GMLOS 3.7   AMLOS 5.1   RW 1.6040

Principal Diagnosis
T78.00XA Anaphylactic reaction d/t unsp food, init enc
T78.01XA Anaphylactic reaction d/t peanuts, init enc
T78.02XA Anaphylactic reaction d/t shellfish (crustaceans), init
T78.03XA Anaphylactic reaction d/t oth fish, init enc
T78.04XA Anaphylactic reaction d/t fruits and vegetables, init
T78.05XA Anaphylactic reaction d/t tree nuts and seeds, init
T78.06XA Anaphylactic reaction d/t food additives, init enc
T78.07XA Anaphylactic reaction d/t milk and dairy products, init
T78.08XA Anaphylactic reaction d/t eggs, init enc
T78.09XA Anaphylactic reaction d/t oth food products, init enc
T78.2XXA Anaphylactic shock, unsp, init enc
T78.3XXA Angioneurotic edema, init enc
T78.40XA Allergy, unsp, init enc
T78.49XA Oth allergy, init enc
T80.5[1,2,9]XA Anaphylactic reaction d/t [administration of bld and bld products, vaccination, oth serum], init enc
T80.6[1,2,9]XA Oth serum reaction d/t [administration of bld and bld products, vaccination, oth serum], init enc
T88.6XXA Anaphyl reaction d/t advrs eff drug/med prop admin, init

---

DRG 916 **Allergic Reactions without MCC**
GMLOS 1.8   AMLOS 2.2   RW 0.5582

Select principal diagnosis listed under DRG 915

Surgical   Medical   CC Indicator   MCC Indicator   Procedure Proxy   PDx MCC PDx acts as own MCC   PDx CC PDx acts as own CC

DRG 917   Poisoning and Toxic Effects of Drugs with MCC

GMLOS 3.5   **AMLOS 4.8**   **RW 1.4065**   ⊤

Principal Diagnosis

M1A.1*	Lead-induced chr gout
T36.0X5A	Adverse effect of penicilins, init enc
T36.0X[1,2,3,4]A	Poison by penicillins, [accid (unintentional), intentional self-harm, assault, undetermined], init enc
T36.1X5A	Adverse effect of cephalospor/oth beta-lactm antibiot, init
T36.1X[1,2,3,4]A	Poison by cephaloporins and oth beta-lactam antibiotics, [accid (unintentional), intentional self-harm, assault, undetermined], init enc
T36.2X5A	Adverse effect of chloramphenicol group, init enc
T36.2X[1,2,3,4]A	Poison by chloramphenicol group, [accid (unintentional), intentional self-harm, assault, undetermined], init enc
T36.3X5A	Adverse effect of macrolides, init enc
T36.3X[1,2,3,4]A	Poison by macrolides, [accid (unintentional), intentional self-harm, assault, undetermined], init enc
T36.4X5A	Adverse effect of tetracyclines, init enc
T36.4X[1,2,3,4]A	Poison by tetracyclines, [accid (unintentional), intentional self-harm, assault, undetermined], init enc
T36.5X5A	Adverse effect of aminoglycosides, init enc
T36.5X[1,2,3,4]A	Poison by aminoglycosides, [accid (unintentional), intentional self-harm, assault, undetermined], init enc
T36.6X5A	Adverse effect of rifampicins, init enc
T36.6X[1,2,3,4]A	Poison by rifampicins, [accid (unintentional), intentional self-harm, assault, undetermined], init enc
T36.7X5A	Adverse effect of antifungal antibiotics, sys used, init
T36.7X[1,2,3,4]A	Poison by antifungal antibiotics, sysically used, [accid (unintentional), intentional self-harm, assault, undetermined], init enc
T36.8X5A	Adverse effect of oth systemic antibiotics, init enc
T36.8X[1,2,3,4]A	Poison by oth sysic antibiotics [accid (unintentional), intentional self-harm, assault, undetermined], init enc
T36.95XA	Adverse effect of unsp systemic antibiotic, init enc
T36.9[1,2,3,4]XA	Poison by unsp sysic antibiotic [accid (unintentional), intentional self-harm, assault, undetermined], init enc
T37.0X5A	Adverse effect of sulfonamides, init enc
T37.0X[1,2,3,4]A	Poison by sulfonamides, [accid (unintentional), intentional self-harm, assault, undetermined], init enc
T37.1X5A	Adverse effect of antimycobacterial drugs, init enc
T37.1X[1,2,3,4]A	Poison by antimycobacterial drugs, [accid (unintentional), intentional self-harm, assault, undetermined], init enc
T37.2X5A	Advrs effect of antimalari/drugs acting on bld protzoa, init
T37.2X[1,2,3,4]A	Poison by antimalarials and drugs acting on oth bld protozoa, [accid (unintentional), intentional self-harm, assault, undetermined], init enc
T37.3X5A	Adverse effect of oth antiprotozoal drugs, init enc
T37.3X[1,2,3,4]A	Poison by oth antiprotozoal drugs, [accid (unintentional), intentional self-harm, assault, undetermined], init enc
T37.4X5A	Adverse effect of anthelminthics, init enc
T37.4X[1,2,3,4]A	Poison by anthelminthics, [accid (unintentional), intentional self-harm, assault, undetermined], init enc
T37.5X5A	Adverse effect of antiviral drugs, init enc
T37.5X[1,2,3,4]A	Poison by antiviral drugs, [accid (unintentional), intentional self-harm, assault, undetermined], init enc
T37.8X5A	Adverse effect of systemic anti-infect/parasit, init
T37.8X[1,2,3,4]A	Poison by oth spec sysic anti-infectives and antiparasitics, [accid (unintentional), intentional self-harm, assault, undetermined], init enc
T37.95XA	Advrs effect of unsp sys anti-infect and antiparasitic, init
T37.9[1,2,3,4]XA	Poison by unsp sysic anti-infectives and antiparasitics, [accid (unintentional), intentional self-harm, assault, undetermined], init enc
T38.0X5A	Adverse effect of glucocort/synth analog, init
T38.0X[1,2,3,4]A	Poison by glucocorticoids and synth analogues, [accid (unintentional), intentional self-harm, assault, undetermined], init enc
T38.1X5A	Adverse effect of thyroid hormones and substitutes, init
T38.1X[1,2,3,4]A	Poison by thyroid hormones and subs, [accid (unintentional), intentional self-harm, assault, undetermined], init enc
T38.2X5A	Adverse effect of antithyroid drugs, init enc
T38.2X[1,2,3,4]A	Poison by antithyroid drugs, [accid (unintentional), intentional self-harm, assault, undetermined], init enc
T38.3X5A	Adverse effect of insulin and oral hypoglycemic drugs, init
T38.3X[1,2,3,4]A	Poison by insulin and oral hypoglycemic (antidiabetic) drugs, [accid (unintentional), intentional self-harm, assault, undetermined], init enc
T38.4X5A	Adverse effect of oral contraceptives, init enc
T38.4X[1,2,3,4]A	Poison by oral contraceptives, [accid (unintentional), intentional self-harm, assault, undetermined], init enc
T38.5X5A	Adverse effect of oth estrogens and progestogens, init
T38.5X[1,2,3,4]A	Poison by oth estrogens and progestogens, [accid (unintentional), intentional self-harm, assault, undetermined], init enc
T38.6X5A	Adverse effect of antigonadtr/antiestr/antiandrg, NEC, init
T38.6X[1,2,3,4]A	Poison by antigonadotrophins, antiestrogens, antiandrogens, NEC, [accid (unintentional), intentional self-harm, assault, undetermined], init enc
T38.7X5A	Adverse effect of androgens and anabolic congeners, init
T38.7X[1,2,3,4]A	Poison by androgens and anabolic congeners, sysically used, [accid (unintentional), intentional self-harm, assault, undetermined], init enc
T38.805A	Adverse effect of unsp hormones and synth sub, init
T38.80[1,2,3,4]A	Poison by unsp hormones and synth subs, [accid (unintentional), intentional self-harm, assault, undetermined], init enc
T38.815A	Adverse effect of ant pituitary hormones, init enc
T38.81[1,2,3,4]A	Poison by ant pituitary (adenohypophyseal) hormones, [accid (unintentional), intentional self-harm, assault, undetermined], init enc
T38.895A	Adverse effect of hormones and synth substitutes, init
T38.89[1,2,3,4]A	Poison by oth hormones and synth subs, [accid (unintentional), intentional self-harm, assault, undetermined], init enc
T38.905A	Adverse effect of unsp hormone antagonists, init enc
T38.90[1,2,3,4]A	Poison by unsp hormone antagonists, [accid (unintentional), intentional self-harm, assault, undetermined], init enc
T38.995A	Adverse effect of oth hormone antagonists, init enc
T38.99[1,2,3,4]A	Poison by oth hormone antagonists, [accid (unintentional), intentional self-harm, assault, undetermined], init enc
T39.015A	Adverse effect of aspirin, init enc
T39.095A	Adverse effect of salicylates, init enc
T39.0[1,9][1,2,3,4]A	Poison by [aspirin, salicylates], [accid (unintentional), intentional self-harm, assault, undetermined], init enc
T39.1X5A	Adverse effect of 4-Aminophenol derivatives, init enc
T39.1X[1,2,3,4]A	Poison by 4-Aminophenol derivatives, [accid (unintentional), intentional self-harm, assault, undetermined], init enc
T39.2X5A	Adverse effect of pyrazolone derivatives, init enc
T39.2X[1,2,3,4]A	Poison by pyrazolone derivatives, [accid (unintentional), intentional self-harm, assault, undetermined], init enc
T39.315A	Adverse effect of propionic acid derivatives, init enc
T39.31[1,2,3,4]A	Poison by propionic acid derivatives, [accid (unintentional), intentional self-harm, assault, undetermined], init enc
T39.395A	Adverse effect of nonsteroidal anti-inflam drugs, init
T39.39[1,2,3,4]A	Poison by oth nonsteroidal anti-inflam drugs (NSAID), [accid (unintentional), intentional self-harm, assault, undetermined], init enc
T39.4X5A	Adverse effect of antirheumatics, NEC, init
T39.4X[1,2,3,4]A	Poison by antirheumatics, NEC, [accid (unintentional), intentional self-harm, assault, undetermined], init enc
T39.8X5A	Adverse effect of nonopioid analges/antipyret, NEC, init
T39.8X[1,2,3,4]A	Poison by oth nonopiod analgesics and antipyretics, [accid (unintentional), intentional self-harm, assault, undetermined], init enc
T39.95XA	Adverse effect of unsp nonopi analgs/antipyr/antirheu, init
T39.9[1,2,3,4]XA	Poison by unsp nonopiod analgesic, antipyretic and antirheumatic, [accid (unintentional), intentional self-harm, assault, undetermined], init enc
T40.0X5A	Adverse effect of opium, init enc
T40.0X[1,2,3,4]A	Poison by opium, [accid (unintentional), intentional self-harm, assault, undetermined], init enc
T40.1X[1,2,3,4]A	Poison by and adverse effect of heroin, [accid (unintentional), intentional self-harm, assault, undetermined], init enc
T40.2X5A	Adverse effect of oth opioids, init enc
T40.2X[1,2,3,4]A	Poison by oth opiods, [accid (unintentional), intentional self-harm, assault, undetermined], init enc
T40.3X5A	Adverse effect of methadone, init enc
T40.3X[1,2,3,4]A	Poison by methadone, [accid (unintentional), intentional self-harm, assault, undetermined], init enc
T40.4X5A	Adverse effect of oth synth narcotics, init enc
T40.4X[1,2,3,4]A	Poison by oth synth narcotics, [accid (unintentional), intentional self-harm, assault, undetermined], init enc
T40.5X5A	Adverse effect of cocaine, init enc
T40.5X[1,2,3,4]A	Poison by cocaine, [accid (unintentional), intentional self-harm, assault, undetermined], init enc
T40.605A	Adverse effect of unsp narcotics, init enc
T40.60[1,2,3,4]A	Poison by unsp narcotics, [accid (unintentional), intentional self-harm, assault, undetermined], init enc

⊤ **Transfer DRG**   SP **Special Payment**   * **Code Range**   **6th and 7th Character of ZZ = No Device, No Qualifier ZX = No Device, Diagnostic**

362   MS-DRG Version 33.0   © 2015 Optum360, LLC

T40.695A	Adverse effect of oth narcotics, init enc
T40.69[1,2,3,4]A	Poison by spec narcotics, [accid (unintentional), intentional self-harm, assault, undetermined], init enc
T40.7X5A	Adverse effect of cannabis (derivatives), init enc
T40.7X[1,2,3,4]A	Poison by cannabis (derivatives), [accid (unintentional), intentional self-harm, assault, undetermined], init enc
T40.8X[1,2,3,4]A	Poison by and adverse effect of lysergide (LSD), [accid (unintentional), intentional self-harm, assault, undetermined], init enc
T40.905A	Adverse effect of unsp psychodysleptics, init enc
T40.90[1,2,3,4]A	Poison by unsp psychodysleptics (hallucinogens), [accid (unintentional), intentional self-harm, assault, undetermined], init enc
T40.995A	Adverse effect of oth psychodysleptics, init enc
T40.99[1,2,3,4]A	Poison by oth psychodysleptics (hallucinogens), [accid (unintentional), intentional self-harm, assault, undetermined], init enc
T41.0X5A	Adverse effect of inhaled anesthetics, init enc
T41.0X[1,2,3,4]A	Poison by inhaled anesthetics, [accid (unintentional), intentional self-harm, assault, undetermined], init enc
T41.1X5A	Adverse effect of intravenous anesthetics, init enc
T41.1X[1,2,3,4]A	Poison by intravenous anesthetics, [accid (unintentional), intentional self-harm, assault, undetermined], init enc
T41.205A	Adverse effect of unsp general anesthetics, init enc
T41.20[1,2,3,4]A	Poison by unsp general anesthetics, [accid (unintentional), intentional self-harm, assault, undetermined], init enc
T41.295A	Adverse effect of oth general anesthetics, init enc
T41.29[1,2,3,4]A	Poison by oth general anesthetics, [accid (unintentional), intentional self-harm, assault, undetermined], init enc
T41.3X5A	Adverse effect of local anesthetics, init enc
T41.3X[1,2,3,4]A	Poison by local anesthetics, [accid (unintentional), intentional self-harm, assault, undetermined], init enc
T41.45XA	Adverse effect of unsp anesthetic, init enc
T41.4[1,2,3,4]XA	Poison by unsp anesthetic, [accid (unintentional), intentional self-harm, assault, undetermined], init enc
T41.5X5A	Adverse effect of therapeutic gases, init enc
T41.5X[1,2,3,4]A	Poison by therapeutic gases, [accid (unintentional), intentional self-harm, assault, undetermined], init enc
T42.0X5A	Adverse effect of hydantoin derivatives, init enc
T42.0X[1,2,3,4]A	Poison by hydantoin derivatives, [accid (unintentional), intentional self-harm, assault, undetermined], init enc
T42.1X5A	Adverse effect of iminostilbenes, init enc
T42.1X[1,2,3,4]A	Poison by iminostilbenes, [accid (unintentional), intentional self-harm, assault, undetermined], init enc
T42.2X5A	Adverse effect of succinimides and oxazolidinediones, init
T42.2X[1,2,3,4]A	Poison by succinimides and oxazolidinediones, [accid (unintentional), intentional self-harm, assault, undetermined], init enc
T42.3X5A	Adverse effect of barbiturates, init enc
T42.3X[1,2,3,4]A	Poison by barbituates, [accid (unintentional), intentional self-harm, assault, undetermined], init enc
T42.4X5A	Adverse effect of benzodiazepines, init enc
T42.4X[1,2,3,4]A	Poison by benzodiazepines, [accid (unintentional), intentional self-harm, assault, undetermined], init enc
T42.5X5A	Adverse effect of mixed antiepileptics, init enc
T42.5X[1,2,3,4]A	Poison by mixed antiepileptics, [accid (unintentional), intentional self-harm, assault, undetermined], init enc
T42.6X5A	Adverse effect of antiepileptic and sed-hypntc drugs, init
T42.6X[1,2,3,4]A	Poison by oth antiepileptic and sedative-hypnotic drugs, [accid (unintentional), intentional self-harm, assault, undetermined], init enc
T42.75XA	Adverse effect of unsp antieplptc and sed-hypntc drugs, init
T42.7[1,2,3,4]XA	Poison by unsp antiepileptic and sedative-hypnotic drugs, [accid (unintentional), intentional self-harm, assault, undetermined], init enc
T42.8X5A	Adverse effect of antiparkns drug/centr musc-tone depr, init
T42.8X[1,2,3,4]A	Poison by antiparkinsonism drugs and oth central muscle-tone depressants, [accid (unintentional), intentional self-harm, assault, undetermined], init enc
T43.015A	Adverse effect of tricyclic antidepressants, init enc
T43.01[1,2,3,4]A	Poison by tricyclic antidepressants, [accid (unintentional), intentional self-harm, assault, undetermined], init enc
T43.025A	Adverse effect of tetracyclic antidepressants, init enc
T43.02[1,2,3,4]A	Poison by tetracyclic antidepressants, [accid (unintentional), intentional self-harm, assault, undetermined], init enc
T43.1X5A	Adverse effect of MAO inhib antidepressants, init
T43.1X[1,2,3,4]A	Poison by monoamine-oxidase-inhibitor antidepressants, [accid (unintentional), intentional self-harm, assault, undetermined], init enc
T43.205A	Adverse effect of unsp antidepressants, init enc

T43.20[1,2,3,4]A	Poison by unsp antidepressants, [accid (unintentional), intentional self-harm, assault, undetermined], init enc
T43.215A	Advrs effect of slctv seroton/norepineph reup inhibtr, init
T43.21[1,2,3,4]A	Poison by selective serotonin and norepinephrine reuptake inhibitors, [accid (unintentional), intentional self-harm, assault, undetermined], init enc
T43.225A	Adverse effect of selective serotonin reuptake inhibtr, init
T43.22[1,2,3,4]A	Poison by selective serotonin reuptake inhibitors, [accid (unintentional), intentional self-harm, assault, undetermined], init enc
T43.295A	Adverse effect of oth antidepressants, init enc
T43.29[1,2,3,4]A	Poison by oth antidepressants, [accid (unintentional), intentional self-harm, assault, undetermined], init enc
T43.3X5A	Adverse effect of phenothiazine antipsychot/neurolept, init
T43.3X[1,2,3,4]A	Poison by phenothiazine antipsychotics and neuroleptics, [accid (unintentional), intentional self-harm, assault, undetermined], init enc
T43.4X5A	Adverse effect of butyrophen/thiothixen neuroleptics, init
T43.4X[1,2,3,4]A	Poison by butyrophenone and thiothixene neuroleptics, [accid (unintentional), intentional self-harm, assault, undetermined], init enc
T43.505A	Adverse effect of unsp antipsychotics and neuroleptics, init
T43.50[1,2,3,4]A	Poison by unsp antipsychotics and neuroleptics, [accid (unintentional), intentional self-harm, assault, undetermined], init enc
T43.595A	Adverse effect of oth antipsychotics and neuroleptics, init
T43.59[1,2,3,4]A	Poison by oth antipsychotics and neuroleptics, [accid (unintentional), intentional self-harm, assault, undetermined], init enc
T43.605A	Adverse effect of unsp psychostimulants, init enc
T43.60[1,2,3,4]A	Poison by unsp psychostimulants, [accid (unintentional), intentional self-harm, assault, undetermined], init enc
T43.615A	Adverse effect of caffeine, init enc
T43.61[1,2,3,4]A	Poison by caffeine, [accid (unintentional), intentional self-harm, assault, undetermined], init enc
T43.625A	Adverse effect of amphetamines, init enc
T43.62[1,2,3,4]A	Poison by amphetamines, [accid (unintentional), intentional self-harm, assault, undetermined], init enc
T43.635A	Adverse effect of methylphenidate, init enc
T43.63[1,2,3,4]A	Poison by methylphenidate, [accid (unintentional), intentional self-harm, assault, undetermined], init enc
T43.695A	Adverse effect of oth psychostimulants, init enc
T43.69[1,2,3,4]A	Poison by oth psychostimulants, [accid (unintentional), intentional self-harm, assault, undetermined], init enc
T43.8X5A	Adverse effect of oth psychotropic drugs, init enc
T43.8X[1,2,3,4]A	Poison by oth psychotropic drugs, [accid (unintentional), intentional self-harm, assault, undetermined], init enc
T43.95XA	Adverse effect of unsp psychotropic drug, init enc
T43.9[1,2,3,4]XA	Poison by unsp psychotropic drug, [accid (unintentional), intentional self-harm, assault, undetermined], init enc
T44.0X5A	Adverse effect of anticholinesterase agents, init enc
T44.0X[1,2,3,4]A	Poison by anticholinesterase agents, [accid (unintentional), intentional self-harm, assault, undetermined], init enc
T44.1X5A	Adverse effect of oth parasympathomimetics, init enc
T44.1X[1,2,3,4]A	Poison by parasympathomimetics (cholinergics), [accid (unintentional), intentional self-harm, assault, undetermined], init enc
T44.2X5A	Adverse effect of ganglionic blocking drugs, init enc
T44.2X[1,2,3,4]A	Poison by ganglionic blocking drugs, [accid (unintentional), intentional self-harm, assault, undetermined], init enc
T44.3X5A	Adverse effect of parasympatholytics and spasmolytics, init
T44.3X[1,2,3,4]A	Poison by oth parasympatholytics (anticholinergics and antimuscarinics) and spasmolytics, [accid (unintentional), intentional self-harm, assault, undetermined], init enc
T44.4X5A	Adverse effect of predom alpha-adrenocpt agonists, init
T44.4X[1,2,3,4]A	Poison by predominantly alpha-adrenoreceptor agonists, [accid (unintentional), intentional self-harm, assault, undetermined], init enc
T44.5X5A	Adverse effect of predom beta-adrenocpt agonists, init
T44.5X[1,2,3,4]A	Poison by predominantly beta-adrenoreceptor agonists, [accid (unintentional), intentional self-harm, assault, undetermined], init enc
T44.6X5A	Adverse effect of alpha-adrenoreceptor antagonists, init
T44.6X[1,2,3,4]A	Poison by predominantly alpha-adrenoreceptor antagonists, [accid (unintentional), intentional self-harm, assault, undetermined], init enc
T44.7X5A	Adverse effect of beta-adrenoreceptor antagonists, init
T44.7X[1,2,3,4]A	Poison by predominantly beta-adrenoreceptor antagonists, [accid (unintentional), intentional self-harm, assault, undetermined], init enc

Surgical	**Medical**	**CC Indicator**	**MCC Indicator**	**Procedure Proxy**	**PDx MCC** PDx acts as own MCC	**PDx CC** PDx acts as own CC

T44.8X5A	Adverse effect of centr-acting/adren-neurn-block agnt, init
T44.8X[1,2,3,4]A	Poison by centrally-acting and adrenergic-neuron-blocking agents, [accid (unintentional), intentional self-harm, assault, undetermined], init enc
T44.905A	Advrs effect of unsp drugs affecting the autonm nervous sys, init
T44.90[1,2,3,4]A	Poison by unsp drugs primarily affecting the autonomic nervous sys, [accid (unintentional), intentional self-harm, assault, undetermined], init enc
T44.995A	Adverse effect of drug affecting the autonomic nervous sys, init
T44.99[1,2,3,4]A	Poison by oth drug primarily affecting the autonomic nervous sys, [accid (unintentional), intentional self-harm, assault, undetermined], init enc
T45.0X5A	Adverse effect of antiallergic and antiemetic drugs, init
T45.0X[1,2,3,4]A	Poison by antiallergic and antiemetic drugs, [accid (unintentional), intentional self-harm, assault, undetermined], init enc
T45.1X5A	Adverse effect of antineoplastic and immunosup drugs, init
T45.1X[1,2,3,4]A	Poison by antineoplastic and immunosuppressive drugs, [accid (unintentional), intentional self-harm, assault, undetermined], init enc
T45.2X5A	Adverse effect of vitamins, init enc
T45.2X[1,2,3,4]A	Poison by vitamins, [accid (unintentional), intentional self-harm, assault, undetermined], init enc
T45.3X5A	Adverse effect of enzymes, init enc
T45.3X[1,2,3,4]A	Poison by enzymes, [accid (unintentional), intentional self-harm, assault, undetermined], init enc
T45.4X5A	Adverse effect of iron and its compounds, init enc
T45.4X[1,2,3,4]A	Poison by iron and its compounds, [accid (unintentional), intentional self-harm, assault, undetermined], init enc
T45.515A	Adverse effect of anticoagulants, init enc
T45.51[1,2,3,4]A	Poison by anticoagulants, [accid (unintentional), intentional self-harm, assault, undetermined], init enc
T45.525A	Adverse effect of antithrombotic drugs, init enc
T45.52[1,2,3,4]A	Poison by antithrombotic drugs, [accid (unintentional), intentional self-harm, assault, undetermined], init enc
T45.605A	Adverse effect of unsp fibrinolysis-affecting drugs, init
T45.60[1,2,3,4]A	Poison by unsp fibrinolysis-affecting drugs, [accid (unintentional), intentional self-harm, assault, undetermined], init enc
T45.615A	Adverse effect of thrombolytic drugs, init enc
T45.61[1,2,3,4]A	Poison by thrombolytic drug, [accid (unintentional), intentional self-harm, assault, undetermined], init enc
T45.625A	Adverse effect of hemostatic drug, init enc
T45.62[1,2,3,4]A	Poison by hemostatic drug, [accid (unintentional), intentional self-harm, assault, undetermined], init enc
T45.695A	Adverse effect of oth fibrinolysis-affecting drugs, init
T45.69[1,2,3,4]A	Poison by oth fibrinolysis-affecting drug, [accid (unintentional), intentional self-harm, assault, undetermined], init enc
T45.7X5A	Adverse effect of anticoag antag, vit K and oth coag, init
T45.7X[1,2,3,4]A	Poison by anticoagulant antagonists, vitamin K and oth coagulants, [accid (unintentional), intentional self-harm, assault, undetermined], init enc
T45.8X5A	Adverse effect of prim systemic and hematolog agents, init
T45.8X[1,2,3,4]A	Poison by oth primarily sysic and hematological agents, [accid (unintentional), intentional self-harm, assault, undetermined], init enc
T45.95XA	Adverse effect of unsp prim sys and hematolog agent, init
T45.9[1,2,3,4]XA	Poison by unsp primarily sysic and hematological agents, [accid (unintentional), intentional self-harm, assault, undetermined], init enc
T46.0X5A	Adverse effect of cardi-stim glycos/drug simlar act, init
T46.0X[1,2,3,4]A	Poison by cardiac stimulant glycosides and drugs of similar action, [accid (unintentional), intentional self-harm, assault, undetermined], init enc
T46.1X5A	Adverse effect of calcium-channel blockers, init enc
T46.1X[1,2,3,4]A	Poison by calcium-channel blockers, [accid (unintentional), intentional self-harm, assault, undetermined], init enc
T46.2X5A	Adverse effect of oth antidysrhythmic drugs, init enc
T46.2X[1,2,3,4]A	Poison by antidysrhythmic drugs, [accid (unintentional), intentional self-harm, assault, undetermined], init enc
T46.3X5A	Adverse effect of coronary vasodilators, init enc
T46.3X[1,2,3,4]A	Poison by coronary vasodilators, [accid (unintentional), intentional self-harm, assault, undetermined], init enc
T46.4X5A	Adverse effect of angiotens-convert-enzyme inhibitors, init
T46.4X[1,2,3,4]A	Poison by angiotensin-converting-enzyme inhibitors, [accid (unintentional), intentional self-harm, assault, undetermined], init enc

T46.5X5A	Adverse effect of oth antihypertensive drugs, init enc
T46.5X[1,2,3,4]A	Poison by oth antihypertensive drugs, [accid (unintentional), intentional self-harm, assault, undetermined], init enc
T46.6X5A	Adverse effect of antihyperlip and antiarterio drugs, init
T46.6X[1,2,3,4]A	Poison by antihyperlipidemic and antiarteriosclerotic drugs, [accid (unintentional), intentional self-harm, assault, undetermined], init enc
T46.7X5A	Adverse effect of peripheral vasodilators, init enc
T46.7X[1,2,3,4]A	Poison by peripheral vasodilators, [accid (unintentional), intentional self-harm, assault, undetermined], init enc
T46.8X5A	Adverse effect of antivaric drugs, incl* scler agents, init
T46.8X[1,2,3,4]A	Poison by antivaricose drugs, incl* sclerosing agents, [accid (unintentional), intentional self-harm, assault, undetermined], init enc
T46.905A	Adverse effect of unsp agents affecting the cardiovasc sys, init
T46.90[1,2,3,4]A	Poison by unsp agents primarily affecting the cardiovascular sys, [accid (unintentional), intentional self-harm, assault, undetermined], init enc
T46.995A	Adverse effect of agents affected the cardiovascular sys, init
T46.99[1,2,3,4]A	Poison by oth agent primarily affecting the cardiovascular sys, [accid (unintentional), intentional self-harm, assault, undetermined], init enc
T47.0X5A	Adverse effect of histamine H2-receptor blockers, init
T47.0X[1,2,3,4]A	Poison by histamine H2-receptor blockers, [accid (unintentional), intentional self-harm, assault, undetermined], init enc
T47.1X5A	Adverse effect of antacids and anti-gstrc-sec drugs, init
T47.1X[1,2,3,4]A	Poison by oth antacids and anti-gastric-secretion drugs, [accid (unintentional), intentional self-harm, assault, undetermined], init enc
T47.2X5A	Adverse effect of stimulant laxatives, init enc
T47.2X[1,2,3,4]A	Poison by stimulant laxatives, [accid (unintentional), intentional self-harm, assault, undetermined], init enc
T47.3X5A	Adverse effect of saline and osmotic laxatives, init enc
T47.3X[1,2,3,4]A	Poison by saline and osmotic laxatives, [accid (unintentional), intentional self-harm, assault, undetermined], init enc
T47.4X5A	Adverse effect of oth laxatives, init enc
T47.4X[1,2,3,4]A	Poison by oth laxatives, [accid (unintentional), intentional self-harm, assault, undetermined], init enc
T47.5X5A	Adverse effect of digestants, init enc
T47.5X[1,2,3,4]A	Poison by digestants, [accid (unintentional), intentional self-harm, assault, undetermined], init enc
T47.6X5A	Adverse effect of antidiarrheal drugs, init enc
T47.6X[1,2,3,4]A	Poison by antidiarrheal drugs, [accid (unintentional), intentional self-harm, assault, undetermined], init enc
T47.7X5A	Adverse effect of emetics, init enc
T47.7X[1,2,3,4]A	Poison by emetics, [accid (unintentional), intentional self-harm, assault, undetermined], init enc
T47.8X5A	Adverse effect of agents primarily affecting GI sys, init
T47.8X[1,2,3,4]A	Poison by oth agents primarily affecting gastrointestinal sys, [accid (unintentional), intentional self-harm, assault, undetermined], init enc
T47.95XA	Adverse effect of unsp agents affected the GI sys, init
T47.9[1,2,3,4]XA	Poison by unsp agents primarily affecting gastrointestinal sys, [accid (unintentional), intentional self-harm, assault, undetermined], init enc
T48.0X5A	Adverse effect of oxytocic drugs, init enc
T48.0X[1,2,3,4]A	Poison by oxytocic drugs, [accid (unintentional), intentional self-harm, assault, undetermined], init enc
T48.1X5A	Adverse effect of skeletal muscle relaxants, init enc
T48.1X[1,2,3,4]A	Poison by skeletal muscle relaxants (neuromuscular blocking agents), [accid (unintentional), intentional self-harm, assault, undetermined], init enc
T48.205A	Adverse effect of unsp drugs acting on muscles, init enc
T48.20[1,2,3,4]A	Poison by unsp drugs working on muscles, [accid (unintentional), intentional self-harm, assault, undetermined], init enc
T48.295A	Adverse effect of oth drugs acting on muscles, init enc
T48.29[1,2,3,4]A	Poison by oth drugs working on muscles, [accid (unintentional), intentional self-harm, assault, undetermined], init enc
T48.3X5A	Adverse effect of antitussives, init enc
T48.3X[1,2,3,4]A	Poison by antitussives, [accid (unintentional), intentional self-harm, assault, undetermined], init enc
T48.4X5A	Adverse effect of expectorants, init enc
T48.4X[1,2,3,4]A	Poison by expectorants, [accid (unintentional), intentional self-harm, assault, undetermined], init enc
T48.5X5A	Adverse effect of oth anti-common-cold drugs, init enc

Code	Description
T48.5X[1,2,3,4]A	Poison by oth anti-common-cold drugs, [accid (unintentional), intentional self-harm, assault, undetermined], init enc
T48.6X5A	Adverse effect of antiasthmatics, init enc
T48.6X[1,2,3,4]A	Poison by antiasthmatics, [accid (unintentional), intentional self-harm, assault, undetermined], init enc
T48.905A	Advrs effect of unsp agents prim act on the resp sys, init
T48.90[1,2,3,4]A	Poison by unsp agents primarily acting on the respiratory sys, [accid (unintentional), intentional self-harm, assault, undetermined], init enc
T48.995A	Adverse effect of agents prim acting on the resp sys, init
T48.99[1,2,3,4]A	Poison by oth agents primarily acting on the respiratory sys, [accid (unintentional), intentional self-harm, assault, undetermined], init enc
T49.0X5A	Adverse effect of local antifung/infect/inflamm drugs, init
T49.0X[1,2,3,4]A	Poison by local antifungal, anti-infective and anti-inflam drugs, [accid (unintentional), intentional self-harm, assault, undetermined], init enc
T49.1X5A	Adverse effect of antipruritics, init enc
T49.1X[1,2,3,4]A	Poison by antipruritics, [accid (unintentional), intentional self-harm, assault, undetermined], init enc
T49.2X5A	Adverse effect of local astringents/detergents, init
T49.2X[1,2,3,4]A	Poison by local astringents and local detergents, [accid (unintentional), intentional self-harm, assault, undetermined], init enc
T49.3X5A	Adverse effect of emollients, demulcents and protect, init
T49.3X[1,2,3,4]A	Poison by emollients, demulcents and protectants, [accid (unintentional), intentional self-harm, assault, undetermined], init enc
T49.4X5A	Adverse effect of keratolyt/keratplst/hair trmt drug, init
T49.4X[1,2,3,4]A	Poison by keratolytics, keratoplastics, and oth hair tx drugs, [accid (unintentional), intentional self-harm, assault, undetermined], init enc
T49.5X5A	Adverse effect of opth drugs and preparations, init
T49.6X5A	Adverse effect of otorhino drugs and preparations, init
T49.6X[1,2,3,4]A	Poison by otorhinolaryngological drugs and preparations, [accid (unintentional), intentional self-harm, assault, undetermined], init enc
T49.7X5A	Adverse effect of dental drugs, topically applied, init
T49.7X[1,2,3,4]A	Poison by dental drugs, topically applied, [accid (unintentional), intentional self-harm, assault, undetermined], init enc
T49.8X5A	Adverse effect of oth topical agents, init enc
T49.8X[1,2,3,4]A	Poison by oth topical agents, [accid (unintentional), intentional self-harm, assault, undetermined], init enc
T49.95XA	Adverse effect of unsp topical agent, init enc
T49.9[1,2,3,4]XA	Poison by unsp topical agent, [accid (unintentional), intentional self-harm, assault, undetermined], init enc
T50.0X5A	Adverse effect of mineralocorticoids and their antag, init
T50.0X[1,2,3,4]A	Poison by mineralocorticoids and their antagonists, [accid (unintentional), intentional self-harm, assault, undetermined], init enc
T50.1X5A	Adverse effect of loop diuretics, init enc
T50.1X[1,2,3,4]A	Poison by loop (hugh ceiling) diuretics, [accid (unintentional), intentional self-harm, assault, undetermined], init enc
T50.2X5A	Advrs eff of crbnc-anhydr inhibtr, benzo/oth diuretc, init
T50.2X[1,2,3,4]A	Poison by carbonic-anhydrase inhibitors, benzothiadiazides and oth diuretics, [accid (unintentional), intentional self-harm, assault, undetermined], init enc
T50.3X5A	Adverse effect of electrolytic/caloric/wtr-bal agnt, init
T50.3X[1,2,3,4]A	Poison by eletrolytic, caloric and water-balance agents, [accid (unintentional), intentional self-harm, assault, undetermined], init enc
T50.4X5A	Adverse effect of drugs affecting uric acid metabolism, init
T50.4X[1,2,3,4]A	Poison by drugs affecting uric acid metabolism, [accid (unintentional), intentional self-harm, assault, undetermined], init enc
T50.5X5A	Adverse effect of appetite depressants, init enc
T50.5X[1,2,3,4]A	Poison by appetite depressants, [accid (unintentional), intentional self-harm, assault, undetermined], init enc
T50.6X5A	Adverse effect of antidotes and chelating agents, init
T50.6X[1,2,3,4]A	Poison by antidotes and chelating agents, [accid (unintentional), intentional self-harm, assault, undetermined], init enc
T50.7X5A	Adverse effect of analeptics and opioid receptor antag, init
T50.7X[1,2,3,4]A	Poison by analeptics and opiod receptor antagonists, [accid (unintentional), intentional self-harm, assault, undetermined], init enc
T50.8X5A	Adverse effect of diagnostic agents, init enc
T50.8X[1,2,3,4]A	Poison by dx agents, [accid (unintentional), intentional self-harm, assault, undetermined], init enc
T50.905A	Adverse effect of unsp drug/meds/biol subst, init
T50.90[1,2,3,4]A	Poison by unsp drugs, medicaments and biological substances, [accid (unintentional), intentional self-harm, assault, undetermined], init enc
T50.995A	Adverse effect of drug/meds/biol subst, init
T50.99[1,2,3,4]A	Poison by oth drugs, medicaments and biological substances, [accid (unintentional), intentional self-harm, assault, undetermined], init enc
T50.A15A	Advrs effect of pertuss vaccine, incl* combin w pertuss, init
T50.A1[1,2,3,4]A	Poison by pertussis vaccine, incl* combinations w/ a pertussis component, [accid (unintentional), intentional self-harm, assault, undetermined], init enc
T50.A25A	Adverse effect of mixed bact vaccines w/o a pertuss, init
T50.A2[1,2,3,4]A	Poison by mixed bacterial vaccines w/o a pertussis component, [accid (unintentional), intentional self-harm, assault, undetermined], init enc
T50.A95A	Adverse effect of oth bacterial vaccines, init enc
T50.A9[1,2,3,4]A	Poison by oth bacterial vaccines, [accid (unintentional), intentional self-harm, assault, undetermined], init enc
T50.B15A	Adverse effect of smallpox vaccines, init enc
T50.B1[1,2,3,4]A	Poison by smpox vaccines, [accid (unintentional), intentional self-harm, assault, undetermined], init enc
T50.B95A	Adverse effect of oth viral vaccines, init enc
T50.B9[1,2,3,4]A	Poison by oth viral vaccines, [accid (unintentional), intentional self-harm, assault, undetermined], init enc
T50.Z15A	Adverse effect of immunoglobulin, init enc
T50.Z1[1,2,3,4]A	Poison by immunoglobin, [accid (unintentional), intentional self-harm, assault, undetermined], init enc
T50.Z95A	Adverse effect of vaccines and biological substances, init
T50.Z9[1,2,3,4]A	Poison by oth vaccines and biological substances, [accid (unintentional), intentional self-harm, assault, undetermined], init enc
T51.0X[1,2,3,4]A	Txc effct of ethanol, [accid (unintentional), intentional self-harm, assault, undetermined], init enc
T51.1X[1,2,3,4]A	Txc effct of methanol, [accid (unintentional), intentional self-harm, assault, undetermined], init enc
T51.2X[1,2,3,4]A	Txc effct of 2-Propanol, [accid (unintentional), intentional self-harm, assault, undetermined], init enc
T51.3X[1,2,3,4]A	Txc effct of fusel oil, [accid (unintentional), intentional self-harm, assault, undetermined], init enc
T51.8X[1,2,3,4]A	Txc effct of oth alcohols, [accid (unintentional), intentional self-harm, assault, undetermined], init enc
T51.9[1,2,3,4]XA	Txc effct of unsp alcohol, [accid (unintentional), intentional self-harm, assault, undetermined], init enc
T52.0X[1,2,3,4]A	Txc effct of petroleum products, [accid (unintentional), intentional self-harm, assault, undetermined], init enc
T52.1X[1,2,3,4]A	Txc effct of benzene [accid (unintentional), intentional self-harm, assault, undetermined], init enc
T52.2X[1,2,3,4]A	Txc effct of homologues of benzene, [accid (unintentional), intentional self-harm, assault, undetermined], init enc
T52.3X[1,2,3,4]A	Txc effct of glycoles, [accid (unintentional), intentional self-harm, assault, undetermined], init enc
T52.4X[1,2,3,4]A	Txc effct of ketones, [accid (unintentional), intentional self-harm, assault, undetermined], init enc
T52.8X[1,2,3,4]A	Txc effct of oth organic solvents, [accid (unintentional), intentional self-harm, assault, undetermined], init enc
T52.9[1,2,3,4]XA	Txc effct of unsp organic solvent, [accid (unintentional), intentional self-harm, assault, undetermined], init enc
T53.0X[1,2,3,4]A	Txc effct of carbon tetrachloride, [accid (unintentional), intentional self-harm, assault, undetermined], init enc
T53.1X[1,2,3,4]A	Txc effct of chloroform, [accid (unintentional), intentional self-harm, assault, undetermined], init enc
T53.2X[1,2,3,4]A	Txc effct of trichloroethylene, [accid (unintentional), intentional self-harm, assault, undetermined], init enc
T53.3X[1,2,3,4]A	Txc effct of tetrachloroethylene, [accid (unintentional), intentional self-harm, assault, undetermined], init enc
T53.4X[1,2,3,4]A	Txc effct of dichloromethane, [accid (unintentional), intentional self-harm, assault, undetermined], init enc
T53.5X[1,2,3,4]A	Txc effct of chlorofluorocarbons, [accid (unintentional), intentional self-harm, assault, undetermined], init enc
T53.6X[1,2,3,4]A	Txc effct of oth halogen derivatives of aliphatic hydrocarbons, [accid (unintentional), intentional self-harm, assault, undetermined], init enc
T53.7X[1,2,3,4]A	Txc effct of oth halogen derivatives of aromatic hydrocarbons, [accid (unintentional), intentional self-harm, assault, undetermined], init enc

Surgical   **Medical**   **CC Indicator**   **MCC Indicator**   **Procedure Proxy**   **PDxMCC** PDx acts as own MCC   **PDxCC** PDx acts as own CC

T53.9[1,2,3,4]XA Txc effct of unsp halogen derivatives of aliphatic and aromatic hydrocarbons, [accid (unintentional), intentional self-harm, assault, undetermined], init enc

T54.0X[1,2,3,4]A Txc effct of phenol and phenol homologues, [accid (unintentional), intentional self-harm, assault, undetermined], init enc

T54.1X[1,2,3,4]A Txc effct of oth corrosive organic compound, [accid (unintentional), intentional self-harm, assault, undetermined], init enc

T54.2X[1,2,3,4]A Txc effct of corrosive acids and acid-like substances, [accid (unintentional), intentional self-harm, assault, undetermined], init enc

T54.3X[1,2,3,4]A Txc effct of corrosive alkalis and alkali-like substances, [accid (unintentional), intentional self-harm, assault, undetermined], init enc

T54.9[1,2,3,4]XA Txc effct of unsp corrosive substance, [accid (unintentional), intentional self-harm, assault, undetermined], init enc

T55.0X[1,2,3,4]A Txc effct of soaps, [accid (unintentional), intentional self-harm, assault, undetermined], init enc

T55.1X[1,2,3,4]A Txc effct of detergents, [accid (unintentional), intentional self-harm, assault, undetermined], init enc

T56.0X[1,2,3,4]A Txc effct of lead and its compounds, [accid (unintentional), intentional self-harm, assault, undetermined], init enc

T56.1X[1,2,3,4]A Txc effct of mercury and its compounds, [accid (unintentional), intentional self-harm, assault, undetermined], init enc

T56.2X[1,2,3,4]A Txc effct of chromium and its compounds, [accid (unintentional), intentional self-harm, assault, undetermined], init enc

T56.3X[1,2,3,4]A Txc effct of cadmium and its compounds, [accid (unintentional), intentional self-harm, assault, undetermined], init enc

T56.4X[1,2,3,4]A Txc effct of copper and its compounds, [accid (unintentional), intentional self-harm, assault, undetermined], init enc

T56.5X[1,2,3,4]A Txc effct of zinc and its compounds, [accid (unintentional), intentional self-harm, assault, undetermined], init enc

T56.6X[1,2,3,4]A Txc effct of tin and its compounds, [accid (unintentional), intentional self-harm, assault, undetermined], init enc

T56.7X[1,2,3,4]A Txc effct of beryllium and its compounds, [accid (unintentional), intentional self-harm, assault, undetermined], init enc

T56.81[1,2,3,4]A Txc effct of thallium and its compounds, [accid (unintentional), intentional self-harm, assault, undetermined], init enc

T56.89[1,2,3,4]A Txc effct of oth metals, [accid (unintentional), intentional self-harm, assault, undetermined], init enc

T56.9[1,2,3,4]XA Txc effct of unsp metal, [accid (unintentional), intentional self-harm, assault, undetermined], init enc

T57.0X[1,2,3,4]A Txc effct of arsenic and its compounds, [accid (unintentional), intentional self-harm, assault, undetermined], init enc

T57.1X[1,2,3,4]A Txc effct of phosphorus and its compounds, [accid (unintentional), intentional self-harm, assault, undetermined], init enc

T57.2X[1,2,3,4]A Txc effct of manganese and its compounds, [accid (unintentional), intentional self-harm, assault, undetermined], init enc

T57.3X[1,2,3,4]A Txc effct of hydrogen cyanide, [accid (unintentional), intentional self-harm, assault, undetermined], init enc

T57.8X[1,2,3,4]A Txc effct of oth spec inorganic substances, [accid (unintentional), intentional self-harm, assault, undetermined], init enc

T57.9[1,2,3,4]XA Txc effct of unsp inorganic substance, [accid (unintentional), intentional self-harm, assault, undetermined], init enc

T58.0[1,2,3,4]XA Txc effct of carbon monoxide from motor vehicle exhaust, [accid (unintentional), intentional self-harm, assault, undetermined], init enc

T58.1[1,2,3,4]XA Txc effct of carbon monoxide from utility gas, [accid (unintentional), intentional self-harm, assault, undetermined], init enc

T58.2X[1,2,3,4]A Txc effct of carbon monoxide from incomplete combustion of oth domestic fuels, [accid (unintentional), intentional self-harm, assault, undetermined], init enc

T58.8X[1,2,3,4]A Txc effct of carbon monoxide from oth source, [accid (unintentional), intentional self-harm, assault, undetermined], init enc

T58.9[1,2,3,4]XA Txc effct of carbon monoxide from unsp source, [accid (unintentional), intentional self-harm, assault, undetermined], init enc

T59.0X[1,2,3,4]A Txc effct of nitrogen oxides, [accid (unintentional), intentional self-harm, assault, undetermined], init enc

T59.1X[1,2,3,4]A Txc effct of sulfur dioxide, [accid (unintentional), intentional self-harm, assault, undetermined], init enc

T59.2X[1,2,3,4]A Txc effct of formaldehyde, [accid (unintentional), intentional self-harm, assault, undetermined], init enc

T59.3X[1,2,3,4]A Txc effct of lacrimogenic gas, [accid (unintentional), intentional self-harm, assault, undetermined], init enc

T59.4X[1,2,3,4]A Txc effct of chlorine gas, [accid (unintentional), intentional self-harm, assault, undetermined], init enc

T59.5X[1,2,3,4]A Txc effct of fluorine gas and hydrogen fluoride, [accid (unintentional), intentional self-harm, assault, undetermined], init enc

T59.6X[1,2,3,4]A Txc effct of hydrogen sulfide, [accid (unintentional), intentional self-harm, assault, undetermined], init enc

T59.7X[1,2,3,4]A Txc effct of carbon dioxide, [accid (unintentional), intentional self-harm, assault, undetermined], init enc

T59.81[1,2,3,4]A Txc effct of smoke, [accid (unintentional), intentional self-harm, assault, undetermined], init enc

T59.89[1,2,3,4]A Txc effct of oth spec gases, fumes and vapors, [accid (unintentional), intentional self-harm, assault, undetermined], init enc

T59.9[1,2,3,4]XA Txc effct of unsp gases, fumes and vapors, [accid (unintentional), intentional self harm, assault, undetermined], init enc

T60.0X[1,2,3,4]A Txc effct of organophosphate and carbamate insecticides, [accid (unintentional), intentional self-harm, assault, undetermined], init enc

T60.1X[1,2,3,4]A Txc effct of halogenated insecticides, [accid (unintentional), intentional self-harm, assault, undetermined], init enc

T60.2X[1,2,3,4]A Txc effct of oth insecticides, [accid (unintentional), intentional self-harm, assault, undetermined], init enc

T60.3X[1,2,3,4]A Txc effct of herbicides and fungicides, [accid (unintentional), intentional self-harm, assault, undetermined], init enc

T60.4X[1,2,3,4]A Txc effct of rodenticides, [accid (unintentional), intentional self-harm, assault, undetermined], init enc

T60.8X[1,2,3,4]A Txc effct of oth pesticides, [accid (unintentional), intentional self-harm, assault, undetermined], init enc

T60.9[1,2,3,4]XA Txc effct of unsp pesticides, [accid (unintentional), intentional self-harm, assault, undetermined], init enc

T61.0[1,2,3,4]XA Ciguatera fish poison, [accid (unintentional), intentional self-harm, assault, undetermined], init enc

T61.1[1,2,3,4]XA Scombroid fish poison, [accid (unintentional), intentional self-harm, assault, undetermined], init enc

T61.77[1,2,3,4]A Oth fish poison, [accid (unintentional), intentional self-harm, assault, undetermined], init enc

T61.78[1,2,3,4]A Oth shellfish poison, [accid (unintentional), intentional self-harm, assault, undetermined], init enc

T61.8X[1,2,3,4]A Txc effct of oth seafood, [accid (unintentional), intentional self-harm, assault, undetermined], init enc

T61.9[1,2,3,4]XA Txc effct of unsp seafood, [accid (unintentional), intentional self-harm, assault, undetermined], init enc

T62.0X[1,2,3,4]A Txc effct of ingested mushrooms, [accid (unintentional), intentional self-harm, assault, undetermined], init enc

T62.1X[1,2,3,4]A Txc effct of ingested berries, [accid (unintentional), intentional self-harm, assault, undetermined], init enc

T62.2X[1,2,3,4]A Txc effct of oth ingested (parts of) plant(s), [accid (unintentional), intentional self-harm, assault, undetermined], init enc

T62.8X[1,2,3,4]A Txc effct of oth spec noxious substances eaten as food, [accid (unintentional), intentional self-harm, assault, undetermined], init enc

T62.9[1,2,3,4]XA Txc effct of unsp noxious substances eaten as food, [accid (unintentional), intentional self-harm, assault, undetermined], init enc

T63.00[1,2,3,4]A Txc effct of unsp snake venom, [accid (unintentional), intentional self-harm, assault, undetermined], init enc

T63.01[1,2,3,4]A Txc effct of rattlesnake venom, [accid (unintentional), intentional self-harm, assault, undetermined], init enc

T63.02[1,2,3,4]A Txc effct of coral snake venom, [accid (unintentional), intentional self-harm, assault, undetermined], init enc

T63.03[1,2,3,4]A Txc effct of taipan venom, [accid (unintentional), intentional self-harm, assault, undetermined], init enc

T63.04[1,2,3,4]A Txc effct of cobra venom, [accid (unintentional), intentional self-harm, assault, undetermined], init enc

T63.06[1,2,3,4]A Txc effct of venom of oth North and South American snake, [accid (unintentional), intentional self-harm, assault, undetermined], init enc

T63.07[1,2,3,4]A Txc effct of venom of oth Australian snake, [accid (unintentional), intentional self-harm, assault, undetermined], init enc

---

T Transfer DRG   SP Special Payment   * Code Range   6th and 7th Character of ZZ = No Device, No Qualifier ZX = No Device, Diagnostic

MS-DRG Version 33.0

T63.08[1,2,3,4]A Txc effct of venom of oth African and Asian snake, [accid (unintentional), intentional self-harm, assault, undetermined], init enc

T63.09[1,2,3,4]A Txc effct of venom of oth snake, [accid (unintentional), intentional self-harm, assault, undetermined], init enc

T63.11[1,2,3,4]A Txc effct of venom of gila monster, [accid (unintentional), intentional self-harm, assault, undetermined], init enc

T63.12[1,2,3,4]A Txc effct of venom of oth venomous lizard, [accid (unintentional), intentional self-harm, assault, undetermined], init enc

T63.19[1,2,3,4]A Txc effct of venom of oth reptiles, [accid (unintentional), intentional self-harm, assault, undetermined], init enc

T63.2X[1,2,3,4]A Txc effct of venom of scorpion, [accid (unintentional), intentional self-harm, assault, undetermined], init enc

T63.30[1,2,3,4]A Txc effct of unsp spider venom, [accid (unintentional), intentional self-harm, assault, undetermined], init enc

T63.31[1,2,3,4]A Txc effct of venom of black widow spider, [accid (unintentional), intentional self-harm, assault, undetermined], init enc

T63.32[1,2,3,4]A Txc effct of venom of tarantula, [accid (unintentional), intentional self-harm, assault, undetermined], init enc

T63.33[1,2,3,4]A Txc effct of venom of brown recluse spider, [accid (unintentional), intentional self-harm, assault, undetermined], init enc

T63.39[1,2,3,4]A Txc effct of venom of oth spider, [accid (unintentional), intentional self-harm, assault, undetermined], init enc

T63.41[1,2,3,4]A Txc effct of venom of centipedes and venomous millipedes, [accid (unintentional), intentional self-harm, assault, undetermined], init enc

T63.42[1,2,3,4]A Txc effct of venom of ants, [accid (unintentional), intentional self-harm, assault, undetermined], init enc

T63.43[1,2,3,4]A Txc effct of venom of caterpillars, [accid (unintentional), intentional self-harm, assault, undetermined], init enc

T63.44[1,2,3,4]A Txc effct of venom of bees, [accid (unintentional), intentional self-harm, assault, undetermined], init enc

T63.45[1,2,3,4]A Txc effct of venom of hornets, [accid (unintentional), intentional self-harm, assault, undetermined], init enc

T63.46[1,2,3,4]A Txc effct of venom of wasps, [accid (unintentional), intentional self-harm, assault, undetermined], init enc

T63.48[1,2,3,4]A Txc effct of venom of oth arthropod, [accid (unintentional), intentional self-harm, assault, undetermined], init enc

T63.51[1,2,3,4]A Txc effct of contact w/ stingray, [accid (unintentional), intentional self-harm, assault, undetermined], init enc

T63.59[1,2,3,4]A Txc effct of contact w/ oth venomous fish, [accid (unintentional), intentional self-harm, assault, undetermined], init enc

T63.61[1,2,3,4]A Txc effct of contact w/ Portugese Man-o-war, [accid (unintentional), intentional self-harm, assault, undetermined], init enc

T63.62[1,2,3,4]A Txc effct of contact w/ oth jellyfish, [accid (unintentional), intentional self-harm, assault, undetermined], init enc

T63.63[1,2,3,4]A Txc effct of contact w/ sea anemone, [accid (unintentional), intentional self-harm, assault, undetermined], init enc

T63.69[1,2,3,4]A Txc effct of contact w/ oth venomous marine animals, [accid (unintentional), intentional self-harm, assault, undetermined], init enc

T63.71[1,2,3,4]A Txc effct of contact w/ venomous marine plant, [accid (unintentional), intentional self-harm, assault, undetermined], init enc

T63.79[1,2,3,4]A Txc effct of contact w/ oth venomous plant, [accid (unintentional), intentional self-harm, assault, undetermined], init enc

T63.81[1,2,3,4]A Txc effct of contact w/ venomous frog, [accid (unintentional), intentional self-harm, assault, undetermined], init enc

T63.82[1,2,3,4]A Txc effct of contact w/ venomous toad, [accid (unintentional), intentional self-harm, assault, undetermined], init enc

T63.83[1,2,3,4]A Txc effct of contact w/ oth venomous amphibian, [accid (unintentional), intentional self-harm, assault, undetermined], init enc

T63.89[1,2,3,4]A Txc effct of contact w/ oth venomous animals, [accid (unintentional), intentional self-harm, assault, undetermined], init enc

T63.9[1,2,3,4]XA Txc effct of contact w/ unsp venomous animal, [accid (unintentional), intentional self-harm, assault, undetermined], init enc

T64.0[1,2,3,4]XA Txc effct of aflatoxin, [accid (unintentional), intentional self-harm, assault, undetermined], init enc

T64.8[1,2,3,4]XA Txc effct of oth mycotoxin food contaminants, [accid (unintentional), intentional self-harm, assault, undetermined], init enc

T65.0X[1,2,3,4]A Txc effct of cyanides, [accid (unintentional), intentional self-harm, assault, undetermined], init enc

T65.1X[1,2,3,4]A Txc effct of strychnine, [accid (unintentional), intentional self-harm, assault, undetermined], init enc

T65.21[1,2,3,4]A Txc effct of chewing tobacco, [accid (unintentional), intentional self-harm, assault, undetermined], init enc

T65.22[1,2,3,4]A Txc effct of tobacco cigarettes, [accid (unintentional), intentional self-harm, assault, undetermined], init enc

T65.29[1,2,3,4]A Txc effct of oth tobacco and nicotine, [accid (unintentional), intentional self-harm, assault, undetermined], init enc

T65.3X[1,2,3,4]A Txc effct of nitroderivatives and amnioderivatives of benzene and its homologues, [accid (unintentional), intentional self-harm, assault, undetermined], init enc

T65.4X[1,2,3,4]A Txc effct of carbon disulfide, [accid (unintentional), intentional self-harm, assault, undetermined], init enc

T65.5X[1,2,3,4]A Txc effct of nitroglycerin and oth nitric acids amd esters, [accid (unintentional), intentional self-harm, assault, undetermined], init enc

T65.6X[1,2,3,4]A Txc effct of paints and dyes, NEC, [accid (unintentional), intentional self-harm, assault, undetermined], init enc

T65.81[1,2,3,4]A Txc effct of latex, [accid (unintentional), intentional self-harm, assault, undetermined], init enc

T65.82[1,2,3,4]A Txc effct of harmful algae and algae toxins, [accid (unintentional), intentional self-harm, assault, undetermined], init enc

T65.83[1,2,3,4]A Txc effct of fiberglass, NEC, [accid (unintentional), intentional self-harm, assault, undetermined], init enc

T65.89[1,2,3,4]A Txc effct of oth spec substances, [accid (unintentional), intentional self-harm, assault, undetermined], init enc

T65.9[1,2,3,4]XA Txc effct of unsp substance, [accid (unintentional), intentional self-harm, assault, undetermined], init enc

T78.41XA Arthus phenomenon, init enc

T88.52XA Failed mod sedation during procedure, init enc

T88.59XA Oth comp of anesthesia, init enc

DRG 918 **Poisoning and Toxic Effects of Drugs without MCC**
GMLOS 2.2 AMLOS 2.9 RW 0.6859 ⊤

Select principal diagnosis listed under DRG 917

DRG 919 **Complications of Treatment with MCC**
GMLOS 4.5 AMLOS 6.2 RW 1.7611

Principal Diagnosis

D47.Z1 Post-transplant lymphoproliferative d/o (PTLD)
D78* Intraop and postprocedural comp of the spleen
E36* Intraoperative comp of endocrine sys
E89.8* Oth postproc endocrine and metabolic comp and d/o
G96.11 Dural tear
G97.4* Accid punc & lac of a nervous sys org dur proc
G97.5* Postproc hemor/hemtom of a nervous sys org fol a procedure
H59.01* Keratopathy (bullous aphakic) following cataract surgery
H59.03* Cystoid macular edema following cataract surgery
H59.09* Oth d/o of the eye following cataract surgery
H59.1* Intraop hemor/hemtom of eye and adnexa comp a procedure
H59.2* Accid punc & lac of eye and adnexa during a procedure
H59.3* Postproc hemor/hemtom of eye and adnexa fol a procedure
H59.8* Oth intraop & postproc comp and d/o of eye and adnx, NEC
H95.2* Intraop hemor/hemtom of ear/mastd compl a procedure
H95.3* Accid punc & lac of ear/mastd during a procedure
H95.4* Postproc hemor/hemtom of ear/mastd following a procedure
H95.8* Oth intraop and postproc comp and d/o of ear/mastd, NEC
I97.3 Postprocedural hypertension
I97.4* Intraop hemor/hemtom of a circ sys org comp a procedure
I97.5* Accid punc & lac of a circ sys org dur proc
I97.6* Postproc hemor/hemtom of a circ sys org fol a procedure
J95.6* Intraop hemor/hemtom of a resp sys org comp a procedure
J95.7* Accid punc & lac of a respiratory sys org dur proc
J95.830 Postproc hemor/hemtom of a resp sys org fol a resp sys proc
J95.831 Postproc hemor/hemtom of a resp sys org fol oth procedure
K91.6* Intraop hemor/hemtom of a dgstv sys org comp a procedure
K91.7* Accid punc & lac of a digestive sys org dur proc
K91.840 Postproc hemor/hemtom of dgstv sys org fol a dgstv sys proc
K91.841 Postproc hemor/hemtom of a dgstv sys org fol oth procedure
L76* Intraop and postprocedural comp of skin, SQ
M96.8* Oth intraop and postproc comp and d/o of ms sys, NEC
N98.1 Hyperstimulation of ovaries
N98.2 Comp of attempt introduce of fertilized ovum fol in vitro

---

Surgical   Medical   CC Indicator   MCC Indicator   Procedure Proxy   PDxMCC PDx acts as own MCC   PDxCC PDx acts as own CC

Code	Description
N98.3	Comp of attempted introduction of embryo in embryo transfer
N98.8	Oth comp associated with artfcl fertilization
N98.9	Comp associated with artfcl fertilization, unsp
N99.6*	Intraop hemor/hemtom of a GU sys org comp a procedure
N99.7*	Accid punc & lac of a GU sys org dur proc
N99.820	Postproc hemor/hemtom of a GU sys org fol a GU sys procedure
N99.821	Postproc hemor/hemtom of a GU sys org fol oth procedure
T81.1[0,1,2,9]XA	Postprocedural [unsp, cardiogenic, septic, oth] shock, init enc
T81.3[0,1,2,3]XA	Disruption of [unsp wnd, ext operation (surgical) wnd, int operation (surgical) wnd, traum inj wnd rpr], init enc
T81.5[0,1,2,3,9][0,1,2,3,4,5,6,7,8,9]A	[Unsp comp, Adhesions, Obstruction, Perforation, Oth comps] d/t FB accidally lt in body following [surgical operation, inf or transfusion, kidney dialysis, injectionor immunization, endo exam, heart catheterization, aspiration punc or oth catheterization, rmvl of catheter or packing, oth procedure, unsp procedure], init enc
T81.6[0,1,9]XA	[Unsp acute reaction, Aseptic peritonitis, Oth acute reaction] d/t foreign substance accidally lt during a procedure, init enc
T81.81XA	Comp of inhalation therapy, init enc
T81.82XA	Emphysema (SQ) resulting from a procedure, init
T81.83XA	Persistent postprocedural fistula, init enc
T81.89XA	Oth comp of procedures, NEC, init
T81.9XXA	Unsp comp of procedure, init enc
T85.3[1,2,9][0,1]A	[Breakdown (mech), Displac, Oth mech comp] of prosthetic orbit of [rt, lt] eye, init enc
T85.5[1,2,9][0,1,8]A	[Breakdown (mech), Displac, Oth mech comp] of [bile duct prosthesis, esophageal anti-reflux dev, oth gastrointestinal prosthetic devs, implants and grafts], init enc
T85.63[0,1,3,8]A	Leakage of [epidural and subdural inf catheter, intraperitoneal dialysis catheter, insulin pump, oth spec int prosthetic devs, implants and grafts], init enc
T85.69[0,1,2,3,4,8] A	Oth mech comp of [epidural and subdural inf catheter, intraperitoneal dialysis catheter, permanent sutures, artfcl skin graft and decellularized allodermis, insulin pump, oth spec int prosthetic devs, implants and grafts], init enc
T85.6[1,2][0,1,2,3,4,8]A	[Breakdown (mech), Displac] of [epidural and subdural inf catheter, intraperitoneal dialysis catheter, permanent sutures, artfcl skin graft and decellularized allodermis, insulin pump, oth spec int prosthetic devs, implants and grafts], init enc
T85.7[1,2,9]XA	Infxn and inflam reaction d/t [peritoneal dialysis catheter, insulin pump, oth int prosthetic devs, implants and grafts], init enc
T85.8[1,2,3,4,5,6,9]XA	[Embolism, Fibrosis, Hemor, Pain, Stenosis, Thrombosis, Oth spec comp] d/t int prosthetic devs, implants and grafts, NEC, init enc
T85.9XXA	Unsp comp of int prosth dev/grft, init
T86.5	Comp of stem cell transplant
T86.82*	Comp of skin graft (allograft) (autograft)
T86.83*	Comp of bone graft
T86.84[2,8,9]	[Infxn, Oth comp, Unsp comp] of corneal transplant
T86.85*	Comp of intestine transplant
T86.9*	Comp of unsp transplanted organ and tissue
T88.4XXA	Failed or difficult intubation, init enc
T88.7XXA	Unsp adverse effect of drug or medicament, init enc
T88.8XXA	Oth comp of surgical and medical care, NEC, init
T88.9XXA	Comp of surgical and medical care, unsp, init enc

DRG 920   Complications of Treatment with CC

GMLOS 3.1	AMLOS 4.0	RW 0.9991

Select principal diagnosis listed under DRG 919

DRG 921   Complications of Treatment without CC/MCC

GMLOS 2.3	AMLOS 2.8	RW 0.6960

Select principal diagnosis listed under DRG 919

DRG 922   Other Injury, Poisoning and Toxic Effect Diagnoses with MCC

GMLOS 4.0	AMLOS 6.0	RW 1.5833

Principal Diagnosis

Code	Description
T33.01[1,2,9][A,S]	Superf frostbite of [rt, lt, unsp] ear, [init enc, seq]
T33.0[2,9]X[A,S]	Superf frostbite of [nose, oth part of head], [init enc, seq]
T33.4[0,1,2]X[A,S]	Superf frostbite of [unsp, rt, lt] arm, [init enc, seq]
T33.51[1,2,9][A,S]	Superf frostbite of [rt, lt, unsp] wrist, [init enc, seq]

Code	Description
T33.52[1,2,9][A,S]	Superf frostbite of [rt, lt, unsp] hand, [init enc, seq]
T33.53[1,2,9][A,S]	Superf frostbite of [rt, lt, unsp] fingers, [init enc, seq]
T33.6[0,1,2]X[A,S]	Superf frostbite of [unsp, rt, lt] hip & thigh, [init enc, seq]
T33.7[0,1,2]X[A,S]	Superf frostbite of [unsp, rt, lt] knee and lwr leg, [init enc, seq]
T33.81[1,2,9][A,S]	Superf frostbite of [rt, lt, unsp] ankle, [init enc, seq]
T33.82[1,2,9][A,S]	Superf frostbite of [rt, lt, unsp] foot, [init enc, seq]
T33.83[1,2,9][A,S]	Superf frostbite of [rt, lt, unsp] toe(s), [init enc, seq]
T33.9[0,9]X[A,S]	Superf frostbite of [unsp, oth] sites, [init enc, seq]
T33.[1,2,3]XX[A,S]	Superf frostbite of [neck, thorax, abd wall, lwr back and pelvis], [init enc, seq]
T34.01[1,2,9][A,S]	Frostbite w/ tissue necrosis of [rt, lt, unsp] ear, [init enc, seq]
T34.0[2,9]X[A,S]	Frostbite w/ tissue necrosis of [nose, oth part of head], [init enc, seq]
T34.4[0,1,2]X[A,S]	Frostbite w/ tissue necrosis of [unsp, rt, lt] arm, [init enc, seq]
T34.51[1,2,9][A,S]	Frostbite w/ tissue necrosis of [rt, lt, unsp] wrist, [init enc, seq]
T34.52[1,2,9][A,S]	Frostbite w/ tissue necrosis of [rt, lt, unsp] hand, [init enc, seq]
T34.53[1,2,9][A,S]	Frostbite w/ tissue necrosis of [rt, lt, unsp] fingers, [init enc, seq]
T34.6[0,1,2]X[A,S]	Frostbite w/ tissue necrosis of [unsp, rt, lt] hip & thigh, [init enc, seq]
T34.7[0,1,2]X[A,S]	Frostbite w/ tissue necrosis of [unsp, rt, lt] knee and lwr leg, [init enc, seq]
T34.81[1,2,9][A,S]	Frostbite w/ tissue necrosis of [rt, lt, unsp] ankle, [init enc, seq]
T34.82[1,2,9][A,S]	Frostbite w/ tissue necrosis of [rt, lt, unsp] foot, [init enc, seq]
T34.83[1,2,9][A,S]	Frostbite w/ tissue necrosis of [rt, lt, unsp] toe(s), [init enc, seq]
T34.9[0,9]X[A,S]	Frostbite w/ tissue necrosis of [unsp, oth] sites, [init enc, seq]
T34.[1,2,3]XX[A,S]	Frostbite w/ tissue necrosis of [neck, thorax, abd wall, lwrback and pelvis], [init enc, seq]
T36.0X5S	Adverse effect of penicillins, seq
T36.0X[1,2,3,4]S	Poison by penicillins, [accid (unintentional), intentional self-harm, assault, undetermined], seq
T36.1X5S	Advrs effect of cephalospor/oth beta-lactm antibiot, seq
T36.1X[1,2,3,4]S	Poison by cephaloporins and oth beta-lactam antibiotics, [accid (unintentional), intentional self-harm, assault, undetermined], seq
T36.2X5S	Adverse effect of chloramphenicol group, seq
T36.2X[1,2,3,4]S	Poison by chloramphenicol group, [accid (unintentional), intentional self-harm, assault, undetermined], seq
T36.3X5S	Adverse effect of macrolides, seq
T36.3X[1,2,3,4]S	Poison by macrolides, [accid (unintentional), intentional self-harm, assault, undetermined], seq
T36.4X5S	Adverse effect of tetracyclines, seq
T36.4X[1,2,3,4]S	Poison by tetracyclines, [accid (unintentional), intentional self-harm, assault, undetermined], seq
T36.5X5S	Adverse effect of aminoglycosides, seq
T36.5X[1,2,3,4]S	Poison by aminoglycosides, [accid (unintentional), intentional self-harm, assault, undetermined], seq
T36.6X5S	Adverse effect of rifampicins, seq
T36.6X[1,2,3,4]S	Poison by rifampicins, [accid (unintentional), intentional self-harm, assault, undetermined], seq
T36.7X5S	Adverse effect of antifungal antibiotics, sys used, seq
T36.7X[1,2,3,4]S	Poison by antifungal antibiotics, sysically used, [accid (unintentional), intentional self-harm, assault, undetermined], seq
T36.8X5S	Adverse effect of oth systemic antibiotics, seq
T36.8X[1,2,3,4]S	Poison by oth sysic antibiotics [accid (unintentional), intentional self-harm, assault, undetermined], seq
T36.95XS	Adverse effect of unsp systemic antibiotic, seq
T36.9[1,2,3,4]XS	Poison by unsp sysic antibiotic [accid (unintentional), intentional self-harm, assault, undetermined], seq
T37.0X5S	Adverse effect of sulfonamides, seq
T37.0X[1,2,3,4]S	Poison by sulfonamides, [accid (unintentional), intentional self-harm, assault, undetermined], seq
T37.1X5S	Adverse effect of antimycobacterial drugs, seq
T37.1X[1,2,3,4]S	Poison by antimycobacterial drugs, [accid (unintentional), intentional self-harm, assault, undetermined], seq
T37.2X5S	Advrs effect of antimalari/drugs acting on bld protzoa, seq
T37.2X[1,2,3,4]S	Poison by antimalarials and drugs acting on oth bld protozoa, [accid (unintentional), intentional self-harm, assault, undetermined], seq
T37.3X5S	Adverse effect of oth antiprotozoal drugs, seq
T37.3X[1,2,3,4]S	Poison by oth antiprotozoal drugs, [accid (unintentional), intentional self-harm, assault, undetermined], seq
T37.4X5S	Adverse effect of anthelminthics, seq
T37.4X[1,2,3,4]S	Poison by anthelminthics, [accid (unintentional), intentional self-harm, assault, undetermined], seq
T37.5X5S	Adverse effect of antiviral drugs, seq
T37.5X[1,2,3,4]S	Poison by antiviral drugs, [accid (unintentional), intentional self-harm, assault, undetermined], seq
T37.8X5S	Adverse effect of systemic anti-infect/parasit, seq

Ⓣ Transfer DRG   ⓢⓟ Special Payment   * Code Range   **6th and 7th Character of ZZ = No Device, No Qualifier ZX = No Device, Diagnostic**

368   MS-DRG Version 33.0   © 2015 Optum360, LLC

Code	Description
T37.8X[1,2,3,4]S	Poison by oth spec sysic anti-infectives and antiparasitics, [accid (unintentional), intentional self-harm, assault, undetermined], seq
T37.95XS	Advrs effect of unsp sys anti-infect and antiparasitic, seq
T37.9[1,2,3,4]XS	Poison by unsp sysic anti-infectives and antiparasitics, [accid (unintentional), intentional self-harm, assault, undetermined], seq
T38.0X5S	Adverse effect of glucocort/synth analog, seq
T38.0X[1,2,3,4]S	Poison by glucocorticoids and synth analogues, [accid (unintentional), intentional self-harm, assault, undetermined], seq
T38.1X5S	Adverse effect of thyroid hormones and substitutes, seq
T38.1X[1,2,3,4]S	Poison by thyroid hormones and subs, [accid (unintentional), intentional self-harm, assault, undetermined], seq
T38.2X5S	Adverse effect of antithyroid drugs, seq
T38.2X[1,2,3,4]S	Poison by antithyroid drugs, [accid (unintentional), intentional self-harm, assault, undetermined], seq
T38.3X5S	Advrs effect of insulin and oral hypoglycemic drugs, seq
T38.3X[1,2,3,4]S	Poison by insulin and oral hypoglycemic (antidiabetic) drugs, [accid (unintentional), intentional self-harm, assault, undetermined], seq
T38.4X5S	Adverse effect of oral contraceptives, seq
T38.4X[1,2,3,4]S	Poison by oral contraceptives, [accid (unintentional), intentional self-harm, assault, undetermined], seq
T38.5X5S	Adverse effect of oth estrogens and progestogens, seq
T38.5X[1,2,3,4]S	Poison by oth estrogens and progestogens, [accid (unintentional), intentional self-harm, assault, undetermined], seq
T38.6X5S	Advrs effect of antigonadtr/antiestr/antiandrg, NEC, seq
T38.6X[1,2,3,4]S	Poison by antigonadotrophins, antiestrogens, antiandrogens, NEC, [accid (unintentional), intentional self-harm, assault, undetermined], seq
T38.7X5S	Adverse effect of androgens and anabolic congeners, seq
T38.7X[1,2,3,4]S	Poison by androgens and anabolic congeners, sysically used, [accid (unintentional), intentional self-harm, assault, undetermined], seq
T38.805S	Adverse effect of unsp hormones and synth sub, seq
T38.80[1,2,3,4]S	Poison by unsp hormones and synth subs, [accid (unintentional), intentional self-harm, assault, undetermined], seq
T38.815S	Adverse effect of ant pituitary hormones, seq
T38.81[1,2,3,4]S	Poison by ant pituitary (adenohypophyseal) hormones, [accid (unintentional), intentional self-harm, assault, undetermined], seq
T38.895S	Adverse effect of hormones and synth sub, seq
T38.89[1,2,3,4]S	Poison by oth hormones and synth subs, [accid (unintentional), intentional self-harm, assault, undetermined], seq
T38.905S	Adverse effect of unsp hormone antagonists, seq
T38.90[1,2,3,4]S	Poison by unsp hormone antagonists, [accid (unintentional), intentional self-harm, assault, undetermined], seq
T38.995S	Adverse effect of oth hormone antagonists, seq
T38.99[1,2,3,4]S	Poison by oth hormone antagonists, [accid (unintentional), intentional self-harm, assault, undetermined], seq
T39.0[1,9]5S	Adverse effect of [aspirin, salicylates], seq
T39.0[1,9][1,2,3,4]S	Poison by [aspirin, salicylates], [accid (unintentional), intentional self-harm, assault, undetermined], seq
T39.1X5S	Adverse effect of 4-Aminophenol derivatives, seq
T39.1X[1,2,3,4]S	Poison by 4-Aminophenol derivatives, [accid (unintentional), intentional self-harm, assault, undetermined], seq
T39.2X5S	Adverse effect of pyrazolone derivatives, seq
T39.2X[1,2,3,4]S	Poison by pyrazolone derivatives, [accid (unintentional), intentional self-harm, assault, undetermined], seq
T39.315S	Adverse effect of propionic acid derivatives, seq
T39.31[1,2,3,4]S	Poison by propionic acid derivatives, [accid (unintentional), intentional self-harm, assault, undetermined], seq
T39.395S	Adverse effect of nonsteroidal anti-inflam drugs, seq
T39.39[1,2,3,4]S	Poison by oth nonsteroidal anti-inflam drugs (NSAID), [accid (unintentional), intentional self-harm, assault, undetermined], seq
T39.4X5S	Adverse effect of antirheumatics, NEC, seq
T39.4X[1,2,3,4]S	Poison by antirheumatics, NEC, [accid (unintentional), intentional self-harm, assault, undetermined], seq
T39.8X5S	Adverse effect of nonopioid analges/antipyret, NEC, seq
T39.8X[1,2,3,4]S	Poison by oth nonopiod analgesics and antipyretics, [accid (unintentional), intentional self-harm, assault, undetermined], seq
T39.95XS	Advrs effect of unsp nonopi analgs/antipyr/antirheu, seq
T39.9[1,2,3,4]XS	Poison by unsp nonopiod analgesic, antipyretic and antirheumatic, [accid (unintentional), intentional self-harm, assault, undetermined], seq
T40.0X5S	Adverse effect of opium, seq
T40.0X[1,2,3,4]S	Poison by opium, [accid (unintentional), intentional self-harm, assault, undetermined], seq
T40.1X[1,2,3,4]S	Poison by and adverse effect of heroin, [accid (unintentional), intentional self-harm, assault, undetermined], seq
T40.2X5S	Adverse effect of oth opioids, seq
T40.2X[1,2,3,4]S	Poison by oth opiods, [accid (unintentional), intentional self-harm, assault, undetermined], seq
T40.3X5S	Adverse effect of methadone, seq
T40.3X[1,2,3,4]S	Poison by methadone, [accid (unintentional), intentional self-harm, assault, undetermined], seq
T40.4X5S	Adverse effect of oth synth narcotics, seq
T40.4X[1,2,3,4]S	Poison by oth synth narcotics, [accid (unintentional), intentional self-harm, assault, undetermined], seq
T40.5X5S	Adverse effect of cocaine, seq
T40.5X[1,2,3,4]S	Poison by cocaine, [accid (unintentional), intentional self-harm, assault, undetermined], seq
T40.605S	Adverse effect of unsp narcotics, seq
T40.60[1,2,3,4]S	Poison by unsp narcotics, [accid (unintentional), intentional self-harm, assault, undetermined], seq
T40.695S	Adverse effect of oth narcotics, seq
T40.69[1,2,3,4]S	Poison by spec narcotics, [accid (unintentional), intentional self-harm, assault, undetermined], seq
T40.7X5S	Adverse effect of cannabis (derivatives), seq
T40.7X[1,2,3,4]S	Poison by cannabis (derivatives), [accid (unintentional), intentional self-harm, assault, undetermined], seq
T40.8X[1,2,3,4]S	Poison by and adverse effect of lysergide (LSD), [accid (unintentional), intentional self-harm, assault, undetermined], seq
T40.905S	Adverse effect of unsp psychodysleptics, seq
T40.90[1,2,3,4]S	Poison by unsp psychodysleptics (hallucinogens), [accid (unintentional), intentional self-harm, assault, undetermined], seq
T40.995S	Adverse effect of oth psychodysleptics, seq
T40.99[1,2,3,4]S	Poison by oth psychodysleptics (hallucinogens), [accid (unintentional), intentional self-harm, assault, undetermined], seq
T41.0X5S	Adverse effect of inhaled anesthetics, seq
T41.0X[1,2,3,4]S	Poison by inhaled anesthetics, [accid (unintentional), intentional self-harm, assault, undetermined], seq
T41.1X5S	Adverse effect of intravenous anesthetics, seq
T41.1X[1,2,3,4]S	Poison by intravenous anesthetics, [accid (unintentional), intentional self-harm, assault, undetermined], seq
T41.205S	Adverse effect of unsp general anesthetics, seq
T41.20[1,2,3,4]S	Poison by unsp general anesthetics, [accid (unintentional), intentional self-harm, assault, undetermined], seq
T41.295S	Adverse effect of oth general anesthetics, seq
T41.29[1,2,3,4]S	Poison by oth general anesthetics, [accid (unintentional), intentional self-harm, assault, undetermined], seq
T41.3X5S	Adverse effect of local anesthetics, seq
T41.3X[1,2,3,4]S	Poison by local anesthetics, [accid (unintentional), intentional self-harm, assault, undetermined], seq
T41.45XS	Adverse effect of unsp anesthetic, seq
T41.4[1,2,3,4]XS	Poison by unsp anesthetic, [accid (unintentional), intentional self-harm, assault, undetermined], seq
T41.5X5S	Adverse effect of therapeutic gases, seq
T41.5X[1,2,3,4]S	Poison by therapeutic gases, [accid (unintentional), intentional self-harm, assault, undetermined], seq
T42.0X5S	Adverse effect of hydantoin derivatives, seq
T42.0X[1,2,3,4]S	Poison by hydantoin derivatives, [accid (unintentional), intentional self-harm, assault, undetermined], seq
T42.1X5S	Adverse effect of iminostilbenes, seq
T42.1X[1,2,3,4]S	Poison by iminostilbenes, [accid (unintentional), intentional self-harm, assault, undetermined], seq
T42.2X5S	Advrs effect of succinimides and oxazolidinediones, seq
T42.2X[1,2,3,4]S	Poison by succinimides and oxazolidinediones, [accid (unintentional), intentional self-harm, assault, undetermined], seq
T42.3X5S	Adverse effect of barbiturates, seq
T42.3X[1,2,3,4]S	Poison by barbituates, [accid (unintentional), intentional self-harm, assault, undetermined], seq
T42.4X5S	Adverse effect of benzodiazepines, seq
T42.4X[1,2,3,4]S	Poison by benzodiazepines, [accid (unintentional), intentional self-harm, assault, undetermined], seq
T42.5X5S	Adverse effect of mixed antiepileptics, seq
T42.5X[1,2,3,4]S	Poison by mixed antiepileptics, [accid (unintentional), intentional self-harm, assault, undetermined], seq

MDC 21: Injuries, Poisonings And Toxic Effects Of Drugs—MEDICAL

Surgical   **Medical**   **CC Indicator**   **MCC Indicator**   **Procedure Proxy**   **PDxMCC PDx acts as own MCC**   **PDxCC PDx acts as own CC**

T42.6X5S	Adverse effect of antieplptc and sed-hypntc drugs, seq
T42.6X[1,2,3,4]S	Poison by oth antiepileptic and sedative-hypnotic drugs, [accid (unintentional), intentional self-harm, assault, undetermined], seq
T42.75XS	Advrs effect of unsp antieplptc and sed-hypntc drugs, seq
T42.7[1,2,3,4]XS	Poison by unsp antiepileptic and sedative-hypnotic drugs, [accid (unintentional), intentional self-harm, assault, undetermined], seq
T42.8X5S	Advrs effect of antiparkns drug/centr musc-tone depr, seq
T42.8X[1,2,3,4]S	Poison by antiparkinsonism drugs and oth central muscle-tone depressants, [accid (unintentional), intentional self-harm, assault, undetermined], seq
T43.015S	Adverse effect of tricyclic antidepressants, seq
T43.01[1,2,3,4]S	Poison by tricyclic antidepressants, [accid (unintentional), intentional self-harm, assault, undetermined], seq
T43.025S	Adverse effect of tetracyclic antidepressants, seq
T43.02[1,2,3,4]S	Poison by tetracyclic antidepressants, [accid (unintentional), intentional self-harm, assault, undetermined], seq
T43.1X5S	Adverse effect of MAO inhib antidepressants, seq
T43.1X[1,2,3,4]S	Poison by monoamine-oxidase-inhibitor antidepressants, [accid (unintentional), intentional self-harm, assault, undetermined], seq
T43.205S	Adverse effect of unsp antidepressants, seq
T43.20[1,2,3,4]S	Poison by unsp antidepressants, [accid (unintentional), intentional self-harm, assault, undetermined], seq
T43.215S	Advrs effect of slctv seroton/norepineph reup inhibtr, seq
T43.21[1,2,3,4]S	Poison by selective serotonin and norepinephrine reuptake inhibitors, [accid (unintentional), intentional self-harm, assault, undetermined], seq
T43.225S	Adverse effect of slctv serotonin reuptake inhibtr, seq
T43.22[1,2,3,4]S	Poison by selective serotonin reuptake inhibitors, [accid (unintentional), intentional self-harm, assault, undetermined], seq
T43.295S	Adverse effect of oth antidepressants, seq
T43.29[1,2,3,4]S	Poison by oth antidepressants, [accid (unintentional), intentional self-harm, assault, undetermined], seq
T43.3X5S	Adverse effect of phenothiaz antipsychot/neurolept, seq
T43.3X[1,2,3,4]S	Poison by phenothiazine antipsychotics and neuroleptics, [accid (unintentional), intentional self-harm, assault, undetermined], seq
T43.4X5S	Adverse effect of butyrophen/thiothixen neuroleptc, seq
T43.4X[1,2,3,4]S	Poison by butyrophenone and thiothixene neuroleptics, [accid (unintentional), intentional self-harm, assault, undetermined], seq
T43.505S	Adverse effect of unsp antipsychot/neurolept, seq
T43.50[1,2,3,4]S	Poison by unsp antipsychotics and neuroleptics, [accid (unintentional), intentional self-harm, assault, undetermined], seq
T43.595S	Adverse effect of antipsychotics and neuroleptics, seq
T43.59[1,2,3,4]S	Poison by oth antipsychotics and neuroleptics, [accid (unintentional), intentional self-harm, assault, undetermined], seq
T43.605S	Adverse effect of unsp psychostimulants, seq
T43.60[1,2,3,4]S	Poison by unsp psychostimulants, [accid (unintentional), intentional self-harm, assault, undetermined], seq
T43.615S	Adverse effect of caffeine, seq
T43.61[1,2,3,4]S	Poison by caffeine, [accid (unintentional), intentional self-harm, assault, undetermined], seq
T43.625S	Adverse effect of amphetamines, seq
T43.62[1,2,3,4]S	Poison by amphetamines, [accid (unintentional), intentional self-harm, assault, undetermined], seq
T43.635S	Adverse effect of methylphenidate, seq
T43.63[1,2,3,4]S	Poison by methylphenidate, [accid (unintentional), intentional self-harm, assault, undetermined], seq
T43.695S	Adverse effect of oth psychostimulants, seq
T43.69[1,2,3,4]S	Poison by oth psychostimulants, [accid (unintentional), intentional self-harm, assault, undetermined], seq
T43.8X5S	Adverse effect of oth psychotropic drugs, seq
T43.8X[1,2,3,4]S	Poison by oth psychotropic drugs, [accid (unintentional), intentional self-harm, assault, undetermined], seq
T43.95XS	Adverse effect of unsp psychotropic drug, seq
T43.9[1,2,3,4]XS	Poison by unsp psychotropic drug, [accid (unintentional), intentional self-harm, assault, undetermined], seq
T44.0X5S	Adverse effect of anticholinesterase agents, seq
T44.0X[1,2,3,4]S	Poison by anticholinesterase agents, [accid (unintentional), intentional self-harm, assault, undetermined], seq
T44.1X5S	Adverse effect of oth parasympathomimetics, seq
T44.1X[1,2,3,4]S	Poison by parasympathomimetics (cholinergics), [accid (unintentional), intentional self-harm, assault, undetermined], seq
T44.2X5S	Adverse effect of ganglionic blocking drugs, seq
T44.2X[1,2,3,4]S	Poison by ganglionic blocking drugs, [accid (unintentional), intentional self-harm, assault, undetermined], seq
T44.3X5S	Adverse effect of parasympath and spasmolytics, seq
T44.3X[1,2,3,4]S	Poison by oth parasympatholytics (anticholinergics and antimuscarinics) and spasmolytics, [accid (unintentional), intentional self-harm, assault, undetermined], seq
T44.4X5S	Adverse effect of predom alpha-adrenocpt agonists, seq
T44.4X[1,2,3,4]S	Poison by predominantly alpha-adrenoreceptor agonists, [accid (unintentional), intentional self-harm, assault, undetermined], seq
T44.5X5S	Adverse effect of predom beta-adrenocpt agonists, seq
T44.5X[1,2,3,4]S	Poison by predominantly beta-adrenoreceptor agonists, [accid (unintentional), intentional self-harm, assault, undetermined], seq
T44.6X5S	Adverse effect of alpha-adrenoreceptor antagonists, seq
T44.6X[1,2,3,4]S	Poison by predominantly alpha-adrenoreceptor antagonists, [accid (unintentional), intentional self-harm, assault, undetermined], seq
T44.7X5S	Adverse effect of beta-adrenoreceptor antagonists, seq
T44.7X[1,2,3,4]S	Poison by predominantly beta-adrenoreceptor antagonists, [accid (unintentional), intentional self-harm, assault, undetermined], seq
T44.8X5S	Advrs effect of centr-acting/adren-neurn-block agnt, seq
T44.8X[1,2,3,4]S	Poison by centrally-acting and adrenergic-neuron-blocking agents, [accid (unintentional), intentional self-harm, assault, undetermined], seq
T44.905S	Advrs effect of unsp drugs affected the autonm nrv sys, seq
T44.90[1,2,3,4]S	Poison by unsp drugs primarily affecting the autonomic nervous sys, [accid (unintentional), intentional self-harm, assault, undetermined], seq
T44.995S	Adverse effect of drug affected the autonm nervous sys, seq
T44.99[1,2,3,4]S	Poison by oth drug primarily affecting the autonomic nervous sys, [accid (unintentional), intentional self-harm, assault, undetermined], seq
T45.0X5S	Adverse effect of antiallergic and antiemetic drugs, seq
T45.0X[1,2,3,4]S	Poison by antiallergic and antiemetic drugs, [accid (unintentional), intentional self-harm, assault, undetermined], seq
T45.1X5S	Adverse effect of antineopl and immunosup drugs, seq
T45.1X[1,2,3,4]S	Poison by antineoplastic and immunosuppressive drugs, [accid (unintentional), intentional self-harm, assault, undetermined], seq
T45.2X5S	Adverse effect of vitamins, seq
T45.2X[1,2,3,4]S	Poison by vitamins, [accid (unintentional), intentional self-harm, assault, undetermined], seq
T45.3X5S	Adverse effect of enzymes, seq
T45.3X[1,2,3,4]S	Poison by enzymes, [accid (unintentional), intentional self-harm, assault, undetermined], seq
T45.4X5S	Adverse effect of iron and its compounds, seq
T45.4X[1,2,3,4]S	Poison by iron and its compounds, [accid (unintentional), intentional self-harm, assault, undetermined], seq
T45.515S	Adverse effect of anticoagulants, seq
T45.51[1,2,3,4]S	Poison by anticoagulants, [accid (unintentional), intentional self-harm, assault, undetermined], seq
T45.525S	Adverse effect of antithrombotic drugs, seq
T45.52[1,2,3,4]S	Poison by antithrombotic drugs, [accid (unintentional), intentional self-harm, assault, undetermined], seq
T45.605S	Adverse effect of unsp fibrinolysis-affecting drugs, seq
T45.60[1,2,3,4]S	Poison by unsp fibrinolysis-affecting drugs, [accid (unintentional), intentional self-harm, assault, undetermined], seq
T45.615S	Adverse effect of thrombolytic drugs, seq
T45.61[1,2,3,4]S	Poison by thrombolytic drug, [accid (unintentional), intentional self-harm, assault, undetermined], seq
T45.625S	Adverse effect of hemostatic drug, seq
T45.62[1,2,3,4]S	Poison by hemostatic drug, [accid (unintentional), intentional self-harm, assault, undetermined], seq
T45.695S	Adverse effect of oth fibrinolysis-affecting drugs, seq
T45.69[1,2,3,4]S	Poison by oth fibrinolysis-affecting drug, [accid (unintentional), intentional self-harm, assault, undetermined], seq
T45.7X5S	Advrs effect of anticoag antag, vit K and oth coag, seq
T45.7X[1,2,3,4]S	Poison by anticoagulant antagonists, vitamin K and oth coagulants, [accid (unintentional), intentional self-harm, assault, undetermined], seq
T45.8X5S	Adverse effect of prim sys and hematolog agents, seq
T45.8X[1,2,3,4]S	Poison by oth primarily sysic and hematological agents, [accid (unintentional), intentional self-harm, assault, undetermined], seq

---

Ⓣ **Transfer DRG**   Ⓢ **Special Payment**   * **Code Range**   **6th and 7th Character of ZZ = No Device, No Qualifier ZX = No Device, Diagnostic**

T45.95XS	Adverse effect of unsp prim sys and hematolog agent, seq
T45.9[1,2,3,4]XS	Poison by unsp primarily sysic and hematological agents, [accid (unintentional), intentional self-harm, assault, undetermined], seq
T46.0X5S	Adverse effect of cardi-stim glycos/drug simlar act, seq
T46.0X[1,2,3,4]S	Poison by cardiac stimulant glycosides and drugs of similar action, [accid (unintentional), intentional self-harm, assault, undetermined], seq
T46.1X5S	Adverse effect of calcium-channel blockers, seq
T46.1X[1,2,3,4]S	Poison by calcium-channel blockers, [accid (unintentional), intentional self-harm, assault, undetermined], seq
T46.2X5S	Adverse effect of oth antidysrhythmic drugs, seq
T46.2X[1,2,3,4]S	Poison by antidysrythmic drugs, [accid (unintentional), intentional self-harm, assault, undetermined], seq
T46.3X5S	Adverse effect of coronary vasodilators, seq
T46.3X[1,2,3,4]S	Poison by coronary vasodilators, [accid (unintentional), intentional self-harm, assault, undetermined], seq
T46.4X5S	Adverse effect of angiotens-convert-enzyme inhibtr, seq
T46.4X[1,2,3,4]S	Poison by angiotensin-converting-enzyme inhibitors, [accid (unintentional), intentional self-harm, assault, undetermined], seq
T46.5X5S	Adverse effect of oth antihypertensive drugs, seq
T46.5X[1,2,3,4]S	Poison by oth antihypertensive drugs, [accid (unintentional), intentional self-harm, assault, undetermined], seq
T46.6X5S	Advrs effect of antihyperlip and antiarterio drugs, seq
T46.6X[1,2,3,4]S	Poison by antihyperlipidemic and antiarteriosclerotic drugs, [accid (unintentional), intentional self-harm, assault, undetermined], seq
T46.7X5S	Adverse effect of peripheral vasodilators, seq
T46.7X[1,2,3,4]S	Poison by peripheral vasodilators, [accid (unintentional), intentional self-harm, assault, undetermined], seq
T46.8X5S	Adverse effect of antivaric drugs, incl* scler agents, seq
T46.8X[1,2,3,4]S	Poison by antivaricose drugs, incl* sclerosing agents, [accid (unintentional), intentional self-harm, assault, undetermined], seq
T46.905S	Advrs effect of unsp agents affected the cardiovasc sys, seq
T46.90[1,2,3,4]S	Poison by unsp agents primarily affecting the cardiovascular sys, [accid (unintentional), intentional self-harm, assault, undetermined], seq
T46.995S	Adverse effect of agents affected the cardiovascular sys, seq
T46.99[1,2,3,4]S	Poison by oth agent primarily affecting the cardiovascular sys, [accid (unintentional), intentional self-harm, assault, undetermined], seq
T47.0X5S	Adverse effect of histamine H2-receptor blockers, seq
T47.0X[1,2,3,4]S	Poison by histamine H2-receptor blockers, [accid (unintentional), intentional self-harm, assault, undetermined], seq
T47.1X5S	Adverse effect of antacids and anti-gstrc-sec drugs, seq
T47.1X[1,2,3,4]S	Poison by oth antacids and anti-gastric-secretion drugs, [accid (unintentional), intentional self-harm, assault, undetermined], seq
T47.2X5S	Adverse effect of stimulant laxatives, seq
T47.2X[1,2,3,4]S	Poison by stimulant laxatives, [accid (unintentional), intentional self-harm, assault, undetermined], seq
T47.3X5S	Adverse effect of saline and osmotic laxatives, seq
T47.3X[1,2,3,4]S	Poison by saline and osmotic laxatives, [accid (unintentional), intentional self-harm, assault, undetermined], seq
T47.4X5S	Adverse effect of oth laxatives, seq
T47.4X[1,2,3,4]S	Poison by oth laxatives, [accid (unintentional), intentional self-harm, assault, undetermined], seq
T47.5X5S	Adverse effect of digestants, seq
T47.5X[1,2,3,4]S	Poison by digestants, [accid (unintentional), intentional self-harm, assault, undetermined], seq
T47.6X5S	Adverse effect of antidiarrheal drugs, seq
T47.6X[1,2,3,4]S	Poison by antidiarrheal drugs, [accid (unintentional), intentional self-harm, assault, undetermined], seq
T47.7X5S	Adverse effect of emetics, seq
T47.7X[1,2,3,4]S	Poison by emetics, [accid (unintentional), intentional self-harm, assault, undetermined], seq
T47.8X5S	Adverse effect of agents primarily affecting GI sys, seq
T47.8X[1,2,3,4]S	Poison by oth agents primarily affecting gastrointestinal sys, [accid (unintentional), intentional self-harm, assault, undetermined], seq
T47.95XS	Adverse effect of unsp agents affected the GI sys, seq
T47.9[1,2,3,4]XS	Poison by unsp agents primarily affecting gastrointestinal sys, [accid (unintentional), intentional self-harm, assault, undetermined], seq
T48.0X5S	Adverse effect of oxytocic drugs, seq
T48.0X[1,2,3,4]S	Poison by oxytocic drugs, [accid (unintentional), intentional self-harm, assault, undetermined], seq

T48.1X5S	Adverse effect of skeletal muscle relaxants, seq
T48.1X[1,2,3,4]S	Poison by skeletal muscle relaxants (neuromuscular blocking agents), [accid (unintentional), intentional self-harm, assault, undetermined], seq
T48.205S	Adverse effect of unsp drugs acting on muscles, seq
T48.20[1,2,3,4]S	Poison by unsp drugs working on muscles, [accid (unintentional), intentional self-harm, assault, undetermined], seq
T48.295S	Adverse effect of oth drugs acting on muscles, seq
T48.29[1,2,3,4]S	Poison by oth drugs working on muscles, [accid (unintentional), intentional self-harm, assault, undetermined], seq
T48.3X5S	Adverse effect of antitussives, seq
T48.3X[1,2,3,4]S	Poison by antitussives, [accid (unintentional), intentional self-harm, assault, undetermined], seq
T48.4X5S	Adverse effect of expectorants, seq
T48.4X[1,2,3,4]S	Poison by expectorants, [accid (unintentional), intentional self-harm, assault, undetermined], seq
T48.5X5S	Adverse effect of oth anti-common-cold drugs, seq
T48.5X[1,2,3,4]S	Poison by oth anti-common-cold drugs, [accid (unintentional), intentional self-harm, assault, undetermined], seq
T48.6X5S	Adverse effect of antiasthmatics, seq
T48.6X[1,2,3,4]S	Poison by antiasthmatics, [accid (unintentional), intentional self-harm, assault, undetermined], seq
T48.905S	Advrs effect of unsp agents prim act on the resp sys, seq
T48.90[1,2,3,4]S	Poison by unsp agents primarily acting on the respiratory sys, [accid (unintentional), intentional self-harm, assault, undetermined], seq
T48.995S	Advrs effect of agents prim acting on the resp sys, seq
T48.99[1,2,3,4]S	Poison by oth agents primarily acting on the respiratory sys, [accid (unintentional), intentional self-harm, assault, undetermined], seq
T49.0X5S	Advrs effect of local antifung/infect/inflamm drugs, seq
T49.0X[1,2,3,4]S	Poison by local antifungal, anti-infective and anti-inflam drugs, [accid (unintentional), intentional self-harm, assault, undetermined], seq
T49.1X5S	Adverse effect of antipruritics, seq
T49.1X[1,2,3,4]S	Poison by antipruritics, [accid (unintentional), intentional self-harm, assault, undetermined], seq
T49.2X5S	Adverse effect of local astringents/detergents, seq
T49.2X[1,2,3,4]S	Poison by local astringents and local detergents, [accid (unintentional), intentional self-harm, assault, undetermined], seq
T49.3X5S	Advrs effect of emollients, demulcents and protect, seq
T49.3X[1,2,3,4]S	Poison by emollients, demulcents and protectants, [accid (unintentional), intentional self-harm, assault, undetermined], seq
T49.4X5S	Advrs effect of keratolyt/keratplst/hair trmt drug, seq
T49.4X[1,2,3,4]S	Poison by keratolytics, keratoplastics, and oth hair tx drugs, [accid (unintentional), intentional self-harm, assault, undetermined], seq
T49.5X5S	Adverse effect of opth drugs and preparations, seq
T49.5X[1,2,3,4]S	Poison by ophthalmological drugs and preparations, [accid (unintentional), intentional self-harm, assault, undetermined], seq
T49.6X5S	Adverse effect of otorhino drugs and preparations, seq
T49.6X[1,2,3,4]S	Poison by otorhinolaryngological drugs and preparations, [accid (unintentional), intentional self-harm, assault, undetermined], seq
T49.7X5S	Adverse effect of dental drugs, topically applied, seq
T49.7X[1,2,3,4]S	Poison by dental drugs, topically applied, [accid (unintentional), intentional self-harm, assault, undetermined], seq
T49.8X5S	Adverse effect of oth topical agents, seq
T49.8X[1,2,3,4]S	Poison by oth topical agents, [accid (unintentional), intentional self-harm, assault, undetermined], seq
T49.95XS	Adverse effect of unsp topical agent, seq
T49.9[1,2,3,4]XS	Poison by unsp topical agent, [accid (unintentional), intentional self-harm, assault, undetermined], seq
T50.0X5S	Adverse effect of mineralocorticoids and antag, seq
T50.0X[1,2,3,4]S	Poison by mineralocorticoids and their antagonists, [accid (unintentional), intentional self-harm, assault, undetermined], seq
T50.1X5S	Adverse effect of loop [high-ceiling] diuretics, seq
T50.1X[1,2,3,4]S	Poison by loop (hugh ceiling) diuretics, [accid (unintentional), intentional self-harm, assault, undetermined], seq
T50.2X5S	Advrs eff of crbnc-anhydr inhibtr, benzo/oth diuretc, seq

---

Surgical **Medical** **CC Indicator** **MCC Indicator** **Procedure Proxy** **PDxMCC** **PDx acts as own MCC** **PDxCC** **PDx acts as own CC**

T50.2X[1,2,3,4]S — Poison by carbonic-anhydrase inhibitors, benzothiadiazides and oth diuretics, [accid (unintentional), intentional self-harm, assault, undetermined], seq

T50.3X5S — Adverse effect of electrolytic/caloric/wtr-bal agnt, seq

T50.3X[1,2,3,4]S — Poison by eletrolytic, caloric and water-balance agents, [accid (unintentional), intentional self-harm, assault, undetermined], seq

T50.4X5S — Adverse effect of drugs affecting uric acid metab, seq

T50.4X[1,2,3,4]S — Poison by drugs affecting uric acid metabolism, [accid (unintentional), intentional self-harm, assault, undetermined], seq

T50.5X5S — Adverse effect of appetite depressants, seq

T50.5X[1,2,3,4]S — Poison by appetite depressants, [accid (unintentional), intentional self-harm, assault, undetermined], seq

T50.6X5S — Adverse effect of antidotes and chelating agents, seq

T50.6X[1,2,3,4]S — Poison by antidotes and chelating agents, [accid (unintentional), intentional self-harm, assault, undetermined], seq

T50.7X5S — Advrs effect of analeptics and opioid receptor antag, seq

T50.7X[1,2,3,4]S — Poison by analeptics and opiod receptor antagonists, [accid (unintentional), intentional self-harm, assault, undetermined], seq

T50.8X5S — Adverse effect of diagnostic agents, seq

T50.8X[1,2,3,4]S — Poison by dx agents, [accid (unintentional), intentional self-harm, assault, undetermined], seq

T50.905S — Adverse effect of unsp drug/meds/biol subst, seq

T50.90[1,2,3,4]S — Poison by unsp drugs, medicaments and biological substances, [accid (unintentional), intentional self-harm, assault, undetermined], seq

T50.995S — Adverse effect of drug/meds/biol subst, seq

T50.99[1,2,3,4]S — Poison by oth drugs, medicaments and biological substances, [accid (unintentional), intentional self-harm, assault, undetermined], init encoun

T50.A15S — Advrs effect of pertuss vaccine, incl* combin w pertuss, seq

T50.A1[1,2,3,4]S — Poison by pertussis vaccine, incl* combinations w/ a pertussis component, [accid (unintentional), intentional self-harm, assault, undetermined], seq

T50.A25S — Adverse effect of mixed bact vaccines w/o a pertuss, seq

T50.A2[1,2,3,4]S — Poison by mixed bacterial vaccines w/o a pertussis component, [accid (unintentional), intentional self-harm, assault, undetermined], seq

T50.A95S — Adverse effect of oth bacterial vaccines, seq

T50.A9[1,2,3,4]S — Poison by oth bacterial vaccines, [accid (unintentional), intentional self-harm, assault, undetermined], seq

T50.B15S — Adverse effect of smallpox vaccines, seq

T50.B1[1,2,3,4]S — Poison by smpox vaccines, [accid (unintentional), intentional self-harm, assault, undetermined], seq

T50.B95S — Adverse effect of oth viral vaccines, seq

T50.B9[1,2,3,4]S — Poison by oth viral vaccines, [accid (unintentional), intentional self-harm, assault, undetermined], seq

T50.Z15S — Adverse effect of immunoglobulin, seq

T50.Z1[1,2,3,4]S — Poison by immunoglobin, [accid (unintentional), intentional self-harm, assault, undetermined], seq

T50.Z95S — Adverse effect of vaccines and biolg substances, seq

T50.Z9[1,2,3,4]S — Poison by oth vaccines and biological substances, [accid (unintentional), intentional self-harm, assault, undetermined], seq

T51.0X[1,2,3,4]S — Txc effct of ethanol, [accid (unintentional), intentional self-harm, assault, undetermined], seq

T51.1X[1,2,3,4]S — Txc effct of methanol, [accid (unintentional), intentional self-harm, assault, undetermined], seq

T51.2X[1,2,3,4]S — Txc effct of 2-Propanol, [accid (unintentional), intentional self-harm, assault, undetermined], seq

T51.3X[1,2,3,4]S — Txc effct of fusel oil, [accid (unintentional), intentional self-harm, assault, undetermined], seq

T51.8X[1,2,3,4]S — Txc effct of oth alcohols, [accid (unintentional), intentional self-harm, assault, undetermined], seq

T51.9[1,2,3,4]XS — Txc effct of unsp alcohol, [accid (unintentional), intentional self-harm, assault, undetermined], seq

T52.0X[1,2,3,4]S — Txc effct of petroleum products, [accid (unintentional), intentional self-harm, assault, undetermined], seq

T52.1X[1,2,3,4]S — Txc effct of benzene [accid (unintentional), intentional self-harm, assault, undetermined], seq

T52.2X[1,2,3,4]S — Txc effct of homologues of benzene, [accid (unintentional), intentional self-harm, assault, undetermined], seq

T52.3X[1,2,3,4]S — Txc effct of glycoles, [accid (unintentional), intentional self-harm, assault, undetermined], seq

T52.4X[1,2,3,4]S — Txc effct of ketones, [accid (unintentional), intentional self-harm, assault, undetermined], seq

T52.8X[1,2,3,4]S — Txc effct of oth organic solvents, [accid (unintentional), intentional self-harm, assault, undetermined], seq

T52.9[1,2,3,4]XS — Txc effct of unsp organic solvent, [accid (unintentional), intentional self-harm, assault, undetermined], seq

T53.0X[1,2,3,4]S — Txc effct of carbon tetrachloride, [accid (unintentional), intentional self-harm, assault, undetermined], seq

T53.1X[1,2,3,4]S — Txc effct of chloroform, [accid (unintentional), intentional self-harm, assault, undetermined], seq

T53.2X[1,2,3,4]S — Txc effct of trichloroethylene, [accid (unintentional), intentional self-harm, assault, undetermined], seq

T53.3X[1,2,3,4]S — Txc effct of tetrachloroethylene, [accid (unintentional), intentional self-harm, assault, undetermined], seq

T53.4X[1,2,3,4]S — Txc effct of dichloromethane, [accid (unintentional), intentional self-harm, assault, undetermined], seq

T53.5X[1,2,3,4]S — Txc effct of chlorofluorocarbons, [accid (unintentional), intentional self-harm, assault, undetermined], seq

T53.6X[1,2,3,4]S — Txc effct of oth halogen derivatives of aliphatic hydrocarbons, [accid (unintentional), intentional self-harm, assault, undetermined], seq

T53.7X[1,2,3,4]S — Txc effct of oth halogen derivatives of aromatic hydrocarbons, [accid (unintentional), intentional self-harm, assault, undetermined], seq

T53.9[1,2,3,4]XS — Txc effct of unsp halogen derivatives of aliphatic and aromatic hydrocarbons, [accid (unintentional), intentional self-harm, assault, undetermined], seq

T54.0X[1,2,3,4]S — Txc effct of phenol and phenol homologues, [accid (unintentional), intentional self-harm, assault, undetermined], seq

T54.1X[1,2,3,4]S — Txc effct of oth corrosive organic compound, [accid (unintentional), intentional self-harm, assault, undetermined], seq

T54.2X[1,2,3,4]S — Txc effct of corrosive acids and acid-like substances, [accid (unintentional), intentional self-harm, assault, undetermined], seq

T54.3X[1,2,3,4]S — Txc effct of corrosive alkalis and alkali-like substances, [accid (unintentional), intentional self-harm, assault, undetermined], seq

T54.9[1,2,3,4]XS — Txc effct of unsp corrosive substance, [accid (unintentional), intentional self-harm, assault, undetermined], seq

T55.0X[1,2,3,4]S — Txc effct of soaps, [accid (unintentional), intentional self-harm, assault, undetermined], seq

T55.1X[1,2,3,4]S — Txc effct of detergents, [accid (unintentional), intentional self-harm, assault, undetermined], seq

T56.0X[1,2,3,4]S — Txc effct of lead and its compounds, [accid (unintentional), intentional self-harm, assault, undetermined], seq

T56.1X[1,2,3,4]S — Txc effct of mercury and its compounds, [accid (unintentional), intentional self-harm, assault, undetermined], seq

T56.2X[1,2,3,4]S — Txc effct of chromium and its compounds, [accid (unintentional), intentional self-harm, assault, undetermined], seq

T56.3X[1,2,3,4]S — Txc effct of cadmium and its compounds, [accid (unintentional), intentional self-harm, assault, undetermined], seq

T56.4X[1,2,3,4]S — Txc effct of copper and its compounds, [accid (unintentional), intentional self-harm, assault, undetermined], seq

T56.5X[1,2,3,4]S — Txc effct of zinc and its compounds, [accid (unintentional), intentional self-harm, assault, undetermined], seq

T56.6X[1,2,3,4]S — Txc effct of tin and its compounds, [accid (unintentional), intentional self-harm, assault, undetermined], seq

T56.7X[1,2,3,4]S — Txc effct of beryllium and its compounds, [accid (unintentional), intentional self-harm, assault, undetermined], seq

T56.81[1,2,3,4]S — Txc effct of thallium and its compounds, [accid (unintentional), intentional self-harm, assault, undetermined], seq

T56.89[1,2,3,4]S — Txc effct of oth metals, [accid (unintentional), intentional self-harm, assault, undetermined], seq

T56.9[1,2,3,4]XS — Txc effct of unsp metal, [accid (unintentional), intentional self-harm, assault, undetermined], seq

T57.0X[1,2,3,4]S — Txc effct of arsenic and its compounds, [accid (unintentional), intentional self-harm, assault, undetermined], seq

T57.1X[1,2,3,4]S — Txc effct of phosphorus and its compounds, [accid (unintentional), intentional self-harm, assault, undetermined], seq

T57.2X[1,2,3,4]S — Txc effct of manganese and its compounds, [accid (unintentional), intentional self-harm, assault, undetermined], seq

T57.3X[1,2,3,4]S — Txc effct of hydrogen cyanide, [accid (unintentional), intentional self-harm, assault, undetermined], seq

---

□T Transfer DRG   SP Special Payment   * Code Range   6th and 7th Character of ZZ = No Device, No Qualifier ZX = No Device, Diagnostic

T57.8X[1,2,3,4]S   Txc effct of oth spec inorganic substances, [accid (unintentional), intentional self-harm, assault, undetermined], seq

T57.9[1,2,3,4]XS   Txc effct of unsp inorganic substance, [accid (unintentional), intentional self-harm, assault, undetermined], seq

T58.0[1,2,3,4]XS   Txc effct of carbon monoxide from motor vehicle exhaust, [accid (unintentional), intentional self-harm, assault, undetermined], seq

T58.1[1,2,3,4]XS   Txc effct of carbon monoxide from utility gas, [accid (unintentional), intentional self-harm, assault, undetermined], seq

T58.2X[1,2,3,4]S   Txc effct of carbon monoxide from incomplete combustion of oth domestic fuels, [accid (unintentional), intentional self-harm, assault, undetermined], seq

T58.8X[1,2,3,4]S   Txc effct of carbon monoxide from oth source, [accid (unintentional), intentional self-harm, assault, undetermined], seq

T58.9[1,2,3,4]XS   Txc effct of carbon monoxide from unsp source, [accid (unintentional), intentional self-harm, assault, undetermined], seq

T59.0X[1,2,3,4]S   Txc effct of nitrogen oxides, [accid (unintentional), intentional self-harm, assault, undetermined], seq

T59.1X[1,2,3,4]S   Txc effct of sulfur dioxide, [accid (unintentional), intentional self-harm, assault, undetermined], seq

T59.2X[1,2,3,4]S   Txc effct of formaldehyde, [accid (unintentional), intentional self-harm, assault, undetermined], seq

T59.3X[1,2,3,4]S   Txc effct of lacrimogenic gas, [accid (unintentional), intentional self-harm, assault, undetermined], seq

T59.4X[1,2,3,4]S   Txc effct of chlorine gas, [accid (unintentional), intentional self-harm, assault, undetermined], seq

T59.5X[1,2,3,4]S   Txc effct of fluorine gas and hydrogen fluoride, [accid (unintentional), intentional self-harm, assault, undetermined], seq

T59.6X[1,2,3,4]S   Txc effct of hydrogen sulfide, [accid (unintentional), intentional self-harm, assault, undetermined], seq

T59.7X[1,2,3,4]S   Txc effct of carbon dioxide, [accid (unintentional), intentional self-harm, assault, undetermined], seq

T59.81[1,2,3,4]S   Txc effct of smoke, [accid (unintentional), intentional self-harm, assault, undetermined], seq

T59.89[1,2,3,4]S   Txc effct of oth spec gases, fumes and vapors, [accid (unintentional), intentional self-harm, assault, undetermined], seq

T59.9[1,2,3,4]XS   Txc effct of unsp gases, fumes and vapors, [accid (unintentional), intentional self-harm, assault, undetermined], seq

T60.0X[1,2,3,4]S   Txc effct of organophosphate and carbamate insecticides, [accid (unintentional), intentional self-harm, assault, undetermined], seq

T60.1X[1,2,3,4]S   Txc effct of halogenated insecticides, [accid (unintentional), intentional self-harm, assault, undetermined], seq

T60.2X[1,2,3,4]S   Txc effct of oth insecticides, [accid (unintentional), intentional self-harm, assault, undetermined], seq

T60.3X[1,2,3,4]S   Txc effct of herbicides and fungicides, [accid (unintentional), intentional self-harm, assault, undetermined], seq

T60.4X[1,2,3,4]S   Txc effct of rodenticides, [accid (unintentional), intentional self-harm, assault, undetermined], seq

T60.8X[1,2,3,4]S   Txc effct of oth pesticides, [accid (unintentional), intentional self-harm, assault, undetermined], seq

T60.9[1,2,3,4]XS   Txc effct of unsp pesticides, [accid (unintentional), intentional self-harm, assault, undetermined], seq

T61.0[1,2,3,4]XS   Ciguatera fish poison, [accid (unintentional), intentional self-harm, assault, undetermined], seq

T61.1[1,2,3,4]XS   Scombroid fish poison, [accid (unintentional), intentional self-harm, assault, undetermined], seq

T61.77[1,2,3,4]S   Oth fish poison, [accid (unintentional), intentional self-harm, assault, undetermined], seq

T61.78[1,2,3,4]S   Oth shellfish poison, [accid (unintentional), intentional self-harm, assault, undetermined], seq

T61.8X[1,2,3,4]S   Txc effct of oth seafood, [accid (unintentional), intentional self-harm, assault, undetermined], seq

T61.9[1,2,3,4]XS   Txc effct of unsp seafood, [accid (unintentional), intentional self-harm, assault, undetermined], seq

T62.0X[1,2,3,4]S   Txc effct of ingested mushrooms, [accid (unintentional), intentional self-harm, assault, undetermined], seq

T62.1X[1,2,3,4]S   Txc effct of ingested berries, [accid (unintentional), intentional self-harm, assault, undetermined], seq

T62.2X[1,2,3,4]S   Txc effct of oth ingested (parts of) plant(s), [accid (unintentional), intentional self-harm, assault, undetermined], seq

T62.8X[1,2,3,4]S   Txc effct of oth spec noxious substances eaten as food, [accid (unintentional), intentional self-harm, assault, undetermined], seq

T62.9[1,2,3,4]XS   Txc effct of unsp noxious substances eaten as food, [accid (unintentional), intentional self-harm, assault, undetermined], seq

T63.00[1,2,3,4]S   Txc effct of unsp snake venom, [accid (unintentional), intentional self-harm, assault, undetermined], seq

T63.01[1,2,3,4]S   Txc effct of rattlesnake venom, [accid (unintentional), intentional self-harm, assault, undetermined], seq

T63.02[1,2,3,4]S   Txc effct of coral snake venom, [accid (unintentional), intentional self-harm, assault, undetermined], seq

T63.03[1,2,3,4]S   Txc effct of taipan venom, [accid (unintentional), intentional self-harm, assault, undetermined], seq

T63.04[1,2,3,4]S   Txc effct of cobra venom, [accid (unintentional), intentional self-harm, assault, undetermined], seq

T63.06[1,2,3,4]S   Txc effct of venom of oth North and South American snake, [accid (unintentional), intentional self-harm, assault, undetermined], seq

T63.07[1,2,3,4]S   Txc effct of venom of oth Australian snake, [accid (unintentional), intentional self-harm, assault, undetermined], seq

T63.08[1,2,3,4]S   Txc effct of venom of oth African and Asian snake, [accid (unintentional), intentional self-harm, assault, undetermined], seq

T63.09[1,2,3,4]S   Txc effct of venom of oth snake, [accid (unintentional), intentional self-harm, assault, undetermined], seq

T63.11[1,2,3,4]S   Txc effct of venom of gila monster, [accid (unintentional), intentional self-harm, assault, undetermined], seq

T63.12[1,2,3,4]S   Txc effct of venom of oth venomous lizard, [accid (unintentional), intentional self-harm, assault, undetermined], seq

T63.19[1,2,3,4]S   Txc effct of venom of oth reptiles, [accid (unintentional), intentional self-harm, assault, undetermined], seq

T63.2X[1,2,3,4]S   Txc effct of venom of scorpion, [accid (unintentional), intentional self-harm, assault, undetermined], seq

T63.30[1,2,3,4]S   Txc effct of unsp spider venom, [accid (unintentional), intentional self-harm, assault, undetermined], seq

T63.31[1,2,3,4]S   Txc effct of venom of black widow spider, [accid (unintentional), intentional self-harm, assault, undetermined], seq

T63.32[1,2,3,4]S   Txc effct of venom of tarantula, [accid (unintentional), intentional self-harm, assault, undetermined], seq

T63.33[1,2,3,4]S   Txc effct of venom of brown recluse spider, [accid (unintentional), intentional self-harm, assault, undetermined], seq

T63.39[1,2,3,4]S   Txc effct of venom of oth spider, [accid (unintentional), intentional self-harm, assault, undetermined], seq

T63.41[1,2,3,4]S   Txc effct of venom of centipedes and venomous millipedes, [accid (unintentional), intentional self-harm, assault, undetermined], seq

T63.42[1,2,3,4]S   Txc effct of venom of ants, [accid (unintentional), intentional self-harm, assault, undetermined], seq

T63.43[1,2,3,4]S   Txc effct of venom of caterpillars, [accid (unintentional), intentional self-harm, assault, undetermined], seq

T63.44[1,2,3,4]S   Txc effct of venom of bees, [accid (unintentional), intentional self-harm, assault, undetermined], seq

T63.45[1,2,3,4]S   Txc effct of venom of hornets, [accid (unintentional), intentional self-harm, assault, undetermined], seq

T63.46[1,2,3,4]S   Txc effct of venom of wasps, [accid (unintentional), intentional self-harm, assault, undetermined], seq

T63.48[1,2,3,4]S   Txc effct of venom of oth arthropod, [accid (unintentional), intentional self-harm, assault, undetermined], seq

T63.51[1,2,3,4]S   Txc effct of contact w/ stingray, [accid (unintentional), intentional self-harm, assault, undetermined], seq

T63.59[1,2,3,4]S   Txc effct of contact w/ oth venomous fish, [accid (unintentional), intentional self-harm, assault, undetermined], seq

T63.61[1,2,3,4]S   Txc effct of contact w/ Portugese Man-o-war, [accid (unintentional), intentional self-harm, assault, undetermined], seq

T63.62[1,2,3,4]S   Txc effct of contact w/ oth jellyfish, [accid (unintentional), intentional self-harm, assault, undetermined], seq

T63.63[1,2,3,4]S   Txc effct of contact w/ sea anemone, [accid (unintentional), intentional self-harm, assault, undetermined], seq

T63.69[1,2,3,4]S   Txc effct of contact w/ oth venomous marine animals, [accid (unintentional), intentional self-harm, assault, undetermined], seq

Surgical   **Medical**   **CC Indicator**   **MCC Indicator**   **Procedure Proxy**   PDxMCC **PDx acts as own MCC**   PDxCC **PDx acts as own CC**

T63.71[1,2,3,4]S	Txc effct of contact w/ venomous marine plant, [accid (unintentional), intentional self-harm, assault, undetermined], seq	T71.1[1,2,3,5,6,9][1,2,3,4][A,S]	Asphyxiation d/t [smothing under pillow, plastic bag, being trapped in bed linens, smothing under anoth person's body, smothing in furniture, hanging, mech threat to breathing d/t oth causes], [accid, intentional self-harm, assault, undetermined], [init enc, seq]
T63.79[1,2,3,4]S	Txc effct of contact w/ oth venomous plant, [accid (unintentional), intentional self-harm, assault, undetermined], seq		
T63.81[1,2,3,4]S	Txc effct of contact w/ venomous frog, [accid (unintentional), intentional self-harm, assault, undetermined], seq	T71.29X[A,S]	Asphyxiation d/t being trapped in oth low oxygen environment, [init enc, seq]
T63.82[1,2,3,4]S	Txc effct of contact w/ venomous toad, [accid (unintentional), intentional self-harm, assault, undetermined], seq	T71.2[0,1]X[A,S]	Asphyxiation d/t [sysic oxygen deficiency d/t low oxygen content in ambient air d/t unsp cause, cave-in or falling earth], [init enc, seq]
T63.83[1,2,3,4]S	Txc effct of contact w/ oth venomous amphibian, [accid (unintentional), intentional self-harm, assault, undetermined], seq	T71.2[2,3][1,2,3,4][A,S]	Asphyxiation d/t being trapped in a [car trunk, (discarded) refrigerator], [accid, intentional self-harm, assault, undetermined], [init enc, seq]
T63.89[1,2,3,4]S	Txc effct of contact w/ oth venomous animals, [accid (unintentional), intentional self-harm, assault, undetermined], seq	T71.9XX[A,S]	Asphyxiation d/t unsp cause, [init enc, seq]
		T73.0XX[A,S]	Starvation, [init enc, seq]
T63.9[1,2,3,4]XS	Txc effct of contact w/ unsp venomous animal, [accid (unintentional), intentional self-harm, assault, undetermined], seq	T73.1XX[A,S]	Deprivation of water, [init enc, seq]
		T73.2XX[A,S]	Exhaustion d/t exposure, [init enc, seq]
		T73.3XX[A,S]	Exhaustion d/t excessive exertion, [init enc, seq]
T64.0[1,2,3,4]XS	Txc effct of aflatoxin, [accid (unintentional), intentional self-harm, assault, undetermined], seq	T73.8XX[A,S]	Oth effects of deprivation, [init enc, seq]
		T73.9XX[A,S]	Effect of deprivation, unsp, [init enc, seq]
T64.8[1,2,3,4]XS	Txc effct of oth mycotoxin food contaminants, [accid (unintentional), intentional self-harm, assault, undetermined], seq	T74.0[1,2]X[A,S]	[Adult, Child] neglect or abandonment, confirmed, [init enc, seq]
		T74.1[1,2]X[A,S]	[Adult, Child] physical abuse, confirmed, [init enc, seq]
T65.0X[1,2,3,4]S	Txc effct of cyanides, [accid (unintentional), intentional self-harm, assault, undetermined], seq	T74.2[1,2]X[A,S]	[Adult, Child] sexual abuse, confirmed, [init enc, seq]
		T74.3[1,2]X[A,S]	[Adult, Child] psychological abuse, confirmed, [init enc, seq]
T65.1X[1,2,3,4]S	Txc effct of strychnine, [accid (unintentional), intentional self-harm, assault, undetermined], seq	T74.4XX[A,S]	Shaken infant synd, [init enc, seq]
		T74.9[1,2]X[A,S]	Unsp [adult, child] maltx, confirmed, [init enc, seq]
T65.21[1,2,3,4]S	Txc effct of chewing tobacco, [accid (unintentional), intentional self-harm, assault, undetermined], seq	T75.0[0,1,9]X[A,S]	[Unsp effects of, Shock d/t being struck by, Unsp effects of] lightning, [init enc, seq]
T65.22[1,2,3,4]S	Txc effct of tobacco cigarettes, [accid (unintentional), intentional self-harm, assault, undetermined], seq	T75.1XX[A,S]	Unsp effects of drowning and nonfatal submersion, [init enc, seq]
T65.29[1,2,3,4]S	Txc effct of oth tobacco and nicotine, [accid (unintentional), intentional self-harm, assault, undetermined], seq	T75.20X[A,S]	Unsp effects of vibration, [init enc, seq]
		T75.21X[A,S]	Pneumatic hammer synd, [init enc, seq]
T65.3X[1,2,3,4]S	Txc effct of nitroderivatives and amnioderivatives of benzene and its homologues, [accid (unintentional), intentional self-harm, assault, undetermined], seq	T75.22X[A,S]	Traum vasospastic synd, [init enc, seq]
		T75.23X[A,S]	Vertigo from infrasound, [init enc, seq]
		T75.29X[A,S]	Oth effects of vibration, [init enc, seq]
T65.4X[1,2,3,4]S	Txc effct of carbon disulfide, [accid (unintentional), intentional self-harm, assault, undetermined], seq	T75.3XXS	Motion sickness, seq
		T75.4XX[A,S]	Electrocution, [init enc, seq]
T65.5X[1,2,3,4]S	Txc effct of nitroglycerin and oth nitric acids amd esters, [accid (unintentional), intentional self-harm, assault, undetermined], seq	T75.89X[A,S]	Oth spec effects of ext causes, [init enc, seq]
		T75.8[1,2]X[A,S]	Effects of [abnormal gravitation [G] forces, weightlessness], [init enc, seq]
T65.6X[1,2,3,4]S	Txc effct of paints and dyes, NEC, [accid (unintentional), intentional self-harm, assault, undetermined], seq	T76.0[1,2]X[A,S]	[Adult, Child] neglect or abandonment, suspected, [init enc, seq]
T65.81[1,2,3,4]S	Txc effct of latex, [accid (unintentional), intentional self-harm, assault, undetermined], seq	T76.1[1,2]X[A,S]	[Adult, Child] physical abuse, suspected, [init enc, seq]
		T76.2[1,2]X[A,S]	[Adult, Child] sexual abuse, suspected, [init enc, seq]
T65.82[1,2,3,4]S	Txc effct of harmful algae and algae toxins, [accid (unintentional), intentional self-harm, assault, undetermined], seq	T76.3[1,2]X[A,S]	[Adult, Child] psychological abuse, suspected, [init enc, seq]
		T76.9[1,2]X[A,S]	Unsp [adult, child] maltx, suspected, [init enc, seq]
T65.83[1,2,3,4]S	Txc effct of fiberglass, NEC, [accid (unintentional), intentional self-harm, assault, undetermined], seq	T78.0[0,1,2,3,4,5,6,7,8,9]XS	Anaphylactic reaction d/t [unsp food, peanuts, shellfish (crustaceans), oth fish, fruits and vegetables, tree nuts and seeds, food additives, milk and dairy products, eggs, oth food products], seq
T65.89[1,2,3,4]S	Txc effct of oth spec substances, [accid (unintentional), intentional self-harm, assault, undetermined], seq		
		T78.1XX[A,S]	Oth adverse food reactions, NEC, [init enc, seq]
T65.9[1,2,3,4]XS	Txc effct of unsp substance, [accid (unintentional), intentional self-harm, assault, undetermined], seq	T78.2XXS	Anaphylactic shock, unsp, seq
		T78.3XXS	Angioneurotic edema, seq
T66.XXX[A,S]	Radiation sickness, unsp, [init enc, seq]	T78.40XS	Allergy, unsp, seq
T67.[0,1,2,3,4,5,6,7]XX[A,S]	Heat [stroke and sunstroke, syncope, cramp, exhaustion anhydrotic, exhaustion d/t salt depletion, exhaustion unsp, fatigue transient, edema], [init enc, seq]	T78.41XS	Arthus phenomenon, seq
		T78.49XS	Oth allergy, seq
		T78.8XX[A,S]	Oth adverse effects, NEC, [init enc, seq]
T67.[8,9]XX[A,S]	[Oth, Unsp] effects of heat and light, [init enc, seq]	T79.2XXA	Traum secondary and recurrent hemor and seroma, init
T68.XXX[A,S]	Hypothmia, [init enc, seq]	T79.4XXA	Traum shock, init enc
T69.01[1,2,9][A,S]	Immersion hand, [rt, lt, unsp] hand, [init enc, seq]	T79.A0XA	Compartment synd, unsp, init enc
T69.02[1,2,9][A,S]	Immersion foot, [rt, lt, unsp] foot, [init enc, seq]	T79.A1[1,2,9]A	Traum compartment synd of [rt, lt, unsp] upr extr, init enc
T69.1XX[A,S]	Chilblains, [init enc, seq]	T79.A2[1,2,9]A	Traum compartment synd of [rt, lt, unsp] lwr extr, init enc
T69.[8,9]XX[A,S]	[Oth spec, Unsp] effects of reduced temperature, [init enc, seq]	T79.A3[9]XA	Traum compartment synd of [abd, oth sites], init enc
T70.2[0,9]X[A,S]	[Unsp, Oth] effects of high altitude, [init enc, seq]	T79.[8,9]XXA	[Oth, Unsp] early comps of trauma, init enc
T70.3XX[A,S]	Caisson dz [decompression sickness], [init enc, seq]	T80.21[1,2,8,9]S	[Bldstream, Local, Oth, Unsp] infxn d/t central venous catheter, seq
T70.4XX[A,S]	Effects of high-pressure fluids, [init enc, seq]		
T70.8XX[A,S]	Oth effects of air pressure and water pressure, [init enc, seq]	T80.22XS	Acute infxn fol transfs,infusn,inject bld/products, seq
T70.9XX[A,S]	Effect of air pressure and water pressure, unsp, [init enc, seq]	T80.29XS	Infxn fol oth inf, transfs and theraputc inject, seq
T70.[0,1]XXS	[Otitic, Sinus] barotrauma, seq	T80.30XS	ABO incompat react d/t tranfs of bld/bld prod, unsp, seq
T71.141A	Asphyx d/t smothr under another person's body, acc, init	T80.31[0,1,9]S	ABO incompatibility w/ [acute, delayed, unsp] hemolytic transfusion reaction, seq
T71.141S	Asphyx d/t smothr under another person's body, acc, seq		
T71.143A	Asphyx d/t smothr under another person's body, asslt, init	T80.39XS	Oth ABO incompat react d/t tranfs of bld/bld prod, seq
T71.143S	Asphyx d/t smothr under another person's body, asslt, seq	T80.40XS	Rh incompat react d/t tranfs of bld/bld prod, unsp, seq
T71.144A	Asphyx d/t smothr under another person's body, undet, init	T80.41[0,1,9]S	Rh incompatibility w/ [acute, delayed, unsp] hemolytic transfusion reaction, seq
T71.144S	Asphyx d/t smothr under another person's body, undet, seq		
		T80.49XS	Oth Rh incompat react d/t tranfs of bld/bld prod, seq
		T80.5[1,2,9]XS	Anaphylactic reaction d/t [administration of bld and bld products, vaccination, oth serum], seq

---

Ⓣ **Transfer DRG**　　　ⓈⓅ **Special Payment**　　　***Code Range**　　　**6th and 7th Character of ZZ = No Device, No Qualifier ZX = No Device, Diagnostic**

T80.6[1,2,9]XS Oth serum reaction d/t [administration of bld and bld products, vaccination, oth serum], seq

T80.81[0,8]S Extravasation of [vesicant antineoplastic chemothapy, oth vesicant agent], seq

T80.89XS Oth comp fol inf, tranfs and theraputc inject, seq

T80.90XS Unsp comp fol inf and theraputc injection, seq

T80.91[0,1,9]S [Acute, Delayed, Unsp] hemolytic transfusion reaction, unsp incompatibility, seq

T80.92XS Unsp transfusion reaction, seq

T80.A0XS Non-ABO incompat react d/t tranfs of bld/bld prod,unsp, seq

T80.A1[0,1,9]S Non-ABO incompatibility w/ [acute, delayed, hemolytic] hemolytic transfusion reaction, seq

T80.A9XS Oth non-ABO incompat react d/t tranfs of bld/bld prod, seq

T80.[0,1]XXS [Air embolism, Vascular comps] following inf, transfusion and therapeutic injection, seq

T81.1[0,1,2,9]XS Postprocedural [unsp, cardiogenic, septic, oth] shock, seq

T81.30XS Disruption of wnd, unsp, seq

T81.33XS Disruption of traum inj wnd repair, seq

T81.3[1,2]XS Disruption of [ext, int] operation (surgical) wnd, NEC, seq

T81.4XXS Infxn following a procedure, seq

T81.5[0,1,2,3,9][0,1,2,3,4,5,6,7,8,9]S[Unsp comp, Adhesions, Obstruction, Perforation, Oth comps] d/t FB accidally lt in body following [surgical operation, inf or transfusion, kidney dialysis, injectionor immunization, endo exam, heart catheterization, aspiration punc or oth catheterization, rmvl of catheter or packing, oth procedure, unsp procedure], seq

T81.6[0,1,9]XS [Unsp acute reaction, Aseptic peritonitis, Oth acute reaction] d/t foreign substance accidally lt during a procedure, seq

T81.71[0,1,8,9]S Comp of [mesenteric, renal, oth, unsp] artery following a procedure, NEC, seq

T81.72XS Comp of vein following a procedure, NEC, seq

T81.81XS Comp of inhalation therapy, seq

T81.82XS Emphysema (SQ) resulting from a procedure, seq

T81.83XS Persistent postprocedural fistula, seq

T81.89XS Oth comp of procedures, NEC, seq

T81.9XXS Unsp comp of procedure, seq

T82.0[1,2,3,9]XS [Breakdown (mech), Displac, Leakage, Oth mech] comp of heart valve prosthesis, seq

T82.11[0,1,8,9]S Breakdown (mech) of [cardiac electrode, cardiac pulse generator, oth cardiac electronic dev, unsp cardiac electronic dev], seq

T82.12[0,1,8,9]S Displac of [cardiac electrode, cardiac pulse generator, oth cardiac electronic dev, unsp cardiac electronic dev], seq

T82.19[0,1,8,9]S Oth mech comp of [cardiac electrode, cardiac pulse generator, oth cardiac electronic dev, unsp cardiac electronic dev], seq

T82.21[1,2,3,8]S [Breakdown (mech), Displac, Leakage, Oth mech comp] of coronary artery bypass graft, seq

T82.22[1,2,3,8]S [Breakdown (mech), Displac, Leakage, Oth mech comp] of biological heart valve graft, seq

T82.31[0,1,2,8,9]S Breakdown (mech) of [aortic (bifurcation) graft (replace), carotid arterial graft (bypass), femor arterial graft (bypass), oth vascular grafts, unsp vascular grafts], seq

T82.32[0,1,2,8,9]S Displac of [aortic (bifurcation) graft (replace), carotid arterial graft (bypass), femor arterial graft (bypass), oth vascular grafts, unsp vascular grafts], seq

T82.33[0,1,2,8,9]S Leakage of [aortic (bifurcation) graft (replace), carotid arterial graft (bypass), femor arterial graft (bypass), oth vascular grafts, unsp vascular grafts], seq

T82.39[0,1,2,8,9]S Oth mech comp of [aortic (bifurcation) graft (replace), carotid arterial graft (bypass), femor arterial graft (bypass), oth vascular grafts, unsp vascular grafts], seq

T82.4[1,2,3,9]XS [Breakdown (mech), Displac, Leakage, Oth mech comp] of vascular dialysis catheter, seq

T82.51[0,1,2,3,4,5,8,9]S Breakdown (mech) of [surgically created arteriovenous fistula, surgically created arteriovenous shunt, artfcl heart, balloon (counterpulsation) dev, inf catheter, umbrella dev, oth cardiac/vascular dev, unsp cardiac/vascular dev], seq

T82.52[0,1,2,3,4,5,8,9]S Displac of [surgically created arteriovenous fistula, surgically created arteriovenous shunt, artfcl heart, balloon (counterpulsation) dev, inf catheter, umbrella dev, oth cardiac/vascular dev, unsp cardiac/vascular dev], seq

T82.53[0,1,2,3,4,5,8,9]S Leakage of [surgically created arteriovenous fistula, surgically created arteriovenous shunt, artfcl heart, balloon (counterpulsation) dev, inf catheter, umbrella dev, oth cardiac/vascular dev, unsp cardiac/vascular dev], seq

T82.59[0,1,2,3,4,5,8,9]S Oth mech comp of [surgically created arteriovenous fistula, surgically created arteriovenous shunt, artfcl heart, balloon (counterpulsation) dev, inf catheter, umbrella dev, oth cardiac/vascular dev, unsp cardiac/vascular dev], seq

T82.6XXS Infect/inflm reaction d/t cardiac valve prosth, seq

T82.7XXS Infect/inflm react d/t oth cardi/vasc dev/implnt/grft, seq

T82.8[1,2,3,4,5,6,9][7,8]S [Embolism, Fibrosis, Hemor, Pain, Stenosis, Thrombosis, Oth spec comp] of [cardiac, vascular] prosthetic devs, implants and grafts, seq

T82.9XXS Unsp comp of cardiac and vascular prosth dev/grft, seq

T83.0[1,2,3,9][0,8]S [Breakdown (mech), Displac, Leakage, Oth mech comp] of [cystostomy, oth indwelling urethral] catheter, seq

T83.1[1,2,9][0,1,2,8]S [Breakdown (mech), Displac, Oth mech comp] of [urinary electronic stimulator, urinary sphincter implant, urinary stent, oth urinary devs], seq

T83.2[1,2,3,9]XS [Breakdown (mech), Displac, Leakage, Oth mech comp] of graft of urinary organ, seq

T83.3[1,2,9]XS [Breakdown (mech), Displac, Oth mech comp] of intrauterine contraceptive dev, seq

T83.4[1,2,9][0,8]S [Breakdown (mech), Displac, Oth mech comp] of [penile (implanted) prosthesis, oth prosthetic devs, implants and grafts of genital tract], seq

T83.5[1,9]XS Infxn and inflam reaction d/t [indwelling urinary catheter, prosthetic dev, implant and graft in urinary sys], seq

T83.6XXS Infect/inflm react d/t prosth dev/grft in genitl trct, seq

T83.7[1,2][1,8]S [Erosion, Exposure] of [implanted vaginal mesh, implanted mesh] and oth prosthetic materials to surrounding organ or tissue, seq

T83.8[1,2,3,4,5,6,9]XS[Embolism, Fibrosis, Hemor, Pain, Stenosis, Thrombosis, Oth spec comp] of genitourinary prosthetic devs, implants and grafts, seq

T83.9XXS Unsp comp of genitourinary prosth dev/grft, seq

T84.01[0,1,2,3,8,9]S Broken int [rt hip, lt hip, rt knee, lt knee, oth site, unsp site] prosthesis, seq

T84.02[0,1]S Disloc of int [rt, lt] hip prosthesis, seq

T84.02[2,3]S Instability of int [rt, lt] knee prosthesis, seq

T84.02[8,9]S Disloc of [oth, unsp] int jt prosthesis, seq

T84.03[0,1,2,3,8,9]S Mech loosening of [rt hip, lt hip, rt knee, lt knee, oth site, unsp site] prosthesis, seq

T84.04[0,1,2,3,8,9]S Periprosthetic fx around int prosthetic [rt hip, lt hip, rt knee, lt knee, oth, unsp] jt, seq

T84.05[0,1,2,3,8,9]S Periprosthetic osteolysis of int prosthetic [rt hip, lt hip, rt knee, lt knee, oth, unsp] jt, seq

T84.06[0,1,2,3,8,9]S Wear of articular bearing surface of int prosthetic [rt hip, lt hip, rt knee, lt knee, oth, unsp] jt, seq

T84.09[0,1,2,3,8,9]S Oth mech comp of int prosthetic [rt hip, lt hip, rt knee, lt knee, oth, unsp] jt, seq

T84.11[0,1,2,3,4,5,6,7,9]S Breakdown (mech) of int fix dev of [rt humerus, lt humerus, bone of rt forearm, bone of lt forearm, rt femur, lt femur, bone of rt lwr leg, bone of lt lwr leg, unsp bone of limb], seq

T84.12[0,1,2,3,4,5,6,7,9]S Displac of int fix dev of [rt humerus, lt humerus, bone of rt forearm, bone of lt forearm, rt femur, lt femur, bone of rt lwr leg, bone of lt lwr leg, unsp bone of limb], seq

T84.19[0,1,2,3,4,5,6,7,9]S Oth mech comp of int fix dev of [rt humerus, lt humerus, bone of rt forearm, bone of lt forearm, rt femur, lt femur, bone of rt lwr leg, bone of lt lwr leg, unsp bone of limb], seq

T84.21[0,3,6,8]S Breakdown (mech) of int fix dev of [bones of hand and fingers, bones of foot and toes, vertebrae, oth bones], seq

T84.22[0,3,6,8]S Displac of int fix dev of [bones of hand and fingers, bones of foot and toes, vertebrae, oth bones], seq

T84.29[0,3,6,8]S Oth mech comp of int fix dev of [bones of hand and fingers, bones of foot and toes, vertebrae, oth bones], seq

T84.3[1,2,9][0,8]S [Breakdown (mech), Displac, Oth mech comp] of [electronic bone stimulator, oth bone dev(s), implants and grafts], seq

T84.4[1,2,9][0,8]S [Breakdown (mech), Displac, Oth mech comp] of [muscle and tndn graft, oth int orthopedic dev(s), implants and graft], seq

T84.5[0,1,2,3,4,9]XS Infxn and inflam reaction d/t [unsp int jt, int rt hip, int lt hip, int rt knee, int lt knee, oth int jt] prosthesis, seq

T84.60XS Infect/inflm reaction d/t int fix of unsp site, seq

T84.61[0,1,2,3,4,5,9]S Infxn and inflam reaction d/t int fix dev of [rt humerus, lt humerus, rt radius, lt radius, rt ulna, lt ulna, unsp bone of arm], seq

T84.62[0,1,2,3,4,5,9]S Infxn and inflam reaction d/t int fix dev of [rt femur, lt femur, rt tibia, lt tibia, rt fibula, lt fibula, unsp bone of leg], seq

T84.63XS Infect/inflm reaction d/t int fix of spine, seq

T84.69XS Infect/inflm reaction d/t int fix of site, seq

T84.7XXS Infect/inflm react d/t oth int orth prosth dev/grft, seq

T84.8[1,2,3,4,5,6,9]XS [Embolism, Fibrosis, Hemor, Pain, Stenosis, Thrombosis, Oth spec comp] d/t int orthopedic prosthetic devs, implants and grafts, seq

T84.9XXS Unsp comp of int orthopedic prosth dev/grft, seq

T85.0[1,2,3,9]XS [Breakdown (mech), Displac, Leakage, Oth mech comp] of ventricular intracranial (communicating) shunt, seq

---

Surgical   **Medical**   CC Indicator   **MCC Indicator**   Procedure Proxy   PDxMCC **PDx acts as own MCC**   PDxCC **PDx acts as own CC**

T85.11[0,1,2,8]S	Breakdown (mech) of implanted electronic neurostimulator (electrode) of [brain, peripheral nerve, spinal cord, oth nervous sys], seq
T85.12[0,1,2,8]S	Displac of implanted electronic neurostimulator (electrode) of [brain, peripheral nerve, spinal cord, oth nervous sys], seq
T85.19[0,1,2,9]S	Oth mech comp of implanted electronic neurostimulator (electrode) of [brain, peripheral nerve, spinal cord, oth nervous sys], seq
T85.2[1,2,9]XS	[Breakdown (mech), Displac, Oth mech comp] of intraocular lens, seq
T85.318S	Breakdown (mech) of ocular prosth dev/grft, seq
T85.31[0,1]S	Breakdown (mech) of prosthetic orbit of [rt, lt] eye, seq
T85.328S	Displac of ocular prosth dev/grft, seq
T85.32[0,1]S	Displac of prosthetic orbit of [rt, lt] eye, seq
T85.398S	Mech compl of ocular prosth dev/grft, seq
T85.39[0,1]S	Oth mech comp of prosthetic orbit of [rt, lt] eye, seq
T85.4[1,2,3,4,9]XS	[Breakdown (mech), Displac, Leakage, Capsular contracture, Oth mech comp] of breast prosthesis and implant, seq
T85.5[1,2,9][0,1,8]S	[Breakdown (mech), Displac, Oth mech comp] of [bile duct prosthesis, esophageal anti-reflux dev, oth gastrointestinal prosthetic devs, implants and grafts], seq
T85.63[0,1,3,8]S	Leakage of [epidural and subdural inf catheter, intraperitoneal dialysis catheter, insulin pump, oth spec int prosthetic devs, implants and grafts], seq
T85.69[0,1,2,3,4,8]S	Oth mech comp of [epidural and subdural inf catheter, intraperitoneal dialysis catheter, permanent sutures, artfcl skin graft and decellularized allodermis, insulin pump, oth spec int prosthetic devs, implants and grafts], seq
T85.6[1,2][0,1,2,3,4,8]S	[Breakdown (mech), Displac] of [epidural and subdural inf catheter, intraperitoneal dialysis catheter, permanent sutures, artfcl skin graft and decellularized allodermis, insulin pump, oth spec int prosthetic devs, implants and grafts], seq
T85.7[1,2,9]XS	Infxn and inflam reaction d/t [peritoneal dialysis catheter, insulin pump, oth int prosthetic devs, implants and grafts], seq
T85.8[1,2,3,4,5,6,9]XS	[Embolism, Fibrosis, Hemor, Pain, Stenosis, Thrombosis, Oth spec comp] d/t int prosthetic devs, implants and grafts, NEC, seq
T85.9XXS	Unsp comp of int prosth dev/grft, seq
T88.0XXS	Infxn following immunization, seq
T88.1XXS	Oth comp following immunization, NEC, seq
T88.2XX[A,S]	Shock d/t anesthesia, [init enc, seq]
T88.3XX[A,S]	Malig hyperthermia d/t anesthesia, [init enc, seq]
T88.4XXS	Failed or difficult intubation, seq
T88.51XA	Hypothermia following anesthesia, init enc
T88.51XS	Hypothermia following anesthesia, seq
T88.52XS	Failed mod sedation during procedure, seq
T88.59XS	Oth comp of anesthesia, seq
T88.6XXS	Anaphyl react d/t advrs eff drug/med prop admin, seq
T88.7XXS	Unsp adverse effect of drug or medicament, seq
T88.8XXS	Oth comp of surgical and medical care, NEC, seq
T88.9XXS	Comp of surgical and medical care, unsp, seq
Z04.[1,2,3]	Enc for exam and observation following [transport, work, oth] accid

---

DRG 923 **Other Injury, Poisoning and Toxic Effect Diagnoses without MCC**

GMLOS 2.5	AMLOS 3.5	RW 0.8117

Select principal diagnosis listed under DRG 922

[T] **Transfer DRG**   [SP] **Special Payment**   * **Code Range**   **6th and 7th Character of ZZ = No Device, No Qualifier ZX = No Device, Diagnostic**

376

MS-DRG Version 33.0

© 2015 Optum360, LLC

SURGICAL

▲**DRG 927** **Extensive Burns or Full Thickness Burns with Mechanical Ventilation >96 Hours with Skin Graft**

GMLOS 23.5 **AMLOS 30.6** **RW 15.9672**

Full-Thickness Burns with MV >96 hrs

Principal or Secondary Diagnosis

T20.30XA	Burn third degree of head, face, and neck, unsp site, init
T20.31[1,2,9]A	Burn of 3rd degree of [rt, lt, unsp] ear (any part, except ear drum), init enc
T20.39XA	Burn of 3rd deg mu sites of head, face, and neck, init
T20.3[2,3,4,5,6,7]XA	Burn of 3rd degree of [lip(s), chin, nose (septum), scalp (any part), forehead and cheek, neck], init enc
T20.70XA	Corrosion third degree of head, face, and neck, unsp site, init
T20.71[1,2,9]A	Corrosion of 3rd degree of [rt, lt, unsp] ear (any part, except ear drum), init enc
T20.79XA	Corrosion of 3rd deg mu sites of head, face, and neck, init
T20.7[2,3,4,5,6,7]XA	Corrosion of 3rd degree of [lip(s), chin, nose (septum), scalp (any part), forehead and cheek, neck], init enc
T21.3[0,1,2,3,4,5,6,7,9]XA	Burn of 3rd degree of [trunk, unsp site, chest wall, abd wall, upr back, lwr back, buttock, male genital rgn, femal genital rgn, oth site of trunk], init enc
T21.7[0,1,2,3,4,5,6,7,9]XA	Corrosion of 3rd degree of [trunk, unsp site, chest wall, abd wall, upr back, lwr back, buttock, male genital rgn, femal genital rgn, oth site of trunk], init enc
T22.30XA	Burn third deg of shldr/up lmb, ex wrs/hnd, unsp site, init
T22.31[1,2,9]A	Burn of 3rd degree of [rt, lt, unsp] forearm, init enc
T22.32[1,2,9]A	Burn of 3rd degree of [rt, lt, unsp] elbow, init enc
T22.33[1,2,9]A	Burn of 3rd degree of [rt, lt, unsp] upr arm, init enc
T22.34[1,2,9]A	Burn of 3rd degree of [rt, lt, unsp] axilla, init enc
T22.35[1,2,9]A	Burn of 3rd degree of [rt, lt, unsp] shldr, init enc
T22.36[1,2,9]A	Burn of 3rd degree of [rt, lt, unsp] scapular rgn, init enc
T22.39[1,2,9]A	Burn of 3rd degree of multi sites of [rt, lt, unsp] shldr and upr limb, except wrist and hand, init enc
T22.70XA	Corrosion 3rd deg of shldr/up lmb, ex wrs/hnd, unsp site, init
T22.71[1,2,9]A	Corrosion of 3rd degree of [rt, lt, unsp] forearm, init enc
T22.72[1,2,9]A	Corrosion of 3rd degree of [rt, lt, unsp] elbow, init enc
T22.73[1,2,9]A	Corrosion of 3rd degree of [rt, lt, unsp] upr arm, init enc
T22.74[1,2,9]A	Corrosion of 3rd degree of [rt, lt, unsp] axilla, init enc
T22.75[1,2,9]A	Corrosion of 3rd degree of [rt, lt, unsp] shldr, init enc
T22.76[1,2,9]A	Corrosion of 3rd degree of [rt, lt, unsp] scapular rgn, init enc
T22.79[1,2,9]A	Corrosion of 3rd degree of multi sites of [rt, lt, unsp] shldr and upr limb, except wrist and hand, init enc
T23.30[1,2,9]A	Burn of 3rd degree of [rt, lt, unsp] hand, unsp site, init enc
T23.31[1,2,9]A	Burn of 3rd degree of [rt, lt, unsp] thumb (nail), init enc
T23.32[1,2,9]A	Burn of 3rd degree of single [rt, lt, unsp] finger (nail) except thumb, init enc
T23.33[1,2,9]A	Burn of 3rd degree of multi [rt, lt, unsp] fingers (nail), not incl* thumb, init enc
T23.34[1,2,9]A	Burn of 3rd degree of multi [rt, lt, unsp] fingers (nail), incl* thumb, init enc
T23.35[1,2,9]A	Burn of 3rd degree of [rt, lt, unsp] palm, init enc
T23.36[1,2,9]A	Burn of 3rd degree of back of [rt, lt, unsp] hand, init enc
T23.37[1,2,9]A	Burn of 3rd degree of [rt, lt, unsp] wrist, init enc
T23.39[1,2,9]A	Burn of 3rd degree of multi sites of [rt, lt, unsp] wrist and hand, init enc
T23.70[1,2,9]A	Corrosion of 3rd degree of [rt, lt, unsp] hand, unsp site, init enc
T23.71[1,2,9]A	Corrosion of 3rd degree of [rt, lt, unsp] thumb (nail), init enc
T23.72[1,2,9]A	Corrosion of 3rd degree of single [rt, lt, unsp] finger (nail) except thumb, init enc
T23.73[1,2,9]A	Corrosion of 3rd degree of multi [rt, lt, unsp] fingers (nail), not incl* thumb, init enc
T23.74[1,2,9]A	Corrosion of 3rd degree of multi [rt, lt, unsp] fingers (nail), incl* thumb, init enc
T23.75[1,2,9]A	Corrosion of 3rd degree of [rt, lt, unsp] palm, init enc
T23.76[1,2,9]A	Corrosion of 3rd degree of back of [rt, lt, unsp] hand, init enc
T23.77[1,2,9]A	Corrosion of 3rd degree of [rt, lt, unsp] wrist, init enc
T23.79[1,2,9]A	Corrosion of 3rd degree of multi sites of [rt, lt, unsp] wrist and hand, init enc
T24.30[1,2,9]A	Burn of 3rd degree of unsp site of [rt, lt, unsp] lwr limb, except ankle and foot, init enc
T24.31[1,2,9]A	Burn of 3rd degree of [rt, lt, unsp] thigh, init enc
T24.32[1,2,9]A	Burn of 3rd degree of [rt, lt, unsp] knee, init enc
T24.33[1,2,9]A	Burn of 3rd degree of [rt, lt, unsp] lwr leg, init enc
T24.39[1,2,9]A	Burn of 3rd degree of multi sites of [rt, lt, unsp] lwr limb, except ankle and foot, init enc
T24.70[1,2,9]A	Corrosion of 3rd degree of unsp site of [rt, lt, unsp] lwr limb, except ankle and foot, init enc
T24.71[1,2,9]A	Corrosion of 3rd degree of [rt, lt, unsp] thigh, init enc
T24.72[1,2,9]A	Corrosion of 3rd degree of [rt, lt, unsp] knee, init enc
T24.73[1,2,9]A	Corrosion of 3rd degree of [rt, lt, unsp] lwr leg, init enc
T24.79[1,2,9]A	Corrosion of 3rd degree of multi sites of [rt, lt, unsp] lwr limb, except ankle and foot, init enc
T25.31[1,2,9]A	Burn of 3rd degree of [rt, lt, unsp] ankle, init enc
T25.32[1,2,9]A	Burn of 3rd degree of [rt, lt, unsp] foot, init enc
T25.33[1,2,9]A	Burn of 3rd degree of [rt, lt, unsp] toe(s) (nail), init enc
T25.39[1,2,9]A	Burn of 3rd degree of multi sites of [rt, lt, unsp] ankle and foot, init enc
T25.71[1,2,9]A	Corrosion of 3rd degree of [rt, lt, unsp] ankle, init enc
T25.72[1,2,9]A	Corrosion of 3rd degree of [rt, lt, unsp] foot, init enc
T25.73[1,2,9]A	Corrosion of 3rd degree of [rt, lt, unsp] toe(s) (nail), init enc
T25.79[1,2,9]A	Corrosion of 3rd degree of multi sites of [rt, lt, unsp] ankle and foot, init enc
T26.2[0,1,2]XA	Burn w/ resulting rupture and destr of [unsp, rt, lt] eyeball, init enc
T31.11	Burns of 10-19% of body surface w 10-19% third degree burns
T32.11	Corrosion 10-19% of body surface w 10-19% third degree corrosion

AND

Nonoperating Room Procedures

5A1955Z	Respiratory Ventilation, > 96 Consecutive Hrs

AND

Operating Room Procedures

0H80XZZ	Div of Scalp Skin, Ext Appr
0H81XZZ	Div of Face Skin, Ext Appr
0H84XZZ	Div of Neck Skin, Ext Appr
0HB5XZZ	Exc of Chest Skin, Ext Appr
0HB6XZZ	Exc of Back Skin, Ext Appr
0HB7XZZ	Exc of Abd Skin, Ext Appr
0HB8XZZ	Exc of Buttock Skin, Ext Appr
0HBAXZZ	Exc of Genitalia Skin, Ext Appr
0HBBXZZ	Exc of Rt Upr Arm Skin, Ext Appr
0HBCXZZ	Exc of Lt Upr Arm Skin, Ext Appr
0HBDXZZ	Exc of Rt Lwr Arm Skin, Ext Appr
0HBEXZZ	Exc of Lt Lwr Arm Skin, Ext Appr
0HBFXZZ	Exc of Rt Hand Skin, Ext Appr
0HBGXZZ	Exc of Lt Hand Skin, Ext Appr
0HBHXZZ	Exc of Rt Upr Leg Skin, Ext Appr
0HBJXZZ	Exc of Lt Upr Leg Skin, Ext Appr
0HBKXZZ	Exc of Rt Lwr Leg Skin, Ext Appr
0HBLXZZ	Exc of Lt Lwr Leg Skin, Ext Appr
0HBMXZZ	Exc of Rt Foot Skin, Ext Appr
0HBNXZZ	Exc of Lt Foot Skin, Ext Appr
0HR0XJZ	Replace of Scalp Skin with Synth Sub, Extern Appr
0HR0X[7,J,K][3,4]	Replace/Skin, Scalp, Ext, [Auto Tissue Sub, Synth Sub, Nonauto Tissue Sub], [Full Thickness, Partial Thickness]
0HR1XJZ	Replace of Face Skin with Synth Sub, Extern Appr
0HR1X[7,J,K][3,4]	Replace/Skin, Face, Ext, [Auto Tissue Sub, Synth Sub, Nonauto Tissue Sub], [Full Thickness, Partial Thickness]
0HR4XJZ	Replace of Neck Skin with Synth Sub, Extern Appr
0HR4X[7,J,K][3,4]	Replace/Skin, Neck, Ext, [Auto Tissue Sub, Synth Sub, Nonauto Tissue Sub], [Full Thickness, Partial Thickness]
0HR5XJZ	Replace of Chest Skin with Synth Sub, Extern Appr
0HR5X[7,J,K][3,4]	Replace/Skin, Chest, Ext, [Auto Tissue Sub, Synth Sub, Nonauto Tissue Sub], [Full Thickness, Partial Thickness]
0HR6XJZ	Replace of Back Skin with Synth Sub, Extern Appr
0HR6X[7,J,K][3,4]	Replace/Skin, Back, Ext, [Auto Tissue Sub, Synth Sub, Nonauto Tissue Sub], [Full Thickness, Partial Thickness]
0HR7XJZ	Replace of Abd Skin with Synth Sub, Extern Appr
0HR7X[7,J,K][3,4]	Replace/Skin, Abd, Ext, [Auto Tissue Sub, Synth Sub, Nonauto Tissue Sub], [Full Thickness, Partial Thickness]
0HR8XJZ	Replace of Buttock Skin with Synth Sub, Extern Appr
0HR8X[7,J,K][3,4]	Replace/Skin, Buttock, Ext, [Auto Tissue Sub, Synth Sub, Nonauto Tissue Sub], [Full Thickness, Partial Thickness]

Surgical	Medical	CC Indicator	MCC Indicator	Procedure Proxy	PDxMCC **PDx acts as own MCC**	PDxCC **PDx acts as own CC**

0HRAXJZ	Replace of Genitalia Skin with Synth Sub, Extern Appr
0HRAX[7,J,K][3,4]	Replace/Skin, Genitalia, Ext, [Auto Tissue Sub, Synth Sub, Nonauto Tissue Sub], [Full Thickness, Partial Thickness]
0HRBXJZ	Replace of Rt Up Arm Skin with Synth Sub, Extern Appr
0HRBX[7,J,K][3,4]	Replace/Skin, Rt Upr Arm, Ext, [Auto Tissue Sub, Synth Sub, Nonauto Tissue Sub], [Full Thickness, Partial Thickness]
0HRCXJZ	Replace of Lt Up Arm Skin with Synth Sub, Extern Appr
0HRCX[7,J,K][3,4]	Replace/Skin, Lt Upr Arm, Ext, [Auto Tissue Sub, Synth Sub, Nonauto Tissue Sub], [Full Thickness, Partial Thickness]
0HRDXJZ	Replace of Rt Low Arm Skin with Synth Sub, Extern Appr
0HRDX[7,J,K][3,4]	Replace/Skin, Rt Lwr Arm, Ext, [Auto Tissue Sub, Synth Sub, Nonauto Tissue Sub], [Full Thickness, Partial Thickness]
0HREXJZ	Replace of Lt Low Arm Skin with Synth Sub, Extern Appr
0HREX[7,J,K][3,4]	Replace/Skin, Lt Lwr Arm, Ext, [Auto Tissue Sub, Synth Sub, Nonauto Tissue Sub], [Full Thickness, Partial Thickness]
0HRFXJZ	Replace of Rt Hand Skin with Synth Sub, Extern Appr
0HRFX[7,J,K][3,4]	Replace/Skin, Rt Hand, Ext, [Auto Tissue Sub, Synth Sub, Nonauto Tissue Sub], [Full Thickness, Partial Thickness]
0HRGXJZ	Replace of Lt Hand Skin with Synth Sub, Extern Appr
0HRGX[7,J,K][3,4]	Replace/Skin, Lt Hand, Ext, [Auto Tissue Sub, Synth Sub, Nonauto Tissue Sub], [Full Thickness, Partial Thickness]
0HRHXJZ	Replace of Rt Up Leg Skin with Synth Sub, Extern Appr
0HRHX[7,J,K][3,4]	Replace/Skin, Rt Upr Leg, Ext, [Auto Tissue Sub, Synth Sub, Nonauto Tissue Sub], [Full Thickness, Partial Thickness]
0HRJXJZ	Replace of Lt Up Leg Skin with Synth Sub, Extern Appr
0HRJX[7,J,K][3,4]	Replace/Skin, Lt Upr Leg, Ext, [Auto Tissue Sub, Synth Sub, Nonauto Tissue Sub], [Full Thickness, Partial Thickness]
0HRKXJZ	Replace of Rt Low Leg Skin with Synth Sub, Extern Appr
0HRKX[7,J,K][3,4]	Replace/Skin, Rt Lwr Leg, Ext, [Auto Tissue Sub, Synth Sub, Nonauto Tissue Sub], [Full Thickness, Partial Thickness]
0HRLXJZ	Replace of Lt Low Leg Skin with Synth Sub, Extern Appr
0HRLX[7,J,K][3,4]	Replace/Skin, Lt Lwr Leg, Ext, [Auto Tissue Sub, Synth Sub, Nonauto Tissue Sub], [Full Thickness, Partial Thickness]
0HRMXJZ	Replace of Rt Foot Skin with Synth Sub, Extern Appr
0HRMX[7,J,K][3,4]	Replace/Skin, Rt Foot, Ext, [Auto Tissue Sub, Synth Sub, Nonauto Tissue Sub], [Full Thickness, Partial Thickness]
0HRNXJZ	Replace of Lt Foot Skin with Synth Sub, Extern Appr
0HRNX[7,J,K][3,4]	Replace/Skin, Lt Foot, Ext, [Auto Tissue Sub, Synth Sub, Nonauto Tissue Sub], [Full Thickness, Partial Thickness]
0HRTX[7,K]Z	Replace/Breast, Rt, Ext, [Auto Tissue Sub, Nonauto Tissue Sub], NQ
0HRUX[7,K]Z	Replace/Breast, Lt, Ext, [Auto Tissue Sub, Nonauto Tissue Sub], NQ
0HRVX[7,K]Z	Replace/Breast, Bilat, Ext, [Auto Tissue Sub, Nonauto Tissue Sub], NQ
0HX0XZZ	Transfer Scalp Skin, Ext Appr
0HX1XZZ	Transfer Face Skin, Ext Appr
0HX4XZZ	Transfer Neck Skin, Ext Appr
0HX5XZZ	Transfer Chest Skin, Ext Appr
0HX6XZZ	Transfer Back Skin, Ext Appr
0HX7XZZ	Transfer Abd Skin, Ext Appr
0HX8XZZ	Transfer Buttock Skin, Ext Appr
0HX9XZZ	Transfer Perineum Skin, Ext Appr
0HXAXZZ	Transfer Genitalia Skin, Ext Appr
0HXBXZZ	Transfer Rt Upr Arm Skin, Ext Appr
0HXCXZZ	Transfer Lt Upr Arm Skin, Ext Appr
0HXDXZZ	Transfer Rt Lwr Arm Skin, Ext Appr
0HXEXZZ	Transfer Lt Lwr Arm Skin, Ext Appr
0HXFXZZ	Transfer Rt Hand Skin, Ext Appr
0HXGXZZ	Transfer Lt Hand Skin, Ext Appr
0HXHXZZ	Transfer Rt Upr Leg Skin, Ext Appr
0HXJXZZ	Transfer Lt Upr Leg Skin, Ext Appr
0HXKXZZ	Transfer Rt Lwr Leg Skin, Ext Appr
0HXLXZZ	Transfer Lt Lwr Leg Skin, Ext Appr
0HXMXZZ	Transfer Rt Foot Skin, Ext Appr
0HXNXZZ	Transfer Lt Foot Skin, Ext Appr
0JH0[0,3]NZ	Insert/SQ Tissue & Fascia, Scalp, [Opn, Perc], Tissue Expander, NQ
0JH1[0,3]NZ	Insert/SQ Tissue & Fascia, Face, [Opn, Perc], Tissue Expander, NQ
0JH4[0,3]NZ	Insert/SQ Tissue & Fascia, Ant Neck, [Opn, Perc], Tissue Expander, NQ
0JH5[0,3]NZ	Insert/SQ Tissue & Fascia, Post Neck, [Opn, Perc], Tissue Expander, NQ
0JH6[0,3]NZ	Insert/SQ Tissue & Fascia, Chest, [Opn, Perc], Tissue Expander, NQ
0JH7[0,3]NZ	Insert/SQ Tissue & Fascia, Back, [Opn, Perc], Tissue Expander, NQ
0JH8[0,3]NZ	Insert/SQ Tissue & Fascia, Abd, [Opn, Perc], Tissue Expander, NQ
0JH9[0,3]NZ	Insert/SQ Tissue & Fascia, Buttock, [Opn, Perc], Tissue Expander, NQ
0JHB[0,3]NZ	Insert/SQ Tissue & Fascia, Perineum, [Opn, Perc], Tissue Expander, NQ
0JHC[0,3]NZ	Insert/SQ Tissue & Fascia, Genitalia, [Opn, Perc], Tissue Expander, NQ
0JHD[0,3]NZ	Insert/SQ Tissue & Fascia, Rt Upr Arm, [Opn, Perc], Tissue Expander, NQ
0JHF[0,3]NZ	Insert/SQ Tissue & Fascia, Lt Upr Arm, [Opn, Perc], Tissue Expander, NQ
0JHG[0,3]NZ	Insert/SQ Tissue & Fascia, Rt Lwr Arm, [Opn, Perc], Tissue Expander, NQ
0JHH[0,3]NZ	Insert/SQ Tissue & Fascia, Lt Lwr Arm, [Opn, Perc], Tissue Expander, NQ
0JHJ[0,3]NZ	Insert/SQ Tissue & Fascia, Rt Hand, [Opn, Perc], Tissue Expander, NQ
0JHK[0,3]NZ	Insert/SQ Tissue & Fascia, Lt Hand, [Opn, Perc], Tissue Expander, NQ
0JHL[0,3]NZ	Insert/SQ Tissue & Fascia, Rt Upr Leg, [Opn, Perc], Tissue Expander, NQ
0JHM[0,3]NZ	Insert/SQ Tissue & Fascia, Lt Upr Leg, [Opn, Perc], Tissue Expander, NQ
0JHN[0,3]NZ	Insert/SQ Tissue & Fascia, Rt Lwr Leg, [Opn, Perc], Tissue Expander, NQ
0JHP[0,3]NZ	Insert/SQ Tissue & Fascia, Lt Lwr Leg, [Opn, Perc], Tissue Expander, NQ
0JHQ[0,3]NZ	Insert/SQ Tissue & Fascia, Rt Foot, [Opn, Perc], Tissue Expander, NQ
0JHR[0,3]NZ	Insert/SQ Tissue & Fascia, Lt Foot, [Opn, Perc], Tissue Expander, NQ
0JX0[0,3]Z[B,C]	Transfer/SQ Tissue & Fascia, Scalp, [Opn, Perc], No Dev, [Skin and SQ Tissue, Skin, SQ Tissue & Fascia]
0JX1[0,3]Z[B,C]	Transfer/SQ Tissue & Fascia, Face, [Opn, Perc], No Dev, [Skin and SQ Tissue, Skin, SQ Tissue & Fascia]
0JX4[0,3]Z[B,C]	Transfer/SQ Tissue & Fascia, Ant Neck, [Opn, Perc], No Dev, [Skin and SQ Tissue, Skin, SQ Tissue & Fascia]
0JX5[0,3]Z[B,C]	Transfer/SQ Tissue & Fascia, Post Neck, [Opn, Perc], No Dev, [Skin and SQ Tissue, Skin, SQ Tissue & Fascia]
0JX6[0,3]Z[B,C]	Transfer/SQ Tissue & Fascia, Chest, [Opn, Perc], No Dev, [Skin and SQ Tissue, Skin, SQ Tissue & Fascia]
0JX7[0,3]Z[B,C]	Transfer/SQ Tissue & Fascia, Back, [Opn, Perc], No Dev, [Skin and SQ Tissue, Skin, SQ Tissue & Fascia]
0JX8[0,3]Z[B,C]	Transfer/SQ Tissue & Fascia, Abd, [Opn, Perc], No Dev, [Skin and SQ Tissue, Skin, SQ Tissue & Fascia]
0JX9[0,3]Z[B,C]	Transfer/SQ Tissue & Fascia, Buttock, [Opn, Perc], No Dev, [Skin and SQ Tissue, Skin, SQ Tissue & Fascia]
0JXB[0,3]Z[B,C]	Transfer/SQ Tissue & Fascia, Perineum, [Opn, Perc], No Dev, [Skin and SQ Tissue, Skin, SQ Tissue & Fascia]
0JXC[0,3]Z[B,C]	Transfer/SQ Tissue & Fascia, Genitalia, [Opn, Perc], No Dev, [Skin and SQ Tissue, Skin, SQ Tissue & Fascia]
0JXD[0,3]Z[B,C]	Transfer/SQ Tissue & Fascia, Rt Upr Arm, [Opn, Perc], No Dev, [Skin and SQ Tissue, Skin, SQ Tissue & Fascia]
0JXF[0,3]Z[B,C]	Transfer/SQ Tissue & Fascia, Lt Upr Arm, [Opn, Perc], No Dev, [Skin and SQ Tissue, Skin, SQ Tissue & Fascia]
0JXG[0,3]Z[B,C]	Transfer/SQ Tissue & Fascia, Rt Lwr Arm, [Opn, Perc], No Dev, [Skin and SQ Tissue, Skin, SQ Tissue & Fascia]
0JXH[0,3]Z[B,C]	Transfer/SQ Tissue & Fascia, Lt Lwr Arm, [Opn, Perc], No Dev, [Skin and SQ Tissue, Skin, SQ Tissue & Fascia]
0JXJ[0,3]Z[B,C]	Transfer/SQ Tissue & Fascia, Rt Hand, [Opn, Perc], No Dev, [Skin and SQ Tissue, Skin, SQ Tissue & Fascia]
0JXK[0,3]Z[B,C]	Transfer/SQ Tissue & Fascia, Lt Hand, [Opn, Perc], No Dev, [Skin and SQ Tissue, Skin, SQ Tissue & Fascia]
0JXL[0,3]Z[B,C]	Transfer/SQ Tissue & Fascia, Rt Upr Leg, [Opn, Perc], No Dev, [Skin and SQ Tissue, Skin, SQ Tissue & Fascia]
0JXM[0,3]Z[B,C]	Transfer/SQ Tissue & Fascia, Lt Upr Leg, [Opn, Perc], No Dev, [Skin and SQ Tissue, Skin, SQ Tissue & Fascia]
0JXN[0,3]Z[B,C]	Transfer/SQ Tissue & Fascia, Rt Lwr Leg, [Opn, Perc], No Dev, [Skin and SQ Tissue, Skin, SQ Tissue & Fascia]
0JXP[0,3]Z[B,C]	Transfer/SQ Tissue & Fascia, Lt Lwr Leg, [Opn, Perc], No Dev, [Skin and SQ Tissue, Skin, SQ Tissue & Fascia]
0JXQ[0,3]Z[B,C]	Transfer/SQ Tissue & Fascia, Rt Foot, [Opn, Perc], No Dev, [Skin and SQ Tissue, Skin, SQ Tissue & Fascia]
0JXR[0,3]Z[B,C]	Transfer/SQ Tissue & Fascia, Lt Foot, [Opn, Perc], No Dev, [Skin and SQ Tissue, Skin, SQ Tissue & Fascia]
0WU0[0,4]7Z	Supl/Head, [Opn, Perc Endo], Auto Tissue Sub, NQ
0WU2[0,4]7Z	Supl/Face, [Opn, Perc Endo], Auto Tissue Sub, NQ
0WU6[0,4]7Z	Supl/Neck, [Opn, Perc Endo], Auto Tissue Sub, NQ
0WUK[0,4]7Z	Supl/Upr Back, [Opn, Perc Endo], Auto Tissue Sub, NQ
0WUL[0,4]7Z	Supl/Lwr Back, [Opn, Perc Endo], Auto Tissue Sub, NQ
0XU2[0,4]7Z	Supl/Shldr Rgn, Rt, [Opn, Perc Endo], Auto Tissue Sub, NQ

Ⓣ **Transfer DRG**   ⓈⓅ **Special Payment**   * **Code Range**   **6th and 7th Character of ZZ = No Device, No Qualifier ZX = No Device, Diagnostic**

ØXU3[Ø,4]7Z	Supl/Shldr Rgn, Lt, [Opn, Perc Endo], Auto Tissue Sub, NQ
ØXU4[Ø,4]7Z	Supl/Axilla, Rt, [Opn, Perc Endo], Auto Tissue Sub, NQ
ØXU5[Ø,4]7Z	Supl/Axilla, Lt, [Opn, Perc Endo], Auto Tissue Sub, NQ
ØXU6[Ø,4]7Z	Supl/Upr Extr, Rt, [Opn, Perc Endo], Auto Tissue Sub, NQ
ØXU7[Ø,4]7Z	Supl/Upr Extr, Lt, [Opn, Perc Endo], Auto Tissue Sub, NQ
ØXU8[Ø,4]7Z	Supl/Upr Arm, Rt, [Opn, Perc Endo], Auto Tissue Sub, NQ
ØXU9[Ø,4]7Z	Supl/Upr Arm, Lt, [Opn, Perc Endo], Auto Tissue Sub, NQ
ØXUB[Ø,4]7Z	Supl/Elbow Rgn, Rt, [Opn, Perc Endo], Auto Tissue Sub, NQ
ØXUC[Ø,4]7Z	Supl/Elbow Rgn, Lt, [Opn, Perc Endo], Auto Tissue Sub, NQ
ØXUD[Ø,4]7Z	Supl/Lwr Arm, Rt, [Opn, Perc Endo], Auto Tissue Sub, NQ
ØXUF[Ø,4]7Z	Supl/Lwr Arm, Lt, [Opn, Perc Endo], Auto Tissue Sub, NQ
ØXUG[Ø,4]7Z	Supl/Wrist Rgn, Rt, [Opn, Perc Endo], Auto Tissue Sub, NQ
ØXUH[Ø,4]7Z	Supl/Wrist Rgn, Lt, [Opn, Perc Endo], Auto Tissue Sub, NQ
ØXUJ[Ø,4]7Z	Supl/Hand, Rt, [Opn, Perc Endo], Auto Tissue Sub, NQ
ØXUK[Ø,4]7Z	Supl/Hand, Lt, [Opn, Perc Endo], Auto Tissue Sub, NQ
ØXUL[Ø,4]7Z	Supl/Thumb, Rt, [Opn, Perc Endo], Auto Tissue Sub, NQ
ØXUM[Ø,4]7Z	Supl/Thumb, Lt, [Opn, Perc Endo], Auto Tissue Sub, NQ
ØXUN[Ø,4]7Z	Supl/Index Finger, Rt, [Opn, Perc Endo], Auto Tissue Sub, NQ
ØXUP[Ø,4]7Z	Supl/Index Finger, Lt, [Opn, Perc Endo], Auto Tissue Sub, NQ
ØXUQ[Ø,4]7Z	Supl/Mid Finger, Rt, [Opn, Perc Endo], Auto Tissue Sub, NQ
ØXUR[Ø,4]7Z	Supl/Mid Finger, Lt, [Opn, Perc Endo], Auto Tissue Sub, NQ
ØXUS[Ø,4]7Z	Supl/Ring Finger, Rt, [Opn, Perc Endo], Auto Tissue Sub, NQ
ØXUT[Ø,4]7Z	Supl/Ring Finger, Lt, [Opn, Perc Endo], Auto Tissue Sub, NQ
ØXUV[Ø,4]7Z	Supl/Little Finger, Rt, [Opn, Perc Endo], Auto Tissue Sub, NQ
ØXUW[Ø,4]7Z	Supl/Little Finger, Lt, [Opn, Perc Endo], Auto Tissue Sub, NQ

OR

Extensive Burns

Principal or Secondary Diagnosis

T31.2[1,2]	Burns involving 20-29% of body surface w/ [10-19, 20-29]% 3rd degree burns
T31.3[1,2,3]	Burns involving 30-39% of body surface w/ [10-19, 20-29, 30-39]% 3rd degree burns
T31.4[1,2,3,4]	Burns involving 40-49% of body surface w/ [10-19, 20-29, 30-39, 40-49]% 3rd degree burns
T31.5[1,2,3,4,5]	Burns involving 50-59% of body surface w/ [10-19, 20-29, 30-39, 40-49, 50-59]% 3rd degree burns
T31.6[1,2,3,4,5,6]	Burns involving 60-69% of body surface w/ [10-19, 20-29, 30-39, 40-49, 50-59, 60-69]% 3rd degree burns
T31.7[1,2,3,4,5,6,7]	Burns involving 70-79% of body surface w/ [10-19, 20-29, 30-39, 40-49, 50-59, 60-69, 70-79]% 3rd degree burns
T31.8[1,2,3,4,5,6,7,8]	Burns involving 80-89% of body surface w/ [10-19, 20-29, 30-39, 40-49, 50-59, 60-69, 70-79, 80-89]% 3rd degree burns
T31.9[1,2,3,4,5,6,7,8,9]	Burns involving 90% or more of body surface w/ [10-19, 20-29, 30-39, 40-49, 50-59, 60-69, 70-79, 80-89, 90 or more]% 3rd degree burns
T32.2[1,2]	Corrosions involving 20-29% of body surface w/ [10-19, 20-29]% 3rd degree burns
T32.3[1,2,3]	Corrosions involving 30-39% of body surface w/ [10-19, 20-29, 30-39]% 3rd degree burns
T32.4[1,2,3,4]	Corrosions involving 40-49% of body surface w/ [10-19, 20-29, 30-39, 40-49]% 3rd degree burns
T32.5[1,2,3,4,5]	Corrosions involving 50-59% of body surface w/ [10-19, 20-29, 30-39, 40-49, 50-59]% 3rd degree burns
T32.6[1,2,3,4,5,6]	Corrosions involving 60-69% of body surface w/ [10-19, 20-29, 30-39, 40-49, 50-59, 60-69]% 3rd degree burns
T32.7[1,2,3,4,5,6,7]	Corrosions involving 70-79% of body surface w/ [10-19, 20-29, 30-39, 40-49, 50-59, 60-69, 70-79]% 3rd degree burns
T32.8[1,2,3,4,5,6,7,8]	Corrosions involving 80-89% of body surface w/ [10-19, 20-29, 30-39, 40-49, 50-59, 60-69, 70-79, 80-89]% 3rd degree burns
T32.9[1,2,3,4,5,6,7,8,9]	Corrosions involving 90% or more of body surface w/ [10-19, 20-29, 30-39, 40-49, 50-59, 60-69, 70-79, 80-89, 90 or more]% 3rd degree burns

---

DRG 928 Full Thickness Burn with Skin Graft or Inhalation Injury with CC/MCC

GMLOS 11.3   AMLOS 15.4   RW 5.7399

Principal or Secondary Diagnosis

T20.30XA	Burn 3rd degree of head, face, and neck, unsp site, init
T20.31[1,2,9]A	Burn of 3rd degree of [rt, lt, unsp] ear (any part, except ear drum), init enc
T20.39XA	Burn of 3rd deg mu sites of head, face, and neck, init
T20.3[2,3,4,5,6,7]XA	Burn of 3rd degree of [lip(s), chin, nose (septum), scalp (any part), forehead and cheek, neck], init enc
T20.70XA	Corrosion 3rd degree of head, face, and neck, unsp site, init
T20.71[1,2,9]A	Corrosion of 3rd degree of [rt, lt, unsp] ear (any part, except ear drum), init enc

T20.79XA	Corrosion of 3rd deg mu sites of head, face, and neck, init
T20.7[2,3,4,5,6,7]XA	Corrosion of 3rd degree of [lip(s), chin, nose (septum), scalp (any part), forehead and cheek, neck], init enc
T21.3[0,1,2,3,4,5,6,7,9]XA	Burn of 3rd degree of [trunk, unsp site, chest wall, abd wall, upr back, lwr back, buttock, male genital rgn, femal genital rgn, oth site of trunk], init enc
T21.7[0,1,2,3,4,5,6,7,9]XA	Corrosion of 3rd degree of [trunk, unsp site, chest wall, abd wall, upr back, lwr back, buttock, male genital rgn, femal genital rgn, oth site of trunk], init enc
T22.30XA	Burn 3rd deg of shldr/up lmb, ex wrs/hnd, unsp site, init
T22.31[1,2,9]A	Burn of 3rd degree of [rt, lt, unsp] forearm, init enc
T22.32[1,2,9]A	Burn of 3rd degree of [rt, lt, unsp] elbow, init enc
T22.33[1,2,9]A	Burn of 3rd degree of [rt, lt, unsp] upr arm, init enc
T22.34[1,2,9]A	Burn of 3rd degree of [rt, lt, unsp] axilla, init enc
T22.35[1,2,9]A	Burn of 3rd degree of [rt, lt, unsp] shldr, init enc
T22.36[1,2,9]A	Burn of 3rd degree of [rt, lt, unsp] scapular rgn, init enc
T22.39[1,2,9]A	Burn of 3rd degree of multi sites of [rt, lt, unsp] shldr and upr limb, except wrist and hand, init enc
T22.70XA	Corrosion 3rd deg of shldr/up lmb, ex wrs/hnd, unsp site, init
T22.71[1,2,9]A	Corrosion of 3rd degree of [rt, lt, unsp] forearm, init enc
T22.72[1,2,9]A	Corrosion of 3rd degree of [rt, lt, unsp] elbow, init enc
T22.73[1,2,9]A	Corrosion of 3rd degree of [rt, lt, unsp] upr arm, init enc
T22.74[1,2,9]A	Corrosion of 3rd degree of [rt, lt, unsp] axilla, init enc
T22.75[1,2,9]A	Corrosion of 3rd degree of [rt, lt, unsp] shldr, init enc
T22.76[1,2,9]A	Corrosion of 3rd degree of [rt, lt, unsp] scapular rgn, init enc
T22.79[1,2,9]A	Corrosion of 3rd degree of multi sites of [rt, lt, unsp] shldr and upr limb, except wrist and hand, init enc
T23.30[1,2,9]A	Burn of 3rd degree of [rt, lt, unsp] hand, unsp site, init enc
T23.31[1,2,9]A	Burn of 3rd degree of [rt, lt, unsp] thumb (nail), init enc
T23.32[1,2,9]A	Burn of 3rd degree of single [rt, lt, unsp] finger (nail) except thumb, init enc
T23.33[1,2,9]A	Burn of 3rd degree of multi [rt, lt, unsp] fingers (nail), not incl* thumb, init enc
T23.34[1,2,9]A	Burn of 3rd degree of multi [rt, lt, unsp] fingers (nail), incl* thumb, init enc
T23.35[1,2,9]A	Burn of 3rd degree of [rt, lt, unsp] palm, init enc
T23.36[1,2,9]A	Burn of 3rd degree of back of [rt, lt, unsp] hand, init enc
T23.37[1,2,9]A	Burn of 3rd degree of [rt, lt, unsp] wrist, init enc
T23.39[1,2,9]A	Burn of 3rd degree of multi sites of [rt, lt, unsp] wrist and hand, init enc
T23.70[1,2,9]A	Corrosion of 3rd degree of [rt, lt, unsp] hand, unsp site, init enc
T23.71[1,2,9]A	Corrosion of 3rd degree of [rt, lt, unsp] thumb (nail), init enc
T23.72[1,2,9]A	Corrosion of 3rd degree of single [rt, lt, unsp] finger (nail) except thumb, init enc
T23.73[1,2,9]A	Corrosion of 3rd degree of multi [rt, lt, unsp] fingers (nail), not incl* thumb, init enc
T23.74[1,2,9]A	Corrosion of 3rd degree of multi [rt, lt, unsp] fingers (nail), incl* thumb, init enc
T23.75[1,2,9]A	Corrosion of 3rd degree of [rt, lt, unsp] palm, init enc
T23.76[1,2,9]A	Corrosion of 3rd degree of back of [rt, lt, unsp] hand, init enc
T23.77[1,2,9]A	Corrosion of 3rd degree of [rt, lt, unsp] wrist, init enc
T23.79[1,2,9]A	Corrosion of 3rd degree of multi sites of [rt, lt, unsp] wrist and hand, init enc
T24.30[1,2,9]A	Burn of 3rd degree of unsp site of [rt, lt, unsp] lwr limb, except ankle and foot, init enc
T24.31[1,2,9]A	Burn of 3rd degree of [rt, lt, unsp] thigh, init enc
T24.32[1,2,9]A	Burn of 3rd degree of [rt, lt, unsp] knee, init enc
T24.33[1,2,9]A	Burn of 3rd degree of [rt, lt, unsp] lwr leg, init enc
T24.39[1,2,9]A	Burn of 3rd degree of multi sites of [rt, lt, unsp] lwr limb, except ankle and foot, init enc
T24.70[1,2,9]A	Corrosion of 3rd degree of unsp site of [rt, lt, unsp] lwr limb, except ankle and foot, init enc
T24.71[1,2,9]A	Corrosion of 3rd degree of [rt, lt, unsp] thigh, init enc
T24.72[1,2,9]A	Corrosion of 3rd degree of [rt, lt, unsp] knee, init enc
T24.73[1,2,9]A	Corrosion of 3rd degree of [rt, lt, unsp] lwr leg, init enc
T24.79[1,2,9]A	Corrosion of 3rd degree of multi sites of [rt, lt, unsp] lwr limb, except ankle and foot, init enc
T25.31[1,2,9]A	Burn of 3rd degree of [rt, lt, unsp] ankle, init enc
T25.32[1,2,9]A	Burn of 3rd degree of [rt, lt, unsp] foot, init enc
T25.33[1,2,9]A	Burn of 3rd degree of [rt, lt, unsp] toe(s) (nail), init enc
T25.39[1,2,9]A	Burn of 3rd degree of multi sites of [rt, lt, unsp] ankle and foot, init enc
T25.71[1,2,9]A	Corrosion of 3rd degree of [rt, lt, unsp] ankle, init enc
T25.72[1,2,9]A	Corrosion of 3rd degree of [rt, lt, unsp] foot, init enc
T25.73[1,2,9]A	Corrosion of 3rd degree of [rt, lt, unsp] toe(s) (nail), init enc
T25.79[1,2,9]A	Corrosion of 3rd degree of multi sites of [rt, lt, unsp] ankle and foot, init enc
T26.2[0,1,2]XA	Burn w/ resulting rupture and destr of [unsp, rt, lt] eyeball, init enc
T31.11	Burns of 10-19% of body surface w 10-19% 3rd degree burns

MDC 22: Burns—SURGICAL

T32.11	Corrosion 1Ø-19% of body surface w 1Ø-19% 3rd degree corrosion

AND

Operating Room Procedures

ØH8ØXZZ	Div of Scalp Skin, Ext Appr
ØH81XZZ	Div of Face Skin, Ext Appr
ØH84XZZ	Div of Neck Skin, Ext Appr
ØHB5XZZ	Exc of Chest Skin, Ext Appr
ØHB6XZZ	Exc of Back Skin, Ext Appr
ØHB7XZZ	Exc of Abd Skin, Ext Appr
ØHB8XZZ	Exc of Buttock Skin, Ext Appr
ØHBAXZZ	Exc of Genitalia Skin, Ext Appr
ØHBBXZZ	Exc of Rt Upr Arm Skin, Ext Appr
ØHBCXZZ	Exc of Lt Upr Arm Skin, Ext Appr
ØHBDXZZ	Exc of Rt Lwr Arm Skin, Ext Appr
ØHBEXZZ	Exc of Lt Lwr Arm Skin, Ext Appr
ØHBFXZZ	Exc of Rt Hand Skin, Ext Appr
ØHBGXZZ	Exc of Lt Hand Skin, Ext Appr
ØHBHXZZ	Exc of Rt Upr Leg Skin, Ext Appr
ØHBJXZZ	Exc of Lt Upr Leg Skin, Ext Appr
ØHBKXZZ	Exc of Rt Lwr Leg Skin, Ext Appr
ØHBLXZZ	Exc of Lt Lwr Leg Skin, Ext Appr
ØHBMXZZ	Exc of Rt Foot Skin, Ext Appr
ØHBNXZZ	Exc of Lt Foot Skin, Ext Appr
ØHRØ*	Replace/Skin, Scalp
ØHR1*	Replace/Skin, Face
ØHR4*	Replace/Skin, Neck
ØHR5*	Replace/Skin, Chest
ØHR6*	Replace/Skin, Back
ØHR7*	Replace/Skin, Abd
ØHR8*	Replace/Skin, Buttock
ØHRA*	Replace/Skin, Genitalia
ØHRB*	Replace/Skin, Rt Upr Arm
ØHRC*	Replace/Skin, Lt Upr Arm
ØHRD*	Replace/Skin, Rt Lwr Arm
ØHRE*	Replace/Skin, Lt Lwr Arm
ØHRF*	Replace/Skin, Rt Hand
ØHRG*	Replace/Skin, Lt Hand
ØHRH*	Replace/Skin, Rt Upr Leg
ØHRJ*	Replace/Skin, Lt Upr Leg
ØHRK*	Replace/Skin, Rt Lwr Leg
ØHRL*	Replace/Skin, Lt Lwr Leg
ØHRM*	Replace/Skin, Rt Foot
ØHRN*	Replace/Skin, Lt Foot
ØHRTX[7,K]Z	Replace/Breast, Rt, Ext, [Auto Tissue Sub, Nonauto Tissue Sub], NQ
ØHRUX[7,K]Z	Replace/Breast, Lt, Ext, [Auto Tissue Sub, Nonauto Tissue Sub], NQ
ØHRVX[7,K]Z	Replace/Breast, Bilat, Ext, [Auto Tissue Sub, Nonauto Tissue Sub], NQ
ØHXØXZZ	Transfer Scalp Skin, Ext Appr
ØHX1XZZ	Transfer Face Skin, Ext Appr
ØHX4XZZ	Transfer Neck Skin, Ext Appr
ØHX5XZZ	Transfer Chest Skin, Ext Appr
ØHX6XZZ	Transfer Back Skin, Ext Appr
ØHX7XZZ	Transfer Abd Skin, Ext Appr
ØHX8XZZ	Transfer Buttock Skin, Ext Appr
ØHX9XZZ	Transfer Perineum Skin, Ext Appr
ØHXAXZZ	Transfer Genitalia Skin, Ext Appr
ØHXBXZZ	Transfer Rt Upr Arm Skin, Ext Appr
ØHXCXZZ	Transfer Lt Upr Arm Skin, Ext Appr
ØHXDXZZ	Transfer Rt Lwr Arm Skin, Ext Appr
ØHXEXZZ	Transfer Lt Lwr Arm Skin, Ext Appr
ØHXFXZZ	Transfer Rt Hand Skin, Ext Appr
ØHXGXZZ	Transfer Lt Hand Skin, Ext Appr
ØHXHXZZ	Transfer Rt Upr Leg Skin, Ext Appr
ØHXJXZZ	Transfer Lt Upr Leg Skin, Ext Appr
ØHXKXZZ	Transfer Rt Lwr Leg Skin, Ext Appr
ØHXLXZZ	Transfer Lt Lwr Leg Skin, Ext Appr
ØHXMXZZ	Transfer Rt Foot Skin, Ext Appr
ØHXNXZZ	Transfer Lt Foot Skin, Ext Appr
ØJHØ*	Insert/SQ Tissue & Fascia, Scalp
ØJH1*	Insert/SQ Tissue & Fascia, Face
ØJH4*	Insert/SQ Tissue & Fascia, Ant Neck
ØJH5*	Insert/SQ Tissue & Fascia, Posterior Neck
ØJH6[Ø,3]NZ	Insert/SQ Tissue & Fascia, Chest, [Opn, Perc], Tissue Expander, NQ
ØJH7[Ø,3]NZ	Insert/SQ Tissue & Fascia, Back, [Opn, Perc], Tissue Expander, NQ
ØJH8[Ø,3]NZ	Insert/SQ Tissue & Fascia, Abd, [Opn, Perc], Tissue Expander, NQ
ØJH9*	Insert/SQ Tissue & Fascia, Buttock
ØJHB*	Insert/SQ Tissue & Fascia, Perineum
ØJHC*	Insert/SQ Tissue & Fascia, Pelvic Region
ØJHD[Ø,3]NZ	Insert/SQ Tissue & Fascia, Rt Upr Arm, [Opn, Perc], Tissue Expander, NQ
ØJHF[Ø,3]NZ	Insert/SQ Tissue & Fascia, Lt Upr Arm, [Opn, Perc], Tissue Expander, NQ
ØJHG[Ø,3]NZ	Insert/SQ Tissue & Fascia, Rt Lwr Arm, [Opn, Perc], Tissue Expander, NQ
ØJHH[Ø,3]NZ	Insert/SQ Tissue & Fascia, Lt Lwr Arm, [Opn, Perc], Tissue Expander, NQ
ØJHJ*	Insert/SQ Tissue & Fascia, Rt Hand
ØJHK*	Insert/SQ Tissue & Fascia, Lt Hand
ØJHL[Ø,3]NZ	Insert/SQ Tissue & Fascia, Rt Upr Leg, [Opn, Perc], Tissue Expander, NQ
ØJHM[Ø,3]NZ	Insert/SQ Tissue & Fascia, Lt Upr Leg, [Opn, Perc], Tissue Expander, NQ
ØJHN[Ø,3]NZ	Insert/SQ Tissue & Fascia, Rt Lwr Leg, [Opn, Perc], Tissue Expander, NQ
ØJHP[Ø,3]NZ	Insert/SQ Tissue & Fascia, Lt Lwr Leg, [Opn, Perc], Tissue Expander, NQ
ØJHQ*	Insert/SQ Tissue & Fascia, Rt Foot
ØJHR*	Insert/SQ Tissue & Fascia, Lt Foot
ØJXØ[Ø,3]Z[B,C]	Transfer/SQ Tissue & Fascia, Scalp, [Opn, Perc], No Dev, [Skin and SQ Tissue, Skin, SQ Tissue & Fascia]
ØJX1[Ø,3]Z[B,C]	Transfer/SQ Tissue & Fascia, Face, [Opn, Perc], No Dev, [Skin and SQ Tissue, Skin, SQ Tissue & Fascia]
ØJX4[Ø,3]Z[B,C]	Transfer/SQ Tissue & Fascia, Ant Neck, [Opn, Perc], No Dev, [Skin and SQ Tissue, Skin, SQ Tissue & Fascia]
ØJX5[Ø,3]Z[B,C]	Transfer/SQ Tissue & Fascia, Post Neck, [Opn, Perc], No Dev, [Skin and SQ Tissue, Skin, SQ Tissue & Fascia]
ØJX6[Ø,3]Z[B,C]	Transfer/SQ Tissue & Fascia, Chest, [Opn, Perc], No Dev, [Skin and SQ Tissue, Skin, SQ Tissue & Fascia]
ØJX7[Ø,3]Z[B,C]	Transfer/SQ Tissue & Fascia, Back, [Opn, Perc], No Dev, [Skin and SQ Tissue, Skin, SQ Tissue & Fascia]
ØJX8[Ø,3]Z[B,C]	Transfer/SQ Tissue & Fascia, Abd, [Opn, Perc], No Dev, [Skin and SQ Tissue, Skin, SQ Tissue & Fascia]
ØJX9[Ø,3]Z[B,C]	Transfer/SQ Tissue & Fascia, Buttock, [Opn, Perc], No Dev, [Skin and SQ Tissue, Skin, SQ Tissue & Fascia]
ØJXB[Ø,3]Z[B,C]	Transfer/SQ Tissue & Fascia, Perineum, [Opn, Perc], No Dev, [Skin and SQ Tissue, Skin, SQ Tissue & Fascia]
ØJXC[Ø,3]Z[B,C]	Transfer/SQ Tissue & Fascia, Genitalia, [Opn, Perc], No Dev, [Skin and SQ Tissue, Skin, SQ Tissue & Fascia]
ØJXD[Ø,3]Z[B,C]	Transfer/SQ Tissue & Fascia, Rt Upr Arm, [Opn, Perc], No Dev, [Skin and SQ Tissue, Skin, SQ Tissue & Fascia]
ØJXF[Ø,3]Z[B,C]	Transfer/SQ Tissue & Fascia, Lt Upr Arm, [Opn, Perc], No Dev, [Skin and SQ Tissue, Skin, SQ Tissue & Fascia]
ØJXG[Ø,3]Z[B,C]	Transfer/SQ Tissue & Fascia, Rt Lwr Arm, [Opn, Perc], No Dev, [Skin and SQ Tissue, Skin, SQ Tissue & Fascia]
ØJXH[Ø,3]Z[B,C]	Transfer/SQ Tissue & Fascia, Lt Lwr Arm, [Opn, Perc], No Dev, [Skin and SQ Tissue, Skin, SQ Tissue & Fascia]
ØJXJ[Ø,3]Z[B,C]	Transfer/SQ Tissue & Fascia, Rt Hand, [Opn, Perc], No Dev, [Skin and SQ Tissue, Skin, SQ Tissue & Fascia]
ØJXK[Ø,3]Z[B,C]	Transfer/SQ Tissue & Fascia, Lt Hand, [Opn, Perc], No Dev, [Skin and SQ Tissue, Skin, SQ Tissue & Fascia]
ØJXL[Ø,3]Z[B,C]	Transfer/SQ Tissue & Fascia, Rt Upr Leg, [Opn, Perc], No Dev, [Skin and SQ Tissue, Skin, SQ Tissue & Fascia]
ØJXM[Ø,3]Z[B,C]	Transfer/SQ Tissue & Fascia, Lt Upr Leg, [Opn, Perc], No Dev, [Skin and SQ Tissue, Skin, SQ Tissue & Fascia]
ØJXN[Ø,3]Z[B,C]	Transfer/SQ Tissue & Fascia, Rt Lwr Leg, [Opn, Perc], No Dev, [Skin and SQ Tissue, Skin, SQ Tissue & Fascia]
ØJXP[Ø,3]Z[B,C]	Transfer/SQ Tissue & Fascia, Lt Lwr Leg, [Opn, Perc], No Dev, [Skin and SQ Tissue, Skin, SQ Tissue & Fascia]
ØJXQ[Ø,3]Z[B,C]	Transfer/SQ Tissue & Fascia, Rt Foot, [Opn, Perc], No Dev, [Skin and SQ Tissue, Skin, SQ Tissue & Fascia]
ØJXR[Ø,3]Z[B,C]	Transfer/SQ Tissue & Fascia, Lt Foot, [Opn, Perc], No Dev, [Skin and SQ Tissue, Skin, SQ Tissue & Fascia]
ØWUØ[Ø,4]7Z	Supl/Head, [Opn, Perc Endo], Auto Tissue Sub, NQ
ØWU2[Ø,4]7Z	Supl/Face, [Opn, Perc Endo], Auto Tissue Sub, NQ
ØWU6[Ø,4]7Z	Supl/Neck, [Opn, Perc Endo], Auto Tissue Sub, NQ
ØWUK[Ø,4]7Z	Supl/Upr Back, [Opn, Perc Endo], Auto Tissue Sub, NQ
ØWUL[Ø,4]7Z	Supl/Lwr Back, [Opn, Perc Endo], Auto Tissue Sub, NQ
ØXU2[Ø,4]7Z	Supl/Shldr Rgn, Rt, [Opn, Perc Endo], Auto Tissue Sub, NQ
ØXU3[Ø,4]7Z	Supl/Shldr Rgn, Lt, [Opn, Perc Endo], Auto Tissue Sub, NQ
ØXU4[Ø,4]7Z	Supl/Axilla, Rt, [Opn, Perc Endo], Auto Tissue Sub, NQ
ØXU5[Ø,4]7Z	Supl/Axilla, Lt, [Opn, Perc Endo], Auto Tissue Sub, NQ
ØXU6[Ø,4]7Z	Supl/Upr Extr, Rt, [Opn, Perc Endo], Auto Tissue Sub, NQ
ØXU7[Ø,4]7Z	Supl/Upr Extr, Lt, [Opn, Perc Endo], Auto Tissue Sub, NQ

T **Transfer DRG**   SP **Special Payment**   * **Code Range**   **6th and 7th Character of ZZ = No Device, No Qualifier ZX = No Device, Diagnostic**

ØXU8[0,4]7Z	Supl/Upr Arm, Rt, [Opn, Perc Endo], Auto Tissue Sub, NQ
ØXU9[0,4]7Z	Supl/Upr Arm, Lt, [Opn, Perc Endo], Auto Tissue Sub, NQ
ØXUB[0,4]7Z	Supl/Elbow Rgn, Rt, [Opn, Perc Endo], Auto Tissue Sub, NQ
ØXUC[0,4]7Z	Supl/Elbow Rgn, Lt, [Opn, Perc Endo], Auto Tissue Sub, NQ
ØXUD[0,4]7Z	Supl/Lwr Arm, Rt, [Opn, Perc Endo], Auto Tissue Sub, NQ
ØXUF[0,4]7Z	Supl/Lwr Arm, Lt, [Opn, Perc Endo], Auto Tissue Sub, NQ
ØXUG[0,4]7Z	Supl/Wrist Rgn, Rt, [Opn, Perc Endo], Auto Tissue Sub, NQ
ØXUH[0,4]7Z	Supl/Wrist Rgn, Lt, [Opn, Perc Endo], Auto Tissue Sub, NQ
ØXUJ[0,4]7Z	Supl/Hand, Rt, [Opn, Perc Endo], Auto Tissue Sub, NQ
ØXUK[0,4]7Z	Supl/Hand, Lt, [Opn, Perc Endo], Auto Tissue Sub, NQ
ØXUL[0,4]7Z	Supl/Thumb, Rt, [Opn, Perc Endo], Auto Tissue Sub, NQ
ØXUM[0,4]7Z	Supl/Thumb, Lt, [Opn, Perc Endo], Auto Tissue Sub, NQ
ØXUN[0,4]7Z	Supl/Index Finger, Rt, [Opn, Perc Endo], Auto Tissue Sub, NQ
ØXUP[0,4]7Z	Supl/Index Finger, Lt, [Opn, Perc Endo], Auto Tissue Sub, NQ
ØXUQ[0,4]7Z	Supl/Mid Finger, Rt, [Opn, Perc Endo], Auto Tissue Sub, NQ
ØXUR[0,4]7Z	Supl/Mid Finger, Lt, [Opn, Perc Endo], Auto Tissue Sub, NQ
ØXUS[0,4]7Z	Supl/Ring Finger, Rt, [Opn, Perc Endo], Auto Tissue Sub, NQ
ØXUT[0,4]7Z	Supl/Ring Finger, Lt, [Opn, Perc Endo], Auto Tissue Sub, NQ
ØXUV[0,4]7Z	Supl/Little Finger, Rt, [Opn, Perc Endo], Auto Tissue Sub, NQ
ØXUW[0,4]7Z	Supl/Little Finger, Lt, [Opn, Perc Endo], Auto Tissue Sub, NQ

OR

Secondary Diagnosis

J70.5	Respiratory conditions d/t smoke inhalation
J95.1	Acute pulmn insufficiency following thoracic surgery
J95.2	Acute pulmn insufficiency following nonthoracic surgery
J95.3	Chr pulmn insufficiency following surgery
J95.82*	Postprocedural respiratory failure
J96.0*	Acute respiratory failure
J96.2*	Acute and chr respiratory failure
J96.9*	Respiratory failure, unsp
T27.0XXA	Burn of larynx and trachea, init enc
T27.1XXA	Burn involving larynx and trachea with lung, init enc
T27.2XXA	Burn of oth parts of respiratory tract, init enc
T27.3XXA	Burn of respiratory tract, part unsp, init enc
T27.4XXA	Corrosion of larynx and trachea, init enc
T27.5XXA	Corrosion involving larynx and trachea w lung, init enc
T27.6XXA	Corrosion of oth parts of respiratory tract, init enc
T27.7XXA	Corrosion of respiratory tract, part unsp, init enc
T59.81[1,2,3,4]A	Txc effct of smoke, [accid (unintentional), intentional self-harm, assault, undetermined], init enc
T59.89[1,2,3,4]A	Txc effct of oth spec gases, fumes and vapors, [accid (unintentional), intentional self-harm, assault, undetermined], init enc
T59.9[1,2,3,4]XA	Txc effct of unsp gases, fumes and vapors, [accid (unintentional), intentional self harm, assault, undetermined], init enc

DRG 929 **Full Thickness Burn with Skin Graft or Inhalation Injury without CC/MCC**
GMLOS 5.5   **AMLOS 7.5**   **RW 2.4661**

Select prinicpal or secondary diagnosis AND EITHER operating room procedure OR secondary diagnosis of inhalation injury listed under DRG 928

MEDICAL

▲DRG 933 **Extensive Burns or Full Thickness Burns with Mechanical Ventilation >96 Hours without Skin Graft**
GMLOS 2.6   **AMLOS 5.9**   **RW 2.8685**

Full-Thickness Burns with MV >96 hrs

Principal or Secondary Diagnosis

T20.30XA	Burn 3rd degree of head, face, and neck, unsp site, init
T20.31[1,2,9]A	Burn of 3rd degree of [rt, lt, unsp] ear (any part, except ear drum), init enc
T20.39XA	Burn of 3rd deg mu sites of head, face, and neck, init
T20.3[2,3,4,5,6,7]XA	Burn of 3rd degree of [lip(s), chin, nose (septum), scalp (any part), forehead and cheek, neck], init enc
T20.70XA	Corrosion 3rd degree of head, face, and neck, unsp site, init
T20.71[1,2,9]A	Corrosion of 3rd degree of [rt, lt, unsp] ear (any part, except ear drum), init enc
T20.79XA	Corrosion of 3rd deg mu sites of head, face, and neck, init
T20.7[2,3,4,5,6,7]XA	Corrosion of 3rd degree of [lip(s), chin, nose (septum), scalp (any part), forehead and cheek, neck], init enc

T21.3[0,1,2,3,4,5,6,7,9]XA	Burn of 3rd degree of [trunk, unsp site, chest wall, abd wall, upr back, lwr back, buttock, male genital rgn, femal genital rgn, oth site of trunk], init enc
T21.7[0,1,2,3,4,5,6,7,9]XA	Corrosion of 3rd degree of [trunk, unsp site, chest wall, abd wall, upr back, lwr back, buttock, male genital rgn, femal genital rgn, oth site of trunk], init enc
T22.30XA	Burn 3rd deg of shldr/up lmb, ex wrs/hnd, unsp site, init
T22.31[1,2,9]A	Burn of 3rd degree of [rt, lt, unsp] forearm, init enc
T22.32[1,2,9]A	Burn of 3rd degree of [rt, lt, unsp] elbow, init enc
T22.33[1,2,9]A	Burn of 3rd degree of [rt, lt, unsp] upr arm, init enc
T22.34[1,2,9]A	Burn of 3rd degree of [rt, lt, unsp] axilla, init enc
T22.35[1,2,9]A	Burn of 3rd degree of [rt, lt, unsp] shldr, init enc
T22.36[1,2,9]A	Burn of 3rd degree of [rt, lt, unsp] scapular rgn, init enc
T22.39[1,2,9]A	Burn of 3rd degree of multi sites of [rt, lt, unsp] shldr and upr limb, except wrist and hand, init enc
T22.70XA	Corrosion 3rd deg of shldr/up lmb, ex wrs/hnd, unsp site, init
T22.71[1,2,9]A	Corrosion of 3rd degree of [rt, lt, unsp] forearm, init enc
T22.72[1,2,9]A	Corrosion of 3rd degree of [rt, lt, unsp] elbow, init enc
T22.73[1,2,9]A	Corrosion of 3rd degree of [rt, lt, unsp] upr arm, init enc
T22.74[1,2,9]A	Corrosion of 3rd degree of [rt, lt, unsp] axilla, init enc
T22.75[1,2,9]A	Corrosion of 3rd degree of [rt, lt, unsp] shldr, init enc
T22.76[1,2,9]A	Corrosion of 3rd degree of [rt, lt, unsp] scapular rgn, init enc
T22.79[1,2,9]A	Corrosion of 3rd degree of multi sites of [rt, lt, unsp] shldr and upr limb, except wrist and hand, init enc
T23.30[1,2,9]A	Burn of 3rd degree of [rt, lt, unsp] hand, unsp site, init enc
T23.31[1,2,9]A	Burn of 3rd degree of [rt, lt, unsp] thumb (nail), init enc
T23.32[1,2,9]A	Burn of 3rd degree of single [rt, lt, unsp] finger (nail) except thumb, init enc
T23.33[1,2,9]A	Burn of 3rd degree of multi [rt, lt, unsp] fingers (nail), not incl* thumb, init enc
T23.34[1,2,9]A	Burn of 3rd degree of multi [rt, lt, unsp] fingers (nail), incl* thumb, init enc
T23.35[1,2,9]A	Burn of 3rd degree of [rt, lt, unsp] palm, init enc
T23.36[1,2,9]A	Burn of 3rd degree of back of [rt, lt, unsp] hand, init enc
T23.37[1,2,9]A	Burn of 3rd degree of [rt, lt, unsp] wrist, init enc
T23.39[1,2,9]A	Burn of 3rd degree of multi sites of [rt, lt, unsp] wrist and hand, init enc
T23.70[1,2,9]A	Corrosion of 3rd degree of [rt, lt, unsp] hand, unsp site, init enc
T23.71[1,2,9]A	Corrosion of 3rd degree of [rt, lt, unsp] thumb (nail), init enc
T23.72[1,2,9]A	Corrosion of 3rd degree of single [rt, lt, unsp] finger (nail) except thumb, init enc
T23.73[1,2,9]A	Corrosion of 3rd degree of multi [rt, lt, unsp] fingers (nail), not incl* thumb, init enc
T23.74[1,2,9]A	Corrosion of 3rd degree of multi [rt, lt, unsp] fingers (nail), incl* thumb, init enc
T23.75[1,2,9]A	Corrosion of 3rd degree of [rt, lt, unsp] palm, init enc
T23.76[1,2,9]A	Corrosion of 3rd degree of back of [rt, lt, unsp] hand, init enc
T23.77[1,2,9]A	Corrosion of 3rd degree of [rt, lt, unsp] wrist, init enc
T23.79[1,2,9]A	Corrosion of 3rd degree of multi sites of [rt, lt, unsp] wrist and hand, init enc
T24.30[1,2,9]A	Burn of 3rd degree of unsp site of [rt, lt, unsp] lwr limb, except ankle and foot, init enc
T24.31[1,2,9]A	Burn of 3rd degree of [rt, lt, unsp] thigh, init enc
T24.32[1,2,9]A	Burn of 3rd degree of [rt, lt, unsp] knee, init enc
T24.33[1,2,9]A	Burn of 3rd degree of [rt, lt, unsp] lwr leg, init enc
T24.39[1,2,9]A	Burn of 3rd degree of multi sites of [rt, lt, unsp] lwr limb, except ankle and foot, init enc
T24.70[1,2,9]A	Corrosion of 3rd degree of unsp site of [rt, lt, unsp] lwr limb, except ankle and foot, init enc
T24.71[1,2,9]A	Corrosion of 3rd degree of [rt, lt, unsp] thigh, init enc
T24.72[1,2,9]A	Corrosion of 3rd degree of [rt, lt, unsp] knee, init enc
T24.73[1,2,9]A	Corrosion of 3rd degree of [rt, lt, unsp] lwr leg, init enc
T24.79[1,2,9]A	Corrosion of 3rd degree of multi sites of [rt, lt, unsp] lwr limb, except ankle and foot, init enc
T25.31[1,2,9]A	Burn of 3rd degree of [rt, lt, unsp] ankle, init enc
T25.32[1,2,9]A	Burn of 3rd degree of [rt, lt, unsp] foot, init enc
T25.33[1,2,9]A	Burn of 3rd degree of [rt, lt, unsp] toe(s) (nail), init enc
T25.39[1,2,9]A	Burn of 3rd degree of multi sites of [rt, lt, unsp] ankle and foot, init enc
T25.71[1,2,9]A	Corrosion of 3rd degree of [rt, lt, unsp] ankle, init enc
T25.72[1,2,9]A	Corrosion of 3rd degree of [rt, lt, unsp] foot, init enc
T25.73[1,2,9]A	Corrosion of 3rd degree of [rt, lt, unsp] toe(s) (nail), init enc
T25.79[1,2,9]A	Corrosion of 3rd degree of multi sites of [rt, lt, unsp] ankle and foot, init enc
T26.2[0,1,2]XA	Burn w/ resulting rupture and destr of [unsp, rt, lt] eyeball, init enc
T31.11	Burns of 10-19% of body surface w 10-19% 3rd degree burns
T32.11	Corrosion 10-19% of body surface w 10-19% 3rd degree corrosion

MDC 22: Burns—MEDICAL

MDC 22: Burns—MEDICAL

AND

Nonoperating Room Procedure

5A1955Z   Respiratory Ventilation, > 96 Consecutive Hrs
OR

Extensive Burns

Principal or Secondary Diagnosis

T31.2[1,2]   Burns involving 20-29% of body surface w/ [10-19, 20-29]% 3rd degree burns
T31.3[1,2,3]   Burns involving 30-39% of body surface w/ [10-19, 20-29, 30-39]% 3rd degree burns
T31.4[1,2,3,4]   Burns involving 40-49% of body surface w/ [10-19, 20-29, 30-39, 40-49]% 3rd degree burns
T31.5[1,2,3,4,5]   Burns involving 50-59% of body surface w/ [10-19, 20-29, 30-39, 40-49, 50-59]% 3rd degree burns
T31.6[1,2,3,4,5,6]   Burns involving 60-69% of body surface w/ [10-19, 20-29, 30-39, 40-49, 50-59, 60-69]% 3rd degree burns
T31.7[1,2,3,4,5,6,7]   Burns involving 70-79% of body surface w/ [10-19, 20-29, 30-39, 40-49, 50-59, 60-69, 70-79]% 3rd degree burns
T31.8[1,2,3,4,5,6,7,8]   Burns involving 80-89% of body surface w/ [10-19, 20-29, 30-39, 40-49, 50-59, 60-69, 70-79, 80-89]% 3rd degree burns
T31.9[1,2,3,4,5,6,7,8,9]   Burns involving 90% or more of body surface w/ [10-19, 20-29, 30-39, 40-49, 50-59, 60-69, 70-79, 80-89, 90 or more]% 3rd degree burns
T32.2[1,2]   Corrosions involving 20-29% of body surface w/ [10-19, 20-29]% 3rd degree burns
T32.3[1,2,3]   Corrosions involving 30-39% of body surface w/ [10-19, 20-29, 30-39]% 3rd degree burns
T32.4[1,2,3,4]   Corrosions involving 40-49% of body surface w/ [10-19, 20-29, 30-39, 40-49]% 3rd degree burns
T32.5[1,2,3,4,5]   Corrosions involving 50-59% of body surface w/ [10-19, 20-29, 30-39, 40-49, 50-59]% 3rd degree burns
T32.6[1,2,3,4,5,6]   Corrosions involving 60-69% of body surface w/ [10-19, 20-29, 30-39, 40-49, 50-59, 60-69]% 3rd degree burns
T32.7[1,2,3,4,5,6,7]   Corrosions involving 70-79% of body surface w/ [10-19, 20-29, 30-39, 40-49, 50-59, 60-69, 70-79]% 3rd degree burns
T32.8[1,2,3,4,5,6,7,8]   Corrosions involving 80-89% of body surface w/ [10-19, 20-29, 30-39, 40-49, 50-59, 60-69, 70-79, 80-89]% 3rd degree burns
T32.9[1,2,3,4,5,6,7,8,9]   Corrosions involving 90% or more of body surface w/ [10-19, 20-29, 30-39, 40-49, 50-59, 60-69, 70-79, 80-89, 90 or more]% 3rd degree burns

---

DRG 934   **Full Thickness Burn without Skin Graft or Inhalation Injury**
        GMLOS 4.2   **AMLOS 6.2**   **RW 1.6716**

Principal or Secondary Diagnosis

T20.30XA   Burn 3rd degree of head, face, and neck, unsp site, init
T20.31[1,2,9]A   Burn of 3rd degree of [rt, lt, unsp] ear (any part, except ear drum), init enc
T20.39XA   Burn of 3rd deg mu sites of head, face, and neck, init
T20.3[2,3,4,5,6,7]XA   Burn of 3rd degree of [lip(s), chin, nose (septum), scalp (any part), forehead and cheek, neck], init enc
T20.70XA   Corrosion 3rd degree of head, face, and neck, unsp site, init
T20.71[1,2,9]A   Corrosion of 3rd degree of [rt, lt, unsp] ear (any part, except ear drum), init enc
T20.79XA   Corrosion of 3rd deg mu sites of head, face, and neck, init
T20.7[2,3,4,5,6,7]XA   Corrosion of 3rd degree of [lip(s), chin, nose (septum), scalp (any part), forehead and cheek, neck], init enc
T21.3[0,1,2,3,4,5,6,7,9]XA   Burn of 3rd degree of [trunk, unsp site, chest wall, abd wall, upr back, lwr back, buttock, male genital rgn, femal genital rgn, oth site of trunk], init enc
T21.7[0,1,2,3,4,5,6,7,9]XA   Corrosion of 3rd degree of [trunk, unsp site, chest wall, abd wall, upr back, lwr back, buttock, male genital rgn, femal genital rgn, oth site of trunk], init enc
T22.30XA   Burn 3rd deg of shldr/up lmb, ex wrs/hnd, unsp site, init
T22.31[1,2,9]A   Burn of 3rd degree of [rt, lt, unsp] forearm, init enc
T22.32[1,2,9]A   Burn of 3rd degree of [rt, lt, unsp] elbow, init enc
T22.33[1,2,9]A   Burn of 3rd degree of [rt, lt, unsp] upr arm, init enc
T22.34[1,2,9]A   Burn of 3rd degree of [rt, lt, unsp] axilla, init enc
T22.35[1,2,9]A   Burn of 3rd degree of [rt, lt, unsp] shldr, init enc
T22.36[1,2,9]A   Burn of 3rd degree of [rt, lt, unsp] scapular rgn, init enc
T22.39[1,2,9]A   Burn of 3rd degree of multi sites of [rt, lt, unsp] shldr and upr limb, except wrist and hand, init enc
T22.70XA   Corrosion 3rd deg of shldr/up lmb, ex wrs/hnd, unsp site, init
T22.71[1,2,9]A   Corrosion of 3rd degree of [rt, lt, unsp] forearm, init enc
T22.72[1,2,9]A   Corrosion of 3rd degree of [rt, lt, unsp] elbow, init enc
T22.73[1,2,9]A   Corrosion of 3rd degree of [rt, lt, unsp] upr arm, init enc

T22.74[1,2,9]A   Corrosion of 3rd degree of [rt, lt, unsp] axilla, init enc
T22.75[1,2,9]A   Corrosion of 3rd degree of [rt, lt, unsp] shldr, init enc
T22.76[1,2,9]A   Corrosion of 3rd degree of [rt, lt, unsp] scapular rgn, init enc
T22.79[1,2,9]A   Corrosion of 3rd degree of multi sites of [rt, lt, unsp] shldr and upr limb, except wrist and hand, init enc
T23.30[1,2,9]A   Burn of 3rd degree of [rt, lt, unsp] hand, unsp site, init enc
T23.31[1,2,9]A   Burn of 3rd degree of [rt, lt, unsp] thumb (nail), init enc
T23.32[1,2,9]A   Burn of 3rd degree of single [rt, lt, unsp] finger (nail) except thumb, init enc
T23.33[1,2,9]A   Burn of 3rd degree of multi [rt, lt, unsp] fingers (nail), not incl* thumb, init enc
T23.34[1,2,9]A   Burn of 3rd degree of multi [rt, lt, unsp] fingers (nail), incl* thumb, init enc
T23.35[1,2,9]A   Burn of 3rd degree of [rt, lt, unsp] palm, init enc
T23.36[1,2,9]A   Burn of 3rd degree of back of [rt, lt, unsp] hand, init enc
T23.37[1,2,9]A   Burn of 3rd degree of [rt, lt, unsp] wrist, init enc
T23.39[1,2,9]A   Burn of 3rd degree of multi sites of [rt, lt, unsp] wrist and hand, init enc
T23.70[1,2,9]A   Corrosion of 3rd degree of [rt, lt, unsp] hand, unsp site, init enc
T23.71[1,2,9]A   Corrosion of 3rd degree of [rt, lt, unsp] thumb (nail), init enc
T23.72[1,2,9]A   Corrosion of 3rd degree of single [rt, lt, unsp] finger (nail) except thumb, init enc
T23.73[1,2,9]A   Corrosion of 3rd degree of multi [rt, lt, unsp] fingers (nail), not incl* thumb, init enc
T23.74[1,2,9]A   Corrosion of 3rd degree of multi [rt, lt, unsp] fingers (nail), incl* thumb, init enc
T23.75[1,2,9]A   Corrosion of 3rd degree of [rt, lt, unsp] palm, init enc
T23.76[1,2,9]A   Corrosion of 3rd degree of back of [rt, lt, unsp] hand, init enc
T23.77[1,2,9]A   Corrosion of 3rd degree of [rt, lt, unsp] wrist, init enc
T23.79[1,2,9]A   Corrosion of 3rd degree of multi sites of [rt, lt, unsp] wrist and hand, init enc
T24.30[1,2,9]A   Burn of 3rd degree of unsp site of [rt, lt, unsp] lwr limb, except ankle and foot, init enc
T24.31[1,2,9]A   Burn of 3rd degree of [rt, lt, unsp] thigh, init enc
T24.32[1,2,9]A   Burn of 3rd degree of [rt, lt, unsp] knee, init enc
T24.33[1,2,9]A   Burn of 3rd degree of [rt, lt, unsp] lwr leg, init enc
T24.39[1,2,9]A   Burn of 3rd degree of multi sites of [rt, lt, unsp] lwr limb, except ankle and foot, init enc
T24.70[1,2,9]A   Corrosion of 3rd degree of unsp site of [rt, lt, unsp] lwr limb, except ankle and foot, init enc
T24.71[1,2,9]A   Corrosion of 3rd degree of [rt, lt, unsp] thigh, init enc
T24.72[1,2,9]A   Corrosion of 3rd degree of [rt, lt, unsp] knee, init enc
T24.73[1,2,9]A   Corrosion of 3rd degree of [rt, lt, unsp] lwr leg, init enc
T24.79[1,2,9]A   Corrosion of 3rd degree of multi sites of [rt, lt, unsp] lwr limb, except ankle and foot, init enc
T25.31[1,2,9]A   Burn of 3rd degree of [rt, lt, unsp] ankle, init enc
T25.32[1,2,9]A   Burn of 3rd degree of [rt, lt, unsp] foot, init enc
T25.33[1,2,9]A   Burn of 3rd degree of [rt, lt, unsp] toe(s) (nail), init enc
T25.39[1,2,9]A   Burn of 3rd degree of multi sites of [rt, lt, unsp] ankle and foot, init enc
T25.71[1,2,9]A   Corrosion of 3rd degree of [rt, lt, unsp] ankle, init enc
T25.72[1,2,9]A   Corrosion of 3rd degree of [rt, lt, unsp] foot, init enc
T25.73[1,2,9]A   Corrosion of 3rd degree of [rt, lt, unsp] toe(s) (nail), init enc
T25.79[1,2,9]A   Corrosion of 3rd degree of multi sites of [rt, lt, unsp] ankle and foot, init enc
T26.2[0,1,2]XA   Burn w/ resulting rupture and destr of [unsp, rt, lt] eyeball, init enc
T31.11   Burns of 10-19% of body surface w 10-19% 3rd degree burns
T32.11   Corrosion 10-19% of body surface w 10-19% 3rd degree corrosion

---

DRG 935   **Nonextensive Burns**
        GMLOS 3.4   **AMLOS 5.1**   **RW 1.5141**

Principal or Secondary Diagnosis

T20.00XA   Burn of unsp degree of head, face, and neck, unsp site, init
T20.01[1,2,9]A   Burn of unsp degree of [rt, lt, unsp] ear [any part, except ear drum], init enc
T20.09XA   Burn of unsp deg mult sites of head, face, and neck, init
T20.0[2,3,4]XA   Burn of unsp degree of [lip(s), chin, nose (septum)], init enc
T20.0[5,6,7]XA   Burn of unsp degree of [scalp [any part], forehead and cheek, neck], init enc
T20.10XA   Burn first degree of head, face, and neck, unsp site, init
T20.11[1,2,9]A   Burn of 1st degree of [rt, lt, unsp] ear [any part, except ear drum], init enc
T20.19XA   Burn of first deg mult sites of head, face, and neck, init
T20.1[2,3,4]XA   Burn of 1st degree of [lip(s), chin, nose (septum)], init enc
T20.1[5,6,7]XA   Burn of 1st degree of [scalp [any part], forehead and cheek, neck], init enc

---

T Transfer DRG   SP Special Payment   * Code Range   6th and 7th Character of ZZ = No Device, No Qualifier ZX = No Device, Diagnostic

Code	Description
T20.20XA	Burn 2nd degree of head, face, and neck, unsp site, init
T20.21[1,2,9]A	Burn of 2nd degree of [rt, lt, unsp] ear [any part, except ear drum], init enc
T20.29XA	Burn of 2nd deg mul sites of head, face, and neck, init
T20.2[2,3,4]XA	Burn of 2nd degree of [lip(s), chin, nose (septum)], init enc
T20.2[5,6,7]XA	Burn of 2nd degree of [scalp [any part], forehead and cheek, neck], init enc
T20.40XA	Corrosion unsp degree of head, face, and neck, unsp site, init
T20.41[1,2,9]A	Corrosion of unsp degree of [rt, lt, unsp] ear [any part, except ear drum], init enc
T20.49XA	Corrosion unsp deg mult sites of head, face, and neck, init
T20.4[2,3,4]XA	Corrosion of unsp degree of [lip(s), chin, nose (septum)], init enc
T20.4[5,6,7]XA	Corrosion of unsp degree of [scalp [any part], forehead and cheek, neck], init enc
T20.50XA	Corrosion first degree of head, face, and neck, unsp site, init
T20.51[1,2,9]A	Corrosion of 1st degree of [rt, lt, unsp] ear [any part, except ear drum], init enc
T20.59XA	Corrosion first deg mult sites of head, face, and neck, init
T20.5[2,3,4]XA	Corrosion of 1st degree of [lip(s), chin, nose (septum)], init enc
T20.5[5,6,7]XA	Corrosion of 1st degree of [scalp [any part], forehead and cheek, neck], init enc
T20.60XA	Corrosion 2nd deg of head, face, and neck, unsp site, init
T20.61[1,2,9]A	Corrosion of 2nd degree of [rt, lt, unsp] ear [any part, except ear drum], init enc
T20.69XA	Corrosion of 2nd deg mul sites of head, face, and neck, init
T20.6[2,3,4]XA	Corrosion of 2nd degree of [lip(s), chin, nose (septum)], init enc
T20.6[5,6,7]XA	Corrosion of 2nd degree of [scalp [any part], forehead and cheek, neck], init enc
T21.0[0,1,2,3,4,5,6,7,9]XA	Burn of unsp degree of [unsp site of trunk, chest wall, abd wall, upr back, lwr back, buttock, male genital rgn, female genital rgn, oth site of trunk], init enc
T21.1[0,1,2,3,4,5,6,7,9]XA	Burn of 1st degree of [unsp site of trunk, chest wall, abd wall, upr back, lwr back, buttock, male genital rgn, female genital rgn, oth site of trunk], init enc
T21.2[0,1,2,3,4,5,6,7,9]XA	Burn of 2nd degree of [unsp site of trunk, chest wall, abd wall, upr back, lwr back, buttock, male genital rgn, female genital rgn, oth site of trunk], init enc
T21.4[0,1,2,3,4,5,6,7,9]XA	Corrosion of unsp degree of [unsp site of trunk, chest wall, abd wall, upr back, lwr back, buttock, male genital rgn, female genital rgn, oth site of trunk], init enc
T21.5[0,1,2,3,4,5,6,7,9]XA	Corrosion of 1st degree of [unsp site of trunk, chest wall, abd wall, upr back, lwr back, buttock, male genital rgn, female genital rgn, oth site of trunk], init enc
T21.6[0,1,2,3,4,5,6,7,9]XA	Corrosion of 2nd degree of [unsp site of trunk, chest wall, abd wall, upr back, lwr back, buttock, male genital rgn, female genital rgn, oth site of trunk], init enc
T22.00XA	Burn unsp deg of shldr/up lmb, ex wrs/hnd, unsp site, init
T22.01[1,2,9]A	Burn of unsp degree of [rt, lt, unsp] forearm, init enc
T22.02[1,2,9]A	Burn of unsp degree of [rt, lt, unsp] elbow, init enc
T22.03[1,2,9]A	Burn of unsp degree of [rt, lt, unsp] upr arm, init enc
T22.04[1,2,9]A	Burn of unsp degree of [rt, lt, unsp] axilla, init enc
T22.05[1,2,9]A	Burn of unsp degree of [rt, lt, unsp] shldr, init enc
T22.06[1,2,9]A	Burn of unsp degree of [rt, lt, unsp] scapular rgn, init enc
T22.09[1,2,9]A	Burn of unsp degree of multi sites of [rt, lt, unsp] shldr and upr limb, except wrist and hand, init enc
T22.10XA	Burn first deg of shldr/up lmb, ex wrs/hnd, unsp site, init
T22.11[1,2,9]A	Burn of 1st degree of [rt, lt, unsp] forearm, init enc
T22.12[1,2,9]A	Burn of 1st degree of [rt, lt, unsp] elbow, init enc
T22.13[1,2,9]A	Burn of 1st degree of [rt, lt, unsp] upr arm, init enc
T22.14[1,2,9]A	Burn of 1st degree of [rt, lt, unsp] axilla, init enc
T22.15[1,2,9]A	Burn of 1st degree of [rt, lt, unsp] shldr, init enc
T22.16[1,2,9]A	Burn of 1st degree of [rt, lt, unsp] scapular rgn, init enc
T22.19[1,2,9]A	Burn of 1st degree of multi sites of [rt, lt, unsp] shldr and upr limb, except wrist and hand, init enc
T22.20XA	Burn 2nd deg of shldr/up lmb, ex wrs/hnd, unsp site, init
T22.21[1,2,9]A	Burn of 2nd degree of [rt, lt, unsp] forearm, init enc
T22.22[1,2,9]A	Burn of 2nd degree of [rt, lt, unsp] elbow, init enc
T22.23[1,2,9]A	Burn of 2nd degree of [rt, lt, unsp] upr arm, init enc
T22.24[1,2,9]A	Burn of 2nd degree of [rt, lt, unsp] axilla, init enc
T22.25[1,2,9]A	Burn of 2nd degree of [rt, lt, unsp] shldr, init enc
T22.26[1,2,9]A	Burn of 2nd degree of [rt, lt, unsp] scapular rgn, init enc
T22.29[1,2,9]A	Burn of 2nd degree of multi sites of [rt, lt, unsp] shldr and upr limb, except wrist and hand, init enc
T22.40XA	Corrosion unsp deg of shldr/up lmb, ex wrs/hnd, unsp site, init
T22.41[1,2,9]A	Corrosion of unsp degree of [rt, lt, unsp] forearm, init enc
T22.42[1,2,9]A	Corrosion of unsp degree of [rt, lt, unsp] elbow, init enc
T22.43[1,2,9]A	Corrosion of unsp degree of [rt, lt, unsp] upr arm, init enc
T22.44[1,2,9]A	Corrosion of unsp degree of [rt, lt, unsp] axilla, init enc
T22.45[1,2,9]A	Corrosion of unsp degree of [rt, lt, unsp] shldr, init enc
T22.46[1,2,9]A	Corrosion of unsp degree of [rt, lt, unsp] scapular rgn, init enc
T22.49[1,2,9]A	Corrosion of unsp degree of multi sites of [rt, lt, unsp] shldr and upr limb, except wrist and hand, init enc
T22.50XA	Corrosion first deg of shldr/up lmb, ex wrs/hnd unsp site, init
T22.51[1,2,9]A	Corrosion of 1st degree of [rt, lt, unsp] forearm, init enc
T22.52[1,2,9]A	Corrosion of 1st degree of [rt, lt, unsp] elbow, init enc
T22.53[1,2,9]A	Corrosion of 1st degree of [rt, lt, unsp] upr arm, init enc
T22.54[1,2,9]A	Corrosion of 1st degree of [rt, lt, unsp] axilla, init enc
T22.55[1,2,9]A	Corrosion of 1st degree of [rt, lt, unsp] shldr, init enc
T22.56[1,2,9]A	Corrosion of 1st degree of [rt, lt, unsp] scapular rgn, init enc
T22.59[1,2,9]A	Corrosion of 1st degree of multi sites of [rt, lt, unsp] shldr and upr limb, except wrist and hand, init enc
T22.60XA	Corrosion 2nd deg of shldr/up lmb, ex wrs/hnd, unsp site, init
T22.61[1,2,9]A	Corrosion of 2nd degree of [rt, lt, unsp] forearm, init enc
T22.62[1,2,9]A	Corrosion of 2nd degree of [rt, lt, unsp] elbow, init enc
T22.63[1,2,9]A	Corrosion of 2nd degree of [rt, lt, unsp] upr arm, init enc
T22.64[1,2,9]A	Corrosion of 2nd degree of [rt, lt, unsp] axilla, init enc
T22.65[1,2,9]A	Corrosion of 2nd degree of [rt, lt, unsp] shldr, init enc
T22.66[1,2,9]A	Corrosion of 2nd degree of [rt, lt, unsp] scapular rgn, init enc
T22.69[1,2,9]A	Corrosion of 2nd degree of multi sites of [rt, lt, unsp] shldr and upr limb, except wrist and hand, init enc
T23.00[1,2,9]A	Burn of unsp degree of [rt, lt, unsp] hand, unsp site, init enc
T23.01[1,2,9]A	Burn of unsp degree of [rt, lt, unsp] thumb (nail), init enc
T23.02[1,2,9]A	Burn of unsp degree of single [rt, lt, unsp] finger (nail) except thumb, init enc
T23.03[1,2,9]A	Burn of unsp degree of multi [rt, lt, unsp] fingers (nail), not incl* thumb, init enc
T23.04[1,2,9]A	Burn of unsp degree of multi [rt, lt, unsp] fingers (nail), incl* thumb, init enc
T23.05[1,2,9]A	Burn of unsp degree of [rt, lt, unsp] palm, init enc
T23.06[1,2,9]A	Burn of unsp degree of back of [rt, lt, unsp] hand, init enc
T23.07[1,2,9]A	Burn of unsp degree of [rt, lt, unsp] wrist, init enc
T23.09[1,2,9]A	Burn of unsp degree of multi sites of [rt, lt, unsp] wrist and hand, init enc
T23.10[1,2,9]A	Burn of 1st degree of [rt, lt, unsp] hand, unsp site, init enc
T23.11[1,2,9]A	Burn of 1st degree of [rt, lt, unsp] thumb (nail), init enc
T23.12[1,2,9]A	Burn of 1st degree of single [rt, lt, unsp] finger (nail) except thumb, init enc
T23.13[1,2,9]A	Burn of 1st degree of multi [rt, lt, unsp] fingers (nail), not incl* thumb, init enc
T23.14[1,2,9]A	Burn of 1st degree of multi [rt, lt, unsp] fingers (nail), incl* thumb, init enc
T23.15[1,2,9]A	Burn of 1st degree of [rt, lt, unsp] palm, init enc
T23.16[1,2,9]A	Burn of 1st degree of back of [rt, lt, unsp] hand, init enc
T23.17[1,2,9]A	Burn of 1st degree of [rt, lt, unsp] wrist, init enc
T23.19[1,2,9]A	Burn of 1st degree of multi sites of [rt, lt, unsp] wrist and hand, init enc
T23.20[1,2,9]A	Burn of 2nd degree of [rt, lt, unsp] hand, unsp site, init enc
T23.21[1,2,9]A	Burn of 2nd degree of [rt, lt, unsp] thumb (nail), init enc
T23.22[1,2,9]A	Burn of 2nd degree of single [rt, lt, unsp] finger (nail) except thumb, init enc
T23.23[1,2,9]A	Burn of 2nd degree of multi [rt, lt, unsp] fingers (nail), not incl* thumb, init enc
T23.24[1,2,9]A	Burn of 2nd degree of multi [rt, lt, unsp] fingers (nail), incl* thumb, init enc
T23.25[1,2,9]A	Burn of 2nd degree of [rt, lt, unsp] palm, init enc
T23.26[1,2,9]A	Burn of 2nd degree of back of [rt, lt, unsp] hand, init enc
T23.27[1,2,9]A	Burn of 2nd degree of [rt, lt, unsp] wrist, init enc
T23.29[1,2,9]A	Burn of 2nd degree of multi sites of [rt, lt, unsp] wrist and hand, init enc
T23.40[1,2,9]A	Corrosion of unsp degree of [rt, lt, unsp] hand, unsp site, init enc
T23.41[1,2,9]A	Corrosion of unsp degree of [rt, lt, unsp] thumb (nail), init enc
T23.42[1,2,9]A	Corrosion of unsp degree of single [rt, lt, unsp] finger (nail) except thumb, init enc
T23.43[1,2,9]A	Corrosion of unsp degree of multi [rt, lt, unsp] fingers (nail), not incl* thumb, init enc
T23.44[1,2,9]A	Corrosion of unsp degree of multi [rt, lt, unsp] fingers (nail), incl* thumb, init enc
T23.45[1,2,9]A	Corrosion of unsp degree of [rt, lt, unsp] palm, init enc
T23.46[1,2,9]A	Corrosion of unsp degree of back of [rt, lt, unsp] hand, init enc
T23.47[1,2,9]A	Corrosion of unsp degree of [rt, lt, unsp] wrist, init enc
T23.49[1,2,9]A	Corrosion of unsp degree of multi sites of [rt, lt, unsp] wrist and hand, init enc
T23.50[1,2,9]A	Corrosion of 1st degree of [rt, lt, unsp] hand, unsp site, init enc
T23.51[1,2,9]A	Corrosion of 1st degree of [rt, lt, unsp] thumb (nail), init enc
T23.52[1,2,9]A	Corrosion of 1st degree of single [rt, lt, unsp] finger (nail) except thumb, init enc

Surgical   **Medical**   **CC Indicator**   **MCC Indicator**   **Procedure Proxy**   **PDxMCC PDx acts as own MCC**   **PDxCC PDx acts as own CC**

MDC 22: Burns—MEDICAL

MDC 22: Burns—MEDICAL

T23.53[1,2,9]A	Corrosion of 1st degree of multi [rt, lt, unsp] fingers (nail), not incl* thumb, init enc
T23.54[1,2,9]A	Corrosion of 1st degree of multi [rt, lt, unsp] fingers (nail), incl* thumb, init enc
T23.55[1,2,9]A	Corrosion of 1st degree of [rt, lt, unsp] palm, init enc
T23.56[1,2,9]A	Corrosion of 1st degree of back of [rt, lt, unsp] hand, init enc
T23.57[1,2,9]A	Corrosion of 1st degree of [rt, lt, unsp] wrist, init enc
T23.59[1,2,9]A	Corrosion of 1st degree of multi sites of [rt, lt, unsp] wrist and hand, init enc
T23.60[1,2,9]A	Corrosion of 2nd degree of [rt, lt, unsp] hand, unsp site, init enc
T23.61[1,2,9]A	Corrosion of 2nd degree of [rt, lt, unsp] thumb (nail), init enc
T23.62[1,2,9]A	Corrosion of 2nd degree of single [rt, lt, unsp] finger (nail) except thumb, init enc
T23.63[1,2,9]A	Corrosion of 2nd degree of multi [rt, lt, unsp] fingers (nail), not incl* thumb, init enc
T23.64[1,2,9]A	Corrosion of 2nd degree of multi [rt, lt, unsp] fingers (nail), incl* thumb, init enc
T23.65[1,2,9]A	Corrosion of 2nd degree of [rt, lt, unsp] palm, init enc
T23.66[1,2,9]A	Corrosion of 2nd degree of back of [rt, lt, unsp] hand, init enc
T23.67[1,2,9]A	Corrosion of 2nd degree of [rt, lt, unsp] wrist, init enc
T23.69[1,2,9]A	Corrosion of 2nd degree of multi sites of [rt, lt, unsp] wrist and hand, init enc
T24.00[1,2,9]A	Burn of unsp degree of unsp site of [rt, lt, unsp] lwr limb, except ankle and foot, init enc
T24.01[1,2,9]A	Burn of unsp degree of [rt, lt, unsp] thigh, init enc
T24.02[1,2,9]A	Burn of unsp degree of [rt, lt, unsp] knee, init enc
T24.03[1,2,9]A	Burn of unsp degree of [rt, lt, unsp] lwr leg, init enc
T24.09[1,2,9]A	Burn of unsp degree of multi sites of [rt, lt, unsp] lwr limb, except ankle and foot, init enc
T24.10[1,2,9]A	Burn of 1st degree of unsp site of [rt, lt, unsp] lwr limb, except ankle and foot, init enc
T24.11[1,2,9]A	Burn of 1st degree of [rt, lt, unsp] thigh, init enc
T24.12[1,2,9]A	Burn of 1st degree of [rt, lt, unsp] knee, init enc
T24.13[1,2,9]A	Burn of 1st degree of [rt, lt, unsp] lwr leg, init enc
T24.19[1,2,9]A	Burn of 1st degree of multi sites of [rt, lt, unsp] lwr limb, except ankle and foot, init enc
T24.20[1,2,9]A	Burn of 2nd degree of unsp site of [rt, lt, unsp] lwr limb, except ankle and foot, init enc
T24.21[1,2,9]A	Burn of 2nd degree of [rt, lt, unsp] thigh, init enc
T24.22[1,2,9]A	Burn of 2nd degree of [rt, lt, unsp] knee, init enc
T24.23[1,2,9]A	Burn of 2nd degree of [rt, lt, unsp] lwr leg, init enc
T24.29[1,2,9]A	Burn of 2nd degree of multi sites of [rt, lt, unsp] lwr limb, except ankle and foot, init enc
T24.40[1,2,9]A	Corrosion of unsp degree of unsp site of [rt, lt, unsp] lwr limb, except ankle and foot, init enc
T24.41[1,2,9]A	Corrosion of unsp degree of [rt, lt, unsp] thigh, init enc
T24.42[1,2,9]A	Corrosion of unsp degree of [rt, lt, unsp] knee, init enc
T24.43[1,2,9]A	Corrosion of unsp degree of [rt, lt, unsp] lwr leg, init enc
T24.49[1,2,9]A	Corrosion of unsp degree of multi sites of [rt, lt, unsp] lwr limb, except ankle and foot, init enc
T24.50[1,2,9]A	Corrosion of 1st degree of unsp site of [rt, lt, unsp] lwr limb, except ankle and foot, init enc
T24.51[1,2,9]A	Corrosion of 1st degree of [rt, lt, unsp] thigh, init enc
T24.52[1,2,9]A	Corrosion of 1st degree of [rt, lt, unsp] knee, init enc
T24.53[1,2,9]A	Corrosion of 1st degree of [rt, lt, unsp] lwr leg, init enc
T24.59[1,2,9]A	Corrosion of 1st degree of multi sites of [rt, lt, unsp] lwr limb, except ankle and foot, init enc
T24.60[1,2,9]A	Corrosion of 2nd degree of unsp site of [rt, lt, unsp] lwr limb, except ankle and foot, init enc
T24.61[1,2,9]A	Corrosion of 2nd degree of [rt, lt, unsp] thigh, init enc
T24.62[1,2,9]A	Corrosion of 2nd degree of [rt, lt, unsp] knee, init enc
T24.63[1,2,9]A	Corrosion of 2nd degree of [rt, lt, unsp] lwr leg, init enc
T24.69[1,2,9]A	Corrosion of 2nd degree of multi sites of [rt, lt, unsp] lwr limb, except ankle and foot, init enc
T25.01[1,2,9]A	Burn of unsp degree of [rt, lt, unsp] ankle, init enc
T25.02[1,2,9]A	Burn of unsp degree of [rt, lt, unsp] foot, init enc
T25.03[1,2,9]A	Burn of unsp degree of [rt, lt, unsp] toe(s) (nail), init enc
T25.09[1,2,9]A	Burn of unsp degree of multi sites of [rt, lt, unsp] ankle and foot, init enc
T25.11[1,2,9]A	Burn of 1st degree of [rt, lt, unsp] ankle, init enc
T25.12[1,2,9]A	Burn of 1st degree of [rt, lt, unsp] foot, init enc
T25.13[1,2,9]A	Burn of 1st degree of [rt, lt, unsp] toe(s) (nail), init enc
T25.19[1,2,9]A	Burn of 1st degree of multi sites of [rt, lt, unsp] ankle and foot, init enc
T25.21[1,2,9]A	Burn of 2nd degree of [rt, lt, unsp] ankle, init enc
T25.22[1,2,9]A	Burn of 2nd degree of [rt, lt, unsp] foot, init enc
T25.23[1,2,9]A	Burn of 2nd degree of [rt, lt, unsp] toe(s) (nail), init enc
T25.29[1,2,9]A	Burn of 2nd degree of multi sites of [rt, lt, unsp] ankle and foot, init enc
T25.41[1,2,9]A	Corrosion of unsp degree of [rt, lt, unsp] ankle, init enc
T25.42[1,2,9]A	Corrosion of unsp degree of [rt, lt, unsp] foot, init enc
T25.43[1,2,9]A	Corrosion of unsp degree of [rt, lt, unsp] toe(s) (nail), init enc
T25.49[1,2,9]A	Corrosion of unsp degree of multi sites of [rt, lt, unsp] ankle and foot, init enc
T25.51[1,2,9]A	Corrosion of 1st degree of [rt, lt, unsp] ankle, init enc
T25.52[1,2,9]A	Corrosion of 1st degree of [rt, lt, unsp] foot, init enc
T25.53[1,2,9]A	Corrosion of 1st degree of [rt, lt, unsp] toe(s) (nail), init enc
T25.59[1,2,9]A	Corrosion of 1st degree of multi sites of [rt, lt, unsp] ankle and foot, init enc
T25.61[1,2,9]A	Corrosion of 2nd degree of [rt, lt, unsp] ankle, init enc
T25.62[1,2,9]A	Corrosion of 2nd degree of [rt, lt, unsp] foot, init enc
T25.63[1,2,9]A	Corrosion of 2nd degree of [rt, lt, unsp] toe(s) (nail), init enc
T25.69[1,2,9]A	Corrosion of 2nd degree of multi sites of [rt, lt, unsp] ankle and foot, init enc
T28.3XXA	Burn of int genitourinary organs, init enc
T28.40XA	Burn of unsp int organ, init enc
T28.41[1,2,9]A	Burn of [rt, lt, unsp] ear drum, init enc
T28.49XA	Burn of oth int organ, init enc
T28.8XXA	Corrosion of int genitourinary organs, init enc
T28.90XA	Corrosions of unsp int organs, init enc
T28.91[1,2,9]A	Corrosion of [rt, lt, unsp] ear drum, init enc
T28.99XA	Corrosions of oth int organs, init enc
T30.0	Burn of unsp body region, unsp degree
T30.4	Corrosion of unsp body region, unsp degree
T31.0	Burns involving < 10% of body surface
T31.[1,2,3,4,5,6,7,8,9]0	Burns involving [10-19, 20-29, 30-39, 40-49, 50-59, 60-69, 70-79, 80-89, 90 or more]% of body surface w/ 0% to 9% 3rd degree burns
T32.0	Corrosions involving < 10% of body surface
T32.[1,2,3,4,5,6,7,8,9]0	Burns involving [10-19, 20-29, 30-39, 40-49, 50-59, 60-69, 70-79, 80-89, 90 or more]% of body surface w/ 0% to 9% 3rd degree corrosions

---

[T] **Transfer DRG**   [SP] **Special Payment**   *** Code Range**   **6th and 7th Character of ZZ = No Device, No Qualifier ZX = No Device, Diagnostic**

384   MS-DRG Version 33.0   © 2015 Optum360, LLC

SURGICAL

DRG 939   O.R. Procedure with Diagnoses of Other Contact with Health Services with MCC
GMLOS 6.2   **AMLOS 9.1**   **RW 2.9866**

Select any operating room procedure

DRG 940   O.R. Procedure with Diagnoses of Other Contact with Health Services with CC
GMLOS 3.7   **AMLOS 5.2**   **RW 1.9107**

Select any operating room procedure

DRG 941   O.R. Procedure with Diagnoses of Other Contact with Health Services without CC/MCC
GMLOS 2.1   **AMLOS 2.7**   **RW 1.3589**

Select any operating room procedure

MEDICAL

DRG 945   Rehabilitation with CC/MCC
GMLOS 8.8   **AMLOS 10.9**   **RW 1.2781**   ⊤

Principal Diagnosis

Z44.8	Enc for fit/adjst of ext prosthetic devices
Z44.9	Enc for fit/adjst of unsp ext prosthetic device

OR

Rehabilitation Procedures

F00*	Phys Rehab & Diag Audiology, Rehab, Speech Assess
F01*	Phys Rehab & Diag Audiology, Rehab, Motor/Nrv Assess
F02*	Phys Rehab & Diag Audiology, Rehab, ADL Assess
F06*	Phys Rehab & Diag Audiology, Rehab, Speech Trmt
F07*	Phys Rehab & Diag Audiology, Rehab, Motor Trmt
F08*	Phys Rehab & Diag Audiology, Rehab, ADL Trmt
F09*	Phys Rehab & Diag Audiology, Rehab, Hear Trmt
F0B*	Phys Rehab & Diag Audiology, Rehab, Cochlear Impl Trmt
F0C*	Phys Rehab & Diag Audiology, Rehab, Vestib Trmt
F0D*	Phys Rehab & Diag Audiology, Rehab, Device Fit
F0F*	Phys Rehab & Diag Audiology, Rehab, Caregiver Train

AND

Any principal diagnosis from MDC 23 except the following

Z45.1	Enc for adjustment and management of inf pump
Z45.2	Enc for adjustment and management of VAD
Z46.82	Enc for fit/adjst of non-vascular catheter
Z48.03	Enc for change or rmvl of drains
Z48.1	Enc for planned postprocedural wnd closure
Z48.2*	Enc for aftercare following organ transplant
Z48.3	Aftercare following surgery for neoplasm
Z48.8*	Enc for oth spec postprocedural aftercare
Z51.81	Enc for therapeutic drug lvl monitoring

DRG 946   Rehabilitation without CC/MCC
GMLOS 6.8   **AMLOS 7.8**   **RW 1.0151**   ⊤

Select principal diagnosis OR rehabilitation procedures AND principal diagnosis listed under DRG 945

DRG 947   Signs and Symptoms with MCC
GMLOS 3.5   **AMLOS 4.7**   **RW 1.1323**   ⊤

Principal Diagnosis

E07.81	Sick-euthyroid synd
E79.0	Hyperuricemia w/o signs of inflam arthrit and tophaceous dis
G89.1*	Acute pain, NEC
G89.3	Neoplasm related pain (acute) (chr)
G93.3	Postviral fatigue synd
P09	Abnormal findings on neonatal screening
R18*	Ascites
R23.0	Cyanosis
R23.1	Pallor
R23.2	Flushing
R41.0	Disorientation, unsp
R41.1	Anterograde amnesia
R41.2	Retrograde amnesia
R41.3	Oth amnesia
R41.82	Altered mental status, unsp
R41.9	Unsp symptoms and signs w cognitive functions and awareness
R45.83	Excessive crying of child, adolescent or adult
R45.84	Anhedonia
R52	Pain, unsp
R53.0	Neoplastic (malig) related fatigue
R53.1	Weakness
R53.8*	Oth malaise and fatigue
R60*	Edema, NEC
R64	Cachexia
R68.0	Hypothermia, not associated w low environmental temperature
R68.11	Excessive crying of infant (baby)
R68.12	Fussy infant (baby)
R68.81	Early satiety
R68.83	Chills (w/o fever)
R68.89	Oth general symptoms and signs
R70*	Elev erythro sedim and abnormality of plasma viscosity
R74*	Abnormal serum enzyme levels
R77*	Oth abnormalities of plasma proteins
R78.1	Finding of opiate drug in bld
R78.2	Finding of cocaine in bld
R78.3	Finding of hallucinogen in bld
R78.4	Finding of oth drugs of addictive potential in bld
R78.5	Finding of oth psychotropic drug in bld
R78.6	Finding of steroid agent in bld
R78.7*	Finding of abnormal lvl of heavy metals in bld
R78.89	Finding of oth substances, not normally found in bld
R78.9	Finding of unsp substance, not normally found in bld
R79*	Oth abnormal findings of bld chemistry
R82.1	Myoglobinuria
R84*	Abnormal findings in specimens from resp org/thrx
R85.0	Abn lev enzymes in specimens from dgstv org/abd cav
R85.1	Abn lev hormones in specimens from dgstv org/abd cav
R85.2	Abn lev drug/meds/biol subst in specmn fr dgstv org/abd cav
R85.3	Abn lev substance nonmed source in specmn fr dgstv org/abd cav
R85.4	Abnormal immunolog findings in specmn from dgstv org/abd cav
R85.5	Abn microbiolog findings in specmn from dgstv org/abd cav
R85.69	Abn cytolog findings in specmn from oth dgstv org/abd cav
R85.7	Abnormal histolog findings in specmn from dgstv org/abd cav
R85.89	Oth abnormal findings in specimens from dgstv org/abd cav
R85.9	Unsp abnormal finding in specimens from dgstv org/abd cav
R87.0	Abn lev enzymes in specimens from female genital organs
R87.1	Abn lev hormones in specimens from female genital organs
R87.2	Abn lev drug/meds/biol subst in specmn from fem gntl organs
R87.3	Abn lev substance nonmed source in specmn from fem gntl organs
R87.4	Abn immunolog findings in specmn from female genital organs

| Surgical | Medical | CC Indicator | MCC Indicator | Procedure Proxy | PDxMCC PDx acts as own MCC | PDxCC PDx acts as own CC |

© 2015 Optum360, LLC   MS-DRG Version 33.0   385

R87.5	Abn microbiolog find in specmn from female genital organs
R87.61[8,9]	[Oth, Unsp] abnormal cytological findings on specimens from cervix uteri
R87.629	Unsp abnormal cytological findings in specimens from vagina
R87.69	Abn cytolog find in specmn from oth female genital organs
R87.7	Abn histolog findings in specmn from female genital organs
R87.89	Oth abnormal findings in specmn from female genital organs
R87.9	Unsp abnormal finding in specmn from female genital organs
R88*	Abnormal findings in oth body fluids and substances
R89.0	Abnormal lvl of enzymes in specimens from oth org/tiss
R89.1	Abnormal lvl of hormones in specimens from oth org/tiss
R89.2	Abn lev drug/meds/biol subst in specmn from oth org/tiss
R89.3	Abn lev substance nonmed source in specmn from oth org/tiss
R89.4	Abnormal immunolog findings in specimens from oth org/tiss
R89.5	Abnormal microbiolog findings in specimens from oth org/tiss
R89.6	Abnormal cytological findings in specmn from oth org/tiss
R89.7	Abnormal histolog findings in specimens from oth org/tiss
R89.8	Oth abnormal findings in specimens from oth org/tiss
R90.89	Oth abnormal findings on diagnostic imaging of cnsl
R93.9	Dx imaging inconclusive d/t excess body fat of patient
R97*	Abnormal tumor markers

DRG 948   Signs and Symptoms without MCC
GMLOS 2.7   AMLOS 3.3   RW 0.7356   T

Select principal diagnosis listed under DRG 947

DRG 949   Aftercare with CC/MCC
GMLOS 3.3   AMLOS 5.1   RW 1.1197

Principal Diagnosis

S00.0[0,1,2,3,4,5,6,7]XD	[Unsp superf inj, Abrasion, Blister (nonthermal), Contsn, Ext constriction of part, Superf FB, Insect bite (nonvenomous), Oth superf bite] of scalp, subsq enc
S00.1[0,1,2]XD	Contsn of [unsp, rt, lt] eyelid and periocular area, subsq enc
S00.2[0,1,2,4,5,6,7][1,2,9]D	[Unsp superf inj, Abrasion, Blister (nonthermal), Ext constriction, Superf FB, Insect bite (nonvenomous), Oth superf bite] of [rt, lt, unsp] eyelid and periocular area, subsq enc
S00.3[0,1,2,3,4,5,6,7]XD	[Unsp superf inj, Abrasion, Blister (nonthermal), Contsn, Ext constriction, Superf FB, Insect bite (nonvenomous), Oth superf bite] of nose, subsq enc
S00.4[0,1,2,3,4,5,6,7][1,2,9]D	[Unsp superf inj, Abrasion, Blister (nonthermal), Contsn, Ext constriction, Superf FB, Insect bite (nonvenomous), Oth superf bite] of [rt, lt, unsp] ear, subsq enc
S00.5[0,1,2,3,4,5,6,7][1,2]D	[Unsp superf inj, Abrasion, Blister (nonthermal), Contsn, Ext constriction, Superf FB, Insect bite (nonvenomous), Oth superf bite] of [lip, oral cavity], subsq enc
S00.8[0,1,2,3,4,5,6,7]XD	[Unsp superf inj, Abrasion, Blister (nonthermal), Contsn, Ext constriction, Superf FB, Insect bite (nonvenomous), Oth superf bite] of oth part of head, subsq enc
S00.9[0,1,2,3,4,5,6,7]XD	[Unsp superf inj, Abrasion, Blister (nonthermal), Contsn, Ext constriction, Superf FB, Insect bite (nonvenomous), Oth superf bite] of unsp part of head, subsq enc
S01.0[0,1,2,3,4,5]XD	[Unsp opn wnd, Lac w/o FB, Lac w/ FB, Punc wnd w/o FB, Punc wnd w/ FB, Opn bite] of scalp, subsq enc
S01.1[0,1,2,3,4,5][1,2,9]D	[Unsp opn wnd, Lac w/o FB, Lac w/ FB, Punc wnd w/o FB, Punc wnd w/ FB, Opn bite] of [rt, lt, unsp] eyelid and periocular area, subsq enc
S01.2[0,1,2,3,4,5]XD	[Unsp opn wnd, Lac w/o FB, Lac w/ FB, Punc wnd w/o FB, Punc wnd w/ FB, Opn bite] of nose, subsq enc
S01.3[0,1,2,3,4,5][1,2,9]D	[Unsp opn wnd, Lac w/o FB, Lac w/ FB, Punc wnd w/o FB, Punc wnd w/ FB, Opn bite] of [rt, lt, unsp] ear, subsq enc
S01.4[0,1,2,3,4,5][1,2,9]D	[Unsp opn wnd, Lac w/o FB, Lac w/ FB, Punc wnd w/o FB, Punc wnd w/ FB, Opn bite] of [rt, lt, unsp] cheek and temporomandibular area, subsq enc
S01.5[0,1,2,3,4,5][1,2]D	[Unsp opn wnd, Lac w/o FB, Lac w/ FB, Punc wnd w/o FB, Punc wnd w/ FB, Opn bite] of [lip, oral cavity], subsq enc
S01.8[0,1,2,3,4,5]XD	[Unsp opn wnd, Lac w/o FB, Lac w/ FB, Punc wnd w/o FB, Punc wnd w/ FB, Opn bite] of oth part of head, subsq enc
S01.9[0,1,2,3,4,5]XD	[Unsp opn wnd, Lac w/o FB, Lac w/ FB, Punc wnd w/o FB, Punc wnd w/ FB, Opn bite] of unsp part of head, subsq enc
S03.4XXD	Sprain of jaw, subsq enc
S03.[0,1,2]XXD	Disloc of [jaw, septal cartilage of nose, tooth], subsq enc
S03.[8,9]XXD	Sprain of jts and lgmts of [oth, unsp] parts of head, subsq enc
S04.01[1,2,9]D	Inj of optic nerve, [rt, lt, unsp] eye, subsq enc
S04.02XD	Inj of optic chiasm, subsq enc

S04.03[1,2,9]D	Inj of optic tract and pathways, [rt, lt, unsp] eye, subsq enc
S04.04[1,2,9]D	Inj of visual cortex, [rt, lt, unsp] eye, subsq enc
S04.1[0,1,2]XD	Inj of visual cortex of [rt, lt, unsp] eye, subsq enc
S04.2[0,1,2]XD	Inj of trochlear nerve, [unsp, rt, lt] side, subsq enc
S04.3[0,1,2]XD	Inj of trigeminal nerve, [unsp, rt, lt] side, subsq enc
S04.4[0,1,2]XD	Inj of abducent nerve, [unsp, rt, lt] side, subsq enc
S04.5[0,1,2]XD	Inj of facial nerve, [unsp, rt, lt] side, subsq enc
S04.6[0,1,2]XD	Inj of acoustic nerve, [unsp, rt, lt] side, subsq enc
S04.7[0,1,2]XD	Inj of accessory nerve, [unsp, rt, lt] side, subsq enc
S04.8[1,9][1,2,9]D	Inj of [olfactory (1st), oth cranial] nerve(s), [rt, lt, unsp] side, subsq enc
S04.9XXD	Inj of unsp cranial nerve, subsq enc
S05.0[0,1,2]XD	Inj of conjunctiva and corneal abrasion w/o FB, [rt, lt, unsp] eye, subsq enc
S05.1[0,1,2]XD	Contsn of eyeball and orbital tissues, [rt, lt, unsp] eye, subsq enc
S05.2[0,1,2]XD	Ocular lac and rupture w/ prolapse or loss of intraocular tissue, [rt, lt, unsp] eye, subsq enc
S05.3[0,1,2]XD	Ocular lac w/o prolapse or loss of intraocular tissue, [rt, lt, unsp] eye, subsq enc
S05.4[0,1,2]XD	Penetrating wnd of orbit w/ or w/o FB, [unsp, rt, lt] eye, subsq enc
S05.5[0,1,2]XD	Penetrating wnd w/ FB of [unsp, rt, lt] eyeball, subsq enc
S05.6[0,1,2]XD	Penetrating wnd w/o FB of [unsp, rt, lt] eyeball, subsq enc
S05.7[0,1,2]XD	Avulsion of [unsp, rt, lt] eye, subsq enc
S05.8X[1,2,9]D	Oth injuries of [rt, lt, unsp] eye and orbit, subsq enc
S05.9[0,1,2]XD	Unsp inj of [unsp, rt, lt] eye and orbit, subsq enc
S06.0X0D	Concussion w/o LOC, subs enc
S06.0X[1,2,3,4]D	Concussion w/ LOC of [30 min or less, 31-59 min, 1 hr to 5 hrs 59 min, 6 hrs to 24 hrs], subsq enc
S06.0X[5,6]D	Concussion w/ LOC of [> 24 hrs w/ return to pre-existing conscious lvl, > 24 hrs w/o return to pre-existing conscious lvl w/ patient surviving], subsq enc
S06.0X[7,8,9]D	Concussion w/ LOC of [any dur w/ death d/t brain inj prior to regain cnscness, any dur w/ death d/t oth cause prior to regain cnscness, unsp dur], subsq enc
S06.1X0D	Traum cerebral edema w/o LOC, subs
S06.1X[1,2,3,4]D	Traum cerebral edema w/ LOC of [30 min or less, 31 min to 59 min, 1 hr to 5 hrs 59 min, 6 hrs to 24 hrs], subsq enc
S06.1X[5,6]D	Traum cerebral edema w/ LOC [> 24 hrs w/ return to pre-existing conscious lvl, > 24 hrs w/o return to pre-existing conscious lvl w/ patient surviving], subsq enc
S06.1X[7,8,9]D	Traum cerebral edema w/ LOC of [any dur w/ death d/t brain inj prior to regain cnscness, any dur w/ death d/t oth cause prior to regain cnscness, unsp dur], subsq enc
S06.2X0D	Diffuse TBI w/o LOC, subs
S06.2X[1,2,3,4]D	Diffuse traum brain inj w/ LOC of [30 min or less, 31-59 min, 1 hr to 5 hrs 59 min, 6 hrs to 24 hrs], subsq enc
S06.2X[5,6]D	Diffuse traum brain inj w/ LOC of [> 24 hrs w/ return to pre-existing conscious lvl, > 24 hrs w/o return to pre-existing conscious lvl w/ patient surviving], subsq enc
S06.2X[7,8,9]D	Diffuse traum brain inj w/ LOC of [any dur w/ death d/t brain inj prior to regain cnscness, any dur w/ death d/t oth cause prior to regain cnscness, unsp dur], subsq enc
S06.300D	Unsp focal TBI w/o LOC, subs
S06.30[1,2,3,4]D	Unsp focal traum brain inj w/ LOC of [30 min or less, 31 min to 59 min, 1 hr to 5 hrs 59 min, 6 hrs to 24 hrs], subsq enc
S06.30[5,6]D	Unsp focal traum brain inj w/ LOC [> 24 hrs w/ return to pre-existing conscious lvl, > 24 hrs w/o return to pre-existing conscious lvl w/ patient surviving], subsq enc
S06.30[7,8,9]D	Unsp focal traum brain inj w/ LOC of [any dur w/ death d/t brain inj prior to regain cnscness, any dur w/ death d/t oth cause prior to regain cnscness, unsp dur], subsq enc
S06.310D	Contus/lac rt cerebrum w/o LOC, subs
S06.31[1,2,3,4]D	Contsn and lac of rt cerebrum w/ LOC of [30 min or less, 31 min to 59 min, 1 hr to 5 hrs 59 min, 6 hrs to 24 hrs], subsq enc
S06.31[5,6]D	Contsn and lac of rt cerebrum w/ LOC [> 24 hrs w/ return to pre-existing conscious lvl, > 24 hrs w/o return to pre-existing conscious lvl w/ patient surviving], subsq enc
S06.31[7,8,9]D	Contsn and lac of rt cerebrum w/ LOC of [any dur w/ death d/t brain inj prior to regain cnscness, any dur w/ death d/t oth cause prior to regain cnscness, unsp dur], subsq enc
S06.320D	Contus/lac lt cerebrum w/o LOC, subs
S06.32[1,2,3,4]D	Contsn and lac of lt cerebrum w/ LOC of [30 min or less, 31 min to 59 min, 1 hr to 5 hrs 59 min, 6 hrs to 24 hrs], subsq enc
S06.32[5,6]D	Contsn and lac of lt cerebrum w/ LOC [> 24 hrs w/ return to pre-existing conscious lvl, > 24 hrs w/o return to pre-existing conscious lvl w/ patient surviving], subsq enc

---

T **Transfer DRG**   SP **Special Payment**   * **Code Range**   **6th and 7th Character of ZZ = No Device, No Qualifier ZX = No Device, Diagnostic**

MS-DRG Version 33.0

S06.32[7,8,9]D	Contsn and lac of lt cerebrum w/ LOC of [any dur w/ death d/t brain inj prior to regain cnscness, any dur w/ death d/t oth cause prior to regain cnscness, unsp dur], subsq enc
S06.330D	Contus/lac cereb, w/o LOC, subs
S06.33[1,2,3,4]D	Contsn and lac of unsp cerebrum w/ LOC of [30 min or less, 31 min to 59 min, 1 hr to 5 hrs 59 min, 6 hrs to 24 hrs], subsq enc
S06.33[5,6]D	Contsn and lac of unsp cerebrum w/ LOC [> 24 hrs w/ return to pre-existing conscious lvl, > 24 hrs w/o return to pre-existing conscious lvl w/ patient surviving], subsq enc
S06.33[7,8,9]D	Contsn and lac of unsp cerebrum w/ LOC of [any dur w/ death d/t brain inj prior to regain cnscness, any dur w/ death d/t oth cause prior to regain cnscness, unsp dur], subsq enc
S06.340D	Traum hemor rt cerebrum w/o LOC, subs
S06.34[1,2,3,4]D	Traum hemor of rt cerebrum w/ LOC of [30 min or less, 31 min to 59 min, 1 hr to 5 hrs 59 min, 6 hrs to 24 hrs], subsq enc
S06.34[5,6]D	Traum hemor of rt cerebrum w/ LOC [> 24 hrs w/ return to pre-existing conscious lvl, > 24 hrs w/o return to pre-existing conscious lvl w/ patient surviving], subsq enc
S06.34[7,8,9]D	Traum hemor of rt cerebrum w/ LOC of [any dur w/ death d/t brain inj prior to regain cnscness, any dur w/ death d/t oth cause prior to regain cnscness, unsp dur], subsq enc
S06.350D	Traum hemor lt cerebrum w/o LOC, subs
S06.35[1,2,3,4]D	Traum hemor of lt cerebrum w/ LOC of [30 min or less, 31 min to 59 min, 1 hr to 5 hrs 59 min, 6 hrs to 24 hrs], subsq enc
S06.35[5,6]D	Traum hemor of lt cerebrum w/ LOC [> 24 hrs w/ return to pre-existing conscious lvl, > 24 hrs w/o return to pre-existing conscious lvl w/ patient surviving], subsq enc
S06.35[7,8,9]D	Traum hemor of lt cerebrum w/ LOC of [any dur w/ death d/t brain inj prior to regain cnscness, any dur w/ death d/t oth cause prior to regain cnscness, unsp dur], subsq enc
S06.360D	Traum hemor cereb, w/o LOC, subs
S06.36[1,2,3,4]D	Traum hemor of cerebrum, unsp, w/ LOC of [30 min or less, 31 min to 59 min, 1 hr to 5 hrs 59 min, 6 hrs to 24 hrs], subsq enc
S06.36[5,6]D	Traum hemor of cerebrum, unsp, w/ LOC [> 24 hrs w/ return to pre-existing conscious lvl, > 24 hrs w/o return to pre-existing conscious lvl w/ patient surviving], subsq enc
S06.36[7,8,9]D	Traum hemor of cerebrum, unsp, w/ LOC of [any dur w/ death d/t brain inj prior to regain cnscness, any dur w/ death d/t oth cause prior to regain cnscness, unsp dur], subsq enc
S06.370D	Contus/lac/hem crblm w/o LOC, subs
S06.37[1,2,3,4]D	Contsn, lac, and hemor of cerebellum w/ LOC of [30 min or less, 31 min to 59 min, 1 hr to 5 hrs 59 min, 6 hrs to 24 hrs], subsq enc
S06.37[5,6]D	Contsn, lac, and hemor of cerebellum w/ LOC [> 24 hrs w/ return to pre-existing conscious lvl, > 24 hrs w/o return to pre-existing conscious lvl w/ patient surviving], subsq enc
S06.37[7,8,9]D	Contsn, lac, and hemor of cerebellum w/ LOC of [any dur w/ death d/t brain inj prior to regain cnscness, any dur w/ death d/t oth cause prior to regain cnscness, unsp dur], subsq enc
S06.380D	Contus/lac/hem brainstem w/o LOC, subs
S06.38[1,2,3,4]D	Contsn, lac, and hemor of brainstem w/ LOC of [30 min or less, 31 min to 59 min, 1 hr to 5 hrs 59 min, 6 hrs to 24 hrs], subsq enc
S06.38[5,6]D	Contsn, lac, and hemor of brainstem w/ LOC [> 24 hrs w/ return to pre-existing conscious lvl, > 24 hrs w/o return to pre-existing conscious lvl w/ patient surviving], subsq enc
S06.38[7,8,9]D	Contsn, lac, and hemor of brainstem w/ LOC of [any dur w/ death d/t brain inj prior to regain cnscness, any dur w/ death d/t oth cause prior to regain cnscness, unsp dur], subsq enc
S06.4X0D	Epidural hemor w/o LOC, subs enc
S06.4X[1,2,3,4]D	Epidural hemor w/ LOC of [30 min or less, 31-59 min, 1 hr to 5 hrs 59 min, 6 hrs to 24 hrs], subsq enc
S06.4X[5,6]D	Epidural hemor w/ LOC of [> 24 hrs w/ return to pre-existing conscious lvl, > 24 hrs w/o return to pre-existing conscious lvl w/ patient surviving], subsq enc
S06.4X[7,8,9]D	Epidural hemor w/ LOC of [any dur w/ death d/t brain inj prior to regain cnscness, any dur w/ death d/t oth cause prior to regain cnscness, unsp dur], subsq enc
S06.5X0D	Traum subdr hem w/o LOC, subs
S06.5X[1,2,3,4]D	Traum subdural hemor w/ LOC of [30 min or less, 31-59 min, 1 hr to 5 hrs 59 min, 6 hrs to 24 hrs], subsq enc
S06.5X[5,6]D	Traum subdural hemor w/ LOC of [> 24 hrs w/ return to pre-existing conscious lvl, > 24 hrs w/o return to pre-existing conscious lvl w/ patient surviving], subsq enc
S06.5X[7,8,9]D	Traum subdural hemor w/ LOC of [any dur w/ death d/t brain inj prior to regain cnscness, any dur w/ death d/t oth cause prior to regain cnscness, unsp dur], subsq enc
S06.6X0D	Traum subrac hem w/o LOC, subs
S06.6X[1,2,3,4]D	Traum subarachnoid hemor w/ LOC of [30 min or less, 31-59 min, 1 hr to 5 hrs 59 min, 6 hrs to 24 hrs], subsq enc
S06.6X[5,6]D	Traum subarachnoid hemor w/ LOC of [> 24 hrs w/ return to pre-existing conscious lvl, > 24 hrs w/o return to pre-existing conscious lvl w/ patient surviving], subsq enc
S06.6X[7,8,9]D	Traum subarachnoid hemor w/ LOC of [any dur w/ death d/t brain inj prior to regain cnscness, any dur w/ death d/t oth cause prior to regain cnscness, unsp dur], subsq enc
S06.810D	Inj of Rt int carotid, intcr w/o LOC, subs
S06.81[1,2,3,4]D	Inj of rt int carotid artery, intracranial portion, NEC w/ LOC of [30 min or less, 31-59 min, 1 hr to 5 hrs 59 min, 6 hrs to 24 hrs], subsq enc
S06.81[5,6]D	Inj of rt int carotid artery, intracranial portion, NEC w/ LOC of [> 24 hrs w/ return to pre-existing conscious lvl, > 24 hrs w/o return to pre-existing conscious lvl w/ patient surviving], subsq enc
S06.81[7,8,9]D	Inj of rt int carotid artery, intracranial portion, NEC w/ LOC of [any dur w/ death d/t brain inj prior to regain cnscness, any dur w/ death d/t oth cause prior to regain cnscness, unsp dur], subsq enc
S06.820D	Inj of Lt int carotid, intcr w/o LOC, subs
S06.82[1,2,3,4]D	Inj of lt int carotid artery, intracranial portion, NEC w/ LOC of [30 min or less, 31-59 min, 1 hr to 5 hrs 59 min, 6 hrs to 24 hrs], subsq enc
S06.82[5,6]D	Inj of lt int carotid artery, intracranial portion, NEC w/ LOC of > 24 hrs [w/ return to pre-existing conscious lvl, w/o return to pre-existing conscious lvl w/ patient surviving], subsq enc
S06.82[7,8,9]D	Inj of lt int carotid artery, intracranial portion, NEC w/ LOC of [any dur w/ death d/t brain inj prior to regain cnscness, any dur w/ death d/t oth cause prior to regain cnscness, unsp dur], subsq enc
S06.890D	Intcran inj w/o LOC, subs enc
S06.89[1,2,3,4]D	Oth spec intracranial inj w/ LOC of [30 min or less, 31-59 min, 1 hr to 5 hrs 59 min, 6 hrs to 24 hrs], subsq enc
S06.89[5,6]D	Oth spec intracranial inj w/ LOC of [> 24 hrs w/ return to pre-existing conscious lvl, > 24 hrs w/o return to pre-existing conscious lvl w/ patient surviving], subsq enc
S06.89[7,8,9]D	Oth spec intracranial inj w/ LOC of [any dur w/ death d/t brain inj prior to regain cnscness, any dur w/ death d/t oth cause prior to regain cnscness, unsp dur], subsq enc
S06.9X0D	Unsp intracranial inj w/o LOC, subs
S06.9X[1,2,3,4]D	Unsp intracranial inj w/ LOC of [30 min or less, 31-59 min, 1 hr to 5 hrs 59 min, 6 hrs to 24 hrs], subsq enc
S06.9X[5,6]D	Unsp intracranial inj w/ LOC of > 24 hrs [w/ return to pre-existing conscious lvl, w/o return to pre-existing conscious lvl w/ patient surviving], subsq enc
S06.9X[7,8,9]D	Unsp intracranial inj w/ LOC of [any dur w/ death d/t brain inj prior to regain cnscness, any dur w/ death d/t oth cause prior to regain cnscness, unsp dur], subsq enc
S07.[0,1,8,9]XXD	Crushing inj of [face, skull, oth parts of head, head part unsp], subsq enc
S08.0XXD	Avulsion of scalp, subsq enc
S08.1[1,2][1,2,9]D	[Complete, Partial] traum amp of [rt, lt, unsp] ear, subsq enc
S08.81[1,2]	[Complete, Partial] traum amp of nose, subsq enc
S08.89XD	Traum amp of oth parts of head, subs enc
S09.0XXD	Inj of bld vessels of head, NEC, subs
S09.1[0,1,2,9]XD	[Unsp inj, strain, lac, oth spec inj] of muscle and tndn of head, subsq enc
S09.2[0,1,2]XD	Traum rupture of [unsp, rt, lt] ear drum, subsq enc
S09.30[1,2,9]D	Unsp inj of [rt, lt, unsp] mid and inner ear, subsq enc
S09.31[1,2,3,9]D	Primary blast inj of [rt, lt, bilat, unsp] ear, subsq enc
S09.39[1,2,9]D	Oth spec inj of [rt, lt, unsp] mid and inner ear, subsq enc
S09.8XXD	Oth spec injuries of head, subsq enc
S09.9[0,1,2,3]XD	Unsp inj of [head, ear, nose, face], subsq enc
S10.0XXD	Contsn of throat, subsq enc
S10.1[0,1,2,4,5,6,7]XD	[Unsp superf injuries, Abrasion, Blister, Ext constriction of part, Superf FB, Insect bite (nonvenomous), Oth superf bite] of throat, subsq enc
S10.83XD	Contsn of oth spec part of neck, subs enc
S10.8[0,1,2,4,5,6,7]XD	[Unsp superf injuries, Abrasion, Blister, Ext constriction of part, Superf FB, Insect bite (nonvenomous), Oth superf bite] of neck, subsq enc
S10.93XD	Contsn of unsp part of neck, subs enc
S10.9[0,1,2,4,5,6,7]XD	[Unsp superf injuries, Abrasion, Blister, Ext constriction of part, Superf FB, Insect bite (nonvenomous), Oth superf bite] of unsp part of neck, subsq enc
S11.01[1,2,3,4,5,9]D	[Lac w/o FB, Lac w/ FB, Punc wnd w/o FB, Punc wnd w/ FB, Opn bite, Unsp opn wnd], of larynx, subsq enc
S11.02[1,2,3,4,5,9]D	[Lac w/o FB, Lac w/ FB, Punc wnd w/o FB, Punc wnd w/ FB, Opn bite, Unsp opn wnd], of trachea, subsq enc
S11.03[1,2,3,4,5,9]D	[Lac w/o FB, Lac w/ FB, Punc wnd w/o FB, Punc wnd w/ FB, Opn bite, Unsp opn wnd], of vocal cord, subsq enc

Surgical	Medical	CC Indicator	MCC Indicator	Procedure Proxy	PDxMCC PDx acts as own MCC	PDxCC PDx acts as own CC

MDC 23: Factors Influencing Health Status And Other Contacts With Health Services—MEDICAL

Code	Description
S11.1[0,1,2,3,4,5]XD	[Unsp opn wnd, Lac w/o FB, Lac w/ FB, Punc wnd w/o FB of thyroid gland, Punc wnd w/ FB, Opn bite] of thyroid gland, subsq enc
S11.2[0,1,2,3,4,5]XD	[Unsp opn wnd, Lac w/o FB, Lac w/ FB, Punc wnd w/o FB of thyroid gland, Punc wnd w/ FB, Opn bite] of pharynx and cervical esophagus, subsq enc
S11.8[0,1,2,3,4,5,9]XD	[Unsp opn wnd, Lac w/o FB, Lac w/ FB, Punc wnd w/o FB of thyroid gland, Punc wnd w/ FB, Opn bite] of oth spec part of neck, subsq enc
S11.9[0,1,2,3,4,5]XD	[Unsp opn wnd, Lac w/o FB, Lac w/ FB, Punc wnd w/o FB of thyroid gland, Punc wnd w/ FB, Opn bite] of unsp part of neck, subsq enc
S13.0XXD	Traum rupture of cervical intervertebral disc, subs
S13.10[0,1]D	[Sublux, Disloc] of unsp cervical vertebrae, subsq enc
S13.11[0,1]D	[Sublux, Disloc] of C0/C1 cervical vertebrae, subsq enc
S13.12[0,1]D	[Sublux, Disloc] of C1/C2 cervical vertebrae, subsq enc
S13.13[0,1]D	[Sublux, Disloc] of C2/C3 cervical vertebrae, subsq enc
S13.14[0,1]D	[Sublux, Disloc] of C3/C4 cervical vertebrae, subsq enc
S13.15[0,1]D	[Sublux, Disloc] of C4/C5 cervical vertebrae, subsq enc
S13.16[0,1]D	[Sublux, Disloc] of C5/C6 cervical vertebrae, subsq enc
S13.17[0,1]D	[Sublux, Disloc] of C6/C7 cervical vertebrae, subsq enc
S13.18[0,1]D	[Sublux, Disloc] of C7/T1 cervical vertebrae, subsq enc
S13.2[0,9]XD	Disloc of [unsp, oth] parts of neck, subsq enc
S13.4XXD	Sprain of lgmt of cervical spine, subsq enc
S13.5XXD	Sprain of thyroid region, subsq enc
S13.8XXD	Sprain of jts and lgmt of oth prt neck, subs enc
S13.9XXD	Sprain of jts and lgmt of unsp parts of neck, subs
S14.0XXD	Concussion and edema of cervical spinal cord, subs enc
S14.10[1,2,3,4,5,6,7,8,9]D	Unsp inj at [C1, C2, C3, C4, C5, C6, C7, C8, unsp] lvl of cervical spinal cord, subsq enc
S14.11[1,2,3,4,5,6,7,8,9]D	Complete lesion at [C1, C2, C3, C4, C5, C6, C7, C8, unsp] lvl of cervical spinal cord, subsq enc
S14.12[1,2,3,4,5,6,7,8,9]D	Central cord synd at [C1, C2, C3, C4, C5, C6, C7, C8, unsp] lvl of cervical spinal cord, subsq enc
S14.13[1,2,3,4,5,6,7,8,9]D	Ant cord synd at [C1, C2, C3, C4, C5, C6, C7, C8, unsp] lvl of cervical spinal cord, subsq enc
S14.14[1,2,3,4,5,6,7,8,9]D	Brown-Sequard synd at [C1, C2, C3, C4, C5, C6, C7, C8, unsp] lvl of cervical spinal cord, subsq enc
S14.15[1,2,3,4,5,6,7,8,9]D	Oth incomplete lesion at [C1, C2, C3, C4, C5, C6, C7, C8, unsp] lvl of cervical spinal cord, subsq enc
S14.[2,3,4,5,8,9]XXD	Inj of [nerve root of cervical spine, brachial plexus, peripheral nerves of neck, cervical sympathetic nerves, oth spec nerves of neck, unsp nerves of neck], subsq enc
S15.00[1,2,9]D	Unsp inj of [rt, lt, unsp] carotid artery, subsq enc
S15.01[1,2,9]D	Minor lac of [rt, lt, unsp] carotid artery, subsq enc
S15.02[1,2,9]D	Major lac of [rt, lt, unsp] carotid artery, subsq enc
S15.09[1,2,9]D	Oth spec inj of [rt, lt, unsp] carotid artery, subsq enc
S15.10[1,2,9]D	Unsp inj of [rt, lt, unsp] vert artery, subsq enc
S15.11[1,2,9]D	Minor lac of [rt, lt, unsp] vert artery, subsq enc
S15.12[1,2,9]D	Major lac of [rt, lt, unsp] vert artery, subsq enc
S15.19[1,2,9]D	Oth spec inj of [rt, lt, unsp] vert artery, subsq enc
S15.20[1,2,9]D	Unsp inj of [rt, lt, unsp] ext jugular vein, subsq enc
S15.21[1,2,9]D	Minor lac of [rt, lt, unsp] ext jugular vein, subsq enc
S15.22[1,2,9]D	Major lac of [rt, lt, unsp] ext jugular vein, subsq enc
S15.29[1,2,9]D	Oth spec inj of [rt, lt, unsp] ext jugular vein, subsq enc
S15.30[1,2,9]D	Unsp inj of [rt, lt, unsp] int jugular vein, subsq enc
S15.31[1,2,9]D	Minor lac of [rt, lt, unsp] int jugular vein, subsq enc
S15.32[1,2,9]D	Major lac of [rt, lt, unsp] int jugular vein, subsq enc
S15.39[1,2,9]D	Oth spec inj of [rt, lt, unsp] int jugular vein, subsq enc
S15.8XXD	Inj of oth bld vessels at neck lvl, subs enc
S15.9XXD	Inj of unsp bld vessel at neck lvl, subs enc
S16.[1,2,8,9]XXD	[Strain, Lac, Oth spec inj, Unsp inj] of muscle, fascia and tndn at neck lvl, subsq enc
S17.0XXD	Crushing inj of larynx and trachea, subsq enc
S17.8XXD	Crushing inj of oth parts of neck, subsq enc
S17.9XXD	Crushing inj of neck, part unsp, subs enc
S19.8[0,1,2,3,4,5,9]XD	Oth spec injuries of [unsp part of neck, larynx, cervical trachea, vocal cord, thyroid gland, pharynx and cervical esophagus, oth spec part of neck], unspifed inj of neck, subsq enc
S19.9XXD	Unsp inj of neck, subsq enc
S20.0[0,1,2]XD	Contsn of breast, [unsp, rt, lt] breast, subsq enc
S20.10[1,2,9]D	Unsp superf injuries of breast, [rt, lt, unsp] breast, subsq enc
S20.11[1,2,9]D	Abrasion of breast, [rt, lt, unsp] breast, subsq enc
S20.12[1,2,9]D	Blister (nonthermal) of breast, [rt, lt, unsp] breast, subsq enc
S20.14[1,2,9]D	Ext constriction of part of breast, [rt, lt, unsp] breast, subsq enc
S20.15[1,2,9]D	Superf FB of breast, [rt, lt, unsp] breast, subsq enc
S20.16[1,2,9]D	Insect bite (nonvenomous) of breast, [rt, lt, unsp] breast, subsq enc
S20.17[1,2,9]D	Oth superf bite of breast, [rt, lt, unsp] breast, subsq enc
S20.20XD	Contsn of thorax, unsp, subsq enc
S20.21[1,2,9]D	Contsn of [rt, lt, unsp] front wall of thorax, subsq enc
S20.22[1,2,9]D	Contsn of [rt, lt, unsp] back wall of thorax, subsq enc
S20.30[1,2,9]D	Unsp superf injuries of [rt, lt, unsp] front wall of thorax, subsq enc
S20.31[1,2,9]D	Abrasion of [rt, lt, unsp] front wall of thorax, subsq enc
S20.32[1,2,9]D	Blister (nonthermal) of [rt, lt, unsp] front wall of thorax, subsq enc
S20.34[1,2,9]D	Ext constriction of [rt, lt, unsp] front wall of thorax, subsq enc
S20.35[1,2,9]D	Superf FB of [rt, lt, unsp] front wall of thorax, subsq enc
S20.36[1,2,9]D	Insect bite (nonvenomous) of [rt, lt, unsp] front wall of thorax, subsq enc
S20.37[1,2,9]D	Oth superf bite of [rt, lt, unsp] front wall of thorax, subsq enc
S20.40[1,2,9]D	Unsp superf injuries of [rt, lt, unsp] back wall of thorax, subsq enc
S20.41[1,2,9]D	Abrasion of [rt, lt, unsp] back wall of thorax, subsq enc
S20.42[1,2,9]D	Blister (nonthermal) of [rt, lt, unsp] back wall of thorax, subsq enc
S20.44[1,2,9]D	Ext constriction of [rt, lt, unsp] back wall of thorax, subsq enc
S20.45[1,2,9]D	Superf FB of [rt, lt, unsp] back wall of thorax, subsq enc
S20.46[1,2,9]D	Insect bite (nonvenomous) of [rt, lt, unsp] back wall of thorax, subsq enc
S20.47[1,2,9]D	Oth superf bite of [rt, lt, unsp] back wall of thorax, subsq enc
S20.9[0,1,2,4,5,6,7]XD	[Unsp superf inj, Abrasion, Blister (nonthermal), Ext constriction, Superf FB, Insect bite (nonvenomous), Oth superf bite] of unsp parts of thorax, subsq enc
S21.00[1,2,9]D	Unsp opn wnd of [rt, lt, unsp] breast, subsq enc
S21.01[1,2,9]D	Lac w/o FB of [rt, lt, unsp] breast, subsq enc
S21.02[1,2,9]D	Lac w/ FB of [rt, lt, unsp] breast, subsq enc
S21.03[1,2,9]D	Punc wnd w/o FB of [rt, lt, unsp] breast, subsq enc
S21.04[1,2,9]D	Punc wnd w/ FB of [rt, lt, unsp] breast, subsq enc
S21.05[1,2,9]D	Opn bite of [rt, lt, unsp] breast, subsq enc
S21.10[1,2,9]D	Unsp opn wnd of [rt, lt, unpsecified] front wall of thorax w/o penetration into thoracic cavity, subsq enc
S21.11[1,2,9]D	Lac w/o FB of [rt, lt, unpsecified] front wall of thorax w/o penetration into thoracic cavity, subsq enc
S21.12[1,2,9]D	Lac w/ FB of [rt, lt, unpsecified] front wall of thorax w/o penetration into thoracic cavity, subsq enc
S21.13[1,2,9]D	Punc wnd w/o FB of [rt, lt, unpsecified] front wall of thorax w/o penetration into thoracic cavity, subsq enc
S21.14[1,2,9]D	Punc wnd w/ FB of [rt, lt, unpsecified] front wall of thorax w/o penetration into thoracic cavity, subsq enc
S21.15[1,2,9]D	Opn wnd w/ FB of [rt, lt, unpsecified] front wall of thorax w/o penetration into thoracic cavity, subsq enc
S21.20[1,2,9]D	Unsp opn wnd of [rt, lt, unpsecified] back wall of thorax w/o penetration into thoracic cavity, subsq enc
S21.21[1,2,9]D	Lac w/o FB of [rt, lt, unpsecified] back wall of thorax w/o penetration into thoracic cavity, subsq enc
S21.22[1,2,9]D	Lac w/ FB of [rt, lt, unpsecified] back wall of thorax w/o penetration into thoracic cavity, subsq enc
S21.23[1,2,9]D	Punc wnd w/o FB of [rt, lt, unpsecified] back wall of thorax w/o penetration into thoracic cavity, subsq enc
S21.24[1,2,9]D	Punc wnd w/ FB of [rt, lt, unpsecified] back wall of thorax w/o penetration into thoracic cavity, subsq enc
S21.25[1,2,9]D	Opn wnd w/ FB of [rt, lt, unpsecified] back wall of thorax w/o penetration into thoracic cavity, subsq enc
S21.30[1,2,9]D	Unsp opn wnd of [rt, lt, unpsecified] front wall of thorax w/ penetration into thoracic cavity, subsq enc
S21.31[1,2,9]D	Lac w/o FB of [rt, lt, unpsecified] front wall of thorax w/ penetration into thoracic cavity, subsq enc
S21.32[1,2,9]D	Lac w/ FB of [rt, lt, unpsecified] front wall of thorax w/ penetration into thoracic cavity, subsq enc
S21.33[1,2,9]D	Punc wnd w/o FB of [rt, lt, unpsecified] front wall of thorax w/ penetration into thoracic cavity, subsq enc
S21.34[1,2,9]D	Punc wnd w/ FB of [rt, lt, unpsecified] front wall of thorax w/ penetration into thoracic cavity, subsq enc
S21.35[1,2,9]D	Opn bite of [rt, lt, unpsecified] front wall of thorax w/ penetration into thoracic cavity, subsq enc
S21.40[1,2,9]D	Unsp opn wnd of [rt, lt, unpsecified] back wall of thorax w/ penetration into thoracic cavity, subsq enc
S21.41[1,2,9]D	Lac w/o FB of [rt, lt, unpsecified] back wall of thorax w/ penetration into thoracic cavity, subsq enc
S21.42[1,2,9]D	Lac w/ FB of [rt, lt, unpsecified] back wall of thorax w/ penetration into thoracic cavity, subsq enc
S21.43[1,2,9]D	Punc wnd w/o FB of [rt, lt, unpsecified] back wall of thorax w/ penetration into thoracic cavity, subsq enc
S21.44[1,2,9]D	Punc wnd w/ FB of [rt, lt, unpsecified] back wall of thorax w/ penetration into thoracic cavity, subsq enc

---

☐ **Transfer DRG**   ⓈⓅ **Special Payment**   * **Code Range**   **6th and 7th Character of ZZ = No Device, No Qualifier ZX = No Device, Diagnostic**

S21.45[1,2,9]D   Opn wnd w/ FB of [rt, lt, unspecified] back wall of thorax w/ penetration into thoracic cavity, subsq enc

S21.9[0,1,2,3,4,5]XD   [Unsp opn wnd, Lac w/ FB, Lac w/ FB, Punc wnd w/o FB, Punc wnd w/ FB, Opn bite] of unsp part of thorax, subsq enc

S23.0XXD   Traum rupture of thoracic intervertebral disc, subs

S23.10[0,1]D   [Sublux, Disclocation] of unsp thoracic vertebra, subsq enc

S23.11[0,1]D   [Sublux, Disloc] of T1/T2 thoracic vertebra, subsq enc

S23.12[0,1,2,3]D   [Sublux, Disloc] of [T2/T3, T3/T4] thoracic vertebra, subsq enc

S23.13[0,1,2,3]D   [Sublux, Disloc] of [T4/T5, T5/T6] thoracic vertebra, subsq enc

S23.14[0,1,2,3]D   [Sublux, Disloc] of [T6/T7, T7/T8] thoracic vertebra, subsq enc

S23.15[0,1,2,3]D   [Sublux, Disloc] of [T8/T9, T9/T10] thoracic vertebra, subsq enc

S23.16[0,1,2,3]D   [Sublux, Disloc] of [T10/T11, T11/T12] thoracic vertebra, subsq enc

S23.17[0,1]D   [Sublux, Disloc] of T12/L1 thoracic vertebra, subsq enc

S23.2[0,9]XD   Disloc of [unsp part, oth parts] of thorax, subsq enc

S23.3XXD   Sprain of lgmt of thoracic spine, subsq enc

S23.41XD   Sprain of ribs, subsq enc

S23.42[0,1,8,9]D   Sprain of [sternoclavicular (jt) (lgmt), chondrosternal jt], Oth sprain of sternum, Unsp sprain of sternum, subsq enc

S23.8XXD   Sprain of oth spec parts of thorax, subs enc

S23.9XXD   Sprain of unsp parts of thorax, subsq enc

S24.0XXD   Concussion and edema of thoracic spinal cord, subs enc

S24.10[1,2,3,4,9]D   Unsp inj at (T1, T2-T6, T7-T10, T11-T12, unsp) lvl of thoracic spinal cord, subsq enc

S24.11[1,2,3,4,9]D   Complete lesion at [T1, T2-T6, T7-T10, T11-T12, unsp) lvl of thoracic spinal cord, subsq enc

S24.13[1,2,3,4,9]D   Ant cord synd at [T1, T2-T6, T7-T10, T11-T12, unsp) lvl of thoracic spinal cord, subsq enc

S24.14[1,2,3,4,9]D   Brown-Sequard synd at [T1, T2-T6, T7-T10, T11-T12, unsp] lvl of thoracic spinal cord, subsq enc

S24.15[1,2,3,4,9]D   Oth incomplete lesion at [T1, T2-T6, T7-T10, T11-T12, unsp] lvl of thoracic spinal cord, subsq enc

S24.2XXD   Inj of nerve root of thoracic spine, subsq enc

S24.3XXD   Inj of peripheral nerves of thorax, subsq enc

S24.4XXD   Inj of thoracic sympathetic nervous sys, subs enc

S24.8XXD   Inj of oth spec nerves of thorax, subs enc

S24.9XXD   Inj of unsp nerve of thorax, subsq enc

S25.0[0,1,2,9]XD   [Unsp inj, Minor lac, Major lac, Oth spec inj] of thoracic aorta, subsq enc

S25.10[1,2,9]D   Unsp inj of [rt, lt, unsp] innominate or subclavian artery, subsq enc

S25.11[1,2,9]D   Minor lac of [rt, lt, unsp] innominate or subclavian artery, subsq enc

S25.12[1,2,9]D   Major lac of [rt, lt, unsp] innominate or subclavian artery, subsq enc

S25.19[1,2,9]D   Oth spec inj of [rt, lt, unsp] innominate or subclavian artery, subsq enc

S25.2[0,1,2,9]XD   [Unsp inj, Minor lac, Major lac, Oth spec inj] of superior vena cava, subsq enc

S25.30[1,2,9]D   Unsp inj of [rt, lt, unsp] innominate or subclavian vein, subsq enc

S25.31[1,2,9]D   Minor lac of [rt, lt, unsp] innominate or subclavian vein, subsq enc

S25.32[1,2,9]D   Major lac of [rt, lt, unsp] innominate or subclavian vein, subsq enc

S25.39[1,2,9]D   Oth spec inj of [rt, lt, unsp] innominate or subclavian vein, subsq enc

S25.40[1,2,9]D   Unsp inj of [rt, lt, unsp] pulmn bld vessels, subsq enc

S25.41[1,2,9]D   Minor lac of [rt, lt, unsp] pulmn bld vessels, subsq enc

S25.42[1,2,9]D   Major lac of [rt, lt, unsp] pulmn bld vessels, subsq enc

S25.49[1,2,9]D   Oth spec inj of [rt, lt, unsp] pulmn bld vessels, subsq enc

S25.50[1,2,9]D   Unsp inj of intercostal bld vessels, [rt, lt, unsp] side, subsq enc

S25.51[1,2,9]D   Lac of intercostal bld vessels, [rt, lt, unsp] side, subsq enc

S25.59[1,2,9]D   Oth spec inj of intercostal bld vessels, [rt, lt, unsp] side, subsq enc

S25.80[1,2,9]D   Unsp inj of oth bld vessels of thorax, [rt, lt, unsp] side, subsq enc

S25.81[1,2,9]D   Lac of oth bld vessels of thorax, [rt, lt, unsp] side, subsq enc

S25.89[1,2,9]D   Oth spec inj of oth bld vessels of thorax, [rt, lt, unsp] side, subsq enc

S25.9[0,1,9]XD   [Unsp inj, Lac, Oth spec inj] of unsp bld vessel of thorax, subsq enc

S26.02[0,1,2]D   [Mild, Mod, Major] lac of heart w/ hemopericardium, subsq enc

S26.09XD   Oth inj of heart with hemopericardium, subs enc

S26.0[0,1]XD   [Unsp inj, Contsn] of heart w/ hemopericardium, subsq enc

S26.1[0,1,2,9]XD   [Unsp inj, Contsn, Lac, Oth inj] of heart w/o hemopericardium, subsq enc

S26.9[0,1,2,9]XD   [Unsp inj, Contsn, Lac, Oth inj] unsp, w/ or w/o hemopericardium, subsq enc

S27.0XXD   Traum pneumothorax, subsq enc

S27.1XXD   Traum hemothorax, subsq enc

S27.2XXD   Traum hemopneumothorax, subsq enc

S27.30[1,2,9]D   Unsp inj of lung, [unilat, bilat, unsp], subsq enc

S27.31[1,2,9]D   Primary blast inj of lung, [unilat, bilat, unsp], subsq enc

S27.32[1,2,9]D   Contsn of lung, [unilat, bilat, unsp], subsq enc

S27.33[1,2,9]D   Lac of lung, [unilat, bilat, unsp], subsq enc

S27.39[1,2,9]D   Oth injuries of lung, [unilat, bilat, unsp], subsq enc

S27.40[1,2,9]D   Unsp inj of bronchus, [unilat, bilat, unsp], subsq enc

S27.41[1,2,9]D   Primary blast inj of bronchus, [unilat, bilat, unsp], subsq enc

S27.42[1,2,9]D   Contsn of bronchus, [unilat, bilat, unsp], subsq enc

S27.43[1,2,9]D   Lac of bronchus, [unilat, bilat, unsp], subsq enc

S27.49[1,2,9]D   Oth injuries of bronchus, [unilat, bilat, unsp], subsq enc

S27.5[0,1,2,3,9]XD   [Unsp inj, Primary blast inj, Contsn, Lac, Oth inj] of thoracic trachea, subsq enc

S27.6[0,3,9]XD   [Unsp inj, Lac, Oth inj] of pleura, subsq enc

S27.80[2,3,8,9]D   [Contsn, Lac, Oth inj, Unsp inj] of diaphragm, subsq enc

S27.81[2,3,8,9]D   [Contsn, Lac, Oth inj, Unsp inj] of esophagus [thoracic part], subsq enc

S27.89[2,3,8,9]D   [Contsn, Lac, Oth inj, Unsp inj] of oth spec intrathoracic organs, subsq enc

S27.9XXD   Inj of unsp intrathoracic organ, subs enc

S28.0XXD   Crushed chest, subsq enc

S28.1XXD   Traum amp of part of thorax, except breast, subs

S28.21[1,2,9]D   Complete traum amp of [rt, lt, unsp] breast, subsq enc

S28.22[1,2,9]D   Partial traum amp of [rt, lt, unsp] breast, subsq enc

S29.00[1,2,9]D   Unsp inj of muscle and tndn of [front, back, unsp] wall of thorax, subsq enc

S29.01[1,2,9]D   Strain of muscle and tndn of [front, back, unsp] wall of thorax, subsq enc

S29.02[1,2,9]D   Lac of muscle and tndn of [front, back, unsp] wall of thorax, subsq enc

S29.09[1,2,9]D   Oth inj of muscle and tndn of [front, back, unsp] wall of thorax, subsq enc

S29.8XXD   Oth spec injuries of thorax, subsq enc

S29.9XXD   Unsp inj of thorax, subsq enc

S30.0XXD   Contsn of lwr back and pelvis, subsq enc

S30.1XXD   Contsn of abd wall, subsq enc

S30.201D   Contsn of unsp ext genital organ, male, subs enc

S30.202D   Contsn of unsp ext genital organ, female, subs

S30.2[1,2,3]XD   Contsn of [penis, scrotum and testes, vagina and vulva], subsq enc

S30.3XXD   Contsn of anus, subsq enc

S30.81[0,1,2,3,4,5,6,7]D   Abrasion of [lwr back and pelvis, abd wall, penis, scrotum and testes, vagina and vulva, unsp ext genital organs male, unsp ext genital organs female, anus], subsq enc

S30.82[0,1,2,3,4,5,6,7]D   Blister [nonthermal] of [lwr back and pelvis, abd wall, penis, scrotum and testes, vagina and vulva, unsp ext genital organs male, unsp ext genital organs female, anus], subsq enc

S30.84[0,1,2,3,4,5,6]D   Ext constriction of [lwr back and pelvis, abd wall, penis, scrotum and testes, vagina and vulva, unsp ext genital organs male, unsp ext genital organs female], subsq enc

S30.85[0,1,2,3,4,5,6,7]D   Superf FB of [lwr back and pelvis, abd wall, penis, scrotum and testes, vagina and vulva, unsp ext genital organs male, unsp ext genital organs female, anus], subsq enc

S30.86[0,1,2,3,4,5,6,7]D   Insect bite [nonvenomous] of [lwr back and pelvis, abd wall, penis, scrotum and testes, vagina and vulva, unsp ext genital organs male, unsp ext genital organs female, anus], subsq enc

S30.87[0,1,2,3,4,5,6,7]D   Oth superf bite of [lwr back and pelvis, abd wall, penis, scrotum and testes, vagina and vulva, unsp ext genital organs male, unsp ext genital organs female, anus], subsq enc

S30.9[1,2,3,4,5,6,7,8]XD   Unsp superf inj of [lwr back and pelvis, abd wall, penis, scrotum and testes, vagina and vulva, unsp ext genital organs male, unsp ext genital organs female, anus], subsq enc

S31.00[0,1]D   Unsp opn wnd of lwr back and pelvis [w/o, w/] penetration into retroperitoneum, subsq enc

S31.01[0,1]D   Lac w/o FB of lwr back and pelvis [w/o, w/] penetration into retroperitoneum, subsq enc

S31.02[0,1]D   Lac w/ FB of lwr back and pelvis [w/o, w/] penetration into retroperitoneum, subsq enc

S31.03[0,1]D   Punc wnd w/o FB of lwr back and pelvis [w/o, w/] penetration into retroperitoneum, subsq enc

S31.04[0,1]D   Punc wnd w/ FB of lwr back and pelvis [w/o, w/] penetration into retroperitoneum, subsq enc

S31.05[0,1]D   Opn bite of lwr back and pelvis [w/o,w/] penetration into retroperitoneum, subsq enc

---

Surgical   **Medical**   **CC Indicator**   **MCC Indicator**   **Procedure Proxy**   **PDx MCC** PDx acts as own MCC   **PDx CC** PDx acts as own CC

MDC 23: Factors Influencing Health Status And Other Contacts With Health Services—MEDICAL

S31.10[0,1,2,3,4,5,9]D Unsp opn wnd of abd wall, [rt upr quadrant, lt upr quadrant, epigastric rgn, rt lwr quadrant, lt lwr quadrant, periumbilic rgn, unsp quadrant], w/o penetration into peritoneal cavity, subsq enc

S31.11[0,1,2,3,4,5,9]D Lac w/o FB, [rt upr quadrant, lt upr quadrant, epigastric rgn, rt lwr quadrant, lt lwr quadrant, periumbilic rgn, unsp quadrant], w/o penetration into peritoneal cavity, subsq enc

S31.12[0,1,2,3,4,5,9]D Lac of abd wall w/ FB, [rt upr quadrant, lt upr quadrant, epigastric rgn, rt lwr quadrant, lt lwr quadrant, periumbilic rgn, unsp quadrant], w/o penetration into peritoneal cavity, subsq enc

S31.13[0,1,2,3,4,5,9]D Punc wnd of abd wall w/o FB, [rt upr quadrant, lt upr quadrant, epigastric rgn, rt lwr quadrant, lt lwr quadrant, periumbilic rgn, unsp quadrant], w/o penetration into peritoneal cavity, subsq enc

S31.14[0,1,2,3,4,5,9]D Punc wnd of abd wall w/ FB, [rt upr quadrant, lt upr quadrant, epigastric rgn, rt lwr quadrant, lt lwr quadrant, periumbilic rgn, unsp quadrant], w/o penetration into peritoneal cavity, subsq enc

S31.15[0,1,2,3,4,5,9]D Opn bite of abd wall w/ FB, [rt upr quadrant, lt upr quadrant, epigastric rgn, rt lwr quadrant, lt lwr quadrant, periumbilic rgn, unsp quadrant], w/o penetration into peritoneal cavity, subsq enc

S31.2[0,1,2,3,4,5]XD [Unsp opn wnd, Lac w/o FB, Lac w/ FB, Punc wnd w/o FB, Punc wnd w/ FB, Opn bite] of penis, subsq enc

S31.3[0,1,2,3,4,5]XD [Unsp opn wnd, Lac w/o FB, Lac w/ FB, Punc wnd w/o FB, Punc wnd w/ FB, Opn bite] of scrotum and testes, subsq enc

S31.4[0,1,2,3,4,5]XD [Unsp opn wnd, Lac w/o FB, Lac w/ FB, Punc wnd w/o FB, Punc wnd w/ FB, Opn bite] of vagina and vulva, subsq enc

S31.50[1,2]D Unsp opn wnd of unsp ext genital organs, [male, female], subsq enc

S31.51[1,2]D Lac w/o FB of unsp ext genital organs, [male, female], subsq enc

S31.52[1,2]D Lac w/ FB of unsp ext genital organs, [male, female], subsq enc

S31.53[1,2]D Punc wnd w/o FB of unsp ext genital organs, [male, female], subsq enc

S31.54[1,2]D Punc wnd w/ FB of unsp ext genital organs, [male, female], subsq enc

S31.55[1,2]D Opn bite of unsp ext genital organs, [male, female], subsq enc

S31.60[0,1,2,3,4,5,9]D Unsp opn wnd of abd wall, [rt upr quadrant, lt upr quadrant, epigastric rgn, rt lwr quadrant, lt lwr quadrant, periumbilic rgn, unsp quadrant], w/ penetration into peritoneal cavity, subsq enc

S31.61[0,1,2,3,4,5,9]D Lac w/o FB, [rt upr quadrant, lt upr quadrant, epigastric rgn, rt lwr quadrant, lt lwr quadrant, periumbilic rgn, unsp quadrant], w/ penetration into peritoneal cavity, subsq enc

S31.62[0,1,2,3,4,5,9]D Lac of abd wall w/ FB, [rt upr quadrant, lt upr quadrant, epigastric rgn, rt lwr quadrant, lt lwr quadrant, periumbilic rgn, unsp quadrant], w/ penetration into peritoneal cavity, subsq enc

S31.63[0,1,2,3,4,5,9]D Punc wnd of abd wall w/o FB, [rt upr quadrant, lt upr quadrant, epigastric rgn, rt lwr quadrant, lt lwr quadrant, periumbilic rgn, unsp quadrant], w/ penetration into peritoneal cavity, subsq enc

S31.64[0,1,2,3,4,5,9]D Punc wnd of abd wall w/ FB, [rt upr quadrant, lt upr quadrant, epigastric rgn, rt lwr quadrant, lt lwr quadrant, periumbilic rgn, unsp quadrant], w/ penetration into peritoneal cavity, subsq enc

S31.65[0,1,2,3,4,5,9]D Opn bite of abd wall w/ FB, [rt upr quadrant, lt upr quadrant, epigastric rgn, rt lwr quadrant, lt lwr quadrant, periumbilic rgn, unsp quadrant], w/ penetration into peritoneal cavity, subsq enc

S31.80[1,2,3,4,5,9]D [Lac w/o FB, Lac w/ FB, Punc wnd w/o FB, Punc wnd w/ FB, Opn bite, Unsp opn wnd] of unsp buttock, subsq enc

S31.81[1,2,3,4,5,9]D [Lac w/o FB, Lac w/ FB, Punc wnd w/o FB, Punc wnd w/ FB, Opn bite, Unsp opn wnd] of rt buttock, subsq enc

S31.82[1,2,3,4,5,9]D [Lac w/o FB, Lac w/ FB, Punc wnd w/o FB, Punc wnd w/ FB, Opn bite, Unsp opn wnd] of lt buttock, subsq enc

S31.83[1,2,3,4,5,9]D [Lac w/o FB, Lac w/ FB, Punc wnd w/o FB, Punc wnd w/ FB, Opn bite, Unsp opn wnd] of anus, subsq enc

S33.0XXD Traum rupture of lumbar intervertebral disc, subs enc
S33.10[0,1]D [Sublux, Disloc] of unsp lumbar vertebra, subsq enc
S33.11[0,1]D [Sublux, Disloc] of L1/L2 lumbar vertebra, subsq enc
S33.12[0,1]D [Sublux, Disloc] of L2/L3 lumbar vertebra, subsq enc
S33.13[0,1]D [Sublux, Disloc] of L3/L4 lumbar vertebra, subsq enc
S33.14[0,1]D [Sublux, Disloc] of L4/L5 lumbar vertebra, subsq enc
S33.2XXD Disloc of sacroiliac and sacrococcygeal jt, subs
S33.30XD Disloc of unsp parts of lumbar spine and pelvis, subs
S33.39XD Disloc of oth prt lumbar spine and pelvis, subs enc

S33.4XXD Traum rupture of symphysis pubis, subsq enc
S33.5XXD Sprain of lgmt of lumbar spine, subsq enc
S33.6XXD Sprain of sacroiliac jt, subsq enc
S33.8XXD Sprain of oth parts of lumbar spine and pelvis, subs enc
S33.9XXD Sprain of unsp parts of lumbar spine and pelvis, subs enc
S34.0[1,2]XD Concussion and edema of [lumbar, sacral] spinal cord, subsq enc
S34.10[1,2,3,4,5,unsp]D Unsp inj to [L1, L2, L3, L4, L5, unsp] lvl of lumbar spinal cord, subsq enc
S34.11[1,2,3,4,5,9]D Complete lesion of [L1, L2, L3, L4, L5, unsp] lvl of lumbar spinal cord, subsq enc
S34.12[1,2,3,4,5,9]D Incomplete lesion of [L1, L2, L3, L4, L5, unsp] lvl of lumbar spinal cord, subsq enc
S34.13[1,2,9]D [Complete lesion, Incomplete lesion, Unsp inj] of sacral spinal cord, subsq enc
S34.2[1,2]XD Inj of nerve root of [lumbar, sacral] spine, subsq enc
S34.3XXD Inj of cauda equina, subsq enc
S34.4XXD Inj of lumbosacral plexus, subsq enc
S34.5XXD Inj of lumbar, sacral and pelvic sympathetic nerves, subs
S34.6XXD Inj prph nerve(s) at abd, low back and pelvis lvl, subs
S34.8XXD Inj of nerves at abd, low back and pelvis lvl, subs
S34.9XXD Inj unsp nerves at abd, low back and pelvis lvl, subs
S35.0[0,1,2,9]XD [Minor lac, Major lac, Oth inj] of abd aorta, subsq enc
S35.1[0,1,2,9]XD [Unsp inj, Minor lac, Major lac, Oth inj] of inferior vena cava, subsq enc
S35.21[1,2,8,9]D [Minor lac, Major lac, Oth inj, Unsp inj] of celiac artery, subsq enc
S35.22[1,2,8,9]D [Minor lac, Major lac, Oth inj, Unsp inj] of superior mesenteric artery, subsq enc
S35.23[1,2,8,9]D [Minor lac, Major lac, Oth inj, Unsp inj] of inferior mesenteric artery, subsq enc
S35.29[1,2,8,9]D [Minor lac, Major lac, Oth inj, Unsp inj] of celiac and mesenteric artery, subsq enc
S35.31[1,8,9]D [Lac, Oth spec inj, Unsp inj] of portal vein, subsq enc
S35.32[1,8,9]D [Lac, Oth spec inj, Unsp inj] of splenic vein, subsq enc
S35.33[1,8,9]D [Lac, Oth spec inj, Unsp inj] of superior mesenteric vein, subsq enc
S35.34[1,8,9]D [Lac, Oth spec inj, Unsp inj] of inferior mesenteric vein, subsq enc
S35.40[1,2,3,4,5,6]D Unsp inj of [rt renal artery, lt renal artery, unsp renal artery, rt renal vein, lt renal vein, unsp renal vein], subsq enc
S35.41[1,2,3,4,5,6]D Lac of [rt renal artery, lt renal artery, unsp renal artery, rt renal vein, lt renal vein, unsp renal vein], subsq enc
S35.49[1,2,3,4,5,6]D Oth spec inj of [rt renal artery, lt renal artery, unsp renal artery, rt renal vein, lt renal vein, unsp renal vein], subsq enc
S35.50XD Inj of unsp iliac bld vessel(s), subs enc
S35.51[1,2,3,4,5,6]D Inj of [rt iliac artery, lt iliac artery, unsp iliac artery, rt iliac vein, lt iliac vein, unsp iliac vein] subsq enc
S35.53[1,2,3,4,5,6]D Inj of [rt uterine artery, lt uterine artery, unsp uterine artery, rt uterine vein, lt uterine vein, unsp uterine vein] subsq enc
S35.59XD Inj of oth iliac bld vessels, subsq enc
S35.8X[1,8,9]D [Lac, Oth spec inj, Unsp inj] of oth bld vessels at abd, lwr back and pelvis lvl, subsq enc
S35.9[0,1,9]XD [Unsp inj, Lac, Oth spec inj] of unsp bld vessel at abd, lwr back and pelvis lvl, subsq enc
S36.00XD Unsp inj of spleen, subsq enc
S36.02[0,1,9]D [Minor, Major, Unsp] contsn of spleen, subsq enc
S36.03[0,1,2,9]D [Superf (capsular), Mod, Major, Unsp] lac of spleen, subsq enc
S36.09XD Oth inj of spleen, subsq enc
S36.11[2,3,4,5,6,8,9]D [Contsn, Lac, Minor lac, Mod lac, Major lac, Oth inj, Unsp inj] of liver, subsq enc
S36.12[2,3,8,9]D [Contsn, lac, Oth inj, Unsp inj] of gallbladder, subsq enc
S36.13XD Inj of bile duct, subsq enc
S36.20[0,1,2,9]D Unsp inj of [head, body, tail, unsp part] of pancreas, subsq enc
S36.22[0,1,2,9]D Contsn of [head, body, tail, unsp part] of pancreas, subsq enc
S36.23[0,1,2,9]D Lac of [head, body, tail, unsp part] of pancreas, subsq enc
S36.24[0,1,2,9]D Minor lac of [head, body, tail, unsp part] of pancreas, subsq enc
S36.25[0,1,2,9]D Mod lac of [head, body, tail, unsp part] of pancreas, subsq enc
S36.26[0,1,2,9]D Major lac of [head, body, tail, unsp part] of pancreas, subsq enc
S36.29[0,1,2,9]D Oth inj of [head, body, tail, unsp part] of pancreas, subsq enc
S36.3[0,2,3,9]XD [Unsp inj, Contsn, Lac, Oth inj] of stomach, subsq enc
S36.40[0,8,9]D Unsp inj of [duodenum, oth part of sm intestine, unsp part of sm intestine], subsq enc
S36.41[0,8,9]D Primary blast inj of [duodenum, oth part of sm intestine, unsp part of sm intestine], subsq enc
S36.42[0,8,9]D Contsn of [duodenum, oth part of sm intestine, unsp part of sm intestine], subsq enc

---

T **Transfer DRG**   SP **Special Payment**   * **Code Range**   **6th and 7th Character of ZZ = No Device, No Qualifier ZX = No Device, Diagnostic**

MS-DRG Version 33.0
© 2015 Optum360, LLC

Code	Description
S36.43[0,8,9]D	Lac of [duodenum, oth part of sm intestine, unsp part of sm intestine], subsq enc
S36.49[0,8,9]D	Oth inj of [duodenum, oth part of sm intestine, unsp part of sm intestine], subsq enc
S36.50[0,1,2,3,8,9]D	Unsp inj of [ascending [rt] colon, transv colon, descending [lt] colon, sigmoid colon, oth part of colon,unsp part of colon], subsq enc
S36.51[0,1,2,3,8,9]D	Primary blast inj of [ascending [rt] colon, transv colon, descending [lt] colon, sigmoid colon, oth part of colon,unsp part of colon], subsq enc
S36.52[0,1,2,3,8,9]D	Contsn of [ascending [rt] colon, transv colon, descending [lt] colon, sigmoid colon, oth part of colon,unsp part of colon], subsq enc
S36.53[0,1,2,3,8,9]D	Lac of [ascending [rt] colon, transv colon, descending [lt] colon, sigmoid colon, oth part of colon,unsp part of colon], subsq enc
S36.59[0,1,2,3,8,9]D	Oth inj of [ascending [rt] colon, transv colon, descending [lt] colon, sigmoid colon, oth part of colon,unsp part of colon], subsq enc
S36.6[0,1,2,3,9]XD	[Unsp inj, Primary blast inj, Contsn, Lac, Oth inj] of rectum, subsq enc
S36.81XD	Inj of peritoneum, subsq enc
S36.89[2,3,8,9]D	[Contsn, Lac, Oth inj, Unsp inj] of oth intra-abd organs, subsq enc
S36.9[0,2,3,9]XD	[Unsp inj, Contsn, Lac, Oth inj] of unsp intra-abd organ, subsq enc
S37.00[1,2,9]D	Unsp inj of [rt, lt, unsp] kidney, subsq enc
S37.01[1,2,9]D	Minor contsn of [rt, lt, unsp] kidney, subsq enc
S37.02[1,2,9]D	Major contsn of [rt, lt, unsp] kidney, subsq enc
S37.03[1,2,9]D	Lac of [rt, lt, unsp] kidney, subsq enc
S37.04[1,2,9]D	Minor lac of [rt, lt, unsp] kidney, subsq enc
S37.05[1,2,9]D	Mod lac of [rt, lt, unsp] kidney, subsq enc
S37.06[1,2,9]D	Major lac of [rt, lt, unsp] kidney, subsq enc
S37.09[1,2,9]D	Oth inj of [rt, lt, unsp] kidney, subsq enc
S37.1[0,2,3,9]XD	[Unsp inj, Contsn, Lac, Oth inj] of ureter, subsq enc
S37.2[0,2,3,9]XD	[Unsp inj, Contsn, Lac, Oth inj] of bladder, subsq enc
S37.3[0,2,3,9]XD	[Unsp inj, Contsn, Lac, Oth inj] of urethra, subsq enc
S37.40[1,2,9]D	Unsp inj of ovary, [unilat, bilat, unsp], subsq enc
S37.42[1,2,9]D	Contsn of ovary, [unilat, bilat, unsp], subsq enc
S37.43[1,2,9]D	Lac of ovary, [unilat, bilat, unsp], subsq enc
S37.49[1,2,9]D	Oth inj of ovary, [unilat, bilat, unsp], subsq enc
S37.50[1,2,9]D	Unsp inj of fallopian tube, [unilat, bilat, unsp] subsq enc
S37.51[1,2,9]D	Primary blast inj of fallopian tube, [unilat, bilat, unsp] subsq enc
S37.52[1,2,9]D	Contsn of fallopian tube, [unilat, bilat, unsp] subsq enc
S37.53[1,2,9]D	Lac of fallopian tube, [unilat, bilat, unsp] subsq enc
S37.59[1,2,9]D	Oth inj of fallopian tube, [unilat, bilat, unsp] subsq enc
S37.6[0,2,3,9]XD	[Unsp inj, Contsn, Lac, Oth inj] of uterus, subsq enc
S37.81[2,3,8,9]D	[Contsn, Lac, Oth inj, Unsp inj] of adrenal gland, subsq enc
S37.82[2,3,8,9]D	[Contsn, Lac, Oth inj, Unsp inj] of prostate, subsq enc
S37.89[2,3,8,9]D	[Contsn, Lac, Oth inj, Unsp inj] of oth urinary and pelvic organ, subsq enc
S37.9[0,2,3,9]XD	[Unsp inj, Contsn, Lac, Oth inj] of unsp urinary and pelvic organ, subsq enc
S38.00[1,2]D	Crushing inj of unsp ext genital organs, [male, female] subsq enc
S38.0[1,2,3]XD	Crushing inj of [penis, scrotum and testis, vulva] subsq enc
S38.1XXD	Crushing inj of abd, lwr back, and pelvis, subs
S38.21[1,2]D	[Complete, Partial] traum amp of female ext genital organs, subsq enc
S38.22[1,2]D	[Complete, Partial] traum amp of penis, subsq enc
S38.23[1,2]D	[Complete, Partial] traum amp of scrotum and testis, subsq enc
S38.3XXD	Transection (partial) of abd, subsq enc
S39.00[1,2,3]D	Unsp inj of muscle, fascia and tndn of [abd, lwr back, pelvis], subsq enc
S39.01[1,2,3]D	Strain of muscle, fascia and tndn of [abd, lwr back, pelvis], subsq enc
S39.02[1,2,3]D	Lac of muscle, fascia and tndn of [abd, lwr back, pelvis], subsq enc
S39.09[1,2,3]D	Oth inj of muscle, fascia and tndn of [abd, lwr back, pelvis], subsq enc
S39.84[0,8]D	[Fx of corpus cavernosum penis, Oth spec injuries of ext genitals], subsq enc
S39.8[1,2,3]XD	Oth spec injuries of [abd, lwr back, pelvis], subsq enc
S39.9[1,2,3,4]XD	Unsp inj of [abd, lwr back, pelvis, ext genitals] subsq enc
S40.01[1,2,9]D	Contsn of [rt, lt, unsp] shldr, subsq enc
S40.02[1,2,9]D	Contsn of [rt, lt, unsp] upr arm, subsq enc
S40.21[1,2,9]D	Abrasion of [rt, lt, unsp] shldr, subsq enc
S40.22[1,2,9]D	Blister (nonthermal) of [rt, lt, unsp] shldr, subsq enc
S40.24[1,2,9]D	Ext constriction of [rt, lt, unsp] shldr, subsq enc
S40.25[1,2,9]D	Superf FB of [rt, lt, unsp] shldr, subsq enc
S40.26[1,2,9]D	Insect bite (nonvenomous) of [rt, lt, unsp] shldr, subsq enc
S40.27[1,2,9]D	Oth superf bite of [rt, lt, unsp] shldr, subsq enc
S40.81[1,2,9]D	Abrasion of [rt, lt, unsp] shldr, subsq enc
S40.82[1,2,9]D	Blister (nonthermal) of [rt, lt, unsp] upr arm, subsq enc
S40.84[1,2,9]D	Ext constriction of [rt, lt, unsp] upr arm, subsq enc
S40.85[1,2,9]D	Superf FB of [rt, lt, unsp] upr arm, subsq enc
S40.86[1,2,9]D	Insect bite (nonvenomous) of [rt, lt, unsp] upr arm, subsq enc
S40.87[1,2,9]D	Oth superf bite of [rt, lt, unsp] upr arm, subsq enc
S40.91[1,2,9]D	Unsp superf inj of [rt, lt, unsp] shldr, subsq enc
S40.92[1,2,9]D	Unsp superf inj of [rt, lt, unsp] upr arm, subsq enc
S41.00[1,2,9]D	Unsp opn wnd of [rt, lt, unsp] shldr, subsq enc
S41.01[1,2,9]D	Lac w/o FB of [rt, lt, unsp] shldr, subsq enc
S41.02[1,2,9]D	Lac w/ FB of [rt, lt, unsp] shldr, subsq enc
S41.03[1,2,9]D	Punc wnd w/o FB of [rt, lt, unsp] shldr, subsq enc
S41.04[1,2,9]D	Punc wnd w/ FB of [rt, lt, unsp] shldr, subsq enc
S41.05[1,2,9]D	Opn bite of [rt, lt, unsp] shldr, subsq enc
S41.10[1,2,9]D	Unsp opn wnd of [rt, lt, unsp] upr arm, subsq enc
S41.11[1,2,9]D	Lac w/o FB of [rt, lt, unsp] upr arm, subsq enc
S41.12[1,2,9]D	Lac w/ FB of [rt, lt, unsp] upr arm, subsq enc
S41.13[1,2,9]D	Punc wnd w/o FB of [rt, lt, unsp] upr arm, subsq enc
S41.14[1,2,9]D	Punc wnd w/ FB of [rt, lt, unsp] upr arm, subsq enc
S41.15[1,2,9]D	Opn bite of [rt, lt, unsp] upr arm, subsq enc
S43.00[1,2,3,4,5,6]D	Unsp sublux of [rt, lt, unsp] shldr jt, Unsp disloc of [rt, lt, unsp] shldr jt, subsq enc
S43.01[1,2,3,4,5,6]D	Ant sublux of [rt, lt, unsp] humerus, Ant disloc of [rt, lt, unsp] humerus subsq enc
S43.02[1,2,3,4,5,6]D	Post sublux of [rt, lt, unsp] humerus, Post disloc of [rt, lt, unsp] humerus subsq enc
S43.03[1,2,3,4,5,6]D	Inferior sublux of [rt, lt, unsp] humerus, Inferior disloc of [rt, lt, unsp] humerus subsq enc
S43.08[1,2,3,4,5,6]D	Oth sublux of [rt, lt, unsp] humerus, Oth disloc of [rt, lt, unsp] humerus subsq enc
S43.10[1,2,9]D	Unsp disloc of [rt, lt, unsp] acromioclavicular jt, subsq enc
S43.11[1,2,9]D	Sublux of [rt, lt, unsp] acromioclavicular jt, subsq enc
S43.12[1,2,9]D	Disloc of [rt, lt, unsp] acromioclavicular jt, 100%-200% displac, subsq enc
S43.13[1,2,9]D	Disloc of [rt, lt, unsp] acromioclavicular jt, > 200% displac, subsq enc
S43.14[1,2,9]D	Inferior disloc of [rt, lt, unsp] acromioclavicular jt, subsq enc
S43.15[1,2,9]D	Post disloc of [rt, lt, unsp] acromioclavicular jt, subsq enc
S43.20[1,2,3,4,5,6]D	Unsp sublux of [rt, lt, unsp] sternoclavicular jt, Unsp disloc of [rt, lt, unsp] sternoclavicular jt, subsq enc
S43.21[1,2,3,4,5,6]D	Ant sublux of [rt, lt, unsp] sternoclavicular jt, Ant disloc of [rt, lt, unsp] sternoclavicular jt, subsq enc
S43.22[1,2,3,4,5,6]D	Post sublux of [rt, lt, unsp] sternoclavicular jt, Post disloc of [rt, lt, unsp] sternoclavicular jt, subsq enc
S43.30[1,2,3]D	Sublux of unsp parts of [rt, lt, unsp] shldr girdle, subsq enc
S43.30[4,5,6]D	Disloc of unsp parts of [rt, lt, unsp] shldr girdle, subsq enc
S43.31[1,2,3]D	Sublux of [rt, lt, unsp] scapula, subsq enc
S43.31[4,5,6]D	Disloc of [rt, lt, unsp] scapula, subsq enc
S43.39[1,2,3]D	Sublux of oth parts of [rt, lt, unsp] shldr girdle, subsq enc
S43.39[4,5,6]D	Disloc of oth parts of [rt, lt, unsp] shldr girdle, subsq enc
S43.40[1,2,9]D	Unsp sprain of [rt, lt, unsp] shldr jt, subsq enc
S43.41[1,2,9]D	Sprain of [rt, lt, unsp] coracohumeral (lgmt), subsq enc
S43.42[1,2,9]D	Sprain of [rt, lt, unsp] rotator cuff capsule, subsq enc
S43.43[1,2,9]D	Superior glenoid labrum lesion of [rt, lt, unsp] shldr, subsq enc
S43.49[1,2,9]D	Oth sprain of [rt, lt, unpecified] shldr jt, subsq enc
S43.5[0,1,2]XD	Sprain of [unsp, rt, lt] acromioclavicular jt, subsq enc
S43.6[0,1,2]XD	Sprain of [unsp, rt, lt] sternoclavicular jt, subsq enc
S43.8[0,1,2]XD	Sprain of oth spec parts of [unsp, rt, lt] shldr girdle, subsq enc
S43.9[0,1,2]XD	Sprain of unsp parts of [unsp, rt, lt] shldr girdle, subsq enc
S44.0[0,1,2]XD	Inj of ulnar nerve at upr arm lvl, [unsp, rt, lt] arm, subsq enc
S44.1[0,1,2]XD	Inj of median nerve at upr arm lvl, [unsp, rt, lt] arm, subsq enc
S44.2[0,1,2]XD	Inj of radial nerve at upr arm lvl, [unsp, rt, lt] arm, subsq enc
S44.3[0,1,2]XD	Inj of axillary nerve, [unsp, rt, lt] arm, subsq enc
S44.4[0,1,2]XD	Inj of musculocutaneous nerve, [unsp, rt, lt] arm, subsq enc
S44.5[0,1,2]XD	Inj of cutaneous sensory nerve at shldr and upr arm lvl, [unsp, rt, lt] arm, subsq enc
S44.8X[1,2,9]D	Inj of oth nerves at shldr and upr arm lvl, [rt,lt, unsp] arm, subsq enc
S44.9[0,1,2]XD	Inj of unsp nerve at shldr and upr arm lvl, [unsp, rt, lt] arm, subsq enc
S45.00[1,2,9]D	Unsp inj of axillary artery, [rt, lt, unsp] side, subsq enc
S45.0[1,9][1,2,9]D	[Lac, Oth spec inj] of axillary artery, [rt, lt, unsp] side, subsq enc
S45.10[1,2,9]D	Unsp inj of brachial artery, [rt, lt, unsp] side, subsq enc
S45.11[1,2,9]D	Lac of brachial artery, [rt, lt, unsp] side, subsq enc
S45.19[1,2,9]D	Oth spec inj of brachial artery, [rt, lt, unsp] side, subsq enc

---

Surgical   **Medical**   **CC Indicator**   **MCC Indicator**   **Procedure Proxy**   PDxMCC **PDx acts as own MCC**   PDxCC **PDx acts as own CC**

MDC 23: Factors Influencing Health Status And Other Contacts With Health Services—MEDICAL

S45.20[1,2,9]D	Unsp inj of axillary or brachial vein, [rt, lt, unsp] side, subsq enc
S45.21[1,2,9]D	Lac of axillary or brachial vein, [rt, lt, unsp] side, subsq enc
S45.29[1,2,9]D	Oth spec inj of axillary or brachial vein, [rt, lt, unsp] side, subsq enc
S45.30[1,2,9]D	Unsp inj of superf vein at shldr and upr arm lvl, [rt, lt, unsp] arm, subsq enc
S45.31[1,2,9]D	Lac of superf vein at shldr and upr arm lvl, [rt, lt, unsp] arm, subsq enc
S45.39[1,2,9]D	Oth spec inj of superf vein at shldr and upr arm lvl, [rt, lt, unsp] arm, subsq enc
S45.80[1,2,9]D	Unsp inj of muscle(s) and tndn(s) of the rotator cuff of [rt, lt, unsp] shldr, subsq enc
S45.81[1,2,9]D	Lac of oth spec bld vessels at shldr and upr arm lvl, [rt, lt, unsp] arm, subsq enc
S45.89[1,2,9]D	Oth spec inj of oth spec bld vessels at shldr and upr arm lvl, [rt, lt, unsp] arm, subsq enc
S45.90[1,2,9]D	Unsp inj of unsp bld vessel at shldr and upr arm lvl, [rt, lt, unsp] arm, subsq enc
S45.91[1,2,9]D	Oth spec inj of brachial artery, [rt, lt, unsp] side, subsq enc
S45.99[1,2,9]D	Oth spec inj of unsp bld vessel at shldr and upr arm lvl, [rt, lt, unsp] arm, subsq enc
S46.00[1,2,9]D	Unsp inj of muscle(s) and tndn(s) of the rotator cuff of [rt, lt, unsp] shldr, subsq enc
S46.01[1,2,9]D	Strain of muscle(s) and tndn(s) of the rotator cuff of [rt, lt, unsp] shldr, subsq enc
S46.02[1,2,9]D	Lac of muscle(s) and tndn(s) of the rotator cuff of [rt, lt, unsp] shldr, subsq enc
S46.09[1,2,9]D	Oth inj of muscle(s) and tndn(s) of the rotator cuff of [rt, lt, unsp] shldr, subsq enc
S46.10[1,2,9]D	Unsp inj of muscle, fascia and tndn of long head of biceps, [rt, lt, unsp] arm, subsq enc
S46.11[1,2,9]D	Strain of muscle, fascia and tndn of long head of biceps, [rt, lt, unsp] arm, subsq enc
S46.12[1,2,9]D	Lac of muscle, fascia and tndn of long head of biceps, [rt, lt, unsp] arm, subsq enc
S46.19[1,2,9]D	Oth inj of muscle, fascia and tndn of long head of biceps, [rt, lt, unsp] arm, subsq enc
S46.20[1,2,9]D	Unsp inj of muscle, fascia and tndn of oth parts of biceps, [rt, lt, unsp] arm, subsq enc
S46.21[1,2,9]D	Strain of muscle, fascia and tndn of oth parts of biceps, [rt, lt, unsp] arm, subsq enc
S46.22[1,2,9]D	Lac of muscle, fascia and tndn of oth parts of biceps, [rt, lt, unsp] arm, subsq enc
S46.29[1,2,9]D	Oth inj of muscle, fascia and tndn of oth parts of biceps, [rt, lt, unsp] arm, subsq enc
S46.30[1,2,9]D	Unsp inj of muscle, fascia and tndn of triceps, [rt, lt, unsp] arm, subsq enc
S46.31[1,2,9]D	Strain of muscle, fascia and tndn of triceps, [rt, lt, unsp] arm, subsq enc
S46.32[1,2,9]D	Lac of muscle, fascia and tndn of triceps, [rt, lt, unsp] arm, subsq enc
S46.39[1,2,9]D	Oth inj of muscle, fascia and tndn of triceps, [rt, lt, unsp] arm, subsq enc
S46.80[1,2,9]D	Unsp inj of oth muscles, fascia and tndns at shldr and upr arm lvl, [rt, lt, unsp] arm, subsq enc
S46.81[1,2,9]D	Strain of oth muscles, fascia and tndns at shldr and upr arm lvl, [rt, lt, unsp] arm, subsq enc
S46.82[1,2,9]D	Lac of oth muscles, fascia and tndns at shldr and upr arm lvl, [rt, lt, unsp] arm, subsq enc
S46.89[1,2,9]D	Oth inj of oth muscles, fascia and tndns at shldr and upr arm lvl, [rt, lt, unsp] arm, subsq enc
S46.90[1,2,9]D	Unsp inj of unsp muscle, fascia and tndn at shldr and upr arm lvl, [rt, lt, unsp] arm, subsq enc
S46.91[1,2,9]D	Strain of unsp muscle, fascia and tndn at shldr and upr arm lvl, [rt, lt, unsp] arm, subsq enc
S46.92[1,2,9]D	Lac of unsp muscle, fascia and tndn at shldr and upr arm lvl, [rt, lt, unsp] arm, subsq enc
S46.99[1,2,9]D	Oth inj of unsp muscle, fascia and tndn at shldr and upr arm lvl, [rt, lt, unsp] arm, subsq enc
S47.1XXD	Crushing inj of rt shldr and upr arm, subs enc
S47.2XXD	Crushing inj of lt shldr and upr arm, subs enc
S47.9XXD	Crushing inj of shldr and upr arm, unsp arm, subs
S48.01[1,2,9]D	Complete traum amp at [rt, lt, unsp] shldr jt, subsq enc
S48.02[1,2,9]D	Partial traum amp at [rt, lt, unsp] shldr jt, subsq enc
S48.11[1,2,9]D	Complete traum amp at lvl between [rt, lt, unsp] shldr and elbow, subsq enc
S48.12[1,2,9]D	Partial traum amp at lvl between [rt, lt, unsp] shldr and elbow, subsq enc
S48.91[1,2,9]D	Complete traum amp of [rt, lt, unsp] shldr and upr arm, lvl unsp, subsq enc
S48.92[1,2,9]D	Partial traum amp of [rt, lt, unsp] shldr and upr arm, lvl unsp, subsq enc
S49.8[0,1,2]XD	Oth spec injuries of [unsp, rt, lt] shldr and upr arm, subsq enc
S49.9[0,1,2]XD	Unsp inj of [unsp, rt, lt] shldr and upr arm, subsq enc
S50.0[0,1,2]XD	Contsn of [rt, lt, unsp] elbow, subsq enc
S50.1[0,1,2]XD	Contsn of [rt, lt, unsp] forearm, subsq enc
S50.31[1,2,9]D	Abrasion of [rt, lt, unsp] elbow, subsq enc
S50.32[1,2,9]D	Blister (nonthermal) of [rt, lt, unsp] elbow, subsq enc
S50.34[1,2,9]D	Ext constriction of [rt, lt, unsp] elbow, subsq enc
S50.35[1,2,9]D	Superf FB of [rt, lt, unsp] elbow, subsq enc
S50.36[1,2,9]D	Insect bite (nonvenomous) of [rt, lt, unsp] elbow, subsq enc
S50.37[1,2,9]D	Oth superf bite of [rt, lt, unsp] elbow, subsq enc
S50.81[1,2,9]D	Abrasion of [rt, lt, unsp] forearm, subsq enc
S50.82[1,2,9]D	Blister (nonthermal) of [rt, lt, unsp] forearm, subsq enc
S50.84[1,2,9]D	Ext constriction of [rt, lt, unsp] forearm, subsq enc
S50.85[1,2,9]D	Superf FB of [rt, lt, unsp] forearm, subsq enc
S50.86[1,2,9]D	Insect bite (nonvenomous) of [rt, lt, unsp] forearm, subsq enc
S50.87[1,2,9]D	Oth superf bite of [rt, lt, unsp] forearm, subsq enc
S50.90[1,2,9]D	Unsp superf inj of [rt, lt, unsp] elbow, subsq enc
S50.91[1,2,9]D	Unsp superf inj of [rt, lt, unsp] forearm, subsq enc
S51.00[1,2,9]D	Unsp opn wnd of [rt, lt, unsp] elbow, subsq enc
S51.01[1,2,9]D	Lac w/o FB of [rt, lt, unsp] elbow, subsq enc
S51.02[1,2,9]D	Lac w/ FB of [rt, lt, unsp] elbow, subsq enc
S51.03[1,2,9]D	Punc wnd w/o FB of [rt, lt, unsp] elbow, subsq enc
S51.04[1,2,9]D	Punc wnd w/ FB of [rt, lt, unsp] elbow, subsq enc
S51.05[1,2,9]D	Opn bite of [rt, lt, unsp] elbow, subsq enc
S51.80[1,2,9]D	Unsp opn wnd of [rt, lt, unsp] forearm, subsq enc
S51.81[1,2,9]D	Lac w/o FB of [rt, lt, unsp] forearm, subsq enc
S51.82[1,2,9]D	Lac w/ FB of [rt, lt, unsp] forearm, subsq enc
S51.83[1,2,9]D	Punc wnd w/o FB of [rt, lt, unsp] forearm, subsq enc
S51.84[1,2,9]D	Punc wnd w/ FB of [rt, lt, unsp] forearm, subsq enc
S51.85[1,2,9]D	Opn bite of [rt, lt, unsp] forearm, subsq enc
S53.00[1,2,3]D	Unsp sublux of [rt, lt, unsp] radial head, subsq enc
S53.00[4,5,6]D	Unsp disloc of [rt, lt, unsp] radial head, subsq enc
S53.01[1,2,3]D	Ant sublux of [rt, lt, unsp] radial head, subsq enc
S53.01[4,5,6]D	Ant disloc of [rt, lt, unsp] radial head, subsq enc
S53.02[1,2,3]D	Post sublux of [rt, lt, unsp] radial head, subsq enc
S53.02[4,5,6]D	Post disloc of [rt, lt, unsp] radial head, subsq enc
S53.03[1,2,3]D	Nursemaid's elbow, [rt, lt, unsp] elbow, subsq enc
S53.09[1,2,3]D	Oth sublux of [rt, lt, unsp] radial head, subsq enc
S53.09[4,5,6]D	Oth disloc of [rt, lt, unsp] radial head, subsq enc
S53.10[1,2,3]D	Unsp sublux of [rt, lt, unsp] ulnohumeral jt, subsq enc
S53.10[4,5,6]D	Unsp disloc of [rt, lt, unsp] ulnohumeral jt, subsq enc
S53.11[1,2,3]D	Ant sublux of [rt, lt, unsp] ulnohumeral jt, subsq enc
S53.11[4,5,6]D	Ant disloc of [rt, lt, unsp] ulnohumeral jt, subsq enc
S53.12[1,2,3]D	Post sublux of [rt, lt, unsp] ulnohumeral jt, subsq enc
S53.12[4,5,6]D	Post disloc of [rt, lt, unsp] ulnohumeral jt, subsq enc
S53.13[1,2,3]D	Med sublux of [rt, lt, unsp] ulnohumeral jt, subsq enc
S53.13[4,5,6]D	Med disloc of [rt, lt, unsp] ulnohumeral jt, subsq enc
S53.14[1,2,3]D	Lat sublux of [rt, lt, unsp] ulnohumeral jt, subsq enc
S53.14[4,5,6]D	Lat disloc of [rt, lt, unsp] ulnohumeral jt, subsq enc
S53.19[1,2,3]D	Oth sublux of [rt, lt, unsp] ulnohumeral jt, subsq enc
S53.19[4,5,6]D	Oth disloc of [rt, lt, unsp] ulnohumeral jt, subsq enc
S53.2[0,1,2]XD	Traum rupture of [unsp, rt, lt] radial collat lgmt, subsq enc
S53.3[0,1,2]XD	Traum rupture of [unsp, rt, lt] ulnar collat lgmt, subsq enc
S53.40[1,2,9]D	Unsp sprain of [rt, lt, unsp] elbow, subsq enc
S53.41[1,2,9]D	Radiohumeral (jt) sprain of [rt, lt, unsp] elbow, subsq enc
S53.42[1,2,9]D	Ulnohumeral sprain of [rt, lt, unsp] elbow, subsq enc
S53.43[1,2,9]D	Radial collat lgmt sprain of [rt, lt, unsp] elbow, subsq enc
S53.44[1,2,9]D	Ulnar collat lgmt sprain of [rt, lt, unsp] elbow, subsq enc
S53.49[1,2,9]D	Oth sprain of [rt, lt, unsp] elbow, subsq enc
S54.0[0,1,2]XD	Inj of ulnar nerve at forearm lvl, [unsp, rt, lt] arm, subsq enc
S54.1[0,1,2]XD	Inj of median nerve at forearm lvl, [unsp, rt, lt] arm, subsq enc
S54.2[0,1,2]XD	Inj of radial nerve at forearm lvl, [unsp, rt, lt] arm, subsq enc
S54.3[0,1,2]XD	Inj of cutaneous sensory nerve at forearm lvl, [unsp, rt, lt] arm, subsq enc
S54.8X[1,2,9]D	Unsp inj of oth nerves at forearm lvl, [rt, lt, unsp] arm, subsq enc
S54.9[0,1,2]XD	Inj of unsp nerve at forearm lvl, [unsp, rt, lt] arm, subsq enc
S55.00[1,2,9]D	Unsp inj of ulnar artery at forearm lvl, [rt, lt, unsp] arm, subsq enc
S55.01[1,2,9]D	Lac of ulnar artery at forearm lvl, [rt, lt, unsp] arm, subsq enc
S55.09[1,2,9]D	Oth spec inj of ulnar artery at forearm lvl, [rt, lt, unsp] arm, subsq enc
S55.10[1,2,9]D	Unsp inj of radial artery at forearm lvl, [rt, lt, unsp] arm, subsq enc
S55.11[1,2,9]D	Lac of radial artery at forearm lvl, [rt, lt, unsp] arm, subsq enc

---

T Transfer DRG   SP Special Payment   * Code Range   **6th and 7th Character of ZZ = No Device, No Qualifier ZX = No Device, Diagnostic**

392   MS-DRG Version 33.0   © 2015 Optum360, LLC

S55.19[1,2,9]D Oth spec inj of radial artery at forearm lvl, [rt, lt, unsp] arm, subsq enc
S55.20[1,2,9]D Unsp inj of vein at forearm lvl, [rt, lt, unsp] arm, subsq enc
S55.21[1,2,9]D Lac of vein at forearm lvl, [rt, lt, unsp] arm, subsq enc
S55.29[1,2,9]D Oth spec inj of vein at forearm lvl, [rt, lt, unsp] arm, subsq enc
S55.80[1,2,9]D Unsp inj of oth bld vessels at forearm lvl, [rt, lt, unsp] arm, subsq enc
S55.81[1,2,9]D Lac of oth bld vessels at forearm lvl, [rt, lt, unsp] arm, subsq enc
S55.89[1,2,9]D Oth spec inj of oth bld vessels at forearm lvl, [rt, lt, unsp] arm, subsq enc
S55.90[1,2,9]D Unsp inj of unsp bld vessels at forearm lvl, [rt, lt, unsp] arm, subsq enc
S55.91[1,2,9]D Lac of unsp bld vessels at forearm lvl, [rt, lt, unsp] arm, subsq enc
S55.99[1,2,9]D Oth spec inj of unsp bld vessels at forearm lvl, [rt, lt, unsp] arm, subsq enc
S56.00[1,2,9]D Unsp inj of flexor muscle, fascia and tndn of [rt, lt, unsp] thumb at forearm lvl, subsq enc
S56.01[1,2,9]D Strain of flexor muscle, fascia and tndn of [rt, lt, unsp] thumb at forearm lvl, subsq enc
S56.02[1,2,9]D Lac of flexor muscle, fascia and tndn of [rt, lt, unsp] thumb at forearm lvl, subsq enc
S56.09[1,2,9]D Oth inj of flexor muscle, fascia and tndn of [rt, lt, unsp] thumb at forearm lvl, subsq enc
S56.109D Unsp inj flexor musc/fasc/tend unsp fngr at forearm lv, subs
S56.10[1,2]D Unsp inj of flexor muscle, fascia and tndn of [rt, lt] index finger at forearm lvl, subsq enc
S56.10[3,4]D Unsp inj of flexor muscle, fascia and tndn of [rt, lt] mid finger at forearm lvl, subsq enc
S56.10[5,6]D Unsp inj of flexor muscle, fascia and tndn of [rt, lt] ring finger at forearm lvl, subsq enc
S56.10[7,8]D Unsp inj of flexor muscle, fascia and tndn of [rt, lt] little finger at forearm lvl, subsq enc
S56.119D Strain flexor musc/fasc/tend of unsp fngr at forearm lv, subs
S56.11[1,2]D Strain of flexor muscle, fascia and tndn of [rt, lt] index finger at forearm lvl, subsq enc
S56.11[3,4]D Strain of flexor muscle, fascia and tndn of [rt, lt] mid finger at forearm lvl, subsq enc
S56.11[5,6]D Strain of flexor muscle, fascia and tndn of [rt, lt] ring finger at forearm lvl, subsq enc
S56.11[7,8]D Strain of flexor muscle, fascia and tndn of [rt, lt] little finger at forearm lvl, subsq enc
S56.129D Lacerat flexor musc/fasc/tend unsp finger at forearm lv, subs
S56.12[1,2]D Lac of flexor muscle, fascia and tndn of [rt, lt] index finger at forearm lvl, subsq enc
S56.12[3,4]D Lac of flexor muscle, fascia and tndn of [rt, lt] mid finger at forearm lvl, subsq enc
S56.12[5,6]D Lac of flexor muscle, fascia and tndn of [rt, lt] ring finger at forearm lvl, subsq enc
S56.12[7,8]D Lac of flexor muscle, fascia and tndn of [rt, lt] little finger at forearm lvl, subsq enc
S56.199D Inj flexor musc/fasc/tend unsp finger at forearm lvl, subs
S56.19[1,2]D Oth inj of flexor muscle, fascia and tndn of [rt, lt] index finger at forearm lvl, subsq enc
S56.19[3,4]D Oth inj of flexor muscle, fascia and tndn of [rt, lt] mid finger at forearm lvl, subsq enc
S56.19[5,6]D Oth inj of flexor muscle, fascia and tndn of [rt, lt] ring finger at forearm lvl, subsq enc
S56.19[7,8]D Oth inj of flexor muscle, fascia and tndn of [rt, lt] little finger at forearm lvl, subsq enc
S56.20[1,2,9]D Unsp inj of oth flexor muscle, fascia and tndn at forearm lvl, [rt, lt, unsp] arm, subsq enc
S56.21[1,2,9]D Strain of oth flexor muscle, fascia and tndn at forearm lvl, [rt, lt, unsp] arm, subsq enc
S56.22[1,2,9]D Lac of oth flexor muscle, fascia and tndn at forearm lvl, [rt, lt, unsp] arm, subsq enc
S56.29[1,2,9]D Oth inj of oth flexor muscle, fascia and tndn at forearm lvl, [rt, lt, unsp] arm, subsq enc
S56.30[1,2,9]D Unsp inj of extensor or abductor muscles, fascia and tndns of [rt, lt, unsp] thumb at forearm lvl, subsq enc
S56.31[1,2,9]D Strain of extensor or abductor muscles, fascia and tndns of [rt, lt, unsp] thumb at forearm lvl, subsq enc
S56.32[1,2,9]D Lac of extensor or abductor muscles, fascia and tndns of [rt, lt, unsp] thumb at forearm lvl, subsq enc
S56.39[1,2,9]D Oth inj of extensor or abductor muscles, fascia and tndns of [rt, lt, unsp] thumb at forearm lvl, subsq enc
S56.409D Unsp inj extn musc/fasc/tend unsp finger at forearm lv, subs
S56.40[1,2]D Unsp inj of extensor muscle, fascia and tndn of [rt, lt] index finger at forearm lvl, subsq enc

S56.40[3,4]D Unsp inj of extensor muscle, fascia and tndn of [rt, lt] mid finger at forearm lvl, subsq enc
S56.40[5,6]D Unsp inj of extensor muscle, fascia and tndn of [rt, lt] ring finger at forearm lvl, subsq enc
S56.40[7,8]D Unsp inj of extensor muscle, fascia and tndn of [rt, lt] little finger at forearm lvl, subsq enc
S56.419D Strain extn musc/fasc/tend fngr,unsp fngr at forarm lv, subs
S56.41[1,2]D Strain of extensor muscle, fascia and tndn of [rt, lt] index finger at forearm lvl, subsq enc
S56.41[3,4]D Strain of extensor muscle, fascia and tndn of [rt, lt] mid finger at forearm lvl, subsq enc
S56.41[5,6]D Strain of extensor muscle, fascia and tndn of [rt, lt] ring finger at forearm lvl, subsq enc
S56.41[7,8]D Strain of extensor muscle, fascia and tndn of [rt, lt] little finger at forearm lvl, subsq enc
S56.429D Lacerat extn musc/fasc/tend unsp finger at forarm lv, subs
S56.42[1,2]D Lac of extensor muscle, fascia and tndn of [rt, lt] index finger at forearm lvl, subsq enc
S56.42[3,4]D Lac of extensor muscle, fascia and tndn of [rt, lt] mid finger at forearm lvl, subsq enc
S56.42[5,6]D Lac of extensor muscle, fascia and tndn of [rt, lt] ring finger at forearm lvl, subsq enc
S56.42[7,8]D Lac of extensor muscle, fascia and tndn of [rt, lt] little finger at forearm lvl, subsq enc
S56.499D Inj extensor musc/fasc/tend unsp finger at forarm lv, subs
S56.49[1,2]D Oth inj of extensor muscle, fascia and tndn of [rt, lt] index finger at forearm lvl, subsq enc
S56.49[3,4]D Oth inj of extensor muscle, fascia and tndn of [rt, lt] mid finger at forearm lvl, subsq enc
S56.49[5,6]D Oth inj of extensor muscle, fascia and tndn of [rt, lt] ring finger at forearm lvl, subsq enc
S56.49[7,8]D Oth inj of extensor muscle, fascia and tndn of [rt, lt] little finger at forearm lvl, subsq enc
S56.50[1,2,9]D Unsp inj of oth extensor muscle, fascia and tndn at forearm lvl, [rt, lt, unsp] arm, subsq enc
S56.51[1,2,9]D Strain of oth extensor muscle, fascia and tndn at forearm lvl, [rt, lt, unsp] arm, subsq enc
S56.52[1,2,9]D Lac of oth extensor muscle, fascia and tndn at forearm lvl, [rt, lt, unsp] arm, subsq enc
S56.59[1,2,9]D Oth inj of oth extensor muscle, fascia and tndn at forearm lvl, [rt, lt, unsp] arm, subsq enc
S56.80[1,2,9]D Unsp inj of oth muscles, fascia and tndns at forearm lvl, [rt, lt, unsp] arm, subsq enc
S56.81[1,2,9]D Strain of oth muscles, fascia and tndns at forearm lvl, [rt, lt, unsp] arm, subsq enc
S56.82[1,2,9]D Lac of oth muscles, fascia and tndns at forearm lvl, [rt, lt, unsp] arm, subsq enc
S56.89[1,2,9]D Oth inj of oth muscles, fascia and tndns at forearm lvl, [rt, lt, unsp] arm, subsq enc
S56.90[1,2,9]D Unsp inj of unsp muscles, fascia and tndns at forearm lvl, [rt, lt, unsp] arm, subsq enc
S56.91[1,2,9]D Strain of unsp muscles, fascia and tndns at forearm lvl, [rt, lt, unsp] arm, subsq enc
S56.92[1,2,9]D Lac of unsp muscles, fascia and tndns at forearm lvl, [rt, lt, unsp] arm, subsq enc
S56.99[1,2,9]D Oth inj of unsp muscles, fascia and tndns at forearm lvl, [rt, lt, unsp] arm, subsq enc
S57.0[0,1,2]XD Crushing inj of [unsp, rt, lt] elbow, subsq enc
S57.8[0,1,2]XD Crushing inj of [unsp, rt, lt] forearm, subsq enc
S58.01[1,2,9]D Complete traum amp at elbow lvl, [rt, lt, unsp] arm, subsq enc
S58.02[1,2,9]D Partial traum amp at elbow lvl, [rt, lt, unsp] arm, subsq enc
S58.11[1,2,9]D Complete traum amp at lvl between elbow and wrist, [rt, lt, unsp] arm, subsq enc
S58.12[1,2,9]D Partial traum amp at lvl between elbow and wrist, [rt, lt, unsp] arm, subsq enc
S58.91[1,2,9]D Complete traum amp of [rt, lt, unsp] forearm, lvl unsp, subsq enc
S58.92[1,2,9]D Partial traum amp of [rt, lt, unsp] forearm, lvl unsp, subsq enc
S59.80[1,2,9]D Oth spec injuries of [rt, lt, unsp] elbow, subsq enc
S59.81[1,2,9]D Oth spec injuries [rt, lt, unsp] forearm, subsq enc
S59.90[1,2,9]D Unsp inj of [rt, lt, unsp] elbow, subsq enc
S59.91[1,2,9]D Unsp inj of [rt, lt, unsp] forearm, subsq enc
S60.00XD Contsn of unsp finger w/o damage to nail, subs enc
S60.01[1,2,9]D Contsn of [rt, lt, unsp] thumb w/o damage to nail, subsq enc
S60.02[1,2,9]D Contsn of [rt, lt, unsp] index finger w/o damage to nail, subsq enc
S60.03[1,2,9]D Contsn of [rt, lt, unsp] mid finger w/o damage to nail, subsq enc
S60.04[1,2,9]D Contsn of [rt, lt, unsp] ring finger w/o damage to nail, subsq enc

Surgical   **Medical**   **CC Indicator**   **MCC Indicator**   **Procedure Proxy**   PDx MCC **PDx acts as own MCC**   PDx CC **PDx acts as own CC**

Code	Description
S60.05[1,2,9]D	Contsn of [rt, lt, unsp] little finger w/o damage to nail, subsq enc
S60.10XD	Contsn of unsp finger with damage to nail, subs enc
S60.11[1,2,9]D	Contsn of [rt, lt, unsp] thumb w/ damage to nail, subsq enc
S60.12[1,2,9]D	Contsn of [rt, lt, unsp] index finger w/ damage to nail, subsq enc
S60.13[1,2,9]D	Contsn of [rt, lt, unsp] mid finger w/ damage to nail, subsq enc
S60.14[1,2,9]D	Contsn of [rt, lt, unsp] ring finger w/ damage to nail, subsq enc
S60.15[1,2,9]D	Contsn of [rt, lt, unsp] little finger w/ damage to nail, subsq enc
S60.21[1,2,9]D	Contsn of [rt, lt, unsp] wrist, subsq enc
S60.22[1,2,9]D	Contsn of [rt, lt, unsp] hand, subsq enc
S60.31[1,2,9]D	Abrasion of [rt, lt, unsp] thumb, subsq enc
S60.32[1,2,9]D	Blister (nonthermal) of [rt, lt, unsp] thumb, subsq enc
S60.34[1,2,9]D	Ext constriction of [rt, lt, unsp] thumb, subsq enc
S60.35[1,2,9]D	Superf FB of [rt, lt, unsp] thumb, subsq enc
S60.36[1,2,9]D	Insect bite (nonvenomous) of [rt, lt, unsp] thumb, subsq enc
S60.37[1,2,9]D	Oth superf bite of [rt, lt, unsp] thumb, subsq enc
S60.39[1,2,9]D	Oth superf injuries of [rt, lt, unsp] thumb, subsq enc
S60.41[0,1]D	Abrasion of [rt, lt] index finger, subsq enc
S60.41[2,3]D	Abrasion of [rt, lt] mid finger, subsq enc
S60.41[4,5]D	Abrasion of [rt, lt] ring finger, subsq enc
S60.41[6,7]D	Abrasion of [rt, lt] little finger, subsq enc
S60.41[8,9]D	Abrasion of [oth, unsp] finger, subsq enc
S60.42[0,1]D	Blister (nonthermal) of [rt, lt] index finger, subsq enc
S60.42[2,3]D	Blister (nonthermal) of [rt, lt] mid finger, subsq enc
S60.42[4,5]D	Blister (nonthermal) of [rt, lt] ring finger, subsq enc
S60.42[6,7]D	Blister (nonthermal) of [rt, lt] little finger, subsq enc
S60.42[8,9]D	Blister (nonthermal) of [oth, unsp] finger, subsq enc
S60.44[0,1]D	Ext constriction of [rt, lt] index finger, subsq enc
S60.44[2,3]D	Ext constriction of [rt, lt] mid finger, subsq enc
S60.44[4,5]D	Ext constriction of [rt, lt] ring finger, subsq enc
S60.44[6,7]D	Ext constriction of [rt, lt] little finger, subsq enc
S60.44[8,9]D	Ext constriction of [oth, unsp] finger, subsq enc
S60.45[0,1]D	Superf FB of [rt, lt] index finger, subsq enc
S60.45[2,3]D	Superf FB of [rt, lt] mid finger, subsq enc
S60.45[4,5]D	Superf FB of [rt, lt] ring finger, subsq enc
S60.45[6,7]D	Superf FB of [rt, lt] little finger, subsq enc
S60.45[8,9]D	Superf FB of [oth, unsp] finger, subsq enc
S60.46[0,1]D	Insect bite (nonvenomous) of [rt, lt] index finger, subsq enc
S60.46[2,3]D	Insect bite (nonvenomous) of [rt, lt] mid finger, subsq enc
S60.46[4,5]D	Insect bite (nonvenomous) of [rt, lt] ring finger, subsq enc
S60.46[6,7]D	Insect bite (nonvenomous) of [rt, lt] little finger, subsq enc
S60.46[8,9]D	Insect bite (nonvenomous) of [oth, unsp] finger, subsq enc
S60.47[0,1]D	Oth superf bite of [rt, lt] index finger, subsq enc
S60.47[2,3]D	Oth superf bite of [rt, lt] mid finger, subsq enc
S60.47[4,5]D	Oth superf bite of [rt, lt] ring finger, subsq enc
S60.47[6,7]D	Oth superf bite of [rt, lt] little finger, subsq enc
S60.47[8,9]D	Oth superf bite of [oth, unsp] finger, subsq enc
S60.51[1,2,9]D	Abrasion of [rt, lt, unsp] hand, subsq enc
S60.52[1,2,9]D	Blister (nonthermal) of [rt, lt, unsp] hand, subsq enc
S60.54[1,2,9]D	Ext constriction of [rt, lt, unsp] hand, subsq enc
S60.55[1,2,9]D	Superf FB of [rt, lt, unsp] hand, subsq enc
S60.56[1,2,9]D	Insect bite (nonvenomous) of [rt, lt, unsp] hand, subsq enc
S60.57[1,2,9]D	Oth superf bite of hand of [rt, lt, unsp] hand, subsq enc
S60.81[1,2,9]D	Abrasion of [rt, lt, unsp] wrist, subsq enc
S60.82[1,2,9]D	Blister (nonthermal) of [rt, lt, unsp] wrist, subsq enc
S60.84[1,2,9]D	Ext constriction of [rt, lt, unsp] wrist, subsq enc
S60.85[1,2,9]D	Superf FB of [rt, lt, unsp] wrist, subsq enc
S60.86[1,2,9]D	Insect bite (nonvenomous) of [rt, lt, unsp] wrist, subsq enc
S60.87[1,2,9]D	Oth superf bite of [rt, lt, unsp] wrist, subsq enc
S60.91[1,2,9]D	Unsp superf inj of [rt, lt, unsp] wrist, subsq enc
S60.92[1,2,9]D	Unsp superf inj of [rt, lt, unsp] hand, subsq enc
S60.93[1,2,9]D	Unsp superf inj of [rt, lt, unsp] thumb, subsq enc
S60.94[0,1]D	Unsp superf inj of [rt, lt] index finger, subsq enc
S60.94[2,3]D	Unsp superf inj of [rt, lt] mid finger, subsq enc
S60.94[4,5]D	Unsp superf inj of [rt, lt] ring finger, subsq enc
S60.94[6,7]D	Unsp superf inj of [rt, lt] little finger, subsq enc
S60.94[8,9]D	Unsp superf inj of [oth, unsp] finger, subsq enc
S61.00[1,2,9]D	Unsp opn wnd of [rt, lt, unsp] thumb w/o damage to nail, subsq enc
S61.01[1,2,9]D	Lac w/o FB of [rt, lt, unsp] thumb w/o damage to nail, subsq enc
S61.02[1,2,9]D	Lac w/ FB of [rt, lt, unsp] thumb w/o damage to nail, subsq enc
S61.03[1,2,9]D	Punc wnd w/o FB of [rt, lt, unsp] thumb w/o damage to nail, subsq enc
S61.04[1,2,9]D	Punc wnd w/ FB of [rt, lt, unsp] thumb w/o damage to nail, subsq enc
S61.05[1,2,9]D	Opn wnd of [rt, lt, unsp] thumb w/o damage to nail, subsq enc
S61.10[1,2,9]D	Unsp opn wnd of [rt, lt, unsp] thumb w/ damage to nail, subsq enc
S61.11[1,2,9]D	Lac w/o FB of [rt, lt, unsp] thumb w/ damage to nail, subsq enc
S61.12[1,2,9]D	Lac w/ FB of [rt, lt, unsp] thumb w/ damage to nail, subsq enc
S61.13[1,2,9]D	Punc wnd w/o FB of [rt, lt, unsp] thumb w/ damage to nail, subsq enc
S61.14[1,2,9]D	Punc wnd w/ FB of [rt, lt, unsp] thumb w/ damage to nail, subsq enc
S61.15[1,2,9]D	Opn wnd of [rt, lt, unsp] thumb w/ damage to nail, subsq enc
S61.20[0,1]D	Unsp opn wnd of [rt, lt] index finger w/o damage to nail, subsq enc
S61.20[2,3]D	Unsp opn wnd of [rt, lt] mid finger w/o damage to nail, subsq enc
S61.20[4,5]D	Unsp opn wnd of [rt, lt] ring finger w/o damage to nail, subsq enc
S61.20[6,7]D	Unsp opn wnd of [rt, lt] little finger w/o damage to nail, subsq enc
S61.20[8,9]D	Unsp opn wnd of [oth, unsp] finger w/o damage to nail, subsq enc
S61.21[0,1]D	Lac w/o FB of [rt, lt] index finger w/o damage to nail, subsq enc
S61.21[2,3]D	Lac w/o FB of [rt, lt] mid finger w/o damage to nail, subsq enc
S61.21[4,5]D	Lac w/o FB of [rt, lt] ring finger w/o damage to nail, subsq enc
S61.21[6,7]D	Lac w/o FB of [rt, lt] little finger w/o damage to nail, subsq enc
S61.21[8,9]D	Lac w/o FB of [oth, unsp] finger w/o damage to nail, subsq enc
S61.22[0,1]D	Lac w/ FB of [rt, lt] index finger w/o damage to nail, subsq enc
S61.22[2,3]D	Lac w/ FB of [rt, lt] mid finger w/o damage to nail, subsq enc
S61.22[4,5]D	Lac w/ FB of [rt, lt] ring finger w/o damage to nail, subsq enc
S61.22[6,7]D	Lac w/ FB of [rt, lt] little finger w/o damage to nail, subsq enc
S61.22[8,9]D	Lac w/ FB of [oth, unsp] finger w/o damage to nail, subsq enc
S61.23[0,1]D	Punc wnd w/o FB of [rt, lt] index finger w/o damage to nail, subsq enc
S61.23[2,3]D	Punc wnd w/o FB of [rt, lt] mid finger w/o damage to nail, subsq enc
S61.23[4,5]D	Punc wnd w/o FB of [rt, lt] ring finger w/o damage to nail, subsq enc
S61.23[6,7]D	Punc wnd w/o FB of [rt, lt] little finger w/o damage to nail, subsq enc
S61.23[8,9]D	Punc wnd w/o FB of [oth, unsp] finger w/o damage to nail, subsq enc
S61.24[0,1]D	Punc wnd w/ FB of [rt, lt] index finger w/o damage to nail, subsq enc
S61.24[2,3]D	Punc wnd w/ FB of [rt, lt] mid finger w/o damage to nail, subsq enc
S61.24[4,5]D	Punc wnd w/ FB of [rt, lt] ring finger w/o damage to nail, subsq enc
S61.24[6,7]D	Punc wnd w/ FB of [rt, lt] little finger w/o damage to nail, subsq enc
S61.24[8,9]D	Punc wnd w/ FB of [oth, unsp] finger w/o damage to nail, subsq enc
S61.25[0,1]D	Opn bite of [rt, lt] index finger w/o damage to nail, subsq enc
S61.25[2,3]D	Opn bite of [rt, lt] mid finger w/o damage to nail, subsq enc
S61.25[4,5]D	Opn bite of [rt, lt] ring finger w/o damage to nail, subsq enc
S61.25[6,7]D	Opn bite of [rt, lt] little finger w/o damage to nail, subsq enc
S61.25[8,9]D	Opn bite of [oth, unsp] finger w/o damage to nail, subsq enc
S61.30[0,1]D	Unsp opn wnd of [rt, lt] index finger w/ damage to nail, subsq enc
S61.30[2,3]D	Unsp opn wnd of [rt, lt] mid finger w/ damage to nail, subsq enc
S61.30[4,5]D	Unsp opn wnd of [rt, lt] ring finger w/ damage to nail, subsq enc
S61.30[6,7]D	Unsp opn wnd of [rt, lt] little finger w/ damage to nail, subsq enc
S61.30[8,9]D	Unsp opn wnd of [oth, unsp] finger w/ damage to nail, subsq enc
S61.31[0,1]D	Lac w/o FB of [rt, lt] index finger w/ damage to nail, subsq enc
S61.31[2,3]D	Lac w/o FB of [rt, lt] mid finger w/ damage to nail, subsq enc
S61.31[4,5]D	Lac w/o FB of [rt, lt] ring finger w/ damage to nail, subsq enc
S61.31[6,7]D	Lac w/o FB of [rt, lt] little finger w/ damage to nail, subsq enc
S61.31[8,9]D	Lac w/o FB of [oth, unsp] finger w/ damage to nail, subsq enc
S61.32[0,1]D	Lac w/ FB of [rt, lt] index finger w/ damage to nail, subsq enc
S61.32[2,3]D	Lac w/ FB of [rt, lt] mid finger w/ damage to nail, subsq enc
S61.32[4,5]D	Lac w/ FB of [rt, lt] ring finger w/ damage to nail, subsq enc
S61.32[6,7]D	Lac w/ FB of [rt, lt] little finger w/ damage to nail, subsq enc
S61.32[8,9]D	Lac w/ FB of [oth, unsp] finger w/ damage to nail, subsq enc
S61.33[0,1]D	Punc wnd w/o FB of [rt, lt] index finger w/ damage to nail, subsq enc
S61.33[2,3]D	Punc wnd w/o FB of [rt, lt] mid finger w/ damage to nail, subsq enc

---

T **Transfer DRG**　　SP **Special Payment**　　＊ **Code Range**　　**6th and 7th Character of ZZ = No Device, No Qualifier ZX = No Device, Diagnostic**

Code	Description	Code	Description
S61.33[4,5]D	Punc wnd w/o FB of [rt, lt] ring finger w/ damage to nail, subsq enc	S63.21[4,5]D	Sublux of metacarpophalangeal jt of [rt, lt] ring finger, subsq enc
S61.33[6,7]D	Punc wnd w/o FB of [rt, lt] little finger w/ damage to nail, subsq enc	S63.21[6,7]D	Sublux of metacarpophalangeal jt of [rt, lt] little finger, subsq enc
S61.33[8,9]D	Punc wnd w/o FB of [oth, unsp] finger w/ damage to nail, subsq enc	S63.21[8,9]D	Sublux of metacarpophalangeal jt of [oth, unsp] finger, subsq enc
S61.34[0,1]D	Punc wnd w/ FB of [rt, lt] index finger w/ damage to nail, subsq enc	S63.22[0,1]D	Sublux of unsp interphalangeal jt of [rt, lt] index finger, subsq enc
S61.34[2,3]D	Punc wnd w/ FB of [rt, lt] mid finger w/ damage to nail, subsq enc	S63.22[2,3]D	Sublux of unsp interphalangeal jt of [rt, lt] mid finger, subsq enc
S61.34[4,5]D	Punc wnd w/ FB of [rt, lt] ring finger w/ damage to nail, subsq enc	S63.22[4,5]D	Sublux of unsp interphalangeal jt of [rt, lt] ring finger, subsq enc
S61.34[6,7]D	Punc wnd w/ FB of [rt, lt] little finger w/ damage to nail, subsq enc	S63.22[6,7]D	Sublux of unsp interphalangeal jt of [rt, lt] little finger, subsq enc
S61.34[8,9]D	Punc wnd w/ FB of [oth, unsp] finger w/ damage to nail, subsq enc	S63.22[8,9]D	Sublux of unsp interphalangeal jt of [oth, unsp] finger, subsq enc
S61.35[0,1]D	Opn bite of [rt, lt] index finger w/ damage to nail, subsq enc	S63.23[0,1]D	Sublux of proximal interphalangeal jt of [rt, lt] index finger, subsq enc
S61.35[2,3]D	Opn bite of [rt, lt] mid finger w/ damage to nail, subsq enc	S63.23[2,3]D	Sublux of proximal interphalangeal jt of [rt, lt] mid finger, subsq enc
S61.35[4,5]D	Opn bite of [rt, lt] ring finger w/ damage to nail, subsq enc		
S61.35[6,7]D	Opn bite of [rt, lt] little finger w/ damage to nail, subsq enc	S63.23[4,5]D	Sublux of proximal interphalangeal jt of [rt, lt] ring finger, subsq enc
S61.35[8,9]D	Opn bite of [oth, unsp] finger w/ damage to nail, subsq enc	S63.23[6,7]D	Sublux of proximal interphalangeal jt of [rt, lt] little finger, subsq enc
S61.40[1,2,9]D	Unsp opn wnd of [rt, lt, unsp] hand, subsq enc		
S61.41[1,2,9]D	Lac w/o FB of [rt, lt, unsp] hand, subsq enc	S63.23[8,9]D	Sublux of proximal interphalangeal jt of [oth, unsp] finger, subsq enc
S61.42[1,2,9]D	Lac w/ FB of [rt, lt, unsp] hand, subsq enc	S63.24[0,1]D	Sublux of distal interphalangeal jt of [rt, lt] index finger, subsq enc
S61.43[1,2,9]D	Punc wnd w/o FB of [rt, lt, unsp] hand, subsq enc		
S61.44[1,2,9]D	Punc wnd w/ FB of [rt, lt, unsp] hand, subsq enc	S63.24[2,3]D	Sublux of distal interphalangeal jt of [rt, lt] mid finger, subsq enc
S61.45[1,2,9]D	Opn bite of [rt, lt, unsp] hand, subsq enc	S63.24[4,5]D	Sublux of distal interphalangeal jt of [rt, lt] ring finger, subsq enc
S61.50[1,2,9]D	Unsp opn wnd of [rt, lt, unsp] wrist, subsq enc		
S61.51[1,2,9]D	Lac w/o FB of [rt, lt, unsp] wrist, subsq enc	S63.24[6,7]D	Sublux of distal interphalangeal jt of [rt, lt] little finger, subsq enc
S61.52[1,2,9]D	Lac w/ FB of [rt, lt, unsp] wrist, subsq enc		
S61.53[1,2,9]D	Punc wnd w/o FB of [rt, lt, unsp] wrist, subsq enc	S63.24[8,9]D	Sublux of distal interphalangeal jt of [oth, unsp] finger, subsq enc
S61.54[1,2,9]D	Punc wnd w/ FB of [rt, lt, unsp] wrist, subsq enc		
S61.55[1,2,9]D	Opn bite of [rt, lt, unsp] wrist, subsq enc	S63.25[0,1]D	Unsp disloc of [rt, lt] index finger, subsq enc
S63.00[1,2,3]D	Unsp sublux of [rt, lt] wrist and hand, subsq enc	S63.25[2,3]D	Unsp disloc of [rt, lt] mid finger, subsq enc
S63.00[4,5,6]D	Unsp disloc of [rt, lt] wrist and hand, subsq enc	S63.25[4,5]D	Unsp disloc of [rt, lt] ring finger, subsq enc
S63.01[1,2,3]D	Sublux of distal radioulnar jt of [rt, lt] wrist, subsq enc	S63.25[6,7]D	Unsp disloc of [rt, lt] little finger, subsq enc
S63.01[4,5,6]D	Disloc of distal radioulnar jt of [rt, lt] wrist, subsq enc	S63.25[8,9]D	Unsp disloc of [oth, unsp] finger, subsq enc
S63.02[1,2,3]D	Sublux of radiocarpal jt of [rt, lt] wrist, subsq enc	S63.26[0,1]D	Disloc of metacarpophalangeal jt of [rt, lt] index finger, subsq enc
S63.02[4,5,6]D	Disloc of radiocarpal jt of [rt, lt] wrist, subsq enc		
S63.03[1,2,3]D	Sublux of midcarpal jt of [rt, lt] wrist, subsq enc	S63.26[2,3]D	Disloc of metacarpophalangeal jt of [rt, lt] mid finger, subsq enc
S63.03[4,5,6]D	Disloc of midcarpal jt of [rt, lt] wrist, subsq enc		
S63.04[1,2,3]D	Sublux of carpometacarpal jt of [rt, lt] thumb, subsq enc	S63.26[4,5]D	Disloc of metacarpophalangeal jt of [rt, lt] ring finger, subsq enc
S63.04[4,5,6]D	Disloc of carpometacarpal jt of [rt, lt] thumb, subsq enc		
S63.05[1,2,3]D	Sublux of oth carpometacarpal jt of [rt, lt] hand, subsq enc	S63.26[6,7]D	Disloc of metacarpophalangeal jt of [rt, lt] little finger, subsq enc
S63.05[4,5,6]D	Disloc of oth carpometacarpal jt of [rt, lt] hand, subsq enc	S63.26[8,9]D	Disloc of metacarpophalangeal jt of [oth, unsp] finger, subsq enc
S63.06[1,2,3]D	Sublux of metacarpal (bone), proximal end of [rt, lt] hand, subsq enc	S63.27[0,1]D	Disloc of unsp interphalangeal jt of [rt, lt] index finger, subsq enc
S63.06[4,5,6]D	Disloc of metacarpal (bone), proximal end of [rt, lt] hand, subsq enc	S63.27[2,3]D	Disloc of unsp interphalangeal jt of [rt, lt] mid finger, subsq enc
S63.07[1,2,3]D	Sublux of distal end of [rt, lt] ulna, subsq enc		
S63.07[4,5,6]D	Disloc of distal end of [rt, lt] ulna, subsq enc	S63.27[4,5]D	Disloc of unsp interphalangeal jt of [rt, lt] ring finger, subsq enc
S63.09[1,2,3]D	Oth sublux of [rt, lt] wrist and hand, subsq enc		
S63.09[4,5,6]D	Oth disloc of [rt, lt] wrist and hand, subsq enc	S63.27[6,7]D	Disloc of unsp interphalangeal jt of [rt, lt] little finger, subsq enc
S63.10[1,2,3]D	Unsp sublux of [rt, lt, unsp] thumb, subsq enc		
S63.10[4,5,6]D	Unsp disloc of [rt, lt, unsp] thumb, subsq enc	S63.27[8,9]D	Disloc of unsp interphalangeal jt of [oth, unsp] finger, subsq enc
S63.11[1,2,3]D	Sublux of metacarpophalangeal jt of [rt, lt, unsp] thumb, subsq enc	S63.28[0,1]D	Disloc of proximal interphalangeal jt of [rt, lt] index finger, subsq enc
S63.11[4,5,6]D	Disloc of metacarpophalangeal jt of [rt, lt, unsp] thumb, subsq enc	S63.28[2,3]D	Disloc of proximal interphalangeal jt of [rt, lt] mid finger, subsq enc
S63.12[1,2,3]D	Sublux of unsp interphalangeal jt of [rt, lt, unsp] thumb, subsq enc	S63.28[4,5]D	Disloc of proximal interphalangeal jt of [rt, lt] ring finger, subsq enc
S63.12[4,5,6]D	Disloc of unsp interphalangeal jt of [rt, lt, unsp] thumb, subsq enc	S63.28[6,7]D	Disloc of proximal interphalangeal jt of [rt, lt] little finger, subsq enc
S63.13[1,2,3]D	Sublux of proximal interphalangeal jt of [rt, lt, unsp] thumb, subsq enc	S63.28[8,9]D	Disloc of proximal interphalangeal jt of [oth, unsp] finger, subsq enc
S63.13[4,5,6]D	Disloc of proximal interphalangeal jt of [rt, lt, unsp] thumb, subsq enc	S63.29[0,1]D	Disloc of distal interphalangeal jt of [rt, lt] index finger, subsq enc
S63.14[1,2,3]D	Sublux of distal interphalangeal jt of [rt, lt, unsp] thumb, subsq enc	S63.29[2,3]D	Disloc of distal interphalangeal jt of [rt, lt] mid finger, subsq enc
S63.14[4,5,6]D	Disloc of distal interphalangeal jt of [rt, lt, unsp] thumb, subsq enc		
S63.20[0,1]D	Unsp sublux of [rt, lt] index finger, subsq enc	S63.29[4,5]D	Disloc of distal interphalangeal jt of [rt, lt] ring finger, subsq enc
S63.20[2,3]D	Unsp sublux of [rt, lt] mid finger, subsq enc		
S63.20[4,5]D	Unsp sublux of [rt, lt] ring finger, subsq enc	S63.29[6,7]D	Disloc of distal interphalangeal jt of [rt, lt] little finger, subsq enc
S63.20[6,7]D	Unsp sublux of [rt, lt] little finger, subsq enc		
S63.20[8,9]D	Unsp sublux of [oth, unsp] finger, subsq enc		
S63.21[0,1]D	Sublux of metacarpophalangeal jt of [rt, lt] index finger, subsq enc		
S63.21[2,3]D	Sublux of metacarpophalangeal jt of [rt, lt] mid finger, subsq enc		

Surgical	Medical	CC Indicator	MCC Indicator	Procedure Proxy	**PDx MCC** PDx acts as own MCC	**PDx CC** PDx acts as own CC

S63.29[8,9]D	Disloc of distal interphalangeal jt of [oth, unsp] finger, subsq enc
S63.30[1,2,9]D	Traum rupture of unsp lgmt of [rt, lt, unsp] wrist, subsq enc
S63.31[1,2,9]D	Traum rupture of collat lgmt of [rt, lt, unsp] wrist, subsq enc
S63.32[1,2,9]D	Traum rupture of [rt, lt, unsp] radiocarpal lgmt, subsq enc
S63.33[1,2,9]D	Traum rupture of [rt, lt, unsp] ulnocarpal (palmar) lgmt, subsq enc
S63.39[1,2,9]D	Traum rupture of oth lgmt of [rt, lt, unsp] wrist, subsq enc
S63.40[0,1]D	Traum rupture of unsp lgmt of [rt, lt] index finger at metacarpophalangeal and interphalangeal jt, subsq enc
S63.40[2,3]D	Traum rupture of unsp lgmt of [rt, lt] mid finger at metacarpophalangeal and interphalangeal jt, subsq enc
S63.40[4,5]D	Traum rupture of unsp lgmt of [rt, lt] ring finger at metacarpophalangeal and interphalangeal jt, subsq enc
S63.40[6,7]D	Traum rupture of unsp lgmt of [rt, lt] little finger at metacarpophalangeal and interphalangeal jt, subsq enc
S63.40[8,9]D	Traum rupture of unsp lgmt of [oth, unsp] finger at metacarpophalangeal and interphalangeal jt, subsq enc
S63.41[0,1]D	Traum rupture of collat lgmt of [rt, lt] index finger at metacarpophalangeal and interphalangeal jt, subsq enc
S63.41[2,3]D	Traum rupture of collat lgmt of [rt, lt] mid finger at metacarpophalangeal and interphalangeal jt, subsq enc
S63.41[4,5]D	Traum rupture of collat lgmt of [rt, lt] ring finger at metacarpophalangeal and interphalangeal jt, subsq enc
S63.41[6,7]D	Traum rupture of collat lgmt of [rt, lt] little finger at metacarpophalangeal and interphalangeal jt, subsq enc
S63.41[8,9]D	Traum rupture of collat lgmt of [oth, unsp] finger at metacarpophalangeal and interphalangeal jt, subsq enc
S63.42[0,1]D	Traum rupture of palmar lgmt of [rt, lt] index finger at metacarpophalangeal and interphalangeal jt, subsq enc
S63.42[2,3]D	Traum rupture of palmar lgmt of [rt, lt] mid finger at metacarpophalangeal and interphalangeal jt, subsq enc
S63.42[4,5]D	Traum rupture of palmar lgmt of [rt, lt] ring finger at metacarpophalangeal and interphalangeal jt, subsq enc
S63.42[6,7]D	Traum rupture of palmar lgmt of [rt, lt] little finger at metacarpophalangeal and interphalangeal jt, subsq enc
S63.42[8,9]D	Traum rupture of palmar lgmt of [oth, unsp] finger at metacarpophalangeal and interphalangeal jt, subsq enc
S63.43[0,1]D	Traum rupture of volar plate of [rt, lt] index finger at metacarpophalangeal and interphalangeal jt, subsq enc
S63.43[2,3]D	Traum rupture of volar plate of [rt, lt] mid finger at metacarpophalangeal and interphalangeal jt, subsq enc
S63.43[4,5]D	Traum rupture of volar plate of [rt, lt] ring finger at metacarpophalangeal and interphalangeal jt, subsq enc
S63.43[6,7]D	Traum rupture of volar plate of [rt, lt] little finger at metacarpophalangeal and interphalangeal jt, subsq enc
S63.43[8,9]D	Traum rupture of volar plate of [oth, unsp] finger at metacarpophalangeal and interphalangeal jt, subsq enc
S63.49[0,1]D	Traum rupture of oth lgmt of [rt, lt] index finger at metacarpophalangeal and interphalangeal jt, subsq enc
S63.49[2,3]D	Traum rupture of oth lgmt of [rt, lt] mid finger at metacarpophalangeal and interphalangeal jt, subsq enc
S63.49[4,5]D	Traum rupture of oth lgmt of [rt, lt] ring finger at metacarpophalangeal and interphalangeal jt, subsq enc
S63.49[6,7]D	Traum rupture of oth lgmt of [rt, lt] little finger at metacarpophalangeal and interphalangeal jt, subsq enc
S63.49[8,9]D	Traum rupture of oth lgmt of [oth, unsp] finger at metacarpophalangeal and interphalangeal jt, subsq enc
S63.50[1,2,9]D	Unsp sprain of [rt, lt, unsp] wrist, subsq enc
S63.51[1,2,9]D	Sprain of carpal jt of [rt, lt, unsp] wrist, subsq enc
S63.52[1,2,9]D	Sprain of radiocarpal jt of [rt, lt, unsp] wrist, subsq enc
S63.59[1,2,9]D	Oth spec sprain of [rt, lt, unsp] wrist, subsq enc
S63.60[1,2,9]D	Unsp sprain of [rt, lt, unsp] thumb, subsq enc
S63.61[0,1]D	Unsp sprain of [rt, lt] index finger, subsq enc
S63.61[2,3]D	Unsp sprain of [rt, lt] mid finger, subsq enc
S63.61[4,5]D	Unsp sprain of [rt, lt] ring finger, subsq enc
S63.61[6,7]D	Unsp sprain of [rt, lt] little finger, subsq enc
S63.61[8,9]D	Unsp sprain of [oth, unsp] finger, subsq enc
S63.62[1,2,9]D	Sprain of interphalangeal jt of [rt, lt, unsp] thumb, subsq enc
S63.63[0,1]D	Sprain of interphalangeal jt of [rt, lt] index finger, subsq enc
S63.63[2,3]D	Sprain of interphalangeal jt of [rt, lt] mid finger, subsq enc
S63.63[4,5]D	Sprain of interphalangeal jt of [rt, lt] ring finger, subsq enc
S63.63[6,7]D	Sprain of interphalangeal jt of [rt, lt] little finger, subsq enc
S63.63[8,9]D	Sprain of interphalangeal jt of [oth, unsp] finger, subsq enc
S63.64[1,2,9]D	Sprain of metacarpophalangeal jt of [rt, lt, unsp] thumb, subsq enc
S63.65[0,1]D	Sprain of metacarpophalangeal jt of [rt, lt] index finger, subsq enc
S63.65[2,3]D	Sprain of metacarpophalangeal jt of [rt, lt] mid finger, subsq enc
S63.65[4,5]D	Sprain of metacarpophalangeal jt of [rt, lt] ring finger, subsq enc
S63.65[6,7]D	Sprain of metacarpophalangeal jt of [rt, lt] little finger, subsq enc
S63.65[8,9]D	Sprain of metacarpophalangeal jt of [oth, unsp] finger, subsq enc
S63.68[1,2,9]D	Oth sprain of [rt, lt, unsp] thumb, subsq enc
S63.69[0,1]D	Oth sprain of [rt, lt] index finger, subsq enc
S63.69[2,3]D	Oth sprain of [rt, lt] mid finger, subsq enc
S63.69[4,5]D	Oth sprain of [rt, lt] ring finger, subsq enc
S63.69[6,7]D	Oth sprain of [rt, lt] little finger, subsq enc
S63.69[8,9]D	Oth sprain of [oth, unsp] finger, subsq enc
S63.8X[1,2,9]D	Sprain of oth part of [rt, lt, unsp] wrist and hand, subsq enc
S63.9[0,1,2]XD	Sprain of unsp part of [unsp, rt, lt] wrist and hand, subsq enc
S64.0[0,1,2]XD	Inj of ulnar nerve at wrist and hand lvl of [unsp, rt, lt] arm, subsq enc
S64.1[0,1,2]XD	Inj of median nerve at wrist and hand lvl of [unsp, rt, lt] arm, subsq enc
S64.2[0,1,2]XD	Inj of radial nerve at wrist and hand lvl of [unsp, rt, lt] arm, subsq enc
S64.3[0,1,2]XD	Inj of digital nerve of [unsp, rt, lt] thumb, subsq enc
S64.40XD	Inj of digital nerve of unsp finger, subs enc
S64.498D	Inj of digital nerve of oth finger, subs enc
S64.49[0,1]D	Inj of digital nerve of [rt, lt] index finger, subsq enc
S64.49[2,3]D	Inj of digital nerve of [rt, lt] mid finger, subsq enc
S64.49[4,5]D	Inj of digital nerve of [rt, lt] ring finger, subsq enc
S64.49[6,7]D	Inj of digital nerve of [rt, lt] little finger, subsq enc
S64.8X[1,2,9]D	Inj of oth nerves at wrist and hand lvl of [rt, lt, unsp] arm, subsq enc
S64.9[0,1,2]XD	Inj of unsp nerve at wrist and hand lvl of [unsp, rt, lt] arm, subsq enc
S65.00[1,2,9]D	Unsp inj of ulnar artery at wrist and hand lvl of [rt, lt, unsp] arm, subsq enc
S65.01[1,2,9]D	Lac of ulnar artery at wrist and hand lvl of [rt, lt, unsp] arm, subsq enc
S65.09[1,2,9]D	Oth spec inj of ulnar artery at wrist and hand lvl of [rt, lt, unsp] arm, subsq enc
S65.10[1,2,9]D	Unsp inj of radial artery at wrist and hand lvl of [rt, lt, unsp] arm, subsq enc
S65.11[1,2,9]D	Lac of radial artery at wrist and hand lvl of [rt, lt, unsp] arm, subsq enc
S65.19[1,2,9]D	Oth spec inj of radial artery at wrist and hand lvl of [rt, lt, unsp] arm, subsq enc
S65.20[1,2,9]D	Unsp inj of superf palmar arch of [rt, lt, unsp] hand, subsq enc
S65.21[1,2,9]D	Lac of superf palmar arch of [rt, lt, unsp] hand, subsq enc
S65.29[1,2,9]D	Oth spec inj of superf palmar arch of [rt, lt, unsp] hand, subsq enc
S65.30[1,2,9]D	Unsp inj of deep palmar arch of [rt, lt, unsp] hand, subsq enc
S65.31[1,2,9]D	Lac of deep palmar arch of [rt, lt, unsp] hand, subsq enc
S65.39[1,2,9]D	Oth spec inj of deep palmar arch of [rt, lt, unsp] hand, subsq enc
S65.40[1,2,9]D	Unsp inj of bld vessel of [rt, lt, unsp] thumb, subsq enc
S65.41[1,2,9]D	Lac of bld vessel of [rt, lt, unsp] thumb, subsq enc
S65.49[1,2,9]D	Oth spec inj of bld vessel of [rt, lt, unsp] thumb, subsq enc
S65.50[0,1]D	Unsp inj of bld vessel of [rt, lt] index finger, subsq enc
S65.50[2,3]D	Unsp inj of bld vessel of [rt, lt] mid finger, subsq enc
S65.50[4,5]D	Unsp inj of bld vessel of [rt, lt] ring finger, subsq enc
S65.50[6,7]D	Unsp inj of bld vessel of [rt, lt] little finger, subsq enc
S65.50[8,9]D	Unsp inj of bld vessel of [oth, unsp] finger, subsq enc
S65.51[0,1]D	Lac of bld vessel of [rt, lt] index finger, subsq enc
S65.51[2,3]D	Lac of bld vessel of [rt, lt] mid finger, subsq enc
S65.51[4,5]D	Lac of bld vessel of [rt, lt] ring finger, subsq enc
S65.51[6,7]D	Lac of bld vessel of [rt, lt] little finger, subsq enc
S65.51[8,9]D	Lac of bld vessel of [oth, unsp] finger, subsq enc
S65.59[0,1]D	Oth spec inj of bld vessel of [rt, lt] index finger, subsq enc
S65.59[2,3]D	Oth spec inj of bld vessel of [rt, lt] mid finger, subsq enc
S65.59[4,5]D	Oth spec inj of bld vessel of [rt, lt] ring finger, subsq enc
S65.59[6,7]D	Oher spec inj of bld vessel of [rt, lt] little finger, subsq enc
S65.59[8,9]D	Oth spec inj of bld vessel of [oth, unsp] finger, subsq enc
S65.80[1,2,9]D	Unsp inj of oth bld vessels at wrist and hand lvl of [rt, lt, unsp] arm, subsq enc
S65.81[1,2,9]D	Lac of oth bld vessels at wrist and hand lvl of [rt, lt, unsp] arm, subsq enc
S65.89[1,2,9]D	Oth spec inj of oth bld vessels at wrist and hand lvl of [rt, lt, unsp] arm, subsq enc
S65.90[1,2,9]D	Unsp inj of unsp bld vessel at wrist and hand lvl of [rt, lt, unsp] arm, subsq enc
S65.91[1,2,9]D	Lac of unsp bld vessel at wrist and hand lvl of [rt, lt, unsp] arm, subsq enc

---

T **Transfer DRG**   **SP** **Special Payment**   *** Code Range**   **6th and 7th Character of ZZ = No Device, No Qualifier ZX = No Device, Diagnostic**

MDC 23: Factors Influencing Health Status And Other Contacts With Health Services—MEDICAL

S65.99[1,2,9]D — Oth spec inj of unsp bld vessel at wrist and hand lvl of [rt, lt, unsp] arm, subsq enc

S66.00[1,2,9]D — Unsp inj of long flexor muscle, fascia and tndn of [rt, lt, unsp] thumb at wrist and hand lvl, subsq enc

S66.01[1,2,9]D — Strain of long flexor muscle, fascia and tndn of [rt, lt, unsp] thumb at wrist and hand lvl, subsq enc

S66.02[1,2,9]D — Lac of long flexor muscle, fascia and tndn of [rt, lt, unsp] thumb at wrist and hand lvl, subsq enc

S66.09[1,2,9]D — Oth spec inj of long flexor muscle, fascia and tndn of [rt, lt, unsp] thumb at wrist and hand lvl, subsq enc

S66.10[0,1]D — Unsp inj of flexor muscle, fascia and tndn of [rt, lt] index finger at wrist and hand lvl, subsq enc

S66.10[2,3]D — Unsp inj of flexor muscle, fascia and tndn of [rt, lt] mid finger at wrist and hand lvl, subsq enc

S66.10[4,5]D — Unsp inj of flexor muscle, fascia and tndn of [rt, lt] ring finger at wrist and hand lvl, subsq enc

S66.10[6,7]D — Unsp inj of flexor muscle, fascia and tndn of [rt, lt] little finger at wrist and hand lvl, subsq enc

S66.10[8,9]D — Unsp inj of flexor muscle, fascia and tndn of [oth, unsp] finger at wrist and hand lvl, subsq enc

S66.11[0,1]D — Strain of flexor muscle, fascia and tndn of [rt, lt] index finger at wrist and hand lvl, subsq enc

S66.11[2,3]D — Strain of flexor muscle, fascia and tndn of [rt, lt] mid finger at wrist and hand lvl, subsq enc

S66.11[4,5]D — Strain of flexor muscle, fascia and tndn of [rt, lt] ring finger at wrist and hand lvl, subsq enc

S66.11[6,7]D — Strain of flexor muscle, fascia and tndn of [rt, lt] little finger at wrist and hand lvl, subsq enc

S66.11[8,9]D — Strain of flexor muscle, fascia and tndn of [oth, unsp] finger at wrist and hand lvl, subsq enc

S66.12[0,1]D — Lac of flexor muscle, fascia and tndn of [rt, lt] index finger at wrist and hand lvl, subsq enc

S66.12[2,3]D — Lac of flexor muscle, fascia and tndn of [rt, lt] mid finger at wrist and hand lvl, subsq enc

S66.12[4,5]D — Lac of flexor muscle, fascia and tndn of [rt, lt] ring finger at wrist and hand lvl, subsq enc

S66.12[6,7]D — Lac of flexor muscle, fascia and tndn of [rt, lt] little finger at wrist and hand lvl, subsq enc

S66.12[8,9]D — Lac of flexor muscle, fascia and tndn of [oth, unsp] finger at wrist and hand lvl, subsq enc

S66.19[0,1]D — Oth inj of flexor muscle, fascia and tndn of [rt, lt] index finger at wrist and hand lvl, subsq enc

S66.19[2,3]D — Oth inj of flexor muscle, fascia and tndn of [rt, lt] mid finger at wrist and hand lvl, subsq enc

S66.19[4,5]D — Oth inj of flexor muscle, fascia and tndn of [rt, lt] ring finger at wrist and hand lvl, subsq enc

S66.19[6,7]D — Oth inj of flexor muscle, fascia and tndn of [rt, lt] little finger at wrist and hand lvl, subsq enc

S66.19[8,9]D — Oth inj of flexor muscle, fascia and tndn of [oth, unsp] finger at wrist and hand lvl, subsq enc

S66.20[1,2,9]D — Unsp inj of extensor muscle, fascia and tndn of [rt, lt, unsp] thumb at wrist and hand lvl, subsq enc

S66.21[1,2,9]D — Strain of extensor muscle, fascia and tndn of [rt, lt, unsp] thumb at wrist and hand lvl, subsq enc

S66.22[1,2,9]D — Lac of extensor muscle, fascia and tndn of [rt, lt, unsp] thumb at wrist and hand lvl, subsq enc

S66.29[1,2,9]D — Oth spec inj of extensor muscle, fascia and tndn of [rt, lt, unsp] thumb at wrist and hand lvl, subsq enc

S66.30[0,1]D — Unsp inj of extensor muscle, fascia and tndn of [rt, lt] index finger at wrist and hand lvl, subsq enc

S66.30[2,3]D — Unsp inj of extensor muscle, fascia and tndn of [rt, lt] mid finger at wrist and hand lvl, subsq enc

S66.30[4,5]D — Unsp inj of extensor muscle, fascia and tndn of [rt, lt] ring finger at wrist and hand lvl, subsq enc

S66.30[6,7]D — Unsp inj of extensor muscle, fascia and tndn of [rt, lt] little finger at wrist and hand lvl, subsq enc

S66.30[8,9]D — Unsp inj of extensor muscle, fascia and tndn of [oth, unsp] finger at wrist and hand lvl, subsq enc

S66.31[0,1]D — Strain of extensor muscle, fascia and tndn of [rt, lt] index finger at wrist and hand lvl, subsq enc

S66.31[2,3]D — Strain of extensor muscle, fascia and tndn of [rt, lt] mid finger at wrist and hand lvl, subsq enc

S66.31[4,5]D — Strain of extensor muscle, fascia and tndn of [rt, lt] ring finger at wrist and hand lvl, subsq enc

S66.31[6,7]D — Strain of extensor muscle, fascia and tndn of [rt, lt] little finger at wrist and hand lvl, subsq enc

S66.31[8,9]D — Strain of extensor muscle, fascia and tndn of [oth, unsp] finger at wrist and hand lvl, subsq enc

S66.32[0,1]D — Lac of extensor muscle, fascia and tndn of [rt, lt] index finger at wrist and hand lvl, subsq enc

S66.32[2,3]D — Lac of extensor muscle, fascia and tndn of [rt, lt] mid finger at wrist and hand lvl, subsq enc

S66.32[4,5]D — Lac of extensor muscle, fascia and tndn of [rt, lt] ring finger at wrist and hand lvl, subsq enc

S66.32[6,7]D — Lac of extensor muscle, fascia and tndn of [rt, lt] little finger at wrist and hand lvl, subsq enc

S66.32[8,9]D — Lac of extensor muscle, fascia and tndn of [oth, unsp] finger at wrist and hand lvl, subsq enc

S66.39[0,1]D — Unsp inj of extensor muscle, fascia and tndn of [rt, lt] index finger at wrist and hand lvl, subsq enc

S66.39[2,3]D — Unsp inj of extensor muscle, fascia and tndn of [rt, lt] mid finger at wrist and hand lvl, subsq enc

S66.39[4,5]D — Unsp inj of extensor muscle, fascia and tndn of [rt, lt] ring finger at wrist and hand lvl, subsq enc

S66.39[6,7]D — Unsp inj of extensor muscle, fascia and tndn of [rt, lt] little finger at wrist and hand lvl, subsq enc

S66.39[8,9]D — Unsp inj of extensor muscle, fascia and tndn of [oth, unsp] finger at wrist and hand lvl, subsq enc

S66.4[0,1,2,9][1,2,9]D — [Unsp inj, Strain, Lac, Oth spec inj] of intrinsic muscle, fascia and tndn of [rt, lt, unsp] thumb at wrist and hand lvl, subsq enc

S66.5[0,1,2,9][0,1,2,3,4,5,6,7,8,9]D — [Unsp inj, Strain, Lac, Oth inj] of intrinsic muscle, fascia and tndn of [rt index, lt index, rt mid, lt mid, rt ring, lt ring, rt little, lt little, oth, unsp] finger at wrist and hand lvl, subsq enc

S66.[8,9][0,1,2,9][1,2,9]D — [Unsp inj, Strain, Lac, Oth inj] of [oth spec, unsp] muscles, fascia and tndns at wrist and hand lvl, [rt, lt, unsp] hand, subsq enc

S67.0[0,1,2]XD — Crushing inj of [unsp, rt, lt] thumb, subsq enc

S67.10XD — Crushing inj of unsp finger(s), subs enc

S67.19[0,1,2,3,4,5,6,7,8]D — Crushing inj of [rt index, lt index, rt ring, lt ring, rt mid, lt mid, rt little, lt little, oth] finger, subsq enc

S67.2[0,1,2]XD — Crushing inj of [unsp, rt, lt] hand, subsq enc

S67.3[0,1,2]XD — Crushing inj of [unsp, rt, lt] wrist, subsq enc

S67.4[0,1,2]XD — Crushing inj of [unsp, rt, lt] wrist and hand, subsq enc

S67.9[0,1,2]XD — Crushing inj of unsp parts of [unsp, rt, lt] hand and fingers, subsq enc

S68.0[1,2][1,2,9]D — [Complete, Partial] traum metacarpophalangeal amp of [rt, lt, unsp] thumb, subsq enc

S68.1[1,2][0,1,2,3,4,5,6,7,8,9]D — [Complete, Partial] traum metacarpophalangeal amp of [rt index, lt index, rt mid, lt mid, rt ring, lt ring, rt little, lt little, oth, unsp] finger, subsq enc

S68.4[1,2][1,2,9]D — [Complete, Partial] traum amp of [rt, lt, unsp] hand at wrist lvl, subsq enc

S68.5[1,2][1,2,9]D — [Complete, Partial] traum transphalangeal amp of [rt, lt, unsp] thumb, subsq enc

S68.6[1,2][0,1,2,3,4,5,6,7,8,9]D — [Complete, Partial] traum transphalangeal amp of [rt index, lt index, rt mid, lt mid, rt ring, lt ring, rt little, lt little, oth, unsp] finger, subsq enc

S68.7[1,2][1,2,9]D — [Complete, Partial] traum transmetacarpal amp of [rt, lt, unsp] hand, subsq enc

S69.[8,9][0,1,2]XD — [Oth spec, Unsp] injuries of [unsp, rt, lt] wrist, hand and finger(s), subsq enc

S70.0[0,1,2]XD — Contsn of [unsp, rt, lt] hip, subsq enc

S70.1[0,1,2]XD — Contsn of [unsp, rt, lt] thigh, subsq enc

S70.2[1,2,4,5,6,7][1,2,9]D — [Abrasion, Blister (nonthermal), Ext constriction, Superf FB, Insect bite (nonvenomous), Oth superf bite], [rt, lt, unsp] hip, subsq enc

S70.3[1,2,4,5,6,7][1,2,9]D — [Abrasion, Blister (nonthermal), Ext constriction, Superf FB, Insect bite (nonvenomous), Oth superf bite], [rt, lt, unsp] thigh, subsq enc

S70.9[1,2][1,2,9]D — Unsp superf inj of [rt, lt, unsp] [hip, thigh], subsq enc

S71.0[0,1,2,3,4,5][1,2,9]D — [Unsp opn wnd, Lac w/o FB, Lac w/ FB, Punc wnd w/o FB, Punc wnd w/ FB, Opn bite], [rt, lt, unsp] hip, subsq enc

S71.1[0,1,2,3,4,5][1,2,9]D — [Unsp opn wnd, Lac w/o FB, Lac w/ FB, Punc wnd w/o FB, Punc wnd w/ FB, Opn bite], [rt, lt, unsp] thigh, subsq enc

S73.00[1,2,3]D — Unsp sublux of [rt, lt, unsp] hip, subsq enc

S73.00[4,5,6]D — Unsp disloc of [rt, lt, unsp] hip, subsq enc

S73.01[1,2,3]D — Post sublux of [rt, lt, unsp] hip, subsq enc

S73.01[4,5,6]D — Post disloc of [rt, lt, unsp] hip, subsq enc

S73.02[1,2,3]D — Obturator sublux of [rt, lt, unsp] hip, subsq enc

S73.02[4,5,6]D — Obturator disloc of [rt, lt, unsp] hip, subsq enc

S73.03[1,2,3]D — Oth ant sublux of [rt, lt, unsp] hip, subsq enc

S73.03[4,5,6]D — Oth ant disloc of [rt, lt, unsp] hip, subsq enc

S73.04[1,2,3]D — Central sublux of [rt, lt, unsp] hip, subsq enc

S73.04[4,5,6]D — Central disloc of [rt, lt, unsp] hip, subsq enc

S73.1[0,1,2,9][1,2,9]D — [Unsp, Iliofemoral lgmt, Ischiocapsular lgmt, Oth] sprain of [rt, lt, unsp] hip, subsq enc

S74.8X[1,2,9]D — Inj of oth nerves at hip & thigh lvl, [unsp, rt, lt] leg, subsq enc

S74.9[0,1,2]XD — Inj of unsp nerve at hip & thigh lvl, [unsp, rt, lt] leg, subsq enc

---

Surgical   **Medical**   **CC Indicator**   **MCC Indicator**   **Procedure Proxy**   **PDxMCC** PDx acts as own MCC   **PDxCC** PDx acts as own CC

S74.[Ø,1,2][Ø,1,2]XD Inj of [sciatic, femor, cutaneous sensory] nerve at hip & thigh lvl, [unsp, rt, lt] leg, subsq enc
S75.Ø[Ø,1,2,9][1,2,9]D [Unsp inj, Minor lac, Major lac, Oth spec inj] of femor artery, [rt, lt, unsp] leg, subsq enc
S75.1[Ø,1,2,9][1,2,9]D [Unsp inj, Minor lac, Major lac, Oth spec inj] of femor vein at hip & thigh lvl, [rt, lt, unsp] leg, subsq enc
S75.2[Ø,1,2,9][1,2,9]D [Unsp inj, Minor lac, Major lac, Oth spec inj] of greater saphenous vein at hip & thigh lvl, [rt, lt, unsp] leg, subsq enc
S75.8[Ø,1,9][1,2,9]D [Unsp inj, Lac, Oth spec inj] of oth bld vessels at hip & thigh lvl, [rt, lt, unsp] leg, subsq enc
S75.9[Ø,1,9][1,2,9]D [Unsp inj, Lac, Oth spec inj] of unsp bld vessel at hip & thigh lvl, [rt, lt, unsp] leg, subsq enc
S76.Ø[Ø,1,2,9][1,2,9]D [Unsp inj, Strain, Lac, Oth spec inj] of muscle, fascia and tndn of [rt, lt, unsp] hip, subsq enc
S76.1[Ø,1,2,9][1,2,9]D [Unsp inj, Strain, Lac, Oth spec inj] of [rt, lt, unsp] quadriceps muscle, fascia and tndn, subsq enc
S76.2[Ø,1,2,9][1,2,9]D [Unsp inj, Strain, Lac, Oth inj] of adductor muscle, fascia and tndn of [rt, lt, unsp] thigh, subsq enc
S76.3[Ø,1,2,9][1,2,9]D [Unsp inj, Strain, Lac, Oth spec inj] of muscle, fascia and tndn of the post muscle group at thigh lvl, [rt, lt, unsp] thigh, subsq enc
S76.8[Ø,1,2,9][1,2,9]D [Unsp inj, Strain, Lac, Oth inj] of oth spec muscles, fascia and tndns at thigh lvl, [rt, lt, unsp] thigh, subsq enc
S76.9[Ø,1,2,9][1,2,9]D [Unsp inj, Strain, Lac, Oth spec inj] of unsp muscles, fascia and tndns at thigh lvl, [rt, lt, unsp] thigh, subsq enc
S77.[Ø,1,2][Ø,1,2]XD Crushing inj of [unsp, rt, lt] [hip, thigh, hip w/ thigh], subsq enc
S78.Ø[1,2][1,2,9]D [Complete, Partial] traum amp at [rt, lt, unsp] hip jt, subsq enc
S78.1[1,2][1,2,9]D [Complete, Partial] traum amp at lvl between [rt, lt, unsp] hip and knee, subsq enc
S78.9[1,2][1,2,9]D [Complete, Partial] traum amp of [rt, lt, unsp] hip & thigh, lvl unsp, subsq enc
S79.[8,9][1,2][1,2,9]D [Oth spec, Unsp] injuries of [rt, lt, unsp] [hip, thigh], subsq enc
S80.Ø[Ø,1,2]XD Contsn of [unsp, rt, lt] knee, subsq enc
S80.1[Ø,1,2]XD Contsn of [unsp, rt, lt] lwr leg, subsq enc
S80.2[1,2,4,5,6,7][1,2,9]D [Abrasion, Blister (nonthermal), Ext constriction, Superf FB, Insect bite (nonvenomous), Oth superf bite] of [rt, lt, unsp] knee, subsq enc
S80.8[1,2,4,5,6,7][1,2,9]D [Abrasion, Blister (nonthermal), Ext constriction, Superf FB, Insect bite (nonvenomous), Oth superf bite] of [rt, lt, unsp] lwr leg, subsq enc
S80.9[1,2][1,2,9]D Unsp superf inj of [rt, lt, unsp] [knee, lwr leg], subsq enc
S81.Ø[Ø,1,2,3,4,5][1,2,9]D [Unsp opn wnd, Lac w/o FB, Lac w/ FB, Punc wnd w/o FB, Punc wnd w/ FB, Opn bite] [rt, lt, unsp] knee, subsq enc
S81.8[Ø,1,2,3,4,5][1,2,9]D [Unsp opn wnd, Lac w/o FB, Lac w/ FB, Punc wnd w/o FB, Punc wnd w/ FB, Opn bite] [rt, lt, unsp] lwr leg, subsq enc
S83.ØØ[1,2,3]D Unsp sublux of [rt, lt, unsp] patella, subsq enc
S83.ØØ[4,5,6]D Unsp disloc of [rt, lt, unsp] patella, subsq enc
S83.Ø1[1,2,3]D Lat sublux of [rt, lt, unsp] patella, subsq enc
S83.Ø1[4,5,6]D Lat disloc of [rt, lt, unsp] patella, subsq enc
S83.Ø9[1,2,3]D Oth sublux of [rt, lt, unsp] patella, subsq enc
S83.Ø9[4,5,6]D Oth disloc of [rt, lt, unsp] patella, subsq enc
S83.10[1,2,3]D Unsp sublux of [rt, lt, unsp] knee, subsq enc
S83.10[4,5,6]D Unsp disloc of [rt, lt, unsp] knee, subsq enc
S83.11[1,2,3]D Ant sublux of proximal end of tibia, [rt, lt, unsp] knee, subsq enc
S83.11[4,5,6]D Ant disloc of proximal end of tibia, [rt, lt, unsp] knee, subsq enc
S83.12[1,2,3]D Post sublux of proximal end of tibia, [rt, lt, unsp] knee, subsq enc
S83.12[4,5,6]D Post disloc of proximal end of tibia, [rt, lt, unsp] knee, subsq enc
S83.13[1,2,3]D Med sublux of proximal end of tibia, [rt, lt, unsp] knee, subsq enc
S83.13[4,5,6]D Med disloc of proximal end of tibia, [rt, lt, unsp] knee, subsq enc
S83.14[1,2,3]D Lat sublux of proximal end of tibia, [rt, lt, unsp] knee, subsq enc
S83.14[4,5,6]D Lat disloc of proximal end of tibia, [rt, lt, unsp] knee, subsq enc
S83.19[1,2,3]D Oth sublux of [rt, lt, unsp] knee, subsq enc
S83.19[4,5,6]D Oth disloc of [rt, lt, unsp] knee, subsq enc
S83.20[Ø,1,2]D Bucket-handle tear of unsp meniscus, current inj, [rt, lt, unsp] knee, subsq enc
S83.20[3,4,5]D Oth tear of unsp meniscus, current inj, [rt, lt, unsp] knee, subsq enc
S83.20[6,7,9]D Unsp tear of unsp meniscus, current inj, [rt, lt, unsp] knee, subsq enc
S83.21[1,2,9]D Bucket-handle tear of med meniscus, current inj, [rt, lt, unsp] knee, subsq enc

S83.22[1,2,9]D Peripheral tear of med meniscus, current inj, [rt, lt, unsp] knee, subsq enc
S83.23[1,2,9]D Complex tear of med meniscus, current inj, [rt, lt, unsp] knee, subsq enc
S83.24[1,2,9]D Oth tear of med meniscus, current inj, [rt, lt, unsp] knee, subsq enc
S83.25[1,2,9]D Bucket-handle tear of lat meniscus, current inj, [rt, lt, unsp] knee, subsq enc
S83.26[1,2,9]D Peripheral tear of lat meniscus, current inj, [rt, lt, unsp] knee, subsq enc
S83.27[1,2,9]D Complex tear of lat meniscus, current inj, [rt, lt, unsp] knee, subsq enc
S83.28[1,2,9]D Oth tear of lat meniscus, current inj, [rt, lt, unsp] knee, subsq enc
S83.3[Ø,1,2]XD Tear of articular cartilage of [unsp, rt, lt] knee, current, subsq enc
S83.4[Ø,1,2][1,2,9]D Sprain of [unsp, med, lat] collat lgmt of [rt, lt, unsp] knee, subsq enc
S83.5[Ø,1,2][1,2,9]D Sprain of [unsp, ant, post] cruciate lgmt of [rt, lt, unsp] knee, subsq enc
S83.6[Ø,1,2]XD Sprain of the superior tibiofibular jt and lgmt, [unsp, rt, lt] knee, subsq enc
S83.8X[1,2,9]D Sprain of oth spec parts of [rt, lt, unsp] knee, subsq enc
S83.9[Ø,1,2]XD Sprain of unsp site of [unsp, rt, lt] knee, subsq enc
S84.8Ø[1,2,9]D Inj of oth nerves at lwr leg lvl, [rt, lt, unsp] leg, subsq enc
S84.9[Ø,1,2]XD Inj of unsp nerve at lwr leg lvl, [unsp, rt, lt] leg, subsq enc
S84.[Ø,1,2][Ø,1,2]XD Inj of [tibial, peroneal, cutaneous sensory] nerve at lwr leg lvl, [unsp, rt, lt] leg, subsq enc
S85.Ø[Ø,1,9][1,2,9]D [Unsp inj, Lac, Oth spec inj] of popliteal artery, [rt, lt, unsp] leg, subsq enc
S85.1[Ø,1,2][1,2,9]D [Unsp inj, Lac, Oth spec inj] of unsp tibial artery, [rt, lt, unsp] leg, subsq enc
S85.1[3,4,5][1,2,9]D [Unsp inj, Lac, Oth spec inj] of ant tibial artery, [rt, lt, unsp] leg, subsq enc
S85.1[6,7,8][1,2,9]D [Unsp inj, Lac, Oth spec inj] of post tibial artery, [rt, lt, unsp] leg, subsq enc
S85.2[Ø,1,9][1,2,9]D [Unsp inj, Lac, Oth spec inj] of peroneal artery, [rt, lt, unsp] leg, subsq enc
S85.3[Ø,1,9][1,2,9]D [Unsp inj, Lac, Oth spec inj] of greater saphenous vein at lwr leg lvl, [rt, lt, unsp] leg, subsq enc
S85.4[Ø,1,9][1,2,9]D [Unsp inj, Lac, Oth spec inj] of lesser saphenous vein at lwr leg lvl, [rt, lt, unsp] leg, subsq enc
S85.5[Ø,1,9][1,2,9]D [Unsp inj, Lac, Oth spec inj] of popliteal vein, [rt, lt, unsp] leg, subsq enc
S85.8[Ø,1,9][1,2,9]D [Unsp inj, Lac, Oth spec inj] of oth bood vessels at lwr leg lvl, [rt, lt, unsp] leg, subsq enc
S85.9[Ø,1,9][1,2,9]D [Unsp inj, Lac, Oth spec inj] of unsp bood vessels at lwr leg lvl, [rt, lt, unsp] leg, subsq enc
S86.Ø[Ø,1,2,9][1,2,9]D [Unsp inj, Strain, Lac, Oth spec inj] of [rt, lt, unsp] Achilles tndn, subsq enc
S86.1[Ø,1,2,9][1,2,9]D [Unsp inj, Strain, Lac, Oth spec inj] of oth muscle(s) and tndn(s) of post muscle group at lwr leg lvl, [rt, lt, unsp] leg, subsq enc
S86.2[Ø,1,2,9][1,2,9]D [Unsp inj, Strain, Lac, Oth spec inj] of oth muscle(s) and tndn(s) of ant muscle group at lwr leg lvl, [rt, lt, unsp] leg, subsq enc
S86.3[Ø,1,2,9][1,2,9]D [Unsp inj, Strain, Lac, Oth spec inj] of oth muscle(s) and tndn(s) of peroneal muscle group at lwr leg lvl, [rt, lt, unsp] leg, subsq enc
S86.8[Ø,1,2,9][1,2,9]D [Unsp inj, Strain, Lac, Oth spec inj] of oth muscle(s) and tndn(s) at lwr leg lvl, [rt, lt, unsp] leg, subsq enc
S86.9[Ø,1,2,9][1,2,9]D [Unsp inj, Strain, Lac, Oth spec inj] of unsp muscle(s) and tndn(s) at lwr leg lvl, [rt, lt, unsp] leg, subsq enc
S87.Ø[Ø,1,2]XD Crushing inj of [unsp, rt, lt] knee, subsq enc
S87.8[Ø,1,2]XD Crushing inj of [unsp, rt, lt] lwr leg, subsq enc
S88.Ø[1,2][1,2,9]D [Complete, Partial] traum amp at knee lvl, [rt, lt, unsp] lwr leg, subsq enc
S88.1[1,2][1,2,9]D [Complete, Partial] traum amp at lvl between knee and ankle, [rt, lt, unsp] lwr leg, subsq enc
S88.9[1,2][1,2,9]D [Complete, Partial] traum amp of [rt, lt, unsp] lwr leg, lvl unsp, subsq enc
S89.[8,9][Ø,1,2]XD [Oth spec injuries, Unsp inj] of [unsp, rt, lt] lwr leg, subsq enc
S90.Ø[Ø,1,2]XD Contsn of [unsp, rt, lt] ankle, subsq enc
S90.1[1,2][1,2,9]D Contsn of [rt, lt, unsp] [great, lesser] toe(s) w/o damage to nail, subsq enc
S90.2[1,2][1,2,9]D Contsn of [rt, lt, unsp] [great, lesser] toe(s) w/ damage to nail, subsq enc
S90.3[Ø,1,2]XD Contsn of [unsp, rt, lt] foot, subsq enc
S90.41[1,2,3]D Abrasion, [rt, lt, unsp] great toe, subsq enc
S90.41[4,5,6]D Abrasion, [rt, lt, unsp] lesser toe(s), subsq enc

S90.42[1,2,3]D	Blister (nonthermal), [rt, lt, unsp] great toe, subsq enc
S90.42[4,5,6]D	Blister (nonthermal), [rt, lt, unsp] lesser toe(s), subsq enc
S90.44[1,2,3]D	Ext constriction, [rt, lt, unsp] great toe, subsq enc
S90.44[4,5,6]D	Ext constriction, [rt, lt, unsp] lesser toe(s), subsq enc
S90.45[1,2,3]D	Superf FB, [rt, lt, unsp] great toe, subsq enc
S90.45[4,5,6]D	Superf FB, [rt, lt, unsp] lesser toe(s), subsq enc
S90.46[1,2,3]D	Insect bite (nonvenomous), [rt, lt, unsp] great toe, subsq enc
S90.46[4,5,6]D	Insect bite (nonvenomous), [rt, lt, unsp] lesser toe(s), subsq enc
S90.47[1,2,3]D	Oth superf bite of [rt, lt, unsp] great toe, subsq enc
S90.47[4,5,6]D	Oth superf bite of [rt, lt, unsp] lesser toe(s), subsq enc
S90.5[1,2,4,5,6,7][1,2,9]D	[Abrasion, Blister (nonthermal), Ext constriction, Superf FB, Insect bite (nonvenomous), Oth superf bite], [rt, lt, unsp] ankle, subsq enc
S90.8[1,2,4,5,6,7][1,2,9]D	[Abrasion, Blister (nonthermal), Ext constriction, Superf FB, Insect bite (nonvenomous), Oth superf bite], [rt, lt, unsp] foot, subsq enc
S90.91[1,2,9]D	Unsp superf inj of [rt, lt, unsp] ankle, subsq enc
S90.92[1,2,9]D	Unsp superf inj of [rt, lt, unsp] foot, subsq enc
S90.93[1,2,3]D	Unsp superf inj of [rt, lt, unsp] great toe, subsq enc
S90.93[4,5,6]D	Unsp superf inj of [rt, lt, unsp] lesser toe(s), subsq enc
S91.00[1,2,9]D	Unsp opn wnd, [rt, lt, unsp] ankle, subsq enc
S91.05[1,2,9]D	Opn bite, [rt, lt, unsp] ankle, subsq enc
S91.0[1,2][1,2,9]D	Lac [w/o, w/] FB, [rt, lt, unsp] ankle, subsq enc
S91.0[3,4][1,2,9]D	Punc wnd [w/o, w/] FB, [rt, lt, unsp] ankle, subsq enc
S91.109D	Unsp opn wnd of unsp toe(s) w/o damage to nail, subs
S91.10[1,2,3]D	Unsp opn wnd of [rt, lt, unsp] great toe w/o damage to nail, subsq enc
S91.10[4,5,6]D	Unsp opn wnd of [rt, lt, unsp] lesser toe(s) w/o damage to nail, subsq enc
S91.119D	Lac w/o fb of unsp toe w/o damage to nail, subs
S91.11[1,2,3]D	Lac w/o FB of [rt, lt, unsp] great toe w/o damage to nail, subsq enc
S91.11[4,5,6]D	Lac w/o FB of [rt, lt, unsp] lesser toe(s) w/o damage to nail, subsq enc
S91.129D	Lac w fb of unsp toe(s) w/o damage to nail, subs
S91.12[1,2,3]D	Lac w/ FB of [rt, lt, unsp] great toe w/o damage to nail, subsq enc
S91.12[4,5,6]D	Lac w/ FB of [rt, lt, unsp] lesser toe(s) w/o damage to nail, subsq enc
S91.139D	Punc w/o fb of unsp toe(s) w/o damage to nail, subs
S91.13[1,2,3]D	Punc wnd w/o FB of [rt, lt, unsp] great toe w/o damage to nail, subsq enc
S91.13[4,5,6]D	Punc wnd w/o FB of [rt, lt, unsp] lesser toe(s) w/o damage to nail, subsq enc
S91.149D	Punc w FB of unsp toe(s) w/o damage to nail, subs
S91.14[1,2,3]D	Punc wnd w/ FB of [rt, lt, unsp] great toe w/o damage to nail, subsq enc
S91.14[4,5,6]D	Punc wnd w/ FB of [rt, lt, unsp] lesser toe(s) w/o damage to nail, subsq enc
S91.159D	Opn bite of unsp toe(s) w/o damage to nail, subs enc
S91.15[1,2,3]D	Opn bite of [rt, lt, unsp] great toe w/o damage to nail, subsq enc
S91.15[4,5,6]D	Opn bite of [rt, lt, unsp] lesser toe(s) w/o damage to nail, subsq enc
S91.209D	Unsp opn wnd of unsp toe(s) w damage to nail, subs enc
S91.20[1,2,3]D	Unsp opn wnd of [rt, lt, unsp] great toe w/ damage to nail, subsq enc
S91.20[4,5,6]D	Unsp opn wnd of [rt, lt, unsp] lesser toe(s) w/ damage to nail, subsq enc
S91.219D	Lac w/o fb of unsp toe(s) w damage to nail, subs
S91.21[1,2,3]D	Lac w/o FB of [rt, lt, unsp] great toe w/ damage to nail, subsq enc
S91.21[4,5,6]D	Lac w/o FB of [rt, lt, unsp] lesser toe(s) w/ damage to nail, subsq enc
S91.229D	Lac w fb of unsp toe(s) w damage to nail, subs
S91.22[1,2,3]D	Lac w/ FB of [rt, lt, unsp] great toe w/ damage to nail, subsq enc
S91.22[4,5,6]D	Lac w/ FB of [rt, lt, unsp] lesser toe(s) w/ damage to nail, subsq enc
S91.239D	Punc w/o FB of unsp toe(s) w damage to nail, subs
S91.23[1,2,3]D	Punc wnd w/o FB of [rt, lt, unsp] great toe w/ damage to nail, subsq enc
S91.23[4,5,6]D	Punc wnd w/o FB of [rt, lt, unsp] lesser toe(s) w/ damage to nail, subsq enc
S91.249D	Punc w FB of unsp toe(s) w damage to nail, subs
S91.24[1,2,3]D	Punc wnd w/ FB of [rt, lt, unsp] great toe w/ damage to nail, subsq enc
S91.24[4,5,6]D	Punc wnd w/ FB of [rt, lt, unsp] lesser toe(s) w/ damage to nail, subsq enc
S91.259D	Opn bite of unsp toe(s) with damage to nail, subs enc
S91.25[1,2,3]D	Opn bite of [rt, lt, unsp] great toe w/ damage to nail, subsq enc
S91.25[4,5,6]D	Opn bite of [rt, lt, unsp] lesser toe(s) w/ damage to nail, subsq enc
S91.30[1,2,9]D	Unsp opn wnd, [rt, lt, unsp] foot, subsq enc
S91.31[1,2,9]D	Lac w/o FB, [rt, lt, unsp] foot, subsq enc
S91.32[1,2,9]D	Lac w/ FB, [rt, lt, unsp] foot, subsq enc
S91.33[1,2,9]D	Punc wnd w/o FB, [rt, lt, unsp] foot, subsq enc
S91.34[1,2,9]D	Punc wnd w/ FB, [rt, lt, unsp] foot, subsq enc
S91.35[1,2,9]D	Opn bite, [rt, lt, unsp] foot, subsq enc
S93.0[1,2,3]XD	Sublux of [rt, lt, unsp] ankle jt, subsq enc
S93.0[4,5,6]XD	Disloc of [rt, lt, unsp] ankle jt, subsq enc
S93.10[1,2,3]D	Unsp sublux of [rt, lt, unsp] toe(s), subsq enc
S93.10[4,5,6]D	Unsp disloc of [rt, lt, unsp] toe(s), subsq enc
S93.119D	Disloc of interphalangeal jt of unsp toe(s), subs
S93.11[1,2,3]D	Disloc of interphalangeal jt of [rt, lt, unsp] great toe, subsq enc
S93.11[4,5,6]D	Disloc of interphalangeal jt of [rt, lt, unsp] lesser toe(s), subsq enc
S93.129D	Disloc of MTP jt of unsp toe(s), subs
S93.12[1,2,3]D	Disloc of metatarsophalangeal jt of [rt, lt, unsp] great toe, subsq enc
S93.12[4,5,6]D	Disloc of metatarsophalangeal jt of [rt, lt, unsp] lesser toe(s), subsq enc
S93.139D	Sublux of interphalangeal jt of unsp toe(s), subs
S93.13[1,2,3]D	Sublux of interphalangeal jt of [rt, lt, unsp] great toe, subsq enc
S93.13[4,5,6]D	Sublux of interphalangeal jt of [rt, lt, unsp] lesser toe(s), subsq enc
S93.149D	Sublux of MTP jt of unsp toe(s), subs
S93.14[1,2,3]D	Sublux of metatarsophalangeal jt of [rt, lt, unsp] great toe, subsq enc
S93.14[4,5,6]D	Sublux of metatarsophalangeal jt of [rt, lt, unsp] lesser toe(s), subsq enc
S93.30[1,2,3]D	Unsp sublux of [rt, lt, unsp] foot, subsq enc
S93.30[4,5,6]D	Unsp disloc of [rt, lt, unsp] foot, subsq enc
S93.31[1,2,3]D	Sublux of tarsal jt of [rt, lt, unsp] foot, subsq enc
S93.31[4,5,6]D	Disloc of tarsal jt of [rt, lt, unsp] foot, subsq enc
S93.32[1,2,3]D	Sublux of tarsometatarsal jt of [rt, lt, unsp] foot, subsq enc
S93.32[4,5,6]D	Disloc of tarsometatarsal jt of [rt, lt, unsp] foot, subsq enc
S93.33[1,2,3]D	Oth sublux of [rt, lt, unsp] foot, subsq enc
S93.33[4,5,6]D	Oth disloc of [rt, lt, unsp] foot, subsq enc
S93.4[0,1,2,3,9][1,2,9]D	Sprain of [unsp, calcaneofibular, deltoid, tibiofibular, oth] lgmt of [rt, lt, unsp] ankle, subsq enc
S93.509D	Unsp sprain of unsp toe(s), subs enc
S93.50[1,2,3]D	Unsp strain of [rt, lt, unsp] great toe, subsq enc
S93.50[4,5,6]D	Unsp strain of [rt, lt, unsp] lesser toe(s), subsq enc
S93.519D	Sprain of interphalangeal jt of unsp toe(s), subs enc
S93.51[1,2,3]D	Strain of interphalangeal jt of [rt, lt, unsp] great toe, subsq enc
S93.51[4,5,6]D	Strain of interphalangeal jt of [rt, lt, unsp] lesser toe(s), subsq enc
S93.529D	Sprain of metatarsophalangeal jt of unsp toe(s), subs
S93.52[1,2,3]D	Strain of metatarsophalangeal jt of [rt, lt, unsp] great toe, subsq enc
S93.52[4,5,6]D	Strain of metatarsophalangeal jt of [rt, lt, unsp] lesser toe(s), subsq enc
S93.60[1,2,9]D	Unsp sprain of [rt, lt, unsp] foot, subsq enc
S93.61[1,2,9]D	Sprain of tarsal lgmt of [rt, lt, unsp] foot, subsq enc
S93.62[1,2,9]D	Sprain of tarsometatarsal lgmt of [rt, lt, unsp] foot, subsq enc
S93.69[1,2,9]D	Oth sprain of [rt, lt, unsp] foot, subsq enc
S94.8X[1,2,9]D	Inj of oth nerves at ankle and foot lvl, [unsp, rt, lt] leg, subsq enc
S94.9[0,1,2]XD	Inj of unsp nerve at ankle and foot lvl, [unsp leg, rt, lt], subsq enc
S94.[0,1,2,3][0,1,2]XD	Inj of [lat plantar, med plantar, deep peroneal, cutaneous sensory] nerve, [unsp, rt, lt] leg, subsq enc
S95.0[0,1,9][1,2,9]D	[Unsp inj, Lac, Oth spec inj] of dorsal artery of [rt, lt, unsp] foot, subsq enc
S95.1[0,1,9][1,2,9]D	[Unsp inj, Lac, Oth spec inj] of plantar artery of [rt, lt, unsp] foot, subsq enc
S95.2[0,1,9][1,2,9]D	[Unsp inj, Lac, Oth spec inj] of dorsal vein of [rt, lt, unsp] foot, subsq enc
S95.8[0,1,9][1,2,9]D	[Unsp inj, Lac, Oth spec inj] of oth bld vessels at ankle and foot lvl, [rt, lt, unsp] leg, subsq enc
S95.9[0,1,9][1,2,9]D	[Unsp inj, Lac, Oth spec inj] of unsp bld vessel at ankle and foot lvl, [rt, lt, unsp] leg, subsq enc
S96.0[0,1,2,9][1,2,9]D	[Unsp inj, Strain, Lac, Oth inj] of muscle and tndn of long flexor muscle of toe at ankle and foot lvl, [rt, lt, unsp] foot, subsq enc

Surgical   **Medical**   **CC Indicator**   **MCC Indicator**   **Procedure Proxy**   PDxMCC **PDx acts as own MCC**   PDxCC **PDx acts as own CC**

© 2015 Optum360, LLC   MS-DRG Version 33.0   399

MDC 23: Factors Influencing Health Status And Other Contacts With Health Services—MEDICAL

MDC 23: Factors Influencing Health Status And Other Contacts With Health Services—MEDICAL

Code	Description
S96.1[0,1,2,9][1,2,9]D	[Unsp inj, Strain, Lac, Oth inj] of muscle and tndn of long extensor muscle of toe at ankle and foot lvl, [rt, lt, unsp] foot, subsq enc
S96.2[0,1,2,9][1,2,9]D	[Unsp inj, Strain, Lac, Oth inj] of intrinsic muscle and tndn at ankle and foot lvl, [rt, lt, unsp] foot, subsq enc
S96.8[0,1,2,9][1,2,9]D	[Unsp inj, Strain, Lac, Oth inj] of oth spec muscles and tndns at ankle and foot lvl, [rt, lt, unsp] foot, subsq enc
S96.9[0,1,2,9][1,2,9]D	[Unsp inj, Strain, Lac, Oth inj] of unsp muscle and tndn at ankle and foot lvl, [rt, lt, unsp] foot, subsq enc
S97.0[0,1,2]XD	Crushing inj of [unsp, rt, lt] ankle, subsq enc
S97.10[1,2,9]D	Crushing inj of unsp [rt, lt, unsp] toe(s), subsq enc
S97.11[1,2,9]D	Crushing inj of [rt, lt, unsp] great toe, subsq enc
S97.12[1,2,9]D	Crushing inj of [rt, lt, unsp] lesser toe(s), subsq enc
S97.8[0,1,2]XD	Crushing inj of [unsp, rt, lt] foot, subsq enc
S98.0[1,2][1,2,9]D	[Complete, Partial] traum amp of [rt, lt, unsp] foot at ankle lvl, subsq enc
S98.1[1,2][1,2,9]D	[Complete, Partial] traum amp of [rt, lt, unsp] great toe, subsq enc
S98.1[3,4][1,2,9]D	[Complete, Partial] traum amp of one [rt, lt, unsp] lesser toe, subsq enc
S98.2[1,2][1,2,9]D	[Complete, Partial] traum amp of two or more [rt, lt, unsp] lesser toes, subsq enc
S98.3[1,2][1,2,9]D	[Complete, Partial] traum amp of [rt, lt, unsp] midfoot, subsq enc
S98.9[1,2][1,2,9]D	[Complete, Partial] traum amp of [rt, lt, unsp] foot, lvl unsp, subsq enc
S99.81[1,2,9]D	Oth spec injuries of [rt, lt, unsp] ankle, subsq enc
S99.82[1,2,9]D	Oth spec injuries of [rt, lt, unsp] foot, subsq enc
S99.91[1,2,9]D	Unsp inj of [rt, lt, unsp] ankle, subsq enc
S99.92[1,2,9]D	Unsp inj of [rt, lt, unsp] foot, subsq enc
T15.[0,1,8,9][0,1,2]XD	FB in [cornea, conjunctival sac, oth and multi parts of ext eye, ext eye part unsp], [unsp, rt, lt] eye, subsq enc
T16.[1,2,9]XXD	FB in [rt, lt, unsp] ear, subsq enc
T17.2[0,1,2,9][0,8]D	[Unsp FB, Gastric contents, Food, Oth foreign object] in pharynx causing [asphyxiation, oth inj], subsq enc
T17.3[0,1,2,9][0,8]D	[Unsp FB, Gastric contents, Food, Oth foreign object] in larynx causing [asphyxiation, oth inj], subsq enc
T17.4[0,1,2,9][0,8]D	[Unsp FB, Gastric contents, Food, Oth foreign object] in trachea causing [asphyxiation, oth inj], subsq enc
T17.5[0,1,2,9][0,8]D	[Unsp FB, Gastric contents, Food, Oth foreign object] in bronchus causing [asphyxiation, oth inj], subsq enc
T17.8[0,1,2,9][0,8]D	[Unsp FB, Gastric contents, Food, Oth foreign object] in oth parts of respiratory tract causing [asphyxiation, oth inj], subsq enc
T17.9[0,1,2,9][0,8]D	[Unsp FB, Gastric contents, Food, Oth foreign object] in respiratory tract, part unsp causing [asphyxiation, oth inj], subsq enc
T17.[0,1]XXD	FB in [nasal sinus, nostril], subsq enc
T18.0XXD	FB in mouth, subsq enc
T18.1[0,1,2,9][0,8]D	[Unsp FB, Gastric contents, Food, Oth foreign object] in esophagus causing [compression of trachea, oth inj], subsq enc
T18.[2,3,4,5,8,9]XXD	FB in [stomach, sm intestine, colon, anus and rectum, oth parts of alimentary tract, alimentary tract part unsp], subsq enc
T19.[0,1,2,3,4,8,9]XXD	FB in [urethra, bladder, vulva and vagina, uterus, penis, oth parts of genitourinary tract, genitourinary tract part unsp], subsq enc
T20.00XD	Burn of unsp degree of head, face, and neck, unsp site, subs
T20.01[1,2,9]D	Burn of unsp degree of [rt, lt, unsp] ear [any part, except ear drum], subsq enc
T20.09XD	Burn of unsp deg mult sites of head, face, and neck, subs
T20.0[2,3,4]XD	Burn of unsp degree of [lip(s), chin, nose (septum)], subsq enc
T20.0[5,6,7]XD	Burn of unsp degree of [scalp [any part], forehead and cheek, neck], subsq enc
T20.10XD	Burn first degree of head, face, and neck, unsp site, subs
T20.11[1,2,9]D	Burn of 1st degree of [rt, lt, unsp] ear [any part, except ear drum], subsq enc
T20.19XD	Burn of first deg mult sites of head, face, and neck, subs
T20.1[2,3,4]XD	Burn of 1st degree of [lip(s), chin, nose (septum)], subsq enc
T20.1[5,6,7]XD	Burn of 1st degree of [scalp [any part], forehead and cheek, neck], subsq enc
T20.20XD	Burn 2nd degree of head, face, and neck, unsp site, subs
T20.21[1,2,9]D	Burn of 2nd degree of [rt, lt, unsp] ear [any part, except ear drum], subsq enc
T20.29XD	Burn of 2nd deg mul sites of head, face, and neck, subs
T20.2[2,3,4]XD	Burn of 2nd degree of [lip(s), chin, nose (septum)], subsq enc
T20.2[5,6,7]XD	Burn of 2nd degree of [scalp [any part], forehead and cheek, neck], subsq enc
T20.30XD	Burn 3rd degree of head, face, and neck, unsp site, subs
T20.31[1,2,9]D	Burn of 3rd degree of [rt, lt, unsp] ear [any part, except ear drum], subsq enc
T20.39XD	Burn of 3rd deg mu sites of head, face, and neck, subs
T20.3[2,3,4]XD	Burn of 3rd degree of [lip(s), chin, nose (septum)], subsq enc
T20.3[5,6,7]XD	Burn of 3rd degree of [scalp [any part], forehead and cheek, neck], subsq enc
T20.40XD	Corrosion unsp degree of head, face, and neck, unsp site, subs
T20.41[1,2,9]D	Corrosion of unsp degree of [rt, lt, unsp] ear [any part, except ear drum], subsq enc
T20.49XD	Corrosion unsp deg mult sites of head, face, and neck, subs
T20.4[2,3,4]XD	Corrosion of unsp degree of [lip(s), chin, nose (septum)], subsq enc
T20.4[5,6,7]XD	Corrosion of unsp degree of [scalp [any part], forehead and cheek, neck], subsq enc
T20.50XD	Corrosion first degree of head, face, and neck, unsp site, subs
T20.51[1,2,9]D	Corrosion of 1st degree of [rt, lt, unsp] ear [any part, except ear drum], subsq enc
T20.59XD	Corrosion first deg mult sites of head, face, and neck, subs
T20.5[2,3,4]XD	Corrosion of 1st degree of [lip(s), chin, nose (septum)], subsq enc
T20.5[5,6,7]XD	Corrosion of 1st degree of [scalp [any part], forehead and cheek, neck], subsq enc
T20.60XD	Corrosion 2nd deg of head, face, and neck, unsp site, subs
T20.61[1,2,9]D	Corrosion of 2nd degree of [rt, lt, unsp] ear [any part, except ear drum], subsq enc
T20.69XD	Corrosion of 2nd deg mul sites of head, face, and neck, subs
T20.6[2,3,4]XD	Corrosion of 2nd degree of [lip(s), chin, nose (septum)], subsq enc
T20.6[5,6,7]XD	Corrosion of 2nd degree of [scalp [any part], forehead and cheek, neck], subsq enc
T20.70XD	Corrosion 3rd degree of head, face, and neck, unsp site, subs
T20.71[1,2,9]D	Corrosion of 3rd degree of [rt, lt, unsp] ear [any part, except ear drum], subsq enc
T20.79XD	Corrosion of 3rd deg mu sites of head, face, and neck, subs
T20.7[2,3,4]XD	Corrosion of 3rd degree of [lip(s), chin, nose (septum)], subsq enc
T20.7[5,6,7]XD	Corrosion of 3rd degree of [scalp [any part], forehead and cheek, neck], subsq enc
T21.0[0,1,2,3,4,5,6,7,9]XD	Burn of unsp degree of [unsp site of trunk, chest wall, abd wall, upr back, lwr back, buttock, male genital rgn, female genital rgn, oth site of trunk], subsq enc
T21.1[0,1,2,3,4,5,6,7,9]XD	Burn of 1st degree of [unsp site of trunk, chest wall, abd wall, upr back, lwr back, buttock, male genital rgn, female genital rgn, oth site of trunk], subsq enc
T21.2[0,1,2,3,4,5,6,7,9]XD	Burn of 2nd degree of [unsp site of trunk, chest wall, abd wall, upr back, lwr back, buttock, male genital rgn, female genital rgn, oth site of trunk], subsq enc
T21.3[0,1,2,3,4,5,6,7,9]XD	Burn of 3rd degree of [unsp site of trunk, chest wall, abd wall, upr back, lwr back, buttock, male genital rgn, female genital rgn, oth site of trunk], subsq enc
T21.4[0,1,2,3,4,5,6,7,9]XD	Corrosion of unsp degree of [unsp site of trunk, chest wall, abd wall, upr back, lwr back, buttock, male genital rgn, female genital rgn, oth site of trunk], subsq enc
T21.5[0,1,2,3,4,5,6,7,9]XD	Corrosion of 1st degree of [unsp site of trunk, chest wall, abd wall, upr back, lwr back, buttock, male genital rgn, female genital rgn, oth site of trunk], subsq enc
T21.6[0,1,2,3,4,5,6,7,9]XD	Corrosion of 2nd degree of [unsp site of trunk, chest wall, abd wall, upr back, lwr back, buttock, male genital rgn, female genital rgn, oth site of trunk], subsq enc
T21.7[0,1,2,3,4,5,6,7,9]XD	Corrosion of 3rd degree of [unsp site of trunk, chest wall, abd wall, upr back, lwr back, buttock, male genital rgn, female genital rgn, oth site of trunk], subsq enc
T22.00XD	Burn unsp deg of shldr/up lmb, ex wrs/hnd, unsp site, subs
T22.01[1,2,9]D	Burn of unsp degree of [rt, lt, unsp] forearm, subsq enc
T22.02[1,2,9]D	Burn of unsp degree of [rt, lt, unsp] elbow, subsq enc
T22.03[1,2,9]D	Burn of unsp degree of [rt, lt, unsp] upr arm, subsq enc
T22.04[1,2,9]D	Burn of unsp degree of [rt, lt, unsp] axilla, subsq enc
T22.05[1,2,9]D	Burn of unsp degree of [rt, lt, unsp] shldr, subsq enc
T22.06[1,2,9]D	Burn of unsp degree of [rt, lt, unsp] scapular rgn, subsq enc
T22.09[1,2,9]D	Burn of unsp degree of multi sites of [rt, lt, unsp] shldr and upr limb, except wrist and hand, subsq enc
T22.10XD	Burn first deg of shldr/up lmb, ex wrs/hnd, unsp site, subs
T22.11[1,2,9]D	Burn of 1st degree of [rt, lt, unsp] forearm, subsq enc
T22.12[1,2,9]D	Burn of 1st degree of [rt, lt, unsp] elbow, subsq enc
T22.13[1,2,9]D	Burn of 1st degree of [rt, lt, unsp] upr arm, subsq enc
T22.14[1,2,9]D	Burn of 1st degree of [rt, lt, unsp] axilla, subsq enc
T22.15[1,2,9]D	Burn of 1st degree of [rt, lt, unsp] shldr, subsq enc
T22.16[1,2,9]D	Burn of 1st degree of [rt, lt, unsp] scapular rgn, subsq enc
T22.19[1,2,9]D	Burn of 1st degree of multi sites of [rt, lt, unsp] shldr and upr limb, except wrist and hand, subsq enc

T Transfer DRG   SP Special Payment   * Code Range   6th and 7th Character of ZZ = No Device, No Qualifier ZX = No Device, Diagnostic

400   MS-DRG Version 33.0   © 2015 Optum360, LLC

Code	Description
T22.20XD	Burn 2nd deg of shldr/up lmb, ex wrs/hnd, unsp site, subs
T22.21[1,2,9]D	Burn of 2nd degree of [rt, lt, unsp] forearm, subsq enc
T22.22[1,2,9]D	Burn of 2nd degree of [rt, lt, unsp] elbow, subsq enc
T22.23[1,2,9]D	Burn of 2nd degree of [rt, lt, unsp] upr arm, subsq enc
T22.24[1,2,9]D	Burn of 2nd degree of [rt, lt, unsp] axilla, subsq enc
T22.25[1,2,9]D	Burn of 2nd degree of [rt, lt, unsp] shldr, subsq enc
T22.26[1,2,9]D	Burn of 2nd degree of [rt, lt, unsp] scapular rgn, subsq enc
T22.29[1,2,9]D	Burn of 2nd degree of multi sites of [rt, lt, unsp] shldr and upr limb, except wrist and hand, subsq enc
T22.30XD	Burn 3rd deg of shldr/up lmb, ex wrs/hnd, unsp site, subs
T22.31[1,2,9]D	Burn of 3rd degree of [rt, lt, unsp] forearm, subsq enc
T22.32[1,2,9]D	Burn of 3rd degree of [rt, lt, unsp] elbow, subsq enc
T22.33[1,2,9]D	Burn of 3rd degree of [rt, lt, unsp] upr arm, subsq enc
T22.34[1,2,9]D	Burn of 3rd degree of [rt, lt, unsp] axilla, subsq enc
T22.35[1,2,9]D	Burn of 3rd degree of [rt, lt, unsp] shldr, subsq enc
T22.36[1,2,9]D	Burn of 3rd degree of [rt, lt, unsp] scapular rgn, subsq enc
T22.39[1,2,9]D	Burn of 3rd degree of multi sites of [rt, lt, unsp] shldr and upr limb, except wrist and hand, subsq enc
T22.40XD	Corrosion unsp deg of shldr/up lmb, ex wrs/hnd, unsp site, subs
T22.41[1,2,9]D	Corrosion of unsp degree of [rt, lt, unsp] forearm, subsq enc
T22.42[1,2,9]D	Corrosion of unsp degree of [rt, lt, unsp] elbow, subsq enc
T22.43[1,2,9]D	Corrosion of unsp degree of [rt, lt, unsp] upr arm, subsq enc
T22.44[1,2,9]D	Corrosion of unsp degree of [rt, lt, unsp] axilla, subsq enc
T22.45[1,2,9]D	Corrosion of unsp degree of [rt, lt, unsp] shldr, subsq enc
T22.46[1,2,9]D	Corrosion of unsp degree of [rt, lt, unsp] scapular rgn, subsq enc
T22.49[1,2,9]D	Corrosion of unsp degree of multi sites of [rt, lt, unsp] shldr and upr limb, except wrist and hand, subsq enc
T22.50XD	Corrosion first deg of shldr/up lmb, ex wrs/hnd unsp site, subs
T22.51[1,2,9]D	Corrosion of 1st degree of [rt, lt, unsp] forearm, subsq enc
T22.52[1,2,9]D	Corrosion of 1st degree of [rt, lt, unsp] elbow, subsq enc
T22.53[1,2,9]D	Corrosion of 1st degree of [rt, lt, unsp] upr arm, subsq enc
T22.54[1,2,9]D	Corrosion of 1st degree of [rt, lt, unsp] axilla, subsq enc
T22.55[1,2,9]D	Corrosion of 1st degree of [rt, lt, unsp] shldr, subsq enc
T22.59[1,2,9]D	Corrosion of 1st degree of multi sites of [rt, lt, unsp] shldr and upr limb, except wrist and hand, subsq enc
T22.60XD	Corrosion 2nd deg of shldr/up lmb, ex wrs/hnd, unsp site, subs
T22.61[1,2,9]D	Corrosion of 2nd degree of [rt, lt, unsp] forearm, subsq enc
T22.62[1,2,9]D	Corrosion of 2nd degree of [rt, lt, unsp] elbow, subsq enc
T22.63[1,2,9]D	Corrosion of 2nd degree of [rt, lt, unsp] upr arm, subsq enc
T22.64[1,2,9]D	Corrosion of 2nd degree of [rt, lt, unsp] axilla, subsq enc
T22.65[1,2,9]D	Corrosion of 2nd degree of [rt, lt, unsp] shldr, subsq enc
T22.66[1,2,9]D	Corrosion of 2nd degree of [rt, lt, unsp] scapular rgn, subsq enc
T22.69[1,2,9]D	Corrosion of 2nd degree of multi sites of [rt, lt, unsp] shldr and upr limb, except wrist and hand, subsq enc
T22.70XD	Corrosion 3rd deg of shldr/up lmb, ex wrs/hnd, unsp site, subs
T22.71[1,2,9]D	Corrosion of 3rd degree of [rt, lt, unsp] forearm, subsq enc
T22.72[1,2,9]D	Corrosion of 3rd degree of [rt, lt, unsp] elbow, subsq enc
T22.73[1,2,9]D	Corrosion of 3rd degree of [rt, lt, unsp] upr arm, subsq enc
T22.74[1,2,9]D	Corrosion of 3rd degree of [rt, lt, unsp] axilla, subsq enc
T22.75[1,2,9]D	Corrosion of 3rd degree of [rt, lt, unsp] shldr, subsq enc
T22.76[1,2,9]D	Corrosion of 3rd degree of [rt, lt, unsp] scapular rgn, subsq enc
T22.79[1,2,9]D	Corrosion of 3rd degree of multi sites of [rt, lt, unsp] shldr and upr limb, except wrist and hand, subsq enc
T23.00[1,2,9]D	Burn of unsp degree of [rt, lt, unsp] hand, unsp site, subsq enc
T23.01[1,2,9]D	Burn of unsp degree of [rt, lt, unsp] thumb (nail), subsq enc
T23.02[1,2,9]D	Burn of unsp degree of single [rt, lt, unsp] finger (nail) except thumb, subsq enc
T23.03[1,2,9]D	Burn of unsp degree of multi [rt, lt, unsp] fingers (nail), not incl* thumb, subsq enc
T23.04[1,2,9]D	Burn of unsp degree of multi [rt, lt, unsp] fingers (nail), incl* thumb, subsq enc
T23.05[1,2,9]D	Burn of unsp degree of [rt, lt, unsp] palm, subsq enc
T23.06[1,2,9]D	Burn of unsp degree of back of [rt, lt, unsp] hand, subsq enc
T23.07[1,2,9]D	Burn of unsp degree of [rt, lt, unsp] wrist, subsq enc
T23.09[1,2,9]D	Burn of unsp degree of multi sites of [rt, lt, unsp] wrist and hand, subsq enc
T23.10[1,2,9]D	Burn of 1st degree of [rt, lt, unsp] hand, unsp site, subsq enc
T23.11[1,2,9]D	Burn of 1st degree of [rt, lt, unsp] thumb (nail), subsq enc
T23.12[1,2,9]D	Burn of 1st degree of single [rt, lt, unsp] finger (nail) except thumb, subsq enc
T23.13[1,2,9]D	Burn of 1st degree of multi [rt, lt, unsp] fingers (nail), not incl* thumb, subsq enc
T23.14[1,2,9]D	Burn of 1st degree of multi [rt, lt, unsp] fingers (nail), incl* thumb, subsq enc
T23.15[1,2,9]D	Burn of 1st degree of [rt, lt, unsp] palm, subsq enc
T23.16[1,2,9]D	Burn of 1st degree of back of [rt, lt, unsp] hand, subsq enc
T23.17[1,2,9]D	Burn of 1st degree of [rt, lt, unsp] wrist, subsq enc
T23.19[1,2,9]D	Burn of 1st degree of multi sites of [rt, lt, unsp] wrist and hand, subsq enc
T23.20[1,2,9]D	Burn of 2nd degree of [rt, lt, unsp] hand, unsp site, subsq enc
T23.21[1,2,9]D	Burn of 2nd degree of [rt, lt, unsp] thumb (nail), subsq enc
T23.22[1,2,9]D	Burn of 2nd degree of single [rt, lt, unsp] finger (nail) except thumb, subsq enc
T23.23[1,2,9]D	Burn of 2nd degree of multi [rt, lt, unsp] fingers (nail), not incl* thumb, subsq enc
T23.24[1,2,9]D	Burn of 2nd degree of multi [rt, lt, unsp] fingers (nail), incl* thumb, subsq enc
T23.25[1,2,9]D	Burn of 2nd degree of [rt, lt, unsp] palm, subsq enc
T23.26[1,2,9]D	Burn of 2nd degree of back of [rt, lt, unsp] hand, subsq enc
T23.27[1,2,9]D	Burn of 2nd degree of [rt, lt, unsp] wrist, subsq enc
T23.29[1,2,9]D	Burn of 2nd degree of multi sites of [rt, lt, unsp] wrist and hand, subsq enc
T23.30[1,2,9]D	Burn of 3rd degree of [rt, lt, unsp] hand, unsp site, subsq enc
T23.31[1,2,9]D	Burn of 3rd degree of [rt, lt, unsp] thumb (nail), subsq enc
T23.32[1,2,9]D	Burn of 3rd degree of single [rt, lt, unsp] finger (nail) except thumb, subsq enc
T23.33[1,2,9]D	Burn of 3rd degree of multi [rt, lt, unsp] fingers (nail), not incl* thumb, subsq enc
T23.34[1,2,9]D	Burn of 3rd degree of multi [rt, lt, unsp] fingers (nail), incl* thumb, subsq enc
T23.35[1,2,9]D	Burn of 3rd degree of [rt, lt, unsp] palm, subsq enc
T23.36[1,2,9]D	Burn of 3rd degree of back of [rt, lt, unsp] hand, subsq enc
T23.37[1,2,9]D	Burn of 3rd degree of [rt, lt, unsp] wrist, subsq enc
T23.39[1,2,9]D	Burn of 3rd degree of multi sites of [rt, lt, unsp] wrist and hand, subsq enc
T23.40[1,2,9]D	Corrosion of unsp degree of [rt, lt, unsp] hand, unsp site, subsq enc
T23.41[1,2,9]D	Corrosion of unsp degree of [rt, lt, unsp] thumb (nail), subsq enc
T23.42[1,2,9]D	Corrosion of unsp degree of single [rt, lt, unsp] finger (nail) except thumb, subsq enc
T23.43[1,2,9]D	Corrosion of unsp degree of multi [rt, lt, unsp] fingers (nail), not incl* thumb, subsq enc
T23.44[1,2,9]D	Corrosion of unsp degree of multi [rt, lt, unsp] fingers (nail), incl* thumb, subsq enc
T23.45[1,2,9]D	Corrosion of unsp degree of [rt, lt, unsp] palm, subsq enc
T23.46[1,2,9]D	Corrosion of unsp degree of back of [rt, lt, unsp] hand, subsq enc
T23.47[1,2,9]D	Corrosion of unsp degree of [rt, lt, unsp] wrist, subsq enc
T23.49[1,2,9]D	Corrosion of unsp degree of multi sites of [rt, lt, unsp] wrist and hand, subsq enc
T23.50[1,2,9]D	Corrosion of 1st degree of [rt, lt, unsp] hand, unsp site, subsq enc
T23.51[1,2,9]D	Corrosion of 1st degree of [rt, lt, unsp] thumb (nail), subsq enc
T23.52[1,2,9]D	Corrosion of 1st degree of single [rt, lt, unsp] finger (nail) except thumb, subsq enc
T23.53[1,2,9]D	Corrosion of 1st degree of multi [rt, lt, unsp] fingers (nail), not incl* thumb, subsq enc
T23.54[1,2,9]D	Corrosion of 1st degree of multi [rt, lt, unsp] fingers (nail), incl* thumb, subsq enc
T23.55[1,2,9]D	Corrosion of 1st degree of [rt, lt, unsp] palm, subsq enc
T23.56[1,2,9]D	Corrosion of 1st degree of back of [rt, lt, unsp] hand, subsq enc
T23.57[1,2,9]D	Corrosion of 1st degree of [rt, lt, unsp] wrist, subsq enc
T23.59[1,2,9]D	Corrosion of 1st degree of multi sites of [rt, lt, unsp] wrist and hand, subsq enc
T23.60[1,2,9]D	Corrosion of 2nd degree of [rt, lt, unsp] hand, unsp site, subsq enc
T23.61[1,2,9]D	Corrosion of 2nd degree of [rt, lt, unsp] thumb (nail), subsq enc
T23.62[1,2,9]D	Corrosion of 2nd degree of single [rt, lt, unsp] finger (nail) except thumb, subsq enc
T23.63[1,2,9]D	Corrosion of 2nd degree of multi [rt, lt, unsp] fingers (nail), not incl* thumb, subsq enc
T23.64[1,2,9]D	Corrosion of 2nd degree of multi [rt, lt, unsp] fingers (nail), incl* thumb, subsq enc
T23.65[1,2,9]D	Corrosion of 2nd degree of [rt, lt, unsp] palm, subsq enc
T23.66[1,2,9]D	Corrosion of 2nd degree of back of [rt, lt, unsp] hand, subsq enc
T23.67[1,2,9]D	Corrosion of 2nd degree of [rt, lt, unsp] wrist, subsq enc
T23.69[1,2,9]D	Corrosion of 2nd degree of multi sites of [rt, lt, unsp] wrist and hand, subsq enc
T23.70[1,2,9]D	Corrosion of 3rd degree of [rt, lt, unsp] hand, unsp site, subsq enc
T23.71[1,2,9]D	Corrosion of 3rd degree of [rt, lt, unsp] thumb (nail), subsq enc
T23.72[1,2,9]D	Corrosion of 3rd degree of single [rt, lt, unsp] finger (nail) except thumb, subsq enc

Surgical   **Medical**   **CC Indicator**   **MCC Indicator**   **Procedure Proxy**   PDx MCC **PDx acts as own MCC**   PDx CC **PDx acts as own CC**

MDC 23: Factors Influencing Health Status And Other Contacts With Health Services—MEDICAL

Code	Description
T23.73[1,2,9]D	Corrosion of 3rd degree of multi [rt, lt, unsp] fingers (nail), not incl* thumb, subsq enc
T23.74[1,2,9]D	Corrosion of 3rd degree of multi [rt, lt, unsp] fingers (nail), incl* thumb, subsq enc
T23.75[1,2,9]D	Corrosion of 3rd degree of [rt, lt, unsp] palm, subsq enc
T23.76[1,2,9]D	Corrosion of 3rd degree of back of [rt, lt, unsp] hand, subsq enc
T23.77[1,2,9]D	Corrosion of 3rd degree of [rt, lt, unsp] wrist, subsq enc
T23.79[1,2,9]D	Corrosion of 3rd degree of multi sites of [rt, lt, unsp] wrist and hand, subsq enc
T24.00[1,2,9]D	Burn of unsp degree of unsp site of [rt, lt, unsp] lwr limb, except ankle and foot, subsq enc
T24.01[1,2,9]D	Burn of unsp degree of [rt, lt, unsp] thigh, subsq enc
T24.02[1,2,9]D	Burn of unsp degree of [rt, lt, unsp] knee, subsq enc
T24.03[1,2,9]D	Burn of unsp degree of [rt, lt, unsp] lwr leg, subsq enc
T24.09[1,2,9]D	Burn of unsp degree of multi sites of [rt, lt, unsp] lwr limb, except ankle and foot, subsq enc
T24.10[1,2,9]D	Burn of 1st degree of unsp site of [rt, lt, unsp] lwr limb, except ankle and foot, subsq enc
T24.11[1,2,9]D	Burn of 1st degree of [rt, lt, unsp] thigh, subsq enc
T24.12[1,2,9]D	Burn of 1st degree of [rt, lt, unsp] knee, subsq enc
T24.13[1,2,9]D	Burn of 1st degree of [rt, lt, unsp] lwr leg, subsq enc
T24.19[1,2,9]D	Burn of 1st degree of multi sites of [rt, lt, unsp] lwr limb, except ankle and foot, subsq enc
T24.20[1,2,9]D	Burn of 2nd degree of unsp site of [rt, lt, unsp] lwr limb, except ankle and foot, subsq enc
T24.21[1,2,9]D	Burn of 2nd degree of [rt, lt, unsp] thigh, subsq enc
T24.22[1,2,9]D	Burn of 2nd degree of [rt, lt, unsp] knee, subsq enc
T24.23[1,2,9]D	Burn of 2nd degree of [rt, lt, unsp] lwr leg, subsq enc
T24.29[1,2,9]D	Burn of 2nd degree of multi sites of [rt, lt, unsp] lwr limb, except ankle and foot, subsq enc
T24.30[1,2,9]D	Burn of 3rd degree of unsp site of [rt, lt, unsp] lwr limb, except ankle and foot, subsq enc
T24.31[1,2,9]D	Burn of 3rd degree of [rt, lt, unsp] thigh, subsq enc
T24.32[1,2,9]D	Burn of 3rd degree of [rt, lt, unsp] knee, subsq enc
T24.33[1,2,9]D	Burn of 3rd degree of [rt, lt, unsp] lwr leg, subsq enc
T24.39[1,2,9]D	Burn of 3rd degree of multi sites of [rt, lt, unsp] lwr limb, except ankle and foot, subsq enc
T24.40[1,2,9]D	Corrosion of unsp degree of unsp site of [rt, lt, unsp] lwr limb, except ankle and foot, subsq enc
T24.41[1,2,9]D	Corrosion of unsp degree of [rt, lt, unsp] thigh, subsq enc
T24.42[1,2,9]D	Corrosion of unsp degree of [rt, lt, unsp] knee, subsq enc
T24.43[1,2,9]D	Corrosion of unsp degree of [rt, lt, unsp] lwr leg, subsq enc
T24.49[1,2,9]D	Corrosion of unsp degree of multi sites of [rt, lt, unsp] lwr limb, except ankle and foot, subsq enc
T24.50[1,2,9]D	Corrosion of 1st degree of unsp site of [rt, lt, unsp] lwr limb, except ankle and foot, subsq enc
T24.51[1,2,9]D	Corrosion of 1st degree of [rt, lt, unsp] thigh, subsq enc
T24.52[1,2,9]D	Corrosion of 1st degree of [rt, lt, unsp] knee, subsq enc
T24.53[1,2,9]D	Corrosion of 1st degree of [rt, lt, unsp] lwr leg, subsq enc
T24.59[1,2,9]D	Corrosion of 1st degree of multi sites of [rt, lt, unsp] lwr limb, except ankle and foot, subsq enc
T24.60[1,2,9]D	Corrosion of 2nd degree of unsp site of [rt, lt, unsp] lwr limb, except ankle and foot, subsq enc
T24.61[1,2,9]D	Corrosion of 2nd degree of [rt, lt, unsp] thigh, subsq enc
T24.62[1,2,9]D	Corrosion of 2nd degree of [rt, lt, unsp] knee, subsq enc
T24.63[1,2,9]D	Corrosion of 2nd degree of [rt, lt, unsp] lwr leg, subsq enc
T24.69[1,2,9]D	Corrosion of 2nd degree of multi sites of [rt, lt, unsp] lwr limb, except ankle and foot, subsq enc
T24.70[1,2,9]D	Corrosion of 3rd degree of unsp site of [rt, lt, unsp] lwr limb, except ankle and foot, subsq enc
T24.71[1,2,9]D	Corrosion of 3rd degree of [rt, lt, unsp] thigh, subsq enc
T24.72[1,2,9]D	Corrosion of 3rd degree of [rt, lt, unsp] knee, subsq enc
T24.73[1,2,9]D	Corrosion of 3rd degree of [rt, lt, unsp] lwr leg, subsq enc
T24.79[1,2,9]D	Corrosion of 3rd degree of multi sites of [rt, lt, unsp] lwr limb, except ankle and foot, subsq enc
T25.01[1,2,9]D	Burn of unsp degree of [rt, lt, unsp] ankle, subsq enc
T25.02[1,2,9]D	Burn of unsp degree of [rt, lt, unsp] foot, subsq enc
T25.03[1,2,9]D	Burn of unsp degree of [rt, lt, unsp] toe(s) (nail), subsq enc
T25.09[1,2,9]D	Burn of unsp degree of multi sites of [rt, lt, unsp] ankle and foot, subsq enc
T25.11[1,2,9]D	Burn of 1st degree of [rt, lt, unsp] ankle, subsq enc
T25.12[1,2,9]D	Burn of 1st degree of [rt, lt, unsp] foot, subsq enc
T25.13[1,2,9]D	Burn of 1st degree of [rt, lt, unsp] toe(s) (nail), subsq enc
T25.19[1,2,9]D	Burn of 1st degree of multi sites of [rt, lt, unsp] ankle and foot, subsq enc
T25.21[1,2,9]D	Burn of 2nd degree of [rt, lt, unsp] ankle, subsq enc
T25.22[1,2,9]D	Burn of 2nd degree of [rt, lt, unsp] foot, subsq enc
T25.23[1,2,9]D	Burn of 2nd degree of [rt, lt, unsp] toe(s) (nail), subsq enc
T25.29[1,2,9]D	Burn of 2nd degree of multi sites of [rt, lt, unsp] ankle and foot, subsq enc
T25.31[1,2,9]D	Burn of 3rd degree of [rt, lt, unsp] ankle, subsq enc
T25.32[1,2,9]D	Burn of 3rd degree of [rt, lt, unsp] foot, subsq enc
T25.33[1,2,9]D	Burn of 3rd degree of [rt, lt, unsp] toe(s) (nail), subsq enc
T25.39[1,2,9]D	Burn of 3rd degree of multi sites of [rt, lt, unsp] ankle and foot, subsq enc
T25.41[1,2,9]D	Corrosion of unsp degree of [rt, lt, unsp] ankle, subsq enc
T25.42[1,2,9]D	Corrosion of unsp degree of [rt, lt, unsp] foot, subsq enc
T25.43[1,2,9]D	Corrosion of unsp degree of [rt, lt, unsp] toe(s) (nail), subsq enc
T25.49[1,2,9]D	Corrosion of unsp degree of multi sites of [rt, lt, unsp] ankle and foot, subsq enc
T25.51[1,2,9]D	Corrosion of 1st degree of [rt, lt, unsp] ankle, subsq enc
T25.52[1,2,9]D	Corrosion of 1st degree of [rt, lt, unsp] foot, subsq enc
T25.53[1,2,9]D	Corrosion of 1st degree of [rt, lt, unsp] toe(s) (nail), subsq enc
T25.59[1,2,9]D	Corrosion of 1st degree of multi sites of [rt, lt, unsp] ankle and foot, subsq enc
T25.61[1,2,9]D	Corrosion of 2nd degree of [rt, lt, unsp] ankle, subsq enc
T25.62[1,2,9]D	Corrosion of 2nd degree of [rt, lt, unsp] foot, subsq enc
T25.63[1,2,9]D	Corrosion of 2nd degree of [rt, lt, unsp] toe(s) (nail), subsq enc
T25.69[1,2,9]D	Corrosion of 2nd degree of multi sites of [rt, lt, unsp] ankle and foot, subsq enc
T25.71[1,2,9]D	Corrosion of 3rd degree of [rt, lt, unsp] ankle, subsq enc
T25.72[1,2,9]D	Corrosion of 3rd degree of [rt, lt, unsp] foot, subsq enc
T25.73[1,2,9]D	Corrosion of 3rd degree of [rt, lt, unsp] toe(s) (nail), subsq enc
T25.79[1,2,9]D	Corrosion of 3rd degree of multi sites of [rt, lt, unsp] ankle and foot, subsq enc
T26.0[0,1,2]XD	Burn of [unsp, rt, lt] eyelid and periocular area, subsq enc
T26.1[0,1,2]XD	Burn of cornea and conjunctival sac, [unsp, rt, lt] eye, subsq enc
T26.2[0,1,2]XD	Burn w/ resulting rupture and destr of [unsp, rt, lt] eyeball, subsq enc
T26.3[0,1,2]XD	Burns of oth spec parts of [unsp, rt, lt] eye and adnexa, subsq enc
T26.4[0,1,2]XD	Burn of [unsp, rt, lt] eye and adnexa, part unsp, subsq enc
T26.5[0,1,2]XD	Burn of [unsp, rt, lt] eyelid and periocular area, subsq enc
T26.6[0,1,2]XD	Corrosion of cornea and conjunctival sac, [unsp, rt, lt] eye, subsq enc
T26.7[0,1,2]XD	Corrosion w/ resulting rupture and destr of [unsp, rt, lt] eyeball, subsq enc
T26.8[0,1,2]XD	Corrosions of oth spec parts of [unsp, rt, lt] eye and adnexa, subsq enc
T26.9[0,1,2]XD	Corrosions of [unsp, rt, lt] eye and adnexa, part unsp, subsq enc
T27.0XXD	Burn of larynx and trachea, subsq enc
T27.1XXD	Burn involving larynx and trachea with lung, subsq enc
T27.2XXD	Burn of oth parts of respiratory tract, subs enc
T27.3XXD	Burn of respiratory tract, part unsp, subs enc
T27.4XXD	Corrosion of larynx and trachea, subsq enc
T27.5XXD	Corrosion involving larynx and trachea w lung, subs enc
T27.6XXD	Corrosion of oth parts of respiratory tract, subs enc
T27.7XXD	Corrosion of respiratory tract, part unsp, subs enc
T28.0XXD	Burn of mouth and pharynx, subsq enc
T28.1XXD	Burn of esophagus, subsq enc
T28.2XXD	Burn of oth parts of alimentary tract, subs enc
T28.3XXD	Burn of int genitourinary organs, subsq enc
T28.40XD	Burn of unsp int organ, subsq enc
T28.41[1,2,9]D	Burn of [rt, lt, unsp] ear drum, subsq enc
T28.49XD	Burn of oth int organ, subsq enc
T28.5XXD	Corrosion of mouth and pharynx, subsq enc
T28.6XXD	Corrosion of esophagus, subsq enc
T28.7XXD	Corrosion of oth parts of alimentary tract, subs enc
T28.8XXD	Corrosion of int genitourinary organs, subs enc
T28.90XD	Corrosions of unsp int organs, subs enc
T28.91[1,2,9]D	Corrosion of [rt, lt, unsp] ear drum, subsq enc
T28.99XD	Corrosions of oth int organs, subsq enc
T33.01[1,2,9]D	Superf frostbite of [rt, lt, unsp] ear, subsq enc
T33.02XD	Superf frostbite of nose, subsq enc
T33.09XD	Superf frostbite of oth part of head, subs enc
T33.1XXD	Superf frostbite of neck, subsq enc
T33.2XXD	Superf frostbite of thorax, subsq enc
T33.3XXD	Superfic frostbite of abd wall, lwr back and pelvis, subs
T33.4[0,1,2]XD	Superf frostbite of [unsp, rt, lt] arm, subsq enc
T33.51[1,2,9]D	Superf frostbite of [rt, lt, unsp] wrist, subsq enc
T33.52[1,2,9]D	Superf frostbite of [rt, lt, unsp] hand, subsq enc
T33.53[1,2,9]D	Superf frostbite of [rt, lt, unsp] fingers, subsq enc
T33.6[0,1,2]XD	Superf frostbite of [unsp, rt, lt] hip & thigh, subsq enc
T33.7[0,1,2]XD	Superf frostbite of [unsp, rt, lt] knee and lwr leg, subsq enc
T33.81[1,2,9]D	Superf frostbite of [rt, lt, unsp] ankle, subsq enc

T Transfer DRG   SP Special Payment   * Code Range   6th and 7th Character of ZZ = No Device, No Qualifier ZX = No Device, Diagnostic

402

MS-DRG Version 33.0

© 2015 Optum360, LLC

Code	Description
T33.82[1,2,9]D	Superf frostbite of [rt, lt, unsp] foot, subsq enc
T33.83[1,2,9]D	Superf frostbite of [rt, lt, unsp] toe(s), subsq enc
T33.9[0,9]XD	Superf frostbite of [unsp, oth] sites, subsq enc
T34.01[1,2,9]D	Frostbite w/ tissue necrosis of [rt, lt, unsp] ear, subsq enc
T34.02XD	Frostbite with tissue necrosis of nose, subsq enc
T34.09XD	Frostbite w tissue necrosis of oth part of head, subs enc
T34.1XXD	Frostbite with tissue necrosis of neck, subsq enc
T34.2XXD	Frostbite with tissue necrosis of thorax, subs enc
T34.3XXD	Frstbte w tissue necros abd wall, low back and pelvis, subs
T34.4[0,1,2]XD	Frostbite w/ tissue necrosis of [unsp, rt, lt] arm, subsq enc
T34.51[1,2,9]D	Frostbite w/ tissue necrosis of [rt, lt, unsp] wrist, subsq enc
T34.52[1,2,9]D	Frostbite w/ tissue necrosis of [rt, lt, unsp] hand, subsq enc
T34.53[1,2,9]D	Frostbite w/ tissue necrosis of [rt, lt, unsp] fingers, subsq enc
T34.6[0,1,2]XD	Frostbite w/ tissue necrosis of [unsp, rt, lt] hip & thigh, subsq enc
T34.7[0,1,2]XD	Frostbite w/ tissue necrosis of [unsp, rt, lt] knee and lwr leg, subsq enc
T34.81[1,2,9]D	Frostbite w/ tissue necrosis of [rt, lt, unsp] ankle, subsq enc
T34.82[1,2,9]D	Frostbite w/ tissue necrosis of [rt, lt, unsp] foot, subsq enc
T34.83[1,2,9]D	Frostbite w/ tissue necrosis of [rt, lt, unsp] toe(s), subsq enc
T34.9[0,9]XD	Frostbite w/ tissue necrosis of [unsp, oth] sites, subsq enc
T36.0X5D	Adverse effect of penicillins, subsq enc
T36.0X6*	Underdosing of penicillins
T36.0X[1,2,3,4]D	Poison by penicillins, [accid (unintentional), intentional self-harm, assault, undetermined], subsq enc
T36.1X5D	Adverse effect of cephalospor/oth beta-lactm antibiot, subs
T36.1X6*	Underdosing of cephalospor/oth beta-lactm antibiotics
T36.1X[1,2,3,4]D	Poison by cephaloporins and oth beta-lactam antibiotics, [accid (unintentional), intentional self-harm, assault, undetermined], subsq enc
T36.2X5D	Adverse effect of chloramphenicol group, subs enc
T36.2X6*	Underdosing of chloramphenicol group
T36.2X[1,2,3,4]D	Poison by chloramphenicol group, [accid (unintentional), intentional self-harm, assault, undetermined], subsq enc
T36.3X5D	Adverse effect of macrolides, subsq enc
T36.3X6*	Underdosing of macrolides
T36.3X[1,2,3,4]D	Poison by macrolides, [accid (unintentional), intentional self-harm, assault, undetermined], subsq enc
T36.4X5D	Adverse effect of tetracyclines, subsq enc
T36.4X6*	Underdosing of tetracyclines
T36.4X[1,2,3,4]D	Poison by tetracyclines, [accid (unintentional), intentional self-harm, assault, undetermined], subsq enc
T36.5X5D	Adverse effect of aminoglycosides, subsq enc
T36.5X6*	Underdosing of aminoglycosides
T36.5X[1,2,3,4]D	Poison by aminoglycosides, [accid (unintentional), intentional self-harm, assault, undetermined], subsq enc
T36.6X5D	Adverse effect of rifampicins, subsq enc
T36.6X6*	Underdosing of rifampicins
T36.6X[1,2,3,4]D	Poison by rifampicins, [accid (unintentional), intentional self-harm, assault, undetermined], subsq enc
T36.7X5D	Adverse effect of antifungal antibiotics, sys used, subs
T36.7X6*	Underdosing of antifungal antibiotics, systemically used
T36.7X[1,2,3,4]D	Poison by antifungal antibiotics, sysically used, [accid (unintentional), intentional self-harm, assault, undetermined], subsq enc
T36.8X5D	Adverse effect of oth systemic antibiotics, subs enc
T36.8X6*	Underdosing of oth systemic antibiotics
T36.8X[1,2,3,4]D	Poison by oth sysic antibiotics [accid (unintentional), intentional self-harm, assault, undetermined], subsq enc
T36.95XD	Adverse effect of unsp systemic antibiotic, subs enc
T36.96*	Underdosing of unsp systemic antibiotic
T36.9[1,2,3,4]XD	Poison by unsp sysic antibiotic [accid (unintentional), intentional self-harm, assault, undetermined], subsq enc
T37.0X5D	Adverse effect of sulfonamides, subsq enc
T37.0X6*	Underdosing of sulfonamides
T37.0X[1,2,3,4]D	Poison by sulfonamides, [accid (unintentional), intentional self-harm, assault, undetermined], subsq enc
T37.1X5D	Adverse effect of antimycobacterial drugs, subs enc
T37.1X6*	Underdosing of antimycobacterial drugs
T37.1X[1,2,3,4]D	Poison by antimycobacterial drugs, [accid (unintentional), intentional self-harm, assault, undetermined], subsq enc
T37.2X5D	Advrs effect of antimalari/drugs acting on bld protzoa, subs
T37.2X6*	Underdosing of antimalarials and drugs acting on bld protzoa
T37.2X[1,2,3,4]D	Poison by antimalarials and drugs acting on oth bld protzoa, [accid (unintentional), intentional self-harm, assault, undetermined], subsq enc
T37.3X5D	Adverse effect of oth antiprotozoal drugs, subs enc
T37.3X6*	Underdosing of oth antiprotozoal drugs
T37.3X[1,2,3,4]D	Poison by oth antiprotozoal drugs, [accid (unintentional), intentional self-harm, assault, undetermined], subsq enc
T37.4X5D	Adverse effect of anthelminthics, subsq enc
T37.4X6*	Underdosing of anthelminthics
T37.4X[1,2,3,4]D	Poison by anthelminthics, [accid (unintentional), intentional self-harm, assault, undetermined], subsq enc
T37.5X5D	Adverse effect of antiviral drugs, subsq enc
T37.5X6*	Underdosing of antiviral drugs
T37.5X[1,2,3,4]D	Poison by antiviral drugs, [accid (unintentional), intentional self-harm, assault, undetermined], subsq enc
T37.8X5D	Adverse effect of systemic anti-infect/parasit, subs
T37.8X6*	Underdosing of systemic anti-infectives and antiparasitics
T37.8X[1,2,3,4]D	Poison by oth spec sysic anti-infectives and antiparasitics, [accid (unintentional), intentional self-harm, assault, undetermined], subsq enc
T37.95XD	Advrs effect of unsp sys anti-infect and antiparasitic, subs
T37.96*	Underdosing of unsp systemic anti-infect/parasit
T37.9[1,2,3,4]XD	Poison by unsp sysic anti-infectives and antiparasitics, [accid (unintentional), intentional self-harm, assault, undetermined], subsq enc
T38.0X5D	Adverse effect of glucocort/synth analog, subs
T38.0X6*	Underdosing of glucocorticoids and synth analogues
T38.0X[1,2,3,4]D	Poison by glucocorticoids and synth analogues, [accid (unintentional), intentional self-harm, assault, undetermined], subsq enc
T38.1X5D	Adverse effect of thyroid hormones and substitutes, subs
T38.1X6*	Underdosing of thyroid hormones and substitutes
T38.1X[1,2,3,4]D	Poison by thyroid hormones and subs, [accid (unintentional), intentional self-harm, assault, undetermined], subsq enc
T38.2X5D	Adverse effect of antithyroid drugs, subsq enc
T38.2X6*	Underdosing of antithyroid drugs
T38.2X[1,2,3,4]D	Poison by antithyroid drugs, [accid (unintentional), intentional self-harm, assault, undetermined], subsq enc
T38.3X5D	Adverse effect of insulin and oral hypoglycemic drugs, subs
T38.3X6*	Underdosing of insulin and oral hypoglycemic drugs
T38.3X[1,2,3,4]D	Poison by insulin and oral hypoglycemic (antidiabetic) drugs, [accid (unintentional), intentional self-harm, assault, undetermined], subsq enc
T38.4X5D	Adverse effect of oral contraceptives, subsq enc
T38.4X6*	Underdosing of oral contraceptives
T38.4X[1,2,3,4]D	Poison by oral contraceptives, [accid (unintentional), intentional self-harm, assault, undetermined], subsq enc
T38.5X5D	Adverse effect of oth estrogens and progestogens, subs
T38.5X6*	Underdosing of oth estrogens and progestogens
T38.5X[1,2,3,4]D	Poison by oth estrogens and progestogens, [accid (unintentional), intentional self-harm, assault, undetermined], subsq enc
T38.6X5D	Adverse effect of antigonadtr/antiestr/antiandrg, NEC, subs
T38.6X6*	Underdosing of antigonadtr/antiestr/antiandrg, NEC
T38.6X[1,2,3,4]D	Poison by antigonadotrophins, antiestrogens, antiandrogens, NEC, [accid (unintentional), intentional self-harm, assault, undetermined], subsq enc
T38.7X5D	Adverse effect of androgens and anabolic congeners, subs
T38.7X6*	Underdosing of androgens and anabolic congeners
T38.7X[1,2,3,4]D	Poison by androgens and anabolic congeners, sysically used, [accid (unintentional), intentional self-harm, assault, undetermined], subsq enc
T38.805D	Adverse effect of unsp hormones and synth sub, subs
T38.806*	Underdosing of unsp hormones and synth substitutes
T38.80[1,2,3,4]D	Poison by unsp hormones and synth subs, [accid (unintentional), intentional self-harm, assault, undetermined], subsq enc
T38.815D	Adverse effect of ant pituitary hormones, subs enc
T38.816*	Underdosing of ant pituitary hormones
T38.81[1,2,3,4]D	Poison by ant pituitary (adenohypophyseal) hormones, [accid (unintentional), intentional self-harm, assault, undetermined], subsq enc
T38.895D	Adverse effect of hormones and synth substitutes, subs
T38.896*	Underdosing of oth hormones and synth substitutes
T38.89[1,2,3,4]D	Poison by oth hormones and synth subs, [accid (unintentional), intentional self-harm, assault, undetermined], subsq enc
T38.905D	Adverse effect of unsp hormone antagonists, subs enc
T38.906*	Underdosing of unsp hormone antagonists
T38.90[1,2,3,4]D	Poison by unsp hormone antagonists, [accid (unintentional), intentional self-harm, assault, undetermined], subsq enc
T38.995D	Adverse effect of oth hormone antagonists, subs enc
T38.996*	Underdosing of oth hormone antagonists
T38.99[1,2,3,4]D	Poison by oth hormone antagonists, [accid (unintentional), intentional self-harm, assault, undetermined], subsq enc
T39.015D	Adverse effect of aspirin, subsq enc
T39.016*	Underdosing of aspirin

Surgical   **Medical**   **CC Indicator**   **MCC Indicator**   **Procedure Proxy**   **PDx MCC** PDx acts as own MCC   **PDx CC** PDx acts as own CC

© 2015 Optum360, LLC   MS-DRG Version 33.0   **403**

T39.01[1,2,3,4]D	Poison by aspirin, [accid (unintentional), intentional self-harm, assault, undetermined], subsq enc
T39.095D	Adverse effect of salicylates, subsq enc
T39.096*	Underdosing of salicylates
T39.09[1,2,3,4]D	Poison by salicylates, [accid (unintentional), intentional self-harm, assault, undetermined], subsq enc
T39.1X5D	Adverse effect of 4-Aminophenol derivatives, subs enc
T39.1X6*	Underdosing of 4-Aminophenol derivatives
T39.1X[1,2,3,4]D	Poison by 4-Aminophenol derivatives, [accid (unintentional), intentional self-harm, assault, undetermined], subsq enc
T39.2X5D	Adverse effect of pyrazolone derivatives, subs enc
T39.2X6*	Underdosing of pyrazolone derivatives
T39.2X[1,2,3,4]D	Poison by pyrazolone derivatives, [accid (unintentional), intentional self-harm, assault, undetermined], subsq enc
T39.315D	Adverse effect of propionic acid derivatives, subs enc
T39.316*	Underdosing of propionic acid derivatives
T39.31[1,2,3,4]D	Poison by propionic acid derivatives, [accid (unintentional), intentional self-harm, assault, undetermined], subsq enc
T39.395D	Adverse effect of nonsteroidal anti-inflam drugs, subs
T39.396*	Underdosing of nonsteroidal anti-inflam drugs
T39.39[1,2,3,4]D	Poison by oth nonsteroidal anti-inflam drugs (NSAID), [accid (unintentional), intentional self-harm, assault, undetermined], subsq enc
T39.4X5D	Adverse effect of antirheumatics, NEC, subs
T39.4X6*	Underdosing of antirheumatics, NEC
T39.4X[1,2,3,4]D	Poison by antirheumatics, NEC, [accid (unintentional), intentional self-harm, assault, undetermined], subsq enc
T39.8X5D	Adverse effect of nonopioid analges/antipyret, NEC, subs
T39.8X6*	Underdosing of nonopioid analges/antipyret, NEC
T39.8X[1,2,3,4]D	Poison by oth nonopiod analgesics and antipyretics, [accid (unintentional), intentional self-harm, assault, undetermined], subsq enc
T39.95XD	Adverse effect of unsp nonopi analgs/antipyr/antirheu, subs
T39.96*	Underdosing of unsp nonopi analgs/antipyr/antirheu
T39.9[1,2,3,4]XD	Poison by unsp nonopiod analgesic, antipyretic and antirheumatic, [accid (unintentional), intentional self-harm, assault, undetermined], subsq enc
T40.0X5D	Adverse effect of opium, subsq enc
T40.0X6*	Underdosing of opium
T40.0X[1,2,3,4]D	Poison by opium, [accid (unintentional), intentional self-harm, assault, undetermined], subsq enc
T40.1X[1,2,3,4]D	Poison by and adverse effect of heroin, [accid (unintentional), intentional self-harm, assault, undetermined], subsq enc
T40.2X5D	Adverse effect of oth opioids, subsq enc
T40.2X6*	Underdosing of oth opioids
T40.2X[1,2,3,4]D	Poison by oth opiods, [accid (unintentional), intentional self-harm, assault, undetermined], subsq enc
T40.3X5D	Adverse effect of methadone, subsq enc
T40.3X6*	Underdosing of methadone
T40.3X[1,2,3,4]D	Poison by methadone, [accid (unintentional), intentional self-harm, assault, undetermined], subsq enc
T40.4X5D	Adverse effect of oth synth narcotics, subs enc
T40.4X6*	Underdosing of oth synth narcotics
T40.4X[1,2,3,4]D	Poison by oth synth narcotics, [accid (unintentional), intentional self-harm, assault, undetermined], subsq enc
T40.5X5D	Adverse effect of cocaine, subsq enc
T40.5X6*	Underdosing of cocaine
T40.5X[1,2,3,4]D	Poison by cocaine, [accid (unintentional), intentional self-harm, assault, undetermined], subsq enc
T40.605D	Adverse effect of unsp narcotics, subs enc
T40.606*	Underdosing of unsp narcotics
T40.60[1,2,3,4]D	Poison by unsp narcotics, [accid (unintentional), intentional self-harm, assault, undetermined], subsq enc
T40.695D	Adverse effect of oth narcotics, subsq enc
T40.696*	Underdosing of oth narcotics
T40.69[1,2,3,4]D	Poison by spec narcotics, [accid (unintentional), intentional self-harm, assault, undetermined], subsq enc
T40.7X5D	Adverse effect of cannabis (derivatives), subs enc
T40.7X6*	Underdosing of cannabis (derivatives)
T40.7X[1,2,3,4]D	Poison by cannabis (derivatives), [accid (unintentional), intentional self-harm, assault, undetermined], subsq enc
T40.8X[1,2,3,4]D	Poison by and adverse effect of lysergide (LSD), [accid (unintentional), intentional self-harm, assault, undetermined], subsq enc
T40.905D	Adverse effect of unsp psychodysleptics, subs enc
T40.906*	Underdosing of unsp psychodysleptics
T40.90[1,2,3,4]D	Poison by unsp psychodysleptics (hallucinogens), [accid (unintentional), intentional self-harm, assault, undetermined], subsq enc
T40.995D	Adverse effect of oth psychodysleptics, subs enc
T40.996*	Underdosing of oth psychodysleptics
T40.99[1,2,3,4]D	Poison by oth psychodysleptics (hallucinogens), [accid (unintentional), intentional self-harm, assault, undetermined], subsq enc
T41.0X5D	Adverse effect of inhaled anesthetics, subsq enc
T41.0X6*	Underdosing of inhaled anesthetics
T41.0X[1,2,3,4]D	Poison by inhaled anesthetics, [accid (unintentional), intentional self-harm, assault, undetermined], subsq enc
T41.1X5D	Adverse effect of intravenous anesthetics, subs enc
T41.1X6*	Underdosing of intravenous anesthetics
T41.1X[1,2,3,4]D	Poison by intravenous anesthetics, [accid (unintentional), intentional self-harm, assault, undetermined], subsq enc
T41.205D	Adverse effect of unsp general anesthetics, subs enc
T41.206*	Underdosing of unsp general anesthetics
T41.20[1,2,3,4]D	Poison by unsp general anesthetics, [accid (unintentional), intentional self-harm, assault, undetermined], subsq enc
T41.295D	Adverse effect of oth general anesthetics, subs enc
T41.296*	Underdosing of oth general anesthetics
T41.29[1,2,3,4]D	Poison by oth general anesthetics, [accid (unintentional), intentional self-harm, assault, undetermined], subsq enc
T41.3X5D	Adverse effect of local anesthetics, subsq enc
T41.3X6*	Underdosing of local anesthetics
T41.3X[1,2,3,4]D	Poison by local anesthetics, [accid (unintentional), intentional self-harm, assault, undetermined], subsq enc
T41.45XD	Adverse effect of unsp anesthetic, subs enc
T41.46*	Underdosing of unsp anesthetics
T41.4[1,2,3,4]XD	Poison by unsp anesthetic, [accid (unintentional), intentional self-harm, assault, undetermined], subsq enc
T41.5X5D	Adverse effect of therapeutic gases, subsq enc
T41.5X6*	Underdosing of therapeutic gases
T41.5X[1,2,3,4]D	Poison by therapeutic gases, [accid (unintentional), intentional self-harm, assault, undetermined], subsq enc
T42.0X5D	Adverse effect of hydantoin derivatives, subs enc
T42.0X6*	Underdosing of hydantoin derivatives
T42.0X[1,2,3,4]D	Poison by hydantoin derivatives, [accid (unintentional), intentional self-harm, assault, undetermined], subsq enc
T42.1X5D	Adverse effect of iminostilbenes, subsq enc
T42.1X6*	Underdosing of iminostilbenes
T42.1X[1,2,3,4]D	Poison by iminostilbenes, [accid (unintentional), intentional self-harm, assault, undetermined], subsq enc
T42.2X5D	Adverse effect of succinimides and oxazolidinediones, subs
T42.2X6*	Underdosing of succinimides and oxazolidinediones
T42.2X[1,2,3,4]D	Poison by succinimides and oxazolidinediones, [accid (unintentional), intentional self-harm, assault, undetermined], subsq enc
T42.3X5D	Adverse effect of barbiturates, subsq enc
T42.3X6*	Underdosing of barbiturates
T42.3X[1,2,3,4]D	Poison by barbituates, [accid (unintentional), intentional self-harm, assault, undetermined], subsq enc
T42.4X5D	Adverse effect of benzodiazepines, subsq enc
T42.4X6*	Underdosing of benzodiazepines
T42.4X[1,2,3,4]D	Poison by benzodiazepines, [accid (unintentional), intentional self-harm, assault, undetermined], subsq enc
T42.5X5D	Adverse effect of mixed antiepileptics, subsq enc
T42.5X6*	Underdosing of mixed antiepileptics
T42.5X[1,2,3,4]D	Poison by mixed antiepileptics, [accid (unintentional), intentional self-harm, assault, undetermined], subsq enc
T42.6X5D	Adverse effect of antiepileptic and sed-hypntc drugs, subs
T42.6X6*	Underdosing of oth antiepileptic and sedative-hypnotic drugs
T42.6X[1,2,3,4]D	Poison by oth antiepileptic and sedative-hypnotic drugs, [accid (unintentional), intentional self-harm, assault, undetermined], subsq enc
T42.75XD	Adverse effect of unsp antieplptc and sed-hypntc drugs, subs
T42.76*	Underdosing of unsp antiepileptic and sed-hypntc drugs
T42.7[1,2,3,4]XD	Poison by unsp antiepileptic and sedative-hypnotic drugs, [accid (unintentional), intentional self-harm, assault, undetermined], subsq enc
T42.8X5D	Adverse effect of antiparkns drug/centr musc-tone depr, subs
T42.8X6*	Underdosing of antiparkns drug/centr muscle-tone depressants
T42.8X[1,2,3,4]D	Poison by antiparkinsonism drugs and oth central muscle-tone depressants, [accid (unintentional), intentional self-harm, assault, undetermined], subsq enc
T43.015D	Adverse effect of tricyclic antidepressants, subs enc
T43.016*	Underdosing of tricyclic antidepressants
T43.01[1,2,3,4]D	Poison by tricyclic antidepressants, [accid (unintentional), intentional self-harm, assault, undetermined], subsq enc
T43.025D	Adverse effect of tetracyclic antidepressants, subs enc
T43.026*	Underdosing of tetracyclic antidepressants

T Transfer DRG   SP Special Payment   * Code Range   6th and 7th Character of ZZ = No Device, No Qualifier ZX = No Device, Diagnostic

404   MS-DRG Version 33.0   © 2015 Optum360, LLC

T43.02[1,2,3,4]D	Poison by tetracyclic antidepressants, [accid (unintentional), intentional self-harm, assault, undetermined], subsq enc
T43.1X5D	Adverse effect of MAO inhib antidepressants, subs
T43.1X6*	Underdosing of monoamine-oxidase-inhibitor antidepressants
T43.1X[1,2,3,4]D	Poison by monoamine-oxidase-inhibitor antidepressants, [accid (unintentional), intentional self-harm, assault, undetermined], subsq enc
T43.205D	Adverse effect of unsp antidepressants, subs enc
T43.206*	Underdosing of unsp antidepressants
T43.20[1,2,3,4]D	Poison by unsp antidepressants, [accid (unintentional), intentional self-harm, assault, undetermined], subsq enc
T43.215D	Advrs effect of slctv seroton/norepineph reup inhibtr, subs
T43.216*	Underdosing of selective seroton/norepineph reup inhibitors
T43.21[1,2,3,4]D	Poison by selective serotonin and norepinephrine reuptake inhibitors, [accid (unintentional), intentional self-harm, assault, undetermined], subsq enc
T43.225D	Adverse effect of selective serotonin reuptake inhibtr, subs
T43.226*	Underdosing of selective serotonin reuptake inhibitors
T43.22[1,2,3,4]D	Poison by selective serotonin reuptake inhibitors, [accid (unintentional), intentional self-harm, assault, undetermined], subsq enc
T43.295D	Adverse effect of oth antidepressants, subs enc
T43.296*	Underdosing of oth antidepressants
T43.29[1,2,3,4]D	Poison by oth antidepressants, [accid (unintentional), intentional self-harm, assault, undetermined], subsq enc
T43.3X5D	Adverse effect of phenothiazine antipsychot/neurolept, subs
T43.3X6*	Underdosing of phenothiazine antipsychotics and neuroleptics
T43.3X[1,2,3,4]D	Poison by phenothiazine antipsychotics and neuroleptics, [accid (unintentional), intentional self-harm, assault, undetermined], subsq enc
T43.4X5D	Adverse effect of butyrophen/thiothixen neuroleptics, subs
T43.4X6*	Underdosing of butyrophenone and thiothixene neuroleptics
T43.4X[1,2,3,4]D	Poison by butyrophenone and thiothixene neuroleptics, [accid (unintentional), intentional self-harm, assault, undetermined], subsq enc
T43.505D	Adverse effect of unsp antipsychotics and neuroleptics, subs
T43.506*	Underdosing of unsp antipsychotics and neuroleptics
T43.50[1,2,3,4]D	Poison by unsp antipsychotics and neuroleptics, [accid (unintentional), intentional self-harm, assault, undetermined], subsq enc
T43.595D	Adverse effect of oth antipsychotics and neuroleptics, subs
T43.596*	Underdosing of oth antipsychotics and neuroleptics
T43.59[1,2,3,4]D	Poison by oth antipsychotics and neuroleptics, [accid (unintentional), intentional self-harm, assault, undetermined], subsq enc
T43.605D	Adverse effect of unsp psychostimulants, subs enc
T43.606*	Underdosing of unsp psychostimulants
T43.60[1,2,3,4]D	Poison by unsp psychostimulants, [accid (unintentional), intentional self-harm, assault, undetermined], subsq enc
T43.615D	Adverse effect of caffeine, subs enc
T43.616*	Underdosing of caffeine
T43.61[1,2,3,4]D	Poison by caffeine, [accid (unintentional), intentional self-harm, assault, undetermined], subsq enc
T43.625D	Adverse effect of amphetamines, subsq enc
T43.626*	Underdosing of amphetamines
T43.62[1,2,3,4]D	Poison by amphetamines, [accid (unintentional), intentional self-harm, assault, undetermined], subsq enc
T43.635D	Adverse effect of methylphenidate, subsq enc
T43.636*	Underdosing of methylphenidate
T43.63[1,2,3,4]D	Poison by methylphenidate, [accid (unintentional), intentional self-harm, assault, undetermined], subsq enc
T43.695D	Adverse effect of oth psychostimulants, subs enc
T43.696*	Underdosing of oth psychostimulants
T43.69[1,2,3,4]D	Poison by oth psychostimulants, [accid (unintentional), intentional self-harm, assault, undetermined], subsq enc
T43.8X5D	Adverse effect of oth psychotropic drugs, subs enc
T43.8X6*	Underdosing of oth psychotropic drugs
T43.8X[1,2,3,4]D	Poison by oth psychotropic drugs, [accid (unintentional), intentional self-harm, assault, undetermined], subsq enc
T43.95XD	Adverse effect of unsp psychotropic drug, subs enc
T43.96*	Underdosing of unsp psychotropic drug
T43.9[1,2,3,4]XD	Poison by unsp psychotropic drug, [accid (unintentional), intentional self-harm, assault, undetermined], subsq enc
T44.0X5D	Adverse effect of anticholinesterase agents, subs enc
T44.0X6*	Underdosing of anticholinesterase agents
T44.0X[1,2,3,4]D	Poison by anticholinesterase agents, [accid (unintentional), intentional self-harm, assault, undetermined], subsq enc
T44.1X5D	Adverse effect of oth parasympathomimetics, subs enc
T44.1X6*	Underdosing of oth parasympathomimetics
T44.1X[1,2,3,4]D	Poison by parasympathomimetics (cholinergics), [accid (unintentional), intentional self-harm, assault, undetermined], subsq enc
T44.2X5D	Adverse effect of ganglionic blocking drugs, subs enc
T44.2X6*	Underdosing of ganglionic blocking drugs
T44.2X[1,2,3,4]D	Poison by ganglionic blocking drugs, [accid (unintentional), intentional self-harm, assault, undetermined], subsq enc
T44.3X5D	Adverse effect of parasympatholytics and spasmolytics, subs
T44.3X6*	Underdosing of oth parasympatholytics and spasmolytics
T44.3X[1,2,3,4]D	Poison by oth parasympatholytics (anticholinergics and antimuscarinics) and spasmolytics, [accid (unintentional), intentional self-harm, assault, undetermined], subsq enc
T44.4X5D	Adverse effect of predom alpha-adrenocpt agonists, subs
T44.4X6*	Underdosing of predominantly alpha-adrenoreceptor agonists
T44.4X[1,2,3,4]D	Poison by predominantly alpha-adrenoreceptor agonists, [accid (unintentional), intentional self-harm, assault, undetermined], subsq enc
T44.5X5D	Adverse effect of predom beta-adrenocpt agonists, subs
T44.5X6*	Underdosing of predominantly beta-adrenoreceptor agonists
T44.5X[1,2,3,4]D	Poison by predominantly beta-adrenoreceptor agonists, [accid (unintentional), intentional self-harm, assault, undetermined], subsq enc
T44.6X5D	Adverse effect of alpha-adrenoreceptor antagonists, subs
T44.6X6*	Underdosing of alpha-adrenoreceptor antagonists
T44.6X[1,2,3,4]D	Poison by predominantly alpha-adrenoreceptor antagonists, [accid (unintentional), intentional self-harm, assault, undetermined], subsq enc
T44.7X5D	Adverse effect of beta-adrenoreceptor antagonists, subs
T44.7X6*	Underdosing of beta-adrenoreceptor antagonists
T44.7X[1,2,3,4]D	Poison by predominantly beta-adrenoreceptor antagonists, [accid (unintentional), intentional self-harm, assault, undetermined], subsq enc
T44.8X5D	Adverse effect of centr-acting/adren-neurn-block agnt, subs
T44.8X6*	Underdosing of centr-acting/adren-neurn-block agnt
T44.8X[1,2,3,4]D	Poison by centrally-acting and adrenergic-neuron-blocking agents, [accid (unintentional), intentional self-harm, assault, undetermined], subsq enc
T44.905D	Advrs effect of unsp drugs affecting the autonm nervous sys, subs
T44.906*	Underdosing of unsp drugs affecting the autonomic nervous sys
T44.90[1,2,3,4]D	Poison by unsp drugs primarily affecting the autonomic nervous sys, [accid (unintentional), intentional self-harm, assault, undetermined], subsq enc
T44.995D	Adverse effect of drug affecting the autonomic nervous sys, subs
T44.996*	Underdosing of drug affecting the autonomic nervous sys
T44.99[1,2,3,4]D	Poison by oth drug primarily affecting the autonomic nervous sys, [accid (unintentional), intentional self-harm, assault, undetermined], subsq enc
T45.0X5D	Adverse effect of antiallergic and antiemetic drugs, subs
T45.0X6*	Underdosing of antiallergic and antiemetic drugs
T45.0X[1,2,3,4]D	Poison by antiallergic and antiemetic drugs, [accid (unintentional), intentional self-harm, assault, undetermined], subsq enc
T45.1X5D	Adverse effect of antineoplastic and immunosup drugs, subs
T45.1X6*	Underdosing of antineoplastic and immunosuppressive drugs
T45.1X[1,2,3,4]D	Poison by antineoplastic and immunosuppressive drugs, [accid (unintentional), intentional self-harm, assault, undetermined], subsq enc
T45.2X5D	Adverse effect of vitamins, subsq enc
T45.2X6*	Underdosing of vitamins
T45.2X[1,2,3,4]D	Poison by vitamins, [accid (unintentional), intentional self-harm, assault, undetermined], subsq enc
T45.3X5D	Adverse effect of enzymes, subsq enc
T45.3X6*	Underdosing of enzymes
T45.3X[1,2,3,4]D	Poison by enzymes, [accid (unintentional), intentional self-harm, assault, undetermined], subsq enc
T45.4X5D	Adverse effect of iron and its compounds, subs enc
T45.4X6*	Underdosing of iron and its compounds
T45.4X[1,2,3,4]D	Poison by iron and its compounds, [accid (unintentional), intentional self-harm, assault, undetermined], subsq enc
T45.515D	Adverse effect of anticoagulants, subsq enc
T45.516*	Underdosing of anticoagulants
T45.51[1,2,3,4]D	Poison by anticoagulants, [accid (unintentional), intentional self-harm, assault, undetermined], subsq enc
T45.525D	Adverse effect of antithrombotic drugs, subsq enc
T45.526*	Underdosing of antithrombotic drugs

Surgical   **Medical**   **CC Indicator**   **MCC Indicator**   **Procedure Proxy**   **PDxMCC** PDx acts as own MCC   **PDxCC** PDx acts as own CC

MDC 23: Factors Influencing Health Status And Other Contacts With Health Services—MEDICAL

T45.52[1,2,3,4]D	Poison by antithrombotic drugs, [accid (unintentional), intentional self-harm, assault, undetermined], subsq enc
T45.605D	Adverse effect of unsp fibrinolysis-affecting drugs, subs
T45.606*	Underdosing of unsp fibrinolysis-affecting drugs
T45.60[1,2,3,4]D	Poison by unsp fibrinolysis-affecting drugs, [accid (unintentional), intentional self-harm, assault, undetermined], subsq enc
T45.615D	Adverse effect of thrombolytic drugs, subsq enc
T45.616*	Underdosing of thrombolytic drugs
T45.61[1,2,3,4]D	Poison by thrombolytic drug, [accid (unintentional), intentional self-harm, assault, undetermined], subsq enc
T45.625D	Adverse effect of hemostatic drug, subsq enc
T45.626*	Underdosing of hemostatic drugs
T45.62[1,2,3,4]D	Poison by hemostatic drug, [accid (unintentional), intentional self-harm, assault, undetermined], subsq enc
T45.695D	Adverse effect of oth fibrinolysis-affecting drugs, subs
T45.696*	Underdosing of oth fibrinolysis-affecting drugs
T45.69[1,2,3,4]D	Poison by oth fibrinolysis-affecting drug, [accid (unintentional), intentional self-harm, assault, undetermined], subsq enc
T45.7X5D	Adverse effect of anticoag antag, vit K and oth coag, subs
T45.7X6*	Undrdose of anticoag antagonist, vitamin K and oth coag
T45.7X[1,2,3,4]D	Poison by anticoagulant antagonists, vitamin K and oth coagulants, [accid (unintentional), intentional self-harm, assault, undetermined], subsq enc
T45.8X5D	Adverse effect of prim systemic and hematolog agents, subs
T45.8X6*	Underdosing of primarily systemic and hematological agents
T45.8X[1,2,3,4]D	Poison by oth primarily sysic and hematological agents, [accid (unintentional), intentional self-harm, assault, undetermined], subsq enc
T45.95XD	Adverse effect of unsp prim sys and hematolog agent, subs
T45.96*	Underdosing of unsp primarily systemic and hematolog agent
T45.9[1,2,3,4]XD	Poison by unsp primarily sysic and hematological agents, [accid (unintentional), intentional self-harm, assault, undetermined], subsq enc
T46.0X5D	Adverse effect of cardi-stim glycos/drug simlar act, subs
T46.0X6*	Underdosing of cardi-stim glycos/drug simlar act
T46.0X[1,2,3,4]D	Poison by cardiac stimulant glycosides and drugs of similar action, [accid (unintentional), intentional self-harm, assault, undetermined], subsq enc
T46.1X5D	Adverse effect of calcium-channel blockers, subs enc
T46.1X6*	Underdosing of calcium-channel blockers
T46.1X[1,2,3,4]D	Poison by calcium-channel blockers, [accid (unintentional), intentional self-harm, assault, undetermined], subsq enc
T46.2X5D	Adverse effect of oth antidysrhythmic drugs, subs enc
T46.2X6*	Underdosing of oth antidysrhythmic drugs
T46.2X[1,2,3,4]D	Poison by antidysrythmic drugs, [accid (unintentional), intentional self-harm, assault, undetermined], subsq enc
T46.3X5D	Adverse effect of coronary vasodilators, subs enc
T46.3X6*	Underdosing of coronary vasodilators
T46.3X[1,2,3,4]D	Poison by coronary vasodilators, [accid (unintentional), intentional self-harm, assault, undetermined], subsq enc
T46.4X5D	Adverse effect of angiotens-convert-enzyme inhibitors, subs
T46.4X6*	Underdosing of angiotensin-converting-enzyme inhibitors
T46.4X[1,2,3,4]D	Poison by angiotensin-converting-enzyme inhibitors, [accid (unintentional), intentional self-harm, assault, undetermined], subsq enc
T46.5X5D	Adverse effect of oth antihypertensive drugs, subs enc
T46.5X6*	Underdosing of oth antihypertensive drugs
T46.5X[1,2,3,4]D	Poison by oth antihypertensive drugs, [accid (unintentional), intentional self-harm, assault, undetermined], subsq enc
T46.6X5D	Adverse effect of antihyperlip and antiarterio drugs, subs
T46.6X6*	Underdosing of antihyperlipidemic and antiarterio drugs
T46.6X[1,2,3,4]D	Poison by antihyperlipidemic and antiarteriosclerotic drugs, [accid (unintentional), intentional self-harm, assault, undetermined], subsq enc
T46.7X5D	Adverse effect of peripheral vasodilators, subs enc
T46.7X6*	Underdosing of peripheral vasodilators
T46.7X[1,2,3,4]D	Poison by peripheral vasodilators, [accid (unintentional), intentional self-harm, assault, undetermined], subsq enc
T46.8X5D	Adverse effect of antivaric drugs, incl* scler agents, subs
T46.8X6*	Underdosing of antivaric drugs, incl* sclerosing agents
T46.8X[1,2,3,4]D	Poison by antivaricose drugs, incl* sclerosing agents, [accid (unintentional), intentional self-harm, assault, undetermined], subsq enc
T46.905D	Adverse effect of unsp agents affecting the cardiovasc sys, subs
T46.906*	Underdosing of unsp agents affecting the cardiovascular sys
T46.90[1,2,3,4]D	Poison by unsp agents primarily affecting the cardiovascular sys, [accid (unintentional), intentional self-harm, assault, undetermined], subsq enc
T46.995D	Adverse effect of agents affecting the cardiovascular sys, subs
T46.996*	Underdosing of agents affecting the cardiovascular sys
T46.99[1,2,3,4]D	Poison by oth agent primarily affecting the cardiovascular sys, [accid (unintentional), intentional self-harm, assault, undetermined], subsq enc
T47.0X5D	Adverse effect of histamine H2-receptor blockers, subs
T47.0X6*	Underdosing of histamine H2-receptor blockers
T47.0X[1,2,3,4]D	Poison by histamine H2-receptor blockers, [accid (unintentional), intentional self-harm, assault, undetermined], subsq enc
T47.1X5D	Adverse effect of antacids and anti-gstrc-sec drugs, subs
T47.1X6*	Underdosing of oth antacids and anti-gastric-secretion drugs
T47.1X[1,2,3,4]D	Poison by oth antacids and anti-gastric-secretion drugs, [accid (unintentional), intentional self-harm, assault, undetermined], subsq enc
T47.2X5D	Adverse effect of stimulant laxatives, subsq enc
T47.2X6*	Underdosing of stimulant laxatives
T47.2X[1,2,3,4]D	Poison by stimulant laxatives, [accid (unintentional), intentional self-harm, assault, undetermined], subsq enc
T47.3X5D	Adverse effect of saline and osmotic laxatives, subs enc
T47.3X6*	Underdosing of saline and osmotic laxatives
T47.3X[1,2,3,4]D	Poison by saline and osmotic laxatives, [accid (unintentional), intentional self-harm, assault, undetermined], subsq enc
T47.4X5D	Adverse effect of oth laxatives, subsq enc
T47.4X6*	Underdosing of oth laxatives
T47.4X[1,2,3,4]D	Poison by oth laxatives, [accid (unintentional), intentional self-harm, assault, undetermined], subsq enc
T47.5X5D	Adverse effect of digestants, subsq enc
T47.5X6*	Underdosing of digestants
T47.5X[1,2,3,4]D	Poison by digestants, [accid (unintentional), intentional self-harm, assault, undetermined], subsq enc
T47.6X5D	Adverse effect of antidiarrheal drugs, subsq enc
T47.6X6*	Underdosing of antidiarrheal drugs
T47.6X[1,2,3,4]D	Poison by antidiarrheal drugs, [accid (unintentional), intentional self-harm, assault, undetermined], subsq enc
T47.7X5D	Adverse effect of emetics, subsq enc
T47.7X6*	Underdosing of emetics
T47.7X[1,2,3,4]D	Poison by emetics, [accid (unintentional), intentional self-harm, assault, undetermined], subsq enc
T47.8X5D	Adverse effect of agents primarily affecting GI sys, subs
T47.8X6*	Underdosing of agents primarily affecting GI sys
T47.8X[1,2,3,4]D	Poison by oth agents primarily affecting gastrointestinal sys, [accid (unintentional), intentional self-harm, assault, undetermined], subsq enc
T47.95XD	Adverse effect of unsp agents affecting the GI sys, subs
T47.96*	Underdosing of unsp agents primarily affecting the GI sys
T47.9[1,2,3,4]XD	Poison by unsp agents primarily affecting gastrointestinal sys, [accid (unintentional), intentional self-harm, assault, undetermined], subsq enc
T48.0X5D	Adverse effect of oxytocic drugs, subsq enc
T48.0X6*	Underdosing of oxytocic drugs
T48.0X[1,2,3,4]D	Poison by oxytocic drugs, [accid (unintentional), intentional self-harm, assault, undetermined], subsq enc
T48.1X5D	Adverse effect of skeletal muscle relaxants, subs enc
T48.1X6*	Underdosing of skeletal muscle relaxants
T48.1X[1,2,3,4]D	Poison by skeletal muscle relaxants (neuromuscular blocking agents), [accid (unintentional), intentional self-harm, assault, undetermined], subsq enc
T48.205D	Adverse effect of unsp drugs acting on muscles, subs enc
T48.206*	Underdosing of unsp drugs acting on muscles
T48.20[1,2,3,4]D	Poison by unsp drugs working on muscles, [accid (unintentional), intentional self-harm, assault, undetermined], subsq enc
T48.295D	Adverse effect of oth drugs acting on muscles, subs enc
T48.296*	Underdosing of oth drugs acting on muscles
T48.29[1,2,3,4]D	Poison by oth drugs working on muscles, [accid (unintentional), intentional self-harm, assault, undetermined], subsq enc
T48.3X5D	Adverse effect of antitussives, subsq enc
T48.3X6*	Underdosing of antitussives
T48.3X[1,2,3,4]D	Poison by antitussives, [accid (unintentional), intentional self-harm, assault, undetermined], subsq enc
T48.4X5D	Adverse effect of expectorants, subsq enc
T48.4X6*	Underdosing of expectorants
T48.4X[1,2,3,4]D	Poison by expectorants, [accid (unintentional), intentional self-harm, assault, undetermined], subsq enc
T48.5X5D	Adverse effect of oth anti-common-cold drugs, subs enc

---

T Transfer DRG   SP Special Payment   * Code Range   **6th and 7th Character of ZZ = No Device, No Qualifier ZX = No Device, Diagnostic**

MS-DRG Version 33.0

© 2015 Optum360, LLC

Code	Description
T48.5X6*	Underdosing of oth anti-common-cold drugs
T48.5X[1,2,3,4]D	Poison by oth anti-common-cold drugs, [accid (unintentional), intentional self-harm, assault, undetermined], subsq enc
T48.6X5D	Adverse effect of antiasthmatics, subsq enc
T48.6X6*	Underdosing of antiasthmatics
T48.6X[1,2,3,4]D	Poison by antiasthmatics, [accid (unintentional), intentional self-harm, assault, undetermined], subsq enc
T48.905D	Advrs effect of unsp agents prim act on the resp sys, subs
T48.906*	Underdosing of unsp agents primarily acting on the resp sys
T48.90[1,2,3,4]D	Poison by unsp agents primarily acting on the respiratory sys, [accid (unintentional), intentional self-harm, undetermined], subsq enc
T48.995D	Adverse effect of agents prim acting on the resp sys, subs
T48.996*	Underdosing of agents primarily acting on the resp sys
T48.99[1,2,3,4]D	Poison by oth agents primarily acting on the respiratory sys, [accid (unintentional), intentional self-harm, assault, undetermined], subsq enc
T49.0X5D	Adverse effect of local antifung/infect/inflamm drugs, subs
T49.0X6*	Underdosing of local antifung/infect/inflamm drugs
T49.0X[1,2,3,4]D	Poison by local antifungal, anti-infective and anti-inflam drugs, [accid (unintentional), intentional self-harm, assault, undetermined], subsq enc
T49.1X5D	Adverse effect of antipruritics, subsq enc
T49.1X6*	Underdosing of antipruritics
T49.1X[1,2,3,4]D	Poison by antipruritics, [accid (unintentional), intentional self-harm, assault, undetermined], subsq enc
T49.2X5D	Adverse effect of local astringents/detergents, subs
T49.2X6*	Underdosing of local astringents and local detergents
T49.2X[1,2,3,4]D	Poison by local astringents and local detergents, [accid (unintentional), intentional self-harm, assault, undetermined], subsq enc
T49.3X5D	Adverse effect of emollients, demulcents and protect, subs
T49.3X6*	Underdosing of emollients, demulcents and protectants
T49.3X[1,2,3,4]D	Poison by emollients, demulcents and protectants, [accid (unintentional), intentional self-harm, assault, undetermined], subsq enc
T49.4X5D	Adverse effect of keratolyt/keratplst/hair trmt drug, subs
T49.4X6*	Underdosing of keratolyt/keratplst/hair trmt drug
T49.4X[1,2,3,4]D	Poison by keratolytics, keratoplastics, and oth hair tx drugs, [accid (unintentional), intentional self-harm, assault, undetermined], subsq enc
T49.5X5D	Adverse effect of opth drugs and preparations, subs
T49.5X6*	Underdosing of ophthalmological drugs and preparations
T49.5X[1,2,3,4]D	Poison by ophthalmological drugs and preparations, [accid (unintentional), intentional self-harm, assault, undetermined], subsq enc
T49.6X5D	Adverse effect of otorhino drugs and preparations, subs
T49.6X6*	Underdosing of otorhinolaryngological drugs and preparations
T49.6X[1,2,3,4]D	Poison by otorhinolaryngological drugs and preparations, [accid (unintentional), intentional self-harm, assault, undetermined], subsq enc
T49.7X5D	Adverse effect of dental drugs, topically applied, subs
T49.7X6*	Underdosing of dental drugs, topically applied
T49.7X[1,2,3,4]D	Poison by dental drugs, topically applied, [accid (unintentional), intentional self-harm, assault, undetermined], subsq enc
T49.8X5D	Adverse effect of oth topical agents, subsq enc
T49.8X6*	Underdosing of oth topical agents
T49.8X[1,2,3,4]D	Poison by oth topical agents, [accid (unintentional), intentional self-harm, assault, undetermined], subsq enc
T49.95XD	Adverse effect of unsp topical agent, subs enc
T49.96*	Underdosing of unsp topical agent
T49.9[1,2,3,4]XD	Poison by unsp topical agent, [accid (unintentional), intentional self-harm, assault, undetermined], subsq enc
T50.0X5D	Adverse effect of mineralocorticoids and their antag, subs
T50.0X6*	Underdosing of mineralocorticoids and their antagonists
T50.0X[1,2,3,4]D	Poison by mineralocorticoids and their antagonists, [accid (unintentional), intentional self-harm, assault, undetermined], subsq enc
T50.1X5D	Adverse effect of loop diuretics, subsq enc
T50.1X6*	Underdosing of loop [high-ceiling] diuretics
T50.1X[1,2,3,4]D	Poison by loop (hugh ceiling) diuretics, [accid (unintentional), intentional self-harm, assault, undetermined], subsq enc
T50.2X5D	Advrs eff of crbnc-anhydr inhibtr, benzo/oth diuretc, subs
T50.2X6*	Underdosing of crbnc-anhydr inhibtr, benzo/oth diuretc
T50.2X[1,2,3,4]D	Poison by carbonic-anhydrase inhibitors, benzothiadiazides and oth diuretics, [accid (unintentional), intentional self-harm, assault, undetermined], subsq enc
T50.3X5D	Adverse effect of electrolytic/caloric/wtr-bal agnt, subs
T50.3X6*	Underdosing of electrolytic/caloric/wtr-bal agnt
T50.3X[1,2,3,4]D	Poison by eletrolytic, caloric and water-balance agents, [accid (unintentional), intentional self-harm, assault, undetermined], subsq enc
T50.4X5D	Adverse effect of drugs affecting uric acid metabolism, subs
T50.4X6*	Underdosing of drugs affecting uric acid metabolism
T50.4X[1,2,3,4]D	Poison by drugs affecting uric acid metabolism, [accid (unintentional), intentional self-harm, assault, undetermined], subsq enc
T50.5X5D	Adverse effect of appetite depressants, subsq enc
T50.5X6*	Underdosing of appetite depressants
T50.5X[1,2,3,4]D	Poison by appetite depressants, [accid (unintentional), intentional self-harm, assault, undetermined], subsq enc
T50.6X5D	Adverse effect of antidotes and chelating agents, subs
T50.6X6*	Underdosing of antidotes and chelating agents
T50.6X[1,2,3,4]D	Poison by antidotes and chelating agents, [accid (unintentional), intentional self-harm, assault, undetermined], subsq enc
T50.7X5D	Adverse effect of analeptics and opioid receptor antag, subs
T50.7X6*	Underdosing of analeptics and opioid receptor antagonists
T50.7X[1,2,3,4]D	Poison by analeptics and opiod receptor antagonists, [accid (unintentional), intentional self-harm, assault, undetermined], subsq enc
T50.8X5D	Adverse effect of diagnostic agents, subsq enc
T50.8X6*	Underdosing of diagnostic agents
T50.8X[1,2,3,4]D	Poison by dx agents, [accid (unintentional), intentional self-harm, assault, undetermined], subsq enc
T50.905D	Adverse effect of unsp drug/meds/biol subst, subs
T50.906*	Underdosing of unsp drug/meds/biol subst
T50.90[1,2,3,4]D	Poison by unsp drugs, medicaments and biological substances, [accid (unintentional), intentional self-harm, assault, undetermined], subsq enc
T50.995D	Adverse effect of drug/meds/biol subst, subs
T50.996*	Underdosing of drugs, medicaments and biological substances
T50.99[1,2,3,4]D	Poison by oth drugs, medicaments and biological substances, [accid (unintentional), intentional self-harm, assault, undetermined], subsq enc
T50.A15D	Advrs effect of pertuss vaccine, incl* combin w pertuss, subs
T50.A16*	Underdosing of pertussis vaccine, incl* combin w pertuss
T50.A1[1,2,3,4]D	Poison by pertussis vaccine, incl* combinations w/ a pertussis component, [accid (unintentional), intentional self-harm, assault, undetermined], subsq enc
T50.A25D	Adverse effect of mixed bact vaccines w/o a pertuss, subs
T50.A26*	Underdosing of mixed bacterial vaccines w/o a pertuss
T50.A2[1,2,3,4]D	Poison by mixed bacterial vaccines w/o a pertussis component, [accid (unintentional), intentional self-harm, assault, undetermined], subsq enc
T50.A95D	Adverse effect of oth bacterial vaccines, subs enc
T50.A96*	Underdosing of oth bacterial vaccines
T50.A9[1,2,3,4]D	Poison by oth bacterial vaccines, [accid (unintentional), intentional self-harm, assault, undetermined], subsq enc
T50.B15D	Adverse effect of smallpox vaccines, subsq enc
T50.B16*	Underdosing of smallpox vaccines
T50.B1[1,2,3,4]D	Poison by smpox vaccines, [accid (unintentional), intentional self-harm, assault, undetermined], subsq enc
T50.B95D	Adverse effect of oth viral vaccines, subsq enc
T50.B96*	Underdosing of oth viral vaccines
T50.B9[1,2,3,4]D	Poison by oth viral vaccines, [accid (unintentional), intentional self-harm, assault, undetermined], subsq enc
T50.Z15D	Adverse effect of immunoglobulin, subsq enc
T50.Z16*	Underdosing of immunoglobulin
T50.Z1[1,2,3,4]D	Poison by immunoglobin, [accid (unintentional), intentional self-harm, assault, undetermined], subsq enc
T50.Z95D	Adverse effect of vaccines and biological substances, subs
T50.Z96*	Underdosing of oth vaccines and biological substances
T50.Z9[1,2,3,4]D	Poison by oth vaccines and biological substances, [accid (unintentional), intentional self-harm, assault, undetermined], subsq enc
T51.0X[1,2,3,4]D	Txc effct of ethanol, [accid (unintentional), intentional self-harm, assault, undetermined], subsq enc
T51.1X[1,2,3,4]D	Txc effct of methanol, [accid (unintentional), intentional self-harm, assault, undetermined], subsq enc
T51.2X[1,2,3,4]D	Txc effct of 2-Propanol, [accid (unintentional), intentional self-harm, assault, undetermined], subsq enc
T51.3X[1,2,3,4]D	Txc effct of fusel oil, [accid (unintentional), intentional self-harm, assault, undetermined], subsq enc
T51.8X[1,2,3,4]D	Txc effct of oth alcohols, [accid (unintentional), intentional self-harm, assault, undetermined], subsq enc

Surgical	**Medical**	**CC Indicator**	**MCC Indicator**	**Procedure Proxy**	PDxMCC **PDx acts as own MCC**	PDxCC **PDx acts as own CC**

T51.9[1,2,3,4]XD Txc effct of unsp alcohol, [accid (unintentional), intentional self-harm, assault, undetermined], subsq enc

T52.0X[1,2,3,4]D Txc effct of petroleum products, [accid (unintentional), intentional self-harm, assault, undetermined], subsq enc

T52.1X[1,2,3,4]D Txc effct of benzene [accid (unintentional), intentional self-harm, assault, undetermined], subsq enc

T52.2X[1,2,3,4]D Txc effct of homologues of benzene, [accid (unintentional), intentional self-harm, assault, undetermined], subsq enc

T52.3X[1,2,3,4]D Txc effct of glycoles, [accid (unintentional), intentional self-harm, assault, undetermined], subsq enc

T52.4X[1,2,3,4]D Txc effct of ketones, [accid (unintentional), intentional self-harm, assault, undetermined], subsq enc

T52.8X[1,2,3,4]D Txc effct of oth organic solvents, [accid (unintentional), intentional self-harm, assault, undetermined], subsq enc

T52.9[1,2,3,4]XD Txc effct of unsp organic solvent, [accid (unintentional), intentional self-harm, assault, undetermined], subsq enc

T53.0X[1,2,3,4]D Txc effct of carbon tetrachloride, [accid (unintentional), intentional self-harm, assault, undetermined], subsq enc

T53.1X[1,2,3,4]D Txc effct of chloroform, [accid (unintentional), intentional self-harm, assault, undetermined], subsq enc

T53.2X[1,2,3,4]D Txc effct of trichloroethylene, [accid (unintentional), intentional self-harm, assault, undetermined], subsq enc

T53.3X[1,2,3,4]D Txc effct of tetrachloroethylene, [accid (unintentional), intentional self-harm, assault, undetermined], subsq enc

T53.4X[1,2,3,4]D Txc effct of dichloromethane, [accid (unintentional), intentional self-harm, assault, undetermined], subsq enc

T53.5X[1,2,3,4]D Txc effct of chlorofluorocarbons, [accid (unintentional), intentional self-harm, assault, undetermined], subsq enc

T53.6X[1,2,3,4]D Txc effct of oth halogen derivatives of aliphatic hydrocarbons, [accid (unintentional), intentional self-harm, assault, undetermined], subsq enc

T53.7X[1,2,3,4]D Txc effct of oth halogen derivatives of aromatic hydrocarbons, [accid (unintentional), intentional self-harm, assault, undetermined], subsq enc

T53.9[1,2,3,4]XD Txc effct of unsp halogen derivatives of aliphatic and aromatic hydrocarbons, [accid (unintentional), intentional self-harm, assault, undetermined], subsq enc

T54.0X[1,2,3,4]D Txc effct of phenol and phenol homologues, [accid (unintentional), intentional self-harm, assault, undetermined], subsq enc

T54.1X[1,2,3,4]D Txc effct of oth corrosive organic compound, [accid (unintentional), intentional self-harm, assault, undetermined], subsq enc

T54.2X[1,2,3,4]D Txc effct of corrosive acids and acid-like substances, [accid (unintentional), intentional self-harm, assault, undetermined], subsq enc

T54.3X[1,2,3,4]D Txc effct of corrosive alkalis and alkali-like substances, [accid (unintentional), intentional self-harm, assault, undetermined], subsq enc

T54.9[1,2,3,4]XD Txc effct of unsp corrosive substance, [accid (unintentional), intentional self-harm, assault, undetermined], subsq enc

T55.0X[1,2,3,4]D Txc effct of soaps, [accid (unintentional), intentional self-harm, assault, undetermined], subsq enc

T55.1X[1,2,3,4]D Txc effct of detergents, [accid (unintentional), intentional self-harm, assault, undetermined], subsq enc

T56.0X[1,2,3,4]D Txc effct of lead and its compounds, [accid (unintentional), intentional self-harm, assault, undetermined], subsq enc

T56.1X[1,2,3,4]D Txc effct of mercury and its compounds, [accid (unintentional), intentional self-harm, assault, undetermined], subsq enc

T56.2X[1,2,3,4]D Txc effct of chromium and its compounds, [accid (unintentional), intentional self-harm, assault, undetermined], subsq enc

T56.3X[1,2,3,4]D Txc effct of cadmium and its compounds, [accid (unintentional), intentional self-harm, assault, undetermined], subsq enc

T56.4X[1,2,3,4]D Txc effct of copper and its compounds, [accid (unintentional), intentional self-harm, assault, undetermined], subsq enc

T56.5X[1,2,3,4]D Txc effct of zinc and its compounds, [accid (unintentional), intentional self-harm, assault, undetermined], subsq enc

T56.6X[1,2,3,4]D Txc effct of tin and its compounds, [accid (unintentional), intentional self-harm, assault, undetermined], subsq enc

T56.7X[1,2,3,4]D Txc effct of beryllium and its compounds, [accid (unintentional), intentional self-harm, assault, undetermined], subsq enc

T56.81[1,2,3,4]D Txc effct of thallium and its compounds, [accid (unintentional), intentional self-harm, assault, undetermined], subsq enc

T56.89[1,2,3,4]D Txc effct of oth metals, [accid (unintentional), intentional self-harm, assault, undetermined], subsq enc

T56.9[1,2,3,4]XD Txc effct of unsp metal, [accid (unintentional), intentional self-harm, assault, undetermined], subsq enc

T57.0X[1,2,3,4]D Txc effct of arsenic and its compounds, [accid (unintentional), intentional self-harm, assault, undetermined], subsq enc

T57.1X[1,2,3,4]D Txc effct of phosphorus and its compounds, [accid (unintentional), intentional self-harm, assault, undetermined], subsq enc

T57.2X[1,2,3,4]D Txc effct of manganese and its compounds, [accid (unintentional), intentional self-harm, assault, undetermined], subsq enc

T57.3X[1,2,3,4]D Txc effct of hydrogen cyanide, [accid (unintentional), intentional self-harm, assault, undetermined], subsq enc

T57.8X[1,2,3,4]D Txc effct of oth spec inorganic substances, [accid (unintentional), intentional self-harm, assault, undetermined], subsq enc

T57.9[1,2,3,4]XD Txc effct of unsp inorganic substance, [accid (unintentional), intentional self-harm, assault, undetermined], subsq enc

T58.0[1,2,3,4]XD Txc effct of carbon monoxide from motor vehicle exhaust, [accid (unintentional), intentional self-harm, assault, undetermined], subsq enc

T58.1[1,2,3,4]XD Txc effct of carbon monoxide from utility gas, [accid (unintentional), intentional self-harm, assault, undetermined], subsq enc

T58.2X[1,2,3,4]D Txc effct of carbon monoxide from incomplete combustion of oth domestic fuels, [accid (unintentional), intentional self-harm, assault, undetermined], subsq enc

T58.8X[1,2,3,4]D Txc effct of carbon monoxide from oth source, [accid (unintentional), intentional self-harm, assault, undetermined], subsq enc

T58.9[1,2,3,4]XD Txc effct of carbon monoxide from unsp source, [accid (unintentional), intentional self-harm, assault, undetermined], subsq enc

T59.0X[1,2,3,4]D Txc effct of nitrogen oxides, [accid (unintentional), intentional self-harm, assault, undetermined], subsq enc

T59.1X[1,2,3,4]D Txc effct of sulfur dioxide, [accid (unintentional), intentional self-harm, assault, undetermined], subsq enc

T59.2X[1,2,3,4]D Txc effct of formaldehyde, [accid (unintentional), intentional self-harm, assault, undetermined], subsq enc

T59.3X[1,2,3,4]D Txc effct of lacrimogenic gas, [accid (unintentional), intentional self-harm, assault, undetermined], subsq enc

T59.4X[1,2,3,4]D Txc effct of chlorine gas, [accid (unintentional), intentional self-harm, assault, undetermined], subsq enc

T59.5X[1,2,3,4]D Txc effct of fluorine gas and hydrogen fluoride, [accid (unintentional), intentional self-harm, assault, undetermined], subsq enc

T59.6X[1,2,3,4]D Txc effct of hydrogen sulfide, [accid (unintentional), intentional self-harm, assault, undetermined], subsq enc

T59.7X[1,2,3,4]D Txc effct of carbon dioxide, [accid (unintentional), intentional self-harm, assault, undetermined], subsq enc

T59.81[1,2,3,4]D Txc effct of smoke, [accid (unintentional), intentional self-harm, assault, undetermined], subsq enc

T59.89[1,2,3,4]D Txc effct of oth spec gases, fumes and vapors, [accid (unintentional), intentional self-harm, assault, undetermined], subsq enc

T59.9[1,2,3,4]XD Txc effct of unsp gases, fumes and vapors, [accid (unintentional), intentional self-harm, assault, undetermined], subsq enc

T60.0X[1,2,3,4]D Txc effct of organophosphate and carbamate insecticides, [accid (unintentional), intentional self-harm, assault, undetermined], subsq enc

T60.1X[1,2,3,4]D Txc effct of halogenated insecticides, [accid (unintentional), intentional self-harm, assault, undetermined], subsq enc

T60.2X[1,2,3,4]D Txc effct of oth insecticides, [accid (unintentional), intentional self-harm, assault, undetermined], subsq enc

T60.3X[1,2,3,4]D Txc effct of herbicides and fungicides, [accid (unintentional), intentional self-harm, assault, undetermined], subsq enc

T60.4X[1,2,3,4]D Txc effct of rodenticides, [accid (unintentional), intentional self-harm, assault, undetermined], subsq enc

T60.8X[1,2,3,4]D Txc effct of oth pesticides, [accid (unintentional), intentional self-harm, assault, undetermined], subsq enc

T60.9[1,2,3,4]XD Txc effct of unsp pesticides, [accid (unintentional), intentional self-harm, assault, undetermined], subsq enc

T61.0[1,2,3,4]XD Ciguatera fish poison, [accid (unintentional), intentional self-harm, assault, undetermined], subsq enc

T61.1[1,2,3,4]XD Scombroid fish poison, [accid (unintentional), intentional self-harm, assault, undetermined], subsq enc

T61.77[1,2,3,4]D Oth fish poison, [accid (unintentional), intentional self-harm, assault, undetermined], subsq enc

T61.78[1,2,3,4]D Oth shellfish poison, [accid (unintentional), intentional self-harm, assault, undetermined], subsq enc

---

T Transfer DRG   SP Special Payment   * Code Range   6th and 7th Character of ZZ = No Device, No Qualifier ZX = No Device, Diagnostic

T61.8X[1,2,3,4]D Txc effct of oth seafood, [accid (unintentional), intentional self-harm, assault, undetermined], subsq enc

T61.9[1,2,3,4]XD Txc effct of unsp seafood, [accid (unintentional), intentional self-harm, assault, undetermined], subsq enc

T62.0X[1,2,3,4]D Txc effct of ingested mushrooms, [accid (unintentional), intentional self-harm, assault, undetermined], subsq enc

T62.1X[1,2,3,4]D Txc effct of ingested berries, [accid (unintentional), intentional self-harm, assault, undetermined], subsq enc

T62.2X[1,2,3,4]D Txc effct of oth ingested (parts of) plant(s), [accid (unintentional), intentional self-harm, assault, undetermined], subsq enc

T62.8X[1,2,3,4]D Txc effct of oth spec noxious substances eaten as food, [accid (unintentional), intentional self-harm, assault, undetermined], subsq enc

T62.9[1,2,3,4]XD Txc effct of unsp noxious substances eaten as food, [accid (unintentional), intentional self-harm, assault, undetermined], subsq enc

T63.00[1,2,3,4]D Txc effct of unsp snake venom, [accid (unintentional), intentional self-harm, assault, undetermined], subsq enc

T63.01[1,2,3,4]D Txc effct of rattlesnake venom, [accid (unintentional), intentional self-harm, assault, undetermined], subsq enc

T63.02[1,2,3,4]D Txc effct of coral snake venom, [accid (unintentional), intentional self-harm, assault, undetermined], subsq enc

T63.03[1,2,3,4]D Txc effct of taipan venom, [accid (unintentional), intentional self-harm, assault, undetermined], subsq enc

T63.04[1,2,3,4]D Txc effct of cobra venom, [accid (unintentional), intentional self-harm, assault, undetermined], subsq enc

T63.06[1,2,3,4]D Txc effct of venom of oth North and South American snake, [accid (unintentional), intentional self-harm, assault, undetermined], subsq enc

T63.07[1,2,3,4]D Txc effct of venom of oth Australian snake, [accid (unintentional), intentional self-harm, assault, undetermined], subsq enc

T63.08[1,2,3,4]D Txc effct of venom of oth African and Asian snake, [accid (unintentional), intentional self-harm, assault, undetermined], subsq enc

T63.09[1,2,3,4]D Txc effct of venom of oth snake, [accid (unintentional), intentional self-harm, assault, undetermined], subsq enc

T63.11[1,2,3,4]D Txc effct of venom of gila monster, [accid (unintentional), intentional self-harm, assault, undetermined], subsq enc

T63.12[1,2,3,4]D Txc effct of venom of oth venomous lizard, [accid (unintentional), intentional self-harm, assault, undetermined], subsq enc

T63.19[1,2,3,4]D Txc effct of venom of oth reptiles, [accid (unintentional), intentional self-harm, assault, undetermined], subsq enc

T63.2X[1,2,3,4]D Txc effct of venom of scorpion, [accid (unintentional), intentional self-harm, assault, undetermined], subsq enc

T63.30[1,2,3,4]D Txc effct of unsp spider venom, [accid (unintentional), intentional self-harm, assault, undetermined], subsq enc

T63.31[1,2,3,4]D Txc effct of venom of black widow spider, [accid (unintentional), intentional self-harm, assault, undetermined], subsq enc

T63.32[1,2,3,4]D Txc effct of venom of tarantula, [accid (unintentional), intentional self-harm, assault, undetermined], subsq enc

T63.33[1,2,3,4]D Txc effct of venom of brown recluse spider, [accid (unintentional), intentional self-harm, assault, undetermined], subsq enc

T63.39[1,2,3,4]D Txc effct of venom of oth spider, [accid (unintentional), intentional self-harm, assault, undetermined], subsq enc

T63.41[1,2,3,4]D Txc effct of venom of centipedes and venomous millipedes, [accid (unintentional), intentional self-harm, assault, undetermined], subsq enc

T63.42[1,2,3,4]D Txc effct of venom of ants, [accid (unintentional), intentional self-harm, assault, undetermined], subsq enc

T63.43[1,2,3,4]D Txc effct of venom of caterpillars, [accid (unintentional), intentional self-harm, assault, undetermined], subsq enc

T63.44[1,2,3,4]D Txc effct of venom of bees, [accid (unintentional), intentional self-harm, assault, undetermined], subsq enc

T63.45[1,2,3,4]D Txc effct of venom of hornets, [accid (unintentional), intentional self-harm, assault, undetermined], subsq encount

T63.46[1,2,3,4]D Txc effct of venom of wasps, [accid (unintentional), intentional self-harm, assault, undetermined], subsq enc

T63.48[1,2,3,4]D Txc effct of venom of oth arthropod, [accid (unintentional), intentional self-harm, assault, undetermined], subsq enc

T63.51[1,2,3,4]D Txc effct of contact w/ stingray, [accid (unintentional), intentional self-harm, assault, undetermined], subsq enc

T63.59[1,2,3,4]D Txc effct of contact w/ oth venomous fish, [accid (unintentional), intentional self-harm, assault, undetermined], subsq enc

T63.61[1,2,3,4]D Txc effct of contact w/ Portugese Man-o-war, [accid (unintentional), intentional self-harm, assault, undetermined], subsq enc

T63.62[1,2,3,4]D Txc effct of contact w/ oth jellyfish, [accid (unintentional), intentional self-harm, assault, undetermined], subsq enc

T63.63[1,2,3,4]D Txc effct of contact w/ sea anemone, [accid (unintentional), intentional self-harm, assault, undetermined], subsq enc

T63.69[1,2,3,4]D Txc effct of contact w/ oth venomous marine animals, [accid (unintentional), intentional self-harm, assault, undetermined], subsq enc

T63.71[1,2,3,4]D Txc effct of contact w/ venomous marine plant, [accid (unintentional), intentional self-harm, assault, undetermined], subsq enc

T63.79[1,2,3,4]D Txc effct of contact w/ oth venomous plant, [accid (unintentional), intentional self-harm, assault, undetermined], subsq enc

T63.81[1,2,3,4]D Txc effct of contact w/ venomous frog, [accid (unintentional), intentional self-harm, assault, undetermined], subsq enc

T63.82[1,2,3,4]D Txc effct of contact w/ venomous toad, [accid (unintentional), intentional self-harm, assault, undetermined], subsq enc

T63.83[1,2,3,4]D Txc effct of contact w/ oth venomous amphibian, [accid (unintentional), intentional self-harm, assault, undetermined], subsq enc

T63.89[1,2,3,4]D Txc effct of contact w/ oth venomous animals, [accid (unintentional), intentional self-harm, assault, undetermined], subsq enc

T63.9[1,2,3,4]XD Txc effct of contact w/ unsp venomous animal, [accid (unintentional), intentional self-harm, assault, undetermined], subsq enc

T64.0[1,2,3,4]XD Txc effct of aflatoxin, [accid (unintentional), intentional self-harm, assault, undetermined], subsq enc

T64.8[1,2,3,4]XD Txc effct of oth mycotoxin food contaminants, [accid (unintentional), intentional self-harm, assault, undetermined], subsq enc

T65.0X[1,2,3,4]D Txc effct of cyanides, [accid (unintentional), intentional self-harm, assault, undetermined], subsq enc

T65.1X[1,2,3,4]D Txc effct of strychnine, [accid (unintentional), intentional self-harm, assault, undetermined], subsq enc

T65.21[1,2,3,4]D Txc effct of chewing tobacco, [accid (unintentional), intentional self-harm, assault, undetermined], subsq enc

T65.22[1,2,3,4]D Txc effct of tobacco cigarettes, [accid (unintentional), intentional self-harm, assault, undetermined], subsq enc

T65.29[1,2,3,4]D Txc effct of oth tobacco and nicotine, [accid (unintentional), intentional self-harm, assault, undetermined], subsq enc

T65.3X[1,2,3,4]D Txc effct of nitroderivatives and amnioderivatives of benzene and its homologues, [accid (unintentional), intentional self-harm, assault, undetermined], subsq enc

T65.4X[1,2,3,4]D Txc effct of carbon disulfide, [accid (unintentional), intentional self-harm, assault, undetermined], subsq enc

T65.5X[1,2,3,4]D Txc effct of nitroglycerin and oth nitric acids amd esters, [accid (unintentional), intentional self-harm, assault, undetermined], subsq enc

T65.6X[1,2,3,4]D Txc effct of paints and dyes, NEC, [accid (unintentional), intentional self-harm, assault, undetermined], subsq enc

T65.81[1,2,3,4]D Txc effct of latex, [accid (unintentional), intentional self-harm, assault, undetermined], subsq enc

T65.82[1,2,3,4]D Txc effct of harmful algae and algae toxins, [accid (unintentional), intentional self-harm, assault, undetermined], subsq enc

T65.83[1,2,3,4]D Txc effct of fiberglass, NEC, [accid (unintentional), intentional self-harm, assault, undetermined], subsq enc

T65.89[1,2,3,4]D Txc effct of oth spec substances, [accid (unintentional), intentional self-harm, assault, undetermined], subsq enc

T65.9[1,2,3,4]XD Txc effct of unsp substance, [accid (unintentional), intentional self-harm, assault, undetermined], subsq enc

T66.XXXD Radiation sickness, unsp, subsq enc

T67.8XXD Oth effects of heat and light, subsq enc

T67.9XXD Effect of heat and light, unsp, subsq enc

T67.[0,1,2,3,4,5,6,7]XXDHeat [stroke and sunstroke, syncope, cramp, exhaustion anhydrotic, exhaustion d/t salt depletion, exhaustion unsp, fatigue transient, edema], subsq enc

T68.XXXD Hypothermia, subsq enc

T69.01[1,2,9]D Immersion hand, [rt, lt, unsp] hand, subsq enc

T69.02[1,2,9]D Immersion foot, [rt, lt, unsp] foot, subsq enc

T69.1XXD Chilblains, subsq enc

T69.[8,9]XXD [Oth spec, Unsp] effects of reduced temperature, subsq enc

T70.0XXD Otitic barotrauma, subsq enc

T70.1XXD Sinus barotrauma, subsq enc

T70.20XD Unsp effects of high altitude, subsq enc

T70.29XD Oth effects of high altitude, subsq enc

Surgical   **Medical**   **CC Indicator**   **MCC Indicator**   **Procedure Proxy**   **PDx MCC** **PDx acts as own MCC**   **PDx CC** **PDx acts as own CC**

MDC 23: Factors Influencing Health Status And Other Contacts With Health Services—MEDICAL

T70.3XXD	Caisson dz, subsq enc
T70.4XXD	Effects of high-pressure fluids, subsq enc
T70.8XXD	Oth effects of air pressure and water pressure, subs enc
T70.9XXD	Effect of air pressure and water pressure, unsp, subs enc
T71.141D	Asphyx d/t smothr under another person's body, acc, subs
T71.143D	Asphyx d/t smothr under another person's body, asslt, subs
T71.144D	Asphyx d/t smothr under another person's body, undet, subs
T71.1[1,2,3,5,6,9][1,2,3,4]D	Asphyxiation d/t [smothing under pillow, plastic bag, being trapped in bed linens, smothing under anoth person's body, smothing in furniture, hanging, mech threat to breathing d/t oth causes], [accid, intentional self-harm, assault, undetermined], subsq enc
T71.20XD	Asphyx d/t sys oxy defic d/t low oxy in air unsp cause, subs
T71.21XD	Asphyxiation d/t cave-in or falling earth, subs enc
T71.29XD	Asphyx d/t being trap in oth low oxygen environment, subs
T71.2[2,3][1,2,3,4]D	Asphyxiation d/t being trapped in a [car trunk, (discarded) refrigerator], [accid, intentional self-harm, assault, undetermined], subsq enc
T71.9XXD	Asphyxiation d/t unsp cause, subsq enc
T73.0XXD	Starvation, subsq enc
T73.1XXD	Deprivation of water, subsq enc
T73.2XXD	Exhaustion d/t exposure, subsq enc
T73.3XXD	Exhaustion d/t excessive exertion, subsq enc
T73.8XXD	Oth effects of deprivation, subsq enc
T73.9XXD	Effect of deprivation, unsp, subsq enc
T74.0[1,2]XD	[Adult, Child] neglect or abandonment, confirmed, subsq enc
T74.1[1,2]XD	[Adult, Child] physical abuse, confirmed, subsq enc
T74.2[1,2]XD	[Adult, Child] sexual abuse, confirmed, subsq enc
T74.3[1,2]XD	[Adult, Child] psychological abuse, confirmed, subsq enc
T74.4XXD	Shaken infant synd, subsq enc
T74.9[1,2]XD	Unsp [adult, child] maltx, confirmed, subsq enc
T75.0[0,1,9]XD	[Unsp effects of, Shock d/t being struck by, Unsp effects of] lightning, subsq enc
T75.1XXD	Unsp effects of drowning and nonfatal submersion, subs
T75.20XD	Unsp effects of vibration, subsq enc
T75.21XD	Pneumatic hammer synd, subsq enc
T75.22XD	Traum vasospastic synd, subsq enc
T75.23XD	Vertigo from infrasound, subsq enc
T75.29XD	Oth effects of vibration, subsq enc
T75.3XXD	Motion sickness, subsq enc
T75.4XXD	Electrocution, subsq enc
T75.89XD	Oth spec effects of ext causes, subs enc
T75.8[1,2]XD	Effects of [abnormal gravitation [G] forces, weightlessness], subsq enc
T76.0[1,2]XD	[Adult, Child] neglect or abandonment, suspected, subsq enc
T76.1[1,2]XD	[Adult, Child] physical abuse, suspected, subsq enc
T76.2[1,2]XD	[Adult, Child] sexual abuse, suspected, subsq enc
T76.3[1,2]XD	[Adult, Child] psychological abuse, suspected, subsq enc
T76.9[1,2]XD	Unsp [adult, child] maltx, suspected, subsq enc
T78.0[0,1,2,3,4,5,6,7,8,9]XD	Anaphylactic reaction d/t [unsp food, peanuts, shellfish (crustaceans), oth fish, fruits and vegetables, tree nuts and seeds, food additives, milk and dairy products, eggs, oth food products], subsq enc
T78.1XXD	Oth adverse food reactions, NEC, subs
T78.2XXD	Anaphylactic shock, unsp, subsq enc
T78.3XXD	Angioneurotic edema, subsq enc
T78.40XD	Allergy, unsp, subsq enc
T78.41XD	Arthus phenomenon, subsq enc
T78.49XD	Oth allergy, subsq enc
T78.8XXD	Oth adverse effects, NEC, subs enc
T79.A0XD	Compartment synd, unsp, subsq enc
T79.A1[1,2,9]D	Traum compartment synd of [rt, lt, unsp] upr extr, subsq enc
T79.A2[1,2,9]D	Traum compartment synd of [rt, lt, unsp] lwr extr, subsq enc
T79.A[3,9]XD	Traum compartment synd of [abd, oth sites], subsq enc
T79.[0,1]XXD	[Air, Fat] embolism (traum), subsq enc
T79.[2,4,5,6,7]XXD	Traum [2ndary and recurrent hemor and seroma, shock, anuria, ischemia of muscle, SQ emphysema], subsq enc
T79.[8,9]XXD	[Oth, Unsp] early comps of trauma, subsq enc
T80.0XXD	Air embolism fol inf, transfs and theraputc inject, subs
T80.1XXD	Vascular comp fol infusn, transfs and theraputc inject, subs
T80.21[1,2,8,9]D	[Bldstream, Local, Oth, Unsp] infxn d/t central venous catheter, subsq enc
T80.22XD	Acute infxn fol transfs,infusn,inject bld/products, subs
T80.29XD	Infxn fol oth inf, transfusion and theraputc inject, subs
T80.30XD	ABO incompat react d/t tranfs of bld/bld prod, unsp, subs
T80.31[0,1,9]D	ABO incompatibility w/ [acute, delayed, unsp] hemolytic transfusion reaction, subsq enc
T80.39XD	Oth ABO incompat react d/t tranfs of bld/bld prod, subs
T80.40XD	Rh incompat react d/t tranfs of bld/bld prod, unsp, subs

T80.41[0,1,9]D	Rh incompatibility w/ [acute, delayed, unsp] hemolytic transfusion reaction, subsq enc
T80.49XD	Oth Rh incompat reaction d/t tranfs of bld/bld prod, subs
T80.5[1,2,9]XD	Anaphylactic reaction d/t [administration of bld and bld products, vaccination, oth serum], subsq enc
T80.6[1,2,9]XD	Oth serum reaction d/t [administration of bld and bld products, vaccination, oth serum], subsq enc
T80.81[0,8]D	Extravasation of [vesicant antineoplastic chemothapy, oth vesicant agent], subsq enc
T80.89XD	Oth comp fol inf, transfusion and theraputc inject, subs
T80.90XD	Unsp comp following inf and therapeutic injection, subs
T80.91[0,1,9]D	[Acute, Delayed, Unsp] hemolytic transfusion reaction, unsp incompatibility, subsq enc
T80.92XD	Unsp transfusion reaction, subsq enc
T80.A0XD	Non-ABO incompat react d/t tranfs of bld/bld prod,unsp, subs
T80.A1[0,1,9]D	Non-ABO incompatibility w/ [acute, delayed, hemolytic] hemolytic transfusion reaction, subsq enc
T80.A9XD	Oth non-ABO incompat react d/t tranfs of bld/bld prod, subs
T81.1[0,1,2,9]XD	Postprocedural [unsp, cardiogenic, septic, oth] shock, subsq enc
T81.3[0,1,2,3]XD	Disruption of [unsp wnd, ext operation (surgical) wnd, int operation (surgical) wnd, traum inj wnd rpr], subsq enc
T81.4XXD	Infxn following a procedure, subsq enc
T81.5[0,1,2,3,9][0,1,2,3,4,5,6,7,8,9]D	[Unsp comp, Adhesions, Obstruction, Perforation, Oth comps] d/t FB accidally lt in body following [surgical operation, inf or transfusion, kidney dialysis, injectionor immunization, endo exam, heart catheterization, aspiration punc or oth catheterization, rmvl of catheter or packing, oth procedure, unsp procedure], subsq enc
T81.6[0,1,9]XD	[Unsp acute reaction, Aseptic peritonitis, Oth acute reaction] d/t foreign substance accidally lt during a procedure, subsq enc
T81.71[0,1,8,9]D	Comp of [mesenteric, renal, oth, unsp] artery following a procedure, NEC, subsq enc
T81.72XD	Comp of vein following a procedure, NEC, subs
T81.81XD	Comp of inhalation therapy, subsq enc
T81.82XD	Emphysema (SQ) resulting from a procedure, subs
T81.83XD	Persistent postprocedural fistula, subsq enc
T81.89XD	Oth comp of procedures, NEC, subs
T81.9XXD	Unsp comp of procedure, subsq enc
T82.0[1,2,3,9]XD	[Breakdown (mech), Displac, Leakage, Oth mech] comp of heart valve prosthesis, subsq enc
T82.11[0,1,8,9]D	Breakdown (mech) of [cardiac electrode, cardiac pulse generator, oth cardiac electronic dev, unsp cardiac electronic dev], subsq enc
T82.12[0,1,8,9]D	Displac of [cardiac electrode, cardiac pulse generator, oth cardiac electronic dev, unsp cardiac electronic dev], subsq enc
T82.19[0,1,8,9]D	Oth mech comp of [cardiac electrode, cardiac pulse generator, oth cardiac electronic dev, unsp cardiac electronic dev], subsq enc
T82.21[1,2,3,8]D	[Breakdown (mech), Displac, Leakage, Oth mech comp] of coronary artery bypass graft, subsq enc
T82.22[1,2,3,8]D	[Breakdown (mech), Displac, Leakage, Oth mech comp] of biological heart valve graft, subsq enc
T82.31[0,1,2,8,9]D	Breakdown (mech) of [aortic (bifurcation) graft (replace), carotid arterial graft (bypass), femor arterial graft (bypass), oth vascular grafts, unsp vascular grafts], subsq enc
T82.32[0,1,2,8,9]D	Displac of [aortic (bifurcation) graft (replace), carotid arterial graft (bypass), femor arterial graft (bypass), oth vascular grafts, unsp vascular grafts], subsq
T82.33[0,1,2,8,9]D	Leakage of [aortic (bifurcation) graft (replace), carotid arterial graft (bypass), femor arterial graft (bypass), oth vascular grafts, unsp vascular grafts], subsq enc
T82.39[0,1,2,8,9]D	Oth mech comp of [aortic (bifurcation) graft (replace), carotid arterial graft (bypass), femor arterial graft (bypass), oth vascular grafts, unsp vascular grafts], subsq enc
T82.4[1,2,3,9]XD	[Breakdown (mech), Displac, Leakage, Oth mech comp] of vascular dialysis catheter, subsq enc
T82.51[0,1,2,3,4,5,8,9]D	Breakdown (mech) of [surgically created arteriovenous fistula, surgically created arteriovenous shunt, artfcl heart, balloon (counterpulsation) dev, inf catheter, umbrella dev, oth cardiac/vascular dev, unsp cardiac/vascular dev], subsq enc
T82.52[0,1,2,3,4,5,8,9]D	Displac of [surgically created arteriovenous fistula, surgically created arteriovenous shunt, artfcl heart, balloon (counterpulsation) dev, inf catheter, umbrella dev, oth cardiac/vascular dev, unsp cardiac/vascular dev], subsq enc
T82.53[0,1,2,3,4,5,8,9]D	Leakage of [surgically created arteriovenous fistula, surgically created arteriovenous shunt, artfcl heart, balloon (counterpulsation) dev, inf catheter, umbrella dev, oth cardiac/vascular dev, unsp cardiac/vascular dev], subsq enc

---

[T] **Transfer DRG**　　　[SP] **Special Payment**　　　***Code Range**　　　**6th and 7th Character of ZZ = No Device, No Qualifier ZX = No Device, Diagnostic**

T82.59[0,1,2,3,4,5,8,9]D	Oth mech comp of [surgically created arteriovenous fistula, surgically created arteriovenous shunt, artfcl heart, balloon (counterpulsation) dev, inf catheter, umbrella dev, oth cardiac/vascular dev, unsp cardiac/vascular dev], subsq enc
T82.6XXD	Infect/inflm reaction d/t cardiac valve prosthesis, subs
T82.7XXD	Infect/inflm react d/t oth cardi/vasc dev/implnt/grft, subs
T82.8[1,2,3,4,5,6,9][7,8]D	[Embolism, Fibrosis, Hemor, Pain, Stenosis, Thrombosis, Oth spec comp] of [cardiac, vascular] prosthetic devs, implants and grafts, subsq enc
T82.9XXD	Unsp comp of cardiac and vascular prosth dev/grft, subs
T83.0[1,2,3,9][0,8]D	[Breakdown (mech), Displac, Leakage, Oth mech comp] of [cystostomy, oth indwelling urethral] catheter, subsq enc
T83.1[1,2,9][0,1,2,8]D	[Breakdown (mech), Displac, Oth mech comp] of [urinary electronic stimulator, urinary sphincter implant, urinary stent, oth urinary devs], subsq enc
T83.2[1,2,3,9]XD	[Breakdown (mech), Displac, Leakage, Oth mech comp] of graft of urinary organ, subsq enc
T83.3[1,2,9]XD	[Breakdown (mech), Displac, Oth mech comp] of intrauterine contraceptive dev, subsq enc
T83.4[1,2,9][0,8]D	[Breakdown (mech), Displac, Oth mech comp] of [penile (implanted) prosthesis, oth prosthetic devs, implants and grafts of genital tract], subsq enc
T83.5[1,9]XD	Infxn and inflam reaction d/t [indwelling urinary catheter, prosthetic dev, implant and graft in urinary sys], subsq enc
T83.6XXD	Infect/inflm react d/t prosth dev/grft in genitl trct, subs
T83.7[1,2][1,8]D	[Erosion, Exposure] of [implanted vaginal mesh, implanted mesh] and oth prosthetic materials to surrounding organ or tissue, subsq enc
T83.8[1,2,3,4,5,6,9]XD	[Embolism, Fibrosis, Hemor, Pain, Stenosis, Thrombosis, Oth spec comp] of genitourinary prosthetic devs, implants and grafts, subsq enc
T83.9XXD	Unsp comp of genitourinary prosth dev/grft, subs
T84.01[0,1,2,3,8,9]D	Broken int [rt hip, lt hip, rt knee, lt knee, oth site, unsp site] prosthesis, subsq enc
T84.02[0,1]D	Disloc of int [rt, lt] hip prosthesis, subsq enc
T84.02[2,3]D	Instability of int [rt, lt] knee prosthesis, subsq enc
T84.02[8,9]D	Disloc of [oth, unsp] int jt prosthesis, subsq enc
T84.03[0,1,2,3,8,9]D	Mech loosening of [rt hip, lt hip, rt knee, lt knee, oth site, unsp site] prosthesis, subsq enc
T84.05[0,1,2,3,8,9]D	Periprosthetic osteolysis [rt hip, lt hip, rt knee, lt knee, oth site, unsp site] prosthesis, subsq enc
T84.06[0,1,2,3,8,9]D	Wear of articular bearing surface of int prosthetic [rt hip, lt hip, rt knee, lt knee, oth site, unsp site] jt, subsq enc
T84.09[0,1,2,3,8,9]D	Oth mech comp of [rt hip, lt hip, rt knee, lt knee, oth jt, unsp jt] prosthesis, subsq enc
T84.11[0,1,2,3,4,5,6,7,9]D	Breakdown (mech) of int fix dev of [rt humerus, lt humerus, bone of rt forearm, bone of lt forearm, rt femur, lt femur, bone of rt lwr leg, bone of lt lwr leg, unsp bone of limb], subsq enc
T84.12[0,1,2,3,4,5,6,7,9]D	Displac of int fix dev of [rt humerus, lt humerus, bone of rt forearm, bone of lt forearm, rt femur, lt femur, bone of rt lwr leg, bone of lt lwr leg, unsp bone of limb], subsq enc
T84.19[0,1,2,3,4,5,6,7,9]D	Oth mech comp of int fix dev of [rt humerus, lt humerus, bone of rt forearm, bone of lt forearm, rt femur, lt femur, bone of rt lwr leg, bone of lt lwr leg, unsp bone of limb], subsq enc
T84.21[0,3,6,8]D	Breakdown (mech) of int fix dev of [bones of hand and fingers, bones of foot and toes, vertebrae, oth bones], subsq enc
T84.22[0,3,6,8]D	Displac of int fix dev of [bones of hand and fingers, bones of foot and toes, vertebrae, oth bones], subsq enc
T84.29[0,3,6,8]D	Oth mech comp of int fix dev of [bones of hand and fingers, bones of foot and toes, vertebrae, oth bones], subsq enc
T84.3[1,2,9][0,8]D	[Breakdown (mech), Displac, Oth mech comp] of [electronic bone stimulator, oth bone dev(s), implants and grafts], subsq enc
T84.4[1,2,9][0,8]D	[Breakdown (mech), Displac, Oth mech comp] of [muscle and tndn graft, oth int orthopedic dev(s), implants and graft], subsq enc
T84.5[0,1,2,3,4,9]XD	Infxn and inflam reaction d/t [unsp int jt, int rt hip, int lt hip, int rt knee, int lt knee, oth int jt] prosthesis, subsq enc
T84.60XD	Infect/inflm reaction d/t int fix of unsp site, subs
T84.61[0,1,2,3,4,5,9]D	Infxn and inflam reaction d/t int fix dev of [rt humerus, lt humerus, rt radius, lt radius, rt ulna, lt ulna, unsp bone of arm], subsq enc
T84.62[0,1,2,3,4,5,9]D	Infxn and inflam reaction d/t int fix dev of [rt femur, lt femur, rt tibia, lt tibia, rt fibula, lt fibula, unsp bone of leg], subsq enc
T84.6[3,9]XD	Infxn and inflam reaction d/t int fix dev of [spine, oth site], subsq enc
T84.7XXD	Infect/inflm react d/t oth int orth prosth dev/grft, subs
T84.8[1,2,3,4,5,6,9]XD	[Embolism, Fibrosis, Hemor, Pain, Stenosis, Thrombosis, Oth spec comp] d/t int orthopedic prosthetic devs, implants and grafts, subsq enc
T84.9XXD	Unsp comp of int orthopedic prosth dev/grft, subs
T85.0[1,2,3,9]XD	[Breakdown (mech), Displac, Leakage, Oth mech comp] of ventricular intracranial (communicating) shunt, subsq enc
T85.11[0,1,2,8]D	Breakdown (mech) of implanted electronic neurostimulator (electrode) of [brain, peripheral nerve, spinal cord, oth nervous sys], subsq enc
T85.12[0,1,2,8]D	Displac of implanted electronic neurostimulator (electrode) of [brain, peripheral nerve, spinal cord, oth nervous sys], subsq enc
T85.19[0,1,2,9]D	Oth mech comp of implanted electronic neurostimulator (electrode) of [brain, peripheral nerve, spinal cord, oth nervous sys], subsq enc
T85.2[1,2,9]XD	[Breakdown (mech), Displac, Oth mech comp] of intraocular lens, subsq enc
T85.318D	Breakdown (mech) of ocular prosth dev/grft, subs
T85.31[0,1]D	Breakdown (mech) of prosthetic orbit of [rt, lt] eye, subsq enc
T85.328D	Displac of ocular prosth dev/grft, subs
T85.32[0,1]D	Displac of prosthetic orbit of [rt, lt] eye, subsq enc
T85.398D	Mech compl of ocular prosth dev/grft, subs
T85.39[0,1]D	Oth mech comp of prosthetic orbit of [rt, lt] eye, subsq enc
T85.4[1,2,3,4,9]XD	[Breakdown (mech), Displac, Leakage, Capsular contracture, Oth mech comp] of breast prosthesis and implant, subsq enc
T85.5[1,2,9][0,1,8]D	[Breakdown (mech), Displac, Oth mech comp] of [bile duct prosthesis, esophageal anti-reflux dev, oth gastrointestinal prosthetic devs, implants and grafts], subsq enc
T85.63[0,1,3,8]D	Leakage of [epidural and subdural inf catheter, intraperitoneal dialysis catheter, insulin pump, oth spec int prosthetic devs, implants and grafts], subsq enc
T85.69[0,1,2,3,4,8]D	Oth mech comp of [epidural and subdural inf catheter, intraperitoneal dialysis catheter, permanent sutures, artfcl skin graft and decellularized allodermis, insulin pump, oth spec int prosthetic devs, implants and grafts], subsq enc
T85.6[1,2][0,1,2,3,4,8]D	[Breakdown (mech), Displac] of [epidural and subdural inf catheter, intraperitoneal dialysis catheter, permanent sutures, artfcl skin graft and decellularized allodermis, insulin pump, oth spec int prosthetic devs, implants and grafts], subsq enc
T85.7[1,2,9]XD	Infxn and inflam reaction d/t [peritoneal dialysis catheter, insulin pump, oth int prosthetic devs, implants and grafts], subsq enc
T85.8[1,2,3,4,5,6,9]XD	[Embolism, Fibrosis, Hemor, Pain, Stenosis, Thrombosis, Oth spec comp] d/t int prosthetic devs, implants and grafts, NEC, subsq enc
T85.9XXD	Unsp comp of int prosth dev/grft, subs
T88.0XXD	Infxn following immunization, subsq enc
T88.1XXD	Oth comp following immunization, NEC, subs
T88.2XXD	Shock d/t anesthesia, subsq enc
T88.3XXD	Malig hyperthermia d/t anesthesia, subs enc
T88.4XXD	Failed or difficult intubation, subsq enc
T88.51XD	Hypothermia following anesthesia, subsq enc
T88.52XD	Failed mod sedation during procedure, subs enc
T88.59XD	Oth comp of anesthesia, subsq enc
T88.6XXD	Anaphyl reaction d/t advrs eff drug/med prop admin, subs
T88.7XXD	Unsp adverse effect of drug or medicament, subs enc
T88.8XXD	Oth comp of surgical and medical care, NEC, subs
T88.9XXD	Comp of surgical and medical care, unsp, subs enc
Z45.1	Enc for adjustment and management of inf pump
Z45.2	Enc for adjustment and management of VAD
Z46.82	Enc for fit/adjst of non-vascular catheter
Z48.03	Enc for change or rmvl of drains
Z48.1	Enc for planned postprocedural wnd closure
Z48.2*	Enc for aftercare following organ transplant
Z48.3	Aftercare following surgery for neoplasm
Z48.8*	Enc for oth spec postprocedural aftercare
Z51.8*	Enc for oth spec aftercare
Z79.0*	Long term (current) use of antocoag/antithrom/angiplate
Z79.1	Long term (current) use of non-steroidal non-inflam (NSAID)
Z79.2	Long term (current) use of antibiotics
Z79.3	Long term (current) use of hormonal contraceptives
Z79.4	Long term (current) use of insulin
Z79.5*	Long term (current) use of steroids
Z79.82	Long term (current) use of aspirin
Z79.83	Long term (current) use of bisphosphonates
Z79.891	Long term (current) use of opiate analgesic
Z79.899	Oth long term (current) drug therapy
Z92.2*	Personal history of drug therapy

Surgical **Medical** **CC Indicator** **MCC Indicator** **Procedure Proxy** **PDxMCC PDx acts as own MCC** **PDxCC PDx acts as own CC**

DRG 950   Aftercare without CC/MCC

| GMLOS 2.3 | AMLOS 2.9 | RW 0.5798 |

Select any principal diagnosis listed under DRG 949

DRG 951   Oth Factors Influencing Health Status

| GMLOS 2.7 | AMLOS 6.0 | RW 0.9885 |

Principal Diagnosis

Code	Description
F17.2[0,1,2,9][0,1]	Nicotine dependence, [unsp, cigarettes, chewing tobacco, oth tobacco product], [uncomp, in remission]
J95.850	Mechanical comp of respirator
P00.2	Newborn affected by maternal infec/parastc dz
P00.89	Newborn affected by oth maternal conditions
Q89.9	Congenital malformation, unsp
Q92*	Oth trisomies and partial trisomies of the autosomes, NEC
Q93.0	Whole chromosome monosomy,nonmosaic (meiotic nondisjunction)
Q93.1	Whole chromosome monosomy, mosaic (mitotic nondisjunction)
Q93.2	Chromosome replaced with ring, dicentric or isochromosome
Q95*	Balanced rearrangements and structural markers, NEC
Q99.9	Chromosomal abnormality, unsp
R40.21[3,4][0,1,2,3,4]	Coma scale, eyes opn, [to sound, spontaneous], [unsp time, in the field (EMT or ambulance), at arrival to emergency department, at hospital admission, 24 hrs or more after hospital admission]
R40.22[3,4,5][0,1,2,3,4]	Coma scale, best verbal response, [inappropriate words, confused conversation, oriented], [unsp time, in the field (EMT or ambulance), at arrival to emergency department, at hospital admission, 24 hrs or more after hospital admission]
R40.23[3,5,6][0,1,2,3,4]	Coma scale, best motor response, [abnormal, localizes pain, obeys commands], [unsp time, in the field (EMT or ambulance), at arrival to emergency department, at hospital admission, 24 hrs or more after hospital admission]
R40.244	Oth coma,w/o Glasgow coma scale score,or w/part score report
R40.24[1,2,3]	Glasgow coma scale score [13-15, 9-12, 3-8]
R41.83	Borderline intellectual functioning
R44.8	Oth symptoms and signs w general sensations and perceptions
R44.9	Unsp symptoms and signs w general sensations and perceptions
R45.850	Homicidal ideations
R46*	Symptoms and signs involving appearance and behav
R68.13	Apparent life threatening event in infant (ALTE)
R68.19	Oth nonspecific symptoms peculiar to infancy
R68.82	Decreased libido
R69	Illness, unsp
R99	Ill-defined and unknown cause of mortality
Z00*	Enc for general exam w/o complaint, susp or reprtd dx
Z01*	Enc for oth sp exam w/o complaint, suspected or reprtd dx
Z02*	Enc for administrative exam
Z03*	Enc for medical obs for susp dz and cond ruled out
Z04.4*	Enc for exam and observation following alleged rape
Z04.6	Enc for general psychiatric exam, requested by authority
Z04.7*	Enc for exam and obs following alleged physical abuse
Z04.8	Enc for exam and observation for oth reasons
Z04.9	Enc for exam and observation for unsp reason
Z09	Enc for f/u exam aft tx for cond oth than malig neoplm
Z11*	Enc for screening for infec/parastc dz
Z12*	Enc for screening for malig neoplasms
Z13*	Enc for screening for oth dz and d/o
Z14*	Genetic carrier
Z15*	Genetic susceptibility to dz
Z17*	Estrogen receptor status
Z18*	Retained FB fragments
Z20*	Contact w and (suspected) exposure to communicable dz
Z22.0	Carrier of typhoid
Z22.1	Carrier of oth intestinal infectious dz
Z22.2	Carrier of diphtheria
Z22.3*	Carrier of oth spec bacterial dz
Z22.4	Carrier of infections w sexl mode of transmiss
Z22.6	Carrier of human T-lymphotropic virus type-1 infxn
Z22.8	Carrier of oth infectious dz
Z22.9	Carrier of infectious dz, unsp
Z23	Enc for immunization
Z28*	Immunization not carried out and underimmunization status
Z30.0*	Enc for general counseling and advice on contraception
Z30.4*	Enc for surveillance of contraceptives

Code	Description
Z30.8	Enc for oth contraceptive management
Z30.9	Enc for contraceptive management, unsp
Z31.4*	Enc for procreative investigation and testing
Z31.5	Enc for genetic counseling
Z31.6*	Enc for general counseling and advice on procreation
Z31.8*	Enc for oth procreative management
Z31.9	Enc for procreative management, unsp
Z32*	Enc for preg test and chldbrth and childcare instruction
Z33.1	Pregnant state, incidental
Z34*	Enc for supervision of normal preg
Z36	Enc for antenatal screening of mother
Z37*	Outcome of delivery
Z39.1	Enc for care and exam of lactating mother
Z39.2	Enc for routine postpartum follow-up
Z3A*	Weeks of gestation
Z40.0[0,9]	Enc for prophylactic rmvl of [unsp, oth] organ
Z40.8	Enc for oth prophylactic surgery
Z40.9	Enc for prophylactic surgery, unsp
Z41.3	Enc for ear piercing
Z41.8	Enc for oth proc for purpose oth than remedy health state
Z41.9	Enc for proc for purpose oth than remedy hlth state, unsp
Z43.8	Enc for attention to oth artfcl openings
Z43.9	Enc for attention to unsp artfcl Opng
Z44.2*	Enc for fitting and adjustment of artfcl eye
Z44.3*	Enc for fit/adjst of ext breast prosthesis
Z45.8*	Enc for adjustment and management of implanted devices
Z45.9	Enc for adjust and management of unsp implanted device
Z46.0	Enc for fit/adjst of spectacles and contact lenses
Z46.1	Enc for fitting and adjustment of hearing aid
Z46.3	Enc for fit/adjst of dental prosthetic device
Z46.4	Enc for fitting and adjustment of orthodontic device
Z46.81	Enc for fitting and adjustment of insulin pump
Z46.89	Enc for fitting and adjustment of oth devices
Z46.9	Enc for fitting and adjustment of unsp device
Z48.00	Enc for change or rmvl of nonsurg wnd dressing
Z48.01	Enc for change or rmvl of surgical wnd dressing
Z48.02	Enc for rmvl of sutures
Z51.5	Enc for palliative care
Z52.0*	Bld donor
Z52.3	Bone marrow donor
Z52.5	Cornea donor
Z52.8*	Donor of oth spec organs or tissues
Z52.9	Donor of unsp organ or tissue
Z53*	Persons enc hlth serv for spec proc & tx, not crd out
Z55*	Problems related to education and literacy
Z56*	Problems related to employment and unemployment
Z57*	Occupational exposure to risk factors
Z59*	Problems related to housing and economic circumstances
Z60*	Problems related to social environment
Z62*	Problems related to upbringing
Z63*	Oth prob rel to prim support group, incl* family circumstances
Z64.4	Discord with counselors
Z65*	Problems related to oth psychosocial circumstances
Z66	Do not resuscitate
Z67*	Bld type
Z68.1	Body mass index (BMI) 19 or less, adult
Z68.2*	Body mass index (BMI) 20-29, adult
Z68.3*	Body mass index (BMI) 30-39, adult
Z68.5*	Body mass index (BMI) pediatric
Z69*	Enc for mental health serv for victim and perp of abuse
Z70*	Counseling related to sexual attitude, behav and orientn
Z71*	Persons enc health serv for oth cnsl and med advice, NEC
Z72.0	Tobacco use
Z72.3	Lack of physical exercise
Z72.4	Inappropriate diet and eating habits
Z72.5*	High risk sexual behav
Z72.6	Gambling and betting
Z72.820	Sleep deprivation
Z72.821	Inadequate sleep hygiene
Z72.89	Oth problems related to lifestyle
Z72.9	Problem related to lifestyle, unsp
Z73*	Problems related to life management difficulty
Z74*	Problems related to care provider dependency
Z75*	Problems related to medical facilities and oth health care
Z76*	Persons encountering health services in oth circumstances
Z77*	Oth contact w and (suspected) exposures hazardous to health
Z78*	Oth spec health status
Z79.810	Lng trm (crnt) use of slctv estrog receptor modulators
Z79.811	Long term (current) use of aromatase inhibitors

T Transfer DRG   SP Special Payment   * Code Range   6th and 7th Character of ZZ = No Device, No Qualifier ZX = No Device, Diagnostic

Z79.818	Lng trm (crnt) use of agnt affecting estrog recpt & estrog levels
Z79.890	Hormone replace therapy (postmenopausal)
Z80*	Family history of primary malig neoplasm
Z81*	Family history of mental and behavioral d/o
Z82*	Fam hx of certain disabil & chr dis (leading to disablement)
Z83*	Family history of oth specific d/o
Z84*	Family history of oth conditions
Z86*	Personal history of certain oth dz
Z87.0*	Personal history of dz of the respiratory sys
Z87.1*	Personal history of dz of the digestive sys
Z87.2	Personal history of dz of the skin, SQ
Z87.3*	Personal history of dz of the ms sys and conn tiss
Z87.411	Personal history of vaginal dysplasia
Z87.412	Personal history of vulvar dysplasia
Z87.42	Personal history of oth dz of the female genital tract
Z87.430	Personal history of prostatic dysplasia
Z87.438	Personal history of oth dz of male genital organs
Z87.440	Personal history of urinary (tract) infections
Z87.441	Personal history of nephrotic synd
Z87.442	Personal history of urinary calculi
Z87.448	Personal history of oth dz of urinary sys
Z87.5*	Personal history of comp of preg, chldbrth and the puerp
Z87.7*	Personal history of (corrected) congenital malformations
Z87.81	Personal history of (healed) traum fx
Z87.820	Personal history of traum brain inj
Z87.821	Personal history of retained FB fully removed
Z87.828	Personal history of oth (healed) physical inj and trauma
Z87.891	Personal history of nicotine dependence
Z87.892	Personal history of anaphylaxis
Z87.898	Personal history of oth spec conditions
Z88*	Allergy status to drug/meds/biol subst
Z89*	Acquired absence of limb
Z90.02	Acquired absence of larynx
Z90.09	Acquired absence of oth part of head and neck
Z90.1*	Acquired absence of breast and nipple
Z90.3	Acquired absence of stomach [part of]
Z90.4*	Acquired absence of oth spec parts of digestive tract
Z90.5	Acquired absence of kidney
Z90.8*	Acquired absence of oth organs
Z91*	Personal risk factors, NEC
Z92.0	Personal history of contraception
Z92.3	Personal history of irradiation
Z92.8*	Personal history of oth medical tx
Z93*	Artfcl Opng status
Z94.82	Intestine transplant status
Z94.89	Oth transplanted organ and tissue status
Z94.9	Transplanted organ and tissue status, unsp
Z95.0	Presence of cardiac pacemaker
Z95.1	Presence of aortocoronary bypass graft
Z95.5	Presence of coronary angioplasty implant and graft
Z95.810	Presence of automatic (implantable) cardiac defibrillator
Z95.818	Presence of oth cardiac implants and grafts
Z95.9	Presence of cardiac and vascular implant and graft, unsp
Z96.2*	Presence of otological and audiological implants
Z96.3	Presence of artfcl larynx
Z96.4*	Presence of endocrine implants
Z96.5	Presence of tooth-root and mandibular implants
Z96.8*	Presence of oth spec functional implants
Z96.9	Presence of functional implant, unsp
Z97.2	Presence of dental prosthetic device (complete) (partial)
Z97.3	Presence of spectacles and contact lenses
Z97.4	Presence of ext hearing-aid
Z97.5	Presence of (intrauterine) contraceptive device
Z97.8	Presence of oth spec devices
Z98*	Oth postprocedural states
Z99*	Dependence on enabling machines and devices, NEC

Surgical   **Medical**   **CC Indicator**   **MCC Indicator**   **Procedure Proxy**   **PDxMCC** **PDx acts as own MCC**   **PDxCC** **PDx acts as own CC**

SURGICAL

DRG 955 **Craniotomy for Multiple Significant Trauma**
  GMLOS 8.4   AMLOS 11.9   RW 5.6773

Select the principal diagnosis from the Trauma Diagnosis List located in DRG 963

AND

At least two different diagnoses from two different Significant Trauma Body Site Categories located in DRG 963

AND

Operating Room Procedures

0016[0,3][7,J,K]B	Bypass/Cerebral Ventricle, [Opn, Perc], [Auto Tissue Sub, Synth Sub, Nonauto Tissue Sub], Cerebral Cisterns
0050*	Destr/Brain
0051*	Destr/Cerebral Meninges
0052*	Destr/Dura Mater
0056*	Destr/Cerebral Ventricle
0057*	Destr/Cerebral Hemisphere
0058*	Destr/Basal Ganglia
0059*	Destr/Thalamus
005A*	Destr/Hypothalamus
005B*	Destr/Pons
005C*	Destr/Cerebellum
005D*	Destr/Medulla Oblongata
0080*	Div/Brain
0087*	Div/Cerebral Hemisphere
0088*	Div/Basal Ganglia
0090[0,3,4][0,Z]Z	Drain/Brain, [Opn, Perc, Perc Endo], [Drain Dev, No Dev], NQ
00910[0,Z]Z	Drain/Cerebral Meninges, Opn, [Drain Dev, No Dev], NQ
00920[0,Z]Z	Drain/Dura Mater, Opn, [Drain Dev, No Dev], NQ
0093[0,3,4][0,Z]Z	Drain/Epidural Space, [Opn, Perc, Perc Endo], [Drain Dev, No Dev], NQ
00940[0,Z]Z	Drain/Subdural Space, Opn, [Drain Dev, No Dev], NQ
00950[0,Z]Z	Drain/Subarachnoid Space, Opn, [Drain Dev, No Dev], NQ
00960ZZ	Drain of Cerebral Ventricle, Opn Appr
0096[0,3,4]0Z	Drain/Cerebral Ventricle, [Opn, Perc, Perc Endo], Drain Dev, NQ
0097[0,3,4][0,Z]Z	Drain/Cerebral Hemisphere, [Opn, Perc, Perc Endo], [Drain Dev, No Dev], NQ
0098[0,3,4][0,Z]Z	Drain/Basal Ganglia, [Opn, Perc, Perc Endo], [Drain Dev, No Dev], NQ
0099[0,3,4][0,Z]Z	Drain/Thalamus, [Opn, Perc, Perc Endo], [Drain Dev, No Dev], NQ
009A[0,3,4][0,Z]Z	Drain/Hypothalamus, [Opn, Perc, Perc Endo], [Drain Dev, No Dev], NQ
009B[0,3,4][0,Z]Z	Drain/Pons, [Opn, Perc, Perc Endo], [Drain Dev, No Dev], NQ
009C[0,3,4][0,Z]Z	Drain/Cerebellum, [Opn, Perc, Perc Endo], [Drain Dev, No Dev], NQ
009D[0,3,4][0,Z]Z	Drain/Medulla Oblongata, [Opn, Perc, Perc Endo], [Drain Dev, No Dev], NQ
00B0[0,3,4]ZZ	Exc/Brain, [Opn, Perc, Perc Endo]
00B1[0,3,4]ZZ	Exc/Cerebral Meninges, [Opn, Perc, Perc Endo]
00B2[0,3,4]ZZ	Exc/Dura Mater, [Opn, Perc, Perc Endo]
00B6[0,3,4]ZZ	Exc/Cerebral Ventricle, [Opn, Perc, Perc Endo]
00B7[0,3,4]ZZ	Exc/Cerebral Hemisphere, [Opn, Perc, Perc Endo]
00B8[0,3,4]ZZ	Exc/Basal Ganglia, [Opn, Perc, Perc Endo]
00B9[0,3,4]ZZ	Exc/Thalamus, [Opn, Perc, Perc Endo]
00BA[0,3,4]ZZ	Exc/Hypothalamus, [Opn, Perc, Perc Endo]
00BB[0,3,4]ZZ	Exc/Pons, [Opn, Perc, Perc Endo]
00BC[0,3,4]ZZ	Exc/Cerebellum, [Opn, Perc, Perc Endo]
00BD[0,3,4]ZZ	Exc/Medulla Oblongata, [Opn, Perc, Perc Endo]
00C0*	Extir/Brain
00C1*	Extir/Cerebral Meninges
00C2*	Extir/Dura Mater
00C4*	Extir/Subdural Space
00C5*	Extir/Subarachnoid Space
00C6*	Extir/Cerebral Ventricle
00C7*	Extir/Cerebral Hemisphere
00C8*	Extir/Basal Ganglia
00C9*	Extir/Thalamus
00CA*	Extir/Hypothalamus
00CB*	Extir/Pons
00CC*	Extir/Cerebellum
00CD*	Extir/Medulla Oblongata
00D1*	Extract/Cerebral Meninges
00D2*	Extract/Dura Mater
00F3[0,3,4]ZZ	Fragmn/Epidural Space, [Opn, Perc, Perc Endo]
00F4[0,3,4]ZZ	Fragmn/Subdural Space, [Opn, Perc, Perc Endo]
00F5[0,3,4]ZZ	Fragmn/Subarachnoid Space, [Opn, Perc, Perc Endo]
00F6[0,3,4]ZZ	Fragmn/Cerebral Ventricle, [Opn, Perc, Perc Endo]
00H0[0,3,4][2,3]Z	Insert/Brain, [Opn, Perc, Perc Endo], [Monitoring Dev, Inf Dev], NQ
00H6[0,3,4][2,3]Z	Insert/Cerebral Ventricle, [Opn, Perc, Perc Endo], [Monitoring Dev, Inf Dev], NQ
00J00ZZ	Inspect of Brain, Opn Appr
00N6*	Rls/Cerebral Ventricle
00N8*	Rls/Basal Ganglia
00N9*	Rls/Thalamus
00NA*	Rls/Hypothalamus
00NB*	Rls/Pons
00NC*	Rls/Cerebellum
00ND*	Rls/Medulla Oblongata
00NK*	Rls/Trigeminal Nerve
00P0[0,3,4][0,2,3,7,J,K]Z	Rmvl/Brain, [Opn, Perc, Perc Endo], [Drain Dev, Monitoring Dev, Inf Dev, Auto Tissue Sub, Synth Sub, Nonauto Tissue Sub], NQ
00P6X2Z	Rmvl of Monitor Dev from Cereb Ventricle, Extern Appr
00P6[0,3,4][0,2,3]Z	Rmvl/Cerebral Ventricle, [Opn, Perc, Perc Endo], [Drain Dev, Monitoring Dev, Inf Dev], NQ
00Q0*	Repair/Brain
00Q1*	Repair/Cerebral Meninges
00Q2*	Repair/Dura Mater
00Q6*	Repair/Cerebral Ventricle
00Q7*	Repair/Cerebral Hemisphere
00Q8*	Repair/Basal Ganglia
00Q9*	Repair/Thalamus
00QA*	Repair/Hypothalamus
00QB*	Repair/Pons
00QC*	Repair/Cerebellum
00QD*	Repair/Medulla Oblongata
00T*	Central Nervous Sys, Resect
00U1*	Supl/Cerebral Meninges
00U2*	Supl/Dura Mater
00W00[0,2,3,7,M]Z	Rev/Brain, Opn, [Drain Dev, Monitoring Dev, Inf Dev, Auto Tissue Sub, Neurostimulator Lead], NQ
00W0[3,4][0,2,3,7,J,K,M]Z	Rev/Brain, [Perc, Perc Endo], [Drain Dev, Monitoring Dev, Inf Dev, Auto Tissue Sub, Synth Sub, Nonauto Tissue Sub, Neurostimulator Lead], NQ
00W6[0,3,4][0,2,3,M]Z	Rev/Cerebral Ventricle, [Opn, Perc, Perc Endo], [Drain Dev, Monitoring Dev, Inf Dev, Neurostimulator Lead], NQ
03LG[0,3,4][C,Z]Z	Occlsn/Intracranial Artery, [Opn, Perc, Perc Endo], [Extralum Dev, No Dev], NQ
05LL*	Occlsn/Intracranial Vein
0N50*	Destr/Skull
0N51*	Destr/Frontal Bone, Rt
0N52*	Destr/Frontal Bone, Lt
0N53*	Destr/Parietal Bone, Rt
0N54*	Destr/Parietal Bone, Lt
0N55*	Destr/Temporal Bone, Rt
0N56*	Destr/Temporal Bone, Lt
0N57*	Destr/Occipital Bone, Rt
0N58*	Destr/Occipital Bone, Lt
0N90[0,3,4][0,Z]Z	Drain/Skull, [Opn, Perc, Perc Endo], [Drain Dev, No Dev], NQ
0N91[0,3,4][0,Z]Z	Drain/Frontal Bone, Rt, [Opn, Perc, Perc Endo], [Drain Dev, No Dev], NQ
0N92[0,3,4][0,Z]Z	Drain/Frontal Bone, Lt, [Opn, Perc, Perc Endo], [Drain Dev, No Dev], NQ
0N93[0,3,4][0,Z]Z	Drain/Parietal Bone, Rt, [Opn, Perc, Perc Endo], [Drain Dev, No Dev], NQ
0N94[0,3,4][0,Z]Z	Drain/Parietal Bone, Lt, [Opn, Perc, Perc Endo], [Drain Dev, No Dev], NQ
0N95[0,3,4][0,Z]Z	Drain/Temporal Bone, Rt, [Opn, Perc, Perc Endo], [Drain Dev, No Dev], NQ
0N96[0,3,4][0,Z]Z	Drain/Temporal Bone, Lt, [Opn, Perc, Perc Endo], [Drain Dev, No Dev], NQ

Ⓣ Transfer DRG   ⓢ Special Payment   * Code Range   6th and 7th Character of ZZ = No Device, No Qualifier ZX = No Device, Diagnostic

0N97[0,3,4][0,Z]Z	Drain/Occipital Bone, Rt, [Opn, Perc, Perc Endo], [Drain Dev, No Dev], NQ
0N98[0,3,4][0,Z]Z	Drain/Occipital Bone, Lt, [Opn, Perc, Perc Endo], [Drain Dev, No Dev], NQ
0NB0[0,3,4]ZZ	Exc/Skull, [Opn, Perc, Perc Endo]
0NB1[0,3,4]ZZ	Exc/Frontal Bone, Rt, [Opn, Perc, Perc Endo]
0NB2[0,3,4]ZZ	Exc/Frontal Bone, Lt, [Opn, Perc, Perc Endo]
0NB3[0,3,4]ZZ	Exc/Parietal Bone, Rt, [Opn, Perc, Perc Endo]
0NB4[0,3,4]ZZ	Exc/Parietal Bone, Lt, [Opn, Perc, Perc Endo]
0NB5[0,3,4]ZZ	Exc/Temporal Bone, Rt, [Opn, Perc, Perc Endo]
0NB6[0,3,4]ZZ	Exc/Temporal Bone, Lt, [Opn, Perc, Perc Endo]
0NB7[0,3,4]ZZ	Exc/Occipital Bone, Rt, [Opn, Perc, Perc Endo]
0NB8[0,3,4]ZZ	Exc/Occipital Bone, Lt, [Opn, Perc, Perc Endo]
0NC1*	Extir/Frontal Bone, Rt
0NC2*	Extir/Frontal Bone, Lt
0NC3*	Extir/Parietal Bone, Rt
0NC4*	Extir/Parietal Bone, Lt
0NC5*	Extir/Temporal Bone, Rt
0NC6*	Extir/Temporal Bone, Lt
0NC7*	Extir/Occipital Bone, Rt
0NC8*	Extir/Occipital Bone, Lt
0NH0[0,3,4]4Z	Insert/Skull, [Opn, Perc, Perc Endo], Int Fix Dev, NQ
0NH1*	Insert/Frontal Bone, Rt
0NH2*	Insert/Frontal Bone, Lt
0NH3*	Insert/Parietal Bone, Rt
0NH4*	Insert/Parietal Bone, Lt
0NH5[0,3,4]4Z	Insert/Temporal Bone, Rt, [Opn, Perc, Perc Endo], Int Fix Dev, NQ
0NH6[0,3,4]4Z	Insert/Temporal Bone, Lt, [Opn, Perc, Perc Endo], Int Fix Dev, NQ
0NH7*	Insert/Occipital Bone, Rt
0NH8*	Insert/Occipital Bone, Lt
0NN1*	Rls/Frontal Bone, Rt
0NN2*	Rls/Frontal Bone, Lt
0NN3*	Rls/Parietal Bone, Rt
0NN4*	Rls/Parietal Bone, Lt
0NN5*	Rls/Temporal Bone, Rt
0NN6*	Rls/Temporal Bone, Lt
0NN7*	Rls/Occipital Bone, Rt
0NN8*	Rls/Occipital Bone, Lt
0NQ0*	Repair/Skull
0NQ1*	Repair/Frontal Bone, Rt
0NQ2*	Repair/Frontal Bone, Lt
0NQ3*	Repair/Parietal Bone, Rt
0NQ4*	Repair/Parietal Bone, Lt
0NQ5*	Repair/Temporal Bone, Rt
0NQ6*	Repair/Temporal Bone, Lt
0NQ7*	Repair/Occipital Bone, Rt
0NQ8*	Repair/Occipital Bone, Lt
0NR0*	Replace/Skull
0NR1[0,3,4]JZ	Replace/Frontal Bone, Rt, [Opn, Perc, Perc Endo], Synth Sub, NQ
0NR2[0,3,4]JZ	Replace/Frontal Bone, Lt, [Opn, Perc, Perc Endo], Synth Sub, NQ
0NR3[0,3,4]JZ	Replace/Parietal Bone, Rt, [Opn, Perc, Perc Endo], Synth Sub, NQ
0NR4[0,3,4]JZ	Replace/Parietal Bone, Lt, [Opn, Perc, Perc Endo], Synth Sub, NQ
0NR5[0,3,4]JZ	Replace/Temporal Bone, Rt, [Opn, Perc, Perc Endo], Synth Sub, NQ
0NR6[0,3,4]JZ	Replace/Temporal Bone, Lt, [Opn, Perc, Perc Endo], Synth Sub, NQ
0NR7[0,3,4]JZ	Replace/Occipital Bone, Rt, [Opn, Perc, Perc Endo], Synth Sub, NQ
0NR8[0,3,4]JZ	Replace/Occipital Bone, Lt, [Opn, Perc, Perc Endo], Synth Sub, NQ
0NS0*	Repos/Skull
0NS1*	Repos/Frontal Bone, Rt
0NS2*	Repos/Frontal Bone, Lt
0NS3*	Repos/Parietal Bone, Rt
0NS4*	Repos/Parietal Bone, Lt
0NS5*	Repos/Temporal Bone, Rt
0NS6*	Repos/Temporal Bone, Lt
0NS7*	Repos/Occipital Bone, Rt
0NS8*	Repos/Occipital Bone, Lt
0NT10ZZ	Resect of Rt Frontal Bone, Opn Appr
0NT20ZZ	Resect of Lt Frontal Bone, Opn Appr
0NT30ZZ	Resect of Rt Parietal Bone, Opn Appr
0NT40ZZ	Resect of Lt Parietal Bone, Opn Appr
0NT50ZZ	Resect of Rt Temporal Bone, Opn Appr

0NT60ZZ	Resect of Lt Temporal Bone, Opn Appr
0NT70ZZ	Resect of Rt Occipital Bone, Opn Appr
0NT80ZZ	Resect of Lt Occipital Bone, Opn Appr
0NU0[0,3,4]JZ	Supl/Skull, [Opn, Perc, Perc Endo], Synth Sub, NQ
0NU1[0,3,4]JZ	Supl/Frontal Bone, Rt, [Opn, Perc, Perc Endo], Synth Sub, NQ
0NU2[0,3,4]JZ	Supl/Frontal Bone, Lt, [Opn, Perc, Perc Endo], Synth Sub, NQ
0NU3[0,3,4]JZ	Supl/Parietal Bone, Rt, [Opn, Perc, Perc Endo], Synth Sub, NQ
0NU4[0,3,4]JZ	Supl/Parietal Bone, Lt, [Opn, Perc, Perc Endo], Synth Sub, NQ
0NU5[0,3,4]JZ	Supl/Temporal Bone, Rt, [Opn, Perc, Perc Endo], Synth Sub, NQ
0NU6[0,3,4]JZ	Supl/Temporal Bone, Lt, [Opn, Perc, Perc Endo], Synth Sub, NQ
0NU7[0,3,4]JZ	Supl/Occipital Bone, Rt, [Opn, Perc, Perc Endo], Synth Sub, NQ
0NU8[0,3,4]JZ	Supl/Occipital Bone, Lt, [Opn, Perc, Perc Endo], Synth Sub, NQ
0W910[0,Z]Z	Drain/Cranial Cavity, Opn, [Drain Dev, No Dev], NQ
0WC1[0,3,4]ZZ	Extir/Cranial Cavity, [Opn, Perc, Perc Endo]
0WF1[0,3,4]ZZ	Fragmn/Cranial Cavity, [Opn, Perc, Perc Endo]
0WJ10ZZ	Inspect of Cranial Cavity, Opn Appr

OR

Select a principal diagnosis from one Significant Trauma Body Site Category located in DRG 963

AND

Two or more significant trauma diagnoses from different Significant Trauma Body Site Categories located in DRG 963

AND

Any operating room procedure listed above

DRG 956 **Limb Reattachment, Hip and Femur Procedures for Multiple Significant Trauma**

GMLOS 6.4	AMLOS 7.8	RW 3.7116	T

Select principal diagnosis from Trauma Diagnosis List located in DRG 963

AND

At least two different diagnoses from two different Significant Trauma Body Site Categories located in DRG 963

AND

Operating Room Procedures

0L8J*	Div/Hip Tndn, Rt
0L8K*	Div/Hip Tndn, Lt
0Q86*	Div/Upr Femur, Rt
0Q87*	Div/Upr Femur, Lt
0Q88*	Div/Femor Shaft, Rt
0Q89*	Div/Femor Shaft, Lt
0Q8B*	Div/Lwr Femur, Rt
0Q8C*	Div/Lwr Femur, Lt
0QC6*	Extir/Upr Femur, Rt
0QC7*	Extir/Upr Femur, Lt
0QC8*	Extir/Femor Shaft, Rt
0QC9*	Extir/Femor Shaft, Lt
0QCB*	Extir/Lwr Femur, Rt
0QCC*	Extir/Lwr Femur, Lt
0QH6[0,3,4][4,5,6,B,C,D]Z	Insert/Upr Femur, Rt, [Opn, Perc, Perc Endo], [Int Fix Dev, Ext Fix Dev, Int Fix Dev, Intramedullary Int Fix Dev, Ext Fix Dev, Monop, Ext Fix Dev, Ring, Ext Fix Dev, Hybrid], NQ
0QH7[0,3,4][4,5,6,B,C,D]Z	Insert/Upr Femur, Lt, [Opn, Perc, Perc Endo], [Int Fix Dev, Ext Fix Dev, Int Fix Dev, Intramedullary Int Fix Dev, Ext Fix Dev, Monop, Ext Fix Dev, Ring, Ext Fix Dev, Hybrid], NQ
0QH8[0,3,4][4,5,6,B,C,D]Z	Insert/Femor Shaft, Rt, [Opn, Perc, Perc Endo], [Int Fix Dev, Ext Fix Dev, Int Fix Dev, Intramedullary Int Fix Dev, Ext Fix Dev, Monop, Ext Fix Dev, Ring, Ext Fix Dev, Hybrid], NQ
0QH9[0,3,4][4,5,6,B,C,D]Z	Insert/Femor Shaft, Lt, [Opn, Perc, Perc Endo], [Int Fix Dev, Ext Fix Dev, Int Fix Dev, Intramedullary Int Fix Dev, Ext Fix Dev, Monop, Ext Fix Dev, Ring, Ext Fix Dev, Hybrid], NQ
0QHB[0,3,4][4,5,6,B,C,D]Z	Insert/Lwr Femur, Rt, [Opn, Perc, Perc Endo], [Int Fix Dev, Ext Fix Dev, Int Fix Dev, Intramedullary Int Fix Dev, Ext Fix Dev, Monop, Ext Fix Dev, Ring, Ext Fix Dev, Hybrid], NQ
0QHC[0,3,4][4,5,6,B,C,D]Z	Insert/Lwr Femur, Lt, [Opn, Perc, Perc Endo], [Int Fix Dev, Ext Fix Dev, Int Fix Dev, Intramedullary Int Fix Dev, Ext Fix Dev, Monop, Ext Fix Dev, Ring, Ext Fix Dev, Hybrid], NQ
0QN6*	Rls/Upr Femur, Rt
0QN7*	Rls/Upr Femur, Lt
0QN8*	Rls/Femor Shaft, Rt
0QN9*	Rls/Femor Shaft, Lt
0QNB*	Rls/Lwr Femur, Rt
0QNC*	Rls/Lwr Femur, Lt
0QQ6*	Repair/Upr Femur, Rt
0QQ7*	Repair/Upr Femur, Lt

Surgical **Medical** **CC Indicator** **MCC Indicator** **Procedure Proxy** **PDx MCC** PDx acts as own MCC **PDx CC** PDx acts as own CC

© 2015 Optum360, LLC | MS-DRG Version 33.0 | 415

MDC 24: Multiple Significant Trauma—SURGICAL

MDC 24: Multiple Significant Trauma—SURGICAL

0QQ8*	Repair/Femor Shaft, Rt
0QQ9*	Repair/Femor Shaft, Lt
0QQB*	Repair/Lwr Femur, Rt
0QQC*	Repair/Lwr Femur, Lt
0QR6*	Replace/Upr Femur, Rt
0QR7*	Replace/Upr Femur, Lt
0QR8*	Replace/Femor Shaft, Rt
0QR9*	Replace/Femor Shaft, Lt
0QRB*	Replace/Lwr Femur, Rt
0QRC*	Replace/Lwr Femur, Lt
0QS60ZZ	Repos Rt Upr Femur, Opn Appr
0QS6[0,3,4][4,5,6,B,C,D]Z	Repos/Upr Femur, Rt, [Opn, Perc, Perc Endo], [Int Fix Dev, Ext Fix Dev, Int Fix Dev, Intramedullary Int Fix Dev, Ext Fix Dev, Monop, Ext Fix Dev, Ring, Ext Fix Dev, Hybrid], NQ
0QS70ZZ	Repos Lt Upr Femur, Opn Appr
0QS7[0,3,4][4,5,6,B,C,D]Z	Repos/Upr Femur, Lt, [Opn, Perc, Perc Endo], [Int Fix Dev, Ext Fix Dev, Int Fix Dev, Intramedullary Int Fix Dev, Ext Fix Dev, Monop, Ext Fix Dev, Ring, Ext Fix Dev, Hybrid], NQ
0QS80ZZ	Repos Rt Femor Shaft, Opn Appr
0QS8[0,3,4][4,5,6,B,C,D]Z	Repos/Femor Shaft, Rt, [Opn, Perc, Perc Endo], [Int Fix Dev, Ext Fix Dev, Int Fix Dev, Intramedullary Int Fix Dev, Ext Fix Dev, Monop, Ext Fix Dev, Ring, Ext Fix Dev, Hybrid], NQ
0QS90ZZ	Repos Lt Femor Shaft, Opn Appr
0QS9[0,3,4][4,5,6,B,C,D]Z	Repos/Femor Shaft, Lt, [Opn, Perc, Perc Endo], [Int Fix Dev, Ext Fix Dev, Int Fix Dev, Intramedullary Int Fix Dev, Ext Fix Dev, Monop, Ext Fix Dev, Ring, Ext Fix Dev, Hybrid], NQ
0QSB0ZZ	Repos Rt Lwr Femur, Opn Appr
0QSB[0,3,4][4,5,6,B,C,D]Z	Repos/Lwr Femur, Rt, [Opn, Perc, Perc Endo], [Int Fix Dev, Ext Fix Dev, Int Fix Dev, Intramedullary Int Fix Dev, Ext Fix Dev, Monop, Ext Fix Dev, Ring, Ext Fix Dev, Hybrid], NQ
0QSC0ZZ	Repos Lt Lwr Femur, Opn Appr
0QSC[0,3,4][4,5,6,B,C,D]Z	Repos/Lwr Femur, Lt, [Opn, Perc, Perc Endo], [Int Fix Dev, Ext Fix Dev, Int Fix Dev, Intramedullary Int Fix Dev, Ext Fix Dev, Monop, Ext Fix Dev, Ring, Ext Fix Dev, Hybrid], NQ
0QT60ZZ	Resect of Rt Upr Femur, Opn Appr
0QT70ZZ	Resect of Lt Upr Femur, Opn Appr
0QT80ZZ	Resect of Rt Femor Shaft, Opn Appr
0QT90ZZ	Resect of Lt Femor Shaft, Opn Appr
0QTB0ZZ	Resect of Rt Lwr Femur, Opn Appr
0QTC0ZZ	Resect of Lt Lwr Femur, Opn Appr
0QU6*	Supl/Upr Femur, Rt
0QU7*	Supl/Upr Femur, Lt
0QU8*	Supl/Femor Shaft, Rt
0QU9*	Supl/Femor Shaft, Lt
0QUB*	Supl/Lwr Femur, Rt
0QUC*	Supl/Lwr Femur, Lt
0SB9[0,3,4]ZZ	Exc/Hip Jt, Rt, [Opn, Perc, Perc Endo]
0SBB[0,3,4]ZZ	Exc/Hip Jt, Lt, [Opn, Perc, Perc Endo]
0SG9*	Fusion/Hip Jt, Rt
0SGB*	Fusion/Hip Jt, Lt
0SN9[0,3,4]ZZ	Rls/Hip Jt, Rt, [Opn, Perc, Perc Endo]
0SNB[0,3,4]ZZ	Rls/Hip Jt, Lt, [Opn, Perc, Perc Endo]
0SP909Z	Rmvl of Liner from Rt Hip Jt, Opn Appr
0SP9[0,3,4]JZ	Rmvl/Hip Jt, Rt, [Opn, Perc, Perc Endo], Synth Sub, NQ
0SPB09Z	Rmvl of Liner from Lt Hip Jt, Opn Appr
0SPB[0,3,4]JZ	Rmvl/Hip Jt, Lt, [Opn, Perc, Perc Endo], Synth Sub, NQ
0SQ9*	Repair/Hip Jt, Rt
0SQB*	Repair/Hip Jt, Lt
0SR9*	Replace/Hip Jt, Rt
0SRA*	Replace/Hip Jt, Acetabular Surface, Rt
0SRB*	Replace/Hip Jt, Lt
0SRE*	Replace/Hip Jt, Acetabular Surface, Lt
0SRR*	Replace/Hip Jt, Femor Surface, Rt
0SRS*	Replace/Hip Jt, Femor Surface, Lt
0SS90[4,5,Z]Z	Repos/Hip Jt, Rt, Opn, [Int Fix Dev, Ext Fix Dev, No Dev], NQ
0SSB0[4,5,Z]Z	Repos/Hip Jt, Lt, Opn, [Int Fix Dev, Ext Fix Dev, No Dev], NQ
0ST90ZZ	Resect of Rt Hip Jt, Opn Appr
0STB0ZZ	Resect of Lt Hip Jt, Opn Appr
0SU90BZ	Supl Rt Hip Jt with Resurf Dev, Opn Appr
0SUA0BZ	Supl Rt Hip Jt, Acetab with Resurf Dev, Opn Appr
0SUB0BZ	Supl Lt Hip Jt with Resurf Dev, Opn Appr
0SUE0BZ	Supl Lt Hip Jt, Acetab with Resurf Dev, Opn Appr
0SUR0BZ	Supl Rt Hip Jt, Femor with Resurf Dev, Opn Appr
0SUS0BZ	Supl Lt Hip Jt, Femor with Resurf Dev, Opn Appr
0SW9[0,3,4]JZ	Rev/Hip Jt, Rt, [Opn, Perc, Perc Endo], Synth Sub, NQ
0SWB[0,3,4]JZ	Rev/Hip Jt, Lt, [Opn, Perc, Perc Endo], Synth Sub, NQ
0XM00ZZ	Reattach of Rt Forequarter, Opn Appr
0XM10ZZ	Reattach of Lt Forequarter, Opn Appr
0XM20ZZ	Reattach of Rt Shldr Region, Opn Appr
0XM30ZZ	Reattach of Lt Shldr Region, Opn Appr

0XM40ZZ	Reattach of Rt Axilla, Opn Appr
0XM50ZZ	Reattach of Lt Axilla, Opn Appr
0XM60ZZ	Reattach of Rt Upr Extr, Opn Appr
0XM70ZZ	Reattach of Lt Upr Extr, Opn Appr
0XM80ZZ	Reattach of Rt Upr Arm, Opn Appr
0XM90ZZ	Reattach of Lt Upr Arm, Opn Appr
0XMB0ZZ	Reattach of Rt Elbow Region, Opn Appr
0XMC0ZZ	Reattach of Lt Elbow Region, Opn Appr
0XMD0ZZ	Reattach of Rt Lwr Arm, Opn Appr
0XMF0ZZ	Reattach of Lt Lwr Arm, Opn Appr
0XMG0ZZ	Reattach of Rt Wrist Region, Opn Appr
0XMH0ZZ	Reattach of Lt Wrist Region, Opn Appr
0XMJ0ZZ	Reattach of Rt Hand, Opn Appr
0XMK0ZZ	Reattach of Lt Hand, Opn Appr
0YM70ZZ	Reattach of Rt Femor Region, Opn Appr
0YM80ZZ	Reattach of Lt Femor Region, Opn Appr
0YMC0ZZ	Reattach of Rt Upr Leg, Opn Appr
0YMD0ZZ	Reattach of Lt Upr Leg, Opn Appr
0YMF0ZZ	Reattach of Rt Knee Region, Opn Appr
0YMG0ZZ	Reattach of Lt Knee Region, Opn Appr
0YMH0ZZ	Reattach of Rt Lwr Leg, Opn Appr
0YMJ0ZZ	Reattach of Lt Lwr Leg, Opn Appr
0YMK0ZZ	Reattach of Rt Ankle Region, Opn Appr
0YML0ZZ	Reattach of Lt Ankle Region, Opn Appr
0YMM0ZZ	Reattach of Rt Foot, Opn Appr
0YMN0ZZ	Reattach of Lt Foot, Opn Appr

OR

Select a principal diagnosis from one Significant Trauma Body Site Category located in DRG 963

AND

Two or more significant trauma diagnoses from different Significant Trauma Body Site Categories located in DRG 963

AND

Any operating room procedure listed above

DRG 957 **Other O.R. Procedures for Multiple Significant Trauma with MCC**

GMLOS 9.4   **AMLOS 13.3**   **RW 6.5504**

Select principal diagnosis from Trauma Diagnosis List located in DRG 963

AND

At least two different diagnoses from two different Significant Trauma Body Site Categories located in DRG 963

AND

Any operating procedure from MDC 21

EXCLUDING

Pacemaker leads and devices and any procedure listed under DRGs 955 and 956

OR

Select a principal diagnosis from one Significant Trauma Body Site Category located in DRG 963

AND

Two or more significant trauma diagnoses from different Significant Trauma Body Site Categories located in DRG 963

AND

Any operating room procedure listed from MDC 21

EXCLUDING

Pacemaker leads and devices and any procedure listed under DRGs 955 and 956

T Transfer DRG   SP Special Payment   * Code Range   6th and 7th Character of ZZ = No Device, No Qualifier ZX = No Device, Diagnostic

DRG 958 Other O.R. Procedures for Multiple Significant Trauma with CC
GMLOS 6.9 **AMLOS 8.4** **RW 3.8565**

Select principal diagnosis from Trauma Diagnosis List located in DRG 963
AND

At least two different diagnoses from two different Significant Trauma Body Site Categories located in DRG 963
AND

Any operating room procedure from MDC 21

EXCLUDING

Pacemaker leads and devices and any procedure listed under DRGs 955 and 956
OR

Select a principal diagnosis from one Significant Trauma Body Site Category located in DRG 963
AND

Two or more significant trauma diagnoses from different Significant Trauma Body Site Categories located in DRG 963
AND

Any operating room procedure from MDC 21

EXCLUDING

Pacemaker leads and devices and any procedure listed under DRGs 955 and 956

DRG 959 Other O.R. Procedures for Multiple Significant Trauma without CC/MCC
GMLOS 4.2 **AMLOS 4.8** **RW 2.1705**

Select principal diagnosis from Trauma Diagnosis List located in DRG 963
AND

At least two different diagnoses from two different Significant Trauma Body Site Categories located in DRG 963
AND

Any operating room procedure from MDC 21

EXCLUDING

Pacemaker leads and devices and any procedure listed under DRGs 955 and 956
OR

Select a principal diagnosis from one Significant Trauma Body Site Category located in DRG 963
AND

Two or more significant trauma diagnoses from different Significant Trauma Body Site Categories located in DRG 963
AND

Any operating room procedure from MDC 21

EXCLUDING

Pacemaker leads and devices and any procedure listed under DRGs 955 and 956

MEDICAL

DRG 963 Other Multiple Significant Trauma with MCC
GMLOS 5.4 **AMLOS 8.0** **RW 2.6295**

Select principal diagnosis from the Trauma Diagnosis List located below
AND

At least two different diagnoses from two different Significant Trauma Body Site Categories located below
OR

Select a principal diagnosis from one Significant Trauma Body Site Category located below
AND

Two or more significant trauma diagnoses from different Significant Trauma Body Site Categories located below

Trauma Diagnosis

M99.1[0,1,2,3,4,5,6,7,8,9] Sublux complex (vert) of [head rgn, cervical rgn, thoracic rgn, lumbar rgn, sacral rgn, pelvic rgn, lwr extr, upr extr, rib cage, abdial and oth rgns]

S00.0[0,1,2,3,4,5,6,7]XA [Unsp superf inj, Abrasion, Blister (nonthermal), Contsn, Ext constriction, Superf FB, Insect bite (nonvenomous), Oth superf bite] of scalp, init enc

S00.1[0,1,2]XA Contsn of [unsp, rt, lt] eyelid and periocular area, init enc

S00.2[0,1,2,4,5,6,7][1,2,9]A [Unsp superf inj, Abrasion, Blister (nonthermal), Ext constriction, Superf FB, Insect bite (nonvenomous), Oth superf bite] of [rt, lt, unsp] eyelid and periocular area, init enc

S00.3[0,1,2,3,4,5,6,7]XA [Unsp superf inj, Abrasion, Blister (nonthermal), Contsn, Ext constriction, Superf FB, Insect bite (nonvenomous), Oth superf bite] of nose, init enc

S00.4[0,1,2,3,4,5,6,7][1,2,9]A [Unsp superf inj, Abrasion, Blister (nonthermal), Contsn, Ext constriction, Superf FB, Insect bite (nonvenomous), Oth superf bite] of [rt, lt, unsp] ear, init enc

S00.5[0,1,2,3,4,5,6,7][1,2]A [Unsp superf inj, Abrasion, Blister (nonthermal), Contsn, Ext constriction, Superf FB, Insect bite (nonvenomous), Oth superf bite] of [lip, oral cavity], init enc

S00.8[0,1,2,3,4,5,6,7]XA [Unsp superf inj, Abrasion, Blister (nonthermal), Contsn, Ext constriction, Superf FB, Insect bite (nonvenomous, Oth superf bite] of oth part of head, init enc

S00.9[0,1,2,3,4,5,6,7]XA [Unsp superf inj, Abrasion, Blister (nonthermal), Contsn, Ext constriction, Superf FB, Insect bite (nonvenomous), Oth superf bite] of unsp part of head, init enc

S01.0[0,1,2,3,4,5]XA [Unsp opn wnd, Lac w/o FB, Lac w/ FB, Punc wnd w/o FB, Punc wnd w/ FB, Opn bite] of scalp, init enc

S01.1[0,1,2,3,4,5][1,2,9]A [Unsp opn wnd, Lac w/o FB, Lac w/ FB, Punc wnd w/o FB, Punc wnd w/ FB, Opn bite] of [rt, lt, unsp] eyelid and periocular area, init enc

S01.2[0,1,2,3,4,5]XA [Unsp opn wnd, Lac w/o FB, Lac w/ FB, Punc wnd w/o FB, Punc wnd w/ FB, Opn bite] of nose, init enc

S01.3[0,1,2,3,4,5][1,2,9]A [Unsp opn wnd, Lac w/o FB, Lac w/ FB, Punc wnd w/o FB, Punc wnd w/ FB, Opn bite] of [rt, lt, unsp] ear, init enc

S01.4[0,1,2,3,4,5][1,2,9]A [Unsp opn wnd, Lac w/o FB, Lac w/ FB, Punc wnd w/o FB, Punc wnd w/ FB, Opn bite] of [rt, lt, unsp] cheek and temporomandibular area, init enc

S01.5[0,1,2,3,4,5][1,2]A [Unsp opn wnd, Lac w/o FB, Lac w/ FB, Punc wnd w/o FB, Punc wnd w/ FB, Opn bite] of [lip, oral cavity], init enc

S01.8[0,1,2,3,4,5]XA [Unsp opn wnd, Lac w/o FB, Lac w/ FB, Punc wnd w/o FB, Punc wnd w/ FB, Opn bite] of oth part of head, init enc

S01.9[0,1,2,3,4,5]XA [Unsp opn wnd, Lac w/o FB, Lac w/ FB, Punc wnd w/o FB, Punc wnd w/ FB, Opn bite] of unsp part of head, init enc

S02.0XX[A,B] Fx of vault of skull, init enc for [clsd, opn] fx

S02.10X[A,B] Unsp fx of base of skull, init enc for [clsd, opn] fx

S02.11[0,1,2,3][A,B] [Type I, Type II, Type III, Unsp] occipital condyle fx, init enc for [clsd, opn] fx

S02.11[8,9][A,B] [Oth, Unsp] fx of occiput, init enc for [clsd, opn] fx

S02.19X[A,B] Oth fx of base of skull, init enc for [clsd, opn] fx

S02.2XX[A,B] Fx of nasal bones, init enc for [clsd, opn] fx

S02.3XX[A,B] Fx of orbital floor, init enc for [clsd, opn] fx

S02.40[0,1,2][A,B] [Malar, Maxillary, Zygomatic] fx, unsp, init enc for [clsd, opn] fx

S02.41[1,2,3][A,B] [LeFort I fx, LeFort II fx, LeFort III fx], init enc for [clsd, opn] fx

S02.42X[A,B] Fx of alveolus of maxilla, init enc for [clsd, opn] fx

S02.5XX[A,B] Fx of tooth (traum), init enc for [clsd, opn] fx

S02.600[A,B] Fx of unsp part of body of mandible, init enc for [clsd, opn] fx

S02.609[A,B] Fx of mandible, unsp, init enc for [clsd, opn] fx

S02.6[1,2,3]X[A,B] Fx of [condylar, subcondylar, coronoid] process of mandible, init enc for [clsd, opn] fx

S02.6[4,5,6,7,9]X[A,B] Fx of [ramus, angle, symphysis, alveolus, oth spec site] of mandible, init enc for [clsd, opn] fx

S02.8XX[A,B] Fxs of oth spec skull and facial bones, init enc for [clsd, opn] fx

S02.91X[A,B] Unsp fx of skull, init enc for [clsd, opn] fx

S02.92X[A,B] Unsp fx of facial bones, init enc for [clsd, opn] fx

S03.4XXA Sprain of jaw, init enc

S03.[0,1,2]XXA Disloc of [jaw, septal cartilage of nose, tooth], init enc

S03.[8,9]XXA Sprain of jts and lgmts of [oth, unsp] parts of head, init enc

S04.01[1,2,9]A Inj of optic nerve, [rt, lt, unsp] eye, init enc

S04.02XA Inj of optic chiasm, init enc

S04.0[3,4][1,2,9]A Inj of [optic tract and pathways, visual cortex], [rt, lt, unsp] eye, init enc

S04.8[1,9][1,2,9]A Inj of [olfactory (1st), oth cranial] nerve(s), [rt, lt, unsp] side, init enc

S04.9XXA Inj of unsp cranial nerve, init enc

S04.[1,2,3,4,5,6,7][0,1,2]XA Inj of [oculomotor, trochlear, trigeminal, abducent, facial, acoustic, accessory] nerve, [unsp, rt, lt] side, init enc

| Surgical | Medical | CC Indicator | MCC Indicator | Procedure Proxy | PDxMCC PDx acts as own MCC | PDxCC PDx acts as own CC |

S05.0[0,1,2]XA	Inj of conjunctiva and corneal abrasion w/o FB, [unsp, rt, lt] eye, init enc
S05.1[0,1,2]XA	Contsn of eyeball and orbital tissues, [unsp, rt, lt] eye, init enc
S05.2[0,1,2]XA	Ocular lac and rupture w/ prolapse or loss of intraocular tissue, [unsp, rt, lt] eye, init enc
S05.3[0,1,2]XA	Ocular lac w/o prolapse or loss of intraocular tissue, [unsp, rt, lt] eye, init enc
S05.4[0,1,2]XA	Penetrating wnd of orbit w/ or w/o FB, [unsp, rt, lt] eye, init enc
S05.5[0,1,2]XA	Penetrating wnd w/ FB of [unsp, rt, lt] eyeball, init enc
S05.6[0,1,2]XA	Penetrating wnd w/o FB of [unsp, rt, lt] eyeball, init enc
S05.7[0,1,2]XA	Avulsion of [unsp, rt, lt] eye, init enc
S05.8X[1,2,9]A	Oth injuries of [rt, lt, unsp] eye and orbit, init enc
S05.9[0,1,2]XA	Unsp inj of [unsp, rt, lt] eye and orbit, init enc
S06.0X0A	Concussion w/o LOC, init enc
S06.0X[1,2,3,4]A	Concussion w/ LOC of [30 min or less, 31 min to 59 min, 1 hr to 5 hrs 59 min, 6 hrs to 24 hrs], init enc
S06.0X[5,6]A	Concussion w/ LOC > 24 hrs [w/, w/o] return to pre-existing conscious lvl, init enc
S06.0X[7,8,9]A	Concussion w/ LOC of [any dur w/ death d/t brain inj prior to regain cnscness, any dur w/ death d/t oth cause prior to regain cnscness, unsp dur], init enc
S06.1X0A	Traum cerebral edema w/o LOC, init **PDxMCC**
S06.1X[1,2,3,4]A	Traum cerebral edema w/ LOC of [30 min or less, 31min to 59 min, 1 hr to 5 hrs 59 min, 6 hrs to 24 hrs], init enc
S06.1X[5,6]A	Traum cerebral edema w/ LOC > 24 hrs [w/ return to pre-existing conscious lvl, w/o return to pre-existing conscious lvl w/ patient surviving], init enc
S06.1X[7,8,9]A	Traum cerebral edema w/ LOC of [any dur w/ death d/t brain inj prior to regain cnscness, any dur w/ death d/t oth cause prior to regain cnscness, unsp dur], init enc
S06.2X0A	Diffuse TBI w/o LOC, init
S06.2X[1,2,3,4]A	Diffuse traum brain inj w/ LOC of [30 min or less, 31 min to 59 min, 1 hr to 5 hrs 59 min, 6 hrs to 24 hrs], init enc
S06.2X[5,6]A	Diffuse traum brain inj w/ LOC > 24 hrs [w/ return to pre-existing conscious lvl, w/o return to pre-existing conscious lvl w/ patient surviving], init enc
S06.2X[7,8,9]A	Diffuse traum brain inj w/ LOC of [any dur w/ death d/t brain inj prior to regain cnscness, any dur w/ death d/t oth cause prior to regain cnscness, unsp dur], init enc
S06.300A	Unsp focal TBI w/o LOC, init
S06.30[1,2,3,4]A	Unsp focal traum brain inj w/ LOC of [30 min or less, 31 min to 59 min, 1 hr to 5 hrs 59 min, 6 hrs to 24 hrs], init enc
S06.30[5,6]A	Unsp focal traum brain inj w/ LOC > 24 hrs [w/ return to pre-existing conscious lvl, w/o return to pre-existing conscious lvl w/ patient surviving], init enc
S06.30[7,8,9]A	Unsp focal traum brain inj w/ LOC of [any dur w/ death d/t brain inj prior to regain cnscness, any dur w/ death d/t oth cause prior to regain cnscness, unsp dur], init enc
S06.310A	Contus/lac rt cerebrum w/o LOC, init
S06.31[1,2,3,4]A	Contsn and lac of rt cerebrum w/ LOC of [30 min or less, 31 min to 59 min, 1 hr to 5 hrs 59 min, 6 hrs to 24 hrs], init enc
S06.31[5,6]A	Contsn and lac of rt cerebrum w/ LOC > 24 hrs [w/ return to pre-existing conscious lvl, w/o return to pre-existing conscious lvl w/ patient surviving], init enc
S06.31[7,8,9]A	Contsn and lac of rt cerebrum w/ LOC of [any dur w/ death d/t brain inj prior to regain cnscness, any dur w/ death d/t oth cause prior to regain cnscness, unsp dur], init enc
S06.320A	Contus/lac lt cerebrum w/o LOC, init
S06.32[1,2,3,4]A	Contsn and lac of lt cerebrum w/ LOC of [30 min or less, 31 min to 59 min, 1 hr to 5 hrs 59 min, 6 hrs to 24 hrs], init enc
S06.32[5,6]A	Contsn and lac of lt cerebrum w/ LOC > 24 hrs [w/ return to pre-existing conscious lvl, w/o return to pre-existing conscious lvl w/ patient surviving], init enc
S06.32[7,8,9]A	Contsn and lac of lt cerebrum w/ LOC of [any dur w/ death d/t brain inj prior to regain cnscness, any dur w/ death d/t oth cause prior to regain cnscness, unsp dur], init enc
S06.330A	Contus/lac cereb, w/o LOC, init
S06.33[1,2,3,4]A	Contsn and lac of cerebrum, unsp, w/ LOC of [30 min or less, 31 min to 59 min, 1 hr to 5 hrs 59 min, 6 hrs to 24 hrs], init enc
S06.33[5,6]A	Contsn and lac of cerebrum, unsp, w/ LOC > 24 hrs [w/ return to pre-existing conscious lvl, w/o return to pre-existing conscious lvl w/ patient surviving], init enc
S06.33[7,8,9]A	Contsn and lac of cerebrum, unsp, w/ LOC of [any dur w/ death d/t brain inj prior to regain cnscness, any dur w/ death d/t oth cause prior to regain cnscness, unsp dur], init enc
S06.340A	Traum hemor rt cerebrum w/o LOC, init
S06.34[1,2,3,4]A	Traum hemor of rt cerebrum w/ LOC of [30 min or less, 31 min to 59 min, 1 hr to 5 hrs 59 min, 6 hrs to 24 hrs], init enc
S06.34[5,6]A	Traum hemor of rt cerebrum w/ LOC > 24 hrs [w/ return to pre-existing conscious lvl, w/o return to pre-existing conscious lvl w/ patient surviving], init enc
S06.34[7,8,9]A	Traum hemor of rt cerebrum w/ LOC of [any dur w/ death d/t brain inj prior to regain cnscness, any dur w/ death d/t oth cause prior to regain cnscness, unsp dur], init enc
S06.350A	Traum hemor lt cerebrum w/o LOC, init
S06.35[1,2,3,4]A	Traum hemor of lt cerebrum w/ LOC of [30 min or less, 31 min to 59 min, 1 hr to 5 hrs 59 min, 6 hrs to 24 hrs], init enc
S06.35[5,6]A	Traum hemor of lt cerebrum w/ LOC > 24 hrs [w/ return to pre-existing conscious lvl, w/o return to pre-existing conscious lvl w/ patient surviving], init enc
S06.35[7,8,9]A	Traum hemor of lt cerebrum w/ LOC of [any dur w/ death d/t brain inj prior to regain cnscness, any dur w/ death d/t oth cause prior to regain cnscness, unsp dur], init enc
S06.360A	Traum hemor cereb, w/o LOC, init
S06.36[1,2,3,4]A	Traum hemor of cerebrum, unsp, w/ LOC of [30 min or less, 31 min to 59 min, 1 hr to 5 hrs 59 min, 6 hrs to 24 hrs], init enc
S06.36[5,6]A	Traum hemor of cerebrum, unsp, w/ LOC > 24 hrs [w/ return to pre-existing conscious lvl, w/o return to pre-existing conscious lvl w/ patient surviving], init enc
S06.36[7,8,9]A	Traum hemor of cerebrum, unsp, w/ LOC of [any dur w/ death d/t brain inj prior to regain cnscness, any dur w/ death d/t oth cause prior to regain cnscness, unsp dur], init enc
S06.370A	Contus/lac/hem crblm w/o LOC, init
S06.37[1,2,3,4]A	Contsn, lac, and hemor of cerebellum w/ LOC of [30 min or less, 31 min to 59 min, 1 hr to 5 hrs 59 min, 6 hrs to 24 hrs], init enc
S06.37[5,6]A	Contsn, lac, and hemor of cerebellum w/ LOC > 24 hrs [w/ return to pre-existing conscious lvl, w/o return to pre-existing conscious lvl w/ patient surviving], init enc
S06.37[7,8,9]A	Contsn, lac, and hemor of cerebellum w/ LOC of [any dur w/ death d/t brain inj prior to regain cnscness, any dur w/ death d/t oth cause prior to regain cnscness, unsp dur], init enc
S06.380A	Contus/lac/hem brainstem w/o LOC, init
S06.38[1,2,3,4]A	Contsn, lac, and hemor of brainstem w/ LOC of [30 min or less, 31 min to 59 min, 1 hr to 5 hrs 59 min, 6 hrs to 24 hrs], init enc
S06.38[5,6]A	Contsn, lac, and hemor of brainstem w/ LOC > 24 hrs [w/ return to pre-existing conscious lvl, w/o return to pre-existing conscious lvl w/ patient surviving], init enc
S06.38[7,8,9]A	Contsn, lac, and hemor of brainstem w/ LOC of [any dur w/ death d/t brain inj prior to regain cnscness, any dur w/ death d/t oth cause prior to regain cnscness, unsp dur], init enc
S06.4X0A	Epidural hemor w/o LOC, init enc
S06.4X[1,2,3,4]A	Epidural hemor w/ LOC of [30 min or less, 31 min to 59 min, 1 hr to 5 hrs 59 min, 6 hrs to 24 hrs], init enc
S06.4X[5,6]A	Epidural hemor w/ LOC > 24 hrs [w/ return to pre-existing conscious lvl, w/o return to pre-existing conscious lvl w/ patient surviving], init enc
S06.4X[7,8,9]A	Epidural hemor w/ LOC of [any dur w/ death d/t brain inj prior to regain cnscness, any dur w/ death d/t oth cause prior to regain cnscness, unsp dur], init enc
S06.5X0A	Traum subdr hem w/o LOC, init
S06.5X[1,2,3,4]A	Traum subdural hemor w/ LOC of [30 min or less, 31 min to 59 min, 1 hr to 5 hrs 59 min, 6 hrs to 24 hrs], init enc
S06.5X[5,6]A	Traum subdural hemor w/ LOC > 24 hrs [w/ return to pre-existing conscious lvl, w/o return to pre-existing conscious lvl w/ patient surviving], init enc
S06.5X[7,8,9]A	Traum subdural hemor w/ LOC of [any dur w/ death d/t brain inj prior to regain cnscness, any dur w/ death d/t oth cause prior to regain cnscness, unsp dur], init enc
S06.6X0A	Traum subrac hem w/o LOC, init
S06.6X[1,2,3,4]A	Traum subarachnoid hemor w/ LOC of [30 min or less, 31 min to 59 min, 1 hr to 5 hrs 59 min, 6 hrs to 24 hrs], init enc
S06.6X[5,6]A	Traum subarachnoid hemor w/ LOC > 24 hrs [w/ return to pre-existing conscious lvl, w/o return to pre-existing conscious lvl w/ patient surviving], init enc
S06.6X[7,8,9]A	Traum subarachnoid hemor w/ LOC of [any dur w/ death d/t brain inj prior to regain cnscness, any dur w/ death d/t oth cause prior to regain cnscness, unsp dur], init enc
S06.810A	Inj of Rt int carotid, intcr w/o LOC, init
S06.81[1,2,3,4]A	Inj of rt int carotid artery, intracranial portion, NEC, w/ LOC of [30 min or less, 31 min to 59 min, 1 hr to 5 hrs 59 min, 6 hrs to 24 hrs], init enc
S06.81[5,6]A	Inj of rt int carotid artery, intracranial portion, NEC, w/ LOC > 24 hrs [w/ return to pre-existing conscious lvl, w/o return to pre-existing conscious lvl w/ patient surviving], init enc

T **Transfer DRG**   SP **Special Payment**   * **Code Range**   **6th and 7th Character of ZZ = No Device, No Qualifier ZX = No Device, Diagnostic**

418   MS-DRG Version 33.0   © 2015 Optum360, LLC

Code	Description
S06.81[7,8,9]A	Inj of rt int carotid artery, intracranial portion, NEC w/ LOC of [any dur w/ death d/t brain inj prior to regain cnscness, any dur w/ death d/t oth cause prior to regain cnscness, unsp dur], init enc
S06.820A	Inj of Lt int carotid, intcr w/o LOC, init
S06.82[1,2,3,4]A	Inj of lt int carotid artery, intracranial portion, NEC, w/ LOC of [3Ø min or less, 31 min to 59 min, 1 hr to 5 hrs 59 min, 6 hrs to 24 hrs], init enc
S06.82[5,6]A	Inj of lt int carotid artery, intracranial portion, NEC, w/ LOC > 24 hrs [w/ return to pre-existing conscious lvl, w/o return to pre-existing conscious lvl w/ patient surviving], init enc
S06.82[7,8,9]A	Inj of lt int carotid artery, intracranial portion, NEC w/ LOC of [any dur w/ death d/t brain inj prior to regain cnscness, any dur w/ death d/t oth cause prior to regain cnscness, unsp dur], init enc
S06.890A	Intcran inj w/o LOC, init enc
S06.89[1,2,3,4]A	Oth spec intracranial inj w/ LOC of [3Ø min or less, 31 min to 59 min, 1 hr to 5 hrs 59 min, 6 hrs to 24 hrs], init enc
S06.89[5,6]A	Oth spec intracranial inj w/ LOC > 24 hrs [w/ return to pre-existing conscious lvl, w/o return to pre-existing conscious lvl w/ patient surviving], init enc
S06.89[7,8,9]A	Oth spec intracranial inj w/ LOC of [any dur w/ death d/t brain inj prior to regain cnscness, any dur w/ death d/t oth cause prior to regain cnscness, unsp dur], init enc
S06.9XØA	Unsp intracranial inj w/o LOC, init
S06.9X[1,2,3,4]A	Unsp intracranial inj w/ LOC of [3Ø min or less, 31 min to 59 min, 1 hr to 5 hrs 59 min, 6 hrs to 24 hrs], init enc
S06.9X[5,6]A	Unsp intracranial inj w/ LOC > 24 hrs [w/ return to pre-existing conscious lvl, w/o return to pre-existing conscious lvl w/ patient surviving], init enc
S06.9X[7,8,9]A	Unsp intracranial inj w/ LOC of [any dur w/ death d/t brain inj prior to regain cnscness, any dur w/ death d/t oth cause prior to regain cnscness, unsp dur], init enc
S07.ØXXA	Crushing inj of face, init enc
S07.1XXA	Crushing inj of skull, init enc
S07.8XXA	Crushing inj of oth parts of head, init enc
S07.9XXA	Crushing inj of head, part unsp, init enc
S08.ØXXA	Avulsion of scalp, init enc
S08.1[1,2][1,2,9]A	[Complete, Partial] traum amp of [rt, lt, unsp] ear, init enc
S08.81[1,2]A	[Complete, Partial] traum amp of nose, init enc
S08.89XA	Traum amp of oth parts of head, init enc
S09.ØXXA	Inj of bld vessels of head, NEC, init
S09.1[Ø,1,2,9]XA	[Unsp inj, Strain, Lac, Oth spec inj] of muscle and tndn of head, init enc
S09.2[Ø,1,2]XA	Traum rupture of [unsp, rt, lt] ear drum, init enc
S09.30[1,2,9]A	Unsp inj of [rt, lt, unsp] mid and inner ear, init enc
S09.31[1,2,3,9]A	Primary blast inj of [rt, lt, bilat, unsp] ear, init enc
S09.39[1,2,9]A	Oth spec inj of [rt, lt, unsp] mid and inner ear, init enc
S09.8XXA	Oth spec injuries of head, init enc
S09.9[Ø,1,2,3]XA	Unsp inj of [head, ear, nose, face], init enc
S10.ØXXA	Contsn of throat, init enc
S10.1[Ø,1,2,4,5,6,7]XA	[Unsp superf injuries, Abrasion, Blister (nonthermal), Ext constriction of part, Superf FB, Insect bite (nonvenomous, Oth superf bite] of throat, init enc
S10.8[Ø,1,2,3,4,5,6,7]XA	[Unsp superf inj, Abrasion, Blister (nonthermal), Contsn, Ext constriction, Superf FB, Insect bite, Oth superf bite] of oth spec part of neck, init enc
S10.9[Ø,1,2,3,4,5,6,7]XA	[Unsp superf inj, Abrasion, Blister (nonthermal), Contsn, Ext constriction, Superf FB, Insect bite, Oth superf bite] of unsp part of neck, init enc
S11.Ø1[1,2,3,4,5,9]A	[Lac w/o FB, Lac w/ FB, Punc wnd w/o FB, Punc wnd w/ FB, Opn bite, Unsp opn wnd] of larynx, init enc
S11.Ø2[1,2,3,4,5,9]A	[Lac w/o FB, Lac w/ FB, Punc wnd w/o FB, Punc wnd w/ FB, Opn bite, Unsp opn wnd] of trachea, init enc
S11.Ø3[1,2,3,4,5,9]A	[Lac w/o FB, Lac w/ FB, Punc wnd w/o FB, Punc wnd w/ FB, Opn bite, Unsp opn wnd] of vocal cord, init enc
S11.1[Ø,1,2,3,4,5]XA	[Unsp opn wnd, Lac w/o FB, Lac w/ FB, Punc wnd w/o FB, Punc wnd w/ FB, Opn bite] of thyroid gland, init enc
S11.2[Ø,1,2,3,4,5]XA	[Unsp opn wnd, Lac w/o FB, Lac w/ FB, Punc wnd w/o FB, Punc wnd w/ FB, Opn bite] of pharynx and cervical esophagus, init enc
S11.8[Ø,1,2,3,4,5,9]XA	[Unsp opn wnd, Lac w/o FB, Lac w/ FB, Punc wnd w/o FB, Punc wnd w/ FB, Opn bite, Oth opn wnd] of oth spec part of neck, init enc
S11.9[Ø,1,2,3,4,5]XA	[Unsp opn wnd, Lac w/o FB, Lac w/ FB, Punc wnd w/o FB, Punc wnd w/ FB, Opn bite] of unsp part of neck, init enc
S12.ØØ[Ø,1][A,B]	Unsp [disp, nondisp] fx of 1st cervical vertebra, init enc for [clsd, opn] fx
S12.Ø3[Ø,1][A,B]	[Disp, Nondisp] post arch fx of 1st cervical vertebra, init enc for [clsd, opn] fx
S12.Ø4[Ø,1][A,B]	[Disp, Nondisp] lat mass fx of 1st cervical vertebra, init enc for [clsd, opn] fx
S12.Ø9[Ø,1][A,B]	Oth [disp, nondisp] fx of 1st cervical vertebra, init enc for [clsd, opn] fx
S12.Ø[1,2]X[A,B]	[Stable, Unstable] burst fx of 1st cervical vertebra, init enc for [clsd, opn] fx
S12.10[Ø,1][A,B]	Unsp [disp, nondisp] fx of 2nd cervical vertebra, init enc for [clsd, opn] fx
S12.11[Ø,1,2][A,B]	[Ant disp, Post disp, Nondisp] Type II dens fx, init enc for [clsd. opn] fx
S12.12[Ø,1][A,B]	Oth [disp, nondisp] dens fx, init enc for [clsd, opn] fx
S12.13[Ø,1][A,B]	Unsp traum [disp, nondisp] spondylolisthesis of 2nd cervical vertebra, init enc for [clsd, opn] fx
S12.14X[A,B]	Type III traum spondylolisthesis of 2nd cervical vertebra, init enc for [clsd, opn] fx
S12.15[Ø,1][A,B]	Oth traum [disp, nondisp] spondylolisthesis of 2nd cervical vertebra, init enc for [clsd, opn] fx
S12.19[Ø,1][A,B]	Oth [disp, nondisp] fx of 2nd cervical vertebra, init enc for [clsd,opn] fx
S12.20[Ø,1][A,B]	Unsp [disp, nondisp] fx of 3rd cervical vertebra, init enc for [clsd, opn] fx
S12.23[Ø,1][A,B]	Unsp traum [disp, nondisp] spondylolisthesis of 3rd cervical vertebra, init enc for [clsd, opn] fx
S12.24X[A,B]	Type III traum spondylolisthesis of 3rd cervical vertebra, init enc for [clsd, opn] fx
S12.25[Ø,1][A,B]	Oth traum [disp, nondisp] spondylolisthesis of 3rd cervical vertebra, init enc for [clsd, opn] fx
S12.29[Ø,1][A,B]	Oth [disp, nondisp] fx of 3rd cervical vertebra, init enc for [clsd, opn] fx
S12.30[Ø,1][A,B]	Unsp [disp, nondisp] fx of 4th cervical vertebra, init enc for [clsd, opn] fx
S12.33[Ø,1][A,B]	Unsp traum [disp, nondisp] spondylolisthesis of 4th cervical vertebra, init enc for [clsd, opn] fx
S12.34X[A,B]	Type III traum spondylolisthesis of 4th cervical vertebra, init enc for [clsd, opn] fx
S12.35[Ø,1][A,B]	Oth traum [disp, nondisp] spondylolisthesis of 4th cervical vertebra, init enc for [clsd, opn] fx
S12.39[Ø,1][A,B]	Oth [disp, nondisp] fx of 4th cervical vertebra, init enc for [clsd, opn] fx
S12.40[Ø,1][A,B]	Unsp [disp, nondisp] fx of 5th cervical vertebra, init enc for [clsd, opn] fx
S12.43[Ø,1][A,B]	Unsp traum [disp, nondisp] spondylolisthesis of 5th cervical vertebra, init enc for [clsd, opn] fx
S12.44X[A,B]	Type III traum spondylolisthesis of 5th cervical vertebra, init enc for [clsd, opn] fx
S12.45[Ø,1][A,B]	Oth traum [disp, nondisp] spondylolisthesis of 5th cervical vertebra, init enc for [clsd, opn] fx
S12.49[Ø,1][A,B]	Oth [disp, nondisp] fx of 5th cervical vertebra, init enc for [clsd, opn] fx
S12.50[Ø,1][A,B]	Unsp [disp, nondisp] fx of 6th cervical vertebra, init enc for [clsd, opn] fx
S12.53[Ø,1][A,B]	Unsp traum [disp, nondisp] spondylolisthesis of 6th cervical vertebra, init enc for [clsd, opn] fx
S12.54X[A,B]	Type III traum spondylolisthesis of 6th cervical vertebra, init enc for [clsd, opn] fx
S12.55[Ø,1][A,B]	Oth traum [disp, nondisp] spondylolisthesis of 6th cervical vertebra, init enc for [clsd, opn] fx
S12.59[Ø,1][A,B]	Oth [disp, nondisp] fx of 6th cervical vertebra, init enc for [clsd, opn] fx
S12.60[Ø,1][A,B]	Unsp [disp, nondisp] fx of 7th cervical vertebra, init enc for [clsd, opn] fx
S12.63[Ø,1][A,B]	Unsp traum [disp, nondisp] spondylolisthesis of 7th cervical vertebra, init enc for [clsd, opn] fx
S12.64X[A,B]	Type III traum spondylolisthesis of 7th cervical vertebra, init enc for [clsd, opn] fx
S12.65[Ø,1][A,B]	Oth traum [disp, nondisp] spondylolisthesis of 7th cervical vertebra, init enc for [clsd, opn] fx
S12.69[Ø,1][A,B]	Oth [disp, nondisp] fx of 7th cervical vertebra, init enc for [clsd, opn] fx
S12.8XXA	Fx of oth parts of neck, init enc
S12.9XXA	Fx of neck, unsp, init enc
S13.ØXXA	Traum rupture of cervical intervertebral disc, init
S13.1[Ø,1,2,3,4,5,6,7,8][Ø,1]A	[Sublux, Disloc] of [unsp, CØ/C1, C1/C2, C2/C3, C3/C4, C4/C5, C5/C6, C6/C7, C7/T1] cervical vertebrae, init enc
S13.2[Ø,9]XA	Disloc of [unsp, oth] parts of neck, init enc
S13.[4,5,8,9]XXA	Sprain of [lgmts of cervical spine, thyroid rgn, jts and lgmts of oth parts of neck, jts and lgmts of unsp parts of neck], init enc
S14.ØXXA	Concussion and edema of cervical spinal cord, init enc
S14.10[1,2,3,4,5,6,7,8,9]A	Unsp inj at [C1, C2, C3, C4, C5, C6, C7, C8, unsp] lvl of cervical spinal cord, init enc

Surgical　　**Medical**　　**CC Indicator**　　**MCC Indicator**　　**Procedure Proxy**　　PDxMCC **PDx acts as own MCC**　　PDxCC **PDx acts as own CC**

© 2015 Optum360, LLC　　　　　　　　　　　　　MS-DRG Version 33.0　　　　　　　　　　　　　　　**419**

MDC 24: Multiple Significant Trauma—MEDICAL

S14.11[1,2,3,4,5,6,7,8,9]A Complete lesion at [C1,C2, C3, C4, C5, C6, C7, C8, unsp] lvl of cervical spinal cord, init enc

S14.12[1,2,3,4,5,6,7,8,9]A Central cord synd at [C1, C2, C3, C4, C5, C6, C7, C8, unsp] lvl of cervical spinal cord, init enc

S14.13[1,2,3,4,5,6,7,8,9]A Ant cord synd at [C1, C2, C3, C4, C5, C6, C7, C8, unsp] lvl of cervical spinal cord, init enc

S14.14[1,2,3,4,5,6,7,8,9]A Brown-Sequard synd at [C1, C2, C3, C4, C5, C6, C7, C8, unsp] lvl of cervical spinal cord, init enc

S14.15[1,2,3,4,5,6,7,8,9]A Oth incomplete lesion at [C1, C2, C3, C4, C5, C6, C7, C8, unsp] lvl of cervical spinal cord, init enc

S14.[2,3,4,5,8,9]XXA Inj of [nerve root of cervical spine, brachial plexus, peripheral nerves of neck, cervical sympathetic nerves, oth spec nerves of neck, unsp nerves of neck], init enc

S15.0[0,1,2,9][1,2,9]A [Unsp inj, Minor lac, Major lac, Oth spec inj] of [rt, lt, unsp] carotid artery, init enc

S15.1[0,1,2,9][1,2,9]A [Unsp inj, Minor lac, Major lac, Oth spec inj] of [rt, lt, unsp] vert artery, init enc

S15.2[0,1,2,9][1,2,9]A [Unsp inj, Minor lac, Major lac, Oth spec inj] of [rt, lt, unsp] ext jugular vein, init enc

S15.3[0,1,2,9][1,2,9]A [Unsp inj, Minor lac, Major lac, Oth spec inj] of [rt, lt, unsp] int jugular vein, init enc

S15.[8,9]XXA Inj of [oth spec, unsp] bld vessel(s) at neck lvl, init enc

S16.[1,2,8,9]XXA [Strain, Lac, Oth spec inj, Unsp inj] of muscle, fascia and tndn at neck lvl, init enc

S17.[0,8,9]XXA Crushing inj of [larynx and trachea, oth spec parts of neck, unsp part of neck], init enc

S19.8[0,1,2,3,4,5,9]XA Oth spec injuries of [unsp part of neck, larynx, cervical trachea, vocal cord, thyroid gland, pharynx and cervical esophagus, oth spec part of neck], init enc

S19.9XXA Unsp inj of neck, init enc

S20.0[0,1,2]XA Contsn of [unsp, rt, lt] breast, init enc

S20.1[0,1,2,4,5,6,7][1,2,9]A [Unsp superf injuries, Abrasion, Blister (nonthermal), Ext constriction of part, Superf FB, Insect bite, Oth superf bite] of breast, [rt, lt, unsp] breast, init enc

S20.20XA Contsn of thorax, unsp, init enc

S20.2[1,2][1,2,9]A Contsn of [front, back][rt, lt, unsp] wall of thorax, init enc

S20.3[0,1,2,4,5,6,7][1,2,9]A [Unsp superf injuries, Abrasion, Blister (nonthermal), Ext constriction, Superf FB, Insect bite (nonvenomous), Oth superf bite] of [rt, lt, unsp] front wall of thorax, init enc

S20.4[0,1,2,4,5,6,7][1,2,9]A [Unsp superf injuries, Abrasion, Blister (nonthermal), Ext constriction, Superf FB, Insect bite (nonvenomous), Oth superf bite] of [rt, lt, unsp] back wall of thorax, init enc

S20.9[0,1,2,4,5,6,7]XA [Unsp superf inj, Abrasion, Blister (nonthermal), Ext constriction, Superf FB, Insect bite (nonvenomous), Oth superf bite] of unsp parts of thorax, init enc

S21.0[0,1,2,3,4,5][1,2,9]A [Unsp opn wnd, Lac w/o FB, Lac w/ FB, Punc wnd w/o FB, Punc wnd w/ FB, Opn bite] of [rt, lt, unsp] breast, init enc

S21.1[0,1,2,3,4,5][1,2,9]A [Unsp opn wnd, Lac w/o FB, Lac w/ FB, Punc wnd w/o FB, Punc wnd w/ FB, Opn bite] of [rt, lt, unsp] front wall of thorax w/o penetration into thoracic cavity, init enc

S21.2[0,1,2,3,4,5][1,2,9]A [Unsp opn wnd, Lac w/o FB, Lac w/ FB, Punc wnd w/o FB, Punc wnd w/ FB, Opn bite] of [rt, lt, unsp] back wall of thorax w/o penetration into thoracic cavity, init enc

S21.3[0,1,2,3,4,5][1,2,9]A [Unsp opn wnd, Lac w/o FB, Lac w/ FB, Punc wnd w/o FB, Punc wnd w/ FB, Opn bite] of [rt, lt, unsp] front wall of thorax w/ penetration into thoracic cavity, init enc

S21.4[0,1,2,3,4,5][1,2,9]A [Unsp opn wnd, Lacertion w/o FB, Lac w/ FB, Punc wnd w/o FB, Punc wnd w/ FB, Opn bite] of [rt, lt, unsp] back wall of thorax w/ penetration into thoracic cavity, init enc

S21.9[0,1,2,3,4,5]XA [Unsp opn wnd, Lac w/o FB, Lac w/ FB, Punc wnd w/o FB, Punc wnd w/ FB, Opn bite] of unsp part of thorax, init enc

S22.00[0,1,2,8,9][A,B] [Wedge compression, Stable burst, Unstable burst, Oth, Unsp] fx of unsp thoracic vertebra, init enc for [clsd, opn] fx

S22.01[0,1,2,8,9][A,B] [Wedge compression, Stable burst, Unstable burst, Oth, Unsp] fx of 1st thoracic vertebra, init enc for [clsd, opn] fx

S22.02[0,1,2,8,9][A,B] [Wedge compression, Stable burst, Unstable burst, Oth, Unsp] fx of 2nd thoracic vertebra, init enc for [clsd, opn] fx

S22.03[0,1,2,8,9][A,B] [Wedge compression, Stable burst, Unstable burst, Oth, Unsp] fx of 3rd thoracic vertebra, init enc for [clsd, opn] fx

S22.04[0,1,2,8,9][A,B] [Wedge compression, Stable burst, Unstable burst, Oth, Unsp] fx of 4th thoracic vertebra, init enc for [clsd, opn] fx

S22.052A Unstable burst fx of T5-T6 vertebra, init for clos fx

S22.052B Unstable burst fx of T5-T6 vertebra, init for opn fx

S22.05[0,1,8,9][A,B] [Wedge compression, Stable burst, Unstable burst, Oth, Unsp] fx of T5-T6 vertebra, init enc for [clsd, opn] fx

S22.06[0,1,2,8,9][A,B] [Wedge compression, Stable burst, Unstable burst, Oth, Unsp] fx of T7-T8 vertebra, init enc for [clsd, opn] fx

S22.07[0,1,2,8,9][A,B] [Wedge compression, Stable burst, Unstable burst, Oth, Unsp] fx of T9-T10 vertebra, init enc for [clsd, opn] fx

S22.08[0,1,2,8,9][A,B] [Wedge compression, Stable burst, Unstable burst, Oth, Unsp] fx of T11-T12 vertebra, init enc for [clsd, opn] fx

S22.2[0,1,2,3,4]X[A,B] [Unsp fx of sternum, Fx of manubrium, Fx of body of sternum, Sternal manubrial dissociation, Fx of xiphoid process], init enc for [clsd, opn] fx

S22.3[1,2,9]X[A,B] Fx of one rib, [rt, lt, unsp] side, init enc for [clsd, opn] fx

S22.4[1,2,3,9]X[A,B] Multi fxs of ribs, [rt, lt, unsp] side, init enc for [clsd, opn] fx

S22.5XX[A,B] Flail chest, init enc for [clsd, opn] fx

S22.9XX[A,B] Fx of bony thorax, part unsp, init enc for [clsd, opn] fx

S23.0XXA Traum rupture of thoracic intervertebral disc, init

S23.10[0,1]A [Sublux, Disloc] of unsp thoracic vertebra, init enc

S23.11[0,1]A [Sublux, Disloc] of T1/T2 thoracic vertebrae, init enc

S23.12[0,1]A [Sublux, Disloc] of T2/T3 thoracic vertebrae, init enc

S23.12[2,3]A [Sublux, Disloc] of T3/T4 thoracic vertebrae, init enc

S23.13[0,1]A [Sublux, Disloc] of T4/T5 thoracic vertebrae, init enc

S23.13[2,3]A [Sublux, Disloc] of T5/T6 thoracic vertebrae, init enc

S23.14[0,1]A [Sublux, Disloc] of T6/T7 thoracic vertebrae, init enc

S23.14[2,3]A [Sublux, Disloc] of T7/T8 thoracic vertebrae, init enc

S23.15[0,1]A [Sublux, Disloc] of T8/T9 thoracic vertebrae, init enc

S23.15[2,3]A [Sublux, Disloc] of T9/T10 thoracic vertebrae, init enc

S23.16[0,1]A [Sublux, Disloc] of T10/T11 thoracic vertebrae, init enc

S23.16[2,3,]A [Sublux, Disloc] of T11/T12 thoracic vertebrae, init enc

S23.17[0,1]A [Sublux, Disloc] of T12/L1 thoracic vertebrae, init enc

S23.2[0,9]XA Disloc of [unsp, oth] part(s) of thorax, init enc

S23.3XXA Sprain of lgmt of thoracic spine, init enc

S23.41XA Sprain of ribs, init enc

S23.42[0,1]A Sprain of [sternoclavicular (jt) (lgmt), chondrosternal jt], init enc

S23.42[8,9]A [Oth, Unsp] sprain of sternum, init enc

S23.[8,9]XXA Sprain of [oth spec, unsp] parts of thorax, init enc

S24.0XXA Concussion and edema of thoracic spinal cord, init enc

S24.10[1,2,3,4,9]A Unsp inj at [T1, T2-T6, T7-T10, T11-T12, unsp] lvl of thoracic spinal cord, init enc

S24.11[1,2,3,4,9]A Complete lesion at [T1, T2-T6, T7-T10, T11-T12, unsp] lvl of thoracic spinal cord, init enc

S24.13[1,2,3,4,9]A Ant cord synd at [T1, T2-T6, T7-T10, T11-T12, unsp] lvl of thoracic spinal cord, init enc

S24.14[1,2,3,4,9]A Brown-Sequard synd at [T1, T2-T6, T7-T10, T11-T12, unsp] lvl of thoracic spinal cord, init enc

S24.15[1,2,3,4,9]A Oth incomplete lesion at [T1, T2-6, T7-T10, T11-T12, unsp] lvl of thoracic spinal cord, init enc

S24.2XXA Inj of nerve root of thoracic spine, init enc

S24.3XXA Inj of peripheral nerves of thorax, init enc

S24.4XXA Inj of thoracic sympathetic nervous sys, init enc

S24.[8,9]XXA Inj of [oth spec, unsp] nerve(s) of thorax, init enc

S25.0[0,1,2,9]XA [Unsp inj, Minor lac, Major lac, Oth spec inj] of thoracic aorta, init enc

S25.1[0,1,2,9][1,2,9]A [Unsp inj, Minor lac, Major lac, Oth spec inj] of [rt, lt, unsp] innominate or subclavian artery, init enc

S25.2[0,1,2,9]XA [Unsp inj, Minor lac, Major lac, Oth spec inj] of superior vena cava, init enc

S25.3[0,1,2,9][1,2,9]A [Unsp inj, Minor lac, Major lac, Oth spec inj] of [rt, lt, unsp] innominate or subclavian vein, init enc

S25.4[0,1,2,9][1,2,9]A [Unsp inj, Minor lac, Major lac, Oth spec inj] of [rt, lt, unsp] pulmn bld vessels, init enc

S25.5[0,1,9][1,2,9]A [Unsp inj, Lac, Oth spec inj] of intercostal bld vessels, [rt, lt, unsp] side, init enc

S25.8[0,1,9][1,2,9]A [Unsp inj, Lac, Oth spec inj] of oth bld vessels of thorax, [rt, lt, unsp] side, init enc

S25.9[0,1,9]XA [Unsp inj, Lac, Oth spec inj] of unsp bld vessel of thorax, init enc

S26.02[0,1,2]A [Mild, Mod, Major] lac of heart w/ hemopericardium, init enc

S26.09XA Oth inj of heart with hemopericardium, init enc

S26.0[0,1]XA [Unsp inj, Contsn] of heart w/ hemopericardium, init enc

S26.1[0,1,2,9]XA [Unsp inj, Contsn, Lac, Oth inj] of heart w/o hemopericardium, init enc

S26.9[0,1,2,9]XA [Unsp inj, Contsn, Lac, Oth inj] of heart, unsp w/ or w/o hemopericardium, init enc

S27.3[0,1,2,3,9][1,2,9]A [Unsp inj, Primary blast inj, Contsn, Lac, Oth injuries] of lung, [unilat, bilat, unsp], init enc

S27.4[0,1,2,3,9][1,2,9]A [Unsp inj, Primary blast inj, Contsn, Lac, Oth inj] of bronchus, [unilat, bilat, unsp], init enc

S27.5[0,1,2,3,9]XA [Unsp inj, Primary blast inj, Contsn, Lac, Oth inj] of thoracic trachea, init enc

S27.6[0,3,9]XA [Unsp inj, Lac, Oth inj] of pleura, init enc

S27.80[2,3,8,9]A [Contsn, Lac, Oth inj, Unsp inj] of diaphragm, init enc

S27.81[2,3,8,9]A [Contsn, Lac, Oth inj, Unsp inj] of esophagus (thoracic part), init enc

S27.89[2,3,8,9]A [Contsn, Lac, Oth inj, Unsp inj] of oth spec intrathoracic organs, init enc

T Transfer DRG   SP Special Payment   * Code Range   6th and 7th Character of ZZ = No Device, No Qualifier ZX = No Device, Diagnostic

420   MS-DRG Version 33.0   © 2015 Optum360, LLC

Code	Description
S27.9XXA	Inj of unsp intrathoracic organ, init enc
S27.[0,1,2]XXA	Traum [pneumothorax, hemothorax, hemopneumothorax], init enc
S28.0XXA	Crushed chest, init enc
S28.1XXA	Traum amp of part of thorax, except breast, init
S28.2[1,2][1,2,9]A	[Complete, Partial] traum amp of [rt, lt, unsp] breast, init enc
S29.0[0,1,2,9][1,2,9]A	[Unsp inj, Strain, Lac, Oth inj] of muscle and tndn of [front, back, unsp] wall of thorax, init enc
S29.[8,9]XXA	[Oth spec injuries, Unsp inj] of thorax, init enc
S30.20[1,2]A	Contsn of unsp ext genital organ, [male, female], init enc
S30.2[1,2,3]XA	Contsn of [penis, scrotum and testes, vagina and vulva], init enc
S30.3XXA	Contsn of anus, init enc
S30.8[1,2,4,5,6,7][0,1,2,3,4,5,6,7]A	[Abrasion, Blister (nonthermal), Ext constriction, Superf FB, Insect bite (nonvenomous), Oth superf bite] of [lwr back and pelvis, abd wall, penis, scrotum and testes, vagina and vulva, unsp ext genital organs [male, female], anus], init enc
S30.9[1,2,3,4,5,6,7,8]XA	Unsp superf inj of [lwr back and pelvis, abd wall, penis, scrotum and testes, vagina and vulva, unsp ext genital organs [male, female], anus], init enc
S30.[0,1]XXA	Contsn of [lwr back and pelvis, abd wall], init enc
S31.0[0,1,2,3,4,5][0,1]A	[Unsp opn wnd, Lac w/o FB, Lac w/ FB, Punc wnd w/o FB, Punc wnd w/ FB, Opn bite] of lwr back and pelvis [w/o, w/] penetration into retroperitoneum, init enc
S31.1[0,1,2,3,4,5][0,1,2,3,4,5,9]A	[Unsp opn wnd, Lac w/o FB, Lac w/ FB, Punc wnd w/o FB, Punc wnd w/ FB, Opn bite] of abd wall, [rt upr quadrant, lt upr quadrant, epigastric rgn, rt lwr quadrant, lt lwr quadrant, periumbilic rgn, unsp quadrant] w/o penetration into peritoneal cavity, init enc
S31.2[0,1,2,3,4,5]XA	[Unsp opn wnd, Lac w/o FB, Lac w/ FB, Punc wnd w/o FB, Punc wnd w/ FB, Opn bite], of penis, init enc
S31.3[0,1,2,3,4,5]XA	[Unsp opn wnd, Lac w/o FB, Lac w/ FB, Punc wnd w/o FB, Punc wnd w/ FB, Opn bite], of scrotum and testes, init enc
S31.4[0,1,2,3,4,5]XA	[Unsp opn wnd, Lac w/o FB, Lac w/ FB, Punc wnd w/o FB, Punc wnd w/ FB, Opn bite] of vagina and vulva, init enc
S31.5[0,1,2,3,4,5][1,2]A	[Unsp opn wnd, Lac w/o FB, Lac w/ FB, Punc wnd w/o FB, Punc wnd w/ FB, Opn bite] of unsp ext genital organs, [male, female], init enc
S31.6[0,1,2,3,4,5][0,1,2,3,4,5,9]A	[Unsp opn wnd, Lac w/o FB, Lac w/ FB, Punc wnd w/o FB, Punc wnd w/ FB, Opn bite] of abd wall, [rt upr quadrant, lt upr quadrant, epigastric rgn, rt lwr quadrant, lt lwr quadrant, periumbilic rgn, unsp quadrant] w/ penetration into peritoneal cavity, init enc
S31.83[1,2,3,4,5,9]A	[Lac w/o FB, Lac w/ FB, Punc wnd w/o FB, Punc w/ FB, Opn bite, Unsp opn wnd] of anus, init enc
S31.8[0,1,2][1,2,3,4,5,9]A	[Lac w/o FB, Lac w/ FB, Punc wnd w/o FB, Punc wnd w/ FB, Opn bite, Unsp opn wnd] of [unsp, rt, lt] buttock, init enc
S32.00[0,1,2,8,9][A,B]	[Wedge compression, Stable burst, Unstable burst, Oth, Unsp] fx of unsp lumbar vertebra, init enc for [clsd, opn] fx
S32.01[0,1,2,8,9][A,B]	[Wedge compression, Stable burst, Unstable burst, Oth, Unsp] fx of 1st lumbar vertebra, init enc for [clsd, opn] fx
S32.02[0,1,2,8,9][A,B]	[Wedge compression, Stable burst, Unstable burst, Oth, Unsp] fx of 2nd lumbar vertebra, init enc for [clsd, opn] fx
S32.03[0,1,2,8,9][A,B]	[Wedge compression, Stable burst, Unstable burst, Oth, Unsp] fx of 3rd lumbar vertebra, init enc for [clsd, opn] fx
S32.04[0,1,2,8,9][A,B]	[Wedge compression, Stable burst, Unstable burst, Oth, Unsp] fx of 4th lumbar vertebra, init enc for [clsd, opn] fx
S32.05[0,1,2,8,9][A,B]	[Wedge compression, Stable burst, Unstable burst, Oth, Unsp] fx of 5th lumbar vertebra, init enc for [clsd, opn] fx
S32.10X[A,B]	Unsp fx of sacrum, init enc for [clsd, opn] fx
S32.11[0,1,2,9][A,B]	[Nondisp Zone I, Minimally disp Zone I, Severely disp Zone I, Unsp Zone I] fx of sacrum, init enc for [clsd, opn] fx
S32.12[0,1,2,9][A,B]	[Nondisp Zone II, Minimally disp Zone II, Severely disp Zone II, Unsp Zone II] fx of sacrum, init enc for [clsd, opn] fx
S32.13[0,1,2,9][A,B]	[Nondisp Zone III, Minimally disp Zone III, Severely disp Zone III, Unsp Zone III] fx of sacrum, init enc for [clsd, opn] fx
S32.1[4,5,6,7,9]X[A,B]	[Type 1, Type 2, Type 3, Type 4, Oth] fx of sacrum, init enc for [clsd, opn] fx
S32.2XX[A,B]	Fx of coccyx, init enc for [clsd, opn] fx
S32.30[1,2,9][A,B]	Unsp fx of [rt, lt, unsp] ilium, init enc for [clsd, opn] fx
S32.31[1,2,3,4,5,6][A,B]	[Disp, Nondisp] avulsion fx of [rt, lt, unsp] ilium, init enc for [clsd, opn] fx
S32.39[1,2,9][A,B]	Oth fx of ilium [rt, lt, unsp] init enc for [clsd, opn] fx
S32.40[1,2,9][A,B]	Unsp fx of acetab [rt, lt, unsp] init enc for [clsd, opn] fx
S32.41[1,2,3,4,5,6][A,B]	[Disp, Nondisp] fx of ant wall of [rt, lt, unsp] acetab, init enc for [clsd, opn] fx
S32.42[1,2,3,4,5,6][A,B]	[Disp, Nondisp] fx of post wall of [rt, lt, unsp] acetab, init enc for [clsd, opn] fx
S32.43[1,2,3,4,5,6][A,B]	[Disp, Nondisp] fx of ant column [iliopubic] of [rt, lt, unsp] acetab, init enc for [clsd, opn] fx
S32.44[1,2,3,4,5,6][A,B]	[Disp, Nondisp] fx of post column [ilioischial] of [rt, lt, unsp] acetab, init enc for [clsd, opn] fx
S32.45[1,2,3,4,5,6][A,B]	[Disp, Nondisp] transv fx of [rt, lt, unsp] acetab, init enc for [clsd, opn] fx
S32.46[1,2,3,4,5,6][A,B]	[Disp, Nondisp] associated transv-post fx of [rt, lt, unsp] acetab, init enc for [clsd, opn] fx
S32.47[1,2,3,4,5,6][A,B]	[Disp, Nondisp] fx of med wall of [rt, lt, unsp] acetab, init enc for [clsd, opn] fx
S32.48[1,2,3,4,5,6][A,B]	[Disp, Nondisp] dome fx of [rt, lt, unsp] acetab, init enc for [clsd, opn] fx
S32.491A	Oth fx of rt acetabulum, init for clos fx
S32.491B	Oth fx of rt acetabulum, init for opn fx
S32.492A	Oth fx of lt acetabulum, init for clos fx
S32.492B	Oth fx of lt acetabulum, init for opn fx
S32.499A	Oth fx of unsp acetabulum, init for clos fx
S32.499B	Oth fx of unsp acetabulum, init for opn fx
S32.50[1,2,9][A,B]	Unsp fx of pubis [rt, lt, unsp] init enc for [clsd, opn] fx
S32.51[1,2,9][A,B]	Fx of superior rim of pubis [rt, lt, unsp] init enc for [clsd, opn] fx
S32.59[1,2,9][A,B]	Oth spec fx of pubis [rt, lt, unsp] init enc for [clsd, opn] fx
S32.60[1,2,9][A,B]	Unsp fx of ischium [rt, lt, unsp], init enc for [clsd, opn] fx
S32.61[1,2,3,4,5,6][A,B]	[Disp, Nondisp] avulsion fx of [rt, lt, unsp] ischium, init enc for [clsd, opn] fx
S32.69[1,2,9][A,B]	Oth spec fx of ischium [rt, lt, unsp] init enc for [clsd, opn] fx
S32.81[0,1][A,B]	Multi fxs of pelvis w/ [stable, unstable] disruption of pelvic ring, init enc for [clsd, opn] fx
S32.82XA	Multi fx of pelvis w/o disrupt of pelvic ring, init
S32.82XB	Mult fx of pelvis w/o disrupt of pelv ring, init for opn fx
S32.89X[A,B]	Fx of oth parts of pelvis, init enc for [clsd, opn] fx
S32.9XX[A,B]	Fx of unsp parts of lumbosacral spine and pelvis, init enc for [clsd, opn] fx
S33.0XXA	Traum rupture of lumbar intervertebral disc, init enc
S33.1[0,1,2,3,4][0,1]A	[Sublux, Disloc] of [unsp, L1/L2, L2/L3, L3/L4, L4/L5] lumbar vertebra, init enc
S33.2XXA	Disloc of sacroiliac and sacrococcygeal jt, init
S33.3[0,9]XA	Disloc of [unsp, oth] parts of lumbar spine and pelvis, init enc
S33.4XXA	Traum rupture of symphysis pubis, init enc
S33.5XXA	Sprain of lgmt of lumbar spine, init enc
S33.6XXA	Sprain of sacroiliac jt, init enc
S33.[8,9]XXA	Sprain of [oth, unsp] parts of lumbar spine and pelvis, init enc
S34.0[1,2]XA	Concussion and edema of [lumbar, sacral] spinal cord, init enc
S34.10[1,2,3,4,5,9]A	Unsp inj to [L1, L2, L3, L4, L5, unsp] lvl of lumbar spinal cord, init enc
S34.13[1,2,9]A	[Complete lesion, Incomplete lesion, Unsp inj] (of) (to) sacral spinal cord, init enc
S34.1[1,2][1,2,3,4,5,9]A	[Complete, Incomplete] lesion of [L1, L2, L3, L4, L5, unsp] lvl of lumbar spinal cord, init enc
S34.2[1,2]XA	Inj of nerve root of [lumbar, sacral] spine, init enc
S34.5XXA	Inj of lumbar, sacral and pelvic sympathetic nerves, init
S34.[3,4]XXA	Inj of [cauda equina, lumbosacral plexus], init enc
S34.[6,8,9]XXA	Inj of [peripheral, oth, unsp] nerve(s) at abd, lwr back and pelvis lvl, init enc
S35.0[0,1,2,9]XA	[Unsp inj, Minor lac, Major lac, Oth inj] of abd aorta, init enc
S35.1[0,1,2,9]XA	[Unsp inj, Minor lac, Major lac, Oth inj] of inferior vena cava, init enc
S35.21[1,2,8,9]A	[Minor lac, Major lac, Oth inj, Unsp inj] of celiac artery, init enc
S35.29[1,2,8,9]A	[Minor lac, Major lac, Oth inj, Unsp inj] of branches of celiac and mesenteric artery, init enc
S35.2[2,3][1,2,8,9]A	[Minor lac, Major lac, Oth inj, Unsp inj] of [superior, inferior] mesenteric artery, init enc
S35.31[1,8,9]A	[Lac, Oth, Unsp] of portal vein, init enc
S35.32[1,8,9]A	[Lac, Oth, Unsp] of splenic vein, init enc
S35.3[3,4][1,8,9]A	[Lac, Oth spec inj, Unsp inj] of [superior, inferior] mesenteric vein, init enc
S35.4[0,1,9][1,2,3,4,5,6]A	[Unsp inj, Lac, Oth spec inj] of [rt renal artery, lt renal artery, unsp renal artery, rt renal vein, lt renal vein, unsp renal vein], init enc
S35.50XA	Inj of unsp iliac bld vessel(s), init enc
S35.51[1,2,3,4,5,6]A	Inj of [rt iliac artery, lt iliac artery, unsp iliac artery, rt iliac vein, lt iliac vein, unsp iliac vein], init enc
S35.53[1,2,3,4,5,6]A	Inj of [rt uterine artery, lt uterine artery, unsp uterine artery, rt uterine vein, lt uterine vein, unsp uterine vein], init enc
S35.59XA	Inj of oth iliac bld vessels, init enc
S35.8X[1,8,9]A	[Lac, Oth spec, Unsp inj] of oth bld vessels at abd, lwr back and pelvis lvl, init enc
S35.9[0,1,9]XA	[Unsp inj, Lac, Oth spec inj] of unsp bld vessel at abd, lwr back and pelvis lvl, init enc
S36.00XA	Unsp inj of spleen, init enc

Surgical   **Medical**   **CC Indicator**   **MCC Indicator**   **Procedure Proxy**   **PDxMCC** PDx acts as own MCC   **PDxCC** PDx acts as own CC

MDC 24: Multiple Significant Trauma—MEDICAL

S36.02[0,1,9]A   [Minor, Major, Unsp] contsn of spleen, init enc
S36.03[0,1,2,9]A   [Superf (capsular), Mod, Major, Unsp] lac of spleen, init enc
S36.09XA   Oth inj of spleen, init enc
S36.11[2,3,4,5,6,8,9]A [Contsn, Lac (unsp degree), Minor lac, Mod lac, Major lac, Oth inj, Unsp inj] of liver, init enc
S36.12[2,3,8,9]A   [Contsn, Lac, Oth inj, Unsp inj] of gallbladder, init enc
S36.13XA   Inj of bile duct, init enc
S36.2[0,2,3,4,5,6,9][0,1,2,9]A [Unsp inj, Contsn, Lac (unsp degree), Minor lac, Mod lac, Major lac, Oth inj] of [head, body, tail, unsp part] of pancreas, init enc
S36.3[0,2,3,9]XA   [Unsp inj, Contsn, Lac, Oth inj] of stomach, init enc
S36.4[0,1,2,3,9][0,8,9]A [Unsp inj, Primary blast, Contsn, Lac, Oth inj] of [duodenum, oth part of sm intestine, unsp part of sm intestine], init enc
S36.5[0,1,2,3,9][0,1,2,3,8,9]A [Unsp inj, Primary blast inj, Contsn, Lac, Oth inj] of [ascending [rt], transv, descending (lt), sigmoid, oth part, unsp part] (of) colon, init enc
S36.6[0,1,2,3,9]XA [Unsp inj, Primary blast inj, Contsn, Lac, Oth inj] of rectum, init enc
S36.81XA   Inj of peritoneum, init enc
S36.89[2,3,8,9]A   [Contsn, Lac, Oth inj, Unsp inj] of oth intra-abd organs, init enc
S36.9[0,2,3,9]XA   [Unsp inj, Contsn, Lac, Oth inj] of unsp intra-abd organ, init enc
S37.0[0,1,2,3,4,5,6,9][1,2,9]A [Unsp inj, Minor contsn, Major contsn, Lac (unsp degree), Minor lac, Mod lac, Major lac, Oth inj] of [rt, lt, unsp] kidney, init enc
S37.1[0,2,3,9]XA   [Unsp inj, Contsn, Lac, Oth inj] of ureter, init enc
S37.2[0,2,3,9]XA   [Unsp inj, Contsn, Lac, Oth inj] of bladder, init enc
S37.3[0,2,3,9]XA   [Unsp inj, Contsn, Lac, Oth inj] of urethra, init enc
S37.6[0,2,3,9]XA   [Unsp inj, Contsn, Lac, Oth Inj] of uterus, init enc
S37.81[2,3,8,9]A   [Contsn, Lac, Oth inj, Unsp inj] of adrenal gland, init enc
S37.89[2,3,8,9]A   [Contsn, Lac, Oth inj, Unsp inj] of oth urinary and pelvic organ, init enc
S37.9[0,2,3,9]XA   [Unsp inj, Contsn, Lac, Oth inj] of unsp urinary and pelvic organ, init enc
S38.00[1,2]A   Crushing inj of unsp ext genital organs, [male, female], init enc
S38.0[1,2,3]XA   Crushing inj of [penis, scrotum and testis, vulva], init enc
S38.1XXA   Crushing inj of abd, lwr back, and pelvis, init
S38.21[1,2]A   [Complete, Partial] traum amp of female ext genital organs, init enc
S38.2[2,3][1,2]A   [Complete, Partial] traum amp of [penis, scrotum and testis], init enc
S38.3XXA   Transection (partial) of abd, init enc
S39.001A   Unsp inj of muscle, fascia and tndn of abd, init
S39.002A   Unsp inj of muscle, fascia and tndn of lwr back, init
S39.003A   Unsp inj of muscle, fascia and tndn of pelvis, init
S39.011A   Strain of muscle, fascia and tndn of abd, init enc
S39.012A   Strain of muscle, fascia and tndn of lwr back, init
S39.013A   Strain of muscle, fascia and tndn of pelvis, init enc
S39.021A   Lac of muscle, fascia and tndn of abd, init
S39.022A   Lac of muscle, fascia and tndn of lwr back, init
S39.023A   Lac of muscle, fascia and tndn of pelvis, init
S39.091A   Inj muscle, fascia and tndn of abd, init enc
S39.092A   Inj muscle, fascia and tndn of lwr back, init enc
S39.093A   Inj muscle, fascia and tndn of pelvis, init enc
S39.840A   Fx of corpus cavernosum penis, init enc
S39.848A   Oth spec injuries of ext genitals, init enc
S39.8[1,2,3]XA   Oth spec injuries of [abd, lwr back, pelvis], init enc
S39.9[1,2,3,4]XA   Unsp inj of [abd, lwr back, pelvis, ext genitals], init enc
S40.0[1,2][1,2,9]A Contsn of [rt, lt, unsp] [shldr, upr arm], init enc
S40.2[1,2,4,5,6,7][1,2,9]A [Abrasion, Blister (nonthermal), Ext constriction, Superf FB, Insect bite (nonvenomous), Oth superf bite] of [rt, lt, unsp] shldr, init enc
S40.8[1,2,4,5,6,7][1,2,9]A [Abrasion, Blister (nonthermal), Ext constriction, Superf FB, Insect bite (nonvenomous), Oth superf bite] of [rt, lt, unsp] upr arm, init enc
S40.9[1,2][1,2,9]A Unsp superf inj of [rt, lt, unsp] [shldr, upr arm], init enc
S41.0[0,1,2,3,4,5][1,2,9]A [Unsp opn wnd, Lac w/o FB, Lac w/ FB, Punc wnd w/o FB, Punc wnd w/ FB, Opn bite] of [rt, lt, unsp] shldr, init enc
S41.1[0,1,2,3,4,5][1,2,9]A [Unsp opn wnd, Lac w/o FB, Lac w/ FB, Punc wnd w/o FB, Punc wnd w/ FB, Opn bite] of [rt, lt, unsp] upr arm, init enc
S42.00[1,2,9][A,B] Fx of unsp part of clavicle [rt, lt, unsp] init enc for fx [clsd, opn]
S42.01[1,2,3,4,5,6,7,8,9][A,B] [Ant disp, Post disp, Nondisp] fx of sternal end of [rt, lt, unsp] clavicle, init enc for [clsd, opn] fx
S42.02[1,2,3,4,5,6][A,B] [Disp, Nondisp] fx of shaft of [rt, lt, unsp] clavicle, init enc for [clsd, opn] fx
S42.03[1,2,3,4,5,6][A,B] [Disp, Nondisp] fx of lat end of [rt, lt, unsp] clavicle, init enc for [clsd, opn] fx

S42.10[1,2,9][A,B] Fx of unsp part of scapula, [rt, lt, unsp] shldr, init enc for [clsd, opn] fx
S42.11[1,2,3,4,5,6][A,B] [Disp, Nondisp] fx of body of scapula, [rt, lt, unsp] shldr, init enc for [clsd, opn] fx
S42.12[1,2,3,4,5,6][A,B] [Disp, Nondisp] fx of acromial process, [rt, lt, unsp] shldr, init enc for [clsd, opn] fx
S42.13[1,2,3,4,5,6][A,B] [Disp, Nondisp] fx of coracoid process, [rt, lt, unsp] shldr, init enc for [clsd, opn] fx
S42.14[1,2,3,4,5,6][A,B] [Disp, Disp] fx of glenoid cavity of scapula, [rt, lt, unsp] shldr, init enc for [clsd, opn] fx
S42.15[1,2,3,4,5,6][A,B] [Disp, Nondisp] fx of neck of scapula, [rt, lt, unsp] shldr, init enc for [clsd, opn] fx
S42.19[1,2,9][A,B] Fx of oth part of scapula, [rt, lt, unsp] shldr, init enc for [clsd, opn] fx
S42.20[1,2,9][A,B] Unsp fx of upr end of [rt, lt, unsp] humerus, init enc for [clsd, opn] fx
S42.21[1,2,3,4,5,6][A,B] Unsp [disp, nondisp] fx of surgical neck of [rt, lt, unsp] humerus, init enc for [clsd, opn] fx
S42.22[1,2,3,4,5,6][A,B] 2-part [disp, nondisp] fx of surgical neck of [rt, lt, unsp] humerus, init enc for [clsd, opn] fx
S42.23[1,2,9][A,B] 3-part fx of surgical neck of [rt, lt, unsp] humerus, init enc for [clsd, opn] fx
S42.24[1,2,9][A,B] 4-part fx of surgical neck of [rt, lt, unsp] humerus, init enc for [clsd, opn] fx
S42.25[1,2,3,4,5,6][A,B] [Disp, Nondisp] fx of greater tuberosity of [rt, lt, unsp] humerus, init enc for [clsd, opn] fx
S42.26[1,2,3,4,5,6][A,B] [Disp, Nondisp] fx of lesser tuberosity of [rt, lt, unsp] humerus, init enc for [clsd, opn] fx
S42.27[1,2,9]A   Torus fx of upr end of humerus [rt, lt, unsp] init enc for clsd fx
S42.29[1,2,3,4,5,6][A,B] Oth [disp, nondisp] fx of upr end of [rt, lt, unsp] humerus, init enc for [clsd, opn] fx
S42.30[1,2,9][A,B] Unsp fx of shaft of humerus [rt, lt, unsp] arm, init enc for [clsd, opn] fx
S42.31[1,2,9]A   Greenstick fx of shaft of humerus, [rt, lt, unsp] arm, init enc for clsd fx
S42.32[1,2,3,4,5,6][A,B] [Disp, Nondisp] transv fx of shaft of humerus, [rt, lt, unsp] arm, init enc for [clsd, opn] fx
S42.33[1,2,3,4,5,6][A,B] [Disp, Nondisp] oblique fx of shaft of humerus, [rt, lt, unsp] arm, init enc for [clsd, opn] fx
S42.34[1,2,3,4,5,6][A,B] [Disp, Nondisp] spiral fx of shaft of humerus, [rt, lt, unsp] arm, init enc for [clsd, opn] fx
S42.35[1,2,3,4,5,6][A,B] [Disp, Nondisp] comm fx of shaft of humerus, [rt, lt, unsp] arm, init enc for [clsd, opn] fx
S42.36[1,2,3,4,5,6][A,B] [Disp, Nondisp] seg fx of shaft of humerus, [rt, lt, unsp] arm, init enc for [clsd, opn] fx
S42.39[1,2,9][A,B] Oth fx of shaft of [rt, lt, unsp] humerus, init enc for [clsd, opn] fx
S42.40[1,2,9][A,B] Unsp fx of lwr end of [rt, lt, unsp] humerus, init enc for [clsd, opn] fx
S42.41[1,2,3,4,5,6][A,B] [Disp, Nondisp] simple supracondylar fx w/o intercondylar fx of [rt, lt, unsp] humerus, init enc for [clsd, opn] fx
S42.42[1,2,3,4,5,6][A,B] [Disp, Nondisp] comm supracondylar fx w/o intercondylar fx of [rt, lt, unsp] humerus, init enc for [clsd, opn] fx
S42.43[1,2,3,4,5,6][A,B] [Disp, Nondisp] fx (avulsion) of lat epicondyle of [rt, lt, unsp] humerus, init enc for [clsd, opn] fx
S42.44[1,2,3,4,5,6,7,8,9][A,B] [Disp, Nondisp, Incarcerated] fx (avulsion) of med epicondyle of [rt, lt, unsp] humerus, init enc for [clsd, opn] fx
S42.45[1,2,3,4,5,6][A,B] [Disp, Nondisp] fx of lat condyle of [rt, lt, unsp] humerus, init enc for [clsd, opn] fx
S42.46[1,2,3,4,5,6][A,B] [Disp, Nondisp] fx of med condyle of [rt, lt, unsp] humerus, init enc for [clsd, opn] fx
S42.47[1,2,3,4,5,6][A,B] [Disp, Nondisp] transcondylar fx of [rt, lt, unsp] humerus, init enc for [clsd, opn] fx
S42.48[1,2,9]A   Torus fx of lwr end of [rt, lt, unsp] humerus, init enc for clsd fx
S42.49[1,2,3,4,5,6][A,B] Oth [disp, nondisp] fx of lwr end of [rt, lt, unsp] humerus, init enc for [clsd, opn] fx
S42.9[0,1,2]X[A,B] Fx of [unsp, rt, lt] shldr girdle, part unsp, init enc for [clsd, opn] fx
S43.00[1,2,3,4,5,6]A Unsp [sublux, disloc] of [rt, lt, unsp] shldr jt, init enc
S43.08[1,2,3,4,5,6]A Oth [sublux, disloc] of [rt, lt, unsp] shldr jt, init enc
S43.0[1,2,3][1,2,3,4,5,6]A [Ant, Post, Inferior] [sublux, disloc] of [rt, lt, unsp] humerus, init enc
S43.1[0,1][1,2,9]A [Unsp disloc, Sublux] of [rt, lt, unsp] acromioclavicular jt, init enc
S43.1[2,3][1,2,9]A Disloc of [rt, lt, unsp] acromioclavicular jt, [100%-200%, > 200%] displac, init enc
S43.1[4,5][1,2,9]A [Inferior, Post] disloc of [rt, lt, unsp] acromioclavicular jt, init enc

S43.2[0,1,2][1,2,3,4,5,6] [Unsp, Ant, Post] [sublux, disloc] of [rt, lt, unsp] sternoclavicular jt, init enc

S43.30[1,2,3,4,5,6]A [Sublux, Disloc] of unsp parts of [rt, lt, unsp] shldr girdle, init enc

S43.31[1,2,3,4,5,6]A [Sublux, Disloc] of [rt, lt, unsp] scapula, init enc

S43.39[1,2,3,4,5,6]A [Sublux, Disloc] of oth parts of [rt, lt, unsp] shldr girdle, init enc

S43.43[1,2,9]A Superior glenoid labrum lesion of [rt, lt, unsp] shldr, init enc

S43.49[1,2,9]A Oth sprain of [rt, lt, unsp] shldr jt, init enc

S43.4[0,1,2][1,2,9]A [Unsp sprain, Sprain] of [rt, lt, unsp] [shldr jt, coracohumeral (lgmt), rotator cuff capsule], init enc

S43.[5,6][0,1,2]XA Sprain of [unsp, rt, lt] [acromioclavicular, sternoclavicular] jt, init enc

S43.[8,9][0,1,2]XA Sprain of [oth spec, unsp] parts of [unsp, rt, lt] shldr girdle, init enc

S44.8X1A Inj of nerves at shldr/up arm, rt arm, init

S44.8X2A Inj of nerves at shldr/up arm, lt arm, init

S44.8X9A Inj of nerves at shldr/up arm, unsp arm, init

S44.[0,1,2][0,1,2]XA Inj of [ulnar, median, radial] nerve at upr arm lvl, [unsp, rt, lt] arm, init enc

S44.[3,4][0,1,2]XA Inj of [axillary, musculocutaneous] nerve, [unsp, rt, lt] arm, init enc

S44.[5,8,9][0,1,2]XA Inj of [cutaneous sensory, oth, unsp] nerve(s) at shldr and upr arm lvl, [unsp, rt, lt] arm, init enc

S45.0[0,1,9][1,2,9]A [Unsp inj, Lac, Oth spec inj] of axillary artery, [rt, lt, unsp] side, init enc

S45.1[0,1,9][1,2,9] A [Unsp inj, Lac, Oth spec inj] of brachial artery, [rt, lt, unsp] side, init enc

S45.2[0,1,9][1,2,9]A [Unsp inj, Lac, Oth spec inj] of axillary or brachial vein, [rt, lt, unsp] side, init enc

S45.3[0,1,9][1,2,9]A [Unsp inj, Lac, Oth spec inj] of superf vein at shldr and upr arm lvl, [rt, lt, unsp] arm, init enc

S45.8[0,1,9][1,2,9]A [Unsp inj, Lac, Oth spec inj] of oth spec bld vessels at shldr and upr arm lvl, [rt, lt, unsp] arm, init enc

S45.9[0,1,9][1,2,9]A [Unsp inj, Lac, Oth spec inj] of unsp bld vessel at shldr and upr arm lvl, [rt, lt, unsp] arm, init enc

S46.0[0,1,2,9][1,2,9]A [Unsp inj, Strain, Lac, Oth inj] of muscle(s) and tndn(s) of the rotator cuff of [rt, lt, unsp] shldr, init enc

S46.1[0,1,2,9][1,2,9]A [Unsp inj, Strain, Lac, Oth inj] of muscle, fascia and tndn of long head of biceps, [rt, lt, unsp] arm, init enc

S46.2[0,1,2,9][1,2,9]A [Unsp inj, Strain, Lac, Oth inj] of muscle, fascia and tndn of oth parts of biceps, [rt, lt, unsp] arm, init enc

S46.3[0,1,2,9][1,2,9]A [Unsp inj, Strain, Lac, oth inj] of muscle, fascia and tndn of triceps, [rt, lt, unsp] arm, init enc

S46.[8,9][0,1,2,9][1,2,9]A [Unsp inj, Strain, Lac, Oth inj] of [oth, unsp] muscle(s), fascia and tndn(s) at shldr and upr arm lvl, [rt, lt, unsp] arm, init enc

S47.[1,2,9]XXA Crushing inj of [rt, lt, unsp] shldr and upr arm, init enc

S48.0[1,2][1,2,9]A [Complete, Partial] traum amp at [rt, lt, unsp] shldr jt, init enc

S48.1[1,2][1,2,9]A [Complete, Partial] traum amp at lvl between [rt, lt, unsp] shldr and elbow, init enc

S48.9[1,2][1,2,9]A [Complete, Partial] traum amp of [rt, lt, unsp] shldr and upr arm, lvl unsp, init enc

S49.0[0,1,2,3,4,9][1,2,9]A [Unsp, Salter-Harris Type I, Salter-Harris Type II, Salter-Harris Type III, Salter-Harris Type IV, Oth] physeal fx of upr end of humerus, [rt, lt, unsp] arm, init enc for clsd fx

S49.1[0,1,2,3,4,9][1,2,9]A [Unsp, Salter-Harris Type I, Salter-Harris Type II, Salter-Harris Type III, Salter-Harris Type IV, Oth] physeal fx of lwr end of humerus, [rt, lt, unsp] arm, init enc for clsd fx

S49.[8,9][0,1,2]XA [Oth spec injuries, Unsp inj] of shldr and upr arm, [unsp, rt, lt] arm, init enc

S50.3[1,2,4,5,6,7][1,2,9]A [Abrasion, Blister (nonthermal), Ext constriction, Superf FB, Insect bite (nonvenomous), Oth superf bite] of [rt, lt, unsp] elbow, init enc

S50.8[1,2,4,5,6,7][1,2,9]A [Abrasion, Blister (nonthermal), Ext constriction, Superf FB, Insect bite (nonvenomous), Oth superf bite] of [rt, lt, unsp] forearm, init enc

S50.9[0,1][1,2,9]A Unsp superf inj of [rt, lt, unsp] [elbow, forearm], init enc

S50.[0,1][0,1,2]XA Contsn of [unsp, rt, lt] [elbow, forearm], init enc

S51.0[0,1,2,3,4,5][1,2,9]A [Unsp opn wnd, Lac w/o FB, Lac w/ FB, Punc wnd w/o FB, Punc wnd w/ FB, Opn bite] of [rt, lt, unsp] elbow, init enc

S51.8[0,1,2,3,4,5][1,2,9]A [Unsp opn wnd, Lac w/o FB, Lac w/ FB, Punc wnd w/o FB, Punc wnd w/ FB, Opn bite] of [rt, lt, unsp] forearm, init enc

S52.00[1,2,9][A,B,C] Unsp fx of upr end of [rt, lt, unsp] ulna, init enc for [clsd fx, opn fx type I or II, opn fx type IIIA, IIIB, or IIIC]

S52.01[1,2,9]A Torus fx of upr end of [rt, lt, unsp] ulna, init enc for clsd fx

S52.02[1,2,3,4,5,6][A,B,C] [Disp, Nondisp] fx of olecranon process w/o intraarticular extension of [rt, lt, unsp] ulna, init enc for [clsd fx, opn fx type I or II, opn fx type IIIA, IIIB, or IIIC]

S52.03[1,2,3,4,5,6][A,B,C] [Disp, Nondisp] fx of olecranon process w/ intraarticular extension of [rt, lt, unsp] ulna, init enc for [clsd fx, opn fx type I or II, opn fx type IIIA, IIIb, or IIIC]

S52.04[1,2,3,4,5,6][A,B,C] [Disp, Nondisp] fx of coronoid process of [rt, lt, unsp] ulna, init enc for [clsd fx, opn fx type I or II, opn fx type IIIA, IIIB, or IIIC]

S52.09[1,2,9][A,B,C] Oth fx of upr end of [rt, lt, unsp] ulna, init enc for [clsd fx, opn fx type I or II, opn fx type I or II, opn fx type IIIA, IIIB, or IIIC]

S52.10[1,2,9][A,B,C] Unsp fx of upr end of [rt, lt, unsp] radius, init enc for [clsd fx, opn fx type I or II, opn fx type IIIA, IIIB, or IIIC]

S52.11[1,2,9]A Torus fx of upr end of [rt, lt, unsp] radius, init enc for clsd fx

S52.12[1,2,3,4,5,6][A,B,C] [Disp, Nondisp] fx of head of [rt, lt, unsp] radius, init enc for [clsd fx, opn type I or II, opn fx IIIA, IIIB, or IIIC]

S52.13[1,2,3,4,5,6][A,B,C] [Disp, Nondisp] fx of neck of [rt, lt, unsp] radius, init enc for [clsd fx, opn fx type I or II, opn fx type IIIA, IIIB, or IIIC]

S52.18[1,2,9][A,B,C] Oth fx of upr end of [rt, lt, unsp] radius, init enc for [clsd fx, opn fx type I or II, opn fx type IIIA, IIIB, or IIIC]

S52.20[1,2,9][A,B,C] Unsp fx of shaft of [rt, lt, unsp] ulna, init enc for [clsd fx, opn fx type I or II, opn fx type IIIA, IIIB, or IIIC]

S52.21[1,2,9]A Greenstick fx of shaft of [rt, lt, unsp] ulna, init enc for clsd fx

S52.22[1,2,3,4,5,6][A,B,C] [Disp, Nondisp] transv fx of shaft of [rt, lt, unsp] ulna, init enc for [clsd fx, opn fx type I or II, opn fx type IIIA, IIIB, or IIIC]

S52.23[1,2,3,4,5,6][A,B,C] [Disp, Nondisp] oblique fx of shaft of [rt, lt, unsp] ulna, init enc for [clsd fx, opn fx type I or II, opn fx type IIIA, IIIB, or IIIC]

S52.24[1,2,3,4,5,6][A,B,C] [Disp, Nondisp] spiral fx of shaft of ulna, [rt, lt, unsp] arm, init enc for [clsd fx, opn fx type I or type II, opn fx type IIIA, IIIB, or IIIC]

S52.25[1,2,3,4,5,6][A,B,C] [Disp, Nondisp] comm fx of shaft of ulna, [rt, lt, unsp] arm, init enc for [clsd fx, opn fx type I or II, opn fx type IIIA, IIIB, or IIIC]

S52.26[1,2,3,4,5,6][A,B,C] [Disp, Nondisp] seg fx of shaft of ulna, [rt, lt, unsp] arm, init enc for [clsd fx, opn fx type I or II, opn fx type IIIA, IIIB, or IIIC]

S52.27[1,2,9][A,B,C] Monteggia's fx of [rt, lt, unsp] ulna, init enc for [clsd fx, opn fx type I or II, opn fx type IIIA, IIIB, or IIIC]

S52.28[1,2,3][A,B,C] Bent bone of [rt, lt, unsp] ulna, init enc for [clsd fx, opn fx type I or II, opn fx type IIIA, IIIB, or IIIC]

S52.29[1,2,9][A,B,C] Oth fx of shaft of [rt, lt, unsp] ulna, init enc for [clsd fx, opn fx type I or II, opn fx type IIIA, IIIB, or IIIC]

S52.30[1,2,9][A,B,C] Unsp fx of shaft of [rt, lt, unsp] radius, init enc for [clsd fx, opn fx type I or II, opn fx type IIIA, IIIB, or IIIC]

S52.31[1,2,9]A Greenstick fx of shaft of radius, [rt, lt, unsp] arm, init enc for clsd fx

S52.32[1,2,3,4,5,6][A,B,C] [Disp, Nondisp] transv fx of shaft of [rt, lt, unsp] radius, init enc for [clsd fx, opn fx type I or II, opn fx type IIIA, IIIB, or IIIC]

S52.33[1,2,3,4,5,6][A,B,C] [Disp, Nondisp] oblique fx of shaft of [rt, lt, unsp] radius, init enc for [clsd fx, opn fx type I or II, opn fx type IIIA, IIIB, or IIIC]

S52.34[1,2,3,4,5,6][A,B,C][Disp, Nondisp] spiral fx of shaft of radius, [rt, lt, unsp] arm, init enc for [clsd fx, opn fx type I or II, opn fx type IIIA, IIIB, or IIIC]

S52.35[1,2,3,4,5,6][A,B,C] [Disp, Nondisp] comm fx of shaft of radius, [rt, lt, unsp] arm, init enc for [clsd fx, opn fx type I or II, opn fx type IIIA, IIIB, or IIIC]

S52.36[1,2,3,4,5,6][A,B,C] [Disp, Nondisp] seg fx of shaft of radius, [rt, lt, unsp] arm, init enc for [clsd fx, opn fx type I or II, opn fx fx type IIIA, IIIB, or IIIC]

S52.37[1,2,9][A,B,C] Galeazzi's fx of [rt, lt, unsp] radius, init enc for [clsd fx, opn fx type I or II, opn fx type IIIA, IIIB, or IIIC]

S52.38[1,2,9][A,B,C] Bent bone of [rt, lt, unsp] radius, init enc for [clsd fx, opn fx type I or II, opn fx type IIIA, IIIB, or IIIC]

S52.39[1,2,9][A,B,C] Oth fx of shaft of radius [rt, lt, unsp] arm, init enc for [clsd fx, opn fx type I or II, opn fx type IIIA, IIIB, or IIIC]

S52.50[1,2,9][A,B,C] Unsp fx of the lwr end of [rt, lt, unsp] radius, init enc for [clsd fx, opn fx type I or II, opn fx type IIIA, IIIB, or IIIC]

S52.51[1,2,3,4,5,6][A,B,C] [Disp, Nondisp] fx of [rt, lt, unsp] radial styloid process, init enc for [clsd fx, opn fx type I or II, opn fx type IIIA, IIIB, or IIIC]

S52.52[1,2,9]A Torus fx of lwr end of [rt, lt, unsp] radius, init enc for clsd fx

S52.53[1,2,9][A,B,C] Colles' fx of [rt, lt, unsp] radius, init enc for [clsd fx, opn fx type I or II, opn fx type IIIA, IIIB, or IIIC]

S52.54[1,2,9][A,B,C] Smith's fx of [rt, lt, unsp] radius, init enc for [clsd fx, opn fx type I or II, opn fx type IIIA, IIIB, or IIIC]

S52.55[1,2,9][A,B,C] Oth extraarticular fx of lwr end of [rt, lt, unsp] radius, init enc for [clsd fx, opn fx type I or II, opn fx type IIIA, IIIB, or IIIC]

S52.56[1,2,9][A,B,C] Barton's fx of [rt, lt, unsp] radius, init enc for [clsd fx, opn fx type I or II, opn fx type IIIA, IIIB, or IIIC]

Surgical   **Medical**   **CC Indicator**   **MCC Indicator**   **Procedure Proxy**   PDxMCC **PDx acts as own MCC**   PDxCC **PDx acts as own CC**

MDC 24: Multiple Significant Trauma—MEDICAL

S52.57[1,2,9][A,B,C] Oth intraarticular fxs of lwr end of [rt, lt, unsp] radius, init enc for [clsd fx, opn fx type I or II, opn fx type IIIA, IIIB, or IIIC]

S52.59[1,2,9][A,B,C] Oth fxs of lwr end of [rt, lt, unsp] radius, init enc for [clsd fx, opn fx type I or II, opn fx type IIIA, IIIB, or IIIC]

S52.60[1,2,9][A,B,C] Unsp fx of lwr end of [rt, lt, unsp] ulna, init enc for [clsd fx, opn fx type I or II, opn fx type IIIA, IIIB, IIIC]

S52.61[1,2,3,4,5,6][A,B,C] [Disp, Nondisp] fx of [rt, lt, unsp] ulna styloid process, init enc for [clsd fx, opn fx type I or II, opn fx type IIIA, IIIB, or IIIC]

S52.62[1,2,9]A Torus fx of lwr end of [rt, lt, unsp] ulna, init enc for clsd fx

S52.69[1,2,9][A,B,C] Oth fx of lwr end of [rt, lt, unsp] ulna, init enc for [clsd fx, opn fx type I or II, opn fx type IIIA, IIIB, or IIIC]

S52.9[0,1,2]X[A,B,C] Oth fx of [unsp, rt, lt] forearm, init enc for [clsd fx, opn fx type I or II, opn fx type IIIA, IIIB, IIIC]

S53.0[0,1,2,3,9][1,2,3,4,5,6]A [Unsp, Ant, Post, Nursemaid's, Oth] [sublux, disloc] of [rt, lt, unsp] radial head, init enc

S53.1[0,1,2,3,4,9][1,2,3,4,5,6]A [Unsp, Ant, Post, Med, Lat, Oth] [sublux, disloc] of [rt, lt, unsp] ulnohumeral jt, init enc

S53.4[0,1,2,3,4,9][1,2,9]A [Unsp, Radiohumeral (jt), Ulnohumeral (jt), Radial collat lgmt, Ulnar collat lgmt, Oth] sprain of [rt, lt, unsp] elbow, init enc

S53.[2,3][0,1,2]XA Traum rupture of [unsp, rt, lt] [radial, ulnar] collat lgmt, init enc

S54.01XA Inj of ulnar nerve at forearm lvl, rt arm, init

S54.11XA Inj of median nerve at forearm lvl, rt arm, init

S54.21XA Inj of radial nerve at forearm lvl, rt arm, init

S54.31XA Inj of cutan sensory nerve at forarm lv, rt arm, init

S54.8X[1,2,9]A Unsp inj oth nerves at forearm lvl, [rt, lt, unsp] arm, init enc

S54.9[0,1,2]XA Inj of unsp nerve at forearm lvl, [unsp, rt, lt] arm, init enc

S54.[0,1,2,3][0,2,3]XA Inj of [ulnar, median, radial, cutaneous sensory] nerve at forearm lvl, [unsp, rt, lt] arm, init enc

S55.[0,1,2,8,9][0,1,9][1,2,9]A [Unsp inj, Lac, Oth spec inj] of [ulnar artery, radial artery, vein, oth bld vessels, unsp bld vessel] at forearm lvl, [rt, lt, unsp] arm, init enc

S56.0[0,1,2,9][1,2,9]A [Unsp inj, Strain, Lac, Oth inj] of flexor muscle, fascia and tndn of [rt, lt, unsp] thumb at forearm lvl, init enc

S56.1[0,1,2,9][1,2,3,4,5,6,7,8,9]A [Unsp inj, Strain, Lac, Oth inj] of flexor muscle, fascia and tndn of (of finger) [rt, lt] [index, mid, ring, little, unsp] finger at forearm lvl, init enc

S56.2[0,1,2,9][1,2,9]A [Unsp inj, Strain, Lac, Oth inj] of oth flexor muscle, fascia and tndn at forearm lvl, [rt, lt, unsp] arm, init enc

S56.3[0,1,2,9][1,2,9]A [Unsp inj, Strain, Lac, Oth inj] of extensor or abductor muscles, fascia and tndns of [rt, lt, unsp] thumb at forearm lvl, init enc

S56.4[0,1,2,9][1,2,3,,4,5,6,7,8,9]A [Unsp inj, Strain, Lac, Oth inj] of extensor muscle, fascia and tndn of (of finger,) [rt, lt] [index, mid, ring, little, unsp] finger at forearm lvl, init enc

S56.5[0,1,2,9][1,2,9]A [Unsp inj, Strain, Lac, Oth inj] of oth extensor muscle, fascia and tndn at forearm lvl, [rt, lt, unsp] arm, init enc

S56.[8,9][0,1,2,9][1,2,9]A [Unsp inj, Strain, Lac, Oth inj] of [oth, unsp] muscles, fascia and tndns at forearm lvl, [rt, lt, unsp] arm, init enc

S57.[0,8][0,1,2]XA Crushing inj of [unsp, rt, lt] [elbow, forearm], init enc

S58.0[1,2][1,2,9]A [Complete, Partial] traum amp at elbow lvl, [rt, lt, unsp] arm, init enc

S58.1[1,2][1,2,9]A [Complete, Partial] traum amp at lvl between elbow and wrist, [rt, lt, unsp] arm, init enc

S58.9[1,2][1,2,9]A [Complete, Partial] traum amp of [rt, lt, unsp] forearm, lvl unsp, init enc

S59.0[0,1,2,3,4,9][1,2,9]A [Unsp, Salter-HarrisType I, Salter-Harris Type II, Salter-Harris Type III, Salter-Harris Type IV, Oth] physeal fx of lwr end of ulna, [rt, lt, unsp] arm, init enc for clsd fx

S59.1[0,1,2,3,4,9][1,2,9]A [Unsp, Salter-Harris Type I, Salter-Harris Type II, Salter-Harris III, Salter-Harris IV, Oth] physeal fx of upr end of radius, [rt, lt, unsp] arm, init enc for clsd fx

S59.2[0,1,2,3,4,9][1,2,9]A [Unsp, Salter-Harris Type I, Salter-Harris Type II, Salter-Harris Type III, Salter-Harris Type IV, Oth] physeal fx of lwr end of radius, [rt, lt, unsp] arm, init enc for clsd fx

S59.[8,9][0,1][1,2,9]A [Oth spec injuries, Unsp inj] of [rt, lt, unsp] [elbow, forearm], init enc

S60.00XA Contsn of unsp finger w/o damage to nail, init enc

S60.0[1,2,3,4,5][1,2,9]A Contsn of [rt, lt, unsp] [thumb, index finger, mid finger, ring finger, little finger] w/o damage to nail, init enc

S60.10XA Contsn of unsp finger with damage to nail, init enc

S60.1[1,2,3,4,5][1,2,9]A Contsn of [rt, lt, unsp] [thumb, index finger, mid finger, ring finger, little finger] w/ damage to nail, init enc

S60.2[1,2][1,2,9]A Contsn of [rt, lt, unsp] [wrist, hand], init enc

S60.3[1,2,4,5,6,7,9][1,2,9]A [Abrasion, Blister (nonthermal), Ext constriction, Superf FB, Insect bite (nonvenomous), Oth superf bite, Oth superf injuries] of [rt, lt, unsp] thumb, init enc

S60.4[1,2,4,5,6,7][0,1,2,3,4,5,6,7,8,9]A [Abrasion, Blister (nonthermal), Ext constriction, Superf FB, Insect bite (nonvenomous), Oth superf bite] of [rt index, lt index, rt mid, lt mid, rt ring, lt ring, rt little, lt little, oth, unsp] finger, init enc

S60.5[1,2,4,5,6,7][1,2,9]A [Abrasion, Blister (nonthermal), Ext constriction, Superf FB, Insect bite (nonvenomous), Oth superf bite] of [rt, lt, unsp] hand, init enc

S60.8[1,2,4,5,6,7][1,2,9]A [Abrasion, Blister (nonthermal), Ext constriction, Superf FB, Insect bite (nonvenomous), Oth superf bite] of [rt, lt, unsp] wrist, init enc

S60.940A Unsp superf inj of rt index finger, init enc

S60.943A Unsp superf inj of lt mid finger, init enc

S60.944A Unsp superf inj of rt ring finger, init enc

S60.945A Unsp superf inj of lt ring finger, init enc

S60.946A Unsp superf inj of rt little finger, init enc

S60.947A Unsp superf inj of lt little finger, init enc

S60.948A Unsp superf inj of oth finger, init enc

S60.9[1,2,3,4][1,2,9]A Unsp superf inj of [rt, lt, unsp] [wrist, hand, thumb, index finger, mid finger, ring finger, little finger, oth finger, unsp finger], init enc

S61.0[0,1,2,3,4,5][1,2,9]A [Unsp opn wnd, Lac w/o FB, Lac w/ FB, Punc wnd w/o FB, Punc wnd w/ FB, Opn bite] of [rt, lt, unsp] thumb w/o damage to nail, init enc

S61.1[0,1,2,3,4,5][1,2,9]A [Unsp opn wnd, Lac w/o FB, Lac w/ FB, Punc wnd w/o FB, Punc wnd w/ FB, Opn bite] of [rt, lt, unsp] thumb w/ damage to nail, init enc

S61.2[0,1,2,3,4,5][0,1,2,3,4,5,6,7,8,9]A [Unsp opn wnd, Lac w/o FB, Lac w/ FB, Punc wnd w/o FB, Punc wnd w/ FB, Opn bite] of [rt index finger, lt index finger, rt mid finger, lt mid finger, rt ring finger, lt ring finger, rt little finger, lt little finger, oth finger, unsp finger] w/o damage to nail, init enc

S61.3[0,1,2,3,4,5][0,1,2,3,4,5,6,7,8,9]A [Unsp opn wnd, Lac w/o FB, Lac w/ FB, Punc wnd w/o FB, Punc wnd w/ FB, Opn bite] of [rt index finger, lt index finger, rt mid finger, lt mid finger, rt ring finger, lt ring finger, rt little finger, lt little finger, oth finger, unsp finger] w/ damage to nail, init enc

S61.[4,5][0,1,2,3,4,5][1,2,9]A [Unsp opn wnd, Lac w/o FB, Lac w/ FB, Punc wnd w/o FB, Punc wnd w/ FB, Opn bite] of [rt, lt, unsp] [hand, wrist], init enc

S62.00[1,2,9][A,B] Unsp fx of navicular [scaphoid] bone of [rt, lt, unsp] wrist, init enc for [clsd, opn] fx

S62.01[1,2,3,4,5,6][A,B] [Disp, Nondisp] fx of distal pole of navicular [scaphoid] bone of [rt, lt, unsp] wrist, init enc for [clsd, opn] fx

S62.02[1,2,3,4,5,6][A,B] [Disp, Nondisp] fx of mid 3rd of navicular [scaphoid] bone of [rt, lt, unsp] wrist, init enc for [clsd, opn] fx

S62.03[1,2,3,4,5,6][A,B] [Disp, Nondisp] fx of proximal 3rd of navicular [scaphoid] bone of [rt, lt, unsp] wrist, init enc for [clsd, opn] fx

S62.10[1,2,9][A,B] Fx of unsp carpal bone, [rt, lt, unsp] wrist, init enc for [clsd, opn] fx

S62.11[1,2,3,4,,5,6][A,B] [Disp, Nondisp] fx of triquetrum [cuneiform] bone, [rt, lt, unsp] wrist, init enc for [clsd, opn] fx

S62.12[1,2,3,4,5,6][A,B] [Disp, Nondisp] fx of lunate [semilunar], [rt, lt, unsp] wrist, init enc for [clsd, opn] fx

S62.13[1,2,3,4,5,6][A,B] [Disp, Nondisp] fx of capitate [os magnum] bone, [rt, lt, unsp] wrist, init enc for [clsd, opn] fx

S62.14[1,2,3,4,5,6][A,B] [Disp, Nondisp] fx of body of hamate [unciform] bone, [rt, lt, unsp] wrist, init enc for [clsd, opn] fx

S62.15[1,2,3,4,5,6][A,B] [Disp, Nondisp] fx of hook process of hamate [unciform] bone, [rt, lt, unsp] wrist, init enc for [clsd, opn] fx

S62.16[1,2,3,4,5,6][A,B] [Disp, Nondisp] fx of pisiform, [rt, lt, unsp] wrist, init enc for [clsd, opn] fx

S62.17[1,2,3,4,5,6][A,B] [Disp, Nondisp] fx of trapezium [lgr multangular], [rt, lt, unsp] wrist, init enc for [clsd, opn] fx

S62.18[1,2,3,4,5,6][A,B] [Disp, Nondisp] fx of trapezoid [smer multangular], [rt, lt, unsp] wrist, init enc for [clsd, opn] fx

S62.20[1,2,9][A,B] Unsp fx of 1st metacarpal bone, [rt, lt, unsp] hand, init enc for [clsd, opn] fx

S62.21[1,2,3][A,B] Bennett's fx, [rt, lt, unsp] hand, init enc for [clsd, opn] fx

S62.22[1,2,3,4,5,6][A,B] [Disp, Nondisp] Rolando's fx, [rt, lt, unsp] hand, init enc for [clsd, opn] fx

S62.23[1,2,3,4,5,6][A,B] Oth [disp, nondisp] fx of base of 1st metacarpal bone, [rt, lt, unsp] hand, init enc for [clsd, opn] fx

S62.24[1,2,3,4,5,6][A,B] [Disp, Nondisp] fx of shaft of 1st metacarpal bone, [rt, lt, unsp] hand, init enc for [clsd, opn] fx

S62.25[1,2,3,4,5,6][A,B] [Disp, Nondisp] fx of neck of 1st metacarpal bone, [rt, lt, unsp] hand, init enc for [clsd, opn] fx

S62.29[1,2,9][A,B] Oth fx of 1st metacarpal bone, [rt, lt, unsp] hand, init enc for [clsd, opn] fx

S62.30[0,1,2,3,4,5,6,7,8,9][A,B] Unsp fx of [2nd, 3rd, 4th, 5th, oth, unsp] metacarpal bone, (rt, lt) hand, init enc for [clsd, opn] fx

---

T Transfer DRG   SP Special Payment   * Code Range   6th and 7th Character of ZZ = No Device, No Qualifier ZX = No Device, Diagnostic

424   MS-DRG Version 33.0   © 2015 Optum360, LLC

S62.31[0,1,2,3,4,5,6,7,8,9][A,B] Disp fx of base of [2nd, 3rd, 4th, 5th, oth, unsp] metacarpal bone, (rt, lt) hand, init enc for [clsd, opn] fx
S62.32[0,1,2,3,4,5,6,7,8,9][A,B] Disp fx of shaft of [2nd, 3rd, 4th, 5th, oth, unsp] metacarpal bone, (rt, lt) hand, init enc for [clsd, opn] fx
S62.33[0,1,2,3,4,5,6,7,8,9][A,B] Disp fx of neck of [2nd, 3rd, 4th, 5th, oth, unsp] metacarpal bone, (rt, lt) hand, init enc for [clsd, opn] fx
S62.34[0,1,2,3,4,5,6,7,8,9][A,B] Nondisp fx of base of [2nd, 3rd, 4th, 5th, oth, unsp] metacarpal bone, (rt, lt) hand, init enc for [clsd, opn] fx
S62.35[0,1,2,3,4,5,6,7,8,9][A,B] Nondisp fx of shaft of [2nd, 3rd, 4th, 5th, oth, unsp] metacarpal bone, (rt, lt) hand, init enc for [clsd, opn] fx
S62.36[0,1,2,3,4,5,6,7,8,9][A,B] Nondisp fx of neck of [2nd, 3rd, 4th, 5th, oth, unsp] metacarpal bone, (rt, lt) hand, init enc for [clsd, opn] fx
S62.39[0,1,2,3,4,5,6,7,8,9][A,B] Oth fx of [2nd, 3rd, 4th, 5th, oth, unsp] metacarpal bone, (rt, lt) hand, init enc for [clsd, opn] fx
S62.50[1,2,9][A,B] Fx of unsp phalanx of [rt, lt, unsp] thumb, init enc for [clsd, opn] fx
S62.51[1,2,3,4,5,6][A,B] [Disp, Nondisp] fx of proximal phalanx of [rt, lt, unsp] thumb, init enc for [clsd, opn] fx
S62.52[1,2,3,4,5,6][A,B] [Disp, Nondisp] fx of distal phalanx of [rt, lt, unsp] thumb, init enc for [clsd, opn] fx
S62.60[0,1,2,3,4,5,6,7,8,9][A,B] Fx of unsp phalanx of [rt index, lt index, rt mid, lt mid, rt ring, lt ring, rt little, lt little, oth, unsp] finger, init enc for [clsd, opn] fx
S62.61[0,1,2,3,4,5,6,7,8,9] [A,B] Disp fx of proximal phalanx of [rt index, lt index, rt mid, lt mid, rt ring, lt ring, rt little, lt little, oth, unsp] finger, init enc for [clsd, opn] fx
S62.62[0,1,2,3,4,5,6,7,8,9] [A,B] Disp fx of med phalanx of [rt index, lt index, rt mid, lt mid, rt ring, lt ring, rt little, lt little, oth, unsp] finger, init enc for [clsd, opn] fx
S62.63[0,1,2,3,4,5,6,7,8,9] [A,B] Disp fx of distal phalanx of [rt index, lt index, rt mid, lt mid, rt ring, lt ring, rt little, lt little, oth, unsp] finger, init enc for [clsd, opn] fx
S62.64[0,1,2,3,4,5,6,7,8,9] [A,B] Nondisp fx of proximal phalanx of [rt index, lt index, rt mid, lt mid, rt ring, lt ring, rt little, lt little, oth, unsp] finger, init enc for [clsd, opn] fx
S62.65[0,1,2,3,4,5,6,7,8,9] [A,B] Nondisp fx of med phalanx of [rt index, lt index, rt mid, lt mid, rt ring, lt ring, rt little, lt little, oth, unsp] finger, init enc for [clsd, opn] fx
S62.66[0,1,2,3,4,5,6,7,8,9] [A,B] Nondisp fx of distal phalanx of [rt index, lt index, rt mid, lt mid, rt ring, lt ring, rt little, lt little, oth, unsp] finger, init enc for [clsd, opn] fx
S62.9[0,1,2]X[A,B] Unsp fx of [unsp, rt, lt] wrist and hand, init enc for [clsd, opn] fx
S63.00[1,2,3,4,5,6]A Unsp [sublux, disloc] of [rt, lt, unsp] wrist and hand, init enc
S63.04[1,2,3,4,5,6]A [Sublux, Disloc] of carpometacarpal jt of [rt, lt, unsp] thumb, init enc
S63.05[1,2,3,4,5,6]A [Sublux, Disloc] of oth carpometacarpal jt of [rt, lt, unsp] hand, init enc
S63.06[1,2,3,4,5,6]A [Sublux, Disloc] of metacarpal (bone), proximal end of [rt, lt, unsp] hand, init enc
S63.07[1,2,3,4,5,6]A [Sublux, Disloc] of distal end of [rt, lt, unsp] ulna, init enc
S63.09[1,2,3,4,5,6]A Oth [sublux, disloc] of [rt, lt, unsp] wrist and hand, init enc
S63.0[1,2,3][1,2,3,4,5,6]A [Sublux, Disloc] of [distal radioulnar, radiocarpal, midcarpal] jt of [rt, lt, unsp] wrist, init enc
S63.10[1,2,3,4,5,6]A Unsp [sublux, disloc] of [rt, lt, unsp] thumb, init enc
S63.1[1,2,3,4][1,2,3,4,5,6]A [Sublux, Disloc] of [metacarpophalangeal, unsp interphalangeal, proximal interphalangeal, distal interphalangeal] jt of [rt, lt, unsp] thumb, init enc
S63.20[0,1,2,3,4,5,6,7,8,9]A Unsp sublux of [rt index, lt index, rt mid, lt mid, rt ring, lt ring, rt little, lt little, oth, unsp] finger, init enc
S63.25[0,1,2,3,4,5,6,7,8,9]A Unsp disloc of [rt index, lt index, rt mid, lt mid, rt ring, lt ring, rt little, lt little, oth, unsp] finger, init enc
S63.2[1,2,3,4][0,1,2,3,4,5,6,7,8,9]A Sublux of [metacarpophalangeal, unsp interphalangeal, proximal interphalangeal, distal interphalangeal] jt of [rt, lt, oth, unsp] index finger, init enc
S63.2[6,7,8,9][0,1,2,3,4,5,6,7,8,9]A Disloc of [metacarpophalangeal, unsp interphalangeal, proximal interphalangeal, distal interphalangeal] jt of [rt index, lt index, rt mid, lt mid, rt ring, lt ring, rt little, lt little, oth, unsp] finger, init enc
S63.39[1,2,9]A Traum rupture of oth lgmt of [rt, lt, unsp] wrist, init enc
S63.3[0,1][1,2,9]A Traum rupture of [unsp, collat] lgmt of [rt, lt, unsp] wrist, init enc
S63.3[2,3][1,2,9]A Traum rupture of [rt, lt, unsp] [radiocarpal, ulnocarpal (palmar] lgmt, init enc
S63.43[0,1,2,3,4,5,6,7,8,9]A Traum rupture of volar plate of [rt index, lt index, rt mid, lt mid, rt ring, lt ring, rt little, lt little, oth, unsp] finger at metacarpophalangeal and interphalangeal jt, init enc
S63.49[0,1,2,3,4,5,6,7,8,9]A Traum rupture of oth lgmt of [rt index, lt index, rt mid, lt mid, rt ring, lt ring, rt little, lt little, oth, unsp] finger at metacarpophalangeal and interphalangeal jt, init enc

S63.4[0,1,2][0,1,2,3,4,5,6,7,8,9]A Traum rupture of [unsp, collat, palmar] lgmt of [rt index, lt index, rt mid, lt mid, rt ring, lt ring, rt little, lt little, oth, unsp] finger at metacarpophalangeal and interphalangeal jt, init enc
S63.50[1,2,9]A Unsp sprain of [rt, lt, unsp] wrist, init enc
S63.59[1,2,9]A Oth spec sprain of [rt, lt, unsp] wrist, init enc
S63.5[1,2][1,2,9]A Sprain of [carpal, radiocarpal] jt of [rt, lt, unsp] wrist, init enc
S63.60[1,2,9]A Unsp sprain of [rt, lt, unsp] thumb, init enc
S63.61[0,1,2,3,4,5,6,7,8,9]A Unsp sprain of [rt index, lt index, rt mid, lt mid, rt ring, lt ring, rt little, lt little, oth, unsp] finger, init enc
S63.62[1,2,9]A Sprain of interphalangeal jt of [rt, lt, unsp] thumb, init enc
S63.63[0,1,2,3,4,5,6,7,8,9]A Sprain of interphalangeal jt of [rt index, lt index, rt mid, lt mid, rt ring, lt ring, rt little, lt little, oth, unsp] finger, init enc
S63.64[1,2,9]A Sprain of metacarpophalangeal jt of [rt, lt, unsp] thumb, init enc
S63.65[0,1,2,3,4,5,6,7,8,9]A Sprain of metacarpophalangeal jt of [rt index, lt index, rt mid, lt mid, rt ring, lt ring, rt little, lt little, oth, unsp] finger, init enc
S63.68[1,2,9]A Oth sprain of [rt, lt, unsp] thumb, init enc
S63.69[0,1,2,3,4,5,6,7,8,9]A Oth sprain of [rt index, lt index, rt mid, lt mid, rt ring, lt ring, rt little, lt little, oth, unsp] finger, init enc
S63.8X[1,2,9]A Sprain of oth part of [rt, lt, unsp] wrist and hand, init enc
S63.90XA Sprain of unsp part of unsp wrist and hand, init enc
S63.91XA Sprain of unsp part of rt wrist and hand, init enc
S63.92XA Sprain of unsp part of lt wrist and hand, init enc
S64.3[0,1,2]XA Inj of digital nerve of [unsp, rt, lt] thumb, init enc
S64.40XA Inj of digital nerve of unsp finger, init enc
S64.49[0,1,2,3,4,5,6,7,8]A Inj of digital nerve of [rt index, lt index, rt mid, lt mid, rt ring, lt ring, rt little, lt little, oth] finger, init enc
S64.8X[1,2,9]A Inj of oth nerves at wrist and hand lvl of [rt, lt, unsp] arm, init enc
S64.9[0,1,2]XA Inj of unsp nerve at wrist and hand lvl of [unsp, rt, lt] arm, init enc
S64.[0,1,2][0,1,2]XA Inj of [ulnar, median, radial] nerve at wrist and hand lvl of [unsp, rt, lt] arm, init enc
S65.4[0,1,9][1,2,9]A [Unsp inj, Lac, Oth spec inj] of bld vessel of [rt, lt, unsp] thumb, init enc
S65.5[0,1,9][0,1,2,3,4,5,6,7,8,9]A [Unsp inj, Lac, Oth spec inj] of bld vessel of [rt index, lt index, rt mid, lt mid, rt ring, lt ring, rt little, lt little, oth, unsp] finger, init enc
S65.[0,1][0,1,9][1,2,9]A [Unsp inj, Lac, Oth spec inj] of [ulnar, radial] artery at wrist and hand lvl of [rt, lt, unsp] arm, init enc
S65.[2,3][0,1,9][1,2,9]A [Unsp inj, Lac, Oth spec inj] of [superf, deep] palmar arch of [rt, lt, unsp] hand, init enc
S65.[8,9][0,1,9][1,2,9]A [Unsp inj, Lac, Oth spec inj] of oth bld vessels at wrist and hand lvl of [rt, lt, unsp] arm, init enc
S66.0[0,1,2,9][1,2,9]A [Unsp inj, Strain, Lac, Oth spec inj] of long flexor muscle, fascia and tndn of [rt, lt, unsp] thumb at wrist and hand lvl, init enc
S66.1[0,1,2,9][0,1,2,3,4,5,6,7,8,9]A [Unsp inj, Strain, Lac, Oth inj] of flexor muscle, fascia and tndn of [rt index, lt index, rt mid, lt mid, rt ring, lt ring, rt little, lt little, oth, unsp] finger at wrist and hand lvl, init enc
S66.291A Inj extensor musc/fasc/tend rt thumb at wrs/hnd lv, init
S66.292A Inj extensor musc/fasc/tend lt thumb at wrs/hnd lv, init
S66.299A Inj extensor musc/fasc/tend thmb at wrs/hnd lv, init
S66.2[0,1,9][1,2,9]A [Unsp inj, Strain, Lac, oth spec inj] of extensor muscle, fascia and tndn of [rt, lt, unsp] thumb at wrist and hand lvl, init enc
S66.3[0,1,2,9][0,1,2,3,4,5,6,7,8,9]A [Unsp inj, Strain, Lac, Oth inj] of extensor muscle, fascia and tndn of [rt index, lt index, rt mid, lt mid, rt ring, lt ring, rt little, lt little, oth, unsp] finger at wrist and hand lvl, init enc
S66.4[0,1,2,9][1,2,9]A [Unsp inj, Strain, Lac, Oth spec inj] of intrinsic muscle, fascia and tndn of [rt, lt, unsp] thumb at wrist and hand lvl, init enc
S66.5[0,1,2,9][0,1,2,3,4,5,6,7,8,9]A [Unsp inj, Strain, Lac, Oth inj] of intrinsic muscle, fascia and tndn of [rt index, lt index, rt mid, lt mid, rt ring, lt ring, rt little, lt little, oth, unsp] finger at wrist and hand lvl, init enc
S66.[8,9][0,1,2,9][1,2,9]A [Unsp inj, Strain, Lac, Oth inj] of [oth spec, unsp] muscles, fascia and tndns at wrist and hand lvl, [rt, lt, unsp] hand, init enc
S67.0[0,1,2]XA Crushing inj of [unsp, rt, lt] thumb, init enc
S67.10XA Crushing inj of unsp finger(s), init enc
S67.19[0,1,2,3,4,5,6,7,8]A Crushing inj of [rt index, lt index, rt ring, lt ring, rt mid, lt mid, rt little, lt little, oth] finger, init enc
S67.2[0,1,2]XA Crushing inj of [unsp, rt, lt] hand, init enc
S67.3[0,1,2]XA Crushing inj of [unsp, rt, lt] wrist, init enc
S67.4[0,1,2]XA Crushing inj of [unsp, rt, lt] wrist and hand, init enc

Surgical   **Medical**   **CC Indicator**   **MCC Indicator**   **Procedure Proxy**   [PDxMCC] **PDx acts as own MCC**   [PDxCC] **PDx acts as own CC**

S67.9[0,1,2]XA Crushing inj of unsp parts of [unsp, rt, lt] hand and fingers, init enc

S68.0[1,2][1,2,9]A [Complete, Partial] traum metacarpophalangeal amp of [rt, lt, unsp] thumb, init enc

S68.1[1,2][0,1,2,3,4,5,6,7,8,9]A[Complete, Partial] traum metacarpophalangeal amp of [rt index, lt index, rt mid, lt mid, rt ring, lt ring, rt little, lt little, oth, unsp] finger, init enc

S68.4[1,2][1,2,9]A [Complete, Partial] traum amp of [rt, lt, unsp] hand at wrist lvl, init enc

S68.5[1,2][1,2,9]A [Complete, Partial] traum transphalangeal amp of [rt, lt, unsp] thumb, init enc

S68.6[1,2][0,1,2,3,4,5,6,7,8,9]A [Complete, Partial] traum transphalangeal amp of [rt index, lt index, rt mid, lt mid, rt ring, lt ring, rt little, lt little, oth, unsp] finger, init enc

S68.7[1,2][1,2,9]A [Complete, Partial] traum transmetacarpal amp of [rt, lt, unsp] hand, init enc

S69.[8,9][0,1,2]XA [Oth spec injuries, Unsp inj] of [unsp, rt, lt] wrist, hand and finger(s), init enc

S70.2[1,2,4,5,6,7][1,2,9]A [Abrasion, Blister (nonthermal), Ext constriction, Superf FB, Insect bite (nonvenomous), Oth superf bite], [rt, lt, unsp] hip, init enc

S70.3[1,2,4,5,6,7][1,2,9]A [Abrasion, Blister (nonthermal), Ext constriction, Superf FB, Insect bite (nonvenomous), Oth superf bite], [rt, lt, unsp] thigh, init enc

S70.9[1,2][1,2,9]A Unsp superf inj of [rt, lt, unsp] [hip, thigh], init enc

S70.[0,1][0,1,2]XA Contsn of [unsp, rt, lt] [hip, thigh], init enc

S71.0[0,1,2,3,4,5][1,2,9]A [Unsp opn wnd, Lac w/o FB, Lac w/ FB, Punc wnd w/o FB, Punc wnd w/ FB, Opn bite], [rt, lt, unsp] hip, init enc

S71.111A Lac w/o FB, rt thigh, init enc
S71.112A Lac w/o FB, lt thigh, init enc
S71.119A Lac w/o FB, unsp thigh, init enc
S71.121A Lac with FB, rt thigh, init enc
S71.122A Lac with FB, lt thigh, init enc
S71.129A Lac with FB, unsp thigh, init enc

S71.1[0,12,3,4,5][1,2,9]A [Unsp opn wnd, Lac w/o FB, Lac w/ FB, Punc wnd w/o FB, Punc wnd w/ FB, Opn bite], [rt, lt, unsp] thigh, init enc

S72.00[1,2,9][A,B,C] Fx of unsp part of neck of [rt, lt, unsp] femur, init enc for [clsd fx, opn fx type I or II, opn fx type IIIA, IIIB, or IIIC]

S72.01[1,2,9][A,B,C] Unsp intracapsular fx of [rt, lt, unsp] femur, init enc for [clsd fx, opn fx type I or II, opn fx type IIIA, IIIB, or IIIC]

S72.02[1,2,3,4,5,6][A,B,C] [Disp, Nondisp] fx of epiphysis (separation) (upr) of [rt, lt, unsp] femur, init enc for [clsd fx, opn fx type I or II, opn fx type IIIA, IIIB, or IIIC]

S72.03[1,2,3,4,5,6][A,B,C][Disp, Nondisp] midcervical fx of [rt, lt, unsp] femur, init enc for [clsd fx, opn fx type I or II, opn fx type IIIA, IIIB, or IIIC]

S72.04[1,2,3,4,5,6][A,B,C][Disp, Nondisp] fx of base of neck of [rt, lt, unsp] femur, init enc for [clsd fx, opn fx type I or II, opn fx type IIIA, IIIB, or IIIC]

S72.05[1,2,9][A,B,C] Unsp fx of head of [rt, lt, unsp] femur, init enc for [clsd fx, opn fx type I or II, opn fx type IIIA, IIIB, or IIIC]

S72.06[1,2,3,4,5,6][A,B,C] [Disp, Nondisp] articular fx of head of [rt, lt, unsp] femur, init enc for [clsd fx, opn fx type I or II, opn fx type IIIA, IIIB, or IIIC]

S72.09[1,2,9][A,B,C] Oth fx of head and neck of [rt, lt, unsp] femur, init enc for [clsd fx, opn fx type I or II, opn fx type IIIA, IIIB, or IIIC]

S72.10[1,2,9][A,B,C] Unsp trochanteric fx of [rt, lt, unsp] femur, init enc for [clsd fx, opn fx type I or II, opn fx type IIIA, IIIB, or IIIC]

S72.11[1,2,3,4,5,6][A,B,C] [Disp, Nondisp] fx of greater trochanter of [rt, lt, unsp] femur, init enc for [clsd fx, opn fx type I or II, opn fx type IIIA, IIIB, or IIIC]

S72.12[1,2,3,4,5,6][A,B,C] [Disp, Nondisp] fx of lesser trochanter of [rt, lt, unsp] femur, init enc for [clsd fx, opn fx type I or II, opn fx type IIIA, IIIB, or IIIC]

S72.13[1,2,3,4,5,6][A,B,C] [Disp, Nondisp] apophyseal fx of [rt, lt, unsp] femur, init enc for [clsd fx, opn fx type I or II, opn fx type IIIA, IIIB, or IIIC]

S72.14[1,2,3,4,5,6][A,B,C] [Disp, Nondisp] intertrochanteric fx of [rt, lt, unsp] femur, init enc for [clsd fx, opn fx type I or II, opn fx type IIIA, IIIB, or IIIC]

S72.2[1,2,3,4,5,6]X[A,B,C] [Disp, Nondisp] subtrochanteric fx of [rt, lt, unsp] femur, init enc for [clsd fx, opn fx type I or II, opn fx type IIIA, IIIB, IIIC]

S72.30[1,2,9][A,B,C] Unsp fx of shaft of [rt, lt, unsp] femur, init enc for [clsd fx, opn fx type I or II, opn fx type IIIA, IIIB, or IIIC]

S72.32[1,2,3,4,5,6][A,B,C] [Disp, Nondisp] transv fx of shaft of [rt, lt, unsp] femur, init enc for [clsd fx,opn fx type I or II, opn fx type IIIA, IIIB, or IIIC]

S72.33[1,2,3,4,5,6][A,B,C] [Disp, Nondisp] oblique fx of shaft of [rt, lt, unsp] femur, init enc for [clsd fx, opn fx type I or II, opn fx type IIIA, IIIB, or IIIC]

S72.34[1,2,3,4,5,6][A,B,C] [Disp, Nondisp] spiral fx of shaft of [rt, lt, unsp] femur, init enc for [clsd fx, opn fx type I or II, opn fx type IIIA, IIIB, or IIIC]

S72.35[1,2,3,4,5,6][A,B,C] [Disp, Nondisp] comm fx of shaft of [rt, lt, unsp] femur, init enc for [clsd fx, opn fx type I or II, opn fx type IIIA, IIIB, IIIC]

S72.36[1,2,3,4,5,6][A,B,C] [Disp, Nondisp] seg fx of shaft of [rt, lt, unsp] femur, init enc for [clsd fx, opn fx type I or II, opn fx type IIIA, IIIB, or IIIC]

S72.39[1,2,9][A,B,C] Oth fx of shaft of [rt, lt, unsp] femur, init enc for [clsd fx, opn fx type I or II, opn fx type IIIA, IIIB, or IIIC]

S72.40[1,2,9][A,B,C] Unsp fx of lwr end of [rt, lt, unsp] femur, init enc for [clsd fx, opn fx type I or II, opn fx type IIIA, IIIB, or IIIC]

S72.41[1,2,3,4,5,6][A,B,C] [Disp, Nondisp] unsp condyle fx of lwr end of [rt, lt, unsp] femur, init enc for [clsd fx, opn fx type I or II, opn fx type IIIA, IIIB, or IIIC]

S72.42[1,2,3,4,5,6][A,B,C] [Disp, Nondisp] fx of lat condyle of [rt, lt, unsp] femur, init enc for [clsd fx, opn fx type I or II, opn fx type IIIA, IIIB, or IIIC]

S72.43[1,2,3,4,5,6][A,B,C] [Disp, Nondisp] fx of med condyle of [rt, lt, unsp] femur, init enc for [clsd fx, opn fx type I or II, opn fx type IIIA, IIIB, or IIIC]

S72.44[1,2,3,4,5,6][A,B,C] [Disp, Nondisp] fx of lwr epiphysis (separation) of [rt, lt, unsp] femur, init enc for [clsd fx, opn fx type I or II, opn fx type IIIA, IIIB, or IIIC]

S72.45[1,2,3,4,5,6][A,B,C] [Disp, Nondisp] supracondylar fx w/o intracondylar extension of lwr end of [rt, lt, unsp] femur, init enc for [clsd fx, opn fx type I or II, opn fx type IIIA, IIIB, or IIIC]

S72.46[1,2,3,4,5,6][A,B,C] [Disp, Nondisp] supracondylar fx w/ intracondylar extension of lwr end of [rt, lt, unsp] femur, init enc for [clsd fx, opn fx type I or II, opn fx type IIIA, IIIB, or IIIC]

S72.47[1,2,9]A Torus fx of lwr end of [rt, lt, unsp] femur, init enc for clsd fx

S72.49[1,2,9][A,B,C] Oth fx of lwr end of [rt, lt, unsp] femur, init enc for [clsd fx, opn fx type I or II, opn fx type IIIA, IIIB, or IIIC]

S72.8X[1,2,9][A,B,C] Oth fx of [rt, lt, unsp] femur, init enc for [clsd fx, opn fx type I or II, opn fx type IIIA, IIIB, or IIIC]

S72.9[0,1,2]X[A,B,C] Unsp fx of [unsp, rt lt] femur, init enc for [clsd fx, opn fx type I or II, opn fx type IIIA, IIIB, or IIIC]

S73.00[1,2,3,4,5,6]A Unsp [sublux, disloc] of [rt, lt, unsp] hip, init enc
S73.01[1,2,3,4,5,6]A Post [sublux, disloc] of [rt, lt, unsp] hip, init enc
S73.02[1,2,3,4,5,6]A Obturator [sublux, disloc] of [rt, lt, unsp] hip, init enc
S73.03[1,2,3,4,5,6]A Oth ant [sublux, disloc] of [rt, lt, unsp] hip, init enc
S73.04[1,2,3,4,5,6]A Central [sublux, disloc] of [rt, lt, unsp] hip, init enc
S73.10[1,2,9]A Unsp sprain of [rt, lt, unsp] hip, init enc
S73.19[1,2,9]A Oth sprain of [rt, lt, unsp] hip, init enc
S73.1[1,2][1,2,9]A [Iliofemoral, Ischiocapsular] lgmt sprain of [rt, lt, unsp] hip, init enc

S74.8X[1,2,9]A Inj of oth nerves at hip & thigh lvl, [rt, lt, unsp] leg, init enc
S74.9[0,1,2]XA Inj of unsp nerve at hip & thigh lvl, [unsp, rt, lt] leg, init enc
S74.[0,1,2][0,1,2]XA Inj of [sciatic, femor, cutaneous sensory] nerve at hip & thigh lvl, [unsp, rt, lt] leg, init enc

S75.0[0,1,2,9][1,2,9]A [Unsp inj, Minor lac, Major lac, Oth spec inj] of femor artery, [rt, lt, unsp] leg, init enc

S75.1[0,1,2,9][1,2,9]A [Unsp inj, Minor lac, Major lac, Oth spec inj] of femor vein at hip & thigh lvl, [rt, lt, unsp] leg, init enc

S75.2[0,1,2,9][1,2,9]A [Unsp inj, Minor lac, Major lac, Oth spec inj] of greater saphenous vein at hip & thigh lvl, [rt, lt, unsp] leg, init enc

S75.8[0,1,9][1,2,9]A [Unsp inj, Lac, Oth spec inj] of oth bld vessels at hip & thigh lvl, [rt, lt, unsp] leg, init enc

S75.9[0,1,9][1,2,9]A [Unsp inj, Lac, Oth spec inj] of unsp bld vessel at hip & thigh lvl, [rt, lt, unsp] leg, init enc

S76.0[0,1,2,9][1,2,9]A [Unsp inj, Strain, Lac, Oth spec inj] of muscle, fascia and tndn of [rt, lt, unsp] hip, init enc

S76.1[0,1,2,9][1,2,9]A [Unsp inj, Strain, Lac, Oth spec inj] of [rt, lt, unsp] quadriceps muscle, fascia and tndn, init enc

S76.2[0,1,2,9][1,2,9]A [Unsp inj, Strain, Lac, Oth inj] of adductor muscle, fascia and tndn of [rt, lt, unsp] thigh, init enc

S76.3[0,1,2,9][1,2,9]A [Unsp inj, Strain, Lac, Oth inj] of muscle, fascia and tndn of the post muscle group at thigh lvl, [rt, lt, unsp] thigh, init enc

S76.8[0,1,2,9][1,2,9]A [Unsp inj, Strain, Lac, Oth inj] of oth spec muscles, fascia and tndns at thigh lvl, [rt, lt, unsp] thigh, init enc

S76.9[0,1,2,9][1,2,9]A [Unsp inj, Strain, Lac, Oth spec inj] of unsp muscles, fascia and tndns at thigh lvl, [rt, lt, unsp] thigh, init enc

S77.[0,1,2][0,1,2]XA Crushing inj of [unsp, rt, lt] [hip, thigh, hip w/ thigh], init enc

S78.0[1,2][1,2,9]A [Complete, Partial] traum amp at [rt, lt, unsp] hip jt, init enc

S78.1[1,2][1,2,9]A [Complete, Partial] traum amp at lvl between [rt, lt, unsp] hip and knee, init enc

S78.9[1,2][1,2,9]A [Complete, Partial] traum amp of [rt, lt, unsp] hip & thigh, lvl unsp, init enc

S79.00[1,2,9]A Unsp physeal fx of upr end of [rt, lt, unsp] femur, init enc for clsd fx

---

T Transfer DRG   SP Special Payment   * Code Range   6th and 7th Character of ZZ = No Device, No Qualifier ZX = No Device, Diagnostic

426   MS-DRG Version 33.0   © 2015 Optum360, LLC

S79.01[1,2,9]A Salter-Harris Type I physeal fx of upr end of [rt, lt, unsp] femur, init enc for clsd fx

S79.09[1,2,9]A Oth physeal fx of upr end of [rt, lt, unsp] femur, init enc for clsd fx

S79.10[1,2,9]A Unsp physeal fx of lwr end of [rt, lt, unsp] femur, inital enc for clsd fx

S79.19[1,2,9]A Oth physeal fx of lwr end of [rt, lt, unsp] femur, inital enc for clsd fx

S79.1[1,2,3,4][1,2,9]ASalter-Harris [Type I, Type II, Type III, Type IV] physeal fx of lwr end of [rt, lt, unsp] femur, init enc for clsd fx

S79.8[1,2][1,2,9]A Oth spec injuries of [rt, lt, unsp] [hip, thigh], init enc

S79.9[1,2][1,2,9]A Unsp inj of [rt, lt, unsp] [hip, thigh], init enc

S80.8[1,2,4,5,6,7][1,2,9]A [Abrasion, Blister (nonthermal), Ext constriction, Superf FB, Insect bite (nonvenomous), Oth superf bite] [rt, lt, unsp] lwr leg, init enc

S80.9[1,2][1,2,9]A Unsp superf inj of [rt, lt, unsp] [knee, lwr leg], init enc

S80.[0,1][0,1,2]XA Contsn of [unsp, rt, lt] [knee, lwr leg], init enc

S80.[2,8][1,2,4,5,6,7][1,2,9]A [Abrasion, Blister (nonthermal), Superf FB, Insect bite (nonvenomous), Oth superf bite] [rt, lt, unsp] knee, init enc

S81.0[0,1,2,3,4,5][1,2,9]A [Unsp opn wnd, Lac w/o FB, Lac w/ FB, Punc wnd w/o FB, Punc wnd w/ FB, Opn bite] [rt, lt, unsp] knee, init enc

S81.8[0,1,2,3,4,5][1,2,9]A [Unsp opn wnd, Lac w/o FB, Lac w/ FB, Punc wnd w/o FB, Punc wnd w/ FB, Opn bite] [rt, lt, unsp] lwr leg, init enc

S82.00[1,2,9][A,B,C]Unsp fx of [rt, lt, unsp] patella, init enc for [clsd fx, opn fx type I or II, opn fx type IIIA, IIIB, or IIIC]

S82.01[1,2,3,4,5,6][A,B,C] [Disp, Nondisp] osteochondral fx of [rt, lt, unsp] patella, init enc for [clsd fx, opn fx type I or II, opn fx type IIIA, IIIB, or IIIC]

S82.02[1,2,3,4,5,6][A,B,C] [Disp, Nondisp] longitudinal fx of [rt, lt, unsp] patella, init enc for [clsd fx, opn fx type I or II, opn fx type IIIA, IIIB, or IIIC]

S82.03[1,2,3,4,5,6][A,B,C] [Disp, Nondisp] transv fx of [rt, lt, unsp] patella, init enc for [clsd fx, opn fx type I or II, opn fx type IIIA, IIIB, or IIIC]

S82.04[1,2,3,4,5,6][A,B,C] [Disp, Nondisp] comm fx of [rt, lt, unsp] patella, init enc for [clsd fx, opn fx type I or II, opn fx type IIIA, IIIB, or IIIC]

S82.09[1,2,9][A,B,C] Oth fx of [rt, lt, unsp] patella, init enc for [clsd fx, opn fx type I or II, opn fx type IIIA, IIIB, or IIIC]

S82.10[1,2,9][A,B,C] Unsp fx of upr end of [rt, lt, unsp] tibia, init enc for [clsd fx, fx type I or II, opn fx type IIIA, IIIB, or IIIC]

S82.11[1,2,3,4,5,6][A,B,C] [Disp, Nondisp] fx of [rt, lt, unsp] tibial spine, init enc for [clsd fx, opn fx type I or II, opn fx type IIIA, IIIB, or IIIC]

S82.12[1,2,3,4,5,6][A,B,C] [Disp, Nondisp] fx of lat condyle of [rt, lt, unsp] tibia, init enc for [clsd fx, opn fx type I or II, opn fx type IIIA, IIIB, or IIIC]

S82.13[1,2,3,4,5,6][A,B,C] [Disp, Nondisp] fx of med condyle of [rt, lt, unsp] tibia, init enc for [clsd fx, opn fx type I or II, opn fx type IIIA, IIIB, or IIIC]

S82.14[1,2,3,4,5,6][A,B,C] [Disp, Nondisp] bicondylar fx of [rt, lt, unsp] tibia, init enc for [clsd fx, opn fx type I or II, opn fx type IIIA, IIIB, or IIIC]

S82.15[1,2,3,4,5,6][A,B,C] [Disp, Nondisp] fx of [rt, lt, unsp] tibial tuberosity, init enc for [clsd fx, opn fx type I or II, opn fx type IIIA, IIIB, IIIC]

S82.16[1,2,9]A Torus fx of upr end of [rt, lt, unsp] tibia, init enc for clsd fx

S82.19[1,2,9][A,B,C] Oth fx of upr end of [rt, lt, unsp] tibia, init enc for [clsd fx, opn fx type I or II, opn fx type IIIA, IIIB, or IIIC]

S82.20[1,2,9][A,B,C] Unsp fx of shaft of [rt, lt, unsp] tibia, init enc for [clsd fx, opn fx type I or II, opn fx type IIIA, IIIB, or IIIC]

S82.22[1,2,3][A,B,C] Disp transv fx of shaft of [rt, lt, unsp] tibia, [init enc for clsd fx, init enc for opn fx type I or II, init enc for opn fx type IIIA, IIIB, or IIIC]

S82.22[4,5,6][A,B,C]Nondisp transv fx of shaft of [rt, lt, unsp] tibia, [init enc for clsd fx, init enc for opn fx type I or II, init enc for opn fx type IIIA, IIIB, or IIIC]

S82.23[1,2,3][A,B,C] Disp oblique fx of shaft of [rt, lt, unsp] tibia, [init enc for clsd fx, init enc for opn fx type I or II, init enc for opn fx type IIIA, IIIB, or IIIC]

S82.23[4,5,6][A,B,C] Nondisp oblique fx of shaft of [rt, lt, unsp] tibia, [init enc for clsd fx, init enc for opn fx type I or II, init enc for opn fx type IIIA, IIIB, or IIIC]

S82.24[1,2,3][A,B,C] Disp spiral fx of shaft of [rt, lt, unsp] tibia, [init enc for clsd fx, init enc for opn fx type I or II, init enc for opn fx type IIIA, IIIB, or IIIC]

S82.24[4,5,6][A,B,C] Nondisp spiral fx of shaft of [rt, lt, unsp] tibia, [init enc for clsd fx, init enc for opn fx type I or II, init enc for opn fx type IIIA, IIIB, or IIIC]

S82.25[1,2,3][A,B,C] Disp comm fx of shaft of [rt, lt, unsp] tibia, [init enc for clsd fx, init enc for opn fx type I or II, init enc for opn fx type IIIA, IIIB, or IIIC]

S82.25[4,5,6][A,B,C] Nondisp comm fx of shaft of [rt, lt, unsp] tibia, [init enc for clsd fx, init enc for opn fx type I or II, init enc for opn fx type IIIA, IIIB, or IIIC]

S82.26[1,2,3][A,B,C] Disp seg fx of shaft of [rt, lt, unsp] tibia, [init enc for clsd fx, init enc for opn fx type I or II, init enc for opn fx type IIIA, IIIB, or IIIC]

S82.26[4,5,6][A,B,C] Nondisp seg fx of shaft of [rt, lt, unsp] tibia, [init enc for clsd fx, init enc for opn fx type I or II, init enc for opn fx type IIIA, IIIB, or IIIC]

S82.29[1,2,9][A,B,C] Oth fx of shaft of [rt, lt, unsp] tibia, [init enc for clsd fx, init enc for opn fx type I or II, init enc for opn fx type IIIA, IIIB, or IIIC]

S82.30[1,2,9][A,B,C] Unsp fx of lwr end of [rt, lt, unsp] tibia, [init enc for clsd fx, init enc for opn fx type I or II, init enc for opn fx type IIIA, IIIB, or IIIC]

S82.31[1,2,9]A Torus fx of lwr end of [rt, lt, unsp] tibia, init enc for clsd fx

S82.39[1,2,9][A,B,C] Oth fx of lwr end of [rt, lt, unsp] tibia, [init enc for clsd fx, init enc for opn fx type I or II, init enc for opn fx type IIIA, IIIB, or IIIC]

S82.40[1,2,9][A,B,C] Unsp fx of shaft of [rt, lt, unsp] fibula, [init enc for clsd fx, init enc for opn fx type I or II, init enc for opn fx type IIIA, IIIB, or IIIC]

S82.42[1,2,3][A,B,C] Disp transv fx of shaft of [rt, lt, unsp] fibula, [init enc for clsd fx, init enc for opn fx type I or II, init enc for opn fx type IIIA, IIIB, or IIIC]

S82.42[4,5,6][A,B,C] Nondisp transv fx of shaft of [rt, lt, unsp] fibula, [init enc for clsd fx, init enc for opn fx type I or II, init enc for opn fx type IIIA, IIIB, or IIIC]

S82.43[1,2,3][A,B,C] Disp oblique fx of shaft of [rt, lt, unsp] fibula, [init enc for clsd fx, init enc for opn fx type I or II, init enc for opn fx type IIIA, IIIB, or IIIC]

S82.43[4,5,6][A,B,C] Nondisp oblique fx of shaft of [rt, lt, unsp] fibula, [init enc for clsd fx, init enc for opn fx type I or II, init enc for opn fx type IIIA, IIIB, or IIIC]

S82.44[1,2,3][A,B,C] Disp spiral fx of shaft of [rt, lt, unsp] fibula, [init enc for clsd fx, init enc for opn fx type I or II, init enc for opn fx type IIIA, IIIB, or IIIC]

S82.44[4,5,6][A,B,C] Nondisp spiral fx of shaft of [rt, lt, unsp] fibula, [init enc for clsd fx, init enc for opn fx type I or II, init enc for opn fx type IIIA, IIIB, or IIIC]

S82.45[1,2,3][A,B,C] Disp comm fx of shaft of [rt, lt, unsp] fibula, [init enc for clsd fx, init enc for opn fx type I or II, init enc for opn fx type IIIA, IIIB, or IIIC]

S82.45[4,5,6][A,B,C] Nondisp comm fx of shaft of [rt, lt, unsp] fibula, [init enc for clsd fx, init enc for opn fx type I or II, init enc for opn fx type IIIA, IIIB, or IIIC]

S82.46[1,2,3][A,B,C] Disp seg fx of shaft of [rt, lt, unsp] fibula, [init enc for clsd fx, init enc for opn fx type I or II, init enc for opn fx type IIIA, IIIB, or IIIC]

S82.46[4,5,6][A,B,C] Nondisp seg fx of shaft of [rt, lt, unsp] fibula, [init enc for clsd fx, init enc for opn fx type I or II, init enc for opn fx type IIIA, IIIB, or IIIC]

S82.49[1,2,9][A,B,C] Oth fx of shaft of [rt, lt, unsp] fibula, [init enc for clsd fx, init enc for opn fx type I or II, init enc for opn fx type IIIA, IIIB, or IIIC]

S82.5[1,2,3]X[A,B,C] Disp fx of med malleolus of [rt, lt, unsp] tibia, [init enc for clsd fx, init enc for opn fx type I or II, init enc for opn fx type I or II]

S82.5[4,5,6]X[A,B,C] Nondisp fx of med malleolus of [rt, lt, unsp] tibia, [init enc for clsd fx, init enc for opn fx type I or II, init enc for opn fx type I or II]

S82.6[1,2,3]X[A,B,C] Disp fx of lat malleolus of [rt, lt, unsp] tibia, [init enc for clsd fx, init enc for opn fx type I or II, init enc for opn fx type I or II]

S82.6[4,5,6]X[A,B,C] Nondisp fx of lat malleolus of [rt, lt, unsp] tibia, [init enc for clsd fx, init enc for opn fx type I or II, init enc for opn fx type I or II]

S82.81[1,2,9]A Torus fx of upr end of [rt, lt, unsp] fibula, init enc for clsd fx

S82.82[1,2,9]A Torus fx of lwr end of [rt, lt, unsp] fibula, init enc for clsd fx

S82.83[1,2,9][A,B,C] Oth fx of upr and lwr end of [rt, lt, unsp] fibula, [init enc for clsd fx, init enc for opn fx type I or II, init enc for opn fx type IIIA, IIIB, or IIIC]

S82.84[1,2,3][A,B,C] Disp bimalleolar fx of [rt, lt, unsp] lwr leg, [init enc for clsd fx, init enc for opn fx type I or II, init enc for opn fx type I or II]

S82.84[4,5,6][A,B,C] Nondisp bimalleolar fx of [rt, lt, unsp] lwr leg, [init enc for clsd fx, init enc for opn fx type I or II, init enc for opn fx type I or II]

S82.85[1,2,3][A,B,C] Disp trimalleolar fx of [rt, lt, unsp] lwr leg, [init enc for clsd fx, init enc for opn fx type I or II, init enc for opn fx type I or II]

Surgical   **Medical**   **CC Indicator**   **MCC Indicator**   **Procedure Proxy**   **PDxMCC PDx acts as own MCC**   **PDxCC PDx acts as own CC**

© 2015 Optum360, LLC   MS-DRG Version 33.0   **427**

S82.85[4,5,6][A,B,C] Nondisp trimalleolar fx of [rt, lt, unsp] lwr leg, [init enc for clsd fx, init enc for opn fx type I or II, init enc for opn fx type I or II]

S82.86[1,2,3][A,B,C] Disp Maisonneuve's fx of [rt, lt, unsp] leg, [init enc for clsd fx, init enc for opn fx type I or II, init enc for opn fx type I or II]

S82.86[4,5,6][A,B,C] Nondisp Maisonneuve's fx of [rt, lt, unsp] leg, [init enc for clsd fx, init enc for opn fx type I or II, init enc for opn fx type I or II]

S82.87[1,2,3][A,B,C] Disp pilon fx of [rt, lt, unsp] tibia, [init enc for clsd fx, init enc for opn fx type I or II, init enc for opn fx type I or II]

S82.87[4,5,6][A,B,C] Nondisp pilon fx of [rt, lt, unsp] tibia, [init enc for clsd fx, init enc for opn fx type I or II, init enc for opn fx type I or II]

S82.89[1,2,9][A,B,C] Oth fx of [rt, lt, unsp] lwr leg, [init enc for clsd fx, init enc for opn fx type I or II, init enc for opn fx type I or II]

S82.9[0,1,2]X[A,B,C] Unsp fx of [unsp, rt, lt] lwr leg, [init enc for clsd fx, init enc for opn fx type I or II, init enc for opn fx type I or II]

S83.00[1,2,3]A Unsp sublux of [rt, lt, unsp] patella, init enc
S83.00[4,5,6]A Unsp disloc of [rt, lt, unsp] patella, init enc
S83.01[1,2,3]A Lat sublux of [rt, lt, unsp] patella, init enc
S83.01[4,5,6]A Lat disloc of [rt, lt, unsp] patella, init enc
S83.09[1,2,3]A Oth sublux of [rt, lt, unsp] patella, init enc
S83.09[4,5,6]A Oth disloc of [rt, lt, unsp] patella, init enc
S83.10[1,2,3]A Unsp sublux of [rt, lt, unsp] knee, init enc
S83.10[4,5,6]A Unsp disloc of [rt, lt, unsp] knee, init enc
S83.11[1,2,3]A Ant sublux of proximal end of tibia, [rt, lt, unsp] knee, init enc
S83.11[4,5,6]A Ant disloc of proximal end of tibia, [rt, lt, unsp] knee, init enc
S83.12[1,2,3]A Post sublux of proximal end of tibia, [rt, lt, unsp] knee, init enc
S83.12[4,5,6]A Post disloc of proximal end of tibia, [rt, lt, unsp] knee, init enc
S83.13[1,2,3]A Med sublux of proximal end of tibia, [rt, lt, unsp] knee, init enc
S83.13[4,5,6]A Med disloc of proximal end of tibia, [rt, lt, unsp] knee, init enc
S83.14[1,2,3]A Lat sublux of proximal end of tibia, [rt, lt, unsp] knee, init enc
S83.14[4,5,6]A Lat disloc of proximal end of tibia, [rt, lt, unsp] knee, init enc
S83.19[1,2,3]A Oth sublux of [rt, lt, unsp] knee, init enc
S83.19[4,5,6]A Oth disloc of [rt, lt, unsp] knee, init enc
S83.20[0,1,2]A Bucket-handle tear of unsp meniscus, current inj, [rt, lt, unsp] knee, init enc
S83.20[3,4,5]A Oth tear of unsp meniscus, current inj, [rt, lt, unsp] knee, init enc
S83.20[6,7,9]A Unsp tear of unsp meniscus, current inj, [rt, lt, unsp] knee, init enc
S83.21[1,2,9]A Bucket-handle tear of med meniscus, current inj, [rt, lt, unsp] knee, init enc
S83.22[1,2,9]A Peripheral tear of med meniscus, current inj, [rt, lt, unsp] knee, init enc
S83.23[1,2,9]A Complex tear of med meniscus, current inj, [rt, lt, unsp] knee, init enc
S83.24[1,2,9]A Oth tear of med meniscus, current inj, [rt, lt, unsp] knee, init enc
S83.25[1,2,9]A Bucket-handle tear of lat meniscus, current inj, [rt, lt, unsp] knee, init enc
S83.26[1,2,9]A Peripheral tear of lat meniscus, current inj, [rt, lt, unsp] knee, init enc
S83.27[1,2,9]A Complex tear of lat meniscus, current inj, [rt, lt, unsp] knee, init enc
S83.28[1,2,9]A Oth tear of lat meniscus, current inj, [rt, lt, unsp] knee, init enc
S83.3[0,1,2]XA Tear of articular cartilage of [unsp, rt, lt] knee, current, init enc
S83.4[0,1,2][1,2,9]A Sprain of [unsp, med, lat] collat lgmt of [rt, lt, unsp] knee, init enc
S83.5[0,1,2][1,2,9]A Sprain of [unsp, ant, post] cruciate lgmt of [rt, lt, unsp] knee, init enc
S83.6[0,1,2]XA Sprain of the superior tibiofibular jt and lgmt, [unsp, rt, lt] knee, init enc
S83.8X[1,2,9]A Sprain of oth spec parts of [rt, lt, unsp] knee, init enc
S83.9[0,1,2]XA Sprain of unsp site of [unsp, rt, lt] knee, init enc
S84.0[0,1,2]XA Inj of tibial nerve at lwr leg lvl, [unsp, rt, lt] leg, init enc
S84.1[0,1,2]XA Inj of peroneal nerve at lwr leg lvl, [unsp, rt, lt] leg, init enc
S84.2[0,1,2]XA Inj of cutaneous sensory nerve at lwr leg lvl, [unsp, rt, lt] leg, init enc
S84.80[1,2,9]A Inj of oth nerves at lwr leg lvl, [rt, lt, unsp] leg, init enc
S84.9[0,1,2]XA Inj of unsp nerve at lwr leg lvl, [unsp, rt, lt] leg, init enc
S85.0[0,1,9][1,2,9]A [Unsp inj, Lac, Oth spec inj] of popliteal artery, [rt, lt, unsp] leg, init enc
S85.1[0,1,2][1,2,9]A [Unsp inj, Lac, Oth spec inj] of unsp tibial artery, [rt, lt, unsp] leg, init enc
S85.1[3,4,5][1,2,9]A [Unsp inj, Lac, Oth spec inj] of ant tibial artery, [rt, lt, unsp] leg, init enc
S85.1[6,7,8][1,2,9]A [Unsp inj, Lac, Oth spec inj] of post tibial artery, [rt, lt, unsp] leg, init enc
S85.2[0,1,9][1,2,9]A [Unsp inj, Lac, Oth spec inj] of peroneal artery, [rt, lt, unsp] leg, init enc

S85.3[0,1,9][1,2,9]A [Unsp inj, Lac, Oth spec inj] of greater saphenous vein at lwr leg lvl, [rt, lt, unsp] leg, init enc
S85.4[0,1,9][1,2,9]A [Unsp inj, Lac, Oth spec inj] of lesser saphenous vein at lwr leg lvl, [rt, lt, unsp] leg, init enc
S85.5[0,1,9][1,2,9]A [Unsp inj, Lac, Oth spec inj] of popliteal vein, [rt, lt, unsp] leg, init enc
S85.8[0,1,9][1,2,9]A [Unsp inj, Lac, Oth spec inj] of oth bood vessels at lwr leg lvl, [rt, lt, unsp] leg, init enc
S85.9[0,1,9][1,2,9]A [Unsp inj, Lac, Oth spec inj] of unsp bood vessels at lwr leg lvl, [rt, lt, unsp] leg, init enc
S86.0[0,1,2,9][1,2,9]A [Unsp inj, Strain, Lac, Oth spec inj] of [rt, lt, unsp] Achilles tndn, init enc
S86.1[0,1,2,9][1,2,9]A [Unsp inj, Strain, Lac, Oth spec inj] of oth muscle(s) and tndn(s) of post muscle group at lwr leg lvl, [rt, lt, unsp] leg, init enc
S86.2[0,1,2,9][1,2,9]A [Unsp inj, Strain, Lac, Oth spec inj] of oth muscle(s) and tndn(s) of ant muscle group at lwr leg lvl, [rt, lt, unsp] leg, init enc
S86.3[0,1,2,9][1,2,9]A [Unsp inj, Strain, Lac, Oth spec inj] of oth muscle(s) and tndn(s) of peroneal muscle group at lwr leg lvl, [rt, lt, unsp] leg, init enc
S86.8[0,1,2,9][1,2,9]A [Unsp inj, Strain, Lac, Oth spec inj] of oth muscle(s) and tndn(s) at lwr leg lvl, [rt, lt, unsp] leg, init enc
S86.9[0,1,2,9][1,2,9]A [Unsp inj, Strain, Lac, Oth spec inj] of unsp muscle(s) and tndn(s) at lwr leg lvl, [rt, lt, unsp] leg, init enc
S87.0[0,1,2]XA Crushing inj of [unsp, rt, lt] knee, init enc
S87.8[0,1,2]XA Crushing inj of [unsp, rt, lt] lwr leg, init enc
S88.0[1,2][1,2,9]A [Complete, Partial] traum amp at knee lvl, [rt, lt, unsp] lwr leg, init enc
S88.1[1,2][1,2,9]A [Complete, Partial] traum amp at lvl between knee and ankle, [rt, lt, unsp] lwr leg, init enc
S88.9[1,2][1,2,9]A [Complete, Partial] traum amp of [rt, lt, unsp] lwr leg, lvl unsp, init enc
S89.00[1,2,9]A Unsp physeal fx of upr end of [rt, lt, unsp] tibia, init enc for clsd fx
S89.09[1,2,9]A Oth physeal fx of upr end of [rt, lt, unsp] tibia, init enc for clsd fx
S89.0[1,2,3,4][1,2,9]A Salter-Harris Type [I, II, III, IV] physeal fx of upr end of [rt, lt, unsp] tibia, init enc for clsd fx
S89.10[1,2,9]A Unsp physeal fx of lwr end of [rt, lt, unsp] tibia, init enc for clsd fx
S89.19[1,2,9]A Oth physeal fx of lwr end of [rt, lt, unsp] tibia, init enc for clsd fx
S89.1[1,2,3,4][1,2,9]A Salter-Harris Type [I, II, III, IV] physeal fx of lwr end of [rt, lt, unsp] tibia, init enc for clsd fx
S89.2[0,1,2,9][1,2,9]A [Unsp, Salter-Harris Type I, Salter-Harris Type II, Oth] physeal fx of upr end of [rt, lt, unsp] fibula, init enc for clsd fx
S89.3[0,1,2,9][1,2,9]A [Unsp, Salter-Harris Type I, Salter-Harris Type II, Oth] physeal fx of lwr end of [rt, lt, unsp] fibula, init enc for clsd fx
S89.8[0,1,2]XA Oth spec injuries of [unsp, rt, lt] lwr leg, init enc
S89.9[0,1,2]XA Unsp inj of [unsp, rt, lt] lwr leg, init enc
S90.0[0,1,2]XA Contsn of [unsp, rt, lt] ankle, init enc
S90.1[1,2][1,2,9]A Contsn of [rt, lt, unsp] [great, lesser] toe(s) w/o damage to nail, init enc
S90.2[1,2][1,2,9]A Contsn of [rt, lt, unsp] [great, lesser] toe(s) w/ damage to nail, init enc
S90.3[0,1,2]XA Contsn of [unsp, rt, lt] foot, init enc
S90.41[1,2,3]A Abrasion, [rt, lt, unsp] great toe, init enc
S90.41[4,5,6]A Abrasion, [rt, lt, unsp] lesser toe(s), init enc
S90.42[1,2,3]A Blister (nonthermal), [rt, lt, unsp] great toe, init enc
S90.42[4,5,6]A Blister (nonthermal), [rt, lt, unsp] lesser toe(s), init enc
S90.44[1,2,3]A Ext constriction, [rt, lt, unsp] great toe, init enc
S90.44[4,5,6]A Ext constriction, [rt, lt, unsp] lesser toe(s), init enc
S90.45[1,2,3]A Superf FB, [rt, lt, unsp] great toe, init enc
S90.45[4,5,6]A Superf FB, [rt, lt, unsp] lesser toe(s), init enc
S90.46[1,2,3]A Insect bite (nonvenomous), [rt, lt, unsp] great toe, init enc
S90.46[4,5,6]A Insect bite (nonvenomous), [rt, lt, unsp] lesser toe(s), init enc
S90.47[1,2,3]A Oth superf bite of [rt, lt, unsp] great toe, init enc
S90.47[4,5,6]A Oth superf bite of [rt, lt, unsp] lesser toe(s), init enc
S90.5[1,2,4,5,6,7][1,2,9]A [Abrasion, Blister (nonthermal), Ext constriction, Superf FB, Insect bite (nonvenomous), Oth superf bite], [rt, lt, unsp] ankle, init enc
S90.8[1,2,4,5,6,7][1,2,9]A [Abrasion, Blister (nonthermal), Ext constriction, Superf FB, Insect bite (nonvenomous), Oth superf bite], [rt, lt, unsp] foot, init enc
S90.91[1,2,9]A Unsp superf inj of [rt, lt, unsp] ankle, init enc
S90.92[1,2,9]A Unsp superf inj of [rt, lt, unsp] foot, init enc
S90.93[1,2,3]A Unsp superf inj of [rt, lt, unsp] great toe, init enc
S90.93[4,5,6]A Unsp superf inj of [rt, lt, unsp] lesser toe(s), init enc
S91.00[1,2,9]A Unsp opn wnd, [rt, lt, unsp] ankle, init enc

T Transfer DRG   SP Special Payment   * Code Range   6th and 7th Character of ZZ = No Device, No Qualifier ZX = No Device, Diagnostic

S91.01[1,2,9]A Lac w/o FB, [rt, lt, unsp] ankle, init enc
S91.02[1,2,9]A Lac w/ FB, [rt, lt, unsp] ankle, init enc
S91.03[1,2,9]A Punc wnd w/o FB, [rt, lt, unsp] ankle, init enc
S91.04[1,2,9]A Punc wnd w/ FB, [rt, lt, unsp] ankle, init enc
S91.05[1,2,9]A Opn bite, [rt, lt, unsp] ankle, init enc
S91.10[1,2,3]A Unsp opn wnd of [rt, lt, unsp] great toe w/o damage to nail, init enc
S91.10[4,5,6]A Unsp opn wnd of [rt, lt, unsp] lesser toe(s) w/o damage to nail, init enc
S91.11[1,2,3]A Lac w/o FB of [rt, lt, unsp] great toe w/o damage to nail, init enc
S91.11[4,5,6]A Lac w/o FB of [rt, lt, unsp] lesser toe(s) w/o damage to nail, init enc
S91.12[1,2,3]A Lac w/ FB of [rt, lt, unsp] great toe w/o damage to nail, init enc
S91.12[4,5,6]A Lac w/ FB of [rt, lt, unsp] lesser toe(s) w/o damage to nail, init enc
S91.13[1,2,3]A Punc wnd w/o FB of [rt, lt, unsp] great toe w/o damage to nail, init enc
S91.13[4,5,6]A Punc wnd w/o FB of [rt, lt, unsp] lesser toe(s) w/o damage to nail, init enc
S91.14[1,2,3]A Punc wnd w/ FB of [rt, lt, unsp] great toe w/o damage to nail, init enc
S91.14[4,5,6]A Punc wnd w/ FB of [rt, lt, unsp] lesser toe(s) w/o damage to nail, init enc
S91.15[1,2,3]A Opn bite of [rt, lt, unsp] great toe w/o damage to nail, init enc
S91.15[4,5,6]A Opn bite of [rt, lt, unsp] lesser toe(s) w/o damage to nail, init enc
S91.20[1,2,3]A Unsp opn wnd of [rt, lt, unsp] great toe w/ damage to nail, init enc
S91.20[4,5,6]A Unsp opn wnd of [rt, lt, unsp] lesser toe(s) w/ damage to nail, init enc
S91.21[1,2,3]A Lac w/o FB of [rt, lt, unsp] great toe w/ damage to nail, init enc
S91.21[4,5,6]A Lac w/o FB of [rt, lt, unsp] lesser toe(s) w/ damage to nail, init enc
S91.22[1,2,3]A Lac w/ FB of [rt, lt, unsp] great toe w/ damage to nail, init enc
S91.23[1,2,3]A Punc wnd w/o FB of [rt, lt, unsp] great toe w/ damage to nail, init enc
S91.23[4,5,6]A Punc wnd w/o FB of [rt, lt, unsp] lesser toe(s) w/ damage to nail, init enc
S91.24[1,2,3]A Punc wnd w/ FB of [rt, lt, unsp] great toe w/ damage to nail, init enc
S91.24[4,5,6]A Punc wnd w/ FB of [rt, lt, unsp] lesser toe(s) w/ damage to nail, init enc
S91.25[1,2,3]A Opn bite of [rt, lt, unsp] great toe w/ damage to nail, init enc
S91.25[4,5,6]A Opn bite of [rt, lt, unsp] lesser toe(s) w/ damage to nail, init enc
S91.30[1,2,9]A Unsp opn wnd, [rt, lt, unsp] foot, init enc
S91.31[1,2,9]A Lac w/o FB, [rt, lt, unsp] foot, init enc
S91.32[1,2,9]A Lac w/ FB, [rt, lt, unsp] foot, init enc
S91.33[1,2,9]A Punc wnd w/o FB, [rt, lt, unsp] foot, init enc
S91.34[1,2,9]A Punc wnd w/ FB, [rt, lt, unsp] foot, init enc
S91.35[1,2,9]A Opn bite, [rt, lt, unsp] foot, init enc
S92.00[1,2,9][A,B] Unsp fx of [rt, lt, unsp] calcaneus, init enc for [clsd, opn] fx
S92.01[1,2,3][A,B] Disp fx of body of [rt, lt, unsp] calcaneus, init enc for [clsd, opn] fx
S92.01[4,5,6][A,B] Nondisp fx of body of [rt, lt, unsp] calcaneus, init enc for [clsd, opn] fx
S92.02[1,2,3][A,B] Disp fx of ant process of [rt, lt, unsp] calcaneus, init enc for [clsd, opn] fx
S92.02[4,5,6][A,B] Nondisp fx of ant process of [rt, lt, unsp] calcaneus, init enc for [clsd, opn] fx
S92.03[1,2,3][A,B] Disp avulsion fx of tuberosity of [rt, lt, unsp] calcaneus, init enc for [clsd, opn] fx
S92.03[4,5,6][A,B] Nondisp avulsion fx of tuberosity of [rt, lt, unsp] calcaneus, init enc for [clsd, opn] fx
S92.04[1,2,3][A,B] Disp oth fx of tuberosity of [rt, lt, unsp] calcaneus, init enc for [clsd, opn] fx
S92.04[4,5,6][A,B] Nondisp oth fx of tuberosity of [rt, lt, unsp] calcaneus, init enc for [clsd, opn] fx
S92.05[1,2,3][A,B] Disp oth extraarticular fx of [rt, lt, unsp] calcaneus, init enc for [clsd, opn] fx
S92.05[4,5,6][A,B] Nondisp oth extraarticular fx of [rt, lt, unsp] calcaneus, init enc for [clsd, opn] fx
S92.06[1,2,3][A,B] Disp intraarticular fx of [rt, lt, unsp] calcaneus, init enc for [clsd, opn] fx
S92.06[4,5,6][A,B] Nondisp intraarticular fx of [rt, lt, unsp] calcaneus, init enc for [clsd, opn] fx
S92.10[1,2,9][A,B] Unsp fx of [rt, lt, unsp] talus, init enc for [clsd, opn] fx
S92.11[1,2,3][A,B] Disp fx of neck of [rt, lt, unsp] talus, init enc for [clsd, opn] fx

S92.11[4,5,6][A,B] Nondisp fx of neck of [rt, lt, unsp] talus, init enc for [clsd, opn] fx
S92.12[1,2,3][A,B] Disp fx of body of [rt, lt, unsp] talus, init enc for [clsd, opn] fx
S92.12[4,5,6][A,B] Nondisp fx of body of [rt, lt, unsp] talus, init enc for [clsd, opn] fx
S92.13[1,2,3][A,B] Disp fx of post process of [rt, lt, unsp] talus, init enc for [clsd, opn] fx
S92.13[4,5,6][A,B] Nondisp fx of post process of [rt, lt, unsp] talus, init enc for [clsd, opn] fx
S92.14[1,2,3][A,B] Disp dome fx of [rt, lt, unsp] talus, init enc for [clsd, opn] fx
S92.14[4,5,6][A,B] Nondisp dome fx of [rt, lt, unsp] talus, init enc for [clsd, opn] fx
S92.15[1,2,3][A,B] Disp avulsion fx (chip fx) of [rt, lt, unsp] talus, init enc for [clsd, opn] fx
S92.15[4,5,6][A,B] Nondisp avulsion fx (chip fx) of [rt, lt, unsp] talus, init enc for [clsd, opn] fx
S92.19[1,2,9][A,B] Oth fx of [rt, lt, unsp] talus, init enc for [clsd, opn] fx
S92.20[1,2,9][A,B] Fx of unsp tarsal bone(s) of [rt, lt, unsp] foot, init enc for [clsd, opn] fx
S92.21[1,2,3][A,B] Disp fx of cuboid bone of [rt, lt, unsp] foot, init enc for [clsd, opn] fx
S92.21[4,5,6][A,B] Nondisp fx of cuboid bone of [rt, lt, unsp] foot, init enc for [clsd, opn] fx
S92.22[1,2,3][A,B] Disp fx of lat cuneiform of [rt, lt, unsp] foot, init enc for [clsd, opn] fx
S92.22[4,5,6][A,B] Nondisp fx of lat cuneiform of [rt, lt, unsp] foot, init enc for [clsd, opn] fx
S92.23[1,2,3][A,B] Disp fx of intermediate cuneiform of [rt, lt, unsp] foot, init enc for [clsd, opn] fx
S92.23[4,5,6][A,B] Nondisp fx of intermediate cuneiform of [rt, lt, unsp] foot, init enc for [clsd, opn] fx
S92.24[1,2,3][A,B] Disp fx of med cuneiform of [rt, lt, unsp] foot, init enc for [clsd, opn] fx
S92.24[4,5,6][A,B] Nondisp fx of med cuneiform of [rt, lt, unsp] foot, init enc for [clsd, opn] fx
S92.25[1,2,3][A,B] Disp fx of navicular (scaphoid) of [rt, lt, unsp] foot, init enc for [clsd, opn] fx
S92.25[4,5,6][A,B] Nondisp fx of navicular (scaphoid) of [rt, lt, unsp] foot, init enc for [clsd, opn] fx
S92.30[1,2,9][A,B] Fx of unsp metatarsal bone(s), [rt, lt, unsp] foot, init enc for [clsd, opn] fx
S92.31[1,2,3][A,B] Disp fx of 1st metatarsal bone, [rt, lt, unsp] foot, init enc for [clsd, opn] fx
S92.31[4,5,6][A,B] Nondisp fx of 1st metatarsal bone, [rt, lt, unsp] foot, init enc for [clsd, opn] fx
S92.32[1,2,3][A,B] Disp fx of 2nd metatarsal bone, [rt, lt, unsp] foot, init enc for [clsd, opn] fx
S92.32[4,5,6][A,B] Nondisp fx of 2nd metatarsal bone, [rt, lt, unsp] foot, init enc for [clsd, opn] fx
S92.33[1,2,3][A,B] Disp fx of 3rd metatarsal bone, [rt, lt, unsp] foot, init enc for [clsd, opn] fx
S92.33[4,5,6][A,B] Nondisp fx of 3rd metatarsal bone, [rt, lt, unsp] foot, init enc for [clsd, opn] fx
S92.34[1,2,3][A,B] Disp fx of 4th metatarsal bone, [rt, lt, unsp] foot, init enc for [clsd, opn] fx
S92.34[4,5,6][A,B] Nondisp fx of 4th metatarsal bone, [rt, lt, unsp] foot, init enc for [clsd, opn] fx
S92.35[1,2,3][A,B] Disp fx of 5th metatarsal bone, [rt, lt, unsp] foot, init enc for [clsd, opn] fx
S92.35[4,5,6][A,B] Nondisp fx of 5th metatarsal bone, [rt, lt, unsp] foot, init enc for [clsd, opn] fx
S92.40[1,2,3][A,B] Disp unsp fx of [rt, lt, unsp] great toe, init enc for [clsd, opn] fx
S92.40[4,5,6][A,B] Nondisp unsp fx of [rt, lt, unsp] great toe, init enc for [clsd, opn] fx
S92.41[1,2,3][A,B] Disp fx of proximal phalanx of [rt, lt, unsp] great toe, init enc for [clsd, opn] fx
S92.41[4,5,6][A,B] Nondisp fx of proximal phalanx of [rt, lt, unsp] great toe, init enc for [clsd, opn] fx
S92.42[1,2,3][A,B] Disp fx of distal phalanx of [rt, lt, unsp] great toe, init enc for [clsd, opn] fx
S92.42[4,5,6][A,B] Nondisp fx of distal phalanx of [rt, lt, unsp] great toe, init enc for [clsd, opn] fx
S92.49[1,2,9][A,B] Oth fx of [rt, lt, unsp] great toe, init enc for [clsd, opn] fx
S92.50[1,2,3][A,B] Disp unsp fx of [rt, lt, unsp] lesser toe(s), init enc for [clsd, opn] fx
S92.50[4,5,6][A,B] Nondisp unsp fx of [rt, lt, unsp] lesser toe(s), init enc for [clsd, opn] fx
S92.51[1,2,3][A,B] Disp fx of proximal phalanx of [rt, lt, unsp] lesser toe(s), init enc for [clsd, opn] fx
S92.51[4,5,6][A,B] Nondisp fx of proximal phalanx of [rt, lt, unsp] lesser toe(s), init enc for [clsd, opn] fx

Surgical **Medical** **CC Indicator** **MCC Indicator** **Procedure Proxy** **PDxMCC PDx acts as own MCC** **PDxCC PDx acts as own CC**

MDC 24: Multiple Significant Trauma—MEDICAL

Code	Description
S92.52[1,2,3][A,B]	Disp fx of med phalanx of [rt, lt, unsp] lesser toe(s), init enc for [clsd, opn] fx
S92.52[4,5,6][A,B]	Nondisp fx of med phalanx of [rt, lt, unsp] lesser toe(s), init enc for [clsd, opn] fx
S92.53[1,2,3][A,B]	Disp fx of distal phalanx of [rt, lt, unsp] lesser toe(s), init enc for [clsd, opn] fx
S92.53[4,5,6][A,B]	Nondisp fx of distal phalanx of [rt, lt, unsp] lesser toe(s), init enc for [clsd, opn] fx
S92.59[1,2,9][A,B]	Oth fx of [rt, lt, unsp] lesser toe(s), init enc for [clsd, opn] fx
S92.90[1,2,9][A,B]	Unsp fx of [rt, lt, unsp] foot, init enc for [clsd, opn] fx
S92.91[1,2,9][A,B]	Unsp fx of [rt, lt, unsp] toe(s), init enc for [clsd, opn] fx
S93.0[1,2,3]XA	Sublux of [rt, lt, unsp] ankle jt, init enc
S93.0[4,5,6]XA	Disloc of [rt, lt, unsp] ankle jt, init enc
S93.10[1,2,3]A	Unsp sublux of [rt, lt, unsp] toe(s), init enc
S93.10[4,5,6]A	Unsp disloc of [rt, lt, unsp] toe(s), init enc
S93.119A	Disloc of interphalangeal jt of unsp toe(s), init
S93.11[1,2,3]A	Disloc of interphalangeal jt of [rt, lt, unsp] great toe, init enc
S93.11[4,5,6]A	Disloc of interphalangeal jt of [rt, lt, unsp] lesser toe(s), init enc
S93.129A	Disloc of MTP jt of unsp toe(s), init
S93.12[1,2,3]A	Disloc of metatarsophalangeal jt of [rt, lt, unsp] great toe, init enc
S93.12[4,5,6]A	Disloc of metatarsophalangeal jt of [rt, lt, unsp] lesser toe(s), init enc
S93.139A	Sublux of interphalangeal jt of unsp toe(s), init
S93.13[1,2,3]A	Sublux of interphalangeal jt of [rt, lt, unsp] great toe, init enc
S93.13[4,5,6]A	Sublux of interphalangeal jt of [rt, lt, unsp] lesser toe(s), init enc
S93.149A	Sublux of MTP jt of unsp toe(s), init
S93.14[1,2,3]A	Sublux of metatarsophalangeal jt of [rt, lt, unsp] great toe, init enc
S93.14[4,5,6]A	Sublux of metatarsophalangeal jt of [rt, lt, unsp] lesser toe(s), init enc
S93.30[1,2,3]A	Unsp sublux of [rt, lt, unsp] foot, init enc
S93.30[4,5,6]A	Unsp disloc of [rt, lt, unsp] foot, init enc
S93.31[1,2,3]A	Sublux of tarsal jt of [rt, lt, unsp] foot, init enc
S93.31[4,5,6]A	Disloc of tarsal jt of [rt, lt, unsp] foot, init enc
S93.32[1,2,3]A	Sublux of tarsometatarsal jt of [rt, lt, unsp] foot, init enc
S93.32[4,5,6]A	Disloc of tarsometatarsal jt of [rt, lt, unsp] foot, init enc
S93.33[1,2,3]A	Oth sublux of [rt, lt, unsp] foot, init enc
S93.33[4,5,6]A	Oth disloc of [rt, lt, unsp] foot, init enc
S93.4[0,1,2,3,9][1,2,9]A	Sprain of [unsp, calcaneofibular, deltoid, tibiofibular, oth] lgmt of [rt, lt, unsp] ankle, init enc
S93.509A	Unsp sprain of unsp toe(s), init enc
S93.50[1,2,3]A	Unsp strain of [rt, lt, unsp] great toe, init enc
S93.50[4,5,6]A	Unsp strain of [rt, lt, unsp] lesser toe(s), init enc
S93.519A	Sprain of interphalangeal jt of unsp toe(s), init enc
S93.51[1,2,3]A	Strain of interphalangeal jt of [rt, lt, unsp] great toe, init enc
S93.51[4,5,6]A	Strain of interphalangeal jt of [rt, lt, unsp] lesser toe(s), init enc
S93.529A	Sprain of metatarsophalangeal jt of unsp toe(s), init
S93.52[1,2,3]A	Strain of metatarsophalangeal jt of [rt, lt, unsp] great toe, init enc
S93.52[4,5,6]A	Strain of metatarsophalangeal jt of [rt, lt, unsp] lesser toe(s), init enc
S93.60[1,2,9]A	Unsp sprain of [rt, lt, unsp] foot, init enc
S93.61[1,2,9]A	Sprain of tarsal lgmt of [rt, lt, unsp] foot, init enc
S93.62[1,2,9]A	Sprain of tarsometatarsal lgmt of [rt, lt, unsp] foot, init enc
S93.69[1,2,9]A	Oth sprain of [rt, lt, unsp] foot, init enc
S94.8X[1,2,9]A	Inj of oth nerves at ankle and foot lvl, [unsp leg, rt, lt], init enc
S94.9[0,1,2]XA	Inj of unsp nerve at ankle and foot lvl, [unsp leg, rt, lt], init enc
S94.[0,1,2,3][0,1,2]XA	Inj of [lat plantar, med plantar, deep peroneal, cutaneous sensory] nerve, [unsp, rt, lt] leg, init enc
S95.0[0,1,9][1,2,9]A	[Unsp inj, Lac, Oth spec inj] of dorsal artery of [rt, lt, unsp] foot, init enc
S95.1[0,1,9][1,2,9]A	[Unsp inj, Lac, Oth spec inj] of plantar artery of [rt, lt, unsp] foot, init enc
S95.2[0,1,9][1,2,9]A	[Unsp inj, Lac, Oth spec inj] of dorsal vein of [rt, lt, unsp] foot, init enc
S95.8[0,1,9][1,2,9]A	[Unsp inj, Lac, Oth spec inj] of oth bld vessels at ankle and foot lvl, [rt, lt, unsp] leg, init enc
S95.9[0,1,9][1,2,9]A	[Unsp inj, Lac, Oth spec inj] of unsp bld vessel at ankle and foot lvl, [rt, lt, unsp] leg, init enc
S96.0[0,1,2,9][1,2,9]A	[Unsp inj, Strain, Lac, Oth inj] of muscle and tndn of long flexor muscle of toe at ankle and foot lvl, [rt, lt, unsp] foot, init enc
S96.1[0,1,2,9][1,2,9]A	[Unsp inj, Strain, Lac, Oth inj] of muscle and tndn of long extensor muscle of toe at ankle and foot lvl, [rt, lt, unsp] foot, init enc
S96.2[0,1,2,9][1,2,9]A	[Unsp inj, Strain, Lac, Oth inj] of intrinsic muscle and tndn at ankle and foot lvl, [rt, lt, unsp] foot, init enc
S96.8[0,1,2,9][1,2,9]A	[Unsp inj, Strain, Lac, Oth inj] of oth spec muscles and tndns at ankle and foot lvl, [rt, lt, unsp] foot, init enc
S96.9[0,1,2,9][1,2,9]A	[Unsp inj, Strain, Lac, Oth inj] of unsp muscle and tndn at ankle and foot lvl, [rt, lt, unsp] foot, init enc
S97.0[0,1,2]XA	Crushing inj of [unsp, rt, lt] ankle, init enc
S97.1[0,1,2][1,2,9]A	Crushing inj of [unsp rt, unsp lt, unsp, rt great, lt great, unsp great, rt lesser, lt lesser, unsp lesser] toe(s), init enc
S97.8[0,1,2]XA	Crushing inj of [unsp, rt, lt] foot, init enc
S98.0[1,2][1,2,9]A	[Complete, Partial] traum amp of [rt, lt, unsp] foot at ankle lvl, init enc
S98.1[1,2][1,2,9]A	[Complete, Partial] traum amp of [rt, lt, unsp] great toe, init enc
S98.1[3,4][1,2,9]A	[Complete, Partial] traum amp of one [rt, lt, unsp] lesser toe, init enc
S98.2[1,2][1,2,9]A	[Complete, Partial] traum amp of two or more [rt, lt, unsp] lesser toes, init enc
S98.3[1,2][1,2,9]A	[Complete, Partial] traum amp of [rt, lt, unsp] midfoot, init enc
S98.9[1,2][1,2,9]A	[Complete, Partial] traum amp of [rt, lt, unsp] foot, lvl unsp, init enc
S99.81[1,2,9]A	Oth spec injuries of [rt, lt, unsp] ankle, init enc
S99.82[1,2,9]A	Oth spec injuries of [rt, lt, unsp] foot, init enc
S99.91[1,2,9]A	Unsp inj of [rt, lt, unsp] ankle, init enc
S99.92[1,2,9]A	Unsp inj of [rt, lt, unsp] foot, init enc
T07	Unsp multi injuries
T14.8	Oth inj of unsp body region
T14.90	Inj, unsp
T14.91	Suicide attempt
T79.0XXA	Air embolism (traum), init enc
T79.1XXA	Fat embolism (traum), init enc
T79.2XXA	Traum secondary and recurrent hemor and seroma, init
T79.4XXA	Traum shock, init enc
T79.5XXA	Traum anuria, init enc
T79.6XXA	Traum ischemia of muscle, init enc
T79.7XXA	Traum SQ emphysema, init enc
T79.8XXA	Oth early comp of trauma, init enc
T79.9XXA	Unsp early comp of trauma, init enc
T79.A0XA	Compartment synd, unsp, init enc
T79.A1[1,2,9]A	Traum compartment synd of [rt, lt, unsp] upr extr, init enc
T79.A2[1,2,9]A	Traum compartment synd of [rt, lt, unsp] lwr extr, init enc
T79.A[3,9]XA	Traum compartment synd of [abd, oth sites], init enc

Significant Trauma Body Site Category 1 - Head

Code	Description
S02.10XB	Unsp fx of base of skull, init for opn fx
S02.91X[A,B]	Unsp fx of skull, init enc for [clsd, opn] fx
S06.0X[3,4]A	Concussion w/ LOC of [1 hr to 5 hrs 59 min, 6 hrs to 24 hrs], init enc
S06.0X[5,6]A	Concussion w/ LOC > 24 hrs [w/, w/o] return to pre-existing conscious lvl, init enc
S06.1X0A	Traum cerebral edema w/o LOC, init PDx MCC
S06.1X[1,2,3,4]A	Traum cerebral edema w/ LOC of [30 min or less, 31 min to 59 min, 1 hr to 5 hrs 59 min, 6 hrs to 24 hrs], init enc
S06.1X[5,6]A	Traum cerebral edema w/ LOC > 24 hrs [w/ return to pre-existing conscious lvl, w/o return to pre-existing conscious lvl w/ patient surviving], init enc
S06.1X[7,8,9]A	Traum cerebral edema w/ LOC of [any dur w/ death d/t brain inj prior to regain cnscness, any dur w/ death d/t oth cause prior to regain cnscness, unsp dur], init enc
S06.2X0A	Diffuse TBI w/o LOC, init
S06.2X[1,2,3,4]A	Diffuse traum brain inj w/ LOC of [30 min or less, 31 min to 59 min, 1 hr to 5 hrs 59 min, 6 hrs to 24 hrs], init enc
S06.2X[5,6]A	Diffuse traum brain inj w/ LOC > 24 hrs [w/ return to pre-existing conscious lvl, w/o return to pre-existing conscious lvl w/ patient surviving], init enc
S06.2X[7,8,9]A	Diffuse traum brain inj w/ LOC of [any dur w/ death d/t brain inj prior to regain cnscness, any dur w/ death d/t oth cause prior to regain cnscness, unsp dur], init enc
S06.300A	Unsp focal TBI w/o LOC, init
S06.30[1,2,3,4]A	Unsp focal traum brain inj w/ LOC of [30 min or less, 31 min to 59 min, 1 hr to 5 hrs 59 min, 6 hrs to 24 hrs], init enc
S06.30[5,6]A	Unsp focal traum brain inj w/ LOC > 24 hrs [w/ return to pre-existing conscious lvl, w/o return to pre-existing conscious lvl w/ patient surviving], init enc
S06.30[7,8,9]A	Unsp focal traum brain inj w/ LOC of [any dur w/ death d/t brain inj prior to regain cnscness, any dur w/ death d/t oth cause prior to regain cnscness, unsp dur], init enc
S06.310A	Contus/lac rt cerebrum w/o LOC, init
S06.31[1,2,3,4]A	Contsn and lac of rt cerebrum w/ LOC of [30 min or less, 31 min to 59 min, 1 hr to 5 hrs 59 min, 6 hrs to 24 hrs], init enc

T Transfer DRG   SP Special Payment   * Code Range   **6th and 7th Character of ZZ = No Device, No Qualifier ZX = No Device, Diagnostic**

430   MS-DRG Version 33.0   © 2015 Optum360, LLC

S06.31[5,6]A   Contsn and lac of rt cerebrum w/ LOC > 24 hrs [w/ return to pre-existing conscious lvl, w/o return to pre-existing conscious lvl w/ patient surviving], init enc

S06.31[7,8,9]A   Contsn and lac of rt cerebrum w/ LOC of [any dur w/ death d/t brain inj prior to regain cnscness, any dur w/ death d/t oth cause prior to regain cnscness, unsp dur], init enc

S06.320A   Contus/lac lt cerebrum w/o LOC, init

S06.32[1,2,3,4]A   Contsn and lac of lt cerebrum w/ LOC of [30 min or less, 31 min to 59 min, 1 hr to 5 hrs 59 min, 6 hrs to 24 hrs], init enc

S06.32[5,6]A   Contsn and lac of lt cerebrum w/ LOC > 24 hrs [w/ return to pre-existing conscious lvl, w/o return to pre-existing conscious lvl w/ patient surviving], init enc

S06.32[7,8,9]A   Contsn and lac of lt cerebrum w/ LOC of [any dur w/ death d/t brain inj prior to regain cnscness, any dur w/ death d/t oth cause prior to regain cnscness, unsp dur], init enc

S06.330A   Contus/lac cereb, w/o LOC, init

S06.33[1,2,3,4]A   Contsn and lac of cerebrum, unsp, w/ LOC of [30 min or less, 31 min to 59 min, 1 hr to 5 hrs 59 min, 6 hrs to 24 hrs], init enc

S06.33[5,6]A   Contsn and lac of cerebrum, unsp, w/ LOC > 24 hrs [w/ return to pre-existing conscious lvl, w/o return to pre-existing conscious lvl w/ patient surviving], init enc

S06.33[7,8,9]A   Contsn and lac of cerebrum, unsp, w/ LOC of [any dur w/ death d/t brain inj prior to regain cnscness, any dur w/ death d/t oth cause prior to regain cnscness, unsp dur], init enc

S06.340A   Traum hemor rt cerebrum w/o LOC, init

S06.34[1,2,3,4]A   Traum hemor of rt cerebrum w/ LOC of [30 min or less, 31 min to 59 min, 1 hr to 5 hrs 59 min, 6 hrs to 24 hrs], init enc

S06.34[5,6]A   Traum hemor of rt cerebrum w/ LOC > 24 hrs [w/ return to pre-existing conscious lvl, w/o return to pre-existing conscious lvl w/ patient surviving], init enc

S06.34[7,8,9]A   Traum hemor of rt cerebrum w/ LOC of [any dur w/ death d/t brain inj prior to regain cnscness, any dur w/ death d/t oth cause prior to regain cnscness, unsp dur], init enc

S06.350A   Traum hemor lt cerebrum w/o LOC, init

S06.35[1,2,3,4]A   Traum hemor of lt cerebrum w/ LOC of [30 min or less, 31 min to 59 min, 1 hr to 5 hrs 59 min, 6 hrs to 24 hrs], init enc

S06.35[5,6]A   Traum hemor of lt cerebrum w/ LOC > 24 hrs [w/ return to pre-existing conscious lvl, w/o return to pre-existing conscious lvl w/ patient surviving], init enc

S06.35[7,8,9]A   Traum hemor of lt cerebrum w/ LOC of [any dur w/ death d/t brain inj prior to regain cnscness, any dur w/ death d/t oth cause prior to regain cnscness, unsp dur], init enc

S06.360A   Traum hemor cereb, w/o LOC, init

S06.36[1,2,3,4]A   Traum hemor of cerebrum, unsp, w/ LOC of [30 min or less, 31 min to 59 min, 1 hr to 5 hrs 59 min, 6 hrs to 24 hrs], init enc

S06.36[5,6]A   Traum hemor of cerebrum, unsp, w/ LOC > 24 hrs [w/ return to pre-existing conscious lvl, w/o return to pre-existing conscious lvl w/ patient surviving], init enc

S06.36[7,8,9]A   Traum hemor of cerebrum, unsp, w/ LOC of [any dur w/ death d/t brain inj prior to regain cnscness, any dur w/ death d/t oth cause prior to regain cnscness, unsp dur], init enc

S06.370A   Contus/lac/hem crblm w/o LOC, init

S06.37[1,2,3,4]A   Contsn, lac, and hemor of cerebellum w/ LOC of [30 min or less, 31 min to 59 min, 1 hr to 5 hrs 59 min, 6 hrs to 24 hrs], init enc

S06.37[5,6]A   Contsn, lac, and hemor of cerebellum w/ LOC > 24 hrs [w/ return to pre-existing conscious lvl, w/o return to pre-existing conscious lvl w/ patient surviving], init enc

S06.37[7,8,9]A   Contsn, lac, and hemor of cerebellum w/ LOC of [any dur w/ death d/t brain inj prior to regain cnscness, any dur w/ death d/t oth cause prior to regain cnscness, unsp dur], init enc

S06.380A   Contus/lac/hem brainstem w/o LOC, init

S06.38[1,2,3,4]A   Contsn, lac, and hemor of brainstem w/ LOC of [30 min or less, 31 min to 59 min, 1 hr to 5 hrs 59 min, 6 hrs to 24 hrs], init enc

S06.38[5,6]A   Contsn, lac, and hemor of brainstem w/ LOC > 24 hrs [w/ return to pre-existing conscious lvl, w/o return to pre-existing conscious lvl w/ patient surviving], init enc

S06.38[7,8,9]A   Contsn, lac, and hemor of brainstem w/ LOC of [any dur w/ death d/t brain inj prior to regain cnscness, any dur w/ death d/t oth cause prior to regain cnscness, unsp dur], init enc

S06.4X0A   Epidural hemor w/o LOC, init enc

S06.4X[1,2,3,4]A   Epidural hemor w/ LOC of [30 min or less, 31 min to 59 min, 1 hr to 5 hrs 59 min, 6 hrs to 24 hrs], init enc

S06.4X[5,6]A   Epidural hemor w/ LOC > 24 hrs [w/ return to pre-existing conscious lvl, w/o return to pre-existing conscious lvl w/ patient surviving], init enc

S06.4X[7,8,9]A   Epidural hemor w/ LOC of [any dur w/ death d/t brain inj prior to regain cnscness, any dur w/ death d/t oth cause prior to regain cnscness, unsp dur], init enc

S06.5X0A   Traum subdr hem w/o LOC, init

S06.5X[1,2,3,4]A   Traum subdural hemor w/ LOC of [30 min or less, 31 min to 59 min, 1 hr to 5 hrs 59 min, 6 hrs to 24 hrs], init enc

S06.5X[5,6]A   Traum subdural hemor w/ LOC > 24 hrs [w/ return to pre-existing conscious lvl, w/o return to pre-existing conscious lvl w/ patient surviving], init enc

S06.5X[7,8,9]A   Traum subdural hemor w/ LOC of [any dur w/ death d/t brain inj prior to regain cnscness, unsp dur], init enc

S06.6X0A   Traum subrac hem w/o LOC, init

S06.6X[1,2,3,4]A   Traum subarachnoid hemor w/ LOC of [30 min or less, 31 min to 59 min, 1 hr to 5 hrs 59 min, 6 hrs to 24 hrs], init enc

S06.6X[5,6]A   Traum subarachnoid hemor w/ LOC > 24 hrs [w/ return to pre-existing conscious lvl, w/o return to pre-existing conscious lvl w/ patient surviving], init enc

S06.6X[7,8,9]A   Traum subarachnoid hemor w/ LOC of [any dur w/ death d/t brain inj prior to regain cnscness, any dur w/ death d/t oth cause prior to regain cnscness, unsp dur], init enc

S06.810A   Inj of Rt int carotid, intcr w/o LOC, init

S06.81[1,2,3,4]A   Inj of rt int carotid artery, intracranial portion, NEC, w/ LOC of [30 min or less, 31 min to 59 min, 1 hr to 5 hrs 59 min, 6 hrs to 24 hrs], init enc

S06.81[5,6]A   Inj of rt int carotid artery, intracranial portion, NEC, w/ LOC > 24 hrs [w/ return to pre-existing conscious lvl, w/o return to pre-existing conscious lvl w/ patient surviving], init enc

S06.81[7,8,9]A   Inj of rt int carotid artery, intracranial portion, NEC w/ LOC of [any dur w/ death d/t brain inj prior to regain cnscness, any dur w/ death d/t oth cause prior to regain cnscness, unsp dur], init enc

S06.820A   Inj of Lt int carotid, intcr w/o LOC, init

S06.82[1,2,3,4]A   Inj of lt int carotid artery, intracranial portion, NEC, w/ LOC of [30 min or less, 31 min to 59 min, 1 hr to 5 hrs 59 min, 6 hrs to 24 hrs], init enc

S06.82[5,6]A   Inj of lt int carotid artery, intracranial portion, NEC, w/ LOC > 24 hrs [w/ return to pre-existing conscious lvl, w/o return to pre-existing conscious lvl w/ patient surviving], init enc

S06.82[7,8,9]A   Inj of lt int carotid artery, intracranial portion, NEC w/ LOC of [any dur w/ death d/t brain inj prior to regain cnscness, any dur w/ death d/t oth cause prior to regain cnscness, unsp dur], init enc

S06.890A   Intcran inj w/o LOC, init enc

S06.89[1,2,3,4]A   Oth spec intracranial inj w/ LOC of [30 min or less, 31 min to 59 min, 1 hr to 5 hrs 59 min, 6 hrs to 24 hrs], init enc

S06.89[5,6]A   Oth spec intracranial inj w/ LOC > 24 hrs [w/ return to pre-existing conscious lvl, w/o return to pre-existing conscious lvl w/ patient surviving], init enc

S06.89[7,8,9]A   Oth spec intracranial inj w/ LOC of [any dur w/ death d/t brain inj prior to regain cnscness, any dur w/ death d/t oth cause prior to regain cnscness, unsp dur], init enc

S06.9X0A   Unsp intracranial inj w/o LOC, init

S06.9X[1,2,3,4]A   Unsp intracranial inj w/ LOC of [30 min or less, 31 min to 59 min, 1 hr to 5 hrs 59 min, 6 hrs to 24 hrs], init enc

S06.9X[5,6]A   Unsp intracranial inj w/ LOC > 24 hrs [w/ return to pre-existing conscious lvl, w/o return to pre-existing conscious lvl w/ patient surviving], init enc

S06.9X[7,8,9]A   Unsp intracranial inj w/ LOC of [any dur w/ death d/t brain inj prior to regain cnscness, any dur w/ death d/t oth cause prior to regain cnscness, unsp dur], init enc

S07.[0,1,8,9]XXA   Crushing inj of [face, skull, oth parts of head, head part unsp], init enc

S15.00[1,2]A   Unsp inj of [rt, lt] carotid artery, init enc

S15.0[1,2,9][1,2,9]A   [Minor lac, Major lac, Oth spec inj] of [rt, lt, unsp] carotid artery, init enc

S15.2[0,1,2,9][1,2,9]A   [Unsp inj, Minor lac, Major lac, Oth spec inj] of [rt, lt, unsp] ext jugular vein, init enc

S15.3[0,1,2,9][1,2,9]A   [Unsp inj, Minor lac, Major lac, Oth spec inj] of [rt, lt, unsp] int jugular vein, init enc

S15.8XXA   Inj of oth bld vessels at neck lvl, init enc

S17.[0,8,9]XXA   Crushing inj of [larynx and trachea, oth spec parts of neck, unsp part of neck], init enc

Significant Trauma Body Site Category 2 - Chest

S11.0[1,2,3][2,4]A   [Lac, Punc wnd] of [larynx, trachea, vocal cord] w/ FB, init enc

S12.8XXA   Fx of oth parts of neck, init enc

S21.30[1,2,9]A   Unsp opn wnd of [rt, lt, unsp] front wall of thorax w/ penetration into thoracic cavity, init enc

S21.35[1,2,9]A   Opn bite of [rt, lt, unsp] front wall of thorax w/ penetration into thoracic cavity, init enc

S21.3[1,2][1,2,9]A   Lac [w/o, w/] FB of [rt, lt, unsp] front wall of thorax w/ penetration into thoracic cavity, init enc

---

Surgical   **Medical**   **CC Indicator**   **MCC Indicator**   **Procedure Proxy**   **PDxMCC** **PDx acts as own MCC**   **PDxCC** **PDx acts as own CC**

MDC 24: Multiple Significant Trauma—MEDICAL

S21.3[3,4][1,2,9]A Punc wnd [w/o, w/] FB of [rt, lt, unsp] front wall of thorax w/ penetration into thoracic cavity, init enc
S21.40[1,2,9]A Unsp opn wnd of [rt, lt, unsp] back wall of thorax w/ penetration into thoracic cavity, init enc
S21.45[1,2,9]A Opn bite of [rt, lt, unsp] back wall of thorax w/ penetration into thoracic cavity, init enc
S21.4[1,2][1,2,9]A Lac [w/o, w/] FB of [rt, lt, unsp] back wall of thorax w/ penetration into thoracic cavity, init enc
S21.4[3,4][1,2,9]A Punc wnd [w/o, w/] FB of [rt, lt, unsp] back wall of thorax w/ penetration into thoracic cavity, init enc
S22.2[0,1,2,3,4]XB [Unsp fx of sternum, Fx of manubrium, Fx of body of sternum, Sternal manubrial dissociation, Fx of xiphoid process], init enc for opn fx
S22.41X[A,B] Multi fxs of ribs, rt side, init enc for [clsd, opn] fx
S22.42XB Multi fractures of ribs, lt side, init for opn fx
S22.5XX[A,B] Flail chest, init enc for [clsd, opn] fx
S25.0[0,1,2,9]XA [Unsp inj, Minor lac, Major lac, Oth spec inj] of thoracic aorta, init enc
S25.1[0,1,2,9][1,2,9]A [Unsp inj, Minor lac, Major lac, Oth spec inj] of [rt, lt, unsp] innominate or subclavian artery, init enc
S25.2[0,1,2,9]XA [Unsp inj, Minor lac, Major lac, Oth spec inj] of superior vena cava, init enc
S25.3[0,1,2,9][1,2,9]A [Unsp inj, Minor lac, Major lac, Oth spec inj] of [rt, lt, unsp] innominate or subclavian vein, init enc
S25.4[0,1,2,9][1,2,9]A [Unsp inj, Minor lac, Major lac, Oth spec inj] of [rt, lt, unsp] pulmn bld vessels, init enc
S25.8[0,1,9][1,2,9]A [Unsp inj, Lac, Oth spec inj] of oth bld vessels of thorax, [rt, lt, unsp] side, init enc
S25.9[0,1,9]XA [Unsp inj, Lac, Oth spec inj] of unsp bld vessel of thorax, init enc
S26.02[0,1,2]A [Mild, Mod, Major] lac of heart w/ hemopericardium, init enc
S26.09XA Oth inj of heart with hemopericardium, init enc
S26.0[0,1]XA [Unsp inj, Contsn] of heart w/ hemopericardium, init enc
S26.1[0,1,2,9]XA [Unsp inj, Contsn, Lac, Oth inj] of heart w/o hemopericardium, init enc
S26.9[0,1,2,9]XA [Unsp inj, Contsn, Lac, Oth inj] of heart, unsp w/ or w/o hemopericardium, init enc
S27.3[0,1,2,3,9][1,2,9]A [Unsp inj, Primary blast inj, Contsn, Lac, Oth injuries] of lung, [unilat, bilat, unsp], init enc
S27.4[0,1,2,3,9][1,2,9]A [Unsp inj, Primary blast inj, Contsn, Lac, Oth inj] of bronchus, [unilat, bilat, unsp], init enc
S27.5[0,1,2,3,9]XA [Unsp inj, Primary blast inj, Contsn, Lac, Oth inj] of thoracic trachea, init enc
S27.6[0,3,9]XA [Unsp inj, Lac, Oth inj] of pleura, init enc
S27.80[2,3,8,9]A [Contsn, Lac, Oth inj, Unsp inj] of diaphragm, init enc
S27.81[2,3,8,9]A [Contsn, Lac, Oth inj, Unsp inj] of esophagus (thoracic part), init enc
S27.89[2,3,8,9]A [Contsn, Lac, Oth inj, Unsp inj] of oth spec intrathoracic organs, init enc
S27.9XXA Inj of unsp intrathoracic organ, init enc
S27.[0,1,2]XXA Traum [pneumothorax, hemothorax, hemopneumothorax], init enc
T79.[0,1]XXA [Air, Fat] embolism (traum), init enc

Significant Trauma Body Site Category 3 - Abdomen

S31.0[0,1,2,3,4,5]1A [Unsp opn wnd, Lac w/o FB, Lac w/ FB, Punc wnd w/o FB, Punc wnd w/ FB, Opn bite] of lwr back and pelvis w/ penetration into retroperitoneum, init enc
S31.6[0,1,2,3,4,5][0,1,2,3,4,5,9]A [Unsp opn wnd, Lac w/o FB, Lac w/ FB, Punc wnd w/o FB, Punc wnd w/ FB, Opn bite] of abd wall, [rt upr quadrant, lt upr quadrant, epigastric rgn, rt lwr quadrant, lt lwr quadrant, periumbilic rgn, unsp quadrant] w/ penetration into peritoneal cavity, init enc
S35.0[0,1,2,9]XA [Unsp inj, Minor lac, Major lac, Oth inj] of abd aorta, init enc
S35.1[0,1,2,9]XA [Unsp inj, Minor lac, Major lac, Oth inj] of inferior vena cava, init enc
S35.21[1,2,8,9]A [Minor lac, Major lac, Oth inj, Unsp inj] of celiac artery, init enc
S35.22[1,2,8,9]A [Minor lac, Major lac, Oth inj, Unsp inj] of superior mesenteric artery, init enc
S35.23[1,2,8,9]A [Minor lac, Major lac, Oth inj, Unsp inj] of inferior mesenteric artery, init enc
S35.29[1,2,8,9]A [Minor lac, Major lac, Oth inj, Unsp inj] of branches of celiac and mesenteric artery, init enc
S35.3[1,2,3,4][1,8,9]A [Lac, Oth spec inj, Unsp inj] of [portal, splenic, superior mesenteric, inferior mesenteric] vein, init enc
S35.4[0,1,9][1,2,3,4,5,6]A [Unsp inj, Lac, Oth spec inj] of [rt renal artery, lt renal artery, unsp renal artery, rt renal vein, lt renal vein, unsp renal vein], init enc
S35.50XA Inj of unsp iliac bld vessel(s), init enc

S35.51[1,2,3,4,5,6]A Inj of [rt iliac artery, lt iliac artery, unsp iliac artery, rt iliac vein, rt iliac vein, unsp iliac vein], init enc
S35.53[1,2,3,4,5,6]A Inj of [rt uterine artery, lt uterine artery, unsp uterine artery, rt uterine vein, rt uterine vein, unsp uterine vein], init enc
S35.59XA Inj of oth iliac bld vessels, init enc
S35.8X[1,8,9]A [Lac, Oth spec, Unsp inj] of oth bld vessels at abd, lwr back and pelvis lvl, init enc
S35.9[0,1,9]XA [Unsp inj, Lac, Oth spec inj] of unsp bld vessel at abd, lwr back and pelvis lvl, init enc
S36.00XA Unsp inj of spleen, init enc
S36.02[0,1,9]A [Minor, Major, Unsp] contsn of spleen, init enc
S36.03[0,1,2,9]A [Superf (capsular), Mod, Major, Unsp] lac of spleen, init enc
S36.09XA Oth inj of spleen, init enc
S36.11[2,3,4,5,6,8,9]A [Contsn, Lac (unsp degree), Minor lac, Mod lac, Major lac, Oth inj, Unsp inj] of liver, init enc
S36.12[2,3,8,9]A [Contsn, Lac, Oth inj, Unsp inj] of gallbladder, init enc
S36.13XA Inj of bile duct, init enc
S36.20[0,1,2,9]A Unsp inj of [head, body, tail, unsp part] of pancreas, init enc
S36.22[0,1,2,9]A Contsn of [head, body, tail, unsp part] of pancreas, init enc
S36.23[0,1,2,9]A Lac of [head, body, tail, unsp part] of pancreas, unsp degree, init enc
S36.24[0,1,2,9]A Minor lac of [head, body, tail, unsp part] of pancreas, init enc
S36.25[0,1,2,9]A Mod lac of [head, body, tail, unsp part] of pancreas, init enc
S36.26[0,1,2,9]A Major lac of [head, body, tail, unsp part] of pancreas, init enc
S36.29[0,1,2,9]A Oth inj of [head, body, tail, unsp part] of pancreas, init enc
S36.3[0,2,3,9]XA [Unsp inj, Contsn, Lac, Oth inj] of stomach, init enc
S36.4[0,1,2,3,9][0,8,9]A [Unsp inj, Primary blast, Contsn, Lac, Oth inj] of [duodenum, oth part of sm intestine, unsp part of sm intestine], init enc
S36.50[0,1,2,3,8,9]A Unsp inj of [ascending [rt] colon, transv colon, descending [lt] colon, sigmoid colon, oth part of colon, unsp part of colon], init enc
S36.51[0,1,2,3,8,9]A Primary blast inj of [ascending [rt] colon, transv colon, descending [lt] colon, sigmoid colon, oth part of colon, unsp part of colon], init enc
S36.52[0,1,2,3,8,9]A Contsn of [ascending [rt] colon, transv colon, descending [lt] colon, sigmoid colon, oth part of colon, unsp part of colon], init enc
S36.53[0,1,2,3,8,9]A Lac of [ascending [rt] colon, transv colon, descending [lt] colon, sigmoid colon, oth part of colon, unsp part of colon], init enc
S36.59[0,1,2,3,8,9]A Oth inj of [ascending [rt] colon, transv colon, descending [lt] colon, sigmoid colon, oth part of colon, unsp part of colon], init enc
S36.6[0,1,2,3,9]XA [Unsp inj, Primary blast inj, Contsn, Lac, Oth inj] of rectum, init enc
S36.89[2,3,8,9]A [Contsn, Lac, Oth inj, Unsp inj] of oth intra-abd organs, init enc
T79.A3XA Traum compartment synd of abd, init enc

Significant Trauma Body Site Category 4 - Kidney

S37.0[0,1,2,3,4,5,6,9][1,2,9]A [Unsp inj, Minor contsn, Major contsn, Lac (unsp degree), Minor lac, Mod lac, Major lac, Oth inj] of [rt, lt, unsp] kidney, init enc
S37.81[2,3,8,9]A [Contsn, Lac, Oth inj, Unsp inj] of adrenal gland, init enc

Significant Trauma Body Site Category 5 - Urinary

S37.1[0,2,3,9]XA [Unsp inj, Contsn, Lac, Oth inj] of ureter, init enc
S37.2[0,2,3,9]XA [Unsp inj, Contsn, Lac, Oth inj] of bladder, init enc
S37.3[0,2,3,9]XA [Unsp inj, Contsn, Lac, Oth inj] of urethra, init enc
S37.6[0,2,3,9]XA [Unsp inj, Contsn, Lac, Oth Inj] of uterus, init enc
S37.89[2,3,8,9]A [Contsn, Lac, Oth inj, Unsp inj] of oth urinary and pelvic organ, init enc
S37.9[0,2,3,9]XA [Unsp inj, Contsn, Lac, Oth inj] of unsp urinary and pelvic organ, init enc

Significant Trauma Body Site Category 6 - Pelvis and Spine

M99.1[0,1] Sublux complex (vert) of [head, cervical] rgn
S13.0XXA Traum rupture of cervical intervertebral disc, init
S13.1[0,1,2,3,4,5,6,7,8][0,1]A [Sublux, Disloc] of [unsp, C0/C1, C1/C2, C2/C3, C3/C4, C4/C5, C5/C6, C6/C7, C7/T1] cervical vertebrae, init enc
S13.2[0,9]XA Disloc of [unsp, oth] parts of neck, init enc
S14.0XXA Concussion and edema of cervical spinal cord, init enc
S14.10[1,2,3,4,5,6,7,8,9]A Unsp inj at [C1, C2, C3, C4, C5, C6, C7, C8, unsp] lvl of cervical spinal cord, init enc
S14.11[1,2,3,4,5,6,7,8,9]A Complete lesion at [C1,C2, C3, C4, C5, C6, C7, C8, unsp] lvl of cervical spinal cord, init enc
S14.12[1,2,3,4,5,6,7,8,9]A Central cord synd at [C1, C2, C3, C4, C5, C6, C7, C8, unsp] lvl of cervical spinal cord, init enc
S14.13[1,2,3,4,5,6,7,8,9]A Ant cord synd at [C1, C2, C3, C4, C5, C6, C7, C8, unsp] lvl of cervical spinal cord, init enc

S14.14[1,2,3,4,5,6,7,8,9]A Brown-Sequard synd at [C1, C2, C3, C4, C5, C6, C7, C8, unsp] lvl of cervical spinal cord, init enc

S14.15[1,2,3,4,5,6,7,8,9]A Oth incomplete lesion at [C1, C2, C3, C4, C5, C6, C7, C8, unsp] lvl of cervical spinal cord, init enc

S22.9XXB Fx of bony thorax, part unsp, init for opn fx

S24.0XXA Concussion and edema of thoracic spinal cord, init enc

S24.10[1,2,3,4,9]A Unsp inj at [T1, T2-T6, T7-T10, T11-T12, unsp] lvl of thoracic spinal cord, init enc

S24.11[1,2,3,4,9]A Complete lesion at [T1, T2-T6, T7-T10, T11-T12, unsp] lvl of thoracic spinal cord, init enc

S24.13[1,2,3,4,9]A Ant cord synd at [T1, T2-T6, T7-T10, T11-T12, unsp] lvl of thoracic spinal cord, init enc

S24.14[1,2,3,4,9]A Brown-Sequard synd at [T1, T2-T6, T7-T10, T11-T12, unsp] lvl of thoracic spinal cord, init enc

S24.15[1,2,3,4,9]A Oth incomplete lesion at [T1, T2-6, T7-T10, T11-T12, unsp] lvl of thoracic spinal cord, init enc

S24.3XXA Inj of peripheral nerves of thorax, init enc

S24.8XXA Inj of oth spec nerves of thorax, init enc

S24.9XXA Inj of unsp nerve of thorax, init enc

S28.0XXA Crushed chest, init enc

S32.10X[A,B] Unsp fx of sacrum, init enc for [clsd, opn] fx

S32.11[0,1,2,9][A,B] [Nondisp Zone I, Minimally disp Zone I, Severely disp Zone I, Unsp Zone I] fx of sacrum, init enc for [clsd, opn] fx

S32.12[0,1,2,9][A,B] [Nondisp Zone II, Minimally disp Zone II, Severely disp Zone II, Unsp Zone II] fx of sacrum, init enc for [clsd, opn] fx

S32.13[0,1,2,9][A,B] [Nondisp Zone III, Minimally disp Zone III, Severely disp Zone III, Unsp Zone III] fx of sacrum, init enc for [clsd, opn] fx

S32.1[4,5,6,7,9]X[A,B] [Type 1, Type 2, Type 3, Type 4, Oth] fx of sacrum, init enc for [clsd, opn] fx

S32.2XX[A,B] Fx of coccyx, init enc for [clsd, opn] fx

S32.30[1,2,9][A,B] Unsp fx of [rt, lt, unsp] ilium, init enc for [clsd, opn] fx

S32.31[1,2,3,4,5,6][A,B][Disp, Nondisp] avulsion fx of [rt, lt, unsp] ilium, init enc for [clsd, opn] fx

S32.39[1,2,9][A,B] Oth fx of ilium [rt, lt, unsp] init enc for [clsd, opn] fx

S32.40[1,2,9][A,B] Unsp fx of acetab [rt, lt, unsp] init enc for [clsd, opn] fx

S32.41[1,2,3][A,B] Disp fx of ant wall of acetab [rt, lt, unsp] init enc for [clsd fx, opn fx]

S32.41[4,5,6][A,B] Nondisp fx of ant wall of acetab [rt, lt, unsp] init enc for [clsd fx, opn fx]

S32.42[1,2,3][A,B] Disp fx of post wall of [rt, lt, unsp] acetab, init enc for [clsd, opn] fx

S32.42[4,5,6][A,B] Nondisp fx of post wall of acetab [rt, lt, unsp] init enc for [clsd fx, opn fx]

S32.43[1,2,3][A,B] Disp fx of ant column [iliopubic] of acetab [rt, lt, unsp] init enc for [clsd fx, opn fx]

S32.43[4,5,6][A,B] Nondisp fx of ant column [iliopubic] of acetab [rt, lt, unsp] init enc for [clsd fx, opn fx

S32.44[1,2,3][A,B] Disp fx of post column [ilioischial] of acetab [rt, lt, unsp] init enc for [clsd fx, opn fx

S32.44[4,5,6][A,B] Nondisp fx of post column [ilioischial] of acetab [rt, lt, unsp] init enc for [clsd fx, opn fx

S32.45[1,2,3][A,B] Disp transv fx of acetab [rt, lt, unsp] init enc for [clsd fx, opn fx]

S32.45[4,5,6][A,B] Nondisp transv fx of acetab [rt, lt, unsp] init enc for [clsd fx, opn fx]

S32.46[1,2,3][A,B] Disp associated transv-post fx of acetab [rt, lt, unsp] init enc for [clsd fx, opn fx]

S32.46[4,5,6][A,B] Nondisp associated transv-post fx of acetab [rt, lt, unsp] init enc for [clsd, opn] fx

S32.47[1,2,3][A,B] Disp fx of med wall of acetab [rt, lt, unsp] init enc for [clsd fx, opn fx]

S32.47[4,5,6][A,B] Nondisp fx of med wall of [rt, lt, unsp] acetab, init enc for [clsd, opn] fx

S32.48[1,2,3][A,B] Disp dome fx of [rt, lt, unsp] acetab, init enc for [clsd, opn] fx

S32.48[4,5,6][A,B] Nondisp dome fx of [rt, lt, unsp] acetab, init enc for [clsd, opn] fx

S32.491A Oth fx of rt acetabulum, init for clos fx

S32.491B Oth fx of rt acetabulum, init for opn fx

S32.492A Oth fx of lt acetabulum, init for clos fx

S32.492B Oth fx of lt acetabulum, init for opn fx

S32.499A Oth fx of unsp acetabulum, init for clos fx

S32.499B Oth fx of unsp acetabulum, init for opn fx

S32.50[1,2,9][A,B] Unsp fx of pubis [rt, lt, unsp] init enc for [clsd, opn] fx

S32.51[1,2,9][A,B] Fx of superior rim of pubis [rt, lt, unsp] init enc for [clsd, opn] fx

S32.59[1,2,9][A,B] Oth spec fx of pubis [rt, lt, unsp] init enc for [clsd, opn] fx

S32.60[1,2,9][A,B] Unsp fx of ischium [rt, lt, unsp], init enc for [clsd, opn] fx

S32.61[1,2,3,4,5,6][A,B] [Disp, Nondisp] avulsion fx of [rt, lt, unsp] ischium, init enc for [clsd, opn] fx

S32.69[1,2,9][A,B] Oth spec fx of ischium [rt, lt, unsp] init enc for [clsd, opn] fx

S32.81[0,1][A,B] Multi fxs of pelvis w/ [stable, unstable] disruption of pelvic ring, init enc for [clsd, opn] fx

S32.82XA Multi fx of pelvis w/o disrupt of pelvic ring, init

S32.82XB Mult fx of pelvis w/o disrupt of pelv ring, init for opn fx

S32.89X[A,B] Fx of oth parts of pelvis, init enc for [clsd, opn] fx

S32.9XX[A,B] Fx of unsp parts of lumbosacral spine and pelvis, init enc for [clsd, opn] fx

S34.0[1,2]XA Concussion and edema of [lumbar, sacral] spinal cord, init enc

S34.10[1,2,3,4,5,9]A Unsp inj to [L1, L2, L3, L4, L5, unsp] lvl of lumbar spinal cord, init enc

S34.11[1,2,3,4,5,9]A Complete lesion of [L1, L2, L3, L4, L5, unsp] lvl of lumbar spinal cord, init enc

S34.12[1,2,3,4,5,9]A Incomplete lesion of [L1, L2, L3, L4, L5, unsp] lvl of lumbar spinal cord, init enc

S34.13[1,2,9]A [Complete lesion, Incomplete lesion, Unsp inj] (of) (to) sacral spinal cord, init enc

S34.[3,4]XXA Inj of [cauda equina, lumbosacral plexus], init enc

S34.[6,8,9]XXA Inj of [peripheral, oth, unsp] nerve(s) at abd, lwr back and pelvis lvl, init enc

S36.81XA Inj of peritoneum, init enc

S38.1XXA Crushing inj of abd, lwr back, and pelvis, init

Significant Trauma Body Site Category 7 - Upr Limb

S14.3XXA Inj of brachial plexus, init enc

S42.20[1,2,9]B Unsp fx of upr end of [rt, lt, unsp] humerus, init enc for opn fx

S42.211B Unsp disp fx of surgical neck of Rt humerus, init for opn fx

S42.212B Unsp disp fx of surgical neck of Lt humerus, init for opn fx

S42.213B Unsp disp fx of surg neck of unsp humerus, init for opn fx

S42.214B Unsp nondisp fx of surg neck of Rt humerus, init for opn fx

S42.215B Unsp nondisp fx of surg neck of Lt humerus, init for opn fx

S42.216B Unsp nondisp fx of surg neck of unsp humer, init for opn fx

S42.22[1,2,3]B 2-part disp fx of surgical neck of [rt, lt, unsp] humerus, init enc for opn fx

S42.22[4,5,6]B 2-part nondisp fx of surgical neck of [rt, lt, unsp] humerus, init enc for opn fx

S42.23[1,2,9]B 3-part fx of surgical neck of [rt, lt, unsp] humerus, init enc for opn fx

S42.24[1,2,9]B 4-part fx of surgical neck of [rt, lt, unsp] humerus, init enc for opn fx

S42.25[1,2,3]B Disp fx of greater tuberosity of [rt, lt, unsp] humerus, init enc for opn fx

S42.25[4,5,6]B Nondisp fx of greater tuberosity of [rt, lt, unsp] humerus, init enc for opn fx

S42.26[1,2,3]B Disp fx of lesser tuberosity of [rt, lt, unsp] humerus, init enc for opn fx

S42.26[4,5,6]B Nondisp fx of lesser tuberosity of [rt, lt, unsp] humerus, init enc for opn fx

S42.29[1,2,3]B Oth disp fx of upr end of [rt, lt, unsp] humerus, init enc for opn fx

S42.29[4,5,6]B Oth nondisp fx of upr end of [rt, lt, unsp] humerus, init enc for opn fx

S42.30[1,2,9]B Unsp fx of shaft of humerus [rt, lt, unsp] arm, init enc for opn fx

S42.32[1,2,3]B Disp transv fx of shaft of [rt, lt, unsp] humerus, init enc for opn fx

S42.32[4,5,6]B Nondisp transv fx of shaft of [rt, lt, unsp] humerus, init enc for opn fx

S42.33[1,2,3]B Disp oblique fx of shaft of [rt, lt, unsp] humerus, init enc for opn fx

S42.33[4,5,6]B Nondisp oblique fx of shaft of [rt, lt, unsp] humerus, init enc for opn fx

S42.34[1,2,3]B Disp spiral fx of shaft of [rt, lt, unsp] humerus, init enc for opn fx

S42.34[4,5,6]B Nondisp spiral fx of shaft of [rt, lt, unsp] humerus, init enc for opn fx

S42.35[1,2,3]B Disp comm fx of shaft of [rt, lt, unsp] humerus, init enc for opn fx

S42.35[4,5,6]B Nondisp comm fx of shaft of [rt, lt, unsp] humerus, init enc for opn fx

S42.36[1,2,3]B Disp seg fx of shaft of [rt, lt, unsp] humerus, init enc for opn fx

S42.36[4,5,6]B Nondisp seg fx of shaft of [rt, lt, unsp] humerus, init enc for opn fx

S42.39[1,2,9]B Oth fx of shaft of [rt, lt, unsp] humerus, init enc for opn fx

S42.40[1,2,9]B Unsp fx of lwr end of [rt, lt, unsp] humerus, init enc for opn fx

S42.41[1,2,3]B Disp simple supracondylar fx w/o intercondylar fx of [rt, lt, unsp] humerus, init enc for opn fx

S42.41[4,5,6]B Nondisp simple supracondylar fx w/o intercondylar fx of [rt, lt, unsp] humerus, init enc for opn fx

S42.42[1,2,3]B Disp comm supracondylar fx w/o intercondylar fx of [rt, lt, unsp] humerus, init enc for opn fx

---

Surgical   **Medical**   **CC Indicator**   **MCC Indicator**   **Procedure Proxy**   **PDxMCC** **PDx acts as own MCC**   **PDxCC PDx acts as own CC**

MDC 24: Multiple Significant Trauma—MEDICAL

S42.42[4,5,6]B	Nondisp comm supracondylar fx w/o intercondylar fx of [rt, lt, unsp] humerus, init enc for opn fx
S42.43[1,2,3]B	Disp fx (avulsion) of lat epicondyle of [rt, lt, unsp] humerus, init enc for opn fx
S42.43[4,5,6]B	Nondisp fx (avulsion) of lat epicondyle of [rt, lt, unsp] humerus, init enc for opn fx
S42.447B	Incarcerated fx of med epicondyl of Rt humer, init for opn fx
S42.448B	Incarcerated fx of med epicondyl of Lt humer, init for opn fx
S42.449B	Incarcerated fx of med epicondyl of unsp humer, 7thB
S42.44[1,2,3]B	Disp fx (avulsion) of med epicondyle of [rt, lt, unsp] humerus, init enc for opn fx
S42.44[4,5,6]B	Nondisp fx (avulsion) of med epicondyle of [rt, lt, unsp] humerus, init enc for opn fx
S42.45[1,2,3]B	Disp fx of lat condyle of [rt, lt, unsp] humerus, init enc for opn fx
S42.45[4,5,6]B	Nondisp fx of lat condyle of [rt, lt, unsp] humerus, init enc for opn fx
S42.46[1,2,3]B	Disp fx of med condyle of [rt, lt, unsp] humerus, init enc for opn fx
S42.46[4,5,6]B	Nondisp fx of med condyle of [rt, lt, unsp] humerus, init enc for opn fx
S42.47[1,2,3]B	Disp transcondylar fx of [rt, lt, unsp] humerus, init enc for opn fx
S42.47[4,5,6]B	Nondisp transcondylar fx of [rt, lt, unsp] humerus, init enc for opn fx
S42.49[1,2,3]B	Oth disp fx of lwr end of [rt, lt, unsp] humerus, init enc for opn fx
S42.49[4,5,6]B	Oth nondisp fx of lwr end of [rt, lt, unsp] humerus, init enc for opn fx
S42.9[0,1,2]XB	Fx of [unsp, rt, lt] shldr girdle, part unsp, init enc for opn fx
S44.0[0,1,2]XA	Inj of ulnar nerve at upr arm lvl, [unsp, rt, lt] arm, init enc
S44.1[0,1,2]XA	Inj of median nerve at upr arm lvl, [unsp, rt, lt] arm, init enc
S44.2[0,1,2]XA	Inj of radial nerve at upr arm lvl, [unsp, rt, lt] arm, init enc
S44.3[0,1,2]XA	Inj of axillary nerve at upr arm lvl, [unsp, rt, lt] arm, init enc
S44.8X[1,2]A	Inj of oth nerves at shldr and upr arm lvl, [rt,lt] arm, init enc
S45.0[0,1,9][1,2,9]A	[Unsp inj, Lac, Oth spec inj] of axillary artery, [rt, lt, unsp] side, init enc
S45.1[0,1,9][1,2,9]A	[Unsp inj, Lac, Oth spec inj] of brachial artery, [rt, lt, unsp] side, init enc
S45.2[0,1,9][1,2,9]A	[Unsp inj, Lac, Oth spec inj] of axillary or brachial vein, [rt, lt, unsp] side, init enc
S45.3[0,1,9][1,2,9]A	[Unsp inj, Lac, Oth spec inj] of superf vein at shldr and upr arm lvl, [rt, lt, unsp] arm, init enc
S45.8[0,1,9][1,2,9]A	[Unsp inj, Lac, Oth spec inj] of oth spec bld vessels at shldr and upr arm lvl, [rt, lt, unsp] arm, init enc
S45.9[0,1,9][1,2,9]A	[Unsp inj, Lac, Oth spec inj] of unsp bld vessel at shldr and upr arm lvl, [rt, lt, unsp] arm, init enc
S47.[1,2,9]XXA	Crushing inj of [rt, lt, unsp] shldr and upr arm, init enc
S48.0[1,2][1,2,9]A	[Complete, Partial] traum amp at [rt, lt, unsp] shldr jt, init enc
S48.1[1,2][1,2,9]A	[Complete, Partial] traum amp at lvl between [rt, lt, unsp] shldr and elbow, init enc
S48.9[1,2][1,2,9]A	[Complete, Partial] traum amp of [rt, lt, unsp] shldr and upr arm, lvl unsp, init enc
S52.00[1,2,9][B,C]	Unsp fx of upr end of [rt, lt, unsp] ulna, init enc for opn fx [type I or II, type IIIA, IIIB, or IIIC]
S52.02[1,2,3][B,C]	Disp fx of olecranon process w/o intraarticular extension of [rt, lt, unsp] ulna, init enc for fx opn fx type [I or II, IIIA IIIB or IIIC]
S52.02[4,5,6][B,C]	Nondisp fx of olecranon process w/o intraarticular extension of [rt, lt, unsp] ulna, init enc for fx opn fx type [I or II, IIIA IIIB or IIIC]
S52.03[1,2,3][B,C]	Disp fx of olecranon process w/ intraarticular extension of [rt, lt, unsp] ulna, init enc for opn fx type [I or II, IIIA IIIB or IIIC]
S52.03[4,5,6][B,C]	Nondisp fx of olecranon process w/ intraarticular extension of [rt, lt, unsp] ulna, init enc for opn fx type [I or II, IIIA IIIB or IIIC]
S52.04[1,2,3][B,C]	Disp fx of coronoid process of [rt, lt, unsp] ulna, init enc for opn fx type [I or II, IIIA IIIB or IIIC]
S52.04[4,5,6][B,C]	Nondisp fx of coronoid process of [rt, lt, unsp] ulna, init enc for opn fx type [I or II, IIIA IIIB or IIIC]
S52.09[1,2,9][B,C]	Oth fx of upr end of [rt, lt, unsp] ulna, init enc for opn fx type [I or II, IIIA IIIB or IIIC]
S52.10[1,2,9][B,C]	Unsp fx of upr end of [rt, lt, unsp] radius, init enc for opn fx type [I or II, IIIA IIIB or IIIC]
S52.12[1,2,3][B,C]	Disp fx of head of [rt, lt, unsp] radius, init enc for opn fx type [I or II, IIIA IIIB or IIIC]
S52.12[4,5,6][B,C]	Nondisp fx of head of [rt, lt, unsp] radius, init enc for opn fx type [I or II, IIIA IIIB or IIIC]
S52.13[1,2,3][B,C]	Disp fx of neck of [rt, lt, unsp] radius, init enc for opn fx type [I or II, IIIA IIIB or IIIC]

S52.13[4,5,6][B,C]	Nondisp fx of neck of [rt, lt, unsp] radius, init enc for opn fx type [I or II, IIIA IIIB or IIIC]
S52.18[1,2,9][B,C]	Oth fx of upr end of [rt, lt, unsp] radius, init enc for opn fx type [I or II, IIIA IIIB or IIIC]
S52.20[1,2,9][B,C]	Unsp fx of shaft of [rt, lt, unsp] ulna, init enc for opn fx type [I or II, IIIA IIIB or IIIC]
S52.22[1,2,3][B,C]	Disp transv fx of [rt, lt, unsp] ulna, init enc for opn fx type [I or II, IIIA IIIB or IIIC]
S52.22[4,5,6][B,C]	Nondisp transv fx of [rt, lt, unsp] ulna, init enc for opn fx type [I or II, IIIA IIIB or IIIC]
S52.23[1,2,3][B,C]	Disp oblique fx of [rt, lt, unsp] ulna, init enc for opn fx type [I or II, IIIA IIIB or IIIC]
S52.23[4,5,6][B,C]	Nondisp oblique fx of [rt, lt, unsp] ulna, init enc for opn fx type [I or II, IIIA IIIB or IIIC]
S52.24[1,2,3][B,C]	Disp spiral fx of [rt, lt, unsp] ulna, init enc for opn fx type [I or II, IIIA IIIB or IIIC]
S52.24[4,5,6][B,C]	Nondisp spiral fx of [rt, lt, unsp] ulna, init enc for opn fx type [I or II, IIIA IIIB or IIIC]
S52.25[1,2,3][B,C]	Disp comm fx of [rt, lt, unsp] ulna, init enc for opn fx [type I or II, IIIA IIIB or IIIC]
S52.25[4,5,6][B,C]	Nondisp comm fx of [rt, lt, unsp] ulna, init enc for opn fx [type I or II, IIIA IIIB or IIIC]
S52.26[1,2,3][B,C]	Disp semental fx of shaft of [rt, lt, unsp] ulna, init enc for opn fx type [I or II, IIIA IIIB or IIIC]
S52.26[4,5,6][B,C]	Nondisp semental fx of shaft of [rt, lt, unsp] ulna, init enc for opn fx type [I or II, IIIA IIIB or IIIC]
S52.27[1,2,9][B,C]	Monteggia's fx of [rt, lt, unsp] ulna, init enc for opn fx type [I or II, IIIA IIIB or IIIC]
S52.28[1,2,3][B,C]	Bent bone of [rt, lt, unsp] ulna, init enc for opn fx type [I or II, IIIA IIIB or IIIC]
S52.29[1,2,9][B,C]	Oth fx of shaft of [rt, lt, unsp] ulna, init enc for opn fx type [I or II, IIIA IIIB or IIIC]
S52.30[1,2,9][B,C]	Unsp fx of shaft of [rt, lt, unsp] radius, init enc for opn fx type [I or II, IIIA IIIB or IIIC]
S52.32[1,2,3][B,C]	Disp transv fx of shaft of [rt, lt, unsp] radius, init enc for opn fx type [I or II, IIIA IIIB or IIIC]
S52.32[4,5,6][B,C]	Nondisp transv fx of shaft of [rt, lt, unsp] radius, init enc for opn fx type [I or II, IIIA IIIB or IIIC]
S52.33[1,2,3][B,C]	Disp oblique fx of shaft of [rt, lt, unsp] radius, init enc for opn fx type [I or II, IIIA IIIB or IIIC]
S52.33[4,5,6][B,C]	Nondisp oblique fx of shaft of [rt, lt, unsp] radius, init enc for opn fx type [I or II, IIIA IIIB or IIIC]
S52.34[1,2,3][B,C]	Disp spiral fx of shaft of [rt, lt, unsp] radius, init enc for opn fx type [I or II, IIIA IIIB or IIIC]
S52.34[4,5,6][B,C]	Nondisp spiral fx of shaft of [rt, lt, unsp] radius, init enc for opn fx type [I or II, IIIA IIIB or IIIC]
S52.35[1,2,3][B,C]	Disp comm fx of shaft of [rt, lt, unsp] radius, init enc for opn fx type [I or II, IIIA IIIB or IIIC]
S52.35[4,5,6][B,C]	Nondisp comm fx of shaft of [rt, lt, unsp] radius, init enc for opn fx type [I or II, IIIA IIIB or IIIC]
S52.36[1,2,3][B,C]	Disp seg fx of shaft of [rt, lt, unsp] radius, init enc for opn fx type [I or II, IIIA IIIB or IIIC]
S52.36[4,5,6][B,C]	Nondisp seg fx of shaft of [rt, lt, unsp] radius, init enc for opn fx type [I or II, IIIA IIIB or IIIC]
S52.37[1,2,9][B,C]	Galeazzi's fx of [rt, lt, unsp] radius, init enc for opn fx type [I or II, IIIA IIIB or IIIC]
S52.38[1,2,9][B,C]	Bent bone of [rt, lt, unsp] radius, init enc for opn fx type [I or II, IIIA IIIB or IIIC]
S52.39[1,2,9][B,C]	Oth fx of shaft of radius [rt, lt, unsp] arm, init enc for opn fx type [I or II, IIIA IIIB or IIIC]
S52.50[1,2,9][B,C]	Unsp fx of the lwr end of [rt, lt, unsp] radius, init enc for opn fx type [I or II, IIIA IIIB or IIIC]
S52.51[1,2,3][B,C]	Disp fx of [rt, lt, unsp] radial styloid process, init enc for opn fx type [I or II, IIIA IIIB or IIIC]
S52.51[4,5,6][B,C]	Nondisp fx of [rt, lt, unsp] radial styloid process, init enc for opn fx type [I or II, IIIA IIIB or IIIC]
S52.53[1,2,9][B,C]	Colles' fx of [rt, lt, unsp] radius, init enc for opn fx type [I or II, IIIA IIIB or IIIC]
S52.54[1,2,9][B,C]	Smith's fx of [rt, lt, unsp] radius, init enc for opn fx type [I or II, IIIA IIIB or IIIC]
S52.55[1,2,9][B,C]	Oth extraarticular fx of lwr end of [rt, lt, unsp] radius, init enc for opn fx type [I or II, IIIA IIIB or IIIC]
S52.56[1,2,9][B,C]	Barton's fx of [rt, lt, unsp] radius, init enc for opn fx type [I or II, IIIA IIIB or IIIC]
S52.57[1,2,9][B,C]	Oth intraarticular fxs of lwr end of [rt, lt, unsp] radius, init enc for opn fx type [I or II, IIIA IIIB or IIIC]
S52.59[1,2,9][B,C]	Oth fxs of lwr end of [rt, lt, unsp] radius, init enc for opn fx type [I or II, IIIA IIIB or IIIC]
S52.60[1,2,9][B,C]	Unsp fx of lwr end of [rt, lt, unsp] ulna, init enc for opn fx type [I or II, IIIA IIIB IIIC]

ⓣ **Transfer DRG**   ⓢⓟ **Special Payment**   *** Code Range**   **6th and 7th Character of ZZ = No Device, No Qualifier ZX = No Device, Diagnostic**

S52.61[1,2,3][B,C] Disp fx of [rt, lt, unsp] ulna styloid process, init enc for fx opn fx type [I or II, IIIA IIIB IIIC]

S52.61[4,5,6][B,C] Nondisp fx of [rt, lt, unsp] ulna styloid process, init enc for fx opn fx type [I or II, IIIA IIIB IIIC]

S52.69[1,2,9][B,C] Oth fx of lwr end of [rt, lt, unsp] ulna, init enc for opn fx type [I or II, IIIA IIIB or IIIC]

S52.9[0,1,2]X[B,C] Oth fx of [unsp, rt, lt] forearm, init enc for opn fx type [I or II, IIIA IIIB IIIC]

S54.0[0,1,2]XA Inj of ulnar nerve at forearm lvl, [unsp, rt, lt] arm, init enc

S54.1[0,1,2]XA Inj of median nerve at forearm lvl, [unsp, rt, lt] arm, init enc

S54.2[0,1,2]XA Inj of radial nerve at forearm lvl, [unsp, rt, lt] arm, init enc

S54.8X1A Unsp inj of oth nerves at forearm lvl, rt arm, init

S54.8X2A Unsp inj of oth nerves at forearm lvl, lt arm, init

S54.8X9A Unsp inj of oth nerves at forearm lvl, unsp arm, init

S55.0[0,1,9][1,2,9]A [Unsp inj, Lac, Oth spec inj] of ulnar artery at forearm lvl, [rt, lt, unsp] arm, init enc

S55.1[0,1,9][1,2,9]A [Unsp inj, Lac, Oth spec inj] of radial artery at forearm lvl, [rt, lt, unsp] arm, init enc

S55.2[0,1,9][1,2,9]A [Unsp inj, Lac, Oth spec inj] of vein at forearm lvl, [rt, lt, unsp] arm, init enc

S55.8[0,1,9][1,2,9]A [Unsp inj, Lac, Oth spec inj] of oth bld vessels at forearm lvl, [rt, lt, unsp] arm, init enc

S55.9[0,1,9][1,2,9]A [Unsp inj, Lac, Oth spec inj] of unsp bld vessel at forearm lvl, [rt, lt, unsp] arm, init enc

S57.[0,8][0,1,2]XA Crushing inj of [unsp, rt, lt] [elbow, forearm], init enc

S58.0[1,2][1,2,9]A [Complete, Partial] traum amp at elbow lvl, [rt, lt, unsp] arm, init enc

S58.1[1,2][1,2,9]A [Complete, Partial] traum amp at lvl between elbow and wrist, [rt, lt, unsp] arm, init enc

S58.9[1,2][1,2,9]A [Complete, Partial] traum amp of [rt, lt, unsp] forearm, lvl unsp, init enc

S62.90XB Unsp fx of unsp wrist and hand, init for opn fx

S64.0[0,1,2]XA Inj of ulnar nerve at wrist and hand lvl of [unsp, rt, lt] arm, init enc

S64.1[0,1,2]XA Inj of median nerve at wrist and hand lvl of [unsp, rt, lt] arm, init enc

S64.2[0,1,2]XA Inj of radial nerve at wrist and hand lvl of [unsp, rt, lt] arm, init enc

S64.8X[1,2,9]A Inj of oth nerves at wrist and hand lvl of [rt, lt, unsp] arm, init enc

S65.0[0,1,9][1,2,9]A [Unsp inj, Lac, Oth spec inj] of ulnar artery at wrist and hand lvl of [rt, lt, unsp] arm, init enc

S65.1[0,1,9][1,2,9]A [Unsp inj, Lac, Oth spec inj] of radial artery at wrist and hand lvl of [rt, lt, unsp] arm, init enc

S65.8[0,1,9][1,2,9]A [Unsp inj, Lac, Oth spec inj] of oth bld vessels at wrist and hand lvl of [rt, lt, unsp] arm, init enc

S65.9[0,1,9][1,2,9]A [Unsp inj, Lac, Oth spec inj] of unsp bld vessels at wrist and hand lvl of [rt, lt, unsp] arm, init enc

S68.4[1,2][1,2,9]A [Complete, Partial] traum amp of [rt, lt, unsp] hand at wrist lvl, init enc

S68.7[1,2][1,2,9]A [Complete, Partial] traum transmetacarpal amp of [rt, lt, unsp] hand, init enc

T79.6XXA Traum ischemia of muscle, init enc

T79.A1[1,2,9]A Traum compartment synd of [rt, lt, unsp] upr extr, init enc

Significant Trauma Body Site Category 8 - Lwr Limb

S72.00[1,2,9][A,B,C] Fx of unsp part of neck of [rt, lt, unsp] femur, init enc for [clsd fx, opn fx type I or II, opn fx type IIIA, IIIB, or IIIC]

S72.01[1,2,9][A,B,C] Unsp intracapsular fx of [rt, lt, unsp] femur, init enc for [clsd fx, opn fx type I or II, opn fx type IIIA, IIIB, or IIIC]

S72.02[1,2,3][A,B,C] Disp fx of epiphysis (separation) (upr) of [rt, lt, unsp] femur, init enc for [clsd fx, opn fx type I or II or NOS, or opn fx type IIIA, IIIB, or IIIC]

S72.02[4,5,6][A,B,C] Nondisp fx of epiphysis (separation) (upr) of [rt, lt, unsp] femur, init enc for [clsd fx, opn fx type I or II or NOS, or opn fx type IIIA, IIIB, or IIIC]

S72.03[1,2,3][A,B,C] Disp midcervical fx of [rt, lt, unsp] femur, init enc for [clsd fx, opn fx type I or II or NOS, or opn fx type IIIA, IIIB, or IIIC]

S72.03[4,5,6][A,B,C] Nondisp midcervical fx of [rt, lt, unsp] femur, init enc for [clsd fx, opn fx type I or II or NOS, or opn fx type IIIA, IIIB, or IIIC]

S72.04[1,2,3][A,B,C] Disp fx of base of neck of [rt, lt, unsp] femur, init enc for opn fx type [I or II, IIIA IIIB or IIIC]

S72.04[4,5,6][A,B,C] Nondisp fx of base of neck of [rt, lt, unsp] femur, init enc for opn fx type [I or II, IIIA IIIB or IIIC]

S72.05[1,2,9][A,B,C] Unsp fx of head of [rt, lt, unsp] femur, init enc for [clsd fx, opn fx type I or II, opn fx type IIIA, IIIB, or IIIC]

S72.06[1,2,3][A,B,C] Disp articular fx of head of [rt, lt, unsp] femur, init enc for fx [clsd, opn fx type I or II or NOS, or opn fx type IIIA, IIIB, or IIIC]

S72.06[4,5,6][A,B,C] Nondisp articular fx of head of femur [rt, lt, unsp] init enc for fx [clsd, opn fx type I or II or NOS, or opn fx type IIIA, IIIB, or IIIC]

S72.09[1,2,9][A,B,C] Oth fx of head and neck of [rt, lt, unsp] femur, init enc for [clsd fx, opn fx type I or II, opn fx type IIIA, IIIB, or IIIC]

S72.10[1,2,9][A,B,C] Unsp trochanteric fx of [rt, lt, unsp] femur, init enc for [clsd fx, opn fx type I or II, opn fx type IIIA, IIIB, or IIIC]

S72.11[1,2,3][A,B,C] Disp fx of greater trochanter of [rt, lt, unsp] femur, init enc for fx [clsd, opn fx type I or II or NOS, or opn fx type IIIA, IIIB, or IIIC]

S72.11[4,5,6][A,B,C] Nondisp fx of greater trochanter of femur [rt, lt, unsp] init enc for fx [clsd, opn fx type I or II or NOS, or opn fx type IIIA, IIIB, or IIIC]

S72.12[1,2,3][A,B,C] Disp fx of lesser trochanter of [rt, lt, unsp] femur, init enc for [clsd fx, opn fx type I or II or NOS, or opn fx type IIIA, IIIB, or IIIC]

S72.12[4,5,6][A,B,C] Nondisp fx of lesser trochanter of [rt, lt, unsp] femur, init enc for [clsd fx, opn fx type I or II or NOS, or opn fx type IIIA, IIIB, or IIIC]

S72.13[1,2,3][A,B,C] Disp apophyseal fx of [rt, lt, unsp] femur, init enc for [clsd fx, opn fx type I or II or NOS, or opn fx type IIIA, IIIB, or IIIC]

S72.13[4,5,6][A,B,C] Nondisp apophyseal fx of [rt, lt, unsp] femur, init enc for [clsd fx, opn fx type I or II or NOS, or opn fx type IIIA, IIIB, or IIIC]

S72.14[1,2,3][A,B,C] Disp intertrochanteric fx of [rt, lt, unsp] femur, init enc for [clsd fx, opn fx type I or II or NOS, or opn fx type IIIA, IIIB, or IIIC]

S72.14[4,5,6][A,B,C] Nondisp intertrochanteric fx of [rt, lt, unsp] femur, init enc for [clsd fx, opn fx type I or II or NOS, or opn fx type IIIA, IIIB, or IIIC]

S72.2[1,2,3]X[A,B,C] Disp subtrochanteric fx of [rt, lt, unsp] femur, init enc for [clsd fractrure, opn fx type I or II or NOS, or opn fx type IIIA, IIIB, or IIIC]

S72.2[4,5,6]X[A,B,C] Nondisp subtrochanteric fx of [rt, lt, unsp] femur, init enc for [clsd fractrure, opn fx type I or II or NOS, or opn fx type IIIA, IIIB, or IIIC]

S72.30[1,2,9][A,B,C] Unsp fx of shaft of [rt, lt, unsp] femur, init enc for [clsd fx, opn fx type I or II, opn fx type IIIA, IIIB, or IIIC]

S72.32[1,2,3][A,B,C] Disp transv fx of shaft of [rt, lt, unsp] femur, init enc for [clsd fx, opn fx type I or II, opn fx type IIIA, IIIB, or IIIC]

S72.32[4,5,6][A,B,C] Nondisp transv fx of shaft of [rt, lt, unsp] femur, init enc for [clsd fx, opn fx type I or II, opn fx type IIIA, IIIB, or IIIC]

S72.33[1,2,3][A,B,C] Disp oblique fx of shaft of [rt, lt, unsp] femur, init enc for [clsd fx, opn fx type I or II , opn fx type IIIA, IIIB, or IIIC]

S72.33[4,5,6][A,B,C] Nondisp oblique fx of shaft of [rt, lt, unsp] femur, init enc for [clsd fx, opn fx type I or II, opn fx type IIIA, IIIB, or IIIC]

S72.34[1,2,3][A,B,C] Disp spiral fx of shaft of [rt, lt, unsp] femur, init enc for [clsd fx, opn fx type I or II, opn fx type IIIA, IIIB, or IIIC]

S72.34[4,5,6][A,B,C] Nondisp spiral fx of shaft of [rt, lt, unsp] femur, init enc for [clsd fx, opn fx type I or II, opn fx type IIIA, IIIB, or IIIC]

S72.35[1,2,3][A,B,C] Disp comm fx of shaft of [rt, lt, unsp] femur, init enc for [clsd fx, opn fx type I or II, opn fx type IIIA, IIIB, or IIIC]

S72.35[4,5,6][A,B,C] Nondisp comm fx of shaft of femur [rt, lt, unsp], init enc for [clsd fx, opn fx type I or II or NOS, opn fx type IIIA, IIIB, or IIIC]

S72.36[1,2,3][A,B,C] Disp seg fx of shaft of [rt, lt, unsp] femur, init enc for [clsd fx, opn fx type I or II, opn fx type IIIA, IIIB, or IIIC]

S72.36[4,5,6][A,B,C] Nondisp seg fx of shaft of [rt, lt, unsp] femur, init enc for [clsd fx, opn fx type I or II, opn fx type IIIA, IIIB, or IIIC]

S72.39[1,2,9][A,B,C] Oth fx of shaft of [rt, lt, unsp] femur, init enc for [clsd fx, opn fx type I or II, opn fx type IIIA, IIIB, or IIIC]

S72.40[1,2,9][A,B,C] Unsp fx of lwr end of [rt, lt, unsp] femur, init enc for [clsd fx, opn fx type I or II, opn fx type IIIA, IIIB, or IIIC]

S72.41[1,2,3][A,B,C] Disp unsp condyle fx of lwr end of [rt, lt, unsp] femur, init enc for [clsd fx, opn fx type I or II, opn fx type IIIA, IIIB, or IIIC]

S72.41[4,5,6][A,B,C] Nondisp unsp condyle fx of lwr end of [rt, lt, unsp] femur, init enc for [clsd fx, opn fx type I or II, opn fx type IIIA, IIIB, or IIIC]

S72.42[1,2,3][A,B,C] Disp fx of lat condyle of [rt, lt, unsp] femur, init enc for [clsd fx, opn fx type I or II, opn fx type IIIA, IIIB, or IIIC]

S72.42[4,5,6][A,B,C] Nondisp fx of lat condyle of [rt, lt, unsp] femur, init enc for [clsd fx, opn fx type I or II, opn fx type IIIA, IIIB, or IIIC]

S72.43[1,2,3][A,B,C] Disp fx of med condyle of [rt, lt, unsp] femur, init enc for [clsd fx, opn fx type I or II, opn fx type IIIA, IIIB, or IIIC]

S72.43[4,5,6][A,B,C] Nondisp fx of med condyle of [rt, lt, unsp] femur, init enc for [clsd fx, opn fx type I or II, opn fx type IIIA, IIIB, or IIIC]

S72.44[1,2,3][A,B,C] Disp fx of lwr epiphysis (separation) of [rt, lt, unsp] femur, init enc for [clsd fx, opn fx type I or II, opn fx type IIIA, IIIB, or IIIC]

S72.44[4,5,6][A,B,C] Nondisp fx of lwr epiphysis (separation) of [rt, lt, unsp] femur, init enc for [clsd fx, opn fx type I or II, opn fx type IIIA, IIIB, or IIIC]

Surgical　**Medical**　**CC Indicator**　**MCC Indicator**　**Procedure Proxy**　PDx MCC **PDx acts as own MCC**　PDx CC **PDx acts as own CC**

© 2015 Optum360, LLC　MS-DRG Version 33.0　**435**

MDC 24: Multiple Significant Trauma—MEDICAL

S72.45[1,2,3][A,B,C] Disp supracondylar fx w/o intracondylar extension of lwr end of [rt, lt, unsp] femur, init enc for [clsd fx, opn fx type I or II, opn fx type IIIA, IIIB, or IIIC]

S72.45[4,5,6][A,B,C] Nondisp supracondylar fx w/o intracondylar extension of lwr end of [rt, lt, unsp] femur, init enc for [clsd fx, opn fx type I or II, opn fx type IIIA, IIIB, or IIIC]

S72.46[1,2,3][A,B,C] Disp supracondylar fx w/ intracondylar extension of lwr end of [rt, lt, unsp] femur, init enc for [clsd fx, opn fx type I or II, opn fx type IIIA, IIIB, or IIIC]

S72.46[4,5,6][A,B,C] Nondisp supracondylar fx w/ intracondylar extension of lwr end of [rt, lt, unsp] femur, init enc for [clsd fx, opn fx type I or II, opn fx type IIIA, IIIB, or IIIC]

S72.47[1,2,9]A Torus fx of lwr end of [rt, lt, unsp] femur, init enc for clsd fx

S72.49[1,2,9][A,B,C] Oth fx of lwr end of [rt, lt, unsp] femur, init enc for [clsd fx, opn fx type I or II, opn fx type IIIA, IIIB, or IIIC]

S72.8X[1,2,9][A,B,C] Oth fx of [rt, lt, unsp] femur, init enc for [clsd fx, opn fx type I or II, opn fx type IIIA, IIIB, or IIIC]

S72.9[0,1,2]X[A,B,C] Unsp fx of [unsp, rt lt] femur, init enc for [clsd fx, opn fx type I or II, opn fx type IIIA, IIIB, or IIIC]

S74.0[0,1,2]XA Inj of sciatic nerve at hip & thigh lvl, [unsp, rt, lt] leg, init enc

S74.1[0,1,2]XA Inj of femor nerve at hip & thigh lvl, [unsp, rt, lt] leg, init enc

S74.8X[1,2,9]A Inj of oth nerves at hip & thigh lvl, [rt, lt, unsp] leg, init enc

S74.9[0,1,2]XA Inj of unsp nerve at hip & thigh lvl, [unsp, rt, lt] leg, init enc

S75.0[0,1,2,9][1,2,9]A [Unsp inj, Minor lac, Major lac, Oth spec inj] of femor artery, [rt, lt, unsp] leg, init enc

S75.1[0,1,2,9][1,2,9]A [Unsp inj, Minor lac, Major lac, Oth spec inj] of femor vein at hip & thigh lvl, [rt, lt, unsp] leg, init enc

S75.8[0,1,9][1,2,9]A [Unsp inj, Lac, Oth spec inj] of oth bld vessels at hip & thigh lvl, [rt, lt, unsp] leg, init enc

S77.[0,1,2][0,1,2]XA Crushing inj of [unsp, rt, lt] [hip, thigh, hip w/ thigh], init enc

S78.0[1,2][1,2,9]A [Complete, Partial] traum amp at [rt, lt, unsp] hip jt, init enc

S78.1[1,2][1,2,9]A [Complete, Partial] traum amp at lvl between [rt, lt, unsp] hip and knee, init enc

S78.9[1,2][1,2,9]A [Complete, Partial] traum amp of [rt, lt, unsp] hip & thigh, lvl unsp, init enc

S79.00[1,2,9]A Unsp physeal fx of upr end of [rt, lt, unsp] femur, init enc for clsd fx

S79.01[1,2,9]A Salter-Harris Type I physeal fx of upr end of [rt, lt, unsp] femur, init enc for clsd fx

S79.09[1,2,9]A Oth physeal fx of upr end of [rt, lt, unsp] femur, init enc for clsd fx

S79.10[1,2,9]A Unsp physeal fx of lwr end of [rt, lt, unsp] femur, inital enc for clsd fx

S79.19[1,2,9]A Oth physeal fx of lwr end of [rt, lt, unsp] femur, inital enc for clsd fx

S79.1[1,2,3,4][1,2,9]A Salter-Harris [Type I, Type II, Type III, Type IV] physeal fx of lwr end of [rt, lt, unsp] femur, init enc for clsd fx

S82.10[1,2,9][B,C] Unsp fx of upr end of [rt, lt, unsp] tibia, init enc for opn fx type [I or II, IIIA IIIB or IIIC]

S82.11[1,2,3][B,C] Disp fx of [rt, lt, unsp] tibial spine, init enc for opn fx type [I or II, IIIA IIIB or IIIC]

S82.11[4,5,6][B,C] Nondisp fx of [rt, lt, unsp] tibial spine, init enc for opn fx type [I or II, IIIA IIIB or IIIC]

S82.12[1,2,3][B,C] Disp fx of lat condyle of [rt, lt, unsp] tibia, init enc for opn fx type [I or II, IIIA IIIB or IIIC]

S82.12[4,5,6][B,C] Nondisp fx of lat condyle of [rt, lt, unsp] tibia, init enc for opn fx type [I or II, IIIA IIIB or IIIC]

S82.13[1,2,3][B,C] Disp fx of med condyle of [rt, lt, unsp] tibia, init enc for opn fx type [I or II, IIIA IIIB or IIIC]

S82.13[4,5,6][B,C] Nondisp fx of med condyle of [rt, lt, unsp] tibia, init enc for opn fx type [I or II, IIIA IIIB or IIIC]

S82.14[1,2,3][B,C] Disp bicondylar fx of [rt, lt, unsp] tibia, init enc for opn fx type [I or II, IIIA IIIB or IIIC]

S82.14[4,5,6][B,C] Nondisp bicondylar fx of [rt, lt, unsp] tibia, init enc for opn fx type [I or II, IIIA IIIB or IIIC]

S82.15[1,2,3][B,C] Disp fx of [rt, lt, unsp] tibial tuberosity, init enc for opn fx type [I or II, IIIA IIIB or IIIC]

S82.15[4,5,6][B,C] Nondisp fx of [rt, lt, unsp] tibial tuberosity, init enc for opn fx type [I or II, IIIA IIIB or IIIC]

S82.16[1,2,9]A Torus fx of upr end of [rt, lt, unsp] tibia, init enc for clsd fx

S82.19[1,2,9][B,C] Oth fx of upr end of [rt, lt, unsp] tibia, init enc for opn fx type [I or II, IIIA IIIB or IIIC]

S82.20[1,2,9][B,C] Unsp fx of shaft of [rt, lt, unsp] tibia, init enc for opn fx type [I or II, IIIA IIIB or IIIC]

S82.22[1,2,3][B,C] Disp transv fx of shaft of [rt, lt, unsp] tibia, init enc for opn fx type [I or II, IIIA IIIB or IIIC]

S82.22[4,5,6][B,C] Nondisp transv fx of shaft of [rt, lt, unsp] tibia, init enc for opn fx type [I or II, IIIA IIIB or IIIC]

S82.23[1,2,3][B,C] Disp oblique fx of shaft of [rt, lt, unsp] tibia, init enc for opn fx type [I or II, IIIA IIIB or IIIC]

S82.23[4,5,6][B,C] Nondisp oblique fx of shaft of [rt, lt, unsp] tibia, init enc for opn fx type [I or II, IIIA IIIB or IIIC]

S82.24[1,2,3][B,C] Disp spiral fx of shaft of [rt, lt, unsp] tibia, init enc for opn fx type [I or II, IIIA IIIB or IIIC]

S82.24[4,5,6][B,C] Nondisp spiral fx of shaft of [rt, lt, unsp] tibia, init enc for opn fx type [I or II, IIIA IIIB or IIIC]

S82.25[1,2,3][B,C] Disp comm fx of shaft of [rt, lt, unsp] tibia, init enc for opn fx type [I or II, IIIA IIIB or IIIC]

S82.25[4,5,6][B,C] Nondisp comm fx of shaft of [rt, lt, unsp] tibia, init enc for opn fx type [I or II, IIIA IIIB or IIIC]

S82.26[1,2,3][B,C] Disp seg fx of shaft of [rt, lt, unsp] tibia, init enc for opn fx type [I or II, IIIA IIIB or IIIC]

S82.26[4,5,6][B,C] Nondisp seg fx of shaft of [rt, lt, unsp] tibia, init enc for opn fx type [I or II, IIIA IIIB or IIIC]

S82.29[1,2,9][B,C] Oth fx of shaft of [rt, lt, unsp] tibia, init enc for opn fx type [I or II, IIIA IIIB or IIIC]

S82.31[1,2,9]A Torus fx of lwr end of [rt, lt, unsp] tibia, init enc for clsd fx

S82.40[1,2,9][B,C] Unsp fx of shaft of [rt, lt, unsp] fibula, init enc for opn fx type [I or II, IIIA IIIB or IIIC]

S82.42[1,2,3][B,C] Disp transv fx of shaft of [rt, lt, unsp] fibula, init enc for opn fx type [I or II, IIIA IIIB or IIIC]

S82.42[4,5,6][B,C] Nondisp transv fx of shaft of [rt, lt, unsp] fibula, init enc for opn fx type [I or II, IIIA IIIB or IIIC]

S82.43[1,2,3][B,C] Disp oblique fx of shaft of [rt, lt, unsp] fibula, init enc for opn fx type [I or II, IIIA IIIB or IIIC]

S82.43[4,5,6][B,C] Nondisp oblique fx of shaft of [rt, lt, unsp] fibula, init enc for opn fx type [I or II, IIIA IIIB or IIIC]

S82.44[1,2,3][B,C] Disp spiral fx of shaft of [rt, lt, unsp] fibula, init enc for opn fx type [I or II, IIIA IIIB or IIIC]

S82.44[4,5,6][B,C] Nondisp spiral fx of shaft of [rt, lt, unsp] fibula, init enc for opn fx type [I or II, IIIA IIIB or IIIC]

S82.45[1,2,3][B,C] Disp comm fx of shaft of [rt, lt, unsp] fibula, init enc for opn fx type [I or II, IIIA IIIB or IIIC]

S82.45[4,5,6][B,C] Nondisp comm fx of shaft of [rt, lt, unsp] fibula, init enc for opn fx type [I or II, IIIA IIIB or IIIC]

S82.46[1,2,3][B,C] Disp seg fx of shaft of [rt, lt, unsp] fibula, init enc for opn fx type [I or II, IIIA IIIB or IIIC]

S82.46[4,5,6][B,C] Nondisp seg fx of shaft of [rt, lt, unsp] fibula, init enc for opn fx type [I or II, IIIA IIIB or IIIC]

S82.49[1,2,9][B,C] Oth fx of shaft of [rt, lt, unsp] fibula, init enc for opn fx type [I or II, IIIA IIIB or IIIC]

S82.81[1,2,9]A Torus fx of upr end of [rt, lt, unsp] fibula, init enc for clsd fx

S82.82[1,2,9]A Torus fx of lwr end of [rt, lt, unsp] fibula, init enc for clsd fx

S82.83[1,2,9][B,C] Oth fx of upr and lwr end of [rt, lt, unsp] fibula, init enc for opn fx type [I or II, IIIA IIIB or IIIC]

S82.86[1,2,3][B,C] Disp Maisonneuve's fx of [rt, lt, unsp] leg, init enc for opn fx type [I or II, IIIA IIIB or IIIC]

S82.86[4,5,6][B,C] Nondisp Maisonneuve's fx of [rt, lt, unsp] leg, init enc for opn fx type [I or II, IIIA IIIB or IIIC]

S84.0[0,1,2]XA Inj of tibial nerve at lwr leg lvl, [unsp, rt, lt] leg, init enc

S84.1[0,1,2]XA Inj of peroneal nerve at lwr leg lvl, [unsp, rt, lt] leg, init enc

S84.80[1,2,9]A Inj of oth nerves at lwr leg lvl, [rt, lt, unsp] leg, init enc

S84.9[0,1,2]XA Inj of unsp nerve at lwr leg lvl, [unsp, rt, lt] leg, init enc

S85.0[0,1,9][1,2,9]A [Unsp inj, Lac, Oth spec inj] of popliteal artery, [rt, lt, unsp] leg, init enc

S85.1[0,1,2][1,2,9]A [Unsp inj, Lac, Oth spec inj] of unsp tibial artery, [rt, lt, unsp] leg, init enc

S85.1[3,4,5][1,2,9]A [Unsp inj, Lac, Oth spec inj] of ant tibial artery, [rt, lt, unsp] leg, init enc

S85.1[6,7,8][1,2,9]A [Unsp inj, Lac, Oth spec inj] of post tibial artery, [rt, lt, unsp] leg, init enc

S85.2[0,1,9][1,2,9]A [Unsp inj, Lac, Oth spec inj] of peroneal artery, [rt, lt, unsp] leg, init enc

S85.5[0,1,9][1,2,9]A [Unsp inj, Lac, Oth spec inj] of popliteal vein, [rt, lt, unsp] leg, init enc

S85.8[0,1,9][1,2,9]A [Unsp inj, Lac, Oth spec inj] of oth bood vessels at lwr leg lvl, [rt, lt, unsp] leg, init enc

S87.0[0,1,2]XA Crushing inj of [unsp, rt, lt] knee, init enc

S87.8[0,1,2]XA Crushing inj of [unsp, rt, lt] lwr leg, init enc

S88.0[1,2][1,2,9]A [Complete, Partial] traum amp at knee lvl, [rt, lt, unsp] lwr leg, init enc

S88.1[1,2][1,2,9]A [Complete, Partial] traum amp at lvl between knee and ankle, [rt, lt, unsp] lwr leg, init enc

S88.9[1,2][1,2,9]A [Complete, Partial] traum amp of [rt, lt, unsp] lwr leg, lvl unsp, init enc

S94.2[0,1,2]XA Inj of deep peroneal nerve at ankle and foot lvl, [unsp, rt, lt] leg, init enc

S94.8X[1,2,9]A Inj of oth nerves at ankle and foot lvl, [unsp leg, rt, lt], init enc

S94.9[0,1,2]XA Inj of unsp nerve at ankle and foot lvl, [unsp leg, rt, lt], init enc

---

Ⓣ **Transfer DRG**   ⓢⓟ **Special Payment**   * **Code Range**   **6th and 7th Character of ZZ = No Device, No Qualifier ZX = No Device, Diagnostic**

S95.0[0,1,9][1,2,9]A [Unsp inj, Lac, Oth spec inj] of dorsal artery of [rt, lt, unsp] foot, init enc
S95.2[0,1,9][1,2,9]A [Unsp inj, Lac, Oth spec inj] of dorsal vein of [rt, lt, unsp] foot, init enc
S95.8[0,1,9][1,2,9]A [Unsp inj, Lac, Oth spec inj] of oth bld vessels at ankle and foot lvl, [rt, lt, unsp] leg, init enc
S98.0[1,2][1,2,9]A [Complete, Partial] traum amp of [rt, lt, unsp] foot at ankle lvl, init enc
S98.3[1,2][1,2,9]A [Complete, Partial] traum amp of [rt, lt, unsp] midfoot, init enc
S98.9[1,2][1,2,9]A [Complete, Partial] traum amp of [rt, lt, unsp] foot, lvl unsp, init enc
T79.A2[1,2,9]A   Traum compartment synd of [rt, lt, unsp] lwr extr, init enc

DRG 964   Other Multiple Significant Trauma with CC
GMLOS 4.1   AMLOS 5.0   RW 1.4205

Select principal diagnosis from Trauma Diagnosis List located in DRG 963
AND

At least two different diagnoses from two different Significant Trauma Body Site Categories located in DRG 963
OR

Select a principal diagnosis from one Significant Trauma Body Site Category located in DRG 963
AND

Two or more significant trauma diagnoses from different Significant Trauma Body Site Categories located in DRG 963

DRG 965   Other Multiple Significant Trauma without CC/MCC
GMLOS 3.0   AMLOS 3.5   RW 0.9217

Select principal diagnosis from Trauma Diagnosis List located in DRG 963
AND

At least two different diagnoses from two different Significant Trauma Body Site Categories located in DRG 963
OR

Select a principal diagnosis from one Significant Trauma Body Site Category located in DRG 963
AND

Two or more significant trauma diagnoses from different Significant Trauma Body Site Categories located in DRG 963

MDC 25
Human Immunodeficiency Virus Infections

SURGICAL

DRG 969 HIV with Extensive O.R. Procedure with MCC
GMLOS 11.2   AMLOS 15.1   RW 5.0291

Principal Diagnosis

B20   Human immunodef virus [HIV] dz
AND

Any operating procedures excluding nonextensive operating room procedures (those procedures assigned to DRGs 987 - 989)
OR

Secondary Diagnosis

B20   Human immunodef virus [HIV] dz
AND

Principal diagnosis of any major or significant HIV-related condition listed in DRG 974 or DRG 977
AND

Any operating procedures excluding nonextensive operating room procedures (those procedures assigned to DRGs 987 - 989)

DRG 970 HIV with Extensive O.R. Procedure without MCC
GMLOS 5.1   AMLOS 6.9   RW 2.7871

Principal Diagnosis

B20   Human immunodeficiency virus [HIV] dz
AND

Any operating procedures excluding nonextensive operating room procedures (those procedures assigned to DRGs 987 - 989)
OR

Secondary Diagnosis

B20   Human immunodeficiency virus [HIV] dz
AND

Principal diagnosis of any major or significant HIV-related condition listed in DRG 974 or DRG 977
AND

Any operating procedures excluding nonextensive operating room procedures (those procedures assigned to DRGs 987 - 989)

MEDICAL

DRG 974 HIV with Major Related Condition with MCC
GMLOS 6.6   AMLOS 9.2   RW 2.6531

Principal or Secondary Diagnosis

B20   Human immunodef virus [HIV] dz
AND

Major HIV-related Diagnosis

A02.1	Salmonella sepsis
A02.2*	Localized salmonella infections
A02.8	Oth spec salmonella infections
A02.9	Salmonella infxn, unsp
A07.3	Isosporiasis
A15*	Respiratory tuberculosis
A17*	Tuberculosis of nervous sys
A18*	Tuberculosis of oth organs
A19*	Miliary tuberculosis
A31.2	Dissem mycobacterium avium-intracellulare complex (DMAC)
A31.8	Oth mycobacterial infections
A31.9	Mycobacterial infxn, unsp
A40.9	Streptococcal sepsis, unsp
A41*	Oth sepsis
A42*	Actinomycosis

A43*	Nocardiosis
A48.1	Legionnaires' dz
A60.0[0,1,4,9]	Herpesviral infxn of [unsp urogenital sys, penis, vulvovaginitis, oth urogenital tract]
A60.1	Herpesviral infxn of perianal skin and rectum
A60.9	Anogenital herpesviral infxn, unsp
A81.2	Progressive multifocal leukoencephalopathy
A81.82	Gerstmann-Straussler-Scheinker synd
A81.83	Fatal familial insomnia
A81.89	Oth atypical virus infections of central nervous sys
A81.9	Atypical virus infxn of central nervous sys, unsp
A85.0	Enteroviral encephalitis
A85.1	Adenoviral encephalitis
A85.8	Oth spec viral encephalitis
A86	Unsp viral encephalitis
A88.8	Oth spec viral infections of central nervous sys
A89	Unsp viral infxn of central nervous sys
B00.0	Eczema herpeticum
B00.1	Herpesviral vesicular dermatitis
B00.2	Herpesviral gingivostomatitis and pharyngotonsillitis
B00.3	Herpesviral meningitis
B00.4	Herpesviral encephalitis
B00.5*	Herpesviral ocular dz
B00.7	Disseminated herpesviral dz
B00.81	Herpesviral hepatitis
B00.89	Oth herpesviral infxn
B00.9	Herpesviral infxn, unsp
B02.0	Zoster encephalitis
B02.1	Zoster meningitis
B02.2[1,2,3,9]	Postherpetic [geniculate ganglionitis, trigeminal neuralgia, polyneuropathy, oth nervous sys involvement]
B02.3*	Zoster ocular dz
B02.7	Disseminated zoster
B02.8	Zoster with oth comp
B02.9	Zoster w/o comp
B10.0*	Oth human herpesvirus encephalitis
B25.8	Oth cytomegaloviral dz
B25.9	Cytomegaloviral dz, unsp
B37.0	Candidal stomatitis
B37.1	Pulmn candidiasis
B37.2	Candidiasis of skin and nail
B37.5	Candidal meningitis
B37.6	Candidal endocarditis
B37.8*	Candidiasis of oth sites
B37.9	Candidiasis, unsp
B38*	Coccidioidomycosis
B39*	Histoplasmosis
B45.0	Pulmn cryptococcosis
B45.2	Cutaneous cryptococcosis
B45.3	Osseous cryptococcosis
B45.7	Disseminated cryptococcosis
B45.8	Oth forms of cryptococcosis
B45.9	Cryptococcosis, unsp
B47.1	Actinomycetoma
B47.9	Mycetoma, unsp
B48.8	Oth spec mycoses
B58*	Toxoplasmosis
B59	Pneumocystosis
B60.8	Oth spec protozoal dz
B78.0	Intestinal strongyloidiasis
B78.7	Disseminated strongyloidiasis
B78.9	Strongyloidiasis, unsp
B99.8	Oth infectious dz
C46*	Kaposi's sarcoma
C82.5*	Diffuse follicle center lymphoma
C83.0*	Sm cell B-cell lymphoma
C83.1*	Mantle cell lymphoma
C83.3*	Diffuse large B-cell lymphoma
C83.7*	Burkitt lymphoma
C83.8*	Oth non-follicular lymphoma
C83.9*	Non-follicular (diffuse) lymphoma, unsp
C84.4*	Peripheral T-cell lymphoma, not classified
C84.6*	Anaplastic large cell lymphoma, ALK-positive
C84.7*	Anaplastic large cell lymphoma, ALK-negative
C84.9*	Mature T/NK-cell lymphomas, unsp

T Transfer DRG   SP Special Payment   * Code Range   6th and 7th Character of ZZ = No Device, No Qualifier ZX = No Device, Diagnostic

438   MS-DRG Version 33.0   © 2015 Optum360, LLC

C84.A*	Cutaneous T-cell lymphoma, unsp
C84.Z*	Oth mature T/NK-cell lymphomas
C85*	Oth and unsp types of non-Hodgkin lymphoma
C86*	Oth spec types of T/NK-cell lymphoma
C88.4	Extrnod mrgnl zn B-cell lymph of mucosa-assoc lymphoid tiss
F03.90	Unsp dementia w/o behavioral disturbance
F06.8	Oth mental d/o d/t known physiological condition
F07.9	Unsp personality & behavrl d/o d/t known physiol cond
F09	Unsp mental d/o d/t known physiological condition
F28	Oth psych d/o not d/t a sub or known physiol cond
F29	Unsp psychosis not d/t a substance or known physiol cond
G04.8*	Oth encephalitis, myelitis and encephalomyelitis
G04.9*	Encephalitis, myelitis and encephalomyelitis, unsp
G36.9	Acute disseminated demyelination, unsp
G37.4	Subacute necrotizing myelitis of central nervous sys
G37.9	Demyelinating dz of central nervous sys, unsp
G93.4*	Oth and unsp encephalopathy
G93.9	D/o of brain, unsp
G95.2*	Oth and unsp cord compression
G95.9	Dz of spinal cord, unsp
G96.9	D/o of central nervous sys, unsp
G98.8	Oth d/o of nervous sys
I33*	Acute and subacute endocarditis
I40*	Acute myocarditis
I67.3	Progressive vascular leukoencephalopathy
I67.83	Posterior reversible encephalopathy synd
J09.X1	Flu d/t ident novel flu A virus w pneumonia
J10.08	Flu d/t oth ident flu virus w oth pneumonia
J12.3	Human metapneumovirus pneumonia
J12.8*	Oth viral pneumonia
J12.9	Viral pneumonia, unsp
J13	Pneumonia d/t Streptococcus pneumoniae
J14	Pneumonia d/t Hemophilus influenzae
J15.0	Pneumonia d/t Klebsiella pneumoniae
J15.1	Pneumonia d/t Pseudomonas
J15.2*	Pneumonia d/t staphylococcus
J15.3	Pneumonia d/t streptococcus, group B
J15.4	Pneumonia d/t oth streptococci
J15.5	Pneumonia d/t Escherichia coli
J15.6	Pneumonia d/t oth aerobic Gram-negative bacteria
J15.8	Pneumonia d/t oth spec bacteria
J15.9	Unsp bacterial pneumonia
J18.1	Lobar pneumonia, unsp organism
J18.8	Oth pneumonia, unsp organism
J18.9	Pneumonia, unsp organism
L08.1	Erythrasma

DRG 975 **HIV with Major Related Condition with CC**
GMLOS 4.5　　　AMLOS 6.0　　　RW 1.3589

Select principal AND secondary diagnoses listed under DRG 974

DRG 976 **HIV with Major Related Condition without CC/MCC**
GMLOS 3.3　　　AMLOS 4.1　　　RW 0.9073

Select principal AND secondary diagnoses listed under DRG 974

DRG 977 **HIV with or without Other Related Condition**
GMLOS 3.5　　　AMLOS 4.7　　　RW 1.1577

Any combination of principal or secondary diagnoses including
B20	Human immunodef virus [HIV] dz

MDC 25: Human Immunodeficiency Virus Infections—MEDICAL

Surgical　　**Medical**　　**CC Indicator**　　**MCC Indicator**　　**Procedure Proxy**　　🅿🅳🆇🅼🅲🅲 PDx acts as own MCC　　🅿🅳🆇🅲🅲 PDx acts as own CC

© 2015 Optum360, LLC　　　　MS-DRG Version 33.0　　　　**439**

DRGs Associated with All MDCs

SURGICAL

DRG 981   Extensive O.R. Procedure Unrelated to Principal Diagnosis with MCC

GMLOS 9.5   AMLOS 12.5   RW 4.8532   [T]

Discharges with all operating room procedures not listed for DRG 984 and DRG 987 that are unrelated to principal diagnosis

DRG 982   Extensive O.R. Procedure Unrelated to Principal Diagnosis with CC

GMLOS 5.4   AMLOS 7.1   RW 2.7416   [T]

Discharges with all operating room procedures not listed for DRG 984 and DRG 987 that are unrelated to principal diagnosis

DRG 983   Extensive O.R. Procedure Unrelated to Principal Diagnosis without CC/MCC

GMLOS 2.8   AMLOS 3.6   RW 1.7615   [T]

Discharges with all operating room procedures not listed for DRG 984 and DRG 987 that are unrelated to principal diagnosis

DRG 984   Prostatic O.R. Procedure Unrelated to Principal Diagnosis with MCC

GMLOS 9.3   AMLOS 12.2   RW 3.3844

Operating Room Procedures

0V50[7,8]ZZ	Destr/Prostate, [Via Natrl or Artfcl Opng, Via Natrl or Artfcl Opng Endo]
0V900ZX	Drain of Prostate, Opn Appr, Diagnostic
0V90[0,7,8]0Z	Drain, Prostate w/ Drain Dev [Opn, Via Natrl or Artfcl Opng, Via Natrl or Artfcl Opng Endo]
0V90[0,7,8]ZZ	Drain, Prostate [Opn, Via Natrl or Artfcl Opng, Via Natrl or Artfcl Opng Endo]
0VB00ZX	Exc of Prostate, Opn Appr, Diagnostic
0VB0[0,3,4,7,8]ZZ	Exc/Prostate, [Opn, Perc, Perc Endo, Via Natrl or Artfcl Opng, Via Natrl or Artfcl Opng Endo]
0VC0*	Extir/Prostate
0VJ4[0,3,4]ZZ	Inspect/Prostate and Seminal Vesicles, [Opn, Perc, Perc Endo]
0VN0*	Rls/Prostate
0VP40[0,1,3,7,J,K]	Rmvl of [Drain Dev, Radioact Elmt, Inf Dev, Auto Tissue Sub, Synth Sub, Nonauto Tissue Sub] from Prostate and Seminal Vesicles, Opn
0VP43[0,1,3,7,J,K]Z	Rmvl of [Drain Dev, Radioact Elmt, Inf Dev, Auto Tissue Sub, Synth Sub, Nonauto Tissue Sub], from Prostate and Seminal Vesicles, Perc
0VP44[0,1,3,7,J,K]Z	Rmvl of [Drain Dev, Radioact Elmt, Inf Dev, Auto Tissue Sub, Synth Sub, Nonauto Tissue Sub] from Prostate and Seminal Vesicles, Perc Endo
0VP47[0,1,3,7,J,K]Z	Rmvl of [Drain Dev, Radioact Elmt, Inf Dev, Auto Tissue Sub, Synth Sub, Nonauto Tissue Sub] from Prostate and Seminal Vesicles, Via Natrl or Artfcl Opng
0VP48[0,1,3,7,J,K]Z	Rmvl of [Drain Dev, Radioact Elmt, Inf Dev, Auto Tissue Sub, Synth Sub, Nonauto Tissue Sub] from Prostate and Seminal Vesicles, Via Natrl or Artfcl Opng Endo
0VQ0*	Repair/Prostate
0VT0[4,7,8]ZZ	Resect/Prostate, [Perc Endo, Via Natrl or Artfcl Opng, Via Natrl or Artfcl Opng Endo]
0VW40[0,3,7,J,K]Z	Rev of [Drain Dev, Inf Dev, Auto Tissue Sub, Synth Sub, Nonauto Tissue Sub] in Prostate and Seminal Vesicles, Opn
0VW43[0,3,7,J,K]Z	Rev of [Drain Dev, Inf Dev, Auto Tissue Sub, Synth Sub, Nonauto Tissue Sub] in Prostate and Seminal Vesicles, Perc
0VW44[0,3,7,J,K]Z	Rev of [Drain Dev, Inf Dev, Auto Tissue Sub, Synth Sub, Nonauto Tissue Sub] in Prostate and Seminal Vesicles, Perc Endo
0VW47[0,3,7,J,K]Z	Rev of [Drain Dev, Inf Dev, Auto Tissue Sub, Synth Sub, Nonauto Tissue Sub] in Prostate and Seminal Vesicles, Via Natrl or Artfcl Opng
0VW48[0,3,7,J,K]Z	Rev of [Drain Dev, Inf Dev, Auto Tissue Sub, Synth Sub, Nonauto Tissue Sub] in Prostate and Seminal Vesicles, Via Natrl or Artfcl Opng Endo

DRG 985   Prostatic O.R. Procedure Unrelated to Principal Diagnosis with CC

GMLOS 4.8   AMLOS 6.7   RW 1.9339

Select operating room procedures listed under DRG 984

DRG 986   Prostatic O.R. Procedure Unrelated to Principal Diagnosis without CC/MCC

GMLOS 2.4   AMLOS 3.4   RW 1.2079

Select operating room procedures listed under DRG 984

DRG 987   Nonextensive O.R. Procedure Unrelated to Principal Diagnosis with MCC

GMLOS 8.0   AMLOS 10.5   RW 3.2123   [T]

Operating Room Procedures

00BF[0,3,4]ZZ	Exc/Olfactory Nerve, [Opn, Perc, Perc Endo]
00BG[0,3,4]ZZ	Exc/Optic Nerve, [Opn, Perc, Perc Endo]
00BH[0,3,4]ZZ	Exc/Oculomotor Nerve, [Opn, Perc, Perc Endo]
00BJ[0,3,4]ZZ	Exc/Trochlear Nerve, [Opn, Perc, Perc Endo]
00BK[0,3,4]ZZ	Exc/Trigeminal Nerve, [Opn, Perc, Perc Endo]
00BL[0,3,4]ZZ	Exc/Abducens Nerve, [Opn, Perc, Perc Endo]
00BM[0,3,4]ZZ	Exc/Facial Nerve, [Opn, Perc, Perc Endo]
00BN[3,4]ZZ	Exc/Acoustic Nerve, [Perc, Perc Endo]
00BP[0,3,4]ZZ	Exc/Glossopharyngeal Nerve, [Opn, Perc, Perc Endo]
00BQ[0,3,4]ZZ	Exc/Vagus Nerve, [Opn, Perc, Perc Endo]
00BR[0,3,4]ZZ	Exc/Accessory Nerve, [Opn, Perc, Perc Endo]
00BS[0,3,4]ZZ	Exc/Hypoglossal Nerve, [Opn, Perc, Perc Endo]
00DF[0,3,4]ZZ	Extract/Olfactory Nerve, [Opn, Perc, Perc Endo]
00DG[0,3,4]ZZ	Extract/Optic Nerve, [Opn, Perc, Perc Endo]
00DH[0,3,4]ZZ	Extract/Oculomotor Nerve, [Opn, Perc, Perc Endo]
00DJ[0,3,4]ZZ	Extract/Trochlear Nerve, [Opn, Perc, Perc Endo]
00DK[0,3,4]ZZ	Extract/Trigeminal Nerve, [Opn, Perc, Perc Endo]
00DL[0,3,4]ZZ	Extract/Abducens Nerve, [Opn, Perc, Perc Endo]
00DM[0,3,4]ZZ	Extract/Facial Nerve, [Opn, Perc, Perc Endo]
00DN[0,3,4]ZZ	Extract/Acoustic Nerve, [Opn, Perc, Perc Endo]
00DP[0,3,4]ZZ	Extract/Glossopharyngeal Nerve, [Opn, Perc, Perc Endo]
00DQ[0,3,4]ZZ	Extract/Vagus Nerve, [Opn, Perc, Perc Endo]
00DR[0,3,4]ZZ	Extract/Accessory Nerve, [Opn, Perc, Perc Endo]
00DS[0,3,4]ZZ	Extract/Hypoglossal Nerve, [Opn, Perc, Perc Endo]
00NF[0,3,4]ZZ	Rls/Olfactory Nerve, [Opn, Perc, Perc Endo]
00NG[0,3,4]ZZ	Rls/Optic Nerve, [Opn, Perc, Perc Endo]
00NH[0,3,4]ZZ	Rls/Oculomotor Nerve, [Opn, Perc, Perc Endo]
00NJ[0,3,4]ZZ	Rls/Trochlear Nerve, [Opn, Perc, Perc Endo]
00NK[0,3,4]ZZ	Rls/Trigeminal Nerve, [Opn, Perc, Perc Endo]
00NL[0,3,4]ZZ	Rls/Abducens Nerve, [Opn, Perc, Perc Endo]
00NM[0,3,4]ZZ	Rls/Facial Nerve, [Opn, Perc, Perc Endo]
00NN[0,3,4]ZZ	Rls/Acoustic Nerve, [Opn, Perc, Perc Endo]
00NP[0,3,4]ZZ	Rls/Glossopharyngeal Nerve, [Opn, Perc, Perc Endo]
00NQ[0,3,4]ZZ	Rls/Vagus Nerve, [Opn, Perc, Perc Endo]
00NR[0,3,4]ZZ	Rls/Accessory Nerve, [Opn, Perc, Perc Endo]
00NS[0,3,4]ZZ	Rls/Hypoglossal Nerve, [Opn, Perc, Perc Endo]
015N[0,3,4]ZZ	Destr/Lumbar Sympathetic Nerve, [Opn, Perc, Perc Endo]
01B0[0,3,4]ZZ	Exc/Cervical Plexus, [Opn, Perc, Perc Endo]
01B1[0,3,4]ZZ	Exc/Cervical Nerve, [Opn, Perc, Perc Endo]
01B2[0,3,4]ZZ	Exc/Phrenic Nerve, [Opn, Perc, Perc Endo]
01B3[0,3,4]ZZ	Exc/Brachial Plexus, [Opn, Perc, Perc Endo]
01B4[0,3,4]ZZ	Exc/Ulnar Nerve, [Opn, Perc, Perc Endo]
01B5[0,3,4]ZZ	Exc/Median Nerve, [Opn, Perc, Perc Endo]
01B6[0,3,4]ZZ	Exc/Radial Nerve, [Opn, Perc, Perc Endo]
01B8[0,3,4]ZZ	Exc/Thoracic Nerve, [Opn, Perc, Perc Endo]
01B9[0,3,4]ZZ	Exc/Lumbar Plexus, [Opn, Perc, Perc Endo]
01BA[0,3,4]ZZ	Exc/Lumbosacral Plexus, [Opn, Perc, Perc Endo]
01BB[0,3,4]ZZ	Exc/Lumbar Nerve, [Opn, Perc, Perc Endo]
01BC[0,3,4]ZZ	Exc/Pudendal Nerve, [Opn, Perc, Perc Endo]
01BD[0,3,4]ZZ	Exc/Femor Nerve, [Opn, Perc, Perc Endo]
01BF[0,3,4]ZZ	Exc/Sciatic Nerve, [Opn, Perc, Perc Endo]
01BG[0,3,4]ZZ	Exc/Tibial Nerve, [Opn, Perc, Perc Endo]

[T] **Transfer DRG**   [SP] **Special Payment**   * **Code Range**   **6th and 7th Character of ZZ = No Device, No Qualifier ZX = No Device, Diagnostic**

01BH[0,3,4]ZZ	Exc/Peroneal Nerve, [Opn, Perc, Perc Endo]
01BN[0,3,4]ZZ	Exc/Lumbar Sympathetic Nerve, [Opn, Perc, Perc Endo]
01BQ[0,3,4]ZZ	Exc/Sacral Plexus, [Opn, Perc, Perc Endo]
01BR[0,3,4]ZZ	Exc/Sacral Nerve, [Opn, Perc, Perc Endo]
01D0[0,3,4]ZZ	Extract/Cervical Plexus, [Opn, Perc, Perc Endo]
01D1[0,3,4]ZZ	Extract/Cervical Nerve, [Opn, Perc, Perc Endo]
01D2[0,3,4]ZZ	Extract/Phrenic Nerve, [Opn, Perc, Perc Endo]
01D3[0,3,4]ZZ	Extract/Brachial Plexus, [Opn, Perc, Perc Endo]
01D4[0,3,4]ZZ	Extract/Ulnar Nerve, [Opn, Perc, Perc Endo]
01D5[0,3,4]ZZ	Extract/Median Nerve, [Opn, Perc, Perc Endo]
01D6[0,3,4]ZZ	Extract/Radial Nerve, [Opn, Perc, Perc Endo]
01D8[0,3,4]ZZ	Extract/Thoracic Nerve, [Opn, Perc, Perc Endo]
01D9[0,3,4]ZZ	Extract/Lumbar Plexus, [Opn, Perc, Perc Endo]
01DA[0,3,4]ZZ	Extract/Lumbosacral Plexus, [Opn, Perc, Perc Endo]
01DB[0,3,4]ZZ	Extract/Lumbar Nerve, [Opn, Perc, Perc Endo]
01DC[0,3,4]ZZ	Extract/Pudendal Nerve, [Opn, Perc, Perc Endo]
01DD[0,3,4]ZZ	Extract/Femor Nerve, [Opn, Perc, Perc Endo]
01DF[0,3,4]ZZ	Extract/Sciatic Nerve, [Opn, Perc, Perc Endo]
01DG[0,3,4]ZZ	Extract/Tibial Nerve, [Opn, Perc, Perc Endo]
01DH[0,3,4]ZZ	Extract/Peroneal Nerve, [Opn, Perc, Perc Endo]
01DN[0,3,4]ZZ	Extract/Lumbar Sympathetic Nerve, [Opn, Perc, Perc Endo]
01DQ[0,3,4]ZZ	Extract/Sacral Plexus, [Opn, Perc, Perc Endo]
01DR[0,3,4]ZZ	Extract/Sacral Nerve, [Opn, Perc, Perc Endo]
01N0[0,3,4]ZZ	Rls/Cervical Plexus, [Opn, Perc, Perc Endo]
01N1[0,3,4]ZZ	Rls/Cervical Nerve, [Opn, Perc, Perc Endo]
01N2[0,3,4]ZZ	Rls/Phrenic Nerve, [Opn, Perc, Perc Endo]
01N3[0,3,4]ZZ	Rls/Brachial Plexus, [Opn, Perc, Perc Endo]
01N4[0,3,4]ZZ	Rls/Ulnar Nerve, [Opn, Perc, Perc Endo]
01N5[0,3,4]ZZ	Rls/Median Nerve, [Opn, Perc, Perc Endo]
01N6[0,3,4]ZZ	Rls/Radial Nerve, [Opn, Perc, Perc Endo]
01N8[0,3,4]ZZ	Rls/Thoracic Nerve, [Opn, Perc, Perc Endo]
01N9[0,3,4]ZZ	Rls/Lumbar Plexus, [Opn, Perc, Perc Endo]
01NA[0,3,4]ZZ	Rls/Lumbosacral Plexus, [Opn, Perc, Perc Endo]
01NB[0,3,4]ZZ	Rls/Lumbar Nerve, [Opn, Perc, Perc Endo]
01NC[0,3,4]ZZ	Rls/Pudendal Nerve, [Opn, Perc, Perc Endo]
01ND[0,3,4]ZZ	Rls/Femor Nerve, [Opn, Perc, Perc Endo]
01NF[0,3,4]ZZ	Rls/Sciatic Nerve, [Opn, Perc, Perc Endo]
01NG[0,3,4]ZZ	Rls/Tibial Nerve, [Opn, Perc, Perc Endo]
01NH[0,3,4]ZZ	Rls/Peroneal Nerve, [Opn, Perc, Perc Endo]
01NQ[0,3,4]ZZ	Rls/Sacral Plexus, [Opn, Perc, Perc Endo]
01NR[0,3,4]ZZ	Rls/Sacral Nerve, [Opn, Perc, Perc Endo]
02BP[0,3,4]ZX	Exc/Pulmn Trunk, [Opn, Perc, Perc Endo]
02BQ[0,3,4]ZX	Exc/Pulmn Artery, Rt, [Opn, Perc, Perc Endo]
02BR[0,3,4]ZX	Exc/Pulmn Artery, Lt, [Opn, Perc, Perc Endo]
02BS[0,3,4]ZX	Exc/Pulmn Vein, Rt, [Opn, Perc, Perc Endo]
02BT[0,3,4]ZX	Exc/Pulmn Vein, Lt, [Opn, Perc, Perc Endo]
02BV[0,3,4]ZX	Exc/Superior Vena Cava, [Opn, Perc, Perc Endo]
02BW[0,3,4]ZX	Exc/Thoracic Aorta, [Opn, Perc, Perc Endo]
0390[0,3,4]ZX	Drain/Int Mammary Artery, Rt, [Opn, Perc, Perc Endo]
0391[0,3,4]ZX	Drain/Int Mammary Artery, Lt, [Opn, Perc, Perc Endo]
0392[0,3,4]ZX	Drain/Innominate Artery, [Opn, Perc, Perc Endo]
0393[0,3,4]ZX	Drain/Subclavian Artery, Rt, [Opn, Perc, Perc Endo]
0394[0,3,4]ZX	Drain/Subclavian Artery, Lt, [Opn, Perc, Perc Endo]
0395[0,3,4]ZX	Drain/Axillary Artery, Rt, [Opn, Perc, Perc Endo]
0396[0,3,4]ZX	Drain/Axillary Artery, Lt, [Opn, Perc, Perc Endo]
0397[0,3,4]ZX	Drain/Brachial Artery, Rt, [Opn, Perc, Perc Endo]
0398[0,3,4]ZX	Drain/Brachial Artery, Lt, [Opn, Perc, Perc Endo]
0399[0,3,4]ZX	Drain/Ulnar Artery, Rt, [Opn, Perc, Perc Endo]
039A[0,3,4]ZX	Drain/Ulnar Artery, Lt, [Opn, Perc, Perc Endo]
039B[0,3,4]ZX	Drain/Radial Artery, Rt, [Opn, Perc, Perc Endo]
039C[0,3,4]ZX	Drain/Radial Artery, Lt, [Opn, Perc, Perc Endo]
039D[0,3,4]ZX	Drain/Hand Artery, Rt, [Opn, Perc, Perc Endo]
039F[0,3,4]ZX	Drain/Hand Artery, Lt, [Opn, Perc, Perc Endo]
039G[0,3,4]ZX	Drain/Intracranial Artery, [Opn, Perc, Perc Endo]
039H[0,3,4]ZX	Drain/Common Carotid Artery, Rt, [Opn, Perc, Perc Endo]
039J[0,3,4]ZX	Drain/Common Carotid Artery, Lt, [Opn, Perc, Perc Endo]
039K[0,3,4]ZX	Drain/Int Carotid Artery, Rt, [Opn, Perc, Perc Endo]
039L[0,3,4]ZX	Drain/Int Carotid Artery, Lt, [Opn, Perc, Perc Endo]
039M[0,3,4]ZX	Drain/Ext Carotid Artery, Rt, [Opn, Perc, Perc Endo]
039N[0,3,4]ZX	Drain/Ext Carotid Artery, Lt, [Opn, Perc, Perc Endo]
039P[0,3,4]ZX	Drain/Vert Artery, Rt, [Opn, Perc, Perc Endo]
039Q[0,3,4]ZX	Drain/Vert Artery, Lt, [Opn, Perc, Perc Endo]
039R[0,3,4]ZX	Drain/Face Artery, [Opn, Perc, Perc Endo]
039S[0,3,4]ZX	Drain/Temporal Artery, Rt, [Opn, Perc, Perc Endo]
039T[0,3,4]ZX	Drain/Temporal Artery, Lt, [Opn, Perc, Perc Endo]
039U[0,3,4]ZX	Drain/Thyroid Artery, Rt, [Opn, Perc, Perc Endo]
039V[0,3,4]ZX	Drain/Thyroid Artery, Lt, [Opn, Perc, Perc Endo]
039Y[0,3,4]ZX	Drain/Upr Artery, [Opn, Perc, Perc Endo]
03B0[0,3,4]ZX	Exc/Int Mammary Artery, Rt, [Opn, Perc, Perc Endo]
03B1[0,3,4]ZX	Exc/Int Mammary Artery, Lt, [Opn, Perc, Perc Endo]

03B2[0,3,4]ZX	Exc/Innominate Artery, [Opn, Perc, Perc Endo]
03B3[0,3,4]ZX	Exc/Subclavian Artery, Rt, [Opn, Perc, Perc Endo]
03B4[0,3,4]ZX	Exc/Subclavian Artery, Lt, [Opn, Perc, Perc Endo]
03B5[0,3,4]ZX	Exc/Axillary Artery, Rt, [Opn, Perc, Perc Endo]
03B6[0,3,4]ZX	Exc/Axillary Artery, Lt, [Opn, Perc, Perc Endo]
03B7[0,3,4]ZX	Exc/Brachial Artery, Rt, [Opn, Perc, Perc Endo]
03B8[0,3,4]ZX	Exc/Brachial Artery, Lt, [Opn, Perc, Perc Endo]
03B9[0,3,4]ZX	Exc/Ulnar Artery, Rt, [Opn, Perc, Perc Endo]
03BA[0,3,4]ZX	Exc/Ulnar Artery, Lt, [Opn, Perc, Perc Endo]
03BB[0,3,4]ZX	Exc/Radial Artery, Rt, [Opn, Perc, Perc Endo]
03BC[0,3,4]ZX	Exc/Radial Artery, Lt, [Opn, Perc, Perc Endo]
03BD[0,3,4]ZX	Exc/Hand Artery, Rt, [Opn, Perc, Perc Endo]
03BF[0,3,4]ZX	Exc/Hand Artery, Lt, [Opn, Perc, Perc Endo]
03BG[0,3,4]ZX	Exc/Intracranial Artery, [Opn, Perc, Perc Endo]
03BH[0,3,4]ZX	Exc/Common Carotid Artery, Rt, [Opn, Perc, Perc Endo]
03BJ[0,3,4]ZX	Exc/Common Carotid Artery, Lt, [Opn, Perc, Perc Endo]
03BK[0,3,4]ZX	Exc/Int Carotid Artery, Rt, [Opn, Perc, Perc Endo]
03BL[0,3,4]ZX	Exc/Int Carotid Artery, Lt, [Opn, Perc, Perc Endo]
03BM[0,3,4]ZX	Exc/Ext Carotid Artery, Rt, [Opn, Perc, Perc Endo]
03BN[0,3,4]ZX	Exc/Ext Carotid Artery, Lt, [Opn, Perc, Perc Endo]
03BP[0,3,4]ZX	Exc/Vert Artery, Rt, [Opn, Perc, Perc Endo]
03BQ[0,3,4]ZX	Exc/Vert Artery, Lt, [Opn, Perc, Perc Endo]
03BR[0,3,4]ZX	Exc/Face Artery, [Opn, Perc, Perc Endo]
03BS[0,3,4]ZX	Exc/Temporal Artery, Rt, [Opn, Perc, Perc Endo]
03BT[0,3,4]ZX	Exc/Temporal Artery, Lt, [Opn, Perc, Perc Endo]
03BU[0,3,4]ZX	Exc/Thyroid Artery, Rt, [Opn, Perc, Perc Endo]
03BV[0,3,4]ZX	Exc/Thyroid Artery, Lt, [Opn, Perc, Perc Endo]
03BY[0,3,4]ZX	Exc/Upr Artery, [Opn, Perc, Perc Endo]
03WY[0,3,4][7,K]Z	Rev/Upr Artery, [Opn, Perc, Perc Endo], [Auto Tissue Sub, Nonauto Tissue Sub], NQ
0490[0,3,4]ZX	Drain/Abd Aorta, [Opn, Perc, Perc Endo]
0491[0,3,4]ZX	Drain/Celiac Artery, [Opn, Perc, Perc Endo]
0492[0,3,4]ZX	Drain/Gastric Artery, [Opn, Perc, Perc Endo]
0493[0,3,4]ZX	Drain/Hepatic Artery, [Opn, Perc, Perc Endo]
0494[0,3,4]ZX	Drain/Splenic Artery, [Opn, Perc, Perc Endo]
0495[0,3,4]ZX	Drain/Superior Mesenteric Artery, [Opn, Perc, Perc Endo]
0496[0,3,4]ZX	Drain/Colic Artery, Rt, [Opn, Perc, Perc Endo]
0497[0,3,4]ZX	Drain/Colic Artery, Lt, [Opn, Perc, Perc Endo]
0498[0,3,4]ZX	Drain/Colic Artery, Mid, [Opn, Perc, Perc Endo]
0499[0,3,4]ZX	Drain/Renal Artery, Rt, [Opn, Perc, Perc Endo]
049A[0,3,4]ZX	Drain/Renal Artery, Lt, [Opn, Perc, Perc Endo]
049B[0,3,4]ZX	Drain/Inferior Mesenteric Artery, [Opn, Perc, Perc Endo]
049C[0,3,4]ZX	Drain/Common Iliac Artery, Rt, [Opn, Perc, Perc Endo]
049D[0,3,4]ZX	Drain/Common Iliac Artery, Lt, [Opn, Perc, Perc Endo]
049E[0,3,4]ZX	Drain/Int Iliac Artery, Rt, [Opn, Perc, Perc Endo]
049F[0,3,4]ZX	Drain/Int Iliac Artery, Lt, [Opn, Perc, Perc Endo]
049H[0,3,4]ZX	Drain/Ext Iliac Artery, Rt, [Opn, Perc, Perc Endo]
049J[0,3,4]ZX	Drain/Ext Iliac Artery, Lt, [Opn, Perc, Perc Endo]
049K[0,3,4]ZX	Drain/Femor Artery, Rt, [Opn, Perc, Perc Endo]
049L[0,3,4]ZX	Drain/Femor Artery, Lt, [Opn, Perc, Perc Endo]
049M[0,3,4]ZX	Drain/Popliteal Artery, Rt, [Opn, Perc, Perc Endo]
049N[0,3,4]ZX	Drain/Popliteal Artery, Lt, [Opn, Perc, Perc Endo]
049P[0,3,4]ZX	Drain/Ant Tibial Artery, Rt, [Opn, Perc, Perc Endo]
049Q[0,3,4]ZX	Drain/Ant Tibial Artery, Lt, [Opn, Perc, Perc Endo]
049R[0,3,4]ZX	Drain/Post Tibial Artery, Rt, [Opn, Perc, Perc Endo]
049S[0,3,4]ZX	Drain/Post Tibial Artery, Lt, [Opn, Perc, Perc Endo]
049T[0,3,4]ZX	Drain/Peroneal Artery, Rt, [Opn, Perc, Perc Endo]
049U[0,3,4]ZX	Drain/Peroneal Artery, Lt, [Opn, Perc, Perc Endo]
049V[0,3,4]ZX	Drain/Foot Artery, Rt, [Opn, Perc, Perc Endo]
049W[0,3,4]ZX	Drain/Foot Artery, Lt, [Opn, Perc, Perc Endo]
049Y[0,3,4]ZX	Drain/Lwr Artery, [Opn, Perc, Perc Endo]
04B0[0,3,4]ZX	Exc/Abd Aorta, [Opn, Perc, Perc Endo]
04B1[0,3,4]ZX	Exc/Celiac Artery, [Opn, Perc, Perc Endo]
04B2[0,3,4]ZX	Exc/Gastric Artery, [Opn, Perc, Perc Endo]
04B3[0,3,4]ZX	Exc/Hepatic Artery, [Opn, Perc, Perc Endo]
04B4[0,3,4]ZX	Exc/Splenic Artery, [Opn, Perc, Perc Endo]
04B5[0,3,4]ZX	Exc/Superior Mesenteric Artery, [Opn, Perc, Perc Endo]
04B6[0,3,4]ZX	Exc/Colic Artery, Rt, [Opn, Perc, Perc Endo]
04B7[0,3,4]ZX	Exc/Colic Artery, Lt, [Opn, Perc, Perc Endo]
04B8[0,3,4]ZX	Exc/Colic Artery, Mid, [Opn, Perc, Perc Endo]
04B9[0,3,4]ZX	Exc/Renal Artery, Rt, [Opn, Perc, Perc Endo]
04BA[0,3,4]ZX	Exc/Renal Artery, Lt, [Opn, Perc, Perc Endo]
04BB[0,3,4]ZX	Exc/Inferior Mesenteric Artery, [Opn, Perc, Perc Endo]
04BC[0,3,4]ZX	Exc/Common Iliac Artery, Rt, [Opn, Perc, Perc Endo]
04BD[0,3,4]ZX	Exc/Common Iliac Artery, Lt, [Opn, Perc, Perc Endo]
04BE[0,3,4]ZX	Exc/Int Iliac Artery, Rt, [Opn, Perc, Perc Endo]
04BF[0,3,4]ZX	Exc/Int Iliac Artery, Lt, [Opn, Perc, Perc Endo]
04BH[0,3,4]ZX	Exc/Ext Iliac Artery, Rt, [Opn, Perc, Perc Endo]
04BJ[0,3,4]ZX	Exc/Ext Iliac Artery, Lt, [Opn, Perc, Perc Endo]
04BK[0,3,4]ZX	Exc/Femor Artery, Rt, [Opn, Perc, Perc Endo]

DRGs Associated with All MDCs—SURGICAL

Surgical   **Medical**   **CC Indicator**   **MCC Indicator**   **Procedure Proxy**   PDx MCC **PDx acts as own MCC**   PDx CC **PDx acts as own CC**

DRGs Associated with All MDCs—SURGICAL

04BL[Ø,3,4]ZX	Exc/Femor Artery, Lt, [Opn, Perc, Perc Endo]
04BM[Ø,3,4]ZX	Exc/Popliteal Artery, Rt, [Opn, Perc, Perc Endo]
04BN[Ø,3,4]ZX	Exc/Popliteal Artery, Lt, [Opn, Perc, Perc Endo]
04BP[Ø,3,4]ZX	Exc/Ant Tibial Artery, Rt, [Opn, Perc, Perc Endo]
04BQ[Ø,3,4]ZX	Exc/Ant Tibial Artery, Lt, [Opn, Perc, Perc Endo]
04BR[Ø,3,4]ZX	Exc/Post Tibial Artery, Rt, [Opn, Perc, Perc Endo]
04BS[Ø,3,4]ZX	Exc/Post Tibial Artery, Lt, [Opn, Perc, Perc Endo]
04BT[Ø,3,4]ZX	Exc/Peroneal Artery, Rt, [Opn, Perc, Perc Endo]
04BU[Ø,3,4]ZX	Exc/Peroneal Artery, Lt, [Opn, Perc, Perc Endo]
04BV[Ø,3,4]ZX	Exc/Foot Artery, Rt, [Opn, Perc, Perc Endo]
04BW[Ø,3,4]ZX	Exc/Foot Artery, Lt, [Opn, Perc, Perc Endo]
04BY[Ø,3,4]ZX	Exc/Lwr Artery, [Opn, Perc, Perc Endo]
04L1[Ø,3,4][C,D,Z]Z	Occlsn/Celiac Artery, [Opn, Perc, Perc Endo], [Extralum Dev, Intralum Dev, No Dev], NQ
04L2[Ø,3,4][C,Z]Z	Occlsn/Gastric Artery, [Opn, Perc, Perc Endo], [Extralum Dev, No Dev], NQ
04L2[Ø,4]DZ	Occlsn/Gastric Artery, [Opn, Perc Endo], Intralum Dev, NQ
04L3[Ø,3,4][C,D,Z]Z	Occlsn/Hepatic Artery, [Opn, Perc, Perc Endo], [Extralum Dev, Intralum Dev, No Dev], NQ
04L4[Ø,3,4][C,D,Z]Z	Occlsn/Splenic Artery, [Opn, Perc, Perc Endo], [Extralum Dev, Intralum Dev, No Dev], NQ
04L5[Ø,3,4][C,D,Z]Z	Occlsn/Superior Mesenteric Artery, [Opn, Perc, Perc Endo], [Extralum Dev, Intralum Dev, No Dev], NQ
04L6[Ø,3,4][C,D,Z]Z	Occlsn/Colic Artery, Rt, [Opn, Perc, Perc Endo], [Extralum Dev, Intralum Dev, No Dev], NQ
04L7[Ø,3,4][C,D,Z]Z	Occlsn/Colic Artery, Lt, [Opn, Perc, Perc Endo], [Extralum Dev, Intralum Dev, No Dev], NQ
04L8[Ø,3,4][C,D,Z]Z	Occlsn/Colic Artery, Mid, [Opn, Perc, Perc Endo], [Extralum Dev, Intralum Dev, No Dev], NQ
04L9[Ø,3,4][C,D,Z]Z	Occlsn/Renal Artery, Rt, [Opn, Perc, Perc Endo], [Extralum Dev, Intralum Dev, No Dev], NQ
04LA[Ø,3,4][C,D,Z]Z	Occlsn/Renal Artery, Lt, [Opn, Perc, Perc Endo], [Extralum Dev, Intralum Dev, No Dev], NQ
04LB[Ø,3,4][C,D,Z]Z	Occlsn/Inferior Mesenteric Artery, [Opn, Perc, Perc Endo], [Extralum Dev, Intralum Dev, No Dev], NQ
04LC[Ø,3,4][C,Z]Z	Occlsn/Common Iliac Artery, Rt, [Opn, Perc, Perc Endo], [Extralum Dev, No Dev], NQ
04LD[Ø,3,4][C,Z]Z	Occlsn/Common Iliac Artery, Lt, [Opn, Perc, Perc Endo], [Extralum Dev, No Dev], NQ
04LE[Ø,3,4][C,Z]Z	Occlsn/Int Iliac Artery, Rt, [Opn, Perc, Perc Endo], [Extralum Dev, No Dev], NQ
04LF[Ø,3,4][C,Z]Z	Occlsn/Int Iliac Artery, Lt, [Opn, Perc, Perc Endo], [Extralum Dev, No Dev], NQ
04LH[Ø,3,4][C,Z]Z	Occlsn/Ext Iliac Artery, Rt, [Opn, Perc, Perc Endo], [Extralum Dev, No Dev], NQ
04LJ[Ø,3,4][C,Z]Z	Occlsn/Ext Iliac Artery, Lt, [Opn, Perc, Perc Endo], [Extralum Dev, No Dev], NQ
04PY[Ø,3,4][7,J,K]Z	Rmvl/Lwr Artery, [Opn, Perc, Perc Endo], [Auto Tissue Sub, Synth Sub, Nonauto Tissue Sub], NQ
04WY[Ø,3,4][7,J,K]Z	Rev/Lwr Artery, [Opn, Perc, Perc Endo], [Auto Tissue Sub, Synth Sub, Nonauto Tissue Sub], NQ
0590[Ø,3,4]ZX	Drain/Azygos Vein, [Opn, Perc, Perc Endo]
0591[Ø,3,4]ZX	Drain/Hemiazygos Vein, [Opn, Perc, Perc Endo]
0593[Ø,3,4]ZX	Drain/Innominate Vein, Rt, [Opn, Perc, Perc Endo]
0594[Ø,3,4]ZX	Drain/Innominate Vein, Lt, [Opn, Perc, Perc Endo]
0595[Ø,3,4]ZX	Drain/Subclavian Vein, Rt, [Opn, Perc, Perc Endo]
0596[Ø,3,4]ZX	Drain/Subclavian Vein, Lt, [Opn, Perc, Perc Endo]
0597[Ø,3,4]ZX	Drain/Axillary Vein, Rt, [Opn, Perc, Perc Endo]
0598[Ø,3,4]ZX	Drain/Axillary Vein, Lt, [Opn, Perc, Perc Endo]
0599[Ø,3,4]ZX	Drain/Brachial Vein, Rt, [Opn, Perc, Perc Endo]
059A[Ø,3,4]ZX	Drain/Brachial Vein, Lt, [Opn, Perc, Perc Endo]
059B[Ø,3,4]ZX	Drain/Basilic Vein, Rt, [Opn, Perc, Perc Endo]
059C[Ø,3,4]ZX	Drain/Basilic Vein, Lt, [Opn, Perc, Perc Endo]
059D[Ø,3,4]ZX	Drain/Cephalic Vein, Rt, [Opn, Perc, Perc Endo]
059F[Ø,3,4]ZX	Drain/Cephalic Vein, Lt, [Opn, Perc, Perc Endo]
059G[Ø,3,4]ZX	Drain/Hand Vein, Rt, [Opn, Perc, Perc Endo]
059H[Ø,3,4]ZX	Drain/Hand Vein, Lt, [Opn, Perc, Perc Endo]
059L[Ø,3,4]ZX	Drain/Intracranial Vein, [Opn, Perc, Perc Endo]
059M[Ø,3,4]ZX	Drain/Int Jugular Vein, Rt, [Opn, Perc, Perc Endo]
059N[Ø,3,4]ZX	Drain/Int Jugular Vein, Lt, [Opn, Perc, Perc Endo]
059P[Ø,3,4]ZX	Drain/Ext Jugular Vein, Rt, [Opn, Perc, Perc Endo]
059Q[Ø,3,4]ZX	Drain/Ext Jugular Vein, Lt, [Opn, Perc, Perc Endo]
059R[Ø,3,4]ZX	Drain/Vert Vein, Rt, [Opn, Perc, Perc Endo]
059S[Ø,3,4]ZX	Drain/Vert Vein, Lt, [Opn, Perc, Perc Endo]
059T[Ø,3,4]ZX	Drain/Face Vein, Rt, [Opn, Perc, Perc Endo]
059V[Ø,3,4]ZX	Drain/Face Vein, Lt, [Opn, Perc, Perc Endo]
059Y[Ø,3,4]ZX	Drain/Upr Vein, [Opn, Perc, Perc Endo]
05BØ[Ø,3,4]ZX	Exc/Azygos Vein, [Opn, Perc, Perc Endo]
05B1[Ø,3,4]ZX	Exc/Hemiazygos Vein, [Opn, Perc, Perc Endo]
05B3[Ø,3,4]ZX	Exc/Innominate Vein, Rt, [Opn, Perc, Perc Endo]

05B4[Ø,3,4]ZX	Exc/Innominate Vein, Lt, [Opn, Perc, Perc Endo]
05B5[Ø,3,4]ZX	Exc/Subclavian Vein, Rt, [Opn, Perc, Perc Endo]
05B6[Ø,3,4]ZX	Exc/Subclavian Vein, Lt, [Opn, Perc, Perc Endo]
05B7[Ø,3,4]ZX	Exc/Axillary Vein, Rt, [Opn, Perc, Perc Endo]
05B8[Ø,3,4]ZX	Exc/Axillary Vein, Lt, [Opn, Perc, Perc Endo]
05B9[Ø,3,4]ZX	Exc/Brachial Vein, Rt, [Opn, Perc, Perc Endo]
05BA[Ø,3,4]ZX	Exc/Brachial Vein, Lt, [Opn, Perc, Perc Endo]
05BB[Ø,3,4]ZX	Exc/Basilic Vein, Rt, [Opn, Perc, Perc Endo]
05BC[Ø,3,4]ZX	Exc/Basilic Vein, Lt, [Opn, Perc, Perc Endo]
05BD[Ø,3,4]ZX	Exc/Cephalic Vein, Rt, [Opn, Perc, Perc Endo]
05BF[Ø,3,4]ZX	Exc/Cephalic Vein, Lt, [Opn, Perc, Perc Endo]
05BG[Ø,3,4]ZX	Exc/Hand Vein, Rt, [Opn, Perc, Perc Endo]
05BH[Ø,3,4]ZX	Exc/Hand Vein, Lt, [Opn, Perc, Perc Endo]
05BL[Ø,3,4]ZX	Exc/Intracranial Vein, [Opn, Perc, Perc Endo]
05BM[Ø,3,4]ZX	Exc/Int Jugular Vein, Rt, [Opn, Perc, Perc Endo]
05BN[Ø,3,4]ZX	Exc/Int Jugular Vein, Lt, [Opn, Perc, Perc Endo]
05BP[Ø,3,4]ZX	Exc/Ext Jugular Vein, Rt, [Opn, Perc, Perc Endo]
05BQ[Ø,3,4]ZX	Exc/Ext Jugular Vein, Lt, [Opn, Perc, Perc Endo]
05BR[Ø,3,4]ZX	Exc/Vert Vein, Rt, [Opn, Perc, Perc Endo]
05BS[Ø,3,4]ZX	Exc/Vert Vein, Lt, [Opn, Perc, Perc Endo]
05BT[Ø,3,4]ZX	Exc/Face Vein, Rt, [Opn, Perc, Perc Endo]
05BV[Ø,3,4]ZX	Exc/Face Vein, Lt, [Opn, Perc, Perc Endo]
05BY[Ø,3,4]ZX	Exc/Upr Vein, [Opn, Perc, Perc Endo]
05PY[Ø,3,4][7,J,K]Z	Rmvl/Upr Vein, [Opn, Perc, Perc Endo], [Auto Tissue Sub, Synth Sub, Nonauto Tissue Sub], NQ
05WY[Ø,3,4][7,J,K]Z	Rev/Upr Vein, [Opn, Perc, Perc Endo], [Auto Tissue Sub, Synth Sub, Nonauto Tissue Sub], NQ
065Y[Ø,3,4]ZC	Destr/Lwr Vein, [Opn, Perc, Perc Endo], No Dev, Hemorrhoidal Plexus
069Ø[Ø,3,4]ZX	Drain/Inferior Vena Cava, [Opn, Perc, Perc Endo]
0691[Ø,3,4]ZX	Drain/Splenic Vein, [Opn, Perc, Perc Endo]
0692[Ø,3,4]ZX	Drain/Gastric Vein, [Opn, Perc, Perc Endo]
0693[Ø,3,4]ZX	Drain/Esophageal Vein, [Opn, Perc, Perc Endo]
0694[Ø,3,4]ZX	Drain/Hepatic Vein, [Opn, Perc, Perc Endo]
0695[Ø,3,4]ZX	Drain/Superior Mesenteric Vein, [Opn, Perc, Perc Endo]
0696[Ø,3,4]ZX	Drain/Inferior Mesenteric Vein, [Opn, Perc, Perc Endo]
0697[Ø,3,4]ZX	Drain/Colic Vein, [Opn, Perc, Perc Endo]
0698[Ø,3,4]ZX	Drain/Portal Vein, [Opn, Perc, Perc Endo]
0699[Ø,3,4]ZX	Drain/Renal Vein, Rt, [Opn, Perc, Perc Endo]
069B[Ø,3,4]ZX	Drain/Renal Vein, Lt, [Opn, Perc, Perc Endo]
069C[Ø,3,4]ZX	Drain/Common Iliac Vein, Rt, [Opn, Perc, Perc Endo]
069D[Ø,3,4]ZX	Drain/Common Iliac Vein, Lt, [Opn, Perc, Perc Endo]
069F[Ø,3,4]ZX	Drain/Ext Iliac Vein, Rt, [Opn, Perc, Perc Endo]
069G[Ø,3,4]ZX	Drain/Ext Iliac Vein, Lt, [Opn, Perc, Perc Endo]
069H[Ø,3,4]ZX	Drain/Hypogastric Vein, Rt, [Opn, Perc, Perc Endo]
069J[Ø,3,4]ZX	Drain/Hypogastric Vein, Lt, [Opn, Perc, Perc Endo]
069M[Ø,3,4]ZX	Drain/Femor Vein, Rt, [Opn, Perc, Perc Endo]
069N[Ø,3,4]ZX	Drain/Femor Vein, Lt, [Opn, Perc, Perc Endo]
069P[Ø,3,4]ZX	Drain/Greater Saphenous Vein, Rt, [Opn, Perc, Perc Endo]
069Q[Ø,3,4]ZX	Drain/Greater Saphenous Vein, Lt, [Opn, Perc, Perc Endo]
069R[Ø,3,4]ZX	Drain/Lesser Saphenous Vein, Rt, [Opn, Perc, Perc Endo]
069S[Ø,3,4]ZX	Drain/Lesser Saphenous Vein, Lt, [Opn, Perc, Perc Endo]
069T[Ø,3,4]ZX	Drain/Foot Vein, Rt, [Opn, Perc, Perc Endo]
069V[Ø,3,4]ZX	Drain/Foot Vein, Lt, [Opn, Perc, Perc Endo]
069Y[Ø,3,4]ZX	Drain/Lwr Vein, [Opn, Perc, Perc Endo]
06BØ[Ø,3,4]ZX	Exc/Inferior Vena Cava, [Opn, Perc, Perc Endo]
06B1[Ø,3,4]ZX	Exc/Splenic Vein, [Opn, Perc, Perc Endo]
06B2[Ø,3,4]ZX	Exc/Gastric Vein, [Opn, Perc, Perc Endo]
06B3[Ø,3,4]ZX	Exc/Esophageal Vein, [Opn, Perc, Perc Endo]
06B4[Ø,3,4]ZX	Exc/Hepatic Vein, [Opn, Perc, Perc Endo]
06B5[Ø,3,4]ZX	Exc/Superior Mesenteric Vein, [Opn, Perc, Perc Endo]
06B6[Ø,3,4]ZX	Exc/Inferior Mesenteric Vein, [Opn, Perc, Perc Endo]
06B7[Ø,3,4]ZX	Exc/Colic Vein, [Opn, Perc, Perc Endo]
06B8[Ø,3,4]ZX	Exc/Portal Vein, [Opn, Perc, Perc Endo]
06B9[Ø,3,4]ZX	Exc/Renal Vein, Rt, [Opn, Perc, Perc Endo]
06BB[Ø,3,4]ZX	Exc/Renal Vein, Lt, [Opn, Perc, Perc Endo]
06BC[Ø,3,4]ZX	Exc/Common Iliac Vein, Rt, [Opn, Perc, Perc Endo]
06BD[Ø,3,4]ZX	Exc/Common Iliac Vein, Lt, [Opn, Perc, Perc Endo]
06BF[Ø,3,4]ZX	Exc/Ext Iliac Vein, Rt, [Opn, Perc, Perc Endo]
06BG[Ø,3,4]ZX	Exc/Ext Iliac Vein, Lt, [Opn, Perc, Perc Endo]
06BH[Ø,3,4]ZX	Exc/Hypogastric Vein, Rt, [Opn, Perc, Perc Endo]
06BJ[Ø,3,4]ZX	Exc/Hypogastric Vein, Lt, [Opn, Perc, Perc Endo]
06BM[Ø,3,4]ZX	Exc/Femor Vein, Rt, [Opn, Perc, Perc Endo]
06BN[Ø,3,4]ZX	Exc/Femor Vein, Lt, [Opn, Perc, Perc Endo]
06BP[Ø,3,4]ZX	Exc/Greater Saphenous Vein, Rt, [Opn, Perc, Perc Endo]
06BQ[Ø,3,4]ZX	Exc/Greater Saphenous Vein, Lt, [Opn, Perc, Perc Endo]
06BR[Ø,3,4]ZX	Exc/Lesser Saphenous Vein, Rt, [Opn, Perc, Perc Endo]
06BS[Ø,3,4]ZX	Exc/Lesser Saphenous Vein, Lt, [Opn, Perc, Perc Endo]
06BT[Ø,3,4]ZX	Exc/Foot Vein, Rt, [Opn, Perc, Perc Endo]
06BV[Ø,3,4]ZX	Exc/Foot Vein, Lt, [Opn, Perc, Perc Endo]

Ⓣ **Transfer DRG**   ⓢ **Special Payment**   * **Code Range**   **6th and 7th Character of ZZ = No Device, No Qualifier ZX = No Device, Diagnostic**

06BY[0,3,4]Z[C,X]	Exc/Lwr Vein, [Opn, Perc, Perc Endo], No Dev, [Hemorrhoidal Plexus, Dx]
06CM[0,3,4]ZZ	Extir/Femor Vein, Rt, [Opn, Perc, Perc Endo]
06CN[0,3,4]ZZ	Extir/Femor Vein, Lt, [Opn, Perc, Perc Endo]
06CP[0,3,4]ZZ	Extir/Greater Saphenous Vein, Rt, [Opn, Perc, Perc Endo]
06CQ[0,3,4]ZZ	Extir/Greater Saphenous Vein, Lt, [Opn, Perc, Perc Endo]
06CR[0,3,4]ZZ	Extir/Lesser Saphenous Vein, Rt, [Opn, Perc, Perc Endo]
06CS[0,3,4]ZZ	Extir/Lesser Saphenous Vein, Lt, [Opn, Perc, Perc Endo]
06CT[0,3,4]ZZ	Extir/Foot Vein, Rt, [Opn, Perc, Perc Endo]
06CV[0,3,4]ZZ	Extir/Foot Vein, Lt, [Opn, Perc, Perc Endo]
06DM[0,3,4]ZZ	Extract/Femor Vein, Rt, [Opn, Perc, Perc Endo]
06DN[0,3,4]ZZ	Extract/Femor Vein, Lt, [Opn, Perc, Perc Endo]
06DP[0,3,4]ZZ	Extract/Greater Saphenous Vein, Rt, [Opn, Perc, Perc Endo]
06DQ[0,3,4]ZZ	Extract/Greater Saphenous Vein, Lt, [Opn, Perc, Perc Endo]
06DR[0,3,4]ZZ	Extract/Lesser Saphenous Vein, Rt, [Opn, Perc, Perc Endo]
06DS[0,3,4]ZZ	Extract/Lesser Saphenous Vein, Lt, [Opn, Perc, Perc Endo]
06DT[0,3,4]ZZ	Extract/Foot Vein, Rt, [Opn, Perc, Perc Endo]
06DV[0,3,4]ZZ	Extract/Foot Vein, Lt, [Opn, Perc, Perc Endo]
06DY[0,3,4]ZZ	Extract/Lwr Vein, [Opn, Perc, Perc Endo]
06HY[0,3,4]2Z	Insert/Lwr Vein, [Opn, Perc, Perc Endo], Monitoring Dev, NQ
06LY[0,3,4][C,D,Z]C	Occlsn/Lwr Vein, [Opn, Perc, Perc Endo], [Extralum Dev, Intralum Dev, No Dev], Hemorrhoidal Plexus
06PY[0,3,4][0,2,3,7,C,D,J,K]Z	Rmvl/Lwr Vein, [Opn, Perc, Perc Endo], [Drain Dev, Monitoring Dev, Inf Dev, Auto Tissue Sub, Extralum Dev, Intralum Dev, Synth Sub, Nonauto Tissue Sub], NQ
06WY[0,3,4][0,2,3,7,C,D,J,K]Z	Rev/Lwr Vein, [Opn, Perc, Perc Endo], [Drain Dev, Monitoring Dev, Inf Dev, Auto Tissue Sub, Extralum Dev, Intralum Dev, Synth Sub, Nonauto Tissue Sub], NQ
0790[0,3,4]ZX	Drain/Lymphatic, Head, [Opn, Perc, Perc Endo]
0790[0,3,4][0,Z]Z	Drain/Lymphatic, Head, [Opn, Perc, Perc Endo], [Drain Dev, No Dev], NQ
0791[0,3,4]ZX	Drain/Lymphatic, Rt Neck, [Opn, Perc, Perc Endo]
0791[0,3,4][0,Z]Z	Drain/Lymphatic, Rt Neck, [Opn, Perc, Perc Endo], [Drain Dev, No Dev], NQ
0792[0,3,4]ZX	Drain/Lymphatic, Lt Neck, [Opn, Perc, Perc Endo]
0792[0,3,4][0,Z]Z	Drain/Lymphatic, Lt Neck, [Opn, Perc, Perc Endo], [Drain Dev, No Dev], NQ
0793[0,3,4]ZX	Drain/Lymphatic, Rt Upr Extr, [Opn, Perc, Perc Endo]
0793[0,3,4][0,Z]Z	Drain/Lymphatic, Rt Upr Extr, [Opn, Perc, Perc Endo], [Drain Dev, No Dev], NQ
0794[0,3,4]ZX	Drain/Lymphatic, Lt Upr Extr, [Opn, Perc, Perc Endo]
0794[0,3,4][0,Z]Z	Drain/Lymphatic, Lt Upr Extr, [Opn, Perc, Perc Endo], [Drain Dev, No Dev], NQ
0795[0,3,4]ZX	Drain/Lymphatic, Rt Axillary, [Opn, Perc, Perc Endo]
0795[0,3,4][0,Z]Z	Drain/Lymphatic, Rt Axillary, [Opn, Perc, Perc Endo], [Drain Dev, No Dev], NQ
0796[0,3,4]ZX	Drain/Lymphatic, Lt Axillary, [Opn, Perc, Perc Endo]
0796[0,3,4][0,Z]Z	Drain/Lymphatic, Lt Axillary, [Opn, Perc, Perc Endo], [Drain Dev, No Dev], NQ
0797[0,3,4]ZX	Drain/Lymphatic, Thorax, [Opn, Perc, Perc Endo]
0797[0,3,4][0,Z]Z	Drain/Lymphatic, Thorax, [Opn, Perc, Perc Endo], [Drain Dev, No Dev], NQ
0798[0,3,4]ZX	Drain/Lymphatic, Int Mammary, Rt, [Opn, Perc, Perc Endo]
0798[0,3,4][0,Z]Z	Drain/Lymphatic, Int Mammary, Rt, [Opn, Perc, Perc Endo], [Drain Dev, No Dev], NQ
0799[0,3,4]ZX	Drain/Lymphatic, Int Mammary, Lt, [Opn, Perc, Perc Endo]
0799[0,3,4][0,Z]Z	Drain/Lymphatic, Int Mammary, Lt, [Opn, Perc, Perc Endo], [Drain Dev, No Dev], NQ
079B[0,3,4]ZX	Drain/Lymphatic, Mesenteric, [Opn, Perc, Perc Endo]
079B[0,3,4][0,Z]Z	Drain/Lymphatic, Mesenteric, [Opn, Perc, Perc Endo], [Drain Dev, No Dev], NQ
079C[0,3,4]ZX	Drain/Lymphatic, Pelvis, [Opn, Perc, Perc Endo]
079C[0,3,4][0,Z]Z	Drain/Lymphatic, Pelvis, [Opn, Perc, Perc Endo], [Drain Dev, No Dev], NQ
079D[0,3,4]ZX	Drain/Lymphatic, Aortic, [Opn, Perc, Perc Endo]
079D[0,3,4][0,Z]Z	Drain/Lymphatic, Aortic, [Opn, Perc, Perc Endo], [Drain Dev, No Dev], NQ
079F[0,3,4]ZX	Drain/Lymphatic, Rt Lwr Extr, [Opn, Perc, Perc Endo]
079F[0,3,4][0,Z]Z	Drain/Lymphatic, Rt Lwr Extr, [Opn, Perc, Perc Endo], [Drain Dev, No Dev], NQ
079G[0,3,4]ZX	Drain/Lymphatic, Lt Lwr Extr, [Opn, Perc, Perc Endo]
079G[0,3,4][0,Z]Z	Drain/Lymphatic, Lt Lwr Extr, [Opn, Perc, Perc Endo], [Drain Dev, No Dev], NQ
079H[0,3,4]ZX	Drain/Lymphatic, Rt Inguinal, [Opn, Perc, Perc Endo]
079H[0,3,4][0,Z]Z	Drain/Lymphatic, Rt Inguinal, [Opn, Perc, Perc Endo], [Drain Dev, No Dev], NQ
079J[0,3,4]ZX	Drain/Lymphatic, Lt Inguinal, [Opn, Perc, Perc Endo]
079J[0,3,4][0,Z]Z	Drain/Lymphatic, Lt Inguinal, [Opn, Perc, Perc Endo], [Drain Dev, No Dev], NQ
079K[0,3,4]ZX	Drain/Thoracic Duct, [Opn, Perc, Perc Endo]
079L[0,3,4]ZX	Drain/Cisterna Chyli, [Opn, Perc, Perc Endo]
07B0[0,3,4]Z[X,Z]	Exc/Lymphatic, Head, [Opn, Perc, Perc Endo], No Dev, [Dx, NQ]
07B1[0,3,4]Z[X,Z]	Exc/Lymphatic, Rt Neck, [Opn, Perc, Perc Endo], No Dev, [Dx, NQ]
07B2[0,3,4]Z[X,Z]	Exc/Lymphatic, Lt Neck, [Opn, Perc, Perc Endo], No Dev, [Dx, NQ]
07B3[0,3,4]Z[X,Z]	Exc/Lymphatic, Rt Upr Extr, [Opn, Perc, Perc Endo], No Dev, [Dx, NQ]
07B4[0,3,4]Z[X,Z]	Exc/Lymphatic, Lt Upr Extr, [Opn, Perc, Perc Endo], No Dev, [Dx, NQ]
07B5[0,3,4]Z[X,Z]	Exc/Lymphatic, Rt Axillary, [Opn, Perc, Perc Endo], No Dev, [Dx, NQ]
07B6[0,3,4]Z[X,Z]	Exc/Lymphatic, Lt Axillary, [Opn, Perc, Perc Endo], No Dev, [Dx, NQ]
07B7[0,3,4]Z[X,Z]	Exc/Lymphatic, Thorax, [Opn, Perc, Perc Endo], No Dev, [Dx, NQ]
07B8[0,3,4]ZX	Exc/Lymphatic, Int Mammary, Rt, [Opn, Perc, Perc Endo]
07B9[0,3,4]ZX	Exc/Lymphatic, Int Mammary, Lt, [Opn, Perc, Perc Endo]
07BB[0,3,4]Z[X,Z]	Exc/Lymphatic, Mesenteric, [Opn, Perc, Perc Endo], No Dev, [Dx, NQ]
07BC[0,3,4]Z[X,Z]	Exc/Lymphatic, Pelvis, [Opn, Perc, Perc Endo], No Dev, [Dx, NQ]
07BD[0,3,4]Z[X,Z]	Exc/Lymphatic, Aortic, [Opn, Perc, Perc Endo], No Dev, [Dx, NQ]
07BF[0,3,4]Z[X,Z]	Exc/Lymphatic, Rt Lwr Extr, [Opn, Perc, Perc Endo], No Dev, [Dx, NQ]
07BG[0,3,4]Z[X,Z]	Exc/Lymphatic, Lt Lwr Extr, [Opn, Perc, Perc Endo], No Dev, [Dx, NQ]
07BH[0,3,4]Z[X,Z]	Exc/Lymphatic, Rt Inguinal, [Opn, Perc, Perc Endo], No Dev, [Dx, NQ]
07BJ[0,3,4]Z[X,Z]	Exc/Lymphatic, Lt Inguinal, [Opn, Perc, Perc Endo], No Dev, [Dx, NQ]
07BK[0,3,4]ZX	Exc/Thoracic Duct, [Opn, Perc, Perc Endo]
07BL[0,3,4]ZX	Exc/Cisterna Chyli, [Opn, Perc, Perc Endo]
07C0[0,3,4]ZZ	Extir/Lymphatic, Head, [Opn, Perc, Perc Endo]
07C1[0,3,4]ZZ	Extir/Lymphatic, Rt Neck, [Opn, Perc, Perc Endo]
07C2[0,3,4]ZZ	Extir/Lymphatic, Lt Neck, [Opn, Perc, Perc Endo]
07C3[0,3,4]ZZ	Extir/Lymphatic, Rt Upr Extr, [Opn, Perc, Perc Endo]
07C4[0,3,4]ZZ	Extir/Lymphatic, Lt Upr Extr, [Opn, Perc, Perc Endo]
07C5[0,3,4]ZZ	Extir/Lymphatic, Rt Axillary, [Opn, Perc, Perc Endo]
07C6[0,3,4]ZZ	Extir/Lymphatic, Lt Axillary, [Opn, Perc, Perc Endo]
07C7[0,3,4]ZZ	Extir/Lymphatic, Thorax, [Opn, Perc, Perc Endo]
07C8[0,3,4]ZZ	Extir/Lymphatic, Int Mammary, Rt, [Opn, Perc, Perc Endo]
07C9[0,3,4]ZZ	Extir/Lymphatic, Int Mammary, Lt, [Opn, Perc, Perc Endo]
07CB[0,3,4]ZZ	Extir/Lymphatic, Mesenteric, [Opn, Perc, Perc Endo]
07CC[0,3,4]ZZ	Extir/Lymphatic, Pelvis, [Opn, Perc, Perc Endo]
07CD[0,3,4]ZZ	Extir/Lymphatic, Aortic, [Opn, Perc, Perc Endo]
07CF[0,3,4]ZZ	Extir/Lymphatic, Rt Lwr Extr, [Opn, Perc, Perc Endo]
07CG[0,3,4]ZZ	Extir/Lymphatic, Lt Lwr Extr, [Opn, Perc, Perc Endo]
07CH[0,3,4]ZZ	Extir/Lymphatic, Rt Inguinal, [Opn, Perc, Perc Endo]
07CJ[0,3,4]ZZ	Extir/Lymphatic, Lt Inguinal, [Opn, Perc, Perc Endo]
07CK[0,3,4]ZZ	Extir/Thoracic Duct, [Opn, Perc, Perc Endo]
07CL[0,3,4]ZZ	Extir/Cisterna Chyli, [Opn, Perc, Perc Endo]
07JK[0,3,4]ZZ	Inspect/Thoracic Duct, [Opn, Perc, Perc Endo]
07JL[0,3,4]ZZ	Inspect/Cisterna Chyli, [Opn, Perc, Perc Endo]
07JN[0,3,4]ZZ	Inspect/Lymphatic, [Opn, Perc, Perc Endo]
07PN[0,3,4][0,3,C,D]Z	Rmvl/Lymphatic, [Opn, Perc, Perc Endo], [Drain Dev, Inf Dev, Extralum Dev, Intralum Dev], NQ
07WN[0,3,4][0,3,C,D]Z	Rev/Lymphatic, [Opn, Perc, Perc Endo], [Drain Dev, Inf Dev, Extralum Dev, Intralum Dev], NQ
08123[K,Z]4	Bypass/Ant Chamber, Rt, Perc, [Nonauto Tissue Sub, No Dev], Sclera
08133[K,Z]4	Bypass/Ant Chamber, Lt, Perc, [Nonauto Tissue Sub, No Dev], Sclera
081X[0,3][J,K,Z]3	Bypass/Lacrimal Duct, Rt, [Opn, Perc], [Synth Sub, Nonauto Tissue Sub, No Dev], Nasal Cavity
081Y[0,3][J,K,Z]3	Bypass/Lacrimal Duct, Lt, [Opn, Perc], [Synth Sub, Nonauto Tissue Sub, No Dev], Nasal Cavity
0850XZZ	Destr of Rt Eye, Ext Appr
0851XZZ	Destr of Lt Eye, Ext Appr
08523ZZ	Destr of Rt Ant Chamber, Perc Appr
08533ZZ	Destr of Lt Ant Chamber, Perc Appr
08543ZZ	Destr of Rt Vitreous, Perc Appr
08553ZZ	Destr of Lt Vitreous, Perc Appr
0856XZZ	Destr of Rt Sclera, Ext Appr
0857XZZ	Destr of Lt Sclera, Ext Appr
0858XZZ	Destr of Rt Cornea, Ext Appr
0859XZZ	Destr of Lt Cornea, Ext Appr
085A[0,3]ZZ	Destr/Choroid, Rt, [Opn, Perc]
085B[0,3]ZZ	Destr/Choroid, Lt, [Opn, Perc]
085C3ZZ	Destr of Rt Iris, Perc Appr

DRGs Associated with All MDCs—SURGICAL

Surgical	**Medical**	**CC Indicator**	**MCC Indicator**	**Procedure Proxy**	**PDx·MCC** PDx acts as own MCC	**PDx·CC** PDx acts as own CC

Ø85D3ZZ	Destr of Lt Iris, Perc Appr
Ø85E3ZZ	Destr of Rt Retina, Perc Appr
Ø85F3ZZ	Destr of Lt Retina, Perc Appr
Ø85G3ZZ	Destr of Rt Retinal Vessel, Perc Appr
Ø85H3ZZ	Destr of Lt Retinal Vessel, Perc Appr
Ø85J3ZZ	Destr of Rt Lens, Perc Appr
Ø85K3ZZ	Destr of Lt Lens, Perc Appr
Ø85L[Ø,3]ZZ	Destr/Extraocular Muscle, Rt, [Opn, Perc]
Ø85M[Ø,3]ZZ	Destr/Extraocular Muscle, Lt, [Opn, Perc]
Ø85N[Ø,3,X]ZZ	Destr/Upr Eyelid, Rt, [Opn, Perc, Ext]
Ø85P[Ø,3,X]ZZ	Destr/Upr Eyelid, Lt, [Opn, Perc, Ext]
Ø85Q[Ø,3,X]ZZ	Destr/Lwr Eyelid, Rt, [Opn, Perc, Ext]
Ø85R[Ø,3,X]ZZ	Destr/Lwr Eyelid, Lt, [Opn, Perc, Ext]
Ø85SXZZ	Destr of Rt Conjunctiva, Ext Appr
Ø85TXZZ	Destr of Lt Conjunctiva, Ext Appr
Ø85V[Ø,3]ZZ	Destr/Lacrimal Gland, Rt, [Opn, Perc]
Ø85W[Ø,3]ZZ	Destr/Lacrimal Gland, Lt, [Opn, Perc]
Ø85X[Ø,3,7,8]ZZ	Destr/Lacrimal Duct, Rt, [Opn, Perc, Via Natrl or Artfcl Opng, Via Natrl or Artfcl Opng Endo]
Ø85Y[Ø,3,7,8]ZZ	Destr/Lacrimal Duct, Lt, [Opn, Perc, Via Natrl or Artfcl Opng, Via Natrl or Artfcl Opng Endo]
Ø87X[Ø,3,7,8][D,Z]Z	Dilation/Lacrimal Duct, Rt, [Opn, Perc, Via Natrl or Artfcl Opng, Via Natrl or Artfcl Opng Endo], [Intralum Dev, No Dev], NQ
Ø87Y[Ø,3,7,8][D,Z]Z	Dilation/Lacrimal Duct, Lt, [Opn, Perc, Via Natrl or Artfcl Opng, Via Natrl or Artfcl Opng Endo], [Intralum Dev, No Dev], NQ
Ø89ØXZX	Drain of Rt Eye, Ext Appr, Diagnostic
Ø89ØX[Ø,Z]Z	Drain/Eye, Rt, Ext, [Drain Dev, No Dev], NQ
Ø891XZX	Drain of Lt Eye, Ext Appr, Diagnostic
Ø891X[Ø,Z]Z	Drain/Eye, Lt, Ext, [Drain Dev, No Dev], NQ
Ø8923ZX	Drain of Rt Ant Chamber, Perc Appr, Diagn
Ø8923[Ø,Z]Z	Drain/Ant Chamber, Rt, Perc, [Drain Dev, No Dev], NQ
Ø8933ZX	Drain of Lt Ant Chamber, Perc Appr, Diagn
Ø8933[Ø,Z]Z	Drain/Ant Chamber, Lt, Perc, [Drain Dev, No Dev], NQ
Ø8943ZX	Drain of Rt Vitreous, Perc Appr, Diagn
Ø8943[Ø,Z]Z	Drain/Vitreous, Rt, Perc, [Drain Dev, No Dev], NQ
Ø8953ZX	Drain of Lt Vitreous, Perc Appr, Diagnostic
Ø8953[Ø,Z]Z	Drain/Vitreous, Lt, Perc, [Drain Dev, No Dev], NQ
Ø896XZX	Drain of Rt Sclera, Ext Appr, Diagnostic
Ø896X[Ø,Z]Z	Drain/Sclera, Rt, Ext, [Drain Dev, No Dev], NQ
Ø897XZX	Drain of Lt Sclera, Ext Appr, Diagnostic
Ø897X[Ø,Z]Z	Drain/Sclera, Lt, Ext, [Drain Dev, No Dev], NQ
Ø898XZX	Drain of Rt Cornea, Ext Appr, Diagnostic
Ø898X[Ø,Z]Z	Drain/Cornea, Rt, Ext, [Drain Dev, No Dev], NQ
Ø899XZX	Drain of Lt Cornea, Ext Appr, Diagnostic
Ø899X[Ø,Z]Z	Drain/Cornea, Lt, Ext, [Drain Dev, No Dev], NQ
Ø89A[Ø,3]ZX	Drain/Choroid, Rt, [Opn, Perc]
Ø89A[Ø,3][Ø,Z]Z	Drain/Choroid, Rt, [Opn, Perc], [Drain Dev, No Dev], NQ
Ø89B[Ø,3]ZX	Drain/Choroid, Lt, [Opn, Perc]
Ø89B[Ø,3][Ø,Z]Z	Drain/Choroid, Lt, [Opn, Perc], [Drain Dev, No Dev], NQ
Ø89C3ZX	Drain of Rt Iris, Perc Appr, Diagnostic
Ø89C3[Ø,Z]Z	Drain/Iris, Rt, Perc, [Drain Dev, No Dev], NQ
Ø89D3ZX	Drain of Lt Iris, Perc Appr, Diagnostic
Ø89D3[Ø,Z]Z	Drain/Iris, Lt, Perc, [Drain Dev, No Dev], NQ
Ø89E3ZX	Drain of Rt Retina, Perc Appr, Diagnostic
Ø89E3[Ø,Z]Z	Drain/Retina, Rt, Perc, [Drain Dev, No Dev], NQ
Ø89F3ZX	Drain of Lt Retina, Perc Appr, Diagnostic
Ø89F3[Ø,Z]Z	Drain/Retina, Lt, Perc, [Drain Dev, No Dev], NQ
Ø89G3ZX	Drain of Rt Retinal Vessel, Perc Appr, Diagn
Ø89G3[Ø,Z]Z	Drain/Retinal Vessel, Rt, Perc, [Drain Dev, No Dev], NQ
Ø89H3ZX	Drain of Lt Retinal Vessel, Perc Appr, Diagn
Ø89H3[Ø,Z]Z	Drain/Retinal Vessel, Lt, Perc, [Drain Dev, No Dev], NQ
Ø89J3ZX	Drain of Rt Lens, Perc Appr, Diagnostic
Ø89J3[Ø,Z]Z	Drain/Lens, Rt, Perc, [Drain Dev, No Dev], NQ
Ø89K3ZX	Drain of Lt Lens, Perc Appr, Diagnostic
Ø89K3[Ø,Z]Z	Drain/Lens, Lt, Perc, [Drain Dev, No Dev], NQ
Ø89L[Ø,3]ZX	Drain/Extraocular Muscle, Rt, [Opn, Perc]
Ø89L[Ø,3][Ø,Z]Z	Drain/Extraocular Muscle, Rt, [Opn, Perc], [Drain Dev, No Dev], NQ
Ø89M[Ø,3]ZX	Drain/Extraocular Muscle, Lt, [Opn, Perc]
Ø89M[Ø,3][Ø,Z]Z	Drain/Extraocular Muscle, Lt, [Opn, Perc], [Drain Dev, No Dev], NQ
Ø89N[Ø,3,X]ZX	Drain/Upr Eyelid, Rt, [Opn, Perc, Ext]
Ø89P[Ø,3,X]ZX	Drain/Upr Eyelid, Lt, [Opn, Perc, Ext]
Ø89Q[Ø,3,X]ZX	Drain/Lwr Eyelid, Rt, [Opn, Perc, Ext]
Ø89R[Ø,3,X]ZX	Drain/Lwr Eyelid, Lt, [Opn, Perc, Ext]
Ø89SXZX	Drain of Rt Conjunctiva, Ext Appr, Diagnostic
Ø89SX[Ø,Z]Z	Drain/Conjunctiva, Rt, Ext, [Drain Dev, No Dev], NQ
Ø89TXZX	Drain of Lt Conjunctiva, Ext Appr, Diagnostic

Ø89TX[Ø,Z]Z	Drain/Conjunctiva, Lt, Ext, [Drain Dev, No Dev], NQ
Ø89V[Ø,3]ZX	Drain/Lacrimal Gland, Rt, [Opn, Perc]
Ø89V[Ø,3][Ø,Z]Z	Drain/Lacrimal Gland, Rt, [Opn, Perc], [Drain Dev, No Dev], NQ
Ø89W[Ø,3]ZX	Drain/Lacrimal Gland, Lt, [Opn, Perc]
Ø89W[Ø,3][Ø,Z]Z	Drain/Lacrimal Gland, Lt, [Opn, Perc], [Drain Dev, No Dev], NQ
Ø89X[Ø,3,7,8]ZX	Drain/Lacrimal Duct, Rt, [Opn, Perc, Via Natrl or Artfcl Opng, Via Natrl or Artfcl Opng Endo]
Ø89X[Ø,3,7,8][Ø,Z]Z	Drain/Lacrimal Duct, Rt, [Opn, Perc, Via Natrl or Artfcl Opng, Via Natrl or Artfcl Opng Endo], [Drain Dev, No Dev], NQ
Ø89Y[Ø,3,7,8]ZX	Drain/Lacrimal Duct, Lt, [Opn, Perc, Via Natrl or Artfcl Opng, Via Natrl or Artfcl Opng Endo]
Ø89Y[Ø,3,7,8][Ø,Z]Z	Drain/Lacrimal Duct, Lt, [Opn, Perc, Via Natrl or Artfcl Opng, Via Natrl or Artfcl Opng Endo], [Drain Dev, No Dev], NQ
Ø8BØ[Ø,3,X]Z[X,Z]	Exc/Eye, Rt, [Opn, Perc, Ext], No Dev, [Dx, NQ]
Ø8B1[Ø,3,X]Z[X,Z]	Exc/Eye, Lt, [Opn, Perc, Ext], No Dev, [Dx, NQ]
Ø8B43Z[X,Z]	Exc/Vitreous, Rt, Perc, No Dev, [Dx, NQ]
Ø8B53Z[X,Z]	Exc/Vitreous, Lt, Perc, No Dev, [Dx, NQ]
Ø8B6XZ[X,Z]	Exc/Sclera, Rt, Ext, No Dev, [Dx, NQ]
Ø8B7XZ[X,Z]	Exc/Sclera, Lt, Ext, No Dev, [Dx, NQ]
Ø8B8XZ[X,Z]	Exc/Cornea, Rt, Ext, No Dev, [Dx, NQ]
Ø8B9XZ[X,Z]	Exc/Cornea, Lt, Ext, No Dev, [Dx, NQ]
Ø8BA[Ø,3]Z[X,Z]	Exc/Choroid, Rt, [Opn, Perc], No Dev, [Dx, NQ]
Ø8BB[Ø,3]Z[X,Z]	Exc/Choroid, Lt, [Opn, Perc], No Dev, [Dx, NQ]
Ø8BC3Z[X,Z]	Exc/Iris, Rt, Perc, No Dev, [Dx, NQ]
Ø8BD3Z[X,Z]	Exc/Iris, Lt, Perc, No Dev, [Dx, NQ]
Ø8BE3Z[X,Z]	Exc/Retina, Rt, Perc, No Dev, [Dx, NQ]
Ø8BF3Z[X,Z]	Exc/Retina, Lt, Perc, No Dev, [Dx, NQ]
Ø8BJ3Z[X,Z]	Exc/Lens, Rt, Perc, No Dev, [Dx, NQ]
Ø8BK3Z[X,Z]	Exc/Lens, Lt, Perc, No Dev, [Dx, NQ]
Ø8BL[Ø,3]Z[X,Z]	Exc/Extraocular Muscle, Rt, [Opn, Perc], No Dev, [Dx, NQ]
Ø8BM[Ø,3]Z[X,Z]	Exc/Extraocular Muscle, Lt, [Opn, Perc], No Dev, [Dx, NQ]
Ø8BN[Ø,3,X]Z[X,Z]	Exc/Upr Eyelid, Rt, [Opn, Perc, Ext], No Dev, [Dx, NQ]
Ø8BP[Ø,3,X]Z[X,Z]	Exc/Upr Eyelid, Lt, [Opn, Perc, Ext], No Dev, [Dx, NQ]
Ø8BQ[Ø,3,X]Z[X,Z]	Exc/Lwr Eyelid, Rt, [Opn, Perc, Ext], No Dev, [Dx, NQ]
Ø8BR[Ø,3,X]Z[X,Z]	Exc/Lwr Eyelid, Lt, [Opn, Perc, Ext], No Dev, [Dx, NQ]
Ø8BSXZ[X,Z]	Exc/Conjunctiva, Rt, Ext, No Dev, [Dx, NQ]
Ø8BTXZ[X,Z]	Exc/Conjunctiva, Lt, Ext, No Dev, [Dx, NQ]
Ø8BV[Ø,3]Z[X,Z]	Exc/Lacrimal Gland, Rt, [Opn, Perc], No Dev, [Dx, NQ]
Ø8BW[Ø,3]Z[X,Z]	Exc/Lacrimal Gland, Lt, [Opn, Perc], No Dev, [Dx, NQ]
Ø8BX[Ø,3,7,8]Z[X,Z]	Exc/Lacrimal Duct, Rt, [Opn, Perc, Via Natrl or Artfcl Opng, Via Natrl or Artfcl Opng Endo], No Dev, [Dx, NQ]
Ø8BY[Ø,3,7,8]Z[X,Z]	Exc/Lacrimal Duct, Lt, [Opn, Perc, Via Natrl or Artfcl Opng, Via Natrl or Artfcl Opng Endo], No Dev, [Dx, NQ]
Ø8CØXZZ	Extir of Matter from Rt Eye, Ext Appr
Ø8C1XZZ	Extir of Matter from Lt Eye, Ext Appr
Ø8C23ZZ	Extir of Matter from Rt Ant Chamber, Perc Appr
Ø8C33ZZ	Extir of Matter from Lt Ant Chamber, Perc Appr
Ø8C4[3,X]ZZ	Extir/Vitreous, Rt, [Perc, Ext]
Ø8C5[3,X]ZZ	Extir/Vitreous, Lt, [Perc, Ext]
Ø8C8XZZ	Extir of Matter from Rt Cornea, Ext Appr
Ø8C9XZZ	Extir of Matter from Lt Cornea, Ext Appr
Ø8CA[Ø,3,X]ZZ	Extir/Choroid, Rt, [Opn, Perc, Ext]
Ø8CB[Ø,3,X]ZZ	Extir/Choroid, Lt, [Opn, Perc, Ext]
Ø8CC[3,X]ZZ	Extir/Iris, Rt, [Perc, Ext]
Ø8CD[3,X]ZZ	Extir/Iris, Lt, [Perc, Ext]
Ø8CE[3,X]ZZ	Extir/Retina, Rt, [Perc, Ext]
Ø8CF[3,X]ZZ	Extir/Retina, Lt, [Perc, Ext]
Ø8CG[3,X]ZZ	Extir/Retinal Vessel, Rt, [Perc, Ext]
Ø8CH[3,X]ZZ	Extir/Retinal Vessel, Lt, [Perc, Ext]
Ø8CJ[3,X]ZZ	Extir/Lens, Rt, [Perc, Ext]
Ø8CK[3,X]ZZ	Extir/Lens, Lt, [Perc, Ext]
Ø8CL[Ø,3,X]ZZ	Extir/Extraocular Muscle, Rt, [Opn, Perc, Ext]
Ø8CM[Ø,3,X]ZZ	Extir/Extraocular Muscle, Lt, [Opn, Perc, Ext]
Ø8CSXZZ	Extir of Matter from Rt Conjunctiva, Extern Appr
Ø8CTXZZ	Extir of Matter from Lt Conjunctiva, Extern Appr
Ø8CV[Ø,3,X]ZZ	Extir/Lacrimal Gland, Rt, [Opn, Perc, Ext]
Ø8CW[Ø,3,X]ZZ	Extir/Lacrimal Gland, Lt, [Opn, Perc, Ext]
Ø8CX[Ø,3,7,8]ZZ	Extir/Lacrimal Duct, Rt, [Opn, Perc, Via Natrl or Artfcl Opng Endo]
Ø8CY[Ø,3,7,8]ZZ	Extir/Lacrimal Duct, Lt, [Opn, Perc, Via Natrl or Artfcl Opng Endo]
Ø8D8XZ[X,Z]	Extract/Cornea, Rt, Ext, No Dev, [Dx, NQ]
Ø8D9XZ[X,Z]	Extract/Cornea, Lt, Ext, No Dev, [Dx, NQ]
Ø8DJ3ZZ	Extract of Rt Lens, Perc Appr
Ø8DK3ZZ	Extract of Lt Lens, Perc Appr
Ø8F43ZZ	Fragmn in Rt Vitreous, Perc Appr
Ø8F53ZZ	Fragmn in Lt Vitreous, Perc Appr
Ø8HØ[3,X][1,3]Z	Insert/Eye, Rt, [Perc, Ext], [Radioact Elmt, Inf Dev], NQ
Ø8H1[3,X][1,3]Z	Insert/Eye, Lt, [Perc, Ext], [Radioact Elmt, Inf Dev], NQ
Ø8JØXZZ	Inspect of Rt Eye, Ext Appr

T Transfer DRG   SP Special Payment   * Code Range   6th and 7th Character of ZZ = No Device, No Qualifier ZX = No Device, Diagnostic

MS-DRG Version 33.0

© 2015 Optum360, LLC

Code	Description
08J1XZZ	Inspect of Lt Eye, Ext Appr
08JJXZZ	Inspect of Rt Lens, Ext Appr
08JKXZZ	Inspect of Lt Lens, Ext Appr
08JL[0,X]ZZ	Inspect/Extraocular Muscle, Rt, [Opn, Ext]
08JM[0,X]ZZ	Inspect/Extraocular Muscle, Lt, [Opn, Ext]
08LX[0,3,7,8][D,Z]Z	Occlsn/Lacrimal Duct, Rt, [Opn, Perc, Via Natrl or Artfcl Opng, Via Natrl or Artfcl Opng Endo], [Intralum Dev, No Dev], NQ
08LX[0,3]CZ	Occlsn/Lacrimal Duct, Rt, [Opn, Perc], Extralum Dev, NQ
08LY[0,3,7,8][D,Z]Z	Occlsn/Lacrimal Duct, Lt, [Opn, Perc, Via Natrl or Artfcl Opng, Via Natrl or Artfcl Opng Endo], [Intralum Dev, No Dev], NQ
08LY[0,3]CZ	Occlsn/Lacrimal Duct, Lt, [Opn, Perc], Extralum Dev, NQ
08MNXZZ	Reattach of Rt Upr Eyelid, Ext Appr
08MPXZZ	Reattach of Lt Upr Eyelid, Ext Appr
08MQXZZ	Reattach of Rt Lwr Eyelid, Ext Appr
08MRXZZ	Reattach of Lt Lwr Eyelid, Ext Appr
08N0XZZ	Rls Rt Eye, Ext Appr
08N1XZZ	Rls Lt Eye, Ext Appr
08N23ZZ	Rls Rt Ant Chamber, Perc Appr
08N33ZZ	Rls Lt Ant Chamber, Perc Appr
08N43ZZ	Rls Rt Vitreous, Perc Appr
08N53ZZ	Rls Lt Vitreous, Perc Appr
08N6XZZ	Rls Rt Sclera, Ext Appr
08N7XZZ	Rls Lt Sclera, Ext Appr
08N8XZZ	Rls Rt Cornea, Ext Appr
08N9XZZ	Rls Lt Cornea, Ext Appr
08NA[0,3]ZZ	Rls/Choroid, Rt, [Opn, Perc]
08NB[0,3]ZZ	Rls/Choroid, Lt, [Opn, Perc]
08NC3ZZ	Rls Rt Iris, Perc Appr
08ND3ZZ	Rls Lt Iris, Perc Appr
08NE3ZZ	Rls Rt Retina, Perc Appr
08NF3ZZ	Rls Lt Retina, Perc Appr
08NG3ZZ	Rls Rt Retinal Vessel, Perc Appr
08NH3ZZ	Rls Lt Retinal Vessel, Perc Appr
08NJ3ZZ	Rls Rt Lens, Perc Appr
08NK3ZZ	Rls Lt Lens, Perc Appr
08NL[0,3]ZZ	Rls/Extraocular Muscle, Rt, [Opn, Perc]
08NM[0,3]ZZ	Rls/Extraocular Muscle, Lt, [Opn, Perc]
08NN[0,3,X]ZZ	Rls/Upr Eyelid, Rt, [Opn, Perc, Ext]
08NP[0,3,X]ZZ	Rls/Upr Eyelid, Lt, [Opn, Perc, Ext]
08NQ[0,3,X]ZZ	Rls/Lwr Eyelid, Rt, [Opn, Perc, Ext]
08NR[0,3,X]ZZ	Rls/Lwr Eyelid, Lt, [Opn, Perc, Ext]
08NSXZZ	Rls Rt Conjunctiva, Ext Appr
08NTXZZ	Rls Lt Conjunctiva, Ext Appr
08NV[0,3]ZZ	Rls/Lacrimal Gland, Rt, [Opn, Perc]
08NW[0,3]ZZ	Rls/Lacrimal Gland, Lt, [Opn, Perc]
08NX[0,3,7,8]ZZ	Rls/Lacrimal Duct, Rt, [Opn, Perc, Via Natrl or Artfcl Opng, Via Natrl or Artfcl Opng Endo]
08NY[0,3,7,8]ZZ	Rls/Lacrimal Duct, Lt, [Opn, Perc, Via Natrl or Artfcl Opng, Via Natrl or Artfcl Opng Endo]
08P0X[1,7,J,K]Z	Rmvl/Eye, Rt, Ext, [Radioact Elmt, Auto Tissue Sub, Synth Sub, Nonauto Tissue Sub], NQ
08P0[0,3,7,8][0,1,3,7,C,D,J,K]Z	Rmvl/Eye, Rt, [Opn, Perc, Via Natrl or Artfcl Opng, Via Natrl or Artfcl Opng Endo], [Drain Dev, Radioact Elmt, Inf Dev, Auto Tissue Sub, Extralum Dev, Intralum Dev, Synth Sub, Nonauto Tissue Sub], NQ
08P1X[7,J,K]Z	Rmvl/Eye, Lt, Ext, [Auto Tissue Sub, Synth Sub, Nonauto Tissue Sub], NQ
08P1[0,3,7,8][0,1,3,7,C,D,J,K]Z	Rmvl/Eye, Lt, [Opn, Perc, Via Natrl or Artfcl Opng, Via Natrl or Artfcl Opng Endo], [Drain Dev, Radioact Elmt, Inf Dev, Auto Tissue Sub, Extralum Dev, Intralum Dev, Synth Sub, Nonauto Tissue Sub], NQ
08PJ3JZ	Rmvl of Synth Sub from Rt Lens, Perc Appr
08PK3JZ	Rmvl of Synth Sub from Lt Lens, Perc Appr
08PL[0,3][0,7,J,K]Z	Rmvl/Extraocular Muscle, Rt, [Opn, Perc], [Drain Dev, Auto Tissue Sub, Synth Sub, Nonauto Tissue Sub], NQ
08PM[0,3][0,7,J,K]Z	Rmvl/Extraocular Muscle, Lt, [Opn, Perc], [Drain Dev, Auto Tissue Sub, Synth Sub, Nonauto Tissue Sub], NQ
08Q0XZZ	Repair Rt Eye, Ext Appr
08Q1XZZ	Repair Lt Eye, Ext Appr
08Q23ZZ	Repair Rt Ant Chamber, Perc Appr
08Q33ZZ	Repair Lt Ant Chamber, Perc Appr
08Q43ZZ	Repair Rt Vitreous, Perc Appr
08Q53ZZ	Repair Lt Vitreous, Perc Appr
08Q6XZZ	Repair Rt Sclera, Ext Appr
08Q7XZZ	Repair Lt Sclera, Ext Appr
08Q8XZZ	Repair Rt Cornea, Ext Appr
08Q9XZZ	Repair Lt Cornea, Ext Appr
08QA[0,3]ZZ	Rpr/Choroid, Rt, [Opn, Perc]
08QB[0,3]ZZ	Rpr/Choroid, Lt, [Opn, Perc]
08QC3ZZ	Repair Rt Iris, Perc Appr
08QD3ZZ	Repair Lt Iris, Perc Appr
08QE3ZZ	Repair Rt Retina, Perc Appr
08QF3ZZ	Repair Lt Retina, Perc Appr
08QG3ZZ	Repair Rt Retinal Vessel, Perc Appr
08QH3ZZ	Repair Lt Retinal Vessel, Perc Appr
08QJ3ZZ	Repair Rt Lens, Perc Appr
08QK3ZZ	Repair Lt Lens, Perc Appr
08QL[0,3]ZZ	Rpr/Extraocular Muscle, Rt, [Opn, Perc]
08QM[0,3]ZZ	Rpr/Extraocular Muscle, Lt, [Opn, Perc]
08QSXZZ	Repair Rt Conjunctiva, Ext Appr
08QTXZZ	Repair Lt Conjunctiva, Ext Appr
08QV[0,3]ZZ	Rpr/Lacrimal Gland, Rt, [Opn, Perc]
08QW[0,3]ZZ	Rpr/Lacrimal Gland, Lt, [Opn, Perc]
08QX[0,3,7,8]ZZ	Rpr/Lacrimal Duct, Rt, [Opn, Perc, Via Natrl or Artfcl Opng, Via Natrl or Artfcl Opng Endo]
08QY[0,3,7,8]ZZ	Rpr/Lacrimal Duct, Lt, [Opn, Perc, Via Natrl or Artfcl Opng, Via Natrl or Artfcl Opng Endo]
08R0[0,3][7,J,K]Z	Replace/Eye, Rt, [Opn, Perc], [Auto Tissue Sub, Synth Sub, Nonauto Tissue Sub], NQ
08R1[0,3][7,J,K]Z	Replace/Eye, Lt, [Opn, Perc], [Auto Tissue Sub, Synth Sub, Nonauto Tissue Sub], NQ
08R43[7,J,K]Z	Replace/Vitreous, Rt, Perc, [Auto Tissue Sub, Synth Sub, Nonauto Tissue Sub], NQ
08R53[7,J,K]Z	Replace/Vitreous, Lt, Perc, [Auto Tissue Sub, Synth Sub, Nonauto Tissue Sub], NQ
08R6X[7,J,K]Z	Replace/Sclera, Rt, Ext, [Auto Tissue Sub, Synth Sub, Nonauto Tissue Sub], NQ
08R7X[7,J,K]Z	Replace/Sclera, Lt, Ext, [Auto Tissue Sub, Synth Sub, Nonauto Tissue Sub], NQ
08R8[3,X][7,J,K]Z	Replace/Cornea, Rt, [Perc, Ext], [Auto Tissue Sub, Synth Sub, Nonauto Tissue Sub], NQ
08R9[3,X][7,J,K]Z	Replace/Cornea, Lt, [Perc, Ext], [Auto Tissue Sub, Synth Sub, Nonauto Tissue Sub], NQ
08RA[0,3][7,J,K]Z	Replace/Choroid, Rt, [Opn, Perc], [Auto Tissue Sub, Synth Sub, Nonauto Tissue Sub], NQ
08RB[0,3][7,J,K]Z	Replace/Choroid, Lt, [Opn, Perc], [Auto Tissue Sub, Synth Sub, Nonauto Tissue Sub], NQ
08RC3[7,J,K]Z	Replace/Iris, Rt, Perc, [Auto Tissue Sub, Synth Sub, Nonauto Tissue Sub], NQ
08RD3[7,J,K]Z	Replace/Iris, Lt, Perc, [Auto Tissue Sub, Synth Sub, Nonauto Tissue Sub], NQ
08RG3[7,J,K]Z	Replace/Retinal Vessel, Rt, Perc, [Auto Tissue Sub, Synth Sub, Nonauto Tissue Sub], NQ
08RH3[7,J,K]Z	Replace/Retinal Vessel, Lt, Perc, [Auto Tissue Sub, Synth Sub, Nonauto Tissue Sub], NQ
08RJ30Z	Replace of Rt Lens with Intraoc Telescp, Perc Appr
08RJ3[7,J,K]Z	Replace/Lens, Rt, Perc, [Auto Tissue Sub, Synth Sub, Nonauto Tissue Sub], NQ
08RK30Z	Replace of Lt Lens with Intraoc Telescp, Perc Appr
08RK3[7,J,K]Z	Replace/Lens, Lt, Perc, [Auto Tissue Sub, Synth Sub, Nonauto Tissue Sub], NQ
08RN[0,3,X][7,J,K]Z	Replace/Upr Eyelid, Rt, [Opn, Perc, Ext], [Auto Tissue Sub, Synth Sub, Nonauto Tissue Sub], NQ
08RP[0,3,X][7,J,K]Z	Replace/Upr Eyelid, Lt, [Opn, Perc, Ext], [Auto Tissue Sub, Synth Sub, Nonauto Tissue Sub], NQ
08RQ[0,3,X][7,J,K]Z	Replace/Lwr Eyelid, Rt, [Opn, Perc, Ext], [Auto Tissue Sub, Synth Sub, Nonauto Tissue Sub], NQ
08RR[0,3,X][7,J,K]Z	Replace/Lwr Eyelid, Lt, [Opn, Perc, Ext], [Auto Tissue Sub, Synth Sub, Nonauto Tissue Sub], NQ
08RSX[7,J,K]Z	Replace/Conjunctiva, Rt, Ext, [Auto Tissue Sub, Synth Sub, Nonauto Tissue Sub], NQ
08RTX[7,J,K]Z	Replace/Conjunctiva, Lt, Ext, [Auto Tissue Sub, Synth Sub, Nonauto Tissue Sub], NQ
08RX[0,3,7,8][7,J,K]Z	Replace/Lacrimal Duct, Rt, [Opn, Perc, Via Natrl or Artfcl Opng, Via Natrl or Artfcl Opng Endo], [Auto Tissue Sub, Synth Sub, Nonauto Tissue Sub], NQ
08RY[0,3,7,8][7,J,K]Z	Replace/Lacrimal Duct, Lt, [Opn, Perc, Via Natrl or Artfcl Opng, Via Natrl or Artfcl Opng Endo], [Auto Tissue Sub, Synth Sub, Nonauto Tissue Sub], NQ
08SC3ZZ	Repos Rt Iris, Perc Appr
08SD3ZZ	Repos Lt Iris, Perc Appr
08SG3ZZ	Repos Rt Retinal Vessel, Perc Appr
08SH3ZZ	Repos Lt Retinal Vessel, Perc Appr
08SJ3ZZ	Repos Rt Lens, Perc Appr
08SK3ZZ	Repos Lt Lens, Perc Appr
08SL[0,3]ZZ	Repos/Extraocular Muscle, Rt, [Opn, Perc]
08SM[0,3]ZZ	Repos/Extraocular Muscle, Lt, [Opn, Perc]
08SN[0,3,X]ZZ	Repos/Upr Eyelid, Rt, [Opn, Perc, Ext]
08SP[0,3,X]ZZ	Repos/Upr Eyelid, Lt, [Opn, Perc, Ext]
08SQ[0,3,X]ZZ	Repos/Lwr Eyelid, Rt, [Opn, Perc, Ext]

Surgical   Medical   CC Indicator   MCC Indicator   Procedure Proxy   PDx MCC PDx acts as own MCC   PDx CC PDx acts as own CC

DRGs Associated with All MDCs—SURGICAL

08SR[0,3,X]ZZ	Repos/Lwr Eyelid, Lt, [Opn, Perc, Ext]
08SV[0,3]ZZ	Repos/Lacrimal Gland, Rt, [Opn, Perc]
08SW[0,3]ZZ	Repos/Lacrimal Gland, Lt, [Opn, Perc]
08SX[0,3,7,8]ZZ	Repos/Lacrimal Duct, Rt, [Opn, Perc, Via Natrl or Artfcl Opng, Via Natrl or Artfcl Opng Endo]
08SY[0,3,7,8]ZZ	Repos/Lacrimal Duct, Lt, [Opn, Perc, Via Natrl or Artfcl Opng, Via Natrl or Artfcl Opng Endo]
08T0XZZ	Resect of Rt Eye, Ext Appr
08T1XZZ	Resect of Lt Eye, Ext Appr
08T43ZZ	Resect of Rt Vitreous, Perc Appr
08T53ZZ	Resect of Lt Vitreous, Perc Appr
08T8XZZ	Resect of Rt Cornea, Ext Appr
08T9XZZ	Resect of Lt Cornea, Ext Appr
08TC3ZZ	Resect of Rt Iris, Perc Appr
08TD3ZZ	Resect of Lt Iris, Perc Appr
08TJ3ZZ	Resect of Rt Lens, Perc Appr
08TK3ZZ	Resect of Lt Lens, Perc Appr
08TL[0,3]ZZ	Resect/Extraocular Muscle, Rt, [Opn, Perc]
08TM[0,3]ZZ	Resect/Extraocular Muscle, Lt, [Opn, Perc]
08TN[0,X]ZZ	Resect/Upr Eyelid, Rt, [Opn, Ext]
08TP[0,X]ZZ	Resect/Upr Eyelid, Lt, [Opn, Ext]
08TQ[0,X]ZZ	Resect/Lwr Eyelid, Rt, [Opn, Ext]
08TR[0,X]ZZ	Resect/Lwr Eyelid, Lt, [Opn, Ext]
08TV[0,3]ZZ	Resect/Lacrimal Gland, Rt, [Opn, Perc]
08TW[0,3]ZZ	Resect/Lacrimal Gland, Lt, [Opn, Perc]
08TX[0,3,7,8]ZZ	Resect/Lacrimal Duct, Rt, [Opn, Perc, Via Natrl or Artfcl Opng, Via Natrl or Artfcl Opng Endo]
08TY[0,3,7,8]ZZ	Resect/Lacrimal Duct, Lt, [Opn, Perc, Via Natrl or Artfcl Opng, Via Natrl or Artfcl Opng Endo]
08U0[0,3][7,J,K]Z	Supl/Eye, Rt, [Opn, Perc], [Auto Tissue Sub, Synth Sub, Nonauto Tissue Sub], NQ
08U1[0,3][7,J,K]Z	Supl/Eye, Lt, [Opn, Perc], [Auto Tissue Sub, Synth Sub, Nonauto Tissue Sub], NQ
08U8[0,3,X][7,J,K]Z	Supl/Cornea, Rt, [Opn, Perc, Ext], [Auto Tissue Sub, Synth Sub, Nonauto Tissue Sub], NQ
08U9[0,3,X][7,J,K]Z	Supl/Cornea, Lt, [Opn, Perc, Ext], [Auto Tissue Sub, Synth Sub, Nonauto Tissue Sub], NQ
08UC[0,3][7,J,K]Z	Supl/Iris, Rt, [Opn, Perc], [Auto Tissue Sub, Synth Sub, Nonauto Tissue Sub], NQ
08UD[0,3][7,J,K]Z	Supl/Iris, Lt, [Opn, Perc], [Auto Tissue Sub, Synth Sub, Nonauto Tissue Sub], NQ
08UE[0,3][7,J,K]Z	Supl/Retina, Rt, [Opn, Perc], [Auto Tissue Sub, Synth Sub, Nonauto Tissue Sub], NQ
08UF[0,3][7,J,K]Z	Supl/Retina, Lt, [Opn, Perc], [Auto Tissue Sub, Synth Sub, Nonauto Tissue Sub], NQ
08UG[0,3][7,J,K]Z	Supl/Retinal Vessel, Rt, [Opn, Perc], [Auto Tissue Sub, Synth Sub, Nonauto Tissue Sub], NQ
08UH[0,3][7,J,K]Z	Supl/Retinal Vessel, Lt, [Opn, Perc], [Auto Tissue Sub, Synth Sub, Nonauto Tissue Sub], NQ
08UL[0,3][7,J,K]Z	Supl/Extraocular Muscle, Rt, [Opn, Perc], [Auto Tissue Sub, Synth Sub, Nonauto Tissue Sub], NQ
08UM[0,3][7,J,K]Z	Supl/Extraocular Muscle, Lt, [Opn, Perc], [Auto Tissue Sub, Synth Sub, Nonauto Tissue Sub], NQ
08UN[0,3,X][7,J,K]Z	Supl/Upr Eyelid, Rt, [Opn, Perc, Ext], [Auto Tissue Sub, Synth Sub, Nonauto Tissue Sub], NQ
08UP[0,3,X][7,J,K]Z	Supl/Upr Eyelid, Lt, [Opn, Perc, Ext], [Auto Tissue Sub, Synth Sub, Nonauto Tissue Sub], NQ
08UQ[0,3,X][7,J,K]Z	Supl/Lwr Eyelid, Rt, [Opn, Perc, Ext], [Auto Tissue Sub, Synth Sub, Nonauto Tissue Sub], NQ
08UR[0,3,X][7,J,K]Z	Supl/Lwr Eyelid, Lt, [Opn, Perc, Ext], [Auto Tissue Sub, Synth Sub, Nonauto Tissue Sub], NQ
08UX[0,3,7,8][7,J,K]Z	Supl/Lacrimal Duct, Rt, [Opn, Perc, Via Natrl or Artfcl Opng, Via Natrl or Artfcl Opng Endo], [Auto Tissue Sub, Synth Sub, Nonauto Tissue Sub], NQ
08UY[0,3,7,8][7,J,K]Z	Supl/Lacrimal Duct, Lt, [Opn, Perc, Via Natrl or Artfcl Opng, Via Natrl or Artfcl Opng Endo], [Auto Tissue Sub, Synth Sub, Nonauto Tissue Sub], NQ
08VX[0,3,7,8][D,Z]Z	Restrict/Lacrimal Duct, Rt, [Opn, Perc, Via Natrl or Artfcl Opng, Via Natrl or Artfcl Opng Endo], [Intralum Dev, No Dev], NQ
08VX[0,3]CZ	Restrict/Lacrimal Duct, Rt, [Opn, Perc], Extralum Dev, NQ
08VY[0,3,7,8][D,Z]Z	Restrict/Lacrimal Duct, Lt, [Opn, Perc, Via Natrl or Artfcl Opng, Via Natrl or Artfcl Opng Endo], [Intralum Dev, No Dev], NQ
08VY[0,3]CZ	Restrict/Lacrimal Duct, Lt, [Opn, Perc], Extralum Dev, NQ
08W0[0,3,7,8][0,3,7,C,D,J,K]Z	Rev/Eye, Rt, [Opn, Perc, Via Natrl or Artfcl Opng, Via Natrl or Artfcl Opng Endo], [Drain Dev, Inf Dev, Auto Tissue Sub, Extralum Dev, Intralum Dev, Synth Sub, Nonauto Tissue Sub], NQ
08W1[0,3,7,8][0,3,7,C,D,J,K]Z	Rev/Eye, Lt, [Opn, Perc, Via Natrl or Artfcl Opng, Via Natrl or Artfcl Opng Endo], [Drain Dev, Inf Dev, Auto Tissue Sub, Extralum Dev, Intralum Dev, Synth Sub, Nonauto Tissue Sub], NQ
08WJ3JZ	Rev of Synth Sub in Rt Lens, Perc Appr
08WK3JZ	Rev of Synth Sub in Lt Lens, Perc Appr
08WL[0,3][0,7,J,K]Z	Rev/Extraocular Muscle, Rt, [Opn, Perc], [Drain Dev, Auto Tissue Sub, Synth Sub, Nonauto Tissue Sub], NQ
08WM[0,3][0,7,J,K]Z	Rev/Extraocular Muscle, Lt, [Opn, Perc], [Drain Dev, Auto Tissue Sub, Synth Sub, Nonauto Tissue Sub], NQ
08XL[0,3]ZZ	Transfer/Extraocular Muscle, Rt, [Opn, Perc]
08XM[0,3]ZZ	Transfer/Extraocular Muscle, Lt, [Opn, Perc]
0900[0,3,4,X][7,J,K,Z]Z	Alter/Ext Ear, Rt, [Opn, Perc, Perc Endo, Ext], [Auto Tissue Sub, Synth Sub, Nonauto Tissue Sub, No Dev], NQ
0901[0,3,4,X][7,J,K,Z]Z	Alter/Ext Ear, Lt, [Opn, Perc, Perc Endo, Ext], [Auto Tissue Sub, Synth Sub, Nonauto Tissue Sub, No Dev], NQ
0902[0,3,4,X][7,J,K,Z]Z	Alter/Ext Ear, Bilat, [Opn, Perc, Perc Endo, Ext], [Auto Tissue Sub, Synth Sub, Nonauto Tissue Sub, No Dev], NQ
090K[0,3,4,X][7,J,K,Z]Z	Alter/Nose, [Opn, Perc, Perc Endo, Ext], [Auto Tissue Sub, Synth Sub, Nonauto Tissue Sub, No Dev], NQ
09590ZZ	Destr of Rt Auditory Ossicle, Opn Appr
095A0ZZ	Destr of Lt Auditory Ossicle, Opn Appr
095U[0,3,4]ZZ	Destr/Ethmoid Sinus, Rt, [Opn, Perc, Perc Endo]
095V[0,3,4]ZZ	Destr/Ethmoid Sinus, Lt, [Opn, Perc, Perc Endo]
098L[0,3,4,7,8]ZZ	Div/Nasal Turbinate, [Opn, Perc, Perc Endo, Via Natrl or Artfcl Opng, Via Natrl or Artfcl Opng Endo]
099500Z	Drain of Rt Mid Ear with Drain Dev, Opn Appr
09950ZX	Drain of Rt Mid Ear, Opn Appr, Diagnostic
099600Z	Drain of Lt Mid Ear with Drain Dev, Opn Appr
09960ZX	Drain of Lt Mid Ear, Opn Appr, Diagnostic
0997[0,3,4,7,8]0Z	Drain/Tympanic Membrane, Rt, [Opn, Perc, Perc Endo, Via Natrl or Artfcl Opng, Via Natrl or Artfcl Opng Endo], Drain Dev, NQ
0997[0,3,4,7,8]ZX	Drain/Tympanic Membrane, Rt, [Opn, Perc, Perc Endo, Via Natrl or Artfcl Opng, Via Natrl or Artfcl Opng Endo]
0998[0,3,4,7,8]0Z	Drain/Tympanic Membrane, Lt, [Opn, Perc, Perc Endo, Via Natrl or Artfcl Opng, Via Natrl or Artfcl Opng Endo], Drain Dev, NQ
0998[0,3,4,7,8]ZX	Drain/Tympanic Membrane, Lt, [Opn, Perc, Perc Endo, Via Natrl or Artfcl Opng, Via Natrl or Artfcl Opng Endo]
09990ZX	Drain of Rt Auditory Ossicle, Opn Appr, Diagn
099A0ZX	Drain of Lt Auditory Ossicle, Opn Appr, Diagnostic
099B[0,3,4]ZX	Drain/Mastoid Sinus, Rt, [Opn, Perc, Perc Endo]
099B[0,3,4][0,Z]Z	Drain/Mastoid Sinus, Rt, [Opn, Perc, Perc Endo], [Drain Dev, No Dev], NQ
099C[0,3,4]ZX	Drain/Mastoid Sinus, Lt, [Opn, Perc, Perc Endo]
099C[0,3,4][0,Z]Z	Drain/Mastoid Sinus, Lt, [Opn, Perc, Perc Endo], [Drain Dev, No Dev], NQ
099D0ZX	Drain of Rt Inner Ear, Opn Appr, Diagnostic
099E0ZX	Drain of Lt Inner Ear, Opn Appr, Diagnostic
099F[0,3,4,7,8]ZX	Drain/Eustachian Tube, Rt, [Opn, Perc, Perc Endo, Via Natrl or Artfcl Opng, Via Natrl or Artfcl Opng Endo]
099G[0,3,4,7,8]ZX	Drain/Eustachian Tube, Lt, [Opn, Perc, Perc Endo, Via Natrl or Artfcl Opng, Via Natrl or Artfcl Opng Endo]
09B50Z[X,Z]	Exc/Mid Ear, Rt, Opn, No Dev, [Dx, NQ]
09B60Z[X,Z]	Exc/Mid Ear, Lt, Opn, No Dev, [Dx, NQ]
09B7[0,3,4,7,8]Z[X,Z]	Exc/Tympanic Membrane, Rt, [Opn, Perc, Perc Endo, Via Natrl or Artfcl Opng, Via Natrl or Artfcl Opng Endo], No Dev, [Dx, NQ]
09B8[0,3,4,7,8]Z[X,Z]	Exc/Tympanic Membrane, Lt, [Opn, Perc, Perc Endo, Via Natrl or Artfcl Opng, Via Natrl or Artfcl Opng Endo], No Dev, [Dx, NQ]
09B90Z[X,Z]	Exc/Auditory Ossicle, Rt, Opn, No Dev, [Dx, NQ]
09BA0Z[X,Z]	Exc/Auditory Ossicle, Lt, Opn, No Dev, [Dx, NQ]
09BB[0,3,4]ZX	Exc/Mastoid Sinus, Rt, [Opn, Perc, Perc Endo]
09BC[0,3,4]ZX	Exc/Mastoid Sinus, Lt, [Opn, Perc, Perc Endo]
09BD0ZX	Exc of Rt Inner Ear, Opn Appr, Diagnostic
09BE0ZX	Exc of Lt Inner Ear, Opn Appr, Diagnostic
09BL[0,3,4,7,8]ZZ	Exc/Nasal Turbinate, [Opn, Perc, Perc Endo, Via Natrl or Artfcl Opng, Via Natrl or Artfcl Opng Endo]
09BM[0,3,4]ZZ	Exc/Nasal Septum, [Opn, Perc, Perc Endo]
09BU[0,3,4]ZZ	Exc/Ethmoid Sinus, Rt, [Opn, Perc, Perc Endo]
09BV[0,3,4]ZZ	Exc/Ethmoid Sinus, Lt, [Opn, Perc, Perc Endo]
09C50ZZ	Extir of Matter from Rt Mid Ear, Opn Appr
09C60ZZ	Extir of Matter from Lt Mid Ear, Opn Appr
09CB[0,3,4]ZZ	Extir/Mastoid Sinus, Rt, [Opn, Perc, Perc Endo]
09CC[0,3,4]ZZ	Extir/Mastoid Sinus, Lt, [Opn, Perc, Perc Endo]
09D90ZZ	Extract of Rt Auditory Ossicle, Opn Appr
09DA0ZZ	Extract of Lt Auditory Ossicle, Opn Appr

T **Transfer DRG**   SP **Special Payment**   * **Code Range**   **6th and 7th Character of ZZ = No Device, No Qualifier ZX = No Device, Diagnostic**

MS-DRG Version 33.0

© 2015 Optum360, LLC

09DL[0,3,4,7,8]ZZ Extract/Nasal Turbinate, [Opn, Perc, Perc Endo, Via Natrl or Artfcl Opng, Via Natrl or Artfcl Opng Endo]
09DM[0,3,4]ZZ Extract/Nasal Septum, [Opn, Perc, Perc Endo]
09DU[0,3,4]ZZ Extract/Ethmoid Sinus, Rt, [Opn, Perc, Perc Endo]
09DV[0,3,4]ZZ Extract/Ethmoid Sinus, Lt, [Opn, Perc, Perc Endo]
09J7[0,3,4,7,X]ZZ Inspect/Tympanic Membrane, Rt, [Opn, Perc, Perc Endo, Via Natrl or Artfcl Opng, Ext]
09J8[0,3,4,7,X]ZZ Inspect/Tympanic Membrane, Lt, [Opn, Perc, Perc Endo, Via Natrl or Artfcl Opng, Ext]
09JD[0,3,4,X]ZZ Inspect/Inner Ear, Rt, [Opn, Perc, Perc Endo, Ext]
09JE[0,3,4,X]ZZ Inspect/Inner Ear, Lt, [Opn, Perc, Perc Endo, Ext]
09M0XZZ Reattach of Rt Ext Ear, Ext Appr
09M1XZZ Reattach of Lt Ext Ear, Ext Appr
09MKXZZ Reattach of Nose, Ext Appr
09N0[0,3,4,X]ZZ Rls/Ext Ear, Rt, [Opn, Perc, Perc Endo, Ext]
09N1[0,3,4,X]ZZ Rls/Ext Ear, Lt, [Opn, Perc, Perc Endo, Ext]
09N3[0,3,4,7,8,X]ZZ Rls/Ext Auditory Canal, Rt, [Opn, Perc, Perc Endo, Via Natrl or Artfcl Opng, Via Natrl or Artfcl Opng Endo, Ext]
09N4[0,3,4,7,8,X]ZZ Rls/Ext Auditory Canal, Lt, [Opn, Perc, Perc Endo, Via Natrl or Artfcl Opng, Via Natrl or Artfcl Opng Endo, Ext]
09N50ZZ Rls Rt Mid Ear, Opn Appr
09N60ZZ Rls Lt Mid Ear, Opn Appr
09Q0[0,3,4]ZZ Rpr/Ext Ear, Rt, [Opn, Perc, Perc Endo]
09Q1[0,3,4]ZZ Rpr/Ext Ear, Lt, [Opn, Perc, Perc Endo]
09Q2[0,3,4]ZZ Rpr/Ext Ear, Bilat, [Opn, Perc, Perc Endo]
09Q3[0,3,4,7,8]ZZ Rpr/Ext Auditory Canal, Rt, [Opn, Perc, Perc Endo, Via Natrl or Artfcl Opng, Via Natrl or Artfcl Opng Endo]
09Q4[0,3,4,7,8]ZZ Rpr/Ext Auditory Canal, Lt, [Opn, Perc, Perc Endo, Via Natrl or Artfcl Opng, Via Natrl or Artfcl Opng Endo]
09Q50ZZ Repair Rt Mid Ear, Opn Appr
09Q60ZZ Repair Lt Mid Ear, Opn Appr
09Q7[0,3,4,7,8]ZZ Rpr/Tympanic Membrane, Rt, [Opn, Perc, Perc Endo, Via Natrl or Artfcl Opng, Via Natrl or Artfcl Opng Endo]
09Q8[0,3,4,7,8]ZZ Rpr/Tympanic Membrane, Lt, [Opn, Perc, Perc Endo, Via Natrl or Artfcl Opng, Via Natrl or Artfcl Opng Endo]
09QK[0,3,4,X]ZZ Rpr/Nose, [Opn, Perc, Perc Endo, Ext]
09QL[0,3,4,7,8]ZZ Rpr/Nasal Turbinate, [Opn, Perc, Perc Endo, Via Natrl or Artfcl Opng, Via Natrl or Artfcl Opng Endo]
09QM[0,3,4]ZZ Rpr/Nasal Septum, [Opn, Perc, Perc Endo]
09R0[0,X][7,J,K]Z Replace/Ext Ear, Rt, [Opn, Ext], [Auto Tissue Sub, Synth Sub, Nonauto Tissue Sub], NQ
09R1[0,X][7,J,K]Z Replace/Ext Ear, Lt, [Opn, Ext], [Auto Tissue Sub, Synth Sub, Nonauto Tissue Sub], NQ
09R2[0,X][7,J,K]Z Replace/Ext Ear, Bilat, [Opn, Ext], [Auto Tissue Sub, Synth Sub, Nonauto Tissue Sub], NQ
09R50[7,J,K]Z Replace/Mid Ear, Rt, Opn, [Auto Tissue Sub, Synth Sub, Nonauto Tissue Sub], NQ
09R60[7,J,K]Z Replace/Mid Ear, Lt, Opn, [Auto Tissue Sub, Synth Sub, Nonauto Tissue Sub], NQ
09R90[7,J,K]Z Replace/Auditory Ossicle, Rt, Opn, [Auto Tissue Sub, Synth Sub, Nonauto Tissue Sub], NQ
09RA0[7,J,K]Z Replace/Auditory Ossicle, Lt, Opn, [Auto Tissue Sub, Synth Sub, Nonauto Tissue Sub], NQ
09RK[0,X][7,J,K]Z Replace/Nose, [Opn, Ext], [Auto Tissue Sub, Synth Sub, Nonauto Tissue Sub], NQ
09RL[0,3,4,7,8][7,J,K]Z Replace/Nasal Turbinate, [Opn, Perc, Perc Endo, Via Natrl or Artfcl Opng, Via Natrl or Artfcl Opng Endo], [Auto Tissue Sub, Synth Sub, Nonauto Tissue Sub], NQ
09RM[0,3,4][7,J,K]Z Replace/Nasal Septum, [Opn, Perc, Perc Endo], [Auto Tissue Sub, Synth Sub, Nonauto Tissue Sub], NQ
09RN[0,7,8][7,J,K]Z Replace/Nasopharynx, [Opn, Via Natrl or Artfcl Opng, Via Natrl or Artfcl Opng Endo], [Auto Tissue Sub, Synth Sub, Nonauto Tissue Sub], NQ
09S0[0,4,X]ZZ Repos/Ext Ear, Rt, [Opn, Perc Endo, Ext]
09S1[0,4,X]ZZ Repos/Ext Ear, Lt, [Opn, Perc Endo, Ext]
09S2[0,4,X]ZZ Repos/Ext Ear, Bilat, [Opn, Perc Endo, Ext]
09S7[0,4,7,8]ZZ Repos/Tympanic Membrane, Rt, [Opn, Perc Endo, Via Natrl or Artfcl Opng, Via Natrl or Artfcl Opng Endo]
09S8[0,4,7,8]ZZ Repos/Tympanic Membrane, Lt, [Opn, Perc Endo, Via Natrl or Artfcl Opng, Via Natrl or Artfcl Opng Endo]
09SK[0,4,X]ZZ Repos/Nose, [Opn, Perc Endo, Ext]
09SL[0,4,7,8]ZZ Repos/Nasal Turbinate, [Opn, Perc Endo, Via Natrl or Artfcl Opng, Via Natrl or Artfcl Opng Endo]
09SM[0,4]ZZ Repos/Nasal Septum, [Opn, Perc Endo]
09T0[0,4,X]ZZ Resect/Ext Ear, Rt, [Opn, Perc Endo, Ext]
09T1[0,4,X]ZZ Resect/Ext Ear, Lt, [Opn, Perc Endo, Ext]
09T90ZZ Resect of Rt Auditory Ossicle, Opn Appr
09TA0ZZ Resect of Lt Auditory Ossicle, Opn Appr
09TL[0,4,7,8]ZZ Resect/Nasal Turbinate, [Opn, Perc Endo, Via Natrl or Artfcl Opng, Via Natrl or Artfcl Opng Endo]

09TM[0,4]ZZ Resect/Nasal Septum, [Opn, Perc Endo]
09TU[0,4]ZZ Resect/Ethmoid Sinus, Rt, [Opn, Perc Endo]
09TV[0,4]ZZ Resect/Ethmoid Sinus, Lt, [Opn, Perc Endo]
09U0[0,X][7,J,K]Z Supl/Ext Ear, Rt, [Opn, Ext], [Auto Tissue Sub, Synth Sub, Nonauto Tissue Sub], NQ
09U1[0,X][7,J,K]Z Supl/Ext Ear, Lt, [Opn, Ext], [Auto Tissue Sub, Synth Sub, Nonauto Tissue Sub], NQ
09U2[0,X][7,J,K]Z Supl/Ext Ear, Bilat, [Opn, Ext], [Auto Tissue Sub, Synth Sub, Nonauto Tissue Sub], NQ
09U50[7,J,K]Z Supl/Mid Ear, Rt, Opn, [Auto Tissue Sub, Synth Sub, Nonauto Tissue Sub], NQ
09U60[7,J,K]Z Supl/Mid Ear, Lt, Opn, [Auto Tissue Sub, Synth Sub, Nonauto Tissue Sub], NQ
09U7[0,7,8][7,J,K]Z Supl/Tympanic Membrane, Rt, [Opn, Via Natrl or Artfcl Opng, Via Natrl or Artfcl Opng Endo], [Auto Tissue Sub, Synth Sub, Nonauto Tissue Sub], NQ
09U8[0,7,8][7,J,K]Z Supl/Tympanic Membrane, Lt, [Opn, Via Natrl or Artfcl Opng, Via Natrl or Artfcl Opng Endo], [Auto Tissue Sub, Synth Sub, Nonauto Tissue Sub], NQ
09U90[7,J,K]Z Supl/Auditory Ossicle, Rt, Opn, [Auto Tissue Sub, Synth Sub, Nonauto Tissue Sub], NQ
09UA0[7,J,K]Z Supl/Auditory Ossicle, Lt, Opn, [Auto Tissue Sub, Synth Sub, Nonauto Tissue Sub], NQ
09UK[0,X][7,J,K]Z Supl/Nose, [Opn, Ext], [Auto Tissue Sub, Synth Sub, Nonauto Tissue Sub], NQ
09UL[0,3,4,7,8][7,J,K]Z Supl/Nasal Turbinate, [Opn, Perc, Perc Endo, Via Natrl or Artfcl Opng, Via Natrl or Artfcl Opng Endo], [Auto Tissue Sub, Synth Sub, Nonauto Tissue Sub], NQ
09UM[0,3,4][7,J,K]Z Supl/Nasal Septum, [Opn, Perc, Perc Endo], [Auto Tissue Sub, Synth Sub, Nonauto Tissue Sub], NQ
09UN[0,7,8][7,J,K]Z Supl/Nasopharynx, [Opn, Via Natrl or Artfcl Opng, Via Natrl or Artfcl Opng Endo], [Auto Tissue Sub, Synth Sub, Nonauto Tissue Sub], NQ
0B9C8ZX Drain of Rt Upr Lung Lobe, Endo, Diagn
0B9D8ZX Drain of Rt Mid Lung Lobe, Endo, Diagn
0B9F8ZX Drain of Rt Lwr Lung Lobe, Endo, Diagn
0B9G8ZX Drain of Lt Upr Lung Lobe, Endo, Diagn
0B9H8ZX Drain of Lung Lingula, Endo, Diagn
0B9J8ZX Drain of Lt Lwr Lung Lobe, Endo, Diagn
0B9K8ZX Drain of Rt Lung, Endo, Diagn
0B9L8ZX Drain of Lt Lung, Endo, Diagn
0B9M8ZX Drain of Bilat Lungs, Endo, Diagn
0BBC[7,8]ZX Exc/Upr Lung Lobe, Rt, [Via Natrl or Artfcl Opng, Via Natrl or Artfcl Opng Endo]
0BBD[7,8]ZX Exc/Mid Lung Lobe, Rt, [Via Natrl or Artfcl Opng, Via Natrl or Artfcl Opng Endo]
0BBF[7,8]ZX Exc/Lwr Lung Lobe, Rt, [Via Natrl or Artfcl Opng, Via Natrl or Artfcl Opng Endo]
0BBG[7,8]ZX Exc/Upr Lung Lobe, Lt, [Via Natrl or Artfcl Opng, Via Natrl or Artfcl Opng Endo]
0BBH[7,8]ZX Exc/Lung Lingula, [Via Natrl or Artfcl Opng, Via Natrl or Artfcl Opng Endo]
0BBJ[7,8]ZX Exc/Lwr Lung Lobe, Lt, [Via Natrl or Artfcl Opng, Via Natrl or Artfcl Opng Endo]
0BBK[7,8]ZX Exc/Lung, Rt, [Via Natrl or Artfcl Opng, Via Natrl or Artfcl Opng Endo]
0BBL[7,8]ZX Exc/Lung, Lt, [Via Natrl or Artfcl Opng, Via Natrl or Artfcl Opng Endo]
0BBM[4,7,8]ZX Exc/Lungs, Bilat, [Perc Endo, Via Natrl or Artfcl Opng, Via Natrl or Artfcl Opng Endo]
0BH0[0,3,4,7,8]1Z Insert/Tracheobronchial Tree, [Opn, Perc, Perc Endo, Via Natrl or Artfcl Opng, Via Natrl or Artfcl Opng Endo], Radioact Elmt, NQ
0BHK[0,3,4,7,8]1Z Insert/Lung, Rt, [Opn, Perc, Perc Endo, Via Natrl or Artfcl Opng, Via Natrl or Artfcl Opng Endo], Radioact Elmt, NQ
0BHL[0,3,4,7,8]1Z Insert/Lung, Lt, [Opn, Perc, Perc Endo, Via Natrl or Artfcl Opng, Via Natrl or Artfcl Opng Endo], Radioact Elmt, NQ
0C00X[7,J,K,Z]Z Alter/Upr Lip, Ext, [Auto Tissue Sub, Synth Sub, Nonauto Tissue Sub, No Dev], NQ
0C01X[7,J,K,Z]Z Alter/Lwr Lip, Ext, [Auto Tissue Sub, Synth Sub, Nonauto Tissue Sub, No Dev], NQ
0C50[0,3,X]ZZ Destr/Upr Lip, [Opn, Perc, Ext]
0C51[0,3,X]ZZ Destr/Lwr Lip, [Opn, Perc, Ext]
0C52[0,3,X]ZZ Destr/Hard Palate, [Opn, Perc, Ext]
0C53[0,3,X]ZZ Destr/Soft Palate, [Opn, Perc, Ext]
0C54[0,3,X]ZZ Destr/Buccal Mucosa, [Opn, Perc, Ext]
0C57[0,3,X]ZZ Destr/Tongue, [Opn, Perc, Ext]
0C58[0,3]ZZ Destr/Parotid Gland, Rt, [Opn, Perc]
0C59[0,3]ZZ Destr/Parotid Gland, Lt, [Opn, Perc]
0C5B[0,3]ZZ Destr/Parotid Duct, Rt, [Opn, Perc]

Surgical **Medical** **CC Indicator** **MCC Indicator** **Procedure Proxy** PDxMCC **PDx acts as own MCC** PDxCC **PDx acts as own CC**

© 2015 Optum360, LLC MS-DRG Version 33.0 **447**

DRGs Associated with All MDCs—SURGICAL

0C5C[0,3]ZZ	Destr/Parotid Duct, Lt, [Opn, Perc]
0C5D[0,3]ZZ	Destr/Sublingual Gland, Rt, [Opn, Perc]
0C5F[0,3]ZZ	Destr/Sublingual Gland, Lt, [Opn, Perc]
0C5G[0,3]ZZ	Destr/Submaxillary Gland, Rt, [Opn, Perc]
0C5H[0,3]ZZ	Destr/Submaxillary Gland, Lt, [Opn, Perc]
0C5J[0,3]ZZ	Destr/Minor Salivary Gland, [Opn, Perc]
0C5N[0,3,X]ZZ	Destr/Uvula, [Opn, Perc, Ext]
0C5S[0,3,4,7,8]ZZ	Destr/Larynx, [Opn, Perc, Perc Endo, Via Natrl or Artfcl Opng, Via Natrl or Artfcl Opng Endo]
0C5T[0,3,4,7,8]ZZ	Destr/Vocal Cord, Rt, [Opn, Perc, Perc Endo, Via Natrl or Artfcl Opng, Via Natrl or Artfcl Opng Endo]
0C5V[0,3,4,7,8]ZZ	Destr/Vocal Cord, Lt, [Opn, Perc, Perc Endo, Via Natrl or Artfcl Opng, Via Natrl or Artfcl Opng Endo]
0C7S[0,3,4,7,8][D,Z]Z	Dilation/Larynx, [Opn, Perc, Perc Endo, Via Natrl or Artfcl Opng, Via Natrl or Artfcl Opng Endo], [Intralum Dev, No Dev], NQ
0C92[0,3,X]ZX	Drain/Hard Palate, [Opn, Perc, Ext]
0C93[0,3,X]ZX	Drain/Soft Palate, [Opn, Perc, Ext]
0C980ZX	Drain of Rt Parotid Gland, Opn Appr, Diagnostic
0C990ZX	Drain of Lt Parotid Gland, Opn Appr, Diagnostic
0C9B0ZX	Drain of Rt Parotid Duct, Opn Appr, Diagnostic
0C9C0ZX	Drain of Lt Parotid Duct, Opn Appr, Diagnostic
0C9D0ZX	Drain of Rt Sublingual Gland, Opn Appr, Diagn
0C9F0ZX	Drain of Lt Sublingual Gland, Opn Appr, Diagnostic
0C9G0ZX	Drain of Rt Submaxillary Gland, Opn Appr, Diagn
0C9H0ZX	Drain of Lt Submaxillary Gland, Opn Appr, Diagn
0C9J0ZX	Drain of Minor Salivary Gland, Opn Appr, Diagnostic
0C9N[0,3,X]ZX	Drain/Uvula, [Opn, Perc, Ext]
0C9N[0,3,X][0,Z]Z	Drain/Uvula, [Opn, Perc, Ext], [Drain Dev, No Dev], NQ
0C9P[0,3,X]ZX	Drain/Tonsils, [Opn, Perc, Ext]
0C9Q[0,3,X]ZX	Drain/Adenoids, [Opn, Perc, Ext]
0CB0[0,3,X]ZZ	Exc/Upr Lip, [Opn, Perc, Ext]
0CB1[0,3,X]ZZ	Exc/Lwr Lip, [Opn, Perc, Ext]
0CB2[0,3,X]Z[X,Z]	Exc/Hard Palate, [Opn, Perc, Ext], No Dev, [Dx, NQ]
0CB3[0,3,X]Z[X,Z]	Exc/Soft Palate, [Opn, Perc, Ext], No Dev, [Dx, NQ]
0CB4[0,3,X]ZZ	Exc/Buccal Mucosa, [Opn, Perc, Ext]
0CB80ZX	Exc of Rt Parotid Gland, Opn Appr, Diagnostic
0CB8[0,3]ZZ	Exc/Parotid Gland, Rt, [Opn, Perc]
0CB90ZX	Exc of Lt Parotid Gland, Opn Appr, Diagnostic
0CB9[0,3]ZZ	Exc/Parotid Gland, Lt, [Opn, Perc]
0CBB0ZX	Exc of Rt Parotid Duct, Opn Appr, Diagnostic
0CBB[0,3]ZZ	Exc/Parotid Duct, Rt, [Opn, Perc]
0CBC0ZX	Exc of Lt Parotid Duct, Opn Appr, Diagnostic
0CBC[0,3]ZZ	Exc/Parotid Duct, Lt, [Opn, Perc]
0CBD0ZX	Exc of Rt Sublingual Gland, Opn Appr, Diagn
0CBD[0,3]ZZ	Exc/Sublingual Gland, Rt, [Opn, Perc]
0CBF0ZX	Exc of Lt Sublingual Gland, Opn Appr, Diagnostic
0CBF[0,3]ZZ	Exc/Sublingual Gland, Lt, [Opn, Perc]
0CBG0ZX	Exc of Rt Submaxillary Gland, Opn Appr, Diagn
0CBG[0,3]ZZ	Exc/Submaxillary Gland, Rt, [Opn, Perc]
0CBH0ZX	Exc of Lt Submaxillary Gland, Opn Appr, Diagn
0CBH[0,3]ZZ	Exc/Submaxillary Gland, Lt, [Opn, Perc]
0CBJ0ZX	Exc of Minor Salivary Gland, Opn Appr, Diagnostic
0CBJ[0,3]ZZ	Exc/Minor Salivary Gland, [Opn, Perc]
0CBN[0,3,X]Z[X,Z]	Exc/Uvula, [Opn, Perc, Ext], No Dev, [Dx, NQ]
0CBP[0,3,X]ZX	Exc/Tonsils, [Opn, Perc, Ext]
0CBQ[0,3,X]ZX	Exc/Adenoids, [Opn, Perc, Ext]
0CC0[0,3]ZZ	Extir/Upr Lip, [Opn, Perc]
0CC1[0,3]ZZ	Extir/Lwr Lip, [Opn, Perc]
0CC4[0,3]ZZ	Extir/Buccal Mucosa, [Opn, Perc]
0CCN[0,3]ZZ	Extir/Uvula, [Opn, Perc]
0CDT[0,3,4,7,8]ZZ	Extract/Vocal Cord, Rt, [Opn, Perc, Perc Endo, Via Natrl or Artfcl Opng, Via Natrl or Artfcl Opng Endo]
0CDV[0,3,4,7,8]ZZ	Extract/Vocal Cord, Lt, [Opn, Perc, Perc Endo, Via Natrl or Artfcl Opng, Via Natrl or Artfcl Opng Endo]
0CH7[0,3,X]1Z	Insert/Tongue, [Opn, Perc, Ext], Radioact Elmt, NQ
0CM00ZZ	Reattach of Upr Lip, Opn Appr
0CM10ZZ	Reattach of Lwr Lip, Opn Appr
0CM30ZZ	Reattach of Soft Palate, Opn Appr
0CMN0ZZ	Reattach of Uvula, Opn Appr
0CN2[0,3,X]ZZ	Rls/Hard Palate, [Opn, Perc, Ext]
0CN3[0,3,X]ZZ	Rls/Soft Palate, [Opn, Perc, Ext]
0CN4[0,3,X]ZZ	Rls/Buccal Mucosa, [Opn, Perc, Ext]
0CNN[0,3,X]ZZ	Rls/Uvula, [Opn, Perc, Ext]
0CPS[0,3,7,8]JZ	Rmvl/Larynx, [Opn, Perc, Via Natrl or Artfcl Opng, Via Natrl or Artfcl Opng Endo], Synth Sub, NQ
0CPY[0,3][0,1,7,D,J,K]Z	Rmvl/Mouth and Throat, [Opn, Perc], [Drain Dev, Radioact Elmt, Auto Tissue Sub, Intralum Dev, Synth Sub, Nonauto Tissue Sub], NQ
0CQ0[0,3]ZZ	Rpr/Upr Lip, [Opn, Perc]

0CQ1[0,3]ZZ	Rpr/Lwr Lip, [Opn, Perc]
0CQ4[0,3,X]ZZ	Rpr/Buccal Mucosa, [Opn, Perc, Ext]
0CQN[0,3,X]ZZ	Rpr/Uvula, [Opn, Perc, Ext]
0CR0[0,3,X][7,J,K]Z	Replace/Upr Lip, [Opn, Perc, Ext], [Auto Tissue Sub, Synth Sub, Nonauto Tissue Sub], NQ
0CR1[0,3,X][7,J,K]Z	Replace/Lwr Lip, [Opn, Perc, Ext], [Auto Tissue Sub, Synth Sub, Nonauto Tissue Sub], NQ
0CR4[0,3,X][7,J,K]Z	Replace/Buccal Mucosa, [Opn, Perc, Ext], [Auto Tissue Sub, Synth Sub, Nonauto Tissue Sub], NQ
0CRM[0,7,8][7,J,K]Z	Replace/Pharynx, [Opn, Via Natrl or Artfcl Opng, Via Natrl or Artfcl Opng Endo], [Auto Tissue Sub, Synth Sub, Nonauto Tissue Sub], NQ
0CRN[0,3,X][7,J,K]Z	Replace/Uvula, [Opn, Perc, Ext], [Auto Tissue Sub, Synth Sub, Nonauto Tissue Sub], NQ
0CRT[0,7,8]JZ	Replace/Vocal Cord, Rt, [Opn, Via Natrl or Artfcl Opng, Via Natrl or Artfcl Opng Endo], Synth Sub, NQ
0CRV87Z	Replace of Lt Vocal Cord with Autol Sub, Endo
0CRV[0,7]JZ	Replace/Vocal Cord, Lt, [Opn, Via Natrl or Artfcl Opng], Synth Sub, NQ
0CS0[0,X]ZZ	Repos/Upr Lip, [Opn, Ext]
0CS1[0,X]ZZ	Repos/Lwr Lip, [Opn, Ext]
0CSN[0,X]ZZ	Repos/Uvula, [Opn, Ext]
0CT0[0,X]ZZ	Resect/Upr Lip, [Opn, Ext]
0CT1[0,X]ZZ	Resect/Lwr Lip, [Opn, Ext]
0CT2[0,X]ZZ	Resect/Hard Palate, [Opn, Ext]
0CT3[0,X]ZZ	Resect/Soft Palate, [Opn, Ext]
0CT80ZZ	Resect of Rt Parotid Gland, Opn Appr
0CT90ZZ	Resect of Lt Parotid Gland, Opn Appr
0CTB0ZZ	Resect of Rt Parotid Duct, Opn Appr
0CTC0ZZ	Resect of Lt Parotid Duct, Opn Appr
0CTD0ZZ	Resect of Rt Sublingual Gland, Opn Appr
0CTF0ZZ	Resect of Lt Sublingual Gland, Opn Appr
0CTG0ZZ	Resect of Rt Submaxillary Gland, Opn Appr
0CTH0ZZ	Resect of Lt Submaxillary Gland, Opn Appr
0CTJ0ZZ	Resect of Minor Salivary Gland, Opn Appr
0CTN[0,X]ZZ	Resect/Uvula, [Opn, Ext]
0CTP[0,X]ZZ	Resect/Tonsils, [Opn, Ext]
0CU0[0,3,X][7,J,K]Z	Supl/Upr Lip, [Opn, Perc, Ext], [Auto Tissue Sub, Synth Sub, Nonauto Tissue Sub], NQ
0CU1[0,3,X][7,J,K]Z	Supl/Lwr Lip, [Opn, Perc, Ext], [Auto Tissue Sub, Synth Sub, Nonauto Tissue Sub], NQ
0CU4[0,3,X][7,J,K]Z	Supl/Buccal Mucosa, [Opn, Perc, Ext], [Auto Tissue Sub, Synth Sub, Nonauto Tissue Sub], NQ
0CUM[0,7,8][7,J,K]Z	Supl/Pharynx, [Opn, Via Natrl or Artfcl Opng, Via Natrl or Artfcl Opng Endo], [Auto Tissue Sub, Synth Sub, Nonauto Tissue Sub], NQ
0CUN[0,3,X][7,J,K]Z	Supl/Uvula, [Opn, Perc, Ext], [Auto Tissue Sub, Synth Sub, Nonauto Tissue Sub], NQ
0CWY37Z	Rev of Autol Sub in Mouth/Throat, Perc Appr
0CWY[0,3][0,1,D,J,K]Z	Rev/Mouth and Throat, [Opn, Perc], [Drain Dev, Radioact Elmt, Intralum Dev, Synth Sub, Nonauto Tissue Sub], NQ
0CX0[0,X]ZZ	Transfer/Upr Lip, [Opn, Ext]
0CX1[0,X]ZZ	Transfer/Lwr Lip, [Opn, Ext]
0CX3[0,X]ZZ	Transfer/Soft Palate, [Opn, Ext]
0CX4[0,X]ZZ	Transfer/Buccal Mucosa, [Opn, Ext]
0CX5[0,X]ZZ	Transfer/Upr Gingiva, [Opn, Ext]
0CX6[0,X]ZZ	Transfer/Lwr Gingiva, [Opn, Ext]
0D56[0,3,7]ZZ	Destr/Stomach, [Opn, Perc, Via Natrl or Artfcl Opng]
0D57[0,3,7]ZZ	Destr/Stomach, Pylorus, [Opn, Perc, Via Natrl or Artfcl Opng]
0D58[0,3,4,7,8]ZZ	Destr/Sm Intestine, [Opn, Perc, Perc Endo, Via Natrl or Artfcl Opng, Via Natrl or Artfcl Opng Endo]
0D59[0,3,7]ZZ	Destr/Duodenum, [Opn, Perc, Via Natrl or Artfcl Opng]
0D5A[0,3,4,7,8]ZZ	Destr/Jejunum, [Opn, Perc, Perc Endo, Via Natrl or Artfcl Opng, Via Natrl or Artfcl Opng Endo]
0D5B[0,3,4,7,8]ZZ	Destr/Ileum, [Opn, Perc, Perc Endo, Via Natrl or Artfcl Opng, Via Natrl or Artfcl Opng Endo]
0D5C[0,3,4,7,8]ZZ	Destr/Ileocecal Valve, [Opn, Perc, Perc Endo, Via Natrl or Artfcl Opng, Via Natrl or Artfcl Opng Endo]
0D5E[0,3,7]ZZ	Destr/Lg Intestine, [Opn, Perc, Via Natrl or Artfcl Opng]
0D5F[0,3,7]ZZ	Destr/Lg Intestine, Rt, [Opn, Perc, Via Natrl or Artfcl Opng]
0D5G[0,3,7]ZZ	Destr/Lg Intestine, Lt, [Opn, Perc, Via Natrl or Artfcl Opng]
0D5H[0,3,7]ZZ	Destr/Cecum, [Opn, Perc, Via Natrl or Artfcl Opng]
0D5K[0,3,7]ZZ	Destr/Ascending Colon, [Opn, Perc, Via Natrl or Artfcl Opng]
0D5L[0,3,7]ZZ	Destr/Transv Colon, [Opn, Perc, Via Natrl or Artfcl Opng]
0D5M[0,3,7]ZZ	Destr/Descending Colon, [Opn, Perc, Via Natrl or Artfcl Opng]
0D5N[0,3,7]ZZ	Destr/Sigmoid Colon, [Opn, Perc, Via Natrl or Artfcl Opng]
0D5Q[0,3,7,X]ZZ	Destr/Anus, [Opn, Perc, Via Natrl or Artfcl Opng, Ext]
0D5R[0,3]ZZ	Destr/Anal Sphincter, [Opn, Perc]
0D5S[0,3,4]ZZ	Destr/Greater Omentum, [Opn, Perc, Perc Endo]
0D5T[0,3,4]ZZ	Destr/Lesser Omentum, [Opn, Perc, Perc Endo]

T Transfer DRG   **SP** Special Payment   * Code Range   6th and 7th Character of ZZ = No Device, No Qualifier ZX = No Device, Diagnostic

0D5V[0,3,4]ZZ	Destr/Mesentery, [Opn, Perc, Perc Endo]
0D5W[0,3,4]ZZ	Destr/Peritoneum, [Opn, Perc, Perc Endo]
0D8R[0,3]ZZ	Div/Anal Sphincter, [Opn, Perc]
0D960ZX	Drain of Stomach, Opn Appr, Diagnostic
0D970ZX	Drain of Stomach, Pylorus, Opn Appr, Diagnostic
0D9E0ZX	Drain of Large Intestine, Opn Appr, Diagnostic
0D9F0ZX	Drain of Rt Large Intestine, Opn Appr, Diagnostic
0D9G0ZX	Drain of Lt Large Intestine, Opn Appr, Diagnostic
0D9H0ZX	Drain of Cecum, Opn Appr, Diagnostic
0D9K0ZX	Drain of Ascending Colon, Opn Appr, Diagnostic
0D9L0ZX	Drain of Transv Colon, Opn Appr, Diagnostic
0D9M0ZX	Drain of Descending Colon, Opn Appr, Diagnostic
0D9N0ZX	Drain of Sigmoid Colon, Opn Appr, Diagnostic
0D9P0ZX	Drain of Rectum, Opn Appr, Diagnostic
0D9R[0,3,4][0,Z]Z	Drain/Anal Sphincter, [Opn, Perc, Perc Endo], [Drain Dev, No Dev], NQ
0DB60ZX	Exc of Stomach, Opn Appr, Diagnostic
0DB70ZX	Exc of Stomach, Pylorus, Opn Appr, Diagnostic
0DB8[3,7,8]ZZ	Exc/Sm Intestine, [Perc, Via Natrl or Artfcl Opng, Via Natrl or Artfcl Opng Endo]
0DB9[0,3]ZZ	Exc/Duodenum, [Opn, Perc]
0DBA[0,3,4,7,8]ZZ	Exc/Jejunum, [Opn, Perc, Perc Endo, Via Natrl or Artfcl Opng, Via Natrl or Artfcl Opng Endo]
0DBB[0,3,4,7,8]ZZ	Exc/Ileum, [Opn, Perc, Perc Endo, Via Natrl or Artfcl Opng, Via Natrl or Artfcl Opng Endo]
0DBC[0,3,4,7,8]ZZ	Exc/Ileocecal Valve, [Opn, Perc, Perc Endo, Via Natrl or Artfcl Opng, Via Natrl or Artfcl Opng Endo]
0DBE0ZX	Exc of Large Intestine, Opn Appr, Diagnostic
0DBE7ZZ	Exc of Large Intestine, Via Opng
0DBF0ZX	Exc of Rt Large Intestine, Opn Appr, Diagnostic
0DBF7ZZ	Exc of Rt Large Intestine, Via Opng
0DBG0ZX	Exc of Lt Large Intestine, Opn Appr, Diagnostic
0DBG7ZZ	Exc of Lt Large Intestine, Via Opng
0DBH0ZX	Exc of Cecum, Opn Appr, Diagnostic
0DBH7ZZ	Exc of Cecum, Via Natrl or Artfcl Opng
0DBK0ZX	Exc of Ascending Colon, Opn Appr, Diagnostic
0DBK7ZZ	Exc of Ascending Colon, Via Opng
0DBL0ZX	Exc of Transv Colon, Opn Appr, Diagnostic
0DBL7ZZ	Exc of Transv Colon, Via Opng
0DBM0ZX	Exc of Descending Colon, Opn Appr, Diagnostic
0DBM7ZZ	Exc of Descending Colon, Via Opng
0DBN0ZX	Exc of Sigmoid Colon, Opn Appr, Diagnostic
0DBN7ZZ	Exc of Sigmoid Colon, Via Natrl or Artfcl Opng
0DBP0ZX	Exc of Rectum, Opn Appr, Diagnostic
0DBP[3,7]ZZ	Exc/Rectum, [Perc, Via Natrl or Artfcl Opng]
0DBQ[0,3,4,7,8,X]ZZ	Exc/Anus, [Opn, Perc, Perc Endo, Via Natrl or Artfcl Opng, Via Natrl or Artfcl Opng Endo, Ext]
0DBR[0,3,4]ZZ	Exc/Anal Sphincter, [Opn, Perc, Perc Endo]
0DBS[0,3,4]ZZ	Exc/Greater Omentum, [Opn, Perc, Perc Endo]
0DBT[0,3,4]ZZ	Exc/Lesser Omentum, [Opn, Perc, Perc Endo]
0DBV[0,3,4]ZZ	Exc/Mesentery, [Opn, Perc, Perc Endo]
0DBW[0,3,4]ZZ	Exc/Peritoneum, [Opn, Perc, Perc Endo]
0DCR[0,3,4]ZZ	Extir/Anal Sphincter, [Opn, Perc, Perc Endo]
0DH5[0,3,4,7,8]1Z	Insert/Esophagus, [Opn, Perc, Perc Endo, Via Natrl or Artfcl Opng, Via Natrl or Artfcl Opng Endo], Radioact Elmt, NQ
0DHP[0,3,4,7,8]1Z	Insert/Rectum, [Opn, Perc, Perc Endo, Via Natrl or Artfcl Opng, Via Natrl or Artfcl Opng Endo], Radioact Elmt, NQ
0DJD4ZZ	Inspect of Lwr Intestinal Tract, Perc Endo Appr
0DJU[3,4]ZZ	Inspect/Omentum, [Perc, Perc Endo]
0DJV[3,4]ZZ	Inspect/Mesentery, [Perc, Perc Endo]
0DJW[3,4]ZZ	Inspect/Peritoneum, [Perc, Perc Endo]
0DNP[0,3,4,7,8]ZZ	Rls/Rectum, [Opn, Perc, Perc Endo, Via Natrl or Artfcl Opng, Via Natrl or Artfcl Opng Endo]
0DNR[0,3,4]ZZ	Rls/Anal Sphincter, [Opn, Perc, Perc Endo]
0DP64[3,C]Z	Rmvl/Stomach, Perc Endo, [Inf Dev, Extralum Dev], NQ
0DQ64ZZ	Repair Stomach, Perc Endo Appr
0DQR[0,3,4]ZZ	Rpr/Anal Sphincter, [Opn, Perc, Perc Endo]
0DQW[0,3,4]ZZ	Rpr/Peritoneum, [Opn, Perc, Perc Endo]
0DRR[0,4][7,J,K]Z	Replace/Anal Sphincter, [Opn, Perc Endo], [Auto Tissue Sub, Synth Sub, Nonauto Tissue Sub], NQ
0DTQ[0,4,7,8]ZZ	Resect/Anus, [Opn, Perc Endo, Via Natrl or Artfcl Opng, Via Natrl or Artfcl Opng Endo]
0DTR[0,4]ZZ	Resect/Anal Sphincter, [Opn, Perc Endo]
0DTS[0,4]ZZ	Resect/Greater Omentum, [Opn, Perc Endo]
0DTT[0,4]ZZ	Resect/Lesser Omentum, [Opn, Perc Endo]
0DUR[0,4][7,J,K]Z	Supl/Anal Sphincter, [Opn, Perc Endo], [Auto Tissue Sub, Synth Sub, Nonauto Tissue Sub], NQ
0DV44[C,D,Z]Z	Restrict/Esophagogastric Junction, Perc Endo, [Extralum Dev, Intralum Dev, No Dev], NQ
0DV64CZ	Restrict of Stomach with Extralum Dev, Perc Endo Appr
0DW64[3,C]Z	Rev/Stomach, Perc Endo, [Inf Dev, Extralum Dev], NQ
0FHB[0,3,4,7,8]1Z	Insert/Hepatobiliary Duct, [Opn, Perc, Perc Endo, Via Natrl or Artfcl Opng, Via Natrl or Artfcl Opng Endo], Radioact Elmt, NQ
0FHD[0,3,4,7,8]1Z	Insert/Pancreatic Duct, [Opn, Perc, Perc Endo, Via Natrl or Artfcl Opng, Via Natrl or Artfcl Opng Endo], Radioact Elmt, NQ
0FJ04ZZ	Inspect of Liver, Perc Endo Appr
0FJ44ZZ	Inspect of Gallbladder, Perc Endo Appr
0FJD4ZZ	Inspect of Pancreatic Duct, Perc Endo Appr
0FJG4ZZ	Inspect of Pancreas, Perc Endo Appr
0FL50[C,D,Z]Z	Occlsn/Hepatic Duct, Rt, Opn, [Extralum Dev, Intralum Dev, No Dev], NQ
0FL60[C,D,Z]Z	Occlsn/Hepatic Duct, Lt, Opn, [Extralum Dev, Intralum Dev, No Dev], NQ
0FL80[C,D,Z]Z	Occlsn/Cystic Duct, Opn, [Extralum Dev, Intralum Dev, No Dev], NQ
0FL90[C,D,Z]Z	Occlsn/Common Bile Duct, Opn, [Extralum Dev, Intralum Dev, No Dev], NQ
0FM40ZZ	Reattach of Gallbladder, Opn Appr
0FR5[0,4]JZ	Replace/Hepatic Duct, Rt, [Opn, Perc Endo], Synth Sub, NQ
0FR6[0,4]JZ	Replace/Hepatic Duct, Lt, [Opn, Perc Endo], Synth Sub, NQ
0FR8[0,4]JZ	Replace/Cystic Duct, [Opn, Perc Endo], Synth Sub, NQ
0FR9[0,4]JZ	Replace/Common Bile Duct, [Opn, Perc Endo], Synth Sub, NQ
0FS4[0,4]ZZ	Repos/Gallbladder, [Opn, Perc Endo]
0FT44ZZ	Resect of Gallbladder, Perc Endo Appr
0FV50[C,D,Z]Z	Restrict/Hepatic Duct, Rt, Opn, [Extralum Dev, Intralum Dev, No Dev], NQ
0FV60[C,D,Z]Z	Restrict/Hepatic Duct, Lt, Opn, [Extralum Dev, Intralum Dev, No Dev], NQ
0FV80[C,D,Z]Z	Restrict/Cystic Duct, Opn, [Extralum Dev, Intralum Dev, No Dev], NQ
0FV90[C,D,Z]Z	Restrict/Common Bile Duct, Opn, [Extralum Dev, Intralum Dev, No Dev], NQ
0H0T[0,3,X][7,J,K]Z	Alter/Breast, Rt, [Opn, Perc, Ext], [Auto Tissue Sub, Synth Sub, Nonauto Tissue Sub], NQ
0H0U[0,3,X][7,J,K]Z	Alter/Breast, Lt, [Opn, Perc, Ext], [Auto Tissue Sub, Synth Sub, Nonauto Tissue Sub], NQ
0H0V[0,3,X][7,J,K]Z	Alter/Breast, Bilat, [Opn, Perc, Ext], [Auto Tissue Sub, Synth Sub, Nonauto Tissue Sub], NQ
0H5T[0,3,7,8,X]ZZ	Destr/Breast, Rt, [Opn, Perc, Via Natrl or Artfcl Opng, Via Natrl or Artfcl Opng Endo, Ext]
0H5U[0,3,7,8,X]ZZ	Destr/Breast, Lt, [Opn, Perc, Via Natrl or Artfcl Opng, Via Natrl or Artfcl Opng Endo, Ext]
0H5V[0,3,7,8,X]ZZ	Destr/Breast, Bilat, [Opn, Perc, Via Natrl or Artfcl Opng, Via Natrl or Artfcl Opng Endo, Ext]
0H89XZZ	Div of Perineum Skin, Ext Appr
0H99X[0,Z]Z	Drain/Skin, Perineum, Ext, [Drain Dev, No Dev], NQ
0H9T0ZX	Drain of Rt Breast, Opn Appr, Diagnostic
0H9U0ZX	Drain of Lt Breast, Opn Appr, Diagnostic
0H9V0ZX	Drain of Bilat Breast, Opn Appr, Diagnostic
0H9W0ZX	Drain of Rt Nipple, Opn Appr, Diagnostic
0H9X0ZX	Drain of Lt Nipple, Opn Appr, Diagnostic
0HBT0ZX	Exc of Rt Breast, Opn Appr, Diagnostic
0HBT[0,3,7,8,X]ZZ	Exc/Breast, Rt, [Opn, Perc, Via Natrl or Artfcl Opng, Via Natrl or Artfcl Opng Endo, Ext]
0HBU0ZX	Exc of Lt Breast, Opn Appr, Diagnostic
0HBU[0,3,7,8,X]ZZ	Exc/Breast, Lt, [Opn, Perc, Via Natrl or Artfcl Opng, Via Natrl or Artfcl Opng Endo, Ext]
0HBV0ZX	Exc of Bilat Breast, Opn Appr, Diagnostic
0HBV[0,3,7,8,X]ZZ	Exc/Breast, Bilat, [Opn, Perc, Via Natrl or Artfcl Opng, Via Natrl or Artfcl Opng Endo, Ext]
0HBW0ZX	Exc of Rt Nipple, Opn Appr, Diagnostic
0HBX0ZX	Exc of Lt Nipple, Opn Appr, Diagnostic
0HBY0ZX	Exc of Supernumerary Breast, Opn Appr, Diagnostic
0HHT[0,3,7,8,X]1Z	Insert/Breast, Rt, [Opn, Perc, Via Natrl or Artfcl Opng, Via Natrl or Artfcl Opng Endo, Ext], Radioact Elmt, NQ
0HHT[0,3,7,8]NZ	Insert/Breast, Rt, [Opn, Perc, Via Natrl or Artfcl Opng, Via Natrl or Artfcl Opng Endo], Tissue Expander, NQ
0HHU[0,3,7,8,X]1Z	Insert/Breast, Lt, [Opn, Perc, Via Natrl or Artfcl Opng, Via Natrl or Artfcl Opng Endo, Ext], Radioact Elmt, NQ
0HHU[0,3,7,8]NZ	Insert/Breast, Lt, [Opn, Perc, Via Natrl or Artfcl Opng, Via Natrl or Artfcl Opng Endo], Tissue Expander, NQ
0HHV[0,3,7,8,X]1Z	Insert/Breast, Bilat, [Opn, Perc, Via Natrl or Artfcl Opng, Via Natrl or Artfcl Opng Endo, Ext], Radioact Elmt, NQ
0HHV[0,3,7,8]NZ	Insert/Breast, Bilat, [Opn, Perc, Via Natrl or Artfcl Opng, Via Natrl or Artfcl Opng Endo], Tissue Expander, NQ
0HHW[0,3,7,8,X]1Z	Insert/Nipple, Rt, [Opn, Perc, Via Natrl or Artfcl Opng, Via Natrl or Artfcl Opng Endo, Ext], Radioact Elmt, NQ
0HHW[0,3,7,8]NZ	Insert/Nipple, Rt, [Opn, Perc, Via Natrl or Artfcl Opng, Via Natrl or Artfcl Opng Endo], Tissue Expander, NQ

Surgical **Medical** **CC Indicator** **MCC Indicator** **Procedure Proxy** **PDxMCC** PDx acts as own MCC **PDxCC** PDx acts as own CC

DRGs Associated with All MDCs—SURGICAL

ØHHX[Ø,3,7,8,X]1Z	Insert/Nipple, Lt, [Opn, Perc, Via Natrl or Artfcl Opng, Via Natrl or Artfcl Opng Endo], Radioact Elmt, NQ
ØHHX[Ø,3,7,8]NZ	Insert/Nipple, Lt, [Opn, Perc, Via Natrl or Artfcl Opng, Via Natrl or Artfcl Opng Endo], Tissue Expander, NQ
ØHM1XZZ	Reattach of Face Skin, Ext Appr
ØHM2XZZ	Reattach of Rt Ear Skin, Ext Appr
ØHM3XZZ	Reattach of Lt Ear Skin, Ext Appr
ØHM4XZZ	Reattach of Neck Skin, Ext Appr
ØHM5XZZ	Reattach of Chest Skin, Ext Appr
ØHM6XZZ	Reattach of Back Skin, Ext Appr
ØHM7XZZ	Reattach of Abd Skin, Ext Appr
ØHM8XZZ	Reattach of Buttock Skin, Ext Appr
ØHM9XZZ	Reattach of Perineum Skin, Ext Appr
ØHMAXZZ	Reattach of Genitalia Skin, Ext Appr
ØHMBXZZ	Reattach of Rt Upr Arm Skin, Ext Appr
ØHMCXZZ	Reattach of Lt Upr Arm Skin, Ext Appr
ØHMDXZZ	Reattach of Rt Lwr Arm Skin, Ext Appr
ØHMEXZZ	Reattach of Lt Lwr Arm Skin, Ext Appr
ØHMFXZZ	Reattach of Rt Hand Skin, Ext Appr
ØHMGXZZ	Reattach of Lt Hand Skin, Ext Appr
ØHMHXZZ	Reattach of Rt Upr Leg Skin, Ext Appr
ØHMJXZZ	Reattach of Lt Upr Leg Skin, Ext Appr
ØHMKXZZ	Reattach of Rt Lwr Leg Skin, Ext Appr
ØHMLXZZ	Reattach of Lt Lwr Leg Skin, Ext Appr
ØHMMXZZ	Reattach of Rt Foot Skin, Ext Appr
ØHMNXZZ	Reattach of Lt Foot Skin, Ext Appr
ØHNØXZZ	Rls Scalp Skin, Ext Appr
ØHN1XZZ	Rls Face Skin, Ext Appr
ØHN2XZZ	Rls Rt Ear Skin, Ext Appr
ØHN3XZZ	Rls Lt Ear Skin, Ext Appr
ØHN4XZZ	Rls Neck Skin, Ext Appr
ØHN5XZZ	Rls Chest Skin, Ext Appr
ØHN6XZZ	Rls Back Skin, Ext Appr
ØHN7XZZ	Rls Abd Skin, Ext Appr
ØHN8XZZ	Rls Buttock Skin, Ext Appr
ØHN9XZZ	Rls Perineum Skin, Ext Appr
ØHNAXZZ	Rls Genitalia Skin, Ext Appr
ØHNBXZZ	Rls Rt Upr Arm Skin, Ext Appr
ØHNCXZZ	Rls Lt Upr Arm Skin, Ext Appr
ØHNDXZZ	Rls Rt Lwr Arm Skin, Ext Appr
ØHNEXZZ	Rls Lt Lwr Arm Skin, Ext Appr
ØHNFXZZ	Rls Rt Hand Skin, Ext Appr
ØHNGXZZ	Rls Lt Hand Skin, Ext Appr
ØHNHXZZ	Rls Rt Upr Leg Skin, Ext Appr
ØHNJXZZ	Rls Lt Upr Leg Skin, Ext Appr
ØHNKXZZ	Rls Rt Lwr Leg Skin, Ext Appr
ØHNLXZZ	Rls Lt Lwr Leg Skin, Ext Appr
ØHNMXZZ	Rls Rt Foot Skin, Ext Appr
ØHNNXZZ	Rls Lt Foot Skin, Ext Appr
ØHNQXZZ	Rls Finger Nail, Ext Appr
ØHNRXZZ	Rls Toe Nail, Ext Appr
ØHPT[Ø,3][J,N]Z	Rmvl/Breast, Rt, [Opn, Perc], [Synth Sub, Tissue Expander], NQ
ØHPU[Ø,3][J,N]Z	Rmvl/Breast, Lt, [Opn, Perc], [Synth Sub, Tissue Expander], NQ
ØHR2XJZ	Replace of Rt Ear Skin with Synth Sub, Extern Appr
ØHR2X[7,J,K][3,4]	Replace/Skin, Rt Ear, Ext, [Auto Tissue Sub, Synth Sub, Nonauto Tissue Sub], [Full Thickness, Partial Thickness]
ØHR3XJZ	Replace of Lt Ear Skin with Synth Sub, Extern Appr
ØHR3X[7,J,K][3,4]	Replace/Skin, Lt Ear, Ext, [Auto Tissue Sub, Synth Sub, Nonauto Tissue Sub], [Full Thickness, Partial Thickness]
ØHR9XJZ	Replace of Perineum Skin with Synth Sub, Extern Appr
ØHR9X[7,J,K][3,4]	Replace/Skin, Perineum, Ext, [Auto Tissue Sub, Synth Sub, Nonauto Tissue Sub], [Full Thickness, Partial Thickness]
ØHRFX74	Replace Rt Hand Skin w Autol Sub, Part Thick, Extern
ØHRGX74	Replace Lt Hand Skin w Autol Sub, Part Thick, Extern
ØHRSX[J,K]Z	Replace/Hair, Ext, [Synth Sub, Nonauto Tissue Sub], NQ
ØHWT[Ø,3]JZ	Rev/Breast, Rt, [Opn, Perc], Synth Sub, NQ
ØHWU[Ø,3]JZ	Rev/Breast, Lt, [Opn, Perc], Synth Sub, NQ
ØHX2XZZ	Transfer Rt Ear Skin, Ext Appr
ØHX3XZZ	Transfer Lt Ear Skin, Ext Appr
ØJØ1[Ø,3]ZZ	Alter/SQ Tissue & Fascia, Face, [Opn, Perc]
ØJØ4[Ø,3]ZZ	Alter/SQ Tissue & Fascia, Ant Neck, [Opn, Perc]
ØJØ5[Ø,3]ZZ	Alter/SQ Tissue & Fascia, Post Neck, [Opn, Perc]
ØJØ6[Ø,3]ZZ	Alter/SQ Tissue & Fascia, Chest, [Opn, Perc]
ØJØ7[Ø,3]ZZ	Alter/SQ Tissue & Fascia, Back, [Opn, Perc]
ØJØ8[Ø,3]ZZ	Alter/SQ Tissue & Fascia, Abd, [Opn, Perc]
ØJØ9[Ø,3]ZZ	Alter/SQ Tissue & Fascia, Buttock, [Opn, Perc]
ØJØD[Ø,3]ZZ	Alter/SQ Tissue & Fascia, Rt Upr Arm, [Opn, Perc]
ØJØF[Ø,3]ZZ	Alter/SQ Tissue & Fascia, Lt Upr Arm, [Opn, Perc]
ØJØG[Ø,3]ZZ	Alter/SQ Tissue & Fascia, Rt Lwr Arm, [Opn, Perc]
ØJØH[Ø,3]ZZ	Alter/SQ Tissue & Fascia, Lt Lwr Arm, [Opn, Perc]

ØJØL[Ø,3]ZZ	Alter/SQ Tissue & Fascia, Rt Upr Leg, [Opn, Perc]
ØJØM[Ø,3]ZZ	Alter/SQ Tissue & Fascia, Lt Upr Leg, [Opn, Perc]
ØJØN[Ø,3]ZZ	Alter/SQ Tissue & Fascia, Rt Lwr Leg, [Opn, Perc]
ØJØP[Ø,3]ZZ	Alter/SQ Tissue & Fascia, Lt Lwr Leg, [Opn, Perc]
ØJ81[Ø,3]ZZ	Div/SQ Tissue & Fascia, Face, [Opn, Perc]
ØJ8J[Ø,3]ZZ	Div/SQ Tissue & Fascia, Rt Hand, [Opn, Perc]
ØJ8K[Ø,3]ZZ	Div/SQ Tissue & Fascia, Lt Hand, [Opn, Perc]
ØJ9ØØZZ	Drain of Scalp SQ/Fascia, Opn Appr
ØJ94ØZZ	Drain of Ant Neck SQ/Fascia, Opn Appr
ØJ95ØZZ	Drain of Post Neck SQ/Fascia, Opn Appr
ØJ96ØZZ	Drain of Chest SQ/Fascia, Opn Appr
ØJ97ØZZ	Drain of Back SQ/Fascia, Opn Appr
ØJ98ØZZ	Drain of Abd SQ/Fascia, Opn Appr
ØJ99ØZZ	Drain of Buttock SQ/Fascia, Opn Appr
ØJ9BØZZ	Drain of Perineum SQ/Fascia, Opn Appr
ØJ9CØZZ	Drain of Pelvic SQ/Fascia, Opn Appr
ØJ9DØZZ	Drain of Rt Up Arm SQ/Fascia, Opn Appr
ØJ9FØZZ	Drain of Lt Up Arm SQ/Fascia, Opn Appr
ØJ9GØZZ	Drain of Rt Low Arm SQ/Fascia, Opn Appr
ØJ9HØZZ	Drain of Lt Low Arm SQ/Fascia, Opn Appr
ØJ9J3ZZ	Drain of Rt Hand SQ/Fascia, Perc Appr
ØJ9J[Ø,3]ØZ	Drain/SQ Tissue & Fascia, Rt Hand, [Opn, Perc], Drain Dev, NQ
ØJ9J[Ø,3]ZZ	Drain/SQ Tissue & Fascia, Rt Hand, [Opn, Perc]
ØJ9KØØZ	Drain of Lt Hand SQ/Fascia with Drain Dev, Opn Appr
ØJ9KØZZ	Drain of Lt Hand SQ/Fascia, Opn Appr
ØJ9K3ØZ	Drain of Lt Hand SQ/Fascia with Drain Dev, Perc Appr
ØJ9K3ZZ	Drain of Lt Hand SQ/Fascia, Perc Appr
ØJ9LØZZ	Drain of Rt Up Leg SQ/Fascia, Opn Appr
ØJ9MØZZ	Drain of Lt Up Leg SQ/Fascia, Opn Appr
ØJ9NØZZ	Drain of Rt Low Leg SQ/Fascia, Opn Appr
ØJ9PØZZ	Drain of Lt Low Leg SQ/Fascia, Opn Appr
ØJ9QØZZ	Drain of Rt Foot SQ/Fascia, Opn Appr
ØJ9RØZZ	Drain of Lt Foot SQ/Fascia, Opn Appr
ØJBØ3ZZ	Exc of Scalp SQ/Fascia, Perc Appr
ØJB13ZZ	Exc of Face SQ/Fascia, Perc Appr
ØJB43ZZ	Exc of Ant Neck SQ/Fascia, Perc Appr
ØJB53ZZ	Exc of Post Neck SQ/Fascia, Perc Appr
ØJB63ZZ	Exc of Chest SQ/Fascia, Perc Appr
ØJB73ZZ	Exc of Back SQ/Fascia, Perc Appr
ØJB83ZZ	Exc of Abd SQ/Fascia, Perc Appr
ØJB93ZZ	Exc of Buttock SQ/Fascia, Perc Appr
ØJBB3ZZ	Exc of Perineum SQ/Fascia, Perc Appr
ØJBC3ZZ	Exc of Pelvic SQ/Fascia, Perc Appr
ØJBD3ZZ	Exc of Rt Up Arm SQ/Fascia, Perc Appr
ØJBF3ZZ	Exc of Lt Up Arm SQ/Fascia, Perc Appr
ØJBG3ZZ	Exc of Rt Low Arm SQ/Fascia, Perc Appr
ØJBH3ZZ	Exc of Lt Low Arm SQ/Fascia, Perc Appr
ØJBJ[Ø,3]ZZ	Exc/SQ Tissue & Fascia, Rt Hand, [Opn, Perc]
ØJBK[Ø,3]ZZ	Exc/SQ Tissue & Fascia, Lt Hand, [Opn, Perc]
ØJBL3ZZ	Exc of Rt Up Leg SQ/Fascia, Perc Appr
ØJBM3ZZ	Exc of Lt Up Leg SQ/Fascia, Perc Appr
ØJBN3ZZ	Exc of Rt Low Leg SQ/Fascia, Perc Appr
ØJBP3ZZ	Exc of Lt Low Leg SQ/Fascia, Perc Appr
ØJBQ3ZZ	Exc of Rt Foot SQ/Fascia, Perc Appr
ØJBR3ZZ	Exc of Lt Foot SQ/Fascia, Perc Appr
ØJHS[Ø,3]1Z	Insert/SQ Tissue & Fascia, Head and Neck, [Opn, Perc], Radioact Elmt, NQ
ØJHT[Ø,3]1Z	Insert/SQ Tissue & Fascia, Trunk, [Opn, Perc], Radioact Elmt, NQ
ØJHV[Ø,3]1Z	Insert/SQ Tissue & Fascia, Upr Extr, [Opn, Perc], Radioact Elmt, NQ
ØJHW[Ø,3]1Z	Insert/SQ Tissue & Fascia, Lwr Extr, [Opn, Perc], Radioact Elmt, NQ
ØJPT[Ø,3]PZ	Rmvl/SQ Tissue & Fascia, Trunk, [Opn, Perc], Cardiac Rhythm Related Dev, NQ
ØJQ1[Ø,3]ZZ	Rpr/SQ Tissue & Fascia, Face, [Opn, Perc]
ØJQ4[Ø,3]ZZ	Rpr/SQ Tissue & Fascia, Ant Neck, [Opn, Perc]
ØJQ5[Ø,3]ZZ	Rpr/SQ Tissue & Fascia, Post Neck, [Opn, Perc]
ØJQ6[Ø,3]ZZ	Rpr/SQ Tissue & Fascia, Chest, [Opn, Perc]
ØJQ7[Ø,3]ZZ	Rpr/SQ Tissue & Fascia, Back, [Opn, Perc]
ØJQ8[Ø,3]ZZ	Rpr/SQ Tissue & Fascia, Abd, [Opn, Perc]
ØJQ9[Ø,3]ZZ	Rpr/SQ Tissue & Fascia, Buttock, [Opn, Perc]
ØJQB[Ø,3]ZZ	Rpr/SQ Tissue & Fascia, Perineum, [Opn, Perc]
ØJQD[Ø,3]ZZ	Rpr/SQ Tissue & Fascia, Rt Upr Arm, [Opn, Perc]
ØJQF[Ø,3]ZZ	Rpr/SQ Tissue & Fascia, Lt Upr Arm, [Opn, Perc]
ØJQG[Ø,3]ZZ	Rpr/SQ Tissue & Fascia, Rt Lwr Arm, [Opn, Perc]
ØJQH[Ø,3]ZZ	Rpr/SQ Tissue & Fascia, Lt Lwr Arm, [Opn, Perc]
ØJQJ[Ø,3]ZZ	Rpr/SQ Tissue & Fascia, Rt Hand, [Opn, Perc]
ØJQK[Ø,3]ZZ	Rpr/SQ Tissue & Fascia, Lt Hand, [Opn, Perc]
ØJQL[Ø,3]ZZ	Rpr/SQ Tissue & Fascia, Rt Upr Leg, [Opn, Perc]

T **Transfer DRG**   SP **Special Payment**   * **Code Range**   **6th and 7th Character of ZZ = No Device, No Qualifier ZX = No Device, Diagnostic**

Code	Description
ØJQM[Ø,3]ZZ	Rpr/SQ Tissue & Fascia, Lt Upr Leg, [Opn, Perc]
ØJQN[Ø,3]ZZ	Rpr/SQ Tissue & Fascia, Rt Lwr Leg, [Opn, Perc]
ØJQP[Ø,3]ZZ	Rpr/SQ Tissue & Fascia, Lt Lwr Leg, [Opn, Perc]
ØJQQ[Ø,3]ZZ	Rpr/SQ Tissue & Fascia, Rt Foot, [Opn, Perc]
ØJQR[Ø,3]ZZ	Rpr/SQ Tissue & Fascia, Lt Foot, [Opn, Perc]
ØK5Ø[Ø,3,4]ZZ	Destr/Head Muscle, [Opn, Perc, Perc Endo]
ØK51[Ø,3,4]ZZ	Destr/Facial Muscle, [Opn, Perc, Perc Endo]
ØK52[Ø,3,4]ZZ	Destr/Neck Muscle, Rt, [Opn, Perc, Perc Endo]
ØK53[Ø,3,4]ZZ	Destr/Neck Muscle, Lt, [Opn, Perc, Perc Endo]
ØK54[Ø,3,4]ZZ	Destr/Tongue, Palate, Pharynx Muscle, [Opn, Perc, Perc Endo]
ØK55[Ø,3,4]ZZ	Destr/Shldr Muscle, Rt, [Opn, Perc, Perc Endo]
ØK56[Ø,3,4]ZZ	Destr/Shldr Muscle, Lt, [Opn, Perc, Perc Endo]
ØK57[Ø,3,4]ZZ	Destr/Upr Arm Muscle, Rt, [Opn, Perc, Perc Endo]
ØK58[Ø,3,4]ZZ	Destr/Upr Arm Muscle, Lt, [Opn, Perc, Perc Endo]
ØK59[Ø,3,4]ZZ	Destr/Lwr Arm and Wrist Muscle, Rt, [Opn, Perc, Perc Endo]
ØK5B[Ø,3,4]ZZ	Destr/Lwr Arm and Wrist Muscle, Lt, [Opn, Perc, Perc Endo]
ØK5F[Ø,3,4]ZZ	Destr/Trunk Muscle, Rt, [Opn, Perc, Perc Endo]
ØK5G[Ø,3,4]ZZ	Destr/Trunk Muscle, Lt, [Opn, Perc, Perc Endo]
ØK5H[Ø,3,4]ZZ	Destr/Thorax Muscle, Rt, [Opn, Perc, Perc Endo]
ØK5J[Ø,3,4]ZZ	Destr/Thorax Muscle, Lt, [Opn, Perc, Perc Endo]
ØK5K[Ø,3,4]ZZ	Destr/Abd Muscle, Rt, [Opn, Perc, Perc Endo]
ØK5L[Ø,3,4]ZZ	Destr/Abd Muscle, Lt, [Opn, Perc, Perc Endo]
ØK5M[Ø,3,4]ZZ	Destr/Perineum Muscle, [Opn, Perc, Perc Endo]
ØK5N[Ø,3,4]ZZ	Destr/Hip Muscle, Rt, [Opn, Perc, Perc Endo]
ØK5P[Ø,3,4]ZZ	Destr/Hip Muscle, Lt, [Opn, Perc, Perc Endo]
ØK5Q[Ø,3,4]ZZ	Destr/Upr Leg Muscle, Rt, [Opn, Perc, Perc Endo]
ØK5R[Ø,3,4]ZZ	Destr/Upr Leg Muscle, Lt, [Opn, Perc, Perc Endo]
ØK5S[Ø,3,4]ZZ	Destr/Lwr Leg Muscle, Rt, [Opn, Perc, Perc Endo]
ØK5T[Ø,3,4]ZZ	Destr/Lwr Leg Muscle, Lt, [Opn, Perc, Perc Endo]
ØK5V[Ø,3,4]ZZ	Destr/Foot Muscle, Rt, [Opn, Perc, Perc Endo]
ØK5W[Ø,3,4]ZZ	Destr/Foot Muscle, Lt, [Opn, Perc, Perc Endo]
ØK9ØØZX	Drain of Head Muscle, Opn Appr, Diagnostic
ØK9Ø[Ø,3,4]ØZ	Drain/Head Muscle, [Opn, Perc, Perc Endo], Drain Dev, NQ
ØK9Ø[Ø,4]ZZ	Drain/Head Muscle, [Opn, Perc Endo]
ØK91ØZX	Drain of Facial Muscle, Opn Appr, Diagnostic
ØK91[Ø,3,4]ØZ	Drain/Facial Muscle, [Opn, Perc, Perc Endo], Drain Dev, NQ
ØK91[Ø,4]ZZ	Drain/Facial Muscle, [Opn, Perc Endo]
ØK92ØZX	Drain of Rt Neck Muscle, Opn Appr, Diagnostic
ØK92[Ø,3,4]ØZ	Drain/Neck Muscle, Rt, [Opn, Perc, Perc Endo], Drain Dev, NQ
ØK92[Ø,4]ZZ	Drain/Neck Muscle, Rt, [Opn, Perc Endo]
ØK93ØZX	Drain of Lt Neck Muscle, Opn Appr, Diagnostic
ØK93[Ø,3,4]ØZ	Drain/Neck Muscle, Lt, [Opn, Perc, Perc Endo], Drain Dev, NQ
ØK93[Ø,4]ZZ	Drain/Neck Muscle, Lt, [Opn, Perc Endo]
ØK94ØZX	Drain of Tongue/Palate/Phar Muscle, Opn Appr, Diagn
ØK94[Ø,3,4]ØZ	Drain/Tongue, Palate, Pharynx Muscle, [Opn, Perc, Perc Endo], Drain Dev, NQ
ØK94[Ø,4]ZZ	Drain/Tongue, Palate, Pharynx Muscle, [Opn, Perc Endo]
ØK95ØZX	Drain of Rt Shldr Muscle, Opn Appr, Diagnostic
ØK95[Ø,3,4]ØZ	Drain/Shldr Muscle, Rt, [Opn, Perc, Perc Endo], Drain Dev, NQ
ØK95[Ø,4]ZZ	Drain/Shldr Muscle, Rt, [Opn, Perc Endo]
ØK96ØZX	Drain of Lt Shldr Muscle, Opn Appr, Diagnostic
ØK96[Ø,3,4]ØZ	Drain/Shldr Muscle, Lt, [Opn, Perc, Perc Endo], Drain Dev, NQ
ØK96[Ø,4]ZZ	Drain/Shldr Muscle, Lt, [Opn, Perc Endo]
ØK97ØZX	Drain of Rt Upr Arm Muscle, Opn Appr, Diagn
ØK97[Ø,3,4]ØZ	Drain/Upr Arm Muscle, Rt, [Opn, Perc, Perc Endo], Drain Dev, NQ
ØK97[Ø,4]ZZ	Drain/Upr Arm Muscle, Rt, [Opn, Perc Endo]
ØK98ØZX	Drain of Lt Upr Arm Muscle, Opn Appr, Diagnostic
ØK98[Ø,3,4]ØZ	Drain/Upr Arm Muscle, Lt, [Opn, Perc, Perc Endo], Drain Dev, NQ
ØK98[Ø,4]ZZ	Drain/Upr Arm Muscle, Lt, [Opn, Perc Endo]
ØK99ØZX	Drain of Rt Low Arm & Wrist Muscle, Opn Appr, Diagn
ØK99[Ø,3,4]ØZ	Drain/Lwr Arm and Wrist Muscle, Rt, [Opn, Perc, Perc Endo], Drain Dev, NQ
ØK99[Ø,4]ZZ	Drain/Lwr Arm and Wrist Muscle, Rt, [Opn, Perc Endo]
ØK9BØZX	Drain of Lt Low Arm & Wrist Muscle, Opn Appr, Diagn
ØK9B[Ø,3,4]ØZ	Drain/Lwr Arm and Wrist Muscle, Lt, [Opn, Perc, Perc Endo], Drain Dev, NQ
ØK9B[Ø,4]ZZ	Drain/Lwr Arm and Wrist Muscle, Lt, [Opn, Perc Endo]
ØK9CØZX	Drain of Rt Hand Muscle, Opn Appr, Diagnostic
ØK9DØZX	Drain of Lt Hand Muscle, Opn Appr, Diagnostic
ØK9FØZX	Drain of Rt Trunk Muscle, Opn Appr, Diagnostic
ØK9F[Ø,3,4]ØZ	Drain/Trunk Muscle, Rt, [Opn, Perc, Perc Endo], Drain Dev, NQ
ØK9F[Ø,4]ZZ	Drain/Trunk Muscle, Rt, [Opn, Perc Endo]
ØK9GØZX	Drain of Lt Trunk Muscle, Opn Appr, Diagnostic
ØK9G[Ø,3,4]ØZ	Drain/Trunk Muscle, Lt, [Opn, Perc, Perc Endo], Drain Dev, NQ
ØK9G[Ø,4]ZZ	Drain/Trunk Muscle, Lt, [Opn, Perc Endo]
ØK9HØZX	Drain of Rt Thorax Muscle, Opn Appr, Diagnostic
ØK9H[Ø,3,4]ØZ	Drain/Thorax Muscle, Rt, [Opn, Perc, Perc Endo], Drain Dev, NQ
ØK9H[Ø,4]ZZ	Drain/Thorax Muscle, Rt, [Opn, Perc Endo]
ØK9JØZX	Drain of Lt Thorax Muscle, Opn Appr, Diagnostic
ØK9J[Ø,3,4]ØZ	Drain/Thorax Muscle, Lt, [Opn, Perc, Perc Endo], Drain Dev, NQ
ØK9J[Ø,4]ZZ	Drain/Thorax Muscle, Lt, [Opn, Perc Endo]
ØK9KØZX	Drain of Rt Abd Muscle, Opn Appr, Diagnostic
ØK9K[Ø,3,4]ØZ	Drain/Abd Muscle, Rt, [Opn, Perc, Perc Endo], Drain Dev, NQ
ØK9K[Ø,4]ZZ	Drain/Abd Muscle, Rt, [Opn, Perc Endo]
ØK9LØZX	Drain of Lt Abd Muscle, Opn Appr, Diagnostic
ØK9L[Ø,3,4]ØZ	Drain/Abd Muscle, Lt, [Opn, Perc, Perc Endo], Drain Dev, NQ
ØK9L[Ø,4]ZZ	Drain/Abd Muscle, Lt, [Opn, Perc Endo]
ØK9MØZX	Drain of Perineum Muscle, Opn Appr, Diagnostic
ØK9M[Ø,3,4]ØZ	Drain/Perineum Muscle, [Opn, Perc, Perc Endo], Drain Dev, NQ
ØK9M[Ø,4]ZZ	Drain/Perineum Muscle, [Opn, Perc Endo]
ØK9NØZX	Drain of Rt Hip Muscle, Opn Appr, Diagnostic
ØK9N[Ø,3,4]ØZ	Drain/Hip Muscle, Rt, [Opn, Perc, Perc Endo], Drain Dev, NQ
ØK9N[Ø,4]ZZ	Drain/Hip Muscle, Rt, [Opn, Perc Endo]
ØK9PØZX	Drain of Lt Hip Muscle, Opn Appr, Diagnostic
ØK9P[Ø,3,4]ØZ	Drain/Hip Muscle, Lt, [Opn, Perc, Perc Endo], Drain Dev, NQ
ØK9P[Ø,4]ZZ	Drain/Hip Muscle, Lt, [Opn, Perc Endo]
ØK9QØZX	Drain of Rt Upr Leg Muscle, Opn Appr, Diagn
ØK9Q[Ø,3,4]ØZ	Drain/Upr Leg Muscle, Rt, [Opn, Perc, Perc Endo], Drain Dev, NQ
ØK9Q[Ø,4]ZZ	Drain/Upr Leg Muscle, Rt, [Opn, Perc Endo]
ØK9RØZX	Drain of Lt Upr Leg Muscle, Opn Appr, Diagnostic
ØK9R[Ø,3,4]ØZ	Drain/Upr Leg Muscle, Lt, [Opn, Perc, Perc Endo], Drain Dev, NQ
ØK9R[Ø,4]ZZ	Drain/Upr Leg Muscle, Lt, [Opn, Perc Endo]
ØK9SØZX	Drain of Rt Lwr Leg Muscle, Opn Appr, Diagn
ØK9S[Ø,3,4]ØZ	Drain/Lwr Leg Muscle, Rt, [Opn, Perc, Perc Endo], Drain Dev, NQ
ØK9S[Ø,4]ZZ	Drain/Lwr Leg Muscle, Rt, [Opn, Perc Endo]
ØK9TØZX	Drain of Lt Lwr Leg Muscle, Opn Appr, Diagnostic
ØK9T[Ø,3,4]ØZ	Drain/Lwr Leg Muscle, Lt, [Opn, Perc, Perc Endo], Drain Dev, NQ
ØK9T[Ø,4]ZZ	Drain/Lwr Leg Muscle, Lt, [Opn, Perc Endo]
ØK9VØZX	Drain of Rt Foot Muscle, Opn Appr, Diagnostic
ØK9V[Ø,3,4]ØZ	Drain/Foot Muscle, Rt, [Opn, Perc, Perc Endo], Drain Dev, NQ
ØK9V[Ø,4]ZZ	Drain/Foot Muscle, Rt, [Opn, Perc Endo]
ØK9WØZX	Drain of Lt Foot Muscle, Opn Appr, Diagnostic
ØK9W[Ø,3,4]ØZ	Drain/Foot Muscle, Lt, [Opn, Perc, Perc Endo], Drain Dev, NQ
ØK9W[Ø,4]ZZ	Drain/Foot Muscle, Lt, [Opn, Perc Endo]
ØKBØØZX	Exc of Head Muscle, Opn Appr, Diagnostic
ØKB1ØZX	Exc of Facial Muscle, Opn Appr, Diagnostic
ØKB2ØZX	Exc of Rt Neck Muscle, Opn Appr, Diagnostic
ØKB3ØZX	Exc of Lt Neck Muscle, Opn Appr, Diagnostic
ØKB4ØZX	Exc of Tongue/Palate/Phar Muscle, Opn Appr, Diagn
ØKB5ØZX	Exc of Rt Shldr Muscle, Opn Appr, Diagnostic
ØKB6ØZX	Exc of Lt Shldr Muscle, Opn Appr, Diagnostic
ØKB7ØZX	Exc of Rt Upr Arm Muscle, Opn Appr, Diagn
ØKB8ØZX	Exc of Lt Upr Arm Muscle, Opn Appr, Diagnostic
ØKB9ØZX	Exc of Rt Low Arm & Wrist Muscle, Opn Appr, Diagn
ØKBBØZX	Exc of Lt Low Arm & Wrist Muscle, Opn Appr, Diagn
ØKBCØZX	Exc of Rt Hand Muscle, Opn Appr, Diagnostic
ØKBDØZX	Exc of Lt Hand Muscle, Opn Appr, Diagnostic
ØKBFØZX	Exc of Rt Trunk Muscle, Opn Appr, Diagnostic
ØKBGØZX	Exc of Lt Trunk Muscle, Opn Appr, Diagnostic
ØKBHØZX	Exc of Rt Thorax Muscle, Opn Appr, Diagnostic
ØKBJØZX	Exc of Lt Thorax Muscle, Opn Appr, Diagnostic
ØKBKØZX	Exc of Rt Abd Muscle, Opn Appr, Diagnostic
ØKBLØZX	Exc of Lt Abd Muscle, Opn Appr, Diagnostic
ØKBMØZX	Exc of Perineum Muscle, Opn Appr, Diagnostic
ØKBNØZX	Exc of Rt Hip Muscle, Opn Appr, Diagnostic
ØKBPØZX	Exc of Lt Hip Muscle, Opn Appr, Diagnostic
ØKBQØZX	Exc of Rt Upr Leg Muscle, Opn Appr, Diagn
ØKBRØZX	Exc of Lt Upr Leg Muscle, Opn Appr, Diagnostic
ØKBSØZX	Exc of Rt Lwr Leg Muscle, Opn Appr, Diagn
ØKBTØZX	Exc of Lt Lwr Leg Muscle, Opn Appr, Diagnostic
ØKBVØZX	Exc of Rt Foot Muscle, Opn Appr, Diagnostic
ØKBWØZX	Exc of Lt Foot Muscle, Opn Appr, Diagnostic
ØKCØ[Ø,3,4]ZZ	Extir/Head Muscle, [Opn, Perc, Perc Endo]
ØKC1[Ø,3,4]ZZ	Extir/Facial Muscle, [Opn, Perc, Perc Endo]
ØKC2[Ø,3,4]ZZ	Extir/Neck Muscle, Rt, [Opn, Perc, Perc Endo]
ØKC3[Ø,3,4]ZZ	Extir/Neck Muscle, Lt, [Opn, Perc, Perc Endo]
ØKC4[Ø,3,4]ZZ	Extir/Tongue, Palate, Pharynx Muscle, [Opn, Perc, Perc Endo]
ØKC5[Ø,3,4]ZZ	Extir/Shldr Muscle, Rt, [Opn, Perc, Perc Endo]
ØKC6[Ø,3,4]ZZ	Extir/Shldr Muscle, Lt, [Opn, Perc, Perc Endo]
ØKC7[Ø,3,4]ZZ	Extir/Upr Arm Muscle, Rt, [Opn, Perc, Perc Endo]
ØKC8[Ø,3,4]ZZ	Extir/Upr Arm Muscle, Lt, [Opn, Perc, Perc Endo]
ØKC9[Ø,3,4]ZZ	Extir/Lwr Arm and Wrist Muscle, Rt, [Opn, Perc, Perc Endo]
ØKCB[Ø,3,4]ZZ	Extir/Lwr Arm and Wrist Muscle, Lt, [Opn, Perc, Perc Endo]
ØKCF[Ø,3,4]ZZ	Extir/Trunk Muscle, Rt, [Opn, Perc, Perc Endo]

Surgical   **Medical**   **CC Indicator**   **MCC Indicator**   **Procedure Proxy**   🟥**PDxMCC** **PDx acts as own MCC**   🟥**PDxCC** **PDx acts as own CC**

DRGs Associated with All MDCs—SURGICAL

ØKCG[Ø,3,4]ZZ	Extir/Trunk Muscle, Lt, [Opn, Perc, Perc Endo]
ØKCH[Ø,3,4]ZZ	Extir/Thorax Muscle, Rt, [Opn, Perc, Perc Endo]
ØKCJ[Ø,3,4]ZZ	Extir/Thorax Muscle, Lt, [Opn, Perc, Perc Endo]
ØKCK[Ø,3,4]ZZ	Extir/Abd Muscle, Rt, [Opn, Perc, Perc Endo]
ØKCL[Ø,3,4]ZZ	Extir/Abd Muscle, Lt, [Opn, Perc, Perc Endo]
ØKCM[Ø,3,4]ZZ	Extir/Perineum Muscle, [Opn, Perc, Perc Endo]
ØKCN[Ø,3,4]ZZ	Extir/Hip Muscle, Rt, [Opn, Perc, Perc Endo]
ØKCP[Ø,3,4]ZZ	Extir/Hip Muscle, Lt, [Opn, Perc, Perc Endo]
ØKCQ[Ø,3,4]ZZ	Extir/Upr Leg Muscle, Rt, [Opn, Perc, Perc Endo]
ØKCR[Ø,3,4]ZZ	Extir/Upr Leg Muscle, Lt, [Opn, Perc, Perc Endo]
ØKCS[Ø,3,4]ZZ	Extir/Lwr Leg Muscle, Rt, [Opn, Perc, Perc Endo]
ØKCT[Ø,3,4]ZZ	Extir/Lwr Leg Muscle, Lt, [Opn, Perc, Perc Endo]
ØKCV[Ø,3,4]ZZ	Extir/Foot Muscle, Rt, [Opn, Perc, Perc Endo]
ØKCW[Ø,3,4]ZZ	Extir/Foot Muscle, Lt, [Opn, Perc, Perc Endo]
ØKPX[Ø,3,4][Ø,7,J,K]Z	Rmvl/Upr Muscle, [Opn, Perc, Perc Endo], [Drain Dev, Auto Tissue Sub, Synth Sub, Nonauto Tissue Sub], NQ
ØKPY[Ø,3,4][Ø,7,J,K]Z	Rmvl/Lwr Muscle, [Opn, Perc, Perc Endo], [Drain Dev, Auto Tissue Sub, Synth Sub, Nonauto Tissue Sub], NQ
ØKQØ[Ø,3,4]ZZ	Rpr/Head Muscle, [Opn, Perc, Perc Endo]
ØKQ1[Ø,3,4]ZZ	Rpr/Facial Muscle, [Opn, Perc, Perc Endo]
ØKQ2[Ø,3,4]ZZ	Rpr/Neck Muscle, Rt, [Opn, Perc, Perc Endo]
ØKQ3[Ø,3,4]ZZ	Rpr/Neck Muscle, Lt, [Opn, Perc, Perc Endo]
ØKQ4[Ø,3,4]ZZ	Rpr/Tongue, Palate, Pharynx Muscle, [Opn, Perc, Perc Endo]
ØKQ5[Ø,3,4]ZZ	Rpr/Shldr Muscle, Rt, [Opn, Perc, Perc Endo]
ØKQ6[Ø,3,4]ZZ	Rpr/Shldr Muscle, Lt, [Opn, Perc, Perc Endo]
ØKQ7[Ø,3,4]ZZ	Rpr/Upr Arm Muscle, Rt, [Opn, Perc, Perc Endo]
ØKQ8[Ø,3,4]ZZ	Rpr/Upr Arm Muscle, Lt, [Opn, Perc, Perc Endo]
ØKQ9[Ø,3,4]ZZ	Rpr/Lwr Arm and Wrist Muscle, Rt, [Opn, Perc, Perc Endo]
ØKQB[Ø,3,4]ZZ	Rpr/Lwr Arm and Wrist Muscle, Lt, [Opn, Perc, Perc Endo]
ØKQC[Ø,3,4]ZZ	Rpr/Hand Muscle, Rt, [Opn, Perc, Perc Endo]
ØKQD[Ø,3,4]ZZ	Rpr/Hand Muscle, Lt, [Opn, Perc, Perc Endo]
ØKQF[Ø,3,4]ZZ	Rpr/Trunk Muscle, Rt, [Opn, Perc, Perc Endo]
ØKQG[Ø,3,4]ZZ	Rpr/Trunk Muscle, Lt, [Opn, Perc, Perc Endo]
ØKQH[Ø,3,4]ZZ	Rpr/Thorax Muscle, Rt, [Opn, Perc, Perc Endo]
ØKQJ[Ø,3,4]ZZ	Rpr/Thorax Muscle, Lt, [Opn, Perc, Perc Endo]
ØKQK[Ø,3,4]ZZ	Rpr/Abd Muscle, Rt, [Opn, Perc, Perc Endo]
ØKQL[Ø,3,4]ZZ	Rpr/Abd Muscle, Lt, [Opn, Perc, Perc Endo]
ØKQM[Ø,3,4]ZZ	Rpr/Perineum Muscle, [Opn, Perc, Perc Endo]
ØKQN[Ø,3,4]ZZ	Rpr/Hip Muscle, Rt, [Opn, Perc, Perc Endo]
ØKQP[Ø,3,4]ZZ	Rpr/Hip Muscle, Lt, [Opn, Perc, Perc Endo]
ØKQS[Ø,3,4]ZZ	Rpr/Lwr Leg Muscle, Rt, [Opn, Perc, Perc Endo]
ØKQT[Ø,3,4]ZZ	Rpr/Lwr Leg Muscle, Lt, [Opn, Perc, Perc Endo]
ØKQV[Ø,3,4]ZZ	Rpr/Foot Muscle, Rt, [Opn, Perc, Perc Endo]
ØKQW[Ø,3,4]ZZ	Rpr/Foot Muscle, Lt, [Opn, Perc, Perc Endo]
ØKWX[Ø,3,4][Ø,7,J,K,M]Z	Rev/Upr Muscle, [Opn, Perc, Perc Endo], [Drain Dev, Auto Tissue Sub, Synth Sub, Nonauto Tissue Sub, Stimulator Lead], NQ
ØKWY[Ø,3,4][Ø,7,J,K,M]Z	Rev/Lwr Muscle, [Opn, Perc, Perc Endo], [Drain Dev, Auto Tissue Sub, Synth Sub, Nonauto Tissue Sub, Stimulator Lead], NQ
ØL57[Ø,3,4]ZZ	Destr/Hand Tndn, Rt, [Opn, Perc, Perc Endo]
ØL58[Ø,3,4]ZZ	Destr/Hand Tndn, Lt, [Opn, Perc, Perc Endo]
ØL8Ø[Ø,3,4]ZZ	Div/Head and Neck Tndn, [Opn, Perc, Perc Endo]
ØL81[Ø,3,4]ZZ	Div/Shldr Tndn, Rt, [Opn, Perc, Perc Endo]
ØL82[Ø,3,4]ZZ	Div/Shldr Tndn, Lt, [Opn, Perc, Perc Endo]
ØL83[Ø,3,4]ZZ	Div/Upr Arm Tndn, Rt, [Opn, Perc, Perc Endo]
ØL84[Ø,3,4]ZZ	Div/Upr Arm Tndn, Lt, [Opn, Perc, Perc Endo]
ØL85[Ø,3,4]ZZ	Div/Lwr Arm and Wrist Tndn, Rt, [Opn, Perc, Perc Endo]
ØL86[Ø,3,4]ZZ	Div/Lwr Arm and Wrist Tndn, Lt, [Opn, Perc, Perc Endo]
ØL87[Ø,3,4]ZZ	Div/Hand Tndn, Rt, [Opn, Perc, Perc Endo]
ØL88[Ø,3,4]ZZ	Div/Hand Tndn, Lt, [Opn, Perc, Perc Endo]
ØL89[Ø,3,4]ZZ	Div/Trunk Tndn, Rt, [Opn, Perc, Perc Endo]
ØL8B[Ø,3,4]ZZ	Div/Trunk Tndn, Lt, [Opn, Perc, Perc Endo]
ØL8C[Ø,3,4]ZZ	Div/Thorax Tndn, Rt, [Opn, Perc, Perc Endo]
ØL8D[Ø,3,4]ZZ	Div/Thorax Tndn, Lt, [Opn, Perc, Perc Endo]
ØL8F[Ø,3,4]ZZ	Div/Abd Tndn, Rt, [Opn, Perc, Perc Endo]
ØL8G[Ø,3,4]ZZ	Div/Abd Tndn, Lt, [Opn, Perc, Perc Endo]
ØL8H[Ø,3,4]ZZ	Div/Perineum Tndn, [Opn, Perc, Perc Endo]
ØL8L[Ø,3,4]ZZ	Div/Upr Leg Tndn, Rt, [Opn, Perc, Perc Endo]
ØL8M[Ø,3,4]ZZ	Div/Upr Leg Tndn, Lt, [Opn, Perc, Perc Endo]
ØL8Q[Ø,3,4]ZZ	Div/Knee Tndn, Rt, [Opn, Perc, Perc Endo]
ØL8R[Ø,3,4]ZZ	Div/Knee Tndn, Lt, [Opn, Perc, Perc Endo]
ØL8S[Ø,3,4]ZZ	Div/Ankle Tndn, Rt, [Opn, Perc, Perc Endo]
ØL8T[Ø,3,4]ZZ	Div/Ankle Tndn, Lt, [Opn, Perc, Perc Endo]
ØL8V[Ø,3,4]ZZ	Div/Foot Tndn, Rt, [Opn, Perc, Perc Endo]
ØL8W[Ø,3,4]ZZ	Div/Foot Tndn, Lt, [Opn, Perc, Perc Endo]
ØL9ØØZX	Drain of Head and Neck Tndn, Opn Appr, Diagnostic
ØL9Ø[Ø,3,4][Ø,Z]Z	Drain/Head and Neck Tndn, [Opn, Perc, Perc Endo], [Drain Dev, No Dev], NQ
ØL91ØZX	Drain of Rt Shldr Tndn, Opn Appr, Diagnostic
ØL91[Ø,3,4][Ø,Z]Z	Drain/Shldr Tndn, Rt, [Opn, Perc, Perc Endo], [Drain Dev, No Dev], NQ
ØL92ØZX	Drain of Lt Shldr Tndn, Opn Appr, Diagnostic
ØL92[Ø,3,4][Ø,Z]Z	Drain/Shldr Tndn, Lt, [Opn, Perc, Perc Endo], [Drain Dev, No Dev], NQ
ØL93ØZX	Drain of Rt Upr Arm Tndn, Opn Appr, Diagn
ØL93[Ø,3,4][Ø,Z]Z	Drain/Upr Arm Tndn, Rt, [Opn, Perc, Perc Endo], [Drain Dev, No Dev], NQ
ØL94ØZX	Drain of Lt Upr Arm Tndn, Opn Appr, Diagnostic
ØL94[Ø,3,4][Ø,Z]Z	Drain/Upr Arm Tndn, Lt, [Opn, Perc, Perc Endo], [Drain Dev, No Dev], NQ
ØL95ØZX	Drain of Rt Low Arm & Wrist Tndn, Opn Appr, Diagn
ØL95[Ø,3,4][Ø,Z]Z	Drain/Lwr Arm and Wrist Tndn, Rt, [Opn, Perc, Perc Endo], [Drain Dev, No Dev], NQ
ØL96ØZX	Drain of Lt Low Arm & Wrist Tndn, Opn Appr, Diagn
ØL96[Ø,3,4][Ø,Z]Z	Drain/Lwr Arm and Wrist Tndn, Lt, [Opn, Perc, Perc Endo], [Drain Dev, No Dev], NQ
ØL97ØZX	Drain of Rt Hand Tndn, Opn Appr, Diagnostic
ØL97ØZZ	Drain of Rt Hand Tndn, Opn Appr
ØL97[Ø,3,4]ØZ	Drain/Hand Tndn, Rt, [Opn, Perc, Perc Endo], Drain Dev, NQ
ØL98ØZX	Drain of Lt Hand Tndn, Opn Appr, Diagnostic
ØL98ØZZ	Drain of Lt Hand Tndn, Opn Appr
ØL98[Ø,3,4]ØZ	Drain/Hand Tndn, Lt, [Opn, Perc, Perc Endo], Drain Dev, NQ
ØL99ØZX	Drain of Rt Trunk Tndn, Opn Appr, Diagnostic
ØL99[Ø,3,4][Ø,Z]Z	Drain/Trunk Tndn, Rt, [Opn, Perc, Perc Endo], [Drain Dev, No Dev], NQ
ØL9BØZX	Drain of Lt Trunk Tndn, Opn Appr, Diagnostic
ØL9B[Ø,3,4][Ø,Z]Z	Drain/Trunk Tndn, Lt, [Opn, Perc, Perc Endo], [Drain Dev, No Dev], NQ
ØL9CØZX	Drain of Rt Thorax Tndn, Opn Appr, Diagnostic
ØL9C[Ø,3,4][Ø,Z]Z	Drain/Thorax Tndn, Rt, [Opn, Perc, Perc Endo], [Drain Dev, No Dev], NQ
ØL9DØZX	Drain of Lt Thorax Tndn, Opn Appr, Diagnostic
ØL9D[Ø,3,4][Ø,Z]Z	Drain/Thorax Tndn, Lt, [Opn, Perc, Perc Endo], [Drain Dev, No Dev], NQ
ØL9FØZX	Drain of Rt Abd Tndn, Opn Appr, Diagnostic
ØL9F[Ø,3,4][Ø,Z]Z	Drain/Abd Tndn, Rt, [Opn, Perc, Perc Endo], [Drain Dev, No Dev], NQ
ØL9GØZX	Drain of Lt Abd Tndn, Opn Appr, Diagnostic
ØL9G[Ø,3,4][Ø,Z]Z	Drain/Abd Tndn, Lt, [Opn, Perc, Perc Endo], [Drain Dev, No Dev], NQ
ØL9HØZX	Drain of Perineum Tndn, Opn Appr, Diagnostic
ØL9H[Ø,3,4][Ø,Z]Z	Drain/Perineum Tndn, [Opn, Perc, Perc Endo], [Drain Dev, No Dev], NQ
ØL9JØZX	Drain of Rt Hip Tndn, Opn Appr, Diagnostic
ØL9J[Ø,3,4][Ø,Z]Z	Drain/Hip Tndn, Rt, [Opn, Perc, Perc Endo], [Drain Dev, No Dev], NQ
ØL9KØZX	Drain of Lt Hip Tndn, Opn Appr, Diagnostic
ØL9K[Ø,3,4][Ø,Z]Z	Drain/Hip Tndn, Lt, [Opn, Perc, Perc Endo], [Drain Dev, No Dev], NQ
ØL9LØZX	Drain of Rt Upr Leg Tndn, Opn Appr, Diagn
ØL9L[Ø,3,4][Ø,Z]Z	Drain/Upr Leg Tndn, Rt, [Opn, Perc, Perc Endo], [Drain Dev, No Dev], NQ
ØL9MØZX	Drain of Lt Upr Leg Tndn, Opn Appr, Diagnostic
ØL9M[Ø,3,4][Ø,Z]Z	Drain/Upr Leg Tndn, Lt, [Opn, Perc, Perc Endo], [Drain Dev, No Dev], NQ
ØL9NØZX	Drain of Rt Lwr Leg Tndn, Opn Appr, Diagn
ØL9N[Ø,3,4][Ø,Z]Z	Drain/Lwr Leg Tndn, Rt, [Opn, Perc, Perc Endo], [Drain Dev, No Dev], NQ
ØL9PØZX	Drain of Lt Lwr Leg Tndn, Opn Appr, Diagnostic
ØL9P[Ø,3,4][Ø,Z]Z	Drain/Lwr Leg Tndn, Lt, [Opn, Perc, Perc Endo], [Drain Dev, No Dev], NQ
ØL9QØZX	Drain of Rt Knee Tndn, Opn Appr, Diagnostic
ØL9Q[Ø,3,4][Ø,Z]Z	Drain/Knee Tndn, Rt, [Opn, Perc, Perc Endo], [Drain Dev, No Dev], NQ
ØL9RØZX	Drain of Lt Knee Tndn, Opn Appr, Diagnostic
ØL9R[Ø,3,4][Ø,Z]Z	Drain/Knee Tndn, Lt, [Opn, Perc, Perc Endo], [Drain Dev, No Dev], NQ
ØL9SØZX	Drain of Rt Ankle Tndn, Opn Appr, Diagnostic
ØL9S[Ø,3,4][Ø,Z]Z	Drain/Ankle Tndn, Rt, [Opn, Perc, Perc Endo], [Drain Dev, No Dev], NQ
ØL9TØZX	Drain of Lt Ankle Tndn, Opn Appr, Diagnostic
ØL9T[Ø,3,4][Ø,Z]Z	Drain/Ankle Tndn, Lt, [Opn, Perc, Perc Endo], [Drain Dev, No Dev], NQ
ØL9VØZX	Drain of Rt Foot Tndn, Opn Appr, Diagnostic
ØL9V[Ø,3,4][Ø,Z]Z	Drain/Foot Tndn, Rt, [Opn, Perc, Perc Endo], [Drain Dev, No Dev], NQ
ØL9WØZX	Drain of Lt Foot Tndn, Opn Appr, Diagnostic
ØL9W[Ø,3,4][Ø,Z]Z	Drain/Foot Tndn, Lt, [Opn, Perc, Perc Endo], [Drain Dev, No Dev], NQ

T **Transfer DRG**   SP **Special Payment**   * **Code Range**   **6th and 7th Character of ZZ = No Device, No Qualifier ZX = No Device, Diagnostic**

MS-DRG Version 33.0

ØLBØØZX	Exc of Head and Neck Tndn, Opn Appr, Diagnostic
ØLB1ØZX	Exc of Rt Shldr Tndn, Opn Appr, Diagnostic
ØLB2ØZX	Exc of Lt Shldr Tndn, Opn Appr, Diagnostic
ØLB3ØZX	Exc of Rt Upr Arm Tndn, Opn Appr, Diagn
ØLB4ØZX	Exc of Lt Upr Arm Tndn, Opn Appr, Diagnostic
ØLB5ØZX	Exc of Rt Low Arm & Wrist Tndn, Opn Appr, Diagn
ØLB6ØZX	Exc of Lt Low Arm & Wrist Tndn, Opn Appr, Diagn
ØLB7ØZX	Exc of Rt Hand Tndn, Opn Appr, Diagnostic
ØLB8ØZX	Exc of Lt Hand Tndn, Opn Appr, Diagnostic
ØLB9ØZX	Exc of Rt Trunk Tndn, Opn Appr, Diagnostic
ØLBBØZX	Exc of Lt Trunk Tndn, Opn Appr, Diagnostic
ØLBCØZX	Exc of Rt Thorax Tndn, Opn Appr, Diagnostic
ØLBDØZX	Exc of Lt Thorax Tndn, Opn Appr, Diagnostic
ØLBFØZX	Exc of Rt Abd Tndn, Opn Appr, Diagnostic
ØLBGØZX	Exc of Lt Abd Tndn, Opn Appr, Diagnostic
ØLBHØZX	Exc of Perineum Tndn, Opn Appr, Diagnostic
ØLBJØZX	Exc of Rt Hip Tndn, Opn Appr, Diagnostic
ØLBKØZX	Exc of Lt Hip Tndn, Opn Appr, Diagnostic
ØLBLØZX	Exc of Rt Upr Leg Tndn, Opn Appr, Diagn
ØLBMØZX	Exc of Lt Upr Leg Tndn, Opn Appr, Diagnostic
ØLBNØZX	Exc of Rt Lwr Leg Tndn, Opn Appr, Diagn
ØLBPØZX	Exc of Lt Lwr Leg Tndn, Opn Appr, Diagnostic
ØLBQØZX	Exc of Rt Knee Tndn, Opn Appr, Diagnostic
ØLBRØZX	Exc of Lt Knee Tndn, Opn Appr, Diagnostic
ØLBSØZX	Exc of Rt Ankle Tndn, Opn Appr, Diagnostic
ØLBTØZX	Exc of Lt Ankle Tndn, Opn Appr, Diagnostic
ØLBVØZX	Exc of Rt Foot Tndn, Opn Appr, Diagnostic
ØLBWØZX	Exc of Lt Foot Tndn, Opn Appr, Diagnostic
ØLCØ[Ø,3,4]ZZ	Extir/Head and Neck Tndn, [Opn, Perc, Perc Endo]
ØLC1[Ø,3,4]ZZ	Extir/Shldr Tndn, Rt, [Opn, Perc, Perc Endo]
ØLC2[Ø,3,4]ZZ	Extir/Shldr Tndn, Lt, [Opn, Perc, Perc Endo]
ØLC3[Ø,3,4]ZZ	Extir/Upr Arm Tndn, Rt, [Opn, Perc, Perc Endo]
ØLC4[Ø,3,4]ZZ	Extir/Upr Arm Tndn, Lt, [Opn, Perc, Perc Endo]
ØLC5[Ø,3,4]ZZ	Extir/Lwr Arm and Wrist Tndn, Rt, [Opn, Perc, Perc Endo]
ØLC6[Ø,3,4]ZZ	Extir/Lwr Arm and Wrist Tndn, Lt, [Opn, Perc, Perc Endo]
ØLC7[Ø,3,4]ZZ	Extir/Hand Tndn, Rt, [Opn, Perc, Perc Endo]
ØLC8[Ø,3,4]ZZ	Extir/Hand Tndn, Lt, [Opn, Perc, Perc Endo]
ØLC9[Ø,3,4]ZZ	Extir/Trunk Tndn, Rt, [Opn, Perc, Perc Endo]
ØLCB[Ø,3,4]ZZ	Extir/Trunk Tndn, Lt, [Opn, Perc, Perc Endo]
ØLCC[Ø,3,4]ZZ	Extir/Thorax Tndn, Rt, [Opn, Perc, Perc Endo]
ØLCD[Ø,3,4]ZZ	Extir/Thorax Tndn, Lt, [Opn, Perc, Perc Endo]
ØLCF[Ø,3,4]ZZ	Extir/Abd Tndn, Rt, [Opn, Perc, Perc Endo]
ØLCG[Ø,3,4]ZZ	Extir/Abd Tndn, Lt, [Opn, Perc, Perc Endo]
ØLCH[Ø,3,4]ZZ	Extir/Perineum Tndn, [Opn, Perc, Perc Endo]
ØLCJ[Ø,3,4]ZZ	Extir/Hip Tndn, Rt, [Opn, Perc, Perc Endo]
ØLCK[Ø,3,4]ZZ	Extir/Hip Tndn, Lt, [Opn, Perc, Perc Endo]
ØLCL[Ø,3,4]ZZ	Extir/Upr Leg Tndn, Rt, [Opn, Perc, Perc Endo]
ØLCM[Ø,3,4]ZZ	Extir/Upr Leg Tndn, Lt, [Opn, Perc, Perc Endo]
ØLCN[Ø,3,4]ZZ	Extir/Lwr Leg Tndn, Rt, [Opn, Perc, Perc Endo]
ØLCP[Ø,3,4]ZZ	Extir/Lwr Leg Tndn, Lt, [Opn, Perc, Perc Endo]
ØLCQ[Ø,3,4]ZZ	Extir/Knee Tndn, Rt, [Opn, Perc, Perc Endo]
ØLCR[Ø,3,4]ZZ	Extir/Knee Tndn, Lt, [Opn, Perc, Perc Endo]
ØLCS[Ø,3,4]ZZ	Extir/Ankle Tndn, Rt, [Opn, Perc, Perc Endo]
ØLCT[Ø,3,4]ZZ	Extir/Ankle Tndn, Lt, [Opn, Perc, Perc Endo]
ØLCV[Ø,3,4]ZZ	Extir/Foot Tndn, Rt, [Opn, Perc, Perc Endo]
ØLCW[Ø,3,4]ZZ	Extir/Foot Tndn, Lt, [Opn, Perc, Perc Endo]
ØLJX[Ø,3,4]ZZ	Inspect/Upr Tndn, [Opn, Perc, Perc Endo]
ØLPX[Ø,3,4][Ø,7,J,K]Z	Rmvl/Upr Tndn, [Opn, Perc, Perc Endo], [Drain Dev, Auto Tissue Sub, Synth Sub, Nonauto Tissue Sub], NQ
ØLPY[Ø,3,4][Ø,7,J,K]Z	Rmvl/Lwr Tndn, [Opn, Perc, Perc Endo], [Drain Dev, Auto Tissue Sub, Synth Sub, Nonauto Tissue Sub], NQ
ØLQ1[Ø,3,4]ZZ	Rpr/Shldr Tndn, Rt, [Opn, Perc, Perc Endo]
ØLQ2[Ø,3,4]ZZ	Rpr/Shldr Tndn, Lt, [Opn, Perc, Perc Endo]
ØLQ7[Ø,3,4]ZZ	Rpr/Hand Tndn, Rt, [Opn, Perc, Perc Endo]
ØLQ8[Ø,3,4]ZZ	Rpr/Hand Tndn, Lt, [Opn, Perc, Perc Endo]
ØLQQ[Ø,3,4]ZZ	Rpr/Knee Tndn, Rt, [Opn, Perc, Perc Endo]
ØLQR[Ø,3,4]ZZ	Rpr/Knee Tndn, Lt, [Opn, Perc, Perc Endo]
ØLQS[Ø,3,4]ZZ	Rpr/Ankle Tndn, Rt, [Opn, Perc, Perc Endo]
ØLQT[Ø,3,4]ZZ	Rpr/Ankle Tndn, Lt, [Opn, Perc, Perc Endo]
ØLWX[Ø,3,4][Ø,7,J,K]Z	Rev/Upr Tndn, [Opn, Perc, Perc Endo], [Drain Dev, Auto Tissue Sub, Synth Sub, Nonauto Tissue Sub], NQ
ØLWY[Ø,3,4][Ø,7,J,K]Z	Rev/Lwr Tndn, [Opn, Perc, Perc Endo], [Drain Dev, Auto Tissue Sub, Synth Sub, Nonauto Tissue Sub], NQ
ØM5N[Ø,3,4]ZZ	Destr/Knee Bursa & Lgmt, Rt, [Opn, Perc, Perc Endo]
ØM5P[Ø,3,4]ZZ	Destr/Knee Bursa & Lgmt, Lt, [Opn, Perc, Perc Endo]
ØM5S[Ø,3,4]ZZ	Destr/Foot Bursa & Lgmt, Rt, [Opn, Perc, Perc Endo]
ØM5T[Ø,3,4]ZZ	Destr/Foot Bursa & Lgmt, Lt, [Opn, Perc, Perc Endo]
ØM8Ø[Ø,3,4]ZZ	Div/Head and Neck Bursa & Lgmt, [Opn, Perc, Perc Endo]
ØM81[Ø,3,4]ZZ	Div/Shldr Bursa & Lgmt, Rt, [Opn, Perc, Perc Endo]
ØM82[Ø,3,4]ZZ	Div/Shldr Bursa & Lgmt, Lt, [Opn, Perc, Perc Endo]
ØM83[Ø,3,4]ZZ	Div/Elbow Bursa & Lgmt, Rt, [Opn, Perc, Perc Endo]
ØM84[Ø,3,4]ZZ	Div/Elbow Bursa & Lgmt, Lt, [Opn, Perc, Perc Endo]
ØM89[Ø,3,4]ZZ	Div/Upr Extr Bursa & Lgmt, Rt, [Opn, Perc, Perc Endo]
ØM8B[Ø,3,4]ZZ	Div/Upr Extr Bursa & Lgmt, Lt, [Opn, Perc, Perc Endo]
ØM8C[Ø,3,4]ZZ	Div/Trunk Bursa & Lgmt, Rt, [Opn, Perc, Perc Endo]
ØM8D[Ø,3,4]ZZ	Div/Trunk Bursa & Lgmt, Lt, [Opn, Perc, Perc Endo]
ØM8F[Ø,3,4]ZZ	Div/Thorax Bursa & Lgmt, Rt, [Opn, Perc, Perc Endo]
ØM8G[Ø,3,4]ZZ	Div/Thorax Bursa & Lgmt, Lt, [Opn, Perc, Perc Endo]
ØM8H[Ø,3,4]ZZ	Div/Abd Bursa & Lgmt, Rt, [Opn, Perc, Perc Endo]
ØM8J[Ø,3,4]ZZ	Div/Abd Bursa & Lgmt, Lt, [Opn, Perc, Perc Endo]
ØM8K[Ø,3,4]ZZ	Div/Perineum Bursa & Lgmt, [Opn, Perc, Perc Endo]
ØM8L[Ø,3,4]ZZ	Div/Hip Bursa & Lgmt, Rt, [Opn, Perc, Perc Endo]
ØM8M[Ø,3,4]ZZ	Div/Hip Bursa & Lgmt, Lt, [Opn, Perc, Perc Endo]
ØM8N[Ø,3,4]ZZ	Div/Knee Bursa & Lgmt, Rt, [Opn, Perc, Perc Endo]
ØM8P[Ø,3,4]ZZ	Div/Knee Bursa & Lgmt, Lt, [Opn, Perc, Perc Endo]
ØM8Q[Ø,3,4]ZZ	Div/Ankle Bursa & Lgmt, Rt, [Opn, Perc, Perc Endo]
ØM8R[Ø,3,4]ZZ	Div/Ankle Bursa & Lgmt, Lt, [Opn, Perc, Perc Endo]
ØM8S[Ø,3,4]ZZ	Div/Foot Bursa & Lgmt, Rt, [Opn, Perc, Perc Endo]
ØM8T[Ø,3,4]ZZ	Div/Foot Bursa & Lgmt, Lt, [Opn, Perc, Perc Endo]
ØM8V[Ø,3,4]ZZ	Div/Lwr Extr Bursa & Lgmt, Rt, [Opn, Perc, Perc Endo]
ØM8W[Ø,3,4]ZZ	Div/Lwr Extr Bursa & Lgmt, Lt, [Opn, Perc, Perc Endo]
ØM9ØØ[Ø,Z]Z	Drain/Head and Neck Bursa & Lgmt, Opn, [Drain Dev, No Dev], NQ
ØM91Ø[Ø,Z]Z	Drain/Shldr Bursa & Lgmt, Rt, Opn, [Drain Dev, No Dev], NQ
ØM92Ø[Ø,Z]Z	Drain/Shldr Bursa & Lgmt, Lt, Opn, [Drain Dev, No Dev], NQ
ØM93Ø[Ø,Z]Z	Drain/Elbow Bursa & Lgmt, Rt, Opn, [Drain Dev, No Dev], NQ
ØM94Ø[Ø,Z]Z	Drain/Elbow Bursa & Lgmt, Lt, Opn, [Drain Dev, No Dev], NQ
ØM99ØZX	Drain of Rt Up Extrem Bursa/Lig, Opn Appr, Diagn
ØM99Ø[Ø,Z]Z	Drain/Upr Extr Bursa & Lgmt, Rt, Opn, [Drain Dev, No Dev], NQ
ØM9BØZX	Drain of Lt Up Extrem Bursa/Lig, Opn Appr, Diagn
ØM9BØ[Ø,Z]Z	Drain/Upr Extr Bursa & Lgmt, Lt, Opn, [Drain Dev, No Dev], NQ
ØM9CØ[Ø,Z]Z	Drain/Trunk Bursa & Lgmt, Rt, Opn, [Drain Dev, No Dev], NQ
ØM9DØ[Ø,Z]Z	Drain/Trunk Bursa & Lgmt, Lt, Opn, [Drain Dev, No Dev], NQ
ØM9FØ[Ø,Z]Z	Drain/Thorax Bursa & Lgmt, Rt, Opn, [Drain Dev, No Dev], NQ
ØM9GØ[Ø,Z]Z	Drain/Thorax Bursa & Lgmt, Lt, Opn, [Drain Dev, No Dev], NQ
ØM9HØZX	Drain of Rt Abd Bursa/Lig, Opn Appr, Diagn
ØM9HØ[Ø,Z]Z	Drain/Abd Bursa & Lgmt, Rt, Opn, [Drain Dev, No Dev], NQ
ØM9JØZX	Drain of Lt Abd Bursa/Lig, Opn Appr, Diagn
ØM9JØ[Ø,Z]Z	Drain/Abd Bursa & Lgmt, Lt, Opn, [Drain Dev, No Dev], NQ
ØM9KØZX	Drain of Perineum Bursa/Lig, Opn Appr, Diagn
ØM9KØ[Ø,Z]Z	Drain/Perineum Bursa & Lgmt, Opn, [Drain Dev, No Dev], NQ
ØM9LØ[Ø,Z]Z	Drain/Hip Bursa & Lgmt, Rt, Opn, [Drain Dev, No Dev], NQ
ØM9MØ[Ø,Z]Z	Drain/Hip Bursa & Lgmt, Lt, Opn, [Drain Dev, No Dev], NQ
ØM9NØZZ	Drain of Rt Knee Bursa & Lgmt, Opn Appr
ØM9N[Ø,3,4]ØZ	Drain/Knee Bursa & Lgmt, Rt, [Opn, Perc, Perc Endo], Drain Dev, NQ
ØM9PØZZ	Drain of Lt Knee Bursa & Lgmt, Opn Appr
ØM9P[Ø,3,4]ØZ	Drain/Knee Bursa & Lgmt, Lt, [Opn, Perc, Perc Endo], Drain Dev, NQ
ØM9QØ[Ø,Z]Z	Drain/Ankle Bursa & Lgmt, Rt, Opn, [Drain Dev, No Dev], NQ
ØM9RØ[Ø,Z]Z	Drain/Ankle Bursa & Lgmt, Lt, Opn, [Drain Dev, No Dev], NQ
ØM9SØZZ	Drain of Rt Foot Bursa & Lgmt, Opn Appr
ØM9S[Ø,3,4]ØZ	Drain/Foot Bursa & Lgmt, Rt, [Opn, Perc, Perc Endo], Drain Dev, NQ
ØM9TØZZ	Drain of Lt Foot Bursa & Lgmt, Opn Appr
ØM9T[Ø,3,4]ØZ	Drain/Foot Bursa & Lgmt, Lt, [Opn, Perc, Perc Endo], Drain Dev, NQ
ØM9VØZX	Drain of Rt Low Extrem Bursa/Lig, Opn Appr, Diagn
ØM9VØ[Ø,Z]Z	Drain/Lwr Extr Bursa & Lgmt, Rt, Opn, [Drain Dev, No Dev], NQ
ØM9WØZX	Drain of Lt Low Extrem Bursa/Lig, Opn Appr, Diagn
ØM9WØ[Ø,Z]Z	Drain/Lwr Extr Bursa & Lgmt, Lt, Opn, [Drain Dev, No Dev], NQ
ØMBØ[Ø,3,4]ZZ	Exc/Head and Neck Bursa & Lgmt, [Opn, Perc, Perc Endo]
ØMB1[Ø,3,4]ZZ	Exc/Shldr Bursa & Lgmt, Rt, [Opn, Perc, Perc Endo]
ØMB2[Ø,3,4]ZZ	Exc/Shldr Bursa & Lgmt, Lt, [Opn, Perc, Perc Endo]
ØMB3[Ø,3,4]ZZ	Exc/Elbow Bursa & Lgmt, Rt, [Opn, Perc, Perc Endo]
ØMB4[Ø,3,4]ZZ	Exc/Elbow Bursa & Lgmt, Lt, [Opn, Perc, Perc Endo]
ØMB5[Ø,3,4]ZZ	Exc/Wrist Bursa & Lgmt, Rt, [Opn, Perc, Perc Endo]
ØMB6[Ø,3,4]ZZ	Exc/Wrist Bursa & Lgmt, Lt, [Opn, Perc, Perc Endo]
ØMB9ØZX	Exc of Rt Up Extrem Bursa/Lig, Opn Appr, Diagn
ØMB9[Ø,3,4]ZZ	Exc/Upr Extr Bursa & Lgmt, Rt, [Opn, Perc, Perc Endo]
ØMBB[Ø,3,4]ZZ	Exc/Upr Extr Bursa & Lgmt, Lt, [Opn, Perc, Perc Endo]
ØMBC[Ø,3,4]ZZ	Exc/Trunk Bursa & Lgmt, Rt, [Opn, Perc, Perc Endo]
ØMBD[Ø,3,4]ZZ	Exc/Trunk Bursa & Lgmt, Lt, [Opn, Perc, Perc Endo]
ØMBF[Ø,3,4]ZZ	Exc/Thorax Bursa & Lgmt, Rt, [Opn, Perc, Perc Endo]
ØMBG[Ø,3,4]ZZ	Exc/Thorax Bursa & Lgmt, Lt, [Opn, Perc, Perc Endo]
ØMBHØZX	Exc of Rt Abd Bursa/Lig, Opn Appr, Diagn
ØMBH[Ø,3,4]ZZ	Exc/Abd Bursa & Lgmt, Rt, [Opn, Perc, Perc Endo]
ØMBJØZX	Exc of Lt Abd Bursa/Lig, Opn Appr, Diagn
ØMBJ[Ø,3,4]ZZ	Exc/Abd Bursa & Lgmt, Lt, [Opn, Perc, Perc Endo]
ØMBKØZX	Exc of Perineum Bursa/Lig, Opn Appr, Diagn

DRGs Associated with All MDCs—SURGICAL

ØMBK[Ø,3,4]ZZ   Exc/Perineum Bursa & Lgmt, [Opn, Perc, Perc Endo]
ØMBL[Ø,3,4]ZZ   Exc/Hip Bursa & Lgmt, Rt, [Opn, Perc, Perc Endo]
ØMBM[Ø,3,4]ZZ   Exc/Hip Bursa & Lgmt, Lt, [Opn, Perc, Perc Endo]
ØMBN[Ø,3,4]ZZ   Exc/Knee Bursa & Lgmt, Rt, [Opn, Perc, Perc Endo]
ØMBP[Ø,3,4]ZZ   Exc/Knee Bursa & Lgmt, Lt, [Opn, Perc, Perc Endo]
ØMBQ[Ø,3,4]ZZ   Exc/Ankle Bursa & Lgmt, Rt, [Opn, Perc, Perc Endo]
ØMBR[Ø,3,4]ZZ   Exc/Ankle Bursa & Lgmt, Lt, [Opn, Perc, Perc Endo]
ØMBS[Ø,3,4]ZZ   Exc/Foot Bursa & Lgmt, Rt, [Opn, Perc, Perc Endo]
ØMBT[Ø,3,4]ZZ   Exc/Foot Bursa & Lgmt, Lt, [Opn, Perc, Perc Endo]
ØMBVØZX   Exc of Rt Low Extrem Bursa/Lig, Opn Appr, Diagn
ØMBV[Ø,3,4]ZZ   Exc/Lwr Extr Bursa & Lgmt, Rt, [Opn, Perc, Perc Endo]
ØMBWØZX   Exc of Lt Low Extrem Bursa/Lig, Opn Appr, Diagn
ØMBW[Ø,3,4]ZZ   Exc/Lwr Extr Bursa & Lgmt, Lt, [Opn, Perc, Perc Endo]
ØMCØ[Ø,3,4]ZZ   Extir/Head and Neck Bursa & Lgmt, [Opn, Perc, Perc Endo]
ØMC1[Ø,3,4]ZZ   Extir/Shldr Bursa & Lgmt, Rt, [Opn, Perc, Perc Endo]
ØMC2[Ø,3,4]ZZ   Extir/Shldr Bursa & Lgmt, Lt, [Opn, Perc, Perc Endo]
ØMC3[Ø,3,4]ZZ   Extir/Elbow Bursa & Lgmt, Rt, [Opn, Perc, Perc Endo]
ØMC4[Ø,3,4]ZZ   Extir/Elbow Bursa & Lgmt, Lt, [Opn, Perc, Perc Endo]
ØMC9[Ø,3,4]ZZ   Extir/Upr Extr Bursa & Lgmt, Rt, [Opn, Perc, Perc Endo]
ØMCB[Ø,3,4]ZZ   Extir/Upr Extr Bursa & Lgmt, Lt, [Opn, Perc, Perc Endo]
ØMCC[Ø,3,4]ZZ   Extir/Trunk Bursa & Lgmt, Rt, [Opn, Perc, Perc Endo]
ØMCD[Ø,3,4]ZZ   Extir/Trunk Bursa & Lgmt, Lt, [Opn, Perc, Perc Endo]
ØMCF[Ø,3,4]ZZ   Extir/Thorax Bursa & Lgmt, Rt, [Opn, Perc, Perc Endo]
ØMCG[Ø,3,4]ZZ   Extir/Thorax Bursa & Lgmt, Lt, [Opn, Perc, Perc Endo]
ØMCH[Ø,3,4]ZZ   Extir/Abd Bursa & Lgmt, Rt, [Opn, Perc, Perc Endo]
ØMCJ[Ø,3,4]ZZ   Extir/Abd Bursa & Lgmt, Lt, [Opn, Perc, Perc Endo]
ØMCK[Ø,3,4]ZZ   Extir/Perineum Bursa & Lgmt, [Opn, Perc, Perc Endo]
ØMCL[Ø,3,4]ZZ   Extir/Hip Bursa & Lgmt, Rt, [Opn, Perc, Perc Endo]
ØMCM[Ø,3,4]ZZ   Extir/Hip Bursa & Lgmt, Lt, [Opn, Perc, Perc Endo]
ØMCN[Ø,3,4]ZZ   Extir/Knee Bursa & Lgmt, Rt, [Opn, Perc, Perc Endo]
ØMCP[Ø,3,4]ZZ   Extir/Knee Bursa & Lgmt, Lt, [Opn, Perc, Perc Endo]
ØMCQ[Ø,3,4]ZZ   Extir/Ankle Bursa & Lgmt, Rt, [Opn, Perc, Perc Endo]
ØMCR[Ø,3,4]ZZ   Extir/Ankle Bursa & Lgmt, Lt, [Opn, Perc, Perc Endo]
ØMCS[Ø,3,4]ZZ   Extir/Foot Bursa & Lgmt, Rt, [Opn, Perc, Perc Endo]
ØMCT[Ø,3,4]ZZ   Extir/Foot Bursa & Lgmt, Lt, [Opn, Perc, Perc Endo]
ØMCV[Ø,3,4]ZZ   Extir/Lwr Extr Bursa & Lgmt, Rt, [Opn, Perc, Perc Endo]
ØMCW[Ø,3,4]ZZ   Extir/Lwr Extr Bursa & Lgmt, Lt, [Opn, Perc, Perc Endo]
ØMDØ[Ø,3,4]ZZ   Extract/Head and Neck Bursa & Lgmt, [Opn, Perc, Perc Endo]
ØMD1[Ø,3,4]ZZ   Extract/Shldr Bursa & Lgmt, Rt, [Opn, Perc, Perc Endo]
ØMD2[Ø,3,4]ZZ   Extract/Shldr Bursa & Lgmt, Lt, [Opn, Perc, Perc Endo]
ØMD3[Ø,3,4]ZZ   Extract/Elbow Bursa & Lgmt, Rt, [Opn, Perc, Perc Endo]
ØMD4[Ø,3,4]ZZ   Extract/Elbow Bursa & Lgmt, Lt, [Opn, Perc, Perc Endo]
ØMD5[Ø,3,4]ZZ   Extract/Wrist Bursa & Lgmt, Rt, [Opn, Perc, Perc Endo]
ØMD6[Ø,3,4]ZZ   Extract/Wrist Bursa & Lgmt, Lt, [Opn, Perc, Perc Endo]
ØMD9[Ø,3,4]ZZ   Extract/Upr Extr Bursa & Lgmt, Rt, [Opn, Perc, Perc Endo]
ØMDB[Ø,3,4]ZZ   Extract/Upr Extr Bursa & Lgmt, Lt, [Opn, Perc, Perc Endo]
ØMDC[Ø,3,4]ZZ   Extract/Trunk Bursa & Lgmt, Rt, [Opn, Perc, Perc Endo]
ØMDD[Ø,3,4]ZZ   Extract/Trunk Bursa & Lgmt, Lt, [Opn, Perc, Perc Endo]
ØMDF[Ø,3,4]ZZ   Extract/Thorax Bursa & Lgmt, Rt, [Opn, Perc, Perc Endo]
ØMDG[Ø,3,4]ZZ   Extract/Thorax Bursa & Lgmt, Lt, [Opn, Perc, Perc Endo]
ØMDH[Ø,3,4]ZZ   Extract/Abd Bursa & Lgmt, Rt, [Opn, Perc, Perc Endo]
ØMDJ[Ø,3,4]ZZ   Extract/Abd Bursa & Lgmt, Lt, [Opn, Perc, Perc Endo]
ØMDK[Ø,3,4]ZZ   Extract/Perineum Bursa & Lgmt, [Opn, Perc, Perc Endo]
ØMDL[Ø,3,4]ZZ   Extract/Hip Bursa & Lgmt, Rt, [Opn, Perc, Perc Endo]
ØMDM[Ø,3,4]ZZ   Extract/Hip Bursa & Lgmt, Lt, [Opn, Perc, Perc Endo]
ØMDN[Ø,3,4]ZZ   Extract/Knee Bursa & Lgmt, Rt, [Opn, Perc, Perc Endo]
ØMDP[Ø,3,4]ZZ   Extract/Knee Bursa & Lgmt, Lt, [Opn, Perc, Perc Endo]
ØMDQ[Ø,3,4]ZZ   Extract/Ankle Bursa & Lgmt, Rt, [Opn, Perc, Perc Endo]
ØMDR[Ø,3,4]ZZ   Extract/Ankle Bursa & Lgmt, Lt, [Opn, Perc, Perc Endo]
ØMDS[Ø,3,4]ZZ   Extract/Foot Bursa & Lgmt, Rt, [Opn, Perc, Perc Endo]
ØMDT[Ø,3,4]ZZ   Extract/Foot Bursa & Lgmt, Lt, [Opn, Perc, Perc Endo]
ØMDV[Ø,3,4]ZZ   Extract/Lwr Extr Bursa & Lgmt, Rt, [Opn, Perc, Perc Endo]
ØMDW[Ø,3,4]ZZ   Extract/Lwr Extr Bursa & Lgmt, Lt, [Opn, Perc, Perc Endo]
ØMPX[Ø,3,4][7,K]Z   Rmvl/Upr Bursa & Lgmt, [Opn, Perc, Perc Endo], [Auto Tissue Sub, Nonauto Tissue Sub], NQ
ØMPY[Ø,3,4][7,K]Z   Rmvl/Lwr Bursa & Lgmt, [Opn, Perc, Perc Endo], [Auto Tissue Sub, Nonauto Tissue Sub], NQ
ØMTØ[Ø,4]ZZ   Resect/Head and Neck Bursa & Lgmt, [Opn, Perc Endo]
ØMT1[Ø,4]ZZ   Resect/Shldr Bursa & Lgmt, Rt, [Opn, Perc Endo]
ØMT2[Ø,4]ZZ   Resect/Shldr Bursa & Lgmt, Lt, [Opn, Perc Endo]
ØMT3[Ø,4]ZZ   Resect/Elbow Bursa & Lgmt, Rt, [Opn, Perc Endo]
ØMT4[Ø,4]ZZ   Resect/Elbow Bursa & Lgmt, Lt, [Opn, Perc Endo]
ØMT5[Ø,4]ZZ   Resect/Wrist Bursa & Lgmt, Rt, [Opn, Perc Endo]
ØMT6[Ø,4]ZZ   Resect/Wrist Bursa & Lgmt, Lt, [Opn, Perc Endo]
ØMT9[Ø,4]ZZ   Resect/Upr Extr Bursa & Lgmt, Rt, [Opn, Perc Endo]
ØMTB[Ø,4]ZZ   Resect/Upr Extr Bursa & Lgmt, Lt, [Opn, Perc Endo]
ØMTC[Ø,4]ZZ   Resect/Trunk Bursa & Lgmt, Rt, [Opn, Perc Endo]
ØMTD[Ø,4]ZZ   Resect/Trunk Bursa & Lgmt, Lt, [Opn, Perc Endo]
ØMTF[Ø,4]ZZ   Resect/Thorax Bursa & Lgmt, Rt, [Opn, Perc Endo]
ØMTG[Ø,4]ZZ   Resect/Thorax Bursa & Lgmt, Lt, [Opn, Perc Endo]
ØMTH[Ø,4]ZZ   Resect/Abd Bursa & Lgmt, Rt, [Opn, Perc Endo]
ØMTJ[Ø,4]ZZ   Resect/Abd Bursa & Lgmt, Lt, [Opn, Perc Endo]
ØMTK[Ø,4]ZZ   Resect/Perineum Bursa & Lgmt, [Opn, Perc Endo]
ØMTL[Ø,4]ZZ   Resect/Hip Bursa & Lgmt, Rt, [Opn, Perc Endo]
ØMTM[Ø,4]ZZ   Resect/Hip Bursa & Lgmt, Lt, [Opn, Perc Endo]
ØMTN[Ø,4]ZZ   Resect/Knee Bursa & Lgmt, Rt, [Opn, Perc Endo]
ØMTP[Ø,4]ZZ   Resect/Knee Bursa & Lgmt, Lt, [Opn, Perc Endo]
ØMTQ[Ø,4]ZZ   Resect/Ankle Bursa & Lgmt, Rt, [Opn, Perc Endo]
ØMTR[Ø,4]ZZ   Resect/Ankle Bursa & Lgmt, Lt, [Opn, Perc Endo]
ØMTS[Ø,4]ZZ   Resect/Foot Bursa & Lgmt, Rt, [Opn, Perc Endo]
ØMTT[Ø,4]ZZ   Resect/Foot Bursa & Lgmt, Lt, [Opn, Perc Endo]
ØMTV[Ø,4]ZZ   Resect/Lwr Extr Bursa & Lgmt, Rt, [Opn, Perc Endo]
ØMTW[Ø,4]ZZ   Resect/Lwr Extr Bursa & Lgmt, Lt, [Opn, Perc Endo]
ØMWX[Ø,3,4][Ø,7,J,K]Z   Rev/Upr Bursa & Lgmt, [Opn, Perc, Perc Endo], [Drain Dev, Auto Tissue Sub, Synth Sub, Nonauto Tissue Sub], NQ
ØMWY[Ø,3,4][Ø,7,J,K]Z   Rev/Lwr Bursa & Lgmt, [Opn, Perc, Perc Endo], [Drain Dev, Auto Tissue Sub, Synth Sub, Nonauto Tissue Sub], NQ
ØN5B[Ø,3,4]ZZ   Destr/Nasal Bone, [Opn, Perc, Perc Endo]
ØN5C[Ø,3,4]ZZ   Destr/Sphenoid Bone, Rt, [Opn, Perc, Perc Endo]
ØN5D[Ø,3,4]ZZ   Destr/Sphenoid Bone, Lt, [Opn, Perc, Perc Endo]
ØN5F[Ø,3,4]ZZ   Destr/Ethmoid Bone, Rt, [Opn, Perc, Perc Endo]
ØN5G[Ø,3,4]ZZ   Destr/Ethmoid Bone, Lt, [Opn, Perc, Perc Endo]
ØN5H[Ø,3,4]ZZ   Destr/Lacrimal Bone, Rt, [Opn, Perc, Perc Endo]
ØN5J[Ø,3,4]ZZ   Destr/Lacrimal Bone, Lt, [Opn, Perc, Perc Endo]
ØN5K[Ø,3,4]ZZ   Destr/Palatine Bone, Rt, [Opn, Perc, Perc Endo]
ØN5L[Ø,3,4]ZZ   Destr/Palatine Bone, Lt, [Opn, Perc, Perc Endo]
ØN5M[Ø,3,4]ZZ   Destr/Zygomatic Bone, Rt, [Opn, Perc, Perc Endo]
ØN5N[Ø,3,4]ZZ   Destr/Zygomatic Bone, Lt, [Opn, Perc, Perc Endo]
ØN5P[Ø,3,4]ZZ   Destr/Orbit, Rt, [Opn, Perc, Perc Endo]
ØN5Q[Ø,3,4]ZZ   Destr/Orbit, Lt, [Opn, Perc, Perc Endo]
ØN5R[Ø,3,4]ZZ   Destr/Maxilla, Rt, [Opn, Perc, Perc Endo]
ØN5S[Ø,3,4]ZZ   Destr/Maxilla, Lt, [Opn, Perc, Perc Endo]
ØN5T[Ø,3,4]ZZ   Destr/Mandible, Rt, [Opn, Perc, Perc Endo]
ØN5V[Ø,3,4]ZZ   Destr/Mandible, Lt, [Opn, Perc, Perc Endo]
ØN5X[Ø,3,4]ZZ   Destr/Hyoid Bone, [Opn, Perc, Perc Endo]
ØN8P[Ø,3,4]ZZ   Div/Orbit, Rt, [Opn, Perc, Perc Endo]
ØN8Q[Ø,3,4]ZZ   Div/Orbit, Lt, [Opn, Perc, Perc Endo]
ØN9C[Ø,3,4]ZX   Drain/Sphenoid Bone, Rt, [Opn, Perc, Perc Endo]
ØN9D[Ø,3,4]ZX   Drain/Sphenoid Bone, Lt, [Opn, Perc, Perc Endo]
ØN9F[Ø,3,4]ZX   Drain/Ethmoid Bone, Rt, [Opn, Perc, Perc Endo]
ØN9G[Ø,3,4]ZX   Drain/Ethmoid Bone, Lt, [Opn, Perc, Perc Endo]
ØN9H[Ø,3,4]ZX   Drain/Lacrimal Bone, Rt, [Opn, Perc, Perc Endo]
ØN9J[Ø,3,4]ZX   Drain/Lacrimal Bone, Lt, [Opn, Perc, Perc Endo]
ØN9K[Ø,3,4]ZX   Drain/Palatine Bone, Rt, [Opn, Perc, Perc Endo]
ØN9L[Ø,3,4]ZX   Drain/Palatine Bone, Lt, [Opn, Perc, Perc Endo]
ØN9M[Ø,3,4]ZX   Drain/Zygomatic Bone, Rt, [Opn, Perc, Perc Endo]
ØN9N[Ø,3,4]ZX   Drain/Zygomatic Bone, Lt, [Opn, Perc, Perc Endo]
ØN9P[Ø,3,4]ØZ   Drain/Orbit, Rt, [Opn, Perc, Perc Endo], Drain Dev, NQ
ØN9P[Ø,3,4]ZX   Drain/Orbit, Rt, [Opn, Perc, Perc Endo]
ØN9P[Ø,4]ZZ   Drain/Orbit, Rt, [Opn, Perc Endo]
ØN9Q[Ø,3,4]ØZ   Drain/Orbit, Lt, [Opn, Perc, Perc Endo], Drain Dev, NQ
ØN9Q[Ø,3,4]ZX   Drain/Orbit, Lt, [Opn, Perc, Perc Endo]
ØN9Q[Ø,4]ZZ   Drain/Orbit, Lt, [Opn, Perc Endo]
ØN9R[Ø,3,4]ZX   Drain/Maxilla, Rt, [Opn, Perc, Perc Endo]
ØN9S[Ø,3,4]ZX   Drain/Maxilla, Lt, [Opn, Perc, Perc Endo]
ØN9T[Ø,3,4]ZX   Drain/Mandible, Rt, [Opn, Perc, Perc Endo]
ØN9V[Ø,3,4]ZX   Drain/Mandible, Lt, [Opn, Perc, Perc Endo]
ØN9X[Ø,3,4]ZX   Drain/Hyoid Bone, [Opn, Perc, Perc Endo]
ØNBC[Ø,3,4]ZX   Exc/Sphenoid Bone, Rt, [Opn, Perc, Perc Endo]
ØNBD[Ø,3,4]ZX   Exc/Sphenoid Bone, Lt, [Opn, Perc, Perc Endo]
ØNBF[Ø,3,4]ZX   Exc/Ethmoid Bone, Rt, [Opn, Perc, Perc Endo]
ØNBG[Ø,3,4]ZX   Exc/Ethmoid Bone, Lt, [Opn, Perc, Perc Endo]
ØNBH[Ø,3,4]ZX   Exc/Lacrimal Bone, Rt, [Opn, Perc, Perc Endo]
ØNBJ[Ø,3,4]ZX   Exc/Lacrimal Bone, Lt, [Opn, Perc, Perc Endo]
ØNBK[Ø,3,4]ZX   Exc/Palatine Bone, Rt, [Opn, Perc, Perc Endo]
ØNBL[Ø,3,4]ZX   Exc/Palatine Bone, Lt, [Opn, Perc, Perc Endo]
ØNBM[Ø,3,4]ZX   Exc/Zygomatic Bone, Rt, [Opn, Perc, Perc Endo]
ØNBN[Ø,3,4]ZX   Exc/Zygomatic Bone, Lt, [Opn, Perc, Perc Endo]
ØNBP[Ø,3,4]Z[X,Z]   Exc/Orbit, Rt, [Opn, Perc, Perc Endo], No Dev, [Dx, NQ]
ØNBQ[Ø,3,4]Z[X,Z]   Exc/Orbit, Lt, [Opn, Perc, Perc Endo], No Dev, [Dx, NQ]
ØNBX[Ø,3,4]ZX   Exc/Hyoid Bone, [Opn, Perc, Perc Endo]
ØNNX[Ø,3,4]ZZ   Rls/Hyoid Bone, [Opn, Perc, Perc Endo]
ØNPW[Ø,3,4]JZ   Rmvl/Facial Bone, [Opn, Perc, Perc Endo], Synth Sub, NQ
ØNQB[Ø,3,4,X]ZZ   Rpr/Nasal Bone, [Opn, Perc, Perc Endo, Ext]
ØNQP[Ø,3,4,X]ZZ   Rpr/Orbit, Rt, [Opn, Perc, Perc Endo, Ext]
ØNQQ[Ø,3,4,X]ZZ   Rpr/Orbit, Lt, [Opn, Perc, Perc Endo, Ext]
ØNRB[Ø,3,4][7,J,K]Z   Replace/Nasal Bone, [Opn, Perc, Perc Endo], [Auto Tissue Sub, Synth Sub, Nonauto Tissue Sub], NQ
ØNRP[Ø,3,4][7,J]Z   Replace/Orbit, Rt, [Opn, Perc, Perc Endo], [Auto Tissue Sub, Synth Sub], NQ

Ⓣ **Transfer DRG**   ⓈⓅ **Special Payment**   * **Code Range**   **6th and 7th Character of ZZ = No Device, No Qualifier ZX = No Device, Diagnostic**

ØNRQ[Ø,3,4][7,J]Z	Replace/Orbit, Lt, [Opn, Perc, Perc Endo], [Auto Tissue Sub, Synth Sub], NQ
ØNSBØ[4,Z]Z	Repos/Nasal Bone, Opn, [Int Fix Dev, No Dev], NQ
ØNUB[Ø,3,4][7,J,K]Z	Supl/Nasal Bone, [Opn, Perc, Perc Endo], [Auto Tissue Sub, Synth Sub, Nonauto Tissue Sub], NQ
ØNUP[Ø,3,4]JZ	Supl/Orbit, Rt, [Opn, Perc, Perc Endo], Synth Sub, NQ
ØNUQ[Ø,3,4]JZ	Supl/Orbit, Lt, [Opn, Perc, Perc Endo], Synth Sub, NQ
ØP5Ø[Ø,3,4]ZZ	Destr/Sternum, [Opn, Perc, Perc Endo]
ØP51[Ø,3,4]ZZ	Destr/Rib, Rt, [Opn, Perc, Perc Endo]
ØP52[Ø,3,4]ZZ	Destr/Rib, Lt, [Opn, Perc, Perc Endo]
ØP53[Ø,3,4]ZZ	Destr/Cervical Vertebra, [Opn, Perc, Perc Endo]
ØP54[Ø,3,4]ZZ	Destr/Thoracic Vertebra, [Opn, Perc, Perc Endo]
ØP55[Ø,3,4]ZZ	Destr/Scapula, Rt, [Opn, Perc, Perc Endo]
ØP56[Ø,3,4]ZZ	Destr/Scapula, Lt, [Opn, Perc, Perc Endo]
ØP57[Ø,3,4]ZZ	Destr/Glenoid Cavity, Rt, [Opn, Perc, Perc Endo]
ØP58[Ø,3,4]ZZ	Destr/Glenoid Cavity, Lt, [Opn, Perc, Perc Endo]
ØP59[Ø,3,4]ZZ	Destr/Clavicle, Rt, [Opn, Perc, Perc Endo]
ØP5B[Ø,3,4]ZZ	Destr/Clavicle, Lt, [Opn, Perc, Perc Endo]
ØP5C[Ø,3,4]ZZ	Destr/Humeral Head, Rt, [Opn, Perc, Perc Endo]
ØP5D[Ø,3,4]ZZ	Destr/Humeral Head, Lt, [Opn, Perc, Perc Endo]
ØP5F[Ø,3,4]ZZ	Destr/Humeral Shaft, Rt, [Opn, Perc, Perc Endo]
ØP5G[Ø,3,4]ZZ	Destr/Humeral Shaft, Lt, [Opn, Perc, Perc Endo]
ØP5H[Ø,3,4]ZZ	Destr/Radius, Rt, [Opn, Perc, Perc Endo]
ØP5J[Ø,3,4]ZZ	Destr/Radius, Lt, [Opn, Perc, Perc Endo]
ØP5K[Ø,3,4]ZZ	Destr/Ulna, Rt, [Opn, Perc, Perc Endo]
ØP5L[Ø,3,4]ZZ	Destr/Ulna, Lt, [Opn, Perc, Perc Endo]
ØP5M[Ø,3,4]ZZ	Destr/Carpal, Rt, [Opn, Perc, Perc Endo]
ØP5N[Ø,3,4]ZZ	Destr/Carpal, Lt, [Opn, Perc, Perc Endo]
ØP5P[Ø,3,4]ZZ	Destr/Metacarpal, Rt, [Opn, Perc, Perc Endo]
ØP5Q[Ø,3,4]ZZ	Destr/Metacarpal, Lt, [Opn, Perc, Perc Endo]
ØP5R[Ø,3,4]ZZ	Destr/Thumb Phalanx, Rt, [Opn, Perc, Perc Endo]
ØP5S[Ø,3,4]ZZ	Destr/Thumb Phalanx, Lt, [Opn, Perc, Perc Endo]
ØP5T[Ø,3,4]ZZ	Destr/Finger Phalanx, Rt, [Opn, Perc, Perc Endo]
ØP5V[Ø,3,4]ZZ	Destr/Finger Phalanx, Lt, [Opn, Perc, Perc Endo]
ØP9Ø[Ø,3,4]ZX	Drain/Sternum, [Opn, Perc, Perc Endo]
ØP91[Ø,3,4]ZX	Drain/Rib, Rt, [Opn, Perc, Perc Endo]
ØP92[Ø,3,4]ZX	Drain/Rib, Lt, [Opn, Perc, Perc Endo]
ØP93[Ø,3,4]ZX	Drain/Cervical Vertebra, [Opn, Perc, Perc Endo]
ØP94[Ø,3,4]ZX	Drain/Thoracic Vertebra, [Opn, Perc, Perc Endo]
ØP95[Ø,3,4]ZX	Drain/Scapula, Rt, [Opn, Perc, Perc Endo]
ØP96[Ø,3,4]ZX	Drain/Scapula, Lt, [Opn, Perc, Perc Endo]
ØP97[Ø,3,4]ZX	Drain/Glenoid Cavity, Rt, [Opn, Perc, Perc Endo]
ØP98[Ø,3,4]ZX	Drain/Glenoid Cavity, Lt, [Opn, Perc, Perc Endo]
ØP99[Ø,3,4]ZX	Drain/Clavicle, Rt, [Opn, Perc, Perc Endo]
ØP9B[Ø,3,4]ZX	Drain/Clavicle, Lt, [Opn, Perc, Perc Endo]
ØP9C[Ø,3,4]ZX	Drain/Humeral Head, Rt, [Opn, Perc, Perc Endo]
ØP9D[Ø,3,4]ZX	Drain/Humeral Head, Lt, [Opn, Perc, Perc Endo]
ØP9F[Ø,3,4]ZX	Drain/Humeral Shaft, Rt, [Opn, Perc, Perc Endo]
ØP9G[Ø,3,4]ZX	Drain/Humeral Shaft, Lt, [Opn, Perc, Perc Endo]
ØP9H[Ø,3,4]ZX	Drain/Radius, Rt, [Opn, Perc, Perc Endo]
ØP9J[Ø,3,4]ZX	Drain/Radius, Lt, [Opn, Perc, Perc Endo]
ØP9K[Ø,3,4]ZX	Drain/Ulna, Rt, [Opn, Perc, Perc Endo]
ØP9L[Ø,3,4]ZX	Drain/Ulna, Lt, [Opn, Perc, Perc Endo]
ØP9M[Ø,3,4]ZX	Drain/Carpal, Rt, [Opn, Perc, Perc Endo]
ØP9N[Ø,3,4]ZX	Drain/Carpal, Lt, [Opn, Perc, Perc Endo]
ØP9P[Ø,3,4]ZX	Drain/Metacarpal, Rt, [Opn, Perc, Perc Endo]
ØP9Q[Ø,3,4]ZX	Drain/Metacarpal, Lt, [Opn, Perc, Perc Endo]
ØP9R[Ø,3,4]ZX	Drain/Thumb Phalanx, Rt, [Opn, Perc, Perc Endo]
ØP9S[Ø,3,4]ZX	Drain/Thumb Phalanx, Lt, [Opn, Perc, Perc Endo]
ØP9T[Ø,3,4]ZX	Drain/Finger Phalanx, Rt, [Opn, Perc, Perc Endo]
ØP9V[Ø,3,4]ZX	Drain/Finger Phalanx, Lt, [Opn, Perc, Perc Endo]
ØPBØ[Ø,3,4]ZX	Exc/Sternum, [Opn, Perc, Perc Endo]
ØPB1[Ø,3,4]ZX	Exc/Rib, Rt, [Opn, Perc, Perc Endo]
ØPB2[Ø,3,4]ZX	Exc/Rib, Lt, [Opn, Perc, Perc Endo]
ØPB3[Ø,3,4]ZX	Exc/Cervical Vertebra, [Opn, Perc, Perc Endo]
ØPB4[Ø,3,4]ZX	Exc/Thoracic Vertebra, [Opn, Perc, Perc Endo]
ØPB5[Ø,3,4]ZX	Exc/Scapula, Rt, [Opn, Perc, Perc Endo]
ØPB6[Ø,3,4]ZX	Exc/Scapula, Lt, [Opn, Perc, Perc Endo]
ØPB7[Ø,3,4]ZX	Exc/Glenoid Cavity, Rt, [Opn, Perc, Perc Endo]
ØPB8[Ø,3,4]ZX	Exc/Glenoid Cavity, Lt, [Opn, Perc, Perc Endo]
ØPB9[Ø,3,4]ZX	Exc/Clavicle, Rt, [Opn, Perc, Perc Endo]
ØPBB[Ø,3,4]ZX	Exc/Clavicle, Lt, [Opn, Perc, Perc Endo]
ØPBC[Ø,3,4]ZX	Exc/Humeral Head, Rt, [Opn, Perc, Perc Endo]
ØPBD[Ø,3,4]ZX	Exc/Humeral Head, Lt, [Opn, Perc, Perc Endo]
ØPBF[Ø,3,4]ZX	Exc/Humeral Shaft, Rt, [Opn, Perc, Perc Endo]
ØPBG[Ø,3,4]ZX	Exc/Humeral Shaft, Lt, [Opn, Perc, Perc Endo]
ØPBH[Ø,3,4]ZX	Exc/Radius, Rt, [Opn, Perc, Perc Endo]
ØPBJ[Ø,3,4]ZX	Exc/Radius, Lt, [Opn, Perc, Perc Endo]
ØPBK[Ø,3,4]ZX	Exc/Ulna, Rt, [Opn, Perc, Perc Endo]
ØPBL[Ø,3,4]ZX	Exc/Ulna, Lt, [Opn, Perc, Perc Endo]
ØPBM[Ø,3,4]ZX	Exc/Carpal, Rt, [Opn, Perc, Perc Endo]
ØPBN[Ø,3,4]ZX	Exc/Carpal, Lt, [Opn, Perc, Perc Endo]
ØPBP[Ø,3,4]ZX	Exc/Metacarpal, Rt, [Opn, Perc, Perc Endo]
ØPBQ[Ø,3,4]ZX	Exc/Metacarpal, Lt, [Opn, Perc, Perc Endo]
ØPBR[Ø,3,4]ZX	Exc/Thumb Phalanx, Rt, [Opn, Perc, Perc Endo]
ØPBS[Ø,3,4]ZX	Exc/Thumb Phalanx, Lt, [Opn, Perc, Perc Endo]
ØPBT[Ø,3,4]ZX	Exc/Finger Phalanx, Rt, [Opn, Perc, Perc Endo]
ØPBV[Ø,3,4]ZX	Exc/Finger Phalanx, Lt, [Opn, Perc, Perc Endo]
ØPPØ[Ø,3,4][4,7,J,K]Z	Rmvl/Sternum, [Opn, Perc, Perc Endo], [Int Fix Dev, Auto Tissue Sub, Synth Sub, Nonauto Tissue Sub], NQ
ØPP1[Ø,3,4][4,7,J,K]Z	Rmvl/Rib, Rt, [Opn, Perc, Perc Endo], [Int Fix Dev, Auto Tissue Sub, Synth Sub, Nonauto Tissue Sub], NQ
ØPP2[Ø,3,4][4,7,J,K]Z	Rmvl/Rib, Lt, [Opn, Perc, Perc Endo], [Int Fix Dev, Auto Tissue Sub, Synth Sub, Nonauto Tissue Sub], NQ
ØPP3[Ø,3,4][4,7,J,K]Z	Rmvl/Cervical Vertebra, [Opn, Perc, Perc Endo], [Int Fix Dev, Auto Tissue Sub, Synth Sub, Nonauto Tissue Sub], NQ
ØPP4[Ø,3,4][4,7,J,K]Z	Rmvl/Thoracic Vertebra, [Opn, Perc, Perc Endo], [Int Fix Dev, Auto Tissue Sub, Synth Sub, Nonauto Tissue Sub], NQ
ØPP5[Ø,3,4][4,7,J,K]Z	Rmvl/Scapula, Rt, [Opn, Perc, Perc Endo], [Int Fix Dev, Auto Tissue Sub, Synth Sub, Nonauto Tissue Sub], NQ
ØPP6[Ø,3,4][4,7,J,K]Z	Rmvl/Scapula, Lt, [Opn, Perc, Perc Endo], [Int Fix Dev, Auto Tissue Sub, Synth Sub, Nonauto Tissue Sub], NQ
ØPP7[Ø,3,4][4,7,J,K]Z	Rmvl/Glenoid Cavity, Rt, [Opn, Perc, Perc Endo], [Int Fix Dev, Auto Tissue Sub, Synth Sub, Nonauto Tissue Sub], NQ
ØPP8[Ø,3,4][4,7,J,K]Z	Rmvl/Glenoid Cavity, Lt, [Opn, Perc, Perc Endo], [Int Fix Dev, Auto Tissue Sub, Synth Sub, Nonauto Tissue Sub], NQ
ØPP9[Ø,3,4][4,7,J,K]Z	Rmvl/Clavicle, Rt, [Opn, Perc, Perc Endo], [Int Fix Dev, Auto Tissue Sub, Synth Sub, Nonauto Tissue Sub], NQ
ØPPB[Ø,3,4][4,7,J,K]Z	Rmvl/Clavicle, Lt, [Opn, Perc, Perc Endo], [Int Fix Dev, Auto Tissue Sub, Synth Sub, Nonauto Tissue Sub], NQ
ØPPC[Ø,3,4][4,5,7,J,K]Z	Rmvl/Humeral Head, Rt, [Opn, Perc, Perc Endo], [Int Fix Dev, Ext Fix Dev, Auto Tissue Sub, Synth Sub, Nonauto Tissue Sub], NQ
ØPPD[Ø,3,4][4,5,7,J,K]Z	Rmvl/Humeral Head, Lt, [Opn, Perc, Perc Endo], [Int Fix Dev, Ext Fix Dev, Auto Tissue Sub, Synth Sub, Nonauto Tissue Sub], NQ
ØPPF[Ø,3,4][4,5,7,J,K]Z	Rmvl/Humeral Shaft, Rt, [Opn, Perc, Perc Endo], [Int Fix Dev, Ext Fix Dev, Auto Tissue Sub, Synth Sub, Nonauto Tissue Sub], NQ
ØPPG[Ø,3,4][4,5,7,J,K]Z	Rmvl/Humeral Shaft, Lt, [Opn, Perc, Perc Endo], [Int Fix Dev, Ext Fix Dev, Auto Tissue Sub, Synth Sub, Nonauto Tissue Sub], NQ
ØPPH[Ø,3,4][4,5,7,J,K]Z	Rmvl/Radius, Rt, [Opn, Perc, Perc Endo], [Int Fix Dev, Ext Fix Dev, Auto Tissue Sub, Synth Sub, Nonauto Tissue Sub], NQ
ØPPJ[Ø,3,4][4,5,7,J,K]Z	Rmvl/Radius, Lt, [Opn, Perc, Perc Endo], [Int Fix Dev, Ext Fix Dev, Auto Tissue Sub, Synth Sub, Nonauto Tissue Sub], NQ
ØPPK[Ø,3,4][4,5,7,J,K]Z	Rmvl/Ulna, Rt, [Opn, Perc, Perc Endo], [Int Fix Dev, Ext Fix Dev, Auto Tissue Sub, Synth Sub, Nonauto Tissue Sub], NQ
ØPPL[Ø,3,4][4,5,7,J,K]Z	Rmvl/Ulna, Lt, [Opn, Perc, Perc Endo], [Int Fix Dev, Ext Fix Dev, Auto Tissue Sub, Synth Sub, Nonauto Tissue Sub], NQ
ØPPM[Ø,3,4][4,5,7,J,K]Z	Rmvl/Carpal, Rt, [Opn, Perc, Perc Endo], [Int Fix Dev, Ext Fix Dev, Auto Tissue Sub, Synth Sub, Nonauto Tissue Sub], NQ
ØPPN[Ø,3,4][4,5,7,J,K]Z	Rmvl/Carpal, Lt, [Opn, Perc, Perc Endo], [Int Fix Dev, Ext Fix Dev, Auto Tissue Sub, Synth Sub, Nonauto Tissue Sub], NQ
ØPPP[Ø,3,4][4,5,7,J,K]Z	Rmvl/Metacarpal, Rt, [Opn, Perc, Perc Endo], [Int Fix Dev, Ext Fix Dev, Auto Tissue Sub, Synth Sub, Nonauto Tissue Sub], NQ
ØPPQ[Ø,3,4][4,5,7,J,K]Z	Rmvl/Metacarpal, Lt, [Opn, Perc, Perc Endo], [Int Fix Dev, Ext Fix Dev, Auto Tissue Sub, Synth Sub, Nonauto Tissue Sub], NQ
ØPPR[Ø,3,4][4,5,7,J,K]Z	Rmvl/Thumb Phalanx, Rt, [Opn, Perc, Perc Endo], [Int Fix Dev, Ext Fix Dev, Auto Tissue Sub, Synth Sub, Nonauto Tissue Sub], NQ
ØPPS[Ø,3,4][4,5,7,J,K]Z	Rmvl/Thumb Phalanx, Lt, [Opn, Perc, Perc Endo], [Int Fix Dev, Ext Fix Dev, Auto Tissue Sub, Synth Sub, Nonauto Tissue Sub], NQ
ØPPT[Ø,3,4][4,5,7,J,K]Z	Rmvl/Finger Phalanx, Rt, [Opn, Perc, Perc Endo], [Int Fix Dev, Ext Fix Dev, Auto Tissue Sub, Synth Sub, Nonauto Tissue Sub], NQ
ØPPV[Ø,3,4][4,5,7,J,K]Z	Rmvl/Finger Phalanx, Lt, [Opn, Perc, Perc Endo], [Int Fix Dev, Ext Fix Dev, Auto Tissue Sub, Synth Sub, Nonauto Tissue Sub], NQ
ØPPY[Ø,3,4][Ø,M]Z	Rmvl/Upr Bone, [Opn, Perc, Perc Endo], [Drain Dev, Bone Growth Stimulator], NQ
ØPRH[Ø,3,4][7,K]Z	Replace/Radius, Rt, [Opn, Perc, Perc Endo], [Auto Tissue Sub, Nonauto Tissue Sub], NQ
ØPRJ[Ø,3,4][7,K]Z	Replace/Radius, Lt, [Opn, Perc, Perc Endo], [Auto Tissue Sub, Nonauto Tissue Sub], NQ
ØPRK[Ø,3,4][7,K]Z	Replace/Ulna, Rt, [Opn, Perc, Perc Endo], [Auto Tissue Sub, Nonauto Tissue Sub], NQ

Surgical **Medical** **CC Indicator** **MCC Indicator** **Procedure Proxy** PDxMCC **PDx acts as own MCC** PDxCC **PDx acts as own CC**

DRGs Associated with All MDCs—SURGICAL

0PRL[0,3,4][7,K]Z	Replace/Ulna, Lt, [Opn, Perc, Perc Endo], [Auto Tissue Sub, Nonauto Tissue Sub], NQ
0PSH[3,4][4,6]Z	Repos/Radius, Rt, [Perc, Perc Endo], [Int Fix Dev, Intramedullary Int Fix Dev], NQ
0PSJ[3,4][4,6]Z	Repos/Radius, Lt, [Perc, Perc Endo], [Int Fix Dev, Intramedullary Int Fix Dev], NQ
0PSK[3,4][4,6]Z	Repos/Ulna, Rt, [Perc, Perc Endo], [Int Fix Dev, Intramedullary Int Fix Dev], NQ
0PSL[3,4][4,6]Z	Repos/Ulna, Lt, [Perc, Perc Endo], [Int Fix Dev, Intramedullary Int Fix Dev], NQ
0PUH[0,3,4][7,K]Z	Supl/Radius, Rt, [Opn, Perc, Perc Endo], [Auto Tissue Sub, Nonauto Tissue Sub], NQ
0PUJ[0,3,4][7,K]Z	Supl/Radius, Lt, [Opn, Perc, Perc Endo], [Auto Tissue Sub, Nonauto Tissue Sub], NQ
0PUK[0,3,4][7,K]Z	Supl/Ulna, Rt, [Opn, Perc, Perc Endo], [Auto Tissue Sub, Nonauto Tissue Sub], NQ
0PUL[0,3,4][7,K]Z	Supl/Ulna, Lt, [Opn, Perc, Perc Endo], [Auto Tissue Sub, Nonauto Tissue Sub], NQ
0Q50[0,3,4]ZZ	Destr/Lumbar Vertebra, [Opn, Perc, Perc Endo]
0Q51[0,3,4]ZZ	Destr/Sacrum, [Opn, Perc, Perc Endo]
0Q52[0,3,4]ZZ	Destr/Pelvic Bone, Rt, [Opn, Perc, Perc Endo]
0Q53[0,3,4]ZZ	Destr/Pelvic Bone, Lt, [Opn, Perc, Perc Endo]
0Q54[0,3,4]ZZ	Destr/Acetab, Rt, [Opn, Perc, Perc Endo]
0Q55[0,3,4]ZZ	Destr/Acetab, Lt, [Opn, Perc, Perc Endo]
0Q56[0,3,4]ZZ	Destr/Upr Femur, Rt, [Opn, Perc, Perc Endo]
0Q57[0,3,4]ZZ	Destr/Upr Femur, Lt, [Opn, Perc, Perc Endo]
0Q58[0,3,4]ZZ	Destr/Femor Shaft, Rt, [Opn, Perc, Perc Endo]
0Q59[0,3,4]ZZ	Destr/Femor Shaft, Lt, [Opn, Perc, Perc Endo]
0Q5B[0,3,4]ZZ	Destr/Lwr Femur, Rt, [Opn, Perc, Perc Endo]
0Q5C[0,3,4]ZZ	Destr/Lwr Femur, Lt, [Opn, Perc, Perc Endo]
0Q5D[0,3,4]ZZ	Destr/Patella, Rt, [Opn, Perc, Perc Endo]
0Q5F[0,3,4]ZZ	Destr/Patella, Lt, [Opn, Perc, Perc Endo]
0Q5G[0,3,4]ZZ	Destr/Tibia, Rt, [Opn, Perc, Perc Endo]
0Q5H[0,3,4]ZZ	Destr/Tibia, Lt, [Opn, Perc, Perc Endo]
0Q5J[0,3,4]ZZ	Destr/Fibula, Rt, [Opn, Perc, Perc Endo]
0Q5K[0,3,4]ZZ	Destr/Fibula, Lt, [Opn, Perc, Perc Endo]
0Q5L[0,3,4]ZZ	Destr/Tarsal, Rt, [Opn, Perc, Perc Endo]
0Q5M[0,3,4]ZZ	Destr/Tarsal, Lt, [Opn, Perc, Perc Endo]
0Q5N[0,3,4]ZZ	Destr/Metatarsal, Rt, [Opn, Perc, Perc Endo]
0Q5P[0,3,4]ZZ	Destr/Metatarsal, Lt, [Opn, Perc, Perc Endo]
0Q5Q[0,3,4]ZZ	Destr/Toe Phalanx, Rt, [Opn, Perc, Perc Endo]
0Q5R[0,3,4]ZZ	Destr/Toe Phalanx, Lt, [Opn, Perc, Perc Endo]
0Q5S[0,3,4]ZZ	Destr/Coccyx, [Opn, Perc, Perc Endo]
0Q8L[0,3,4]ZZ	Div/Tarsal, Rt, [Opn, Perc, Perc Endo]
0Q8M[0,3,4]ZZ	Div/Tarsal, Lt, [Opn, Perc, Perc Endo]
0Q8N[0,3,4]ZZ	Div/Metatarsal, Rt, [Opn, Perc, Perc Endo]
0Q8P[0,3,4]ZZ	Div/Metatarsal, Lt, [Opn, Perc, Perc Endo]
0Q90[0,3,4]ZX	Drain/Lumbar Vertebra, [Opn, Perc, Perc Endo]
0Q91[0,3,4]ZX	Drain/Sacrum, [Opn, Perc, Perc Endo]
0Q92[0,3,4]ZX	Drain/Pelvic Bone, Rt, [Opn, Perc, Perc Endo]
0Q93[0,3,4]ZX	Drain/Pelvic Bone, Lt, [Opn, Perc, Perc Endo]
0Q94[0,3,4]ZX	Drain/Acetab, Rt, [Opn, Perc, Perc Endo]
0Q95[0,3,4]ZX	Drain/Acetab, Lt, [Opn, Perc, Perc Endo]
0Q96[0,3,4]ZX	Drain/Upr Femur, Rt, [Opn, Perc, Perc Endo]
0Q97[0,3,4]ZX	Drain/Upr Femur, Lt, [Opn, Perc, Perc Endo]
0Q98[0,3,4]ZX	Drain/Femor Shaft, Rt, [Opn, Perc, Perc Endo]
0Q99[0,3,4]ZX	Drain/Femor Shaft, Lt, [Opn, Perc, Perc Endo]
0Q9B[0,3,4]ZX	Drain/Lwr Femur, Rt, [Opn, Perc, Perc Endo]
0Q9C[0,3,4]ZX	Drain/Lwr Femur, Lt, [Opn, Perc, Perc Endo]
0Q9D[0,3,4]ZX	Drain/Patella, Rt, [Opn, Perc, Perc Endo]
0Q9F[0,3,4]ZX	Drain/Patella, Lt, [Opn, Perc, Perc Endo]
0Q9G[0,3,4]ZX	Drain/Tibia, Rt, [Opn, Perc, Perc Endo]
0Q9H[0,3,4]ZX	Drain/Tibia, Lt, [Opn, Perc, Perc Endo]
0Q9J[0,3,4]ZX	Drain/Fibula, Rt, [Opn, Perc, Perc Endo]
0Q9K[0,3,4]ZX	Drain/Fibula, Lt, [Opn, Perc, Perc Endo]
0Q9L[0,3,4]ZX	Drain/Tarsal, Rt, [Opn, Perc, Perc Endo]
0Q9M[0,3,4]ZX	Drain/Tarsal, Lt, [Opn, Perc, Perc Endo]
0Q9N[0,3,4]ZX	Drain/Metatarsal, Rt, [Opn, Perc, Perc Endo]
0Q9P[0,3,4]ZX	Drain/Metatarsal, Lt, [Opn, Perc, Perc Endo]
0Q9Q[0,3,4]ZX	Drain/Toe Phalanx, Rt, [Opn, Perc, Perc Endo]
0Q9R[0,3,4]ZX	Drain/Toe Phalanx, Lt, [Opn, Perc, Perc Endo]
0Q9S[0,3,4]ZX	Drain/Coccyx, [Opn, Perc, Perc Endo]
0QB0[0,3,4]ZX	Exc/Lumbar Vertebra, [Opn, Perc, Perc Endo]
0QB1[0,3,4]ZX	Exc/Sacrum, [Opn, Perc, Perc Endo]
0QB2[0,3,4]ZX	Exc/Pelvic Bone, Rt, [Opn, Perc, Perc Endo]
0QB3[0,3,4]ZX	Exc/Pelvic Bone, Lt, [Opn, Perc, Perc Endo]
0QB4[0,3,4]ZX	Exc/Acetab, Rt, [Opn, Perc, Perc Endo]
0QB5[0,3,4]ZX	Exc/Acetab, Lt, [Opn, Perc, Perc Endo]
0QB6[0,3,4]ZX	Exc/Upr Femur, Rt, [Opn, Perc, Perc Endo]
0QB7[0,3,4]ZX	Exc/Upr Femur, Lt, [Opn, Perc, Perc Endo]
0QB8[0,3,4]ZX	Exc/Femor Shaft, Rt, [Opn, Perc, Perc Endo]
0QB9[0,3,4]ZX	Exc/Femor Shaft, Lt, [Opn, Perc, Perc Endo]
0QBB[0,3,4]ZX	Exc/Lwr Femur, Rt, [Opn, Perc, Perc Endo]
0QBC[0,3,4]ZX	Exc/Lwr Femur, Lt, [Opn, Perc, Perc Endo]
0QBD[0,3,4]ZX	Exc/Patella, Rt, [Opn, Perc, Perc Endo]
0QBF[0,3,4]ZX	Exc/Patella, Lt, [Opn, Perc, Perc Endo]
0QBG[0,3,4]ZX	Exc/Tibia, Rt, [Opn, Perc, Perc Endo]
0QBH[0,3,4]ZX	Exc/Tibia, Lt, [Opn, Perc, Perc Endo]
0QBJ[0,3,4]ZX	Exc/Fibula, Rt, [Opn, Perc, Perc Endo]
0QBK[0,3,4]ZX	Exc/Fibula, Lt, [Opn, Perc, Perc Endo]
0QBL[0,3,4]Z[X,Z]	Exc/Tarsal, Rt, [Opn, Perc, Perc Endo], No Dev, [Dx, NQ]
0QBM[0,3,4]Z[X,Z]	Exc/Tarsal, Lt, [Opn, Perc, Perc Endo], No Dev, [Dx, NQ]
0QBN[0,3,4]Z[X,Z]	Exc/Metatarsal, Rt, [Opn, Perc, Perc Endo], No Dev, [Dx, NQ]
0QBP[0,3,4]Z[X,Z]	Exc/Metatarsal, Lt, [Opn, Perc, Perc Endo], No Dev, [Dx, NQ]
0QBQ[0,3,4]ZX	Exc/Toe Phalanx, Rt, [Opn, Perc, Perc Endo]
0QBR[0,3,4]ZX	Exc/Toe Phalanx, Lt, [Opn, Perc, Perc Endo]
0QBS[0,3,4]ZX	Exc/Coccyx, [Opn, Perc, Perc Endo]
0QP0[0,3,4][4,7,J,K]Z	Rmvl/Lumbar Vertebra, [Opn, Perc, Perc Endo], [Int Fix Dev, Auto Tissue Sub, Synth Sub, Nonauto Tissue Sub], NQ
0QP1[0,3,4][4,7,J,K]Z	Rmvl/Sacrum, [Opn, Perc, Perc Endo], [Int Fix Dev, Auto Tissue Sub, Synth Sub, Nonauto Tissue Sub], NQ
0QP2[0,3,4][4,5,7,J,K]Z	Rmvl/Pelvic Bone, Rt, [Opn, Perc, Perc Endo], [Int Fix Dev, Ext Fix Dev, Auto Tissue Sub, Synth Sub, Nonauto Tissue Sub], NQ
0QP3[0,3,4][4,5,7,J,K]Z	Rmvl/Pelvic Bone, Lt, [Opn, Perc, Perc Endo], [Int Fix Dev, Ext Fix Dev, Auto Tissue Sub, Synth Sub, Nonauto Tissue Sub], NQ
0QP4[0,3,4][4,7,J,K]Z	Rmvl/Acetab, Rt, [Opn, Perc, Perc Endo], [Int Fix Dev, Auto Tissue Sub, Synth Sub, Nonauto Tissue Sub], NQ
0QP5[0,3,4][4,7,J,K]Z	Rmvl/Acetab, Lt, [Opn, Perc, Perc Endo], [Int Fix Dev, Auto Tissue Sub, Synth Sub, Nonauto Tissue Sub], NQ
0QP6[0,3,4][4,5,7,J,K]Z	Rmvl/Upr Femur, Rt, [Opn, Perc, Perc Endo], [Int Fix Dev, Ext Fix Dev, Auto Tissue Sub, Synth Sub, Nonauto Tissue Sub], NQ
0QP7[0,3,4][4,5,7,J,K]Z	Rmvl/Upr Femur, Lt, [Opn, Perc, Perc Endo], [Int Fix Dev, Ext Fix Dev, Auto Tissue Sub, Synth Sub, Nonauto Tissue Sub], NQ
0QP8[0,3,4][4,5,7,J,K]Z	Rmvl/Femor Shaft, Rt, [Opn, Perc, Perc Endo], [Int Fix Dev, Ext Fix Dev, Auto Tissue Sub, Synth Sub, Nonauto Tissue Sub], NQ
0QP9[0,3,4][4,5,7,J,K]Z	Rmvl/Femor Shaft, Lt, [Opn, Perc, Perc Endo], [Int Fix Dev, Ext Fix Dev, Auto Tissue Sub, Synth Sub, Nonauto Tissue Sub], NQ
0QPB[0,3,4][4,5,7,J,K]Z	Rmvl/Lwr Femur, Rt, [Opn, Perc, Perc Endo], [Int Fix Dev, Ext Fix Dev, Auto Tissue Sub, Synth Sub, Nonauto Tissue Sub], NQ
0QPC[0,3,4][4,5,7,J,K]Z	Rmvl/Lwr Femur, Lt, [Opn, Perc, Perc Endo], [Int Fix Dev, Ext Fix Dev, Auto Tissue Sub, Synth Sub, Nonauto Tissue Sub], NQ
0QPD[0,3,4][4,5,7,J,K]Z	Rmvl/Patella, Rt, [Opn, Perc, Perc Endo], [Int Fix Dev, Ext Fix Dev, Auto Tissue Sub, Synth Sub, Nonauto Tissue Sub], NQ
0QPF[0,3,4][4,5,7,J,K]Z	Rmvl/Patella, Lt, [Opn, Perc, Perc Endo], [Int Fix Dev, Ext Fix Dev, Auto Tissue Sub, Synth Sub, Nonauto Tissue Sub], NQ
0QPG[0,3,4][4,5,7,J,K]Z	Rmvl/Tibia, Rt, [Opn, Perc, Perc Endo], [Int Fix Dev, Ext Fix Dev, Auto Tissue Sub, Synth Sub, Nonauto Tissue Sub], NQ
0QPH[0,3,4][4,5,7,J,K]Z	Rmvl/Tibia, Lt, [Opn, Perc, Perc Endo], [Int Fix Dev, Ext Fix Dev, Auto Tissue Sub, Synth Sub, Nonauto Tissue Sub], NQ
0QPJ[0,3,4][4,5,7,J,K]Z	Rmvl/Fibula, Rt, [Opn, Perc, Perc Endo], [Int Fix Dev, Ext Fix Dev, Auto Tissue Sub, Synth Sub, Nonauto Tissue Sub], NQ
0QPK[0,3,4][4,5,7,J,K]Z	Rmvl/Fibula, Lt, [Opn, Perc, Perc Endo], [Int Fix Dev, Ext Fix Dev, Auto Tissue Sub, Synth Sub, Nonauto Tissue Sub], NQ
0QPL[0,3,4][4,5,7,J,K]Z	Rmvl/Tarsal, Rt, [Opn, Perc, Perc Endo], [Int Fix Dev, Ext Fix Dev, Auto Tissue Sub, Synth Sub, Nonauto Tissue Sub], NQ
0QPM[0,3,4][4,5,7,J,K]Z	Rmvl/Tarsal, Lt, [Opn, Perc, Perc Endo], [Int Fix Dev, Ext Fix Dev, Auto Tissue Sub, Synth Sub, Nonauto Tissue Sub], NQ
0QPN[0,3,4][4,5,7,J,K]Z	Rmvl/Metatarsal, Rt, [Opn, Perc, Perc Endo], [Int Fix Dev, Ext Fix Dev, Auto Tissue Sub, Synth Sub, Nonauto Tissue Sub], NQ
0QPP[0,3,4][4,5,7,J,K]Z	Rmvl/Metatarsal, Lt, [Opn, Perc, Perc Endo], [Int Fix Dev, Ext Fix Dev, Auto Tissue Sub, Synth Sub, Nonauto Tissue Sub], NQ
0QPQ[0,3,4][4,5,7,J,K]Z	Rmvl/Toe Phalanx, Rt, [Opn, Perc, Perc Endo], [Int Fix Dev, Ext Fix Dev, Auto Tissue Sub, Synth Sub, Nonauto Tissue Sub], NQ
0QPR[0,3,4][4,5,7,J,K]Z	Rmvl/Toe Phalanx, Lt, [Opn, Perc, Perc Endo], [Int Fix Dev, Ext Fix Dev, Auto Tissue Sub, Synth Sub, Nonauto Tissue Sub], NQ
0QPS[0,3,4][4,7,J,K]Z	Rmvl/Coccyx, [Opn, Perc, Perc Endo], [Int Fix Dev, Auto Tissue Sub, Synth Sub, Nonauto Tissue Sub], NQ

Ⓣ **Transfer DRG**   ⓈⓅ **Special Payment**   * **Code Range**   **6th and 7th Character of ZZ = No Device, No Qualifier ZX = No Device, Diagnostic**

ØQPY[Ø,3,4][Ø,M]Z Rmvl/Lwr Bone, [Opn, Perc, Perc Endo], [Drain Dev, Bone Growth Stimulator], NQ
ØQTLØZZ Resect of Rt Tarsal, Opn Appr
ØQTMØZZ Resect of Lt Tarsal, Opn Appr
ØQTNØZZ Resect of Rt Metatarsal, Opn Appr
ØQTPØZZ Resect of Lt Metatarsal, Opn Appr
ØR5C[Ø,3,4]ZZ Destr/Temporomandibular Jt, Rt, [Opn, Perc, Perc Endo]
ØR5D[Ø,3,4]ZZ Destr/Temporomandibular Jt, Lt, [Opn, Perc, Perc Endo]
ØR9C[Ø,3,4]ZX Drain/Temporomandibular Jt, Rt, [Opn, Perc, Perc Endo]
ØR9D[Ø,3,4]ZX Drain/Temporomandibular Jt, Lt, [Opn, Perc, Perc Endo]
ØRBC[Ø,3,4]Z[X,Z] Exc/Temporomandibular Jt, Rt, [Opn, Perc, Perc Endo], No Dev, [Dx, NQ]
ØRBD[Ø,3,4]Z[X,Z] Exc/Temporomandibular Jt, Lt, [Opn, Perc, Perc Endo], No Dev, [Dx, NQ]
ØRBE[Ø,3,4]ZZ Exc/Sternoclavicular Jt, Rt, [Opn, Perc, Perc Endo]
ØRBF[Ø,3,4]ZZ Exc/Sternoclavicular Jt, Lt, [Opn, Perc, Perc Endo]
ØRBG[Ø,3,4]ZZ Exc/Acromioclavicular Jt, Rt, [Opn, Perc, Perc Endo]
ØRBH[Ø,3,4]ZZ Exc/Acromioclavicular Jt, Lt, [Opn, Perc, Perc Endo]
ØRBJ[Ø,3,4]ZZ Exc/Shldr Jt, Rt, [Opn, Perc, Perc Endo]
ØRBK[Ø,3,4]ZZ Exc/Shldr Jt, Lt, [Opn, Perc, Perc Endo]
ØRBL[Ø,3,4]ZZ Exc/Elbow Jt, Rt, [Opn, Perc, Perc Endo]
ØRBM[Ø,3,4]ZZ Exc/Elbow Jt, Lt, [Opn, Perc, Perc Endo]
ØRBN[Ø,3,4]ZZ Exc/Wrist Jt, Rt, [Opn, Perc, Perc Endo]
ØRBP[Ø,3,4]ZZ Exc/Wrist Jt, Lt, [Opn, Perc, Perc Endo]
ØRBQ[Ø,3,4]ZZ Exc/Carpal Jt, Rt, [Opn, Perc, Perc Endo]
ØRBR[Ø,3,4]ZZ Exc/Carpal Jt, Lt, [Opn, Perc, Perc Endo]
ØRBS[Ø,3,4]ZZ Exc/Metacarpocarpal Jt, Rt, [Opn, Perc, Perc Endo]
ØRBT[Ø,3,4]ZZ Exc/Metacarpocarpal Jt, Lt, [Opn, Perc, Perc Endo]
ØRBU[Ø,3,4]ZZ Exc/Metacarpophalangeal Jt, Rt, [Opn, Perc, Perc Endo]
ØRBV[Ø,3,4]ZZ Exc/Metacarpophalangeal Jt, Lt, [Opn, Perc, Perc Endo]
ØRBW[Ø,3,4]ZZ Exc/Finger Phalangeal Jt, Rt, [Opn, Perc, Perc Endo]
ØRBX[Ø,3,4]ZZ Exc/Finger Phalangeal Jt, Lt, [Opn, Perc, Perc Endo]
ØRQE[Ø,3,4,X]ZZ Rpr/Sternoclavicular Jt, Rt, [Opn, Perc, Perc Endo, Ext]
ØRQF[Ø,3,4,X]ZZ Rpr/Sternoclavicular Jt, Lt, [Opn, Perc, Perc Endo, Ext]
ØRQG[Ø,3,4,X]ZZ Rpr/Acromioclavicular Jt, Rt, [Opn, Perc, Perc Endo, Ext]
ØRQH[Ø,3,4,X]ZZ Rpr/Acromioclavicular Jt, Lt, [Opn, Perc, Perc Endo, Ext]
ØRQJ[Ø,3,4,X]ZZ Rpr/Shldr Jt, Rt, [Opn, Perc, Perc Endo, Ext]
ØRQK[Ø,3,4,X]ZZ Rpr/Shldr Jt, Lt, [Opn, Perc, Perc Endo, Ext]
ØRUE[Ø,3,4][7,J,K]Z Supl/Sternoclavicular Jt, Rt, [Opn, Perc, Perc Endo], [Auto Tissue Sub, Synth Sub, Nonauto Tissue Sub], NQ
ØRUF[Ø,3,4][7,J,K]Z Supl/Sternoclavicular Jt, Lt, [Opn, Perc, Perc Endo], [Auto Tissue Sub, Synth Sub, Nonauto Tissue Sub], NQ
ØRUG[Ø,3,4][7,J,K]Z Supl/Acromioclavicular Jt, Rt, [Opn, Perc, Perc Endo], [Auto Tissue Sub, Synth Sub, Nonauto Tissue Sub], NQ
ØRUH[Ø,3,4][7,J,K]Z Supl/Acromioclavicular Jt, Lt, [Opn, Perc, Perc Endo], [Auto Tissue Sub, Synth Sub, Nonauto Tissue Sub], NQ
ØRUJ[Ø,3,4][7,J,K]Z Supl/Shldr Jt, Rt, [Opn, Perc, Perc Endo], [Auto Tissue Sub, Synth Sub, Nonauto Tissue Sub], NQ
ØRUK[Ø,3,4][7,J,K]Z Supl/Shldr Jt, Lt, [Opn, Perc, Perc Endo], [Auto Tissue Sub, Synth Sub, Nonauto Tissue Sub], NQ
ØS5C[Ø,3,4]ZZ Destr/Knee Jt, Rt, [Opn, Perc, Perc Endo]
ØS5D[Ø,3,4]ZZ Destr/Knee Jt, Lt, [Opn, Perc, Perc Endo]
ØS5H[Ø,3,4]ZZ Destr/Tarsal Jt, Rt, [Opn, Perc, Perc Endo]
ØS5J[Ø,3,4]ZZ Destr/Tarsal Jt, Lt, [Opn, Perc, Perc Endo]
ØS5K[Ø,3,4]ZZ Destr/Metatarsal-Tarsal Jt, Rt, [Opn, Perc, Perc Endo]
ØS5L[Ø,3,4]ZZ Destr/Metatarsal-Tarsal Jt, Lt, [Opn, Perc, Perc Endo]
ØS5M[Ø,3,4]ZZ Destr/Metatarsal-Phalangeal Jt, Rt, [Opn, Perc, Perc Endo]
ØS5N[Ø,3,4]ZZ Destr/Metatarsal-Phalangeal Jt, Lt, [Opn, Perc, Perc Endo]
ØS5P[Ø,3,4]ZZ Destr/Toe Phalangeal Jt, Rt, [Opn, Perc, Perc Endo]
ØS5Q[Ø,3,4]ZZ Destr/Toe Phalangeal Jt, Lt, [Opn, Perc, Perc Endo]
ØS9C[Ø,Z]Z Drain/Knee Jt, Rt, Opn, [Drain Dev, No Dev], NQ
ØS9DØ[Ø,Z]Z Drain/Knee Jt, Lt, Opn, [Drain Dev, No Dev], NQ
ØS9HØ[Ø,Z]Z Drain/Tarsal Jt, Rt, Opn, [Drain Dev, No Dev], NQ
ØS9JØ[Ø,Z]Z Drain/Tarsal Jt, Lt, Opn, [Drain Dev, No Dev], NQ
ØS9KØ[Ø,Z]Z Drain/Metatarsal-Tarsal Jt, Rt, Opn, [Drain Dev, No Dev], NQ
ØS9LØ[Ø,Z]Z Drain/Metatarsal-Tarsal Jt, Lt, Opn, [Drain Dev, No Dev], NQ
ØS9MØ[Ø,Z]Z Drain/Metatarsal-Phalangeal Jt, Rt, Opn, [Drain Dev, No Dev], NQ
ØS9NØ[Ø,Z]Z Drain/Metatarsal-Phalangeal Jt, Lt, Opn, [Drain Dev, No Dev], NQ
ØS9PØ[Ø,Z]Z Drain/Toe Phalangeal Jt, Rt, Opn, [Drain Dev, No Dev], NQ
ØS9QØ[Ø,Z]Z Drain/Toe Phalangeal Jt, Lt, Opn, [Drain Dev, No Dev], NQ
ØSBC[Ø,3,4]ZZ Exc/Knee Jt, Rt, [Opn, Perc, Perc Endo]
ØSBD[Ø,3,4]ZZ Exc/Knee Jt, Lt, [Opn, Perc, Perc Endo]
ØSBF[Ø,3,4]ZZ Exc/Ankle Jt, Rt, [Opn, Perc, Perc Endo]
ØSBG[Ø,3,4]ZZ Exc/Ankle Jt, Lt, [Opn, Perc, Perc Endo]
ØSBH[Ø,3,4]ZZ Exc/Tarsal Jt, Rt, [Opn, Perc, Perc Endo]
ØSBJ[Ø,3,4]ZZ Exc/Tarsal Jt, Lt, [Opn, Perc, Perc Endo]
ØSBK[Ø,3,4]ZZ Exc/Metatarsal-Tarsal Jt, Rt, [Opn, Perc, Perc Endo]
ØSBL[Ø,3,4]ZZ Exc/Metatarsal-Tarsal Jt, Lt, [Opn, Perc, Perc Endo]

ØSBM[Ø,3,4]ZZ Exc/Metatarsal-Phalangeal Jt, Rt, [Opn, Perc, Perc Endo]
ØSBN[Ø,3,4]ZZ Exc/Metatarsal-Phalangeal Jt, Lt, [Opn, Perc, Perc Endo]
ØSBP[Ø,3,4]ZZ Exc/Toe Phalangeal Jt, Rt, [Opn, Perc, Perc Endo]
ØSBQ[Ø,3,4]ZZ Exc/Toe Phalangeal Jt, Lt, [Opn, Perc, Perc Endo]
ØSCC[Ø,3,4]ZZ Extir/Knee Jt, Rt, [Opn, Perc, Perc Endo]
ØSCD[Ø,3,4]ZZ Extir/Knee Jt, Lt, [Opn, Perc, Perc Endo]
ØSCH[Ø,3,4]ZZ Extir/Tarsal Jt, Rt, [Opn, Perc, Perc Endo]
ØSCJ[Ø,3,4]ZZ Extir/Tarsal Jt, Lt, [Opn, Perc, Perc Endo]
ØSCK[Ø,3,4]ZZ Extir/Metatarsal-Tarsal Jt, Rt, [Opn, Perc, Perc Endo]
ØSCL[Ø,3,4]ZZ Extir/Metatarsal-Tarsal Jt, Lt, [Opn, Perc, Perc Endo]
ØSCM[Ø,3,4]ZZ Extir/Metatarsal-Phalangeal Jt, Rt, [Opn, Perc, Perc Endo]
ØSCN[Ø,3,4]ZZ Extir/Metatarsal-Phalangeal Jt, Lt, [Opn, Perc, Perc Endo]
ØSCP[Ø,3,4]ZZ Extir/Toe Phalangeal Jt, Rt, [Opn, Perc, Perc Endo]
ØSCQ[Ø,3,4]ZZ Extir/Toe Phalangeal Jt, Lt, [Opn, Perc, Perc Endo]
ØSGP[Ø,3,4][4,5,7,J,K,Z]Z Fusion/Toe Phalangeal Jt, Rt, [Opn, Perc, Perc Endo], [Int Fix Dev, Ext Fix Dev, Auto Tissue Sub, Synth Sub, Nonauto Tissue Sub, No Dev], NQ
ØSGQ[Ø,3,4][4,5,7,J,K,Z]ZF usion/Toe Phalangeal Jt, Lt, [Opn, Perc, Perc Endo], [Int Fix Dev, Ext Fix Dev, Auto Tissue Sub, Synth Sub, Nonauto Tissue Sub, No Dev], NQ
ØSHC[Ø,3,4][4,5]Z Insert/Knee Jt, Rt, [Opn, Perc, Perc Endo], [Int Fix Dev, Ext Fix Dev], NQ
ØSHD[Ø,3,4][4,5]Z Insert/Knee Jt, Lt, [Opn, Perc, Perc Endo], [Int Fix Dev, Ext Fix Dev], NQ
ØSHH[Ø,3,4][4,5]Z Insert/Tarsal Jt, Rt, [Opn, Perc, Perc Endo], [Int Fix Dev, Ext Fix Dev], NQ
ØSHJ[Ø,3,4][4,5]Z Insert/Tarsal Jt, Lt, [Opn, Perc, Perc Endo], [Int Fix Dev, Ext Fix Dev], NQ
ØSHK[Ø,3,4][4,5]Z Insert/Metatarsal-Tarsal Jt, Rt, [Opn, Perc, Perc Endo], [Int Fix Dev, Ext Fix Dev], NQ
ØSHL[Ø,3,4][4,5]Z Insert/Metatarsal-Tarsal Jt, Lt, [Opn, Perc, Perc Endo], [Int Fix Dev, Ext Fix Dev], NQ
ØSHM[Ø,3,4][4,5]Z Insert/Metatarsal-Phalangeal Jt, Rt, [Opn, Perc, Perc Endo], [Int Fix Dev, Ext Fix Dev], NQ
ØSHN[Ø,3,4][4,5]Z Insert/Metatarsal-Phalangeal Jt, Lt, [Opn, Perc, Perc Endo], [Int Fix Dev, Ext Fix Dev], NQ
ØSHP[Ø,3,4][4,5]Z Insert/Toe Phalangeal Jt, Rt, [Opn, Perc, Perc Endo], [Int Fix Dev, Ext Fix Dev], NQ
ØSHQ[Ø,3,4][4,5]Z Insert/Toe Phalangeal Jt, Lt, [Opn, Perc, Perc Endo], [Int Fix Dev, Ext Fix Dev], NQ
ØSJC[Ø,4]ZZ Inspect/Knee Jt, Rt, [Opn, Perc Endo]
ØSJD[Ø,4]ZZ Inspect/Knee Jt, Lt, [Opn, Perc Endo]
ØSJHØZZ Inspect of Rt Tarsal Jt, Opn Appr
ØSJJØZZ Inspect of Lt Tarsal Jt, Opn Appr
ØSJKØZZ Inspect of Rt Metatarsal-Tarsal Jt, Opn Appr
ØSJLØZZ Inspect of Lt Metatarsal-Tarsal Jt, Opn Appr
ØSJMØZZ Inspect of Rt Metatarsophal Jt, Opn Appr
ØSJNØZZ Inspect of Lt Metatarsophal Jt, Opn Appr
ØSJPØZZ Inspect of Rt Toe Phalangeal Jt, Opn Appr
ØSJQØZZ Inspect of Lt Toe Phalangeal Jt, Opn Appr
ØSNC[Ø,3,4]ZZ Rls/Knee Jt, Rt, [Opn, Perc, Perc Endo]
ØSND[Ø,3,4]ZZ Rls/Knee Jt, Lt, [Opn, Perc, Perc Endo]
ØSPC[Ø,3,4][Ø,3,4,5,7,K]Z Rmvl/Knee Jt, Rt, [Opn, Perc, Perc Endo], [Drain Dev, Inf Dev, Int Fix Dev, Ext Fix Dev, Auto Tissue Sub, Nonauto Tissue Sub], NQ
ØSPD[Ø,3,4][Ø,3,4,5,7,K]Z Rmvl/Knee Jt, Lt, [Opn, Perc, Perc Endo], [Drain Dev, Inf Dev, Int Fix Dev, Ext Fix Dev, Auto Tissue Sub, Nonauto Tissue Sub], NQ
ØSPH[Ø,3,4][Ø,3,4,5,7,K]Z Rmvl/Tarsal Jt, Rt, [Opn, Perc, Perc Endo], [Drain Dev, Inf Dev, Int Fix Dev, Ext Fix Dev, Auto Tissue Sub, Nonauto Tissue Sub], NQ
ØSPJ[Ø,3,4][Ø,3,4,5,7,K]Z Rmvl/Tarsal Jt, Lt, [Opn, Perc, Perc Endo], [Drain Dev, Inf Dev, Int Fix Dev, Ext Fix Dev, Auto Tissue Sub, Nonauto Tissue Sub], NQ
ØSPK[Ø,3,4][Ø,3,4,5,7,K]Z Rmvl/Metatarsal-Tarsal Jt, Rt, [Opn, Perc, Perc Endo], [Drain Dev, Inf Dev, Int Fix Dev, Ext Fix Dev, Auto Tissue Sub, Nonauto Tissue Sub], NQ
ØSPL[Ø,3,4][Ø,3,4,5,7,K]Z Rmvl/Metatarsal-Tarsal Jt, Lt, [Opn, Perc, Perc Endo], [Drain Dev, Inf Dev, Int Fix Dev, Ext Fix Dev, Auto Tissue Sub, Nonauto Tissue Sub], NQ
ØSPM[Ø,3,4][Ø,3,4,5,7,K]Z Rmvl/Metatarsal-Phalangeal Jt, Rt, [Opn, Perc, Perc Endo], [Drain Dev, Inf Dev, Int Fix Dev, Ext Fix Dev, Auto Tissue Sub, Nonauto Tissue Sub], NQ
ØSPN[Ø,3,4][Ø,3,4,5,7,K]Z Rmvl/Metatarsal-Phalangeal Jt, Lt, [Opn, Perc, Perc Endo], [Drain Dev, Inf Dev, Int Fix Dev, Ext Fix Dev, Auto Tissue Sub, Nonauto Tissue Sub], NQ
ØSPP[Ø,3,4][Ø,3,4,5,7,K]Z Rmvl/Toe Phalangeal Jt, Rt, [Opn, Perc, Perc Endo], [Drain Dev, Inf Dev, Int Fix Dev, Ext Fix Dev, Auto Tissue Sub, Nonauto Tissue Sub], NQ

Surgical **Medical** **CC Indicator** **MCC Indicator** **Procedure Proxy** **PDx MCC** PDx acts as own MCC **PDx CC** PDx acts as own CC

ØSPQ[Ø,3,4][Ø,3,4,5,7,K]Z Rmvl/Toe Phalangeal Jt, Lt, [Opn, Perc, Perc Endo], [Drain Dev, Inf Dev, Int Fix Dev, Ext Fix Dev, Auto Tissue Sub, Nonauto Tissue Sub], NQ

ØSRHØ[7,J,K]Z Replace/Tarsal Jt, Rt, Opn, [Auto Tissue Sub, Synth Sub, Nonauto Tissue Sub], NQ

ØSRJØ[7,J,K]Z Replace/Tarsal Jt, Lt, Opn, [Auto Tissue Sub, Synth Sub, Nonauto Tissue Sub], NQ

ØSRKØ[7,J,K]Z Replace/Metatarsal-Tarsal Jt, Rt, Opn, [Auto Tissue Sub, Synth Sub, Nonauto Tissue Sub], NQ

ØSRLØ[7,J,K]Z Replace/Metatarsal-Tarsal Jt, Lt, Opn, [Auto Tissue Sub, Synth Sub, Nonauto Tissue Sub], NQ

ØSRMØ[7,J,K]Z Replace/Metatarsal-Phalangeal Jt, Rt, Opn, [Auto Tissue Sub, Synth Sub, Nonauto Tissue Sub], NQ

ØSRNØ[7,J,K]Z Replace/Metatarsal-Phalangeal Jt, Lt, Opn, [Auto Tissue Sub, Synth Sub, Nonauto Tissue Sub], NQ

ØSRPØ[7,J,K]Z Replace/Toe Phalangeal Jt, Rt, Opn, [Auto Tissue Sub, Synth Sub, Nonauto Tissue Sub], NQ

ØSRQØ[7,J,K]Z Replace/Toe Phalangeal Jt, Lt, Opn, [Auto Tissue Sub, Synth Sub, Nonauto Tissue Sub], NQ

ØSTHØZZ Resect of Rt Tarsal Jt, Opn Appr

ØSTJØZZ Resect of Lt Tarsal Jt, Opn Appr

ØSTKØZZ Resect of Rt Metatarsal-Tarsal Jt, Opn Appr

ØSTLØZZ Resect of Lt Metatarsal-Tarsal Jt, Opn Appr

ØSTMØZZ Resect of Rt Metatarsophal Jt, Opn Appr

ØSTNØZZ Resect of Lt Metatarsal-Phalangeal Jt, Opn Appr

ØSTPØZZ Resect of Rt Toe Phalangeal Jt, Opn Appr

ØSTQØZZ Resect of Lt Toe Phalangeal Jt, Opn Appr

ØSWCØ9Z Rev of Liner in Rt Knee Jt, Opn Appr

ØSWC[Ø,3,4][Ø,3,4,5,7,8,K]Z R ev/Knee Jt, Rt, [Opn, Perc, Perc Endo], [Drain Dev, Inf Dev, Int Fix Dev, Ext Fix Dev, Auto Tissue Sub, Spacer, Nonauto Tissue Sub], NQ

ØSWDØ9Z Rev of Liner in Lt Knee Jt, Opn Appr

ØSWD[Ø,3,4][Ø,3,4,5,7,8,K]Z Rev/Knee Jt, Lt, [Opn, Perc, Perc Endo], [Drain Dev, Inf Dev, Int Fix Dev, Ext Fix Dev, Auto Tissue Sub, Spacer, Nonauto Tissue Sub], NQ

ØSWH[Ø,3,4][Ø,3,4,5,7,8,K]Z Rev/Tarsal Jt, Rt, [Opn, Perc, Perc Endo], [Drain Dev, Inf Dev, Int Fix Dev, Ext Fix Dev, Auto Tissue Sub, Spacer, Nonauto Tissue Sub], NQ

ØSWJ[Ø,3,4][Ø,3,4,5,7,8,K]Z Rev/Tarsal Jt, Lt, [Opn, Perc, Perc Endo], [Drain Dev, Inf Dev, Int Fix Dev, Ext Fix Dev, Auto Tissue Sub, Spacer, Nonauto Tissue Sub], NQ

ØSWK[Ø,3,4][Ø,3,4,5,7,8,K]Z Rev/Metatarsal-Tarsal Jt, Rt, [Opn, Perc, Perc Endo], [Drain Dev, Inf Dev, Int Fix Dev, Ext Fix Dev, Auto Tissue Sub, Spacer, Nonauto Tissue Sub], NQ

ØSWL[Ø,3,4][Ø,3,4,5,7,8,K]Z Rev/Metatarsal-Tarsal Jt, Lt, [Opn, Perc, Perc Endo], [Drain Dev, Inf Dev, Int Fix Dev, Ext Fix Dev, Auto Tissue Sub, Spacer, Nonauto Tissue Sub], NQ

ØSWM[Ø,3,4][Ø,3,4,5,7,8,K]Z Rev/Metatarsal-Phalangeal Jt, Rt, [Opn, Perc, Perc Endo], [Drain Dev, Inf Dev, Int Fix Dev, Ext Fix Dev, Auto Tissue Sub, Spacer, Nonauto Tissue Sub], NQ

ØSWN[Ø,3,4][Ø,3,4,5,7,8,K]Z Rev/Metatarsal-Phalangeal Jt, Lt, [Opn, Perc, Perc Endo], [Drain Dev, Inf Dev, Int Fix Dev, Ext Fix Dev, Auto Tissue Sub, Spacer, Nonauto Tissue Sub], NQ

ØSWP[Ø,3,4][Ø,3,4,5,7,8,K]Z Rev/Toe Phalangeal Jt, Rt, [Opn, Perc, Perc Endo], [Drain Dev, Inf Dev, Int Fix Dev, Ext Fix Dev, Auto Tissue Sub, Spacer, Nonauto Tissue Sub], NQ

ØSWQ[Ø,3,4][Ø,3,4,5,7,8,K]Z Rev/Toe Phalangeal Jt, Lt, [Opn, Perc, Perc Endo], [Drain Dev, Inf Dev, Int Fix Dev, Ext Fix Dev, Auto Tissue Sub, Spacer, Nonauto Tissue Sub], NQ

ØT5B[Ø,3,4,7,8]ZZ Destr/Bladder, [Opn, Perc, Perc Endo, Via Natrl or Artfcl Opng, Via Natrl or Artfcl Opng Endo]

ØT5C[Ø,3,4,7,8]ZZ Destr/Bladder Neck, [Opn, Perc, Perc Endo, Via Natrl or Artfcl Opng, Via Natrl or Artfcl Opng Endo]

ØT76[Ø,3,4,7,8]ZZ Dilation/Ureter, Rt, [Opn, Perc, Perc Endo, Via Natrl or Artfcl Opng, Via Natrl or Artfcl Opng Endo]

ØT77[Ø,3,4,7,8]ZZ Dilation/Ureter, Lt, [Opn, Perc, Perc Endo, Via Natrl or Artfcl Opng, Via Natrl or Artfcl Opng Endo]

ØT7D[Ø,3,4]ZZ Dilation/Urethra, [Opn, Perc, Perc Endo]

ØT8C[Ø,3,4]ZZ Div/Bladder Neck, [Opn, Perc, Perc Endo]

ØT93[7,8]ØZ Drain/Kidney Pelvis, Rt, [Via Natrl or Artfcl Opng, Via Natrl or Artfcl Opng Endo], Drain Dev, NQ

ØT94[7,8]ØZ Drain/Kidney Pelvis, Lt, [Via Natrl or Artfcl Opng, Via Natrl or Artfcl Opng Endo], Drain Dev, NQ

ØT96[Ø,3,4,7,8]ZZ Drain/Ureter, Rt, [Opn, Perc, Perc Endo, Via Natrl or Artfcl Opng, Via Natrl or Artfcl Opng Endo]

ØT97[Ø,3,4,7,8]ZZ Drain/Ureter, Lt, [Opn, Perc, Perc Endo, Via Natrl or Artfcl Opng, Via Natrl or Artfcl Opng Endo]

ØT98[Ø,3,4,7,8]ZZ Drain/Ureters, Bilat, [Opn, Perc, Perc Endo, Via Natrl or Artfcl Opng, Via Natrl or Artfcl Opng Endo]

ØT9B[3,4,7,8]ZX Drain/Bladder, [Perc, Perc Endo, Via Natrl or Artfcl Opng, Via Natrl or Artfcl Opng Endo]

ØT9C[3,4,7,8]ZX Drain/Bladder Neck, [Perc, Perc Endo, Via Natrl or Artfcl Opng, Via Natrl or Artfcl Opng Endo]

ØT9D[Ø,3,4]ØZ Drain/Urethra, [Opn, Perc, Perc Endo], Drain Dev, NQ

ØTBB[3,4,7,8]ZX Exc/Bladder, [Perc, Perc Endo, Via Natrl or Artfcl Opng, Via Natrl or Artfcl Opng Endo]

ØTBB[7,8]ZZ Exc/Bladder, [Via Natrl or Artfcl Opng, Via Natrl or Artfcl Opng Endo]

ØTBC[3,4,7,8]ZX Exc/Bladder Neck, [Perc, Perc Endo, Via Natrl or Artfcl Opng, Via Natrl or Artfcl Opng Endo]

ØTBC[7,8]ZZ Exc/Bladder Neck, [Via Natrl or Artfcl Opng, Via Natrl or Artfcl Opng Endo]

ØTC3[7,8]ZZ Extir/Kidney Pelvis, Rt, [Via Natrl or Artfcl Opng, Via Natrl or Artfcl Opng Endo]

ØTC4[7,8]ZZ Extir/Kidney Pelvis, Lt, [Via Natrl or Artfcl Opng, Via Natrl or Artfcl Opng Endo]

ØTC6[Ø,3,4,7,8]ZZ Extir/Ureter, Rt, [Opn, Perc, Perc Endo, Via Natrl or Artfcl Opng, Via Natrl or Artfcl Opng Endo]

ØTC7[Ø,3,4,7,8]ZZ Extir/Ureter, Lt, [Opn, Perc, Perc Endo, Via Natrl or Artfcl Opng, Via Natrl or Artfcl Opng Endo]

ØTCD[Ø,3,4]ZZ Extir/Urethra, [Opn, Perc, Perc Endo]

ØTH9[Ø,3,4,7,8]2Z Insert/Ureter, [Opn, Perc, Perc Endo, Via Natrl or Artfcl Opng, Via Natrl or Artfcl Opng Endo], Monitoring Dev, NQ

ØTHD[Ø,3,4,7,8,X]2Z Insert/Urethra, [Opn, Perc, Perc Endo, Via Natrl or Artfcl Opng, Via Natrl or Artfcl Opng Endo, Ext], Monitoring Dev, NQ

ØTJ9[Ø,3,7]ZZ Inspect/Ureter, [Opn, Perc, Via Natrl or Artfcl Opng]

ØTJB[3,4]ZZ Inspect/Bladder, [Perc, Perc Endo]

ØTJDØZZ Inspect of Urethra, Opn Appr

ØTLD[Ø,3,4,7,8,X][D,Z]Z Occlsn/Urethra, [Opn, Perc, Perc Endo, Via Natrl or Artfcl Opng, Via Natrl or Artfcl Opng Endo, Ext], [Intralum Dev, No Dev], NQ

ØTLD[Ø,3,4,X]CZ Occlsn/Urethra, [Opn, Perc, Perc Endo, Ext], Extralum Dev, NQ

ØTND[Ø,3,4,7,8,X]ZZ Rls/Urethra, [Opn, Perc, Perc Endo, Via Natrl or Artfcl Opng, Via Natrl or Artfcl Opng Endo, Ext]

ØTP9[Ø,3,4,7,8][Ø,2,3,7,C,D,J,K]ZRmvl/Ureter, [Opn, Perc, Perc Endo, Via Natrl or Artfcl Opng, Via Natrl or Artfcl Opng Endo], [Drain Dev, Monitoring Dev, Inf Dev, Auto Tissue Sub, Extralum Dev, Intralum Dev, Synth Sub, Nonauto Tissue Sub], NQ

ØTPB[Ø,3,4,7,8,X]MZ Rmvl/Bladder, [Opn, Perc, Perc Endo, Via Natrl or Artfcl Opng, Via Natrl or Artfcl Opng Endo, Ext], Stimulator Lead, NQ

ØTPDXLZ Rmvl of Artif Sphincter from Urethra, Extern Appr

ØTPD[Ø,3,4,7,8][Ø,2,3,7,C,D,J,K,L]Z Rmvl/Urethra, [Opn, Perc, Perc Endo, Via Natrl or Artfcl Opng, Via Natrl or Artfcl Opng Endo], [Drain Dev, Monitoring Dev, Inf Dev, Auto Tissue Sub, Extralum Dev, Intralum Dev, Synth Sub, Nonauto Tissue Sub, Artfcl Sphincter], NQ

ØTUC[Ø,4,7,8]JZ Supl/Bladder Neck, [Opn, Perc Endo, Via Natrl or Artfcl Opng, Via Natrl or Artfcl Opng Endo], Synth Sub, NQ

ØTW9[Ø,3,4,7,8][Ø,2,3,7,C,D,J,K,M]Z Rev/Ureter, [Opn, Perc, Perc Endo, Via Natrl or Artfcl Opng, Via Natrl or Artfcl Opng Endo], [Drain Dev, Monitoring Dev, Inf Dev, Auto Tissue Sub, Extralum Dev, Intralum Dev, Synth Sub, Nonauto Tissue Sub, Stimulator Lead], NQ

ØTWD[Ø,3,4,7,8][Ø,2,3,7,C,D,J,K,L]Z Rev/Urethra, [Opn, Perc, Perc Endo, Via Natrl or Artfcl Opng, Via Natrl or Artfcl Opng Endo], [Drain Dev, Monitoring Dev, Inf Dev, Auto Tissue Sub, Extralum Dev, Intralum Dev, Synth Sub, Nonauto Tissue Sub, Artfcl Sphincter], NQ

ØU57[Ø,3,4,7,8]ZZ Destr/Fallopian Tubes, Bilat, [Opn, Perc, Perc Endo, Via Natrl or Artfcl Opng, Via Natrl or Artfcl Opng Endo]

ØU59[Ø,3,4,7,8]ZZ Destr/Uterus, [Opn, Perc, Perc Endo, Via Natrl or Artfcl Opng, Via Natrl or Artfcl Opng Endo]

ØU5C[Ø,3,4,7,8]ZZ Destr/Cervix, [Opn, Perc, Perc Endo, Via Natrl or Artfcl Opng, Via Natrl or Artfcl Opng Endo]

ØU5F[Ø,3,4,7,8]ZZ Destr/Cul-de-sac, [Opn, Perc, Perc Endo, Via Natrl or Artfcl Opng, Via Natrl or Artfcl Opng Endo]

ØU5G[Ø,3,4,7,8,X]ZZ Destr/Vagina, [Opn, Perc, Perc Endo, Via Natrl or Artfcl Opng, Via Natrl or Artfcl Opng Endo, Ext]

ØU5J[Ø,X]ZZ Destr/Clitoris, [Opn, Ext]

ØU5KXZZ Destr of Hymen, Ext Appr

ØU5K[Ø,3,4,7,8]ZZ Destr/Hymen, [Opn, Perc, Perc Endo, Via Natrl or Artfcl Opng, Via Natrl or Artfcl Opng Endo]

ØU5L[Ø,X]ZZ Destr/Vestibular Gland, [Opn, Ext]

ØU5M[Ø,X]ZZ Destr/Vulva, [Opn, Ext]

ØU94[3,4]ZX Drain/Uterine Supporting Structure, [Perc, Perc Endo]

ØU99[3,4,7,8]ZX Drain/Uterus, [Perc, Perc Endo, Via Natrl or Artfcl Opng, Via Natrl or Artfcl Opng Endo]

ØU9C[Ø,3,4,7,8]ZX Drain/Cervix, [Opn, Perc, Perc Endo, Via Natrl or Artfcl Opng, Via Natrl or Artfcl Opng Endo]

T Transfer DRG   SP Special Payment   * Code Range   6th and 7th Character of ZZ = No Device, No Qualifier ZX = No Device, Diagnostic

ØU9C[Ø,3,4,7,8][Ø,Z]Z Drain/Cervix, [Opn, Perc, Perc Endo, Via Natrl or Artfcl Opng, Via Natrl or Artfcl Opng Endo], [Drain Dev, No Dev], NQ

ØU9F[Ø,3,4,7,8]ZX Drain/Cul-de-sac, [Opn, Perc, Perc Endo, Via Natrl or Artfcl Opng, Via Natrl or Artfcl Opng Endo]

ØU9G[Ø,3,4,7,8,X]ZX Drain/Vagina, [Opn, Perc, Perc Endo, Via Natrl or Artfcl Opng, Via Natrl or Artfcl Opng Endo, Ext]

ØU9G[Ø,3,4,7,8,X][Ø,Z]Z Drain/Vagina, [Opn, Perc, Perc Endo, Via Natrl or Artfcl Opng, Via Natrl or Artfcl Opng Endo, Ext], [Drain Dev, No Dev], NQ

ØU9J[Ø,X]ZX Drain/Clitoris, [Opn, Ext]

ØU9J[Ø,X][Ø,Z]Z Drain/Clitoris, [Opn, Ext], [Drain Dev, No Dev], NQ

ØU9KXZX Drain of Hymen, Ext Appr, Diagnostic

ØU9K[Ø,3,4,7,8]ZX Drain/Hymen, [Opn, Perc, Perc Endo, Via Natrl or Artfcl Opng, Via Natrl or Artfcl Opng Endo]

ØU9L[Ø,X]ZX Drain/Vestibular Gland, [Opn, Ext]

ØU9M[Ø,X]ZX Drain/Vulva, [Opn, Ext]

ØU9M[Ø,X][Ø,Z]Z Drain/Vulva, [Opn, Ext], [Drain Dev, No Dev], NQ

ØUB4[3,4,7,8]ZX Exc/Uterine Supporting Structure, [Perc, Perc Endo, Via Natrl or Artfcl Opng, Via Natrl or Artfcl Opng Endo]

ØUB9[Ø,3,4,7,8]ZZ Exc/Uterus, [Opn, Perc, Perc Endo, Via Natrl or Artfcl Opng, Via Natrl or Artfcl Opng Endo]

ØUB9[3,4,7,8]ZX Exc/Uterus, [Perc, Perc Endo, Via Natrl or Artfcl Opng, Via Natrl or Artfcl Opng Endo]

ØUBC[Ø,3,4,7,8]Z[X,Z] Exc/Cervix, [Opn, Perc, Perc Endo, Via Natrl or Artfcl Opng, Via Natrl or Artfcl Opng Endo], No Dev, [Dx, NQ]

ØUBF[Ø,3,4,7,8]Z[X,Z] Exc/Cul-de-sac, [Opn, Perc, Perc Endo, Via Natrl or Artfcl Opng, Via Natrl or Artfcl Opng Endo], No Dev, [Dx, NQ]

ØUBG[Ø,3,4,7,8,X]Z[X,Z] Exc/Vagina, [Opn, Perc, Perc Endo, Via Natrl or Artfcl Opng, Via Natrl or Artfcl Opng Endo, Ext], No Dev, [Dx, NQ]

ØUBJ[Ø,X]Z[X,Z] Exc/Clitoris, [Opn, Ext], No Dev, [Dx, NQ]

ØUBKXZX Exc of Hymen, Ext Appr, Diagnostic

ØUBKXZZ Exc of Hymen, Ext Appr

ØUBK[Ø,3,4,7,8]Z[X,Z] Exc/Hymen, [Opn, Perc, Perc Endo, Via Natrl or Artfcl Opng, Via Natrl or Artfcl Opng Endo], No Dev, [Dx, NQ]

ØUBL[Ø,X]Z[X,Z] Exc/Vestibular Gland, [Opn, Ext], No Dev, [Dx, NQ]

ØUBM[Ø,X]ZX Exc/Vulva, [Opn, Ext]

ØUCG[Ø,3,4]ZZ Extir/Vagina, [Opn, Perc, Perc Endo]

ØUCJ[Ø,X]ZZ Extir/Clitoris, [Opn, Ext]

ØUCL[Ø,X]ZZ Extir/Vestibular Gland, [Opn, Ext]

ØUCMØZZ Extir of Matter from Vulva, Opn Appr

ØUDB[7,8]Z[X,Z] Extract/Endometrium, [Via Natrl or Artfcl Opng, Via Natrl or Artfcl Opng Endo], No Dev, [Dx, NQ]

ØUHC[Ø,3,4,7,8]1Z Insert/Cervix, [Opn, Perc, Perc Endo, Via Natrl or Artfcl Opng, Via Natrl or Artfcl Opng Endo], Radioact Elmt, NQ

ØUHG[Ø,3,4,7,8,X]1Z Insert/Vagina, [Opn, Perc, Perc Endo, Via Natrl or Artfcl Opng, Via Natrl or Artfcl Opng Endo, Ext], Radioact Elmt, NQ

ØUHH[Ø,3,4,7,8]3Z Insert/Vagina and Cul-de-sac, [Opn, Perc, Perc Endo, Via Natrl or Artfcl Opng, Via Natrl or Artfcl Opng Endo], Inf Dev, NQ

ØUJH[Ø,3,4,7]ZZ Inspect/Vagina and Cul-de-sac, [Opn, Perc, Perc Endo, Via Natrl or Artfcl Opng]

ØUJMØZZ Inspect of Vulva, Opn Appr

ØUL5[Ø,3,4,7,8][D,Z]Z Occlsn/Fallopian Tube, Rt, [Opn, Perc, Perc Endo, Via Natrl or Artfcl Opng, Via Natrl or Artfcl Opng Endo], [Intralum Dev, No Dev], NQ

ØUL5[Ø,3,4]CZ Occlsn/Fallopian Tube, Rt, [Opn, Perc, Perc Endo], Extralum Dev, NQ

ØUL6[Ø,3,4,7,8][D,Z]Z Occlsn/Fallopian Tube, Lt, [Opn, Perc, Perc Endo, Via Natrl or Artfcl Opng, Via Natrl or Artfcl Opng Endo], [Intralum Dev, No Dev], NQ

ØUL6[Ø,3,4]CZ Occlsn/Fallopian Tube, Lt, [Opn, Perc, Perc Endo], Extralum Dev, NQ

ØUL7[Ø,3,4,7,8][D,Z]Z Occlsn/Fallopian Tubes, Bilat, [Opn, Perc, Perc Endo, Via Natrl or Artfcl Opng, Via Natrl or Artfcl Opng Endo], [Intralum Dev, No Dev], NQ

ØUL7[Ø,3,4]CZ Occlsn/Fallopian Tubes, Bilat, [Opn, Perc, Perc Endo], Extralum Dev, NQ

ØUMJXZZ Reattach of Clitoris, Ext Appr

ØUMKXZZ Reattach of Hymen, Ext Appr

ØUMK[Ø,4]ZZ Reattach/Hymen, [Opn, Perc Endo]

ØUMMXZZ Reattach of Vulva, Ext Appr

ØUNJ[Ø,X]ZZ Rls/Clitoris, [Opn, Ext]

ØUNKXZZ Rls Hymen, Ext Appr

ØUNK[Ø,3,4,7,8]ZZ Rls/Hymen, [Opn, Perc, Perc Endo, Via Natrl or Artfcl Opng, Via Natrl or Artfcl Opng Endo]

ØUNL[Ø,X]ZZ Rls/Vestibular Gland, [Opn, Ext]

ØUPDØCZ Rmvl of Extralum Dev from Uterus & Cervix, Opn Appr

ØUPH[Ø,3,4,7,8][Ø,1,3,7,D,J,K]Z Rmvl/Vagina and Cul-de-sac, [Opn, Perc, Perc Endo, Via Natrl or Artfcl Opng, Via Natrl or Artfcl Opng Endo], [Drain Dev, Radioact Elmt, Inf Dev, Auto Tissue Sub, Intralum Dev, Synth Sub, Nonauto Tissue Sub], NQ

ØUPMØ[Ø,7,J,K]Z Rmvl/Vulva, Opn, [Drain Dev, Auto Tissue Sub, Synth Sub, Nonauto Tissue Sub], NQ

ØUQJ[Ø,X]ZZ Rpr/Clitoris, [Opn, Ext]

ØUQKXZZ Repair Hymen, Ext Appr

ØUQK[Ø,3,4,7,8]ZZ Rpr/Hymen, [Opn, Perc, Perc Endo, Via Natrl or Artfcl Opng, Via Natrl or Artfcl Opng Endo]

ØUQL[Ø,X]ZZ Rpr/Vestibular Gland, [Opn, Ext]

ØUT9[7,8,F]ZZ Resect/Uterus, [Via Natrl or Artfcl Opng, Via Natrl or Artfcl Opng Endo, Via Natrl or Artfcl Opng w/ Perc Endo Assistance]

ØUTJ[Ø,X]ZZ Resect/Clitoris, [Opn, Ext]

ØUTKXZZ Resect of Hymen, Ext Appr

ØUTK[Ø,4,7,8]ZZ Resect/Hymen, [Opn, Perc Endo, Via Natrl or Artfcl Opng, Via Natrl or Artfcl Opng Endo]

ØUTL[Ø,X]ZZ Resect/Vestibular Gland, [Opn, Ext]

ØUUJ[Ø,X][7,J,K]Z Supl/Clitoris, [Opn, Ext], [Auto Tissue Sub, Synth Sub, Nonauto Tissue Sub], NQ

ØUUM[Ø,X][7,J,K]Z Supl/Vulva, [Opn, Ext], [Auto Tissue Sub, Synth Sub, Nonauto Tissue Sub], NQ

ØUWD[Ø,3,4,7,8]CZ Rev/Uterus and Cervix, [Opn, Perc, Perc Endo, Via Natrl or Artfcl Opng, Via Natrl or Artfcl Opng Endo], Extralum Dev, NQ

ØUWH[Ø,3,4,7,8][Ø,1,3,7,D,J,K]Z Rev/Vagina and Cul-de-sac, [Opn, Perc, Perc Endo, Via Natrl or Artfcl Opng, Via Natrl or Artfcl Opng Endo], [Drain Dev, Radioact Elmt, Inf Dev, Auto Tissue Sub, Intralum Dev, Synth Sub, Nonauto Tissue Sub], NQ

ØUWMØ[Ø,7,J,K]Z Rev/Vulva, Opn, [Drain Dev, Auto Tissue Sub, Synth Sub, Nonauto Tissue Sub], NQ

ØV5F[Ø,3,4]ZZ Destr/Spermatic Cord, Rt, [Opn, Perc, Perc Endo]

ØV5G[Ø,3,4]ZZ Destr/Spermatic Cord, Lt, [Opn, Perc, Perc Endo]

ØV5H[Ø,3,4]ZZ Destr/Spermatic Cords, Bilat, [Opn, Perc, Perc Endo]

ØV5J[Ø,3,4]ZZ Destr/Epididymis, Rt, [Opn, Perc, Perc Endo]

ØV5K[Ø,3,4]ZZ Destr/Epididymis, Lt, [Opn, Perc, Perc Endo]

ØV5L[Ø,3,4]ZZ Destr/Epididymis, Bilat, [Opn, Perc, Perc Endo]

ØV5S[Ø,3,4,X]ZZ Destr/Penis, [Opn, Perc, Perc Endo, Ext]

ØV5T[Ø,3,4,X]ZZ Destr/Prepuce, [Opn, Perc, Perc Endo, Ext]

ØV9S[Ø,3,4,X]ZX Drain/Penis, [Opn, Perc, Perc Endo, Ext]

ØV9S[Ø,3,4,X][Ø,Z]Z Drain/Penis, [Opn, Perc, Perc Endo, Ext], [Drain Dev, No Dev], NQ

ØV9T[Ø,3,4,X]ZX Drain/Prepuce, [Opn, Perc, Perc Endo, Ext]

ØV9T[Ø,3,4,X][Ø,Z]Z Drain/Prepuce, [Opn, Perc, Perc Endo, Ext], [Drain Dev, No Dev], NQ

ØVB6ØZZ Exc of Rt Tunica Vaginalis, Opn Appr

ØVB7ØZZ Exc of Lt Tunica Vaginalis, Opn Appr

ØVBF[Ø,3,4]ZZ Exc/Spermatic Cord, Rt, [Opn, Perc, Perc Endo]

ØVBG[Ø,3,4]ZZ Exc/Spermatic Cord, Lt, [Opn, Perc, Perc Endo]

ØVBH[Ø,3,4]ZZ Exc/Spermatic Cords, Bilat, [Opn, Perc, Perc Endo]

ØVBJ[Ø,3,4]ZZ Exc/Epididymis, Rt, [Opn, Perc, Perc Endo]

ØVBK[Ø,3,4]ZZ Exc/Epididymis, Lt, [Opn, Perc, Perc Endo]

ØVBL[Ø,3,4]ZZ Exc/Epididymis, Bilat, [Opn, Perc, Perc Endo]

ØVBS[Ø,3,4,X]Z[X,Z] Exc/Penis, [Opn, Perc, Perc Endo, Ext], No Dev, [Dx, NQ]

ØVBT[Ø,3,4,X]Z[X,Z] Exc/Prepuce, [Opn, Perc, Perc Endo, Ext], No Dev, [Dx, NQ]

ØVCS[Ø,3,4]ZZ Extir/Penis, [Opn, Perc, Perc Endo]

ØVCT[Ø,3,4,X]ZZ Extir/Prepuce, [Opn, Perc, Perc Endo, Ext]

ØVHØ[Ø,3,4,7,8]1Z Insert/Prostate, [Opn, Perc, Perc Endo, Via Natrl or Artfcl Opng, Via Natrl or Artfcl Opng Endo], Radioact Elmt, NQ

ØVJM[Ø,3,4]ZZ Inspect/Epididymis and Spermatic Cord, [Opn, Perc, Perc Endo]

ØVJR[Ø,3,4]ZZ Inspect/Vas Deferens, [Opn, Perc, Perc Endo]

ØVNS[Ø,3,4]ZZ Rls/Penis, [Opn, Perc, Perc Endo]

ØVPS[Ø,3,4,7,8][Ø,3,7,J,K]Z Rmvl/Penis, [Opn, Perc, Perc Endo, Via Natrl or Artfcl Opng, Via Natrl or Artfcl Opng Endo], [Drain Dev, Inf Dev, Auto Tissue Sub, Synth Sub, Nonauto Tissue Sub], NQ

ØVQS[Ø,3,4]ZZ Rpr/Penis, [Opn, Perc, Perc Endo]

ØVQT[Ø,3,4,X]ZZ Rpr/Prepuce, [Opn, Perc, Perc Endo, Ext]

ØVTF[Ø,4]ZZ Resect/Spermatic Cord, Rt, [Opn, Perc Endo]

ØVTG[Ø,4]ZZ Resect/Spermatic Cord, Lt, [Opn, Perc Endo]

ØVTH[Ø,4]ZZ Resect/Spermatic Cords, Bilat, [Opn, Perc Endo]

ØVUS[Ø,4]JZ Supl/Penis, [Opn, Perc Endo], Synth Sub, NQ

ØVUT[Ø,4,X][7,J,K]Z Supl/Prepuce, [Opn, Perc Endo, Ext], [Auto Tissue Sub, Synth Sub, Nonauto Tissue Sub], NQ

ØVWS[Ø,3,4,7,8][Ø,3,7,J,K]Z Rev/Penis, [Opn, Perc, Perc Endo, Via Natrl or Artfcl Opng, Via Natrl or Artfcl Opng Endo], [Drain Dev, Inf Dev, Auto Tissue Sub, Synth Sub, Nonauto Tissue Sub], NQ

ØW00[Ø,3,4][7,J,K,Z]Z Alter/Head, [Opn, Perc, Perc Endo], [Auto Tissue Sub, Synth Sub, Nonauto Tissue Sub, No Dev], NQ

ØW02[Ø,3,4][7,J,K,Z]Z Alter/Face, [Opn, Perc, Perc Endo], [Auto Tissue Sub, Synth Sub, Nonauto Tissue Sub, No Dev], NQ

ØW06[Ø,3,4][7,J,K,Z]Z Alter/Neck, [Opn, Perc, Perc Endo], [Auto Tissue Sub, Synth Sub, Nonauto Tissue Sub, No Dev], NQ

ØW08[Ø,3,4][7,J,K,Z]Z Alter/Chest Wall, [Opn, Perc, Perc Endo], [Auto Tissue Sub, Synth Sub, Nonauto Tissue Sub, No Dev], NQ

DRGs Associated with All MDCs—SURGICAL

Surgical   Medical   CC Indicator   MCC Indicator   Procedure Proxy   PDxMCC PDx acts as own MCC   PDxCC PDx acts as own CC

DRGs Associated with All MDCs—SURGICAL

0W0F[0,3,4][7,J,K,Z]Z Alter/Abd Wall, [Opn, Perc, Perc Endo], [Auto Tissue Sub, Synth Sub, Nonauto Tissue Sub, No Dev], NQ

0W0K[0,3,4][7,J,K,Z]Z Alter/Upr Back, [Opn, Perc, Perc Endo], [Auto Tissue Sub, Synth Sub, Nonauto Tissue Sub, No Dev], NQ

0W0L[0,3,4][7,J,K,Z]Z Alter/Lwr Back, [Opn, Perc, Perc Endo], [Auto Tissue Sub, Synth Sub, Nonauto Tissue Sub, No Dev], NQ

0W0M[0,3,4][7,J,K,Z]Z Alter/Perineum, Male, [Opn, Perc, Perc Endo], [Auto Tissue Sub, Synth Sub, Nonauto Tissue Sub, No Dev], NQ

0W0N[0,3,4][7,J,K,Z]Z Alter/Perineum, Female, [Opn, Perc, Perc Endo], [Auto Tissue Sub, Synth Sub, Nonauto Tissue Sub, No Dev], NQ

0W9F[0,3,4]ZX Drain/Abd Wall, [Opn, Perc, Perc Endo]

0W9G[0,3,4]ZX Drain/Peritoneal Cavity, [Opn, Perc, Perc Endo]

0W9H[0,3,4]ZX Drain/Retroperitoneum, [Opn, Perc, Perc Endo]

0W9J[0,3,4]ZX Drain/Pelvic Cavity, [Opn, Perc, Perc Endo]

0W9N[0,3,4][0,Z]Z Drain/Perineum, Female, [Opn, Perc, Perc Endo], [Drain Dev, No Dev], NQ

0WB0[0,3,4,X]ZZ Exc/Head, [Opn, Perc, Perc Endo, Ext]

0WB2[0,3,4,X]ZZ Exc/Face, [Opn, Perc, Perc Endo, Ext]

0WB4[0,3,4,X]ZZ Exc/Upr Jaw, [Opn, Perc, Perc Endo, Ext]

0WB5[0,3,4,X]ZZ Exc/Lwr Jaw, [Opn, Perc, Perc Endo, Ext]

0WB6[0,3,4,X]ZZ Exc/Neck, [Opn, Perc, Perc Endo, Ext]

0WB8[0,3,4,X]ZZ Exc/Chest Wall, [Opn, Perc, Perc Endo, Ext]

0WBC[0,3,4]ZZ Exc/Mediastinum, [Opn, Perc, Perc Endo]

0WBFXZ2 Exc of Abd Wall, Stoma, Ext Appr

0WBF[0,3,4,X]Z[X,Z] Exc/Abd Wall, [Opn, Perc, Perc Endo, Ext], No Dev, [Dx, NQ]

0WBK[0,3,4,X]ZZ Exc/Upr Back, [Opn, Perc, Perc Endo, Ext]

0WBL[0,3,4,X]ZZ Exc/Lwr Back, [Opn, Perc, Perc Endo, Ext]

0WBM[0,3,4,X]ZZ Exc/Perineum, Male, [Opn, Perc, Perc Endo, Ext]

0WBN[0,3,4,X]Z[X,Z] Exc/Perineum, Female, [Opn, Perc, Perc Endo, Ext], No Dev, [Dx, NQ]

0WC3[0,3,4]ZZ Extir/Oral Cavity and Throat, [Opn, Perc, Perc Endo]

0WF3[0,3,4]ZZ Fragmn/Oral Cavity and Throat, [Opn, Perc, Perc Endo]

0WH0[0,3,4]1Z Insert/Head, [Opn, Perc, Perc Endo], Radioact Elmt, NQ

0WH1[0,3,4]1Z Insert/Cranial Cavity, [Opn, Perc, Perc Endo], Radioact Elmt, NQ

0WH2[0,3,4]1Z Insert/Face, [Opn, Perc, Perc Endo], Radioact Elmt, NQ

0WH3[0,3,4][1,3,Y]Z Insert/Oral Cavity and Throat, [Opn, Perc, Perc Endo], [Radioact Elmt, Inf Dev, Oth Dev], NQ

0WH4[0,3,4]1Z Insert/Upr Jaw, [Opn, Perc, Perc Endo], Radioact Elmt, NQ

0WH5[0,3,4]1Z Insert/Lwr Jaw, [Opn, Perc, Perc Endo], Radioact Elmt, NQ

0WH6[0,3,4]1Z Insert/Neck, [Opn, Perc, Perc Endo], Radioact Elmt, NQ

0WH8[0,3,4]1Z Insert/Chest Wall, [Opn, Perc, Perc Endo], Radioact Elmt, NQ

0WH9[0,3,4]1Z Insert/Pleural Cavity, Rt, [Opn, Perc, Perc Endo], Radioact Elmt, NQ

0WHB[0,3,4]1Z Insert/Pleural Cavity, Lt, [Opn, Perc, Perc Endo], Radioact Elmt, NQ

0WHC[0,3,4]1Z Insert/Mediastinum, [Opn, Perc, Perc Endo], Radioact Elmt, NQ

0WHD[0,3,4]1Z Insert/Pericardial Cavity, [Opn, Perc, Perc Endo], Radioact Elmt, NQ

0WHF[0,3,4]1Z Insert/Abd Wall, [Opn, Perc, Perc Endo], Radioact Elmt, NQ

0WHG[0,3,4]1Z Insert/Peritoneal Cavity, [Opn, Perc, Perc Endo], Radioact Elmt, NQ

0WHH[0,3,4]1Z Insert/Retroperitoneum, [Opn, Perc, Perc Endo], Radioact Elmt, NQ

0WHJ[0,3,4]1Z Insert/Pelvic Cavity, [Opn, Perc, Perc Endo], Radioact Elmt, NQ

0WHK[0,3,4]1Z Insert/Upr Back, [Opn, Perc, Perc Endo], Radioact Elmt, NQ

0WHL[0,3,4]1Z Insert/Lwr Back, [Opn, Perc, Perc Endo], Radioact Elmt, NQ

0WHM[0,3,4]1Z Insert/Perineum, Male, [Opn, Perc, Perc Endo], Radioact Elmt, NQ

0WHN[0,3,4][1,3,Y]Z Insert/Perineum, Female, [Opn, Perc, Perc Endo], [Radioact Elmt, Inf Dev, Oth Dev], NQ

0WHP[0,3,4,7,8]1Z Insert/Gastrointestinal Tract, [Opn, Perc, Perc Endo, Via Natrl or Artfcl Opng, Via Natrl or Artfcl Opng Endo], Radioact Elmt, NQ

0WHQ[0,3,4,7,8]1Z Insert/Respiratory Tract, [Opn, Perc, Perc Endo, Via Natrl or Artfcl Opng, Via Natrl or Artfcl Opng Endo], Radioact Elmt, NQ

0WHR[0,3,4,7,8]1Z Insert/Genitourinary Tract, [Opn, Perc, Perc Endo, Via Natrl or Artfcl Opng, Via Natrl or Artfcl Opng Endo], Radioact Elmt, NQ

0WJF[3,4]ZZ Inspect/Abd Wall, [Perc, Perc Endo]

0WJG[3,4]ZZ Inspect/Peritoneal Cavity, [Perc, Perc Endo]

0WJH[3,4]ZZ Inspect/Retroperitoneum, [Perc, Perc Endo]

0WJJ[3,4]ZZ Inspect/Pelvic Cavity, [Perc, Perc Endo]

0WJP[3,4,7,8]ZZ Inspect/Gastrointestinal Tract, [Perc, Perc Endo, Via Natrl or Artfcl Opng, Via Natrl or Artfcl Opng Endo]

0WJR[3,4,7,8]ZZ Inspect/Genitourinary Tract, [Perc, Perc Endo, Via Natrl or Artfcl Opng, Via Natrl or Artfcl Opng Endo]

0WM20ZZ Reattach of Face, Opn Appr

0WM40ZZ Reattach of Upr Jaw, Opn Appr

0WM50ZZ Reattach of Lwr Jaw, Opn Appr

0WM60ZZ Reattach of Neck, Opn Appr

0WMK0ZZ Reattach of Upr Back, Opn Appr

0WML0ZZ Reattach of Lwr Back, Opn Appr

0WMM0ZZ Reattach Male Perineum, Opn Appr

0WMN0ZZ Reattach of Female Perineum, Opn Appr

0WPMXJZ Rmvl of Synth Sub from Male Perineum, Extern Appr

0WPM[0,3,4,X][7,K]Z Rmvl/Perineum, Male, [Opn, Perc, Perc Endo, Ext], [Auto Tissue Sub, Nonauto Tissue Sub], NQ

0WPN[0,3,4][0,1,3,7,J,K,Y]Z Rmvl/Perineum, Female, [Opn, Perc, Perc Endo], [Drain Dev, Radioact Elmt, Inf Dev, Auto Tissue Sub, Synth Sub, Nonauto Tissue Sub, Oth Dev], NQ

0WQ0[0,3,4,X]ZZ Rpr/Head, [Opn, Perc, Perc Endo, Ext]

0WQ2[0,3,4,X]ZZ Rpr/Face, [Opn, Perc, Perc Endo, Ext]

0WQ4[0,3,4,X]ZZ Rpr/Upr Jaw, [Opn, Perc, Perc Endo, Ext]

0WQ5[0,3,4,X]ZZ Rpr/Lwr Jaw, [Opn, Perc, Perc Endo, Ext]

0WQ6[0,3,4,X]ZZ Rpr/Neck, [Opn, Perc, Perc Endo, Ext]

0WQF0ZZ Repair Abd Wall, Opn Appr

0WQFXZ2 Repair Abd Wall, Stoma, Ext Appr

0WQK[0,3,4,X]ZZ Rpr/Upr Back, [Opn, Perc, Perc Endo, Ext]

0WQL[0,3,4,X]ZZ Rpr/Lwr Back, [Opn, Perc, Perc Endo, Ext]

0WQM[0,3,4,X]ZZ Rpr/Perineum, Male, [Opn, Perc, Perc Endo, Ext]

0WQN[0,3,4]ZZ Rpr/Perineum, Female, [Opn, Perc, Perc Endo]

0WU0[0,4][7,J,K]Z Supl/Head, [Opn, Perc, Perc Endo], [Auto Tissue Sub, Synth Sub, Nonauto Tissue Sub], NQ

0WU2[0,4][J,K]Z Supl/Face, [Opn, Perc, Perc Endo], [Synth Sub, Nonauto Tissue Sub], NQ

0WU6[0,4][7,J,K]Z Supl/Neck, [Opn, Perc, Perc Endo], [Auto Tissue Sub, Synth Sub, Nonauto Tissue Sub], NQ

0WUF0[7,J,K]Z Supl/Abd Wall, Opn, [Auto Tissue Sub, Synth Sub, Nonauto Tissue Sub], NQ

0WUK[0,4][7,J,K]Z Supl/Upr Back, [Opn, Perc, Perc Endo], [Auto Tissue Sub, Synth Sub, Nonauto Tissue Sub], NQ

0WUL[0,4][7,J,K]Z Supl/Lwr Back, [Opn, Perc, Perc Endo], [Auto Tissue Sub, Synth Sub, Nonauto Tissue Sub], NQ

0WUM[0,4][7,J,K]Z Supl/Perineum, Male, [Opn, Perc, Perc Endo], [Auto Tissue Sub, Synth Sub, Nonauto Tissue Sub], NQ

0WUN[0,4][7,J,K]Z Supl/Perineum, Female, [Opn, Perc, Perc Endo], [Auto Tissue Sub, Synth Sub, Nonauto Tissue Sub], NQ

0WWM[0,3,4][7,K]Z Rev/Perineum, Male, [Opn, Perc, Perc Endo], [Auto Tissue Sub, Nonauto Tissue Sub], NQ

0WWN[0,3,4][0,1,3,7,J,K,Y]Z Rev/Perineum, Female, [Opn, Perc, Perc Endo], [Drain Dev, Radioact Elmt, Inf Dev, Auto Tissue Sub, Synth Sub, Nonauto Tissue Sub, Oth Dev], NQ

0X02[0,3,4][7,J,K,Z]Z Alter/Shldr Rgn, Rt, [Opn, Perc, Perc Endo], [Auto Tissue Sub, Synth Sub, Nonauto Tissue Sub, No Dev], NQ

0X03[0,3,4][7,J,K,Z]Z Alter/Shldr Rgn, Lt, [Opn, Perc, Perc Endo], [Auto Tissue Sub, Synth Sub, Nonauto Tissue Sub, No Dev], NQ

0X04[0,3,4][7,J,K,Z]Z Alter/Axilla, Rt, [Opn, Perc, Perc Endo], [Auto Tissue Sub, Synth Sub, Nonauto Tissue Sub, No Dev], NQ

0X05[0,3,4][7,J,K,Z]Z Alter/Axilla, Lt, [Opn, Perc, Perc Endo], [Auto Tissue Sub, Synth Sub, Nonauto Tissue Sub, No Dev], NQ

0X06[0,3,4][7,J,K,Z]Z Alter/Upr Extr, Rt, [Opn, Perc, Perc Endo], [Auto Tissue Sub, Synth Sub, Nonauto Tissue Sub, No Dev], NQ

0X07[0,3,4][7,J,K,Z]Z Alter/Upr Extr, Lt, [Opn, Perc, Perc Endo], [Auto Tissue Sub, Synth Sub, Nonauto Tissue Sub, No Dev], NQ

0X08[0,3,4][7,J,K,Z]Z Alter/Upr Arm, Rt, [Opn, Perc, Perc Endo], [Auto Tissue Sub, Synth Sub, Nonauto Tissue Sub, No Dev], NQ

0X09[0,3,4][7,J,K,Z]Z Alter/Upr Arm, Lt, [Opn, Perc, Perc Endo], [Auto Tissue Sub, Synth Sub, Nonauto Tissue Sub, No Dev], NQ

0X0B[0,3,4][7,J,K,Z]Z Alter/Elbow Rgn, Rt, [Opn, Perc, Perc Endo], [Auto Tissue Sub, Synth Sub, Nonauto Tissue Sub, No Dev], NQ

0X0C[0,3,4][7,J,K,Z]Z Alter/Elbow Rgn, Lt, [Opn, Perc, Perc Endo], [Auto Tissue Sub, Synth Sub, Nonauto Tissue Sub, No Dev], NQ

0X0D[0,3,4][7,J,K,Z]Z Alter/Lwr Arm, Rt, [Opn, Perc, Perc Endo], [Auto Tissue Sub, Synth Sub, Nonauto Tissue Sub, No Dev], NQ

0X0F[0,3,4][7,J,K,Z]Z Alter/Lwr Arm, Lt, [Opn, Perc, Perc Endo], [Auto Tissue Sub, Synth Sub, Nonauto Tissue Sub, No Dev], NQ

0X0G[0,3,4][7,J,K,Z]Z Alter/Wrist Rgn, Rt, [Opn, Perc, Perc Endo], [Auto Tissue Sub, Synth Sub, Nonauto Tissue Sub, No Dev], NQ

0X0H[0,3,4][7,J,K,Z]Z Alter/Wrist Rgn, Lt, [Opn, Perc, Perc Endo], [Auto Tissue Sub, Synth Sub, Nonauto Tissue Sub, No Dev], NQ

0X6N0Z[0,1,2,3] Detach/Index Finger, Rt, Opn, No Dev, [Complete, High, Mid, Low]

0X6P0Z[0,1,2,3] Detach/Index Finger, Lt, Opn, No Dev, [Complete, High, Mid, Low]

0X6Q0Z[0,1,2,3] Detach/Mid Finger, Rt, Opn, No Dev, [Complete, High, Mid, Low]

0X6R0Z[0,1,2,3] Detach/Mid Finger, Lt, Opn, No Dev, [Complete, High, Mid, Low]

0X6S0Z[0,1,2,3] Detach/Ring Finger, Rt, Opn, No Dev, [Complete, High, Mid, Low]

T **Transfer DRG**   SP **Special Payment**   * **Code Range**   **6th and 7th Character of ZZ = No Device, No Qualifier ZX = No Device, Diagnostic**

ØX6TØZ[Ø,1,2,3]	Detach/Ring Finger, Lt, Opn, No Dev, [Complete, High, Mid, Low]
ØX6VØZ[Ø,1,2,3]	Detach/Little Finger, Rt, Opn, No Dev, [Complete, High, Mid, Low]
ØX6WØZ[Ø,1,2,3]	Detach/Little Finger, Lt, Opn, No Dev, [Complete, High, Mid, Low]
ØXB2[Ø,3,4]ZZ	Exc/Shldr Rgn, Rt, [Opn, Perc, Perc Endo]
ØXB3[Ø,3,4]ZZ	Exc/Shldr Rgn, Lt, [Opn, Perc, Perc Endo]
ØXB4[Ø,3,4]ZZ	Exc/Axilla, Rt, [Opn, Perc, Perc Endo]
ØXB5[Ø,3,4]ZZ	Exc/Axilla, Lt, [Opn, Perc, Perc Endo]
ØXB6[Ø,3,4]ZZ	Exc/Upr Extr, Rt, [Opn, Perc, Perc Endo]
ØXB7[Ø,3,4]ZZ	Exc/Upr Extr, Lt, [Opn, Perc, Perc Endo]
ØXB8[Ø,3,4]ZZ	Exc/Upr Arm, Rt, [Opn, Perc, Perc Endo]
ØXB9[Ø,3,4]ZZ	Exc/Upr Arm, Lt, [Opn, Perc, Perc Endo]
ØXBB[Ø,3,4]ZZ	Exc/Elbow Rgn, Rt, [Opn, Perc, Perc Endo]
ØXBC[Ø,3,4]ZZ	Exc/Elbow Rgn, Lt, [Opn, Perc, Perc Endo]
ØXBD[Ø,3,4]ZZ	Exc/Lwr Arm, Rt, [Opn, Perc, Perc Endo]
ØXBF[Ø,3,4]ZZ	Exc/Lwr Arm, Lt, [Opn, Perc, Perc Endo]
ØXBG[Ø,3,4]ZZ	Exc/Wrist Rgn, Rt, [Opn, Perc, Perc Endo]
ØXBH[Ø,3,4]ZZ	Exc/Wrist Rgn, Lt, [Opn, Perc, Perc Endo]
ØXBJ[Ø,3,4]ZZ	Exc/Hand, Rt, [Opn, Perc, Perc Endo]
ØXBK[Ø,3,4]ZZ	Exc/Hand, Lt, [Opn, Perc, Perc Endo]
ØXH2[Ø,3,4]1Z	Insert/Shldr Rgn, Rt, [Opn, Perc, Perc Endo], Radioact Elmt, NQ
ØXH3[Ø,3,4]1Z	Insert/Shldr Rgn, Lt, [Opn, Perc, Perc Endo], Radioact Elmt, NQ
ØXH4[Ø,3,4]1Z	Insert/Axilla, Rt, [Opn, Perc, Perc Endo], Radioact Elmt, NQ
ØXH5[Ø,3,4]1Z	Insert/Axilla, Lt, [Opn, Perc, Perc Endo], Radioact Elmt, NQ
ØXH6[Ø,3,4]1Z	Insert/Upr Extr, Rt, [Opn, Perc, Perc Endo], Radioact Elmt, NQ
ØXH7[Ø,3,4]1Z	Insert/Upr Extr, Lt, [Opn, Perc, Perc Endo], Radioact Elmt, NQ
ØXH8[Ø,3,4]1Z	Insert/Upr Arm, Rt, [Opn, Perc, Perc Endo], Radioact Elmt, NQ
ØXH9[Ø,3,4]1Z	Insert/Upr Arm, Lt, [Opn, Perc, Perc Endo], Radioact Elmt, NQ
ØXHB[Ø,3,4]1Z	Insert/Elbow Rgn, Rt, [Opn, Perc, Perc Endo], Radioact Elmt, NQ
ØXHC[Ø,3,4]1Z	Insert/Elbow Rgn, Lt, [Opn, Perc, Perc Endo], Radioact Elmt, NQ
ØXHD[Ø,3,4]1Z	Insert/Lwr Arm, Rt, [Opn, Perc, Perc Endo], Radioact Elmt, NQ
ØXHF[Ø,3,4]1Z	Insert/Lwr Arm, Lt, [Opn, Perc, Perc Endo], Radioact Elmt, NQ
ØXHG[Ø,3,4]1Z	Insert/Wrist Rgn, Rt, [Opn, Perc, Perc Endo], Radioact Elmt, NQ
ØXHH[Ø,3,4]1Z	Insert/Wrist Rgn, Lt, [Opn, Perc, Perc Endo], Radioact Elmt, NQ
ØXHJ[Ø,3,4]1Z	Insert/Hand, Rt, [Opn, Perc, Perc Endo], Radioact Elmt, NQ
ØXHK[Ø,3,4]1Z	Insert/Hand, Lt, [Opn, Perc, Perc Endo], Radioact Elmt, NQ
ØXU2[Ø,4][7,J,K]Z	Supl/Shldr Rgn, Rt, [Opn, Perc Endo], [Auto Tissue Sub, Synth Sub, Nonauto Tissue Sub], NQ
ØXU3[Ø,4][7,J,K]Z	Supl/Shldr Rgn, Lt, [Opn, Perc Endo], [Auto Tissue Sub, Synth Sub, Nonauto Tissue Sub], NQ
ØXU4[Ø,4][7,J,K]Z	Supl/Axilla, Rt, [Opn, Perc Endo], [Auto Tissue Sub, Synth Sub, Nonauto Tissue Sub], NQ
ØXU5[Ø,4][7,J,K]Z	Supl/Axilla, Lt, [Opn, Perc Endo], [Auto Tissue Sub, Synth Sub, Nonauto Tissue Sub], NQ
ØXU6[Ø,4][7,J,K]Z	Supl/Upr Extr, Rt, [Opn, Perc Endo], [Auto Tissue Sub, Synth Sub, Nonauto Tissue Sub], NQ
ØXU7[Ø,4][7,J,K]Z	Supl/Upr Extr, Lt, [Opn, Perc Endo], [Auto Tissue Sub, Synth Sub, Nonauto Tissue Sub], NQ
ØXU8[Ø,4][7,J,K]Z	Supl/Upr Arm, Rt, [Opn, Perc Endo], [Auto Tissue Sub, Synth Sub, Nonauto Tissue Sub], NQ
ØXU9[Ø,4][7,J,K]Z	Supl/Upr Arm, Lt, [Opn, Perc Endo], [Auto Tissue Sub, Synth Sub, Nonauto Tissue Sub], NQ
ØXUB[Ø,4][7,J,K]Z	Supl/Elbow Rgn, Rt, [Opn, Perc Endo], [Auto Tissue Sub, Synth Sub, Nonauto Tissue Sub], NQ
ØXUC[Ø,4][7,J,K]Z	Supl/Elbow Rgn, Lt, [Opn, Perc Endo], [Auto Tissue Sub, Synth Sub, Nonauto Tissue Sub], NQ
ØXUD[Ø,4][7,J,K]Z	Supl/Lwr Arm, Rt, [Opn, Perc Endo], [Auto Tissue Sub, Synth Sub, Nonauto Tissue Sub], NQ
ØXUF[Ø,4][7,J,K]Z	Supl/Lwr Arm, Lt, [Opn, Perc Endo], [Auto Tissue Sub, Synth Sub, Nonauto Tissue Sub], NQ
ØXUG[Ø,4][7,J,K]Z	Supl/Wrist Rgn, Rt, [Opn, Perc Endo], [Auto Tissue Sub, Synth Sub, Nonauto Tissue Sub], NQ
ØXUH[Ø,4][7,J,K]Z	Supl/Wrist Rgn, Lt, [Opn, Perc Endo], [Auto Tissue Sub, Synth Sub, Nonauto Tissue Sub], NQ
ØXUJ[Ø,4][7,J,K]Z	Supl/Hand, Rt, [Opn, Perc Endo], [Auto Tissue Sub, Synth Sub, Nonauto Tissue Sub], NQ
ØXUK[Ø,4][7,J,K]Z	Supl/Hand, Lt, [Opn, Perc Endo], [Auto Tissue Sub, Synth Sub, Nonauto Tissue Sub], NQ
ØXUL[Ø,4][7,J,K]Z	Supl/Thumb, Rt, [Opn, Perc Endo], [Auto Tissue Sub, Synth Sub, Nonauto Tissue Sub], NQ
ØXUM[Ø,4][7,J,K]Z	Supl/Thumb, Lt, [Opn, Perc Endo], [Auto Tissue Sub, Synth Sub, Nonauto Tissue Sub], NQ
ØXUN[Ø,4][7,J,K]Z	Supl/Index Finger, Rt, [Opn, Perc Endo], [Auto Tissue Sub, Synth Sub, Nonauto Tissue Sub], NQ
ØXUP[Ø,4][7,J,K]Z	Supl/Index Finger, Lt, [Opn, Perc Endo], [Auto Tissue Sub, Synth Sub, Nonauto Tissue Sub], NQ
ØXUQ[Ø,4][7,J,K]Z	Supl/Mid Finger, Rt, [Opn, Perc Endo], [Auto Tissue Sub, Synth Sub, Nonauto Tissue Sub], NQ
ØXUR[Ø,4][7,J,K]Z	Supl/Mid Finger, Lt, [Opn, Perc Endo], [Auto Tissue Sub, Nonauto Tissue Sub], NQ
ØXUS[Ø,4][7,J,K]Z	Supl/Ring Finger, Rt, [Opn, Perc Endo], [Auto Tissue Sub, Synth Sub, Nonauto Tissue Sub], NQ
ØXUT[Ø,4][7,J,K]Z	Supl/Ring Finger, Lt, [Opn, Perc Endo], [Auto Tissue Sub, Synth Sub, Nonauto Tissue Sub], NQ
ØXUV[Ø,4][7,J,K]Z	Supl/Little Finger, Rt, [Opn, Perc Endo], [Auto Tissue Sub, Synth Sub, Nonauto Tissue Sub], NQ
ØXUW[Ø,4][7,J,K]Z	Supl/Little Finger, Lt, [Opn, Perc Endo], [Auto Tissue Sub, Synth Sub, Nonauto Tissue Sub], NQ
ØY00[Ø,3,4][7,J,K,Z]Z	Alter/Buttock, Rt, [Opn, Perc, Perc Endo], [Auto Tissue Sub, Synth Sub, Nonauto Tissue Sub, No Dev], NQ
ØY01[Ø,3,4][7,J,K,Z]Z	Alter/Buttock, Lt, [Opn, Perc, Perc Endo], [Auto Tissue Sub, Synth Sub, Nonauto Tissue Sub, No Dev], NQ
ØY09[Ø,3,4][7,J,K,Z]Z	Alter/Lwr Extr, Rt, [Opn, Perc, Perc Endo], [Auto Tissue Sub, Synth Sub, Nonauto Tissue Sub, No Dev], NQ
ØY0B[Ø,3,4][7,J,K,Z]Z	Alter/Lwr Extr, Lt, [Opn, Perc, Perc Endo], [Auto Tissue Sub, Synth Sub, Nonauto Tissue Sub, No Dev], NQ
ØY0C[Ø,3,4][7,J,K,Z]Z	Alter/Upr Leg, Rt, [Opn, Perc, Perc Endo], [Auto Tissue Sub, Synth Sub, Nonauto Tissue Sub, No Dev], NQ
ØY0D[Ø,3,4][7,J,K,Z]Z	Alter/Upr Leg, Lt, [Opn, Perc, Perc Endo], [Auto Tissue Sub, Synth Sub, Nonauto Tissue Sub, No Dev], NQ
ØY0F[Ø,3,4][7,J,K,Z]Z	Alter/Knee Rgn, Rt, [Opn, Perc, Perc Endo], [Auto Tissue Sub, Synth Sub, Nonauto Tissue Sub, No Dev], NQ
ØY0G[Ø,3,4][7,J,K,Z]Z	Alter/Knee Rgn, Lt, [Opn, Perc, Perc Endo], [Auto Tissue Sub, Synth Sub, Nonauto Tissue Sub, No Dev], NQ
ØY0H[Ø,3,4][7,J,K,Z]Z	Alter/Lwr Leg, Rt, [Opn, Perc, Perc Endo], [Auto Tissue Sub, Synth Sub, Nonauto Tissue Sub, No Dev], NQ
ØY0J[Ø,3,4][7,J,K,Z]Z	Alter/Lwr Leg, Lt, [Opn, Perc, Perc Endo], [Auto Tissue Sub, Synth Sub, Nonauto Tissue Sub, No Dev], NQ
ØY0K[Ø,3,4][7,J,K,Z]Z	Alter/Ankle Rgn, Rt, [Opn, Perc, Perc Endo], [Auto Tissue Sub, Synth Sub, Nonauto Tissue Sub, No Dev], NQ
ØY0L[Ø,3,4][7,J,K,Z]Z	Alter/Ankle Rgn, Lt, [Opn, Perc, Perc Endo], [Auto Tissue Sub, Synth Sub, Nonauto Tissue Sub, No Dev], NQ
ØY95[Ø,3,4]ZX	Drain/Inguinal Rgn, Rt, [Opn, Perc, Perc Endo]
ØY96[Ø,3,4]ZX	Drain/Inguinal Rgn, Lt, [Opn, Perc, Perc Endo]
ØYB0[Ø,3,4]ZZ	Exc/Buttock, Rt, [Opn, Perc, Perc Endo]
ØYB1[Ø,3,4]ZZ	Exc/Buttock, Lt, [Opn, Perc, Perc Endo]
ØYB5[Ø,3,4]Z[X,Z]	Exc/Inguinal Rgn, Rt, [Opn, Perc, Perc Endo], No Dev, [Dx, NQ]
ØYB6[Ø,3,4]Z[X,Z]	Exc/Inguinal Rgn, Lt, [Opn, Perc, Perc Endo], No Dev, [Dx, NQ]
ØYB7[Ø,3,4]Z[X,Z]	Exc/Femor Rgn, Rt, [Opn, Perc, Perc Endo], No Dev, [Dx, NQ]
ØYB8[Ø,3,4]Z[X,Z]	Exc/Femor Rgn, Lt, [Opn, Perc, Perc Endo], No Dev, [Dx, NQ]
ØYB9[Ø,3,4]ZZ	Exc/Lwr Extr, Rt, [Opn, Perc, Perc Endo]
ØYBB[Ø,3,4]ZZ	Exc/Lwr Extr, Lt, [Opn, Perc, Perc Endo]
ØYBC[Ø,3,4]ZZ	Exc/Upr Leg, Rt, [Opn, Perc, Perc Endo]
ØYBD[Ø,3,4]ZZ	Exc/Upr Leg, Lt, [Opn, Perc, Perc Endo]
ØYBF[Ø,3,4]ZZ	Exc/Knee Rgn, Rt, [Opn, Perc, Perc Endo]
ØYBG[Ø,3,4]ZZ	Exc/Knee Rgn, Lt, [Opn, Perc, Perc Endo]
ØYBH[Ø,3,4]ZZ	Exc/Lwr Leg, Rt, [Opn, Perc, Perc Endo]
ØYBJ[Ø,3,4]ZZ	Exc/Lwr Leg, Lt, [Opn, Perc, Perc Endo]
ØYBK[Ø,3,4]ZZ	Exc/Ankle Rgn, Rt, [Opn, Perc, Perc Endo]
ØYBL[Ø,3,4]ZZ	Exc/Ankle Rgn, Lt, [Opn, Perc, Perc Endo]
ØYBM[Ø,3,4]ZZ	Exc/Foot, Rt, [Opn, Perc, Perc Endo]
ØYBN[Ø,3,4]ZZ	Exc/Foot, Lt, [Opn, Perc, Perc Endo]
ØYH0[Ø,3,4]1Z	Insert/Buttock, Rt, [Opn, Perc, Perc Endo], Radioact Elmt, NQ
ØYH1[Ø,3,4]1Z	Insert/Buttock, Lt, [Opn, Perc, Perc Endo], Radioact Elmt, NQ
ØYH5[Ø,3,4]1Z	Insert/Inguinal Rgn, Rt, [Opn, Perc, Perc Endo], Radioact Elmt, NQ
ØYH6[Ø,3,4]1Z	Insert/Inguinal Rgn, Lt, [Opn, Perc, Perc Endo], Radioact Elmt, NQ
ØYH7[Ø,3,4]1Z	Insert/Femor Rgn, Rt, [Opn, Perc, Perc Endo], Radioact Elmt, NQ
ØYH8[Ø,3,4]1Z	Insert/Femor Rgn, Lt, [Opn, Perc, Perc Endo], Radioact Elmt, NQ
ØYH9[Ø,3,4]1Z	Insert/Lwr Extr, Rt, [Opn, Perc, Perc Endo], Radioact Elmt, NQ
ØYHB[Ø,3,4]1Z	Insert/Lwr Extr, Lt, [Opn, Perc, Perc Endo], Radioact Elmt, NQ
ØYHC[Ø,3,4]1Z	Insert/Upr Leg, Rt, [Opn, Perc, Perc Endo], Radioact Elmt, NQ
ØYHD[Ø,3,4]1Z	Insert/Upr Leg, Lt, [Opn, Perc, Perc Endo], Radioact Elmt, NQ
ØYHF[Ø,3,4]1Z	Insert/Knee Rgn, Rt, [Opn, Perc, Perc Endo], Radioact Elmt, NQ
ØYHG[Ø,3,4]1Z	Insert/Knee Rgn, Lt, [Opn, Perc, Perc Endo], Radioact Elmt, NQ
ØYHH[Ø,3,4]1Z	Insert/Lwr Leg, Rt, [Opn, Perc, Perc Endo], Radioact Elmt, NQ
ØYHJ[Ø,3,4]1Z	Insert/Lwr Leg, Lt, [Opn, Perc, Perc Endo], Radioact Elmt, NQ
ØYHK[Ø,3,4]1Z	Insert/Ankle Rgn, Rt, [Opn, Perc, Perc Endo], Radioact Elmt, NQ
ØYHL[Ø,3,4]1Z	Insert/Ankle Rgn, Lt, [Opn, Perc, Perc Endo], Radioact Elmt, NQ
ØYHM[Ø,3,4]1Z	Insert/Foot, Rt, [Opn, Perc, Perc Endo], Radioact Elmt, NQ
ØYHN[Ø,3,4]1Z	Insert/Foot, Lt, [Opn, Perc, Perc Endo], Radioact Elmt, NQ
ØYJ5[3,4]ZZ	Inspect/Inguinal Rgn, Rt, [Perc, Perc Endo]
ØYJ6[3,4]ZZ	Inspect/Inguinal Rgn, Lt, [Perc, Perc Endo]

Surgical   **Medical**   **CC Indicator**   **MCC Indicator**   **Procedure Proxy**   **PDxMCC** PDx acts as own MCC   **PDxCC** PDx acts as own CC

DRGs Associated with All MDCs—SURGICAL

ØYJ7[3,4]ZZ	Inspect/Femor Rgn, Rt, [Perc, Perc Endo]
ØYJ8[3,4]ZZ	Inspect/Femor Rgn, Lt, [Perc, Perc Endo]
ØYJA[3,4]ZZ	Inspect/Inguinal Rgn, Bilat, [Perc, Perc Endo]
ØYJE[3,4]ZZ	Inspect/Inguinal Rgn, Bilat, [Perc, Perc Endo]
ØYMØØZZ	Reattach of Rt Buttock, Opn Appr
ØYM1ØZZ	Reattach of Lt Buttock, Opn Appr
ØYQ5[Ø,3,4]ZZ	Rpr/Inguinal Rgn, Rt, [Opn, Perc, Perc Endo]
ØYQ6[Ø,3,4]ZZ	Rpr/Inguinal Rgn, Lt, [Opn, Perc, Perc Endo]
ØYQ7[Ø,3,4]ZZ	Rpr/Femor Rgn, Rt, [Opn, Perc, Perc Endo]
ØYQ8[Ø,3,4]ZZ	Rpr/Femor Rgn, Lt, [Opn, Perc, Perc Endo]
ØYQA[Ø,3,4]ZZ	Rpr/Inguinal Rgn, Bilat, [Opn, Perc, Perc Endo]
ØYQE[Ø,3,4]ZZ	Rpr/Femor Rgn, Bilat, [Opn, Perc, Perc Endo]
ØYUØ[Ø,4][7,J,K]Z	Supl/Buttock, Rt, [Opn, Perc Endo], [Auto Tissue Sub, Synth Sub, Nonauto Tissue Sub], NQ
ØYU1[Ø,4][7,J,K]Z	Supl/Buttock, Lt, [Opn, Perc Endo], [Auto Tissue Sub, Synth Sub, Nonauto Tissue Sub], NQ
ØYU5Ø[7,J,K]Z	Supl/Inguinal Rgn, Rt, Opn, [Auto Tissue Sub, Synth Sub, Nonauto Tissue Sub], NQ
ØYU6Ø[7,J,K]Z	Supl/Inguinal Rgn, Lt, Opn, [Auto Tissue Sub, Synth Sub,. Nonauto Tissue Sub], NQ
ØYU7[Ø,4][7,J,K]Z	Supl/Femor Rgn, Rt, [Opn, Perc Endo], [Auto Tissue Sub, Synth Sub, Nonauto Tissue Sub], NQ
ØYU8[Ø,4][7,J,K]Z	Supl/Femor Rgn, Lt, [Opn, Perc Endo], [Auto Tissue Sub, Synth Sub, Nonauto Tissue Sub], NQ
ØYU9[Ø,4][7,J,K]Z	Supl/Lwr Extr, Rt, [Opn, Perc Endo], [Auto Tissue Sub, Synth Sub, Nonauto Tissue Sub], NQ
ØYUAØ[7,J,K]Z	Supl/Inguinal Rgn, Bilat, Opn, [Auto Tissue Sub, Synth Sub, Nonauto Tissue Sub], NQ
ØYUB[Ø,4][7,J,K]Z	Supl/Lwr Extr, Lt, [Opn, Perc Endo], [Auto Tissue Sub, Synth Sub, Nonauto Tissue Sub], NQ
ØYUC[Ø,4][7,J,K]Z	Supl/Upr Leg, Rt, [Opn, Perc Endo], [Auto Tissue Sub, Synth Sub, Nonauto Tissue Sub], NQ
ØYUD[Ø,4][7,J,K]Z	Supl/Upr Leg, Lt, [Opn, Perc Endo], [Auto Tissue Sub, Synth Sub, Nonauto Tissue Sub], NQ
ØYUE[Ø,4][7,J,K]Z	Supl/Femor Rgn, Bilat, [Opn, Perc Endo], [Auto Tissue Sub, Synth Sub, Nonauto Tissue Sub], NQ
ØYUF[Ø,4][7,J,K]Z	Supl/Knee Rgn, Rt, [Opn, Perc Endo], [Auto Tissue Sub, Synth Sub, Nonauto Tissue Sub], NQ
ØYUG[Ø,4][7,J,K]Z	Supl/Knee Rgn, Lt, [Opn, Perc Endo], [Auto Tissue Sub, Synth Sub, Nonauto Tissue Sub], NQ
ØYUH[Ø,4][7,J,K]Z	Supl/Lwr Leg, Rt, [Opn, Perc Endo], [Auto Tissue Sub, Synth Sub, Nonauto Tissue Sub], NQ
ØYUJ[Ø,4][7,J,K]Z	Supl/Lwr Leg, Lt, [Opn, Perc Endo], [Auto Tissue Sub, Synth Sub, Nonauto Tissue Sub], NQ
ØYUK[Ø,4][7,J,K]Z	Supl/Ankle Rgn, Rt, [Opn, Perc Endo], [Auto Tissue Sub, Synth Sub, Nonauto Tissue Sub], NQ
ØYUL[Ø,4][7,J,K]Z	Supl/Ankle Rgn, Lt, [Opn, Perc Endo], [Auto Tissue Sub, Synth Sub, Nonauto Tissue Sub], NQ
ØYUM[Ø,4][7,J,K]Z	Supl/Foot, Rt, [Opn, Perc Endo], [Auto Tissue Sub, Synth Sub, Nonauto Tissue Sub], NQ
ØYUN[Ø,4][7,J,K]Z	Supl/Foot, Lt, [Opn, Perc Endo], [Auto Tissue Sub, Synth Sub, Nonauto Tissue Sub], NQ
ØYUP[Ø,4][7,J,K]Z	Supl/1st Toe, Rt, [Opn, Perc Endo], [Auto Tissue Sub, Synth Sub, Nonauto Tissue Sub], NQ
ØYUQ[Ø,4][7,J,K]Z	Supl/1st Toe, Lt, [Opn, Perc Endo], [Auto Tissue Sub, Synth Sub, Nonauto Tissue Sub], NQ
ØYUR[Ø,4][7,J,K]Z	Supl/2nd Toe, Rt, [Opn, Perc Endo], [Auto Tissue Sub, Synth Sub, Nonauto Tissue Sub], NQ
ØYUS[Ø,4][7,J,K]Z	Supl/2nd Toe, Lt, [Opn, Perc Endo], [Auto Tissue Sub, Synth Sub, Nonauto Tissue Sub], NQ
ØYUT[Ø,4][7,J,K]Z	Supl/3rd Toe, Rt, [Opn, Perc Endo], [Auto Tissue Sub, Synth Sub, Nonauto Tissue Sub], NQ
ØYUU[Ø,4][7,J,K]Z	Supl/3rd Toe, Lt, [Opn, Perc Endo], [Auto Tissue Sub, Synth Sub, Nonauto Tissue Sub], NQ
ØYUV[Ø,4][7,J,K]Z	Supl/4th Toe, Rt, [Opn, Perc Endo], [Auto Tissue Sub, Synth Sub, Nonauto Tissue Sub], NQ
ØYUW[Ø,4][7,J,K]Z	Supl/4th Toe, Lt, [Opn, Perc Endo], [Auto Tissue Sub, Synth Sub, Nonauto Tissue Sub], NQ
ØYUX[Ø,4][7,J,K]Z	Supl/5th Toe, Rt, [Opn, Perc Endo], [Auto Tissue Sub, Synth Sub, Nonauto Tissue Sub], NQ
ØYUY[Ø,4][7,J,K]Z	Supl/5th Toe, Lt, [Opn, Perc Endo], [Auto Tissue Sub, Synth Sub, Nonauto Tissue Sub], NQ
1ØAØ[7,8]ZZ	Abortion/Products of Conception, [Via Natrl or Artfcl Opng, Via Natrl or Artfcl Opng Endo]
3EØC3GC	Introduction of Oth Therap Subst into Eye, Perc Appr
3EØC3SF	Introduction of Oth Gas into Eye, Perc Appr
3EØC3[3,B,H,K,M,T]Z	Introduction/Eye, Perc, [Anti-inflam, Local Anesthetic, Radioact Substance, Oth Dx Substance, Pigment, Destr Agent], NQ
3EØC729	Introduction of Oth Anti-infective into Eye, Via Opng

3EØC7GC	Introduction of Oth Therap Subst into Eye, Via Opng
3EØC7SF	Introduction of Oth Gas into Eye, Via Opng
3EØC7[3,B,H,K,M,T]Z	Introduction/Eye, Via Natrl or Artfcl Opng, [Anti-inflam, Local Anesthetic, Radioact Substance, Oth Dx Substance, Pigment, Destr Agent], NQ
3EØCX29	Introduction of Oth Anti-infect into Eye, Extern Appr
3EØCXGC	Introduction of Oth Therap Subst into Eye, Extern Appr
3EØCXSF	Introduction of Oth Gas into Eye, Ext Appr
3EØCX[3,B,H,K,M,T]Z	Introduction/Eye, Ext, [Anti-inflam, Local Anesthetic, Radioact Substance, Oth Dx Substance, Pigment, Destr Agent], NQ
3EØG3GC	Introduction of Oth Therap Subst into Up GI, Perc Appr
3E1N[3,7,8]8[X,Z]	Irrigation/Male Reproductive, [Perc, Via Natrl or Artfcl Opng, Via Natrl or Artfcl Opng Endo], Irrigating Substance, [Dx, NQ]
4AØ6[Ø,3][5,B]Z	Measurement/Lymphatic, [Opn, Perc], [Flow, Pressure], NQ
4A16[Ø,3][5,B]Z	Monitoring/Lymphatic, [Opn, Perc], [Flow, Pressure], NQ
XR2GØ21	Monitor Rt Knee Jt w Intraop Knee Sens, Opn, New Tech 1
XR2HØ21	Monitor Lt Knee Jt w Intraop Knee Sens, Opn, New Tech 1

OR

ØUT2ØZZ	Resect of Bilat Ovaries, Opn Appr

AND

ØUT7ØZZ	Resect of Bilat Fallopian Tubes, Opn Appr

OR

ØMQS[Ø,3,4]ZZ	Rpr/Foot Bursa & Lgmt, Rt, [Opn, Perc, Perc Endo]
ØMQT[Ø,3,4]ZZ	Rpr/Foot Bursa & Lgmt, Lt, [Opn, Perc, Perc Endo]

AND

ØQ8N[Ø,3,4]ZZ	Div/Metatarsal, Rt, [Opn, Perc, Perc Endo]
ØQ8P[Ø,3,4]ZZ	Div/Metatarsal, Lt, [Opn, Perc, Perc Endo]
ØQBN[Ø,3,4]ZZ	Exc/Metatarsal, Rt, [Opn, Perc, Perc Endo]
ØQBP[Ø,3,4]ZZ	Exc/Metatarsal, Lt, [Opn, Perc, Perc Endo]
ØSGMØZZ	Fusion of Rt Metatarsal-Phalangeal Jt, Opn Appr
ØSGM3ZZ	Fusion of Rt Metatarsal-Phalangeal Jt, Perc Appr
ØSGM4ZZ	Fusion of Rt Metatarsophal Jt, Perc Endo Appr
ØSGNØZZ	Fusion of Lt Metatarsal-Phalangeal Jt, Opn Appr
ØSGN3ZZ	Fusion of Lt Metatarsal-Phalangeal Jt, Perc Appr
ØSGN4ZZ	Fusion of Lt Metatarsophal Jt, Perc Endo Appr

OR

Nonoperating Room Procedures

BFØ3ØZZ	Radiography of Gallbladder & Bile Duct using H Osm Contrast
BFØ31ZZ	Radiography of Gallbladder & Bile Duct using Lt Osm Contrast
BFØ3YZZ	Radiography of Gallbladder & Bile Duct using Oth Contrast
BFØCØZZ	Plain Radiography of Hepatobil Sys, All using H Osm Contrast
BFØC1ZZ	Plain Radiography of Hepatobil Sys, All using Lt Osm Contrast
BFØCYZZ	Plain Radiography of Hepatobil Sys, All using Oth Contrast
XR2GØ21	Monitor Rt Knee Jt w Intraop Knee Sens, Opn, New Tech 1
XR2HØ21	Monitor Lt Knee Jt w Intraop Knee Sens, Opn, New Tech 1

DRG 988   Nonextensive O.R. Procedure Unrelated to Principal Diagnosis with CC

GMLOS 4.6   AMLOS 6.1   RW 1.7533   T

Select operating room procedures or procedure combinations or nonoperating room procedures listed under DRG 987

DRG 989   Nonextensive O.R. Procedure Unrelated to Principal Diagnosis without CC/MCC

GMLOS 2.2   AMLOS 3.Ø   RW 1.Ø425   T

Select operating room procedures or procedure combinations or nonoperating room procedures listed under DRG 987

DRG 999   Ungroupable

GMLOS Ø.Ø   AMLOS Ø.Ø   RW Ø.ØØØØ

Discharges with invalid ICD-10-CM principal diagnosis, sex, or discharge status field (s) missing or invalid and necessary for DRG assignment.

Ⓣ **Transfer DRG**   Ⓢ **Special Payment**   * **Code Range**   **6th and 7th Character of ZZ = No Device, No Qualifier ZX = No Device, Diagnostic**

S35.23[1,2,8,9]A	[Minor lac, Major lac, Oth inj, Unsp inj] of inferior mesenteric artery, init enc **432**
S42.22[1,2,3,4,5, 6][A,B]	2-part [disp, nondisp] fx of surgical neck of [rt, lt, unsp] humerus, init enc for [clsd, opn] fx **422**
S42.22[1,2,3]B	2-part disp fx of surgical neck of [rt, lt, unsp] humerus, init enc for opn fx **433**
S42.22[4,5,6]B	2-part nondisp fx of surgical neck of [rt, lt, unsp] humerus, init enc for opn fx **433**
S42.23[1,2,9] [A,B]	3-part fx of surgical neck of [rt, lt, unsp] humerus, init enc for [clsd, opn] fx **185, 422**
S42.23[1,2,9]B	3-part fx of surgical neck of [rt, lt, unsp] humerus, init enc for opn fx **433**
S42.24[1,2,9] [A,B]	4-part fx of surgical neck of [rt, lt, unsp] humerus, init enc for [clsd, opn] fx **185, 422**
S42.24[1,2,9]B	4-part fx of surgical neck of [rt, lt, unsp] humerus, init enc for opn fx **433**
Q99.1	46, XX true hermaphrodite **261, 265, 270**
A42.1	Abd actinomycosis **114**
R10*	Abd and pelvic pain **116**
R19.3*	Abd rigidity **117**
Q53.21	Abd testis, bilat **289**
Q53.11	Abd testis, unilat **289**
R87.69	Abn cytolog find in specmn from oth female genital organs **386**
R85.69	Abn cytolog findings in specmn from oth dgstv org/abd cav **385**
R93.5	Abn findings on dx imaging of abd regions, incl* retroperiton **116**
R87.7	Abn histolog findings in specmn from female genital organs **386**
R87.4	Abn immunolog findings in specmn from female genital organs **385**
R89.2	Abn lev drug/meds/biol subst in specimens from oth org/tiss **386**
R85.2	Abn lev drug/meds/biol subst in specmn fr dgstv org/abd cav **385**
R87.2	Abn lev drug/meds/biol subst in specmn from fem gntl organs **385**
R85.0	Abn lev enzymes in specimens from dgstv org/abd cav **385**
R87.0	Abn lev enzymes in specimens from female genital organs **385**
R85.1	Abn lev hormones in specimens from dgstv org/abd cav **385**
R87.1	Abn lev hormones in specimens from female genital organs **385**
R85.3	Abn lev substance nonmed source in specmn fr dgstv org/abd cav **385**
R87.3	Abn lev substance nonmed source in specmn from fem gntl organs **385**
R89.3	Abn lev substance nonmed source in specmn from oth org/tiss **386**
R87.5	Abn microbiolog find in specmn from female genital organs **386**
R85.5	Abn microbiolog findings in specmn from dgstv org/abd cav **385**
R92*	Abnormal and inconclusive findings on dx imaging of breast **224**
R94.120	Abnormal auditory function study **58, 289**
R03*	Abnormal bld-pressure reading, w/o diagnosis **103**
R19.1*	Abnormal bowel sounds **116**
R85.61*	Abnormal cytologic smear of anus **117**
R89.6	Abnormal cytological findings in specimens from oth org/tiss **386**
R90.81	Abnormal echoencephalogram **39**
R94.110	Abnormal electro-oculogram [EOG] **46**
R94.131	Abnormal electromyogram [EMG] **195**
R94.111	Abnormal electroretinogram [ERG] **46**
R83*	Abnormal findings in cerebrospinal fluid **39**
R88*	Abnormal findings in oth body fluids and substances **386**
R86*	Abnormal findings in specimens from male genital organs **261**
R84*	Abnormal findings in specimens from resp org/thrx **385**
O28*	Abnormal findings on antenatal screening of mother **277, 279**
R82.8	Abnormal findings on cytolog and histolog exam of urine **255**
R93.8	Abnormal findings on diagnostic imaging of body structures **102**
R93.4	Abnormal findings on diagnostic imaging of urinary organs **255**
R93.[6,7]	Abnormal findings on dx imaging of [limbs, oth parts of musculoskeletal sys] **195**
R93.1	Abnormal findings on dx imaging of heart and cor circ **102**
R93.2	Abnormal findings on dx imaging of liver and biliary tract **124**
R93.3	Abnormal findings on dx imaging of prt digestive tract **116**
R93.0	Abnormal findings on dx imaging of skull and head, NEC **39**
R82.7	Abnormal findings on microbiological exam of urine **255**
P09	Abnormal findings on neonatal screening **385**
O99.814	Abnormal glucose compl childbirth **275**
O99.810	Abnormal glucose compl preg **277**
O99.815	Abnormal glucose compl the puerperium **276**
O99.8[1,2,3,4]4	Abnormal glucose, Streptococcus B carrier state, Oth infxn carrier state, Bariatric surgery status] compl childbirth **273**
O99.8[1,2,3,4]5	Abnormal glucose, Streptococcus B carrier state, Oth infxn carrier state, Bariatric surgery status] compl the puerperium **272**
K04.3	Abnormal hard tissue formation in pulp **4**
R89.7	Abnormal histolog findings in specimens from oth org/tiss **289, 386**
R85.7	Abnormal histolog findings in specmn from dgstv org/abd cav **385**
R89.4	Abnormal immunolog findings in specimens from oth org/tiss **386**
R85.4	Abnormal immunolog findings in specmn from dgstv org/abd cav **385**
R76.9	Abnormal immunological finding in serum, unsp **294**
H02.51*	Abnormal innervation synd **45**
R25*	Abnormal involuntary movements **38**
R89.0	Abnormal lvl of enzymes in specimens from oth org/tiss **386**
R89.1	Abnormal lvl of hormones in specimens from oth org/tiss **386**
R89.5	Abnormal microbiolog findings in specimens from oth org/tiss **386**
R94.113	Abnormal oculomotor study **46**
R29.3	Abnormal posture **38**
O02.9	Abnormal product of conception, unsp **277, 279**
R29.2	Abnormal reflex **38**
R94.130	Abnormal response to nerve stimulation, unsp **39**
R94.3*	Abnormal results of cardiovascular function studies **103**
R94.0*	Abnormal results of function studies of cnsl **39**
R94.8	Abnormal results of function studies of organs and systems **255**
R94.4	Abnormal results of kidney function studies **255**
R94.5	Abnormal results of liver function studies **124**
R94.7	Abnormal results of oth endocrine function studies **247**
R94.1[1,2,3]8	Abnormal results of oth function studies of [eye, ear and oth special senses, peripheral nervous sys] **39**
R94.2	Abnormal results of pulmn function studies **69**
R94.6	Abnormal results of thyroid function studies **247**
R74*	Abnormal serum enzyme levels **385**
R09.3	Abnormal sputum **69**
R97*	Abnormal tumor markers **386**
R82.6	Abnormal urine levels of substances chiefly nonmed source **255**
R94.121	Abnormal vestibular function study **58**
R94.112	Abnormal visually evoked potential [VEP] **46**
O62*	Abnormalities of forces of labor **278, 280**
K00.2	Abnormalities of size and form of teeth **4**
O76	Abnormality in fetal heart rate and rhythm comp labor and delivery **278, 280**
R71*	Abnormality of red bld cells **293**
T80.30XA	ABO incompat react d/t tranfs of bld/bld prod, unsp, init **287, 293**
T80.30XS	ABO incompat react d/t tranfs of bld/bld prod, unsp, seq **374**
T80.30XD	ABO incompat react d/t tranfs of bld/bld prod, unsp, subs **410**
T80.310A	ABO incompatibility w acute hemolytic transfs react, init **293**
T80.311A	ABO incompatibility w delayed hemolytic transfs react, init **293**
T80.319A	ABO incompatibility w hemolytic transfs react, unsp, init **293**
T80.31[0,1,9]A	ABO incompatibility w/ [acute, delayed, unsp] hemolytic transfusion reaction, init enc **287**
T80.31[0,1,9]S	ABO incompatibility w/ [acute, delayed, unsp] hemolytic transfusion reaction, seq **374**
T80.31[0,1,9]D	ABO incompatibility w/ [acute, delayed, unsp] hemolytic transfusion reaction, subsq enc **410**
P55.1	ABO isoimmunization of newborn **288**
S00.51[1,2][A,S]	Abrasion of [lip, oral cavity], [init enc, seq] **224**
S30.81[0,1,2,3,4, 5,6,7]D	Abrasion of [lwr back and pelvis, abd wall, penis, scrotum and testes, vagina and vulva, unsp ext genital organs male, unsp ext genital organs female, anus], subsq enc **389**
S60.41[8,9][A,S]	Abrasion of [oth, unsp] finger, [init enc, seq] **228**
S60.41[8,9]D	Abrasion of [oth, unsp] finger, subsq enc **394**
S30.81[2,3][A,S]	Abrasion of [penis, scrotum and testes], [init enc, seq] **226**
S20.41[1,2,9] [A,S]	Abrasion of [rt, lt, unsp] back wall of thorax, [init enc, seq] **225**

Code	Description
S20.41[1,2,9]D	Abrasion of [rt, lt, unsp] back wall of thorax, subsq enc **388**
S00.41[1,2,9] [A,S]	Abrasion of [rt, lt, unsp] ear, [init enc, seq] **224**
S50.31[1,2,9] [A,S]	Abrasion of [rt, lt, unsp] elbow, [init enc, seq] **227**
S50.31[1,2,9]D	Abrasion of [rt, lt, unsp] elbow, subsq enc **392**
S00.21[1,2,9]A	Abrasion of [rt, lt, unsp] eyelid and periocular area, init enc **46**
S00.21[1,2,9]S	Abrasion of [rt, lt, unsp] eyelid and periocular area, seq **224**
S50.81[1,2,9] [A,S]	Abrasion of [rt, lt, unsp] forearm, [init enc, seq] **227**
S50.81[1,2,9]D	Abrasion of [rt, lt, unsp] forearm, subsq enc **392**
S20.31[1,2,9] [A,S]	Abrasion of [rt, lt, unsp] front wall of thorax, [init enc, seq] **225**
S20.31[1,2,9]D	Abrasion of [rt, lt, unsp] front wall of thorax, subsq enc **388**
S60.51[1,2,9] [A,S]	Abrasion of [rt, lt, unsp] hand, [init enc, seq] **228**
S60.51[1,2,9]D	Abrasion of [rt, lt, unsp] hand, subsq enc **394**
S40.21[1,2,9] [A,S]	Abrasion of [rt, lt, unsp] shldr, [init enc, seq] **227**
S40.21[1,2,9]D	Abrasion of [rt, lt, unsp] shldr, subsq enc **391**
S40.81[1,2,9]D	Abrasion of [rt, lt, unsp] shldr, subsq enc **391**
S60.31[1,2,9] [A,S]	Abrasion of [rt, lt, unsp] thumb, [init enc, seq] **227**
S60.31[1,2,9]D	Abrasion of [rt, lt, unsp] thumb, subsq enc **394**
S40.81[1,2,9] [A,S]	Abrasion of [rt, lt, unsp] upr arm, [init enc, seq] **227**
S60.81[1,2,9] [A,S]	Abrasion of [rt, lt, unsp] wrist, [init enc, seq] **228**
S60.81[1,2,9]D	Abrasion of [rt, lt, unsp] wrist, subsq enc **394**
S60.41[0,1][A,S]	Abrasion of [rt, lt] index finger, [init enc, seq] **228**
S60.41[0,1]D	Abrasion of [rt, lt] index finger, subsq enc **394**
S60.41[6,7][A,S]	Abrasion of [rt, lt] little finger, [init enc, seq] **228**
S60.41[6,7]D	Abrasion of [rt, lt] little finger, subsq enc **394**
S60.41[2,3][A,S]	Abrasion of [rt, lt] mid finger, [init enc, seq] **228**
S60.41[2,3]D	Abrasion of [rt, lt] mid finger, subsq enc **394**
S60.41[4,5][A,S]	Abrasion of [rt, lt] ring finger, [init enc, seq] **228**
S60.41[4,5]D	Abrasion of [rt, lt] ring finger, subsq enc **394**
S30.811[A,S]	Abrasion of abd wall, [init enc, seq] **226**
S30.817[A,S]	Abrasion of anus, [init enc, seq] **226**
S20.11[1,2,9] [A,S]	Abrasion of breast, [rt, lt, unsp] breast, [init enc, seq] **225**
S20.11[1,2,9]D	Abrasion of breast, [rt, lt, unsp] breast, subsq enc **388**
S30.810[A,S]	Abrasion of lwr back and pelvis, [init enc, seq] **226**
S00.01X[A,S]	Abrasion of scalp, [init enc, seq] **224**
K03.1	Abrasion of teeth **4**
S30.81[5,6][A,S]	Abrasion of unsp ext genital organs, [male, female], [init enc, seq] **226**
S30.814[A,S]	Abrasion of vagina and vulva, [init enc, seq] **226**
S90.51[1,2,9] [A,S]	Abrasion, [rt, lt, unsp] ankle, [init enc, seq] **230**
S90.81[1,2,9] [A,S]	Abrasion, [rt, lt, unsp] foot, [init enc, seq] **230**
S90.41[1,2,3] [A,S]	Abrasion, [rt, lt, unsp] great toe, [init enc, seq] **230**
S90.41[1,2,3]A	Abrasion, [rt, lt, unsp] great toe, init enc **428**
S90.41[1,2,3]D	Abrasion, [rt, lt, unsp] great toe, subsq enc **398**
S70.21[1,2,9] [A,S]	Abrasion, [rt, lt, unsp] hip, [init enc, seq] **229**
S80.21[1,2,9] [A,S]	Abrasion, [rt, lt, unsp] knee, [init enc, seq] **229**
S90.41[4,5,6] [A,S]	Abrasion, [rt, lt, unsp] lesser toe(s), [init enc, seq] **230**
S90.41[4,5,6]A	Abrasion, [rt, lt, unsp] lesser toe(s), init enc **428**
S90.41[4,5,6]D	Abrasion, [rt, lt, unsp] lesser toe(s), subsq enc **398**
S80.81[1,2,9] [A,S]	Abrasion, [rt, lt, unsp] lwr leg, [init enc, seq] **229**
S70.31[1,2,9] [A,S]	Abrasion, [rt, lt, unsp] thigh, [init enc, seq] **229**
S60.3[1,2,4,5,6,7, 9][1,2,9]A	Abrasion, Blister (nonthermal), Ext constriction, Superf FB, Insect bite (nonvenomous), Oth superf bite, Oth superf injuries] of [rt, lt, unsp] thumb, init enc **424**
S80.[2,8] [1,2,4,5,6,7] [1,2,9]A	Abrasion, Blister (nonthermal), Ext constriction, Superf FB, Insect bite (nonvenomous), Oth superf bite] [rt, lt, unsp] knee, init enc **427**
S80.8[1,2,4,5,6,7] [1,2,9]A	Abrasion, Blister (nonthermal), Ext constriction, Superf FB, Insect bite (nonvenomous), Oth superf bite] [rt, lt, unsp] lwr leg, init enc **427**
S30.8[1,2,4,5,6,7] [0,1,2,3,4,5,6,7] A	Abrasion, Blister (nonthermal), Ext constriction, Superf FB, Insect bite (nonvenomous), Oth superf bite] of [lwr back and pelvis, abd wall, penis, scrotum and testes, vagina and vulva, unsp ext genital organs [male, female], anus], init enc **421**
S60.4[1,2,4,5,6,7] [0,1,2,3,4,5,6,7, 8,9]A	Abrasion, Blister (nonthermal), Ext constriction, Superf FB, Insect bite (nonvenomous), Oth superf bite] of [rt index, lt index, rt mid, lt mid, rt ring, lt ring, rt little, lt little, oth, unsp] finger, init enc **424**
S50.3[1,2,4,5,6,7] [1,2,9]A	Abrasion, Blister (nonthermal), Ext constriction, Superf FB, Insect bite (nonvenomous), Oth superf bite] of [rt, lt, unsp] elbow, init enc **423**
S50.8[1,2,4,5,6,7] [1,2,9]A	Abrasion, Blister (nonthermal), Ext constriction, Superf FB, Insect bite (nonvenomous), Oth superf bite] of [rt, lt, unsp] forearm, init enc **423**
S60.5[1,2,4,5,6,7] [1,2,9]A	Abrasion, Blister (nonthermal), Ext constriction, Superf FB, Insect bite (nonvenomous), Oth superf bite] of [rt, lt, unsp] hand, init enc **424**
S80.2[1,2,4,5,6,7] [1,2,9]D	Abrasion, Blister (nonthermal), Ext constriction, Superf FB, Insect bite (nonvenomous), Oth superf bite] of [rt, lt, unsp] knee, subsq enc **398**
S80.8[1,2,4,5,6,7] [1,2,9]D	Abrasion, Blister (nonthermal), Ext constriction, Superf FB, Insect bite (nonvenomous), Oth superf bite] of [rt, lt, unsp] lwr leg, subsq enc **398**
S40.2[1,2,4,5,6,7] [1,2,9]A	Abrasion, Blister (nonthermal), Ext constriction, Superf FB, Insect bite (nonvenomous), Oth superf bite] of [rt, lt, unsp] shldr, init enc **422**
S40.8[1,2,4,5,6,7] [1,2,9]A	Abrasion, Blister (nonthermal), Ext constriction, Superf FB, Insect bite (nonvenomous), Oth superf bite] of [rt, lt, unsp] upr arm, init enc **422**
S60.8[1,2,4,5,6,7] [1,2,9]A	Abrasion, Blister (nonthermal), Ext constriction, Superf FB, Insect bite (nonvenomous), Oth superf bite] of [rt, lt, unsp] wrist, init enc **424**
S90.5[1,2,4,5,6,7] [1,2,9]A	[Abrasion, Blister (nonthermal), Ext constriction, Superf FB, Insect bite (nonvenomous), Oth superf bite], [rt, lt, unsp] ankle, init enc **428**
S90.5[1,2,4,5,6,7] [1,2,9]D	Abrasion, Blister (nonthermal), Ext constriction, Superf FB, Insect bite (nonvenomous), Oth superf bite], [rt, lt, unsp] ankle, subsq enc **399**
S90.8[1,2,4,5,6,7] [1,2,9]A	[Abrasion, Blister (nonthermal), Ext constriction, Superf FB, Insect bite (nonvenomous), Oth superf bite], [rt, lt, unsp] foot, init enc **428**
S90.8[1,2,4,5,6,7] [1,2,9]D	Abrasion, Blister (nonthermal), Ext constriction, Superf FB, Insect bite (nonvenomous), Oth superf bite], [rt, lt, unsp] foot, subsq enc **399**
S70.2[1,2,4,5,6,7] [1,2,9]A	Abrasion, Blister (nonthermal), Ext constriction, Superf FB, Insect bite (nonvenomous), Oth superf bite], [rt, lt, unsp] hip, init enc **426**
S70.2[1,2,4,5,6,7] [1,2,9]D	Abrasion, Blister (nonthermal), Ext constriction, Superf FB, Insect bite (nonvenomous), Oth superf bite], [rt, lt, unsp] hip, subsq enc **397**
S70.3[1,2,4,5,6,7] [1,2,9]A	Abrasion, Blister (nonthermal), Ext constriction, Superf FB, Insect bite (nonvenomous), Oth superf bite], [rt, lt, unsp] thigh, init enc **426**
S70.3[1,2,4,5,6,7] [1,2,9]D	Abrasion, Blister (nonthermal), Ext constriction, Superf FB, Insect bite (nonvenomous), Oth superf bite], [rt, lt, unsp] thigh, subsq enc **397**
K61*	Abscess of anal and rectal regions **117, 284**
N75.1	Abscess of Bartholin's gland **269**
O91.1[2,3]	Abscess of breast associated w/ [the puerperium, lactation] **272**
O91.11[1,2,3]	Abscess of breast associated w/ preg, [1st, 2nd, 3rd] trmstr **274, 278**
O91.13	Abscess of breast associated with lactation **276**
O91.12	Abscess of breast associated with the puerperium **274, 276**
K63.0	Abscess of intestine **114**
K75.0	Abscess of liver **284**
J85*	Abscess of lung and mediastinum **67, 284**
K11.3	Abscess of salivary gland **4**
D73.3	Abscess of spleen **294**
E32.1	Abscess of thymus **283, 294**
N76.4	Abscess of vulva **269**
J34.0	Abscess, furuncle and carbuncle of nose **289**
N91*	Absent, scanty and rare menstruation **265, 270**

B60.10	Acanthamebiasis, unsp 309	
L83	Acanthosis nigricans 234	
Q17.0	Accessory auricle 289	
Q33.1	Accessory lobe of lung 69	
I97.5*	Accid punc & lac of a circ sys org dur proc 284, 367	
K91.7*	Accid punc & lac of a digestive sys org dur proc 284, 367	
N99.7*	Accid punc & lac of a GU sys org dur proc 285, 368	
G97.4*	Accid punc & lac of a nervous sys org dur proc 283, 367	
J95.7*	Accid punc & lac of a respiratory sys org dur proc 284, 367	
E36.1*	Accid punc & lac of an endo sys org during a procedure 283	
H95.3*	Accid punc & lac of ear/mastd during a procedure 283, 367	
H59.2*	Accid punc & lac of eye and adnexa during a procedure 283, 367	
L76.1*	Accid punc & lac of skin, SQ during a procedure 284	
D78.1*	Accid punc & lac of the spleen during a procedure 283	
M96.82[0,1]	Accid punc and lac of a musculoskeletal structure during [a musculoskeletal sys, oth] procedure 285	
R82.4	Acetonuria 247	
K22.0	Achalasia of cardia 116	
K31.83	Achlorhydria 116	
Q77.0	Achondrogenesis 195	
Q77.4	Achondroplasia 195	
H53.51	Achromatopsia 46	
L70*	Acne 234	
M21.5[1,2][1,2,9]	Acquired [clawhand, clubhand], [rt, lt, unsp] hand 34	
Z90.1*	Acquired absence of breast and nipple 413	
Z90.01	Acquired absence of eye 47	
Z90.7*	Acquired absence of genital organ(s) 265, 270	
Z90.5	Acquired absence of kidney 413	
Z90.02	Acquired absence of larynx 413	
Z89*	Acquired absence of limb 413	
Z90.2	Acquired absence of lung [part of] 70	
Z90.8*	Acquired absence of oth organs 413	
Z90.09	Acquired absence of oth part of head and neck 413	
Z90.6	Acquired absence of oth parts of urinary tract 256	
Z90.4*	Acquired absence of oth spec parts of digestive tract 413	
Z90.79	Acquired absence of other genital organ(s) 261	
Z90.3	Acquired absence of stomach [part of] 413	
M21.53[1,2,9]	Acquired clawfoot, [rt, lt, unsp] foot 34	
M21.54[1,2,9]	Acquired clubfoot, [rt, lt, unsp] foot 193	
D68.4	Acquired coagulation factor deficiency 294	
H53.52	Acquired color vision deficiency 45	
M20.6[0,1,2]	Acquired deformities of toe(s), unsp, [unsp, rt, lt] foot 193	
M95.4	Acquired deformity of chest and rib 194	
M95.9	Acquired deformity of musculoskeletal sys, unsp 194	
M95.3	Acquired deformity of neck 194	
M95.0	Acquired deformity of nose 58	
M95.5	Acquired deformity of pelvis 194	
L12.3*	Acquired epidermolysis bullosa 223	
D59.9	Acquired hemolytic anemia, unsp 283, 293	
D68.311	Acquired hemophilia 294	
P91.1	Acquired periventricular cysts of newborn 282	
D60.9	Acquired pure red cell aplasia, unsp 293	
H61.3*	Acquired stenosis of ext ear canal 58	
L40.2	Acrodermatitis continua 223	
B47.1	Actinomycetoma 308, 438	
A42*	Actinomycosis 438	
A42.9	Actinomycosis, unsp 308	
A42.7	Actinomycotic sepsis 282, 309	
H04.3[2,3][1,2,3,9]	Acute [dacryocystitis, lacrimal canaliculitis] of [rt, lt, bilat, unsp] lacrimal passage 45	
A06.0	Acute amebic dysentery 114	
J96.2*	Acute and chr respiratory failure 381	
I33*	Acute and subacute endocarditis 283, 439	
I33.9	Acute and subacute endocarditis, unsp 99	
K72.0*	Acute and subacute hepatic failure 284	
I33.0	Acute and subacute infective endocarditis 99	
K04.4	Acute apical periodontitis of pulpal origin 4	
K35.2	Acute appendicitis with generalized peritonitis 108, 114	
K35.3	Acute appendicitis with localized peritonitis 108, 114	
J21*	Acute bronchiolitis 69	

J20*	Acute bronchitis 69
I67.81	Acute cerebrovascular insufficiency 33
B57.1	Acute Chagas' dz w/o heart involvement 308
B57.0	Acute Chagas' dz with heart involvement 103
I24.0	Acute coronary thrombosis not resulting in myocardial infrc 102
N30.0*	Acute cystitis 255, 285
H04.01[1,2,3,9]	Acute dacryoadenitis, [rt, lt, bilat, unsp] lacrimal gland 45
K31.0	Acute dilatation of stomach 116, 284
G36.9	Acute disseminated demyelination, unsp 439
G04.0*	Acute disseminated encephalitis & encephalomyelitis (ADEM) 11, 15, 41
K26.3	Acute duodenal ulcer w/o hemor or perforation 115
K26.2	Acute duodenal ulcer with both hemor and perforation 115
K26.0	Acute duodenal ulcer with hemor 115
K26.1	Acute duodenal ulcer with perforation 115
I82.4*	Acute embolism and thrombosis of deep veins of low extrm 100
I82.6*	Acute embolism and thrombosis of veins of upr extr 100
J05.1*	Acute epiglottitis 3
C94.0*	Acute erythroid leukemia 304, 305
K25.3	Acute gastric ulcer w/o hemor or perforation 115
K25.2	Acute gastric ulcer with both hemor and perforation 115
K25.0	Acute gastric ulcer with hemor 115
K25.1	Acute gastric ulcer with perforation 115
K29.01	Acute gastritis with bleeding 115
K28.2	Acute gastrojejunal ulcer w both hemor and perforation 115
K28.3	Acute gastrojejunal ulcer w/o hemor or perforation 115
K28.0	Acute gastrojejunal ulcer with hemor 115
K28.1	Acute gastrojejunal ulcer with perforation 115
K05.0*	Acute gingivitis 4
D89.810	Acute graft-versus-host dz 293
M86.06[1,2,9]	Acute hematogenous osteomyelitis, [rt, lt, unsp] tibia & fibula 131
M86.08	Acute hematogenous osteomyelitis, oth sites 125
T80.910A	Acute hemolytic transfs react, unsp incompatibility, init 293
B15*	Acute hepatitis A 124
B16*	Acute hepatitis B 124, 283
T80.22XA	Acute infxn fol tranfs,infusn,inject bld/products, init 287, 307, 309
T80.22XS	Acute infxn fol tranfs,infusn,inject bld/products, seq 374
T80.22XD	Acute infxn fol tranfs,infusn,inject bld/products, subs 410
I24.9	Acute ischemic heart dz, unsp 102
N17*	Acute kidney failure 254, 285
J04.0	Acute laryngitis 3, 57
J06.0	Acute laryngopharyngitis 4
J04.2	Acute laryngotracheitis 3, 57
C95.0*	Acute leukemia of unsp cell type 304, 305
L04*	Acute lymphadenitis 284
L04.0	Acute lymphadenitis of face, head and neck 294
L04.3	Acute lymphadenitis of lwr limb 294
L04.8	Acute lymphadenitis of oth sites 294
L04.1	Acute lymphadenitis of trunk 294
L04.2	Acute lymphadenitis of upr limb 294
L04.9	Acute lymphadenitis, unsp 294
C91.0*	Acute lymphoblastic leukemia [ALL] 304, 305
H70.0*	Acute mastoiditis 57
C94.2*	Acute megakaryoblastic leukemia 303, 305
A39.2	Acute meningococcemia 309
C93.0*	Acute monoblastic/monocytic leukemia 304, 305
C92.0*	Acute myeloblastic leukemia 304, 305
C92.6*	Acute myeloid leukemia with 11q23-abnormality 304, 305
C92.A*	Acute myeloid leukemia with multilineage dysplasia 304, 305
C92.5*	Acute myelomonocytic leukemia 304, 305
I40*	Acute myocarditis 103, 439
H73.0*	Acute myringitis 57
J00	Acute nasopharyngitis [common cold] 3, 57
G04.3*	Acute necrotizing hemorrhagic encephalopathy 11, 15, 41
N00*	Acute nephritic synd 256, 285
A80.4	Acute nonparalytic poliomyelitis 307
J05.0	Acute obstructive laryngitis [croup] 3
J05*	Acute obstructive laryngitis [croup] and epiglottitis 57
D89.812	Acute on chr graft-versus-host dz 293
G89.1*	Acute pain, NEC 385

T46.995S	Adverse effect of agents affected the cardiovascular sys, seq 371
T46.995D	Adverse effect of agents affecting the cardiovascular sys, subs 406
T48.995A	Adverse effect of agents prim acting on the resp sys, init 365
T48.995D	Adverse effect of agents prim acting on the resp sys, subs 407
T47.8X5A	Adverse effect of agents primarily affecting GI sys, init 287, 364
T47.8X5S	Adverse effect of agents primarily affecting GI sys, seq 371
T47.8X5D	Adverse effect of agents primarily affecting GI sys, subs 406
T44.6X5A	Adverse effect of alpha-adrenoreceptor antagonists, init 287, 363
T44.6X5S	Adverse effect of alpha-adrenoreceptor antagonists, seq 370
T44.6X5D	Adverse effect of alpha-adrenoreceptor antagonists, subs 405
T36.5X5A	Adverse effect of aminoglycosides, init enc 286, 362
T36.5X5S	Adverse effect of aminoglycosides, seq 368
T36.5X5D	Adverse effect of aminoglycosides, subsq enc 403
T43.625A	Adverse effect of amphetamines, init enc 363
T43.625S	Adverse effect of amphetamines, seq 370
T43.625D	Adverse effect of amphetamines, subsq enc 405
T50.7X5A	Adverse effect of analeptics and opioid receptor antag, init 287, 365
T50.7X5D	Adverse effect of analeptics and opioid receptor antag, subs 407
T38.7X5A	Adverse effect of androgens and anabolic congeners, init 286, 362
T38.7X5S	Adverse effect of androgens and anabolic congeners, seq 369
T38.7X5D	Adverse effect of androgens and anabolic congeners, subs 403
T46.4X5A	Adverse effect of angiotens-convert-enzyme inhibitors, init 287, 364
T46.4X5D	Adverse effect of angiotens-convert-enzyme inhibitors, subs 406
T46.4X5S	Adverse effect of angiotens-convert-enzyme inhibtr, seq 371
T38.815A	Adverse effect of ant pituitary hormones, init enc 362
T38.815S	Adverse effect of ant pituitary hormones, seq 369
T38.815D	Adverse effect of ant pituitary hormones, subs enc 403
T47.1X5A	Adverse effect of antacids and anti-gstrc-sec drugs, init 287, 364
T47.1X5S	Adverse effect of antacids and anti-gstrc-sec drugs, seq 371
T47.1X5D	Adverse effect of antacids and anti-gstrc-sec drugs, subs 406
T37.4X5A	Adverse effect of anthelminthics, init enc 286, 362
T37.4X5S	Adverse effect of anthelminthics, seq 368
T37.4X5D	Adverse effect of anthelminthics, subsq enc 403
T45.0X5A	Adverse effect of antiallergic and antiemetic drugs, init 287, 364
T45.0X5S	Adverse effect of antiallergic and antiemetic drugs, seq 370
T45.0X5D	Adverse effect of antiallergic and antiemetic drugs, subs 405
T48.6X5A	Adverse effect of antiasthmatics, init enc 287, 365
T48.6X5S	Adverse effect of antiasthmatics, seq 371
T48.6X5D	Adverse effect of antiasthmatics, subsq enc 407
T44.0X5A	Adverse effect of anticholinesterase agents, init enc 287, 363
T44.0X5S	Adverse effect of anticholinesterase agents, seq 370
T44.0X5D	Adverse effect of anticholinesterase agents, subs enc 405
T45.7X5A	Adverse effect of anticoag antag, vit K and oth coag, init 287, 364
T45.7X5D	Adverse effect of anticoag antag, vit K and oth coag, subs 406
T45.515A	Adverse effect of anticoagulants, init enc 364
T45.515S	Adverse effect of anticoagulants, seq 370
T45.515D	Adverse effect of anticoagulants, subsq enc 405
T47.6X5A	Adverse effect of antidiarrheal drugs, init enc 287, 364
T47.6X5S	Adverse effect of antidiarrheal drugs, seq 371
T47.6X5D	Adverse effect of antidiarrheal drugs, subsq enc 406
T50.6X5A	Adverse effect of antidotes and chelating agents, init 287, 365
T50.6X5S	Adverse effect of antidotes and chelating agents, seq 372
T50.6X5D	Adverse effect of antidotes and chelating agents, subs 407
T42.6X5A	Adverse effect of antiepileptic and sed-hypntc drugs, init 287, 363
T42.6X5D	Adverse effect of antiepileptic and sed-hypntc drugs, subs 404
T42.6X5S	Adverse effect of antieplptc and sed-hypntc drugs, seq 370
T36.7X5A	Adverse effect of antifungal antibiotics, sys used, init 286, 362
T36.7X5S	Adverse effect of antifungal antibiotics, sys used, seq 368
T36.7X5D	Adverse effect of antifungal antibiotics, sys used, subs 403
T38.6X5A	Adverse effect of antigonadtr/antiestr/antiandrg, NEC, init 286, 362
T38.6X5D	Adverse effect of antigonadtr/antiestr/antiandrg, NEC, subs 403
T46.6X5A	Adverse effect of antihyperlip and antiarterio drugs, init 287, 364
T46.6X5D	Adverse effect of antihyperlip and antiarterio drugs, subs 406
T37.1X5A	Adverse effect of antimycobacterial drugs, init enc 286, 362
T37.1X5S	Adverse effect of antimycobacterial drugs, seq 368
T37.1X5D	Adverse effect of antimycobacterial drugs, subs enc 403
T45.1X5A	Adverse effect of antineoplastic and immunosup drugs, init 287, 364
T45.1X5S	Adverse effect of antineoplastic and immunosup drugs, seq 370
T45.1X5D	Adverse effect of antineoplastic and immunosup drugs, subs 405
T42.8X5A	Adverse effect of antiparkns drug/centr musc-tone depr, init 287, 363
T42.8X5D	Adverse effect of antiparkns drug/centr musc-tone depr, subs 404
T49.1X5A	Adverse effect of antipruritics, init enc 287, 365
T49.1X5S	Adverse effect of antipruritics, seq 371
T49.1X5D	Adverse effect of antipruritics, subsq enc 407
T43.595S	Adverse effect of antipsychotics and neuroleptics, seq 370
T39.4X5A	Adverse effect of antirheumatics, NEC, init 286, 362
T39.4X5S	Adverse effect of antirheumatics, NEC, seq 369
T39.4X5D	Adverse effect of antirheumatics, NEC, subs 404
T45.525A	Adverse effect of antithrombotic drugs, init enc 364
T45.525S	Adverse effect of antithrombotic drugs, seq 370
T45.525D	Adverse effect of antithrombotic drugs, subsq enc 405
T38.2X5A	Adverse effect of antithyroid drugs, init enc 286, 362
T38.2X5S	Adverse effect of antithyroid drugs, seq 369
T38.2X5D	Adverse effect of antithyroid drugs, subsq enc 403
T48.3X5A	Adverse effect of antitussives, init enc 287, 364
T48.3X5S	Adverse effect of antitussives, seq 371
T48.3X5D	Adverse effect of antitussives, subsq enc 406
T46.8X5A	Adverse effect of antivaric drugs, incl* scler agents, init 287, 364
T46.8X5S	Adverse effect of antivaric drugs, incl* scler agents, seq 371
T46.8X5D	Adverse effect of antivaric drugs, incl* scler agents, subs 406
T37.5X5A	Adverse effect of antiviral drugs, init enc 286, 362
T37.5X5S	Adverse effect of antiviral drugs, seq 368
T37.5X5D	Adverse effect of antiviral drugs, subsq enc 403
T50.5X5A	Adverse effect of appetite depressants, init enc 287, 365
T50.5X5S	Adverse effect of appetite depressants, seq 372
T50.5X5D	Adverse effect of appetite depressants, subsq enc 407
T39.015A	Adverse effect of aspirin, init enc 362
T39.015D	Adverse effect of aspirin, subsq enc 403
T42.3X5A	Adverse effect of barbiturates, init enc 287, 363
T42.3X5S	Adverse effect of barbiturates, seq 369
T42.3X5D	Adverse effect of barbiturates, subsq enc 404
T42.4X5A	Adverse effect of benzodiazepines, init enc 287, 363
T42.4X5S	Adverse effect of benzodiazepines, seq 369
T42.4X5D	Adverse effect of benzodiazepines, subsq enc 404
T44.7X5A	Adverse effect of beta-adrenoreceptor antagonists, init 287, 363
T44.7X5S	Adverse effect of beta-adrenoreceptor antagonists, seq 370
T44.7X5D	Adverse effect of beta-adrenoreceptor antagonists, subs 405
T43.4X5S	Adverse effect of butyrophen/thiothixen neuroleptc, seq 370
T43.4X5A	Adverse effect of butyrophen/thiothixen neuroleptics, init 287, 363
T43.4X5D	Adverse effect of butyrophen/thiothixen neuroleptics, subs 405
T43.615A	Adverse effect of caffeine, init enc 363
T43.615S	Adverse effect of caffeine, seq 370
T43.615D	Adverse effect of caffeine, subsq enc 405
T46.1X5A	Adverse effect of calcium-channel blockers, init enc 287, 364
T46.1X5S	Adverse effect of calcium-channel blockers, seq 371
T46.1X5D	Adverse effect of calcium-channel blockers, subs enc 406
T40.7X5A	Adverse effect of cannabis (derivatives), init enc 286, 363
T40.7X5S	Adverse effect of cannabis (derivatives), seq 369
T40.7X5D	Adverse effect of cannabis (derivatives), subs enc 404
T46.0X5A	Adverse effect of cardi-stim glycos/drug simlar act, init 287, 364
T46.0X5S	Adverse effect of cardi-stim glycos/drug simlar act, seq 371
T46.0X5D	Adverse effect of cardi-stim glycos/drug simlar act, subs 406
T44.8X5A	Adverse effect of centr-acting/adren-neurn-block agnt, init 287, 364
T44.8X5D	Adverse effect of centr-acting/adren-neurn-block agnt, subs 405
T36.1X5A	Adverse effect of cephalospor/oth beta-lactm antibiot, init 286, 362
T36.1X5D	Adverse effect of cephalospor/oth beta-lactm antibiot, subs 403
T36.2X5A	Adverse effect of chloramphenicol group, init enc 286, 362
T36.2X5S	Adverse effect of chloramphenicol group, seq 368
T36.2X5D	Adverse effect of chloramphenicol group, subs enc 403
T40.5X5A	Adverse effect of cocaine, init enc 286, 362
T40.5X5S	Adverse effect of cocaine, seq 369

T40.5X5D	Adverse effect of cocaine, subsq enc 404
T46.3X5A	Adverse effect of coronary vasodilators, init enc 287, 364
T46.3X5S	Adverse effect of coronary vasodilators, seq 371
T46.3X5D	Adverse effect of coronary vasodilators, sub enc 406
T49.7X5A	Adverse effect of dental drugs, topically applied, init 287, 365
T49.7X5S	Adverse effect of dental drugs, topically applied, seq 371
T49.7X5D	Adverse effect of dental drugs, topically applied, subs 407
T50.8X5A	Adverse effect of diagnostic agents, init enc 287, 365
T50.8X5S	Adverse effect of diagnostic agents, seq 372
T50.8X5D	Adverse effect of diagnostic agents, subsq enc 407
T47.5X5A	Adverse effect of digestants, init enc 287, 364
T47.5X5S	Adverse effect of digestants, seq 371
T47.5X5D	Adverse effect of digestants, subsq enc 406
T44.995S	Adverse effect of drug affected the autonm nervous sys, seq 370
T44.995A	Adverse effect of drug affecting the autonomic nervous sys, init 364
T44.995D	Adverse effect of drug affecting the autonomic nervous sys, subs 405
T50.995A	Adverse effect of drug/meds/biol subst, init 365
T50.995S	Adverse effect of drug/meds/biol subst, seq 372
T50.995D	Adverse effect of drug/meds/biol subst, subs 407
T50.4X5S	Adverse effect of drugs affecting uric acid metab, seq 372
T50.4X5A	Adverse effect of drugs affecting uric acid metabolism, init 287, 365
T50.4X5D	Adverse effect of drugs affecting uric acid metabolism, subs 407
T50.3X5A	Adverse effect of electrolytic/caloric/wtr-bal agnt, init enc 287, 365
T50.3X5S	Adverse effect of electrolytic/caloric/wtr-bal agnt, seq 372
T50.3X5D	Adverse effect of electrolytic/caloric/wtr-bal agnt, subs 407
T47.7X5A	Adverse effect of emetics, init enc 287, 364
T47.7X5S	Adverse effect of emetics, seq 371
T47.7X5D	Adverse effect of emetics, subsq enc 406
T49.3X5A	Adverse effect of emollients, demulcents and protect, init 287, 365
T49.3X5D	Adverse effect of emollients, demulcents and protect, subs 407
T45.3X5A	Adverse effect of enzymes, init enc 287, 364
T45.3X5S	Adverse effect of enzymes, seq 370
T45.3X5D	Adverse effect of enzymes, subsq enc 405
T48.4X5A	Adverse effect of expectorants, init enc 287, 364
T48.4X5S	Adverse effect of expectorants, seq 371
T48.4X5D	Adverse effect of expectorants, subsq enc 406
T44.2X5A	Adverse effect of ganglionic blocking drugs, init enc 287, 363
T44.2X5S	Adverse effect of ganglionic blocking drugs, seq 370
T44.2X5D	Adverse effect of ganglionic blocking drugs, subs enc 405
T38.0X5A	Adverse effect of glucocort/synth analog, init 286, 362
T38.0X5S	Adverse effect of glucocort/synth analog, seq 369
T38.0X5D	Adverse effect of glucocort/synth analog, subs 403
T45.625A	Adverse effect of hemostatic drug, init enc 364
T45.625S	Adverse effect of hemostatic drug, seq 370
T45.625D	Adverse effect of hemostatic drug, subsq enc 406
T47.0X5A	Adverse effect of histamine H2-receptor blockers, init 287, 364
T47.0X5S	Adverse effect of histamine H2-receptor blockers, seq 371
T47.0X5D	Adverse effect of histamine H2-receptor blockers, subs 406
T38.895S	Adverse effect of hormones and synth sub, seq 369
T38.895A	Adverse effect of hormones and synth substitutes, init 362
T38.895D	Adverse effect of hormones and synth substitutes, subs 403
T42.0X5A	Adverse effect of hydantoin derivatives, init enc 287, 363
T42.0X5S	Adverse effect of hydantoin derivatives, seq 369
T42.0X5D	Adverse effect of hydantoin derivatives, subsq enc 404
T42.1X5A	Adverse effect of iminostilbenes, init enc 287, 363
T42.1X5S	Adverse effect of iminostilbenes, seq 369
T42.1X5D	Adverse effect of iminostilbenes, subsq enc 404
T50.Z15A	Adverse effect of immunoglobulin, init enc 365
T50.Z15S	Adverse effect of immunoglobulin, seq 372
T50.Z15D	Adverse effect of immunoglobulin, subsq enc 407
T41.0X5A	Adverse effect of inhaled anesthetics, init enc 286, 363
T41.0X5S	Adverse effect of inhaled anesthetics, seq 369
T41.0X5D	Adverse effect of inhaled anesthetics, subsq enc 404
T38.3X5A	Adverse effect of insulin and oral hypoglycemic drugs, init 286, 362
T38.3X5D	Adverse effect of insulin and oral hypoglycemic drugs, subs 403
T41.1X5A	Adverse effect of intravenous anesthetics, init enc 286, 363

T41.1X5S	Adverse effect of intravenous anesthetics, seq 369
T41.1X5D	Adverse effect of intravenous anesthetics, subs enc 404
T45.4X5A	Adverse effect of iron and its compounds, init enc 287, 364
T45.4X5S	Adverse effect of iron and its compounds, seq 370
T45.4X5D	Adverse effect of iron and its compounds, subs enc 405
T49.4X5A	Adverse effect of keratolyt/keratplst/hair trmt drug, init 287, 365
T49.4X5D	Adverse effect of keratolyt/keratplst/hair trmt drug, subs 407
T41.3X5A	Adverse effect of local anesthetics, init enc 287, 363
T41.3X5S	Adverse effect of local anesthetics, seq 369
T41.3X5D	Adverse effect of local anesthetics, subsq enc 404
T49.0X5A	Adverse effect of local antifung/infect/inflamm drugs, init 287, 365
T49.0X5D	Adverse effect of local antifung/infect/inflamm drugs, subs 407
T49.2X5A	Adverse effect of local astringents/detergents, init 287, 365
T49.2X5S	Adverse effect of local astringents/detergents, seq 371
T49.2X5D	Adverse effect of local astringents/detergents, subs 407
T50.1X5S	Adverse effect of loop [high-ceiling] diuretics, seq 371
T50.1X5A	Adverse effect of loop diuretics, init enc 287, 365
T50.1X5D	Adverse effect of loop diuretics, subsq enc 407
T36.3X5A	Adverse effect of macrolides, init enc 286, 362
T36.3X5S	Adverse effect of macrolides, seq 368
T36.3X5D	Adverse effect of macrolides, subsq enc 403
T43.1X5A	Adverse effect of MAO inhib antidepressants, init enc 287, 363
T43.1X5S	Adverse effect of MAO inhib antidepressants, seq 370
T43.1X5D	Adverse effect of MAO inhib antidepressants, subs 405
T40.3X5A	Adverse effect of methadone, init enc 286, 362
T40.3X5S	Adverse effect of methadone, seq 369
T40.3X5D	Adverse effect of methadone, subsq enc 404
T43.635A	Adverse effect of methylphenidate, init enc 363
T43.635S	Adverse effect of methylphenidate, seq 370
T43.635D	Adverse effect of methylphenidate, subsq enc 405
T50.0X5S	Adverse effect of mineralocorticoids and antag, seq 371
T50.0X5A	Adverse effect of mineralocorticoids and their antag, init 287, 365
T50.0X5D	Adverse effect of mineralocorticoids and their antag, subs 407
T42.5X5A	Adverse effect of mixed antiepileptics, init enc 287, 363
T42.5X5S	Adverse effect of mixed antiepileptics, seq 369
T42.5X5D	Adverse effect of mixed antiepileptics, subsq enc 404
T50.A25A	Adverse effect of mixed bact vaccines w/o a pertuss, init 365
T50.A25S	Adverse effect of mixed bact vaccines w/o a pertuss, seq 372
T50.A25D	Adverse effect of mixed bact vaccines w/o a pertuss, subs 407
T39.8X5A	Adverse effect of nonopioid analges/antipyret, NEC, init 286, 362
T39.8X5S	Adverse effect of nonopioid analges/antipyret, NEC, seq 369
T39.8X5D	Adverse effect of nonopioid analges/antipyret, NEC, subs 404
T39.395A	Adverse effect of nonsteroidal anti-inflam drugs, init 362
T39.395S	Adverse effect of nonsteroidal anti-inflam drugs, seq 369
T39.395D	Adverse effect of nonsteroidal anti-inflam drugs, subs 404
T40.0X5A	Adverse effect of opium, init enc 286, 362
T40.0X5S	Adverse effect of opium, seq 369
T40.0X5D	Adverse effect of opium, subsq enc 404
T49.5X5A	Adverse effect of opth drugs and preparations, init 287, 365
T49.5X5S	Adverse effect of opth drugs and preparations, seq 371
T49.5X5D	Adverse effect of opth drugs and preparations, subs 407
T38.4X5A	Adverse effect of oral contraceptives, init enc 286, 362
T38.4X5S	Adverse effect of oral contraceptives, seq 369
T38.4X5D	Adverse effect of oral contraceptives, subsq enc 403
T48.5X5A	Adverse effect of oth anti-common-cold drugs, init enc 287, 364
T48.5X5S	Adverse effect of oth anti-common-cold drugs, seq 371
T48.5X5D	Adverse effect of oth anti-common-cold drugs, subs enc 406
T43.295A	Adverse effect of oth antidepressants, init enc 363
T43.295S	Adverse effect of oth antidepressants, seq 370
T43.295D	Adverse effect of oth antidepressants, subs enc 405
T46.2X5A	Adverse effect of oth antidysrhythmic drugs, init enc 287, 364
T46.2X5S	Adverse effect of oth antidysrhythmic drugs, seq 371
T46.2X5D	Adverse effect of oth antidysrhythmic drugs, subs enc 406
T46.5X5A	Adverse effect of oth antihypertensive drugs, init enc 287, 364
T46.5X5S	Adverse effect of oth antihypertensive drugs, seq 371
T46.5X5D	Adverse effect of oth antihypertensive drugs, subs enc 406
T37.3X5A	Adverse effect of oth antiprotozoal drugs, init enc 286, 362
T37.3X5S	Adverse effect of oth antiprotozoal drugs, seq 368
T37.3X5D	Adverse effect of oth antiprotozoal drugs, subs 403

T43.595A	Adverse effect of oth antipsychotics and neuroleptics, init 363
T43.595D	Adverse effect of oth antipsychotics and neuroleptics, subs 405
T50.A95A	Adverse effect of oth bacterial vaccines, init enc 365
T50.A95S	Adverse effect of oth bacterial vaccines, seq 372
T50.A95D	Adverse effect of oth bacterial vaccines, subs enc 407
T48.295A	Adverse effect of oth drugs acting on muscles, init enc 364
T48.295S	Adverse effect of oth drugs acting on muscles, seq 371
T48.295D	Adverse effect of oth drugs acting on muscles, subs enc 406
T38.5X5A	Adverse effect of oth estrogens and progestogens, init 286, 362
T38.5X5S	Adverse effect of oth estrogens and progestogens, seq 369
T38.5X5D	Adverse effect of oth estrogens and progestogens, subs 403
T45.695A	Adverse effect of oth fibrinolysis-affecting drugs, init 364
T45.695S	Adverse effect of oth fibrinolysis-affecting drugs, seq 370
T45.695D	Adverse effect of oth fibrinolysis-affecting drugs, subs 406
T41.295A	Adverse effect of oth general anesthetics, init enc 363
T41.295S	Adverse effect of oth general anesthetics, seq 369
T41.295D	Adverse effect of oth general anesthetics, subs enc 404
T38.995A	Adverse effect of oth hormone antagonists, init enc 362
T38.995S	Adverse effect of oth hormone antagonists, seq 369
T38.995D	Adverse effect of oth hormone antagonists, subs enc 403
T47.4X5A	Adverse effect of oth laxatives, init enc 287, 364
T47.4X5S	Adverse effect of oth laxatives, seq 371
T47.4X5D	Adverse effect of oth laxatives, subsq enc 406
T40.695A	Adverse effect of oth narcotics, init enc 363
T40.695S	Adverse effect of oth narcotics, seq 369
T40.695D	Adverse effect of oth narcotics, subsq enc 404
T40.2X5A	Adverse effect of oth opioids, init enc 286, 362
T40.2X5S	Adverse effect of oth opioids, seq 369
T40.2X5D	Adverse effect of oth opioids, subsq enc 404
T44.1X5A	Adverse effect of oth parasympathomimetics, init enc 287, 363
T44.1X5S	Adverse effect of oth parasympathomimetics, seq 370
T44.1X5D	Adverse effect of oth parasympathomimetics, subs enc 405
T40.995A	Adverse effect of oth psychodysleptics, init enc 363
T40.995S	Adverse effect of oth psychodysleptics, seq 369
T40.995D	Adverse effect of oth psychodysleptics, subs enc 404
T43.695A	Adverse effect of oth psychostimulants, init enc 363
T43.695S	Adverse effect of oth psychostimulants, seq 370
T43.695D	Adverse effect of oth psychostimulants, subs enc 405
T43.8X5A	Adverse effect of oth psychotropic drugs, init enc 287, 363
T43.8X5S	Adverse effect of oth psychotropic drugs, seq 370
T43.8X5D	Adverse effect of oth psychotropic drugs, subs enc 405
T40.4X5A	Adverse effect of oth synth narcotics, init enc 286, 362
T40.4X5S	Adverse effect of oth synth narcotics, seq 369
T40.4X5D	Adverse effect of oth synth narcotics, subs enc 404
T36.8X5A	Adverse effect of oth systemic antibiotics, init enc 286, 362
T36.8X5S	Adverse effect of oth systemic antibiotics, seq 368
T36.8X5D	Adverse effect of oth systemic antibiotics, subs enc 403
T49.8X5A	Adverse effect of oth topical agents, init enc 287, 365
T49.8X5S	Adverse effect of oth topical agents, seq 371
T49.8X5D	Adverse effect of oth topical agents, subsq enc 407
T50.B95A	Adverse effect of oth viral vaccines, init enc 365
T50.B95S	Adverse effect of oth viral vaccines, seq 372
T50.B95D	Adverse effect of oth viral vaccines, subsq enc 407
T49.6X5A	Adverse effect of otorhino drugs and preparations, init 287, 365
T49.6X5S	Adverse effect of otorhino drugs and preparations, seq 371
T49.6X5D	Adverse effect of otorhino drugs and preparations, subs 407
T48.0X5A	Adverse effect of oxytocic drugs, init enc 287, 364
T48.0X5S	Adverse effect of oxytocic drugs, seq 371
T48.0X5D	Adverse effect of oxytocic drugs, subsq enc 406
T44.3X5S	Adverse effect of parasympath and spasmolytics, seq 370
T44.3X5A	Adverse effect of parasympatholytics and spasmolytics, init 287, 363
T44.3X5D	Adverse effect of parasympatholytics and spasmolytics, subs 405
T36.0X5A	Adverse effect of penicillins, init enc 286, 362
T36.0X5S	Adverse effect of penicillins, seq 368
T36.0X5D	Adverse effect of penicillins, subsq enc 403
T46.7X5A	Adverse effect of peripheral vasodilators, init enc 287, 364
T46.7X5S	Adverse effect of peripheral vasodilators, seq 371
T46.7X5D	Adverse effect of peripheral vasodilators, subsq enc 406
T43.3X5S	Adverse effect of phenothiaz antipsychot/neurolept, seq 370
T43.3X5A	Adverse effect of phenothiazine antipsychot/neurolept, init 287, 363
T43.3X5D	Adverse effect of phenothiazine antipsychot/neurolept, subs 405
T44.4X5A	Adverse effect of predom alpha-adrenocpt agonists, init 287, 363
T44.4X5S	Adverse effect of predom alpha-adrenocpt agonists, seq 370
T44.4X5D	Adverse effect of predom alpha-adrenocpt agonists, subs 405
T44.5X5A	Adverse effect of predom beta-adrenocpt agonists, init 287, 363
T44.5X5S	Adverse effect of predom beta-adrenocpt agonists, seq 370
T44.5X5D	Adverse effect of predom beta-adrenocpt agonists, subs 405
T45.8X5S	Adverse effect of prim sys and hematolog agents, seq 370
T45.8X5A	Adverse effect of prim systemic and hematolog agents, init 287, 364
T45.8X5D	Adverse effect of prim systemic and hematolog agents, subs 406
T39.315A	Adverse effect of propionic acid derivatives, init enc 362
T39.315S	Adverse effect of propionic acid derivatives, seq 369
T39.315D	Adverse effect of propionic acid derivatives, subs enc 404
T39.2X5A	Adverse effect of pyrazolone derivatives, init enc 286, 362
T39.2X5S	Adverse effect of pyrazolone derivatives, seq 369
T39.2X5D	Adverse effect of pyrazolone derivatives, subs enc 404
T36.6X5A	Adverse effect of rifampicins, init enc 286, 362
T36.6X5S	Adverse effect of rifampicins, seq 368
T36.6X5D	Adverse effect of rifampicins, subsq enc 403
T39.095A	Adverse effect of salicylates, init enc 362
T39.095D	Adverse effect of salicylates, subsq enc 404
T47.3X5A	Adverse effect of saline and osmotic laxatives, init enc 287, 364
T47.3X5S	Adverse effect of saline and osmotic laxatives, seq 371
T47.3X5D	Adverse effect of saline and osmotic laxatives, subs enc 406
T43.225A	Adverse effect of selective serotonin reuptake inhibtr, init 363
T43.225D	Adverse effect of selective serotonin reuptake inhibtr, subs 405
T48.1X5A	Adverse effect of skeletal muscle relaxants, init enc 287, 364
T48.1X5S	Adverse effect of skeletal muscle relaxants, seq 371
T48.1X5D	Adverse effect of skeletal muscle relaxants, subs enc 406
T43.225S	Adverse effect of slctv serotonin reuptake inhibtr, seq 370
T50.B15A	Adverse effect of smallpox vaccines, init enc 365
T50.B15S	Adverse effect of smallpox vaccines, seq 372
T50.B15D	Adverse effect of smallpox vaccines, subsq enc 407
T47.2X5A	Adverse effect of stimulant laxatives, init enc 287, 364
T47.2X5S	Adverse effect of stimulant laxatives, seq 371
T47.2X5D	Adverse effect of stimulant laxatives, subsq enc 406
T42.2X5A	Adverse effect of succinimides and oxazolidinediones, init 287, 363
T42.2X5D	Adverse effect of succinimides and oxazolidinediones, subs 404
T37.0X5A	Adverse effect of sulfonamides, init enc 286, 362
T37.0X5S	Adverse effect of sulfonamides, seq 368
T37.0X5D	Adverse effect of sulfonamides, subsq enc 403
T37.8X5A	Adverse effect of systemic anti-infect/parasit, init 286, 362
T37.8X5S	Adverse effect of systemic anti-infect/parasit, seq 368
T37.8X5D	Adverse effect of systemic anti-infect/parasit, subs 403
T43.025A	Adverse effect of tetracyclic antidepressants, init enc 363
T43.025S	Adverse effect of tetracyclic antidepressants, seq 370
T43.025D	Adverse effect of tetracyclic antidepressants, subs enc 404
T36.4X5A	Adverse effect of tetracyclines, init enc 286, 362
T36.4X5S	Adverse effect of tetracyclines, seq 368
T36.4X5D	Adverse effect of tetracyclines, subsq enc 403
T41.5X5A	Adverse effect of therapeutic gases, init enc 287, 363
T41.5X5S	Adverse effect of therapeutic gases, seq 369
T41.5X5D	Adverse effect of therapeutic gases, subsq enc 404
T45.615A	Adverse effect of thrombolytic drugs, init enc 364
T45.615S	Adverse effect of thrombolytic drugs, seq 370
T45.615D	Adverse effect of thrombolytic drugs, subsq enc 406
T38.1X5A	Adverse effect of thyroid hormones and substitutes, init 286, 362
T38.1X5S	Adverse effect of thyroid hormones and substitutes, seq 369
T38.1X5D	Adverse effect of thyroid hormones and substitutes, subs 403
T43.015A	Adverse effect of tricyclic antidepressants, init enc 363
T43.015S	Adverse effect of tricyclic antidepressants, seq 370
T43.015D	Adverse effect of tricyclic antidepressants, subs enc 404
T47.95XA	Adverse effect of unsp agents affected the GI sys, init 287, 364
T47.95XS	Adverse effect of unsp agents affected the GI sys, seq 371
T46.905A	Adverse effect of unsp agents affecting the cardiovasc sys, init 364

Code	Description
T46.905D	Adverse effect of unsp agents affecting the cardiovasc sys, subs 406
T47.95XD	Adverse effect of unsp agents affecting the GI sys, subs 406
T41.45XA	Adverse effect of unsp anesthetic, init enc 287, 363
T41.45XS	Adverse effect of unsp anesthetic, seq 369
T41.45XD	Adverse effect of unsp anesthetic, subs enc 404
T43.205A	Adverse effect of unsp antidepressants, init enc 287, 363
T43.205S	Adverse effect of unsp antidepressants, seq 370
T43.205D	Adverse effect of unsp antidepressants, subs enc 405
T42.75XA	Adverse effect of unsp antieplptc and sed-hypntc drugs, init 287, 363
T42.75XD	Adverse effect of unsp antieplptc and sed-hypntc drugs, subs 404
T43.505S	Adverse effect of unsp antipsychot/neurolept, seq 370
T43.505A	Adverse effect of unsp antipsychotics and neuroleptics, init 363
T43.505D	Adverse effect of unsp antipsychotics and neuroleptics, subs 405
T50.905A	Adverse effect of unsp drug/meds/biol subst, init 365
T50.905S	Adverse effect of unsp drug/meds/biol subst, seq 372
T50.905D	Adverse effect of unsp drug/meds/biol subst, subs 407
T48.205A	Adverse effect of unsp drugs acting on muscles, init enc 364
T48.205S	Adverse effect of unsp drugs acting on muscles, seq 371
T48.205D	Adverse effect of unsp drugs acting on muscles, subs enc 406
T45.605A	Adverse effect of unsp fibrinolysis-affecting drugs, init 364
T45.605S	Adverse effect of unsp fibrinolysis-affecting drugs, seq 370
T45.605D	Adverse effect of unsp fibrinolysis-affecting drugs, subs 406
T41.205A	Adverse effect of unsp general anesthetics, init enc 363
T41.205S	Adverse effect of unsp general anesthetics, seq 369
T41.205D	Adverse effect of unsp general anesthetics, subs enc 404
T38.905A	Adverse effect of unsp hormone antagonists, init enc 362
T38.905S	Adverse effect of unsp hormone antagonists, seq 369
T38.905D	Adverse effect of unsp hormone antagonists, subs enc 403
T38.805A	Adverse effect of unsp hormones and synth sub, init 362
T38.805S	Adverse effect of unsp hormones and synth sub, seq 369
T38.805D	Adverse effect of unsp hormones and synth sub, subs 403
T40.605A	Adverse effect of unsp narcotics, init enc 362
T40.605S	Adverse effect of unsp narcotics, seq 369
T40.605D	Adverse effect of unsp narcotics, subs enc 404
T39.95XA	Adverse effect of unsp nonopi analgs/antipyr/antirheu, init 286, 362
T39.95XD	Adverse effect of unsp nonopi analgs/antipyr/antirheu, subs 404
T45.95XA	Adverse effect of unsp prim sys and hematolog agent, init 287, 364
T45.95XS	Adverse effect of unsp prim sys and hematolog agent, seq 371
T45.95XD	Adverse effect of unsp prim sys and hematolog agent, subs 406
T40.905A	Adverse effect of unsp psychodysleptics, init enc 363
T40.905S	Adverse effect of unsp psychodysleptics, seq 369
T40.905D	Adverse effect of unsp psychodysleptics, subs enc 404
T43.605A	Adverse effect of unsp psychostimulants, init enc 363
T43.605S	Adverse effect of unsp psychostimulants, seq 370
T43.605D	Adverse effect of unsp psychostimulants, subs enc 405
T43.95XA	Adverse effect of unsp psychotropic drug, init enc 287, 363
T43.95XS	Adverse effect of unsp psychotropic drug, seq 370
T43.95XD	Adverse effect of unsp psychotropic drug, subs enc 405
T36.95XA	Adverse effect of unsp systemic antibiotic, init enc 286, 362
T36.95XS	Adverse effect of unsp systemic antibiotic, seq 368
T36.95XD	Adverse effect of unsp systemic antibiotic, subs enc 403
T49.95XA	Adverse effect of unsp topical agent, init enc 287, 365
T49.95XS	Adverse effect of unsp topical agent, seq 371
T49.95XD	Adverse effect of unsp topical agent, subs enc 407
T50.Z95S	Adverse effect of vaccines and biolg substances, seq 372
T50.Z95A	Adverse effect of vaccines and biological substances, init 365
T50.Z95D	Adverse effect of vaccines and biological substances, subs 407
T45.2X5A	Adverse effect of vitamins, init enc 287, 364
T45.2X5S	Adverse effect of vitamins, seq 370
T45.2X5D	Adverse effect of vitamins, subsq enc 405
T50.2X5A	Advrs eff of crbnc-anhydr inhibtr, benzo/oth diuretc, init 287, 365
T50.2X5S	Advrs eff of crbnc-anhydr inhibtr, benzo/oth diuretc, seq 371
T50.2X5D	Advrs eff of crbnc-anhydr inhibtr, benzo/oth diuretc, subs 407
T48.995S	Advrs effect of agents prim acting on the resp sys, seq 371
T50.7X5S	Advrs effect of analeptics and opioid receptor antag, seq 372
T45.7X5S	Advrs effect of anticoag antag, vit K and oth coag, seq 370
T38.6X5S	Advrs effect of antigonadtr/antiestr/antiandrg, NEC, seq 369
T46.6X5S	Advrs effect of antihyperlip and antiarterio drugs, seq 371
T37.2X5A	Advrs effect of antimalari/drugs acting on bld protzoa, init 286, 362
T37.2X5S	Advrs effect of antimalari/drugs acting on bld protzoa, seq 368
T37.2X5D	Advrs effect of antimalari/drugs acting on bld protzoa, subs 403
T42.8X5S	Advrs effect of antiparkns drug/centr musc-tone depr, seq 370
T44.8X5S	Advrs effect of centr-acting/adren-neurn-block agnt, seq 370
T36.1X5S	Advrs effect of cephalospor/oth beta-lactm antibiot, seq 368
T49.3X5S	Advrs effect of emollients, demulcents and protect, seq 371
T38.3X5S	Advrs effect of insulin and oral hypoglycemic drugs, seq 369
T49.4X5S	Advrs effect of keratolyt/keratplst/hair trmt drug, seq 371
T49.0X5S	Advrs effect of local antifung/infect/inflamm drugs, seq 371
T50.A15A	Advrs effect of pertuss vaccine, incl* combin w pertuss, init 365
T50.A15S	Advrs effect of pertuss vaccine, incl* combin w pertuss, seq 372
T50.A15D	Advrs effect of pertuss vaccine, incl* combin w pertuss, subs 407
T43.215A	Advrs effect of slctv seroton/norepineph reup inhibtr, init 363
T43.215S	Advrs effect of slctv seroton/norepineph reup inhibtr, seq 370
T43.215D	Advrs effect of slctv seroton/norepineph reup inhibtr, subs 405
T42.2X5S	Advrs effect of succinimides and oxazolidinediones, seq 369
T46.905S	Advrs effect of unsp agents affected the cardiovasc sys, seq 371
T48.905A	Advrs effect of unsp agents prim act on the resp sys, init 365
T48.905S	Advrs effect of unsp agents prim act on the resp sys, seq 371
T48.905D	Advrs effect of unsp agents prim act on the resp sys, subs 407
T42.75XS	Advrs effect of unsp antieplptc and sed-hypntc drugs, seq 370
T44.905S	Advrs effect of unsp drugs affected the autonm nrv sys, seq 370
T44.905A	Advrs effect of unsp drugs affecting the autonm nervous sys, init 364
T44.905D	Advrs effect of unsp drugs affecting the autonm nervous sys, subs 405
T39.95XS	Advrs effect of unsp nonopi analgs/antipyr/antirheu, seq 369
T37.95XA	Advrs effect of unsp sys anti-infect and antiparasitic, init 286, 362
T37.95XS	Advrs effect of unsp sys anti-infect and antiparasitic, seq 369
T37.95XD	Advrs effect of unsp sys anti-infect and antiparasitic, subs 403
B56*	African trypanosomiasis 308
Z47.3*	Aftercare following explantation of jt prosthesis 184
Z47.1	Aftercare following jt replace surgery 184
Z48.3	Aftercare following surgery for neoplasm 385, 411
O92.3	Agalactia 272, 276
H25*	Age-related cataract 46
R41.81	Age-related cognitive decline 310
M80.00XA	Age-related osteopor w current path fx, unsp site, init 163, 285
M80.08XS	Age-related osteopor w current path fx, verteb, seq 165
M80.08XA	Age-related osteopor w current path fx, vertebra(e), init 125, 163, 285
M80.07[1,2,9][D,G,S]	Age-related osteoporosis w/ current path fx, [rt, lt, unsp] ankle and foot, [subsq enc for fx w/ routine healing, subsq enc for fx w/ delayed healing, seq] 168
M80.07[1,2,9]A	Age-related osteoporosis w/ current path fx, [rt, lt, unsp] ankle and foot, init enc for fx 163, 285
M80.07[1,2,9][K,P]	Age-related osteoporosis w/ current path fx, [rt, lt, unsp] ankle and foot, subsq enc for fx w/ [nonu, malu] 194
M80.05[1,2,9][D,G,S]	Age-related osteoporosis w/ current path fx, [rt, lt, unsp] femur, [subsq enc for fx w/ routine healing, subsq enc for fx w/ delayed healing, seq] 168
M80.05[1,2,9]A	Age-related osteoporosis w/ current path fx, [rt, lt, unsp] femur, init enc for fx 163, 285
M80.05[1,2,9][K,P]	Age-related osteoporosis w/ current path fx, [rt, lt, unsp] femur, subsq enc for fx w/ [nonu, malu] 194
M80.03[1,2,9][D,G,S]	Age-related osteoporosis w/ current path fx, [rt, lt, unsp] forearm, [subsq enc for fx w/ routine healing, subsq enc for fx w/ delayed healing, seq] 168
M80.03[1,2,9]A	Age-related osteoporosis w/ current path fx, [rt, lt, unsp] forearm, init enc for fx 163, 285
M80.03[1,2,9][K,P]	Age-related osteoporosis w/ current path fx, [rt, lt, unsp] forearm, subsq enc for fx w/ [nonu, malu] 194
M80.04[1,2,9][D,G,S]	Age-related osteoporosis w/ current path fx, [rt, lt, unsp] hand, [subsq enc for fx w/ routine healing, subsq enc for fx w/ delayed healing, seq] 168
M80.04[1,2,9]A	Age-related osteoporosis w/ current path fx, [rt, lt, unsp] hand, init enc for fx 163, 285
M80.04[1,2,9][K,P]	Age-related osteoporosis w/ current path fx, [rt, lt, unsp] hand, subsq enc for fx w/ [nonu, malu] 194

Code	Description
M80.02[1,2,9] [D,G,S]	Age-related osteoporosis w/ current path fx, [rt, lt, unsp] humerus, [subsq enc for fx w/ routine healing, subsq enc for fx w/ delayed healing, seq] 168
M80.02[1,2,9]A	Age-related osteoporosis w/ current path fx, [rt, lt, unsp] humerus, init enc for fx 163, 285
M80.02[1,2,9] [K,P]	Age-related osteoporosis w/ current path fx, [rt, lt, unsp] humerus, subsq enc for fx w/ [nonu, malu] 194
M80.06[1,2,9] [D,G,S]	Age-related osteoporosis w/ current path fx, [rt, lt, unsp] lwr leg, [subsq enc for fx w/ routine healing, subsq enc for fx w/ delayed healing, seq] 168
M80.06[1,2,9]A	Age-related osteoporosis w/ current path fx, [rt, lt, unsp] lwr leg, init enc for fx 163, 285
M80.06[1,2,9] [K,P]	Age-related osteoporosis w/ current path fx, [rt, lt, unsp] lwr leg, subsq enc for fx w/ [nonu, malu] 194
M80.01[1,2,9] [D,G,S]	Age-related osteoporosis w/ current path fx, [rt, lt, unsp] shldr, [subsq enc for fx w/ routine healing, subsq enc for fx w/ delayed healing, seq] 168
M80.01[1,2,9]A	Age-related osteoporosis w/ current path fx, [rt, lt, unsp] shldr, init enc for fx 163, 285
M80.01[1,2,9] [K,P]	Age-related osteoporosis w/ current path fx, [rt, lt, unsp] shldr, subsq enc for fx w/ [nonu, malu] 194
M80.00X[D,G,S]	Age-related osteoporosis w/ current path fx, unsp site, [subsq enc for fx w/ routine healing, subsq enc for fx w/ delayed healing, seq] 168
M80.00X[K,P]	Age-related osteoporosis w/ current path fx, unsp site, subsq enc for fx w/ [nonu, malu] 194
M80.08X[D,G]	Age-related osteoporosis w/ current path fx, vertebra(e), [subsq enc for fx w/ routine healing, subsq enc for fx w/ delayed healing] 168
M80.08X[K,P]	Age-related osteoporosis w/ current path fx, vertebra(e), subsq enc for fx w/ [nonu, malu] 194
R54	Age-related physical debility 310
Q33.3	Agenesis of lung 69
Q44.0	Agenesis, aplasia and hypoplasia of gallbladder 124
Q45.0	Agenesis, aplasia and hypoplasia of pancreas 124
K05.2*	Aggressive periodontitis 4
R48.1	Agnosia 311
D70.1	Agranulocytosis secondary to cancer chemotherapy 293
L94.6	Ainhum 309
T79.0XXA	Air embolism (traum), init enc 66, 287, 430
T80.0XXA	Air embolism fol inf, tranfs and theraputc inject, init 66, 287
T80.0XXD	Air embolism fol inf, tranfs and theraputc inject, subs 410
O88.02	Air embolism in childbirth 274
O88.01[1,2,3]	Air embolism in preg, [1st, 2nd, 3rd] trmstr 274
O88.03	Air embolism in the puerperium 274, 276
T80.[0,1]XXS	Air embolism, Vascular comps) following inf, transfusion and therapeutic injection, seq 375
O88.[0,1,2,3,8]2	Air, Amniotic fluid, Thrombo-, Pyemic and septic, Oth] embolism in childbirth 273
O88.[0,1,2,3,8] 1[1,2,3]	Air, Amniotic fluid, Thrombo-, Pyemic and septic, Oth] embolism in preg, [1st, 2nd, 3rd] trmstr 278, 280
O88.[0,1,2,3,8]3	Air, Amniotic fluid, Thrombo-, Pyemic and septic, Oth] embolism in the puerperium 272
O88.[0,1,2,3,8]19	Air, Amniotic fluid, Thrombo-, Pyemic and septic, Oth] embolism, unsp trmstr 281
T79.[0,1]XXA	[Air, Fat] embolism (traum), init enc 432
T79.[0,1]XXS	[Air, Fat] embolism (traum), seq 361
T79.[0,1]XXD	[Air, Fat] embolism (traum), subsq enc 410
J66*	Airway dz d/t specific organic dust 68
O99.31[1,2,3]	Alcohol use compl preg, [1st, 2nd, 3rd] trmstr 277, 278
O99.315	Alcohol use compl the puerperium 276
O99.3[1,2,3,4,5]0	Alcohol use, Drug use, Smoking (tobacco), Oth mental d/o, Dz of the nervous sys] compl preg, childbirth and puerperium, unsp trmstr 281
O99.3[1,2,3,4]4	Alcohol use, Drug use, Smoking (tobacco), Oth mental d/o] compl childbirth 273, 275
O99.3[1,2,3,4]5	Alcohol use, Drug use, Smoking (tobacco), Oth mental d/o] compl the puerperium 272
K70.3*	Alcoholic cirrhosis of liver 123
K70.0	Alcoholic fatty liver 124
K70.2	Alcoholic fibrosis and sclerosis of liver 123
K29.21	Alcoholic gastritis with bleeding 115
K70.4*	Alcoholic hepatic failure 123
K70.1*	Alcoholic hepatitis 123

Code	Description
K70.9	Alcoholic liver dz, unsp 123
G72.1	Alcoholic myopathy 38
M89.0*	Algoneurodystrophy 194
K52.2	Allergic and dietetic gastroenteritis and colitis 116
B44.81	Allergic bronchopulmonary aspergillosis 68
L23*	Allergic contact dermatitis 233
L50.0	Allergic urticaria 284
Z88*	Allergy status to drug/meds/biol subst 413
T78.40XA	Allergy, unsp, init enc 361
T78.40XS	Allergy, unsp, seq 374
T78.40XD	Allergy, unsp, subsq enc 410
B48.2	Allescheriasis 283
L63*	Alopecia areata 234
E88.01	Alpha-1-antitrypsin deficiency 247
D56.[0,1,2,5,8,9]	Alpha, Beta, Delta-beta, Hemoglobin E-beta, Oth, Unsp] thalassemia 283
R41.82	Altered mental status, unsp 385
M27.3	Alveolitis of jaws 4
G30*	Alzheimer's dz 32
G45.3	Amaurosis fugax 45
H53.0*	Amblyopia ex anopsia 46
A06.9	Amebiasis, unsp 308
A06.6	Amebic brain abscess 10, 14, 41
A06.8*	Amebic infxn of oth sites 308
A06.4	Amebic liver abscess 124
A06.5	Amebic lung abscess 67
A06.2	Amebic nondysenteric colitis 114
A06.3	Ameboma of intestine 308
F04	Amnestic d/o d/t known physiological condition 310
O88.12	Amniotic fluid embolism in childbirth 274
O88.11[1,2,3]	Amniotic fluid embolism in preg, [1st, 2nd, 3rd] trmstr 274
O88.13	Amniotic fluid embolism in the puerperium 274, 276
E85*	Amyloidosis 164
R85.8[1,2]	Anal [high, low] risk human papillomavirus (HPV) DNA test positive 117
K62.0	Anal polyp 117
K62.2	Anal prolapse 117
K59.4	Anal spasm 116
T88.6XXS	Anaphylactic react d/t advrs eff drug/med prop admin, seq 376
T80.5[1,2,9]XA	Anaphylactic reaction d/t [administration of bld and bld products, vaccination, oth serum], init enc 287, 361
T80.5[1,2,9]XS	Anaphylactic reaction d/t [administration of bld and bld products, vaccination, oth serum], seq 374
T80.5[1,2,9]XD	Anaphylactic reaction d/t [administration of bld and bld products, vaccination, oth serum], subsq enc 410
T78.0[0,1,2,3,4,5, 6,7,8,9]XS	Anaphylactic reaction d/t [unsp food, peanuts, shellfish (crustaceans), oth fish, fruits and vegetables, tree nuts and seeds, food additives, milk and dairy products, eggs, oth food products], seq 374
T78.0[0,1,2,3,4,5, 6,7,8,9]XD	Anaphylactic reaction d/t [unsp food, peanuts, shellfish (crustaceans), oth fish, fruits and vegetables, tree nuts and seeds, food additives, milk and dairy products, eggs, oth food products], subsq enc 410
T88.6XXA	Anaphylactic reaction d/t advrs eff drug/med prop admin, init 361
T88.6XXD	Anaphylactic reaction d/t advrs eff drug/med prop admin, subs 411
T78.08XA	Anaphylactic reaction d/t eggs, init enc 361
T78.06XA	Anaphylactic reaction d/t food additives, init enc 361
T78.04XA	Anaphylactic reaction d/t fruits and vegetables, init enc 361
T78.07XA	Anaphylactic reaction d/t milk and dairy products, init 361
T78.03XA	Anaphylactic reaction d/t oth fish, init enc 361
T78.09XA	Anaphylactic reaction d/t oth food products, init enc 361
T78.01XA	Anaphylactic reaction d/t peanuts, init enc 361
T78.02XA	Anaphylactic reaction d/t shellfish (crustaceans), init 361
T78.05XA	Anaphylactic reaction d/t tree nuts and seeds, init 361
T78.00XA	Anaphylactic reaction d/t unsp food, init enc 361
T78.2XXA	Anaphylactic shock, unsp, init enc 361
T78.2XXS	Anaphylactic shock, unsp, seq 374
T78.2XXD	Anaphylactic shock, unsp, subsq enc 410
C84.7*	Anaplastic large cell lymphoma, ALK-negative 438
C84.6*	Anaplastic large cell lymphoma, ALK-positive 438

L64*	Androgenic alopecia 234
O99.Ø1[1,2,3]	Anemia compl preg, [1st, 2nd, 3rd] trmstr 277, 278
O99.Ø19	Anemia compl preg, unsp trmstr 281
O99.Ø3	Anemia compl the puerperium 276
D55*	Anemia d/t enzyme d/o 293
D63*	Anemia in chr dz classified elsw 293
P61.2	Anemia of prematurity 282
O99.[Ø,1]2	Anemia, Oth dzs of the bld and bld-forming organs and certain d/o involving the immune mech] compl childbirth 273, 275
O99.[Ø,1]3	Anemia, Oth dzs of the bld and bld-forming organs and certain d/o involving the immune mech] compl the puerperium 272
Q00*	Anencephaly and similar malformations 38, 285
I72.[Ø,1,3,4,8,9]	Aneurysm of [carotid, upr extr, iliac, lwr extr, oth spec, unsp] artery 100
I25.3	Aneurysm of heart 103, 283
I72.2	Aneurysm of renal artery 256
M85.5*	Aneurysmal bone cyst 167
I20*	Angina pectoris 102
K55.2Ø	Angiodysplasia of colon w/o hemor 117
K55.21	Angiodysplasia of colon with hemor 115
K31.819	Angiodysplasia of stomach and duodenum w/o bleeding 116
K31.811	Angiodysplasia of stomach and duodenum with bleeding 115
T78.3XXA	Angioneurotic edema, init enc 361
T78.3XXS	Angioneurotic edema, seq 374
T78.3XXD	Angioneurotic edema, subsq enc 410
B83.2	Angiostrongyliasis d/t Parastrongylus cantonensis 309
R45.84	Anhedonia 385
B81.Ø	Anisakiasis 116
H57.Ø2	Anisocoria 45
H52.3*	Anisometropia and aniseikonia 46
Q38.1	Ankyloglossia 5, 59
M48.1*	Ankylosing hyperostosis [Forestier] 165
M45*	Ankylosing spondylitis 164
M24.6*	Ankylosis of jt 167
KØ3.5	Ankylosis of teeth 4
Q45.1	Annular pancreas 124
KØØ.Ø	Anodontia 4
A63.Ø	Anogenital (venereal) warts 233
A6Ø.9	Anogenital herpesviral infxn, unsp 261, 264, 269, 438
L29.3	Anogenital pruritus, unsp 261, 264, 269
M26.2*	Anomalies of dental arch relationship 4
M26.1*	Anomalies of jaw-cranial base relationship 4
M26.3*	Anomalies of tooth position of fully erupted tooth or teeth 4
Q26.5	Anomalous portal venous connection 100
Q26.4	Anomalous pulmn venous connection, unsp 102
Q11*	Anophthalmos, microphthalmos and macrophthalmos 46
F5Ø.Ø*	Anorexia nervosa 310
G93.1	Anoxic brain damage, NEC 38, 283
G46.1	Ant cerebral artery synd 33
S14.13[1,2,3,4,5, 6,7,8,9][A,S]	Ant cord synd at [C1, C2, C3, C4, C5, C6, C7, C8, unsp] lvl of cervical spinal cord, [init enc, seq] 32
S14.13[1,2,3,4,5, 6,7,8,9]A	Ant cord synd at [C1, C2, C3, C4, C5, C6, C7, C8, unsp] lvl of cervical spinal cord, init enc 420, 432
S14.13[1,2,3,4,5, 6,7,8,9]D	Ant cord synd at [C1, C2, C3, C4, C5, C6, C7, C8, unsp] lvl of cervical spinal cord, subsq enc 388
S24.13[1,2,3,4,9] D	Ant cord synd at [T1, T2-T6, T7-T10, T11-T12, unsp] lvl of thoracic spinal cord, subsq enc 389
S24.13[1,2,3,4,9] [A,S]	Ant cord synd at [T1, T2-T6, T7-T10, T11-T12, unsp] lvl of thoracic spinal cord, [init enc, seq] 32
S24.13[1,2,3,4,9] A	Ant cord synd at [T1, T2-T6, T7-T10, T11-T12, unsp] lvl of thoracic spinal cord, init enc 420, 433
S53.Ø1[4,5,6]D	Ant disloc of [rt, lt, unsp] radial head, subsq enc 392
S43.21[4,5,6]A	Ant disloc of [rt, lt, unsp] sternoclavicular jt, init enc 67
S43.21[4,5,6]S	Ant disloc of [rt, lt, unsp] sternoclavicular jt, seq 185
S53.11[4,5,6]D	Ant disloc of [rt, lt, unsp] ulnohumeral jt, subsq enc 392
S43.Ø1[4,5,6] [A,S]	Ant disloc of humerus [rt, lt, unsp] [init enc, seq] 185
S83.11[4,5,6] [A,S]	Ant disloc of proximal end of tibia, [rt, lt, unsp] knee, [init enc, seq] 191
S83.11[4,5,6]A	Ant disloc of proximal end of tibia, [rt, lt, unsp] knee, init enc 428

S83.11[4,5,6]D	Ant disloc of proximal end of tibia, [rt, lt, unsp] knee, subsq enc 398
S53.Ø1[4,5,6] [A,S]	Ant disloc of radial head [unsp, rt, lt] [init enc, seq] 186
S53.11[4,5,6] [A,S]	Ant disloc of ulnohumeral jt [rt, lt, unsp] [init enc, seq] 186
S42.Ø1[1,2,3] [A,B]	Ant disp fx of if sternal end of clavicle [rt, lt, unsp] init enc for fx [clsd, opn] 184
S42.Ø1[1,2,3] [D,G,S]	Ant disp fx of sternal end of [rt, lt, unsp] clavicle, [subsq enc for fx w/ routine healing, subsq enc for fx w/ delayed healing, seq] 170
S42.Ø1[1,2,3] [K,P]	Ant disp fx of sternal end of [rt, lt, unsp] clavicle, subsq enc for fx w/ [nonu, malu] 196
S42.Ø1[1,2,3,4,5, 6,7,8,9][A,B]	Ant disp, Post disp, Nondisp] fx of sternal end of [rt, lt, unsp] clavicle, init enc for [clsd, opn] fx 422
S12.11[Ø,1,2] [A,B]	Ant disp, Post disp, Nondisp] Type II dens fx, init enc for [clsd. opn] fx 419
S12.11[Ø,1,2] [D,G]	Ant disp, Post disp, Nondisp] Type II dens fx, subsq enc for fx w/ [routine, delayed] healing 169
S12.11[Ø,1,2]K	Ant disp, Post disp, Nondisp] Type II dens fx, subsq enc for fx w/ nonu 195
S43.Ø1[1,2,3,4,5, 6]D	Ant sublux of [rt, lt, unsp] humerus, Ant disloc of [rt, lt, unsp] humerus subsq enc 391
S53.Ø1[1,2,3]D	Ant sublux of [rt, lt, unsp] radial head, subsq enc 392
S43.21[1,2,3,4,5, 6]D	Ant sublux of [rt, lt, unsp] sternoclavicular jt, Ant disloc of [rt, lt, unsp] sternoclavicular jt, subsq enc 391
S43.21[1,2,3]A	Ant sublux of [rt, lt, unsp] sternoclavicular jt, init enc 67
S43.21[1,2,3]S	Ant sublux of [rt, lt, unsp] sternoclavicular jt, seq 185
S53.11[1,2,3]D	Ant sublux of [rt, lt, unsp] ulnohumeral jt, subsq enc 392
S43.Ø1[1,2,3] [A,S]	Ant sublux of humerus [rt, lt, unsp] [init enc, seq] 185
S83.11[1,2,3] [A,S]	Ant sublux of proximal end of tibia, [rt, lt, unsp] knee, [init enc, seq] 191
S83.11[1,2,3]A	Ant sublux of proximal end of tibia, [rt, lt, unsp] knee, init enc 428
S83.11[1,2,3]D	Ant sublux of proximal end of tibia, [rt, lt, unsp] knee, subsq enc 398
S53.Ø1[1,2,3] [A,S]	Ant sublux of radial head [unsp, rt, lt] [init enc, seq] 186
S53.11[1,2,3] [A,S]	Ant sublux of ulnohumeral jt [rt, lt, unsp] [init enc, seq] 186
S43.Ø[1,2,3] [1,2,3,4,5,6]A	Ant, Post, Inferior] [sublux, disloc] of [rt, lt, unsp] humerus, init enc 422
O46.Ø[Ø,1,2,9]9	Antepartum hemor w/ [coagulation defect unsp, afibrinogenemia, disseminated intrascular coagulation, ohter coagulation defect], unsp trmstr 281
O46.Ø[Ø,1,2,9] [1,2,3]	Antepartum hemor w/ [coagulation defect unsp, afibrinogenemia, disseminated intravascular coagulation, oth coagulation defect], [1st, 2nd, 3rd] trmstr 274, 278
O46.Ø*	Antepartum hemor with coagulation defect 277
O46.9[1,2,3]	Antepartum hemor, unsp, [1st, 2nd, 3rd] trmstr 274, 278, 280
O46.9Ø	Antepartum hemor, unsp, unsp trmstr 281
R41.1	Anterograde amnesia 385
A22.7	Anthrax sepsis 309
A22.9	Anthrax, unsp 308
D8Ø.6	Antibody defic w near-norm immunoglob or w hyperimmunoglob 293
D68.312	Antiphospholipid antibody with hemorrhagic d/o 294
R34	Anuria and oliguria 254
I71*	Aortic aneurysm and dissection 100
M31.4	Aortic arch synd [Takayasu] 164
R13*	Aphagia and dysphagia 116
D61.2	Aplastic anemia d/t oth ext agents 293
D61.9	Aplastic anemia, unsp 293
L75*	Apocrine sweat d/o 234
R68.13	Apparent life threatening event in infant (ALTE) 412
R48.2	Apraxia 311
A96*	Arenaviral hemorrhagic fever 307
H57.Ø1	Argyll Robertson pupil, atypical 32
KØ2.3	Arrested dental caries 4
I74*	Arterial embolism and thrombosis 100, 284
I77.3	Arterial fibromuscular dysplasia 100
I77.Ø	Arteriovenous fistula, acquired 100
Q28.2	Arteriovenous malformation of cerebral vessels 38
Q28.[Ø,1]	Arteriovenous, Oth] malformation(s) of precerebral vessels 100

I77.6	Arteritis, unsp 164	
Z93*	Artfcl Opng status 413	
M00.8*	Arthritis and polyarthritis d/t oth bacteria 164	
M00.86[1,2,9]	Arthritis d/t oth bacteria, [rt, lt, unsp] knee 131	
L40.5*	Arthropathic psoriasis 164	
M14*	Arthropathies in oth dz classified elsw 167	
M02.0*	Arthropathy following intestinal bypass 166	
M36.4	Arthropathy in hypersensitivity reactions classd elsw 167	
M36.1	Arthropathy in neoplastic dz 167	
M36.3	Arthropathy in oth bld d/o 167	
A85.2	Arthropod-borne viral encephalitis, unsp 10, 15	
T78.41XA	Arthus phenomenon, init enc 287, 367	
T78.41XS	Arthus phenomenon, seq 374	
T78.41XD	Arthus phenomenon, subsq enc 410	
B77*	Ascariasis 116	
R18*	Ascites 385	
E54	Ascorbic acid deficiency 246	
F84.5	Asperger's synd 311	
B44.9	Aspergillosis, unsp 283, 308	
R09.0*	Asphyxia and hypoxemia 69	
T71.1[1,2,3,5,6,9][1,2,3,4][A,S]	Asphyxiation d/t [smothing under pillow, plastic bag, being trapped in bed linens, smothing under anoth person's body, smothing in furniture, hanging, mech threat to breathing d/t oth causes], [accid, intentional self-harm, assault, undetermined], [init enc, seq] 374	
T71.1[1,2,3,5,6,9][1,2,3,4]D	Asphyxiation d/t [smothing under pillow, plastic bag, being trapped in bed linens, smothing under anoth person's body, smothing in furniture, hanging, mech threat to breathing d/t oth causes], [accid, intentional self-harm, assault, undetermined], subsq enc 410	
T71.2[0,1]X[A,S]	Asphyxiation d/t [sysic oxygen deficiency d/t low oxygen content in ambient air d/t unsp cause, cave-in or falling earth], [init enc, seq] 374	
T71.29XD	Asphyxiation d/t being trap in oth low oxygen environment, subs 410	
T71.2[2,3][1,2,3,4][A,S]	Asphyxiation d/t being trapped in a [car trunk, (discarded) refrigerator], [accid, intentional self-harm, assault, undetermined], [init enc, seq] 374	
T71.2[2,3][1,2,3,4]D	Asphyxiation d/t being trapped in a [car trunk, (discarded) refrigerator], [accid, intentional self-harm, assault, undetermined], subsq enc 410	
T71.29X[A,S]	Asphyxiation d/t being trapped in oth low oxygen environment, [init enc, seq] 374	
T71.21XD	Asphyxiation d/t cave-in or falling earth, subs enc 410	
T71.141A	Asphyxiation d/t smothr under another person's body, acc, init 374	
T71.141S	Asphyxiation d/t smothr under another person's body, acc, seq 374	
T71.141D	Asphyxiation d/t smothr under another person's body, acc, subs 410	
T71.143A	Asphyxiation d/t smothr under another person's body, asslt, init 374	
T71.143S	Asphyxiation d/t smothr under another person's body, asslt, seq 374	
T71.143D	Asphyxiation d/t smothr under another person's body, asslt, subs 410	
T71.144A	Asphyxiation d/t smothr under another person's body, undet, init 374	
T71.144S	Asphyxiation d/t smothr under another person's body, undet, seq 374	
T71.144D	Asphyxiation d/t smothr under another person's body, undet, subs 410	
T71.20XD	Asphyxiation d/t sys oxy defic d/t low oxy in air unsp cause, subs 410	
T71.9XX[A,S]	Asphyxiation d/t unsp cause, [init enc, seq] 374	
T71.9XXD	Asphyxiation d/t unsp cause, subsq enc 410	
O29.019	Aspirat pneumonitis d/t anesth during preg, unsp trmstr 280	
O29.01[1,2,3]	Aspiration pneumonitis d/t anesthesia during preg, [1st, 2nd, 3rd] trmstr 277	
J45*	Asthma 69	
H52.2*	Astigmatism 46	
Z21	Asymptomatic human immunodef virus infxn status 308	
A52.2	Asymptomatic neurosyphilis 41	
I83.9*	Asymptomatic varicose veins of lwr extremities 100	

G80.4	Ataxic cerebral palsy 38	
R26.0	Ataxic gait 38	
J98.11	Atelectasis 284	
I75.0*	Atheroembolism of extremities 100	
I75.81	Atheroembolism of kidney 256	
I75.89	Atheroembolism of oth site 100	
I70.0	Atherosclerosis of aorta 100	
I70.26[1,2,3,8,9]	Atherosclerosis of native arteries of extremities w/ gangrene, [rt leg, lt leg, bilat legs, oth extr, unsp extr] 284	
I70.2*	Atherosclerosis of native arteries of the extremities 100	
I70.8	Atherosclerosis of oth arteries 100	
I70.1	Atherosclerosis of renal artery 256	
I25.1*	Atherosclerotic heart dz of native coronary artery 102	
G80.3	Athetoid cerebral palsy 32	
I70.4*	Athscl auto vein bypass graft(s) of the extremities 100	
I25.7*	Athscl CABG and cor art of transplanted heart w ang pctrs 102	
I70.5*	Athscl nonauto bio bypass graft(s) of the extremities 100	
I70.6*	Athscl nonbiological bypass graft(s) of the extremities 100	
I70.7*	Athscl type of bypass graft(s) of the extremities 100	
I70.3*	Athscl unsp type bypass graft(s) of the extremities 100	
L20*	Atopic dermatitis 233	
Q44.2	Atresia of bile ducts 124	
I48*	Atrial fibrillation and flutter 102, 283	
I23.1	Atrial septal defect as current comp following AMI 103	
I44*	Atrioventricular and lt bundle-branch block 102	
I44.2	Atrioventricular block, complete 283	
L90*	Atrophic d/o of skin 234	
K08.2*	Atrophy of edentulous alveolar ridge 4	
N26.1	Atrophy of kidney (terminal) 256	
K11.0	Atrophy of salivary gland 4	
E03.4	Atrophy of thyroid (acquired) 3, 247	
K14.4	Atrophy of tongue papillae 4	
O66.5	Attempted application of vacuum extractor and forceps 273, 275	
R41.840	Attention and concentration deficit 311	
F90*	Attention-deficit hyperactivity d/o 311	
R87.61[0,1,2,3,4,5,6]	Atyp Sq Cells Undet Significance (Asc-us),atyp Sq Cells Cannot Exclude Hi G Sq Intraepithelial Les (Asc-h),l G Sq Intraepithelial Les (Lgsil),hi G Sq Intraepithelial Les (Hgsil),cytol Evidence Mal,unsatisfactory Cytol,satisfactory C Smer But Lacking Transformation Zone] Smer C 265, 270	
R87.62[0,1,2,3,4,5]	Atyp Sq Cells Undet Significance (Asc-us),atyp Sq Cells Cannot Exclude Hi G Sq Intraepithelial Les (Asc-h),l G Sq Intraepithelial Les (Lgsil),hi G Sq Intraepithelial Les (Hgsil),cytol Evidence Mal,unsatisfactory Cytol] Smer Vag 265, 270	
C92.2*	Atypical chr myeloid leukemia, BCR/ABL-negative 303, 305	
A81*	Atypical virus infections of central nervous sys 32	
A81.9	Atypical virus infxn of central nervous sys, unsp 438	
R44.0	Auditory hallucinations 310	
H93.21[1,2,3,9]	Auditory recruitment, [rt, lt, bilat, unsp] ear 58	
A83.4	Australian encephalitis 10, 15	
F84.0	Autistic d/o 310	
D89.82	Autoimmune lymphoproliferative synd [ALPS] 164	
E06.3	Autoimmune thyroiditis 3	
G90.4	Autonomic dysreflexia 34	
G99.0	Autonomic neuropathy in dz classified elsw 34	
S05.7[0,1,2]XA	Avulsion of [unsp, rt, lt] eye, init enc 47, 418	
S05.7[0,1,2]XS	Avulsion of [unsp, rt, lt] eye, seq 359	
S05.7[0,1,2]XD	Avulsion of [unsp, rt, lt] eye, subsq enc 386	
S08.0XX[A,S]	Avulsion of scalp, [init enc, seq] 225	
S08.0XXA	Avulsion of scalp, init enc 419	
S08.0XXD	Avulsion of scalp, subsq enc 387	
B60.0	Babesiosis 309	
R78.81	Bacteremia 285, 309	
A05.9	Bacterial foodborne intoxication, unsp 116	
A49*	Bacterial infxn of unsp site 308	
G00*	Bacterial meningitis, NEC 41, 283	
G00.9	Bacterial meningitis, unsp 11, 15	
G04.2	Bacterial meningoencephalitis and meningomyelitis, NEC 11, 15, 41, 283	
J15*	Bacterial pneumonia, NEC 284	
P36*	Bacterial sepsis of newborn 282	

Q95*	Balanced rearrangements and structural markers, NEC 412
N48.1	Balanitis 261
N15.0	Balkan nephropathy 256
O99.840	Bariatric surgery status comp preg, unsp trmstr 281
O99.844	Bariatric surgery status compl childbirth 275
O99.84[1,2,3]	Bariatric surgery status compl preg, [1st, 2nd, 3rd] trmstr 278, 280
O99.845	Bariatric surgery status compl the puerperium 276
K22.7*	Barrett's esophagus 115
E78.7[1,2]	Barth, Smith-Lemli-Opitz] synd 193
S52.56[1,2,9] [D,E,F,G,H,J,S]	Barton's fx of [rt, lt, unsp] radius, [subsq enc for clsd fx w/ routine healing, subsq enc for opn fx type I or II w/ routine healing, subsq enc for opn fx type IIIA, IIIB, or IIIC w/ routine healing, subsq enc for clsd fx w/ delayed healing, subsq enc for opn fx type I or II w/ delayed healing, subsq enc for opn fx type I or II w/ delayed healing, seq] 174
S52.56[1,2,9] [A,B,C]	Barton's fx of [rt, lt, unsp] radius, init enc for [clsd fx, opn fx type I or II, opn fx type IIIA, IIIB, or IIIC] 186, 423
S52.56[1,2,9] [B,C]	Barton's fx of [rt, lt, unsp] radius, init enc for opn fx type [I or II, IIIA IIIB or IIIC] 434
S52.56[1,2,9] [K,M,N,P,Q,R]	Barton's fx of [rt, lt, unsp] radius, subsq enc for [clsd fx w/ nonu, opn fx type I or II w/ nonu, opn fx type IIIA, IIIB, or IIIC w/ nonu, clsd fx w/ malu, opn fx type I or II w/ malu, opn fx type IIIA, IIIB, or IIIC w/ malu] 198
A44*	Bartonellosis 308
M35.2	Behcet's dz 164
D17.0	Ben lipomatous neoplm of skin, SQ of head, face and neck 233
R80.3	Bence Jones proteinuria 255
R01.0	Benign and innocent cardiac murmurs 102
D3A.02[0,1,2,3,4, 5,6,9]	Benign carcinoid tumor of the [appendix, cecum, ascending colon, descending colon, sigmoid colon, rectum, unsp portion of lg intestine] 117
D3A.01[0,1,2,9]	Benign carcinoid tumor of the [duodenum, jejunum, ileum, unsp portion of sm intestine] 117
D3A.09[2,4,5,6]	Benign carcinoid tumor of the [stomach, foregut NOS, midgut NOS, hindgut NOS] 117
D3A.090	Benign carcinoid tumor of the bronchus and lung 67
D3A.093	Benign carcinoid tumor of the kidney 248, 255
D3A.091	Benign carcinoid tumor of the thymus 294
D3A.00	Benign carcinoid tumor of unsp site 304, 306
D3A.098	Benign carcinoid tumors of oth sites 304, 306
N47.4	Benign cyst of prepuce 289
G93.2	Benign intracranial hypertension 41
D17.5	Benign lipomatous neoplasm of intra-abd organs 117
D17.4	Benign lipomatous neoplasm of intrathoracic organs 67
D17.71	Benign lipomatous neoplasm of kidney 117
D17.72	Benign lipomatous neoplasm of oth genitourinary organ 233
D17.79	Benign lipomatous neoplasm of oth sites 233
D17.3*	Benign lipomatous neoplasm of skin, SQ of and unsp sites 233
D17.2*	Benign lipomatous neoplasm of skin, SQ of limb 233
D17.1	Benign lipomatous neoplasm of skin, SQ of trunk 233
D17.6	Benign lipomatous neoplasm of spermatic cord 261
D17.9	Benign lipomatous neoplasm, unsp 233
N60*	Benign mammary dysplasia 224
D16.[4,6,8,9]	Benign neoplasm of [bones of skull and face, vert column, pelvic bones, sacrum and coccyx, unsp bone and articular cartilage] 193
D16.[2,3][0,1,2]	Benign neoplasm of [long, short] bones of [unsp, rt, lt] lwr limb 193
D16.[0,1][0,1,2]	Benign neoplasm of [scapula and long, short] bones of [unsp, rt, lt] upr limb 193
D35.0*	Benign neoplasm of adrenal gland 247
D35.6	Benign neoplasm of aortic body and oth paraganglia 32
D16.4	Benign neoplasm of bones of skull and face 3
D33*	Benign neoplasm of brain and oth prt central nervous sys 32
D24*	Benign neoplasm of breast 233
D14.3*	Benign neoplasm of bronchus and lung 67
D35.5	Benign neoplasm of carotid body 32
D12*	Benign neoplasm of colon, rectum, anus and anal canal 117
D21.0	Benign neoplasm of connctv/soft tiss of head, face and neck 193
D21.[3,4,5,6,9]	Benign neoplasm of connective and oth soft tissue of [thorax, abd, pelvis, unsp trunk, unsp connective and oth soft tissue] 193
D21.2[0,1,2]	Benign neoplasm of connective and oth soft tissue of [unsp, rt, lt] lwr limb, incl* hip 193
D21.1[0,1,2]	Benign neoplasm of connective and oth soft tissue of [unsp, rt, lt] upr limb, incl* shldr 193
D35.3	Benign neoplasm of craniopharyngeal duct 247
D13.2	Benign neoplasm of duodenum 117
D35.9	Benign neoplasm of endocrine gland, unsp 247
D13.7	Benign neoplasm of endocrine pancreas 247
D13.0	Benign neoplasm of esophagus 117
D13.5	Benign neoplasm of extrahepatic bile ducts 124
D31*	Benign neoplasm of eye and adnexa 45
D10.2	Benign neoplasm of floor of mouth 3, 59
D15.1	Benign neoplasm of heart 103
D10.7	Benign neoplasm of hypopharynx 3, 58
D13.9	Benign neoplasm of ill-defined sites within the dgstv sys 117
D15.9	Benign neoplasm of intrathoracic organ, unsp 67
D14.1	Benign neoplasm of larynx 3, 58
D10.0	Benign neoplasm of lip 3, 59
D13.4	Benign neoplasm of liver 124
D16.5	Benign neoplasm of lwr jaw bone 3, 59
D36.0	Benign neoplasm of lymph nodes 294
D11.9	Benign neoplasm of major salivary gland, unsp 3
D11*	Benign neoplasm of major salivary glands 58
D29*	Benign neoplasm of male genital organs 261
D15.2	Benign neoplasm of mediastinum 67
D32*	Benign neoplasm of meninges 32
D19.7	Benign neoplasm of mesothelial tissue of oth sites 304, 305
D19.1	Benign neoplasm of mesothelial tissue of peritoneum 117
D19.0	Benign neoplasm of mesothelial tissue of pleura 67
D19.9	Benign neoplasm of mesothelial tissue, unsp 304, 305
D14.0	Benign neoplasm of mid ear, nasl cav and accessory sinuses 3, 58
D10.6	Benign neoplasm of nasopharynx 3, 58
D28*	Benign neoplasm of oth and unsp female genital organs 264, 270
D13.3*	Benign neoplasm of oth and unsp parts of sm intestine 117
D11.7	Benign neoplasm of oth major salivary glands 3
D10.5	Benign neoplasm of oth parts of oropharynx 3, 58
D35.7	Benign neoplasm of oth spec endocrine glands 247
D15.7	Benign neoplasm of oth spec intrathoracic organs 67
D36.7	Benign neoplasm of oth spec sites 304, 306
D27*	Benign neoplasm of ovary 264, 270
D13.6	Benign neoplasm of pancreas 124
D35.1	Benign neoplasm of parathyroid gland 247
D11.0	Benign neoplasm of parotid gland 3
D36.1[0,1,2,3,4,5, 6,7]	Benign neoplasm of peripheral nerves and autonomic nervous sys of [unsp site, face head and neck, upr limb incl* shldr, lwr limb incl* hip, thorax, abd, pelvis, unsp trunk] 193
D10.9	Benign neoplasm of pharynx, unsp 3, 58
D35.4	Benign neoplasm of pineal gland 32
D35.2	Benign neoplasm of pituitary gland 247
D14.4	Benign neoplasm of respiratory sys, unsp 67
D16.7	Benign neoplasm of ribs, sternum and clavicle 67
D13.1	Benign neoplasm of stomach 117
D15.0	Benign neoplasm of thymus 294
D34	Benign neoplasm of thyroid gland 3, 247
D10.1	Benign neoplasm of tongue 3, 59
D10.4	Benign neoplasm of tonsil 3, 58
D14.2	Benign neoplasm of trachea 67
D30*	Benign neoplasm of urinary organs 248, 255
D16.6	Benign neoplasm of vert column 125
D36.9	Benign neoplasm, unsp site 304, 306
D20*	Benign neoplm of soft tissue of retroperiton and peritoneum 117
G03.2	Benign recurrent meningitis [Mollaret] 35
G25.83	Benign shuddering attacks 38
S62.21[1,2,3] [D,G,S]	Bennett's fx, [rt, lt, unsp] hand, [subsq enc for fx w/ routine healing, subsq enc for fx w/ delayed healing, seq] 175
S62.21[1,2,3] [A,B]	Bennett's fx, [rt, lt, unsp] hand, init enc for [clsd, opn] fx 187, 424
S62.21[1,2,3] [K,P]	Bennett's fx, [rt, lt, unsp] hand, subsq enc for fx w/ [nonu, malu] 199

Code	Description
S52.38[1,2,9] [D,E,F,G,H,J,S]	Bent bone of [rt, lt, unsp] radius, [subsq enc for clsd fx w/ routine healing, subsq enc for opn fx type I or II w/ routine healing, subsq enc for opn fx type I or II w/ routine healing, subsq enc for clsd fx w/ delayed healing, subsq enc for opn fx type I or II w/ delayed healing, subsq enc for opn fx type IIIA, IIIB, or IIIC w/ delayed healing, seq] 173
S52.38[1,2,9] [A,B,C]	Bent bone of [rt, lt, unsp] radius, init enc for [clsd fx, opn fx type I or II, opn fx type IIIA, IIIB, or IIIC] 186, 423
S52.38[1,2,9] [B,C]	Bent bone of [rt, lt, unsp] radius, init enc for opn fx type [I or II, IIIA IIIB or IIIC] 434
S52.38[1,2,9] [K,M,N,P,Q,R]	Bent bone of [rt, lt, unsp] radius, subsq enc for [clsd fx w/ nonu, opn fx type I or II w/ nonu, opn fx type IIIA, IIIB, or IIIC w/ nonu, clsd fx w/ malu, opn fx type I or II w/ malu, opn fx type IIIA, IIIB, or IIIC w/ malu] 198
S52.28[1,2,3] [D,E,F,G,H,J,S]	Bent bone of [rt, lt, unsp] ulna, [subsq enc for clsd fx w/ routine healing, subsq enc for opn fx type I or II w/ routine healing, subsq enc for opn fx type I or II w/ routine healing, subsq enc for clsd fx w/ delayed healing, subsq enc for opn fx type I or II w/ delayed healing, subsq enc for opn fx type IIIA, IIIB, or IIIC w/ delayed healing, seq] 173
S52.28[1,2,3] [A,B,C]	Bent bone of [rt, lt, unsp] ulna, init enc for [clsd fx, opn fx type I or II, opn fx type IIIA, IIIB, or IIIC] 186, 423
S52.28[1,2,3] [B,C]	Bent bone of [rt, lt, unsp] ulna, init enc for opn fx type [I or II, IIIA IIIB or IIIC] 434
S52.28[1,2,3] [K,M,N,P,Q,R]	Bent bone of [rt, lt, unsp] ulna, subsq enc for [clsd fx w/ nonu, opn fx type I or II w/ nonu, opn fx type IIIA, IIIB, or IIIC w/ nonu, clsd fx w/ malu, opn fx type I or II w/ malu, opn fx type IIIA, IIIB, or IIIC w/ malu] 198
I45.2	Bifascicular block 283
K41.[0,1]0	Bilat femor hernia, w/ [obstruction w/o gangrene, gangrene], not spec as recurrent 284
K40.[0,1]0	Bilat inguinal hernia, w/ [obstruction w/o gangrene, gangrene], not spec as recurrent 284
K74.5	Biliary cirrhosis, unsp 123
R11.14	Bilious vomiting 116
P92.01	Bilious vomiting of newborn 282
R82.2	Biliuria 124
M99.9	Biomechanical lesion, unsp 194
D81.810	Biotinidase deficiency 247
F31*	Bipolar d/o 311
P11.9	Birth inj to central nervous sys, unsp 282
P11.3	Birth inj to facial nerve 288
P11.4	Birth inj to oth cranial nerves 282
P14.9	Birth inj to peripheral nervous sys, unsp 282
P12.9	Birth inj to scalp, unsp 289
P13*	Birth inj to skeleton 288
P11.5	Birth inj to spine and spinal cord 282
P14.8	Birth injuries to oth parts of peripheral nervous sys 282
N33	Bladder d/o in dz classified elsw 256
N32.0	Bladder-neck obstruction 285
B40*	Blastomycosis 283, 308
Z52.0*	Bld donor 412
Z67*	Bld type 412
T80.21[1,2,8,9]A	[Bldstream, Local, Oth, Unsp] infxn d/t central venous catheter, init enc 103
T80.21[1,2,8,9]S	Bldstream, Local, Oth, Unsp] infxn d/t central venous catheter, seq 374
T80.21[1,2,8,9]D	Bldstream, Local, Oth, Unsp] infxn d/t central venous catheter, subsq enc 410
H02.3*	Blepharochalasis 45
H02.52*	Blepharophimosis 45
G24.5	Blepharospasm 45
O02.0	Blighted ovum and nonhydatidiform mole 277, 279
K90.2	Blind loop synd, NEC 116
H54*	Blindness and low vision 46
S00.52[1,2]S	Blister (nonthermal) of [lip, oral cavity], seq 224
S60.42[8,9]S	Blister (nonthermal) of [oth, unsp] finger, seq 228
S60.42[8,9]D	Blister (nonthermal) of [oth, unsp] finger, subsq enc 394
S30.82[2,3]S	Blister (nonthermal) of [penis, scrotum and testes], seq 226
S20.42[1,2,9]S	Blister (nonthermal) of [rt, lt, unsp] back wall of thorax, seq 225
S20.42[1,2,9]D	Blister (nonthermal) of [rt, lt, unsp] back wall of thorax, subsq enc 388
S00.42[1,2,9]S	Blister (nonthermal) of [rt, lt, unsp] ear, seq 224
S50.32[1,2,9]S	Blister (nonthermal) of [rt, lt, unsp] elbow, seq 227

Code	Description
S50.32[1,2,9]D	Blister (nonthermal) of [rt, lt, unsp] elbow, subsq enc 392
S00.22[1,2,9]A	Blister (nonthermal) of [rt, lt, unsp] eyelid and periocular area, init enc 46
S00.22[1,2,9]S	Blister (nonthermal) of [rt, lt, unsp] eyelid and periocular area, seq 224
S50.82[1,2,9]S	Blister (nonthermal) of [rt, lt, unsp] forearm, seq 227
S50.82[1,2,9]D	Blister (nonthermal) of [rt, lt, unsp] forearm, subsq enc 392
S20.32[1,2,9]S	Blister (nonthermal) of [rt, lt, unsp] front wall of thorax, seq 225
S20.32[1,2,9]D	Blister (nonthermal) of [rt, lt, unsp] front wall of thorax, subsq enc 388
S60.52[1,2,9]S	Blister (nonthermal) of [rt, lt, unsp] hand, seq 228
S60.52[1,2,9]D	Blister (nonthermal) of [rt, lt, unsp] hand, subsq enc 394
S40.22[1,2,9] [A,S]	Blister (nonthermal) of [rt, lt, unsp] shldr, [init enc, seq] 227
S40.22[1,2,9]D	Blister (nonthermal) of [rt, lt, unsp] shldr, subsq enc 391
S60.32[1,2,9]S	Blister (nonthermal) of [rt, lt, unsp] thumb, seq 228
S60.32[1,2,9]D	Blister (nonthermal) of [rt, lt, unsp] thumb, subsq enc 394
S40.82[1,2,9] [A,S]	Blister (nonthermal) of [rt, lt, unsp] upr arm, [init enc, seq] 227
S40.82[1,2,9]D	Blister (nonthermal) of [rt, lt, unsp] upr arm, subsq enc 391
S60.82[1,2,9]S	Blister (nonthermal) of [rt, lt, unsp] wrist, seq 228
S60.82[1,2,9]D	Blister (nonthermal) of [rt, lt, unsp] wrist, subsq enc 394
S60.42[0,1]S	Blister (nonthermal) of [rt, lt] index finger, seq 228
S60.42[0,1]D	Blister (nonthermal) of [rt, lt] index finger, subsq enc 394
S60.42[6,7]S	Blister (nonthermal) of [rt, lt] little finger, seq 228
S60.42[6,7]D	Blister (nonthermal) of [rt, lt] little finger, subsq enc 394
S60.42[2,3]S	Blister (nonthermal) of [rt, lt] mid finger, seq 228
S60.42[2,3]D	Blister (nonthermal) of [rt, lt] mid finger, subsq enc 394
S60.42[4,5]S	Blister (nonthermal) of [rt, lt] ring finger, seq 228
S60.42[4,5]D	Blister (nonthermal) of [rt, lt] ring finger, subsq enc 394
S30.821S	Blister (nonthermal) of abd wall, seq 226
S30.827S	Blister (nonthermal) of anus, seq 226
S20.12[1,2,9]S	Blister (nonthermal) of breast, [rt, lt, unsp] breast, seq 225
S20.12[1,2,9]D	Blister (nonthermal) of breast, [rt, lt, unsp] breast, subsq enc 388
S30.820S	Blister (nonthermal) of lwr back and pelvis, seq 226
S00.32XS	Blister (nonthermal) of nose, seq 224
S00.82XS	Blister (nonthermal) of oth part of head, seq 224
S10.82XS	Blister (nonthermal) of oth part of neck, seq 225
S00.02XS	Blister (nonthermal) of scalp, seq 224
S10.12XS	Blister (nonthermal) of throat, seq 225
S30.82[5,6]S	Blister (nonthermal) of unsp ext genital organs, [male, female], seq 226
S00.92XS	Blister (nonthermal) of unsp part of head, seq 224
S10.92XS	Blister (nonthermal) of unsp part of neck, seq 225
S20.92XS	Blister (nonthermal) of unsp parts of thorax, seq 225
S30.824S	Blister (nonthermal) of vagina and vulva, seq 226
S90.52[1,2,9]S	Blister (nonthermal), [rt, lt, unsp] ankle, seq 230
S90.82[1,2,9]S	Blister (nonthermal), [rt, lt, unsp] foot, seq 230
S90.42[1,2,3]A	Blister (nonthermal), [rt, lt, unsp] great toe, init enc 428
S90.42[1,2,3]S	Blister (nonthermal), [rt, lt, unsp] great toe, seq 230
S90.42[1,2,3]D	Blister (nonthermal), [rt, lt, unsp] great toe, subsq enc 399
S70.22[1,2,9]S	Blister (nonthermal), [rt, lt, unsp] hip, seq 229
S80.22[1,2,9]S	Blister (nonthermal), [rt, lt, unsp] knee, seq 229
S90.42[4,5,6]A	Blister (nonthermal), [rt, lt, unsp] lesser toe(s), init enc 428
S90.42[4,5,6]S	Blister (nonthermal), [rt, lt, unsp] lesser toe(s), seq 230
S90.42[4,5,6]D	Blister (nonthermal), [rt, lt, unsp] lesser toe(s), subsq enc 399
S80.82[1,2,9]S	Blister (nonthermal), [rt, lt, unsp] lwr leg, seq 229
S70.32[1,2,9]S	Blister (nonthermal), [rt, lt, unsp] thigh, seq 229
S00.5[2,6][1,2]A	Blister (nonthermal), Insect bite (nonvenomous)] of [lip, oral cavity], init enc 234
S30.8[2,6] [0,1,2,3,4,5,6,7] A	Blister (nonthermal), Insect bite (nonvenomous)] of [lwr back and pelvis, abd wall, penis, scrotum and testes, vagina and vulva, unsp ext genital organs, male, unsp ext genital organs, female, anus], init enc 234
S00.[8,9][2,6]XA	Blister (nonthermal), Insect bite (nonvenomous)] of [oth, unsp] part of head, init enc 234
S60.4[2,6] [0,1,2,3,4,5,6,7, 8,9]A	Blister (nonthermal), Insect bite (nonvenomous)] of [rt index, lt index, rt mid, lt mid, rt ring, lt ring, rt little, lt little] finger, init enc 234
S90.5[2,6][1,2,9] A	Blister (nonthermal), Insect bite (nonvenomous)] of [rt, lt, unsp] ankle, init enc 234

S20.4[2,6][1,2,9]A	Blister (nonthermal), Insect bite (nonvenomous)] of [rt, lt, unsp] back wall of thorax, init enc 234
S00.4[2,6][1,2,9]A	Blister (nonthermal), Insect bite (nonvenomous)] of [rt, lt, unsp] ear, init enc 234
S50.3[2,6][1,2,9]A	Blister (nonthermal), Insect bite (nonvenomous)] of [rt, lt, unsp] elbow, init enc 234
S90.8[2,6][1,2,9]A	Blister (nonthermal), Insect bite (nonvenomous)] of [rt, lt, unsp] foot, init enc 234
S50.8[2,6][1,2,9]A	Blister (nonthermal), Insect bite (nonvenomous)] of [rt, lt, unsp] forearm, init enc 234
S20.3[2,6][1,2,9]A	Blister (nonthermal), Insect bite (nonvenomous)] of [rt, lt, unsp] front wall of thorax, init enc 234
S90.4[2,6][1,2,3]A	Blister (nonthermal), Insect bite (nonvenomous)] of [rt, lt, unsp] great toe, init enc 234
S60.5[2,6][1,2,9]A	Blister (nonthermal), Insect bite (nonvenomous)] of [rt, lt, unsp] hand, init enc 234
S70.2[2,6][1,2,9]A	Blister (nonthermal), Insect bite (nonvenomous)] of [rt, lt, unsp] hip, init enc 234
S80.2[2,6][1,2,9]A	Blister (nonthermal), Insect bite (nonvenomous)] of [rt, lt, unsp] knee, init enc 234
S90.4[2,6][4,5,6]A	Blister (nonthermal), Insect bite (nonvenomous)] of [rt, lt, unsp] lesser toe(s), init enc 234
S80.8[2,6][1,2,9]A	Blister (nonthermal), Insect bite (nonvenomous)] of [rt, lt, unsp] lwr leg, init enc 234
S70.3[2,6][1,2,9]A	Blister (nonthermal), Insect bite (nonvenomous)] of [rt, lt, unsp] thigh, init enc 234
S60.3[2,6][1,2,9]A	Blister (nonthermal), Insect bite (nonvenomous)] of [rt, lt, unsp] thumb, init enc 234
S60.8[2,6][1,2,9]A	Blister (nonthermal), Insect bite (nonvenomous)] of [rt, lt, unsp] wrist, init enc 234
S20.1[2,6][1,2,9]A	Blister (nonthermal), Insect bite (nonvenomous)] of breast, [rt, lt, unsp] breast, init enc 234
S00.3[2,6]XA	Blister (nonthermal), Insect bite (nonvenomous)] of nose, init enc 234
S10.8[2,6]XA	Blister (nonthermal), Insect bite (nonvenomous)] of oth spec part of neck, init enc 234
S00.0[2,6]XA	Blister (nonthermal), Insect bite (nonvenomous)] of scalp, init enc 234
S10.1[2,6]XA	Blister (nonthermal), Insect bite (nonvenomous)] of throat, init enc 234
S10.9[2,6]XA	Blister (nonthermal), Insect bite (nonvenomous)] of unsp part of neck, init enc 234
S20.9[2,6]XA	Blister (nonthermal), Insect bite (nonvenomous)] of unsp parts of thorax, init enc 234
S30.82[0,1,2,3,4,5,6,7]D	Blister [nonthermal] of [lwr back and pelvis, abd wall, penis, scrotum and testes, vagina and vulva, unsp ext genital organs male, unsp ext genital organs female, anus], subsq enc 389
Z68.1	Body mass index (BMI) 19 or less, adult 412
Z68.2*	Body mass index (BMI) 20-29, adult 412
Z68.3*	Body mass index (BMI) 30-39, adult 412
Z68.4*	Body mass index (BMI) 40 or greater, adult 247
Z68.5*	Body mass index (BMI) pediatric 412
A66.6	Bone and jt lesions of yaws 164
Z52.2*	Bone donor 205
Z52.3	Bone marrow donor 412
Z94.81	Bone marrow transplant status 294
Z94.6	Bone transplant status 205
R41.83	Borderline intellectual functioning 412
A05.1	Botulism food poison 308
R00.1	Bradycardia, unsp 102
G93.82	Brain death 35
G46.3	Brain stem stroke synd 33
A48.4	Brazilian purpuric fever 308
T82.31[0,1,2,8,9]S	Breakdown (mech) of [aortic (bifurcation) graft (replace), carotid arterial graft (bypass), femor arterial graft (bypass), oth vascular grafts, unsp vascular grafts], seq 375
T82.31[0,1,2,8,9]D	Breakdown (mech) of [aortic (bifurcation) graft (replace), carotid arterial graft (bypass), femor arterial graft (bypass), oth vascular grafts, unsp vascular grafts], subsq enc 410
T82.11[0,1,8,9]S	Breakdown (mech) of [cardiac electrode, cardiac pulse generator, oth cardiac electronic dev, unsp cardiac electronic dev], seq 375
T82.11[0,1,8,9]D	Breakdown (mech) of [cardiac electrode, cardiac pulse generator, oth cardiac electronic dev, unsp cardiac electronic dev], subsq enc 410
T82.51[0,1,2,3,4,5,8,9]A	Breakdown (mech) of [surgically created arteriovenous fistula, surgically created arteriovenous shunt, artfcl heart, balloon (counterpulsation) dev, inf catheter, umbrella dev, oth cardiac/vascular dev, unsp cardiac/vascular dev], init enc 103
T82.51[0,1,2,3,4,5,8,9]S	Breakdown (mech) of [surgically created arteriovenous fistula, surgically created arteriovenous shunt, artfcl heart, balloon (counterpulsation) dev, inf catheter, umbrella dev, oth cardiac/vascular dev, unsp cardiac/vascular dev], seq 375
T82.51[0,1,2,3,4,5,8,9]D	Breakdown (mech) of [surgically created arteriovenous fistula, surgically created arteriovenous shunt, artfcl heart, balloon (counterpulsation) dev, inf catheter, umbrella dev, oth cardiac/vascular dev, unsp cardiac/vascular dev], subsq enc 410
T82.110A	Breakdown (mech) of cardiac electrode, init enc 102
T82.118A	Breakdown (mech) of cardiac electronic device, init 103
T85.11[0,1,2,8]A	Breakdown (mech) of implanted electronic neurostimulator (electrode) of [brain, peripheral nerve, spinal cord, oth nervous sys], init enc 40
T85.11[0,1,2,8]S	Breakdown (mech) of implanted electronic neurostimulator (electrode) of [brain, peripheral nerve, spinal cord, oth nervous sys], seq 376
T85.11[0,1,2,8]D	Breakdown (mech) of implanted electronic neurostimulator (electrode) of [brain, peripheral nerve, spinal cord, oth nervous sys], subsq enc 411
T84.21[0,3,6,8]A	Breakdown (mech) of int fix dev of [bones of hand and fingers, bones of foot and toes, vertebrae, oth bones], init enc 183
T84.21[0,3,6,8]S	Breakdown (mech) of int fix dev of [bones of hand and fingers, bones of foot and toes, vertebrae, oth bones], seq 375
T84.21[0,3,6,8]D	Breakdown (mech) of int fix dev of [bones of hand and fingers, bones of foot and toes, vertebrae, oth bones], subsq enc 411
T84.11[0,1,2,3,4,5,6,7,9]A	Breakdown (mech) of int fix dev of [rt humerus, lt humerus, bone of rt forearm, bone of lt forearm, rt femur, lt femur, bone of rt lwr leg, bone of lt lwr leg, unsp bone of limb], init enc 183
T84.11[0,1,2,3,4,5,6,7,9]S	Breakdown (mech) of int fix dev of [rt humerus, lt humerus, bone of rt forearm, bone of lt forearm, rt femur, lt femur, bone of rt lwr leg, bone of lt lwr leg, unsp bone of limb], seq 375
T84.11[0,1,2,3,4,5,6,7,9]D	Breakdown (mech) of int fix dev of [rt humerus, lt humerus, bone of rt forearm, bone of lt forearm, rt femur, lt femur, bone of rt lwr leg, bone of lt lwr leg, unsp bone of limb], subsq enc 411
T85.318S	Breakdown (mech) of ocular prosth dev/grft, seq 376
T85.318D	Breakdown (mech) of ocular prosth dev/grft, subs 411
T85.31[0,1]S	Breakdown (mech) of prosthetic orbit of [rt, lt] eye, seq 376
T85.31[0,1]D	Breakdown (mech) of prosthetic orbit of [rt, lt] eye, subsq enc 411
T85.4[1,2,3,4,9]XS	[Breakdown (mech), Displac, Leakage, Capsular contracture, Oth mech comp] of breast prosthesis and implant, seq 376
T85.4[1,2,3,4,9]XD	[Breakdown (mech), Displac, Leakage, Capsular contracture, Oth mech comp] of breast prosthesis and implant, subsq enc 411
T82.3[1,2,3,9][0,1,2,8,9]A	[Breakdown (mech), Displac, Leakage, Oth mech comp] of [aortic (bifurcation) graft (replace), carotid arterial graft (bypass), femor arterial graft (bypass), oth vascular grafts, unsp vascular graft], init enc 103
T83.0[1,2,3,9][0,8]S	[Breakdown (mech), Displac, Leakage, Oth mech comp] of [cystostomy, oth indwelling urethral] catheter, seq 375
T82.22[1,2,3,8]A	[Breakdown (mech), Displac, Leakage, Oth mech comp] of biological heart valve graft, init enc 103
T82.22[1,2,3,8]S	[Breakdown (mech), Displac, Leakage, Oth mech comp] of biological heart valve graft, seq 375
T82.22[1,2,3,8]D	[Breakdown (mech), Displac, Leakage, Oth mech comp] of biological heart valve graft, subsq enc 410
T82.21[1,2,3,8]A	[Breakdown (mech), Displac, Leakage, Oth mech comp] of coronary artery bypass graft, init enc 103
T82.21[1,2,3,8]S	[Breakdown (mech), Displac, Leakage, Oth mech comp] of coronary artery bypass graft, seq 375
T82.21[1,2,3,8]D	[Breakdown (mech), Displac, Leakage, Oth mech comp] of coronary artery bypass graft, subsq enc 410
T83.0[1,2,3,9][0,8]A	[Breakdown (mech), Displac, Leakage, Oth mech comp] of cystostomy, oth indwelling urethral] catheter, init enc 256
T83.0[1,2,3,9][0,8]D	[Breakdown (mech), Displac, Leakage, Oth mech comp] of cystostomy, oth indwelling urethral] catheter, subsq enc 411
T83.2[1,2,3,9]XA	[Breakdown (mech), Displac, Leakage, Oth mech comp] of graft of urinary organ, init enc 256
T83.2[1,2,3,9]XS	[Breakdown (mech), Displac, Leakage, Oth mech comp] of graft of urinary organ, seq 375
T83.2[1,2,3,9]XD	[Breakdown (mech), Displac, Leakage, Oth mech comp] of graft of urinary organ, subsq enc 411
T82.4[1,2,3,9]XA	[Breakdown (mech), Displac, Leakage, Oth mech comp] of vascular dialysis catheter, init enc 103

Code	Description
T82.4[1,2,3,9]XS	[Breakdown (mech), Displac, Leakage, Oth mech comp] of vascular dialysis catheter, seq **375**
T82.4[1,2,3,9]XD	[Breakdown (mech), Displac, Leakage, Oth mech comp] of vascular dialysis catheter, subsq enc **410**
T85.Ø[1,2,3,9]XS	[Breakdown (mech), Displac, Leakage, Oth mech comp] of ventricular intracranial (communicating) shunt, seq **375**
T85.Ø[1,2,3,9]XD	[Breakdown (mech), Displac, Leakage, Oth mech comp] of ventricular intracranial (communicating) shunt, subsq enc **411**
T82.Ø[1,2,3,9]XA	[Breakdown (mech), Displac, Leakage, Oth mech] comp of heart valve prosthesis, init enc **102**
T82.Ø[1,2,3,9]XS	[Breakdown (mech), Displac, Leakage, Oth mech] comp of heart valve prosthesis, seq **375**
T82.Ø[1,2,3,9]XD	[Breakdown (mech), Displac, Leakage, Oth mech] comp of heart valve prosthesis, subsq enc **410**
T85.Ø[1,2,3]XA	[Breakdown (mech), Displac, Leakage] of ventricular intracranial (communicating) shunt, init enc **40**
T85.5[1,2,9] [Ø,1,8]A	[Breakdown (mech), Displac, Oth mech comp] of [bile duct prosthesis, esophageal anti-reflux dev, oth gastrointestinal prosthetic devs, implants and grafts], init enc **368**
T85.5[1,2,9] [Ø,1,8]S	[Breakdown (mech), Displac, Oth mech comp] of [bile duct prosthesis, esophageal anti-reflux dev, oth gastrointestinal prosthetic devs, implants and grafts], seq **376**
T85.5[1,2,9] [Ø,1,8]D	[Breakdown (mech), Displac, Oth mech comp] of [bile duct prosthesis, esophageal anti-reflux dev, oth gastrointestinal prosthetic devs, implants and grafts], subsq enc **411**
T84.3[1,2,9][Ø,8] A	[Breakdown (mech), Displac, Oth mech comp] of [electronic bone stimulator, oth bone dev(s), implants and grafts], init enc **183**
T84.3[1,2,9][Ø,8]S	[Breakdown (mech), Displac, Oth mech comp] of [electronic bone stimulator, oth bone dev(s), implants and grafts], seq **375**
T84.3[1,2,9][Ø,8] D	[Breakdown (mech), Displac, Oth mech comp] of [electronic bone stimulator, oth bone dev(s), implants and grafts], subsq enc **411**
T84.4[1,2,9][Ø,8] A	[Breakdown (mech), Displac, Oth mech comp] of [muscle and tndn graft, oth int orthopedic dev(s), implants and graft], init enc **183**
T84.4[1,2,9][Ø,8]S	[Breakdown (mech), Displac, Oth mech comp] of [muscle and tndn graft, oth int orthopedic dev(s), implants and graft], seq **375**
T84.4[1,2,9][Ø,8] D	[Breakdown (mech), Displac, Oth mech comp] of [muscle and tndn graft, oth int orthopedic dev(s), implants and graft], subsq enc **411**
T83.4[1,2,9][Ø,8] A	[Breakdown (mech), Displac, Oth mech comp] of [penile (implanted) prosthesis, oth prosthetic devs, implants and grafts of genital tract], init enc **256**
T83.4[1,2,9][Ø,8]S	[Breakdown (mech), Displac, Oth mech comp] of [penile (implanted) prosthesis, oth prosthetic devs, implants and grafts of genital tract], seq **375**
T83.4[1,2,9][Ø,8] D	[Breakdown (mech), Displac, Oth mech comp] of [penile (implanted) prosthesis, oth prosthetic devs, implants and grafts of genital tract], subsq enc **411**
T83.1[1,2,9] [Ø,1,2,8] A	[Breakdown (mech), Displac, Oth mech comp] of [urinary electronic stimulator, urinary sphincter implant, urinary stent, oth urinary devs], init enc **256**
T83.1[1,2,9] [Ø,1,2,8]S	[Breakdown (mech), Displac, Oth mech comp] of [urinary electronic stimulator, urinary sphincter implant, urinary stent, oth urinary devs], seq **375**
T83.1[1,2,9] [Ø,1,2,8]D	[Breakdown (mech), Displac, Oth mech comp] of [urinary electronic stimulator, urinary sphincter implant, urinary stent, oth urinary devs], subsq enc **411**
T85.2[1,2,9]XA	[Breakdown (mech), Displac, Oth mech comp] of intraocular lens, init enc **47**
T85.2[1,2,9]XS	[Breakdown (mech), Displac, Oth mech comp] of intraocular lens, seq **376**
T85.2[1,2,9]XD	[Breakdown (mech), Displac, Oth mech comp] of intraocular lens, subsq enc **411**
T83.3[1,2,9]XA	[Breakdown (mech), Displac, Oth mech comp] of intrauterine contraceptive dev, init enc **265, 270**
T83.3[1,2,9]XS	[Breakdown (mech), Displac, Oth mech comp] of intrauterine contraceptive dev, seq **375**
T83.3[1,2,9]XD	[Breakdown (mech), Displac, Oth mech comp] of intrauterine contraceptive dev, subsq enc **411**
T85.3[1,2,9]8A	[Breakdown (mech), Displac, Oth mech comp] of oth ocular prosthetic devs, implants and grafts, init enc **47**
T85.3[1,2,9][Ø,1] A	[Breakdown (mech), Displac, Oth mech comp] of prosthetic orbit of [rt, lt] eye, init enc **368**
T85.6[1,2] [Ø,1,2,3,4,8]A	[Breakdown (mech), Displac] of [epidural and subdural inf catheter, intraperitoneal dialysis catheter, permanent sutures, artfcl skin graft and decellularized allodermis, insulin pump, oth spec int prosthetic devs, implants and grafts], init enc **368**
T85.6[1,2] [Ø,1,2,3,4,8]S	[Breakdown (mech), Displac] of [epidural and subdural inf catheter, intraperitoneal dialysis catheter, permanent sutures, artfcl skin graft and decellularized allodermis, insulin pump, oth spec int prosthetic devs, implants and grafts], seq **376**
T85.6[1,2] [Ø,1,2,3,4,8]D	[Breakdown (mech), Displac] of [epidural and subdural inf catheter, intraperitoneal dialysis catheter, permanent sutures, artfcl skin graft and decellularized allodermis, insulin pump, oth spec int prosthetic devs, implants and grafts], subsq enc **411**
T85.41XA	Breakdown of breast prosthesis and implant, init **224**
T82.111A	Breakdown of cardiac pulse generator (battery), init **102**
T82.119A	Breakdown of unsp cardiac electronic device, init **103**
P83.4	Breast engorgement of newborn **288**
F23	Brief psychotic d/o **310**
T84.Ø1[Ø,1,2,3,8, 9]A	Broken int [rt hip, lt hip, rt knee, lt knee, oth site, unsp site] prosthesis, init enc **183**
T84.Ø1[Ø,1,2,3,8, 9]S	Broken int [rt hip, lt hip, rt knee, lt knee, oth site, unsp site] prosthesis, seq **375**
T84.Ø1[Ø,1,2,3,8, 9]D	Broken int [rt hip, lt hip, rt knee, lt knee, oth site, unsp site] prosthesis, subsq enc **411**
J47*	Bronchiectasis **68**
J68.[Ø,2,3]	[Bronchitis and pneumonitis, Upr respiratory inflam NEC, Oth acute and subacute respiratory conditions] d/t chemicals, gases, fumes and vapors **69**
J4Ø	Bronchitis, not spec as acute or chr **69**
J18.[Ø,1,8]	[Broncho-, Lobar, Oth] pneumonia, unsp organism **284**
J18.Ø	Bronchopneumonia, unsp organism **68**
S14.14[1,2,3,4,5, 6,7,8,9][A,S]	Brown-Sequard synd at [C1, C2, C3, C4, C5, C6, C7, C8, unsp] lvl of cervical spinal cord, [init enc, seq] **32**
S14.14[1,2,3,4,5, 6,7,8,9]A	Brown-Sequard synd at [C1, C2, C3, C4, C5, C6, C7, C8, unsp] lvl of cervical spinal cord, init enc **420, 433**
S14.14[1,2,3,4,5, 6,7,8,9]D	Brown-Sequard synd at [C1, C2, C3, C4, C5, C6, C7, C8, unsp] lvl of cervical spinal cord, subsq enc **388**
S24.14[1,2,3,4,9] [A,S]	Brown-Sequard synd at [T1, T2-T6, T7-T1Ø, T11-T12, unsp] lvl of thoracic spinal cord, [init enc, seq] **32**
S24.14[1,2,3,4,9] A	Brown-Sequard synd at [T1, T2-T6, T7-T1Ø, T11-T12, unsp] lvl of thoracic spinal cord, init enc **420, 433**
S24.14[1,2,3,4,9] D	Brown-Sequard synd at [T1, T2-T6, T7-T1Ø, T11-T12, unsp] lvl of thoracic spinal cord, subsq enc **389**
A23*	Brucellosis **308**
P12.3	Bruising of scalp d/t birth inj **288**
A2Ø.Ø	Bubonic plague **308**
S83.25[1,2,9] [A,S]	Bucket-handle tear of lat meniscus, current inj, [rt, lt, unsp] knee, [init enc, seq] **192**
S83.25[1,2,9]A	Bucket-handle tear of lat meniscus, current inj, [rt, lt, unsp] knee, init enc **428**
S83.25[1,2,9]D	Bucket-handle tear of lat meniscus, current inj, [rt, lt, unsp] knee, subsq enc **398**
S83.21[1,2,9] [A,S]	Bucket-handle tear of med meniscus, current inj, [rt, lt, unsp] knee, [init enc, seq] **192**
S83.21[1,2,9]A	Bucket-handle tear of med meniscus, current inj, [rt, lt, unsp] knee, init enc **428**
S83.21[1,2,9]D	Bucket-handle tear of med meniscus, current inj, [rt, lt, unsp] knee, subsq enc **398**
S83.2Ø[Ø,1,2] [A,S]	Bucket-handle tear of unsp meniscus, current inj, [rt, lt, unsp] knee, [init enc, seq] **191**
S83.2Ø[Ø,1,2]A	Bucket-handle tear of unsp meniscus, current inj, [rt, lt, unsp] knee, init enc **428**
S83.2Ø[Ø,1,2]D	Bucket-handle tear of unsp meniscus, current inj, [rt, lt, unsp] knee, subsq enc **398**
I82.Ø	Budd-Chiari synd **124**
F5Ø.2	Bulimia nervosa **311**
L14	Bullous d/o in dz classified elsw **223**
L13.9	Bullous d/o, unsp **223**
L12.Ø	Bullous pemphigoid **223**
C83.7*	Burkitt lymphoma **438**
C83.71	Burkitt lymphoma, lymph nodes of head, face, and neck **3**
T27.[Ø,1,2,3]XXA	Burn [of larynx and trachea, involving larynx and trachea w/ lung, of oth parts of respiratory tract, respiratory tract part unsp], init enc **70**
T22.2ØXA	Burn 2nd deg of shldr/up lmb, ex wrs/hnd, unsp site, init **383**
T22.2ØXS	Burn 2nd deg of shldr/up lmb, ex wrs/hnd, unsp site, seq **231**
T22.2ØXD	Burn 2nd deg of shldr/up lmb, ex wrs/hnd, unsp site, subs **401**
T2Ø.2ØXA	Burn 2nd degree of head, face, and neck, unsp site, init **383**
T2Ø.2ØXS	Burn 2nd degree of head, face, and neck, unsp site, seq **230**

Code	Description
T20.20XD	Burn 2nd degree of head, face, and neck, unsp site, subs 400
T22.30XA	Burn 3rd deg of shldr/up lmb, ex wrs/hnd, unsp site, init 377, 379, 381, 382
T22.30XS	Burn 3rd deg of shldr/up lmb, ex wrs/hnd, unsp site, seq 231
T22.30XD	Burn 3rd deg of shldr/up lmb, ex wrs/hnd, unsp site, subs 401
T20.30XA	Burn 3rd degree of head, face, and neck, unsp site, init 377, 379, 381, 382
T20.30XS	Burn 3rd degree of head, face, and neck, unsp site, seq 230
T20.30XD	Burn 3rd degree of head, face, and neck, unsp site, subs 400
T20.19XS	Burn first deg mult sites of head, face, and neck, seq 230
T22.10XA	Burn first deg of shldr/up lmb, ex wrs/hnd, unsp site, init 383
T22.10XS	Burn first deg of shldr/up lmb, ex wrs/hnd, unsp site, seq 231
T22.10XD	Burn first deg of shldr/up lmb, ex wrs/hnd, unsp site, subs 400
T20.10XA	Burn first degree of head, face, and neck, unsp site, init 382
T20.10XS	Burn first degree of head, face, and neck, unsp site, seq 230
T20.10XD	Burn first degree of head, face, and neck, unsp site, subs 400
T27.1XXA	Burn involving larynx and trachea with lung, init enc 381
T27.1XXS	Burn involving larynx and trachea with lung, seq 233
T27.1XXD	Burn involving larynx and trachea with lung, subs enc 402
T27.[2,3]XXS	Burn of [oth, unsp] parts of respiratory tract, seq 233
T28.41[1,2,9]A	Burn of [rt, lt, unsp] ear drum, init enc 384
T28.41[1,2,9]S	Burn of [rt, lt, unsp] ear drum, seq 233
T28.41[1,2,9]D	Burn of [rt, lt, unsp] ear drum, subsq enc 402
T26.4[0,1,2]XA	Burn of [unsp, rt, lt] eye and adnexa, part unsp, init enc 47
T26.4[0,1,2]XS	Burn of [unsp, rt, lt] eye and adnexa, part unsp, seq 233
T26.4[0,1,2]XD	Burn of [unsp, rt, lt] eye and adnexa, part unsp, subsq enc 402
T26.0[0,1,2]XA	Burn of [unsp, rt, lt] eyelid and periocular area, init enc 47
T26.0[0,1,2]XS	Burn of [unsp, rt, lt] eyelid and periocular area, seq 233
T26.0[0,1,2]XD	Burn of [unsp, rt, lt] eyelid and periocular area, subsq enc 402
T26.5[0,1,2]XD	Burn of [unsp, rt, lt] eyelid and periocular area, subsq enc 402
T21.1[1,2]XS	Burn of 1st degree of [chest, abd] wall, seq 231
T20.1[2,3,4]XA	Burn of 1st degree of [lip(s), chin, nose (septum)], init enc 382
T20.1[2,3,4]XS	Burn of 1st degree of [lip(s), chin, nose (septum)], seq 230
T20.1[2,3,4]XD	Burn of 1st degree of [lip(s), chin, nose (septum)], subsq enc 400
T21.1[6,7]XS	Burn of 1st degree of [male, female] genital rgn, seq 231
T25.11[1,2,9]A	Burn of 1st degree of [rt, lt, unsp] ankle, init enc 384
T25.11[1,2,9]S	Burn of 1st degree of [rt, lt, unsp] ankle, seq 232
T25.11[1,2,9]D	Burn of 1st degree of [rt, lt, unsp] ankle, subsq enc 402
T22.14[1,2,9]A	Burn of 1st degree of [rt, lt, unsp] axilla, init enc 383
T22.14[1,2,9]S	Burn of 1st degree of [rt, lt, unsp] axilla, seq 231
T22.14[1,2,9]D	Burn of 1st degree of [rt, lt, unsp] axilla, subsq enc 400
T20.11[1,2,9]A	Burn of 1st degree of [rt, lt, unsp] ear [any part, except ear drum], init enc 382
T20.11[1,2,9]S	Burn of 1st degree of [rt, lt, unsp] ear [any part, except ear drum], seq 230
T20.11[1,2,9]D	Burn of 1st degree of [rt, lt, unsp] ear [any part, except ear drum], subsq enc 400
T22.12[1,2,9]A	Burn of 1st degree of [rt, lt, unsp] elbow, init enc 383
T22.12[1,2,9]S	Burn of 1st degree of [rt, lt, unsp] elbow, seq 231
T22.12[1,2,9]D	Burn of 1st degree of [rt, lt, unsp] elbow, subsq enc 400
T25.12[1,2,9]A	Burn of 1st degree of [rt, lt, unsp] foot, init enc 384
T25.12[1,2,9]S	Burn of 1st degree of [rt, lt, unsp] foot, seq 232
T25.12[1,2,9]D	Burn of 1st degree of [rt, lt, unsp] foot, subsq enc 402
T22.11[1,2,9]A	Burn of 1st degree of [rt, lt, unsp] forearm, init enc 383
T22.11[1,2,9]S	Burn of 1st degree of [rt, lt, unsp] forearm, seq 231
T22.11[1,2,9]D	Burn of 1st degree of [rt, lt, unsp] forearm, subsq enc 400
T23.10[1,2,9]A	Burn of 1st degree of [rt, lt, unsp] hand, unsp site, init enc 383
T23.10[1,2,9]S	Burn of 1st degree of [rt, lt, unsp] hand, unsp site, seq 231
T23.10[1,2,9]D	Burn of 1st degree of [rt, lt, unsp] hand, unsp site, subsq enc 401
T24.12[1,2,9]A	Burn of 1st degree of [rt, lt, unsp] knee, init enc 384
T24.12[1,2,9]S	Burn of 1st degree of [rt, lt, unsp] knee, seq 232
T24.12[1,2,9]D	Burn of 1st degree of [rt, lt, unsp] knee, subsq enc 402
T24.13[1,2,9]A	Burn of 1st degree of [rt, lt, unsp] lwr leg, init enc 384
T24.13[1,2,9]S	Burn of 1st degree of [rt, lt, unsp] lwr leg, seq 232
T24.13[1,2,9]D	Burn of 1st degree of [rt, lt, unsp] lwr leg, subsq enc 402
T23.15[1,2,9]A	Burn of 1st degree of [rt, lt, unsp] palm, init enc 383
T23.15[1,2,9]S	Burn of 1st degree of [rt, lt, unsp] palm, seq 231
T23.15[1,2,9]D	Burn of 1st degree of [rt, lt, unsp] palm, subsq enc 401
T22.16[1,2,9]A	Burn of 1st degree of [rt, lt, unsp] scapular rgn, init enc 383
T22.16[1,2,9]S	Burn of 1st degree of [rt, lt, unsp] scapular rgn, seq 231
T22.16[1,2,9]D	Burn of 1st degree of [rt, lt, unsp] scapular rgn, subsq enc 400
T22.15[1,2,9]A	Burn of 1st degree of [rt, lt, unsp] shldr, init enc 383
T22.15[1,2,9]S	Burn of 1st degree of [rt, lt, unsp] shldr, seq 231
T22.15[1,2,9]D	Burn of 1st degree of [rt, lt, unsp] shldr, subsq enc 400
T24.11[1,2,9]A	Burn of 1st degree of [rt, lt, unsp] thigh, init enc 384
T24.11[1,2,9]S	Burn of 1st degree of [rt, lt, unsp] thigh, seq 232
T24.11[1,2,9]D	Burn of 1st degree of [rt, lt, unsp] thigh, subsq enc 402
T23.11[1,2,9]A	Burn of 1st degree of [rt, lt, unsp] thumb (nail), init enc 383
T23.11[1,2,9]S	Burn of 1st degree of [rt, lt, unsp] thumb (nail), seq 231
T23.11[1,2,9]D	Burn of 1st degree of [rt, lt, unsp] thumb (nail), subsq enc 401
T25.13[1,2,9]A	Burn of 1st degree of [rt, lt, unsp] toe(s) (nail), init enc 384
T25.13[1,2,9]S	Burn of 1st degree of [rt, lt, unsp] toe(s) (nail), seq 232
T25.13[1,2,9]D	Burn of 1st degree of [rt, lt, unsp] toe(s) (nail), subsq enc 402
T22.13[1,2,9]A	Burn of 1st degree of [rt, lt, unsp] upr arm, init enc 383
T22.13[1,2,9]S	Burn of 1st degree of [rt, lt, unsp] upr arm, seq 231
T22.13[1,2,9]D	Burn of 1st degree of [rt, lt, unsp] upr arm, subsq enc 400
T23.17[1,2,9]A	Burn of 1st degree of [rt, lt, unsp] wrist, init enc 383
T23.17[1,2,9]S	Burn of 1st degree of [rt, lt, unsp] wrist, seq 231
T23.17[1,2,9]D	Burn of 1st degree of [rt, lt, unsp] wrist, subsq enc 401
T20.1[5,6,7]XA	Burn of 1st degree of [scalp [any part], forehead and cheek, neck], init enc 382
T20.1[5,6,7]XS	Burn of 1st degree of [scalp [any part], forehead and cheek, neck], seq 230
T20.1[5,6,7]XD	Burn of 1st degree of [scalp [any part], forehead and cheek, neck], subsq enc 400
T21.1[0,1,2,3,4,5,6,7,9]XA	Burn of 1st degree of [unsp site of trunk, chest wall, abd wall, upr back, lwr back, buttock, male genital rgn, female genital rgn, oth site of trunk], init enc 383
T21.1[0,1,2,3,4,5,6,7,9]XD	Burn of 1st degree of [unsp site of trunk, chest wall, abd wall, upr back, lwr back, buttock, male genital rgn, female genital rgn, oth site of trunk], subsq enc 400
T21.1[3,4,5]XS	Burn of 1st degree of [upr back, lwr back, buttock], seq 231
T23.16[1,2,9]A	Burn of 1st degree of back of [rt, lt, unsp] hand, init enc 383
T23.16[1,2,9]S	Burn of 1st degree of back of [rt, lt, unsp] hand, seq 231
T23.16[1,2,9]D	Burn of 1st degree of back of [rt, lt, unsp] hand, subsq enc 401
T23.14[1,2,9]A	Burn of 1st degree of multi [rt, lt, unsp] fingers (nail), incl* thumb, init enc 383
T23.14[1,2,9]S	Burn of 1st degree of multi [rt, lt, unsp] fingers (nail), incl* thumb, seq 231
T23.14[1,2,9]D	Burn of 1st degree of multi [rt, lt, unsp] fingers (nail), incl* thumb, subsq enc 401
T23.13[1,2,9]A	Burn of 1st degree of multi [rt, lt, unsp] fingers (nail), not incl* thumb, init enc 383
T23.13[1,2,9]S	Burn of 1st degree of multi [rt, lt, unsp] fingers (nail), not incl* thumb, seq 231
T23.13[1,2,9]D	Burn of 1st degree of multi [rt, lt, unsp] fingers (nail), not incl* thumb, subsq enc 401
T25.19[1,2,9]S	Burn of 1st degree of multi sites of [rt, lt, unsp] ankle & foot, seq 232
T25.19[1,2,9]A	Burn of 1st degree of multi sites of [rt, lt, unsp] ankle and foot, init enc 384
T25.19[1,2,9]D	Burn of 1st degree of multi sites of [rt, lt, unsp] ankle and foot, subsq enc 402
T24.19[1,2,9]A	Burn of 1st degree of multi sites of [rt, lt, unsp] lwr limb, except ankle and foot, init enc 384
T24.19[1,2,9]S	Burn of 1st degree of multi sites of [rt, lt, unsp] lwr limb, except ankle and foot, seq 232
T24.19[1,2,9]D	Burn of 1st degree of multi sites of [rt, lt, unsp] lwr limb, except ankle and foot, subsq enc 402
T22.19[1,2,9]A	Burn of 1st degree of multi sites of [rt, lt, unsp] shldr and upr limb, except wrist and hand, init enc 383
T22.19[1,2,9]S	Burn of 1st degree of multi sites of [rt, lt, unsp] shldr and upr limb, except wrist and hand, seq 231
T22.19[1,2,9]D	Burn of 1st degree of multi sites of [rt, lt, unsp] shldr and upr limb, except wrist and hand, subsq enc 400
T23.19[1,2,9]A	Burn of 1st degree of multi sites of [rt, lt, unsp] wrist and hand, init enc 383
T23.19[1,2,9]S	Burn of 1st degree of multi sites of [rt, lt, unsp] wrist and hand, seq 231
T23.19[1,2,9]D	Burn of 1st degree of multi sites of [rt, lt, unsp] wrist and hand, subsq enc 401
T23.12[1,2,9]A	Burn of 1st degree of single [rt, lt, unsp] finger (nail) except thumb, init enc 383

T23.12[1,2,9]S	Burn of 1st degree of single [rt, lt, unsp] finger (nail) except thumb, seq **231**
T23.12[1,2,9]D	Burn of 1st degree of single [rt, lt, unsp] finger (nail) except thumb, subsq enc **401**
T24.10[1,2,9]A	Burn of 1st degree of unsp site of [rt, lt, unsp] lwr limb, except ankle and foot, init enc **384**
T24.10[1,2,9]S	Burn of 1st degree of unsp site of [rt, lt, unsp] lwr limb, except ankle and foot, seq **232**
T24.10[1,2,9]D	Burn of 1st degree of unsp site of [rt, lt, unsp] lwr limb, except ankle and foot, subsq enc **402**
T20.29XA	Burn of 2nd deg mul sites of head, face, and neck, init **383**
T20.29XS	Burn of 2nd deg mul sites of head, face, and neck, seq **230**
T20.29XD	Burn of 2nd deg mul sites of head, face, and neck, subs **400**
T21.2[1,2]XS	Burn of 2nd degree of [chest, abd] wall, seq **231**
T20.2[2,3,4]XA	Burn of 2nd degree of [lip(s), chin, nose (septum)], init enc **383**
T20.2[2,3,4]XS	Burn of 2nd degree of [lip(s), chin, nose (septum)], seq **230**
T20.2[2,3,4]XD	Burn of 2nd degree of [lip(s), chin, nose (septum)], subsq enc **400**
T21.2[6,7]XS	Burn of 2nd degree of [male, female] genital rgn, seq **231**
T25.21[1,2,9]A	Burn of 2nd degree of [rt, lt, unsp] ankle, init enc **384**
T25.21[1,2,9]S	Burn of 2nd degree of [rt, lt, unsp] ankle, seq **232**
T25.21[1,2,9]D	Burn of 2nd degree of [rt, lt, unsp] ankle, subsq enc **402**
T22.24[1,2,9]A	Burn of 2nd degree of [rt, lt, unsp] axilla, init enc **383**
T22.24[1,2,9]S	Burn of 2nd degree of [rt, lt, unsp] axilla, seq **231**
T22.24[1,2,9]D	Burn of 2nd degree of [rt, lt, unsp] axilla, subsq enc **401**
T20.21[1,2,9]A	Burn of 2nd degree of [rt, lt, unsp] ear [any part, except ear drum], init enc **383**
T20.21[1,2,9]S	Burn of 2nd degree of [rt, lt, unsp] ear [any part, except ear drum], seq **230**
T20.21[1,2,9]D	Burn of 2nd degree of [rt, lt, unsp] ear [any part, except ear drum], subsq enc **400**
T22.22[1,2,9]A	Burn of 2nd degree of [rt, lt, unsp] elbow, init enc **383**
T22.22[1,2,9]S	Burn of 2nd degree of [rt, lt, unsp] elbow, seq **231**
T22.22[1,2,9]D	Burn of 2nd degree of [rt, lt, unsp] elbow, subsq enc **401**
T25.22[1,2,9]A	Burn of 2nd degree of [rt, lt, unsp] foot, init enc **384**
T25.22[1,2,9]S	Burn of 2nd degree of [rt, lt, unsp] foot, seq **232**
T25.22[1,2,9]D	Burn of 2nd degree of [rt, lt, unsp] foot, subsq enc **402**
T22.21[1,2,9]A	Burn of 2nd degree of [rt, lt, unsp] forearm, init enc **383**
T22.21[1,2,9]S	Burn of 2nd degree of [rt, lt, unsp] forearm, seq **231**
T22.21[1,2,9]D	Burn of 2nd degree of [rt, lt, unsp] forearm, subsq enc **401**
T23.20[1,2,9]A	Burn of 2nd degree of [rt, lt, unsp] hand, unsp site, init enc **383**
T23.20[1,2,9]S	Burn of 2nd degree of [rt, lt, unsp] hand, unsp site, seq **231**
T23.20[1,2,9]D	Burn of 2nd degree of [rt, lt, unsp] hand, unsp site, subsq enc **401**
T24.22[1,2,9]A	Burn of 2nd degree of [rt, lt, unsp] knee, init enc **384**
T24.22[1,2,9]S	Burn of 2nd degree of [rt, lt, unsp] knee, seq **232**
T24.22[1,2,9]D	Burn of 2nd degree of [rt, lt, unsp] knee, subsq enc **402**
T24.23[1,2,9]A	Burn of 2nd degree of [rt, lt, unsp] lwr leg, init enc **384**
T24.23[1,2,9]S	Burn of 2nd degree of [rt, lt, unsp] lwr leg, seq **232**
T24.23[1,2,9]D	Burn of 2nd degree of [rt, lt, unsp] lwr leg, subsq enc **402**
T23.25[1,2,9]A	Burn of 2nd degree of [rt, lt, unsp] palm, init enc **383**
T23.25[1,2,9]S	Burn of 2nd degree of [rt, lt, unsp] palm, seq **232**
T23.25[1,2,9]D	Burn of 2nd degree of [rt, lt, unsp] palm, subsq enc **401**
T22.26[1,2,9]A	Burn of 2nd degree of [rt, lt, unsp] scapular rgn, init enc **383**
T22.26[1,2,9]S	Burn of 2nd degree of [rt, lt, unsp] scapular rgn, seq **231**
T22.26[1,2,9]D	Burn of 2nd degree of [rt, lt, unsp] scapular rgn, subsq enc **401**
T22.25[1,2,9]A	Burn of 2nd degree of [rt, lt, unsp] shldr, init enc **383**
T22.25[1,2,9]S	Burn of 2nd degree of [rt, lt, unsp] shldr, seq **231**
T22.25[1,2,9]D	Burn of 2nd degree of [rt, lt, unsp] shldr, subsq enc **400**
T24.21[1,2,9]A	Burn of 2nd degree of [rt, lt, unsp] thigh, init enc **384**
T24.21[1,2,9]S	Burn of 2nd degree of [rt, lt, unsp] thigh, seq **232**
T24.21[1,2,9]D	Burn of 2nd degree of [rt, lt, unsp] thigh, subsq enc **402**
T23.21[1,2,9]A	Burn of 2nd degree of [rt, lt, unsp] thumb (nail), init enc **383**
T23.21[1,2,9]S	Burn of 2nd degree of [rt, lt, unsp] thumb (nail), seq **231**
T23.21[1,2,9]D	Burn of 2nd degree of [rt, lt, unsp] thumb (nail), subsq enc **401**
T25.23[1,2,9]A	Burn of 2nd degree of [rt, lt, unsp] toe(s) (nail), init enc **384**
T25.23[1,2,9]S	Burn of 2nd degree of [rt, lt, unsp] toe(s) (nail), seq **232**
T25.23[1,2,9]D	Burn of 2nd degree of [rt, lt, unsp] toe(s) (nail), subsq enc **402**
T22.23[1,2,9]A	Burn of 2nd degree of [rt, lt, unsp] upr arm, init enc **383**
T22.23[1,2,9]S	Burn of 2nd degree of [rt, lt, unsp] upr arm, seq **231**
T22.23[1,2,9]D	Burn of 2nd degree of [rt, lt, unsp] upr arm, subsq enc **401**
T23.27[1,2,9]A	Burn of 2nd degree of [rt, lt, unsp] wrist, init enc **383**
T23.27[1,2,9]S	Burn of 2nd degree of [rt, lt, unsp] wrist, seq **232**

T23.27[1,2,9]D	Burn of 2nd degree of [rt, lt, unsp] wrist, subsq enc **401**
T20.2[5,6,7]XA	Burn of 2nd degree of [scalp [any part], forehead and cheek, neck], init enc **383**
T20.2[5,6,7]XD	Burn of 2nd degree of [scalp [any part], forehead and cheek, neck], subsq enc **400**
T20.2[5,6,7]XS	Burn of 2nd degree of [scalp [any part], forehead and cheek, neck], seq **230**
T21.2[0,1,2,3,4,5, 6,7,9]XA	Burn of 2nd degree of [unsp site of trunk, chest wall, abd wall, upr back, lwr back, buttock, male genital rgn, female genital rgn, oth site of trunk], init enc **383**
T21.2[0,1,2,3,4,5, 6,7,9]XD	Burn of 2nd degree of [unsp site of trunk, chest wall, abd wall, upr back, lwr back, buttock, male genital rgn, female genital rgn, oth site of trunk], subsq enc **400**
T21.2[3,4,5]XS	Burn of 2nd degree of [upr back, lwr back, buttock], seq **231**
T23.26[1,2,9]A	Burn of 2nd degree of back of [rt, lt, unsp] hand, init enc **383**
T23.26[1,2,9]S	Burn of 2nd degree of back of [rt, lt, unsp] hand, seq **232**
T23.26[1,2,9]D	Burn of 2nd degree of back of [rt, lt, unsp] hand, subsq enc **401**
T23.24[1,2,9]A	Burn of 2nd degree of multi [rt, lt, unsp] fingers (nail), incl* thumb, init enc **383**
T23.24[1,2,9]S	Burn of 2nd degree of multi [rt, lt, unsp] fingers (nail), incl* thumb, seq **232**
T23.24[1,2,9]D	Burn of 2nd degree of multi [rt, lt, unsp] fingers (nail), incl* thumb, subsq enc **401**
T23.23[1,2,9]A	Burn of 2nd degree of multi [rt, lt, unsp] fingers (nail), not incl* thumb, init enc **383**
T23.23[1,2,9]S	Burn of 2nd degree of multi [rt, lt, unsp] fingers (nail), not incl* thumb, seq **232**
T23.23[1,2,9]D	Burn of 2nd degree of multi [rt, lt, unsp] fingers (nail), not incl* thumb, subsq enc **401**
T25.29[1,2,9]A	Burn of 2nd degree of multi sites of [rt, lt, unsp] ankle and foot, init enc **384**
T25.29[1,2,9]S	Burn of 2nd degree of multi sites of [rt, lt, unsp] ankle and foot, seq **232**
T25.29[1,2,9]D	Burn of 2nd degree of multi sites of [rt, lt, unsp] ankle and foot, subsq enc **402**
T24.29[1,2,9]A	Burn of 2nd degree of multi sites of [rt, lt, unsp] lwr limb, except ankle and foot, init enc **384**
T24.29[1,2,9]S	Burn of 2nd degree of multi sites of [rt, lt, unsp] lwr limb, except ankle and foot, seq **232**
T24.29[1,2,9]D	Burn of 2nd degree of multi sites of [rt, lt, unsp] lwr limb, except ankle and foot, subsq enc **402**
T22.29[1,2,9]A	Burn of 2nd degree of multi sites of [rt, lt, unsp] shldr and upr limb, except wrist and hand, init enc **383**
T22.29[1,2,9]S	Burn of 2nd degree of multi sites of [rt, lt, unsp] shldr and upr limb, except wrist and hand, seq **231**
T22.29[1,2,9]D	Burn of 2nd degree of multi sites of [rt, lt, unsp] shldr and upr limb, except wrist and hand, subsq enc **401**
T23.29[1,2,9]A	Burn of 2nd degree of multi sites of [rt, lt, unsp] wrist and hand, init enc **383**
T23.29[1,2,9]S	Burn of 2nd degree of multi sites of [rt, lt, unsp] wrist and hand, seq **232**
T23.29[1,2,9]D	Burn of 2nd degree of multi sites of [rt, lt, unsp] wrist and hand, subsq enc **401**
T21.29XS	Burn of 2nd degree of oth site of trunk, seq **231**
T23.22[1,2,9]A	Burn of 2nd degree of single [rt, lt, unsp] finger (nail) except thumb, init enc **383**
T23.22[1,2,9]S	Burn of 2nd degree of single [rt, lt, unsp] finger (nail) except thumb, seq **232**
T23.22[1,2,9]D	Burn of 2nd degree of single [rt, lt, unsp] finger (nail) except thumb, subsq enc **401**
T21.20XS	Burn of 2nd degree of trunk, unsp site, seq **231**
T24.20[1,2,9]A	Burn of 2nd degree of unsp site of [rt, lt, unsp] lwr limb, except ankle and foot, init enc **384**
T24.20[1,2,9]S	Burn of 2nd degree of unsp site of [rt, lt, unsp] lwr limb, except ankle and foot, seq **232**
T24.20[1,2,9]D	Burn of 2nd degree of unsp site of [rt, lt, unsp] lwr limb, except ankle and foot, subsq enc **402**
T20.39XA	Burn of 3rd deg mu sites of head, face, and neck, init **377, 379, 381, 382**
T20.39XS	Burn of 3rd deg mu sites of head, face, and neck, seq **230**
T20.39XD	Burn of 3rd deg mu sites of head, face, and neck, subs **400**
T21.3[1,2]XS	Burn of 3rd degree of [chest, abd] wall, seq **231**
T20.3[2,3,4,5,6,7] XA	Burn of 3rd degree of [lip(s), chin, nose (septum), scalp (any part), forehead and cheek, neck], init enc **377, 379, 381, 382**
T20.3[2,3,4]XS	Burn of 3rd degree of [lip(s), chin, nose (septum)], seq **230**

T20.3[2,3,4]XD	Burn of 3rd degree of [lip(s), chin, nose (septum)], subsq enc 400
T21.3[6,7]XS	Burn of 3rd degree of [male, female] genital rgn, seq 231
T25.31[1,2,9]A	Burn of 3rd degree of [rt, lt, unsp] ankle, init enc 377, 379, 381, 382
T25.31[1,2,9]S	Burn of 3rd degree of [rt, lt, unsp] ankle, seq 232
T25.31[1,2,9]D	Burn of 3rd degree of [rt, lt, unsp] ankle, subsq enc 402
T22.34[1,2,9]A	Burn of 3rd degree of [rt, lt, unsp] axilla, init enc 377, 379, 381, 382
T22.34[1,2,9]S	Burn of 3rd degree of [rt, lt, unsp] axilla, seq 231
T22.34[1,2,9]D	Burn of 3rd degree of [rt, lt, unsp] axilla, subsq enc 401
T20.31[1,2,9]A	Burn of 3rd degree of [rt, lt, unsp] ear (any part, except ear drum), init enc 377, 379, 381, 382
T20.31[1,2,9]S	Burn of 3rd degree of [rt, lt, unsp] ear (any part, except ear drum), seq 230
T20.31[1,2,9]D	Burn of 3rd degree of [rt, lt, unsp] ear [any part, except ear drum], subsq enc 400
T22.32[1,2,9]A	Burn of 3rd degree of [rt, lt, unsp] elbow, init enc 377, 379, 381, 382
T22.32[1,2,9]S	Burn of 3rd degree of [rt, lt, unsp] elbow, seq 231
T22.32[1,2,9]D	Burn of 3rd degree of [rt, lt, unsp] elbow, subsq enc 401
T25.32[1,2,9]A	Burn of 3rd degree of [rt, lt, unsp] foot, init enc 377, 379, 381, 382
T25.32[1,2,9]S	Burn of 3rd degree of [rt, lt, unsp] foot, seq 232
T25.32[1,2,9]D	Burn of 3rd degree of [rt, lt, unsp] foot, subsq enc 402
T22.31[1,2,9]A	Burn of 3rd degree of [rt, lt, unsp] forearm, init enc 377, 379, 381, 382
T22.31[1,2,9]S	Burn of 3rd degree of [rt, lt, unsp] forearm, seq 231
T22.31[1,2,9]D	Burn of 3rd degree of [rt, lt, unsp] forearm, subsq enc 401
T23.30[1,2,9]A	Burn of 3rd degree of [rt, lt, unsp] hand, unsp site, init enc 377, 379, 381, 382
T23.30[1,2,9]S	Burn of 3rd degree of [rt, lt, unsp] hand, unsp site, seq 232
T23.30[1,2,9]D	Burn of 3rd degree of [rt, lt, unsp] hand, unsp site, subsq enc 401
T24.32[1,2,9]A	Burn of 3rd degree of [rt, lt, unsp] knee, init enc 377, 379, 381, 382
T24.32[1,2,9]S	Burn of 3rd degree of [rt, lt, unsp] knee, seq 232
T24.32[1,2,9]D	Burn of 3rd degree of [rt, lt, unsp] knee, subsq enc 402
T24.33[1,2,9]A	Burn of 3rd degree of [rt, lt, unsp] lwr leg, init enc 377, 379, 381, 382
T24.33[1,2,9]S	Burn of 3rd degree of [rt, lt, unsp] lwr leg, seq 232
T24.33[1,2,9]D	Burn of 3rd degree of [rt, lt, unsp] lwr leg, subsq enc 402
T23.35[1,2,9]A	Burn of 3rd degree of [rt, lt, unsp] palm, init enc 377, 379, 381, 382
T23.35[1,2,9]S	Burn of 3rd degree of [rt, lt, unsp] palm, seq 232
T23.35[1,2,9]D	Burn of 3rd degree of [rt, lt, unsp] palm, subsq enc 401
T22.36[1,2,9]A	Burn of 3rd degree of [rt, lt, unsp] scapular rgn, init enc 377, 379, 381, 382
T22.36[1,2,9]S	Burn of 3rd degree of [rt, lt, unsp] scapular rgn, seq 231
T22.36[1,2,9]D	Burn of 3rd degree of [rt, lt, unsp] scapular rgn, subsq enc 401
T22.35[1,2,9]A	Burn of 3rd degree of [rt, lt, unsp] shldr, init enc 377, 379, 381, 382
T22.35[1,2,9]S	Burn of 3rd degree of [rt, lt, unsp] shldr, seq 231
T22.35[1,2,9]D	Burn of 3rd degree of [rt, lt, unsp] shldr, subsq enc 401
T24.31[1,2,9]A	Burn of 3rd degree of [rt, lt, unsp] thigh, init enc 377, 379, 381, 382
T24.31[1,2,9]S	Burn of 3rd degree of [rt, lt, unsp] thigh, seq 232
T24.31[1,2,9]D	Burn of 3rd degree of [rt, lt, unsp] thigh, subsq enc 402
T23.31[1,2,9]A	Burn of 3rd degree of [rt, lt, unsp] thumb (nail), init enc 377, 379, 381, 382
T23.31[1,2,9]S	Burn of 3rd degree of [rt, lt, unsp] thumb (nail), seq 232
T23.31[1,2,9]D	Burn of 3rd degree of [rt, lt, unsp] thumb (nail), subsq enc 401
T25.33[1,2,9]A	Burn of 3rd degree of [rt, lt, unsp] toe(s) (nail), init enc 377, 379, 381, 382
T25.33[1,2,9]S	Burn of 3rd degree of [rt, lt, unsp] toe(s) (nail), seq 232
T25.33[1,2,9]D	Burn of 3rd degree of [rt, lt, unsp] toe(s) (nail), subsq enc 402
T22.33[1,2,9]A	Burn of 3rd degree of [rt, lt, unsp] upr arm, init enc 377, 379, 381, 382
T22.33[1,2,9]S	Burn of 3rd degree of [rt, lt, unsp] upr arm, seq 231
T22.33[1,2,9]D	Burn of 3rd degree of [rt, lt, unsp] upr arm, subsq enc 401
T23.37[1,2,9]A	Burn of 3rd degree of [rt, lt, unsp] wrist, init enc 377, 379, 381, 382
T23.37[1,2,9]S	Burn of 3rd degree of [rt, lt, unsp] wrist, seq 232
T23.37[1,2,9]D	Burn of 3rd degree of [rt, lt, unsp] wrist, subsq enc 401
T20.3[5,6,7]XS	Burn of 3rd degree of [scalp [any part], forehead and cheek, neck], seq 230
T20.3[5,6,7]XD	Burn of 3rd degree of [scalp [any part], forehead and cheek, neck], subsq enc 400
T21.3[0,1,2,3,4,5, 6,7,9]XA	Burn of 3rd degree of [trunk, unsp site, chest wall, abd wall, upr back, lwr back, buttock, male genital rgn, femal genital rgn, oth site of trunk], init enc 377, 379, 381, 382
T21.3[0,1,2,3,4,5, 6,7,9]XD	Burn of 3rd degree of [unsp site of trunk, chest wall, abd wall, upr back, lwr back, buttock, male genital rgn, female genital rgn, oth site of trunk], subsq enc 400
T21.3[3,4,5]XS	Burn of 3rd degree of [upr back, lwr back, buttock], seq 231
T23.36[1,2,9]A	Burn of 3rd degree of back of [rt, lt, unsp] hand, init enc 377, 379, 381, 382
T23.36[1,2,9]S	Burn of 3rd degree of back of [rt, lt, unsp] hand, seq 232
T23.36[1,2,9]D	Burn of 3rd degree of back of [rt, lt, unsp] hand, subsq enc 401
T23.34[1,2,9]A	Burn of 3rd degree of multi [rt, lt, unsp] fingers (nail), incl* thumb, init enc 377, 379, 381, 382
T23.34[1,2,9]S	Burn of 3rd degree of multi [rt, lt, unsp] fingers (nail), incl* thumb, seq 232
T23.34[1,2,9]D	Burn of 3rd degree of multi [rt, lt, unsp] fingers (nail), incl* thumb, subsq enc 401
T23.33[1,2,9]A	Burn of 3rd degree of multi [rt, lt, unsp] fingers (nail), not incl* thumb, init enc 377, 379, 381, 382
T23.33[1,2,9]S	Burn of 3rd degree of multi [rt, lt, unsp] fingers (nail), not incl* thumb, seq 232
T23.33[1,2,9]D	Burn of 3rd degree of multi [rt, lt, unsp] fingers (nail), not incl* thumb, subsq enc 401
T25.39[1,2,9]S	Burn of 3rd degree of multi sites of [rt, lt, unsp] ankle & foot, seq 232
T25.39[1,2,9]A	Burn of 3rd degree of multi sites of [rt, lt, unsp] ankle and foot, init enc 377, 379, 381, 382
T25.39[1,2,9]D	Burn of 3rd degree of multi sites of [rt, lt, unsp] ankle and foot, subsq enc 402
T24.39[1,2,9]A	Burn of 3rd degree of multi sites of [rt, lt, unsp] lwr limb, except ankle and foot, init enc 377, 379, 381, 382
T24.39[1,2,9]S	Burn of 3rd degree of multi sites of [rt, lt, unsp] lwr limb, except ankle and foot, seq 232
T24.39[1,2,9]D	Burn of 3rd degree of multi sites of [rt, lt, unsp] lwr limb, except ankle and foot, subsq enc 402
T22.39[1,2,9]A	Burn of 3rd degree of multi sites of [rt, lt, unsp] shldr and upr limb, except wrist and hand, init enc 377, 379, 381, 382
T22.39[1,2,9]S	Burn of 3rd degree of multi sites of [rt, lt, unsp] shldr and upr limb, except wrist and hand, seq 231
T22.39[1,2,9]D	Burn of 3rd degree of multi sites of [rt, lt, unsp] shldr and upr limb, except wrist and hand, subsq enc 401
T23.39[1,2,9]A	Burn of 3rd degree of multi sites of [rt, lt, unsp] wrist and hand, init enc 377, 379, 381, 382
T23.39[1,2,9]S	Burn of 3rd degree of multi sites of [rt, lt, unsp] wrist and hand, seq 232
T23.39[1,2,9]D	Burn of 3rd degree of multi sites of [rt, lt, unsp] wrist and hand, subsq enc 401
T21.39XS	Burn of 3rd degree of oth site of trunk, seq 231
T23.32[1,2,9]A	Burn of 3rd degree of single [rt, lt, unsp] finger (nail) except thumb, init enc 377, 379, 381, 382
T23.32[1,2,9]S	Burn of 3rd degree of single [rt, lt, unsp] finger (nail) except thumb, seq 232
T23.32[1,2,9]D	Burn of 3rd degree of single [rt, lt, unsp] finger (nail) except thumb, subsq enc 401
T21.30XS	Burn of 3rd degree of trunk, unsp site, seq 231
T24.30[1,2,9]A	Burn of 3rd degree of unsp site of [rt, lt, unsp] lwr limb, except ankle and foot, init enc 377, 379, 381, 382
T24.30[1,2,9]S	Burn of 3rd degree of unsp site of [rt, lt, unsp] lwr limb, except ankle and foot, seq 232
T24.30[1,2,9]D	Burn of 3rd degree of unsp site of [rt, lt, unsp] lwr limb, except ankle and foot, subsq enc 402
T26.1[0,1,2]XA	Burn of cornea and conjunctival sac, [unsp, rt, lt] eye, init enc 47
T26.1[0,1,2]XS	Burn of cornea and conjunctival sac, [unsp, rt, lt] eye, seq 233
T26.1[0,1,2]XD	Burn of cornea and conjunctival sac, [unsp, rt, lt] eye, subsq enc 402
T28.1XXA	Burn of esophagus, init enc 114
T28.1XXS	Burn of esophagus, seq 233
T28.1XXD	Burn of esophagus, subsq enc 402
T20.19XA	Burn of first deg mult sites of head, face, and neck, init 382
T20.19XD	Burn of first deg mult sites of head, face, and neck, subs 400
T21.19XS	Burn of first degree of oth site of trunk, seq 231
T21.10XS	Burn of first degree of trunk, unsp site, seq 231
T28.3XXA	Burn of int genitourinary organs, init enc 384
T28.3XXS	Burn of int genitourinary organs, seq 233
T28.3XXD	Burn of int genitourinary organs, subsq enc 402
T27.0XXA	Burn of larynx and trachea, init enc 381
T27.0XXS	Burn of larynx and trachea, seq 233

Code	Description
T27.0XXD	Burn of larynx and trachea, subsq enc 402
T28.0XXA	Burn of mouth and pharynx, init enc 6, 58
T28.0XXS	Burn of mouth and pharynx, seq 233
T28.0XXD	Burn of mouth and pharynx, subsq enc 402
T28.49XA	Burn of oth int organ, init enc 384
T28.49XS	Burn of oth int organ, seq 233
T28.49XD	Burn of oth int organ, subsq enc 402
T28.2XXS	Burn of oth parts of alimentary tract, seq 233
T28.2XXD	Burn of oth parts of alimentary tract, subs enc 402
T27.2XXA	Burn of oth parts of respiratory tract, init enc 381
T27.2XXD	Burn of oth parts of respiratory tract, subs enc 402
T27.3XXA	Burn of respiratory tract, part unsp, init enc 381
T27.3XXD	Burn of respiratory tract, part unsp, subs enc 402
T30.0	Burn of unsp body region, unsp degree 384
T20.09XA	Burn of unsp deg mult sites of head, face, and neck, init 382
T20.09XS	Burn of unsp deg mult sites of head, face, and neck, seq 230
T20.09XD	Burn of unsp deg mult sites of head, face, and neck, subs 400
T21.0[1,2]XS	Burn of unsp degree of [chest, abd] wall, seq 231
T20.0[2,3,4]XA	Burn of unsp degree of [lip(s), chin, nose (septum)], init enc 382
T20.0[2,3,4]XS	Burn of unsp degree of [lip(s), chin, nose (septum)], seq 230
T20.0[2,3,4]XD	Burn of unsp degree of [lip(s), chin, nose (septum)], subsq enc 400
T21.0[6,7]XS	Burn of unsp degree of [male, female] genital rgn, seq 231
T25.01[1,2,9]A	Burn of unsp degree of [rt, lt, unsp] ankle, init enc 384
T25.01[1,2,9]S	Burn of unsp degree of [rt, lt, unsp] ankle, seq 232
T25.01[1,2,9]D	Burn of unsp degree of [rt, lt, unsp] ankle, subsq enc 402
T22.04[1,2,9]A	Burn of unsp degree of [rt, lt, unsp] axilla, init enc 383
T22.04[1,2,9]S	Burn of unsp degree of [rt, lt, unsp] axilla, seq 231
T22.04[1,2,9]D	Burn of unsp degree of [rt, lt, unsp] axilla, subsq enc 400
T20.01[1,2,9]A	Burn of unsp degree of [rt, lt, unsp] ear [any part, except ear drum], init enc 382
T20.01[1,2,9]S	Burn of unsp degree of [rt, lt, unsp] ear [any part, except ear drum], seq 230
T20.01[1,2,9]D	Burn of unsp degree of [rt, lt, unsp] ear [any part, except ear drum], subsq enc 400
T22.02[1,2,9]A	Burn of unsp degree of [rt, lt, unsp] elbow, init enc 383
T22.02[1,2,9]S	Burn of unsp degree of [rt, lt, unsp] elbow, seq 231
T22.02[1,2,9]D	Burn of unsp degree of [rt, lt, unsp] elbow, subsq enc 400
T25.02[1,2,9]A	Burn of unsp degree of [rt, lt, unsp] foot, init enc 384
T25.02[1,2,9]S	Burn of unsp degree of [rt, lt, unsp] foot, seq 232
T25.02[1,2,9]D	Burn of unsp degree of [rt, lt, unsp] foot, subsq enc 402
T22.01[1,2,9]A	Burn of unsp degree of [rt, lt, unsp] forearm, init enc 383
T22.01[1,2,9]S	Burn of unsp degree of [rt, lt, unsp] forearm, seq 231
T22.01[1,2,9]D	Burn of unsp degree of [rt, lt, unsp] forearm, subsq enc 400
T23.00[1,2,9]A	Burn of unsp degree of [rt, lt, unsp] hand, unsp site, init enc 383
T23.00[1,2,9]S	Burn of unsp degree of [rt, lt, unsp] hand, unsp site, seq 231
T23.00[1,2,9]D	Burn of unsp degree of [rt, lt, unsp] hand, unsp site, subsq enc 401
T24.02[1,2,9]A	Burn of unsp degree of [rt, lt, unsp] knee, init enc 384
T24.02[1,2,9]S	Burn of unsp degree of [rt, lt, unsp] knee, seq 232
T24.02[1,2,9]D	Burn of unsp degree of [rt, lt, unsp] knee, subsq enc 402
T24.03[1,2,9]A	Burn of unsp degree of [rt, lt, unsp] lwr leg, init enc 384
T24.03[1,2,9]S	Burn of unsp degree of [rt, lt, unsp] lwr leg, seq 232
T24.03[1,2,9]D	Burn of unsp degree of [rt, lt, unsp] lwr leg, subsq enc 402
T23.05[1,2,9]A	Burn of unsp degree of [rt, lt, unsp] palm, init enc 383
T23.05[1,2,9]S	Burn of unsp degree of [rt, lt, unsp] palm, seq 231
T23.05[1,2,9]D	Burn of unsp degree of [rt, lt, unsp] palm, subsq enc 401
T22.06[1,2,9]A	Burn of unsp degree of [rt, lt, unsp] scapular rgn, init enc 383
T22.06[1,2,9]S	Burn of unsp degree of [rt, lt, unsp] scapular rgn, seq 231
T22.06[1,2,9]D	Burn of unsp degree of [rt, lt, unsp] scapular rgn, subsq enc 400
T22.05[1,2,9]A	Burn of unsp degree of [rt, lt, unsp] shldr, init enc 383
T22.05[1,2,9]S	Burn of unsp degree of [rt, lt, unsp] shldr, seq 231
T22.05[1,2,9]D	Burn of unsp degree of [rt, lt, unsp] shldr, subsq enc 400
T24.01[1,2,9]A	Burn of unsp degree of [rt, lt, unsp] thigh, init enc 384
T24.01[1,2,9]S	Burn of unsp degree of [rt, lt, unsp] thigh, seq 232
T24.01[1,2,9]D	Burn of unsp degree of [rt, lt, unsp] thigh, subsq enc 402
T23.01[1,2,9]A	Burn of unsp degree of [rt, lt, unsp] thumb (nail), init enc 383
T23.01[1,2,9]S	Burn of unsp degree of [rt, lt, unsp] thumb (nail), seq 231
T23.01[1,2,9]D	Burn of unsp degree of [rt, lt, unsp] thumb (nail), subsq enc 401
T25.03[1,2,9]A	Burn of unsp degree of [rt, lt, unsp] toe(s) (nail), init enc 384
T25.03[1,2,9]S	Burn of unsp degree of [rt, lt, unsp] toe(s) (nail), seq 232
T25.03[1,2,9]D	Burn of unsp degree of [rt, lt, unsp] toe(s) (nail), subsq enc 402
T22.03[1,2,9]A	Burn of unsp degree of [rt, lt, unsp] upr arm, init enc 383
T22.03[1,2,9]S	Burn of unsp degree of [rt, lt, unsp] upr arm, seq 231
T22.03[1,2,9]D	Burn of unsp degree of [rt, lt, unsp] upr arm, subsq enc 400
T23.07[1,2,9]A	Burn of unsp degree of [rt, lt, unsp] wrist, init enc 383
T23.07[1,2,9]S	Burn of unsp degree of [rt, lt, unsp] wrist, seq 231
T23.07[1,2,9]D	Burn of unsp degree of [rt, lt, unsp] wrist, subsq enc 401
T20.0[5,6,7]XS	Burn of unsp degree of [scalp [any part], forehead and cheek, neck], seq 230
T20.0[5,6,7]XD	Burn of unsp degree of [scalp [any part], forehead and cheek, neck], subsq enc 400
T20.0[5,6,7]XA	Burn of unsp degree of [scalp [any part], forehead and cheek, neck], init enc 382
T21.0[0,1,2,3,4,5,6,7,9]XA	Burn of unsp degree of [unsp site of trunk, chest wall, abd wall, upr back, lwr back, buttock, male genital rgn, female genital rgn, oth site of trunk], init enc 383
T21.0[0,1,2,3,4,5,6,7,9]XD	Burn of unsp degree of [unsp site of trunk, chest wall, abd wall, upr back, lwr back, buttock, male genital rgn, female genital rgn, oth site of trunk], subsq enc 400
T21.0[3,4,5]XS	Burn of unsp degree of [upr back, lwr back, buttock], seq 231
T23.06[1,2,9]A	Burn of unsp degree of back of [rt, lt, unsp] hand, init enc 383
T23.06[1,2,9]S	Burn of unsp degree of back of [rt, lt, unsp] hand, seq 231
T23.06[1,2,9]D	Burn of unsp degree of back of [rt, lt, unsp] hand, subsq enc 401
T20.00XA	Burn of unsp degree of head, face, and neck, unsp site, init 382
T20.00XD	Burn of unsp degree of head, face, and neck, unsp site, subs 400
T23.04[1,2,9]A	Burn of unsp degree of multi [rt, lt, unsp] fingers (nail), incl* thumb, init enc 383
T23.04[1,2,9]S	Burn of unsp degree of multi [rt, lt, unsp] fingers (nail), incl* thumb, seq 231
T23.04[1,2,9]D	Burn of unsp degree of multi [rt, lt, unsp] fingers (nail), incl* thumb, subsq enc 401
T23.03[1,2,9]A	Burn of unsp degree of multi [rt, lt, unsp] fingers (nail), not incl* thumb, init enc 383
T23.03[1,2,9]S	Burn of unsp degree of multi [rt, lt, unsp] fingers (nail), not incl* thumb, seq 231
T23.03[1,2,9]D	Burn of unsp degree of multi [rt, lt, unsp] fingers (nail), not incl* thumb, subsq enc 401
T25.09[1,2,9]A	Burn of unsp degree of multi sites of [rt, lt, unsp] ankle and foot, init enc 384
T25.09[1,2,9]S	Burn of unsp degree of multi sites of [rt, lt, unsp] ankle and foot, seq 232
T25.09[1,2,9]D	Burn of unsp degree of multi sites of [rt, lt, unsp] ankle and foot, subsq enc 402
T24.09[1,2,9]A	Burn of unsp degree of multi sites of [rt, lt, unsp] lwr limb, except ankle and foot, init enc 384
T24.09[1,2,9]S	Burn of unsp degree of multi sites of [rt, lt, unsp] lwr limb, except ankle and foot, seq 232
T24.09[1,2,9]D	Burn of unsp degree of multi sites of [rt, lt, unsp] lwr limb, except ankle and foot, subsq enc 402
T22.09[1,2,9]A	Burn of unsp degree of multi sites of [rt, lt, unsp] shldr and upr limb, except wrist and hand, init enc 383
T22.09[1,2,9]S	Burn of unsp degree of multi sites of [rt, lt, unsp] shldr and upr limb, except wrist and hand, seq 231
T22.09[1,2,9]D	Burn of unsp degree of multi sites of [rt, lt, unsp] shldr and upr limb, except wrist and hand, subsq enc 400
T23.09[1,2,9]A	Burn of unsp degree of multi sites of [rt, lt, unsp] wrist and hand, init enc 383
T23.09[1,2,9]S	Burn of unsp degree of multi sites of [rt, lt, unsp] wrist and hand, seq 231
T23.09[1,2,9]D	Burn of unsp degree of multi sites of [rt, lt, unsp] wrist and hand, subsq enc 401
T21.09XS	Burn of unsp degree of oth site of trunk, seq 231
T23.02[1,2,9]A	Burn of unsp degree of single [rt, lt, unsp] finger (nail) except thumb, init enc 383
T23.02[1,2,9]S	Burn of unsp degree of single [rt, lt, unsp] finger (nail) except thumb, seq 231
T23.02[1,2,9]D	Burn of unsp degree of single [rt, lt, unsp] finger (nail) except thumb, subsq enc 401
T21.00XS	Burn of unsp degree of trunk, unsp site, seq 231
T24.00[1,2,9]A	Burn of unsp degree of unsp site of [rt, lt, unsp] lwr limb, except ankle and foot, init enc 384
T24.00[1,2,9]S	Burn of unsp degree of unsp site of [rt, lt, unsp] lwr limb, except ankle and foot, seq 232
T24.00[1,2,9]D	Burn of unsp degree of unsp site of [rt, lt, unsp] lwr limb, except ankle and foot, subsq enc 402

Code	Description
T28.40XA	Burn of unsp int organ, init enc 384
T28.40XS	Burn of unsp int organ, seq 233
T28.40XD	Burn of unsp int organ, subsq enc 402
T22.00XA	Burn unsp deg of shldr/up lmb, ex wrs/hnd, unsp site, init 383
T22.00XS	Burn unsp deg of shldr/up lmb, ex wrs/hnd, unsp site, seq 231
T22.00XD	Burn unsp deg of shldr/up lmb, ex wrs/hnd, unsp site, subs 400
T20.00XS	Burn unsp degree of head, face, and neck, unsp site, seq 230
T26.2[0,1,2]XA	Burn w/ resulting rupture and destr of [unsp, rt, lt] eyeball, init enc 47, 377, 379, 381, 382
T26.2[0,1,2]XS	Burn w/ resulting rupture and destr of [unsp, rt, lt] eyeball, seq 233
T26.2[0,1,2]XD	Burn w/ resulting rupture and destr of [unsp, rt, lt] eyeball, subsq enc 402
T28.[2,7]XXA	[Burn, Corrosion] of oth parts of alimentary tract, init enc 118
T31.[1,2,3,4,5,6, 7,8,9]0	Burns involving [10-19, 20-29, 30-39, 40-49, 50-59, 60-69, 70-79, 80-89, 90 or more]% of body surface w/ 0% to 9% 3rd degree burns 384
T32.[1,2,3,4,5,6, 7,8,9]0	Burns involving [10-19, 20-29, 30-39, 40-49, 50-59, 60-69, 70-79, 80-89, 90 or more]% of body surface w/ 0% to 9% 3rd degree corrosions 384
T31.2[1,2]	Burns involving 20-29% of body surface w/ [10-19, 20-29]% 3rd degree burns 379, 382
T31.3[1,2,3]	Burns involving 30-39% of body surface w/ [10-19, 20-29, 30-39]% 3rd degree burns 379, 382
T31.0	Burns involving < 10% of body surface 384
T31.4[1,2,3,4]	Burns involving 40-49% of body surface w/ [10-19, 20-29, 30-39, 40-49]% 3rd degree burns 379, 382
T31.5[1,2,3,4,5]	Burns involving 50-59% of body surface w/ [10-19, 20-29, 30-39, 40-49, 50-59]% 3rd degree burns 379, 382
T31.6[1,2,3,4,5,6]	Burns involving 60-69% of body surface w/ [10-19, 20-29, 30-39, 40-49, 50-59, 60-69]% 3rd degree burns 379, 382
T31.7[1,2,3,4,5,6, 7]	Burns involving 70-79% of body surface w/ [10-19, 20-29, 30-39, 40-49, 50-59, 60-69, 70-79]% 3rd degree burns 379, 382
T31.8[1,2,3,4,5,6, 7,8]	Burns involving 80-89% of body surface w/ [10-19, 20-29, 30-39, 40-49, 50-59, 60-69, 70-79, 80-89]% 3rd degree burns 379, 382
T31.9[1,2,3,4,5, 6,7,8,9]	Burns involving 90% or more of body surface w/ [10-19, 20-29, 30-39, 40-49, 50-59, 60-69, 70-79, 80-89, 90 or more]% 3rd degree burns 379, 382
T31.11	Burns of 10-19% of body surface w 10-19% 3rd degree burns 377, 379, 381, 382
T26.3[0,1,2]XA	Burns of oth spec parts of [unsp, rt, lt] eye and adnexa, init enc 47
T26.3[0,1,2]XS	Burns of oth spec parts of [unsp, rt, lt] eye and adnexa, seq 233
T26.3[0,1,2]XD	Burns of oth spec parts of [unsp, rt, lt] eye and adnexa, subsq enc 402
M70.1*	Bursitis of hand 167
S12.0[1,2]X[A,B,S]	Burst fx of 1st cervical vertebra, [stable, unstable], [init enc for clsd fx, init enc for opn fx, seq] 165
R64	Cachexia 385
L81.3	Cafe au lait spots 289
T70.3XX[A,S]	Caisson dz [decompression sickness], [init enc, seq] 374
T70.3XXD	Caisson dz, subsq enc 410
M77.3*	Calcaneal spur 194
M61*	Calcification and ossification of muscle 167
L94.2	Calcinosis cutis 234
N20*	Calculus of kidney and ureter 255
N21*	Calculus of lwr urinary tract 255
N42.0	Calculus of prostate 261
N22	Calculus of urinary tract in dz classified elsw 255
A83.5	California encephalitis 10, 15
B37.8[1,2,4]	Candidal [esophagitis, enteritis, otitis externa] 283
B37.83	Candidal cheilitis 2, 59
B37.41	Candidal cystitis and urethritis 264, 269
B37.6	Candidal endocarditis 99, 283, 438
B37.82	Candidal enteritis 116
B37.81	Candidal esophagitis 114
B37.5	Candidal meningitis 11, 15, 41, 283, 438
B37.84	Candidal otitis externa 58
B37.7	Candidal sepsis 309
B37.0	Candidal stomatitis 2, 59, 438
B37.8*	Candidiasis of oth sites 438
B37.4*	Candidiasis of oth urogenital sites 261
B37.2	Candidiasis of skin and nail 233, 438

Code	Description
B37.3	Candidiasis of vulva and vagina 264, 269
B37.9	Candidiasis, unsp 308, 438
T85.44XA	Capsular contracture of breast implant, init enc 224
H40.14*	Capsular glaucoma with pseudoexfoliation of lens 46
P12.81	Caput succedaneum 289
D01.3	Carcinoma in situ of anus and anal canal 115
D09.0	Carcinoma in situ of bladder 248, 255
D05*	Carcinoma in situ of breast 223
D02.2*	Carcinoma in situ of bronchus and lung 67
D06*	Carcinoma in situ of cervix uteri 263, 269
D01.0	Carcinoma in situ of colon 115
D01.9	Carcinoma in situ of digestive organ, unsp 115
D07.0	Carcinoma in situ of endometrium 263, 269
D00.1	Carcinoma in situ of esophagus 115
D09.2*	Carcinoma in situ of eye 45
D02.0	Carcinoma in situ of larynx 3, 57
D00.0*	Carcinoma in situ of lip, oral cavity and pharynx 3, 57
D01.5	Carcinoma in situ of liver, gallbladder and bile ducts 123
D07.3*	Carcinoma in situ of oth and unsp female genital organs 263, 269
D07.6*	Carcinoma in situ of oth and unsp male genital organs 258, 260
D01.4*	Carcinoma in situ of oth and unsp parts of intestine 115
D09.1*	Carcinoma in situ of oth and unsp urinary organs 248, 255
D02.3	Carcinoma in situ of oth parts of respiratory sys 67
D01.7	Carcinoma in situ of oth spec digestive organs 115
D09.8	Carcinoma in situ of oth spec sites 304, 305
D07.4	Carcinoma in situ of penis 258, 260
D07.5	Carcinoma in situ of prostate 258, 260
D01.1	Carcinoma in situ of rectosigmoid junction 115
D01.2	Carcinoma in situ of rectum 115
D02.4	Carcinoma in situ of respiratory sys, unsp 67
D04.1*	Carcinoma in situ of skin of eyelid, incl* canthus 45
D04.0	Carcinoma in situ of skin of lip 233
D04.7*	Carcinoma in situ of skin of lwr limb, incl* hip 233
D04.3*	Carcinoma in situ of skin of oth and unsp parts of face 233
D04.8	Carcinoma in situ of skin of oth sites 233
D04.4	Carcinoma in situ of skin of scalp and neck 233
D04.5	Carcinoma in situ of skin of trunk 233
D04.6*	Carcinoma in situ of skin of upr limb, incl* shldr 233
D04.9	Carcinoma in situ of skin, unsp 233
D00.2	Carcinoma in situ of stomach 115
D09.3	Carcinoma in situ of thyroid and oth endocrine glands 304, 305
D02.1	Carcinoma in situ of trachea 67
D07.2	Carcinoma in situ of vagina 263, 269
D07.1	Carcinoma in situ of vulva 263, 269
D04.2*	Carcinoma in situ skin of ear and ext auricular canal 233
D09.9	Carcinoma in situ, unsp 304, 305
O29.1[1,2]9	Cardiac [arrest, failure] d/t anesthesia druing preg, unsp trmstr 280
O29.1[1,2][1,2,3]	Cardiac [arrest, failure] d/t anesthesia during preg, [1st, 2nd, 3rd] trmstr 277
I46*	Cardiac arrest 99, 283
P29.81	Cardiac arrest of newborn 282
R01.1	Cardiac murmur, unsp 102
I51.0	Cardiac septal defect, acquired 103
R57.0	Cardiogenic shock 72, 99
I51.7	Cardiomegaly 102
I42*	Cardiomyopathy 103
I43	Cardiomyopathy in dz classified elsw 103, 283
P29.9	Cardiovasc d/o origin in the perinatal period, unsp 288
A52.00	Cardiovascular syphilis, unsp 103
G45.1	Carotid artery synd (hemispheric) 33
Z22.2	Carrier of diphtheria 412
Z22.6	Carrier of human T-lymphotropic virus type-1 infxn 412
Z22.4	Carrier of infections w sexl mode of transmiss 412
Z22.9	Carrier of infectious dz, unsp 412
Z22.8	Carrier of oth infectious dz 412
Z22.1	Carrier of oth intestinal infectious dz 412
Z22.3*	Carrier of oth spec bacterial dz 412
Z22.0	Carrier of typhoid 412
Z22.5*	Carrier of viral hepatitis 124
A28.1	Cat-scratch dz 294

H59.02*	Cataract (lens) fragments in eye following cataract surgery 46
H28	Cataract in dz classified elsw 46
G83.4	Cauda equina synd 34
M95.1*	Cauliflwr ear 58
I77.4	Celiac artery compression synd 116
K90.0	Celiac dz 116
K12.2	Cellulitis and abscess of mouth 4
L03*	Cellulitis and acute lymphangitis 206, 224
L03.2*	Cellulitis and acute lymphangitis of face and neck 4, 284
L03.1*	Cellulitis and acute lymphangitis of oth parts of limb 284
L03.8*	Cellulitis and acute lymphangitis of oth sites 284
L03.3*	Cellulitis and acute lymphangitis of trunk 284
L03.9*	Cellulitis and acute lymphangitis, unsp 284
H05.0[1,2,3,4][1,2,3,9]	[Cellulitis, Osteomyelitis, Periostitis, Tenonitis] of [rt, lt, bilat, unsp] orbit 45
A20.1	Cellulocutaneous plague 308
S73.04[1,2,3,4,5,6]A	Central [sublux, disloc] of [rt, lt, unsp] hip, init enc 426
H93.25	Central auditory processing d/o 311
S14.12[1,2,3,4,5,6,7,8,9][A,S]	Central cord synd at [C1, C2, C3, C4, C5, C6, C7, C8, unsp] lvl of cervical spinal cord, [init enc, seq] 32
S14.12[1,2,3,4,5,6,7,8,9]A	Central cord synd at [C1, C2, C3, C4, C5, C6, C7, C8, unsp] lvl of cervical spinal cord, init enc 420, 432
S14.12[1,2,3,4,5,6,7,8,9]D	Central cord synd at [C1, C2, C3, C4, C5, C6, C7, C8, unsp] lvl of cervical spinal cord, subsq enc 388
G37.1	Central demyelination of corpus callosum 33
S73.04[4,5,6]A	Central disloc of [rt, lt, unsp] hip, init enc 162
S73.04[4,5,6]S	Central disloc of [rt, lt, unsp] hip, seq 190
S73.04[4,5,6]D	Central disloc of [rt, lt, unsp] hip, subsq enc 397
A84.1	Central European tick-borne encephalitis 10, 15
K76.2	Central hemorrhagic necrosis of liver 124, 284
G89.0	Central pain synd 38
G37.2	Central pontine myelinolysis 33
G47.37	Central sleep apnea in conditions classified elsw 38
S73.04[1,2,3]A	Central sublux of [rt, lt, unsp] hip, init enc 162
S73.04[1,2,3]S	Central sublux of [rt, lt, unsp] hip, seq 190
S73.04[1,2,3]D	Central sublux of [rt, lt, unsp] hip, subsq enc 397
P12.0	Cephalhematoma d/t birth inj 288
B65.3	Cercarial dermatitis 233
G32.81	Cerebellar ataxia in dz classified elsw 32
G46.4	Cerebellar stroke synd 33
I68.0	Cerebral amyloid angiopathy 33
I67.1	Cerebral aneurysm, nonruptured 38
O29.219	Cerebral anoxia d/t anesth during preg, unsp trmstr 280
O29.21[1,2,3]	Cerebral anoxia d/t anesthesia during preg, [1st, 2nd, 3rd] trmstr 277
I68.2	Cerebral arteritis in oth dz classified elsw 41
I67.7	Cerebral arteritis, NEC 41
I67.2	Cerebral atherosclerosis 33
B45.1	Cerebral cryptococcosis 11, 15, 41
G93.0	Cerebral cysts 38
G93.6	Cerebral edema 35
P11.0	Cerebral edema d/t birth inj 282
I63*	Cerebral infarction 33, 284
I63.4*	Cerebral infarction d/t embolism of cerebral arteries 11, 15
I63.1*	Cerebral infarction d/t embolism of precerebral arteries 11, 15
I63.3*	Cerebral infarction d/t thrombosis of cerebral arteries 11, 15
I63.0*	Cerebral infarction d/t thrombosis of precerb arteries 11, 15
I63.9	Cerebral infarction, unsp 11, 15
I63.6	Cerebral infrc d/t cerebral venous thombos, nonpyogenic 11, 15
I63.5*	Cerebral infrc d/t unsp occlsn or stenosis of cerebral art 11, 15
I63.2*	Cerebral infrc d/t unsp occlsn or stenosis of precerb art 11, 15
I67.82	Cerebral ischemia 33
G80.9	Cerebral palsy, unsp 38
O22.5[1,2,3]	Cerebral venous thrombosis in preg, [1st, 2nd, 3rd] trmstr 273, 277
O22.50	Cerebral venous thrombosis in preg, unsp trmstr 280
O87.3	Cerebral venous thrombosis in the puerperium 274
G96.0	Cerebrospinal fluid leak 38, 283
G97.0	Cerebrospinal fluid leak from spinal punc 38, 283
I67.9	Cerebrovascular dz, unsp 33

R87.81[0,1]	Cervical [high, low] risk human papillomavirus (HPV) DNA test positive 265, 270
M50.13	Cervical disc d/o w radiculopathy, cervicothor region 165
M50.12	Cervical disc d/o w radiculopathy, mid-cervical region 165
M50.10	Cervical disc d/o w radiculopathy, unsp cervical region 165
M50.0*	Cervical disc d/o with myelopathy 165
M50.9*	Cervical disc d/o, unsp 165
Q76.5	Cervical rib 195
O26.87[2,3]	Cervical shortening, [2nd, 3rd] trmstr 277, 279
O26.879	Cervical shortening, unsp trmstr 280
M54.2	Cervicalgia 165
M53.1	Cervicobrachial synd 34
M53.0	Cervicocranial synd 34
A42.2	Cervicofacial actinomycosis 233
B57.3*	Chagas' dz (chr) with digestive sys involvement 308
B57.2	Chagas' dz (chr) with heart involvement 103
B57.4*	Chagas' dz (chr) with nervous sys involvement 308
B57.5	Chagas' dz (chr) with oth organ involvement 309
A57	Chancroid 261, 264, 269
R19.4	Change in bowel habit 116
R23.4	Changes in skin texture 234
A52.16	Charcot's arthropathy (tabetic) 32
K13.1	Cheek and lip biting 4
J95.4	Chemical pneumonitis d/t anesthesia 69, 284
R07.1	Chest pain on breathing 69
R07.9	Chest pain, unsp 103
P12.1	Chignon (from vacuum extract) d/t birth inj 288
A92.0	Chikungunya virus dz 307
T69.1XX[A,S]	Chilblains, [init enc, seq] 374
T69.1XXD	Chilblains, subsq enc 409
Z72.810	Child and adolescent antisocial behav 310
F93.9	Childhood emotional d/o, unsp 311
F80.81	Childhood onset fluency d/o 38
R68.83	Chills (w/o fever) 385
Q99.0	Chimera 46, XX/46, XY 261, 265, 270
A70	Chlamydia psittaci infections 307
A56.0[0,1,9]	Chlamydial [infxn of lwr genitourinary tract unsp, cystitis and urethritis, oth infxn of lwr genitourinary tract] 261
A74.0	Chlamydial conjunctivitis 45
A56.3	Chlamydial infxn of anus and rectum 116
A56.2	Chlamydial infxn of genitourinary tract, unsp 261, 264, 269
A56.0*	Chlamydial infxn of lwr genitourinary tract 264, 269
A56.1*	Chlamydial infxn of pelviperitoneum and oth GU organs 255
A56.4	Chlamydial infxn of pharynx 2, 57
A74.9	Chlamydial infxn, unsp 307
A55	Chlamydial lymphogranuloma (venereum) 261, 264, 269
L81.1	Chloasma 289
K83.0	Cholangitis 284
K81*	Cholecystitis 124
Q44.4	Choledochal cyst 124
K80*	Cholelithiasis 124
K65.3	Choleperitonitis 117
A00*	Cholera 114
H71*	Cholesteatoma of mid ear 58
H61.03[1,2,3,9]	Chondritis of [rt, lt, bilat, unsp] ext ear 193
M94.0	Chondrocostal junction synd [Tietze] 69
Q77.3	Chondrodysplasia punctata 195
Q77.6	Chondroectodermal dysplasia 195
M94.3*	Chondrolysis 194
M94.2*	Chondromalacia 167
O41.1[2,4][1,2,3,9][0,1,2,3,4,5,9]	[Chorioamnionitis, Placentitis], [1st, 2nd, 3rd, unsp] trmstr, fetus [N/A or unsp, 1, 2, 3, 4, 5, oth] 278
H32	Chorioretinal d/o in dz classified elsw 46
H30*	Chorioretinal inflam 46
D60.0	Chr acquired pure red cell aplasia 293
J70.1	Chr and oth pulmn manifestations d/t radiation 68
K04.5	Chr apical periodontitis 4
K29.41	Chr atrophic gastritis with bleeding 115
L12.2	Chr bullous dz of childhood 233

D73.2	Chr congestive splenomegaly 294	
K26.7	Chr duodenal ulcer w/o hemor or perforation 115	
J35.9	Chr dz of tonsils and adenoids, unsp 4, 58	
I82.5*	Chr embolism and thrombosis of deep veins of low extrm 100	
I82.7*	Chr embolism and thrombosis of veins of upr extr 100	
H04.03[1,2,3,9]	Chr enlrgment of [rt, lt, bilat, unsp] lacrimal gland 45	
K25.7	Chr gastric ulcer w/o hemor or perforation 115	
K28.7	Chr gastrojejunal ulcer w/o hemor or perforation 115	
K05.1*	Chr gingivitis 4	
M1A.3*	Chr gout d/t renal impairment 167	
M1A.9*	Chr gout, unsp 167	
D89.811	Chr graft-versus-host dz 293	
K73*	Chr hepatitis, NEC 124	
H05.1*	Chr inflam d/o of orbit 45	
H04.4*	Chr inflam of lacrimal passages 45	
M23.5*	Chr instability of knee 193	
A06.1	Chr intestinal amebiasis 114	
I25.9	Chr ischemic heart dz, unsp 102	
N18*	Chr kidney dz (CKD) 254	
N18.1	Chr kidney dz, stage 1 2	
N18.2	Chr kidney dz, stage 2 (mild) 2	
N18.3	Chr kidney dz, stage 3 (mod) 2	
N18.4	Chr kidney dz, stage 4 (severe) 2	
N18.5	Chr kidney dz, stage 5 2	
N18.9	Chr kidney dz, unsp 2	
J37.0	Chr laryngitis 4	
J37*	Chr laryngitis and laryngotracheitis 57	
J37.1	Chr laryngotracheitis 4	
C95.1*	Chr leukemia of unsp cell type 303, 305	
I88.1	Chr lymphadenitis, except mesenteric 294	
C91.1*	Chr lymphocytic leukemia of B-cell type 303, 305	
H70.1*	Chr mastoiditis 57	
G03.1	Chr meningitis 41	
A39.3	Chr meningococcemia 309	
M86.36[1,2,9]	Chr multifocal osteomyelitis, [rt, lt, unsp] tibia & fibula 131	
M86.38	Chr multifocal osteomyelitis, oth site 125	
C92.1*	Chr myeloid leukemia, BCR/ABL-positive 303, 305	
C93.1*	Chr myelomonocytic leukemia 303, 305	
D47.1	Chr myeloproliferative dz 295, 303, 305	
H73.1*	Chr myringitis 57	
J31.1	Chr nasopharyngitis 4	
N03*	Chr nephritic synd 256	
N11.1	Chr obstructive pyelonephritis 255	
K26.6	Chr or unsp duodenal ulcer w both hemor and perf 115	
K26.4	Chr or unsp duodenal ulcer with hemor 115	
K26.5	Chr or unsp duodenal ulcer with perforation 115	
K25.6	Chr or unsp gastric ulcer w both hemor and perf 115	
K25.4	Chr or unsp gastric ulcer with hemor 115	
K25.5	Chr or unsp gastric ulcer with perforation 115	
K28.6	Chr or unsp gastrojejunal ulcer w both hemor and perf 115	
K28.4	Chr or unsp gastrojejunal ulcer with hemor 115	
K28.5	Chr or unsp gastrojejunal ulcer with perforation 115	
K27.6	Chr or unsp peptic ulcer, site unsp, w both hemor and perf 115	
K27.4	Chr or unsp peptic ulcer, site unsp, with hemor 115	
K27.5	Chr or unsp peptic ulcer, site unsp, with perforation 115	
M86.46[1,2,9]	Chr osteomyelitis w/ draining sinus, [rt, lt, unsp] tibia & fibula 131	
M86.48	Chr osteomyelitis with draining sinus, oth site 125	
G89.4	Chr pain synd 38	
G89.2*	Chr pain, NEC 38	
N73.1	Chr parametritis and pelvic cellulitis 269	
K76.1	Chr passive congestion of liver 124	
K27.7	Chr peptic ulcer, site unsp, w/o hemor or perf 115	
K05.3*	Chr periodontitis 4	
J31.2	Chr pharyngitis 4	
B38.1	Chr pulmn coccidioidomycosis 67	
I27.82	Chr pulmn embolism 66, 283	
B39.1	Chr pulmn histoplasmosis capsulati 67	
J95.3	Chr pulmn insufficiency following surgery 68, 284, 381	
J68.4	Chr resp cond d/t chemicals, gases, fumes and vapors 68	
P27*	Chr respiratory dz origin in the perinatal period 68	

I09.2	Chr rheumatic pericarditis 103	
J31*	Chr rhinitis, nasopharyngitis and pharyngitis 57	
J32*	Chr sinusitis 57	
K29.31	Chr superf gastritis with bleeding 115	
E06.2	Chr thyroiditis with transient thyrotoxicosis 3	
J35.0*	Chr tonsillitis and adenoiditis 4, 57	
N11.9	Chr tubulo-interstitial nephritis, unsp 255, 285	
K55.1	Chr vascular d/o of intestine 117	
I87.3*	Chr venous hypertension (idiopathic) 100	
B18*	Chr viral hepatitis 124, 283	
B43*	Chromomycosis and pheomycotic abscess 308	
Q99.9	Chromosomal abnormality, unsp 412	
Q93.2	Chromosome replaced with ring, dicentric or isochromosome 412	
J94.0	Chylous effusion 68, 284	
R82.0	Chyluria 255, 285	
L66*	Cicatricial alopecia [scarring hair loss] 234	
L12.1	Cicatricial pemphigoid 223	
T61.0[1,2,3,4]XA	Ciguatera fish poison, [accid (unintentional), intentional self-harm, assault, undetermined], init enc 366	
T61.0[1,2,3,4]XS	Ciguatera fish poison, [accid (unintentional), intentional self-harm, assault, undetermined], seq 373	
T61.0[1,2,3,4]XD	Ciguatera fish poison, [accid (unintentional), intentional self-harm, assault, undetermined], subsq enc 408	
G47.2*	Circadian rhythm sleep d/o 3, 38	
O43.11[1,2,3]	Circumvallate placenta, [1st, 2nd, 3rd] trmstr 278	
O43.119	Circumvallate placenta, unsp trmstr 281	
Q37.4	Cleft hard and soft palate with bilat cleft lip 5	
Q37.5	Cleft hard and soft palate with unilat cleft lip 5	
Q35.1	Cleft hard palate 4	
Q37.0	Cleft hard palate with bilat cleft lip 5	
Q35.5	Cleft hard palate with cleft soft palate 4	
Q37.1	Cleft hard palate with unilat cleft lip 5	
Q36*	Cleft lip 59	
Q36.0	Cleft lip, bilat 5	
Q36.1	Cleft lip, median 5	
Q36.9	Cleft lip, unilat 5	
Q35*	Cleft palate 59	
Q37*	Cleft palate with cleft lip 59	
Q35.9	Cleft palate, unsp 5	
Q35.3	Cleft soft palate 4	
Q37.2	Cleft soft palate with bilat cleft lip 5	
Q37.3	Cleft soft palate with unilat cleft lip 5	
Q35.7	Cleft uvula 4	
R29.4	Clicking hip 167	
B66.1	Clonorchiasis 124	
R68.3	Clubbing of fingers 69	
Z20.7	Cntct w & expsr to pediculosis, acariasis & oth infestations 289	
D68.9	Coagulation defect, unsp 294	
J60	Coalworker's pneumoconiosis 68	
F14.23	Cocaine dependence with withdrawal 283	
B38*	Coccidioidomycosis 438	
B38.4	Coccidioidomycosis meningitis 11, 15, 41, 283	
B38.9	Coccidioidomycosis, unsp 308	
R41.841	Cognitive communication deficit 310	
P80.0	Cold inj synd 288	
M48.5[2,3]X[D,G]	Collapsed vertebra, NEC, [cervical, cervicothoracic] rgn, subsq enc for fx w/ [routine, delayed] healing 168	
M48.5[6,7]X[D,G]	Collapsed vertebra, NEC, [lumbar, lumbosacral] rgn, subsq enc for fx w/ [routine, delayed] healing 168	
M48.5[4,5]X[D,G]	Collapsed vertebra, NEC, [thoracic, thoracolumbar] rgn, subsq enc for fx w/ [routine, delayed] healing 168	
M48.5[0,1,2,3,4,5,6,7,8]XA	Collapsed vertebra, NEC, [unsp, occipito-atlanto-axial, cervical, cervicothoracic, thoracic, thoracolumbar, lumbar, lumbosacral, sacral and sacrococcygeal] rgn, init enc for fx 125, 163, 284	
M48.5[0,1,2,3,4,5,6,7,8]XS	Collapsed vertebra, NEC, [unsp, occipito-atlanto-axial, cervical, cervicothoracic, thoracic, thoracolumbar, lumbar, lumbosacral, sacral and sacrococcygeal] rgn, seq 165	
M48.51X[D,G]	Collapsed vertebra, NEC, occipito-atlanto-axial rgn, subsq enc for fx w/ [routine, delayed] healing 168	
M48.58X[D,G]	Collapsed vertebra, NEC, sacral and sacrococcygeal rgn, subsq enc for fx w/ [routine, delayed] healing 168	

Code	Description
M48.50X[D,G]	Collapsed vertebra, NEC, site unsp, subsq enc for fx w/ [routine, delayed] healing 167
S52.53[1,2,9] [D,E,F,G,H,J,S]	Colles' fx of [rt, lt, unsp] radius, [subsq enc for clsd fx w/ routine healing, subsq enc for opn fx type I or II w/ routine healing, subsq enc for opn fx type I or II w/ routine healing, subsq enc for clsd fx w/ delayed healing, subsq enc for opn fx type I or II w/ delayed healing, subsq enc for opn fx type IIIA, IIIB, or IIIC w/ delayed healing, seq] 174
S52.53[1,2,9] [A,B,C]	Colles' fx of [rt, lt, unsp] radius, init enc for [clsd fx, opn fx type I or II, opn fx type IIIA, IIIB, or IIIC] 186, 423
S52.53[1,2,9] [B,C]	Colles' fx of [rt, lt, unsp] radius, init enc for opn fx type [I or II, IIIA IIIB or IIIC] 434
S52.53[1,2,9] [K,M,N,P,Q,R]	Colles' fx of [rt, lt, unsp] radius, subsq enc for [clsd fx w/ nonu, opn fx type I or II w/ nonu, opn fx type IIIA, IIIB, or IIIC w/ nonu, clsd fx w/ malu, opn fx type I or II w/ malu, opn fx type IIIA, IIIB, or IIIC w/ malu] 198
H47.31*	Coloboma of optic disc 46
D83.0	Com variab immunodef w predom abnlt of B-cell nums & function 294
D83.1	Com variab immunodef w predom immunoreg T-cell d/o 294
R40.23[3,5,6] [0,1,2,3,4]	Coma scale, best motor response, [abnormal, localizes pain, obeys commands], [unsp time, in the field (EMT or ambulance), at arrival to emergency department, at hospital admission, 24 hrs or more after hospital admission] 412
R40.23[1,2,4] [0,1,2,3,4]	Coma scale, best motor response, [none, extension, flexion w/drawal], [unsp time, in the field (EMT or ambulance), at arrival to emergency department, at hospital admission, 24 hrs or more after hospital admission] 285
R40.232 [0,1,2,3,4]	Coma scale, best motor response, extension [unsp time, in the field (EMT or ambulance), at arrival to ED, at hospital admission, 24 hrs or more after hospital admission 35
R40.234 [0,1,2,3,4]	Coma scale, best motor response, flexion w/drawal [unsp time, in the field (EMT or ambulance), at arrival to ED, at hospital admission, 24 hrs or more after hospital admission 35
R40.231 [0,1,2,3,4]	Coma scale, best motor response, none [unsp time, in the field (EMT or ambulance), at arrival to ED, at hospital admission, 24 hrs or more after hospital admission] 35
R40.22[3,4,5] [0,1,2,3,4]	Coma scale, best verbal response, [inappropriate words, confused conversation, oriented], [unsp time, in the field (EMT or ambulance), at arrival to emergency department, at hospital admission, 24 hrs or more after hospital admission] 412
R40.22[1,2] [0,1,2,3,4]	Coma scale, best verbal response, [none, incomprhensible words, [unsp time, in the field (EMT or ambulance), at arrival to emergency department, at hospital admission, 24 hrs or more after hospital admission] 285
R40.222 [0,1,2,3,4]	Coma scale, best verbal response, incomprehensible words [unsp time, in the field (EMT or ambulance), at arrival to ED, at hospital admission, 24 hrs or more after hospital admission] 35
R40.221 [0,1,2,3,4]	Coma scale, best verbal response, none [unsp time, in the field (EMT or ambulance), at arrival to ED, at hospital admission, 24 hrs or more after hospital admission] 35
R40.21[1,2] [0,1,2,3,4]	Coma scale, eyes opn, [never, to pain], [unsp time, in the field (EMT or ambulance), at arrival to emergency department, at hospital admission, 24 hrs or more after hospital admission] 285
R40.21[3,4] [0,1,2,3,4]	Coma scale, eyes opn, [to sound, spontaneous], [unsp time, in the field (EMT or ambulance), at arrival to emergency department, at hospital admission, 24 hrs or more after hospital admission] 412
R40.211 [0,1,2,3,4]	Coma scale, eyes opn, never [unsp time, in the field (EMT or ambulance), at arrival to ED, at hospital admission, 24 hrs or more after hospital admission] 35
R40.212 [0,1,2,3,4]	Coma scale, eyes opn, to pain [unsp time, in the field (EMT or ambulance), at arrival to ED, at hospital admission, 24 hrs or more after hospital admission] 35
D81.9	Combined immunodef, unsp 293
D83.2	Common variable immunodef w autoantibodies to B- or T-cells 294
D83.9	Common variable immunodef, unsp 294
N98.9	Comp associated with artfcl fertilization, unsp 368
O04*	Comp following (induced) termination of preg 272, 276
O08*	Comp following ectopic and molar preg 272, 275
T81.71[0,1,8,9]A	Comp of [mesenteric, renal, oth, unsp] artery following a procedure, NEC, init enc 287
T81.71[0,1,8,9]S	Comp of [mesenteric, renal, oth, unsp] artery following a procedure, NEC, seq 375
T81.71[0,1,8,9]D	Comp of [mesenteric, renal, oth, unsp] artery following a procedure, NEC, subsq enc 410
T81.71[8,9]A	Comp of [oth, unsp] artery following a procedure, NEC, init enc 101

Code	Description
O74*	Comp of anesthesia during labor and delivery 273, 274
O29*	Comp of anesthesia during preg 276
O89*	Comp of anesthesia during the puerperium 272, 276
K94*	Comp of artfcl openings of the digestive sys 117
N98.2	Comp of attempt introduce of fertilized ovum fol in vitro 367
N98.3	Comp of attempted introduction of embryo in embryo transfer 368
K95*	Comp of bariatric procedures 117
T86.83*	Comp of bone graft 368
T86.0*	Comp of bone marrow transplant 293
T86.2*	Comp of heart transplant 103
T86.3*	Comp of heart-lung transplant 103
T81.81XA	Comp of inhalation therapy, init enc 368
T81.81XS	Comp of inhalation therapy, seq 375
T81.81XD	Comp of inhalation therapy, subsq enc 410
T86.85*	Comp of intestine transplant 124
T86.1*	Comp of kidney transplant 256
O75.9	Comp of labor and delivery, unsp 278, 280
T86.4*	Comp of liver transplant 124
T81.710A	Comp of mesent art following a procedure, NEC, init 118
T87.2	Comp of oth reattached body part 184
T87.1X[1,2,9]	Comp of reattached (part of) [rt, lt, unsp] lwr extr 184
T87.0X[1,2,9]	Comp of reattached (part of) [rt, lt, unsp] upr extr 184
T81.711A	Comp of renal artery following a procedure, NEC, init 256
T86.82*	Comp of skin graft (allograft) (autograft) 368
T86.5	Comp of stem cell transplant 368
N99.5*	Comp of stoma of urinary tract 256
T88.9XXA	Comp of surgical and medical care, unsp, init enc 368
T88.9XXS	Comp of surgical and medical care, unsp, seq 376
T88.9XXD	Comp of surgical and medical care, unsp, subs enc 411
O90*	Comp of the puerperium, unsp 272, 276
T86.9*	Comp of unsp transplanted organ and tissue 368
T81.72XA	Comp of vein following a procedure, NEC, init 101, 287
T81.72XS	Comp of vein following a procedure, NEC, seq 375
T81.72XD	Comp of vein following a procedure, NEC, subs 410
P96.5	Comp to newborn d/t (fetal) intrauterine procedure 288
T79.A0XA	Compartment synd, unsp, init enc 374, 430
T79.A0XS	Compartment synd, unsp, seq 361
T79.A0XD	Compartment synd, unsp, subsq enc 410
J98.3	Compensatory emphysema 69
S14.11[1,2,3,4,5, 6,7,8,9][A,S]	Complete lesion at [C1, C2, C3, C4, C5, C6, C7, C8, unsp] lvl of cervical spinal cord, [init enc, seq] 32
S14.11[1,2,3,4,5, 6,7,8,9]D	Complete lesion at [C1, C2, C3, C4, C5, C6, C7, C8, unsp] lvl of cervical spinal cord, subsq enc 388
S14.11[1,2,3,4,5, 6,7,8,9]A	Complete lesion at [C1,C2, C3, C4, C5, C6, C7, C8, unsp] lvl of cervical spinal cord, init enc 420, 432
S24.11[1,2,3,4,9] D	Complete lesion at [T1, T2-T6, T7-T10, T11-T12, unsp] lvl of thoracic spinal cord, subsq enc 389
S24.11[1,2,3,4,9] [A,S]	Complete lesion at [T1, T2-T6, T7-T10, T11-T12, unsp] lvl of thoracic spinal cord, [init enc, seq] 32
S24.11[1,2,3,4,9] A	Complete lesion at [T1, T2-T6, T7-T10, T11-T12, unsp] lvl of thoracic spinal cord, init enc 420, 433
S34.11[1,2,3,4,5, 9][A,S]	Complete lesion inj to [L1, L2, L3, L4, L5, unsp] lvl of lumbar spinal cord, [init enc, seq] 32
S34.11[1,2,3,4,5, 9]A	Complete lesion of [L1, L2, L3, L4, L5, unsp] lvl of lumbar spinal cord, init enc 433
S34.11[1,2,3,4,5, 9]D	Complete lesion of [L1, L2, L3, L4, L5, unsp] lvl of lumbar spinal cord, subsq enc 390
S34.13[1,2,9]A	[Complete lesion, Incomplete lesion, Unsp inj] (of) (to) sacral spinal cord, init enc 421, 433
S34.13[1,2,9]D	[Complete lesion, Incomplete lesion, Unsp inj] of sacral spinal cord, subsq enc 390
S34.13[1,2,9] [A,S]	[Complete lesion, Incomplete lesion, Unsp inj] to sacral spinal cord, [init enc, seq] 32
K08.1*	Complete loss of teeth 4
S48.01[1,2,9]D	Complete traum amp at [rt, lt, unsp] shldr jt, subsq enc 392
S58.01[1,2,9]D	Complete traum amp at elbow lvl, [rt, lt, unsp] arm, subsq enc 393
S48.11[1,2,9]D	Complete traum amp at lvl between [rt, lt, unsp] shldr and elbow, subsq enc 392
S58.11[1,2,9]D	Complete traum amp at lvl between elbow and wrist, [rt, lt, unsp] arm, subsq enc 393

S28.21[1,2,9] [A,S]	Complete traum amp of [rt, lt, unsp] breast, [init enc, seq] 226
S28.21[1,2,9]D	Complete traum amp of [rt, lt, unsp] breast, subsq enc 389
S08.11[1,2,9]A	Complete traum amp of [rt, lt, unsp] ear, init enc 58
S58.91[1,2,9]D	Complete traum amp of [rt, lt, unsp] forearm, lvl unsp, subsq enc 393
S48.91[1,2,9]D	Complete traum amp of [rt, lt, unsp] shldr and upr arm, lvl unsp, subsq enc 392
S08.811A	Complete traum amp of nose, init enc 5
S68.11[0,1,2,3,4, 5,6,7,8,9]S	Complete traum metacarpophalangeal amp of [rt index, lt index, rt mid, lt mid, rt ring, lt ring, rt little, lt little, oth, unsp] finger, seq 176
S68.61[0,1,2,3,4, 5,6,7,8,9]S	Complete traum transphalangeal amp of [rt index, lt index, rt mid, lt mid, rt ring, lt ring, rt little, lt little, oth, unsp] finger, seq 176
S34.1[1,2] [1,2,3,4,5,9]A	[Complete, Incomplete] lesion of [L1, L2, L3, L4, L5, unsp] lvl of lumbar spinal cord, init enc 421
S78.9[1,2][1,2,9]S	[Complete, Partial] traum amp at [rt, lt, unsp] hip & thigh, lvl unsp, seq 179
S78.0[1,2][1,2,9] A	[Complete, Partial] traum amp at [rt, lt, unsp] hip jt, init enc 360, 426, 436
S78.0[1,2][1,2,9]S	[Complete, Partial] traum amp at [rt, lt, unsp] hip jt, seq 179
S78.0[1,2][1,2,9] D	[Complete, Partial] traum amp at [rt, lt, unsp] hip jt, subsq enc 398
S48.0[1,2][1,2,9] A	[Complete, Partial] traum amp at [rt, lt, unsp] shldr jt, init enc 359, 423, 434
S48.0[1,2][1,2,9]S	[Complete, Partial] traum amp at [rt, lt, unsp] shldr jt, seq 171
S58.0[1,2][1,2,9] A	[Complete, Partial] traum amp at elbow lvl, [rt, lt, unsp] arm, init enc 360, 424, 435
S58.0[1,2][1,2,9]S	[Complete, Partial] traum amp at elbow lvl, [rt, lt, unsp] arm, seq 174
S88.0[1,2][1,2,9] A	[Complete, Partial] traum amp at knee lvl, [rt, lt, unsp] lwr leg, init enc 361, 428, 436
S88.0[1,2][1,2,9]S	[Complete, Partial] traum amp at knee lvl, [rt, lt, unsp] lwr leg, seq 182
S88.9[1,2][1,2,9]S	[Complete, Partial] traum amp at knee lvl, [rt, lt, unsp] lwr leg, seq 182
S88.0[1,2][1,2,9] D	[Complete, Partial] traum amp at knee lvl, [rt, lt, unsp] lwr leg, subsq enc 398
S78.1[1,2][1,2,9] A	[Complete, Partial] traum amp at lvl between [rt, lt, unsp] hip and knee, init enc 360, 426, 436
S78.1[1,2][1,2,9]S	[Complete, Partial] traum amp at lvl between [rt, lt, unsp] hip and knee, seq 179
S78.1[1,2][1,2,9] D	[Complete, Partial] traum amp at lvl between [rt, lt, unsp] hip and knee, subsq enc 398
S48.1[1,2][1,2,9] A	[Complete, Partial] traum amp at lvl between [rt, lt, unsp] shldr and elbow, init enc 359, 423, 434
S48.1[1,2][1,2,9]S	[Complete, Partial] traum amp at lvl between [rt, lt, unsp] shldr and elbow, seq 171
S58.1[1,2][1,2,9] A	[Complete, Partial] traum amp at lvl between elbow and wrist, [rt, lt, unsp] arm, init enc 360, 424, 435
S58.1[1,2][1,2,9]S	[Complete, Partial] traum amp at lvl between elbow and wrist, [rt, lt, unsp] arm, seq 174
S88.1[1,2][1,2,9] A	[Complete, Partial] traum amp at lvl between knee and ankle, [rt, lt, unsp] lwr leg, init enc 361, 428, 436
S88.1[1,2][1,2,9] D	[Complete, Partial] traum amp at lvl between knee and ankle, [rt, lt, unsp] lwr leg, subsq enc 398
S38.2[2,3][1,2]S	[Complete, Partial] traum amp of [penis, scrotum and testes], seq 227
S38.2[2,3][1,2]A	[Complete, Partial] traum amp of [penis, scrotum and testis], init enc 422
S28.2[1,2][1,2,9] A	[Complete, Partial] traum amp of [rt, lt, unsp] breast, init enc 421
S08.1[1,2][1,2,9] A	[Complete, Partial] traum amp of [rt, lt, unsp] ear, init enc 419
S08.1[1,2][1,2,9]S	[Complete, Partial] traum amp of [rt, lt, unsp] ear, seq 225
S08.1[1,2][1,2,9] D	[Complete, Partial] traum amp of [rt, lt, unsp] ear, subsq enc 387
S98.0[1,2][1,2,9] A	[Complete, Partial] traum amp of [rt, lt, unsp] foot at ankle lvl, init enc 361, 430, 437
S98.0[1,2] [1,2,9]S	[Complete, Partial] traum amp of [rt, lt, unsp] foot at ankle lvl, seq 183
S98.0[1,2] [1,2,9]D	[Complete, Partial] traum amp of [rt, lt, unsp] foot at ankle lvl, subsq enc 400
S98.9[1,2][1,2,9] A	[Complete, Partial] traum amp of [rt, lt, unsp] foot, lvl unsp, init enc 361, 430, 437

S98.9[1,2] [1,2,9]S	[Complete, Partial] traum amp of [rt, lt, unsp] foot, lvl unsp, seq 183
S98.9[1,2][1,2,9] D	[Complete, Partial] traum amp of [rt, lt, unsp] foot, lvl unsp, subsq enc 400
S58.9[1,2][1,2,9] A	[Complete, Partial] traum amp of [rt, lt, unsp] forearm, lvl unsp, init enc 360, 424, 435
S58.9[1,2][1,2,9]S	[Complete, Partial] traum amp of [rt, lt, unsp] forearm, lvl unsp, seq 174
S98.1[1,2][1,2,9] A	[Complete, Partial] traum amp of [rt, lt, unsp] great toe, init enc 361, 430
S98.1[1,2][1,2,9]S	[Complete, Partial] traum amp of [rt, lt, unsp] great toe, seq 183
S98.1[1,2] [1,2,9]D	[Complete, Partial] traum amp of [rt, lt, unsp] great toe, subsq enc 400
S68.4[1,2][1,2,9] A	[Complete, Partial] traum amp of [rt, lt, unsp] hand at wrist lvl, init enc 360, 426, 435
S68.4[1,2][1,2,9]S	[Complete, Partial] traum amp of [rt, lt, unsp] hand at wrist lvl, seq 176
S68.4[1,2][1,2,9] D	[Complete, Partial] traum amp of [rt, lt, unsp] hand at wrist lvl, subsq enc 397
S78.9[1,2][1,2,9] A	[Complete, Partial] traum amp at [rt, lt, unsp] hip & thigh, lvl unsp, init enc 360, 426, 436
S78.9[1,2][1,2,9] D	[Complete, Partial] traum amp at [rt, lt, unsp] hip & thigh, lvl unsp, subsq enc 398
S88.9[1,2][1,2,9] A	[Complete, Partial] traum amp of [rt, lt, unsp] lwr leg, lvl unsp, init enc 361, 428, 436
S88.1[1,2][1,2,9]S	[Complete, Partial] traum amp of [rt, lt, unsp] lwr leg, lvl unsp, seq 182
S88.9[1,2][1,2,9] D	[Complete, Partial] traum amp of [rt, lt, unsp] lwr leg, lvl unsp, subsq enc 398
S98.3[1,2][1,2,9] A	[Complete, Partial] traum amp of [rt, lt, unsp] midfoot, init enc 361, 430, 437
S98.3[1,2][1,2,9]S	[Complete, Partial] traum amp of [rt, lt, unsp] midfoot, seq 183
S98.3[1,2][1,2,9] D	[Complete, Partial] traum amp of [rt, lt, unsp] midfoot, subsq enc 400
S48.9[1,2][1,2,9] A	[Complete, Partial] traum amp of [rt, lt, unsp] shldr and upr arm, lvl unsp, init enc 359, 423, 434
S48.9[1,2][1,2,9]S	[Complete, Partial] traum amp of [rt, lt, unsp] shldr and upr arm, lvl unsp, seq 171
S38.21[1,2]A	[Complete, Partial] traum amp of female ext genital organs, init enc 265, 270, 422
S38.21[1,2]S	[Complete, Partial] traum amp of female ext genital organs, seq 227
S38.21[1,2]D	[Complete, Partial] traum amp of female ext genital organs, subsq enc 391
S08.81[1,2]A	[Complete, Partial] traum amp of nose, init enc 58, 419
S08.81[1,2]S	[Complete, Partial] traum amp of nose, seq 225
S08.81[1,2]D	[Complete, Partial] traum amp of nose, subsq enc 387
S98.1[3,4][1,2,9] A	[Complete, Partial] traum amp of one [rt, lt, unsp] lesser toe, init enc 361, 430
S98.1[3,4][1,2,9]S	[Complete, Partial] traum amp of one [rt, lt, unsp] lesser toe, seq 183
S98.1[3,4][1,2,9] D	[Complete, Partial] traum amp of one [rt, lt, unsp] lesser toe, subsq enc 400
S38.22[1,2]A	[Complete, Partial] traum amp of penis, init enc 261
S38.22[1,2]D	[Complete, Partial] traum amp of penis, subsq enc 391
S38.23[1,2]A	[Complete, Partial] traum amp of scrotum and testis, init enc 261
S38.23[1,2]D	[Complete, Partial] traum amp of scrotum and testis, subsq enc 391
S98.2[1,2][1,2,9] A	[Complete, Partial] traum amp of two or more [rt, lt, unsp] lesser toes, init enc 361, 430
S98.2[1,2][1,2,9]S	[Complete, Partial] traum amp of two or more [rt, lt, unsp] lesser toes, seq 183
S98.2[1,2][1,2,9] D	[Complete, Partial] traum amp of two or more [rt, lt, unsp] lesser toes, subsq enc 400
S68.1[1,2] [0,1,2,3,4,5,6,7, 8,9]A	[Complete, Partial] traum metacarpophalangeal amp of [rt index, lt index, rt mid, lt mid, rt ring, lt ring, rt little, lt little, oth, unsp] finger, init enc 360, 426
S68.1[1,2] [0,1,2,3,4,5,6,7, 8,9]D	[Complete, Partial] traum metacarpophalangeal amp of [rt index, lt index, rt mid, lt mid, rt ring, lt ring, rt little, lt little, oth, unsp] finger, subsq enc 397
S68.0[1,2][1,2,9] A	[Complete, Partial] traum metacarpophalangeal amp of [rt, lt, unsp] thumb, init enc 360, 426
S68.0[1,2][1,2,9]S	[Complete, Partial] traum metacarpophalangeal amp of [rt, lt, unsp] thumb, seq 176

Code	Description
S68.0[1,2][1,2,9]D	Complete, Partial] traum metacarpophalangeal amp of [rt, lt, unsp] thumb, subsq enc 397
S68.7[1,2][1,2,9]A	[Complete, Partial] traum transmetacarpal amp of [rt, lt, unsp] hand, init enc 360, 426, 435
S68.7[1,2][1,2,9]S	[Complete, Partial] traum transmetacarpal amp of [rt, lt, unsp] hand, seq 176
S68.7[1,2][1,2,9]D	[Complete, Partial] traum transmetacarpal amp of [rt, lt, unsp] hand, subsq enc 397
S68.6[1,2][0,1,2,3,4,5,6,7,8,9]A	[Complete, Partial] traum transphalangeal amp of [rt index, lt index, rt mid, lt mid, rt ring, lt ring, rt little, lt little, oth, unsp] finger, init enc 360, 426
S68.6[1,2][0,1,2,3,4,5,6,7,8,9]D	[Complete, Partial] traum transphalangeal amp of [rt index, lt index, rt mid, lt mid, rt ring, lt ring, rt little, lt little, oth, unsp] finger, subsq enc 397
S68.5[1,2][1,2,9]A	[Complete, Partial] traum transphalangeal amp of [rt, lt, unsp] thumb, init enc 360, 426
S68.5[1,2][1,2,9]S	[Complete, Partial] traum transphalangeal amp of [rt, lt, unsp] thumb, seq 176
S68.5[1,2][1,2,9]D	[Complete, Partial] traum transphalangeal amp of [rt, lt, unsp] thumb, subsq enc 397
G90.5*	Complex regional pain synd I (CRPS I) 34
S83.27[1,2,9][A,S]	Complex tear of lat meniscus, current inj, [rt, lt, unsp] knee, [init enc, seq] 192
S83.27[1,2,9]A	Complex tear of lat meniscus, current inj, [rt, lt, unsp] knee, init enc 428
S83.27[1,2,9]D	Complex tear of lat meniscus, current inj, [rt, lt, unsp] knee, subsq enc 398
S83.23[1,2,9][A,S]	Complex tear of med meniscus, current inj, [rt, lt, unsp] knee, [init enc, seq] 192
S83.23[1,2,9]A	Complex tear of med meniscus, current inj, [rt, lt, unsp] knee, init enc 428
S83.23[1,2,9]D	Complex tear of med meniscus, current inj, [rt, lt, unsp] knee, subsq enc 398
G93.5	Compression of brain 35
I87.1	Compression of vein 100
G37.5	Concentric sclerosis [Balo] of central nervous sys 33
S34.0[1,2]X[A,S]	Concussion and edema of [lumbar, sacral] spinal cord, [init enc, seq] 32
S34.0[1,2]XA	Concussion and edema of [lumbar, sacral] spinal cord, init enc 421, 433
S34.0[1,2]XD	Concussion and edema of [lumbar, sacral] spinal cord, subsq enc 390
S14.0XX[A,S]	Concussion and edema of cervical spinal cord, [init enc, seq] 32
S14.0XXA	Concussion and edema of cervical spinal cord, init enc 419, 432
S14.0XXD	Concussion and edema of cervical spinal cord, subs enc 388
S24.0XX[A,S]	Concussion and edema of thoracic spinal cord, [init enc, seq] 32
S24.0XXA	Concussion and edema of thoracic spinal cord, init enc 420, 433
S24.0XXD	Concussion and edema of thoracic spinal cord, subs enc 389
S06.0X[5,6]A	Concussion w/ LOC > 24 hrs [w/, w/o] return to pre-existing conscious lvl, init enc 38, 418, 430
S06.0X[5,6]S	Concussion w/ LOC of [> 24 hrs w/ return to pre-existing conscious lvl, > 24 hrs w/o return to pre-existing conscious lvl w/ patient surviving], seq 39
S06.0X[5,6]D	Concussion w/ LOC of [> 24 hrs w/ return to pre-existing conscious lvl, > 24 hrs w/o return to pre-existing conscious lvl w/ patient surviving], subsq enc 386
S06.0X[3,4]A	Concussion w/ LOC of [1 hr to 5 hrs 59 min, 6 hrs to 24 hrs], init enc 430
S06.0X[1,2,3,4]A	Concussion w/ LOC of [30 min or less, 31 min to 59 min, 1 hr to 5 hrs 59 min, 6 hrs to 24 hrs], init enc 38, 418
S06.0X[1,2,3,4]S	Concussion w/ LOC of [30 min or less, 31-59 min, 1 hr to 5 hrs 59 min, 6 hrs to 24 hrs], seq 39
S06.0X[1,2,3,4]D	Concussion w/ LOC of [30 min or less, 31-59 min, 1 hr to 5 hrs 59 min, 6 hrs to 24 hrs], subsq enc 386
S06.0X[7,8,9]A	Concussion w/ LOC of [any dur w/ death d/t brain inj prior to regain cnscness, any dur w/ death d/t oth cause prior to regain cnscness, unsp dur], init enc 38, 418
S06.0X[7,8,9]S	Concussion w/ LOC of [any dur w/ death d/t brain inj prior to regain cnscness, any dur w/ death d/t oth cause prior to regain cnscness, unsp dur], seq 39
S06.0X[7,8,9]D	Concussion w/ LOC of [any dur w/ death d/t brain inj prior to regain cnscness, any dur w/ death d/t oth cause prior to regain cnscness, unsp dur], subsq enc 386
S06.0X0A	Concussion w/o LOC, init enc 38, 418
S06.0X0D	Concussion w/o LOC, subs enc 386
S06.0X0S	Concussion without LOC, seq 39
P83.9	Condition of the integument specific to newborn, unsp 288
P96.9	Condition originating in the perinatal period, unsp 288
F91*	Conduct d/o 311
H90*	Conductive and sensorineural hearing loss 58
G47.51	Confusional arousals 38
Q62*	Congen defects of renal pelvis and congen malform of ureter 256
Q50*	Congen malform of ovaries, fallopian tubes & broad lgmt 265, 270
Q86*	Congen malform syndromes d/t known exogenous causes, NEC 288
Q89.0*	Congenital absence and malformations of spleen 294
Q64.5	Congenital absence of bladder and urethra 256
Q42*	Congenital absence, atresia and stenosis of large intestine 117
Q41*	Congenital absence, atresia and stenosis of sm intestine 117
D70.0	Congenital agranulocytosis 293
G70.2	Congenital and developmental myasthenia 34
P61.3	Congenital anemia from fetal bld loss 288
Q68.3	Congenital bowing of femur 195
Q68.5	Congenital bowing of long bones of leg, unsp 195
Q68.4	Congenital bowing of tibia & fibula 195
Q33.4	Congenital bronchiectasis 68
Q32.2	Congenital bronchomalacia 4
G47.35	Congenital central alveolar hypoventilation synd 38
Q67.1	Congenital compression facies 195
Q33.0	Congenital cystic lung 69
Q66*	Congenital deformities of feet 194
Q65*	Congenital deformities of hip 194
Q68.1	Congenital deformity of finger(s) and hand 195
Q68.2	Congenital deformity of knee 195
Q67.5	Congenital deformity of spine 126, 195
Q68.0	Congenital deformity of sternocleidomastoid muscle 195
Q79.0	Congenital diaphragmatic hernia 69
Q64.6	Congenital diverticulum of bladder 256
Q67.0	Congenital facial asymmetry 194
P37.3	Congenital falciparum malaria 282
Q43.6	Congenital fistula of rectum and anus 117
Q24.6	Congenital heart block 102
P83.5	Congenital hydrocele 288
Q03*	Congenital hydrocephalus 38, 285
P94.1	Congenital hypertonia 288
Q33.6	Congenital hypoplasia and dysplasia of lung 69
E03.1	Congenital hypothyroidism w/o goiter 247
E03.0	Congenital hypothyroidism with diffuse goiter 247
P94.2	Congenital hypotonia 288
Q80*	Congenital ichthyosis 234
P37.9	Congenital infectious or parasitic dz, unsp 282
E00*	Congenital iodine-deficiency synd 247
Q76.41[1,2,3,4,5,9]	Congenital kyphosis [occipito-atlanto-axial, cervical, cervicothoracic, thoracic, thoracolumbar, unsp] rgn 165
Q31.5	Congenital laryngomalacia 4
Q12*	Congenital lens malformations 46
Q76.42*	Congenital lordosis 126
Q76.42[5,6,7,8,9]	Congenital lordosis, [thoracolumbar, lumbar, lumbosacral, sacral and sacrococcygeal, unsp] rgn 195
Q16*	Congenital malform of ear causing impairment of hearing 58
Q10*	Congenital malform of eyelid, lacrimal apparatus and orbit 46
Q76.9	Congenital malformation of bony thorax, unsp 69
Q45.9	Congenital malformation of digestive sys, unsp 117
Q18.9	Congenital malformation of face and neck, unsp 234
Q26.9	Congenital malformation of great vein, unsp 102
Q24.9	Congenital malformation of heart, unsp 102
Q43.9	Congenital malformation of intestine, unsp 117
Q31.9	Congenital malformation of larynx, unsp 4
Q33.9	Congenital malformation of lung, unsp 69
Q82.9	Congenital malformation of skin, unsp 289
Q76.7	Congenital malformation of sternum 69
Q64.9	Congenital malformation of urinary sys, unsp 256
Q87.3	Congenital malformation syndromes involving early overgrowth 195

Q87.[0,1,2]	Congenital malformation synds predominantly [affecting facial appearance, associated w/ short stature, involving limbs] 195
Q89.9	Congenital malformation, unsp 412
Q89.1	Congenital malformations of adrenal gland 247
Q13*	Congenital malformations of ant segment of eye 46
Q23*	Congenital malformations of aortic and mitral valves 102
Q83*	Congenital malformations of breast 224
Q20*	Congenital malformations of cardiac chambers and connections 102
Q21*	Congenital malformations of cardiac septa 102
Q39*	Congenital malformations of esophagus 114
Q25*	Congenital malformations of great arteries 102
Q43.3	Congenital malformations of intestinal fix 117
Q31*	Congenital malformations of larynx 58
Q38.0	Congenital malformations of lips, NEC 5, 59
Q30*	Congenital malformations of nose 58
Q89.2	Congenital malformations of oth endocrine glands 247
Q38.5	Congenital malformations of palate, NEC 117
Q14*	Congenital malformations of posterior segment of eye 46
Q22*	Congenital malformations of pulmn and tricuspid valves 102
Q38.4	Congenital malformations of salivary glands and ducts 5, 58
Q32*	Congenital malformations of trachea and bronchus 58
Q51*	Congenital malformations of uterus and cervix 265, 270
Q45.2	Congenital pancreatic cyst 124
Q66.52	Congenital pes planus, lt foot 289
Q66.51	Congenital pes planus, rt foot 289
Q66.50	Congenital pes planus, unsp foot 289
Q38.7	Congenital pharyngeal pouch 5, 58
P23*	Congenital pneumonia 282
Q64.2	Congenital posterior urethral valves 256
P96.0	Congenital renal failure 288
Q76.3	Congenital scoliosis d/t congenital bony malformation 126, 195
Q76.2	Congenital spondylolisthesis 165
Q44.3	Congenital stenosis and stricture of bile ducts 124
Q32.3	Congenital stenosis of bronchus 4
Q26.0	Congenital stenosis of vena cava 102
Q24.4	Congenital subaortic stenosis 102
Q31.1	Congenital subglottic stenosis 4
A50.9	Congenital syphilis, unsp 308
P37.1	Congenital toxoplasmosis 282
Q32.0	Congenital tracheomalacia 4
P37.0	Congenital tuberculosis 282
Q66.82	Congenital vertical talus deformity, lt foot 289
Q66.81	Congenital vertical talus deformity, rt foot 289
Q66.80	Congenital vertical talus deformity, unsp foot 289
P35*	Congenital viral dz 282
H55.0[1,3,9]	[Congenital, Visual deprivation, Oth forms] nystagmus 46
N42.1	Congestion and hemor of prostate 261
O30.02[1,2,3]	Conjoined twin preg, [1st, 2nd, 3rd] trmstr 277
O30.029	Conjoined twin preg, unsp trmstr 280
Q89.4	Conjoined twins 117, 285
H10*	Conjunctivitis 45
B60.1[2,3]	[Conjunctivitis, Keratoconjunctivitis] d/t Acanthamoeba 45
M99.7*	Connective tiss and disc stenosis of intervertebral foramina 165
M99.4*	Connective tissue stenosis of neural canal 165
H05.24[1,2,3,9]	Constant exophthalmos, [rt, lt, bilat, unsp] eye 45
K59.0*	Constipation 116
D61.0*	Constitutional aplastic anemia 293
Z20*	Contact w and (suspected) exposure to communicable dz 412
Z20.818	Contact w and exposure to oth bact communicable dz 289
Z20.89	Contact w and exposure to oth communicable dz 289
Z20.09	Contact w and exposure to oth intestinal infectious dz 289
Z20.810	Contact with and (suspected) exposure to anthrax 289
O31.[1,2,3] 0X[0,1,2,3,4,5,9]	Continuing preg after [spontaneous abortion, intrauterine death, elective fetal reduction] of one fetus or more, unsp trmstr, fetus [N/A or unsp, 1, 2, 3, 4, 5, oth] 281
O31.3[1,2,3] X[0,1,2,3,4,5,9]	Continuing preg after elective fetal reduction of one fetus or more, [1st, 2nd, 3rd] trmstr, fetus [N/A or unsp, 1, 2, 3, 4, 5, oth] 278, 279
O31.2[1,2,3] X[0,1,2,3,4,5,9]	Continuing preg after intrauterine death of one fetus or more, [1st, 2nd, 3rd] trmstr, fetus [N/A or unsp, 1, 2, 3, 4, 5, oth] 278, 279

O31.1[1,2,3] X[0,1,2,3,4,5,9]	Continuing preg after spontaneous abortion of one fetus or more, [1st, 2nd, 3rd] trmstr, fetus [N/A or unsp, 1, 2, 3, 4, 5, oth] 278, 279
M24.5*	Contracture of jt 194
M62.4*	Contracture of muscle 167
S06.3[1,2,3]5A	Contsn and lac of [rt, lt, unsp] cerebrum w/ LOC > 24 hrs w/ return to pre-existing conscious lvl, init enc 11, 15
S06.3[1,2,3]6A	Contsn and lac of [rt, lt, unsp] cerebrum w/ LOC > 24 hrs w/o return to pre-existing conscious lvl, w/ patient surviving, init enc 11, 15
S06.3[1,2,3]3A	Contsn and lac of [rt, lt, unsp] cerebrum w/ LOC, 1 to 5 hrs 59 min, init enc 11, 15
S06.3[1,2,3]2A	Contsn and lac of [rt, lt, unsp] cerebrum w/ LOC, 31 to 59 min, init enc 11, 15
S06.3[1,2,3]4A	Contsn and lac of [rt, lt, unsp] cerebrum w/ LOC, 6 to 24 hrs, init enc 11, 15
S06.3[1,2,3]8A	Contsn and lac of [rt, lt, unsp] cerebrum w/ LOC, any dur w/ death d/t oth cause prior to regain cnscness, init enc 11, 15
S06.3[1,2,3]7A	Contsn and lac of [rt, lt, unsp] cerebrum w/ LOC, any dur, w/ death d/t brain inj prior to regain cnscness, init enc 11, 15
S06.3[1,2,3]9A	Contsn and lac of [rt, lt, unsp] cerebrum w/ LOC, unsp dur, init enc 11, 15
S06.3[1,2,3]0A	Contsn and lac of [rt, lt, unsp] cerebrum w/o LOC, init enc 11, 15
S06.33[5,6]A	Contsn and lac of cerebrum, unsp, w/ LOC > 24 hrs [w/ return to pre-existing conscious lvl, w/o return to pre-existing conscious lvl w/ patient surviving], init enc 36, 418, 431
S06.33[5,6]S	Contsn and lac of cerebrum, unsp, w/ LOC of [> 24 hrs w/ return to pre-existing conscious lvl, > 24 hrs w/o return to pre-existing conscious lvl w/ patient surviving], seq 39
S06.33[3,4,5,6]A	Contsn and lac of cerebrum, unsp, w/ LOC of [1 hr to 5 hrs 59 min, 6 hrs to 24 hrs, > 24 hrs w/ return to pre-existing conscious lvl, > 24 hrs w/o return to pre-existing conscious lvl patient surviving], init enc 35
S06.33[1,2,3,4]A	Contsn and lac of cerebrum, unsp, w/ LOC of [30 min or less, 31 min to 59 min, 1 hr to 5 hrs 59 min, 6 hrs to 24 hrs], init enc 36, 418, 431
S06.33[1,2,3,4]S	Contsn and lac of cerebrum, unsp, w/ LOC of [30 min or less, 31-59 min, 1 hr to 5 hrs 59 min, 6 hrs to 24 hrs], seq 39
S06.33[7,8,9]A	Contsn and lac of cerebrum, unsp, w/ LOC of [any dur w/ death d/t brain inj prior to regain cnscness, any dur w/ death d/t oth cause prior to regain cnscness, unsp dur], init enc 35, 36, 418, 431
S06.33[7,8,9]S	Contsn and lac of cerebrum, unsp, w/ LOC of [any dur w/ death d/t brain inj prior to regain cnscness, any dur w/ death d/t oth cause prior to regain cnscness, unsp dur], seq 39
S06.32[5,6]D	Contsn and lac of lt cerebrum w/ LOC [> 24 hrs w/ return to pre-existing conscious lvl, > 24 hrs w/o return to pre-existing conscious lvl w/ patient surviving], subsq enc 386
S06.32[5,6]A	Contsn and lac of lt cerebrum w/ LOC > 24 hrs [w/ return to pre-existing conscious lvl, w/o return to pre-existing conscious lvl w/ patient surviving], init enc 36, 418, 431
S06.32[5,6]S	Contsn and lac of lt cerebrum w/ LOC of [> 24 hrs w/ return to pre-existing conscious lvl, > 24 hrs w/o return to pre-existing conscious lvl w/ patient surviving], seq 39
S06.32[3,4,5,6]A	Contsn and lac of lt cerebrum w/ LOC of [1 hr to 5 hrs 59 min, 6 hrs to 24 hrs, > 24 hrs w/ return to pre-existing conscious lvl, > 24 hrs w/o return to pre-existing conscious lvl patient surviving], init enc 35
S06.32[1,2,3,4]A	Contsn and lac of lt cerebrum w/ LOC of [30 min or less, 31 min to 59 min, 1 hr to 5 hrs 59 min, 6 hrs to 24 hrs], init enc 36, 418, 431
S06.32[1,2,3,4]D	Contsn and lac of lt cerebrum w/ LOC of [30 min or less, 31 min to 59 min, 1 hr to 5 hrs 59 min, 6 hrs to 24 hrs], subsq enc 386
S06.32[1,2,3,4]S	Contsn and lac of lt cerebrum w/ LOC of [30 min or less, 31-59 min, 1 hr to 5 hrs 59 min, 6 hrs to 24 hrs], seq 39
S06.32[7,8,9]A	Contsn and lac of lt cerebrum w/ LOC of [any dur w/ death d/t brain inj prior to regain cnscness, any dur w/ death d/t oth cause prior to regain cnscness, unsp dur], init enc 35, 36, 418, 431
S06.32[7,8,9]S	Contsn and lac of lt cerebrum w/ LOC of [any dur w/ death d/t brain inj prior to regain cnscness, any dur w/ death d/t oth cause prior to regain cnscness, unsp dur], seq 39
S06.32[7,8,9]D	Contsn and lac of lt cerebrum w/ LOC of [any dur w/ death d/t brain inj prior to regain cnscness, any dur w/ death d/t oth cause prior to regain cnscness, unsp dur], subsq enc 387
S06.31[5,6]D	Contsn and lac of rt cerebrum w/ LOC [> 24 hrs w/ return to pre-existing conscious lvl, > 24 hrs w/o return to pre-existing conscious lvl w/ patient surviving], subsq enc 386
S06.31[5,6]A	Contsn and lac of rt cerebrum w/ LOC > 24 hrs [w/ return to pre-existing conscious lvl, w/o return to pre-existing conscious lvl w/ patient surviving], init enc 36, 418, 431

S06.31[5,6]S	Contsn and lac of rt cerebrum w/ LOC of [> 24 hrs w/ return to pre-existing conscious lvl, > 24 hrs w/o return to pre-existing conscious lvl w/ patient surviving], seq 39
S06.31[3,4,5,6]A	Contsn and lac of rt cerebrum w/ LOC of [1 hr to 5 hrs 59 min, 6 hrs to 24 hrs, > 24 hrs w/ return to pre-existing conscious lvl, > 24 hrs w/o return to pre-existing conscious lvl patient surviving], init enc 35
S06.31[1,2,3,4]A	Contsn and lac of rt cerebrum w/ LOC of [30 min or less, 31 min to 59 min, 1 hr to 5 hrs 59 min, 6 hrs to 24 hrs], init enc 36, 418, 430
S06.31[1,2,3,4]D	Contsn and lac of rt cerebrum w/ LOC of [30 min or less, 31 min to 59 min, 1 hr to 5 hrs 59 min, 6 hrs to 24 hrs], subsq enc 386
S06.31[1,2,3,4]S	Contsn and lac of rt cerebrum w/ LOC of [30 min or less, 31-59 min, 1 hr to 5 hrs 59 min, 6 hrs to 24 hrs], seq 39
S06.31[7,8,9]A	Contsn and lac of rt cerebrum w/ LOC of [any dur w/ death d/t brain inj prior to regain cnscness, any dur w/ death d/t oth cause prior to regain cnscness, unsp dur], init enc 35, 36, 418, 431
S06.31[7,8,9]S	Contsn and lac of rt cerebrum w/ LOC of [any dur w/ death d/t brain inj prior to regain cnscness, any dur w/ death d/t oth cause prior to regain cnscness, unsp dur], seq 39
S06.31[7,8,9]D	Contsn and lac of rt cerebrum w/ LOC of [any dur w/ death d/t brain inj prior to regain cnscness, any dur w/ death d/t oth cause prior to regain cnscness, unsp dur], subsq enc 386
S06.33[5,6]D	Contsn and lac of unsp cerebrum w/ LOC [> 24 hrs w/ return to pre-existing conscious lvl, > 24 hrs w/o return to pre-existing conscious lvl w/ patient surviving], subsq enc 387
S06.33[1,2,3,4]D	Contsn and lac of unsp cerebrum w/ LOC of [30 min or less, 31 min to 59 min, 1 hr to 5 hrs 59 min, 6 hrs to 24 hrs], subsq enc 387
S06.33[7,8,9]D	Contsn and lac of unsp cerebrum w/ LOC of [any dur w/ death d/t brain inj prior to regain cnscness, any dur w/ death d/t oth cause prior to regain cnscness, unsp dur], subsq enc 387
S06.3[1,2,3]1A	Contsn and lac, [Rt, Lt, Unsp] cerebrum w/ LOC, 30 min or less, init enc 11, 15
S36.52[0,1,2,3,8,9]A	Contsn of [ascending [rt] colon, transv colon, descending [lt] colon, sigmoid colon, oth part of colon,unsp part of colon], init enc 432
S36.52[0,1,2,3,8,9]D	Contsn of [ascending [rt] colon, transv colon, descending [lt] colon, sigmoid colon, oth part of colon,unsp part of colon], subsq enc 391
S36.42[0,8,9]D	Contsn of [duodenum, oth part of sm intestine, unsp part of sm intestine], subsq enc 390
S20.2[1,2][1,2,9]A	Contsn of [front, back][rt, lt, unsp] wall of thorax, init enc 420
S36.22[0,1,2,9]A	Contsn of [head, body, tail, unsp part] of pancreas, init enc 124, 432
S36.22[0,1,2,9]S	Contsn of [head, body, tail, unsp part] of pancreas, seq 117
S36.22[0,1,2,9]D	Contsn of [head, body, tail, unsp part] of pancreas, subsq enc 390
S00.53[1,2][A,S]	Contsn of [lip, oral cavity], [init enc, seq] 224
S30.[0,1]XXA	Contsn of [lwr back and pelvis, abd wall], init enc 421
S30.2[1,2,3]XA	Contsn of [penis, scrotum and testes, vagina and vulva], init enc 421
S30.2[1,2,3]XD	Contsn of [penis, scrotum and testes, vagina and vulva], subsq enc 389
S90.2[1,2][1,2,9]A	Contsn of [rt, lt, unsp] [great, lesser] toe(s) w/ damage to nail, init enc 428
S90.2[1,2][1,2,9]D	Contsn of [rt, lt, unsp] [great, lesser] toe(s) w/ damage to nail, subsq enc 398
S90.1[1,2][1,2,9]A	Contsn of [rt, lt, unsp] [great, lesser] toe(s) w/o damage to nail, init enc 428
S90.1[1,2][1,2,9]D	Contsn of [rt, lt, unsp] [great, lesser] toe(s) w/o damage to nail, subsq enc 398
S40.0[1,2][1,2,9]A	Contsn of [rt, lt, unsp] [shldr, upr arm], init enc 422
S60.1[1,2,3,4,5][1,2,9]A	Contsn of [rt, lt, unsp] [thumb, index finger, mid finger, ring finger, little finger] w/ damage to nail, init enc 424
S60.0[1,2,3,4,5][1,2,9]A	Contsn of [rt, lt, unsp] [thumb, index finger, mid finger, ring finger, little finger] w/o damage to nail, init enc 424
S60.2[1,2][1,2,9]A	Contsn of [rt, lt, unsp] [wrist, hand], init enc 424
S20.22[1,2,9][A,S]	Contsn of [rt, lt, unsp] back wall of thorax, [init enc, seq] 225
S20.22[1,2,9]D	Contsn of [rt, lt, unsp] back wall of thorax, subsq enc 388
S00.43[1,2,9][A,S]	Contsn of [rt, lt, unsp] ear, [init enc, seq] 224
S50.0[0,1,2]XD	Contsn of [rt, lt, unsp] elbow, subsq enc 392
S50.1[0,1,2]XD	Contsn of [rt, lt, unsp] forearm, subsq enc 392
S20.21[1,2,9][A,S]	Contsn of [rt, lt, unsp] front wall of thorax, [init enc, seq] 225
S20.21[1,2,9]D	Contsn of [rt, lt, unsp] front wall of thorax, subsq enc 388
S90.21[1,2,9][A,S]	Contsn of [rt, lt, unsp] great toe w/ damage to nail, [init enc, seq] 230
S90.11[1,2,9][A,S]	Contsn of [rt, lt, unsp] great toe w/o damage to nail, [init enc, seq] 230
S60.22[1,2,9][A,S]	Contsn of [rt, lt, unsp] hand, [init enc, seq] 227
S60.22[1,2,9]D	Contsn of [rt, lt, unsp] hand, subsq enc 394
S60.12[1,2,9][A,S]	Contsn of [rt, lt, unsp] index finger w/ damage to nail, [init enc, seq] 227
S60.12[1,2,9]D	Contsn of [rt, lt, unsp] index finger w/ damage to nail, subsq enc 394
S60.02[1,2,9][A,S]	Contsn of [rt, lt, unsp] index finger w/o damage to nail, [init enc, seq] 227
S60.02[1,2,9]D	Contsn of [rt, lt, unsp] index finger w/o damage to nail, subsq enc 393
S90.22[1,2,9][A,S]	Contsn of [rt, lt, unsp] lesser toe(s) w/ damage to nail, [init enc, seq] 230
S90.12[1,2,9][A,S]	Contsn of [rt, lt, unsp] lesser toe(s) w/o damage to nail, [init enc, seq] 230
S60.15[1,2,9][A,S]	Contsn of [rt, lt, unsp] little finger w/ damage to nail, [init enc, seq] 227
S60.15[1,2,9]D	Contsn of [rt, lt, unsp] little finger w/ damage to nail, subsq enc 394
S60.05[1,2,9][A,S]	Contsn of [rt, lt, unsp] little finger w/o damage to nail, [init enc, seq] 227
S60.05[1,2,9]D	Contsn of [rt, lt, unsp] little finger w/o damage to nail, subsq enc 394
S60.13[1,2,9][A,S]	Contsn of [rt, lt, unsp] mid finger w/ damage to nail, [init enc, seq] 227
S60.13[1,2,9]D	Contsn of [rt, lt, unsp] mid finger w/ damage to nail, subsq enc 394
S60.03[1,2,9][A,S]	Contsn of [rt, lt, unsp] mid finger w/o damage to nail, [init enc, seq] 227
S60.03[1,2,9]D	Contsn of [rt, lt, unsp] mid finger w/o damage to nail, subsq enc 393
S60.14[1,2,9][A,S]	Contsn of [rt, lt, unsp] ring finger w/ damage to nail, [init enc, seq] 227
S60.14[1,2,9]D	Contsn of [rt, lt, unsp] ring finger w/ damage to nail, subsq enc 394
S60.04[1,2,9][A,S]	Contsn of [rt, lt, unsp] ring finger w/o damage to nail, [init enc, seq] 227
S60.04[1,2,9]D	Contsn of [rt, lt, unsp] ring finger w/o damage to nail, subsq enc 393
S40.01[1,2,9][A,S]	Contsn of [rt, lt, unsp] shldr, [init enc, seq] 227
S40.01[1,2,9]D	Contsn of [rt, lt, unsp] shldr, subsq enc 391
S60.11[1,2,9][A,S]	Contsn of [rt, lt, unsp] thumb w/ damage to nail, [init enc, seq] 227
S60.11[1,2,9]D	Contsn of [rt, lt, unsp] thumb w/ damage to nail, subsq enc 394
S60.01[1,2,9][A,S]	Contsn of [rt, lt, unsp] thumb w/o damage to nail, [init enc, seq] 227
S60.01[1,2,9]D	Contsn of [rt, lt, unsp] thumb w/o damage to nail, subsq enc 393
S40.02[1,2,9][A,S]	Contsn of [rt, lt, unsp] upr arm, [init enc, seq] 227
S40.02[1,2,9]D	Contsn of [rt, lt, unsp] upr arm, subsq enc 391
S60.21[1,2,9][A,S]	Contsn of [rt, lt, unsp] wrist, [init enc, seq] 227
S60.21[1,2,9]D	Contsn of [rt, lt, unsp] wrist, subsq enc 394
S30.2[02,3X]A	Contsn of [unsp ext genital organ female, vagina and vulva] init enc 265, 270
S50.[0,1][0,1,2]XA	Contsn of [unsp, rt, lt] [elbow, forearm], init enc 423
S70.[0,1][0,1,2]XA	Contsn of [unsp, rt, lt] [hip, thigh], init enc 426
S80.[0,1][0,1,2]XA	Contsn of [unsp, rt, lt] [knee, lwr leg], init enc 427
S90.0[0,1,2]X[A,S]	Contsn of [unsp, rt, lt] ankle, [init enc, seq] 229
S90.0[0,1,2]XA	Contsn of [unsp, rt, lt] ankle, init enc 428
S90.0[0,1,2]XD	Contsn of [unsp, rt, lt] ankle, subsq enc 398
S20.0[0,1,2]X[A,S]	Contsn of [unsp, rt, lt] breast, [init enc, seq] 225
S20.0[0,1,2]XA	Contsn of [unsp, rt, lt] breast, init enc 420

Code	Description
S50.0[0,1,2]X[A,S]	Contsn of [unsp, rt, lt] elbow, [init enc, seq] 227
S00.1[0,1,2]XA	Contsn of [unsp, rt, lt] eyelid and periocular area, init enc 46, 417
S00.1[0,1,2]XS	Contsn of [unsp, rt, lt] eyelid and periocular area, seq 224
S00.1[0,1,2]XD	Contsn of [unsp, rt, lt] eyelid and periocular area, subsq enc 386
S90.3[0,1,2]X[A,S]	Contsn of [unsp, rt, lt] foot, [init enc, seq] 230
S90.3[0,1,2]XA	Contsn of [unsp, rt, lt] foot, init enc 428
S90.3[0,1,2]XD	Contsn of [unsp, rt, lt] foot, subsq enc 398
S50.1[0,1,2]X[A,S]	Contsn of [unsp, rt, lt] forearm, [init enc, seq] 227
S70.0[0,1,2]X[A,S]	Contsn of [unsp, rt, lt] hip, [init enc, seq] 229
S70.0[0,1,2]XD	Contsn of [unsp, rt, lt] hip, subsq enc 397
S80.0[0,1,2]X[A,S]	Contsn of [unsp, rt, lt] knee, [init enc, seq] 229
S80.0[0,1,2]XD	Contsn of [unsp, rt, lt] knee, subsq enc 398
S80.1[0,1,2]X[A,S]	Contsn of [unsp, rt, lt] lwr leg, [init enc, seq] 229
S80.1[0,1,2]XD	Contsn of [unsp, rt, lt] lwr leg, subsq enc 398
S70.1[0,1,2]X[A,S]	Contsn of [unsp, rt, lt] thigh, [init enc, seq] 229
S70.1[0,1,2]XD	Contsn of [unsp, rt, lt] thigh, subsq enc 397
S30.1XX[A,S]	Contsn of abd wall, [init enc, seq] 226
S30.1XXD	Contsn of abd wall, subsq enc 389
S30.3XX[A,S]	Contsn of anus, [init enc, seq] 226
S30.3XXA	Contsn of anus, init enc 421
S30.3XXD	Contsn of anus, subsq enc 389
S36.520[A,S]	Contsn of ascending [rt] colon, [init enc, seq] 118
S20.0[0,1,2]XD	Contsn of breast, [unsp, rt, lt] breast, subsq enc 388
S27.42[1,2,9]A	Contsn of bronchus, [unilat, bilat, unsp], init enc 67
S27.42[1,2,9]S	Contsn of bronchus, [unilat, bilat, unsp], seq 69
S27.42[1,2,9]D	Contsn of bronchus, [unilat, bilat, unsp], subsq enc 389
S36.522[A,S]	Contsn of descending [lt] colon, [init enc, seq] 118
S36.420[A,S]	Contsn of duodenum, [init enc, seq] 117
S05.1[0,1,2]XD	Contsn of eyeball and orbital tissues, [rt, lt, unsp] eye, subsq enc 386
S05.1[0,1,2]XA	Contsn of eyeball and orbital tissues, [unsp, rt, lt] eye, init enc 46, 418
S05.1[0,1,2]XS	Contsn of eyeball and orbital tissues, [unsp, rt, lt] eye, seq 225
S37.52[1,2,9]D	Contsn of fallopian tube, [unilat, bilat, unsp] subsq enc 391
S37.52[1,2,9]A	Contsn of fallopian tube, [unilat, bilat, unsp], init enc 265, 270
S37.52[1,2,9]S	Contsn of fallopian tube, [unilat, bilat, unsp], seq 265, 270
S36.122A	Contsn of gallbladder, init enc 124
S36.112A	Contsn of liver, init enc 124
S36.112S	Contsn of liver, seq 117
S27.32[1,2,9]D	Contsn of lung, [unilat, bilat, unsp], subsq enc 389
S27.322[A,S]	Contsn of lung, bilat, [init enc, seq] 69
S27.321[A,S]	Contsn of lung, unilat, [init enc, seq] 69
S27.329[A,S]	Contsn of lung, unsp, [init enc, seq] 69
S30.0XX[A,S]	Contsn of lwr back and pelvis, [init enc, seq] 226
S30.0XXD	Contsn of lwr back and pelvis, subsq enc 389
S36.528[A,S]	Contsn of oth part of colon, [init enc, seq] 118
S36.428[A,S]	Contsn of oth part of sm intestine, [init enc, seq] 117
S27.892[A,S]	Contsn of oth spec intrathoracic organs, [init enc, seq] 69
S10.83XD	Contsn of oth spec part of neck, subs enc 387
S37.42[1,2,9]A	Contsn of ovary, [unilat, bilat, unsp], init enc 265, 270
S37.42[1,2,9]S	Contsn of ovary, [unilat, bilat, unsp], seq 265, 270
S37.42[1,2,9]D	Contsn of ovary, [unilat, bilat, unsp], subsq enc 391
S30.21XA	Contsn of penis, init enc 261
S30.21XS	Contsn of penis, seq 226
S36.62X[A,S]	Contsn of rectum, [init enc, seq] 118
S00.03X[A,S]	Contsn of scalp, [init enc, seq] 224
S30.22XA	Contsn of scrotum and testes, init enc 261
S30.22XS	Contsn of scrotum and testes, seq 226
S36.523[A,S]	Contsn of sigmoid colon, [init enc, seq] 118
S36.32X[A,S]	Contsn of stomach, [init enc, seq] 117
S27.52X[A,S]	Contsn of thoracic trachea, [init enc, seq] 69
S20.20X[A,S]	Contsn of thorax, unsp, [init enc, seq] 225
S20.20XA	Contsn of thorax, unsp, init enc 420
S20.20XD	Contsn of thorax, unsp, subsq enc 388
S10.0XX[A,S]	Contsn of throat, [init enc, seq] 225
S10.0XXA	Contsn of throat, init enc 419
S10.0XXD	Contsn of throat, subsq enc 387
S36.521[A,S]	Contsn of transv colon, [init enc, seq] 118
S30.20[1,2]A	Contsn of unsp ext genital organ, [male, female], init enc 421
S30.20[1,2]S	Contsn of unsp ext genital organ, [male, female], seq 226
S30.202D	Contsn of unsp ext genital organ, female, subs 389
S30.201A	Contsn of unsp ext genital organ, male, init enc 261
S30.201D	Contsn of unsp ext genital organ, male, subs enc 389
S60.10X[A,S]	Contsn of unsp finger w/ damage to nail, [init enc, seq] 227
S60.00X[A,S]	Contsn of unsp finger w/o damage to nail, [init enc, seq] 227
S60.00XA	Contsn of unsp finger w/o damage to nail, init enc 424
S60.00XD	Contsn of unsp finger w/o damage to nail, subs enc 393
S60.10XA	Contsn of unsp finger with damage to nail, init enc 424
S60.10XD	Contsn of unsp finger with damage to nail, subs enc 394
S36.92X[A,S]	Contsn of unsp intra-abd organ, [init enc, seq] 118
S36.529[A,S]	Contsn of unsp part of colon, [init enc, seq] 118
S10.93XD	Contsn of unsp part of neck, subsq enc 387
S36.429[A,S]	Contsn of unsp part of sm intestine, [init enc, seq] 117
S30.23XS	Contsn of vagina and vulva, seq 226
S00.3[3,4]X[A,S]	[Contsn, Ext constriction] of nose, [init enc, seq] 224
S00.8[3,4]X[A,S]	[Contsn, ext constriction] of oth part of head, [init enc, seq] 224
S10.8[3,4]X[A,S]	[Contsn, ext constriction] of oth spec part of neck, [init enc, seq] 225
S00.9[3,4]X[A,S]	[Contsn, ext constriction] of unsp part of head, [init enc, seq] 224
S10.9[3,4]X[A,S]	[Contsn, ext constriction] of unsp part of neck, [init enc, seq] 225
S36.11[2,3,4,5,6,8,9]A	[Contsn, Lac (unsp degree), Minor lac, Mod lac, Major lac, Oth inj, Unsp inj] of liver, init enc 422, 432
S06.38[5,6]S	Contsn, lac and hemor of brainstem w/ LOC of [> 24 hrs w/ return to pre-existing conscious lvl, > 24 hrs w/o return to pre-existing conscious lvl w/ patient surviving], seq 39
S06.38[3,4,5,6]A	Contsn, lac and hemor of brainstem w/ LOC of [1 hr to 5 hrs 59 min, 6 hrs to 24 hrs, > 24 hrs w/ return to pre-existing conscious lvl, > 24 hrs w/o return to pre-existing conscious lvl patient surviving], init enc 35
S06.38[1,2,3,4]S	Contsn, lac and hemor of brainstem w/ LOC of [30 min or less, 31-59 min, 1 hr to 5 hrs 59 min, 6 hrs to 24 hrs], seq 39
S06.38[7,8,9]S	Contsn, lac and hemor of brainstem w/ LOC of [any dur w/ death d/t brain inj prior to regain cnscness, any dur w/ death d/t oth cause prior to regain cnscness, unsp dur], seq 39
S06.37[5,6]S	Contsn, lac and hemor of cerebellum w/ LOC of [> 24 hrs w/ return to pre-existing conscious lvl, > 24 hrs w/o return to pre-existing conscious lvl w/ patient surviving], seq 39
S06.37[3,4,5,6]A	Contsn, lac and hemor of cerebellum w/ LOC of [1 hr to 5 hrs 59 min, 6 hrs to 24 hrs, > 24 hrs w/ return to pre-existing conscious lvl, > 24 hrs w/o return to pre-existing conscious lvl patient surviving], init enc 35
S06.37[1,2,3,4]S	Contsn, lac and hemor of cerebellum w/ LOC of [30 min or less, 31-59 min, 1 hr to 5 hrs 59 min, 6 hrs to 24 hrs], seq 39
S06.37[7,8,9]S	Contsn, lac and hemor of cerebellum w/ LOC of [any dur w/ death d/t brain inj prior to regain cnscness, any dur w/ death d/t oth cause prior to regain cnscness, unsp dur], seq 39
S06.38[5,6]D	Contsn, lac, and hemor of brainstem w/ LOC [> 24 hrs w/ return to pre-existing conscious lvl, > 24 hrs w/o return to pre-existing conscious lvl w/ patient surviving], subsq enc 387
S06.38[5,6]A	Contsn, lac, and hemor of brainstem w/ LOC > 24 hrs [w/ return to pre-existing conscious lvl, w/o return to pre-existing conscious lvl w/ patient surviving], init enc 36, 418, 431
S06.38[1,2,3,4]A	Contsn, lac, and hemor of brainstem w/ LOC of [30 min or less, 31 min to 59 min, 1 hr to 5 hrs 59 min, 6 hrs to 24 hrs], init enc 36, 418, 431
S06.38[1,2,3,4]D	Contsn, lac, and hemor of brainstem w/ LOC of [30 min or less, 31 min to 59 min, 1 hr to 5 hrs 59 min, 6 hrs to 24 hrs], subsq enc 387
S06.38[7,8,9]A	Contsn, lac, and hemor of brainstem w/ LOC of [any dur w/ death d/t brain inj prior to regain cnscness, any dur w/ death d/t oth cause prior to regain cnscness, unsp dur], init enc 35, 36, 418, 431
S06.38[7,8,9]D	Contsn, lac, and hemor of brainstem w/ LOC of [any dur w/ death d/t brain inj prior to regain cnscness, any dur w/ death d/t oth cause prior to regain cnscness, unsp dur], subsq enc 387
S06.37[5,6]D	Contsn, lac, and hemor of cerebellum w/ LOC [> 24 hrs w/ return to pre-existing conscious lvl, > 24 hrs w/o return to pre-existing conscious lvl w/ patient surviving], subsq enc 387
S06.37[5,6]A	Contsn, lac, and hemor of cerebellum w/ LOC > 24 hrs [w/ return to pre-existing conscious lvl, w/o return to pre-existing conscious lvl w/ patient surviving], init enc 36, 418, 431

Code	Description
S06.37[1,2,3,4]A	Contsn, lac, and hemor of cerebellum w/ LOC of [30 min or less, 31 min to 59 min, 1 hr to 5 hrs 59 min, 6 hrs to 24 hrs], init enc 36, 418, 431
S06.37[1,2,3,4]D	Contsn, lac, and hemor of cerebellum w/ LOC of [30 min or less, 31 min to 59 min, 1 hr to 5 hrs 59 min, 6 hrs to 24 hrs], subsq enc 387
S06.37[7,8,9]A	Contsn, lac, and hemor of cerebellum w/ LOC of [any dur w/ death d/t brain inj prior to regain cnscness, any dur w/ death d/t oth cause prior to regain cnscness, unsp dur], init enc 35, 36, 418, 431
S06.37[7,8,9]D	Contsn, lac, and hemor of cerebellum w/ LOC of [any dur w/ death d/t brain inj prior to regain cnscness, any dur w/ death d/t oth cause prior to regain cnscness, unsp dur], subsq enc 387
S36.11[2,3,4,5,6, 8,9]D	[Contsn, Lac, Minor lac, Mod lac, Major lac, Oth inj, Unsp inj] of liver, subsq enc 390
S37.81[2,3,8,9]A	[Contsn, Lac, Oth inj, Unsp inj] of adrenal gland, init enc 247, 422, 432
S37.81[2,3,8,9]S	[Contsn, Lac, Oth inj, Unsp inj] of adrenal gland, seq 261, 265, 270
S37.81[2,3,8,9]D	[Contsn, Lac, Oth inj, Unsp inj] of adrenal gland, subsq enc 391
S27.80[2,3,8,9]A	[Contsn, Lac, Oth inj, Unsp inj] of diaphragm, init enc 67, 420, 432
S27.80[2,3,8,9]S	[Contsn, Lac, Oth inj, Unsp inj] of diaphragm, seq 69
S27.80[2,3,8,9]D	[Contsn, Lac, Oth inj, Unsp inj] of diaphragm, subsq enc 389
S27.81[2,3,8,9]A	[Contsn, Lac, Oth inj, Unsp inj] of esophagus (thoracic part), init enc 114, 420, 432
S27.81[2,3,8,9]D	[Contsn, Lac, Oth inj, Unsp inj] of esophagus [thoracic part], subsq enc 389
S27.81[2,3,8,9]S	[Contsn, Lac, Oth inj, Unsp inj] of esophagus, seq 69
S36.12[2,3,8,9]A	[Contsn, Lac, Oth inj, Unsp inj] of gallbladder, init enc 422, 432
S36.12[2,3,8,9]S	[Contsn, Lac, Oth inj, Unsp inj] of gallbladder, seq 117
S36.12[2,3,8,9]D	[Contsn, Lac, Oth inj, Unsp inj] of gallbladder, subsq enc 390
S36.89[2,3,8,9]A	[Contsn, Lac, Oth inj, Unsp inj] of oth intra-abd organs, init enc 359, 422, 432
S36.89[2,3,8,9]S	[Contsn, Lac, Oth inj, Unsp inj] of oth intra-abd organs, seq 118
S36.89[2,3,8,9]D	[Contsn, Lac, Oth inj, Unsp inj] of oth intra-abd organs, subsq enc 391
S27.89[2,3,8,9]A	[Contsn, Lac, Oth inj, Unsp inj] of oth spec intrathoracic organs, init enc 420, 432
S27.89[2,3,8,9]D	[Contsn, Lac, Oth inj, Unsp inj] of oth spec intrathoracic organs, subsq enc 389
S37.89[2,3,8,9]A	[Contsn, Lac, Oth inj, Unsp inj] of oth urinary and pelvic organ, init enc 261, 265, 270, 422, 432
S37.89[2,3,8,9]S	[Contsn, Lac, Oth inj, Unsp inj] of oth urinary and pelvic organ, seq 261, 265, 270
S37.89[2,3,8,9]D	[Contsn, Lac, Oth inj, Unsp inj] of oth urinary and pelvic organ, subsq enc 391
S37.82[2,3,8,9]A	[Contsn, Lac, Oth inj, Unsp inj] of prostate, init enc 261
S37.82[2,3,8,9]S	[Contsn, Lac, Oth inj, Unsp inj] of prostate, seq 261
S37.82[2,3,8,9]D	[Contsn, Lac, Oth inj, Unsp inj] of prostate, subsq enc 391
S06.331A	Contus/lac cereb, w LOC of 30 min or less, init 37
S06.332A	Contus/lac cereb, w LOC of 31-59 min, init 37
S06.330A	Contus/lac cereb, w/o LOC, init 36, 37, 418, 431
S06.330S	Contus/lac cereb, w/o LOC, seq 39
S06.330D	Contus/lac cereb, w/o LOC, subs 387
S06.321A	Contus/lac lt cerebrum w LOC of 30 min or less, init 37
S06.322A	Contus/lac lt cerebrum w LOC of 31-59 min, init 37
S06.320A	Contus/lac lt cerebrum w/o LOC, init 36, 37, 418, 431
S06.320S	Contus/lac lt cerebrum w/o LOC, seq 39
S06.320D	Contus/lac lt cerebrum w/o LOC, subs 386
S06.311A	Contus/lac rt cerebrum w LOC of 30 min or less, init 37
S06.312A	Contus/lac rt cerebrum w LOC of 31-59 min, init 37
S06.310A	Contus/lac rt cerebrum w/o LOC, init 36, 37, 418, 430
S06.310S	Contus/lac rt cerebrum w/o LOC, seq 39
S06.310D	Contus/lac rt cerebrum w/o LOC, subs 386
S06.385A	Contus/lac/hem brainstem w LOC >24 hr w ret consc lev, init 11, 15
S06.383A	Contus/lac/hem brainstem w LOC of 1-5 hrs 59 min, init 11, 15
S06.381A	Contus/lac/hem brainstem w LOC of 30 min or less, init 11, 15, 37
S06.382A	Contus/lac/hem brainstem w LOC of 31-59 min, init 11, 15, 37
S06.384A	Contus/lac/hem brainstem w LOC of 6 hrs to 24 hrs, init 11, 15
S06.389A	Contus/lac/hem brainstem w LOC of unsp dur, init 11, 15, 37
S06.380A	Contus/lac/hem brainstem w/o LOC, init 11, 15, 36, 37, 418, 431
S06.380S	Contus/lac/hem brainstem w/o LOC, seq 39
S06.380D	Contus/lac/hem brainstem w/o LOC, subs 387
S06.386A	Contus/lac/hem brnst w LOC >24 hr w/o ret consc w surv, init 11, 15
S06.387A	Contus/lac/hem brnst w LOC w dth d/t brain inj bf consc,init 11, 15
S06.388A	Contus/lac/hem brnst w LOC w dth d/t oth cause bf consc,init 11, 15
S06.375A	Contus/lac/hem crblm w LOC >24 hr w ret consc lev, init 11, 15
S06.376A	Contus/lac/hem crblm w LOC >24 hr w/o ret consc w surv, init 11, 15
S06.373A	Contus/lac/hem crblm w LOC of 1-5 hrs 59 min, init 11, 15
S06.371A	Contus/lac/hem crblm w LOC of 30 min or less, init 11, 15, 37
S06.372A	Contus/lac/hem crblm w LOC of 31-59 min, init 11, 15, 37
S06.374A	Contus/lac/hem crblm w LOC of 6 hrs to 24 hrs, init 11, 15
S06.379A	Contus/lac/hem crblm w LOC of unsp dur, init 11, 15, 37
S06.377A	Contus/lac/hem crblm w LOC w dth d/t brain inj bf consc,init 11, 15
S06.378A	Contus/lac/hem crblm w LOC w dth d/t oth cause bf consc,init 11, 15
S06.370A	Contus/lac/hem crblm w/o LOC, init 11, 15, 36, 37, 418, 431
S06.370S	Contus/lac/hem crblm w/o LOC, seq 39
S06.370D	Contus/lac/hem crblm w/o LOC, subs 387
H51.1*	Convergence insufficiency and excess 46
F44.7	Conversion d/o with mixed symptom presentation 310
F44.4	Conversion d/o with motor symptom or deficit 310
F44.5	Conversion d/o with seizures or convulsions 310
F44.6	Conversion d/o with sensory symptom or deficit 310
P90	Convulsions of newborn 282
R56*	Convulsions, NEC 41
I27.81	Cor pulmonale (chr) 103
Q24.2	Cor triatriatum 102
Z52.5	Cornea donor 412
H16.31[1,2,3,9]	Corneal abscess, [rt, lt, bilat, unsp] eye 45
H16.4*	Corneal neovascularization 46
H17*	Corneal scars and opacities 46
T86.84[0,1]	Corneal transplant [rejection, failure] 47
Z94.7	Corneal transplant status 47
H16.03[1,2,3,9]	Corneal ulcer w/ hypopyon, [rt, lt, bilat, unsp] eye 45
L84	Corns and callosities 234
I25.4*	Coronary artery aneurysm and dissection 103
T27.[4,5,6,7]XXA	Corrosion [of larynx and trachea, involving larynx and trachea w/ lung, of oth parts of respiratory tract, respiratory tract part unsp], init enc 70
T32.11	Corrosion 10-19% of body surface w 10-19% 3rd degree corrosion 377, 380, 381, 382
T32.11	Corrosion 10-19% of body surface w 10-19% third degree corrosion 377
T20.69XS	Corrosion 2nd deg mul sites of head, face, and neck, seq 231
T20.60XA	Corrosion 2nd deg of head, face, and neck, unsp site, init 383
T20.60XS	Corrosion 2nd deg of head, face, and neck, unsp site, seq 231
T20.60XD	Corrosion 2nd deg of head, face, and neck, unsp site, subs 400
T22.60XA	Corrosion 2nd deg of shldr/up lmb, ex wrs/hnd, unsp site, init 383
T22.60XS	Corrosion 2nd deg of shldr/up lmb, ex wrs/hnd, unsp site, seq 231
T22.60XD	Corrosion 2nd deg of shldr/up lmb, ex wrs/hnd, unsp site, subs 401
T20.79XS	Corrosion 3rd deg mu sites of head, face, and neck, seq 231
T22.70XA	Corrosion 3rd deg of shldr/up lmb, ex wrs/hnd, unsp site, init 377, 379, 381, 382
T22.70XS	Corrosion 3rd deg of shldr/up lmb, ex wrs/hnd, unsp site, seq 231
T22.70XD	Corrosion 3rd deg of shldr/up lmb, ex wrs/hnd, unsp site, subs 401
T20.70XA	Corrosion 3rd degree of head, face, and neck, unsp site, init 377, 379, 381, 382
T20.70XS	Corrosion 3rd degree of head, face, and neck, unsp site, seq 231
T20.70XD	Corrosion 3rd degree of head, face, and neck, unsp site, subs 400
T20.59XA	Corrosion first deg mult sites of head, face, and neck, init 383
T20.59XS	Corrosion first deg mult sites of head, face, and neck, seq 231
T20.59XD	Corrosion first deg mult sites of head, face, and neck, subs 400
T22.50XA	Corrosion first deg of shldr/up lmb, ex wrs/hnd unsp site, init 383
T22.50XS	Corrosion first deg of shldr/up lmb, ex wrs/hnd unsp site, seq 231
T22.50XD	Corrosion first deg of shldr/up lmb, ex wrs/hnd unsp site, subs 401
T20.50XA	Corrosion first degree of head, face, and neck, unsp site, init 383
T20.50XS	Corrosion first degree of head, face, and neck, unsp site, seq 230
T20.50XD	Corrosion first degree of head, face, and neck, unsp site, subs 400
T27.5XXA	Corrosion involving larynx and trachea w lung, init enc 381
T27.5XXD	Corrosion involving larynx and trachea w lung, subs enc 402
T27.5XXS	Corrosion involving larynx and trachea with lung, seq 233

T27.[6,7]XXS	Corrosion of [oth, unsp] parts of respiratory tract, seq 233
T28.91[1,2,9]A	Corrosion of [rt, lt, unsp] ear drum, init enc 384
T28.91[1,2,9]D	Corrosion of [rt, lt, unsp] ear drum, subsq enc 402
T26.9[0,1,2]XA	Corrosion of [unsp, rt, lt] eye and adnexa, part unsp, init enc 47
T26.9[0,1,2]XS	Corrosion of [unsp, rt, lt] eye and adnexa, part unsp, seq 233
T26.5[0,1,2]XA	Corrosion of [unsp, rt, lt] eyelid and periocular area, init enc 47
T26.5[0,1,2]XS	Corrosion of [unsp, rt, lt] eyelid and periocular area, seq 233
T21.5[1,2]XS	Corrosion of 1st degree of [chest, abd] wall, seq 231
T20.5[2,3,4]XA	Corrosion of 1st degree of [lip(s), chin, nose (septum)], init enc 383
T20.5[2,3,4]XS	Corrosion of 1st degree of [lip(s), chin, nose (septum)], seq 231
T20.5[2,3,4]XD	Corrosion of 1st degree of [lip(s), chin, nose (septum)], subsq enc 400
T21.5[6,7]XS	Corrosion of 1st degree of [male, female] genital rgn, seq 231
T25.51[1,2,9]A	Corrosion of 1st degree of [rt, lt, unsp] ankle, init enc 384
T25.51[1,2,9]S	Corrosion of 1st degree of [rt, lt, unsp] ankle, seq 232
T25.51[1,2,9]D	Corrosion of 1st degree of [rt, lt, unsp] ankle, subsq enc 402
T22.54[1,2,9]A	Corrosion of 1st degree of [rt, lt, unsp] axilla, init enc 383
T22.54[1,2,9]S	Corrosion of 1st degree of [rt, lt, unsp] axilla, seq 231
T22.54[1,2,9]D	Corrosion of 1st degree of [rt, lt, unsp] axilla, subsq enc 401
T20.51[1,2,9]A	Corrosion of 1st degree of [rt, lt, unsp] ear [any part, except ear drum], init enc 383
T20.51[1,2,9]S	Corrosion of 1st degree of [rt, lt, unsp] ear [any part, except ear drum], seq 231
T20.51[1,2,9]D	Corrosion of 1st degree of [rt, lt, unsp] ear [any part, except ear drum], subsq enc 400
T22.52[1,2,9]A	Corrosion of 1st degree of [rt, lt, unsp] elbow, init enc 383
T22.52[1,2,9]S	Corrosion of 1st degree of [rt, lt, unsp] elbow, seq 231
T22.52[1,2,9]D	Corrosion of 1st degree of [rt, lt, unsp] elbow, subsq enc 401
T25.52[1,2,9]A	Corrosion of 1st degree of [rt, lt, unsp] foot, init enc 384
T25.52[1,2,9]S	Corrosion of 1st degree of [rt, lt, unsp] foot, seq 232
T25.52[1,2,9]D	Corrosion of 1st degree of [rt, lt, unsp] foot, subsq enc 402
T22.51[1,2,9]A	Corrosion of 1st degree of [rt, lt, unsp] forearm, init enc 383
T22.51[1,2,9]S	Corrosion of 1st degree of [rt, lt, unsp] forearm, seq 231
T22.51[1,2,9]D	Corrosion of 1st degree of [rt, lt, unsp] forearm, subsq enc 401
T23.50[1,2,9]A	Corrosion of 1st degree of [rt, lt, unsp] hand, unsp site, init enc 383
T23.50[1,2,9]S	Corrosion of 1st degree of [rt, lt, unsp] hand, unsp site, seq 232
T23.50[1,2,9]D	Corrosion of 1st degree of [rt, lt, unsp] hand, unsp site, subsq enc 401
T24.52[1,2,9]A	Corrosion of 1st degree of [rt, lt, unsp] knee, init enc 384
T24.52[1,2,9]S	Corrosion of 1st degree of [rt, lt, unsp] knee, seq 232
T24.52[1,2,9]D	Corrosion of 1st degree of [rt, lt, unsp] knee, subsq enc 402
T24.53[1,2,9]A	Corrosion of 1st degree of [rt, lt, unsp] lwr leg, init enc 384
T24.53[1,2,9]S	Corrosion of 1st degree of [rt, lt, unsp] lwr leg, seq 232
T24.53[1,2,9]D	Corrosion of 1st degree of [rt, lt, unsp] lwr leg, subsq enc 402
T23.55[1,2,9]A	Corrosion of 1st degree of [rt, lt, unsp] palm, init enc 384
T23.55[1,2,9]S	Corrosion of 1st degree of [rt, lt, unsp] palm, seq 232
T23.55[1,2,9]D	Corrosion of 1st degree of [rt, lt, unsp] palm, subsq enc 401
T22.56[1,2,9]A	Corrosion of 1st degree of [rt, lt, unsp] scapular rgn, init enc 383
T22.56[1,2,9]S	Corrosion of 1st degree of [rt, lt, unsp] scapular rgn, seq 231
T22.56[1,2,9]D	Corrosion of 1st degree of [rt, lt, unsp] scapular rgn, subsq enc 401
T22.55[1,2,9]A	Corrosion of 1st degree of [rt, lt, unsp] shldr, init enc 383
T22.55[1,2,9]S	Corrosion of 1st degree of [rt, lt, unsp] shldr, seq 231
T22.55[1,2,9]D	Corrosion of 1st degree of [rt, lt, unsp] shldr, subsq enc 401
T24.51[1,2,9]A	Corrosion of 1st degree of [rt, lt, unsp] thigh, init enc 384
T24.51[1,2,9]S	Corrosion of 1st degree of [rt, lt, unsp] thigh, seq 232
T24.51[1,2,9]D	Corrosion of 1st degree of [rt, lt, unsp] thigh, subsq enc 402
T23.51[1,2,9]A	Corrosion of 1st degree of [rt, lt, unsp] thumb (nail), init enc 383
T23.51[1,2,9]S	Corrosion of 1st degree of [rt, lt, unsp] thumb (nail), seq 232
T23.51[1,2,9]D	Corrosion of 1st degree of [rt, lt, unsp] thumb (nail), subsq enc 401
T25.53[1,2,9]A	Corrosion of 1st degree of [rt, lt, unsp] toe(s) (nail), init enc 384
T25.53[1,2,9]S	Corrosion of 1st degree of [rt, lt, unsp] toe(s) (nail), seq 232
T25.53[1,2,9]D	Corrosion of 1st degree of [rt, lt, unsp] toe(s) (nail), subsq enc 402
T22.53[1,2,9]A	Corrosion of 1st degree of [rt, lt, unsp] upr arm, init enc 383
T22.53[1,2,9]S	Corrosion of 1st degree of [rt, lt, unsp] upr arm, seq 231
T22.53[1,2,9]D	Corrosion of 1st degree of [rt, lt, unsp] upr arm, subsq enc 401
T23.57[1,2,9]A	Corrosion of 1st degree of [rt, lt, unsp] wrist, init enc 384
T23.57[1,2,9]S	Corrosion of 1st degree of [rt, lt, unsp] wrist, seq 232
T23.57[1,2,9]D	Corrosion of 1st degree of [rt, lt, unsp] wrist, subsq enc 401
T20.5[5,6,7]XS	Corrosion of 1st degree of [scalp [any part], cheek, neck], seq 231
T20.5[5,6,7]XA	Corrosion of 1st degree of [scalp [any part], forehead and cheek, neck], init enc 383
T20.5[5,6,7]XD	Corrosion of 1st degree of [scalp [any part], forehead and cheek, neck], subsq enc 400
T21.5[0,1,2,3,4,5, 6,7,9]XA	Corrosion of 1st degree of [unsp site of trunk, chest wall, abd wall, upr back, lwr back, buttock, male genital rgn, female genital rgn, oth site of trunk], init enc 383
T21.5[0,1,2,3,4,5, 6,7,9]XD	Corrosion of 1st degree of [unsp site of trunk, chest wall, abd wall, upr back, lwr back, buttock, male genital rgn, female genital rgn, oth site of trunk], subsq enc 400
T21.5[3,4,5]XS	Corrosion of 1st degree of [upr back, lwr back, buttock], seq 231
T23.56[1,2,9]A	Corrosion of 1st degree of back of [rt, lt, unsp] hand, init enc 384
T23.56[1,2,9]S	Corrosion of 1st degree of back of [rt, lt, unsp] hand, seq 232
T23.56[1,2,9]D	Corrosion of 1st degree of back of [rt, lt, unsp] hand, subsq enc 401
T23.54[1,2,9]A	Corrosion of 1st degree of multi [rt, lt, unsp] fingers (nail), incl* thumb, init enc 384
T23.54[1,2,9]S	Corrosion of 1st degree of multi [rt, lt, unsp] fingers (nail), incl* thumb, seq 232
T23.54[1,2,9]D	Corrosion of 1st degree of multi [rt, lt, unsp] fingers (nail), incl* thumb, subsq enc 401
T23.53[1,2,9]A	Corrosion of 1st degree of multi [rt, lt, unsp] fingers (nail), not incl* thumb, init enc 384
T23.53[1,2,9]S	Corrosion of 1st degree of multi [rt, lt, unsp] fingers (nail), not incl* thumb, seq 232
T23.53[1,2,9]D	Corrosion of 1st degree of multi [rt, lt, unsp] fingers (nail), not incl* thumb, subsq enc 401
T25.59[1,2,9]A	Corrosion of 1st degree of multi sites of [rt, lt, unsp] ankle and foot, init enc 384
T25.59[1,2,9]S	Corrosion of 1st degree of multi sites of [rt, lt, unsp] ankle and foot, seq 233
T25.59[1,2,9]D	Corrosion of 1st degree of multi sites of [rt, lt, unsp] ankle and foot, subsq enc 402
T24.59[1,2,9]A	Corrosion of 1st degree of multi sites of [rt, lt, unsp] lwr limb, except ankle and foot, init enc 384
T24.59[1,2,9]S	Corrosion of 1st degree of multi sites of [rt, lt, unsp] lwr limb, except ankle and foot, seq 232
T24.59[1,2,9]D	Corrosion of 1st degree of multi sites of [rt, lt, unsp] lwr limb, except ankle and foot, subsq enc 402
T22.59[1,2,9]A	Corrosion of 1st degree of multi sites of [rt, lt, unsp] shldr and upr limb, except wrist and hand, init enc 383
T22.59[1,2,9]S	Corrosion of 1st degree of multi sites of [rt, lt, unsp] shldr and upr limb, except wrist and hand, seq 231
T22.59[1,2,9]D	Corrosion of 1st degree of multi sites of [rt, lt, unsp] shldr and upr limb, except wrist and hand, subsq enc 401
T23.59[1,2,9]A	Corrosion of 1st degree of multi sites of [rt, lt, unsp] wrist and hand, init enc 384
T23.59[1,2,9]S	Corrosion of 1st degree of multi sites of [rt, lt, unsp] wrist and hand, seq 232
T23.59[1,2,9]D	Corrosion of 1st degree of multi sites of [rt, lt, unsp] wrist and hand, subsq enc 401
T23.52[1,2,9]A	Corrosion of 1st degree of single [rt, lt, unsp] finger (nail) except thumb, init enc 383
T23.52[1,2,9]S	Corrosion of 1st degree of single [rt, lt, unsp] finger (nail) except thumb, seq 232
T23.52[1,2,9]D	Corrosion of 1st degree of single [rt, lt, unsp] finger (nail) except thumb, subsq enc 401
T24.50[1,2,9]A	Corrosion of 1st degree of unsp site of [rt, lt, unsp] lwr limb, except ankle and foot, init enc 384
T24.50[1,2,9]S	Corrosion of 1st degree of unsp site of [rt, lt, unsp] lwr limb, except ankle and foot, seq 232
T24.50[1,2,9]D	Corrosion of 1st degree of unsp site of [rt, lt, unsp] lwr limb, except ankle and foot, subsq enc 402
T20.69XA	Corrosion of 2nd deg mul sites of head, face, and neck, init 383
T20.69XD	Corrosion of 2nd deg mul sites of head, face, and neck, subs 400
T23.66[1,2,9]S	Corrosion of 2nd degree back of [rt, lt, unsp] hand, seq 232
T21.6[1,2]XS	Corrosion of 2nd degree of [chest, abd] wall, seq 231
T20.6[2,3,4]XA	Corrosion of 2nd degree of [lip(s), chin, nose (septum)], init enc 383
T20.6[2,3,4]XS	Corrosion of 2nd degree of [lip(s), chin, nose (septum)], seq 231
T20.6[2,3,4]XD	Corrosion of 2nd degree of [lip(s), chin, nose (septum)], subsq enc 400
T21.6[6,7]XS	Corrosion of 2nd degree of [male, female] genital rgn, seq 231
T25.69[1,2,9]S	Corrosion of 2nd degree of [rt, lt, unsp] ankle and foot, seq 233
T25.61[1,2,9]A	Corrosion of 2nd degree of [rt, lt, unsp] ankle, init enc 384

Code	Description
T25.61[1,2,9]S	Corrosion of 2nd degree of [rt, lt, unsp] ankle, seq 233
T25.61[1,2,9]D	Corrosion of 2nd degree of [rt, lt, unsp] ankle, subsq enc 402
T22.64[1,2,9]A	Corrosion of 2nd degree of [rt, lt, unsp] axilla, init enc 383
T22.64[1,2,9]S	Corrosion of 2nd degree of [rt, lt, unsp] axilla, seq 231
T22.64[1,2,9]D	Corrosion of 2nd degree of [rt, lt, unsp] axilla, subsq enc 401
T20.61[1,2,9]A	Corrosion of 2nd degree of [rt, lt, unsp] ear [any part, except ear drum], init enc 383
T20.61[1,2,9]S	Corrosion of 2nd degree of [rt, lt, unsp] ear [any part, except ear drum], seq 231
T20.61[1,2,9]D	Corrosion of 2nd degree of [rt, lt, unsp] ear [any part, except ear drum], subsq enc 400
T22.62[1,2,9]A	Corrosion of 2nd degree of [rt, lt, unsp] elbow, init enc 383
T22.62[1,2,9]S	Corrosion of 2nd degree of [rt, lt, unsp] elbow, seq 231
T22.62[1,2,9]D	Corrosion of 2nd degree of [rt, lt, unsp] elbow, subsq enc 401
T25.62[1,2,9]A	Corrosion of 2nd degree of [rt, lt, unsp] foot, init enc 384
T25.62[1,2,9]S	Corrosion of 2nd degree of [rt, lt, unsp] foot, seq 233
T25.62[1,2,9]D	Corrosion of 2nd degree of [rt, lt, unsp] foot, subsq enc 402
T22.61[1,2,9]A	Corrosion of 2nd degree of [rt, lt, unsp] forearm, init enc 383
T22.61[1,2,9]S	Corrosion of 2nd degree of [rt, lt, unsp] forearm, seq 231
T22.61[1,2,9]D	Corrosion of 2nd degree of [rt, lt, unsp] forearm, subsq enc 401
T23.60[1,2,9]A	Corrosion of 2nd degree of [rt, lt, unsp] hand, unsp site, init enc 384
T23.60[1,2,9]S	Corrosion of 2nd degree of [rt, lt, unsp] hand, unsp site, seq 232
T23.60[1,2,9]D	Corrosion of 2nd degree of [rt, lt, unsp] hand, unsp site, subsq enc 401
T24.62[1,2,9]A	Corrosion of 2nd degree of [rt, lt, unsp] knee, init enc 384
T24.62[1,2,9]S	Corrosion of 2nd degree of [rt, lt, unsp] knee, seq 232
T24.62[1,2,9]D	Corrosion of 2nd degree of [rt, lt, unsp] knee, subsq enc 402
T24.63[1,2,9]A	Corrosion of 2nd degree of [rt, lt, unsp] lwr leg, init enc 384
T24.63[1,2,9]S	Corrosion of 2nd degree of [rt, lt, unsp] lwr leg, seq 232
T24.63[1,2,9]D	Corrosion of 2nd degree of [rt, lt, unsp] lwr leg, subsq enc 402
T23.65[1,2,9]A	Corrosion of 2nd degree of [rt, lt, unsp] palm, init enc 384
T23.65[1,2,9]S	Corrosion of 2nd degree of [rt, lt, unsp] palm, seq 232
T23.65[1,2,9]D	Corrosion of 2nd degree of [rt, lt, unsp] palm, subsq enc 401
T22.66[1,2,9]A	Corrosion of 2nd degree of [rt, lt, unsp] scapular rgn, init enc 383
T22.66[1,2,9]S	Corrosion of 2nd degree of [rt, lt, unsp] scapular rgn, seq 231
T22.66[1,2,9]D	Corrosion of 2nd degree of [rt, lt, unsp] scapular rgn, subsq enc 401
T22.65[1,2,9]A	Corrosion of 2nd degree of [rt, lt, unsp] shldr, init enc 383
T22.65[1,2,9]S	Corrosion of 2nd degree of [rt, lt, unsp] shldr, seq 231
T22.65[1,2,9]D	Corrosion of 2nd degree of [rt, lt, unsp] shldr, subsq enc 401
T24.61[1,2,9]A	Corrosion of 2nd degree of [rt, lt, unsp] thigh, init enc 384
T24.61[1,2,9]S	Corrosion of 2nd degree of [rt, lt, unsp] thigh, seq 232
T24.61[1,2,9]D	Corrosion of 2nd degree of [rt, lt, unsp] thigh, subsq enc 402
T23.61[1,2,9]A	Corrosion of 2nd degree of [rt, lt, unsp] thumb (nail), init enc 384
T23.61[1,2,9]S	Corrosion of 2nd degree of [rt, lt, unsp] thumb (nail), seq 232
T23.61[1,2,9]D	Corrosion of 2nd degree of [rt, lt, unsp] thumb (nail), subsq enc 401
T25.63[1,2,9]A	Corrosion of 2nd degree of [rt, lt, unsp] toe(s) (nail), init enc 384
T25.63[1,2,9]S	Corrosion of 2nd degree of [rt, lt, unsp] toe(s) (nail), seq 233
T25.63[1,2,9]D	Corrosion of 2nd degree of [rt, lt, unsp] toe(s) (nail), subsq enc 402
T22.63[1,2,9]A	Corrosion of 2nd degree of [rt, lt, unsp] upr arm, init enc 383
T22.63[1,2,9]S	Corrosion of 2nd degree of [rt, lt, unsp] upr arm, seq 231
T22.63[1,2,9]D	Corrosion of 2nd degree of [rt, lt, unsp] upr arm, subsq enc 401
T23.67[1,2,9]A	Corrosion of 2nd degree of [rt, lt, unsp] wrist, init enc 384
T23.67[1,2,9]S	Corrosion of 2nd degree of [rt, lt, unsp] wrist, seq 232
T23.67[1,2,9]D	Corrosion of 2nd degree of [rt, lt, unsp] wrist, subsq enc 401
T20.6[5,6,7]XA	Corrosion of 2nd degree of [scalp [any part], forehead and cheek, neck], init enc 383
T20.6[5,6,7]XS	Corrosion of 2nd degree of [scalp [any part], forehead and cheek, neck], seq 231
T20.6[5,6,7]XD	Corrosion of 2nd degree of [scalp [any part], forehead and cheek, neck], subsq enc 400
T21.6[0,1,2,3,4,5,6,7,9]XA	Corrosion of 2nd degree of [unsp site of trunk, chest wall, abd wall, upr back, lwr back, buttock, male genital rgn, female genital rgn, oth site of trunk], init enc 383
T21.6[0,1,2,3,4,5,6,7,9]XD	Corrosion of 2nd degree of [unsp site of trunk, chest wall, abd wall, upr back, lwr back, buttock, male genital rgn, female genital rgn, oth site of trunk], subsq enc 400
T21.6[3,4,5]XS	Corrosion of 2nd degree of [upr back, lwr back, buttock], seq 231
T23.66[1,2,9]A	Corrosion of 2nd degree of back of [rt, lt, unsp] hand, init enc 384
T23.66[1,2,9]D	Corrosion of 2nd degree of back of [rt, lt, unsp] hand, subsq enc 401
T23.64[1,2,9]A	Corrosion of 2nd degree of multi [rt, lt, unsp] fingers (nail), incl* thumb, init enc 384
T23.64[1,2,9]S	Corrosion of 2nd degree of multi [rt, lt, unsp] fingers (nail), incl* thumb, seq 232
T23.64[1,2,9]D	Corrosion of 2nd degree of multi [rt, lt, unsp] fingers (nail), incl* thumb, subsq enc 401
T23.63[1,2,9]A	Corrosion of 2nd degree of multi [rt, lt, unsp] fingers (nail), not incl* thumb, init enc 384
T23.63[1,2,9]S	Corrosion of 2nd degree of multi [rt, lt, unsp] fingers (nail), not incl* thumb, seq 232
T23.63[1,2,9]D	Corrosion of 2nd degree of multi [rt, lt, unsp] fingers (nail), not incl* thumb, subsq enc 401
T25.69[1,2,9]A	Corrosion of 2nd degree of multi sites of [rt, lt, unsp] ankle and foot, init enc 384
T25.69[1,2,9]D	Corrosion of 2nd degree of multi sites of [rt, lt, unsp] ankle and foot, subsq enc 402
T24.69[1,2,9]A	Corrosion of 2nd degree of multi sites of [rt, lt, unsp] lwr limb, except ankle and foot, init enc 384
T24.69[1,2,9]S	Corrosion of 2nd degree of multi sites of [rt, lt, unsp] lwr limb, except ankle and foot, seq 232
T24.69[1,2,9]D	Corrosion of 2nd degree of multi sites of [rt, lt, unsp] lwr limb, except ankle and foot, subsq enc 402
T22.69[1,2,9]A	Corrosion of 2nd degree of multi sites of [rt, lt, unsp] shldr and upr limb, except wrist and hand, init enc 383
T22.69[1,2,9]S	Corrosion of 2nd degree of multi sites of [rt, lt, unsp] shldr and upr limb, except wrist and hand, seq 231
T22.69[1,2,9]D	Corrosion of 2nd degree of multi sites of [rt, lt, unsp] shldr and upr limb, except wrist and hand, subsq enc 401
T23.69[1,2,9]A	Corrosion of 2nd degree of multi sites of [rt, lt, unsp] wrist and hand, init enc 384
T23.69[1,2,9]S	Corrosion of 2nd degree of multi sites of [rt, lt, unsp] wrist and hand, seq 232
T23.69[1,2,9]D	Corrosion of 2nd degree of multi sites of [rt, lt, unsp] wrist and hand, subsq enc 401
T21.69XS	Corrosion of 2nd degree of oth site of trunk, seq 231
T23.62[1,2,9]A	Corrosion of 2nd degree of single [rt, lt, unsp] finger (nail) except thumb, init enc 384
T23.62[1,2,9]S	Corrosion of 2nd degree of single [rt, lt, unsp] finger (nail) except thumb, seq 232
T23.62[1,2,9]D	Corrosion of 2nd degree of single [rt, lt, unsp] finger (nail) except thumb, subsq enc 401
T21.60XS	Corrosion of 2nd degree of trunk, unsp site, seq 231
T24.60[1,2,9]A	Corrosion of 2nd degree of unsp site of [rt, lt, unsp] lwr limb, except ankle and foot, init enc 384
T24.60[1,2,9]S	Corrosion of 2nd degree of unsp site of [rt, lt, unsp] lwr limb, except ankle and foot, seq 232
T24.60[1,2,9]D	Corrosion of 2nd degree of unsp site of [rt, lt, unsp] lwr limb, except ankle and foot, subsq enc 402
T20.79XA	Corrosion of 3rd deg mu sites of head, face, and neck, init 377, 379, 381, 382
T20.79XD	Corrosion of 3rd deg mu sites of head, face, and neck, subs 400
T21.7[1,2]XS	Corrosion of 3rd degree of [chest, abd] wall, seq 231
T20.7[2,3,4,5,6,7]XA	Corrosion of 3rd degree of [lip(s), chin, nose (septum), scalp (any part), forehead and cheek, neck], init enc 377, 379, 381, 382
T20.7[2,3,4]XS	Corrosion of 3rd degree of [lip(s), chin, nose (septum)], seq 231
T20.7[2,3,4]XD	Corrosion of 3rd degree of [lip(s), chin, nose (septum)], subsq enc 400
T21.7[6,7]XS	Corrosion of 3rd degree of [male, female] genital rgn, seq 231
T25.71[1,2,9]A	Corrosion of 3rd degree of [rt, lt, unsp] ankle, init enc 377, 379, 381, 382
T25.71[1,2,9]S	Corrosion of 3rd degree of [rt, lt, unsp] ankle, seq 233
T25.71[1,2,9]D	Corrosion of 3rd degree of [rt, lt, unsp] ankle, subsq enc 402
T22.74[1,2,9]A	Corrosion of 3rd degree of [rt, lt, unsp] axilla, init enc 377, 379, 381, 382
T22.74[1,2,9]S	Corrosion of 3rd degree of [rt, lt, unsp] axilla, seq 231
T22.74[1,2,9]D	Corrosion of 3rd degree of [rt, lt, unsp] axilla, subsq enc 401
T20.71[1,2,9]A	Corrosion of 3rd degree of [rt, lt, unsp] ear (any part, except ear drum), init enc 377, 379, 381, 382
T20.71[1,2,9]S	Corrosion of 3rd degree of [rt, lt, unsp] ear [any part, except ear drum], seq 231
T20.71[1,2,9]D	Corrosion of 3rd degree of [rt, lt, unsp] ear [any part, except ear drum], subsq enc 400
T22.72[1,2,9]A	Corrosion of 3rd degree of [rt, lt, unsp] elbow, init enc 377, 379, 381, 382

T22.72[1,2,9]S	Corrosion of 3rd degree of [rt, lt, unsp] elbow, seq **231**
T22.72[1,2,9]D	Corrosion of 3rd degree of [rt, lt, unsp] elbow, subsq enc **401**
T25.72[1,2,9]A	Corrosion of 3rd degree of [rt, lt, unsp] foot, init enc **377, 379, 381, 382**
T25.72[1,2,9]S	Corrosion of 3rd degree of [rt, lt, unsp] foot, seq **233**
T25.72[1,2,9]D	Corrosion of 3rd degree of [rt, lt, unsp] foot, subsq enc **402**
T22.71[1,2,9]A	Corrosion of 3rd degree of [rt, lt, unsp] forearm, init enc **377, 379, 381, 382**
T22.71[1,2,9]S	Corrosion of 3rd degree of [rt, lt, unsp] forearm, seq **231**
T22.71[1,2,9]D	Corrosion of 3rd degree of [rt, lt, unsp] forearm, subsq enc **401**
T23.70[1,2,9]A	Corrosion of 3rd degree of [rt, lt, unsp] hand, unsp site, init enc **377, 379, 381, 382**
T23.70[1,2,9]S	Corrosion of 3rd degree of [rt, lt, unsp] hand, unsp site, seq **232**
T23.70[1,2,9]D	Corrosion of 3rd degree of [rt, lt, unsp] hand, unsp site, subsq enc **401**
T24.72[1,2,9]A	Corrosion of 3rd degree of [rt, lt, unsp] knee, init enc **377, 379, 381, 382**
T24.72[1,2,9]S	Corrosion of 3rd degree of [rt, lt, unsp] knee, seq **232**
T24.72[1,2,9]D	Corrosion of 3rd degree of [rt, lt, unsp] knee, subsq enc **402**
T24.73[1,2,9]A	Corrosion of 3rd degree of [rt, lt, unsp] lwr leg, init enc **377, 379, 381, 382**
T24.73[1,2,9]S	Corrosion of 3rd degree of [rt, lt, unsp] lwr leg, seq **232**
T24.73[1,2,9]D	Corrosion of 3rd degree of [rt, lt, unsp] lwr leg, subsq enc **402**
T23.75[1,2,9]A	Corrosion of 3rd degree of [rt, lt, unsp] palm, init enc **377, 379, 381, 382**
T23.75[1,2,9]S	Corrosion of 3rd degree of [rt, lt, unsp] palm, seq **232**
T23.75[1,2,9]D	Corrosion of 3rd degree of [rt, lt, unsp] palm, subsq enc **402**
T22.76[1,2,9]A	Corrosion of 3rd degree of [rt, lt, unsp] scapular rgn, init enc **377, 379, 381, 382**
T22.76[1,2,9]S	Corrosion of 3rd degree of [rt, lt, unsp] scapular rgn, seq **231**
T22.76[1,2,9]D	Corrosion of 3rd degree of [rt, lt, unsp] scapular rgn, subsq enc **401**
T22.75[1,2,9]A	Corrosion of 3rd degree of [rt, lt, unsp] shldr, init enc **377, 379, 381, 382**
T22.75[1,2,9]S	Corrosion of 3rd degree of [rt, lt, unsp] shldr, seq **231**
T22.75[1,2,9]D	Corrosion of 3rd degree of [rt, lt, unsp] shldr, subsq enc **401**
T24.71[1,2,9]A	Corrosion of 3rd degree of [rt, lt, unsp] thigh, init enc **377, 379, 381, 382**
T24.71[1,2,9]S	Corrosion of 3rd degree of [rt, lt, unsp] thigh, seq **232**
T24.71[1,2,9]D	Corrosion of 3rd degree of [rt, lt, unsp] thigh, subsq enc **402**
T23.71[1,2,9]A	Corrosion of 3rd degree of [rt, lt, unsp] thumb (nail), init enc **377, 379, 381, 382**
T23.71[1,2,9]S	Corrosion of 3rd degree of [rt, lt, unsp] thumb (nail), seq **232**
T23.71[1,2,9]D	Corrosion of 3rd degree of [rt, lt, unsp] thumb (nail), subsq enc **401**
T25.73[1,2,9]A	Corrosion of 3rd degree of [rt, lt, unsp] toe(s) (nail), init enc **377, 379, 381, 382**
T25.73[1,2,9]S	Corrosion of 3rd degree of [rt, lt, unsp] toe(s) (nail), seq **233**
T25.73[1,2,9]D	Corrosion of 3rd degree of [rt, lt, unsp] toe(s) (nail), subsq enc **402**
T22.73[1,2,9]A	Corrosion of 3rd degree of [rt, lt, unsp] upr arm, init enc **377, 379, 381, 382**
T22.73[1,2,9]S	Corrosion of 3rd degree of [rt, lt, unsp] upr arm, seq **231**
T22.73[1,2,9]D	Corrosion of 3rd degree of [rt, lt, unsp] upr arm, subsq enc **401**
T23.77[1,2,9]A	Corrosion of 3rd degree of [rt, lt, unsp] wrist, init enc **377, 379, 381, 382**
T23.77[1,2,9]S	Corrosion of 3rd degree of [rt, lt, unsp] wrist, seq **232**
T23.77[1,2,9]D	Corrosion of 3rd degree of [rt, lt, unsp] wrist, subsq enc **402**
T20.7[5,6,7]XS	Corrosion of 3rd degree of [scalp [any part], forehead and cheek, neck], seq **231**
T20.7[5,6,7]XD	Corrosion of 3rd degree of [scalp [any part], forehead and cheek, neck], subsq enc **400**
T21.7[0,1,2,3,4,5, 6,7,9]XA	Corrosion of 3rd degree of [trunk, unsp site, chest wall, abd wall, upr back, lwr back, buttock, male genital rgn, femal genital rgn, oth site of trunk], init enc **377, 379, 381, 382**
T21.7[0,1,2,3,4,5, 6,7,9]XD	Corrosion of 3rd degree of [unsp site of trunk, chest wall, abd wall, upr back, lwr back, buttock, male genital rgn, female genital rgn, oth site of trunk], subsq enc **400**
T21.7[3,4,5]XS	Corrosion of 3rd degree of [upr back, lwr back, buttock], seq **231**
T23.76[1,2,9]A	Corrosion of 3rd degree of back of [rt, lt, unsp] hand, init enc **377, 379, 381, 382**
T23.76[1,2,9]S	Corrosion of 3rd degree of back of [rt, lt, unsp] hand, seq **232**
T23.76[1,2,9]D	Corrosion of 3rd degree of back of [rt, lt, unsp] hand, subsq enc **402**
T23.74[1,2,9]A	Corrosion of 3rd degree of multi [rt, lt, unsp] fingers (nail), incl* thumb, init enc **377, 379, 381, 382**
T23.74[1,2,9]S	Corrosion of 3rd degree of multi [rt, lt, unsp] fingers (nail), incl* thumb, seq **232**
T23.74[1,2,9]D	Corrosion of 3rd degree of multi [rt, lt, unsp] fingers (nail), incl* thumb, subsq enc **402**
T23.73[1,2,9]A	Corrosion of 3rd degree of multi [rt, lt, unsp] fingers (nail), not incl* thumb, init enc **377, 379, 381, 382**
T23.73[1,2,9]S	Corrosion of 3rd degree of multi [rt, lt, unsp] fingers (nail), not incl* thumb, seq **232**
T23.73[1,2,9]D	Corrosion of 3rd degree of multi [rt, lt, unsp] fingers (nail), not incl* thumb, subsq enc **402**
T25.79[1,2,9]A	Corrosion of 3rd degree of multi sites of [rt, lt, unsp] ankle and foot, init enc **377, 379, 381, 382**
T25.79[1,2,9]S	Corrosion of 3rd degree of multi sites of [rt, lt, unsp] ankle and foot, seq **233**
T25.79[1,2,9]D	Corrosion of 3rd degree of multi sites of [rt, lt, unsp] ankle and foot, subsq enc **402**
T24.79[1,2,9]A	Corrosion of 3rd degree of multi sites of [rt, lt, unsp] lwr limb, except ankle and foot, init enc **377, 379, 381, 382**
T24.79[1,2,9]S	Corrosion of 3rd degree of multi sites of [rt, lt, unsp] lwr limb, except ankle and foot, seq **232**
T24.79[1,2,9]D	Corrosion of 3rd degree of multi sites of [rt, lt, unsp] lwr limb, except ankle and foot, subsq enc **402**
T22.79[1,2,9]A	Corrosion of 3rd degree of multi sites of [rt, lt, unsp] shldr and upr limb, except wrist and hand, init enc **377, 379, 381, 382**
T22.79[1,2,9]S	Corrosion of 3rd degree of multi sites of [rt, lt, unsp] shldr and upr limb, except wrist and hand, seq **231**
T22.79[1,2,9]D	Corrosion of 3rd degree of multi sites of [rt, lt, unsp] shldr and upr limb, except wrist and hand, subsq enc **401**
T23.79[1,2,9]A	Corrosion of 3rd degree of multi sites of [rt, lt, unsp] wrist and hand, init enc **377, 379, 381, 382**
T23.79[1,2,9]S	Corrosion of 3rd degree of multi sites of [rt, lt, unsp] wrist and hand, seq **232**
T23.79[1,2,9]D	Corrosion of 3rd degree of multi sites of [rt, lt, unsp] wrist and hand, subsq enc **402**
T21.79XS	Corrosion of 3rd degree of oth site of trunk, seq **231**
T23.72[1,2,9]A	Corrosion of 3rd degree of single [rt, lt, unsp] finger (nail) except thumb, init enc **377, 379, 381, 382**
T23.72[1,2,9]S	Corrosion of 3rd degree of single [rt, lt, unsp] finger (nail) except thumb, seq **232**
T23.72[1,2,9]D	Corrosion of 3rd degree of single [rt, lt, unsp] finger (nail) except thumb, subsq enc **401**
T21.70XS	Corrosion of 3rd degree of trunk, unsp site, seq **231**
T24.70[1,2,9]A	Corrosion of 3rd degree of unsp site of [rt, lt, unsp] lwr limb, except ankle and foot, init enc **377, 379, 381, 382**
T24.70[1,2,9]S	Corrosion of 3rd degree of unsp site of [rt, lt, unsp] lwr limb, except ankle and foot, seq **232**
T24.70[1,2,9]D	Corrosion of 3rd degree of unsp site of [rt, lt, unsp] lwr limb, except ankle and foot, subsq enc **402**
T26.6[0,1,2]XA	Corrosion of cornea and conjunctival sac, [unsp, rt, lt] eye, init enc **47**
T26.6[0,1,2]XS	Corrosion of cornea and conjunctival sac, [unsp, rt, lt] eye, seq **233**
T26.6[0,1,2]XD	Corrosion of cornea and conjunctival sac, [unsp, rt, lt] eye, subsq enc **402**
T28.6XXA	Corrosion of esophagus, init enc **114**
T28.6XXS	Corrosion of esophagus, seq **233**
T28.6XXD	Corrosion of esophagus, subsq enc **402**
T21.59XS	Corrosion of first degree of oth site of trunk, seq **231**
T21.50XS	Corrosion of first degree of trunk, unsp site, seq **231**
T28.8XXA	Corrosion of int genitourinary organs, init enc **384**
T28.8XXS	Corrosion of int genitourinary organs, seq **233**
T28.8XXD	Corrosion of int genitourinary organs, subs enc **402**
T27.4XXA	Corrosion of larynx and trachea, init enc **381**
T27.4XXS	Corrosion of larynx and trachea, seq **233**
T27.4XXD	Corrosion of larynx and trachea, subsq enc **402**
T28.5XXA	Corrosion of mouth and pharynx, init enc **6, 58**
T28.5XXS	Corrosion of mouth and pharynx, seq **233**
T28.5XXD	Corrosion of mouth and pharynx, subsq enc **402**
T28.7XXS	Corrosion of oth parts of alimentary tract, seq **233**
T28.7XXD	Corrosion of oth parts of alimentary tract, subs enc **402**
T27.6XXA	Corrosion of oth parts of respiratory tract, init enc **381**
T27.6XXD	Corrosion of oth parts of respiratory tract, subs enc **402**
T26.8[0,1,2]XS	Corrosion of oth spec parts of [unsp, rt, lt] eye and adnexa, seq **233**
T27.7XXA	Corrosion of respiratory tract, part unsp, init enc **381**

Code	Description
T27.7XXD	Corrosion of respiratory tract, part unsp, subs enc 402
T30.4	Corrosion of unsp body region, unsp degree 384
T21.4[1,2]XS	Corrosion of unsp degree of [chest, abd] wall, seq 231
T20.4[2,3,4]XA	Corrosion of unsp degree of [lip(s), chin, nose (septum)], init enc 383
T20.4[2,3,4]XS	Corrosion of unsp degree of [lip(s), chin, nose (septum)], seq 230
T20.4[2,3,4]XD	Corrosion of unsp degree of [lip(s), chin, nose (septum)], subsq enc 400
T21.4[6,7]XS	Corrosion of unsp degree of [male, female] genital rgn, seq 231
T25.41[1,2,9]A	Corrosion of unsp degree of [rt, lt, unsp] ankle, init enc 384
T25.41[1,2,9]S	Corrosion of unsp degree of [rt, lt, unsp] ankle, seq 232
T25.41[1,2,9]D	Corrosion of unsp degree of [rt, lt, unsp] ankle, subsq enc 402
T22.44[1,2,9]A	Corrosion of unsp degree of [rt, lt, unsp] axilla, init enc 383
T22.44[1,2,9]S	Corrosion of unsp degree of [rt, lt, unsp] axilla, seq 231
T22.44[1,2,9]D	Corrosion of unsp degree of [rt, lt, unsp] axilla, subsq enc 401
T20.41[1,2,9]A	Corrosion of unsp degree of [rt, lt, unsp] ear [any part, except ear drum], init enc 383
T20.41[1,2,9]S	Corrosion of unsp degree of [rt, lt, unsp] ear [any part, except ear drum], seq 230
T20.41[1,2,9]D	Corrosion of unsp degree of [rt, lt, unsp] ear [any part, except ear drum], subsq enc 400
T22.42[1,2,9]A	Corrosion of unsp degree of [rt, lt, unsp] elbow, init enc 383
T22.42[1,2,9]S	Corrosion of unsp degree of [rt, lt, unsp] elbow, seq 231
T22.42[1,2,9]D	Corrosion of unsp degree of [rt, lt, unsp] elbow, subsq enc 401
T25.42[1,2,9]A	Corrosion of unsp degree of [rt, lt, unsp] foot, init enc 384
T25.42[1,2,9]S	Corrosion of unsp degree of [rt, lt, unsp] foot, seq 232
T25.42[1,2,9]D	Corrosion of unsp degree of [rt, lt, unsp] foot, subsq enc 402
T22.41[1,2,9]A	Corrosion of unsp degree of [rt, lt, unsp] forearm, init enc 383
T22.41[1,2,9]S	Corrosion of unsp degree of [rt, lt, unsp] forearm, seq 231
T22.41[1,2,9]D	Corrosion of unsp degree of [rt, lt, unsp] forearm, subsq enc 401
T23.40[1,2,9]A	Corrosion of unsp degree of [rt, lt, unsp] hand, unsp site, init enc 383
T23.40[1,2,9]S	Corrosion of unsp degree of [rt, lt, unsp] hand, unsp site, seq 232
T23.40[1,2,9]D	Corrosion of unsp degree of [rt, lt, unsp] hand, unsp site, subsq enc 401
T24.42[1,2,9]A	Corrosion of unsp degree of [rt, lt, unsp] knee, init enc 384
T24.42[1,2,9]S	Corrosion of unsp degree of [rt, lt, unsp] knee, seq 232
T24.42[1,2,9]D	Corrosion of unsp degree of [rt, lt, unsp] knee, subsq enc 402
T24.43[1,2,9]A	Corrosion of unsp degree of [rt, lt, unsp] lwr leg, init enc 384
T24.43[1,2,9]S	Corrosion of unsp degree of [rt, lt, unsp] lwr leg, seq 232
T24.43[1,2,9]D	Corrosion of unsp degree of [rt, lt, unsp] lwr leg, subsq enc 402
T23.45[1,2,9]A	Corrosion of unsp degree of [rt, lt, unsp] palm, init enc 383
T23.45[1,2,9]S	Corrosion of unsp degree of [rt, lt, unsp] palm, seq 232
T23.45[1,2,9]D	Corrosion of unsp degree of [rt, lt, unsp] palm, subsq enc 401
T22.46[1,2,9]A	Corrosion of unsp degree of [rt, lt, unsp] scapular rgn, init enc 383
T22.46[1,2,9]S	Corrosion of unsp degree of [rt, lt, unsp] scapular rgn, seq 231
T22.46[1,2,9]D	Corrosion of unsp degree of [rt, lt, unsp] scapular rgn, subsq enc 401
T22.45[1,2,9]A	Corrosion of unsp degree of [rt, lt, unsp] shldr, init enc 383
T22.45[1,2,9]S	Corrosion of unsp degree of [rt, lt, unsp] shldr, seq 231
T22.45[1,2,9]D	Corrosion of unsp degree of [rt, lt, unsp] shldr, subsq enc 401
T24.41[1,2,9]A	Corrosion of unsp degree of [rt, lt, unsp] thigh, init enc 384
T24.41[1,2,9]S	Corrosion of unsp degree of [rt, lt, unsp] thigh, seq 232
T24.41[1,2,9]D	Corrosion of unsp degree of [rt, lt, unsp] thigh, subsq enc 402
T23.41[1,2,9]A	Corrosion of unsp degree of [rt, lt, unsp] thumb (nail), init enc 383
T23.41[1,2,9]S	Corrosion of unsp degree of [rt, lt, unsp] thumb (nail), seq 232
T23.41[1,2,9]D	Corrosion of unsp degree of [rt, lt, unsp] thumb (nail), subsq enc 401
T25.43[1,2,9]A	Corrosion of unsp degree of [rt, lt, unsp] toe(s) (nail), init enc 384
T25.43[1,2,9]S	Corrosion of unsp degree of [rt, lt, unsp] toe(s) (nail), seq 232
T25.43[1,2,9]D	Corrosion of unsp degree of [rt, lt, unsp] toe(s) (nail), subsq enc 402
T22.43[1,2,9]A	Corrosion of unsp degree of [rt, lt, unsp] upr arm, init enc 383
T22.43[1,2,9]S	Corrosion of unsp degree of [rt, lt, unsp] upr arm, seq 231
T22.43[1,2,9]D	Corrosion of unsp degree of [rt, lt, unsp] upr arm, subsq enc 401
T23.47[1,2,9]A	Corrosion of unsp degree of [rt, lt, unsp] wrist, init enc 383
T23.47[1,2,9]S	Corrosion of unsp degree of [rt, lt, unsp] wrist, seq 232
T23.47[1,2,9]D	Corrosion of unsp degree of [rt, lt, unsp] wrist, subsq enc 401
T20.4[5,6,7]XA	Corrosion of unsp degree of [scalp [any part], forehead and cheek, neck], init enc 383
T20.4[5,6,7]XS	Corrosion of unsp degree of [scalp [any part], forehead and cheek, neck], seq 230
T20.4[5,6,7]XD	Corrosion of unsp degree of [scalp [any part], forehead and cheek, neck], subsq enc 400
T21.4[0,1,2,3,4,5,6,7,9]XA	Corrosion of unsp degree of [unsp site of trunk, chest wall, abd wall, upr back, lwr back, buttock, male genital rgn, female genital rgn, oth site of trunk], init enc 383
T21.4[0,1,2,3,4,5,6,7,9]XD	Corrosion of unsp degree of [unsp site of trunk, chest wall, abd wall, upr back, lwr back, buttock, male genital rgn, female genital rgn, oth site of trunk], subsq enc 400
T21.4[3,4,5]XS	Corrosion of unsp degree of [upr back, lwr back, buttock], seq 231
T23.46[1,2,9]A	Corrosion of unsp degree of back of [rt, lt, unsp] hand, init enc 383
T23.46[1,2,9]S	Corrosion of unsp degree of back of [rt, lt, unsp] hand, seq 232
T23.46[1,2,9]D	Corrosion of unsp degree of back of [rt, lt, unsp] hand, subsq enc 401
T23.44[1,2,9]A	Corrosion of unsp degree of multi [rt, lt, unsp] fingers (nail), incl* thumb, init enc 383
T23.44[1,2,9]S	Corrosion of unsp degree of multi [rt, lt, unsp] fingers (nail), incl* thumb, seq 232
T23.44[1,2,9]D	Corrosion of unsp degree of multi [rt, lt, unsp] fingers (nail), incl* thumb, subsq enc 401
T23.43[1,2,9]A	Corrosion of unsp degree of multi [rt, lt, unsp] fingers (nail), not incl* thumb, init enc 383
T23.43[1,2,9]S	Corrosion of unsp degree of multi [rt, lt, unsp] fingers (nail), not incl* thumb, seq 232
T23.43[1,2,9]D	Corrosion of unsp degree of multi [rt, lt, unsp] fingers (nail), not incl* thumb, subsq enc 401
T25.49[1,2,9]A	Corrosion of unsp degree of multi sites of [rt, lt, unsp] ankle and foot, init enc 384
T25.49[1,2,9]S	Corrosion of unsp degree of multi sites of [rt, lt, unsp] ankle and foot, seq 232
T25.49[1,2,9]D	Corrosion of unsp degree of multi sites of [rt, lt, unsp] ankle and foot, subsq enc 402
T24.49[1,2,9]A	Corrosion of unsp degree of multi sites of [rt, lt, unsp] lwr limb, except ankle and foot, init enc 384
T24.49[1,2,9]S	Corrosion of unsp degree of multi sites of [rt, lt, unsp] lwr limb, except ankle and foot, seq 232
T24.49[1,2,9]D	Corrosion of unsp degree of multi sites of [rt, lt, unsp] lwr limb, except ankle and foot, subsq enc 402
T22.49[1,2,9]A	Corrosion of unsp degree of multi sites of [rt, lt, unsp] shldr and upr limb, except wrist and hand, init enc 383
T22.49[1,2,9]S	Corrosion of unsp degree of multi sites of [rt, lt, unsp] shldr and upr limb, except wrist and hand, seq 231
T22.49[1,2,9]D	Corrosion of unsp degree of multi sites of [rt, lt, unsp] shldr and upr limb, except wrist and hand, subsq enc 401
T23.49[1,2,9]A	Corrosion of unsp degree of multi sites of [rt, lt, unsp] wrist and hand, init enc 383
T23.49[1,2,9]S	Corrosion of unsp degree of multi sites of [rt, lt, unsp] wrist and hand, seq 232
T23.49[1,2,9]D	Corrosion of unsp degree of multi sites of [rt, lt, unsp] wrist and hand, subsq enc 401
T21.49XS	Corrosion of unsp degree of oth site of trunk, seq 231
T23.42[1,2,9]A	Corrosion of unsp degree of single [rt, lt, unsp] finger (nail) except thumb, init enc 383
T23.42[1,2,9]S	Corrosion of unsp degree of single [rt, lt, unsp] finger (nail) except thumb, seq 232
T23.42[1,2,9]D	Corrosion of unsp degree of single [rt, lt, unsp] finger (nail) except thumb, subsq enc 401
T21.40XS	Corrosion of unsp degree of trunk, unsp site, seq 231
T24.40[1,2,9]A	Corrosion of unsp degree of unsp site of [rt, lt, unsp] lwr limb, except ankle and foot, init enc 384
T24.40[1,2,9]S	Corrosion of unsp degree of unsp site of [rt, lt, unsp] lwr limb, except ankle and foot, seq 232
T24.40[1,2,9]D	Corrosion of unsp degree of unsp site of [rt, lt, unsp] lwr limb, except ankle and foot, subsq enc 402
T20.49XA	Corrosion unsp deg mult sites of head, face, and neck, init 383
T20.49XS	Corrosion unsp deg mult sites of head, face, and neck, seq 230
T20.49XD	Corrosion unsp deg mult sites of head, face, and neck, subs 400
T22.40XA	Corrosion unsp deg of shldr/up lmb, ex wrs/hnd, unsp site, init 383
T22.40XS	Corrosion unsp deg of shldr/up lmb, ex wrs/hnd, unsp site, seq 231
T22.40XD	Corrosion unsp deg of shldr/up lmb, ex wrs/hnd, unsp site, subs 401
T20.40XA	Corrosion unsp degree of head, face, and neck, unsp site, init 383
T20.40XS	Corrosion unsp degree of head, face, and neck, unsp site, seq 230
T20.40XD	Corrosion unsp degree of head, face, and neck, unsp site, subs 400

T26.7[0,1,2]XA	Corrosion w/ resulting rupture and destr of [unsp, rt, lt] eyeball, init enc 47
T26.7[0,1,2]XS	Corrosion w/ resulting rupture and destr of [unsp, rt, lt] eyeball, seq 233
T26.7[0,1,2]XD	Corrosion w/ resulting rupture and destr of [unsp, rt, lt] eyeball, subsq enc 402
T32.2[1,2]	Corrosions involving 20-29% of body surface w/ [10-19, 20-29]% 3rd degree burns 379, 382
T32.3[1,2,3]	Corrosions involving 30-39% of body surface w/ [10-19, 20-29, 30-39]% 3rd degree burns 379, 382
T32.0	Corrosions involving < 10% of body surface 384
T32.4[1,2,3,4]	Corrosions involving 40-49% of body surface w/ [10-19, 20-29, 30-39, 40-49]% 3rd degree burns 379, 382
T32.5[1,2,3,4,5]	Corrosions involving 50-59% of body surface w/ [10-19, 20-29, 30-39, 40-49, 50-59]% 3rd degree burns 379, 382
T32.6[1,2,3,4,5,6]	Corrosions involving 60-69% of body surface w/ [10-19, 20-29, 30-39, 40-49, 50-59, 60-69]% 3rd degree burns 379, 382
T32.7[1,2,3,4,5,6,7]	Corrosions involving 70-79% of body surface w/ [10-19, 20-29, 30-39, 40-49, 50-59, 60-69, 70-79]% 3rd degree burns 379, 382
T32.8[1,2,3,4,5,6,7,8]	Corrosions sinvoling 80-89% of body surface w/ [10-19, 20-29, 30-39, 40-49, 50-59, 60-69, 70-79, 80-89]% 3rd degree burns 379, 382
T32.9[1,2,3,4,5,6,7,8,9]	Corrosions involving 90% or more of body surface w/ [10-19, 20-29, 30-39, 40-49, 50-59, 60-69, 70-79, 80-89, 90 or more]% 3rd degree burns 379, 382
T28.91[1,2,9]S	Corrosions of [rt, lt, unsp] ear drum, seq 233
T26.9[0,1,2]XD	Corrosions of [unsp, rt, lt] eye and adnexa, part unsp, subsq enc 402
T28.99XA	Corrosions of oth int organs, init enc 384
T28.99XS	Corrosions of oth int organs, seq 233
T28.99XD	Corrosions of oth int organs, subsq enc 402
T26.8[0,1,2]XA	Corrosions of oth spec parts of [unsp, rt, lt] eye and adnexa, init enc 47
T26.8[0,1,2]XD	Corrosions of oth spec parts of [unsp, rt, lt] eye and adnexa, subsq enc 402
T28.90XA	Corrosions of unsp int organs, init enc 384
T28.90XS	Corrosions of unsp int organs, seq 233
T28.90XD	Corrosions of unsp int organs, subs enc 402
R05	Cough 69
Z70*	Counseling related to sexual attitude, behav and orientn 412
B08.010	Cowpox 307
M34.1	CR(E)ST synd 164
O92.13	Cracked nipple associated with lactation 276
O92.119	Cracked nipple associated with preg, unsp trmstr 281
O92.12	Cracked nipple associated with the puerperium 276
O92.1[2,3]	Cracked nipple assoicated w/ [the puerperium, lactation] 272
G53	Cranial nerve d/o in dz classified elsw 34
M70.0*	Crepitant synovitis (acute) (chr) of hand and wrist 167
E80.5	Crigler-Najjar synd 124
A98.0	Crimean-Congo hemorrhagic fever 307
K50*	Crohn's dz [regional enteritis] 116
N13.5	Crossing vessel and stricture of ureter w/o hydronephrosis 255
S28.0XXA	Crushed chest, init enc 359, 421, 433
S28.0XXS	Crushed chest, seq 225
S28.0XXD	Crushed chest, subsq enc 389
S07.[0,1,8,9]XXA	Crushing inj of [face, skull, oth parts of head, head part unsp], init enc 359, 431
S07.[0,1,8,9]XXD	Crushing inj of [face, skull, oth parts of head, head part unsp], subsq enc 387
S07.[0,1,8]XXS	Crushing inj of [face, skull, oth parts of head], seq 225
S17.[0,8,9]XXA	Crushing inj of [larynx and trachea, oth spec parts of neck, unsp part of neck], init enc 359, 420, 431
S38.0[1,2]XS	Crushing inj of [penis, scrotum and testes], seq 227
S38.0[1,2,3]XD	Crushing inj of [penis, scrotum and testis, vulva] subsq enc 391
S38.0[1,2,3]XA	Crushing inj of [penis, scrotum and testis, vulva], init enc 422
S67.19[0,1,2,3,4,5,6,7,8]A	Crushing inj of [rt index, lt index, rt ring, lt ring, rt mid, lt mid, rt little, lt little, oth] finger, init enc 360, 425
S67.19[0,1,2,3,4,5,6,7,8]D	Crushing inj of [rt index, lt index, rt ring, lt ring, rt mid, lt mid, rt little, lt little, oth] finger, subsq enc 397
S97.11[1,2,9]S	Crushing inj of [rt, lt, unsp] great toe, seq 230
S97.11[1,2,9]D	Crushing inj of [rt, lt, unsp] great toe, subsq enc 400
S97.12[1,2,9]S	Crushing inj of [rt, lt, unsp] lesser toe(s), seq 230
S97.12[1,2,9]D	Crushing inj of [rt, lt, unsp] lesser toe(s), subsq enc 400
S47.[1,2,9]XXA	Crushing inj of [rt, lt, unsp] shldr and upr arm, init enc 359, 423, 434
S47.[1,2,9]XXS	Crushing inj of [rt, lt, unsp] shldr and upr arm, seq 227
S67.19[0,1]S	Crushing inj of [rt, lt] index finger, seq 229
S67.19[6,7]S	Crushing inj of [rt, lt] little finger, seq 229
S67.19[2,3]S	Crushing inj of [rt, lt] mid finger, seq 229
S67.19[4,5]S	Crushing inj of [rt, lt] ring finger, seq 229
S38.0[02,3X]A	Crushing inj of [unsp ext genital organs female, vulva] init enc 265, 270
S97.1[0,1,2][1,2,9]A	Crushing inj of [unsp rt, unsp lt, unsp, rt great, lt great, unsp great, rt lesser, lt lesser, unsp lesser] toe(s), init enc 361, 430
S57.[0,8][0,1,2]XA	Crushing inj of [unsp, rt, lt] [elbow, forearm], init enc 424, 435
S77.[0,1,2][0,1,2]XA	Crushing inj of [unsp, rt, lt] [hip, thigh, hip w/ thigh], init enc 426, 436
S77.[0,1,2][0,1,2]XD	Crushing inj of [unsp, rt, lt] [hip, thigh, hip w/ thigh], subsq enc 398
S97.0[0,1,2]XA	Crushing inj of [unsp, rt, lt] ankle, init enc 361, 430
S97.0[0,1,2]XS	Crushing inj of [unsp, rt, lt] ankle, seq 230
S97.0[0,1,2]XD	Crushing inj of [unsp, rt, lt] ankle, subsq enc 400
S57.0[0,1,2]XS	Crushing inj of [unsp, rt, lt] elbow, seq 227
S57.0[0,1,2]XD	Crushing inj of [unsp, rt, lt] elbow, subsq enc 393
S97.8[0,1,2]XA	Crushing inj of [unsp, rt, lt] foot, init enc 361, 430
S97.8[0,1,2]XS	Crushing inj of [unsp, rt, lt] foot, seq 230
S97.8[0,1,2]XD	Crushing inj of [unsp, rt, lt] foot, subsq enc 400
S57.8[0,1,2]XS	Crushing inj of [unsp, rt, lt] forearm, seq 227
S57.8[0,1,2]XD	Crushing inj of [unsp, rt, lt] forearm, subsq enc 393
S67.2[0,1,2]XA	Crushing inj of [unsp, rt, lt] hand, init enc 360, 425
S67.2[0,1,2]XS	Crushing inj of [unsp, rt, lt] hand, seq 229
S67.2[0,1,2]XD	Crushing inj of [unsp, rt, lt] hand, subsq enc 397
S77.2[0,1,2]XA	Crushing inj of [unsp, rt, lt] hip w/ thigh, intial enc 360
S77.2[0,1,2]XS	Crushing inj of [unsp, rt, lt] hip w/ thigh, seq 229
S77.0[0,1,2]XA	Crushing inj of [unsp, rt, lt] hip, intial enc 360
S77.0[0,1,2]XS	Crushing inj of [unsp, rt, lt] hip, seq 229
S87.0[0,1,2]XA	Crushing inj of [unsp, rt, lt] knee, init enc 361, 428, 436
S87.0[0,1,2]XS	Crushing inj of [unsp, rt, lt] knee, seq 229
S87.0[0,1,2]XD	Crushing inj of [unsp, rt, lt] knee, subsq enc 398
S87.8[0,1,2]XA	Crushing inj of [unsp, rt, lt] lwr leg, init enc 361, 428, 436
S87.8[0,1,2]XS	Crushing inj of [unsp, rt, lt] lwr leg, seq 229
S87.8[0,1,2]XD	Crushing inj of [unsp, rt, lt] lwr leg, subsq enc 398
S67.9[0,1,2]XS	Crushing inj of [unsp, rt, lt] part(s) of unsp wrist, hand and fingers, seq 229
S77.1[0,1,2]XA	Crushing inj of [unsp, rt, lt] thigh, intial enc 360
S77.1[0,1,2]XS	Crushing inj of [unsp, rt, lt] thigh, seq 229
S67.0[0,1,2]XA	Crushing inj of [unsp, rt, lt] thumb, init enc 360, 425
S67.0[0,1,2]XS	Crushing inj of [unsp, rt, lt] thumb, seq 229
S67.0[0,1,2]XD	Crushing inj of [unsp, rt, lt] thumb, subsq enc 397
S67.4[0,1,2]XA	Crushing inj of [unsp, rt, lt] wrist and hand, init enc 360, 425
S67.4[0,1,2]XS	Crushing inj of [unsp, rt, lt] wrist and hand, seq 229
S67.4[0,1,2]XD	Crushing inj of [unsp, rt, lt] wrist and hand, subsq enc 397
S67.3[0,1,2]XA	Crushing inj of [unsp, rt, lt] wrist, init enc 360, 425
S67.3[0,1,2]XS	Crushing inj of [unsp, rt, lt] wrist, seq 229
S67.3[0,1,2]XD	Crushing inj of [unsp, rt, lt] wrist, subsq enc 397
S38.1XXA	Crushing inj of abd, lwr back, and pelvis, init 359, 422, 433
S38.1XXS	Crushing inj of abd, lwr back, and pelvis, seq 227
S38.1XXD	Crushing inj of abd, lwr back, and pelvis, subs 391
S07.0XXA	Crushing inj of face, init enc 5, 419
S07.9XXA	Crushing inj of head, part unsp, init enc 5, 419
S07.9XXS	Crushing inj of head, part unsp, seq 225
S17.0XXA	Crushing inj of larynx and trachea, init enc 5
S17.0XXS	Crushing inj of larynx and trachea, seq 225
S17.0XXD	Crushing inj of larynx and trachea, subsq enc 388
S57.02XA	Crushing inj of lt elbow, init enc 360
S57.82XA	Crushing inj of lt forearm, init enc 360
S47.2XXD	Crushing inj of lt shldr and upr arm, subs enc 392
S17.9XXA	Crushing inj of neck, part unsp, init enc 5
S17.9XXS	Crushing inj of neck, part unsp, seq 225
S17.9XXD	Crushing inj of neck, part unsp, subs enc 388
S67.198S	Crushing inj of oth finger, seq 229
S07.8XXA	Crushing inj of oth parts of head, init enc 5, 419
S17.8XXA	Crushing inj of oth parts of neck, init enc 5

S17.8XXD	Crushing inj of oth parts of neck, subs enc 388
S17.8XXS	Crushing inj of oth spec parts of neck, seq 225
S38.01XA	Crushing inj of penis, init enc 261
S57.01XA	Crushing inj of rt elbow, init enc 360
S57.81XA	Crushing inj of rt forearm, init enc 360
S47.1XXD	Crushing inj of rt shldr and upr arm, subs enc 392
S38.02XA	Crushing inj of scrotum and testis, init enc 261
S47.9XXD	Crushing inj of shldr and upr arm, unsp arm, subs 392
S07.1XXA	Crushing inj of skull, init enc 5, 419
S97.10[1,2,9]S	Crushing inj of unsp [rt, lt, unsp] toe(s), seq 230
S97.10[1,2,9]D	Crushing inj of unsp [rt, lt, unsp] toe(s), subsq enc 400
S57.00XA	Crushing inj of unsp elbow, init enc 360
S38.00[1,2]D	Crushing inj of unsp ext genital organs, [male, female] subsq enc 391
S38.00[1,2]A	Crushing inj of unsp ext genital organs, [male, female], init enc 422
S38.00[1,2]S	Crushing inj of unsp ext genital organs, [male, female], seq 227
S38.001A	Crushing inj of unsp ext genital organs, male, init enc 261
S67.10XA	Crushing inj of unsp finger(s), init enc 360, 425
S67.10XS	Crushing inj of unsp finger(s), seq 229
S67.10XD	Crushing inj of unsp finger(s), subs enc 397
S57.80XA	Crushing inj of unsp forearm, init enc 360
S67.9[0,1,2]XA	Crushing inj of unsp parts of [unsp, rt, lt] hand and fingers, init enc 360, 426
S67.9[0,1,2]XD	Crushing inj of unsp parts of [unsp, rt, lt] hand and fingers, subsq enc 397
S38.03XS	Crushing inj of vulva, seq 227
D89.1	Cryoglobulinemia 295, 304, 305
B45*	Cryptococcosis 283
B45.9	Cryptococcosis, unsp 438
E24*	Cushing's synd 247
C82.61	Cutan folicl center lymphoma, nodes of head, face, and neck 3
C84.A1	Cutan T-cell lymphoma, unsp nodes of head, face, and neck 3
L02.21[1,2,3,4,5,6,9]	Cutaneous abscess of [abd wall, back (any part, except buttock), chest wall, groin, perineum, umbilicus, trunk unsp] 206
L02.[0,1]1	Cutaneous abscess of [face, neck] 284
L02.41[3,4,5,6,9]	Cutaneous abscess of [rt upr, lt upr, rt lwr, lt lwr, unsp] limb 206
L02.61[1,2,9]	Cutaneous abscess of [rt, lt, unsp] foot 206
L02.51[1,2,9]	Cutaneous abscess of [rt, lt, unsp] hand 206
L02.41[1,2]	Cutaneous abscess of [rt, lt] axilla 206
L02.31	Cutaneous abscess of buttock 206, 284
L02.01	Cutaneous abscess of face 4, 206
L02.61*	Cutaneous abscess of foot 284
L02.51*	Cutaneous abscess of hand 284
L02.811	Cutaneous abscess of head [any part, except face] 206
L02.41*	Cutaneous abscess of limb 284
L02.11	Cutaneous abscess of neck 4, 206
L02.818	Cutaneous abscess of oth sites 206
L02.81*	Cutaneous abscess of oth sites 284
L02.21*	Cutaneous abscess of trunk 284
L02*	Cutaneous abscess, furuncle and carbuncle 224
L02.91	Cutaneous abscess, unsp 206, 284
A06.7	Cutaneous amebiasis 233
A22.0	Cutaneous anthrax 233
B38.3	Cutaneous coccidioidomycosis 233
B45.2	Cutaneous cryptococcosis 438
A36.3	Cutaneous diphtheria 233
A26.0	Cutaneous erysipeloid 308
A32.0	Cutaneous listeriosis 308
A31.1	Cutaneous mycobacterial infxn 233
A43.1	Cutaneous nocardiosis 233
B78.1	Cutaneous strongyloidiasis 224
C84.A*	Cutaneous T-cell lymphoma, unsp 439
B55.[1,2]	[Cutaneous, Mucocutaneous] leishmaniasis 233
R23.0	Cyanosis 385
P28.2	Cyanotic attacks of newborn 288
D70.4	Cyclic neutropenia 293
F34.0	Cyclothymic d/o 310
J34.1	Cyst and mucocele of nose and nasal sinus 289
H05.81[1,2,3,9]	Cyst of [rt, lt, bilat, unsp] orbit 45
N75.0	Cyst of Bartholin's gland 270

N28.1	Cyst of kidney, acquired 256
H33.11[1,2,3,9]	Cyst of ora serrata, [rt, lt, bilat, unsp] eye 46
K09.9	Cyst of oral region, unsp 4
N42.83	Cyst of prostate 260
D73.4	Cyst of spleen 294
K86.[2,3]	[Cyst, Pseudocyst] of pancreas 284
Q44.6	Cystic dz of liver 124
E84.19	Cystic fibrosis with oth intestinal manifestations 117
E84.8	Cystic fibrosis with oth manifestations 246
E84.0	Cystic fibrosis with pulmn manifestations 67
E84.9	Cystic fibrosis, unsp 246
Q61*	Cystic kidney dz 256
M23.0*	Cystic meniscus 184
B69*	Cysticercosis 114
N30.9*	Cystitis, unsp 255, 285
H59.03*	Cystoid macular edema following cataract surgery 367
K09*	Cysts of oral region, NEC 59
B25.9	Cytomegaloviral dz, unsp 307, 438
B25.1	Cytomegaloviral hepatitis 124
B25.2	Cytomegaloviral pancreatitis 124, 283
B25.0	Cytomegaloviral pneumonitis 67
D89.9	D/o involving the immune mechanism, unsp 294
H93.3*	D/o of acoustic nerve 58
O41.9[1,2,3]X[0,1,2,3,4,5,9]	D/o of amniotic fluid and membranes, unsp, [1st, 2nd, 3rd] trmstr, fetus [N/A or unsp, 1, 2, 3, 4, 5, oth] 278, 280
O41.90X[0,1,2,3,4,5,9]	D/o of amniotic fluid and membranes, unsp, unsp trmstr, fetus [N/A or unsp, 1, 2, 3, 4, 5, oth] 281
E70*	D/o of aromatic amino-acid metabolism 247
I79*	D/o of art, arterioles and capilare in dis classd elsw 100
I77.9	D/o of arteries and arterioles, unsp 100
E80.7	D/o of bilirubin metabolism, unsp 124
M85.9	D/o of bone density and structure, unsp 194
M89.9	D/o of bone, unsp 194
G93.9	D/o of brain, unsp 33, 439
E71*	D/o of branched-chain amino-acid metab & fatty-acid metab 247
E83.5*	D/o of calcium metabolism 246
E74.9	D/o of carbohydrate metabolism, unsp 247
M94.9	D/o of cartilage, unsp 194
G96.9	D/o of central nervous sys, unsp 33, 439
M84.9	D/o of continuity of bone, unsp 194
E83.0*	D/o of copper metabolism 247
J98.6	D/o of diaphragm 69
E35	D/o of endocrine glands in dz classd elsw 3, 247
K23	D/o of esophagus in dz classified elsw 116
H62*	D/o of ext ear in dz classified elsw 58
H61.9*	D/o of ext ear, unsp 58
E74.1*	D/o of fructose metabolism 116
E74.2*	D/o of galactose metabolism 247
K87	D/o of GB, biliary trac and pancreas in dis classd elsw 124
K06.9	D/o of gingiva and edentulous alveolar ridge, unsp 4
E77*	D/o of glycoprotein metabolism 247
E76*	D/o of glycosaminoglycan metabolism 247
H22	D/o of iris and ciliary body in dz classd elsw 46
E83.1*	D/o of iron metabolism 247
N28.9	D/o of kidney and ureter, unsp 256
H04.9	D/o of lacrimal sys, unsp 45
M24.2*	D/o of lgmt 167
E78.9	D/o of lipoprotein metabolism, unsp 247
E83.4*	D/o of magnesium metabolism 246
N51	D/o of male genital organs in dz classd elsw 261
E83.9	D/o of mineral metabolism, unsp 247
M63*	D/o of muscle in dz classified elsw 167
P94.9	D/o of muscle tone of newborn, unsp 288
M62.9	D/o of muscle, unsp 167
H47.4*	D/o of optic chiasm 38
H47.0*	D/o of optic nerve, NEC 45
G52*	D/o of oth cranial nerves 34
H47.5*	D/o of oth visual pathways 38
E16.9	D/o of pancreatic int secretion, unsp 247
M22*	D/o of patella 184

N48.9	D/o of penis, unsp 261	
K67	D/o of peritoneum in infectious dz classd elsw 114, 284	
E83.3*	D/o of phosphorus metabolism and phosphatases 247	
L81.9	D/o of pigmentation, unsp 289	
N47*	D/o of prepuce 261	
N42.9	D/o of prostate, unsp 261	
E30*	D/o of puberty, NEC 247	
E79.9	D/o of purine and pyrimidine metabolism, unsp 247	
E74.4	D/o of pyruvate metabolism and gluconeogenesis 247	
K68*	D/o of retroperitoneum 284	
H15*	D/o of sclera 46	
K08.9	D/o of teeth and supporting structures, unsp 4	
G90.9	D/o of the autonomic nervous sys, unsp 34	
E07.9	D/o of thyroid, unsp 3, 247	
K00*	D/o of tooth development and eruption 59	
K00.9	D/o of tooth development, unsp 4	
G50*	D/o of trigeminal nerve 34	
N39.9	D/o of urinary sys, unsp 256	
I87.9	D/o of vein, unsp 102	
H81*	D/o of vestibular function 57	
H47.6*	D/o of visual cortex 38	
H43*	D/o of vitreous body 46	
D72.9	D/o of white bld cells, unsp 294	
E83.2	D/o of zinc metabolism 224	
N25*	D/o resulting from impaired renal tubular function 256	
F94*	D/o social w onset specific to childhood and adolescence 311	
H53.11	Day blindness 46	
O36.81[2,3,9] [0,1,2,3,4,5,9]	Decreased fetal movements [2nd, 3rd, unsp] trmstr, fetus [N/A or unsp, 1, 2, 3, 4, 5, oth] 278, 279	
R68.82	Decreased libido 412	
O22.3[1,2,3]	Deep phlebothrombosis in preg, [1st, 2nd, 3rd] trmstr 273, 277	
O22.30	Deep phlebothrombosis in preg, unsp trmstr 280	
O87.1	Deep phlebothrombosis in the puerperium 274	
D84.1	Defects in the complement sys 247	
E80.3	Defects of catalase and peroxidase 247	
E53*	Deficiency of oth B group vitamins 246	
E61*	Deficiency of oth nutrient elements 246	
N47.3	Deficient foreskin 289	
M43.9	Deforming dorsopathy, unsp 125, 164	
N65*	Deformity and disproportion of reconstructed breast 224	
H05.3*	Deformity of orbit 45	
H44.5*	Degenerated conditions of globe 46	
H21.2*	Degeneration of iris and ciliary body 46	
H93.0*	Degenerative and vascular d/o of ear 58	
H44.2*	Degenerative myopia 46	
O72.2	Delayed and secondary postpartum hemor 272, 274, 276	
O75.5	Delayed delivery after artfcl rupture of membranes 273, 275	
T80.911A	Delayed hemolytic transfs react, unsp incompatibility, init 293	
P96.82	Delayed separation of umbilical cord 289	
Q93.9	Deletion from autosomes, unsp 310	
Q93.3	Deletion of short arm of chromosome 4 310	
Q93.4	Deletion of short arm of chromosome 5 310	
Q93.7	Deletions with oth complex rearrangements 310	
F05	Delirium d/t known physiological condition 310	
F22	Delusional d/o 310	
F02*	Dementia in oth dz classified elsw 310	
R45.3	Demoralization and apathy 310	
G37.9	Demyelinating dz of central nervous sys, unsp 33, 439	
A90	Dengue fever [classical dengue] 307	
A91	Dengue hemorrhagic fever 307	
M26.7*	Dental alveolar anomalies 4	
K02*	Dental caries 59	
K02.5*	Dental caries on pit and fissure surface 4	
K02.6*	Dental caries on smooth surface 4	
K02.9	Dental caries, unsp 4	
K02.7	Dental root caries 4	
M26*	Dentofacial anomalies [incl* malocclusion] 59	
M26.9	Dentofacial anomaly, unsp 4	
M26.5*	Dentofacial functional abnormalities 4	
Z99*	Dependence on enabling machines and devices, NEC 413	

F48.1	Depersonalization-derealization synd 310	
K03.6	Deposits [accretions] on teeth 4	
T73.1XX[A,S]	Deprivation of water, [init enc, seq] 374	
T73.1XXD	Deprivation of water, subsq enc 410	
M23.2*	Derangement of meniscus d/t old tear or inj 184	
L27*	Dermatitis d/t substances taken internally 233	
L13.0	Dermatitis herpetiformis 233	
M36.0	Dermato(poly)myositis in neoplastic dz 164	
B35*	Dermatophytosis 233	
M33*	Dermatopolymyositis 164	
H53.53	Deuteranomaly 46	
K09.1	Developmental (nonodontogenic) cysts of oral region 4	
M27.0	Developmental d/o of jaws 4	
F80.9	Developmental d/o of speech and language, unsp 311	
K09.0	Developmental odontogenic cysts 4	
J34.2	Deviated nasal septum 4	
Q24.0	Dextrocardia 102	
D82.1	Di George's synd 293	
E08.5*	Diabetes d/t underlying condition w circulatory comp 1, 2, 100	
E08.65	Diabetes d/t underlying condition w hyperglycemia 246	
E08.0*	Diabetes d/t underlying condition w hyperosmolarity 1, 2, 246	
E08.2*	Diabetes d/t underlying condition w kidney comp 1, 2, 256	
E08.4*	Diabetes d/t underlying condition w neurological comp 1, 2, 34	
E08.3*	Diabetes d/t underlying condition w ophthalmic comp 1, 2, 45	
E08.63*	Diabetes d/t underlying condition w oral comp 246	
E08.6*	Diabetes d/t underlying condition w oth comp 1, 2	
E08.69	Diabetes d/t underlying condition w oth comp 246	
E08.618	Diabetes d/t underlying condition w oth diabetic arthrop 246	
E08.62*	Diabetes d/t underlying condition w skin comp 246	
E08.8	Diabetes d/t underlying condition w unsp comp 1, 2, 246	
E08.9	Diabetes d/t underlying condition w/o comp 1, 2, 246	
E08.610	Diabetes d/t undrl cond w diabetic neuropathic arthrop 34	
E23.2	Diabetes insipidus 283	
E08.64*	Diabetes mellitus d/t underlying condition w hypoglycemia 246	
E08.1*	Diabetes mellitus d/t underlying condition w ketoacidosis 1, 2, 246	
L22	Diaper dermatitis 233, 289	
K44.9	Diaphragmatic hernia w/o obstruction or gangrene 116	
K44.1	Diaphragmatic hernia with gangrene 117	
K44.0	Diaphragmatic hernia with obstruction, w/o gangrene 116	
K44.[0,1]	Diaphragmatic hernia, w/ [obstruction w/o gangrene, gangrene], not spec as recurrent 284	
R19.7	Diarrhea, unsp 116	
Q77.5	Diastrophic dysplasia 195	
B66.2	Dicroceliasis 309	
E58	Dietary calcium deficiency 246	
E59	Dietary selenium deficiency 246	
E60	Dietary zinc deficiency 246	
K31.82	Dieulafoy lesion (hemorrhagic) of stomach and duodenum 115	
R26.2	Difficulty in walking, NEC 167	
M35.4	Diffuse (eosinophilic) fasciitis 167	
C82.51	Diffuse folicl center lymph, nodes of head, face, and neck 3	
C82.5*	Diffuse follicle center lymphoma 438	
H16.3[2,3,9] [1,2,3,9]	[Diffuse interstitial, Sclerosing, Oth interstitial and deep] keratitis, [rt, lt, bilat, unsp] eye 46	
C83.3*	Diffuse large B-cell lymphoma 438	
C83.31	Diffuse large B-cell lymphoma, nodes of head, face, and neck 3	
G37.0	Diffuse sclerosis of central nervous sys 33	
S06.2X1A	Diffuse TBI w LOC of 30 min or less, init 37	
S06.2X2A	Diffuse TBI w LOC of 31-59 min, init 37	
S06.2X0A	Diffuse TBI w/o LOC, init 36, 37, 418, 430	
S06.2X0S	Diffuse TBI w/o LOC, seq 39	
S06.2X0D	Diffuse TBI w/o LOC, subs 386	
S06.2X[5,6]A	Diffuse traum brain inj w/ LOC > 24 hrs [w/ return to pre-existing conscious lvl, w/o return to pre-existing conscious lvl w/ patient surviving], init enc 36, 418, 430	
S06.2X[5,6]S	Diffuse traum brain inj w/ LOC of [> 24 hrs w/ return to pre-existing conscious lvl, > 24 hrs w/o return to pre-existing conscious lvl w/ patient surviving], seq 39	
S06.2X[5,6]D	Diffuse traum brain inj w/ LOC of [> 24 hrs w/ return to pre-existing conscious lvl, > 24 hrs w/o return to pre-existing conscious lvl w/ patient surviving], subsq enc 386	

S06.2X[3,4,5,6]A	Diffuse traum brain inj w/ LOC of [1 hr to 5 hrs 59 min, 6 hrs to 24 hrs, > 24 hrs w/ return to pre-existing conscious lvl, > 24 hrs w/o return to pre-existing conscious lvl patient surviving], init enc 35
S06.2X[1,2,3,4]A	Diffuse traum brain inj w/ LOC of [30 min or less, 31 min to 59 min, 1 hr to 5 hrs 59 min, 6 hrs to 24 hrs], init enc 36, 418, 430
S06.2X[1,2,3,4]S	Diffuse traum brain inj w/ LOC of [30 min or less, 31-59 min, 1 hr to 5 hrs 59 min, 6 hrs to 24 hrs], seq 39
S06.2X[1,2,3,4]D	Diffuse traum brain inj w/ LOC of [30 min or less, 31-59 min, 1 hr to 5 hrs 59 min, 6 hrs to 24 hrs], subsq enc 386
S06.2X[7,8,9]A	Diffuse traum brain inj w/ LOC of [any dur w/ death d/t brain inj prior to regain cnscness, any dur w/ death d/t oth cause prior to regain cnscness, unsp dur], init enc 35, 36, 418, 430
S06.2X[7,8,9]S	Diffuse traum brain inj w/ LOC of [any dur w/ death d/t brain inj prior to regain cnscness, any dur w/ death d/t oth cause prior to regain cnscness, unsp dur], seq 39
S06.2X[7,8,9]D	Diffuse traum brain inj w/ LOC of [any dur w/ death d/t brain inj prior to regain cnscness, any dur w/ death d/t oth cause prior to regain cnscness, unsp dur], subsq enc 386
A36.9	Diphtheria, unsp 308
A36.8[2,3,4]	Diphtheritic [radiculomyelitis, polyneuritis, tubulo-interstitial nephropathy] 308
A36.81	Diphtheritic cardiomyopathy 103
A36.86	Diphtheritic conjunctivitis 45
A36.85	Diphtheritic cystitis 255
B70.0	Diphyllobothriasis 116
H93.22[1,2,3,9]	Diplacusis, [rt, lt, bilat, unsp] ear 58
G83.0	Diplegia of upr limbs 32
H53.2	Diplopia 45
M01*	Direct infect of jt in infec/parastc dis classd elsw 164
M46.4*	Discitis, unsp 164
Q68.6	Discoid meniscus 184
Z64.4	Discord with counselors 412
S03.[0,1,2]XXA	Disloc of [jaw, septal cartilage of nose, tooth], init enc 417
S03.[0,1,2]XXD	Disloc of [jaw, septal cartilage of nose, tooth], subsq enc 386
S63.2[6,7,8,9] [0,1,2,3,4,5,6,7, 8,9]A	Disloc of [metacarpophalangeal, unsp interphalangeal, proximal interphalangeal, distal interphalangeal] jt of [rt index, lt index, rt mid, lt mid, rt ring, lt ring, rt little, lt little, oth, unsp] finger, init enc 425
T84.02[8,9]A	Disloc of [oth, unsp] int jt prosthesis, init enc 183
T84.02[8,9]S	Disloc of [oth, unsp] int jt prosthesis, seq 375
T84.02[8,9]D	Disloc of [oth, unsp] int jt prosthesis, subsq enc 411
S43.1[2,3][1,2,9] A	Disloc of [rt, lt, unsp] acromioclavicular jt, [100%-200%, > 200%] displac, init enc 422
S43.13[1,2,9]D	Disloc of [rt, lt, unsp] acromioclavicular jt, > 200% displac, subsq enc 391
S43.12[1,2,9]D	Disloc of [rt, lt, unsp] acromioclavicular jt, 100%-200% displac, subsq enc 391
S93.0[4,5,6] X[A,S]	Disloc of [rt, lt, unsp] ankle jt, [init enc, seq] 193
S93.0[4,5,6]XA	Disloc of [rt, lt, unsp] ankle jt, init enc 430
S93.0[4,5,6]XD	Disloc of [rt, lt, unsp] ankle jt, subsq enc 399
S43.31[4,5,6]D	Disloc of [rt, lt, unsp] scapula, subsq enc 391
S23.2[0,9]XD	Disloc of [unsp part, oth parts] of thorax, subsq enc 389
S23.2[0,9]XS	Disloc of [unsp, oth] part of thorax, seq 184
S23.2[0,9]XA	Disloc of [unsp, oth] part(s) of thorax, init enc 420
S33.3[0,9]XA	Disloc of [unsp, oth] parts of lumbar spine and pelvis, init enc 421
S13.2[0,9]XA	Disloc of [unsp, oth] parts of neck, init enc 165, 419, 432
S13.2[0,9]XS	Disloc of [unsp, oth] parts of neck, seq 184
S13.2[0,9]XD	Disloc of [unsp, oth] parts of neck, subsq enc 388
S43.13[1,2,9] [A,S]	Disloc of acromioclavicular jt, > 200% displac [rt, lt, unsp] [init enc, seq] 185
S43.12[1,2,9] [A,S]	Disloc of acromioclavicular jt, 100%-200% displac [rt, lt, unsp] [init enc, seq] 185
S63.04[4,5,6] [A,S]	Disloc of carpometacarpal jt of [rt, lt, unsp] thumb, [init enc, seq] 188
S63.04[4,5,6]D	Disloc of carpometacarpal jt of [rt, lt] thumb, subsq enc 395
S63.07[4,5,6] [A,S]	Disloc of distal end of [rt, lt, unsp] ulna, [init enc, seq] 188
S63.07[4,5,6]D	Disloc of distal end of [rt, lt] ulna, subsq enc 395
S63.29[8,9][A,S]	Disloc of distal interphalangeal jt of [oth, unsp] finger, [init enc, seq] 189
S63.29[8,9]D	Disloc of distal interphalangeal jt of [oth, unsp] finger, subsq enc 396

S63.14[4,5,6] [A,S]	Disloc of distal interphalangeal jt of [rt, lt, unsp] thumb, [init enc, seq] 189
S63.14[4,5,6]D	Disloc of distal interphalangeal jt of [rt, lt, unsp] thumb, subsq enc 395
S63.29[0,1][A,S]	Disloc of distal interphalangeal jt of [rt, lt] index finger, [init enc, seq] 189
S63.29[0,1]D	Disloc of distal interphalangeal jt of [rt, lt] index finger, subsq enc 395
S63.29[6,7][A,S]	Disloc of distal interphalangeal jt of [rt, lt] little finger, [init enc, seq] 189
S63.29[6,7]D	Disloc of distal interphalangeal jt of [rt, lt] little finger, subsq enc 395
S63.29[2,3][A,S]	Disloc of distal interphalangeal jt of [rt, lt] mid finger, [init enc, seq] 189
S63.29[2,3]D	Disloc of distal interphalangeal jt of [rt, lt] mid finger, subsq enc 395
S63.29[4,5][A,S]	Disloc of distal interphalangeal jt of [rt, lt] ring finger, [init enc, seq] 189
S63.29[4,5]D	Disloc of distal interphalangeal jt of [rt, lt] ring finger, subsq enc 395
S63.01[4,5,6] [A,S]	Disloc of distal radioulnar jt of [rt, lt, unsp] wrist, [init enc, seq] 188
S63.01[4,5,6]D	Disloc of distal radioulnar jt of [rt, lt] wrist, subsq enc 395
T84.02[0,1]A	Disloc of int [rt, lt] hip prosthesis, init enc 183
T84.02[0,1]S	Disloc of int [rt, lt] hip prosthesis, seq 375
T84.02[0,1]D	Disloc of int [rt, lt] hip prosthesis, subsq enc 411
S93.11[1,2,3] [A,S]	Disloc of interphalangeal jt of [rt, lt, unsp] great toe, [init enc, seq] 193
S93.11[1,2,3]A	Disloc of interphalangeal jt of [rt, lt, unsp] great toe, init enc 430
S93.11[1,2,3]D	Disloc of interphalangeal jt of [rt, lt, unsp] great toe, subsq enc 399
S93.11[4,5,6] [A,S]	Disloc of interphalangeal jt of [rt, lt, unsp] lesser toe(s), [init enc, seq] 193
S93.11[4,5,6]A	Disloc of interphalangeal jt of [rt, lt, unsp] lesser toe(s), init enc 430
S93.11[4,5,6]D	Disloc of interphalangeal jt of [rt, lt, unsp] lesser toe(s), subsq enc 399
S93.119[A,S]	Disloc of interphalangeal jt of unsp toe(s), [init enc, seq] 193
S93.119A	Disloc of interphalangeal jt of unsp toe(s), init 430
S93.119D	Disloc of interphalangeal jt of unsp toe(s), subs 399
S03.0XXA	Disloc of jaw, init enc 5, 59
S03.0XXS	Disloc of jaw, seq 184
S63.06[4,5,6] [A,S]	Disloc of metacarpal (bone), proximal end of [rt, lt, unsp] hand, [init enc, seq] 188
S63.06[4,5,6]D	Disloc of metacarpal (bone), proximal end of [rt, lt] hand, subsq enc 395
S63.26[8,9][A,S]	Disloc of metacarpophalangeal jt of [oth, unsp] finger, [init enc, seq] 189
S63.26[8,9]D	Disloc of metacarpophalangeal jt of [oth, unsp] finger, subsq enc 395
S63.11[4,5,6] [A,S]	Disloc of metacarpophalangeal jt of [rt, lt, unsp] thumb, [init enc, seq] 189
S63.11[4,5,6]D	Disloc of metacarpophalangeal jt of [rt, lt, unsp] thumb, subsq enc 395
S63.26[0,1][A,S]	Disloc of metacarpophalangeal jt of [rt, lt] index finger, [init enc, seq] 189
S63.26[0,1]D	Disloc of metacarpophalangeal jt of [rt, lt] index finger, subsq enc 395
S63.26[6,7][A,S]	Disloc of metacarpophalangeal jt of [rt, lt] little finger, [init enc, seq] 189
S63.26[6,7]D	Disloc of metacarpophalangeal jt of [rt, lt] little finger, subsq enc 395
S63.26[2,3][A,S]	Disloc of metacarpophalangeal jt of [rt, lt] mid finger, [init enc, seq] 189
S63.26[2,3]D	Disloc of metacarpophalangeal jt of [rt, lt] mid finger, subsq enc 395
S63.26[4,5][A,S]	Disloc of metacarpophalangeal jt of [rt, lt] ring finger, [init enc, seq] 189
S63.26[4,5]D	Disloc of metacarpophalangeal jt of [rt, lt] ring finger, subsq enc 395
S93.12[1,2,3] [A,S]	Disloc of metatarsophalangeal jt of [rt, lt, unsp] great toe, [init enc, seq] 193
S93.12[1,2,3]A	Disloc of metatarsophalangeal jt of [rt, lt, unsp] great toe, init enc 430
S93.12[1,2,3]D	Disloc of metatarsophalangeal jt of [rt, lt, unsp] great toe, subsq enc 399

S93.12[4,5,6] [A,S]	Disloc of metatarsophalangeal jt of [rt, lt, unsp] lesser toe(s), [init enc, seq] 193
S93.12[4,5,6]A	Disloc of metatarsophalangeal jt of [rt, lt, unsp] lesser toe(s), init enc 430
S93.12[4,5,6]D	Disloc of metatarsophalangeal jt of [rt, lt, unsp] lesser toe(s), subsq enc 399
S93.129[A,S]	Disloc of metatarsophalangeal jt of unsp toe(s), [init enc, seq] 193
S63.03[4,5,6] [A,S]	Disloc of midcarpal jt of [rt, lt, unsp] wrist, [init enc, seq] 188
S63.03[4,5,6]D	Disloc of midcarpal jt of [rt, lt] wrist, subsq enc 395
S93.129A	Disloc of MTP jt of unsp toe(s), init 430
S93.129D	Disloc of MTP jt of unsp toe(s), subs 399
S33.3[0,9]X[A,S]	Disloc of of parts of lumbar spine and pelvis [unsp, oth] [Init enc, seq] 184
S63.05[4,5,6] [A,S]	Disloc of oth carpometacarpal jt of [rt, lt, unsp] hand, [init enc, seq] 188
S63.05[4,5,6]D	Disloc of oth carpometacarpal jt of [rt, lt] hand, subsq enc 395
S43.39[4,5,6]D	Disloc of oth parts of [rt, lt, unsp] shldr girdle, subsq enc 391
S43.39[4,5,6] [A,S]	Disloc of oth parts of shldr girdle [rt, lt, unsp] [init enc, seq] 185
S23.29XA	Disloc of oth parts of thorax, init enc 166
S33.39XD	Disloc of oth prt lumbar spine and pelvis, subs enc 390
S63.28[8,9][A,S]	Disloc of proximal interphalangeal jt of [oth, unsp] finger, [init enc, seq] 189
S63.28[8,9]D	Disloc of proximal interphalangeal jt of [oth, unsp] finger, subsq enc 395
S63.13[4,5,6] [A,S]	Disloc of proximal interphalangeal jt of [rt, lt, unsp] thumb, [init enc, seq] 189
S63.13[4,5,6]D	Disloc of proximal interphalangeal jt of [rt, lt, unsp] thumb, subsq enc 395
S63.28[0,1][A,S]	Disloc of proximal interphalangeal jt of [rt, lt] index finger, [init enc, seq] 189
S63.28[0,1]D	Disloc of proximal interphalangeal jt of [rt, lt] index finger, subsq enc 395
S63.28[6,7][A,S]	Disloc of proximal interphalangeal jt of [rt, lt] little finger, [init enc, seq] 189
S63.28[6,7]D	Disloc of proximal interphalangeal jt of [rt, lt] little finger, subsq enc 395
S63.28[2,3][A,S]	Disloc of proximal interphalangeal jt of [rt, lt] mid finger, [init enc, seq] 189
S63.28[2,3]D	Disloc of proximal interphalangeal jt of [rt, lt] mid finger, subsq enc 395
S63.28[4,5][A,S]	Disloc of proximal interphalangeal jt of [rt, lt] ring finger, [init enc, seq] 189
S63.28[4,5]D	Disloc of proximal interphalangeal jt of [rt, lt] ring finger, subsq enc 395
S63.02[4,5,6] [A,S]	Disloc of radiocarpal jt of [rt, lt, unsp] wrist, [init enc, seq] 188
S63.02[4,5,6]D	Disloc of radiocarpal jt of [rt, lt] wrist, subsq enc 395
S33.2XXA	Disloc of sacroiliac and sacrococcygeal jt, init 166, 421
S33.2XXS	Disloc of sacroiliac and sacrococcygeal jt, seq 184
S33.2XXD	Disloc of sacroiliac and sacrococcygeal jt, subs 390
S43.31[4,5,6] [A,S]	Disloc of scapula [rt, lt, unsp] [init enc, seq] 185
S03.1XXA	Disloc of septal cartilage of nose, init enc 184
S03.1XXS	Disloc of septal cartilage of nose, seq 184
S93.31[4,5,6] [A,S]	Disloc of tarsal jt of [rt, lt, unsp] foot, [init enc, seq] 193
S93.31[4,5,6]A	Disloc of tarsal jt of [rt, lt, unsp] foot, init enc 430
S93.31[4,5,6]D	Disloc of tarsal jt of [rt, lt, unsp] foot, subsq enc 399
S93.32[4,5,6] [A,S]	Disloc of tarsometatarsal jt of [rt, lt, unsp] foot, [init enc, seq] 193
S93.32[4,5,6]A	Disloc of tarsometatarsal jt of [rt, lt, unsp] foot, init enc 430
S93.32[4,5,6]D	Disloc of tarsometatarsal jt of [rt, lt, unsp] foot, subsq enc 399
S03.2XXA	Disloc of tooth, init enc 59
S03.2XXS	Disloc of tooth, seq 224
S63.27[8,9][A,S]	Disloc of unsp interphalangeal jt of [oth, unsp] finger, [init enc, seq] 189
S63.27[8,9]D	Disloc of unsp interphalangeal jt of [oth, unsp] finger, subsq enc 395
S63.12[4,5,6] [A,S]	Disloc of unsp interphalangeal jt of [rt, lt, unsp] thumb, [init enc, seq] 189
S63.12[4,5,6]D	Disloc of unsp interphalangeal jt of [rt, lt, unsp] thumb, subsq enc 395
S63.27[0,1][A,S]	Disloc of unsp interphalangeal jt of [rt, lt] index finger, [init enc, seq] 189
S63.27[0,1]D	Disloc of unsp interphalangeal jt of [rt, lt] index finger, subsq enc 395
S63.27[6,7][A,S]	Disloc of unsp interphalangeal jt of [rt, lt] little finger, [init enc, seq] 189
S63.27[6,7]D	Disloc of unsp interphalangeal jt of [rt, lt] little finger, subsq enc 395
S63.27[2,3][A,S]	Disloc of unsp interphalangeal jt of [rt, lt] mid finger, [init enc, seq] 189
S63.27[2,3]D	Disloc of unsp interphalangeal jt of [rt, lt] mid finger, subsq enc 395
S63.27[4,5][A,S]	Disloc of unsp interphalangeal jt of [rt, lt] ring finger, [init enc, seq] 189
S63.27[4,5]D	Disloc of unsp interphalangeal jt of [rt, lt] ring finger, subsq enc 395
S23.20XA	Disloc of unsp part of thorax, init enc 166
S43.30[4,5,6]D	Disloc of unsp parts of [rt, lt, unsp] shldr girdle, subsq enc 391
S33.30XD	Disloc of unsp parts of lumbar spine and pelvis, subs 390
S43.30[4,5,6] [A,S]	Disloc of unsp parts of shldr girdle [rt, lt, unsp] [init enc, seq] 185
R41.0	Disorientation, unsp 385
S42.22[1,2,3] [A,B]	Disp 2-part fx of surgical neck of humerus [rt, lt, unsp] init enc for fx, clsd, opn] 184
S72.13[1,2,3] [D,E,F,G,H,J,S]	Disp apophyseal fx of [rt, lt, unsp] femur, [subsq enc for clsd fx w/ routine healing, subsq enc for opn fx type I or II w/ routine healing, subsq enc for opn fx type IIIA, IIIB, or IIIC w/ routine healing, subsq enc for clsd fx w/ delayed healing, subsq enc for opn fx type I or II w/ delayed healing, subsq enc for opn fx type IIIA, IIIB, or IIIC w/ delayed healing, seq] 177
S72.13[1,2,3] [A,B,C]	Disp apophyseal fx of [rt, lt, unsp] femur, init enc for [clsd fx, opn fx type I or II or NOS, or opn fx type IIIA, IIIB, or IIIC] 162, 286, 435
S72.13[1,2,3] [K,M,N,P,Q,R]	Disp apophyseal fx of [rt, lt, unsp] femur, subsq enc for [clsd fx w/ nonu, opn fx type I or II w/ nonu, opn fx type IIIA, IIIB, or IIIC w/ nonu, clsd fx w/ malu, opn fx type I or II w/ malu, opn fx type IIIA, IIIB, or IIIC w/ malu] 201
S72.06[1,2,3] [D,E,F,G,H,J,S]	Disp articular fx of head of [rt, lt, unsp] femur, [subsq enc for clsd fx w/ routine healing, subsq enc for opn fx type I or II w/ routine healing, subsq enc for opn fx type IIIA, IIIB, or IIIC w/ routine healing, subsq enc for clsd fx w/ delayed healing, subsq enc for opn fx type I or II w/ delayed healing, subsq enc for opn fx type IIIA, IIIB, or IIIC w/ delayed healing, seq] 177
S72.06[1,2,3] [A,B,C]	Disp articular fx of head of [rt, lt, unsp] femur, init enc for fx [clsd, opn fx type I or II or NOS, or opn fx type IIIA, IIIB, or IIIC] 162, 286, 435
S72.06[1,2,3] [K,M,N,P,Q,R]	Disp articular fx of head of [rt, lt, unsp] femur, subsq enc for [clsd fx w/ nonu, opn fx type I or II w/ nonu, opn fx type IIIA, IIIB, or IIIC w/ nonu, clsd fx w/ malu, opn fx type I or II w/ malu, opn fx type IIIA, IIIB, or IIIC w/ malu] 201
S32.46[1,2,3]S	Disp associated transv-post fx of [rt, lt, unsp] acetab, seq 166
S32.46[1,2,3] [D,G]	Disp associated transv-post fx of [rt, lt, unsp] acetab, subsq enc for fx w/ [routine, delayed] healing 170
S32.46[1,2,3]K	Disp associated transv-post fx of [rt, lt, unsp] acetab, subsq enc for fx w/ nonu 196
S32.46[1,2,3] [A,B]	Disp associated transv-post fx of acetab [rt, lt, unsp] init enc for [clsd fx, opn fx] 162, 433
S92.15[1,2,3] [D,G,S]	Disp avulsion fx (chip fx) of [rt, lt, unsp] talus, [subsq enc for fx w/ routine healing, subsq enc for fx w/ delayed healing, seq] 182
S92.15[1,2,3] [A,B]	Disp avulsion fx (chip fx) of [rt, lt, unsp] talus, init enc for [clsd, opn] fx 192, 429
S92.15[1,2,3] [K,P]	Disp avulsion fx (chip fx) of [rt, lt, unsp] talus, subsq enc for fx w/ [nonu, malu] 204
S32.31[1,2,3]S	Disp avulsion fx of [rt, lt, unsp] ilium, seq 166
S32.31[1,2,3] [D,G]	Disp avulsion fx of [rt, lt, unsp] ilium, subsq enc for fx w/ [routine, delayed] healing 170
S32.31[1,2,3]K	Disp avulsion fx of [rt, lt, unsp] ilium, subsq enc for fx w/ nonu 196
S32.61[1,2,3] [D,G]	Disp avulsion fx of [rt, lt, unsp] ischium, subsq enc for fx w/ [routine, delayed] healing 170
S32.61[1,2,3]K	Disp avulsion fx of [rt, lt, unsp] ischium, subsq enc for fx w/ nonu 196
S32.31[1,2,3] [A,B]	Disp avulsion fx of ilium [rt, lt, unsp] init enc for [clsd fx, opn fx] 162
S32.61[1,2,3] [A,B]	Disp avulsion fx of ischium [rt, lt, unsp] init enc for [clsd fx, opn fx] 162
S32.61[1,2,3]S	Disp avulsion fx of ischium [rt, lt, unsp] init enc for fx, seq 166

S92.03[1,2,3] [D,G,S] Disp avulsion fx of tuberosity of [rt, lt, unsp] calcaneus, [subsq enc for fx w/ routine healing, subsq enc for fx w/ delayed healing, seq] **182**

S92.03[1,2,3] [A,B] Disp avulsion fx of tuberosity of [rt, lt, unsp] calcaneus, init enc for [clsd, opn] fx **192, 429**

S92.03[1,2,3] [K,P] Disp avulsion fx of tuberosity of [rt, lt, unsp] calcaneus, subsq enc for fx w/ [nonu, malu] **204**

S82.14[1,2,3] [A,B,C] Disp bicondylar fx of [rt, lt, unsp] tibia, [init enc for clsd fx, init enc for opn fx type I or II, init enc for opn fx type IIIA, IIIB, or IIIC] **190**

S82.14[1,2,3] [D,E,F,G,H,J,S] Disp bicondylar fx of [rt, lt, unsp] tibia, [subsq enc for clsd fx w/ routine healing, subsq enc for opn fx type I or II w/ routine healing, subsq enc for opn fx type IIIA, IIIB, or IIIC w/ routine healing, subsq enc for clsd fx w/ delayed healing, subsq enc for opn fx type I or II w/ delayed healing, subsq enc for opn fx type IIIA, IIIB, or IIIC w/ delayed healing, seq] **180**

S82.14[1,2,3] [B,C] Disp bicondylar fx of [rt, lt, unsp] tibia, init enc for opn fx type [I or II, IIIA IIIB or IIIC] **436**

S82.14[1,2,3] [K,M,N,P,Q,R] Disp bicondylar fx of [rt, lt, unsp] tibia, subsq enc for [clsd fx w/ nonu, opn fx type I or II w/ nonu, opn fx type IIIA, IIIB, or IIIC w/ nonu, clsd fx w/ malu, opn fx type I or II w/ malu, opn fx type I or II w/ malu] **202**

S82.84[1,2,3] [A,B,C] Disp bimalleolar fx of [rt, lt, unsp] lwr leg, [init enc for clsd fx, init enc for opn fx type I or II, init enc for opn fx type I or II] **191, 427**

S82.84[1,2,3] [D,E,F,G,H,J,S] Disp bimalleolar fx of [rt, lt, unsp] lwr leg, [subsq enc for clsd fx w/ routine healing, subsq enc for opn fx type I or II w/ routine healing, subsq enc for opn fx type IIIA, IIIB, or IIIC w/ routine healing, subsq enc for clsd fx w/ delayed healing, subsq enc for opn fx type I or II w/ delayed healing, subsq enc for opn fx type IIIA, IIIB, or IIIC w/ delayed healing, seq] **181**

S82.84[1,2,3] [K,M,N,P,Q,R] Disp bimalleolar fx of [rt, lt, unsp] lwr leg, subsq enc for [clsd fx w/ nonu, opn fx type I or II w/ nonu, opn fx type IIIA, IIIB, or IIIC w/ nonu, clsd fx w/ malu, opn fx type I or II w/ malu, opn fx type I or II w/ malu] **203**

S82.04[1,2,3] [A,B,C] Disp comm fx of [rt, lt, unsp] patella, [init enc for clsd fx, init enc for opn fx type I or II, init enc for opn fx type IIIA, IIIB, or IIIC] **190**

S82.04[1,2,3] [D,E,F,G,H,J,S] Disp comm fx of [rt, lt, unsp] patella, [subsq enc for clsd fx w/ routine healing, subsq enc for opn fx type I or II w/ routine healing, subsq enc for opn fx type IIIA, IIIB, or IIIC w/ routine healing, subsq enc for clsd fx w/ delayed healing, subsq enc for opn fx type I or II w/ delayed healing, seq] **179**

S82.04[1,2,3] [K,M,N,P,Q,R] Disp comm fx of [rt, lt, unsp] patella, subsq enc for [clsd fx w/ nonu, opn fx type I or II w/ nonu, opn fx type IIIA, IIIB, or IIIC w/ nonu, clsd fx w/ malu, opn fx type I or II w/ malu, opn fx type I or II w/ malu] **202**

S52.25[1,2,3] [B,C] Disp comm fx of [rt, lt, unsp] ulna, init enc for opn fx [type I or II, IIIA IIIB or IIIC] **434**

S72.35[1,2,3] [D,E,F,G,H,J,S] Disp comm fx of shaft of [rt, lt, unsp] femur, [subsq enc for clsd fx w/ routine healing, subsq enc for opn fx type I or II w/ routine healing, subsq enc for opn fx type IIIA, IIIB, or IIIC w/ routine healing, subsq enc for clsd fx w/ delayed healing, subsq enc for opn fx type I or II w/ delayed healing, subsq enc for opn fx type IIIA, IIIB, or IIIC w/ delayed healing, seq] **178**

S72.35[1,2,3] [A,B,C] Disp comm fx of shaft of [rt, lt, unsp] femur, init enc for [clsd fx, opn fx type I or II, opn fx type IIIA, IIIB, or IIIC] **161, 286, 435**

S72.35[1,2,3] [K,M,N,P,Q,R] Disp comm fx of shaft of [rt, lt, unsp] femur, subsq enc for [clsd fx w/ nonu, opn fx type I or II w/ nonu, opn fx type IIIA, IIIB, or IIIC w/ nonu, clsd fx w/ malu, opn fx type I or II w/ malu, opn fx type IIIA, IIIB, or IIIC w/ malu] **201**

S82.45[1,2,3] [A,B,C] Disp comm fx of shaft of [rt, lt, unsp] fibula, [init enc for clsd fx, init enc for opn fx type I or II, init enc for opn fx type IIIA, IIIB, or IIIC] **191, 427**

S82.45[1,2,3] [D,E,F,G,H,J,S] Disp comm fx of shaft of [rt, lt, unsp] fibula, [subsq enc for clsd fx w/ routine healing, subsq enc for opn fx type I or II w/ routine healing, subsq enc for opn fx type IIIA, IIIB, or IIIC w/ routine healing, subsq enc for clsd fx w/ delayed healing, subsq enc for opn fx type I or II w/ delayed healing, subsq enc for opn fx type IIIA, IIIB, or IIIC w/ delayed healing, seq] **181**

S82.45[1,2,3] [B,C] Disp comm fx of shaft of [rt, lt, unsp] fibula, init enc for opn fx type [I or II, IIIA IIIB or IIIC] **436**

S82.45[1,2,3] [K,M,N,P,Q,R] Disp comm fx of shaft of [rt, lt, unsp] fibula, subsq enc for [clsd fx w/ nonu, opn fx type I or II w/ nonu, opn fx type IIIA, IIIB, or IIIC w/ nonu, clsd fx w/ malu, opn fx type I or II w/ malu, opn fx type I or II w/ malu] **203**

S42.35[1,2,3] [D,G,S] Disp comm fx of shaft of [rt, lt, unsp] humerus, [subsq enc for fx w/ routine healing, subsq enc for fx w/ delayed healing, seq] **171**

S42.35[1,2,3]B Disp comm fx of shaft of [rt, lt, unsp] humerus, init enc for opn fx **433**

S52.35[1,2,3] [D,E,F,G,H,J,S] Disp comm fx of shaft of [rt, lt, unsp] radius, [subsq enc for clsd fx w/ routine healing, subsq enc for opn fx type I or II w/ routine healing, subsq enc for clsd fx w/ delayed healing, subsq enc for opn fx type I or II w/ delayed healing, subsq enc for opn fx type IIIA, IIIB, or IIIC w/ delayed healing, seq] **173**

S52.35[1,2,3] [B,C] Disp comm fx of shaft of [rt, lt, unsp] radius, init enc for opn fx type [I or II, IIIA IIIB or IIIC] **434**

S82.25[1,2,3] [A,B,C] Disp comm fx of shaft of [rt, lt, unsp] tibia, [init enc for clsd fx, init enc for opn fx type I or II, init enc for opn fx type IIIA, IIIB, or IIIC] **191, 427**

S82.25[1,2,3] [D,E,F,G,H,J,S] Disp comm fx of shaft of [rt, lt, unsp] tibia, [subsq enc for clsd fx w/ routine healing, subsq enc for opn fx type I or II w/ routine healing, subsq enc for opn fx type IIIA, IIIB, or IIIC w/ routine healing, subsq enc for clsd fx w/ delayed healing, subsq enc for opn fx type I or II w/ delayed healing, subsq enc for opn fx type IIIA, IIIB, or IIIC w/ delayed healing, seq] **180**

S82.25[1,2,3] [B,C] Disp comm fx of shaft of [rt, lt, unsp] tibia, init enc for opn fx type [I or II, IIIA IIIB or IIIC] **436**

S82.25[1,2,3] [K,M,N,P,Q,R] Disp comm fx of shaft of [rt, lt, unsp] tibia, subsq enc for [clsd fx w/ nonu, opn fx type I or II w/ nonu, opn fx type IIIA, IIIB, or IIIC w/ nonu, clsd fx w/ malu, opn fx type I or II w/ malu, opn fx type I or II w/ malu] **203**

S52.25[1,2,3] [D,E,F,G,H,J,S] Disp comm fx of shaft of [rt, lt, unsp] ulna, [subsq enc for clsd fx w/ routine healing, subsq enc for opn fx type I or II w/ routine healing, subsq enc for opn fx type IIIA, IIIB, or IIIC w/ routine healing, subsq enc for clsd fx w/ delayed healing, subsq enc for opn fx type I or II w/ delayed healing, subsq enc for opn fx type IIIA, IIIB, or IIIC w/ delayed healing, seq] **173**

S42.35[1,2,3] [A,B] Disp comm fx of shaft of humerus [rt, lt, unsp] init enc for fx [clsd, opn] **185**

S42.35[1,2,3] [K,P] Disp comm fx of shaft of humerus, [rt, lt, unsp] arm, subsq enc for fx w/ [nonu, malu] **197**

S52.35[1,2,3] [A,B,C] Disp comm fx of shaft of radius [rt, lt, unsp] init enc for [clsd fx, opn fx type I or II or opn fx NOS, opn fx type IIIA, IIIB, or IIIC] **186**

S52.35[1,2,3] [K,M,N,P,Q,R] Disp comm fx of shaft of radius, [rt, lt, unsp] arm, subsq enc for [clsd fx w/ nonu, opn fx type I or II w/ nonu, opn fx type IIIA, IIIB, or IIIC w/ nonu, clsd fx w/ malu, opn fx type I or II w/ malu, opn fx type IIIA, IIIB, or IIIC w/ malu] **198**

S52.25[1,2,3] [K,M,N,P,Q,R] Disp comm fx of shaft of ulna, [rt, lt, unsp] arm, subsq enc for [clsd fx w/ nonu, opn fx type I or II w/ nonu, opn fx type IIIA, IIIB, or IIIC w/ nonu, clsd fx w/ malu, opn fx type I or II w/ malu, opn fx type IIIA, IIIB, or IIIC w/ malu] **198**

S52.25[1,2,3] [A,B,C] Disp comm fx of ulna [rt, lt, unsp] init enc for [clsd fx, opn fx type I or II or opn fx NOS, opn fx type IIIA, IIIB, or IIIC] **186**

S42.42[1,2,3] [D,G,S] Disp comm supracondylar fx w/o intercondylar fx of [rt, lt, unsp] humerus, [subsq enc for fx w/ routine healing, subsq enc for fx w/ delayed healing, seq] **171**

S42.42[1,2,3]B Disp comm supracondylar fx w/o intercondylar fx of [rt, lt, unsp] humerus, init enc for opn fx **433**

S42.42[1,2,3] [K,P] Disp comm supracondylar fx w/o intercondylar fx of [rt, lt, unsp] humerus, subsq enc for fx w/ [nonu, malu] **197**

S42.42[1,2,3] [A,B] Disp comm supracondylar fx w/o intercondylar fx of humerus [rt, lt, unsp] init enc for fx [clsd, opn] **185**

S32.48[1,2,3] [A,B] Disp dome fx of [rt, lt, unsp] acetab, init enc for [clsd, opn] fx **162, 433**

S32.48[1,2,3]S Disp dome fx of [rt, lt, unsp] acetab, seq **166**

S32.48[1,2,3] [D,G] Disp dome fx of [rt, lt, unsp] acetab, subsq enc for fx w/ [routine, delayed] healing **170**

S32.48[1,2,3]K Disp dome fx of [rt, lt, unsp] acetab, subsq enc for fx w/ nonu **196**

S92.14[1,2,3] [D,G,S] Disp dome fx of [rt, lt, unsp] talus, [subsq enc for fx w/ routine healing, subsq enc for fx w/ delayed healing, seq] **182**

S92.14[1,2,3] [A,B] Disp dome fx of [rt, lt, unsp] talus, init enc for [clsd, opn] fx **192, 429**

S92.14[1,2,3] [K,P] Disp dome fx of [rt, lt, unsp] talus, subsq enc for fx w/ [nonu, malu] **204**

S42.43[1,2,3] [D,G,S] Disp fx (avulsion) of lat epicondyle of [rt, lt, unsp] humerus, [subsq enc for fx w/ routine healing, subsq enc for fx w/ delayed healing, seq] **171**

S42.43[1,2,3]B Disp fx (avulsion) of lat epicondyle of [rt, lt, unsp] humerus, init enc for opn fx **434**

S42.43[1,2,3] [K,P] Disp fx (avulsion) of lat epicondyle of [rt, lt, unsp] humerus, subsq enc for fx w/ [nonu, malu] **197**

S42.43[1,2,3] [A,B] Disp fx (avulsion) of lat epicondyle of humerus [rt, lt, unsp] init enc for fx [clsd, opn] **185**

S42.44[1,2,3] [D,G,S]	Disp fx (avulsion) of med epicondyle of [rt, lt, unsp] humerus, [subsq enc for fx w/ routine healing, subsq enc for fx w/ delayed healing, seq] 171
S42.44[1,2,3]B	Disp fx (avulsion) of med epicondyle of [rt, lt, unsp] humerus, init enc for opn fx 434
S42.44[1,2,3] [K,P]	Disp fx (avulsion) of med epicondyle of [rt, lt, unsp] humerus, subsq enc for fx w/ [nonu, malu] 197
S42.44[1,2,3] [A,B]	Disp fx (avulsion) of med epicondyle of humerus [rt, lt, unsp] init enc for fx [clsd, opn] 185
S52.51[1,2,3] [D,E,F,G,H,J,S]	Disp fx of [rt, lt, unsp] radial styloid process, [subsq enc for clsd fx w/ routine healing, subsq enc for opn fx type I or II w/ routine healing, subsq enc for opn fx type IIIA, IIIB, or IIIC w/ routine healing, subsq enc for clsd fx w/ delayed healing, subsq enc for opn fx type I or II w/ delayed healing, subsq enc for opn fx type IIIA, IIIB, or IIIC w/ delayed healing, seq] 173
S52.51[1,2,3] [A,B,C]	Disp fx of [rt, lt, unsp] radial styloid process, init enc for [clsd fx, opn fx type I or II or opn fx NOS, opn fx type IIIA, IIIB, or IIIC] 186
S52.51[1,2,3] [B,C]	Disp fx of [rt, lt, unsp] radial styloid process, init enc for opn fx type [I or II, IIIA IIIB or IIIC] 434
S52.51[1,2,3] [K,M,N,P,Q,R]	Disp fx of [rt, lt, unsp] radial styloid process, subsq enc for [clsd fx w/ nonu, opn fx type I or II w/ nonu, opn fx type IIIA, IIIB, or IIIC w/ nonu, clsd fx w/ malu, opn fx type I or II w/ malu, opn fx type IIIA, IIIB, or IIIC w/ malu] 198
S82.11[1,2,3] [A,B,C]	Disp fx of [rt, lt, unsp] tibial spine, [init enc for clsd fx, init enc for opn fx type I or II, init enc for opn fx type IIIA, IIIB, or IIIC] 190
S82.11[1,2,3] [D,E,F,G,H,J,S]	Disp fx of [rt, lt, unsp] tibial spine, [subsq enc for clsd fx w/ routine healing, subsq enc for opn fx type I or II w/ routine healing, subsq enc for opn fx type IIIA, IIIB, or IIIC w/ routine healing, subsq enc for clsd fx w/ delayed healing, subsq enc for opn fx type I or II w/ delayed healing, subsq enc for opn fx type I or II w/ delayed healing, seq] 179
S82.11[1,2,3] [B,C]	Disp fx of [rt, lt, unsp] tibial spine, init enc for opn fx type [I or II, IIIA IIIB or IIIC] 436
S82.11[1,2,3] [K,M,N,P,Q,R]	Disp fx of [rt, lt, unsp] tibial spine, subsq enc for [clsd fx w/ nonu, opn fx type I or II w/ nonu, opn fx type IIIA, IIIB, or IIIC w/ nonu, clsd fx w/ malu, opn fx type I or II w/ malu, opn fx type I or II w/ malu] 202
S82.15[1,2,3] [A,B,C]	Disp fx of [rt, lt, unsp] tibial tuberosity, [init enc for clsd fx, init enc for opn fx type I or II, init enc for opn fx type IIIA, IIIB, or IIIC] 191
S82.15[1,2,3] [D,E,F,G,H,J,S]	Disp fx of [rt, lt, unsp] tibial tuberosity, [subsq enc for clsd fx w/ routine healing, subsq enc for opn fx type I or II w/ routine healing, subsq enc for opn fx type IIIA, IIIB, or IIIC w/ routine healing, subsq enc for clsd fx w/ delayed healing, subsq enc for opn fx type I or II w/ delayed healing, subsq enc for opn fx type I or II w/ delayed healing, seq] 180
S82.15[1,2,3] [B,C]	Disp fx of [rt, lt, unsp] tibial tuberosity, init enc for opn fx type [I or II, IIIA IIIB or IIIC] 436
S82.15[1,2,3] [K,M,N,P,Q,R]	Disp fx of [rt, lt, unsp] tibial tuberosity, subsq enc for [clsd fx w/ nonu, opn fx type I or II w/ nonu, opn fx type IIIA, IIIB, or IIIC w/ nonu, clsd fx w/ malu, opn fx type I or II w/ malu, opn fx type I or II w/ malu] 202
S52.61[1,2,3] [D,E,F,G,H,J,S]	Disp fx of [rt, lt, unsp] ulna styloid process, [subsq enc for clsd fx w/ routine healing, subsq enc for opn fx type I or II w/ routine healing, subsq enc for opn fx type IIIA, IIIB, or IIIC w/ routine healing, subsq enc for clsd fx w/ delayed healing, subsq enc for opn fx type I or II w/ delayed healing, subsq enc for opn fx type I or II w/ delayed healing, seq] 174
S52.61[1,2,3] [B,C]	Disp fx of [rt, lt, unsp] ulna styloid process, init enc for opn fx type [I or II, IIIA IIIB IIIC] 435
S52.61[1,2,3] [K,M,N,P,Q,R]	Disp fx of [rt, lt, unsp] ulna styloid process, subsq enc for [clsd fx w/ nonu, opn fx type I or II w/ nonu, opn fx type IIIA, IIIB, or IIIC w/ nonu, clsd fx w/ malu, opn fx type I or II w/ malu, opn fx type IIIA, IIIB, or IIIC w/ malu] 198
S92.31[1,2,3] [D,G,S]	Disp fx of 1st metatarsal bone, [rt, lt, unsp] foot, [subsq enc for fx w/ routine healing, subsq enc for fx w/ delayed healing, seq] 183
S92.31[1,2,3] [A,B]	Disp fx of 1st metatarsal bone, [rt, lt, unsp] foot, init enc for [clsd, opn] fx 192, 429
S92.31[1,2,3] [K,P]	Disp fx of 1st metatarsal bone, [rt, lt, unsp] foot, subsq enc for fx w/ [nonu, malu] 204
S92.32[1,2,3] [D,G,S]	Disp fx of 2nd metatarsal bone, [rt, lt, unsp] foot, [subsq enc for fx w/ routine healing, subsq enc for fx w/ delayed healing, seq] 183
S92.32[1,2,3] [A,B]	Disp fx of 2nd metatarsal bone, [rt, lt, unsp] foot, init enc for [clsd, opn] fx 192, 429
S92.32[1,2,3] [K,P]	Disp fx of 2nd metatarsal bone, [rt, lt, unsp] foot, subsq enc for fx w/ [nonu, malu] 204
S92.33[1,2,3] [D,G,S]	Disp fx of 3rd metatarsal bone, [rt, lt, unsp] foot, [subsq enc for fx w/ routine healing, subsq enc for fx w/ delayed healing, seq] 183
S92.33[1,2,3] [A,B]	Disp fx of 3rd metatarsal bone, [rt, lt, unsp] foot, init enc for [clsd, opn] fx 192, 429
S92.33[1,2,3] [K,P]	Disp fx of 3rd metatarsal bone, [rt, lt, unsp] foot, subsq enc for fx w/ [nonu, malu] 204
S92.34[1,2,3] [D,G,S]	Disp fx of 4th metatarsal bone, [rt, lt, unsp] foot, [subsq enc for fx w/ routine healing, subsq enc for fx w/ delayed healing, seq] 183
S92.34[1,2,3] [A,B]	Disp fx of 4th metatarsal bone, [rt, lt, unsp] foot, init enc for [clsd, opn] fx 192, 429
S92.34[1,2,3] [K,P]	Disp fx of 4th metatarsal bone, [rt, lt, unsp] foot, subsq enc for fx w/ [nonu, malu] 204
S92.35[1,2,3] [D,G,S]	Disp fx of 5th metatarsal bone, [rt, lt, unsp] foot, [subsq enc for fx w/ routine healing, subsq enc for fx w/ delayed healing, seq] 183
S92.35[1,2,3] [A,B]	Disp fx of 5th metatarsal bone, [rt, lt, unsp] foot, init enc for [clsd, opn] fx 192, 429
S92.35[1,2,3] [K,P]	Disp fx of 5th metatarsal bone, [rt, lt, unsp] foot, subsq enc for fx w/ [nonu, malu] 204
S42.12[1,2,3] [A,B]	Disp fx of acromial process [rt, lt, unsp] init enc for fx [clsd, opn] 184
S42.12[1,2,3] [D,G,S]	Disp fx of acromial process, [rt, lt, unsp] shldr, [subsq enc for fx w/ routine healing, subsq enc for fx w/ delayed healing, seq] 170
S42.12[1,2,3] [K,P]	Disp fx of acromial process, [rt, lt, unsp] shldr, subsq enc for fx w/ [nonu, malu] 196
S32.43[1,2,3]S	Disp fx of ant column (iliopubic) of [rt, lt, unsp] acetab, seq 166
S32.43[1,2,3] [D,G]	Disp fx of ant column (iliopubic) of [rt, lt, unsp] acetab, subsq enc for fx w/ [routine, delayed] healing 170
S32.43[1,2,3]K	Disp fx of ant column (iliopubic) of [rt, lt, unsp] acetab, subsq enc for fx w/ nonu 196
S32.43[1,2,3] [A,B]	Disp fx of ant column [iliopubic] of acetab [rt, lt, unsp] init enc for [clsd fx, opn fx] 162, 433
S92.02[1,2,3] [D,G,S]	Disp fx of ant process of [rt, lt, unsp] calcaneus, [subsq enc for fx w/ routine healing, subsq enc for fx w/ delayed healing, seq] 182
S92.02[1,2,3] [A,B]	Disp fx of ant process of [rt, lt, unsp] calcaneus, init enc for [clsd, opn] fx 192, 429
S92.02[1,2,3] [K,P]	Disp fx of ant process of [rt, lt, unsp] calcaneus, subsq enc for fx w/ [nonu, malu] 204
S32.41[1,2,3]S	Disp fx of ant wall of [rt, lt, unsp] acetab, seq 166
S32.41[1,2,3] [D,G]	Disp fx of ant wall of [rt, lt, unsp] acetab, subsq enc for fx w/ [routine, delayed] healing 170
S32.41[1,2,3]K	Disp fx of ant wall of [rt, lt, unsp] acetab, subsq enc for fx w/ nonu 196
S32.41[1,2,3] [A,B]	Disp fx of ant wall of acetab [rt, lt, unsp] init enc for [clsd fx, opn fx] 162, 433
S62.31[0,1,2,3,4, 5,6,7,8,9][A,B]	Disp fx of base of [2nd, 3rd, 4th, 5th, oth, unsp] metacarpal bone, (rt, lt) hand, init enc for [clsd, opn] fx 425
S62.31[8,9] [D,G,S]	Disp fx of base of [oth, unsp] metacarpal bone, [subsq enc for fx w/ routine healing, subsq enc for fx w/ delayed healing, seq] 175
S62.31[8,9][K,P]	Disp fx of base of [oth, unsp] metacarpal bone, subsq enc for fx w/ [nonu, malu] 199
S62.31[0,1][A,B]	Disp fx of base of 2nd metacarpal bone of hand [rt, lt] init enc for fx [clsd, opn] 187
S62.31[0,1] [D,G,S]	Disp fx of base of 2nd metacarpal bone, [rt, lt] hand, [subsq enc for fx w/ routine healing, subsq enc for fx w/ delayed healing, seq] 175
S62.31[0,1][K,P]	Disp fx of base of 2nd metacarpal bone, [rt, lt] hand, subsq enc for fx w/ [nonu, malu] 199
S62.31[2,3][A,B]	Disp fx of base of 3rd metacarpal bone of hand [rt, lt] init enc for fx [clsd, opn] 187
S62.31[2,3] [D,G,S]	Disp fx of base of 3rd metacarpal bone, [rt, lt] hand, [subsq enc for fx w/ routine healing, subsq enc for fx w/ delayed healing, seq] 175
S62.31[2,3][K,P]	Disp fx of base of 3rd metacarpal bone, [rt, lt] hand, subsq enc for fx w/ [nonu, malu] 199
S62.31[4,5][A,B]	Disp fx of base of 4th metacarpal bone of hand [rt, lt] init enc for fx [clsd, opn] 187
S62.31[4,5] [D,G,S]	Disp fx of base of 4th metacarpal bone, [rt, lt] hand, [subsq enc for fx w/ routine healing, subsq enc for fx w/ delayed healing, seq] 175
S62.31[4,5][K,P]	Disp fx of base of 4th metacarpal bone, [rt, lt] hand, subsq enc for fx w/ [nonu, malu] 199
S62.31[6,7][A,B]	Disp fx of base of 5th metacarpal bone of hand [rt, lt] init enc for fx [clsd, opn] 187
S62.31[6,7] [D,G,S]	Disp fx of base of 5th metacarpal bone, [rt, lt] hand, [subsq enc for fx w/ routine healing, subsq enc for fx w/ delayed healing, seq] 175
S62.31[6,7][K,P]	Disp fx of base of 5th metacarpal bone, [rt, lt] hand, subsq enc for fx w/ [nonu, malu] 199
S62.31[8,9][A,B]	Disp fx of base of metacarpal bone of hand [oth, unsp] init enc for fx [clsd, opn] 187

Code	Description
S72.04[1,2,3] [D,E,F,G,H,J,S]	Disp fx of base of neck of [rt, lt, unsp] femur, [subsq enc for clsd fx w/ routine healing, subsq enc for opn fx type I or II w/ routine healing, subsq enc for opn fx type IIIA, IIIB, or IIIC w/ routine healing, subsq enc for clsd fx w/ delayed healing, subsq enc for opn fx type I or II w/ delayed healing, subsq enc for opn fx type IIIA, IIIB, or IIIC w/ delayed healing, seq] **177**
S72.04[1,2,3] [A,B,C]	Disp fx of base of neck of [rt, lt, unsp] femur, init enc for opn fx type [I or II, IIIA IIIB or IIIC] **162, 286, 435**
S72.04[1,2,3] [K,M,N,P,Q,R]	Disp fx of base of neck of [rt, lt, unsp] femur, subsq enc for [clsd fx w/ nonu, opn fx type I or II w/ nonu, opn fx type IIIA, IIIB, or IIIC w/ nonu, clsd fx w/ malu, opn fx type I or II w/ malu, opn fx type IIIA, IIIB, or IIIC w/ malu] **201**
S92.01[1,2,3] [D,G,S]	Disp fx of body of [rt, lt, unsp] calcaneus, [subsq enc for fx w/ routine healing, subsq enc for fx w/ delayed healing, seq] **182**
S92.01[1,2,3] [A,B]	Disp fx of body of [rt, lt, unsp] calcaneus, init enc for [clsd, opn] fx **192, 429**
S92.01[1,2,3] [K,P]	Disp fx of body of [rt, lt, unsp] calcaneus, subsq enc for fx w/ [nonu, malu] **204**
S92.12[1,2,3] [D,G,S]	Disp fx of body of [rt, lt, unsp] talus, [subsq enc for fx w/ routine healing, subsq enc for fx w/ delayed healing, seq] **182**
S92.12[1,2,3] [A,B]	Disp fx of body of [rt, lt, unsp] talus, init enc for [clsd, opn] fx **192, 429**
S92.12[1,2,3] [K,P]	Disp fx of body of [rt, lt, unsp] talus, subsq enc for fx w/ [nonu, malu] **204**
S62.14[1,2,3] [D,G,S]	Disp fx of body of hamate (unciform) bone, [rt, lt, unsp] wrist, [subsq enc for fx w/ routine healing, subsq enc for fx w/ delayed healing, seq] **175**
S62.14[1,2,3] [K,P]	Disp fx of body of hamate (unciform) bone, [rt, lt, unsp] wrist, subsq enc for fx w/ [nonu, malu] **199**
S62.14[1,2,3] [A,B]	Disp fx of body of mate [unciform] bone of wrist [rt, lt, unsp] init enc for fx [clsd, opn **187**
S42.11[1,2,3] [A,B,K,P]	Disp fx of body of scapula, [rt, lt, unsp] shldr, [init enc for clsd fx, init enc for opn fx, subsq enc for fx w/ nonu, subsq enc for fx w/ malu] **196**
S42.11[1,2,3] [D,G,S]	Disp fx of body of scapula, [rt, lt, unsp] shldr, [subsq enc for fx w/ routine healing, subsq enc for fx w/ delayed healing, seq] **170**
S62.13[1,2,3] [D,G,S]	Disp fx of capitate (os magnum) bone, [rt, lt, unsp] wrist, [subsq enc for fx w/ routine healing, subsq enc for fx w/ delayed healing, seq] **175**
S62.13[1,2,3] [K,P]	Disp fx of capitate (os magnum) bone, [rt, lt, unsp] wrist, subsq enc for fx w/ [nonu, malu] **199**
S62.13[1,2,3] [A,B]	Disp fx of capitate [os magnum] bone of wrist [rt, lt, unsp] init enc for fx [clsd, opn] **187**
S42.13[1,2,3] [A,B]	Disp fx of coracoid process of shldr [rt, lt, unsp] init enc for fx [clsd, opn] **184**
S42.13[1,2,3] [D,G,S]	Disp fx of coracoid process, [rt, lt, unsp] shldr, [subsq enc for fx w/ routine healing, subsq enc for fx w/ delayed healing, seq] **170**
S42.13[1,2,3] [K,P]	Disp fx of coracoid process, [rt, lt, unsp] shldr, subsq enc for fx w/ [nonu, malu] **196**
S52.04[1,2,3] [D,E,F,G,H,J,S]	Disp fx of coronoid process of [rt, lt, unsp] ulna, [subsq enc for clsd fx w/ routine healing, subsq enc for opn fx type I or II w/ routine healing, subsq enc for opn fx type IIIA, IIIB, or IIIC w/ routine healing, subsq enc for clsd fx w/ delayed healing, subsq enc for opn fx type I or II w/ delayed healing, subsq enc for opn fx type IIIA, IIIB, or IIIC w/ delayed healing, seq] **172**
S52.04[1,2,3] [B,C]	Disp fx of coronoid process of [rt, lt, unsp] ulna, init enc for opn fx type [I or II, IIIA IIIB or IIIC] **434**
S52.04[1,2,3] [K,M,N,P,Q,R]	Disp fx of coronoid process of [rt, lt, unsp] ulna, subsq enc for [clsd fx w/ nonu, opn fx type I or II w/ nonu, opn fx type IIIA, IIIB, or IIIC w/ nonu, clsd fx w/ malu, opn fx type I or II w/ malu, opn fx type IIIA, IIIB, or IIIC w/ malu] **197**
S52.04[1,2,3] [A,B,C]	Disp fx of coronoid process of ulna [rt, lt, unsp] init enc for fx [clsd fx, opn fx type I or II or opn fx NOS, opn fx type IIIA, IIIB, or IIIC] **186**
S92.21[1,2,3] [D,G,S]	Disp fx of cuboid bone of [rt, lt, unsp] foot, [subsq enc for fx w/ routine healing, subsq enc for fx w/ delayed healing, seq] **182**
S92.21[1,2,3] [A,B]	Disp fx of cuboid bone of [rt, lt, unsp] foot, init enc for [clsd, opn] fx **192, 429**
S92.21[1,2,3] [K,P]	Disp fx of cuboid bone of [rt, lt, unsp] foot, subsq enc for fx w/ [nonu, malu] **204**
S92.53[1,2,3] [K,P]	Disp fx of distal phalanx [rt, lt, unsp] lesser toe(s), subsq enc for fx w/ [nonu, malu] **204**
S62.63[8,9] [D,G,S]	Disp fx of distal phalanx of [oth, unsp] finger, [subsq enc for fx w/ routine healing, subsq enc for fx w/ delayed healing, seq] **176**
S62.63[8,9][A,B]	Disp fx of distal phalanx of [oth, unsp] finger, init enc for [clsd, opn] fx **188**
S62.63[8,9][K,P]	Disp fx of distal phalanx of [oth, unsp] finger, subsq enc for fx w/ [nonu, malu] **200**
S62.63[0,1,2,3,4, 5,6,7,8,9] [A,B]	Disp fx of distal phalanx of [rt index, lt index, rt mid, lt mid, rt ring, lt ring, rt little, lt little, oth, unsp] finger, init enc for [clsd, opn] fx **425**
S92.42[1,2,3] [D,G,S]	Disp fx of distal phalanx of [rt, lt, unsp] great toe, [subsq enc for fx w/ routine healing, subsq enc for fx w/ delayed healing, seq] **183**
S92.42[1,2,3] [A,B]	Disp fx of distal phalanx of [rt, lt, unsp] great toe, init enc for [clsd, opn] fx **192, 429**
S92.42[1,2,3] [K,P]	Disp fx of distal phalanx of [rt, lt, unsp] great toe, subsq enc for fx w/ [nonu, malu] **204**
S92.53[1,2,3] [D,G,S]	Disp fx of distal phalanx of [rt, lt, unsp] lesser toe(s), [subsq enc for fx w/ routine healing, subsq enc for fx w/ delayed healing, seq] **183**
S92.53[1,2,3] [A,B]	Disp fx of distal phalanx of [rt, lt, unsp] lesser toe(s), init enc for [clsd, opn] fx **193, 430**
S62.52[1,2,3] [D,G,S]	Disp fx of distal phalanx of [rt, lt, unsp] thumb, [subsq enc for fx w/ routine healing, subsq enc for fx w/ delayed healing, seq] **176**
S62.52[1,2,3] [A,B]	Disp fx of distal phalanx of [rt, lt, unsp] thumb, init enc for [clsd, opn] fx **188**
S62.52[1,2,3] [K,P]	Disp fx of distal phalanx of [rt, lt, unsp] thumb, subsq enc for fx w/ [nonu, malu] **200**
S62.63[0,1] [D,G,S]	Disp fx of distal phalanx of [rt, lt] index finger, [subsq enc for fx w/ routine healing, subsq enc for fx w/ delayed healing, seq] **176**
S62.63[0,1][A,B]	Disp fx of distal phalanx of [rt, lt] index finger, init enc for [clsd, opn] fx **188**
S62.63[0,1][K,P]	Disp fx of distal phalanx of [rt, lt] index finger, subsq enc for fx w/ [nonu, malu] **200**
S62.63[6,7] [D,G,S]	Disp fx of distal phalanx of [rt, lt] little finger, [subsq enc for fx w/ routine healing, subsq enc for fx w/ delayed healing, seq] **176**
S62.63[6,7][A,B]	Disp fx of distal phalanx of [rt, lt] little finger, init enc for [clsd, opn] fx **188**
S62.63[6,7][K,P]	Disp fx of distal phalanx of [rt, lt] little finger, subsq enc for fx w/ [nonu, malu] **200**
S62.63[2,3] [D,G,S]	Disp fx of distal phalanx of [rt, lt] mid finger, [subsq enc for fx w/ routine healing, subsq enc for fx w/ delayed healing, seq] **176**
S62.63[2,3][A,B]	Disp fx of distal phalanx of [rt, lt] mid finger, init enc for [clsd, opn] fx **188**
S62.63[2,3][K,P]	Disp fx of distal phalanx of [rt, lt] mid finger, subsq enc for fx w/ [nonu, malu] **200**
S62.63[4,5] [D,G,S]	Disp fx of distal phalanx of [rt, lt] ring finger, [subsq enc for fx w/ routine healing, subsq enc for fx w/ delayed healing, seq] **176**
S62.63[4,5][A,B]	Disp fx of distal phalanx of [rt, lt] ring finger, init enc for [clsd, opn] fx **188**
S62.63[4,5][K,P]	Disp fx of distal phalanx of [rt, lt] ring finger, subsq enc for fx w/ [nonu, malu] **200**
S62.01[1,2,3] [D,G,S]	Disp fx of distal pole of navicular (scaphoid) bone of [rt, lt, unsp] wrist, [subsq enc for fx w/ routine healing, subsq enc for fx w/ delayed healing, seq] **174**
S62.01[1,2,3] [K,P]	Disp fx of distal pole of navicular (scaphoid) bone of [rt, lt, unsp] wrist, subsq enc for fx w/ [nonu, malu] **199**
S62.01[1,2,3] [A,B]	Disp fx of distal pole of navicular [scaphoid] bone of wrist [rt, lt, unsp] init enc for fx [clsd, opn] **187**
S72.02[1,2,3] [D,E,F,G,H,J,S]	Disp fx of epiphysis (separation) (upr) of [rt, lt, unsp] femur, [subsq enc for clsd fx w/ routine healing, subsq enc for opn fx type I or II w/ routine healing, subsq enc for opn fx type IIIA, IIIB, or IIIC w/ routine healing, subsq enc for clsd fx w/ delayed healing, subsq enc for opn fx type I or II w/ delayed healing, subsq enc for opn fx type IIIA, IIIB, or IIIC w/ delayed healing, seq] **177**
S72.02[1,2,3] [A,B,C]	Disp fx of epiphysis (separation) (upr) of [rt, lt, unsp] femur, init enc for [clsd fx, opn fx type I or II or NOS, or opn fx type IIIA, IIIB, or IIIC] **162, 286, 435**
S72.02[1,2,3] [K,M,N,P,Q,R]	Disp fx of epiphysis (separation) (upr) of [rt, lt, unsp] femur, subsq enc for [clsd fx w/ nonu, opn fx type I or II w/ nonu, opn fx type IIIA, IIIB, or IIIC w/ nonu, clsd fx w/ malu, opn fx type I or II w/ malu, opn fx type IIIA, IIIB, or IIIC w/ malu] **200**
S42.14[1,2,3] [A,B]	Disp fx of glenoid cavity of scapula [rt, lt, unsp] init enc for fx [clsd, opn] **184**
S42.14[1,2,3] [D,G,S]	Disp fx of glenoid cavity of scapula, [rt, lt, unsp] shldr, [subsq enc for fx w/ routine healing, subsq enc for fx w/ delayed healing, seq] **170**
S42.14[1,2,3] [K,P]	Disp fx of glenoid cavity of scapula, [rt, lt, unsp] shldr, subsq enc for fx w/ [nonu, malu] **196**
S72.11[1,2,3] [D,E,F,G,H,J,S]	Disp fx of greater trochanter of [rt, lt, unsp] femur, [subsq enc for clsd fx w/ routine healing, subsq enc for opn fx type I or II w/ routine healing, subsq enc for opn fx type IIIA, IIIB, or IIIC w/ routine healing, subsq enc for clsd fx w/ delayed healing, subsq enc for opn fx type I or II w/ delayed healing, subsq enc for opn fx type IIIA, IIIB, or IIIC w/ delayed healing, seq] **177**

S72.11[1,2,3] [A,B,C]	Disp fx of greater trochanter of [rt, lt, unsp] femur, init enc for fx [clsd, opn fx type I or II or NOS, or opn fx type IIIA, IIIB, or IIIC] 162, 286, 435
S72.11[1,2,3] [K,M,N,P,Q,R]	Disp fx of greater trochanter of [rt, lt, unsp] femur, subsq enc for [clsd fx w/ nonu, opn fx type I or II w/ nonu, opn fx type IIIA, IIIB, or IIIC w/ nonu, clsd fx w/ malu, opn fx type I or II w/ malu, opn fx type IIIA, IIIB, or IIIC w/ malu] 201
S42.25[1,2,3] [D,G,S]	Disp fx of greater tuberosity of [rt, lt, unsp] humerus, [subsq enc for fx w/ routine healing, subsq enc for fx w/ delayed healing, seq] 171
S42.25[1,2,3]B	Disp fx of greater tuberosity of [rt, lt, unsp] humerus, init enc for opn fx 433
S42.25[1,2,3] [K,P]	Disp fx of greater tuberosity of [rt, lt, unsp] humerus, subsq enc for fx w/ [nonu, malu] 196
S42.25[1,2,3] [A,B]	Disp fx of greater tuberosity of humerus [rt, lt, unsp] init enc for fx [clsd, opn] 185
S52.12[1,2,3] [D,E,F,G,H,J,S]	Disp fx of head of [rt, lt, unsp] radius, [subsq enc for clsd fx w/ routine healing, subsq enc for opn fx type I or II w/ routine healing, subsq enc for opn fx type IIIA, IIIB, or IIIC w/ routine healing, subsq enc for clsd fx w/ delayed healing, subsq enc for opn fx type I or II w/ delayed healing, subsq enc for opn fx type IIIA, IIIB, or IIIC w/ delayed healing, seq] 172
S52.12[1,2,3] [A,B,C]	Disp fx of head of [rt, lt, unsp] radius, init enc for [clsd fx, opn fx type I or II or opn fx NOS, opn fx type IIIA, IIIB, or IIIC] 186
S52.12[1,2,3] [B,C]	Disp fx of head of [rt, lt, unsp] radius, init enc for opn fx type [I or II, IIIA IIIB or IIIC] 434
S52.12[1,2,3] [K,M,N,P,Q,R]	Disp fx of head of [rt, lt, unsp] radius, subsq enc for [clsd fx w/ nonu, opn fx type I or II w/ nonu, opn fx type IIIA, IIIB, or IIIC w/ nonu, clsd fx w/ malu, opn fx type I or II w/ malu, opn fx type IIIA, IIIB, or IIIC w/ malu] 197
S62.15[1,2,3] [D,G,S]	Disp fx of hook process of hamate (unciform) bone, [rt, lt, unsp] wrist, [subsq enc for fx w/ routine healing, subsq enc for fx w/ delayed healing, seq] 175
S62.15[1,2,3] [K,P]	Disp fx of hook process of hamate (unciform) bone, [rt, lt, unsp] wrist, subsq enc for fx w/ [nonu, malu] 199
S62.15[1,2,3] [A,B]	Disp fx of hook process of hamate [unciform] bone of wrist [rt, lt, unsp] init enc for fx [clsd, opn] 187
S92.23[1,2,3] [D,G,S]	Disp fx of intermediate cuneiform of [rt, lt, unsp] foot, [subsq enc for fx w/ routine healing, subsq enc for fx w/ delayed healing, seq] 182
S92.23[1,2,3] [A,B]	Disp fx of intermediate cuneiform of [rt, lt, unsp] foot, init enc for [clsd, opn] fx 192, 429
S92.23[1,2,3] [K,P]	Disp fx of intermediate cuneiform of [rt, lt, unsp] foot, subsq enc for fx w/ [nonu, malu] 204
S72.42[1,2,3] [D,E,F,G,H,J,S]	Disp fx of lat condyle of [rt, lt, unsp] femur, [subsq enc for clsd fx w/ routine healing, subsq enc for opn fx type I or II w/ routine healing, subsq enc for opn fx type IIIA, IIIB, or IIIC w/ routine healing, subsq enc for clsd fx w/ delayed healing, subsq enc for opn fx type I or II w/ delayed healing, subsq enc for opn fx type IIIA, IIIB, or IIIC w/ delayed healing, seq] 178
S72.42[1,2,3] [A,B,C]	Disp fx of lat condyle of [rt, lt, unsp] femur, init enc for [clsd fx, opn fx type I or II, opn fx type IIIA, IIIB, or IIIC] 161, 435
S72.42[1,2,3] [K,M,N,P,Q,R]	Disp fx of lat condyle of [rt, lt, unsp] femur, subsq enc for [clsd fx w/ nonu, opn fx type I or II w/ nonu, opn fx type IIIA, IIIB, or IIIC w/ nonu, clsd fx w/ malu, opn fx type I or II w/ malu, opn fx type IIIA, IIIB, or IIIC w/ malu] 201
S42.45[1,2,3] [D,G,S]	Disp fx of lat condyle of [rt, lt, unsp] humerus, [subsq enc for fx w/ routine healing, subsq enc for fx w/ delayed healing, seq] 171
S42.45[1,2,3]B	Disp fx of lat condyle of [rt, lt, unsp] humerus, init enc for opn fx 434
S42.45[1,2,3] [K,P]	Disp fx of lat condyle of [rt, lt, unsp] humerus, subsq enc for fx w/ [nonu, malu] 197
S82.12[1,2,3] [A,B,C]	Disp fx of lat condyle of [rt, lt, unsp] tibia, [init enc for clsd fx, init enc for opn fx type I or II, init enc for opn fx type IIIA, IIIB, or IIIC] 190
S82.12[1,2,3] [D,E,F,G,H,J,S]	Disp fx of lat condyle of [rt, lt, unsp] tibia, [subsq enc for clsd fx w/ routine healing, subsq enc for opn fx type I or II w/ routine healing, subsq enc for opn fx type IIIA, IIIB, or IIIC w/ routine healing, subsq enc for clsd fx w/ delayed healing, subsq enc for opn fx type I or II w/ delayed healing, subsq enc for opn fx type I or II w/ delayed healing, seq] 179
S82.12[1,2,3] [B,C]	Disp fx of lat condyle of [rt, lt, unsp] tibia, init enc for opn fx type [I or II, IIIA IIIB or IIIC] 436
S82.12[1,2,3] [K,M,N,P,Q,R]	Disp fx of lat condyle of [rt, lt, unsp] tibia, subsq enc for [clsd fx w/ nonu, opn fx type I or II w/ nonu, opn fx type IIIA, IIIB, or IIIC w/ nonu, clsd fx w/ malu, opn fx type I or II w/ malu, opn fx type I or II w/ malu] 202
S42.45[1,2,3] [A,B]	Disp fx of lat condyle of humerus [rt, lt, unsp] init enc for fx [clsd, opn] 185
S92.22[1,2,3] [D,G,S]	Disp fx of lat cuneiform of [rt, lt, unsp] foot, [subsq enc for fx w/ routine healing, subsq enc for fx w/ delayed healing, seq] 182
S92.22[1,2,3] [A,B]	Disp fx of lat cuneiform of [rt, lt, unsp] foot, init enc for [clsd, opn] fx 192, 429
S92.22[1,2,3] [K,P]	Disp fx of lat cuneiform of [rt, lt, unsp] foot, subsq enc for fx w/ [nonu, malu] 204
S42.03[1,2,3] [D,G,S]	Disp fx of lat end of [rt, lt, unsp] clavicle, [subsq enc for fx w/ routine healing, subsq enc for fx w/ delayed healing, seq] 170
S42.03[1,2,3] [K,P]	Disp fx of lat end of [rt, lt, unsp] clavicle, subsq enc for fx w/ [nonu, malu] 196
S42.03[1,2,3] [A,B]	Disp fx of lat end of clavicle [rt, lt, unsp] init enc for fx [clsd, opn] 184
S82.6[1,2,3] X[D,E,F,G,H,J,S]	Disp fx of lat malleolus of [rt, lt, unsp] fibula, [subsq enc for clsd fx w/ routine healing, subsq enc for opn fx type I or II w/ routine healing, subsq enc for opn fx type IIIA, IIIB, or IIIC w/ routine healing, subsq enc for clsd fx w/ delayed healing, subsq enc for opn fx type I or II w/ delayed healing, subsq enc for opn fx type IIIA, IIIB, or IIIC w/ delayed healing, seq] 181
S82.6[1,2,3] X[K,M,N,P,Q,R]	Disp fx of lat malleolus of [rt, lt, unsp] fibula, subsq enc for [clsd fx w/ nonu, opn fx type I or II w/ nonu, opn fx type IIIA, IIIB, or IIIC w/ nonu, clsd fx w/ malu, opn fx type I or II w/ malu, opn fx type I or II w/ malu] 203
S82.6[1,2,3] X[A,B,C]	Disp fx of lat malleolus of [rt, lt, unsp] tibia, [init enc for clsd fx, init enc for opn fx type I or II, init enc for opn fx type I or II] 191, 427
S72.12[1,2,3] [D,E,F,G,H,J,S]	Disp fx of lesser trochanter of [rt, lt, unsp] femur, [subsq enc for clsd fx w/ routine healing, subsq enc for opn fx type I or II w/ routine healing, subsq enc for opn fx type IIIA, IIIB, or IIIC w/ routine healing, subsq enc for clsd fx w/ delayed healing, subsq enc for opn fx type I or II w/ delayed healing, subsq enc for opn fx type IIIA, IIIB, or IIIC w/ delayed healing, seq] 177
S72.12[1,2,3] [A,B,C]	Disp fx of lesser trochanter of [rt, lt, unsp] femur, init enc for [clsd fx, opn fx type I or II or NOS, or opn fx type IIIA, IIIB, or IIIC] 162, 286, 435
S72.12[1,2,3] [K,M,N,P,Q,R]	Disp fx of lesser trochanter of [rt, lt, unsp] femur, subsq enc for [clsd fx w/ nonu, opn fx type I or II w/ nonu, opn fx type IIIA, IIIB, or IIIC w/ nonu, clsd fx w/ malu, opn fx type I or II w/ malu, opn fx type IIIA, IIIB, or IIIC w/ malu] 201
S42.26[1,2,3] [D,G,S]	Disp fx of lesser tuberosity of [rt, lt, unsp] humerus, [subsq enc for fx w/ routine healing, subsq enc for fx w/ delayed healing, seq] 171
S42.26[1,2,3]B	Disp fx of lesser tuberosity of [rt, lt, unsp] humerus, init enc for opn fx 433
S42.26[1,2,3] [K,P]	Disp fx of lesser tuberosity of [rt, lt, unsp] humerus, subsq enc for fx w/ [nonu, malu] 196
S42.26[1,2,3] [A,B]	Disp fx of lesser tuberosity of humerus [rt, lt, unsp] init enc for fx [clsd, opn] 185
S62.12[1,2,3] [D,G,S]	Disp fx of lunate (semilunar), [rt, lt, unsp] wrist, [subsq enc for fx w/ routine healing, subsq enc for fx w/ delayed healing, seq] 174
S62.12[1,2,3] [K,P]	Disp fx of lunate (semilunar), [rt, lt, unsp] wrist, subsq enc for fx w/ [nonu, malu] 199
S62.12[1,2,3] [A,B]	Disp fx of lunate [semilunar] bone of wrist [rt, lt, unsp] init enc for fx [clsd, opn] 187
S72.44[1,2,3] [D,E,F,G,H,J,S]	Disp fx of lwr epiphysis (separation) of [rt, lt, unsp] femur, [subsq enc for clsd fx w/ routine healing, subsq enc for opn fx type I or II w/ routine healing, subsq enc for opn fx type IIIA, IIIB, or IIIC w/ routine healing, subsq enc for clsd fx w/ delayed healing, subsq enc for opn fx type I or II w/ delayed healing, subsq enc for opn fx type I or II w/ delayed healing, seq] 178
S72.44[1,2,3] [A,B,C]	Disp fx of lwr epiphysis (separation) of [rt, lt, unsp] femur, init enc for [clsd fx, opn fx type I or II, opn fx type IIIA, IIIB, or IIIC] 161, 435
S72.44[1,2,3] [K,M,N,P,Q,R]	Disp fx of lwr epiphysis (separation) of [rt, lt, unsp] femur, subsq enc for [clsd fx w/ nonu, opn fx type I or II w/ nonu, opn fx type IIIA, IIIB, or IIIC w/ nonu, clsd fx w/ malu, opn fx type I or II w/ malu, opn fx type IIIA, IIIB, or IIIC w/ malu] 201
S82.13[1,2,3] [D,E,F,G,H,J,S]	Disp fx of med condyle [rt, lt, unsp] tibia, [subsq enc for clsd fx w/ routine healing, subsq enc for opn fx type I or II w/ routine healing, subsq enc for opn fx type IIIA, IIIB, or IIIC w/ routine healing, subsq enc for clsd fx w/ delayed healing, subsq enc for opn fx type I or II w/ delayed healing, subsq enc for opn fx type I or II w/ delayed healing, seq] 179
S72.43[1,2,3] [D,E,F,G,H,J,S]	Disp fx of med condyle of [rt, lt, unsp] femur, [subsq enc for clsd fx w/ routine healing, subsq enc for opn fx type I or II w/ routine healing, subsq enc for opn fx type IIIA, IIIB, or IIIC w/ routine healing, subsq enc for clsd fx w/ delayed healing, subsq enc for opn fx type I or II w/ delayed healing, subsq enc for opn fx type I or II w/ delayed healing, seq] 178
S72.43[1,2,3] [A,B,C]	Disp fx of med condyle of [rt, lt, unsp] femur, init enc for [clsd fx, opn fx type I or II, opn fx type IIIA, IIIB, or IIIC] 161, 435

S72.43[1,2,3] [K,M,N,P,Q,R] Disp fx of med condyle of [rt, lt, unsp] femur, subsq enc for [clsd fx w/ nonu, opn fx type I or II w/ nonu, opn fx type IIIA, IIIB, or IIIC w/ nonu, clsd fx w/ malu, opn fx type I or II w/ malu, opn fx type IIIA, IIIB, or IIIC w/ malu] 201

S42.46[1,2,3] [D,G,S] Disp fx of med condyle of [rt, lt, unsp] humerus, [subsq enc for fx w/ routine healing, subsq enc for fx w/ delayed healing, seq] 171

S42.46[1,2,3]B Disp fx of med condyle of [rt, lt, unsp] humerus, init enc for opn fx 434

S42.46[1,2,3] [K,P] Disp fx of med condyle of [rt, lt, unsp] humerus, subsq enc for fx w/ [nonu, malu] 197

S82.13[1,2,3] [A,B,C] Disp fx of med condyle of [rt, lt, unsp] tibia, [init enc for clsd fx, init enc for opn fx type I or II, init enc for opn fx type IIIA, IIIB, or IIIC] 190

S82.13[1,2,3] [B,C] Disp fx of med condyle of [rt, lt, unsp] tibia, init enc for opn fx type [I or II, IIIA IIIB or IIIC] 436

S82.13[1,2,3] [K,M,N,P,Q,R] Disp fx of med condyle of [rt, lt, unsp] tibia, subsq enc for [clsd fx w/ nonu, opn fx type I or II w/ nonu, opn fx type IIIA, IIIB, or IIIC w/ nonu, clsd fx w/ malu, opn fx type I or II w/ malu, opn fx type I or II w/ malu] 202

S42.46[1,2,3] [A,B] Disp fx of med condyle of humerus [rt, lt, unsp] init enc for fx [clsd, opn] 185

S92.24[1,2,3] [D,G,S] Disp fx of med cuneiform of [rt, lt, unsp] foot, [subsq enc for fx w/ routine healing, subsq enc for fx w/ delayed healing, seq] 183

S92.24[1,2,3] [A,B] Disp fx of med cuneiform of [rt, lt, unsp] foot, init enc for [clsd, opn] fx 192, 429

S92.24[1,2,3] [K,P] Disp fx of med cuneiform of [rt, lt, unsp] foot, subsq enc for fx w/ [nonu, malu] 204

S82.5[1,2,3] X[A,B,C] Disp fx of med malleolus of [rt, lt, unsp] tibia, [init enc for clsd fx, init enc for opn fx type I or II, init enc for opn fx type I or II] 191, 427

S82.5[1,2,3] X[D,E,F,G,H,J,S] Disp fx of med malleolus of [rt, lt, unsp] tibia, [subsq enc for clsd fx w/ routine healing, subsq enc for opn fx type I or II w/ routine healing, subsq enc for opn fx type IIIA, IIIB, or IIIC w/ routine healing, subsq enc for clsd fx w/ delayed healing, subsq enc for opn fx type I or II w/ delayed healing, subsq enc for opn fx type IIIA, IIIB, or IIIC w/ delayed healing, seq] 181

S82.5[1,2,3] X[K,M,N,P,Q,R] Disp fx of med malleolus of [rt, lt, unsp] tibia, subsq enc for [clsd fx w/ nonu, opn fx type I or II w/ nonu, opn fx type IIIA, IIIB, or IIIC w/ nonu, clsd fx w/ malu, opn fx type I or II w/ malu, opn fx type I or II w/ malu] 203

S92.52[1,2,3] [K,P] Disp fx of med phalanx [rt, lt, unsp] lesser toe(s), subsq enc for fx w/ [nonu, malu] 204

S62.62[8,9] [D,G,S] Disp fx of med phalanx of [oth, unsp] finger, [subsq enc for fx w/ routine healing, subsq enc for fx w/ delayed healing, seq] 176

S62.62[8,9][A,B] Disp fx of med phalanx of [oth, unsp] finger, init enc for [clsd, opn] fx 188

S62.62[8,9][K,P] Disp fx of med phalanx of [oth, unsp] finger, subsq enc for fx w/ [nonu, malu] 200

S62.62[0,1,2,3,4, 5,6,7,8,9] [A,B] Disp fx of med phalanx of [rt index, lt index, rt mid, lt mid, rt ring, lt ring, rt little, lt little, oth, unsp] finger, init enc for [clsd, opn] fx 425

S92.52[1,2,3] [D,G,S] Disp fx of med phalanx of [rt, lt, unsp] lesser toe(s), [subsq enc for fx w/ routine healing, subsq enc for fx w/ delayed healing, seq] 183

S92.52[1,2,3] [A,B] Disp fx of med phalanx of [rt, lt, unsp] lesser toe(s), init enc for [clsd, opn] fx 193, 430

S62.62[0,1] [D,G,S] Disp fx of med phalanx of [rt, lt] index finger, [subsq enc for fx w/ routine healing, subsq enc for fx w/ delayed healing, seq] 176

S62.62[0,1][A,B] Disp fx of med phalanx of [rt, lt] index finger, init enc for [clsd, opn] fx 188

S62.62[0,1][K,P] Disp fx of med phalanx of [rt, lt] index finger, subsq enc for fx w/ [nonu, malu] 200

S62.62[6,7] [D,G,S] Disp fx of med phalanx of [rt, lt] little finger, [subsq enc for fx w/ routine healing, subsq enc for fx w/ delayed healing, seq] 176

S62.62[6,7][A,B] Disp fx of med phalanx of [rt, lt] little finger, init enc for [clsd, opn] fx 188

S62.62[6,7][K,P] Disp fx of med phalanx of [rt, lt] little finger, subsq enc for fx w/ [nonu, malu] 200

S62.62[2,3] [D,G,S] Disp fx of med phalanx of [rt, lt] mid finger, [subsq enc for fx w/ routine healing, subsq enc for fx w/ delayed healing, seq] 176

S62.62[2,3][A,B] Disp fx of med phalanx of [rt, lt] mid finger, init enc for [clsd, opn] fx 188

S62.62[2,3][K,P] Disp fx of med phalanx of [rt, lt] mid finger, subsq enc for fx w/ [nonu, malu] 200

S62.62[4,5] [D,G,S] Disp fx of med phalanx of [rt, lt] ring finger, [subsq enc for fx w/ routine healing, subsq enc for fx w/ delayed healing, seq] 176

S62.62[4,5][A,B] Disp fx of med phalanx of [rt, lt] ring finger, init enc for [clsd, opn] fx 188

S62.62[4,5][K,P] Disp fx of med phalanx of [rt, lt] ring finger, subsq enc for fx w/ [nonu, malu] 200

S32.47[1,2,3]S Disp fx of med wall of [rt, lt, unsp] acetab, seq 166

S32.47[1,2,3] [D,G] Disp fx of med wall of [rt, lt, unsp] acetab, subsq enc for fx w/ [routine, delayed] healing 170

S32.47[1,2,3]K Disp fx of med wall of [rt, lt, unsp] acetab, subsq enc for fx w/ nonu 196

S32.47[1,2,3] [A,B] Disp fx of med wall of acetab [rt, lt, unsp] init enc for [clsd fx, opn fx] 162, 433

S62.02[1,2,3] [D,G,S] Disp fx of mid 3rd of navicular (scaphoid) bone of [rt, lt, unsp] wrist, [subsq enc for fx w/ routine healing, subsq enc for fx w/ delayed healing, seq] 174

S62.02[1,2,3] [K,P] Disp fx of mid 3rd of navicular (scaphoid) bone of [rt, lt, unsp] wrist, subsq enc for fx w/ [nonu, malu] 199

S62.02[1,2,3] [A,B] Disp fx of mid 3rd of navicular [scaphoid] bone of wrist [rt, lt, unsp] init enc for fx [clsd, opn] 187

S92.25[1,2,3] [D,G,S] Disp fx of navicular (scaphoid) of [rt, lt, unsp] foot, [subsq enc for fx w/ routine healing, subsq enc for fx w/ delayed healing, seq] 183

S92.25[1,2,3] [A,B] Disp fx of navicular (scaphoid) of [rt, lt, unsp] foot, init enc for [clsd, opn] fx 192, 429

S92.25[1,2,3] [K,P] Disp fx of navicular (scaphoid) of [rt, lt, unsp] foot, subsq enc for fx w/ [nonu, malu] 204

S62.33[0,1,2,3,4, 5,6,7,8,9][A,B] Disp fx of neck of [2nd, 3rd, 4th, 5th, oth, unsp] metacarpal bone, (rt, lt) hand, init enc for [clsd, opn] fx 425

S62.33[8,9] [D,G,S] Disp fx of neck of [oth, unsp] metacarpal bone, [subsq enc for fx w/ routine healing, subsq enc for fx w/ delayed healing, seq] 175

S62.33[8,9][K,P] Disp fx of neck of [oth, unsp] metacarpal bone, subsq enc for fx w/ [nonu, malu] 199

S52.13[1,2,3] [D,E,F,G,H,J,S] Disp fx of neck of [rt, lt, unsp] radius, [subsq enc for clsd fx w/ routine healing, subsq enc for opn fx type I or II w/ routine healing, subsq enc for opn fx type IIIA, IIIB, or IIIC w/ routine healing, subsq enc for clsd fx w/ delayed healing, subsq enc for opn fx type I or II w/ delayed healing, subsq enc for opn fx type IIIA, IIIB, or IIIC w/ delayed healing, seq] 172

S52.13[1,2,3] [B,C] Disp fx of neck of [rt, lt, unsp] radius, init enc for opn fx type [I or II, IIIA IIIB or IIIC] 434

S52.13[1,2,3] [K,M,N,P,Q,R] Disp fx of neck of [rt, lt, unsp] radius, subsq enc for [clsd fx w/ nonu, opn fx type I or II w/ nonu, opn fx type IIIA, IIIB, or IIIC w/ nonu, clsd fx w/ malu, opn fx type I or II w/ malu, opn fx type IIIA, IIIB, or IIIC w/ malu] 197

S92.11[1,2,3] [D,G,S] Disp fx of neck of [rt, lt, unsp] talus, [subsq enc for fx w/ routine healing, subsq enc for fx w/ delayed healing, seq] 182

S92.11[1,2,3] [A,B] Disp fx of neck of [rt, lt, unsp] talus, init enc for [clsd, opn] fx 192, 429

S92.11[1,2,3] [K,P] Disp fx of neck of [rt, lt, unsp] talus, subsq enc for fx w/ [nonu, malu] 204

S62.25[1,2,3] [A,B] Disp fx of neck of 1st metacarpal bone of hand [rt, lt, unsp] init enc for fx [clsd, opn] 187

S62.25[1,2,3] [D,G,S] Disp fx of neck of 1st metacarpal bone, [rt, lt, unsp] hand, [subsq enc for fx w/ routine healing, subsq enc for fx w/ delayed healing, seq] 175

S62.25[1,2,3] [K,P] Disp fx of neck of 1st metacarpal bone, [rt, lt, unsp] hand, subsq enc for fx w/ [nonu, malu] 199

S62.33[0,1][A,B] Disp fx of neck of 2nd metacarpal bone of hand [rt, lt] init enc for [clsd, opn] fx 188

S62.33[0,1] [D,G,S] Disp fx of neck of 2nd metacarpal bone, [rt, lt] hand, [subsq enc for fx w/ routine healing, subsq enc for fx w/ delayed healing, seq] 175

S62.33[0,1][K,P] Disp fx of neck of 2nd metacarpal bone, [rt, lt] hand, subsq enc for fx w/ [nonu, malu] 199

S62.33[2,3][A,B] Disp fx of neck of 3rd metacarpal bone of hand [rt, lt] init enc for fx [clsd, opn] 188

S62.33[2,3] [D,G,S] Disp fx of neck of 3rd metacarpal bone, [rt, lt] hand, [subsq enc for fx w/ routine healing, subsq enc for fx w/ delayed healing, seq] 175

S62.33[2,3][K,P] Disp fx of neck of 3rd metacarpal bone, [rt, lt] hand, subsq enc for fx w/ [nonu, malu] 199

S62.33[4,5][A,B] Disp fx of neck of 4th metacarpal bone of hand [rt, lt] init enc for fx [clsd, opn] 188

S62.33[4,5] [D,G,S] Disp fx of neck of 4th metacarpal bone, [rt, lt] hand, [subsq enc for fx w/ routine healing, subsq enc for fx w/ delayed healing, seq] 175

S62.33[4,5][K,P] Disp fx of neck of 4th metacarpal bone, [rt, lt] hand, subsq enc for fx w/ [nonu, malu] 199

S62.33[6,7][A,B] Disp fx of neck of 5th metacarpal bone of hand [rt, lt] init enc for fx [clsd, opn] 188

S62.33[6,7] [D,G,S] Disp fx of neck of 5th metacarpal bone, [rt, lt] hand, [subsq enc for fx w/ routine healing, subsq enc for fx w/ delayed healing, seq] 175

S62.33[6,7][K,P] Disp fx of neck of 5th metacarpal bone, [rt, lt] hand, subsq enc for fx w/ [nonu, malu] 199

Code	Description
S62.33[8,9][A,B]	Disp fx of neck of metacarpal bone of hand [oth, unsp] init enc for fx [clsd, opn] 188
S52.13[1,2,3] [A,B,C]	Disp fx of neck of radius [rt, lt, unsp] init enc for [clsd fx, opn fx type I or II or opn fx NOS, opn fx type IIIA, IIIB, or IIIC] 186
S42.15[1,2,3] [D,G,S]	Disp fx of neck of scapula, [rt, lt, unsp] shldr, [subsq enc for fx w/ routine healing, subsq enc for fx w/ delayed healing, seq] 170
S42.15[1,2,3] [K,P]	Disp fx of neck of scapula, [rt, lt, unsp] shldr, subsq enc for fx w/ [nonu, malu] 196
S52.03[1,2,3] [D,E,F,G,H,J,S]	Disp fx of olecranon process w/ intraarticular extension of [rt, lt, unsp] ulna, [subsq enc for clsd fx w/ routine healing, subsq enc for opn fx type I or II w/ routine healing, subsq enc for opn fx type IIIA, IIIB, or IIIC w/ routine healing, subsq enc for clsd fx w/ delayed healing, subsq enc for opn fx type I or II w/ delayed healing, subsq enc for opn fx type IIIA, IIIB, or IIIC w/ delayed healing, seq] 172
S52.03[1,2,3] [B,C]	Disp fx of olecranon process w/ intraarticular extension of [rt, lt, unsp] ulna, init enc for opn fx type [I or II, IIIA IIIB or IIIC] 434
S52.03[1,2,3] [K,M,N,P,Q,R]	Disp fx of olecranon process w/ intraarticular extension of [rt, lt, unsp] ulna, subsq enc for [clsd fx w/ nonu, opn fx type I or II w/ nonu, opn fx type IIIA, IIIB, or IIIC w/ nonu, clsd fx w/ malu, opn fx type I or II w/ malu, opn fx type IIIA, IIIB, or IIIC w/ malu] 197
S52.03[1,2,3] [A,B,C]	Disp fx of olecranon process w/ intraarticular extension of ulna [rt, lt, unsp] init enc for fx [clsd fx, opn fx type I or II or opn fx NOS, opn fx type IIIA, IIIB, or IIIC] 186
S52.02[1,2,3] [D,E,F,G,H,J,S]	Disp fx of olecranon process w/o intraarticular extension of [rt, lt, unsp] ulna, [subsq enc for clsd fx w/ routine healing, subsq enc for opn fx type I or II w/ routine healing, subsq enc for opn fx type IIIA, IIIB, or IIIC w/ routine healing, subsq enc for clsd fx w/ delayed healing, subsq enc for opn fx type I or II w/ delayed healing, subsq enc for opn fx type IIIA, IIIB, or IIIC w/ delayed healing, seq] 172
S52.02[1,2,3] [B,C]	Disp fx of olecranon process w/o intraarticular extension of [rt, lt, unsp] ulna, init enc for fx opn fx type [I or II, IIIA IIIB or IIIC] 434
S52.02[1,2,3] [K,M,N,P,Q,R]	Disp fx of olecranon process w/o intraarticular extension of [rt, lt, unsp] ulna, subsq enc for [clsd fx w/ nonu, opn fx type I or II w/ nonu, opn fx type IIIA, IIIB, or IIIC w/ nonu, clsd fx w/ malu, opn fx type I or II w/ malu, opn fx type IIIA, IIIB, or IIIC w/ malu] 197
S52.02[1,2,3] [A,B,C]	Disp fx of olecranon process w/o intraarticular extension of ulna [rt, lt, unsp] init enc for fx [clsd fx, opn fx type I or II or opn fx NOS, opn fx type IIIA, IIIB, or IIIC] 186
S62.16[1,2,3] [A,B]	Disp fx of pisiform bone of wrist [rt, lt, unsp] init enc for fx [clsd, opn] 187
S62.16[1,2,3] [D,G,S]	Disp fx of pisiform, [rt, lt, unsp] wrist, [subsq enc for fx w/ routine healing, subsq enc for fx w/ delayed healing, seq] 175
S62.16[1,2,3] [K,P]	Disp fx of pisiform, [rt, lt, unsp] wrist, subsq enc for fx w/ [nonu, malu] 199
S32.44[1,2,3]S	Disp fx of post column (ilioischial) of [rt, lt, unsp] acetab, seq 166
S32.44[1,2,3] [D,G]	Disp fx of post column (ilioischial) of [rt, lt, unsp] acetab, subsq enc for fx w/ [routine, delayed] healing 170
S32.44[1,2,3]K	Disp fx of post column (ilioischial) of [rt, lt, unsp] acetab, subsq enc for fx w/ nonu 196
S32.44[1,2,3] [A,B]	Disp fx of post column [ilioischial] of acetab [rt, lt, unsp] init enc for [clsd fx, opn fx 162, 433
S92.13[1,2,3] [D,G,S]	Disp fx of post process of [rt, lt, unsp] talus, [subsq enc for fx w/ routine healing, subsq enc for fx w/ delayed healing, seq] 182
S92.13[1,2,3] [A,B]	Disp fx of post process of [rt, lt, unsp] talus, init enc for [clsd, opn] fx 192, 429
S92.13[1,2,3] [K,P]	Disp fx of post process of [rt, lt, unsp] talus, subsq enc for fx w/ [nonu, malu] 204
S32.42[1,2,3] [A,B]	Disp fx of post wall of [rt, lt, unsp] acetab, init enc for [clsd, opn] fx 162, 433
S32.42[1,2,3]S	Disp fx of post wall of [rt, lt, unsp] acetab, seq 166
S32.42[1,2,3] [D,G]	Disp fx of post wall of [rt, lt, unsp] acetab, subsq enc for fx w/ [routine, delayed] healing 170
S32.42[1,2,3]K	Disp fx of post wall of [rt, lt, unsp] acetab, subsq enc for fx w/ nonu 196
S62.03[1,2,3] [D,G,S]	Disp fx of proximal 3rd of navicular (scaphoid) bone of [rt, lt, unsp] wrist, [subsq enc for fx w/ routine healing, subsq enc for fx w/ delayed healing, seq] 174
S62.03[1,2,3] [K,P]	Disp fx of proximal 3rd of navicular (scaphoid) bone of [rt, lt, unsp] wrist, subsq enc for fx w/ [nonu, malu] 199
S62.03[1,2,3] [A,B]	Disp fx of proximal 3rd of navicular [scaphoid] bone of wrist [rt, lt, unsp] init enc for fx [clsd, opn] 187
S92.51[1,2,3] [K,P]	Disp fx of proximal phalanx [rt, lt, unsp] lesser toe(s), subsq enc for fx w/ [nonu, malu] 204
S62.61[8,9] [D,G,S]	Disp fx of proximal phalanx of [oth, unsp] finger, [subsq enc for fx w/ routine healing, subsq enc for fx w/ delayed healing, seq] 176
S62.61[8,9][K,P]	Disp fx of proximal phalanx of [oth, unsp] finger, subsq enc for fx w/ [nonu, malu] 200
S62.61[0,1,2,3,4, 5,6,7,8,9] [A,B]	Disp fx of proximal phalanx of [rt index, lt index, rt mid, lt mid, rt ring, lt ring, rt little, lt little, oth, unsp] finger, init enc for [clsd, opn] fx 425
S92.41[1,2,3] [D,G,S]	Disp fx of proximal phalanx of [rt, lt, unsp] great toe, [subsq enc for fx w/ routine healing, subsq enc for fx w/ delayed healing, seq] 183
S92.41[1,2,3] [A,B]	Disp fx of proximal phalanx of [rt, lt, unsp] great toe, init enc for [clsd, opn] fx 192, 429
S92.41[1,2,3] [K,P]	Disp fx of proximal phalanx of [rt, lt, unsp] great toe, subsq enc for fx w/ [nonu, malu] 204
S92.51[1,2,3] [D,G,S]	Disp fx of proximal phalanx of [rt, lt, unsp] lesser toe(s), [subsq enc for fx w/ routine healing, subsq enc for fx w/ delayed healing, seq] 183
S92.51[1,2,3] [A,B]	Disp fx of proximal phalanx of [rt, lt, unsp] lesser toe(s), init enc for [clsd, opn] fx 193, 429
S62.51[1,2,3] [D,G,S]	Disp fx of proximal phalanx of [rt, lt, unsp] thumb, [subsq enc for fx w/ routine healing, subsq enc for fx w/ delayed healing, seq] 176
S62.51[1,2,3] [A,B]	Disp fx of proximal phalanx of [rt, lt, unsp] thumb, init enc for [clsd, opn] fx 188
S62.51[1,2,3] [K,P]	Disp fx of proximal phalanx of [rt, lt, unsp] thumb, subsq enc for fx w/ [nonu, malu] 200
S62.61[0,1] [D,G,S]	Disp fx of proximal phalanx of [rt, lt] index finger, [subsq enc for fx w/ routine healing, subsq enc for fx w/ delayed healing, seq] 176
S62.61[0,1][A,B]	Disp fx of proximal phalanx of [rt, lt] index finger, init enc for [clsd, opn] fx 188
S62.61[0,1][K,P]	Disp fx of proximal phalanx of [rt, lt] index finger, subsq enc for fx w/ [nonu, malu] 200
S62.61[6,7] [D,G,S]	Disp fx of proximal phalanx of [rt, lt] little finger, [subsq enc for fx w/ routine healing, subsq enc for fx w/ delayed healing, seq] 176
S62.61[6,7][K,P]	Disp fx of proximal phalanx of [rt, lt] little finger, subsq enc for fx w/ [nonu, malu] 200
S62.61[2,3] [D,G,S]	Disp fx of proximal phalanx of [rt, lt] mid finger, [subsq enc for fx w/ routine healing, subsq enc for fx w/ delayed healing, seq] 176
S62.61[2,3][A,B]	Disp fx of proximal phalanx of [rt, lt] mid finger, init enc for [clsd, opn] fx 188
S62.61[2,3][K,P]	Disp fx of proximal phalanx of [rt, lt] mid finger, subsq enc for fx w/ [nonu, malu] 200
S62.61[4,5] [D,G,S]	Disp fx of proximal phalanx of [rt, lt] ring finger, [subsq enc for fx w/ routine healing, subsq enc for fx w/ delayed healing, seq] 176
S62.61[4,5][K,P]	Disp fx of proximal phalanx of [rt, lt] ring finger, subsq enc for fx w/ [nonu, malu] 200
S62.32[0,1,2,3,4, 5,6,7,8,9][A,B]	Disp fx of shaft of [2nd, 3rd, 4th, 5th, oth, unsp] metacarpal bone, (rt, lt) hand, init enc for [clsd, opn] fx 425
S62.32[8,9] [D,G,S]	Disp fx of shaft of [oth, unsp] metacarpal bone, [subsq enc for fx w/ routine healing, subsq enc for fx w/ delayed healing, seq] 175
S62.32[8,9][K,P]	Disp fx of shaft of [oth, unsp] metacarpal bone, subsq enc for fx w/ [nonu, malu] 199
S42.02[1,2,3] [D,G,S]	Disp fx of shaft of [rt, lt, unsp] clavicle, [subsq enc for fx w/ routine healing, subsq enc for fx w/ delayed healing, seq] 170
S42.02[1,2,3] [K,P]	Disp fx of shaft of [rt, lt, unsp] clavicle, subsq enc for fx w/ [nonu, malu] 196
S62.24[1,2,3] [A,B]	Disp fx of shaft of 1st metacarpal bone of hand [rt, lt, unsp] init enc for fx [clsd, opn] 187
S62.24[1,2,3] [D,G,S]	Disp fx of shaft of 1st metacarpal bone, [rt, lt, unsp] hand, [subsq enc for fx w/ routine healing, subsq enc for fx w/ delayed healing, seq] 175
S62.24[1,2,3] [K,P]	Disp fx of shaft of 1st metacarpal bone, [rt, lt, unsp] hand, subsq enc for fx w/ [nonu, malu] 199
S62.32[0,1][A,B]	Disp fx of shaft of 2nd metacarpal bone of hand [rt, lt]] init enc for fx [clsd, opn] 187
S62.32[0,1] [D,G,S]	Disp fx of shaft of 2nd metacarpal bone, [rt, lt] hand, [subsq enc for fx w/ routine healing, subsq enc for fx w/ delayed healing, seq] 175
S62.32[0,1][K,P]	Disp fx of shaft of 2nd metacarpal bone, [rt, lt] hand, subsq enc for fx w/ [nonu, malu] 199
S62.32[2,3][A,B]	Disp fx of shaft of 3rd metacarpal bone of hand [rt, lt]] init enc for fx [clsd, opn] 187
S62.32[2,3] [D,G,S]	Disp fx of shaft of 3rd metacarpal bone, [rt, lt] hand, [subsq enc for fx w/ routine healing, subsq enc for fx w/ delayed healing, seq] 175
S62.32[2,3][K,P]	Disp fx of shaft of 3rd metacarpal bone, [rt, lt] hand, subsq enc for fx w/ [nonu, malu] 199
S62.32[4,5][A,B]	Disp fx of shaft of 4th metacarpal bone of hand [rt, lt] init enc for fx [clsd, opn] 187
S62.32[4,5] [D,G,S]	Disp fx of shaft of 4th metacarpal bone, [rt, lt] hand, [subsq enc for fx w/ routine healing, subsq enc for fx w/ delayed healing, seq] 175

S62.32[4,5][K,P]	Disp fx of shaft of 4th metacarpal bone, [rt, lt] hand, subsq enc for fx w/ [nonu, malu] **199**
S62.32[6,7][A,B]	Disp fx of shaft of 5th metacarpal bone of hand [rt, lt] init enc for fx [clsd, opn] **188**
S62.32[6,7] [D,G,S]	Disp fx of shaft of 5th metacarpal bone, [rt, lt] hand, [subsq enc for fx w/ routine healing, subsq enc for fx w/ delayed healing, seq] **175**
S62.32[6,7][K,P]	Disp fx of shaft of 5th metacarpal bone, [rt, lt] hand, subsq enc for fx w/ [nonu, malu] **199**
S42.02[1,2,3] [A,B]	Disp fx of shaft of clavicle [rt, lt, unsp] init enc for fx [clsd, opn] **184**
S62.32[8,9][A,B]	Disp fx of shaft of metacarpal bone of hand [oth, unsp] init enc for fx [clsd, opn] **188**
S62.17[1,2,3] [D,G,S]	Disp fx of trapezium (lgr multangular), [rt, lt, unsp] wrist, [subsq enc for fx w/ routine healing, subsq enc for fx w/ delayed healing, seq] **175**
S62.17[1,2,3] [K,P]	Disp fx of trapezium (lgr multangular), [rt, lt, unsp] wrist, subsq enc for fx w/ [nonu, malu] **199**
S62.17[1,2,3] [A,B]	Disp fx of trapezium [lgr multangular] bone of wrist [rt, lt, unsp] init enc for fx [clsd, opn] **187**
S62.18[1,2,3] [D,G,S]	Disp fx of trapezoid (smer multangular), [rt, lt, unsp] wrist, [subsq enc for fx w/ routine healing, subsq enc for fx w/ delayed healing, seq] **175**
S62.18[1,2,3] [K,P]	Disp fx of trapezoid (smer multangular), [rt, lt, unsp] wrist, subsq enc for fx w/ [nonu, malu] **199**
S62.18[1,2,3] [A,B]	Disp fx of trapezoid [smer multangular] bone of wrist [rt, lt, unsp] init enc for fx [clsd, opn] **187**
S62.11[1,2,3] [D,G,S]	Disp fx of triquetrum (cuneiform) bone of [rt, lt, unsp] wrist, [subsq enc for fx w/ routine healing, subsq enc for fx w/ delayed healing, seq] **174**
S62.11[1,2,3] [K,P]	Disp fx of triquetrum (cuneiform) bone, [rt, lt, unsp] wrist, subsq enc for fx w/ [nonu, malu] **199**
S62.11[1,2,3] [A,B]	Disp fx of triquetrum [cuneiform] bone of wrist [rt, lt, unsp] init enc for fx [clsd, opn] **187**
S52.61[1,2,3] [A,B,C]	Disp fx of ulna styloid process [rt, lt, unsp] init enc for fx [clsd, opn fx type I or II or opn fx NOS, opn fx type IIIA, IIIB, IIIC] **186**
S62.61[8,9][A,B]	Disp fx proximal phalanx of [oth, unsp] finger, init enc for [clsd, opn] fx **188**
S62.61[6,7][A,B]	Disp fx proximal phalanx of [rt, lt] little finger, init enc for [clsd, opn] fx **188**
S62.61[4,5][A,B]	Disp fx proximal phalanx of [rt, lt] ring finger, init enc for [clsd, opn] fx **188**
S72.14[1,2,3] [D,E,F,G,H,J,S]	Disp intertrochanteric fx of [rt, lt, unsp] femur, [subsq enc for clsd fx w/ routine healing, subsq enc for opn fx type I or II w/ routine healing, subsq enc for opn fx type IIIA, IIIB, or IIIC w/ routine healing, subsq enc for clsd fx w/ delayed healing, subsq enc for opn fx type I or II w/ delayed healing, subsq enc for opn fx type IIIA, IIIB, or IIIC w/ delayed healing, seq] **177**
S72.14[1,2,3] [A,B,C]	Disp intertrochanteric fx of [rt, lt, unsp] femur, init enc for [clsd fx, opn fx type I or II or NOS, or opn fx type IIIA, IIIB, or IIIC] **162, 286, 435**
S72.14[1,2,3] [K,M,N,P,Q,R]	Disp intertrochanteric fx of [rt, lt, unsp] femur, subsq enc for [clsd fx w/ nonu, opn fx type I or II w/ nonu, opn fx type IIIA, IIIB, or IIIC w/ nonu, clsd fx w/ malu, opn fx type I or II w/ malu, opn fx type IIIA, IIIB, or IIIC w/ malu] **201**
S92.06[1,2,3] [D,G,S]	Disp intraarticular fx of [rt, lt, unsp] calcaneus, [subsq enc for fx w/ routine healing, subsq enc for fx w/ delayed healing, seq] **182**
S92.06[1,2,3] [A,B]	Disp intraarticular fx of [rt, lt, unsp] calcaneus, init enc for [clsd, opn] fx **192, 429**
S92.06[1,2,3] [K,P]	Disp intraarticular fx of [rt, lt, unsp] calcaneus, subsq enc for fx w/ [nonu, malu] **204**
S82.02[1,2,3] [A,B,C]	Disp longitudinal fx of [rt, lt, unsp] patella, [init enc for clsd fx, init enc for opn fx type I or II, init enc for opn fx type IIIA, IIIB, or IIIC] **190**
S82.02[1,2,3] [D,E,F,G,H,J,S]	Disp longitudinal fx of [rt, lt, unsp] patella, [subsq enc for clsd fx w/ routine healing, subsq enc for opn fx type I or II w/ routine healing, subsq enc for opn fx type IIIA, IIIB, or IIIC w/ routine healing, subsq enc for clsd fx w/ delayed healing, subsq enc for opn fx type I or II w/ delayed healing, seq] **179**
S82.02[1,2,3] [K,M,N,P,Q,R]	Disp longitudinal fx of [rt, lt, unsp] patella, subsq enc for [clsd fx w/ nonu, opn fx type I or II w/ nonu, opn fx type IIIA, IIIB, or IIIC w/ nonu, clsd fx w/ malu, opn fx type I or II w/ malu] **202**
S82.86[1,2,3] [A,B,C]	Disp Maisonneuve's fx of [rt, lt, unsp] leg, [init enc for clsd fx, init enc for opn fx type I or II, init enc for opn fx type I or II] **191, 428**
S82.86[1,2,3] [D,E,F,G,H,J,S]	Disp Maisonneuve's fx of [rt, lt, unsp] leg, [subsq enc for clsd fx w/ routine healing, subsq enc for opn fx type I or II w/ routine healing, subsq enc for opn fx type IIIA, IIIB, or IIIC w/ routine healing, subsq enc for clsd fx w/ delayed healing, subsq enc for opn fx type I or II w/ delayed healing, subsq enc for opn fx type IIIA, IIIB, or IIIC w/ delayed healing, seq] **181**
S82.86[1,2,3] [B,C]	Disp Maisonneuve's fx of [rt, lt, unsp] leg, init enc for opn fx type [I or II, IIIA IIIB or IIIC] **436**
S82.86[1,2,3] [K,M,N,P,Q,R]	Disp Maisonneuve's fx of [rt, lt, unsp] leg, subsq enc for [clsd fx w/ nonu, opn fx type I or II w/ nonu, opn fx type IIIA, IIIB, or IIIC w/ nonu, clsd fx w/ malu, opn fx type I or II w/ malu, opn fx type I or II w/ malu] **203**
S72.03[1,2,3] [D,E,F,G,H,J,S]	Disp midcervical fx of [rt, lt, unsp] femur, [subsq enc for clsd fx w/ routine healing, subsq enc for opn fx type I or II w/ routine healing, subsq enc for opn fx type IIIA, IIIB, or IIIC w/ routine healing, subsq enc for clsd fx w/ delayed healing, subsq enc for opn fx type I or II w/ delayed healing, subsq enc for opn fx type IIIA, IIIB, or IIIC w/ delayed healing, seq] **177**
S72.03[1,2,3] [A,B,C]	Disp midcervical fx of [rt, lt, unsp] femur, init enc for [clsd fx, opn fx type I or II or NOS, or opn fx type IIIA, IIIB, or IIIC] **162, 286, 435**
S72.03[1,2,3] [K,M,N,P,Q,R]	Disp midcervical fx of [rt, lt, unsp] femur, subsq enc for [clsd fx w/ nonu, opn fx type I or II w/ nonu, opn fx type IIIA, IIIB, or IIIC w/ nonu, clsd fx w/ malu, opn fx type I or II w/ malu, opn fx type IIIA, IIIB, or IIIC w/ malu] **200**
S52.23[1,2,3] [B,C]	Disp oblique fx of [rt, lt, unsp] ulna, init enc for opn fx type [I or II, IIIA IIIB or IIIC] **434**
S72.33[1,2,3] [D,E,F,G,H,J,S]	Disp oblique fx of shaft of [rt, lt, unsp] femur, [subsq enc for clsd fx w/ routine healing, subsq enc for opn fx type I or II w/ routine healing, subsq enc for opn fx type IIIA, IIIB, or IIIC w/ routine healing, subsq enc for clsd fx w/ delayed healing, subsq enc for opn fx type I or II w/ delayed healing, subsq enc for opn fx type IIIA, IIIB, or IIIC w/ delayed healing, seq] **178**
S72.33[1,2,3] [A,B,C]	Disp oblique fx of shaft of [rt, lt, unsp] femur, init enc for [clsd fx, opn fx type I or II , opn fx type IIIA, IIIB, or IIIC] **161, 286, 435**
S72.33[1,2,3] [K,M,N,P,Q,R]	Disp oblique fx of shaft of [rt, lt, unsp] femur, subsq enc for [clsd fx w/ nonu, opn fx type I or II w/ nonu, opn fx type IIIA, IIIB, or IIIC w/ nonu, clsd fx w/ malu, opn fx type I or II w/ malu, opn fx type IIIA, IIIB, or IIIC w/ malu] **201**
S82.43[1,2,3] [A,B,C]	Disp oblique fx of shaft of [rt, lt, unsp] fibula, [init enc for clsd fx, init enc for opn fx type I or II, init enc for opn fx type IIIA, IIIB, or IIIC] **191, 427**
S82.43[1,2,3] [D,E,F,G,H,J,S]	Disp oblique fx of shaft of [rt, lt, unsp] fibula, [subsq enc for clsd fx w/ routine healing, subsq enc for opn fx type I or II w/ routine healing, subsq enc for opn fx type IIIA, IIIB, or IIIC w/ routine healing, subsq enc for clsd fx w/ delayed healing, subsq enc for opn fx type I or II w/ delayed healing, subsq enc for opn fx type IIIA, IIIB, or IIIC w/ delayed healing, seq] **181**
S82.43[1,2,3] [B,C]	Disp oblique fx of shaft of [rt, lt, unsp] fibula, init enc for opn fx type [I or II, IIIA IIIB or IIIC] **436**
S82.43[1,2,3] [K,M,N,P,Q,R]	Disp oblique fx of shaft of [rt, lt, unsp] fibula, subsq enc for [clsd fx w/ nonu, opn fx type I or II w/ nonu, opn fx type IIIA, IIIB, or IIIC w/ nonu, clsd fx w/ malu, opn fx type I or II w/ malu, opn fx type I or II w/ malu] **203**
S42.33[1,2,3] [D,G,S]	Disp oblique fx of shaft of [rt, lt, unsp] humerus, [subsq enc for fx w/ routine healing, subsq enc for fx w/ delayed healing, seq] **171**
S42.33[1,2,3]B	Disp oblique fx of shaft of [rt, lt, unsp] humerus, init enc for opn fx **433**
S52.33[1,2,3] [D,E,F,G,H,J,S]	Disp oblique fx of shaft of [rt, lt, unsp] radius, [subsq enc for clsd fx w/ routine healing, subsq enc for opn fx type I or II w/ routine healing, subsq enc for opn fx type I or II w/ routine healing, subsq enc for clsd fx w/ delayed healing, subsq enc for opn fx type I or II w/ delayed healing, subsq enc for opn fx type IIIA, IIIB, or IIIC w/ delayed healing, seq] **173**
S52.33[1,2,3] [B,C]	Disp oblique fx of shaft of [rt, lt, unsp] radius, init enc for opn fx type [I or II, IIIA IIIB or IIIC] **434**
S52.33[1,2,3] [K,M,N,P,Q,R]	Disp oblique fx of shaft of [rt, lt, unsp] radius, subsq enc for [clsd fx w/ nonu, opn fx type I or II w/ nonu, opn fx type IIIA, IIIB, or IIIC w/ nonu, clsd fx w/ malu, opn fx type I or II w/ malu, opn fx type IIIA, IIIB, or IIIC w/ malu] **198**
S82.23[1,2,3] [A,B,C]	Disp oblique fx of shaft of [rt, lt, unsp] tibia, [init enc for clsd fx, init enc for opn fx type I or II, init enc for opn fx type IIIA, IIIB, or IIIC] **191, 427**
S82.23[1,2,3] [D,E,F,G,H,J,S]	Disp oblique fx of shaft of [rt, lt, unsp] tibia, [subsq enc for clsd fx w/ routine healing, subsq enc for opn fx type I or II w/ routine healing, subsq enc for opn fx type IIIA, IIIB, or IIIC w/ routine healing, subsq enc for clsd fx w/ delayed healing, subsq enc for opn fx type I or II w/ delayed healing, subsq enc for opn fx type IIIA, IIIB, or IIIC w/ delayed healing, seq] **180**

Code	Description
S82.23[1,2,3] [B,C]	Disp oblique fx of shaft of [rt, lt, unsp] tibia, init enc for opn fx type [I or II, IIIA IIIB or IIIC] **436**
S82.23[1,2,3] [K,M,N,P,Q,R]	Disp oblique fx of shaft of [rt, lt, unsp] tibia, subsq enc for [clsd fx w/ nonu, opn fx type I or II w/ nonu, opn fx type IIIA, IIIB, or IIIC w/ nonu, clsd fx w/ malu, opn fx type I or II w/ malu, opn fx type I or II w/ malu] **203**
S52.23[1,2,3] [D,E,F,G,H,J,S]	Disp oblique fx of shaft of [rt, lt, unsp] ulna, [subsq enc for clsd fx w/ routine healing, subsq enc for opn fx type I or II w/ routine healing, subsq enc for opn fx type IIIA, IIIB, or IIIC w/ routine healing, subsq enc for clsd fx w/ delayed healing, subsq enc for opn fx type I or II w/ delayed healing, subsq enc for opn fx type IIIA, IIIB, or IIIC w/ delayed healing, seq] **172**
S52.23[1,2,3] [K,M,N,P,Q,R]	Disp oblique fx of shaft of [rt, lt, unsp] ulna, subsq enc for [clsd fx w/ nonu, opn fx type I or II w/ nonu, opn fx type IIIA, IIIB, or IIIC w/ nonu, clsd fx w/ malu, opn fx type I or II w/ malu, opn fx type IIIA, IIIB, or IIIC w/ malu] **198**
S42.33[1,2,3] [A,B]	Disp oblique fx of shaft of humerus [rt, lt, unsp] init enc for fx [clsd, opn] **185**
S42.33[1,2,3] [K,P]	Disp oblique fx of shaft of humerus, [rt, lt, unsp] arm, subsq enc for fx w/ [nonu, malu] **197**
S52.33[1,2,3] [A,B,C]	Disp oblique fx of shaft of radius [rt, lt, unsp] init enc for [clsd fx, opn fx type I or II or opn fx NOS, opn fx type IIIA, IIIB, or IIIC] **186**
S52.23[1,2,3] [A,B,C]	Disp oblique fx of ulna [rt, lt, unsp] init enc for [clsd fx, opn fx type I or II or opn fx NOS, opn fx type IIIA, IIIB, or IIIC] **186**
S82.01[1,2,3] [A,B,C]	Disp osteochondral fx of [rt, lt, unsp] patella, [init enc for clsd fx, init enc for opn fx type I or II, init enc for opn fx type IIIA, IIIB, or IIIC] **190**
S82.01[1,2,3] [D,E,F,G,H,J,S]	Disp osteochondral fx of [rt, lt, unsp] patella, [subsq enc for clsd fx w/ routine healing, subsq enc for opn fx type I or II w/ routine healing, subsq enc for opn fx type IIIA, IIIB, or IIIC w/ routine healing, subsq enc for clsd fx w/ delayed healing, subsq enc for opn fx type I or II w/ delayed healing, subsq enc for opn fx type I or II w/ delayed healing, seq] **179**
S82.01[1,2,3] [K,M,N,P,Q,R]	Disp osteochondral fx of [rt, lt, unsp] patella, subsq enc for [clsd fx w/ nonu, opn fx type I or II w/ nonu, opn fx type IIIA, IIIB, or IIIC w/ nonu, clsd fx w/ malu, opn fx type I or II w/ malu, opn fx type I or II w/ malu] **202**
S92.05[1,2,3] [D,G,S]	Disp oth extraarticular fx of [rt, lt, unsp] calcaneus, [subsq enc for fx w/ routine healing, subsq enc for fx w/ delayed healing, seq] **182**
S92.05[1,2,3] [A,B]	Disp oth extraarticular fx of [rt, lt, unsp] calcaneus, init enc for [clsd, opn] fx **192, 429**
S92.05[1,2,3] [K,P]	Disp oth extraarticular fx of [rt, lt, unsp] calcaneus, subsq enc for fx w/ [nonu, malu] **204**
S92.04[1,2,3] [D,G,S]	Disp oth fx of tuberosity of [rt, lt, unsp] calcaneus, [subsq enc for fx w/ routine healing, subsq enc for fx w/ delayed healing, seq] **182**
S92.04[1,2,3] [A,B]	Disp oth fx of tuberosity of [rt, lt, unsp] calcaneus, init enc for [clsd, opn] fx **192, 429**
S92.04[1,2,3] [K,P]	Disp oth fx of tuberosity of [rt, lt, unsp] calcaneus, subsq enc for fx w/ [nonu, malu] **204**
S82.87[1,2,3] [A,B,C]	Disp pilon fx of [rt, lt, unsp] tibia, [init enc for clsd fx, init enc for opn fx type I or II, init enc for opn fx type I or II] **191, 428**
S82.87[1,2,3] [D,E,F,G,H,J,S]	Disp pilon fx of [rt, lt, unsp] tibia, [subsq enc for clsd fx w/ routine healing, subsq enc for opn fx type I or II w/ routine healing, subsq enc for opn fx type IIIA, IIIB, or IIIC w/ routine healing, subsq enc for clsd fx w/ delayed healing, subsq enc for opn fx type I or II w/ delayed healing, subsq enc for opn fx type IIIA, IIIB, or IIIC w/ delayed healing, seq] **181**
S82.87[1,2,3] [K,M,N,P,Q,R]	Disp pilon fx of [rt, lt, unsp] tibia, subsq enc for [clsd fx w/ nonu, opn fx type I or II w/ nonu, opn fx type IIIA, IIIB, or IIIC w/ nonu, clsd fx w/ malu, opn fx type I or II w/ malu, opn fx type I or II w/ malu] **203**
S62.22[1,2,3] [A,B]	Disp Rolando's fx of hand [rt, lt, unsp] init enc for fx [clsd, opn] **187**
S62.22[1,2,3] [D,G,S]	Disp Rolando's fx, [rt, lt, unsp] hand, [subsq enc for fx w/ routine healing, subsq enc for fx w/ delayed healing, seq] **175**
S62.22[1,2,3] [K,P]	Disp Rolando's fx, [rt, lt, unsp] hand, subsq enc for fx w/ [nonu, malu] **199**
S72.36[1,2,3] [D,E,F,G,H,J,S]	Disp seg fx of shaft of [rt, lt, unsp] femur, [subsq enc for clsd fx w/ routine healing, subsq enc for opn fx type I or II w/ routine healing, subsq enc for opn fx type IIIA, IIIB, or IIIC w/ routine healing, subsq enc for clsd fx w/ delayed healing, subsq enc for opn fx type I or II w/ delayed healing, subsq enc for opn fx type IIIA, IIIB, or IIIC w/ delayed healing, seq] **178**
S72.36[1,2,3] [A,B,C]	Disp seg fx of shaft of [rt, lt, unsp] femur, init enc for [clsd fx, opn fx type I or II, opn fx type IIIA, IIIB, or IIIC] **161, 286, 435**
S72.36[1,2,3] [K,M,N,P,Q,R]	Disp seg fx of shaft of [rt, lt, unsp] femur, subsq enc for [clsd fx w/ nonu, opn fx type I or II w/ nonu, opn fx type IIIA, IIIB, or IIIC w/ nonu, clsd fx w/ malu, opn fx type I or II w/ malu, opn fx type IIIA, IIIB, or IIIC w/ malu] **201**
S82.46[1,2,3] [A,B,C]	Disp seg fx of shaft of [rt, lt, unsp] fibula, [init enc for clsd fx, init enc for opn fx type I or II, init enc for opn fx type IIIA, IIIB, or IIIC] **191, 427**
S82.46[1,2,3] [D,E,F,G,H,J,S]	Disp seg fx of shaft of [rt, lt, unsp] fibula, [subsq enc for clsd fx w/ routine healing, subsq enc for opn fx type I or II w/ routine healing, subsq enc for opn fx type IIIA, IIIB, or IIIC w/ routine healing, subsq enc for clsd fx w/ delayed healing, subsq enc for opn fx type I or II w/ delayed healing, subsq enc for opn fx type IIIA, IIIB, or IIIC w/ delayed healing, seq] **181**
S82.46[1,2,3] [B,C]	Disp seg fx of shaft of [rt, lt, unsp] fibula, init enc for opn fx type [I or II, IIIA IIIB or IIIC] **436**
S82.46[1,2,3] [K,M,N,P,Q,R]	Disp seg fx of shaft of [rt, lt, unsp] fibula, subsq enc for [clsd fx w/ nonu, opn fx type I or II w/ nonu, opn fx type IIIA, IIIB, or IIIC w/ nonu, clsd fx w/ malu, opn fx type I or II w/ malu, opn fx type I or II w/ malu] **203**
S42.36[1,2,3] [D,G,S]	Disp seg fx of shaft of [rt, lt, unsp] humerus, [subsq enc for fx w/ routine healing, subsq enc for fx w/ delayed healing, seq] **171**
S42.36[1,2,3]B	Disp seg fx of shaft of [rt, lt, unsp] humerus, init enc for opn fx **433**
S52.36[1,2,3] [D,E,F,G,H,J,S]	Disp seg fx of shaft of [rt, lt, unsp] radius, [subsq enc for clsd fx w/ routine healing, subsq enc for opn fx type I or II w/ routine healing, subsq enc for opn fx type I or II w/ routine healing, subsq enc for clsd fx w/ delayed healing, subsq enc for opn fx type I or II w/ delayed healing, subsq enc for opn fx type IIIA, IIIB, or IIIC w/ delayed healing, seq] **173**
S52.36[1,2,3] [B,C]	Disp seg fx of shaft of [rt, lt, unsp] radius, init enc for opn fx type [I or II, IIIA IIIB or IIIC] **434**
S82.26[1,2,3] [A,B,C]	Disp seg fx of shaft of [rt, lt, unsp] tibia, [init enc for clsd fx, init enc for opn fx type I or II, init enc for opn fx type IIIA, IIIB, or IIIC] **191, 427**
S82.26[1,2,3] [D,E,F,G,H,J,S]	Disp seg fx of shaft of [rt, lt, unsp] tibia, [subsq enc for clsd fx w/ routine healing, subsq enc for opn fx type I or II w/ routine healing, subsq enc for opn fx type IIIA, IIIB, or IIIC w/ routine healing, subsq enc for clsd fx w/ delayed healing, subsq enc for opn fx type I or II w/ delayed healing, subsq enc for opn fx type IIIA, IIIB, or IIIC w/ delayed healing, seq] **180**
S82.26[1,2,3] [B,C]	Disp seg fx of shaft of [rt, lt, unsp] tibia, init enc for opn fx type [I or II, IIIA IIIB or IIIC] **436**
S82.26[1,2,3] [K,M,N,P,Q,R]	Disp seg fx of shaft of [rt, lt, unsp] tibia, subsq enc for [clsd fx w/ nonu, opn fx type I or II w/ nonu, opn fx type IIIA, IIIB, or IIIC w/ nonu, clsd fx w/ malu, opn fx type I or II w/ malu, opn fx type I or II w/ malu] **203**
S52.26[1,2,3] [D,E,F,G,H,J,S]	Disp seg fx of shaft of [rt, lt, unsp] ulna, [subsq enc for clsd fx w/ routine healing, subsq enc for opn fx type I or II w/ routine healing, subsq enc for opn fx type IIIA, IIIB, or IIIC w/ routine healing, subsq enc for clsd fx w/ delayed healing, subsq enc for opn fx type I or II w/ delayed healing, subsq enc for opn fx type IIIA, IIIB, or IIIC w/ delayed healing, seq] **173**
S42.36[1,2,3] [A,B]	Disp seg fx of shaft of humerus [rt, lt, unsp] init enc for fx [clsd, opn] **185**
S42.36[1,2,3] [K,P]	Disp seg fx of shaft of humerus, [rt, lt, unsp] arm, subsq enc for fx w/ [nonu, malu] **197**
S52.36[1,2,3] [A,B,C]	Disp seg fx of shaft of radius [rt, lt, unsp] init enc for [clsd fx, opn fx type I or II or opn fx NOS, opn fx type IIIA, IIIB, or IIIC] **186**
S52.36[1,2,3] [K,M,N,P,Q,R]	Disp seg fx of shaft of radius, [rt, lt, unsp] arm, subsq enc for [clsd fx w/ nonu, opn fx type I or II w/ nonu, opn fx type IIIA, IIIB, or IIIC w/ nonu, clsd fx w/ malu, opn fx type IIIA, IIIB, or IIIC w/ malu] **198**
S52.26[1,2,3] [K,M,N,P,Q,R]	Disp seg fx of shaft of ulna, [rt, lt, unsp] arm, subsq enc for [clsd fx w/ nonu, opn fx type I or II w/ nonu, opn fx type IIIA, IIIB, or IIIC w/ nonu, clsd fx w/ malu, opn fx type I or II w/ malu, opn fx type IIIA, IIIB, or IIIC w/ malu] **198**
S52.26[1,2,3] [B,C]	Disp semental fx of shaft of [rt, lt, unsp] ulna, init enc for opn fx type [I or II, IIIA IIIB or IIIC] **434**
S52.26[1,2,3] [A,B,C]	Disp semental fx of shaft of ulna [rt, lt, unsp] init enc for [clsd fx, opn fx type I or II or opn fx NOS, opn fx type IIIA, IIIB, or IIIC] **186**
S42.41[1,2,3] [D,G,S]	Disp simple supracondylar fx w/o intercondylar fx of [rt, lt, unsp] humerus, [subsq enc for fx w/ routine healing, subsq enc for fx w/ delayed healing, seq] **171**
S42.41[1,2,3]B	Disp simple supracondylar fx w/o intercondylar fx of [rt, lt, unsp] humerus, init enc for opn fx **433**
S42.41[1,2,3] [K,P]	Disp simple supracondylar fx w/o intercondylar fx of [rt, lt, unsp] humerus, subsq enc for fx w/ [nonu, malu] **197**
S42.41[1,2,3] [A,B]	Disp simple supracondylar fx w/o intercondylar fx of humerus [rt, lt, unsp] init enc for fx [clsd, opn] **185**

Code	Description
S52.24[1,2,3] [B,C]	Disp spiral fx of [rt, lt, unsp] ulna, init enc for opn fx type [I or II, IIIA IIIB or IIIC] **434**
S72.34[1,2,3] [D,E,F,G,H,J,S]	Disp spiral fx of shaft of [rt, lt, unsp] femur, [subsq enc for clsd fx w/ routine healing, subsq enc for opn fx type I or II w/ routine healing, subsq enc for opn fx type IIIA, IIIB, or IIIC w/ routine healing, subsq enc for clsd fx w/ delayed healing, subsq enc for opn fx type I or II w/ delayed healing, subsq enc for opn fx type IIIA, IIIB, or IIIC w/ delayed healing, seq] **178**
S72.34[1,2,3] [A,B,C]	Disp spiral fx of shaft of [rt, lt, unsp] femur, init enc for [clsd fx, opn fx type I or II, opn fx type IIIA, IIIB, or IIIC] **161, 286, 435**
S72.34[1,2,3] [K,M,N,P,Q,R]	Disp spiral fx of shaft of [rt, lt, unsp] femur, subsq enc for [clsd fx w/ nonu, opn fx type I or II w/ nonu, opn fx type IIIA, IIIB, or IIIC w/ nonu, clsd fx w/ malu, opn fx type I or II w/ malu, opn fx type IIIA, IIIB, or IIIC w/ malu] **201**
S82.44[1,2,3] [A,B,C]	Disp spiral fx of shaft of [rt, lt, unsp] fibula, [init enc for clsd fx, init enc for opn fx type I or II, init enc for opn fx type IIIA, IIIB, or IIIC] **191, 427**
S82.44[1,2,3] [D,E,F,G,H,J,S]	Disp spiral fx of shaft of [rt, lt, unsp] fibula, [subsq enc for clsd fx w/ routine healing, subsq enc for opn fx type I or II w/ routine healing, subsq enc for opn fx type IIIA, IIIB, or IIIC w/ routine healing, subsq enc for clsd fx w/ delayed healing, subsq enc for opn fx type I or II w/ delayed healing, subsq enc for opn fx type IIIA, IIIB, or IIIC w/ delayed healing, seq] **181**
S82.44[1,2,3] [B,C]	Disp spiral fx of shaft of [rt, lt, unsp] fibula, init enc for opn fx type [I or II, IIIA IIIB or IIIC] **436**
S82.44[1,2,3] [K,M,N,P,Q,R]	Disp spiral fx of shaft of [rt, lt, unsp] fibula, subsq enc for [clsd fx w/ nonu, opn fx type I or II w/ nonu, opn fx type IIIA, IIIB, or IIIC w/ nonu, clsd fx w/ malu, opn fx type I or II w/ malu, opn fx type I or II w/ malu] **203**
S42.34[1,2,3] [D,G,S]	Disp spiral fx of shaft of [rt, lt, unsp] humerus, [subsq enc for fx w/ routine healing, subsq enc for fx w/ delayed healing, seq] **171**
S42.34[1,2,3]B	Disp spiral fx of shaft of [rt, lt, unsp] humerus, init enc for opn fx **433**
S52.34[1,2,3] [D,E,F,G,H,J,S]	Disp spiral fx of shaft of [rt, lt, unsp] radius, [subsq enc for clsd fx w/ routine healing, subsq enc for opn fx type I or II w/ routine healing, subsq enc for opn fx type I or II w/ routine healing, subsq enc for clsd fx w/ delayed healing, subsq enc for opn fx type I or II w/ delayed healing, subsq enc for opn fx type IIIA, IIIB, or IIIC w/ delayed healing, seq] **173**
S52.34[1,2,3] [B,C]	Disp spiral fx of shaft of [rt, lt, unsp] radius, init enc for opn fx type [I or II, IIIA IIIB or IIIC] **434**
S82.24[1,2,3] [A,B,C]	Disp spiral fx of shaft of [rt, lt, unsp] tibia, [init enc for clsd fx, init enc for opn fx type I or II, init enc for opn fx type IIIA, IIIB, or IIIC] **191, 427**
S82.24[1,2,3] [D,E,F,G,H,J,S]	Disp spiral fx of shaft of [rt, lt, unsp] tibia, [subsq enc for clsd fx w/ routine healing, subsq enc for opn fx type I or II w/ routine healing, subsq enc for opn fx type IIIA, IIIB, or IIIC w/ routine healing, subsq enc for clsd fx w/ delayed healing, subsq enc for opn fx type I or II w/ delayed healing, subsq enc for opn fx type IIIA, IIIB, or IIIC w/ delayed healing, seq] **180**
S82.24[1,2,3] [B,C]	Disp spiral fx of shaft of [rt, lt, unsp] tibia, init enc for opn fx type [I or II, IIIA IIIB or IIIC] **436**
S82.24[1,2,3] [K,M,N,P,Q,R]	Disp spiral fx of shaft of [rt, lt, unsp] tibia, subsq enc for [clsd fx w/ nonu, opn fx type I or II w/ nonu, opn fx type IIIA, IIIB, or IIIC w/ nonu, clsd fx w/ malu, opn fx type I or II w/ malu, opn fx type I or II w/ malu] **203**
S52.24[1,2,3] [D,E,F,G,H,J,S]	Disp spiral fx of shaft of [rt, lt, unsp] ulna, [subsq enc for clsd fx w/ routine healing, subsq enc for opn fx type I or II w/ routine healing, subsq enc for opn fx type IIIA, IIIB, or IIIC w/ routine healing, subsq enc for clsd fx w/ delayed healing, subsq enc for opn fx type I or II w/ delayed healing, subsq enc for opn fx type IIIA, IIIB, or IIIC w/ delayed healing, seq] **172**
S42.34[1,2,3] [A,B]	Disp spiral fx of shaft of humerus [rt, lt, unsp] init enc for fx [clsd, opn] **185**
S42.34[1,2,3] [K,P]	Disp spiral fx of shaft of humerus, [rt, lt, unsp] arm, subsq enc for fx w/ [nonu, malu] **197**
S52.34[1,2,3] [A,B,C]	Disp spiral fx of shaft of radius [rt, lt, unsp} init enc for [clsd fx, opn fx type I or II or opn fx NOS, opn fx type IIIA, IIIB, or IIIC] **186**
S52.34[1,2,3] [K,M,N,P,Q,R]	Disp spiral fx of shaft of radius, [rt, lt, unsp] arm, subsq enc for [clsd fx w/ nonu, opn fx type I or II w/ nonu, opn fx type IIIA, IIIB, or IIIC w/ nonu, clsd fx w/ malu, opn fx type I or II w/ malu, opn fx type IIIA, IIIB, or IIIC w/ malu] **198**
S52.24[1,2,3] [K,M,N,P,Q,R]	Disp spiral fx of shaft of ulna, [rt, lt, unsp] arm, subsq enc for [clsd fx w/ nonu, opn fx type I or II w/ nonu, opn fx type IIIA, IIIB, or IIIC w/ nonu, clsd fx w/ malu, opn fx type I or II w/ malu, opn fx type IIIA, IIIB, or IIIC w/ malu] **198**
S52.24[1,2,3] [A,B,C]	Disp spiral fx of ulna [rt, lt, unsp} init enc for [clsd fx, opn fx type I or II or opn fx NOS, opn fx type IIIA, IIIB, or IIIC] **186**
S72.2[1,2,3] X[D,E,F,G,H,J,S]	Disp subtrochanteric fx of [rt, lt, unsp] femur, [subsq enc for clsd fx w/ routine healing, subsq enc for opn fx type I or II w/ routine healing, subsq enc for opn fx type IIIA, IIIB, or IIIC w/ routine healing, subsq enc for clsd fx w/ delayed healing, subsq enc for opn fx type I or II w/ delayed healing, subsq enc for opn fx type IIIA, IIIB, or IIIC w/ delayed healing, seq] **177**
S72.2[1,2,3] X[A,B,C]	Disp subtrochanteric fx of [rt, lt, unsp] femur, init enc for [clsd fractrure, opn fx type I or II or NOS, or opn fx type IIIA, IIIB, or IIIC] **162, 286, 435**
S72.2[1,2,3] X[K,M,N,P,Q,R]	Disp subtrochanteric fx of [rt, lt, unsp] femur, subsq enc for [clsd fx w/ nonu, opn fx type I or II w/ nonu, opn fx type IIIA, IIIB, or IIIC w/ nonu, clsd fx w/ malu, opn fx type I or II w/ malu, opn fx type IIIA, IIIB, or IIIC w/ malu] **201**
S72.46[1,2,3] [D,E,F,G,H,J,S]	Disp supracondylar fx w/ intracondylar extension of lwr end of [rt, lt, unsp] femur, [subsq enc for clsd fx w/ routine healing, subsq enc for opn fx type I or II w/ routine healing, subsq enc for opn fx type IIIA, IIIB, or IIIC w/ routine healing, subsq enc for clsd fx w/ delayed healing, subsq enc for opn fx type I or II w/ delayed healing, subsq enc for opn fx type I or II w/ delayed healing, seq] **178**
S72.46[1,2,3] [A,B,C]	Disp supracondylar fx w/ intracondylar extension of lwr end of [rt, lt, unsp] femur, init enc for [clsd fx, opn fx type I or II, opn fx type IIIA, IIIB, or IIIC] **161, 436**
S72.46[1,2,3] [K,M,N,P,Q,R]	Disp supracondylar fx w/ intracondylar extension of lwr end of [rt, lt, unsp] femur, subsq enc for [clsd fx w/ nonu, opn fx type I or II w/ nonu, opn fx type IIIA, IIIB, or IIIC w/ nonu, clsd fx w/ malu, opn fx type I or II w/ malu, opn fx type IIIA, IIIB, or IIIC w/ malu] **202**
S72.45[1,2,3] [D,E,F,G,H,J,S]	Disp supracondylar fx w/o intracondylar extension of lwr end of [rt, lt, unsp] femur, [subsq enc for clsd fx w/ routine healing, subsq enc for opn fx type I or II w/ routine healing, subsq enc for opn fx type IIIA, IIIB, or IIIC w/ routine healing, subsq enc for clsd fx w/ delayed healing, subsq enc for opn fx type I or II w/ delayed healing, subsq enc for opn fx type I or II w/ delayed healing, seq] **178**
S72.45[1,2,3] [A,B,C]	Disp supracondylar fx w/o intracondylar extension of lwr end of [rt, lt, unsp] femur, init enc for [clsd fx, opn fx type I or II, opn fx type IIIA, IIIB, or IIIC] **161, 436**
S72.45[1,2,3] [K,M,N,P,Q,R]	Disp supracondylar fx w/o intracondylar extension of lwr end of [rt, lt, unsp] femur, subsq enc for [clsd fx w/ nonu, opn fx type I or II w/ nonu, opn fx type IIIA, IIIB, or IIIC w/ nonu, clsd fx w/ malu, opn fx type I or II w/ malu, opn fx type IIIA, IIIB, or IIIC w/ malu] **202**
S42.47[1,2,3] [D,G,S]	Disp transcondylar fx of [rt, lt, unsp] humerus, [subsq enc for fx w/ routine healing, subsq enc for fx w/ delayed healing, seq] **171**
S42.47[1,2,3]B	Disp transcondylar fx of [rt, lt, unsp] humerus, init enc for opn fx **434**
S42.47[1,2,3] [K,P]	Disp transcondylar fx of [rt, lt, unsp] humerus, subsq enc for fx w/ [nonu, malu] **197**
S42.47[1,2,3] [A,B]	Disp transcondylar fx of humerus [rt, lt, unsp] init enc for fx [clsd, opn] **185**
S32.45[1,2,3]S	Disp transv fx of [rt, lt, unsp] acetab, seq **166**
S32.45[1,2,3] [D,G]	Disp transv fx of [rt, lt, unsp] acetab, subsq enc for fx w/ [routine, delayed] healing **170**
S32.45[1,2,3]K	Disp transv fx of [rt, lt, unsp] acetab, subsq enc for fx w/ nonu **196**
S82.03[1,2,3] [A,B,C]	Disp transv fx of [rt, lt, unsp] patella, [init enc for clsd fx, init enc for opn fx type I or II, init enc for opn fx type IIIA, IIIB, or IIIC] **190**
S82.03[1,2,3] [D,E,F,G,H,J,S]	Disp transv fx of [rt, lt, unsp] patella, [subsq enc for clsd fx w/ routine healing, subsq enc for opn fx type I or II w/ routine healing, subsq enc for opn fx type IIIA, IIIB, or IIIC w/ routine healing, subsq enc for clsd fx w/ delayed healing, subsq enc for opn fx type I or II w/ delayed healing, subsq enc for opn fx type I or II w/ delayed healing, seq] **179**
S82.03[1,2,3] [K,M,N,P,Q,R]	Disp transv fx of [rt, lt, unsp] patella, subsq enc for [clsd fx w/ nonu, opn fx type I or II w/ nonu, opn fx type IIIA, IIIB, or IIIC w/ nonu, clsd fx w/ malu, opn fx type I or II w/ malu, opn fx type I or II w/ malu] **202**
S52.22[1,2,3] [B,C]	Disp transv fx of [rt, lt, unsp] ulna, init enc for opn fx type [I or II, IIIA IIIB or IIIC] **434**
S32.45[1,2,3] [A,B]	Disp transv fx of acetab [rt, lt, unsp] init enc for [clsd fx, opn fx] **162, 433**
S72.32[1,2,3] [D,E,F,G,H,J,S]	Disp transv fx of shaft of [rt, lt, unsp] femur, [subsq enc for clsd fx w/ routine healing, subsq enc for opn fx type I or II w/ routine healing, subsq enc for opn fx type IIIA, IIIB, or IIIC w/ routine healing, subsq enc for clsd fx w/ delayed healing, subsq enc for opn fx type I or II w/ delayed healing, subsq enc for opn fx type IIIA, IIIB, or IIIC w/ delayed healing, seq] **178**
S72.32[1,2,3] [A,B,C]	Disp transv fx of shaft of [rt, lt, unsp] femur, init enc for [clsd fx, opn fx type I or II, opn fx type IIIA, IIIB, or IIIC] **161, 286, 435**

Code	Description
S72.32[1,2,3] [K,M,N,P,Q,R]	Disp transv fx of shaft of [rt, lt, unsp] femur, subsq enc for [clsd fx w/ nonu, opn fx type I or II w/ nonu, opn fx type IIIA, IIIB, or IIIC w/ nonu, clsd fx w/ malu, opn fx type I or II w/ malu, opn fx type IIIA, IIIB, or IIIC w/ malu] 201
S82.42[1,2,3] [A,B,C]	Disp transv fx of shaft of [rt, lt, unsp] fibula, [init enc for clsd fx, init enc for opn fx type I or II, init enc for opn fx type IIIA, IIIB, or IIIC] 191, 427
S82.42[1,2,3] [D,E,F,G,H,J,S]	Disp transv fx of shaft of [rt, lt, unsp] fibula, [subsq enc for clsd fx w/ routine healing, subsq enc for opn fx type I or II w/ routine healing, subsq enc for opn fx type IIIA, IIIB, or IIIC w/ routine healing, subsq enc for clsd fx w/ delayed healing, subsq enc for opn fx type I or II w/ delayed healing, subsq enc for opn fx type IIIA, IIIB, or IIIC w/ delayed healing, seq] 180
S82.42[1,2,3] [B,C]	Disp transv fx of shaft of [rt, lt, unsp] fibula, init enc for opn fx type [I or II, IIIA IIIB or IIIC] 436
S82.42[1,2,3] [K,M,N,P,Q,R]	Disp transv fx of shaft of [rt, lt, unsp] fibula, subsq enc for [clsd fx w/ nonu, opn fx type I or II w/ nonu, opn fx type IIIA, IIIB, or IIIC w/ nonu, clsd fx w/ malu, opn fx type I or II w/ malu, opn fx type I or II w/ malu] 203
S42.32[1,2,3] [D,G,S]	Disp transv fx of shaft of [rt, lt, unsp] humerus, [subsq enc for fx w/ routine healing, subsq enc for fx w/ delayed healing, seq] 171
S42.32[1,2,3]B	Disp transv fx of shaft of [rt, lt, unsp] humerus, init enc for opn fx 433
S52.32[1,2,3] [D,E,F,G,H,J,S]	Disp transv fx of shaft of [rt, lt, unsp] radius, [subsq enc for clsd fx w/ routine healing, subsq enc for opn fx type I or II w/ routine healing, subsq enc for opn fx type I or II w/ routine healing, subsq enc for clsd fx w/ delayed healing, subsq enc for opn fx type I or II w/ delayed healing, subsq enc for opn fx type IIIA, IIIB, or IIIC w/ delayed healing, seq] 173
S52.32[1,2,3] [B,C]	Disp transv fx of shaft of [rt, lt, unsp] radius, init enc for opn fx type [I or II, IIIA IIIB or IIIC] 434
S52.32[1,2,3] [K,M,N,P,Q,R]	Disp transv fx of shaft of [rt, lt, unsp] radius, subsq enc for [clsd fx w/ nonu, opn fx type I or II w/ nonu, opn fx type IIIA, IIIB, or IIIC w/ nonu, clsd fx w/ malu, opn fx type I or II w/ malu, opn fx type IIIA, IIIB, or IIIC w/ malu] 198
S82.22[1,2,3] [A,B,C]	Disp transv fx of shaft of [rt, lt, unsp] tibia, [init enc for clsd fx, init enc for opn fx type I or II, init enc for opn fx type IIIA, IIIB, or IIIC] 191, 427
S82.22[1,2,3] [D,E,F,G,H,J,S]	Disp transv fx of shaft of [rt, lt, unsp] tibia, [subsq enc for clsd fx w/ routine healing, subsq enc for opn fx type I or II w/ routine healing, subsq enc for opn fx type IIIA, IIIB, or IIIC w/ routine healing, subsq enc for clsd fx w/ delayed healing, subsq enc for opn fx type I or II w/ delayed healing, seq] 180
S82.22[1,2,3] [B,C]	Disp transv fx of shaft of [rt, lt, unsp] tibia, init enc for opn fx type [I or II, IIIA IIIB or IIIC] 436
S82.22[1,2,3] [K,M,N,P,Q,R]	Disp transv fx of shaft of [rt, lt, unsp] tibia, subsq enc for [clsd fx w/ nonu, opn fx type I or II w/ nonu, opn fx type IIIA, IIIB, or IIIC w/ nonu, clsd fx w/ malu, opn fx type I or II w/ malu, opn fx type I or II w/ malu] 202
S52.22[1,2,3] [D,E,F,G,H,J,S]	Disp transv fx of shaft of [rt, lt, unsp] ulna, [subsq enc for clsd fx w/ routine healing, subsq enc for opn fx type I or II w/ routine healing, subsq enc for opn fx type IIIA, IIIB, or IIIC w/ routine healing, subsq enc for clsd fx w/ delayed healing, subsq enc for opn fx type I or II w/ delayed healing, subsq enc for opn fx type IIIA, IIIB, or IIIC w/ delayed healing, seq] 172
S52.22[1,2,3] [K,M,N,P,Q,R]	Disp transv fx of shaft of [rt, lt, unsp] ulna, subsq enc for [clsd fx w/ nonu, opn fx type I or II w/ nonu, opn fx type IIIA, IIIB, or IIIC w/ nonu, clsd fx w/ malu, opn fx type I or II w/ malu, opn fx type IIIA, IIIB, or IIIC w/ malu] 198
S42.32[1,2,3] [A,B]	Disp transv fx of shaft of humerus [rt, lt, unsp] init enc for fx [clsd, opn] 185
S42.32[1,2,3] [K,P]	Disp transv fx of shaft of humerus, [rt, lt, unsp] arm, subsq enc for fx w/ [nonu, malu] 197
S52.32[1,2,3] [A,B,C]	Disp transv fx of shaft of radius [rt, lt, unsp} init enc for [clsd fx, opn fx type I or II or opn fx NOS, opn fx type IIIA, IIIB, or IIIC] 186
S52.22[1,2,3] [A,B,C]	Disp transv fx of ulna {rt, lt, unsp} init enc for [clsd fx, opn fx type I or II or opn fx NOS, opn fx type IIIA, IIIB, or IIIC] 186
S82.85[1,2,3] [A,B,C]	Disp trimalleolar fx of [rt, lt, unsp] lwr leg, [init enc for clsd fx, init enc for opn fx type I or II, init enc for opn fx type I or II] 191, 427
S82.85[1,2,3] [D,E,F,G,H,J,S]	Disp trimalleolar fx of [rt, lt, unsp] lwr leg, [subsq enc for clsd fx w/ routine healing, subsq enc for opn fx type I or II w/ routine healing, subsq enc for opn fx type IIIA, IIIB, or IIIC w/ routine healing, subsq enc for clsd fx w/ delayed healing, subsq enc for opn fx type I or II w/ delayed healing, subsq enc for opn fx type IIIA, IIIB, or IIIC w/ delayed healing, seq] 181
S82.85[1,2,3] [K,M,N,P,Q,R]	Disp trimalleolar fx of [rt, lt, unsp] lwr leg, subsq enc for [clsd fx w/ nonu, opn fx type I or II w/ nonu, opn fx type IIIA, IIIB, or IIIC w/ nonu, clsd fx w/ malu, opn fx type I or II w/ malu, opn fx type I or II w/ malu] 203
S72.41[1,2,3] [D,E,F,G,H,J,S]	Disp unsp condyle fx of lwr end of [rt, lt, unsp] femur, [subsq enc for clsd fx w/ routine healing, subsq enc for opn fx type I or II w/ routine healing, subsq enc for opn fx type IIIA, IIIB, or IIIC w/ routine healing, subsq enc for clsd fx w/ delayed healing, subsq enc for opn fx type I or II w/ delayed healing, subsq enc for opn fx type IIIA, IIIB, or IIIC w/ delayed healing, seq] 178
S72.41[1,2,3] [A,B,C]	Disp unsp condyle fx of lwr end of [rt, lt, unsp] femur, init enc for [clsd fx, opn fx type I or II, opn fx type IIIA, IIIB, or IIIC] 161, 435
S72.41[1,2,3] [K,M,N,P,Q,R]	Disp unsp condyle fx of lwr end of [rt, lt, unsp] femur, subsq enc for [clsd fx w/ nonu, opn fx type I or II w/ nonu, opn fx type IIIA, IIIB, or IIIC w/ nonu, clsd fx w/ malu, opn fx type I or II w/ malu, opn fx type IIIA, IIIB, or IIIC w/ malu] 201
S92.40[1,2,3] [D,G,S]	Disp unsp fx of [rt, lt, unsp] great toe, [subsq enc for fx w/ routine healing, subsq enc for fx w/ delayed healing, seq] 183
S92.40[1,2,3] [A,B]	Disp unsp fx of [rt, lt, unsp] great toe, init enc for [clsd, opn] fx 192, 429
S92.40[1,2,3] [K,P]	Disp unsp fx of [rt, lt, unsp] great toe, subsq enc for fx w/ [nonu, malu] 204
S92.50[1,2,3] [D,G,S]	Disp unsp fx of [rt, lt, unsp] lesser toe(s), [subsq enc for fx w/ routine healing, subsq enc for fx w/ delayed healing, seq] 183
S92.50[1,2,3] [A,B]	Disp unsp fx of [rt, lt, unsp] lesser toe(s), init enc for [clsd, opn] fx 193, 429
S92.50[1,2,3] [K,P]	Disp unsp fx of [rt, lt, unsp] lesser toe(s), subsq enc for fx w/ [nonu, malu] 204
S42.14[1,2,3,4,5,6][A,B]	Disp, Disp] fx of glenoid cavity of scapula, [rt, lt, unsp] shldr, init enc for [clsd, opn] fx 422
S42.44[1,2,3,4,5,6,7,8,9][A,B]	Disp, Nondisp, Incarcerated] fx (avulsion) of med epicondyle of [rt, lt, unsp] humerus, init enc for [clsd, opn] fx 422
S72.13[1,2,3,4,5,6][A,B,C]	Disp, Nondisp] apophyseal fx of [rt, lt, unsp] femur, init enc for [clsd fx, opn fx type I or II, opn fx type IIIA, IIIB, or IIIC] 426
S72.06[1,2,3,4,5,6][A,B,C]	Disp, Nondisp] articular fx of head of [rt, lt, unsp] femur, init enc for [clsd fx, opn fx type I or II, opn fx type IIIA, IIIB, or IIIC] 426
S32.46[1,2,3,4,5,6][A,B]	Disp, Nondisp] associated transv-post fx of [rt, lt, unsp] acetab, init enc for [clsd, opn] fx 421
S32.31[1,2,3,4,5,6][A,B]	Disp, Nondisp] avulsion fx of [rt, lt, unsp] ilium, init enc for [clsd, opn] fx 421, 433
S32.61[1,2,3,4,5,6][A,B]	Disp, Nondisp] avulsion fx of [rt, lt, unsp] ischium, init enc for [clsd, opn] fx 421, 433
S82.14[1,2,3,4,5,6][A,B,C]	Disp, Nondisp] bicondylar fx of [rt, lt, unsp] tibia, init enc for [clsd fx, opn fx type I or II, opn fx type IIIA, IIIB, or IIIC] 427
S82.04[1,2,3,4,5,6][A,B,C]	Disp, Nondisp] comm fx of [rt, lt, unsp] patella, init enc for [clsd fx, opn fx type I or II, opn fx type IIIA, IIIB, or IIIC] 427
S72.35[1,2,3,4,5,6][A,B,C]	Disp, Nondisp] comm fx of shaft of [rt, lt, unsp] femur, init enc for [clsd fx, opn fx type I or II, opn fx type IIIA, IIIB, IIIC] 426
S42.35[1,2,3,4,5,6][A,B]	Disp, Nondisp] comm fx of shaft of humerus, [rt, lt, unsp] arm, init enc for [clsd, opn] fx 422
S52.35[1,2,3,4,5,6][A,B,C]	Disp, Nondisp] comm fx of shaft of radius, [rt, lt, unsp] arm, init enc for [clsd fx, opn fx type I or II, opn fx type IIIA, IIIB, or IIIC] 423
S52.25[1,2,3,4,5,6][A,B,C]	Disp, Nondisp] comm fx of shaft of ulna, [rt, lt, unsp] arm, init enc for [clsd fx, opn fx type I or II, opn fx type IIIA, IIIB, or IIIC] 423
S42.42[1,2,3,4,5,6][A,B]	Disp, Nondisp] comm supracondylar fx w/o intercondylar fx of [rt, lt, unsp] humerus, init enc for [clsd, opn] fx 422
S32.48[1,2,3,4,5,6][A,B]	Disp, Nondisp] dome fx of [rt, lt, unsp] acetab, init enc for [clsd, opn] fx 421
S42.43[1,2,3,4,5,6][A,B]	Disp, Nondisp] fx (avulsion) of lat epicondyle of [rt, lt, unsp] humerus, init enc for [clsd, opn] fx 422
S52.51[1,2,3,4,5,6][A,B,C]	Disp, Nondisp] fx of [rt, lt, unsp] radial styloid process, init enc for [clsd fx, opn fx type I or II, opn fx type IIIA, IIIB, or IIIC] 423
S82.11[1,2,3,4,5,6][A,B,C]	Disp, Nondisp] fx of [rt, lt, unsp] tibial spine, init enc for [clsd fx, opn fx type I or II, opn fx type IIIA, IIIB, or IIIC] 427
S82.15[1,2,3,4,5,6][A,B,C]	Disp, Nondisp] fx of [rt, lt, unsp] tibial tuberosity, init enc for [clsd fx, opn fx type I or II, opn fx type IIIA, IIIB, IIIC] 427
S52.61[1,2,3,4,5,6][A,B,C]	Disp, Nondisp] fx of [rt, lt, unsp] ulna styloid process, init enc for [clsd fx, opn fx type I or II, opn fx type IIIA, IIIB, or IIIC] 424
S42.12[1,2,3,4,5,6][A,B]	Disp, Nondisp] fx of acromial process, [rt, lt, unsp] shldr, init enc for [clsd, opn] fx 422
S32.43[1,2,3,4,5,6][A,B]	Disp, Nondisp] fx of ant column [iliopubic] of [rt, lt, unsp] acetab, init enc for [clsd, opn] fx 421
S32.41[1,2,3,4,5,6][A,B]	Disp, Nondisp] fx of ant wall of [rt, lt, unsp] acetab, init enc for [clsd, opn] fx 421
S72.04[1,2,3,4,5,6][A,B,C]	Disp, Nondisp] fx of base of neck of [rt, lt, unsp] femur, init enc for [clsd fx, opn fx type I or II, opn fx type IIIA, IIIB, or IIIC] 426

S62.14[1,2,3,4,5,6][A,B] Disp, Nondisp] fx of body of hamate [unciform] bone, [rt, lt, unsp] wrist, init enc for [clsd, opn] fx 424

S42.11[1,2,3,4,5,6][A,B] Disp, Nondisp] fx of body of scapula, [rt, lt, unsp] shldr, init enc for [clsd, opn] fx 422

S62.13[1,2,3,4,5,6][A,B] Disp, Nondisp] fx of capitate [os magnum] bone, [rt, lt, unsp] wrist, init enc for [clsd, opn] fx 424

S42.13[1,2,3,4,5,6][A,B] Disp, Nondisp] fx of coracoid process, [rt, lt, unsp] shldr, init enc for [clsd, opn] fx 422

S52.04[1,2,3,4,5,6][A,B,C] Disp, Nondisp] fx of coronoid process of [rt, lt, unsp] ulna, init enc for [clsd fx, opn fx type I or II, opn fx type IIIA, IIIB, or IIIC] 423

S62.52[1,2,3,4,5,6][A,B] Disp, Nondisp] fx of distal phalanx of [rt, lt, unsp] thumb, init enc for [clsd, opn] fx 425

S62.01[1,2,3,4,5,6][A,B] Disp, Nondisp] fx of distal pole of navicular [scaphoid] bone of [rt, lt, unsp] wrist, init enc for [clsd, opn] fx 424

S72.02[1,2,3,4,5,6][A,B,C] Disp, Nondisp] fx of epiphysis (separation) (upr) of [rt, lt, unsp] femur, init enc for [clsd fx, opn fx type I or II, opn fx type IIIA, IIIB, or IIIC] 426

S72.11[1,2,3,4,5,6][A,B,C] Disp, Nondisp] fx of greater trochanter of [rt, lt, unsp] femur, init enc for [clsd fx, opn fx type I or II, opn fx type IIIA, IIIB, or IIIC] 426

S42.25[1,2,3,4,5,6][A,B] Disp, Nondisp] fx of greater tuberosity of [rt, lt, unsp] humerus, init enc for [clsd, opn] fx 422

S52.12[1,2,3,4,5,6][A,B,C] Disp, Nondisp] fx of head of [rt, lt, unsp] radius, init enc for [clsd fx, opn type I or II, opn fx IIIA, IIIB, or IIIC] 423

S62.15[1,2,3,4,5,6][A,B] Disp, Nondisp] fx of hook process of hamate [unciform] bone, [rt, lt, unsp] wrist, init enc for [clsd, opn] fx 424

S72.42[1,2,3,4,5,6][A,B,C] Disp, Nondisp] fx of lat condyle of [rt, lt, unsp] femur, init enc for [clsd fx, opn fx type I or II, opn fx type IIIA, IIIB, or IIIC] 426

S42.45[1,2,3,4,5,6][A,B] Disp, Nondisp] fx of lat condyle of [rt, lt, unsp] humerus, init enc for [clsd, opn] fx 422

S82.12[1,2,3,4,5,6][A,B,C] Disp, Nondisp] fx of lat condyle of [rt, lt, unsp] tibia, init enc for [clsd fx, opn fx type I or II, opn fx type IIIA, IIIB, or IIIC] 427

S42.03[1,2,3,4,5,6][A,B] Disp, Nondisp] fx of lat end of [rt, lt, unsp] clavicle, init enc for [clsd, opn] fx 422

S72.12[1,2,3,4,5,6][A,B,C] Disp, Nondisp] fx of lesser trochanter of [rt, lt, unsp] femur, init enc for [clsd fx, opn fx type I or II, opn fx type IIIA, IIIB, or IIIC] 426

S42.26[1,2,3,4,5,6][A,B] Disp, Nondisp] fx of lesser tuberosity of [rt, lt, unsp] humerus, init enc for [clsd, opn] fx 422

S62.12[1,2,3,4,5,6][A,B] Disp, Nondisp] fx of lunate [semilunar], [rt, lt, unsp] wrist, init enc for [clsd, opn] fx 424

S72.44[1,2,3,4,5,6][A,B,C] Disp, Nondisp] fx of lwr epiphysis (separation) of [rt, lt, unsp] femur, init enc for [clsd fx, opn fx type I or II, opn fx type IIIA, IIIB, or IIIC] 426

S72.43[1,2,3,4,5,6][A,B,C] Disp, Nondisp] fx of med condyle of [rt, lt, unsp] femur, init enc for [clsd fx, opn fx type I or II, opn fx type IIIA, IIIB, or IIIC] 426

S42.46[1,2,3,4,5,6][A,B] Disp, Nondisp] fx of med condyle of [rt, lt, unsp] humerus, init enc for [clsd, opn] fx 422

S82.13[1,2,3,4,5,6][A,B,C] Disp, Nondisp] fx of med condyle of [rt, lt, unsp] tibia, init enc for [clsd fx, opn fx type I or II, opn fx type IIIA, IIIB, or IIIC] 427

S32.47[1,2,3,4,5,6][A,B] Disp, Nondisp] fx of med wall of [rt, lt, unsp] acetab, init enc for [clsd, opn] fx 421

S62.02[1,2,3,4,5,6][A,B] Disp, Nondisp] fx of mid 3rd of navicular [scaphoid] bone of [rt, lt, unsp] wrist, init enc for [clsd, opn] fx 424

S52.13[1,2,3,4,5,6][A,B,C] Disp, Nondisp] fx of neck of [rt, lt, unsp] radius, init enc for [clsd fx, opn fx type I or II, opn fx type IIIA, IIIB, or IIIC] 423

S62.25[1,2,3,4,5,6][A,B] Disp, Nondisp] fx of neck of 1st metacarpal bone, [rt, lt, unsp] hand, init enc for [clsd, opn] fx 424

S42.15[1,2,3,4,5,6][A,B] Disp, Nondisp] fx of neck of scapula, [rt, lt, unsp] shldr, init enc for [clsd, opn] fx 422

S52.03[1,2,3,4,5,6][A,B,C] Disp, Nondisp] fx of olecranon process w/ intraarticular extension of [rt, lt, unsp] ulna, init enc for [clsd fx, opn fx type I or II, opn fx type IIIA, IIIb, or IIIC] 423

S52.02[1,2,3,4,5,6][A,B,C] Disp, Nondisp] fx of olecranon process w/o intraarticular extension of [rt, lt, unsp] ulna, init enc for [clsd fx, opn fx type I or II, opn fx type IIIA, IIIB, or IIIC] 423

S62.16[1,2,3,4,5,6][A,B] Disp, Nondisp] fx of pisiform, [rt, lt, unsp] wrist, init enc for [clsd, opn] fx 424

S32.44[1,2,3,4,5,6][A,B] Disp, Nondisp] fx of post column [ilioischial] of [rt, lt, unsp] acetab, init enc for [clsd, opn] fx 421

S32.42[1,2,3,4,5,6][A,B] Disp, Nondisp] fx of post wall of [rt, lt, unsp] acetab, init enc for [clsd, opn] fx 421

S62.03[1,2,3,4,5,6][A,B] Disp, Nondisp] fx of proximal 3rd of navicular [scaphoid] bone of [rt, lt, unsp] wrist, init enc for [clsd, opn] fx 424

S62.51[1,2,3,4,5,6][A,B] Disp, Nondisp] fx of proximal phalanx of [rt, lt, unsp] thumb, init enc for [clsd, opn] fx 425

S42.02[1,2,3,4,5,6][A,B] Disp, Nondisp] fx of shaft of [rt, lt, unsp] clavicle, init enc for [clsd, opn] fx 422

S62.24[1,2,3,4,5,6][A,B] Disp, Nondisp] fx of shaft of 1st metacarpal bone, [rt, lt, unsp] hand, init enc for [clsd, opn] fx 424

S62.17[1,2,3,4,5,6][A,B] Disp, Nondisp] fx of trapezium [lgr multangular], [rt, lt, unsp] wrist, init enc for [clsd, opn] fx 424

S62.18[1,2,3,4,5,6][A,B] Disp, Nondisp] fx of trapezoid [smer multangular], [rt, lt, unsp] wrist, init enc for [clsd, opn] fx 424

S62.11[1,2,3,4,5,6][A,B] Disp, Nondisp] fx of triquetrum [cuneiform] bone, [rt, lt, unsp] wrist, init enc for [clsd, opn] fx 424

S72.14[1,2,3,4,5,6][A,B,C] Disp, Nondisp] intertrochanteric fx of [rt, lt, unsp] femur, init enc for [clsd fx, opn fx type I or II, opn fx type IIIA, IIIB, or IIIC] 426

S12.04[0,1][A,B] Disp, Nondisp] lat mass fx of 1st cervical vertebra, init enc for [clsd, opn] fx 419

S12.04[0,1][D,G] Disp, Nondisp] lat mass fx of 1st cervical vertebra, subsq enc for fx w/ [routine, delayed] healing 169

S12.04[0,1]K Disp, Nondisp] lat mass fx of 1st cervical vertebra, subsq enc for fx w/ nonu 195

S82.02[1,2,3,4,5,6][A,B,C] Disp, Nondisp] longitudinal fx of [rt, lt, unsp] patella, init enc for [clsd fx, opn fx type I or II, opn fx type IIIA, IIIB, or IIIC] 427

S72.03[1,2,3,4,5,6][A,B,C] Disp, Nondisp] midcervical fx of [rt, lt, unsp] femur, init enc for [clsd fx, opn fx type I or II, opn fx type IIIA, IIIB, or IIIC] 426

S72.33[1,2,3,4,5,6][A,B,C] Disp, Nondisp] oblique fx of shaft of [rt, lt, unsp] femur, init enc for [clsd fx, opn fx type I or II, opn fx type IIIA, IIIB, or IIIC] 426

S52.33[1,2,3,4,5,6][A,B,C] Disp, Nondisp] oblique fx of shaft of [rt, lt, unsp] radius, init enc for [clsd fx, opn fx type I or II, opn fx type IIIA, IIIB, or IIIC] 423

S52.23[1,2,3,4,5,6][A,B,C] Disp, Nondisp] oblique fx of shaft of [rt, lt, unsp] ulna, init enc for [clsd fx, opn fx type I or II, opn fx type IIIA, IIIB, or IIIC] 423

S42.33[1,2,3,4,5,6][A,B] Disp, Nondisp] oblique fx of shaft of humerus, [rt, lt, unsp] arm, init enc for [clsd, opn] fx 422

S82.01[1,2,3,4,5,6][A,B,C] Disp, Nondisp] osteochondral fx of [rt, lt, unsp] patella, init enc for [clsd fx, opn fx type I or II, opn fx type IIIA, IIIB, or IIIC] 427

S12.03[0,1][A,B] Disp, Nondisp] post arch fx of 1st cervical vertebra, init enc for [clsd, opn] fx 419

S12.03[0,1][D,G] Disp, Nondisp] post arch fx of 1st cervical vertebra, subsq enc for fx w/ [routine, delayed] healing 169

S12.03[0,1]K Disp, Nondisp] post arch fx of 1st cervical vertebra, subsq enc for fx w/ nonu 195

S62.22[1,2,3,4,5,6][A,B] Disp, Nondisp] Rolando's fx, [rt, lt, unsp] hand, init enc for [clsd, opn] fx 424

S72.36[1,2,3,4,5,6][A,B,C] Disp, Nondisp] seg fx of shaft of [rt, lt, unsp] femur, init enc for [clsd fx, opn fx type I or II, opn fx type IIIA, IIIB, or IIIC] 426

S42.36[1,2,3,4,5,6][A,B] Disp, Nondisp] seg fx of shaft of humerus, [rt, lt, unsp] arm, init enc for [clsd, opn] fx 422

S52.36[1,2,3,4,5,6][A,B,C] Disp, Nondisp] seg fx of shaft of radius, [rt, lt, unsp] arm, init enc for [clsd fx, opn fx type I or II, opn fx fx type IIIA, IIIB, or IIIC] 423

S52.26[1,2,3,4,5,6][A,B,C] Disp, Nondisp] seg fx of shaft of ulna, [rt, lt, unsp] arm, init enc for [clsd fx, opn fx type I or II, opn fx type IIIA, IIIB, or IIIC] 423

S42.41[1,2,3,4,5,6][A,B] Disp, Nondisp] simple supracondylar fx w/o intercondylar fx of [rt, lt, unsp] humerus, init enc for [clsd, opn] fx 422

S72.34[1,2,3,4,5,6][A,B,C] Disp, Nondisp] spiral fx of shaft of [rt, lt, unsp] femur, init enc for [clsd fx, opn fx type I or II, opn fx type IIIA, IIIB, or IIIC] 426

S42.34[1,2,3,4,5,6][A,B] Disp, Nondisp] spiral fx of shaft of humerus, [rt, lt, unsp] arm, init enc for [clsd, opn] fx 422

S52.34[1,2,3,4,5,6][A,B,C] Disp, Nondisp] spiral fx of shaft of radius, [rt, lt, unsp] arm, init enc for [clsd fx, opn fx type I or II, opn fx type IIIA, IIIB, or IIIC] 423

S52.24[1,2,3,4,5,6][A,B,C] Disp, Nondisp] spiral fx of shaft of ulna, [rt, lt, unsp] arm, init enc for [clsd fx, opn fx type I or type II, opn fx type IIIA, IIIB, or IIIC] 423

S72.2[1,2,3,4,5,6]X[A,B,C] Disp, Nondisp] subtrochanteric fx of [rt, lt, unsp] femur, init enc for [clsd fx, opn fx type I or II, opn fx type IIIA, IIIB, IIIC] 426

S72.46[1,2,3,4,5,6][A,B,C] Disp, Nondisp] supracondylar fx w/ intracondylar extension of lwr end of [rt, lt, unsp] femur, init enc for [clsd fx, opn fx type I or II, opn fx type IIIA, IIIB, or IIIC] 426

S72.45[1,2,3,4,5,6][A,B,C] Disp, Nondisp] supracondylar fx w/o intracondylar extension of lwr end of [rt, lt, unsp] femur, init enc for [clsd fx, opn fx type I or II, opn fx type IIIA, IIIB, or IIIC] 426

S42.47[1,2,3,4,5,6][A,B] Disp, Nondisp] transcondylar fx of [rt, lt, unsp] humerus, init enc for [clsd, opn] fx 422

S32.45[1,2,3,4,5,6][A,B] Disp, Nondisp] transv fx of [rt, lt, unsp] acetab, init enc for [clsd, opn] fx 421

S82.03[1,2,3,4,5,6][A,B,C] Disp, Nondisp] transv fx of [rt, lt, unsp] patella, init enc for [clsd fx, opn fx type I or II, opn fx type IIIA, IIIB, or IIIC] 427

S72.32[1,2,3,4,5,6][A,B,C] Disp, Nondisp] transv fx of shaft of [rt, lt, unsp] femur, init enc for [clsd fx, opn fx type I or II, opn fx type IIIA, IIIB, or IIIC] 426

S52.32[1,2,3,4,5,6][A,B,C] Disp, Nondisp] transv fx of shaft of [rt, lt, unsp] radius, init enc for [clsd fx, opn fx type I or II, opn fx type IIIA, IIIB, or IIIC] 423

S52.22[1,2,3,4,5,6][A,B,C] Disp, Nondisp] transv fx of shaft of [rt, lt, unsp] ulna, init enc for [clsd fx, opn fx type I or II, opn fx type IIIA, IIIB, or IIIC] 423

S42.32[1,2,3,4,5,6][A,B]	Disp, Nondisp] transv fx of shaft of humerus, [rt, lt, unsp] arm, init enc for [clsd, opn] fx 422
S72.41[1,2,3,4,5,6][A,B,C]	Disp, Nondisp] unsp condyle fx of lwr end of [rt, lt, unsp] femur, init enc for [clsd fx, opn fx type I or II, opn fx type IIIA, IIIB, or IIIC] 426
H05.21[1,2,3,9]	Displac (lat) of globe, [rt, lt, bilat, unsp] eye 45
T82.32[0,1,2,8,9]S	Displac of [aortic (bifurcation) graft (replace), carotid arterial graft (bypass), femor arterial graft (bypass), oth vascular grafts, unsp vascular grafts], seq 375
T82.32[0,1,2,8,9]D	Displac of [aortic (bifurcation) graft (replace), carotid arterial graft (bypass), femor arterial graft (bypass), oth vascular grafts, unsp vascular grafts], subsq 410
T82.12[0,1,8,9]S	Displac of [cardiac electrode, cardiac pulse generator, oth cardiac electronic dev, unsp cardiac electronic dev], seq 375
T82.12[0,1,8,9]D	Displac of [cardiac electrode, cardiac pulse generator, oth cardiac electronic dev, unsp cardiac electronic dev], subsq enc 410
T82.52[0,1,2,3,4,5,8,9]A	Displac of [surgically created arteriovenous fistula, surgically created arteriovenous shunt, artfcl heart, balloon (counterpulsation) dev, inf catheter, umbrella dev, oth cardiac/vascular dev, unsp cardiac/vascular dev], init enc 103
T82.52[0,1,2,3,4,5,8,9]S	Displac of [surgically created arteriovenous fistula, surgically created arteriovenous shunt, artfcl heart, balloon (counterpulsation) dev, inf catheter, umbrella dev, oth cardiac/vascular dev, unsp cardiac/vascular dev], seq 375
T82.52[0,1,2,3,4,5,8,9]D	Displac of [surgically created arteriovenous fistula, surgically created arteriovenous shunt, artfcl heart, balloon (counterpulsation) dev, inf catheter, umbrella dev, oth cardiac/vascular dev, unsp cardiac/vascular dev], subsq enc 410
T85.42XA	Displac of breast prosthesis and implant, init enc 224
T82.120A	Displac of cardiac electrode, init enc 102
T82.121A	Displac of cardiac pulse generator (battery), init 102
T85.12[0,1,2,8]A	Displac of implanted electronic neurostimulator (electrode) of [brain, peripheral nerve, spinal cord, oth nervous sys], init enc 40
T85.12[0,1,2,8]S	Displac of implanted electronic neurostimulator (electrode) of [brain, peripheral nerve, spinal cord, oth nervous sys], seq 376
T85.12[0,1,2,8]D	Displac of implanted electronic neurostimulator (electrode) of [brain, peripheral nerve, spinal cord, oth nervous sys], subsq enc 411
T84.22[0,3,6,8]A	Displac of int fix dev of [bones of hand and fingers, bones of foot and toes, vertebrae, oth bones], init enc 183
T84.22[0,3,6,8]S	Displac of int fix dev of [bones of hand and fingers, bones of foot and toes, vertebrae, oth bones], seq 375
T84.22[0,3,6,8]D	Displac of int fix dev of [bones of hand and fingers, bones of foot and toes, vertebrae, oth bones], subsq enc 411
T84.12[0,1,2,3,4,5,6,7,9]A	Displac of int fix dev of [rt humerus, lt humerus, bone of rt forearm, bone of lt forearm, rt femur, lt femur, bone of rt lwr leg, bone of lt lwr leg, unsp bone of limb], init enc 183
T84.12[0,1,2,3,4,5,6,7,9]S	Displac of int fix dev of [rt humerus, lt humerus, bone of rt forearm, bone of lt forearm, rt femur, lt femur, bone of rt lwr leg, bone of lt lwr leg, unsp bone of limb], seq 375
T84.12[0,1,2,3,4,5,6,7,9]D	Displac of int fix dev of [rt humerus, lt humerus, bone of rt forearm, bone of lt forearm, rt femur, lt femur, bone of rt lwr leg, bone of lt lwr leg, unsp bone of limb], subsq enc 411
T85.328S	Displac of ocular prosth dev/grft, seq 376
T85.328D	Displac of ocular prosth dev/grft, subs 411
T82.128A	Displac of oth cardiac electronic device, init enc 103
T85.32[0,1]S	Displac of prosthetic orbit of [rt, lt] eye, seq 376
T85.32[0,1]D	Displac of prosthetic orbit of [rt, lt] eye, subsq enc 411
T82.129A	Displac of unsp cardiac electronic device, init enc 103
T81.3[1,2]XS	Disruption of [ext, int] operation (surgical) wnd, NEC, seq 375
T81.3[0,1,2,3]XA	Disruption of [unsp wnd, ext operation (surgical) wnd, int operation (surgical) wnd, traum inj wnd rpr], init enc 368
T81.3[0,1,2,3]XD	Disruption of [unsp wnd, ext operation (surgical) wnd, int operation (surgical) wnd, traum inj wnd rpr], subsq enc 410
O90.0	Disruption of cesarean delivery wnd 272, 274, 276
O90.1	Disruption of perineal obstetric wnd 272, 274, 276
T81.33XS	Disruption of traum inj wnd repair, seq 375
T81.30XS	Disruption of wnd, unsp, seq 375
I77.7[1,2,4,9]	Dissection of [carotid, iliac, vert, oth] artery 100
I67.0	Dissection of cerebral arteries, nonruptured 100
I77.73	Dissection of renal artery 256
A31.2	Dissem mycobacterium avium-intracellulare complex (DMAC) 308, 438
B38.7	Disseminated coccidioidomycosis 283, 308
B45.7	Disseminated cryptococcosis 438
B00.7	Disseminated herpesviral dz 283, 309, 438

B39.3	Disseminated histoplasmosis capsulati 308
D65	Disseminated intravascular coagulation 283, 294
P60	Disseminated intravascular coagulation of newborn 282
C80.0	Disseminated malig neoplasm, unsp 304, 305
B78.7	Disseminated strongyloidiasis 116, 438
B02.7	Disseminated zoster 283, 307, 438
F44.0	Dissociative amnesia 310
F44.9	Dissociative and conversion d/o, unsp 310
F44.1	Dissociative fugue 310
F44.81	Dissociative identity d/o 310
F44.2	Dissociative stupor 310
P91.9	Disturbance of cerebral status of newborn, unsp 282
K00.6	Disturbances in tooth eruption 4, 289
K00.4	Disturbances in tooth formation 4
K11.7	Disturbances of salivary secretion 4
R20*	Disturbances of skin sensation 38
R43*	Disturbances of smell and taste 39
K57.5[1,3]	[Diverticulosis, Diverticulitis] of both sm and lg intestine w/o perforation or abscess w/ bleeding 115
K57.5[0,2]	[Diverticulosis, Diverticulitis] of both sm and lg intestine w/o perforation or abscess w/o bleeding 116
K57.9[1,3]	[Diverticulosis, Diverticulitis] of intestine, part unsp, w/o perforation or abscess w/ bleeding 115
K57.9[0,2]	[Diverticulosis, Diverticulitis] of intestine, part unsp, w/o perforation or abscess w/o bleeding 116
K57.3[1,3]	[Diverticulosis, Diverticulitis] of lg intestine w/o perforation or abscess w/ bleeding 115
K57.3[0,2]	[Diverticulosis, Diverticulitis] of lg intestine w/o perforation or abscess w/o bleeding 116
K57.1[0,2]	[Diverticulosis, Diverticulitis] of sm intestine w/ perforation and abscess w/o bleeding 116
K57.1[1,3]	[Diverticulosis, Diverticulitis] of sm intestine w/o perforation or abscess w/ bleeding 115
K22.5	Diverticulum of esophagus, acquired 116
R42	Dizziness and giddiness 57
Z66	Do not resuscitate 412
Q67.2	Dolichocephaly 195
Z52.8*	Donor of oth spec organs or tissues 412
Z52.9	Donor of unsp organ or tissue 412
M54.9	Dorsalgia, unsp 165
M53.9	Dorsopathy, unsp 165
Q90*	Down synd 310
B72	Dracunculiasis 309
I24.1	Dressler's synd 103
G24.0*	Drug induced dystonia 38
G25.6*	Drug induced tics and oth tics of organic origin 38
E09.65	Drug or chemical induced diabetes mellitus w hyperglycemia 246
E09.0*	Drug or chemical induced diabetes mellitus w hyperosmolarity 1, 2, 246
E09.9	Drug or chemical induced diabetes mellitus w/o comp 2, 2, 246
E09.64*	Drug or chemical induced diabetes mellitus with hypoglycemia 246
E09.1*	Drug or chemical induced diabetes mellitus with ketoacidosis 1, 2, 246
O99.32[1,2,3]	Drug use compl preg, [1st, 2nd, 3rd] trmstr 277, 278
O99.325	Drug use compl the puerperium 276
N14*	Drug- & heavy-metal-induced tubulo-interstitial & tublr cond 256
D61.1	Drug-induced aplastic anemia 293
D59.0	Drug-induced autoimmune hemolytic anemia 293
G25.4	Drug-induced chorea 32
M1A.2*	Drug-induced chr gout 167
M10.2*	Drug-induced gout 166
E16.0	Drug-induced hypoglycemia w/o coma 247
G72.0	Drug-induced myopathy 38
D59.2	Drug-induced nonautoimmune hemolytic anemia 283, 293
E66.1	Drug-induced obesity 246
E06.4	Drug-induced thyroiditis 3
G25.1	Drug-induced tremor 38
E09.5*	Drug/chem diabetes mellitus w circulatory comp 2, 100
E09.2*	Drug/chem diabetes mellitus w kidney comp 1, 2, 256
E09.4*	Drug/chem diabetes mellitus w neurological comp 1, 2, 34

Code	Description
E09.3*	Drug/chem diabetes mellitus w ophthalmic comp 1, 2, 45
E09.63*	Drug/chem diabetes mellitus w oral comp 246
E09.6*	Drug/chem diabetes mellitus w oth comp 2
E09.69	Drug/chem diabetes mellitus w oth comp 246
E09.618	Drug/chem diabetes mellitus w oth diabetic arthropathy 246
E09.62*	Drug/chem diabetes mellitus w skin comp 246
E09.8	Drug/chem diabetes mellitus w unsp comp 2, 246
E09.610	Drug/chem diabetes w diabetic neuropathic arthropathy 34
H47.3[2,3] [1,2,3,9]	[Drusen, Pseudopapilledema] of optic disc, [rt, lt, bilat, unsp] eye 45
R68.2	Dry mouth, unsp 5, 58
H50.81[1,2]	Duane's synd, [rt, lt] eye 46
K26.9	Duodenal ulcer, unsp as acute or chr, w/o hemor or perf 115
K29.81	Duodenitis with bleeding 115
K29.[8,9]0	[Duodenitis, Unsp gastroduodenitis] w/o bleeding 116
Q43.4	Duplication of intestine 117
G96.11	Dural tear 283, 367
K57.41	Dvtrcli of both sm and lg int w perf and abscess w bleed 115
K57.40	Dvtrcli of both sm and lg int w perf and abscs w/o bleed 116
K57.81	Dvtrcli of intest, part unsp, w perf and abscess w bleeding 115
K57.80	Dvtrcli of intest, part unsp, w perf and abscess w/o bleed 116
K57.21	Dvtrcli of lg int w perforation and abscess w bleeding 115
K57.20	Dvtrcli of lg int w perforation and abscess w/o bleeding 116
K57.01	Dvtrcli of sm int w perforation and abscess w bleeding 115
K57.00	Dvtrcli of sm int w perforation and abscess w/o bleeding 116
R93.9	Dx imaging inconclusive d/t excess body fat of patient 386
E07.1	Dyshormogenetic goiter 247
K22.4	Dyskinesia of esophagus 116
R48.0	Dyslexia and alexia 311
N94.6	Dysmenorrhea, unsp 270
N94.1	Dyspareunia 270
F52.6	Dyspareunia not d/t a substance or known physiol cond 311
N87*	Dysplasia of cervix uteri 265, 270
N42.3	Dysplasia of prostate 261
R06.0*	Dyspnea 69
F34.1	Dysthymic d/o 310
G24.9	Dystonia, unsp 38
K62.9	Dz of anus and rectum, unsp 117
N75*	Dz of Bartholin's gland 265
N75.9	Dz of Bartholin's gland, unsp 269
D75.9	Dz of bld and bld-forming organs, unsp 294
J98.0*	Dz of bronchus, NEC 4, 69
I78.9	Dz of capillaries, unsp 100
K92.9	Dz of digestive sys, unsp 117
K22.9	Dz of esophagus, unsp 116
K03.9	Dz of hard tissues of teeth, unsp 4
K63.9	Dz of intestine, unsp 117
M27.9	Dz of jaws, unsp 4
K13.0	Dz of lips 4
J98.5	Dz of mediastinum, NEC 67, 284
K04*	Dz of pulp and periapical tissues 59
K11.9	Dz of salivary gland, unsp 4
K11*	Dz of salivary glands 58
G95.9	Dz of spinal cord, unsp 38, 439
D73.9	Dz of spleen, unsp 294
K31.9	Dz of stomach and duodenum, unsp 116
O99.[4,5,6,7]2	Dz of the [circulatory, respiratory, digestive, skin and SQ tissue] sys compl childbirth 273
O99.[4,5,6,7]3	Dz of the [circulatory, respiratory, digestive, skin and SQ tissue] sys compl the puerperium 272
O99.419	Dz of the circ sys comp preg, unsp trmstr 281
O99.43	Dz of the circ sys compl the puerperium 274, 276
O99.42	Dz of the circulatory sys compl childbirth 274
O99.41[1,2,3]	Dz of the circulatory sys compl preg, [1st, 2nd, 3rd] trmstr 274, 277, 278
O99.619	Dz of the dgstv sys comp preg, unsp trmstr 281
O99.62	Dz of the digestive sys compl childbirth 275
O99.61[1,2,3]	Dz of the digestive sys compl preg, [1st, 2nd, 3rd] trmstr 277, 278
O99.63	Dz of the digestive sys compl the puerperium 276
O99.350	Dz of the nervous sys comp preg, unsp trmstr 277
O99.354	Dz of the nervous sys compl childbirth 273, 275
O99.35[1,2,3]	Dz of the nervous sys compl preg, [1st, 2nd, 3rd] trmstr 277, 278
O99.355	Dz of the nervous sys compl the puerperium 272, 276
O99.519	Dz of the resp sys comp preg, unsp trmstr 281
O99.53	Dz of the resp sys compl the puerperium 276
O99.52	Dz of the respiratory sys compl childbirth 275
O99.51[1,2,3]	Dz of the respiratory sys compl preg, [1st, 2nd, 3rd] trmstr 277, 278
O99.71[1,2,3]	Dz of the skin and SQ tissue compl preg, [1st, 2nd, 3rd] trmstr 277, 278
O99.719	Dz of the skin, SQ comp preg, unsp trmstr 281
O99.72	Dz of the skin, SQ compl childbirth 275
O99.73	Dz of the skin, SQ compl the puerperium 276
E32.9	Dz of thymus, unsp 294
K14*	Dz of tongue 59
K14.9	Dz of tongue, unsp 4
J39.9	Dz of upr respiratory tract, unsp 4, 57
J38*	Dz of vocal cords and larynx, NEC 58
A50.1	Early congenital syphilis, latent 308
A50.0*	Early congenital syphilis, symptomatic 308
A50.2	Early congenital syphilis, unsp 308
R68.81	Early satiety 385
A51.5	Early syphilis, latent 308
A51.9	Early syphilis, unsp 308
A83.2	Eastern equine encephalitis 10, 15
F50.9	Eating d/o, unsp 311
A98.4	Ebola virus dz 307
L74*	Eccrine sweat d/o 234
B67.90	Echinococcosis, unsp 309
B67.8	Echinococcosis, unsp, of liver 124
B67.2	Echinococcus granulosus infxn of bone 309
B67.0	Echinococcus granulosus infxn of liver 124
B67.1	Echinococcus granulosus infxn of lung 67
B67.32	Echinococcus granulosus infxn, multi sites 309
B67.39	Echinococcus granulosus infxn, oth sites 309
B67.31	Echinococcus granulosus infxn, thyroid gland 247
B67.4	Echinococcus granulosus infxn, unsp 309
B67.5	Echinococcus multilocularis infxn of liver 124
B67.6*	Echinococcus multilocularis infxn, oth and multi sites 309
B67.7	Echinococcus multilocularis infxn, unsp 309
O15.1	Eclampsia in labor 273
O15.0*	Eclampsia in preg 276
O15.0[2,3]	Eclampsia in preg, [2nd, 3rd] trmstr 273, 277
O15.02	Eclampsia in preg, second trmstr 279
O15.03	Eclampsia in preg, third trmstr 279
O15.00	Eclampsia in preg, unsp trmstr 279, 280
O15.2	Eclampsia in the puerperium 272, 273, 275
O15.9	Eclampsia, unsp as to time period 276, 279, 280
Q43.5	Ectopic anus 117
Q53.22	Ectopic perineal testis, bilat 289
Q53.12	Ectopic perineal testis, unilat 289
O00*	Ectopic preg 276
Q53.02	Ectopic testes, bilat 289
Q53.01	Ectopic testis, unilat 289
Q53.00	Ectopic testis, unsp 289
Q33.5	Ectopic tissue in lung 69
H02.1*	Ectropion of eyelid 45
B00.0	Eczema herpeticum 233, 283, 438
J38.4	Edema of larynx 4
H05.2[2,3] [1,2,3,9]	[Edema, Hemor] of [rt, lt, bilat, unsp] orbit 45
R60*	Edema, NEC 385
T70.9XX[A,S]	Effect of air pressure and water pressure, unsp, [init enc, seq] 374
T70.9XXD	Effect of air pressure and water pressure, unsp, subs enc 410
T73.9XX[A,S]	Effect of deprivation, unsp, [init enc, seq] 374
T73.9XXD	Effect of deprivation, unsp, subsq enc 410
T67.9XXD	Effect of heat and light, unsp, subsq enc 409
T75.8[1,2]X[A,S]	Effects of [abnormal gravitation [G] forces, weightlessness], [init enc, seq] 374
T75.8[1,2]XD	Effects of [abnormal gravitation [G] forces, weightlessness], subsq enc 410

T70.4XX[A,S]	Effects of high-pressure fluids, [init enc, seq] **374**	
T70.4XXD	Effects of high-pressure fluids, subsq enc **410**	
M25.4*	Effusion of jt **194**	
Q79.6	Ehlers-Danlos synd **195**	
T75.4XX[A,S]	Electrocution, [init enc, seq] **374**	
T75.4XXD	Electrocution, subsq enc **410**	
R70*	Elev erythro sedim and abnormality of plasma viscosity **385**	
R73*	Elevated bld glucose lvl **247**	
R82.5	Elevated urine levels of drug/meds/biol subst **255**	
K01*	Embedded and impacted teeth **59**	
K01.0	Embedded teeth **4, 289**	
I82.A*	Embolism and thrombosis of axillary vein **100**	
I82.C*	Embolism and thrombosis of int jugular vein **100**	
I82.8*	Embolism and thrombosis of oth spec veins **100**	
I82.3	Embolism and thrombosis of renal vein **256**	
I82.B*	Embolism and thrombosis of subclavian vein **100**	
I82.9*	Embolism and thrombosis of unsp vein **100**	
T82.81[7,8]A	Embolism of [cardiac, vascular] prosthetic devs, implants and grafts, init enc **103**	
T84.8[1,2,3,4,5,6,9]XA	[Embolism, Fibrosis, Hemor, Pain, Stenosis, Thrombosis, Oth spec comp] d/t int orthopedic prosthetic devs, implants and grafts, init enc **184**	
T84.8[1,2,3,4,5,6,9]XS	[Embolism, Fibrosis, Hemor, Pain, Stenosis, Thrombosis, Oth spec comp] d/t int orthopedic prosthetic devs, implants and grafts, seq **375**	
T84.8[1,2,3,4,5,6,9]XD	[Embolism, Fibrosis, Hemor, Pain, Stenosis, Thrombosis, Oth spec comp] d/t int orthopedic prosthetic devs, implants and grafts, subsq enc **411**	
T85.8[1,2,3,4,5,6,9]XA	[Embolism, Fibrosis, Hemor, Pain, Stenosis, Thrombosis, Oth spec comp] d/t int prosthetic devs, implants and grafts, NEC, init enc **368**	
T85.8[1,2,3,4,5,6,9]XS	[Embolism, Fibrosis, Hemor, Pain, Stenosis, Thrombosis, Oth spec comp] d/t int prosthetic devs, implants and grafts, NEC, seq **376**	
T85.8[1,2,3,4,5,6,9]XD	[Embolism, Fibrosis, Hemor, Pain, Stenosis, Thrombosis, Oth spec comp] d/t int prosthetic devs, implants and grafts, NEC, subsq enc **411**	
T82.8[1,2,3,4,5,6,9][7,8]S	[Embolism, Fibrosis, Hemor, Pain, Stenosis, Thrombosis, Oth spec comp] of [cardiac, vascular] prosthetic devs, implants and grafts, seq **375**	
T82.8[1,2,3,4,5,6,9][7,8]D	[Embolism, Fibrosis, Hemor, Pain, Stenosis, Thrombosis, Oth spec comp] of [cardiac, vascular] prosthetic devs, implants and grafts, subsq enc **411**	
T83.8[1,2,3,4,5,6,9]XA	[Embolism, Fibrosis, Hemor, Pain, Stenosis, Thrombosis, Oth spec comp] of genitourinary prosthetic devs, implants and grafts, init enc **256**	
T83.8[1,2,3,4,5,6,9]XS	[Embolism, Fibrosis, Hemor, Pain, Stenosis, Thrombosis, Oth spec comp] of genitourinary prosthetic devs, implants and grafts, seq **375**	
T83.8[1,2,3,4,5,6,9]XD	[Embolism, Fibrosis, Hemor, Pain, Stenosis, Thrombosis, Oth spec comp] of genitourinary prosthetic devs, implants and grafts, subsq enc **411**	
R45.86	Emotional lability **310**	
T81.82XA	Emphysema (SQ) resulting from a procedure, init **368**	
T81.82XS	Emphysema (SQ) resulting from a procedure, seq **375**	
T81.82XD	Emphysema (SQ) resulting from a procedure, subs **410**	
J43*	Emphysema **68**	
Z45.9	Enc for adjust and management of unsp implanted device **412**	
Z45.4*	Enc for adjust and mgmt of implanted nervous sys device **40**	
Z45.3*	Enc for adjust and mgmt of implnt dev of the specl senses **40**	
Z45.0*	Enc for adjustment and management of cardiac device **103**	
Z45.8*	Enc for adjustment and management of implanted devices **412**	
Z45.1	Enc for adjustment and management of inf pump **385, 411**	
Z45.2	Enc for adjustment and management of VAD **385, 411**	
Z02*	Enc for administrative exam **412**	
Z02.82	Enc for adoption services **289**	
Z48.2*	Enc for aftercare following organ transplant **385, 411**	
Z36	Enc for antenatal screening of mother **412**	
Z51.1*	Enc for antineoplastic chemotherapy and immunotherapy **304, 305, 306**	
Z51.0	Enc for antineoplastic radiation therapy **304, 306**	
Z43.7	Enc for attention to artfcl vagina **265, 270**	
Z43.3	Enc for attention to colostomy **118**	
Z43.5	Enc for attention to cystostomy **256**	
Z43.1	Enc for attention to gastrostomy **118**	
Z43.2	Enc for attention to ileostomy **118**	
Z43.8	Enc for attention to oth artfcl openings **412**	
Z43.0	Enc for attention to tracheostomy **70**	
Z43.9	Enc for attention to unsp artfcl Opng **412**	
Z43.4	Enc for attn to oth artif openings of digestive tract **118**	
Z43.6	Enc for attn to oth artif openings of urinary tract **256**	
Z39.1	Enc for care and exam of lactating mother **412**	
Z39.0	Enc for care and exam of mother immediately after del **272, 276**	
Z49*	Enc for care involving renal dialysis **254**	
O82	Enc for cesarean delivery w/o indication **273, 275**	
Z48.03	Enc for change or rmvl of drains **385, 411**	
Z48.00	Enc for change or rmvl of nonsurg wnd dressing **412**	
Z48.01	Enc for change or rmvl of surgical wnd dressing **412**	
Z30.9	Enc for contraceptive management, unsp **412**	
Z41.1	Enc for cosmetic surgery **234**	
Z41.3	Enc for ear piercing **289, 412**	
Z33.2	Enc for elective termination of preg **272, 276**	
Z04.7*	Enc for exam and obs following alleged physical abuse **412**	
Z04.[1,2,3]	Enc for exam and observation following [transport, work, oth] accid **376**	
Z04.4*	Enc for exam and observation following alleged rape **412**	
Z04.8	Enc for exam and observation for oth reasons **412**	
Z04.9	Enc for exam and observation for unsp reason **412**	
Z02.6	Enc for exam for insurance purposes **289**	
Z01.118	Enc for exam of ears and hearing w oth abnormal findings **289**	
Z01.10	Enc for exam of ears and hearing w/o abnormal findings **289**	
Z09	Enc for f/u exam aft tx for cond oth than malig neoplm **412**	
Z46.3	Enc for fit/adjst of dental prosthetic device **412**	
Z46.2	Enc for fit/adjst of dev rel to nrv sys and specl senses **40**	
Z44.3*	Enc for fit/adjst of ext breast prosthesis **412**	
Z44.8	Enc for fit/adjst of ext prosthetic devices **385**	
Z46.59	Enc for fit/adjst of GI appliance and device **118**	
Z46.82	Enc for fit/adjst of non-vascular catheter **385, 411**	
Z46.0	Enc for fit/adjst of spectacles and contact lenses **412**	
Z44.9	Enc for fit/adjst of unsp ext prosthetic device **385**	
Z44.0[0,1,2][1,2,9]	Enc for fitting and adjustment of [unsp, complete, partial][rt, lt, unsp] artfcl arm **184**	
Z44.1[0,1,2][1,2,9]	Enc for fitting and adjustment of [unsp, complete, partial][rt, lt, unsp] artfcl leg **184**	
Z44.2*	Enc for fitting and adjustment of artfcl eye **412**	
Z46.51	Enc for fitting and adjustment of gastric lap band **118**	
Z46.1	Enc for fitting and adjustment of hearing aid **412**	
Z46.81	Enc for fitting and adjustment of insulin pump **412**	
Z46.4	Enc for fitting and adjustment of orthodontic device **412**	
Z46.89	Enc for fitting and adjustment of oth devices **412**	
Z46.9	Enc for fitting and adjustment of unsp device **412**	
Z46.6	Enc for fitting and adjustment of urinary device **256**	
Z08	Enc for follow-up exam after tx for malig neoplasm **304, 305, 306**	
O80	Enc for full-term uncomplicated delivery **273, 275**	
Z30.0*	Enc for general counseling and advice on contraception **412**	
Z31.6*	Enc for general counseling and advice on procreation **412**	
Z00*	Enc for general exam w/o complaint, susp or reprtd dx **412**	
Z04.6	Enc for general psychiatric exam, requested by authority **412**	
Z31.5	Enc for genetic counseling **412**	
Z01.12	Enc for hearing conservation and tx **289**	
Z01.110	Enc for hearing exam following failed hear screening **289**	
Z76.2	Enc for hlth suprvsn and care of healthy infant and child **289**	
Z23	Enc for immunization **289, 412**	
Z03*	Enc for medical obs for susp dz and cond ruled out **412**	
Z69*	Enc for mental health serv for victim and perp of abuse **412**	
Z47.8[1,2]	Enc for orthopedic aftercare following [surgical amp, scoliosis surgery] **184**	
Z02.89	Enc for oth administrative examinations **289**	
Z30.8	Enc for oth contraceptive management **412**	
Z47.89	Enc for oth orthopedic aftercare **184**	
Z41.8	Enc for oth proc for purpose oth than remedy health state **412**	
Z31.8*	Enc for oth procreative management **412**	
Z40.8	Enc for oth prophylactic surgery **412**	
Z01*	Enc for oth sp exam w/o complaint, suspected or reprtd dx **412**	

Code	Description
Z51.8*	Enc for oth spec aftercare 411
Z48.8*	Enc for oth spec postprocedural aftercare 385, 411
Z51.5	Enc for palliative care 412
Z48.1	Enc for planned postprocedural wnd closure 385, 411
Z42*	Enc for plast/recnst surg fol med proc or healed inj 234
Z32*	Enc for preg test and chldbrth and childcare instruction 412
Z41.9	Enc for proc for purpose oth than remedy hlth state, unsp 412
Z31.4*	Enc for procreative investigation and testing 412
Z31.9	Enc for procreative management, unsp 412
Z40.0[0,9]	Enc for prophylactic rmvl of [unsp, oth] organ 412
Z40.01	Enc for prophylactic rmvl of breast 224
Z40.02	Enc for prophylactic rmvl of ovary 265, 270
Z40.9	Enc for prophylactic surgery, unsp 412
Z31.0	Enc for reversal of previous sterilization 261, 265, 270
Z47.2	Enc for rmvl of int fix device 184
Z48.02	Enc for rmvl of sutures 412
Z41.2	Enc for routine and ritual male circumcision 261, 289
Z00.121	Enc for routine child health exam w abnormal findings 289
Z00.129	Enc for routine child health exam w/o abnormal findings 289
Z39.2	Enc for routine postpartum follow-up 412
Z11*	Enc for screening for infec/parastc dz 412
Z12*	Enc for screening for malig neoplasms 412
Z13*	Enc for screening for oth dz and d/o 412
Z13.228	Enc for screening for oth metabolic d/o 289
Z30.2	Enc for sterilization 261, 265, 270
Z34*	Enc for supervision of normal preg 412
Z30.4*	Enc for surveillance of contraceptives 412
Z51.81	Enc for therapeutic drug lvl monitoring 385
G05.3	Encephalitis and encephalomyelitis in dz classd elsw 11, 15
G04.9*	Encephalitis, myelitis and encephalomyelitis, unsp 11, 15, 41, 439
Q01*	Encephalocele 38, 285
Q78.4	Enchondromatosis 195
F98.1	Encopresis not d/t a substance or known physiol condition 311
G05*	Encphlts, myelitis & encephalomyelitis in dis classd elsw 41
N43.0	Encysted hydrocele 261
N18.6	End stage renal dz 2
O99.280	Endo, nutritional and metab dz comp preg, unsp trmstr 281
I39	Endocarditis and heart valve d/o in dis classd elsw 102, 283
I38	Endocarditis, valve unsp 102, 283
O99.285	Endocrine, nutritional and metabolic dz comp the puerp 272, 276
O99.28[1,2,3]	Endocrine, nutritional and metabolic dzs compl preg, [1st, 2nd, 3rd] trmstr 277, 278
N80.6	Endometriosis in cutaneous scar 234
N80.[0,1,2,3,4]	Endometriosis of [uterus, ovary, fallopian tube, pelvic peritoneum, rectovaginal septum and vagina] 270
N80.2	Endometriosis of fallopian tube 265
N80.5	Endometriosis of intestine 116
N80.1	Endometriosis of ovary 265
N80.3	Endometriosis of pelvic peritoneum 265
N80.4	Endometriosis of rectovaginal septum and vagina 265
N80.0	Endometriosis of uterus 265
N80.9	Endometriosis, unsp 265, 270
O86.12	Endometritis following delivery 274
M27.6*	Endosseous dental implant failure 4
R59.9	Enlarged lymph nodes, unsp 294
N40*	Enlarged prostate 260
H05.4*	Enophthalmos 45
B80	Enterobiasis 116
M07*	Enteropathic arthropathies 166
K63.4	Enteroptosis 117
A85.0	Enteroviral encephalitis 438
A88.0	Enteroviral exanthematous fever [Boston exanthem] 34
B08.5	Enteroviral vesicular pharyngitis 2, 57
B08.4	Enteroviral vesicular stomatitis with exanthem 307
M76*	Enthesopathies, lwr limb, excluding foot 167
M77.9	Enthesopathy, unsp 167
H02.0*	Entropion and trichiasis of eyelid 45
F98.0	Enuresis not d/t a substance or known physiol condition 311
D72.1	Eosinophilia 294
L98.3	Eosinophilic cellulitis [Wells] 206, 224, 284

Code	Description
P12.2	Epicranial subaponeurotic hemor d/t birth inj 282
B33.0	Epidemic myalgia 68
A88.1	Epidemic vertigo 38
Q81*	Epidermolysis bullosa 234
Q81.2	Epidermolysis bullosa dystrophica 289
Q81.1	Epidermolysis bullosa letalis 289
Q81.0	Epidermolysis bullosa simplex 289
Q81.9	Epidermolysis bullosa, unsp 289
S06.4X1A	Epidural hemor w LOC of 30 min or less, init 37
S06.4X2A	Epidural hemor w/ LOC of 31-59 min, init 37
S06.4X[5,6]A	Epidural hemor w/ LOC > 24 hrs [w/ return to pre-existing conscious lvl, w/o return to pre-existing conscious lvl w/ patient surviving], init enc 36, 418, 431
S06.4X[5,6]S	Epidural hemor w/ LOC of [> 24 hrs w/ return to pre-existing conscious lvl, > 24 hrs w/o return to pre-existing conscious lvl w/ patient surviving], seq 40
S06.4X[5,6]D	Epidural hemor w/ LOC of [> 24 hrs w/ return to pre-existing conscious lvl, > 24 hrs w/o return to pre-existing conscious lvl w/ patient surviving], subsq enc 387
S06.4X[3,4,5,6]A	Epidural hemor w/ LOC of [1 hr to 5 hrs 59 min, 6 hrs to 24 hrs, > 24 hrs w/ return to pre-existing conscious lvl, > 24 hrs w/o return to pre-existing conscious lvl pt surviving], init enc 35
S06.4X[1,2,3,4]A	Epidural hemor w/ LOC of [30 min or less, 31 min to 59 min, 1 hr to 5 hrs 59 min, 6 hrs to 24 hrs], init enc 36, 418, 431
S06.4X[1,2,3,4]S	Epidural hemor w/ LOC of [30 min or less, 31-59 min, 1 hr to 5 hrs 59 min, 6 hrs to 24 hrs], seq 39
S06.4X[1,2,3,4]D	Epidural hemor w/ LOC of [30 min or less, 31-59 min, 1 hr to 5 hrs 59 min, 6 hrs to 24 hrs], subsq enc 387
S06.4X[7,8,9]A	Epidural hemor w/ LOC of [any dur w/ death d/t brain inj prior to regain cnscness, any dur w/ death d/t oth cause prior to regain cnscness, unsp dur], init enc 35, 37, 418, 431
S06.4X[7,8,9]S	Epidural hemor w/ LOC of [any dur w/ death d/t brain inj prior to regain cnscness, any dur w/ death d/t oth cause prior to regain cnscness, unsp dur], seq 40
S06.4X[7,8,9]D	Epidural hemor w/ LOC of [any dur w/ death d/t brain inj prior to regain cnscness, any dur w/ death d/t oth cause prior to regain cnscness, unsp dur], subsq enc 387
S06.4X0A	Epidural hemor w/o LOC, init enc 36, 37, 418, 431
S06.4X0D	Epidural hemor w/o LOC, subs enc 387
S06.4X0S	Epidural hemor without LOC, seq 39
G40*	Epilepsy and recurrent seizures 41
H04.2*	Epiphora 45
Q64.0	Epispadias 261
R04.0	Epistaxis 57
P14.0	Erb's paralysis d/t birth inj 288
N86	Erosion and ectropion of cervix uteri 265, 270
K03.2	Erosion of teeth 4
T83.7[1,2][1,8]S	[Erosion, Exposure] of [implanted vaginal mesh, implanted mesh] and oth prosthetic materials to surrounding organ or tissue, seq 375
T83.7[1,2][1,8]D	[Erosion, Exposure] of [implanted vaginal mesh, implanted mesh] and oth prosthetic materials to surrounding organ or tissue, subsq enc 411
T83.7[1,2]1A	[Erosion, Exposure] of implanted vaginal mesh and oth prosthetic materials to surrounding organ or tissue, init enc 265, 270
T83.7[1,2]8A	[Erosion, Exposure] of oth implanted mesh and oth prosthetic materials to surrounding organ or tissue, init enc 256
A46	Erysipelas 224
A26.9	Erysipeloid, unsp 308
A26.7	Erysipelothrix sepsis 309
L53.1	Erythema annulare centrifugum 223, 284
L54	Erythema in dz classified elsw 234
B08.3	Erythema infectiosum [fifth dz] 307
L53.2	Erythema marginatum 223, 284
L51*	Erythema multiforme 223
L52	Erythema nodosum 223
L53.9	Erythematous condition, unsp 234
L08.1	Erythrasma 233, 439
K22.2	Esophageal obstruction 116
I85.0*	Esophageal varices 114
K20*	Esophagitis 116
H50.0*	Esotropia 46
D47.3	Essential (hemorrhagic) thrombocythemia 294

Code	Description
T88.4XXA	Failed or difficult intubation, init enc 368
T88.4XXS	Failed or difficult intubation, seq 376
T88.4XXD	Failed or difficult intubation, subsq enc 411
O66.40	Failed trial of labor, unsp 278, 280
P92.6	Failure to thrive in newborn 246
O47*	False labor 276
Z82*	Fam hx of certain disabil & chr dis (leading to disablement) 413
G90.1	Familial dysautonomia [Riley-Day] 38, 283
D75.0	Familial erythrocytosis 294
Z83.3	Family history of diabetes mellitus 289
Z83.49	Family history of endo, nutritional and metabolic dz 289
Z82.0	Family history of epilepsy and oth dis of the nervous sys 289
Z81*	Family history of mental and behavioral d/o 413
Z84*	Family history of oth conditions 413
Z83.1	Family history of oth infectious and parasitic dz 289
Z81.8	Family history of oth mental and behaval d/o 289
Z83*	Family history of oth specific d/o 413
Z80*	Family history of primary malig neoplasm 413
Z82.49	Family hx of ischem heart dis and oth dis of the circ sys 289
A84.0	Far Eastern tick-borne encephalitis 10, 15
B66.3	Fascioliasis 124
B66.5	Fasciolopsiasis 124
T79.1XXA	Fat embolism (traum), init enc 66, 287, 430
A81.83	Fatal familial insomnia 438
M48.4[2,3]X[D,G]	Fatigue fx of vertebra, [cervical, cervicothoracic] rgn, subsq enc for fx w/ [routine, delayed] healing 167
M48.4[6,7]X[D,G]	Fatigue fx of vertebra, [lumbar, lumbosacral] rgn, subsq enc for fx w/ [routine, delayed] healing 167
M48.4[4,5]X[D,G]	Fatigue fx of vertebra, [thoracic, thoracolumbar] rgn, subsq enc for fx w/ [routine, delayed] healing 167
M48.4[0,1,2,3,4, 5,6,7,8]XA	Fatigue fx of vertebra, [unsp, occipito-atlanto-axial, cervical, cervicothoracic, thoracic, thoraccolumbar, lumbar, lumbosacral, sacral and sacrococcygeal] rgn, init enc for fx 163
M48.4[0,1,2,3,4, 5,6,7,8]XS	Fatigue fx of vertebra, [unsp, occipito-atlanto-axial, cervical, cervicothoracic, thoracic, thoracolumbar, lumbar, lumbosacral, sacral and sacrococcygeal] rgn, seq of fx 165
M48.41X[D,G]	Fatigue fx of vertebra, occipito-atlanto-axial rgn, subsq enc for fx w/ [routine, delayed] healing 167
M48.48X[D,G]	Fatigue fx of vertebra, sacral and sacrococcygeal rgn, subsq enc for fx w/ [routine, delayed] healing 167
M48.40X[D,G]	Fatigue fx of vertebra, site unsp, subsq enc for fx w/ [routine, delayed] healing 167
K76.0	Fatty (change of) liver, NEC 124
M60.2*	FB granuloma of soft tissue, NEC 167
L92.3	FB granuloma of the skin and SQ tissue 234
T15.[0,1,8,9] [0,1,2]XD	FB in [cornea, conjunctival sac, oth and multi parts of ext eye, ext eye part unsp], [unsp, rt, lt] eye, subsq enc 400
T17.[0,1]XXS	FB in [nasal sinus, nostril], seq 361
T17.[0,1]XXD	FB in [nasal sinus, nostril], subsq enc 400
T16.[1,2,9]XXS	FB in [rt, lt, unsp] ear, seq 361
T16.[1,2,9]XXD	FB in [rt, lt, unsp] ear, subsq enc 400
T18.[2,3,4,5,8,9] XXS	FB in [stomach, sm intestine, colon, anus and rectum, oth parts of alimentary tract, alimentary tract part unsp], seq 361
T18.[2,3,4,5,8,9] XXD	FB in [stomach, sm intestine, colon, anus and rectum, oth parts of alimentary tract, alimentary tract part unsp], subsq enc 400
T18.[2,3,4,5,8,9] XXA	FB in [stomach, sm intestine, colon, anus and rectum, oth parts of alimentary tract, unsp part of alimentary tract], init enc 118
T19.[0,1,2,3,4, 8,9]XXS	FB in [urethra, bladder, vulva and vagina, uterus, penis, oth parts of genitourinary tract, genitourinary tract part unsp], seq 361
T19.[0,1,2,3,4, 8,9]XXD	FB in [urethra, bladder, vulva and vagina, uterus, penis, oth parts of genitourinary tract, genitourinary tract part unsp], subsq enc 400
T19.1XXA	FB in bladder, init enc 256
T15.1[0,1,2]XA	FB in conjunctival sac, [unsp, rt, lt] eye, init enc 47
T15.1[0,1,2]XS	FB in conjunctival sac, [unsp, rt, lt] eye, seq 361
T15.0[0,1,2]XA	FB in cornea, [unsp, rt, lt] eye, init enc 47
T15.0[0,1,2]XS	FB in cornea, [unsp, rt, lt] eye, seq 361
T16.9XXA	FB in ear, unsp ear, init enc 58
T19.9XXA	FB in genitourinary tract, part unsp, init enc 256
T16.2XXA	FB in lt ear, init enc 58
T18.0XXA	FB in mouth, init enc 6, 59
T18.0XXS	FB in mouth, seq 361

Code	Description
T18.0XXD	FB in mouth, subsq enc 400
T17.0XXA	FB in nasal sinus, init enc 58
T17.1XXA	FB in nostril, init enc 58
T15.8[0,1,2]XA	FB in oth and multi parts of ext eye, [unsp, rt, lt] eye, init enc 47
T15.8[0,1,2]XS	FB in oth and multi parts of ext eye, [unsp, rt, lt] eye, seq 361
T19.8XXA	FB in oth prt genitourinary tract, init enc 256
T19.4XXA	FB in penis, init enc 261
T16.1XXA	FB in rt ear, init enc 58
T19.0XXA	FB in urethra, init enc 256
T19.3XXA	FB in uterus, init enc 265, 270
T19.2XXA	FB in vulva and vagina, init enc 265, 270
T15.9[0,1,2]XA	FB on ext eye, part unsp, [unsp, rt, lt] eye, init enc 47
T15.9[0,1,2]XS	FB on ext eye, part unsp, [unsp, rt, lt] eye, seq 361
L98.2	Febrile neutrophilic dermatosis [Sweet] 234
R15*	Fecal incontinence 116
P92.9	Feeding problem of newborn, unsp 289
R39.14	Feeling of incomplete bladder emptying 285
M05.0*	Felty's synd 164
N73.3	Female acute pelvic peritonitis 269
N73.4	Female chr pelvic peritonitis 269
N81*	Female genital prolapse 265, 270
N82.9	Female genital tract fistula, unsp 265, 270
N82.5	Female genital tract-skin fistulae 265, 270
N97*	Female infertility 265, 270
N74	Female pelvic inflam d/o in dz classd elsw 264, 269
N73.9	Female pelvic inflam dz, unsp 269
N73.6	Female pelvic peritoneal adhesions (postinfective) 270
N73.5	Female pelvic peritonitis, unsp 269
Q56.2	Female pseudohermaphroditism, NEC 265, 270
K41*	Femor hernia 117
O36.82[1,2,3] [0,1,2,3,4,5,9]	Fetal anemia and thrombocytopenia, [1st, 2nd, 3rd] trmstr, fetus [N/A or unsp, 1, 2, 3, 4, 5, oth] 278, 279
O43.019	Fetomaternal placental transfusion synd, unsp trmstr 281
O43.0[1,2][1,2,3]	[Fetomaternal, Fetus-to-fetus] placental transfusion synd, [1st, 2nd, 3rd] trmstr 278, 280
O43.029	Fetus-to-fetus placental transfusion synd, unsp trmstr 281
R50*	Fever of oth and unknown origin 307
M72*	Fibroblastic d/o 167
M79.7	Fibromyalgia 167
T82.82[7,8]A	Fibrosis of [cardiac, vascular] prosthetic devs, implants and grafts, init enc 103
J94.1	Fibrothorax 68
M85.0*	Fibrous dysplasia (monostotic) 167
B74*	Filariasis 309
R78.7*	Finding of abnormal lvl of heavy metals in bld 385
R78.2	Finding of cocaine in bld 385
R78.3	Finding of hallucinogen in bld 385
R78.1	Finding of opiate drug in bld 385
R78.4	Finding of oth drugs of addictive potential in bld 385
R78.5	Finding of oth psychotropic drug in bld 385
R78.89	Finding of oth substances, not normally found in bld 385
R78.6	Finding of steroid agent in bld 385
R78.9	Finding of unsp substance, not normally found in bld 385
K60*	Fissure and fistula of anal and rectal regions 117
K63.2	Fistula of intestine 117
M25.1*	Fistula of jt 167
K11.4	Fistula of salivary gland 4
K31.6	Fistula of stomach and duodenum 116
N82.3	Fistula of vagina to large intestine 117, 285
N82.2	Fistula of vagina to sm intestine 117, 285
N31.2	Flaccid neuropathic bladder, NEC 285
S22.5XX[A,B]	Flail chest, init enc for [clsd, opn] fx 67, 420, 432
S22.5XXS	Flail chest, seq 166
S22.5XX[D,G]	Flail chest, subsq enc for fx w/ [routine, delayed] healing 170
S22.5XXK	Flail chest, subsq enc for fx with nonu 196
M25.2*	Flail jt 194
M21.4[0,1,2]	Flat foot (pes planus) (acquired), [unsp, rt, lt] foot 193
M40.3*	Flatback synd 125
R14*	Flatulence and related conditions 116

Code	Description
M21.2[1,2,3,4,5,6,7][1,2,9]	Flexion deformity, [rt, lt, unsp] [shldr, elbow, wrist, finger jts, hip, knee, ankle and toes] 193
M21.20	Flexion deformity, unsp site 193
J09.X1	Flu d/t ident novel flu A virus w pneumonia 439
J09.X[3,9]	Flu d/t identified novel flu A virus w/ [gastrointestinal, oth] manifestations 308
J09.X[1,2]	Flu d/t identified novel flu A virus w/ [pneumonia, oth respiratory manifestations] 68, 284
J10.2	Flu d/t oth ident flu virus w GI manifest 308
J10.8*	Flu d/t oth ident flu virus w oth manifest 308
J10.08	Flu d/t oth ident flu virus w oth pneumonia 66, 68, 284, 439
J10.1	Flu d/t oth ident flu virus w oth resp manifest 68, 284
J10.01	Flu d/t oth ident flu virus w same oth ident flu virus pn 66, 68
J10.00	Flu d/t oth ident flu virus w unsp type of pneumonia 66, 68
J11.2	Flu d/t unidentified flu virus w GI manifest 308
J11.8*	Flu d/t unidentified flu virus w oth manifest 308
J11.1	Flu d/t unidentified flu virus w oth resp manifest 57
J11.08	Flu d/t unidentified flu virus w spec pneumonia 66
J11.00	Flu d/t unidentified flu virus w unsp type of pneumonia 66
J11.0*	Flu d/t unidentified flu virus with pneumonia 68
B66.9	Fluke infxn, unsp 309
R23.2	Flushing 385
D52*	Folate deficiency anemia 293
C82.21	Foliclar lymph grade III, unsp, nodes of head, face, and nk 3
C82.31	Foliclar lymphoma grade IIIa, nodes of head, face, and neck 3
C82.41	Foliclar lymphoma grade IIIb, nodes of head, face, and neck 3
L72*	Follicular cysts of skin and SQ tissue 234
C82*	Follicular lymphoma 295, 303, 305
C82.01	Follicular lymphoma grade I, nodes of head, face, and neck 3
C82.11	Follicular lymphoma grade II, nodes of head, face, and neck 3
C82.91	Follicular lymphoma, unsp, nodes of head, face, and neck 3
T17.52[0,8]A	Food in bronchus causing [asphyxiation, oth inj], init enc 69
T18.12[0,8]A	Food in esophagus causing [compression of trachea, oth inj], init enc 118
T17.32[0,8]A	Food in larynx causing [asphyxiation, oth inj], init enc 58
T17.320A	Food in larynx causing asphyxiation, init enc 6
T17.328A	Food in larynx causing oth inj, init enc 6
T17.82[0,8]A	Food in oth parts of respiratory tract causing [asphyxiation, oth inj], init enc 70
T17.22[0,8]A	Food in pharynx causing [asphyxiation, oth inj], init enc 58
T17.220A	Food in pharynx causing asphyxiation, init enc 6
T17.228A	Food in pharynx causing oth inj, init enc 6
T17.92[0,8]A	Food in respiratory tract, part unsp causing [asphyxiation, oth inj], init enc 70
T17.42[0,8]A	Food in trachea causing [asphyxiation, oth inj], init enc 69
A05.4	Foodborne Bacillus cereus intoxication 114
A05.2	Foodborne Clostridium perfringens intoxication 114
A05.0	Foodborne staphylococcal intoxication 114
A05.3	Foodborne Vibrio parahaemolyticus intoxication 114
A05.5	Foodborne Vibrio vulnificus intoxication 114
M21.37[1,2,9]	Foot drop, [rt, lt, unsp] foot 193
H47.14[1,2,3,9]	Foster-Kennedy synd, [rt, lt, bilat, unsp] eye 38
S42.24[1,2,9][D,G,S]	Four-part fx of surgical neck of [rt, lt, unsp] humerus, [subsq enc for fx w/ routine healing, subsq enc for fx w/ delayed healing, seq] 171
S42.24[1,2,9][K,P]	Four-part nondisp fx of surgical neck of [rt, lt, unsp] humerus, subsq enc for fx w/ [nonu, malu] 196
H49.1*	Fourth [trochlear] nerve palsy 45
S02.8XXA	Fractures of oth skull and facial bones, init for clos fx 5
S02.8XXB	Fractures of oth skull and facial bones, init for opn fx 5
S02.8XXS	Fractures of oth spec skull and facial bones, seq 39
Q99.2	Fragile X chromosome 310
L81.2	Freckles 289
R41.844	Frontal lobe and executive function deficit 310
T34.09XD	Frostbite w tissue necrosis of oth part of head, subs enc 403
T34.[1,2,3]XX[A,S]	Frostbite w/ tissue necrosis of [neck, thorax, abd wall, lwrback and pelvis], [init enc, seq] 368
T34.0[2,9]X[A,S]	Frostbite w/ tissue necrosis of [nose, oth part of head], [init enc, seq] 368
T34.81[1,2,9][A,S]	Frostbite w/ tissue necrosis of [rt, lt, unsp] ankle, [init enc, seq] 368
T34.81[1,2,9]D	Frostbite w/ tissue necrosis of [rt, lt, unsp] ankle, subsq enc 403

Code	Description
T34.01[1,2,9][A,S]	Frostbite w/ tissue necrosis of [rt, lt, unsp] ear, [init enc, seq] 368
T34.01[1,2,9]D	Frostbite w/ tissue necrosis of [rt, lt, unsp] ear, subsq enc 403
T34.53[1,2,9][A,S]	Frostbite w/ tissue necrosis of [rt, lt, unsp] fingers, [init enc, seq] 368
T34.53[1,2,9]D	Frostbite w/ tissue necrosis of [rt, lt, unsp] fingers, subsq enc 403
T34.82[1,2,9][A,S]	Frostbite w/ tissue necrosis of [rt, lt, unsp] foot, [init enc, seq] 368
T34.82[1,2,9]D	Frostbite w/ tissue necrosis of [rt, lt, unsp] foot, subsq enc 403
T34.52[1,2,9][A,S]	Frostbite w/ tissue necrosis of [rt, lt, unsp] hand, [init enc, seq] 368
T34.52[1,2,9]D	Frostbite w/ tissue necrosis of [rt, lt, unsp] hand, subsq enc 403
T34.83[1,2,9][A,S]	Frostbite w/ tissue necrosis of [rt, lt, unsp] toe(s), [init enc, seq] 368
T34.83[1,2,9]D	Frostbite w/ tissue necrosis of [rt, lt, unsp] toe(s), subsq enc 403
T34.51[1,2,9][A,S]	Frostbite w/ tissue necrosis of [rt, lt, unsp] wrist, [init enc, seq] 368
T34.51[1,2,9]D	Frostbite w/ tissue necrosis of [rt, lt, unsp] wrist, subsq enc 403
T34.9[0,9]X[A,S]	Frostbite w/ tissue necrosis of [unsp, oth] sites, [init enc, seq] 368
T34.9[0,9]XD	Frostbite w/ tissue necrosis of [unsp, oth] sites, subsq enc 403
T34.4[0,1,2]X[A,S]	Frostbite w/ tissue necrosis of [unsp, rt, lt] arm, [init enc, seq] 368
T34.4[0,1,2]XD	Frostbite w/ tissue necrosis of [unsp, rt, lt] arm, subsq enc 403
T34.6[0,1,2]X[A,S]	Frostbite w/ tissue necrosis of [unsp, rt, lt] hip & thigh, [init enc, seq] 368
T34.6[0,1,2]XD	Frostbite w/ tissue necrosis of [unsp, rt, lt] hip & thigh, subsq enc 403
T34.7[0,1,2]X[A,S]	Frostbite w/ tissue necrosis of [unsp, rt, lt] knee and lwr leg, [init enc, seq] 368
T34.7[0,1,2]XD	Frostbite w/ tissue necrosis of [unsp, rt, lt] knee and lwr leg, subsq enc 403
T34.1XXD	Frostbite with tissue necrosis of neck, subsq enc 403
T34.02XD	Frostbite with tissue necrosis of nose, subsq enc 403
T34.2XXD	Frostbite with tissue necrosis of thorax, subs enc 403
T34.3XXD	Frstbte w tissue necros abd wall, low back and pelvis, subs 403
D71	Functional d/o of polymorphonuclear neutrophils 293
K59.1	Functional diarrhea 116
K30	Functional dyspepsia 116
K59.9	Functional intestinal d/o, unsp 116
R53.2	Functional quadriplegia 32
M43.2*	Fusion of spine 164
R68.12	Fussy infant (baby) 385
S02.6[1,2,3,4,5,6,7,9]XK	Fx of [condylar process, subcondylar process, coronoid process, ramus, angle, symphysis, alveolus, oth spec site] of mandible, subsq enc for fx w/ nonu 195
S02.6[1,2,3]XS	Fx of [condylar, subcondylar, coronoid] process of mandible 39
S02.6[1,2,3]X[A,B]	Fx of [condylar, subcondylar, coronoid] process of mandible, init enc for [clsd, opn] fx 417
S02.6[1,2,3]X[D,G]	Fx of [condylar, subcondylar, coronoid] process of mandible, subsq enc for fx w/ [routine, delayed] healing 169
M96.6[6,7][1,2,9]	Fx of [femur, tibia or fibula] following insert of orthopedic implant, jt prosthesis, or bone plate, [rt, lt, unspecified] leg 169
M96.6[2,3][1,2,9]	Fx of [humerus, radius or ulna] following insert of orthopedic implant, jt prosthesis, or bone plate, [rt, lt, unspecified] arm 169
S22.2[1,2]XK	Fx of [manubrium, body of sternum], subsq enc for fx w/ nonu 196
S02.[2,3]XX[D,G]	Fx of [nasal bones, orbital floor], subsq enc for fx w/ [routine, delayed] healing 169
S02.[2,3]XXK	Fx of [nasal bones, orbital floor], subsq enc for fx w/ nonu 195
S12.[8,9]XXD	Fx of [oth parts of neck, neck unsp], subsq enc 169
M96.6[5,9]	Fx of [pelvis, oth bone] following insert of orthopedic implant, jt prosthesis, or bone plate 169
S02.6[4,5,6,7,9]XS	Fx of [ramus, angle, symphysis, alveolus, oth spec site] of mandible 39
S02.6[4,5,6,7,9]X[A,B]	Fx of [ramus, angle, symphysis, alveolus, oth spec site] of mandible, init enc for [clsd, opn] fx 417
S02.6[4,5,6,7,9]X[D,G]	Fx of [ramus, angle, symphysis, alveolus, oth spec site] of mandible, subsq enc for fx w/ [routine, delayed] healing 169
S02.60[0,9]K	Fx of [unsp part of body of mandible, manible unsp], subsq enc for fx w/ nonu 195
S42.9[0,1,2]X[D,G,S]	Fx of [unsp, rt, lt] shldr girdle, part unsp, [subsq enc for fx w/ routine healing, subsq enc for fx w/ delayed healing, seq] 171
S42.9[0,1,2]X[A,B]	Fx of [unsp, rt, lt] shldr girdle, part unsp, init enc for [clsd, opn] fx 185, 422

Code	Description
S42.9[0,1,2]XB	Fx of [unsp, rt, lt] shldr girdle, part unsp, init enc for opn fx **434**
S42.9[0,1,2]X[K,P]	Fx of [unsp, rt, lt] shldr girdle, part unsp, subsq enc for fx w/ [nonu, malu] **197**
S32.01[0,1,2,8,9][A,B,S]	Fx of 1st lumbar vertebra [wedge compression fx, stable burst fx, unstable burst fx, oth fx, unsp fx] [init enc for fx [clsd,opn], seq] **166**
S32.02[0,1,2,8,9][A,B,S]	Fx of 2nd lumbar vertebra [wedge compression fx, stable burst fx, unstable burst fx, oth fx, unsp fx] [init enc for fx [clsd,opn], seq] **166**
S32.03[0,1,2,8,9][A,B,S]	Fx of 3rd lumbar vertebra [wedge compression fx, stable burst fx, unstable burst fx, oth fx, unsp fx] [init enc for fx [clsd,opn], seq] **166**
S32.04[0,1,2,8,9][A,B,S]	Fx of 4th lumbar vertebra [wedge compression fx, stable burst fx, unstable burst fx, oth fx, unsp fx] [init enc for fx [clsd,opn], seq] **166**
S32.05[0,1,2,8,9][A,B,S]	Fx of 5th lumbar vertebra [wedge compression fx, stable burst fx, unstable burst fx, unsp fx] init enc for fx [clsd, opn, seq] **166**
S02.67X[A,B]	Fx of alveolus of mandible, init enc for [clsd, opn] fx **59**
S02.67XA	Fx of alveolus of mandible, init for clos fx **5**
S02.67XB	Fx of alveolus of mandible, init for opn fx **5**
S02.42X[A,B,K]	Fx of alveolus of maxilla, [init enc for clsd fx, init enc for opn fx, subsq enc for fx w/ nonu] **195**
S02.42X[A,B]	Fx of alveolus of maxilla, init enc for [clsd, opn] fx **417**
S02.42XA	Fx of alveolus of maxilla, init for clos fx **5**
S02.42XB	Fx of alveolus of maxilla, init for opn fx **5**
S02.42XS	Fx of alveolus of maxilla, seq **39**
S02.42X[D,G]	Fx of alveolus of maxilla, subsq enc for fx w/ [routine, delayed] healing **169**
S02.65X[A,B]	Fx of angle of mandible, init enc for [clsd, opn] fx **59**
S02.65XB	Fx of angle of mandible, init enc for opn fx **5**
S02.65XA	Fx of angle of mandible, init for clos fx **5**
S22.22X[A,B]	Fx of body of sternum, init enc for [clsd, opn] fx **67**
S22.22XS	Fx of body of sternum, seq **166**
S22.22X[D,G]	Fx of body of sternum, subsq enc for fx w/ [routine, delayed] healing **170**
S22.9XX[A,B,K]	Fx of bony thorax, part unsp, [init enc for clsd fx, init enc for opn fx, subsq enc for fx w/ nonu] **196**
S22.9XX[A,B]	Fx of bony thorax, part unsp, init enc for [clsd, opn] fx **420**
S22.9XXB	Fx of bony thorax, part unsp, init for opn fx **433**
S22.9XXS	Fx of bony thorax, part unsp, seq **166**
S22.9XX[D,G]	Fx of bony thorax, part unsp, subsq enc for fx w/ [routine, delayed] healing **170**
S32.2XX[A,B,S]	Fx of coccyx, [init enc for clsd fx, init enc for opn fx, seq] **166**
S32.2XX[A,B]	Fx of coccyx, init enc for [clsd, opn] fx **421, 433**
S32.2XXK	Fx of coccyx, subs enc for fx with nonu **196**
S32.2XX[D,G]	Fx of coccyx, subsq enc for fx w/ [routine, delayed] healing **170**
S02.61X[A,B]	Fx of condylar process of mandible, init enc for [clsd, opn] fx **59**
S02.61XA	Fx of condylar process of mandible, init for clos fx **5**
S02.61XB	Fx of condylar process of mandible, init for opn fx **5**
S02.63X[A,B]	Fx of coronoid process of mandible, init enc for [clsd, opn] fx **59**
S02.63XA	Fx of coronoid process of mandible, init for clos fx **5**
S02.63XB	Fx of coronoid process of mandible, init for opn fx **5**
S39.840[A,S]	Fx of corpus cavernosum penis, [init enc, seq] **359**
S39.840A	Fx of corpus cavernosum penis, init enc **422**
S39.84[0,8]D	[Fx of corpus cavernosum penis, Oth spec injuries of ext genitals], subsq enc **391**
S02.69XA	Fx of mandible of oth site, init for clos fx **5**
S02.69XB	Fx of mandible of oth site, init for opn fx **5**
S02.69X[A,B]	Fx of mandible of oth spec site, init enc for [clsd, opn] fx **59**
S02.609[A,B]	Fx of mandible, unsp, init enc for [clsd, opn] fx **59, 417**
S02.609A	Fx of mandible, unsp, init enc for clsd fx **5**
S02.609B	Fx of mandible, unsp, init enc for opn fx **5**
S02.609S	Fx of mandible, unsp, seq **39**
S02.609[D,G]	Fx of mandible, unsp, subsq enc for fx w/ [routine, delayed] healing **169**
S22.21X[A,B]	Fx of manubrium, init enc for [clsd, opn] fx **67**
S22.21XS	Fx of manubrium, seq **166**
S22.21X[D,G]	Fx of manubrium, subsq enc for fx w/ [routine, delayed] healing **170**
S02.2XX[A,B]	Fx of nasal bones, init enc for [clsd, opn] fx **58, 417**
S02.2XXS	Fx of nasal bones, seq **39**
S12.9XX[A,S]	Fx of neck, unsp, [init enc for clsd fx, seq] **165**
S12.9XXA	Fx of neck, unsp, init enc **419**
S22.3[1,2,9]X[A,B]	Fx of one rib, [rt, lt, unsp] side, init enc for [clsd, opn] fx **420**
S22.3[1,2,9]XA	Fx of one rib, [rt, lt, unsp] side, init enc for clsd fx **69**
S22.3[1,2,9]XB	Fx of one rib, [rt, lt, unsp] side, init enc for opn fx **67**
S22.3[1,2,9]XS	Fx of one rib, [rt, lt, unsp] side, seq **166**
S22.3[1,2,9]X[D,G]	Fx of one rib, [rt, lt, unsp] side, subsq enc for fx w/ [routine, delayed] healing **170**
S22.3[1,2,9]XK	Fx of one rib, [rt, lt, unsp] side, subsq enc for fx w/ nonu **196**
S02.3X[A,B]	Fx of orbital floor, init enc for [clsd, opn] fx **46, 417**
S02.3XXA	Fx of orbital floor, init enc for clsd fx **5**
S02.3XXB	Fx of orbital floor, init enc for opn fx **5**
S02.3XXS	Fx of orbital floor, seq **39**
S42.19[1,2,9][A,B,K,P]	Fx of oth part of scapula, [rt, lt, unsp] shldr, [init enc for clsd fx, init enc for opn fx, subsq enc for fx w/ nonu, subsq enc for fx w/ malu] **196**
S42.19[1,2,9][D,G,S]	Fx of oth part of scapula, [rt, lt, unsp] shldr, [subsq enc for fx w/ routine healing, subsq enc for fx w/ delayed healing, seq] **171**
S42.19[1,2,9][A,B]	Fx of oth part of scapula, [rt, lt, unsp] shldr, init enc for [clsd, opn] fx **422**
S12.8XXA	Fx of oth parts of neck, init enc **5, 58, 419, 431**
S12.8XXS	Fx of oth parts of neck, seq **165**
S32.89X[A,B]	Fx of oth parts of pelvis, init enc for [clsd, opn] fx **162, 421, 433**
S32.89XS	Fx of oth parts of pelvis, seq **166**
S32.89XK	Fx of oth parts of pelvis, subs for fx w nonu **196**
S32.89X[D,G]	Fx of oth parts of pelvis, subsq enc for fx w/ [routine, delayed] healing **170**
S02.64X[A,B]	Fx of ramus of mandible, init enc for [clsd, opn] fx **59**
S02.64XB	Fx of ramus of mandible, init enc for opn fx **5**
S02.64XA	Fx of ramus of mandible, init for clos fx **5**
S32.1[4,5,6,7,9]X[A,B,S]	Fx of sacrum [type 1, type 2, type 3, type 4, oth] init enc for fx [clsd, opn, seq] **166**
S02.62XA	Fx of subcondylar process of mandible, init **5**
S02.62X[A,B]	Fx of subcondylar process of mandible, init enc for [clsd, opn] fx **59**
S02.62XB	Fx of subcondylar process of mandible, init for opn fx **5**
S32.51[1,2,9]S	Fx of superior rim of [rt, lt, unsp] pubis, seq **166**
S32.51[1,2,9][D,G]	Fx of superior rim of [rt, lt, unsp] pubis, subsq enc for fx w/ [routine, delayed] healing **170**
S32.51[1,2,9]K	Fx of superior rim of [rt, lt, unsp] pubis, subsq enc for fx w/ nonu **196**
S32.51[1,2,9][A,B]	Fx of superior rim of pubis [rt, lt, unsp] init enc for [clsd, opn] fx **162, 421, 433**
S02.66X[A,B]	Fx of symphysis of mandible, init enc for [clsd, opn] fx **59**
S02.66XA	Fx of symphysis of mandible, init for clos fx **5**
S02.66XB	Fx of symphysis of mandible, init for opn fx **5**
S02.5XX[A,B]	Fx of tooth (traum), init enc for [clsd, opn] fx **59, 417**
S02.5XXS	Fx of tooth (Traum), seq **39**
S02.5XXK	Fx of tooth (traum), subs for fx w nonu **195**
S02.5XX[D,G]	Fx of tooth (traum), subsq enc for fx w/ [routine, delayed] healing **169**
S62.10[1,2,9][D,G,S]	Fx of unsp carpal bone, [rt, lt, unsp] wrist, [subsq enc for fx w/ routine healing, subsq enc for fx w/ delayed healing, seq] **174**
S62.10[1,2,9][A,B]	Fx of unsp carpal bone, [rt, lt, unsp] wrist, init enc for [clsd, opn] fx **187, 424**
S62.10[1,2,9][K,P]	Fx of unsp carpal bone, [rt, lt, unsp] wrist, subsq enc for fx w/ [nonu, malu] **199**
S32.00[0,1,2,8,9][A,B,S]	Fx of unsp lumbar vertebra [wedge compression fx, stable burst fx, unstable burst fx, oth fx, unsp fx] [init enc for fx [clsd,opn], seq] **166**
S92.30[1,2,9][K,P]	Fx of unsp metatarsal bone(s) of [rt, lt, unsp] foot, subsq enc for fx w/ [nonu, malu] **204**
S92.30[1,2,9][D,G,S]	Fx of unsp metatarsal bone(s), [rt, lt, unsp] foot, [subsq enc for fx w/ routine healing, subsq enc for fx w/ delayed healing, seq] **183**
S92.30[1,2,9][A,B]	Fx of unsp metatarsal bone(s), [rt, lt, unsp] foot, init enc for [clsd, opn] fx **192, 429**
S42.00[1,2,9][K,P]	Fx of unsp part of [rt, lt, unsp] clavicle, subsq enc for fx w/ [nonu, malu] **196**
S02.600[A,B]	Fx of unsp part of body of mandible, init enc for [clsd, opn] fx **59, 417**
S02.600A	Fx of unsp part of body of mandible, init for clos fx **5**
S02.600B	Fx of unsp part of body of mandible, init for opn fx **5**
S02.600S	Fx of unsp part of body of mandible, seq **39**
S02.600[D,G]	Fx of unsp part of body of mandible, subsq enc for fx w/ [routine, delayed] healing **169**
S42.00[1,2,9][A,B]	Fx of unsp part of clavicle [rt, lt, unsp] init enc for fx [clsd, opn] **184, 422**

Code	Description
S72.00[1,2,9] [D,E,F,G,H,J,S]	Fx of unsp part of neck of [rt, lt, unsp] femur, [subsq enc for clsd fx w/ routine healing, subsq enc for opn fx type I or II w/ routine healing, subsq enc for opn fx type IIIA, IIIB, or IIIC w/ routine healing, subsq enc for clsd fx w/ delayed healing, subsq enc for opn fx type I or II w/ delayed healing, subsq enc for opn fx type IIIA, IIIB, or IIIC w/ delayed healing, seq] 176
S72.00[1,2,9] [A,B,C]	Fx of unsp part of neck of [rt, lt, unsp] femur, init enc for [clsd fx, opn fx type I or II, opn fx type IIIA, IIIB, or IIIC] 162, 286, 426
S72.00[1,2,9] [A,B,C]	Fx of unsp part of neck of [rt, lt, unsp] femur, init enc for [clsd fx, opn fx type I or II, opn fx type IIIA, IIIB, or IIIC] 435
S72.00[1,2,9] [K,M,N,P,Q,R]	Fx of unsp part of neck of [rt, lt, unsp] femur, subsq enc for [clsd fx w/ nonu, opn fx type I or II w/ nonu, opn fx type IIIA, IIIB, or IIIC w/ nonu, clsd fx w/ malu, opn fx type I or II w/ malu, opn fx type IIIA, IIIB, or IIIC w/ malu] 200
S42.10[1,2,9] [D,G,S]	Fx of unsp part of scapula, [rt, lt, unsp] shldr, [subsq enc for fx w/ routine healing, subsq enc for fx w/ delayed healing, seq] 170
S42.10[1,2,9] [A,B]	Fx of unsp part of scapula, [rt, lt, unsp] shldr, init enc for [clsd, opn] fx 184, 422
S42.10[1,2,9] [K,P]	Fx of unsp part of scapula, [rt, lt, unsp] shldr, subsq enc for fx w/ [nonu, malu] 196
S32.9XX[A,B]	Fx of unsp parts of lumbosacral spine and pelvis, init enc for [clsd, opn] fx 162, 421, 433
S32.9XX[D,G]	Fx of unsp parts of lumbosacral spine and pelvis, subsq enc for fx w/ [routine, delayed] healing 170
S62.60[8,9] [D,G,S]	Fx of unsp phalanx of [oth, unsp] finger, [subsq enc for fx w/ routine healing, subsq enc for fx w/ delayed healing, seq] 176
S62.60[8,9][A,B]	Fx of unsp phalanx of [oth, unsp] finger, init enc for [clsd, opn] fx 188
S62.60[8,9][K,P]	Fx of unsp phalanx of [oth, unsp] finger, subsq enc for fx w/ [nonu, malu] 200
S62.60[0,1,2,3,4, 5,6,7,8,9][A,B]	Fx of unsp phalanx of [rt index, lt index, rt mid, lt mid, rt ring, lt ring, rt little, lt little, oth, unsp] finger, init enc for [clsd, opn] fx 425
S62.50[1,2,9] [D,G,S]	Fx of unsp phalanx of [rt, lt, unsp] thumb, [subsq enc for fx w/ routine healing, subsq enc for fx w/ delayed healing, seq] 176
S62.50[1,2,9] [A,B]	Fx of unsp phalanx of [rt, lt, unsp] thumb, init enc for [clsd, opn] fx 188, 425
S62.50[1,2,9] [K,P]	Fx of unsp phalanx of [rt, lt, unsp] thumb, subsq enc for fx w/ [nonu, malu] 200
S62.60[0,1] [D,G,S]	Fx of unsp phalanx of [rt, lt] index finger, [subsq enc for fx w/ routine healing, subsq enc for fx w/ delayed healing, seq] 176
S62.60[0,1][A,B]	Fx of unsp phalanx of [rt, lt] index finger, init enc for [clsd, opn] fx 188
S62.60[0,1][K,P]	Fx of unsp phalanx of [rt, lt] index finger, subsq enc for fx w/ [nonu, malu] 200
S62.60[6,7] [D,G,S]	Fx of unsp phalanx of [rt, lt] little finger, [subsq enc for fx w/ routine healing, subsq enc for fx w/ delayed healing, seq] 176
S62.60[6,7][A,B]	Fx of unsp phalanx of [rt, lt] little finger, init enc for [clsd, opn] fx 188
S62.60[6,7][K,P]	Fx of unsp phalanx of [rt, lt] little finger, subsq enc for fx w/ [nonu, malu] 200
S62.60[2,3] [D,G,S]	Fx of unsp phalanx of [rt, lt] mid finger, [subsq enc for fx w/ routine healing, subsq enc for fx w/ delayed healing, seq] 176
S62.60[2,3][A,B]	Fx of unsp phalanx of [rt, lt] mid finger, init enc for [clsd, opn] fx 188
S62.60[2,3][K,P]	Fx of unsp phalanx of [rt, lt] mid finger, subsq enc for fx w/ [nonu, malu] 200
S62.60[4,5] [D,G,S]	Fx of unsp phalanx of [rt, lt] ring finger, [subsq enc for fx w/ routine healing, subsq enc for fx w/ delayed healing, seq] 176
S62.60[4,5][A,B]	Fx of unsp phalanx of [rt, lt] ring finger, init enc for [clsd, opn] fx 188
S62.60[4,5][K,P]	Fx of unsp phalanx of [rt, lt] ring finger, subsq enc for fx w/ [nonu, malu] 200
S92.20[1,2,9] [D,G,S]	Fx of unsp tarsal bone(s) of [rt, lt, unsp] foot, [subsq enc for fx w/ routine healing, subsq enc for fx w/ delayed healing, seq] 182
S92.20[1,2,9] [A,B]	Fx of unsp tarsal bone(s) of [rt, lt, unsp] foot, init enc for [clsd, opn] fx 192, 429
S92.20[1,2,9] [K,P]	Fx of unsp tarsal bone(s) of [rt, lt, unsp] foot, subsq enc for fx w/ [nonu, malu] 204
S02.0XX[A,B]	Fx of vault of skull, init enc for [clsd, opn] fx 36, 37, 417
S02.0XXS	Fx of vault of skull, seq 39
S02.0XXK	Fx of vault of skull, subs for fx w nonu 195
S02.0XX[D,G]	Fx of vault of skull, subsq enc for fx w/ [routine, delayed] healing 169
S22.24X[A,B]	Fx of xiphoid process, init enc for [clsd, opn] fx 67
S22.24XS	Fx of xiphoid process, seq 166

Code	Description
S22.24XK	Fx of xiphoid process, subs for fx w nonu 196
S22.24X[D,G]	Fx of xiphoid process, subsq enc for fx w/ [routine, delayed] healing 170
S32.9XXK	Fx unsp parts of lumbosacr spin & pelv, 7thK 196
S32.9XXS	Fx unsp parts of lumbosacral spine & pelvis, seq 166
S02.8XX[A,B,K]	Fxs of oth spec skull and facial bones, [init enc for clsd fx, init enc for opn fx, subsq enc for fx w/ nonu] 195
S02.8XX[A,B]	Fxs of oth spec skull and facial bones, init enc for [clsd, opn] fx 417
S02.8XX[D,G]	Fxs of oth spec skull and facial bones, subsq enc for fx w/ [routine, delayed] healing 169
O92.6	Galactorrhea 272, 276
S52.37[1,2,9] [D,E,F,G,H,J,S]	Galeazzi's fx of [rt, lt, unsp] radius, [subsq enc for clsd fx w/ routine healing, subsq enc for opn fx type I or II w/ routine healing, subsq enc for opn fx type I or II w/ routine healing, subsq enc for clsd fx w/ delayed healing, subsq enc for opn fx type I or II w/ delayed healing, subsq enc for opn fx type IIIA, IIIB, or IIIC w/ delayed healing, seq] 173
S52.37[1,2,9] [A,B,C]	Galeazzi's fx of [rt, lt, unsp] radius, init enc for [clsd fx, opn fx type I or II, opn fx type IIIA, IIIB, or IIIC] 186, 423
S52.37[1,2,9] [B,C]	Galeazzi's fx of [rt, lt, unsp] radius, init enc for opn fx type [I or II, IIIA IIIB or IIIC] 434
S52.37[1,2,9] [K,M,N,P,Q,R]	Galeazzi's fx of [rt, lt, unsp] radius, subsq enc for [clsd fx w/ nonu, opn fx type I or II w/ nonu, opn fx type IIIA, IIIB, or IIIC w/ nonu, clsd fx w/ malu, opn fx type I or II w/ malu, opn fx type IIIA, IIIB, or IIIC w/ malu] 198
Z72.6	Gambling and betting 412
A66.5	Gangosa 2, 58
I96	Gangrene, NEC 100, 284
A48.0	Gas gangrene 283, 308
T17.51[0,8]A	Gastric contents in bronchus causing [asphyxiation, oth inj], init enc 69
T18.11[0,8]A	Gastric contents in esophagus causing [compression of trachea, oth inj], init enc 118
T17.31[0,8]A	Gastric contents in larynx causing [asphyxiation, oth inj], init enc 58
T17.310A	Gastric contents in larynx causing asphyxiation, init enc 6
T17.318A	Gastric contents in larynx causing oth inj, init enc 6
T17.81[0,8]A	Gastric contents in oth parts of respiratory tract causing [asphyxiation, oth inj], init enc 70
T17.21[0,8]A	Gastric contents in pharynx causing [asphyxiation, oth inj], init enc 58
T17.210A	Gastric contents in pharynx causing asphyxiation, init 6
T17.218A	Gastric contents in pharynx causing oth inj, init enc 6
T17.91[0,8]A	Gastric contents in respiratory tract, part unsp causing [asphyxiation, oth inj], init enc 70
T17.41[0,8]A	Gastric contents in trachea causing [asphyxiation, oth inj], init enc 69
K31.4	Gastric diverticulum 116
K25.9	Gastric ulcer, unsp as acute or chr, w/o hemor or perf 115
I86.4	Gastric varices 100
K29.71	Gastritis, unsp, with bleeding 115
K22.6	Gastro-esophageal lac-hemor synd 114
K21*	Gastro-esophageal reflux dz 116
K29.91	Gastroduodenitis, unsp, with bleeding 115
K52.0	Gastroenteritis and colitis d/t radiation 117
A22.2	Gastrointestinal anthrax 114
K92.2	Gastrointestinal hemor, unsp 115, 284
K92.81	Gastrointestinal mucositis (ulcerative) 116
A21.3	Gastrointestinal tularemia 114
K28.9	Gastrojejunal ulcer, unsp as acute or chr, w/o hemor or perf 115
K31.84	Gastroparesis 116
Q79.3	Gastroschisis 117, 285
L27.0	Gen skin eruption d/t drugs and meds taken internally 284
F64*	Gender identity d/o 311
A52.17	General paresis 32
K65.0	Generalized (acute) peritonitis 114
H53.48[1,2,3,9]	Generalized contraction of visual field, [rt, lt, bilat, unsp] eye 45
R59.1	Generalized enlarged lymph nodes 294
R61	Generalized hyperhidrosis 294
L40.1	Generalized pustular psoriasis 234
D72.0	Genetic anomalies of leukocytes 293
Z14*	Genetic carrier 412
Z15*	Genetic susceptibility to dz 412

G24.1	Genetic torsion dystonia 32
O22.1[1,2,3]	Genital varices in preg, [1st, 2nd, 3rd] trmstr 277
O22.10	Genital varices in preg, unsp trmstr 280
K14.1	Geographic tongue 4
A81.82	Gerstmann-Straussler-Scheinker synd 438
O13.[1,2,3]	Gestational (preg-induced) hypertension w/o significant proteinuria, [1st, 2nd, 3rd] trmstr 277, 279
O12.[0,1,2][1,2,3]	Gestational [edema, proteinuria, edema w/ proteinuria], [1st, 2nd, 3rd] trmstr 277
O24.42[0,4,9]	Gestational diabetes mellitus in childbirth, [diet, insulin, unsp] controlled 273, 275
O24.41[0,4,9]	Gestational diabetes mellitus in preg, [diet, insulin, unsp] controlled 276, 277
O24.43[0,4,9]	Gestational diabetes mellitus in the puerperium, [diet, insulin, unsp] controlled 272, 275
O12*	Gestational edema and proteinuria w/o hypertension 276
O12.21	Gestational edema with proteinuria, first trmstr 279
O12.22	Gestational edema with proteinuria, second trmstr 279
O12.23	Gestational edema with proteinuria, third trmstr 279
O12.20	Gestational edema with proteinuria, unsp trmstr 279, 280
O12.01	Gestational edema, first trmstr 279
O12.02	Gestational edema, second trmstr 279
O12.03	Gestational edema, third trmstr 279
O12.00	Gestational edema, unsp trmstr 279, 280
O13.9	Gestational hypertension w/o signif proteinuria, unsp trmstr 280
O12.11	Gestational proteinuria, first trmstr 279
O12.12	Gestational proteinuria, second trmstr 279
O12.13	Gestational proteinuria, third trmstr 279
O12.10	Gestational proteinuria, unsp trmstr 279, 280
M31.5	Giant cell arteritis with polymyalgia rheumatica 164
M27.1	Giant cell granuloma, central 4
E80.4	Gilbert synd 124
K06.2	Gingival & edentulous alveolar ridge lesions assoc w trauma 4
K06.1	Gingival enlargement 4
K06.0	Gingival recession 4
K05*	Gingivitis and periodontal dz 59
A24*	Glanders and melioidosis 308
R40.24[1,2,3]	Glasgow coma scale score [13-15, 9-12, 3-8] 412
H42	Glaucoma in dz classified elsw 46
H40.6*	Glaucoma secondary to drugs 46
H40.4*	Glaucoma secondary to eye inflam 46
H40.3*	Glaucoma secondary to eye trauma 46
H40.5*	Glaucoma secondary to oth eye d/o 46
H40.0*	Glaucoma suspect 46
H47.23*	Glaucomatous optic atrophy 46
N08	Glomerular d/o in dz classified elsw 256
K14.0	Glossitis 4
K14.6	Glossodynia 4
E74.0*	Glycogen storage dz 247
R81	Glycosuria 246
E75.0*	GM2 gangliosidosis 32
B83.1	Gnathostomiasis 309
A54.1	Gonocl infxn of lwr GU tract w periureth and acc glnd abcs 261, 264, 269
A54.2[1,4,9]	Gonococcal [infxn of kidney and ureter, female pelvic inflam dz, oth genitourinary infxns] 264, 269
A54.2[1,2,3,9]	Gonococcal [infxn of kidney and ureter, prostatitis, infxn of oth male genital organs, oth genitourinary infxns] 261
A54.0[0,2,3,9]	Gonococcal [infxn of lwr genitourinary tract unsp, vulvovaginitis unsp, cervicitis unsp, infxn of lwr genitourinary tract oth] 264, 269
A54.4[0,2,3,9]	Gonococcal [infxn of musculoskeletal sys unsp, arthritis, osteomyelitis, oth musculoskeletal tissue] 164
A54.82	Gonococcal brain abscess 308
A54.01	Gonococcal cystitis and urethritis, unsp 255
A54.83	Gonococcal heart infxn 103
A54.6	Gonococcal infxn of anus and rectum 116
A54.3*	Gonococcal infxn of eye 45
A54.0[0,9]	Gonococcal infxn of lwr genitourinary tract [unsp, oth] 261
A54.9	Gonococcal infxn, unsp 308
A54.81	Gonococcal meningitis 10, 14, 41
A54.85	Gonococcal peritonitis 114

A54.5	Gonococcal pharyngitis 2, 57
A54.84	Gonococcal pneumonia 308
A54.86	Gonococcal sepsis 309
A54.41	Gonococcal spondylopathy 163
O98.22	Gonorrhea compl childbirth 274
O98.21[1,2,3]	Gonorrhea compl preg, [1st, 2nd, 3rd] trmstr 274, 277
O98.23	Gonorrhea compl the puerperium 274, 276
L94.4	Gottron's papules 234
M10.3*	Gout d/t renal impairment 256
M10.9	Gout, unsp 166
D89.813	Graft-versus-host dz, unsp 293
K13.4	Granuloma and granuloma-like lesions of oral mucosa 4
L92.0	Granuloma annulare 234
L92.2	Granuloma faciale [eosinophilic granuloma of skin] 234
A58	Granuloma inguinale 261, 264, 269
L92.9	Granulomatous d/o of the skin, SQ, unsp 234
K75.3	Granulomatous hepatitis, NEC 284
S42.31[1,2,9] [D,G,S]	Greenstick fx of shaft of [rt, lt, unsp] humerus, [subsq enc for fx w/ routine healing, subsq enc for fx w/ delayed healing, seq] 171
S52.21[1,2,9] [D,G,S]	Greenstick fx of shaft of [rt, lt, unsp] ulna, [subsq enc for fx w/ routine healing, subsq enc for fx w/ delayed healing, seq] 172
S52.21[1,2,9]A	Greenstick fx of shaft of [rt, lt, unsp] ulna, init enc for clsd fx 186, 423
S52.21[1,2,9] [K,P]	Greenstick fx of shaft of [rt, lt, unsp] ulna, subsq enc for fx w/ [nonu, malu] 197
S42.31[1,2,9]A	Greenstick fx of shaft of humerus, [rt, lt, unsp] arm, init enc for clsd fx 185, 422
S42.31[1,2,9] [K,P]	Greenstick fx of shaft of humerus, [rt, lt, unsp] arm, subsq enc for fx w/ [nonu, malu] 197
S52.31[1,2,9] [D,G,S]	Greenstick fx of shaft of radius, [rt, lt, unsp] arm, [subsq enc for fx w/ routine healing, subsq enc for fx w/ delayed healing, seq] 173
S52.31[1,2,9]A	Greenstick fx of shaft of radius, [rt, lt, unsp] arm, init enc for clsd fx 186, 423
S52.31[1,2,9] [K,P]	Greenstick fx of shaft of radius, [rt, lt, unsp] arm, subsq enc for fx w/ [nonu, malu] 198
G61.0	Guillain-Barre synd 41
L40.4	Guttate psoriasis 223
L67*	Hair color and hair shaft abnormalities 234
C91.4*	Hairy cell leukemia 303, 305
C91.40	Hairy cell leukemia not having achieved remission 3
K13.3	Hairy leukoplakia 4
R19.6	Halitosis 58
R44.3	Hallucinations, unsp 310
M20.[1,2,3] [0,1,2]	Hallux [valgus (acquired), rigidus, varus (acquired)], [unsp, rt, lt] foot 193
B33.4	Hantavirus (cardio)-pulmn synd [HPS] [HCPS] 307
R51	Headache 41
Z00.111	Health exam for newborn 8 to 28 days old 289
Z00.110	Health exam for newborn under 8 days old 289
Z94.3	Heart and lungs transplant status 103
I51.9	Heart dz, unsp 102
I50*	Heart failure 72, 99, 283
Z94.1	Heart transplant status 103
R12	Heartburn 116
T67.[0,1,2,3,4, 5,6,7]XX[A,S]	Heat [stroke and sunstroke, syncope, cramp, exhaustion anhydrotic, exhaustion d/t salt depletion, exhaustion unsp, fatigue transient, edema], [init enc, seq] 374
T67.[0,1,2,3,4, 5,6,7]XXD	Heat [stroke and sunstroke, syncope, cramp, exhaustion anhydrotic, exhaustion d/t salt depletion, exhaustion unsp, fatigue transient, edema], subsq enc 409
O14.22	HELLP synd (HELLP), second trmstr 279
O14.23	HELLP synd (HELLP), third trmstr 279
O14.20	HELLP synd (HELLP), unsp trmstr 279, 280
O14.2*	HELLP synd 276
O14.2[2,3]	HELLP synd, [2nd, 3rd] trmstr 277
B83.9	Helminthiasis, unsp 309
D18.0[0,9]	Hemangioma [unsp, oth] site 103
D18.03	Hemangioma of intra-abd structures 116
D18.02	Hemangioma of intracranial structures 38
D18.09	Hemangioma of oth sites 3
D18.01	Hemangioma of skin and SQ tissue 3, 233
D18.00	Hemangioma unsp site 3

Code	Description
M25.0*	Hemarthrosis 167
K92.0	Hematemesis 115, 284
N83.7	Hematoma of broad lgmt 285
O90.2	Hematoma of obstetric wnd 274
R36.1	Hematospermia 261
R31*	Hematuria 255, 285
G81*	Hemiplegia and hemiparesis 32
R82.3	Hemoglobinuria 255
D59.6	Hemoglobinuria d/t hemolysis from oth ext causes 283, 293
P55.9	Hemolytic dz of newborn, unsp 282
T80.919A	Hemolytic transfs react, unsp incompat, unsp ac/delay, init 293
D59.3	Hemolytic-uremic synd 283, 293
I23.0	Hemopericardium as current comp following AMI 103
I31.2	Hemopericardium, NEC 283
K66.1	Hemoperitoneum 284
D76.1	Hemophagocytic lymphohistiocytosis 294
D76.2	Hemophagocytic synd, infxn-associated 294
M36.2	Hemophilic arthropathy 167
G00.0	Hemophilus meningitis 11, 15
R04.2	Hemoptysis 69
R04.8*	Hemor from oth sites in respiratory passages 69
R04.9	Hemor from respiratory passages, unsp 69
R04.1	Hemor from throat 5, 58
O20*	Hemor in early preg 276
T82.83[7,8]A	Hemor of [cardiac, vascular] prosthetic devs, implants and grafts, init enc 103
K62.5	Hemor of anus and rectum 115, 284
N99.5[2,3][0,1,2,8]	[Hemor, Infxn, Malfunction, Oth comp] of [oth ext, oth] stoma of urinary tract 285
R58	Hemor, NEC 103, 285
D68.32	Hemorrhagic d/o d/t extrinsic circulating anticoagulants 294
P53	Hemorrhagic dz of newborn 282
A98.5	Hemorrhagic fever with renal synd 255
K64*	Hemorrhoids and perianal venous thrombosis 117
O22.4[1,2,3]	Hemorrhoids in preg, [1st, 2nd, 3rd] trmstr 277
O22.40	Hemorrhoids in preg, unsp trmstr 280
J94.2	Hemothorax 68, 284
D75.82	Heparin induced thrombocytopenia (HIT) 283, 294
K72*	Hepatic failure, NEC 124
K72.9*	Hepatic failure, unsp 284
K74.0	Hepatic fibrosis 123
K74.2	Hepatic fibrosis with hepatic sclerosis 124
K74.1	Hepatic sclerosis 124
K76.5	Hepatic veno-occlusive dz 124
R16.2	Hepatomegaly with splenomegaly, NEC 124
R16.0	Hepatomegaly, NEC 124
K76.81	Hepatopulmonary synd 69
K76.7	Hepatorenal synd 124, 284
G60.9	Hereditary and idiopathic neuropathy, unsp 34
G11*	Hereditary ataxia 32
D68.2	Hereditary deficiency of oth clotting factors 294
K00.5	Hereditary disturbances in tooth structure, NEC 4
E80.0	Hereditary erythropoietic porphyria 247
D67	Hereditary factor IX deficiency 294
D66	Hereditary factor VIII deficiency 294
D68.1	Hereditary factor XI deficiency 294
I78.0	Hereditary hemorrhagic telangiectasia 100
D80.0	Hereditary hypogammaglobulinemia 294
G60.0	Hereditary motor and sensory neuropathy 34
N07*	Hereditary nephropathy, NEC 256
H47.22	Hereditary optic atrophy 45
Q56.0	Hermaphroditism, NEC 261, 265, 270
O26.4*	Herpes gestationis 276
O26.4[1,2,3]	Herpes gestationis, [1st, 2nd, 3rd] trmstr 277
O26.40	Herpes gestationis, unsp trmstr 280
B00.82	Herpes simplex myelitis 10, 15, 41
A60.0[0,3,4,9]	Herpesviral [infxn of urogenital sys unsp, cervicitis, vulvovaginitis, infxn of oth urogenital tract] 264, 269
B00.4	Herpesviral encephalitis 10, 15, 41, 283, 438
B00.2	Herpesviral gingivostomatitis and pharyngotonsillitis 2, 59, 283, 438
B00.81	Herpesviral hepatitis 116, 283, 438
A60.0[0,1,4,9]	Herpesviral infxn of [unsp urogenital sys, penis, vulvovaginitis, oth urogenital tract] 438
A60.0[0,1,2,9]	Herpesviral infxn of [urogenital sys unsp, penis, oth male genital organs, oth urogenital tract] 261
A60.1	Herpesviral infxn of perianal skin and rectum 261, 264, 269, 438
B00.9	Herpesviral infxn, unsp 233, 438
B00.3	Herpesviral meningitis 10, 15, 34, 283, 438
B00.5*	Herpesviral ocular dz 45, 283, 438
B00.1	Herpesviral vesicular dermatitis 58, 283, 438
H53.47	Heteronymous bilat field defects 45
H50.5*	Heterophoria 46
R06.6	Hiccough 69
G47.32	High altitude periodic breathing 69
Z72.5*	High risk sexual behav 412
Q43.1	Hirschsprung's dz 117
D47.0	Histiocytic and mast cell tumors of uncertain behav 295, 303, 305
C96.A	Histiocytic sarcoma 3, 295, 303, 305
B39*	Histoplasmosis 438
B39.4	Histoplasmosis capsulati, unsp 308
B39.5	Histoplasmosis duboisii 308
B39.9	Histoplasmosis, unsp 308
C81*	Hodgkin lymphoma 295, 303, 305
C81.91	Hodgkin lymphoma, unsp, lymph nodes of head, face, and neck 3
R45.850	Homicidal ideations 412
H53.46[1,2,9]	Homonymous bilat field defects, [rt, lt, unsp] side 45
B76*	Hookworm dz 114
H00*	Hordeolum and chalazion 45
Z79.890	Hormone replace therapy (postmenopausal) 413
G90.2	Horner's synd 34
R45.5	Hostility 310
K31.2	Hourglass stricture and stenosis of stomach 116
O98.71[1,2,3]	Human immunodef virus (HIV) dz compl preg, [1st, 2nd, 3rd] trmstr 274, 277
B20	Human immunodef virus [HIV] dz 438, 438, 439
O98.72	Human immunodef virus dz compl childbirth 274
O98.73	Human immunodef virus dz compl the puerperium 276
J12.3	Human metapneumovirus pneumonia 439
E83.81	Hungry bone synd 246
G10	Huntington's dz 32
O01*	Hydatidiform mole 277, 279
N43.3	Hydrocele, unsp 261
G91*	Hydrocephalus 32
N13.1	Hydronephrosis w ureteral stricture, NEC 255, 285
N13.2	Hydronephrosis with renal & ureteral calculous obstruction 255, 285
P56*	Hydrops fetalis d/t hemolytic dz 282
P83.2	Hydrops fetalis not d/t hemolytic dz 282
N13.4	Hydroureter 255, 285
I12.0	Hyp chr kidney dz w stage 5 chr kidney dz or ESRD 2
I13.0	Hyp hrt & chr kdny dis w hrt fail and stg 1-4/unsp chr kdny 72, 99, 283
I13.2	Hyp hrt & chr kdny dis w hrt fail and w stg 5 chr kdny/ESRD 2, 72, 99, 283
I13.10	Hyp hrt & chr kdny dis w/o hrt fail, w stg 1-4/unsp chr kdny 102
I13.11	Hyp hrt and chr kdny dis w/o hrt fail, w stg 5 chr kdny/ESRD 2, 254
H93.23[1,2,3,9]	Hyperacusis, [rt, lt, bilat, unsp] ear 58
E26*	Hyperaldosteronism 247
K03.4	Hypercementosis 4
E78.3	Hyperchylomicronemia 247
O21.1	Hyperemesis gravidarum with metabolic disturbance 279
E22*	Hyperfunction of pituitary gland 247
D89.2	Hypergammaglobulinemia, unsp 294
D82.4	Hyperimmunoglobulin E [IgE] synd 294
E78.5	Hyperlipidemia, unsp 247
H52.0*	Hypermetropia 46
M35.7	Hypermobility synd 167
M85.2	Hyperostosis of skull 194
E21*	Hyperparathyroidism and oth d/o of parathyroid gland 247

E07.0	Hypersecretion of calcitonin 247
M31.0	Hypersensitivity angiitis 164
J67*	Hypersensitivity pneumonitis d/t organic dust 68
G47.1*	Hypersomnia 311
D73.1	Hypersplenism 294
N98.1	Hyperstimulation of ovaries 367
I12*	Hypertensive chr kidney dz 254
I67.4	Hypertensive encephalopathy 35
I11.9	Hypertensive heart dz w/o heart failure 102
I11.0	Hypertensive heart dz with heart failure 72, 99, 283
L68*	Hypertrichosis 234
L91*	Hypertrophic d/o of skin 234
M79.4	Hypertrophy of (infrapatellar) fat pad 234
J35.2	Hypertrophy of adenoids 4, 58
M89.3*	Hypertrophy of bone 194
N62	Hypertrophy of breast 224
N28.81	Hypertrophy of kidney 256
K11.1	Hypertrophy of salivary gland 4
K14.3	Hypertrophy of tongue papillae 4
J35.1	Hypertrophy of tonsils 4, 58
J35.3	Hypertrophy of tonsils with hypertrophy of adenoids 4, 58
E79.0	Hyperuricemia w/o signs of inflam arthrit and tophaceous dis 385
R06.4	Hyperventilation 69
H21.0*	Hyphema 46
F52.0	Hypoactive sexual desire d/o 311
E23*	Hypofunction and oth d/o of the pituitary gland 247
O92.4	Hypogalactia 272, 276
E16.2	Hypoglycemia, unsp 246
E20.9	Hypoparathyroidism, unsp 247
Q54*	Hypospadias 261
D73.0	Hyposplenism 294
J18.2	Hypostatic pneumonia, unsp organism 68
I95.2	Hypotension d/t drugs 102
I95.3	Hypotension of hemodialysis 102
I95.9	Hypotension, unsp 103
T88.51XA	Hypothermia following anesthesia, init enc 376
T88.51XS	Hypothermia following anesthesia, seq 376
T88.51XD	Hypothermia following anesthesia, subsq enc 411
P80.9	Hypothermia of newborn, unsp 288
R68.0	Hypothermia, not associated w low environmental temperature 385
T68.XXXD	Hypothermia, subsq enc 409
T68.XXX[A,S]	Hypothmia, [init enc, seq] 374
E03.2	Hypothyroidism d/t meds and oth exogenous substances 247
E03.9	Hypothyroidism, unsp 247
H44.4*	Hypotony of eye 46
R57.1	Hypovolemic shock 309
P91.60	Hypoxic ischemic encephalopathy [HIE], unsp 288
P70.3	Iatrogenic neonatal hypoglycemia 282
G47.34	Idio sleep related nonobstructive alveolar hypoventilation 58
D61.3	Idiopathic aplastic anemia 293
M1A.0*	Idiopathic chr gout 167
M10.0*	Idiopathic gout 166
E20.0	Idiopathic hypoparathyroidism 247
I95.0	Idiopathic hypotension 103
G24.2	Idiopathic nonfamilial dystonia 38
G24.4	Idiopathic orofacial dystonia 38
G90.0*	Idiopathic peripheral autonomic neuropathy 34
G60.3	Idiopathic progressive neuropathy 34
H21.3[0,1,2][1,2,3,9]	[Idiopathic, Exudative, Implantation] cysts of iris, ciliary body or ant chamber, [rt, lt, bilat, unsp] eye 46
E20.[0,8,9]	[Idiopathic, Oth, Unsp] hypoparathyroidism 283
K56.7	Ileus, unsp 284
S73.11[1,2,9]A	Iliofemoral lgmt sprain of hip [rt, lt, unsp] init enc 162
S73.1[1,2,9][1,2,9]S	[Iliofemoral lgmt, Ischiocapsular lgmt, Oth] sprain of [rt, lt, unsp] hip, seq 190
S73.1[1,2][1,2,9]A	[Iliofemoral, Ischiocapsular] lgmt sprain of [rt, lt, unsp] hip, init enc 426
R99	Ill-defined and unknown cause of mortality 412
R69	Illness, unsp 412

T69.02[1,2,9][A,S]	Immersion foot, [rt, lt, unsp] foot, [init enc, seq] 374
T69.02[1,2,9]D	Immersion foot, [rt, lt, unsp] foot, subsq enc 409
T69.01[1,2,9][A,S]	Immersion hand, [rt, lt, unsp] hand, [init enc, seq] 374
T69.01[1,2,9]D	Immersion hand, [rt, lt, unsp] hand, subsq enc 409
M62.3	Immobility synd (paraplegic) 167
D89.3	Immune reconstitution synd 294
Z28.02	Immuniz not crd out bec chr illness or cond of patient 289
Z28.03	Immuniz not crd out bec immune compromised state of patient 289
Z28.04	Immuniz not crd out bec patient allergy to vaccine or cmpnt 289
Z28.29	Immuniz not crd out bec patient decision for oth reason 289
Z28.20	Immuniz not crd out bec patient decision for unsp reason 289
Z28.1	Immuniz not crd out because of patient belief/grp pressr 289
Z28.81	Immuniz not crd out d/t patient having had the dz 289
Z28*	Immunization not carried out and underimmunization status 412
Z28.82	Immunization not carried out because of caregiver refusal 289
Z28.09	Immunization not carried out because of oth contraindication 289
Z28.21	Immunization not carried out because of patient refusal 289
Z28.89	Immunization not carried out for oth reason 289
Z28.9	Immunization not carried out for unsp reason 289
Z28.01	Immunization not crd out because of acute illness of patient 289
D82.9	Immunodef associated with major defect, unsp 294
D82.8	Immunodef associated with oth major defects 294
D82.3	Immunodef fol heredit defctv response to Epstein-Barr virus 294
D80.9	Immunodef w/ predominantly antibody defects, unsp 293
D80.5	Immunodef with increased immunoglobulin M [IgM] 294
D82.2	Immunodef with short-limbed stature 294
D84.9	Immunodef, unsp 294
H61.2*	Impacted cerumen 58
K01.1	Impacted teeth 4, 289
L01*	Impetigo 224
F63.9	Impulse d/o, unsp 311
R45.87	Impulsiveness 310
Z72.821	Inadequate sleep hygiene 412
Z72.4	Inappropriate diet and eating habits 412
S42.44[7,8,9][D,G,S]	Incarcerated fx (avulsion) of med epicondyle of [rt, lt, unsp] humerus, [subsq enc for fx w/ routine healing, subsq enc for fx w/ delayed healing, seq] 171
S42.44[7,8,9][K,P]	Incarcerated fx (avulsion) of med epicondyle of [rt, lt, unsp] humerus, subsq enc for fx w/ [nonu, malu] 197
S42.44[7,8,9][A,B]	Incarcerated fx (avulsion) of med epicondyle of humerus [rt, lt, unsp] init enc for fx [clsd, opn] 185
S42.448B	Incarcerated fx of med epicondyl of Lt humer, init for opn fx 434
S42.447B	Incarcerated fx of med epicondyl of Rt humer, init for opn fx 434
S42.449B	Incarcerated fx of med epicondyl of unsp humer, 7thB 434
K43.[0,1]	Incisional hernia, w/ [obstruction w/o gangrene, gangrene], not spec as recurrent 284
S34.12[1,2,3,4,5,9]A	Incomplete lesion of [L1, L2, L3, L4, L5, unsp] lvl of lumbar spinal cord, init enc 433
S34.12[1,2,3,4,5,9]D	Incomplete lesion of [L1, L2, L3, L4, L5, unsp] lvl of lumbar spinal cord, subsq enc 390
S34.12[1,2,3,4,5,9][A,S]	Incomplete lesion to [L1, L2, L3, L4, L5, unsp] lvl of lumbar spinal cord, [init enc, seq] 32
R75	Inconclusive laboratory evidence of human immunodef virus 294
Q82.3	Incontinentia pigmenti 289
E16.4	Increased secretion of gastrin 115
E16.3	Increased secretion of glucagon 247
Q56.4	Indeterminate sex, unsp 261, 265, 270
N48.6	Induration penis plastica 261
A48.51	Infant botulism 283
M41.0*	Infantile idiopathic scoliosis 125
L44.4	Infantile papular acrodermatitis [Gianotti-Crosti] 308
K76.3	Infarction of liver 124, 284
D73.5	Infarction of spleen 294
O23.31	Infect of prt urinary tract in preg, first trmstr 279
T84.629A	Infect/inflm react d/t int fix of unsp bone of leg, init 131
T82.7XXA	Infect/inflm react d/t oth cardi/vasc dev/implnt/grft, init 103
T82.7XXS	Infect/inflm react d/t oth cardi/vasc dev/implnt/grft, seq 375
T82.7XXD	Infect/inflm react d/t oth cardi/vasc dev/implnt/grft, subs 411

T84.7XXA	Infect/inflm react d/t oth int orth prosth dev/grft, init **132, 183**
T84.7XXS	Infect/inflm react d/t oth int orth prosth dev/grft, seq **375**
T84.7XXD	Infect/inflm react d/t oth int orth prosth dev/grft, subs **411**
T83.6XXA	Infect/inflm react d/t prosth dev/grft in genitl trct, init **256**
T83.6XXS	Infect/inflm react d/t prosth dev/grft in genitl trct, seq **375**
T83.6XXD	Infect/inflm react d/t prosth dev/grft in genitl trct, subs **411**
T82.6XXS	Infect/inflm reaction d/t cardiac valve prosth, seq **375**
T82.6XXA	Infect/inflm reaction d/t cardiac valve prosthesis, init **103**
T82.6XXD	Infect/inflm reaction d/t cardiac valve prosthesis, subs **411**
T84.69XA	Infect/inflm reaction d/t int fix of site, init **131**
T84.69XS	Infect/inflm reaction d/t int fix of site, seq **375**
T84.63XA	Infect/inflm reaction d/t int fix of spine, init **131**
T84.63XS	Infect/inflm reaction d/t int fix of spine, seq **375**
T84.60XA	Infect/inflm reaction d/t int fix of unsp site, init **131, 183**
T84.60XS	Infect/inflm reaction d/t int fix of unsp site, seq **375**
T84.60XD	Infect/inflm reaction d/t int fix of unsp site, subs **411**
N43.1	Infected hydrocele **261**
O41.1*	Infection of amniotic sac and membranes **280**
O91.[0,1,2]1[1,2,3]	Infection of nipple, Abscess of breast, Nonpurulent mastitis] associated w preg, [1st, 2nd, 3rd] trmstr **280**
O23.11	Infections of bladder in preg, first trmstr **279**
O23.12	Infections of bladder in preg, second trmstr **279**
O23.13	Infections of bladder in preg, third trmstr **279**
O23.10	Infections of bladder in preg, unsp trmstr **279, 280**
O23.519	Infections of cervix in preg, unsp trmstr **280**
O23*	Infections of genitourinary tract in preg **276**
O23.01	Infections of kidney in preg, first trmstr **279**
O23.02	Infections of kidney in preg, second trmstr **279**
O23.03	Infections of kidney in preg, third trmstr **279**
O23.00	Infections of kidney in preg, unsp trmstr **279, 280**
O23.30	Infections of prt urinary tract in preg, unsp trmstr **279, 280**
O23.21	Infections of urethra in preg, first trmstr **279**
O23.22	Infections of urethra in preg, second trmstr **279**
O23.23	Infections of urethra in preg, third trmstr **279**
O23.20	Infections of urethra in preg, unsp trmstr **279, 280**
A09	Infectious gastroenteritis and colitis, unsp **116**
B27*	Infectious mononucleosis **307**
I40.0	Infective myocarditis **283**
M60.0*	Infective myositis **167**
S43.14[1,2,9]D	Inferior disloc of [rt, lt, unsp] acromioclavicular jt, subsq enc **391**
S43.14[1,2,9][A,S]	Inferior disloc of acromioclavicular jt, > 200% displac {rt, lt, unsp} [init enc, seq] **185**
S43.03[4,5,6][A,S]	Inferior disloc of humerus [rt, lt, unsp] [init enc, seq] **185**
S43.03[1,2,3,4,5,6]D	Inferior sublux of [rt, lt, unsp] humerus, Inferior disloc of [rt, lt, unsp] humerus subsq enc **391**
S43.03[1,2,3][A,S]	Inferior sublux of humerus [rt, lt, unsp] [init enc, seq] **185**
S43.14[4,5][1,2,9]A	[Inferior, Post] disloc of [rt, lt, unsp] acromioclavicular jt, init enc **422**
H59.4*	Inflam (infxn) of postprocedural bleb **46**
G72.4*	Inflam and immune myopathies, NEC **164**
M27.2	Inflam conditions of jaws **4**
N61	Inflam d/o of breast **224**
N49*	Inflam d/o of male genital organs, NEC **261**
N72	Inflam dz of cervix uteri **264, 269**
N41*	Inflam dz of prostate **261**
N71*	Inflam dz of uterus, except cervix **264, 269**
K75.9	Inflam liver dz, unsp **284**
M06.4	Inflam polyarthropathy **166**
G61.9	Inflam polyneuropathy, unsp **34**
T83.5[1,9]XA	Infxn and inflam reaction d/t [indwelling urinary catheter, prosthetic dev, implant and graft in urinary sys], init enc **256**
T83.5[1,9]XS	Infxn and inflam reaction d/t [indwelling urinary catheter, prosthetic dev, implant and graft in urinary sys], seq **375**
T83.5[1,9]XD	Infxn and inflam reaction d/t [indwelling urinary catheter, prosthetic dev, implant and graft in urinary sys], subsq enc **411**
T85.7[1,2,9]XA	Infxn and inflam reaction d/t [peritoneal dialysis catheter, insulin pump, oth int prosthetic devs, implants and grafts], init enc **368**
T85.7[1,2,9]XS	Infxn and inflam reaction d/t [peritoneal dialysis catheter, insulin pump, oth int prosthetic devs, implants and grafts], seq **376**

T85.7[1,2,9]XD	Infxn and inflam reaction d/t [peritoneal dialysis catheter, insulin pump, oth int prosthetic devs, implants and grafts], subsq enc **411**
T84.5[0,1,2,3,4,9]XA	Infxn and inflam reaction d/t [unsp int jt, int rt hip, int lt hip, int rt knee, int lt knee, oth int jt] prosthesis, init enc **131, 183**
T84.5[0,1,2,3,4,9]XS	Infxn and inflam reaction d/t [unsp int jt, int rt hip, int lt hip, int rt knee, int lt knee, oth int jt] prosthesis, seq **375**
T84.5[0,1,2,3,4,9]XD	Infxn and inflam reaction d/t [unsp int jt, int rt hip, int lt hip, int rt knee, int lt knee, oth int jt] prosthesis, subsq enc **411**
T84.62[0,1,2,3,4,5,9]A	Infxn and inflam reaction d/t int fix dev of [rt femur, lt femur, rt tibia, lt tibia, rt fibula, lt fibula, unsp bone of leg], init enc **183**
T84.62[0,1,2,3,4,5,9]S	Infxn and inflam reaction d/t int fix dev of [rt femur, lt femur, rt tibia, lt tibia, rt fibula, lt fibula, unsp bone of leg], seq **375**
T84.62[0,1,2,3,4,5,9]D	Infxn and inflam reaction d/t int fix dev of [rt femur, lt femur, rt tibia, lt tibia, rt fibula, lt fibula, unsp bone of leg], subsq enc **411**
T84.61[0,1,2,3,4,5,9]A	Infxn and inflam reaction d/t int fix dev of [rt humerus, lt humerus, rt radius, lt radius, rt ulna, lt ulna, unsp bone of arm], init enc **183**
T84.61[0,1,2,3,4,5,9]S	Infxn and inflam reaction d/t int fix dev of [rt humerus, lt humerus, rt radius, lt radius, rt ulna, lt ulna, unsp bone of arm], seq **375**
T84.61[0,1,2,3,4,5,9]D	Infxn and inflam reaction d/t int fix dev of [rt humerus, lt humerus, rt radius, lt radius, rt ulna, lt ulna, unsp bone of arm], subsq enc **411**
T84.62[0,1]A	Infxn and inflam reaction d/t int fix dev of [rt, lt] femur, init enc **131**
T84.62[4,5]A	Infxn and inflam reaction d/t int fix dev of [rt, lt] fibula, init enc **131**
T84.62[2,3]A	Infxn and inflam reaction d/t int fix dev of [rt, lt] tibia, init enc **131**
T84.6[3,9]XA	Infxn and inflam reaction d/t int fix dev of [spine, oth site], init enc **183**
T84.6[3,9]XD	Infxn and inflam reaction d/t int fix dev of [spine, oth site], subsq enc **411**
N98.0	Infxn associated with artfcl insemination **285, 307, 309**
T80.29XS	Infxn fol oth inf, tranfs and theraputc inject, seq **374**
T80.29XA	Infxn fol oth inf, transfusion and theraputc inject, init **287, 307, 309**
T80.29XD	Infxn fol oth inf, transfusion and theraputc inject, subs **410**
T81.4XXA	infxn following a procedure, init enc **287, 307**
T81.4XXS	Infxn following a procedure, seq **375**
T81.4XXD	Infxn following a procedure, subsq enc **410**
T88.0XXA	Infxn following immunization, init enc **287, 307, 309**
T88.0XXS	Infxn following immunization, seq **376**
T88.0XXD	Infxn following immunization, subsq enc **411**
O41.10[1,2,3,9][0,1,2,3,4,5,9]	Infxn of amniotic sac and membranes, unsp, [1st, 2nd, 3rd, unsp] trmstr, fetus [N/A or unsp, 1, 2, 3, 4, 5, oth] **278**
T87.4*	infxn of amp stump **205**
O23.5[1,2,9][1,2,3]	[Infxn of cervix, Salpingo-oophoritis, Infxn of oth part of genital tract] in preg, [1st, 2nd, 3rd] trmstr **277**
M46.3*	infxn of intervertebral disc (pyogenic) **163**
O91.0[2,3]	Infxn of nipple associated w/ [the puerperium, lactation] **272, 276**
O91.01[1,2,3]	Infxn of nipple associated w/ preg, [1st, 2nd, 3rd] trmstr **274, 278**
O91.02	infxn of nipple associated with the puerperium **274**
O91.[0,1,2]19	[Infxn of nipple, Abcess of breast, Nonpurulent mastitis] associated w/ preg, unsp trmstr **281**
O86.0	infxn of obstetric surgical wnd **274**
O23.599	Infxn oth prt genital tract in preg, unsp trmstr **280**
P39.9	Infxn specific to the perinatal period, unsp **282**
T86.84[2,8,9]	[Infxn, Oth comp, Unsp comp] of corneal transplant **368**
O23.[0,1,2,3][1,2,3]	Infxns of [kidney, bladder, urethra, oth parts of urinary tract] in preg, [1st, 2nd, 3rd] trmstr **277**
K40*	Inguinal hernia **117**
A66.[0,1,2,3,4]	[Init lesions of, Multi papillomata and wet crab, Oth early skin lesions of, Hyperkeratosis of, Gummata and ulcers of] yaws **233**
S66.292A	Inj extensor musc/fasc/tend lt thumb at wrs/hnd lv, init **425**
S66.291A	Inj extensor musc/fasc/tend rt thumb at wrs/hnd lv, init **425**
S66.299A	Inj extensor musc/fasc/tend thmb at wrs/hnd lv, init **425**
S56.499D	Inj extensor musc/fasc/tend unsp finger at forearm lv, subs **393**
S56.199D	Inj flexor musc/fasc/tend unsp finger at forearm lvl, subs **393**
S06.821A	Inj Lt int carotid, intcr w LOC of 30 min or less, init **37**
S34.5XXS	Inj lumbar, sacral and pelvic sympathetic nerves, seq **40**
S16.8XXA	Inj muscle, fascia and tndn at neck lvl, init enc **5**
S39.091A	Inj muscle, fascia and tndn of abd, init enc **422**
S39.092A	Inj muscle, fascia and tndn of lwr back, init enc **422**
S39.093A	Inj muscle, fascia and tndn of pelvis, init enc **422**
S34.8XXS	Inj nerves at abd, low back and pelvis lvl, seq **40**
S44.[3,4][0,1,2]XA	Inj of [axillary, musculocutaneous] nerve, [unsp, rt, lt] arm, init enc **423**
S34.[3,4]XXA	Inj of [cauda equina, lumbosacral plexus], init enc **421, 433**

S44.[5,8,9][0,1,2]XA	Inj of [cutaneous sensory, oth, unsp] nerve(s) at shldr and upr arm lvl, [unsp, rt, lt] arm, init enc 423
S94.[0,1,2,3][0,1,2]XA	Inj of [lat plantar, med plantar, deep peroneal, cutaneous sensory] nerve, [unsp, rt, lt] leg, init enc 430
S94.[0,1,2,3][0,1,2]XD	Inj of [lat plantar, med plantar, deep peroneal, cutaneous sensory] nerve, [unsp, rt, lt] leg, subsq enc 399
S14.[2,3,4,5,8,9]XXA	Inj of [nerve root of cervical spine, brachial plexus, peripheral nerves of neck, cervical sympathetic nerves, oth spec nerves of neck, unsp nerves of neck], init enc 420
S14.[2,3,4,5,8,9]XXD	Inj of [nerve root of cervical spine, brachial plexus, peripheral nerves of neck, cervical sympathetic nerves, oth spec nerves of neck, unsp nerves of neck], subsq enc 388
S04.[1,2,3,4,5,6,7][0,1,2]XA	Inj of [oculomotor, trochlear, trigeminal, abducent, facial, acoustic, accessory] nerve, [unsp, rt, lt] side, init enc 417
S04.8[1,9][1,2,9]A	Inj of [olfactory (1st), oth cranial] nerve(s), [rt, lt, unsp] side, init enc 417
S04.8[1,9][1,2,9]D	Inj of [olfactory (1st), oth cranial] nerve(s), [rt, lt, unsp] side, subsq enc 386
S04.0[3,4][1,2,9]A	Inj of [optic tract and pathways, visual cortex], [rt, lt, unsp] eye, init enc 417
S15.[8,9]XXA	Inj of [oth spec, unsp] bld vessel(s) at neck lvl, init enc 359, 420
S24.[8,9]XXA	Inj of [oth spec, unsp] nerve(s) of thorax, init enc 420
S15.[8,9]XXS	Inj of [oth, unsp] spec bld vessel(s) at neck lvl, seq 100
S34.[6,8,9]XXA	Inj of [peripheral, oth, unsp] nerve(s) at abd, lwr back and pelvis lvl, init enc 421, 433
S35.51[1,2,3,4,5,6]A	Inj of [rt iliac artery, lt iliac artery, unsp iliac artery, rt iliac vein, lt iliac vein, unsp iliac vein], init enc 421
S35.51[1,2,3,4,5,6]D	Inj of [rt iliac artery, lt iliac artery, unsp iliac artery, rt iliac vein, lt iliac vein, unsp iliac vein] subsq enc 390
S35.51[1,2,3,4,5,6]A	Inj of [rt iliac artery, lt iliac artery, unsp iliac artery, rt iliac vein, lt iliac vein, unsp iliac vein], init enc 359, 432
S35.53[1,2,3,4,5,6]D	Inj of [rt uterine artery, lt uterine artery, unsp uterine artery, rt uterine vein, lt uterine vein, unsp uterine vein] subsq enc 390
S35.53[1,2,3,4,5,6]A	Inj of [rt uterine artery, lt uterine artery, unsp uterine artery, rt uterine vein, rt uterine vein, unsp uterine vein], init enc 359, 421, 432
S35.51[1,2,3]S	Inj of [rt, lt, unsp] iliac artery, seq 100
S35.51[4,5,6]S	Inj of [rt, lt, unsp] iliac vein, seq 100
S35.53[1,2,3]S	Inj of [rt, lt, unsp] uterine artery, seq 100
S35.53[4,5,6]S	Inj of [rt, lt, unsp] uterine vein, seq 100
S74.[0,1,2][0,1,2]XA	Inj of [sciatic, femor, cutaneous sensory] nerve at hip & thigh lvl, [unsp, rt, lt] leg, init enc 426
S74.[0,1,2][0,1,2]XD	Inj of [sciatic, femor, cutaneous sensory] nerve at hip & thigh lvl, [unsp, rt, lt] leg, subsq enc 398
S84.[0,1,2][0,1,2]XD	Inj of [tibial, peroneal, cutaneous sensory] nerve at lwr leg lvl, [unsp, rt, lt] leg, subsq enc 398
S54.[0,1,2,3][0,2,3]XA	Inj of [ulnar, median, radial, cutaneous sensory] nerve at forearm lvl, [unsp, rt, lt] arm, init enc 424
S44.[0,1,2][0,1,2]XA	Inj of [ulnar, median, radial] nerve at upr arm lvl, [unsp, rt, lt] arm, init enc 423
S64.[0,1,2][0,1,2]XA	Inj of [ulnar, median, radial] nerve at wrist and hand lvl of [unsp, rt, lt] arm, init enc 425
S04.4[0,1,2]XA	Inj of abducent nerve, [unsp, rt, lt] side, init enc 34
S04.4[0,1,2]XS	Inj of abducent nerve, [unsp, rt, lt] side, seq 39
S04.4[0,1,2]XD	Inj of abducent nerve, [unsp, rt, lt] side, subsq enc 386
S04.7[0,1,2]XA	Inj of accessory nerve, [unsp, rt, lt] side, init enc 34
S04.7[0,1,2]XS	Inj of accessory nerve, [unsp, rt, lt] side, seq 39
S04.7[0,1,2]XD	Inj of accessory nerve, [unsp, rt, lt] side, subsq enc 386
S04.6[0,1,2]XA	Inj of acoustic nerve, [unsp, rt, lt] side, init enc 58
S04.6[0,1,2]XS	Inj of acoustic nerve, [unsp, rt, lt] side, seq 39
S04.6[0,1,2]XD	Inj of acoustic nerve, [unsp, rt, lt] side, subsq enc 386
S44.3[0,1,2]XA	Inj of axillary nerve at upr arm lvl, [unsp, rt, lt] arm, init enc 34, 434
S44.3[0,1,2]XS	Inj of axillary nerve at upr arm lvl, [unsp, rt, lt] arm, seq 40
S44.3[0,1,2]XD	Inj of axillary nerve, [unsp, rt, lt] arm, subsq enc 391
S36.13XA	Inj of bile duct, init enc 124, 422, 432
S36.13XS	Inj of bile duct, seq 117
S36.13XD	Inj of bile duct, subsq enc 390
S09.0XXA	Inj of bld vessels of head, NEC, init 5, 359, 419
S09.0XXS	Inj of bld vessels of head, NEC, seq 100
S09.0XXD	Inj of bld vessels of head, NEC, subs 387
S14.3XXA	Inj of brachial plexus, init enc 34, 285, 433
S14.3XXS	Inj of brachial plexus, seq 40
S34.3XXA	Inj of cauda equina, init enc 32

S34.3XXS	Inj of cauda equina, seq 40
S34.3XXD	Inj of cauda equina, subsq enc 390
S14.5XXA	Inj of cervical sympathetic nerves, init enc 34
S14.5XXS	Inj of cervical sympathetic nerves, seq 40
S05.0[0,1,2]XD	Inj of conjunctiva and corneal abrasion w/o FB, [rt, lt, unsp] eye, subsq enc 386
S05.0[0,1,2]XA	Inj of conjunctiva and corneal abrasion w/o FB, [unsp, rt, lt] eye, init enc 46, 418
S05.0[0,1,2]XS	Inj of conjunctiva and corneal abrasion w/o FB, [unsp, rt, lt] eye, seq 224
S54.31XA	Inj of cutan sensory nerve at forearm lv, rt arm, init 424
S94.3[0,1,2]XA	Inj of cutaneous sensory nerve at ankle and foot lvl, [unsp, rt, lt] leg, init enc 34
S94.3[0,1,2]XS	Inj of cutaneous sensory nerve at ankle and foot lvl, [unsp, rt, lt] leg, seq 40
S54.3[0,1,2]XA	Inj of cutaneous sensory nerve at forearm lvl, [unsp, rt, lt] arm, init enc 34
S54.3[0,1,2]XS	Inj of cutaneous sensory nerve at forearm lvl, [unsp, rt, lt] arm, seq 40
S54.3[0,1,2]XD	Inj of cutaneous sensory nerve at forearm lvl, [unsp, rt, lt] arm, subsq enc 392
S74.2[0,1,2]XA	Inj of cutaneous sensory nerve at hip & thigh lvl, [unsp, rt, lt] leg, init enc 34
S74.2[0,1,2]XS	Inj of cutaneous sensory nerve at hip & thigh lvl, [unsp, rt, lt] leg, seq 40
S84.2[0,1,2]XA	Inj of cutaneous sensory nerve at lwr leg lvl, [unsp, rt, lt] leg, init enc 34, 428
S84.2[0,1,2]XS	Inj of cutaneous sensory nerve at lwr leg lvl, [unsp, rt, lt] leg, seq 40
S44.5[0,1,2]XA	Inj of cutaneous sensory nerve at shldr and upr arm lvl, [unsp, rt, lt] arm, init enc 34
S44.5[0,1,2]XS	Inj of cutaneous sensory nerve at shldr and upr arm lvl, [unsp, rt, lt] arm, seq 40
S44.5[0,1,2]XD	Inj of cutaneous sensory nerve at shldr and upr arm lvl, [unsp, rt, lt] arm, subsq enc 391
S94.2[0,1,2]XA	Inj of deep peroneal nerve at ankle and foot lvl, [unsp, rt, lt] leg, init enc 34, 436
S94.2[0,1,2]XS	Inj of deep peroneal nerve at ankle and foot lvl, [unsp, rt, lt] leg, seq 40
S64.49[0,1,2,3,4,5,6,7,8]A	Inj of digital nerve of [rt index, lt index, rt mid, lt mid, rt ring, lt ring, rt little, lt little, oth] finger, init enc 34, 425
S64.49[0,1,2,3,4,5,6,7,8]S	Inj of digital nerve of [rt index, lt index, rt mid, lt mid, rt ring, lt ring, rt little, lt little, unsp] finger, seq 40
S64.49[0,1]D	Inj of digital nerve of [rt, lt] index finger, subsq enc 396
S64.49[6,7]D	Inj of digital nerve of [rt, lt] little finger, subsq enc 396
S64.49[2,3]D	Inj of digital nerve of [rt, lt] mid finger, subsq enc 396
S64.49[4,5]D	Inj of digital nerve of [rt, lt] ring finger, subsq enc 396
S64.3[0,1,2]XA	Inj of digital nerve of [unsp, rt, lt] thumb, init enc 34, 425
S64.3[0,1,2]XD	Inj of digital nerve of [unsp, rt, lt] thumb, subsq enc 396
S64.498D	Inj of digital nerve of oth finger, subs enc 396
S64.3[0,1,2]XS	Inj of digital nerve of thumb, [unsp, rt, lt] arm, seq 40
S64.40XA	Inj of digital nerve of unsp finger, init enc 34, 425
S64.40XS	Inj of digital nerve of unsp finger, seq 40
S64.40XD	Inj of digital nerve of unsp finger, subs enc 396
S04.5[0,1,2]XA	Inj of facial nerve, [unsp, rt, lt] side, init enc 34
S04.5[0,1,2]XS	Inj of facial nerve, [unsp, rt, lt] side, seq 39
S04.5[0,1,2]XD	Inj of facial nerve, [unsp, rt, lt] side, subsq enc 386
S74.1[0,1,2]XA	Inj of femor nerve at hip & thigh lvl, [unsp, rt, lt] leg, init enc 34, 436
S74.1[0,1,2]XS	Inj of femor nerve at hip & thigh lvl, [unsp, rt, lt] leg, seq 40
S94.0[0,1,2]XA	Inj of lat plantar nerve, [unsp, rt, lt] leg, init enc 34
S94.0[0,1,2]XS	Inj of lat plantar nerve, [unsp, rt, lt] leg, seq 40
S06.82[3,4,5,6]A	Inj of lt int carotid artery, intracranial, NEC w/ LOC of [1 hr to 5 hrs 59 min, 6 hrs to 24 hrs, > 24 hrs w/ return to pre-existing conscious lvl, > 24 hrs w/o return to pre-existing conscious lvl patient surviving], init enc 36
S06.82[1,2,3,4]S	Inj of lt int carotid artery, intracranial portion, NEC w/ LOC of [30 min or less, 31-59 min, 1 hr to 5 hrs 59 min, 6 hrs to 24 hrs], seq 40
S06.82[1,2,3,4]D	Inj of lt int carotid artery, intracranial portion, NEC w/ LOC of [30 min or less, 31-59 min, 1 hr to 5 hrs 59 min, 6 hrs to 24 hrs], subsq enc 387
S06.82[7,8,9]A	Inj of lt int carotid artery, intracranial portion, NEC w/ LOC of [any dur w/ death d/t brain inj prior to regain cnscness, any dur w/ death d/t oth cause prior to regain cnscness, unsp dur], init enc 36, 37, 419, 431

S06.82[7,8,9]S	Inj of lt int carotid artery, intracranial portion, NEC w/ LOC of [any dur w/ death d/t brain inj prior to regain cnscness, any dur w/ death d/t oth cause prior to regain cnscness, unsp dur], seq **40**
S06.82[7,8,9]D	Inj of lt int carotid artery, intracranial portion, NEC w/ LOC of [any dur w/ death d/t brain inj prior to regain cnscness, any dur w/ death d/t oth cause prior to regain cnscness, unsp dur], subsq enc **387**
S06.82[5,6]S	Inj of lt int carotid artery, intracranial portion, NEC w/ LOC of > 24 hrs [w/ return to pre-existing conscious lvl, w/o return to pre-existing conscious lvl w/ patient surviving], seq **40**
S06.82[5,6]D	Inj of lt int carotid artery, intracranial portion, NEC w/ LOC of > 24 hrs [w/ return to pre-existing conscious lvl, w/o return to pre-existing conscious lvl w/ patient surviving], subsq enc **387**
S06.82[5,6]A	Inj of lt int carotid artery, intracranial portion, NEC, w/ LOC > 24 hrs [w/ return to pre-existing conscious lvl, w/o return to pre-existing conscious lvl w/ patient surviving], init enc **37, 419, 431**
S06.82[1,2,3,4]A	Inj of lt int carotid artery, intracranial portion, NEC, w/ LOC of [30 min or less, 31 min to 59 min, 1 hr to 5 hrs 59 min, 6 hrs to 24 hrs], init enc **37, 419, 431**
S06.822A	Inj of Lt int carotid, intcr w LOC of 31-59 min, init **37**
S06.820A	Inj of Lt int carotid, intcr w/o LOC, init **37, 419, 431**
S06.820S	Inj of Lt int carotid, intcr w/o LOC, seq **40**
S06.820D	Inj of Lt int carotid, intcr w/o LOC, subs **387**
S34.5XXA	Inj of lumbar, sacral and pelvic sympathetic nerves, init **34, 421**
S34.5XXD	Inj of lumbar, sacral and pelvic sympathetic nerves, subs **390**
S34.4XXA	Inj of lumbosacral plexus, init enc **34**
S34.4XXS	Inj of lumbosacral plexus, seq **40**
S34.4XXD	Inj of lumbosacral plexus, subsq enc **390**
S94.1[0,1,2]XA	Inj of med plantar nerve, [unsp, rt, lt] leg, init enc **34**
S94.1[0,1,2]XS	Inj of med plantar nerve, [unsp, rt, lt] leg, seq **40**
S54.1[0,1,2]XA	Inj of median nerve at forearm lvl, [unsp, rt, lt] arm, init enc **34, 435**
S54.1[0,1,2]XS	Inj of median nerve at forearm lvl, [unsp, rt, lt] arm, seq **40**
S54.1[0,1,2]XD	Inj of median nerve at forearm lvl, [unsp, rt, lt] arm, subsq enc **392**
S54.11XA	Inj of median nerve at forearm lvl, rt arm, init **424**
S44.1[0,1,2]XA	Inj of median nerve at upr arm lvl, [unsp, rt, lt] arm, init enc **34, 434**
S44.1[0,1,2]XS	Inj of median nerve at upr arm lvl, [unsp, rt, lt] arm, seq **40**
S44.1[0,1,2]XD	Inj of median nerve at upr arm lvl, [unsp, rt, lt] arm, subsq enc **391**
S64.1[0,1,2]XA	Inj of median nerve at wrist and hand lvl of [unsp, rt, lt] arm, init enc **34, 435**
S64.1[0,1,2]XD	Inj of median nerve at wrist and hand lvl of [unsp, rt, lt] arm, subsq enc **396**
S64.1[0,1,2]XS	Inj of median nerve at wrist and hand lvl, [unsp, rt, lt] arm, seq **40**
S44.4[0,1,2]XA	Inj of musculocutaneous nerve at upr arm lvl, [unsp, rt, lt] arm, init enc **34**
S44.4[0,1,2]XS	Inj of musculocutaneous nerve at upr arm lvl, [unsp, rt, lt] arm, seq **40**
S44.4[0,1,2]XD	Inj of musculocutaneous nerve, [unsp, rt, lt] arm, subsq enc **391**
S34.2[1,2]XA	Inj of nerve root of [lumbar, sacral] spine, init enc **34, 421**
S34.2[1,2]XS	Inj of nerve root of [lumbar, sacral] spine, seq **40**
S34.2[1,2]XD	Inj of nerve root of [lumbar, sacral] spine, subsq enc **390**
S14.2XXA	Inj of nerve root of cervical spine, init enc **34**
S14.2XXS	Inj of nerve root of cervical spine, seq **40**
S24.2XXA	Inj of nerve root of thoracic spine, init enc **34, 420**
S24.2XXS	Inj of nerve root of thoracic spine, seq **40**
S24.2XXD	Inj of nerve root of thoracic spine, subsq enc **389**
S34.8XXA	Inj of nerves at abd, low back and pelvis lvl, init **34**
S34.8XXD	Inj of nerves at abd, low back and pelvis lvl, subs **390**
S94.8X1A	Inj of nerves at ankle and foot lvl, rt leg, init **34**
S44.8X2A	Inj of nerves at shldr/up arm, lt arm, init **34, 423**
S44.8X1A	Inj of nerves at shldr/up arm, rt arm, init **34, 423**
S44.8X9A	Inj of nerves at shldr/up arm, unsp arm, init **34, 423**
S64.8X2A	Inj of nerves at wrist and hand lvl of lt arm, init **34**
S64.8X1A	Inj of nerves at wrist and hand lvl of rt arm, init **34**
S64.8X9A	Inj of nerves at wrist and hand lvl of unsp arm, init **34**
S04.1[0,1,2]XA	Inj of oculomotor nerve, [unsp, rt, lt] side, init enc **34**
S04.1[0,1,2]XS	Inj of oculomotor nerve, [unsp, rt, lt] side, seq **39**
S04.81[1,2,9]A	Inj of olfactory (1st) nerve, [rt, lt, unsp] side, init enc **34**
S04.81[1,2,9]S	Inj of olfactory (1st) nerve, [rt, lt, unsp] side, seq **39**
S04.02X[A,S]	Inj of optic chiasm, [init enc, seq] **39**
S04.02XA	Inj of optic chiasm, init enc **417**
S04.02XD	Inj of optic chiasm, subsq enc **386**
S04.01[1,2,9]A	Inj of optic nerve, [rt, lt, unsp] eye, init enc **46, 417**

S04.01[1,2,9]S	Inj of optic nerve, [rt, lt, unsp] eye, seq **39**
S04.01[1,2,9]D	Inj of optic nerve, [rt, lt, unsp] eye, subsq enc **386**
S04.03[1,2,9]A	Inj of optic tract and pathways, [rt, lt, unsp] eye, init enc **39**
S04.03[1,2,9]S	Inj of optic tract and pathways, [rt, lt, unsp] eye, seq **39**
S04.03[1,2,9]D	Inj of optic tract and pathways, [rt, lt, unsp] eye, subsq enc **386**
S15.8XXA	Inj of oth bld vessels at neck lvl, init enc **5, 431**
S15.8XXD	Inj of oth bld vessels at neck lvl, subs enc **388**
S04.89[1,2,9]A	Inj of oth cranial nerves, [rt, lt, unsp] side, init enc **34**
S04.89[1,2,9]S	Inj of oth cranial nerves, [rt, lt, unsp] side, seq **39**
S35.59XA	Inj of oth iliac bld vessels, init enc **359, 421, 432**
S35.59XS	Inj of oth iliac bld vessels, seq **100**
S35.59XD	Inj of oth iliac bld vessels, subsq enc **390**
S94.8X[1,2,9]A	Inj of oth nerves at ankle and foot lvl, [unsp leg, rt, lt], init enc **430, 436**
S94.8X[1,2,9]S	Inj of oth nerves at ankle and foot lvl, [unsp, rt, lt] leg, seq **40**
S94.8X[1,2,9]D	Inj of oth nerves at ankle and foot lvl, [unsp, rt, lt] leg, subsq enc **399**
S94.8X2A	Inj of oth nerves at ankle and foot lvl, lt leg, init **34**
S94.8X9A	Inj of oth nerves at ankle and foot lvl, unsp leg, init **34**
S54.8X[1,2,9]S	Inj of oth nerves at forearm lvl, [unsp, rt, lt] arm, seq **40**
S74.8X[1,2,9]A	Inj of oth nerves at hip & thigh lvl, [rt, lt, unsp] leg, init enc **426, 436**
S74.8X[1,2,9]S	Inj of oth nerves at hip & thigh lvl, [unsp, rt, lt] leg, seq **40**
S74.8X[1,2,9]D	Inj of oth nerves at hip & thigh lvl, [unsp, rt, lt] leg, subsq enc **397**
S74.8X2A	Inj of oth nerves at hip & thigh lvl, lt leg, init **34**
S74.8X1A	Inj of oth nerves at hip & thigh lvl, rt leg, init **34**
S74.8X9A	Inj of oth nerves at hip & thigh lvl, unsp leg, init **34**
S84.80[1,2,9]A	Inj of oth nerves at lwr leg lvl, [rt, lt, unsp] leg, init enc **428, 436**
S84.80[1,2,9]D	Inj of oth nerves at lwr leg lvl, [rt, lt, unsp] leg, subsq enc **398**
S84.80[1,2,9]S	Inj of oth nerves at lwr leg lvl, [unsp, rt, lt] leg, seq **40**
S84.802A	Inj of oth nerves at lwr leg lvl, lt leg, init **34**
S84.801A	Inj of oth nerves at lwr leg lvl, rt leg, init **34**
S84.809A	Inj of oth nerves at lwr leg lvl, unsp leg, init **34**
S44.8X[1,2,9]D	Inj of oth nerves at shldr and upr arm lvl, [rt, lt, unsp] arm, subsq enc **391**
S44.8X[1,2]A	Inj of oth nerves at shldr and upr arm lvl, [rt, lt] arm, init enc **434**
S44.8X[1,2,9]S	Inj of oth nerves at shldr and upr arm lvl, [unsp, rt, lt] arm, seq **40**
S64.8X[1,2,9]A	Inj of oth nerves at wrist and hand lvl of [rt, lt, unsp] arm, init enc **425, 435**
S64.8X[1,2,9]D	Inj of oth nerves at wrist and hand lvl of [rt, lt, unsp] arm, subsq enc **396**
S64.8X[1,2,9]S	Inj of oth nerves at wrist and hand lvl, [unsp, rt, lt] arm, seq **40**
S14.8XXA	Inj of oth spec nerves of neck, init enc **34**
S14.8XXS	Inj of oth spec nerves of neck, seq **40**
S24.8XXA	Inj of oth spec nerves of thorax, init enc **34, 433**
S24.8XXS	Inj of oth spec nerves of thorax, seq **40**
S24.8XXD	Inj of oth spec nerves of thorax, subs enc **389**
S14.4XXA	Inj of peripheral nerves of neck, init enc **34**
S14.4XXS	Inj of peripheral nerves of neck, seq **40**
S24.3XXA	Inj of peripheral nerves of thorax, init enc **34, 420, 433**
S24.3XXS	Inj of peripheral nerves of thorax, seq **40**
S24.3XXD	Inj of peripheral nerves of thorax, subsq enc **389**
S36.81X[A,S]	Inj of peritoneum, [init enc, seq] **118**
S36.81XA	Inj of peritoneum, init enc **422, 433**
S36.81XD	Inj of peritoneum, subsq enc **391**
S84.1[0,1,2]XA	Inj of peroneal nerve at lwr leg lvl, [unsp, rt, lt] leg, init enc **34, 428, 436**
S84.1[0,1,2]XS	Inj of peroneal nerve at lwr leg lvl, [unsp, rt, lt] leg, seq **40**
S54.2[0,1,2]XA	Inj of radial nerve at forearm lvl, [unsp, rt, lt] arm, init enc **34, 435**
S54.2[0,1,2]XS	Inj of radial nerve at forearm lvl, [unsp, rt, lt] arm, seq **40**
S54.2[0,1,2]XD	Inj of radial nerve at forearm lvl, [unsp, rt, lt] arm, subsq enc **392**
S54.21XA	Inj of radial nerve at forearm lvl, rt arm, init **424**
S44.2[0,1,2]XA	Inj of radial nerve at upr arm lvl, [unsp, rt, lt] arm, init enc **34, 434**
S44.2[0,1,2]XS	Inj of radial nerve at upr arm lvl, [unsp, rt, lt] arm, seq **40**
S44.2[0,1,2]XD	Inj of radial nerve at upr arm lvl, [unsp, rt, lt] arm, subsq enc **391**
S64.2[0,1,2]XA	Inj of radial nerve at wrist and hand lvl of [unsp, rt, lt] arm, init enc **34, 435**
S64.2[0,1,2]XD	Inj of radial nerve at wrist and hand lvl of [unsp, rt, lt] arm, subsq enc **396**
S64.2[0,1,2]XS	Inj of radial nerve at wrist and hand lvl, [unsp, rt, lt] arm, seq **40**

Code	Description
S06.81[5,6]S	Inj of rt int carotid artery, intracranial portion, NEC w/ LOC of [> 24 hrs w/ return to pre-existing conscious lvl, > 24 hrs w/o return to pre-existing conscious lvl w/ patient surviving], seq **40**
S06.81[5,6]D	Inj of rt int carotid artery, intracranial portion, NEC w/ LOC of [> 24 hrs w/ return to pre-existing conscious lvl, > 24 hrs w/o return to pre-existing conscious lvl w/ patient surviving], subsq enc **387**
S06.81[3,4,5,6]A	Inj of rt int carotid artery, intracranial portion, NEC w/ LOC of [1 hr to 5 hrs 59 min, 6 hrs to 24 hrs, > 24 hrs w/ return to pre-existing conscious lvl, > 24 hrs w/o return to pre-existing conscious lvl patient surviving], init enc **36**
S06.81[1,2,3,4]S	Inj of rt int carotid artery, intracranial portion, NEC w/ LOC of [30 min or less, 31-59 min, 1 hr to 5 hrs 59 min, 6 hrs to 24 hrs], seq **40**
S06.81[1,2,3,4]D	Inj of rt int carotid artery, intracranial portion, NEC w/ LOC of [30 min or less, 31-59 min, 1 hr to 5 hrs 59 min, 6 hrs to 24 hrs], subsq enc **387**
S06.81[7,8,9]A	Inj of rt int carotid artery, intracranial portion, NEC w/ LOC of [any dur w/ death d/t brain inj prior to regain cnscness, any dur w/ death d/t oth cause prior to regain cnscness, unsp dur], init enc **36, 37, 419, 431**
S06.81[7,8,9]S	Inj of rt int carotid artery, intracranial portion, NEC w/ LOC of [any dur w/ death d/t brain inj prior to regain cnscness, any dur w/ death d/t oth cause prior to regain cnscness, unsp dur], seq **40**
S06.81[7,8,9]D	Inj of rt int carotid artery, intracranial portion, NEC w/ LOC of [any dur w/ death d/t brain inj prior to regain cnscness, any dur w/ death d/t oth cause prior to regain cnscness, unsp dur], subsq enc **387**
S06.81[5,6]A	Inj of rt int carotid artery, intracranial portion, NEC, w/ LOC > 24 hrs [w/ return to pre-existing conscious lvl, w/o return to pre-existing conscious lvl w/ patient surviving], init enc **37, 418, 431**
S06.81[1,2,3,4]A	Inj of rt int carotid artery, intracranial portion, NEC, w/ LOC of [30 min or less, 31 min to 59 min, 1 hr to 5 hrs 59 min, 6 hrs to 24 hrs], init enc **37, 418, 431**
S06.812A	Inj of Rt int carotid, intcr w LOC of 31-59 min, init **37**
S06.810A	Inj of Rt int carotid, intcr w/o LOC, init **37, 418, 431**
S06.810S	Inj of Rt int carotid, intcr w/o LOC, seq **40**
S06.810D	Inj of Rt int carotid, intcr w/o LOC, subs **387**
P12.4	Inj of scalp of newborn d/t monitoring equipment **289**
S74.0[0,1,2]XA	Inj of sciatic nerve at hip & thigh lvl, [unsp, rt, lt] leg, init enc **34, 436**
S74.0[0,1,2]XS	Inj of sciatic nerve at hip & thigh lvl, [unsp, rt, lt] leg, seq **40**
S24.4XXA	Inj of thoracic sympathetic nervous sys, init enc **34, 420**
S24.4XXS	Inj of thoracic sympathetic nervous sys, seq **40**
S24.4XXD	Inj of thoracic sympathetic nervous sys, subs enc **389**
S84.0[0,1,2]XA	Inj of tibial nerve at lwr leg lvl, [unsp, rt, lt] leg, init enc **34, 428, 436**
S84.0[0,1,2]XS	Inj of tibial nerve at lwr leg lvl, [unsp, rt, lt] leg, seq **40**
S04.3[0,1,2]XA	Inj of trigeminal nerve, [unsp, rt, lt] side, init enc **34**
S04.3[0,1,2]XS	Inj of trigeminal nerve, [unsp, rt, lt] side, seq **39**
S04.3[0,1,2]XD	Inj of trigeminal nerve, [unsp, rt, lt] side, subsq enc **386**
S04.2[0,1,2]XA	Inj of trochlear nerve, [unsp, rt, lt] side, init enc **34**
S04.2[0,1,2]XS	Inj of trochlear nerve, [unsp, rt, lt] side, seq **39**
S04.2[0,1,2]XD	Inj of trochlear nerve, [unsp, rt, lt] side, subsq enc **386**
S54.0[0,1,2]XA	Inj of ulnar nerve at forearm lvl, [unsp, rt, lt] arm, init enc **34, 435**
S54.0[0,1,2]XS	Inj of ulnar nerve at forearm lvl, [unsp, rt, lt] arm, seq **40**
S54.0[0,1,2]XD	Inj of ulnar nerve at forearm lvl, [unsp, rt, lt] arm, subsq enc **392**
S54.01XA	Inj of ulnar nerve at forearm lvl, rt arm, init **424**
S44.0[0,1,2]XA	Inj of ulnar nerve at upr arm lvl, [unsp, rt, lt] arm, init enc **34, 434**
S44.0[0,1,2]XS	Inj of ulnar nerve at upr arm lvl, [unsp, rt, lt] arm, seq **40**
S44.0[0,1,2]XD	Inj of ulnar nerve at upr arm lvl, [unsp, rt, lt] arm, subsq enc **391**
S64.0[0,1,2]XA	Inj of ulnar nerve at wrist and hand lvl of [unsp, rt, lt] arm, init enc **34, 435**
S64.0[0,1,2]XD	Inj of ulnar nerve at wrist and hand lvl of [unsp, rt, lt] arm, subsq enc **396**
S64.0[0,1,2]XS	Inj of ulnar nerve at wrist and hand lvl, [unsp, rt, lt] arm, seq **40**
S15.9XXA	Inj of unsp bld vessel at neck lvl, init enc **5**
S15.9XXD	Inj of unsp bld vessel at neck lvl, subs enc **388**
S04.9XXA	Inj of unsp cranial nerve, init enc **34, 417**
S04.9XXS	Inj of unsp cranial nerve, seq **39**
S04.9XXD	Inj of unsp cranial nerve, subsq enc **386**
S35.50XA	Inj of unsp iliac bld vessel(s), init enc **359, 421, 432**
S35.50XS	Inj of unsp iliac bld vessel(s), seq **100**
S35.50XD	Inj of unsp iliac bld vessel(s), subs enc **390**
S27.9XXA	Inj of unsp intrathoracic organ, init enc **359, 421, 432**
S27.9XXS	Inj of unsp intrathoracic organ, seq **69**
S27.9XXD	Inj of unsp intrathoracic organ, subs enc **389**
S94.9[0,1,2]XA	Inj of unsp nerve at ankle and foot lvl, [unsp leg, rt, lt], init enc **34, 430, 436**
S94.9[0,1,2]XD	Inj of unsp nerve at ankle and foot lvl, [unsp leg, rt, lt], subsq enc **399**
S94.9[0,1,2]XS	Inj of unsp nerve at ankle and foot lvl, [unsp, rt, lt] leg, seq **40**
S54.9[0,1,2]XA	Inj of unsp nerve at forearm lvl, [unsp, rt, lt] arm, init enc **34, 424**
S54.9[0,1,2]XS	Inj of unsp nerve at forearm lvl, [unsp, rt, lt] arm, seq **40**
S54.9[0,1,2]XD	Inj of unsp nerve at forearm lvl, [unsp, rt, lt] arm, subsq enc **392**
S74.9[0,1,2]XA	Inj of unsp nerve at hip & thigh lvl, [unsp, rt, lt] leg, init enc **34, 426, 436**
S74.9[0,1,2]XS	Inj of unsp nerve at hip & thigh lvl, [unsp, rt, lt] leg, seq **40**
S74.9[0,1,2]XD	Inj of unsp nerve at hip & thigh lvl, [unsp, rt, lt] leg, subsq enc **397**
S84.9[0,1,2]XA	Inj of unsp nerve at lwr leg lvl, [unsp, rt, lt] leg, init enc **34, 428, 436**
S84.9[0,1,2]XS	Inj of unsp nerve at lwr leg lvl, [unsp, rt, lt] leg, seq **40**
S84.9[0,1,2]XD	Inj of unsp nerve at lwr leg lvl, [unsp, rt, lt] leg, subsq enc **398**
S44.9[0,1,2]XA	Inj of unsp nerve at shldr and upr arm lvl, [unsp, rt, lt] arm, init enc **34**
S44.9[0,1,2]XS	Inj of unsp nerve at shldr and upr arm lvl, [unsp, rt, lt] arm, seq **40**
S44.9[0,1,2]XD	Inj of unsp nerve at shldr and upr arm lvl, [unsp, rt, lt] arm, subsq enc **391**
S64.9[0,1,2]XA	Inj of unsp nerve at wrist and hand lvl of [unsp, rt, lt] arm, init enc **34, 425**
S64.9[0,1,2]XD	Inj of unsp nerve at wrist and hand lvl of [unsp, rt, lt] arm, subsq enc **396**
S64.9[0,1,2]XS	Inj of unsp nerve at wrist and hand lvl, [unsp, rt, lt] arm, seq **40**
S24.9XXA	Inj of unsp nerve of thorax, init enc **34, 433**
S24.9XXS	Inj of unsp nerve of thorax, seq **40**
S24.9XXD	Inj of unsp nerve of thorax, subsq enc **389**
S14.9XXA	Inj of unsp nerves of neck, init enc **34**
S14.9XXS	Inj of unsp nerves of neck, seq **40**
S04.1[0,1,2]XD	Inj of visual cortex of [rt, lt, unsp] eye, subsq enc **386**
S04.04[1,2,9]A	Inj of visual cortex, [rt, lt, unsp] eye, init enc **39**
S04.04[1,2,9]S	Inj of visual cortex, [rt, lt, unsp] eye, seq **39**
S04.04[1,2,9]D	Inj of visual cortex, [rt, lt, unsp] eye, subsq enc **386**
S34.6XXA	Inj prph nerve(s) at abd, low back and pelvis lvl, init **34**
S34.6XXS	Inj prph nerve(s) at abd, low back and pelvis lvl, seq **40**
S34.6XXD	Inj prph nerve(s) at abd, low back and pelvis lvl, subs **390**
S06.811A	Inj Rt int carotid, intcr w LOC of 30 min or less, init **37**
S34.9XXA	Inj unsp nerves at abd, low back and pelvis lvl, init **34**
S34.9XXS	Inj unsp nerves at abd, low back and pelvis lvl, seq **40**
S34.9XXD	Inj unsp nerves at abd, low back and pelvis lvl, subs **390**
O9A.21[1,2,3]	Inj, poison and certain oth consequences of ext causes compl preg, [1st, 2nd, 3rd] trmstr **277, 278**
T14.90	Inj, unsp **361, 430**
O9A.22	Inj/poisn/oth conseq of ext causes comp childbirth **273, 275**
O9A.219	Inj/poisn/oth conseq of ext causes comp preg, unsp trmstr **281**
O9A.23	Inj/poisn/oth conseq of ext causes comp the puerperium **272, 276**
S60.46[8,9]D	Insect bite (nonenvomous) of [oth, unsp] finger, subsq enc **394**
S60.46[0,1]D	Insect bite (nonenvomous) of [rt, lt] index finger, subsq enc **394**
S60.46[6,7]D	Insect bite (nonenvomous) of [rt, lt] little finger, subsq enc **394**
S60.46[2,3]D	Insect bite (nonenvomous) of [rt, lt] mid finger, subsq enc **394**
S60.46[4,5]D	Insect bite (nonenvomous) of [rt, lt] ring finger, subsq enc **394**
S00.56[1,2]S	Insect bite (nonvenomous) of [lip, oral cavity], seq **224**
S60.46[8,9]S	Insect bite (nonvenomous) of [oth, unsp] finger, seq **228**
S30.86[2,3]S	Insect bite (nonvenomous) of [penis, scrotum and testes], seq **226**
S20.46[1,2,9]S	Insect bite (nonvenomous) of [rt, lt, unsp] back wall of thorax, seq **225**
S20.46[1,2,9]D	Insect bite (nonvenomous) of [rt, lt, unsp] back wall of thorax, subsq enc **388**
S00.46[1,2,9]S	Insect bite (nonvenomous) of [rt, lt, unsp] ear, seq **224**
S50.36[1,2,9]S	Insect bite (nonvenomous) of [rt, lt, unsp] elbow, seq **227**
S50.36[1,2,9]D	Insect bite (nonvenomous) of [rt, lt, unsp] elbow, subsq enc **392**
S00.26[1,2,9]A	Insect bite (nonvenomous) of [rt, lt, unsp] eyelid and periocular area, init enc **46**
S00.26[1,2,9]S	Insect bite (nonvenomous) of [rt, lt, unsp] eyelid and periocular area, seq **224**
S50.86[1,2,9]S	Insect bite (nonvenomous) of [rt, lt, unsp] forearm, seq **227**
S50.86[1,2,9]D	Insect bite (nonvenomous) of [rt, lt, unsp] forearm, subsq enc **392**
S20.36[1,2,9]S	Insect bite (nonvenomous) of [rt, lt, unsp] front wall of thorax, seq **225**
S20.36[1,2,9]D	Insect bite (nonvenomous) of [rt, lt, unsp] front wall of thorax, subsq enc **388**

S60.56[1,2,9]S	Insect bite (nonvenomous) of [rt, lt, unsp] hand, seq 228
S60.56[1,2,9]D	Insect bite (nonvenomous) of [rt, lt, unsp] hand, subsq enc 394
S40.26[1,2,9]A	Insect bite (nonvenomous) of [rt, lt, unsp] shldr, init enc 234
S40.26[1,2,9]S	Insect bite (nonvenomous) of [rt, lt, unsp] shldr, seq 227
S40.26[1,2,9]D	Insect bite (nonvenomous) of [rt, lt, unsp] shldr, subsq enc 391
S60.36[1,2,9]S	Insect bite (nonvenomous) of [rt, lt, unsp] thumb, seq 228
S60.36[1,2,9]D	Insect bite (nonvenomous) of [rt, lt, unsp] thumb, subsq enc 394
S40.86[1,2,9]A	Insect bite (nonvenomous) of [rt, lt, unsp] upr arm, init enc 234
S40.86[1,2,9]S	Insect bite (nonvenomous) of [rt, lt, unsp] upr arm, seq 227
S40.86[1,2,9]D	Insect bite (nonvenomous) of [rt, lt, unsp] upr arm, subsq enc 391
S60.86[1,2,9]S	Insect bite (nonvenomous) of [rt, lt, unsp] wrist, seq 228
S60.86[1,2,9]D	Insect bite (nonvenomous) of [rt, lt, unsp] wrist, subsq enc 394
S60.46[0,1]S	Insect bite (nonvenomous) of [rt, lt] index finger, seq 228
S60.46[6,7]S	Insect bite (nonvenomous) of [rt, lt] little finger, seq 228
S60.46[2,3]S	Insect bite (nonvenomous) of [rt, lt] mid finger, seq 228
S60.46[4,5]S	Insect bite (nonvenomous) of [rt, lt] ring finger, seq 228
S30.861S	Insect bite (nonvenomous) of abd wall, seq 226
S30.867S	Insect bite (nonvenomous) of anus, seq 226
S20.16[1,2,9]S	Insect bite (nonvenomous) of breast, [rt, lt, unsp] breast, seq 225
S20.16[1,2,9]D	Insect bite (nonvenomous) of breast, [rt, lt, unsp] breast, subsq enc 388
S30.860S	Insect bite (nonvenomous) of lwr back and pelvis, seq 226
S00.36XS	Insect bite (nonvenomous) of nose, seq 224
S00.86XS	Insect bite (nonvenomous) of oth part of head, seq 224
S00.06XS	Insect bite (nonvenomous) of scalp, seq 224
S10.16XS	Insect bite (nonvenomous) of throat, seq 225
S30.86[5,6]S	Insect bite (nonvenomous) of unsp ext genital organs, [male, female], seq 226
S00.96XS	Insect bite (nonvenomous) of unsp part of head, seq 224
S20.96XS	Insect bite (nonvenomous) of unsp parts of thorax, seq 225
S30.864S	Insect bite (nonvenomous) of vagina and vulva, seq 226
S90.56[1,2,9]S	Insect bite (nonvenomous), [rt, lt, unsp] ankle, seq 230
S90.86[1,2,9]S	Insect bite (nonvenomous), [rt, lt, unsp] foot, seq 230
S90.46[1,2,3]A	Insect bite (nonvenomous), [rt, lt, unsp] great toe, init enc 428
S90.46[1,2,3]S	Insect bite (nonvenomous), [rt, lt, unsp] great toe, seq 230
S90.46[1,2,3]D	Insect bite (nonvenomous), [rt, lt, unsp] great toe, subsq enc 399
S70.26[1,2,9]S	Insect bite (nonvenomous), [rt, lt, unsp] hip, seq 229
S80.26[1,2,9]S	Insect bite (nonvenomous), [rt, lt, unsp] knee, seq 229
S90.46[4,5,6]A	Insect bite (nonvenomous), [rt, lt, unsp] lesser toe(s), init enc 428
S90.46[4,5,6]S	Insect bite (nonvenomous), [rt, lt, unsp] lesser toe(s), seq 230
S90.46[4,5,6]D	Insect bite (nonvenomous), [rt, lt, unsp] lesser toe(s), subsq enc 399
S80.86[1,2,9]S	Insect bite (nonvenomous), [rt, lt, unsp] lwr leg, seq 229
S70.36[1,2,9]S	Insect bite (nonvenomous), [rt, lt, unsp] thigh, seq 229
S30.86[0,1,2,3,4, 5,6,7]D	Insect bite [nonvenomous] of [lwr back and pelvis, abd wall, penis, scrotum and testes, vagina and vulva, unsp ext genital organs male, unsp ext genital organs female, anus], subsq enc 389
S10.86XS	Insect bite of oth spec part of neck, seq 225
S10.96XS	Insect bite of unsp part of neck, seq 225
G47.0*	Insomnia 311
P59.1	Inspissated bile synd 282
T84.02[2,3]A	Instability of int [rt, lt] knee prosthesis, init enc 183
T84.02[2,3]S	Instability of int [rt, lt] knee prosthesis, seq 375
T84.02[2,3]D	Instability of int [rt, lt] knee prosthesis, subsq enc 411
B83.4	Int hirudiniasis 233
H52.51[1,2,3,9]	Int ophthalmoplegia (complete) (total), [rt, lt, bilat, unsp] eye 45
S06.891A	Intcran inj w LOC of 30 min or less, init 37
S06.892A	Intcran inj w LOC of 31-59 min, init 37
S06.890A	Intcran inj w/o LOC, init enc 37, 419, 431
S06.890D	Intcran inj w/o LOC, subs enc 387
G07	Intcrn & intraspinal abscs & granuloma in dis classd elsw 11, 15, 41, 283
R90.0	Intcrn space-occupying lesion found on dx imaging of cnsl 234
R07.82	Intercostal pain 103
H50.3*	Intermittent heterotropia 46
H05.2[5,6][1,2,3,9]	[Intermittent, Pulsating] exophthalmos, [rt, lt, bilat, unsp] eye 45
H51.2*	Internuclear ophthalmoplegia 38
P25*	Interstit emphysema and rel cond origin in perinat period 282
N30.1*	Interstitial cystitis (chr) 255
J98.2	Interstitial emphysema 68, 284

M60.1*	Interstitial myositis 167
M99.5*	Intervertebral disc stenosis of neural canal 165
B81.3	Intestinal angiostrongyliasis 116
B81.1	Intestinal capillariasis 116
K90.9	Intestinal malabsorption, unsp 116
P76.2	Intestinal obstruction d/t inspissated milk 282
P76.9	Intestinal obstruction of newborn, unsp 288
B78.0	Intestinal strongyloidiasis 116, 438
Z94.82	Intestine transplant status 413
R19.0*	Intra-abd and pelvic swelling, mass and lump 116
P39.2	Intra-amniotic infxn affecting newborn, NEC 282
I51.3	Intracardiac thrombosis, NEC 102
G06.0	Intracranial abscess and granuloma 11, 15
G06*	Intracranial and intraspinal abscess and granuloma 41, 283
G08	Intracranial and intraspinal phlebitis and thrombophlebitis 11, 15, 38
G97.2	Intracranial hypotension following ventricular shunting 38, 283
P10*	Intracranial lac and hemor d/t birth inj 282
P52*	Intracranial nontraumatic hemor of newborn 282
L76*	Intraop and postprocedural comp of skin, SQ 367
D78*	Intraop and postprocedural comp of the spleen 367
I97.4*	Intraop, hemor/hemtom of a circ sys org comp a procedure 367
K91.6*	Intraop hemor/hemtom of a dgstv sys org comp a procedure 367
N99.6*	Intraop hemor/hemtom of a GU sys org comp a procedure 368
G97.3*	Intraop hemor/hemtom of a nervous sys org comp a procedure 38
J95.6*	Intraop hemor/hemtom of a resp sys org comp a procedure 367
H95.2*	Intraop hemor/hemtom of ear/mastd compl a procedure 367
H59.1*	Intraop hemor/hemtom of eye and adnexa comp a procedure 367
I97.7*	Intraoperative cardiac functional disturbances 103, 284
I97.81[0,1]	Intraoperative cerebrovascular infarction during [cardiac, oth] surgery 38
E36*	Intraoperative comp of endocrine sys 367
G06.1	Intraspinal abscess and granuloma 11, 15
K56.1	Intussusception 284
B44.0	Invasive pulmn aspergillosis 67
E01*	Iodine-deficiency related thyroid d/o and allied cond 247
H20*	Iridocyclitis 46
D50*	Iron deficiency anemia 293
N30.4*	Irradiation cystitis 256
R45.4	Irritability and anger 310
K58*	Irritable bowel synd 116
L24*	Irritant contact dermatitis 233
K13.6	Irritative hyperplasia of oral mucosa 4
N28.0	Ischemia and infarction of kidney 256
I25.5	Ischemic cardiomyopathy 102
S73.12[1,2,9]A	Ischiocapsular (lgmt) sprain of hip [rt, lt, unsp] init enc 162
R80.0	Isolated proteinuria 255
N06*	Isolated proteinuria with spec morphological lesion 256
A07.3	Isosporiasis 438
A83.0	Japanese encephalitis 10, 15
R68.84	Jaw pain 5, 59
M25.9	Jt d/o, unsp 167
M24.9	Jt derangement, unsp 194
M41.1*	Juvenile and adolescent idiopathic scoliosis 125
M08*	Juvenile arthritis 164
A50.45	Juvenile general paresis 41
C93.3*	Juvenile myelomonocytic leukemia 303, 305
M91*	Juvenile osteochondrosis of hip and pelvis 167
M42.0*	Juvenile osteochondrosis of spine 125
M30.2	Juvenile polyarteritis 164
C46*	Kaposi's sarcoma 438
C46.[0,1,7,9]	Kaposi's sarcoma of [skin, soft tissue, oth sites, unsp] 233
C46.4	Kaposi's sarcoma of gastrointestinal sites 114
C46.5*	Kaposi's sarcoma of lung 67
C46.3	Kaposi's sarcoma of lymph nodes 295, 303, 305
C46.2	Kaposi's sarcoma of palate 3, 57
Q98.5	Karyotype 47, XYY 265, 270
H49.81*	Kearns-Sayre synd 247
H16.2*	Keratoconjunctivitis 46
L86	Keratoderma in dz classified elsw 234

H59.Ø1*	Keratopathy (bullous aphakic) following cataract surgery 367
P57*	Kernicterus 282
Z52.4	Kidney donor 256
Z94.Ø	Kidney transplant status 2, 256
M48.2*	Kissing spine 165
F63.2	Kleptomania 310
Q76.1	Klippel-Feil synd 195
P14.1	Klumpke's paralysis d/t birth inj 288
E75.23	Krabbe dz 32
E4Ø	Kwashiorkor 246
A98.2	Kyasanur Forest dz 307
I27.1	Kyphoscoliotic heart dz 103
M4Ø*	Kyphosis and lordosis 164
O69.8[1,2,9] X[1,2,3,4,5,9]	Labor and delivery comp by [cord around neck w/o compression, oth cord entanglement w/o compression, oth cord comp], fetus [1, 2, 3, 4, 5, oth] 273, 275
O69.8[1,2]XØ	Labor and delivery comp by [cord around neck, oth cord entanglement], w/o compression, N/A or unsp 278
O68	Labor and delivery comp by abnlt of fetal acid-base balance 273, 275
O69.1*	Labor and delivery comp by cord around neck, w compression 273, 275
O67*	Labor and delivery comp by intrapartum hemor, NEC 273, 274
O69.2*	Labor and delivery comp by oth cord entangle, w compression 273, 275
O69.8[1,2,9]XØ	Labor and delivery complicated by [cord around neck without compression, oth cord entanglement without compression, oth cord comp], N/A or unsp 280
O69.9*	Labor and delivery complicated by cord comp, unsp 273, 275
O69.89XØ	Labor and delivery complicated by oth cord comp, unsp 278
O69.Ø*	Labor and delivery complicated by prolapse of cord 273, 275
O69.3*	Labor and delivery complicated by short cord 273, 275
O69.4*	Labor and delivery complicated by vasa previa 273, 275
O69.5*	Labor and delivery complicated by vascular lesion of cord 273, 275
H83.2*	Labyrinthine dysfunction 57
H83.1*	Labyrinthine fistula 58
H83.Ø*	Labyrinthitis 57
SØ1.5[1,2][1,2]S	Lac [w/o, w/] FB of [lip, oral cavity], seq 224
S21.4[1,2][1,2,9]A	Lac [w/o, w/] FB of [rt, lt, unsp] back wall of thorax w/ penetration into thoracic cavity, init enc 359, 432
S21.4[1,2][1,2,9]S	Lac [w/o, w/] FB of [rt, lt, unsp] back wall of thorax w/ penetration into thoracic cavity, seq 225
SØ1.4[1,2][1,2,9] [A,S]	Lac [w/o, w/] FB of [rt, lt, unsp] cheek and temporomandibular area, [init enc, seq] 224
SØ1.3[1,2][1,2,9]S	Lac [w/o, w/] FB of [rt, lt, unsp] ear, seq 224
SØ1.1[1,2][1,2,9]S	Lac [w/o, w/] FB of [rt, lt, unsp] eyelid and periocular area, seq 224
S21.3[1,2][1,2,9]A	Lac [w/o, w/] FB of [rt, lt, unsp] front wall of thorax w/ penetration into thoracic cavity, init enc 359, 431
S21.3[1,2][1,2,9]S	Lac [w/o, w/] FB of [rt, lt, unsp] front wall of thorax w/ penetration into thoracic cavity, seq 225
S11.Ø1[1,2]A	Lac [w/o, w/] FB of larynx, init enc 58
S31.82[1,2][A,S]	Lac [w/o, w/] FB of lt buttock, [init enc, seq] 227
SØ1.2[1,2]XA	Lac [w/o, w/] FB of nose, init enc 58
SØ1.8[1,2]X[A,S]	Lac [w/o, w/] FB of oth part of head, [init enc, seq] 224
S11.8[1,2]X[A,S]	Lac [w/o, w/] FB of oth spec part of neck, [init enc, seq] 225
S31.2[1,2]XS	Lac [w/o, w/] FB of penis, seq 226
S11.2[1,2]XA	Lac [w/o, w/] FB of pharynx and cervical esophagus, init enc 58
S31.81[1,2][A,S]	Lac [w/o, w/] FB of rt buttock, [init enc, seq] 227
SØ1.Ø[1,2]X[A,S]	Lac [w/o, w/] FB of scalp, [init enc, seq] 224
S11.Ø2[1,2]A	Lac [w/o, w/] FB of trachea, init enc 67
S31.8Ø[1,2][A,S]	Lac [w/o, w/] FB of unsp buttock, [init enc, seq] 227
SØ1.9[1,2]X[A,S]	Lac [w/o, w/] FB of unsp part of head, [init enc, seq] 224
S11.9[1,2]X[A,S]	Lac [w/o, w/] FB of unsp part of neck, [init enc, seq] 225
S31.4[1,2]XS	Lac [w/o, w/] FB of vagina and vulva, seq 226
S11.Ø3[1,2]A	Lac [w/o, w/] FB of vocal cord, init enc 58
S91.Ø[1,2][1,2,9] D	Lac [w/o, w/] FB, [rt, lt, unsp] ankle, subsq enc 399
S36.53[Ø,1,2,3,8, 9]A	Lac of [ascending [rt] colon, transv colon, descending [lt] colon, sigmoid colon, oth part of colon,unsp part of colon], init enc 432
S36.53[Ø,1,2,3,8, 9]D	Lac of [ascending [rt] colon, transv colon, descending [lt] colon, sigmoid colon, oth part of colon,unsp part of colon], subsq enc 391

S36.43[Ø,8,9]D	Lac of [duodenum, oth part of sm intestine, unsp part of sm intestine], subsq enc 391
S36.23[Ø,1,2,9]D	Lac of [head, body, tail, unsp part] of pancreas, subsq enc 390
S36.23[Ø,1,2,9]A	Lac of [head, body, tail, unsp part] of pancreas, unsp degree, init enc 124, 432
S36.23[Ø,1,2,9]S	Lac of [head, body, tail, unsp part] of pancreas, unsp degree, seq 117
S96.[2,8,9] 2[1,2,9]A	Lac of [intrinsic, oth, unsp] muscle and tndn at ankle and foot lvl, [rt, lt, unsp] foot, init enc 204
S86.[8,9]2[1,2,9] A	Lac of [oth, unsp] muscle(s) and tndn(s) at lwr leg lvl, [rt, lt, unsp] leg, init enc 204
S86.[8,9]2[1,2,9]S	Lac of [oth, unsp] muscle(s) and tndn(s) at lwr leg lvl, [rt, lt, unsp] leg, seq 229
S56.[8,9]2[1,2,9] A	Lac of [oth, unsp] muscles, fascia and tndns at forearm lvl, [rt, lt, unsp] arm, init enc 199
S56.[8,9]2[1,2,9]S	Lac of [oth, unsp] muscles, fascia and tndns at forearm lvl, [rt, lt, unsp] arm, seq 227
S46.[8,9]2[1,2,9] A	Lac of [oth, unsp] muscles, fascia and tndns at shldr and upr arm lvl, [rt, lt, unsp] arm, init enc 197
S46.[8,9]2[1,2,9]S	Lac of [oth, unsp] muscles, fascia and tndns at shldr and upr arm lvl, [rt, lt, unsp] arm, seq 227
S66.[8,9]2[1,2,9] A	Lac of [oth, unsp] spec muscles, fascia and tndns at wrist and hand lvl, [rt, lt, unsp] hand, init enc 200
S35.41[1,2,3,4,5, 6]D	Lac of [rt renal artery, lt renal artery, unsp renal artery, rt renal vein, lt renal vein, unsp renal vein], subsq enc 390
S86.Ø2[1,2,9]A	Lac of [rt, lt, unsp] Achilles tndn, init enc 203
S86.Ø2[1,2,9]S	Lac of [rt, lt, unsp] Achilles tndn, seq 229
S37.Ø3[1,2,9]D	Lac of [rt, lt, unsp] kidney, subsq enc 391
S37.Ø3[1,2,9]A	Lac of [rt, lt, unsp] kidney, unsp degree, init enc 256
S37.Ø3[1,2,9]S	Lac of [rt, lt, unsp] kidney, unsp degree, seq 118
S76.12[1,2,9]A	Lac of [rt, lt, unsp] quadriceps muscle, fascia and tndn, init enc 202
S76.12[1,2,9]S	Lac of [rt, lt, unsp] quadriceps muscle, fascia and tndn, seq 229
S35.41[1,2,3]S	Lac of [rt, lt, unsp] renal artery, seq 100
S35.41[4,5,6]S	Lac of [rt, lt, unsp] renal vein, seq 100
S31.62[Ø,1,2,3,4, 5,9]D	Lac of abd wall w/ FB, [rt upr quadrant, lt upr quadrant, epigastric rgn, rt lwr quadrant, lt lwr quadrant, periumbilic rgn, unsp quadrant], w/ penetration into peritoneal cavity, subsq enc 390
S31.12[Ø,1,2,3,4, 5,9]D	Lac of abd wall w/ FB, [rt upr quadrant, lt upr quadrant, epigastric rgn, rt lwr quadrant, lt lwr quadrant, periumbilic rgn, unsp quadrant], w/o penetration into peritoneal cavity, subsq enc 390
S31.12[3,4]S	Lac of abd wall w/ FB, [rt, lt] lwr quadrant w/o penetration into peritoneal cavity, seq 226
S31.12[Ø,1]S	Lac of abd wall w/ FB, [rt, lt] upr quadrant w/o penetration into peritoneal cavity, seq 226
S76.22[1,2,9]A	Lac of adductor muscle, fascia and tndn of [rt, lt, unsp] thigh, init enc 202
S76.22[1,2,9]S	Lac of adductor muscle, fascia and tndn of [rt, lt, unsp] thigh, seq 229
S85.14[1,2,9]S	Lac of ant tibial artery, [rt, lt, unsp] leg, seq 101
S36.53Ø[A,S]	Lac of ascending [rt] colon, [init enc, seq] 118
S45.Ø1[1,2,9]S	Lac of axillary artery, [rt, lt, unsp] side, seq 100
S45.21[1,2,9]S	Lac of axillary or brachial vein, [rt, lt, unsp] side, seq 100
S45.21[1,2,9]D	Lac of axillary or brachial vein, [rt, lt, unsp] side, subsq enc 392
S65.51[8,9]D	Lac of bld vessel of [oth, unsp] finger, subsq enc 396
S65.51[Ø,1,2,3,4, 5,6,7,8,9]S	Lac of bld vessel of [rt index, lt index, rt mid, lt mid, rt ring, lt ring, rt little, lt little, oth, unsp] finger, seq 101
S65.51[1,2,9]S	Lac of bld vessel of [rt, lt, unsp] thumb, seq 101
S65.41[1,2,9]D	Lac of bld vessel of [rt, lt, unsp] thumb, subsq enc 396
S65.51[Ø,1]D	Lac of bld vessel of [rt, lt] index finger, subsq enc 396
S65.51[6,7]D	Lac of bld vessel of [rt, lt] little finger, subsq enc 396
S65.51[2,3]D	Lac of bld vessel of [rt, lt] mid finger, subsq enc 396
S65.51[4,5]D	Lac of bld vessel of [rt, lt] ring finger, subsq enc 396
S45.11[1,2,9]S	Lac of brachial artery, [rt, lt, unsp] side, seq 100
S45.11[1,2,9]D	Lac of brachial artery, [rt, lt, unsp] side, subsq enc 391
S27.43[1,2,9]A	Lac of bronchus, [unilat, bilat, unsp], init enc 67
S27.43[1,2,9]S	Lac of bronchus, [unilat, bilat, unsp], seq 69
S27.43[1,2,9]D	Lac of bronchus, [unilat, bilat, unsp], subsq enc 389
S65.31[1,2,9]S	Lac of deep palmar arch of [rt, lt, unsp] hand, seq 101
S65.31[1,2,9]D	Lac of deep palmar arch of [rt, lt, unsp] hand, subsq enc 396
S36.532[A,S]	Lac of descending [lt] colon, [init enc, seq] 118
S95.Ø1[1,2,9]S	Lac of dorsal artery of [rt, lt, unsp] foot, seq 101
S95.21[1,2,9]S	Lac of dorsal vein of [rt, lt, unsp] foot, seq 101
S36.43Ø[A,S]	Lac of duodenum, [init enc, seq] 118

S66.32[8,9]S	Lac of extensor muscle, fascia and tndn of [oth, unsp] finger at wrist and hand lvl, seq **229**
S66.32[8,9]D	Lac of extensor muscle, fascia and tndn of [oth, unsp] finger at wrist and hand lvl, subsq enc **397**
S66.32[0,1,2,3,4, 5,6,7,8,9]A	Lac of extensor muscle, fascia and tndn of [rt index, lt index, rt mid, lt mid, rt ring, lt ring, rt little, lt little, oth, unsp] finger at wrist and hand lvl, init enc **200**
S56.42[1,2,3,4,5, 6,7,8,9]A	Lac of extensor muscle, fascia and tndn of [rt index, lt index, rt mid, lt mid, rt ring, lt ring, rt little, lt little] finger at forearm lvl, init enc **199**
S56.32[1,2,9]A	Lac of extensor muscle, fascia and tndn of [rt, lt, unsp] thumb at forearm lvl, init enc **199**
S66.22[1,2,9]A	Lac of extensor muscle, fascia and tndn of [rt, lt, unsp] thumb at wrist and hand lvl, init enc **200**
S66.22[1,2,9]S	Lac of extensor muscle, fascia and tndn of [rt, lt, unsp] thumb at wrist and hand lvl, seq **229**
S66.22[1,2,9]D	Lac of extensor muscle, fascia and tndn of [rt, lt, unsp] thumb at wrist and hand lvl, subsq enc **397**
S56.42[1,2]S	Lac of extensor muscle, fascia and tndn of [rt, lt] index finger at forearm lvl, seq **227**
S56.42[1,2]D	Lac of extensor muscle, fascia and tndn of [rt, lt] index finger at forearm lvl, subsq enc **393**
S66.32[0,1]S	Lac of extensor muscle, fascia and tndn of [rt, lt] index finger at wrist and hand lvl, seq **229**
S66.32[0,1]D	Lac of extensor muscle, fascia and tndn of [rt, lt] index finger at wrist and hand lvl, subsq enc **397**
S56.42[7,8]S	Lac of extensor muscle, fascia and tndn of [rt, lt] little finger at forearm lvl, seq **227**
S56.42[7,8]D	Lac of extensor muscle, fascia and tndn of [rt, lt] little finger at forearm lvl, subsq enc **393**
S66.32[6,7]S	Lac of extensor muscle, fascia and tndn of [rt, lt] little finger at wrist and hand lvl, seq **229**
S66.32[6,7]D	Lac of extensor muscle, fascia and tndn of [rt, lt] little finger at wrist and hand lvl, subsq enc **397**
S56.42[3,4]S	Lac of extensor muscle, fascia and tndn of [rt, lt] mid finger at forearm lvl, seq **227**
S56.42[3,4]D	Lac of extensor muscle, fascia and tndn of [rt, lt] mid finger at forearm lvl, subsq enc **393**
S66.32[2,3]S	Lac of extensor muscle, fascia and tndn of [rt, lt] mid finger at wrist and hand lvl, seq **229**
S66.32[2,3]D	Lac of extensor muscle, fascia and tndn of [rt, lt] mid finger at wrist and hand lvl, subsq enc **397**
S56.42[5,6]S	Lac of extensor muscle, fascia and tndn of [rt, lt] ring finger at forearm lvl, seq **227**
S56.42[5,6]D	Lac of extensor muscle, fascia and tndn of [rt, lt] ring finger at forearm lvl, subsq enc **393**
S66.32[4,5]S	Lac of extensor muscle, fascia and tndn of [rt, lt] ring finger at wrist and hand lvl, seq **229**
S66.32[4,5]D	Lac of extensor muscle, fascia and tndn of [rt, lt] ring finger at wrist and hand lvl, subsq enc **397**
S56.32[1,2,9]S	Lac of extensor or abductor muscles, fascia and tndns of [rt, lt, unsp] thumb at forearm lvl, seq **227**
S56.32[1,2,9]D	Lac of extensor or abductor muscles, fascia and tndns of [rt, lt, unsp] thumb at forearm lvl, subsq enc **393**
S37.53[1,2,9]D	Lac of fallopian tube, [unilat, bilat, unsp] subsq enc **391**
S37.53[1,2,9]A	Lac of fallopian tube, [unilat, bilat, unsp], init enc **265, 270**
S37.53[1,2,9]S	Lac of fallopian tube, [unilat, bilat, unsp], seq **265, 270**
S66.12[8,9]S	Lac of flexor muscle, fascia and tndn of [oth, unsp] finger at wrist and hand lvl, seq **229**
S66.12[8,9]D	Lac of flexor muscle, fascia and tndn of [oth, unsp] finger at wrist and hand lvl, subsq enc **397**
S66.12[0,1,2,3,4, 5,6,7,8,9]A	Lac of flexor muscle, fascia and tndn of [rt index, lt index, rt mid, lt mid, rt ring, lt ring, rt little, lt little, oth, unsp] finger at wrist and hand lvl, init enc **200**
S56.12[1,2,3,4,5, 6,7,8,9]A	Lac of flexor muscle, fascia and tndn of [rt index, lt index, rt mid, lt mid, rt ring, lt ring, rt little, lt little] finger at forearm lvl, init enc **199**
S56.02[1,2,9]A	Lac of flexor muscle, fascia and tndn of [rt, lt, unsp] thumb at forearm lvl, init enc **199**
S56.02[1,2,9]S	Lac of flexor muscle, fascia and tndn of [rt, lt, unsp] thumb at forearm lvl, seq **227**
S56.02[1,2,9]D	Lac of flexor muscle, fascia and tndn of [rt, lt, unsp] thumb at forearm lvl, subsq enc **393**
S56.12[1,2]S	Lac of flexor muscle, fascia and tndn of [rt, lt] index finger at forearm lvl, seq **227**
S56.12[1,2]D	Lac of flexor muscle, fascia and tndn of [rt, lt] index finger at forearm lvl, subsq enc **393**
S66.12[0,1]S	Lac of flexor muscle, fascia and tndn of [rt, lt] index finger at wrist and hand lvl, seq **229**
S66.12[0,1]D	Lac of flexor muscle, fascia and tndn of [rt, lt] index finger at wrist and hand lvl, subsq enc **397**
S56.12[7,8]S	Lac of flexor muscle, fascia and tndn of [rt, lt] little finger at forearm lvl, seq **227**
S56.12[7,8]D	Lac of flexor muscle, fascia and tndn of [rt, lt] little finger at forearm lvl, subsq enc **393**
S66.12[6,7]S	Lac of flexor muscle, fascia and tndn of [rt, lt] little finger at wrist and hand lvl, seq **229**
S66.12[6,7]D	Lac of flexor muscle, fascia and tndn of [rt, lt] little finger at wrist and hand lvl, subsq enc **397**
S56.12[3,4]S	Lac of flexor muscle, fascia and tndn of [rt, lt] mid finger at forearm lvl, seq **227**
S56.12[3,4]D	Lac of flexor muscle, fascia and tndn of [rt, lt] mid finger at forearm lvl, subsq enc **393**
S66.12[2,3]S	Lac of flexor muscle, fascia and tndn of [rt, lt] mid finger at wrist and hand lvl, seq **229**
S66.12[2,3]D	Lac of flexor muscle, fascia and tndn of [rt, lt] mid finger at wrist and hand lvl, subsq enc **397**
S56.12[5,6]S	Lac of flexor muscle, fascia and tndn of [rt, lt] ring finger at forearm lvl, seq **227**
S56.12[5,6]D	Lac of flexor muscle, fascia and tndn of [rt, lt] ring finger at forearm lvl, subsq enc **393**
S66.12[4,5]S	Lac of flexor muscle, fascia and tndn of [rt, lt] ring finger at wrist and hand lvl, seq **229**
S66.12[4,5]D	Lac of flexor muscle, fascia and tndn of [rt, lt] ring finger at wrist and hand lvl, subsq enc **397**
S36.123A	Lac of gallbladder, init enc **124**
S85.31[1,2,9]S	Lac of greater saphenous vein at lwr leg lvl, [rt, lt, unsp] leg, seq **101**
S25.51[1,2,9]S	Lac of intercostal bld vessels, [rt, lt, unsp] side, seq **100**
S25.51[1,2,9]D	Lac of intercostal bld vessels, [rt, lt, unsp] side, subsq enc **389**
S96.22[1,2,9]S	Lac of intrinsic muscle and tndn at ankle and foot lvl, [rt, lt, unsp] foot, seq **230**
S66.52[8,9]S	Lac of intrinsic muscle, fascia and tndn of [oth, unsp] finger at wrist and hand lvl, seq **229**
S66.52[0,1,2,3,4, 5,6,7,8,9]A	Lac of intrinsic muscle, fascia and tndn of [rt index, lt index, rt mid, lt mid, rt ring, lt ring, rt little, lt little, oth, unsp] finger at wrist and hand lvl, init enc **200**
S66.42[1,2,9]A	Lac of intrinsic muscle, fascia and tndn of [rt, lt, unsp] thumb at wrist and hand lvl, init enc **200**
S66.42[1,2,9]S	Lac of intrinsic muscle, fascia and tndn of [rt, lt, unsp] thumb at wrist and hand lvl, seq **229**
S66.52[0,1]S	Lac of intrinsic muscle, fascia and tndn of [rt, lt] index finger at wrist and hand lvl, seq **229**
S66.52[6,7]S	Lac of intrinsic muscle, fascia and tndn of [rt, lt] little finger at wrist and hand lvl, seq **229**
S66.52[2,3]S	Lac of intrinsic muscle, fascia and tndn of [rt, lt] mid finger at wrist and hand lvl, seq **229**
S66.52[4,5]S	Lac of intrinsic muscle, fascia and tndn of [rt, lt] ring finger at wrist and hand lvl, seq **229**
S85.41[1,2,9]S	Lac of lesser saphenous vein at lwr leg lvl, [rt, lt, unsp] leg, seq **101**
S36.113S	Lac of liver, unsp degree, seq **117**
S66.02[1,2,9]A	Lac of long flexor muscle, fascia and tndn of [rt, lt, unsp] thumb at wrist and hand lvl, init enc **200**
S66.02[1,2,9]S	Lac of long flexor muscle, fascia and tndn of [rt, lt, unsp] thumb at wrist and hand lvl, seq **229**
S66.02[1,2,9]D	Lac of long flexor muscle, fascia and tndn of [rt, lt, unsp] thumb at wrist and hand lvl, subsq enc **397**
S27.33[1,2,9]A	Lac of lung, [unilat, bilat, unsp], init enc **67**
S27.33[1,2,9]S	Lac of lung, [unilat, bilat, unsp], seq **69**
S27.33[1,2,9]D	Lac of lung, [unilat, bilat, unsp], subsq enc **389**
S29.02[1,2,9] [A,S]	Lac of muscle and tndn of [front, back, unsp] wall of thorax, [init enc, seq] **226**
S29.02[1,2,9]D	Lac of muscle and tndn of [front, back, unsp] wall of thorax, subsq enc **389**
S09.12X[A,S]	Lac of muscle and tndn of head, [init enc, seq] **225**
S96.[0,1]2[1,2,9] A	Lac of muscle and tndn of long [flexor, extensor] muscle of toe at ankle and foot lvl, [rt, lt, unsp] foot, init enc **204**
S96.12[1,2,9]S	Lac of muscle and tndn of long extensor muscle of toe at ankle and foot lvl, [rt, lt, unsp] foot, seq **230**

Code	Description
S96.02[1,2,9]S	Lac of muscle and tndn of long flexor muscle of toe at ankle and foot lvl, [rt, lt, unsp] foot, seq **230**
S16.2XX[A,S]	Lac of muscle, fascia and tndn at neck lvl, [init enc, seq] **225**
S16.2XXA	Lac of muscle, fascia and tndn at neck lvl, init **5**
S39.02[1,2,3]D	Lac of muscle, fascia and tndn of [abd, lwr back, pelvis], subsq enc **391**
S39.02[1,2][A,S]	Lac of muscle, fascia and tndn of [abd, lwr back], [init enc, seq] **227**
S46.[1,2]2[1,2,9]A	Lac of muscle, fascia and tndn of [long head, oth parts] of biceps, [rt, lt, unsp] arm, init enc **197**
S46.[1,2]2[1,2,9]S	Lac of muscle, fascia and tndn of [long head, oth parts] of biceps, [rt, lt, unsp] arm, seq **227**
S76.02[1,2,9]A	Lac of muscle, fascia and tndn of [rt, lt, unsp] hip, init enc **202**
S76.02[1,2,9]S	Lac of muscle, fascia and tndn of [rt, lt, unsp] hip, seq **229**
S39.021A	Lac of muscle, fascia and tndn of abd, init **422**
S46.12[1,2,9]D	Lac of muscle, fascia and tndn of long head of biceps, [rt, lt, unsp] arm, subsq enc **392**
S39.022A	Lac of muscle, fascia and tndn of lwr back, init **422**
S46.22[1,2,9]D	Lac of muscle, fascia and tndn of oth parts of biceps, [rt, lt, unsp] arm, subsq enc **392**
S39.023[A,S]	Lac of muscle, fascia and tndn of pelvis, [init enc, seq] **227**
S39.023A	Lac of muscle, fascia and tndn of pelvis, init **422**
S76.32[1,2,9]A	Lac of muscle, fascia and tndn of the post muscle group at thigh lvl, [rt, lt, unsp] thigh, init enc **202**
S76.32[1,2,9]S	Lac of muscle, fascia and tndn of the post muscle group at thigh lvl, [rt, lt, unsp] thigh, seq **229**
S46.32[1,2,9]A	Lac of muscle, fascia and tndn of triceps, [rt, lt, unsp] arm, init enc **197**
S46.32[1,2,9]S	Lac of muscle, fascia and tndn of triceps, [rt, lt, unsp] arm, seq **227**
S46.32[1,2,9]D	Lac of muscle, fascia and tndn of triceps, [rt, lt, unsp] arm, subsq enc **392**
S86.22[1,2,9]S	Lac of muscle(s) and tndn(s) of ant muscle group at lwr leg lvl, [rt, lt, unsp] leg, seq **229**
S86.32[1,2,9]S	Lac of muscle(s) and tndn(s) of peroneal muscle group at lwr leg lvl, [rt, lt, unsp] leg, seq **229**
S46.02[1,2,9]A	Lac of muscle(s) and tndn(s) of the rotator cuff of [rt, lt, unsp] shldr, init enc **197**
S46.02[1,2,9]S	Lac of muscle(s) and tndn(s) of the rotator cuff of [rt, lt, unsp] shldr, seq **227**
S46.02[1,2,9]D	Lac of muscle(s) and tndn(s) of the rotator cuff of [rt, lt, unsp] shldr, subsq enc **392**
S95.81[1,2,9]S	Lac of oth bld vessels at ankle and foot lvl, [rt, lt, unsp] leg, seq **101**
S55.81[1,2,9]S	Lac of oth bld vessels at forearm lvl, [rt, lt, unsp] arm, seq **101**
S55.81[1,2,9]D	Lac of oth bld vessels at forearm lvl, [rt, lt, unsp] arm, subsq enc **393**
S75.81[1,2,9]S	Lac of oth bld vessels at hip & thigh lvl, [rt, lt, unsp] leg, seq **101**
S85.81[1,2,9]S	Lac of oth bld vessels at lwr leg lvl, [rt, lt, unsp] leg, seq **101**
S65.81[1,2,9]S	Lac of oth bld vessels at wrist and hand lvl of [rt, lt, unsp] arm, seq **101**
S65.81[1,2,9]D	Lac of oth bld vessels at wrist and hand lvl of [rt, lt, unsp] arm, subsq enc **396**
S25.81[1,2,9]S	Lac of oth bld vessels of thorax, [rt, lt, unsp] side, seq **100**
S25.81[1,2,9]D	Lac of oth bld vessels of thorax, [rt, lt, unsp] side, subsq enc **389**
S56.52[1,2,9]A	Lac of oth extensor muscle, fascia and tndn at forearm lvl, [rt, lt, unsp] arm, init enc **199**
S56.52[1,2,9]S	Lac of oth extensor muscle, fascia and tndn at forearm lvl, [rt, lt, unsp] arm, seq **227**
S56.52[1,2,9]D	Lac of oth extensor muscle, fascia and tndn at forearm lvl, [rt, lt, unsp] arm, subsq enc **393**
S56.22[1,2,9]A	Lac of oth flexor muscle, fascia and tndn at forearm lvl, [rt, lt, unsp] arm, init enc **199**
S56.22[1,2,9]S	Lac of oth flexor muscle, fascia and tndn at forearm lvl, [rt, lt, unsp] arm, seq **227**
S56.22[1,2,9]D	Lac of oth flexor muscle, fascia and tndn at forearm lvl, [rt, lt, unsp] arm, subsq enc **393**
S86.[1,2,3]2[1,2,9]A	Lac of oth muscle(s) and tndn(s) of [post, ant, peroneal] muscle group at lwr leg lvl, [rt, lt, unsp] leg, init enc **204**
S86.12[1,2,9]S	Lac of oth muscle(s) and tndn(s) of post muscle group at lwr leg lvl, [rt, lt, unsp] leg, seq **229**
S56.82[1,2,9]D	Lac of oth muscles, fascia and tndns at forearm lvl, [rt, lt, unsp] arm, subsq enc **393**
S46.82[1,2,9]D	Lac of oth muscles, fascia and tndns at shldr and upr arm lvl, [rt, lt, unsp] arm, subsq enc **392**
S36.538[A,S]	Lac of oth part of colon, [init enc, seq] **118**
S36.438[A,S]	Lac of oth part of sm intestine, [init enc, seq] **118**
S45.81[1,2,9]S	Lac of oth spec bld vessels at shldr and upr arm lvl, [rt, lt, unsp] arm, seq **101**
S45.81[1,2,9]D	Lac of oth spec bld vessels at shldr and upr arm lvl, [rt, lt, unsp] arm, subsq enc **392**
S27.893[A,S]	Lac of oth spec intrathoracic organs, [init enc, seq] **69**
S96.82[1,2,9]S	Lac of oth spec muscles and tndns at ankle and foot lvl, [rt, lt, unsp] foot, seq **230**
S76.82[1,2,9]A	Lac of oth spec muscles, fascia and tndns at thigh lvl, [rt, lt, unsp] thigh, init enc **202**
S76.82[1,2,9]S	Lac of oth spec muscles, fascia and tndns at thigh lvl, [rt, lt, unsp] thigh, seq **229**
S66.82[1,2,9]S	Lac of oth spec muscles, fascia and tndns at wrist and hand lvl, [rt, lt, unsp] hand, seq **229**
S37.43[1,2,9]A	Lac of ovary, [unilat, bilat, unsp], init enc **265, 270**
S37.43[1,2,9]S	Lac of ovary, [unilat, bilat, unsp], seq **265, 270**
S37.43[1,2,9]D	Lac of ovary, [unilat, bilat, unsp], subsq enc **391**
S85.21[1,2,9]S	Lac of peroneal artery, [rt, lt, unsp] leg, seq **101**
S95.11[1,2,9]S	Lac of plantar artery of [rt, lt, unsp] foot, seq **101**
S27.63X[A,S]	Lac of pleura, [init enc, seq] **69**
S85.01[1,2,9]S	Lac of popliteal artery, [rt, lt, unsp] leg, seq **101**
S85.51[1,2,9]S	Lac of popliteal vein, [rt, lt, unsp] leg, seq **101**
S85.17[1,2,9]S	Lac of post tibial artery, [rt, lt, unsp] leg, seq **101**
S55.11[1,2,9]S	Lac of radial artery at forearm lvl, [rt, lt, unsp] arm, seq **101**
S55.11[1,2,9]D	Lac of radial artery at forearm lvl, [rt, lt, unsp] arm, subsq enc **392**
S65.11[1,2,9]S	Lac of radial artery at wrist and hand lvl of [rt, lt, unsp] arm, seq **101**
S65.11[1,2,9]D	Lac of radial artery at wrist and hand lvl of [rt, lt, unsp] arm, subsq enc **396**
S36.63X[A,S]	Lac of rectum, [init enc, seq] **118**
S36.533[A,S]	Lac of sigmoid colon, [init enc, seq] **118**
S36.33X[A,S]	Lac of stomach, [init enc, seq] **117**
S65.21[1,2,9]S	Lac of superf palmar arch of [rt, lt, unsp] hand, seq **101**
S65.21[1,2,9]D	Lac of superf palmar arch of [rt, lt, unsp] hand, subsq enc **396**
S45.31[1,2,9]S	Lac of superf vein at shldr and upr arm lvl, [rt, lt, unsp] arm, seq **100**
S45.31[1,2,9]D	Lac of superf vein at shldr and upr arm lvl, [rt, lt, unsp] arm, subsq enc **392**
S27.53X[A,S]	Lac of thoracic trachea, [init enc, seq] **69**
S36.531[A,S]	Lac of transv colon, [init enc, seq] **118**
S55.01[1,2,9]S	Lac of ulnar artery at forearm lvl, [rt, lt, unsp] arm, seq **101**
S55.01[1,2,9]D	Lac of ulnar artery at forearm lvl, [rt, lt, unsp] arm, subsq enc **392**
S65.01[1,2,9]S	Lac of ulnar artery at wrist and hand lvl of [rt, lt, unsp] arm, seq **101**
S65.01[1,2,9]D	Lac of ulnar artery at wrist and hand lvl of [rt, lt, unsp] arm, subsq enc **396**
S95.91[1,2,9]S	Lac of unsp bld vessel at ankle and foot lvl, [rt, lt, unsp] leg, seq **101**
S55.91[1,2,9]S	Lac of unsp bld vessel at forearm lvl, [rt, lt, unsp] arm, seq **101**
S75.91[1,2,9]S	Lac of unsp bld vessel at hip & thigh lvl, [rt, lt, unsp] leg, seq **101**
S85.91[1,2,9]S	Lac of unsp bld vessel at lwr leg lvl, [rt, lt, unsp] leg, seq **101**
S65.91[1,2,9]S	Lac of unsp bld vessel at wrist and hand lvl of [rt, lt, unsp] arm, seq **101**
S65.91[1,2,9]D	Lac of unsp bld vessel at wrist and hand lvl of [rt, lt, unsp] arm, subsq enc **396**
S55.91[1,2,9]D	Lac of unsp bld vessels at forearm lvl, [rt, lt, unsp] arm, subsq enc **393**
S45.91[1,2,9]S	Lac of unsp bld vessels at shldr and upr arm lvl, [rt, lt, unsp] arm, seq **101**
S36.93X[A,S]	Lac of unsp intra-abd organ, [init enc, seq] **118**
S96.92[1,2,9]S	Lac of unsp muscle and tndn at ankle and foot lvl, [rt, lt, unsp] foot, seq **230**
S46.92[1,2,9]D	Lac of unsp muscle, fascia and tndn at shldr and upr arm lvl, [rt, lt, unsp] arm, subsq enc **392**
S66.92[1,2,9]S	Lac of unsp muscle, fascia and tndn at wrist and hand lvl, [rt, lt, unsp] hand, seq **229**
S56.92[1,2,9]D	Lac of unsp muscle, fascia and tndn at forearm lvl, [rt, lt, unsp] arm, subsq enc **393**
S76.92[1,2,9]A	Lac of unsp muscles, fascia and tndns at thigh lvl, [rt, lt, unsp] thigh, init enc **202**
S76.92[1,2,9]S	Lac of unsp muscles, fascia and tndns at thigh lvl, [rt, lt, unsp] thigh, seq **229**
S36.539[A,S]	Lac of unsp part of colon, [init enc, seq] **118**
S36.439[A,S]	Lac of unsp part of sm intestine, [init enc, seq] **118**
S85.11[1,2,9]S	Lac of unsp tibial artery, [rt, lt, unsp] leg, seq **101**
O71.81	Lac of uterus, NEC **273, 275**
S55.21[1,2,9]S	Lac of vein at forearm lvl, [rt, lt, unsp] arm, seq **101**

S55.21[1,2,9]D	Lac of vein at forearm lvl, [rt, lt, unsp] arm, subsq enc **393**
S36.11[3,4,5,6]A	[Lac unsp degree, Minor lac, Mod lac, Major lac] of liver, init enc **124**
S31.622S	Lac w fb of abd wall, epigst rgn w penet perit cav, seq **226**
S31.625S	Lac w fb of abd wall, periumb rgn w penet perit cav, seq **226**
S31.629S	Lac w fb of abd wall, unsp q w penet perit cav, seq **226**
S31.021S	Lac w fb of low back and pelvis w penet retroperiton, seq **226**
S11.82XA	Lac w FB of oth part of neck, init enc **5**
S11.22XA	Lac w fb of pharynx and cervical esophagus, init **5**
S11.92XA	Lac w FB of unsp part of neck, init enc **5**
S91.229S	Lac w fb of unsp toe(s) w damage to nail, seq **230**
S91.229D	Lac w fb of unsp toe(s) w damage to nail, subs **399**
S91.129S	Lac w fb of unsp toe(s) w/o damage to nail, seq **230**
S91.129D	Lac w fb of unsp toe(s) w/o damage to nail, subs **399**
S01.52[1,2]A	Lac w/ FB of [lip, oral cavity] init enc **59**
S61.32[8,9]S	Lac w/ FB of [oth, unsp] finger w/ damage to nail, seq **228**
S61.32[8,9]D	Lac w/ FB of [oth, unsp] finger w/ damage to nail, subsq enc **394**
S61.22[8,9]S	Lac w/ FB of [oth, unsp] finger w/o damage to nail, seq **228**
S61.22[8,9]D	Lac w/ FB of [oth, unsp] finger w/o damage to nail, subsq enc **394**
S21.42[1,2,9]D	Lac w/ FB of [rt, lt, unspecified] back wall of thorax w/ penetration into thoracic cavity, subsq enc **388**
S21.22[1,2,9]D	Lac w/ FB of [rt, lt, unspecified] back wall of thorax w/o penetration into thoracic cavity, subsq enc **388**
S21.32[1,2,9]D	Lac w/ FB of [rt, lt, unspecified] front wall of thorax w/ penetration into thoracic cavity, subsq enc **388**
S21.12[1,2,9]D	Lac w/ FB of [rt, lt, unspecified] front wall of thorax w/o penetration into thoracic cavity, subsq enc **388**
S21.22[1,2,9] [A,S]	Lac w/ FB of [rt, lt, unsp] back wall of thorax w/o penetration into thoracic cavity, [init enc, seq] **225**
S21.02[1,2,9] [A,S]	Lac w/ FB of [rt, lt, unsp] breast, [init enc, seq] **225**
S21.02[1,2,9]D	Lac w/ FB of [rt, lt, unsp] breast, subsq enc **388**
S51.02[1,2,9]S	Lac w/ FB of [rt, lt, unsp] elbow, seq **227**
S51.02[1,2,9]D	Lac w/ FB of [rt, lt, unsp] elbow, subsq enc **392**
S01.12[1,2,9]A	Lac w/ FB of [rt, lt, unsp] eyelid and periocular area, init enc **46**
S51.82[1,2,9]S	Lac w/ FB of [rt, lt, unsp] forearm, seq **227**
S51.82[1,2,9]D	Lac w/ FB of [rt, lt, unsp] forearm, subsq enc **392**
S21.12[1,2,9]S	Lac w/ FB of [rt, lt, unsp] front wall of thorax w/o penetration into thoracic cavity, seq **225**
S91.22[1,2,3]A	Lac w/ FB of [rt, lt, unsp] great toe w/ damage to nail, init enc **429**
S91.22[1,2,3]S	Lac w/ FB of [rt, lt, unsp] great toe w/ damage to nail, seq **230**
S91.22[1,2,3]D	Lac w/ FB of [rt, lt, unsp] great toe w/ damage to nail, subsq enc **399**
S91.12[1,2,3]A	Lac w/ FB of [rt, lt, unsp] great toe w/o damage to nail, init enc **429**
S91.12[1,2,3]S	Lac w/ FB of [rt, lt, unsp] great toe w/o damage to nail, seq **230**
S91.12[1,2,3]D	Lac w/ FB of [rt, lt, unsp] great toe w/o damage to nail, subsq enc **399**
S61.42[1,2,9]S	Lac w/ FB of [rt, lt, unsp] hand, seq **229**
S61.42[1,2,9]D	Lac w/ FB of [rt, lt, unsp] hand, subsq enc **395**
S91.22[4,5,6]S	Lac w/ FB of [rt, lt, unsp] lesser toe(s) w/ damage to nail, seq **230**
S91.22[4,5,6]D	Lac w/ FB of [rt, lt, unsp] lesser toe(s) w/ damage to nail, subsq enc **399**
S91.12[4,5,6]A	Lac w/ FB of [rt, lt, unsp] lesser toe(s) w/o damage to nail, init enc **429**
S91.12[4,5,6]S	Lac w/ FB of [rt, lt, unsp] lesser toe(s) w/o damage to nail, seq **230**
S91.12[4,5,6]D	Lac w/ FB of [rt, lt, unsp] lesser toe(s) w/o damage to nail, subsq enc **399**
S41.02[1,2,9]S	Lac w/ FB of [rt, lt, unsp] shldr, seq **227**
S41.02[1,2,9]D	Lac w/ FB of [rt, lt, unsp] shldr, subsq enc **391**
S61.12[1,2,9]S	Lac w/ FB of [rt, lt, unsp] thumb w/ damage to nail, seq **228**
S61.12[1,2,9]D	Lac w/ FB of [rt, lt, unsp] thumb w/ damage to nail, subsq enc **394**
S61.02[1,2,9]S	Lac w/ FB of [rt, lt, unsp] thumb w/o damage to nail, seq **228**
S61.02[1,2,9]D	Lac w/ FB of [rt, lt, unsp] thumb w/o damage to nail, subsq enc **394**
S41.12[1,2,9]S	Lac w/ FB of [rt, lt, unsp] upr arm, seq **227**
S41.12[1,2,9]D	Lac w/ FB of [rt, lt, unsp] upr arm, subsq enc **391**
S61.52[1,2,9]S	Lac w/ FB of [rt, lt, unsp] wrist, seq **229**
S61.52[1,2,9]D	Lac w/ FB of [rt, lt, unsp] wrist, subsq enc **395**
S61.32[0,1]S	Lac w/ FB of [rt, lt] index finger w/ damage to nail, seq **228**
S61.32[0,1]D	Lac w/ FB of [rt, lt] index finger w/ damage to nail, subsq enc **394**
S61.22[0,1]S	Lac w/ FB of [rt, lt] index finger w/o damage to nail, seq **228**
S61.22[0,1]D	Lac w/ FB of [rt, lt] index finger w/o damage to nail, subsq enc **394**
S61.32[6,7]S	Lac w/ FB of [rt, lt] little finger w/ damage to nail, seq **228**
S61.32[6,7]D	Lac w/ FB of [rt, lt] little finger w/ damage to nail, subsq enc **394**
S61.22[6,7]S	Lac w/ FB of [rt, lt] little finger w/o damage to nail, seq **228**
S61.22[6,7]D	Lac w/ FB of [rt, lt] little finger w/o damage to nail, subsq enc **394**
S61.32[2,3]S	Lac w/ FB of [rt, lt] mid finger w/ damage to nail, seq **228**
S61.32[2,3]D	Lac w/ FB of [rt, lt] mid finger w/ damage to nail, subsq enc **394**
S61.22[2,3]S	Lac w/ FB of [rt, lt] mid finger w/o damage to nail, seq **228**
S61.22[2,3]D	Lac w/ FB of [rt, lt] mid finger w/o damage to nail, subsq enc **394**
S61.32[4,5]S	Lac w/ FB of [rt, lt] ring finger w/ damage to nail, seq **228**
S61.32[4,5]D	Lac w/ FB of [rt, lt] ring finger w/ damage to nail, subsq enc **394**
S61.22[4,5]S	Lac w/ FB of [rt, lt] ring finger w/o damage to nail, seq **228**
S61.22[4,5]D	Lac w/ FB of [rt, lt] ring finger w/o damage to nail, subsq enc **394**
S31.62[0,1,2,3,4,5,9]A	Lac w/ FB of abd wall, [rt upr quadrant, lt upr quadrant, epigastric rgn, rt lwr quadrant, lt lwr quadrant, periumbilic rgn, unsp quadrant] w/ penetration into peritoneal cavity, init enc **117**
S31.62[0,1,3,4]S	Lac w/ FB of abd wall, [rt, lt] [upr, lwr] quadrant w/ penetration into peritoneal cavity, seq **226**
S31.02[0,1]D	Lac w/ FB of lwr back and pelvis [w/o, w/] penetration into retroperitoneum, subsq enc **389**
S31.020[A,S]	Lac w/ FB of lwr back and pelvis w/o penetration into retroperitoneum, [init enc, seq] **226**
S31.52[1,2]D	Lac w/ FB of unsp ext genital organs, [male, female], subsq enc **390**
S91.02[1,2,9]A	Lac w/ FB, [rt, lt, unsp] ankle, init enc **429**
S91.02[1,2,9]S	Lac w/ FB, [rt, lt, unsp] ankle, seq **230**
S91.32[1,2,9]A	Lac w/ FB, [rt, lt, unsp] foot, init enc **429**
S91.32[1,2,9]S	Lac w/ FB, [rt, lt, unsp] foot, seq **230**
S91.32[1,2,9]D	Lac w/ FB, [rt, lt, unsp] foot, subsq enc **399**
S71.02[1,2,9]S	Lac w/ FB, [rt, lt, unsp] hip, seq **229**
S81.02[1,2,9]S	Lac w/ FB, [rt, lt, unsp] knee, seq **229**
S81.82[1,2,9]S	Lac w/ FB, [rt, lt, unsp] lwr leg, seq **229**
S71.12[1,2,9]S	Lac w/ FB, [rt, lt, unsp] thigh, seq **229**
S01.51[1,2]A	Lac w/o FB of [lip, oral cavity] init enc **59**
S61.31[8,9][A,S]	Lac w/o FB of [oth, unsp] finger w/ damage to nail, [init enc, seq] **228**
S61.31[8,9]D	Lac w/o FB of [oth, unsp] finger w/ damage to nail, subsq enc **394**
S61.21[8,9][A,S]	Lac w/o FB of [oth, unsp] finger w/o damage to nail, [init enc, seq] **228**
S61.21[8,9]D	Lac w/o FB of [oth, unsp] finger w/o damage to nail, subsq enc **394**
S21.41[1,2,9]D	Lac w/o FB of [rt, lt, unspecified] back wall of thorax w/ penetration into thoracic cavity, subsq enc **388**
S21.21[1,2,9]D	Lac w/o FB of [rt, lt, unspecified] back wall of thorax w/o penetration into thoracic cavity, subsq enc **388**
S21.31[1,2,9]D	Lac w/o FB of [rt, lt, unspecified] front wall of thorax w/ penetration into thoracic cavity, subsq enc **388**
S21.11[1,2,9]D	Lac w/o FB of [rt, lt, unspecified] front wall of thorax w/o penetration into thoracic cavity, subsq enc **388**
S21.21[1,2,9] [A,S]	Lac w/o FB of [rt, lt, unsp] back wall of thorax w/o penetration into thoracic cavity, [init enc, seq] **225**
S21.01[1,2,9] [A,S]	Lac w/o FB of [rt, lt, unsp] breast, [init enc, seq] **225**
S21.01[1,2,9]D	Lac w/o FB of [rt, lt, unsp] breast, subsq enc **388**
S51.01[1,2,9] [A,S]	Lac w/o FB of [rt, lt, unsp] elbow, [init enc, seq] **227**
S51.01[1,2,9]D	Lac w/o FB of [rt, lt, unsp] elbow, subsq enc **392**
S01.11[1,2,9]A	Lac w/o FB of [rt, lt, unsp] eyelid and periocular area, init enc **46**
S51.81[1,2,9] [A,S]	Lac w/o FB of [rt, lt, unsp] forearm, [init enc, seq] **227**
S51.81[1,2,9]D	Lac w/o FB of [rt, lt, unsp] forearm, subsq enc **392**
S21.11[1,2,9] [A,S]	Lac w/o FB of [rt, lt, unsp] front wall of thorax w/o penetration into thoracic cavity, [init enc, seq] **225**
S91.21[1,2,3] [A,S]	Lac w/o FB of [rt, lt, unsp] great toe w/ damage to nail, [init enc, seq] **230**
S91.21[1,2,3]A	Lac w/o FB of [rt, lt, unsp] great toe w/ damage to nail, init enc **429**
S91.21[1,2,3]D	Lac w/o FB of [rt, lt, unsp] great toe w/ damage to nail, subsq enc **399**
S91.11[1,2,3] [A,S]	Lac w/o FB of [rt, lt, unsp] great toe w/o damage to nail, [init enc, seq] **230**
S91.11[1,2,3]A	Lac w/o FB of [rt, lt, unsp] great toe w/o damage to nail, init enc **429**
S91.11[1,2,3]D	Lac w/o FB of [rt, lt, unsp] great toe w/o damage to nail, subsq enc **399**
S61.41[1,2,9] [A,S]	Lac w/o FB of [rt, lt, unsp] hand, [init enc, seq] **229**
S61.41[1,2,9]D	Lac w/o FB of [rt, lt, unsp] hand, subsq enc **395**

S91.21[4,5,6] [A,S]	Lac w/o FB of [rt, lt, unsp] lesser toe(s) w/ damage to nail, [init enc, seq] 230
S91.21[4,5,6]A	Lac w/o FB of [rt, lt, unsp] lesser toe(s) w/ damage to nail, init enc 429
S91.21[4,5,6]D	Lac w/o FB of [rt, lt, unsp] lesser toe(s) w/ damage to nail, subsq enc 399
S91.11[4,5,6] [A,S]	Lac w/o FB of [rt, lt, unsp] lesser toe(s) w/o damage to nail, [init enc, seq] 230
S91.11[4,5,6]A	Lac w/o FB of [rt, lt, unsp] lesser toe(s) w/o damage to nail, init enc 429
S91.11[4,5,6]D	Lac w/o FB of [rt, lt, unsp] lesser toe(s) w/o damage to nail, subsq enc 399
S41.01[1,2,9] [A,S]	Lac w/o FB of [rt, lt, unsp] shldr, [init enc, seq] 227
S41.01[1,2,9]D	Lac w/o FB of [rt, lt, unsp] shldr, subsq enc 391
S61.11[1,2,9] [A,S]	Lac w/o FB of [rt, lt, unsp] thumb w/ damage to nail, [init enc, seq] 228
S61.11[1,2,9]D	Lac w/o FB of [rt, lt, unsp] thumb w/ damage to nail, subsq enc 394
S61.01[1,2,9] [A,S]	Lac w/o FB of [rt, lt, unsp] thumb w/o damage to nail, [init enc, seq] 228
S61.01[1,2,9]D	Lac w/o FB of [rt, lt, unsp] thumb w/o damage to nail, subsq enc 394
S41.11[1,2,9] [A,S]	Lac w/o FB of [rt, lt, unsp] upr arm, [init enc, seq] 227
S41.11[1,2,9]D	Lac w/o FB of [rt, lt, unsp] upr arm, subsq enc 391
S61.51[1,2,9] [A,S]	Lac w/o FB of [rt, lt, unsp] wrist, [init enc, seq] 229
S61.51[1,2,9]D	Lac w/o FB of [rt, lt, unsp] wrist, subsq enc 395
S61.31[0,1][A,S]	Lac w/o FB of [rt, lt] index finger w/ damage to nail, [init enc, seq] 228
S61.31[0,1]D	Lac w/o FB of [rt, lt] index finger w/ damage to nail, subsq enc 394
S61.21[0,1][A,S]	Lac w/o FB of [rt, lt] index finger w/o damage to nail, [init enc, seq] 228
S61.21[0,1]D	Lac w/o FB of [rt, lt] index finger w/o damage to nail, subsq enc 394
S61.31[6,7][A,S]	Lac w/o FB of [rt, lt] little finger w/ damage to nail, [init enc, seq] 228
S61.31[6,7]D	Lac w/o FB of [rt, lt] little finger w/ damage to nail, subsq enc 394
S61.21[6,7][A,S]	Lac w/o FB of [rt, lt] little finger w/o damage to nail, [init enc, seq] 228
S61.21[6,7]D	Lac w/o FB of [rt, lt] little finger w/o damage to nail, subsq enc 394
S61.31[2,3][A,S]	Lac w/o FB of [rt, lt] mid finger w/ damage to nail, [init enc, seq] 228
S61.31[2,3]D	Lac w/o FB of [rt, lt] mid finger w/ damage to nail, subsq enc 394
S61.21[2,3][A,S]	Lac w/o FB of [rt, lt] mid finger w/o damage to nail, [init enc, seq] 228
S61.21[2,3]D	Lac w/o FB of [rt, lt] mid finger w/o damage to nail, subsq enc 394
S61.31[4,5][A,S]	Lac w/o FB of [rt, lt] ring finger w/ damage to nail, [init enc, seq] 228
S61.31[4,5]D	Lac w/o FB of [rt, lt] ring finger w/ damage to nail, subsq enc 394
S61.21[4,5][A,S]	Lac w/o FB of [rt, lt] ring finger w/o damage to nail, [init enc, seq] 228
S61.21[4,5]D	Lac w/o FB of [rt, lt] ring finger w/o damage to nail, subsq enc 394
S31.61[0,1,2,3,4, 5,9]A	Lac w/o FB of abd wall, [rt upr quadrant, lt upr quadrant, epigastric rgn, rt lwr quadrant, lt lwr quadrant, periumbilic rgn, unsp quadrant] w/ penetration into peritoneal cavity, init enc 117
S31.61[0,1,3,4]S	Lac w/o FB of abd wall, [rt, lt] [upr, lwr] quadrant w/ penetration into peritoneal cavity, seq 226
S31.11[3,4][A,S]	Lac w/o FB of abd wall, [rt, lt] lwr quadrant w/o penetration into peritoneal cavity, [init enc, seq] 226
S31.11[0,1][A,S]	Lac w/o FB of abd wall, [rt, lt] upr quadrant w/o penetration into peritoneal cavity, [init enc, seq] 226
S31.112[A,S]	Lac w/o FB of abd wall, epigastric rgn w/o penetration into peritoneal cavity, [init enc, seq] 226
S31.612S	Lac w/o fb of abd wall, epigst rgn w penet perit cav, seq 226
S31.615S	Lac w/o fb of abd wall, periumb rgn w penet perit cav, seq 226
S31.115[A,S]	Lac w/o FB of abd wall, periumbilic rgn w/o penetration into peritoneal cavity, [init enc, seq] 226
S31.619S	Lac w/o fb of abd wall, unsp q w penet perit cav, seq 226
S31.119[A,S]	Lac w/o FB of abd wall, unsp quadrant w/o penetration into peritoneal cavity, [init enc, seq] 226
S31.831[A,S]	Lac w/o FB of anus, [init enc, seq] 227
S11.011A	Lac w/o FB of larynx, init enc 5
S31.011S	Lac w/o fb of low back and pelvis w penet retroperiton, seq 226

S31.01[0,1]D	Lac w/o FB of lwr back and pelvis [w/o, w/] penetration into retroperitoneum, subsq enc 389
S31.010[A,S]	Lac w/o FB of lwr back and pelvis w/o penetration into retroperitoneum, [init enc, seq] 226
S01.21XA	Lac w/o FB of nose, init enc 5
S11.81XA	Lac w/o FB of oth part of neck, init enc 5
S11.21XA	Lac w/o fb of pharynx and cervical esophagus, init 5
S11.11XA	Lac w/o FB of thyroid gland, init enc 5
S11.021A	Lac w/o FB of trachea, init enc 5
S31.51[1,2]D	Lac w/o FB of unsp ext genital organs, [male, female], subsq enc 390
S11.91XA	Lac w/o FB of unsp part of neck, init 5
S21.91X[A,S]	Lac w/o FB of unsp part of thorax, [init enc, seq] 225
S91.119[A,S]	Lac w/o FB of unsp toe w/o damage to nail, [init enc, seq] 230
S91.119D	Lac w/o fb of unsp toe w/o damage to nail, subs 399
S91.219D	Lac w/o fb of unsp toe(s) w damage to nail, subs 399
S91.219[A,S]	Lac w/o FB of unsp toe(s) w/ damage to nail, [init enc, seq] 230
S11.031A	Lac w/o FB of vocal cord, init enc 5
S31.61[0,1,2,3,4, 5,9]D	Lac w/o FB, [rt upr quadrant, lt upr quadrant, epigastric rgn, rt lwr quadrant, lt lwr quadrant, periumbilic rgn, unsp quadrant], w/ penetration into peritoneal cavity, subsq enc 390
S31.11[0,1,2,3,4, 5,9]D	Lac w/o FB, [rt upr quadrant, lt upr quadrant, epigastric rgn, rt lwr quadrant, lt lwr quadrant, periumbilic rgn, unsp quadrant], w/o penetration into peritoneal cavity, subsq enc 390
S91.01[1,2,9] [A,S]	Lac w/o FB, [rt, lt, unsp] ankle, [init enc, seq] 230
S91.01[1,2,9]A	Lac w/o FB, [rt, lt, unsp] ankle, init enc 429
S91.31[1,2,9] [A,S]	Lac w/o FB, [rt, lt, unsp] foot, [init enc, seq] 230
S91.31[1,2,9]A	Lac w/o FB, [rt, lt, unsp] foot, init enc 429
S91.31[1,2,9]D	Lac w/o FB, [rt, lt, unsp] foot, subsq enc 399
S71.01[1,2,9] [A,S]	Lac w/o FB, [rt, lt, unsp] hip, [init enc, seq] 229
S81.01[1,2,9] [A,S]	Lac w/o FB, [rt, lt, unsp] knee, [init enc, seq] 229
S81.81[1,2,9] [A,S]	Lac w/o FB, [rt, lt, unsp] lwr leg, [init enc, seq] 229
S71.11[1,2,9] [A,S]	Lac w/o FB, [rt, lt, unsp] thigh, [init enc, seq] 229
S31.83[1,2,3,4,5, 9]A	[Lac w/o FB, Lac w/ FB, Punc wnd w/o FB, Punc w/ FB, Opn bite, Unsp opn wnd] of anus, init enc 421
S31.8[0,1,2] [1,2,3,4,5,9]A	[Lac w/o FB, Lac w/ FB, Punc wnd w/o FB, Punc wnd w/ FB, Opn bite, Unsp opn wnd] of [unsp, rt, lt] buttock, init enc 421
S31.83[1,2,3,4,5, 9]D	[Lac w/o FB, Lac w/ FB, Punc wnd w/o FB, Punc wnd w/ FB, Opn bite, Unsp opn wnd] of anus, subsq enc 390
S11.01[1,2,3,4,5, 9]A	[Lac w/o FB, Lac w/ FB, Punc wnd w/o FB, Punc wnd w/ FB, Opn bite, Unsp opn wnd] of larynx, init enc 419
S31.82[1,2,3,4,5, 9]D	[Lac w/o FB, Lac w/ FB, Punc wnd w/o FB, Punc wnd w/ FB, Opn bite, Unsp opn wnd] of lt buttock, subsq enc 390
S31.81[1,2,3,4,5, 9]D	[Lac w/o FB, Lac w/ FB, Punc wnd w/o FB, Punc wnd w/ FB, Opn bite, Unsp opn wnd] of rt buttock, subsq enc 390
S11.02[1,2,3,4,5, 9]A	[Lac w/o FB, Lac w/ FB, Punc wnd w/o FB, Punc wnd w/ FB, Opn bite, Unsp opn wnd] of trachea, init enc 419
S31.80[1,2,3,4,5, 9]D	[Lac w/o FB, Lac w/ FB, Punc wnd w/o FB, Punc wnd w/ FB, Opn bite, Unsp opn wnd] of unsp buttock, subsq enc 390
S11.03[1,2,3,4,5, 9]A	[Lac w/o FB, Lac w/ FB, Punc wnd w/o FB, Punc wnd w/ FB, Opn bite, Unsp opn wnd] of vocal cord, init enc 419
S11.01[1,2,3,4,5, 9]D	[Lac w/o FB, Lac w/ FB, Punc wnd w/o FB, Punc wnd w/ FB, Opn bite, Unsp opn wnd], of larynx, subsq enc 387
S11.02[1,2,3,4,5, 9]D	[Lac w/o FB, Lac w/ FB, Punc wnd w/o FB, Punc wnd w/ FB, Opn bite, Unsp opn wnd], of trachea, subsq enc 387
S11.03[1,2,3,4,5, 9]D	[Lac w/o FB, Lac w/ FB, Punc wnd w/o FB, Punc wnd w/ FB, Opn bite, Unsp opn wnd], of vocal cord, subsq enc 387
S71.112A	Lac w/o FB, lt thigh, init enc 426
S71.111A	Lac w/o FB, rt thigh, init enc 426
S71.119A	Lac w/o FB, unsp thigh, init enc 426
S01.2[1,2,3,4]XS	[Lac w/o, Lac w/, Punc wnd w/o, Punc wnd w/] FB of nose, seq 224
S31.832S	Lac with FB of anus, seq 227
S11.012A	Lac with FB of larynx, init enc 5
S01.22XA	Lac with FB of nose, init enc 5
S11.12XA	Lac with FB of thyroid gland, init enc 5
S11.022A	Lac with FB of trachea, init enc 5
S21.92XS	Lac with FB of unsp part of thorax, seq 225

S11.032A	Lac with FB of vocal cord, init enc 5
S71.122A	Lac with FB, lt thigh, init enc 426
S71.121A	Lac with FB, rt thigh, init enc 426
S71.129A	Lac with FB, unsp thigh, init enc 426
S35.3[1,2,3,4][1,8,9]A	[Lac, Oth spec inj, Unsp inj] of [portal, splenic, superior mesenteric, inferior mesenteric] vein, init enc 359, 432
S35.3[3,4][1,8,9]A	[Lac, Oth spec inj, Unsp inj] of [superior, inferior] mesenteric vein, init enc 421
S35.34[1,8,9]D	[Lac, Oth spec inj, Unsp inj] of inferior mesenteric vein, subsq enc 390
S35.34[1,8,9]S	[Lac, Oth spec inj, Unsp inj] of inferior mesenteric, seq 100
S35.8X[1,8,9]S	[Lac, Oth spec inj, Unsp inj] of oth bld vessels at abd, lwr back and pelvis lvl, seq 100
S35.8X[1,8,9]D	[Lac, Oth spec inj, Unsp inj] of oth bld vessels at abd, lwr back and pelvis lvl, subsq enc 390
S35.31[1,8,9]S	[Lac, Oth spec inj, Unsp inj] of portal vein, seq 100
S35.31[1,8,9]D	[Lac, Oth spec inj, Unsp inj] of portal vein, subsq enc 390
S35.32[1,8,9]S	[Lac, Oth spec inj, Unsp inj] of splenic vein, seq 100
S35.32[1,8,9]D	[Lac, Oth spec inj, Unsp inj] of splenic vein, subsq enc 390
S35.33[1,8,9]S	[Lac, Oth spec inj, Unsp inj] of superior mesenteric vein, seq 100
S35.33[1,8,9]D	[Lac, Oth spec inj, Unsp inj] of superior mesenteric vein, subsq enc 390
S45.0[1,9][1,2,9]D	[Lac, Oth spec inj] of axillary artery, [rt, lt, unsp] side, subsq enc 391
S35.8X[1,8,9]A	[Lac, Oth spec, Unsp inj] of oth bld vessels at abd, lwr back and pelvis lvl, init enc 359, 421, 432
S35.31[1,8,9]A	[Lac, Oth, Unsp] of portal vein, init enc 421
S35.32[1,8,9]A	[Lac, Oth, Unsp] of splenic vein, init enc 421
S11.01[1,2,3,4]S	[Lac, punc wnd] [w/o, w/] FB of larynx, seq 225
S11.2[1,2,3,4]XS	[Lac, punc wnd] [w/o, w/] FB of pharynx and cervical esophagus, seq 225
S31.3[1,2,3,4]XS	[Lac, punc wnd] [w/o, w/] FB of scrotum and testes, seq 226
S11.1[1,2,3,4]XS	[Lac, punc wnd] [w/o, w/] FB of thyroid gland, seq 225
S11.02[1,2,3,4]S	[Lac, punc wnd] [w/o, w/] FB of trachea, seq 225
S11.03[1,2,3,4]S	[Lac, punc wnd] [w/o, w/] FB of vocal cord, seq 225
S11.0[1,2,3][2,4]A	[Lac, punc wnd] of [larynx, trachea, vocal cord] w/ FB, init enc 431
S31.1[2,4][0,1,2,3,4,5,9]A	[Lac, punc wnd] of abd wall w/ FB, [rt upr quadrant, lt upr quadrant, epigastric rgn, rt lwr quadrant, lt lwr quadrant, periumbilic rgn, unsp quadrant], w/o penetration into peritoneal cavity, init enc 359
S91.2[2,4][1,2,3,4,5,6,9]A	[Lac, punc wnd] w/ FB of [rt great, lt great, unsp great, rt lesser, lt lesser, unsp lesser, unsp] toe(s) w/ damage to nail, init enc 361
S91.1[2,4][1,2,3,4,5,6,9]A	[Lac, punc wnd] w/ FB of [rt great, lt great, unsp great, rt lesser, lt lesser, unsp lesser, unsp] toe(s) w/o damage to nail, init enc 361
S61.3[2,4][0,1,2,3,4,5,6,7,8,9]A	[Lac, punc wnd] w/ FB of [rt index, lt index, rt mid, lt mid, rt ring, lt ring, rt little, lt little, oth, unsp] finger w/ damage to nail, init enc 360
S61.2[2,4][0,1,2,3,4,5,6,7,8,9]A	[Lac, punc wnd] w/ FB of [rt index, lt index, rt mid, lt mid, rt ring, lt ring, rt little, lt little, oth, unsp] finger w/o damage to nail, init enc 360
S51.0[2,4][1,2,9]A	[Lac, punc wnd] w/ FB of [rt, lt, unsp] elbow, init enc 359
S91.3[2,4][1,2,9]A	[Lac, punc wnd] w/ FB of [rt, lt, unsp] foot, init enc 361
S51.8[2,4][1,2,9]A	[Lac, punc wnd] w/ FB of [rt, lt, unsp] forearm, init enc 359
S21.1[2,4][1,2,9]A	[Lac, punc wnd] w/ FB of [rt, lt, unsp] front wall of thorax w/o penetration into thoracic cavity, init enc 359
S61.4[2,4][1,2,9]A	[Lac, punc wnd] w/ FB of [rt, lt, unsp] hand, init enc 360
S41.0[2,4][1,2,9]A	[Lac, punc wnd] w/ FB of [rt, lt, unsp] shldr, init enc 359
S61.1[2,4][1,2,9]A	[Lac, punc wnd] w/ FB of [rt, lt, unsp] thumb w/ damage to nail, init enc 360
S61.0[2,4][1,2,9]A	[Lac, punc wnd] w/ FB of [rt, lt, unsp] thumb w/o damage to nail, init enc 360
S41.1[2,4][1,2,9]A	[Lac, punc wnd] w/ FB of [rt, lt, unsp] upr arm, init enc 359
S61.5[2,4][1,2,9]A	[Lac, punc wnd] w/ FB of [rt, lt, unsp] wrist, init enc 360
S31.83[2,4]A	[Lac, punc wnd] w/ FB of anus, init enc 359
S21.9[2,4]XA	[Lac, punc wnd] w/ FB of unsp part of thorax, init enc 359

S91.0[2,4][1,2,9]A	[Lac, punc wnd] w/ FB, [rt, lt, unsp] ankle, init enc 361
S71.0[2,4][1,2,9]A	[Lac, punc wnd] w/ FB, [rt, lt, unsp] hip, init enc 360
S81.0[2,4][1,2,9]A	[Lac, punc wnd] w/ FB, [rt, lt, unsp] knee, init enc 360
S81.8[2,4][1,2,9]A	[Lac, punc wnd] w/ FB, [rt, lt, unsp] lwr leg, init enc 360
S71.1[2,4][1,2,9]A	[Lac, punc wnd] w/ FB, [rt, lt, unsp] thigh, init enc 360
S31.122S	Lacerat abd wall w fb, epigst rgn w/o penet perit cav, seq 226
S31.125S	Lacerat abd wall w fb, periumb rgn w/o penet perit cav, seq 226
S31.129S	Lacerat abd wall w fb, unsp q w/o penet perit cav, seq 226
S56.429S	Lacerat extn musc/fasc/tend unsp finger at forarm lv, seq 227
S56.429D	Lacerat extn musc/fasc/tend unsp finger at forarm lv, subs 393
S56.129S	Lacerat flexor musc/fasc/tend unsp finger at forarm lv, seq 227
S56.129D	Lacerat flexor musc/fasc/tend unsp finger at forarm lv, subs 393
R62*	Lack of expected normal physiol dev in childhood and adults 246
Z72.3	Lack of physical exercise 412
E73*	Lactose intolerance 116
H02.2*	Lagophthalmos 45
G70.81	Lambert-Eaton synd in dz classified elsw 32
G73.1	Lambert-Eaton synd in neoplastic dz 32
G70.80	Lambert-Eaton synd, unsp 32
A36.2	Laryngeal diphtheria 2, 58
Q31.2	Laryngeal hypoplasia 4
J38.5	Laryngeal spasm 4, 284
Q31.3	Laryngocele 4
S83.01[4,5,6][A,S]	Lat disloc of [rt, lt, unsp] patella, [init enc, seq] 191
S83.01[4,5,6]A	Lat disloc of [rt, lt, unsp] patella, init enc 428
S83.01[4,5,6]D	Lat disloc of [rt, lt, unsp] patella, subsq enc 398
S53.14[4,5,6]D	Lat disloc of [rt, lt, unsp] ulnohumeral jt, subsq enc 392
S83.14[4,5,6][A,S]	Lat disloc of proximal end of tibia, [rt, lt, unsp] knee, [init enc, seq] 191
S83.14[4,5,6]A	Lat disloc of proximal end of tibia, [rt, lt, unsp] knee, init enc 428
S83.14[4,5,6]D	Lat disloc of proximal end of tibia, [rt, lt, unsp] knee, subsq enc 398
M77.1*	Lat epicondylitis 167
S12.04[0,1][A,B,S]	Lat mass fx of 1st cervical vertebra [disp, nondisp] init enc for fx [clsd, opn, seq] 165
S83.01[1,2,3][A,S]	Lat sublux of [rt, lt, unsp] patella, [init enc, seq] 191
S83.01[1,2,3]A	Lat sublux of [rt, lt, unsp] patella, init enc 428
S83.01[1,2,3]D	Lat sublux of [rt, lt, unsp] patella, subsq enc 398
S53.14[1,2,3][A,S]	Lat sublux of [rt, lt, unsp] ulnohumeral jt, [init enc, seq] 186
S53.14[4,5,6][A,S]	Lat sublux of [rt, lt, unsp] ulnohumeral jt, [init enc, seq] 186
S53.14[1,2,3]D	Lat sublux of [rt, lt, unsp] ulnohumeral jt, subsq enc 392
S83.14[1,2,3][A,S]	Lat sublux of proximal end of tibia, [rt, lt, unsp] knee, [init enc, seq] 191
S83.14[1,2,3]A	Lat sublux of proximal end of tibia, [rt, lt, unsp] knee, init enc 428
S83.14[1,2,3]D	Lat sublux of proximal end of tibia, [rt, lt, unsp] knee, subsq enc 398
A50.4[0,1,2,3]	Late congenital [unsp neurosyphilis, syphilitic meningitis, syphilitic encephalitis, syphilitic polyneuropathy] 41
A50.6	Late congenital syphilis, latent 308
A50.7	Late congenital syphilis, unsp 308
A50.32	Late congenital syphilitic chorioretinitis 308
A50.31	Late congenital syphilitic interstitial keratitis 45
A50.30	Late congenital syphilitic oculopathy, unsp 308
A50.44	Late congenital syphilitic optic nerve atrophy 308
A67.2	Late lesions of pinta 308
P74.[0,1,2,3,4]	[Late metabolic acidosis, Dehydration, Disturbances of sodium balance, Disturbances of potassium balance, Oth transitory electrolyte disturbances] of newborn 282
O48*	Late preg 278, 280
A52.8	Late syphilis, latent 308
A52.9	Late syphilis, unsp 308
A52.14	Late syphilitic encephalitis 10, 14, 41
A52.13	Late syphilitic meningitis 10, 14, 41
A52.15	Late syphilitic neuropathy 32

Code	Description
A52.71	Late syphilitic oculopathy 45
O21.2	Late vomiting of preg 279
A66.8	Latent yaws 308
M1A.1*	Lead-induced chr gout 362
M10.1*	Lead-induced gout 166
T82.33[0,1,2,8,9]S	Leakage of [aortic (bifurcation) graft (replace), carotid arterial graft (bypass), femor arterial graft (bypass), oth vascular grafts, unsp vascular grafts], seq 375
T82.33[0,1,2,8,9]D	Leakage of [aortic (bifurcation) graft (replace), carotid arterial graft (bypass), femor arterial graft (bypass), oth vascular grafts, unsp vascular grafts], subsq enc 410
T85.63[0,1,3,8]A	Leakage of [epidural and subdural inf catheter, intraperitoneal dialysis catheter, insulin pump, oth spec int prosthetic devs, implants and grafts], init enc 368
T85.63[0,1,3,8]S	Leakage of [epidural and subdural inf catheter, intraperitoneal dialysis catheter, insulin pump, oth spec int prosthetic devs, implants and grafts], seq 376
T85.63[0,1,3,8]D	Leakage of [epidural and subdural inf catheter, intraperitoneal dialysis catheter, insulin pump, oth spec int prosthetic devs, implants and grafts], subsq enc 411
T82.53[0,1,2,3,4,5,8,9]A	Leakage of [surgically created arteriovenous fistula, surgically created arteriovenous shunt, artfcl heart, balloon (counterpulsation) dev, inf catheter, umbrella dev, oth cardiac/vascular dev, unsp cardiac/vascular dev], init enc 103
T82.53[0,1,2,3,4,5,8,9]S	Leakage of [surgically created arteriovenous fistula, surgically created arteriovenous shunt, artfcl heart, balloon (counterpulsation) dev, inf catheter, umbrella dev, oth cardiac/vascular dev, unsp cardiac/vascular dev], seq 375
T82.53[0,1,2,3,4,5,8,9]D	Leakage of [surgically created arteriovenous fistula, surgically created arteriovenous shunt, artfcl heart, balloon (counterpulsation) dev, inf catheter, umbrella dev, oth cardiac/vascular dev, unsp cardiac/vascular dev], subsq enc 410
T85.43XA	Leakage of breast prosthesis and implant, init enc 224
S02.41[1,2,3]S	LeFort [I, II, III] fx, seq 39
S02.41[1,2,3][D,G]	LeFort [I, II, III] fx, subsq enc for fx w/ [routine, delayed] healing 169
S02.41[1,2,3]K	LeFort [I, II, III] fx, subsq enc for fx w/ nonu 195
S02.411[A,B]	LeFort I fx, init enc for [clsd, opn] fx 59
S02.411A	LeFort I fx, init enc for clsd fx 5
S02.411B	LeFort I fx, init enc for opn fx 5
S02.41[1,2,3][A,B]	[LeFort I fx, LeFort II fx, LeFort III fx], init enc for [clsd, opn] fx 417
S02.412[A,B]	LeFort II fx, init enc for [clsd, opn] fx 59
S02.412A	LeFort II fx, init enc for clsd fx 5
S02.412B	LeFort II fx, init enc for opn fx 5
S02.413[A,B]	LeFort III fx, init enc for [clsd, opn] fx 59
S02.413A	LeFort III fx, init enc for clsd fx 5
S02.413B	LeFort III fx, init enc for opn fx 5
A48.1	Legionnaires' dz 66, 67, 283, 438
D25*	Leiomyoma of uterus 264, 270
B55.9	Leishmaniasis, unsp 308
A30*	Leprosy [Hansen's dz] 308
A27.0	Leptospirosis icterohemorrhagica 308
A27.9	Leptospirosis, unsp 308
E79.1	Lesch-Nyhan synd 247
M31.2	Lethal midline granuloma 163
C95*	Leukemia of unsp cell type 295
C95.9*	Leukemia, unsp 303, 305
L81.5	Leukoderma, NEC 289
K13.2*	Leukoplakia and oth disturb of oral epithelium, incl* tongue 4
N48.0	Leukoplakia of penis 261
Q24.1	Levocardia 102
L44.[1,2,3]	Lichen [nitidus, striatus, ruber moniliformis] 234
L43*	Lichen planus 234
L28*	Lichen simplex chronicus and prurigo 233
L94.1	Linear scleroderma 234
E75.6	Lipid storage d/o, unsp 247
E88.1	Lipodystrophy, NEC 247
E88.2	Lipomatosis, NEC 247
E78.6	Lipoprotein deficiency 247
A32.1*	Listerial meningitis and meningoencephalitis 308
A32.7	Listerial sepsis 309
A32.9	Listeriosis, unsp 308
O26.62	Liver and biliary tract d/o in childbirth 273, 275
O26.61*	Liver and biliary tract d/o in preg 276
O26.61[1,2,3]	Liver and biliary tract d/o in preg, [1st, 2nd, 3rd] trmstr 277
O26.619	Liver and biliary tract d/o in preg, unsp trmstr 280
O26.63	Liver and biliary tract d/o in the puerperium 272, 275
K77	Liver d/o in dz classified elsw 124
Z52.6	Liver donor 124
K76.9	Liver dz, unsp 124
Z94.4	Liver transplant status 124
Z79.818	Lng trm (crnt) use of agnt affecting estrog recpt & estrog levels 413
Z79.810	Lng trm (crnt) use of slctv estrog receptor modulators 412
J18.1	Lobar pneumonia, unsp organism 68, 439
D05.[0,1,8,9][0,1,2]	[Lobular, Intraductal, Oth spec type of, Unsp type of] carcinoma in situ of [unsp, rt, lt] breast 221
L08.9	Local infxn of the skin and SQ tissue, unsp 224, 289
E65	Localized adiposity 246
L94.9	Localized connective tissue d/o, unsp 234
R59.0	Localized enlarged lymph nodes 294
A02.2*	Localized salmonella infections 438
A02.20	Localized salmonella infxn, unsp 308
L94.0	Localized scleroderma [morphea] 234
L27.1	Localized skin eruption d/t drugs and meds taken internally 284
R22.0	Localized swelling, mass and lump, head 234
R22.4*	Localized swelling, mass and lump, lwr limb 234
R22.1	Localized swelling, mass and lump, neck 234
R22.2	Localized swelling, mass and lump, trunk 69
R22.9	Localized swelling, mass and lump, unsp 234
R22.3*	Localized swelling, mass and lump, upr limb 234
G83.5	Locked-in state 38
O63*	Long labor 278, 280
Z79.2	Long term (current) use of antibiotics 411
Z79.0*	Long term (current) use of antocoag/antithrom/angiplate 411
Z79.811	Long term (current) use of aromatase inhibitors 412
Z79.82	Long term (current) use of aspirin 411
Z79.83	Long term (current) use of bisphosphonates 411
Z79.3	Long term (current) use of hormonal contraceptives 411
Z79.4	Long term (current) use of insulin 411
Z79.1	Long term (current) use of non-steroidal non-inflam (NSAID) 411
Z79.891	Long term (current) use of opiate analgesic 411
Z79.5*	Long term (current) use of steroids 411
M24.0*	Loose body in jt 193
M23.4*	Loose body in knee 193
M40.5*	Lordosis, unsp 125, 126
R29.890	Loss of height 38
M54.5	Low back pain 165
R45.81	Low self-esteem 310
O26.1*	Low weight gain in preg 276
O26.10	Low weight gain in preg, unsp trmstr 280
H40.12*	Low-tension glaucoma 45
M54.4*	Lumbago with sciatica 165
T86.81[0,1,2]	Lung transplant [rejection, failure, infxn] 70
Z94.2	Lung transplant status 70
L93*	Lupus erythematosus 223
A69.2*	Lyme dz 308
C81.41	Lymp-rich class Hodgkin lymph, nodes of head, face, and neck 3
D18.1	Lymphangioma, any site 294
I89.1	Lymphangitis 224, 284
I89.0	Lymphedema, NEC 233
C83.51	Lymphoblastic lymphoma, nodes of head, face, and neck 3
C81.31	Lymphocy deplet class Hodgkin lymph, nodes of head, face, & nk 3
D84.0	Lymphocyte function antigen-1 [LFA-1] defect 294
C91*	Lymphoid leukemia 295
C91.9*	Lymphoid leukemia, unsp 303, 305
Q18.6	Macrocheilia 59
Q38.2	Macroglossia 5, 59
Q18.4	Macrostomia 59
M26.0*	Major anomalies of jaw size 4
S37.02[1,2,9]S	Major contsn of [rt, lt, unsp] kidney, seq 118
S37.02[1,2,9]D	Major contsn of [rt, lt, unsp] kidney, subsq enc 391
S36.021A	Major contsn of spleen, init enc 294

C32.0	Malig neoplasm of glottis	3
C03*	Malig neoplasm of gum	57
C03.9	Malig neoplasm of gum, unsp	2
C05.0	Malig neoplasm of hard palate	3
C76.0	Malig neoplasm of head, face and neck	3, 57
C38.0	Malig neoplasm of heart	103
C13*	Malig neoplasm of hypopharynx	57
C13.9	Malig neoplasm of hypopharynx, unsp	3
C26.9	Malig neoplasm of ill-defined sites within the dgstv sys	114
C26.0	Malig neoplasm of intestinal tract, part unsp	114
C64*	Malig neoplasm of kidney, except renal pelvis	248, 255
C32.3	Malig neoplasm of laryngeal cartilage	3
C32*	Malig neoplasm of larynx	57
C32.9	Malig neoplasm of larynx, unsp	3
C04.1	Malig neoplasm of lat floor of mouth	2
C11.2	Malig neoplasm of lat wall of nasopharynx	3
C10.2	Malig neoplasm of lat wall of oropharynx	3
C02.4	Malig neoplasm of lingual tonsil	2
C00*	Malig neoplasm of lip	57
C00.9	Malig neoplasm of lip, unsp	2
C00.5	Malig neoplasm of lip, unsp, inner aspect	2
C22*	Malig neoplasm of liver and intrahepatic bile ducts	123
C03.1	Malig neoplasm of lwr gum	2
C76.5*	Malig neoplasm of lwr limb	304, 305
C00.4	Malig neoplasm of lwr lip, inner aspect	2
C39.9	Malig neoplasm of lwr respiratory tract, part unsp	67
C50.3[1,2][1,2,9]	Malig neoplasm of lwr-inner quadrant of [rt, lt, unsp] [female, male] breast	221
C50.5[1,2][1,2,9]	Malig neoplasm of lwr-outer quadrant of [rt, lt, unsp] [female, male] breast	221
C08.9	Malig neoplasm of major salivary gland, unsp	3
C41.1	Malig neoplasm of mandible	3
C31.0	Malig neoplasm of maxillary sinus	3
C38.3	Malig neoplasm of mediastinum, part unsp	67
C70*	Malig neoplasm of meninges	32
C30.1	Malig neoplasm of mid ear	3
C06.9	Malig neoplasm of mouth, unsp	3
C30.0	Malig neoplasm of nasal cavity	3
C30*	Malig neoplasm of nasal cavity and mid ear	57
C11*	Malig neoplasm of nasopharynx	57
C11.9	Malig neoplasm of nasopharynx, unsp	3
C50.0[1,2][1,2,9]	Malig neoplasm of nipple and areola, [rt, lt, unsp] [female, male] breast	221
C10*	Malig neoplasm of oropharynx	57
C10.9	Malig neoplasm of oropharynx, unsp	3
C57*	Malig neoplasm of oth and unsp female genital organs	269
C08*	Malig neoplasm of oth and unsp major salivary glands	57
C63*	Malig neoplasm of oth and unsp male genital organs	258, 260
C24*	Malig neoplasm of oth and unsp parts of biliary tract	123
C06*	Malig neoplasm of oth and unsp parts of mouth	57
C02*	Malig neoplasm of oth and unsp parts of tongue	57
C68*	Malig neoplasm of oth and unsp urinary organs	248, 255
C49*	Malig neoplasm of oth connective and soft tissue	163
C57.7	Malig neoplasm of oth spec female genital organs	263
C76.8	Malig neoplasm of oth spec ill-defined sites	304, 305
C56*	Malig neoplasm of ovary	262, 269
C50.8[1,2][1,2,9]	Malig neoplasm of overlapping sites of [rt, lt, unsp] [female, male] breast	221
C31.8	Malig neoplasm of overlapping sites of accessory sinuses	3
C04.8	Malig neoplasm of overlapping sites of floor of mouth	3
C13.8	Malig neoplasm of overlapping sites of hypopharynx	3
C32.8	Malig neoplasm of overlapping sites of larynx	3
C00.8	Malig neoplasm of overlapping sites of lip	2
C11.8	Malig neoplasm of overlapping sites of nasopharynx	3
C10.8	Malig neoplasm of overlapping sites of oropharynx	3
C05.8	Malig neoplasm of overlapping sites of palate	3
C02.8	Malig neoplasm of overlapping sites of tongue	2
C09.8	Malig neoplasm of overlapping sites of tonsil	3
C06.8*	Malig neoplasm of ovrlp sites of and unsp parts of mouth	3
C57.8	Malig neoplasm of ovrlp sites of female genital organs	263
C48.8	Malig neoplasm of ovrlp sites of retroperiton and peritoneum	114
C05*	Malig neoplasm of palate	57
C05.9	Malig neoplasm of palate, unsp	3
C25*	Malig neoplasm of pancreas	123
C57.3	Malig neoplasm of parametrium	262
C75.0	Malig neoplasm of parathyroid gland	247
C07	Malig neoplasm of parotid gland	3, 57
C76.3	Malig neoplasm of pelvis	258, 260, 263, 269
C60*	Malig neoplasm of penis	258, 260
C48.2	Malig neoplasm of peritoneum, unsp	114
C14.0	Malig neoplasm of pharynx, unsp	3
C75.3	Malig neoplasm of pineal gland	32
C75.1	Malig neoplasm of pituitary gland	247
C58	Malig neoplasm of placenta	263, 269
C38.4	Malig neoplasm of pleura	67
C13.0	Malig neoplasm of postcricoid region	3
C38.2	Malig neoplasm of posterior mediastinum	67
C13.2	Malig neoplasm of posterior wall of hypopharynx	3
C11.1	Malig neoplasm of posterior wall of nasopharynx	3
C10.3	Malig neoplasm of posterior wall of oropharynx	3
C61	Malig neoplasm of prostate	258, 260
C47*	Malig neoplasm of prph nerves and autonomic nervous sys	163
C12	Malig neoplasm of pyriform sinus	3, 57
C19	Malig neoplasm of rectosigmoid junction	114
C20	Malig neoplasm of rectum	114
C65*	Malig neoplasm of renal pelvis	248, 255
C06.2	Malig neoplasm of retromolar area	3
C48.0	Malig neoplasm of retroperitoneum	304, 305
C57.2*	Malig neoplasm of round lgmt	262
C14*	Malig neoplasm of sites in the lip, oral cavity and pharynx	57
C17*	Malig neoplasm of sm intestine	114
C05.1	Malig neoplasm of soft palate	3
C48.1	Malig neoplasm of spec parts of peritoneum	114
C31.3	Malig neoplasm of sphenoid sinus	3
C26.1	Malig neoplasm of spleen	295, 303, 305
C16*	Malig neoplasm of stomach	114
C32.2	Malig neoplasm of subglottis	3
C08.1	Malig neoplasm of sublingual gland	3
C08.0	Malig neoplasm of submandibular gland	3
C11.0	Malig neoplasm of superior wall of nasopharynx	3
C32.1	Malig neoplasm of supraglottis	3
C62*	Malig neoplasm of testis	258, 260
C76.1	Malig neoplasm of thorax	67
C37	Malig neoplasm of thymus	304, 305
C73	Malig neoplasm of thyroid gland	3, 247
C02.9	Malig neoplasm of tongue, unsp	2
C09*	Malig neoplasm of tonsil	57
C09.9	Malig neoplasm of tonsil, unsp	3
C09.0	Malig neoplasm of tonsillar fossa	3
C09.1	Malig neoplasm of tonsillar pillar (ant) (posterior)	3
C33	Malig neoplasm of trachea	67
C50.9[1,2][1,2,9]	Malig neoplasm of unsp site of [rt, lt, unsp] [female, male] breast	221
C03.0	Malig neoplasm of upr gum	2
C76.4*	Malig neoplasm of upr limb	304, 305
C00.3	Malig neoplasm of upr lip, inner aspect	2
C39.0	Malig neoplasm of upr respiratory tract, part unsp	3, 57
C50.2[1,2][1,2,9]	Malig neoplasm of upr-inner quadrant of [rt, lt, unsp] [female, male] breast	221
C50.4[1,2][1,2,9]	Malig neoplasm of upr-outer quadrant of [rt, lt, unsp] [female, male] breast	221
C66*	Malig neoplasm of ureter	248, 255
C57.4	Malig neoplasm of uterine adnexa, unsp	262
C55	Malig neoplasm of uterus, part unsp	263, 269
C05.2	Malig neoplasm of uvula	3
C52	Malig neoplasm of vagina	263, 269
C10.0	Malig neoplasm of vallecula	3
C02.2	Malig neoplasm of ventral surface of tongue	2
C41.2	Malig neoplasm of vert column	125
C06.1	Malig neoplasm of vestibule of mouth	3

Code	Description
C51*	Malig neoplasm of vulva 263, 269
C14.2	Malig neoplasm of Waldeyer's ring 3
C75.8	Malig neoplasm with pluriglandular involvement, unsp 247
C96.9	Malig neoplm of lymphoid, hematpoetc and rel tissue, unsp 3, 295, 303, 305
C38.8	Malig neoplm of ovrlp sites of heart, mediastinum and pleura 67
C14.8	Malig neoplm of ovrlp sites of lip, oral cavity and pharynx 3
C72*	Malig neoplm of spinal cord, cranial nerves and oth prt cnsl 32
G21.0	Malig neuroleptic synd 38
J91.0	Malig pleural effusion 67
C7A.1	Malig poorly differentiated neuroendocrine tumors 304, 305
O25.2	Malnut in childbirth 273, 275
O25.1[1,2,3]	Malnut in preg, [1st, 2nd, 3rd] trmstr 276, 277
O25.10	Malnut in preg, unsp trmstr 280
O25.3	Malnut in the puerperium 272, 275
M26.4	Malocclusion, unsp 4
F30*	Manic episode 311
C83.1*	Mantle cell lymphoma 438
E42	Marasmic kwashiorkor 246
A98.3	Marburg virus dz 307
Q87.4*	Marfan's synd 102
C94.3*	Mast cell leukemia 303, 305
Q82.2	Mastocytosis 289
O33.0	Matern care for disproprtn d/t deformity of matern pelv bone 276
O33.1	Matern care for disproprtn d/t generally contracted pelvis 278, 279
O33.3*	Matern care for disproprtn d/t outlet contrctn of pelvis 278
O33.4*	Matern care for disproprtn of mixed matern and fetal origin 278
O34.2[1,9]	Maternal care d/t uterine scar from [previous cesarean delivery, oth previous surgery] 278
O34.2*	Maternal care d/t uterine scar from previous surgery 279
O36.1[1,9][1,2,3], X[0,1,2,3,4,5,9]	Maternal care for [anti-A (Rh) antibodies, oth isoimmunization], [1st, 2nd, 3rd] trmstr, fetus [N/A or unsp, 1, 2, 3, 4, 5, oth] 278, 279
O36.1[1,9] 9[0,1,2,3,4,5,9]	Maternal care for [anti-A (Rh) antibodies, oth isoimmunization], unsp trmstr, fetus [N/A or unsp, 1, 2, 3, 4, oth] 281
O36.0[1,9] 9[0,1,2,3,4,5,9]	Maternal care for [anti-D (Rh) antibodies, oth isoimmunization], fetus [N/A or unsp, 1,2,3,4,5, oth] 281
O36.0[1,9][1,2,3], [0,1,2,3,4,5,9]	Maternal care for [anti-D (Rh) antibodies, oth rhesus isoimmunization], [1st, 2nd, 3rd] trmstr, fetus [N/A or unsp, 1, 2, 3, 4, 5, oth] 278, 279
O34.[3,4][1,2,3]	Maternal care for [cervical incompetence, oth abnormalities of cervix], [1st, 2nd, 3rd] trmstr 278, 279
O34.[0,1][1,2,3]	Maternal care for [congenital malformation of uterus, benign tumor of corpus uteri], [1st, 2nd, 3rd] trmstr 278, 279
O34.5[1,2,3,9] [1,2,3]	Maternal care for [incarceration, prolapse, retroversion, oth abnormalities] of gravid uterus, [1st, 2nd, 3rd] trmstr 278, 279
O36.5[1,9][1,2,3] [0,1,2,3,4,5,9]	Maternal care for [known or suspected placental insufficiency, oth known or suspected poor fetal growth], [1st, 2nd, 3rd] trmstr, fetus [N/A or unsp, 1, 2, 3, 4, 5, oth] 278, 279
O34.[8,9][1,2,3]	Maternal care for [oth, unsp] abnormalities of pelvic organs, [1st, 2nd, 3rd] trmstr 278, 279
O34.90	Maternal care for abnlt of pelvic organ, unsp, unsp trmstr 281
O34.70	Maternal care for abnlt of vulva and perineum, unsp trmstr 281
O34.[6,7][1,2,3]	Maternal care for abnormality of [vagina, vulva and perineum], [1st, 2nd, 3rd] trmstr 278, 279
O34.60	Maternal care for abnormality of vagina, unsp trmstr 281
O34.10	Maternal care for benign tumor of corpus uteri, unsp trmstr 281
O34.30	Maternal care for cervical incompetence, unsp trmstr 281
O33.6*	Maternal care for disproportion d/t hydrocephalic fetus 278, 279
O33.2	Maternal care for disproportion d/t inlet contraction of pelvis 278, 279
O33.7	Maternal care for disproportion d/t oth fetal deformities 278, 279
O33.3*	Maternal care for disproportion d/t outlet contraction of pelvis 279
O33.5*	Maternal care for disproportion d/t unusually large fetus 278, 279
O33.4*	Maternal care for disproportion of mixed maternal and fetal origin 279
O33.8	Maternal care for disproportion of oth origin 278, 279
O33.9	Maternal care for disproportion, unsp 278, 279
O36.6[1,2,3] X[0,1,2,3,4,5,9]	Maternal care for excessive fetal growth, [1st, 2nd, 3rd] trmstr, fetus [N/A or unsp, 1, 2, 3, 4, 5, oth] 278, 279
O36.60X[0,1,2,3, 4,5,9]	Maternal care for excessive fetal growth, unsp trmstr, fetus [N/A or unsp, 1, 2, 3, 4, 5, oth] 281
O36.829[0,1,2,3, 4,5,9]	Maternal care for fetal anemia and thromboscytopnia, unsp trmstr, fetus [N/A or unsp, 1, 2, 3, 4, 5, oth] 281
O36.9[1,2,3] X[0,1,2,3,4,5,9]	Maternal care for fetal problem, unsp [1st, 2nd, 3rd] trmstr, fetus [N/A or unsp, 1, 2, 3, 4, 5, oth] 278, 280
O36.90X[0,1,2,3, 4,5,9]	Maternal care for fetal problem, unsp, unsp trmstr, fetus [N/A or unsp, 1, 2, 3, 4 5, oth] 281
O36.2[1,2,3] X[0,1,2,3,4,5,9]	Maternal care for hydrops fetalis, [1st, 2nd, 3rd] trmstr, fetus [N/A or unsp, 1, 2, 3, 4, 5, oth] 278, 279
O36.20X[0,1,2,3, 4,5,9]	Maternal care for hydrops fetalis, unsp trmstr, fetus [N/A or unsp, 1, 2, 3, 4, 5, oth] 281
O34.519	Maternal care for incarceration of gravid uterus, unsp trmstr 281
O36.4*	Maternal care for intrauterine death 279
O36.4XX[0,1,2,3, 4,5,9]	Maternal care for intrauterine death, fetus [N/A or unsp, 1, 2, 3, 4, 5, oth] 278
O35*	Maternal care for known or suspected fetal abnlt and damage 278, 279
O36.519[0,1,2,3, 4,5,9]	Maternal care for known or suspected placental insufficiency, unsp trmstr, fetus [N/A or unsp, 1, 2, 3, 4, 5, oth] 281
O32*	Maternal care for malpresentation of fetus 278, 279
O34.40	Maternal care for oth abnlt of cervix, unsp trmstr 281
O34.599	Maternal care for oth abnlt of gravid uterus, unsp trmstr 281
O34.80	Maternal care for oth abnlt of pelvic organs, unsp trmstr 281
O36.599[0,1,2,3, 4,5,9]	Maternal care for oth known or suspected poor fetal growth, unsp trmstr, fetus [N/A or unsp, 1, 2, 3, 4, 5, oth] 281
O36.89[1,2,3] [0,1,2,3,4,5,9]	Maternal care for oth spec fetal problems, [1st, 2nd, 3rd] trmstr, fetus [N/A or unsp, 1, 2, 3, 4, 5, oth] 278, 280
O36.899[0,1,2,3, 4,5,9]	Maternal care for oth spec fetal problems, unsp trmstr, fetus [N/A or unsp, 1, 2, 3, 4, 5, oth] 281
O34.529	Maternal care for prolapse of gravid uterus, unsp trmstr 281
O34.539	Maternal care for retroversion of gravid uterus, unsp trmstr 281
O34.00	Maternal care for unsp congen malform of uterus, unsp trmstr 281
O36.7[1,2,3] X[0,1,2,3,4,5,9]	Maternal care for viable fetus in abd preg, [1st, 2nd, 3rd] trmstr, fetus [N/A or unsp, 1, 2, 3, 4, 5, oth] 278, 279
O36.70X[0,1,2,3, 4,5,9]	Maternal care for viable fetus in abd preg, unsp trmstr, fetus [not appicable or unsp, 1, 2, 3, 4, 5, oth] 281
O75.0	Maternal distress during labor and delivery 272, 276
O75.81	Maternal exhaustion compl labor and delivery 273, 275
O26.5[0,1,2,3]	Maternal hypotension synd, [unsp, 1st, 2nd, 3rd] trmstr 277
O26.5*	Maternal hypotension syndrome 279
C91.A*	Mature B-cell leukemia Burkitt-type 303, 305
C84.91	Mature T/NK-cell lymph, unsp, nodes of head, face, and neck 3
C84*	Mature T/NK-cell lymphomas 295, 303, 305
C84.9*	Mature T/NK-cell lymphomas, unsp 438
S02.401[A,B]	Maxillary fx, unsp, init enc for [clsd, opn] fx 59
S02.401A	Maxillary fx, unsp, init enc for clsd fx 5
S02.401B	Maxillary fx, unsp, init enc for opn fx 5
B05.[0,1,2,3,4]	Measles comp by [encephalitis, meningitis, pneumonia, otitis media, intestinal comps] 283
B05.0	Measles complicated by encephalitis 11, 15, 41
B05.1	Measles complicated by meningitis 307
B05.3	Measles complicated by otitis media 57
B05.2	Measles complicated by pneumonia 67
B05.81	Measles keratitis and keratoconjunctivitis 45
B05.9	Measles w/o comp 307
B05.4	Measles with intestinal comp 307
B05.8*	Measles with oth comp 283
T85.49XA	Mech compl of breast prosthesis and implant, init enc 224
T82.190A	Mech compl of cardiac electrode, init enc 102
T82.191A	Mech compl of cardiac pulse generator (battery), init enc 102
T85.398S	Mech compl of ocular prosth dev/grft, seq 376
T85.398D	Mech compl of ocular prosth dev/grft, subs 411
T82.198A	Mech compl of oth cardiac electronic device, init enc 103
T82.199A	Mech compl of unsp cardiac device, init enc 103
T85.09XA	Mech compl of ventricular intracranial shunt, init 40
T84.03[0,1,2,3,8, 9]A	Mech loosening of [rt hip, lt hip, rt knee, lt knee, oth site, unsp site] prosthesis, init enc 183
T84.03[0,1,2,3,8, 9]S	Mech loosening of [rt hip, lt hip, rt knee, lt knee, oth site, unsp site] prosthesis, seq 375
T84.03[0,1,2,3,8, 9]D	Mech loosening of [rt hip, lt hip, rt knee, lt knee, oth site, unsp site] prosthesis, subsq enc 411
H02.41[1,2,3,9]	Mech ptosis of [rt, lt, bilat, unsp] eyelid 45
J95.850	Mechanical comp of respirator 412

Alphabetic Index to Diseases

H50.6*	Mechanical strabismus 46
Q43.0	Meckel's diverticulum (disp) (hypertrophic) 115
E84.11	Meconium ileus in cystic fibrosis 282
P76.0	Meconium plug synd 282
P96.83	Meconium staining 288
S53.13[4,5,6] [A,S]	Med disloc of [rt, lt, unsp] ulnohumeral jt, [init enc, seq] 186
S53.13[4,5,6]D	Med disloc of [rt, lt, unsp] ulnohumeral jt, subsq enc 392
S83.13[4,5,6] [A,S]	Med disloc of proximal end of tibia, [rt, lt, unsp] knee, [init enc, seq] 191
S83.13[4,5,6]A	Med disloc of proximal end of tibia, [rt, lt, unsp] knee, init enc 428
S83.13[4,5,6]D	Med disloc of proximal end of tibia, [rt, lt, unsp] knee, subsq enc 398
S53.13[1,2,3] [A,S]	Med sublux of [rt, lt, unsp] ulnohumeral jt, [init enc, seq] 186
S53.13[1,2,3]D	Med sublux of [rt, lt, unsp] ulnohumeral jt, subsq enc 392
S83.13[1,2,3] [A,S]	Med sublux of proximal end of tibia, [rt, lt, unsp] knee, [init enc, seq] 191
S83.13[1,2,3]A	Med sublux of proximal end of tibia, [rt, lt, unsp] knee, init enc 428
S83.13[1,2,3]D	Med sublux of proximal end of tibia, [rt, lt, unsp] knee, subsq enc 398
M77.0*	Medial epicondylitis 167
K14.2	Median rhomboid glossitis 4
C85.21	Mediastnl large B-cell lymph, nodes of head, face, and neck 3
K59.3	Megacolon, NEC 117
N28.82	Megaloureter 256
D22.2*	Melanocytic nevi of ear and ext auricular canal 233
D22.1*	Melanocytic nevi of eyelid, incl* canthus 45
D22.0	Melanocytic nevi of lip 233
D22.7*	Melanocytic nevi of lwr limb, incl* hip 233
D22.3*	Melanocytic nevi of oth and unsp parts of face 233
D22.4	Melanocytic nevi of scalp and neck 233
D22.5	Melanocytic nevi of trunk 233
D22.6*	Melanocytic nevi of upr limb, incl* shldr 233
D22.9	Melanocytic nevi, unsp 233
D03.2*	Melanoma in situ of ear and ext auricular canal 223
D03.1*	Melanoma in situ of eyelid, incl* canthus 45
D03.0	Melanoma in situ of lip 223
D03.7*	Melanoma in situ of lwr limb, incl* hip 223
D03.3*	Melanoma in situ of oth and unsp parts of face 223
D03.8	Melanoma in situ of oth sites 223
D03.4	Melanoma in situ of scalp and neck 223
D03.5*	Melanoma in situ of trunk 223
D03.6*	Melanoma in situ of upr limb, incl* shldr 223
D03.9	Melanoma in situ, unsp 223
K92.1	Melena 115, 284
G96.12	Meningeal adhesions (cerebral) (spinal) 38
A17.1	Meningeal tuberculoma 10, 14, 41
R29.1	Meningismus 38
G03.8	Meningitis d/t oth spec causes 41, 283
G01	Meningitis in bacterial dz classified elsw 11, 15, 41, 283
G02	Meningitis in oth infec/parastc dz classd elsw 11, 15, 41, 283
G03.9	Meningitis, unsp 41, 283
A39.5[0,2,3]	Meningococcal [carditis unsp, myocarditis, pericarditis] 103
A39.81	Meningococcal encephalitis 10, 14, 41
A39.51	Meningococcal endocarditis 99
A39.5*	Meningococcal heart dz 282
A39.9	Meningococcal infxn, unsp 309
A39.0	Meningococcal meningitis 10, 14, 41
A39.82	Meningococcal retrobulbar neuritis 45, 282
A39.8[3,4]	[Meningococcal, Postmeningococcal] arthritis 164, 282
A39.4	Meningococcemia, unsp 309
B60.11	Meningoencephalitis d/t Acanthamoeba (culbertsoni) 309
N95*	Menopausal and oth perimenopausal d/o 265, 270
F99	Mental d/o, not otherwise spec 310
C4A*	Merkel cell carcinoma 223
C45.7	Mesothelioma of oth sites 304, 305
C45.2	Mesothelioma of pericardium 103
C45.1	Mesothelioma of peritoneum 114
C45.0	Mesothelioma of pleura 67
C45.9	Mesothelioma, unsp 304, 305
P19*	Metabolic acidemia in newborn 288
E88.9	Metabolic d/o, unsp 247
E75.25	Metachromatic leukodystrophy 32
Q78.5	Metaphyseal dysplasia 195
M77.4*	Metatarsalgia 167
D74*	Methemoglobinemia 293
Q02	Microcephaly 38, 285
Q18.7	Microcheilia 59
M31.7	Microscopic polyangiitis 164
Q18.5	Microstomia 59
G46.0	Mid cerebral artery synd 33
G43*	Migraine 41
J45.[2,3]2	Mild [intermittent, persistent] asthma w/ status asthmaticus 284
O21.0	Mild hyperemesis gravidarum 279
P91.61	Mild hypoxic ischemic encephalopathy [HIE] 288
F70	Mild intellectual disabilities 310
O14.0[2,3]	Mild to mod pre-eclampsia, [2nd, 3rd] trmstr 276
O14.02	Mild to mod pre-eclampsia, second trmstr 279
O14.[0,1,2,9][2,3]	Mild to mod pre-eclampsia, Severe pre-eclampsia, HELLP synd, Unsp pre-eclampsia], [2nd, 3rd] trmstr 273
O14.03	Mild to mod pre-eclampsia, third trmstr 279
O14.00	Mild to mod pre-eclampsia, unsp trmstr 280
O14.[0,1][2,3]	Mild to mod, Severe] pre-eclampsia, [2nd, 3rd] trmstr 277
S26.02[0,1,2]A	Mild, Mod, Major] lac of heart w/ hemopericardium, init enc 103, 420, 432
S26.02[0,1,2]S	Mild, Mod, Major] lac of heart w/ hemopericardium, seq 69
S26.02[0,1,2]D	Mild, Mod, Major] lac of heart w/ hemopericardium, subsq enc 389
A19*	Miliary tuberculosis 308, 438
S37.02[1,2,9]A	Minor contsn of [rt, lt, unsp] kidney, init enc 256
S37.01[1,2,9]S	Minor contsn of [rt, lt, unsp] kidney, seq 118
S37.01[1,2,9]D	Minor contsn of [rt, lt, unsp] kidney, subsq enc 391
S36.020A	Minor contsn of spleen, init enc 294
S36.24[0,1,2,9]A	Minor lac of [head, body, tail, unsp part] of pancreas, init enc 124, 432
S36.24[0,1,2,9]S	Minor lac of [head, body, tail, unsp part] of pancreas, seq 117
S36.24[0,1,2,9]D	Minor lac of [head, body, tail, unsp part] of pancreas, subsq enc 390
S15.01[1,2,9]S	Minor lac of [rt, lt, unsp] carotid artery, seq 100
S15.01[1,2,9]D	Minor lac of [rt, lt, unsp] carotid artery, subsq enc 388
S15.21[1,2,9]S	Minor lac of [rt, lt, unsp] ext jugular vein, seq 100
S15.21[1,2,9]D	Minor lac of [rt, lt, unsp] ext jugular vein, subsq enc 388
S25.11[1,2,9]S	Minor lac of [rt, lt, unsp] innominate or subclavian artery, seq 100
S25.11[1,2,9]D	Minor lac of [rt, lt, unsp] innominate or subclavian artery, subsq enc 389
S25.31[1,2,9]S	Minor lac of [rt, lt, unsp] innominate or subclavian vein, seq 100
S25.31[1,2,9]D	Minor lac of [rt, lt, unsp] innominate or subclavian vein, subsq enc 389
S15.31[1,2,9]S	Minor lac of [rt, lt, unsp] int jugular vein, seq 100
S15.31[1,2,9]D	Minor lac of [rt, lt, unsp] int jugular vein, subsq enc 388
S37.04[1,2,9]S	Minor lac of [rt, lt, unsp] kidney, seq 118
S37.04[1,2,9]D	Minor lac of [rt, lt, unsp] kidney, subsq enc 391
S25.41[1,2,9]S	Minor lac of [rt, lt, unsp] pulmn bld vessels, seq 100
S25.41[1,2,9]D	Minor lac of [rt, lt, unsp] pulmn bld vessels, subsq enc 389
S15.11[1,2,9]S	Minor lac of [rt, lt, unsp] vert artery, seq 100
S15.11[1,2,9]D	Minor lac of [rt, lt, unsp] vert artery, subsq enc 388
S37.04[1,2,9]A	Minor lac of [rt,lt, unsp] kidney, init enc 256
S75.01[1,2,9]S	Minor lac of femor artery, [rt, lt, unsp] leg, seq 101
S75.11[1,2,9]S	Minor lac of femor vein at hip & thigh lvl, [rt, lt, unsp] leg, seq 101
S75.21[1,2,9]S	Minor lac of greater saphenous vein at hip & thigh lvl, [rt, lt, unsp] leg, seq 101
S15.112A	Minor lac of lt vert artery, init enc 5
S15.111A	Minor lac of rt vert artery, init enc 5
S15.119A	Minor lac of unsp vert artery, init enc 5
S35.2[1,2,3,9] [1,2,8,9]A	[Minor lac, Major lac, Oth inj, Unsp inj] of [celiac, superior mesenteric, inferior mesenteric, branches of celiac and mesenteric] artery, init enc 359
S35.2[2,3] [1,2,8,9]A	Minor lac, Major lac, Oth inj, Unsp inj] of [superior, inferior] mesenteric artery, init enc 421
S35.29[1,2,8,9]A	Minor lac, Major lac, Oth inj, Unsp inj] of branches of celiac and mesenteric artery, init enc 421, 432

Code	Description
S35.29[1,2,8,9]S	Minor lac, Major lac, Oth inj, Unsp inj] of branches of celiac and mesenteric artery, seq 100
S35.29[1,2,8,9]D	Minor lac, Major lac, Oth inj, Unsp inj] of celiac and mesenteric artery, subsq enc 390
S35.21[1,2,8,9]A	Minor lac, Major lac, Oth inj, Unsp inj] of celiac artery, init enc 421, 432
S35.21[1,2,8,9]S	Minor lac, Major lac, Oth inj, Unsp inj] of celiac artery, seq 100
S35.21[1,2,8,9]D	Minor lac, Major lac, Oth inj, Unsp inj] of celiac artery, subsq enc 390
S35.23[1,2,8,9]S	Minor lac, Major lac, Oth inj, Unsp inj] of inferior mesenteric artery, seq 100
S35.23[1,2,8,9]D	Minor lac, Major lac, Oth inj, Unsp inj] of inferior mesenteric artery, subsq enc 390
S35.22[1,2,8,9]A	[Minor lac, Major lac, Oth inj, Unsp inj] of superior mesenteric artery, init enc 432
S35.22[1,2,8,9]S	[Minor lac, Major lac, Oth inj, Unsp inj] of superior mesenteric artery, seq 100
S35.22[1,2,8,9]D	[Minor lac, Major lac, Oth inj, Unsp inj] of superior mesenteric artery, subsq enc 390
S35.0[0,1,2,9]XD	[Minor lac, Major lac, Oth inj] of abd aorta, subsq enc 390
S15.0[1,2,9] [1,2,9]A	[Minor lac, Major lac, Oth spec inj] of [rt, lt, unsp] carotid artery, init enc 431
S36.02[0,1,9]A	[Minor, Major, Unsp] contsn of spleen, init enc 286, 422, 432
S36.02[0,1,9]S	[Minor, Major, Unsp] contsn of spleen, seq 117
S36.02[0,1,9]D	[Minor, Major, Unsp] contsn of spleen, subsq enc 390
S36.11[4,5,6]S	[Minor, Mod, Major] lac of liver, seq 117
H57.03	Miosis 45
O02.1	Missed abortion 272, 276
E88.4*	Mitochondrial metabolism d/o 247
N94.0	Mittelschmerz 270
C81.21	Mix cellular class Hodgkin lymph, nodes of head, face, and nk 3
E78.2	Mixed hyperlipidemia 247
B81.4	Mixed intestinal helminthiases 309
F80.2	Mixed receptive-expressive language d/o 311
J41.8	Mixed simple and mucopurulent chr bronchitis 68
F71	Mod intellectual disabilities 310
S36.25[0,1,2,9]A	Mod lac of [head, body, tail, unsp part] of pancreas, init enc 124, 432
S36.25[0,1,2,9]S	Mod lac of [head, body, tail, unsp part] of pancreas, seq 117
S36.25[0,1,2,9]D	Mod lac of [head, body, tail, unsp part] of pancreas, subsq enc 390
S37.05[1,2,9]A	Mod lac of [rt, lt, unsp] kidney, init enc 256
S37.05[1,2,9]S	Mod lac of [rt, lt, unsp] kidney, seq 118
S37.05[1,2,9]D	Mod lac of [rt, lt, unsp] kidney, subsq enc 391
S36.031A	Mod lac of spleen, init enc 294
P91.6[2,3]	Mod, Severe] hypoxic ischemic encephalopathy (HIE) 282
J45.[4,5]2	Mod, Severe] persistent asthma w/ status asthmaticus 284
B08.1	Molluscum contagiosum 233
B04	Monkeypox 307
D47.2	Monoclonal gammopathy 294
C93*	Monocytic leukemia 295
C93.9*	Monocytic leukemia, unsp 303, 305
G57*	Mononeuropathies of lwr limb 34
G56*	Mononeuropathies of upr limb 34
G59	Mononeuropathy in dz classified elsw 34
G83.1*	Monoplegia of lwr limb 38
G83.2*	Monoplegia of upr limb 38
G83.3*	Monoplegia, unsp 38
S52.27[1,2,9] [D,E,F,G,H,J,S]	Monteggia's fx of [rt, lt, unsp] ulna, [subsq enc for clsd fx w/ routine healing, subsq enc for opn fx type I or II w/ routine healing, subsq enc for opn fx type I or II w/ routine healing, subsq enc for clsd fx w/ delayed healing, subsq enc for opn fx type I or II w/ delayed healing, subsq enc for opn fx type IIIA, IIIB, or IIIC w/ delayed healing, seq] 173
S52.27[1,2,9] [A,B,C]	Monteggia's fx of [rt, lt, unsp] ulna, init enc for [clsd fx, opn fx type I or II, opn fx type IIIA, IIIB, or IIIC] 186, 423
S52.27[1,2,9] [B,C]	Monteggia's fx of [rt, lt, unsp] ulna, init enc for opn fx type [I or II, IIIA IIIB or IIIC] 434
S52.27[1,2,9] [K,M,N,P,Q,R]	Monteggia's fx of [rt, lt, unsp] ulna, subsq enc for [clsd fx w/ nonu, opn fx type I or II w/ nonu, opn fx type IIIA, IIIB, or IIIC w/ nonu, clsd fx w/ malu, opn fx type I or II w/ malu, opn fx type IIIA, IIIB, or IIIC w/ malu] 198
E66.2	Morbid (severe) obesity with alveolar hypoventilation 69
A83*	Mosquito-borne viral encephalitis 41
A83.9	Mosquito-borne viral encephalitis, unsp 10, 15
A92.9	Mosquito-borne viral fever, unsp 307
T75.3XXA	Motion sickness, init enc 57
T75.3XXS	Motion sickness, seq 374
T75.3XXD	Motion sickness, subsq enc 410
K00.3	Mottled teeth 4
R06.5	Mouth breathing 58
I67.5	Moyamoya dz 38
L98.5	Mucinosis of the skin 234
K11.6	Mucocele of salivary gland 4
M30.3	Mucocutaneous lymph node synd [Kawasaki] 164
J41.1	Mucopurulent chr bronchitis 68
S32.82XK	Mult fx of pelv w/o disrupt of pelv ring, 7thK 196
S32.82XB	Mult fx of pelvis w/o disrupt of pelv ring, init for opn fx 421, 433
G45.2	Multi and bilat precerebral artery syndromes 33
Q78.6	Multi congenital exostoses 195
Q89.7	Multi congenital malformations, NEC 195
S22.43XB	Multi fractures of ribs, bilat, init for opn fx 432
S22.42XB	Multi fractures of ribs, lt side, init for opn fx 432
S32.82XA	Multi fx of pelvis w/o disrupt of pelvic ring, init 421, 433
S32.82XS	Multi fx of pelvis w/o disrupt of pelvic ring, seq 166
S32.81[0,1][A,B]	Multi fxs of pelvis w/ [stable, unstable] disruption of pelvic ring, init enc for [clsd, opn] fx 162, 421, 433
S32.81[0,1][D,G]	Multi fxs of pelvis w/ [stable, unstable] disruption of pelvic ring, subsq enc for fx w/ [routine, delayed] healing 170
S32.81[0,1]K	Multi fxs of pelvis w/ [stable, unstable] disruption of pelvic ring, subsq enc for fx w/ nonu 196
S32.81[0,1]S	Multi fxs of pelvis w/ disruption of pelvic ring [stable, unstable] init enc for fx, seq 166
S32.82X[A,B]	Multi fxs of pelvis w/o disruption of pelvic ring, init enc for [clsd, opn] fx 162
S32.82X[D,G]	Multi fxs of pelvis w/o disruption of pelvic ring, subsq enc for fx w/ [routine, delayed] healing 170
S22.4[1,2,3,9]XS	Multi fxs of ribs, [rt, lt, bilat, unsp] side, seq 166
S22.4[1,2,3,9] X[D,G]	Multi fxs of ribs, [rt, lt, bilat, unsp] side, subsq enc for fx w/ [routine, delayed] healing 170
S22.4[1,2,3,9]XK	Multi fxs of ribs, [rt, lt, bilat, unsp] side, subsq enc for fx w/ nonu 196
S22.4[1,2,3,9] X[A,B]	Multi fxs of ribs, [rt, lt, unsp] side, init enc for [clsd, opn] fx 420
S22.43X[A,B]	Multi fxs of ribs, bilat, init enc for [clsd, opn] fx 67
S22.42X[A,B]	Multi fxs of ribs, lt side, init enc for [clsd, opn] fx 67
S22.41X[A,B]	Multi fxs of ribs, rt side, init enc for [clsd, opn] fx 67, 432
S22.49X[A,B]	Multi fxs of ribs, unsp side, init enc for [clsd, opn] fx 67
O30.9[1,2,3]	Multi gestation, unsp, [1st, 2nd, 3rd] trmstr 277, 279
O30.90	Multi gestation, unsp, unsp trmstr 281
C90*	Multi myeloma and malig plasma cell neoplasms 295, 303, 305
G35	Multi sclerosis 32
I08*	Multi valve dz 102
G90.3	Multi-sys degeneration of the autonomic nervous sys 32
C96.0	Multifocal and multisystemic Langerhans-cell histiocytosis 3, 304, 305
C96.5	Multifocal and unisystemic Langerhans-cell histiocytosis 247
M35.5	Multifocal fibrosclerosis 164
B26.8[2,3,5]	Mumps [myocarditis, nephritis, arthritis] 307
B26.[0,1,2,3]	Mumps [orchitis, meningitis, encephalitis, pancreatitis] 283
B26.2	Mumps encephalitis 11, 15, 41
B26.81	Mumps hepatitis 124
B26.1	Mumps meningitis 11, 15, 35
B26.0	Mumps orchitis 261
B26.3	Mumps pancreatitis 124
B26.84	Mumps polyneuropathy 34
B26.9	Mumps w/o comp 307
B26.8*	Mumps with oth comp 283
M62.830	Muscle spasm of back 165
M62.831	Muscle spasm of calf 167
M62.5*	Muscle wasting and atrophy, NEC 167
M62.81	Muscle weakness (generalized) 167
M79.1	Myalgia 167
G70.0*	Myasthenia gravis 32
G73.3	Myasthenic syndromes in oth dz classified elsw 32

B47.9	Mycetoma, unsp 233, 438
A31.9	Mycobacterial infxn, unsp 308, 438
C84.01	Mycosis fungoides, lymph nodes of head, face, and neck 3
H16.0[6,7][1,2,3,9]	Mycotic, Perforated] corneal ulcer, [rt, lt, bilat, unsp] eye 45
H57.04	Mydriasis 45
G05.4	Myelitis in dz classified elsw 11, 15
C94.6	Myelodysplastic dz, not classified 303, 305
D46*	Myelodysplastic syndromes 293
D75.81	Myelofibrosis 295, 303, 305
C92*	Myeloid leukemia 295
C92.9*	Myeloid leukemia, unsp 303, 305
C92.3*	Myeloid sarcoma 303, 305
G99.2	Myelopathy in dz classified elsw 38
D61.82	Myelophthisis 295, 303, 305
B87*	Myiasis 233
E79.2	Myoadenylate deaminase deficiency 247
I51.5	Myocardial degeneration 103
I41	Myocarditis in dz classified elsw 103, 283
I51.4	Myocarditis, unsp 103
G25.3	Myoclonus 38
R82.1	Myoglobinuria 385
G70.9	Myoneural d/o, unsp 34
G72.2	Myopathy d/t oth txc agents 38
G73.7	Myopathy in dz classified elsw 38
H05.82[1,2,3,9]	Myopathy of extraocular muscles, [rt, lt, bilat, unsp] orbit 45
G72.9	Myopathy, unsp 38
H52.1*	Myopia 46
M60.9	Myositis, unsp 167
E03.5	Myxedema coma 35, 283
B60.2	Naegleriasis 309
L60*	Nail d/o 234
L62	Nail d/o in dz classified elsw 234
G47.4*	Narcolepsy and cataplexy 38
R09.81	Nasal congestion 58, 289
J34.81	Nasal mucositis (ulcerative) 289
J33*	Nasal polyp 58
A36.1	Nasopharyngeal diphtheria 2, 58
R11.0	Nausea 116
R11.2	Nausea with vomiting, unsp 116
L92.1	Necrobiosis lipoidica, NEC 234
T87.5*	Necrosis of amp stump 205
I77.5	Necrosis of artery 100
K04.1	Necrosis of pulp 4
P77*	Necrotizing enterocolitis of newborn 282
A69.0	Necrotizing ulcerative stomatitis 2, 59
M31.9	Necrotizing vasculopathy, unsp 100
P37.2	Neonatal (disseminated) listeriosis 282
P54.4	Neonatal adrenal hemor 282
P24*	Neonatal aspiration 282
P37.5	Neonatal candidiasis 288
P29.1*	Neonatal cardiac dysrhythmia 288
P29.0	Neonatal cardiac failure 288
P91.4	Neonatal cerebral depression 282
P91.3	Neonatal cerebral irritability 282
P91.0	Neonatal cerebral ischemia 282
P91.2	Neonatal cerebral leukomalacia 38, 285
P91.5	Neonatal coma 282
P39.1	Neonatal conjunctivitis and dacryocystitis 288
P54.5	Neonatal cutaneous hemor 289
P70.2	Neonatal diabetes mellitus 282
P92.5	Neonatal difficulty in feeding at breast 289
P83.1	Neonatal erythema toxicum 289
P72.0	Neonatal goiter, NEC 288
P54.0	Neonatal hematemesis 288
P78.2	Neonatal hematemesis and melena d/t swallowed matern bld 288
P54.9	Neonatal hemor, unsp 288
P29.2	Neonatal hypertension 288
P39.0	Neonatal infective mastitis 282
P59.0	Neonatal jaundice associated with preterm delivery 288

P58*	Neonatal jaundice d/t oth excessive hemolysis 288
P59.3	Neonatal jaundice from breast milk inhibitor 289
P59.2*	Neonatal jaundice from oth and unsp hepatocellular damage 282
P59.8	Neonatal jaundice from oth spec causes 289
P59.9	Neonatal jaundice, unsp 289
P54.1	Neonatal melena 282
P54.2	Neonatal rectal hemor 282
P39.4	Neonatal skin infxn 282
P39.3	Neonatal urinary tract infxn 282
P54.6	Neonatal vaginal hemor 288
P96.1	Neonatal w/drawal symp from matern use of drugs of addiction 282
D48.[1,2]	Neoplasm of uncertain behav of [connective and oth soft tissue, peripheral nerves and autonomic nervous sys] 193
D48.6[0,1,2]	Neoplasm of uncertain behav of [unsp, rt, lt] breast 221
D44.1*	Neoplasm of uncertain behav of adrenal gland 247
D44.7	Neoplasm of uncertain behav of aortic body and oth paraganglia 32
D37.3	Neoplasm of uncertain behav of appendix 115
D48.0	Neoplasm of uncertain behav of bone/artic cartl 125, 163
D43*	Neoplasm of uncertain behav of brain and cnsl 32
D48.6*	Neoplasm of uncertain behav of breast 223
D44.6	Neoplasm of uncertain behav of carotid body 32
D37.4	Neoplasm of uncertain behav of colon 115
D44.4	Neoplasm of uncertain behav of craniopharyngeal duct 247
D37.9	Neoplasm of uncertain behav of digestive organ, unsp 115
D39.9	Neoplasm of uncertain behav of female genital organ, unsp 263
D39*	Neoplasm of uncertain behav of female genital organs 269
D38.0	Neoplasm of uncertain behav of larynx 3, 57
D37.0*	Neoplasm of uncertain behav of lip, oral cavity and pharynx 3, 57
D37.6	Neoplasm of uncertain behav of liver, GB & bile duct 123
D40*	Neoplasm of uncertain behav of male genital organs 258, 260
D38.3	Neoplasm of uncertain behav of mediastinum 67
D42*	Neoplasm of uncertain behav of meninges 32
D37.8	Neoplasm of uncertain behav of oth digestive organs 115
D39.8	Neoplasm of uncertain behav of oth female genital organs 263
D38.5	Neoplasm of uncertain behav of oth respiratory organs 67
D48.7	Neoplasm of uncertain behav of oth spec sites 304, 306
D39.1*	Neoplasm of uncertain behav of ovary 262
D44.2	Neoplasm of uncertain behav of parathyroid gland 247
D48.4	Neoplasm of uncertain behav of peritoneum 115
D44.5	Neoplasm of uncertain behav of pineal gland 32
D44.3	Neoplasm of uncertain behav of pituitary gland 247
D39.2	Neoplasm of uncertain behav of placenta 263
D38.2	Neoplasm of uncertain behav of pleura 67
D37.5	Neoplasm of uncertain behav of rectum 115
D38.6	Neoplasm of uncertain behav of respiratory organ, unsp 67
D48.3	Neoplasm of uncertain behav of retroperitoneum 115
D48.5	Neoplasm of uncertain behav of skin 233
D37.2	Neoplasm of uncertain behav of sm intestine 115
D37.1	Neoplasm of uncertain behav of stomach 115
D38.4	Neoplasm of uncertain behav of thymus 67
D44.0	Neoplasm of uncertain behav of thyroid gland 247
D38.1	Neoplasm of uncertain behav of trachea, bronchus and lung 67
D44.9	Neoplasm of uncertain behav of unsp endocrine gland 247
D41*	Neoplasm of uncertain behav of urinary organs 248, 255
D39.0	Neoplasm of uncertain behav of uterus 263
D48.9	Neoplasm of uncertain behav, unsp 304, 306
D49.4	Neoplasm of unsp behav of bladder 248, 255
D49.2	Neoplasm of unsp behav of bone, soft tissue, and skin 125, 193
D49.6	Neoplasm of unsp behav of brain 32
D49.3	Neoplasm of unsp behav of breast 224
D49.0	Neoplasm of unsp behav of digestive sys 115
D49.5	Neoplasm of unsp behav of oth genitourinary organs 248, 255
D49.8*	Neoplasm of unsp behav of oth spec sites 304, 306
D49.1	Neoplasm of unsp behav of respiratory sys 67
D49.9	Neoplasm of unsp behav of unsp site 304, 306
G89.3	Neoplasm related pain (acute) (chr) 385
R53.0	Neoplastic (malig) related fatigue 385

S72.06[4,5,6] **[A,B,C]**	Nondisp articular fx of head of femur [rt, lt, unsp] init enc for fx [clsd, opn fx type I or II or NOS, or opn fx type IIIA, IIIB, or IIIC] **162, 286, 435**
S32.46[4,5,6]S	Nondisp associated transv-post fx of [rt, lt, unsp] acetab, seq **166**
S32.46[4,5,6] **[D,G]**	Nondisp associated transv-post fx of [rt, lt, unsp] acetab, subsq enc for fx w/ [routine, delayed] healing **170**
S32.46[4,5,6]K	Nondisp associated transv-post fx of [rt, lt, unsp] acetab, subsq enc for fx w/ nonu **196**
S32.46[4,5,6] **[A,B]**	Nondisp associated transv-post fx of acetab [rt, lt, unsp] init enc for [clsd, opn] fx **162, 433**
S92.15[4,5,6] **[D,G,S]**	Nondisp avulsion fx (chip fx) of [rt, lt, unsp] talus, [subsq enc for fx w/ routine healing, subsq enc for fx w/ delayed healing, seq] **182**
S92.15[4,5,6] **[A,B]**	Nondisp avulsion fx (chip fx) of [rt, lt, unsp] talus, init enc for [clsd, opn] fx **192, 429**
S92.15[4,5,6] **[K,P]**	Nondisp avulsion fx (chip fx) of [rt, lt, unsp] talus, subsq enc for fx w/ [nonu, malu] **204**
S32.31[4,5,6]S	Nondisp avulsion fx of [rt, lt, unsp] ilium, seq **166**
S32.31[4,5,6] **[D,G]**	Nondisp avulsion fx of [rt, lt, unsp] ilium, subsq enc for fx w/ [routine, delayed] healing **170**
S32.31[4,5,6]K	Nondisp avulsion fx of [rt, lt, unsp] ilium, subsq enc for fx w/ nonu **196**
S32.61[4,5,6] **[D,G]**	Nondisp avulsion fx of [rt, lt, unsp] ischium, subsq enc for fx w/ [routine, delayed] healing **170**
S32.61[4,5,6]K	Nondisp avulsion fx of [rt, lt, unsp] ischium, subsq enc for fx w/ nonu **196**
S32.31[4,5,6] **[A,B]**	Nondisp avulsion fx of ilium [rt, lt, unsp] init enc for [clsd fx, opn fx] **162**
S32.61[4,5,6] **[A,B]**	Nondisp avulsion fx of ischium [rt, lt, unsp] init enc for [clsd fx, opn fx] **162**
S32.61[4,5,6]S	Nondisp avulsion fx of ischium [rt, lt, unsp] init enc for fx, seq **166**
S92.03[4,5,6] **[D,G,S]**	Nondisp avulsion fx of tuberosity of [rt, lt, unsp] calcaneus, [subsq enc for fx w/ routine healing, subsq enc for fx w/ delayed healing, seq] **182**
S92.03[4,5,6] **[A,B]**	Nondisp avulsion fx of tuberosity of [rt, lt, unsp] calcaneus, init enc for [clsd, opn] fx **192, 429**
S92.03[4,5,6] **[K,P]**	Nondisp avulsion fx of tuberosity of [rt, lt, unsp] calcaneus, subsq enc for fx w/ [nonu, malu] **204**
S82.14[4,5,6] **[A,B,C]**	Nondisp bicondylar fx of [rt, lt, unsp] tibia, [init enc for clsd fx, init enc for opn fx type I or II, init enc for opn fx type IIIA, IIIB, or IIIC] **191**
S82.14[4,5,6] **[D,E,F,G,H,J,S]**	Nondisp bicondylar fx of [rt, lt, unsp] tibia, [subsq enc for clsd fx w/ routine healing, subsq enc for opn fx type I or II w/ routine healing, subsq enc for opn fx type IIIA, IIIB, or IIIC w/ routine healing, subsq enc for clsd fx w/ delayed healing, subsq enc for opn fx type I or II w/ delayed healing, subsq enc for opn fx type I or II w/ delayed healing, seq] **180**
S82.14[4,5,6] **[B,C]**	Nondisp bicondylar fx of [rt, lt, unsp] tibia, init enc for opn fx type [I or II, IIIA IIIB or IIIC] **436**
S82.14[4,5,6] **[K,M,N,P,Q,R]**	Nondisp bicondylar fx of [rt, lt, unsp] tibia, subsq enc for [clsd fx w/ nonu, opn fx type I or II w/ nonu, opn fx type IIIA, IIIB, or IIIC w/ nonu, clsd fx w/ malu, opn fx type I or II w/ malu, opn fx type I or II w/ malu] **202**
S82.84[4,5,6] **[A,B,C]**	Nondisp bimalleolar fx of [rt, lt, unsp] lwr leg, [init enc for clsd fx, init enc for opn fx type I or II, init enc for opn fx type I or II] **191, 427**
S82.84[4,5,6] **[D,E,F,G,H,J,S]**	Nondisp bimalleolar fx of [rt, lt, unsp] lwr leg, [subsq enc for clsd fx w/ routine healing, subsq enc for opn fx type I or II w/ routine healing, subsq enc for opn fx type IIIA, IIIB, or IIIC w/ routine healing, subsq enc for clsd fx w/ delayed healing, subsq enc for opn fx type I or II w/ delayed healing, subsq enc for opn fx type IIIA, IIIB, or IIIC w/ delayed healing, seq] **181**
S82.84[4,5,6] **[K,M,N,P,Q,R]**	Nondisp bimalleolar fx of [rt, lt, unsp] lwr leg, subsq enc for [clsd fx w/ nonu, opn fx type I or II w/ nonu, opn fx type IIIA, IIIB, or IIIC w/ nonu, clsd fx w/ malu, opn fx type I or II w/ malu, opn fx type I or II w/ malu] **203**
S82.04[4,5,6] **[A,B,C]**	Nondisp comm fx of [rt, lt, unsp] patella, [init enc for clsd fx, init enc for opn fx type I or II, init enc for opn fx type IIIA, IIIB, or IIIC] **190**
S82.04[4,5,6] **[D,E,F,G,H,J,S]**	Nondisp comm fx of [rt, lt, unsp] patella, subsq enc for [clsd fx w/ routine healing, subsq enc for opn fx type I or II w/ routine healing, subsq enc for opn fx type IIIA, IIIB, or IIIC w/ routine healing, subsq enc for clsd fx w/ delayed healing, subsq enc for opn fx type I or II w/ delayed healing, subsq enc for opn fx type I or II w/ delayed healing, seq] **179**
S82.04[4,5,6] **[K,M,N,P,Q,R]**	Nondisp comm fx of [rt, lt, unsp] patella, subsq enc for [clsd fx w/ nonu, opn fx type I or II w/ nonu, opn fx type IIIA, IIIB, or IIIC w/ nonu, clsd fx w/ malu, opn fx type I or II w/ malu, opn fx type I or II w/ malu] **202**
S52.25[4,5,6] **[B,C]**	Nondisp comm fx of [rt, lt, unsp] ulna, init enc for opn fx [type I or II, IIIA IIIB or IIIC] **434**
S72.35[4,5,6] **[D,E,F,G,H,J,S]**	Nondisp comm fx of shaft of [rt, lt, unsp] femur, [subsq enc for clsd fx w/ routine healing, subsq enc for opn fx type I or II w/ routine healing, subsq enc for opn fx type IIIA, IIIB, or IIIC w/ routine healing, subsq enc for clsd fx w/ delayed healing, subsq enc for opn fx type I or II w/ delayed healing, subsq enc for opn fx type IIIA, IIIB, or IIIC w/ delayed healing, seq] **178**
S72.35[4,5,6] **[K,M,N,P,Q,R]**	Nondisp comm fx of shaft of [rt, lt, unsp] femur, subsq enc for [clsd fx w/ nonu, opn fx type I or II w/ nonu, opn fx type IIIA, IIIB, or IIIC w/ nonu, clsd fx w/ malu, opn fx type I or II w/ malu, opn fx type IIIA, IIIB, or IIIC w/ malu] **201**
S82.45[4,5,6] **[A,B,C]**	Nondisp comm fx of shaft of [rt, lt, unsp] fibula, [init enc for clsd fx, init enc for opn fx type I or II, init enc for opn fx type IIIA, IIIB, or IIIC] **191, 427**
S82.45[4,5,6] **[D,E,F,G,H,J,S]**	Nondisp comm fx of shaft of [rt, lt, unsp] fibula, [subsq enc for clsd fx w/ routine healing, subsq enc for opn fx type I or II w/ routine healing, subsq enc for opn fx type IIIA, IIIB, or IIIC w/ routine healing, subsq enc for clsd fx w/ delayed healing, subsq enc for opn fx type I or II w/ delayed healing, subsq enc for opn fx type IIIA, IIIB, or IIIC w/ delayed healing, seq] **181**
S82.45[4,5,6] **[B,C]**	Nondisp comm fx of shaft of [rt, lt, unsp] fibula, init enc for opn fx type [I or II, IIIA IIIB or IIIC] **436**
S82.45[4,5,6] **[K,M,N,P,Q,R]**	Nondisp comm fx of shaft of [rt, lt, unsp] fibula, subsq enc for [clsd fx w/ nonu, opn fx type I or II w/ nonu, opn fx type IIIA, IIIB, or IIIC w/ nonu, clsd fx w/ malu, opn fx type I or II w/ malu] **203**
S42.35[4,5,6] **[D,G,S]**	Nondisp comm fx of shaft of [rt, lt, unsp] humerus, [subsq enc for fx w/ routine healing, subsq enc for fx w/ delayed healing, seq] **171**
S42.35[4,5,6]B	Nondisp comm fx of shaft of [rt, lt, unsp] humerus, init enc for opn fx **433**
S52.35[4,5,6] **[D,E,F,G,H,J,S]**	Nondisp comm fx of shaft of [rt, lt, unsp] radius, [subsq enc for clsd fx w/ routine healing, subsq enc for opn fx type I or II w/ routine healing, subsq enc for opn fx type I or II w/ routine healing, subsq enc for clsd fx w/ delayed healing, subsq enc for opn fx type I or II w/ delayed healing, subsq enc for opn fx type IIIA, IIIB, or IIIC w/ delayed healing, seq] **173**
S52.35[4,5,6] **[B,C]**	Nondisp comm fx of shaft of [rt, lt, unsp] radius, init enc for opn fx type [I or II, IIIA IIIB or IIIC] **434**
S82.25[4,5,6] **[A,B,C]**	Nondisp comm fx of shaft of [rt, lt, unsp] tibia, [init enc for clsd fx, init enc for opn fx type I or II, init enc for opn fx type IIIA, IIIB, or IIIC] **191, 427**
S82.25[4,5,6] **[D,E,F,G,H,J,S]**	Nondisp comm fx of shaft of [rt, lt, unsp] tibia, [subsq enc for clsd fx w/ routine healing, subsq enc for opn fx type I or II w/ routine healing, subsq enc for opn fx type IIIA, IIIB, or IIIC w/ routine healing, subsq enc for clsd fx w/ delayed healing, subsq enc for opn fx type I or II w/ delayed healing, subsq enc for opn fx type IIIA, IIIB, or IIIC w/ delayed healing, seq] **180**
S82.25[4,5,6] **[B,C]**	Nondisp comm fx of shaft of [rt, lt, unsp] tibia, init enc for opn fx type [I or II, IIIA IIIB or IIIC] **436**
S82.25[4,5,6] **[K,M,N,P,Q,R]**	Nondisp comm fx of shaft of [rt, lt, unsp] tibia, subsq enc for [clsd fx w/ nonu, opn fx type I or II w/ nonu, opn fx type IIIA, IIIB, or IIIC w/ nonu, clsd fx w/ malu, opn fx type I or II w/ malu, opn fx type I or II w/ malu] **203**
S52.25[4,5,6] **[D,E,F,G,H,J,S]**	Nondisp comm fx of shaft of [rt, lt, unsp] ulna, [subsq enc for clsd fx w/ routine healing, subsq enc for opn fx type I or II w/ routine healing, subsq enc for opn fx type IIIA, IIIB, or IIIC w/ routine healing, subsq enc for clsd fx w/ delayed healing, subsq enc for opn fx type I or II w/ delayed healing, subsq enc for opn fx type IIIA, IIIB, or IIIC w/ delayed healing, seq] **173**
S72.35[4,5,6] **[A,B,C]**	Nondisp comm fx of shaft of femur [rt, lt, unsp], init enc for [clsd fx, opn fx type I or II or NOS, opn fx type IIIA, IIIB, or IIIC] **161, 286, 435**
S42.35[4,5,6] **[A,B]**	Nondisp comm fx of shaft of humerus [rt, lt, unsp] init enc for fx [clsd, opn] **185**
S42.35[4,5,6] **[K,P]**	Nondisp comm fx of shaft of humerus, [rt, lt, unsp] arm, subsq enc for fx w/ [nonu, malu] **197**
S52.35[4,5,6] **[A,B,C]**	Nondisp comm fx of shaft of radius [rt, lt, unsp] init enc for [clsd fx, opn fx type I or II or opn fx NOS, opn fx type IIIA, IIIB, or IIIC] **186**
S52.35[4,5,6] **[K,M,N,P,Q,R]**	Nondisp comm fx of shaft of radius, [rt, lt, unsp] arm, subsq enc for [clsd fx w/ nonu, opn fx type I or II w/ nonu, opn fx type IIIA, IIIB, or IIIC w/ nonu, clsd fx w/ malu, opn fx type I or II w/ malu, opn fx type IIIA, IIIB, or IIIC w/ malu] **198**
S52.25[4,5,6] **[K,M,N,P,Q,R]**	Nondisp comm fx of shaft of ulna, [rt, lt, unsp] arm, subsq enc for [clsd fx w/ nonu, opn fx type I or II w/ nonu, opn fx type IIIA, IIIB, or IIIC w/ nonu, clsd fx w/ malu, opn fx type I or II w/ malu, opn fx type IIIA, IIIB, or IIIC w/ malu] **198**
S52.25[4,5,6] **[A,B,C]**	Nondisp comm fx of ulna [rt, lt, unsp] init enc for [clsd fx, opn fx type I or II or opn fx NOS, opn fx type IIIA, IIIB, or IIIC] **186**

Code	Description
S42.42[4,5,6] [D,G,S]	Nondisp comm supracondylar fx w/o intercondylar fx of [rt, lt, unsp] humerus, [subsq enc for fx w/ routine healing, subsq enc for fx w/ delayed healing, seq] **171**
S42.42[4,5,6]B	Nondisp comm supracondylar fx w/o intercondylar fx of [rt, lt, unsp] humerus, init enc for opn fx **434**
S42.42[4,5,6] [K,P]	Nondisp comm supracondylar fx w/o intercondylar fx of [rt, lt, unsp] humerus, subsq enc for fx w/ [nonu, malu] **197**
S42.42[4,5,6] [A,B]	Nondisp comm supracondylar fx of humerus [rt, lt, unsp] init enc for fx [clsd, opn] **185**
S32.48[4,5,6] [A,B]	Nondisp dome fx of [rt, lt, unsp] acetab, init enc for [clsd, opn] fx **162, 433**
S32.48[4,5,6]S	Nondisp dome fx of [rt, lt, unsp] acetab, seq **166**
S32.48[4,5,6] [D,G]	Nondisp dome fx of [rt, lt, unsp] acetab, subsq enc for fx w/ [routine, delayed] healing **170**
S32.48[4,5,6]K	Nondisp dome fx of [rt, lt, unsp] acetab, subsq enc for fx w/ nonu **196**
S92.14[4,5,6] [D,G,S]	Nondisp dome fx of [rt, lt, unsp] talus, [subsq enc for fx w/ routine healing, subsq enc for fx w/ delayed healing, seq] **182**
S92.14[4,5,6] [A,B]	Nondisp dome fx of [rt, lt, unsp] talus, init enc for [clsd, opn] fx **192, 429**
S92.14[4,5,6] [K,P]	Nondisp dome fx of [rt, lt, unsp] talus, subsq enc for fx w/ [nonu, malu] **204**
S42.43[4,5,6] [D,G,S]	Nondisp fx (avulsion) of lat epicondyle of [rt, lt, unsp] humerus, [subsq enc for fx w/ routine healing, subsq enc for fx w/ delayed healing, seq] **171**
S42.43[4,5,6]B	Nondisp fx (avulsion) of lat epicondyle of [rt, lt, unsp] humerus, init enc for opn fx **434**
S42.43[4,5,6] [K,P]	Nondisp fx (avulsion) of lat epicondyle of [rt, lt, unsp] humerus, subsq enc for fx w/ [nonu, malu] **197**
S42.43[4,5,6] [A,B]	Nondisp fx (avulsion) of lat epicondyle of humerus [rt, lt, unsp] init enc for fx [clsd, opn] **185**
S42.44[4,5,6] [D,G,S]	Nondisp fx (avulsion) of med epicondyle of [rt, lt, unsp] humerus, [subsq enc for fx w/ routine healing, subsq enc for fx w/ delayed healing, seq] **171**
S42.44[4,5,6]B	Nondisp fx (avulsion) of med epicondyle of [rt, lt, unsp] humerus, init enc for opn fx **434**
S42.44[4,5,6] [K,P]	Nondisp fx (avulsion) of med epicondyle of [rt, lt, unsp] humerus, subsq enc for fx w/ [nonu, malu] **197**
S42.44[4,5,6] [A,B]	Nondisp fx (avulsion) of med epicondyle of humerus [rt, lt, unsp] init enc for fx [clsd, opn] **185**
S52.51[4,5,6] [D,E,F,G,H,J,S]	Nondisp fx of [rt, lt, unsp] radial styloid process, [subsq enc for clsd fx w/ routine healing, subsq enc for opn fx type I or II w/ routine healing, subsq enc for opn fx type I or II w/ routine healing, subsq enc for clsd fx w/ delayed healing, subsq enc for opn fx type I or II w/ delayed healing, subsq enc for opn fx type IIIA, IIIB, or IIIC w/ delayed healing, seq] **173**
S52.51[4,5,6] [B,C]	Nondisp fx of [rt, lt, unsp] radial styloid process, init enc for opn fx type [I or II, IIIA IIIB or IIIC] **434**
S52.51[4,5,6] [K,M,N,P,Q,R]	Nondisp fx of [rt, lt, unsp] radial styloid process, subsq enc for [clsd fx w/ nonu, opn fx type I or II w/ nonu, opn fx type IIIA, IIIB, or IIIC w/ nonu, clsd fx w/ malu, opn fx type I or II w/ malu, opn fx type IIIA, IIIB, or IIIC w/ malu] **198**
S82.11[4,5,6] [A,B,C]	Nondisp fx of [rt, lt, unsp] tibial spine, [init enc for clsd fx, init enc for opn fx type I or II, init enc for opn fx type IIIA, IIIB, or IIIC] **190**
S82.11[4,5,6] [D,E,F,G,H,J,S]	Nondisp fx of [rt, lt, unsp] tibial spine, [subsq enc for clsd fx w/ routine healing, subsq enc for opn fx type I or II w/ routine healing, subsq enc for opn fx type IIIA, IIIB, or IIIC w/ routine healing, subsq enc for clsd fx w/ delayed healing, subsq enc for opn fx type I or II w/ delayed healing, seq] **179**
S82.11[4,5,6] [B,C]	Nondisp fx of [rt, lt, unsp] tibial spine, init enc for opn fx type [I or II, IIIA IIIB or IIIC] **436**
S82.11[4,5,6] [K,M,N,P,Q,R]	Nondisp fx of [rt, lt, unsp] tibial spine, subsq enc for [clsd fx w/ nonu, opn fx type I or II w/ nonu, opn fx type IIIA, IIIB, or IIIC w/ nonu, clsd fx w/ malu, opn fx type I or II w/ malu, opn fx type I or II w/ malu] **202**
S82.15[4,5,6] [A,B,C]	Nondisp fx of [rt, lt, unsp] tibial tuberosity, [init enc for clsd fx, init enc for opn fx type I or II, init enc for opn fx type IIIA, IIIB, or IIIC] **191**
S82.15[4,5,6] [D,E,F,G,H,J,S]	Nondisp fx of [rt, lt, unsp] tibial tuberosity, [subsq enc for clsd fx w/ routine healing, subsq enc for opn fx type I or II w/ routine healing, subsq enc for opn fx type IIIA, IIIB, or IIIC w/ routine healing, subsq enc for clsd fx w/ delayed healing, subsq enc for opn fx type I or II w/ delayed healing, subsq enc for opn fx type I or II w/ delayed healing, seq] **180**
S82.15[4,5,6] [B,C]	Nondisp fx of [rt, lt, unsp] tibial tuberosity, init enc for opn fx type [I or II, IIIA IIIB or IIIC] **436**
S82.15[4,5,6] [K,M,N,P,Q,R]	Nondisp fx of [rt, lt, unsp] tibial tuberosity, subsq enc for [clsd fx w/ nonu, opn fx type I or II w/ nonu, opn fx type IIIA, IIIB, or IIIC w/ nonu, clsd fx w/ malu, opn fx type I or II w/ malu, opn fx type I or II w/ malu] **202**
S52.61[4,5,6] [D,E,F,G,H,J,S]	Nondisp fx of [rt, lt, unsp] ulna styloid process, [subsq enc for clsd fx w/ routine healing, subsq enc for opn fx type I or II w/ routine healing, subsq enc for opn fx type IIIA, IIIB, or IIIC w/ routine healing, subsq enc for clsd fx w/ delayed healing, subsq enc for opn fx type I or II w/ delayed healing, subsq enc for opn fx type I or II w/ delayed healing, seq] **174**
S52.61[4,5,6] [B,C]	Nondisp fx of [rt, lt, unsp] ulna styloid process, init enc for fx opn fx type [I or II, IIIA IIIB IIIC] **435**
S52.61[4,5,6] [K,M,N,P,Q,R]	Nondisp fx of [rt, lt, unsp] ulna styloid process, subsq enc for [clsd fx w/ nonu, opn fx type I or II w/ nonu, opn fx type IIIA, IIIB, or IIIC w/ nonu, clsd fx w/ malu, opn fx type I or II w/ malu, opn fx type IIIA, IIIB, or IIIC w/ malu] **199**
S92.31[4,5,6] [D,G,S]	Nondisp fx of 1st metatarsal bone, [rt, lt, unsp] foot, [subsq enc for fx w/ routine healing, subsq enc for fx w/ delayed healing, seq] **183**
S92.31[4,5,6] [A,B]	Nondisp fx of 1st metatarsal bone, [rt, lt, unsp] foot, init enc for [clsd, opn] fx **192, 429**
S92.31[4,5,6] [K,P]	Nondisp fx of 1st metatarsal bone, [rt, lt, unsp] foot, subsq enc for fx w/ [nonu, malu] **204**
S92.32[4,5,6] [D,G,S]	Nondisp fx of 2nd metatarsal bone, [rt, lt, unsp] foot, [subsq enc for fx w/ routine healing, subsq enc for fx w/ delayed healing, seq] **183**
S92.32[4,5,6] [A,B]	Nondisp fx of 2nd metatarsal bone, [rt, lt, unsp] foot, init enc for [clsd, opn] fx **192, 429**
S92.32[4,5,6] [K,P]	Nondisp fx of 2nd metatarsal bone, [rt, lt, unsp] foot, subsq enc for fx w/ [nonu, malu] **204**
S92.33[4,5,6] [D,G,S]	Nondisp fx of 3rd metatarsal bone, [rt, lt, unsp] foot, [subsq enc for fx w/ routine healing, subsq enc for fx w/ delayed healing, seq] **183**
S92.33[4,5,6] [A,B]	Nondisp fx of 3rd metatarsal bone, [rt, lt, unsp] foot, init enc for [clsd, opn] fx **192, 429**
S92.33[4,5,6] [K,P]	Nondisp fx of 3rd metatarsal bone, [rt, lt, unsp] foot, subsq enc for fx w/ [nonu, malu] **204**
S92.34[4,5,6] [D,G,S]	Nondisp fx of 4th metatarsal bone, [rt, lt, unsp] foot, [subsq enc for fx w/ routine healing, subsq enc for fx w/ delayed healing, seq] **183**
S92.34[4,5,6] [A,B]	Nondisp fx of 4th metatarsal bone, [rt, lt, unsp] foot, init enc for [clsd, opn] fx **192, 429**
S92.34[4,5,6] [K,P]	Nondisp fx of 4th metatarsal bone, [rt, lt, unsp] foot, subsq enc for fx w/ [nonu, malu] **204**
S92.35[4,5,6] [D,G,S]	Nondisp fx of 5th metatarsal bone, [rt, lt, unsp] foot, [subsq enc for fx w/ routine healing, subsq enc for fx w/ delayed healing, seq] **183**
S92.35[4,5,6] [A,B]	Nondisp fx of 5th metatarsal bone, [rt, lt, unsp] foot, init enc for [clsd, opn] fx **192, 429**
S92.35[4,5,6] [K,P]	Nondisp fx of 5th metatarsal bone, [rt, lt, unsp] foot, subsq enc for fx w/ [nonu, malu] **204**
S42.12[4,5,6] [A,B]	Nondisp fx of acromial process [rt, lt, unsp] init enc for fx [clsd, opn] **184**
S42.12[4,5,6] [D,G,S]	Nondisp fx of acromial process, [rt, lt, unsp] shldr, [subsq enc for fx w/ routine healing, subsq enc for fx w/ delayed healing, seq] **170**
S42.12[4,5,6] [K,P]	Nondisp fx of acromial process, [rt, lt, unsp] shldr, subsq enc for fx w/ [nonu, malu] **196**
S32.43[4,5,6]S	Nondisp fx of ant column (iliopubic) of [rt, lt, unsp] acetab, seq **166**
S32.43[4,5,6] [D,G]	Nondisp fx of ant column (iliopubic) of [rt, lt, unsp] acetab, subsq enc for fx w/ [routine, delayed] healing **170**
S32.43[4,5,6]K	Nondisp fx of ant column (iliopubic) of [rt, lt, unsp] acetab, subsq enc for fx w/ nonu **196**
S32.43[4,5,6] [A,B]	Nondisp fx of ant column [iliopubic] of acetab [rt, lt, unsp] init enc for [clsd fx, opn fx **162, 433**
S92.02[4,5,6] [D,G,S]	Nondisp fx of ant process of [rt, lt, unsp] calcaneus, [subsq enc for fx w/ routine healing, subsq enc for fx w/ delayed healing, seq] **182**
S92.02[4,5,6] [A,B]	Nondisp fx of ant process of [rt, lt, unsp] calcaneus, init enc for [clsd, opn] fx **192, 429**
S92.02[4,5,6] [K,P]	Nondisp fx of ant process of [rt, lt, unsp] calcaneus, subsq enc for fx w/ [nonu, malu] **204**
S32.41[4,5,6]S	Nondisp fx of ant wall of [rt, lt, unsp] acetab, seq **166**
S32.41[4,5,6] [D,G]	Nondisp fx of ant wall of [rt, lt, unsp] acetab, subsq enc for fx w/ [routine, delayed] healing **170**
S32.41[4,5,6]K	Nondisp fx of ant wall of [rt, lt, unsp] acetab, subsq enc for fx w/ nonu **196**
S32.41[4,5,6] [A,B]	Nondisp fx of ant wall of acetab [rt, lt, unsp] init enc for [clsd fx, opn fx] **162, 433**
S62.34[0,1,2,3,4, 5,6,7,8,9][A,B]	Nondisp fx of base of [2nd, 3rd, 4th, 5th, oth, unsp] metacarpal bone, (rt, lt) hand, init enc for [clsd, opn] fx **425**
S62.34[8,9] [D,G,S]	Nondisp fx of base of [oth, unsp] metacarpal bone, [subsq enc for fx w/ routine healing, subsq enc for fx w/ delayed healing, seq] **175**

Code	Description
S62.34[8,9][K,P]	Nondisp fx of base of [oth, unsp] metacarpal bone, subsq enc for fx w/ [nonu, malu] **200**
S62.34[8,9][A,B]	Nondisp fx of base of [oth,unsp] metacarpal bone, init enc for [clsd, opn] fx **188**
S62.34[0,1][A,B]	Nondisp fx of base of 2nd metacarpal bone, [rt, lt, unsp] hand, init enc for [clsd, opn] fx **188**
S62.34[0,1] [D,G,S]	Nondisp fx of base of 2nd metacarpal bone, [rt, lt] hand, [subsq enc for fx w/ routine healing, subsq enc for fx w/ delayed healing, seq] **175**
S62.34[0,1][K,P]	Nondisp fx of base of 2nd metacarpal bone, [rt, lt] hand, subsq enc for fx w/ [nonu, malu] **199**
S62.34[2,3][A,B]	Nondisp fx of base of 3rd metacarpal bone, [rt, lt, unsp] hand, init enc for [clsd, opn] fx **188**
S62.34[2,3] [D,G,S]	Nondisp fx of base of 3rd metacarpal bone, [rt, lt] hand, [subsq enc for fx w/ routine healing, subsq enc for fx w/ delayed healing, seq] **175**
S62.34[2,3][K,P]	Nondisp fx of base of 3rd metacarpal bone, [rt, lt] hand, subsq enc for fx w/ [nonu, malu] **200**
S62.34[4,5][A,B]	Nondisp fx of base of 4th metacarpal bone, [rt, lt, unsp] hand, init enc for [clsd, opn] fx **188**
S62.34[4,5] [D,G,S]	Nondisp fx of base of 4th metacarpal bone, [rt, lt] hand, [subsq enc for fx w/ routine healing, subsq enc for fx w/ delayed healing, seq] **175**
S62.34[4,5][K,P]	Nondisp fx of base of 4th metacarpal bone, [rt, lt] hand, subsq enc for fx w/ [nonu, malu] **200**
S62.34[6,7][A,B]	Nondisp fx of base of 5th metacarpal bone, [rt, lt, unsp] hand, init enc for [clsd, opn] fx **188**
S62.34[6,7] [D,G,S]	Nondisp fx of base of 5th metacarpal bone, [rt, lt] hand, [subsq enc for fx w/ routine healing, subsq enc for fx w/ delayed healing, seq] **175**
S62.34[6,7][K,P]	Nondisp fx of base of 5th metacarpal bone, [rt, lt] hand, subsq enc for fx w/ [nonu, malu] **200**
S72.04[4,5,6] [D,E,F,G,H,J,S]	Nondisp fx of base of neck of [rt, lt, unsp] femur, [subsq enc for clsd fx w/ routine healing, subsq enc for opn fx type I or II w/ routine healing, subsq enc for opn fx type IIIA, IIIB, or IIIC w/ routine healing, subsq enc for clsd fx w/ delayed healing, subsq enc for opn fx type I or II w/ delayed healing, subsq enc for opn fx type IIIA, IIIB, or IIIC w/ delayed healing, seq] **177**
S72.04[4,5,6] [A,B,C]	Nondisp fx of base of neck of [rt, lt, unsp] femur, init enc for opn fx type [I or II, IIIA IIIB or IIIC] **162, 286, 435**
S72.04[4,5,6] [K,M,N,P,Q,R]	Nondisp fx of base of neck of [rt, lt, unsp] femur, subsq enc for [clsd fx w/ nonu, opn fx type I or II w/ nonu, opn fx type IIIA, IIIB, or IIIC w/ nonu, clsd fx w/ malu, opn fx type I or II w/ malu, opn fx type IIIA, IIIB, or IIIC w/ malu] **178**
S92.01[4,5,6] [D,G,S]	Nondisp fx of body of [rt, lt, unsp] calcaneus, [subsq enc for fx w/ routine healing, subsq enc for fx w/ delayed healing, seq] **182**
S92.01[4,5,6] [A,B]	Nondisp fx of body of [rt, lt, unsp] calcaneus, init enc for [clsd, opn] fx **192, 429**
S92.01[4,5,6] [K,P]	Nondisp fx of body of [rt, lt, unsp] calcaneus, subsq enc for fx w/ [nonu, malu] **204**
S92.12[4,5,6] [D,G,S]	Nondisp fx of body of [rt, lt, unsp] talus, [subsq enc for fx w/ routine healing, subsq enc for fx w/ delayed healing, seq] **182**
S92.12[4,5,6] [A,B]	Nondisp fx of body of [rt, lt, unsp] talus, init enc for [clsd, opn] fx **192, 429**
S92.12[4,5,6] [K,P]	Nondisp fx of body of [rt, lt, unsp] talus, subsq enc for fx w/ [nonu, malu] **204**
S62.14[4,5,6] [D,G,S]	Nondisp fx of body of hamate (unciform) bone, [rt, lt, unsp] wrist, [subsq enc for fx w/ routine healing, subsq enc for fx w/ delayed healing, seq] **175**
S62.14[4,5,6] [K,P]	Nondisp fx of body of hamate (unciform) bone, [rt, lt, unsp] wrist, subsq enc for fx w/ [nonu, malu] **199**
S62.14[4,5,6] [A,B]	Nondisp fx of body of hamate [unciform] bone of wrist [rt, lt, unsp] init enc for fx [clsd, opn **187**
S42.11[4,5,6] [A,B,K,P]	Nondisp fx of body of scapula, [rt, lt, unsp] shldr, [init enc for clsd fx, init enc for opn fx, subsq enc for fx w/ nonu, subsq enc for fx w/ malu] **196**
S42.11[4,5,6] [D,G,S]	Nondisp fx of body of scapula, [rt, lt, unsp] shldr, [subsq enc for fx w/ routine healing, subsq enc for fx w/ delayed healing, seq] **170**
S62.13[4,5,6] [D,G,S]	Nondisp fx of capitate (os magnum) bone, [rt, lt, unsp] wrist, [subsq enc for fx w/ routine healing, subsq enc for fx w/ delayed healing, seq] **175**
S62.13[4,5,6] [K,P]	Nondisp fx of capitate (os magnum) bone, [rt, lt, unsp] wrist, subsq enc for fx w/ [nonu, malu] **199**
S62.13[4,5,6] [A,B]	Nondisp fx of capitate [os magnum] bone of wrist [rt, lt, unsp] init enc for fx [clsd, opn **187**
S42.13[4,5,6] [A,B]	Nondisp fx of coracoid process of shldr [rt, lt, unsp] init enc for fx [clsd, opn] **184**
S42.13[4,5,6] [D,G,S]	Nondisp fx of coracoid process, [rt, lt, unsp] shldr, [subsq enc for fx w/ routine healing, subsq enc for fx w/ delayed healing, seq] **170**
S42.13[4,5,6] [K,P]	Nondisp fx of coracoid process, [rt, lt, unsp] shldr, subsq enc for fx w/ [nonu, malu] **196**
S52.04[4,5,6] [D,E,F,G,H,J,S]	Nondisp fx of coronoid process of [rt, lt, unsp] ulna, [subsq enc for clsd fx w/ routine healing, subsq enc for opn fx type I or II w/ routine healing, subsq enc for opn fx type IIIA, IIIB, or IIIC w/ routine healing, subsq enc for clsd fx w/ delayed healing, subsq enc for opn fx type I or II w/ delayed healing, subsq enc for opn fx type IIIA, IIIB, or IIIC w/ delayed healing, seq] **172**
S52.04[4,5,6] [B,C]	Nondisp fx of coronoid process of [rt, lt, unsp] ulna, init enc for opn fx type [I or II, IIIA IIIB or IIIC] **434**
S52.04[4,5,6] [K,M,N,P,Q,R]	Nondisp fx of coronoid process of [rt, lt, unsp] ulna, subsq enc for [clsd fx w/ nonu, opn fx type I or II w/ nonu, opn fx type IIIA, IIIB, or IIIC w/ nonu, clsd fx w/ malu, opn fx type I or II w/ malu, opn fx type IIIA, IIIB, or IIIC w/ malu] **197**
S52.04[4,5,6] [A,B,C]	Nondisp fx of coronoid process of ulna [rt, lt, unsp] init enc for fx [clsd fx, opn fx type I or II or opn fx NOS, opn fx type IIIA, IIIB, or IIIC] **186**
S92.21[4,5,6] [D,G,S]	Nondisp fx of cuboid bone of [rt, lt, unsp] foot, [subsq enc for fx w/ routine healing, subsq enc for fx w/ delayed healing, seq] **182**
S92.21[4,5,6] [A,B]	Nondisp fx of cuboid bone of [rt, lt, unsp] foot, init enc for [clsd, opn] fx **192, 429**
S92.21[4,5,6] [K,P]	Nondisp fx of cuboid bone of [rt, lt, unsp] foot, subsq enc for fx w/ [nonu, malu] **204**
S92.53[4,5,6] [K,P]	Nondisp fx of distal phalanx [rt, lt, unsp] lesser toe(s), subsq enc for fx w/ [nonu, malu] **204**
S62.66[8,9] [D,G,S]	Nondisp fx of distal phalanx of [oth, unsp] finger, [subsq enc for fx w/ routine healing, subsq enc for fx w/ delayed healing, seq] **176**
S62.66[8,9][A,B]	Nondisp fx of distal phalanx of [oth, unsp] finger, init enc for [clsd, opn] fx **188**
S62.66[8,9][K,P]	Nondisp fx of distal phalanx of [oth, unsp] finger, subsq enc for fx w/ [nonu, malu] **200**
S62.66[0,1,2,3,4, 5,6,7,8,9] [A,B]	Nondisp fx of distal phalanx of [rt index, lt index, rt mid, lt mid, rt ring, lt ring, rt little, lt little, oth, unsp] finger, init enc for [clsd, opn] fx **425**
S92.42[4,5,6] [D,G,S]	Nondisp fx of distal phalanx of [rt, lt, unsp] great toe, [subsq enc for fx w/ routine healing, subsq enc for fx w/ delayed healing, seq] **183**
S92.42[4,5,6] [A,B]	Nondisp fx of distal phalanx of [rt, lt, unsp] great toe, init enc for [clsd, opn] fx **192, 429**
S92.42[4,5,6] [K,P]	Nondisp fx of distal phalanx of [rt, lt, unsp] great toe, subsq enc for fx w/ [nonu, malu] **204**
S92.53[4,5,6] [D,G,S]	Nondisp fx of distal phalanx of [rt, lt, unsp] lesser toe(s), [subsq enc for fx w/ routine healing, subsq enc for fx w/ delayed healing, seq] **183**
S92.53[4,5,6] [A,B]	Nondisp fx of distal phalanx of [rt, lt, unsp] lesser toe(s), init enc for [clsd, opn] fx **193, 430**
S62.52[4,5,6] [D,G,S]	Nondisp fx of distal phalanx of [rt, lt, unsp] thumb, [subsq enc for fx w/ routine healing, subsq enc for fx w/ delayed healing, seq] **176**
S62.52[4,5,6] [A,B]	Nondisp fx of distal phalanx of [rt, lt, unsp] thumb, init enc for [clsd, opn] fx **188**
S62.52[4,5,6] [K,P]	Nondisp fx of distal phalanx of [rt, lt, unsp] thumb, subsq enc for fx w/ [nonu, malu] **200**
S62.66[0,1] [D,G,S]	Nondisp fx of distal phalanx of [rt, lt] index finger, [subsq enc for fx w/ routine healing, subsq enc for fx w/ delayed healing, seq] **176**
S62.66[0,1][A,B]	Nondisp fx of distal phalanx of [rt, lt] index finger, init enc for [clsd, opn] fx **188**
S62.66[0,1][K,P]	Nondisp fx of distal phalanx of [rt, lt] index finger, subsq enc for fx w/ [nonu, malu] **200**
S62.66[6,7] [D,G,S]	Nondisp fx of distal phalanx of [rt, lt] little finger, [subsq enc for fx w/ routine healing, subsq enc for fx w/ delayed healing, seq] **176**
S62.66[6,7][A,B]	Nondisp fx of distal phalanx of [rt, lt] little finger, init enc for [clsd, opn] fx **188**
S62.66[6,7][K,P]	Nondisp fx of distal phalanx of [rt, lt] little finger, subsq enc for fx w/ [nonu, malu] **200**
S62.66[2,3] [D,G,S]	Nondisp fx of distal phalanx of [rt, lt] mid finger, [subsq enc for fx w/ routine healing, subsq enc for fx w/ delayed healing, seq] **176**
S62.66[2,3][A,B]	Nondisp fx of distal phalanx of [rt, lt] mid finger, init enc for [clsd, opn] fx **188**
S62.66[2,3][K,P]	Nondisp fx of distal phalanx of [rt, lt] mid finger, subsq enc for fx w/ [nonu, malu] **200**
S62.66[4,5] [D,G,S]	Nondisp fx of distal phalanx of [rt, lt] ring finger, [subsq enc for fx w/ routine healing, subsq enc for fx w/ delayed healing, seq] **176**

S62.66[4,5][A,B]	Nondisp fx of distal phalanx of [rt, lt] ring finger, init enc for [clsd, opn] fx **188**
S62.66[4,5][K,P]	Nondisp fx of distal phalanx of [rt, lt] ring finger, subsq enc for fx w/ [nonu, malu] **200**
S62.01[4,5,6] [D,G,S]	Nondisp fx of distal pole of navicular (scaphoid) bone of [rt, lt, unsp] wrist, [subsq enc for fx w/ routine healing, subsq enc for fx w/ delayed healing, seq] **174**
S62.01[4,5,6] [K,P]	Nondisp fx of distal pole of navicular (scaphoid) bone of [rt, lt, unsp] wrist, subsq enc for fx w/ [nonu, malu] **199**
S62.01[4,5,6] [A,B]	Nondisp fx of distal pole of navicular [scaphoid] bone of wrist [rt, lt, unsp] init enc for fx [clsd, opn] **187**
S72.02[4,5,6] [D,E,F,G,H,J,S]	Nondisp fx of epiphysis (separation) (upr) of [rt, lt, unsp] femur, [subsq enc for clsd fx w/ routine healing, subsq enc for opn fx type I or II w/ routine healing, subsq enc for opn fx type IIIA, IIIB, or IIIC w/ routine healing, subsq enc for clsd fx w/ delayed healing, subsq enc for opn fx type I or II w/ delayed healing, subsq enc for opn fx type IIIA, IIIB, or IIIC w/ delayed healing, seq] **177**
S72.02[4,5,6] [A,B,C]	Nondisp fx of epiphysis (separation) (upr) of [rt, lt, unsp] femur, init enc for [clsd fx, opn fx type I or II or NOS, or opn fx type IIIA, IIIB, or IIIC] **162, 286, 435**
S72.02[4,5,6] [K,M,N,P,Q,R]	Nondisp fx of epiphysis (separation) (upr) of [rt, lt, unsp] femur, subsq enc for [clsd fx w/ nonu, opn fx type I or II w/ nonu, opn fx type IIIA, IIIB, or IIIC w/ nonu, clsd fx w/ malu, opn fx type I or II w/ malu, opn fx type IIIA, IIIB, or IIIC w/ malu] **200**
S42.14[4,5,6] [A,B]	Nondisp fx of glenoid cavity of scapula [rt, lt, unsp] init enc for fx [clsd, opn] **184**
S42.14[4,5,6] [D,G,S]	Nondisp fx of glenoid cavity of scapula, [rt, lt, unsp] shldr, [subsq enc for fx w/ routine healing, subsq enc for fx w/ delayed healing, seq] **170**
S42.14[4,5,6] [K,P]	Nondisp fx of glenoid cavity of scapula, [rt, lt, unsp] shldr, subsq enc for fx w/ [nonu, malu] **196**
S72.11[4,5,6] [D,E,F,G,H,J,S]	Nondisp fx of greater trochanter of [rt, lt, unsp] femur, [subsq enc for clsd fx w/ routine healing, subsq enc for opn fx type I or II w/ routine healing, subsq enc for opn fx type IIIA, IIIB, or IIIC w/ routine healing, subsq enc for clsd fx w/ delayed healing, subsq enc for opn fx type I or II w/ delayed healing, subsq enc for opn fx type IIIA, IIIB, or IIIC w/ delayed healing, seq] **177**
S72.11[4,5,6] [K,M,N,P,Q,R]	Nondisp fx of greater trochanter of [rt, lt, unsp] femur, subsq enc for [clsd fx w/ nonu, opn fx type I or II w/ nonu, opn fx type IIIA, IIIB, or IIIC w/ nonu, clsd fx w/ malu, opn fx type I or II w/ malu, opn fx type IIIA, IIIB, or IIIC w/ malu] **201**
S72.11[4,5,6] [A,B,C]	Nondisp fx of greater trochanter of femur [rt, lt, unsp] init enc for fx [clsd, opn fx type I or II or NOS, or opn fx type IIIA, IIIB, or IIIC] **162, 286, 435**
S42.25[4,5,6] [D,G,S]	Nondisp fx of greater tuberosity of [rt, lt, unsp] humerus, [subsq enc for fx w/ routine healing, subsq enc for fx w/ delayed healing, seq] **171**
S42.25[4,5,6]B	Nondisp fx of greater tuberosity of [rt, lt, unsp] humerus, init enc for opn fx **433**
S42.25[4,5,6] [K,P]	Nondisp fx of greater tuberosity of [rt, lt, unsp] humerus, subsq enc for fx w/ [nonu, malu] **196**
S42.25[4,5,6] [A,B]	Nondisp fx of greater tuberosity of humerus [rt, lt, unsp] init enc for fx [clsd, opn] **185**
S52.12[4,5,6] [D,E,F,G,H,J,S]	Nondisp fx of head of [rt, lt, unsp] radius, [subsq enc for clsd fx w/ routine healing, subsq enc for opn fx type I or II w/ routine healing, subsq enc for opn fx type IIIA, IIIB, or IIIC w/ routine healing, subsq enc for clsd fx w/ delayed healing, subsq enc for opn fx type I or II w/ delayed healing, subsq enc for opn fx type IIIA, IIIB, or IIIC w/ delayed healing, seq] **172**
S52.12[4,5,6] [B,C]	Nondisp fx of head of [rt, lt, unsp] radius, init enc for opn fx type [I or II, IIIA IIIB or IIIC] **434**
S52.12[4,5,6] [K,M,N,P,Q,R]	Nondisp fx of head of [rt, lt, unsp] radius, subsq enc for [clsd fx w/ nonu, opn fx type I or II w/ nonu, opn fx type IIIA, IIIB, or IIIC w/ nonu, clsd fx w/ malu, opn fx type I or II w/ malu, opn fx type IIIA, IIIB, or IIIC w/ malu] **197**
S52.12[4,5,6] [A,B,C]	Nondisp fx of head of radius [rt, lt, unsp] init enc for [clsd fx, opn fx type I or II or opn fx NOS, or opn fx type IIIA, IIIB, or IIIC] **186**
S62.15[4,5,6] [D,G,S]	Nondisp fx of hook process of hamate (unciform) bone, [rt, lt, unsp] wrist, [subsq enc for fx w/ routine healing, subsq enc for fx w/ delayed healing, seq] **175**
S62.15[4,5,6] [K,P]	Nondisp fx of hook process of hamate (unciform) bone, [rt, lt, unsp] wrist, subsq enc for fx w/ [nonu, malu] **199**
S62.15[4,5,6] [A,B]	Nondisp fx of hook process of hamate [unciform] bone of wrist [rt, lt, unsp] init enc for fx [clsd, opn] **187**
S92.23[4,5,6] [D,G,S]	Nondisp fx of intermediate cuneiform of [rt, lt, unsp] foot, [subsq enc for fx w/ routine healing, subsq enc for fx w/ delayed healing, seq] **183**
S92.23[4,5,6] [A,B]	Nondisp fx of intermediate cuneiform of [rt, lt, unsp] foot, init enc for [clsd, opn] fx **192, 429**
S92.23[4,5,6] [K,P]	Nondisp fx of intermediate cuneiform of [rt, lt, unsp] foot, subsq enc for fx w/ [nonu, malu] **204**
S72.42[4,5,6] [D,E,F,G,H,J,S]	Nondisp fx of lat condyle of [rt, lt, unsp] femur, [subsq enc for clsd fx w/ routine healing, subsq enc for opn fx type I or II w/ routine healing, subsq enc for opn fx type IIIA, IIIB, or IIIC w/ routine healing, subsq enc for clsd fx w/ delayed healing, subsq enc for opn fx type I or II w/ delayed healing, subsq enc for opn fx type IIIA, IIIB, or IIIC w/ delayed healing, seq] **178**
S72.42[4,5,6] [A,B,C]	Nondisp fx of lat condyle of [rt, lt, unsp] femur, init enc for [clsd fx, opn fx type I or II, opn fx type IIIA, IIIB, or IIIC] **161, 435**
S72.42[4,5,6] [K,M,N,P,Q,R]	Nondisp fx of lat condyle of [rt, lt, unsp] femur, subsq enc for [clsd fx w/ nonu, opn fx type I or II w/ nonu, opn fx type IIIA, IIIB, or IIIC w/ nonu, clsd fx w/ malu, opn fx type I or II w/ malu, opn fx type IIIA, IIIB, or IIIC w/ malu] **201**
S42.45[4,5,6] [D,G,S]	Nondisp fx of lat condyle of [rt, lt, unsp] humerus, [subsq enc for fx w/ routine healing, subsq enc for fx w/ delayed healing, seq] **171**
S42.45[4,5,6]B	Nondisp fx of lat condyle of [rt, lt, unsp] humerus, init enc for opn fx **434**
S42.45[4,5,6] [K,P]	Nondisp fx of lat condyle of [rt, lt, unsp] humerus, subsq enc for fx w/ [nonu, malu] **197**
S82.12[4,5,6] [A,B,C]	Nondisp fx of lat condyle of [rt, lt, unsp] tibia, [init enc for clsd fx, init enc for opn fx type I or II, init enc for opn fx type IIIA, IIIB, or IIIC] **190**
S82.12[4,5,6] [D,E,F,G,H,J,S]	Nondisp fx of lat condyle of [rt, lt, unsp] tibia, [subsq enc for clsd fx w/ routine healing, subsq enc for opn fx type I or II w/ routine healing, subsq enc for opn fx type IIIA, IIIB, or IIIC w/ routine healing, subsq enc for clsd fx w/ delayed healing, subsq enc for opn fx type I or II w/ delayed healing, subsq enc for opn fx type I or II w/ delayed healing, seq] **179**
S82.12[4,5,6] [B,C]	Nondisp fx of lat condyle of [rt, lt, unsp] tibia, init enc for opn fx type [I or II, IIIA IIIB or IIIC] **436**
S82.12[4,5,6] [K,M,N,P,Q,R]	Nondisp fx of lat condyle of [rt, lt, unsp] tibia, subsq enc for [clsd fx w/ nonu, opn fx type I or II w/ nonu, opn fx type IIIA, IIIB, or IIIC w/ nonu, clsd fx w/ malu, opn fx type I or II w/ malu, opn fx type I or II w/ malu] **202**
S42.45[4,5,6] [A,B]	Nondisp fx of lat condyle of humerus [rt, lt, unsp] init enc for fx [clsd, opn] **185**
S92.22[4,5,6] [D,G,S]	Nondisp fx of lat cuneiform of [rt, lt, unsp] foot, [subsq enc for fx w/ routine healing, subsq enc for fx w/ delayed healing, seq] **182**
S92.22[4,5,6] [A,B]	Nondisp fx of lat cuneiform of [rt, lt, unsp] foot, init enc for [clsd, opn] fx **192, 429**
S92.22[4,5,6] [K,P]	Nondisp fx of lat cuneiform of [rt, lt, unsp] foot, subsq enc for fx w/ [nonu, malu] **204**
S42.03[4,5,6] [D,G,S]	Nondisp fx of lat end of [rt, lt, unsp] clavicle, [subsq enc for fx w/ routine healing, subsq enc for fx w/ delayed healing, seq] **170**
S42.03[4,5,6] [K,P]	Nondisp fx of lat end of [rt, lt, unsp] clavicle, subsq enc for fx w/ [nonu, malu] **196**
S42.03[4,5,6] [A,B]	Nondisp fx of lat end of clavicle [rt, lt, unsp] init enc for fx [clsd, opn] **184**
S82.6[4,5,6] X[D,E,F,G,H,J,S]	Nondisp fx of lat malleolus of [rt, lt, unsp] fibula, [subsq enc for clsd fx w/ routine healing, subsq enc for opn fx type I or II w/ routine healing, subsq enc for opn fx type IIIA, IIIB, or IIIC w/ routine healing, subsq enc for clsd fx w/ delayed healing, subsq enc for opn fx type I or II w/ delayed healing, subsq enc for opn fx type IIIA, IIIB, or IIIC w/ delayed healing, seq] **181**
S82.6[4,5,6] X[K,M,N,P,Q,R]	Nondisp fx of lat malleolus of [rt, lt, unsp] fibula, subsq enc for [clsd fx w/ nonu, opn fx type I or II w/ nonu, opn fx type IIIA, IIIB, or IIIC w/ nonu, clsd fx w/ malu, opn fx type I or II w/ malu, opn fx type I or II w/ malu] **203**
S82.6[4,5,6] X[A,B,C]	Nondisp fx of lat malleolus of [rt, lt, unsp] tibia, [init enc for clsd fx, init enc for opn fx type I or II, init enc for opn fx type I or II] **191, 427**
S72.12[4,5,6] [D,E,F,G,H,J,S]	Nondisp fx of lesser trochanter of [rt, lt, unsp] femur, [subsq enc for clsd fx w/ routine healing, subsq enc for opn fx type I or II w/ routine healing, subsq enc for opn fx type IIIA, IIIB, or IIIC w/ routine healing, subsq enc for clsd fx w/ delayed healing, subsq enc for opn fx type I or II w/ delayed healing, subsq enc for opn fx type IIIA, IIIB, or IIIC w/ delayed healing, seq] **177**
S72.12[4,5,6] [A,B,C]	Nondisp fx of lesser trochanter of [rt, lt, unsp] femur, init enc for [clsd fx, opn fx type I or II or NOS, or opn fx type IIIA, IIIB, or IIIC] **162, 286, 435**
S72.12[4,5,6] [K,M,N,P,Q,R]	Nondisp fx of lesser trochanter of [rt, lt, unsp] femur, subsq enc for [clsd fx w/ nonu, opn fx type I or II w/ nonu, opn fx type IIIA, IIIB, or IIIC w/ nonu, clsd fx w/ malu, opn fx type I or II w/ malu, opn fx type IIIA, IIIB, or IIIC w/ malu] **201**

S42.26[4,5,6] [D,G,S] Nondisp fx of lesser tuberosity of [rt, lt, unsp] humerus, [subsq enc for fx w/ routine healing, subsq enc for fx w/ delayed healing, seq] **171**

S42.26[4,5,6]B Nondisp fx of lesser tuberosity of [rt, lt, unsp] humerus, init enc for opn fx **433**

S42.26[4,5,6] [K,P] Nondisp fx of lesser tuberosity of [rt, lt, unsp] humerus, subsq enc for fx w/ [nonu, malu] **196**

S42.26[4,5,6] [A,B] Nondisp fx of lesser tuberosity of humerus [rt, lt, unsp] init enc for fx [clsd, opn] **185**

S62.12[4,5,6] [D,G,S] Nondisp fx of lunate (semilunar), [rt, lt, unsp] wrist, [subsq enc for fx w/ routine healing, subsq enc for fx w/ delayed healing, seq] **175**

S62.12[4,5,6] [K,P] Nondisp fx of lunate (semilunar), [rt, lt, unsp] wrist, subsq enc for fx w/ [nonu, malu] **199**

S62.12[4,5,6] [A,B] Nondisp fx of lunate [semilunar] bone of wrist [rt, lt, unsp] init enc for fx [clsd, opn] **187**

S72.44[4,5,6] [D,E,F,G,H,J,S] Nondisp fx of lwr epiphysis (separation) of [rt, lt, unsp] femur, [subsq enc for clsd fx w/ routine healing, subsq enc for opn fx type I or II w/ routine healing, subsq enc for opn fx type IIIA, IIIB, or IIIC w/ routine healing, subsq enc for clsd fx w/ delayed healing, subsq enc for opn fx type I or II w/ delayed healing, subsq enc for opn fx type I or II w/ delayed healing, seq] **178**

S72.44[4,5,6] [A,B,C] Nondisp fx of lwr epiphysis (separation) of [rt, lt, unsp] femur, init enc for [clsd fx, opn fx type I or II, opn fx type IIIA, IIIB, or IIIC] **161, 435**

S72.44[4,5,6] [K,M,N,P,Q,R] Nondisp fx of lwr epiphysis (separation) of [rt, lt, unsp] femur, subsq enc for [clsd fx w/ nonu, opn fx type I or II w/ nonu, opn fx type IIIA, IIIB, or IIIC w/ nonu, clsd fx w/ malu, opn fx type I or II w/ malu, opn fx type IIIA, IIIB, or IIIC w/ malu] **201**

S82.13[4,5,6] [D,E,F,G,H,J,S] Nondisp fx of med condyle [rt, lt, unsp] tibia, [subsq enc for clsd fx w/ routine healing, subsq enc for opn fx type I or II w/ routine healing, subsq enc for opn fx type IIIA, IIIB, or IIIC w/ routine healing, subsq enc for clsd fx w/ delayed healing, subsq enc for opn fx type I or II w/ delayed healing, subsq enc for opn fx type I or II w/ delayed healing, seq] **180**

S72.43[4,5,6] [D,E,F,G,H,J,S] Nondisp fx of med condyle of [rt, lt, unsp] femur, [subsq enc for clsd fx w/ routine healing, subsq enc for opn fx type I or II w/ routine healing, subsq enc for opn fx type IIIA, IIIB, or IIIC w/ routine healing, subsq enc for clsd fx w/ delayed healing, subsq enc for opn fx type I or II w/ delayed healing, subsq enc for opn fx type I or II w/ delayed healing, seq] **178**

S72.43[4,5,6] [A,B,C] Nondisp fx of med condyle of [rt, lt, unsp] femur, init enc for [clsd fx, opn fx type I or II, opn fx type IIIA, IIIB, or IIIC] **161, 435**

S72.43[4,5,6] [K,M,N,P,Q,R] Nondisp fx of med condyle of [rt, lt, unsp] femur, subsq enc for [clsd fx w/ nonu, opn fx type I or II w/ nonu, opn fx type IIIA, IIIB, or IIIC w/ nonu, clsd fx w/ malu, opn fx type I or II w/ malu, opn fx type IIIA, IIIB, or IIIC w/ malu] **201**

S42.46[4,5,6] [D,G,S] Nondisp fx of med condyle of [rt, lt, unsp] humerus, [subsq enc for fx w/ routine healing, subsq enc for fx w/ delayed healing, seq] **171**

S42.46[4,5,6]B Nondisp fx of med condyle of [rt, lt, unsp] humerus, init enc for opn fx **434**

S42.46[4,5,6] [K,P] Nondisp fx of med condyle of [rt, lt, unsp] humerus, subsq enc for fx w/ [nonu, malu] **197**

S82.13[4,5,6] [A,B,C] Nondisp fx of med condyle of [rt, lt, unsp] tibia, [init enc for clsd fx, init enc for opn fx type I or II, init enc for opn fx type IIIA, IIIB, or IIIC] **190**

S82.13[4,5,6] [B,C] Nondisp fx of med condyle of [rt, lt, unsp] tibia, init enc for opn fx type [I or II, IIIA IIIB or IIIC] **436**

S82.13[4,5,6] [K,M,N,P,Q,R] Nondisp fx of med condyle of [rt, lt, unsp] tibia, subsq enc for [clsd fx w/ nonu, opn fx type I or II w/ nonu, opn fx type IIIA, IIIB, or IIIC w/ nonu, clsd fx w/ malu, opn fx type I or II w/ malu, opn fx type I or II w/ malu] **202**

S42.46[4,5,6] [A,B] Nondisp fx of med condyle of humerus [rt, lt, unsp] init enc for fx [clsd, opn] **185**

S92.24[4,5,6] [D,G,S] Nondisp fx of med cuneiform of [rt, lt, unsp] foot, [subsq enc for fx w/ routine healing, subsq enc for fx w/ delayed healing, seq] **183**

S92.24[4,5,6] [A,B] Nondisp fx of med cuneiform of [rt, lt, unsp] foot, init enc for [clsd, opn] fx **192, 429**

S92.24[4,5,6] [K,P] Nondisp fx of med cuneiform of [rt, lt, unsp] foot, subsq enc for fx w/ [nonu, malu] **204**

S82.5[4,5,6] X[A,B,C] Nondisp fx of med malleolus of [rt, lt, unsp] tibia, [init enc for clsd fx, init enc for opn fx type I or II, init enc for opn fx type I or II] **191, 427**

S82.5[4,5,6] X[D,E,F,G,H,J,S] Nondisp fx of med malleolus of [rt, lt, unsp] tibia, [subsq enc for clsd fx w/ routine healing, subsq enc for opn fx type I or II w/ routine healing, subsq enc for opn fx type IIIA, IIIB, or IIIC w/ routine healing, subsq enc for clsd fx w/ delayed healing, subsq enc for opn fx type I or II w/ delayed healing, subsq enc for opn fx type IIIA, IIIB, or IIIC w/ delayed healing, seq] **181**

S82.5[4,5,6] X[K,M,N,P,Q,R] Nondisp fx of med malleolus of [rt, lt, unsp] tibia, subsq enc for [clsd fx w/ nonu, opn fx type I or II w/ nonu, opn fx type IIIA, IIIB, or IIIC w/ nonu, clsd fx w/ malu, opn fx type I or II w/ malu, opn fx type I or II w/ malu] **203**

S92.52[4,5,6] [K,P] Nondisp fx of med phalanx [rt, lt, unsp] lesser toe(s), subsq enc for fx w/ [nonu, malu] **204**

S62.65[8,9] [D,G,S] Nondisp fx of med phalanx of [oth, unsp] finger, [subsq enc for fx w/ routine healing, subsq enc for fx w/ delayed healing, seq] **176**

S62.65[8,9][A,B] Nondisp fx of med phalanx of [oth, unsp] finger, init enc for [clsd, opn] fx **188**

S62.65[8,9][K,P] Nondisp fx of med phalanx of [oth, unsp] finger, subsq enc for fx w/ [nonu, malu] **200**

S62.65[0,1,2,3,4, 5,6,7,8,9] [A,B] Nondisp fx of med phalanx of [rt index, lt index, rt mid, lt mid, rt ring, lt ring, rt little, lt little, oth, unsp] finger, init enc for [clsd, opn] fx **425**

S92.52[4,5,6] [D,G,S] Nondisp fx of med phalanx of [rt, lt, unsp] lesser toe(s), [subsq enc for fx w/ routine healing, subsq enc for fx w/ delayed healing, seq] **183**

S92.52[4,5,6] [A,B] Nondisp fx of med phalanx of [rt, lt, unsp] lesser toe(s), init enc for [clsd, opn] fx **193, 430**

S62.65[0,1] [D,G,S] Nondisp fx of med phalanx of [rt, lt] index finger, [subsq enc for fx w/ routine healing, subsq enc for fx w/ delayed healing, seq] **176**

S62.65[0,1][A,B] Nondisp fx of med phalanx of [rt, lt] index finger, init enc for [clsd, opn] fx **188**

S62.65[0,1][K,P] Nondisp fx of med phalanx of [rt, lt] index finger, subsq enc for fx w/ [nonu, malu] **200**

S62.65[6,7] [D,G,S] Nondisp fx of med phalanx of [rt, lt] little finger, [subsq enc for fx w/ routine healing, subsq enc for fx w/ delayed healing, seq] **176**

S62.65[6,7][A,B] Nondisp fx of med phalanx of [rt, lt] little finger, init enc for [clsd, opn] fx **188**

S62.65[6,7][K,P] Nondisp fx of med phalanx of [rt, lt] little finger, subsq enc for fx w/ [nonu, malu] **200**

S62.65[2,3] [D,G,S] Nondisp fx of med phalanx of [rt, lt] mid finger, [subsq enc for fx w/ routine healing, subsq enc for fx w/ delayed healing, seq] **176**

S62.65[2,3][A,B] Nondisp fx of med phalanx of [rt, lt] mid finger, init enc for [clsd, opn] fx **188**

S62.65[2,3][K,P] Nondisp fx of med phalanx of [rt, lt] mid finger, subsq enc for fx w/ [nonu, malu] **200**

S62.65[4,5] [D,G,S] Nondisp fx of med phalanx of [rt, lt] ring finger, [subsq enc for fx w/ routine healing, subsq enc for fx w/ delayed healing, seq] **176**

S62.65[4,5][A,B] Nondisp fx of med phalanx of [rt, lt] ring finger, init enc for [clsd, opn] fx **188**

S62.65[4,5][K,P] Nondisp fx of med phalanx of [rt, lt] ring finger, subsq enc for fx w/ [nonu, malu] **200**

S32.47[4,5,6] [A,B] Nondisp fx of med wall of [rt, lt, unsp] acetab, init enc for [clsd, opn] fx **162, 433**

S32.47[4,5,6]S Nondisp fx of med wall of [rt, lt, unsp] acetab, seq **166**

S32.47[4,5,6] [D,G] Nondisp fx of med wall of [rt, lt, unsp] acetab, subsq enc for fx w/ [routine, delayed] healing **170**

S32.47[4,5,6]K Nondisp fx of med wall of [rt, lt, unsp] acetab, subsq enc for fx w/ nonu **196**

S62.02[4,5,6] [D,G,S] Nondisp fx of mid 3rd of navicular (scaphoid) bone of [rt, lt, unsp] wrist, [subsq enc for fx w/ routine healing, subsq enc for fx w/ delayed healing, seq] **174**

S62.02[4,5,6] [K,P] Nondisp fx of mid 3rd of navicular (scaphoid) bone of [rt, lt, unsp] wrist, subsq enc for fx w/ [nonu, malu] **199**

S62.02[4,5,6] [A,B] Nondisp fx of mid 3rd of navicular [scaphoid] bone of wrist [rt, lt, unsp] init enc for fx [clsd, opn] **187**

S92.25[4,5,6] [D,G,S] Nondisp fx of navicular (scaphoid) of [rt, lt, unsp] foot, [subsq enc for fx w/ routine healing, subsq enc for fx w/ delayed healing, seq] **183**

S92.25[4,5,6] [A,B] Nondisp fx of navicular (scaphoid) of [rt, lt, unsp] foot, init enc for [clsd, opn] fx **192, 429**

S92.25[4,5,6] [K,P] Nondisp fx of navicular (scaphoid) of [rt, lt, unsp] foot, subsq enc for fx w/ [nonu, malu] **204**

S62.36[0,1,2,3,4, 5,6,7,8,9][A,B] Nondisp fx of neck of [2nd, 3rd, 4th, 5th, oth, unsp] metacarpal bone, (rt, lt) hand, init enc for [clsd, opn] fx **425**

S62.36[8,9] [D,G,S] Nondisp fx of neck of [oth, unsp] metacarpal bone, [subsq enc for fx w/ routine healing, subsq enc for fx w/ delayed healing, seq] **176**

S62.36[8,9][K,P] Nondisp fx of neck of [oth, unsp] metacarpal bone, subsq enc for fx w/ [nonu, malu] **200**

S62.36[8,9][A,B] Nondisp fx of neck of [oth,unsp] metacarpal bone, init enc for [clsd, opn] fx **188**

Code	Description
S52.13[4,5,6] [D,E,F,G,H,J,S]	Nondisp fx of neck of [rt, lt, unsp] radius, [subsq enc for clsd fx w/ routine healing, subsq enc for opn fx type I or II w/ routine healing, subsq enc for opn fx type IIIA, IIIB, or IIIC w/ routine healing, subsq enc for clsd fx w/ delayed healing, subsq enc for opn fx type I or II w/ delayed healing, subsq enc for opn fx type IIIA, IIIB, or IIIC w/ delayed healing, seq] 172
S52.13[4,5,6] [B,C]	Nondisp fx of neck of [rt, lt, unsp] radius, init enc for opn fx type [I or II, IIIA IIIB or IIIC] 434
S52.13[4,5,6] [K,M,N,P,Q,R]	Nondisp fx of neck of [rt, lt, unsp] radius, subsq enc for [clsd fx w/ nonu, opn fx type I or II w/ nonu, opn fx type IIIA, IIIB, or IIIC w/ nonu, clsd fx w/ malu, opn fx type I or II w/ malu, opn fx type IIIA, IIIB, or IIIC w/ malu] 197
S92.11[4,5,6] [D,G,S]	Nondisp fx of neck of [rt, lt, unsp] talus, [subsq enc for fx w/ routine healing, subsq enc for fx w/ delayed healing, seq] 182
S92.11[4,5,6] [A,B]	Nondisp fx of neck of [rt, lt, unsp] talus, init enc for [clsd, opn] fx 192, 429
S92.11[4,5,6] [K,P]	Nondisp fx of neck of [rt, lt, unsp] talus, subsq enc for fx w/ [nonu, malu] 204
S62.25[4,5,6] [A,B]	Nondisp fx of neck of 1st metacarpal bone of hand [rt, lt, unsp] init enc for fx [clsd, opn] 187
S62.25[4,5,6] [D,G,S]	Nondisp fx of neck of 1st metacarpal bone, [rt, lt, unsp] hand, [subsq enc for fx w/ routine healing, subsq enc for fx w/ delayed healing] 175
S62.25[4,5,6] [K,P]	Nondisp fx of neck of 1st metacarpal bone, [rt, lt, unsp] hand, subsq enc for fx w/ [nonu, malu] 199
S62.36[0,1][A,B]	Nondisp fx of neck of 2nd metacarpal bone, [rt, lt, unsp] hand, init enc for [clsd, opn] fx 188
S62.36[0,1] [D,G,S]	Nondisp fx of neck of 2nd metacarpal bone, [rt, lt] hand, [subsq enc for fx w/ routine healing, subsq enc for fx w/ delayed healing, seq] 175
S62.36[0,1][K,P]	Nondisp fx of neck of 2nd metacarpal bone, [rt, lt] hand, subsq enc for fx w/ [nonu, malu] 200
S62.36[2,3][A,B]	Nondisp fx of neck of 3rd metacarpal bone, [rt, lt, unsp] hand, init enc for [clsd, opn] fx 188
S62.36[2,3] [D,G,S]	Nondisp fx of neck of 3rd metacarpal bone, [rt, lt] hand, [subsq enc for fx w/ routine healing, subsq enc for fx w/ delayed healing, seq] 175
S62.36[2,3][K,P]	Nondisp fx of neck of 3rd metacarpal bone, [rt, lt] hand, subsq enc for fx w/ [nonu, malu] 200
S62.36[4,5][A,B]	Nondisp fx of neck of 4th metacarpal bone, [rt, lt, unsp] hand, init enc for [clsd, opn] fx 188
S62.36[4,5] [D,G,S]	Nondisp fx of neck of 4th metacarpal bone, [rt, lt] hand, [subsq enc for fx w/ routine healing, subsq enc for fx w/ delayed healing, seq] 176
S62.36[4,5][K,P]	Nondisp fx of neck of 4th metacarpal bone, [rt, lt] hand, subsq enc for fx w/ [nonu, malu] 200
S62.36[6,7][A,B]	Nondisp fx of neck of 5th metacarpal bone, [rt, lt, unsp] hand, init enc for [clsd, opn] fx 188
S62.36[6,7] [D,G,S]	Nondisp fx of neck of 5th metacarpal bone, [rt, lt] hand, [subsq enc for fx w/ routine healing, subsq enc for fx w/ delayed healing, seq] 176
S62.36[6,7][K,P]	Nondisp fx of neck of 5th metacarpal bone, [rt, lt] hand, subsq enc for fx w/ [nonu, malu] 200
S52.13[4,5,6] [A,B,C]	Nondisp fx of neck of radius [rt, lt, unsp] init enc for [clsd fx, opn fx type I or II or opn fx NOS, opn fx type IIIA, IIIB, or IIIC] 186
S42.15[1,2,3] [A,B]	Nondisp fx of neck of scapula [rt, lt, unsp] init enc for fx [clsd, opn] 184
S42.15[4,5,6] [A,B]	Nondisp fx of neck of scapula [rt, lt, unsp] init enc for fx [clsd, opn] 184
S42.15[4,5,6] [D,G,S]	Nondisp fx of neck of scapula, [rt, lt, unsp] shldr, [subsq enc for fx w/ routine healing, subsq enc for fx w/ delayed healing, seq] 171
S42.15[4,5,6] [K,P]	Nondisp fx of neck of scapula, [rt, lt, unsp] shldr, subsq enc for fx w/ [nonu, malu] 196
S52.03[4,5,6] [D,E,F,G,H,J,S]	Nondisp fx of olecranon process w/ intraarticular extension of [rt, lt, unsp] ulna, [subsq enc for clsd fx w/ routine healing, subsq enc for opn fx type I or II w/ routine healing, subsq enc for opn fx type IIIA, IIIB, or IIIC w/ routine healing, subsq enc for clsd fx w/ delayed healing, subsq enc for opn fx type I or II w/ delayed healing, subsq enc for opn fx type IIIA, IIIB, or IIIC w/ delayed healing, seq] 172
S52.03[4,5,6] [B,C]	Nondisp fx of olecranon process w/ intraarticular extension of [rt, lt, unsp] ulna, init enc for opn fx type [I or II, IIIA IIIB or IIIC] 434
S52.03[4,5,6] [K,M,N,P,Q,R]	Nondisp fx of olecranon process w/ intraarticular extension of [rt, lt, unsp] ulna, subsq enc for [clsd fx w/ nonu, opn fx type I or II w/ nonu, opn fx type IIIA, IIIB, or IIIC w/ nonu, clsd fx w/ malu, opn fx type I or II w/ malu, opn fx type IIIA, IIIB, or IIIC w/ malu] 197

Code	Description
S52.03[4,5,6] [A,B,C]	Nondisp fx of olecranon process w/ intraarticular extension of ulna [rt, lt, unsp] init enc for fx [clsd fx, opn fx type I or II or opn fx NOS, opn fx type IIIA, IIIB, or IIIC] 186
S52.02[4,5,6] [D,E,F,G,H,J,S]	Nondisp fx of olecranon process w/o intraarticular extension of [rt, lt, unsp] ulna, [subsq enc for clsd fx w/ routine healing, subsq enc for opn fx type I or II w/ routine healing, subsq enc for opn fx type IIIA, IIIB, or IIIC w/ routine healing, subsq enc for clsd fx w/ delayed healing, subsq enc for opn fx type I or II w/ delayed healing, subsq enc for opn fx type IIIA, IIIB, or IIIC w/ delayed healing, seq] 172
S52.02[4,5,6] [B,C]	Nondisp fx of olecranon process w/o intraarticular extension of [rt, lt, unsp] ulna, init enc for fx opn fx type [I or II, IIIA IIIB or IIIC] 434
S52.02[4,5,6] [K,M,N,P,Q,R]	Nondisp fx of olecranon process w/o intraarticular extension of [rt, lt, unsp] ulna, subsq enc for [clsd fx w/ nonu, opn fx type I or II w/ nonu, opn fx type IIIA, IIIB, or IIIC w/ nonu, clsd fx w/ malu, opn fx type I or II w/ malu, opn fx type IIIA, IIIB, or IIIC w/ malu] 197
S52.02[4,5,6] [A,B,C]	Nondisp fx of olecranon process w/o intraarticular extension of ulna [rt, lt, unsp] init enc for fx [clsd fx, opn fx type I or II or opn fx NOS, opn fx type IIIA, IIIB, or IIIC] 186
S62.16[4,5,6] [A,B]	Nondisp fx of pisiform bone of wrist [rt, lt, unsp] init enc for fx [clsd, opn] 187
S62.16[4,5,6] [D,G,S]	Nondisp fx of pisiform, [rt, lt, unsp] wrist, [subsq enc for fx w/ routine healing, subsq enc for fx w/ delayed healing, seq] 175
S62.16[4,5,6] [K,P]	Nondisp fx of pisiform, [rt, lt, unsp] wrist, subsq enc for fx w/ [nonu, malu] 199
S32.44[4,5,6]S	Nondisp fx of post column (ilioischial) of [rt, lt, unsp] acetab, seq 166
S32.44[4,5,6] [D,G]	Nondisp fx of post column (ilioischial) of [rt, lt, unsp] acetab, subsq enc for fx w/ [routine, delayed] healing 170
S32.44[4,5,6]K	Nondisp fx of post column (ilioischial) of [rt, lt, unsp] acetab, subsq enc for fx w/ nonu 196
S32.44[4,5,6] [A,B]	Nondisp fx of post column [ilioischial] of acetab [rt, lt, unsp] init enc for [clsd fx, opn fx 162, 433
S92.13[4,5,6] [D,G,S]	Nondisp fx of post process of [rt, lt, unsp] talus, [subsq enc for fx w/ routine healing, subsq enc for fx w/ delayed healing, seq] 182
S92.13[4,5,6] [A,B]	Nondisp fx of post process of [rt, lt, unsp] talus, init enc for [clsd, opn] fx 192, 429
S92.13[4,5,6] [K,P]	Nondisp fx of post process of [rt, lt, unsp] talus, subsq enc for fx w/ [nonu, malu] 204
S32.42[4,5,6]S	Nondisp fx of post wall of [rt, lt, unsp] acetab, seq 166
S32.42[4,5,6] [D,G]	Nondisp fx of post wall of [rt, lt, unsp] acetab, subsq enc for fx w/ [routine, delayed] healing 170
S32.42[4,5,6]K	Nondisp fx of post wall of [rt, lt, unsp] acetab, subsq enc for fx w/ nonu 196
S32.42[4,5,6] [A,B]	Nondisp fx of post wall of acetab [rt, lt, unsp] init enc for [clsd fx, opn fx] 162, 433
S62.03[4,5,6] [D,G,S]	Nondisp fx of proximal 3rd of navicular (scaphoid) bone of [rt, lt, unsp] wrist, [subsq enc for fx w/ routine healing, subsq enc for fx w/ delayed healing, seq] 174
S62.03[4,5,6] [K,P]	Nondisp fx of proximal 3rd of navicular (scaphoid) bone of [rt, lt, unsp] wrist, subsq enc for fx w/ [nonu, malu] 199
S62.03[4,5,6] [A,B]	Nondisp fx of proximal 3rd of navicular [scaphoid] bone of wrist [rt, lt, unsp] init enc for fx [clsd, opn] 187
S92.51[4,5,6] [K,P]	Nondisp fx of proximal phalanx [rt, lt, unsp] lesser toe(s), subsq enc for fx w/ [nonu, malu] 204
S62.64[8,9] [D,G,S]	Nondisp fx of proximal phalanx of [oth, unsp] finger, [subsq enc for fx w/ routine healing, subsq enc for fx w/ delayed healing, seq] 176
S62.64[8,9][A,B]	Nondisp fx of proximal phalanx of [oth, unsp] finger, init enc for [clsd, opn] fx 188
S62.64[8,9][K,P]	Nondisp fx of proximal phalanx of [oth, unsp] finger, subsq enc for fx w/ [nonu, malu] 200
S62.64[0,1,2,3,4, 5,6,7,8,9] [A,B]	Nondisp fx of proximal phalanx of [rt index, lt index, rt mid, lt mid, rt ring, lt ring, rt little, lt little, oth, unsp] finger, init enc for [clsd, opn] fx 425
S92.41[4,5,6] [D,G,S]	Nondisp fx of proximal phalanx of [rt, lt, unsp] great toe, [subsq enc for fx w/ routine healing, subsq enc for fx w/ delayed healing, seq] 183
S92.41[4,5,6] [A,B]	Nondisp fx of proximal phalanx of [rt, lt, unsp] great toe, init enc for [clsd, opn] fx 192, 429
S92.41[4,5,6] [K,P]	Nondisp fx of proximal phalanx of [rt, lt, unsp] great toe, subsq enc for fx w/ [nonu, malu] 204
S92.51[4,5,6] [D,G,S]	Nondisp fx of proximal phalanx of [rt, lt, unsp] lesser toe(s), [subsq enc for fx w/ routine healing, subsq enc for fx w/ delayed healing, seq] 183
S92.51[4,5,6] [A,B]	Nondisp fx of proximal phalanx of [rt, lt, unsp] lesser toe(s), init enc for [clsd, opn] fx 193, 429

S62.51[4,5,6] [D,G,S]	Nondisp fx of proximal phalanx of [rt, lt, unsp] thumb, [subsq enc for fx w/ routine healing, subsq enc for fx w/ delayed healing, seq] **176**
S62.51[4,5,6] [A,B]	Nondisp fx of proximal phalanx of [rt, lt, unsp] thumb, init enc for [clsd, opn] fx **188**
S62.51[4,5,6] [K,P]	Nondisp fx of proximal phalanx of [rt, lt, unsp] thumb, subsq enc for fx w/ [nonu, malu] **200**
S62.64[0,1] [D,G,S]	Nondisp fx of proximal phalanx of [rt, lt] index finger, [subsq enc for fx w/ routine healing, subsq enc for fx w/ delayed healing, seq] **176**
S62.64[0,1][A,B]	Nondisp fx of proximal phalanx of [rt, lt] index finger, init enc for [clsd, opn] fx **188**
S62.64[0,1][K,P]	Nondisp fx of proximal phalanx of [rt, lt] index finger, subsq enc for fx w/ [nonu, malu] **200**
S62.64[6,7] [D,G,S]	Nondisp fx of proximal phalanx of [rt, lt] little finger, [subsq enc for fx w/ routine healing, subsq enc for fx w/ delayed healing, seq] **176**
S62.64[6,7][A,B]	Nondisp fx of proximal phalanx of [rt, lt] little finger, init enc for [clsd, opn] fx **188**
S62.64[6,7][K,P]	Nondisp fx of proximal phalanx of [rt, lt] little finger, subsq enc for fx w/ [nonu, malu] **200**
S62.64[2,3] [D,G,S]	Nondisp fx of proximal phalanx of [rt, lt] mid finger [subsq enc for fx w/ routine healing, subsq enc for fx w/ delayed healing, seq] **176**
S62.64[2,3][A,B]	Nondisp fx of proximal phalanx of [rt, lt] mid finger, init enc for [clsd, opn] fx **188**
S62.64[2,3][K,P]	Nondisp fx of proximal phalanx of [rt, lt] mid finger, subsq enc for fx w/ [nonu, malu] **200**
S62.64[4,5] [D,G,S]	Nondisp fx of proximal phalanx of [rt, lt] ring finger, [subsq enc for fx w/ routine healing, subsq enc for fx w/ delayed healing, seq] **176**
S62.64[4,5][A,B]	Nondisp fx of proximal phalanx of [rt, lt] ring finger, init enc for [clsd, opn] fx **188**
S62.64[4,5][K,P]	Nondisp fx of proximal phalanx of [rt, lt] ring finger, subsq enc for fx w/ [nonu, malu] **200**
S52.51[4,5,6] [A,B]	Nondisp fx of radial styloid process [rt, lt, unsp] init enc for [clsd fx, opn fx type I or II or opn fx NOS, opn fx type IIIA, IIIB, or IIIC] **186**
S62.35[0,1,2,3,4, 5,6,7,8,9][A,B]	Nondisp fx of shaft of [2nd, 3rd, 4th, 5th, oth, unsp] metacarpal bone, (rt, lt) hand, init enc for [clsd, opn] fx **425**
S62.35[8,9] [D,G,S]	Nondisp fx of shaft of [oth, unsp] metacarpal bone, [subsq enc for fx w/ routine healing, subsq enc for fx w/ delayed healing, seq] **175**
S62.35[8,9][K,P]	Nondisp fx of shaft of [oth] metacarpal bone, subsq enc for fx w/ [nonu, malu] **200**
S62.35[8,9][A,B]	Nondisp fx of shaft of [oth,unsp] metacarpal bone, init enc for [clsd, opn] fx **188**
S42.02[4,5,6] [D,G,S]	Nondisp fx of shaft of [rt, lt, unsp] clavicle, [subsq enc for fx w/ routine healing, subsq enc for fx w/ delayed healing, seq] **170**
S42.02[4,5,6] [K,P]	Nondisp fx of shaft of [rt, lt, unsp] clavicle, subsq enc for fx w/ [nonu, malu] **196**
S62.24[4,5,6] [A,B]	Nondisp fx of shaft of 1st metacarpal bone of hand [rt, lt, unsp] init enc for fx [clsd, opn] **187**
S62.24[4,5,6] [D,G,S]	Nondisp fx of shaft of 1st metacarpal bone, [rt, lt, unsp] hand, [subsq enc for fx w/ routine healing, subsq enc for fx w/ delayed healing, seq] **175**
S62.24[4,5,6] [K,P]	Nondisp fx of shaft of 1st metacarpal bone, [rt, lt, unsp] hand, subsq enc for fx w/ [nonu, malu] **199**
S62.35[0,1][A,B]	Nondisp fx of shaft of 2nd metacarpal bone, [rt, lt, unsp] hand, init enc for [clsd, opn] fx **188**
S62.35[0,1] [D,G,S]	Nondisp fx of shaft of 2nd metacarpal bone, [rt, lt] hand, [subsq enc for fx w/ routine healing, subsq enc for fx w/ delayed healing, seq] **175**
S62.35[0,1][K,P]	Nondisp fx of shaft of 2nd metacarpal bone, [rt, lt] hand, subsq enc for fx w/ [nonu, malu] **200**
S62.35[2,3][A,B]	Nondisp fx of shaft of 3rd metacarpal bone, [rt, lt, unsp] hand, init enc for [clsd, opn] fx **188**
S62.35[2,3] [D,G,S]	Nondisp fx of shaft of 3rd metacarpal bone, [rt, lt] hand, [subsq enc for fx w/ routine healing, subsq enc for fx w/ delayed healing, seq] **175**
S62.35[2,3][K,P]	Nondisp fx of shaft of 3rd metacarpal bone, [rt, lt] hand, subsq enc for fx w/ [nonu, malu] **200**
S62.35[4,5][A,B]	Nondisp fx of shaft of 4th metacarpal bone, [rt, lt, unsp] hand, init enc for [clsd, opn] fx **188**
S62.35[4,5] [D,G,S]	Nondisp fx of shaft of 4th metacarpal bone, [rt, lt] hand, [subsq enc for fx w/ routine healing, subsq enc for fx w/ delayed healing, seq] **175**
S62.35[4,5][K,P]	Nondisp fx of shaft of 4th metacarpal bone, [rt, lt] hand, subsq enc for fx w/ [nonu, malu] **200**
S62.35[6,7][A,B]	Nondisp fx of shaft of 5th metacarpal bone, [rt, lt, unsp] hand, init enc for [clsd, opn] fx **188**
S62.35[6,7] [D,G,S]	Nondisp fx of shaft of 5th metacarpal bone, [rt, lt] hand, [subsq enc for fx w/ routine healing, subsq enc for fx w/ delayed healing, seq] **175**
S62.35[6,7][K,P]	Nondisp fx of shaft of 5th metacarpal bone, [rt, lt] hand, subsq enc for fx w/ [nonu, malu] **200**
S42.02[4,5,6] [A,B]	Nondisp fx of shaft of clavicle [rt, lt, unsp] init enc for fx [clsd, opn] **184**
S42.01[7,8,9] [D,G,S]	Nondisp fx of sternal end of [rt, lt, unsp] clavicle, [subsq enc for fx w/ routine healing, subsq enc for fx w/ delayed healing, seq] **170**
S42.01[7,8,9] [K,P]	Nondisp fx of sternal end of [rt, lt, unsp] clavicle, subsq enc for fx w/ [nonu, malu] **196**
S42.01[7,8,9] [A,B]	Nondisp fx of sternal end of clavicle [rt, lt, unsp] init enc for fx [clsd, opn] **184**
S62.17[4,5,6] [D,G,S]	Nondisp fx of trapezium (lgr multangular), [rt, lt, unsp] wrist, [subsq enc for fx w/ routine healing, subsq enc for fx w/ delayed healing, seq] **175**
S62.17[4,5,6] [K,P]	Nondisp fx of trapezium (lgr multangular), [rt, lt, unsp] wrist, subsq enc for fx w/ [nonu, malu] **199**
S62.17[4,5,6] [A,B]	Nondisp fx of trapezium [lgr multangular] bone of wrist [rt, lt, unsp] init enc for fx [clsd, opn] **187**
S62.18[4,5,6] [D,G,S]	Nondisp fx of trapezoid (smer multangular), [rt, lt, unsp] wrist, [subsq enc for fx w/ routine healing, subsq enc for fx w/ delayed healing, seq] **175**
S62.18[4,5,6] [K,P]	Nondisp fx of trapezoid (smer multangular), [rt, lt, unsp] wrist, subsq enc for fx w/ [nonu, malu] **199**
S62.18[4,5,6] [A,B]	Nondisp fx of trapezoid [smer multangular] bone of wrist [rt, lt, unsp] init enc for fx [clsd, opn] **187**
S62.11[4,5,6] [D,G,S]	Nondisp fx of triquetrum (cuneiform) bone of [rt, lt, unsp] wrist, [subsq enc for fx w/ routine healing, subsq enc for fx w/ delayed healing, seq] **174**
S62.11[4,5,6] [K,P]	Nondisp fx of triquetrum (cuneiform) bone, [rt, lt, unsp] wrist, subsq enc for fx w/ [nonu, malu] **199**
S62.11[4,5,6] [A,B]	Nondisp fx of triquetrum [cuneiform] bone of wrist [rt, lt, unsp] init enc for fx [clsd, opn] **187**
S52.61[4,5,6] [A,B,C]	Nondisp fx of ulna styloid process [rt, lt, unsp] init enc for fx [clsd, opn fx type I or II or opn fx NOS, opn fx type IIIA, IIIB, IIIC] **186**
S72.14[4,5,6] [D,E,F,G,H,J,S]	Nondisp intertrochanteric fx of [rt, lt, unsp] femur, [subsq enc for clsd fx w/ routine healing, subsq enc for opn fx type I or II w/ routine healing, subsq enc for opn fx type IIIA, IIIB, or IIIC w/ routine healing, subsq enc for clsd fx w/ delayed healing, subsq enc for opn fx type I or II w/ delayed healing, subsq enc for opn fx type IIIA, IIIB, or IIIC w/ delayed healing, seq] **177**
S72.14[4,5,6] [A,B,C]	Nondisp intertrochanteric fx of [rt, lt, unsp] femur, init enc for [clsd fx, opn fx type I or II or NOS, or opn fx type IIIA, IIIB, or IIIC] **162, 286, 435**
S72.14[4,5,6] [K,M,N,P,Q,R]	Nondisp intertrochanteric fx of [rt, lt, unsp] femur, subsq enc for [clsd fx w/ nonu, opn fx type I or II w/ nonu, opn fx type IIIA, IIIB, or IIIC w/ nonu, clsd fx w/ malu, opn fx type I or II w/ malu, opn fx type IIIA, IIIB, or IIIC w/ malu] **201**
S92.06[4,5,6] [D,G,S]	Nondisp intraarticular fx of [rt, lt, unsp] calcaneus, [subsq enc for fx w/ routine healing, subsq enc for fx w/ delayed healing, seq] **182**
S92.06[4,5,6] [A,B]	Nondisp intraarticular fx of [rt, lt, unsp] calcaneus, init enc for [clsd, opn] fx **192, 429**
S92.06[4,5,6] [K,P]	Nondisp intraarticular fx of [rt, lt, unsp] calcaneus, subsq enc for fx w/ [nonu, malu] **204**
S82.02[4,5,6] [A,B,C]	Nondisp longitudinal fx of [rt, lt, unsp] patella, [init enc for clsd fx, init enc for opn fx type I or II, init enc for opn fx type IIIA, IIIB, or IIIC] **190**
S82.02[4,5,6] [D,E,F,G,H,J,S]	Nondisp longitudinal fx of [rt, lt, unsp] patella, [subsq enc for clsd fx w/ routine healing, subsq enc for opn fx type I or II w/ routine healing, subsq enc for opn fx type IIIA, IIIB, or IIIC w/ routine healing, subsq enc for clsd fx w/ delayed healing, subsq enc for opn fx type I or II w/ delayed healing, seq] **179**
S82.02[4,5,6] [K,M,N,P,Q,R]	Nondisp longitudinal fx of [rt, lt, unsp] patella, subsq enc for [clsd fx w/ nonu, opn fx type I or II w/ nonu, opn fx type IIIA, IIIB, or IIIC w/ nonu, clsd fx w/ malu, opn fx type I or II w/ malu, opn fx type I or II w/ malu] **202**
S82.86[4,5,6] [A,B,C]	Nondisp Maisonneuve's fx of [rt, lt, unsp] leg, [init enc for clsd fx, init enc for opn fx type I or II, init enc for opn fx type I or II] **191, 428**
S82.86[4,5,6] [D,E,F,G,H,J,S]	Nondisp Maisonneuve's fx of [rt, lt, unsp] leg, [subsq enc for clsd fx w/ routine healing, subsq enc for opn fx type I or II w/ routine healing, subsq enc for opn fx type IIIA, IIIB, or IIIC w/ routine healing, subsq enc for clsd fx w/ delayed healing, subsq enc for opn fx type I or II w/ delayed healing, subsq enc for opn fx type IIIA, IIIB, or IIIC w/ delayed healing, seq] **181**

S82.86[4,5,6] [B,C]	Nondisp Maisonneuve's fx of [rt, lt, unsp] leg, init enc for opn fx type [I or II, IIIA IIIB or IIIC] **436**
S82.86[4,5,6] [K,M,N,P,Q,R]	Nondisp Maisonneuve's fx of [rt, lt, unsp] leg, subsq enc for [clsd fx w/ nonu, opn fx type I or II w/ nonu, opn fx type IIIA, IIIB, or IIIC w/ nonu, clsd fx w/ malu, opn fx type I or II w/ malu, opn fx type I or II w/ malu] **203**
S72.03[4,5,6] [D,E,F,G,H,J,S]	Nondisp midcervical fx of [rt, lt, unsp] femur, [subsq enc for clsd fx w/ routine healing, subsq enc for opn fx type I or II w/ routine healing, subsq enc for opn fx type IIIA, IIIB, or IIIC w/ routine healing, subsq enc for clsd fx w/ delayed healing, subsq enc for opn fx type I or II w/ delayed healing, subsq enc for opn fx type IIIA, IIIB, or IIIC w/ delayed healing, seq] **177**
S72.03[4,5,6] [A,B,C]	Nondisp midcervical fx of [rt, lt, unsp] femur, init enc for [clsd fx, opn fx type I or II or NOS, or opn fx type IIIA, IIIB, or IIIC] **162, 286, 435**
S72.03[4,5,6] [K,M,N,P,Q,R]	Nondisp midcervical fx of [rt, lt, unsp] femur, subsq enc for [clsd fx w/ nonu, opn fx type I or II w/ nonu, opn fx type IIIA, IIIB, or IIIC w/ nonu, clsd fx w/ malu, opn fx type I or II w/ malu, opn fx type IIIA, IIIB, or IIIC w/ malu] **201**
S52.23[4,5,6] [B,C]	Nondisp oblique fx of [rt, lt, unsp] ulna, init enc for opn fx type [I or II, IIIA IIIB or IIIC] **434**
S72.33[4,5,6] [D,E,F,G,H,J,S]	Nondisp oblique fx of shaft of [rt, lt, unsp] femur, [subsq enc for clsd fx w/ routine healing, subsq enc for opn fx type I or II w/ routine healing, subsq enc for opn fx type IIIA, IIIB, or IIIC w/ routine healing, subsq enc for clsd fx w/ delayed healing, subsq enc for opn fx type I or II w/ delayed healing, subsq enc for opn fx type IIIA, IIIB, or IIIC w/ delayed healing, seq] **178**
S72.33[4,5,6] [A,B,C]	Nondisp oblique fx of shaft of [rt, lt, unsp] femur, init enc for [clsd fx, opn fx type I or II, opn fx type IIIA, IIIB, or IIIC] **161, 286, 435**
S72.33[4,5,6] [K,M,N,P,Q,R]	Nondisp oblique fx of shaft of [rt, lt, unsp] femur, subsq enc for [clsd fx w/ nonu, opn fx type I or II w/ nonu, opn fx type IIIA, IIIB, or IIIC w/ nonu, clsd fx w/ malu, opn fx type I or II w/ malu, opn fx type IIIA, IIIB, or IIIC w/ malu] **201**
S82.43[4,5,6] [A,B,C]	Nondisp oblique fx of shaft of [rt, lt, unsp] fibula, [init enc for clsd fx, init enc for opn fx type I or II, init enc for opn fx type IIIA, IIIB, or IIIC] **191, 427**
S82.43[4,5,6] [D,E,F,G,H,J,S]	Nondisp oblique fx of shaft of [rt, lt, unsp] fibula, [subsq enc for clsd fx w/ routine healing, subsq enc for opn fx type I or II w/ routine healing, subsq enc for opn fx type IIIA, IIIB, or IIIC w/ routine healing, subsq enc for clsd fx w/ delayed healing, subsq enc for opn fx type I or II w/ delayed healing, subsq enc for opn fx type IIIA, IIIB, or IIIC w/ delayed healing, seq] **181**
S82.43[4,5,6] [B,C]	Nondisp oblique fx of shaft of [rt, lt, unsp] fibula, init enc for opn fx type [I or II, IIIA IIIB or IIIC] **436**
S82.43[4,5,6] [K,M,N,P,Q,R]	Nondisp oblique fx of shaft of [rt, lt, unsp] fibula, subsq enc for [clsd fx w/ nonu, opn fx type I or II w/ nonu, opn fx type IIIA, IIIB, or IIIC w/ nonu, clsd fx w/ malu, opn fx type I or II w/ malu, opn fx type I or II w/ malu] **203**
S42.33[4,5,6] [D,G,S]	Nondisp oblique fx of shaft of [rt, lt, unsp] humerus, [subsq enc for fx w/ routine healing, subsq enc for fx w/ delayed healing, seq] **171**
S42.33[4,5,6]B	Nondisp oblique fx of shaft of [rt, lt, unsp] humerus, init enc for opn fx **433**
S52.33[4,5,6] [D,E,F,G,H,J,S]	Nondisp oblique fx of shaft of [rt, lt, unsp] radius, [subsq enc for clsd fx w/ routine healing, subsq enc for opn fx type I or II w/ routine healing, subsq enc for opn fx type IIIA, IIIB, or IIIC w/ routine healing, subsq enc for clsd fx w/ delayed healing, subsq enc for opn fx type I or II w/ delayed healing, subsq enc for opn fx type IIIA, IIIB, or IIIC w/ delayed healing, seq] **173**
S52.33[4,5,6] [B,C]	Nondisp oblique fx of shaft of [rt, lt, unsp] radius, init enc for opn fx type [I or II, IIIA IIIB or IIIC] **434**
S52.33[4,5,6] [K,M,N,P,Q,R]	Nondisp oblique fx of shaft of [rt, lt, unsp] radius, subsq enc for [clsd fx w/ nonu, opn fx type I or II w/ nonu, opn fx type IIIA, IIIB, or IIIC w/ nonu, clsd fx w/ malu, opn fx type I or II w/ malu, opn fx type IIIA, IIIB, or IIIC w/ malu] **198**
S82.23[4,5,6] [A,B,C]	Nondisp oblique fx of shaft of [rt, lt, unsp] tibia, [init enc for clsd fx, init enc for opn fx type I or II, init enc for opn fx type IIIA, IIIB, or IIIC] **191, 427**
S82.23[4,5,6] [D,E,F,G,H,J,S]	Nondisp oblique fx of shaft of [rt, lt, unsp] tibia, [subsq enc for clsd fx w/ routine healing, subsq enc for opn fx type I or II w/ routine healing, subsq enc for opn fx type IIIA, IIIB, or IIIC w/ routine healing, subsq enc for clsd fx w/ delayed healing, subsq enc for opn fx type I or II w/ delayed healing, subsq enc for opn fx type IIIA, IIIB, or IIIC w/ delayed healing, seq] **180**
S82.23[4,5,6] [B,C]	Nondisp oblique fx of shaft of [rt, lt, unsp] tibia, init enc for opn fx type [I or II, IIIA IIIB or IIIC] **436**

S82.23[4,5,6] [K,M,N,P,Q,R]	Nondisp oblique fx of shaft of [rt, lt, unsp] tibia, subsq enc for [clsd fx w/ nonu, opn fx type I or II w/ nonu, opn fx type IIIA, IIIB, or IIIC w/ nonu, clsd fx w/ malu, opn fx type I or II w/ malu, opn fx type I or II w/ malu] **203**
S52.23[4,5,6] [D,E,F,G,H,J,S]	Nondisp oblique fx of shaft of [rt, lt, unsp] ulna, [subsq enc for clsd fx w/ nonu, opn fx type I or II w/ routine healing, subsq enc for opn fx type IIIA, IIIB, or IIIC w/ routine healing, subsq enc for clsd fx w/ delayed healing, subsq enc for opn fx type I or II w/ delayed healing, subsq enc for opn fx type IIIA, IIIB, or IIIC w/ delayed healing, seq] **172**
S52.23[4,5,6] [K,M,N,P,Q,R]	Nondisp oblique fx of shaft of [rt, lt, unsp] ulna, subsq enc for [clsd fx w/ nonu, opn fx type I or II w/ nonu, opn fx type IIIA, IIIB, or IIIC w/ nonu, clsd fx w/ malu, opn fx type I or II w/ malu, opn fx type IIIA, IIIB, or IIIC w/ malu] **198**
S42.33[4,5,6] [A,B]	Nondisp oblique fx of shaft of humerus [rt, lt, unsp] init enc for fx [clsd, opn] **185**
S42.33[4,5,6] [K,P]	Nondisp oblique fx of shaft of humerus, [rt, lt, unsp] arm, subsq enc for fx w/ [nonu, malu] **197**
S52.33[4,5,6] [A,B,C]	Nondisp oblique fx of shaft of radius [rt, lt, unsp] init enc for [clsd fx, opn fx type I or II or opn fx NOS, opn fx type IIIA, IIIB, or IIIC] **186**
S52.23[4,5,6] [A,B,C]	Nondisp oblique fx of ulna [rt, lt, unsp} init enc for [clsd fx, opn fx type I or II or opn fx NOS, opn fx type IIIA, IIIB, or IIIC] **186**
S82.01[4,5,6] [A,B,C]	Nondisp osteochondral fx of [rt, lt, unsp] patella, [init enc for clsd fx, init enc for opn fx type I or II, init enc for opn fx type IIIA, IIIB, or IIIC] **190**
S82.01[4,5,6] [D,E,F,G,H,J,S]	Nondisp osteochondral fx of [rt, lt, unsp] patella, [subsq enc for clsd fx w/ routine healing, subsq enc for opn fx type I or II w/ routine healing, subsq enc for opn fx type IIIA, IIIB, or IIIC w/ routine healing, subsq enc for clsd fx w/ delayed healing, subsq enc for opn fx type I or II w/ delayed healing, seq] **179**
S82.01[4,5,6] [K,M,N,P,Q,R]	Nondisp osteochondral fx of [rt, lt, unsp] patella, subsq enc for [clsd fx w/ nonu, opn fx type I or II w/ nonu, opn fx type IIIA, IIIB, or IIIC w/ nonu, clsd fx w/ malu, opn fx type I or II w/ malu, opn fx type I or II w/ malu] **202**
S92.05[4,5,6] [D,G,S]	Nondisp oth extraarticular fx of [rt, lt, unsp] calcaneus, [subsq enc for fx w/ routine healing, subsq enc for fx w/ delayed healing, seq] **182**
S92.05[4,5,6] [A,B]	Nondisp oth extraarticular fx of [rt, lt, unsp] calcaneus, init enc for [clsd, opn] fx **192, 429**
S92.05[4,5,6] [K,P]	Nondisp oth extraarticular fx of [rt, lt, unsp] calcaneus, subsq enc for fx w/ [nonu, malu] **204**
S92.04[4,5,6] [D,G,S]	Nondisp oth fx of tuberosity of [rt, lt, unsp] calcaneus, [subsq enc for fx w/ routine healing, subsq enc for fx w/ delayed healing, seq] **182**
S92.04[4,5,6] [A,B]	Nondisp oth fx of tuberosity of [rt, lt, unsp] calcaneus, init enc for [clsd, opn] fx **192, 429**
S92.04[4,5,6] [K,P]	Nondisp oth fx of tuberosity of [rt, lt, unsp] calcaneus, subsq enc for fx w/ [nonu, malu] **204**
S82.87[4,5,6] [A,B,C]	Nondisp pilon fx of [rt, lt, unsp] tibia, [init enc for clsd fx, init enc for opn fx type I or II, init enc for opn fx type I or II] **191, 428**
S82.87[4,5,6] [D,E,F,G,H,J,S]	Nondisp pilon fx of [rt, lt, unsp] tibia, [subsq enc for clsd fx w/ routine healing, subsq enc for opn fx type I or II w/ routine healing, subsq enc for opn fx type IIIA, IIIB, or IIIC w/ routine healing, subsq enc for clsd fx w/ delayed healing, subsq enc for opn fx type I or II w/ delayed healing, subsq enc for opn fx type IIIA, IIIB, or IIIC w/ delayed healing, seq] **181**
S82.87[4,5,6] [K,M,N,P,Q,R]	Nondisp pilon fx of [rt, lt, unsp] tibia, subsq enc for [clsd fx w/ nonu, opn fx type I or II w/ nonu, opn fx type IIIA, IIIB, or IIIC w/ nonu, clsd fx w/ malu, opn fx type I or II w/ malu, opn fx type I or II w/ malu] **203**
S62.22[4,5,6] [D,G,S]	Nondisp Rolando's fx, [rt, lt, unsp] hand, [subsq enc for fx w/ routine healing, subsq enc for fx w/ delayed healing, seq] **175**
S62.22[4,5,6] [A,B]	Nondisp Rolando's fx, [rt, lt, unsp] hand, init enc for [clsd, opn] fx **187**
S62.22[4,5,6] [K,P]	Nondisp Rolando's fx, [rt, lt, unsp] hand, subsq enc for fx w/ [nonu, malu] **199**
S72.36[4,5,6] [D,E,F,G,H,J,S]	Nondisp seg fx of shaft of [rt, lt, unsp] femur, [subsq enc for clsd fx w/ routine healing, subsq enc for opn fx type I or II w/ routine healing, subsq enc for opn fx type IIIA, IIIB, or IIIC w/ routine healing, subsq enc for clsd fx w/ delayed healing, subsq enc for opn fx type I or II w/ delayed healing, subsq enc for opn fx type IIIA, IIIB, or IIIC w/ delayed healing, seq] **178**
S72.36[4,5,6] [A,B,C]	Nondisp seg fx of shaft of [rt, lt, unsp] femur, init enc for [clsd fx, opn fx type I or II, opn fx type IIIA, IIIB, or IIIC] **161, 286, 435**

S72.36[4,5,6] [K,M,N,P,Q,R]	Nondisp seg fx of shaft of [rt, lt, unsp] femur, subsq enc for [clsd fx w/ nonu, opn fx type I or II w/ nonu, opn fx type IIIA, IIIB, or IIIC w/ nonu, clsd fx w/ malu, opn fx type I or II w/ malu, opn fx type IIIA, IIIB, or IIIC w/ malu] 201
S82.46[4,5,6] [A,B,C]	Nondisp seg fx of shaft of [rt, lt, unsp] fibula, [init enc for clsd fx, init enc for opn fx type I or II, init enc for opn fx type IIIA, IIIB, or IIIC] 191, 427
S82.46[4,5,6] [D,E,F,G,H,J,S]	Nondisp seg fx of shaft of [rt, lt, unsp] fibula, [subsq enc for clsd fx w/ routine healing, subsq enc for opn fx type I or II w/ routine healing, subsq enc for opn fx type IIIA, IIIB, or IIIC w/ routine healing, subsq enc for clsd fx w/ delayed healing, subsq enc for opn fx type I or II w/ delayed healing, subsq enc for opn fx type IIIA, IIIB, or IIIC w/ delayed healing, seq] 181
S82.46[4,5,6] [B,C]	Nondisp seg fx of shaft of [rt, lt, unsp] fibula, init enc for opn fx type [I or II, IIIA IIIB or IIIC] 436
S82.46[4,5,6] [K,M,N,P,Q,R]	Nondisp seg fx of shaft of [rt, lt, unsp] fibula, subsq enc for [clsd fx w/ nonu, opn fx type I or II w/ nonu, opn fx type IIIA, IIIB, or IIIC w/ nonu, clsd fx w/ malu, opn fx type I or II w/ malu, opn fx type I or II w/ malu] 203
S42.36[4,5,6] [D,G,S]	Nondisp seg fx of shaft of [rt, lt, unsp] humerus, [subsq enc for fx w/ routine healing, subsq enc for fx w/ delayed healing, seq] 171
S42.36[4,5,6]B	Nondisp seg fx of shaft of [rt, lt, unsp] humerus, init enc for opn fx 433
S52.36[4,5,6] [D,E,F,G,H,J,S]	Nondisp seg fx of shaft of [rt, lt, unsp] radius, [subsq enc for clsd fx w/ routine healing, subsq enc for opn fx type I or II w/ routine healing, subsq enc for opn fx type I or II w/ routine healing, subsq enc for clsd fx w/ delayed healing, subsq enc for opn fx type I or II w/ delayed healing, subsq enc for opn fx type IIIA, IIIB, or IIIC w/ delayed healing, seq] 173
S52.36[4,5,6] [B,C]	Nondisp seg fx of shaft of [rt, lt, unsp] radius, init enc for opn fx type [I or II, IIIA IIIB or IIIC] 434
S82.26[4,5,6] [A,B,C]	Nondisp seg fx of shaft of [rt, lt, unsp] tibia, [init enc for clsd fx, init enc for opn fx type I or II, init enc for opn fx type IIIA, IIIB, or IIIC] 191, 427
S82.26[4,5,6] [D,E,F,G,H,J,S]	Nondisp seg fx of shaft of [rt, lt, unsp] tibia, [subsq enc for clsd fx w/ routine healing, subsq enc for opn fx type I or II w/ routine healing, subsq enc for opn fx type IIIA, IIIB, or IIIC w/ routine healing, subsq enc for clsd fx w/ delayed healing, subsq enc for opn fx type I or II w/ delayed healing, subsq enc for opn fx type IIIA, IIIB, or IIIC w/ delayed healing, seq] 180
S82.26[4,5,6] [B,C]	Nondisp seg fx of shaft of [rt, lt, unsp] tibia, init enc for opn fx type [I or II, IIIA IIIB or IIIC] 436
S82.26[4,5,6] [K,M,N,P,Q,R]	Nondisp seg fx of shaft of [rt, lt, unsp] tibia, subsq enc for [clsd fx w/ nonu, opn fx type I or II w/ nonu, opn fx type IIIA, IIIB, or IIIC w/ nonu, clsd fx w/ malu, opn fx type I or II w/ malu, opn fx type I or II w/ malu] 203
S52.26[4,5,6] [D,E,F,G,H,J,S]	Nondisp seg fx of shaft of [rt, lt, unsp] ulna, [subsq enc for clsd fx w/ routine healing, subsq enc for opn fx type I or II w/ routine healing, subsq enc for opn fx type IIIA, IIIB, or IIIC w/ routine healing, subsq enc for clsd fx w/ delayed healing, subsq enc for opn fx type I or II w/ delayed healing, subsq enc for opn fx type IIIA, IIIB, or IIIC w/ delayed healing, seq] 173
S42.36[4,5,6] [A,B]	Nondisp seg fx of shaft of humerus [rt, lt, unsp] init enc for fx [clsd, opn] 185
S42.36[4,5,6] [K,P]	Nondisp seg fx of shaft of humerus, [rt, lt, unsp] arm, subsq enc for fx w/ [nonu, malu] 197
S52.36[4,5,6] [A,B,C]	Nondisp seg fx of shaft of radius [rt, lt, unsp} init enc for [clsd fx, opn fx type I or II or opn fx NOS, opn fx type IIIA, IIIB, or IIIC] 186
S52.36[4,5,6] [K,M,N,P,Q,R]	Nondisp seg fx of shaft of radius, [rt, lt, unsp] arm, subsq enc for [clsd fx w/ nonu, opn fx type I or II w/ nonu, opn fx type IIIA, IIIB, or IIIC w/ nonu, clsd fx w/ malu, opn fx type I or II w/ malu, opn fx type IIIA, IIIB, or IIIC w/ malu] 198
S52.26[4,5,6] [K,M,N,P,Q,R]	Nondisp seg fx of shaft of ulna, [rt, lt, unsp] arm, subsq enc for [clsd fx w/ nonu, opn fx type I or II w/ nonu, opn fx type IIIA, IIIB, or IIIC w/ nonu, clsd fx w/ malu, opn fx type I or II w/ malu, opn fx type IIIA, IIIB, or IIIC w/ malu] 198
S52.26[4,5,6] [B,C]	Nondisp semental fx of shaft of [rt, lt, unsp] ulna, init enc for opn fx type [I or II, IIIA IIIB or IIIC] 434
S52.26[4,5,6] [A,B,C]	Nondisp semental fx of shaft of ulna [rt, lt, unsp} init enc for [clsd fx, opn fx type I or II or opn fx NOS, opn fx type IIIA, IIIB, or IIIC] 186
S42.41[4,5,6] [D,G,S]	Nondisp simple supracondylar fx w/o intercondylar fx of [rt, lt, unsp] humerus, [subsq enc for fx w/ routine healing, subsq enc for fx w/ delayed healing, seq] 171
S42.41[4,5,6]B	Nondisp simple supracondylar fx w/o intercondylar fx of [rt, lt, unsp] humerus, init enc for opn fx 433
S42.41[4,5,6] [K,P]	Nondisp simple supracondylar fx w/o intercondylar fx of [rt, lt, unsp] humerus, subsq enc for fx w/ [nonu, malu] 197
S42.41[4,5,6] [A,B]	Nondisp simple supracondylar fx w/o intercondylar fx of humerus [rt, lt, unsp] init enc for fx [clsd, opn] 185
S52.24[4,5,6] [B,C]	Nondisp spiral fx of [rt, lt, unsp] ulna, init enc for opn fx type [I or II, IIIA IIIB or IIIC] 434
S72.34[4,5,6] [D,E,F,G,H,J,S]	Nondisp spiral fx of shaft of [rt, lt, unsp] femur, [subsq enc for clsd fx w/ routine healing, subsq enc for opn fx type I or II w/ routine healing, subsq enc for opn fx type IIIA, IIIB, or IIIC w/ routine healing, subsq enc for clsd fx w/ delayed healing, subsq enc for opn fx type I or II w/ delayed healing, subsq enc for opn fx type IIIA, IIIB, or IIIC w/ delayed healing, seq] 178
S72.34[4,5,6] [A,B,C]	Nondisp spiral fx of shaft of [rt, lt, unsp] femur, init enc for [clsd fx, opn fx type I or II, opn fx type IIIA, IIIB, or IIIC] 161, 286
S72.34[4,5,6] [A,B,C]	Nondisp spiral fx of shaft of [rt, lt, unsp] femur, init enc for [clsd fx, opn fx type I or II, opn fx type IIIA, IIIB, or IIIC] 435
S72.34[4,5,6] [K,M,N,P,Q,R]	Nondisp spiral fx of shaft of [rt, lt, unsp] femur, subsq enc for [clsd fx w/ nonu, opn fx type I or II w/ nonu, opn fx type IIIA, IIIB, or IIIC w/ nonu, clsd fx w/ malu, opn fx type I or II w/ malu, opn fx type IIIA, IIIB, or IIIC w/ malu] 201
S82.44[4,5,6] [A,B,C]	Nondisp spiral fx of shaft of [rt, lt, unsp] fibula, [init enc for clsd fx, init enc for opn fx type I or II, init enc for opn fx type IIIA, IIIB, or IIIC] 191, 427
S82.44[4,5,6] [D,E,F,G,H,J,S]	Nondisp spiral fx of shaft of [rt, lt, unsp] fibula, [subsq enc for clsd fx w/ routine healing, subsq enc for opn fx type I or II w/ routine healing, subsq enc for opn fx type IIIA, IIIB, or IIIC w/ routine healing, subsq enc for clsd fx w/ delayed healing, subsq enc for opn fx type I or II w/ delayed healing, subsq enc for opn fx type IIIA, IIIB, or IIIC w/ delayed healing, seq] 181
S82.44[4,5,6] [B,C]	Nondisp spiral fx of shaft of [rt, lt, unsp] fibula, init enc for opn fx type [I or II, IIIA IIIB or IIIC] 436
S82.44[4,5,6] [K,M,N,P,Q,R]	Nondisp spiral fx of shaft of [rt, lt, unsp] fibula, subsq enc for [clsd fx w/ nonu, opn fx type I or II w/ nonu, opn fx type IIIA, IIIB, or IIIC w/ nonu, clsd fx w/ malu, opn fx type I or II w/ malu, opn fx type I or II w/ malu] 203
S42.34[4,5,6] [D,G,S]	Nondisp spiral fx of shaft of [rt, lt, unsp] humerus, [subsq enc for fx w/ routine healing, subsq enc for fx w/ delayed healing, seq] 171
S42.34[4,5,6]B	Nondisp spiral fx of shaft of [rt, lt, unsp] humerus, init enc for opn fx 433
S52.34[4,5,6] [D,E,F,G,H,J,S]	Nondisp spiral fx of shaft of [rt, lt, unsp] radius, [subsq enc for clsd fx w/ routine healing, subsq enc for opn fx type I or II w/ routine healing, subsq enc for clsd fx w/ delayed healing, subsq enc for opn fx type I or II w/ delayed healing, subsq enc for opn fx type IIIA, IIIB, or IIIC w/ delayed healing, seq] 173
S52.34[4,5,6] [B,C]	Nondisp spiral fx of shaft of [rt, lt, unsp] radius, init enc for opn fx type [I or II, IIIA IIIB or IIIC] 434
S82.24[4,5,6] [A,B,C]	Nondisp spiral fx of shaft of [rt, lt, unsp] tibia, [init enc for clsd fx, init enc for opn fx type I or II, init enc for opn fx type IIIA, IIIB, or IIIC] 191, 427
S82.24[4,5,6] [D,E,F,G,H,J,S]	Nondisp spiral fx of shaft of [rt, lt, unsp] tibia, [subsq enc for clsd fx w/ routine healing, subsq enc for opn fx type I or II w/ routine healing, subsq enc for opn fx type IIIA, IIIB, or IIIC w/ routine healing, subsq enc for clsd fx w/ delayed healing, subsq enc for opn fx type I or II w/ delayed healing, subsq enc for opn fx type IIIA, IIIB, or IIIC w/ delayed healing, seq] 180
S82.24[4,5,6] [B,C]	Nondisp spiral fx of shaft of [rt, lt, unsp] tibia, init enc for opn fx type [I or II, IIIA IIIB or IIIC] 436
S82.24[4,5,6] [K,M,N,P,Q,R]	Nondisp spiral fx of shaft of [rt, lt, unsp] tibia, subsq enc for [clsd fx w/ nonu, opn fx type I or II w/ nonu, opn fx type IIIA, IIIB, or IIIC w/ nonu, clsd fx w/ malu, opn fx type I or II w/ malu, opn fx type I or II w/ malu] 203
S52.24[4,5,6] [D,E,F,G,H,J,S]	Nondisp spiral fx of shaft of [rt, lt, unsp] ulna, [subsq enc for clsd fx w/ routine healing, subsq enc for opn fx type I or II w/ routine healing, subsq enc for opn fx type IIIA, IIIB, or IIIC w/ routine healing, subsq enc for clsd fx w/ delayed healing, subsq enc for opn fx type I or II w/ delayed healing, subsq enc for opn fx type IIIA, IIIB, or IIIC w/ delayed healing, seq] 173
S42.34[4,5,6] [A,B]	Nondisp spiral fx of shaft of humerus [rt, lt, unsp] init enc for fx [clsd, opn] 185
S42.34[4,5,6] [K,P]	Nondisp spiral fx of shaft of humerus, [rt, lt, unsp] arm, subsq enc for fx w/ [nonu, malu] 197
S52.34[4,5,6] [A,B,C]	Nondisp spiral fx of shaft of radius [rt, lt, unsp} init enc for [clsd fx, opn fx type I or II or opn fx NOS, opn fx type IIIA, IIIB, or IIIC] 186
S52.34[4,5,6] [K,M,N,P,Q,R]	Nondisp spiral fx of shaft of radius, [rt, lt, unsp] arm, subsq enc for [clsd fx w/ nonu, opn fx type I or II w/ nonu, opn fx type IIIA, IIIB, or IIIC w/ nonu, clsd fx w/ malu, opn fx type I or II w/ malu, opn fx type IIIA, IIIB, or IIIC w/ malu] 198

Code	Description
S52.24[4,5,6] [K,M,N,P,Q,R]	Nondisp spiral fx of shaft of ulna, [rt, lt, unsp] arm, subsq enc for [clsd fx w/ nonu, opn fx type I or II w/ nonu, opn fx type IIIA, IIIB, or IIIC w/ nonu, clsd fx w/ malu, opn fx type I or II w/ malu, opn fx type IIIA, IIIB, or IIIC w/ malu] 198
S52.24[4,5,6] [A,B,C]	Nondisp spiral fx of ulna [rt, lt, unsp} init enc for [clsd fx, opn fx type I or II or opn fx NOS, opn fx type IIIA, IIIB, or IIIC] 186
S72.2[4,5,6] X[D,E,F,G,H,J,S]	Nondisp subtrochanteric fx of [rt, lt, unsp], femur, [subsq enc for clsd fx w/ routine healing, subsq enc for opn fx type I or II w/ routine healing, subsq enc for opn fx type IIIA, IIIB, or IIIC w/ routine healing, subsq enc for clsd fx w/ delayed healing, subsq enc for opn fx type I or II w/ delayed healing, subsq enc for opn fx type IIIA, IIIB, or IIIC w/ delayed healing, seq] 177
S72.2[4,5,6] X[A,B,C]	Nondisp subtrochanteric fx of [rt, lt, unsp] femur, init enc for [clsd fractrure, opn fx type I or II or NOS, or opn fx type IIIA, IIIB, or IIIC] 162, 286, 435
S72.2[4,5,6] X[K,M,N,P,Q,R]	Nondisp subtrochanteric fx of [rt, lt, unsp] femur, subsq enc for [clsd fx w/ nonu, opn fx type I or II w/ nonu, opn fx type IIIA, IIIB, or IIIC w/ nonu, clsd fx w/ malu, opn fx type I or II w/ malu, opn fx type IIIA, IIIB, or IIIC w/ malu] 201
S72.46[4,5,6] [D,E,F,G,H,J,S]	Nondisp supracondylar fx w/ intracondylar extension of lwr end of [rt, lt, unsp] femur, [subsq enc for clsd fx w/ routine healing, subsq enc for opn fx type I or II w/ routine healing, subsq enc for opn fx type IIIA, IIIB, or IIIC w/ routine healing, subsq enc for clsd fx w/ delayed healing, subsq enc for opn fx type I or II w/ delayed healing, subsq enc for opn fx type I or II w/ delayed healing, seq] 179
S72.46[4,5,6] [A,B,C]	Nondisp supracondylar fx w/ intracondylar extension of lwr end of [rt, lt, unsp] femur, init enc for [clsd fx, opn fx type I or II, opn fx type IIIA, IIIB, or IIIC] 161, 436
S72.46[4,5,6] [K,M,N,P,Q,R]	Nondisp supracondylar fx w/ intracondylar extension of lwr end of [rt, lt, unsp] femur, subsq enc for [clsd fx w/ nonu, opn fx type I or II w/ nonu, opn fx type IIIA, IIIB, or IIIC w/ nonu, clsd fx w/ malu, opn fx type I or II w/ malu, opn fx type IIIA, IIIB, or IIIC w/ malu] 202
S72.45[4,5,6] [D,E,F,G,H,J,S]	Nondisp supracondylar fx w/o intracondylar extension of [rt, lt, unsp] femur, [subsq enc for clsd fx w/ routine healing, subsq enc for opn fx type I or II w/ routine healing, subsq enc for opn fx type IIIA, IIIB, or IIIC w/ routine healing, subsq enc for clsd fx w/ delayed healing, subsq enc for opn fx type I or II w/ delayed healing, subsq enc for opn fx type I or II w/ delayed healing, seq] 178
S72.45[4,5,6] [A,B,C]	Nondisp supracondylar fx w/o intracondylar extension of lwr end of [rt, lt, unsp] femur, init enc for [clsd fx, opn fx type I or II, opn fx type IIIA, IIIB, or IIIC] 161, 436
S72.45[4,5,6] [K,M,N,P,Q,R]	Nondisp supracondylar fx w/o intracondylar extension of lwr end of [rt, lt, unsp] femur, subsq enc for [clsd fx w/ nonu, opn fx type I or II w/ nonu, opn fx type IIIA, IIIB, or IIIC w/ nonu, clsd fx w/ malu, opn fx type I or II w/ malu, opn fx type IIIA, IIIB, or IIIC w/ malu] 202
S42.47[4,5,6] [D,G,S]	Nondisp transcondylar fx of [rt, lt, unsp] humerus, [subsq enc for fx w/ routine healing, subsq enc for fx w/ delayed healing, seq] 171
S42.47[4,5,6]B	Nondisp transcondylar fx of [rt, lt, unsp] humerus, init enc for opn fx 434
S42.47[4,5,6] [K,P]	Nondisp transcondylar fx of [rt, lt, unsp] humerus, subsq enc for fx w/ [nonu, malu] 197
S42.47[4,5,6] [A,B]	Nondisp transcondylar fx of humerus [rt, lt, unsp] init enc for fx [clsd, opn] 185
S32.45[4,5,6]S	Nondisp transv fx of [rt, lt, unsp] acetab, seq 166
S32.45[4,5,6] [D,G]	Nondisp transv fx of [rt, lt, unsp] acetab, subsq enc for fx w/ [routine, delayed] healing 170
S32.45[4,5,6]K	Nondisp transv fx of [rt, lt, unsp] acetab, subsq enc for fx w/ nonu 196
S82.03[4,5,6] [A,B,C]	Nondisp transv fx of [rt, lt, unsp] patella, [init enc for clsd fx, init enc for opn fx type I or II, init enc for opn fx type IIIA, IIIB, or IIIC] 190
S82.03[4,5,6] [D,E,F,G,H,J,S]	Nondisp transv fx of [rt, lt, unsp] patella, [subsq enc for clsd fx w/ routine healing, subsq enc for opn fx type I or II w/ routine healing, subsq enc for opn fx type IIIA, IIIB, or IIIC w/ routine healing, subsq enc for clsd fx w/ delayed healing, subsq enc for opn fx type I or II w/ delayed healing, subsq enc for opn fx type I or II w/ delayed healing, seq] 179
S82.03[4,5,6] [K,M,N,P,Q,R]	Nondisp transv fx of [rt, lt, unsp] patella, subsq enc for [clsd fx w/ nonu, opn fx type I or II w/ nonu, opn fx type IIIA, IIIB, or IIIC w/ nonu, clsd fx w/ malu, opn fx type I or II w/ malu, opn fx type I or II w/ malu] 202
S52.22[4,5,6] [B,C]	Nondisp transv fx of [rt, lt, unsp] ulna, init enc for opn fx type [I or II, IIIA IIIB or IIIC] 434
S32.45[4,5,6] [A,B]	Nondisp transv fx of acetab [rt, lt, unsp] init enc for [clsd fx, opn fx] 162, 433
S72.32[4,5,6] [D,E,F,G,H,J,S]	Nondisp transv fx of shaft of [rt, lt, unsp] femur, [subsq enc for clsd fx w/ routine healing, subsq enc for opn fx type I or II w/ routine healing, subsq enc for opn fx type IIIA, IIIB, or IIIC w/ routine healing, subsq enc for clsd fx w/ delayed healing, subsq enc for opn fx type I or II w/ delayed healing, subsq enc for opn fx type IIIA, IIIB, or IIIC w/ delayed healing, seq] 178
S72.32[4,5,6] [A,B,C]	Nondisp transv fx of shaft of [rt, lt, unsp] femur, init enc for [clsd fx, opn fx type I or II, opn fx type IIIA, IIIB, or IIIC] 161, 286, 435
S72.32[4,5,6] [K,M,N,P,Q,R]	Nondisp transv fx of shaft of [rt, lt, unsp] femur, subsq enc for [clsd fx w/ nonu, opn fx type I or II w/ nonu, opn fx type IIIA, IIIB, or IIIC w/ nonu, clsd fx w/ malu, opn fx type I or II w/ malu, opn fx type IIIA, IIIB, or IIIC w/ malu] 201
S82.42[4,5,6] [A,B,C]	Nondisp transv fx of shaft of [rt, lt, unsp] fibula, [init enc for clsd fx, init enc for opn fx type I or II, init enc for opn fx type IIIA, IIIB, or IIIC] 191, 427
S82.42[4,5,6] [D,E,F,G,H,J,S]	Nondisp transv fx of shaft of [rt, lt, unsp] fibula, [subsq enc for clsd fx w/ routine healing, subsq enc for opn fx type I or II w/ routine healing, subsq enc for opn fx type IIIA, IIIB, or IIIC w/ routine healing, subsq enc for clsd fx w/ delayed healing, subsq enc for opn fx type IIIA, IIIB, or IIIC w/ delayed healing, seq] 180
S82.42[4,5,6] [B,C]	Nondisp transv fx of shaft of [rt, lt, unsp] fibula, init enc for opn fx type [I or II, IIIA IIIB or IIIC] 436
S82.42[4,5,6] [K,M,N,P,Q,R]	Nondisp transv fx of shaft of [rt, lt, unsp] fibula, subsq enc for [clsd fx w/ nonu, opn fx type I or II w/ nonu, opn fx type IIIA, IIIB, or IIIC w/ nonu, clsd fx w/ malu, opn fx type I or II w/ malu, opn fx type I or II w/ malu] 203
S42.32[4,5,6] [D,G,S]	Nondisp transv fx of shaft of [rt, lt, unsp] humerus, [subsq enc for fx w/ routine healing, subsq enc for fx w/ delayed healing, seq] 171
S42.32[4,5,6]B	Nondisp transv fx of shaft of [rt, lt, unsp] humerus, init enc for opn fx 433
S52.32[4,5,6] [D,E,F,G,H,J,S]	Nondisp transv fx of shaft of [rt, lt, unsp] radius, [subsq enc for clsd fx w/ routine healing, subsq enc for opn fx type I or II w/ routine healing, subsq enc for clsd fx w/ delayed healing, subsq enc for opn fx type I or II w/ delayed healing, subsq enc for opn fx type IIIA, IIIB, or IIIC w/ delayed healing, seq] 173
S52.32[4,5,6] [B,C]	Nondisp transv fx of shaft of [rt, lt, unsp] radius, init enc for opn fx type [I or II, IIIA IIIB or IIIC] 434
S52.32[4,5,6] [K,M,N,P,Q,R]	Nondisp transv fx of shaft of [rt, lt, unsp] radius, subsq enc for [clsd fx w/ nonu, opn fx type I or II w/ nonu, opn fx type IIIA, IIIB, or IIIC w/ nonu, clsd fx w/ malu, opn fx type I or II w/ malu, opn fx type IIIA, IIIB, or IIIC w/ malu] 198
S82.22[4,5,6] [A,B,C]	Nondisp transv fx of shaft of [rt, lt, unsp] tibia, [init enc for clsd fx, init enc for opn fx type I or II, init enc for opn fx type IIIA, IIIB, or IIIC] 191, 427
S82.22[4,5,6] [D,E,F,G,H,J,S]	Nondisp transv fx of shaft of [rt, lt, unsp] tibia, [subsq enc for clsd fx w/ routine healing, subsq enc for opn fx type I or II w/ routine healing, subsq enc for opn fx type IIIA, IIIB, or IIIC w/ routine healing, subsq enc for clsd fx w/ delayed healing, subsq enc for opn fx type I or II w/ delayed healing, seq] 180
S82.22[4,5,6] [B,C]	Nondisp transv fx of shaft of [rt, lt, unsp] tibia, init enc for opn fx type [I or II, IIIA IIIB or IIIC] 436
S82.22[4,5,6] [K,M,N,P,Q,R]	Nondisp transv fx of shaft of [rt, lt, unsp] tibia, subsq enc for [clsd fx w/ nonu, opn fx type I or II w/ nonu, opn fx type IIIA, IIIB, or IIIC w/ nonu, clsd fx w/ malu, opn fx type I or II w/ malu, opn fx type I or II w/ malu] 202
S52.22[4,5,6] [D,E,F,G,H,J,S]	Nondisp transv fx of shaft of [rt, lt, unsp] ulna, [subsq enc for clsd fx w/ routine healing, subsq enc for opn fx type I or II w/ routine healing, subsq enc for opn fx type IIIA, IIIB, or IIIC w/ routine healing, subsq enc for clsd fx w/ delayed healing, subsq enc for opn fx type I or II w/ delayed healing, subsq enc for opn fx type IIIA, IIIB, or IIIC w/ delayed healing, seq] 172
S52.22[4,5,6] [K,M,N,P,Q,R]	Nondisp transv fx of shaft of [rt, lt, unsp] ulna, subsq enc for [clsd fx w/ nonu, opn fx type I or II w/ nonu, opn fx type IIIA, IIIB, or IIIC w/ nonu, clsd fx w/ malu, opn fx type I or II w/ malu, opn fx type IIIA, IIIB, or IIIC w/ malu] 198
S42.32[4,5,6] [A,B]	Nondisp transv fx of shaft of humerus [rt, lt, unsp] init enc for fx [clsd, opn] 185
S42.32[4,5,6] [K,P]	Nondisp transv fx of shaft of humerus, [rt, lt, unsp] arm, subsq enc for fx w/ [nonu, malu] 197
S52.32[4,5,6] [A,B,C]	Nondisp transv fx of shaft of radius [rt, lt, unsp} init enc for [clsd fx, opn fx type I or II or opn fx NOS, opn fx type IIIA, IIIB, or IIIC] 186
S52.22[4,5,6] [A,B,C]	Nondisp transv fx of ulna {rt, lt, unsp} init enc for [clsd fx, opn fx type I or II or opn fx NOS, opn fx type IIIA, IIIB, or IIIC] 186
S82.85[4,5,6] [A,B,C]	Nondisp trimalleolar fx of [rt, lt, unsp] lwr leg, [init enc for clsd fx, init enc for opn fx type I or II, init enc for opn fx type I or II] 191, 428

Code	Description
S82.85[4,5,6] [D,E,F,G,H,J,S]	Nondisp trimalleolar fx of [rt, lt, unsp] lwr leg, [subsq enc for clsd fx w/ routine healing, subsq enc for opn fx type I or II w/ routine healing, subsq enc for opn fx type IIIA, IIIB, or IIIC w/ routine healing, subsq enc for clsd fx w/ delayed healing, subsq enc for opn fx type I or II w/ delayed healing, subsq enc for opn fx type IIIA, IIIB, or IIIC w/ delayed healing, seq] 181
S82.85[4,5,6] [K,M,N,P,Q,R]	Nondisp trimalleolar fx of [rt, lt, unsp] lwr leg, subsq enc for [clsd fx w/ nonu, opn fx type I or II w/ nonu, opn fx type IIIA, IIIB, or IIIC w/ nonu, clsd fx w/ malu, opn fx type I or II w/ malu, opn fx type I or II w/ malu] 203
S72.41[4,5,6] [D,E,F,G,H,J,S]	Nondisp unsp condyle fx of lwr end of [rt, lt, unsp] femur, [subsq enc for clsd fx w/ routine healing, subsq enc for opn fx type I or II w/ routine healing, subsq enc for opn fx type IIIA, IIIB, or IIIC w/ routine healing, subsq enc for clsd fx w/ delayed healing, subsq enc for opn fx type I or II w/ delayed healing, subsq enc for opn fx type IIIA, IIIB, or IIIC w/ delayed healing, seq] 178
S72.41[4,5,6] [A,B,C]	Nondisp unsp condyle fx of lwr end of [rt, lt, unsp] femur, init enc for [clsd fx, opn fx type I or II, opn fx type IIIA, IIIB, or IIIC] 161, 435
S72.41[4,5,6] [K,M,N,P,Q,R]	Nondisp unsp condyle fx of lwr end of [rt, lt, unsp] femur, subsq enc for [clsd fx w/ nonu, opn fx type I or II w/ nonu, opn fx type IIIA, IIIB, or IIIC w/ nonu, clsd fx w/ malu, opn fx type I or II w/ malu, opn fx type IIIA, IIIB, or IIIC w/ malu] 201
S92.40[4,5,6] [D,G,S]	Nondisp unsp fx of [rt, lt, unsp] great toe, [subsq enc for fx w/ routine healing, subsq enc for fx w/ delayed healing, seq] 183
S92.40[4,5,6] [A,B]	Nondisp unsp fx of [rt, lt, unsp] great toe, init enc for [clsd, opn] fx 192, 429
S92.40[4,5,6] [K,P]	Nondisp unsp fx of [rt, lt, unsp] great toe, subsq enc for fx w/ [nonu, malu] 204
S92.50[4,5,6] [D,G,S]	Nondisp unsp fx of [rt, lt, unsp] lesser toe(s), [subsq enc for fx w/ routine healing, subsq enc for fx w/ delayed healing, seq] 183
S92.50[4,5,6] [A,B]	Nondisp unsp fx of [rt, lt, unsp] lesser toe(s), init enc for [clsd, opn] fx 193, 429
S92.50[4,5,6] [K,P]	Nondisp unsp fx of [rt, lt, unsp] lesser toe(s), subsq enc for fx w/ [nonu, malu] 204
S32.11[0,1,2,9] [A,B]	Nondisp Zone I, Minimally disp Zone I, Severely disp Zone I, Unsp Zone I fx of sacrum, init enc for [clsd, opn] fx 421, 433
S32.12[0,1,2,9] [A,B]	Nondisp Zone II, Minimally disp Zone II, Severely disp Zone II, Unsp Zone II fx of sacrum, init enc for [clsd, opn] fx 421, 433
S32.13[0,1,2,9] [A,B]	Nondisp Zone III, Minimally disp Zone III, Severely disp Zone III, Unsp Zone III fx of sacrum, init enc for [clsd, opn] fx 421, 433
S32.12[0,1,2,9] [D,G]	Nondisp, Minimally disp, Severely disp, Unspecified Zone II fx of sacrum, subsq enc for fx w/ [routine, delayed] healing 170
S32.13[0,1,2,9] [D,G]	Nondisp, Minimally disp, Severely disp, Unspecified Zone III fx of sacrum, subsq enc for fx w/ [routine, delayed] healing 170
S32.11[0,1,2,9] [D,G]	Nondisp, Minimally disp, Severely disp, Unsp Zone I fx of sacrum, subsq enc for fx w/ [routine, delayed] healing 170
S32.11[0,1,2,9]K	Nondisp, Minimally disp, Severely disp, Unsp Zone I fx of sacrum, subsq enc for fx w/ nonu 196
S32.12[0,1,2,9]K	Nondisp, Minimally disp, Severely disp, Unsp Zone II fx of sacrum, subsq enc for fx w/ nonu 196
S32.13[0,1,2,9]K	Nondisp, Minimally disp, Severely disp, Unsp Zone III fx of sacrum, subsq enc for fx w/ nonu 196
D80.1	Nonfamilial hypogammaglobulinemia 294
I89.9	Noninfective d/o of lymphatic vessels and nodes, unsp 294
H61.1*	Noninfective d/o of pinna 58
K52.9	Noninfective gastroenteritis and colitis, unsp 116
P78.3	Noninfective neonatal diarrhea 288
N83*	Noninflammatory d/o of ovary, fallop and broad lgmt 265, 270
N44*	Noninflammatory d/o of testis 261
N11.0	Nonobstructive reflux-associated chr pyelonephritis 255
A48.2	Nonpneumonic Legionnaires' dz [Pontiac fever] 308
F48.9	Nonpsychotic mental d/o, unsp 310
O91.2[2,3]	Nonpurulent mastitis associated w/ [the puerperium, lactation] 272, 276
O91.21[1,2,3]	Nonpurulent mastitis associated w/ preg, [1st, 2nd, 3rd] trmstr 274, 278
O91.22	Nonpurulent mastitis associated with the puerperium 274
G03.0	Nonpyogenic meningitis 41, 283
I67.6	Nonpyogenic thrombosis of intracranial venous sys 38
I35*	Nonrheumatic aortic valve d/o 102
I34*	Nonrheumatic mitral valve d/o 102
I37*	Nonrheumatic pulmn valve d/o 102
I36*	Nonrheumatic tricuspid valve d/o 102
I88.9	Nonspecific lymphadenitis, unsp 294
I88.0	Nonspecific mesenteric lymphadenitis 117

Code	Description
R76.1*	Nonspecific reaction to test for tuberculosis 67
K75.2	Nonspecific reactive hepatitis 284
N34.1	Nonspecific urethritis 261, 264, 269
H65*	Nonsuppurative otitis media 57
E04.1	Nontoxic single thyroid nodule 3
M79.A*	Nontraumatic compartment synd 167
I62.1	Nontraumatic extradural hemor 7
I61.1	Nontraumatic intcrbl hemor in hemisphere, cortical 7, 11, 15
I61.0	Nontraumatic intcrbl hemor in hemisphere, subcortical 7, 11, 15
I61*	Nontraumatic intracerebral hemor 33, 284
I61.3	Nontraumatic intracerebral hemor in brain stem 7, 11, 15
I61.4	Nontraumatic intracerebral hemor in cerebellum 7, 11, 15
I61.2	Nontraumatic intracerebral hemor in hemisphere, unsp 7, 11, 15
I61.5	Nontraumatic intracerebral hemor, intraventricular 7, 11, 15
I61.6	Nontraumatic intracerebral hemor, multi localized 7, 11, 15
I61.9	Nontraumatic intracerebral hemor, unsp 7, 11, 15
I62.9	Nontraumatic intracranial hemor, unsp 7, 11, 15
M62.2*	Nontraumatic ischemic infarction of muscle 167
I60.2*	Nontraumatic subarach hemor from ant communicating artery 7, 11, 15
I60.0*	Nontraumatic subarach hemor from carotid siphon and bifurcation 7, 11, 15
I60.3*	Nontraumatic subarach hemor from posterior communicating artery 7, 11, 15
I60*	Nontraumatic subarachnoid hemor 33, 284
I60.4	Nontraumatic subarachnoid hemor from basilar artery 7, 11, 15
I60.1*	Nontraumatic subarachnoid hemor from mid cerebral artery 7, 11, 15
I60.6	Nontraumatic subarachnoid hemor from oth intracran art 7, 11, 15
I60.7	Nontraumatic subarachnoid hemor from unsp intracran art 7, 11, 15
I60.5*	Nontraumatic subarachnoid hemor from vert artery 7, 11, 15
I60.9	Nontraumatic subarachnoid hemor, unsp 7, 11, 15
I62.0*	Nontraumatic subdural hemor 7
A65	Nonvenereal syphilis 308
S53.03[1,2,3] [A,S]	Nursemaid's elbow [unsp, rt, lt] [init enc, seq] 186
S53.03[1,2,3]D	Nursemaid's elbow, [rt, lt, unsp] elbow, subsq enc 392
E41	Nutritional marasmus 246, 283
A92.1	O'nyong-nyong fever 307
O99.21[1,2,3]	Obesity compl preg, [1st, 2nd, 3rd] trmstr 278, 280
O99.210	Obesity compl preg, unsp trmstr 281
O99.215	Obesity compl the puerperium 272, 276
E66.0*	Obesity d/t excess calories 246
O99.2[1,8]4	Obesity, Endocrine nutritional and metabolic dzs compl childbirth 273, 275
E66.9	Obesity, unsp 246
F42	Obsessive-compulsive d/o 310
O71.6	Obstetric damage to pelvic jts and lgmt 272, 275
O71.7	Obstetric hematoma of pelvis 272, 275
O71.4	Obstetric high vaginal lac alone 272, 275
O71.3	Obstetric lac of cervix 272, 275
O71.9	Obstetric trauma, unsp 272, 276
A34	Obstetrical tetanus 272, 275
O66.[0,1,2,3]	Obstructed labor d/t [shldr dystocia, locked twins, unusually lg fetus, oth abnormalities of fetus] 273, 275
O64*	Obstructed labor d/t malposition and malpresent of fetus 273, 275
O65*	Obstructed labor d/t maternal pelvic abnormality 273, 275
O66.6	Obstructed labor d/t oth multi fetuses 273, 275
O66.9	Obstructed labor, unsp 273, 275
K31.5	Obstruction of duodenum 115
H68.1*	Obstruction of Eustachian tube 58
N13.9	Obstructive and reflux uropathy, unsp 256, 285
G47.33	Obstructive sleep apnea (adult) (pediatric) 58
S73.02[1,2,3,4,5,6]A	Obturator [sublux, disloc] of [rt, lt, unsp] hip, init enc 426
S73.02[4,5,6]A	Obturator disloc of [rt, lt, unsp] hip, init enc 162
S73.02[4,5,6]S	Obturator disloc of [rt, lt, unsp] hip, seq 190
S73.02[4,5,6]D	Obturator disloc of [rt, lt, unsp] hip, subsq enc 397
S73.02[1,2,3]A	Obturator sublux of [rt, lt, unsp] hip, init enc 162
S73.02[1,2,3]S	Obturator sublux of [rt, lt, unsp] hip, seq 190

Code	Description
S31.051S	Opn bite of low back and pelvis w penet retroperiton, seq 226
S31.825[A,S]	Opn bite of lt buttock, [init enc, seq] 227
S31.05[0,1]D	Opn bite of lwr back and pelvis [w/o,w/] penetration into retroperitoneum, subsq enc 389
S31.050[A,S]	Opn bite of lwr back and pelvis w/o penetration into retroperitoneum, [init enc, seq] 226
S01.25XA	Opn bite of nose, init enc 5, 58
S01.25XS	Opn bite of nose, seq 224
S01.85X[A,S]	Opn bite of oth part of head, [init enc, seq] 224
S11.85X[A,S]	Opn bite of oth spec part of neck, [init enc, seq] 225
S11.85XA	Opn bite of oth spec part of neck, init enc 5
S31.25XS	Opn bite of penis, seq 226
S11.25XA	Opn bite of pharynx and cervical esophagus, init enc 5, 58
S11.25XS	Opn bite of pharynx and cervical esophagus, seq 225
S31.815[A,S]	Opn bite of rt buttock, [init enc, seq] 227
S01.05X[A,S]	Opn bite of scalp, [init enc, seq] 224
S31.35XS	Opn bite of scrotum and testes, seq 226
S11.15XA	Opn bite of thyroid gland, init enc 5
S11.15XS	Opn bite of thyroid gland, seq 225
S11.025A	Opn bite of trachea, init enc 5, 67
S11.025S	Opn bite of trachea, seq 225
S31.805[A,S]	Opn bite of unsp buttock, [init enc, seq] 227
S31.55[1,2]D	Opn bite of unsp ext genital organs, [male, female], subsq enc 390
S01.95X[A,S]	Opn bite of unsp part of head, [init enc, seq] 224
S11.95X[A,S]	Opn bite of unsp part of neck, [init enc, seq] 225
S11.95XA	Opn bite of unsp part of neck, init enc 5
S21.95X[A,S]	Opn bite of unsp part of thorax, [init enc, seq] 225
S91.259[A,S]	Opn bite of unsp toe(s) w/ damage to nail, [init enc, seq] 230
S91.159[A,S]	Opn bite of unsp toe(s) w/o damage to nail, [init enc, seq] 230
S91.159D	Opn bite of unsp toe(s) w/o damage to nail, subs enc 399
S91.259D	Opn bite of unsp toe(s) with damage to nail, subs enc 399
S31.45XS	Opn bite of vagina and vulva, seq 226
S11.035A	Opn bite of vocal cord, init enc 5, 58
S11.035S	Opn bite of vocal cord, seq 225
S91.05[1,2,9][A,S]	Opn bite, [rt, lt, unsp] ankle, [init enc, seq] 230
S91.05[1,2,9]A	Opn bite, [rt, lt, unsp] ankle, init enc 429
S91.05[1,2,9]D	Opn bite, [rt, lt, unsp] ankle, subsq enc 399
S51.05[1,2,9][A,S]	Opn bite, [rt, lt, unsp] elbow, [init enc, seq] 227
S91.35[1,2,9][A,S]	Opn bite, [rt, lt, unsp] foot, [init enc, seq] 230
S91.35[1,2,9]A	Opn bite, [rt, lt, unsp] foot, init enc 429
S91.35[1,2,9]D	Opn bite, [rt, lt, unsp] foot, subsq enc 399
S71.05[1,2,9][A,S]	Opn bite, [rt, lt, unsp] hip, [init enc, seq] 229
S81.05[1,2,9][A,S]	Opn bite, [rt, lt, unsp] knee, [init enc, seq] 229
S81.85[1,2,9][A,S]	Opn bite, [rt, lt, unsp] lwr leg, [init enc, seq] 229
S71.15[1,2,9][A,S]	Opn bite, [rt, lt, unsp] thigh, [init enc, seq] 229
S61.15[1,2,9]D	Opn wnd of [rt, lt, unsp] thumb w/ damage to nail, subsq enc 394
S61.05[1,2,9]D	Opn wnd of [rt, lt, unsp] thumb w/o damage to nail, subsq enc 394
S01.4[0,1,2,3,4,5]2A	Opn wnd of lt cheek and temporomandibular area, [unsp, lac w/o FB, lac w/ FB, punc w/o FB, punc w/ FB, bite] init enc 5
S01.4[0,1,2,3,4,5]1A	Opn wnd of rt cheek and temporomandibular area, [unsp, lac w/o FB, lac w/ FB, punc w/o FB, punc w/ FB, bite], init enc 5
S21.45[1,2,9]D	Opn wnd w/ FB of [rt, lt, unspecified] back wall of thorax w/ penetration into thoracic cavity, subsq enc 389
S21.25[1,2,9]D	Opn wnd w/ FB of [rt, lt, unspecified] back wall of thorax w/ penetration into thoracic cavity, subsq enc 388
S21.15[1,2,9]D	Opn wnd w/ FB of [rt, lt, unspecified] front wall of thorax w/o penetration into thoracic cavity, subsq enc 388
H46*	Optic neuritis 45
K12.3*	Oral mucositis (ulcerative) 4
K13.5	Oral submucous fibrosis 4
N45*	Orchitis and epididymitis 261
B08.02	Orf virus dz 233
F52.3*	Orgasmic d/o 311
I95.1	Orthostatic hypotension 102
R80.2	Orthostatic proteinuria, unsp 256

Code	Description
M99.6*	Osseous and sublux stenosis of intervertebral foramina 165
B45.3	Osseous cryptococcosis 438
M99.3*	Osseous stenosis of neural canal 165
M85.3*	Osteitis condensans 167
M88*	Osteitis deformans [Paget's dz of bone] 167
M18*	Osteoarthritis of first carpometacarpal jt 167
M16*	Osteoarthritis of hip 167
M17*	Osteoarthritis of knee 167
Q78.9	Osteochondrodysplasia, unsp 195
Q78.0	Osteogenesis imperfecta 126, 195
M89.5*	Osteolysis 194
M86*	Osteomyelitis 163
M46.2*	Osteomyelitis of vertebra 125, 163
M86.9	Osteomyelitis, unsp 131
D47.4	Osteomyelofibrosis 294
M87*	Osteonecrosis 167
M90*	Osteopathies in dz classified elsw 167
M89.6*	Osteopathy after poliomyelitis 194
Q78.2	Osteopetrosis 195
M25.77[1,2,3]	Osteophyte, [rt, lt, unsp] ankle 167
M25.72[1,2,9]	Osteophyte, [rt, lt, unsp] elbow 167
M25.77[4,5,6]	Osteophyte, [rt, lt, unsp] foot 167
M25.74[1,2,9]	Osteophyte, [rt, lt, unsp] hand 167
M25.75[1,2,9]	Osteophyte, [rt, lt, unsp] hip 167
M25.76[1,2,9]	Osteophyte, [rt, lt, unsp] knee 167
M25.71[1,2,9]	Osteophyte, [rt, lt, unsp] shldr 167
M25.73[1,2,9]	Osteophyte, [rt, lt, unsp] wrist 167
M25.70	Osteophyte, unsp jt 167
M25.78	Osteophyte, vertebrae 164
M81*	Osteoporosis w/o current Path fx 167
H92*	Otalgia and effusion of ear 58
S12.12[0,1][A,B]	Oth [disp, nondisp] dens fx, init enc for [clsd, opn] fx 419
S12.12[0,1][D,G]	Oth [disp, nondisp] dens fx, subsq enc for fx w/ [routine, delayed] healing 169
S12.12[0,1]K	Oth [disp, nondisp] dens fx, subsq enc for fx w/ nonu 195
S12.09[0,1][A,B]	Oth [disp, nondisp] fx of 1st cervical vertebra, init enc for [clsd, opn] fx 419
S12.09[0,1][D,G]	Oth [disp, nondisp] fx of 1st cervical vertebra, subsq enc for fx w/ [routine, delayed] healing 169
S12.09[0,1]K	Oth [disp, nondisp] fx of 1st cervical vertebra, subsq enc for fx w/ nonu 195
S12.19[0,1][A,B]	Oth [disp, nondisp] fx of 2nd cervical vertebra, init enc for [clsd,opn] fx 419
S12.19[0,1][D,G]	Oth [disp, nondisp] fx of 2nd cervical vertebra, subsq enc for fx w/ [routine, delayed] healing 169
S12.19[0,1]K	Oth [disp, nondisp] fx of 2nd cervical vertebra, subsq enc for fx w/ nonu 195
S12.29[0,1][A,B]	Oth [disp, nondisp] fx of 3rd cervical vertebra, init enc for [clsd, opn] fx 419
S12.29[0,1][D,G]	Oth [disp, nondisp] fx of 3rd cervical vertebra, subsq enc for fx w/ [routine, delayed] healing 169
S12.29[0,1]K	Oth [disp, nondisp] fx of 3rd cervical vertebra, subsq enc for fx w/ nonu 195
S12.39[0,1][A,B]	Oth [disp, nondisp] fx of 4th cervical vertebra, init enc for [clsd, opn] fx 419
S12.39[0,1][D,G]	Oth [disp, nondisp] fx of 4th cervical vertebra, subsq enc for fx w/ [routine, delayed] healing 169
S12.39[0,1]K	Oth [disp, nondisp] fx of 4th cervical vertebra, subsq enc for fx w/ nonu 195
S12.49[0,1][A,B]	Oth [disp, nondisp] fx of 5th cervical vertebra, init enc for [clsd, opn] fx 419
S12.49[0,1][D,G]	Oth [disp, nondisp] fx of 5th cervical vertebra, subsq enc for fx w/ [routine, delayed] healing 169
S12.49[0,1]K	Oth [disp, nondisp] fx of 5th cervical vertebra, subsq enc for fx w/ nonu 195
S12.59[0,1][A,B,S]	Oth [disp, nondisp] fx of 6th cervical vertebra, [init enc for clsd fx, init enc for opn fx, seq] 165
S12.59[0,1][A,B]	Oth [disp, nondisp] fx of 6th cervical vertebra, init enc for [clsd, opn] fx 419
S12.59[0,1][D,G]	Oth [disp, nondisp] fx of 6th cervical vertebra, subsq enc for fx w/ [routine, delayed] healing 169
S12.59[0,1]K	Oth [disp, nondisp] fx of 6th cervical vertebra, subsq enc for fx w/ nonu 195

S12.69[Ø,1][A,B,S]	Oth [disp, nondisp] fx of 7th cervical vertebra, [init enc for clsd fx, init enc for opn fx, seq] 165	
S12.69[Ø,1][A,B]	Oth [disp, nondisp] fx of 7th cervical vertebra, init enc for [clsd, opn] fx 419	
S12.69[Ø,1][D,G]	Oth [disp, nondisp] fx of 7th cervical vertebra, subsq enc for fx w/ [routine, delayed] healing 169	
S12.69[Ø,1]K	Oth [disp, nondisp] fx of 7th cervical vertebra, subsq enc for fx w/ nonu 195	
S62.23[1,2,3,4,5,6][A,B]	Oth [disp, nondisp] fx of base of 1st metacarpal bone, [rt, lt, unsp] hand, init enc for [clsd, opn] fx 424	
S42.49[1,2,3,4,5,6][A,B]	Oth [disp, nondisp] fx of lwr end of [rt, lt, unsp] humerus, init enc for [clsd, opn] fx 422	
S42.29[1,2,3,4,5,6][A,B]	Oth [disp, nondisp] fx of upr end of [rt, lt, unsp] humerus, init enc for [clsd, opn] fx 422	
N99.8[1,9]	Oth [intraoperative, postprocedural] comps (and d/o) of genitourinary sys 256	
S43.08[1,2,3,4,5,6]A	Oth [sublux, disloc] of [rt, lt, unsp] shldr jt, init enc 422	
S63.09[1,2,3,4,5,6]A	Oth [sublux, disloc] of [rt, lt, unsp] wrist and hand, init enc 425	
K45*	Oth abd hernia 117	
H93.29[1,2,3,9]	Oth abnormal auditory perceptions, [rt, lt, bilat, unsp] ear 58	
R87.618	Oth abnormal cytolog findings on specimens from cervix uteri 289	
R87.628	Oth abnormal cytological findings on specimens from vagina 265, 270	
R85.89	Oth abnormal findings in specimens from dgstv org/abd cav 385	
R89.8	Oth abnormal findings in specimens from oth org/tiss 386	
R87.89	Oth abnormal findings in specmn from female genital organs 386	
R79*	Oth abnormal findings of bld chemistry 385	
R90.89	Oth abnormal findings on diagnostic imaging of cnsl 386	
N93*	Oth abnormal uterine and vaginal bleeding 265, 270	
R06.8*	Oth abnormalities of breathing 69	
R26.8*	Oth abnormalities of gait and mobility 38	
R00.8	Oth abnormalities of heart beat 103	
R77*	Oth abnormalities of plasma proteins 385	
T80.39XA	Oth ABO incompat react d/t tranfs of bld/bld prod, init 287, 293	
T80.39XS	Oth ABO incompat react d/t tranfs of bld/bld prod, seq 374	
T80.39XD	Oth ABO incompat react d/t tranfs of bld/bld prod, subs 410	
J39.1	Oth abscess of pharynx 4, 57	
B60.19	Oth acanthamebic dz 309	
L11*	Oth acantholytic d/o 233	
M21.6X[1,2,9]	Oth acquired deformities of [rt, lt, unsp] foot 193	
M95.8	Oth acquired deformities of musculoskeletal sys 194	
M95.2	Oth acquired deformity of head 194	
D59.8	Oth acquired hemolytic anemias 283, 293	
D60.8	Oth acquired pure red cell aplasias 293	
G36*	Oth acute disseminated demyelination 33	
M86.16[1,2,9]	Oth acute osteomyelitis, [rt, lt, unsp] tibia & fibula 131	
M86.18	Oth acute osteomyelitis, oth site 125	
I01.8	Oth acute rheumatic heart dz 103	
L56*	Oth acute skin changes d/t ultraviolet radiation 234	
B17*	Oth acute viral hepatitis 124, 283	
T78.8XX[A,S]	Oth adverse effects, NEC, [init enc, seq] 374	
T78.8XXD	Oth adverse effects, NEC, subs enc 410	
T78.1XX[A,S]	Oth adverse food reactions, NEC, [init enc, seq] 374	
T78.1XXD	Oth adverse food reactions, NEC, subs 410	
T78.49XA	Oth allergy, init enc 361	
T78.49XS	Oth allergy, seq 374	
T78.49XD	Oth allergy, subsq enc 410	
R41.3	Oth amnesia 385	
R82.9*	Oth and unsp abnormal findings in urine 255	
K35.8*	Oth and unsp acute appendicitis 117	
H21.5*	Oth and unsp adhes and disruptions of iris and ciliary body 46	
M12*	Oth and unsp arthropathy 167	
P28.1*	Oth and unsp atelectasis of newborn 288	
I70.9*	Oth and unsp atherosclerosis 100	
K74.6*	Oth and unsp cirrhosis of liver 123	
Q64.7*	Oth and unsp congenital malformations of bladder and urethra 256	
G95.2*	Oth and unsp cord compression 38, 439	
M27.4*	Oth and unsp cysts of jaw 4	
H53.3*	Oth and unsp d/o of binocular vision 46	
O92.2*	Oth and unsp d/o of breast assoc w preg and the puerp 272, 276	
I99*	Oth and unsp d/o of circulatory sys 102	
H69*	Oth and unsp d/o of Eustachian tube 58	
O92.7*	Oth and unsp d/o of lactation 272, 276	
N50*	Oth and unsp d/o of male genital organs 261	
J34*	Oth and unsp d/o of nose and nasal sinuses 58	
H44.3*	Oth and unsp degenerative d/o of globe 46	
H02.7*	Oth and unsp degeneratv d/o of eyelid and perioculr area 45	
L30*	Oth and unsp dermatitis 234	
G25.7*	Oth and unsp drug induced movement d/o 32	
K04.9*	Oth and unsp dz of pulp and periapical tissues 4	
P83.3*	Oth and unsp edema specific to newborn 288	
G93.4*	Oth and unsp encephalopathy 33, 439	
E75.1*	Oth and unsp gangliosidosis 32	
H91*	Oth and unsp hearing loss 58	
H50.4*	Oth and unsp heterotropia 46	
N13.3*	Oth and unsp hydronephrosis 255, 285	
B99*	Oth and unsp infectious dz 309	
K56.6*	Oth and unsp intestinal obstruction 284	
M40.2*	Oth and unsp kyphosis 125	
K13.7*	Oth and unsp lesions of oral mucosa 4	
C44.0*	Oth and unsp malig neoplasm of skin of lip 3	
C44.3*	Oth and unsp malig neoplasm skin/ and unsp parts of face 233	
C44.1*	Oth and unsp malig neoplasm skin/ eyelid, incl* canthus 45	
I62*	Oth and unsp nontraumatic intracranial hemor 33, 284	
M19*	Oth and unsp osteoarthritis 167	
D10.3*	Oth and unsp parts of mouth 3, 59	
G62*	Oth and unsp polyneuropathies 34	
E80.2*	Oth and unsp porphyria 247	
H16.1*	Oth and unsp superf keratitis without conjunctivitis 46	
R39*	Oth and unsp symptoms and signs involving the GU sys 255	
A53*	Oth and unsp syphilis 308	
C85*	Oth and unsp types of non-Hodgkin lymphoma 295, 303, 305, 439	
K43.[6,7]	Oth and unsp ventral hernia, w/ [obstruction w/o gangrene, gangrene], not spec as recurrent 284	
D64*	Oth anemias 293	
H57.09	Oth anomalies of pupillary function 45	
S73.03[1,2,3,4,5,6]A	Oth ant [sublux, disloc] of [rt, lt, unsp] hip, init enc 426	
S73.03[4,5,6]A	Oth ant disloc of [rt, lt, unsp] hip, init enc 162	
S73.03[4,5,6]S	Oth ant disloc of [rt, lt, unsp] hip, seq 190	
S73.03[4,5,6]D	Oth ant disloc of [rt, lt, unsp] hip, subsq enc 397	
S73.03[1,2,3]A	Oth ant sublux of [rt, lt, unsp] hip, init enc 162	
S73.03[1,2,3]S	Oth ant sublux of [rt, lt, unsp] hip, seq 190	
S73.03[1,2,3]D	Oth ant sublux of [rt, lt, unsp] hip, subsq enc 397	
O46.8X[1,2,3]	Oth antepartum hemor, [1st, 2nd, 3rd] trmstr 274, 278, 280	
O46.8X9	Oth antepartum hemor, unsp trmstr 281	
F41*	Oth anxiety d/o 310	
D61.89	Oth aplastic anemias and oth bone marrow failure synd 293	
P28.4	Oth apnea of newborn 288	
K36	Oth appendicitis 117	
M13*	Oth arthritis 167	
A93*	Oth arthropod-borne viral fevers, NEC 307	
M24.1[1,2,3,4][1,2,9]	Oth articular cartilage d/o, [rt, lt, unsp] [shldr, elbow, wrist, hand] 184	
M24.17[1,2,3]	Oth articular cartilage d/o, [rt, lt, unsp] ankle 184	
M24.17[4,5,6]	Oth articular cartilage d/o, [rt, lt, unsp] foot 184	
M24.15[1,2,9]	Oth articular cartilage d/o, [rt, lt, unsp] hip 193	
M24.10	Oth articular cartilage d/o, unsp site 193	
Q64.3*	Oth atresia and stenosis of urethra and bladder neck 256	
A81.89	Oth atypical virus infections of central nervous sys 438	
D59.1	Oth autoimmune hemolytic anemias 293	
B96*	Oth bacterial agents as the cause of dz classd elsw 309	
A04*	Oth bacterial intestinal infections 114	
G00.8	Oth bacterial meningitis 11, 15	
F98.8	Oth behav/emotn d/o w onset usly occur in chldhd and adol 311	
D23.1*	Oth benign neoplasm of skin of eyelid, incl* canthus 45	
D23.0	Oth benign neoplasm of skin of lip 233	
D23.7*	Oth benign neoplasm of skin of lwr limb, incl* hip 233	

D23.3*	Oth benign neoplasm of skin of oth and unsp parts of face 233	
D23.4	Oth benign neoplasm of skin of scalp and neck 233	
D23.5	Oth benign neoplasm of skin of trunk 233	
D23.9	Oth benign neoplasm of skin, unsp 233	
D23.2*	Oth benign neoplasm skin/ ear and ext auricular canal 233	
D23.6*	Oth benign neoplasm skin/ upr limb, incl* shldr 233	
D26*	Oth benign neoplasms of uterus 264, 270	
D3A.8	Oth benign neuroendocrine tumors 304, 306	
M99.8[3,4]	Oth biomech lesions [lumbar rgn, sacral rgn] 165	
M99.8[0,1,2,5,6,7,8,9]	Oth biomech lesions of [head, cervical, thoracic, pelvic, lwr extr, upr extr, rib cage, abd and oth] rgn 194	
P15*	Oth birth injuries 288	
P12.89	Oth birth injuries to scalp 289	
P14.3	Oth brachial plexus birth injuries 288	
Q18.2	Oth branchial cleft malformations 58	
M70.3*	Oth bursitis of elbow 167	
M70.7*	Oth bursitis of hip 167	
M70.5*	Oth bursitis of knee 167	
M71*	Oth bursopathies 167	
I49*	Oth cardiac arrhythmias 102	
O29.199	Oth cardiac comp of anesth during preg, unsp trmstr 280	
O29.19[1,2,3]	Oth cardiac comps of anesthesia during preg, [1st, 2nd, 3rd] trmstr 277	
R01.2	Oth cardiac sounds 103	
P29.89	Oth cardiovasc d/o originating in the perinatal period 288	
A52.09	Oth cardiovascular syphilis 103	
H26*	Oth cataract 46	
O29.29[1,2,3]	Oth central nervous sys comps of anesthesia during preg, [1st, 2nd, 3rd] trmstr 277	
I63.8	Oth cerebral infarction 11, 15	
G80.8	Oth cerebral palsy 38	
A52.12	Oth cerebrospinal syphilis 32	
I68.8	Oth cerebrovascular d/o in dz classd elsw 33	
I67.89	Oth cerebrovascular dz 33	
A52.05	Oth cerebrovascular syphilis 103	
I67.848	Oth cerebrovascular vasospasm and vasoconstriction 33	
M50.8*	Oth cervical disc d/o 165	
M50.3*	Oth cervical disc degeneration 165	
M50.2*	Oth cervical disc displac 165	
B71*	Oth cestode infections 114	
H04.6*	Oth changes of lacrimal passages 45	
R07.89	Oth chest pain 103	
F84.3	Oth childhood disintegrative d/o 310	
F93.8	Oth childhood emotional d/o 311	
A74.8*	Oth chlamydial dz 307	
G25.5	Oth chorea 32	
N30.2*	Oth chr cystitis 255	
J35.8	Oth chr dz of tonsils and adenoids 4, 58	
L53.3	Oth chr figurate erythema 223, 284	
M86.56[1,2,9]	Oth chr hematogenous osteomyelitis, [rt, lt, unsp] tibia & fibula 131	
M86.58	Oth chr hematogenous osteomyelitis, oth site 125	
J44*	Oth chr obstructive pulmn dz 68	
M86.66[1,2,9]	Oth chr osteomyelitis, [rt, lt, unsp] tibia & fibula 131	
M86.68	Oth chr osteomyelitis, oth site 125	
E06.5	Oth chr thyroiditis 3	
N11.8	Oth chr tubulo-interstitial nephritis 255	
C81.71	Oth class Hodgkin lymphoma, nodes of head, face, and neck 3	
O29.299	Oth cnsl comp of anesthesia during preg, unsp trmstr 280	
H53.59	Oth color vision deficiencies 46	
R40.244	Oth coma,w/o Glasgow coma scale score,or w/part score report 412	
D81.89	Oth combined immunodeficiencies 293	
D83.8	Oth common variable immunodeficiencies 294	
N98.8	Oth comp associated with artfcl fertilization 368	
T80.89XS	Oth comp fol inf, tranfs and theraputc inject, seq 375	
T80.89XA	Oth comp fol inf, transfusion and theraputc inject, init 287, 293	
T80.89XD	Oth comp fol inf, transfusion and theraputc inject, subs 410	
T88.1XXA	Oth comp following immunization, NEC, init 308	
T88.1XXS	Oth comp following immunization, NEC, seq 376	

T88.1XXD	Oth comp following immunization, NEC, subs 411	
T87.8*	Oth comp of amp stump 205	
O29.8X9	Oth comp of anesthesia during preg, unsp trmstr 280	
O89.8	Oth comp of anesthesia during the puerperium 274	
T88.59XA	Oth comp of anesthesia, init enc 287, 367	
T88.59XS	Oth comp of anesthesia, seq 376	
T88.59XD	Oth comp of anesthesia, subsq enc 411	
K91.858	Oth comp of intestinal pouch 117, 284	
O75.4	Oth comp of obstetric surgery and procedures 273, 274	
T81.89XA	Oth comp of procedures, NEC, init 368	
T81.89XS	Oth comp of procedures, NEC, seq 375	
T81.89XD	Oth comp of procedures, NEC, subs 410	
J95.859	Oth comp of respirator [ventilator] 69, 284	
O29.5X9	Oth comp of spinal and epidural anesth during preg, unsp trmstr 280	
T88.8XXA	Oth comp of surgical and medical care, NEC, init 368	
T88.8XXS	Oth comp of surgical and medical care, NEC, seq 376	
T88.8XXD	Oth comp of surgical and medical care, NEC, subs 411	
O90.8*	Oth comp of the puerperium, NEC 272, 276	
O90.89	Oth comp of the puerperium, NEC 274	
O31.8X[1,2,3][0,1,2,3,4,5,9]	Oth comp specific to multiple gestation, [1st, 2nd, 3rd] trmstr, fetus [N/A or unsp, 1, 2, 3, 4, 5, oth] 278, 279	
O29.8X[1,2,3]	Oth comps of anesthesia during preg, [1st, 2nd, 3rd] trmstr 277	
O29.5X[1,2,3]	Oth comps of spinal and epidural anesthesia during preg, [1st, 2nd, 3rd] trmstr 277	
O31.8X9[0,1,2,3,4,5,9]	Oth comps specific to multi gestation, unsp trmstr, fetus [N/A or unsp, 1, 2, 3, 4, 5, oth] 281	
N94.89	Oth cond assoc w female genital organs and menstrual cycle 270	
P96.89	Oth conditions originating in the perinatal period 288	
M30.8	Oth conditions related to polyarteritis nodosa 164	
I45*	Oth conduction d/o 102	
P61.4	Oth congenital anemias, NEC 288	
Q67.8	Oth congenital deformities of chest 195	
Q67.4	Oth congenital deformities of skull, face and jaw 195	
Q43.2	Oth congenital functional d/o of colon 117	
P37.4	Oth congenital malaria 282	
Q76.49	Oth congenital malform of spine, not associated w scoliosis 165	
Q87.5	Oth congenital malformation syndromes w oth skeletal changes 195	
Q87.8*	Oth congenital malformation syndromes, NEC 195	
Q79.5*	Oth congenital malformations of abd wall 117	
Q44.5	Oth congenital malformations of bile ducts 124	
Q76.8	Oth congenital malformations of bony thorax 69	
Q04*	Oth congenital malformations of brain 38, 285	
Q32.4	Oth congenital malformations of bronchus 4	
Q79.1	Oth congenital malformations of diaphragm 69	
Q17*	Oth congenital malformations of ear 58	
Q15*	Oth congenital malformations of eye 46	
Q52*	Oth congenital malformations of female genitalia 265, 270	
Q44.1	Oth congenital malformations of gallbladder 124	
Q26.8	Oth congenital malformations of great veins 102	
Q84*	Oth congenital malformations of integument 234	
Q63*	Oth congenital malformations of kidney 256	
Q31.8	Oth congenital malformations of larynx 4	
Q74*	Oth congenital malformations of limb(s) 195	
Q44.7	Oth congenital malformations of liver 124	
Q33.8	Oth congenital malformations of lung 69	
Q55*	Oth congenital malformations of male genital organs 261	
Q38.6	Oth congenital malformations of mouth 5, 59	
Q07*	Oth congenital malformations of nervous sys 38, 285	
Q45.3	Oth congenital malformations of pancreas and pancreatic duct 124	
Q27*	Oth congenital malformations of peripheral vascular sys 100	
Q38.8	Oth congenital malformations of pharynx 5, 58	
Q34*	Oth congenital malformations of respiratory sys 69	
Q76.6	Oth congenital malformations of ribs 69	
Q82*	Oth congenital malformations of skin 234	
Q75*	Oth congenital malformations of skull and face bones 195	
Q06*	Oth congenital malformations of spinal cord 38, 285	
Q38.3	Oth congenital malformations of tongue 5, 59	

Q32.1	Oth congenital malformations of trachea **4**	
Q40*	Oth congenital malformations of upr alimentary tract **117**	
Z77*	Oth contact w and (suspected) exposures hazardous to health **412**	
M11*	Oth crystal arthropathies **166**	
I23.8	Oth current comp following AMI **103**	
M85.6*	Oth cyst of bone **167**	
N30.8*	Oth cystitis **255, 285**	
K09.8	Oth cysts of oral region, NEC **4**	
B25.8	Oth cytomegaloviral dz **307, 438**	
H02.59	Oth d/o affecting eyelid function **45**	
E27*	Oth d/o of adrenal gland **247**	
E72*	Oth d/o of amino-acid metabolism **247**	
G90.8	Oth d/o of autonomic nervous sys **34**	
E80.6	Oth d/o of bilirubin metabolism **124**	
N32*	Oth d/o of bladder **256**	
D77	Oth d/o of bld/bld-frm organs in dz classd elsw **294**	
M89.2*	Oth d/o of bone development and growth **194**	
G94	Oth d/o of brain in dz classified elsw **32**	
N64*	Oth d/o of breast **224**	
H31*	Oth d/o of choroid **46**	
H11*	Oth d/o of conjunctiva **45**	
M84.8*	Oth d/o of continuity of bone **194**	
H18*	Oth d/o of cornea **46**	
L81.6	Oth d/o of diminished melanin formation **289**	
H94*	Oth d/o of ear in dz classified elsw **58**	
H95.1*	Oth d/o of ear/mastd following mastoidectomy **58**	
E87*	Oth d/o of fluid, electrolyte and acid-base balance **246, 283**	
K06*	Oth d/o of gingiva and edentulous alveolar ridge **59**	
H44.8*	Oth d/o of globe **46**	
E74.3*	Oth d/o of intestinal carbohydrate absorption **116**	
N29	Oth d/o of kidney and ureter in dz classd elsw **256**	
H04.1*	Oth d/o of lacrimal gland **45**	
H04.8*	Oth d/o of lacrimal sys **45**	
H27*	Oth d/o of lens **46**	
E78.8*	Oth d/o of lipoprotein metabolism **247**	
J98.4	Oth d/o of lung **69**	
G96.19	Oth d/o of meninges, NEC **38**	
H75*	Oth d/o of mid ear and mastoid in dz classd elsw **58**	
H74*	Oth d/o of mid ear mastoid **58**	
E83.89	Oth d/o of mineral metabolism **247**	
P94.8	Oth d/o of muscle tone of newborn **288**	
G98.8	Oth d/o of nervous sys **439**	
G98*	Oth d/o of nervous sys NEC **33**	
H47.39*	Oth d/o of optic disc **46**	
H05.89	Oth d/o of orbit **45**	
G64	Oth d/o of peripheral nervous sys **34**	
K66*	Oth d/o of peritoneum **117**	
L81*	Oth d/o of pigmentation **234**	
E88.09	Oth d/o of plasma-protein metabolism, NEC **304, 306**	
N47.8	Oth d/o of prepuce **289**	
F88	Oth d/o of psychological development **311**	
E79.8	Oth d/o of purine and pyrimidine metabolism **247**	
H52.6	Oth d/o of refraction **46**	
K68.9	Oth d/o of retroperitoneum **114**	
L99	Oth d/o of skin, SQ in dz classd elsw **234**	
L59*	Oth d/o of skin, SQ related to radiation **234**	
M67*	Oth d/o of synovium and tndn **167**	
K08*	Oth d/o of teeth and supporting structures **59**	
H59.09*	Oth d/o of the eye following cataract surgery **367**	
K00.8	Oth d/o of tooth development **4**	
N36*	Oth d/o of urethra **256**	
M20.5X[1,2,9]	Oth deformities of toe(s) (acquired), [rt, lt, unsp] foot **193**	
G23*	Oth degenerative dz of basal ganglia **32**	
G31*	Oth degenerative dz of nervous sys, NEC **32**	
G32.89	Oth degeneratv d/o of nervous sys in dis classd elsw **33**	
Q93.8*	Oth deletions from the autosomes **310**	
Q93.5	Oth deletions of part of a chromosome **310**	
G37.8	Oth demyelinating dz of central nervous sys **33**	
S12.12[0,1] [A,B,S]	Oth dens fx [disp, nondisp] init enc for fx [clsd, opn, seq] **165**	

M26.8*	Oth dentofacial anomalies **4**
F32.8	Oth depressive episodes **311**
F80.89	Oth developmental d/o of speech and language **311**
E13.5*	Oth diabetes mellitus with circulatory comp **2, 100**
E13.610	Oth diabetes mellitus with diabetic neuropathic arthropathy **34**
E13.4*	Oth diabetes mellitus with neurological comp **2, 34**
E13.3*	Oth diabetes mellitus with ophthalmic comp **2, 45**
E13.618	Oth diabetes mellitus with oth diabetic arthropathy **246**
E13.6*	Oth diabetes mellitus with oth spec comp **2**
E13.69	Oth diabetes mellitus with oth spec comp **246**
E13.8	Oth diabetes mellitus with unsp comp **2, 246**
A36.89	Oth diphtheritic comp **308**
O99.119	Oth dis of bld/bld-form org/immun mechnsm comp preg,unsp trmstr **281**
O99.13	Oth dis of the bld/bld-form org/immun mechnsm comp the puerp **276**
O99.11[1,2,3]	Oth diseases of the blood and blood-forming organs and certain d/o involving the immune mechanism comp preg, [1st, 2nd, 3rd] trmstr **278, 280**
S93.33[4,5,6] [A,S]	Oth disloc of [rt, lt, unsp] foot, [init enc, seq] **193**
S93.33[4,5,6]A	Oth disloc of [rt, lt, unsp] foot, init enc **430**
S93.33[4,5,6]D	Oth disloc of [rt, lt, unsp] foot, subsq enc **399**
S83.19[4,5,6] [A,S]	Oth disloc of [rt, lt, unsp] knee, [init enc, seq] **191**
S83.19[4,5,6]A	Oth disloc of [rt, lt, unsp] knee, init enc **428**
S83.19[4,5,6]D	Oth disloc of [rt, lt, unsp] knee, subsq enc **398**
S83.09[4,5,6] [A,S]	Oth disloc of [rt, lt, unsp] patella, [init enc, seq] **191**
S83.09[4,5,6]A	Oth disloc of [rt, lt, unsp] patella, init enc **428**
S83.09[4,5,6]D	Oth disloc of [rt, lt, unsp] patella, subsq enc **398**
S53.09[4,5,6]D	Oth disloc of [rt, lt, unsp] radial head, subsq enc **392**
S53.19[4,5,6] [A,S]	Oth disloc of [rt, lt, unsp] ulnohumeral jt, [init enc, seq] **186**
S53.19[4,5,6]D	Oth disloc of [rt, lt, unsp] ulnohumeral jt, subsq enc **392**
S63.09[4,5,6] [A,S]	Oth disloc of [rt, lt, unsp] wrist and hand, [init enc, seq] **189**
S63.09[4,5,6]D	Oth disloc of [rt, lt] wrist and hand, subsq enc **395**
S53.09[4,5,6] [A,S]	Oth disloc of radial head [unsp, rt, lt] [init enc, seq] **186**
S43.08[4,5,6] [A,S]	Oth disloc of shldr jt [rt, lt, unsp] [init enc, seq] **185**
S42.29[1,2,3] [K,P]	Oth disp fx of [rt, lt, unsp] humerus, subsq enc for fx w/ [nonu, malu] **197**
S62.23[1,2,3] [A,B]	Oth disp fx of base of 1st metacarpal bone of hand [rt, lt, unsp] init enc for fx [clsd, opn] **187**
S62.23[1,2,3] [D,G,S]	Oth disp fx of base of 1st metacarpal bone, [rt, lt, unsp] hand, [subsq enc for fx w/ routine healing, subsq enc for fx w/ delayed healing, seq] **175**
S62.23[1,2,3] [K,P]	Oth disp fx of base of 1st metacarpal bone, [rt, lt, unsp] hand, subsq enc for fx w/ [nonu, malu] **199**
S42.49[1,2,3] [D,G,S]	Oth disp fx of lwr end of [rt, lt, unsp] humerus, [subsq enc for fx w/ routine healing, subsq enc for fx w/ delayed healing, seq] **171**
S42.49[1,2,3]B	Oth disp fx of lwr end of [rt, lt, unsp] humerus, init enc for opn fx **434**
S42.49[1,2,3] [K,P]	Oth disp fx of lwr end of [rt, lt, unsp] humerus, subsq enc for fx w/ [nonu, malu] **197**
S42.49[1,2,3] [A,B]	Oth disp fx of lwr end of humerus [rt, lt, unsp] init enc for fx [clsd, opn] **185**
S42.29[1,2,3] [D,G,S]	Oth disp fx of upr end of [rt, lt, unsp] humerus, [subsq enc for fx w/ routine healing, subsq enc for fx w/ delayed healing, seq] **171**
S42.29[1,2,3] [A,B]	Oth disp fx of upr end of [rt, lt, unsp] humerus, init enc for [clsd, opn] fx **185**
S42.29[1,2,3]B	Oth disp fx of upr end of [rt, lt, unsp] humerus, init enc for opn fx **433**
D89.89	Oth disrd involving the immune mechanism, NEC **294**
K06.8	Oth disrd of gingiva and edentulous alveolar ridge **4**
G99.8	Oth disrd of nervous sys in dz classified elsw **33**
F44.89	Oth dissociative and conversion d/o **311**
P81*	Oth disturbances of temperature regulation of newborn **288**
M54.8*	Oth dorsalgia **165**
D70.2	Oth drug-induced agranulocytosis **293**
G21.1*	Oth drug-induced secondary parkinsonism **32**

G24.8	Oth dystonia 38	
O99.89	Oth dz and conditions compl preg/chldbrth 277, 278	
K38*	Oth dz of appendix 117	
N75.8	Oth dz of Bartholin's gland 270	
K83*	Oth dz of biliary tract 124	
I78.8	Oth dz of capillaries 100	
K82*	Oth dz of gallbladder 124	
K03*	Oth dz of hard tissues of teeth 59	
M27*	Oth dz of jaws 59	
J38.7	Oth dz of larynx 4	
K13*	Oth dz of lip and oral mucosa 59	
K86*	Oth dz of pancreas 124	
I31*	Oth dz of pericardium 103	
J39.2	Oth dz of pharynx 4, 58	
I28*	Oth dz of pulmn vessels 103	
K11.8	Oth dz of salivary glands 4	
D73.8*	Oth dz of spleen 294	
K31.89	Oth dz of stomach and duodenum 116	
E32.8	Oth dz of thymus 294	
K14.8	Oth dz of tongue 4	
J38.3	Oth dz of vocal cords 4	
T79.8XXA	Oth early comp of trauma, init enc 430	
F50.8	Oth eating d/o 311	
B67.99	Oth echinococcosis 309	
T70.8XX[A,S]	Oth effects of air pressure and water pressure, [init enc, seq] 374	
T70.8XXD	Oth effects of air pressure and water pressure, subs enc 410	
T73.8XX[A,S]	Oth effects of deprivation, [init enc, seq] 374	
T73.8XXD	Oth effects of deprivation, subsq enc 410	
T67.8XXD	Oth effects of heat and light, subsq enc 409	
T70.29XD	Oth effects of high altitude, subsq enc 409	
T75.29X[A,S]	Oth effects of vibration, [init enc, seq] 374	
T75.29XD	Oth effects of vibration, subsq enc 410	
O88.82	Oth embolism in childbirth 274	
O88.81[1,2,3]	Oth embolism in preg, [1st, 2nd, 3rd] trmstr 274	
O88.83	Oth embolism in the puerperium 274, 276	
G04.8*	Oth encephalitis, myelitis and encephalomyelitis 11, 15, 41, 439	
E34*	Oth endocrine d/o 247	
N80.8	Oth endometriosis 265, 270	
H44.19	Oth endophthalmitis 45	
M77.8	Oth enthesopathies, NEC 167	
M77.5	Oth enthesopathy of foot 167	
L85*	Oth epidermal thickening 234	
Q81.8	Oth epidermolysis bullosa 289	
S52.55[1,2,9][D,E,F,G,H,J,S]	Oth extraarticular fx of lwr end of [rt, lt, unsp] radius, [subsq enc for clsd fx w/ routine healing, subsq enc for opn fx type I or II w/ routine healing, subsq enc for opn fx type IIIA, IIIB, or IIIC w/ routine healing, subsq enc for clsd fx w/ delayed healing, subsq enc for opn fx type I or II w/ delayed healing, subsq enc for opn fx type I or II w/ delayed healing, seq] 174	
S52.55[1,2,9][A,B,C]	Oth extraarticular fx of lwr end of [rt, lt, unsp] radius, init enc for [clsd fx, opn fx type I or II, opn fx type IIIA, IIIB, or IIIC] 186, 423	
S52.55[1,2,9][B,C]	Oth extraarticular fx of lwr end of [rt, lt, unsp] radius, init enc for opn fx type [I or II, IIIA IIIB or IIIC] 434	
S52.55[1,2,9][K,M,N,P,Q,R]	Oth extraarticular fx of lwr end of [rt, lt, unsp] radius, subsq enc for [clsd fx w/ nonu, opn fx type I or II w/ nonu, opn fx type IIIA, IIIB, or IIIC w/ nonu, clsd fx w/ malu, opn fx type I or II w/ malu, opn fx type IIIA, IIIB, or IIIC w/ malu] 198	
T18.19[0,8]A	Oth FB in esophagus causing [compression of trachea, oth inj], init enc 118	
R19.5	Oth fecal abnormalities 116	
F98.29	Oth feeding d/o of infancy and early childhood 311	
P92.8	Oth feeding problems of newborn 289	
N82.8	Oth female genital tract fistulae 265, 270, 285	
N82.4	Oth female intestinal-genital tract fistulae 117, 285	
N73*	Oth female pelvic inflam dz 264	
N82.1	Oth female urinary-genital tract fistulae 265, 270	
O77*	Oth fetal stress compl labor and delivery 273, 275	
T61.77[1,2,3,4]A	Oth fish poison, [accid (unintentional), intentional self-harm, assault, undetermined], init enc 366	
T61.77[1,2,3,4]S	Oth fish poison, [accid (unintentional), intentional self-harm, assault, undetermined], seq 373	

T61.77[1,2,3,4]D	Oth fish poison, [accid (unintentional), intentional self-harm, assault, undetermined], subsq enc 408	
L73*	Oth follicular d/o 234	
T17.59[0,8]A	Oth foreign object in bronchus causing [asphyxiation, oth inj], init enc 70	
T17.39[0,8]A	Oth foreign object in larynx causing [asphyxiation, oth inj], init enc 58	
T17.390A	Oth foreign object in larynx causing asphyxiation, init 6	
T17.398A	Oth foreign object in larynx causing oth inj, init enc 6	
T17.89[0,8]A	Oth foreign object in oth parts of respiratory tract causing [asphyxiation, oth inj], init enc 70	
T17.29[0,8]A	Oth foreign object in pharynx causing [asphyxiation, oth inj], init enc 58	
T17.290A	Oth foreign object in pharynx causing asphyxiation, init 6	
T17.298A	Oth foreign object in pharynx causing oth inj, init 6	
T17.99[0,8]A	Oth foreign object in respiratory tract, part unsp [in causing asphyxiation, causing oth inj], init enc 70	
T17.49[0,8]A	Oth foreign object in trachea causing [asphyxiation, oth inj], init enc 69	
A42.8*	Oth forms of actinomycosis 308	
I24.8	Oth forms of acute ischemic heart dz 102	
A22.8	Oth forms of anthrax 308	
B44.89	Oth forms of aspergillosis 283, 308	
I25.8*	Oth forms of chr ischemic heart dz 102	
B38.89	Oth forms of coccidioidomycosis 283, 308	
B45.8	Oth forms of cryptococcosis 438	
A26.8	Oth forms of erysipeloid 308	
A27.8*	Oth forms of leptospirosis 10, 14, 41	
A32.8*	Oth forms of listeriosis 308	
A43.8	Oth forms of nocardiosis 308	
A20.8	Oth forms of plague 308	
M41.8*	Oth forms of scoliosis 125	
K12.1	Oth forms of stomatitis 4	
S62.39[0,1,2,3,4,5,6,7,8,9][A,B]	Oth fx of [2nd, 3rd, 4th, 5th, oth, unsp] metacarpal bone, (rt, lt) hand, init enc for [clsd, opn] fx 425	
S62.39[8,9][D,G,S]	Oth fx of [oth, unsp] metacarpal bone, [subsq enc for fx w/ routine healing, subsq enc for fx w/ delayed healing, seq] 176	
S62.39[8,9][K,P]	Oth fx of [oth, unsp] metacarpal bone, subsq enc for fx w/ [nonu, malu] 200	
S62.39[8,9][A,B]	Oth fx of [oth,unsp] metacarpal bone, init enc for [clsd, opn] fx 188	
S72.8X[1,2,9][D,E,F,G,H,J,S]	Oth fx of [rt, lt, unsp] femur, [subsq enc for clsd fx w/ routine healing, subsq enc for opn fx type I or II w/ routine healing, subsq enc for opn fx type IIIA, IIIB, or IIIC w/ routine healing, subsq enc for clsd fx w/ delayed healing, subsq enc for opn fx type I or II w/ delayed healing, subsq enc for opn fx type I or II w/ delayed healing, seq] 179	
S72.8X[1,2,9][A,B,C]	Oth fx of [rt, lt, unsp] femur, init enc for [clsd fx, opn fx type I or II, opn fx type IIIA, IIIB, or IIIC] 161, 286, 426, 436	
S72.8X[1,2,9][K,M,N,P,Q,R]	Oth fx of [rt, lt, unsp] femur, subsq enc for [clsd fx w/ nonu, opn fx type I or II w/ nonu, opn fx type IIIA, IIIB, or IIIC w/ nonu, clsd fx w/ malu, opn fx type I or II w/ malu, opn fx type IIIA, IIIB, or IIIC w/ malu] 202	
S92.49[1,2,9][D,G,S]	Oth fx of [rt, lt, unsp] great toe, [subsq enc for fx w/ routine healing, subsq enc for fx w/ delayed healing, seq] 183	
S92.49[1,2,9][A,B]	Oth fx of [rt, lt, unsp] great toe, init enc for [clsd, opn] fx 192, 429	
S92.49[1,2,9][K,P]	Oth fx of [rt, lt, unsp] great toe, subsq enc for fx w/ [nonu, malu] 204	
S32.39[1,2,9]S	Oth fx of [rt, lt, unsp] ilium, seq 166	
S32.39[1,2,9][D,G]	Oth fx of [rt, lt, unsp] ilium, subsq enc for fx w/ [routine, delayed] healing 170	
S32.39[1,2,9]K	Oth fx of [rt, lt, unsp] ilium, subsq enc for fx w/ nonu 196	
S92.59[1,2,9][D,G,S]	Oth fx of [rt, lt, unsp] lesser toe(s), [subsq enc for fx w/ routine healing, subsq enc for fx w/ delayed healing, seq] 183	
S92.59[1,2,9][A,B]	Oth fx of [rt, lt, unsp] lesser toe(s), init enc for [clsd, opn] fx 193, 430	
S92.59[1,2,9][K,P]	Oth fx of [rt, lt, unsp] lesser toe(s), subsq enc for fx w/ [nonu, malu] 204	
S82.89[1,2,9][A,B,C]	Oth fx of [rt, lt, unsp] lwr leg, [init enc for clsd fx, init enc for opn fx type I or II, init enc for opn fx type I or II] 191, 428	

S82.89[1,2,9] [D,E,F,G,H,J,S]	Oth fx of [rt, lt, unsp] lwr leg, [subsq enc for clsd fx w/ routine healing, subsq enc for opn fx type I or II w/ routine healing, subsq enc for opn fx type IIIA, IIIB, or IIIC w/ routine healing, subsq enc for clsd fx w/ delayed healing, subsq enc for opn fx type I or II w/ delayed healing, subsq enc for opn fx type IIIA, IIIB, or IIIC w/ delayed healing, seq] **182**
S82.89[1,2,9] [K,M,N,P,Q,R]	Oth fx of [rt, lt, unsp] lwr leg, subsq enc for [clsd fx w/ nonu, opn fx type I or II w/ nonu, opn fx type IIIA, IIIB, or IIIC w/ nonu, clsd fx w/ malu, opn fx type I or II w/ malu, opn fx type I or II w/ malu] **203**
S82.09[1,2,9] [D,E,F,G,H,J,S]	Oth fx of [rt, lt, unsp] patella, [subsq enc for clsd fx w/ routine healing, subsq enc for opn fx type I or II w/ routine healing, subsq enc for opn fx type IIIA, IIIB, or IIIC w/ routine healing, subsq enc for clsd fx w/ delayed healing, subsq enc for opn fx type I or II w/ delayed healing, seq] **179**
S82.09[1,2,9] [A,B,C]	Oth fx of [rt, lt, unsp] patella, init enc for [clsd fx, opn fx type I or II, opn fx type IIIA, IIIB, or IIIC] **190, 427**
S82.09[1,2,9] [K,M,N,P,Q,R]	Oth fx of [rt, lt, unsp] patella, subsq enc for [clsd fx w/ nonu, opn fx type I or II w/ nonu, opn fx type IIIA, IIIB, or IIIC w/ nonu, clsd fx w/ malu, opn fx type I or II w/ malu, opn fx type I or II w/ malu] **202**
S92.19[1,2,9] [D,G,S]	Oth fx of [rt, lt, unsp] talus, [subsq enc for fx w/ routine healing, subsq enc for fx w/ delayed healing, seq] **182**
S92.19[1,2,9] [A,B]	Oth fx of [rt, lt, unsp] talus, init enc for [clsd, opn] fx **192, 429**
S92.19[1,2,9] [K,P]	Oth fx of [rt, lt, unsp] talus, subsq enc for fx w/ [nonu, malu] **204**
S52.9[0,1,2] X[A,B,C]	Oth fx of [unsp, rt, lt] forearm, init enc for [clsd fx, opn fx type I or II, opn fx type IIIA, IIIB, IIIC] **186, 424**
S52.9[0,1,2] X[B,C]	Oth fx of [unsp, rt, lt] forearm, init enc for opn fx type [I or II, IIIA IIIB IIIC] **435**
S12.09[0,1] [A,B,S]	Oth fx of 1st cervical vertebra [disp, nondisp] init enc for fx [clsd, opn, seq] **165**
S62.29[1,2,9] [D,G,S]	Oth fx of 1st metacarpal bone, [rt, lt, unsp] hand, [subsq enc for fx w/ routine healing, subsq enc for fx w/ delayed healing, seq] **175**
S62.29[1,2,9] [A,B]	Oth fx of 1st metacarpal bone, [rt, lt, unsp] hand, init enc for [clsd, opn] fx **187, 424**
S62.29[1,2,9] [K,P]	Oth fx of 1st metacarpal bone, [rt, lt, unsp] hand, subsq enc for fx w/ [nonu, malu] **199**
S12.19[0,1] [A,B,S]	Oth fx of 2nd cervical vertebra [disp, nondisp] init enc for fx [clsd, opn, seq] **165**
S62.39[0,1][A,B]	Oth fx of 2nd metacarpal bone, [rt, lt, unsp] hand, init enc for [clsd, opn] fx **188**
S62.39[0,1] [D,G,S]	Oth fx of 2nd metacarpal bone, [rt, lt] hand, [subsq enc for fx w/ routine healing, subsq enc for fx w/ delayed healing, seq] **176**
S62.39[0,1][K,P]	Oth fx of 2nd metacarpal bone, [rt, lt] hand, subsq enc for fx w/ [nonu, malu] **200**
S12.29[0,1] [A,B,S]	Oth fx of 3rd cervical vertebra [disp, nondisp] init enc for fx [clsd, opn, seq] **165**
S62.39[2,3][A,B]	Oth fx of 3rd metacarpal bone, [rt, lt, unsp] hand, init enc for [clsd, opn] fx **188**
S62.39[2,3] [D,G,S]	Oth fx of 3rd metacarpal bone, [rt, lt] hand, [subsq enc for fx w/ routine healing, subsq enc for fx w/ delayed healing, seq] **176**
S62.39[2,3][K,P]	Oth fx of 3rd metacarpal bone, [rt, lt] hand, subsq enc for fx w/ [nonu, malu] **200**
S12.39[0,1] [A,B,S]	Oth fx of 4th cervical vertebra [disp, nondisp] init enc for fx [clsd, opn, seq] **165**
S62.39[4,5][A,B]	Oth fx of 4th metacarpal bone, [rt, lt, unsp] hand, init enc for [clsd, opn] fx **188**
S62.39[4,5][K,P]	Oth fx of 4th metacarpal bone, [rt, lt] hand, subsq enc for fx w/ [nonu, malu] **200**
S12.49[0,1] [A,B,S]	Oth fx of 5th cervical vertebra [disp, nondisp] init enc for fx [clsd, opn, seq] **165**
S62.39[6,7][A,B]	Oth fx of 5th metacarpal bone, [rt, lt, unsp] hand, init enc for [clsd, opn] fx **188**
S62.39[6,7][K,P]	Oth fx of 5th metacarpal bone, [rt, lt] hand, subsq enc for fx w/ [nonu, malu] **200**
S02.19X[A,B]	Oth fx of base of skull, init enc for [clsd, opn] fx **36, 37, 417**
S02.19XS	Oth fx of base of skull, seq **39**
S02.19XK	Oth fx of base of skull, subs for fx w nonu **195**
S02.19X[D,G]	Oth fx of base of skull, subsq enc for fx w/ [routine, delayed] healing **169**

S72.09[1,2,9] [D,E,F,G,H,J,S]	Oth fx of head and neck of [rt, lt, unsp] femur, [subsq enc for clsd fx w/ routine healing, subsq enc for opn fx type I or II w/ routine healing, subsq enc for opn fx type IIIA, IIIB, or IIIC w/ routine healing, subsq enc for clsd fx w/ delayed healing, subsq enc for opn fx type I or II w/ delayed healing, subsq enc for opn fx type IIIA, IIIB, or IIIC w/ delayed healing, seq] **177**
S72.09[1,2,9] [A,B,C]	Oth fx of head and neck of [rt, lt, unsp] femur, init enc for [clsd fx, opn fx type I or II, opn fx type IIIA, IIIB, or IIIC] **162, 286, 426, 435**
S72.09[1,2,9] [K,M,N,P,Q,R]	Oth fx of head and neck of [rt, lt, unsp] femur, subsq enc for [clsd fx w/ nonu, opn fx type I or II w/ nonu, opn fx type IIIA, IIIB, or IIIC w/ nonu, clsd fx w/ malu, opn fx type I or II w/ malu, opn fx type IIIA, IIIB, or IIIC w/ malu] **201**
S32.39[1,2,9] [A,B]	Oth fx of ilium [rt, lt, unsp] init enc for [clsd, opn] fx **162, 421, 433**
S32.492A	Oth fx of lt acetabulum, init for clos fx **421, 433**
S32.492B	Oth fx of lt acetabulum, init for opn fx **421, 433**
S72.49[1,2,9] [D,E,F,G,H,J,S]	Oth fx of lwr end of [rt, lt, unsp] femur, [subsq enc for clsd fx w/ routine healing, subsq enc for opn fx type I or II w/ routine healing, subsq enc for clsd fx w/ delayed healing, subsq enc for opn fx type IIIA, IIIB, or IIIC w/ routine healing, subsq enc for opn fx type I or II w/ delayed healing, seq] **179**
S72.49[1,2,9] [A,B,C]	Oth fx of lwr end of [rt, lt, unsp] femur, init enc for [clsd fx, opn fx type I or II, opn fx type IIIA, IIIB, or IIIC] **161, 426, 436**
S72.49[1,2,9] [K,M,N,P,Q,R]	Oth fx of lwr end of [rt, lt, unsp] femur, subsq enc for [clsd fx w/ nonu, opn fx type I or II w/ nonu, opn fx type IIIA, IIIB, or IIIC w/ nonu, clsd fx w/ malu, opn fx type I or II w/ malu, opn fx type IIIA, IIIB, or IIIC w/ malu] **202**
S82.39[1,2,9] [A,B,C]	Oth fx of lwr end of [rt, lt, unsp] tibia, [init enc for clsd fx, init enc for opn fx type I or II, init enc for opn fx type IIIA, IIIB, or IIIC] **191, 427**
S82.39[1,2,9] [K,M,N,P,Q,R]	Oth fx of lwr end of [rt, lt, unsp] tibia, subsq enc for [clsd fx w/ nonu, opn fx type I or II w/ nonu, opn fx type IIIA, IIIB, or IIIC w/ nonu, clsd fx w/ malu, opn fx type I or II w/ malu, opn fx type I or II w/ malu] **203**
S52.69[1,2,9] [D,E,F,G,H,J,S]	Oth fx of lwr end of [rt, lt, unsp] ulna, [subsq enc for clsd fx w/ routine healing, subsq enc for opn fx type I or II w/ routine healing, subsq enc for opn fx type IIIA, IIIB, or IIIC w/ routine healing, subsq enc for clsd fx w/ delayed healing, subsq enc for opn fx type I or II w/ delayed healing, seq] **174**
S52.69[1,2,9] [A,B,C]	Oth fx of lwr end of [rt, lt, unsp] ulna, init enc for [clsd fx, opn fx type I or II, opn fx type IIIA, IIIB, or IIIC] **186, 424**
S52.69[1,2,9] [B,C]	Oth fx of lwr end of [rt, lt, unsp] ulna, init enc for opn fx type [I or II, IIIA IIIB or IIIC] **435**
S52.69[1,2,9] [K,M,N,P,Q,R]	Oth fx of lwr end of [rt, lt, unsp] ulna, subsq enc for [clsd fx w/ nonu, opn fx type I or II w/ nonu, opn fx type IIIA, IIIB, or IIIC w/ nonu, clsd fx w/ malu, opn fx type I or II w/ malu, opn fx type IIIA, IIIB, or IIIC w/ malu] **199**
S82.39[1,2,9] [D,E,F,G,H,J,S]	Oth fx of lwr end of[rt, lt, unsp] tibia, [subsq enc for clsd fx w/ routine healing, subsq enc for opn fx type I or II w/ routine healing, subsq enc for opn fx type IIIA, IIIB, or IIIC w/ routine healing, subsq enc for clsd fx w/ delayed healing, subsq enc for opn fx type I or II w/ delayed healing, seq] **180**
S62.39[4,5] [D,G,S]	Oth fx of of 4th metacarpal bone, [rt, lt] hand, [subsq enc for fx w/ routine healing, subsq enc for fx w/ delayed healing, seq] **176**
S62.39[6,7] [D,G,S]	Oth fx of of 5th metacarpal bone, [rt, lt] hand, [subsq enc for fx w/ routine healing, subsq enc for fx w/ delayed healing, seq] **176**
S32.491A	Oth fx of rt acetabulum, init for clos fx **421, 433**
S32.491B	Oth fx of rt acetabulum, init for opn fx **421, 433**
S72.39[1,2,9] [D,E,F,G,H,J,S]	Oth fx of shaft of [rt, lt, unsp] femur, [subsq enc for clsd fx w/ routine healing, subsq enc for opn fx type I or II w/ routine healing, subsq enc for opn fx type IIIA, IIIB, or IIIC w/ routine healing, subsq enc for clsd fx w/ delayed healing, subsq enc for opn fx type I or II w/ delayed healing, subsq enc for opn fx type IIIA, IIIB, or IIIC w/ delayed healing, seq] **178**
S72.39[1,2,9] [A,B,C]	Oth fx of shaft of [rt, lt, unsp] femur, init enc for [clsd fx, opn fx type I or II, opn fx type IIIA, IIIB, or IIIC] **161, 286, 435, 426**
S72.39[1,2,9] [K,M,N,P,Q,R]	Oth fx of shaft of [rt, lt, unsp] femur, subsq enc for [clsd fx w/ nonu, opn fx type I or II w/ nonu, opn fx type IIIA, IIIB, or IIIC w/ nonu, clsd fx w/ malu, opn fx type I or II w/ malu, opn fx type IIIA, IIIB, or IIIC w/ malu] **201**
S82.49[1,2,9] [A,B,C]	Oth fx of shaft of [rt, lt, unsp] fibula, [init enc for clsd fx, init enc for opn fx type I or II, init enc for opn fx type IIIA, IIIB, or IIIC] **191, 427**

Code	Description
S82.49[1,2,9] [D,E,F,G,H,J,S]	Oth fx of shaft of [rt, lt, unsp] fibula, [subsq enc for clsd fx w/ routine healing, subsq enc for opn fx type I or II w/ routine healing, subsq enc for opn fx type IIIA, IIIB, or IIIC w/ routine healing, subsq enc for clsd fx w/ delayed healing, subsq enc for opn fx type I or II w/ delayed healing, subsq enc for opn fx type IIIA, IIIB, or IIIC w/ delayed healing, seq] **181**
S82.49[1,2,9] [B,C]	Oth fx of shaft of [rt, lt, unsp] fibula, init enc for opn fx type [I or II, IIIA IIIB or IIIC] **436**
S82.49[1,2,9] [K,M,N,P,Q,R]	Oth fx of shaft of [rt, lt, unsp] fibula, subsq enc for [clsd fx w/ nonu, opn fx type I or II w/ nonu, opn fx type IIIA, IIIB, or IIIC w/ nonu, clsd fx w/ malu, opn fx type I or II w/ malu, opn fx type I or II w/ malu] **203**
S42.39[1,2,9] [D,G,S]	Oth fx of shaft of [rt, lt, unsp] humerus, [subsq enc for fx w/ routine healing, subsq enc for fx w/ delayed healing, seq] **171**
S42.39[1,2,9] [A,B]	Oth fx of shaft of [rt, lt, unsp] humerus, init enc for [clsd, opn] fx **185, 422**
S42.39[1,2,9]B	Oth fx of shaft of [rt, lt, unsp] humerus, init enc for opn fx **433**
S42.39[1,2,9] [K,P]	Oth fx of shaft of [rt, lt, unsp] humerus, subsq enc for fx w/ [nonu, malu] **197**
S52.39[1,2,9] [D,E,F,G,H,J,S]	Oth fx of shaft of [rt, lt, unsp] radius, [subsq enc for clsd fx w/ routine healing, subsq enc for opn fx type I or II w/ routine healing, subsq enc for opn fx type I or II w/ routine healing, subsq enc for clsd fx w/ delayed healing, subsq enc for opn fx type I or II w/ delayed healing, subsq enc for opn fx type IIIA, IIIB, or IIIC w/ delayed healing, seq] **173**
S82.29[1,2,9] [A,B,C]	Oth fx of shaft of [rt, lt, unsp] tibia, [init enc for clsd fx, init enc for opn fx type I or II, init enc for opn fx type IIIA, IIIB, or IIIC] **191, 427**
S82.29[1,2,9] [D,E,F,G,H,J,S]	Oth fx of shaft of [rt, lt, unsp] tibia, [subsq enc for clsd fx w/ routine healing, subsq enc for opn fx type I or II w/ routine healing, subsq enc for opn fx type IIIA, IIIB, or IIIC w/ routine healing, subsq enc for clsd fx w/ delayed healing, subsq enc for opn fx type I or II w/ delayed healing, subsq enc for opn fx type IIIA, IIIB, or IIIC w/ delayed healing, seq] **180**
S82.29[1,2,9] [B,C]	Oth fx of shaft of [rt, lt, unsp] tibia, init enc for opn fx type [I or II, IIIA IIIB or IIIC] **436**
S82.29[1,2,9] [K,M,N,P,Q,R]	Oth fx of shaft of [rt, lt, unsp] tibia, subsq enc for [clsd fx w/ nonu, opn fx type I or II w/ nonu, opn fx type IIIA, IIIB, or IIIC w/ nonu, clsd fx w/ malu, opn fx type I or II w/ malu, opn fx type I or II w/ malu] **203**
S52.29[1,2,9] [D,E,F,G,H,J,S]	Oth fx of shaft of [rt, lt, unsp] ulna, [subsq enc for clsd fx w/ routine healing, subsq enc for opn fx type I or II w/ routine healing, subsq enc for opn fx type I or II w/ routine healing, subsq enc for clsd fx w/ delayed healing, subsq enc for opn fx type I or II w/ delayed healing, subsq enc for opn fx type IIIA, IIIB, or IIIC w/ delayed healing, seq] **173**
S52.29[1,2,9] [A,B,C]	Oth fx of shaft of [rt, lt, unsp] ulna, init enc for [clsd fx, opn fx type I or II, opn fx type IIIA, IIIB, or IIIC] **186, 423**
S52.29[1,2,9] [B,C]	Oth fx of shaft of [rt, lt, unsp] ulna, init enc for opn fx type [I or II, IIIA IIIB or IIIC] **434**
S52.29[1,2,9] [K,M,N,P,Q,R]	Oth fx of shaft of [rt, lt, unsp] ulna, subsq enc for [clsd fx w/ nonu, opn fx type I or II w/ nonu, opn fx type IIIA, IIIB, or IIIC w/ nonu, clsd fx w/ malu, opn fx type I or II w/ malu, opn fx type IIIA, IIIB, or IIIC w/ malu] **198**
S52.39[1,2,9] [A,B,C]	Oth fx of shaft of radius [rt, lt, unsp] arm, init enc for [clsd fx, opn fx type I or II, opn fx type IIIA, IIIB, or IIIC] **186, 423**
S52.39[1,2,9] [B,C]	Oth fx of shaft of radius [rt, lt, unsp] arm, init enc for opn fx type [I or II, IIIA IIIB or IIIC] **434**
S52.39[1,2,9] [K,M,N,P,Q,R]	Oth fx of shaft of radius, [rt, lt, unsp] arm, subsq enc for [clsd fx w/ nonu, opn fx type I or II w/ nonu, opn fx type IIIA, IIIB, or IIIC w/ nonu, clsd fx w/ malu, opn fx type I or II w/ malu, opn fx type IIIA, IIIB, or IIIC w/ malu] **198**
S32.499A	Oth fx of unsp acetabulum, init for clos fx **421, 433**
S32.499B	Oth fx of unsp acetabulum, init for opn fx **421, 433**
S82.83[1,2,9] [A,B,C]	Oth fx of upr and lwr end of [rt, lt, unsp] fibula, [init enc for clsd fx, init enc for opn fx type I or II, init enc for opn fx type IIIA, IIIB, or IIIC] **191, 427**
S82.83[1,2,9] [D,E,F,G,H,J,S]	Oth fx of upr and lwr end of [rt, lt, unsp] fibula, [subsq enc for clsd fx w/ routine healing, subsq enc for opn fx type I or II w/ routine healing, subsq enc for opn fx type IIIA, IIIB, or IIIC w/ routine healing, subsq enc for clsd fx w/ delayed healing, subsq enc for opn fx type I or II w/ delayed healing, subsq enc for opn fx type IIIA, IIIB, or IIIC w/ delayed healing, seq] **181**
S82.83[1,2,9] [B,C]	Oth fx of upr and lwr end of [rt, lt, unsp] fibula, init enc for opn fx type [I or II, IIIA IIIB or IIIC] **436**
S82.83[1,2,9] [K,M,N,P,Q,R]	Oth fx of upr and lwr end of [rt, lt, unsp] fibula, subsq enc for [clsd fx w/ nonu, opn fx type I or II w/ nonu, opn fx type IIIA, IIIB, or IIIC w/ nonu, clsd fx w/ malu, opn fx type I or II w/ malu, opn fx type I or II w/ malu] **203**
S52.18[1,2,9] [D,E,F,G,H,J,S]	Oth fx of upr end of [rt, lt, unsp] radius, [subsq enc for clsd fx w/ routine healing, subsq enc for opn fx type I or II w/ routine healing, subsq enc for opn fx type IIIA, IIIB, or IIIC w/ routine healing, subsq enc for clsd fx w/ delayed healing, subsq enc for opn fx type I or II w/ delayed healing, subsq enc for opn fx type IIIA, IIIB, or IIIC w/ delayed healing, seq] **172**
S52.18[1,2,9] [A,B,C]	Oth fx of upr end of [rt, lt, unsp] radius, init enc for [clsd fx, opn fx type I or II, opn fx type IIIA, IIIB, or IIIC] **186, 423**
S52.18[1,2,9] [B,C]	Oth fx of upr end of [rt, lt, unsp] radius, init enc for opn fx type [I or II, IIIA IIIB or IIIC] **434**
S52.18[1,2,9] [K,M,N,P,Q,R]	Oth fx of upr end of [rt, lt, unsp] radius, subsq enc for [clsd fx w/ nonu, opn fx type I or II w/ nonu, opn fx type IIIA, IIIB, or IIIC w/ nonu, clsd fx w/ malu, opn fx type I or II w/ malu, opn fx type IIIA, IIIB, or IIIC w/ malu] **197**
S82.19[1,2,9] [D,E,F,G,H,J,S]	Oth fx of upr end of [rt, lt, unsp] tibia, [subsq enc for clsd fx w/ routine healing, subsq enc for opn fx type I or II w/ routine healing, subsq enc for opn fx type IIIA, IIIB, or IIIC w/ routine healing, subsq enc for clsd fx w/ delayed healing, subsq enc for opn fx type I or II w/ delayed healing, subsq enc for opn fx type I or II w/ delayed healing, seq] **180**
S82.19[1,2,9] [A,B,C]	Oth fx of upr end of [rt, lt, unsp] tibia, init enc for [clsd fx, opn fx type I or II, opn fx type IIIA, IIIB, or IIIC] **191, 427**
S82.19[1,2,9] [B,C]	Oth fx of upr end of [rt, lt, unsp] tibia, init enc for opn fx type [I or II, IIIA IIIB or IIIC] **436**
S82.19[1,2,9] [K,M,N,P,Q,R]	Oth fx of upr end of [rt, lt, unsp] tibia, subsq enc for [clsd fx w/ nonu, opn fx type I or II w/ nonu, opn fx type IIIA, IIIB, or IIIC w/ nonu, clsd fx w/ malu, opn fx type I or II w/ malu, opn fx type I or II w/ malu] **202**
S52.09[1,2,9] [D,E,F,G,H,J,S]	Oth fx of upr end of [rt, lt, unsp] ulna, [subsq enc for clsd fx w/ routine healing, subsq enc for opn fx type I or II w/ routine healing, subsq enc for opn fx type IIIA, IIIB, or IIIC w/ routine healing, subsq enc for clsd fx w/ delayed healing, subsq enc for opn fx type I or II w/ delayed healing, subsq enc for opn fx type IIIA, IIIB, or IIIC w/ delayed healing, seq] **172**
S52.09[1,2,9] [A,B,C]	Oth fx of upr end of [rt, lt, unsp] ulna, init enc for [clsd fx, opn fx type I or II, opn fx type I or II, opn fx type IIIA, IIIB, or IIIC] **186, 423**
S52.09[1,2,9] [B,C]	Oth fx of upr end of [rt, lt, unsp] ulna, init enc for opn fx type [I or II, IIIA IIIB or IIIC] **434**
S52.09[1,2,9] [K,M,N,P,Q,R]	Oth fx of upr end of [rt, lt, unsp] ulna, subsq enc for [clsd fx w/ nonu, opn fx type I or II w/ nonu, opn fx type IIIA, IIIB, or IIIC w/ nonu, clsd fx w/ malu, opn fx type I or II w/ malu, opn fx type IIIA, IIIB, or IIIC w/ malu] **197**
S52.59[1,2,9] [D,E,F,G,H,J,S]	Oth fxs of lwr end of [rt, lt, unsp] radius, [subsq enc for clsd fx w/ routine healing, subsq enc for opn fx type I or II w/ routine healing, subsq enc for opn fx type IIIA, IIIB, or IIIC w/ routine healing, subsq enc for clsd fx w/ delayed healing, subsq enc for opn fx type I or II w/ delayed healing, subsq enc for opn fx type I or II w/ delayed healing, seq] **174**
S52.59[1,2,9] [A,B,C]	Oth fxs of lwr end of [rt, lt, unsp] radius, init enc for [clsd fx, opn fx type I or II, opn fx type IIIA, IIIB, or IIIC] **186, 424**
S52.59[1,2,9] [B,C]	Oth fxs of lwr end of [rt, lt, unsp] radius, init enc for opn fx type [I or II, IIIA IIIB or IIIC] **434**
S52.59[1,2,9] [K,M,N,P,Q,R]	Oth fxs of lwr end of [rt, lt, unsp] radius, subsq enc for [clsd fx w/ nonu, opn fx type I or II w/ nonu, opn fx type IIIA, IIIB, or IIIC w/ nonu, clsd fx w/ malu, opn fx type I or II w/ malu, opn fx type IIIA, IIIB, or IIIC w/ malu] **198**
K29.61	Oth gastritis with bleeding **115**
R68.89	Oth general symptoms and signs **385**
A52.76	Oth genitourinary symptomatic late syphilis **308**
M31.6	Oth giant cell arteritis **164**
H40.8*	Oth glaucoma **46**
A54.89	Oth gonococcal infections **308**
L92.8	Oth granulomatous d/o of the skin, SQ **224**
R44.2	Oth hallucinations **310**
M20.4[0,1,2]	Oth hammer toe(s) (acquired), [unsp, rt, lt] foot **193**
G44*	Oth headache syndromes **41**
I52	Oth heart d/o in dz classified elsw **102**
P08.1	Oth heavy for gestational age newborn **288**
P55.8	Oth hemolytic dz of newborn **282**
D68.318	Oth hemorrhagic d/o d/t intrns circ anticoag,antib,inhib **294**
G60.8	Oth hereditary and idiopathic neuropathies **34**
D58*	Oth hereditary hemolytic anemias **293**
B00.89	Oth herpesviral infxn **283, 307, 438**
D76.3	Oth histiocytosis syndromes **294**
B10.0*	Oth human herpesvirus encephalitis **11, 15, 41, 283, 438**
B10.8*	Oth human herpesvirus infxn **233**

N43.2	Oth hydrocele 261
E67*	Oth hyperalimentation 246
E78.4	Oth hyperlipidemia 247
M89.4*	Oth hypertrophic osteoarthropathy 167
E16.1	Oth hypoglycemia 247
E20.8	Oth hypoparathyroidism 247
I95.89	Oth hypotension 103
P80.8	Oth hypothermia of newborn 288
M41.2*	Oth idiopathic scoliosis 125
I51.89	Oth ill-defined heart dz 102
O72.1	Oth immediate postpartum hemor 273, 274
D80.8	Oth immunodeficiencies with predominantly antibody defects 293
K56.4*	Oth impaction of intestine 284
F63.8*	Oth impulse d/o 310
S24.15[1,2,3,4,9][A,S]	Oth incomplete inj at [T1, T2-T6, T7-T10, T11-T12, unsp] lvl of thoracic spinal cord, [init enc, seq] 32
S14.15[1,2,3,4,5,6,7,8,9][A,S]	Oth incomplete lesion at [C1, C2, C3, C4, C5, C6, C7, C8, unsp] lvl of cervical spinal cord, [init enc, seq] 32
S14.15[1,2,3,4,5,6,7,8,9]A	Oth incomplete lesion at [C1, C2, C3, C4, C5, C6, C7, C8, unsp] lvl of cervical spinal cord, init enc 420, 433
S14.15[1,2,3,4,5,6,7,8,9]D	Oth incomplete lesion at [C1, C2, C3, C4, C5, C6, C7, C8, unsp] lvl of cervical spinal cord, subsq enc 388
S24.15[1,2,3,4,9]A	Oth incomplete lesion at [T1, T2-6, T7-T10, T11-T12, unsp] lvl of thoracic spinal cord, init enc 420, 433
S24.15[1,2,3,4,9]D	Oth incomplete lesion at [T1, T2-T6, T7-T10, T11-T12, unsp] lvl of thoracic spinal cord, subsq enc 389
O98.32	Oth infections w sexl mode of transmiss comp childbirth 274
O98.33	Oth infections w sexl mode of transmiss comp the puerperium 274, 276
B99.8	Oth infectious dz 438
M46.5*	Oth infective spondylopathies 164
B88*	Oth infestations 233
L98.[6,8,9]	Oth infiltrative, Oth spec, Unsp] d/o of the skin and SQ tissue 234
N48.2*	Oth inflam d/o of penis 261
N47.7	Oth inflam dz of prepuce 289
K75*	Oth inflam liver dz 124
H01*	Oth inflam of eyelid 45
N76*	Oth inflam of vagina and vulva 265
G61.8*	Oth inflam polyneuropathies 34
O99.83[0,4,5]	Oth infxn carrier state compl [preg, childbirth, the puerperium] 274
O99.830	Oth infxn carrier state compl preg 277
O99.835	Oth infxn carrier state compl the puerperium 276
O75.3	Oth infxn during labor 274, 278, 280
O98.31[1,2,3]	Oth infxns w/ a predominantly sexual mode of transmission compl preg, [1st, 2nd, 3rd] trmstr 274, 277
S36.59[0,1,2,3,8,9]A	Oth inj of [ascending [rt] colon, transv colon, descending [lt] colon, sigmoid colon, oth part of colon,unsp part of colon], init enc 432
S36.59[0,1,2,3,8,9]D	Oth inj of [ascending [rt] colon, transv colon, descending [lt] colon, sigmoid colon, oth part of colon,unsp part of colon], subsq enc 391
S36.49[0,8,9]D	Oth inj of [duodenum, oth part of sm intestine, unsp part of sm intestine], subsq enc 391
S36.29[0,1,2,9]A	Oth inj of [head, body, tail, unsp part] of pancreas, init enc 124, 432
S36.29[0,1,2,9]S	Oth inj of [head, body, tail, unsp part] of pancreas, seq 117
S36.29[0,1,2,9]D	Oth inj of [head, body, tail, unsp part] of pancreas, subsq enc 390
S37.09[1,2,9]A	Oth inj of [rt, lt, unsp] kidney, init enc 256
S37.09[1,2,9]S	Oth inj of [rt, lt, unsp] kidney, seq 118
S37.09[1,2,9]D	Oth inj of [rt, lt, unsp] kidney, subsq enc 391
S36.590[A,S]	Oth inj of ascending [rt] colon, [init enc, seq] 118
S27.49[1,2,9]A	Oth inj of bronchus, [unilat, bilat, unsp], init enc 67
S27.49[1,2,9]S	Oth inj of bronchus, [unilat, bilat, unsp], seq 69
S36.592[A,S]	Oth inj of descending [lt] colon, [init enc, seq] 118
S36.490[A,S]	Oth inj of duodenum, [init enc, seq] 118
S56.49[1,2]D	Oth inj of extensor muscle, fascia and tndn of [rt, lt] index finger at forearm lvl, subsq enc 393
S56.49[7,8]D	Oth inj of extensor muscle, fascia and tndn of [rt, lt] little finger at forearm lvl, subsq enc 393
S56.49[3,4]D	Oth inj of extensor muscle, fascia and tndn of [rt, lt] mid finger at forearm lvl, subsq enc 393
S56.49[5,6]D	Oth inj of extensor muscle, fascia and tndn of [rt, lt] ring finger at forearm lvl, subsq enc 393

S56.39[1,2,9]D	Oth inj of extensor or abductor muscles, fascia and tndns of [rt, lt, unsp] thumb at forearm lvl, subsq enc 393
S37.59[1,2,9]D	Oth inj of fallopian tube, [unilat, bilat, unsp] subsq enc 391
S37.59[1,2,9]A	Oth inj of fallopian tube, [unilat, bilat, unsp], init enc 265, 270
S37.59[1,2,9]S	Oth inj of fallopian tube, [unilat, bilat, unsp], seq 265, 270
S66.19[8,9]D	Oth inj of flexor muscle, fascia and tndn of [oth, unsp] finger at wrist and hand lvl, subsq enc 397
S56.09[1,2,9]D	Oth inj of flexor muscle, fascia and tndn of [rt, lt, unsp] thumb at forearm lvl, subsq enc 393
S56.19[1,2]D	Oth inj of flexor muscle, fascia and tndn of [rt, lt] index finger at forearm lvl, subsq enc 393
S66.19[0,1]D	Oth inj of flexor muscle, fascia and tndn of [rt, lt] index finger at wrist and hand lvl, subsq enc 397
S56.19[7,8]D	Oth inj of flexor muscle, fascia and tndn of [rt, lt] little finger at forearm lvl, subsq enc 393
S66.19[6,7]D	Oth inj of flexor muscle, fascia and tndn of [rt, lt] little finger at wrist and hand lvl, subsq enc 397
S56.19[3,4]D	Oth inj of flexor muscle, fascia and tndn of [rt, lt] mid finger at forearm lvl, subsq enc 393
S66.19[2,3]D	Oth inj of flexor muscle, fascia and tndn of [rt, lt] mid finger at wrist and hand lvl, subsq enc 397
S56.19[5,6]D	Oth inj of flexor muscle, fascia and tndn of [rt, lt] ring finger at forearm lvl, subsq enc 393
S66.19[4,5]D	Oth inj of flexor muscle, fascia and tndn of [rt, lt] ring finger at wrist and hand lvl, subsq enc 397
S36.128A	Oth inj of gallbladder, init enc 124
S26.09XA	Oth inj of heart with hemopericardium, init enc 103, 420, 432
S26.09XS	Oth inj of heart with hemopericardium, seq 69
S26.09XD	Oth inj of heart with hemopericardium, subs enc 389
S29.09[1,2,9]D	Oth inj of muscle and tndn of [front, back, unsp] wall of thorax, subsq enc 389
S09.19XA	Oth inj of muscle and tndn of head, init enc 5
S39.09[1,2,3]D	Oth inj of muscle, fascia and tndn of [abd, lwr back, pelvis], subsq enc 391
S46.19[1,2,9]D	Oth inj of muscle, fascia and tndn of long head of biceps, [rt, lt, unsp] arm, subsq enc 392
S46.29[1,2,9]D	Oth inj of muscle, fascia and tndn of oth parts of biceps, [rt, lt, unsp] arm, subsq enc 392
S46.39[1,2,9]D	Oth inj of muscle, fascia and tndn of triceps, [rt, lt, unsp] arm, subsq enc 392
S46.09[1,2,9]D	Oth inj of muscle(s) and tndn(s) of the rotator cuff of [rt, lt, unsp] shldr, subsq enc 392
S56.59[1,2,9]D	Oth inj of oth extensor muscle, fascia and tndn at forearm lvl, [rt, lt, unsp] arm, subsq enc 393
S56.29[1,2,9]D	Oth inj of oth flexor muscle, fascia and tndn at forearm lvl, [rt, lt, unsp] arm, subsq enc 393
S56.89[1,2,9]D	Oth inj of oth muscles, fascia and tndns at forearm lvl, [rt, lt, unsp] arm, subsq enc 393
S46.89[1,2,9]D	Oth inj of oth muscles, fascia and tndns at shldr and upr arm lvl, [rt, lt, unsp] arm, subsq enc 392
S36.598[A,S]	Oth inj of oth part of colon, [init enc, seq] 118
S36.498[A,S]	Oth inj of oth part of sm intestine, [init enc, seq] 118
S27.898[A,S]	Oth inj of oth spec intrathoracic organs, [init enc, seq] 69
S37.49[1,2,9]A	Oth inj of ovary, [unilat, bilat, unsp], init enc 265, 270
S37.49[1,2,9]S	Oth inj of ovary, [unilat, bilat, unsp], seq 265, 270
S37.49[1,2,9]D	Oth inj of ovary, [unilat, bilat, unsp], subsq enc 391
S27.69X[A,S]	Oth inj of pleura, [init enc, seq] 69
S36.69X[A,S]	Oth inj of rectum, [init enc, seq] 118
S15.191A	Oth inj of rt vert artery, init enc 5
S36.593[A,S]	Oth inj of sigmoid colon, [init enc, seq] 118
S36.09XA	Oth inj of spleen, init enc 286, 294, 422, 432
S36.09XS	Oth inj of spleen, seq 117
S36.09XD	Oth inj of spleen, subsq enc 390
S36.39X[A,S]	Oth inj of stomach, [init enc, seq] 117
S27.59X[A,S]	Oth inj of thoracic trachea, [init enc, seq] 69
S36.591[A,S]	Oth inj of transv colon, [init enc, seq] 118
T14.8	Oth inj of unsp body region 230, 430
S36.99X[A,S]	Oth inj of unsp intra-abd organ, [init enc, seq] 118
S46.99[1,2,9]D	Oth inj of unsp muscle, fascia and tndn at shldr and upr arm lvl, [rt, lt, unsp] arm, subsq enc 392
S56.99[1,2,9]D	Oth inj of unsp muscles, fascia and tndns at forearm lvl, [rt, lt, unsp] arm, subsq enc 393
S36.599[A,S]	Oth inj of unsp part of colon, [init enc, seq] 118

Code	Description
S36.499[A,S]	Oth inj of unsp part of sm intestine, [init enc, seq] 118
S15.199A	Oth inj of unsp vert artery, init enc 5
S05.8X[1,2,9]A	Oth injuries of [rt, lt, unsp] eye and orbit, init enc 47, 418
S05.8X[1,2,9]S	Oth injuries of [rt, lt, unsp] eye and orbit, seq 359
S05.8X[1,2,9]D	Oth injuries of [rt, lt, unsp] eye and orbit, subsq enc 386
S27.49[1,2,9]D	Oth injuries of bronchus, [unilat, bilat, unsp], subsq enc 389
S27.39[1,2,9]D	Oth injuries of lung, [unilat, bilat, unsp], subsq enc 389
S27.392[A,S]	Oth injuries of lung, bilat, [init enc, seq] 69
S27.391[A,S]	Oth injuries of lung, unilat, [init enc, seq] 69
S27.399[A,S]	Oth injuries of lung, unsp, [init enc, seq] 69
S19.89XA	Oth injuries of oth spec part of neck, init enc 6
S19.85XA	Oth injuries of pharynx and cervical esophagus, init enc 6
S19.80XA	Oth injuries of unsp part of neck, init enc 5
M25.3*	Oth instability of jt 194
M23.8*	Oth int derangements of knee 184
F78	Oth intellectual disabilities 310
J84.84*	Oth interstitial lung dz of childhood 284
J84*	Oth interstitial pulmn dz 68
K90.89	Oth intestinal malabsorption 116
S52.57[1,2,9] [D,E,F,G,H,J,S]	Oth intraarticular fx of lwr end of [rt, lt, unsp] radius, [subsq enc for clsd fx w/ routine healing, subsq enc for opn fx type I or II w/ routine healing, subsq enc for opn fx type IIIA, IIIB, or IIIC w/ routine healing, subsq enc for clsd fx w/ delayed healing, subsq enc for opn fx type I or II w/ delayed healing, subsq enc for opn fx type I or II w/ delayed healing, seq] 174
S52.57[1,2,9] [K,M,N,P,Q,R]	Oth intraarticular fx of lwr end of [rt, lt, unsp] radius, subsq enc for [clsd fx w/ nonu, opn fx type I or II w/ nonu, opn fx type IIIA, IIIB, or IIIC w/ nonu, clsd fx w/ malu, opn fx type I or II w/ malu, opn fx type IIIA, IIIB, or IIIC w/ malu] 198
S52.57[1,2,9] [A,B,C]	Oth intraarticular fxs of lwr end of [rt, lt, unsp] radius, init enc for [clsd fx, opn fx type I or II, opn fx type IIIA, IIIB, or IIIC] 186, 424
S52.57[1,2,9] [B,C]	Oth intraarticular fxs of lwr end of [rt, lt, unsp] radius, init enc for opn fx type [I or II, IIIA IIIB or IIIC] 434
S06.89[3,4,5,6]A	Oth intracranial inj w/ LOC of [1 hr to 5 hrs 59 min, 6 hrs to 24 hrs, > 24 hrs w/ return to pre-existing conscious lvl, > 24 hrs w/o return to pre-existing conscious lvl patient surviving], init enc 36
S06.890S	Oth intracranial inj w/o LOC, seq 40
H59.8*	Oth intraop & postproc comp and d/o of eye and adnx, NEC 367
H95.8*	Oth intraop and postproc comp and d/o of ear/mastd, NEC 367
M96.8*	Oth intraop and postproc comp and d/o of ms sys, NEC 367
G97.8*	Oth intraop and postproc comp and d/o of nervous sys 38, 283
K91.81	Oth intraoperative comp of digestive sys 117, 284
N99.81	Oth intraoperative comp of genitourinary sys 285
J95.88	Oth intraoperative comp of respiratory sys, NEC 69, 284
I97.88	Oth intraoperative comp of the circ sys, NEC 103, 284
H55.89	Oth irregular eye movements 46
M92*	Oth juvenile osteochondrosis 167
H16.8	Oth keratitis 46
R27*	Oth lack of coordination 38
G46.7	Oth lacunar syndromes 33
A50.49	Oth late congenital neurosyphilis 41
A50.5*	Oth late congenital syphilis, symptomatic 308
A50.39	Oth late congenital syphilitic oculopathy 308
C94*	Oth leukemias of spec cell type 295
E75.5	Oth lipid storage d/o 247
L08.8*	Oth local infections of the skin and SQ tissue 224
H53.45[1,2,3,9]	Oth localized visual field defect, [rt, lt, bilat, unsp] eye 45
Z79.899	Oth long term (current) drug therapy 411
P07.1*	Oth low birth weight newborn 282
C91.Z*	Oth lymphoid leukemia 303, 305
R53.8*	Oth malaise and fatigue 385
N53*	Oth male sexual dysfunction 261
O43.19[1,2,3]	Oth malformation of placenta, [1st, 2nd, 3rd] trmstr 278
O43.199	Oth malformation of placenta, unsp trmstr 281
Q28.3	Oth malformations of cerebral vessels 38
C96.Z	Oth malig neoplm of lymphoid, hematpoetc and related tissue 295, 303, 305
C7A.8	Oth malig neuroendocrine tumors 304, 305
E50.8	Oth manifestations of vitamin A deficiency 246
A66.7	Oth manifestations of yaws 308
H70.8*	Oth mastoiditis and related conditions 58
O98.83	Oth maternal infec/parastc dz comp the puerperium 274, 276
O98.82	Oth maternal infec/parastc dz compl childbirth 274
O98.81[1,2,3]	Oth maternal infectious and parasitic dzs compl preg, [1st, 2nd, 3rd] trmstr 274, 277
C84.Z1	Oth mature T/NK-cell lymph, nodes of head, face, and neck 3
C84.Z*	Oth mature T/NK-cell lymphomas 439
B05.89	Oth measles comp 307
T82.39[0,1,2,8,9]S	Oth mech comp of [aortic (bifurcation) graft (replace), carotid arterial graft (bypass), femor arterial graft (bypass), oth vascular grafts, unsp vascular grafts], seq 375
T82.39[0,1,2,8,9]D	Oth mech comp of [aortic (bifurcation) graft (replace), carotid arterial graft (bypass), femor arterial graft (bypass), oth vascular grafts, unsp vascular grafts], subsq enc 410
T82.19[0,1,8,9]S	Oth mech comp of [cardiac electrode, cardiac pulse generator, oth cardiac electronic dev, unsp cardiac electronic dev], seq 375
T82.19[0,1,8,9]D	Oth mech comp of [cardiac electrode, cardiac pulse generator, oth cardiac electronic dev, unsp cardiac electronic dev], subsq enc 410
T85.69[0,1,2,3,4,8]A	Oth mech comp of [epidural and subdural inf catheter, intraperitoneal dialysis catheter, permanent sutures, artfcl skin graft and decellularized allodermis, insulin pump, oth spec int prosthetic devs, implants and grafts], init enc 368
T85.69[0,1,2,3,4,8]S	Oth mech comp of [epidural and subdural inf catheter, intraperitoneal dialysis catheter, permanent sutures, artfcl skin graft and decellularized allodermis, insulin pump, oth spec int prosthetic devs, implants and grafts], seq 376
T85.69[0,1,2,3,4,8]D	Oth mech comp of [epidural and subdural inf catheter, intraperitoneal dialysis catheter, permanent sutures, artfcl skin graft and decellularized allodermis, insulin pump, oth spec int prosthetic devs, implants and grafts], subsq enc 411
T84.09[0,1,2,3,8,9]A	Oth mech comp of [rt hip, lt hip, rt knee, lt knee, oth jt, unsp jt] prosthesis, init enc 183
T84.09[0,1,2,3,8,9]D	Oth mech comp of [rt hip, lt hip, rt knee, lt knee, oth jt, unsp jt] prosthesis, subsq enc 411
T82.59[0,1,2,3,4,5,8,9]A	Oth mech comp of [surgically created arteriovenous fistula, surgically created arteriovenous shunt, artfcl heart, balloon (counterpulsation) dev, inf catheter, umbrella dev, oth cardiac/vascular dev, unsp cardiac/vascular dev], init enc 103
T82.59[0,1,2,3,4,5,8,9]S	Oth mech comp of [surgically created arteriovenous fistula, surgically created arteriovenous shunt, artfcl heart, balloon (counterpulsation) dev, inf catheter, umbrella dev, oth cardiac/vascular dev, unsp cardiac/vascular dev], seq 375
T82.59[0,1,2,3,4,5,8,9]D	Oth mech comp of [surgically created arteriovenous fistula, surgically created arteriovenous shunt, artfcl heart, balloon (counterpulsation) dev, inf catheter, umbrella dev, oth cardiac/vascular dev, unsp cardiac/vascular dev], subsq enc 411
T85.19[0,1,2,9]A	Oth mech comp of implanted electronic neurostimulator (electrode) of [brain, peripheral nerve, spinal cord, oth nervous sys], init enc 40
T85.19[0,1,2,9]S	Oth mech comp of implanted electronic neurostimulator (electrode) of [brain, peripheral nerve, spinal cord, oth nervous sys], seq 376
T85.19[0,1,2,9]D	Oth mech comp of implanted electronic neurostimulator (electrode) of [brain, peripheral nerve, spinal cord, oth nervous sys], subsq enc 411
T84.29[0,3,6,8]A	Oth mech comp of int fix dev of [bones of hand and fingers, bones of foot and toes, vertebrae, oth bones], init enc 183
T84.29[0,3,6,8]S	Oth mech comp of int fix dev of [bones of hand and fingers, bones of foot and toes, vertebrae, oth bones], seq 375
T84.29[0,3,6,8]D	Oth mech comp of int fix dev of [bones of hand and fingers, bones of foot and toes, vertebrae, oth bones], subsq enc 411
T84.19[0,1,2,3,4,5,6,7,9]A	Oth mech comp of int fix dev of [rt humerus, lt humerus, bone of rt forearm, bone of lt forearm, rt femur, lt femur, bone of rt lwr leg, bone of lt lwr leg, unsp bone of limb], init enc 183
T84.19[0,1,2,3,4,5,6,7,9]S	Oth mech comp of int fix dev of [rt humerus, lt humerus, bone of rt forearm, bone of lt forearm, rt femur, lt femur, bone of rt lwr leg, bone of lt lwr leg, unsp bone of limb], seq 375
T84.19[0,1,2,3,4,5,6,7,9]D	Oth mech comp of int fix dev of [rt humerus, lt humerus, bone of rt forearm, bone of lt forearm, rt femur, lt femur, bone of rt lwr leg, bone of lt lwr leg, unsp bone of limb], subsq enc 411
T84.09[0,1,2,3,8,9]S	Oth mech comp of int prosthetic [rt hip, lt hip, rt knee, lt knee, oth, unsp] jt, seq 375
T85.39[0,1]S	Oth mech comp of prosthetic orbit of [rt, lt] eye, seq 376
T85.39[0,1]D	Oth mech comp of prosthetic orbit of [rt, lt] eye, subsq enc 411
L81.4	Oth melanin hyperpigmentation 289
A39.89	Oth meningococcal infections 309
M23.3*	Oth meniscus derangements 184
O99.34[1,2,3]	Oth mental d/o compl preg, [1st, 2nd, 3rd] trmstr 277, 278

F07.89	Oth personality & behavrl d/o d/t known physiol cond **32**	
F84.8	Oth pervasive developmental d/o **311**	
Q85.8	Oth phakomatoses, NEC **304, 306**	
S79.19[1,2,9][D,G,S]	Oth physeal fx of lwr end of [rt, lt, unsp] femur, [subsq enc for fx w/ routine healing, subsq enc for fx w/ delayed healing, seq] **179**	
S79.19[1,2,9]A	Oth physeal fx of lwr end of [rt, lt, unsp] femur, inital enc for clsd fx **162, 427, 436**	
S79.19[1,2,9][K,P]	Oth physeal fx of lwr end of [rt, lt, unsp] femur, subsq enc for fx w/ [nonu, malu] **202**	
S89.39[1,2,9][D,G,S]	Oth physeal fx of lwr end of [rt, lt, unsp] fibula, [subsq enc for fx w/ routine healing, subsq enc for fx w/ delayed healing, seq] **182**	
S89.39[1,2,9][K,P]	Oth physeal fx of lwr end of [rt, lt, unsp] fibula, subsq enc for fx w/ [nonu, malu] **204**	
S89.19[1,2,9][D,G,S]	Oth physeal fx of lwr end of [rt, lt, unsp] tibia, [subsq enc for fx w/ routine healing, subsq enc for fx w/ delayed healing, seq] **182**	
S89.19[1,2,9]A	Oth physeal fx of lwr end of [rt, lt, unsp] tibia, init enc for clsd fx **192, 428**	
S89.19[1,2,9][K,P]	Oth physeal fx of lwr end of [rt, lt, unsp] tibia, subsq enc for fx w/ [nonu, malu] **204**	
S49.19[1,2,9]A	Oth physeal fx of lwr end of humerus [rt, lt, unsp] init enc **186**	
S49.19[1,2,9][D,G,S]	Oth physeal fx of lwr end of humerus, [rt, lt, unsp] arm, [subsq enc for fx w/ routine healing, subsq enc for fx w/ delayed healing, seq] **172**	
S49.19[1,2,9][K,P]	Oth physeal fx of lwr end of humerus, [rt, lt, unsp] arm, subsq enc for fx w/ [nonu, malu] **197**	
S59.29[1,2,9]A	Oth physeal fx of lwr end of radius [rt, lt, unsp] init enc **187**	
S59.29[1,2,9][D,G,S]	Oth physeal fx of lwr end of radius, [rt, lt, unsp] arm, [subsq enc for fx w/ routine healing, subsq enc for fx w/ delayed healing, seq] **174**	
S59.29[1,2,9][K,P]	Oth physeal fx of lwr end of radius, [rt, lt, unsp] arm, subsq enc for fx w/ [nonu, malu] **199**	
S59.09[1,2,9]A	Oth physeal fx of lwr end of ulna [rt, lt, unsp] init enc **187**	
S59.09[1,2,9][D,G,S]	Oth physeal fx of lwr end of ulna, [rt, lt, unsp] arm, [subsq enc for fx w/ routine healing, subsq enc for fx w/ delayed healing, seq] **174**	
S59.09[1,2,9][K,P]	Oth physeal fx of lwr end of ulna, [rt, lt, unsp] arm, subsq enc for fx w/ [nonu, malu] **199**	
S79.09[1,2,9][D,G,S]	Oth physeal fx of upr end of [rt, lt, unsp] femur, [subsq enc for fx w/ routine healing, subsq enc for fx w/ delayed healing, seq] **179**	
S79.09[1,2,9]A	Oth physeal fx of upr end of [rt, lt, unsp] femur, init enc for clsd fx **162, 286, 427, 436**	
S79.09[1,2,9][K,P]	Oth physeal fx of upr end of [rt, lt, unsp] femur, subsq enc for fx w/ [nonu, malu] **202**	
S89.29[1,2,9][D,G,S]	Oth physeal fx of upr end of [rt, lt, unsp] fibula, [subsq enc for fx w/ routine healing, subsq enc for fx w/ delayed healing, seq] **182**	
S89.29[1,2,9][K,P]	Oth physeal fx of upr end of [rt, lt, unsp] fibula, subsq enc for fx w/ [nonu, malu] **204**	
S89.09[1,2,9][D,G,S]	Oth physeal fx of upr end of [rt, lt, unsp] tibia, [subsq enc for fx w/ routine healing, subsq enc for fx w/ delayed healing, seq] **182**	
S89.09[1,2,9]A	Oth physeal fx of upr end of [rt, lt, unsp] tibia, init enc for clsd fx **192, 428**	
S89.09[1,2,9][K,P]	Oth physeal fx of upr end of [rt, lt, unsp] tibia, subsq enc for fx w/ [nonu, malu] **204**	
S49.09[1,2,9]A	Oth physeal fx of upr end of humerus [rt, lt, unsp], init enc for clsd fx **185**	
S49.09[1,2,9][D,G,S]	Oth physeal fx of upr end of humerus, [rt, lt, unsp] arm, [subsq enc for fx w/ routine healing, subsq enc for fx w/ delayed healing, seq] **172**	
S49.09[1,2,9][K,P]	Oth physeal fx of upr end of humerus, [rt, lt, unsp] arm, subsq enc for fx w/ [nonu, malu] **197**	
S59.19[1,2,9]A	Oth physeal fx of upr end of radius [rt, lt, unsp] init enc **187**	
S59.19[1,2,9][D,G,S]	Oth physeal fx of upr end of radius, [rt, lt, unsp] arm, [subsq enc for fx w/ routine healing, subsq enc for fx w/ delayed healing, seq] **174**	
S59.19[1,2,9][K,P]	Oth physeal fx of upr end of ulna, [rt, lt, unsp] arm, subsq enc for fx w/ [nonu, malu] **199**	
O43.89[1,2,3]	Oth placental d/o, [1st, 2nd, 3rd] trmstr **278**	
O43.899	Oth placental d/o, unsp trmstr **281**	
J18.8	Oth pneumonia, unsp organism **68, 439**	
B02.29	Oth postherpetic nervous sys involvement **33, 283**	
J95.89	Oth postproc comp and d/o of resp sys, NEC **69, 284**	
I97.89	Oth postproc comp and d/o of the circ sys, NEC **103, 284**	
E89.8*	Oth postproc endocrine and metabolic comp and d/o **367**	
I97.1*	Oth postprocedural cardiac functional disturbances **103, 284**	
K91.89	Oth postprocedural comp and d/o of dgstv sys **117, 284**	
N99.89	Oth postprocedural comp and d/o of GU sys **285**	
Z98*	Oth postprocedural states **413**	
O24.819	Oth pre-existing diabetes in preg, unsp trmstr **280**	
O24.82	Oth pre-existing diabetes mellitus in childbirth **273**	
O24.81[1,2,3]	Oth pre-existing diabetes mellitus in preg, [1st, 2nd, 3rd] trmstr **273, 276, 277**	
O24.83	Oth pre-existing diabetes mellitus in the puerperium **272, 275**	
O26.899	Oth preg related conditions, unsp trmstr **280**	
O45.8X[1,2,3]	Oth premature separation of placenta, [1st, 2nd, 3rd] trmstr **273, 278, 280**	
O45.8X9	Oth premature separation of placenta, unsp trmstr **281**	
Z63*	Oth prob rel to prim support group, incl* family circumstances **412**	
Z72.89	Oth problems related to lifestyle **412**	
P84	Oth problems with newborn **288**	
R80.8	Oth proteinuria **255**	
A07*	Oth protozoal intestinal dz **114**	
L29.8	Oth pruritus **234**	
L40.8	Oth psoriasis **223**	
F28	Oth psych d/o not d/t a sub or known physiol cond **311, 439**	
F19.[2,9]3[0,1,2,9]	Oth psychoactive substance [dependence, use unsp] w/ w/drawal [uncomp, delirium, perceptual disturbance, unsp] **283**	
O86*	Oth puerperal infections **272, 276**	
J98.19	Oth pulmn collapse **284**	
O29.099	Oth pulmn comp of anesth during preg, unsp trmstr **280**	
O89.09	Oth pulmn comp of anesthesia during the puerperium **274**	
O29.09[1,2,3]	Oth pulmn comps of anesthesia during preg, [1st, 2nd, 3rd] trmstr **277**	
I26.99	Oth pulmn embolism w/o acute cor pulmonale **66**	
I26.09	Oth pulmn embolism with acute cor pulmonale **66**	
B44.[1,2,7]	Oth pulmn, Tonsillar, Disseminated] aspergillosis **283, 308**	
G97.1	Oth reaction to spinal and lumbar punc **41, 283**	
F43.8	Oth reactions to severe stress **310**	
M02.8*	Oth reactive arthropathies **164**	
M43.4	Oth recurrent atlantoaxial disloc **194**	
M43.5*	Oth recurrent vert disloc **194**	
J68.8	Oth resp cond d/t chemicals, gases, fumes and vapors **68**	
P22.8	Oth respiratory distress of newborn **288**	
H35*	Oth retinal d/o **46**	
H33.8	Oth retinal detachments **46**	
H33.19[1,2,3,9]	Oth retinoschisis and retinal cysts, [rt, lt, bilat, unsp] eye **46**	
K68.19	Oth retroperitoneal abscess **114**	
T80.49XS	Oth Rh incompat react d/t tranfs of bld/bld prod, seq **374**	
T80.49XA	Oth Rh incompat reaction d/t tranfs of bld/bld prod, init **287, 293**	
T80.49XD	Oth Rh incompat reaction d/t tranfs of bld/bld prod, subs **410**	
M05.8*	Oth rheumatoid arthritis with rheumatoid factor **164**	
A79*	Oth rickettsioses **308**	
B06.89	Oth rubella comp **307**	
M62.1*	Oth rupture of muscle (nontraumatic) **167**	
B65.8	Oth schistosomiasis **309**	
M1A.4*	Oth secondary chr gout **167**	
M10.4*	Oth secondary gout **166**	
M40.1*	Oth secondary kyphosis **126**	
C7B.8	Oth secondary neuroendocrine tumors **304, 305**	
G21.8	Oth secondary parkinsonism **32**	
I27.2	Oth secondary pulmn hypertension **103**	
M41.5*	Oth secondary scoliosis **126**	
A51.49	Oth secondary syphilitic conditions **308**	
A41*	Oth sepsis **282, 309, 438**	
T80.6[1,2,9]XA	Oth serum reaction d/t [administration of bld and bld products, vaccination, oth serum], init enc **287, 361**	
T80.6[1,2,9]XS	Oth serum reaction d/t [administration of bld and bld products, vaccination, oth serum], seq **375**	
T80.6[1,2,9]XD	Oth serum reaction d/t [administration of bld and bld products, vaccination, oth serum], subsq enc **410**	
Q97*	Oth sex chromosome abnormalities, female phenotype, NEC **265, 270**	
Q98*	Oth sex chromosome abnormalities, male phenotype, NEC **261**	
F66	Oth sexual d/o **311**	
F52.8	Oth sexual dysfnct not d/t a sub or known physiol cond **311**	
T61.78[1,2,3,4]A	Oth shellfish poison, [accid (unintentional), intentional self-harm, assault, undetermined], init enc **366**	
T61.78[1,2,3,4]S	Oth shellfish poison, [accid (unintentional), intentional self-harm, assault, undetermined], seq **373**	

Code	Description
T61.78[1,2,3,4]D	Oth shellfish poison, [accid (unintentional), intentional self-harm, assault, undetermined], subsq enc 408
R57.8	Oth shock 309
B37.89	Oth sites of candidiasis 308
R23.8	Oth skin changes 234
G47.39	Oth sleep apnea 58
G47.8	Oth sleep d/o 3, 58
G47.69	Oth sleep related movement d/o 58
M70.8*	Oth soft tissue d/o related to use/pressure 167
K45.[Ø,1]	Oth spec abd hernia, w/ [obstruction w/o gangrene, gangrene], not spec as recurrent 284
R76.8	Oth spec abnormal immunological findings in serum 294
OØ2.8*	Oth spec abnormal products of conception 277
M21.8[2,3,5,6] [1,2,9]	Oth spec acquired deformities of [rt, lt, unsp] [upr arm, forearm, thigh, lwr leg] 193
M21.8Ø	Oth spec acquired deformities of unsp limb 193
A48.8	Oth spec bacterial dz 308
AØ5.8	Oth spec bacterial foodborne intoxications 114
A48.5*	Oth spec botulism 308
P11.1	Oth spec brain damage d/t birth inj 288
L13.8	Oth spec bullous d/o 223
Q99.8	Oth spec chromosome abnormalities 261, 265, 270
D68.8	Oth spec coagulation defects 294
T82.89[7,8]A	Oth spec comp of [cardiac, vascular] prosthetic devs, implants and grafts, init enc 103
O75.89	Oth spec comp of labor and delivery 278, 280
P83.8	Oth spec conditions of integument specific to newborn 289
I45.89	Oth spec conduction d/o 283
P37.8	Oth spec congenital infectious and parasitic dz 282
Q89.8	Oth spec congenital malformations 195
Q45.8	Oth spec congenital malformations of digestive sys 117
Q18.8	Oth spec congenital malformations of face and neck 58
Q24.8	Oth spec congenital malformations of heart 102
Q43.8	Oth spec congenital malformations of intestine 117
Q82.8	Oth spec congenital malformations of skin 289
Q64.8	Oth spec congenital malformations of urinary sys 256
Q68.8	Oth spec congenital musculoskeletal deformities 195
F68.8	Oth spec d/o of adult personality and behav 310
O41.8X[1,2,3] [Ø,1,2,3,4,5,9]	Oth spec d/o of amniotic fluid and membranes, [1st, 2nd, 3rd] trmstr, fetus [N/A or unsp, 1, 2, 3, 4, 5, oth] 278, 280
O41.8X9[Ø,1,2,3, 4,5,9]	Oth spec d/o of amniotic fluid and membranes, unsp trmstr, fetus [N/A or unsp, 1, 2, 3, 4, 5, oth] 281
I77.8*	Oth spec d/o of arteries and arterioles 100
H51.8	Oth spec d/o of binocular movement 45
M89.8*	Oth spec d/o of bone 194
M85.8*	Oth spec d/o of bone density and structure 194
G93.89	Oth spec d/o of brain 33
E74.8	Oth spec d/o of carbohydrate metabolism 247
M94.8*	Oth spec d/o of cartilage 194
G96.8	Oth spec d/o of central nervous sys 33
H93.8*	Oth spec d/o of ear 58
H61.8*	Oth spec d/o of ext ear 58
H57.8	Oth spec d/o of eye and adnexa 46
HØ2.8*	Oth spec d/o of eyelid 45
H21.8*	Oth spec d/o of iris and ciliary body 46
N28.89	Oth spec d/o of kidney and ureter 256
M62.89	Oth spec d/o of muscle 167
J34.89	Oth spec d/o of nose and nasal sinuses 289
E16.8	Oth spec d/o of pancreatic int secretion 247
N48.8*	Oth spec d/o of penis 261
L81.8	Oth spec d/o of pigmentation 289
N42.89	Oth spec d/o of prostate 261
KØ8.8	Oth spec d/o of teeth and supporting structures 4
EØ7.89	Oth spec d/o of thyroid 3, 247
H73.8*	Oth spec d/o of tympanic membrane 58
N39.8	Oth spec d/o of urinary sys 256
I87.8	Oth spec d/o of veins 102
D72.8*	Oth spec d/o of white bld cells 294
M43.8*	Oth spec deforming dorsopathies 125, 164
M43.8X9	Oth spec deforming dorsopathies, site unsp 126
E13.9	Oth spec diabetes mellitus w/o comp 2, 246
E13.65	Oth spec diabetes mellitus with hyperglycemia 246
E13.Ø*	Oth spec diabetes mellitus with hyperosmolarity 2, 246
E13.64*	Oth spec diabetes mellitus with hypoglycemia 246
E13.1*	Oth spec diabetes mellitus with ketoacidosis 2, 246
E13.2*	Oth spec diabetes mellitus with kidney comp 2, 256
E13.63*	Oth spec diabetes mellitus with oral comp 246
E13.62*	Oth spec diabetes mellitus with skin comp 246
P91.8	Oth spec disturbances of cerebral status of newborn 282
M53.8*	Oth spec dorsopathies 165
K62.8*	Oth spec dz of anus and rectum 117
D75.89	Oth spec dz of bld and bld-forming organs 294
K22.8	Oth spec dz of esophagus 116
KØ3.8*	Oth spec dz of hard tissues of teeth 4
H83.8*	Oth spec dz of inner ear 57
K63.8*	Oth spec dz of intestine 117
M27.8	Oth spec dz of jaws 4
K76.89	Oth spec dz of liver 124
G95.8*	Oth spec dz of spinal cord 38
K92.89	Oth spec dz of the digestive sys 117
J39.8	Oth spec dz of upr respiratory tract 4, 69
T75.89X[A,S]	Oth spec effects of ext causes, [init enc, seq] 374
T75.89XD	Oth spec effects of ext causes, subs enc 410
L53.8	Oth spec erythematous conditions 234
G25.89	Oth spec extrapyramidal and movement d/o 32
N73.8	Oth spec female pelvic inflam dz 269
B66.8	Oth spec fluke infections 309
G25.2	Oth spec forms of tremor 38
K59.8	Oth spec functional intestinal d/o 116
S32.49[1,2,9] [A,B]	Oth spec fx of [rt, lt, unsp] acetab, init enc for [clsd, opn] fx 162
S32.49[1,2,9]S	Oth spec fx of [rt, lt, unsp] acetab, seq 166
S32.49[1,2,9] [D,G]	Oth spec fx of [rt, lt, unsp] acetab, subsq enc for fx w/ [routine, delayed] healing 170
S32.49[1,2,9]K	Oth spec fx of [rt, lt, unsp] acetab, subsq enc for fx w/ nonu 196
S32.69[1,2,9] [D,G]	Oth spec fx of [rt, lt, unsp] ischium, subsq enc for fx w/ [routine, delayed] healing 170
S32.69[1,2,9]K	Oth spec fx of [rt, lt, unsp] ischium, subsq enc for fx w/ nonu 196
S32.59[1,2,9]S	Oth spec fx of [rt, lt, unsp] pubis, seq 166
S32.59[1,2,9] [D,G]	Oth spec fx of [rt, lt, unsp] pubis, subsq enc for fx w/ [routine, delayed] healing 170
S32.59[1,2,9]K	Oth spec fx of [rt, lt, unsp] pubis, subsq enc for fx w/ nonu 196
S32.69[1,2,9] [A,B]	Oth spec fx of ischium [rt, lt, unsp] init enc for [clsd, opn] fx 162, 421, 433
S32.69[1,2,9]S	Oth spec fx of ischium [rt, lt, unsp] init enc for fx, seq 166
S32.59[1,2,9] [A,B]	Oth spec fx of pubis [rt, lt, unsp] init enc for [clsd, opn] fx 162, 421, 433
Z78*	Oth spec health status 412
B83.8	Oth spec helminthiases 309
EØ3.8	Oth spec hypothyroidism 247
D84.8	Oth spec immunodeficiencies 294
P39.8	Oth spec infections specific to the perinatal period 282
K75.8*	Oth spec inflam liver dz 284
N76.8*	Oth spec inflam of vagina and vulva 269
M46.8*	Oth spec inflam spondylopathies 164
S35.49[1,2,3,4,5, 6]D	Oth spec inj of [rt renal artery, lt renal artery, unsp renal artery, rt renal vein, lt renal vein, unsp renal vein], subsq enc 390
S15.Ø9[1,2,9]S	Oth spec inj of [rt, lt, unsp] carotid artery, seq 100
S15.Ø9[1,2,9]D	Oth spec inj of [rt, lt, unsp] carotid artery, subsq enc 388
S15.29[1,2,9]S	Oth spec inj of [rt, lt, unsp] ext jugular vein, seq 100
S15.29[1,2,9]D	Oth spec inj of [rt, lt, unsp] ext jugular vein, subsq enc 388
S25.19[1,2,9]S	Oth spec inj of [rt, lt, unsp] innominate or subclavian artery, seq 100
S25.19[1,2,9]D	Oth spec inj of [rt, lt, unsp] innominate or subclavian artery, subsq enc 389
S25.39[1,2,9]S	Oth spec inj of [rt, lt, unsp] innominate or subclavian vein, seq 100
S25.39[1,2,9]D	Oth spec inj of [rt, lt, unsp] innominate or subclavian vein, subsq enc 389
S15.39[1,2,9]S	Oth spec inj of [rt, lt, unsp] int jugular vein, seq 100
S15.39[1,2,9]D	Oth spec inj of [rt, lt, unsp] int jugular vein, subsq enc 388
SØ9.39[1,2,9]A	Oth spec inj of [rt, lt, unsp] mid and inner ear, init enc 58, 419

Code	Description
S09.39[1,2,9]D	Oth spec inj of [rt, lt, unsp] mid and inner ear, subsq enc **387**
S25.49[1,2,9]S	Oth spec inj of [rt, lt, unsp] pulmn bld vessels, seq **100**
S25.49[1,2,9]D	Oth spec inj of [rt, lt, unsp] pulmn bld vessels, subsq enc **389**
S35.49[1,2,3]S	Oth spec inj of [rt, lt, unsp] renal artery, seq **100**
S35.49[4,5,6]S	Oth spec inj of [rt, lt, unsp] renal vein, seq **100**
S15.19[1,2,9]S	Oth spec inj of [rt, lt, unsp] vert artery, seq **100**
S15.19[1,2,9]D	Oth spec inj of [rt, lt, unsp] vert artery, subsq enc **388**
S85.15[1,2,9]S	Oth spec inj of ant tibial artery, [rt, lt, unsp] leg, seq **101**
S45.09[1,2,9]S	Oth spec inj of axillary artery, [rt, lt, unsp] side, seq **100**
S45.29[1,2,9]S	Oth spec inj of axillary or brachial vein, [rt, lt, unsp] side, seq **100**
S45.29[1,2,9]D	Oth spec inj of axillary or brachial vein, [rt, lt, unsp] side, subsq enc **392**
S65.59[8,9]D	Oth spec inj of bld vessel of [oth, unsp] finger, subsq enc **396**
S65.59[0,1,2,3,4,5,6,7,8,9]S	Oth spec inj of bld vessel of [rt index, lt index, rt mid, lt mid, rt ring, lt ring, rt little, lt little, oth, unsp] finger, seq **101**
S65.49[1,2,9]S	Oth spec inj of bld vessel of [rt, lt, unsp] thumb, seq **101**
S65.49[1,2,9]D	Oth spec inj of bld vessel of [rt, lt, unsp] thumb, subsq enc **396**
S65.59[0,1]D	Oth spec inj of bld vessel of [rt, lt] index finger, subsq enc **396**
S65.59[2,3]D	Oth spec inj of bld vessel of [rt, lt] mid finger, subsq enc **396**
S65.59[4,5]D	Oth spec inj of bld vessel of [rt, lt] ring finger, subsq enc **396**
S45.19[1,2,9]S	Oth spec inj of brachial artery, [rt, lt, unsp] side, seq **100**
S45.19[1,2,9]D	Oth spec inj of brachial artery, [rt, lt, unsp] side, subsq enc **391**
S45.91[1,2,9]D	Oth spec inj of brachial artery, [rt, lt, unsp] side, subsq enc **392**
S65.39[1,2,9]S	Oth spec inj of deep palmar arch of [rt, lt, unsp] hand, seq **101**
S65.39[1,2,9]D	Oth spec inj of deep palmar arch of [rt, lt, unsp] hand, subsq enc **396**
S95.09[1,2,9]S	Oth spec inj of dorsal artery of [rt, lt, unsp] foot, seq **101**
S95.29[1,2,9]S	Oth spec inj of dorsal vein of [rt, lt, unsp] foot, seq **101**
S66.29[1,2,9]D	Oth spec inj of extensor muscle, fascia and tndn of [rt, lt, unsp] thumb at wrist and hand lvl, subsq enc **397**
S75.09[1,2,9]S	Oth spec inj of femor artery, [rt, lt, unsp] leg, seq **101**
S75.19[1,2,9]S	Oth spec inj of femor vein at hip & thigh lvl, [rt, lt, unsp] leg, seq **101**
S75.29[1,2,9]S	Oth spec inj of greater saphenous vein at hip & thigh lvl, [rt, lt, unsp] leg, seq **101**
S85.39[1,2,9]S	Oth spec inj of greater saphenous vein at lwr leg lvl, [rt, lt, unsp] leg, seq **101**
S25.59[1,2,9]S	Oth spec inj of intercostal bld vessels, [rt, lt, unsp] side, seq **100**
S25.59[1,2,9]D	Oth spec inj of intercostal bld vessels, [rt, lt, unsp] side, subsq enc **389**
S85.49[1,2,9]S	Oth spec inj of lesser saphenous vein at lwr leg lvl, [rt, lt, unsp] leg, seq **101**
S66.09[1,2,9]D	Oth spec inj of long flexor muscle, fascia and tndn of [rt, lt, unsp] thumb at wrist and hand lvl, subsq enc **397**
S15.192A	Oth spec inj of lt vert artery, init enc **5**
S09.19X[A,S]	Oth spec inj of muscle and tndn of head, [init enc, seq] **359**
S95.89[1,2,9]S	Oth spec inj of oth bld vessels at ankle and foot lvl, [rt, lt, unsp] leg, seq **101**
S55.89[1,2,9]S	Oth spec inj of oth bld vessels at forearm lvl, [rt, lt, unsp] arm, seq **101**
S55.89[1,2,9]D	Oth spec inj of oth bld vessels at forearm lvl, [rt, lt, unsp] arm, subsq enc **393**
S75.89[1,2,9]S	Oth spec inj of oth bld vessels at hip & thigh lvl, [rt, lt, unsp] leg, seq **101**
S85.89[1,2,9]S	Oth spec inj of oth bld vessels at lwr leg lvl, [rt, lt, unsp] leg, seq **101**
S65.89[1,2,9]S	Oth spec inj of oth bld vessels at wrist and hand lvl of [rt, lt, unsp] arm, seq **101**
S65.89[1,2,9]D	Oth spec inj of oth bld vessels at wrist and hand lvl of [rt, lt, unsp] arm, subsq enc **396**
S25.89[1,2,9]S	Oth spec inj of oth bld vessels of thorax, [rt, lt, unsp] side, seq **100**
S25.89[1,2,9]D	Oth spec inj of oth bld vessels of thorax, [rt, lt, unsp] side, subsq enc **389**
S45.89[1,2,9]S	Oth spec inj of oth spec bld vessels at shldr and upr arm lvl, [rt, lt, unsp] arm, seq **101**
S45.89[1,2,9]D	Oth spec inj of oth spec bld vessels at shldr and upr arm lvl, [rt, lt, unsp] arm, subsq enc **392**
S85.29[1,2,9]S	Oth spec inj of peroneal artery, [rt, lt, unsp] leg, seq **101**
S95.19[1,2,9]S	Oth spec inj of plantar artery of [rt, lt, unsp] foot, seq **101**
S85.09[1,2,9]S	Oth spec inj of popliteal artery, [rt, lt, unsp] leg, seq **101**
S85.59[1,2,9]S	Oth spec inj of popliteal vein, [rt, lt, unsp] leg, seq **101**
S85.18[1,2,9]S	Oth spec inj of post tibial artery, [rt, lt, unsp] leg, seq **101**
S55.19[1,2,9]S	Oth spec inj of radial artery at forearm lvl, [rt, lt, unsp] arm, seq **101**
S55.19[1,2,9]D	Oth spec inj of radial artery at forearm lvl, [rt, lt, unsp] arm, subsq enc **393**
S65.19[1,2,9]S	Oth spec inj of radial artery at wrist and hand lvl of [rt, lt, unsp] arm, seq **101**
S65.19[1,2,9]D	Oth spec inj of radial artery at wrist and hand lvl of [rt, lt, unsp] arm, subsq enc **396**
S65.29[1,2,9]S	Oth spec inj of superf palmar arch of [rt, lt, unsp] hand, seq **101**
S65.29[1,2,9]D	Oth spec inj of superf palmar arch of [rt, lt, unsp] hand, subsq enc **396**
S45.39[1,2,9]S	Oth spec inj of superf vein at shldr and upr arm lvl, [rt, lt, unsp] arm, seq **101**
S45.39[1,2,9]D	Oth spec inj of superf vein at shldr and upr arm lvl, [rt, lt, unsp] arm, subsq enc **392**
S55.09[1,2,9]S	Oth spec inj of ulnar artery at forearm lvl, [rt, lt, unsp] arm, seq **101**
S55.09[1,2,9]D	Oth spec inj of ulnar artery at forearm lvl, [rt, lt, unsp] arm, subsq enc **392**
S65.09[1,2,9]S	Oth spec inj of ulnar artery at wrist and hand lvl of [rt, lt, unsp] arm, seq **101**
S65.09[1,2,9]D	Oth spec inj of ulnar artery at wrist and hand lvl of [rt, lt, unsp] arm, subsq enc **396**
S95.99[1,2,9]S	Oth spec inj of unsp bld vessel at ankle and foot lvl, [rt, lt, unsp] leg, seq **101**
S55.99[1,2,9]S	Oth spec inj of unsp bld vessel at forearm lvl, [rt, lt, unsp] arm, seq **101**
S75.99[1,2,9]S	Oth spec inj of unsp bld vessel at hip & thigh lvl, [rt, lt, unsp] leg, seq **101**
S85.99[1,2,9]S	Oth spec inj of unsp bld vessel at lwr leg lvl, [rt, lt, unsp] leg, seq **101**
S45.99[1,2,9]D	Oth spec inj of unsp bld vessel at shldr and upr arm lvl, [rt, lt, unsp] arm, subsq enc **392**
S65.99[1,2,9]S	Oth spec inj of unsp bld vessel at wrist and hand lvl of [rt, lt, unsp] arm, seq **101**
S65.99[1,2,9]D	Oth spec inj of unsp bld vessel at wrist and hand lvl of [rt, lt, unsp] arm, subsq enc **397**
S55.99[1,2,9]D	Oth spec inj of unsp bld vessels at forearm lvl, [rt, lt, unsp] arm, subsq enc **393**
S45.99[1,2,9]S	Oth spec inj of unsp bld vessels at shldr and upr arm lvl, [rt, lt, unsp] arm, seq **101**
S85.12[1,2,9]S	Oth spec inj of unsp tibial artery, [rt, lt, unsp] leg, seq **101**
S55.29[1,2,9]S	Oth spec inj of vein at forearm lvl, [rt, lt, unsp] arm, seq **101**
S55.29[1,2,9]D	Oth spec inj of vein at forearm lvl, [rt, lt, unsp] arm, subsq enc **393**
S59.81[1,2,9]D	Oth spec injuries [rt, lt, unsp] forearm, subsq enc **393**
S39.9[1,2,3,4]X[A,S]	Oth spec injuries of [abd, lwr back, pelvis, ext genitals], [init enc, seq] **359**
S39.8[1,2,3]X[A,S]	Oth spec injuries of [abd, lwr back, pelvis], [init enc, seq] **359**
S39.8[1,2,3]XA	Oth spec injuries of [abd, lwr back, pelvis], init enc **422**
S39.8[1,2,3]XD	Oth spec injuries of [abd, lwr back, pelvis], subsq enc **391**
S79.8[1,2][1,2,9]A	Oth spec injuries of [rt, lt, unsp] [hip, thigh], init enc **427**
S99.81[1,2,9][A,S]	Oth spec injuries of [rt, lt, unsp] ankle, [init enc, seq] **361**
S99.81[1,2,9]A	Oth spec injuries of [rt, lt, unsp] ankle, init enc **430**
S99.81[1,2,9]D	Oth spec injuries of [rt, lt, unsp] ankle, subsq enc **400**
S59.80[1,2,9][A,S]	Oth spec injuries of [rt, lt, unsp] elbow, [init enc, seq] **360**
S59.80[1,2,9]D	Oth spec injuries of [rt, lt, unsp] elbow, subsq enc **393**
S99.82[1,2,9][A,S]	Oth spec injuries of [rt, lt, unsp] foot, [init enc, seq] **361**
S99.82[1,2,9]A	Oth spec injuries of [rt, lt, unsp] foot, init enc **430**
S99.82[1,2,9]D	Oth spec injuries of [rt, lt, unsp] foot, subsq enc **400**
S59.81[1,2,9][A,S]	Oth spec injuries of [rt, lt, unsp] forearm, [init enc, seq] **360**
S79.81[1,2,9][A,S]	Oth spec injuries of [rt, lt, unsp] hip, [init enc, seq] **360**
S79.82[1,2,9][A,S]	Oth spec injuries of [rt, lt, unsp] thigh, [init enc, seq] **360**
S19.8[0,1,2,3,4,5,9]X[A,S]	Oth spec injuries of [unsp part of neck, larynx, cervical trachea, vocal cord, thyroid gland, pharynx and cervical esophagus, oth spec part of neck], [init enc, seq] **359**
S19.8[0,1,2,3,4,5,9]XA	Oth spec injuries of [unsp part of neck, larynx, cervical trachea, vocal cord, thyroid gland, pharynx and cervical esophagus, oth spec part of neck], init enc **420**

Code	Description
S19.8[0,1,2,3,4,5,9]XD	Oth spec injuries of [unsp part of neck, larynx, cervical trachea, vocal cord, thyroid gland, pharynx and cervical esophagus, oth spec part of neck], unspifed inj of neck, subsq enc **388**
S89.8[0,1,2]XA	Oth spec injuries of [unsp, rt, lt] lwr leg, init enc **428**
S49.8[0,1,2]XD	Oth spec injuries of [unsp, rt, lt] shldr and upr arm, subsq enc **392**
S19.82XA	Oth spec injuries of cervical trachea, init enc **6**
S39.848[A,S]	Oth spec injuries of ext genitals, [init enc, seq] **359**
S39.848A	Oth spec injuries of ext genitals, init enc **422**
S09.8XX[A,S]	Oth spec injuries of head, [init enc, seq] **359**
S09.8XXA	Oth spec injuries of head, init enc **5, 419**
S09.8XXD	Oth spec injuries of head, subsq enc **387**
S19.81XA	Oth spec injuries of larynx, init enc **5**
S29.8XXD	Oth spec injuries of thorax, subsq enc **389**
S19.84XA	Oth spec injuries of thyroid gland, init enc **6**
S19.83XA	Oth spec injuries of vocal cord, init enc **6**
S59.[8,9][0,1][1,2,9]A	Oth spec injuries, Unsp inj] of [rt, lt, unsp] [elbow, forearm], init enc **424**
S89.[8,9][0,1,2]X[A,S]	[Oth spec injuries, Unsp inj] of [unsp, rt, lt] lwr leg, [init enc, seq] **361**
S89.[8,9][0,1,2]XD	[Oth spec injuries, Unsp inj] of [unsp, rt, lt] lwr leg, subsq enc **398**
S69.[8,9][0,1,2]X[A,S]	[Oth spec injuries, Unsp inj] of [unsp, rt, lt] wrist, hand and finger(s), [init enc, seq] **360**
S69.[8,9][0,1,2]XA	[Oth spec injuries, Unsp inj] of [unsp, rt, lt] wrist, hand and finger(s), init enc **426**
S49.[8,9][0,1,2]X[A,S]	[Oth spec injuries, Unsp inj] of shldr and upr arm, [unsp, rt, lt] arm, [init enc, seq] **359**
S49.[8,9][0,1,2]XA	[Oth spec injuries, Unsp inj] of shldr and upr arm, [unsp, rt, lt] arm, init enc **423**
S29.[8,9]XX[A,S]	[Oth spec injuries, Unsp inj] of thorax, [init enc, seq] **359**
S29.[8,9]XXA	Oth spec injuries, Unsp inj] of thorax, init enc **421**
B81.8	Oth spec intestinal helminthiases **116**
P76.8	Oth spec intestinal obstruction of newborn **288**
S06.89[5,6]A	Oth spec intracranial inj w/ LOC > 24 hrs [w/ return to pre-existing conscious lvl, w/o return to pre-existing conscious lvl w/ patient surviving], init enc **37, 419, 431**
S06.89[5,6]D	Oth spec intracranial inj w/ LOC of [> 24 hrs w/ return to pre-existing conscious lvl, > 24 hrs w/o return to pre-existing conscious lvl w/ patient surviving], subsq enc **387**
S06.89[1,2,3,4]A	Oth spec intracranial inj w/ LOC of [30 min or less, 31 min to 59 min, 1 hr to 5 hrs 59 min, 6 hrs to 24 hrs], init enc **37, 419, 431**
S06.89[1,2,3,4]S	Oth spec intracranial inj w/ LOC of [30 min or less, 31-59 min, 1 hr to 5 hrs 59 min, 6 hrs to 24 hrs], seq **40**
S06.89[1,2,3,4]D	Oth spec intracranial inj w/ LOC of [30 min or less, 31-59 min, 1 hr to 5 hrs 59 min, 6 hrs to 24 hrs], subsq enc **387**
S06.89[7,8,9]A	Oth spec intracranial inj w/ LOC of [any dur w/ death d/t brain inj prior to regain cnscness, any dur w/ death d/t oth cause prior to regain cnscness, unsp dur], init enc **36, 37, 419, 431**
S06.89[7,8,9]S	Oth spec intracranial inj w/ LOC of [any dur w/ death d/t brain inj prior to regain cnscness, any dur w/ death d/t oth cause prior to regain cnscness, unsp dur], seq **40**
S06.89[7,8,9]D	Oth spec intracranial inj w/ LOC of [any dur w/ death d/t brain inj prior to regain cnscness, any dur w/ death d/t oth cause prior to regain cnscness, unsp dur], subsq enc **387**
S06.89[5,6]S	Oth spec intracranial inj w/ LOC of > 24 hrs [w/ return to pre-existing conscious lvl, w/o return to pre-existing conscious lvl w/ patient surviving], seq **40**
M25.8*	Oth spec jt d/o **167**
C94.8*	Oth spec leukemias **303, 305**
L94.8	Oth spec localized connective tissue d/o **234**
B53*	Oth spec malaria **308**
E88.8*	Oth spec metabolic d/o **247**
A92.8	Oth spec mosquito-borne viral fevers **307**
O30.82[1,2,3]	Oth spec multi gestation w/ two or more monoamniotic fetuses, [1st, 2nd, 3rd] trmstr **277**
O30.81[1,2,3]	Oth spec multi gestation w/ two or more monochorionic fetuses, [1st, 2nd, 3rd] trmstr **277**
O30.8[0,1,2,9]9	Oth spec multi gestation, [unsp, two or more monochorionic fetuses, two or more monoamniotic fetuses, unable to determine the number of placenta and amniotic sacs], unsp trmstr **281**
O30.89[1,2,3]	Oth spec multi gestation, unable to determine number of placenta and number of amniotic sacs, [1st, 2nd, 3rd] trmstr **277**
O30.80[1,2,3]	Oth spec multi gestation, unsp number of placenta and unsp number of amniotic sacs, [1st, 2nd, 3rd] trmstr **277**
B48.8	Oth spec mycoses **283, 438**
G70.89	Oth spec myoneural d/o **34**
G72.8*	Oth spec myopathies **38**
M31.8	Oth spec necrotizing vasculopathies **100**
P54.8	Oth spec neonatal hemorrhages **288**
K52.8*	Oth spec noninfective gastroenteritis and colitis **116**
N89.8	Oth spec noninflammatory d/o of vagina **289**
F48.8	Oth spec nonpsychotic mental d/o **310**
O71.89	Oth spec obstetric trauma **272, 276**
O66.8	Oth spec obstructed labor **273, 275**
Q78.8	Oth spec osteochondrodysplasias **195**
L44.8	Oth spec papulosquamous d/o **234**
G83.8*	Oth spec paralytic syndromes **38**
P78.8*	Oth spec perinatal digestive sys d/o **288**
P61.8	Oth spec perinatal hematological d/o **288**
I73.8*	Oth spec peripheral vascular dz **100**
J94.8	Oth spec pleural conditions **68, 284**
A63.8	Oth spec predominantly sexually transmitted dz **261, 264, 269**
O26.89*	Oth spec preg related conditions **276**
O26.89[1,2,3]	Oth spec preg related conditions, [1st, 2nd, 3rd] trmstr **277**
B60.8	Oth spec protozoal dz **309, 438**
O86.8*	Oth spec puerperal infections **274**
I27.89	Oth spec pulmn heart dz **103**
N15.8	Oth spec renal tubulo-interstitial dz **256**
P28.8*	Oth spec respiratory conditions of newborn **288**
J98.8	Oth spec respiratory d/o **69**
I09.89	Oth spec rheumatic heart dz **102**
M06.8*	Oth spec rheumatoid arthritis **164**
A02.8	Oth spec salmonella infections **308, 438**
M79.8*	Oth spec soft tissue d/o **167**
A69.8	Oth spec spirochetal infections **308**
M48.8*	Oth spec spondylopathies **164**
S63.59[1,2,9][A,S]	Oth spec sprain of [rt, lt, unsp] wrist, [init enc, seq] **190**
S63.59[1,2,9]A	Oth spec sprain of [rt, lt, unsp] wrist, init enc **425**
S63.59[1,2,9]D	Oth spec sprain of [rt, lt, unsp] wrist, subsq enc **396**
H50.89	Oth spec strabismus **45**
M35.8	Oth spec systemic involvement of connective tissue **164**
P72.8	Oth spec transitory neonatal endocrine d/o **288**
O71.82	Oth spec trauma to perineum and vulva **272, 275**
C86*	Oth spec types of T/NK-cell lymphoma **295, 303, 305, 439**
N39.4*	Oth spec urinary incontinence **255**
B33.8	Oth spec viral dz **308**
A85.8	Oth spec viral encephalitis **438**
A98.8	Oth spec viral hemorrhagic fevers **307**
A88.8	Oth spec viral infections of central nervous sys **41, 438**
Q28.[8,9]	[Oth spec, Unsp] congenital malformations of circulatory sys **100**
T69.[8,9]XX[A,S]	[Oth spec, Unsp] effects of reduced temperature, [init enc, seq] **374**
T69.[8,9]XXD	[Oth spec, Unsp] effects of reduced temperature, subsq enc **409**
S16.[8,9]XX[A,S]	[Oth spec, Unsp] inj of muscle, fascia and tndn at neck lvl, [init enc, seq] **359**
S79.[8,9][1,2][1,2,9]D	[Oth spec, Unsp] injuries of [rt, lt, unsp] [hip, thigh], subsq enc **398**
S69.[8,9][0,1,2]XD	[Oth spec, Unsp] injuries of [unsp, rt, lt] wrist, hand and finger(s), subsq enc **397**
M24.8*	Oth specific jt derangements, NEC **194**
O02.8*	Oth specified abnormal products of conception **279**
O30.8[0,1,2,9][1,2,3]	Oth specified multiple gestation, [unsp number of placenta and amniotic sacs, two or more monochorionic fetuses, two or more monoamniotic fetuses, unable to determine the number of placenta and amniotic sacs], [1st, 2nd, 3rd] trmstr **279**
E75.29	Oth sphingolipidosis **32**
M23.6*	Oth spontaneous disruption of lgmt(s) of knee **184**
S63.69[8,9][A,S]	Oth sprain of [oth, unsp] finger, [init enc, seq] **190**
S63.69[8,9]D	Oth sprain of [oth, unsp] finger, subsq enc **396**
S63.69[0,1,2,3,4,5,6,7,8,9]A	Oth sprain of [rt index, lt index, rt mid, lt mid, rt ring, lt ring, rt little, lt little, oth, unsp] finger, init enc **425**
S43.49[1,2,9]D	Oth sprain of [rt, lt, unpecified] shldr jt, subsq enc **391**
S53.49[1,2,9]D	Oth sprain of [rt, lt, unsp] elbow, subsq enc **392**
S93.69[1,2,9][A,S]	Oth sprain of [rt, lt, unsp] foot, [init enc, seq] **193**

Code	Description
S93.69[1,2,9]A	Oth sprain of [rt, lt, unsp] foot, init enc 430
S93.69[1,2,9]D	Oth sprain of [rt, lt, unsp] foot, subsq enc 399
S73.19[1,2,9]A	Oth sprain of [rt, lt, unsp] hip, init enc 163, 426
S43.49[1,2,9]A	Oth sprain of [rt, lt, unsp] shldr jt, init enc 423
S63.68[1,2,9] [A,S]	Oth sprain of [rt, lt, unsp] thumb, [init enc, seq] 190
S63.68[1,2,9]A	Oth sprain of [rt, lt, unsp] thumb, init enc 425
S63.68[1,2,9]D	Oth sprain of [rt, lt, unsp] thumb, subsq enc 396
S63.69[0,1][A,S]	Oth sprain of [rt, lt] index finger, [init enc, seq] 190
S63.69[0,1]D	Oth sprain of [rt, lt] index finger, subsq enc 396
S63.69[6,7][A,S]	Oth sprain of [rt, lt] little finger, [init enc, seq] 190
S63.69[6,7]D	Oth sprain of [rt, lt] little finger, subsq enc 396
S63.69[2,3][A,S]	Oth sprain of [rt, lt] mid finger, [init enc, seq] 190
S63.69[2,3]D	Oth sprain of [rt, lt] mid finger, subsq enc 396
S63.69[4,5][A,S]	Oth sprain of [rt, lt] ring finger, [init enc, seq] 190
S63.69[4,5]D	Oth sprain of [rt, lt] ring finger, subsq enc 396
S53.49[1,2,9] [A,S]	Oth sprain of elbow [rt, lt, unsp] [init enc, seq] 187
S43.49[1,2,9] [A,S]	Oth sprain of shldr jt [rt, lt, unsp] [init enc, seq] 185
F15.[2,9]3	Oth stimulant [dependence, use unsp] w/ w/drawal 283
M00.2*	Oth streptococcal arthritis and polyarthritis 164
M00.26[1,2,9]	Oth streptococcal arthritis, [rt, lt, unsp] knee 131
H53.19	Oth subjective visual disturbances 46
S93.33[1,2,3] [A,S]	Oth sublux of [rt, lt, unsp] foot, [init enc, seq] 193
S93.33[1,2,3]A	Oth sublux of [rt, lt, unsp] foot, init enc 430
S93.33[1,2,3]D	Oth sublux of [rt, lt, unsp] foot, subsq enc 399
S43.08[1,2,3,4,5,6]D	Oth sublux of [rt, lt, unsp] humerus, Oth disloc of [rt, lt, unsp] humerus subsq enc 391
S83.19[1,2,3] [A,S]	Oth sublux of [rt, lt, unsp] knee, [init enc, seq] 191
S83.19[1,2,3]A	Oth sublux of [rt, lt, unsp] knee, init enc 428
S83.19[1,2,3]D	Oth sublux of [rt, lt, unsp] knee, subsq enc 398
S83.09[1,2,3] [A,S]	Oth sublux of [rt, lt, unsp] patella, [init enc, seq] 191
S83.09[1,2,3]A	Oth sublux of [rt, lt, unsp] patella, init enc 428
S83.09[1,2,3]D	Oth sublux of [rt, lt, unsp] patella, subsq enc 398
S53.09[1,2,3]D	Oth sublux of [rt, lt, unsp] radial head, subsq enc 392
S53.19[1,2,3] [A,S]	Oth sublux of [rt, lt, unsp] ulnohumeral jt, [init enc, seq] 186
S53.19[1,2,3]D	Oth sublux of [rt, lt, unsp] ulnohumeral jt, subsq enc 392
S63.09[1,2,3] [A,S]	Oth sublux of [rt, lt, unsp] wrist and hand, [init enc, seq] 188
S63.09[1,2,3]D	Oth sublux of [rt, lt] wrist and hand, subsq enc 395
S53.09[1,2,3] [A,S]	Oth sublux of radial head [unsp, rt, lt] [init enc, seq] 186
S43.08[1,2,3] [A,S]	Oth sublux of shldr jt [rt, lt, unsp] [init enc, seq] 185
S00.57[1,2][A,S]	Oth superf bite of [lip, oral cavity], [init enc, seq] 224
S30.87[0,1,2,3,4,5,6,7]D	Oth superf bite of [lwr back and pelvis, abd wall, penis, scrotum and testes, vagina and vulva, unsp ext genital organs male, unsp ext genital organs female, anus], subsq enc 389
S60.47[8,9][A,S]	Oth superf bite of [oth, unsp] finger, [init enc, seq] 228
S60.47[8,9]D	Oth superf bite of [oth, unsp] finger, subsq enc 394
S30.87[2,3][A,S]	Oth superf bite of [penis, scrotum and testes], [init enc, seq] 226
S20.47[1,2,9] [A,S]	Oth superf bite of [rt, lt, unsp] back wall of thorax, [init enc, seq] 225
S20.47[1,2,9]D	Oth superf bite of [rt, lt, unsp] back wall of thorax, subsq enc 388
S00.47[1,2,9] [A,S]	Oth superf bite of [rt, lt, unsp] ear, [init enc, seq] 224
S50.37[1,2,9] [A,S]	Oth superf bite of [rt, lt, unsp] elbow, [init enc, seq] 227
S50.37[1,2,9]D	Oth superf bite of [rt, lt, unsp] elbow, subsq enc 392
S00.27[1,2,9]A	Oth superf bite of [rt, lt, unsp] eyelid and periocular area, init enc 46
S00.27[1,2,9]S	Oth superf bite of [rt, lt, unsp] eyelid and periocular area, seq 224
S90.87[1,2,9] [A,S]	Oth superf bite of [rt, lt, unsp] foot, [init enc, seq] 230
S50.87[1,2,9] [A,S]	Oth superf bite of [rt, lt, unsp] forearm, [init enc, seq] 227
S50.87[1,2,9]D	Oth superf bite of [rt, lt, unsp] forearm, subsq enc 392
S20.37[1,2,9] [A,S]	Oth superf bite of [rt, lt, unsp] front wall of thorax, [init enc, seq] 225
S20.37[1,2,9]D	Oth superf bite of [rt, lt, unsp] front wall of thorax, subsq enc 388
S90.47[1,2,3] [A,S]	Oth superf bite of [rt, lt, unsp] great toe, [init enc, seq] 230
S90.47[1,2,3]A	Oth superf bite of [rt, lt, unsp] great toe, init enc 428
S90.47[1,2,3]D	Oth superf bite of [rt, lt, unsp] great toe, subsq enc 399
S80.27[1,2,9] [A,S]	Oth superf bite of [rt, lt, unsp] knee, [init enc, seq] 229
S90.47[4,5,6] [A,S]	Oth superf bite of [rt, lt, unsp] lesser toe(s), [init enc, seq] 230
S90.47[4,5,6]A	Oth superf bite of [rt, lt, unsp] lesser toe(s), init enc 428
S90.47[4,5,6]D	Oth superf bite of [rt, lt, unsp] lesser toe(s), subsq enc 399
S40.27[1,2,9] [A,S]	Oth superf bite of [rt, lt, unsp] shldr, [init enc, seq] 227
S40.27[1,2,9]D	Oth superf bite of [rt, lt, unsp] shldr, subsq enc 391
S70.37[1,2,9] [A,S]	Oth superf bite of [rt, lt, unsp] thigh, [init enc, seq] 229
S60.37[1,2,9] [A,S]	Oth superf bite of [rt, lt, unsp] thumb, [init enc, seq] 228
S60.37[1,2,9]D	Oth superf bite of [rt, lt, unsp] thumb, subsq enc 394
S40.87[1,2,9] [A,S]	Oth superf bite of [rt, lt, unsp] upr arm, [init enc, seq] 227
S40.87[1,2,9]D	Oth superf bite of [rt, lt, unsp] upr arm, subsq enc 391
S60.87[1,2,9] [A,S]	Oth superf bite of [rt, lt, unsp] wrist, [init enc, seq] 228
S60.87[1,2,9]D	Oth superf bite of [rt, lt, unsp] wrist, subsq enc 394
S60.47[0,1][A,S]	Oth superf bite of [rt, lt] index finger, [init enc, seq] 228
S60.47[0,1]D	Oth superf bite of [rt, lt] index finger, subsq enc 394
S60.47[6,7][A,S]	Oth superf bite of [rt, lt] little finger, [init enc, seq] 228
S60.47[6,7]D	Oth superf bite of [rt, lt] little finger, subsq enc 394
S60.47[2,3][A,S]	Oth superf bite of [rt, lt] mid finger, [init enc, seq] 228
S60.47[2,3]D	Oth superf bite of [rt, lt] mid finger, subsq enc 394
S60.47[4,5][A,S]	Oth superf bite of [rt, lt] ring finger, [init enc, seq] 228
S60.47[4,5]D	Oth superf bite of [rt, lt] ring finger, subsq enc 394
S30.871[A,S]	Oth superf bite of abd wall, [init enc, seq] 226
S90.57[1,2,9] [A,S]	Oth superf bite of ankle, [rt, lt, unsp] ankle, [init enc, seq] 230
S30.877[A,S]	Oth superf bite of anus, [init enc, seq] 226
S20.17[1,2,9] [A,S]	Oth superf bite of breast, [rt, lt, unsp] breast, [init enc, seq] 225
S20.17[1,2,9]D	Oth superf bite of breast, [rt, lt, unsp] breast, subsq enc 388
S60.57[1,2,9] [A,S]	Oth superf bite of hand of [rt, lt, unsp] hand, [init enc, seq] 228
S60.57[1,2,9]D	Oth superf bite of hand of [rt, lt, unsp] hand, subsq enc 394
S70.27[1,2,9] [A,S]	Oth superf bite of hip, [rt, lt, unsp] hip, [init enc, seq] 229
S30.870[A,S]	Oth superf bite of lwr back and pelvis, [init enc, seq] 226
S00.37X[A,S]	Oth superf bite of nose, [init enc, seq] 224
S00.87X[A,S]	Oth superf bite of oth part of head, [init enc, seq] 224
S00.07X[A,S]	Oth superf bite of scalp, [init enc, seq] 224
S10.17X[A,S]	Oth superf bite of throat, [init enc, seq] 225
S30.87[5,6][A,S]	Oth superf bite of unsp ext genital organs, [male, female], [init enc, seq] 226
S00.97X[A,S]	Oth superf bite of unsp part of head, [init enc, seq] 224
S20.97X[A,S]	Oth superf bite of unsp parts of thorax, [init enc, seq] 225
S30.874[A,S]	Oth superf bite of vagina and vulva, [init enc, seq] 226
S80.87[1,2,9] [A,S]	Oth superf bite, [rt, lt, unsp] lwr leg, [init enc, seq] 229
S60.39[1,2,9] [A,S]	Oth superf injuries of [rt, lt, unsp] thumb, [init enc, seq] 228
S60.39[1,2,9]D	Oth superf injuries of [rt, lt, unsp] thumb, subsq enc 394
B36*	Oth superf mycoses 233
R48.8	Oth symbolic dysfunctions 311
A52.79	Oth symptomatic late syphilis 308
A52.19	Oth symptomatic neurosyphilis 32
R45.89	Oth symptoms and signs involving emotional state 310
R09.89	Oth symptoms and signs involving the circ and resp systems 103
R19.8	Oth symptoms and signs involving the dgstv sys and abd 116
R29.898	Oth symptoms and signs involving the musculoskeletal sys 167
R29.818	Oth symptoms and signs involving the nervous sys 38
R41.89	Oth symptoms and signs w cognitive functions & awareness 310

M79.6*	Pain in limb, hand, foot, fingers and toes 167
M54.6	Pain in thoracic spine 165
R07.0	Pain in throat 58
R52	Pain, unsp 385
R23.1	Pallor 385
R00.2	Palpitations 102
H51.0	Palsy (spasm) of conjugate gaze 46
Z94.83	Pancreas transplant status 124
K90.3	Pancreatic steatorrhea 116
D61.81*	Pancytopenia 293
M54.0 [3,4,5,6,7,8,9]	Panniculitis affecting rgns of neck and back [cervicothoracic, thoracic, thoracolumbar, lumbar, lumbosacral, sacral and sacrococcygeal, multi] rgn(s) 165
M54.0[0,1,2]	Panniculitis affecting rgns of neck and back, [unsp, occipito-atlanto-axial, cervical] rgn 234
M79.3	Panniculitis, unsp 234
H44.11*	Panuveitis 46
H47.1[0,1,2]	Papilledema [unsp, associated w/ increased intracranial pressure, associated w/ decreased ocular pressure] 283
H47.12	Papilledema associated with decreased ocular pressure 46
H47.11	Papilledema associated with increased intracranial pressure 38
H47.13	Papilledema associated with retinal d/o 46
L45	Papulosquamous d/o in dz classified elsw 234
L44.9	Papulosquamous d/o, unsp 234
O31.0*	Papyraceous fetus 279
O31.0[0,1,2,3] X[0,1,2,3,4,5,9]	Papyraceous fetus, [unsp, 1st, 2nd, 3rd] trmstr, fetus [N/A or unsp, 1, 2, 3, 4, 5, oth] 278
B41*	Paracoccidioidomycosis 283, 308
B66.4	Paragonimiasis 67
J38.0*	Paralysis of vocal cords and larynx 4, 284
R26.1	Paralytic gait 38
K56.0	Paralytic ileus 284
K56*	Paralytic ileus and intestinal obstruction w/o hernia 116
G83.9	Paralytic synd, unsp 38
G13.0	Paraneoplastic neuromyopathy and neuropathy 34
F65*	Paraphilias 311
N47.2	Paraphimosis 289
G82*	Paraplegia (paraparesis) and quadriplegia (quadriparesis) 32
B08.6*	Parapoxvirus infections 307
L41*	Parapsoriasis 223
H21.33[1,2,3,9]	Parasitic cyst of iris, ciliary body or ant chamber, [rt, lt, bilat, unsp] eye 45
H33.12[1,2,3,9]	Parasitic cyst of retina, [rt, lt, bilat, unsp] eye 45
H44.12[1,2,3,9]	Parasitic endophthalmitis, unsp, [rt, lt, bilat, unsp] eye 45
G47.5*	Parasomnia 3
G47.54	Parasomnia in conditions classified elsw 58
G47.50	Parasomnia, unsp 58
K43.[3,4]	Parastomal hernia, w/ [obstruction w/o gangrene, gangrene], not spec as recurrent 284
B08.04	Paravaccinia, unsp 307
H52.52*	Paresis of accommodation 46
G20	Parkinson's dz 32
D59.5	Paroxysmal nocturnal hemoglobinuria [Marchiafava-Micheli] 283, 293
I47*	Paroxysmal tachycardia 102
Q26.3	Partial anomalous pulmn venous connection 102
K08.4*	Partial loss of teeth 4
S48.02[1,2,9]D	Partial traum amp at [rt, lt, unsp] shldr jt, subsq enc 392
S58.02[1,2,9]D	Partial traum amp at elbow lvl, [rt, lt, unsp] arm, subsq enc 393
S48.12[1,2,9]D	Partial traum amp at lvl between [rt, lt, unsp] shldr and elbow, subsq enc 392
S58.12[1,2,9]D	Partial traum amp at lvl between elbow and wrist, [rt, lt, unsp] arm, subsq enc 393
S28.22[1,2,9] [A,S]	Partial traum amp of [rt, lt, unsp] breast, [init enc, seq] 226
S28.22[1,2,9]D	Partial traum amp of [rt, lt, unsp] breast, subsq enc 389
S58.92[1,2,9]D	Partial traum amp of [rt, lt, unsp] forearm, lvl unsp, subsq enc 393
S48.92[1,2,9]D	Partial traum amp of [rt, lt, unsp] shldr and upr arm, lvl unsp, subsq enc 392
S08.122A	Partial Traum amp of lt ear, init enc 58
S08.812A	Partial traum amp of nose, init enc 5

S08.121A	Partial Traum amp of rt ear, init enc 58
S08.129A	Partial Traum amp of unsp ear, init enc 58
S68.12[0,1,2,3,4, 5,6,7,8,9]S	Partial traum metacarpophalangeal amp of [rt index, lt index, rt mid, lt mid, rt ring, lt ring, rt little, lt little, oth, unsp] finger, seq 176
S68.62[0,1,2,3,4, 5,6,7,8,9]S	Partial traum transphalangeal amp of [rt index, lt index, rt mid, lt mid, rt ring, lt ring, rt little, lt little, oth, unsp] finger, seq 176
A28.0	Pasteurellosis 308
M24.3[1,2,3,4,6] [1,2,9]	Path disloc of [rt, lt, unsp] [shldr, elbow, wrist, hand, knee], NEC 184
M24.37[1,2,3]	Path disloc of [rt, lt, unsp] ankle, NEC 184
M24.37[4,5,6]	Path disloc of [rt, lt, unsp] foot, NEC 184
M24.35[1,2,9]	Path disloc of [rt, lt, unsp] hip, NEC 193
M24.30	Path disloc of unsp jt, NEC 184
M84.47[1,2,3,4,5, 6,7,8,9]A	Path fx [rt ankle, lt ankle, unsp ankle, rt foot, lt foot, unsp foot, rt toe(s), lt toe(s), unsp toe(s)], init enc for fx 163, 285
M84.55[0,1,2,3,9] A	Path fx in neoplastic dz, [pelvis, rt femur, lt femur, unsp femur, unsp hip], init enc for fx 163, 285
M84.57[1,2,3,4,5, 6]A	Path fx in neoplastic dz, [rt ankle, lt ankle, unsp ankle, rt foot, lt foot, unsp foot], init enc for fx 163, 285
M84.56[1,2,3,4,9] [D,G,S]	Path fx in neoplastic dz, [rt tibia, lt tibia, rt fibula, lt fibula, unsp tibia & fibula], [subsq enc for fx w/ routine healing, subsq enc for fx w/ delayed healing, seq] 168
M84.56[1,2,3,4,9] A	Path fx in neoplastic dz, [rt tibia, lt tibia, rt fibula, lt fibula, unsp tibia & fibula], init enc for fx 163, 285
M84.56[1,2,3,4,9] [K,P]	Path fx in neoplastic dz, [rt tibia, lt tibia, rt fibula, lt fibula, unsp tibia & fibula], subsq enc for fx w/ [nonu, malu] 194
M84.53[1,2,3,4,9] [D,G,S]	Path fx in neoplastic dz, [rt ulna, lt ulna, rt radius, lt radius, unsp ulna and radius], [subsq enc for fx w/ routine healing, subsq enc for fx w/ delayed healing, seq] 168
M84.53[1,2,3,4,9] A	Path fx in neoplastic dz, [rt ulna, lt ulna, rt radius, lt radius, unsp ulna and radius], init enc for fx 163, 285
M84.53[1,2,3,4,9] [K,P]	Path fx in neoplastic dz, [rt ulna, lt ulna, rt radius, lt radius, unsp ulna and radius], subsq enc for fx w/ [nonu, malu] 194
M84.57[1,2,3] [D,G,S]	Path fx in neoplastic dz, [rt, lt, unsp] ankle, [subsq enc for fx w/ routine healing, subsq enc for fx w/ delayed healing, seq] 168
M84.57[1,2,3] [K,P]	Path fx in neoplastic dz, [rt, lt, unsp] ankle, subsq enc for fx w/ [nonu, malu] 194
M84.55[1,2,3] [D,G,S]	Path fx in neoplastic dz, [rt, lt, unsp] femur, [subsq enc for fx w/ routine healing, subsq enc for fx w/ delayed healing, seq] 168
M84.55[1,2,3] [K,P]	Path fx in neoplastic dz, [rt, lt, unsp] femur, subsq enc for fx w/ [nonu, malu] 194
M84.57[4,5,6] [D,G,S]	Path fx in neoplastic dz, [rt, lt, unsp] foot, [subsq enc for fx w/ routine healing, subsq enc for fx w/ delayed healing, seq] 168
M84.57[4,5,6] [K,P]	Path fx in neoplastic dz, [rt, lt, unsp] foot, subsq enc for fx w/ [nonu, malu] 194
M84.54[1,2,9] [D,G,S]	Path fx in neoplastic dz, [rt, lt, unsp] hand, [subsq enc for fx w/ routine healing, subsq enc for fx w/ delayed healing, seq] 168
M84.54[1,2,9]A	Path fx in neoplastic dz, [rt, lt, unsp] hand, init enc for fx 163, 285
M84.54[1,2,9] [K,P]	Path fx in neoplastic dz, [rt, lt, unsp] hand, subsq enc for fx w/ [nonu, malu] 194
M84.52[1,2,9] [D,G,S]	Path fx in neoplastic dz, [rt, lt, unsp] humerus, [subsq enc for fx w/ routine healing, subsq enc for fx w/ delayed healing, seq] 168
M84.52[1,2,9]A	Path fx in neoplastic dz, [rt, lt, unsp] humerus, init enc for fx 163, 285
M84.52[1,2,9] [K,P]	Path fx in neoplastic dz, [rt, lt, unsp] humerus, subsq enc for fx w/ [nonu, malu] 194
M84.51[1,2,9] [D,G,S]	Path fx in neoplastic dz, [rt, lt, unsp] shldr, [subsq enc for fx w/ routine healing, subsq enc for fx w/ delayed healing, seq] 168
M84.51[1,2,9]A	Path fx in neoplastic dz, [rt, lt, unsp] shldr, init enc for fx 163, 285
M84.51[1,2,9] [K,P]	Path fx in neoplastic dz, [rt, lt, unsp] shldr, subsq enc for fx w/ [nonu, malu] 194
M84.559[K,P]	Path fx in neoplastic dz, hip, unsp, subsq enc for fx w/ [nonu, malu] 194
M84.58XA	Path fx in neoplastic dz, oth site, init 125, 163, 285
M84.58XS	Path fx in neoplastic dz, oth site, seq 165
M84.550S	Path fx in neoplastic dz, pelvis, seq 165
M84.550[K,P]	Path fx in neoplastic dz, pelvis, subsq enc for fx w/ [nonu, malu] 194
M84.550[D,G]	Path fx in neoplastic dz, pelvis, subsq enc for fx w/ [routine, delayed] healing 168
M84.559[D,G,S]	Path fx in neoplastic dz, unsp hip, [subsq enc for fx w/ routine healing, subsq enc for fx w/ delayed healing, seq] 168
M84.50X[D,G,S]	Path fx in neoplastic dz, unsp site, [subsq enc for fx w/ routine healing, subsq enc for fx w/ delayed healing, seq] 168

M84.50XA	Path fx in neoplastic dz, unsp site, init **163**, **285**
M84.50X[K,P]	Path fx in neoplastic dz, unsp site, subsq enc for fx w/ [nonu, malu] **194**
M84.58X[K,P]	Path fx in neoplastic dz, vertebrae, subsq enc for fx w/ [nonu, malu] **194**
M84.58XG	Path fx in neopltc dis, oth site, subs fx w delay heal **168**
M84.58XD	Path fx in neopltc dis, oth site, subs for fx w routn heal **168**
M84.65[0,1,2,3,9]A	Path fx in oth dz, [pelvis, rt femur, lt femur, unsp femur, hip NOS], init enc for fx **163**, **285**
M84.67[1,2,3,4,5,6]A	Path fx in oth dz, [rt ankle, lt ankle, unsp ankle, rt foot, lt foot, unsp foot], init enc for fx **285**
M84.66[1,2,3,4,9][D,G,S]	Path fx in oth dz, [rt tibia, lt tibia, rt fibula, lt fibula, unsp tibia & fibula], [subsq enc for fx w/ routine healing, subsq enc for fx w/ delayed healing, seq] **169**
M84.66[1,2,3,4,9]A	Path fx in oth dz, [rt tibia, lt tibia, rt fibula, lt fibula, unsp tibia & fibula], init enc for fx **163**, **285**
M84.63[1,2,3,4,9][D,G,S]	Path fx in oth dz, [rt ulna, lt ulna, rt radius, lt radius, unsp ulna and radius], [subsq enc for fx w/ routine healing, subsq enc for fx w/ delayed healing, seq] **168**
M84.63[1,2,3,4,9]A	Path fx in oth dz, [rt ulna, lt ulna, rt radius, lt radius, unsp ulna and radius], init enc for fx **163**, **285**
M84.67[1,2,3][D,G,S]	Path fx in oth dz, [rt, lt, unsp] ankle, [subsq enc for fx w/ routine healing, subsq enc for fx w/ delayed healing, seq] **169**
M84.65[1,2,3][D,G,S]	Path fx in oth dz, [rt, lt, unsp] femur, [subsq enc for fx w/ routine healing, subsq enc for fx w/ delayed healing, seq] **169**
M84.67[4,5,6][D,G,S]	Path fx in oth dz, [rt, lt, unsp] foot, [subsq enc for fx w/ routine healing, subsq enc for fx w/ delayed healing, seq] **169**
M84.64[1,2,9][D,G,S]	Path fx in oth dz, [rt, lt, unsp] hand, [subsq enc for fx w/ routine healing, subsq enc for fx w/ delayed healing, seq] **169**
M84.64[1,2,9]A	Path fx in oth dz, [rt, lt, unsp] hand, init enc for fx **163**, **285**
M84.62[1,2,9][D,G,S]	Path fx in oth dz, [rt, lt, unsp] humerus, [subsq enc for fx w/ routine healing, subsq enc for fx w/ delayed healing, seq] **168**
M84.62[1,2,9]A	Path fx in oth dz, [rt, lt, unsp] humerus, init enc for fx **163**, **285**
M84.61[1,2,9][D,G,S]	Path fx in oth dz, [rt, lt, unsp] shldr, [subsq enc for fx w/ routine healing, subsq enc for fx w/ delayed healing, seq] **168**
M84.61[1,2,9]A	Path fx in oth dz, [rt, lt, unsp] shldr, init enc for fx **163**, **285**
M84.672A	Path fx in oth dz, lt ankle, init **163**
M84.675A	Path fx in oth dz, lt foot, init for fx **163**
M84.68X[D,G,S]	Path fx in oth dz, oth site, [subsq enc for fx w/ routine healing, subsq enc for fx w/ delayed healing, seq] **169**
M84.68XA	Path fx in oth dz, oth site, init for fx **125**, **163**, **285**
M84.68X[K,P]	Path fx in oth dz, oth site, subsq enc for fx w/ [nonu, malu] **194**
M84.650S	Path fx in oth dz, pelvis, seq **165**
M84.650[D,G]	Path fx in oth dz, pelvis, subsq enc for fx w/ [routine, delayed] healing **169**
M84.671A	Path fx in oth dz, rt ankle, init **163**
M84.674A	Path fx in oth dz, rt foot, init **163**
M84.673A	Path fx in oth dz, unsp ankle, init **163**
M84.676A	Path fx in oth dz, unsp foot, init for fx **163**
M84.659[D,G,S]	Path fx in oth dz, unsp hip, [subsq enc for fx w/ routine healing, subsq enc for fx w/ delayed healing, seq] **169**
M84.60X[D,G,S]	Path fx in oth dz, unsp site, [subsq enc for fx w/ routine healing, subsq enc for fx w/ delayed healing, seq] **168**
M84.60XA	Path fx in oth dz, unsp site, init for fx **163**, **285**
M84.66[1,2,3,4,9][K,P]	Path fx in oth dzs, [rt tibia, lt tibia, rt fibula, lt fibula, unsp tibia & fibula], subsq enc for fx w/ [nonu, malu] **194**
M84.63[1,2,3,4,9][K,P]	Path fx in oth dzs, [rt ulna, lt ulna, rt radius, lt radius, unsp ulna and radius], subsq enc for fx w/ [nonu, malu] **194**
M84.67[1,2,3][K,P]	Path fx in oth dzs, [rt, lt, unsp] ankle, subsq enc for fx w/ [nonu, malu] **194**
M84.65[1,2,3][K,P]	Path fx in oth dzs, [rt, lt, unsp] femur, subsq enc for fx w/ [nonu, malu] **194**
M84.67[4,5,6][K,P]	Path fx in oth dzs, [rt, lt, unsp] foot, subsq enc for fx w/ [nonu, malu] **194**
M84.64[1,2,9][K,P]	Path fx in oth dzs, [rt, lt, unsp] hand, subsq enc for fx w/ [nonu, malu] **194**
M84.62[1,2,9][K,P]	Path fx in oth dzs, [rt, lt, unsp] humerus, subsq enc for fx w/ [nonu, malu] **194**
M84.61[1,2,9][K,P]	Path fx in oth dzs, [rt, lt, unsp] shldr, subsq enc for fx w/ [nonu, malu] **194**
M84.659[K,P]	Path fx in oth dzs, hip, unsp, subsq enc for fx w/ [nonu, malu] **194**
M84.650[K,P]	Path fx in oth dzs, pelvis, subsq enc for fx w/ [nonu, malu] **194**
M84.60X[K,P]	Path fx in oth dzs, unsp site, subsq enc for fx w/ [nonu, malu] **194**
M84.45[4,9][K,P]	Path fx, [pelvis, unsp hip], subsq enc for fx w/ [nonu, malu] **194**
M84.45[1,2,3,4,9]A	Path fx, [rt femur, lt femur, unsp femur, pelvis, unsp hip], init enc for fx **163**, **285**
M84.44[1,2,3,4,5,6]A	Path fx, [rt hand, lt hand, unsp hand, rt finger(s), lt finger(s), unsp finger(s)], init enc for fx **163**, **285**
M84.46[1,2,3,4,9][D,G,S]	Path fx, [rt tibia, lt tibia, rt fibula, lt fibula, unsp tibia & fibula], [subsq enc for fx w/ routine healing, subsq enc for fx w/ delayed healing, seq] **168**
M84.46[1,2,3,4,9]A	Path fx, [rt tibia, lt tibia, rt fibula, lt fibula, unsp tibia & fibula], init enc for fx **163**, **285**
M84.46[1,2,3,4,9][K,P]	Path fx, [rt tibia, lt tibia, rt fibula, lt fibula, unsp tibia & fibula], subsq enc for fx w/ [nonu, malu] **194**
M84.43[1,2,3,4,9]A	Path fx, [rt ulna, lt ulna, rt radius, lt radius, unsp radius and ulna], init enc for fx **163**, **285**
M84.43[1,2,3,4,9][D,G,S]	Path fx, [rt ulna, lt ulna, rt radius, lt radius, unsp ulna and radius], [subsq enc for fx w/ routine healing, subsq enc for fx w/ delayed healing, seq] **168**
M84.43[1,2,3,4,9][K,P]	Path fx, [rt ulna, lt ulna, rt radius, lt radius, unsp ulna and radius], subsq enc for fx w/ [nonu, malu] **194**
M84.47[1,2,3][D,G,S]	Path fx, [rt, lt, unsp] ankle, [subsq enc for fx w/ routine healing, subsq enc for fx w/ delayed healing, seq] **168**
M84.47[1,2,3][K,P]	Path fx, [rt, lt, unsp] ankle, subsq enc for fx w/ [nonu, malu] **194**
M84.45[1,2,3][D,G,S]	Path fx, [rt, lt, unsp] femur, [subsq enc for fx w/ routine healing, subsq enc for fx w/ delayed healing, seq] **168**
M84.45[1,2,3][K,P]	Path fx, [rt, lt, unsp] femur, subsq enc for fx w/ [nonu, malu] **194**
M84.44[4,5,6][K,P]	Path fx, [rt, lt, unsp] finger(s), subsq enc for fx w/ [nonu, malu] **194**
M84.44[4,5,6][D,G,S]	Path fx, [rt, lt, unsp] fingers, [subsq enc for fx w/ routine healing, subsq enc for fx w/ delayed healing, seq] **168**
M84.47[4,5,6][D,G,S]	Path fx, [rt, lt, unsp] foot, [subsq enc for fx w/ routine healing, subsq enc for fx w/ delayed healing, seq] **168**
M84.47[4,5,6][K,P]	Path fx, [rt, lt, unsp] foot, subsq enc for fx w/ [nonu, malu] **194**
M84.44[1,2,3][D,G,S]	Path fx, [rt, lt, unsp] hand, [subsq enc for fx w/ routine healing, subsq enc for fx w/ delayed healing, seq] **168**
M84.44[1,2,3][K,P]	Path fx, [rt, lt, unsp] hand, subsq enc for fx w/ [nonu, malu] **194**
M84.42[1,2,9][D,G,S]	Path fx, [rt, lt, unsp] humerus, [subsq enc for fx w/ routine healing, subsq enc for fx w/ delayed healing, seq] **168**
M84.42[1,2,9]A	Path fx, [rt, lt, unsp] humerus, init enc for fx **163**, **285**
M84.42[1,2,9][K,P]	Path fx, [rt, lt, unsp] humerus, subsq enc for fx w/ [nonu, malu] **194**
M84.41[1,2,9][D,G,S]	Path fx, [rt, lt, unsp] shldr, [subsq enc for fx w/ routine healing, subsq enc for fx w/ delayed healing, seq] **168**
M84.41[1,2,9]A	Path fx, [rt, lt, unsp] shldr, init enc for fx **163**, **285**
M84.41[1,2,9][K,P]	Path fx, [rt, lt, unsp] shldr, subsq enc for fx w/ [nonu, malu] **194**
M84.47[7,8,9][K,P]	Path fx, [rt, lt, unsp] toe(s), subsq enc for fx w/ [nonu, malu] **194**
M84.47[7,8,9][D,G,S]	Path fx, [rt, lt, unsp] toes, [subsq enc for fx w/ routine healing, subsq enc for fx w/ delayed healing, seq] **168**
M84.48X[D,G,S]	Path fx, oth site, [subsq enc for fx w/ routine healing, subsq enc for fx w/ delayed healing, seq] **168**
M84.48XA	Path fx, oth site, init enc for fx **163**, **285**
M84.48X[K,P]	Path fx, oth site, subsq enc for fx w/ [nonu, malu] **194**
M84.454[D,G]	Path fx, pelvis, [subsq enc for fx w/ routine healing, subsq enc for fx w/ delayed healing] **168**
M84.454S	Path fx, pelvis, seq **165**
M84.459[D,G,S]	Path fx, unsp hip, [subsq enc for fx w/ routine healing, subsq enc for fx w/ delayed healing, seq] **168**
M84.40X[D,G,S]	Path fx, unsp site, [subsq enc for fx w/ routine healing, subsq enc for fx w/ delayed healing, seq] **168**
M84.40XA	Path fx, unsp site, init enc for fx **163**, **285**
M84.40X[K,P]	Path fx, unsp site, subsq enc for fx w/ [nonu, malu] **194**
F63.0	Path gambling **310**
K03.3	Path resorption of teeth **4**
Q67.7	Pectus carinatum **69**
Q67.6	Pectus excavatum **69**
B85*	Pediculosis and phthiriasis **233**
K76.4	Peliosis hepatis **124**, **284**
I86.2	Pelvic varices **261**, **264**, **270**
L12.9	Pemphigoid, unsp **223**
L10*	Pemphigus **223**

Code	Description
S05.[5,6][0,1,2]XS	Penetrating wnd [w/, w/o FB of [unsp, rt, lt] eyeball, seq 225
S05.4[0,1,2]XA	Penetrating wnd of orbit w/ or w/o FB, [unsp, rt, lt] eye, init enc 47, 418
S05.4[0,1,2]XS	Penetrating wnd of orbit w/ or w/o FB, [unsp, rt, lt] eye, seq 225
S05.4[0,1,2]XD	Penetrating wnd of orbit w/ or w/o FB, [unsp, rt, lt] eye, subsq enc 386
S05.5[0,1,2]XA	Penetrating wnd w/ FB of [unsp, rt, lt] eyeball, init enc 47, 418
S05.5[0,1,2]XD	Penetrating wnd w/ FB of [unsp, rt, lt] eyeball, subsq enc 386
S05.6[0,1,2]XA	Penetrating wnd w/o FB of [unsp, rt, lt] eyeball, init enc 47, 418
S05.6[0,1,2]XD	Penetrating wnd w/o FB of [unsp, rt, lt] eyeball, subsq enc 386
B48.4	Penicillosis 283
K27.9	Peptic ulc, site unsp, unsp as ac or chr, w/o hemor or perf 115
K22.3	Perforation of esophagus 114, 284
K63.1	Perforation of intestine (nontraumatic) 117, 284
H72*	Perforation of tympanic membrane 58
K04.7	Periapical abscess w/o sinus 4
K04.6	Periapical abscess with sinus 4
M77.2*	Periarthritis of wrist 167
I32	Pericarditis in dz classified elsw 103, 283
P78.9	Perinatal digestive sys d/o, unsp 288
P61.9	Perinatal hematological d/o, unsp 288
P78.0	Perinatal intestinal perforation 282
O70*	Perineal lac during delivery 272, 275
R06.3	Periodic breathing 69
G47.61	Periodic limb movement d/o 38
G72.3	Periodic paralysis 38
K05.6	Periodontal dz, unsp 4
K05.4	Periodontosis 4
O90.3	Peripartum cardiomyopathy 272, 274, 276
C84.4*	Peripheral T-cell lymphoma, not classified 438
S83.26[1,2,9][A,S]	Peripheral tear of lat meniscus, current inj, [rt, lt, unsp] knee, [init enc, seq] 192
S83.26[1,2,9]A	Peripheral tear of lat meniscus, current inj, [rt, lt, unsp] knee, init enc 428
S83.26[1,2,9]D	Peripheral tear of lat meniscus, current inj, [rt, lt, unsp] knee, subsq enc 398
S83.22[1,2,9][A,S]	Peripheral tear of med meniscus, current inj, [rt, lt, unsp] knee, [init enc, seq] 192
S83.22[1,2,9]A	Peripheral tear of med meniscus, current inj, [rt, lt, unsp] knee, init enc 428
S83.22[1,2,9]D	Peripheral tear of med meniscus, current inj, [rt, lt, unsp] knee, subsq enc 398
Z95.820	Peripheral vascular angioplasty status w implants and grafts 103
I73.9	Peripheral vascular dz, unsp 100
T84.04[8,9][A,D]	Periprosthetic fx around [oth, unsp] int prosthetic jt, [init, subsq] enc 183
T84.04[0,1,2,3,8,9]S	Periprosthetic fx around int prosthetic [rt hip, lt hip, rt knee, lt knee, oth, unsp] jt, seq 375
T84.04[0,1][A,D]	Periprosthetic fx around int prosthetic [rt, lt] hip jt, [init, subsq] enc 183
T84.04[2,3][A,D]	Periprosthetic fx around int prosthetic [rt, lt] knee jt, [init, subsq] enc 183
T84.05[0,1,2,3,8,9]A	Periprosthetic osteolysis [rt hip, lt hip, rt knee, lt knee, oth site, unsp site] prosthesis, init enc 183
T84.05[0,1,2,3,8,9]D	Periprosthetic osteolysis [rt hip, lt hip, rt knee, lt knee, oth site, unsp site] prosthesis, subsq enc 411
T84.05[0,1,2,3,8,9]S	Periprosthetic osteolysis of int prosthetic [rt hip, lt hip, rt knee, lt knee, oth, unsp] jt, seq 375
M27.5*	Periradicular pathology assoc w previous endodontic tx 4
K65.1	Peritoneal abscess 114
K65*	Peritonitis 284
K65.9	Peritonitis, unsp 114
J36	Peritonsillar abscess 4, 57
Q43.7	Persistent cloaca 117
P29.3	Persistent fetal circulation 282
E32.0	Persistent hyperplasia of thymus 294
Q26.1	Persistent lt superior vena cava 102
F34.9	Persistent mood [affective] d/o, unsp 311
T81.83XA	Persistent postprocedural fistula, init enc 287, 368
T81.83XS	Persistent postprocedural fistula, seq 375
T81.83XD	Persistent postprocedural fistula, subsq enc 410
R80.1	Persistent proteinuria, unsp 255
R40.3	Persistent vegetative state 35, 285
Z87.7*	Personal history of (corrected) congenital malformations 413
Z87.81	Personal history of (healed) traum fx 413
Z87.892	Personal history of anaphylaxis 413
Z86*	Personal history of certain oth dz 413
Z87.410	Personal history of cervical dysplasia 304, 306
Z87.5*	Personal history of comp of preg, chldbrth and the puerp 413
Z92.0	Personal history of contraception 413
Z92.2*	Personal history of drug therapy 411
Z87.1*	Personal history of dz of the digestive sys 413
Z87.3*	Personal history of dz of the ms sys and conn tiss 413
Z87.0*	Personal history of dz of the respiratory sys 413
Z87.2	Personal history of dz of the skin, SQ 413
Z92.3	Personal history of irradiation 413
Z85.6	Personal history of leukemia 306
Z85*	Personal history of malig neoplasm 304
Z85.3	Personal history of malig neoplasm of breast 306
Z85.0*	Personal history of malig neoplasm of digestive organs 306
Z85.4*	Personal history of malig neoplasm of genital organs 306
Z85.21	Personal history of malig neoplasm of larynx 6
Z85.810	Personal history of malig neoplasm of tongue 6
Z85.5*	Personal history of malig neoplasm of urinary tract 306
Z85.9	Personal history of malig neoplasm, unsp 306
Z85.8*	Personal history of malig neoplasms of organs and systems 306
Z85.1*	Personal history of malig neoplm of trachea, bronc and lung 306
Z87.441	Personal history of nephrotic synd 413
Z87.891	Personal history of nicotine dependence 413
Z87.828	Personal history of oth (healed) physical inj and trauma 413
Z87.438	Personal history of oth dz of male genital organs 413
Z87.42	Personal history of oth dz of the female genital tract 413
Z87.448	Personal history of oth dz of urinary sys 413
Z92.8*	Personal history of oth medical tx 413
Z87.898	Personal history of oth spec conditions 413
Z87.430	Personal history of prostatic dysplasia 413
Z87.821	Personal history of retained FB fully removed 413
Z87.890	Personal history of sex reassignment 311
Z87.820	Personal history of traum brain inj 413
Z87.440	Personal history of urinary (tract) infections 413
Z87.442	Personal history of urinary calculi 413
Z87.411	Personal history of vaginal dysplasia 413
Z87.412	Personal history of vulvar dysplasia 413
Z91*	Personal risk factors, NEC 413
F07.0	Personality change d/t known physiological condition 310
Z71*	Persons enc health serv for oth cnsl and med advice, NEC 412
Z53*	Persons enc hlth serv for spec proc & tx, not crd out 412
Z76*	Persons encountering health services in oth circumstances 412
F84.9	Pervasive developmental d/o, unsp 311
H70.2*	Petrositis 57
Q85.9	Phakomatosis, unsp 304, 306
A36.0	Pharyngeal diphtheria 2, 58
N47.1	Phimosis 289
I80.2*	Phlbts and thombophlb of and unsp deep vessels of low extrm 99, 284
I80.0*	Phlebitis and thombophlb of superf vessels of low extrm 100
I80.[8,9]	Phlebitis and thrombophlebitis of [oth, unsp] site(s) 100
I80.1*	Phlebitis and thrombophlebitis of femor vein 99, 284
I80.3	Phlebitis and thrombophlebitis of lwr extremities, unsp 99, 284
K75.1	Phlebitis of portal vein 284
F40*	Phobic anxiety d/o 310
F80.0	Phonological d/o 311
P14.2	Phrenic nerve paralysis d/t birth inj 282
M89.1*	Physeal arrest 194
S49.10[1,2,9][A]	Physeal fx of lwr end of humerus [rt, lt, unsp] init enc 185
O9A.31[1,2,3]	Physical abuse compl preg, [1st, 2nd, 3rd] trmstr 277, 278
O9A.319	Physical abuse compl preg, unsp trmstr 281
O9A.33	Physical abuse compl the puerperium 276
O9A.[3,4,5]2	Physical, Sexual, Psychological] abuse compl childbirth 273, 275
O9A.[3,4,5]3	Physical, Sexual, Psychological] abuse compl the puerperium 272
F98.3	Pica of infancy and childhood 311
H40.13*	Pigmentary glaucoma 46

L81.7	Pigmented purpuric dermatosis **289**
L05*	Pilonidal cyst and sinus **224**
A67.9	Pinta, unsp **308**
L42	Pityriasis rosea **234**
L44.0	Pityriasis rubra pilaris **234**
O43.2[1,2,3]9	Placenta [accreta, increta, percreta], unsp trmstr **281**
O43.21[1,2,3]	Placenta accreta, [frist, 2nd, 3rd] trmstr **272, 273, 275**
O43.22[1,2,3]	Placenta increta, [1st, 2nd, 3rd] trmstr **272, 273, 275**
O43.23[1,2,3]	Placenta precreta, [1st, 2nd, 3rd] trmstr **272, 273, 275**
O44.[0,1][1,2,3]	Placenta previa [spec as w/o hemor, w/ hemor], [1st, 2nd, 3rd] trmstr **273, 278, 280**
O44.00	Placenta previa spec as w/o hemor, unsp trmstr **281**
O44.10	Placenta previa with hemor, unsp trmstr **281**
O43.81[1,2,3]	Placental infarction, [1st, 2nd, 3rd] trmstr **278**
O43.8[1,9][1,2,3]	Placental infarction, Oth placental d/o], [1st, 2nd, 3rd] trmstr **280**
O43.819	Placental infarction, unsp trmstr **281**
Q67.3	Plagiocephaly **195**
A20.3	Plague meningitis **308**
A20.9	Plague, unsp **308**
B50*	Plasmodium falciparum malaria **308**
B52*	Plasmodium malariae malaria **308**
B51*	Plasmodium vivax malaria **308**
J94.9	Pleural condition, unsp **68**
J91.8	Pleural effusion in oth conditions classified elsw **68, 284**
J90	Pleural effusion, NEC **68, 284**
J92*	Pleural plaque **68**
R09.1	Pleurisy **68**
R07.81	Pleurodynia **69**
K14.5	Plicated tongue **4**
T75.21X[A,S]	Pneumatic hammer synd, [init enc, seq] **374**
T75.21XD	Pneumatic hammer synd, subsq enc **410**
M00.1*	Pneumococcal arthritis and polyarthritis **164**
M00.16[1,2,9]	Pneumococcal arthritis, [rt, lt, unsp] knee **131**
G00.1	Pneumococcal meningitis **11, 15**
J65	Pneumoconiosis associated with tuberculosis **68**
J61	Pneumoconiosis d/t asbestos and oth mineral fibers **68**
J62*	Pneumoconiosis d/t dust containing silica **68**
J63*	Pneumoconiosis d/t oth inorganic dusts **68**
B59	Pneumocystosis **67, 283, 438**
J15.5	Pneumonia d/t Escherichia coli **66, 67, 439**
J14	Pneumonia d/t Hemophilus influenzae **68, 284, 439**
J15.0	Pneumonia d/t Klebsiella pneumoniae **66, 67, 439**
J15.7	Pneumonia d/t Mycoplasma pneumoniae **68**
J15.6	Pneumonia d/t oth aerobic Gram-negative bacteria **66, 67, 439**
J16*	Pneumonia d/t oth infectious organisms, NEC **68, 284**
J15.8	Pneumonia d/t oth spec bacteria **66, 67, 439**
J15.4	Pneumonia d/t oth streptococci **68, 439**
J15.1	Pneumonia d/t Pseudomonas **66, 67, 439**
J15.2*	Pneumonia d/t staphylococcus **66, 67, 439**
J13	Pneumonia d/t Streptococcus pneumoniae **68, 284, 439**
J15.3	Pneumonia d/t streptococcus, group B **68, 439**
J17	Pneumonia in dz classified elsw **67**
J18.9	Pneumonia, unsp organism **68, 284, 439**
A20.2	Pneumonic plague **67**
J69.[0,8]	Pneumonitis d/t inhalation of [food and vomit, oth solids and liquids] **284**
J69*	Pneumonitis d/t solids and liquids **67**
J93*	Pneumothorax and air leak **68**
L57.3	Poikiloderma of Civatte **289**
L94.5	Poikiloderma vasculare atrophicans **223**
T39.0[1,9] [1,2,3,4]A	Poison by [aspirin, salicylates], [accid (unintentional), intentional self-harm, assault, undetermined], init enc **362**
T39.0[1,9] [1,2,3,4]S	Poison by [aspirin, salicylates], [accid (unintentional), intentional self-harm, assault, undetermined], seq **369**
T39.1X[1,2,3,4]A	Poison by 4-Aminophenol derivatives, [accid (unintentional), intentional self-harm, assault, undetermined], init enc **362**
T39.1X[1,2,3,4]S	Poison by 4-Aminophenol derivatives, [accid (unintentional), intentional self-harm, assault, undetermined], seq **369**
T39.1X[1,2,3,4]D	Poison by 4-Aminophenol derivatives, [accid (unintentional), intentional self-harm, assault, undetermined], subsq enc **404**

T36.5X[1,2,3,4]A	Poison by aminoglycosides, [accid (unintentional), intentional self-harm, assault, undetermined], init enc **362**
T36.5X[1,2,3,4]S	Poison by aminoglycosides, [accid (unintentional), intentional self-harm, assault, undetermined], seq **368**
T36.5X[1,2,3,4]D	Poison by aminoglycosides, [accid (unintentional), intentional self-harm, assault, undetermined], subsq enc **403**
T43.62[1,2,3,4]A	Poison by amphetamines, [accid (unintentional), intentional self-harm, assault, undetermined], init enc **363**
T43.62[1,2,3,4]S	Poison by amphetamines, [accid (unintentional), intentional self-harm, assault, undetermined], seq **370**
T43.62[1,2,3,4]D	Poison by amphetamines, [accid (unintentional), intentional self-harm, assault, undetermined], subsq enc **405**
T50.7X[1,2,3,4]A	Poison by analeptics and opiod receptor antagonists, [accid (unintentional), intentional self-harm, assault, undetermined], init enc **365**
T50.7X[1,2,3,4]S	Poison by analeptics and opiod receptor antagonists, [accid (unintentional), intentional self-harm, assault, undetermined], seq **372**
T50.7X[1,2,3,4]D	Poison by analeptics and opiod receptor antagonists, [accid (unintentional), intentional self-harm, assault, undetermined], subsq enc **407**
T40.1X[1,2,3,4]A	Poison by and adverse effect of heroin, [accid (unintentional), intentional self-harm, assault, undetermined], init enc **362**
T40.1X[1,2,3,4]S	Poison by and adverse effect of heroin, [accid (unintentional), intentional self-harm, assault, undetermined], seq **369**
T40.1X[1,2,3,4]D	Poison by and adverse effect of heroin, [accid (unintentional), intentional self-harm, assault, undetermined], subsq enc **404**
T40.8X[1,2,3,4]A	Poison by and adverse effect of lysergide (LSD), [accid (unintentional), intentional self-harm, assault, undetermined], init enc **363**
T40.8X[1,2,3,4]S	Poison by and adverse effect of lysergide (LSD), [accid (unintentional), intentional self-harm, assault, undetermined], seq **369**
T40.8X[1,2,3,4]D	Poison by and adverse effect of lysergide (LSD), [accid (unintentional), intentional self-harm, assault, undetermined], subsq enc **404**
T38.7X[1,2,3,4]A	Poison by androgens and anabolic congeners, sysically used, [accid (unintentional), intentional self-harm, assault, undetermined], init enc **362**
T38.7X[1,2,3,4]S	Poison by androgens and anabolic congeners, sysically used, [accid (unintentional), intentional self-harm, assault, undetermined], seq **369**
T38.7X[1,2,3,4]D	Poison by androgens and anabolic congeners, sysically used, [accid (unintentional), intentional self-harm, assault, undetermined], subsq enc **403**
T46.4X[1,2,3,4]A	Poison by angiotensin-converting-enzyme inhibitors, [accid (unintentional), intentional self-harm, assault, undetermined], init enc **364**
T46.4X[1,2,3,4]S	Poison by angiotensin-converting-enzyme inhibitors, [accid (unintentional), intentional self-harm, assault, undetermined], seq **371**
T46.4X[1,2,3,4]D	Poison by angiotensin-converting-enzyme inhibitors, [accid (unintentional), intentional self-harm, assault, undetermined], subsq enc **406**
T38.81[1,2,3,4]A	Poison by ant pituitary (adenohypophyseal) hormones, [accid (unintentional), intentional self-harm, assault, undetermined], init enc **362**
T38.81[1,2,3,4]S	Poison by ant pituitary (adenohypophyseal) hormones, [accid (unintentional), intentional self-harm, assault, undetermined], seq **369**
T38.81[1,2,3,4]D	Poison by ant pituitary (adenohypophyseal) hormones, [accid (unintentional), intentional self-harm, assault, undetermined], subsq enc **403**
T37.4X[1,2,3,4]A	Poison by anthelminthics, [accid (unintentional), intentional self-harm, assault, undetermined], init enc **362**
T37.4X[1,2,3,4]S	Poison by anthelminthics, [accid (unintentional), intentional self-harm, assault, undetermined], seq **368**
T37.4X[1,2,3,4]D	Poison by anthelminthics, [accid (unintentional), intentional self-harm, assault, undetermined], subsq enc **403**
T45.0X[1,2,3,4]A	Poison by antiallergic and antiemetic drugs, [accid (unintentional), intentional self-harm, assault, undetermined], init enc **364**
T45.0X[1,2,3,4]S	Poison by antiallergic and antiemetic drugs, [accid (unintentional), intentional self-harm, assault, undetermined], seq **370**
T45.0X[1,2,3,4]D	Poison by antiallergic and antiemetic drugs, [accid (unintentional), intentional self-harm, assault, undetermined], subsq enc **405**
T48.6X[1,2,3,4]A	Poison by antiasthmatics, [accid (unintentional), intentional self-harm, assault, undetermined], init enc **365**

T48.6X[1,2,3,4]S Poison by antiasthmatics, [accid (unintentional), intentional self-harm, assault, undetermined], seq **371**

T48.6X[1,2,3,4]D Poison by antiasthmatics, [accid (unintentional), intentional self-harm, assault, undetermined], subsq enc **407**

T44.0X[1,2,3,4]A Poison by anticholinesterase agents, [accid (unintentional), intentional self-harm, assault, undetermined], init enc **363**

T44.0X[1,2,3,4]S Poison by anticholinesterase agents, [accid (unintentional), intentional self-harm, assault, undetermined], seq **370**

T44.0X[1,2,3,4]D Poison by anticholinesterase agents, [accid (unintentional), intentional self-harm, assault, undetermined], subsq enc **405**

T45.7X[1,2,3,4]A Poison by anticoagulant antagonists, vitamin K and oth coagulants, [accid (unintentional), intentional self-harm, assault, undetermined], init enc **364**

T45.7X[1,2,3,4]S Poison by anticoagulant antagonists, vitamin K and oth coagulants, [accid (unintentional), intentional self-harm, assault, undetermined], seq **370**

T45.7X[1,2,3,4]D Poison by anticoagulant antagonists, vitamin K and oth coagulants, [accid (unintentional), intentional self-harm, assault, undetermined], subsq enc **406**

T45.51[1,2,3,4]A Poison by anticoagulants, [accid (unintentional), intentional self-harm, assault, undetermined], init enc **364**

T45.51[1,2,3,4]S Poison by anticoagulants, [accid (unintentional), intentional self-harm, assault, undetermined], seq **370**

T45.51[1,2,3,4]D Poison by anticoagulants, [accid (unintentional), intentional self-harm, assault, undetermined], subsq enc **405**

T47.6X[1,2,3,4]A Poison by antidiarrheal drugs, [accid (unintentional), intentional self-harm, assault, undetermined], init enc **364**

T47.6X[1,2,3,4]S Poison by antidiarrheal drugs, [accid (unintentional), intentional self-harm, assault, undetermined], seq **371**

T47.6X[1,2,3,4]D Poison by antidiarrheal drugs, [accid (unintentional), intentional self-harm, assault, undetermined], subsq enc **406**

T50.6X[1,2,3,4]A Poison by antidotes and chelating agents, [accid (unintentional), intentional self-harm, assault, undetermined], init enc **365**

T50.6X[1,2,3,4]S Poison by antidotes and chelating agents, [accid (unintentional), intentional self-harm, assault, undetermined], seq **372**

T50.6X[1,2,3,4]D Poison by antidotes and chelating agents, [accid (unintentional), intentional self-harm, assault, undetermined], subsq enc **407**

T46.2X[1,2,3,4]A Poison by antidysrythmic drugs, [accid (unintentional), intentional self-harm, assault, undetermined], init enc **364**

T46.2X[1,2,3,4]S Poison by antidysrythmic drugs, [accid (unintentional), intentional self-harm, assault, undetermined], seq **371**

T46.2X[1,2,3,4]D Poison by antidysrythmic drugs, [accid (unintentional), intentional self-harm, assault, undetermined], subsq enc **406**

T36.7X[1,2,3,4]A Poison by antifungal antibiotics, sysically used, [accid (unintentional), intentional self-harm, assault, undetermined], init enc **362**

T36.7X[1,2,3,4]S Poison by antifungal antibiotics, sysically used, [accid (unintentional), intentional self-harm, assault, undetermined], seq **368**

T36.7X[1,2,3,4]D Poison by antifungal antibiotics, sysically used, [accid (unintentional), intentional self-harm, assault, undetermined], subsq enc **403**

T38.6X[1,2,3,4]A Poison by antigonadotrophins, antiestrogens, antiandrogens, NEC, [accid (unintentional), intentional self-harm, assault, undetermined], init enc **362**

T38.6X[1,2,3,4]S Poison by antigonadotrophins, antiestrogens, antiandrogens, NEC, [accid (unintentional), intentional self-harm, assault, undetermined], seq **369**

T38.6X[1,2,3,4]D Poison by antigonadotrophins, antiestrogens, antiandrogens, NEC, [accid (unintentional), intentional self-harm, assault, undetermined], subsq enc **403**

T46.6X[1,2,3,4]A Poison by antihyperlipidemic and antiarteriosclerotic drugs, [accid (unintentional), intentional self-harm, assault, undetermined], init enc **364**

T46.6X[1,2,3,4]S Poison by antihyperlipidemic and antiarteriosclerotic drugs, [accid (unintentional), intentional self-harm, assault, undetermined], seq **371**

T46.6X[1,2,3,4]D Poison by antihyperlipidemic and antiarteriosclerotic drugs, [accid (unintentional), intentional self-harm, assault, undetermined], subsq enc **406**

T37.2X[1,2,3,4]A Poison by antimalarials and drugs acting on oth bld protozoa, [accid (unintentional), intentional self-harm, assault, undetermined], init enc **362**

T37.2X[1,2,3,4]S Poison by antimalarials and drugs acting on oth bld protozoa, [accid (unintentional), intentional self-harm, assault, undetermined], seq **368**

T37.2X[1,2,3,4]D Poison by antimalarials and drugs acting on oth bld protozoa, [accid (unintentional), intentional self-harm, assault, undetermined], subsq enc **403**

T37.1X[1,2,3,4]A Poison by antimycobacterial drugs, [accid (unintentional), intentional self-harm, assault, undetermined], init enc **362**

T37.1X[1,2,3,4]S Poison by antimycobacterial drugs, [accid (unintentional), intentional self-harm, assault, undetermined], seq **368**

T37.1X[1,2,3,4]D Poison by antimycobacterial drugs, [accid (unintentional), intentional self-harm, assault, undetermined], subsq enc **403**

T45.1X[1,2,3,4]A Poison by antineoplastic and immunosuppressive drugs, [accid (unintentional), intentional self-harm, assault, undetermined], init enc **364**

T45.1X[1,2,3,4]S Poison by antineoplastic and immunosuppressive drugs, [accid (unintentional), intentional self-harm, assault, undetermined], seq **370**

T45.1X[1,2,3,4]D Poison by antineoplastic and immunosuppressive drugs, [accid (unintentional), intentional self-harm, assault, undetermined], subsq enc **405**

T42.8X[1,2,3,4]A Poison by antiparkinsonism drugs and oth central muscle-tone depressants, [accid (unintentional), intentional self-harm, assault, undetermined], init enc **363**

T42.8X[1,2,3,4]S Poison by antiparkinsonism drugs and oth central muscle-tone depressants, [accid (unintentional), intentional self-harm, assault, undetermined], seq **370**

T42.8X[1,2,3,4]D Poison by antiparkinsonism drugs and oth central muscle-tone depressants, [accid (unintentional), intentional self-harm, assault, undetermined], subsq enc **404**

T49.1X[1,2,3,4]A Poison by antipruritics, [accid (unintentional), intentional self-harm, assault, undetermined], init enc **365**

T49.1X[1,2,3,4]S Poison by antipruritics, [accid (unintentional), intentional self-harm, assault, undetermined], seq **371**

T49.1X[1,2,3,4]D Poison by antipruritics, [accid (unintentional), intentional self-harm, assault, undetermined], subsq enc **407**

T39.4X[1,2,3,4]A Poison by antirheumatics, NEC, [accid (unintentional), intentional self-harm, assault, undetermined], init enc **362**

T39.4X[1,2,3,4]S Poison by antirheumatics, NEC, [accid (unintentional), intentional self-harm, assault, undetermined], seq **369**

T39.4X[1,2,3,4]D Poison by antirheumatics, NEC, [accid (unintentional), intentional self-harm, assault, undetermined], subsq enc **404**

T45.52[1,2,3,4]A Poison by antithrombotic drugs, [accid (unintentional), intentional self-harm, assault, undetermined], init enc **364**

T45.52[1,2,3,4]S Poison by antithrombotic drugs, [accid (unintentional), intentional self-harm, assault, undetermined], seq **370**

T45.52[1,2,3,4]D Poison by antithrombotic drugs, [accid (unintentional), intentional self-harm, assault, undetermined], subsq enc **406**

T38.2X[1,2,3,4]A Poison by antithyroid drugs, [accid (unintentional), intentional self-harm, assault, undetermined], init enc **362**

T38.2X[1,2,3,4]S Poison by antithyroid drugs, [accid (unintentional), intentional self-harm, assault, undetermined], seq **369**

T38.2X[1,2,3,4]D Poison by antithyroid drugs, [accid (unintentional), intentional self-harm, assault, undetermined], subsq enc **403**

T48.3X[1,2,3,4]A Poison by antitussives, [accid (unintentional), intentional self-harm, assault, undetermined], init enc **364**

T48.3X[1,2,3,4]S Poison by antitussives, [accid (unintentional), intentional self-harm, assault, undetermined], seq **371**

T48.3X[1,2,3,4]D Poison by antitussives, [accid (unintentional), intentional self-harm, assault, undetermined], subsq enc **406**

T46.8X[1,2,3,4]A Poison by antivaricose drugs, incl* sclerosing agents, [accid (unintentional), intentional self-harm, assault, undetermined], init enc **364**

T46.8X[1,2,3,4]S Poison by antivaricose drugs, incl* sclerosing agents, [accid (unintentional), intentional self-harm, assault, undetermined], seq **371**

T46.8X[1,2,3,4]D Poison by antivaricose drugs, incl* sclerosing agents, [accid (unintentional), intentional self-harm, assault, undetermined], subsq enc **406**

T37.5X[1,2,3,4]A Poison by antiviral drugs, [accid (unintentional), intentional self-harm, assault, undetermined], init enc **362**

T37.5X[1,2,3,4]S Poison by antiviral drugs, [accid (unintentional), intentional self-harm, assault, undetermined], seq **368**

T37.5X[1,2,3,4]D Poison by antiviral drugs, [accid (unintentional), intentional self-harm, assault, undetermined], subsq enc **403**

T50.5X[1,2,3,4]A Poison by appetite depressants, [accid (unintentional), intentional self-harm, assault, undetermined], init enc **365**

T50.5X[1,2,3,4]S Poison by appetite depressants, [accid (unintentional), intentional self-harm, assault, undetermined], seq **372**

T50.5X[1,2,3,4]D Poison by appetite depressants, [accid (unintentional), intentional self-harm, assault, undetermined], subsq enc **407**

T39.01[1,2,3,4]D Poison by aspirin, [accid (unintentional), intentional self-harm, assault, undetermined], subsq enc **404**

T42.3X[1,2,3,4]A Poison by barbituates, [accid (unintentional), intentional self-harm, assault, undetermined], init enc **363**

T42.3X[1,2,3,4]S Poison by barbituates, [accid (unintentional), intentional self-harm, assault, undetermined], seq **369**

T42.3X[1,2,3,4]D Poison by barbituates, [accid (unintentional), intentional self-harm, assault, undetermined], subsq enc **404**

T42.4X[1,2,3,4]A Poison by benzodiazepines, [accid (unintentional), intentional self-harm, assault, undetermined], init enc **363**

T42.4X[1,2,3,4]S Poison by benzodiazepines, [accid (unintentional), intentional self-harm, assault, undetermined], seq **369**

T42.4X[1,2,3,4]D Poison by benzodiazepines, [accid (unintentional), intentional self-harm, assault, undetermined], subsq enc **404**

T43.4X[1,2,3,4]A Poison by butyrophenone and thiothixene neuroleptics, [accid (unintentional), intentional self-harm, assault, undetermined], init enc **363**

T43.4X[1,2,3,4]S Poison by butyrophenone and thiothixene neuroleptics, [accid (unintentional), intentional self-harm, assault, undetermined], seq **370**

T43.4X[1,2,3,4]D Poison by butyrophenone and thiothixene neuroleptics, [accid (unintentional), intentional self-harm, assault, undetermined], subsq enc **405**

T43.61[1,2,3,4]A Poison by caffeine, [accid (unintentional), intentional self-harm, assault, undetermined], init enc **363**

T43.61[1,2,3,4]S Poison by caffeine, [accid (unintentional), intentional self-harm, assault, undetermined], seq **370**

T43.61[1,2,3,4]D Poison by caffeine, [accid (unintentional), intentional self-harm, assault, undetermined], subsq enc **405**

T46.1X[1,2,3,4]A Poison by calcium-channel blockers, [accid (unintentional), intentional self-harm, assault, undetermined], init enc **364**

T46.1X[1,2,3,4]S Poison by calcium-channel blockers, [accid (unintentional), intentional self-harm, assault, undetermined], seq **371**

T46.1X[1,2,3,4]D Poison by calcium-channel blockers, [accid (unintentional), intentional self-harm, assault, undetermined], subsq enc **406**

T40.7X[1,2,3,4]A Poison by cannabis (derivatives), [accid (unintentional), intentional self-harm, assault, undetermined], init enc **363**

T40.7X[1,2,3,4]S Poison by cannabis (derivatives), [accid (unintentional), intentional self-harm, assault, undetermined], seq **369**

T40.7X[1,2,3,4]D Poison by cannabis (derivatives), [accid (unintentional), intentional self-harm, assault, undetermined], subsq enc **404**

T50.2X[1,2,3,4]A Poison by carbonic-anhydrase inhibitors, benzothiadiazides and oth diuretics, [accid (unintentional), intentional self-harm, assault, undetermined], init enc **365**

T50.2X[1,2,3,4]S Poison by carbonic-anhydrase inhibitors, benzothiadiazides and oth diuretics, [accid (unintentional), intentional self-harm, assault, undetermined], seq **372**

T50.2X[1,2,3,4]D Poison by carbonic-anhydrase inhibitors, benzothiadiazides and oth diuretics, [accid (unintentional), intentional self-harm, assault, undetermined], subsq enc **407**

T46.0X[1,2,3,4]A Poison by cardiac stimulant glycosides and drugs of similar action, [accid (unintentional), intentional self-harm, assault, undetermined], init enc **364**

T46.0X[1,2,3,4]S Poison by cardiac stimulant glycosides and drugs of similar action, [accid (unintentional), intentional self-harm, assault, undetermined], seq **371**

T46.0X[1,2,3,4]D Poison by cardiac stimulant glycosides and drugs of similar action, [accid (unintentional), intentional self-harm, assault, undetermined], subsq enc **406**

T44.8X[1,2,3,4]A Poison by centrally-acting and adrenergic-neuron-blocking agents, [accid (unintentional), intentional self-harm, assault, undetermined], init enc **364**

T44.8X[1,2,3,4]S Poison by centrally-acting and adrenergic-neuron-blocking agents, [accid (unintentional), intentional self-harm, assault, undetermined], seq **370**

T44.8X[1,2,3,4]D Poison by centrally-acting and adrenergic-neuron-blocking agents, [accid (unintentional), intentional self-harm, assault, undetermined], subsq enc **405**

T36.1X[1,2,3,4]A Poison by cephaloporins and oth beta-lactam antibiotics, [accid (unintentional), intentional self-harm, assault, undetermined], init enc **362**

T36.1X[1,2,3,4]S Poison by cephaloporins and oth beta-lactam antibiotics, [accid (unintentional), intentional self-harm, assault, undetermined], seq **368**

T36.1X[1,2,3,4]D Poison by cephaloporins and oth beta-lactam antibiotics, [accid (unintentional), intentional self-harm, assault, undetermined], subsq enc **403**

T36.2X[1,2,3,4]A Poison by chloramphenicol group, [accid (unintentional), intentional self-harm, assault, undetermined], init enc **362**

T36.2X[1,2,3,4]S Poison by chloramphenicol group, [accid (unintentional), intentional self-harm, assault, undetermined], seq **368**

T36.2X[1,2,3,4]D Poison by chloramphenicol group, [accid (unintentional), intentional self-harm, assault, undetermined], subsq enc **403**

T40.5X[1,2,3,4]A Poison by cocaine, [accid (unintentional), intentional self-harm, assault, undetermined], init enc **362**

T40.5X[1,2,3,4]S Poison by cocaine, [accid (unintentional), intentional self-harm, assault, undetermined], seq **369**

T40.5X[1,2,3,4]D Poison by cocaine, [accid (unintentional), intentional self-harm, assault, undetermined], subsq enc **404**

T46.3X[1,2,3,4]A Poison by coronary vasodilators, [accid (unintentional), intentional self-harm, assault, undetermined], init enc **364**

T46.3X[1,2,3,4]S Poison by coronary vasodilators, [accid (unintentional), intentional self-harm, assault, undetermined], seq **371**

T46.3X[1,2,3,4]D Poison by coronary vasodilators, [accid (unintentional), intentional self-harm, assault, undetermined], subsq enc **406**

T49.7X[1,2,3,4]A Poison by dental drugs, topically applied, [accid (unintentional), intentional self-harm, assault, undetermined], init enc **365**

T49.7X[1,2,3,4]S Poison by dental drugs, topically applied, [accid (unintentional), intentional self-harm, assault, undetermined], seq **371**

T49.7X[1,2,3,4]D Poison by dental drugs, topically applied, [accid (unintentional), intentional self-harm, assault, undetermined], subsq enc **407**

T47.5X[1,2,3,4]A Poison by digestants, [accid (unintentional), intentional self-harm, assault, undetermined], init enc **364**

T47.5X[1,2,3,4]S Poison by digestants, [accid (unintentional), intentional self-harm, assault, undetermined], seq **371**

T47.5X[1,2,3,4]D Poison by digestants, [accid (unintentional), intentional self-harm, assault, undetermined], subsq enc **406**

T50.4X[1,2,3,4]A Poison by drugs affecting uric acid metabolism, [accid (unintentional), intentional self-harm, assault, undetermined], init enc **365**

T50.4X[1,2,3,4]S Poison by drugs affecting uric acid metabolism, [accid (unintentional), intentional self-harm, assault, undetermined], seq **372**

T50.4X[1,2,3,4]D Poison by drugs affecting uric acid metabolism, [accid (unintentional), intentional self-harm, assault, undetermined], subsq enc **407**

T50.8X[1,2,3,4]A Poison by dx agents, [accid (unintentional), intentional self-harm, assault, undetermined], init enc **365**

T50.8X[1,2,3,4]S Poison by dx agents, [accid (unintentional), intentional self-harm, assault, undetermined], seq **372**

T50.8X[1,2,3,4]D Poison by dx agents, [accid (unintentional), intentional self-harm, assault, undetermined], subsq enc **407**

T50.3X[1,2,3,4]A Poison by eletrolytic, caloric and water-balance agents, [accid (unintentional), intentional self-harm, assault, undetermined], init enc **365**

T50.3X[1,2,3,4]S Poison by eletrolytic, caloric and water-balance agents, [accid (unintentional), intentional self-harm, assault, undetermined], seq **372**

T50.3X[1,2,3,4]D Poison by eletrolytic, caloric and water-balance agents, [accid (unintentional), intentional self-harm, assault, undetermined], subsq enc **407**

T47.7X[1,2,3,4]A Poison by emetics, [accid (unintentional), intentional self-harm, assault, undetermined], init enc **364**

T47.7X[1,2,3,4]S Poison by emetics, [accid (unintentional), intentional self-harm, assault, undetermined], seq **371**

T47.7X[1,2,3,4]D Poison by emetics, [accid (unintentional), intentional self-harm, assault, undetermined], subsq enc **406**

T49.3X[1,2,3,4]A Poison by emollients, demulcents and protectants, [accid (unintentional), intentional self-harm, assault, undetermined], init enc **365**

T49.3X[1,2,3,4]S Poison by emollients, demulcents and protectants, [accid (unintentional), intentional self-harm, assault, undetermined], seq **371**

T49.3X[1,2,3,4]D Poison by emollients, demulcents and protectants, [accid (unintentional), intentional self-harm, assault, undetermined], subsq enc **407**

T45.3X[1,2,3,4]A Poison by enzymes, [accid (unintentional), intentional self-harm, assault, undetermined], init enc **364**

T45.3X[1,2,3,4]S Poison by enzymes, [accid (unintentional), intentional self-harm, assault, undetermined], seq **370**

T45.3X[1,2,3,4]D Poison by enzymes, [accid (unintentional), intentional self-harm, assault, undetermined], subsq enc **405**

T48.4X[1,2,3,4]A Poison by expectorants, [accid (unintentional), intentional self-harm, assault, undetermined], init enc **364**

T48.4X[1,2,3,4]S Poison by expectorants, [accid (unintentional), intentional self-harm, assault, undetermined], seq **371**

T48.4X[1,2,3,4]D Poison by expectorants, [accid (unintentional), intentional self-harm, assault, undetermined], subsq enc **406**

T44.2X[1,2,3,4]A Poison by ganglionic blocking drugs, [accid (unintentional), intentional self-harm, assault, undetermined], init enc **363**

T44.2X[1,2,3,4]S Poison by ganglionic blocking drugs, [accid (unintentional), intentional self-harm, assault, undetermined], seq **370**

T44.2X[1,2,3,4]D Poison by ganglionic blocking drugs, [accid (unintentional), intentional self-harm, assault, undetermined], subsq enc **405**

T38.0X[1,2,3,4]A Poison by glucocorticoids and synth analogues, [accid (unintentional), intentional self-harm, assault, undetermined], init enc **362**

T38.0X[1,2,3,4]S Poison by glucocorticoids and synth analogues, [accid (unintentional), intentional self-harm, assault, undetermined], seq **369**

T38.0X[1,2,3,4]D Poison by glucocorticoids and synth analogues, [accid (unintentional), intentional self-harm, assault, undetermined], subsq enc **403**

T45.62[1,2,3,4]A Poison by hemostatic drug, [accid (unintentional), intentional self-harm, assault, undetermined], init enc **364**

T45.62[1,2,3,4]S Poison by hemostatic drug, [accid (unintentional), intentional self-harm, assault, undetermined], seq **370**

T45.62[1,2,3,4]D Poison by hemostatic drug, [accid (unintentional), intentional self-harm, assault, undetermined], subsq enc **406**

T47.0X[1,2,3,4]A Poison by histamine H2-receptor blockers, [accid (unintentional), intentional self-harm, assault, undetermined], init enc **364**

T47.0X[1,2,3,4]S Poison by histamine H2-receptor blockers, [accid (unintentional), intentional self-harm, assault, undetermined], seq **371**

T47.0X[1,2,3,4]D Poison by histamine H2-receptor blockers, [accid (unintentional), intentional self-harm, assault, undetermined], subsq enc **406**

T42.0X[1,2,3,4]A Poison by hydantoin derivatives, [accid (unintentional), intentional self-harm, assault, undetermined], init enc **363**

T42.0X[1,2,3,4]S Poison by hydantoin derivatives, [accid (unintentional), intentional self-harm, assault, undetermined], seq **369**

T42.0X[1,2,3,4]D Poison by hydantoin derivatives, [accid (unintentional), intentional self-harm, assault, undetermined], subsq enc **404**

T42.1X[1,2,3,4]A Poison by iminostilbenes, [accid (unintentional), intentional self-harm, assault, undetermined], init enc **363**

T42.1X[1,2,3,4]S Poison by iminostilbenes, [accid (unintentional), intentional self-harm, assault, undetermined], seq **369**

T42.1X[1,2,3,4]D Poison by iminostilbenes, [accid (unintentional), intentional self-harm, assault, undetermined], subsq enc **404**

T50.Z1[1,2,3,4]A Poison by immunoglobin, [accid (unintentional), intentional self-harm, assault, undetermined], init enc **365**

T50.Z1[1,2,3,4]S Poison by immunoglobin, [accid (unintentional), intentional self-harm, assault, undetermined], seq **372**

T50.Z1[1,2,3,4]D Poison by immunoglobin, [accid (unintentional), intentional self-harm, assault, undetermined], subsq enc **407**

T41.0X[1,2,3,4]A Poison by inhaled anesthetics, [accid (unintentional), intentional self-harm, assault, undetermined], init enc **363**

T41.0X[1,2,3,4]S Poison by inhaled anesthetics, [accid (unintentional), intentional self-harm, assault, undetermined], seq **369**

T41.0X[1,2,3,4]D Poison by inhaled anesthetics, [accid (unintentional), intentional self-harm, assault, undetermined], subsq enc **404**

T38.3X[1,2,3,4]A Poison by insulin and oral hypoglycemic (antidiabetic) drugs, [accid (unintentional), intentional self-harm, assault, undetermined], init enc **362**

T38.3X[1,2,3,4]S Poison by insulin and oral hypoglycemic (antidiabetic) drugs, [accid (unintentional), intentional self-harm, assault, undetermined], seq **369**

T38.3X[1,2,3,4]D Poison by insulin and oral hypoglycemic (antidiabetic) drugs, [accid (unintentional), intentional self-harm, assault, undetermined], subsq enc **403**

T41.1X[1,2,3,4]A Poison by intravenous anesthetics, [accid (unintentional), intentional self-harm, assault, undetermined], init enc **363**

T41.1X[1,2,3,4]S Poison by intravenous anesthetics, [accid (unintentional), intentional self-harm, assault, undetermined], seq **369**

T41.1X[1,2,3,4]D Poison by intravenous anesthetics, [accid (unintentional), intentional self-harm, assault, undetermined], subsq enc **404**

T45.4X[1,2,3,4]A Poison by iron and its compounds, [accid (unintentional), intentional self-harm, assault, undetermined], init enc **364**

T45.4X[1,2,3,4]S Poison by iron and its compounds, [accid (unintentional), intentional self-harm, assault, undetermined], seq **370**

T45.4X[1,2,3,4]D Poison by iron and its compounds, [accid (unintentional), intentional self-harm, assault, undetermined], subsq enc **405**

T49.4X[1,2,3,4]A Poison by keratolytics, keratoplastics, and oth hair tx drugs, [accid (unintentional), intentional self-harm, assault, undetermined], init enc **365**

T49.4X[1,2,3,4]S Poison by keratolytics, keratoplastics, and oth hair tx drugs, [accid (unintentional), intentional self-harm, assault, undetermined], seq **371**

T49.4X[1,2,3,4]D Poison by keratolytics, keratoplastics, and oth hair tx drugs, [accid (unintentional), intentional self-harm, assault, undetermined], subsq enc **407**

T41.3X[1,2,3,4]A Poison by local anesthetics, [accid (unintentional), intentional self-harm, assault, undetermined], init enc **363**

T41.3X[1,2,3,4]S Poison by local anesthetics, [accid (unintentional), intentional self-harm, assault, undetermined], seq **369**

T41.3X[1,2,3,4]D Poison by local anesthetics, [accid (unintentional), intentional self-harm, assault, undetermined], subsq enc **404**

T49.0X[1,2,3,4]A Poison by local antifungal, anti-infective and anti-inflam drugs, [accid (unintentional), intentional self-harm, assault, undetermined], init enc **365**

T49.0X[1,2,3,4]S Poison by local antifungal, anti-infective and anti-inflam drugs, [accid (unintentional), intentional self-harm, assault, undetermined], seq **371**

T49.0X[1,2,3,4]D Poison by local antifungal, anti-infective and anti-inflam drugs, [accid (unintentional), intentional self-harm, assault, undetermined], subsq enc **407**

T49.2X[1,2,3,4]A Poison by local astringents and local detergents, [accid (unintentional), intentional self-harm, assault, undetermined], init enc **365**

T49.2X[1,2,3,4]S Poison by local astringents and local detergents, [accid (unintentional), intentional self-harm, assault, undetermined], seq **371**

T49.2X[1,2,3,4]D Poison by local astringents and local detergents, [accid (unintentional), intentional self-harm, assault, undetermined], subsq enc **407**

T50.1X[1,2,3,4]A Poison by loop (hugh ceiling) diuretics, [accid (unintentional), intentional self-harm, assault, undetermined], init enc **365**

T50.1X[1,2,3,4]S Poison by loop (hugh ceiling) diuretics, [accid (unintentional), intentional self-harm, assault, undetermined], seq **371**

T50.1X[1,2,3,4]D Poison by loop (hugh ceiling) diuretics, [accid (unintentional), intentional self-harm, assault, undetermined], subsq enc **407**

T36.3X[1,2,3,4]A Poison by macrolides, [accid (unintentional), intentional self-harm, assault, undetermined], init enc **362**

T36.3X[1,2,3,4]S Poison by macrolides, [accid (unintentional), intentional self-harm, assault, undetermined], seq **368**

T36.3X[1,2,3,4]D Poison by macrolides, [accid (unintentional), intentional self-harm, assault, undetermined], subsq enc **403**

T40.3X[1,2,3,4]A Poison by methadone, [accid (unintentional), intentional self-harm, assault, undetermined], init enc **362**

T40.3X[1,2,3,4]S Poison by methadone, [accid (unintentional), intentional self-harm, assault, undetermined], seq **369**

T40.3X[1,2,3,4]D Poison by methadone, [accid (unintentional), intentional self-harm, assault, undetermined], subsq enc **404**

T43.63[1,2,3,4]A Poison by methylphenidate, [accid (unintentional), intentional self-harm, assault, undetermined], init enc **363**

T43.63[1,2,3,4]S Poison by methylphenidate, [accid (unintentional), intentional self-harm, assault, undetermined], seq **370**

T43.63[1,2,3,4]D Poison by methylphenidate, [accid (unintentional), intentional self-harm, assault, undetermined], subsq enc **405**

T50.0X[1,2,3,4]A Poison by mineralocorticoids and their antagonists, [accid (unintentional), intentional self-harm, assault, undetermined], init enc **365**

T50.0X[1,2,3,4]S Poison by mineralocorticoids and their antagonists, [accid (unintentional), intentional self-harm, assault, undetermined], seq **371**

T50.0X[1,2,3,4]D Poison by mineralocorticoids and their antagonists, [accid (unintentional), intentional self-harm, assault, undetermined], subsq enc **407**

T42.5X[1,2,3,4]A Poison by mixed antiepileptics, [accid (unintentional), intentional self-harm, assault, undetermined], init enc **363**

T42.5X[1,2,3,4]S Poison by mixed antiepileptics, [accid (unintentional), intentional self-harm, assault, undetermined], seq **369**

T42.5X[1,2,3,4]D Poison by mixed antiepileptics, [accid (unintentional), intentional self-harm, assault, undetermined], subsq enc **404**

T50.A2[1,2,3,4]A Poison by mixed bacterial vaccines w/o a pertussis component, [accid (unintentional), intentional self-harm, assault, undetermined], init enc **365**

T50.A2[1,2,3,4]S Poison by mixed bacterial vaccines w/o a pertussis component, [accid (unintentional), intentional self-harm, assault, undetermined], seq **372**

T50.A2[1,2,3,4]D Poison by mixed bacterial vaccines w/o a pertussis component, [accid (unintentional), intentional self-harm, assault, undetermined], subsq enc **407**

T43.1X[1,2,3,4]A Poison by monoamine-oxidase-inhibitor antidepressants, [accid (unintentional), intentional self-harm, assault, undetermined], init enc **363**

T43.1X[1,2,3,4]S Poison by monoamine-oxidase-inhibitor antidepressants, [accid (unintentional), intentional self-harm, assault, undetermined], seq **370**

T43.1X[1,2,3,4]D Poison by monoamine-oxidase-inhibitor antidepressants, [accid (unintentional), intentional self-harm, assault, undetermined], subsq enc **405**

T49.5X[1,2,3,4]A Poison by ophthalmological drugs and preparations, [accid (unintentional), intentional self-harm, assault, undetermined], init enc **47**

T49.5X[1,2,3,4]S Poison by ophthalmological drugs and preparations, [accid (unintentional), intentional self-harm, assault, undetermined], seq **371**

T49.5X[1,2,3,4]D Poison by ophthalmological drugs and preparations, [accid (unintentional), intentional self-harm, assault, undetermined], subsq enc **407**

T40.0X[1,2,3,4]A Poison by opium, [accid (unintentional), intentional self-harm, assault, undetermined], init enc **362**

T40.0X[1,2,3,4]S Poison by opium, [accid (unintentional), intentional self-harm, assault, undetermined], seq **369**

T40.0X[1,2,3,4]D Poison by opium, [accid (unintentional), intentional self-harm, assault, undetermined], subsq enc **404**

T38.4X[1,2,3,4]A Poison by oral contraceptives, [accid (unintentional), intentional self-harm, assault, undetermined], init enc **362**

T38.4X[1,2,3,4]S Poison by oral contraceptives, [accid (unintentional), intentional self-harm, assault, undetermined], seq **369**

T38.4X[1,2,3,4]D Poison by oral contraceptives, [accid (unintentional), intentional self-harm, assault, undetermined], subsq enc **403**

T46.99[1,2,3,4]A Poison by oth agent primarily affecting the cardiovascular sys, [accid (unintentional), intentional self-harm, assault, undetermined], init enc **364**

T46.99[1,2,3,4]S Poison by oth agent primarily affecting the cardiovascular sys, [accid (unintentional), intentional self-harm, assault, undetermined], seq **371**

T46.99[1,2,3,4]D Poison by oth agent primarily affecting the cardiovascular sys, [accid (unintentional), intentional self-harm, assault, undetermined], subsq enc **406**

T48.99[1,2,3,4]A Poison by oth agents primarily acting on the respiratory sys, [accid (unintentional), intentional self-harm, assault, undetermined], init enc **365**

T48.99[1,2,3,4]S Poison by oth agents primarily acting on the respiratory sys, [accid (unintentional), intentional self-harm, assault, undetermined], seq **371**

T48.99[1,2,3,4]D Poison by oth agents primarily acting on the respiratory sys, [accid (unintentional), intentional self-harm, assault, undetermined], subsq enc **407**

T47.8X[1,2,3,4]A Poison by oth agents primarily affecting gastrointestinal sys, [accid (unintentional), intentional self-harm, assault, undetermined], init enc **364**

T47.8X[1,2,3,4]S Poison by oth agents primarily affecting gastrointestinal sys, [accid (unintentional), intentional self-harm, assault, undetermined], seq **371**

T47.8X[1,2,3,4]D Poison by oth agents primarily affecting gastrointestinal sys, [accid (unintentional), intentional self-harm, assault, undetermined], subsq enc **406**

T47.1X[1,2,3,4]A Poison by oth antacids and anti-gastric-secretion drugs, [accid (unintentional), intentional self-harm, assault, undetermined], init enc **364**

T47.1X[1,2,3,4]S Poison by oth antacids and anti-gastric-secretion drugs, [accid (unintentional), intentional self-harm, assault, undetermined], seq **371**

T47.1X[1,2,3,4]D Poison by oth antacids and anti-gastric-secretion drugs, [accid (unintentional), intentional self-harm, assault, undetermined], subsq enc **406**

T48.5X[1,2,3,4]A Poison by oth anti-common-cold drugs, [accid (unintentional), intentional self-harm, assault, undetermined], init enc **365**

T48.5X[1,2,3,4]S Poison by oth anti-common-cold drugs, [accid (unintentional), intentional self-harm, assault, undetermined], seq **371**

T48.5X[1,2,3,4]D Poison by oth anti-common-cold drugs, [accid (unintentional), intentional self-harm, assault, undetermined], subsq enc **407**

T43.29[1,2,3,4]A Poison by oth antidepressants, [accid (unintentional), intentional self-harm, assault, undetermined], init enc **363**

T43.29[1,2,3,4]S Poison by oth antidepressants, [accid (unintentional), intentional self-harm, assault, undetermined], seq **370**

T43.29[1,2,3,4]D Poison by oth antidepressants, [accid (unintentional), intentional self-harm, assault, undetermined], subsq enc **405**

T42.6X[1,2,3,4]A Poison by oth antiepileptic and sedative-hypnotic drugs, [accid (unintentional), intentional self-harm, assault, undetermined], init enc **363**

T42.6X[1,2,3,4]S Poison by oth antiepileptic and sedative-hypnotic drugs, [accid (unintentional), intentional self-harm, assault, undetermined], seq **370**

T42.6X[1,2,3,4]D Poison by oth antiepileptic and sedative-hypnotic drugs, [accid (unintentional), intentional self-harm, assault, undetermined], subsq enc **404**

T46.5X[1,2,3,4]A Poison by oth antihypertensive drugs, [accid (unintentional), intentional self-harm, assault, undetermined], init enc **364**

T46.5X[1,2,3,4]S Poison by oth antihypertensive drugs, [accid (unintentional), intentional self-harm, assault, undetermined], seq **371**

T46.5X[1,2,3,4]D Poison by oth antihypertensive drugs, [accid (unintentional), intentional self-harm, assault, undetermined], subsq enc **406**

T37.3X[1,2,3,4]A Poison by oth antiprotozoal drugs, [accid (unintentional), intentional self-harm, assault, undetermined], init enc **362**

T37.3X[1,2,3,4]S Poison by oth antiprotozoal drugs, [accid (unintentional), intentional self-harm, assault, undetermined], seq **368**

T37.3X[1,2,3,4]D Poison by oth antiprotozoal drugs, [accid (unintentional), intentional self-harm, assault, undetermined], subsq enc **403**

T43.59[1,2,3,4]A Poison by oth antipsychotics and neuroleptics, [accid (unintentional), intentional self-harm, assault, undetermined], init enc **363**

T43.59[1,2,3,4]S Poison by oth antipsychotics and neuroleptics, [accid (unintentional), intentional self-harm, assault, undetermined], seq **370**

T43.59[1,2,3,4]D Poison by oth antipsychotics and neuroleptics, [accid (unintentional), intentional self-harm, assault, undetermined], subsq enc **405**

T50.A9[1,2,3,4]A Poison by oth bacterial vaccines, [accid (unintentional), intentional self-harm, assault, undetermined], init enc **365**

T50.A9[1,2,3,4]S Poison by oth bacterial vaccines, [accid (unintentional), intentional self-harm, assault, undetermined], seq **372**

T50.A9[1,2,3,4]D Poison by oth bacterial vaccines, [accid (unintentional), intentional self-harm, assault, undetermined], subsq enc **407**

T44.99[1,2,3,4]A Poison by oth drug primarily affecting the autonomic nervous sys, [accid (unintentional), intentional self-harm, assault, undetermined], init enc **364**

T44.99[1,2,3,4]S Poison by oth drug primarily affecting the autonomic nervous sys, [accid (unintentional), intentional self-harm, assault, undetermined], seq **370**

T44.99[1,2,3,4]D Poison by oth drug primarily affecting the autonomic nervous sys, [accid (unintentional), intentional self-harm, assault, undetermined], subsq enc **405**

T48.29[1,2,3,4]A Poison by oth drugs working on muscles, [accid (unintentional), intentional self-harm, assault, undetermined], init enc **364**

T48.29[1,2,3,4]S Poison by oth drugs working on muscles, [accid (unintentional), intentional self-harm, assault, undetermined], seq **371**

T48.29[1,2,3,4]D Poison by oth drugs working on muscles, [accid (unintentional), intentional self-harm, assault, undetermined], subsq enc **406**

T50.99[1,2,3,4]A Poison by oth drugs, medicaments and biological substances, [accid (unintentional), intentional self-harm, assault, undetermined], init enc **365**

T50.99[1,2,3,4]S Poison by oth drugs, medicaments and biological substances, [accid (unintentional), intentional self-harm, assault, undetermined], init encoun **372**

T50.99[1,2,3,4]D Poison by oth drugs, medicaments and biological substances, [accid (unintentional), intentional self-harm, assault, undetermined], subsq enc **407**

T38.5X[1,2,3,4]A Poison by oth estrogens and progestogens, [accid (unintentional), intentional self-harm, assault, undetermined], init enc **362**

T38.5X[1,2,3,4]S Poison by oth estrogens and progestogens, [accid (unintentional), intentional self-harm, assault, undetermined], seq **369**

T38.5X[1,2,3,4]D Poison by oth estrogens and progestogens, [accid (unintentional), intentional self-harm, assault, undetermined], subsq enc **403**

T45.69[1,2,3,4]A Poison by oth fibrinolysis-affecting drug, [accid (unintentional), intentional self-harm, assault, undetermined], init enc **364**

T45.69[1,2,3,4]S Poison by oth fibrinolysis-affecting drug, [accid (unintentional), intentional self-harm, assault, undetermined], seq **370**

T45.69[1,2,3,4]D Poison by oth fibrinolysis-affecting drug, [accid (unintentional), intentional self-harm, assault, undetermined], subsq enc **406**

T41.29[1,2,3,4]A Poison by oth general anesthetics, [accid (unintentional), intentional self-harm, assault, undetermined], init enc **363**

T41.29[1,2,3,4]S Poison by oth general anesthetics, [accid (unintentional), intentional self-harm, assault, undetermined], seq **369**

T41.29[1,2,3,4]D Poison by oth general anesthetics, [accid (unintentional), intentional self-harm, assault, undetermined], subsq enc **404**

T38.99[1,2,3,4]A Poison by oth hormone antagonists, [accid (unintentional), intentional self-harm, assault, undetermined], init enc **362**

T38.99[1,2,3,4]S Poison by oth hormone antagonists, [accid (unintentional), intentional self-harm, assault, undetermined], seq **369**

T38.99[1,2,3,4]D Poison by oth hormone antagonists, [accid (unintentional), intentional self-harm, assault, undetermined], subsq enc **403**

T38.89[1,2,3,4]A Poison by oth hormones and synth subs, [accid (unintentional), intentional self-harm, assault, undetermined], init enc **362**

T38.89[1,2,3,4]S Poison by oth hormones and synth subs, [accid (unintentional), intentional self-harm, assault, undetermined], seq **369**

T38.89[1,2,3,4]D Poison by oth hormones and synth subs, [accid (unintentional), intentional self-harm, assault, undetermined], subsq enc **403**

T47.4X[1,2,3,4]A Poison by oth laxatives, [accid (unintentional), intentional self-harm, assault, undetermined], init enc **364**

T47.4X[1,2,3,4]S Poison by oth laxatives, [accid (unintentional), intentional self-harm, assault, undetermined], seq **371**

T47.4X[1,2,3,4]D Poison by oth laxatives, [accid (unintentional), intentional self-harm, assault, undetermined], subsq enc **406**

T39.8X[1,2,3,4]A Poison by oth nonopiod analgesics and antipyretics, [accid (unintentional), intentional self-harm, assault, undetermined], init enc **362**

T39.8X[1,2,3,4]S Poison by oth nonopiod analgesics and antipyretics, [accid (unintentional), intentional self-harm, assault, undetermined], seq **369**

T39.8X[1,2,3,4]D Poison by oth nonopiod analgesics and antipyretics, [accid (unintentional), intentional self-harm, assault, undetermined], subsq enc **404**

T39.39[1,2,3,4]A Poison by oth nonsteroidal anti-inflam drugs (NSAID), [accid (unintentional), intentional self-harm, assault, undetermined], init enc **362**

T39.39[1,2,3,4]S Poison by oth nonsteroidal anti-inflam drugs (NSAID), [accid (unintentional), intentional self-harm, assault, undetermined], seq **369**

T39.39[1,2,3,4]D Poison by oth nonsteroidal anti-inflam drugs (NSAID), [accid (unintentional), intentional self-harm, assault, undetermined], subsq enc **404**

T40.2X[1,2,3,4]A Poison by oth opiods, [accid (unintentional), intentional self-harm, assault, undetermined], init enc **362**

T40.2X[1,2,3,4]S Poison by oth opiods, [accid (unintentional), intentional self-harm, assault, undetermined], seq **369**

T40.2X[1,2,3,4]D Poison by oth opiods, [accid (unintentional), intentional self-harm, assault, undetermined], subsq enc **404**

T44.3X[1,2,3,4]A Poison by oth parasympatholytics (anticholinergics and antimuscarinics) and spasmolytics, [accid (unintentional), intentional self-harm, assault, undetermined], init enc **363**

T44.3X[1,2,3,4]S Poison by oth parasympatholytics (anticholinergics and antimuscarinics) and spasmolytics, [accid (unintentional), intentional self-harm, assault, undetermined], seq **370**

T44.3X[1,2,3,4]D Poison by oth parasympatholytics (anticholinergics and antimuscarinics) and spasmolytics, [accid (unintentional), intentional self-harm, assault, undetermined], subsq enc **405**

T45.8X[1,2,3,4]A Poison by oth primarily sysic and hematological agents, [accid (unintentional), intentional self-harm, assault, undetermined], init enc **364**

T45.8X[1,2,3,4]S Poison by oth primarily sysic and hematological agents, [accid (unintentional), intentional self-harm, assault, undetermined], seq **370**

T45.8X[1,2,3,4]D Poison by oth primarily sysic and hematological agents, [accid (unintentional), intentional self-harm, assault, undetermined], subsq enc **406**

T40.99[1,2,3,4]A Poison by oth psychodysleptics (hallucinogens), [accid (unintentional), intentional self-harm, assault, undetermined], init enc **363**

T40.99[1,2,3,4]S Poison by oth psychodysleptics (hallucinogens), [accid (unintentional), intentional self-harm, assault, undetermined], seq **369**

T40.99[1,2,3,4]D Poison by oth psychodysleptics (hallucinogens), [accid (unintentional), intentional self-harm, assault, undetermined], subsq enc **404**

T43.69[1,2,3,4]A Poison by oth psychostimulants, [accid (unintentional), intentional self-harm, assault, undetermined], init enc **363**

T43.69[1,2,3,4]S Poison by oth psychostimulants, [accid (unintentional), intentional self-harm, assault, undetermined], seq **370**

T43.69[1,2,3,4]D Poison by oth psychostimulants, [accid (unintentional), intentional self-harm, assault, undetermined], subsq enc **405**

T43.8X[1,2,3,4]A Poison by oth psychotropic drugs, [accid (unintentional), intentional self-harm, assault, undetermined], init enc **363**

T43.8X[1,2,3,4]S Poison by oth psychotropic drugs, [accid (unintentional), intentional self-harm, assault, undetermined], seq **370**

T43.8X[1,2,3,4]D Poison by oth psychotropic drugs, [accid (unintentional), intentional self-harm, assault, undetermined], subsq enc **405**

T37.8X[1,2,3,4]A Poison by oth spec sysic anti-infectives and antiparasitics, [accid (unintentional), intentional self-harm, assault, undetermined], init enc **362**

T37.8X[1,2,3,4]S Poison by oth spec sysic anti-infectives and antiparasitics, [accid (unintentional), intentional self-harm, assault, undetermined], seq **369**

T37.8X[1,2,3,4]D Poison by oth spec sysic anti-infectives and antiparasitics, [accid (unintentional), intentional self-harm, assault, undetermined], subsq enc **403**

T40.4X[1,2,3,4]A Poison by oth synth narcotics, [accid (unintentional), intentional self-harm, assault, undetermined], init enc **362**

T40.4X[1,2,3,4]S Poison by oth synth narcotics, [accid (unintentional), intentional self-harm, assault, undetermined], seq **369**

T40.4X[1,2,3,4]D Poison by oth synth narcotics, [accid (unintentional), intentional self-harm, assault, undetermined], subsq enc **404**

T36.8X[1,2,3,4]A Poison by oth sysic antibiotics [accid (unintentional), intentional self-harm, assault, undetermined], init enc **362**

T36.8X[1,2,3,4]S Poison by oth sysic antibiotics [accid (unintentional), intentional self-harm, assault, undetermined], seq **368**

T36.8X[1,2,3,4]D Poison by oth sysic antibiotics [accid (unintentional), intentional self-harm, assault, undetermined], subsq enc **403**

T49.8X[1,2,3,4]A Poison by oth topical agents, [accid (unintentional), intentional self-harm, assault, undetermined], init enc **365**

T49.8X[1,2,3,4]S Poison by oth topical agents, [accid (unintentional), intentional self-harm, assault, undetermined], seq **371**

T49.8X[1,2,3,4]D Poison by oth topical agents, [accid (unintentional), intentional self-harm, assault, undetermined], subsq enc **407**

T50.Z9[1,2,3,4]A Poison by oth vaccines and biological substances, [accid (unintentional), intentional self-harm, assault, undetermined], init enc **365**

T50.Z9[1,2,3,4]S Poison by oth vaccines and biological substances, [accid (unintentional), intentional self-harm, assault, undetermined], seq **372**

T50.Z9[1,2,3,4]D Poison by oth vaccines and biological substances, [accid (unintentional), intentional self-harm, assault, undetermined], subsq enc **407**

T50.B9[1,2,3,4]A Poison by oth viral vaccines, [accid (unintentional), intentional self-harm, assault, undetermined], init enc **365**

T50.B9[1,2,3,4]S Poison by oth viral vaccines, [accid (unintentional), intentional self-harm, assault, undetermined], seq **372**

T50.B9[1,2,3,4]D Poison by oth viral vaccines, [accid (unintentional), intentional self-harm, assault, undetermined], subsq enc **407**

T49.6X[1,2,3,4]A Poison by otorhinolaryngological drugs and preparations, [accid (unintentional), intentional self-harm, assault, undetermined], init enc **365**

T49.6X[1,2,3,4]S Poison by otorhinolaryngological drugs and preparations, [accid (unintentional), intentional self-harm, assault, undetermined], seq **371**

T49.6X[1,2,3,4]D Poison by otorhinolaryngological drugs and preparations, [accid (unintentional), intentional self-harm, assault, undetermined], subsq enc **407**

T48.0X[1,2,3,4]A Poison by oxytocic drugs, [accid (unintentional), intentional self-harm, assault, undetermined], init enc **364**

T48.0X[1,2,3,4]S Poison by oxytocic drugs, [accid (unintentional), intentional self-harm, assault, undetermined], seq **371**

T48.0X[1,2,3,4]D Poison by oxytocic drugs, [accid (unintentional), intentional self-harm, assault, undetermined], subsq enc **406**

T44.1X[1,2,3,4]A Poison by parasympathomimetics (cholinergics), [accid (unintentional), intentional self-harm, assault, undetermined], init enc **363**

T44.1X[1,2,3,4]S Poison by parasympathomimetics (cholinergics), [accid (unintentional), intentional self-harm, assault, undetermined], seq **370**

T44.1X[1,2,3,4]D Poison by parasympathomimetics (cholinergics), [accid (unintentional), intentional self-harm, assault, undetermined], subsq enc **405**

T36.0X[1,2,3,4]A Poison by penicillins, [accid (unintentional), intentional self-harm, assault, undetermined], init enc **362**

T36.0X[1,2,3,4]S Poison by penicillins, [accid (unintentional), intentional self-harm, assault, undetermined], seq **368**

T36.0X[1,2,3,4]D Poison by penicillins, [accid (unintentional), intentional self-harm, assault, undetermined], subsq enc **403**

T46.7X[1,2,3,4]A Poison by peripheral vasodilators, [accid (unintentional), intentional self-harm, assault, undetermined], init enc **364**

T46.7X[1,2,3,4]S Poison by peripheral vasodilators, [accid (unintentional), intentional self-harm, assault, undetermined], seq **371**

T46.7X[1,2,3,4]D Poison by peripheral vasodilators, [accid (unintentional), intentional self-harm, assault, undetermined], subsq enc **406**

T50.A1[1,2,3,4]A Poison by pertussis vaccine, incl* combinations w/ a pertussis component, [accid (unintentional), intentional self-harm, assault, undetermined], init enc **365**

T50.A1[1,2,3,4]S Poison by pertussis vaccine, incl* combinations w/ a pertussis component, [accid (unintentional), intentional self-harm, assault, undetermined], seq **372**

T50.A1[1,2,3,4]D Poison by pertussis vaccine, incl* combinations w/ a pertussis component, [accid (unintentional), intentional self-harm, assault, undetermined], subsq enc **407**

T43.3X[1,2,3,4]A Poison by phenothiazine antipsychotics and neuroleptics, [accid (unintentional), intentional self-harm, assault, undetermined], init enc **363**

T43.3X[1,2,3,4]S Poison by phenothiazine antipsychotics and neuroleptics, [accid (unintentional), intentional self-harm, assault, undetermined], seq **370**

T43.3X[1,2,3,4]D Poison by phenothiazine antipsychotics and neuroleptics, [accid (unintentional), intentional self-harm, assault, undetermined], subsq enc **405**

T44.4X[1,2,3,4]A Poison by predominantly alpha-adrenoreceptor agonists, [accid (unintentional), intentional self-harm, assault, undetermined], init enc **363**

T44.4X[1,2,3,4]S Poison by predominantly alpha-adrenoreceptor agonists, [accid (unintentional), intentional self-harm, assault, undetermined], seq **370**

T44.4X[1,2,3,4]D Poison by predominantly alpha-adrenoreceptor agonists, [accid (unintentional), intentional self-harm, assault, undetermined], subsq enc **405**

T44.6X[1,2,3,4]A Poison by predominantly alpha-adrenoreceptor antagonists, [accid (unintentional), intentional self-harm, assault, undetermined], init enc **363**

T44.6X[1,2,3,4]S Poison by predominantly alpha-adrenoreceptor antagonists, [accid (unintentional), intentional self-harm, assault, undetermined], seq **370**

T44.6X[1,2,3,4]D Poison by predominantly alpha-adrenoreceptor antagonists, [accid (unintentional), intentional self-harm, assault, undetermined], subsq enc **405**

T44.5X[1,2,3,4]A Poison by predominantly beta-adrenoreceptor agonists, [accid (unintentional), intentional self-harm, assault, undetermined], init enc **363**

T44.5X[1,2,3,4]S Poison by predominantly beta-adrenoreceptor agonists, [accid (unintentional), intentional self-harm, assault, undetermined], seq **370**

T44.5X[1,2,3,4]D Poison by predominantly beta-adrenoreceptor agonists, [accid (unintentional), intentional self-harm, assault, undetermined], subsq enc **405**

T44.7X[1,2,3,4]A Poison by predominantly beta-adrenoreceptor antagonists, [accid (unintentional), intentional self-harm, assault, undetermined], init enc **363**

T44.7X[1,2,3,4]S Poison by predominantly beta-adrenoreceptor antagonists, [accid (unintentional), intentional self-harm, assault, undetermined], seq **370**

T44.7X[1,2,3,4]D Poison by predominantly beta-adrenoreceptor antagonists, [accid (unintentional), intentional self-harm, assault, undetermined], subsq enc **405**

T39.31[1,2,3,4]A Poison by propionic acid derivatives, [accid (unintentional), intentional self-harm, assault, undetermined], init enc **362**

T39.31[1,2,3,4]S Poison by propionic acid derivatives, [accid (unintentional), intentional self-harm, assault, undetermined], seq **369**

T39.31[1,2,3,4]D Poison by propionic acid derivatives, [accid (unintentional), intentional self-harm, assault, undetermined], subsq enc **404**

T39.2X[1,2,3,4]A Poison by pyrazolone derivatives, [accid (unintentional), intentional self-harm, assault, undetermined], init enc **362**

T39.2X[1,2,3,4]S Poison by pyrazolone derivatives, [accid (unintentional), intentional self-harm, assault, undetermined], seq **369**

T39.2X[1,2,3,4]D Poison by pyrazolone derivatives, [accid (unintentional), intentional self-harm, assault, undetermined], subsq enc **404**

T36.6X[1,2,3,4]A Poison by rifampicins, [accid (unintentional), intentional self-harm, assault, undetermined], init enc **362**

T36.6X[1,2,3,4]S Poison by rifampicins, [accid (unintentional), intentional self-harm, assault, undetermined], seq **368**

T36.6X[1,2,3,4]D Poison by rifampicins, [accid (unintentional), intentional self-harm, assault, undetermined], subsq enc **403**

T39.09[1,2,3,4]D Poison by salicylates, [accid (unintentional), intentional self-harm, assault, undetermined], subsq enc **404**

T47.3X[1,2,3,4]A Poison by saline and osmotic laxatives, [accid (unintentional), intentional self-harm, assault, undetermined], init enc **364**

T47.3X[1,2,3,4]S Poison by saline and osmotic laxatives, [accid (unintentional), intentional self-harm, assault, undetermined], seq **371**

T47.3X[1,2,3,4]D Poison by saline and osmotic laxatives, [accid (unintentional), intentional self-harm, assault, undetermined], subsq enc **406**

T43.21[1,2,3,4]A Poison by selective serotonin and norepinephrine reuptake inhibitors, [accid (unintentional), intentional self-harm, assault, undetermined], init enc **363**

T43.21[1,2,3,4]S Poison by selective serotonin and norepinephrine reuptake inhibitors, [accid (unintentional), intentional self-harm, assault, undetermined], seq **370**

T43.21[1,2,3,4]D Poison by selective serotonin and norepinephrine reuptake inhibitors, [accid (unintentional), intentional self-harm, assault, undetermined], subsq enc **405**

T43.22[1,2,3,4]A Poison by selective serotonin reuptake inhibitors, [accid (unintentional), intentional self-harm, assault, undetermined], init enc **363**

T43.22[1,2,3,4]S Poison by selective serotonin reuptake inhibitors, [accid (unintentional), intentional self-harm, assault, undetermined], seq **370**

T43.22[1,2,3,4]D Poison by selective serotonin reuptake inhibitors, [accid (unintentional), intentional self-harm, assault, undetermined], subsq enc **405**

T48.1X[1,2,3,4]A Poison by skeletal muscle relaxants (neuromuscular blocking agents), [accid (unintentional), intentional self-harm, assault, undetermined], init enc **364**

T48.1X[1,2,3,4]S Poison by skeletal muscle relaxants (neuromuscular blocking agents), [accid (unintentional), intentional self-harm, assault, undetermined], seq **371**

T48.1X[1,2,3,4]D Poison by skeletal muscle relaxants (neuromuscular blocking agents), [accid (unintentional), intentional self-harm, assault, undetermined], subsq enc **406**

T50.B1[1,2,3,4]A Poison by smpox vaccines, [accid (unintentional), intentional self-harm, assault, undetermined], init enc **365**

T50.B1[1,2,3,4]S Poison by smpox vaccines, [accid (unintentional), intentional self-harm, assault, undetermined], seq **372**

T50.B1[1,2,3,4]D Poison by smpox vaccines, [accid (unintentional), intentional self-harm, assault, undetermined], subsq enc **407**

T40.69[1,2,3,4]A Poison by spec narcotics, [accid (unintentional), intentional self-harm, assault, undetermined], init enc **363**

T40.69[1,2,3,4]S Poison by spec narcotics, [accid (unintentional), intentional self-harm, assault, undetermined], seq **369**

T40.69[1,2,3,4]D Poison by spec narcotics, [accid (unintentional), intentional self-harm, assault, undetermined], subsq enc **404**

T47.2X[1,2,3,4]A Poison by stimulant laxatives, [accid (unintentional), intentional self-harm, assault, undetermined], init enc **364**

T47.2X[1,2,3,4]S Poison by stimulant laxatives, [accid (unintentional), intentional self-harm, assault, undetermined], seq **371**

T47.2X[1,2,3,4]D Poison by stimulant laxatives, [accid (unintentional), intentional self-harm, assault, undetermined], subsq enc **406**

T42.2X[1,2,3,4]A Poison by succinimides and oxazolidinediones, [accid (unintentional), intentional self-harm, assault, undetermined], init enc **363**

T42.2X[1,2,3,4]S Poison by succinimides and oxazolidinediones, [accid (unintentional), intentional self-harm, assault, undetermined], seq **369**

T42.2X[1,2,3,4]D Poison by succinimides and oxazolidinediones, [accid (unintentional), intentional self-harm, assault, undetermined], subsq enc **404**

T37.0X[1,2,3,4]A Poison by sulfonamides, [accid (unintentional), intentional self-harm, assault, undetermined], init enc **362**

T37.0X[1,2,3,4]S Poison by sulfonamides, [accid (unintentional), intentional self-harm, assault, undetermined], seq **368**

T37.0X[1,2,3,4]D Poison by sulfonamides, [accid (unintentional), intentional self-harm, assault, undetermined], subsq enc **403**

T43.02[1,2,3,4]A Poison by tetracyclic antidepressants, [accid (unintentional), intentional self-harm, assault, undetermined], init enc **363**

T43.02[1,2,3,4]S Poison by tetracyclic antidepressants, [accid (unintentional), intentional self-harm, assault, undetermined], seq **370**

T43.02[1,2,3,4]D Poison by tetracyclic antidepressants, [accid (unintentional), intentional self-harm, assault, undetermined], subsq enc **405**

T36.4X[1,2,3,4]A Poison by tetracyclines, [accid (unintentional), intentional self-harm, assault, undetermined], init enc **362**

T36.4X[1,2,3,4]S Poison by tetracyclines, [accid (unintentional), intentional self-harm, assault, undetermined], seq **368**

T36.4X[1,2,3,4]D Poison by tetracyclines, [accid (unintentional), intentional self-harm, assault, undetermined], subsq enc **403**

T41.5X[1,2,3,4]A Poison by therapeutic gases, [accid (unintentional), intentional self-harm, assault, undetermined], init enc **363**

T41.5X[1,2,3,4]S Poison by therapeutic gases, [accid (unintentional), intentional self-harm, assault, undetermined], seq **369**

T41.5X[1,2,3,4]D Poison by therapeutic gases, [accid (unintentional), intentional self-harm, assault, undetermined], subsq enc **404**

T45.61[1,2,3,4]A Poison by thrombolytic drug, [accid (unintentional), intentional self-harm, assault, undetermined], init enc **364**

T45.61[1,2,3,4]S Poison by thrombolytic drug, [accid (unintentional), intentional self-harm, assault, undetermined], seq **370**

T45.61[1,2,3,4]D Poison by thrombolytic drug, [accid (unintentional), intentional self-harm, assault, undetermined], subsq enc **406**

T38.1X[1,2,3,4]A Poison by thyroid hormones and subs, [accid (unintentional), intentional self-harm, assault, undetermined], init enc **362**

T38.1X[1,2,3,4]S Poison by thyroid hormones and subs, [accid (unintentional), intentional self-harm, assault, undetermined], seq **369**

T38.1X[1,2,3,4]D Poison by thyroid hormones and subs, [accid (unintentional), intentional self-harm, assault, undetermined], subsq enc **403**

T43.01[1,2,3,4]A Poison by tricyclic antidepressants, [accid (unintentional), intentional self-harm, assault, undetermined], init enc **363**

T43.01[1,2,3,4]S Poison by tricyclic antidepressants, [accid (unintentional), intentional self-harm, assault, undetermined], seq **370**

T43.01[1,2,3,4]D Poison by tricyclic antidepressants, [accid (unintentional), intentional self-harm, assault, undetermined], subsq enc **404**

T48.90[1,2,3,4]A Poison by unsp agents primarily acting on the respiratory sys, [accid (unintentional), intentional self-harm, assault, undetermined], init enc **365**

T48.90[1,2,3,4]S Poison by unsp agents primarily acting on the respiratory sys, [accid (unintentional), intentional self-harm, assault, undetermined], seq **371**

T48.90[1,2,3,4]D Poison by unsp agents primarily acting on the respiratory sys, [accid (unintentional), intentional self-harm, assault, undetermined], subsq enc **407**

T47.9[1,2,3,4]XA Poison by unsp agents primarily affecting gastrointestinal sys, [accid (unintentional), intentional self-harm, assault, undetermined], init enc **364**

T47.9[1,2,3,4]XS Poison by unsp agents primarily affecting gastrointestinal sys, [accid (unintentional), intentional self-harm, assault, undetermined], seq **371**

T47.9[1,2,3,4]XD Poison by unsp agents primarily affecting gastrointestinal sys, [accid (unintentional), intentional self-harm, assault, undetermined], subsq enc **406**

T46.90[1,2,3,4]A Poison by unsp agents primarily affecting the cardiovascular sys, [accid (unintentional), intentional self-harm, assault, undetermined], init enc **364**

T46.90[1,2,3,4]S Poison by unsp agents primarily affecting the cardiovascular sys, [accid (unintentional), intentional self-harm, assault, undetermined], seq **371**

T46.90[1,2,3,4]D Poison by unsp agents primarily affecting the cardiovascular sys, [accid (unintentional), intentional self-harm, assault, undetermined], subsq enc **406**

T41.4[1,2,3,4]XA Poison by unsp anesthetic, [accid (unintentional), intentional self-harm, assault, undetermined], init enc **363**

T41.4[1,2,3,4]XS Poison by unsp anesthetic, [accid (unintentional), intentional self-harm, assault, undetermined], seq **369**

T41.4[1,2,3,4]XD Poison by unsp anesthetic, [accid (unintentional), intentional self-harm, assault, undetermined], subsq enc **404**

T43.20[1,2,3,4]A Poison by unsp antidepressants, [accid (unintentional), intentional self-harm, assault, undetermined], init enc **363**

T43.20[1,2,3,4]S Poison by unsp antidepressants, [accid (unintentional), intentional self-harm, assault, undetermined], seq **370**

T43.20[1,2,3,4]D Poison by unsp antidepressants, [accid (unintentional), intentional self-harm, assault, undetermined], subsq enc **405**

T42.7[1,2,3,4]XA Poison by unsp antiepileptic and sedative-hypnotic drugs, [accid (unintentional), intentional self-harm, assault, undetermined], init enc **363**

T42.7[1,2,3,4]XS Poison by unsp antiepileptic and sedative-hypnotic drugs, [accid (unintentional), intentional self-harm, assault, undetermined], seq **370**

T42.7[1,2,3,4]XD Poison by unsp antiepileptic and sedative-hypnotic drugs, [accid (unintentional), intentional self-harm, assault, undetermined], subsq enc **404**

T43.50[1,2,3,4]A Poison by unsp antipsychotics and neuroleptics, [accid (unintentional), intentional self-harm, assault, undetermined], init enc **363**

T43.50[1,2,3,4]S Poison by unsp antipsychotics and neuroleptics, [accid (unintentional), intentional self-harm, assault, undetermined], seq **370**

T43.50[1,2,3,4]D Poison by unsp antipsychotics and neuroleptics, [accid (unintentional), intentional self-harm, assault, undetermined], subsq enc **405**

T44.90[1,2,3,4]A Poison by unsp drugs primarily affecting the autonomic nervous sys, [accid (unintentional), intentional self-harm, assault, undetermined], init enc **364**

T44.90[1,2,3,4]S Poison by unsp drugs primarily affecting the autonomic nervous sys, [accid (unintentional), intentional self-harm, assault, undetermined], seq **370**

T44.90[1,2,3,4]D Poison by unsp drugs primarily affecting the autonomic nervous sys, [accid (unintentional), intentional self-harm, assault, undetermined], subsq enc **405**

T48.20[1,2,3,4]A Poison by unsp drugs working on muscles, [accid (unintentional), intentional self-harm, assault, undetermined], init enc **364**

T48.20[1,2,3,4]S Poison by unsp drugs working on muscles, [accid (unintentional), intentional self-harm, assault, undetermined], seq **371**

T48.20[1,2,3,4]D Poison by unsp drugs working on muscles, [accid (unintentional), intentional self-harm, assault, undetermined], subsq enc **406**

T50.90[1,2,3,4]A Poison by unsp drugs, medicaments and biological substances, [accid (unintentional), intentional self-harm, assault, undetermined], init enc **365**

T50.90[1,2,3,4]S Poison by unsp drugs, medicaments and biological substances, [accid (unintentional), intentional self-harm, assault, undetermined], seq **372**

T50.90[1,2,3,4]D Poison by unsp drugs, medicaments and biological substances, [accid (unintentional), intentional self-harm, assault, undetermined], subsq enc **407**

T45.60[1,2,3,4]A Poison by unsp fibrinolysis-affecting drugs, [accid (unintentional), intentional self-harm, assault, undetermined], init enc **364**

T45.60[1,2,3,4]S Poison by unsp fibrinolysis-affecting drugs, [accid (unintentional), intentional self-harm, assault, undetermined], seq **370**

T45.60[1,2,3,4]D Poison by unsp fibrinolysis-affecting drugs, [accid (unintentional), intentional self-harm, assault, undetermined], subsq enc **406**

T41.20[1,2,3,4]A Poison by unsp general anesthetics, [accid (unintentional), intentional self-harm, assault, undetermined], init enc **363**

T41.20[1,2,3,4]S Poison by unsp general anesthetics, [accid (unintentional), intentional self-harm, assault, undetermined], seq **369**

T41.20[1,2,3,4]D Poison by unsp general anesthetics, [accid (unintentional), intentional self-harm, assault, undetermined], subsq enc **404**

T38.90[1,2,3,4]A Poison by unsp hormone antagonists, [accid (unintentional), intentional self-harm, assault, undetermined], init enc **362**

T38.90[1,2,3,4]S Poison by unsp hormone antagonists, [accid (unintentional), intentional self-harm, assault, undetermined], seq **369**

T38.90[1,2,3,4]D Poison by unsp hormone antagonists, [accid (unintentional), intentional self-harm, assault, undetermined], subsq enc **403**

T38.80[1,2,3,4]A Poison by unsp hormones and synth subs, [accid (unintentional), intentional self-harm, assault, undetermined], init enc **362**

T38.80[1,2,3,4]S Poison by unsp hormones and synth subs, [accid (unintentional), intentional self-harm, assault, undetermined], seq **369**

T38.80[1,2,3,4]D Poison by unsp hormones and synth subs, [accid (unintentional), intentional self-harm, assault, undetermined], subsq enc **403**

T40.60[1,2,3,4]A Poison by unsp narcotics, [accid (unintentional), intentional self-harm, assault, undetermined], init enc **362**

Code	Description
T40.60[1,2,3,4]S	Poison by unsp narcotics, [accid (unintentional), intentional self-harm, assault, undetermined], seq 369
T40.60[1,2,3,4]D	Poison by unsp narcotics, [accid (unintentional), intentional self-harm, assault, undetermined], subsq enc 404
T39.9[1,2,3,4]XA	Poison by unsp nonopiod analgesic, antipyretic and antirheumatic, [accid (unintentional), intentional self-harm, assault, undetermined], init enc 362
T39.9[1,2,3,4]XS	Poison by unsp nonopiod analgesic, antipyretic and antirheumatic, [accid (unintentional), intentional self-harm, assault, undetermined], seq 369
T39.9[1,2,3,4]XD	Poison by unsp nonopiod analgesic, antipyretic and antirheumatic, [accid (unintentional), intentional self-harm, assault, undetermined], subsq enc 404
T45.9[1,2,3,4]XA	Poison by unsp primarily sysic and hematological agents, [accid (unintentional), intentional self-harm, assault, undetermined], init enc 364
T45.9[1,2,3,4]XS	Poison by unsp primarily sysic and hematological agents, [accid (unintentional), intentional self-harm, assault, undetermined], seq 371
T45.9[1,2,3,4]XD	Poison by unsp primarily sysic and hematological agents, [accid (unintentional), intentional self-harm, assault, undetermined], subsq enc 406
T40.90[1,2,3,4]A	Poison by unsp psychodysleptics (hallucinogens), [accid (unintentional), intentional self-harm, assault, undetermined], init enc 363
T40.90[1,2,3,4]S	Poison by unsp psychodysleptics (hallucinogens), [accid (unintentional), intentional self-harm, assault, undetermined], seq 369
T40.90[1,2,3,4]D	Poison by unsp psychodysleptics (hallucinogens), [accid (unintentional), intentional self-harm, assault, undetermined], subsq enc 404
T43.60[1,2,3,4]A	Poison by unsp psychostimulants, [accid (unintentional), intentional self-harm, assault, undetermined], init enc 363
T43.60[1,2,3,4]S	Poison by unsp psychostimulants, [accid (unintentional), intentional self-harm, assault, undetermined], seq 370
T43.60[1,2,3,4]D	Poison by unsp psychostimulants, [accid (unintentional), intentional self-harm, assault, undetermined], subsq enc 405
T43.9[1,2,3,4]XA	Poison by unsp psychotropic drug, [accid (unintentional), intentional self-harm, assault, undetermined], init enc 363
T43.9[1,2,3,4]XS	Poison by unsp psychotropic drug, [accid (unintentional), intentional self-harm, assault, undetermined], seq 370
T43.9[1,2,3,4]XD	Poison by unsp psychotropic drug, [accid (unintentional), intentional self-harm, assault, undetermined], subsq enc 405
T37.9[1,2,3,4]XA	Poison by unsp sysic anti-infectives and antiparasitics, [accid (unintentional), intentional self-harm, assault, undetermined], init enc 362
T37.9[1,2,3,4]XS	Poison by unsp sysic anti-infectives and antiparasitics, [accid (unintentional), intentional self-harm, assault, undetermined], seq 369
T37.9[1,2,3,4]XD	Poison by unsp sysic anti-infectives and antiparasitics, [accid (unintentional), intentional self-harm, assault, undetermined], subsq enc 403
T36.9[1,2,3,4]XA	Poison by unsp sysic antibiotic [accid (unintentional), intentional self-harm, assault, undetermined], init enc 362
T36.9[1,2,3,4]XS	Poison by unsp sysic antibiotic [accid (unintentional), intentional self-harm, assault, undetermined], seq 368
T36.9[1,2,3,4]XD	Poison by unsp sysic antibiotic [accid (unintentional), intentional self-harm, assault, undetermined], subsq enc 403
T49.9[1,2,3,4]XA	Poison by unsp topical agent, [accid (unintentional), intentional self-harm, assault, undetermined], init enc 365
T49.9[1,2,3,4]XS	Poison by unsp topical agent, [accid (unintentional), intentional self-harm, assault, undetermined], seq 371
T49.9[1,2,3,4]XD	Poison by unsp topical agent, [accid (unintentional), intentional self-harm, assault, undetermined], subsq enc 407
T45.2X[1,2,3,4]A	Poison by vitamins, [accid (unintentional), intentional self-harm, assault, undetermined], init enc 364
T45.2X[1,2,3,4]S	Poison by vitamins, [accid (unintentional), intentional self-harm, assault, undetermined], seq 370
T45.2X[1,2,3,4]D	Poison by vitamins, [accid (unintentional), intentional self-harm, assault, undetermined], subsq enc 405
M30.0	Polyarteritis nodosa 164
M30.1	Polyarteritis with lung involvement [Churg-Strauss] 163
D89.0	Polyclonal hypergammaglobulinemia 294
P61.1	Polycythemia neonatorum 288
D45	Polycythemia vera 295, 303, 305
Q69*	Polydactyly 195

Code	Description
E31*	Polyglandular dysfunction 247
O40.[1,2,3] XX.[0,1,2,3,4,5,9]	Polyhydramnios, [1st, 2nd, 3rd] trmstr, fetus [N/A or unsp, 1, 2, 3, 4, 5, oth] 278
O40.1*	Polyhydramnios, first trmstr 280
O40.2*	Polyhydramnios, second trmstr 280
O40.3*	Polyhydramnios, third trmstr 280
O40.9*	Polyhydramnios, unsp trmstr 281
M35.3	Polymyalgia rheumatica 164
G63	Polyneuropathy in dz classified elsw 34
M15*	Polyosteoarthritis 167
Q78.1	Polyostotic fibrous dysplasia 195
K63.5	Polyp of colon 117
N84*	Polyp of female genital tract 265, 270
K31.7	Polyp of stomach and duodenum 117
J38.1	Polyp of vocal cord and larynx 4
R35*	Polyuria 255
E80.1	Porphyria cutanea tarda 247
K76.6	Portal hypertension 124
I81	Portal vein thrombosis 124
Q26.6	Portal vein-hepatic artery fistula 100
S73.01[1,2,3,4,5,6]A	Post [sublux, disloc] of [rt, lt, unsp] hip, init enc 426
S12.03[0,1] [A,B,S]	Post arch fx of 1st cervical vertebra [disp, nondisp] init enc for fx [clsd, opn, seq] 165
S43.15[1,2,9]D	Post disloc of [rt, lt, unsp] acromioclavicular jt, subsq enc 391
S73.01[4,5,6]A	Post disloc of [rt, lt, unsp] hip, init enc 162
S73.01[4,5,6]S	Post disloc of [rt, lt, unsp] hip, seq 190
S73.01[4,5,6]D	Post disloc of [rt, lt, unsp] hip, subsq enc 397
S53.02[4,5,6]D	Post disloc of [rt, lt, unsp] radial head, subsq enc 392
S43.22[4,5,6]A	Post disloc of [rt, lt, unsp] sternoclavicular jt, init enc 67
S43.22[4,5,6]S	Post disloc of [rt, lt, unsp] sternoclavicular jt, seq 185
S53.12[4,5,6]D	Post disloc of [rt, lt, unsp] ulnohumeral jt, subsq enc 392
S43.15[1,2,9] [A,S]	Post disloc of acromioclavicular jt, > 200% displac {rt, lt, unsp] [init enc, seq] 185
S43.02[4,5,6] [A,S]	Post disloc of humerus [rt, lt, unsp] [init enc, seq] 185
S83.12[4,5,6] [A,S]	Post disloc of proximal end of tibia, [rt, lt, unsp] knee, [init enc, seq] 191
S83.12[4,5,6]A	Post disloc of proximal end of tibia, [rt, lt, unsp] knee, init enc 428
S83.12[4,5,6]D	Post disloc of proximal end of tibia, [rt, lt, unsp] knee, subsq enc 398
S53.02[4,5,6] [A,S]	Post disloc of radial head [unsp, rt, lt] [init enc, seq] 186
S53.12[4,5,6] [A,S]	Post disloc of ulnohumeral jt [rt, lt, unsp] [init enc, seq] 186
S42.01[4,5,6] [A,B]	Post disp fx of if sternal end of clavicle [rt, lt, unsp] init enc for fx [clsd, opn 184
S42.01[4,5,6] [D,G,S]	Post disp fx of sternal end of [rt, lt, unsp] clavicle, [subsq enc for fx w/ routine healing, subsq enc for fx w/ delayed healing, seq] 170
S42.01[4,5,6] [K,P]	Post disp fx of sternal end of [rt, lt, unsp] clavicle, subsq enc for fx w/ [nonu, malu] 196
S73.01[1,2,3]A	Post sublux of [rt, lt, unsp] hip, init enc 162
S73.01[1,2,3]S	Post sublux of [rt, lt, unsp] hip, seq 190
S73.01[1,2,3]D	Post sublux of [rt, lt, unsp] hip, subsq enc 397
S43.02[1,2,3] [A,S]	Post sublux of [rt, lt, unsp] humerus, [init enc, seq] 185
S43.02[1,2,3,4,5,6]D	Post sublux of [rt, lt, unsp] humerus, Post disloc of [rt, lt, unsp] humerus subsq enc 391
S53.02[1,2,3] [A,S]	Post sublux of [rt, lt, unsp] radial head, [init enc, seq] 186
S53.02[1,2,3]D	Post sublux of [rt, lt, unsp] radial head, subsq enc 392
S43.22[1,2,3]A	Post sublux of [rt, lt, unsp] sternoclavicular jt, init enc 67
S43.22[1,2,3,4,5,6]D	Post sublux of [rt, lt, unsp] sternoclavicular jt, Post disloc of [rt, lt, unsp] sternoclavicular jt, subsq enc 391
S43.22[1,2,3]S	Post sublux of [rt, lt, unsp] sternoclavicular jt, seq 185
S53.12[1,2,3]D	Post sublux of [rt, lt, unsp] ulnohumeral jt, subsq enc 392
S83.12[1,2,3] [A,S]	Post sublux of proximal end of tibia, [rt, lt, unsp] knee, [init enc, seq] 191
S83.12[1,2,3]A	Post sublux of proximal end of tibia, [rt, lt, unsp] knee, init enc 428
S83.12[1,2,3]D	Post sublux of proximal end of tibia, [rt, lt, unsp] knee, subsq enc 398

S53.12[1,2,3] [A,S]	Post sublux of ulnohumeral jt [rt, lt, unsp] [init enc, seq] **186**	
P08.21	Post-term newborn **288**	
D47.Z1	Post-transplant lymphoproliferative d/o (PTLD) **367**	
F43.1*	Post-traum stress d/o (PTSD) **310**	
H70.81[1,2,3,9]	Postauricular fistula, [rt, lt, bilat, unsp] ear(s) **283**	
I97.0	Postcardiotomy synd **103**, **284**	
K91.5	Postcholecystectomy synd **124**	
F07.81	Postconcussional synd **41**	
M02.1*	Postdysenteric arthropathy **166**	
G21.3	Postencephalitic parkinsonism **32**	
G46.2	Posterior cerebral artery synd **33**	
I67.83	Posterior reversible encephalopathy synd **33**, **439**	
K03.7	Posteruptive color changes of dental hard tissues **4**	
K91.1	Postgastric surgery syndromes **116**	
B02.2[1,2,3,9]	Postherpetic [geniculate ganglionitis, trigeminal neuralgia, polyneuropathy, oth nervous sys involvement] **438**	
B02.2[1,2,3]	Postherpetic [geniculate ganglionitis, trigeminal neuralgia, polyneuropathy] **283**	
B02.21	Postherpetic geniculate ganglionitis **33**	
B02.24	Postherpetic myelitis **11**, **15**, **41**	
B02.23	Postherpetic polyneuropathy **33**	
B02.22	Postherpetic trigeminal neuralgia **33**	
M02.2*	Postimmunization arthropathy **166**	
I23.7	Postinfarction angina **103**	
E03.3	Postinfectious hypothyroidism **247**	
L81.0	Postinflammatory hyperpigmentation **289**	
M96.3	Postlaminectomy kyphosis **125**, **165**	
M96.1	Postlaminectomy synd, NEC **165**	
I97.2	Postmastectomy lymphedema synd **224**	
R09.82	Postnasal drip **58**	
O90.4	Postpartum acute kidney failure **272**, **276**	
O72.3	Postpartum coagulation defects **272**, **274**, **276**	
O71.2	Postpartum inversion of uterus **272**, **275**	
O90.6	Postpartum mood disturbance **272**, **276**	
O90.5	Postpartum thyroiditis **272**, **276**	
G14	Postpolio synd **38**	
N99.0	Postprocedural (acute) (chr) kidney failure **256**, **285**	
T81.1[0,1,2,9]XA	Postprocedural [unsp, cardiogenic, septic, oth] shock, init enc **287**, **368**	
T81.1[0,1,2,9]XS	Postprocedural [unsp, cardiogenic, septic, oth] shock, seq **375**	
T81.1[0,1,2,9]XD	Postprocedural [unsp, cardiogenic, septic, oth] shock, subsq enc **410**	
N99.2	Postprocedural adhesions of vagina **265**, **270**	
E89.6	Postprocedural adrenocortical (-medullary) hypofunction **247**	
I97.82[0,1]	Postprocedural cerebrovascular infarction during [cardiac, oth] surgery **38**	
I97.6*	Postprocedural hemor/hemtom of a circ sys org fol a procedure **367**	
K91.841	Postprocedural hemor/hemtom of a dgstv sys org fol oth procedure **367**	
N99.820	Postprocedural hemor/hemtom of a GU sys org fol a GU sys procedure **368**	
N99.821	Postprocedural hemor/hemtom of a GU sys org fol oth procedure **368**	
G97.5*	Postprocedural hemor/hemtom of a nervous sys org fol a procedure **367**	
J95.830	Postprocedural hemor/hemtom of a resp sys org fol a resp sys proc **367**	
J95.831	Postprocedural hemor/hemtom of a resp sys org fol oth procedure **367**	
K91.840	Postprocedural hemor/hemtom of dgstv sys org fol a dgstv sys proc **367**	
H95.4*	Postprocedural hemor/hemtom of ear/mastd following a procedure **367**	
H59.3*	Postprocedural hemor/hemtom of eye and adnexa fol a procedure **367**	
K91.82	Postprocedural hepatic failure **117**, **284**	
K91.83	Postprocedural hepatorenal synd **117**, **284**	
I97.3	Postprocedural hypertension **367**	
E89.1	Postprocedural hypoinsulinemia **2**, **246**	
E89.2	Postprocedural hypoparathyroidism **247**, **283**	

E89.3	Postprocedural hypopituitarism **247**	
I95.81	Postprocedural hypotension **102**	
E89.0	Postprocedural hypothyroidism **247**	
K91.3	Postprocedural intestinal obstruction **117**, **284**	
E89.4*	Postprocedural ovarian failure **264**, **270**	
N99.4	Postprocedural pelvic peritoneal adhesions **117**	
J95.81*	Postprocedural pneumothorax and air leak **68**	
J95.82*	Postprocedural respiratory failure **68**, **381**	
K68.11	Postprocedural retroperitoneal abscess **307**	
J95.5	Postprocedural subglottic stenosis **69**, **284**	
E89.5	Postprocedural testicular hypofunction **247**	
N99.1*	Postprocedural urethral stricture **255**	
M96.2	Postradiation kyphosis **125**, **165**	
M96.5	Postradiation scoliosis **125**, **165**	
M96.4	Postsurgical lordosis **125**, **165**	
K91.2	Postsurgical malabsorption, NEC **116**, **284**	
I87.0*	Postthrombotic synd **100**	
M40.0*	Postural kyphosis **125**	
M40.4*	Postural lordosis **125**	
G93.3	Postviral fatigue synd **385**	
K91.850	Pouchitis **117**, **284**	
I45.6	Pre-excitation synd **283**	
O10.211	Pre-exist hyp chr kidney dz comp preg, first trmstr **278**	
O10.212	Pre-exist hyp chr kidney dz comp preg, second trmstr **278**	
O10.213	Pre-exist hyp chr kidney dz comp preg, third trmstr **278**	
O10.219	Pre-exist hyp chr kidney dz comp preg, unsp trmstr **280**	
O10.32	Pre-exist hyp heart and chr kidney dz comp chldbrth **273**	
O10.33	Pre-exist hyp heart and chr kidney dz comp the puerp **275**	
O10.311	Pre-exist hyp heart and CKD comp preg, first trmstr **278**	
O10.312	Pre-exist hyp heart and CKD comp preg, second trmstr **278**	
O10.313	Pre-exist hyp heart and CKD comp preg, third trmstr **279**	
O10.319	Pre-exist hyp heart and CKD comp preg, unsp trmstr **280**	
O10.111	Pre-exist hyp heart dz comp preg, first trmstr **278**	
O10.112	Pre-exist hyp heart dz comp preg, second trmstr **278**	
O10.113	Pre-exist hyp heart dz comp preg, third trmstr **278**	
O10.119	Pre-exist hyp heart dz comp preg, unsp trmstr **280**	
O10.[0,1,2,3,4,9]2	Pre-existing [essential hypertension, hypertensive heart dz, hypertensive chr kidney dz, hypertensive heart and chr kidney dz, 2ndary hypertension] compl childbirth **273**	
O10.[0,1,2,3,4,9]3	Pre-existing [essential hypertension, hypertensive heart dz, hypertensive chr kidney dz, hypertensive heart and chr kidney dz, 2ndary hypertension] compl the puerperium **272**	
O10.41[1,2,3]	Pre-existing 2ndary hypertension compl preg, [1st, 2nd, 3rd] trmstr **273**, **276**	
O24.[0,1,3]2	Pre-existing diabetes mellitus, [type 1, type 2, type unsp], in childbirth **273**	
O24.[0,1]1[1,2,3]	Pre-existing diabetes mellitus, type [1, 2], in preg, [1st, 2nd, 3rd] trmstr **277**	
O24.02	Pre-existing diabetes mellitus, type 1, in childbirth **273**	
O24.01[1,2,3]	Pre-existing diabetes mellitus, type 1, in preg, [1st, 2nd, 3rd] trmstr **273**, **276**	
O24.03	Pre-existing diabetes mellitus, type 1, in the puerperium **272**, **275**	
O24.12	Pre-existing diabetes mellitus, type 2, in childbirth **273**	
O24.11[1,2,3]	Pre-existing diabetes mellitus, type 2, in preg, [1st, 2nd, 3rd] trmstr **273**, **276**	
O24.13	Pre-existing diabetes mellitus, type 2, in the puerperium **272**, **275**	
O24.019	Pre-existing diabetes, type 1, in preg, unsp trmstr **280**	
O24.119	Pre-existing diabetes, type 2, in preg, unsp trmstr **280**	
O10.011	Pre-existing essential hypertension comp preg, first trmstr **278**	
O10.012	Pre-existing essential hypertension comp preg, second trmstr **278**	
O10.013	Pre-existing essential hypertension comp preg, third trmstr **278**	
O10.019	Pre-existing essential hypertension comp preg, unsp trmstr **280**	
O10.03	Pre-existing essential hypertension comp the puerperium **273**, **275**	
O10.02	Pre-existing essential hypertension compl childbirth **273**	
O10.01[1,2,3]	Pre-existing essential hypertension compl preg, [1st, 2nd, 3rd] trmstr **273**, **276**	
O10.22	Pre-existing hyp chr kidney dz comp childbirth **273**	
O10.23	Pre-existing hyp chr kidney dz comp the puerperium **275**	
O11.1	Pre-existing hypertension w pre-eclampsia, first trmstr **279**	
O11.2	Pre-existing hypertension w pre-eclampsia, second trmstr **279**	

O11.3	Pre-existing hypertension w pre-eclampsia, third trmstr **279**	
O11.[1,2,3]	Pre-existing hypertension w/ pre-eclampsia, [1st, 2nd, 3rd] trmstr **273, 277**	
O11*	Pre-existing hypertension with pre-eclampsia **276**	
O11.9	Pre-existing hypertension with pre-eclampsia, unsp trmstr **279, 280**	
O10.21[1,2,3]	Pre-existing hypertensive chr kidney dz compl preg, [1st, 2nd, 3rd] trmstr **273, 276**	
O10.31[1,2,3]	Pre-existing hypertensive heart and chr kidney dz compl preg, [1st, 2nd, thrid] trmstr **273, 276**	
O10.12	Pre-existing hypertensive heart dz comp childbirth **273**	
O10.13	Pre-existing hypertensive heart dz comp the puerperium **273, 275**	
O10.11[1,2,3]	Pre-existing hypertensive heart dz compl preg, [1st, 2nd, 3rd] trmstr **273, 276**	
O10.412	Pre-existing secondary hypertension comp preg, 2nd trmstr **279**	
O10.411	Pre-existing secondary hypertension comp preg, first trmstr **279**	
O10.413	Pre-existing secondary hypertension comp preg, third trmstr **279**	
O10.419	Pre-existing secondary hypertension comp preg, unsp trmstr **280**	
O10.43	Pre-existing secondary hypertension comp the puerperium **273, 275**	
O10.42	Pre-existing secondary hypertension compl childbirth **273**	
Q18.1	Preauricular sinus and cyst **58**	
R07.2	Precordial pain **103**	
O26.20	Preg care for patient w recurrent preg loss, unsp trmstr **280**	
O26.2[1,2,3]	Preg care for patient w/ recurrent preg loss, [1st, 2nd, 3rd] trmstr **277, 279**	
O26.9[1,2,3]	Preg related conditions, unsp, [1st, 2nd, 3rd] trmstr **276, 277**	
O26.90	Preg related conditions, unsp, unsp trmstr **280**	
O26.81*	Preg related exhaustion and fatigue **276**	
O26.81[1,2,3]	Preg related exhaustion and fatigue, [1st, 2nd, 3rd] trmstr **277**	
O26.819	Preg related exhaustion and fatigue, unsp trmstr **280**	
O26.82[1,2,3]	Preg related peripheral neuritis, [1st,2nd, 3rd] trmstr **276, 277**	
O26.829	Preg related peripheral neuritis, unsp trmstr **280**	
O26.83*	Preg related renal dz **276**	
O26.83[1,2,3]	Preg related renal dz, [1st, 2nd, 3rd] trmstr **277**	
O26.839	Preg related renal dz, unsp trmstr **280**	
O36.80X0	Preg w inconclusive fetal viability, unsp **281**	
O36.80X1	Preg with inconclusive fetal viability, fetus 1 **281**	
O36.80X2	Preg with inconclusive fetal viability, fetus 2 **281**	
O36.80X3	Preg with inconclusive fetal viability, fetus 3 **281**	
O36.80X4	Preg with inconclusive fetal viability, fetus 4 **281**	
O36.80X5	Preg with inconclusive fetal viability, fetus 5 **281**	
O36.80X9	Preg with inconclusive fetal viability, oth fetus **281**	
Z33.1	Pregnant state, incidental **412**	
F52.4	Premature ejaculation **311**	
O42*	Premature rupture of membranes **278, 280**	
O45.0[0,1,2,9][1,2,3]	Premature separation of placenta w/ [coagulation defect unsp, afibrinogenemia, disseminated intravascular coagulation, oth coagulation defect], [1st, 2nd, 3rd] trmstr **273, 278**	
O45.0[0,1,2,9]9	Premature separation of placenta w/ [coagulation defect unsp, afibrinogenemia, disseminated intravascular coagulation, oth coagulation defect], unsp trmstr **281**	
O45.0*	Premature separation of placenta with coagulation defect **276**	
O45.9[1,2,3]	Premature separation of placenta, unsp, [1st, 2nd 3rd] trmstr **273, 278, 280**	
O45.90	Premature separation of placenta, unsp, unsp trmstr **281**	
N94.3	Premenstrual tension synd **270**	
M70.4*	Prepatellar bursitis **167**	
H52.4	Presbyopia **46**	
Z97.5	Presence of (intrauterine) contraceptive device **413**	
Z95.81[1,2]	Presence of [heart assist dev, fully implantable artfcl heart] **103**	
Z95.1	Presence of aortocoronary bypass graft **413**	
Z97.0	Presence of artfcl eye **47**	
Z96.3	Presence of artfcl larynx **413**	
Z97.1*	Presence of artfcl limb (complete) (partial) **205**	
Z95.810	Presence of automatic (implantable) cardiac defibrillator **413**	
Z95.9	Presence of cardiac and vascular implant and graft, unsp **413**	
Z95.0	Presence of cardiac pacemaker **413**	
Z95.5	Presence of coronary angioplasty implant and graft **413**	
Z97.2	Presence of dental prosthetic device (complete) (partial) **413**	
Z96.4*	Presence of endocrine implants **413**	
Z97.4	Presence of ext hearing-aid **413**	
Z96.9	Presence of functional implant, unsp **2, 413**	
Z96.1	Presence of intraocular lens **47**	
Z96.6*	Presence of orthopedic jt implants **205**	
Z95.818	Presence of oth cardiac implants and grafts **413**	
Z96.49	Presence of oth endocrine implants **2**	
Z95.4	Presence of oth heart-valve replace **103**	
Z97.8	Presence of oth spec devices **413**	
Z96.89	Presence of oth spec functional implants **2**	
Z96.8*	Presence of oth spec functional implants **413**	
Z95.828	Presence of oth vascular implants and grafts **103**	
Z96.7	Presence of other bone and tndn implants **205**	
Z96.2*	Presence of otological and audiological implants **413**	
Z95.2	Presence of prosthetic heart valve **103**	
Z97.3	Presence of spectacles and contact lenses **413**	
Z96.5	Presence of tooth-root and mandibular implants **413**	
Z96.0	Presence of urogenital implants **256**	
Z95.3	Presence of xenogenic heart valve **103**	
O29.029	Pressr collapse of lung d/t anesth during preg, unsp trmstr **280**	
O29.02[1,2,3]	Pressure collapse of lung d/t anesthesia during preg, [1st, 2nd, 3rd] trmstr **277**	
L89*	Pressure ulcer **206, 223**	
P07.3*	Preterm [premature] newborn [oth] **282**	
O60.1[2,3]X[0,1,2,3,4,5,9]	Preterm labor 2nd trmstr w/ preterm delivery [2nd, 3rd] trmstr, fetus [N/A or unsp, 1, 2, 3, 4, 5, oth] **273, 275**	
O60.14X[0,1,2,3,4,5,9]	Preterm labor 3rd trmstr w/ preterm delivery, 3rd trmstr, fetus [N/A or unsp, 1, 2, 3, 4, 5, oth] **273, 275**	
O60.10X[0,1,2,3,4,5,9]	Preterm labor w/ preterm delivery, unsp trmstr, fetus [N/A or unsp, 1, 2, 3, 4, 5, oth] **278, 280**	
O60.0*	Preterm labor w/o delivery **276**	
N48.3*	Priapism **261**	
A51.1	Primary anal syphilis **116**	
H40.2*	Primary angle-closure glaucoma **46**	
P28.0	Primary atelectasis of newborn **282**	
K74.3	Primary biliary cirrhosis **123**	
S36.51[0,1,2,3,8,9]A	Primary blast inj of [ascending [rt] colon, transv colon, descending [lt] colon, sigmoid colon, oth part of colon,unsp part of colon], init enc **432**	
S36.51[0,1,2,3,8,9]D	Primary blast inj of [ascending [rt] colon, transv colon, descending [lt] colon, sigmoid colon, oth part of colon,unsp part of colon], subsq enc **391**	
S36.41[0,8,9]D	Primary blast inj of [duodenum, oth part of sm intestine, unsp part of sm intestine], subsq enc **390**	
S09.31[1,2,3,9]A	Primary blast inj of [rt, lt, bilat, unsp] ear, init enc **58, 419**	
S09.31[1,2,3,9]S	Primary blast inj of [rt, lt, bilat, unsp] ear, seq **225**	
S09.31[1,2,3,9]D	Primary blast inj of [rt, lt, bilat, unsp] ear, subsq enc **387**	
S36.510[A,S]	Primary blast inj of ascending [rt] colon, [init enc, seq] **118**	
S27.41[1,2,9]A	Primary blast inj of bronchus, [unilat, bilat, unsp], init enc **67**	
S27.41[1,2,9]S	Primary blast inj of bronchus, [unilat, bilat, unsp], seq **69**	
S27.41[1,2,9]D	Primary blast inj of bronchus, [unilat, bilat, unsp], subsq enc **389**	
S36.512[A,S]	Primary blast inj of descending [lt] colon, [init enc, seq] **118**	
S36.410[A,S]	Primary blast inj of duodenum, [init enc, seq] **117**	
S37.51[1,2,9]D	Primary blast inj of fallopian tube, [unilat, bilat, unsp] subsq enc **391**	
S37.51[1,2,9]A	Primary blast inj of fallopian tube, [unilat, bilat, unsp], init enc **265, 270**	
S37.51[1,2,9]S	Primary blast inj of fallopian tube, [unilat, bilat, unsp], seq **265, 270**	
S27.31[1,2,9]D	Primary blast inj of lung, [unilat, bilat, unsp], subsq enc **389**	
S27.312[A,S]	Primary blast inj of lung, bilat, [init enc, seq] **69**	
S27.311[A,S]	Primary blast inj of lung, unilat, [init enc, seq] **69**	
S27.319[A,S]	Primary blast inj of lung, unsp, [init enc, seq] **69**	
S36.518[A,S]	Primary blast inj of oth part of colon, [init enc, seq] **118**	
S36.418[A,S]	Primary blast inj of oth part of sm intestine, [init enc, seq] **117**	
S36.61X[A,S]	Primary blast inj of rectum, [init enc, seq] **118**	
S36.513[A,S]	Primary blast inj of sigmoid colon, [init enc, seq] **118**	
S27.51X[A,S]	Primary blast inj of thoracic trachea, [init enc, seq] **69**	
S36.511[A,S]	Primary blast inj of transv colon, [init enc, seq] **118**	
S36.519[A,S]	Primary blast inj of unsp part of colon, [init enc, seq] **118**	
S36.419[A,S]	Primary blast inj of unsp part of sm intestine, [init enc, seq] **117**	
G47.31	Primary central sleep apnea **38**	
G71*	Primary d/o of muscles **38**	

N94.4	Primary dysmenorrhea	270
A51.0	Primary genital syphilis	261, 264, 269
H40.11*	Primary opn-angle glaucoma	46
H47.21[1,2,3,9]	Primary optic atrophy, [rt, lt, bilat, unsp] eye	45
I27.0	Primary pulmn hypertension	103
P28.3	Primary sleep apnea of newborn	288
A51.2	Primary syphilis of oth sites	308
D68.5*	Primary thrombophilia	294
H21.3[4,5][1,2,3,9]	Primary, Exudative] cyst of pars plana, [rt, lt, bilat, unsp] eye	46
A67.[0,1,3]	Primary, Intermediate, Mixed] lesions of pinta	233
Z72.9	Problem related to lifestyle, unsp	412
Z74*	Problems related to care provider dependency	412
Z55*	Problems related to education and literacy	412
Z56*	Problems related to employment and unemployment	412
Z59*	Problems related to housing and economic circumstances	412
Z73*	Problems related to life management difficulty	412
Z75*	Problems related to medical facilities and oth health care	412
Z64.1	Problems related to multiparity	265, 270
Z65*	Problems related to oth psychosocial circumstances	412
Z60*	Problems related to social environment	412
Z64.0	Problems related to unwanted preg	272, 276
Z62*	Problems related to upbringing	412
Z53.09	Proc/tx not carried out because of contraindication	289
Z53.01	Proc/tx not carried out d/t patient smoking	289
Z53.1	Proc/tx not crd out bec pt belief and group pressure	289
Z53.29	Proc/tx not crd out bec pt decision for oth reasons	289
Z53.20	Proc/tx not crd out bec pt decision for unsp reasons	289
Z53.21	Proc/tx not crd out d/t pt lv bef seen by hlth care prov	289
Z53.8	Procedure and tx not carried out for oth reasons	289
Z53.9	Procedure and tx not carried out, unsp reason	289
F73	Profound intellectual disabilities	310
Q78.3	Progressive diaphyseal dysplasia	195
H49.4*	Progressive ext ophthalmoplegia	45
A81.2	Progressive multifocal leukoencephalopathy	438
M34.0	Progressive systemic sclerosis	164
I67.3	Progressive vascular leukoencephalopathy	32, 439
R11.12	Projectile vomiting	116
N99.3	Prolapse of vaginal vault after hysterectomy	265, 270
P08.22	Prolonged gestation of newborn	288
C91.3*	Prolymphocytic leukemia of B-cell type	303, 305
C91.6*	Prolymphocytic leukemia of T-cell type	303, 305
B38.81	Prostatic coccidioidomycosis	233
N42.81	Prostatodynia synd	261
N42.82	Prostatosis synd	261
H53.54	Protanomaly	46
E44*	Protein-calorie malnut of mod and mild degree	246, 283
R80.9	Proteinuria, unsp	255
O98.62	Protozoal dz compl childbirth	274
O98.63	Protozoal dz compl the puerperium	274, 276
O98.61[1,2,3]	Protozoal dzs compl preg, [1st, 2nd, 3rd] trmstr	274, 277
M24.7	Protrusio acetabuli	194
Z85.2*	Prsnl history of malig neoplm of resp and intrathoracic organs	306
Z85.7*	Prsnl hx of malig neoplm of lymphoid, hematpoetc & rel tiss	306
Z85.818	Prsnl hx of malig neoplm of site of lip, oral cav, & pharynx	6
Z85.819	Prsnl hx of malig neoplm of unsp site lip, oral cav, & pharynx	6
Q79.4	Prune belly synd	117
O26.86	Pruritic urticarial papules and plaques of preg (PUPPP)	276, 277
L29.0	Pruritus ani	234
L29.1	Pruritus scroti	261
L29.2	Pruritus vulvae	264, 269
L29.9	Pruritus, unsp	234
M96.0	Pseudarthrosis after fusion or arthrodesis	169
F48.2	Pseudobulbar affect	32
B08.03	Pseudocowpox [milker's node]	233
Q56.3	Pseudohermaphroditism, unsp	261, 265, 270
E20.1	Pseudohypoparathyroidism	246
K68.12	Psoas muscle abscess	114
L40.0	Psoriasis vulgaris	223
L40.9	Psoriasis, unsp	223

F54	Psych & behavrl factors assoc w d/o or dis classd elsw	310
O9A.51[1,2,3]	Psychological abuse compl preg, [1st, 2nd, 3rd] trmstr	277, 278
O9A.519	Psychological abuse compl preg, unsp trmstr	281
O9A.53	Psychological abuse compl the puerperium	276
R41.843	Psychomotor deficit	310
H53.16	Psychophysical visual disturbances	46
F53	Puerperal psychosis	310
O85	Puerperal sepsis	272, 274, 276
A42.0	Pulmn actinomycosis	67
A22.1	Pulmn anthrax	67
B37.1	Pulmn candidiasis	67, 283, 438
B38.2	Pulmn coccidioidomycosis, unsp	67
J98.1*	Pulmn collapse	69
B45.0	Pulmn cryptococcosis	438
J81*	Pulmn edema	68
J68.1	Pulmn edema d/t chemicals, gases, fumes and vapors	68
I26*	Pulmn embolism	283
J82	Pulmn eosinophilia, NEC	68
I27.9	Pulmn heart dz, unsp	103
P26*	Pulmn hemor originating in the perinatal period	282
B39.2	Pulmn histoplasmosis capsulati, unsp	67
Q24.3	Pulmn infundibular stenosis	102
A31.0	Pulmn mycobacterial infxn	67
A43.0	Pulmn nocardiosis	67
B58.3	Pulmn toxoplasmosis	67, 283
A21.2	Pulmn tularemia	67
B45.[0,2,3,7,8,9]	Pulmn, Cutaneous, Osseous, Disseminated, Oth forms of, Unsp] cryptococcosis	308
K04.2	Pulp degeneration	4
K04.0	Pulpitis	4
S31.142S	Punc of abd wall w fb, epigst rgn w/o penet perit cav, seq	226
S31.149S	Punc of abd wall w fb, unsp q w/o penet perit cav, seq	226
S31.145S	Punc of abd wl w fb, periumb rgn w/o penet perit cav, seq	226
S31.642S	Punc w fb of abd wall, epigst rgn w penet perit cav, seq	227
S31.645S	Punc w fb of abd wall, periumb rgn w penet perit cav, seq	227
S31.649S	Punc w fb of abd wall, unsp q w penet perit cav, seq	227
S31.041S	Punc w fb of low back and pelvis w penet retroperiton, seq	226
S11.24XA	Punc w FB of pharynx and cervical esophagus, init	5
S21.94XS	Punc w FB of unsp part of thorax, seq	225
S91.249S	Punc w fb of unsp toe(s) w damage to nail, seq	230
S91.249D	Punc w FB of unsp toe(s) w damage to nail, subs	399
S91.149S	Punc w fb of unsp toe(s) w/o damage to nail, seq	230
S91.149D	Punc w FB of unsp toe(s) w/o damage to nail, subs	399
S31.632S	Punc w/o fb of abd wall, epigst rgn w penet perit cav, seq	226
S31.639S	Punc w/o fb of abd wall, unsp q w penet perit cav, seq	226
S31.635S	Punc w/o fb of abd wl, periumb rgn w penet perit cav, seq	226
S31.031S	Punc w/o fb of low back and pelv w penet retroperiton, seq	226
S11.23XA	Punc w/o fb of pharynx and cervical esophagus, init	5
S91.239D	Punc w/o FB of unsp toe(s) w damage to nail, subs	399
S91.139D	Punc w/o fb of unsp toe(s) w/o damage to nail, subs	399
S01.5[3,4][1,2]S	Punc wnd [w/o, w/] FB of [lip, oral cavity], seq	224
S21.4[3,4][1,2,9]A	Punc wnd [w/o, w/] FB of [rt, lt, unsp] back wall of thorax w/ penetration into thoracic cavity, init enc	359, 432
S21.4[3,4][1,2,9]S	Punc wnd [w/o, w/] FB of [rt, lt, unsp] back wall of thorax w/ penetration into thoracic cavity, seq	225
S01.4[3,4][1,2,9][A,S]	Punc wnd [w/o, w/] FB of [rt, lt, unsp] cheek and temporomandibular area, [init enc, seq]	224
S01.3[3,4][1,2,9]S	Punc wnd [w/o, w/] FB of [rt, lt, unsp] ear, seq	224
S01.1[3,4][1,2,9]S	Punc wnd [w/o, w/] FB of [rt, lt, unsp] eyelid and periocular area, seq	224
S21.3[3,4][1,2,9]A	Punc wnd [w/o, w/] FB of [rt, lt, unsp] front wall of thorax w/ penetration into thoracic cavity, init enc	359, 432
S21.3[3,4][1,2,9]S	Punc wnd [w/o, w/] FB of [rt, lt, unsp] front wall of thorax w/ penetration into thoracic cavity, seq	225
S11.01[3,4]A	Punc wnd [w/o, w/] FB of larynx, init enc	58
S31.82[3,4][A,S]	Punc wnd [w/o, w/] FB of lt buttock, [init enc, seq]	227
S01.2[3,4]XA	Punc wnd [w/o, w/] FB of nose, init enc	58
S01.8[3,4]X[A,S]	Punc wnd [w/o, w/] FB of oth part of head, [init enc, seq]	224
S11.8[3,4]X[A,S]	Punc wnd [w/o, w/] FB of oth spec part of neck, [init enc, seq]	225
S31.2[3,4]XS	Punc wnd [w/o, w/] FB of penis, seq	226

Code	Description
S11.2[3,4]XA	Punc wnd [w/o, w/] FB of pharynx and cervical esophagus, init enc **58**
S31.81[3,4][A,S]	Punc wnd [w/o, w/] FB of rt buttock, [init enc, seq] **227**
S01.0[3,4]X[A,S]	Punc wnd [w/o, w/] FB of scalp, [init enc, seq] **224**
S11.02[3,4]A	Punc wnd [w/o, w/] FB of trachea, init enc **67**
S31.80[3,4][A,S]	Punc wnd [w/o, w/] FB of unsp buttock, [init enc, seq] **227**
S01.9[3,4]X[A,S]	Punc wnd [w/o, w/] FB of unsp part of head, [init enc, seq] **224**
S11.9[3,4]X[A,S]	Punc wnd [w/o, w/] FB of unsp part of neck, [init enc, seq] **225**
S31.4[3,4]XS	Punc wnd [w/o, w/] FB of vagina and vulva, seq **226**
S11.03[3,4]A	Punc wnd [w/o, w/] FB of vocal cord, init enc **58**
S91.0[3,4][1,2,9]D	Punc wnd [w/o, w/] FB, [rt, lt, unsp] ankle, subsq enc **399**
S31.64[0,1,2,3,4,5,9]D	Punc wnd of abd wall w/ FB, [rt upr quadrant, lt upr quadrant, epigastric rgn, rt lwr quadrant, lt lwr quadrant, periumbilic rgn, unsp quadrant], w/ penetration into peritoneal cavity, subsq enc **390**
S31.14[0,1,2,3,4,5,9]D	Punc wnd of abd wall w/ FB, [rt upr quadrant, lt upr quadrant, epigastric rgn, rt lwr quadrant, lt lwr quadrant, periumbilic rgn, unsp quadrant], w/o penetration into peritoneal cavity, subsq enc **390**
S31.14[3,4]S	Punc wnd of abd wall w/ FB, [rt, lt] lwr quadrant w/o penetration into peritoneal cavity, seq **226**
S31.14[0,1]S	Punc wnd of abd wall w/ FB, [rt, lt] upr quadrant w/o penetration into peritoneal cavity, seq **226**
S31.63[0,1,2,3,4,5,9]D	Punc wnd of abd wall w/o FB, [rt upr quadrant, lt upr quadrant, epigastric rgn, rt lwr quadrant, lt lwr quadrant, periumbilic rgn, unsp quadrant], w/ penetration into peritoneal cavity, subsq enc **390**
S31.13[0,1,2,3,4,5,9]D	Punc wnd of abd wall w/o FB, [rt upr quadrant, lt upr quadrant, epigastric rgn, rt lwr quadrant, lt lwr quadrant, periumbilic rgn, unsp quadrant], w/o penetration into peritoneal cavity, subsq enc **390**
S31.13[3,4][A,S]	Punc wnd of abd wall w/o FB, [rt, lt] lwr quadrant w/o penetration into peritoneal cavity, [init enc, seq] **226**
S31.13[0,1][A,S]	Punc wnd of abd wall w/o FB, [rt, lt] upr quadrant w/o penetration into peritoneal cavity, [init enc, seq] **226**
S31.132[A,S]	Punc wnd of abd wall w/o FB, epigastric rgn w/o penetration into peritoneal cavity, [init enc, seq] **226**
S31.135[A,S]	Punc wnd of abd wall w/o FB, periumbilic rgn w/o penetration into peritoneal cavity, [init enc, seq] **226**
S31.139[A,S]	Punc wnd of abd wall w/o FB, unsp quadrant w/o penetration into peritoneal cavity, [init enc, seq] **226**
S11.14XA	Punc wnd w FB of thyroid gland, init enc **5**
S11.94XA	Punc wnd w FB of unsp part of neck, init **5**
S11.84XA	Punc wnd w FB oth prt neck, init enc **5**
S01.54[1,2]A	Punc wnd w/ FB of [lip, oral cavity] init enc **59**
S61.34[8,9]S	Punc wnd w/ FB of [oth, unsp] finger w/ damage to nail, seq **229**
S61.34[8,9]D	Punc wnd w/ FB of [oth, unsp] finger w/ damage to nail, subsq enc **395**
S61.24[8,9]S	Punc wnd w/ FB of [oth, unsp] finger w/o damage to nail, seq **228**
S61.24[8,9]D	Punc wnd w/ FB of [oth, unsp] finger w/o damage to nail, subsq enc **394**
S21.44[1,2,9]D	Punc wnd w/ FB of [rt, lt, unpsecified] back wall of thorax w/ penetration into thoracic cavity, subsq enc **388**
S21.24[1,2,9]D	Punc wnd w/ FB of [rt, lt, unpsecified] back wall of thorax w/o penetration into thoracic cavity, subsq enc **388**
S21.34[1,2,9]D	Punc wnd w/ FB of [rt, lt, unpsecified] front wall of thorax w/ penetration into thoracic cavity, subsq enc **388**
S21.14[1,2,9]D	Punc wnd w/ FB of [rt, lt, unpsecified] front wall of thorax w/o penetration into thoracic cavity, subsq enc **388**
S21.24[1,2,9][A,S]	Punc wnd w/ FB of [rt, lt, unsp] back wall of thorax w/o penetration into thoracic cavity, [init enc, seq] **225**
S21.04[1,2,9][A,S]	Punc wnd w/ FB of [rt, lt, unsp] breast, [init enc, seq] **225**
S21.04[1,2,9]D	Punc wnd w/ FB of [rt, lt, unsp] breast, subsq enc **388**
S51.04[1,2,9]S	Punc wnd w/ FB of [rt, lt, unsp] elbow, seq **227**
S51.04[1,2,9]D	Punc wnd w/ FB of [rt, lt, unsp] elbow, subsq enc **392**
S01.14[1,2,9]A	Punc wnd w/ FB of [rt, lt, unsp] eyelid and periocular area, init enc **46**
S51.84[1,2,9]S	Punc wnd w/ FB of [rt, lt, unsp] forearm, seq **227**
S51.84[1,2,9]D	Punc wnd w/ FB of [rt, lt, unsp] forearm, subsq enc **392**
S21.14[1,2,9]S	Punc wnd w/ FB of [rt, lt, unsp] front wall of thorax w/o penetration into thoracic cavity, seq **225**
S91.24[1,2,3]A	Punc wnd w/ FB of [rt, lt, unsp] great toe w/ damage to nail, init enc **429**
S91.24[1,2,3]S	Punc wnd w/ FB of [rt, lt, unsp] great toe w/ damage to nail, seq **230**
S91.24[1,2,3]D	Punc wnd w/ FB of [rt, lt, unsp] great toe w/ damage to nail, subsq enc **399**
S91.14[1,2,3]A	Punc wnd w/ FB of [rt, lt, unsp] great toe w/o damage to nail, init enc **429**
S91.14[1,2,3]S	Punc wnd w/ FB of [rt, lt, unsp] great toe w/o damage to nail, seq **230**
S91.14[1,2,3]D	Punc wnd w/ FB of [rt, lt, unsp] great toe w/o damage to nail, subsq enc **399**
S61.44[1,2,9]S	Punc wnd w/ FB of [rt, lt, unsp] hand, seq **229**
S61.44[1,2,9]D	Punc wnd w/ FB of [rt, lt, unsp] hand, subsq enc **395**
S91.24[4,5,6]A	Punc wnd w/ FB of [rt, lt, unsp] lesser toe(s) w/ damage to nail, init enc **429**
S91.24[4,5,6]S	Punc wnd w/ FB of [rt, lt, unsp] lesser toe(s) w/ damage to nail, seq **230**
S91.24[4,5,6]D	Punc wnd w/ FB of [rt, lt, unsp] lesser toe(s) w/ damage to nail, subsq enc **399**
S91.14[4,5,6]A	Punc wnd w/ FB of [rt, lt, unsp] lesser toe(s) w/o damage to nail, init enc **429**
S91.14[4,5,6]S	Punc wnd w/ FB of [rt, lt, unsp] lesser toe(s) w/o damage to nail, seq **230**
S91.14[4,5,6]D	Punc wnd w/ FB of [rt, lt, unsp] lesser toe(s) w/o damage to nail, subsq enc **399**
S41.04[1,2,9]S	Punc wnd w/ FB of [rt, lt, unsp] shldr, seq **227**
S41.04[1,2,9]D	Punc wnd w/ FB of [rt, lt, unsp] shldr, subsq enc **391**
S61.14[1,2,9]S	Punc wnd w/ FB of [rt, lt, unsp] thumb w/ damage to nail, seq **228**
S61.14[1,2,9]D	Punc wnd w/ FB of [rt, lt, unsp] thumb w/ damage to nail, subsq enc **394**
S61.04[1,2,9]S	Punc wnd w/ FB of [rt, lt, unsp] thumb w/o damage to nail, seq **228**
S61.04[1,2,9]D	Punc wnd w/ FB of [rt, lt, unsp] thumb w/o damage to nail, subsq enc **394**
S41.14[1,2,9]S	Punc wnd w/ FB of [rt, lt, unsp] upr arm, seq **227**
S41.14[1,2,9]D	Punc wnd w/ FB of [rt, lt, unsp] upr arm, subsq enc **391**
S61.54[1,2,9]S	Punc wnd w/ FB of [rt, lt, unsp] wrist, seq **229**
S61.54[1,2,9]D	Punc wnd w/ FB of [rt, lt, unsp] wrist, subsq enc **395**
S61.34[0,1]S	Punc wnd w/ FB of [rt, lt] index finger w/ damage to nail, seq **229**
S61.34[0,1]D	Punc wnd w/ FB of [rt, lt] index finger w/ damage to nail, subsq enc **395**
S61.24[0,1]S	Punc wnd w/ FB of [rt, lt] index finger w/o damage to nail, seq **228**
S61.24[0,1]D	Punc wnd w/ FB of [rt, lt] index finger w/o damage to nail, subsq enc **394**
S61.34[6,7]S	Punc wnd w/ FB of [rt, lt] little finger w/ damage to nail, seq **229**
S61.34[6,7]D	Punc wnd w/ FB of [rt, lt] little finger w/ damage to nail, subsq enc **395**
S61.24[6,7]S	Punc wnd w/ FB of [rt, lt] little finger w/o damage to nail, seq **228**
S61.24[6,7]D	Punc wnd w/ FB of [rt, lt] little finger w/o damage to nail, subsq enc **394**
S61.34[2,3]S	Punc wnd w/ FB of [rt, lt] mid finger w/ damage to nail, seq **229**
S61.34[2,3]D	Punc wnd w/ FB of [rt, lt] mid finger w/ damage to nail, subsq enc **395**
S61.24[2,3]S	Punc wnd w/ FB of [rt, lt] mid finger w/o damage to nail, seq **228**
S61.24[2,3]D	Punc wnd w/ FB of [rt, lt] mid finger w/o damage to nail, subsq enc **394**
S61.34[4,5]S	Punc wnd w/ FB of [rt, lt] ring finger w/ damage to nail, seq **229**
S61.34[4,5]D	Punc wnd w/ FB of [rt, lt] ring finger w/ damage to nail, subsq enc **395**
S61.24[4,5]S	Punc wnd w/ FB of [rt, lt] ring finger w/o damage to nail, seq **228**
S61.24[4,5]D	Punc wnd w/ FB of [rt, lt] ring finger w/o damage to nail, subsq enc **394**
S31.64[0,1,2,3,4,5,9]A	Punc wnd w/ FB of abd wall, [rt upr quadrant, lt upr quadrant, epigastric rgn, rt lwr quadrant, lt lwr quadrant, periumbilic rgn, unsp quadrant] w/ penetration into peritoneal cavity, init enc **117**
S31.64[0,1,3,4]S	Punc wnd w/ FB of abd wall, [rt, lt] [upr, lwr] quadrant w/ penetration into peritoneal cavity, seq **227**
S31.04[0,1]D	Punc wnd w/ FB of lwr back and pelvis [w/o, w/] penetration into retroperitoneum, subsq enc **389**
S31.040[A,S]	Punc wnd w/ FB of lwr back and pelvis w/o penetration into retroperitoneum, [init enc, seq] **226**
S31.54[1,2]D	Punc wnd w/ FB of unsp ext genital organs, [male, female], subsq enc **390**
S91.04[1,2,9]A	Punc wnd w/ FB, [rt, lt, unsp] ankle, init enc **429**

S91.04[1,2,9]S	Punc wnd w/ FB, [rt, lt, unsp] ankle, seq **230**
S91.34[1,2,9]A	Punc wnd w/ FB, [rt, lt, unsp] foot, init enc **429**
S91.34[1,2,9]S	Punc wnd w/ FB, [rt, lt, unsp] foot, seq **230**
S91.34[1,2,9]D	Punc wnd w/ FB, [rt, lt, unsp] foot, subsq enc **399**
S71.04[1,2,9]S	Punc wnd w/ FB, [rt, lt, unsp] hip, seq **229**
S81.04[1,2,9]S	Punc wnd w/ FB, [rt, lt, unsp] knee, seq **229**
S81.84[1,2,9]S	Punc wnd w/ FB, [rt, lt, unsp] lwr leg, seq **229**
S71.14[1,2,9]S	Punc wnd w/ FB, [rt, lt, unsp] thigh, seq **229**
S01.53[1,2]A	Punc wnd w/o FB of [lip, oral cavity] init enc **59**
S61.33[8,9][A,S]	Punc wnd w/o FB of [oth, unsp] finger w/ damage to nail, [init enc, seq] **229**
S61.33[8,9]D	Punc wnd w/o FB of [oth, unsp] finger w/ damage to nail, subsq enc **395**
S61.23[8,9][A,S]	Punc wnd w/o FB of [oth, unsp] finger w/o damage to nail, [init enc, seq] **228**
S61.23[8,9]D	Punc wnd w/o FB of [oth, unsp] finger w/o damage to nail, subsq enc **394**
S21.43[1,2,9]D	Punc wnd w/ FB of [rt, lt, unspecified] back wall of thorax w/ penetration into thoracic cavity, subsq enc **388**
S21.23[1,2,9]D	Punc wnd w/ FB of [rt, lt, unspecified] back wall of thorax w/o penetration into thoracic cavity, subsq enc **388**
S21.33[1,2,9]D	Punc wnd w/ FB of [rt, lt, unspecified] front wall of thorax w/ penetration into thoracic cavity, subsq enc **388**
S21.13[1,2,9]D	Punc wnd w/ FB of [rt, lt, unspecified] front wall of thorax w/o penetration into thoracic cavity, subsq enc **388**
S21.23[1,2,9] [A,S]	Punc wnd w/ FB of [rt, lt, unsp] back wall of thorax w/o penetration into thoracic cavity, [init enc, seq] **225**
S21.03[1,2,9] [A,S]	Punc wnd w/ FB of [rt, lt, unsp] breast, [init enc, seq] **225**
S21.03[1,2,9]D	Punc wnd w/ FB of [rt, lt, unsp] breast, subsq enc **388**
S51.03[1,2,9] [A,S]	Punc wnd w/o FB of [rt, lt, unsp] elbow, [init enc, seq] **227**
S51.03[1,2,9]D	Punc wnd w/o FB of [rt, lt, unsp] elbow, subsq enc **392**
S01.13[1,2,9]A	Punc wnd w/o FB of [rt, lt, unsp] eyelid and periocular area, init enc **46**
S51.83[1,2,9] [A,S]	Punc wnd w/o FB of [rt, lt, unsp] forearm, [init enc, seq] **227**
S51.83[1,2,9]D	Punc wnd w/o FB of [rt, lt, unsp] forearm, subsq enc **392**
S21.13[1,2,9] [A,S]	Punc wnd w/o FB of [rt, lt, unsp] front wall of thorax w/o penetration into thoracic cavity, [init enc, seq] **225**
S91.23[1,2,3] [A,S]	Punc wnd w/o FB of [rt, lt, unsp] great toe w/ damage to nail, [init enc, seq] **230**
S91.23[1,2,3]A	Punc wnd w/o FB of [rt, lt, unsp] great toe w/ damage to nail, init enc **429**
S91.23[1,2,3]D	Punc wnd w/o FB of [rt, lt, unsp] great toe w/ damage to nail, subsq enc **399**
S91.13[1,2,3] [A,S]	Punc wnd w/o FB of [rt, lt, unsp] great toe w/o damage to nail, [init enc, seq] **230**
S91.13[1,2,3]A	Punc wnd w/o FB of [rt, lt, unsp] great toe w/o damage to nail, init enc **429**
S91.13[1,2,3]D	Punc wnd w/o FB of [rt, lt, unsp] great toe w/o damage to nail, subsq enc **399**
S61.43[1,2,9] [A,S]	Punc wnd w/o FB of [rt, lt, unsp] hand, [init enc, seq] **229**
S61.43[1,2,9]D	Punc wnd w/o FB of [rt, lt, unsp] hand, subsq enc **395**
S91.23[4,5,6] [A,S]	Punc wnd w/o FB of [rt, lt, unsp] lesser toe(s) w/ damage to nail, [init enc, seq] **230**
S91.23[4,5,6]A	Punc wnd w/o FB of [rt, lt, unsp] lesser toe(s) w/ damage to nail, init enc **429**
S91.23[4,5,6]D	Punc wnd w/o FB of [rt, lt, unsp] lesser toe(s) w/ damage to nail, subsq enc **399**
S91.13[4,5,6] [A,S]	Punc wnd w/o FB of [rt, lt, unsp] lesser toe(s) w/o damage to nail, [init enc, seq] **230**
S91.13[4,5,6]A	Punc wnd w/o FB of [rt, lt, unsp] lesser toe(s) w/o damage to nail, init enc **429**
S91.13[4,5,6]D	Punc wnd w/o FB of [rt, lt, unsp] lesser toe(s) w/o damage to nail, subsq enc **399**
S41.03[1,2,9] [A,S]	Punc wnd w/o FB of [rt, lt, unsp] shldr, [init enc, seq] **227**
S41.03[1,2,9]D	Punc wnd w/o FB of [rt, lt, unsp] shldr, subsq enc **391**
S61.13[1,2,9] [A,S]	Punc wnd w/o FB of [rt, lt, unsp] thumb w/ damage to nail, [init enc, seq] **228**
S61.13[1,2,9]D	Punc wnd w/o FB of [rt, lt, unsp] thumb w/ damage to nail, subsq enc **394**
S61.03[1,2,9] [A,S]	Punc wnd w/o FB of [rt, lt, unsp] thumb w/o damage to nail, [init enc, seq] **228**
S61.03[1,2,9]D	Punc wnd w/o FB of [rt, lt, unsp] thumb w/o damage to nail, subsq enc **394**
S41.13[1,2,9] [A,S]	Punc wnd w/o FB of [rt, lt, unsp] upr arm, [init enc, seq] **227**
S41.13[1,2,9]D	Punc wnd w/o FB of [rt, lt, unsp] upr arm, subsq enc **391**
S61.53[1,2,9] [A,S]	Punc wnd w/o FB of [rt, lt, unsp] wrist, [init enc, seq] **229**
S61.53[1,2,9]D	Punc wnd w/o FB of [rt, lt, unsp] wrist, subsq enc **395**
S61.33[0,1][A,S]	Punc wnd w/o FB of [rt, lt] index finger w/ damage to nail, [init enc, seq] **228**
S61.33[0,1]D	Punc wnd w/o FB of [rt, lt] index finger w/ damage to nail, subsq enc **394**
S61.23[0,1][A,S]	Punc wnd w/o FB of [rt, lt] index finger w/o damage to nail, [init enc, seq] **228**
S61.23[0,1]D	Punc wnd w/o FB of [rt, lt] index finger w/o damage to nail, subsq enc **394**
S61.33[6,7][A,S]	Punc wnd w/o FB of [rt, lt] little finger w/ damage to nail, [init enc, seq] **229**
S61.33[6,7]D	Punc wnd w/o FB of [rt, lt] little finger w/ damage to nail, subsq enc **395**
S61.23[6,7][A,S]	Punc wnd w/o FB of [rt, lt] little finger w/o damage to nail, [init enc, seq] **228**
S61.23[6,7]D	Punc wnd w/o FB of [rt, lt] little finger w/o damage to nail, subsq enc **394**
S61.33[2,3][A,S]	Punc wnd w/o FB of [rt, lt] mid finger w/ damage to nail, [init enc, seq] **228**
S61.33[2,3]D	Punc wnd w/o FB of [rt, lt] mid finger w/ damage to nail, subsq enc **394**
S61.23[2,3][A,S]	Punc wnd w/o FB of [rt, lt] mid finger w/o damage to nail, [init enc, seq] **228**
S61.23[2,3]D	Punc wnd w/o FB of [rt, lt] mid finger w/o damage to nail, subsq enc **394**
S61.33[4,5][A,S]	Punc wnd w/o FB of [rt, lt] ring finger w/ damage to nail, [init enc, seq] **228**
S61.33[4,5]D	Punc wnd w/o FB of [rt, lt] ring finger w/ damage to nail, subsq enc **395**
S61.23[4,5][A,S]	Punc wnd w/o FB of [rt, lt] ring finger w/o damage to nail, [init enc, seq] **228**
S61.23[4,5]D	Punc wnd w/o FB of [rt, lt] ring finger w/o damage to nail, subsq enc **394**
S31.63[0,1,2,3,4, 5,9]A	Punc wnd w/o FB of abd wall, [rt upr quadrant, lt upr quadrant, epigastric rgn, rt lwr quadrant, lt lwr quadrant, periumbilic rgn, unsp quadrant] w/ penetration into peritoneal cavity, init enc **117**
S31.63[0,1,3,4]S	Punc wnd w/o FB of abd wall, [rt, lt] [upr, lwr] quadrant w/ penetration into peritoneal cavity, seq **227**
S31.833[A,S]	Punc wnd w/o FB of anus, [init enc, seq] **227**
S11.013A	Punc wnd w/o FB of larynx, init enc **5**
S31.03[0,1]D	Punc wnd w/o FB of lwr back and pelvis [w/o, w/] penetration into retroperitoneum, subsq enc **389**
S31.030[A,S]	Punc wnd w/o FB of lwr back and pelvis w/o penetration into retroperitoneum, [init enc, seq] **226**
S01.23XA	Punc wnd w/o FB of nose, init enc **5**
S11.13XA	Punc wnd w/o FB of thyroid gland, init **5**
S11.023A	Punc wnd w/o FB of trachea, init enc **5**
S31.53[1,2]D	Punc wnd w/o FB of unsp ext genital organs, [male, female], subsq enc **390**
S11.93XA	Punc wnd w/o FB of unsp part of neck, init **5**
S21.93X[A,S]	Punc wnd w/o FB of unsp part of thorax, [init enc, seq] **225**
S91.239[A,S]	Punc wnd w/o FB of unsp toe(s) w/ damage to nail, [init enc, seq] **230**
S91.139[A,S]	Punc wnd w/o FB of unsp toe(s) w/o damage to nail, [init enc, seq] **230**
S11.033A	Punc wnd w/o FB of vocal cord, init enc **5**
S11.83XA	Punc wnd w/o FB oth prt neck, init enc **5**
S91.03[1,2,9] [A,S]	Punc wnd w/o FB, [rt, lt, unsp] ankle, [init enc, seq] **230**
S91.03[1,2,9]A	Punc wnd w/o FB, [rt, lt, unsp] ankle, init enc **429**
S91.33[1,2,9] [A,S]	Punc wnd w/o FB, [rt, lt, unsp] foot, [init enc, seq] **230**
S91.33[1,2,9]A	Punc wnd w/o FB, [rt, lt, unsp] foot, init enc **429**
S91.33[1,2,9]D	Punc wnd w/o FB, [rt, lt, unsp] foot, subsq enc **399**

S71.03[1,2,9] [A,S]	Punc wnd w/o FB, [rt, lt, unsp] hip, [init enc, seq] 229	
S81.03[1,2,9] [A,S]	Punc wnd w/o FB, [rt, lt, unsp] knee, [init enc, seq] 229	
S81.83[1,2,9] [A,S]	Punc wnd w/o FB, [rt, lt, unsp] lwr leg, [init enc, seq] 229	
S71.13[1,2,9] [A,S]	Punc wnd w/o FB, [rt, lt, unsp] thigh, [init enc, seq] 229	
S31.834S	Punc wnd with FB of anus, seq 227	
S11.014A	Punc wnd with FB of larynx, init enc 5	
S01.24XA	Punc wnd with FB of nose, init enc 5	
S11.024A	Punc wnd with FB of trachea, init enc 5	
S11.034A	Punc wnd with FB of vocal cord, init enc 5	
H21.4*	Pupillary membranes 46	
E78.0	Pure hypercholesterolemia 247	
E78.1	Pure hyperglyceridemia 247	
G46.5	Pure motor lacunar synd 33	
G46.6	Pure sensory lacunar synd 33	
D81.5	Purine nucleoside phosphorylase [PNP] deficiency 247	
D69*	Purpura and oth hemorrhagic conditions 294	
H44.0*	Purulent endophthalmitis 45	
L40.3	Pustulosis palmaris et plantaris 223	
N28.8[4,5,6]	Pyelitis, Pyeloureteritis, Ureteritis] cystica 255, 285	
O88.32	Pyemic and septic embolism in childbirth 274	
O88.31[1,2,3]	Pyemic and septic embolism in preg, [1st, 2nd, 3rd] trmstr 274	
O88.33	Pyemic and septic embolism in the puerperium 274, 276	
K31.3	Pylorospasm, NEC 116	
L08.0	Pyoderma 224	
L88	Pyoderma gangrenosum 224	
M00.9	Pyogenic arthritis, unsp 164	
L98.0	Pyogenic granuloma 224	
N13.6	Pyonephrosis 255, 285	
J86*	Pyothorax 67, 284	
O75.2	Pyrexia during labor, NEC 274, 278, 280	
O86.4	Pyrexia of unknown origin following delivery 274	
F63.1	Pyromania 311	
A78	Q fever 308	
Z38.64	Quadruplet liveborn infant, delivered by cesarean 289	
Z38.63	Quadruplet liveborn infant, delivered vaginally 289	
O30.2[0,1,2,9] [1,2,3]	Quadruplet preg [unsp, two or more monochorionic fetuses, two or more monoamniotic fetuses, unable to determine the number of placenta and amniotic sacs], [1st, 2nd, 3rd] trmstr 279	
O30.22[1,2,3]	Quadruplet preg w/ two or more monoamniotic fetuses, [1st, 2nd, 3rd] trmstr 277	
O30.21[1,2,3]	Quadruplet preg w/ two or more monochorionic fetuses, [1st, 2nd, 3rd] trmstr 277	
O30.2[0,1,2,9]9	Quadruplet preg, [unsp number of placenta and unsp number of amniotic sacs, two or more monochorionic fetuses, two or more monoamniotic fetuses, unable to determine the number of placenta and amniotic sacs], unsp trmstr 281	
O30.29[1,2,3]	Quadruplet preg, unable to determine number of placenta and number of amniotic sacs, [1st, 2nd, 3rd] trmstr 277	
O30.20[1,2,3]	Quadruplet preg, unsp number of placenta and unsp number of amniotic sacs, [1st, 2nd, 3rd] trmstr 277	
Z38.66	Quintuplet liveborn infant, delivered by cesarean 289	
Z38.65	Quintuplet liveborn infant, delivered vaginally 289	
A82*	Rabies 41	
A82.9	Rabies, unsp 10, 15	
S53.43[1,2,9] [A,S]	Radial collat lgmt sprain [rt, lt, unsp] [init enc, seq] 187	
S53.43[1,2,9]D	Radial collat lgmt sprain of [rt, lt, unsp] elbow, subsq enc 392	
K62.7	Radiation proctitis 117	
T66.XXX[A,S]	Radiation sickness, unsp, [init enc, seq] 374	
T66.XXXD	Radiation sickness, unsp, subsq enc 409	
K04.8	Radicular cyst 4	
M54.1[4,5,6,7]	Radiculopathy [thoracic, thoracolumbar, lumbar, lumbosacral] rgn 165	
M54.1[0,1,2,3,8]	Radiculopathy, [unsp, occipito-atlanto-axial, cervical, cervicothoracic, sacral and sacrococcygeal] rgn 34	
L58*	Radiodermatitis 234	
S53.41[1,2,9] [A,S]	Radiohumeral (jt) sprain [rt, lt, unsp] [init enc, seq] 186	

S53.41[1,2,9]D	Radiohumeral (jt) sprain of [rt, lt, unsp] elbow, subsq enc 392	
R76.0	Raised antibody titer 294	
N01*	Rapidly progressive nephritic synd 256, 285	
R21	Rash and oth nonspecific skin eruption 234	
A25*	Rat-bite fevers 308	
I73.0*	Raynaud's synd 164	
I47.0	Re-entry ventricular arrhythmia 283	
F43.9	Reaction to severe stress, unsp 310	
P93*	Reactions and intoxications d/t drugs administered to NB 282	
M02.9	Reactive arthropathy, unsp 166	
K62.1	Rectal polyp 117	
K62.3	Rectal prolapse 117	
N02*	Recurrent and persistent hematuria 256	
M43.3	Recurrent atlantoaxial disloc with myelopathy 194	
H95.0*	Recurrent cholesteatoma of postmastoidectomy cavity 58	
M24.4[1,2,3] [1,2,9]	Recurrent disloc, [rt, lt, unsp] [shldr, elbow, wrist] 184	
M24.47[1,2,3]	Recurrent disloc, [rt, lt, unsp] ankle 184	
M24.44[4,5,6]	Recurrent disloc, [rt, lt, unsp] finger 184	
M24.47[4,5,6]	Recurrent disloc, [rt, lt, unsp] foot 184	
M24.45[1,2,9]	Recurrent disloc, [rt, lt, unsp] hip 194	
M24.46[1,2,9]	Recurrent disloc, [rt, lt, unsp] knee 184	
M24.47[7,8,9]	Recurrent disloc, [rt, lt, unsp] toes 184	
M24.40	Recurrent disloc, unsp jt 194	
M24.44[1,2,3]	Recurrent disloc,[rt, lt, unsp] hand 184	
G47.53	Recurrent isolated sleep paralysis 38	
K12.0	Recurrent oral aphthae 4	
N96	Recurrent preg loss 265, 270	
Q72*	Reduction defects of lwr limb 195	
Q73*	Reduction defects of unsp limb 195	
Q71*	Reduction defects of upr limb 195	
G60.1	Refsum's dz 38	
P92.1	Regurgitation and rumination of newborn 289	
M02.3*	Reiter's dz 164	
A68*	Relapsing fevers 308	
M35.6	Relapsing panniculitis [Weber-Christian] 234	
M94.1	Relapsing polychondritis 194	
G47.52	REM sleep behav d/o 58	
Q60*	Renal agenesis and oth reduction defects of kidney 256	
N15.1	Renal and perinephric abscess 255, 285	
N26.9	Renal sclerosis, unsp 256	
N16	Renal tubulo-interstitial d/o in dz classd elsw 256	
N15.9	Renal tubulo-interstitial dz, unsp 256	
R29.6	Repeated falls 38	
M79.5	Residual FB in soft tissue 194	
N99.83	Residual ovary synd 265, 270	
H40.15*	Residual stage of opn-angle glaucoma 46	
Z16*	Resistance to antimicrobial drugs 309	
R09.2	Respiratory arrest 69, 285	
P28.9	Respiratory condition of newborn, unsp 288	
J70.[5,8,9]	Respiratory conditions d/t [smoke inhalation, oth spec ext agents, unsp ext agents] 69	
J70.5	Respiratory conditions d/t smoke inhalation 381	
J99	Respiratory d/o in dz classified elsw 68	
J98.9	Respiratory d/o, unsp 69	
P22.9	Respiratory distress of newborn, unsp 288	
P22.0	Respiratory distress synd of newborn 282	
P28.5	Respiratory failure of newborn 282	
J96*	Respiratory failure, NEC 68	
J96.9*	Respiratory failure, unsp 381	
B97.4	Respiratory syncytial virus causing dz classd elsw 283	
A15*	Respiratory tuberculosis 67, 438	
G25.81	Restless legs synd 32	
R45.1	Restlessness and agitation 310	
H05.5*	Retained (old) fb following penetrating wnd of orbit 45	
H44.6*	Retained (old) intraocular FB, magnetic 46	
H44.7*	Retained (old) intraocular FB, nonmagnetic 46	
K91.86	Retained cholelithiasis following cholecystectomy 117, 284	
K08.3	Retained dental root 4	
Z18*	Retained FB fragments 412	

O26.3[1,2,3]	Retained intrauterine contraceptive dev in preg, [1st, 2nd, 3rd] trmstr 277
O26.3*	Retained intrauterine contraceptive device in preg 276
O73*	Retained placenta and membranes, w/o hemor 272, 274
O73.0	Retained placenta w/o hemor 276
O73.1	Retained portions of placenta and membranes, w/o hemor 276
O26.30	Retained uterin contracep dev in preg, unsp trmstr 280
E45	Retarded development following protein-calorie malnut 246
R33*	Retention of urine 255, 285
H33.3*	Retinal breaks without detach 46
H36	Retinal d/o in dz classified elsw 46
H33.0*	Retinal detach with retinal break 46
H34*	Retinal vascular occlusions 45
O92.0[2,3]	Retracted nipple associated w/ [the puerperium, lactation] 272, 276
O92.019	Retracted nipple associated with preg, unsp trmstr 281
O92.[0,1]1[1,2,3]	Retracted, Cracked] nipple associated w/ preg, [1st, 2nd, 3rd] trmstr 278, 280
Q55.22	Retractile testis 289
R41.2	Retrograde amnesia 385
J39.0	Retropharyngeal and parapharyngeal abscess 4, 57, 284
B33.3	Retrovirus infections, NEC 307
F84.2	Rett's synd 32
I67.841	Reversible cerebrovascular vasoconstriction synd 33
G93.7	Reye's synd 38
T80.40XA	Rh incompat react d/t tranfs of bld/bld prod, unsp, init 287, 293
T80.40XS	Rh incompat react d/t tranfs of bld/bld prod, unsp, seq 374
T80.40XD	Rh incompat react d/t tranfs of bld/bld prod, unsp, subs 410
T80.410A	Rh incompatibility w acute hemolytic transfs react, init 293
T80.411A	Rh incompatibility w delayed hemolytic transfs react, init 293
T80.419A	Rh incompatibility w hemolytic transfs react, unsp, init 293
T80.41[0,1,9]A	Rh incompatibility w/ [acute, delayed, unsp] hemolytic transfusion reaction, init enc 287
T80.41[0,1,9]S	Rh incompatibility w/ [acute, delayed, unsp] hemolytic transfusion reaction, seq 374
T80.41[0,1,9]D	Rh incompatibility w/ [acute, delayed, unsp] hemolytic transfusion reaction, subsq enc 410
P55.0	Rh isoimmunization of newborn 288
M62.82	Rhabdomyolysis 167
I06*	Rheumatic aortic valve dz 102
I02*	Rheumatic chorea 103
I09.1	Rheumatic dz of endocardium, valve unsp 102
I00	Rheumatic fever w/o heart involvement 164
I09.9	Rheumatic heart dz, unsp 103
I09.81	Rheumatic heart failure 72, 99, 283
I05*	Rheumatic mitral valve dz 102
I09.0	Rheumatic myocarditis 103
I07*	Rheumatic tricuspid valve dz 102
M79.0	Rheumatism, unsp 167
M05.6*	Rheumatoid arthritis w involvement of oth organs and systems 164
M05.7*	Rheumatoid arthritis w rheumatoid factor w/o org/sys involv 164
M06.0*	Rheumatoid arthritis w/o rheumatoid factor 164
M05.9	Rheumatoid arthritis with rheumatoid factor, unsp 164
M06.9	Rheumatoid arthritis, unsp 164
M06.2*	Rheumatoid bursitis 164
M05.3*	Rheumatoid heart dz with rheumatoid arthritis 164
M05.1*	Rheumatoid lung dz with rheumatoid arthritis 68
M05.4*	Rheumatoid myopathy with rheumatoid arthritis 164
M06.3*	Rheumatoid nodule 164
M05.5*	Rheumatoid polyneuropathy with rheumatoid arthritis 164
M05.2*	Rheumatoid vasculitis with rheumatoid arthritis 164
E55.0	Rickets, active 166
A92.4	Rift Valley fever 307
H16.0[2,4,5][1,2,3,9]	Ring, Marginal, Mooren's] corneal ulcer, [rt, lt, bilat, unsp] eye 46
A83.6	Rocio virus dz 10, 15
L71*	Rosacea 234
B33.1	Ross River dz 307
B06.82	Rubella arthritis 166
B06.01	Rubella encephalitis 41

B06.02	Rubella meningitis 41
B06.81	Rubella pneumonia 307
B06.9	Rubella w/o comp 307
B06.0*	Rubella with neurological comp 283
B06.00	Rubella with neurological comp, unsp 34
B06.8*	Rubella with oth comp 283
F98.21	Rumination d/o of infancy 310
I77.2	Rupture of artery 100
I23.3	Rupture of card wall w/o hemoperic as current comp fol AMI 103
I23.4	Rupture of chord tendne as current comp following AMI 102
I51.1	Rupture of chordae tendineae, NEC 102
I23.5	Rupture of papillary muscle as current comp following AMI 102
I51.2	Rupture of papillary muscle, NEC 102
O71.0[2,3]	Rupture of uterus before onset of labor, [2nd, 3rd] trmstr 278, 280
O71.00	Rupture of uterus before onset of labor, unsp trmstr 273, 275
O71.1	Rupture of uterus during labor 273, 275
Z92.82	S/p admn tPA in diff fac w/n last 24 hr bef adm to crnt fac 33
H55.81	Saccadic eye movements 45
M53.3	Sacrococcygeal d/o, NEC 165
M46.1	Sacroiliitis, NEC 164
I26.92	Saddle embolus of pulmn artery w/o acute cor pulmonale 66
I26.02	Saddle embolus of pulmn artery with acute cor pulmonale 66
A02.23	Salmonella arthritis 164
A02.0	Salmonella enteritis 114
A02.9	Salmonella infxn, unsp 308, 438
A02.21	Salmonella meningitis 10, 14, 41
A02.24	Salmonella osteomyelitis 163
A02.22	Salmonella pneumonia 67
A02.25	Salmonella pyelonephritis 308
A02.1	Salmonella sepsis 309, 438
A02.29	Salmonella with oth localized infxn 308
N70*	Salpingitis and oophoritis 264, 269
O23.529	Salpingo-oophoritis in preg, unsp trmstr 280
S79.1[1,2,3,4][1,2,9]A	Salter-Harris [Type I, Type II, Type III, Type IV] physeal fx of lwr end of [rt, lt, unsp] femur, init enc for clsd fx 427, 436
S79.1[1,2,3,4][1,2,9][K,P]	Salter-Harris Type [I, II, III, IV] physeal fx of lwr end of [rt, lt, unsp] femur, subsq enc for fx w/ [nonu, malu] 202
S89.1[1,2,3,4][1,2,9]A	Salter-Harris Type [I, II, III, IV] physeal fx of lwr end of [rt, lt, unsp] tibia, init enc for clsd fx 192, 428
S89.1[1,2,3,4][1,2,9][K,P]	Salter-Harris Type [I, II, III, IV] physeal fx of lwr end of [rt, lt, unsp] tibia, subsq enc for fx w/ [nonu, malu] 204
S49.1[1,2,3,4][1,2,9][K,P]	Salter-Harris Type [I, II, III, IV] physeal fx of lwr end of humerus, [rt, lt, unsp] arm, subsq enc for fx w/ [nonu, malu] 197
S59.2[1,2,3,4][1,2,9][K,P]	Salter-Harris Type [I, II, III, IV] physeal fx of lwr end of radius, [rt, lt, unsp] arm, subsq enc for fx w/ [nonu, malu] 199
S59.0[1,2,3,4][1,2,9][K,P]	Salter-Harris Type [I, II, III, IV] physeal fx of lwr end of ulna, [rt, lt, unsp] arm, subsq enc for fx w/ [nonu, malu] 199
S89.0[1,2,3,4][1,2,9]A	Salter-Harris Type [I, II, III, IV] physeal fx of upr end of [rt, lt, unsp] tibia, init enc for clsd fx 192, 428
S89.0[1,2,3,4][1,2,9][K,P]	Salter-Harris Type [I, II, III, IV] physeal fx of upr end of [rt, lt, unsp] tibia, subsq enc for fx w/ [nonu, malu] 204
S49.0[1,2,3,4][1,2,9][K,P]	Salter-Harris Type [I, II, III, IV] physeal fx of upr end of humerus, [rt, lt, unsp] arm, subsq enc for fx w/ [nonu, malu] 197
S59.1[1,2,3,4][1,2,9][K,P]	Salter-Harris Type [I, II, III, IV] physeal fx of upr end of ulna, [rt, lt, unsp] arm, subsq enc for fx w/ [nonu, malu] 199
S89.3[1,2][1,2,9][K,P]	Salter-Harris Type [I, II] physeal fx of lwr end of [rt, lt, unsp] fibula, subsq enc for fx w/ [nonu, malu] 204
S89.2[1,2][1,2,9][K,P]	Salter-Harris Type [I, II] physeal fx of upr end of [rt, lt, unsp] fibula, subsq enc for fx w/ [nonu, malu] 204
S79.11[1,2,9][D,G,S]	Salter-Harris Type I physeal fx of lwr end of [rt, lt, unsp] femur, [subsq enc for fx w/ routine healing, subsq enc for fx w/ delayed healing, seq] 179
S89.31[1,2,9][D,G,S]	Salter-Harris Type I physeal fx of lwr end of [rt, lt, unsp] fibula, [subsq enc for fx w/ routine healing, subsq enc for fx w/ delayed healing, seq] 182
S89.11[1,2,9][D,G,S]	Salter-Harris Type I physeal fx of lwr end of [rt, lt, unsp] tibia, [subsq enc for fx w/ routine healing, subsq enc for fx w/ delayed healing, seq] 182
S79.11[1,2,9]A	Salter-Harris Type I physeal fx of lwr end of femur [rt, lt, unsp] inital enc for clsd fx 161
S49.11[1,2,9]A	Salter-Harris Type I physeal fx of lwr end of humerus [rt, lt, unsp] init enc 185

S49.11[1,2,9] [D,G,S]	Salter-Harris Type I physeal fx of lwr end of humerus, [rt, lt, unsp] arm, [subsq enc for fx w/ routine healing, subsq enc for fx w/ delayed healing, seq] **172**
S59.21[1,2,9]A	Salter-Harris Type I physeal fx of lwr end of radius, [rt, lt, unsp] init enc **187**
S59.21[1,2,9] [D,G,S]	Salter-Harris Type I physeal fx of lwr end of radius, [rt, lt, unsp] arm, [subsq enc for fx w/ routine healing, subsq enc for fx w/ delayed healing, seq] **174**
S59.01[1,2,9]A	Salter-Harris Type I physeal fx of lwr end of ulna [rt, lt, unsp] init enc **187**
S59.01[1,2,9] [D,G,S]	Salter-Harris Type I physeal fx of lwr end of ulna, [rt, lt, unsp] arm, [subsq enc for fx w/ routine healing, subsq enc for fx w/ delayed healing, seq] **174**
S79.01[1,2,9] [D,G,S]	Salter-Harris Type I physeal fx of upr end of [rt, lt, unsp] femur, [subsq enc for fx w/ routine healing, subsq enc for fx w/ delayed healing, seq] **179**
S79.01[1,2,9]A	Salter-Harris Type I physeal fx of upr end of [rt, lt, unsp] femur, init enc for clsd fx **162, 286, 427, 436**
S79.01[1,2,9] [K,P]	Salter-Harris Type I physeal fx of upr end of [rt, lt, unsp] femur, subsq enc for fx w/ [nonu, malu] **202**
S89.21[1,2,9] [D,G,S]	Salter-Harris Type I physeal fx of upr end of [rt, lt, unsp] fibula, [subsq enc for fx w/ routine healing, subsq enc for fx w/ delayed healing, seq] **182**
S89.01[1,2,9] [D,G,S]	Salter-Harris Type I physeal fx of upr end of [rt, lt, unsp] tibia, [subsq enc for fx w/ routine healing, subsq enc for fx w/ delayed healing, seq] **182**
S49.01[1,2,9]A	Salter-Harris Type I physeal fx of upr end of humerus [rt, lt, unsp], init enc for clsd fx **185**
S49.01[1,2,9] [D,G,S]	Salter-Harris Type I physeal fx of upr end of humerus, [rt, lt, unsp] arm, [subsq enc for fx w/ routine healing, subsq enc for fx w/ delayed healing, seq] **171**
S59.11[1,2,9]A	Salter-Harris Type I physeal fx of upr end of radius [rt, lt, unsp] init enc **187**
S59.14[1,2,9]A	Salter-Harris Type I physeal fx of upr end of radius [rt, lt, unsp] init enc **187**
S59.11[1,2,9] [D,G,S]	Salter-Harris Type I physeal fx of upr end of radius, [rt, lt, unsp] arm, [subsq enc for fx w/ routine healing, subsq enc for fx w/ delayed healing, seq] **174**
S79.12[1,2,9] [D,G,S]	Salter-Harris Type II physeal fx of lwr end of [rt, lt, unsp] femur, [subsq enc for fx w/ routine healing, subsq enc for fx w/ delayed healing, seq] **179**
S89.32[1,2,9] [D,G,S]	Salter-Harris Type II physeal fx of lwr end of [rt, lt, unsp] fibula, [subsq enc for fx w/ routine healing, subsq enc for fx w/ delayed healing, seq] **182**
S49.12[1,2,9]A	Salter-Harris Type II physeal fx of lwr end of [rt, lt, unsp] humerus, init enc **185**
S89.12[1,2,9] [D,G,S]	Salter-Harris Type II physeal fx of lwr end of [rt, lt, unsp] tibia, [subsq enc for fx w/ routine healing, subsq enc for fx w/ delayed healing, seq] **182**
S79.12[1,2,9]A	Salter-Harris Type II physeal fx of lwr end of femur [rt, lt, unsp] inital enc for clsd fx **161**
S49.12[1,2,9] [D,G,S]	Salter-Harris Type II physeal fx of lwr end of humerus, [rt, lt, unsp] arm, [subsq enc for fx w/ routine healing, subsq enc for fx w/ delayed healing, seq] **172**
S59.22[1,2,9]A	Salter-Harris Type II physeal fx of lwr end of radius [rt, lt, unsp] init enc **187**
S59.22[1,2,9] [D,G,S]	Salter-Harris Type II physeal fx of lwr end of radius, [rt, lt, unsp] arm, [subsq enc for fx w/ routine healing, subsq enc for fx w/ delayed healing, seq] **174**
S59.02[1,2,9]A	Salter-Harris Type II physeal fx of lwr end of ulna [rt, lt, unsp] init enc **187**
S59.02[1,2,9] [D,G,S]	Salter-Harris Type II physeal fx of lwr end of ulna, [rt, lt, unsp] arm, [subsq enc for fx w/ routine healing, subsq enc for fx w/ delayed healing, seq] **174**
S89.22[1,2,9] [D,G,S]	Salter-Harris Type II physeal fx of upr end of [rt, lt, unsp] fibula, [subsq enc for fx w/ routine healing, subsq enc for fx w/ delayed healing, seq] **182**
S49.02[1,2,9]A	Salter-Harris Type II physeal fx of upr end of humerus, init enc for clsd fx **185**
S89.02[1,2,9] [D,G,S]	Salter-Harris Type II physeal fx of upr end of [rt, lt, unsp] tibia, [subsq enc for fx w/ routine healing, subsq enc for fx w/ delayed healing, seq] **182**
S49.02[1,2,9] [D,G,S]	Salter-Harris Type II physeal fx of upr end of humerus, [rt, lt, unsp] arm, [subsq enc for fx w/ routine healing, subsq enc for fx w/ delayed healing, seq] **171**
S59.12[1,2,9]A	Salter-Harris Type II physeal fx of upr end of radius [rt, lt, unsp] init enc **187**
S59.12[1,2,9] [D,G,S]	Salter-Harris Type II physeal fx of upr end of radius, [rt, lt, unsp] arm, [subsq enc for fx w/ routine healing, subsq enc for fx w/ delayed healing, seq] **174**
S79.13[1,2,9] [D,G,S]	Salter-Harris Type III physeal fx of lwr end of [rt, lt, unsp] femur, [subsq enc for fx w/ routine healing, subsq enc for fx w/ delayed healing, seq] **179**
S89.13[1,2,9] [D,G,S]	Salter-Harris Type III physeal fx of lwr end of [rt, lt, unsp] tibia, [subsq enc for fx w/ routine healing, subsq enc for fx w/ delayed healing, seq] **182**
S79.13[1,2,9]A	Salter-Harris Type III physeal fx of lwr end of femur [rt, lt, unsp] inital enc for clsd fx **161**
S49.13[1,2,9]A	Salter-Harris Type III physeal fx of lwr end of humerus [rt, lt, unsp] init enc **185**
S49.13[1,2,9] [D,G,S]	Salter-Harris Type III physeal fx of lwr end of humerus, [rt, lt, unsp] arm, [subsq enc for fx w/ routine healing, subsq enc for fx w/ delayed healing, seq] **172**
S59.23[1,2,9]A	Salter-Harris Type III physeal fx of lwr end of radius [rt, lt, unsp] init enc **187**
S59.23[1,2,9] [D,G,S]	Salter-Harris Type III physeal fx of lwr end of radius, [rt, lt, unsp] arm, [subsq enc for fx w/ routine healing, subsq enc for fx w/ delayed healing, seq] **174**
S59.03[1,2,9]A	Salter-Harris Type III physeal fx of lwr end of ulna [rt, lt, unsp] seq **187**
S59.03[1,2,9] [D,G,S]	Salter-Harris Type III physeal fx of lwr end of ulna, [rt, lt, unsp] arm, [subsq enc for fx w/ routine healing, subsq enc for fx w/ delayed healing, seq] **174**
S89.03[1,2,9] [D,G,S]	Salter-Harris Type III physeal fx of upr end of [rt, lt, unsp] tibia, [subsq enc for fx w/ routine healing, subsq enc for fx w/ delayed healing, seq] **182**
S49.03[1,2,9]A	Salter-Harris Type III physeal fx of upr end of humerus [rt, lt, unsp], init enc for clsd fx **185**
S49.03[1,2,9] [D,G,S]	Salter-Harris Type III physeal fx of upr end of humerus, [rt, lt, unsp] arm, [subsq enc for fx w/ routine healing, subsq enc for fx w/ delayed healing, seq] **171**
S59.13[1,2,9]A	Salter-Harris Type III physeal fx of upr end of radius [rt, lt, unsp] init enc **187**
S59.13[1,2,9] [D,G,S]	Salter-Harris Type III physeal fx of upr end of radius, [rt, lt, unsp] arm, [subsq enc for fx w/ routine healing, subsq enc for fx w/ delayed healing, seq] **174**
S79.14[1,2,9] [D,G,S]	Salter-Harris Type IV physeal fx of lwr end of [rt, lt, unsp] femur, [subsq enc for fx w/ routine healing, subsq enc for fx w/ delayed healing, seq] **179**
S89.14[1,2,9] [D,G,S]	Salter-Harris Type IV physeal fx of lwr end of [rt, lt, unsp] tibia, [subsq enc for fx w/ routine healing, subsq enc for fx w/ delayed healing, seq] **182**
S79.14[1,2,9]A	Salter-Harris Type IV physeal fx of lwr end of femur [rt, lt, unsp] inital enc for clsd fx **162**
S49.14[1,2,9]A	Salter-Harris Type IV physeal fx of lwr end of humerus [rt, lt, unsp] init enc **185**
S49.14[1,2,9] [D,G,S]	Salter-Harris Type IV physeal fx of lwr end of humerus, [rt, lt, unsp] arm, [subsq enc for fx w/ routine healing, subsq enc for fx w/ delayed healing, seq] **172**
S59.24[1,2,9]A	Salter-Harris Type IV physeal fx of lwr end of radius [rt, lt, unsp] init enc **187**
S59.24[1,2,9] [D,G,S]	Salter-Harris Type IV physeal fx of lwr end of radius, [rt, lt, unsp] arm, [subsq enc for fx w/ routine healing, subsq enc for fx w/ delayed healing, seq] **174**
S59.04[1,2,9]A	Salter-Harris Type IV physeal fx of lwr end of ulna [rt, lt, unsp] init enc **187**
S59.04[1,2,9] [D,G,S]	Salter-Harris Type IV physeal fx of lwr end of ulna, [rt, lt, unsp] arm, [subsq enc for fx w/ routine healing, subsq enc for fx w/ delayed healing, seq] **174**
S89.04[1,2,9] [D,G,S]	Salter-Harris Type IV physeal fx of upr end of [rt, lt, unsp] tibia, [subsq enc for fx w/ routine healing, subsq enc for fx w/ delayed healing, seq] **182**
S49.04[1,2,9]A	Salter-Harris Type IV physeal fx of upr end of humerus [rt, lt, unsp], init enc for clsd fx **185**
S49.04[1,2,9] [D,G,S]	Salter-Harris Type IV physeal fx of upr end of humerus, [rt, lt, unsp] arm, [subsq enc for fx w/ routine healing, subsq enc for fx w/ delayed healing, seq] **171**
S59.14[1,2,9] [D,G,S]	Salter-Harris Type IV physeal fx of upr end of radius, [rt, lt, unsp] arm, [subsq enc for fx w/ routine healing, subsq enc for fx w/ delayed healing, seq] **174**
D86*	Sarcoidosis **68**
C96.4	Sarcoma of dendritic cells (accessory cells) **295, 303, 305**
B86	Scabies **233**

Code	Description
A38*	Scarlet fever 308
B65.0	Schistosomiasis d/t Schistosoma haematobium 255
B65.2	Schistosomiasis d/t Schistosoma japonicum 309
B65.1	Schistosomiasis d/t Schistosoma mansoni 124
B65.9	Schistosomiasis, unsp 309
F25*	Schizoaffective d/o 311
F20*	Schizophrenia 310
F21	Schizotypal d/o 310
M54.3*	Sciatica 165
P83.0	Sclerema neonatorum 288
L94.3	Sclerodactyly 234
K65.4	Sclerosing mesenteritis 117
M41*	Scoliosis 164
M41.9	Scoliosis, unsp 125
T61.1[1,2,3,4]XA	Scombroid fish poison, [accid (unintentional), intentional self-harm, assault, undetermined], init enc 366
T61.1[1,2,3,4]XS	Scombroid fish poison, [accid (unintentional), intentional self-harm, assault, undetermined], seq 373
T61.1[1,2,3,4]XD	Scombroid fish poison, [accid (unintentional), intentional self-harm, assault, undetermined], subsq enc 408
H53.41[1,2,3,9]	Scotoma involving central area, [rt, lt, bilat, unsp] eye 45
H53.42*	Scotoma of blind spot area 46
I86.1	Scrotal varices 261
L21*	Seborrheic dermatitis 233
L82*	Seborrheic keratosis 234
C77*	Secondary and unsp malig neoplasm of lymph nodes 295, 303, 305
C77.0	Secondary and unsp malig neoplasm of nodes of head, face and neck 3
K74.4	Secondary biliary cirrhosis 123
C7B.03	Secondary carcinoid tumors of bone 125, 163
C7B.01	Secondary carcinoid tumors of distant lymph nodes 295, 303, 305
C7B.02	Secondary carcinoid tumors of liver 123
C7B.09	Secondary carcinoid tumors of oth sites 304, 305
C7B.04	Secondary carcinoid tumors of peritoneum 115
C7B.00	Secondary carcinoid tumors, unsp site 304, 305
N94.5	Secondary dysmenorrhea 270
I85.10	Secondary esophageal varices w/o bleeding 117
I85.11	Secondary esophageal varices with bleeding 114
I15*	Secondary hypertension 102
C79.7*	Secondary malig neoplasm of adrenal gland 247
C78.8*	Secondary malig neoplasm of and unsp digestive organs 115
C79.4*	Secondary malig neoplasm of and unsp parts of nervous sys 32
C78.3*	Secondary malig neoplasm of and unsp respiratory organs 67
C79.5*	Secondary malig neoplasm of bone and bone marrow 125, 163
C79.3*	Secondary malig neoplasm of brain and cerebral meninges 32
C79.81	Secondary malig neoplasm of breast 221, 223
C79.82	Secondary malig neoplasm of genital organs 258, 260, 263, 269
C79.0*	Secondary malig neoplasm of kidney and renal pelvis 248, 255
C78.5	Secondary malig neoplasm of large intestine and rectum 115
C78.7	Secondary malig neoplasm of liver and intrahepatic bile duct 123
C78.0*	Secondary malig neoplasm of lung 67
C78.1	Secondary malig neoplasm of mediastinum 67
C79.89	Secondary malig neoplasm of oth spec sites 304, 305
C79.6*	Secondary malig neoplasm of ovary 262, 269
C78.2	Secondary malig neoplasm of pleura 67
C78.6	Secondary malig neoplasm of retroperiton and peritoneum 115
C79.2	Secondary malig neoplasm of skin 221, 223
C78.4	Secondary malig neoplasm of sm intestine 115
C79.9	Secondary malig neoplasm of unsp site 304, 305
C79.1*	Secondary malig neoplm of bladder and oth and unsp urinary organs 248, 255
C7B.1	Secondary Merkel cell carcinoma 304, 305
G21.2	Secondary parkinsonism d/t oth ext agents 32
G21.9	Secondary parkinsonism, unsp 32
D75.1	Secondary polycythemia 294
A51.3*	Secondary syphilis of skin and mucous membranes 233
A51.42	Secondary syphilitic female pelvic dz 308
A51.45	Secondary syphilitic hepatitis 124
A51.41	Secondary syphilitic meningitis 10, 14, 41
A51.44	Secondary syphilitic nephritis 308
A51.43	Secondary syphilitic oculopathy 45
A51.46	Secondary syphilitic osteopathy 163
D69.5*	Secondary thrombocytopenia 283
H53.43[1,2,3,9]	Sector or arcuate defects, [rt, lt, bilat, unsp] eye 45
F13.[2,9]3[0,1,2,9]	Sedative, hypnotic or anxiolytic [dependence, use unsp] w/ w/drawal [uncomp, delirium, perceptual disturbance, unsp] 283
M99.0[0,5,6,7,8,9]	Seg and somatic dysfunction [head rgn, pelvic rgn, lwr extr, upr extr, rib cage, abd and oth rgns] 167
M99.0[1,2,3,4]	Seg and somatic dysfunction of [head rgn, thoracic rgn, lumbar rgn, sacral rgn] 165
D80.2	Selective deficiency of immunoglobulin A [IgA] 294
D80.3	Selective deficiency of immunoglobulin G [IgG] subclasses 294
D80.4	Selective deficiency of immunoglobulin M [IgM] 294
F93.0	Separation anxiety d/o of childhood 310
M62.0*	Separation of muscle (nontraumatic) 167
I76	Septic arterial embolism 100, 284
I26.90	Septic pulmn embolism w/o acute cor pulmonale 66
I26.01	Septic pulmn embolism with acute cor pulmonale 66
A20.7	Septicemic plague 309
B90.0	Sequelae of central nervous sys tuberculosis 38
I69*	Sequelae of cerebrovascular dz 32
O94	Sequelae of comp of preg, chldbrth, and the puerperium 281
B90.1	Sequelae of genitourinary tuberculosis 255
E68	Sequelae of hyperalimentation 246
G65*	Sequelae of inflam and txc polyneuropathies 34
G09	Sequelae of inflam dz of central nervous sys 38
B92	Sequelae of leprosy 309
B94.8	Sequelae of oth infectious and parasitic dz 309
E64.8	Sequelae of oth nutritional deficiencies 246
B91	Sequelae of poliomyelitis 38
E64.0	Sequelae of protein-calorie malnut 246, 283
B90.9	Sequelae of respiratory and unsp tuberculosis 68
E64.3	Sequelae of rickets 166
B94.0	Sequelae of trachoma 45
B90.2	Sequelae of tuberculosis of bones and jts 193
B90.8	Sequelae of tuberculosis of oth organs 309
B94.9	Sequelae of unsp infectious and parasitic dz 309
E64.9	Sequelae of unsp nutritional deficiency 246
B94.1	Sequelae of viral encephalitis 38
B94.2	Sequelae of viral hepatitis 309
E64.1	Sequelae of vitamin A deficiency 246
E64.2	Sequelae of vitamin C deficiency 246
Q33.2	Sequestration of lung 69
H33.2*	Serous retinal detach 46
G61.1	Serum neuropathy 34
D81.2	Severe combined immunodef w low or normal B-cell numbers 293
D81.1	Severe combined immunodef w low T- and B-cell numbers 293
D81.0	Severe combined immunodef with reticular dysgenesis 293
F72	Severe intellectual disabilities 310
O14.1*	Severe pre-eclampsia 276
O14.12	Severe pre-eclampsia, second trmstr 279
O14.13	Severe pre-eclampsia, third trmstr 279
O14.10	Severe pre-eclampsia, unsp trmstr 279, 280
O9A.41[1,2,3]	Sexual abuse compl preg, [1st, 2nd, 3rd] trmstr 277, 278
O9A.419	Sexual abuse compl preg, unsp trmstr 281
O9A.43	Sexual abuse compl the puerperium 276
F52.2*	Sexual arousal d/o 311
F52.1	Sexual aversion d/o 311
R37	Sexual dysfunction, unsp 311
A56.8	Sexually transmitted chlamydial infxn of oth sites 261, 264, 269
C84.11	Sezary dz, lymph nodes of head, face, and neck 3
T74.4XX[A,S]	Shaken infant synd, [init enc, seq] 374
T74.4XXD	Shaken infant synd, subsq enc 410
F24	Shared psychotic d/o 310
A03*	Shigellosis 114
M75*	Shldr lesions 167
T88.2XX[A,S]	Shock d/t anesthesia, [init enc, seq] 376
T88.2XXA	Shock d/t anesthesia, init enc 287
T88.2XXD	Shock d/t anesthesia, subsq enc 411

Code	Description
O75.1	Shock during or following labor and delivery 273, 274
R57.9	Shock, unsp 72, 99, 285
Q77.2	Short rib synd 69
K11.2*	Sialoadenitis 4
K11.5	Sialolithiasis 4
M35.0*	Sicca synd [Sjogren] 164
E07.81	Sick-euthyroid synd 385
D57*	Sickle-cell d/o 293
D57.4*	Sickle-cell thalassemia 283
I25.6	Silent myocardial ischemia 102
J41.0	Simple chr bronchitis 69
R56.00	Simple febrile convulsions 285
Z38.1	Single liveborn infant, born outside hospital 289
Z38.01	Single liveborn infant, delivered by cesarean 289
Z38.00	Single liveborn infant, delivered vaginally 289
Z38.2	Single liveborn infant, unsp as to place of birth 289
T70.1XXA	Sinus barotrauma, init enc 57
T70.1XXD	Sinus barotrauma, subsq enc 409
Q18.0	Sinus, fistula and cyst of branchial cleft 58
Q89.3	Situs inversus 117
H49.2*	Sixth [abducent] nerve palsy 45
M85.1*	Skeletal fluorosis 194
L57*	Skin changes d/t chr expsr to nonionizing radiation 234
Z52.1*	Skin donor 234
Z94.5	Skin transplant status 234
G47.3*	Sleep apnea 3
G47.30	Sleep apnea, unsp 58
F51*	Sleep d/o not d/t a substance or known physiol cond 311
G47.9	Sleep d/o, unsp 311
Z72.820	Sleep deprivation 412
G47.63	Sleep related bruxism 58
G47.36	Sleep related hypoventilation in conditions classd elsw 58
G47.62	Sleep related leg cramps 38
G47.6*	Sleep related movement d/o 3
P92.2	Slow feeding of newborn 289
C83.0*	Sm cell B-cell lymphoma 438
C83.01	Sm cell B-cell lymphoma, nodes of head, face, and neck 3
N27*	Sm kidney of unknown cause 256
B03	Smallpox 307
S52.54[1,2,9] [D,E,F,G,H,J,S]	Smith's fx of [rt, lt, unsp] radius, [subsq enc for clsd fx w/ routine healing, subsq enc for opn fx type I or II w/ routine healing, subsq enc for opn fx type I or II w/ routine healing, subsq enc for clsd fx w/ delayed healing, subsq enc for opn fx type I or II w/ delayed healing, subsq enc for opn fx type IIIA, IIIB, or IIIC w/ delayed healing, seq] 174
S52.54[1,2,9] [A,B,C]	Smith's fx of [rt, lt, unsp] radius, init enc for [clsd fx, opn fx type I or II, opn fx type IIIA, IIIB, or IIIC] 186, 423
S52.54[1,2,9] [B,C]	Smith's fx of [rt, lt, unsp] radius, init enc for opn fx type [I or II, IIIA IIIB or IIIC] 434
S52.54[1,2,9] [K,M,N,P,Q,R]	Smith's fx of [rt, lt, unsp] radius, subsq enc for [clsd fx w/ nonu, opn fx type I or II w/ nonu, opn fx type IIIA, IIIB, or IIIC w/ nonu, clsd fx w/ malu, opn fx type I or II w/ malu, opn fx type IIIA, IIIB, or IIIC w/ malu] 198
O99.33[1,2,3]	Smoking (tobacco) compl preg, [1st, 2nd, 3rd] trmstr 278, 280
O99.335	Smoking (tobacco) compl the puerperium 276
R06.7	Sneezing 58
M79.9	Soft tissue d/o, unsp 167
M85.4*	Solitary bone cyst 167
R91.1	Solitary pulmn nodule 69
F45*	Somatoform d/o 310
R40.0	Somnolence 35
B70.1	Sparganosis 114
H52.53*	Spasm of accommodation 46
G24.3	Spasmodic torticollis 38
G80.1	Spastic diplegic cerebral palsy 32
G80.2	Spastic hemiplegic cerebral palsy 32
G80.0	Spastic quadriplegic cerebral palsy 32
F82	Specific developmental d/o of motor function 311
F81*	Specific developmental d/o of scholastic skills 311
F60*	Specific personality d/o 310
F80.4	Speech and language development delay d/t hearing loss 311

Code	Description
R47*	Speech disturbances, NEC 39
N43.4*	Spermatocele of epididymis 261
E75.3	Sphingolipidosis, unsp 247
Q05*	Spina bifida 38, 285
Q76.0	Spina bifida occulta 38
O29.40	Spinal and epidur anesth induce hdache during preg, unsp trmstr 280
O29.4[1,2,3]	Spinal and epidural anesthesia induced headache during preg, [1st, 2nd, 3rd] trmstr 277
M46.0*	Spinal enthesopathy 164
M53.2X[7,8]	Spinal instabilities, [lumbosacral, sacral and sacrococcygeal] rgn 165
M53.2X[1,2,3,4,5, 6,9]	Spinal instabilities, [occipito-atlanto-axial, cervical, cervicothoracic, thoracic, thoracolumbar, lumbar, unsp] rgn 194
G12*	Spinal muscular atrophy and related syndromes 32
M42*	Spinal osteochondrosis 167
M48.0*	Spinal stenosis 164
A69.9	Spirochetal infxn, unsp 308
R16.1	Splenomegaly, NEC 294
Q77.7	Spondyloepiphyseal dysplasia 195
M43.1*	Spondylolisthesis 164
M43.0*	Spondylolysis 164
M49*	Spondylopathies in dz classified elsw 165
M48.9	Spondylopathy, unsp 165
M47*	Spondylosis 164
O03*	Spontaneous abortion 272, 276
K65.2	Spontaneous bacterial peritonitis 114
R23.3	Spontaneous ecchymoses 294
M66*	Spontaneous rupture of synovium and tndn 167
B42*	Sporotrichosis 308
A77*	Spotted fever [tick-borne rickettsioses] 308
O26.85[1,2,3]	Spotting compl preg, [1st, 2nd, 3rd] trmstr 277, 279
O26.859	Spotting compl preg, unsp trmstr 280
S33.[5,6,8,9]XXS	Sprain [lgmts of lumbar spine, sacroiliac jt, oth parts of lumbar spine and pelvis, unsp parts of lumbar spine and pelvis, seq 184
S63.5[1,2][1,2,9]A	Sprain of [carpal, radiocarpal] jt of [rt, lt, unsp] wrist, init enc 425
S13.[4,5,8,9]XXA	Sprain of [lgmts of cervical spine, thyroid rgn, jts and lgmts of oth parts of neck, jts and lgmts of unsp parts of neck], init enc 419
S13.[4,5]XXS	Sprain of [lgmts of cervical spine, thyroid rgn], seq 184
S33.[5,6,8,9]XXA	Sprain of [lgmts of lumbar spine, sacroiliac jt, oth parts of lumbar spine and pelvis, unsp parts of lumbar spine and pelvis] init enc 166
S43.[8,9][0,1,2] XA	Sprain of [oth spec, unsp] parts of [unsp, rt, lt] shldr girdle, init enc 423
S23.[8,9]XXA	Sprain of [oth spec, unsp] parts of thorax, init enc 420
S33.[8,9]XXA	Sprain of [oth, unsp] parts of lumbar spine and pelvis, init enc 421
S43.41[1,2,9]D	Sprain of [rt, lt, unsp] coracohumeral (lgmt), subsq enc 391
S53.40[1,2,9] [A,S]	Sprain of [rt, lt, unsp] elbow, [init enc, seq] 186
S43.42[1,2,9]D	Sprain of [rt, lt, unsp] rotator cuff capsule, subsq enc 391
S23.42[0,1]A	Sprain of [sternoclavicular (jt) (lgmt), chondrosternal jt], init enc 69, 420
S23.42[0,1,8,9]D	Sprain of [sternoclavicular (jt) (lgmt), chondrosternal jt], Oth sprain of sternum, Unsp sprain of sternum, subsq enc 389
S83.5[0,1,2] [1,2,9]A	Sprain of [unsp, ant, post] cruciate lgmt of [rt, lt, unsp] knee, init enc 428
S83.5[0,1,2] [1,2,9]D	Sprain of [unsp, ant, post] cruciate lgmt of [rt, lt, unsp] knee, subsq enc 398
S93.4[0,1,2,3,9] [1,2,9]A	Sprain of [unsp, calcaneofibular, deltoid, tibiofibular, oth] lgmt of [rt, lt, unsp] ankle, init enc 430
S93.4[0,1,2,3,9] [1,2,9]D	Sprain of [unsp, calcaneofibular, deltoid, tibiofibular, oth] lgmt of [rt, lt, unsp] ankle, subsq enc 399
S83.4[0,1,2] [1,2,9]A	Sprain of [unsp, med, lat] collat lgmt of [rt, lt, unsp] knee, init enc 428
S83.4[0,1,2] [1,2,9]D	Sprain of [unsp, med, lat] collat lgmt of [rt, lt, unsp] knee, subsq enc 398
S43.[5,6][0,1,2] XA	Sprain of [unsp, rt, lt] [acromioclavicular, sternoclavicular] jt, init enc 423
S43.5[0,1,2]XD	Sprain of [unsp, rt, lt] acromioclavicular jt, subsq enc 391
S43.6[0,1,2] X[A,S]	Sprain of [unsp, rt, lt] sternoclavicular jt, [init enc, seq] 185
S43.6[0,1,2]XD	Sprain of [unsp, rt, lt] sternoclavicular jt, subsq enc 391

Code	Description
S43.5[0,1,2]X[A,S]	Sprain of acromioclavicular jt [unsp, rt, lt] [init enc, seq] **185**
S83.51[1,2,9][A,S]	Sprain of ant cruciate lgmt of [rt, lt, unsp] knee, [init enc, seq] **192**
S93.41[1,2,9][A,S]	Sprain of calcaneofibular lgmt of [rt, lt, unsp] ankle, [init enc, seq] **193**
S63.51[1,2,9][A,S]	Sprain of carpal jt of [rt, lt, unsp] wrist, [init enc, seq] **190**
S63.51[1,2,9]D	Sprain of carpal jt of [rt, lt, unsp] wrist, subsq enc **396**
S43.41[1,2,9][A,S]	Sprain of coracohumeral (lgmt) [rt, lt, unsp] [init enc, seq] **185**
S93.42[1,2,9][A,S]	Sprain of deltoid lgmt of [rt, lt, unsp] ankle, [init enc, seq] **193**
S63.63[8,9][A,S]	Sprain of interphalangeal jt of [oth, unsp] finger, [init enc, seq] **190**
S63.63[8,9]D	Sprain of interphalangeal jt of [oth, unsp] finger, subsq enc **396**
S63.63[0,1,2,3,4,5,6,7,8,9]A	Sprain of interphalangeal jt of [rt index, lt index, rt mid, lt mid, rt ring, lt ring, rt little, lt little, oth, unsp] finger, init enc **425**
S93.51[1,2,3][A,S]	Sprain of interphalangeal jt of [rt, lt, unsp] great toe, [init enc, seq] **193**
S93.51[4,5,6][A,S]	Sprain of interphalangeal jt of [rt, lt, unsp] lesser toe(s), [init enc, seq] **193**
S63.62[1,2,9][A,S]	Sprain of interphalangeal jt of [rt, lt, unsp] thumb, [init enc, seq] **190**
S63.62[1,2,9]A	Sprain of interphalangeal jt of [rt, lt, unsp] thumb, init enc **425**
S63.62[1,2,9]D	Sprain of interphalangeal jt of [rt, lt, unsp] thumb, subsq enc **396**
S63.63[0,1][A,S]	Sprain of interphalangeal jt of [rt, lt] index finger, [init enc, seq] **190**
S63.63[0,1]D	Sprain of interphalangeal jt of [rt, lt] index finger, subsq enc **396**
S63.63[6,7][A,S]	Sprain of interphalangeal jt of [rt, lt] little finger, [init enc, seq] **190**
S63.63[6,7]D	Sprain of interphalangeal jt of [rt, lt] little finger, subsq enc **396**
S63.63[2,3][A,S]	Sprain of interphalangeal jt of [rt, lt] mid finger, [init enc, seq] **190**
S63.63[2,3]D	Sprain of interphalangeal jt of [rt, lt] mid finger, subsq enc **396**
S63.63[4,5][A,S]	Sprain of interphalangeal jt of [rt, lt] ring finger, [init enc, seq] **190**
S63.63[4,5]D	Sprain of interphalangeal jt of [rt, lt] ring finger, subsq enc **396**
S93.519[A,S]	Sprain of interphalangeal jt of unsp toe(s), [init enc, seq] **193**
S93.519A	Sprain of interphalangeal jt of unsp toe(s), init enc **430**
S93.519D	Sprain of interphalangeal jt of unsp toe(s), subs enc **399**
S03.4XXA	Sprain of jaw, init enc **59, 417**
S03.4XXS	Sprain of jaw, seq **184**
S03.4XXD	Sprain of jaw, subsq enc **386**
S03.8XXS	Sprain of jts and lgmt of oth parts of head, seq **184**
S03.8XXA	Sprain of jts and lgmt of oth prt head, init enc **195**
S13.8XXA	Sprain of jts and lgmt of oth prt neck, init enc **165**
S13.8XXD	Sprain of jts and lgmt of oth prt neck, subs enc **388**
S03.9XXA	Sprain of jts and lgmt of unsp parts of head, init **184**
S03.9XXS	Sprain of jts and lgmt of unsp parts of head, seq **184**
S13.9XXA	Sprain of jts and lgmt of unsp parts of neck, init **165**
S13.9XXD	Sprain of jts and lgmt of unsp parts of neck, subs **388**
S03.[8,9]XXA	Sprain of jts and lgmts of [oth, unsp] parts of head, init enc **417**
S03.[8,9]XXD	Sprain of jts and lgmts of [oth, unsp] parts of head, subsq enc **386**
S13.[8,9]XXS	Sprain of jts and lgmts, parts of neck {oth, unsp] **184**
S83.42[1,2,9][A,S]	Sprain of lat collat lgmt of [rt, lt, unsp] knee, [init enc, seq] **192**
S13.4XXA	Sprain of lgmt of cervical spine, init enc **165**
S13.4XXD	Sprain of lgmt of cervical spine, subsq enc **388**
S33.5XXA	Sprain of lgmt of lumbar spine, init enc **421**
S33.5XXD	Sprain of lgmt of lumbar spine, subsq enc **390**
S23.3XXA	Sprain of lgmt of thoracic spine, init enc **166, 420**
S23.3XXS	Sprain of lgmt of thoracic spine, seq **184**
S23.3XXD	Sprain of lgmt of thoracic spine, subsq enc **389**
S83.41[1,2,9][A,S]	Sprain of med collat lgmt of [rt, lt, unsp] knee, [init enc, seq] **192**
S63.65[8,9][A,S]	Sprain of metacarpophalangeal jt of [oth, unsp] finger, [init enc, seq] **190**
S63.65[8,9]D	Sprain of metacarpophalangeal jt of [oth, unsp] finger, subsq enc **396**
S63.65[0,1,2,3,4,5,6,7,8,9]A	Sprain of metacarpophalangeal jt of [rt index, lt index, rt mid, lt mid, rt ring, lt ring, rt little, lt little, oth, unsp] finger, init enc **425**
S63.64[1,2,9][A,S]	Sprain of metacarpophalangeal jt of [rt, lt, unsp] thumb, [init enc, seq] **190**
S63.64[1,2,9]A	Sprain of metacarpophalangeal jt of [rt, lt, unsp] thumb, init enc **425**
S63.64[1,2,9]D	Sprain of metacarpophalangeal jt of [rt, lt, unsp] thumb, subsq enc **396**
S63.65[0,1][A,S]	Sprain of metacarpophalangeal jt of [rt, lt] index finger, [init enc, seq] **190**
S63.65[0,1]D	Sprain of metacarpophalangeal jt of [rt, lt] index finger, subsq enc **396**
S63.65[6,7][A,S]	Sprain of metacarpophalangeal jt of [rt, lt] little finger, [init enc, seq] **190**
S63.65[6,7]D	Sprain of metacarpophalangeal jt of [rt, lt] little finger, subsq enc **396**
S63.65[2,3][A,S]	Sprain of metacarpophalangeal jt of [rt, lt] mid finger, [init enc, seq] **190**
S63.65[2,3]D	Sprain of metacarpophalangeal jt of [rt, lt] mid finger, subsq enc **396**
S63.65[4,5][A,S]	Sprain of metacarpophalangeal jt of [rt, lt] ring finger, [init enc, seq] **190**
S63.65[4,5]D	Sprain of metacarpophalangeal jt of [rt, lt] ring finger, subsq enc **396**
S93.52[1,2,3][A,S]	Sprain of metatarsophalangeal jt of [rt, lt, unsp] great toe, [init enc, seq] **193**
S93.52[4,5,6][A,S]	Sprain of metatarsophalangeal jt of [rt, lt, unsp] lesser toe(s), [init enc, seq] **193**
S93.529[A,S]	Sprain of metatarsophalangeal jt of unsp toe(s), [init enc, seq] **193**
S93.529A	Sprain of metatarsophalangeal jt of unsp toe(s), init **430**
S93.529D	Sprain of metatarsophalangeal jt of unsp toe(s), subs **399**
S93.49[1,2,9][A,S]	Sprain of oth lgmt of [rt, lt, unsp] ankle, [init enc, seq] **193**
S63.8X[1,2,9][A,S]	Sprain of oth part of [rt, lt, unsp] wrist and hand, [init enc, seq] **190**
S63.8X[1,2,9]A	Sprain of oth part of [rt, lt, unsp] wrist and hand, init enc **425**
S63.8X[1,2,9]D	Sprain of oth part of [rt, lt, unsp] wrist and hand, subsq enc **396**
S33.8XXD	Sprain of oth parts of lumbar spine and pelvis, subs enc **390**
S23.[8,9]XXS	Sprain of oth parts of thorax [oth spec, unsp] **184**
S83.8X[1,2,9][A,S]	Sprain of oth spec parts of [rt, lt, unsp] knee, [init enc, seq] **192**
S83.8X[1,2,9]A	Sprain of oth spec parts of [rt, lt, unsp] knee, init enc **428**
S83.8X[1,2,9]D	Sprain of oth spec parts of [rt, lt, unsp] knee, subsq enc **398**
S43.8[0,1,2]XD	Sprain of oth spec parts of [unsp, rt, lt] shldr girdle, subsq enc **391**
S23.8XXA	Sprain of oth spec parts of thorax, init enc **166**
S23.8XXD	Sprain of oth spec parts of thorax, subs enc **389**
S43.8[0,1,2]X[A,S]	Sprain of oth unsp parts of shldr girdle [unsp, rt, lt] [init enc, seq] **185**
S83.52[1,2,9][A,S]	Sprain of post cruciate lgmt of [rt, lt, unsp] knee, [init enc, seq] **192**
S63.52[1,2,9][A,S]	Sprain of radiocarpal jt of [rt, lt, unsp] wrist, [init enc, seq] **190**
S63.52[1,2,9]D	Sprain of radiocarpal jt of [rt, lt, unsp] wrist, subsq enc **396**
S23.41XA	Sprain of ribs, init enc **69, 420**
S23.41XS	Sprain of ribs, seq **184**
S23.41XD	Sprain of ribs, subsq enc **389**
S43.42[1,2,9][A,S]	Sprain of rotator cuff capsule [rt, lt, unsp] [init enc, seq] **185**
S33.6XXA	Sprain of sacroiliac jt, init enc **421**
S33.6XXD	Sprain of sacroiliac jt, subsq enc **390**
S23.42[0,1,8,9]S	Sprain of sternum [sternoclavicular (jt) (lgmt), chondrosternal jt, oth, unsp], seq **184**
S93.61[1,2,9][A,S]	Sprain of tarsal lgmt of [rt, lt, unsp] foot, [init enc, seq] **193**
S93.61[1,2,9]A	Sprain of tarsal lgmt of [rt, lt, unsp] foot, init enc **430**
S93.61[1,2,9]D	Sprain of tarsal lgmt of [rt, lt, unsp] foot, subsq enc **399**
S93.62[1,2,9][A,S]	Sprain of tarsometatarsal lgmt of [rt, lt, unsp] foot, [init enc, seq] **193**
S93.62[1,2,9]A	Sprain of tarsometatarsal lgmt of [rt, lt, unsp] foot, init enc **430**
S93.62[1,2,9]D	Sprain of tarsometatarsal lgmt of [rt, lt, unsp] foot, subsq enc **399**
S83.6[0,1,2]X[A,S]	Sprain of the superior tibiofibular jt and lgmt, [rt, lt, unsp] knee, [init enc, seq] **192**
S83.6[0,1,2]XA	Sprain of the superior tibiofibular jt and lgmt, [unsp, rt, lt] knee, init enc **428**
S83.6[0,1,2]XD	Sprain of the superior tibiofibular jt and lgmt, [unsp, rt, lt] knee, subsq enc **398**
S13.5XXA	Sprain of thyroid region, init enc **195**
S13.5XXD	Sprain of thyroid region, subsq enc **388**

S66.11[2,3][A,S]	Strain of flexor muscle, fascia and tndn of [rt, lt, unsp] mid finger at wrist and hand lvl, [init enc, seq] 190
S66.11[4,5][A,S]	Strain of flexor muscle, fascia and tndn of [rt, lt, unsp] ring finger at wrist and hand lvl, [init enc, seq] 190
S56.01[1,2,9]D	Strain of flexor muscle, fascia and tndn of [rt, lt, unsp] thumb at forearm lvl, subsq enc 393
S56.119[A,S]	Strain of flexor muscle, fascia and tndn of [rt, lt] finger at forearm lvl, [init enc, seq] 187
S56.11[1,2][A,S]	Strain of flexor muscle, fascia and tndn of [rt, lt] index finger at forearm lvl, [init enc, seq] 187
S56.11[1,2]D	Strain of flexor muscle, fascia and tndn of [rt, lt] index finger at forearm lvl, subsq enc 393
S66.11[0,1]D	Strain of flexor muscle, fascia and tndn of [rt, lt] index finger at wrist and hand lvl, subsq enc 397
S56.11[7,8][A,S]	Strain of flexor muscle, fascia and tndn of [rt, lt] little finger at forearm lvl, [init enc, seq] 187
S56.11[7,8]D	Strain of flexor muscle, fascia and tndn of [rt, lt] little finger at forearm lvl, subsq enc 393
S66.11[6,7]D	Strain of flexor muscle, fascia and tndn of [rt, lt] little finger at wrist and hand lvl, subsq enc 397
S56.11[3,4][A,S]	Strain of flexor muscle, fascia and tndn of [rt, lt] mid finger at forearm lvl, [init enc, seq] 187
S56.11[3,4]D	Strain of flexor muscle, fascia and tndn of [rt, lt] mid finger at forearm lvl, subsq enc 393
S66.11[2,3]D	Strain of flexor muscle, fascia and tndn of [rt, lt] mid finger at wrist and hand lvl, subsq enc 397
S56.11[5,6][A,S]	Strain of flexor muscle, fascia and tndn of [rt, lt] ring finger at forearm lvl, [init enc, seq] 187
S56.11[5,6]D	Strain of flexor muscle, fascia and tndn of [rt, lt] ring finger at forearm lvl, subsq enc 393
S66.11[4,5]D	Strain of flexor muscle, fascia and tndn of [rt, lt] ring finger at wrist and hand lvl, subsq enc 397
S56.01[1,2,9] [A,S]	Strain of flexor muscle, fascial and tndn of thumb at forearm lvl [rt, lt, unsp]][init enc, seq] 187
S93.51[1,2,3]A	Strain of interphalangeal jt of [rt, lt, unsp] great toe, init enc 430
S93.51[1,2,3]D	Strain of interphalangeal jt of [rt, lt, unsp] great toe, subsq enc 399
S93.51[4,5,6]A	Strain of interphalangeal jt of [rt, lt, unsp] lesser toe(s), init enc 430
S93.51[4,5,6]D	Strain of interphalangeal jt of [rt, lt, unsp] lesser toe(s), subsq enc 399
S96.21[1,2,9] [A,S]	Strain of intrinsic muscle and tndn at ankle and foot lvl, [rt, lt, unsp] foot, [init enc, seq] 193
S66.51[8,9][A,S]	Strain of intrinsic muscle, fascia and tndn of [oth, unsp] finger at wrist and hand lvl, [init enc, seq] 190
S66.51[0,1][A,S]	Strain of intrinsic muscle, fascia and tndn of [rt, lt, unsp] index finger at wrist and hand lvl, [init enc, seq] 190
S66.51[6,7][A,S]	Strain of intrinsic muscle, fascia and tndn of [rt, lt, unsp] little finger at wrist and hand lvl, [init enc, seq] 190
S66.51[2,3][A,S]	Strain of intrinsic muscle, fascia and tndn of [rt, lt, unsp] mid finger at wrist and hand lvl, [init enc, seq] 190
S66.51[4,5][A,S]	Strain of intrinsic muscle, fascia and tndn of [rt, lt, unsp] ring finger at wrist and hand lvl, [init enc, seq] 190
S66.41[1,2,9] [A,S]	Strain of intrinsic muscle, fascia and tndn of [rt, lt, unsp] thumb at wrist and hand lvl, [init enc, seq] 190
S66.01[1,2,9] [A,S]	Strain of long flexor muscle, fascia and tndn of [rt, lt, unsp] thumb at wrist and hand lvl, [init enc, seq] 190
S66.01[1,2,9]D	Strain of long flexor muscle, fascia and tndn of [rt, lt, unsp] thumb at wrist and hand lvl, subsq enc 397
S93.52[1,2,3]A	Strain of metatarsophalangeal jt of [rt, lt, unsp] great toe, init enc 430
S93.52[1,2,3]D	Strain of metatarsophalangeal jt of [rt, lt, unsp] great toe, subsq enc 399
S93.52[4,5,6]A	Strain of metatarsophalangeal jt of [rt, lt, unsp] lesser toe(s), init enc 430
S93.52[4,5,6]D	Strain of metatarsophalangeal jt of [rt, lt, unsp] lesser toe(s), subsq enc 399
S76.812A	Strain of musc/fasc/tend at thigh lvl, lt thigh, init 163
S76.811A	Strain of musc/fasc/tend at thigh lvl, rt thigh, init 163
S76.819A	Strain of musc/fasc/tend at thigh lvl, unsp thigh, init 163
S29.01[1,2,9]D	Strain of muscle and tndn of [front, back, unsp] wall of thorax, subsq enc 389
S09.11XA	Strain of muscle and tndn of head, init enc 5, 359
S09.11XS	Strain of muscle and tndn of head, seq 184
S96.11[1,2,9] [A,S]	Strain of muscle and tndn of long extensor muscle of toe at ankle and foot lvl, [rt, lt, unsp] foot, [init enc, seq] 193
S96.01[1,2,9] [A,S]	Strain of muscle and tndn of long flexor muscle of toe at ankle and foot lvl, [rt, lt, unsp] foot, [init enc, seq] 193
S29.01[1,2,9] [A,S]	Strain of muscle and tndn of wall of thorax [front, back, unsp] [Init enc, seq] 184
S16.1XXA	Strain of muscle, fascia and tndn at neck lvl, init 165
S16.1XXS	Strain of muscle, fascia and tndn at neck lvl, seq 184
S39.01[1,2,3]D	Strain of muscle, fascia and tndn of [abd, lwr back, pelvis], subsq enc 391
S76.01[1,2,9]S	Strain of muscle, fascia and tndn of [rt, lt, unsp] hip, seq 190
S39.011A	Strain of muscle, fascia and tndn of abd, init enc 422
S76.01[1,2,9]A	Strain of muscle, fascia and tndn of hip [rt, lt, unsp] init enc 163
S46.11[1,2,9] [A,S]	Strain of muscle, fascia and tndn of long head of biceps [rt, lt, unsp] [init enc, seq] 185
S46.11[1,2,9]D	Strain of muscle, fascia and tndn of long head of biceps, [rt, lt, unsp] arm, subsq enc 392
S39.012A	Strain of muscle, fascia and tndn of lwr back, init 422
S76.31[1,2,9]A	Strain of muscle, fascia and tndn of of the post muscle group at thigh lvl [rt, lt, unsp] init enc 163
S46.21[1,2,9] [A,S]	Strain of muscle, fascia and tndn of oth parts of biceps [rt, lt, unsp] [init enc, seq] 185
S46.21[1,2,9]D	Strain of muscle, fascia and tndn of oth parts of biceps, [rt, lt, unsp] arm, subsq enc 392
S39.013A	Strain of muscle, fascia and tndn of pelvis, init enc 422
S46.31[1,2,9] [A,S]	Strain of muscle, fascia and tndn of triceps [rt, lt, unsp] [init enc, seq] 185
S46.31[1,2,9]D	Strain of muscle, fascia and tndn of triceps, [rt, lt, unsp] arm, subsq enc 392
S39.01[1,2,3] [A,S]	Strain of muscle, fascia, and tndn of [abd, lwr back, pelvis][init enc, seq] 184
S76.31[1,2,9]S	Strain of muscle, fasica and tndn of the post muscle group at thigh lvl, [rt, lt, unsp] thigh, seq 190
S46.01[1,2,9]D	Strain of muscle(s) and tndn(s) of the rotator cuff of [rt, lt, unsp] shldr, subsq enc 392
S46.01[1,2,9] [A,S]	Strain of muscle(s) and tndn(s) of the rotator cuff of shldr [rt, lt, unsp] [init enc, seq] 185
S56.51[1,2,9] [A,S]	Strain of oth extensor muscle, fascia and tndn at forearm lvl, [rt, lt, unsp] arm, [init enc, seq] 187
S56.51[1,2,9]D	Strain of oth extensor muscle, fascia and tndn at forearm lvl, [rt, lt, unsp] arm, subsq enc 393
S56.21[1,2,9] [A,S]	Strain of oth flexor muscle, fascia and tndn at forearm lvl [rt, lt, unspifed] [init enc, seq] 187
S56.21[1,2,9]D	Strain of oth flexor muscle, fascia and tndn at forearm lvl, [rt, lt, unsp] arm, subsq enc 393
S86.81[1,2,9] [A,S]	Strain of oth muscle(s) and tndn(s) at lwr leg lvl, [rt, lt, unsp] leg, [init enc, seq] 192
S86.21[1,2,9] [A,S]	Strain of oth muscle(s) and tndn(s) of ant muscle group at lwr leg lvl, [rt, lt, unsp] leg, [init enc, seq] 192
S86.31[1,2,9] [A,S]	Strain of oth muscle(s) and tndn(s) of peroneal muscle group at lwr leg lvl, [rt, lt, unsp] leg, [init enc, seq] 192
S86.11[1,2,9] [A,S]	Strain of oth muscle(s) and tndn(s) of post muscle group at lwr leg lvl, [rt, lt, unsp] leg, [init enc, seq] 192
S56.81[1,2,9] [A,S]	Strain of oth muscles, fascia and tndns at forearm lvl, [rt, lt, unsp] arm, [init enc, seq] 187
S56.81[1,2,9]D	Strain of oth muscles, fascia and tndns at forearm lvl, [rt, lt, unsp] arm, subsq enc 393
S46.81[1,2,9] [A,S]	Strain of oth muscles, fascia and tndns at shldr and upr arm lvl, [rt, lt, unsp] arm, [init enc, seq] 185
S46.81[1,2,9]D	Strain of oth muscles, fascia and tndns at shldr and upr arm lvl, [rt, lt, unsp] arm, subsq enc 392
S76.81[1,2,9]S	Strain of oth spec muscle, fasica and tndns at thigh lvl, [rt, lt, unsp] thigh, seq 190
S96.81[1,2,9] [A,S]	Strain of oth spec muscles and tndns at ankle and foot lvl, [rt, lt, unsp] foot, [init enc, seq] 193
S96.91[1,2,9] [A,S]	Strain of unsp muscle and tndn at ankle and foot lvl, [rt, lt, unsp] foot, [init enc, seq] 193
S46.91[1,2,9] [A,S]	Strain of unsp muscle, fascia and tndn at shldr and upr arm lvl [rt, lt, unsp] [init enc, seq] 185
S46.91[1,2,9]D	Strain of unsp muscle, fascia and tndn at shldr and upr arm lvl, [rt, lt, unsp] arm, subsq enc 392
S76.91[1,2,9]S	Strain of unsp muscle, fasica and tndns at thigh lvl, [rt, lt, unsp] thigh, seq 190
S86.91[1,2,9] [A,S]	Strain of unsp muscle(s) and tndn(s) at lwr leg lvl, [rt, lt, unsp] leg, [init enc, seq] 192
S56.91[1,2,9] [A,S]	Strain of unsp muscles, fascia and tndns at forearm lvl, [rt, lt, unsp] arm, [init enc, seq] 187

S63.24[0,1]D	Sublux of distal interphalangeal jt of [rt, lt] index finger, subsq enc **395**
S63.24[6,7][A,S]	Sublux of distal interphalangeal jt of [rt, lt] little finger, [init enc, seq] **189**
S63.24[6,7]D	Sublux of distal interphalangeal jt of [rt, lt] little finger, subsq enc **395**
S63.24[2,3][A,S]	Sublux of distal interphalangeal jt of [rt, lt] mid finger, [init enc, seq] **189**
S63.24[2,3]D	Sublux of distal interphalangeal jt of [rt, lt] mid finger, subsq enc **395**
S63.24[4,5][A,S]	Sublux of distal interphalangeal jt of [rt, lt] ring finger, [init enc, seq] **189**
S63.24[4,5]D	Sublux of distal interphalangeal jt of [rt, lt] ring finger, subsq enc **395**
S63.01[1,2,3][A,S]	Sublux of distal radioulnar jt of [rt, lt, unsp] wrist, [init enc, seq] **188**
S63.01[1,2,3]D	Sublux of distal radioulnar jt of [rt, lt] wrist, subsq enc **395**
S93.13[1,2,3][A,S]	Sublux of interphalangeal jt of [rt, lt, unsp] great toe, [init enc, seq] **193**
S93.13[1,2,3]A	Sublux of interphalangeal jt of [rt, lt, unsp] great toe, init enc **430**
S93.13[1,2,3]D	Sublux of interphalangeal jt of [rt, lt, unsp] great toe, subsq enc **399**
S93.13[4,5,6][A,S]	Sublux of interphalangeal jt of [rt, lt, unsp] lesser toe(s), [init enc, seq] **193**
S93.13[4,5,6]A	Sublux of interphalangeal jt of [rt, lt, unsp] lesser toe(s), init enc **430**
S93.13[4,5,6]D	Sublux of interphalangeal jt of [rt, lt, unsp] lesser toe(s), subsq enc **399**
S93.139[A,S]	Sublux of interphalangeal jt of unsp toe(s), [init enc, seq] **193**
S93.139A	Sublux of interphalangeal jt of unsp toe(s), init **430**
S93.139D	Sublux of interphalangeal jt of unsp toe(s), subs **399**
S63.06[1,2,3][A,S]	Sublux of metacarpal (bone), proximal end of [rt, lt, unsp] hand, [init enc, seq] **188**
S63.06[1,2,3]D	Sublux of metacarpal (bone), proximal end of [rt, lt] hand, subsq enc **395**
S63.21[8,9][A,S]	Sublux of metacarpophalangeal jt of [oth, unsp] finger, [init enc, seq] **189**
S63.21[8,9]D	Sublux of metacarpophalangeal jt of [oth, unsp] finger, subsq enc **395**
S63.11[1,2,3][A,S]	Sublux of metacarpophalangeal jt of [rt, lt, unsp] thumb, [init enc, seq] **189**
S63.11[1,2,3]D	Sublux of metacarpophalangeal jt of [rt, lt] thumb, subsq enc **395**
S63.21[0,1][A,S]	Sublux of metacarpophalangeal jt of [rt, lt] index finger, [init enc, seq] **189**
S63.21[0,1]D	Sublux of metacarpophalangeal jt of [rt, lt] index finger, subsq enc **395**
S63.21[6,7][A,S]	Sublux of metacarpophalangeal jt of [rt, lt] little finger, [init enc, seq] **189**
S63.21[6,7]D	Sublux of metacarpophalangeal jt of [rt, lt] little finger, subsq enc **395**
S63.21[2,3][A,S]	Sublux of metacarpophalangeal jt of [rt, lt] mid finger, [init enc, seq] **189**
S63.21[2,3]D	Sublux of metacarpophalangeal jt of [rt, lt] mid finger, subsq enc **395**
S63.21[4,5][A,S]	Sublux of metacarpophalangeal jt of [rt, lt] ring finger, [init enc, seq] **189**
S63.21[4,5]D	Sublux of metacarpophalangeal jt of [rt, lt] ring finger, subsq enc **395**
S93.14[1,2,3][A,S]	Sublux of metatarsophalangeal jt of [rt, lt, unsp] great toe, [init enc, seq] **193**
S93.14[1,2,3]A	Sublux of metatarsophalangeal jt of [rt, lt, unsp] great toe, init enc **430**
S93.14[1,2,3]D	Sublux of metatarsophalangeal jt of [rt, lt, unsp] great toe, subsq enc **399**
S93.14[4,5,6][A,S]	Sublux of metatarsophalangeal jt of [rt, lt, unsp] lesser toe(s), [init enc, seq] **193**
S93.14[4,5,6]A	Sublux of metatarsophalangeal jt of [rt, lt, unsp] lesser toe(s), init enc **430**
S93.14[4,5,6]D	Sublux of metatarsophalangeal jt of [rt, lt, unsp] lesser toe(s), subsq enc **399**
S93.149[A,S]	Sublux of metatarsophalangeal jt of unsp toe(s), [init enc, seq] **193**
S63.03[1,2,3][A,S]	Sublux of midcarpal jt of [rt, lt, unsp] wrist, [init enc, seq] **188**
S63.03[1,2,3]D	Sublux of midcarpal jt of [rt, lt] wrist, subsq enc **395**

S93.149A	Sublux of MTP jt of unsp toe(s), init **430**
S93.149D	Sublux of MTP jt of unsp toe(s), subs **399**
S63.05[1,2,3][A,S]	Sublux of oth carpometacarpal jt of [rt, lt, unsp] hand, [init enc, seq] **188**
S63.05[1,2,3]D	Sublux of oth carpometacarpal jt of [rt, lt] hand, subsq enc **395**
S43.39[1,2,3]D	Sublux of oth parts of [rt, lt, unsp] shldr girdle, subsq enc **391**
S43.39[1,2,3][A,S]	Sublux of oth parts of shldr girdle [rt, lt, unsp] [init enc, seq] **185**
S63.23[8,9][A,S]	Sublux of proximal interphalangeal jt of [oth, unsp] finger, [init enc, seq] **189**
S63.23[8,9]D	Sublux of proximal interphalangeal jt of [oth, unsp] finger, subsq enc **395**
S63.13[1,2,3][A,S]	Sublux of proximal interphalangeal jt of [rt, lt, unsp] thumb, [init enc, seq] **189**
S63.13[1,2,3]D	Sublux of proximal interphalangeal jt of [rt, lt, unsp] thumb, subsq enc **395**
S63.23[0,1][A,S]	Sublux of proximal interphalangeal jt of [rt, lt] index finger, [init enc, seq] **189**
S63.23[0,1]D	Sublux of proximal interphalangeal jt of [rt, lt] index finger, subsq enc **395**
S63.23[6,7][A,S]	Sublux of proximal interphalangeal jt of [rt, lt] little finger, [init enc, seq] **189**
S63.23[6,7]D	Sublux of proximal interphalangeal jt of [rt, lt] little finger, subsq enc **395**
S63.23[2,3][A,S]	Sublux of proximal interphalangeal jt of [rt, lt] mid finger, [init enc, seq] **189**
S63.23[2,3]D	Sublux of proximal interphalangeal jt of [rt, lt] mid finger, subsq enc **395**
S63.23[4,5][A,S]	Sublux of proximal interphalangeal jt of [rt, lt] ring finger, [init enc, seq] **189**
S63.23[4,5]D	Sublux of proximal interphalangeal jt of [rt, lt] ring finger, subsq enc **395**
S63.02[1,2,3][A,S]	Sublux of radiocarpal jt of [rt, lt, unsp] wrist, [init enc, seq] **188**
S63.02[1,2,3]D	Sublux of radiocarpal jt of [rt, lt] wrist, subsq enc **395**
S43.31[1,2,3][A,S]	Sublux of scapula [rt, lt, unsp] [init enc, seq] **185**
O26.72	Sublux of symphysis (pubis) in childbirth **273, 275**
O26.71*	Sublux of symphysis (pubis) in preg **276**
O26.71[1,2,3]	Sublux of symphysis (pubis) in preg, [1st, 2nd, 3rd] trmstr **277**
O26.719	Sublux of symphysis (pubis) in preg, unsp trmstr **280**
O26.73	Sublux of symphysis (pubis) in the puerperium **272, 275**
S93.31[1,2,3][A,S]	Sublux of tarsal jt of [rt, lt, unsp] foot, [init enc, seq] **193**
S93.31[1,2,3]A	Sublux of tarsal jt of [rt, lt, unsp] foot, init enc **430**
S93.31[1,2,3]D	Sublux of tarsal jt of [rt, lt, unsp] foot, subsq enc **399**
S93.32[1,2,3][A,S]	Sublux of tarsometatarsal jt of [rt, lt, unsp] foot, [init enc, seq] **193**
S93.32[1,2,3]A	Sublux of tarsometatarsal jt of [rt, lt, unsp] foot, init enc **430**
S93.32[1,2,3]D	Sublux of tarsometatarsal jt of [rt, lt, unsp] foot, subsq enc **399**
S63.22[8,9][A,S]	Sublux of unsp interphalangeal jt of [oth, unsp] finger, [init enc, seq] **189**
S63.22[8,9]D	Sublux of unsp interphalangeal jt of [oth, unsp] finger, subsq enc **395**
S63.12[1,2,3][A,S]	Sublux of unsp interphalangeal jt of [rt, lt, unsp] thumb, [init enc, seq] **189**
S63.12[1,2,3]D	Sublux of unsp interphalangeal jt of [rt, lt, unsp] thumb, subsq enc **395**
S63.22[0,1][A,S]	Sublux of unsp interphalangeal jt of [rt, lt] index finger, [init enc, seq] **189**
S63.22[0,1]D	Sublux of unsp interphalangeal jt of [rt, lt] index finger, subsq enc **395**
S63.22[6,7][A,S]	Sublux of unsp interphalangeal jt of [rt, lt] little finger, [init enc, seq] **189**
S63.22[6,7]D	Sublux of unsp interphalangeal jt of [rt, lt] little finger, subsq enc **395**
S63.22[2,3][A,S]	Sublux of unsp interphalangeal jt of [rt, lt] mid finger, [init enc, seq] **189**
S63.22[2,3]D	Sublux of unsp interphalangeal jt of [rt, lt] mid finger, subsq enc **395**
S63.22[4,5][A,S]	Sublux of unsp interphalangeal jt of [rt, lt] ring finger, [init enc, seq] **189**
S63.22[4,5]D	Sublux of unsp interphalangeal jt of [rt, lt] ring finger, subsq enc **395**

S43.30[1,2,3]D	Sublux of unsp parts of [rt, lt, unsp] shldr girdle, subsq enc 391
S43.30[1,2,3] [A,S]	Sublux of unsp parts of shldr girdle [rt, lt, unsp] [init enc, seq] 185
M99.2*	Sublux stenosis of neural canal 165
S23.10[0,1]D	[Sublux, Disclocation] of unsp thoracic vertebra, subsq enc 389
S63.0[1,2,3] [1,2,3,4,5,6]A	[Sublux, Disloc] of [distal radioulnar, radiocarpal, midcarpal] jt of [rt, lt, unsp] wrist, init enc 425
S63.1[1,2,3,4] [1,2,3,4,5,6]A	[Sublux, Disloc] of [metacarpophalangeal, unsp interphalangeal, proximal interphalangeal, distal interphalangeal] jt of [rt, lt, unsp] thumb, init enc 425
S43.31[1,2,3,4,5, 6]A	[Sublux, Disloc] of [rt, lt, unsp] scapula, init enc 423
S23.16[0,1,2,3]D	[Sublux, Disloc] of [T10/T11, T11/T12] thoracic vertebra, subsq enc 389
S23.12[0,1,2,3]D	[Sublux, Disloc] of [T2/T3, T3/T4] thoracic vertebra, subsq enc 389
S23.13[0,1,2,3]D	[Sublux, Disloc] of [T4/T5, T5/T6] thoracic vertebra, subsq enc 389
S23.14[0,1,2,3]D	[Sublux, Disloc] of [T6/T7, T7/T8] thoracic vertebra, subsq enc 389
S23.15[0,1,2,3]D	[Sublux, Disloc] of [T8/T9, T9/T10] thoracic vertebra, subsq enc 389
S13.1[0,1,2,3,4,5, 6,7,8][0,1]A	[Sublux, Disloc] of [unsp, C0/C1, C1/C2, C2/C3, C3/C4, C4/C5, C5/C6, C6/C7, C7/T1] cervical vertebrae, init enc 419, 432
S33.1[0,1,2,3,4] [0,1]A	[Sublux, Disloc] of [unsp, L1/L2, L2/L3, L3/L4, L4/L5] lumbar vertebra, init enc 421
S13.11[0,1]A	[Sublux, Disloc] of C0/C1 cervical vertebrae, init enc 165
S13.11[0,1]D	[Sublux, Disloc] of C0/C1 cervical vertebrae, subsq enc 388
S13.11[0,1]S	[Sublux, Disloc] of C0/C1 cervical verterae, seq 184
S13.12[0,1]A	[Sublux, Disloc] of C1/C2 cervical vertebrae, init enc 165
S13.12[0,1]D	[Sublux, Disloc] of C1/C2 cervical vertebrae, subsq enc 388
S13.12[0,1]S	[Sublux, Disloc] of C1/C2 cervical verterae, seq 184
S13.13[0,1]A	[Sublux, Disloc] of C2/C3 cervical vertebrae, init enc 165
S13.13[0,1]D	[Sublux, Disloc] of C2/C3 cervical vertebrae, subsq enc 388
S13.13[0,1]S	[Sublux, Disloc] of C2/C3 cervical verterae, seq 184
S13.14[0,1]A	[Sublux, Disloc] of C3/C4 cervical vertebrae, init enc 165
S13.14[0,1]D	[Sublux, Disloc] of C3/C4 cervical vertebrae, subsq enc 388
S13.14[0,1]S	[Sublux, Disloc] of C3/C4 cervical vertebrae, seq 184
S13.15[0,1]A	[Sublux, Disloc] of C4/C5 cervical vertebrae, init enc 165
S13.15[0,1]D	[Sublux, Disloc] of C4/C5 cervical vertebrae, subsq enc 388
S13.15[0,1]S	[Sublux, Disloc] of C4/C5 cervical verterae, seq 184
S13.16[0,1]A	[Sublux, Disloc] of C5/C6 cervical vertebrae, init enc 165
S13.16[0,1]D	[Sublux, Disloc] of C5/C6 cervical vertebrae, subsq enc 388
S13.16[0,1]S	[Sublux, Disloc] of C5/C6 cervical verterae, seq 184
S13.17[0,1]A	[Sublux, Disloc] of C6/C7 cervical vertebrae, init enc 165
S13.17[0,1]D	[Sublux, Disloc] of C6/C7 cervical vertebrae, subsq enc 388
S13.17[0,1]S	[Sublux, Disloc] of C6/C7 cervical verterae, seq 184
S13.18[0,1]A	[Sublux, Disloc] of C7/T1 cervical vertebrae, init enc 165
S13.18[0,1]D	[Sublux, Disloc] of C7/T1 cervical vertebrae, subsq enc 388
S13.18[0,1]S	[Sublux, Disloc] of C7/T1 cervical verterae, seq 184
S63.04[1,2,3,4,5, 6]A	[Sublux, Disloc] of carpometacarpal jt of [rt, lt, unsp] thumb, init enc 425
S63.07[1,2,3,4,5, 6]A	[Sublux, Disloc] of distal end of [rt, lt, unsp] ulna, init enc 425
S33.11[0,1]S	[Sublux, Disloc] of L1/L2 lumbar vertebra, seq 184
S33.11[0,1]D	[Sublux, Disloc] of L1/L2 lumbar vertebra, subsq enc 390
S33.12[0,1]S	[Sublux, Disloc] of L2/L3 lumbar vertebra, seq 184
S33.12[0,1]D	[Sublux, Disloc] of L2/L3 lumbar vertebra, subsq enc 390
S33.13[0,1]S	[Sublux, Disloc] of L3/L4 lumbar vertebra, seq 184
S33.13[0,1]D	[Sublux, Disloc] of L3/L4 lumbar vertebra, subsq enc 390
S33.14[0,1]S	[Sublux, Disloc] of L4/L5 lumbar vertebra, seq 184
S33.14[0,1]D	[Sublux, Disloc] of L4/L5 lumbar vertebra, subsq enc 390
S63.06[1,2,3,4,5, 6]A	[Sublux, Disloc] of metacarpal (bone), proximal end of [rt, lt, unsp] hand, init enc 425
S63.05[1,2,3,4,5, 6]A	[Sublux, Disloc] of oth carpometacarpal jt of [rt, lt, unsp] hand, init enc 425
S43.39[1,2,3,4,5, 6]A	[Sublux, Disloc] of oth parts of [rt, lt, unsp] shldr girdle, init enc 423
S23.11[0,1]S	[Sublux, Disloc] of T1/T2 thoracic vertebra, seq 184
S23.11[0,1]D	[Sublux, Disloc] of T1/T2 thoracic vertebra, subsq enc 389
S23.11[0,1]A	[Sublux, Disloc] of T1/T2 thoracic vertebrae, init enc 166, 420
S23.16[0,1]S	[Sublux, Disloc] of T10/T11 thoracic vertebra, seq 184
S23.16[0,1]A	[Sublux, Disloc] of T10/T11 thoracic vertebrae, init enc 166, 420
S23.16[2,3]S	[Sublux, Disloc] of T11/T12 thoracic vertebra, seq 184
S23.16[2,3],A	[Sublux, Disloc] of T11/T12 thoracic vertebrae, init enc 420
S23.17[0,1]S	[Sublux, Disloc] of T12/L1 thoracic vertebra, seq 184

S23.17[0,1]D	[Sublux, Disloc] of T12/L1 thoracic vertebra, subsq enc 389
S23.17[0,1]A	[Sublux, Disloc] of T12/L1 thoracic vertebrae, init enc 166, 420
S23.12[0,1]S	[Sublux, Disloc] of T2/T3 thoracic vertebra, seq 184
S23.12[0,1]A	[Sublux, Disloc] of T2/T3 thoracic vertebrae, init enc 166, 420
S23.12[2,3]S	[Sublux, Disloc] of T3/T4 thoracic vertebra, seq 184
S23.12[2,3]A	[Sublux, Disloc] of T3/T4 thoracic vertebrae, init enc 166, 420
S23.13[0,1]S	[Sublux, Disloc] of T4/T5 thoracic vertebra, seq 184
S23.13[0,1]A	[Sublux, Disloc] of T4/T5 thoracic vertebrae, init enc 166, 420
S23.13[2,3]S	[Sublux, Disloc] of T5/T6 thoracic vertebra, seq 184
S23.13[2,3]A	[Sublux, Disloc] of T5/T6 thoracic vertebrae, init enc 166, 420
S23.14[0,1]S	[Sublux, Disloc] of T6/T7 thoracic vertebra, seq 184
S23.14[0,1]A	[Sublux, Disloc] of T6/T7 thoracic vertebrae, init enc 166, 420
S23.14[2,3]S	[Sublux, Disloc] of T7/T8 thoracic vertebra, seq 184
S23.14[2,3]A	[Sublux, Disloc] of T7/T8 thoracic vertebrae, init enc 166, 420
S23.15[0,1]S	[Sublux, Disloc] of T8/T9 thoracic vertebra, seq 184
S23.15[0,1]A	[Sublux, Disloc] of T8/T9 thoracic vertebrae, init enc 166, 420
S23.15[2,3]S	[Sublux, Disloc] of T9/T10 thoracic vertebra, seq 184
S23.15[2,3]A	[Sublux, Disloc] of T9/T10 thoracic vertebrae, init enc 166, 420
S13.10[0,1]A	[Sublux, Disloc] of unsp cervical vertebrae, init enc 165
S13.10[0,1]D	[Sublux, Disloc] of unsp cervical vertebrae, subsq enc 388
S13.10[0,1]S	[Sublux, Disloc] of unsp cervical verterae, seq 184
S33.10[0,1]S	[Sublux, Disloc] of unsp lumbar vertebra, seq 184
S33.10[0,1]D	[Sublux, Disloc] of unsp lumbar vertebra, subsq enc 390
S43.30[1,2,3,4,5, 6]A	[Sublux, Disloc] of unsp parts of [rt, lt, unsp] shldr girdle, init enc 423
S23.10[0,1]A	[Sublux, Disloc] of unsp thoracic vertebra, init enc 166, 420
S23.10[0,1]S	[Sublux, Disloc] of unsp thoracic vertebra, seq 184
H70.01[1,2,3,9]	Subperiosteal abscess of mastoid, [rt, lt, bilat, unsp] ear(s) 283
I22*	Subsq STEMI & NSTEMI mocard infrc 72, 99
R45.851	Suicidal ideations 310
T14.91	Suicide attempt 361, 430
L55*	Sunburn 234
S36.030A	Superf (capsular) lac of spleen, init enc 294
S36.03[0,1,2,9]A	[Superf (capsular), Mod, Major, Unsp] lac of spleen, init enc 286, 422, 432
S36.03[0,1,2,9]S	[Superf (capsular), Mod, Major, Unsp] lac of spleen, seq 117
S36.03[0,1,2,9]D	[Superf (capsular), Mod, Major, Unsp] lac of spleen, subsq enc 390
S00.55[1,2][A,S]	Superf FB of [lip, oral cavity], [init enc, seq] 224
S30.85[0,1,2,3,4, 5,6,7]D	Superf FB of [lwr back and pelvis, abd wall, penis, scrotum and testes, vagina and vulva, unsp ext genital organs male, unsp ext genital organs female, anus], subsq enc 389
S60.45[8,9][A,S]	Superf FB of [oth, unsp] finger, [init enc, seq] 228
S60.45[8,9]D	Superf FB of [oth, unsp] finger, subsq enc 394
S30.85[2,3][A,S]	Superf FB of [penis, scrotum and testes], [init enc, seq] 226
S20.45[1,2,9] [A,S]	Superf FB of [rt, lt, unsp] back wall of thorax, [init enc, seq] 225
S20.45[1,2,9]D	Superf FB of [rt, lt, unsp] back wall of thorax, subsq enc 388
S00.45[1,2,9] [A,S]	Superf FB of [rt, lt, unsp] ear, [init enc, seq] 224
S50.35[1,2,9] [A,S]	Superf FB of [rt, lt, unsp] elbow, [init enc, seq] 227
S50.35[1,2,9]D	Superf FB of [rt, lt, unsp] elbow, subsq enc 392
S00.25[1,2,9]A	Superf FB of [rt, lt, unsp] eyelid and periocular area, init enc 46
S00.25[1,2,9]S	Superf FB of [rt, lt, unsp] eyelid and periocular area, seq 224
S50.85[1,2,9] [A,S]	Superf FB of [rt, lt, unsp] forearm, [init enc, seq] 227
S50.85[1,2,9]D	Superf FB of [rt, lt, unsp] forearm, subsq enc 392
S20.35[1,2,9] [A,S]	Superf FB of [rt, lt, unsp] front wall of thorax, [init enc, seq] 225
S20.35[1,2,9]D	Superf FB of [rt, lt, unsp] front wall of thorax, subsq enc 388
S60.55[1,2,9] [A,S]	Superf FB of [rt, lt, unsp] hand, [init enc, seq] 228
S60.55[1,2,9]D	Superf FB of [rt, lt, unsp] hand, subsq enc 394
S40.25[1,2,9] [A,S]	Superf FB of [rt, lt, unsp] shldr, [init enc, seq] 227
S40.25[1,2,9]D	Superf FB of [rt, lt, unsp] shldr, subsq enc 391
S60.35[1,2,9] [A,S]	Superf FB of [rt, lt, unsp] thumb, [init enc, seq] 228
S60.35[1,2,9]D	Superf FB of [rt, lt, unsp] thumb, subsq enc 394
S40.85[1,2,9] [A,S]	Superf FB of [rt, lt, unsp] upr arm, [init enc, seq] 227
S40.85[1,2,9]D	Superf FB of [rt, lt, unsp] upr arm, subsq enc 391

S60.85[1,2,9][A,S]	Superf FB of [rt, lt, unsp] wrist, [init enc, seq] 228	
S60.85[1,2,9]D	Superf FB of [rt, lt, unsp] wrist, subsq enc 394	
S60.45[0,1][A,S]	Superf FB of [rt, lt] index finger, [init enc, seq] 228	
S60.45[0,1]D	Superf FB of [rt, lt] index finger, subsq enc 394	
S60.45[6,7][A,S]	Superf FB of [rt, lt] little finger, [init enc, seq] 228	
S60.45[6,7]D	Superf FB of [rt, lt] little finger, subsq enc 394	
S60.45[2,3][A,S]	Superf FB of [rt, lt] mid finger, [init enc, seq] 228	
S60.45[2,3]D	Superf FB of [rt, lt] mid finger, subsq enc 394	
S60.45[4,5][A,S]	Superf FB of [rt, lt] ring finger, [init enc, seq] 228	
S60.45[4,5]D	Superf FB of [rt, lt] ring finger, subsq enc 394	
S30.851[A,S]	Superf FB of abd wall, [init enc, seq] 226	
S30.857[A,S]	Superf FB of anus, [init enc, seq] 226	
S20.15[1,2,9][A,S]	Superf FB of breast, [rt, lt, unsp] breast, [init enc, seq] 225	
S20.15[1,2,9]D	Superf FB of breast, [rt, lt, unsp] breast, subsq enc 388	
S30.850[A,S]	Superf FB of lwr back and pelvis, [init enc, seq] 226	
S00.35X[A,S]	Superf FB of nose, [init enc, seq] 224	
S00.85X[A,S]	Superf FB of oth part of head, [init enc, seq] 224	
S00.05X[A,S]	Superf FB of scalp, [init enc, seq] 224	
S10.15X[A,S]	Superf FB of throat, [init enc, seq] 225	
S30.85[5,6][A,S]	Superf FB of unsp ext genital organs, [male, female], [init enc, seq] 226	
S00.95X[A,S]	Superf FB of unsp part of head, [init enc, seq] 224	
S20.95X[A,S]	Superf FB of unsp parts of thorax, [init enc, seq] 225	
S30.854[A,S]	Superf FB of vagina and vulva, [init enc, seq] 226	
S90.55[1,2,9][A,S]	Superf FB, [rt, lt, unsp] ankle, [init enc, seq] 230	
S90.85[1,2,9][A,S]	Superf FB, [rt, lt, unsp] foot, [init enc, seq] 230	
S90.45[1,2,3][A,S]	Superf FB, [rt, lt, unsp] great toe, [init enc, seq] 230	
S90.45[1,2,3]A	Superf FB, [rt, lt, unsp] great toe, init enc 428	
S90.45[1,2,3]D	Superf FB, [rt, lt, unsp] great toe, subsq enc 399	
S70.25[1,2,9][A,S]	Superf FB, [rt, lt, unsp] hip, [init enc, seq] 229	
S80.25[1,2,9][A,S]	Superf FB, [rt, lt, unsp] knee, [init enc, seq] 229	
S90.45[4,5,6][A,S]	Superf FB, [rt, lt, unsp] lesser toe(s), [init enc, seq] 230	
S90.45[4,5,6]A	Superf FB, [rt, lt, unsp] lesser toe(s), init enc 428	
S90.45[4,5,6]D	Superf FB, [rt, lt, unsp] lesser toe(s), subsq enc 399	
S80.85[1,2,9][A,S]	Superf FB, [rt, lt, unsp] lwr leg, [init enc, seq] 229	
S70.35[1,2,9][A,S]	Superf FB, [rt, lt, unsp] thigh, [init enc, seq] 229	
S10.8[5,7]X[A,S]	[Superf FB, oth superf bite] of oth spec part of neck, [init enc, seq] 225	
S10.9[5,7]X[A,S]	[Superf FB, oth superf bite] of unsp part of neck, [init enc, seq] 225	
T33.[1,2,3]XX[A,S]	Superf frostbite of [neck, thorax, abd wall, lwr back and pelvis], [init enc, seq] 368	
T33.0[2,9]X[A,S]	Superf frostbite of [nose, oth part of head], [init enc, seq] 368	
T33.81[1,2,9][A,S]	Superf frostbite of [rt, lt, unsp] ankle, [init enc, seq] 368	
T33.81[1,2,9]D	Superf frostbite of [rt, lt, unsp] ankle, subsq enc 402	
T33.01[1,2,9][A,S]	Superf frostbite of [rt, lt, unsp] ear, [init enc, seq] 368	
T33.01[1,2,9]D	Superf frostbite of [rt, lt, unsp] ear, subsq enc 402	
T33.53[1,2,9][A,S]	Superf frostbite of [rt, lt, unsp] fingers, [init enc, seq] 368	
T33.53[1,2,9]D	Superf frostbite of [rt, lt, unsp] fingers, subsq enc 402	
T33.82[1,2,9][A,S]	Superf frostbite of [rt, lt, unsp] foot, [init enc, seq] 368	
T33.82[1,2,9]D	Superf frostbite of [rt, lt, unsp] foot, subsq enc 403	
T33.52[1,2,9][A,S]	Superf frostbite of [rt, lt, unsp] hand, [init enc, seq] 368	
T33.52[1,2,9]D	Superf frostbite of [rt, lt, unsp] hand, subsq enc 402	
T33.83[1,2,9][A,S]	Superf frostbite of [rt, lt, unsp] toe(s), [init enc, seq] 368	
T33.83[1,2,9]D	Superf frostbite of [rt, lt, unsp] toe(s), subsq enc 403	
T33.51[1,2,9][A,S]	Superf frostbite of [rt, lt, unsp] wrist, [init enc, seq] 368	
T33.51[1,2,9]D	Superf frostbite of [rt, lt, unsp] wrist, subsq enc 402	
T33.9[0,9]X[A,S]	Superf frostbite of [unsp, oth] sites, [init enc, seq] 368	
T33.9[0,9]XD	Superf frostbite of [unsp, oth] sites, subsq enc 403	
T33.4[0,1,2]X[A,S]	Superf frostbite of [unsp, rt, lt] arm, [init enc, seq] 368	
T33.4[0,1,2]XD	Superf frostbite of [unsp, rt, lt] arm, subsq enc 402	
T33.6[0,1,2]X[A,S]	Superf frostbite of [unsp, rt, lt] hip & thigh, [init enc, seq] 368	
T33.6[0,1,2]XD	Superf frostbite of [unsp, rt, lt] hip & thigh, subsq enc 402	
T33.7[0,1,2]X[A,S]	Superf frostbite of [unsp, rt, lt] knee and lwr leg, [init enc, seq] 368	
T33.7[0,1,2]XD	Superf frostbite of [unsp, rt, lt] knee and lwr leg, subsq enc 402	
T33.1XXD	Superf frostbite of neck, subsq enc 402	
T33.02XD	Superf frostbite of nose, subsq enc 402	
T33.09XD	Superf frostbite of oth part of head, subs enc 402	
T33.2XXD	Superf frostbite of thorax, subsq enc 402	
O22.2[1,2,3]	Superf thrombophlebitis in preg, [1st, 2nd, 3rd] trmstr 277	
O22.20	Superf thrombophlebitis in preg, unsp trmstr 280	
T33.3XXD	Superfic frostbite of abd wall, lwr back and pelvis, subs 402	
S43.43[1,2,9]A	Superior glenoid labrum lesion of [rt, lt, unsp] shldr, init enc 423	
S43.43[1,2,9]D	Superior glenoid labrum lesion of [rt, lt, unsp] shldr, subsq enc 391	
S43.43[1,2,9][A,S]	Superior glenoid labrum lesion of shldr [rt, lt, unsp] [init enc, seq] 185	
K00.1	Supernumerary teeth 4	
O09.5*	Supervision of elderly primigravida and multigravida 280	
O09.7*	Supervision of high risk preg d/t social problems 280	
O09.9*	Supervision of high risk preg, unsp 280	
O09.8*	Supervision of oth high risk pregnancies 280	
O09.40	Supervision of preg w grand multiparity, unsp trmstr 280	
O09.4[1,2,3]	Supervision of preg w/ grand multiparity, [1st, 2nd, 3rd] trmstr 277, 279	
O09.0*	Supervision of preg with history of infertility 280	
O09.3*	Supervision of preg with insufficient antenatal care 280	
O09.6*	Supervision of young primigravida and multigravida 280	
O92.5	Suppressed lactation 272, 276	
H66*	Suppurative and unsp otitis media 57	
J04.3*	Supraglottitis, unsp 3, 57	
O09.1*	Suprvsn of preg w history of ectopic or molar preg 280	
O09.2*	Suprvsn of preg w poor reprodctv or obstetric history 280	
J84.83	Surfactant mutations of the lung 284	
A82.0	Sylvatic rabies 10, 15	
R65*	Symp and signs specifically assoc w sys inflam and infxn 309	
H44.13*	Sympathetic uveitis 46	
A52.73	Symptomatic late syphilis of oth respiratory organs 308	
A52.10	Symptomatic neurosyphilis, unsp 32	
R63*	Symptoms and signs concerning food and fluid intake 246	
R46*	Symptoms and signs involving appearance and behav 412	
R55	Syncope and collapse 102	
P70.1	Synd of infant of a diabetic mother 288	
P70.0	Synd of infant of mother with gestational diabetes 288	
Q70*	Syndactyly 195	
B83.3	Syngamiasis 309	
M65*	Synovitis and tenosynovitis 167	
O98.12	Syphilis compl childbirth 274	
O98.11[1,2,3]	Syphilis compl preg, [1st, 2nd, 3rd] trmstr 274, 277	
O98.13	Syphilis compl the puerperium 274, 276	
A52.77	Syphilis of bone and jt 163	
A52.75	Syphilis of kidney and ureter 255	
A52.74	Syphilis of liver and oth viscera 124	
A52.72	Syphilis of lung and bronchus 67	
A52.78	Syphilis of oth musculoskeletal tissue 167	
A52.01	Syphilitic aneurysm of aorta 102	
A52.02	Syphilitic aortitis 102	
A52.04	Syphilitic cerebral arteritis 103	
A52.03	Syphilitic endocarditis 99	
G95.0	Syringomyelia and syringobulbia 32	
G13.8	Systemic atrophy affected cnsl in oth dz classd elsw 32	
G13.2	Systemic atrophy primarily affecting the cnsl in myxedema 32	
M36.8	Systemic d/o of conn tiss in oth dz classd elsw 164	
M35.9	Systemic involvement of connective tissue, unsp 164	
M32*	Systemic lupus erythematosus (SLE) 164	

L87*	Transepidermal elimination d/o 234	
J95.84	Transfusion-related acute lung inj (TRALI) 69	
D60.1	Transient acquired pure red cell aplasia 293	
R40.4	Transient alter of awareness 310	
G45.9	Transient cerebral ischemic attack, unsp 33	
G45.4	Transient global amnesia 33	
D80.7	Transient hypogammaglobulinemia of infancy 294	
P29.4	Transient myocardial ischemia in newborn 288	
P94.0	Transient neonatal myasthenia gravis 282	
P61.5	Transient neonatal neutropenia 288	
P61.0	Transient neonatal thrombocytopenia 282	
R29.5	Transient paralysis 38	
P22.1	Transient tachypnea of newborn 288	
H53.1[2,3][1,2,3,9]	[Transient, Sudden] visual loss, [rt, lt, bilat, unsp] eye 45	
P70.9	Transitory d/o of carbohydrate metab of newborn, unsp 288	
P74.6	Transitory hyperammonemia of newborn 288	
P76.1	Transitory ileus of newborn 288	
P74.9	Transitory metabolic disturbance of newborn, unsp 288	
P71*	Transitory neonatal d/o of calcium and magnesium metab 282	
P72.9	Transitory neonatal endocrine d/o, unsp 288	
P72.1	Transitory neonatal hyperthyroidism 282	
P74.5	Transitory tyrosinemia of newborn 288	
Z94.9	Transplanted organ and tissue status, unsp 413	
T79.[2,4,5,6,7]XXD	Traum [2ndary and recurrent hemor and seroma, shock, anuria, ischemia of muscle, SQ emphysema], subsq enc 410	
S27.[0,1,2]XXA	Traum [pneumothorax, hemothorax, hemopneumothorax], init enc 286, 421, 432	
S27.[0,1,2]XXS	Traum [pneumothorax, hemothorax, hemopneumothorax], seq 69	
S28.1XX[A,S]	Traum amp (partial) of part of thorax, except breast, [init enc, seq] 225	
S08.89X[A,S]	Traum amp of oth parts of head, [init enc, seq] 225	
S08.89XA	Traum amp of oth parts of head, init enc 419	
S08.89XD	Traum amp of oth parts of head, subs enc 387	
S28.1XXA	Traum amp of part of thorax, except breast, init 421	
S28.1XXD	Traum amp of part of thorax, except breast, subs 389	
T79.5XXA	Traum anuria, init enc 254, 287, 430	
T79.5XXS	Traum anuria, seq 361	
S06.1X1A	Traum cerebral edema w LOC of 30 min or less, init 37	
S06.1X2A	Traum cerebral edema w LOC of 31-59 min, init 37	
S06.1X[5,6]D	Traum cerebral edema w/ LOC [> 24 hrs w/ return to pre-existing conscious lvl, > 24 hrs w/o return to pre-existing conscious lvl w/ patient surviving], subsq enc 386	
S06.1X[5,6]A	Traum cerebral edema w/ LOC > 24 hrs [w/ return to pre-existing conscious lvl, w/o return to pre-existing conscious lvl w/ patient surviving], init enc 36, 418, 430	
S06.1X[5,6]S	Traum cerebral edema w/ LOC of [> 24 hrs w/ return to pre-existing conscious lvl, > 24 hrs w/o return to pre-existing conscious lvl w/ patient surviving], seq 39	
S06.1X[3,4,5,6]A	Traum cerebral edema w/ LOC of [1 hr to 5 hrs 59 min, 6 hrs to 24 hrs, > 24 hrs w/ return to pre-existing conscious lvl, > 24 hrs w/o return to pre-existing conscious lvl patient surviving], init enc 35	
S06.1X[1,2,3,4]A	Traum cerebral edema w/ LOC of [30 min or less, 31 min to 59 min, 1 hr to 5 hrs 59 min, 6 hrs to 24 hrs], init enc 36, 418, 430	
S06.1X[1,2,3,4]D	Traum cerebral edema w/ LOC of [30 min or less, 31 min to 59 min, 1 hr to 5 hrs 59 min, 6 hrs to 24 hrs], subsq enc 386	
S06.1X[1,2,3,4]S	Traum cerebral edema w/ LOC of [30 min or less, 31-59 min, 1 hr to 5 hrs 59 min, 6 hrs to 24 hrs], seq 39	
S06.1X[7,8,9]A	Traum cerebral edema w/ LOC of [any dur w/ death d/t brain inj prior to regain cnscness, any dur w/ death d/t oth cause prior to regain cnscness, unsp dur], init enc 35, 36, 418, 430	
S06.1X[7,8,9]S	Traum cerebral edema w/ LOC of [any dur w/ death d/t brain inj prior to regain cnscness, any dur w/ death d/t oth cause prior to regain cnscness, unsp dur], seq 39	
S06.1X[7,8,9]D	Traum cerebral edema w/ LOC of [any dur w/ death d/t brain inj prior to regain cnscness, any dur w/ death d/t oth cause prior to regain cnscness, unsp dur], subsq enc 386	
S06.1X0A	Traum cerebral edema w/o LOC, init 36, 37, 418, 430	
S06.1X0S	Traum cerebral edema w/o LOC, seq 39	
S06.1X0D	Traum cerebral edema w/o LOC, subs 386	
T79.A[3,9]XA	Traum compartment synd of [abd, oth sites], init enc 374, 430	
T79.A[3,9]XS	Traum compartment synd of [abd, oth sites], seq 361	
T79.A[3,9]XD	Traum compartment synd of [abd, oth sites], subsq enc 410	
T79.A2[1,2,9]A	Traum compartment synd of [rt, lt, unsp] lwr extr, init enc 374, 430, 437	
T79.A2[1,2,9]S	Traum compartment synd of [rt, lt, unsp] lwr extr, seq 361	
T79.A2[1,2,9]D	Traum compartment synd of [rt, lt, unsp] lwr extr, subsq enc 410	
T79.A1[1,2,9]A	Traum compartment synd of [rt, lt, unsp] upr extr, init enc 374, 430, 435	
T79.A1[1,2,9]S	Traum compartment synd of [rt, lt, unsp] upr extr, seq 361	
T79.A1[1,2,9]D	Traum compartment synd of [rt, lt, unsp] upr extr, subsq enc 410	
T79.A3XA	Traum compartment synd of abd, init enc 432	
S27.2XXA	Traum hemopneumothorax, init enc 68	
S27.2XXD	Traum hemopneumothorax, subsq enc 389	
S06.361A	Traum hemor cereb, w LOC of 30 min or less, init 37	
S06.362A	Traum hemor cereb, w LOC of 31-59 min, init 37	
S06.360A	Traum hemor cereb, w/o LOC, init 36, 37, 418, 431	
S06.360S	Traum hemor cereb, w/o LOC, seq 39	
S06.360D	Traum hemor cereb, w/o LOC, subs 387	
S06.351A	Traum hemor lt cerebrum w LOC of 30 min or less, init 37	
S06.352A	Traum hemor lt cerebrum w LOC of 31-59 min, init 37	
S06.350A	Traum hemor lt cerebrum w/o LOC, init 36, 37, 418, 431	
S06.350S	Traum hemor lt cerebrum w/o LOC, seq 39	
S06.350D	Traum hemor lt cerebrum w/o LOC, subs 387	
S06.3[4,5,6]5A	Traum hemor of [rt, lt, unsp] cerebrum w/ LOC, > 24 hrs w/ return to pre-existing conscious lvl, init enc 11, 15	
S06.3[4,5,6]6A	Traum hemor of [rt, lt, unsp] cerebrum w/ LOC, > 24 hrs w/o return to pre-existing conscious lvl w/ patient surviving, init enc 11, 15	
S06.3[4,5,6]1A	Traum hemor of [rt, lt, unsp] cerebrum w/ LOC, 30 min or less, init enc 11, 15	
S06.3[4,5,6]2A	Traum hemor of [rt, lt, unsp] cerebrum w/ LOC, 31 to 59 min, init enc 11, 15	
S06.3[4,5,6]4A	Traum hemor of [rt, lt, unsp] cerebrum w/ LOC, 6 to 24 hrs, init enc 11, 15	
S06.3[4,5,6]7A	Traum hemor of [rt, lt, unsp] cerebrum w/ LOC, any dur w/ death d/t brain inj prior to regain cnscness, init enc 11, 15	
S06.3[4,5,6]8A	Traum hemor of [rt, lt, unsp] cerebrum w/ LOC, any dur w/ death d/t oth cause prior to regain cnscness, init enc 11, 15	
S06.3[4,5,6]9A	Traum hemor of [rt, lt, unsp] cerebrum w/ LOC, unsp dur, init enc 11, 15	
S06.3[4,5,6]0A	Traum hemor of [rt, lt, unsp] cerebrum w/o LOC, init enc 11, 15	
S06.3[4,5,6]3A	Traum hemor of [rt, lt, unsp] rt cerebrum w/ LOC, 1 to 5 hrs 59 min, init enc 11, 15	
S06.36[5,6]D	Traum hemor of cerebrum, unsp, w/ LOC [> 24 hrs w/ return to pre-existing conscious lvl, > 24 hrs w/o return to pre-existing conscious lvl w/ patient surviving], subsq enc 387	
S06.36[5,6]A	Traum hemor of cerebrum, unsp, w/ LOC > 24 hrs [w/ return to pre-existing conscious lvl, w/o return to pre-existing conscious lvl w/ patient surviving], init enc 36, 418, 431	
S06.36[5,6]S	Traum hemor of cerebrum, unsp, w/ LOC of [> 24 hrs w/ return to pre-existing conscious lvl, > 24 hrs w/o return to pre-existing conscious lvl w/ patient surviving], seq 39	
S06.36[3,4,5,6]A	Traum hemor of cerebrum, unsp, w/ LOC of [1 hr to 5 hrs 59 min, 6 hrs to 24 hrs, > 24 hrs w/ return to pre-existing conscious lvl, > 24 hrs w/o return to pre-existing conscious lvl patient surviving], init enc 35	
S06.36[1,2,3,4]A	Traum hemor of cerebrum, unsp, w/ LOC of [30 min or less, 31 min to 59 min, 1 hr to 5 hrs 59 min, 6 hrs to 24 hrs], init enc 36, 418, 431	
S06.36[1,2,3,4]D	Traum hemor of cerebrum, unsp, w/ LOC of [30 min or less, 31 min to 59 min, 1 hr to 5 hrs 59 min, 6 hrs to 24 hrs], subsq enc 387	
S06.36[1,2,3,4]S	Traum hemor of cerebrum, unsp, w/ LOC of [30 min or less, 31-59 min, 1 hr to 5 hrs 59 min, 6 hrs to 24 hrs], seq 39	
S06.36[7,8,9]A	Traum hemor of cerebrum, unsp, w/ LOC of [any dur w/ death d/t brain inj prior to regain cnscness, any dur w/ death d/t oth cause prior to regain cnscness, unsp dur], init enc 35, 36, 418, 431	
S06.36[7,8,9]S	Traum hemor of cerebrum, unsp, w/ LOC of [any dur w/ death d/t brain inj prior to regain cnscness, any dur w/ death d/t oth cause prior to regain cnscness, unsp dur], seq 39	
S06.36[7,8,9]D	Traum hemor of cerebrum, unsp, w/ LOC of [any dur w/ death d/t brain inj prior to regain cnscness, any dur w/ death d/t oth cause prior to regain cnscness, unsp dur], subsq enc 387	
S06.35[5,6]D	Traum hemor of lt cerebrum w/ LOC [> 24 hrs w/ return to pre-existing conscious lvl, > 24 hrs w/o return to pre-existing conscious lvl w/ patient surviving], subsq enc 387	
S06.35[5,6]A	Traum hemor of lt cerebrum w/ LOC > 24 hrs [w/ return to pre-existing conscious lvl, w/o return to pre-existing conscious lvl w/ patient surviving], init enc 36, 418, 431	

Code	Description
S06.35[5,6]S	Traum hemor of lt cerebrum w/ LOC of [> 24 hrs w/ return to pre-existing conscious lvl, > 24 hrs w/o return to pre-existing conscious lvl w/ patient surviving], seq **39**
S06.35[3,4,5,6]A	Traum hemor of lt cerebrum w/ LOC of [1 hr to 5 hrs 59 min, 6 hrs to 24 hrs, > 24 hrs w/ return to pre-existing conscious lvl, > 24 hrs w/o return to pre-existing conscious lvl patient surviving], init enc **35**
S06.35[1,2,3,4]A	Traum hemor of lt cerebrum w/ LOC of [30 min or less, 31 min to 59 min, 1 hr to 5 hrs 59 min, 6 hrs to 24 hrs], init enc **36, 418, 431**
S06.35[1,2,3,4]D	Traum hemor of lt cerebrum w/ LOC of [30 min or less, 31 min to 59 min, 1 hr to 5 hrs 59 min, 6 hrs to 24 hrs], subsq enc **387**
S06.35[1,2,3,4]S	Traum hemor of lt cerebrum w/ LOC of [30 min or less, 31-59 min, 1 hr to 5 hrs 59 min, 6 hrs to 24 hrs], seq **39**
S06.35[7,8,9]A	Traum hemor of lt cerebrum w/ LOC of [any dur w/ death d/t brain inj prior to regain cnscness, any dur w/ death d/t oth cause prior to regain cnscness, unsp dur], init enc **35, 36, 418, 431**
S06.35[7,8,9]S	Traum hemor of lt cerebrum w/ LOC of [any dur w/ death d/t brain inj prior to regain cnscness, any dur w/ death d/t oth cause prior to regain cnscness, unsp dur], seq **39**
S06.35[7,8,9]D	Traum hemor of lt cerebrum w/ LOC of [any dur w/ death d/t brain inj prior to regain cnscness, any dur w/ death d/t oth cause prior to regain cnscness, unsp dur], subsq enc **387**
S06.34[5,6]D	Traum hemor of rt cerebrum w/ LOC [> 24 hrs w/ return to pre-existing conscious lvl, > 24 hrs w/o return to pre-existing conscious lvl w/ patient surviving], subsq enc **387**
S06.34[5,6]A	Traum hemor of rt cerebrum w/ LOC > 24 hrs [w/ return to pre-existing conscious lvl, w/o return to pre-existing conscious lvl w/ patient surviving], init enc **36, 418, 431**
S06.34[5,6]S	Traum hemor of rt cerebrum w/ LOC of [> 24 hrs w/ return to pre-existing conscious lvl, > 24 hrs w/o return to pre-existing conscious lvl w/ patient surviving], seq **39**
S06.34[3,4,5,6]A	Traum hemor of rt cerebrum w/ LOC of [1 hr to 5 hrs 59 min, 6 hrs to 24 hrs, > 24 hrs w/ return to pre-existing conscious lvl, > 24 hrs w/o return to pre-existing conscious lvl patient surviving], init enc **35**
S06.34[1,2,3,4]A	Traum hemor of rt cerebrum w/ LOC of [30 min or less, 31 min to 59 min, 1 hr to 5 hrs 59 min, 6 hrs to 24 hrs], init enc **36, 418, 431**
S06.34[1,2,3,4]D	Traum hemor of rt cerebrum w/ LOC of [30 min or less, 31 min to 59 min, 1 hr to 5 hrs 59 min, 6 hrs to 24 hrs], subsq enc **387**
S06.34[1,2,3,4]S	Traum hemor of rt cerebrum w/ LOC of [30 min or less, 31-59 min, 1 hr to 5 hrs 59 min, 6 hrs to 24 hrs], seq **39**
S06.34[7,8,9]A	Traum hemor of rt cerebrum w/ LOC of [any dur w/ death d/t brain inj prior to regain cnscness, any dur w/ death d/t oth cause prior to regain cnscness, unsp dur], init enc **35, 36, 418, 431**
S06.34[7,8,9]S	Traum hemor of rt cerebrum w/ LOC of [any dur w/ death d/t brain inj prior to regain cnscness, any dur w/ death d/t oth cause prior to regain cnscness, unsp dur], seq **39**
S06.34[7,8,9]D	Traum hemor of rt cerebrum w/ LOC of [any dur w/ death d/t brain inj prior to regain cnscness, any dur w/ death d/t oth cause prior to regain cnscness, unsp dur], subsq enc **387**
S06.341A	Traum hemor rt cerebrum w LOC of 30 min or less, init **37**
S06.342A	Traum hemor rt cerebrum w LOC of 31-59 min, init **37**
S06.340A	Traum hemor rt cerebrum w/o LOC, init **36, 37, 418, 431**
S06.340S	Traum hemor rt cerebrum w/o LOC, seq **39**
S06.340D	Traum hemor rt cerebrum w/o LOC, subs **387**
S27.1XXA	Traum hemothorax, init enc **68**
S27.1XXD	Traum hemothorax, subsq enc **389**
T79.6XXA	Traum ischemia of muscle, init enc **204, 430, 435**
T79.6XXS	Traum ischemia of muscle, seq **361**
S27.0XXA	Traum pneumothorax, init enc **68**
S27.0XXD	Traum pneumothorax, subsq enc **389**
S63.3[2,3][1,2,9]A	Traum rupture of [rt, lt, unsp] [radiocarpal, ulnocarpal (palmar) lgmt, init enc **425**
S53.2[0,1,2]X[A,S]	Traum rupture of [rt, lt, unsp] radial collat lgmt, [init enc, seq] **186**
S63.32[1,2,9]D	Traum rupture of [rt, lt, unsp] radiocarpal lgmt, subsq enc **396**
S53.3[0,1,2]X[A,S]	Traum rupture of [rt, lt, unsp] ulnar collat lgmt, [init enc, seq] **186**
S63.33[1,2,9]D	Traum rupture of [rt, lt, unsp] ulnocarpal (palmar) lgmt, subsq enc **396**
S09.2[1,2]XS	Traum rupture of [rt, lt] ear drum, seq **225**
S63.4[0,1,2][0,1,2,3,4,5,6,7,8,9]A	Traum rupture of [unsp, collat, palmar] lgmt of [rt index, lt index, rt mid, lt mid, rt ring, lt ring, rt little, lt little, oth, unsp] finger at metacarpophalangeal and interphalangeal jt, init enc **425**
S63.3[0,1][1,2,9]A	Traum rupture of [unsp, collat] lgmt of [rt, lt, unsp] wrist, init enc **425**
S53.[2,3][0,1,2]XA	Traum rupture of [unsp, rt, lt] [radial, ulnar] collat lgmt, init enc **424**
S09.2[0,1,2]XA	Traum rupture of [unsp, rt, lt] ear drum, init enc **58, 419**
S09.2[0,1,2]XD	Traum rupture of [unsp, rt, lt] ear drum, subsq enc **387**
S53.2[0,1,2]XD	Traum rupture of [unsp, rt, lt] radial collat lgmt, subsq enc **392**
S53.3[0,1,2]XD	Traum rupture of [unsp, rt, lt] ulnar collat lgmt, subsq enc **392**
S13.0XXA	Traum rupture of cervical intervertebral disc, init **165, 419, 432**
S13.0XXS	Traum rupture of cervical intervertebral disc, seq **184**
S13.0XXD	Traum rupture of cervical intervertebral disc, subs **388**
S63.41[8,9][A,S]	Traum rupture of collat lgmt of [oth, unsp] finger at metacarpophalangeal and interphalangeal jt, [init enc, seq] **189**
S63.41[8,9]D	Traum rupture of collat lgmt of [oth, unsp] finger at metacarpophalangeal and interphalangeal jt, subsq enc **396**
S63.31[1,2,9][A,S]	Traum rupture of collat lgmt of [rt, lt, unsp] wrist, [init enc, seq] **189**
S63.31[1,2,9]D	Traum rupture of collat lgmt of [rt, lt, unsp] wrist, subsq enc **396**
S63.41[0,1][A,S]	Traum rupture of collat lgmt of [rt, lt] index finger at metacarpophalangeal and interphalangeal jt, [init enc, seq] **189**
S63.41[0,1]D	Traum rupture of collat lgmt of [rt, lt] index finger at metacarpophalangeal and interphalangeal jt, subsq enc **396**
S63.41[6,7][A,S]	Traum rupture of collat lgmt of [rt, lt] little finger at metacarpophalangeal and interphalangeal jt, [init enc, seq] **189**
S63.41[6,7]D	Traum rupture of collat lgmt of [rt, lt] little finger at metacarpophalangeal and interphalangeal jt, subsq enc **396**
S63.41[2,3][A,S]	Traum rupture of collat lgmt of [rt, lt] mid finger at metacarpophalangeal and interphalangeal jt, [init enc, seq] **189**
S63.41[2,3]D	Traum rupture of collat lgmt of [rt, lt] mid finger at metacarpophalangeal and interphalangeal jt, subsq enc **396**
S63.41[4,5][A,S]	Traum rupture of collat lgmt of [rt, lt] ring finger at metacarpophalangeal and interphalangeal jt, [init enc, seq] **189**
S63.41[4,5]D	Traum rupture of collat lgmt of [rt, lt] ring finger at metacarpophalangeal and interphalangeal jt, subsq enc **396**
S33.0XXA	Traum rupture of lumbar intervertebral disc, init enc **166, 421**
S33.0XXS	Traum rupture of lumbar intervertebral disc, seq **184**
S33.0XXD	Traum rupture of lumbar intervertebral disc, subs enc **390**
S63.49[8,9][A,S]	Traum rupture of oth lgmt of [oth, unsp] finger at metacarpophalangeal and interphalangeal jt, [init enc, seq] **190**
S63.49[8,9]D	Traum rupture of oth lgmt of [oth, unsp] finger at metacarpophalangeal and interphalangeal jt, subsq enc **396**
S63.49[0,1,2,3,4,5,6,7,8,9]A	Traum rupture of oth lgmt of [rt index, lt index, rt mid, lt mid, rt ring, lt ring, rt little, lt little, oth, unsp] finger at metacarpophalangeal and interphalangeal jt, init enc **425**
S63.39[1,2,9][A,S]	Traum rupture of oth lgmt of [rt, lt, unsp] wrist, [init enc, seq] **189**
S63.39[1,2,9]A	Traum rupture of oth lgmt of [rt, lt, unsp] wrist, init enc **425**
S63.39[1,2,9]D	Traum rupture of oth lgmt of [rt, lt, unsp] wrist, subsq enc **396**
S63.49[0,1][A,S]	Traum rupture of oth lgmt of [rt, lt] index finger at metacarpophalangeal and interphalangeal jt, [init enc, seq] **189**
S63.49[0,1]D	Traum rupture of oth lgmt of [rt, lt] index finger at metacarpophalangeal and interphalangeal jt, subsq enc **396**
S63.49[6,7][A,S]	Traum rupture of oth lgmt of [rt, lt] little finger at metacarpophalangeal and interphalangeal jt, [init enc, seq] **190**
S63.49[6,7]D	Traum rupture of oth lgmt of [rt, lt] little finger at metacarpophalangeal and interphalangeal jt, subsq enc **396**
S63.49[2,3][A,S]	Traum rupture of oth lgmt of [rt, lt] mid finger at metacarpophalangeal and interphalangeal jt, [init enc, seq] **190**
S63.49[2,3]D	Traum rupture of oth lgmt of [rt, lt] mid finger at metacarpophalangeal and interphalangeal jt, subsq enc **396**
S63.49[4,5][A,S]	Traum rupture of oth lgmt of [rt, lt] ring finger at metacarpophalangeal and interphalangeal jt, [init enc, seq] **190**
S63.49[4,5]D	Traum rupture of oth lgmt of [rt, lt] ring finger at metacarpophalangeal and interphalangeal jt, subsq enc **396**
S63.42[8,9][A,S]	Traum rupture of palmar lgmt of [oth, unsp] finger at metacarpophalangeal and interphalangeal jt, [init enc, seq] **189**
S63.42[8,9]D	Traum rupture of palmar lgmt of [oth, unsp] finger at metacarpophalangeal and interphalangeal jt, subsq enc **396**
S63.42[0,1][A,S]	Traum rupture of palmar lgmt of [rt, lt] index finger at metacarpophalangeal and interphalangeal jt, [init enc, seq] **189**
S63.42[0,1]D	Traum rupture of palmar lgmt of [rt, lt] index finger at metacarpophalangeal and interphalangeal jt, subsq enc **396**
S63.42[6,7][A,S]	Traum rupture of palmar lgmt of [rt, lt] little finger at metacarpophalangeal and interphalangeal jt, [init enc, seq] **189**
S63.42[6,7]D	Traum rupture of palmar lgmt of [rt, lt] little finger at metacarpophalangeal and interphalangeal jt, subsq enc **396**

Code	Description
S63.42[2,3][A,S]	Traum rupture of palmar lgmt of [rt, lt] mid finger at metacarpophalangeal and interphalangeal jt, [init enc, seq] **189**
S63.42[2,3]D	Traum rupture of palmar lgmt of [rt, lt] mid finger at metacarpophalangeal and interphalangeal jt, subsq enc **396**
S63.42[4,5][A,S]	Traum rupture of palmar lgmt of [rt, lt] ring finger at metacarpophalangeal and interphalangeal jt, [init enc, seq] **189**
S63.42[4,5]D	Traum rupture of palmar lgmt of [rt, lt] ring finger at metacarpophalangeal and interphalangeal jt, subsq enc **396**
S63.32[1,2,9][A,S]	Traum rupture of radiocarpal lgmt of [rt, lt, unsp] wrist, [init enc, seq] **189**
S33.4XXA	Traum rupture of symphysis pubis, init enc **162, 421**
S33.4XXS	Traum rupture of symphysis pubis, seq **184**
S33.4XXD	Traum rupture of symphysis pubis, subsq enc **390**
S23.0XXA	Traum rupture of thoracic intervertebral disc, init **166, 420**
S23.0XXS	Traum rupture of thoracic intervertebral disc, seq **184**
S23.0XXD	Traum rupture of thoracic intervertebral disc, subs **389**
S63.33[1,2,9][A,S]	Traum rupture of ulnocarpal lgmt of [rt, lt, unsp] wrist, [init enc, seq] **189**
S09.20XS	Traum rupture of unsp ear drum, seq **359**
S63.40[8,9][A,S]	Traum rupture of unsp lgmt of [oth, unsp] finger at metacarpophalangeal and interphalangeal jt, [init enc, seq] **189**
S63.40[8,9]D	Traum rupture of unsp lgmt of [oth, unsp] finger at metacarpophalangeal and interphalangeal jt, subsq enc **396**
S63.30[1,2,9][A,S]	Traum rupture of unsp lgmt of [rt, lt, unsp] wrist, [init enc, seq] **189**
S63.30[1,2,9]D	Traum rupture of unsp lgmt of [rt, lt, unsp] wrist, subsq enc **396**
S63.40[0,1][A,S]	Traum rupture of unsp lgmt of [rt, lt] index finger at metacarpophalangeal and interphalangeal jt, [init enc, seq] **189**
S63.40[0,1]D	Traum rupture of unsp lgmt of [rt, lt] index finger at metacarpophalangeal and interphalangeal jt, subsq enc **396**
S63.40[6,7][A,S]	Traum rupture of unsp lgmt of [rt, lt] little finger at metacarpophalangeal and interphalangeal jt, [init enc, seq] **189**
S63.40[6,7]D	Traum rupture of unsp lgmt of [rt, lt] little finger at metacarpophalangeal and interphalangeal jt, subsq enc **396**
S63.40[2,3][A,S]	Traum rupture of unsp lgmt of [rt, lt] mid finger at metacarpophalangeal and interphalangeal jt, [init enc, seq] **189**
S63.40[2,3]D	Traum rupture of unsp lgmt of [rt, lt] mid finger at metacarpophalangeal and interphalangeal jt, subsq enc **396**
S63.40[4,5][A,S]	Traum rupture of unsp lgmt of [rt, lt] ring finger at metacarpophalangeal and interphalangeal jt, [init enc, seq] **189**
S63.40[4,5]D	Traum rupture of unsp lgmt of [rt, lt] ring finger at metacarpophalangeal and interphalangeal jt, subsq enc **396**
S63.43[8,9][A,S]	Traum rupture of volar plate of [oth, unsp] finger at metacarpophalangeal and interphalangeal jt, [init enc, seq] **189**
S63.43[8,9]D	Traum rupture of volar plate of [oth, unsp] finger at metacarpophalangeal and interphalangeal jt, subsq enc **396**
S63.43[0,1,2,3,4,5,6,7,8,9]A	Traum rupture of volar plate of [rt index, lt index, rt mid, lt mid, rt ring, lt ring, rt little, lt little, oth, unsp] finger at metacarpophalangeal and interphalangeal jt, init enc **425**
S63.43[0,1][A,S]	Traum rupture of volar plate of [rt, lt] index finger at metacarpophalangeal and interphalangeal jt, [init enc, seq] **189**
S63.43[0,1]D	Traum rupture of volar plate of [rt, lt] index finger at metacarpophalangeal and interphalangeal jt, subsq enc **396**
S63.43[6,7][A,S]	Traum rupture of volar plate of [rt, lt] little finger at metacarpophalangeal and interphalangeal jt, [init enc, seq] **189**
S63.43[6,7]D	Traum rupture of volar plate of [rt, lt] little finger at metacarpophalangeal and interphalangeal jt, subsq enc **396**
S63.43[2,3][A,S]	Traum rupture of volar plate of [rt, lt] mid finger at metacarpophalangeal and interphalangeal jt, [init enc, seq] **189**
S63.43[2,3]D	Traum rupture of volar plate of [rt, lt] mid finger at metacarpophalangeal and interphalangeal jt, subsq enc **396**
S63.43[4,5][A,S]	Traum rupture of volar plate of [rt, lt] ring finger at metacarpophalangeal and interphalangeal jt, [init enc, seq] **189**
S63.43[4,5]D	Traum rupture of volar plate of [rt, lt] ring finger at metacarpophalangeal and interphalangeal jt, subsq enc **396**
T79.2XXA	Traum secondary and recurrent hemor and seroma, init **287, 374, 430**
T79.2XXS	Traum secondary and recurrent hemor and seroma, seq **361**
T79.4XXA	Traum shock, init enc **287, 374, 430**
T79.4XXS	Traum shock, seq **361**
M48.3*	Traum spondylopathy **165**
T79.7XXA	Traum SQ emphysema, init enc **68, 287, 430**
T79.7XXS	Traum SQ emphysema, seq **361**
S06.6X[5,6]A	Traum subarachnoid hemor w/ LOC > 24 hrs [w/ return to pre-existing conscious lvl, w/o return to pre-existing conscious lvl w/ patient surviving], init enc **37, 418, 431**
S06.6X[5,6]S	Traum subarachnoid hemor w/ LOC of [> 24 hrs w/ return to pre-existing conscious lvl, > 24 hrs w/o return to pre-existing conscious lvl w/ patient surviving], seq **40**
S06.6X[5,6]D	Traum subarachnoid hemor w/ LOC of [> 24 hrs w/ return to pre-existing conscious lvl, > 24 hrs w/o return to pre-existing conscious lvl w/ patient surviving], subsq enc **387**
S06.6X[3,4,5,6]A	Traum subarachnoid hemor w/ LOC of [1 hr to 5 hrs 59 min, 6 hrs to 24 hrs, > 24 hrs w/ return to pre-existing conscious lvl, > 24 hrs w/o return to pre-existing conscious lvl patient surviving], init enc **36**
S06.6X[1,2,3,4]A	Traum subarachnoid hemor w/ LOC of [30 min or less, 31 min to 59 min, 1 hr to 5 hrs 59 min, 6 hrs to 24 hrs], init enc **37, 418, 431**
S06.6X[1,2,3,4]S	Traum subarachnoid hemor w/ LOC of [30 min or less, 31-59 min, 1 hr to 5 hrs 59 min, 6 hrs to 24 hrs], seq **40**
S06.6X[1,2,3,4]D	Traum subarachnoid hemor w/ LOC of [30 min or less, 31-59 min, 1 hr to 5 hrs 59 min, 6 hrs to 24 hrs], subsq enc **387**
S06.6X[7,8,9]A	Traum subarachnoid hemor w/ LOC of [any dur w/ death d/t brain inj prior to regain cnscness, any dur w/ death d/t oth cause prior to regain cnscness, unsp dur], init enc **36, 37, 418, 431**
S06.6X[7,8,9]S	Traum subarachnoid hemor w/ LOC of [any dur w/ death d/t brain inj prior to regain cnscness, any dur w/ death d/t oth cause prior to regain cnscness, unsp dur], seq **40**
S06.6X[7,8,9]D	Traum subarachnoid hemor w/ LOC of [any dur w/ death d/t brain inj prior to regain cnscness, any dur w/ death d/t oth cause prior to regain cnscness, unsp dur], subsq enc **387**
S06.5X1A	Traum subdr hem w LOC of 30 min or less, init **37**
S06.5X2A	Traum subdr hem w LOC of 31-59 min, init **37**
S06.5X0A	Traum subdr hem w/o LOC, init **37, 418, 431**
S06.5X0S	Traum subdr hem w/o LOC, seq **40**
S06.5X0D	Traum subdr hem w/o LOC, subs **387**
S06.5X[5,6]A	Traum subdural hemor w/ LOC > 24 hrs [w/ return to pre-existing conscious lvl, w/o return to pre-existing conscious lvl w/ patient surviving], init enc **37, 418, 431**
S06.5X[5,6]S	Traum subdural hemor w/ LOC of [> 24 hrs w/ return to pre-existing conscious lvl, > 24 hrs w/o return to pre-existing conscious lvl w/ patient surviving], seq **40**
S06.5X[5,6]D	Traum subdural hemor w/ LOC of [> 24 hrs w/ return to pre-existing conscious lvl, > 24 hrs w/o return to pre-existing conscious lvl w/ patient surviving], subsq enc **387**
S06.5X[3,4,5,6]A	Traum subdural hemor w/ LOC of [1 hr to 5 hrs 59 min, 6 hrs to 24 hrs, > 24 hrs w/ return to pre-existing conscious lvl, > 24 hrs w/o return to pre-existing conscious lvl patient surviving], init enc **35**
S06.5X[1,2,3,4]A	Traum subdural hemor w/ LOC of [30 min or less, 31 min to 59 min, 1 hr to 5 hrs 59 min, 6 hrs to 24 hrs], init enc **37, 418, 431**
S06.5X[1,2,3,4]S	Traum subdural hemor w/ LOC of [30 min or less, 31-59 min, 1 hr to 5 hrs 59 min, 6 hrs to 24 hrs], seq **40**
S06.5X[1,2,3,4]D	Traum subdural hemor w/ LOC of [30 min or less, 31-59 min, 1 hr to 5 hrs 59 min, 6 hrs to 24 hrs], subsq enc **387**
S06.5X[7,8,9]A	Traum subdural hemor w/ LOC of [any dur w/ death d/t brain inj prior to regain cnscness, any dur w/ death d/t oth cause prior to regain cnscness, unsp dur], init enc **36, 37, 418, 431**
S06.5X[7,8,9]S	Traum subdural hemor w/ LOC of [any dur w/ death d/t brain inj prior to regain cnscness, any dur w/ death d/t oth cause prior to regain cnscness, unsp dur], seq **40**
S06.5X[7,8,9]D	Traum subdural hemor w/ LOC of [any dur w/ death d/t brain inj prior to regain cnscness, any dur w/ death d/t oth cause prior to regain cnscness, unsp dur], subsq enc **387**
S06.6X5A	Traum subrac hem w LOC >24 hr w ret consc lev, init **11, 15**
S06.6X6A	Traum subrac hem w LOC >24 hr w/o ret consc w surv, init **11, 15**
S06.6X3A	Traum subrac hem w LOC of 1-5 hrs 59 min, init **11, 15**
S06.6X1A	Traum subrac hem w LOC of 30 min or less, init **11, 15, 37**
S06.6X2A	Traum subrac hem w LOC of 31-59 min, init **11, 15, 37**
S06.6X4A	Traum subrac hem w LOC of 6 hrs to 24 hrs, init **11, 15**
S06.6X9A	Traum subrac hem w LOC of unsp dur, init **11, 15**
S06.6X7A	Traum subrac hem w LOC w death d/t brain inj bf cnscr, init **11, 15**
S06.6X8A	Traum subrac hem w LOC w death d/t oth cause bf consc, init **11, 15**
S06.6X0A	Traum subrac hem w/o LOC, init **11, 15, 37, 418, 431**
S06.6X0S	Traum subrac hem w/o LOC, seq **40**
S06.6X0D	Traum subrac hem w/o LOC, subs **387**
T75.22X[A,S]	Traum vasospastic synd, [init enc, seq] **374**
T75.22XD	Traum vasospastic synd, subsq enc **410**

Code	Description
B75	Trichinellosis 309
A59.0[0,2,3,9]	Trichomoniasis [urogenital unsp, prostatitis, cystitis and urethritis, Oth urogenital] 261
A59.0[0,1,3,9]	Trichomoniasis [urogenital unsp, vulvovaginitis, cystitis and urethritis, oth urogenital] 264, 269
A59.8	Trichomoniasis of oth sites 308
A59.9	Trichomoniasis, unsp 308
B81.2	Trichostrongyliasis 116
F63.3	Trichotillomania 310
B79	Trichuriasis 116
I45.3	Trifascicular block 283
N30.3*	Trigonitis 255
Z38.62	Triplet liveborn infant, delivered by cesarean 289
Z38.61	Triplet liveborn infant, delivered vaginally 289
O30.1[0,1,2,9][1,2,3]	Triplet preg [unsp, two or more monochorionic fetuses, two or more monoamniotic fetuses, unable to determine the number of placenta and amniotic sacs], [1st, 2nd, 3rd] trmstr 279
O30.12[1,2,3]	Triplet preg w/ two or more monoamniotic fetuses, [1st, 2nd, 3rd] trmstr 277
O30.11[1,2,3]	Triplet preg w/ two or more monochorionic fetuses, [1st, 2nd, 3rd] trmstr 277
O30.1[0,1,2,9]9	Triplet preg, [unsp number of placenta and unsp number of amniotic sacs, two or more monochorionic fetuses, two or more monoamniotic fetuses, unable to determine the number of placenta and amniotic sacs], unsp trmstr 280
O30.19[1,2,3]	Triplet preg, unable to determine number of placenta and number of amniotic sacs, [1st, 2nd, 3rd] trmstr 277
O30.10[1,2,3]	Triplet preg, unsp number of placenta and unsp number of amniotic sacs, [1st, 2nd, 3rd] trmstr 277
Q91*	Trisomy 18 and Trisomy 13 310
H53.55	Tritanomaly 46
M70.6*	Trochanteric bursitis 167
G04.1	Tropical spastic paraplegia 32
K90.1	Tropical sprue 116
A18.1[6,7,8]	Tuberculosis [of cervix, female pelvic inflam dz, of oth female genital organs] 264, 269
O98.02	Tuberculosis compl childbirth 274
O98.01[1,2,3]	Tuberculosis compl preg, [1st, 2nd, 3rd] trmstr 274, 277
O98.03	Tuberculosis compl the puerperium 274, 276
A18.6	Tuberculosis of (inner) (mid) ear 58
A18.1[0,1,2,3]	Tuberculosis of [genitourinary sys unsp, kidney and ureter, bladder, oth urinary organs] 255
A18.8[2,4,9]	Tuberculosis of [oth endocrine glands, heart, oth sites] 308
A18.1[4,5]	Tuberculosis of [prostate, oth male genital organs] 261
A18.0[1,3]	Tuberculosis of [spine, oth bones] 163
A18.7	Tuberculosis of adrenal glands 247
A18.83	Tuberculosis of digestive tract organs, NEC 114
A18.5*	Tuberculosis of eye 45
A18.3*	Tuberculosis of intestines, peritoneum and mesenteric glands 114
A17*	Tuberculosis of nervous sys 438
A17.9	Tuberculosis of nervous sys, unsp 308
A18*	Tuberculosis of oth organs 438
A18.4	Tuberculosis of skin and SQ tissue 233
A18.01	Tuberculosis of spine 125
A18.85	Tuberculosis of spleen 294
A18.81	Tuberculosis of thyroid gland 247
O98.[0,1,2,3,4,5,6,7,8,9]2	Tuberculosis, Syphilis, Gonorrhea, Oth infxns w/ a predominantly sexual mode of transmission, Viral hepatitis, Oth viral dzs, Protozoal dzs, Human immunodef virus (HIV) dz, Oth maternal infectious and parasitic dzs, Unsp maternal infectious and parasitic dz] compl childbirth 273
O98.[0,1,2,3,4,5,6,7,8,9]3	Tuberculosis, Syphilis, Gonorrhea, Oth infxns w/ a predominantly sexual mode of transmission, Viral hepatitis, Oth viral dzs, Protozoal dzs, Human immunodef virus (HIV) dz, Oth maternal infectious and parasitic dzs, Unsp maternal infectious and parasitic dz] compl the puerperium 272
O98.[0,1,2,3,4,5,6,7,8,9]1[1,2,3]	Tuberculosis, Syphilis, Gonorrhea, Oth infxns w/ predominantly sexual mode of transmission, Viral hepatitis, Oth viral dzs, Protozoal dzs, Human immunodef virus (HIV) dz, Oth maternal infectious and parasitic dzs, Unsp maternal infectious and parasitic dzs] compl preg, [1st, 2nd, 3rd] trmstr 278
O98.[0,1,2,3,4,5,6,7,8,9]19	Tuberculosis, Syphilis, Gonorrhea, Oth sexually transmitted dz, Viral hepatitis, Oth viral dzs, Protozoal dzs, HIV, Oth maternal infectious and parasitic dzs, Unsp maternal infectious and parasitic dzs] compl preg, childbirth and the puerperium, unsp trmstr 281
A18.02	Tuberculous arthritis of oth jts 164
A17.0	Tuberculous meningitis 10, 14, 41
A18.2	Tuberculous peripheral lymphadenopathy 294
Q85.1	Tuberous sclerosis 38
N12	Tubulo-interstitial nephritis, not spcf as acute or chr 255, 285
E88.3	Tumor lysis synd 254, 283
Q96*	Turner's synd 265, 270
Z38.4	Twin liveborn infant, born outside hospital 289
Z38.31	Twin liveborn infant, delivered by cesarean 289
Z38.30	Twin liveborn infant, delivered vaginally 289
Z38.5	Twin liveborn infant, unsp as to place of birth 289
O30.0[0,1,2,3,4,9][1,2,3]	Twin preg, [unsp number of placenta and unsp number of amniotic sacs, monoamniotic/monochorionic, conjoined twin preg, monochorionic/diamniotic, dichorionic/diamniotic, unable to determine number of placenta and amniotic sacs], [1st, 2nd, 3rd] trmstr 279
O30.0[0,1,3,4,9]9	Twin preg, [unsp number of placenta and unsp number of amniotic sacs, monochorionic/monoamniotic, monochorionic/diamniotic, dichorionic/diamniotic, unable to determine number of placenta and number of amniotic sacs], unsp trmstr 280
O30.04[1,2,3]	Twin preg, dichorionic/diamniotic, [1st, 2nd, 3rd] trmstr 277
O30.03[1,2,3]	Twin preg, monochorionic/diamniotic, [1st, 2nd, 3rd] trmstr 277
O30.01[1,2,3]	Twin preg, monochorionic/monoamniotic, [1st, 2nd, 3rd] trmstr 277
O30.09[1,2,3]	Twin preg, unable to determine number of placenta and number of amniotic sacs, [1st, 2nd, 3rd] trmstr 277
O30.00[1,2,3]	Twin preg, unsp number of placenta and unsp number of amniotic sacs, [1st, 2nd, 3rd] trmstr 277
S42.22[1,2,3][D,G,S]	Two-part disp fx of surgical neck of [rt, lt, unsp] humerus, [subsq enc for fx w/ routine healing, subsq enc for fx w/ delayed healing, seq] 171
S42.22[1,2,3][K,P]	Two-part disp fx of surgical neck of [rt, lt, unsp] humerus, subsq enc for fx w/ [nonu, malu] 196
S42.22[4,5,6][D,G,S]	Two-part nondisp fx of surgical neck of [rt, lt, unsp] humerus, [subsq enc for fx w/ routine healing, subsq enc for fx w/ delayed healing, seq] 171
S42.22[4,5,6][K,P]	Two-part nondisp fx of surgical neck of [rt, lt, unsp] humerus, subsq enc for fx w/ [nonu, malu] 196
T51.2X[1,2,3,4]A	Txc effct of 2-Propanol, [accid (unintentional), intentional self-harm, assault, undetermined], init enc 365
T51.2X[1,2,3,4]S	Txc effct of 2-Propanol, [accid (unintentional), intentional self-harm, assault, undetermined], seq 372
T51.2X[1,2,3,4]D	Txc effct of 2-Propanol, [accid (unintentional), intentional self-harm, assault, undetermined], subsq enc 407
T64.0[1,2,3,4]XA	Txc effct of aflatoxin, [accid (unintentional), intentional self-harm, assault, undetermined], init enc 367
T64.0[1,2,3,4]XS	Txc effct of aflatoxin, [accid (unintentional), intentional self-harm, assault, undetermined], seq 374
T64.0[1,2,3,4]XD	Txc effct of aflatoxin, [accid (unintentional), intentional self-harm, assault, undetermined], subsq enc 409
T57.0X[1,2,3,4]A	Txc effct of arsenic and its compounds, [accid (unintentional), intentional self-harm, assault, undetermined], init enc 366
T57.0X[1,2,3,4]S	Txc effct of arsenic and its compounds, [accid (unintentional), intentional self-harm, assault, undetermined], seq 372
T57.0X[1,2,3,4]D	Txc effct of arsenic and its compounds, [accid (unintentional), intentional self-harm, assault, undetermined], subsq enc 408
T52.1X[1,2,3,4]A	Txc effct of benzene [accid (unintentional), intentional self-harm, assault, undetermined], init enc 365
T52.1X[1,2,3,4]S	Txc effct of benzene [accid (unintentional), intentional self-harm, assault, undetermined], seq 372
T52.1X[1,2,3,4]D	Txc effct of benzene [accid (unintentional), intentional self-harm, assault, undetermined], subsq enc 408
T56.7X[1,2,3,4]A	Txc effct of beryllium and its compounds, [accid (unintentional), intentional self-harm, assault, undetermined], init enc 366
T56.7X[1,2,3,4]S	Txc effct of beryllium and its compounds, [accid (unintentional), intentional self-harm, assault, undetermined], seq 372
T56.7X[1,2,3,4]D	Txc effct of beryllium and its compounds, [accid (unintentional), intentional self-harm, assault, undetermined], subsq enc 408
T56.3X[1,2,3,4]A	Txc effct of cadmium and its compounds, [accid (unintentional), intentional self-harm, assault, undetermined], init enc 366

T56.3X[1,2,3,4]S Txc effct of cadmium and its compounds, [accid (unintentional), intentional self-harm, assault, undetermined], seq **372**

T56.3X[1,2,3,4]D Txc effct of cadmium and its compounds, [accid (unintentional), intentional self-harm, assault, undetermined], subsq enc **408**

T59.7X[1,2,3,4]A Txc effct of carbon dioxide, [accid (unintentional), intentional self-harm, assault, undetermined], init enc **366**

T59.7X[1,2,3,4]S Txc effct of carbon dioxide, [accid (unintentional), intentional self-harm, assault, undetermined], seq **373**

T59.7X[1,2,3,4]D Txc effct of carbon dioxide, [accid (unintentional), intentional self-harm, assault, undetermined], subsq enc **408**

T65.4X[1,2,3,4]A Txc effct of carbon disulfide, [accid (unintentional), intentional self-harm, assault, undetermined], init enc **367**

T65.4X[1,2,3,4]S Txc effct of carbon disulfide, [accid (unintentional), intentional self-harm, assault, undetermined], seq **374**

T65.4X[1,2,3,4]D Txc effct of carbon disulfide, [accid (unintentional), intentional self-harm, assault, undetermined], subsq enc **409**

T58.2X[1,2,3,4]A Txc effct of carbon monoxide from incomplete combustion of oth domestic fuels, [accid (unintentional), intentional self-harm, assault, undetermined], init enc **366**

T58.2X[1,2,3,4]S Txc effct of carbon monoxide from incomplete combustion of oth domestic fuels, [accid (unintentional), intentional self-harm, assault, undetermined], seq **373**

T58.2X[1,2,3,4]D Txc effct of carbon monoxide from incomplete combustion of oth domestic fuels, [accid (unintentional), intentional self-harm, assault, undetermined], subsq enc **408**

T58.0[1,2,3,4]XA Txc effct of carbon monoxide from motor vehicle exhaust, [accid (unintentional), intentional self-harm, assault, undetermined], init enc **366**

T58.0[1,2,3,4]XS Txc effct of carbon monoxide from motor vehicle exhaust, [accid (unintentional), intentional self-harm, assault, undetermined], seq **373**

T58.0[1,2,3,4]XD Txc effct of carbon monoxide from motor vehicle exhaust, [accid (unintentional), intentional self-harm, assault, undetermined], subsq enc **408**

T58.8X[1,2,3,4]A Txc effct of carbon monoxide from oth source, [accid (unintentional), intentional self-harm, assault, undetermined], init enc **366**

T58.8X[1,2,3,4]S Txc effct of carbon monoxide from oth source, [accid (unintentional), intentional self-harm, assault, undetermined], seq **373**

T58.8X[1,2,3,4]D Txc effct of carbon monoxide from oth source, [accid (unintentional), intentional self-harm, assault, undetermined], subsq enc **408**

T58.9[1,2,3,4]XA Txc effct of carbon monoxide from unsp source, [accid (unintentional), intentional self-harm, assault, undetermined], init enc **366**

T58.9[1,2,3,4]XS Txc effct of carbon monoxide from unsp source, [accid (unintentional), intentional self-harm, assault, undetermined], seq **373**

T58.9[1,2,3,4]XD Txc effct of carbon monoxide from unsp source, [accid (unintentional), intentional self-harm, assault, undetermined], subsq enc **408**

T58.1[1,2,3,4]XA Txc effct of carbon monoxide from utility gas, [accid (unintentional), intentional self-harm, assault, undetermined], init enc **366**

T58.1[1,2,3,4]XS Txc effct of carbon monoxide from utility gas, [accid (unintentional), intentional self-harm, assault, undetermined], seq **373**

T58.1[1,2,3,4]XD Txc effct of carbon monoxide from utility gas, [accid (unintentional), intentional self-harm, assault, undetermined], subsq enc **408**

T53.0X[1,2,3,4]A Txc effct of carbon tetrachloride, [accid (unintentional), intentional self-harm, assault, undetermined], init enc **365**

T53.0X[1,2,3,4]S Txc effct of carbon tetrachloride, [accid (unintentional), intentional self-harm, assault, undetermined], seq **372**

T53.0X[1,2,3,4]D Txc effct of carbon tetrachloride, [accid (unintentional), intentional self-harm, assault, undetermined], subsq enc **408**

T65.21[1,2,3,4]A Txc effct of chewing tobacco, [accid (unintentional), intentional self-harm, assault, undetermined], init enc **367**

T65.21[1,2,3,4]S Txc effct of chewing tobacco, [accid (unintentional), intentional self-harm, assault, undetermined], seq **374**

T65.21[1,2,3,4]D Txc effct of chewing tobacco, [accid (unintentional), intentional self-harm, assault, undetermined], subsq enc **409**

T59.4X[1,2,3,4]A Txc effct of chlorine gas, [accid (unintentional), intentional self-harm, assault, undetermined], init enc **366**

T59.4X[1,2,3,4]S Txc effct of chlorine gas, [accid (unintentional), intentional self-harm, assault, undetermined], seq **373**

T59.4X[1,2,3,4]D Txc effct of chlorine gas, [accid (unintentional), intentional self-harm, assault, undetermined], subsq enc **408**

T53.5X[1,2,3,4]A Txc effct of chlorofluorocarbons, [accid (unintentional), intentional self-harm, assault, undetermined], init enc **365**

T53.5X[1,2,3,4]S Txc effct of chlorofluorocarbons, [accid (unintentional), intentional self-harm, assault, undetermined], seq **372**

T53.5X[1,2,3,4]D Txc effct of chlorofluorocarbons, [accid (unintentional), intentional self-harm, assault, undetermined], subsq enc **408**

T53.1X[1,2,3,4]A Txc effct of chloroform, [accid (unintentional), intentional self-harm, assault, undetermined], init enc **365**

T53.1X[1,2,3,4]S Txc effct of chloroform, [accid (unintentional), intentional self-harm, assault, undetermined], seq **372**

T53.1X[1,2,3,4]D Txc effct of chloroform, [accid (unintentional), intentional self-harm, assault, undetermined], subsq enc **408**

T56.2X[1,2,3,4]A Txc effct of chromium and its compounds, [accid (unintentional), intentional self-harm, assault, undetermined], init enc **366**

T56.2X[1,2,3,4]S Txc effct of chromium and its compounds, [accid (unintentional), intentional self-harm, assault, undetermined], seq **372**

T56.2X[1,2,3,4]D Txc effct of chromium and its compounds, [accid (unintentional), intentional self-harm, assault, undetermined], subsq enc **408**

T63.04[1,2,3,4]A Txc effct of cobra venom, [accid (unintentional), intentional self-harm, assault, undetermined], init enc **366**

T63.04[1,2,3,4]S Txc effct of cobra venom, [accid (unintentional), intentional self-harm, assault, undetermined], seq **373**

T63.04[1,2,3,4]D Txc effct of cobra venom, [accid (unintentional), intentional self-harm, assault, undetermined], subsq enc **409**

T63.62[1,2,3,4]A Txc effct of contact w/ oth jellyfish, [accid (unintentional), intentional self-harm, assault, undetermined], init enc **367**

T63.62[1,2,3,4]S Txc effct of contact w/ oth jellyfish, [accid (unintentional), intentional self-harm, assault, undetermined], seq **373**

T63.62[1,2,3,4]D Txc effct of contact w/ oth jellyfish, [accid (unintentional), intentional self-harm, assault, undetermined], subsq enc **409**

T63.83[1,2,3,4]A Txc effct of contact w/ oth venomous amphibian, [accid (unintentional), intentional self-harm, assault, undetermined], init enc **367**

T63.83[1,2,3,4]S Txc effct of contact w/ oth venomous amphibian, [accid (unintentional), intentional self-harm, assault, undetermined], seq **374**

T63.83[1,2,3,4]D Txc effct of contact w/ oth venomous amphibian, [accid (unintentional), intentional self-harm, assault, undetermined], subsq enc **409**

T63.89[1,2,3,4]A Txc effct of contact w/ oth venomous animals, [accid (unintentional), intentional self-harm, assault, undetermined], init enc **367**

T63.89[1,2,3,4]S Txc effct of contact w/ oth venomous animals, [accid (unintentional), intentional self-harm, assault, undetermined], seq **374**

T63.89[1,2,3,4]D Txc effct of contact w/ oth venomous animals, [accid (unintentional), intentional self-harm, assault, undetermined], subsq enc **409**

T63.59[1,2,3,4]A Txc effct of contact w/ oth venomous fish, [accid (unintentional), intentional self-harm, assault, undetermined], init enc **367**

T63.59[1,2,3,4]S Txc effct of contact w/ oth venomous fish, [accid (unintentional), intentional self-harm, assault, undetermined], seq **373**

T63.59[1,2,3,4]D Txc effct of contact w/ oth venomous fish, [accid (unintentional), intentional self-harm, assault, undetermined], subsq enc **409**

T63.69[1,2,3,4]A Txc effct of contact w/ oth venomous marine animals, [accid (unintentional), intentional self-harm, assault, undetermined], init enc **367**

T63.69[1,2,3,4]S Txc effct of contact w/ oth venomous marine animals, [accid (unintentional), intentional self-harm, assault, undetermined], seq **373**

T63.69[1,2,3,4]D Txc effct of contact w/ oth venomous marine animals, [accid (unintentional), intentional self-harm, assault, undetermined], subsq enc **409**

T63.79[1,2,3,4]A Txc effct of contact w/ oth venomous plant, [accid (unintentional), intentional self-harm, assault, undetermined], init enc **367**

T63.79[1,2,3,4]S Txc effct of contact w/ oth venomous plant, [accid (unintentional), intentional self-harm, assault, undetermined], seq **374**

T63.79[1,2,3,4]D Txc effct of contact w/ oth venomous plant, [accid (unintentional), intentional self-harm, assault, undetermined], subsq enc **409**

T63.61[1,2,3,4]A Txc effct of contact w/ Portugese Man-o-war, [accid (unintentional), intentional self-harm, assault, undetermined], init enc **367**

T63.61[1,2,3,4]S Txc effct of contact w/ Portugese Man-o-war, [accid (unintentional), intentional self-harm, assault, undetermined], seq **373**

T63.61[1,2,3,4]D Txc effct of contact w/ Portugese Man-o-war, [accid (unintentional), intentional self-harm, assault, undetermined], subsq enc **409**

T63.63[1,2,3,4]A Txc effct of contact w/ sea anemone, [accid (unintentional), intentional self-harm, assault, undetermined], init enc **367**

T63.63[1,2,3,4]S Txc effct of contact w/ sea anemone, [accid (unintentional), intentional self-harm, assault, undetermined], seq **373**

T63.63[1,2,3,4]D Txc effct of contact w/ sea anemone, [accid (unintentional), intentional self-harm, assault, undetermined], subsq enc **409**

T63.51[1,2,3,4]A Txc effct of contact w/ stingray, [accid (unintentional), intentional self-harm, assault, undetermined], init enc **367**

T63.51[1,2,3,4]S Txc effct of contact w/ stingray, [accid (unintentional), intentional self-harm, assault, undetermined], seq **373**

T63.51[1,2,3,4]D Txc effct of contact w/ stingray, [accid (unintentional), intentional self-harm, assault, undetermined], subsq enc **409**

T63.9[1,2,3,4]XA Txc effct of contact w/ unsp venomous animal, [accid (unintentional), intentional self-harm, assault, undetermined], init enc **367**

T63.9[1,2,3,4]XS Txc effct of contact w/ unsp venomous animal, [accid (unintentional), intentional self-harm, assault, undetermined], seq **374**

T63.9[1,2,3,4]XD Txc effct of contact w/ unsp venomous animal, [accid (unintentional), intentional self-harm, assault, undetermined], subsq enc **409**

T63.81[1,2,3,4]A Txc effct of contact w/ venomous frog, [accid (unintentional), intentional self-harm, assault, undetermined], init enc **367**

T63.81[1,2,3,4]S Txc effct of contact w/ venomous frog, [accid (unintentional), intentional self-harm, assault, undetermined], seq **374**

T63.81[1,2,3,4]D Txc effct of contact w/ venomous frog, [accid (unintentional), intentional self-harm, assault, undetermined], subsq enc **409**

T63.71[1,2,3,4]A Txc effct of contact w/ venomous marine plant, [accid (unintentional), intentional self-harm, assault, undetermined], init enc **367**

T63.71[1,2,3,4]S Txc effct of contact w/ venomous marine plant, [accid (unintentional), intentional self-harm, assault, undetermined], seq **374**

T63.71[1,2,3,4]D Txc effct of contact w/ venomous marine plant, [accid (unintentional), intentional self-harm, assault, undetermined], subsq enc **409**

T63.82[1,2,3,4]A Txc effct of contact w/ venomous toad, [accid (unintentional), intentional self-harm, assault, undetermined], init enc **367**

T63.82[1,2,3,4]S Txc effct of contact w/ venomous toad, [accid (unintentional), intentional self-harm, assault, undetermined], seq **374**

T63.82[1,2,3,4]D Txc effct of contact w/ venomous toad, [accid (unintentional), intentional self-harm, assault, undetermined], subsq enc **409**

T56.4X[1,2,3,4]A Txc effct of copper and its compounds, [accid (unintentional), intentional self-harm, assault, undetermined], init enc **366**

T56.4X[1,2,3,4]S Txc effct of copper and its compounds, [accid (unintentional), intentional self-harm, assault, undetermined], seq **372**

T56.4X[1,2,3,4]D Txc effct of copper and its compounds, [accid (unintentional), intentional self-harm, assault, undetermined], subsq enc **408**

T63.02[1,2,3,4]A Txc effct of coral snake venom, [accid (unintentional), intentional self-harm, assault, undetermined], init enc **366**

T63.02[1,2,3,4]S Txc effct of coral snake venom, [accid (unintentional), intentional self-harm, assault, undetermined], seq **373**

T63.02[1,2,3,4]D Txc effct of coral snake venom, [accid (unintentional), intentional self-harm, assault, undetermined], subsq enc **409**

T54.2X[1,2,3,4]A Txc effct of corrosive acids and acid-like substances, [accid (unintentional), intentional self-harm, assault, undetermined], init enc **366**

T54.2X[1,2,3,4]S Txc effct of corrosive acids and acid-like substances, [accid (unintentional), intentional self-harm, assault, undetermined], seq **372**

T54.2X[1,2,3,4]D Txc effct of corrosive acids and acid-like substances, [accid (unintentional), intentional self-harm, assault, undetermined], subsq enc **408**

T54.3X[1,2,3,4]A Txc effct of corrosive alkalis and alkali-like substances, [accid (unintentional), intentional self-harm, assault, undetermined], init enc **366**

T54.3X[1,2,3,4]S Txc effct of corrosive alkalis and alkali-like substances, [accid (unintentional), intentional self-harm, assault, undetermined], seq **372**

T54.3X[1,2,3,4]D Txc effct of corrosive alkalis and alkali-like substances, [accid (unintentional), intentional self-harm, assault, undetermined], subsq enc **408**

T65.0X[1,2,3,4]A Txc effct of cyanides, [accid (unintentional), intentional self-harm, assault, undetermined], init enc **367**

T65.0X[1,2,3,4]S Txc effct of cyanides, [accid (unintentional), intentional self-harm, assault, undetermined], seq **374**

T65.0X[1,2,3,4]D Txc effct of cyanides, [accid (unintentional), intentional self-harm, assault, undetermined], subsq enc **409**

T55.1X[1,2,3,4]A Txc effct of detergents, [accid (unintentional), intentional self-harm, assault, undetermined], init enc **366**

T55.1X[1,2,3,4]S Txc effct of detergents, [accid (unintentional), intentional self-harm, assault, undetermined], seq **372**

T55.1X[1,2,3,4]D Txc effct of detergents, [accid (unintentional), intentional self-harm, assault, undetermined], subsq enc **408**

T53.4X[1,2,3,4]A Txc effct of dichloromethane, [accid (unintentional), intentional self-harm, assault, undetermined], init enc **365**

T53.4X[1,2,3,4]S Txc effct of dichloromethane, [accid (unintentional), intentional self-harm, assault, undetermined], seq **372**

T53.4X[1,2,3,4]D Txc effct of dichloromethane, [accid (unintentional), intentional self-harm, assault, undetermined], subsq enc **408**

T51.0X[1,2,3,4]A Txc effct of ethanol, [accid (unintentional), intentional self-harm, assault, undetermined], init enc **365**

T51.0X[1,2,3,4]S Txc effct of ethanol, [accid (unintentional), intentional self-harm, assault, undetermined], seq **372**

T51.0X[1,2,3,4]D Txc effct of ethanol, [accid (unintentional), intentional self-harm, assault, undetermined], subsq enc **407**

T65.83[1,2,3,4]A Txc effct of fiberglass, NEC, [accid (unintentional), intentional self-harm, assault, undetermined], init enc **367**

T65.83[1,2,3,4]S Txc effct of fiberglass, NEC, [accid (unintentional), intentional self-harm, assault, undetermined], seq **374**

T65.83[1,2,3,4]D Txc effct of fiberglass, NEC, [accid (unintentional), intentional self-harm, assault, undetermined], subsq enc **409**

T59.5X[1,2,3,4]A Txc effct of fluorine gas and hydrogen fluoride, [accid (unintentional), intentional self-harm, assault, undetermined], init enc **366**

T59.5X[1,2,3,4]S Txc effct of fluorine gas and hydrogen fluoride, [accid (unintentional), intentional self-harm, assault, undetermined], seq **373**

T59.5X[1,2,3,4]D Txc effct of fluorine gas and hydrogen fluoride, [accid (unintentional), intentional self-harm, assault, undetermined], subsq enc **408**

T59.2X[1,2,3,4]A Txc effct of formaldehyde, [accid (unintentional), intentional self-harm, assault, undetermined], init enc **366**

T59.2X[1,2,3,4]S Txc effct of formaldehyde, [accid (unintentional), intentional self-harm, assault, undetermined], seq **373**

T59.2X[1,2,3,4]D Txc effct of formaldehyde, [accid (unintentional), intentional self-harm, assault, undetermined], subsq enc **408**

T51.3X[1,2,3,4]A Txc effct of fusel oil, [accid (unintentional), intentional self-harm, assault, undetermined], init enc **365**

T51.3X[1,2,3,4]S Txc effct of fusel oil, [accid (unintentional), intentional self-harm, assault, undetermined], seq **372**

T51.3X[1,2,3,4]D Txc effct of fusel oil, [accid (unintentional), intentional self-harm, assault, undetermined], subsq enc **407**

T52.3X[1,2,3,4]A Txc effct of glycoles, [accid (unintentional), intentional self-harm, assault, undetermined], init enc **365**

T52.3X[1,2,3,4]S Txc effct of glycoles, [accid (unintentional), intentional self-harm, assault, undetermined], seq **372**

T52.3X[1,2,3,4]D Txc effct of glycoles, [accid (unintentional), intentional self-harm, assault, undetermined], subsq enc **408**

T60.1X[1,2,3,4]A Txc effct of halogenated insecticides, [accid (unintentional), intentional self-harm, assault, undetermined], init enc **366**

T60.1X[1,2,3,4]S Txc effct of halogenated insecticides, [accid (unintentional), intentional self-harm, assault, undetermined], seq **373**

T60.1X[1,2,3,4]D Txc effct of halogenated insecticides, [accid (unintentional), intentional self-harm, assault, undetermined], subsq enc **408**

T65.82[1,2,3,4]A Txc effct of harmful algae and algae toxins, [accid (unintentional), intentional self-harm, assault, undetermined], init enc **367**

T65.82[1,2,3,4]S Txc effct of harmful algae and algae toxins, [accid (unintentional), intentional self-harm, assault, undetermined], seq **374**

T65.82[1,2,3,4]D Txc effct of harmful algae and algae toxins, [accid (unintentional), intentional self-harm, assault, undetermined], subsq enc **409**

T60.3X[1,2,3,4]A Txc effct of herbicides and fungicides, [accid (unintentional), intentional self-harm, assault, undetermined], init enc **366**

T60.3X[1,2,3,4]S Txc effct of herbicides and fungicides, [accid (unintentional), intentional self-harm, assault, undetermined], seq **373**

T60.3X[1,2,3,4]D Txc effct of herbicides and fungicides, [accid (unintentional), intentional self-harm, assault, undetermined], subsq enc **408**

T52.2X[1,2,3,4]A Txc effct of homologues of benzene, [accid (unintentional), intentional self-harm, assault, undetermined], init enc **365**

T52.2X[1,2,3,4]S Txc effct of homologues of benzene, [accid (unintentional), intentional self-harm, assault, undetermined], seq **372**

T52.2X[1,2,3,4]D Txc effct of homologues of benzene, [accid (unintentional), intentional self-harm, assault, undetermined], subsq enc **408**

T57.3X[1,2,3,4]A Txc effct of hydrogen cyanide, [accid (unintentional), intentional self-harm, assault, undetermined], init enc **366**

T57.3X[1,2,3,4]S Txc effct of hydrogen cyanide, [accid (unintentional), intentional self-harm, assault, undetermined], seq **372**

T57.3X[1,2,3,4]D Txc effct of hydrogen cyanide, [accid (unintentional), intentional self-harm, assault, undetermined], subsq enc **408**

T59.6X[1,2,3,4]A Txc effct of hydrogen sulfide, [accid (unintentional), intentional self-harm, assault, undetermined], init enc **366**

T59.6X[1,2,3,4]S Txc effct of hydrogen sulfide, [accid (unintentional), intentional self-harm, assault, undetermined], seq **373**

T59.6X[1,2,3,4]D Txc effct of hydrogen sulfide, [accid (unintentional), intentional self-harm, assault, undetermined], subsq enc **408**

T62.1X[1,2,3,4]A Txc effct of ingested berries, [accid (unintentional), intentional self-harm, assault, undetermined], init enc **366**

T62.1X[1,2,3,4]S Txc effct of ingested berries, [accid (unintentional), intentional self-harm, assault, undetermined], seq **373**

T62.1X[1,2,3,4]D Txc effct of ingested berries, [accid (unintentional), intentional self-harm, assault, undetermined], subsq enc **409**

T62.0X[1,2,3,4]A Txc effct of ingested mushrooms, [accid (unintentional), intentional self-harm, assault, undetermined], init enc **366**

T62.0X[1,2,3,4]S Txc effct of ingested mushrooms, [accid (unintentional), intentional self-harm, assault, undetermined], seq **373**

T62.0X[1,2,3,4]D Txc effct of ingested mushrooms, [accid (unintentional), intentional self-harm, assault, undetermined], subsq enc **409**

T52.4X[1,2,3,4]A Txc effct of ketones, [accid (unintentional), intentional self-harm, assault, undetermined], init enc **365**

T52.4X[1,2,3,4]S Txc effct of ketones, [accid (unintentional), intentional self-harm, assault, undetermined], seq **372**

T52.4X[1,2,3,4]D Txc effct of ketones, [accid (unintentional), intentional self-harm, assault, undetermined], subsq enc **408**

T59.3X[1,2,3,4]A Txc effct of lacrimogenic gas, [accid (unintentional), intentional self-harm, assault, undetermined], init enc **366**

T59.3X[1,2,3,4]S Txc effct of lacrimogenic gas, [accid (unintentional), intentional self-harm, assault, undetermined], seq **373**

T59.3X[1,2,3,4]D Txc effct of lacrimogenic gas, [accid (unintentional), intentional self-harm, assault, undetermined], subsq enc **408**

T65.81[1,2,3,4]A Txc effct of latex, [accid (unintentional), intentional self-harm, assault, undetermined], init enc **367**

T65.81[1,2,3,4]S Txc effct of latex, [accid (unintentional), intentional self-harm, assault, undetermined], seq **374**

T65.81[1,2,3,4]D Txc effct of latex, [accid (unintentional), intentional self-harm, assault, undetermined], subsq enc **409**

T56.0X[1,2,3,4]A Txc effct of lead and its compounds, [accid (unintentional), intentional self-harm, assault, undetermined], init enc **366**

T56.0X[1,2,3,4]S Txc effct of lead and its compounds, [accid (unintentional), intentional self-harm, assault, undetermined], seq **372**

T56.0X[1,2,3,4]D Txc effct of lead and its compounds, [accid (unintentional), intentional self-harm, assault, undetermined], subsq enc **408**

T57.2X[1,2,3,4]A Txc effct of manganese and its compounds, [accid (unintentional), intentional self-harm, assault, undetermined], init enc **366**

T57.2X[1,2,3,4]S Txc effct of manganese and its compounds, [accid (unintentional), intentional self-harm, assault, undetermined], seq **372**

T57.2X[1,2,3,4]D Txc effct of manganese and its compounds, [accid (unintentional), intentional self-harm, assault, undetermined], subsq enc **408**

T56.1X[1,2,3,4]A Txc effct of mercury and its compounds, [accid (unintentional), intentional self-harm, assault, undetermined], init enc **366**

T56.1X[1,2,3,4]S Txc effct of mercury and its compounds, [accid (unintentional), intentional self-harm, assault, undetermined], seq **372**

T56.1X[1,2,3,4]D Txc effct of mercury and its compounds, [accid (unintentional), intentional self-harm, assault, undetermined], subsq enc **408**

T51.1X[1,2,3,4]A Txc effct of methanol, [accid (unintentional), intentional self-harm, assault, undetermined], init enc **365**

T51.1X[1,2,3,4]S Txc effct of methanol, [accid (unintentional), intentional self-harm, assault, undetermined], seq **372**

T51.1X[1,2,3,4]D Txc effct of methanol, [accid (unintentional), intentional self-harm, assault, undetermined], subsq enc **407**

T65.3X[1,2,3,4]A Txc effct of nitroderivatives and amnioderivatives of benzene and its homologues, [accid (unintentional), intentional self-harm, assault, undetermined], init enc **367**

T65.3X[1,2,3,4]S Txc effct of nitroderivatives and amnioderivatives of benzene and its homologues, [accid (unintentional), intentional self-harm, assault, undetermined], seq **374**

T65.3X[1,2,3,4]D Txc effct of nitroderivatives and amnioderivatives of benzene and its homologues, [accid (unintentional), intentional self-harm, assault, undetermined], subsq enc **409**

T59.0X[1,2,3,4]A Txc effct of nitrogen oxides, [accid (unintentional), intentional self-harm, assault, undetermined], init enc **366**

T59.0X[1,2,3,4]S Txc effct of nitrogen oxides, [accid (unintentional), intentional self-harm, assault, undetermined], seq **373**

T59.0X[1,2,3,4]D Txc effct of nitrogen oxides, [accid (unintentional), intentional self-harm, assault, undetermined], subsq enc **408**

T65.5X[1,2,3,4]A Txc effct of nitroglycerin and oth nitric acids amd esters, [accid (unintentional), intentional self-harm, assault, undetermined], init enc **367**

T65.5X[1,2,3,4]S Txc effct of nitroglycerin and oth nitric acids amd esters, [accid (unintentional), intentional self-harm, assault, undetermined], seq **374**

T65.5X[1,2,3,4]D Txc effct of nitroglycerin and oth nitric acids amd esters, [accid (unintentional), intentional self-harm, assault, undetermined], subsq enc **409**

T60.0X[1,2,3,4]A Txc effct of organophosphate and carbamate insecticides, [accid (unintentional), intentional self-harm, assault, undetermined], init enc **366**

T60.0X[1,2,3,4]S Txc effct of organophosphate and carbamate insecticides, [accid (unintentional), intentional self-harm, assault, undetermined], seq **373**

T60.0X[1,2,3,4]D Txc effct of organophosphate and carbamate insecticides, [accid (unintentional), intentional self-harm, assault, undetermined], subsq enc **408**

T51.8X[1,2,3,4]A Txc effct of oth alcohols, [accid (unintentional), intentional self-harm, assault, undetermined], init enc **365**

T51.8X[1,2,3,4]S Txc effct of oth alcohols, [accid (unintentional), intentional self-harm, assault, undetermined], seq **372**

T51.8X[1,2,3,4]D Txc effct of oth alcohols, [accid (unintentional), intentional self-harm, assault, undetermined], subsq enc **407**

T54.1X[1,2,3,4]A Txc effct of oth corrosive organic compound, [accid (unintentional), intentional self-harm, assault, undetermined], init enc **366**

T54.1X[1,2,3,4]S Txc effct of oth corrosive organic compound, [accid (unintentional), intentional self-harm, assault, undetermined], seq **372**

T54.1X[1,2,3,4]D Txc effct of oth corrosive organic compound, [accid (unintentional), intentional self-harm, assault, undetermined], subsq enc **408**

T53.6X[1,2,3,4]A Txc effct of oth halogen derivatives of aliphatic hydrocarbons, [accid (unintentional), intentional self-harm, assault, undetermined], init enc **365**

T53.6X[1,2,3,4]S Txc effct of oth halogen derivatives of aliphatic hydrocarbons, [accid (unintentional), intentional self-harm, assault, undetermined], seq **372**

T53.6X[1,2,3,4]D Txc effct of oth halogen derivatives of aliphatic hydrocarbons, [accid (unintentional), intentional self-harm, assault, undetermined], subsq enc **408**

T53.7X[1,2,3,4]A Txc effct of oth halogen derivatives of aromatic hydrocarbons, [accid (unintentional), intentional self-harm, assault, undetermined], init enc **365**

T53.7X[1,2,3,4]S Txc effct of oth halogen derivatives of aromatic hydrocarbons, [accid (unintentional), intentional self-harm, assault, undetermined], seq **372**

T53.7X[1,2,3,4]D Txc effct of oth halogen derivatives of aromatic hydrocarbons, [accid (unintentional), intentional self-harm, assault, undetermined], subsq enc **408**

T62.2X[1,2,3,4]A Txc effct of oth ingested (parts of) plant(s), [accid (unintentional), intentional self-harm, assault, undetermined], init enc **366**

T62.2X[1,2,3,4]S Txc effct of oth ingested (parts of) plant(s), [accid (unintentional), intentional self-harm, assault, undetermined], seq **373**

T62.2X[1,2,3,4]D Txc effct of oth ingested (parts of) plant(s), [accid (unintentional), intentional self-harm, assault, undetermined], subsq enc **409**

T60.2X[1,2,3,4]A Txc effct of oth insecticides, [accid (unintentional), intentional self-harm, assault, undetermined], init enc **366**

T60.2X[1,2,3,4]S Txc effct of oth insecticides, [accid (unintentional), intentional self-harm, assault, undetermined], seq **373**

T60.2X[1,2,3,4]D Txc effct of oth insecticides, [accid (unintentional), intentional self-harm, assault, undetermined], subsq enc **408**

T56.89[1,2,3,4]A Txc effct of oth metals, [accid (unintentional), intentional self-harm, assault, undetermined], init enc **366**

T56.89[1,2,3,4]S Txc effct of oth metals, [accid (unintentional), intentional self-harm, assault, undetermined], seq **372**

T56.89[1,2,3,4]D Txc effct of oth metals, [accid (unintentional), intentional self-harm, assault, undetermined], subsq enc **408**

T64.8[1,2,3,4]XA Txc effct of oth mycotoxin food contaminants, [accid (unintentional), intentional self-harm, assault, undetermined], init enc **367**

T64.8[1,2,3,4]XS Txc effct of oth mycotoxin food contaminants, [accid (unintentional), intentional self-harm, assault, undetermined], seq **374**

T64.8[1,2,3,4]XD Txc effct of oth mycotoxin food contaminants, [accid (unintentional), intentional self-harm, assault, undetermined], subsq enc **409**

T52.8X[1,2,3,4]A Txc effct of oth organic solvents, [accid (unintentional), intentional self-harm, assault, undetermined], init enc **365**

T52.8X[1,2,3,4]S Txc effct of oth organic solvents, [accid (unintentional), intentional self-harm, assault, undetermined], seq **372**

T52.8X[1,2,3,4]D Txc effct of oth organic solvents, [accid (unintentional), intentional self-harm, assault, undetermined], subsq enc **408**

T60.8X[1,2,3,4]A Txc effct of oth pesticides, [accid (unintentional), intentional self-harm, assault, undetermined], init enc **366**

T60.8X[1,2,3,4]S Txc effct of oth pesticides, [accid (unintentional), intentional self-harm, assault, undetermined], seq **373**

T60.8X[1,2,3,4]D Txc effct of oth pesticides, [accid (unintentional), intentional self-harm, assault, undetermined], subsq enc **408**

T61.8X[1,2,3,4]A Txc effct of oth seafood, [accid (unintentional), intentional self-harm, assault, undetermined], init enc **366**

T61.8X[1,2,3,4]S Txc effct of oth seafood, [accid (unintentional), intentional self-harm, assault, undetermined], seq **373**

T61.8X[1,2,3,4]D Txc effct of oth seafood, [accid (unintentional), intentional self-harm, assault, undetermined], subsq enc **409**

T59.89[1,2,3,4]A Txc effct of oth spec gases, fumes and vapors, [accid (unintentional), intentional self-harm, assault, undetermined], init enc **366, 381**

T59.89[1,2,3,4]S Txc effct of oth spec gases, fumes and vapors, [accid (unintentional), intentional self-harm, assault, undetermined], seq **373**

T59.89[1,2,3,4]D Txc effct of oth spec gases, fumes and vapors, [accid (unintentional), intentional self-harm, assault, undetermined], subsq enc **408**

T57.8X[1,2,3,4]A Txc effct of oth spec inorganic substances, [accid (unintentional), intentional self-harm, assault, undetermined], init enc **366**

T57.8X[1,2,3,4]S Txc effct of oth spec inorganic substances, [accid (unintentional), intentional self-harm, assault, undetermined], seq **373**

T57.8X[1,2,3,4]D Txc effct of oth spec inorganic substances, [accid (unintentional), intentional self-harm, assault, undetermined], subsq enc **408**

T62.8X[1,2,3,4]A Txc effct of oth spec noxious substances eaten as food, [accid (unintentional), intentional self-harm, assault, undetermined], init enc **366**

T62.8X[1,2,3,4]S Txc effct of oth spec noxious substances eaten as food, [accid (unintentional), intentional self-harm, assault, undetermined], seq **373**

T62.8X[1,2,3,4]D Txc effct of oth spec noxious substances eaten as food, [accid (unintentional), intentional self-harm, assault, undetermined], subsq enc **409**

T65.89[1,2,3,4]A Txc effct of oth spec substances, [accid (unintentional), intentional self-harm, assault, undetermined], init enc **367**

T65.89[1,2,3,4]S Txc effct of oth spec substances, [accid (unintentional), intentional self-harm, assault, undetermined], seq **374**

T65.89[1,2,3,4]D Txc effct of oth spec substances, [accid (unintentional), intentional self-harm, assault, undetermined], subsq enc **409**

T65.29[1,2,3,4]A Txc effct of oth tobacco and nicotine, [accid (unintentional), intentional self-harm, assault, undetermined], init enc **367**

T65.29[1,2,3,4]S Txc effct of oth tobacco and nicotine, [accid (unintentional), intentional self-harm, assault, undetermined], seq **374**

T65.29[1,2,3,4]D Txc effct of oth tobacco and nicotine, [accid (unintentional), intentional self-harm, assault, undetermined], subsq enc **409**

T65.6X[1,2,3,4]A Txc effct of paints and dyes, NEC, [accid (unintentional), intentional self-harm, assault, undetermined], init enc **367**

T65.6X[1,2,3,4]S Txc effct of paints and dyes, NEC, [accid (unintentional), intentional self-harm, assault, undetermined], seq **374**

T65.6X[1,2,3,4]D Txc effct of paints and dyes, NEC, [accid (unintentional), intentional self-harm, assault, undetermined], subsq enc **409**

T52.0X[1,2,3,4]A Txc effct of petroleum products, [accid (unintentional), intentional self-harm, assault, undetermined], init enc **365**

T52.0X[1,2,3,4]S Txc effct of petroleum products, [accid (unintentional), intentional self-harm, assault, undetermined], seq **372**

T52.0X[1,2,3,4]D Txc effct of petroleum products, [accid (unintentional), intentional self-harm, assault, undetermined], subsq enc **408**

T54.0X[1,2,3,4]A Txc effct of phenol and phenol homologues, [accid (unintentional), intentional self-harm, assault, undetermined], init enc **366**

T54.0X[1,2,3,4]S Txc effct of phenol and phenol homologues, [accid (unintentional), intentional self-harm, assault, undetermined], seq **372**

T54.0X[1,2,3,4]D Txc effct of phenol and phenol homologues, [accid (unintentional), intentional self-harm, assault, undetermined], subsq enc **408**

T57.1X[1,2,3,4]A Txc effct of phosphorus and its compounds, [accid (unintentional), intentional self-harm, assault, undetermined], init enc **366**

T57.1X[1,2,3,4]S Txc effct of phosphorus and its compounds, [accid (unintentional), intentional self-harm, assault, undetermined], seq **372**

T57.1X[1,2,3,4]D Txc effct of phosphorus and its compounds, [accid (unintentional), intentional self-harm, assault, undetermined], subsq enc **408**

T63.01[1,2,3,4]A Txc effct of rattlesnake venom, [accid (unintentional), intentional self-harm, assault, undetermined], init enc **366**

T63.01[1,2,3,4]S Txc effct of rattlesnake venom, [accid (unintentional), intentional self-harm, assault, undetermined], seq **373**

T63.01[1,2,3,4]D Txc effct of rattlesnake venom, [accid (unintentional), intentional self-harm, assault, undetermined], subsq enc **409**

T60.4X[1,2,3,4]A Txc effct of rodenticides, [accid (unintentional), intentional self-harm, assault, undetermined], init enc **366**

T60.4X[1,2,3,4]S Txc effct of rodenticides, [accid (unintentional), intentional self-harm, assault, undetermined], seq **373**

T60.4X[1,2,3,4]D Txc effct of rodenticides, [accid (unintentional), intentional self-harm, assault, undetermined], subsq enc **408**

T59.81[1,2,3,4]A Txc effct of smoke, [accid (unintentional), intentional self-harm, assault, undetermined], init enc **366, 381**

T59.81[1,2,3,4]S Txc effct of smoke, [accid (unintentional), intentional self-harm, assault, undetermined], seq **373**

T59.81[1,2,3,4]D Txc effct of smoke, [accid (unintentional), intentional self-harm, assault, undetermined], subsq enc **408**

T55.0X[1,2,3,4]A Txc effct of soaps, [accid (unintentional), intentional self-harm, assault, undetermined], init enc **366**

T55.0X[1,2,3,4]S Txc effct of soaps, [accid (unintentional), intentional self-harm, assault, undetermined], seq **372**

T55.0X[1,2,3,4]D Txc effct of soaps, [accid (unintentional), intentional self-harm, assault, undetermined], subsq enc **408**

T65.1X[1,2,3,4]A Txc effct of strychnine, [accid (unintentional), intentional self-harm, assault, undetermined], init enc **367**

T65.1X[1,2,3,4]S Txc effct of strychnine, [accid (unintentional), intentional self-harm, assault, undetermined], seq **374**

T65.1X[1,2,3,4]D Txc effct of strychnine, [accid (unintentional), intentional self-harm, assault, undetermined], subsq enc **409**

T59.1X[1,2,3,4]A Txc effct of sulfur dioxide, [accid (unintentional), intentional self-harm, assault, undetermined], init enc **366**

T59.1X[1,2,3,4]S Txc effct of sulfur dioxide, [accid (unintentional), intentional self-harm, assault, undetermined], seq **373**

T59.1X[1,2,3,4]D Txc effct of sulfur dioxide, [accid (unintentional), intentional self-harm, assault, undetermined], subsq enc **408**

T63.03[1,2,3,4]A Txc effct of taipan venom, [accid (unintentional), intentional self-harm, assault, undetermined], init enc **366**

T63.03[1,2,3,4]S Txc effct of taipan venom, [accid (unintentional), intentional self-harm, assault, undetermined], seq **373**

T63.03[1,2,3,4]D Txc effct of taipan venom, [accid (unintentional), intentional self-harm, assault, undetermined], subsq enc **409**

T53.3X[1,2,3,4]A Txc effct of tetrachloroethylene, [accid (unintentional), intentional self-harm, assault, undetermined], init enc **365**

T53.3X[1,2,3,4]S Txc effct of tetrachloroethylene, [accid (unintentional), intentional self-harm, assault, undetermined], seq **372**

T53.3X[1,2,3,4]D Txc effct of tetrachloroethylene, [accid (unintentional), intentional self-harm, assault, undetermined], subsq enc **408**

T56.81[1,2,3,4]A Txc effct of thallium and its compounds, [accid (unintentional), intentional self-harm, assault, undetermined], init enc **366**

T56.81[1,2,3,4]S Txc effct of thallium and its compounds, [accid (unintentional), intentional self-harm, assault, undetermined], seq **372**

T56.81[1,2,3,4]D Txc effct of thallium and its compounds, [accid (unintentional), intentional self-harm, assault, undetermined], subsq enc **408**

T56.6X[1,2,3,4]A Txc effct of tin and its compounds, [accid (unintentional), intentional self-harm, assault, undetermined], init enc **366**

T56.6X[1,2,3,4]S Txc effct of tin and its compounds, [accid (unintentional), intentional self-harm, assault, undetermined], seq **372**

T56.6X[1,2,3,4]D Txc effct of tin and its compounds, [accid (unintentional), intentional self-harm, assault, undetermined], subsq enc **408**

T65.22[1,2,3,4]A Txc effct of tobacco cigarettes, [accid (unintentional), intentional self-harm, assault, undetermined], init enc **367**

T65.22[1,2,3,4]S Txc effct of tobacco cigarettes, [accid (unintentional), intentional self-harm, assault, undetermined], seq **374**

T65.22[1,2,3,4]D Txc effct of tobacco cigarettes, [accid (unintentional), intentional self-harm, assault, undetermined], subsq enc **409**

T53.2X[1,2,3,4]A Txc effct of trichloroethylene, [accid (unintentional), intentional self-harm, assault, undetermined], init enc **365**

T53.2X[1,2,3,4]S Txc effct of trichloroethylene, [accid (unintentional), intentional self-harm, assault, undetermined], seq **372**

T53.2X[1,2,3,4]D Txc effct of trichloroethylene, [accid (unintentional), intentional self-harm, assault, undetermined], subsq enc **408**

T51.9[1,2,3,4]XA Txc effct of unsp alcohol, [accid (unintentional), intentional self-harm, assault, undetermined], init enc **365**

T51.9[1,2,3,4]XS Txc effct of unsp alcohol, [accid (unintentional), intentional self-harm, assault, undetermined], seq **372**

T51.9[1,2,3,4]XD Txc effct of unsp alcohol, [accid (unintentional), intentional self-harm, assault, undetermined], subsq enc **408**

T54.9[1,2,3,4]XA Txc effct of unsp corrosive substance, [accid (unintentional), intentional self-harm, assault, undetermined], init enc **366**

T54.9[1,2,3,4]XS Txc effct of unsp corrosive substance, [accid (unintentional), intentional self-harm, assault, undetermined], seq **372**

T54.9[1,2,3,4]XD Txc effct of unsp corrosive substance, [accid (unintentional), intentional self-harm, assault, undetermined], subsq enc **408**

T59.9[1,2,3,4]XA Txc effct of unsp gases, fumes and vapors, [accid (unintentional), intentional self harm, assault, undetermined], init enc **366, 381**

T59.9[1,2,3,4]XS Txc effct of unsp gases, fumes and vapors, [accid (unintentional), intentional self-harm, assault, undetermined], seq **373**

T59.9[1,2,3,4]XD Txc effct of unsp gases, fumes and vapors, [accid (unintentional), intentional self-harm, assault, undetermined], subsq enc **408**

T53.9[1,2,3,4]XA Txc effct of unsp halogen derivatives of aliphatic and aromatic hydrocarbons, [accid (unintentional), intentional self-harm, assault, undetermined], init enc **366**

T53.9[1,2,3,4]XS Txc effct of unsp halogen derivatives of aliphatic and aromatic hydrocarbons, [accid (unintentional), intentional self-harm, assault, undetermined], seq **372**

T53.9[1,2,3,4]XD Txc effct of unsp halogen derivatives of aliphatic and aromatic hydrocarbons, [accid (unintentional), intentional self-harm, assault, undetermined], subsq enc **408**

T57.9[1,2,3,4]XA Txc effct of unsp inorganic substance, [accid (unintentional), intentional self-harm, assault, undetermined], init enc **366**

T57.9[1,2,3,4]XS Txc effct of unsp inorganic substance, [accid (unintentional), intentional self-harm, assault, undetermined], seq **373**

T57.9[1,2,3,4]XD Txc effct of unsp inorganic substance, [accid (unintentional), intentional self-harm, assault, undetermined], subsq enc **408**

T56.9[1,2,3,4]XA Txc effct of unsp metal, [accid (unintentional), intentional self-harm, assault, undetermined], init enc **366**

T56.9[1,2,3,4]XS Txc effct of unsp metal, [accid (unintentional), intentional self-harm, assault, undetermined], seq **372**

T56.9[1,2,3,4]XD Txc effct of unsp metal, [accid (unintentional), intentional self-harm, assault, undetermined], subsq enc **408**

T62.9[1,2,3,4]XA Txc effct of unsp noxious substances eaten as food, [accid (unintentional), intentional self-harm, assault, undetermined], init enc **366**

T62.9[1,2,3,4]XS Txc effct of unsp noxious substances eaten as food, [accid (unintentional), intentional self-harm, assault, undetermined], seq **373**

T62.9[1,2,3,4]XD Txc effct of unsp noxious substances eaten as food, [accid (unintentional), intentional self-harm, assault, undetermined], subsq enc **409**

T52.9[1,2,3,4]XA Txc effct of unsp organic solvent, [accid (unintentional), intentional self-harm, assault, undetermined], init enc **365**

T52.9[1,2,3,4]XS Txc effct of unsp organic solvent, [accid (unintentional), intentional self-harm, assault, undetermined], seq **372**

T52.9[1,2,3,4]XD Txc effct of unsp organic solvent, [accid (unintentional), intentional self-harm, assault, undetermined], subsq enc **408**

T60.9[1,2,3,4]XA Txc effct of unsp pesticides, [accid (unintentional), intentional self-harm, assault, undetermined], init enc **366**

T60.9[1,2,3,4]XS Txc effct of unsp pesticides, [accid (unintentional), intentional self-harm, assault, undetermined], seq **373**

T60.9[1,2,3,4]XD Txc effct of unsp pesticides, [accid (unintentional), intentional self-harm, assault, undetermined], subsq enc **408**

T61.9[1,2,3,4]XA Txc effct of unsp seafood, [accid (unintentional), intentional self-harm, assault, undetermined], init enc **366**

T61.9[1,2,3,4]XS Txc effct of unsp seafood, [accid (unintentional), intentional self-harm, assault, undetermined], seq **373**

T61.9[1,2,3,4]XD Txc effct of unsp seafood, [accid (unintentional), intentional self-harm, assault, undetermined], subsq enc **409**

T63.00[1,2,3,4]A Txc effct of unsp snake venom, [accid (unintentional), intentional self-harm, assault, undetermined], init enc **366**

T63.00[1,2,3,4]S Txc effct of unsp snake venom, [accid (unintentional), intentional self-harm, assault, undetermined], seq **373**

T63.00[1,2,3,4]D Txc effct of unsp snake venom, [accid (unintentional), intentional self-harm, assault, undetermined], subsq enc **409**

T63.30[1,2,3,4]A Txc effct of unsp spider venom, [accid (unintentional), intentional self-harm, assault, undetermined], init enc **367**

T63.30[1,2,3,4]S Txc effct of unsp spider venom, [accid (unintentional), intentional self-harm, assault, undetermined], seq **373**

T63.30[1,2,3,4]D Txc effct of unsp spider venom, [accid (unintentional), intentional self-harm, assault, undetermined], subsq enc **409**

T65.9[1,2,3,4]XA Txc effct of unsp substance, [accid (unintentional), intentional self-harm, assault, undetermined], init enc **367**

T65.9[1,2,3,4]XS Txc effct of unsp substance, [accid (unintentional), intentional self-harm, assault, undetermined], seq **374**

T65.9[1,2,3,4]XD Txc effct of unsp substance, [accid (unintentional), intentional self-harm, assault, undetermined], subsq enc **409**

T63.42[1,2,3,4]A Txc effct of venom of ants, [accid (unintentional), intentional self-harm, assault, undetermined], init enc **367**

T63.42[1,2,3,4]S Txc effct of venom of ants, [accid (unintentional), intentional self-harm, assault, undetermined], seq **373**

T63.42[1,2,3,4]D Txc effct of venom of ants, [accid (unintentional), intentional self-harm, assault, undetermined], subsq enc **409**

T63.44[1,2,3,4]A Txc effct of venom of bees, [accid (unintentional), intentional self-harm, assault, undetermined], init enc **367**

T63.44[1,2,3,4]S Txc effct of venom of bees, [accid (unintentional), intentional self-harm, assault, undetermined], seq **373**

T63.44[1,2,3,4]D Txc effct of venom of bees, [accid (unintentional), intentional self-harm, assault, undetermined], subsq enc **409**

T63.31[1,2,3,4]A Txc effct of venom of black widow spider, [accid (unintentional), intentional self-harm, assault, undetermined], init enc **367**

T63.31[1,2,3,4]S Txc effct of venom of black widow spider, [accid (unintentional), intentional self-harm, assault, undetermined], seq **373**

T63.31[1,2,3,4]D Txc effct of venom of black widow spider, [accid (unintentional), intentional self-harm, assault, undetermined], subsq enc **409**

T63.33[1,2,3,4]A Txc effct of venom of brown recluse spider, [accid (unintentional), intentional self-harm, assault, undetermined], init enc **367**

T63.33[1,2,3,4]S Txc effct of venom of brown recluse spider, [accid (unintentional), intentional self-harm, assault, undetermined], seq **373**

T63.33[1,2,3,4]D Txc effct of venom of brown recluse spider, [accid (unintentional), intentional self-harm, assault, undetermined], subsq enc **409**

T63.43[1,2,3,4]A Txc effct of venom of caterpillars, [accid (unintentional), intentional self-harm, assault, undetermined], init enc **367**

T63.43[1,2,3,4]S Txc effct of venom of caterpillars, [accid (unintentional), intentional self-harm, assault, undetermined], seq **373**

T63.43[1,2,3,4]D Txc effct of venom of caterpillars, [accid (unintentional), intentional self-harm, assault, undetermined], subsq enc **409**

T63.41[1,2,3,4]A Txc effct of venom of centipedes and venomous millipedes, [accid (unintentional), intentional self-harm, assault, undetermined], init enc **367**

T63.41[1,2,3,4]S Txc effct of venom of centipedes and venomous millipedes, [accid (unintentional), intentional self-harm, assault, undetermined], seq **373**

T63.41[1,2,3,4]D Txc effct of venom of centipedes and venomous millipedes, [accid (unintentional), intentional self-harm, assault, undetermined], subsq enc **409**

T63.11[1,2,3,4]A Txc effct of venom of gila monster, [accid (unintentional), intentional self-harm, assault, undetermined], init enc **367**

T63.11[1,2,3,4]S Txc effct of venom of gila monster, [accid (unintentional), intentional self-harm, assault, undetermined], seq **373**

T63.11[1,2,3,4]D Txc effct of venom of gila monster, [accid (unintentional), intentional self-harm, assault, undetermined], subsq enc **409**

T63.45[1,2,3,4]A Txc effct of venom of hornets, [accid (unintentional), intentional self-harm, assault, undetermined], init enc **367**

T63.45[1,2,3,4]S	Txc effct of venom of hornets, [accid (unintentional), intentional self-harm, assault, undetermined], seq **373**
T63.45[1,2,3,4]D	Txc effct of venom of hornets, [accid (unintentional), intentional self-harm, assault, undetermined], subsq encount **409**
T63.08[1,2,3,4]A	Txc effct of venom of oth African and Asian snake, [accid (unintentional), intentional self-harm, assault, undetermined], init enc **367**
T63.08[1,2,3,4]S	Txc effct of venom of oth African and Asian snake, [accid (unintentional), intentional self-harm, assault, undetermined], seq **373**
T63.08[1,2,3,4]D	Txc effct of venom of oth African and Asian snake, [accid (unintentional), intentional self-harm, assault, undetermined], subsq enc **409**
T63.48[1,2,3,4]A	Txc effct of venom of oth arthropod, [accid (unintentional), intentional self-harm, assault, undetermined], init enc **367**
T63.48[1,2,3,4]S	Txc effct of venom of oth arthropod, [accid (unintentional), intentional self-harm, assault, undetermined], seq **373**
T63.48[1,2,3,4]D	Txc effct of venom of oth arthropod, [accid (unintentional), intentional self-harm, assault, undetermined], subsq enc **409**
T63.07[1,2,3,4]A	Txc effct of venom of oth Australian snake, [accid (unintentional), intentional self-harm, assault, undetermined], init enc **366**
T63.07[1,2,3,4]S	Txc effct of venom of oth Australian snake, [accid (unintentional), intentional self-harm, assault, undetermined], seq **373**
T63.07[1,2,3,4]D	Txc effct of venom of oth Australian snake, [accid (unintentional), intentional self-harm, assault, undetermined], subsq enc **409**
T63.06[1,2,3,4]A	Txc effct of venom of oth North and South American snake, [accid (unintentional), intentional self-harm, assault, undetermined], init enc **366**
T63.06[1,2,3,4]S	Txc effct of venom of oth North and South American snake, [accid (unintentional), intentional self-harm, assault, undetermined], seq **373**
T63.06[1,2,3,4]D	Txc effct of venom of oth North and South American snake, [accid (unintentional), intentional self-harm, assault, undetermined], subsq enc **409**
T63.19[1,2,3,4]A	Txc effct of venom of oth reptiles, [accid (unintentional), intentional self-harm, assault, undetermined], init enc **367**
T63.19[1,2,3,4]S	Txc effct of venom of oth reptiles, [accid (unintentional), intentional self-harm, assault, undetermined], seq **373**
T63.19[1,2,3,4]D	Txc effct of venom of oth reptiles, [accid (unintentional), intentional self-harm, assault, undetermined], subsq enc **409**
T63.09[1,2,3,4]A	Txc effct of venom of oth snake, [accid (unintentional), intentional self-harm, assault, undetermined], init enc **367**
T63.09[1,2,3,4]S	Txc effct of venom of oth snake, [accid (unintentional), intentional self-harm, assault, undetermined], seq **373**
T63.09[1,2,3,4]D	Txc effct of venom of oth snake, [accid (unintentional), intentional self-harm, assault, undetermined], subsq enc **409**
T63.39[1,2,3,4]A	Txc effct of venom of oth spider, [accid (unintentional), intentional self-harm, assault, undetermined], init enc **367**
T63.39[1,2,3,4]S	Txc effct of venom of oth spider, [accid (unintentional), intentional self-harm, assault, undetermined], seq **373**
T63.39[1,2,3,4]D	Txc effct of venom of oth spider, [accid (unintentional), intentional self-harm, assault, undetermined], subsq enc **409**
T63.12[1,2,3,4]A	Txc effct of venom of oth venomous lizard, [accid (unintentional), intentional self-harm, assault, undetermined], init enc **367**
T63.12[1,2,3,4]S	Txc effct of venom of oth venomous lizard, [accid (unintentional), intentional self-harm, assault, undetermined], seq **373**
T63.12[1,2,3,4]D	Txc effct of venom of oth venomous lizard, [accid (unintentional), intentional self-harm, assault, undetermined], subsq enc **409**
T63.2X[1,2,3,4]A	Txc effct of venom of scorpion, [accid (unintentional), intentional self-harm, assault, undetermined], init enc **367**
T63.2X[1,2,3,4]S	Txc effct of venom of scorpion, [accid (unintentional), intentional self-harm, assault, undetermined], seq **373**
T63.2X[1,2,3,4]D	Txc effct of venom of scorpion, [accid (unintentional), intentional self-harm, assault, undetermined], subsq enc **409**
T63.32[1,2,3,4]A	Txc effct of venom of tarantula, [accid (unintentional), intentional self-harm, assault, undetermined], init enc **367**
T63.32[1,2,3,4]S	Txc effct of venom of tarantula, [accid (unintentional), intentional self-harm, assault, undetermined], seq **373**
T63.32[1,2,3,4]D	Txc effct of venom of tarantula, [accid (unintentional), intentional self-harm, assault, undetermined], subsq enc **409**
T63.46[1,2,3,4]A	Txc effct of venom of wasps, [accid (unintentional), intentional self-harm, assault, undetermined], init enc **367**
T63.46[1,2,3,4]S	Txc effct of venom of wasps, [accid (unintentional), intentional self-harm, assault, undetermined], seq **373**
T63.46[1,2,3,4]D	Txc effct of venom of wasps, [accid (unintentional), intentional self-harm, assault, undetermined], subsq enc **409**

T56.5X[1,2,3,4]A	Txc effct of zinc and its compounds, [accid (unintentional), intentional self-harm, assault, undetermined], init enc **366**
T56.5X[1,2,3,4]S	Txc effct of zinc and its compounds, [accid (unintentional), intentional self-harm, assault, undetermined], seq **372**
T56.5X[1,2,3,4]D	Txc effct of zinc and its compounds, [accid (unintentional), intentional self-harm, assault, undetermined], subsq enc **408**
G92	Txc encephalopathy **11**, **15**, **38**, **283**
L53.0	Txc erythema **223**, **284**
K52.1	Txc gastroenteritis and colitis **117**, **284**
K71*	Txc liver dz **124**, **284**
G70.1	Txc myoneural d/o **34**
O29.3X9	Txc reaction to local anesth during preg, unsp trmstr **280**
O29.3X[1,2,3]	Txc reaction to local anesthesia during preg, [1st, 2nd, 3rd] trmstr **277**
A48.3	Txc shock synd **308**
E10.610	Type 1 diabetes mellitus w diabetic neuropathic arthropathy **34**
E10.9	Type 1 diabetes mellitus w/o comp **2**, **246**
E10.5*	Type 1 diabetes mellitus with circulatory comp **2**, **100**
E10.65	Type 1 diabetes mellitus with hyperglycemia **246**
E10.64*	Type 1 diabetes mellitus with hypoglycemia **246**
E10.1*	Type 1 diabetes mellitus with ketoacidosis **2**, **246**
E10.2*	Type 1 diabetes mellitus with kidney comp **2**, **254**, **256**
E10.4*	Type 1 diabetes mellitus with neurological comp **2**, **34**
E10.3*	Type 1 diabetes mellitus with ophthalmic comp **2**, **45**
E10.63*	Type 1 diabetes mellitus with oral comp **246**
E10.618	Type 1 diabetes mellitus with oth diabetic arthropathy **246**
E10.6*	Type 1 diabetes mellitus with oth spec comp **2**
E10.69	Type 1 diabetes mellitus with oth spec comp **246**
E10.62*	Type 1 diabetes mellitus with skin comp **246**
E10.8	Type 1 diabetes mellitus with unsp comp **2**, **246**
S32.1[4,5,6,7,9]X[A,B]	[Type 1, Type 2, Type 3, Type 4, Oth] fx of sacrum, init enc for [clsd, opn] fx **421**, **433**
S32.1[4,5,6,7,9]X[D,G]	[Type 1, Type 2, Type 3, Type 4, Oth] fx of sacrum, subsq enc for fx w/ [routine, delayed] healing **170**
S32.1[4,5,6,7,9]XK	[Type 1, Type 2, Type 3, Type 4, Oth] fx of sacrum, subsq enc for fx w/ nonu **196**
E11.610	Type 2 diabetes mellitus w diabetic neuropathic arthropathy **34**
E11.9	Type 2 diabetes mellitus w/o comp **2**, **246**
E11.5*	Type 2 diabetes mellitus with circulatory comp **2**, **100**
E11.65	Type 2 diabetes mellitus with hyperglycemia **246**
E11.0*	Type 2 diabetes mellitus with hyperosmolarity **2**, **246**
E11.64*	Type 2 diabetes mellitus with hypoglycemia **246**
E11.2*	Type 2 diabetes mellitus with kidney comp **2**, **256**
E11.4*	Type 2 diabetes mellitus with neurological comp **2**, **34**
E11.3*	Type 2 diabetes mellitus with ophthalmic comp **2**, **45**
E11.63*	Type 2 diabetes mellitus with oral comp **246**
E11.618	Type 2 diabetes mellitus with oth diabetic arthropathy **246**
E11.6*	Type 2 diabetes mellitus with oth spec comp **2**
E11.69	Type 2 diabetes mellitus with oth spec comp **246**
E11.62*	Type 2 diabetes mellitus with skin comp **246**
E11.8	Type 2 diabetes mellitus with unsp comp **2**, **246**
S02.11[0,1,2,3][A,B]	[Type I, Type II, Type III, Unsp] occipital condyle fx, init enc for [clsd, opn] fx **417**
S02.11[0,1,2,3]A	[Type I, Type II, Type III, unsp] occipital condyle fx, init enc for clsd fx **36**, **37**
S02.11[0,1,2,3]B	[Type I, Type II, Type III, unsp] occipital condyle fx, init enc for opn fx **36**, **37**
S02.11[0,1,2,3]S	[Type I, Type II, Type III, Unsp] occipital condyle fx, seq **39**
S02.11[0,1,2,3][D,G]	[Type I, Type II, Type III, Unsp] occipital condyle fx, subsq enc for fx w/ [routine, delayed] healing **169**
S02.11[0,1,2,3]K	[Type I, Type II, Type III, Unsp] occipital condyle fx, subsq enc for fx w/ nonu **195**
S12.11[0,1,2][A,B,S]	Type II dens fx [ant disp, post disp, nondisp] init enc for fx [clsd, opn, seq] **165**
S12.14X[A,B]	Type III traum spondylolisthesis of 2nd cervical vertebra, init enc for [clsd, opn] fx **419**
S12.14X[A,B,S]	Type III traum spondylolisthesis of 2nd cervical vertebra, init enc for fx [clsd, opn, seq] **165**
S12.14X[D,G]	Type III traum spondylolisthesis of 2nd cervical vertebra, subsq enc for fx w/ [routine, delayed] healing **169**
S12.24X[A,B]	Type III traum spondylolisthesis of 3rd cervical vertebra, init enc for [clsd, opn] fx **419**

S12.24X[A,B,S]	Type III traum spondylolisthesis of 3rd cervical vertebra, init enc for fx [clsd, opn, seq] 165
S12.24X[D,G]	Type III traum spondylolisthesis of 3rd cervical vertebra, subsq enc for fx w/ [routine, delayed] healing 169
S12.34X[A,B]	Type III traum spondylolisthesis of 4th cervical vertebra, init enc for [clsd, opn] fx 419
S12.34X[A,B,S]	Type III traum spondylolisthesis of 4th cervical vertebra, init enc for fx [clsd, opn, seq] 165
S12.34X[D,G]	Type III traum spondylolisthesis of 4th cervical vertebra, subsq enc for fx w/ [routine, delayed] healing 169
S12.44X[A,B]	Type III traum spondylolisthesis of 5th cervical vertebra, init enc for [clsd, opn] fx 419
S12.44X[A,B,S]	Type III traum spondylolisthesis of 5th cervical vertebra, init enc for fx [clsd, opn, seq] 165
S12.44X[D,G]	Type III traum spondylolisthesis of 5th cervical vertebra, subsq enc for fx w/ [routine, delayed] healing 169
S12.54X[A,B]	Type III traum spondylolisthesis of 6th cervical vertebra, init enc for [clsd, opn] fx 419
S12.54X[A,B,S]	Type III traum spondylolisthesis of 6th cervical vertebra, init enc for fx [clsd, opn, seq] 165
S12.54X[D,G]	Type III traum spondylolisthesis of 6th cervical vertebra, subsq enc for fx w/ [routine, delayed] healing 169
S12.64X[A,B,S]	Type III traum spondylolisthesis of 7th cervical vertebra, init enc for fx [clsd, opn, seq] 165
S12.64X[A,B]	Type III traum spondylolisthesis of 7th cervical vertebra, init enc for [clsd, opn] fx 419
S12.64X[D,G]	Type III traum spondylolisthesis of 7th cervical vertebra, subsq enc for fx w/ [routine, delayed] healing 169
S12.14XK	Type III traum spondylolysis of 2nd cervcal vert, 7thK 195
S12.24XK	Type III traum spondylolysis of 3rd cervcal vert, 7thK 195
S12.34XK	Type III traum spondylolysis of 4th cervcal vert, 7thK 195
S12.44XK	Type III traum spondylolysis of 5th cervcal vert, 7thK 195
S12.64XK	Type III traum spondylolysis of 7th cervcal vert, 7thK 195
S12.54XK	Type III traum spondylolysis of sixth cervcal vert, 7thK 195
A01*	Typhoid and paratyphoid fevers 308
A75*	Typhus fever 308
K62.6	Ulcer of anus and rectum 117
K22.1*	Ulcer of esophagus 115
K63.3	Ulcer of intestine 117
N48.5	Ulcer of penis 261
N76.5	Ulceration of vagina 269
N76.6	Ulceration of vulva 270
N77.0	Ulceration of vulva in dz classified elsw 270
K51*	Ulcerative colitis 116
A21.[0,1,7,8,9]	[Ulceroglandular, Oculoglandular, Generalized, Oth forms, Unsp] tularemia 308
S53.44[1,2,9] [A,S]	Ulnar collat lgmt sprain [rt, lt, unsp] [init enc, seq] 187
S53.44[1,2,9]D	Ulnar collat lgmt sprain of [rt, lt, unsp] elbow, subsq enc 392
S53.42[1,2,9] [A,S]	Ulnohumeral (jt) sprain [rt, lt, unsp] [init enc, seq] 186
S53.42[1,2,9]D	Ulnohumeral sprain of [rt, lt, unsp] elbow, subsq enc 392
P51*	Umbilical hemor of newborn 288
K42*	Umbilical hernia 117
K42.[0,1]	Umbilical hernia, w/ [obstruction w/o gangrene, gangrene], not spec as recurrent 284
P83.6	Umbilical polyp of newborn 289
T39.1X6*	Underdosing of 4-Aminophenol derivatives 404
T46.996*	Underdosing of agents affecting the cardiovascular sys 406
T48.996*	Underdosing of agents primarily acting on the resp sys 407
T47.8X6*	Underdosing of agents primarily affecting GI sys 406
T44.6X6*	Underdosing of alpha-adrenoreceptor antagonists 405
T36.5X6*	Underdosing of aminoglycosides 403
T43.626*	Underdosing of amphetamines 405
T50.7X6*	Underdosing of analeptics and opioid receptor antagonists 407
T38.7X6*	Underdosing of androgens and anabolic congeners 403
T46.4X6*	Underdosing of angiotensin-converting-enzyme inhibitors 406
T38.816*	Underdosing of ant pituitary hormones 403
T37.4X6*	Underdosing of anthelminthics 403
T45.0X6*	Underdosing of antiallergic and antiemetic drugs 405
T48.6X6*	Underdosing of antiasthmatics 407
T44.0X6*	Underdosing of anticholinesterase agents 405

T45.516*	Underdosing of anticoagulants 405
T47.6X6*	Underdosing of antidiarrheal drugs 406
T50.6X6*	Underdosing of antidotes and chelating agents 407
T36.7X6*	Underdosing of antifungal antibiotics, systemically used 403
T38.6X6*	Underdosing of antigonadtr/antiestr/antiandrg, NEC 403
T46.6X6*	Underdosing of antihyperlipidemic and antiarterio drugs 406
T37.2X6*	Underdosing of antimalarials and drugs acting on bld protzoa 403
T37.1X6*	Underdosing of antimycobacterial drugs 403
T45.1X6*	Underdosing of antineoplastic and immunosuppressive drugs 405
T42.8X6*	Underdosing of antiparkns drug/centr muscle-tone depressants 404
T49.1X6*	Underdosing of antipruritics 407
T39.4X6*	Underdosing of antirheumatics, NEC 404
T45.526*	Underdosing of antithrombotic drugs 405
T38.2X6*	Underdosing of antithyroid drugs 403
T48.3X6*	Underdosing of antitussives 406
T46.8X6*	Underdosing of antivaric drugs, incl* sclerosing agents 406
T37.5X6*	Underdosing of antiviral drugs 403
T50.5X6*	Underdosing of appetite depressants 407
T39.016*	Underdosing of aspirin 403
T42.3X6*	Underdosing of barbiturates 404
T42.4X6*	Underdosing of benzodiazepines 404
T44.7X6*	Underdosing of beta-adrenoreceptor antagonists 405
T43.4X6*	Underdosing of butyrophenone and thiothixene neuroleptics 405
T43.616*	Underdosing of caffeine 405
T46.1X6*	Underdosing of calcium-channel blockers 406
T40.7X6*	Underdosing of cannabis (derivatives) 404
T46.0X6*	Underdosing of cardi-stim glycos/drug simlar act 406
T44.8X6*	Underdosing of centr-acting/adren-neurn-block agnt 405
T36.1X6*	Underdosing of cephalospor/oth beta-lactm antibiotics 403
T36.2X6*	Underdosing of chloramphenicol group 403
T40.5X6*	Underdosing of cocaine 404
T46.3X6*	Underdosing of coronary vasodilators 406
T50.2X6*	Underdosing of crbnc-anhydr inhibtr, benzo/oth diuretc 407
T49.7X6*	Underdosing of dental drugs, topically applied 407
T50.8X6*	Underdosing of diagnostic agents 407
T47.5X6*	Underdosing of digestants 406
T44.996*	Underdosing of drug affecting the autonomic nervous sys 405
T50.4X6*	Underdosing of drugs affecting uric acid metabolism 407
T50.996*	Underdosing of drugs, medicaments and biological substances 407
T50.3X6*	Underdosing of electrolytic/caloric/wtr-bal agnt 407
T47.7X6*	Underdosing of emetics 406
T49.3X6*	Underdosing of emollients, demulcents and protectants 407
T45.3X6*	Underdosing of enzymes 405
T48.4X6*	Underdosing of expectorants 406
T44.2X6*	Underdosing of ganglionic blocking drugs 405
T38.0X6*	Underdosing of glucocorticoids and synth analogues 403
T45.626*	Underdosing of hemostatic drugs 406
T47.0X6*	Underdosing of histamine H2-receptor blockers 406
T42.0X6*	Underdosing of hydantoin derivatives 404
T42.1X6*	Underdosing of iminostilbenes 404
T50.Z16*	Underdosing of immunoglobulin 407
T41.0X6*	Underdosing of inhaled anesthetics 404
T38.3X6*	Underdosing of insulin and oral hypoglycemic drugs 403
T41.1X6*	Underdosing of intravenous anesthetics 404
T45.4X6*	Underdosing of iron and its compounds 405
T49.4X6*	Underdosing of keratolyt/keratplst/hair trmt drug 407
T41.3X6*	Underdosing of local anesthetics 404
T49.0X6*	Underdosing of local antifung/infect/inflamm drugs 407
T49.2X6*	Underdosing of local astringents and local detergents 407
T50.1X6*	Underdosing of loop [high-ceiling] diuretics 407
T36.3X6*	Underdosing of macrolides 403
T40.3X6*	Underdosing of methadone 404
T43.636*	Underdosing of methylphenidate 405
T50.0X6*	Underdosing of mineralocorticoids and their antagonists 407
T42.5X6*	Underdosing of mixed antiepileptics 404
T50.A26*	Underdosing of mixed bacterial vaccines w/o a pertuss 407
T43.1X6*	Underdosing of monoamine-oxidase-inhibitor antidepressants 405

T39.8X6*	Underdosing of nonopioid analges/antipyret, NEC 404	
T49.5X6*	Underdosing of ophthalmological drugs and preparations 407	
T40.0X6*	Underdosing of opium 404	
T38.4X6*	Underdosing of oral contraceptives 403	
T47.1X6*	Underdosing of oth antacids and anti-gastric-secretion drugs 406	
T48.5X6*	Underdosing of oth anti-common-cold drugs 407	
T43.296*	Underdosing of oth antidepressants 405	
T46.2X6*	Underdosing of oth antidysrhythmic drugs 406	
T42.6X6*	Underdosing of oth antiepileptic and sedative-hypnotic drugs 404	
T46.5X6*	Underdosing of oth antihypertensive drugs 406	
T37.3X6*	Underdosing of oth antiprotozoal drugs 403	
T43.596*	Underdosing of oth antipsychotics and neuroleptics 405	
T50.A96*	Underdosing of oth bacterial vaccines 407	
T48.296*	Underdosing of oth drugs acting on muscles 406	
T38.5X6*	Underdosing of oth estrogens and progestogens 403	
T45.696*	Underdosing of oth fibrinolysis-affecting drugs 406	
T41.296*	Underdosing of oth general anesthetics 404	
T38.996*	Underdosing of oth hormone antagonists 403	
T38.896*	Underdosing of oth hormones and synth substitutes 403	
T47.4X6*	Underdosing of oth laxatives 406	
T40.696*	Underdosing of oth narcotics 404	
T39.396*	Underdosing of oth nonsteroidal anti-inflam drugs 404	
T40.2X6*	Underdosing of oth opioids 404	
T44.3X6*	Underdosing of oth parasympatholytics and spasmolytics 405	
T44.1X6*	Underdosing of oth parasympathomimetics 405	
T40.996*	Underdosing of oth psychodysleptics 404	
T43.696*	Underdosing of oth psychostimulants 405	
T43.8X6*	Underdosing of oth psychotropic drugs 405	
T40.4X6*	Underdosing of oth synth narcotics 404	
T36.8X6*	Underdosing of oth systemic antibiotics 403	
T49.8X6*	Underdosing of oth topical agents 407	
T50.Z96*	Underdosing of oth vaccines and biological substances 407	
T50.B96*	Underdosing of oth viral vaccines 407	
T49.6X6*	Underdosing of otorhinolaryngological drugs and preparations 407	
T48.0X6*	Underdosing of oxytocic drugs 406	
T36.0X6*	Underdosing of penicillins 403	
T46.7X6*	Underdosing of peripheral vasodilators 406	
T50.A16*	Underdosing of pertussis vaccine, incl* combin w pertuss 407	
T43.3X6*	Underdosing of phenothiazine antipsychotics and neuroleptics 405	
T44.4X6*	Underdosing of predominantly alpha-adrenoreceptor agonists 405	
T44.5X6*	Underdosing of predominantly beta-adrenoreceptor agonists 405	
T45.8X6*	Underdosing of primarily systemic and hematological agents 406	
T39.316*	Underdosing of propionic acid derivatives 404	
T39.2X6*	Underdosing of pyrazolone derivatives 404	
T36.6X6*	Underdosing of rifampicins 403	
T39.096*	Underdosing of salicylates 404	
T47.3X6*	Underdosing of saline and osmotic laxatives 406	
T43.216*	Underdosing of selective seroton/norepineph reup inhibitors 405	
T43.226*	Underdosing of selective serotonin reuptake inhibitors 405	
T48.1X6*	Underdosing of skeletal muscle relaxants 406	
T50.B16*	Underdosing of smallpox vaccines 407	
T47.2X6*	Underdosing of stimulant laxatives 406	
T42.2X6*	Underdosing of succinimides and oxazolidinediones 404	
T37.0X6*	Underdosing of sulfonamides 403	
T37.8X6*	Underdosing of systemic anti-infectives and antiparasitics 403	
T43.026*	Underdosing of tetracyclic antidepressants 404	
T36.4X6*	Underdosing of tetracyclines 403	
T41.5X6*	Underdosing of therapeutic gases 404	
T45.616*	Underdosing of thrombolytic drugs 406	
T38.1X6*	Underdosing of thyroid hormones and substitutes 403	
T43.016*	Underdosing of tricyclic antidepressants 404	
T46.906*	Underdosing of unsp agents affecting the cardiovascular sys 406	
T48.906*	Underdosing of unsp agents primarily acting on the resp sys 407	
T47.96*	Underdosing of unsp agents primarily affecting the GI sys 406	
T41.46*	Underdosing of unsp anesthetics 404	
T43.206*	Underdosing of unsp antidepressants 405	
T42.76*	Underdosing of unsp antiepileptic and sed-hypntc drugs 404	

T43.506*	Underdosing of unsp antipsychotics and neuroleptics 405
T50.906*	Underdosing of unsp drug/meds/biol subst 407
T48.206*	Underdosing of unsp drugs acting on muscles 406
T44.906*	Underdosing of unsp drugs affecting the autonomic nervous sys 405
T45.606*	Underdosing of unsp fibrinolysis-affecting drugs 406
T41.206*	Underdosing of unsp general anesthetics 404
T38.906*	Underdosing of unsp hormone antagonists 403
T38.806*	Underdosing of unsp hormones and synth substitutes 403
T40.606*	Underdosing of unsp narcotics 404
T39.96*	Underdosing of unsp nonopi analgs/antipyr/antirheu 404
T45.96*	Underdosing of unsp primarily systemic and hematolog agent 406
T40.906*	Underdosing of unsp psychodysleptics 404
T43.606*	Underdosing of unsp psychostimulants 405
T43.96*	Underdosing of unsp psychotropic drug 405
T37.96*	Underdosing of unsp systemic anti-infect/parasit 403
T36.96*	Underdosing of unsp systemic antibiotic 403
T49.96*	Underdosing of unsp topical agent 407
T45.2X6*	Underdosing of vitamins 405
P92.3	Underfeeding of newborn 289
Q53*	Undescended and ectopic testicle 261
Q53.9	Undescended testicle, unsp 289
Q53.20	Undescended testicle, unsp, bilat 289
T45.7X6*	Undrdose of anticoag antagonist, vitamin K and oth coag 406
M21.76[1,2,3,4,9]	Unequal limb length (acquired), [rt tibia, lt tibia, rt fibula, lt fibula, unsp tibia & fibula] 193
M21.73[1,2,3,4,9]	Unequal limb length (acquired), [rt ulna, lt ulna, rt radius, lt radius, unsp ulna and radius] 193
M21.75[1,2,9]	Unequal limb length (acquired), [rt, lt, unsp] femur 193
M21.72[1,2,9]	Unequal limb length (acquired), [rt, lt, unsp] humerus 193
M21.70	Unequal limb length (acquired), unsp site 193
R45.2	Unhappiness 310
C96.6	Unifocal Langerhans-cell histiocytosis 247
K41.[3,4]0	Unilat femor hernia, w/ [obstruction w/o gangrene, gangrene], not spec as recurrent 284
K40.[3,4]0	Unilat inguinal hernia, w/ [obstruction w/o gangrene, gangrene], not spec as recurrent 284
S52.9[0,1,2] X[D,E,F,G,H,J,S]	Unpsecified fx of [unsp, rt, lt] forearm, [subsq enc for clsd fx w/ routine healing, subsq enc for opn fx type I or II w/ routine healing, subsq enc for opn fx type IIIA, IIIB, or IIIC w/ routine healing, subsq enc for clsd fx w/ delayed healing, subsq enc for opn fx type I or II w/ delayed healing, subsq enc for opn fx type I or II w/ delayed healing, seq] 174
K08.5*	Unsatisfactory restoration of tooth 4
T74.9[1,2]X[A,S]	Unsp [adult, child] maltx, confirmed, [init enc, seq] 374
T74.9[1,2]XD	Unsp [adult, child] maltx, confirmed, subsq enc 410
T76.9[1,2]X[A,S]	Unsp [adult, child] maltx, suspected, [init enc, seq] 374
T76.9[1,2]XD	Unsp [adult, child] maltx, suspected, subsq enc 410
S12.00[0,1] [A,B,S]	Unsp [disp, nondisp] fx of 1st cervical vertebra, [init enc for clsd fx, init enc for opn fx, seq] 165
S12.00[0,1][A,B]	Unsp [disp, nondisp] fx of 1st cervical vertebra, init enc for [clsd, opn] fx 419
S12.00[0,1][D,G]	Unsp [disp, nondisp] fx of 1st cervical vertebra, subsq enc for fx w/ [routine, delayed] healing 169
S12.00[0,1]K	Unsp [disp, nondisp] fx of 1st cervical vertebra, subsq enc for fx w/ nonu 195
S12.10[0,1][A,B]	Unsp [disp, nondisp] fx of 2nd cervical vertebra, init enc for [clsd, opn] fx 419
S12.10[0,1][D,G]	Unsp [disp, nondisp] fx of 2nd cervical vertebra, subsq enc for fx w/ [routine, delayed] healing 169
S12.20[0,1][A,B]	Unsp [disp, nondisp] fx of 3rd cervical vertebra, init enc for [clsd, opn] fx 419
S12.20[0,1][D,G]	Unsp [disp, nondisp] fx of 3rd cervical vertebra, subsq enc for fx w/ [routine, delayed] healing 169
S12.20[0,1]K	Unsp [disp, nondisp] fx of 3rd cervical vertebra, subsq enc for fx w/ nonu 195
S12.30[0,1][A,B]	Unsp [disp, nondisp] fx of 4th cervical vertebra, init enc for [clsd, opn] fx 419
S12.30[0,1][D,G]	Unsp [disp, nondisp] fx of 4th cervical vertebra, subsq enc for fx w/ [routine, delayed] healing 169
S12.30[0,1]K	Unsp [disp, nondisp] fx of 4th cervical vertebra, subsq enc for fx w/ nonu 195

Code	Description
S12.40[0,1][A,B]	Unsp [disp, nondisp] fx of 5th cervical vertebra, init enc for [clsd, opn] fx **419**
S12.40[0,1][D,G]	Unsp [disp, nondisp] fx of 5th cervical vertebra, subsq enc for fx w/ [routine, delayed] healing **169**
S12.40[0,1]K	Unsp [disp, nondisp] fx of 5th cervical vertebra, subsq enc for fx w/ nonu **195**
S12.50[0,1][A,B]	Unsp [disp, nondisp] fx of 6th cervical vertebra, init enc for [clsd, opn] fx **419**
S12.50[0,1][D,G]	Unsp [disp, nondisp] fx of 6th cervical vertebra, subsq enc for fx w/ [routine, delayed] healing **169**
S12.50[0,1]K	Unsp [disp, nondisp] fx of 6th cervical vertebra, subsq enc for fx w/ nonu **195**
S12.60[0,1][A,B]	Unsp [disp, nondisp] fx of 7th cervical vertebra, init enc for [clsd, opn] fx **419**
S12.60[0,1][D,G]	Unsp [disp, nondisp] fx of 7th cervical vertebra, subsq enc for fx w/ [routine, delayed] healing **169**
S12.60[0,1]K	Unsp [disp, nondisp] fx of 7th cervical vertebra, subsq enc for fx w/ nonu **195**
S42.21[1,2,3,4,5,6][A,B]	Unsp [disp, nondisp] fx of surgical neck of [rt, lt, unsp] humerus, init enc for [clsd, opn] fx **422**
S12.10[0,1]K	Unsp [disp, undisp] fx of 2nd cervical vertebra, subsq enc for fx w/ nonu **195**
S73.00[1,2,3,4,5,6]A	Unsp [sublux, disloc] of [rt, lt, unsp] hip, init enc **426**
S43.00[1,2,3,4,5,6]A	Unsp [sublux, disloc] of [rt, lt, unsp] shldr jt, init enc **422**
S63.10[1,2,3,4,5,6]A	Unsp [sublux, disloc] of [rt, lt, unsp] thumb, init enc **425**
S63.00[1,2,3,4,5,6]A	Unsp [sublux, disloc] of [rt, lt, unsp] wrist and hand, init enc **425**
K46*	Unsp abd hernia **117**
K46.[0,1]	Unsp abd hernia, w/ [obstruction w/o gangrene, gangrene], not spec as recurrent **284**
R87.619	Unsp abnormal cytolog findings in specmn from cervix uteri **289**
R87.629	Unsp abnormal cytological findings in specimens from vagina **289, 386**
R85.9	Unsp abnormal finding in specimens from dgstv org/abd cav **385**
R89.9	Unsp abnormal finding in specimens from oth org/tiss **309**
R87.9	Unsp abnormal finding in specmn from female genital organs **386**
R06.9	Unsp abnormalities of breathing **69**
R26.9	Unsp abnormalities of gait and mobility **38**
R00.9	Unsp abnormalities of heart beat **103**
M21.9[2,3,4,5,6][1,2,9]	Unsp acquired deformity of [rt, lt, unsp] [upr arm, forearm, hand, thigh, lwr leg] **193**
M21.90	Unsp acquired deformity of unsp limb **193**
H05.00	Unsp acute inflam of orbit **45**
J22	Unsp acute lwr respiratory infxn **69**
T81.6[0,1,9]XA	[Unsp acute reaction, Aseptic peritonitis, Oth acute reaction] d/t foreign substance accidally lt during a procedure, init enc **287, 368**
T81.6[0,1,9]XS	[Unsp acute reaction, Aseptic peritonitis, Oth acute reaction] d/t foreign substance accidally lt during a procedure, seq **375**
T81.6[0,1,9]XD	[Unsp acute reaction, Aseptic peritonitis, Oth acute reaction] d/t foreign substance accidally lt during a procedure, subsq enc **410**
T88.7XXA	Unsp adverse effect of drug or medicament, init enc **368**
T88.7XXS	Unsp adverse effect of drug or medicament, seq **376**
T88.7XXD	Unsp adverse effect of drug or medicament, subs enc **411**
H57.00	Unsp anomaly of pupillary function **45**
K37	Unsp appendicitis **117**
A94	Unsp arthropod-borne viral fever **307**
J45.902	Unsp asthma with status asthmaticus **284**
C85.11	Unsp B-cell lymphoma, lymph nodes of head, face, and neck **3**
J15.9	Unsp bacterial pneumonia **68, 439**
F98.9	Unsp behav/emotn d/o w onst usly occur in chldhd and adol **311**
F59	Unsp behavrl synd assoc w physiol disturb and physcl factors **311**
P11.2	Unsp brain damage d/t birth inj **282**
J42	Unsp chr bronchitis **68**
K29.51	Unsp chr gastritis with bleeding **115**
Q37.8	Unsp cleft palate with bilat cleft lip **5**
Q37.9	Unsp cleft palate with unilat cleft lip **5**
H53.50	Unsp color vision deficiencies **46**
R40.20	Unsp coma **35, 285**
T80.90XS	Unsp comp fol inf and theraputc injection, seq **375**
T80.90XA	Unsp comp following inf and therapeutic injection, init **103, 287**
T80.90XD	Unsp comp following inf and therapeutic injection, subs **410**
T87.9	Unsp comp of amp stump **205**
O29.9[1,2,3]	Unsp comp of anesthesia during preg, [1st, 2nd, 3rd] trmstr **277**
O29.90	Unsp comp of anesthesia during preg, unsp trmstr **280**
T82.9XXA	Unsp comp of cardiac and vascular prosth dev/grft, init **103**
T82.9XXS	Unsp comp of cardiac and vascular prosth dev/grft, seq **375**
T82.9XXD	Unsp comp of cardiac and vascular prosth dev/grft, subs **411**
T83.9XXA	Unsp comp of genitourinary prosth dev/grft, init **256**
T83.9XXS	Unsp comp of genitourinary prosth dev/grft, seq **375**
T83.9XXD	Unsp comp of genitourinary prosth dev/grft, subs **411**
T84.9XXA	Unsp comp of int orthopedic prosth dev/grft, init **184**
T84.9XXS	Unsp comp of int orthopedic prosth dev/grft, seq **375**
T84.9XXD	Unsp comp of int orthopedic prosth dev/grft, subs **411**
T85.9XXA	Unsp comp of int prosth dev/grft, init **368**
T85.9XXS	Unsp comp of int prosth dev/grft, seq **376**
T85.9XXD	Unsp comp of int prosth dev/grft, subs **411**
T81.9XXA	Unsp comp of procedure, init enc **287, 368**
T81.9XXS	Unsp comp of procedure, seq **375**
T81.9XXD	Unsp comp of procedure, subsq enc **410**
T81.5[0,1,2,3,9][0,1,2,3,4,5,6,7,8,9]A	[Unsp comp, Adhesions, Obstruction, Perforation, Oth comps] d/t FB accidally lt in body following [surgical operation, inf or transfusion, kidney dialysis, injectionor immunization, endo exam, heart catheterization, aspiration punc or oth catheterization, rmvl of catheter or packing, oth procedure, unsp procedure], init enc **287, 368**
T81.5[0,1,2,3,9][0,1,2,3,4,5,6,7,8,9]S	[Unsp comp, Adhesions, Obstruction, Perforation, Oth comps] d/t FB accidally lt in body following [surgical operation, inf or transfusion, kidney dialysis, injectionor immunization, endo exam, heart catheterization, aspiration punc or oth catheterization, rmvl of catheter or packing, oth procedure, unsp procedure], seq **375**
T81.5[0,1,2,3,9][0,1,2,3,4,5,6,7,8,9]D	[Unsp comp, Adhesions, Obstruction, Perforation, Oth comps] d/t FB accidally lt in body following [surgical operation, inf or transfusion, kidney dialysis, injectionor immunization, endo exam, heart catheterization, aspiration punc or oth catheterization, rmvl of catheter or packing, oth procedure, unsp procedure], subsq enc **410**
N94.9	Unsp cond assoc w female genital organs and menstrual cycle **270**
L25*	Unsp contact dermatitis **233**
S36.029A	Unsp contsn of spleen, init enc **294**
R56.9	Unsp convulsions **285**
F69	Unsp d/o of adult personality and behav **310**
H51.9	Unsp d/o of binocular movement **46**
H93.9*	Unsp d/o of ear **58**
H57.9	Unsp d/o of eye and adnexa **46**
H02.9	Unsp d/o of eyelid **45**
H44.9	Unsp d/o of globe **46**
H21.9	Unsp d/o of iris and ciliary body **46**
J34.9	Unsp d/o of nose and nasal sinuses **289**
H05.9	Unsp d/o of orbit **45**
F89	Unsp d/o of psychological development **311**
H52.7	Unsp d/o of refraction **46**
H73.9*	Unsp d/o of tympanic membrane **58**
H47.9	Unsp d/o of visual pathways **38**
F03*	Unsp dementia **310**
F03.90	Unsp dementia w/o behavioral disturbance **439**
O24.92	Unsp diabetes mellitus in childbirth **273**
O24.91[1,2,3]	Unsp diabetes mellitus in preg, [1st, 2nd, 3rd] trmstr **273, 276, 277**
O24.919	Unsp diabetes mellitus in preg, unsp trmstr **280**
O24.93	Unsp diabetes mellitus in the puerperium **272, 273, 275**
S63.25[8,9][A,S]	Unsp disloc of [oth, unsp] finger, [init enc, seq] **189**
S63.25[8,9]D	Unsp disloc of [oth, unsp] finger, subsq enc **395**
S63.25[0,1,2,3,4,5,6,7,8,9]A	Unsp disloc of [rt index, lt index, rt mid, lt mid, rt ring, lt ring, rt little, lt little, oth, unsp] finger, init enc **425**
S43.10[1,2,9]D	Unsp disloc of [rt, lt, unsp] acromioclavicular jt, subsq enc **391**
S93.30[4,5,6][A,S]	Unsp disloc of [rt, lt, unsp] foot, [init enc, seq] **193**
S93.30[4,5,6]A	Unsp disloc of [rt, lt, unsp] foot, init enc **430**
S93.30[4,5,6]D	Unsp disloc of [rt, lt, unsp] foot, subsq enc **399**
S73.00[4,5,6]A	Unsp disloc of [rt, lt, unsp] hip, init enc **162**
S73.00[4,5,6]S	Unsp disloc of [rt, lt, unsp] hip, seq **190**
S73.00[4,5,6]D	Unsp disloc of [rt, lt, unsp] hip, subsq enc **397**

Code	Description
S83.10[4,5,6] [A,S]	Unsp disloc of [rt, lt, unsp] knee, [init enc, seq] 191
S83.10[4,5,6]A	Unsp disloc of [rt, lt, unsp] knee, init enc 428
S83.10[4,5,6]D	Unsp disloc of [rt, lt, unsp] knee, subsq enc 398
S83.00[4,5,6] [A,S]	Unsp disloc of [rt, lt, unsp] patella, [init enc, seq] 191
S83.00[4,5,6]A	Unsp disloc of [rt, lt, unsp] patella, init enc 428
S83.00[4,5,6]D	Unsp disloc of [rt, lt, unsp] patella, subsq enc 398
S53.00[4,5,6]D	Unsp disloc of [rt, lt, unsp] radial head, subsq enc 392
S43.20[4,5,6]A	Unsp disloc of [rt, lt, unsp] sternoclavicular jt, init enc 67
S43.20[4,5,6]S	Unsp disloc of [rt, lt, unsp] sternoclavicular jt, seq 185
S63.10[4,5,6] [A,S]	Unsp disloc of [rt, lt, unsp] thumb, [init enc, seq] 189
S63.10[4,5,6]D	Unsp disloc of [rt, lt, unsp] thumb, subsq enc 395
S93.10[4,5,6] [A,S]	Unsp disloc of [rt, lt, unsp] toe(s), [init enc, seq] 193
S93.10[4,5,6]A	Unsp disloc of [rt, lt, unsp] toe(s), init enc 430
S93.10[4,5,6]D	Unsp disloc of [rt, lt, unsp] toe(s), subsq enc 399
S53.10[4,5,6]D	Unsp disloc of [rt, lt, unsp] ulnohumeral jt, subsq enc 392
S63.00[4,5,6] [A,S]	Unsp disloc of [rt, lt, unsp] wrist and hand, [init enc, seq] 188
S63.25[0,1][A,S]	Unsp disloc of [rt, lt] index finger, [init enc, seq] 189
S63.25[0,1]D	Unsp disloc of [rt, lt] index finger, subsq enc 395
S63.25[6,7][A,S]	Unsp disloc of [rt, lt] little finger, [init enc, seq] 189
S63.25[6,7]D	Unsp disloc of [rt, lt] little finger, subsq enc 395
S63.25[2,3][A,S]	Unsp disloc of [rt, lt] mid finger, [init enc, seq] 189
S63.25[2,3]D	Unsp disloc of [rt, lt] mid finger, subsq enc 395
S63.25[4,5][A,S]	Unsp disloc of [rt, lt] ring finger, [init enc, seq] 189
S63.25[4,5]D	Unsp disloc of [rt, lt] ring finger, subsq enc 395
S63.00[4,5,6]D	Unsp disloc of [rt, lt] wrist and hand, subsq enc 395
S43.10[1,2,9] [A,S]	Unsp disloc of acromioclavicular jt {rt, lt, unsp] [init enc, seq] 185
S53.00[4,5,6] [A,S]	Unsp disloc of radial head [unsp, rt, lt] [init enc, seq] 186
S43.00[4,5,6] [A,S]	Unsp disloc of shldr jt [rt, lt, unsp] [init enc, seq] 185
S53.10[4,5,6] [A,S]	Unsp disloc of ulnohumeral jt [rt, lt, unsp] [init enc, seq] 186
S43.1[0,1][1,2,9] A	[Unsp disloc, Sublux] of [rt, lt, unsp] acromioclavicular jt, init enc 422
S12.10[0,1] [A,B,S]	Unsp disp fx of 2nd cervical vertebra [disp, nondisp] init enc for fx [clsd, opn, seq] 165
S42.213B	Unsp disp fx of surg neck of unsp humerus, init for opn fx 433
S42.21[1,2,3] [D,G,S]	Unsp disp fx of surgical neck of [rt, lt, unsp] humerus, [subsq enc for fx w/ routine healing, subsq enc for fx w/ delayed healing, seq] 171
S42.21[1,2,3] [K,P]	Unsp disp fx of surgical neck of [rt, lt, unsp] humerus, subsq enc for fx w/ [nonu, malu] 196
S42.21[1,2,3] [A,B]	Unsp disp fx of surgical neck of humerus [rt, lt, unsp] init enc for fx [clsd, opn] 184
S42.212B	Unsp disp fx of surgical neck of Lt humerus, init for opn fx 433
S42.211B	Unsp disp fx of surgical neck of Rt humerus, init for opn fx 433
H83.9*	Unsp dz of inner ear 57
T79.9XXA	Unsp early comp of trauma, init enc 430
T75.1XX[A,S]	Unsp effects of drowning and nonfatal submersion, [init enc, seq] 374
T75.1XXD	Unsp effects of drowning and nonfatal submersion, subs 410
T70.20XD	Unsp effects of high altitude, subsq enc 409
T75.20X[A,S]	Unsp effects of vibration, [init enc, seq] 374
T75.20XD	Unsp effects of vibration, subs enc 410
T75.0[0,1,9] X[A,S]	[Unsp effects of, Shock d/t being struck by, Unsp effects of] lightning, [init enc, seq] 374
T75.0[0,1,9]XD	[Unsp effects of, Shock d/t being struck by, Unsp effects of] lightning, subsq enc 410
H05.20	Unsp exophthalmos 45
T17.50[0,8]A	Unsp FB in bronchus causing [asphyxiation, oth inj], init enc 69
T18.10[0,8]A	Unsp FB in esophagus causing [compression of trachea, oth inj], init enc 118
T17.30[0,8]A	Unsp FB in larynx causing [asphyxiation, oth inj], init enc 58
T17.300A	Unsp FB in larynx causing asphyxiation, init 6
T17.308A	Unsp FB in larynx causing oth inj, init enc 6
T17.80[0,8]A	Unsp FB in oth parts of respiratory tract causing [asphyxiation, oth inj], init enc 70
T17.20[0,8]A	Unsp FB in pharynx causing [asphyxiation, oth inj], init enc 58
T17.200A	Unsp FB in pharynx causing asphyxiation, init 6
T17.208A	Unsp FB in pharynx causing oth inj, init enc 6
T17.90[0,8]A	Unsp FB in respiratory tract, part unsp causing [asphyxiation, oth inj], init enc 70
T17.40[0,8]A	Unsp FB in trachea causing [asphyxiation, oth inj], init enc 69
T17.5[0,1,2,9] [0,8]S	[Unsp FB, Gastric contents, Food, Oth foreign object] in bronchus causing [asphyxiation, oth inj], seq 361
T17.5[0,1,2,9] [0,8]D	[Unsp FB, Gastric contents, Food, Oth foreign object] in bronchus causing [asphyxiation, oth inj], subsq enc 400
T18.1[0,1,2,9] [0,8]S	[Unsp FB, Gastric contents, Food, Oth foreign object] in esophagus causing [compression of trachea, oth inj], seq 361
T18.1[0,1,2,9] [0,8]D	[Unsp FB, Gastric contents, Food, Oth foreign object] in esophagus causing [compression of trachea, oth inj], subsq enc 400
T17.3[0,1,2,9] [0,8]S	[Unsp FB, Gastric contents, Food, Oth foreign object] in larynx causing [asphyxiation, oth inj], seq 361
T17.3[0,1,2,9] [0,8]D	[Unsp FB, Gastric contents, Food, Oth foreign object] in larynx causing [asphyxiation, oth inj], subsq enc 400
T17.8[0,1,2,9] [0,8]S	[Unsp FB, Gastric contents, Food, Oth foreign object] in oth parts of respiratory tract causing [asphyxiation, oth inj], seq 361
T17.8[0,1,2,9] [0,8]D	[Unsp FB, Gastric contents, Food, Oth foreign object] in oth parts of respiratory tract causing [asphyxiation, oth inj], subsq enc 400
T17.2[0,1,2,9] [0,8]S	[Unsp FB, Gastric contents, Food, Oth foreign object] in pharynx causing [asphyxiation, oth inj], seq 361
T17.2[0,1,2,9] [0,8]D	[Unsp FB, Gastric contents, Food, Oth foreign object] in pharynx causing [asphyxiation, oth inj], subsq enc 400
T17.9[0,1,2,9] [0,8]S	[Unsp FB, Gastric contents, Food, Oth foreign object] in respiratory tract, part unsp causing [asphyxiation, oth inj], seq 361
T17.9[0,1,2,9] [0,8]D	[Unsp FB, Gastric contents, Food, Oth foreign object] in respiratory tract, part unsp causing [asphyxiation, oth inj], subsq enc 400
T17.4[0,1,2,9] [0,8]S	[Unsp FB, Gastric contents, Food, Oth foreign object] in trachea causing [asphyxiation, oth inj], seq 361
T17.4[0,1,2,9] [0,8]D	[Unsp FB, Gastric contents, Food, Oth foreign object] in trachea causing [asphyxiation, oth inj], subsq enc 400
S06.301A	Unsp focal TBI w LOC of 30 min or less, init 37
S06.302A	Unsp focal TBI w LOC of 31-59 min, init 37
S06.300A	Unsp focal TBI w/o LOC, init 36, 37, 418, 430
S06.300S	Unsp focal TBI w/o LOC, seq 39
S06.300D	Unsp focal TBI w/o LOC, subs 386
S06.30[5,6]D	Unsp focal traum brain inj w/ LOC [> 24 hrs w/ return to pre-existing conscious lvl, > 24 hrs w/o return to pre-existing conscious lvl w/ patient surviving], subsq enc 386
S06.30[5,6]A	Unsp focal traum brain inj w/ LOC > 24 hrs [w/ return to pre-existing conscious lvl, w/o return to pre-existing conscious lvl w/ patient surviving], init enc 36, 418, 430
S06.30[5,6]S	Unsp focal traum brain inj w/ LOC of [> 24 hrs w/ return to pre-existing conscious lvl, > 24 hrs w/o return to pre-existing conscious lvl w/ patient surviving], seq 39
S06.30[3,4,5,6]A	Unsp focal traum brain inj w/ LOC of [1 hr to 5 hrs 59 min, 6 hrs to 24 hrs, > 24 hrs w/ return to pre-existing conscious lvl, > 24 hrs w/o return to pre-existing conscious lvl patient surviving], init enc 35
S06.30[1,2,3,4]A	Unsp focal traum brain inj w/ LOC of [30 min or less, 31 min to 59 min, 1 hr to 5 hrs 59 min, 6 hrs to 24 hrs], init enc 36, 418, 430
S06.30[1,2,3,4]D	Unsp focal traum brain inj w/ LOC of [30 min or less, 31 min to 59 min, 1 hr to 5 hrs 59 min, 6 hrs to 24 hrs], subsq enc 386
S06.30[1,2,3,4]S	Unsp focal traum brain inj w/ LOC of [30 min or less, 31-59 min, 1 hr to 5 hrs 59 min, 6 hrs to 24 hrs], seq 39
S06.30[7,8,9]A	Unsp focal traum brain inj w/ LOC of [any dur w/ death d/t brain inj prior to regain cnscness, any dur w/ death d/t oth cause prior to regain cnscness, unsp dur], init enc 35, 36, 418, 430
S06.30[7,8,9]S	Unsp focal traum brain inj w/ LOC of [any dur w/ death d/t brain inj prior to regain cnscness, any dur w/ death d/t oth cause prior to regain cnscness, unsp dur], seq 39
S06.30[7,8,9]D	Unsp focal traum brain inj w/ LOC of [any dur w/ death d/t brain inj prior to regain cnscness, any dur w/ death d/t oth cause prior to regain cnscness, unsp dur], subsq enc 386
S62.30[0,1,2,3,4, 5,6,7,8,9][A,B]	Unsp fx of [2nd, 3rd, 4th, 5th, oth, unsp] metacarpal bone, (rt, lt) hand, init enc for [clsd, opn] fx 424
S62.30[8,9] [D,G,S]	Unsp fx of [oth, unsp] metacarpal bone, [subsq enc for fx w/ routine healing, subsq enc for fx w/ delayed healing, seq] 175
S62.30[8,9][K,P]	Unsp fx of [oth, unsp] metacarpal bone, subsq enc for fx w/ [nonu, malu] 199
S32.40[1,2,9]S	Unsp fx of [rt, lt, unsp] acetab, seq 166
S32.40[1,2,9] [D,G]	Unsp fx of [rt, lt, unsp] acetab, subsq enc for fx w/ [routine, delayed] healing 170

S32.40[1,2,9]K	Unsp fx of [rt, lt, unsp] acetab, subsq enc for fx w/ nonu **196**
S92.00[1,2,9] [D,G,S]	Unsp fx of [rt, lt, unsp] calcaneus, [subsq enc for fx w/ routine healing, subsq enc for fx w/ delayed healing, seq] **182**
S92.00[1,2,9] [A,B]	Unsp fx of [rt, lt, unsp] calcaneus, init enc for [clsd, opn] fx **192, 429**
S92.00[1,2,9] [K,P]	Unsp fx of [rt, lt, unsp] calcaneus, subsq enc for fx w/ [nonu, malu] **204**
S92.90[1,2,9] [D,G,S]	Unsp fx of [rt, lt, unsp] foot, [subsq enc for fx w/ routine healing, subsq enc for fx w/ delayed healing, seq] **183**
S92.90[1,2,9] [A,B]	Unsp fx of [rt, lt, unsp] foot, init enc for [clsd, opn] fx **193, 430**
S92.90[1,2,9] [K,P]	Unsp fx of [rt, lt, unsp] foot, subsq enc for fx w/ [nonu, malu] **204**
S32.30[1,2,9] [A,B]	Unsp fx of [rt, lt, unsp] ilium, init enc for [clsd, opn] fx **162, 421, 433**
S32.30[1,2,9]S	Unsp fx of [rt, lt, unsp] ilium, seq **166**
S32.30[1,2,9] [D,G]	Unsp fx of [rt, lt, unsp] ilium, subsq enc for fx w/ [routine, delayed] healing **170**
S32.30[1,2,9]K	Unsp fx of [rt, lt, unsp] ilium, subsq enc for fx w/ nonu **196**
S32.60[1,2,9]S	Unsp fx of [rt, lt, unsp] ischium, seq **166**
S32.60[1,2,9] [D,G]	Unsp fx of [rt, lt, unsp] ischium, subsq enc for fx w/ [routine, delayed] healing **170**
S32.60[1,2,9]K	Unsp fx of [rt, lt, unsp] ischium, subsq enc for fx w/ nonu **196**
S82.9[0,1,2] X[D,E,F,G,H,J,S]	Unsp fx of [rt, lt, unsp] lwr leg, [subsq enc for clsd fx w/ routine healing, subsq enc for opn fx type I or II w/ routine healing, subsq enc for opn fx type IIIA, IIIB, or IIIC w/ routine healing, subsq enc for clsd fx w/ delayed healing, subsq enc for opn fx type I or II w/ delayed healing, subsq enc for opn fx type IIIA, IIIB, or IIIC w/ delayed healing, seq] **182**
S82.00[1,2,9] [D,E,F,G,H,J,S]	Unsp fx of [rt, lt, unsp] patella, [subsq enc for clsd fx w/ routine healing, subsq enc for opn fx type I or II w/ routine healing, subsq enc for opn fx type IIIA, IIIB, or IIIC w/ routine healing, subsq enc for clsd fx w/ delayed healing, subsq enc for opn fx type I or II w/ delayed healing, subsq enc for opn fx type I or II w/ delayed healing, seq] **179**
S82.00[1,2,9] [A,B,C]	Unsp fx of [rt, lt, unsp] patella, init enc for [clsd fx, opn fx type I or II, opn fx type IIIA, IIIB, or IIIC] **190**
S82.00[1,2,9] [A,B,C]	Unsp fx of [rt, lt, unsp] patella, init enc for [clsd fx, opn fx type I or II, opn fx type IIIA, IIIB, or IIIC] **427**
S82.00[1,2,9] [K,M,N,P,Q,R]	Unsp fx of [rt, lt, unsp] patella, subsq enc for [clsd fx w/ nonu, opn fx type I or II w/ nonu, opn fx type IIIA, IIIB, or IIIC w/ nonu, clsd fx w/ malu, opn fx type I or II w/ malu, opn fx type I or II w/ malu] **202**
S32.50[1,2,9]S	Unsp fx of [rt, lt, unsp] pubis, seq **166**
S32.50[1,2,9] [D,G]	Unsp fx of [rt, lt, unsp] pubis, subsq enc for fx w/ [routine, delayed] healing **170**
S32.50[1,2,9]K	Unsp fx of [rt, lt, unsp] pubis, subsq enc for fx w/ nonu **196**
S92.10[1,2,9] [D,G,S]	Unsp fx of [rt, lt, unsp] talus, [subsq enc for fx w/ routine healing, subsq enc for fx w/ delayed healing, seq] **182**
S92.10[1,2,9] [A,B]	Unsp fx of [rt, lt, unsp] talus, init enc for [clsd, opn] fx **192, 429**
S92.10[1,2,9] [K,P]	Unsp fx of [rt, lt, unsp] talus, subsq enc for fx w/ [nonu, malu] **204**
S92.91[1,2,9] [D,G,S]	Unsp fx of [rt, lt, unsp] toe(s), [subsq enc for fx w/ routine healing, subsq enc for fx w/ delayed healing, seq] **183**
S92.91[1,2,9] [A,B]	Unsp fx of [rt, lt, unsp] toe(s), init enc for [clsd, opn] fx **193, 430**
S92.91[1,2,9] [K,P]	Unsp fx of [rt, lt, unsp] toe(s), subsq enc for fx w/ [nonu, malu] **204**
S02.9[1,2]X[D,G]	Unsp fx of [skull, facial bones], subsq enc for fx w/ [routine, delayed] healing **169**
S72.9[0,1,2] X[A,B,C]	Unsp fx of [unsp, rt lt] femur, init enc for [clsd fx, opn fx type I or II, opn fx type IIIA, IIIB, or IIIC] **161, 286, 426, 436**
S72.9[0,1,2] X[D,E,F,G,H,J,S]	Unsp fx of [unsp, rt, lt] femur, [subsq enc for clsd fx w/ routine healing, subsq enc for opn fx type I or II w/ routine healing, subsq enc for opn fx type IIIA, IIIB, or IIIC w/ routine healing, subsq enc for clsd fx w/ delayed healing, subsq enc for opn fx type I or II w/ delayed healing, subsq enc for opn fx type IIIA, IIIB, or IIIC w/ delayed healing, seq] **179**
S72.9[0,1,2] X[K,M,N,P,Q,R]	Unsp fx of [unsp, rt, lt] femur, subsq enc for [clsd fx w/ nonu, opn fx type I or II w/ nonu, opn fx type IIIA, IIIB, or IIIC w/ nonu, clsd fx w/ malu, opn fx type I or II w/ malu, opn fx type IIIA, IIIB, or IIIC w/ malu] **202**
S52.9[0,1,2] X[K,M,N,P,Q,R]	Unsp fx of [unsp, rt, lt] forearm, subsq enc for [clsd fx w/ nonu, opn fx type I or II w/ nonu, opn fx type IIIA, IIIB, or IIIC w/ nonu, clsd fx w/ malu, opn fx type I or II w/ malu, opn fx type IIIA, IIIB, or IIIC w/ malu] **199**
S82.9[0,1,2] X[A,B,C]	Unsp fx of [unsp, rt, lt] lwr leg, [init enc for clsd fx, init enc for opn fx type I or II, init enc for opn fx type I or II] **191, 428**
S82.9[0,1,2] X[K,M,N,P,Q,R]	Unsp fx of [unsp, rt, lt] lwr leg, subsq enc for [clsd fx w/ nonu, opn fx type I or II w/ nonu, opn fx type IIIA, IIIB, or IIIC w/ nonu, clsd fx w/ malu, opn fx type I or II w/ malu, opn fx type I or II w/ malu] **203**
S62.9[0,1,2] X[D,G,S]	Unsp fx of [unsp, rt, lt] wrist and hand, [subsq enc for fx w/ routine healing, subsq enc for fx w/ delayed healing, seq] **176**
S62.9[0,1,2] X[A,B]	Unsp fx of [unsp, rt, lt] wrist and hand, init enc for [clsd, opn] fx **188, 425**
S62.9[0,1,2] X[K,P]	Unsp fx of [unsp, rt, lt] wrist and hand, subsq enc for fx w/ [nonu, malu] **200**
S62.20[1,2,9] [D,G,S]	Unsp fx of 1st metacarpal bone, [rt, lt, unsp] hand, [subsq enc for fx w/ routine healing, subsq enc for fx w/ delayed healing, seq] **175**
S62.20[1,2,9] [A,B]	Unsp fx of 1st metacarpal bone, [rt, lt, unsp] hand, init enc for [clsd, opn] fx **187, 424**
S62.20[1,2,9] [K,P]	Unsp fx of 1st metacarpal bone, [rt, lt, unsp] hand, subsq enc for fx w/ [nonu, malu] **199**
S62.30[0,1][A,B]	Unsp fx of 2nd metacarpal bone of [rt, lt] hand, init enc for fx [clsd, opn] **187**
S62.30[0,1] [D,G,S]	Unsp fx of 2nd metacarpal bone, [rt, lt] hand, [subsq enc for fx w/ routine healing, subsq enc for fx w/ delayed healing, seq] **175**
S62.30[0,1][K,P]	Unsp fx of 2nd metacarpal bone, [rt, lt] hand, subsq enc for fx w/ [nonu, malu] **199**
S12.20[0,1] [A,B,S]	Unsp fx of 3rd cervical vertebra [disp, nondisp] init enc for [clsd, opn, seq] **165**
S62.30[2,3][A,B]	Unsp fx of 3rd metacarpal bone of [rt, lt] hand, init enc for [clsd, opn] fx **187**
S62.30[2,3] [D,G,S]	Unsp fx of 3rd metacarpal bone, [rt, lt] hand, [subsq enc for fx w/ routine healing, subsq enc for fx w/ delayed healing, seq] **175**
S62.30[2,3][K,P]	Unsp fx of 3rd metacarpal bone, [rt, lt] hand, subsq enc for fx w/ [nonu, malu] **199**
S12.30[0,1] [A,B,S]	Unsp fx of 4th cervical vertebra. [disp, nondisp], [init enc clsd fx, init enc for opn fx, seq] **165**
S62.30[4,5][A,B]	Unsp fx of 4th metacarpal bone of [rt, lt] hand, init enc for [clsd, opn] fx **187**
S62.30[4,5] [D,G,S]	Unsp fx of 4th metacarpal bone, [rt, lt] hand, [subsq enc for fx w/ routine healing, subsq enc for fx w/ delayed healing, seq] **175**
S62.30[4,5][K,P]	Unsp fx of 4th metacarpal bone, [rt, lt] hand, subsq enc for fx w/ [nonu, malu] **199**
S12.40[0,1] [A,B,S]	Unsp fx of 5th cervical vertebra [disp, nondisp] init enc for fx [clsd, opn, seq] **165**
S62.30[6,7][A,B]	Unsp fx of 5th metacarpal bone of [rt, lt] hand, init enc for [clsd, opn] fx **187**
S62.30[6,7] [D,G,S]	Unsp fx of 5th metacarpal bone, [rt, lt] hand, [subsq enc for fx w/ routine healing, subsq enc for fx w/ delayed healing, seq] **175**
S62.30[6,7][K,P]	Unsp fx of 5th metacarpal bone, [rt, lt] hand, subsq enc for fx w/ [nonu, malu] **199**
S12.50[0,1] [A,B,S]	Unsp fx of 6th cervical vertebra [disp, nondisp] init enc for fx [clsd, opn, seq] **165**
S12.60[0,1] [A,B,S]	Unsp fx of 6th cervical vertebra [disp, nondisp] init enc for fx [clsd, opn, seq] **165**
S32.40[1,2,9] [A,B]	Unsp fx of acetab [rt, lt, unsp] init enc for [clsd, opn] fx **162, 421, 433**
S02.10X[A,B]	Unsp fx of base of skull, init enc for [clsd, opn] fx **36, 37, 417**
S02.10XB	Unsp fx of base of skull, init for opn fx **430**
S02.10XS	Unsp fx of base of skull, seq **39**
S02.10XK	Unsp fx of base of skull, subs fx w nonu **195**
S02.10X[D,G]	Unsp fx of base of skull, subsq enc for fx w/ [routine, delayed] healing **169**
S02.92X[A,B,K]	Unsp fx of facial bones, [init enc for clsd fx, init enc for opn fx, subsq enc for fx w/ nonu] **195**
S02.92X[A,B]	Unsp fx of facial bones, init enc for [clsd, opn] fx **417**
S02.92XB	Unsp fx of facial bones, init enc for opn fx **5**
S02.92XA	Unsp fx of facial bones, init for clos fx **5**
S02.92XS	Unsp fx of facial bones, seq **39**
S72.05[1,2,9] [D,E,F,G,H,J,S]	Unsp fx of head of [rt, lt, unsp] femur, [subsq enc for clsd fx w/ routine healing, subsq enc for opn fx type I or II w/ routine healing, subsq enc for opn fx type IIIA, IIIB, or IIIC w/ routine healing, subsq enc for clsd fx w/ delayed healing, subsq enc for opn fx type I or II w/ delayed healing, subsq enc for opn fx type IIIA, IIIB, or IIIC w/ delayed healing, seq] **177**
S72.05[1,2,9] [A,B,C]	Unsp fx of head of [rt, lt, unsp] femur, init enc for [clsd fx, opn fx type I or II, opn fx type IIIA, IIIB, or IIIC] **162, 286, 426, 435**

Code	Description
S72.05[1,2,9] [K,M,N,P,Q,R]	Unsp fx of head of [rt, lt, unsp] femur, subsq enc for [clsd fx w/ nonu, opn fx type I or II w/ nonu, opn fx type IIIA, IIIB, or IIIC w/ nonu, clsd fx w/ malu, opn fx type I or II w/ malu, opn fx type IIIA, IIIB, or IIIC w/ malu] **201**
S32.60[1,2,9] [A,B]	Unsp fx of ischium [rt, lt, unsp], init enc for [clsd, opn] fx **162, 421, 433**
S72.40[1,2,9] [D,E,F,G,H,J,S]	Unsp fx of lwr end of [rt, lt, unsp] femur, [subsq enc for clsd fx w/ routine healing, subsq enc for opn fx type I or II w/ routine healing, subsq enc for opn fx type IIIA, IIIB, or IIIC w/ routine healing, subsq enc for clsd fx w/ delayed healing, subsq enc for opn fx type I or II w/ delayed healing, subsq enc for opn fx type IIIA, IIIB, or IIIC w/ delayed healing, seq] **178**
S72.40[1,2,9] [A,B,C]	Unsp fx of lwr end of [rt, lt, unsp] femur, init enc for [clsd fx, opn fx type I or II, opn fx type IIIA, IIIB, or IIIC] **161, 426, 435**
S72.40[1,2,9] [K,M,N,P,Q,R]	Unsp fx of lwr end of [rt, lt, unsp] femur, subsq enc for [clsd fx w/ nonu, opn fx type I or II w/ nonu, opn fx type IIIA, IIIB, or IIIC w/ nonu, clsd fx w/ malu, opn fx type I or II w/ malu, opn fx type IIIA, IIIB, or IIIC w/ malu] **201**
S42.40[1,2,9] [D,G,S]	Unsp fx of lwr end of [rt, lt, unsp] humerus, [subsq enc for fx w/ routine healing, subsq enc for fx w/ delayed healing, seq] **171**
S42.40[1,2,9] [A,B]	Unsp fx of lwr end of [rt, lt, unsp] humerus, init enc for [clsd, opn] fx **185, 422**
S42.40[1,2,9]B	Unsp fx of lwr end of [rt, lt, unsp] humerus, init enc for opn fx **433**
S42.40[1,2,9] [K,P]	Unsp fx of lwr end of [rt, lt, unsp] humerus, subsq enc for fx w/ [nonu, malu] **197**
S52.50[1,2,9] [D,E,F,G,H,J,S]	Unsp fx of lwr end of [rt, lt, unsp] radius, [subsq enc for clsd fx w/ routine healing, subsq enc for opn fx type I or II w/ routine healing, subsq enc for opn fx type I or II w/ routine healing, subsq enc for clsd fx w/ delayed healing, subsq enc for opn fx type I or II w/ delayed healing, subsq enc for opn fx type IIIA, IIIB, or IIIC w/ delayed healing, seq] **173**
S82.30[1,2,9] [A,B,C]	Unsp fx of lwr end of [rt, lt, unsp] tibia, [init enc for clsd fx, init enc for opn fx type I or II, init enc for opn fx type IIIA, IIIB, or IIIC] **191, 427**
S82.30[1,2,9] [D,E,F,G,H,J,S]	Unsp fx of lwr end of [rt, lt, unsp] tibia, [subsq enc for clsd fx w/ routine healing, subsq enc for opn fx type I or II w/ routine healing, subsq enc for opn fx type IIIA, IIIB, or IIIC w/ routine healing, subsq enc for clsd fx w/ delayed healing, subsq enc for opn fx type I or II w/ delayed healing, subsq enc for opn fx type IIIA, IIIB, or IIIC w/ delayed healing, seq] **180**
S82.30[1,2,9] [K,M,N,P,Q,R]	Unsp fx of lwr end of [rt, lt, unsp] tibia, subsq enc for [clsd fx w/ nonu, opn fx type I or II w/ nonu, opn fx type IIIA, IIIB, or IIIC w/ nonu, clsd fx w/ malu, opn fx type I or II w/ malu, opn fx type I or II w/ malu] **203**
S52.60[1,2,9] [D,E,F,G,H,J,S]	Unsp fx of lwr end of [rt, lt, unsp] ulna, [subsq enc for clsd fx w/ routine healing, subsq enc for opn fx type I or II w/ routine healing, subsq enc for opn fx type IIIA, IIIB, or IIIC w/ routine healing, subsq enc for clsd fx w/ delayed healing, subsq enc for opn fx type I or II w/ delayed healing, subsq enc for opn fx type I or II w/ delayed healing, seq] **174**
S52.60[1,2,9] [A,B,C]	Unsp fx of lwr end of [rt, lt, unsp] ulna, init enc for [clsd fx, opn fx type I or II, opn fx type IIIA, IIIB, IIIC] **186, 424**
S52.60[1,2,9] [B,C]	Unsp fx of lwr end of [rt, lt, unsp] ulna, init enc for opn fx type [I or II, IIIA IIIB IIIC] **434**
S52.60[1,2,9] [K,M,N,P,Q,R]	Unsp fx of lwr end of [rt, lt, unsp] ulna, subsq enc for [clsd fx w/ nonu, opn fx type I or II w/ nonu, opn fx type IIIA, IIIB, or IIIC w/ nonu, clsd fx w/ malu, opn fx type I or II w/ malu, opn fx type IIIA, IIIB, or IIIC w/ malu] **198**
S62.00[1,2,9] [D,G,S]	Unsp fx of navicular (scaphoid) bone of [rt, lt, unsp] wrist, [subsq enc for fx w/ routine healing, subsq enc for fx w/ delayed healing, seq] **174**
S62.00[1,2,9] [K,P]	Unsp fx of navicular (scaphoid) bone of [rt, lt, unsp] wrist, subsq enc for fx w/ [nonu, malu] **199**
S62.00[1,2,9] [A,B]	Unsp fx of navicular [scaphoid] bone of [rt, lt, unsp] wrist, init enc for [clsd, opn] fx **187, 424**
S62.30[8,9][A,B]	Unsp fx of oth metacarpal bone of [oth, unsp] hand, init enc for [clsd, opn] fx **187**
S32.50[1,2,9] [A,B]	Unsp fx of pubis [rt, lt, unsp] init enc for [clsd, opn] fx **162, 421, 433**
S32.10X[A,B,S]	Unsp fx of sacrum init enc for fx [clsd, opn, seq] **166**
S32.10X[A,B]	Unsp fx of sacrum, init enc for [clsd, opn] fx **421, 433**
S32.10XK	Unsp fx of sacrum, subs enc for fx w nonu **196**
S32.10X[D,G]	Unsp fx of sacrum, subsq enc for fx w/ [routine, delayed] healing **170**
S72.30[1,2,9] [D,E,F,G,H,J,S]	Unsp fx of shaft of [rt, lt, unsp] femur, [subsq enc for clsd fx w/ routine healing, subsq enc for opn fx type I or II w/ routine healing, subsq enc for opn fx type IIIA, IIIB, or IIIC w/ routine healing, subsq enc for clsd fx w/ delayed healing, subsq enc for opn fx type I or II w/ delayed healing, subsq enc for opn fx type IIIA, IIIB, or IIIC w/ delayed healing, seq] **177**
S72.30[1,2,9] [A,B,C]	Unsp fx of shaft of [rt, lt, unsp] femur, init enc for [clsd fx, opn fx type I or II, opn fx type IIIA, IIIB, or IIIC] **161, 286, 426, 435**
S72.30[1,2,9] [K,M,N,P,Q,R]	Unsp fx of shaft of [rt, lt, unsp] femur, subsq enc for [clsd fx w/ nonu, opn fx type I or II w/ nonu, opn fx type IIIA, IIIB, or IIIC w/ nonu, clsd fx w/ malu, opn fx type I or II w/ malu, opn fx type IIIA, IIIB, or IIIC w/ malu] **201**
S82.40[1,2,9] [A,B,C]	Unsp fx of shaft of [rt, lt, unsp] fibula, [init enc for clsd fx, init enc for opn fx type I or II, init enc for opn fx type IIIA, IIIB, or IIIC] **191, 427**
S82.40[1,2,9] [D,E,F,G,H,J,S]	Unsp fx of shaft of [rt, lt, unsp] fibula, [subsq enc for clsd fx w/ routine healing, subsq enc for opn fx type I or II w/ routine healing, subsq enc for opn fx type IIIA, IIIB, or IIIC w/ routine healing, subsq enc for clsd fx w/ delayed healing, subsq enc for opn fx type I or II w/ delayed healing, subsq enc for opn fx type IIIA, IIIB, or IIIC w/ delayed healing, seq] **180**
S82.40[1,2,9] [B,C]	Unsp fx of shaft of [rt, lt, unsp] fibula, init enc for opn fx type [I or II, IIIA IIIB or IIIC] **436**
S82.40[1,2,9] [K,M,N,P,Q,R]	Unsp fx of shaft of [rt, lt, unsp] fibula, subsq enc for [clsd fx w/ nonu, opn fx type I or II w/ nonu, opn fx type IIIA, IIIB, or IIIC w/ nonu, clsd fx w/ malu, opn fx type I or II w/ malu, opn fx type I or II w/ malu] **203**
S42.30[1,2,9] [D,G,S]	Unsp fx of shaft of [rt, lt, unsp] humerus, [subsq enc for fx w/ routine healing, subsq enc for fx w/ delayed healing, seq] **171**
S52.20[1,2,9] [D,E,F,G,H,J,S]	Unsp fx of shaft of [rt, lt, unsp] radius, [subsq enc for clsd fx w/ routine healing, subsq enc for opn fx type I or II w/ routine healing, subsq enc for opn fx type IIIA, IIIB, or IIIC w/ routine healing, subsq enc for clsd fx w/ delayed healing, subsq enc for opn fx type I or II w/ delayed healing, subsq enc for opn fx type IIIA, IIIB, or IIIC w/ delayed healing, seq] **172**
S52.30[1,2,9] [A,B,C]	Unsp fx of shaft of [rt, lt, unsp] radius, init enc for [clsd fx, opn fx type I or II, opn fx type IIIA, IIIB, or IIIC] **186, 423**
S52.30[1,2,9] [B,C]	Unsp fx of shaft of [rt, lt, unsp] radius, init enc for opn fx type [I or II, IIIA IIIB or IIIC] **434**
S52.30[1,2,9] [K,M,N,P,Q,R]	Unsp fx of shaft of [rt, lt, unsp] radius, subsq enc for [clsd fx w/ nonu, opn fx type I or II w/ nonu, opn fx type IIIA, IIIB, or IIIC w/ nonu, clsd fx w/ malu, opn fx type I or II w/ malu, opn fx type IIIA, IIIB, or IIIC w/ malu] **198**
S82.20[1,2,9] [D,E,F,G,H,J,S]	Unsp fx of shaft of [rt, lt, unsp] tibia, [subsq enc for clsd fx w/ routine healing, subsq enc for opn fx type I or II w/ routine healing, subsq enc for opn fx type IIIA, IIIB, or IIIC w/ routine healing, subsq enc for clsd fx w/ delayed healing, subsq enc for opn fx type I or II w/ delayed healing, subsq enc for opn fx type I or II w/ delayed healing, seq] **180**
S82.20[1,2,9] [A,B,C]	Unsp fx of shaft of [rt, lt, unsp] tibia, init enc for [clsd fx, opn fx type I or II, opn fx type IIIA, IIIB, or IIIC] **191, 427**
S82.20[1,2,9] [B,C]	Unsp fx of shaft of [rt, lt, unsp] tibia, init enc for opn fx type [I or II, IIIA IIIB or IIIC] **436**
S82.20[1,2,9] [K,M,N,P,Q,R]	Unsp fx of shaft of [rt, lt, unsp] tibia, subsq enc for [clsd fx w/ nonu, opn fx type I or II w/ nonu, opn fx type IIIA, IIIB, or IIIC w/ nonu, clsd fx w/ malu, opn fx type I or II w/ malu, opn fx type I or II w/ malu] **202**
S52.30[1,2,9] [D,E,F,G,H,J,S]	Unsp fx of shaft of [rt, lt, unsp] ulna, [subsq enc for clsd fx w/ routine healing, subsq enc for opn fx type I or II w/ routine healing, subsq enc for opn fx type I or II w/ routine healing, subsq enc for clsd fx w/ delayed healing, subsq enc for opn fx type I or II w/ delayed healing, subsq enc for opn fx type IIIA, IIIB, or IIIC w/ delayed healing, seq] **173**
S52.20[1,2,9] [A,B,C]	Unsp fx of shaft of [rt, lt, unsp] ulna, init enc for [clsd fx, opn fx type I or II, opn fx type IIIA, IIIB, or IIIC] **186, 423**
S52.20[1,2,9] [B,C]	Unsp fx of shaft of [rt, lt, unsp] ulna, init enc for opn fx type [I or II, IIIA IIIB or IIIC] **434**
S52.20[1,2,9] [K,M,N,P,Q,R]	Unsp fx of shaft of [rt, lt, unsp] ulna, subsq enc for [clsd fx w/ nonu, opn fx type I or II w/ nonu, opn fx type IIIA, IIIB, or IIIC w/ nonu, clsd fx w/ malu, opn fx type I or II w/ malu, opn fx type IIIA, IIIB, or IIIC w/ malu] **197**
S42.30[1,2,9] [A,B]	Unsp fx of shaft of humerus [rt, lt, unsp] arm, init enc for [clsd, opn] fx **185, 422**
S42.30[1,2,9]B	Unsp fx of shaft of humerus [rt, lt, unsp] arm, init enc for opn fx **433**
S42.30[1,2,9] [K,P]	Unsp fx of shaft of humerus, [rt, lt, unsp] arm, subsq enc for fx w/ [nonu, malu] **197**
S02.91X[A,B]	Unsp fx of skull, init enc for [clsd, opn] fx **36, 37, 417, 430**
S02.91XS	Unsp fx of skull, seq **39**

Code	Description
S02.91XK	Unsp fx of skull, subs enc for fx w nonu **195**
S22.2[0,1,2,3,4]X[A,B]	[Unsp fx of sternum, Fx of manubrium, Fx of body of sternum, Sternal manubrial dissociation, Fx of xiphoid process], init enc for [clsd, opn] fx **420**
S22.2[0,1,2,3,4]XB	[Unsp fx of sternum, Fx of manubrium, Fx of body of sternum, Sternal manubrial dissociation, Fx of xiphoid process], init enc for opn fx **432**
S22.20X[A,B]	Unsp fx of sternum, init enc for [clsd, opn] fx **67**
S22.20XS	Unsp fx of sternum, seq **166**
S22.20XK	Unsp fx of sternum, subs for fx w nonu **196**
S22.20X[D,G]	Unsp fx of sternum, subsq enc for fx w/ [routine, delayed] healing **169**
S52.50[1,2,9][A,B,C]	Unsp fx of the lwr end of [rt, lt, unsp] radius, init enc for [clsd fx, opn fx type I or II, opn fx type IIIA, IIIB, or IIIC] **186, 423**
S52.50[1,2,9][B,C]	Unsp fx of the lwr end of [rt, lt, unsp] radius, init enc for opn fx type [I or II, IIIA IIIB or IIIC] **434**
S52.50[1,2,9][K,M,N,P,Q,R]	Unsp fx of the lwr end of [rt, lt, unsp] radius, subsq enc for [clsd fx w/ nonu, opn fx type I or II w/ nonu, opn fx type IIIA, IIIB, or IIIC w/ nonu, clsd fx w/ malu, opn fx type I or II w/ malu, opn fx type IIIA, IIIB, or IIIC w/ malu] **198**
S62.90XB	Unsp fx of unsp wrist and hand, init for opn fx **435**
S42.20[1,2,9][D,G,S]	Unsp fx of upr end of [rt, lt, unsp] humerus, [subsq enc for fx w/ routine healing, subsq enc for fx w/ delayed healing, seq] **171**
S42.20[1,2,9][A,B]	Unsp fx of upr end of [rt, lt, unsp] humerus, init enc for [clsd, opn] fx **184, 422**
S42.20[1,2,9]B	Unsp fx of upr end of [rt, lt, unsp] humerus, init enc for opn fx **433**
S42.20[1,2,9][K,P]	Unsp fx of upr end of [rt, lt, unsp] humerus, subsq enc for fx w/ [nonu, malu] **196**
S52.10[1,2,9][A,B,C]	Unsp fx of upr end of [rt, lt, unsp] radius, init enc for [clsd fx, opn fx type I or II, opn fx type IIIA, IIIB, or IIIC] **186, 423**
S52.10[1,2,9][B,C]	Unsp fx of upr end of [rt, lt, unsp] radius, init enc for opn fx type [I or II, IIIA IIIB or IIIC] **434**
S52.10[1,2,9][K,M,N,P,Q,R]	Unsp fx of upr end of [rt, lt, unsp] radius, subsq enc for [clsd fx w/ nonu, opn fx type I or II w/ nonu, opn fx type IIIA, IIIB, or IIIC w/ nonu, clsd fx w/ malu, opn fx type I or II w/ malu, opn fx type IIIA, IIIB, or IIIC w/ malu] **197**
S82.10[1,2,9][D,E,F,G,H,J,S]	Unsp fx of upr end of [rt, lt, unsp] tibia, [subsq enc for clsd fx w/ routine healing, subsq enc for opn fx type I or II w/ routine healing, subsq enc for opn fx type IIIA, IIIB, or IIIC w/ routine healing, subsq enc for clsd fx w/ delayed healing, subsq enc for opn fx type I or II w/ delayed healing, subsq enc for opn fx type I or II w/ delayed healing, seq] **179**
S82.10[1,2,9][A,B,C]	Unsp fx of upr end of [rt, lt, unsp] tibia, init enc for [clsd fx, fx type I or II, opn fx type IIIA, IIIB, or IIIC] **190, 427**
S82.10[1,2,9][B,C]	Unsp fx of upr end of [rt, lt, unsp] tibia, init enc for opn fx type [I or II, IIIA IIIB or IIIC] **436**
S82.10[1,2,9][K,M,N,P,Q,R]	Unsp fx of upr end of [rt, lt, unsp] tibia, subsq enc for [clsd fx w/ nonu, opn fx type I or II w/ nonu, opn fx type IIIA, IIIB, or IIIC w/ nonu, clsd fx w/ malu, opn fx type I or II w/ malu] **202**
S52.00[1,2,9][D,E,F,G,H,J,S]	Unsp fx of upr end of [rt, lt, unsp] ulna, [subsq enc for clsd fx w/ routine healing, subsq enc for opn fx type I or II w/ routine healing, subsq enc for opn fx type IIIA, IIIB, or IIIC w/ routine healing, subsq enc for clsd fx w/ delayed healing, subsq enc for opn fx type I or II w/ delayed healing, subsq enc for opn fx type IIIA, IIIB, or IIIC w/ delayed healing, seq] **172**
S52.10[1,2,9][D,E,F,G,H,J,S]	Unsp fx of upr end of [rt, lt, unsp] ulna, [subsq enc for clsd fx w/ routine healing, subsq enc for opn fx type I or II w/ routine healing, subsq enc for opn fx type IIIA, IIIB, or IIIC w/ routine healing, subsq enc for clsd fx w/ delayed healing, subsq enc for opn fx type I or II w/ delayed healing, subsq enc for opn fx type IIIA, IIIB, or IIIC w/ delayed healing, seq] **172**
S52.00[1,2,9][A,B,C]	Unsp fx of upr end of [rt, lt, unsp] ulna, init enc for [clsd fx, opn fx type I or II, opn fx type IIIA, IIIB, or IIIC] **186, 423**
S52.00[1,2,9][B,C]	Unsp fx of upr end of [rt, lt, unsp] ulna, init enc for opn fx [type I or II, type IIIA, IIIB, or IIIC] **434**
S52.00[1,2,9][K,M,N,P,Q,R]	Unsp fx of upr end of [rt, lt, unsp] ulna, subsq enc for [clsd fx w/ nonu, opn fx type I or II w/ nonu, opn fx type IIIA, IIIB, or IIIC w/ nonu, clsd fx w/ malu, opn fx type I or II w/ malu, opn fx type IIIA, IIIB, or IIIC w/ malu] **197**
O23.9[1,2,3]	Unsp genitourinary tract infxn in preg, [1st, 2nd, 3rd] trmstr **277**
H40.9	Unsp glaucoma **46**
O23.90	Unsp GU tract infxn in preg, unsp trmstr **280**
M46.9*	Unsp inflam spondylopathy **164**
O23.4[1,2,3]	Unsp infxn of urinary tract in preg, [1st, 2nd, 3rd] trmstr **277**
O23.40	Unsp infxn of urinary tract in preg, unsp trmstr **280**

Code	Description
S14.10[1,2,3,4,5,6,7,8,9][A,S]	Unsp inj at [C1, C2, C3, C4, C5, C6, C7, C8, unsp] lvl of cervical spinal cord [init enc, seq] **32**
S14.10[1,2,3,4,5,6,7,8,9]A	Unsp inj at [C1, C2, C3, C4, C5, C6, C7, C8, unsp] lvl of cervical spinal cord, init enc **419, 432**
S14.10[1,2,3,4,5,6,7,8,9]D	Unsp inj at [C1, C2, C3, C4, C5, C6, C7, C8, unsp] lvl of cervical spinal cord, subsq enc **388**
S24.10[1,2,3,4,9]D	Unsp inj at [T1, T2-T6, T7-T10, T11-T12, unsp) lvl of thoracic spinal cord, subsq enc **389**
S24.10[1,2,3,4,9][A,S]	Unsp inj at [T1, T2-T6, T7-T10, T11-T12, unsp) lvl of thoracic spinal cord, [init enc, seq] **32**
S24.10[1,2,3,4,9]A	Unsp inj at [T1, T2-T6, T7-T10, T11-T12, unsp) lvl of thoracic spinal cord, init enc **420, 433**
S56.409D	Unsp inj extn musc/fasc/tend unsp finger at forarm lv, subs **393**
S56.109D	Unsp inj flexor musc/fasc/tend unsp fngr at forarm lv, subs **393**
S39.9[1,2,3,4]XD	Unsp inj of [abd, lwr back, pelvis, ext genitals] subsq enc **391**
S39.9[1,2,3,4]XA	Unsp inj of [abd, lwr back, pelvis, ext genitals], init enc **422**
S36.50[0,1,2,3,8,9]A	Unsp inj of [ascending [rt] colon, transv colon, descending [lt] colon, sigmoid colon, oth part of colon,unsp part of colon], init enc **432**
S36.50[0,1,2,3,8,9]D	Unsp inj of [ascending [rt] colon, transv colon, descending [lt] colon, sigmoid colon, oth part of colon,unsp part of colon], subsq enc **391**
S36.40[0,8,9]D	Unsp inj of [duodenum, oth part of sm intestine, unsp part of sm intestine], subsq enc **390**
S36.20[0,1,2,9]A	[Unsp inj of [head, body, tail, unsp part] of pancreas, init enc **124, 432**
S36.20[0,1,2,9]S	Unsp inj of [head, body, tail, unsp part] of pancreas, seq **117**
S36.20[0,1,2,9]D	Unsp inj of [head, body, tail, unsp part] of pancreas, subsq enc **390**
S09.9[0,1,2,3]XA	Unsp inj of [head, ear, nose, face], init enc **419**
S09.9[0,1,2,3]XD	Unsp inj of [head, ear, nose, face], subsq enc **387**
S09.9[2,3]X[A,S]	Unsp inj of [nose, face], [init enc, seq] **359**
S35.40[1,2,3,4,5,6]D	Unsp inj of [rt renal artery, lt renal artery, unsp renal artery, rt renal vein, lt renal vein, unsp renal vein], subsq enc **390**
S79.9[1,2][1,2,9]A	Unsp inj of [rt, lt, unsp] [hip, thigh], init enc **427**
S99.91[1,2,9][A,S]	Unsp inj of [rt, lt, unsp] ankle, [init enc, seq] **361**
S99.91[1,2,9]A	Unsp inj of [rt, lt, unsp] ankle, init enc **430**
S99.91[1,2,9]D	Unsp inj of [rt, lt, unsp] ankle, subsq enc **400**
S15.00[1,2,9]S	Unsp inj of [rt, lt, unsp] carotid artery, seq **100**
S15.00[1,2,9]D	Unsp inj of [rt, lt, unsp] carotid artery, subsq enc **388**
S59.90[1,2,9][A,S]	Unsp inj of [rt, lt, unsp] elbow, [init enc, seq] **360**
S59.90[1,2,9]D	Unsp inj of [rt, lt, unsp] elbow, subsq enc **393**
S15.20[1,2,9]S	Unsp inj of [rt, lt, unsp] ext jugular vein, seq **100**
S15.20[1,2,9]D	Unsp inj of [rt, lt, unsp] ext jugular vein, subsq enc **388**
S99.92[1,2,9][A,S]	Unsp inj of [rt, lt, unsp] foot, [init enc, seq] **361**
S99.92[1,2,9]A	Unsp inj of [rt, lt, unsp] foot, init enc **430**
S99.92[1,2,9]D	Unsp inj of [rt, lt, unsp] foot, subsq enc **400**
S59.91[1,2,9][A,S]	Unsp inj of [rt, lt, unsp] forearm, [init enc, seq] **360**
S59.91[1,2,9]D	Unsp inj of [rt, lt, unsp] forearm, subsq enc **393**
S79.91[1,2,9][A,S]	Unsp inj of [rt, lt, unsp] hip, [init enc, seq] **360**
S25.10[1,2,9]S	Unsp inj of [rt, lt, unsp] innominate or subclavian artery, seq **100**
S25.10[1,2,9]D	Unsp inj of [rt, lt, unsp] innominate or subclavian artery, subsq enc **389**
S25.30[1,2,9]S	Unsp inj of [rt, lt, unsp] innominate or subclavian vein, seq **100**
S25.30[1,2,9]D	Unsp inj of [rt, lt, unsp] innominate or subclavian vein, subsq enc **389**
S15.30[1,2,9]S	Unsp inj of [rt, lt, unsp] int jugular vein, seq **100**
S15.30[1,2,9]D	Unsp inj of [rt, lt, unsp] int jugular vein, subsq enc **388**
S37.00[1,2,9]A	Unsp inj of [rt, lt, unsp] kidney, init enc **256**
S37.01[1,2,9]A	Unsp inj of [rt, lt, unsp] kidney, init enc **256**
S37.00[1,2,9]S	Unsp inj of [rt, lt, unsp] kidney, seq **118**
S37.00[1,2,9]D	Unsp inj of [rt, lt, unsp] kidney, subsq enc **391**
S09.30[1,2,9]A	Unsp inj of [rt, lt, unsp] mid and inner ear, init enc **58, 419**
S09.30[1,2,9]D	Unsp inj of [rt, lt, unsp] mid and inner ear, subsq enc **387**
S25.40[1,2,9]S	Unsp inj of [rt, lt, unsp] pulmn bld vessels, seq **100**
S25.40[1,2,9]D	Unsp inj of [rt, lt, unsp] pulmn bld vessels, subsq enc **389**
S35.40[1,2,3]S	Unsp inj of [rt, lt, unsp] renal artery, seq **100**
S35.40[4,5,6]S	Unsp inj of [rt, lt, unsp] renal vein, seq **100**

Code	Description
S79.92[1,2,9] [A,S]	Unsp inj of [rt, lt, unsp] thigh, [init enc, seq] **360**
S15.10[1,2,9]S	Unsp inj of [rt, lt, unsp] vert artery, seq **100**
S15.10[1,2,9]D	Unsp inj of [rt, lt, unsp] vert artery, subsq enc **388**
S15.00[1,2]A	Unsp inj of [rt, lt] carotid artery, init enc **431**
S05.9[0,1,2]XA	Unsp inj of [unsp, rt, lt] eye and orbit, init enc **47, 418**
S05.9[0,1,2]XS	Unsp inj of [unsp, rt, lt] eye and orbit, seq **359**
S05.9[0,1,2]XD	Unsp inj of [unsp, rt, lt] eye and orbit, subsq enc **386**
S89.9[0,1,2]XA	Unsp inj of [unsp, rt, lt] lwr leg, init enc **428**
S49.9[0,1,2]XD	Unsp inj of [unsp, rt, lt] shldr and upr arm, subsq enc **392**
S85.13[1,2,9]S	Unsp inj of ant tibial artery, [rt, lt, unsp] leg, seq **101**
S36.500[A,S]	Unsp inj of ascending [rt] colon, [init enc, seq] **118**
S45.00[1,2,9]S	Unsp inj of axillary artery, [rt, lt, unsp] side, seq **100**
S45.00[1,2,9]D	Unsp inj of axillary artery, [rt, lt, unsp] side, subsq enc **391**
S45.20[1,2,9]S	Unsp inj of axillary or brachial vein, [rt, lt, unsp] side, seq **100**
S45.20[1,2,9]D	Unsp inj of axillary or brachial vein, [rt, lt, unsp] side, subsq enc **392**
S65.50[8,9]D	Unsp inj of bld vessel of [oth, unsp] finger, subsq enc **396**
S65.50[0,1,2,3,4, 5,6,7,8,9]S	Unsp inj of bld vessel of [rt index, lt index, rt mid, lt mid, rt ring, lt ring, rt little, lt little, oth, unsp] finger, seq **101**
S65.40[1,2,9]S	Unsp inj of bld vessel of [rt, lt, unsp] thumb, seq **101**
S65.40[1,2,9]D	Unsp inj of bld vessel of [rt, lt, unsp] thumb, subsq enc **396**
S65.50[0,1]D	Unsp inj of bld vessel of [rt, lt] index finger, subsq enc **396**
S65.50[6,7]D	Unsp inj of bld vessel of [rt, lt] little finger, subsq enc **396**
S65.50[2,3]D	Unsp inj of bld vessel of [rt, lt] mid finger, subsq enc **396**
S65.50[4,5]D	Unsp inj of bld vessel of [rt, lt] ring finger, subsq enc **396**
S45.10[1,2,9]S	Unsp inj of brachial artery, [rt, lt, unsp] side, seq **100**
S45.10[1,2,9]D	Unsp inj of brachial artery, [rt, lt, unsp] side, subsq enc **391**
S27.40[1,2,9]A	Unsp inj of bronchus, [unilat, bilat, unsp], init enc **67**
S27.40[1,2,9]S	Unsp inj of bronchus, [unilat, bilat, unsp], seq **69**
S27.40[1,2,9]D	Unsp inj of bronchus, [unilat, bilat, unsp] subsq enc **389**
S65.30[1,2,9]S	Unsp inj of deep palmar arch of [rt, lt, unsp] hand, seq **101**
S65.30[1,2,9]D	Unsp inj of deep palmar arch of [rt, lt, unsp] hand, subsq enc **396**
S36.502[A,S]	Unsp inj of descending [lt] colon, [init enc, seq] **118**
S95.00[1,2,9]S	Unsp inj of dorsal artery of [rt, lt, unsp] foot, seq **101**
S95.20[1,2,9]S	Unsp inj of dorsal vein of [rt, lt, unsp] foot, seq **101**
S36.400[A,S]	Unsp inj of duodenum, [init enc, seq] **117**
S09.91XA	Unsp inj of ear, init enc **58**
S09.91XS	Unsp inj of ear, seq **359**
S66.30[8,9]D	Unsp inj of extensor muscle, fascia and tndn of [oth, unsp] finger at wrist and hand lvl, subsq enc **397**
S66.39[8,9]D	Unsp inj of extensor muscle, fascia and tndn of [oth, unsp] finger at wrist and hand lvl, subsq enc **397**
S66.20[1,2,9]D	Unsp inj of extensor muscle, fascia and tndn of [rt, lt, unsp] thumb at wrist and hand lvl, subsq enc **397**
S56.40[1,2]D	Unsp inj of extensor muscle, fascia and tndn of [rt, lt] index finger at forearm lvl, subsq enc **393**
S66.30[0,1]D	Unsp inj of extensor muscle, fascia and tndn of [rt, lt] index finger at wrist and hand lvl, subsq enc **397**
S66.39[0,1]D	Unsp inj of extensor muscle, fascia and tndn of [rt, lt] index finger at wrist and hand lvl, subsq enc **397**
S56.40[7,8]D	Unsp inj of extensor muscle, fascia and tndn of [rt, lt] little finger at forearm lvl, subsq enc **393**
S66.30[6,7]D	Unsp inj of extensor muscle, fascia and tndn of [rt, lt] little finger at wrist and hand lvl, subsq enc **397**
S66.39[6,7]D	Unsp inj of extensor muscle, fascia and tndn of [rt, lt] little finger at wrist and hand lvl, subsq enc **397**
S56.40[3,4]D	Unsp inj of extensor muscle, fascia and tndn of [rt, lt] mid finger at forearm lvl, subsq enc **393**
S66.30[2,3]D	Unsp inj of extensor muscle, fascia and tndn of [rt, lt] mid finger at wrist and hand lvl, subsq enc **397**
S66.39[2,3]D	Unsp inj of extensor muscle, fascia and tndn of [rt, lt] mid finger at wrist and hand lvl, subsq enc **397**
S56.40[5,6]D	Unsp inj of extensor muscle, fascia and tndn of [rt, lt] ring finger at forearm lvl, subsq enc **393**
S66.30[4,5]D	Unsp inj of extensor muscle, fascia and tndn of [rt, lt] ring finger at wrist and hand lvl, subsq enc **397**
S66.39[4,5]D	Unsp inj of extensor muscle, fascia and tndn of [rt, lt] ring finger at wrist and hand lvl, subsq enc **397**
S56.30[1,2,9]D	Unsp inj of extensor or abductor muscles, fascia and tndns of [rt, lt, unsp] thumb at forearm lvl, subsq enc **393**
S09.93XA	Unsp inj of face, init enc **5**
S37.50[1,2,9]D	Unsp inj of fallopian tube, [unilat, bilat, unsp] subsq enc **391**
S37.50[1,2,9]A	Unsp inj of fallopian tube, [unilat, bilat, unsp], init enc **265, 270**
S37.50[1,2,9]S	Unsp inj of fallopian tube, [unilat, bilat, unsp], seq **265, 270**
S75.00[1,2,9]S	Unsp inj of femor artery, [rt, lt, unsp] leg, seq **101**
S75.10[1,2,9]S	Unsp inj of femor vein at hip & thigh lvl, [rt, lt, unsp] leg, seq **101**
S66.10[8,9]D	Unsp inj of flexor muscle, fascia and tndn of [oth, unsp] finger at wrist and hand lvl, subsq enc **397**
S56.00[1,2,9]D	Unsp inj of flexor muscle, fascia and tndn of [rt, lt, unsp] thumb at forearm lvl, subsq enc **393**
S56.10[1,2]D	Unsp inj of flexor muscle, fascia and tndn of [rt, lt] index finger at forearm lvl, subsq enc **393**
S66.10[0,1]D	Unsp inj of flexor muscle, fascia and tndn of [rt, lt] index finger at wrist and hand lvl, subsq enc **397**
S56.10[7,8]D	Unsp inj of flexor muscle, fascia and tndn of [rt, lt] little finger at forearm lvl, subsq enc **393**
S66.10[6,7]D	Unsp inj of flexor muscle, fascia and tndn of [rt, lt] little finger at wrist and hand lvl, subsq enc **397**
S56.10[3,4]D	Unsp inj of flexor muscle, fascia and tndn of [rt, lt] mid finger at forearm lvl, subsq enc **393**
S66.10[2,3]D	Unsp inj of flexor muscle, fascia and tndn of [rt, lt] mid finger at wrist and hand lvl, subsq enc **397**
S56.10[5,6]D	Unsp inj of flexor muscle, fascia and tndn of [rt, lt] ring finger at forearm lvl, subsq enc **393**
S66.10[4,5]D	Unsp inj of flexor muscle, fascia and tndn of [rt, lt] ring finger at wrist and hand lvl, subsq enc **397**
S36.129A	Unsp inj of gallbladder, init enc **124**
S75.20[1,2,9]S	Unsp inj of greater saphenous vein at hip & thigh lvl, [rt, lt, unsp] leg, seq **101**
S85.30[1,2,9]S	Unsp inj of greater saphenous vein at lwr leg lvl, [rt, lt, unsp] leg, seq **101**
S09.90X[A,S]	Unsp inj of head, [init enc, seq] **359**
S09.90XA	Unsp inj of head, init enc **5**
S25.50[1,2,9]S	Unsp inj of intercostal bld vessels, [rt, lt, unsp] side, seq **100**
S25.50[1,2,9]D	Unsp inj of intercostal bld vessels, [rt, lt, unsp] side, subsq enc **389**
S85.40[1,2,9]S	Unsp inj of lesser saphenous vein at lwr leg lvl, [rt, lt, unsp] leg, seq **101**
S66.00[1,2,9]D	Unsp inj of long flexor muscle, fascia and tndn of [rt, lt, unsp] thumb at wrist and hand lvl, subsq enc **397**
S15.102A	Unsp inj of lt vert artery, init enc **5**
S27.30[1,2,9]D	Unsp inj of lung, [unilat, bilat, unsp], subsq enc **389**
S27.302[A,S]	Unsp inj of lung, bilat, [init enc, seq] **69**
S27.301[A,S]	Unsp inj of lung, unilat, [init enc, seq] **69**
S27.309[A,S]	Unsp inj of lung, unsp, [init enc, seq] **69**
S29.00[1,2,9]D	Unsp inj of muscle and tndn of [front, back, unsp] wall of thorax, subsq enc **389**
S09.10X[A,S]	Unsp inj of muscle and tndn of head, [init enc, seq] **359**
S09.10XA	Unsp inj of muscle and tndn of head, init enc **5**
S16.9XXA	Unsp inj of muscle, fascia and tndn at neck lvl, init **5**
S39.00[1,2,3]D	Unsp inj of muscle, fascia and tndn of [abd, lwr back, pelvis], subsq enc **391**
S39.001A	Unsp inj of muscle, fascia and tndn of abd, init **422**
S46.10[1,2,9]D	Unsp inj of muscle, fascia and tndn of long head of biceps, [rt, lt, unsp] arm, subsq enc **392**
S39.002A	Unsp inj of muscle, fascia and tndn of lwr back, init **422**
S46.20[1,2,9]D	Unsp inj of muscle, fascia and tndn of oth parts of biceps, [rt, lt, unsp] arm, subsq enc **392**
S39.003A	Unsp inj of muscle, fascia and tndn of pelvis, init **422**
S46.30[1,2,9]D	Unsp inj of muscle, fascia and tndn of triceps, [rt, lt, unsp] arm, subsq enc **392**
S45.80[1,2,9]D	Unsp inj of muscle(s) and tndn(s) of the rotator cuff of [rt, lt, unsp] shldr, subsq enc **392**
S46.00[1,2,9]D	Unsp inj of muscle(s) and tndn(s) of the rotator cuff of [rt, lt, unsp] shldr, subsq enc **392**
S19.9XX[A,S]	Unsp inj of neck, [init enc, seq] **359**
S19.9XXA	Unsp inj of neck, init enc **6, 420**
S19.9XXD	Unsp inj of neck, subsq enc **388**
S09.92XA	Unsp inj of nose, init enc **5**
S95.80[1,2,9]S	Unsp inj of oth bld vessels at ankle and foot lvl, [rt, lt, unsp] leg, seq **101**
S55.80[1,2,9]S	Unsp inj of oth bld vessels at forearm lvl, [rt, lt, unsp] arm, seq **101**
S55.80[1,2,9]D	Unsp inj of oth bld vessels at forearm lvl, [rt, lt, unsp] arm, subsq enc **393**
S75.80[1,2,9]S	Unsp inj of oth bld vessels at hip & thigh lvl, [rt, lt, unsp] leg, seq **101**

Code	Description
S85.80[1,2,9]S	Unsp inj of oth bld vessels at lwr leg lvl, [rt, lt, unsp] leg, seq **101**
S65.80[1,2,9]S	Unsp inj of oth bld vessels at wrist and hand lvl of [rt, lt, unsp] arm, seq **101**
S65.80[1,2,9]D	Unsp inj of oth bld vessels at wrist and hand lvl of [rt, lt, unsp] arm, subsq enc **396**
S25.80[1,2,9]S	Unsp inj of oth bld vessels of thorax, [rt, lt, unsp] side, seq **100**
S25.80[1,2,9]D	Unsp inj of oth bld vessels of thorax, [rt, lt, unsp] side, subsq enc **389**
S56.50[1,2,9]D	Unsp inj of oth extensor muscle, fascia and tndn at forearm lvl, [rt, lt, unsp] arm, subsq enc **393**
S56.20[1,2,9]D	Unsp inj of oth flexor muscle, fascia and tndn at forearm lvl, [rt, lt, unsp] arm, subsq enc **393**
S56.80[1,2,9]D	Unsp inj of oth muscles, fascia and tndns at forearm lvl, [rt, lt, unsp] arm, subsq enc **393**
S46.80[1,2,9]D	Unsp inj of oth muscles, fascia and tndns at shldr and upr arm lvl, [rt, lt, unsp] arm, subsq enc **392**
S54.8X[1,2,9]A	Unsp inj of oth nerves at forearm lvl, [rt, lt, unsp] arm, init enc **424**
S54.8X[1,2,9]D	Unsp inj of oth nerves at forearm lvl, [rt, lt, unsp] arm, subsq enc **392**
S54.8X2A	Unsp inj of oth nerves at forearm lvl, lt arm, init **34, 435**
S54.8X1A	Unsp inj of oth nerves at forearm lvl, rt arm, init **34, 435**
S54.8X9A	Unsp inj of oth nerves at forearm lvl, unsp arm, init **34, 435**
S36.508[A,S]	Unsp inj of oth part of colon, [init enc, seq] **118**
S36.408[A,S]	Unsp inj of oth part of sm intestine, [init enc, seq] **117**
S45.80[1,2,9]S	Unsp inj of oth spec bld vessels at shldr and upr arm lvl, [rt, lt, unsp] arm, seq **101**
S27.899[A,S]	Unsp inj of oth spec intrathoracic organs, [init enc, seq] **69**
S37.40[1,2,9]A	Unsp inj of ovary, [unilat, bilat, unsp], init enc **265, 270**
S37.40[1,2,9]S	Unsp inj of ovary, [unilat, bilat, unsp], seq **265, 270**
S37.40[1,2,9]D	Unsp inj of ovary, [unilat, bilat, unsp], subsq enc **391**
S85.20[1,2,9]S	Unsp inj of peroneal artery, [rt, lt, unsp] leg, seq **101**
S95.10[1,2,9]S	Unsp inj of plantar artery of [rt, lt, unsp] foot, seq **101**
S27.60X[A,S]	Unsp inj of pleura, [init enc, seq] **69**
S85.00[1,2,9]S	Unsp inj of popliteal artery, [rt, lt, unsp] leg, seq **101**
S85.50[1,2,9]S	Unsp inj of popliteal vein, [rt, lt, unsp] leg, seq **101**
S85.16[1,2,9]S	Unsp inj of post tibial artery, [rt, lt, unsp] leg, seq **101**
S55.10[1,2,9]S	Unsp inj of radial artery at forearm lvl, [rt, lt, unsp] arm, seq **101**
S55.10[1,2,9]D	Unsp inj of radial artery at forearm lvl, [rt, lt, unsp] arm, subsq enc **392**
S65.10[1,2,9]S	Unsp inj of radial artery at wrist and hand lvl of [rt, lt, unsp] arm, seq **101**
S65.10[1,2,9]D	Unsp inj of radial artery at wrist and hand lvl of [rt, lt, unsp] arm, subsq enc **396**
S36.60X[A,S]	Unsp inj of rectum, [init enc, seq] **118**
S15.101A	Unsp inj of rt vert artery, init enc **5**
S36.503[A,S]	Unsp inj of sigmoid colon, [init enc, seq] **118**
S36.00XA	Unsp inj of spleen, init enc **286, 294, 421, 432**
S36.00XS	Unsp inj of spleen, seq **117**
S36.00XD	Unsp inj of spleen, subsq enc **390**
S36.30X[A,S]	Unsp inj of stomach, [init enc, seq] **117**
S65.20[1,2,9]S	Unsp inj of superf palmar arch of [rt, lt, unsp] hand, seq **101**
S65.20[1,2,9]D	Unsp inj of superf palmar arch of [rt, lt, unsp] hand, subsq enc **396**
S45.30[1,2,9]S	Unsp inj of superf vein at shldr and upr arm lvl, [rt, lt, unsp] arm, seq **100**
S45.30[1,2,9]D	Unsp inj of superf vein at shldr and upr arm lvl, [rt, lt, unsp] arm, subsq enc **392**
S27.50X[A,S]	Unsp inj of thoracic trachea, [init enc, seq] **69**
S29.9XXD	Unsp inj of thorax, subsq enc **389**
S36.501[A,S]	Unsp inj of transv colon, [init enc, seq] **118**
S55.00[1,2,9]S	Unsp inj of ulnar artery at forearm lvl, [rt, lt, unsp] arm, seq **101**
S55.00[1,2,9]D	Unsp inj of ulnar artery at forearm lvl, [rt, lt, unsp] arm, subsq enc **392**
S65.00[1,2,9]S	Unsp inj of ulnar artery at wrist and hand lvl of [rt, lt, unsp] arm, seq **101**
S65.00[1,2,9]D	Unsp inj of ulnar artery at wrist and hand lvl of [rt, lt, unsp] arm, subsq enc **396**
S95.90[1,2,9]S	Unsp inj of unsp bld vessel at ankle and foot lvl, [rt, lt, unsp] leg, seq **101**
S55.90[1,2,9]S	Unsp inj of unsp bld vessel at forearm lvl, [rt, lt, unsp] arm, seq **101**
S75.90[1,2,9]S	Unsp inj of unsp bld vessel at hip & thigh lvl, [rt, lt, unsp] leg, seq **101**
S85.90[1,2,9]S	Unsp inj of unsp bld vessel at lwr leg lvl, [rt, lt, unsp] leg, seq **101**
S45.90[1,2,9]D	Unsp inj of unsp bld vessel at shldr and upr arm lvl, [rt, lt, unsp] arm, subsq enc **392**
S65.90[1,2,9]S	Unsp inj of unsp bld vessel at wrist and hand lvl of [rt, lt, unsp] arm, seq **101**
S65.90[1,2,9]D	Unsp inj of unsp bld vessel at wrist and hand lvl of [rt, lt, unsp] arm, subsq enc **396**
S55.90[1,2,9]D	Unsp inj of unsp bld vessels at forearm lvl, [rt, lt, unsp] arm, subsq enc **393**
S45.90[1,2,9]S	Unsp inj of unsp bld vessels at shldr and upr arm lvl, [rt, lt, unsp] arm, seq **101**
S36.90X[A,S]	Unsp inj of unsp intra-abd organ, [init enc, seq] **118**
S46.90[1,2,9]D	Unsp inj of unsp muscle, fascia and tndn at shldr and upr arm lvl, [rt, lt, unsp] arm, subsq enc **392**
S56.90[1,2,9]D	Unsp inj of unsp muscles, fascia and tndns at forearm lvl, [rt, lt, unsp] arm, subsq enc **393**
S36.509[A,S]	Unsp inj of unsp part of colon, [init enc, seq] **118**
S36.409[A,S]	Unsp inj of unsp part of sm intestine, [init enc, seq] **117**
S85.10[1,2,9]S	Unsp inj of unsp tibial artery, [rt, lt, unsp] leg, seq **101**
S15.109A	Unsp inj of unsp vert artery, init enc **5**
S55.20[1,2,9]S	Unsp inj of vein at forearm lvl, [rt, lt, unsp] arm, seq **101**
S55.20[1,2,9]D	Unsp inj of vein at forearm lvl, [rt, lt, unsp] arm, subsq enc **393**
S34.10[1,2,3,4,5,9][A,S]	[Unsp inj to [L1, L2, L3, L4, L5, unsp] lvl of lumbar spinal cord, [init enc, seq] **32**
S34.10[1,2,3,4,5,9]A	[Unsp inj to [L1, L2, L3, L4, L5, unsp] lvl of lumbar spinal cord, init enc **421, 433**
S34.10[1,2,3,4,5,9]D	[Unsp inj to [L1, L2, L3, L4, L5, unsp] lvl of lumbar spinal cord, subsq enc **390**
S36.2[0,2,3,4,5,6,9][0,1,2,9]A	Unsp inj, Contsn, Lac (unsp degree), Minor lac, Mod lac, Major lac, Oth inj] of [head, body, tail, unsp part] of pancreas, init enc **422**
S37.2[0,2,3,9]XA	[Unsp inj, Contsn, Lac, Oth inj] of bladder, init enc **256, 422, 432**
S37.2[0,2,3,9]XS	[Unsp inj, Contsn, Lac, Oth inj] of bladder, seq **261, 265, 270**
S37.2[0,2,3,9]XD	[Unsp inj, Contsn, Lac, Oth inj] of bladder, subsq enc **391**
S26.1[0,1,2,9]XA	[Unsp inj, Contsn, Lac, Oth inj] of heart w/o hemopericardium, init enc **103, 420, 432**
S26.1[0,1,2,9]XS	[Unsp inj, Contsn, Lac, Oth inj] of heart w/o hemopericardium, seq **69**
S26.1[0,1,2,9]XD	[Unsp inj, Contsn, Lac, Oth inj] of heart w/o hemopericardium, subsq enc **389**
S26.9[0,1,2,9]XA	[Unsp inj, Contsn, Lac, Oth inj] of heart, unsp w/ or w/o hemopericardium, init enc **103, 420, 432**
S26.9[0,1,2,9]XS	[Unsp inj, Contsn, Lac, Oth inj] of heart, unsp w/ or w/o hemopericardium, seq **69**
S36.3[0,2,3,9]XA	[Unsp inj, Contsn, Lac, Oth inj] of stomach, init enc **422, 432**
S36.3[0,2,3,9]XD	[Unsp inj, Contsn, Lac, Oth inj] of stomach, subsq enc **390**
S36.9[0,2,3,9]XA	[Unsp inj, Contsn, Lac, Oth inj] of unsp intra-abd organ, init enc **422**
S36.9[0,2,3,9]XD	[Unsp inj, Contsn, Lac, Oth inj] of unsp intra-abd organ, subsq enc **391**
S37.9[0,2,3,9]XA	[Unsp inj, Contsn, Lac, Oth inj] of unsp urinary and pelvic organ, init enc **261, 265, 270, 422, 432**
S37.9[0,2,3,9]XS	[Unsp inj, Contsn, Lac, Oth inj] of unsp urinary and pelvic organ, seq **261, 265, 270**
S37.9[0,2,3,9]XD	[Unsp inj, Contsn, Lac, Oth inj] of unsp urinary and pelvic organ, subsq enc **391**
S37.1[0,2,3,9]XA	[Unsp inj, Contsn, Lac, Oth inj] of ureter, init enc **256, 422, 432**
S37.1[0,2,3,9]XS	[Unsp inj, Contsn, Lac, Oth inj] of ureter, seq **261, 265, 270**
S37.1[0,2,3,9]XD	[Unsp inj, Contsn, Lac, Oth inj] of ureter, subsq enc **391**
S37.3[0,2,3,9]XA	[Unsp inj, Contsn, Lac, Oth inj] of urethra, init enc **256, 422, 432**
S37.3[0,2,3,9]XS	[Unsp inj, Contsn, Lac, Oth inj] of urethra, seq **261, 265, 270**
S37.3[0,2,3,9]XD	[Unsp inj, Contsn, Lac, Oth inj] of urethra, subsq enc **391**
S37.6[0,2,3,9]XA	[Unsp inj, Contsn, Lac, Oth Inj] of uterus, init enc **265, 270, 422, 432**
S37.6[0,2,3,9]XS	[Unsp inj, Contsn, Lac, Oth Inj] of uterus, seq **265, 270**
S37.6[0,2,3,9]XD	[Unsp inj, Contsn, Lac, Oth inj] of uterus, subsq enc **391**
S26.9[0,1,2,9]XD	[Unsp inj, Contsn, Lac, Oth inj] unsp, w/ or w/o hemopericardium, subsq enc **389**
S26.0[0,1]XA	[Unsp inj, Contsn] of heart w/ hemopericardium, init enc **103, 420, 432**
S26.0[0,1]XS	[Unsp inj, Contsn] of heart w/ hemopericardium, seq **69**
S26.0[0,1]XD	[Unsp inj, Contsn] of heart w/ hemopericardium, subsq enc **389**
S27.6[0,3,9]XA	[Unsp inj, Lac, Oth inj] of pleura, init enc **420, 432**
S27.6[0,3,9]XD	[Unsp inj, Lac, Oth inj] of pleura, subsq enc **389**
S35.4[0,1,9][1,2,3,4,5,6]A	[Unsp inj, Lac, Oth spec inj] of [rt renal artery, lt renal artery, unsp renal artery, rt renal vein, lt renal vein, unsp renal vein], init enc **359, 421, 432**

Code	Description
S65.[2,3][Ø,1,9][1,2,9]A	[Unsp inj, Lac, Oth spec inj] of [superf, deep] palmar arch of [rt, lt, unsp] hand, init enc **425**
S55.[Ø,1,2,8,9][Ø,1,9][1,2,9]A	[Unsp inj, Lac, Oth spec inj] of [ulnar artery, radial artery, vein, oth bld vessels, unsp bld vessel] at forearm lvl, [rt, lt, unsp] arm, init enc **424**
S65.[Ø,1][Ø,1,9][1,2,9]A	[Unsp inj, Lac, Oth spec inj] of [ulnar, radial] artery at wrist and hand lvl of [rt, lt, unsp] arm, init enc **425**
S85.1[3,4,5][1,2,9]A	[Unsp inj, Lac, Oth spec inj] of ant tibial artery, [rt, lt, unsp] leg, init enc **360, 428, 436**
S85.1[3,4,5][1,2,9]D	[Unsp inj, Lac, Oth spec inj] of ant tibial artery, [rt, lt, unsp] leg, subsq enc **398**
S45.Ø[Ø,1,9][1,2,9]A	[Unsp inj, Lac, Oth spec inj] of axillary artery, [rt, lt, unsp] side, init enc **359, 423, 434**
S45.2[Ø,1,9][1,2,9]A	[Unsp inj, Lac, Oth spec inj] of axillary or brachial vein, [rt, lt, unsp] side, init enc **359, 423, 434**
S65.5[Ø,1,9][Ø,1,2,3,4,5,6,7,8,9]A	[Unsp inj, Lac, Oth spec inj] of bld vessel of [rt index, lt index, rt mid, lt mid, rt ring, lt ring, rt little, lt little, oth, unsp] finger, init enc **360, 425**
S65.4[Ø,1,9][1,2,9]A	[Unsp inj, Lac, Oth spec inj] of bld vessel of [rt, lt, unsp] thumb, init enc **360, 425**
S45.1[Ø,1,9][1,2,9]A	[Unsp inj, Lac, Oth spec inj] of brachial artery, [rt, lt, unsp] side, init enc **359, 434**
S45.1[Ø,1,9][1,2,9] A	[Unsp inj, Lac, Oth spec inj] of brachial artery, [rt, lt, unsp] side, init enc **423**
S65.3[Ø,1,9][1,2,9]A	[Unsp inj, Lac, Oth spec inj] of deep palmar arch of [rt, lt, unsp] hand, init enc **360**
S95.Ø[Ø,1,9][1,2,9]A	[Unsp inj, Lac, Oth spec inj] of dorsal artery of [rt, lt, unsp] foot, init enc **361, 430, 437**
S95.Ø[Ø,1,9][1,2,9]D	[Unsp inj, Lac, Oth spec inj] of dorsal artery of [rt, lt, unsp] foot, subsq enc **399**
S95.2[Ø,1,9][1,2,9]A	[Unsp inj, Lac, Oth spec inj] of dorsal vein of [rt, lt, unsp] foot, init enc **361, 430, 437**
S95.2[Ø,1,9][1,2,9]D	[Unsp inj, Lac, Oth spec inj] of dorsal vein of [rt, lt, unsp] foot, subsq enc **399**
S85.3[Ø,1,9][1,2,9]A	[Unsp inj, Lac, Oth spec inj] of greater saphenous vein at lwr leg lvl, [rt, lt, unsp] leg, init enc **361, 428**
S85.3[Ø,1,9][1,2,9]D	[Unsp inj, Lac, Oth spec inj] of greater saphenous vein at lwr leg lvl, [rt, lt, unsp] leg, subsq enc **398**
S25.5[Ø,1,9][1,2,9]A	[Unsp inj, Lac, Oth spec inj] of intercostal bld vessels, [rt, lt, unsp] side, init enc **359, 420**
S85.4[Ø,1,9][1,2,9]A	[Unsp inj, Lac, Oth spec inj] of lesser saphenous vein at lwr leg lvl, [rt, lt, unsp] leg, init enc **361, 428**
S85.4[Ø,1,9][1,2,9]D	[Unsp inj, Lac, Oth spec inj] of lesser saphenous vein at lwr leg lvl, [rt, lt, unsp] leg, subsq enc **398**
S95.8[Ø,1,9][1,2,9]A	[Unsp inj, Lac, Oth spec inj] of oth bld vessels at ankle and foot lvl, [rt, lt, unsp] leg, init enc **361, 430, 437**
S95.8[Ø,1,9][1,2,9]D [	[Unsp inj, Lac, Oth spec inj] of oth bld vessels at ankle and foot lvl, [rt, lt, unsp] leg, subsq enc **399**
S55.8[Ø,1,9][1,2,9]A	[Unsp inj, Lac, Oth spec inj] of oth bld vessels at forearm lvl, [rt, lt, unsp] arm, init enc **359, 435**
S75.8[Ø,1,9][1,2,9]A	[Unsp inj, Lac, Oth spec inj] of oth bld vessels at hip & thigh lvl, [rt, lt, unsp] leg, init enc **360, 426, 436**
S75.8[Ø,1,9][1,2,9]D	[Unsp inj, Lac, Oth spec inj] of oth bld vessels at hip & thigh lvl, [rt, lt, unsp] leg, subsq enc **398**
S65.8[Ø,1,9][1,2,9]A	[Unsp inj, Lac, Oth spec inj] of oth bld vessels at wrist and hand lvl of [rt, lt, unsp] arm, init enc **360, 435**
S65.[8,9][Ø,1,9][1,2,9]A	[Unsp inj, Lac, Oth spec inj] of oth bld vessels at wrist and hand lvl of [rt, lt, unsp] arm, init enc **425**
S25.8[Ø,1,9][1,2,9]A	[Unsp inj, Lac, Oth spec inj] of oth bld vessels of thorax, [rt, lt, unsp] side, init enc **359, 420, 432**
S85.8[Ø,1,9][1,2,9]A	[Unsp inj, Lac, Oth spec inj] of oth bood vessels at lwr leg lvl, [rt, lt, unsp] leg, init enc **361, 428, 436**
S85.8[Ø,1,9][1,2,9]D	[Unsp inj, Lac, Oth spec inj] of oth bood vessels at lwr leg lvl, [rt, lt, unsp] leg, subsq enc **398**
S45.8[Ø,1,9][1,2,9]A	[Unsp inj, Lac, Oth spec inj] of oth spec bld vessels at shldr and upr arm lvl, [rt, lt, unsp] arm, init enc **359, 423, 434**
S85.2[Ø,1,9][1,2,9]A	[Unsp inj, Lac, Oth spec inj] of peroneal artery, [rt, lt, unsp] leg, init enc **361, 428, 436**
S85.2[Ø,1,9][1,2,9]D	[Unsp inj, Lac, Oth spec inj] of peroneal artery, [rt, lt, unsp] leg, subsq enc **398**
S95.1[Ø,1,9][1,2,9]A	[Unsp inj, Lac, Oth spec inj] of plantar artery of [rt, lt, unsp] foot, init enc **361, 430**
S95.1[Ø,1,9][1,2,9]D	[Unsp inj, Lac, Oth spec inj] of plantar artery of [rt, lt, unsp] foot, subsq enc **399**
S85.Ø[Ø,1,9][1,2,9]A	[Unsp inj, Lac, Oth spec inj] of popliteal artery, [rt, lt, unsp] leg, init enc **360, 428, 436**
S85.Ø[Ø,1,9][1,2,9]D	[Unsp inj, Lac, Oth spec inj] of popliteal artery, [rt, lt, unsp] leg, subsq enc **398**
S85.5[Ø,1,9][1,2,9]A	[Unsp inj, Lac, Oth spec inj] of popliteal vein, [rt, lt, unsp] leg, init enc **361, 428, 436**
S85.5[Ø,1,9][1,2,9]D	[Unsp inj, Lac, Oth spec inj] of popliteal vein, [rt, lt, unsp] leg, subsq enc **398**
S85.1[6,7,8][1,2,9]A	[Unsp inj, Lac, Oth spec inj] of post tibial artery, [rt, lt, unsp] leg, init enc **360, 436**
S85.1[6,7,8][1,2,9]A	[Unsp inj, Lac, Oth spec inj] of post tibial artery, [rt, lt, unsp] leg, init enc **428**
S85.1[6,7,8][1,2,9]D	[Unsp inj, Lac, Oth spec inj] of post tibial artery, [rt, lt, unsp] leg, subsq enc **398**
S55.1[Ø,1,9][1,2,9]A	[Unsp inj, Lac, Oth spec inj] of radial artery at forearm lvl, [rt, lt, unsp] arm, init enc **359, 435**
S65.1[Ø,1,9][1,2,9]A	[Unsp inj, Lac, Oth spec inj] of radial artery at wrist and hand lvl of [rt, lt, unsp] arm, init enc **360, 435**
S65.2[Ø,1,9][1,2,9]A	[Unsp inj, Lac, Oth spec inj] of superf palmar arch of [rt, lt, unsp] hand, init enc **360**
S45.3[Ø,1,9][1,2,9]A	[Unsp inj, Lac, Oth spec inj] of superf vein at shldr and upr arm lvl, [rt, lt, unsp] arm, init enc **359, 423, 434**
S55.Ø[Ø,1,9][1,2,9]A	[Unsp inj, Lac, Oth spec inj] of ulnar artery at forearm lvl, [rt, lt, unsp] arm, init enc **359, 435**
S65.Ø[Ø,1,9][1,2,9]A	[Unsp inj, Lac, Oth spec inj] of ulnar artery at wrist and hand lvl of [rt, lt, unsp] arm, init enc **360, 435**
S35.9[Ø,1,9]XA	[Unsp inj, Lac, Oth spec inj] of unsp bld vessel at abd, lwr back and pelvis lvl, init enc **359, 421, 432**
S35.9[Ø,1,9]XS	[Unsp inj, Lac, Oth spec inj] of unsp bld vessel at abd, lwr back and pelvis lvl, seq **100**
S35.9[Ø,1,9]XD	[Unsp inj, Lac, Oth spec inj] of unsp bld vessel at abd, lwr back and pelvis lvl, subsq enc **390**
S95.9[Ø,1,9][1,2,9]A	[Unsp inj, Lac, Oth spec inj] of unsp bld vessel at ankle and foot lvl, [rt, lt, unsp] leg, init enc **361, 430**
S95.9[Ø,1,9][1,2,9]D	[Unsp inj, Lac, Oth spec inj] of unsp bld vessel at ankle and foot lvl, [rt, lt, unsp] leg, subsq enc **399**
S55.9[Ø,1,9][1,2,9]A	[Unsp inj, Lac, Oth spec inj] of unsp bld vessel at forearm lvl, [rt, lt, unsp] arm, init enc **360, 435**
S75.9[Ø,1,9][1,2,9]A	[Unsp inj, Lac, Oth spec inj] of unsp bld vessel at hip & thigh lvl, [rt, lt, unsp] leg, init enc **360, 426**
S75.9[Ø,1,9][1,2,9]D	[Unsp inj, Lac, Oth spec inj] of unsp bld vessel at hip & thigh lvl, [rt, lt, unsp] leg, subsq enc **398**
S45.9[Ø,1,9][1,2,9]A	[Unsp inj, Lac, Oth spec inj] of unsp bld vessel at shldr and upr arm lvl, [rt, lt, unsp] arm, init enc **359, 423, 434**
S25.9[Ø,1,9]XA	[Unsp inj, Lac, Oth spec inj] of unsp bld vessel of thorax, init enc **359, 420, 432**
S25.9[Ø,1,9]XS	[Unsp inj, Lac, Oth spec inj] of unsp bld vessel of thorax, seq **100**
S25.9[Ø,1,9]XD	[Unsp inj, Lac, Oth spec inj] of unsp bld vessel of thorax, subsq enc **389**
S65.9[Ø,1,9][1,2,9]A	[Unsp inj, Lac, Oth spec inj] of unsp bld vessels at wrist and hand lvl of [rt, lt, unsp] arm, init enc **360, 435**
S85.9[Ø,1,9][1,2,9]A	[Unsp inj, Lac, Oth spec inj] of unsp bood vessels at lwr leg lvl, [rt, lt, unsp] leg, init enc **361, 428**
S85.9[Ø,1,9][1,2,9]D	[Unsp inj, Lac, Oth spec inj] of unsp bood vessels at lwr leg lvl, [rt, lt, unsp] leg, subsq enc **398**
S85.1[Ø,1,2][1,2,9]A	[Unsp inj, Lac, Oth spec inj] of unsp tibial artery, [rt, lt, unsp] leg, init enc **360, 428, 436**
S85.1[Ø,1,2][1,2,9]D	[Unsp inj, Lac, Oth spec inj] of unsp tibial artery, [rt, lt, unsp] leg, subsq enc **398**
S55.2[Ø,1,9][1,2,9]A	[Unsp inj, Lac, Oth spec inj] of vein at forearm lvl, [rt, lt, unsp] arm, init enc **359, 435**
S37.Ø[Ø,1,2,3,4,5,6,9][1,2,9]A	Unsp inj, Minor contsn, Major contsn, Lac (unsp degree), Minor lac, Mod lac, Major lac, Oth inj] of [rt, lt, unsp] kidney, init enc **422, 432**
S35.Ø[Ø,1,2,9]XA	[Unsp inj, Minor lac, Major lac, Oth inj] of abd aorta, init enc **286, 359, 421, 432**
S35.1[Ø,1,2,9]XA	[Unsp inj, Minor lac, Major lac, Oth inj] of inferior vena cava, init enc **286, 359, 421, 432**
S35.1[Ø,1,2,9]XD	[Unsp inj, Minor lac, Major lac, Oth inj] of inferior vena cava, subsq enc **390**
S15.Ø[Ø,1,2,9][1,2,9]A	[Unsp inj, Minor lac, Major lac, Oth spec inj] of [rt, lt, unsp] carotid artery, init enc **285, 359, 420**
S15.2[Ø,1,2,9][1,2,9]A	[Unsp inj, Minor lac, Major lac, Oth spec inj] of [rt, lt, unsp] ext jugular vein, init enc **285, 359, 420, 431**
S25.1[Ø,1,2,9][1,2,9]A	[Unsp inj, Minor lac, Major lac, Oth spec inj] of [rt, lt, unsp] innominate or subclavian artery, init enc **285, 359, 420, 432**
S25.3[Ø,1,2,9][1,2,9]A	[Unsp inj, Minor lac, Major lac, Oth spec inj] of [rt, lt, unsp] innominate or subclavian vein, init enc **286, 359, 420, 432**

S15.3[0,1,2,9][1,2,9]A [Unsp inj, Minor lac, Major lac, Oth spec inj] of [rt, lt, unsp] int jugular vein, init enc 285, 359, 431

S25.4[0,1,2,9][1,2,9]A [Unsp inj, Minor lac, Major lac, Oth spec inj] of [rt, lt, unsp] pulmn bld vessels, init enc 286, 359, 420, 432

S15.1[0,1,2,9][1,2,9]A [Unsp inj, Minor lac, Major lac, Oth spec inj] of [rt, lt, unsp] vert artery, init enc 359, 420

S35.0[0,1,2,9]XS [Unsp inj, Minor lac, Major lac, Oth spec inj] of abd aorta, seq 100

S75.0[0,1,2,9][1,2,9]A [Unsp inj, Minor lac, Major lac, Oth spec inj] of femer artery, [rt, lt, unsp] leg, init enc 360, 426, 436

S75.0[0,1,2,9][1,2,9]D [Unsp inj, Minor lac, Major lac, Oth spec inj] of femer artery, [rt, lt, unsp] leg, subsq enc 398

S75.1[0,1,2,9][1,2,9]A [Unsp inj, Minor lac, Major lac, Oth spec inj] of femer vein at hip & thigh lvl, [rt, lt, unsp] leg, init enc 360, 426, 436

S75.1[0,1,2,9][1,2,9]D [Unsp inj, Minor lac, Major lac, Oth spec inj] of femer vein at hip & thigh lvl, [rt, lt, unsp] leg, subsq enc 398

S75.2[0,1,2,9][1,2,9]A [Unsp inj, Minor lac, Major lac, Oth spec inj] of greater saphenous vein at hip & thigh lvl, [rt, lt, unsp] leg, init enc 360, 426

S75.2[0,1,2,9][1,2,9]D [Unsp inj, Minor lac, Major lac, Oth spec inj] of greater saphenous vein at hip & thigh lvl, [rt, lt, unsp] leg, subsq enc 398

S35.1[0,1,2,9]XS [Unsp inj, Minor lac, Major lac, Oth spec inj] of inferior vena cava, seq 100

S25.2[0,1,2,9]XA [Unsp inj, Minor lac, Major lac, Oth spec inj] of superior vena cava, init enc 286, 359, 420, 432

S25.2[0,1,2,9]XS [Unsp inj, Minor lac, Major lac, Oth spec inj] of superior vena cava, seq 100

S25.2[0,1,2,9]XD [Unsp inj, Minor lac, Major lac, Oth spec inj] of superior vena cava, subsq enc 389

S25.0[0,1,2,9]XA [Unsp inj, Minor lac, Major lac, Oth spec inj] of thoracic aorta, init enc 285, 420

S25.0[0,1,2,9]XA [Unsp inj, Minor lac, Major lac, Oth spec inj] of thoracic aorta, init enc 359, 432

S25.0[0,1,2,9]XS [Unsp inj, Minor lac, Major lac, Oth spec inj] of thoracic aorta, seq 100

S25.0[0,1,2,9]XD [Unsp inj, Minor lac, Major lac, Oth spec inj] of thoracic aorta, subsq enc 389

S36.5[0,1,2,3,9][0,1,2,3,8,9]A [Unsp inj, Primary blast inj, Contsn, Lac, Oth inj] of [ascending [rt], transv, descending (lt), sigmoid, oth part, unsp part] (of) colon, init enc 422

S27.4[0,1,2,3,9][1,2,9]A [Unsp inj, Primary blast inj, Contsn, Lac, Oth inj] of bronchus, [unilat, bilat, unsp], init enc 420, 432

S36.6[0,1,2,3,9]XA [Unsp inj, Primary blast inj, Contsn, Lac, Oth inj] of rectum, init enc 422, 432

S36.6[0,1,2,3,9]XD [Unsp inj, Primary blast inj, Contsn, Lac, Oth inj] of rectum, subsq enc 391

S27.5[0,1,2,3,9]XA [Unsp inj, Primary blast inj, Contsn, Lac, Oth inj] of thoracic trachea, init enc 420, 432

S27.5[0,1,2,3,9]XD [Unsp inj, Primary blast inj, Contsn, Lac, Oth inj] of thoracic trachea, subsq enc 389

S27.3[0,1,2,3,9][1,2,9]A [Unsp inj, Primary blast inj, Contsn, Lac, Oth injuries] of lung, [unilat, bilat, unsp], init enc 420, 432

S36.4[0,1,2,3,9][0,8,9]A [Unsp inj, Primary blast, Contsn, Lac, Oth inj] of [duodenum, oth part of sm intestine, unsp part of sm intestine], init enc 422, 432

S66.[8,9][0,1,2,9][1,2,9]A [Unsp inj, Strain, Lac, Oth inj] of [oth spec, unsp] muscles, fascia and tndns at wrist and hand lvl, [rt, lt, unsp] hand, init enc 425

S66.[8,9][0,1,2,9][1,2,9]D [Unsp inj, Strain, Lac, Oth inj] of [oth spec, unsp] muscles, fascia and tndns at wrist and hand lvl, [rt, lt, unsp] hand, subsq enc 397

S46.[8,9][0,1,2,9][1,2,9]A [Unsp inj, Strain, Lac, Oth inj] of [oth, unsp] muscle(s), fascia and tndn(s) at shldr and upr arm lvl, [rt, lt, unsp] arm, init enc 423

S56.[8,9][0,1,2,9][1,2,9]A [Unsp inj, Strain, Lac, Oth inj] of [oth, unsp] muscles, fascia and tndns at forearm lvl, [rt, lt, unsp] arm, init enc 424

S76.2[0,1,2,9][1,2,9]A [Unsp inj, Strain, Lac, Oth inj] of adductor muscle, fascia and tndn of [rt, lt, unsp] thigh, init enc 426

S76.2[0,1,2,9][1,2,9]D [Unsp inj, Strain, Lac, Oth inj] of adductor muscle, fascia and tndn of [rt, lt, unsp] thigh, subsq enc 398

S56.4[0,1,2,9][1,2,3,,4,5,6,7,8,9]A [Unsp inj, Strain, Lac, Oth inj] of extensor muscle, fascia and tndn, of (of finger,) [rt, lt] [index, mid, ring, little, unsp] finger at forearm lvl, init enc 424

S66.3[0,1,2,9][0,1,2,3,4,5,6,7,8,9]A [Unsp inj, Strain, Lac, Oth inj] of [rt index, lt index, rt mid, lt mid, rt ring, lt ring, rt little, lt little, oth, unsp] finger at wrist and hand lvl, init enc 425

S56.3[0,1,2,9][1,2,9]A [Unsp inj, Strain, Lac, Oth inj] of extensor or abductor muscles, fascia and tndns of [rt, lt, unsp] thumb at forearm lvl, init enc 424

S56.1[0,1,2,9][1,2,3,4,5,6,7,8,9]A [Unsp inj, Strain, Lac, Oth inj] of flexor muscle, fascia and tndn of (of finger) [rt, lt] [index, mid, ring, little, unsp] finger at forearm lvl, init enc 424

S66.1[0,1,2,9][0,1,2,3,4,5,6,7,8,9]A [Unsp inj, Strain, Lac, Oth inj] of flexor muscle, fascia and tndn of [rt index, lt index, rt mid, lt mid, rt ring, lt ring, rt little, lt little, oth, unsp] finger at wrist and hand lvl, init enc 425

S56.0[0,1,2,9][1,2,9]A [Unsp inj, Strain, Lac, Oth inj] of flexor muscle, fascia and tndn of [rt, lt, unsp] thumb at forearm lvl, init enc 424

S96.2[0,1,2,9][1,2,9]A [Unsp inj, Strain, Lac, Oth inj] of intrinsic muscle and tndn at ankle and foot lvl, [rt, lt, unsp] foot, init enc 430

S96.2[0,1,2,9][1,2,9]D [Unsp inj, Strain, Lac, Oth inj] of intrinsic muscle and tndn at ankle and foot lvl, [rt, lt, unsp] foot, subsq 400

S66.5[0,1,2,9][0,1,2,3,4,5,6,7,8,9]A [Unsp inj, Strain, Lac, Oth inj] of intrinsic muscle, fascia and tndn of [rt index, lt index, rt mid, lt mid, rt ring, lt ring, rt little, lt little, oth, unsp] finger at wrist and hand lvl, init enc 425

S66.5[0,1,2,9][0,1,2,3,4,5,6,7,8,9]D [Unsp inj, Strain, Lac, Oth inj] of intrinsic muscle, fascia and tndn of [rt index, lt index, rt mid, lt mid, rt ring, lt ring, rt little, lt little, oth, unsp] finger at wrist and hand lvl, subsq enc 397

S29.0[0,1,2,9][1,2,9]A [Unsp inj, Strain, Lac, Oth inj] of muscle and tndn of [front, back, unsp] wall of thorax, init enc 421

S96.1[0,1,2,9][1,2,9]A [Unsp inj, Strain, Lac, Oth inj] of muscle and tndn of long extensor muscle of toe at ankle and foot lvl, [rt, lt, unsp] foot, init enc 430

S96.1[0,1,2,9][1,2,9]D [Unsp inj, Strain, Lac, Oth inj] of muscle and tndn of long extensor muscle of toe at ankle and foot lvl, [rt, lt, unsp] foot, subsq enc 400

S96.0[0,1,2,9][1,2,9]A [Unsp inj, Strain, Lac, Oth inj] of muscle and tndn of long flexor muscle of toe at ankle and foot lvl, [rt, lt, unsp] foot, init enc 430

S96.0[0,1,2,9][1,2,9]D [Unsp inj, Strain, Lac, Oth inj] of muscle and tndn of long flexor muscle of toe at ankle and foot lvl, [rt, lt, unsp] foot, subsq enc 399

S46.1[0,1,2,9][1,2,9]A [Unsp inj, Strain, Lac, Oth inj] of muscle, fascia and tndn of long head of biceps, [rt, lt, unsp] arm, init enc 423

S46.2[0,1,2,9][1,2,9]A [Unsp inj, Strain, Lac, Oth inj] of muscle, fascia and tndn of oth parts of biceps, [rt, lt, unsp] arm, init enc 423

S46.3[0,1,2,9][1,2,9]A [Unsp inj, Strain, Lac, Oth inj] of muscle, fascia and tndn of triceps, [rt, lt, unsp] arm, init enc 423

S46.0[0,1,2,9][1,2,9]A [Unsp inj, Strain, Lac, Oth inj] of muscle(s) and tndn(s) of the rotator cuff of [rt, lt, unsp] shldr, init enc 423

S56.5[0,1,2,9][1,2,9]A [Unsp inj, Strain, Lac, Oth inj] of oth extensor muscle, fascia and tndn at forearm lvl, [rt, lt, unsp] arm, init enc 424

S56.2[0,1,2,9][1,2,9]A [Unsp inj, Strain, Lac, Oth inj] of oth flexor muscle, fascia and tndn at forearm lvl, [rt, lt, unsp] arm, init enc 424

S96.8[0,1,2,9][1,2,9]A [Unsp inj, Strain, Lac, Oth inj] of oth spec muscles and tndns at ankle and foot lvl, [rt, lt, unsp] foot, init enc 430

S96.8[0,1,2,9][1,2,9]D [Unsp inj, Strain, Lac, Oth inj] of oth spec muscles and tndns at ankle and foot lvl, [rt, lt, unsp] foot, subsq enc 400

S76.8[0,1,2,9][1,2,9]A [Unsp inj, Strain, Lac, Oth inj] of oth spec muscles, fascia and tndns at thigh lvl, [rt, lt, unsp] thigh, init enc 426

S76.8[0,1,2,9][1,2,9]D [Unsp inj, Strain, Lac, Oth inj] of oth spec muscles, fascia and tndns at thigh lvl, [rt, lt, unsp] thigh, subsq enc 398

S96.9[0,1,2,9][1,2,9]A [Unsp inj, Strain, Lac, Oth inj] of unsp muscle and tndn at ankle and foot lvl, [rt, lt, unsp] foot, init enc 430

S96.9[0,1,2,9][1,2,9]D [Unsp inj, Strain, Lac, Oth inj] of unsp muscle and tndn at ankle and foot lvl, [rt, lt, unsp] foot, subsq enc 400

S86.0[0,1,2,9][1,2,9]A [Unsp inj, Strain, Lac, Oth spec inj] of [rt, lt, unsp] Achilles tndn, init enc 428

S86.0[0,1,2,9][1,2,9]D [Unsp inj, Strain, Lac, Oth spec inj] of [rt, lt, unsp] Achilles tndn, subsq enc 398

S76.1[0,1,2,9][1,2,9]A [Unsp inj, Strain, Lac, Oth inj] of [rt, lt, unsp] quadriceps muscle, fascia and tndn, init enc 426

S76.1[0,1,2,9][1,2,9]D [Unsp inj, Strain, Lac, Oth inj] of [rt, lt, unsp] quadriceps muscle, fascia and tndn, subsq enc 398

S66.2[0,1,9][1,2,9]A [Unsp inj, Strain, Lac, oth spec inj] of extensor muscle, fascia and tndn of [rt, lt, unsp] thumb at wrist and hand lvl, init enc 425

S66.4[0,1,2,9][1,2,9]A [Unsp inj, Strain, Lac, Oth inj] of intrinsic muscle, fascia and tndn of [rt, lt, unsp] thumb at wrist and hand lvl, init enc 425

S66.4[0,1,2,9][1,2,9]D [Unsp inj, Strain, Lac, Oth spec inj] of intrinsic muscle, fascia and tndn of [rt, lt, unsp] thumb at wrist and hand lvl, subsq 397

S66.0[0,1,2,9][1,2,9]A [Unsp inj, Strain, Lac, Oth spec inj] of long flexor muscle, fascia and tndn of [rt, lt, unsp] thumb at wrist and hand lvl, init enc 425

S09.1[0,1,2,9]XA [Unsp inj, Strain, Lac, Oth spec inj] of muscle and tndn of head, init enc 419

S09.1[0,1,2,9]XD [Unsp inj, strain, lac, oth inj] of muscle and tndn of head, subsq enc 387

S76.0[0,1,2,9][1,2,9]A [Unsp inj, Strain, Lac, Oth spec inj] of muscle, fascia and tndn of [rt, lt, unsp] hip, init enc 426

S76.0[0,1,2,9][1,2,9]D [Unsp inj, Strain, Lac, Oth spec inj] of muscle, fascia and tndn of [rt, lt, unsp] hip, subsq enc 398

S76.3[0,1,2,9][1,2,9]A [Unsp inj, Strain, Lac, Oth spec inj] of muscle, fascia and tndn of the post muscle group at thigh lvl, [rt, lt, unsp] thigh, init enc 426

S76.3[0,1,2,9][1,2,9]D	[Unsp inj, Strain, Lac, Oth spec inj] of muscle, fascia and tndn of the post muscle group at thigh lvl, [rt, lt, unsp] thigh, subsq enc 398
S86.8[0,1,2,9][1,2,9]A	[Unsp inj, Strain, Lac, Oth spec inj] of oth muscle(s) and tndn(s) at lwr leg lvl, [rt, lt, unsp] leg, init enc 428
S86.8[0,1,2,9][1,2,9]D	[Unsp inj, Strain, Lac, Oth spec inj] of oth muscle(s) and tndn(s) at lwr leg lvl, [rt, lt, unsp] leg, subsq enc 398
S86.2[0,1,2,9][1,2,9]A	[Unsp inj, Strain, Lac, Oth spec inj] of oth muscle(s) and tndn(s) of ant muscle group at lwr leg lvl, [rt, lt, unsp] leg, init enc 428
S86.2[0,1,2,9][1,2,9]D	[Unsp inj, Strain, Lac, Oth spec inj] of oth muscle(s) and tndn(s) of ant muscle group at lwr leg lvl, [rt, lt, unsp] leg, subsq enc 398
S86.3[0,1,2,9][1,2,9]A	[Unsp inj, Strain, Lac, Oth spec inj] of oth muscle(s) and tndn(s) of peroneal muscle group at lwr leg lvl, [rt, lt, unsp] leg, init enc 428
S86.3[0,1,2,9][1,2,9]D	[Unsp inj, Strain, Lac, Oth spec inj] of oth muscle(s) and tndn(s) of peroneal muscle group at lwr leg lvl, [rt, lt, unsp] leg, subsq enc 398
S86.1[0,1,2,9][1,2,9]A	[Unsp inj, Strain, Lac, Oth spec inj] of oth muscle(s) and tndn(s) of post muscle group at lwr leg lvl, [rt, lt, unsp] leg, init enc 428
S86.1[0,1,2,9][1,2,9]D	[Unsp inj, Strain, Lac, Oth spec inj] of oth muscle(s) and tndn(s) of post muscle group at lwr leg lvl, [rt, lt, unsp] leg, subsq enc 398
S86.9[0,1,2,9][1,2,9]A	[Unsp inj, Strain, Lac, Oth spec inj] of unsp muscle(s) and tndn(s) at lwr leg lvl, [rt, lt, unsp] leg, init enc 428
S86.9[0,1,2,9][1,2,9]D	[Unsp inj, Strain, Lac, Oth spec inj] of unsp muscle(s) and tndn(s) at lwr leg lvl, [rt, lt, unsp] leg, subsq enc 398
S76.9[0,1,2,9][1,2,9]A	[Unsp inj, Strain, Lac, Oth spec inj] of unsp muscles, fascia and tndns at thigh lvl, [rt, lt, unsp] thigh, init enc 426
S76.9[0,1,2,9][1,2,9]D	[Unsp inj, Strain, Lac, Oth spec inj] of unsp muscles, fascia and tndns at thigh lvl, [rt, lt, unsp] thigh, subsq enc 398
M23.9*	Unsp int derangement of knee 184
F79	Unsp intellectual disabilities 310
H16.30[1,2,3,9]	Unsp interstitial keratitis, [rt, lt, bilat, unsp] eye 46
B82*	Unsp intestinal parasitism 116
S72.01[1,2,9][D,E,F,G,H,J,S]	Unsp intracapsular fx of [rt, lt, unsp] femur, [subsq enc for clsd fx w/ routine healing, subsq enc for opn fx type I or II w/ routine healing, subsq enc for opn fx type IIIA, IIIB, or IIIC w/ routine healing, subsq enc for clsd fx w/ delayed healing, subsq enc for opn fx type I or II w/ delayed healing, subsq enc for opn fx type IIIA, IIIB, or IIIC w/ delayed healing, seq] 176
S72.01[1,2,9][A,B,C]	Unsp intracapsular fx of [rt, lt, unsp] femur, init enc for [clsd fx, opn fx type I or II, opn fx type IIIA, IIIB, or IIIC] 162, 286, 426
S72.01[1,2,9][A,B,C]	Unsp intracapsular fx of [rt, lt, unsp] femur, init enc for [clsd fx, opn fx type I or II, opn fx type IIIA, IIIB, or IIIC] 435
S72.01[1,2,9][K,M,N,P,Q,R]	Unsp intracapsular fx of [rt, lt, unsp] femur, subsq enc for [clsd fx w/ nonu, opn fx type I or II w/ nonu, opn fx type IIIA, IIIB, or IIIC w/ nonu, clsd fx w/ malu, opn fx type I or II w/ malu, opn fx type IIIA, IIIB, or IIIC w/ malu] 200
S06.9X1A	Unsp intracranial inj w LOC of 30 min or less, init 37
S06.9X2A	Unsp intracranial inj w LOC of 31-59 min, init 37
S06.9X[5,6]A	Unsp intracranial inj w/ LOC > 24 hrs [w/ return to pre-existing conscious lvl, w/o return to pre-existing conscious lvl w/ patient surviving], init enc 37, 419, 431
S06.9X[3,4,5,6]A	Unsp intracranial inj w/ LOC of [1 hr to 5 hrs 59 min, 6 hrs to 24 hrs, >24 hrs w/ return to pre-existing conscious lvl, > 24 hrs w/o return to pre-existing conscious lvl patient surviving], init enc 36
S06.9X[1,2,3,4]A	Unsp intracranial inj w/ LOC of [30 min or less, 31 min to 59 min, 1 hr to 5 hrs 59 min, 6 hrs to 24 hrs], init enc 37, 419, 431
S06.9X[1,2,3,4]S	Unsp intracranial inj w/ LOC of [30 min or less, 31-59 min, 1 hr to 5 hrs 59 min, 6 hrs to 24 hrs], seq 40
S06.9X[1,2,3,4]D	Unsp intracranial inj w/ LOC of [30 min or less, 31-59 min, 1 hr to 5 hrs 59 min, 6 hrs to 24 hrs], subsq enc 387
S06.9X[7,8,9]A	Unsp intracranial inj w/ LOC of [any dur w/ death d/t brain inj prior to regain cnscness, any dur w/ death d/t oth cause prior to regain cnscness, unsp dur], init enc 36, 37, 419, 431
S06.9X[7,8,9]S	Unsp intracranial inj w/ LOC of [any dur w/ death d/t brain inj prior to regain cnscness, any dur w/ death d/t oth cause prior to regain cnscness, unsp dur], seq 40
S06.9X[7,8,9]D	Unsp intracranial inj w/ LOC of [any dur w/ death d/t brain inj prior to regain cnscness, any dur w/ death d/t oth cause prior to regain cnscness, unsp dur], subsq enc 387
S06.9X[5,6]S	Unsp intracranial inj w/ LOC of > 24 hrs [w/ return to pre-existing conscious lvl, w/o return to pre-existing conscious lvl w/ patient surviving], seq 40
S06.9X[5,6]D	Unsp intracranial inj w/ LOC of > 24 hrs [w/ return to pre-existing conscious lvl, w/o return to pre-existing conscious lvl w/ patient surviving], subsq enc 387
S06.9X0A	Unsp intracranial inj w/o LOC, init 37, 419, 431
S06.9X0S	Unsp intracranial inj w/o LOC, seq 40
S06.9X0D	Unsp intracranial inj w/o LOC, subs 387
R17	Unsp jaundice 124
H16.9	Unsp keratitis 46
N19	Unsp kidney failure 254
S36.039A	Unsp lac of spleen, init enc 294
N63	Unsp lump in breast 224
B54	Unsp malaria 308
O43.1[0,1,9][1,2,3]	[Unsp malformation of, Circumvallate, Oth malformation of] placenta, [1st, 2nd, 3rd] trmstr 280
C44.5[0,1,2,9][0,1,9]	[Unsp malig neoplasm, Basal cell carcinoma, Squamous cell ca, Oth spec malig neoplasm] of [anal skin, skin of breast, skin of oth part of trunk] 233
C44.8[0,1,2,9]	[Unsp malig neoplasm, Basal cell carcinoma, Squamous cell ca, Oth spec malig neoplasm] of overlapping sites of skin 233
C44.2[0,1,2,9][1,2,9]	[Unsp malig neoplasm, Basal cell carcinoma, Squamous cell ca, Oth spec malig neoplasm] of skin of [unsp, rt, lt] ear and ext auricular canal 233
C44.7[0,1,2,9][1,2,9]	[Unsp malig neoplasm, Basal cell carcinoma, Squamous cell ca, Oth spec malig neoplasm] of skin of [unsp, rt, lt] lwr limb, incl* hip 233
C44.6[0,1,2,9][1,2,9]	[Unsp malig neoplasm, Basal cell carcinoma, Squamous cell ca, Oth spec malig neoplasm] of skin of [unsp, rt, lt] upr limb, incl* shldr 233
C44.4[0,1,2,9]	[Unsp malig neoplasm, Basal cell carcinoma, Squamous cell ca, Oth spec malig neoplasm] of skin of scalp and neck 233
C44.9[0,1,2,9]	[Unsp malig neoplasm, Basal cell carcinoma, Squamous cell ca, Oth spec malig neoplasm] of skin, unsp 233
C44.0[0,1,2,9]	[Unsp malig neoplasm, Basal cell carcinoma, Squamous cell carcinoma, Oth spec malig neoplasm] of skin of lip 233
H70.9*	Unsp mastoiditis 57
O16*	Unsp maternal hypertension 273
O16.[1,2,3]	Unsp maternal hypertension, [1st, 2nd, 3rd] trmstr 276, 277
O16.1	Unsp maternal hypertension, first trmstr 279
O16.2	Unsp maternal hypertension, second trmstr 279
O16.3	Unsp maternal hypertension, third trmstr 279
O16.9	Unsp maternal hypertension, unsp trmstr 280
O98.93	Unsp maternal infec/parastc dz comp the puerperium 274, 276
O98.92	Unsp maternal infec/parastc dz compl childbirth 274
O98.91[1,2,3]	Unsp maternal infectious and parasitic dz compl preg, [1st, 2nd, 3rd] trmstr 274, 277
F09	Unsp mental d/o d/t known physiological condition 310, 439
F39	Unsp mood [affective] d/o 311
T07	Unsp multi injuries 230, 430
B49	Unsp mycosis 308
H73.2*	Unsp myringitis 57
N05*	Unsp nephritic synd 256
S42.215B	Unsp nondisp fx of surg neck of Lt humerus, init for opn fx 433
S42.214B	Unsp nondisp fx of surg neck of Rt humerus, init for opn fx 433
S42.216B	Unsp nondisp fx of surg neck of unsp humer, init for opn fx 433
S42.21[4,5,6][D,G,S]	Unsp nondisp fx of surgical neck of [rt, lt, unsp] humerus, [subsq enc for fx w/ routine healing, subsq enc for fx w/ delayed healing, seq] 171
S42.21[4,5,6][K,P]	Unsp nondisp fx of surgical neck of [rt, lt, unsp] humerus, subsq enc for fx w/ [nonu, malu] 196
S42.21[4,5,6][A,B]	Unsp nondisp fx of surgical neck of humerus [rt, lt, unsp] init enc for fx [clsd, opn] 184
S31.602S	Unsp opn wnd abd wall, epigst rgn w penet perit cav, seq 226
S31.605S	Unsp opn wnd abd wall, periumb rgn w penet perit cav, seq 226
S31.609S	Unsp opn wnd abd wall, unsp q w penet perit cav, seq 226
S31.001S	Unsp opn wnd low back and pelvis w penet retroperiton, seq 226
S01.50[1,2]A	Unsp opn wnd of [lip, oral cavity] init enc 59
S01.50[1,2]S	Unsp opn wnd of [lip, oral cavity], seq 224
S61.30[8,9][A,S]	Unsp opn wnd of [oth, unsp] finger w/ damage to nail, [init enc, seq] 228
S61.30[8,9]D	Unsp opn wnd of [oth, unsp] finger w/ damage to nail, subsq enc 394
S61.20[8,9][A,S]	Unsp opn wnd of [oth, unsp] finger w/o damage to nail, [init enc, seq] 228
S61.20[8,9]D	Unsp opn wnd of [oth, unsp] finger w/o damage to nail, subsq enc 394
S31.[2,3]0XS	Unsp opn wnd of [penis, scrotum and testes], seq 227
S21.40[1,2,9]D	Unsp opn wnd of [rt, lt, unspecified] back wall of thorax w/ penetration into thoracic cavity, subsq enc 388

S21.20[1,2,9]D	Unsp opn wnd of [rt, lt, unspecified] back wall of thorax w/o penetration into thoracic cavity, subsq enc **388**
S21.30[1,2,9]D	Unsp opn wnd of [rt, lt, unspecified] front wall of thorax w/ penetration into thoracic cavity, subsq enc **388**
S21.10[1,2,9]D	Unsp opn wnd of [rt, lt, unspecified] front wall of thorax w/o penetration into thoracic cavity, subsq enc **388**
S21.40[1,2,9]A	Unsp opn wnd of [rt, lt, unsp] back wall of thorax w/ penetration into thoracic cavity, init enc **359, 432**
S21.40[1,2,9]S	Unsp opn wnd of [rt, lt, unsp] back wall of thorax w/ penetration into thoracic cavity, seq **225**
S21.20[1,2,9] [A,S]	Unsp opn wnd of [rt, lt, unsp] back wall of thorax w/o penetration into thoracic cavity, [init enc, seq] **225**
S21.00[1,2,9] [A,S]	Unsp opn wnd of [rt, lt, unsp] breast, [init enc, seq] **225**
S21.00[1,2,9]D	Unsp opn wnd of [rt, lt, unsp] breast, subsq enc **388**
S01.40[1,2,9] [A,S]	Unsp opn wnd of [rt, lt, unsp] cheek and temporomandibular area, [init enc, seq] **224**
S01.30[1,2,9]S	Unsp opn wnd of [rt, lt, unsp] ear, seq **224**
S51.00[1,2,9] [A,S]	Unsp opn wnd of [rt, lt, unsp] elbow, [init enc, seq] **227**
S51.00[1,2,9]D	Unsp opn wnd of [rt, lt, unsp] elbow, subsq enc **392**
S01.10[1,2,9]A	Unsp opn wnd of [rt, lt, unsp] eyelid and periocular area, init enc **46**
S01.10[1,2,9]S	Unsp opn wnd of [rt, lt, unsp] eyelid and periocular area, seq **224**
S51.80[1,2,9] [A,S]	Unsp opn wnd of [rt, lt, unsp] forearm, [init enc, seq] **227**
S51.80[1,2,9]D	Unsp opn wnd of [rt, lt, unsp] forearm, subsq enc **392**
S21.30[1,2,9]A	Unsp opn wnd of [rt, lt, unsp] front wall of thorax w/ penetration into thoracic cavity, init enc **359, 431**
S21.30[1,2,9]S	Unsp opn wnd of [rt, lt, unsp] front wall of thorax w/ penetration into thoracic cavity, seq **225**
S21.10[1,2,9] [A,S]	Unsp opn wnd of [rt, lt, unsp] front wall of thorax w/o penetration into thoracic cavity, [init enc, seq] **225**
S91.20[1,2,3] [A,S]	Unsp opn wnd of [rt, lt, unsp] great toe w/ damage to nail, [init enc, seq] **230**
S91.20[1,2,3]A	Unsp opn wnd of [rt, lt, unsp] great toe w/ damage to nail, init enc **429**
S91.20[1,2,3]D	Unsp opn wnd of [rt, lt, unsp] great toe w/ damage to nail, subsq enc **399**
S91.10[1,2,3] [A,S]	Unsp opn wnd of [rt, lt, unsp] great toe w/o damage to nail, [init enc, seq] **230**
S91.10[1,2,3]A	Unsp opn wnd of [rt, lt, unsp] great toe w/o damage to nail, init enc **429**
S91.10[1,2,3]D	Unsp opn wnd of [rt, lt, unsp] great toe w/o damage to nail, subsq enc **399**
S61.40[1,2,9] [A,S]	Unsp opn wnd of [rt, lt, unsp] hand, [init enc, seq] **229**
S61.40[1,2,9]D	Unsp opn wnd of [rt, lt, unsp] hand, subsq enc **395**
S91.20[4,5,6] [A,S]	Unsp opn wnd of [rt, lt, unsp] lesser toe(s) w/ damage to nail, [init enc, seq] **230**
S91.20[4,5,6]A	Unsp opn wnd of [rt, lt, unsp] lesser toe(s) w/ damage to nail, init enc **429**
S91.20[4,5,6]D	Unsp opn wnd of [rt, lt, unsp] lesser toe(s) w/ damage to nail, subsq enc **399**
S91.10[4,5,6] [A,S]	Unsp opn wnd of [rt, lt, unsp] lesser toe(s) w/o damage to nail, [init enc, seq] **230**
S91.10[4,5,6]A	Unsp opn wnd of [rt, lt, unsp] lesser toe(s) w/o damage to nail, init enc **429**
S91.10[4,5,6]D	Unsp opn wnd of [rt, lt, unsp] lesser toe(s) w/o damage to nail, subsq enc **399**
S41.00[1,2,9] [A,S]	Unsp opn wnd of [rt, lt, unsp] shldr, [init enc, seq] **227**
S41.00[1,2,9]D	Unsp opn wnd of [rt, lt, unsp] shldr, subsq enc **391**
S61.10[1,2,9] [A,S]	Unsp opn wnd of [rt, lt, unsp] thumb w/ damage to nail, [init enc, seq] **228**
S61.10[1,2,9]D	Unsp opn wnd of [rt, lt, unsp] thumb w/ damage to nail, subsq enc **394**
S61.00[1,2,9] [A,S]	Unsp opn wnd of [rt, lt, unsp] thumb w/o damage to nail, [init enc, seq] **228**
S61.00[1,2,9]D	Unsp opn wnd of [rt, lt, unsp] thumb w/o damage to nail, subsq enc **394**
S41.10[1,2,9] [A,S]	Unsp opn wnd of [rt, lt, unsp] upr arm, [init enc, seq] **227**
S41.10[1,2,9]D	Unsp opn wnd of [rt, lt, unsp] upr arm, subsq enc **391**
S61.50[1,2,9] [A,S]	Unsp opn wnd of [rt, lt, unsp] wrist, [init enc, seq] **229**

S61.50[1,2,9]D	Unsp opn wnd of [rt, lt, unsp] wrist, subsq enc **395**
S61.30[0,1][A,S]	Unsp opn wnd of [rt, lt] index finger w/ damage to nail, [init enc, seq] **228**
S61.30[0,1]D	Unsp opn wnd of [rt, lt] index finger w/ damage to nail, subsq enc **394**
S61.20[0,1][A,S]	Unsp opn wnd of [rt, lt] index finger w/o damage to nail, [init enc, seq] **228**
S61.20[0,1]D	Unsp opn wnd of [rt, lt] index finger w/o damage to nail, subsq enc **394**
S61.30[6,7][A,S]	Unsp opn wnd of [rt, lt] little finger w/ damage to nail, [init enc, seq] **228**
S61.30[6,7]D	Unsp opn wnd of [rt, lt] little finger w/ damage to nail, subsq enc **394**
S61.20[6,7][A,S]	Unsp opn wnd of [rt, lt] little finger w/o damage to nail, [init enc, seq] **228**
S61.20[6,7]D	Unsp opn wnd of [rt, lt] little finger w/o damage to nail, subsq enc **394**
S61.30[2,3][A,S]	Unsp opn wnd of [rt, lt] mid finger w/ damage to nail, [init enc, seq] **228**
S61.30[2,3]D	Unsp opn wnd of [rt, lt] mid finger w/ damage to nail, subsq enc **394**
S61.20[2,3][A,S]	Unsp opn wnd of [rt, lt] mid finger w/o damage to nail, [init enc, seq] **228**
S61.20[2,3]D	Unsp opn wnd of [rt, lt] mid finger w/o damage to nail, subsq enc **394**
S61.30[4,5][A,S]	Unsp opn wnd of [rt, lt] ring finger w/ damage to nail, [init enc, seq] **228**
S61.30[4,5]D	Unsp opn wnd of [rt, lt] ring finger w/ damage to nail, subsq enc **394**
S61.20[4,5][A,S]	Unsp opn wnd of [rt, lt] ring finger w/o damage to nail, [init enc, seq] **228**
S61.20[4,5]D	Unsp opn wnd of [rt, lt] ring finger w/o damage to nail, subsq enc **394**
S31.60[0,1,2,3,4, 5,9]A	Unsp opn wnd of abd wall, [rt upr quadrant, lt upr quadrant, epigastric rgn, rt lwr quadrant, lt lwr quadrant, periumbilic rgn, unsp quadrant] w/ penetration into peritoneal cavity, init enc **117**
S31.60[0,1,2,3,4, 5,9]D	Unsp opn wnd of abd wall, [rt upr quadrant, lt upr quadrant, epigastric rgn, rt lwr quadrant, lt lwr quadrant, periumbilic rgn, unsp quadrant], w/ penetration into peritoneal cavity, subsq enc **390**
S31.10[0,1,2,3,4, 5,9]D	Unsp opn wnd of abd wall, [rt upr quadrant, lt upr quadrant, epigastric rgn, rt lwr quadrant, lt lwr quadrant, periumbilic rgn, unsp quadrant], w/o penetration into peritoneal cavity, subsq enc **390**
S31.60[0,1,3,4]S	Unsp opn wnd of abd wall, [rt, lt] [upr, lwr] quadrant w/ penetration into peritoneal cavity, seq **226**
S31.10[3,4][A,S]	Unsp opn wnd of abd wall, [rt, lt] lwr quadrant w/o penetration into peritoneal cavity, [init enc, seq] **226**
S31.10[0,1][A,S]	Unsp opn wnd of abd wall, [rt, lt] upr quadrant w/o penetration into peritoneal cavity, [init enc, seq] **226**
S31.102[A,S]	Unsp opn wnd of abd wall, epigastric rgn w/o penetration into peritoneal cavity, [init enc, seq] **226**
S31.105[A,S]	Unsp opn wnd of abd wall, periumbilic rgn w/o penetration into peritoneal cavity, [init enc, seq] **226**
S31.109[A,S]	Unsp opn wnd of abd wall, unsp quadrant w/o penetration into peritoneal cavity, [init enc, seq] **226**
S31.839[A,S]	Unsp opn wnd of anus, [init enc, seq] **227**
S11.019A	Unsp opn wnd of larynx, init enc **5, 58**
S11.019S	Unsp opn wnd of larynx, seq **225**
S31.829[A,S]	Unsp opn wnd of lt buttock, [init enc, seq] **227**
S31.00[0,1]D	Unsp opn wnd of lwr back and pelvis [w/o, w/] penetration into retroperitoneum, subsq enc **389**
S31.000[A,S]	Unsp opn wnd of lwr back and pelvis w/o penetration into retroperitoneum, [init enc, seq] **226**
S01.20XA	Unsp opn wnd of nose, init enc **5, 58**
S01.20XS	Unsp opn wnd of nose, seq **224**
S01.80X[A,S]	Unsp opn wnd of oth part of head, [init enc, seq] **224**
S11.80XA	Unsp opn wnd of oth part of neck, init enc **5**
S11.80X[A,S]	Unsp opn wnd of oth spec part of neck, [init enc, seq] **225**
S11.20XA	Unsp opn wnd of pharynx and cervical esophagus, init **5, 58**
S11.20XS	Unsp opn wnd of pharynx and cervical esophagus, seq **225**
S31.819[A,S]	Unsp opn wnd of rt buttock, [init enc, seq] **227**
S01.00X[A,S]	Unsp opn wnd of scalp, [init enc, seq] **224**
S11.10XA	Unsp opn wnd of thyroid gland, init enc **5**

S11.10XS	Unsp opn wnd of thyroid gland, seq **225**
S11.029A	Unsp opn wnd of trachea, init enc **5, 67**
S11.029S	Unsp opn wnd of trachea, seq **225**
S31.809[A,S]	Unsp opn wnd of unsp buttock, [init enc, seq] **227**
S31.50[1,2]D	Unsp opn wnd of unsp ext genital organs, [male, female], subsq enc **390**
S01.90X[A,S]	Unsp opn wnd of unsp part of head, [init enc, seq] **224**
S11.90X[A,S]	Unsp opn wnd of unsp part of neck, [init enc, seq] **225**
S11.90XA	Unsp opn wnd of unsp part of neck, init enc **5**
S21.90X[A,S]	Unsp opn wnd of unsp part of thorax, [init enc, seq] **225**
S91.209D	Unsp opn wnd of unsp toe(s) w damage to nail, subs enc **399**
S91.209[A,S]	Unsp opn wnd of unsp toe(s) w/ damage to nail, [init enc, seq] **230**
S91.109[A,S]	Unsp opn wnd of unsp toe(s) w/o damage to nail, [init enc, seq] **230**
S91.109D	Unsp opn wnd of unsp toe(s) w/o damage to nail, subs **399**
S31.40XS	Unsp opn wnd of vagina and vulva, seq **226**
S11.039A	Unsp opn wnd of vocal cord, init enc **5, 58**
S11.039S	Unsp opn wnd of vocal cord, seq **225**
S91.00[1,2,9][A,S]	Unsp opn wnd, [rt, lt, unsp] ankle, [init enc, seq] **230**
S91.00[1,2,9]A	Unsp opn wnd, [rt, lt, unsp] ankle, init enc **428**
S91.00[1,2,9]D	Unsp opn wnd, [rt, lt, unsp] ankle, subsq enc **399**
S91.30[1,2,9][A,S]	Unsp opn wnd, [rt, lt, unsp] foot, [init enc, seq] **230**
S91.30[1,2,9]A	Unsp opn wnd, [rt, lt, unsp] foot, init enc **429**
S91.30[1,2,9]D	Unsp opn wnd, [rt, lt, unsp] foot, subsq enc **399**
S71.00[1,2,9][A,S]	Unsp opn wnd, [rt, lt, unsp] hip, [init enc, seq] **229**
S81.00[1,2,9][A,S]	Unsp opn wnd, [rt, lt, unsp] knee, [init enc, seq] **229**
S81.80[1,2,9][A,S]	Unsp opn wnd, [rt, lt, unsp] lwr leg, [init enc, seq] **229**
S71.10[1,2,9][A,S]	Unsp opn wnd, [rt, lt, unsp] thigh, [init enc, seq] **229**
S01.4[0,1,2,3,4,5]9A	Unsp opn wnd, Lac w/o FB, Lac w/ FB, Punc w/o FB, Punc w/ FB, Bite] of unsp cheek and temporomandibular area, init enc **5**
S11.8[0,1,2,3,4,5,9]XD	[Unsp opn wnd, Lac w/o FB, Lac w/ FB, Punc wnd w/o FB of thyroid gland, Punc wnd w/ FB, Opn bite] of oth spec part of neck, subsq enc **388**
S11.2[0,1,2,3,4,5]XD	[Unsp opn wnd, Lac w/o FB, Lac w/ FB, Punc wnd w/o FB of thyroid gland, Punc wnd w/ FB, Opn bite] of pharynx and cervical esophagus, subsq enc **388**
S11.1[0,1,2,3,4,5]XD	[Unsp opn wnd, Lac w/o FB, Lac w/ FB, Punc wnd w/o FB of thyroid gland, Punc wnd w/ FB, Opn bite] of thyroid gland, subsq enc **388**
S11.9[0,1,2,3,4,5]XD	[Unsp opn wnd, Lac w/o FB, Lac w/ FB, Punc wnd w/o FB of thyroid gland, Punc wnd w/ FB, Opn bite] of unsp part of neck, subsq enc **388**
S11.8[0,1,2,3,4,5,9]XA	[Unsp opn wnd, Lac w/o FB, Lac w/ FB, Punc wnd w/o FB, Punc wnd w/ FB, Opn bite, Oth opn wnd] of oth spec part of neck, init enc **419**
S81.0[0,1,2,3,4,5][1,2,9]A	[Unsp opn wnd, Lac w/o FB, Lac w/ FB, Punc wnd w/o FB, Punc wnd w/ FB, Opn bite] [rt, lt, unsp] knee, init enc **427**
S81.0[0,1,2,3,4,5][1,2,9]D	[Unsp opn wnd, Lac w/o FB, Lac w/ FB, Punc wnd w/o FB, Punc wnd w/ FB, Opn bite] [rt, lt, unsp] knee, subsq enc **398**
S81.8[0,1,2,3,4,5][1,2,9]A	[Unsp opn wnd, Lac w/o FB, Lac w/ FB, Punc wnd w/o FB, Punc wnd w/ FB, Opn bite] [rt, lt, unsp] lwr leg, init enc **427**
S81.8[0,1,2,3,4,5][1,2,9]D	[Unsp opn wnd, Lac w/o FB, Lac w/ FB, Punc wnd w/o FB, Punc wnd w/ FB, Opn bite] [rt, lt, unsp] lwr leg, subsq enc **398**
S01.5[0,1,2,3,4,5][1,2]A	[Unsp opn wnd, Lac w/o FB, Lac w/ FB, Punc wnd w/o FB, Punc wnd w/ FB, Opn bite] of [lip, oral cavity], init enc **417**
S01.5[0,1,2,3,4,5][1,2]D	[Unsp opn wnd, Lac w/o FB, Lac w/ FB, Punc wnd w/o FB, Punc wnd w/ FB, Opn bite] of [lip, oral cavity], subsq enc **386**
S61.3[0,1,2,3,4,5][0,1,2,3,4,5,6,7,8,9]A	[Unsp opn wnd, Lac w/o FB, Lac w/ FB, Punc wnd w/o FB, Punc wnd w/ FB, Opn bite] of [rt index finger, lt index finger, rt mid finger, lt mid finger, rt ring finger, lt ring finger, rt little finger, lt little finger, oth finger, unsp finger] w/ damage to nail, init enc **424**
S61.2[0,1,2,3,4,5][0,1,2,3,4,5,6,7,8,9]A	[Unsp opn wnd, Lac w/o FB, Lac w/ FB, Punc wnd w/o FB, Punc wnd w/ FB, Opn bite] of [rt index finger, lt index finger, rt mid finger, lt mid finger, rt ring finger, lt ring finger, rt little finger, lt little finger, oth finger, unsp finger] w/o damage to nail, init enc **424**
S61.[4,5][0,1,2,3,4,5][1,2,9]A	[Unsp opn wnd, Lac w/o FB, Lac w/ FB, Punc wnd w/o FB, Punc wnd w/ FB, Opn bite] of [rt, lt, unsp] [hand, wrist], init enc **424**
S21.2[0,1,2,3,4,5][1,2,9]A	[Unsp opn wnd, Lac w/o FB, Lac w/ FB, Punc wnd w/o FB, Punc wnd w/ FB, Opn bite] of [rt, lt, unsp] back wall of thorax w/o penetration into thoracic cavity, init enc **420**

S21.0[0,1,2,3,4,5][1,2,9]A	[Unsp opn wnd, Lac w/o FB, Lac w/ FB, Punc wnd w/o FB, Punc wnd w/ FB, Opn bite] of [rt, lt, unsp] breast, init enc **420**
S01.4[0,1,2,3,4,5][1,2,9]A	[Unsp opn wnd, Lac w/o FB, Lac w/ FB, Punc wnd w/o FB, Punc wnd w/ FB, Opn bite] of [rt, lt, unsp] cheek and temporomandibular area, init enc **417**
S01.4[0,1,2,3,4,5][1,2,9]D	[Unsp opn wnd, Lac w/o FB, Lac w/ FB, Punc wnd w/o FB, Punc wnd w/ FB, Opn bite] of [rt, lt, unsp] cheek and temporomandibular area, subsq enc **386**
S01.3[0,1,2,3,4,5][1,2,9]A	[Unsp opn wnd, Lac w/o FB, Lac w/ FB, Punc wnd w/o FB, Punc wnd w/ FB, Opn bite] of [rt, lt, unsp] ear, init enc **58, 417**
S01.3[0,1,2,3,4,5][1,2,9]D	[Unsp opn wnd, Lac w/o FB, Lac w/ FB, Punc wnd w/o FB, Punc wnd w/ FB, Opn bite] of [rt, lt, unsp] ear, subsq enc **386**
S51.0[0,1,2,3,4,5][1,2,9]A	[Unsp opn wnd, Lac w/o FB, Lac w/ FB, Punc wnd w/o FB, Punc wnd w/ FB, Opn bite] of [rt, lt, unsp] elbow, init enc **423**
S01.1[0,1,2,3,4,5][1,2,9]A	[Unsp opn wnd, Lac w/o FB, Lac w/ FB, Punc wnd w/o FB, Punc wnd w/ FB, Opn bite] of [rt, lt, unsp] eyelid and periocular area, init enc **417**
S01.1[0,1,2,3,4,5][1,2,9]D	[Unsp opn wnd, Lac w/o FB, Lac w/ FB, Punc wnd w/o FB, Punc wnd w/ FB, Opn bite] of [rt, lt, unsp] eyelid and periocular area, subsq enc **386**
S51.8[0,1,2,3,4,5][1,2,9]A	[Unsp opn wnd, Lac w/o FB, Lac w/ FB, Punc wnd w/o FB, Punc wnd w/ FB, Opn bite] of [rt, lt, unsp] forearm, init enc **423**
S21.3[0,1,2,3,4,5][1,2,9]A	[Unsp opn wnd, Lac w/o FB, Lac w/ FB, Punc wnd w/o FB, Punc wnd w/ FB, Opn bite] of [rt, lt, unsp] front wall of thorax w/ penetration into thoracic cavity, init enc **420**
S21.1[0,1,2,3,4,5][1,2,9]A	[Unsp opn wnd, Lac w/o FB, Lac w/ FB, Punc wnd w/o FB, Punc wnd w/ FB, Opn bite] of [rt, lt, unsp] front wall of thorax w/o penetration into thoracic cavity, init enc **420**
S41.0[0,1,2,3,4,5][1,2,9]A	[Unsp opn wnd, Lac w/o FB, Lac w/ FB, Punc wnd w/o FB, Punc wnd w/ FB, Opn bite] of [rt, lt, unsp] shldr, init enc **422**
S61.1[0,1,2,3,4,5][1,2,9]A	[Unsp opn wnd, Lac w/o FB, Lac w/ FB, Punc wnd w/o FB, Punc wnd w/ FB, Opn bite] of [rt, lt, unsp] thumb w/ damage to nail, init enc **424**
S61.0[0,1,2,3,4,5][1,2,9]A	[Unsp opn wnd, Lac w/o FB, Lac w/ FB, Punc wnd w/o FB, Punc wnd w/ FB, Opn bite] of [rt, lt, unsp] thumb w/o damage to nail, init enc **424**
S41.1[0,1,2,3,4,5][1,2,9]A	[Unsp opn wnd, Lac w/o FB, Lac w/ FB, Punc wnd w/o FB, Punc wnd w/ FB, Opn bite] of [rt, lt, unsp] upr arm, init enc **422**
S31.6[0,1,2,3,4,5][0,1,2,3,4,5,9]A	[Unsp opn wnd, Lac w/o FB, Lac w/ FB, Punc wnd w/o FB, Punc wnd w/ FB, Opn bite] of abd wall, [rt upr quadrant, lt upr quadrant, epigastric rgn, rt lwr quadrant, lt lwr quadrant, periumbilic rgn, unsp quadrant] w/ penetration into peritoneal cavity, init enc **421, 432**
S31.1[0,1,2,3,4,5][0,1,2,3,4,5,9]A	[Unsp opn wnd, Lac w/o FB, Lac w/ FB, Punc wnd w/o FB, Punc wnd w/ FB, Opn bite] of abd wall, [rt upr quadrant, lt upr quadrant, epigastric rgn, rt lwr quadrant, lt lwr quadrant, periumbilic rgn, unsp quadrant] w/o penetration into peritoneal cavity, init enc **421**
S01.5[0,1,2,3,4,5]1A	[Unsp opn wnd, Lac w/o FB, Lac w/ FB, Punc wnd w/o FB, Punc wnd w/ FB, Opn bite] of lip, init enc **5**
S31.0[0,1,2,3,4,5][0,1]A	[Unsp opn wnd, Lac w/o FB, Lac w/ FB, Punc wnd w/o FB, Punc wnd w/ FB, Opn bite] of lwr back and pelvis [w/o, w/] penetration into retroperitoneum, init enc **421**
S31.0[0,1,2,3,4,5]1A	[Unsp opn wnd, Lac w/o FB, Lac w/ FB, Punc wnd w/o FB, Punc wnd w/ FB, Opn bite] of lwr back and pelvis w/ penetration into retroperitoneum, init enc **256, 432**
S01.2[0,1,2,3,4,5]XA	[Unsp opn wnd, Lac w/o FB, Lac w/ FB, Punc wnd w/o FB, Punc wnd w/ FB, Opn bite] of nose, init enc **417**
S01.2[0,1,2,3,4,5]XD	[Unsp opn wnd, Lac w/o FB, Lac w/ FB, Punc wnd w/o FB, Punc wnd w/ FB, Opn bite] of nose, subsq enc **386**
S01.5[0,1,2,3,4,5]2A	[Unsp opn wnd, Lac w/o FB, Lac w/ FB, Punc wnd w/o FB, Punc wnd w/ FB, Opn bite] of oral cavity, init enc **5**
S01.8[0,1,2,3,4,5]XA	[Unsp opn wnd, Lac w/o FB, Lac w/ FB, Punc wnd w/o FB, Punc wnd w/ FB, Opn bite] of oth part of head, init enc **417**
S01.8[0,1,2,3,4,5]XD	[Unsp opn wnd, Lac w/o FB, Lac w/ FB, Punc wnd w/o FB, Punc wnd w/ FB, Opn bite] of oth part of head, subsq enc **386**
S31.2[0,1,2,3,4,5]XD	[Unsp opn wnd, Lac w/o FB, Lac w/ FB, Punc wnd w/o FB, Punc wnd w/ FB, Opn bite] of penis, subsq enc **390**
S11.2[0,1,2,3,4,5]XA	[Unsp opn wnd, Lac w/o FB, Lac w/ FB, Punc wnd w/o FB, Punc wnd w/ FB, Opn bite] of pharynx and cervical esophagus, init enc **419**
S01.0[0,1,2,3,4,5]XA	[Unsp opn wnd, Lac w/o FB, Lac w/ FB, Punc wnd w/o FB, Punc wnd w/ FB, Opn bite] of scalp, init enc **417**
S01.0[0,1,2,3,4,5]XD	[Unsp opn wnd, Lac w/o FB, Lac w/ FB, Punc wnd w/o FB, Punc wnd w/ FB, Opn bite] of scalp, subsq enc **386**
S31.3[0,1,2,3,4,5]XD	[Unsp opn wnd, Lac w/o FB, Lac w/ FB, Punc wnd w/o FB, Punc wnd w/ FB, Opn bite] of scrotum and testes, subsq enc **390**

Code	Description
S11.1[0,1,2,3,4,5]XA	[Unsp opn wnd, Lac w/o FB, Lac w/ FB, Punc wnd w/o FB, Punc wnd w/ FB, Opn bite] of thyroid gland, init enc 247, 419
S31.5[0,1,2,3,4,5][1,2]A	[Unsp opn wnd, Lac w/o FB, Lac w/ FB, Punc wnd w/o FB, Punc wnd w/ FB, Opn bite] of unsp ext genital organs, [male, female], init enc 421
S31.5[0,1,2,3,4,5]2A	[Unsp opn wnd, Lac w/o FB, Lac w/ FB, Punc wnd w/o FB, Punc wnd w/ FB, Opn bite] of unsp ext genital organs, female, init enc 265, 270
S31.5[0,1,2,3,4,5]2S	[Unsp opn wnd, Lac w/o FB, Lac w/ FB, Punc wnd w/o FB, Punc wnd w/ FB, Opn bite] of unsp ext genital organs, female, seq 265, 270
S01.9[0,1,2,3,4,5]XA	[Unsp opn wnd, Lac w/o FB, Lac w/ FB, Punc wnd w/o FB, Punc wnd w/ FB, Opn bite] of unsp part of head, init enc 417
S01.9[0,1,2,3,4,5]XD	[Unsp opn wnd, Lac w/o FB, Lac w/ FB, Punc wnd w/o FB, Punc wnd w/ FB, Opn bite] of unsp part of head, subsq enc 386
S11.9[0,1,2,3,4,5]XA	[Unsp opn wnd, Lac w/o FB, Lac w/ FB, Punc wnd w/o FB, Punc wnd w/ FB, Opn bite] of unsp part of neck, init enc 419
S21.9[0,1,2,3,4,5]XA	[Unsp opn wnd, Lac w/o FB, Lac w/ FB, Punc wnd w/o FB, Punc wnd w/ FB, Opn bite] of unsp part of thorax, init enc 420
S21.9[0,1,2,3,4,5]XD	[Unsp opn wnd, Lac w/o FB, Lac w/ FB, Punc wnd w/o FB, Punc wnd w/ FB, Opn bite] of unsp part of thorax, subsq enc 389
S31.4[0,1,2,3,4,5]XA	[Unsp opn wnd, Lac w/o FB, Lac w/ FB, Punc wnd w/o FB, Punc wnd w/ FB, Opn bite] of vagina and vulva, init enc 265, 270, 421
S31.4[0,1,2,3,4,5]XD	[Unsp opn wnd, Lac w/o FB, Lac w/ FB, Punc wnd w/o FB, Punc wnd w/ FB, Opn bite] of vagina and vulva, subsq enc 390
S71.0[0,1,2,3,4,5][1,2,9]A	[Unsp opn wnd, Lac w/o FB, Lac w/ FB, Punc wnd w/o FB, Punc wnd w/ FB, Opn bite], [rt, lt, unsp] hip, init enc 426
S71.0[0,1,2,3,4,5][1,2,9]D	[Unsp opn wnd, Lac w/o FB, Lac w/ FB, Punc wnd w/o FB, Punc wnd w/ FB, Opn bite], [rt, lt, unsp] hip, subsq enc 397
S71.1[0,1,2,3,4,5][1,2,9]A	[Unsp opn wnd, Lac w/o FB, Lac w/ FB, Punc wnd w/o FB, Punc wnd w/ FB, Opn bite], [rt, lt, unsp] thigh, init enc 426
S71.1[0,1,2,3,4,5][1,2,9]D	[Unsp opn wnd, Lac w/o FB, Lac w/ FB, Punc wnd w/o FB, Punc wnd w/ FB, Opn bite], [rt, lt, unsp] thigh, subsq enc 397
S31.2[0,1,2,3,4,5]XA	[Unsp opn wnd, Lac w/o FB, Lac w/ FB, Punc wnd w/o FB, Punc wnd w/ FB, Opn bite], of penis, init enc 261, 421
S31.3[0,1,2,3,4,5]XA	[Unsp opn wnd, Lac w/o FB, Lac w/ FB, Punc wnd w/o FB, Punc wnd w/ FB, Opn bite], of scrotum and testes, init enc 261, 421
S31.5[0,1,2,3,4,5]1A	[Unsp opn wnd, Lac w/o FB, Lac w/ FB, Punc wnd w/o FB, Punc wnd w/ FB, Opn bite], of unsp ext genital organs, male, init enc 261
S31.5[0,1,2,3,4,5]1S	[Unsp opn wnd, Lac w/o FB, Lac w/ FB, Punc wnd w/o FB, Punc wnd w/ FB, Opn bite], of unsp ext genital organs, male, seqe 261
S21.4[0,1,2,3,4,5][1,2,9]A	[Unsp opn wnd, Lacertion w/o FB, Lac w/ FB, Punc wnd w/o FB, Punc wnd w/ FB, Opn bite] of [rt, lt, unsp] back wall of thorax w/ penetration into thoracic cavity, init enc 420
H40.10*	Unsp opn-angle glaucoma 46
H47.20	Unsp optic atrophy 45
H47.10	Unsp papilledema 38
H49.9	Unsp paralytic strabismus 45
N73.2	Unsp parametritis and pelvic cellulitis 269
B89	Unsp parasitic dz 309
H61.00[1,2,3,9]	Unsp perichondritis of [rt, lt, bilat, unsp] ext ear 57
F07.9	Unsp personality & behavrl d/o d/t known physiol cond 310, 439
S79.10[1,2,9][D,G,S]	Unsp physeal fx of lwr end of [rt, lt, unsp] femur, [subsq enc for fx w/ routine healing, subsq enc for fx w/ delayed healing, seq] 179
S79.10[1,2,9]A	Unsp physeal fx of lwr end of [rt, lt, unsp] femur, inital enc for clsd fx 161, 427, 436
S79.10[1,2,9][K,P]	Unsp physeal fx of lwr end of [rt, lt, unsp] femur, subsq enc for fx w/ [nonu, malu] 202
S89.30[1,2,9][D,G,S]	Unsp physeal fx of lwr end of [rt, lt, unsp] fibula, [subsq enc for fx w/ routine healing, subsq enc for fx w/ delayed healing, seq] 182
S89.30[1,2,9][K,P]	Unsp physeal fx of lwr end of [rt, lt, unsp] fibula, subsq enc for fx w/ [nonu, malu] 204
S89.10[1,2,9][D,G,S]	Unsp physeal fx of lwr end of [rt, lt, unsp] tibia, [subsq enc for fx w/ routine healing, subsq enc for fx w/ delayed healing, seq] 182
S89.10[1,2,9]A	Unsp physeal fx of lwr end of [rt, lt, unsp] tibia, init enc for clsd fx 192, 428
S89.10[1,2,9][K,P]	Unsp physeal fx of lwr end of [rt, lt, unsp] tibia, subsq enc for fx w/ [nonu, malu] 204
S49.10[1,2,9][D,G,S]	Unsp physeal fx of lwr end of humerus, [rt, lt, unsp] arm, [subsq enc for fx w/ routine healing, subsq enc for fx w/ delayed healing, seq] 172
S49.10[1,2,9][K,P]	Unsp physeal fx of lwr end of humerus, [rt, lt, unsp] arm, subsq enc for fx w/ [nonu, malu] 197
S59.20[1,2,9]A	Unsp physeal fx of lwr end of radius [rt, lt, unsp] init enc 187
S59.20[1,2,9][D,G,S]	Unsp physeal fx of lwr end of radius, [rt, lt, unsp] arm, [subsq enc for fx w/ routine healing, subsq enc for fx w/ delayed healing, seq] 174
S59.20[1,2,9][K,P]	Unsp physeal fx of lwr end of radius, [rt, lt, unsp] arm, subsq enc for fx w/ [nonu, malu] 199
S59.00[1,2,9]A	Unsp physeal fx of lwr end of ulna [rt, lt, unsp] init enc 187
S59.00[1,2,9][D,G,S]	Unsp physeal fx of lwr end of ulna, [rt, lt, unsp] arm, [subsq enc for fx w/ routine healing, subsq enc for fx w/ delayed healing, seq] 174
S59.00[1,2,9][K,P]	Unsp physeal fx of lwr end of ulna, [rt, lt, unsp] arm, subsq enc for fx w/ [nonu, malu] 199
S79.00[1,2,9][D,G,S]	Unsp physeal fx of upr end of [rt, lt, unsp] femur, [subsq enc for fx w/ routine healing, subsq enc for fx w/ delayed healing, seq] 179
S79.00[1,2,9]A	Unsp physeal fx of upr end of [rt, lt, unsp] femur, init enc for clsd fx 162, 286, 426, 436
S79.00[1,2,9][K,P]	Unsp physeal fx of upr end of [rt, lt, unsp] femur, subsq enc for fx w/ [nonu, malu] 202
S89.20[1,2,9][D,G,S]	Unsp physeal fx of upr end of [rt, lt, unsp] fibula, [subsq enc for fx w/ routine healing, subsq enc for fx w/ delayed healing, seq] 182
S89.20[1,2,9][K,P]	Unsp physeal fx of upr end of [rt, lt, unsp] fibula, subsq enc for fx w/ [nonu, malu] 204
S89.00[1,2,9][D,G,S]	Unsp physeal fx of upr end of [rt, lt, unsp] tibia, [subsq enc for fx w/ routine healing, subsq enc for fx w/ delayed healing, seq] 182
S89.00[1,2,9]A	Unsp physeal fx of upr end of [rt, lt, unsp] tibia, init enc for clsd fx 192, 428
S89.00[1,2,9][K,P]	Unsp physeal fx of upr end of [rt, lt, unsp] tibia, subsq enc for fx w/ [nonu, malu] 204
S49.00[1,2,9]A	Unsp physeal fx of upr end of humerus [rt, lt, unsp], init enc for clsd fx 185
S49.00[1,2,9][D,G,S]	Unsp physeal fx of upr end of humerus, [rt, lt, unsp] arm, [subsq enc for fx w/ routine healing, subsq enc for fx w/ delayed healing, seq] 171
S49.00[1,2,9][K,P]	Unsp physeal fx of upr end of humerus, [rt, lt, unsp] arm, subsq enc for fx w/ [nonu, malu] 197
S59.10[1,2,9]A	Unsp physeal fx of upr end of radius [rt, lt, unsp] init enc 187
S59.10[1,2,9][D,G,S]	Unsp physeal fx of upr end of radius, [rt, lt, unsp] arm, [subsq enc for fx w/ routine healing, subsq enc for fx w/ delayed healing, seq] 174
S59.10[1,2,9][K,P]	Unsp physeal fx of upr end of ulna, [rt, lt, unsp] arm, subsq enc for fx w/ [nonu, malu] 199
O43.9[1,2,3]	Unsp placental d/o, [1st, 2nd, 3rd] trmstr 278, 280
O43.90	Unsp placental d/o, unsp trmstr 281
J64	Unsp pneumoconiosis 68
O14.9[2,3]	Unsp pre-eclampsia, [2nd, thrid] trmstr 276, 277
O14.92	Unsp pre-eclampsia, second trmstr 279
O14.93	Unsp pre-eclampsia, third trmstr 279
O14.90	Unsp pre-eclampsia, unsp trmstr 280
O24.319	Unsp pre-existing diabetes in preg, unsp trmstr 280
O24.32	Unsp pre-existing diabetes mellitus in childbirth 273
O24.31[1,2,3]	Unsp pre-existing diabetes mellitus in preg, [1st, 2nd, 3rd] trmstr 273, 276, 277
O24.33	Unsp pre-existing diabetes mellitus in the puerperium 272, 275
O10.911	Unsp pre-existing hypertension comp preg, first trmstr 279
O10.912	Unsp pre-existing hypertension comp preg, second trmstr 279
O10.913	Unsp pre-existing hypertension comp preg, third trmstr 279
O10.919	Unsp pre-existing hypertension comp preg, unsp trmstr 280
O10.92	Unsp pre-existing hypertension compl childbirth 273
O10.91[1,2,3]	Unsp pre-existing hypertension compl preg, [1st, 2nd, 3rd] trmstr 273, 276, 277
O10.93	Unsp pre-existing hypertension compl the puerperium 275
E46	Unsp protein-calorie malnut 246, 283
B64	Unsp protozoal dz 309
F29	Unsp psychosis not d/t a substance or known physiol cond 311, 439
N23	Unsp renal colic 255
J68.9	Unsp resp cond d/t chemicals, gases, fumes and vapors 68
H33.10[1,2,3,9]	Unsp retinoschisis, [rt, lt, bilat, unsp] eye 46
E43	Unsp severe protein-calorie malnut 246, 283
F52.9	Unsp sexual dysfnct not d/t a sub or known physiol cond 311
A64	Unsp sexually transmitted dz 261, 264, 269
R23.9	Unsp skin changes 234
M70.9*	Unsp soft tissue d/o related to use/pressure 167
S63.61[8,9][A,S]	Unsp sprain of [oth, unsp] finger, [init enc, seq] 190
S63.61[8,9]D	Unsp sprain of [oth, unsp] finger, subsq enc 396

S63.61[0,1,2,3,4, 5,6,7,8,9]A	Unsp sprain of [rt index, lt index, rt mid, lt mid, rt ring, lt ring, rt little, lt ringer, oth, unsp] finger, init enc **425**
S53.40[1,2,9]D	Unsp sprain of [rt, lt, unsp] elbow, subsq enc **392**
S93.60[1,2,9] [A,S]	Unsp sprain of [rt, lt, unsp] foot, [init enc, seq] **193**
S93.60[1,2,9]A	Unsp sprain of [rt, lt, unsp] foot, init enc **430**
S93.60[1,2,9]D	Unsp sprain of [rt, lt, unsp] foot, subsq enc **399**
S73.10[1,2,9]A	Unsp sprain of [rt, lt, unsp] hip, init enc **162, 426**
S73.10[1,2,9]S	Unsp sprain of [rt, lt, unsp] hip, seq **190**
S43.40[1,2,9]D	Unsp sprain of [rt, lt, unsp] shldr jt, subsq enc **391**
S63.60[1,2,9] [A,S]	Unsp sprain of [rt, lt, unsp] thumb, [init enc, seq] **190**
S63.60[1,2,9]A	Unsp sprain of [rt, lt, unsp] thumb, init enc **425**
S63.60[1,2,9]D	Unsp sprain of [rt, lt, unsp] thumb, subsq enc **396**
S63.50[1,2,9] [A,S]	Unsp sprain of [rt, lt, unsp] wrist, [init enc, seq] **190**
S63.50[1,2,9]A	Unsp sprain of [rt, lt, unsp] wrist, init enc **425**
S63.50[1,2,9]D	Unsp sprain of [rt, lt, unsp] wrist, subsq enc **396**
S63.61[0,1][A,S]	Unsp sprain of [rt, lt] index finger, [init enc, seq] **190**
S63.61[0,1]D	Unsp sprain of [rt, lt] index finger, subsq enc **396**
S63.61[6,7][A,S]	Unsp sprain of [rt, lt] little finger, [init enc, seq] **190**
S63.61[6,7]D	Unsp sprain of [rt, lt] little finger, subsq enc **396**
S63.61[2,3][A,S]	Unsp sprain of [rt, lt] mid finger, [init enc, seq] **190**
S63.61[2,3]D	Unsp sprain of [rt, lt] mid finger, subsq enc **396**
S63.61[4,5][A,S]	Unsp sprain of [rt, lt] ring finger, [init enc, seq] **190**
S63.61[4,5]D	Unsp sprain of [rt, lt] ring finger, subsq enc **396**
S43.40[1,2,9] [A,S]	Unsp sprain of shldr [rt, lt, unsp] [init enc, seq] **185**
S93.509A	Unsp sprain of unsp toe(s), init enc **430**
S93.509D	Unsp sprain of unsp toe(s), subs enc **399**
S43.4[0,1,2] [1,2,9]A	[Unsp sprain, Sprain] of [rt, lt, unsp] [shldr jt, coracohumeral (lgmt), rotator cuff capsule], init enc **423**
H50.9	Unsp strabismus **46**
S93.50[1,2,3] [A,S]	Unsp strain of [rt, lt, unsp] great toe, [init enc, seq] **193**
S93.50[1,2,3]A	Unsp strain of [rt, lt, unsp] great toe, init enc **430**
S93.50[1,2,3]D	Unsp strain of [rt, lt, unsp] great toe, subsq enc **399**
S93.50[4,5,6] [A,S]	Unsp strain of [rt, lt, unsp] lesser toe(s), [init enc, seq] **193**
S93.50[4,5,6]A	Unsp strain of [rt, lt, unsp] lesser toe(s), init enc **430**
S93.50[4,5,6]D	Unsp strain of [rt, lt, unsp] lesser toe(s), subsq enc **399**
S93.509[A,S]	Unsp strain of unsp toe(s), [init enc, seq] **193**
H53.10	Unsp subjective visual disturbances **46**
S63.20[8,9][A,S]	Unsp sublux of [oth, unsp] finger, [init enc, seq] **189**
S63.20[8,9]D	Unsp sublux of [oth, unsp] finger, subsq enc **395**
S63.20[0,1,2,3,4, 5,6,7,8,9]A	Unsp sublux of [rt index, lt index, rt mid, lt mid, rt ring, lt ring, rt little, lt little, oth, unsp] finger, init enc **425**
S93.30[1,2,3] [A,S]	Unsp sublux of [rt, lt, unsp] foot, [init enc, seq] **193**
S93.30[1,2,3]A	Unsp sublux of [rt, lt, unsp] foot, init enc **430**
S93.30[1,2,3]D	Unsp sublux of [rt, lt, unsp] foot, subsq enc **399**
S73.00[1,2,3]A	Unsp sublux of [rt, lt, unsp] hip, init enc **162**
S73.00[1,2,3]S	Unsp sublux of [rt, lt, unsp] hip, seq **190**
S73.00[1,2,3]D	Unsp sublux of [rt, lt, unsp] hip, subsq enc **397**
S83.10[1,2,3] [A,S]	Unsp sublux of [rt, lt, unsp] knee, [init enc, seq] **191**
S83.10[1,2,3]A	Unsp sublux of [rt, lt, unsp] knee, init enc **428**
S83.10[1,2,3]D	Unsp sublux of [rt, lt, unsp] knee, subsq enc **398**
S83.00[1,2,3] [A,S]	Unsp sublux of [rt, lt, unsp] patella, [init enc, seq] **191**
S83.00[1,2,3]A	Unsp sublux of [rt, lt, unsp] patella, init enc **428**
S83.00[1,2,3]D	Unsp sublux of [rt, lt, unsp] patella, subsq enc **398**
S53.00[1,2,3]D	Unsp sublux of [rt, lt, unsp] radial head, subsq enc **392**
S43.00[1,2,3,4,5, 6]D	Unsp sublux of [rt, lt, unsp] shldr jt, Unsp disloc of [rt, lt, unsp] shldr jt, subsq enc **391**
S43.20[1,2,3]A	Unsp sublux of [rt, lt, unsp] sternoclavicular jt, init enc **67**
S43.20[1,2,3]S	Unsp sublux of [rt, lt, unsp] sternoclavicular jt, seq **185**
S43.20[1,2,3,4,5, 6]D	Unsp sublux of [rt, lt, unsp] sternoclavicular jt, Unsp disloc of [rt, lt, unsp] sternoclavicular jt, subsq enc **391**
S63.10[1,2,3] [A,S]	Unsp sublux of [rt, lt, unsp] thumb, [init enc, seq] **189**
S63.10[1,2,3]D	Unsp sublux of [rt, lt, unsp] thumb, subsq enc **395**

S93.10[1,2,3] [A,S]	Unsp sublux of [rt, lt, unsp] toe(s), [init enc, seq] **193**
S93.10[1,2,3]A	Unsp sublux of [rt, lt, unsp] toe(s), init enc **430**
S93.10[1,2,3]D	Unsp sublux of [rt, lt, unsp] toe(s), subsq enc **399**
S53.10[1,2,3]D	Unsp sublux of [rt, lt, unsp] ulnohumeral jt, subsq enc **392**
S63.00[1,2,3] [A,S]	Unsp sublux of [rt, lt, unsp] wrist and hand, [init enc, seq] **188**
S63.20[0,1][A,S]	Unsp sublux of [rt, lt] index finger, [init enc, seq] **189**
S63.20[0,1]D	Unsp sublux of [rt, lt] index finger, subsq enc **395**
S63.20[6,7][A,S]	Unsp sublux of [rt, lt] little finger, [init enc, seq] **189**
S63.20[6,7]D	Unsp sublux of [rt, lt] little finger, subsq enc **395**
S63.20[2,3][A,S]	Unsp sublux of [rt, lt] mid finger, [init enc, seq] **189**
S63.20[2,3]D	Unsp sublux of [rt, lt] mid finger, subsq enc **395**
S63.20[4,5][A,S]	Unsp sublux of [rt, lt] ring finger, [init enc, seq] **189**
S63.20[4,5]D	Unsp sublux of [rt, lt] ring finger, subsq enc **395**
S63.00[1,2,3]D	Unsp sublux of [rt, lt] wrist and hand, subsq enc **395**
S53.00[1,2,3] [A,S]	Unsp sublux of radial head [unsp, rt, lt] [init enc, seq] **186**
S43.00[1,2,3] [A,S]	Unsp sublux of shldr jt [rt, lt, unsp] [init enc, seq] **185**
S53.10[1,2,3] [A,S]	Unsp sublux of ulnohumeral jt [rt, lt, unsp] [init enc, seq] **186**
S00.50[1,2][A,S]	Unsp superf inj of [lip, oral cavity], [init enc, seq] **224**
S30.9[1,2,3,4,5,6, 7,8]XA	Unsp superf inj of [lwr back and pelvis, abd wall, penis, scrotum and testes, vagina and vulva, unsp ext genital organs [male, female], anus], init enc **421**
S30.9[1,2,3,4,5,6, 7,8]XD	Unsp superf inj of [lwr back and pelvis, abd wall, penis, scrotum and testes, vagina and vulva, unsp ext genital organs male, unsp ext genital organs female, anus], subsq enc **389**
S60.94[8,9][A,S]	Unsp superf inj of [oth, unsp] finger, [init enc, seq] **228**
S60.94[8,9]D	Unsp superf inj of [oth, unsp] finger, subsq enc **394**
S30.9[3,4]X[A,S]	Unsp superf inj of [penis, scrotum and testes], [init enc, seq] **226**
S50.9[0,1][1,2,9] A	Unsp superf inj of [rt, lt, unsp] [elbow, forearm], init enc **423**
S70.9[1,2][1,2,9] A	Unsp superf inj of [rt, lt, unsp] [hip, thigh], init enc **426**
S70.9[1,2][1,2,9] D	Unsp superf inj of [rt, lt, unsp] [hip, thigh], subsq enc **397**
S80.9[1,2][1,2,9] A	Unsp superf inj of [rt, lt, unsp] [knee, lwr leg], init enc **427**
S80.9[1,2][1,2,9] D	Unsp superf inj of [rt, lt, unsp] [knee, lwr leg], subsq enc **398**
S40.9[1,2][1,2,9] A	Unsp superf inj of [rt, lt, unsp] [shldr, upr arm], init enc **422**
S60.9[1,2,3,4] [1,2,9]A	Unsp superf inj of [rt, lt, unsp] [wrist, hand, thumb, index finger, mid finger, ring finger, little finger, oth finger, unsp finger], init enc **424**
S90.91[1,2,9] [A,S]	Unsp superf inj of [rt, lt, unsp] ankle, [init enc, seq] **230**
S90.91[1,2,9]A	Unsp superf inj of [rt, lt, unsp] ankle, init enc **428**
S90.91[1,2,9]D	Unsp superf inj of [rt, lt, unsp] ankle, subsq enc **399**
S00.40[1,2,9] [A,S]	Unsp superf inj of [rt, lt, unsp] ear, [init enc, seq] **224**
S50.90[1,2,9] [A,S]	Unsp superf inj of [rt, lt, unsp] elbow, [init enc, seq] **227**
S50.90[1,2,9]D	Unsp superf inj of [rt, lt, unsp] elbow, subsq enc **392**
S00.20[1,2,9]A	Unsp superf inj of [rt, lt, unsp] eyelid and periocular area, init enc **46**
S00.20[1,2,9]S	Unsp superf inj of [rt, lt, unsp] eyelid and periocular area, seq **224**
S90.92[1,2,9] [A,S]	Unsp superf inj of [rt, lt, unsp] foot, [init enc, seq] **230**
S90.92[1,2,9]A	Unsp superf inj of [rt, lt, unsp] foot, init enc **428**
S90.92[1,2,9]D	Unsp superf inj of [rt, lt, unsp] foot, subsq enc **399**
S50.91[1,2,9] [A,S]	Unsp superf inj of [rt, lt, unsp] forearm, [init enc, seq] **227**
S50.91[1,2,9]D	Unsp superf inj of [rt, lt, unsp] forearm, subsq enc **392**
S90.93[1,2,3] [A,S]	Unsp superf inj of [rt, lt, unsp] great toe, [init enc, seq] **230**
S90.93[1,2,3]A	Unsp superf inj of [rt, lt, unsp] great toe, init enc **428**
S90.93[1,2,3]D	Unsp superf inj of [rt, lt, unsp] great toe, subsq enc **399**
S60.92[1,2,9] [A,S]	Unsp superf inj of [rt, lt, unsp] hand, [init enc, seq] **228**
S60.92[1,2,9]D	Unsp superf inj of [rt, lt, unsp] hand, subsq enc **394**

Code	Description
S70.91[1,2,9] [A,S]	Unsp superf inj of [rt, lt, unsp] hip, [init enc, seq] 229
S80.91[1,2,9] [A,S]	Unsp superf inj of [rt, lt, unsp] knee, [init enc, seq] 229
S90.93[4,5,6] [A,S]	Unsp superf inj of [rt, lt, unsp] lesser toe(s), [init enc, seq] 230
S90.93[4,5,6]A	Unsp superf inj of [rt, lt, unsp] lesser toe(s), init enc 428
S90.93[4,5,6]D	Unsp superf inj of [rt, lt, unsp] lesser toe(s), subsq enc 399
S80.92[1,2,9] [A,S]	Unsp superf inj of [rt, lt, unsp] lwr leg, [init enc, seq] 229
S40.91[1,2,9] [A,S]	Unsp superf inj of [rt, lt, unsp] shldr, [init enc, seq] 227
S40.91[1,2,9]D	Unsp superf inj of [rt, lt, unsp] shldr, subsq enc 391
S70.92[1,2,9] [A,S]	Unsp superf inj of [rt, lt, unsp] thigh, [init enc, seq] 229
S60.93[1,2,9] [A,S]	Unsp superf inj of [rt, lt, unsp] thumb, [init enc, seq] 228
S60.93[1,2,9]D	Unsp superf inj of [rt, lt, unsp] thumb, subsq enc 394
S40.92[1,2,9] [A,S]	Unsp superf inj of [rt, lt, unsp] upr arm, [init enc, seq] 227
S40.92[1,2,9]D	Unsp superf inj of [rt, lt, unsp] upr arm, subsq enc 391
S60.91[1,2,9] [A,S]	Unsp superf inj of [rt, lt, unsp] wrist, [init enc, seq] 228
S60.91[1,2,9]D	Unsp superf inj of [rt, lt, unsp] wrist, subsq enc 394
S60.94[0,1][A,S]	Unsp superf inj of [rt, lt] index finger, [init enc, seq] 228
S60.94[0,1]D	Unsp superf inj of [rt, lt] index finger, subsq enc 394
S60.94[6,7][A,S]	Unsp superf inj of [rt, lt] little finger, [init enc, seq] 228
S60.94[6,7]D	Unsp superf inj of [rt, lt] little finger, subsq enc 394
S60.94[2,3][A,S]	Unsp superf inj of [rt, lt] mid finger, [init enc, seq] 228
S60.94[2,3]D	Unsp superf inj of [rt, lt] mid finger, subsq enc 394
S60.94[4,5][A,S]	Unsp superf inj of [rt, lt] ring finger, [init enc, seq] 228
S60.94[4,5]D	Unsp superf inj of [rt, lt] ring finger, subsq enc 394
S30.92X[A,S]	Unsp superf inj of abd wall, [init enc, seq] 226
S30.98X[A,S]	Unsp superf inj of anus, [init enc, seq] 226
S60.947A	Unsp superf inj of lt little finger, init enc 424
S60.943A	Unsp superf inj of lt mid finger, init enc 424
S60.945A	Unsp superf inj of lt ring finger, init enc 424
S30.91X[A,S]	Unsp superf inj of lwr back and pelvis, [init enc, seq] 226
S60.948A	Unsp superf inj of oth finger, init enc 424
S60.940A	Unsp superf inj of rt index finger, init enc 424
S60.946A	Unsp superf inj of rt little finger, init enc 424
S60.944A	Unsp superf inj of rt ring finger, init enc 424
S00.00X[A,S]	Unsp superf inj of scalp, [init enc, seq] 224
S30.9[6,7]X[A,S]	Unsp superf inj of unsp ext genital organs, [male, female], [init enc, seq] 226
S30.95X[A,S]	Unsp superf inj of vagina and vulva, [init enc, seq] 226
S00.0[0,1,2,3,4,5, 6,7]XD	[Unsp superf inj, Abrasion, Blister (nonthermal), Contsn, Ext constriction of part, Superf FB, Insect bite (nonvenomous), Oth superf bite] of scalp, subsq enc 386
S00.8[0,1,2,3,4,5, 6,7]XA	[Unsp superf inj, Abrasion, Blister (nonthermal), Contsn, Ext constriction, Superf FB, Insect bite (nonvenomous, Oth superf bite] of oth part of head, init enc 417
S00.5[0,1,2,3,4,5, 6,7][1,2]A	[Unsp superf inj, Abrasion, Blister (nonthermal), Contsn, Ext constriction, Superf FB, Insect bite (nonvenomous), Oth superf bite] of [lip, oral cavity], init enc 417
S00.5[0,1,2,3,4,5, 6,7][1,2]D	[Unsp superf inj, Abrasion, Blister (nonthermal), Contsn, Ext constriction, Superf FB, Insect bite (nonvenomous), Oth superf bite] of [lip, oral cavity], subsq enc 386
S00.4[0,1,2,3,4,5, 6,7][1,2,9]A	[Unsp superf inj, Abrasion, Blister (nonthermal), Contsn, Ext constriction, Superf FB, Insect bite (nonvenomous), Oth superf bite] of [rt, lt, unsp] ear, init enc 417
S00.4[0,1,2,3,4,5, 6,7][1,2,9]D	[Unsp superf inj, Abrasion, Blister (nonthermal), Contsn, Ext constriction, Superf FB, Insect bite (nonvenomous), Oth superf bite] of [rt, lt, unsp] ear, subsq enc 386
S00.3[0,1,2,3,4,5, 6,7]XD	[Unsp superf inj, Abrasion, Blister (nonthermal), Contsn, Ext constriction, Superf FB, Insect bite (nonvenomous), Oth superf bite] of nose, subsq enc 386
S00.8[0,1,2,3,4,5, 6,7]XD	[Unsp superf inj, Abrasion, Blister (nonthermal), Contsn, Ext constriction, Superf FB, Insect bite (nonvenomous), Oth superf bite] of oth part of head, subsq enc 386
S00.0[0,1,2,3,4,5, 6,7]XA	[Unsp superf inj, Abrasion, Blister (nonthermal), Contsn, Ext constriction, Superf FB, Insect bite (nonvenomous), Oth superf bite] of scalp, init enc 417
S00.9[0,1,2,3,4,5, 6,7]XA	[Unsp superf inj, Abrasion, Blister (nonthermal), Contsn, Ext constriction, Superf FB, Insect bite (nonvenomous), Oth superf bite] of unsp part of head, init enc 417
S00.9[0,1,2,3,4,5, 6,7]XD	[Unsp superf inj, Abrasion, Blister (nonthermal), Contsn, Ext constriction, Superf FB, Insect bite (nonvenomous), Oth superf bite] of unsp part of head, subsq enc 386
S10.8[0,1,2,3,4,5, 6,7]XA	[Unsp superf inj, Abrasion, Blister (nonthermal), Contsn, Ext constriction, Superf FB, Insect bite, Oth superf bite] of oth spec part of neck, init enc 419
S10.9[0,1,2,3,4,5, 6,7]XA	[Unsp superf inj, Abrasion, Blister (nonthermal), Contsn, Ext constriction, Superf FB, Insect bite, Oth superf bite] of unsp part of neck, init enc 419
S00.2[0,1,2,4,5,6, 7][1,2,9]A	[Unsp superf inj, Abrasion, Blister (nonthermal), Ext constriction, Superf FB, Insect bite (nonvenomous), Oth superf bite] of [rt, lt, unsp] eyelid and periocular area, init enc 417
S00.2[0,1,2,4,5,6, 7][1,2,9]D	[Unsp superf inj, Abrasion, Blister (nonthermal), Ext constriction, Superf FB, Insect bite (nonvenomous), Oth superf bite] of [rt, lt, unsp] eyelid and periocular area, subsq enc 386
S20.9[0,1,2,4,5,6, 7]XA	[Unsp superf inj, Abrasion, Blister (nonthermal), Ext constriction, Superf FB, Insect bite (nonvenomous), Oth superf bite] of unsp parts of thorax, init enc 420
S20.9[0,1,2,4,5,6, 7]XD	[Unsp superf inj, Abrasion, Blister (nonthermal), Ext constriction, Superf FB, Insect bite (nonvenomous), Oth superf bite] of unsp parts of thorax, subsq enc 388
S00.3[0,1,2,3,4,5, 6,7]XA	[Unsp superf inj, Abrasion, Blister, Contsn, Ext constriction, Superf FB, Insect bite (nonvenomous), Oth superf bite] of nose, init enc 417
S00.3[0,1]X[A,S]	[Unsp superf inj, abrasion] of nose, [init enc, seq] 224
S00.8[0,1]X[A,S]	[Unsp superf inj, abrasion] of oth part of head, [init enc, seq] 224
S10.8[0,1]X[A,S]	[Unsp superf inj, abrasion] of oth spec part of neck, [init enc, seq] 225
S00.9[0,1]X[A,S]	[Unsp superf inj, abrasion] of unsp part of head, [init enc, seq] 224
S10.9[0,1]X[A,S]	[Unsp superf inj, abrasion] of unsp part of neck, [init enc, seq] 225
S20.9[0,1]X[A,S]	[Unsp superf inj, abrasion] of unsp parts of thorax, [init enc, seq] 225
S20.40[1,2,9] [A,S]	[Unsp superf injuries of [rt, lt, unsp] back wall of thorax, [init enc, seq] 225
S20.40[1,2,9]D	Unsp superf injuries of [rt, lt, unsp] back wall of thorax, subsq enc 388
S20.30[1,2,9] [A,S]	Unsp superf injuries of [rt, lt, unsp] front wall of thorax, [init enc, seq] 225
S20.30[1,2,9]D	Unsp superf injuries of [rt, lt, unsp] front wall of thorax, subsq enc 388
S20.10[1,2,9] [A,S]	Unsp superf injuries of breast, [rt, lt, unsp] breast, [init enc, seq] 225
S20.10[1,2,9]D	Unsp superf injuries of breast, [rt, lt, unsp] breast, subsq enc 388
S10.1[0,1,2,4,5,6, 7]XA	[Unsp superf injuries, Abrasion, Blister (nonthermal), Ext constriction of part, Superf FB, Insect bite (nonvenomous, Oth superf bite] of throat, init enc 419
S20.1[0,1,2,4,5,6, 7][1,2,9]A	[Unsp superf injuries, Abrasion, Blister (nonthermal), Ext constriction of part, Superf FB, Insect bite, Oth superf bite] of breast, [rt, lt, unsp] breast, init enc 420
S20.4[0,1,2,4,5,6, 7][1,2,9]A	[Unsp superf injuries, Abrasion, Blister (nonthermal), Ext constriction, Superf FB, Insect bite (nonvenomous), Oth superf bite] of [rt, lt, unsp] back wall of thorax, init enc 420
S20.3[0,1,2,4,5,6, 7][1,2,9]A	[Unsp superf injuries, Abrasion, Blister (nonthermal), Ext constriction, Superf FB, Insect bite (nonvenomous), Oth superf bite] of [rt, lt, unsp] front wall of thorax, init enc 420
S10.8[0,1,2,4,5,6, 7]XD	[Unsp superf injuries, Abrasion, Blister, Ext constriction of part, Superf FB, Insect bite (nonvenomous), Oth superf bite] of neck, subsq enc 387
S10.1[0,1,2,4,5,6, 7]XD	[Unsp superf injuries, Abrasion, Blister, Ext constriction of part, Superf FB, Insect bite (nonvenomous), Oth superf bite] of throat, subsq enc 387
S10.9[0,1,2,4,5,6, 7]XD	[Unsp superf injuries, Abrasion, Blister, Ext constriction of part, Superf FB, Insect bite (nonvenomous), Oth superf bite] of unsp part of neck, subsq enc 387
S10.1[0,1]X[A,S]	[Unsp superf injuries, abrasion] of throat, [init enc, seq] 225
R48.9	Unsp symbolic dysfunctions 311
R29.9*	Unsp symptoms & signs involving the nervous and ms systems 38
R41.9	Unsp symptoms and signs w cognitive functions and awareness 385
R44.9	Unsp symptoms and signs w general sensations and perceptions 412
S83.20[6,7,9] [A,S]	Unsp tear of unsp meniscus, current inj, [rt, lt, unsp] knee, [init enc, seq] 192

Code	Description
S56.0[0,9][1,2,9] [A,S]	[Unsp, Oth] inj of flexor muscle, fascia and tndn of [rt, lt, unsp] thumb at forearm lvl, [init enc, seq] 360
S96.2[0,9][1,2,9] [A,S]	[Unsp, Oth] inj of intrinsic muscle and tndn at ankle and foot lvl, [rt, lt, unsp] foot, [init enc, seq] 361
S29.0[0,9][1,2,9] [A,S]	[Unsp, Oth] inj of muscle and tndn of [front, back, unsp] wall of thorax, [init enc, seq] 359
S96.1[0,9][1,2,9] [A,S]	[Unsp, Oth] inj of muscle and tndn of long extensor muscle of toe at ankle and foot lvl, [rt, lt, unsp] foot, [init enc, seq] 361
S96.0[0,9][1,2,9] [A,S]	[Unsp, Oth] inj of muscle and tndn of long flexor muscle of toe at ankle and foot lvl, [rt, lt, unsp] foot, [init enc, seq] 361
S39.0[0,9][1,2,3] [A,S]	[Unsp, Oth] inj of muscle, fascia and tndn of [abd, lwr back, pelvis], [init enc, seq] 359
S46.1[0,9][1,2,9] [A,S]	[Unsp, Oth] inj of muscle, fascia and tndn of long head of biceps, [rt, lt, unsp] arm, [init enc, seq] 359
S46.2[0,9][1,2,9] [A,S]	[Unsp, Oth] inj of muscle, fascia and tndn of oth part of biceps, [rt, lt, unsp] arm, [init enc, seq] 359
S46.3[0,9][1,2,9] [A,S]	[Unsp, Oth] inj of muscle, fascia and tndn of triceps, [rt, lt, unsp] arm, [init enc, seq] 359
S46.0[0,9][1,2,9] [A,S]	[Unsp, Oth] inj of muscle(s) and tndn(s) of the rotator cuff of [rt, lt, unsp] shldr, [init enc, seq] 359
S56.5[0,9][1,2,9] [A,S]	[Unsp, Oth] inj of oth extensor muscle, fascia and tndn at forearm lvl, [rt, lt, unsp] arm, [init enc, seq] 360
S56.2[0,9][1,2,9] [A,S]	[Unsp, Oth] inj of oth flexor muscle, fascia and tndn at forearm lvl, [rt, lt, unsp] arm, [init enc, seq] 360
S56.8[0,9][1,2,9] [A,S]	[Unsp, Oth] inj of oth muscles, fascia and tndns at forearm lvl, [rt, lt, unsp] arm, [init enc, seq] 360
S46.8[0,9][1,2,9] [A,S]	[Unsp, Oth] inj of oth muscles, fascia and tndns at shldr and upr arm lvl, [rt, lt, unsp] arm, [init enc, seq] 359
S96.8[0,9][1,2,9] [A,S]	[Unsp, Oth] inj of oth spec muscles and tndns at ankle and foot lvl, [rt, lt, unsp] foot, [init enc, seq] 361
S96.9[0,9][1,2,9] [A,S]	[Unsp, Oth] inj of unsp muscle and tndn at ankle and foot lvl, [rt, lt, unsp] foot, [init enc, seq] 361
S56.9[0,9][1,2,9] [A,S]	[Unsp, Oth] inj of unsp muscles, fascia and tndns at forearm lvl, [rt, lt, unsp] arm, [init enc, seq] 360
S46.9[0,9][1,2,9] [A,S]	[Unsp, Oth] inj of unsp muscles, fascia and tndns at shldr and upr arm lvl, [rt, lt, unsp] arm, [init enc, seq] 359
H04.3[0,1] [1,2,3,9]	[Unsp, Phlegmonous] dacryocystitis of [rt, lt, bilat, unsp] lacrimal passage 45
S53.4[0,1,2,3,4,9] [1,2,9]A	[Unsp, Radiohumeral (jt), Ulnohumeral (jt), Radial collat lgmt, Ulnar collat lgmt, Oth] sprain of [rt, lt, unsp] elbow, init enc 424
S89.3[0,1,2,9] [1,2,9]A	[Unsp, Salter-Harris Type I, Salter-Harris Type II, Oth] physeal fx of lwr end of [rt, lt, unsp] fibula, init enc for clsd fx 192, 428
S89.2[0,1,2,9] [1,2,9]A	[Unsp, Salter-Harris Type I, Salter-Harris Type II, Oth] physeal fx of upr end of [rt, lt, unsp] fibula, init enc for clsd fx 192, 428
S59.1[0,1,2,3,4,9] [1,2,9]A	[Unsp, Salter-Harris Type I, Salter-Harris Type II, Salter-Harris III, Salter-Harris IV, Oth] physeal fx of upr end of radius, [rt, lt, unsp] arm, init enc for clsd fx 424
S49.1[0,1,2,3,4,9] [1,2,9]A	[Unsp, Salter-Harris Type I, Salter-Harris Type II, Salter-Harris Type III, Salter-Harris Type IV, Oth] physeal fx of lwr end of humerus, [rt, lt, unsp] arm, init enc for clsd fx 423
S59.2[0,1,2,3,4,9] [1,2,9]A	[Unsp, Salter-Harris Type I, Salter-Harris Type II, Salter-Harris Type III, Salter-Harris Type IV, Oth] physeal fx of lwr end of radius, [rt, lt, unsp] arm, init enc for clsd fx 424
S49.0[0,1,2,3,4,9] [1,2,9]A	[Unsp, Salter-Harris Type I, Salter-Harris Type II, Salter-Harris Type III, Salter-Harris Type IV, Oth] physeal fx of upr end of humerus, [rt, lt, unsp] arm, init enc for clsd fx 423
S59.0[0,1,2,3,4,9] [1,2,9]A	[Unsp, Salter-HarrisType I, Salter-Harris Type II, Salter-Harris Type III, Salter-Harris Type IV, Oth] physeal fx of lwr end of ulna, [rt, lt, unsp] arm, init enc for clsd fx 424
S22.052A	Unstable burst fx of T5-T6 vertebra, init for clos fx 420
S22.052B	Unstable burst fx of T5-T6 vertebra, init for opn fx 420
J39.3	Upr respiratory tract hypersensitivity reaction, site unsp 4, 57
A82.1	Urban rabies 10, 15
N34.0	Urethral abscess 255, 285
N37	Urethral d/o in dz classified elsw 255
R36.0	Urethral discharge w/o bld 255
R36.9	Urethral discharge, unsp 255
N35*	Urethral stricture 255
N34.3	Urethral synd, unsp 255
N39.0	Urinary tract infxn, site not spec 255, 285
L50*	Urticaria 234
O26.84[1,2,3]	Uterine size-date discrepancy, [1st, 2nd, 3rd] trmstr 277, 279
O26.849	Uterine size-date discrepancy, unsp trmstr 280
B08.011	Vaccinia not from vaccine 307

Code	Description
R87.82[0,1]	Vaginal [high, low] risk human papillomavirus (HPV) DNA test positive 265, 270
N94.2	Vaginismus 270
F52.5	Vaginismus not d/t a substance or known physiol condition 264, 270
N77.1	Vaginitis, vulvitis and vulvovaginitis in dis classd elsw 269
M21.0[2,5,6,7] [1,2,9]	Valgus deformity, NEC, [rt, lt, unsp] [elbow, hip, knee, ankle] 193
M21.00	Valgus deformity, NEC, unsp site 193
B01.11	Varicella encephalitis and encephalomyelitis 283
B01.1*	Varicella encephalitis, myelitis and encephalomyelitis 41
B01.81	Varicella keratitis 283
B01.0	Varicella meningitis 283, 307
B01.12	Varicella myelitis 11, 15
B01.2	Varicella pneumonia 67, 283
B01.9	Varicella w/o comp 283, 307
B01.8*	Varicella with oth comp 307
O22.00	Varicose veins of low extrm in preg, unsp trmstr 280
O22.0[1,2,3]	Varicose veins of lwr extr in preg, [1st, 2nd, 3rd] trmstr 277
I83.2*	Varicose veins of lwr extremities w ulc and inflam 100
I83.1*	Varicose veins of lwr extremities with inflam 100
I83.8*	Varicose veins of lwr extremities with oth comp 100
I83.0*	Varicose veins of lwr extremities with ulcer 100
O22.[0,1,2,3,4,5] [1,2,3]	Varicose veins of lwr extremity, Genital varices, Superficial thrombophlebitis, Hemorrhoids, Cerebral venous thrombosis] in preg, [1st, 2nd, 3rd] trmstr 279
I86.8	Varicose veins of oth spec sites 100
M21.1[2,5,6,7] [1,2,9]	Varus deformity, NEC, [rt, lt, unsp] [elbow, hip, knee, ankle] 193
M21.10	Varus deformity, NEC, unsp site 193
T80.1XXA	Vascular comp fol infusn, tranfs and theraputc inject, init 103, 287
T80.1XXD	Vascular comp fol infusn, tranfs and theraputc inject, subs 410
K55.9	Vascular d/o of intestine, unsp 117
F01*	Vascular dementia 310
G95.1*	Vascular myelopathies 38
G21.4	Vascular parkinsonism 32
L95*	Vasculitis limited to skin, NEC 234
J30*	Vasomotor and allergic rhinitis 57
O43.121	Velamentous insert of umbilical cord, first trmstr 281
O43.122	Velamentous insert of umbilical cord, second trmstr 281
O43.123	Velamentous insert of umbilical cord, third trmstr 281
O43.129	Velamentous insert of umbilical cord, unsp trmstr 281
A92.2	Venezuelan equine fever 10, 15, 41
O87*	Venous comp and hemorrhoids in the puerperium 272, 276
O22.9[1,2,3]	Venous comp in preg, unsp, [1st, 2nd, 3rd] trmstr 277, 279
O22.90	Venous comp in preg, unsp, unsp trmstr 280
I87.2	Venous insufficiency (chr) (peripheral) 100
J95.851	Ventilator associated pneumonia 69, 284
K43*	Ventral hernia 117
I49.0[1,2]	Ventricular [fibrillation, flutter] 283
Q21.0	Ventricular septal defect 285
I23.2	Ventricular septal defect as current comp following AMI 103
I47.2	Ventricular tachycardia 283
G45.0	Vertebro-basilar artery synd 33
H50.2*	Vertical strabismus 46
H82*	Vertiginous syndromes in dz classified elsw 57
T75.23X[A,S]	Vertigo from infrasound, [init enc, seq] 374
T75.23XD	Vertigo from infrasound, subsq enc 410
N32.2	Vesical fistula, NEC 285
N32.1	Vesicointestinal fistula 285
N13.7*	Vesicoureteral-reflux 256
N82.0	Vesicovaginal fistula 265, 270
R45.6	Violent behav 310
B33.2[0,2,3]	Viral [carditis unsp, myocarditis, pericarditis] 103
B97*	Viral agents as the cause of dz classified elsw 308
A08*	Viral and oth spec intestinal infections 116
B33.24	Viral cardiomyopathy 307
B30*	Viral conjunctivitis 45
B33.21	Viral endocarditis 102
O98.42	Viral hepatitis compl childbirth 274

O98.41[1,2,3]	Viral hepatitis compl preg, [1st, 2nd, 3rd] trmstr 274, 277
O98.43	Viral hepatitis compl the puerperium 274, 276
B34*	Viral infxn of unsp site 308
A87*	Viral meningitis 34
J12*	Viral pneumonia, NEC 68
J12.9	Viral pneumonia, unsp 439
B07*	Viral warts 233
B83.0	Visceral larva migrans 309
B55.0	Visceral leishmaniasis 308
R19.2	Visible peristalsis 116
H53.7*	Vision sensitivity deficiencies 46
R48.3	Visual agnosia 46
H53.14[1,2,3,9]	Visual discomfort, [rt, lt, bilat, unsp] eye 46
H53.15	Visual distortions of shape and size 46
R44.1	Visual hallucinations 46
R41.842	Visuospatial deficit 39
E50.1	Vitamin A deficiency w Bitot's spot and conjunctival xerosis 45
E50.0	Vitamin A deficiency with conjunctival xerosis 45
E50.3	Vitamin A deficiency with corneal ulceration and xerosis 45
E50.2	Vitamin A deficiency with corneal xerosis 45
E50.4	Vitamin A deficiency with keratomalacia 45
E50.5	Vitamin A deficiency with night blindness 45
E50.6	Vitamin A deficiency with xerophthalmic scars of cornea 45
E50.9	Vitamin A deficiency, unsp 246
D51*	Vitamin B12 deficiency anemia 293
E55.9	Vitamin D deficiency, unsp 246
L80	Vitiligo 234, 289
R49*	Voice and resonance d/o 58
E86*	Volume depletion 246, 283
K56.2	Volvulus 284
K91.0	Vomiting following gastrointestinal surgery 116
R11.13	Vomiting of fecal matter 117
O21.9	Vomiting of preg, unsp 279
R11.11	Vomiting w/o nausea 116
R11.10	Vomiting, unsp 116
D68.0	Von Willebrand's dz 294
I86.3	Vulval varices 264, 270
N94.810	Vulvar vestibulitis 269
N77*	Vulvovaginal ulceration and inflam in dz classd elsw 265
A39.1	Waterhouse-Friderichsen synd 282, 309
R53.1	Weakness 385
T84.06[0,1,2,3,8,9]A	Wear of articular bearing surface of int prosthetic [rt hip, lt hip, rt knee, lt knee, oth site, unsp site] jt, init enc 183
T84.06[0,1,2,3,8,9]D	Wear of articular bearing surface of int prosthetic [rt hip, lt hip, rt knee, lt knee, oth site, unsp site] jt, subsq enc 411
T84.06[0,1,2,3,8,9]S	Wear of articular bearing surface of int prosthetic [rt hip, lt hip, rt knee, lt knee, oth, unsp] jt, seq 375
Q31.0	Web of larynx 4
Q18.3	Webbing of neck 234
S32.01[0,1,2,8,9][D,G]	[Wedge compression, Stable burst, Unstable burst, Oth, Unsp] fx of 1st lumbar vertebra, subsq enc for fx w/ [routine, delayed] healing 170
S32.01[0,1,2,8,9]K	[Wedge compression, Stable burst, Unstable burst, Oth, Unsp] fx of 1st lumbar vertebra, subsq enc for fx w/ nonu 196
S22.01[0,1,2,8,9][A,B,S]	[Wedge compression, Stable burst, Unstable burst, Oth, Unsp] fx of 1st thoracic vertebra, [init enc for clsd fx, init enc for opn fx, seq] 166
S22.01[0,1,2,8,9][A,B]	[Wedge compression, Stable burst, Unstable burst, Oth, Unsp] fx of 1st thoracic vertebra, init enc for [clsd, opn] fx 420
S22.01[0,1,2,8,9][D,G]	[Wedge compression, Stable burst, Unstable burst, Oth, Unsp] fx of 1st thoracic vertebra, subsq enc for fx w/ [routine, delayed] healing 169
S22.01[0,1,2,8,9]K	[Wedge compression, Stable burst, Unstable burst, Oth, Unsp] fx of 1st thoracic vertebra, subsq enc for fx w/ nonu 195
S32.02[0,1,2,8,9][A,B]	[Wedge compression, Stable burst, Unstable burst, Oth, Unsp] fx of 2nd lumbar vertebra, init enc for [clsd, opn] fx 421
S32.02[0,1,2,8,9][D,G]	[Wedge compression, Stable burst, Unstable burst, Oth, Unsp] fx of 2nd lumbar vertebra, subsq enc for fx w/ [routine, delayed] healing 170
S32.02[0,1,2,8,9]K	[Wedge compression, Stable burst, Unstable burst, Oth, Unsp] fx of 2nd lumbar vertebra, subsq enc for fx w/ nonu 196
S22.02[0,1,2,8,9][A,B,S]	[Wedge compression, Stable burst, Unstable burst, Oth, Unsp] fx of 2nd thoracic vertebra, [init enc for clsd fx, init enc for opn fx, seq] 166
S22.02[0,1,2,8,9][A,B]	[Wedge compression, Stable burst, Unstable burst, Oth, Unsp] fx of 2nd thoracic vertebra, init enc for [clsd, opn] fx 420
S22.02[0,1,2,8,9][D,G]	[Wedge compression, Stable burst, Unstable burst, Oth, Unsp] fx of 2nd thoracic vertebra, subsq enc for fx w/ [routine, delayed] healing 169
S22.02[0,1,2,8,9]K	[Wedge compression, Stable burst, Unstable burst, Oth, Unsp] fx of 2nd thoracic vertebra, subsq enc for fx w/ nonu 195
S32.03[0,1,2,8,9][A,B]	[Wedge compression, Stable burst, Unstable burst, Oth, Unsp] fx of 3rd lumbar vertebra, init enc for [clsd, opn] fx 421
S32.03[0,1,2,8,9][D,G]	[Wedge compression, Stable burst, Unstable burst, Oth, Unsp] fx of 3rd lumbar vertebra, subsq enc for fx w/ [routine, delayed] healing 170
S32.03[0,1,2,8,9]K	[Wedge compression, Stable burst, Unstable burst, Oth, Unsp] fx of 3rd lumbar vertebra, subsq enc for fx w/ nonu 196
S22.03[0,1,2,8,9][A,B,S]	[Wedge compression, Stable burst, Unstable burst, Oth, Unsp] fx of 3rd thoracic vertebra, [init enc for clsd fx, init enc for opn fx, seq] 166
S22.03[0,1,2,8,9][A,B]	[Wedge compression, Stable burst, Unstable burst, Oth, Unsp] fx of 3rd thoracic vertebra, init enc for [clsd, opn] fx 420
S22.03[0,1,2,8,9][D,G]	[Wedge compression, Stable burst, Unstable burst, Oth, Unsp] fx of 3rd thoracic vertebra, subsq enc for fx w/ [routine, delayed] healing 169
S22.03[0,1,2,8,9]K	[Wedge compression, Stable burst, Unstable burst, Oth, Unsp] fx of 3rd thoracic vertebra, subsq enc for fx w/ nonu 195
S32.04[0,1,2,8,9][A,B]	[Wedge compression, Stable burst, Unstable burst, Oth, Unsp] fx of 4th lumbar vertebra, init enc for [clsd, opn] fx 421
S32.04[0,1,2,8,9][D,G]	[Wedge compression, Stable burst, Unstable burst, Oth, Unsp] fx of 4th lumbar vertebra, subsq enc for fx w/ [routine, delayed] healing 170
S32.04[0,1,2,8,9]K	[Wedge compression, Stable burst, Unstable burst, Oth, Unsp] fx of 4th lumbar vertebra, subsq enc for fx w/ nonu 196
S22.04[0,1,2,8,9][A,B,S]	[Wedge compression, Stable burst, Unstable burst, Oth, Unsp] fx of 4th thoracic vertebra, [init enc for clsd fx, init enc for opn fx, seq] 166
S22.04[0,1,2,8,9][A,B]	[Wedge compression, Stable burst, Unstable burst, Oth, Unsp] fx of 4th thoracic vertebra, init enc for [clsd, opn] fx 420
S22.04[0,1,2,8,9][D,G]	[Wedge compression, Stable burst, Unstable burst, Oth, Unsp] fx of 4th thoracic vertebra, subsq enc for fx w/ [routine, delayed] healing 169
S22.04[0,1,2,8,9]K	[Wedge compression, Stable burst, Unstable burst, Oth, Unsp] fx of 4th thoracic vertebra, subsq enc for fx w/ nonu 195
S32.05[0,1,2,8,9][A,B]	[Wedge compression, Stable burst, Unstable burst, Oth, Unsp] fx of 5th lumbar vertebra, init enc for [clsd, opn] fx 421
S32.05[0,1,2,8,9][D,G]	[Wedge compression, Stable burst, Unstable burst, Oth, Unsp] fx of 5th lumbar vertebra, subsq enc for fx w/ [routine, delayed] healing 170
S32.05[0,1,2,8,9]K	[Wedge compression, Stable burst, Unstable burst, Oth, Unsp] fx of 5th lumbar vertebra, subsq enc for fx w/ nonu 196
S32.08[0,1,2,8,9][A,B,S]	[Wedge compression, Stable burst, Unstable burst, Oth, Unsp] fx of T11-T12 thoracic vertebra, [init enc for clsd fx, init enc for opn fx, seq] 166
S22.08[0,1,2,8,9][A,B]	[Wedge compression, Stable burst, Unstable burst, Oth, Unsp] fx of T11-T12 vertebra, init enc for [clsd, opn] fx 420
S22.08[0,1,2,8,9][D,G]	[Wedge compression, Stable burst, Unstable burst, Oth, Unsp] fx of T11-T12 vertebra, subsq enc for fx w/ [routine, delayed] healing 169
S22.08[0,1,2,8,9]K	[Wedge compression, Stable burst, Unstable burst, Oth, Unsp] fx of T11-T12 vertebra, subsq enc for fx w/ nonu 196
S22.05[0,1,2,8,9][A,B,S]	[Wedge compression, Stable burst, Unstable burst, Oth, Unsp] fx of T5-T6 vertebra, [init enc for clsd fx, init enc for opn fx, seq] 166
S22.05[0,1,8,9][A,B]	[Wedge compression, Stable burst, Unstable burst, Oth, Unsp] fx of T5-T6 vertebra, init enc for [clsd, opn] fx 420
S22.05[0,1,2,8,9][D,G]	[Wedge compression, Stable burst, Unstable burst, Oth, Unsp] fx of T5-T6 vertebra, subsq enc for fx w/ [routine, delayed] healing 169
S22.05[0,1,2,8,9]K	[Wedge compression, Stable burst, Unstable burst, Oth, Unsp] fx of T5-T6 vertebra, subsq enc for fx w/ nonu 196
S22.06[0,1,2,8,9][A,B,S]	[Wedge compression, Stable burst, Unstable burst, Oth, Unsp] fx of T7-T8 thoracic vertebra, [init enc for clsd fx, init enc for opn fx, seq] 166
S22.06[0,1,2,8,9][A,B]	[Wedge compression, Stable burst, Unstable burst, Oth, Unsp] fx of T7-T8 vertebra, init enc for [clsd, opn] fx 420
S22.06[0,1,2,8,9][D,G]	[Wedge compression, Stable burst, Unstable burst, Oth, Unsp] fx of T7-T8 vertebra, subsq enc for fx w/ [routine, delayed] healing 169

S22.06[Ø,1,2,8,9] K	[Wedge compression, Stable burst, Unstable burst, Oth, Unsp] fx of T7-T8 vertebra, subsq enc for fx w/ nonu **196**
S22.07[Ø,1,2,8,9] [A,B,S]	[Wedge compression, Stable burst, Unstable burst, Oth, Unsp] fx of T9-T1Ø thoracic vertebra, [init enc for clsd fx, init enc for opn fx, seq] **166**
S22.07[Ø,1,2,8,9] [A,B]	[Wedge compression, Stable burst, Unstable burst, Oth, Unsp] fx of T9-T1Ø vertebra, init enc for [clsd, opn] fx **420**
S22.07[Ø,1,2,8,9] [D,G]	[Wedge compression, Stable burst, Unstable burst, Oth, Unsp] fx of T9-T1Ø vertebra, subsq enc for fx w/ [routine, delayed] healing **169**
S22.07[Ø,1,2,8,9] K	[Wedge compression, Stable burst, Unstable burst, Oth, Unsp] fx of T9-T1Ø vertebra, subsq enc for fx w/ nonu **196**
S32.00[Ø,1,2,8,9] [A,B]	[Wedge compression, Stable burst, Unstable burst, Oth, Unsp] fx of unsp lumbar vertebra, init enc for [clsd, opn] fx **421**
S32.00[Ø,1,2,8,9] [D,G]	[Wedge compression, Stable burst, Unstable burst, Oth, Unsp] fx of unsp lumbar vertebra, subsq enc for fx w/ [routine, delayed] healing **170**
S32.00[Ø,1,2,8,9] K	[Wedge compression, Stable burst, Unstable burst, Oth, Unsp] fx of unsp lumbar vertebra, subsq enc for fx w/ nonu **196**
S22.00[Ø,1,2,8,9] [A,B,S]	[Wedge compression, Stable burst, Unstable burst, Oth, Unsp] fx of unsp thoracic vertebra, [init enc for clsd fx, init enc for opn fx, seq] **166**
S22.00[Ø,1,2,8,9] [A,B]	[Wedge compression, Stable burst, Unstable burst, Oth, Unsp] fx of unsp thoracic vertebra, init enc for [clsd, opn] fx **420**
S22.00[Ø,1,2,8,9] [D,G]	[Wedge compression, Stable burst, Unstable burst, Oth, Unsp] fx of unsp thoracic vertebra, subsq enc for fx w/ [routine, delayed] healing **169**
S22.00[Ø,1,2,8,9] K	[Wedge compression, Stable burst, Unstable burst, Oth, Unsp] fx of unsp thoracic vertebra, subsq enc for fx w/ nonu **195**
S32.01[Ø,1,2,8,9] [A,B]	[Wedge compression, Stable burst, Unstable burst, Oth, Unsp] fx of 1st lumbar vertebra, init enc for [clsd, opn] fx **421**
Z3A*	Weeks of gestation **412**
M31.3*	Wegener's granulomatosis **163**
A92.3*	West Nile virus infxn **307**
A83.1	Western equine encephalitis **10, 15**
R06.2	Wheezing **69**
K90.81	Whipple's dz **117**
R90.82	White matter dz, unsp **39**
Q93.1	Whole chromosome monosomy, mosaic (mitotic nondisjunction) **412**
Q93.Ø	Whole chromosome monosomy,nonmosaic (meiotic nondisjunction) **412**
A37*	Whooping cough **69**
P96.3	Wide cranial sutures of newborn **288**
D82.Ø	Wiskott-Aldrich synd **293**
P96.2	Withdrawal symptoms from therapeutic use of drugs in newborn **282**
R45.82	Worries **310**
M21.33[1,2,9]	Wrist drop, [Rt, Lt, Unsp] Wrist **34**
H02.6*	Xanthelasma of eyelid **233**
Q82.1	Xeroderma pigmentosum **289**
B08.7*	Yatapoxvirus infections **307**
A66.9	Yaws, unsp **308**
A95*	Yellow fever **307**
S32.11[Ø,1,2,9] [A,B,S]	Zone I fx of sacrum [nondisp, minimally disp, severely disp, unsp] init enc for fx [clsd, opn, seq] **166**
S32.12[Ø,1,2,9] [A,B,S]	Zone II fx of sacrum [nondisp, minimally disp, severely disp, unsp] init enc for fx [clsd, opn, seq] **166**
S32.13[Ø,1,2,9] [A,B,S]	Zone III fx of sacrum [nondisp, minimally disp, severely disp, unsp] init enc for fx [clsd, opn, seq] **166**
A28.9	Zoonotic bacterial dz, unsp **308**
B02.Ø	Zoster encephalitis **33, 283, 438**
B02.1	Zoster meningitis **35, 283, 438**
B02.3*	Zoster ocular dz **45, 283, 438**
B02.9	Zoster w/o comp **223, 283, 438**
B02.8	Zoster with oth comp **283, 307, 438**
S02.402[A,B]	Zygomatic fx, unsp, init enc for [clsd, opn] fx **59**
S02.402A	Zygomatic fx, unsp, init enc for clsd fx **5**
S02.402B	Zygomatic fx, unsp, init enc for opn fx **5**
B46*	Zygomycosis **283, 308**

Numeric Index to Diseases

Code	Page
A00*	114
A01*	308
A02.0	114
A02.1	309, 438
A02.2*	438
A02.20	308
A02.21	10, 14, 41
A02.22	67
A02.23	164
A02.24	163
A02.25	308
A02.29	308
A02.8	308, 438
A02.9	308, 438
A03*	114
A04*	114
A05.0	114
A05.1	308
A05.2	114
A05.3	114
A05.4	114
A05.5	114
A05.8	114
A05.9	116
A06.0	114
A06.1	114
A06.2	114
A06.3	308
A06.4	124
A06.5	67
A06.6	10, 14, 41
A06.7	233
A06.8*	308
A06.9	308
A07.3	438
A07*	114
A08*	116
A09	116
A15*	67, 438
A17.0	10, 14, 41
A17.1	10, 14, 41
A17.8*	10, 14, 41
A17.9	308
A17*	438
A18.0[1,3]	163
A18.01	125
A18.02	164
A18.09	164
A18.1[0,1,2,3]	255
A18.1[4,5]	261
A18.1[6,7,8]	264, 269
A18.2	294
A18.3*	114
A18.4	233
A18.5*	45
A18.6	58
A18.7	247
A18.8[2,4,9]	308
A18.81	247
A18.83	114
A18.85	294
A18*	438
A19*	308, 438
A20.0	308
A20.1	308
A20.2	67

Code	Page
A20.3	308
A20.7	309
A20.8	308
A20.9	308
A21.[0,1,7,8,9]	308
A21.2	67
A21.3	114
A22.0	233
A22.1	67
A22.2	114
A22.7	309
A22.8	308
A22.9	308
A23*	308
A24*	308
A25*	308
A26.0	308
A26.7	309
A26.8	308
A26.9	308
A27.0	308
A27.8*	10, 14, 41
A27.9	308
A28.0	308
A28.1	294
A28.2	308
A28.8	308
A28.9	308
A30*	308
A31.0	67
A31.1	233
A31.2	308, 438
A31.8	308, 438
A31.9	308, 438
A32.0	308
A32.1*	308
A32.7	309
A32.8*	308
A32.9	308
A33	288
A34	272, 275
A35	282, 308
A36.0	2, 58
A36.1	2, 58
A36.2	2, 58
A36.3	233
A36.8[2,3,4]	308
A36.81	103
A36.85	255
A36.86	45
A36.89	308
A36.9	308
A37*	69
A38*	308
A39.0	10, 14, 41
A39.1	282, 309
A39.2	309
A39.3	309
A39.4	309
A39.5[0,2,3]	103
A39.5*	282
A39.51	99
A39.8[3,4]	164, 282
A39.81	10, 14, 41
A39.82	45, 282
A39.89	309

Code	Page
A39.9	309
A40.9	282, 438
A40*	309
A41*	282, 309, 438
A42.0	67
A42.1	114
A42.2	233
A42.7	282, 309
A42.8*	308
A42.9	308
A42*	438
A43.0	67
A43.1	233
A43.8	308
A43.9	308
A43*	438
A44*	308
A46	224
A48.0	283, 308
A48.1	66, 67, 283, 438
A48.2	308
A48.3	308
A48.4	308
A48.5*	308
A48.51	283
A48.8	308
A49*	308
A50.0*	308
A50.1	308
A50.2	308
A50.30	308
A50.31	45
A50.32	308
A50.39	308
A50.4[0,1,2,3]	41
A50.44	308
A50.45	41
A50.49	41
A50.5*	308
A50.6	308
A50.7	308
A50.9	308
A51.0	261, 264, 269
A51.1	116
A51.2	308
A51.3*	233
A51.41	10, 14, 41
A51.42	308
A51.43	45
A51.44	308
A51.45	124
A51.46	163
A51.49	308
A51.5	308
A51.9	308
A52.00	103
A52.01	102
A52.02	102
A52.03	99
A52.04	103
A52.05	103
A52.06	103
A52.09	103
A52.10	32
A52.11	32
A52.12	32

Code	Page
A52.13	10, 14, 41
A52.14	10, 14, 41
A52.15	32
A52.16	32
A52.17	32
A52.19	32
A52.2	41
A52.3	32
A52.71	45
A52.72	67
A52.73	308
A52.74	124
A52.75	255
A52.76	308
A52.77	163
A52.78	167
A52.79	308
A52.8	308
A52.9	308
A53*	308
A54.0[0,2,3,9]	264, 269
A54.0[0,9]	261
A54.01	255
A54.1	261, 264, 269
A54.2[1,2,3,9]	261
A54.2[1,4,9]	264, 269
A54.3*	45
A54.4[0,2,3,9]	164
A54.41	163
A54.5	2, 57
A54.6	116
A54.81	10, 14, 41
A54.82	308
A54.83	103
A54.84	308
A54.85	114
A54.86	309
A54.89	308
A54.9	308
A55	261, 264, 269
A56.0[0,1,9]	261
A56.0*	264, 269
A56.1*	255
A56.2	261, 264, 269
A56.3	116
A56.4	2, 57
A56.8	261, 264, 269
A57	261, 264, 269
A58	261, 264, 269
A59.0[0,1,3,9]	264, 269
A59.0[0,2,3,9]	261
A59.8	308
A59.9	308
A60.0[0,1,2,9]	261
A60.0[0,1,4,9]	438
A60.0[0,3,4,9]	264, 269
A60.1	261, 264, 269, 438
A60.9	261, 264, 269, 438
A63.0	233
A63.8	261, 264, 269
A64	261, 264, 269
A65	308
A66.[0,1,2,3,4]	233
A66.5	2, 58
A66.6	164
A66.7	308

Code	Page	Code	Page	Code	Page	Code	Page
A66.8	308	A92.4	307	B06.9	307	B37.81	114
A66.9	308	A92.8	307	B07*	233	B37.82	116
A67.[0,1,3]	233	A92.9	307	B08.010	307	B37.83	2, 59
A67.2	308	A93*	307	B08.011	307	B37.84	58
A67.9	308	A94	307	B08.02	233	B37.89	308
A68*	308	A95*	307	B08.03	233	B37.9	308, 438
A69.0	2, 59	A96*	307	B08.04	307	B38.0	67
A69.1	2, 57	A98.0	307	B08.09	307	B38.1	67
A69.2*	308	A98.1	307	B08.1	233	B38.2	67
A69.8	308	A98.2	307	B08.2*	283, 307	B38.3	233
A69.9	308	A98.3	307	B08.3	307	B38.4	11, 15, 41, 283
A70	307	A98.4	307	B08.4	307	B38.7	283, 308
A71*	45	A98.5	255	B08.5	2, 57	B38.81	233
A74.0	45	A98.8	307	B08.6*	307	B38.89	283, 308
A74.8*	307	A99	307	B08.7*	307	B38.9	308
A74.9	307	B00.0	233, 283, 438	B08.8	307	B38*	438
A75*	308	B00.1	58, 283, 438	B09	307	B39.[0,1,2]	283
A77*	308	B00.2	2, 59, 283, 438	B10.0*	11, 15, 41, 283, 438	B39.0	67
A78	308	B00.3	10, 15, 34, 283, 438	B10.8*	233	B39.1	67
A79*	308	B00.4	10, 15, 41, 283, 438	B15*	124	B39.2	67
A80.0	10, 15, 41	B00.5*	45, 283, 438	B16*	124, 283	B39.3	308
A80.1	10, 15, 41	B00.7	283, 309, 438	B17*	124, 283	B39.4	308
A80.2	10, 15, 41	B00.81	116, 283, 438	B18*	124, 283	B39.5	308
A80.3*	10, 15, 41	B00.82	10, 15, 41	B19.0	283	B39.9	308
A80.4	307	B00.89	283, 307, 438	B19.1*	283	B39*	438
A80.9	10, 15, 41	B00.9	233, 438	B19.9	283	B40*	283, 308
A81.1	283	B01.0	283, 307	B19*	124	B41*	283, 308
A81.2	438	B01.1*	41	B20	438, 439	B42*	308
A81.82	438	B01.11	283	B25.0	67	B43*	308
A81.83	438	B01.12	11, 15	B25.1	124	B44.[1,2,7]	283, 308
A81.89	438	B01.2	67, 283	B25.2	124, 283	B44.0	67
A81.9	438	B01.8*	307	B25.8	307, 438	B44.81	68
A81*	32	B01.81	283	B25.9	307, 438	B44.89	283, 308
A82.0	10, 15	B01.89	283	B26.[0,1,2,3]	283	B44.9	283, 308
A82.1	10, 15	B01.9	283, 307	B26.0	261	B45.[0,2,3,7,8,9]	308
A82.9	10, 15	B02.0	33, 283, 438	B26.1	11, 15, 35	B45.0	438
A82*	41	B02.1	35, 283, 438	B26.2	11, 15, 41	B45.1	11, 15, 41
A83.0	10, 15	B02.2[1,2,3,9]	438	B26.3	124	B45.2	438
A83.1	10, 15	B02.2[1,2,3]	283	B26.8[2,3,5]	307	B45.3	438
A83.2	10, 15	B02.21	33	B26.8*	283	B45.7	438
A83.3	10, 15	B02.22	33	B26.81	124	B45.8	438
A83.4	10, 15	B02.23	33	B26.84	34	B45.9	438
A83.5	10, 15	B02.24	11, 15, 41	B26.89	307	B45*	283
A83.6	10, 15	B02.29	33, 283	B26.9	307	B46*	283, 308
A83.8	10, 15	B02.3*	45, 283, 438	B27*	307	B47.0	283, 308
A83.9	10, 15	B02.7	283, 307, 438	B30*	45	B47.1	308, 438
A83*	41	B02.8	283, 307, 438	B33.0	68	B47.9	233, 438
A84.0	10, 15	B02.9	223, 283, 438	B33.1	307	B48.2	283
A84.1	10, 15	B03	307	B33.2[0,2,3]	103	B48.4	283
A84.8	10, 15	B04	307	B33.21	102	B48.8	283, 438
A84.9	10, 15	B05.[0,1,2,3,4]	283	B33.24	307	B48*	308
A84*	41	B05.0	11, 15, 41	B33.3	307	B49	308
A85.0	438	B05.1	307	B33.4	307	B50*	308
A85.1	438	B05.2	67	B33.8	308	B51*	308
A85.2	10, 15	B05.3	57	B34*	308	B52*	308
A85.8	438	B05.4	307	B35*	233	B53*	308
A85*	41	B05.8*	283	B36*	233	B54	308
A86	41, 438	B05.81	45	B37.0	2, 59, 438	B55.[1,2]	233
A87*	34	B05.89	307	B37.1	67, 283, 438	B55.0	308
A88.0	34	B05.9	307	B37.2	233, 438	B55.9	308
A88.1	38	B06.0*	283	B37.3	264, 269	B56*	308
A88.8	41, 438	B06.00	34	B37.4*	261	B57.0	103
A89	41, 438	B06.01	41	B37.41	264, 269	B57.1	308
A90	307	B06.02	41	B37.49	264, 269	B57.2	103
A91	307	B06.09	41	B37.5	11, 15, 41, 283, 438	B57.3*	308
A92.0	307	B06.8*	283	B37.6	99, 283, 438	B57.4*	308
A92.1	307	B06.81	307	B37.7	309	B57.5	309
A92.2	10, 15, 41	B06.82	166	B37.8[1,2,4]	283	B58.0*	283
A92.3*	307	B06.89	307	B37.8*	438	B58.00	309

Code	Page	Code	Page	Code	Page	Code	Page
B58.01	45	B81.4	309	C06.2	3	C32.8	3
B58.09	45	B81.8	116	C06.8*	3	C32.9	3
B58.1	124, 283	B82*	116	C06.9	3	C32*	57
B58.2	11, 15, 41, 283	B83.0	309	C06*	57	C33	67
B58.3	67, 283	B83.1	309	C07	3, 57	C34*	67
B58.8*	283	B83.2	309	C08.0	3	C37	304, 305
B58.81	103	B83.3	309	C08.1	3	C38.0	103
B58.82	309	B83.4	233	C08.9	3	C38.1	67
B58.83	309	B83.8	309	C08*	57	C38.2	67
B58.89	309	B83.9	309	C09.0	3	C38.3	67
B58.9	309	B85*	233	C09.1	3	C38.4	67
B58*	438	B86	233	C09.8	3	C38.8	67
B59	67, 283, 438	B87*	233	C09.9	3	C39.0	3, 57
B60.0	309	B88*	233	C09*	57	C39.9	67
B60.1[2,3]	45	B89	309	C10.0	3	C40*	163
B60.10	309	B90.0	38	C10.1	3	C41.1	3
B60.11	309	B90.1	255	C10.2	3	C41.2	125
B60.19	309	B90.2	193	C10.3	3	C41*	163
B60.2	309	B90.8	309	C10.4	3	C43.0	223
B60.8	309, 438	B90.9	68	C10.8	3	C43.1*	45
B64	309	B91	38	C10.9	3	C43.2*	223
B65.0	255	B92	309	C10*	57	C43.3*	223
B65.1	124	B94.0	45	C11.0	3	C43.4	223
B65.2	309	B94.1	38	C11.1	3	C43.5*	223
B65.3	233	B94.2	309	C11.2	3	C43.6*	223
B65.8	309	B94.8	309	C11.3	3	C43.7*	223
B65.9	309	B94.9	309	C11.8	3	C43.8	223
B66.0	124	B95*	309	C11.9	3	C43.9	223
B66.1	124	B96*	309	C11*	57	C44.0[0,1,2,9]	233
B66.2	309	B97.4	283	C12	3, 57	C44.0*	3
B66.3	124	B97*	308	C13.0	3	C44.1*	45
B66.4	67	B99.8	438	C13.1	3	C44.2[0,1,2,9][1,2,9]	233
B66.5	124	B99*	309	C13.2	3	C44.3*	233
B66.8	309	C00.0	2	C13.8	3	C44.4[0,1,2,9]	233
B66.9	309	C00.1	2	C13.9	3	C44.5[0,1,2,9][0,1,9]	233
B67.0	124	C00.2	2	C13*	57	C44.6[0,1,2,9][1,2,9]	233
B67.1	67	C00.3	2	C14.0	3	C44.7[0,1,2,9][1,2,9]	233
B67.2	309	C00.4	2	C14.2	3	C44.8[0,1,2,9]	233
B67.31	247	C00.5	2	C14.8	3	C44.9[0,1,2,9]	233
B67.32	309	C00.6	2	C14*	57	C45.0	67
B67.39	309	C00.8	2	C15*	114	C45.1	114
B67.4	309	C00.9	2	C16*	114	C45.2	103
B67.5	124	C00*	57	C17*	114	C45.7	304, 305
B67.6*	309	C01	2, 57	C18.1	108	C45.9	304, 305
B67.7	309	C02.0	2	C18*	114	C46.[0,1,7,9]	233
B67.8	124	C02.1	2	C19	114	C46.2	3, 57
B67.90	309	C02.2	2	C20	114	C46.3	295, 303, 305
B67.99	309	C02.3	2	C21*	114	C46.4	114
B68*	116	C02.4	2	C22*	123	C46.5*	67
B69*	114	C02.8	2	C23	123	C46*	438
B70.0	116	C02.9	2	C24*	123	C47*	163
B70.1	114	C02*	57	C25*	123	C48.0	304, 305
B71*	114	C03.0	2	C26.0	114	C48.1	114
B72	309	C03.1	2	C26.1	295, 303, 305	C48.2	114
B73*	309	C03.9	2	C26.9	114	C48.8	114
B74*	309	C03*	57	C30.0	3	C49*	163
B75	309	C04.0	2	C30.1	3	C4A*	223
B76*	114	C04.1	2	C30*	57	C50.0[1,2][1,2,9]	221
B77*	116	C04.8	3	C31.0	3	C50.1[1,2][1,2,9]	221
B78.0	116, 438	C04.9	3	C31.1	3	C50.2[1,2][1,2,9]	221
B78.1	224	C04*	57	C31.2	3	C50.3[1,2][1,2,9]	221
B78.7	116, 438	C05.0	3	C31.3	3	C50.4[1,2][1,2,9]	221
B78.9	116, 438	C05.1	3	C31.8	3	C50.5[1,2][1,2,9]	221
B79	116	C05.2	3	C31.9	3	C50.6[1,2][1,2,9]	221
B80	116	C05.8	3	C31*	57	C50.8[1,2][1,2,9]	221
B81.0	116	C05.9	3	C32.0	3	C50.9[1,2][1,2,9]	221
B81.1	116	C05*	57	C32.1	3	C50*	223
B81.2	116	C06.0	3	C32.2	3	C51*	263, 269
B81.3	116	C06.1	3	C32.3	3	C52	263, 269

Code	Page	Code	Page	Code	Page	Code	Page
D89.811	293	E09.69	246	E27*	247	E75.1*	32
D89.812	293	E09.8	2, 246	E28*	264, 270	E75.2[1,2]	247
D89.813	293	E09.9	2, 246	E29*	247	E75.23	32
D89.82	164	E10.1*	2, 246	E30*	247	E75.24*	247
D89.89	294	E10.2*	2, 254, 256	E31*	247	E75.25	32
D89.9	294	E10.3*	2, 45	E32.0	294	E75.29	32
E00*	247	E10.4*	2, 34	E32.1	283, 294	E75.3	247
E01*	247	E10.5*	2, 100	E32.8	294	E75.4	32
E02	247	E10.6*	2	E32.9	294	E75.5	247
E03.0	247	E10.610	34	E34*	247	E75.6	247
E03.1	247	E10.618	246	E35	3, 247	E76*	247
E03.2	247	E10.62*	246	E36.1*	283	E77*	247
E03.3	247	E10.63*	246	E36*	367	E78.0	247
E03.4	3, 247	E10.64*	246	E40	246	E78.1	247
E03.5	35, 283	E10.65	246	E41	246, 283	E78.2	247
E03.8	247	E10.69	246	E42	246	E78.3	247
E03.9	247	E10.8	2, 246	E43	246, 283	E78.4	247
E04.1	3	E10.9	2, 246	E44*	246, 283	E78.5	247
E04*	247	E11.0*	2, 246	E45	246	E78.6	247
E05.0*	3	E11.2*	2, 256	E46	246, 283	E78.7[0,9]	247
E05.1*	3	E11.3*	2, 45	E50.0	45	E78.7[1,2]	193
E05.2*	3	E11.4*	2, 34	E50.1	45	E78.8*	247
E05.3*	3	E11.5*	2, 100	E50.2	45	E78.9	247
E05.4*	3	E11.6*	2	E50.3	45	E79.0	385
E05.8*	3	E11.610	34	E50.4	45	E79.1	247
E05.9*	3	E11.618	246	E50.5	45	E79.2	247
E05*	247	E11.62*	246	E50.6	45	E79.8	247
E06.0	3	E11.63*	246	E50.7	45	E79.9	247
E06.1	3	E11.64*	246	E50.8	246	E80.0	247
E06.2	3	E11.65	246	E50.9	246	E80.1	247
E06.3	3	E11.69	246	E51*	246	E80.2*	247
E06.4	3	E11.8	2, 246	E52	246	E80.3	247
E06.5	3	E11.9	2, 246	E53*	246	E80.4	124
E06.9	3	E13.0*	2, 246	E54	246	E80.5	124
E06*	247	E13.1*	2, 246	E55.0	166	E80.6	124
E07.0	247	E13.2*	2, 256	E55.9	246	E80.7	124
E07.1	247	E13.3*	2, 45	E56*	246	E83.0*	247
E07.81	385	E13.4*	2, 34	E58	246	E83.1*	247
E07.89	3, 247	E13.5*	2, 100	E59	246	E83.2	224
E07.9	3, 247	E13.6*	2	E60	246	E83.3*	247
E08.0*	1, 2, 246	E13.610	34	E61*	246	E83.4*	246
E08.1*	1, 2, 246	E13.618	246	E63*	246	E83.5*	246
E08.2*	1, 2, 256	E13.62*	246	E64.0	246, 283	E83.81	246
E08.3*	1, 2, 45	E13.63*	246	E64.1	246	E83.89	247
E08.4*	1, 2, 34	E13.64*	246	E64.2	246	E83.9	247
E08.5*	1, 2, 100	E13.65	246	E64.3	166	E84.0	67
E08.6*	1, 2	E13.69	246	E64.8	246	E84.11	282
E08.610	34	E13.8	2, 246	E64.9	246	E84.19	117
E08.618	246	E13.9	2, 246	E65	246	E84.8	246
E08.62*	246	E15	246, 283	E66.0*	246	E84.9	246
E08.63*	246	E16.0	247	E66.1	246	E85*	164
E08.64*	246	E16.1	247	E66.2	69	E86*	246, 283
E08.65	246	E16.2	246	E66.3	246	E87*	246, 283
E08.69	246	E16.3	247	E66.8	246	E88.01	247
E08.8	1, 2, 246	E16.4	115	E66.9	246	E88.09	304, 306
E08.9	1, 2, 246	E16.8	247	E67*	246	E88.1	247
E09.0*	1, 2, 246	E16.9	247	E68	246	E88.2	247
E09.1*	1, 2, 246	E20.[0,8,9]	283	E70*	247	E88.3	254, 283
E09.2*	1, 2, 256	E20.0	247	E71*	247	E88.4*	247
E09.3*	1, 2, 45	E20.1	246	E72*	247	E88.8*	247
E09.4*	1, 2, 34	E20.8	247	E73*	116	E88.9	247
E09.5*	2, 100	E20.9	247	E74.0*	247	E89.0	247
E09.6*	2	E21*	247	E74.1*	116	E89.1	2, 246
E09.610	34	E22*	247	E74.2*	247	E89.2	247, 283
E09.618	246	E23.2	283	E74.3*	116	E89.3	247
E09.62*	246	E23*	247	E74.4	247	E89.4*	264, 270
E09.63*	246	E24*	247	E74.8	247	E89.5	247
E09.64*	246	E25*	247	E74.9	247	E89.6	247
E09.65	246	E26*	247	E75.0*	32	E89.8*	367

Code	Page	Code	Page	Code	Page	Code	Page
F01*	310	F48.1	310	F98.29	311	G25.7*	32
F02*	310	F48.2	32	F98.3	311	G25.81	32
F03.90	439	F48.8	310	F98.4	311	G25.82	38
F03*	310	F48.9	310	F98.5	311	G25.83	38
F04	310	F50.0*	310	F98.8	311	G25.89	32
F05	310	F50.2	311	F98.9	311	G25.9	32
F06.8	439	F50.8	311	F99	310	G26	32
F06*	310	F50.9	311	G00.0	11, 15	G30*	32
F07.0	310	F51*	311	G00.1	11, 15	G31*	32
F07.81	41	F52.0	311	G00.2	11, 15	G32.0	38
F07.89	32	F52.1	311	G00.3	11, 15	G32.81	32
F07.9	310, 439	F52.2*	311	G00.8	11, 15	G32.89	33
F09	310, 439	F52.3*	311	G00.9	11, 15	G35	32
F11.[2,9]3	283	F52.4	311	G00*	41, 283	G36.9	439
F13.[2,9]3[0,1,2,9]	283	F52.5	264, 270	G01	11, 15, 41, 283	G36*	33
F14.23	283	F52.6	311	G02	11, 15, 41, 283	G37.0	33
F15.[2,9]3	283	F52.8	311	G03.0	41, 283	G37.1	33
F17.2[0,1,2,9][0,1]	412	F52.9	311	G03.1	41	G37.2	33
F17.2[0,1,2,9]3	283	F53	310	G03.2	35	G37.3	11, 15, 41
F19.[2,9]3[0,1,2,9]	283	F54	310	G03.8	41, 283	G37.4	11, 15, 41, 439
F20*	310	F59	311	G03.9	41, 283	G37.5	33
F21	310	F60*	310	G04.0*	11, 15, 41	G37.8	33
F22	310	F63.0	310	G04.1	32	G37.9	33, 439
F23	310	F63.1	311	G04.2	11, 15, 41, 283	G40*	41
F24	310	F63.2	310	G04.3*	11, 15, 41	G43*	41
F25*	311	F63.3	310	G04.8*	11, 15, 41, 439	G44*	41
F28	311, 439	F63.8*	310	G04.9*	11, 15, 41, 439	G45.0	33
F29	311, 439	F63.9	311	G05.3	11, 15	G45.1	33
F30*	311	F64*	311	G05.4	11, 15	G45.2	33
F31*	311	F65*	311	G05*	41	G45.3	45
F32.0	311	F66	311	G06.0	11, 15	G45.4	33
F32.1	311	F68.1[0,2]	310	G06.1	11, 15	G45.8	33
F32.2	311	F68.11	310	G06.2	11, 15	G45.9	33
F32.3	311	F68.13	310	G06*	41, 283	G46.0	33
F32.4	311	F68.8	310	G07	11, 15, 41, 283	G46.1	33
F32.5	311	F69	310	G08	11, 15, 38	G46.2	33
F32.8	311	F70	310	G09	38	G46.3	33
F32.9	310	F71	310	G10	32	G46.4	33
F33*	311	F72	310	G11*	32	G46.5	33
F34.0	310	F73	310	G12*	32	G46.6	33
F34.1	310	F78	310	G13.0	34	G46.7	33
F34.8	311	F79	310	G13.1	34	G46.8	33
F34.9	311	F80.0	311	G13.2	32	G47.0*	311
F39	311	F80.1	311	G13.8	32	G47.1*	311
F40*	310	F80.2	311	G14	38	G47.2*	3, 38
F41*	310	F80.4	311	G20	32	G47.3*	3
F42	310	F80.81	38	G21.0	38	G47.30	58
F43.0	310	F80.89	311	G21.1*	32	G47.31	38
F43.1*	310	F80.9	311	G21.2	32	G47.32	69
F43.20	310	F81*	311	G21.3	32	G47.33	58
F43.21	310	F82	311	G21.4	32	G47.34	58
F43.22	310	F84.0	310	G21.8	32	G47.35	38
F43.23	310	F84.2	32	G21.9	32	G47.36	58
F43.24	310	F84.3	310	G23*	32	G47.37	38
F43.25	310	F84.5	311	G24.0*	38	G47.39	58
F43.29	310	F84.8	311	G24.1	32	G47.4*	38
F43.8	310	F84.9	311	G24.2	38	G47.5*	3
F43.9	310	F88	311	G24.3	38	G47.50	58
F44.0	310	F89	311	G24.4	38	G47.51	38
F44.1	310	F90*	311	G24.5	45	G47.52	38
F44.2	310	F91*	311	G24.8	38	G47.53	38
F44.4	310	F93.0	310	G24.9	38	G47.54	58
F44.5	310	F93.8	311	G25.0	38	G47.59	58
F44.6	310	F93.9	311	G25.1	38	G47.6*	3
F44.7	310	F94*	311	G25.2	38	G47.61	38
F44.81	310	F95*	38	G25.3	38	G47.62	38
F44.89	311	F98.0	311	G25.4	32	G47.63	58
F44.9	310	F98.1	311	G25.5	32	G47.69	58
F45*	310	F98.21	310	G25.6*	38	G47.8	3, 58

Code	Page	Code	Page	Code	Page	Code	Page
I67.5	38	I82.8*	100	J05.1*	3	J37.1	4
I67.6	38	I82.9*	100	J05*	57	J37*	57
I67.7	41	I82.A*	100	J06.0	4	J38.0*	4, 284
I67.81	33	I82.B*	100	J06.9	4	J38.1	4
I67.82	33	I82.C*	100	J06*	57	J38.2	4
I67.83	33, 439	I83.0*	100	J09.X[1,2]	68, 284	J38.3	4
I67.841	33	I83.1*	100	J09.X[3,9]	308	J38.4	4
I67.848	33	I83.2*	100	J09.X1	439	J38.5	4, 284
I67.89	33	I83.8*	100	J10.00	66, 68	J38.6	4
I67.9	33	I83.9*	100	J10.01	66, 68	J38.7	4
I68.0	33	I85.0*	114	J10.08	66, 68, 284, 439	J38*	58
I68.2	41	I85.10	117	J10.1	68, 284	J39.0	4, 57, 284
I68.8	33	I85.11	114	J10.2	308	J39.1	4, 57
I69*	32	I86.0	100	J10.8*	308	J39.2	4, 58
I70.0	100	I86.1	261	J11.0*	68	J39.3	4, 57
I70.1	256	I86.2	261, 264, 270	J11.00	66	J39.8	4, 69
I70.2*	100	I86.3	264, 270	J11.08	66	J39.9	4, 57
I70.26[1,2,3,8,9]	284	I86.4	100	J11.1	57	J40	69
I70.3*	100	I86.8	100	J11.2	308	J41.0	69
I70.4*	100	I87.0*	100	J11.8*	308	J41.1	68
I70.5*	100	I87.1	100	J12.3	439	J41.8	68
I70.6*	100	I87.2	100	J12.8*	439	J42	68
I70.7*	100	I87.3*	100	J12.9	439	J43*	68
I70.8	100	I87.8	102	J12*	68	J44*	68
I70.9*	100	I87.9	102	J13	68, 284, 439	J45.[2,3]2	284
I71*	100	I88.0	117	J14	68, 284, 439	J45.[4,5]2	284
I72.[0,1,3,4,8,9]	100	I88.1	294	J15.0	66, 67, 439	J45.902	284
I72.2	256	I88.8	294	J15.1	66, 67, 439	J45*	69
I73.0*	164	I88.9	294	J15.2*	66, 67, 439	J47*	68
I73.1	100	I89.0	233	J15.3	68, 439	J60	68
I73.8*	100	I89.1	224, 284	J15.4	68, 439	J61	68
I73.9	100	I89.8	294	J15.5	66, 67, 439	J62*	68
I74*	100, 284	I89.9	294	J15.6	66, 67, 439	J63*	68
I75.0*	100	I95.0	103	J15.7	68	J64	68
I75.81	256	I95.1	102	J15.8	66, 67, 439	J65	68
I75.89	100	I95.2	102	J15.9	68, 439	J66*	68
I76	100, 284	I95.3	102	J15*	284	J67*	68
I77.0	100	I95.81	102	J16*	68, 284	J68.[0,2,3]	69
I77.1	100	I95.89	103	J17	67	J68.1	68
I77.2	100	I95.9	103	J18.[0,1,8]	284	J68.4	68
I77.3	100	I96	100, 284	J18.0	68	J68.8	68
I77.4	116	I97.0	103, 284	J18.1	68, 439	J68.9	68
I77.5	100	I97.1*	103, 284	J18.2	68	J69.[0,8]	284
I77.6	164	I97.2	224	J18.8	68, 439	J69*	67
I77.7[1,2,4,9]	100	I97.3	367	J18.9	68, 284, 439	J70.[2,3,4]	69
I77.73	256	I97.4*	367	J20*	69	J70.[5,8,9]	69
I77.8*	100	I97.5*	284, 367	J21*	69	J70.0	69, 284
I77.9	100	I97.6*	367	J22	69	J70.1	68
I78.0	100	I97.7*	103, 284	J30*	57	J70.5	381
I78.1	233	I97.81[0,1]	38	J31.1	4	J80	69
I78.8	100	I97.82[0,1]	38	J31.2	4	J81.0	284
I78.9	100	I97.88	103, 284	J31*	57	J81*	68
I79*	100	I97.89	103, 284	J32*	57	J82	68
I80.[8,9]	100	I99*	102	J33*	58	J84.83	284
I80.0*	100	J00	3, 57	J34.0	289	J84.84*	284
I80.1*	99, 284	J01*	57	J34.1	289	J84*	68
I80.2*	99, 284	J02.0	3	J34.2	4	J85*	67, 284
I80.3	99, 284	J02.8	3	J34.81	289	J86*	67, 284
I81	124	J02.9	3	J34.89	289	J90	68, 284
I82.0	124	J02*	57	J34.9	289	J91.0	67
I82.1	100	J03.0*	3	J34*	58	J91.8	68, 284
I82.21[0,1]	100	J03.8*	3	J35.0*	4, 57	J92*	68
I82.22[0,1]	99, 284	J03.9*	3	J35.1	4, 58	J93*	68
I82.29[0,1]	100	J03*	57	J35.2	4, 58	J94.0	68, 284
I82.3	256	J04.0	3, 57	J35.3	4, 58	J94.1	68
I82.4*	100	J04.1*	69	J35.8	4, 58	J94.2	68, 284
I82.5*	100	J04.2	3, 57	J35.9	4, 58	J94.8	68, 284
I82.6*	100	J04.3*	3, 57	J36	4, 57	J94.9	68
I82.7*	100	J05.0	3	J37.0	4	J95.0*	4, 69

Code	Page	Code	Page	Code	Page	Code	Page
J95.1	68, 284, 381	K04.5	4	K20*	116	K31.811	115
J95.2	68, 284, 381	K04.6	4	K21*	116	K31.819	116
J95.3	68, 284, 381	K04.7	4	K22.0	116	K31.82	115
J95.4	69, 284	K04.8	4	K22.1*	115	K31.83	116
J95.5	69, 284	K04.9*	4	K22.2	116	K31.84	116
J95.6*	367	K04*	59	K22.3	114, 284	K31.89	116
J95.7*	284, 367	K05.0*	4	K22.4	116	K31.9	116
J95.81*	68	K05.1*	4	K22.5	116	K35.2	108, 114
J95.82*	68, 381	K05.2*	4	K22.6	114	K35.3	108, 114
J95.830	367	K05.3*	4	K22.7*	115	K35.8*	117
J95.831	367	K05.4	4	K22.8	116	K36	117
J95.84	69	K05.5	4	K22.9	116	K37	117
J95.850	412	K05.6	4	K23	116	K38*	117
J95.851	69, 284	K05*	59	K25.0	115	K40.[0,1]0	284
J95.859	69, 284	K06.0	4	K25.1	115	K40.[3,4]0	284
J95.88	69, 284	K06.1	4	K25.2	115	K40*	117
J95.89	69, 284	K06.2	4	K25.3	115	K41.[0,1]0	284
J96.0*	381	K06.8	4	K25.4	115	K41.[3,4]0	284
J96.2*	381	K06.9	4	K25.5	115	K41*	117
J96.9*	381	K06*	59	K25.6	115	K42.[0,1]	284
J96*	68	K08.0	4	K25.7	115	K42*	117
J98.0*	4, 69	K08.1*	4	K25.9	115	K43.[0,1]	284
J98.1*	69	K08.2*	4	K26.0	115	K43.[3,4]	284
J98.11	284	K08.3	4	K26.1	115	K43.[6,7]	284
J98.19	284	K08.4*	4	K26.2	115	K43*	117
J98.2	68, 284	K08.5*	4	K26.3	115	K44.[0,1]	284
J98.3	69	K08.8	4	K26.4	115	K44.0	116
J98.4	69	K08.9	4	K26.5	115	K44.1	117
J98.5	67, 284	K08*	59	K26.6	115	K44.9	116
J98.6	69	K09.0	4	K26.7	115	K45.[0,1]	284
J98.8	69	K09.1	4	K26.9	115	K45*	117
J98.9	69	K09.8	4	K27.0	115	K46.[0,1]	284
J99	68	K09.9	4	K27.1	115	K46*	117
K00.0	4	K09*	59	K27.2	115	K50*	116
K00.1	4	K11.0	4	K27.3	115	K51*	116
K00.2	4	K11.1	4	K27.4	115	K52.0	117
K00.3	4	K11.2*	4	K27.5	115	K52.1	117, 284
K00.4	4	K11.3	4	K27.6	115	K52.2	116
K00.5	4	K11.4	4	K27.7	115	K52.8*	116
K00.6	4, 289	K11.5	4	K27.9	115	K52.9	116
K00.7	4	K11.6	4	K28.0	115	K55.0	117, 284
K00.8	4	K11.7	4	K28.1	115	K55.1	117
K00.9	4	K11.8	4	K28.2	115	K55.20	117
K00*	59	K11.9	4	K28.3	115	K55.21	115
K01.0	4, 289	K11*	58	K28.4	115	K55.8	117
K01.1	4, 289	K12.0	4	K28.5	115	K55.9	117
K01*	59	K12.1	4	K28.6	115	K56.0	284
K02.3	4	K12.2	4	K28.7	115	K56.1	284
K02.5*	4	K12.3*	4	K28.9	115	K56.2	284
K02.6*	4	K12*	59	K29.[0,2,3,4,5,6,7]0	116	K56.4*	284
K02.7	4	K13.0	4	K29.[8,9]0	116	K56.6*	284
K02.9	4	K13.1	4	K29.01	115	K56.7	284
K02*	59	K13.2*	4	K29.21	115	K56*	116
K03.0	4	K13.3	4	K29.31	115	K57.00	116
K03.1	4	K13.4	4	K29.41	115	K57.01	115
K03.2	4	K13.5	4	K29.51	115	K57.1[0,2]	116
K03.3	4	K13.6	4	K29.61	115	K57.1[1,3]	115
K03.4	4	K13.7*	4	K29.71	115	K57.20	116
K03.5	4	K13*	59	K29.81	115	K57.21	115
K03.6	4	K14.0	4	K29.91	115	K57.3[0,2]	116
K03.7	4	K14.1	4	K30	116	K57.3[1,3]	115
K03.8*	4	K14.2	4	K31.0	116, 284	K57.40	116
K03.9	4	K14.3	4	K31.1	115	K57.41	115
K03*	59	K14.4	4	K31.2	116	K57.5[0,2]	116
K04.0	4	K14.5	4	K31.3	116	K57.5[1,3]	115
K04.1	4	K14.6	4	K31.4	116	K57.80	116
K04.2	4	K14.8	4	K31.5	115	K57.81	115
K04.3	4	K14.9	4	K31.6	116	K57.9[0,2]	116
K04.4	4	K14*	59	K31.7	117	K57.9[1,3]	115

Code	Page	Code	Page	Code	Page	Code	Page
K58*	116	K75*	124	L02.81*	284	L44.9	234
K59.0*	116	K76.0	124	L02.811	206	L45	234
K59.1	116	K76.1	124	L02.818	206	L49*	234
K59.2	116	K76.2	124, 284	L02.91	206, 284	L50.0	284
K59.3	117	K76.3	124, 284	L02*	224	L50*	284
K59.4	116	K76.4	124, 284	L03.1*	284	L51*	223
K59.8	116	K76.5	124	L03.2*	4, 284	L52	223
K59.9	116	K76.6	124	L03.3*	284	L53.0	223, 284
K60*	117	K76.7	124, 284	L03.8*	284	L53.1	223, 284
K61*	117, 284	K76.81	69	L03.9*	284	L53.2	223, 284
K62.0	117	K76.89	124	L03*	206, 224	L53.3	223, 284
K62.1	117	K76.9	124	L04.0	294	L53.8	234
K62.2	117	K77	124	L04.1	294	L53.9	234
K62.3	117	K80*	124	L04.2	294	L54	234
K62.4	117	K81*	124	L04.3	294	L55*	234
K62.5	115, 284	K82*	124	L04.8	294	L56*	234
K62.6	117	K83.0	284	L04.9	294	L57.3	289
K62.7	117	K83*	124	L04*	284	L57*	234
K62.8*	117	K85*	124, 284	L05*	224	L58*	234
K62.9	117	K86.[2,3]	284	L08.0	224	L59*	234
K63.0	114	K86*	124	L08.1	233, 439	L60*	234
K63.1	117, 284	K87	124	L08.8*	224	L62	234
K63.2	117	K90.0	116	L08.9	224, 289	L63*	234
K63.3	117	K90.1	116	L10*	223	L64*	234
K63.4	117	K90.2	116	L11*	233	L65*	234
K63.5	117	K90.3	116	L12.0	223	L66*	234
K63.8*	117	K90.4	116	L12.1	223	L67*	234
K63.9	117	K90.81	117	L12.2	233	L68*	234
K64*	117	K90.89	116	L12.3*	223	L70*	234
K65.0	114	K90.9	116	L12.8	223	L71*	234
K65.1	114	K91.0	116	L12.9	223	L72*	234
K65.2	114	K91.1	116	L13.0	233	L73*	234
K65.3	117	K91.2	116, 284	L13.1	233	L74*	234
K65.4	117	K91.3	117, 284	L13.8	223	L75*	234
K65.8	114	K91.5	124	L13.9	223	L76.1*	284
K65.9	114	K91.6*	367	L14	223	L76*	367
K65*	284	K91.7*	284, 367	L20*	233	L80	234, 289
K66.1	284	K91.81	117, 284	L21*	233	L81.0	289
K66*	117	K91.82	117, 284	L22	233, 289	L81.1	289
K67	114, 284	K91.83	117, 284	L23*	233	L81.2	289
K68.11	307	K91.840	367	L24*	233	L81.3	289
K68.12	114	K91.841	367	L25*	233	L81.4	289
K68.19	114	K91.850	117, 284	L26	233	L81.5	289
K68.9	114	K91.858	117, 284	L27.0	284	L81.6	289
K68*	284	K91.86	117, 284	L27.1	284	L81.7	289
K70.0	124	K91.89	117, 284	L27*	233	L81.8	289
K70.1*	123	K92.0	115, 284	L28*	233	L81.9	289
K70.2	123	K92.1	115, 284	L29.0	234	L81*	234
K70.3*	123	K92.2	115, 284	L29.1	261	L82*	234
K70.4*	123	K92.81	116	L29.2	264, 269	L83	234
K70.9	123	K92.89	117	L29.3	261, 264, 269	L84	234
K71*	124, 284	K92.9	117	L29.8	234	L85*	234
K72.0*	284	K94*	117	L29.9	234	L86	234
K72.9*	284	K95*	117	L30*	234	L87*	234
K72*	124	L00	223	L40.0	223	L88	224
K73*	124	L01*	224	L40.1	234	L89*	206, 223
K74.0	123	L02.[0,1]1	284	L40.2	223	L90*	234
K74.1	124	L02.01	4, 206	L40.3	223	L91*	234
K74.2	124	L02.11	4, 206	L40.4	223	L92.0	234
K74.3	123	L02.21[1,2,3,4,5,6,9]	206	L40.5*	164	L92.1	234
K74.4	123	L02.21*	284	L40.8	223	L92.2	234
K74.5	123	L02.31	206, 284	L40.9	223	L92.3	234
K74.6*	123	L02.41[1,2]	206	L41*	223	L92.8	224
K75.0	284	L02.41[3,4,5,6,9]	206	L42	234	L92.9	234
K75.1	284	L02.41*	284	L43*	234	L93*	223
K75.2	284	L02.51[1,2,9]	206	L44.[1,2,3]	234	L94.0	234
K75.3	284	L02.51*	284	L44.0	234	L94.1	234
K75.8*	284	L02.61[1,2,9]	206	L44.4	308	L94.2	234
K75.9	284	L02.61*	284	L44.8	234	L94.3	234

Code	Page	Code	Page	Code	Page	Code	Page
L94.4	234	M06.8*	164	M24.30	184	M31.6	164
L94.5	223	M06.9	164	M24.35[1,2,9]	193	M31.7	164
L94.6	309	M07*	166	M24.37[1,2,3]	184	M31.8	100
L94.8	234	M08*	164	M24.37[4,5,6]	184	M31.9	100
L94.9	234	M10.0*	166	M24.4[1,2,3][1,2,9]	184	M32*	164
L95*	234	M10.1*	166	M24.40	194	M33*	164
L97*	206, 223	M10.2*	166	M24.44[1,2,3]	184	M34.0	164
L98.[6,8,9]	234	M10.3*	256	M24.44[4,5,6]	184	M34.1	164
L98.0	224	M10.4*	166	M24.45[1,2,9]	194	M34.2	164
L98.1	234	M10.9	166	M24.46[1,2,9]	184	M34.81	68
L98.2	234	M11*	166	M24.47[1,2,3]	184	M34.82	164
L98.3	206, 224, 284	M12*	167	M24.47[4,5,6]	184	M34.83	34
L98.4*	206, 223	M13*	167	M24.47[7,8,9]	184	M34.89	164
L98.5	234	M14*	167	M24.5*	194	M34.9	164
L99	234	M15*	167	M24.6*	167	M35.0*	164
M00.00	164	M16*	167	M24.7	194	M35.1	164
M00.011	164	M17*	167	M24.8*	194	M35.2	164
M00.012	164	M18*	167	M24.9	194	M35.3	164
M00.019	164	M19*	167	M25.0*	167	M35.4	167
M00.021	164	M1A.0*	167	M25.1*	167	M35.5	164
M00.022	164	M1A.1*	362	M25.2*	194	M35.6	234
M00.029	164	M1A.2*	167	M25.3*	194	M35.7	167
M00.031	164	M1A.3*	167	M25.4*	194	M35.8	164
M00.032	164	M1A.4*	167	M25.5*	167	M35.9	164
M00.039	164	M1A.9*	167	M25.6*	167	M36.0	164
M00.041	164	M20.[1,2,3][0,1,2]	193	M25.70	167	M36.1	167
M00.042	164	M20.0[0,1,2,3,9][1,2,9]	193	M25.71[1,2,9]	167	M36.2	167
M00.049	164	M20.4[0,1,2]	193	M25.72[1,2,9]	167	M36.3	167
M00.051	164	M20.5X[1,2,9]	193	M25.73[1,2,9]	167	M36.4	167
M00.052	164	M20.6[0,1,2]	193	M25.74[1,2,9]	167	M36.8	164
M00.059	164	M21.0[2,5,6,7][1,2,9]	193	M25.75[1,2,9]	167	M40.0*	125
M00.06*	131	M21.00	193	M25.76[1,2,9]	167	M40.1*	126
M00.061	164	M21.1[2,5,6,7][1,2,9]	193	M25.77[1,2,3]	167	M40.2*	125
M00.062	164	M21.10	193	M25.77[4,5,6]	167	M40.3*	125
M00.069	164	M21.2[1,2,3,4,5,6,7][1,2,9]	193	M25.78	164	M40.4*	125
M00.071	164	M21.20	193	M25.8*	167	M40.5*	125, 126
M00.072	164	M21.33[1,2,9]	34	M25.9	167	M40*	164
M00.079	164	M21.37[1,2,9]	193	M26.0*	4	M41.0*	125
M00.08	164	M21.4[0,1,2]	193	M26.1*	4	M41.1*	125
M00.09	164	M21.5[1,2][1,2,9]	34	M26.2*	4	M41.2*	125
M00.1*	164	M21.53[1,2,9]	34	M26.3*	4	M41.3*	125
M00.16[1,2,9]	131	M21.54[1,2,9]	193	M26.4	4	M41.4*	126
M00.2*	164	M21.6X[1,2,9]	193	M26.5*	4	M41.5*	126
M00.26[1,2,9]	131	M21.70	193	M26.6*	4	M41.8*	125
M00.8*	164	M21.72[1,2,9]	193	M26.7*	4	M41.9	125
M00.86[1,2,9]	131	M21.73[1,2,3,4,9]	193	M26.8*	4	M41*	164
M00.9	164	M21.75[1,2,9]	193	M26.9	4	M42.0*	125
M01*	164	M21.76[1,2,3,4,9]	193	M26*	59	M42*	167
M02.0*	166	M21.8[2,3,5,6][1,2,9]	193	M27.0	4	M43.0*	164
M02.1*	166	M21.80	193	M27.1	4	M43.1*	164
M02.2*	166	M21.9[2,3,4,5,6][1,2,9]	193	M27.2	4	M43.2*	164
M02.3*	164	M21.90	193	M27.3	4	M43.3	194
M02.8*	164	M22*	184	M27.4*	4	M43.4	194
M02.9	166	M23.0*	184	M27.5*	4	M43.5*	194
M05.0*	164	M23.2*	184	M27.6*	4	M43.6	164
M05.1*	68	M23.3*	184	M27.8	4	M43.8*	125, 164
M05.2*	164	M23.4*	193	M27.9	4	M43.8X9	126
M05.3*	164	M23.5*	193	M27*	59	M43.9	125, 164
M05.4*	164	M23.6*	184	M30.0	164	M45*	164
M05.5*	164	M23.8*	184	M30.1	163	M46.0*	164
M05.6*	164	M23.9*	184	M30.2	164	M46.1	164
M05.7*	164	M24.0*	193	M30.3	164	M46.2*	125, 163
M05.8*	164	M24.1[1,2,3,4][1,2,9]	184	M30.8	164	M46.3*	163
M05.9	164	M24.10	193	M31.0	164	M46.4*	164
M06.0*	164	M24.15[1,2,9]	193	M31.1	164	M46.5*	164
M06.1	164	M24.17[1,2,3]	184	M31.2	163	M46.8*	164
M06.2*	164	M24.17[4,5,6]	184	M31.3*	163	M46.9*	164
M06.3*	164	M24.2*	167	M31.4	164	M47*	164
M06.4	166	M24.3[1,2,3,4,6][1,2,9]	184	M31.5	164	M48.0*	164

Numeric Index to Diseases

Code	Page	Code	Page	Code	Page	Code	Page
P11.2	282	P54.0	288	P83.3*	288	Q18.6	59
P11.3	288	P54.1	282	P83.4	288	Q18.7	59
P11.4	282	P54.2	282	P83.5	288	Q18.8	58
P11.5	282	P54.3	282	P83.6	289	Q18.9	234
P11.9	282	P54.4	282	P83.8	289	Q20*	102
P12.0	288	P54.5	289	P83.9	288	Q21.0	285
P12.1	288	P54.6	288	P84	288	Q21*	102
P12.2	282	P54.8	288	P90	282	Q22*	102
P12.3	288	P54.9	288	P91.0	282	Q23*	102
P12.4	289	P55.0	288	P91.1	282	Q24.0	102
P12.81	289	P55.1	288	P91.2	38, 285	Q24.1	102
P12.89	289	P55.8	282	P91.3	282	Q24.2	102
P12.9	289	P55.9	288	P91.4	282	Q24.3	102
P13*	288	P56*	282	P91.5	282	Q24.4	102
P14.0	288	P57*	282	P91.6[2,3]	282	Q24.5	102
P14.1	288	P58*	288	P91.60	288	Q24.6	102
P14.2	282	P59.0	288	P91.61	288	Q24.8	102
P14.3	288	P59.1	282	P91.8	282	Q24.9	102
P14.8	282	P59.2*	282	P91.9	282	Q25*	102
P14.9	282	P59.3	289	P92.01	282	Q26.0	102
P15*	288	P59.8	289	P92.09	289	Q26.1	102
P19*	288	P59.9	289	P92.1	289	Q26.2	102
P22.0	282	P60	282	P92.2	289	Q26.3	102
P22.1	288	P61.0	282	P92.3	289	Q26.4	102
P22.8	288	P61.1	288	P92.4	289	Q26.5	100
P22.9	288	P61.2	282	P92.5	289	Q26.6	100
P23*	282	P61.3	288	P92.6	246	Q26.8	102
P24*	282	P61.4	288	P92.8	289	Q26.9	102
P25*	282	P61.5	288	P92.9	289	Q27*	100
P26*	282	P61.6	282	P93*	282	Q28.[0,1]	100
P27*	68	P61.8	288	P94.0	282	Q28.[8,9]	100
P28.0	282	P61.9	288	P94.1	288	Q28.2	38
P28.1*	288	P70.0	288	P94.2	288	Q28.3	38
P28.2	288	P70.1	288	P94.8	288	Q30*	58
P28.3	288	P70.2	282	P94.9	288	Q31.0	4
P28.4	288	P70.3	282	P95	288	Q31.1	4
P28.5	282	P70.4	282	P96.0	288	Q31.2	4
P28.8*	288	P70.8	288	P96.1	282	Q31.3	4
P28.9	288	P70.9	288	P96.2	282	Q31.5	4
P29.0	288	P71*	282	P96.3	288	Q31.8	4
P29.1*	288	P72.0	288	P96.5	288	Q31.9	4
P29.2	288	P72.1	282	P96.81	288	Q31*	58
P29.3	282	P72.2	288	P96.82	289	Q32.0	4
P29.4	288	P72.8	288	P96.83	288	Q32.1	4
P29.81	282	P72.9	288	P96.89	288	Q32.2	4
P29.89	288	P74.[0,1,2,3,4]	282	P96.9	288	Q32.3	4
P29.9	288	P74.5	288	Q00*	38, 285	Q32.4	4
P35*	282	P74.6	288	Q01*	38, 285	Q32*	58
P36*	282	P74.8	288	Q02	38, 285	Q33.0	69
P37.0	282	P74.9	288	Q03*	38, 285	Q33.1	69
P37.1	282	P76.0	282	Q04*	38, 285	Q33.2	69
P37.2	282	P76.1	288	Q05*	38, 285	Q33.3	69
P37.3	282	P76.2	282	Q06*	38, 285	Q33.4	68
P37.4	282	P76.8	288	Q07*	38, 285	Q33.5	69
P37.5	288	P76.9	288	Q10*	46	Q33.6	69
P37.8	282	P77*	282	Q11*	46	Q33.8	69
P37.9	282	P78.0	282	Q12*	46	Q33.9	69
P38*	282	P78.1	288	Q13*	46	Q34*	69
P39.0	282	P78.2	288	Q14*	46	Q35.1	4
P39.1	288	P78.3	288	Q15*	46	Q35.3	4
P39.2	282	P78.8*	288	Q16*	58	Q35.5	4
P39.3	282	P78.9	288	Q17.0	289	Q35.7	4
P39.4	282	P80.0	288	Q17*	58	Q35.9	5
P39.8	282	P80.8	288	Q18.0	58	Q35*	59
P39.9	282	P80.9	288	Q18.1	58	Q36.0	5
P50*	282	P81*	288	Q18.2	58	Q36.1	5
P51*	288	P83.0	288	Q18.3	234	Q36.9	5
P52*	282	P83.1	289	Q18.4	59	Q36*	59
P53	282	P83.2	282	Q18.5	59	Q37.0	5

Code	Page	Code	Page	Code	Page	Code	Page
S00.03X[A,S]	224	S00.96XS	224	S01.9[0,1,2,3,4,5]XD	386	S02.42XS	39
S00.04X[A,S]	224	S00.97X[A,S]	224	S01.9[1,2]X[A,S]	224	S02.5XX[A,B]	59, 417
S00.05X[A,S]	224	S01.0[0,1,2,3,4,5]XA	417	S01.9[3,4]X[A,S]	224	S02.5XX[D,G]	169
S00.06XS	224	S01.0[0,1,2,3,4,5]XD	386	S01.90X[A,S]	224	S02.5XXK	195
S00.07X[A,S]	224	S01.0[1,2]X[A,S]	224	S01.95X[A,S]	224	S02.5XXS	39
S00.1[0,1,2]XA	46, 417	S01.0[3,4]X[A,S]	224	S02.[2,3]XX[D,G]	169	S02.6[1,2,3,4,5,6,7,9]XK	195
S00.1[0,1,2]XD	386	S01.00X[A,S]	224	S02.[2,3]XXK	195	S02.6[1,2,3]X[A,B]	417
S00.1[0,1,2]XS	224	S01.05X[A,S]	224	S02.0XX[A,B]	36, 37, 417	S02.6[1,2,3]X[D,G]	169
S00.2[0,1,2,4,5,6,7][1,2,9]A	417	S01.1[0,1,2,3,4,5][1,2,9]A	417	S02.0XX[D,G]	169	S02.6[1,2,3]XS	39
S00.2[0,1,2,4,5,6,7][1,2,9]D	386	S01.1[0,1,2,3,4,5][1,2,9]D	386	S02.0XXK	195	S02.6[4,5,6,7,9]X[A,B]	417
S00.20[1,2,9]A	46	S01.1[1,2][1,2,9]S	224	S02.0XXS	39	S02.6[4,5,6,7,9]X[D,G]	169
S00.20[1,2,9]S	224	S01.1[3,4][1,2,9]S	224	S02.10X[A,B]	36, 37, 417	S02.6[4,5,6,7,9]XS	39
S00.21[1,2,9]A	46	S01.10[1,2,9]A	46	S02.10X[D,G]	169	S02.60[0,9]K	195
S00.21[1,2,9]S	224	S01.10[1,2,9]S	224	S02.10XB	430	S02.600[A,B]	59, 417
S00.22[1,2,9]A	46	S01.11[1,2,9]A	46	S02.10XK	195	S02.600[D,G]	169
S00.22[1,2,9]S	224	S01.12[1,2,9]A	46	S02.10XS	39	S02.600A	5
S00.24[1,2,9]A	46	S01.13[1,2,9]A	46	S02.11[0,1,2,3][A,B]	417	S02.600B	5
S00.24[1,2,9]S	224	S01.14[1,2,9]A	46	S02.11[0,1,2,3][D,G]	169	S02.600S	39
S00.25[1,2,9]A	46	S01.15[1,2,9]A	46	S02.11[0,1,2,3]A	36, 37	S02.609[A,B]	59, 417
S00.25[1,2,9]S	224	S01.15[1,2,9]S	224	S02.11[0,1,2,3]B	36, 37	S02.609[D,G]	169
S00.26[1,2,9]A	46	S01.2[0,1,2,3,4,5]XA	417	S02.11[0,1,2,3]K	195	S02.609A	5
S00.26[1,2,9]S	224	S01.2[0,1,2,3,4,5]XD	386	S02.11[0,1,2,3]S	39	S02.609B	5
S00.27[1,2,9]A	46	S01.2[1,2,3,4]XS	224	S02.11[8,9][A,B]	417	S02.609S	39
S00.27[1,2,9]S	224	S01.2[1,2]XA	58	S02.11[8,9][D,G]	169	S02.61X[A,B]	59
S00.3[0,1,2,3,4,5,6,7]XA	417	S01.2[3,4]XA	58	S02.11[8,9]A	36, 37	S02.61XA	5
S00.3[0,1,2,3,4,5,6,7]XD	386	S01.20XA	5, 58	S02.11[8,9]B	36, 37	S02.61XB	5
S00.3[0,1]X[A,S]	224	S01.20XS	224	S02.11[8,9]K	195	S02.62X[A,B]	59
S00.3[2,6]XA	234	S01.21XA	5	S02.11[8,9]S	39	S02.62XA	5
S00.3[3,4]X[A,S]	224	S01.22XA	5	S02.19X[A,B]	36, 37, 417	S02.62XB	5
S00.32XS	224	S01.23XA	5	S02.19X[D,G]	169	S02.63X[A,B]	59
S00.35X[A,S]	224	S01.24XA	5	S02.19XK	195	S02.63XA	5
S00.36XS	224	S01.25XA	5, 58	S02.19XS	39	S02.63XB	5
S00.37X[A,S]	224	S01.25XS	224	S02.2XX[A,B]	58, 417	S02.64X[A,B]	59
S00.4[0,1,2,3,4,5,6,7][1,2,9]A	417	S01.3[0,1,2,3,4,5][1,2,9]A	58, 417	S02.2XXS	39	S02.64XA	5
S00.4[0,1,2,3,4,5,6,7][1,2,9]D	386	S01.3[0,1,2,3,4,5][1,2,9]D	386	S02.3XX[A,B]	46, 417	S02.64XB	5
S00.4[2,6][1,2,9]A	234	S01.3[1,2][1,2,9]S	224	S02.3XXA	5	S02.65X[A,B]	59
S00.40[1,2,9][A,S]	224	S01.3[3,4][1,2,9]S	224	S02.3XXB	5	S02.65XA	5
S00.41[1,2,9][A,S]	224	S01.30[1,2,9]S	224	S02.3XXS	39	S02.65XB	5
S00.42[1,2,9]S	224	S01.35[1,2,9]S	224	S02.40[0,1,2][A,B]	417	S02.66X[A,B]	59
S00.43[1,2,9][A,S]	224	S01.4[0,1,2,3,4,5][1,2,9]A	417	S02.40[0,1,2][D,G]	169	S02.66XA	5
S00.44[1,2,9][A,S]	224	S01.4[0,1,2,3,4,5][1,2,9]D	386	S02.40[0,1,2]K	195	S02.66XB	5
S00.45[1,2,9][A,S]	224	S01.4[0,1,2,3,4,5]1A	5	S02.40[0,1,2]S	39	S02.67X[A,B]	59
S00.46[1,2,9]S	224	S01.4[0,1,2,3,4,5]2A	5	S02.400[A,B]	59	S02.67XA	5
S00.47[1,2,9][A,S]	224	S01.4[0,1,2,3,4,5]9A	5	S02.400A	5	S02.67XB	5
S00.5[0,1,2,3,4,5,6,7][1,2]A	417	S01.4[1,2][1,2,9][A,S]	224	S02.400B	5	S02.69X[A,B]	59
S00.5[0,1,2,3,4,5,6,7][1,2]D	386	S01.4[3,4][1,2,9][A,S]	224	S02.401[A,B]	59	S02.69XA	5
S00.5[2,6][1,2]A	234	S01.40[1,2,9][A,S]	224	S02.401A	5	S02.69XB	5
S00.50[1,2][A,S]	224	S01.45[1,2,9][A,S]	224	S02.401B	5	S02.8XX[A,B,K]	195
S00.51[1,2][A,S]	224	S01.5[0,1,2,3,4,5][1,2]A	417	S02.402[A,B]	59	S02.8XX[A,B]	417
S00.52[1,2]S	224	S01.5[0,1,2,3,4,5][1,2]D	386	S02.402A	5	S02.8XX[D,G]	169
S00.53[1,2][A,S]	224	S01.5[0,1,2,3,4,5]1A	5	S02.402B	5	S02.8XXA	5
S00.54[1,2][A,S]	224	S01.5[0,1,2,3,4,5]2A	5	S02.41[1,2,3][A,B]	417	S02.8XXB	5
S00.55[1,2][A,S]	224	S01.5[1,2][1,2]S	224	S02.41[1,2,3][D,G]	169	S02.8XXS	39
S00.56[1,2]S	224	S01.5[3,4][1,2]S	224	S02.41[1,2,3]K	195	S02.9[1,2]X[D,G]	169
S00.57[1,2][A,S]	224	S01.50[1,2]A	59	S02.41[1,2,3]S	39	S02.91X[A,B]	36, 37, 417, 430
S00.8[0,1,2,3,4,5,6,7]XA	417	S01.50[1,2]S	224	S02.411[A,B]	59	S02.91XK	195
S00.8[0,1,2,3,4,5,6,7]XD	386	S01.51[1,2]A	59	S02.411A	5	S02.91XS	39
S00.8[0,1]X[A,S]	224	S01.52[1,2]A	59	S02.411B	5	S02.92X[A,B,K]	195
S00.8[3,4]X[A,S]	224	S01.53[1,2]A	59	S02.412[A,B]	59	S02.92X[A,B]	417
S00.82XS	224	S01.54[1,2]A	59	S02.412A	5	S02.92XA	5
S00.85X[A,S]	224	S01.55[1,2]A	59	S02.412B	5	S02.92XB	5
S00.86XS	224	S01.55[1,2]S	224	S02.413[A,B]	59	S02.92XS	39
S00.87X[A,S]	224	S01.8[0,1,2,3,4,5]XA	417	S02.413A	5	S03.[0,1,2]XXA	417
S00.9[0,1,2,3,4,5,6,7]XA	417	S01.8[0,1,2,3,4,5]XD	386	S02.413B	5	S03.[0,1,2]XXD	386
S00.9[0,1,2,3,4,5,6,7]XD	386	S01.8[1,2]X[A,S]	224	S02.42X[A,B,K]	195	S03.[8,9]XXA	417
S00.9[0,1]X[A,S]	224	S01.8[3,4]X[A,S]	224	S02.42X[A,B]	417	S03.[8,9]XXD	386
S00.9[3,4]X[A,S]	224	S01.80X[A,S]	224	S02.42X[D,G]	169	S03.0XXA	5, 59
S00.92XS	224	S01.85X[A,S]	224	S02.42XA	5	S03.0XXS	184
S00.95X[A,S]	224	S01.9[0,1,2,3,4,5]XA	417	S02.42XB	5	S03.1XXA	184

Code	Page	Code	Page	Code	Page	Code	Page
S03.1XXS	184	S05.5[0,1,2]XA	47, 418	S06.3[4,5,6]3A	11, 15	S06.34[1,2,3,4]S	39
S03.2XXA	59	S05.5[0,1,2]XD	386	S06.3[4,5,6]4A	11, 15	S06.34[3,4,5,6]A	35
S03.2XXS	224	S05.6[0,1,2]XA	47, 418	S06.3[4,5,6]5A	11, 15	S06.34[5,6]A	36, 418, 431
S03.4XXA	59, 417	S05.6[0,1,2]XD	386	S06.3[4,5,6]6A	11, 15	S06.34[5,6]D	387
S03.4XXD	386	S05.7[0,1,2]XA	47, 418	S06.3[4,5,6]7A	11, 15	S06.34[5,6]S	39
S03.4XXS	184	S05.7[0,1,2]XD	386	S06.3[4,5,6]8A	11, 15	S06.34[7,8,9]A	35, 36, 418, 431
S03.8XXA	195	S05.7[0,1,2]XS	359	S06.3[4,5,6]9A	11, 15	S06.34[7,8,9]D	387
S03.8XXS	184	S05.8X[1,2,9]A	47, 418	S06.30[1,2,3,4]A	36, 418, 430	S06.34[7,8,9]S	39
S03.9XXA	184	S05.8X[1,2,9]D	386	S06.30[1,2,3,4]D	386	S06.340A	36, 37, 418, 431
S03.9XXS	184	S05.8X[1,2,9]S	359	S06.30[1,2,3,4]S	39	S06.340D	387
S04.[1,2,3,4,5,6,7][0,1,2]XA	417	S05.9[0,1,2]XA	47, 418	S06.30[3,4,5,6]A	35	S06.340S	39
S04.0[3,4][1,2,9]A	417	S05.9[0,1,2]XD	386	S06.30[5,6]A	36, 418, 430	S06.341A	37
S04.01[1,2,9]A	46, 417	S05.9[0,1,2]XS	359	S06.30[5,6]D	386	S06.342A	37
S04.01[1,2,9]D	386	S06.0X[1,2,3,4]A	38, 418	S06.30[5,6]S	39	S06.35[1,2,3,4]A	36, 418, 431
S04.01[1,2,9]S	39	S06.0X[1,2,3,4]D	386	S06.30[7,8,9]A	35, 36, 418, 430	S06.35[1,2,3,4]D	387
S04.02X[A,S]	39	S06.0X[1,2,3,4]S	39	S06.30[7,8,9]D	386	S06.35[1,2,3,4]S	39
S04.02XA	417	S06.0X[3,4]A	430	S06.30[7,8,9]S	39	S06.35[3,4,5,6]A	35
S04.02XD	386	S06.0X[5,6]A	38, 418, 430	S06.300A	36, 37, 418, 430	S06.35[5,6]A	36, 418, 431
S04.03[1,2,9]A	39	S06.0X[5,6]D	386	S06.300D	386	S06.35[5,6]D	387
S04.03[1,2,9]D	386	S06.0X[5,6]S	39	S06.300S	39	S06.35[5,6]S	39
S04.03[1,2,9]S	39	S06.0X[7,8,9]A	38, 418	S06.301A	37	S06.35[7,8,9]A	35, 36, 418, 431
S04.04[1,2,9]A	39	S06.0X[7,8,9]D	386	S06.302A	37	S06.35[7,8,9]D	387
S04.04[1,2,9]D	386	S06.0X[7,8,9]S	39	S06.31[1,2,3,4]A	36, 418, 430	S06.35[7,8,9]S	39
S04.04[1,2,9]S	39	S06.0X0A	38, 418	S06.31[1,2,3,4]D	386	S06.350A	36, 37, 418, 431
S04.1[0,1,2]XA	34	S06.0X0D	386	S06.31[1,2,3,4]S	39	S06.350D	387
S04.1[0,1,2]XD	386	S06.0X0S	39	S06.31[3,4,5,6]A	35	S06.350S	39
S04.1[0,1,2]XS	39	S06.1X[1,2,3,4]A	36, 418, 430	S06.31[5,6]A	36, 418, 431	S06.351A	37
S04.2[0,1,2]XA	34	S06.1X[1,2,3,4]D	386	S06.31[5,6]D	386	S06.352A	37
S04.2[0,1,2]XD	386	S06.1X[1,2,3,4]S	39	S06.31[5,6]S	39	S06.36[1,2,3,4]A	36, 418, 431
S04.2[0,1,2]XS	39	S06.1X[3,4,5,6]A	35	S06.31[7,8,9]A	35, 36, 418, 431	S06.36[1,2,3,4]D	387
S04.3[0,1,2]XA	34	S06.1X[5,6]A	36, 418, 430	S06.31[7,8,9]D	386	S06.36[1,2,3,4]S	39
S04.3[0,1,2]XD	386	S06.1X[5,6]D	386	S06.31[7,8,9]S	39	S06.36[3,4,5,6]A	35
S04.3[0,1,2]XS	39	S06.1X[5,6]S	39	S06.310A	36, 37, 418, 430	S06.36[5,6]A	36, 418, 431
S04.4[0,1,2]XA	34	S06.1X[7,8,9]A	35, 36, 418, 430	S06.310D	386	S06.36[5,6]D	387
S04.4[0,1,2]XD	386	S06.1X[7,8,9]D	386	S06.310S	39	S06.36[5,6]S	39
S04.4[0,1,2]XS	39	S06.1X[7,8,9]S	39	S06.311A	37	S06.36[7,8,9]A	35, 36, 418, 431
S04.5[0,1,2]XA	34	S06.1X0A	36, 37, 418, 430	S06.312A	37	S06.36[7,8,9]D	387
S04.5[0,1,2]XD	386	S06.1X0D	386	S06.32[1,2,3,4]A	36, 418, 431	S06.36[7,8,9]S	39
S04.5[0,1,2]XS	39	S06.1X0S	39	S06.32[1,2,3,4]D	386	S06.360A	36, 37, 418, 431
S04.6[0,1,2]XA	58	S06.1X1A	37	S06.32[1,2,3,4]S	39	S06.360D	387
S04.6[0,1,2]XD	386	S06.1X2A	37	S06.32[3,4,5,6]A	35	S06.360S	39
S04.6[0,1,2]XS	39	S06.2X[1,2,3,4]A	36, 418, 430	S06.32[5,6]A	36, 418, 431	S06.361A	37
S04.7[0,1,2]XA	34	S06.2X[1,2,3,4]D	386	S06.32[5,6]D	386	S06.362A	37
S04.7[0,1,2]XD	386	S06.2X[1,2,3,4]S	39	S06.32[5,6]S	39	S06.37[1,2,3,4]A	36, 418, 431
S04.7[0,1,2]XS	39	S06.2X[3,4,5,6]A	35	S06.32[7,8,9]A	35, 36, 418, 431	S06.37[1,2,3,4]D	387
S04.8[1,9][1,2,9]A	417	S06.2X[5,6]A	36, 418, 430	S06.32[7,8,9]D	387	S06.37[1,2,3,4]S	39
S04.8[1,9][1,2,9]D	386	S06.2X[5,6]D	386	S06.32[7,8,9]S	39	S06.37[3,4,5,6]A	35
S04.81[1,2,9]A	34	S06.2X[5,6]S	39	S06.320A	36, 37, 418, 431	S06.37[5,6]A	36, 418, 431
S04.81[1,2,9]S	39	S06.2X[7,8,9]A	35, 36, 418, 430	S06.320D	386	S06.37[5,6]D	387
S04.89[1,2,9]A	34	S06.2X[7,8,9]D	386	S06.320S	39	S06.37[5,6]S	39
S04.89[1,2,9]S	39	S06.2X[7,8,9]S	39	S06.321A	37	S06.37[7,8,9]A	35, 36, 418, 431
S04.9XXA	34, 417	S06.2X0A	36, 37, 418, 430	S06.322A	37	S06.37[7,8,9]D	387
S04.9XXD	386	S06.2X0D	386	S06.33[1,2,3,4]A	36, 418, 431	S06.37[7,8,9]S	39
S04.9XXS	39	S06.2X0S	39	S06.33[1,2,3,4]D	387	S06.370A	11, 15, 36, 37, 418, 431
S05.[2,3][0,1,2]XS	225	S06.2X1A	37	S06.33[1,2,3,4]S	39	S06.370D	387
S05.[5,6][0,1,2]XS	225	S06.2X2A	37	S06.33[3,4,5,6]A	35	S06.370S	39
S05.0[0,1,2]XA	46, 418	S06.3[1,2,3]0A	11, 15	S06.33[5,6]A	36, 418, 431	S06.371A	11, 15, 37
S05.0[0,1,2]XD	386	S06.3[1,2,3]1A	11, 15	S06.33[5,6]D	387	S06.372A	11, 15, 37
S05.0[0,1,2]XS	224	S06.3[1,2,3]2A	11, 15	S06.33[5,6]S	39	S06.373A	11, 15
S05.1[0,1,2]XA	46, 418	S06.3[1,2,3]3A	11, 15	S06.33[7,8,9]A	35, 36, 418, 431	S06.374A	11, 15
S05.1[0,1,2]XD	386	S06.3[1,2,3]4A	11, 15	S06.33[7,8,9]D	387	S06.375A	11, 15
S05.1[0,1,2]XS	225	S06.3[1,2,3]5A	11, 15	S06.33[7,8,9]S	39	S06.376A	11, 15
S05.2[0,1,2]XA	47, 418	S06.3[1,2,3]6A	11, 15	S06.330A	36, 37, 418, 431	S06.377A	11, 15
S05.2[0,1,2]XD	386	S06.3[1,2,3]7A	11, 15	S06.330D	387	S06.378A	11, 15
S05.3[0,1,2]XA	47, 418	S06.3[1,2,3]8A	11, 15	S06.330S	39	S06.379A	11, 15, 37
S05.3[0,1,2]XD	386	S06.3[1,2,3]9A	11, 15	S06.331A	37	S06.38[1,2,3,4]A	36, 418, 431
S05.4[0,1,2]XA	47, 418	S06.3[4,5,6]0A	11, 15	S06.332A	37	S06.38[1,2,3,4]D	387
S05.4[0,1,2]XD	386	S06.3[4,5,6]1A	11, 15	S06.34[1,2,3,4]A	36, 418, 431	S06.38[1,2,3,4]S	39
S05.4[0,1,2]XS	225	S06.3[4,5,6]2A	11, 15	S06.34[1,2,3,4]D	387	S06.38[3,4,5,6]A	35

Code	Page	Code	Page	Code	Page	Code	Page
S06.38[5,6]A	36, 418, 431	S06.6X9A	11, 15	S08.0XX[A,S]	225	S10.8[2,6]XA	234
S06.38[5,6]D	387	S06.81[1,2,3,4]A	37, 418, 431	S08.0XXA	419	S10.8[3,4]X[A,S]	225
S06.38[5,6]S	39	S06.81[1,2,3,4]D	387	S08.0XXD	387	S10.8[5,7]X[A,S]	225
S06.38[7,8,9]A	35, 36, 418, 431	S06.81[1,2,3,4]S	40	S08.1[1,2][1,2,9]A	419	S10.82XS	225
S06.38[7,8,9]D	387	S06.81[3,4,5,6]A	36	S08.1[1,2][1,2,9]D	387	S10.83XD	387
S06.38[7,8,9]S	39	S06.81[5,6]A	37, 418, 431	S08.1[1,2][1,2,9]S	225	S10.86XS	225
S06.380A	11, 15, 36, 37, 418, 431	S06.81[5,6]D	387	S08.11[1,2,9]A	58	S10.9[0,1,2,3,4,5,6,7]XA	419
S06.380D	387	S06.81[5,6]S	40	S08.121A	58	S10.9[0,1,2,4,5,6,7]XD	387
S06.380S	39	S06.81[7,8,9]A	36, 37, 419, 431	S08.122A	58	S10.9[0,1]X[A,S]	225
S06.381A	11, 15, 37	S06.81[7,8,9]D	387	S08.129A	58	S10.9[2,6]XA	234
S06.382A	11, 15, 37	S06.81[7,8,9]S	40	S08.81[1,2]A	58, 419	S10.9[3,4]X[A,S]	225
S06.383A	11, 15	S06.810A	37, 418, 431	S08.81[1,2]D	387	S10.9[5,7]X[A,S]	225
S06.384A	11, 15	S06.810D	387	S08.81[1,2]S	225	S10.92XS	225
S06.385A	11, 15	S06.810S	40	S08.811A	5	S10.93XD	387
S06.386A	11, 15	S06.811A	37	S08.812A	5	S10.96XS	225
S06.387A	11, 15	S06.812A	37	S08.89X[A,S]	225	S11.0[1,2,3][2,4]A	431
S06.388A	11, 15	S06.82[1,2,3,4]A	37, 419, 431	S08.89XA	419	S11.01[1,2,3,4,5,9]A	419
S06.389A	11, 15, 37	S06.82[1,2,3,4]D	387	S08.89XD	387	S11.01[1,2,3,4,5,9]D	387
S06.4X[1,2,3,4]A	36, 418, 431	S06.82[1,2,3,4]S	40	S09.0XXA	5, 359, 419	S11.01[1,2,3,4]S	225
S06.4X[1,2,3,4]D	387	S06.82[3,4,5,6]A	36	S09.0XXD	387	S11.01[1,2]A	58
S06.4X[1,2,3,4]S	39	S06.82[5,6]A	37, 419, 431	S09.0XXS	100	S11.01[3,4]A	58
S06.4X[3,4,5,6]A	35	S06.82[5,6]D	387	S09.1[0,1,2,9]XA	419	S11.011A	5
S06.4X[5,6]A	36, 418, 431	S06.82[5,6]S	40	S09.1[0,1,2,9]XD	387	S11.012A	5
S06.4X[5,6]D	387	S06.82[7,8,9]A	36, 37, 419, 431	S09.10X[A,S]	359	S11.013A	5
S06.4X[5,6]S	40	S06.82[7,8,9]D	387	S09.10XA	5	S11.014A	5
S06.4X[7,8,9]A	35, 37, 418, 431	S06.82[7,8,9]S	40	S09.11XA	5, 359	S11.015A	5, 58
S06.4X[7,8,9]D	387	S06.820A	37, 419, 431	S09.11XS	184	S11.015S	225
S06.4X[7,8,9]S	40	S06.820D	387	S09.12X[A,S]	225	S11.019A	5, 58
S06.4X0A	36, 37, 418, 431	S06.820S	40	S09.19X[A,S]	359	S11.019S	225
S06.4X0D	387	S06.821A	37	S09.19XA	5	S11.02[1,2,3,4,5,9]A	419
S06.4X0S	39	S06.822A	37	S09.2[0,1,2]XA	58, 419	S11.02[1,2,3,4,5,9]D	387
S06.4X1A	37	S06.89[1,2,3,4]A	37, 419, 431	S09.2[0,1,2]XD	387	S11.02[1,2,3,4]S	225
S06.4X2A	37	S06.89[1,2,3,4]D	387	S09.2[1,2]XS	225	S11.02[1,2]A	67
S06.5X[1,2,3,4]A	37, 418, 431	S06.89[1,2,3,4]S	40	S09.20XS	359	S11.02[3,4]A	67
S06.5X[1,2,3,4]D	387	S06.89[3,4,5,6]A	36	S09.3[0,9][1,2,9]S	359	S11.021A	5
S06.5X[1,2,3,4]S	40	S06.89[5,6]A	37, 419, 431	S09.30[1,2,9]A	58, 419	S11.022A	5
S06.5X[3,4,5,6]A	35	S06.89[5,6]D	387	S09.30[1,2,9]D	387	S11.023A	5
S06.5X[5,6]A	37, 418, 431	S06.89[5,6]S	40	S09.31[1,2,3,9]A	58, 419	S11.024A	5
S06.5X[5,6]D	387	S06.89[7,8,9]A	36, 37, 419, 431	S09.31[1,2,3,9]D	387	S11.025A	5, 67
S06.5X[5,6]S	40	S06.89[7,8,9]D	387	S09.31[1,2,3,9]S	225	S11.025S	225
S06.5X[7,8,9]A	36, 37, 418, 431	S06.89[7,8,9]S	40	S09.39[1,2,9]A	58, 419	S11.029A	5, 67
S06.5X[7,8,9]D	387	S06.890A	37, 419, 431	S09.39[1,2,9]D	387	S11.029S	225
S06.5X[7,8,9]S	40	S06.890D	387	S09.8XX[A,S]	359	S11.03[1,2,3,4,5,9]A	419
S06.5X0A	37, 418, 431	S06.890S	40	S09.8XXA	5, 419	S11.03[1,2,3,4,5,9]D	387
S06.5X0D	387	S06.891A	37	S09.8XXD	387	S11.03[1,2,3,4]S	225
S06.5X0S	40	S06.892A	37	S09.9[0,1,2,3]XA	419	S11.03[1,2]A	58
S06.5X1A	37	S06.9X[1,2,3,4]A	37, 419, 431	S09.9[0,1,2,3]XD	387	S11.03[3,4]A	58
S06.5X2A	37	S06.9X[1,2,3,4]D	387	S09.9[2,3]X[A,S]	359	S11.031A	5
S06.6X[1,2,3,4]A	37, 419, 431	S06.9X[1,2,3,4]S	40	S09.90X[A,S]	359	S11.032A	5
S06.6X[1,2,3,4]D	387	S06.9X[3,4,5,6]A	36	S09.90XA	5	S11.033A	5
S06.6X[1,2,3,4]S	40	S06.9X[5,6]A	37, 419, 431	S09.91XA	58	S11.034A	5
S06.6X[3,4,5,6]A	36	S06.9X[5,6]D	387	S09.91XS	359	S11.035A	5, 58
S06.6X[5,6]A	37, 418, 431	S06.9X[5,6]S	40	S09.92XA	5	S11.035S	225
S06.6X[5,6]D	387	S06.9X[7,8,9]A	36, 37, 419, 431	S09.93XA	5	S11.039A	5, 58
S06.6X[5,6]S	40	S06.9X[7,8,9]D	387	S10.0XX[A,S]	225	S11.039S	225
S06.6X[7,8,9]A	36, 37, 418, 431	S06.9X[7,8,9]S	40	S10.0XXA	419	S11.1[0,1,2,3,4,5]XA	247, 419
S06.6X[7,8,9]D	387	S06.9X0A	37, 419, 431	S10.0XXD	387	S11.1[0,1,2,3,4,5]XD	388
S06.6X[7,8,9]S	40	S06.9X0D	387	S10.1[0,1,2,4,5,6,7]XA	419	S11.1[1,2,3,4]XS	225
S06.6X0A	11, 15, 37, 418, 431	S06.9X0S	40	S10.1[0,1,2,4,5,6,7]XD	387	S11.10XA	5
S06.6X0D	387	S06.9X1A	37	S10.1[0,1]X[A,S]	225	S11.10XS	225
S06.6X0S	40	S06.9X2A	37	S10.1[2,6]XA	234	S11.11XA	5
S06.6X1A	11, 15, 37	S07.[0,1,8,9]XXA	359, 431	S10.12XS	225	S11.12XA	5
S06.6X2A	11, 15, 37	S07.[0,1,8,9]XXD	387	S10.14X[A,S]	225	S11.13XA	5
S06.6X3A	11, 15	S07.[0,1,8]XXS	225	S10.15X[A,S]	225	S11.14XA	5
S06.6X4A	11, 15	S07.0XXA	5, 419	S10.16XS	225	S11.15XA	5
S06.6X5A	11, 15	S07.1XXA	5, 419	S10.17X[A,S]	225	S11.15XS	225
S06.6X6A	11, 15	S07.8XXA	5, 419	S10.8[0,1,2,3,4,5,6,7]XA	419	S11.2[0,1,2,3,4,5]XA	419
S06.6X7A	11, 15	S07.9XXA	5, 419	S10.8[0,1,2,4,5,6,7]XD	387	S11.2[0,1,2,3,4,5]XD	388
S06.6X8A	11, 15	S07.9XXS	225	S10.8[0,1]X[A,S]	225	S11.2[1,2,3,4]XS	225

Numeric Index to Diseases

Code	Page	Code	Page	Code	Page	Code	Page
S28.21[1,2,9][A,S]	226	S30.86[5,6]S	226	S31.14[3,4]S	226	S31.65[0,1,2,3,4,5,9]D	390
S28.21[1,2,9]D	389	S30.860S	226	S31.142S	226	S31.65[0,1,3,4]S	227
S28.22[1,2,9][A,S]	226	S30.861S	226	S31.145S	226	S31.652S	227
S28.22[1,2,9]D	389	S30.864S	226	S31.149S	226	S31.655S	227
S29.[8,9]XX[A,S]	359	S30.867S	226	S31.15[0,1,2,3,4,5,9]D	390	S31.659S	227
S29.[8,9]XXA	421	S30.87[0,1,2,3,4,5,6,7]D	389	S31.15[0,1][A,S]	226	S31.8[0,1,2][1,2,3,4,5,9]A	421
S29.0[0,1,2,9][1,2,9]A	421	S30.87[2,3][A,S]	226	S31.15[3,4][A,S]	226	S31.80[1,2,3,4,5,9]D	390
S29.0[0,9][1,2,9][A,S]	359	S30.87[5,6][A,S]	226	S31.152[A,S]	226	S31.80[1,2][A,S]	227
S29.00[1,2,9]D	389	S30.870[A,S]	226	S31.155[A,S]	226	S31.80[3,4][A,S]	227
S29.01[1,2,9][A,S]	184	S30.871[A,S]	226	S31.159[A,S]	226	S31.805[A,S]	227
S29.01[1,2,9]D	389	S30.874[A,S]	226	S31.2[0,1,2,3,4,5]XA	261, 421	S31.809[A,S]	227
S29.02[1,2,9][A,S]	226	S30.877[A,S]	226	S31.2[0,1,2,3,4,5]XD	390	S31.81[1,2,3,4,5,9]D	390
S29.02[1,2,9]D	389	S30.9[1,2,3,4,5,6,7,8]XA	421	S31.2[1,2]XS	226	S31.81[1,2][A,S]	227
S29.09[1,2,9]D	389	S30.9[1,2,3,4,5,6,7,8]XD	389	S31.2[3,4]XS	226	S31.81[3,4][A,S]	227
S29.8XXD	389	S30.9[3,4]X[A,S]	226	S31.25XS	226	S31.815[A,S]	227
S29.9XXD	389	S30.9[6,7]X[A,S]	226	S31.3[0,1,2,3,4,5]XA	261, 421	S31.819[A,S]	227
S30.[0,1]XXA	421	S30.91X[A,S]	226	S31.3[0,1,2,3,4,5]XD	390	S31.82[1,2,3,4,5,9]D	390
S30.0XX[A,S]	226	S30.92X[A,S]	226	S31.3[1,2,3,4]XS	226	S31.82[1,2][A,S]	227
S30.0XXD	389	S30.95X[A,S]	226	S31.35XS	226	S31.82[3,4][A,S]	227
S30.1XX[A,S]	226	S30.98X[A,S]	226	S31.4[0,1,2,3,4,5]XA	265, 270, 421	S31.825[A,S]	227
S30.1XXD	389	S31.[2,3]0XS	227	S31.4[0,1,2,3,4,5]XD	390	S31.829[A,S]	227
S30.2[02,3X]A	265, 270	S31.0[0,1,2,3,4,5][0,1]A	421	S31.4[1,2]XS	226	S31.83[1,2,3,4,5,9]A	421
S30.2[1,2,3]XA	421	S31.0[0,1,2,3,4,5]1A	256, 432	S31.4[3,4]XS	226	S31.83[1,2,3,4,5,9]D	390
S30.2[1,2,3]XD	389	S31.00[0,1]D	389	S31.40XS	226	S31.83[2,4]A	359
S30.20[1,2]A	421	S31.000[A,S]	226	S31.45XS	226	S31.831[A,S]	227
S30.20[1,2]S	226	S31.001S	226	S31.5[0,1,2,3,4,5][1,2]A	421	S31.832S	227
S30.201A	261	S31.01[0,1]D	389	S31.5[0,1,2,3,4,5]1A	261	S31.833[A,S]	227
S30.201D	389	S31.010[A,S]	226	S31.5[0,1,2,3,4,5]1S	261	S31.834S	227
S30.202D	389	S31.011S	226	S31.5[0,1,2,3,4,5]2A	265, 270	S31.835[A,S]	227
S30.21XA	261	S31.02[0,1]D	389	S31.5[0,1,2,3,4,5]2S	265, 270	S31.839[A,S]	227
S30.21XS	226	S31.020[A,S]	226	S31.50[1,2]D	390	S32.00[0,1,2,8,9][A,B,S]	166
S30.22XA	261	S31.021S	226	S31.51[1,2]D	390	S32.00[0,1,2,8,9][A,B]	421
S30.22XS	226	S31.03[0,1]D	389	S31.52[1,2]D	390	S32.00[0,1,2,8,9][D,G]	170
S30.23XS	226	S31.030[A,S]	226	S31.53[1,2]D	390	S32.00[0,1,2,8,9]K	196
S30.3XX[A,S]	226	S31.031S	226	S31.54[1,2]D	390	S32.01[0,1,2,8,9][A,B,S]	166
S30.3XXA	421	S31.04[0,1]D	389	S31.55[1,2]D	390	S32.01[0,1,2,8,9][A,B]	421
S30.3XXD	389	S31.040[A,S]	226	S31.6[0,1,2,3,4,5]	421, 432	S32.01[0,1,2,8,9][D,G]	170
S30.8[1,2,4,5,6,7]	421	S31.041S	226	[0,1,2,3,4,5,9]A		S32.01[0,1,2,8,9]K	196
[0,1,2,3,4,5,6,7]A		S31.05[0,1]D	389	S31.60[0,1,2,3,4,5,9]A	117	S32.02[0,1,2,8,9][A,B,S]	166
S30.8[2,6][0,1,2,3,4,5,6,7]A	234	S31.050[A,S]	226	S31.60[0,1,2,3,4,5,9]D	390	S32.02[0,1,2,8,9][A,B]	421
S30.81[0,1,2,3,4,5,6,7]D	389	S31.051S	226	S31.60[0,1,3,4]S	226	S32.02[0,1,2,8,9][D,G]	170
S30.81[2,3][A,S]	226	S31.1[0,1,2,3,4,5][0,1,2,3,4,5,9]A	421	S31.602S	226	S32.02[0,1,2,8,9]K	196
S30.81[5,6][A,S]	226	S31.1[2,4][0,1,2,3,4,5,9]A	359	S31.605S	226	S32.03[0,1,2,8,9][A,B,S]	166
S30.810[A,S]	226	S31.10[0,1,2,3,4,5,9]D	390	S31.609S	226	S32.03[0,1,2,8,9][A,B]	421
S30.811[A,S]	226	S31.10[0,1][A,S]	226	S31.61[0,1,2,3,4,5,9]A	117	S32.03[0,1,2,8,9][D,G]	170
S30.814[A,S]	226	S31.10[3,4][A,S]	226	S31.61[0,1,2,3,4,5,9]D	390	S32.03[0,1,2,8,9]K	196
S30.817[A,S]	226	S31.102[A,S]	226	S31.61[0,1,3,4]S	226	S32.04[0,1,2,8,9][A,B,S]	166
S30.82[0,1,2,3,4,5,6,7]D	389	S31.105[A,S]	226	S31.612S	226	S32.04[0,1,2,8,9][A,B]	421
S30.82[2,3]S	226	S31.109[A,S]	226	S31.615S	226	S32.04[0,1,2,8,9][D,G]	170
S30.82[5,6]S	226	S31.11[0,1,2,3,4,5,9]D	390	S31.619S	226	S32.04[0,1,2,8,9]K	196
S30.820S	226	S31.11[0,1][A,S]	226	S31.62[0,1,2,3,4,5,9]A	117	S32.05[0,1,2,8,9][A,B,S]	166
S30.821S	226	S31.11[3,4][A,S]	226	S31.62[0,1,2,3,4,5,9]D	390	S32.05[0,1,2,8,9][A,B]	421
S30.824S	226	S31.112[A,S]	226	S31.62[0,1,3,4]S	226	S32.05[0,1,2,8,9][D,G]	170
S30.827S	226	S31.115[A,S]	226	S31.622S	226	S32.05[0,1,2,8,9]K	196
S30.84[0,1,2,3,4,5,6]D	389	S31.119[A,S]	226	S31.625S	226	S32.1[4,5,6,7,9]X[A,B,S]	166
S30.84[2,3][A,S]	226	S31.12[0,1,2,3,4,5,9]D	390	S31.629S	226	S32.1[4,5,6,7,9]X[A,B]	421, 433
S30.84[5,6][A,S]	226	S31.12[0,1]S	226	S31.63[0,1,2,3,4,5,9]A	117	S32.1[4,5,6,7,9]X[D,G]	170
S30.840[A,S]	226	S31.12[3,4]S	226	S31.63[0,1,2,3,4,5,9]D	390	S32.1[4,5,6,7,9]XK	196
S30.841[A,S]	226	S31.122S	226	S31.63[0,1,3,4]S	227	S32.10X[A,B,S]	166
S30.844[A,S]	226	S31.125S	226	S31.632S	226	S32.10X[A,B]	421, 433
S30.85[0,1,2,3,4,5,6,7]D	389	S31.129S	226	S31.635S	226	S32.10X[D,G]	170
S30.85[2,3][A,S]	226	S31.13[0,1,2,3,4,5,9]D	390	S31.639S	226	S32.10XK	196
S30.85[5,6][A,S]	226	S31.13[0,1][A,S]	226	S31.64[0,1,2,3,4,5,9]A	117	S32.11[0,1,2,9][A,B,S]	166
S30.850[A,S]	226	S31.13[3,4][A,S]	226	S31.64[0,1,2,3,4,5,9]D	390	S32.11[0,1,2,9][A,B]	421, 433
S30.851[A,S]	226	S31.132[A,S]	226	S31.64[0,1,3,4]S	227	S32.11[0,1,2,9][D,G]	170
S30.854[A,S]	226	S31.135[A,S]	226	S31.642S	227	S32.11[0,1,2,9]K	196
S30.857[A,S]	226	S31.139[A,S]	226	S31.645S	227	S32.12[0,1,2,9][A,B,S]	166
S30.86[0,1,2,3,4,5,6,7]D	389	S31.14[0,1,2,3,4,5,9]D	390	S31.649S	227	S32.12[0,1,2,9][A,B]	421, 433
S30.86[2,3]S	226	S31.14[0,1]S	226	S31.65[0,1,2,3,4,5,9]A	117	S32.12[0,1,2,9][D,G]	170

Code	Page	Code	Page	Code	Page	Code	Page
S42.39[1,2,9][D,G,S]	171	S42.47[1,2,3][D,G,S]	171	S43.22[1,2,3,4,5,6]D	391	S44.9[0,1,2]XD	391
S42.39[1,2,9][K,P]	197	S42.47[1,2,3][K,P]	197	S43.22[1,2,3]A	67	S44.9[0,1,2]XS	40
S42.39[1,2,9]B	433	S42.47[1,2,3]B	434	S43.22[1,2,3]S	185	S45.0[0,1,9][1,2,9]A	359, 423, 434
S42.40[1,2,9][A,B]	185, 422	S42.47[4,5,6][A,B]	185	S43.22[4,5,6]A	67	S45.0[1,9][1,2,9]D	391
S42.40[1,2,9][D,G,S]	171	S42.47[4,5,6][D,G,S]	171	S43.22[4,5,6]S	185	S45.00[1,2,9]D	391
S42.40[1,2,9][K,P]	197	S42.47[4,5,6][K,P]	197	S43.30[1,2,3,4,5,6]A	423	S45.00[1,2,9]S	100
S42.40[1,2,9]B	433	S42.47[4,5,6]B	434	S43.30[1,2,3][A,S]	185	S45.01[1,2,9]S	100
S42.41[1,2,3,4,5,6][A,B]	422	S42.48[1,2,9][D,G,S]	171	S43.30[1,2,3]D	391	S45.09[1,2,9]S	100
S42.41[1,2,3][A,B]	185	S42.48[1,2,9][K,P]	197	S43.30[4,5,6][A,S]	185	S45.1[0,1,9][1,2,9]A	359, 423, 434
S42.41[1,2,3][D,G,S]	171	S42.48[1,2,9]A	185, 422	S43.30[4,5,6]D	391	S45.10[1,2,9]D	391
S42.41[1,2,3][K,P]	197	S42.49[1,2,3,4,5,6][A,B]	422	S43.31[1,2,3,4,5,6]A	423	S45.10[1,2,9]S	100
S42.41[1,2,3]B	433	S42.49[1,2,3][A,B]	185	S43.31[1,2,3][A,S]	185	S45.11[1,2,9]D	391
S42.41[4,5,6][A,B]	185	S42.49[1,2,3][D,G,S]	171	S43.31[1,2,3]D	391	S45.11[1,2,9]S	100
S42.41[4,5,6][D,G,S]	171	S42.49[1,2,3][K,P]	197	S43.31[4,5,6][A,S]	185	S45.19[1,2,9]D	391
S42.41[4,5,6][K,P]	197	S42.49[1,2,3]B	434	S43.31[4,5,6]D	391	S45.19[1,2,9]S	100
S42.41[4,5,6]B	433	S42.49[4,5,6][A,B]	185	S43.39[1,2,3,4,5,6]A	423	S45.2[0,1,9][1,2,9]A	359, 423, 434
S42.42[1,2,3,4,5,6][A,B]	422	S42.49[4,5,6][D,G,S]	171	S43.39[1,2,3][A,S]	185	S45.20[1,2,9]D	392
S42.42[1,2,3][A,B]	185	S42.49[4,5,6][K,P]	197	S43.39[1,2,3]D	391	S45.20[1,2,9]S	100
S42.42[1,2,3][D,G,S]	171	S42.49[4,5,6]B	434	S43.39[4,5,6][A,S]	185	S45.21[1,2,9]D	392
S42.42[1,2,3][K,P]	197	S42.9[0,1,2]X[A,B]	185, 422	S43.39[4,5,6]D	391	S45.21[1,2,9]S	100
S42.42[1,2,3]B	433	S42.9[0,1,2]X[D,G,S]	171	S43.4[0,1,2][1,2,9]A	423	S45.29[1,2,9]D	392
S42.42[4,5,6][A,B]	185	S42.9[0,1,2]X[K,P]	197	S43.40[1,2,9][A,S]	185	S45.29[1,2,9]S	100
S42.42[4,5,6][D,G,S]	171	S42.9[0,1,2]XB	434	S43.40[1,2,9]D	391	S45.3[0,1,9][1,2,9]A	359, 423, 434
S42.42[4,5,6][K,P]	197	S43.[5,6][0,1,2]XA	423	S43.41[1,2,9][A,S]	185	S45.30[1,2,9]D	392
S42.42[4,5,6]B	434	S43.[8,9][0,1,2]XA	423	S43.41[1,2,9]D	391	S45.30[1,2,9]S	100
S42.43[1,2,3,4,5,6][A,B]	422	S43.0[1,2,3][1,2,3,4,5,6]A	422	S43.42[1,2,9][A,S]	185	S45.31[1,2,9]D	392
S42.43[1,2,3][A,B]	185	S43.00[1,2,3,4,5,6]A	422	S43.42[1,2,9]D	391	S45.31[1,2,9]S	100
S42.43[1,2,3][D,G,S]	171	S43.00[1,2,3,4,5,6]D	391	S43.43[1,2,9][A,S]	185	S45.39[1,2,9]D	392
S42.43[1,2,3][K,P]	197	S43.00[1,2,3][A,S]	185	S43.43[1,2,9]A	423	S45.39[1,2,9]S	101
S42.43[1,2,3]B	434	S43.00[4,5,6][A,S]	185	S43.43[1,2,9]D	391	S45.8[0,1,9][1,2,9]A	359, 423, 434
S42.43[4,5,6][A,B]	185	S43.01[1,2,3,4,5,6]D	391	S43.49[1,2,9][A,S]	185	S45.80[1,2,9]D	392
S42.43[4,5,6][D,G,S]	171	S43.01[1,2,3][A,S]	185	S43.49[1,2,9]A	423	S45.80[1,2,9]S	101
S42.43[4,5,6][K,P]	197	S43.01[4,5,6][A,S]	185	S43.49[1,2,9]D	391	S45.81[1,2,9]D	392
S42.43[4,5,6]B	434	S43.02[1,2,3,4,5,6]D	391	S43.5[0,1,2]X[A,S]	185	S45.81[1,2,9]S	101
S42.44[1,2,3,4,5,6,7,8,9][A,B]	422	S43.02[1,2,3][A,S]	185	S43.5[0,1,2]XD	391	S45.89[1,2,9]D	392
S42.44[1,2,3][A,B]	185	S43.02[4,5,6][A,S]	185	S43.6[0,1,2]X[A,S]	185	S45.89[1,2,9]S	101
S42.44[1,2,3][D,G,S]	171	S43.03[1,2,3,4,5,6]D	391	S43.6[0,1,2]XD	391	S45.9[0,1,9][1,2,9]A	359, 423, 434
S42.44[1,2,3][K,P]	197	S43.03[1,2,3][A,S]	185	S43.8[0,1,2]X[A,S]	185	S45.90[1,2,9]D	392
S42.44[1,2,3]B	434	S43.03[4,5,6][A,S]	185	S43.8[0,1,2]XD	391	S45.90[1,2,9]S	101
S42.44[4,5,6][A,B]	185	S43.08[1,2,3,4,5,6]A	422	S43.9[0,1,2]X[A,S]	185	S45.91[1,2,9]D	392
S42.44[4,5,6][D,G,S]	171	S43.08[1,2,3,4,5,6]D	391	S43.9[0,1,2]XD	391	S45.91[1,2,9]S	101
S42.44[4,5,6][K,P]	197	S43.08[1,2,3][A,S]	185	S44.[0,1,2][0,1,2]XA	423	S45.99[1,2,9]D	392
S42.44[4,5,6]B	434	S43.08[4,5,6][A,S]	185	S44.[3,4][0,1,2]XA	423	S45.99[1,2,9]S	101
S42.44[7,8,9][A,B]	185	S43.1[0,1][1,2,9]A	422	S44.[5,8,9][0,1,2]XA	423	S46.[1,2]2[1,2,9]A	197
S42.44[7,8,9][D,G,S]	171	S43.1[2,3][1,2,9]A	422	S44.0[0,1,2]XA	34, 434	S46.[1,2]2[1,2,9]S	227
S42.44[7,8,9][K,P]	197	S43.1[4,5][1,2,9]A	422	S44.0[0,1,2]XD	391	S46.[8,9][0,1,2,9][1,2,9]A	423
S42.447B	434	S43.10[1,2,9][A,S]	185	S44.0[0,1,2]XS	40	S46.[8,9]2[1,2,9]A	197
S42.448B	434	S43.10[1,2,9]D	391	S44.1[0,1,2]XA	34, 434	S46.[8,9]2[1,2,9]S	227
S42.449B	434	S43.11[1,2,9][A,S]	185	S44.1[0,1,2]XD	391	S46.0[0,1,2,9][1,2,9]A	423
S42.45[1,2,3,4,5,6][A,B]	422	S43.11[1,2,9]D	391	S44.1[0,1,2]XS	40	S46.0[0,9][1,2,9][A,S]	359
S42.45[1,2,3][A,B]	185	S43.12[1,2,9][A,S]	185	S44.2[0,1,2]XA	34, 434	S46.00[1,2,9]D	392
S42.45[1,2,3][D,G,S]	171	S43.12[1,2,9]D	391	S44.2[0,1,2]XD	391	S46.01[1,2,9][A,S]	185
S42.45[1,2,3][K,P]	197	S43.13[1,2,9][A,S]	185	S44.2[0,1,2]XS	40	S46.01[1,2,9]D	392
S42.45[1,2,3]B	434	S43.13[1,2,9]D	391	S44.3[0,1,2]XA	34, 434	S46.02[1,2,9]A	197
S42.45[4,5,6][A,B]	185	S43.14[1,2,9][A,S]	185	S44.3[0,1,2]XD	391	S46.02[1,2,9]D	392
S42.45[4,5,6][D,G,S]	171	S43.14[1,2,9]D	391	S44.3[0,1,2]XS	40	S46.02[1,2,9]S	227
S42.45[4,5,6][K,P]	197	S43.15[1,2,9][A,S]	185	S44.4[0,1,2]XA	34	S46.09[1,2,9]D	392
S42.45[4,5,6]B	434	S43.15[1,2,9]D	391	S44.4[0,1,2]XD	391	S46.1[0,1,2,9][1,2,9]A	423
S42.46[1,2,3,4,5,6][A,B]	422	S43.2[0,1,2][1,2,3,4,5,6]	423	S44.4[0,1,2]XS	40	S46.1[0,9][1,2,9][A,S]	359
S42.46[1,2,3][A,B]	185	S43.20[1,2,3,4,5,6]D	391	S44.5[0,1,2]XA	34	S46.10[1,2,9]D	392
S42.46[1,2,3][D,G,S]	171	S43.20[1,2,3]A	67	S44.5[0,1,2]XD	391	S46.11[1,2,9][A,S]	185
S42.46[1,2,3][K,P]	197	S43.20[1,2,3]S	185	S44.5[0,1,2]XS	40	S46.11[1,2,9]D	392
S42.46[1,2,3]B	434	S43.20[4,5,6]A	67	S44.8X[1,2,9]D	391	S46.12[1,2,9]D	392
S42.46[4,5,6][A,B]	185	S43.20[4,5,6]S	185	S44.8X[1,2,9]S	40	S46.19[1,2,9]D	392
S42.46[4,5,6][D,G,S]	171	S43.21[1,2,3,4,5,6]D	391	S44.8X[1,2]A	434	S46.2[0,1,2,9][1,2,9]A	423
S42.46[4,5,6][K,P]	197	S43.21[1,2,3]A	67	S44.8X1A	34, 423	S46.2[0,9][1,2,9][A,S]	359
S42.46[4,5,6]B	434	S43.21[1,2,3]S	185	S44.8X2A	34, 423	S46.20[1,2,9]D	392
S42.47[1,2,3,4,5,6][A,B]	422	S43.21[4,5,6]A	67	S44.8X9A	34, 423	S46.21[1,2,9][A,S]	185
S42.47[1,2,3][A,B]	185	S43.21[4,5,6]S	185	S44.9[0,1,2]XA	34	S46.21[1,2,9]D	392

Code	Page	Code	Page	Code	Page	Code	Page
S62.12[1,2,3][K,P]	199	S62.24[1,2,3][K,P]	199	S62.33[4,5][A,B]	188	S62.39[6,7][K,P]	200
S62.12[4,5,6][A,B]	187	S62.24[4,5,6][A,B]	187	S62.33[4,5][D,G,S]	175	S62.39[8,9][A,B]	188
S62.12[4,5,6][D,G,S]	175	S62.24[4,5,6][D,G,S]	175	S62.33[4,5][K,P]	199	S62.39[8,9][D,G,S]	176
S62.12[4,5,6][K,P]	199	S62.24[4,5,6][K,P]	199	S62.33[6,7][A,B]	188	S62.39[8,9][K,P]	200
S62.13[1,2,3,4,5,6][A,B]	424	S62.25[1,2,3,4,5,6][A,B]	424	S62.33[6,7][D,G,S]	175	S62.50[1,2,9][A,B]	188, 425
S62.13[1,2,3][A,B]	187	S62.25[1,2,3][A,B]	187	S62.33[6,7][K,P]	199	S62.50[1,2,9][D,G,S]	176
S62.13[1,2,3][D,G,S]	175	S62.25[1,2,3][D,G,S]	175	S62.33[8,9][A,B]	188	S62.50[1,2,9][K,P]	200
S62.13[1,2,3][K,P]	199	S62.25[1,2,3][K,P]	199	S62.33[8,9][D,G,S]	175	S62.51[1,2,3,4,5,6][A,B]	425
S62.13[4,5,6][A,B]	187	S62.25[4,5,6][A,B]	187	S62.33[8,9][K,P]	199	S62.51[1,2,3][A,B]	188
S62.13[4,5,6][D,G,S]	175	S62.25[4,5,6][D,G,S]	175	S62.34[0,1,2,3,4,5,6,7,8,9][A,B]	425	S62.51[1,2,3][D,G,S]	176
S62.13[4,5,6][K,P]	199	S62.25[4,5,6][K,P]	199	S62.34[0,1][A,B]	188	S62.51[1,2,3][K,P]	200
S62.14[1,2,3,4,5,6][A,B]	424	S62.29[1,2,9][A,B]	187, 424	S62.34[0,1][D,G,S]	175	S62.51[4,5,6][A,B]	188
S62.14[1,2,3][A,B]	187	S62.29[1,2,9][D,G,S]	175	S62.34[0,1][K,P]	199	S62.51[4,5,6][D,G,S]	176
S62.14[1,2,3][D,G,S]	175	S62.29[1,2,9][K,P]	199	S62.34[2,3][A,B]	188	S62.51[4,5,6][K,P]	200
S62.14[1,2,3][K,P]	199	S62.30[0,1,2,3,4,5,6,7,8,9][A,B]	424	S62.34[2,3][D,G,S]	175	S62.52[1,2,3,4,5,6][A,B]	425
S62.14[4,5,6][A,B]	187	S62.30[0,1][A,B]	187	S62.34[2,3][K,P]	200	S62.52[1,2,3][A,B]	188
S62.14[4,5,6][D,G,S]	175	S62.30[0,1][D,G,S]	175	S62.34[4,5][A,B]	188	S62.52[1,2,3][D,G,S]	176
S62.14[4,5,6][K,P]	199	S62.30[0,1][K,P]	199	S62.34[4,5][D,G,S]	175	S62.52[1,2,3][K,P]	200
S62.15[1,2,3,4,5,6][A,B]	424	S62.30[2,3][A,B]	187	S62.34[4,5][K,P]	200	S62.52[4,5,6][A,B]	188
S62.15[1,2,3][A,B]	187	S62.30[2,3][D,G,S]	175	S62.34[6,7][A,B]	188	S62.52[4,5,6][D,G,S]	176
S62.15[1,2,3][D,G,S]	175	S62.30[2,3][K,P]	199	S62.34[6,7][D,G,S]	175	S62.52[4,5,6][K,P]	200
S62.15[1,2,3][K,P]	199	S62.30[4,5][A,B]	187	S62.34[6,7][K,P]	200	S62.60[0,1,2,3,4,5,6,7,8,9][A,B]	425
S62.15[4,5,6][A,B]	187	S62.30[4,5][D,G,S]	175	S62.34[8,9][A,B]	188	S62.60[0,1][A,B]	188
S62.15[4,5,6][D,G,S]	175	S62.30[4,5][K,P]	199	S62.34[8,9][D,G,S]	175	S62.60[0,1][D,G,S]	176
S62.15[4,5,6][K,P]	199	S62.30[6,7][A,B]	187	S62.34[8,9][K,P]	200	S62.60[0,1][K,P]	200
S62.16[1,2,3,4,5,6][A,B]	424	S62.30[6,7][D,G,S]	175	S62.35[0,1,2,3,4,5,6,7,8,9][A,B]	425	S62.60[2,3][A,B]	188
S62.16[1,2,3][A,B]	187	S62.30[6,7][K,P]	199	S62.35[0,1][A,B]	188	S62.60[2,3][D,G,S]	176
S62.16[1,2,3][D,G,S]	175	S62.30[8,9][A,B]	187	S62.35[0,1][D,G,S]	175	S62.60[2,3][K,P]	200
S62.16[1,2,3][K,P]	199	S62.30[8,9][D,G,S]	175	S62.35[0,1][K,P]	200	S62.60[4,5][A,B]	188
S62.16[4,5,6][A,B]	187	S62.30[8,9][K,P]	199	S62.35[2,3][A,B]	188	S62.60[4,5][D,G,S]	176
S62.16[4,5,6][D,G,S]	175	S62.31[0,1,2,3,4,5,6,7,8,9][A,B]	425	S62.35[2,3][D,G,S]	175	S62.60[4,5][K,P]	200
S62.16[4,5,6][K,P]	199	S62.31[0,1][A,B]	187	S62.35[2,3][K,P]	200	S62.60[6,7][A,B]	188
S62.17[1,2,3,4,5,6][A,B]	424	S62.31[0,1][D,G,S]	175	S62.35[4,5][A,B]	188	S62.60[6,7][D,G,S]	176
S62.17[1,2,3][A,B]	187	S62.31[0,1][K,P]	199	S62.35[4,5][D,G,S]	175	S62.60[6,7][K,P]	200
S62.17[1,2,3][D,G,S]	175	S62.31[2,3][A,B]	187	S62.35[4,5][K,P]	200	S62.60[8,9][A,B]	188
S62.17[1,2,3][K,P]	199	S62.31[2,3][D,G,S]	175	S62.35[6,7][A,B]	188	S62.60[8,9][D,G,S]	176
S62.17[4,5,6][A,B]	187	S62.31[2,3][K,P]	199	S62.35[6,7][D,G,S]	175	S62.60[8,9][K,P]	200
S62.17[4,5,6][D,G,S]	175	S62.31[4,5][A,B]	187	S62.35[6,7][K,P]	200	S62.61[0,1,2,3,4,5,6,7,8,9][A,B]	425
S62.17[4,5,6][K,P]	199	S62.31[4,5][D,G,S]	175	S62.35[8,9][A,B]	188	S62.61[0,1][A,B]	188
S62.18[1,2,3,4,5,6][A,B]	424	S62.31[4,5][K,P]	199	S62.35[8,9][D,G,S]	175	S62.61[0,1][D,G,S]	176
S62.18[1,2,3][A,B]	187	S62.31[6,7][A,B]	187	S62.35[8,9][K,P]	200	S62.61[0,1][K,P]	200
S62.18[1,2,3][D,G,S]	175	S62.31[6,7][D,G,S]	175	S62.36[0,1,2,3,4,5,6,7,8,9][A,B]	425	S62.61[2,3][A,B]	188
S62.18[1,2,3][K,P]	199	S62.31[6,7][K,P]	199	S62.36[0,1][A,B]	188	S62.61[2,3][D,G,S]	176
S62.18[4,5,6][A,B]	187	S62.31[8,9][A,B]	187	S62.36[0,1][D,G,S]	175	S62.61[2,3][K,P]	200
S62.18[4,5,6][D,G,S]	175	S62.31[8,9][D,G,S]	175	S62.36[0,1][K,P]	200	S62.61[4,5][A,B]	188
S62.18[4,5,6][K,P]	199	S62.31[8,9][K,P]	199	S62.36[2,3][A,B]	188	S62.61[4,5][D,G,S]	176
S62.20[1,2,9][A,B]	187, 424	S62.32[0,1,2,3,4,5,6,7,8,9][A,B]	425	S62.36[2,3][D,G,S]	175	S62.61[4,5][K,P]	200
S62.20[1,2,9][D,G,S]	175	S62.32[0,1][A,B]	187	S62.36[2,3][K,P]	200	S62.61[6,7][A,B]	188
S62.20[1,2,9][K,P]	199	S62.32[0,1][D,G,S]	175	S62.36[4,5][A,B]	188	S62.61[6,7][D,G,S]	176
S62.21[1,2,3][A,B]	187, 424	S62.32[0,1][K,P]	199	S62.36[4,5][D,G,S]	176	S62.61[6,7][K,P]	200
S62.21[1,2,3][D,G,S]	175	S62.32[2,3][A,B]	187	S62.36[4,5][K,P]	200	S62.61[8,9][A,B]	188
S62.21[1,2,3][K,P]	199	S62.32[2,3][D,G,S]	175	S62.36[6,7][A,B]	188	S62.61[8,9][D,G,S]	176
S62.22[1,2,3,4,5,6][A,B]	424	S62.32[2,3][K,P]	199	S62.36[6,7][D,G,S]	176	S62.61[8,9][K,P]	200
S62.22[1,2,3][A,B]	187	S62.32[4,5][A,B]	187	S62.36[6,7][K,P]	200	S62.62[0,1,2,3,4,5,6,7,8,9][A,B]	425
S62.22[1,2,3][D,G,S]	175	S62.32[4,5][D,G,S]	175	S62.36[8,9][A,B]	188	S62.62[0,1][A,B]	188
S62.22[1,2,3][K,P]	199	S62.32[4,5][K,P]	199	S62.36[8,9][D,G,S]	176	S62.62[0,1][D,G,S]	176
S62.22[4,5,6][A,B]	187	S62.32[6,7][A,B]	188	S62.36[8,9][K,P]	200	S62.62[0,1][K,P]	200
S62.22[4,5,6][D,G,S]	175	S62.32[6,7][D,G,S]	175	S62.39[0,1,2,3,4,5,6,7,8,9][A,B]	425	S62.62[2,3][A,B]	188
S62.22[4,5,6][K,P]	199	S62.32[6,7][K,P]	199	S62.39[0,1][A,B]	188	S62.62[2,3][D,G,S]	176
S62.23[1,2,3,4,5,6][A,B]	424	S62.32[8,9][A,B]	188	S62.39[0,1][D,G,S]	176	S62.62[2,3][K,P]	200
S62.23[1,2,3][A,B]	187	S62.32[8,9][D,G,S]	175	S62.39[0,1][K,P]	200	S62.62[4,5][A,B]	188
S62.23[1,2,3][D,G,S]	175	S62.32[8,9][K,P]	199	S62.39[2,3][A,B]	188	S62.62[4,5][D,G,S]	176
S62.23[1,2,3][K,P]	199	S62.33[0,1,2,3,4,5,6,7,8,9][A,B]	425	S62.39[2,3][D,G,S]	176	S62.62[4,5][K,P]	200
S62.23[4,5,6][A,B]	187	S62.33[0,1][A,B]	188	S62.39[2,3][K,P]	200	S62.62[6,7][A,B]	188
S62.23[4,5,6][D,G,S]	175	S62.33[0,1][D,G,S]	175	S62.39[4,5][A,B]	188	S62.62[6,7][D,G,S]	176
S62.23[4,5,6][K,P]	199	S62.33[0,1][K,P]	199	S62.39[4,5][D,G,S]	176	S62.62[6,7][K,P]	200
S62.24[1,2,3,4,5,6][A,B]	424	S62.33[2,3][A,B]	188	S62.39[4,5][K,P]	200	S62.62[8,9][A,B]	188
S62.24[1,2,3][A,B]	187	S62.33[2,3][D,G,S]	175	S62.39[6,7][A,B]	188	S62.62[8,9][D,G,S]	176
S62.24[1,2,3][D,G,S]	175	S62.33[2,3][K,P]	199	S62.39[6,7][D,G,S]	176	S62.62[8,9][K,P]	200

Code	Page
S66.31[Ø,1]D	397
S66.31[2,3][A,S]	190
S66.31[2,3]D	397
S66.31[4,5][A,S]	190
S66.31[4,5]D	397
S66.31[6,7][A,S]	190
S66.31[6,7]D	397
S66.31[8,9][A,S]	190
S66.31[8,9]D	397
S66.32[Ø,1,2,3,4,5,6,7,8,9]A	200
S66.32[Ø,1]D	397
S66.32[Ø,1]S	229
S66.32[2,3]D	397
S66.32[2,3]S	229
S66.32[4,5]D	397
S66.32[4,5]S	229
S66.32[6,7]D	397
S66.32[6,7]S	229
S66.32[8,9]D	397
S66.32[8,9]S	229
S66.39[Ø,1]D	397
S66.39[2,3]D	397
S66.39[4,5]D	397
S66.39[6,7]D	397
S66.39[8,9]D	397
S66.4[Ø,1,2,9][1,2,9]A	425
S66.4[Ø,1,2,9][1,2,9]D	397
S66.4[Ø,9][1,2,9][A,S]	360
S66.41[1,2,9][A,S]	190
S66.42[1,2,9]A	200
S66.42[1,2,9]S	229
S66.5[Ø,1,2,9][Ø,1,2,3,4,5,6,7,8,9]D	397
S66.5[Ø,1,2,9][Ø,1,2,3,4,5,6,7,8,9]A	425
S66.5[Ø,9][Ø,1,2,3,4,5,6,7,8,9][A,S]	360
S66.51[Ø,1][A,S]	190
S66.51[2,3][A,S]	190
S66.51[4,5][A,S]	190
S66.51[6,7][A,S]	190
S66.51[8,9][A,S]	190
S66.52[Ø,1,2,3,4,5,6,7,8,9]A	200
S66.52[Ø,1]S	229
S66.52[2,3]S	229
S66.52[4,5]S	229
S66.52[6,7]S	229
S66.52[8,9]S	229
S66.8[Ø,9][1,2,9][A,S]	360
S66.82[1,2,9]S	229
S66.9[Ø,9][1,2,9][A,S]	360
S66.92[1,2,9]S	229
S67.0[Ø,1,2]XA	360, 425
S67.0[Ø,1,2]XD	397
S67.0[Ø,1,2]XS	229
S67.10XA	360, 425
S67.10XD	397
S67.10XS	229
S67.19[Ø,1,2,3,4,5,6,7,8]A	360, 425
S67.19[Ø,1,2,3,4,5,6,7,8]D	397
S67.19[Ø,1]S	229
S67.19[2,3]S	229
S67.19[4,5]S	229
S67.19[6,7]S	229
S67.198S	229
S67.2[Ø,1,2]XA	360, 425
S67.2[Ø,1,2]XD	397
S67.2[Ø,1,2]XS	229
S67.3[Ø,1,2]XA	360, 425
S67.3[Ø,1,2]XD	397
S67.3[Ø,1,2]XS	229
S67.4[Ø,1,2]XA	360, 425
S67.4[Ø,1,2]XD	397
S67.4[Ø,1,2]XS	229
S67.9[Ø,1,2]XA	360, 426
S67.9[Ø,1,2]XD	397
S67.9[Ø,1,2]XS	229
S68.0[1,2][1,2,9]A	360, 426
S68.0[1,2][1,2,9]D	397
S68.0[1,2][1,2,9]S	176
S68.1[1,2][Ø,1,2,3,4,5,6,7,8,9]A	360, 426
S68.1[1,2][Ø,1,2,3,4,5,6,7,8,9]D	397
S68.11[Ø,1,2,3,4,5,6,7,8,9]S	176
S68.12[Ø,1,2,3,4,5,6,7,8,9]S	176
S68.4[1,2][1,2,9]A	360, 426, 435
S68.4[1,2][1,2,9]D	397
S68.4[1,2][1,2,9]S	176
S68.5[1,2][1,2,9]A	360, 426
S68.5[1,2][1,2,9]D	397
S68.5[1,2][1,2,9]S	176
S68.6[1,2][Ø,1,2,3,4,5,6,7,8,9]A	360, 426
S68.6[1,2][Ø,1,2,3,4,5,6,7,8,9]D	397
S68.61[Ø,1,2,3,4,5,6,7,8,9]S	176
S68.62[Ø,1,2,3,4,5,6,7,8,9]S	176
S68.7[1,2][1,2,9]A	360, 426, 435
S68.7[1,2][1,2,9]D	397
S68.7[1,2][1,2,9]S	176
S69.[8,9][Ø,1,2]X[A,S]	360
S69.[8,9][Ø,1,2]XA	426
S69.[8,9][Ø,1,2]XD	397
S70.[Ø,1][Ø,1,2]XA	426
S70.0[Ø,1,2]X[A,S]	229
S70.0[Ø,1,2]XD	397
S70.1[Ø,1,2]X[A,S]	229
S70.1[Ø,1,2]XD	397
S70.2[1,2,4,5,6,7][1,2,9]A	426
S70.2[1,2,4,5,6,7][1,2,9]D	397
S70.2[2,6][1,2,9]A	234
S70.21[1,2,9][A,S]	229
S70.22[1,2,9]S	229
S70.24[1,2,9][A,S]	229
S70.25[1,2,9][A,S]	229
S70.26[1,2,9]S	229
S70.27[1,2,9][A,S]	229
S70.3[1,2,4,5,6,7][1,2,9]A	426
S70.3[1,2,4,5,6,7][1,2,9]D	397
S70.3[2,6][1,2,9]A	234
S70.31[1,2,9][A,S]	229
S70.32[1,2,9]S	229
S70.34[1,2,9][A,S]	229
S70.35[1,2,9][A,S]	229
S70.36[1,2,9]S	229
S70.37[1,2,9][A,S]	229
S70.9[1,2][1,2,9]A	426
S70.9[1,2][1,2,9]D	397
S70.91[1,2,9][A,S]	229
S70.92[1,2,9][A,S]	229
S71.0[Ø,1,2,3,4,5][1,2,9]A	426
S71.0[Ø,1,2,3,4,5][1,2,9]D	397
S71.0[2,4][1,2,9]A	360
S71.00[1,2,9][A,S]	229
S71.01[1,2,9][A,S]	229
S71.02[1,2,9]S	229
S71.03[1,2,9][A,S]	229
S71.04[1,2,9]S	229
S71.05[1,2,9][A,S]	229
S71.1[Ø,1,2,3,4,5][1,2,9]D	397
S71.1[Ø,12,3,4,5][1,2,9]A	426
S71.1[2,4][1,2,9]A	360
S71.10[1,2,9][A,S]	229
S71.11[1,2,9][A,S]	229
S71.111A	426
S71.112A	426
S71.119A	426
S71.12[1,2,9]S	229
S71.121A	426
S71.122A	426
S71.129A	426
S71.13[1,2,9][A,S]	229
S71.14[1,2,9]S	229
S71.15[1,2,9][A,S]	229
S72.00[1,2,9][A,B,C]	162, 286, 426, 435
S72.00[1,2,9][D,E,F,G,H,J,S]	176
S72.00[1,2,9][K,M,N,P,Q,R]	200
S72.01[1,2,9][A,B,C]	162, 286, 426, 435
S72.01[1,2,9][D,E,F,G,H,J,S]	176
S72.01[1,2,9][K,M,N,P,Q,R]	200
S72.02[1,2,3,4,5,6][A,B,C]	426
S72.02[1,2,3][A,B,C]	162, 286, 435
S72.02[1,2,3][D,E,F,G,H,J,S]	177
S72.02[1,2,3][K,M,N,P,Q,R]	200
S72.02[4,5,6][A,B,C]	162, 286, 435
S72.02[4,5,6][D,E,F,G,H,J,S]	177
S72.02[4,5,6][K,M,N,P,Q,R]	200
S72.03[1,2,3,4,5,6][A,B,C]	426
S72.03[1,2,3][A,B,C]	162, 286, 435
S72.03[1,2,3][D,E,F,G,H,J,S]	177
S72.03[1,2,3][K,M,N,P,Q,R]	200
S72.03[4,5,6][A,B,C]	162, 286, 435
S72.03[4,5,6][D,E,F,G,H,J,S]	177
S72.03[4,5,6][K,M,N,P,Q,R]	201
S72.04[1,2,3,4,5,6][A,B,C]	426
S72.04[1,2,3][A,B,C]	162, 286, 435
S72.04[1,2,3][D,E,F,G,H,J,S]	177
S72.04[1,2,3][K,M,N,P,Q,R]	201
S72.04[4,5,6][A,B,C]	162, 286, 435
S72.04[4,5,6][D,E,F,G,H,J,S]	177
S72.04[4,5,6][K,M,N,P,Q,R]	201
S72.05[1,2,9][A,B,C]	162, 286, 426, 435
S72.05[1,2,9][D,E,F,G,H,J,S]	177
S72.05[1,2,9][K,M,N,P,Q,R]	201
S72.06[1,2,3,4,5,6][A,B,C]	426
S72.06[1,2,3][A,B,C]	162, 286, 435
S72.06[1,2,3][D,E,F,G,H,J,S]	177
S72.06[1,2,3][K,M,N,P,Q,R]	201
S72.06[4,5,6][A,B,C]	162, 286, 435
S72.06[4,5,6][D,E,F,G,H,J,S]	177
S72.06[4,5,6][K,M,N,P,Q,R]	201
S72.09[1,2,9][A,B,C]	162, 286, 426, 435
S72.09[1,2,9][D,E,F,G,H,J,S]	177
S72.09[1,2,9][K,M,N,P,Q,R]	201
S72.10[1,2,9][A,B,C]	162, 286, 426, 435
S72.10[1,2,9][D,E,F,G,H,J,S]	177
S72.10[1,2,9][K,M,N,P,Q,R]	201
S72.11[1,2,3,4,5,6][A,B,C]	426
S72.11[1,2,3][A,B,C]	162, 286, 435
S72.11[1,2,3][D,E,F,G,H,J,S]	177
S72.11[1,2,3][K,M,N,P,Q,R]	201
S72.11[4,5,6][A,B,C]	162, 286, 435
S72.11[4,5,6][D,E,F,G,H,J,S]	177
S72.11[4,5,6][K,M,N,P,Q,R]	201
S72.12[1,2,3,4,5,6][A,B,C]	426
S72.12[1,2,3][A,B,C]	162, 286, 435
S72.12[1,2,3][D,E,F,G,H,J,S]	177
S72.12[1,2,3][K,M,N,P,Q,R]	201
S72.12[4,5,6][A,B,C]	162, 286, 435
S72.12[4,5,6][D,E,F,G,H,J,S]	177
S72.12[4,5,6][K,M,N,P,Q,R]	201
S72.13[1,2,3,4,5,6][A,B,C]	426
S72.13[1,2,3][A,B,C]	162, 286, 435
S72.13[1,2,3][D,E,F,G,H,J,S]	177
S72.13[1,2,3][K,M,N,P,Q,R]	201
S72.13[4,5,6][A,B,C]	162, 286, 435
S72.13[4,5,6][D,E,F,G,H,J,S]	177
S72.13[4,5,6][K,M,N,P,Q,R]	201
S72.14[1,2,3,4,5,6][A,B,C]	426
S72.14[1,2,3][A,B,C]	162, 286, 435
S72.14[1,2,3][D,E,F,G,H,J,S]	177
S72.14[1,2,3][K,M,N,P,Q,R]	201
S72.14[4,5,6][A,B,C]	162, 286, 435
S72.14[4,5,6][D,E,F,G,H,J,S]	177
S72.14[4,5,6][K,M,N,P,Q,R]	201
S72.2[1,2,3,4,5,6]X[A,B,C]	426
S72.2[1,2,3]X[A,B,C]	162, 286, 435
S72.2[1,2,3]X[D,E,F,G,H,J,S]	177
S72.2[1,2,3]X[K,M,N,P,Q,R]	201
S72.2[4,5,6]X[A,B,C]	162, 286, 435
S72.2[4,5,6]X[D,E,F,G,H,J,S]	177
S72.2[4,5,6]X[K,M,N,P,Q,R]	201
S72.30[1,2,9][A,B,C]	
S72.30[1,2,9][A,B,C]	161, 286, 426, 435
S72.30[1,2,9][D,E,F,G,H,J,S]	177
S72.30[1,2,9][K,M,N,P,Q,R]	201
S72.32[1,2,3,4,5,6][A,B,C]	426
S72.32[1,2,3][A,B,C]	161, 286, 435
S72.32[1,2,3][D,E,F,G,H,J,S]	178
S72.32[1,2,3][K,M,N,P,Q,R]	201
S72.32[4,5,6][A,B,C]	161, 286, 435
S72.32[4,5,6][D,E,F,G,H,J,S]	178
S72.32[4,5,6][K,M,N,P,Q,R]	201
S72.33[1,2,3,4,5,6][A,B,C]	426
S72.33[1,2,3][A,B,C]	161, 286, 435
S72.33[1,2,3][D,E,F,G,H,J,S]	178
S72.33[1,2,3][K,M,N,P,Q,R]	201
S72.33[4,5,6][A,B,C]	161, 286, 435
S72.33[4,5,6][D,E,F,G,H,J,S]	178
S72.33[4,5,6][K,M,N,P,Q,R]	201
S72.34[1,2,3,4,5,6][A,B,C]	426
S72.34[1,2,3][A,B,C]	161, 286, 435
S72.34[1,2,3][D,E,F,G,H,J,S]	178
S72.34[1,2,3][K,M,N,P,Q,R]	201
S72.34[4,5,6][A,B,C]	161, 286, 435
S72.34[4,5,6][D,E,F,G,H,J,S]	178
S72.34[4,5,6][K,M,N,P,Q,R]	201
S72.35[1,2,3,4,5,6][A,B,C]	426
S72.35[1,2,3][A,B,C]	161, 286, 435
S72.35[1,2,3][D,E,F,G,H,J,S]	178
S72.35[1,2,3][K,M,N,P,Q,R]	201
S72.35[4,5,6][A,B,C]	161, 286, 435
S72.35[4,5,6][D,E,F,G,H,J,S]	178
S72.35[4,5,6][K,M,N,P,Q,R]	201
S72.36[1,2,3,4,5,6][A,B,C]	426
S72.36[1,2,3][A,B,C]	161, 286, 435
S72.36[1,2,3][D,E,F,G,H,J,S]	178
S72.36[1,2,3][K,M,N,P,Q,R]	201
S72.36[4,5,6][A,B,C]	161, 286, 435
S72.36[4,5,6][D,E,F,G,H,J,S]	178
S72.36[4,5,6][K,M,N,P,Q,R]	201
S72.39[1,2,9][A,B,C]	161, 286, 426, 435
S72.39[1,2,9][D,E,F,G,H,J,S]	178
S72.39[1,2,9][K,M,N,P,Q,R]	201
S72.40[1,2,9][A,B,C]	161, 426, 435
S72.40[1,2,9][D,E,F,G,H,J,S]	178
S72.40[1,2,9][K,M,N,P,Q,R]	201
S72.41[1,2,3,4,5,6][A,B,C]	426

Numeric Index to Diseases

Code	Page	Code	Page	Code	Page	Code	Page
S83.11[1,2,3][A,S]	191	S83.41[1,2,9][A,S]	192	S85.5[0,1,9][1,2,9]D	398	S89.02[1,2,9][D,G,S]	182
S83.11[1,2,3]A	428	S83.42[1,2,9][A,S]	192	S85.50[1,2,9]S	101	S89.03[1,2,9][D,G,S]	182
S83.11[1,2,3]D	398	S83.5[0,1,2][1,2,9]A	428	S85.51[1,2,9]S	101	S89.04[1,2,9][D,G,S]	182
S83.11[4,5,6][A,S]	191	S83.5[0,1,2][1,2,9]D	398	S85.59[1,2,9]S	101	S89.09[1,2,9][D,G,S]	182
S83.11[4,5,6]A	428	S83.50[1,2,9][A,S]	192	S85.8[0,1,9][1,2,9]A	361, 428, 436	S89.09[1,2,9][K,P]	204
S83.11[4,5,6]D	398	S83.51[1,2,9][A,S]	192	S85.8[0,1,9][1,2,9]D	398	S89.09[1,2,9]A	192, 428
S83.12[1,2,3][A,S]	191	S83.52[1,2,9][A,S]	192	S85.80[1,2,9]S	101	S89.1[1,2,3,4][1,2,9][K,P]	204
S83.12[1,2,3]A	428	S83.6[0,1,2]X[A,S]	192	S85.81[1,2,9]S	101	S89.1[1,2,3,4][1,2,9]A	192, 428
S83.12[1,2,3]D	398	S83.6[0,1,2]XA	428	S85.89[1,2,9]S	101	S89.10[1,2,9][D,G,S]	182
S83.12[4,5,6][A,S]	191	S83.6[0,1,2]XD	398	S85.9[0,1,9][1,2,9]A	361, 428	S89.10[1,2,9][K,P]	204
S83.12[4,5,6]A	428	S83.8X[1,2,9][A,S]	192	S85.9[0,1,9][1,2,9]D	398	S89.10[1,2,9]A	192, 428
S83.12[4,5,6]D	398	S83.8X[1,2,9]A	428	S85.90[1,2,9]S	101	S89.11[1,2,9][D,G,S]	182
S83.13[1,2,3][A,S]	191	S83.8X[1,2,9]D	398	S85.91[1,2,9]S	101	S89.12[1,2,9][D,G,S]	182
S83.13[1,2,3]A	428	S83.9[0,1,2]X[A,S]	192	S85.99[1,2,9]S	101	S89.13[1,2,9][D,G,S]	182
S83.13[1,2,3]D	398	S83.9[0,1,2]XA	428	S86.[1,2,3]2[1,2,9]A	204	S89.14[1,2,9][D,G,S]	182
S83.13[4,5,6][A,S]	191	S83.9[0,1,2]XD	398	S86.[8,9]2[1,2,9]A	204	S89.19[1,2,9][D,G,S]	182
S83.13[4,5,6]A	428	S84.[0,1,2][0,1,2]XD	398	S86.[8,9]2[1,2,9]S	229	S89.19[1,2,9][K,P]	204
S83.13[4,5,6]D	398	S84.0[0,1,2]XA	34, 428, 436	S86.0[0,1,2,9][1,2,9]A	428	S89.19[1,2,9]A	192, 428
S83.14[1,2,3][A,S]	191	S84.0[0,1,2]XS	40	S86.0[0,1,2,9][1,2,9]D	398	S89.2[0,1,2,9][1,2,9]A	192, 428
S83.14[1,2,3]A	428	S84.1[0,1,2]XA	34, 428, 436	S86.0[0,9][1,2,9][A,S]	361	S89.2[1,2][1,2,9][K,P]	204
S83.14[1,2,3]D	398	S84.1[0,1,2]XS	40	S86.01[1,2,9][A,S]	192	S89.20[1,2,9][D,G,S]	182
S83.14[4,5,6][A,S]	191	S84.2[0,1,2]XA	34, 428	S86.02[1,2,9]A	203	S89.20[1,2,9][K,P]	204
S83.14[4,5,6]A	428	S84.2[0,1,2]XS	40	S86.02[1,2,9]S	229	S89.21[1,2,9][D,G,S]	182
S83.14[4,5,6]D	398	S84.80[1,2,9]A	428, 436	S86.1[0,1,2,9][1,2,9]A	428	S89.22[1,2,9][D,G,S]	182
S83.19[1,2,3][A,S]	191	S84.80[1,2,9]D	398	S86.1[0,1,2,9][1,2,9]D	398	S89.29[1,2,9][D,G,S]	182
S83.19[1,2,3]A	428	S84.80[1,2,9]S	40	S86.1[0,9][1,2,9][A,S]	361	S89.29[1,2,9][K,P]	204
S83.19[1,2,3]D	398	S84.801A	34	S86.11[1,2,9][A,S]	192	S89.3[0,1,2,9][1,2,9]A	192, 428
S83.19[4,5,6][A,S]	191	S84.802A	34	S86.12[1,2,9]S	229	S89.3[1,2][1,2,9][K,P]	204
S83.19[4,5,6]A	428	S84.809A	34	S86.2[0,1,2,9][1,2,9]A	428	S89.30[1,2,9][D,G,S]	182
S83.19[4,5,6]D	398	S84.9[0,1,2]XA	34, 428, 436	S86.2[0,1,2,9][1,2,9]D	398	S89.30[1,2,9][K,P]	204
S83.20[0,1,2][A,S]	191	S84.9[0,1,2]XD	398	S86.2[0,9][1,2,9][A,S]	361	S89.31[1,2,9][D,G,S]	182
S83.20[0,1,2]A	428	S84.9[0,1,2]XS	40	S86.21[1,2,9][A,S]	192	S89.32[1,2,9][D,G,S]	182
S83.20[0,1,2]D	398	S85.0[0,1,9][1,2,9]A	360, 428, 436	S86.22[1,2,9]S	229	S89.39[1,2,9][D,G,S]	182
S83.20[3,4,5][A,S]	192	S85.0[0,1,9][1,2,9]D	398	S86.3[0,1,2,9][1,2,9]A	428	S89.39[1,2,9][K,P]	204
S83.20[3,4,5]A	428	S85.00[1,2,9]S	101	S86.3[0,1,2,9][1,2,9]D	398	S89.8[0,1,2]XA	428
S83.20[3,4,5]D	398	S85.01[1,2,9]S	101	S86.3[0,9][1,2,9][A,S]	361	S89.9[0,1,2]XA	428
S83.20[6,7,9][A,S]	192	S85.09[1,2,9]S	101	S86.31[1,2,9][A,S]	192	S90.0[0,1,2]X[A,S]	229
S83.20[6,7,9]A	428	S85.1[0,1,2][1,2,9]A	360, 428, 436	S86.32[1,2,9]S	229	S90.0[0,1,2]XA	428
S83.20[6,7,9]D	398	S85.1[0,1,2][1,2,9]D	398	S86.8[0,1,2,9][1,2,9]A	428	S90.0[0,1,2]XD	398
S83.21[1,2,9][A,S]	192	S85.1[3,4,5][1,2,9]A	360, 428, 436	S86.8[0,1,2,9][1,2,9]D	398	S90.1[1,2][1,2,9]A	428
S83.21[1,2,9]A	428	S85.1[3,4,5][1,2,9]D	398	S86.8[0,9][1,2,9][A,S]	361	S90.1[1,2][1,2,9]D	398
S83.21[1,2,9]D	398	S85.1[6,7,8][1,2,9]A	428	S86.81[1,2,9][A,S]	192	S90.11[1,2,9][A,S]	230
S83.22[1,2,9][A,S]	192	S85.1[6,7,8][1,2,9]A	360, 436	S86.9[0,1,2,9][1,2,9]A	428	S90.12[1,2,9][A,S]	230
S83.22[1,2,9]A	428	S85.1[6,7,8][1,2,9]D	398	S86.9[0,1,2,9][1,2,9]D	398	S90.2[1,2][1,2,9]A	428
S83.22[1,2,9]D	398	S85.10[1,2,9]S	101	S86.9[0,9][1,2,9][A,S]	361	S90.2[1,2][1,2,9]D	398
S83.23[1,2,9][A,S]	192	S85.11[1,2,9]S	101	S86.91[1,2,9][A,S]	192	S90.21[1,2,9][A,S]	230
S83.23[1,2,9]A	428	S85.12[1,2,9]S	101	S87.0[0,1,2]XA	361, 428, 436	S90.22[1,2,9][A,S]	230
S83.23[1,2,9]D	398	S85.13[1,2,9]S	101	S87.0[0,1,2]XD	398	S90.3[0,1,2]X[A,S]	230
S83.24[1,2,9][A,S]	192	S85.14[1,2,9]S	101	S87.0[0,1,2]XS	229	S90.3[0,1,2]XA	428
S83.24[1,2,9]A	428	S85.15[1,2,9]S	101	S87.8[0,1,2]XA	361, 428, 436	S90.3[0,1,2]XD	398
S83.24[1,2,9]D	398	S85.16[1,2,9]S	101	S87.8[0,1,2]XD	398	S90.4[2,6][1,2,3]A	234
S83.25[1,2,9][A,S]	192	S85.17[1,2,9]S	101	S87.8[0,1,2]XS	229	S90.4[2,6][4,5,6]A	234
S83.25[1,2,9]A	428	S85.18[1,2,9]S	101	S88.0[1,2][1,2,9]A	361, 428, 436	S90.41[1,2,3][A,S]	230
S83.25[1,2,9]D	398	S85.2[0,1,9][1,2,9]A	361, 428, 436	S88.0[1,2][1,2,9]D	398	S90.41[1,2,3]A	428
S83.26[1,2,9][A,S]	192	S85.2[0,1,9][1,2,9]D	398	S88.0[1,2][1,2,9]S	182	S90.41[1,2,3]D	398
S83.26[1,2,9]A	428	S85.20[1,2,9]S	101	S88.1[1,2][1,2,9]A	361, 428, 436	S90.41[4,5,6][A,S]	230
S83.26[1,2,9]D	398	S85.21[1,2,9]S	101	S88.1[1,2][1,2,9]D	398	S90.41[4,5,6]A	428
S83.27[1,2,9][A,S]	192	S85.29[1,2,9]S	101	S88.1[1,2][1,2,9]S	182	S90.41[4,5,6]D	398
S83.27[1,2,9]A	428	S85.3[0,1,9][1,2,9]A	361, 428	S88.9[1,2][1,2,9]A	361, 428, 436	S90.42[1,2,3]A	428
S83.27[1,2,9]D	398	S85.3[0,1,9][1,2,9]D	398	S88.9[1,2][1,2,9]D	398	S90.42[1,2,3]D	399
S83.28[1,2,9][A,S]	192	S85.30[1,2,9]S	101	S88.9[1,2][1,2,9]S	182	S90.42[1,2,3]S	230
S83.28[1,2,9]A	428	S85.31[1,2,9]S	101	S89.[8,9][0,1,2]X[A,S]	361	S90.42[4,5,6]A	428
S83.28[1,2,9]D	398	S85.39[1,2,9]S	101	S89.[8,9][0,1,2]XD	398	S90.42[4,5,6]D	399
S83.3[0,1,2]X[A,S]	192	S85.4[0,1,9][1,2,9]A	361, 428	S89.0[1,2,3,4][1,2,9][K,P]	204	S90.42[4,5,6]S	230
S83.3[0,1,2]XA	428	S85.4[0,1,9][1,2,9]D	398	S89.0[1,2,3,4][1,2,9]A	192, 428	S90.44[1,2,3][A,S]	230
S83.3[0,1,2]XD	398	S85.40[1,2,9]S	101	S89.00[1,2,9][D,G,S]	182	S90.44[1,2,3]A	428
S83.4[0,1,2][1,2,9]A	428	S85.41[1,2,9]S	101	S89.00[1,2,9][K,P]	204	S90.44[1,2,3]D	399
S83.4[0,1,2][1,2,9]D	398	S85.49[1,2,9]S	101	S89.00[1,2,9]A	192, 428	S90.44[4,5,6][A,S]	230
S83.40[1,2,9][A,S]	192	S85.5[0,1,9][1,2,9]A	361, 428, 436	S89.01[1,2,9][D,G,S]	182	S90.44[4,5,6]A	428

Code	Page	Code	Page	Code	Page	Code	Page
S92.23[4,5,6][D,G,S]	183	S92.50[1,2,3][D,G,S]	183	S93.139A	430	S93.60[1,2,9][A,S]	193
S92.23[4,5,6][K,P]	204	S92.50[1,2,3][K,P]	204	S93.139D	399	S93.60[1,2,9]A	430
S92.24[1,2,3][A,B]	192, 429	S92.50[4,5,6][A,B]	193, 429	S93.14[1,2,3][A,S]	193	S93.60[1,2,9]D	399
S92.24[1,2,3][D,G,S]	183	S92.50[4,5,6][D,G,S]	183	S93.14[1,2,3]A	430	S93.61[1,2,9][A,S]	193
S92.24[1,2,3][K,P]	204	S92.50[4,5,6][K,P]	204	S93.14[1,2,3]D	399	S93.61[1,2,9]A	430
S92.24[4,5,6][A,B]	192, 429	S92.51[1,2,3][A,B]	193, 429	S93.14[4,5,6][A,S]	193	S93.61[1,2,9]D	399
S92.24[4,5,6][D,G,S]	183	S92.51[1,2,3][D,G,S]	183	S93.14[4,5,6]A	430	S93.62[1,2,9][A,S]	193
S92.24[4,5,6][K,P]	204	S92.51[1,2,3][K,P]	204	S93.14[4,5,6]D	399	S93.62[1,2,9]A	430
S92.25[1,2,3][A,B]	192, 429	S92.51[4,5,6][A,B]	193, 429	S93.149[A,S]	193	S93.62[1,2,9]D	399
S92.25[1,2,3][D,G,S]	183	S92.51[4,5,6][D,G,S]	183	S93.149A	430	S93.69[1,2,9][A,S]	193
S92.25[1,2,3][K,P]	204	S92.51[4,5,6][K,P]	204	S93.149D	399	S93.69[1,2,9]A	430
S92.25[4,5,6][A,B]	192, 429	S92.52[1,2,3][A,B]	193, 430	S93.30[1,2,3][A,S]	193	S93.69[1,2,9]D	399
S92.25[4,5,6][D,G,S]	183	S92.52[1,2,3][D,G,S]	183	S93.30[1,2,3]A	430	S94.[0,1,2,3][0,1,2]XA	430
S92.25[4,5,6][K,P]	204	S92.52[1,2,3][K,P]	204	S93.30[1,2,3]D	399	S94.[0,1,2,3][0,1,2]XD	399
S92.30[1,2,9][A,B]	192, 429	S92.52[4,5,6][A,B]	193, 430	S93.30[4,5,6][A,S]	193	S94.0[0,1,2]XA	34
S92.30[1,2,9][D,G,S]	183	S92.52[4,5,6][D,G,S]	183	S93.30[4,5,6]A	430	S94.0[0,1,2]XS	40
S92.30[1,2,9][K,P]	204	S92.52[4,5,6][K,P]	204	S93.30[4,5,6]D	399	S94.1[0,1,2]XA	34
S92.31[1,2,3][A,B]	192, 429	S92.53[1,2,3][A,B]	193, 430	S93.31[1,2,3][A,S]	193	S94.1[0,1,2]XS	40
S92.31[1,2,3][D,G,S]	183	S92.53[1,2,3][D,G,S]	183	S93.31[1,2,3]A	430	S94.2[0,1,2]XA	34, 436
S92.31[1,2,3][K,P]	204	S92.53[1,2,3][K,P]	204	S93.31[1,2,3]D	399	S94.2[0,1,2]XS	40
S92.31[4,5,6][A,B]	192, 429	S92.53[4,5,6][A,B]	193, 430	S93.31[4,5,6][A,S]	193	S94.3[0,1,2]XA	34
S92.31[4,5,6][D,G,S]	183	S92.53[4,5,6][D,G,S]	183	S93.31[4,5,6]A	430	S94.3[0,1,2]XS	40
S92.31[4,5,6][K,P]	204	S92.53[4,5,6][K,P]	204	S93.31[4,5,6]D	399	S94.8X[1,2,9]A	430, 436
S92.32[1,2,3][A,B]	192, 429	S92.59[1,2,9][A,B]	193, 430	S93.32[1,2,3][A,S]	193	S94.8X[1,2,9]D	399
S92.32[1,2,3][D,G,S]	183	S92.59[1,2,9][D,G,S]	183	S93.32[1,2,3]A	430	S94.8X[1,2,9]S	40
S92.32[1,2,3][K,P]	204	S92.59[1,2,9][K,P]	204	S93.32[1,2,3]D	399	S94.8X1A	34
S92.32[4,5,6][A,B]	192, 429	S92.90[1,2,9][A,B]	193, 430	S93.32[4,5,6][A,S]	193	S94.8X2A	34
S92.32[4,5,6][D,G,S]	183	S92.90[1,2,9][D,G,S]	183	S93.32[4,5,6]A	430	S94.8X9A	34
S92.32[4,5,6][K,P]	204	S92.90[1,2,9][K,P]	204	S93.32[4,5,6]D	399	S94.9[0,1,2]XA	34, 430, 436
S92.33[1,2,3][A,B]	192, 429	S92.91[1,2,9][A,B]	193, 430	S93.33[1,2,3][A,S]	193	S94.9[0,1,2]XD	399
S92.33[1,2,3][D,G,S]	183	S92.91[1,2,9][D,G,S]	183	S93.33[1,2,3]A	430	S94.9[0,1,2]XS	40
S92.33[1,2,3][K,P]	204	S92.91[1,2,9][K,P]	204	S93.33[1,2,3]D	399	S95.0[0,1,9][1,2,9]A	361, 430, 437
S92.33[4,5,6][A,B]	192, 429	S93.0[1,2,3]X[A,S]	193	S93.33[4,5,6][A,S]	193	S95.0[0,1,9][1,2,9]D	399
S92.33[4,5,6][D,G,S]	183	S93.0[1,2,3]XA	430	S93.33[4,5,6]A	430	S95.00[1,2,9]S	101
S92.33[4,5,6][K,P]	204	S93.0[1,2,3]XD	399	S93.33[4,5,6]D	399	S95.01[1,2,9]S	101
S92.34[1,2,3][A,B]	192, 429	S93.0[4,5,6]X[A,S]	193	S93.4[0,1,2,3,9][1,2,9]A	430	S95.09[1,2,9]S	101
S92.34[1,2,3][D,G,S]	183	S93.0[4,5,6]XA	430	S93.4[0,1,2,3,9][1,2,9]D	399	S95.1[0,1,9][1,2,9]A	361, 430
S92.34[1,2,3][K,P]	204	S93.0[4,5,6]XD	399	S93.40[1,2,9][A,S]	193	S95.1[0,1,9][1,2,9]D	399
S92.34[4,5,6][A,B]	192, 429	S93.10[1,2,3][A,S]	193	S93.41[1,2,9][A,S]	193	S95.10[1,2,9]S	101
S92.34[4,5,6][D,G,S]	183	S93.10[1,2,3]A	430	S93.42[1,2,9][A,S]	193	S95.11[1,2,9]S	101
S92.34[4,5,6][K,P]	204	S93.10[1,2,3]D	399	S93.43[1,2,9][A,S]	193	S95.19[1,2,9]S	101
S92.35[1,2,3][A,B]	192, 429	S93.10[4,5,6][A,S]	193	S93.49[1,2,9][A,S]	193	S95.2[0,1,9][1,2,9]A	361, 430, 437
S92.35[1,2,3][D,G,S]	183	S93.10[4,5,6]A	430	S93.50[1,2,3][A,S]	193	S95.2[0,1,9][1,2,9]D	399
S92.35[1,2,3][K,P]	204	S93.10[4,5,6]D	399	S93.50[1,2,3]A	430	S95.20[1,2,9]S	101
S92.35[4,5,6][A,B]	192, 429	S93.11[1,2,3][A,S]	193	S93.50[1,2,3]D	399	S95.21[1,2,9]S	101
S92.35[4,5,6][D,G,S]	183	S93.11[1,2,3]A	430	S93.50[4,5,6][A,S]	193	S95.29[1,2,9]S	101
S92.35[4,5,6][K,P]	204	S93.11[1,2,3]D	399	S93.50[4,5,6]A	430	S95.8[0,1,9][1,2,9]A	361, 430, 437
S92.40[1,2,3][A,B]	192, 429	S93.11[4,5,6][A,S]	193	S93.50[4,5,6]D	399	S95.8[0,1,9][1,2,9]D [	399
S92.40[1,2,3][D,G,S]	183	S93.11[4,5,6]A	430	S93.509[A,S]	193	S95.80[1,2,9]S	101
S92.40[1,2,3][K,P]	204	S93.11[4,5,6]D	399	S93.509A	430	S95.81[1,2,9]S	101
S92.40[4,5,6][A,B]	192, 429	S93.119[A,S]	193	S93.509D	399	S95.89[1,2,9]S	101
S92.40[4,5,6][D,G,S]	183	S93.119A	430	S93.51[1,2,3][A,S]	193	S95.9[0,1,9][1,2,9]A	361, 430
S92.40[4,5,6][K,P]	204	S93.119D	399	S93.51[1,2,3]A	430	S95.9[0,1,9][1,2,9]D	399
S92.41[1,2,3][A,B]	192, 429	S93.12[1,2,3][A,S]	193	S93.51[1,2,3]D	399	S95.90[1,2,9]S	101
S92.41[1,2,3][D,G,S]	183	S93.12[1,2,3]A	430	S93.51[4,5,6][A,S]	193	S95.91[1,2,9]S	101
S92.41[1,2,3][K,P]	204	S93.12[1,2,3]D	399	S93.51[4,5,6]A	430	S95.99[1,2,9]S	101
S92.41[4,5,6][A,B]	192, 429	S93.12[4,5,6][A,S]	193	S93.51[4,5,6]D	399	S96.[0,1]2[1,2,9]A	204
S92.41[4,5,6][D,G,S]	183	S93.12[4,5,6]A	430	S93.519[A,S]	193	S96.[2,8,9]2[1,2,9]A	204
S92.41[4,5,6][K,P]	204	S93.12[4,5,6]D	399	S93.519A	430	S96.0[0,1,2,9][1,2,9]A	430
S92.42[1,2,3][A,B]	192, 429	S93.129[A,S]	193	S93.519D	399	S96.0[0,1,2,9][1,2,9]D	399
S92.42[1,2,3][D,G,S]	183	S93.129A	430	S93.52[1,2,3][A,S]	193	S96.0[0,9][1,2,9][A,S]	361
S92.42[1,2,3][K,P]	204	S93.129D	399	S93.52[1,2,3]A	430	S96.01[1,2,9][A,S]	193
S92.42[4,5,6][A,B]	192, 429	S93.13[1,2,3][A,S]	193	S93.52[1,2,3]D	399	S96.02[1,2,9]S	230
S92.42[4,5,6][D,G,S]	183	S93.13[1,2,3]A	430	S93.52[4,5,6][A,S]	193	S96.1[0,1,2,9][1,2,9]A	430
S92.42[4,5,6][K,P]	204	S93.13[1,2,3]D	399	S93.52[4,5,6]A	430	S96.1[0,1,2,9][1,2,9]D	400
S92.49[1,2,9][A,B]	192, 429	S93.13[4,5,6][A,S]	193	S93.52[4,5,6]D	399	S96.1[0,9][1,2,9][A,S]	361
S92.49[1,2,9][D,G,S]	183	S93.13[4,5,6]A	430	S93.529[A,S]	193	S96.11[1,2,9][A,S]	193
S92.49[1,2,9][K,P]	204	S93.13[4,5,6]D	399	S93.529A	430	S96.12[1,2,9]S	230
S92.50[1,2,3][A,B]	193, 429	S93.139[A,S]	193	S93.529D	399	S96.2[0,1,2,9][1,2,9]A	430

Numeric Index to Diseases

Code	Page	Code	Page	Code	Page	Code	Page
S96.2[0,1,2,9][1,2,9]D	400	T15.9[0,1,2]XS	361	T18.1[0,1,2,9][0,8]S	361	T20.31[1,2,9]S	230
S96.2[0,9][1,2,9][A,S]	361	T16.[1,2,9]XXD	400	T18.10[0,8]A	118	T20.39XA	377,379,381,382
S96.21[1,2,9][A,S]	193	T16.[1,2,9]XXS	361	T18.11[0,8]A	118	T20.39XD	400
S96.22[1,2,9]S	230	T16.1XXA	58	T18.12[0,8]A	118	T20.39XS	230
S96.8[0,1,2,9][1,2,9]A	430	T16.2XXA	58	T18.19[0,8]A	118	T20.4[2,3,4]XA	383
S96.8[0,1,2,9][1,2,9]D	400	T16.9XXA	58	T19.[0,1,2,3,4,8,9]XXD	400	T20.4[2,3,4]XD	400
S96.8[0,9][1,2,9][A,S]	361	T17.[0,1]XXD	400	T19.[0,1,2,3,4,8,9]XXS	361	T20.4[2,3,4]XS	230
S96.81[1,2,9][A,S]	193	T17.[0,1]XXS	361	T19.0XXA	256	T20.4[5,6,7]XA	383
S96.82[1,2,9]S	230	T17.0XXA	58	T19.1XXA	256	T20.4[5,6,7]XD	400
S96.9[0,1,2,9][1,2,9]A	430	T17.1XXA	58	T19.2XXA	265,270	T20.4[5,6,7]XS	230
S96.9[0,1,2,9][1,2,9]D	400	T17.2[0,1,2,9][0,8]D	400	T19.3XXA	265,270	T20.40XA	383
S96.9[0,9][1,2,9][A,S]	361	T17.2[0,1,2,9][0,8]S	361	T19.4XXA	261	T20.40XD	400
S96.91[1,2,9][A,S]	193	T17.20[0,8]A	58	T19.8XXA	256	T20.40XS	230
S96.92[1,2,9]S	230	T17.200A	6	T19.9XXA	256	T20.41[1,2,9]A	383
S97.0[0,1,2]XA	361,430	T17.208A	6	T20.0[2,3,4]XA	382	T20.41[1,2,9]D	400
S97.0[0,1,2]XD	400	T17.21[0,8]A	58	T20.0[2,3,4]XD	400	T20.41[1,2,9]S	230
S97.0[0,1,2]XS	230	T17.210A	6	T20.0[2,3,4]XS	230	T20.49XA	383
S97.1[0,1,2][1,2,9]A	361,430	T17.218A	6	T20.0[5,6,7]XA	382	T20.49XD	400
S97.10[1,2,9]D	400	T17.22[0,8]A	58	T20.0[5,6,7]XD	400	T20.49XS	230
S97.10[1,2,9]S	230	T17.220A	6	T20.0[5,6,7]XS	230	T20.5[2,3,4]XA	383
S97.11[1,2,9]D	400	T17.228A	6	T20.00XA	382	T20.5[2,3,4]XD	400
S97.11[1,2,9]S	230	T17.29[0,8]A	58	T20.00XD	400	T20.5[2,3,4]XS	231
S97.12[1,2,9]D	400	T17.290A	6	T20.00XS	230	T20.5[5,6,7]XA	383
S97.12[1,2,9]S	230	T17.298A	6	T20.01[1,2,9]A	382	T20.5[5,6,7]XD	400
S97.8[0,1,2]XA	361,430	T17.3[0,1,2,9][0,8]D	400	T20.01[1,2,9]D	400	T20.5[5,6,7]XS	231
S97.8[0,1,2]XD	400	T17.3[0,1,2,9][0,8]S	361	T20.01[1,2,9]S	230	T20.50XA	383
S97.8[0,1,2]XS	230	T17.30[0,8]A	58	T20.09XA	382	T20.50XD	400
S98.0[1,2][1,2,9]A	361,430,437	T17.300A	6	T20.09XD	400	T20.50XS	230
S98.0[1,2][1,2,9]D	400	T17.308A	6	T20.09XS	230	T20.51[1,2,9]A	383
S98.0[1,2][1,2,9]S	183	T17.31[0,8]A	58	T20.1[2,3,4]XA	382	T20.51[1,2,9]D	400
S98.1[1,2][1,2,9]A	361,430	T17.310A	6	T20.1[2,3,4]XD	400	T20.51[1,2,9]S	231
S98.1[1,2][1,2,9]D	400	T17.318A	6	T20.1[2,3,4]XS	230	T20.59XA	383
S98.1[1,2][1,2,9]S	183	T17.32[0,8]A	58	T20.1[5,6,7]XA	382	T20.59XD	400
S98.1[3,4][1,2,9]A	361,430	T17.320A	6	T20.1[5,6,7]XD	400	T20.59XS	231
S98.1[3,4][1,2,9]D	400	T17.328A	6	T20.1[5,6,7]XS	230	T20.6[2,3,4]XA	383
S98.1[3,4][1,2,9]S	183	T17.39[0,8]A	58	T20.10XA	382	T20.6[2,3,4]XD	400
S98.2[1,2][1,2,9]A	361,430	T17.390A	6	T20.10XD	400	T20.6[2,3,4]XS	231
S98.2[1,2][1,2,9]D	400	T17.398A	6	T20.10XS	230	T20.6[5,6,7]XA	383
S98.2[1,2][1,2,9]S	183	T17.4[0,1,2,9][0,8]D	400	T20.11[1,2,9]A	382	T20.6[5,6,7]XD	400
S98.3[1,2][1,2,9]A	361,430,437	T17.4[0,1,2,9][0,8]S	361	T20.11[1,2,9]D	400	T20.6[5,6,7]XS	231
S98.3[1,2][1,2,9]D	400	T17.40[0,8]A	69	T20.11[1,2,9]S	230	T20.60XA	383
S98.3[1,2][1,2,9]S	183	T17.41[0,8]A	69	T20.19XA	382	T20.60XD	400
S98.9[1,2][1,2,9]A	361,430,437	T17.42[0,8]A	69	T20.19XD	400	T20.60XS	231
S98.9[1,2][1,2,9]D	400	T17.49[0,8]A	69	T20.19XS	230	T20.61[1,2,9]A	383
S98.9[1,2][1,2,9]S	183	T17.5[0,1,2,9][0,8]D	400	T20.2[2,3,4]XA	383	T20.61[1,2,9]D	400
S99.81[1,2,9][A,S]	361	T17.5[0,1,2,9][0,8]S	361	T20.2[2,3,4]XD	400	T20.61[1,2,9]S	231
S99.81[1,2,9]A	430	T17.50[0,8]A	69	T20.2[2,3,4]XS	230	T20.69XA	383
S99.81[1,2,9]D	400	T17.51[0,8]A	69	T20.2[5,6,7]XA	383	T20.69XD	400
S99.82[1,2,9][A,S]	361	T17.52[0,8]A	69	T20.2[5,6,7]XD	400	T20.69XS	231
S99.82[1,2,9]A	430	T17.59[0,8]A	70	T20.2[5,6,7]XS	230	T20.7[2,3,4,5,6,7]XA	377,379,381,382
S99.82[1,2,9]D	400	T17.8[0,1,2,9][0,8]D	400	T20.20XA	383	T20.7[2,3,4]XD	400
S99.91[1,2,9][A,S]	361	T17.8[0,1,2,9][0,8]S	361	T20.20XD	400	T20.7[2,3,4]XS	231
S99.91[1,2,9]A	430	T17.80[0,8]A	70	T20.20XS	230	T20.7[5,6,7]XD	400
S99.91[1,2,9]D	400	T17.81[0,8]A	70	T20.21[1,2,9]A	383	T20.7[5,6,7]XS	231
S99.92[1,2,9][A,S]	361	T17.82[0,8]A	70	T20.21[1,2,9]D	400	T20.70XA	377,379,381,382
S99.92[1,2,9]A	430	T17.89[0,8]A	70	T20.21[1,2,9]S	230	T20.70XD	400
S99.92[1,2,9]D	400	T17.9[0,1,2,9][0,8]D	400	T20.29XA	383	T20.70XS	231
T07	230,430	T17.9[0,1,2,9][0,8]S	361	T20.29XD	400	T20.71[1,2,9]A	377,379,381,382
T14.8	230,430	T17.90[0,8]A	70	T20.29XS	230	T20.71[1,2,9]D	400
T14.90	361,430	T17.91[0,8]A	70	T20.3[2,3,4,5,6,7]XA	377,379,381,382	T20.71[1,2,9]S	231
T14.91	361,430	T17.92[0,8]A	70	T20.3[2,3,4]XD	400	T20.79XA	377,379,381,382
T15.[0,1,8,9][0,1,2]XD	400	T17.99[0,8]A	70	T20.3[2,3,4]XS	230	T20.79XD	400
T15.0[0,1,2]XA	47	T18.[2,3,4,5,8,9]XXA	118	T20.3[5,6,7]XD	400	T20.79XS	231
T15.0[0,1,2]XS	361	T18.[2,3,4,5,8,9]XXD	400	T20.3[5,6,7]XS	230	T21.0[0,1,2,3,4,5,6,7,9]XA	383
T15.1[0,1,2]XA	47	T18.[2,3,4,5,8,9]XXS	361	T20.30XA	377,379,381,382	T21.0[0,1,2,3,4,5,6,7,9]XD	400
T15.1[0,1,2]XS	361	T18.0XXA	6,59	T20.30XD	400	T21.0[1,2]XS	231
T15.8[0,1,2]XA	47	T18.0XXD	400	T20.30XS	230	T21.0[3,4,5]XS	231
T15.8[0,1,2]XS	361	T18.0XXS	361	T20.31[1,2,9]A	377,379,381,382	T21.0[6,7]XS	231
T15.9[0,1,2]XA	47	T18.1[0,1,2,9][0,8]D	400	T20.31[1,2,9]D	400	T21.00XS	231

Code	Page	Code	Page	Code	Page	Code	Page
T21.09XS	231	T22.05[1,2,9]A	383	T22.34[1,2,9]A	377, 379, 381, 382	T22.63[1,2,9]A	383
T21.1[0,1,2,3,4,5,6,7,9]XA	383	T22.05[1,2,9]D	400	T22.34[1,2,9]D	401	T22.63[1,2,9]D	401
T21.1[0,1,2,3,4,5,6,7,9]XD	400	T22.05[1,2,9]S	231	T22.34[1,2,9]S	231	T22.63[1,2,9]S	231
T21.1[1,2]XS	231	T22.06[1,2,9]A	383	T22.35[1,2,9]A	377, 379, 381, 382	T22.64[1,2,9]A	383
T21.1[3,4,5]XS	231	T22.06[1,2,9]D	400	T22.35[1,2,9]D	401	T22.64[1,2,9]D	401
T21.1[6,7]XS	231	T22.06[1,2,9]S	231	T22.35[1,2,9]S	231	T22.64[1,2,9]S	231
T21.10XS	231	T22.09[1,2,9]A	383	T22.36[1,2,9]A	377, 379, 381, 382	T22.65[1,2,9]A	383
T21.19XS	231	T22.09[1,2,9]D	400	T22.36[1,2,9]D	401	T22.65[1,2,9]D	401
T21.2[0,1,2,3,4,5,6,7,9]XA	383	T22.09[1,2,9]S	231	T22.36[1,2,9]S	231	T22.65[1,2,9]S	231
T21.2[0,1,2,3,4,5,6,7,9]XD	400	T22.10XA	383	T22.39[1,2,9]A	377, 379, 381, 382	T22.66[1,2,9]A	383
T21.2[1,2]XS	231	T22.10XD	400	T22.39[1,2,9]D	401	T22.66[1,2,9]D	401
T21.2[3,4,5]XS	231	T22.10XS	231	T22.39[1,2,9]S	231	T22.66[1,2,9]S	231
T21.2[6,7]XS	231	T22.11[1,2,9]A	383	T22.40XA	383	T22.69[1,2,9]A	383
T21.20XS	231	T22.11[1,2,9]D	400	T22.40XD	401	T22.69[1,2,9]D	401
T21.29XS	231	T22.11[1,2,9]S	231	T22.40XS	231	T22.69[1,2,9]S	231
T21.3[0,1,2,3,4,5,6,7,9]XA	377, 379, 381, 382	T22.12[1,2,9]A	383	T22.41[1,2,9]A	383	T22.70XA	377, 379, 381, 382
T21.3[0,1,2,3,4,5,6,7,9]XA	379, 381	T22.12[1,2,9]D	400	T22.41[1,2,9]D	401	T22.70XD	401
T21.3[0,1,2,3,4,5,6,7,9]XD	400	T22.12[1,2,9]S	231	T22.41[1,2,9]S	231	T22.70XS	231
T21.3[1,2]XS	231	T22.13[1,2,9]A	383	T22.42[1,2,9]A	383	T22.71[1,2,9]A	377, 379, 381, 382
T21.3[3,4,5]XS	231	T22.13[1,2,9]D	400	T22.42[1,2,9]D	401	T22.71[1,2,9]D	401
T21.3[6,7]XS	231	T22.13[1,2,9]S	231	T22.42[1,2,9]S	231	T22.71[1,2,9]S	231
T21.30XS	231	T22.14[1,2,9]A	383	T22.43[1,2,9]A	383	T22.72[1,2,9]A	377, 379, 381, 382
T21.39XS	231	T22.14[1,2,9]D	400	T22.43[1,2,9]D	401	T22.72[1,2,9]D	401
T21.4[0,1,2,3,4,5,6,7,9]XA	383	T22.14[1,2,9]S	231	T22.43[1,2,9]S	231	T22.72[1,2,9]S	231
T21.4[0,1,2,3,4,5,6,7,9]XD	400	T22.15[1,2,9]A	383	T22.44[1,2,9]A	383	T22.73[1,2,9]A	377, 379, 381, 382
T21.4[1,2]XS	231	T22.15[1,2,9]D	400	T22.44[1,2,9]D	401	T22.73[1,2,9]D	401
T21.4[3,4,5]XS	231	T22.15[1,2,9]S	231	T22.44[1,2,9]S	231	T22.73[1,2,9]S	231
T21.4[6,7]XS	231	T22.16[1,2,9]A	383	T22.45[1,2,9]A	383	T22.74[1,2,9]A	377, 379, 381, 382
T21.40XS	231	T22.16[1,2,9]D	400	T22.45[1,2,9]D	401	T22.74[1,2,9]D	401
T21.49XS	231	T22.16[1,2,9]S	231	T22.45[1,2,9]S	231	T22.74[1,2,9]S	231
T21.5[0,1,2,3,4,5,6,7,9]XA	383	T22.19[1,2,9]A	383	T22.46[1,2,9]A	383	T22.75[1,2,9]A	377, 379, 381, 382
T21.5[0,1,2,3,4,5,6,7,9]XD	400	T22.19[1,2,9]D	400	T22.46[1,2,9]D	401	T22.75[1,2,9]D	401
T21.5[1,2]XS	231	T22.19[1,2,9]S	231	T22.46[1,2,9]S	231	T22.75[1,2,9]S	231
T21.5[3,4,5]XS	231	T22.20XA	383	T22.49[1,2,9]A	383	T22.76[1,2,9]A	377, 379, 381, 382
T21.5[6,7]XS	231	T22.20XD	401	T22.49[1,2,9]D	401	T22.76[1,2,9]D	401
T21.50XS	231	T22.20XS	231	T22.49[1,2,9]S	231	T22.76[1,2,9]S	231
T21.59XS	231	T22.21[1,2,9]A	383	T22.50XA	383	T22.79[1,2,9]A	377, 379, 381, 382
T21.6[0,1,2,3,4,5,6,7,9]XA	383	T22.21[1,2,9]D	401	T22.50XD	401	T22.79[1,2,9]D	401
T21.6[0,1,2,3,4,5,6,7,9]XD	400	T22.21[1,2,9]S	231	T22.50XS	231	T22.79[1,2,9]S	231
T21.6[1,2]XS	231	T22.22[1,2,9]A	383	T22.51[1,2,9]A	383	T23.00[1,2,9]A	383
T21.6[3,4,5]XS	231	T22.22[1,2,9]D	401	T22.51[1,2,9]D	401	T23.00[1,2,9]D	401
T21.6[6,7]XS	231	T22.22[1,2,9]S	231	T22.51[1,2,9]S	231	T23.00[1,2,9]S	231
T21.60XS	231	T22.23[1,2,9]A	383	T22.52[1,2,9]A	383	T23.01[1,2,9]A	383
T21.69XS	231	T22.23[1,2,9]D	401	T22.52[1,2,9]D	401	T23.01[1,2,9]D	401
T21.7[0,1,2,3,4,5,6,7,9]XA	377, 379, 381	T22.23[1,2,9]S	231	T22.52[1,2,9]S	231	T23.01[1,2,9]S	231
T21.7[0,1,2,3,4,5,6,7,9]XA	382	T22.24[1,2,9]A	383	T22.53[1,2,9]A	383	T23.02[1,2,9]A	383
T21.7[0,1,2,3,4,5,6,7,9]XD	400	T22.24[1,2,9]D	401	T22.53[1,2,9]D	401	T23.02[1,2,9]D	401
T21.7[1,2]XS	231	T22.24[1,2,9]S	231	T22.53[1,2,9]S	231	T23.02[1,2,9]S	231
T21.7[3,4,5]XS	231	T22.25[1,2,9]A	383	T22.54[1,2,9]A	383	T23.03[1,2,9]A	383
T21.7[6,7]XS	231	T22.25[1,2,9]D	401	T22.54[1,2,9]D	401	T23.03[1,2,9]D	401
T21.70XS	231	T22.25[1,2,9]S	231	T22.54[1,2,9]S	231	T23.03[1,2,9]S	231
T21.79XS	231	T22.26[1,2,9]A	383	T22.55[1,2,9]A	383	T23.04[1,2,9]A	383
T22.00XA	383	T22.26[1,2,9]D	401	T22.55[1,2,9]D	401	T23.04[1,2,9]D	401
T22.00XD	400	T22.26[1,2,9]S	231	T22.55[1,2,9]S	231	T23.04[1,2,9]S	231
T22.00XS	231	T22.29[1,2,9]A	383	T22.56[1,2,9]A	383	T23.05[1,2,9]A	383
T22.01[1,2,9]A	383	T22.29[1,2,9]D	401	T22.56[1,2,9]D	401	T23.05[1,2,9]D	401
T22.01[1,2,9]D	400	T22.29[1,2,9]S	231	T22.56[1,2,9]S	231	T23.05[1,2,9]S	231
T22.01[1,2,9]S	231	T22.30XA	377, 379, 381, 382	T22.59[1,2,9]A	383	T23.06[1,2,9]A	383
T22.02[1,2,9]A	383	T22.30XD	401	T22.59[1,2,9]D	401	T23.06[1,2,9]D	401
T22.02[1,2,9]D	400	T22.30XS	231	T22.59[1,2,9]S	231	T23.06[1,2,9]S	231
T22.02[1,2,9]S	231	T22.31[1,2,9]A	377, 379, 381, 382	T22.60XA	383	T23.07[1,2,9]A	383
T22.03[1,2,9]A	383	T22.31[1,2,9]D	401	T22.60XD	401	T23.07[1,2,9]D	401
T22.03[1,2,9]D	400	T22.31[1,2,9]S	231	T22.60XS	231	T23.07[1,2,9]S	231
T22.03[1,2,9]S	231	T22.32[1,2,9]A	377, 379, 381, 382	T22.61[1,2,9]A	383	T23.09[1,2,9]A	383
T22.04[1,2,9]A	383	T22.32[1,2,9]D	401	T22.61[1,2,9]D	401	T23.09[1,2,9]D	401
T22.04[1,2,9]D	400	T22.32[1,2,9]S	231	T22.61[1,2,9]S	231	T23.09[1,2,9]S	231
T22.04[1,2,9]S	231	T22.33[1,2,9]A	377, 379, 381, 382	T22.62[1,2,9]A	383	T23.10[1,2,9]A	383
		T22.33[1,2,9]D	401	T22.62[1,2,9]D	401	T23.10[1,2,9]D	401
		T22.33[1,2,9]S	231	T22.62[1,2,9]S	231	T23.10[1,2,9]S	231

Numeric Index to Diseases

Code	Page	Code	Page	Code	Page	Code	Page
T23.11[1,2,9]A	383	T23.36[1,2,9]A	377, 379, 381, 382	T23.62[1,2,9]A	384	T24.12[1,2,9]A	384
T23.11[1,2,9]D	401	T23.36[1,2,9]D	401	T23.62[1,2,9]D	401	T24.12[1,2,9]D	402
T23.11[1,2,9]S	231	T23.36[1,2,9]S	232	T23.62[1,2,9]S	232	T24.12[1,2,9]S	232
T23.12[1,2,9]A	383	T23.37[1,2,9]A	377, 379, 381, 382	T23.63[1,2,9]A	384	T24.13[1,2,9]A	384
T23.12[1,2,9]D	401	T23.37[1,2,9]D	401	T23.63[1,2,9]D	401	T24.13[1,2,9]D	402
T23.12[1,2,9]S	231	T23.37[1,2,9]S	232	T23.63[1,2,9]S	232	T24.13[1,2,9]S	232
T23.13[1,2,9]A	383	T23.39[1,2,9]A	377, 379, 381, 382	T23.64[1,2,9]A	384	T24.19[1,2,9]A	384
T23.13[1,2,9]D	401	T23.39[1,2,9]D	401	T23.64[1,2,9]D	401	T24.19[1,2,9]D	402
T23.13[1,2,9]S	231	T23.39[1,2,9]S	232	T23.64[1,2,9]S	232	T24.19[1,2,9]S	232
T23.14[1,2,9]A	383	T23.40[1,2,9]A	383	T23.65[1,2,9]A	384	T24.20[1,2,9]A	384
T23.14[1,2,9]D	401	T23.40[1,2,9]D	401	T23.65[1,2,9]D	401	T24.20[1,2,9]D	402
T23.14[1,2,9]S	231	T23.40[1,2,9]S	232	T23.65[1,2,9]S	232	T24.20[1,2,9]S	232
T23.15[1,2,9]A	383	T23.41[1,2,9]A	383	T23.66[1,2,9]A	384	T24.21[1,2,9]A	384
T23.15[1,2,9]D	401	T23.41[1,2,9]D	401	T23.66[1,2,9]D	401	T24.21[1,2,9]D	402
T23.15[1,2,9]S	231	T23.41[1,2,9]S	232	T23.66[1,2,9]S	232	T24.21[1,2,9]S	232
T23.16[1,2,9]A	383	T23.42[1,2,9]A	383	T23.67[1,2,9]A	384	T24.22[1,2,9]A	384
T23.16[1,2,9]D	401	T23.42[1,2,9]D	401	T23.67[1,2,9]D	401	T24.22[1,2,9]D	402
T23.16[1,2,9]S	231	T23.42[1,2,9]S	232	T23.67[1,2,9]S	232	T24.22[1,2,9]S	232
T23.17[1,2,9]A	383	T23.43[1,2,9]A	383	T23.69[1,2,9]A	384	T24.23[1,2,9]A	384
T23.17[1,2,9]D	401	T23.43[1,2,9]D	401	T23.69[1,2,9]D	401	T24.23[1,2,9]D	402
T23.17[1,2,9]S	231	T23.43[1,2,9]S	232	T23.69[1,2,9]S	232	T24.23[1,2,9]S	232
T23.19[1,2,9]A	383	T23.44[1,2,9]A	383	T23.70[1,2,9]A	377, 379, 381, 382	T24.29[1,2,9]A	384
T23.19[1,2,9]D	401	T23.44[1,2,9]D	401	T23.70[1,2,9]D	401	T24.29[1,2,9]D	402
T23.19[1,2,9]S	231	T23.44[1,2,9]S	232	T23.70[1,2,9]S	232	T24.29[1,2,9]S	232
T23.20[1,2,9]A	383	T23.45[1,2,9]A	383	T23.71[1,2,9]A	377, 379, 381, 382	T24.30[1,2,9]A	377, 379, 381, 382
T23.20[1,2,9]D	401	T23.45[1,2,9]D	401	T23.71[1,2,9]D	401	T24.30[1,2,9]D	402
T23.20[1,2,9]S	231	T23.45[1,2,9]S	232	T23.71[1,2,9]S	232	T24.30[1,2,9]S	232
T23.21[1,2,9]A	383	T23.46[1,2,9]A	383	T23.72[1,2,9]A	377, 379, 381, 382	T24.31[1,2,9]A	377, 379, 381, 382
T23.21[1,2,9]D	401	T23.46[1,2,9]D	401	T23.72[1,2,9]D	401	T24.31[1,2,9]D	402
T23.21[1,2,9]S	231	T23.46[1,2,9]S	232	T23.72[1,2,9]S	232	T24.31[1,2,9]S	232
T23.22[1,2,9]A	383	T23.47[1,2,9]A	383	T23.73[1,2,9]A	377, 379, 381, 382	T24.32[1,2,9]A	377, 379, 381, 382
T23.22[1,2,9]D	401	T23.47[1,2,9]D	401	T23.73[1,2,9]D	402	T24.32[1,2,9]D	402
T23.22[1,2,9]S	232	T23.47[1,2,9]S	232	T23.73[1,2,9]S	232	T24.32[1,2,9]S	232
T23.23[1,2,9]A	383	T23.49[1,2,9]A	383	T23.74[1,2,9]A	377, 379, 381, 382	T24.33[1,2,9]A	377, 379, 381, 382
T23.23[1,2,9]D	401	T23.49[1,2,9]D	401	T23.74[1,2,9]D	402	T24.33[1,2,9]D	402
T23.23[1,2,9]S	232	T23.49[1,2,9]S	232	T23.74[1,2,9]S	232	T24.33[1,2,9]S	232
T23.24[1,2,9]A	383	T23.50[1,2,9]A	383	T23.75[1,2,9]A	377, 379, 381, 382	T24.39[1,2,9]A	377, 379, 381, 382
T23.24[1,2,9]D	401	T23.50[1,2,9]D	401	T23.75[1,2,9]D	402	T24.39[1,2,9]D	402
T23.24[1,2,9]S	232	T23.50[1,2,9]S	232	T23.75[1,2,9]S	232	T24.39[1,2,9]S	232
T23.25[1,2,9]A	383	T23.51[1,2,9]A	383	T23.76[1,2,9]A	377, 379, 381, 382	T24.40[1,2,9]A	384
T23.25[1,2,9]D	401	T23.51[1,2,9]D	401	T23.76[1,2,9]D	402	T24.40[1,2,9]D	402
T23.25[1,2,9]S	232	T23.51[1,2,9]S	232	T23.76[1,2,9]S	232	T24.40[1,2,9]S	232
T23.26[1,2,9]A	383	T23.52[1,2,9]A	383	T23.77[1,2,9]A	377, 379, 381, 382	T24.41[1,2,9]A	384
T23.26[1,2,9]D	401	T23.52[1,2,9]D	401	T23.77[1,2,9]D	402	T24.41[1,2,9]D	402
T23.26[1,2,9]S	232	T23.52[1,2,9]S	232	T23.77[1,2,9]S	232	T24.41[1,2,9]S	232
T23.27[1,2,9]A	383	T23.53[1,2,9]A	384	T23.79[1,2,9]A	377, 379, 381, 382	T24.42[1,2,9]A	384
T23.27[1,2,9]D	401	T23.53[1,2,9]D	401	T23.79[1,2,9]D	402	T24.42[1,2,9]D	402
T23.27[1,2,9]S	232	T23.53[1,2,9]S	232	T23.79[1,2,9]S	232	T24.42[1,2,9]S	232
T23.29[1,2,9]A	383	T23.54[1,2,9]A	384	T24.00[1,2,9]A	384	T24.43[1,2,9]A	384
T23.29[1,2,9]D	401	T23.54[1,2,9]D	401	T24.00[1,2,9]D	402	T24.43[1,2,9]D	402
T23.29[1,2,9]S	232	T23.54[1,2,9]S	232	T24.00[1,2,9]S	232	T24.43[1,2,9]S	232
T23.30[1,2,9]A	377, 379, 381, 382	T23.55[1,2,9]A	384	T24.01[1,2,9]A	384	T24.49[1,2,9]A	384
T23.30[1,2,9]D	401	T23.55[1,2,9]D	401	T24.01[1,2,9]D	402	T24.49[1,2,9]D	402
T23.30[1,2,9]S	232	T23.55[1,2,9]S	232	T24.01[1,2,9]S	232	T24.49[1,2,9]S	232
T23.31[1,2,9]A	377, 379, 381, 382	T23.56[1,2,9]A	384	T24.02[1,2,9]A	384	T24.50[1,2,9]A	384
T23.31[1,2,9]D	401	T23.56[1,2,9]D	401	T24.02[1,2,9]D	402	T24.50[1,2,9]D	402
T23.31[1,2,9]S	232	T23.56[1,2,9]S	232	T24.02[1,2,9]S	232	T24.50[1,2,9]S	232
T23.32[1,2,9]A	377, 379, 381, 382	T23.57[1,2,9]A	384	T24.03[1,2,9]A	384	T24.51[1,2,9]A	384
T23.32[1,2,9]D	401	T23.57[1,2,9]D	401	T24.03[1,2,9]D	402	T24.51[1,2,9]D	402
T23.32[1,2,9]S	232	T23.57[1,2,9]S	232	T24.03[1,2,9]S	232	T24.51[1,2,9]S	232
T23.33[1,2,9]A	377, 379, 381, 382	T23.59[1,2,9]A	384	T24.09[1,2,9]A	384	T24.52[1,2,9]A	384
T23.33[1,2,9]D	401	T23.59[1,2,9]D	401	T24.09[1,2,9]D	402	T24.52[1,2,9]D	402
T23.33[1,2,9]S	232	T23.59[1,2,9]S	232	T24.09[1,2,9]S	232	T24.52[1,2,9]S	232
T23.34[1,2,9]A	377, 379, 381, 382	T23.60[1,2,9]A	384	T24.10[1,2,9]A	384	T24.53[1,2,9]A	384
T23.34[1,2,9]D	401	T23.60[1,2,9]D	401	T24.10[1,2,9]D	402	T24.53[1,2,9]D	402
T23.34[1,2,9]S	232	T23.60[1,2,9]S	232	T24.10[1,2,9]S	232	T24.53[1,2,9]S	232
T23.35[1,2,9]A	377, 379, 381, 382	T23.61[1,2,9]A	384	T24.11[1,2,9]A	384	T24.59[1,2,9]A	384
T23.35[1,2,9]D	401	T23.61[1,2,9]D	401	T24.11[1,2,9]D	402	T24.59[1,2,9]D	402
T23.35[1,2,9]S	232	T23.61[1,2,9]S	232	T24.11[1,2,9]S	232	T24.59[1,2,9]S	232

Code	Page	Code	Page	Code	Page	Code	Page
T34.01[1,2,9][A,S]	368	T36.6X[1,2,3,4]A	362	T37.5X6*	403	T38.7X5S	369
T34.01[1,2,9]D	403	T36.6X[1,2,3,4]D	403	T37.8X[1,2,3,4]A	362	T38.7X6*	403
T34.02XD	403	T36.6X[1,2,3,4]S	368	T37.8X[1,2,3,4]D	403	T38.8[0,1,9]5A	286
T34.09XD	403	T36.6X5A	286, 362	T37.8X[1,2,3,4]S	369	T38.80[1,2,3,4]A	362
T34.1XXD	403	T36.6X5D	403	T37.8X5A	286, 362	T38.80[1,2,3,4]D	403
T34.2XXD	403	T36.6X5S	368	T37.8X5D	403	T38.80[1,2,3,4]S	369
T34.3XXD	403	T36.6X6*	403	T37.8X5S	368	T38.805A	362
T34.4[0,1,2]X[A,S]	368	T36.7X[1,2,3,4]A	362	T37.8X6*	403	T38.805D	403
T34.4[0,1,2]XD	403	T36.7X[1,2,3,4]D	403	T37.9[1,2,3,4]XA	362	T38.805S	369
T34.51[1,2,9][A,S]	368	T36.7X[1,2,3,4]S	368	T37.9[1,2,3,4]XD	403	T38.806*	403
T34.51[1,2,9]D	403	T36.7X5A	286, 362	T37.9[1,2,3,4]XS	369	T38.81[1,2,3,4]A	362
T34.52[1,2,9][A,S]	368	T36.7X5D	403	T37.95XA	286, 362	T38.81[1,2,3,4]D	403
T34.52[1,2,9]D	403	T36.7X5S	368	T37.95XD	403	T38.81[1,2,3,4]S	369
T34.53[1,2,9][A,S]	368	T36.7X6*	403	T37.95XS	369	T38.815A	362
T34.53[1,2,9]D	403	T36.8X[1,2,3,4]A	362	T37.96*	403	T38.815D	403
T34.6[0,1,2]X[A,S]	368	T36.8X[1,2,3,4]D	403	T38.0X[1,2,3,4]A	362	T38.815S	369
T34.6[0,1,2]XD	403	T36.8X[1,2,3,4]S	368	T38.0X[1,2,3,4]D	403	T38.816*	403
T34.7[0,1,2]X[A,S]	368	T36.8X5A	286, 362	T38.0X[1,2,3,4]S	369	T38.89[1,2,3,4]A	362
T34.7[0,1,2]XD	403	T36.8X5D	403	T38.0X5A	286, 362	T38.89[1,2,3,4]D	403
T34.81[1,2,9][A,S]	368	T36.8X5S	368	T38.0X5D	403	T38.89[1,2,3,4]S	369
T34.81[1,2,9]D	403	T36.8X6*	403	T38.0X5S	369	T38.895A	362
T34.82[1,2,9][A,S]	368	T36.9[1,2,3,4]XA	362	T38.0X6*	403	T38.895D	403
T34.82[1,2,9]D	403	T36.9[1,2,3,4]XD	403	T38.1X[1,2,3,4]A	362	T38.895S	369
T34.83[1,2,9][A,S]	368	T36.9[1,2,3,4]XS	368	T38.1X[1,2,3,4]D	403	T38.896*	403
T34.83[1,2,9]D	403	T36.95XA	286, 362	T38.1X[1,2,3,4]S	369	T38.9[0,9]5A	286
T34.9[0,9]X[A,S]	368	T36.95XD	403	T38.1X5A	286, 362	T38.90[1,2,3,4]A	362
T34.9[0,9]XD	403	T36.95XS	368	T38.1X5D	403	T38.90[1,2,3,4]D	403
T36.0X[1,2,3,4]A	362	T36.96*	403	T38.1X5S	369	T38.90[1,2,3,4]S	369
T36.0X[1,2,3,4]D	403	T37.0X[1,2,3,4]A	362	T38.1X6*	403	T38.905A	362
T36.0X[1,2,3,4]S	368	T37.0X[1,2,3,4]D	403	T38.2X[1,2,3,4]A	362	T38.905D	403
T36.0X5A	286, 362	T37.0X[1,2,3,4]S	368	T38.2X[1,2,3,4]D	403	T38.905S	369
T36.0X5D	403	T37.0X5A	286, 362	T38.2X[1,2,3,4]S	369	T38.906*	403
T36.0X5S	368	T37.0X5D	403	T38.2X5A	286, 362	T38.99[1,2,3,4]A	362
T36.0X6*	403	T37.0X5S	368	T38.2X5D	403	T38.99[1,2,3,4]D	403
T36.1X[1,2,3,4]A	362	T37.0X6*	403	T38.2X5S	369	T38.99[1,2,3,4]S	369
T36.1X[1,2,3,4]D	403	T37.1X[1,2,3,4]A	362	T38.2X6*	403	T38.995A	362
T36.1X[1,2,3,4]S	368	T37.1X[1,2,3,4]D	403	T38.3X[1,2,3,4]A	362	T38.995D	403
T36.1X5A	286, 362	T37.1X[1,2,3,4]S	368	T38.3X[1,2,3,4]D	403	T38.995S	369
T36.1X5D	403	T37.1X5A	286, 362	T38.3X[1,2,3,4]S	369	T38.996*	403
T36.1X5S	368	T37.1X5D	403	T38.3X5A	286, 362	T39.0[1,9][1,2,3,4]A	362
T36.1X6*	403	T37.1X5S	368	T38.3X5D	403	T39.0[1,9][1,2,3,4]S	369
T36.2X[1,2,3,4]A	362	T37.1X6*	403	T38.3X5S	369	T39.0[1,9]5A	286
T36.2X[1,2,3,4]D	403	T37.2X[1,2,3,4]A	362	T38.3X6*	403	T39.0[1,9]5S	369
T36.2X[1,2,3,4]S	368	T37.2X[1,2,3,4]D	403	T38.4X[1,2,3,4]A	362	T39.01[1,2,3,4]D	404
T36.2X5A	286, 362	T37.2X[1,2,3,4]S	368	T38.4X[1,2,3,4]D	403	T39.015A	362
T36.2X5D	403	T37.2X5A	286, 362	T38.4X[1,2,3,4]S	369	T39.015D	403
T36.2X5S	368	T37.2X5D	403	T38.4X5A	286, 362	T39.016*	403
T36.2X6*	403	T37.2X5S	368	T38.4X5D	403	T39.09[1,2,3,4]D	404
T36.3X[1,2,3,4]A	362	T37.2X6*	403	T38.4X5S	369	T39.095A	362
T36.3X[1,2,3,4]D	403	T37.3X[1,2,3,4]A	362	T38.4X6*	403	T39.095D	404
T36.3X[1,2,3,4]S	368	T37.3X[1,2,3,4]D	403	T38.5X[1,2,3,4]A	362	T39.096*	404
T36.3X5A	286, 362	T37.3X[1,2,3,4]S	368	T38.5X[1,2,3,4]D	403	T39.1X[1,2,3,4]A	362
T36.3X5D	403	T37.3X5A	286, 362	T38.5X[1,2,3,4]S	369	T39.1X[1,2,3,4]D	404
T36.3X5S	368	T37.3X5D	403	T38.5X5A	286, 362	T39.1X[1,2,3,4]S	369
T36.3X6*	403	T37.3X5S	368	T38.5X5D	403	T39.1X5A	286, 362
T36.4X[1,2,3,4]A	362	T37.3X6*	403	T38.5X5S	369	T39.1X5D	404
T36.4X[1,2,3,4]D	403	T37.4X[1,2,3,4]A	362	T38.5X6*	403	T39.1X5S	369
T36.4X[1,2,3,4]S	368	T37.4X[1,2,3,4]D	403	T38.6X[1,2,3,4]A	362	T39.1X6*	404
T36.4X5A	286, 362	T37.4X[1,2,3,4]S	368	T38.6X[1,2,3,4]D	403	T39.2X[1,2,3,4]A	362
T36.4X5D	403	T37.4X5A	286, 362	T38.6X[1,2,3,4]S	369	T39.2X[1,2,3,4]D	404
T36.4X5S	368	T37.4X5D	403	T38.6X5A	286, 362	T39.2X[1,2,3,4]S	369
T36.4X6*	403	T37.4X5S	368	T38.6X5D	403	T39.2X5A	286, 362
T36.5X[1,2,3,4]A	362	T37.4X6*	403	T38.6X5S	369	T39.2X5D	404
T36.5X[1,2,3,4]D	403	T37.5X[1,2,3,4]A	362	T38.6X6*	403	T39.2X5S	369
T36.5X[1,2,3,4]S	368	T37.5X[1,2,3,4]D	403	T38.7X[1,2,3,4]A	362	T39.2X6*	404
T36.5X5A	286, 362	T37.5X[1,2,3,4]S	368	T38.7X[1,2,3,4]D	403	T39.3[1,9]5A	286
T36.5X5D	403	T37.5X5A	286, 362	T38.7X[1,2,3,4]S	369	T39.31[1,2,3,4]A	362
T36.5X5S	368	T37.5X5D	403	T38.7X5A	286, 362	T39.31[1,2,3,4]D	404
T36.5X6*	403	T37.5X5S	368	T38.7X5D	403	T39.31[1,2,3,4]S	369

Code	Page	Code	Page	Code	Page	Code	Page
T39.315A	362	T40.5X6*	404	T41.296*	404	T42.6X5S	370
T39.315D	404	T40.6[0,9]5A	286	T41.3X[1,2,3,4]A	363	T42.6X6*	404
T39.315S	369	T40.60[1,2,3,4]A	362	T41.3X[1,2,3,4]D	404	T42.7[1,2,3,4]XA	363
T39.316*	404	T40.60[1,2,3,4]D	404	T41.3X[1,2,3,4]S	369	T42.7[1,2,3,4]XD	404
T39.39[1,2,3,4]A	362	T40.60[1,2,3,4]S	369	T41.3X5A	287, 363	T42.7[1,2,3,4]XS	370
T39.39[1,2,3,4]D	404	T40.605A	362	T41.3X5D	404	T42.75XA	287, 363
T39.39[1,2,3,4]S	369	T40.605D	404	T41.3X5S	369	T42.75XD	404
T39.395A	362	T40.605S	369	T41.3X6*	404	T42.75XS	370
T39.395D	404	T40.606*	404	T41.4[1,2,3,4]XA	363	T42.76*	404
T39.395S	369	T40.69[1,2,3,4]A	363	T41.4[1,2,3,4]XD	404	T42.8X[1,2,3,4]A	363
T39.396*	404	T40.69[1,2,3,4]D	404	T41.4[1,2,3,4]XS	369	T42.8X[1,2,3,4]D	404
T39.4X[1,2,3,4]A	362	T40.69[1,2,3,4]S	369	T41.45XA	287, 363	T42.8X[1,2,3,4]S	370
T39.4X[1,2,3,4]D	404	T40.695A	363	T41.45XD	404	T42.8X5A	287, 363
T39.4X[1,2,3,4]S	369	T40.695D	404	T41.45XS	369	T42.8X5D	404
T39.4X5A	286, 362	T40.695S	369	T41.46*	404	T42.8X5S	370
T39.4X5D	404	T40.696*	404	T41.5X[1,2,3,4]A	363	T42.8X6*	404
T39.4X5S	369	T40.7X[1,2,3,4]A	363	T41.5X[1,2,3,4]D	404	T43.0[1,2]5A	287
T39.4X6*	404	T40.7X[1,2,3,4]D	404	T41.5X[1,2,3,4]S	369	T43.01[1,2,3,4]A	363
T39.8X[1,2,3,4]A	362	T40.7X[1,2,3,4]S	369	T41.5X5A	287, 363	T43.01[1,2,3,4]D	404
T39.8X[1,2,3,4]D	404	T40.7X5A	286, 363	T41.5X5D	404	T43.01[1,2,3,4]S	370
T39.8X[1,2,3,4]S	369	T40.7X5D	404	T41.5X5S	369	T43.015A	363
T39.8X5A	286, 362	T40.7X5S	369	T41.5X6*	404	T43.015D	404
T39.8X5D	404	T40.7X6*	404	T42.0X[1,2,3,4]A	363	T43.015S	370
T39.8X5S	369	T40.8X[1,2,3,4]A	363	T42.0X[1,2,3,4]D	404	T43.016*	404
T39.8X6*	404	T40.8X[1,2,3,4]D	404	T42.0X[1,2,3,4]S	369	T43.02[1,2,3,4]A	363
T39.9[1,2,3,4]XA	362	T40.8X[1,2,3,4]S	369	T42.0X5A	287, 363	T43.02[1,2,3,4]D	405
T39.9[1,2,3,4]XD	404	T40.9[0,9]5A	286	T42.0X5D	404	T43.02[1,2,3,4]S	370
T39.9[1,2,3,4]XS	369	T40.90[1,2,3,4]A	363	T42.0X5S	369	T43.025A	363
T39.95XA	286, 362	T40.90[1,2,3,4]D	404	T42.0X6*	404	T43.025D	404
T39.95XD	404	T40.90[1,2,3,4]S	369	T42.1X[1,2,3,4]A	363	T43.025S	370
T39.95XS	369	T40.905A	363	T42.1X[1,2,3,4]D	404	T43.026*	404
T39.96*	404	T40.905D	404	T42.1X[1,2,3,4]S	369	T43.1X[1,2,3,4]A	363
T40.0X[1,2,3,4]A	362	T40.905S	369	T42.1X5A	287, 363	T43.1X[1,2,3,4]D	405
T40.0X[1,2,3,4]D	404	T40.906*	404	T42.1X5D	404	T43.1X[1,2,3,4]S	370
T40.0X[1,2,3,4]S	369	T40.99[1,2,3,4]A	363	T42.1X5S	369	T43.1X5A	287, 363
T40.0X5A	286, 362	T40.99[1,2,3,4]D	404	T42.1X6*	404	T43.1X5D	405
T40.0X5D	404	T40.99[1,2,3,4]S	369	T42.2X[1,2,3,4]A	363	T43.1X5S	370
T40.0X5S	369	T40.995A	363	T42.2X[1,2,3,4]D	404	T43.1X6*	405
T40.0X6*	404	T40.995D	404	T42.2X[1,2,3,4]S	369	T43.2[1,2,9]5A	287
T40.1X[1,2,3,4]A	362	T40.995S	369	T42.2X5A	287, 363	T43.20[1,2,3,4]A	363
T40.1X[1,2,3,4]D	404	T40.996*	404	T42.2X5D	404	T43.20[1,2,3,4]D	405
T40.1X[1,2,3,4]S	369	T41.0X[1,2,3,4]A	363	T42.2X5S	369	T43.20[1,2,3,4]S	370
T40.2X[1,2,3,4]A	362	T41.0X[1,2,3,4]D	404	T42.2X6*	404	T43.205A	287, 363
T40.2X[1,2,3,4]D	404	T41.0X[1,2,3,4]S	369	T42.3X[1,2,3,4]A	363	T43.205D	405
T40.2X[1,2,3,4]S	369	T41.0X5A	286, 363	T42.3X[1,2,3,4]D	404	T43.205S	370
T40.2X5A	286, 362	T41.0X5D	404	T42.3X[1,2,3,4]S	369	T43.206*	405
T40.2X5D	404	T41.0X5S	369	T42.3X5A	287, 363	T43.21[1,2,3,4]A	363
T40.2X5S	369	T41.0X6*	404	T42.3X5D	404	T43.21[1,2,3,4]D	405
T40.2X6*	404	T41.1X[1,2,3,4]A	363	T42.3X5S	369	T43.21[1,2,3,4]S	370
T40.3X[1,2,3,4]A	362	T41.1X[1,2,3,4]D	404	T42.3X6*	404	T43.215A	363
T40.3X[1,2,3,4]D	404	T41.1X[1,2,3,4]S	369	T42.4X[1,2,3,4]A	363	T43.215D	405
T40.3X[1,2,3,4]S	369	T41.1X5A	286, 363	T42.4X[1,2,3,4]D	404	T43.215S	370
T40.3X5A	286, 362	T41.1X5D	404	T42.4X[1,2,3,4]S	369	T43.216*	405
T40.3X5D	404	T41.1X5S	369	T42.4X5A	287, 363	T43.22[1,2,3,4]A	363
T40.3X5S	369	T41.1X6*	404	T42.4X5D	404	T43.22[1,2,3,4]D	405
T40.3X6*	404	T41.2[0,9]5A	286	T42.4X5S	369	T43.22[1,2,3,4]S	370
T40.4X[1,2,3,4]A	362	T41.20[1,2,3,4]A	363	T42.4X6*	404	T43.225A	363
T40.4X[1,2,3,4]D	404	T41.20[1,2,3,4]D	404	T42.5X[1,2,3,4]A	363	T43.225D	405
T40.4X[1,2,3,4]S	369	T41.20[1,2,3,4]S	369	T42.5X[1,2,3,4]D	404	T43.225S	370
T40.4X5A	286, 362	T41.205A	363	T42.5X[1,2,3,4]S	369	T43.226*	405
T40.4X5D	404	T41.205D	404	T42.5X5A	287, 363	T43.29[1,2,3,4]A	363
T40.4X5S	369	T41.205S	369	T42.5X5D	404	T43.29[1,2,3,4]D	405
T40.4X6*	404	T41.206*	404	T42.5X5S	369	T43.29[1,2,3,4]S	370
T40.5X[1,2,3,4]A	362	T41.29[1,2,3,4]A	363	T42.5X6*	404	T43.295A	363
T40.5X[1,2,3,4]D	404	T41.29[1,2,3,4]D	404	T42.6X[1,2,3,4]A	363	T43.295D	405
T40.5X[1,2,3,4]S	369	T41.29[1,2,3,4]S	369	T42.6X[1,2,3,4]D	404	T43.295S	370
T40.5X5A	286, 362	T41.295A	363	T42.6X[1,2,3,4]S	370	T43.296*	405
T40.5X5D	404	T41.295D	404	T42.6X5A	287, 363	T43.3X[1,2,3,4]A	363
T40.5X5S	369	T41.295S	369	T42.6X5D	404	T43.3X[1,2,3,4]D	405

Code	Page	Code	Page	Code	Page	Code	Page
T46.3X[1,2,3,4]A	364	T47.1X5S	371	T48.1X5D	406	T49.1X[1,2,3,4]D	407
T46.3X[1,2,3,4]D	406	T47.1X6*	406	T48.1X5S	371	T49.1X[1,2,3,4]S	371
T46.3X[1,2,3,4]S	371	T47.2X[1,2,3,4]A	364	T48.1X6*	406	T49.1X5A	287, 365
T46.3X5A	287, 364	T47.2X[1,2,3,4]D	406	T48.2[0,9]5A	287	T49.1X5D	407
T46.3X5D	406	T47.2X[1,2,3,4]S	371	T48.20[1,2,3,4]A	364	T49.1X5S	371
T46.3X5S	371	T47.2X5A	287, 364	T48.20[1,2,3,4]D	406	T49.1X6*	407
T46.3X6*	406	T47.2X5D	406	T48.20[1,2,3,4]S	371	T49.2X[1,2,3,4]A	365
T46.4X[1,2,3,4]A	364	T47.2X5S	371	T48.205A	364	T49.2X[1,2,3,4]D	407
T46.4X[1,2,3,4]D	406	T47.2X6*	406	T48.205D	406	T49.2X[1,2,3,4]S	371
T46.4X[1,2,3,4]S	371	T47.3X[1,2,3,4]A	364	T48.205S	371	T49.2X5A	287, 365
T46.4X5A	287, 364	T47.3X[1,2,3,4]D	406	T48.206*	406	T49.2X5D	407
T46.4X5D	406	T47.3X[1,2,3,4]S	371	T48.29[1,2,3,4]A	364	T49.2X5S	371
T46.4X5S	371	T47.3X5A	287, 364	T48.29[1,2,3,4]D	406	T49.2X6*	407
T46.4X6*	406	T47.3X5D	406	T48.29[1,2,3,4]S	371	T49.3X[1,2,3,4]A	365
T46.5X[1,2,3,4]A	364	T47.3X5S	371	T48.295A	364	T49.3X[1,2,3,4]D	407
T46.5X[1,2,3,4]D	406	T47.3X6*	406	T48.295D	406	T49.3X[1,2,3,4]S	371
T46.5X[1,2,3,4]S	371	T47.4X[1,2,3,4]A	364	T48.295S	371	T49.3X5A	287, 365
T46.5X5A	287, 364	T47.4X[1,2,3,4]D	406	T48.296*	406	T49.3X5D	407
T46.5X5D	406	T47.4X[1,2,3,4]S	371	T48.3X[1,2,3,4]A	364	T49.3X5S	371
T46.5X5S	371	T47.4X5A	287, 364	T48.3X[1,2,3,4]D	406	T49.3X6*	407
T46.5X6*	406	T47.4X5D	406	T48.3X[1,2,3,4]S	371	T49.4X[1,2,3,4]A	365
T46.6X[1,2,3,4]A	364	T47.4X5S	371	T48.3X5A	287, 364	T49.4X[1,2,3,4]D	407
T46.6X[1,2,3,4]D	406	T47.4X6*	406	T48.3X5D	406	T49.4X[1,2,3,4]S	371
T46.6X[1,2,3,4]S	371	T47.5X[1,2,3,4]A	364	T48.3X5S	371	T49.4X5A	287, 365
T46.6X5A	287, 364	T47.5X[1,2,3,4]D	406	T48.3X6*	406	T49.4X5D	407
T46.6X5D	406	T47.5X[1,2,3,4]S	371	T48.4X[1,2,3,4]A	364	T49.4X5S	371
T46.6X5S	371	T47.5X5A	287, 364	T48.4X[1,2,3,4]D	406	T49.4X6*	407
T46.6X6*	406	T47.5X5D	406	T48.4X[1,2,3,4]S	371	T49.5X[1,2,3,4]A	47
T46.7X[1,2,3,4]A	364	T47.5X5S	371	T48.4X5A	287, 364	T49.5X[1,2,3,4]D	407
T46.7X[1,2,3,4]D	406	T47.5X6*	406	T48.4X5D	406	T49.5X[1,2,3,4]S	371
T46.7X[1,2,3,4]S	371	T47.6X[1,2,3,4]A	364	T48.4X5S	371	T49.5X5A	287, 365
T46.7X5A	287, 364	T47.6X[1,2,3,4]D	406	T48.4X6*	406	T49.5X5D	407
T46.7X5D	406	T47.6X[1,2,3,4]S	371	T48.5X[1,2,3,4]A	365	T49.5X5S	371
T46.7X5S	371	T47.6X5A	287, 364	T48.5X[1,2,3,4]D	407	T49.5X6*	407
T46.7X6*	406	T47.6X5D	406	T48.5X[1,2,3,4]S	371	T49.6X[1,2,3,4]A	365
T46.8X[1,2,3,4]A	364	T47.6X5S	371	T48.5X5A	287, 364	T49.6X[1,2,3,4]D	407
T46.8X[1,2,3,4]D	406	T47.6X6*	406	T48.5X5D	406	T49.6X[1,2,3,4]S	371
T46.8X[1,2,3,4]S	371	T47.7X[1,2,3,4]A	364	T48.5X5S	371	T49.6X5A	287, 365
T46.8X5A	287, 364	T47.7X[1,2,3,4]D	406	T48.5X6*	407	T49.6X5D	407
T46.8X5D	406	T47.7X[1,2,3,4]S	371	T48.6X[1,2,3,4]A	365	T49.6X5S	371
T46.8X5S	371	T47.7X5A	287, 364	T48.6X[1,2,3,4]D	407	T49.6X6*	407
T46.8X6*	406	T47.7X5D	406	T48.6X[1,2,3,4]S	371	T49.7X[1,2,3,4]A	365
T46.9[0,9]5A	287	T47.7X5S	371	T48.6X5A	287, 365	T49.7X[1,2,3,4]D	407
T46.90[1,2,3,4]A	364	T47.7X6*	406	T48.6X5D	407	T49.7X[1,2,3,4]S	371
T46.90[1,2,3,4]D	406	T47.8X[1,2,3,4]A	364	T48.6X5S	371	T49.7X5A	287, 365
T46.90[1,2,3,4]S	371	T47.8X[1,2,3,4]D	406	T48.6X6*	407	T49.7X5D	407
T46.905A	364	T47.8X[1,2,3,4]S	371	T48.9[0,9]5A	287	T49.7X5S	371
T46.905D	406	T47.8X5A	287, 364	T48.90[1,2,3,4]A	365	T49.7X6*	407
T46.905S	371	T47.8X5D	406	T48.90[1,2,3,4]D	407	T49.8X[1,2,3,4]A	365
T46.906*	406	T47.8X5S	371	T48.90[1,2,3,4]S	371	T49.8X[1,2,3,4]D	407
T46.99[1,2,3,4]A	364	T47.8X6*	406	T48.905A	365	T49.8X[1,2,3,4]S	371
T46.99[1,2,3,4]D	406	T47.9[1,2,3,4]XA	364	T48.905D	407	T49.8X5A	287, 365
T46.99[1,2,3,4]S	371	T47.9[1,2,3,4]XD	406	T48.905S	371	T49.8X5D	407
T46.995A	364	T47.9[1,2,3,4]XS	371	T48.906*	407	T49.8X5S	371
T46.995D	406	T47.95XA	287, 364	T48.99[1,2,3,4]A	365	T49.8X6*	407
T46.995S	371	T47.95XD	406	T48.99[1,2,3,4]D	407	T49.9[1,2,3,4]XA	365
T46.996*	406	T47.95XS	371	T48.99[1,2,3,4]S	371	T49.9[1,2,3,4]XD	407
T47.0X[1,2,3,4]A	364	T47.96*	406	T48.995A	365	T49.9[1,2,3,4]XS	371
T47.0X[1,2,3,4]D	406	T48.0X[1,2,3,4]A	364	T48.995D	407	T49.95XA	287, 365
T47.0X[1,2,3,4]S	371	T48.0X[1,2,3,4]D	406	T48.995S	371	T49.95XD	407
T47.0X5A	287, 364	T48.0X[1,2,3,4]S	371	T48.996*	407	T49.95XS	371
T47.0X5D	406	T48.0X5A	287, 364	T49.0X[1,2,3,4]A	365	T49.96*	407
T47.0X5S	371	T48.0X5D	406	T49.0X[1,2,3,4]D	407	T50.0X[1,2,3,4]A	365
T47.0X6*	406	T48.0X5S	371	T49.0X[1,2,3,4]S	371	T50.0X[1,2,3,4]D	407
T47.1X[1,2,3,4]A	364	T48.0X6*	406	T49.0X5A	287, 365	T50.0X[1,2,3,4]S	371
T47.1X[1,2,3,4]D	406	T48.1X[1,2,3,4]A	364	T49.0X5D	407	T50.0X5A	287, 365
T47.1X[1,2,3,4]S	371	T48.1X[1,2,3,4]D	406	T49.0X5S	371	T50.0X5D	407
T47.1X5A	287, 364	T48.1X[1,2,3,4]S	371	T49.0X6*	407	T50.0X5S	371
T47.1X5D	406	T48.1X5A	287, 364	T49.1X[1,2,3,4]A	365	T50.0X6*	407

Code	Page	Code	Page	Code	Page	Code	Page
T50.1X[1,2,3,4]A	365	T50.995S	372	T51.9[1,2,3,4]XA	365	T55.1X[1,2,3,4]A	366
T50.1X[1,2,3,4]D	407	T50.996*	407	T51.9[1,2,3,4]XD	408	T55.1X[1,2,3,4]D	408
T50.1X[1,2,3,4]S	371	T50.A[1,2,9]5A	287	T51.9[1,2,3,4]XS	372	T55.1X[1,2,3,4]S	372
T50.1X5A	287, 365	T50.A1[1,2,3,4]A	365	T52.0X[1,2,3,4]A	365	T56.0X[1,2,3,4]A	366
T50.1X5D	407	T50.A1[1,2,3,4]D	407	T52.0X[1,2,3,4]D	408	T56.0X[1,2,3,4]D	408
T50.1X5S	371	T50.A1[1,2,3,4]S	372	T52.0X[1,2,3,4]S	372	T56.0X[1,2,3,4]S	372
T50.1X6*	407	T50.A15A	365	T52.1X[1,2,3,4]A	365	T56.1X[1,2,3,4]A	366
T50.2X[1,2,3,4]A	365	T50.A15D	407	T52.1X[1,2,3,4]D	408	T56.1X[1,2,3,4]D	408
T50.2X[1,2,3,4]D	407	T50.A15S	372	T52.1X[1,2,3,4]S	372	T56.1X[1,2,3,4]S	372
T50.2X[1,2,3,4]S	372	T50.A16*	407	T52.2X[1,2,3,4]A	365	T56.2X[1,2,3,4]A	366
T50.2X5A	287, 365	T50.A2[1,2,3,4]A	365	T52.2X[1,2,3,4]D	408	T56.2X[1,2,3,4]D	408
T50.2X5D	407	T50.A2[1,2,3,4]D	407	T52.2X[1,2,3,4]S	372	T56.2X[1,2,3,4]S	372
T50.2X5S	371	T50.A2[1,2,3,4]S	372	T52.3X[1,2,3,4]A	365	T56.3X[1,2,3,4]A	366
T50.2X6*	407	T50.A25A	365	T52.3X[1,2,3,4]D	408	T56.3X[1,2,3,4]D	408
T50.3X[1,2,3,4]A	365	T50.A25D	407	T52.3X[1,2,3,4]S	372	T56.3X[1,2,3,4]S	372
T50.3X[1,2,3,4]D	407	T50.A25S	372	T52.4X[1,2,3,4]A	365	T56.4X[1,2,3,4]A	366
T50.3X[1,2,3,4]S	372	T50.A26*	407	T52.4X[1,2,3,4]D	408	T56.4X[1,2,3,4]D	408
T50.3X5A	287, 365	T50.A9[1,2,3,4]A	365	T52.4X[1,2,3,4]S	372	T56.4X[1,2,3,4]S	372
T50.3X5D	407	T50.A9[1,2,3,4]D	407	T52.8X[1,2,3,4]A	365	T56.5X[1,2,3,4]A	366
T50.3X5S	372	T50.A9[1,2,3,4]S	372	T52.8X[1,2,3,4]D	408	T56.5X[1,2,3,4]D	408
T50.3X6*	407	T50.A95A	365	T52.8X[1,2,3,4]S	372	T56.5X[1,2,3,4]S	372
T50.4X[1,2,3,4]A	365	T50.A95D	407	T52.9[1,2,3,4]XA	365	T56.6X[1,2,3,4]A	366
T50.4X[1,2,3,4]D	407	T50.A95S	372	T52.9[1,2,3,4]XD	408	T56.6X[1,2,3,4]D	408
T50.4X[1,2,3,4]S	372	T50.A96*	407	T52.9[1,2,3,4]XS	372	T56.6X[1,2,3,4]S	372
T50.4X5A	287, 365	T50.B[1,9]5A	287	T53.0X[1,2,3,4]A	365	T56.7X[1,2,3,4]A	366
T50.4X5D	407	T50.B1[1,2,3,4]A	365	T53.0X[1,2,3,4]D	408	T56.7X[1,2,3,4]D	408
T50.4X5S	372	T50.B1[1,2,3,4]D	407	T53.0X[1,2,3,4]S	372	T56.7X[1,2,3,4]S	372
T50.4X6*	407	T50.B1[1,2,3,4]S	372	T53.1X[1,2,3,4]A	365	T56.81[1,2,3,4]A	366
T50.5X[1,2,3,4]A	365	T50.B15A	365	T53.1X[1,2,3,4]D	408	T56.81[1,2,3,4]D	408
T50.5X[1,2,3,4]D	407	T50.B15D	407	T53.1X[1,2,3,4]S	372	T56.81[1,2,3,4]S	372
T50.5X[1,2,3,4]S	372	T50.B15S	372	T53.2X[1,2,3,4]A	365	T56.89[1,2,3,4]A	366
T50.5X5A	287, 365	T50.B16*	407	T53.2X[1,2,3,4]D	408	T56.89[1,2,3,4]D	408
T50.5X5D	407	T50.B9[1,2,3,4]A	365	T53.2X[1,2,3,4]S	372	T56.89[1,2,3,4]S	372
T50.5X5S	372	T50.B9[1,2,3,4]D	407	T53.3X[1,2,3,4]A	365	T56.9[1,2,3,4]XA	366
T50.5X6*	407	T50.B9[1,2,3,4]S	372	T53.3X[1,2,3,4]D	408	T56.9[1,2,3,4]XD	408
T50.6X[1,2,3,4]A	365	T50.B95A	365	T53.3X[1,2,3,4]S	372	T56.9[1,2,3,4]XS	372
T50.6X[1,2,3,4]D	407	T50.B95S	372	T53.4X[1,2,3,4]A	365	T57.0X[1,2,3,4]A	366
T50.6X[1,2,3,4]S	372	T50.B96*	407	T53.4X[1,2,3,4]D	408	T57.0X[1,2,3,4]D	408
T50.6X5A	287, 365	T50.Z[1,9]5A	287	T53.4X[1,2,3,4]S	372	T57.0X[1,2,3,4]S	372
T50.6X5D	407	T50.Z1[1,2,3,4]A	365	T53.5X[1,2,3,4]A	365	T57.1X[1,2,3,4]A	366
T50.6X5S	372	T50.Z1[1,2,3,4]D	407	T53.5X[1,2,3,4]D	408	T57.1X[1,2,3,4]D	408
T50.6X6*	407	T50.Z1[1,2,3,4]S	372	T53.5X[1,2,3,4]S	372	T57.1X[1,2,3,4]S	372
T50.7X[1,2,3,4]A	365	T50.Z15A	365	T53.6X[1,2,3,4]A	365	T57.2X[1,2,3,4]A	366
T50.7X[1,2,3,4]D	407	T50.Z15D	407	T53.6X[1,2,3,4]D	408	T57.2X[1,2,3,4]D	408
T50.7X[1,2,3,4]S	372	T50.Z15S	372	T53.6X[1,2,3,4]S	372	T57.2X[1,2,3,4]S	372
T50.7X5A	287, 365	T50.Z16*	407	T53.7X[1,2,3,4]A	365	T57.3X[1,2,3,4]A	366
T50.7X5D	407	T50.Z9[1,2,3,4]A	365	T53.7X[1,2,3,4]D	408	T57.3X[1,2,3,4]D	408
T50.7X5S	372	T50.Z9[1,2,3,4]D	407	T53.7X[1,2,3,4]S	372	T57.3X[1,2,3,4]S	372
T50.7X6*	407	T50.Z9[1,2,3,4]S	372	T53.9[1,2,3,4]XA	366	T57.8X[1,2,3,4]A	366
T50.8X[1,2,3,4]A	365	T50.Z95A	365	T53.9[1,2,3,4]XD	408	T57.8X[1,2,3,4]D	408
T50.8X[1,2,3,4]D	407	T50.Z95D	407	T53.9[1,2,3,4]XS	372	T57.8X[1,2,3,4]S	373
T50.8X[1,2,3,4]S	372	T50.Z95S	372	T54.0X[1,2,3,4]A	366	T57.9[1,2,3,4]XA	366
T50.8X5A	287, 365	T50.Z96*	407	T54.0X[1,2,3,4]D	408	T57.9[1,2,3,4]XD	408
T50.8X5D	407	T51.0X[1,2,3,4]A	365	T54.0X[1,2,3,4]S	372	T57.9[1,2,3,4]XS	373
T50.8X5S	372	T51.0X[1,2,3,4]D	407	T54.1X[1,2,3,4]A	366	T58.0[1,2,3,4]XA	366
T50.8X6*	407	T51.0X[1,2,3,4]S	372	T54.1X[1,2,3,4]D	408	T58.0[1,2,3,4]XD	408
T50.9[0,9]5A	287	T51.1X[1,2,3,4]A	365	T54.1X[1,2,3,4]S	372	T58.0[1,2,3,4]XS	373
T50.90[1,2,3,4]A	365	T51.1X[1,2,3,4]D	407	T54.2X[1,2,3,4]A	366	T58.1[1,2,3,4]XA	366
T50.90[1,2,3,4]D	407	T51.1X[1,2,3,4]S	372	T54.2X[1,2,3,4]D	408	T58.1[1,2,3,4]XD	408
T50.90[1,2,3,4]S	372	T51.2X[1,2,3,4]A	365	T54.2X[1,2,3,4]S	372	T58.1[1,2,3,4]XS	373
T50.905A	365	T51.2X[1,2,3,4]D	407	T54.3X[1,2,3,4]A	366	T58.2X[1,2,3,4]A	366
T50.905D	407	T51.2X[1,2,3,4]S	372	T54.3X[1,2,3,4]D	408	T58.2X[1,2,3,4]D	408
T50.905S	372	T51.3X[1,2,3,4]A	365	T54.3X[1,2,3,4]S	372	T58.2X[1,2,3,4]S	373
T50.906*	407	T51.3X[1,2,3,4]D	407	T54.9[1,2,3,4]XA	366	T58.8X[1,2,3,4]A	366
T50.99[1,2,3,4]A	365	T51.3X[1,2,3,4]S	372	T54.9[1,2,3,4]XD	408	T58.8X[1,2,3,4]D	408
T50.99[1,2,3,4]D	407	T51.8X[1,2,3,4]A	365	T54.9[1,2,3,4]XS	372	T58.8X[1,2,3,4]S	373
T50.99[1,2,3,4]S	372	T51.8X[1,2,3,4]D	407	T55.0X[1,2,3,4]A	366	T58.9[1,2,3,4]XA	366
T50.995A	365	T51.8X[1,2,3,4]S	372	T55.0X[1,2,3,4]D	408	T58.9[1,2,3,4]XD	408
T50.995D	407			T55.0X[1,2,3,4]S	372	T58.9[1,2,3,4]XS	373

Code	Page	Code	Page	Code	Page	Code	Page
T59.0X[1,2,3,4]A	366	T61.9[1,2,3,4]XA	366	T63.39[1,2,3,4]A	367	T65.0X[1,2,3,4]A	367
T59.0X[1,2,3,4]D	408	T61.9[1,2,3,4]XD	409	T63.39[1,2,3,4]D	409	T65.0X[1,2,3,4]D	409
T59.0X[1,2,3,4]S	373	T61.9[1,2,3,4]XS	373	T63.39[1,2,3,4]S	373	T65.0X[1,2,3,4]S	374
T59.1X[1,2,3,4]A	366	T62.0X[1,2,3,4]A	366	T63.41[1,2,3,4]A	367	T65.1X[1,2,3,4]A	367
T59.1X[1,2,3,4]D	408	T62.0X[1,2,3,4]D	409	T63.41[1,2,3,4]D	409	T65.1X[1,2,3,4]D	409
T59.1X[1,2,3,4]S	373	T62.0X[1,2,3,4]S	373	T63.41[1,2,3,4]S	373	T65.1X[1,2,3,4]S	374
T59.2X[1,2,3,4]A	366	T62.1X[1,2,3,4]A	366	T63.42[1,2,3,4]A	367	T65.21[1,2,3,4]A	367
T59.2X[1,2,3,4]D	408	T62.1X[1,2,3,4]D	409	T63.42[1,2,3,4]D	409	T65.21[1,2,3,4]D	409
T59.2X[1,2,3,4]S	373	T62.1X[1,2,3,4]S	373	T63.42[1,2,3,4]S	373	T65.21[1,2,3,4]S	374
T59.3X[1,2,3,4]A	366	T62.2X[1,2,3,4]A	366	T63.43[1,2,3,4]A	367	T65.22[1,2,3,4]A	367
T59.3X[1,2,3,4]D	408	T62.2X[1,2,3,4]D	409	T63.43[1,2,3,4]D	409	T65.22[1,2,3,4]D	409
T59.3X[1,2,3,4]S	373	T62.2X[1,2,3,4]S	373	T63.43[1,2,3,4]S	373	T65.22[1,2,3,4]S	374
T59.4X[1,2,3,4]A	366	T62.8X[1,2,3,4]A	366	T63.44[1,2,3,4]A	367	T65.29[1,2,3,4]A	367
T59.4X[1,2,3,4]D	408	T62.8X[1,2,3,4]D	409	T63.44[1,2,3,4]D	409	T65.29[1,2,3,4]D	409
T59.4X[1,2,3,4]S	373	T62.8X[1,2,3,4]S	373	T63.44[1,2,3,4]S	373	T65.29[1,2,3,4]S	374
T59.5X[1,2,3,4]A	366	T62.9[1,2,3,4]XA	366	T63.45[1,2,3,4]A	367	T65.3X[1,2,3,4]A	367
T59.5X[1,2,3,4]D	408	T62.9[1,2,3,4]XD	409	T63.45[1,2,3,4]D	409	T65.3X[1,2,3,4]D	409
T59.5X[1,2,3,4]S	373	T62.9[1,2,3,4]XS	373	T63.45[1,2,3,4]S	373	T65.3X[1,2,3,4]S	374
T59.6X[1,2,3,4]A	366	T63.00[1,2,3,4]A	366	T63.46[1,2,3,4]A	367	T65.4X[1,2,3,4]A	367
T59.6X[1,2,3,4]D	408	T63.00[1,2,3,4]D	409	T63.46[1,2,3,4]D	409	T65.4X[1,2,3,4]D	409
T59.6X[1,2,3,4]S	373	T63.00[1,2,3,4]S	373	T63.46[1,2,3,4]S	373	T65.4X[1,2,3,4]S	374
T59.7X[1,2,3,4]A	366	T63.01[1,2,3,4]A	366	T63.48[1,2,3,4]A	367	T65.5X[1,2,3,4]A	367
T59.7X[1,2,3,4]D	408	T63.01[1,2,3,4]D	409	T63.48[1,2,3,4]D	409	T65.5X[1,2,3,4]D	409
T59.7X[1,2,3,4]S	373	T63.01[1,2,3,4]S	373	T63.48[1,2,3,4]S	373	T65.5X[1,2,3,4]S	374
T59.81[1,2,3,4]A	366, 381	T63.02[1,2,3,4]A	366	T63.51[1,2,3,4]A	367	T65.6X[1,2,3,4]A	367
T59.81[1,2,3,4]D	408	T63.02[1,2,3,4]D	409	T63.51[1,2,3,4]D	409	T65.6X[1,2,3,4]D	409
T59.81[1,2,3,4]S	373	T63.02[1,2,3,4]S	373	T63.51[1,2,3,4]S	373	T65.6X[1,2,3,4]S	374
T59.89[1,2,3,4]A	366, 381	T63.03[1,2,3,4]A	366	T63.59[1,2,3,4]A	367	T65.81[1,2,3,4]A	367
T59.89[1,2,3,4]D	408	T63.03[1,2,3,4]D	409	T63.59[1,2,3,4]D	409	T65.81[1,2,3,4]D	409
T59.89[1,2,3,4]S	373	T63.03[1,2,3,4]S	373	T63.59[1,2,3,4]S	373	T65.81[1,2,3,4]S	374
T59.9[1,2,3,4]XA	366, 381	T63.04[1,2,3,4]A	366	T63.61[1,2,3,4]A	367	T65.82[1,2,3,4]A	367
T59.9[1,2,3,4]XD	408	T63.04[1,2,3,4]D	409	T63.61[1,2,3,4]D	409	T65.82[1,2,3,4]D	409
T59.9[1,2,3,4]XS	373	T63.04[1,2,3,4]S	373	T63.61[1,2,3,4]S	373	T65.82[1,2,3,4]S	374
T60.0X[1,2,3,4]A	366	T63.06[1,2,3,4]A	366	T63.62[1,2,3,4]A	367	T65.83[1,2,3,4]A	367
T60.0X[1,2,3,4]D	408	T63.06[1,2,3,4]D	409	T63.62[1,2,3,4]D	409	T65.83[1,2,3,4]D	409
T60.0X[1,2,3,4]S	373	T63.06[1,2,3,4]S	373	T63.62[1,2,3,4]S	373	T65.83[1,2,3,4]S	374
T60.1X[1,2,3,4]A	366	T63.07[1,2,3,4]A	366	T63.63[1,2,3,4]A	367	T65.89[1,2,3,4]A	367
T60.1X[1,2,3,4]D	408	T63.07[1,2,3,4]D	409	T63.63[1,2,3,4]D	409	T65.89[1,2,3,4]D	409
T60.1X[1,2,3,4]S	373	T63.07[1,2,3,4]S	373	T63.63[1,2,3,4]S	373	T65.89[1,2,3,4]S	374
T60.2X[1,2,3,4]A	366	T63.08[1,2,3,4]A	367	T63.69[1,2,3,4]A	367	T65.9[1,2,3,4]XA	367
T60.2X[1,2,3,4]D	408	T63.08[1,2,3,4]D	409	T63.69[1,2,3,4]D	409	T65.9[1,2,3,4]XD	409
T60.2X[1,2,3,4]S	373	T63.08[1,2,3,4]S	373	T63.69[1,2,3,4]S	373	T65.9[1,2,3,4]XS	374
T60.3X[1,2,3,4]A	366	T63.09[1,2,3,4]A	367	T63.71[1,2,3,4]A	367	T66.XXX[A,S]	374
T60.3X[1,2,3,4]D	408	T63.09[1,2,3,4]D	409	T63.71[1,2,3,4]D	409	T66.XXXD	409
T60.3X[1,2,3,4]S	373	T63.09[1,2,3,4]S	373	T63.71[1,2,3,4]S	374	T67.[0,1,2,3,4,5,6,7]XX[A,S]	374
T60.4X[1,2,3,4]A	366	T63.11[1,2,3,4]A	367	T63.79[1,2,3,4]A	367	T67.[0,1,2,3,4,5,6,7]XXD	409
T60.4X[1,2,3,4]D	408	T63.11[1,2,3,4]D	409	T63.79[1,2,3,4]D	409	T67.[8,9]XX[A,S]	374
T60.4X[1,2,3,4]S	373	T63.11[1,2,3,4]S	373	T63.79[1,2,3,4]S	374	T67.8XXD	409
T60.8X[1,2,3,4]A	366	T63.12[1,2,3,4]A	367	T63.81[1,2,3,4]A	367	T67.9XXD	409
T60.8X[1,2,3,4]D	408	T63.12[1,2,3,4]D	409	T63.81[1,2,3,4]D	409	T68.XXX[A,S]	374
T60.8X[1,2,3,4]S	373	T63.12[1,2,3,4]S	373	T63.81[1,2,3,4]S	374	T68.XXXD	409
T60.9[1,2,3,4]XA	366	T63.19[1,2,3,4]A	367	T63.82[1,2,3,4]A	367	T69.[8,9]XX[A,S]	374
T60.9[1,2,3,4]XD	408	T63.19[1,2,3,4]D	409	T63.82[1,2,3,4]D	409	T69.[8,9]XXD	409
T60.9[1,2,3,4]XS	373	T63.19[1,2,3,4]S	373	T63.82[1,2,3,4]S	374	T69.01[1,2,9][A,S]	374
T61.0[1,2,3,4]XA	366	T63.2X[1,2,3,4]A	367	T63.83[1,2,3,4]A	367	T69.01[1,2,9]D	409
T61.0[1,2,3,4]XD	408	T63.2X[1,2,3,4]D	409	T63.83[1,2,3,4]D	409	T69.02[1,2,9][A,S]	374
T61.0[1,2,3,4]XS	373	T63.2X[1,2,3,4]S	373	T63.83[1,2,3,4]S	374	T69.02[1,2,9]D	409
T61.1[1,2,3,4]XA	366	T63.30[1,2,3,4]A	367	T63.89[1,2,3,4]A	367	T69.1XX[A,S]	374
T61.1[1,2,3,4]XD	408	T63.30[1,2,3,4]D	409	T63.89[1,2,3,4]D	409	T69.1XXD	409
T61.1[1,2,3,4]XS	373	T63.30[1,2,3,4]S	373	T63.89[1,2,3,4]S	374	T70.[0,1]XXS	374
T61.77[1,2,3,4]A	366	T63.31[1,2,3,4]A	367	T63.9[1,2,3,4]XA	367	T70.0XXA	57
T61.77[1,2,3,4]D	408	T63.31[1,2,3,4]D	409	T63.9[1,2,3,4]XD	409	T70.0XXD	409
T61.77[1,2,3,4]S	373	T63.31[1,2,3,4]S	373	T63.9[1,2,3,4]XS	374	T70.1XXA	57
T61.78[1,2,3,4]A	366	T63.32[1,2,3,4]A	367	T64.0[1,2,3,4]XA	367	T70.1XXD	409
T61.78[1,2,3,4]D	408	T63.32[1,2,3,4]D	409	T64.0[1,2,3,4]XD	409	T70.2[0,9]X[A,S]	374
T61.78[1,2,3,4]S	373	T63.32[1,2,3,4]S	373	T64.0[1,2,3,4]XS	374	T70.20XD	409
T61.8X[1,2,3,4]A	366	T63.33[1,2,3,4]A	367	T64.8[1,2,3,4]XA	367	T70.29XD	409
T61.8X[1,2,3,4]D	409	T63.33[1,2,3,4]D	409	T64.8[1,2,3,4]XD	409	T70.3XX[A,S]	374
T61.8X[1,2,3,4]S	373	T63.33[1,2,3,4]S	373	T64.8[1,2,3,4]XS	374	T70.3XXD	410

Code	Page	Code	Page	Code	Page	Code	Page
T70.4XX[A,S]	374	T75.8[1,2]X[A,S]	374	T79.A0XA	374, 430	T80.911A	293
T70.4XXD	410	T75.8[1,2]XD	410	T79.A0XD	410	T80.919A	293
T70.8XX[A,S]	374	T75.89X[A,S]	374	T79.A0XS	361	T80.92XA	287, 293
T70.8XXD	410	T75.89XD	410	T79.A1[1,2,9]A	374, 430, 435	T80.92XD	410
T70.9XX[A,S]	374	T76.0[1,2]X[A,S]	374	T79.A1[1,2,9]D	410	T80.92XS	375
T70.9XXD	410	T76.0[1,2]XD	410	T79.A1[1,2,9]S	361	T80.A0XA	287, 293
T71.1[1,2,3,5,6,9][1,2,3,4][A,S]	374	T76.1[1,2]X[A,S]	374	T79.A2[1,2,9]A	374, 430, 437	T80.A0XD	410
T71.1[1,2,3,5,6,9][1,2,3,4]D	410	T76.1[1,2]XD	410	T79.A2[1,2,9]D	410	T80.A0XS	375
T71.141A	374	T76.2[1,2]X[A,S]	374	T79.A2[1,2,9]S	361	T80.A1[0,1,9]A	287
T71.141D	410	T76.2[1,2]XD	410	T79.A3XA	432	T80.A1[0,1,9]D	410
T71.141S	374	T76.3[1,2]X[A,S]	374	T80.[0,1]XXS	375	T80.A1[0,1,9]S	375
T71.143A	374	T76.3[1,2]XD	410	T80.0XXA	66, 287	T80.A10A	293
T71.143D	410	T76.9[1,2]X[A,S]	374	T80.0XXD	410	T80.A11A	294
T71.143S	374	T76.9[1,2]XD	410	T80.1XXA	103, 287	T80.A19A	294
T71.144A	374	T78.0[0,1,2,3,4,5,6,7,8,9]XD	410	T80.1XXD	410	T80.A9XA	287, 294
T71.144D	410	T78.0[0,1,2,3,4,5,6,7,8,9]XS	374	T80.21[1,2,8,9]A	103	T80.A9XD	410
T71.144S	374	T78.00XA	361	T80.21[1,2,8,9]D	410	T80.A9XS	375
T71.2[0,1]X[A,S]	374	T78.01XA	361	T80.21[1,2,8,9]S	374	T81.1[0,1,2,9]XA	287, 368
T71.2[2,3][1,2,3,4][A,S]	374	T78.02XA	361	T80.22XA	287, 307, 309	T81.1[0,1,2,9]XD	410
T71.2[2,3][1,2,3,4]D	410	T78.03XA	361	T80.22XD	410	T81.1[0,1,2,9]XS	375
T71.20XD	410	T78.04XA	361	T80.22XS	374	T81.3[0,1,2,3]XA	368
T71.21XD	410	T78.05XA	361	T80.29XA	287, 307, 309	T81.3[0,1,2,3]XD	410
T71.29X[A,S]	374	T78.06XA	361	T80.29XD	410	T81.3[1,2]XS	375
T71.29XD	410	T78.07XA	361	T80.29XS	374	T81.30XS	375
T71.9XX[A,S]	374	T78.08XA	361	T80.30XA	287, 293	T81.33XS	375
T71.9XXD	410	T78.09XA	361	T80.30XD	410	T81.4XXA	287, 307
T73.0XX[A,S]	374	T78.1XX[A,S]	374	T80.30XS	374	T81.4XXD	410
T73.0XXD	410	T78.1XXD	410	T80.31[0,1,9]A	287	T81.4XXS	375
T73.1XX[A,S]	374	T78.2XXA	361	T80.31[0,1,9]D	410	T81.5[0,1,2,3,9][0,1,2,3,4,5,6,7,8,9]A	287, 368
T73.1XXD	410	T78.2XXD	410	T80.31[0,1,9]S	374	T81.5[0,1,2,3,9][0,1,2,3,4,5,6,7,8,9]S	375
T73.2XX[A,S]	374	T78.2XXS	374	T80.310A	293	T81.5[0,1,2,3,9][0,1,2,3,4,5,6,7,8,9]D	410
T73.2XXD	410	T78.3XXA	361	T80.311A	293	T81.6[0,1,9]XA	287, 368
T73.3XX[A,S]	374	T78.3XXD	410	T80.319A	293	T81.6[0,1,9]XD	410
T73.3XXD	410	T78.3XXS	374	T80.39XA	287, 293	T81.6[0,1,9]XS	375
T73.8XX[A,S]	374	T78.40XA	361	T80.39XD	410	T81.71[0,1,8,9]A	287
T73.8XXD	410	T78.40XD	410	T80.39XS	374	T81.71[0,1,8,9]D	410
T73.9XX[A,S]	374	T78.40XS	374	T80.40XA	287, 293	T81.71[0,1,8,9]S	375
T73.9XXD	410	T78.41XA	287, 367	T80.40XD	410	T81.71[8,9]A	101
T74.0[1,2]X[A,S]	374	T78.41XD	410	T80.40XS	374	T81.710A	118
T74.0[1,2]XD	410	T78.41XS	374	T80.41[0,1,9]A	287	T81.711A	256
T74.1[1,2]X[A,S]	374	T78.49XA	361	T80.41[0,1,9]D	410	T81.72XA	101, 287
T74.1[1,2]XD	410	T78.49XD	410	T80.41[0,1,9]S	374	T81.72XD	410
T74.2[1,2]X[A,S]	374	T78.49XS	374	T80.410A	293	T81.72XS	375
T74.2[1,2]XD	410	T78.8XX[A,S]	374	T80.411A	293	T81.81XA	368
T74.3[1,2]X[A,S]	374	T78.8XXD	410	T80.419A	293	T81.81XD	410
T74.3[1,2]XD	410	T79.[0,1]XXA	432	T80.49XA	287, 293	T81.81XS	375
T74.4XX[A,S]	374	T79.[0,1]XXD	410	T80.49XD	410	T81.82XA	368
T74.4XXD	410	T79.[0,1]XXS	361	T80.49XS	374	T81.82XD	410
T74.9[1,2]X[A,S]	374	T79.[2,4,5,6,7]XXD	410	T80.5[1,2,9]XA	287, 361	T81.82XS	375
T74.9[1,2]XD	410	T79.[8,9]XXA	374	T80.5[1,2,9]XD	410	T81.83XA	287, 368
T75.0[0,1,9]X[A,S]	374	T79.[8,9]XXD	410	T80.5[1,2,9]XS	374	T81.83XD	410
T75.0[0,1,9]XD	410	T79.[8,9]XXS	361	T80.6[1,2,9]XA	287, 361	T81.83XS	375
T75.1XX[A,S]	374	T79.0XXA	66, 287, 430	T80.6[1,2,9]XD	410	T81.89XA	368
T75.1XXD	410	T79.1XXA	66, 287, 430	T80.6[1,2,9]XS	375	T81.89XD	410
T75.20X[A,S]	374	T79.2XXA	287, 374, 430	T80.81[0,8]A	287	T81.89XS	375
T75.20XD	410	T79.2XXS	361	T80.81[0,8]D	410	T81.9XXA	287, 368
T75.21X[A,S]	374	T79.4XXA	287, 374, 430	T80.81[0,8]S	375	T81.9XXD	410
T75.21XD	410	T79.4XXS	361	T80.810A	103	T81.9XXS	375
T75.22X[A,S]	374	T79.5XXA	254, 287, 430	T80.818A	103	T82.0[1,2,3,9]XA	102
T75.22XD	410	T79.5XXS	361	T80.89XA	287, 293	T82.0[1,2,3,9]XD	410
T75.23X[A,S]	374	T79.6XXA	204, 430, 435	T80.89XD	410	T82.0[1,2,3,9]XS	375
T75.23XD	410	T79.6XXS	361	T80.89XS	375	T82.11[0,1,8,9]D	410
T75.29X[A,S]	374	T79.7XXA	68, 287, 430	T80.90XA	103, 287	T82.11[0,1,8,9]S	375
T75.29XD	410	T79.7XXS	361	T80.90XD	410	T82.110A	102
T75.3XXA	57	T79.8XXA	430	T80.90XS	375	T82.111A	102
T75.3XXD	410	T79.9XXA	430	T80.91[0,1,9]A	287	T82.118A	103
T75.3XXS	374	T79.A[3,9]XA	374, 430	T80.91[0,1,9]D	410		
T75.4XX[A,S]	374	T79.A[3,9]XD	410	T80.91[0,1,9]S	375		
T75.4XXD	410	T79.A[3,9]XS	361	T80.910A	293		

Code	Page	Code	Page	Code	Page	Code	Page
T82.119A	103	T83.2[1,2,3,9]XD	411	T84.29[0,3,6,8]D	411	T85.398S	376
T82.12[0,1,8,9]D	410	T83.2[1,2,3,9]XS	375	T84.29[0,3,6,8]S	375	T85.4[1,2,3,4,9]XD	411
T82.12[0,1,8,9]S	375	T83.3[1,2,9]XA	265, 270	T84.3[1,2,9][0,8]A	183	T85.4[1,2,3,4,9]XS	376
T82.120A	102	T83.3[1,2,9]XD	411	T84.3[1,2,9][0,8]D	411	T85.41XA	224
T82.121A	102	T83.3[1,2,9]XS	375	T84.3[1,2,9][0,8]S	375	T85.42XA	224
T82.128A	103	T83.4[1,2,9][0,8]A	256	T84.4[1,2,9][0,8]A	183	T85.43XA	224
T82.129A	103	T83.4[1,2,9][0,8]D	411	T84.4[1,2,9][0,8]D	411	T85.44XA	224
T82.19[0,1,8,9]D	410	T83.4[1,2,9][0,8]S	375	T84.4[1,2,9][0,8]S	375	T85.49XA	224
T82.19[0,1,8,9]S	375	T83.5[1,9]XA	256	T84.5[0,1,2,3,4,9]XA	131, 183	T85.5[1,2,9][0,1,8]A	368
T82.190A	102	T83.5[1,9]XD	411	T84.5[0,1,2,3,4,9]XD	411	T85.5[1,2,9][0,1,8]D	411
T82.191A	102	T83.5[1,9]XS	375	T84.5[0,1,2,3,4,9]XS	375	T85.5[1,2,9][0,1,8]S	376
T82.198A	103	T83.6XXA	256	T84.6[3,9]XA	183	T85.6[1,2][0,1,2,3,4,8]A	368
T82.199A	103	T83.6XXD	411	T84.6[3,9]XD	411	T85.6[1,2][0,1,2,3,4,8]D	411
T82.21[1,2,3,8]A	103	T83.6XXS	375	T84.60XA	131, 183	T85.6[1,2][0,1,2,3,4,8]S	376
T82.21[1,2,3,8]D	410	T83.7[1,2][1,8]D	411	T84.60XD	411	T85.63[0,1,3,8]A	368
T82.21[1,2,3,8]S	375	T83.7[1,2][1,8]S	375	T84.60XS	375	T85.63[0,1,3,8]D	411
T82.22[1,2,3,8]A	103	T83.7[1,2]1A	265, 270	T84.61[0,1,2,3,4,5,9]A	183	T85.63[0,1,3,8]S	376
T82.22[1,2,3,8]D	410	T83.7[1,2]8A	256	T84.61[0,1,2,3,4,5,9]D	411	T85.69[0,1,2,3,4,8] A	368
T82.22[1,2,3,8]S	375	T83.8[1,2,3,4,5,6,9]XA	256	T84.61[0,1,2,3,4,5,9]S	375	T85.69[0,1,2,3,4,8]D	411
T82.3[1,2,3,9][0,1,2,8,9]A	103	T83.8[1,2,3,4,5,6,9]XD	411	T84.62[0,1,2,3,4,5,9]A	183	T85.69[0,1,2,3,4,8]S	376
T82.31[0,1,2,8,9]D	410	T83.8[1,2,3,4,5,6,9]XS	375	T84.62[0,1,2,3,4,5,9]D	411	T85.7[1,2,9]XA	368
T82.31[0,1,2,8,9]S	375	T83.9XXA	256	T84.62[0,1,2,3,4,5,9]S	375	T85.7[1,2,9]XD	411
T82.32[0,1,2,8,9]D	410	T83.9XXD	411	T84.62[0,1]A	131	T85.7[1,2,9]XS	376
T82.32[0,1,2,8,9]S	375	T83.9XXS	375	T84.62[2,3]A	131	T85.8[1,2,3,4,5,6,9]XA	368
T82.33[0,1,2,8,9]D	410	T84.01[0,1,2,3,8,9]A	183	T84.62[4,5]A	131	T85.8[1,2,3,4,5,6,9]XD	411
T82.33[0,1,2,8,9]S	375	T84.01[0,1,2,3,8,9]D	411	T84.629A	131	T85.8[1,2,3,4,5,6,9]XS	376
T82.39[0,1,2,8,9]D	410	T84.01[0,1,2,3,8,9]S	375	T84.63XA	131	T85.9XXA	368
T82.39[0,1,2,8,9]S	375	T84.02[0,1]A	183	T84.63XS	375	T85.9XXD	411
T82.4[1,2,3,9]XA	103	T84.02[0,1]D	411	T84.69XA	131	T85.9XXS	376
T82.4[1,2,3,9]XD	410	T84.02[0,1]S	375	T84.69XS	375	T86.0*	293
T82.4[1,2,3,9]XS	375	T84.02[2,3]A	183	T84.7XXA	132, 183	T86.1*	256
T82.51[0,1,2,3,4,5,8,9]A	103	T84.02[2,3]D	411	T84.7XXD	411	T86.2*	103
T82.51[0,1,2,3,4,5,8,9]D	410	T84.02[2,3]S	375	T84.7XXS	375	T86.3*	103
T82.51[0,1,2,3,4,5,8,9]S	375	T84.02[8,9]A	183	T84.8[1,2,3,4,5,6,9]XA	184	T86.4*	124
T82.52[0,1,2,3,4,5,8,9]A	103	T84.02[8,9]D	411	T84.8[1,2,3,4,5,6,9]XD	411	T86.5	368
T82.52[0,1,2,3,4,5,8,9]D	410	T84.02[8,9]S	375	T84.8[1,2,3,4,5,6,9]XS	375	T86.81[0,1,2]	70
T82.52[0,1,2,3,4,5,8,9]S	375	T84.03[0,1,2,3,8,9]A	183	T84.9XXA	184	T86.81[8,9]	70
T82.53[0,1,2,3,4,5,8,9]A	103	T84.03[0,1,2,3,8,9]D	411	T84.9XXD	411	T86.82*	368
T82.53[0,1,2,3,4,5,8,9]D	410	T84.03[0,1,2,3,8,9]S	375	T84.9XXS	375	T86.83*	368
T82.53[0,1,2,3,4,5,8,9]S	375	T84.04[0,1,2,3,8,9]S	375	T85.0[1,2,3,9]XD	411	T86.84[0,1]	47
T82.59[0,1,2,3,4,5,8,9]A	103	T84.04[0,1][A,D]	183	T85.0[1,2,3,9]XS	375	T86.84[2,8,9]	368
T82.59[0,1,2,3,4,5,8,9]D	411	T84.04[2,3][A,D]	183	T85.0[1,2,3]XA	40	T86.85*	368
T82.59[0,1,2,3,4,5,8,9]S	375	T84.04[8,9][A,D]	183	T85.09XA	40	T86.89[0,1,2]	124
T82.6XXA	103	T84.05[0,1,2,3,8,9]A	183	T85.11[0,1,2,8]A	40	T86.89[8,9]	124
T82.6XXD	411	T84.05[0,1,2,3,8,9]D	411	T85.11[0,1,2,8]D	411	T86.9*	368
T82.6XXS	375	T84.05[0,1,2,3,8,9]S	375	T85.11[0,1,2,8]S	376	T87.0X[1,2,9]	184
T82.7XXA	103	T84.06[0,1,2,3,8,9]A	183	T85.12[0,1,2,8]A	40	T87.1X[1,2,9]	184
T82.7XXD	411	T84.06[0,1,2,3,8,9]D	411	T85.12[0,1,2,8]D	411	T87.2	184
T82.7XXS	375	T84.06[0,1,2,3,8,9]S	375	T85.12[0,1,2,8]S	376	T87.3*	204
T82.8[1,2,3,4,5,6,9][7,8]D	411	T84.09[0,1,2,3,8,9]A	183	T85.19[0,1,2,9]A	40	T87.4*	205
T82.8[1,2,3,4,5,6,9][7,8]S	375	T84.09[0,1,2,3,8,9]D	411	T85.19[0,1,2,9]D	411	T87.5*	205
T82.81[7,8]A	103	T84.09[0,1,2,3,8,9]S	375	T85.19[0,1,2,9]S	376	T87.8*	205
T82.82[7,8]A	103	T84.11[0,1,2,3,4,5,6,7,9]A	183	T85.2[1,2,9]XA	47	T87.9	205
T82.83[7,8]A	103	T84.11[0,1,2,3,4,5,6,7,9]D	411	T85.2[1,2,9]XD	411	T88.0XXA	287, 307, 309
T82.84[7,8]A	103	T84.11[0,1,2,3,4,5,6,7,9]S	375	T85.2[1,2,9]XS	376	T88.0XXD	411
T82.85[7,8]A	103	T84.12[0,1,2,3,4,5,6,7,9]A	183	T85.3[1,2,9][0,1]A	368	T88.0XXS	376
T82.86[7,8]A	103	T84.12[0,1,2,3,4,5,6,7,9]D	411	T85.3[1,2,9]8A	47	T88.1XXA	308
T82.89[7,8]A	103	T84.12[0,1,2,3,4,5,6,7,9]S	375	T85.31[0,1]D	411	T88.1XXD	411
T82.9XXA	103	T84.19[0,1,2,3,4,5,6,7,9]A	183	T85.31[0,1]S	376	T88.1XXS	376
T82.9XXD	411	T84.19[0,1,2,3,4,5,6,7,9]D	411	T85.318D	411	T88.2XX[A,S]	376
T82.9XXS	375	T84.19[0,1,2,3,4,5,6,7,9]S	375	T85.318S	376	T88.2XXA	287
T83.0[1,2,3,9][0,8]A	256	T84.21[0,3,6,8]A	183	T85.32[0,1]D	411	T88.2XXD	411
T83.0[1,2,3,9][0,8]D	411	T84.21[0,3,6,8]D	411	T85.32[0,1]S	376	T88.3XX[A,S]	376
T83.0[1,2,3,9][0,8]S	375	T84.21[0,3,6,8]S	375	T85.328D	411	T88.3XXD	411
T83.1[1,2,9][0,1,2,8] A	256	T84.22[0,3,6,8]A	183	T85.328S	376	T88.4XXA	368
T83.1[1,2,9][0,1,2,8]D	411	T84.22[0,3,6,8]D	411	T85.39[0,1]D	411	T88.4XXD	411
T83.1[1,2,9][0,1,2,8]S	375	T84.22[0,3,6,8]S	375	T85.39[0,1]S	376	T88.4XXS	376
T83.2[1,2,3,9]XA	256	T84.29[0,3,6,8]A	183	T85.398D	411	T88.51XA	376

Code	Page	Code	Page	Code	Page	Code	Page
T88.51XD	411	Z28.01	289	Z43.5	256	Z57*	412
T88.51XS	376	Z28.02	289	Z43.6	256	Z59*	412
T88.52XA	367	Z28.03	289	Z43.7	265, 270	Z60*	412
T88.52XD	411	Z28.04	289	Z43.8	412	Z62*	412
T88.52XS	376	Z28.09	289	Z43.9	412	Z63*	412
T88.59XA	287, 367	Z28.1	289	Z44.0[0,1,2][1,2,9]	184	Z64.0	272, 276
T88.59XD	411	Z28.20	289	Z44.1[0,1,2][1,2,9]	184	Z64.1	265, 270
T88.59XS	376	Z28.21	289	Z44.2*	412	Z64.4	412
T88.6XXA	361	Z28.29	289	Z44.3*	412	Z65*	412
T88.6XXD	411	Z28.81	289	Z44.8	385	Z66	412
T88.6XXS	376	Z28.82	289	Z44.9	385	Z67*	412
T88.7XXA	368	Z28.89	289	Z45.0*	103	Z68.1	412
T88.7XXD	411	Z28.9	289	Z45.1	385, 411	Z68.2*	412
T88.7XXS	376	Z28*	412	Z45.2	385, 411	Z68.3*	412
T88.8XXA	368	Z30.0*	412	Z45.3*	40	Z68.4*	247
T88.8XXD	411	Z30.2	261, 265, 270	Z45.4*	40	Z68.5*	412
T88.8XXS	376	Z30.4*	412	Z45.8*	412	Z69*	412
T88.9XXA	368	Z30.8	412	Z45.9	412	Z70*	412
T88.9XXD	411	Z30.9	412	Z46.0	412	Z71*	412
T88.9XXS	376	Z31.0	261, 265, 270	Z46.1	412	Z72.0	412
Z00.110	289	Z31.4*	412	Z46.2	40	Z72.3	412
Z00.111	289	Z31.5	412	Z46.3	412	Z72.4	412
Z00.121	289	Z31.6*	412	Z46.4	412	Z72.5*	412
Z00.129	289	Z31.8*	412	Z46.51	118	Z72.6	412
Z00*	412	Z31.9	412	Z46.59	118	Z72.810	310
Z01.10	289	Z32*	412	Z46.6	256	Z72.811	310
Z01.110	289	Z33.1	412	Z46.81	412	Z72.820	412
Z01.118	289	Z33.2	272, 276	Z46.82	385, 411	Z72.821	412
Z01.12	289	Z34*	412	Z46.89	412	Z72.89	412
Z01*	412	Z36	412	Z46.9	412	Z72.9	412
Z02.6	289	Z37*	273, 275, 412	Z47.1	184	Z73*	412
Z02.82	289	Z38.00	289	Z47.2	184	Z74*	412
Z02.89	289	Z38.01	289	Z47.3*	184	Z75*	412
Z02*	412	Z38.1	289	Z47.8[1,2]	184	Z76.2	289
Z03*	412	Z38.2	289	Z47.89	184	Z76*	412
Z04.[1,2,3]	376	Z38.30	289	Z48.00	412	Z77*	412
Z04.4*	412	Z38.31	289	Z48.01	412	Z78*	412
Z04.6	412	Z38.4	289	Z48.02	412	Z79.0*	411
Z04.7*	412	Z38.5	289	Z48.03	385, 411	Z79.1	411
Z04.8	412	Z38.61	289	Z48.1	385, 411	Z79.2	411
Z04.9	412	Z38.62	289	Z48.2*	385, 411	Z79.3	411
Z08	304, 305, 306	Z38.63	289	Z48.3	385, 411	Z79.4	411
Z09	412	Z38.64	289	Z48.8*	385, 411	Z79.5*	411
Z11*	412	Z38.65	289	Z49*	254	Z79.810	412
Z12*	412	Z38.66	289	Z51.0	304, 306	Z79.811	412
Z13.228	289	Z38.68	289	Z51.1*	304, 305, 306	Z79.818	413
Z13*	412	Z38.69	289	Z51.5	412	Z79.82	411
Z14*	412	Z38.7	289	Z51.8*	411	Z79.83	411
Z15*	412	Z38.8	289	Z51.81	385	Z79.890	413
Z16*	309	Z39.0	272, 276	Z52.0*	412	Z79.891	411
Z17*	412	Z39.1	412	Z52.1*	234	Z79.899	411
Z18*	412	Z39.2	412	Z52.2*	205	Z80*	413
Z20.09	289	Z3A*	412	Z52.3	412	Z81.8	289
Z20.7	289	Z40.0[0,9]	412	Z52.4	256	Z81*	413
Z20.810	289	Z40.01	224	Z52.5	412	Z82.0	289
Z20.818	289	Z40.02	265, 270	Z52.6	124	Z82.49	289
Z20.89	289	Z40.8	412	Z52.8*	412	Z82*	413
Z20*	412	Z40.9	412	Z52.9	412	Z83.1	289
Z21	308	Z41.1	234	Z53.01	289	Z83.3	289
Z22.0	412	Z41.2	261, 289	Z53.09	289	Z83.49	289
Z22.1	412	Z41.3	289, 412	Z53.1	289	Z83*	413
Z22.2	412	Z41.8	412	Z53.20	289	Z84*	413
Z22.3*	412	Z41.9	412	Z53.21	289	Z85.0*	306
Z22.4	412	Z42*	234	Z53.29	289	Z85.1*	306
Z22.5*	124	Z43.0	70	Z53.8	289	Z85.2*	306
Z22.6	412	Z43.1	118	Z53.9	289	Z85.21	6
Z22.8	412	Z43.2	118	Z53*	412	Z85.3	306
Z22.9	412	Z43.3	118	Z55*	412	Z85.4*	306
Z23	289, 412	Z43.4	118	Z56*	412	Z85.5*	306

Code	Page	Code	Page	Code	Page	Code	Page
Z85.6	306	Z87.828	413	Z94.2	70	Z96.4*	413
Z85.7*	306	Z87.890	311	Z94.3	103	Z96.49	2
Z85.8*	306	Z87.891	413	Z94.4	124	Z96.5	413
Z85.810	6	Z87.892	413	Z94.5	234	Z96.6*	205
Z85.818	6	Z87.898	413	Z94.6	205	Z96.7	205
Z85.819	6	Z88*	413	Z94.7	47	Z96.8*	413
Z85.9	306	Z89*	413	Z94.81	294	Z96.89	2
Z85*	304	Z90.01	47	Z94.82	413	Z96.9	2, 413
Z86*	413	Z90.02	413	Z94.83	124	Z97.0	47
Z87.0*	413	Z90.09	413	Z94.84	294	Z97.1*	205
Z87.1*	413	Z90.1*	413	Z94.89	413	Z97.2	413
Z87.2	413	Z90.2	70	Z94.9	413	Z97.3	413
Z87.3*	413	Z90.3	413	Z95.0	413	Z97.4	413
Z87.410	304, 306	Z90.4*	413	Z95.1	413	Z97.5	413
Z87.411	413	Z90.5	413	Z95.2	103	Z97.8	413
Z87.412	413	Z90.6	256	Z95.3	103	Z98*	413
Z87.42	413	Z90.7*	265, 270	Z95.4	103	Z99*	413
Z87.430	413	Z90.79	261	Z95.5	413		
Z87.438	413	Z90.8*	413	Z95.81[1,2]	103		
Z87.440	413	Z91*	413	Z95.810	413		
Z87.441	413	Z92.0	413	Z95.818	413		
Z87.442	413	Z92.2*	411	Z95.820	103		
Z87.448	413	Z92.3	413	Z95.828	103		
Z87.5*	413	Z92.8*	413	Z95.9	413		
Z87.7*	413	Z92.82	33	Z96.0	256		
Z87.81	413	Z93*	413	Z96.1	47		
Z87.820	413	Z94.0	2, 256	Z96.2*	413		
Z87.821	413	Z94.1	103	Z96.3	413		

Code	Description
ØYØC[Ø,3,4][7,J,K,Z]Z	Alter/Upr Leg, Rt, [Opn, Perc, Perc Endo], [Auto Tissue Sub, Synth Sub, Nonauto Tissue Sub, No Dev], NQ 218, 461
ØCØØX[7,J,K,Z]Z	Alter/Upr Lip, Ext, [Auto Tissue Sub, Synth Sub, Nonauto Tissue Sub, No Dev], NQ 210, 447
ØXØH[Ø,3,4][7,J,K,Z]Z	Alter/Wrist Rgn, Lt, [Opn, Perc, Perc Endo], [Auto Tissue Sub, Synth Sub, Nonauto Tissue Sub, No Dev], NQ 218, 460
ØXØG[Ø,3,4][7,J,K,Z]Z	Alter/Wrist Rgn, Rt, [Opn, Perc, Perc Endo], [Auto Tissue Sub, Synth Sub, Nonauto Tissue Sub, No Dev], NQ 218, 460
ØWØ*	Anatomical Regions, General, Alter 355
ØWM*	Anatomical Regions, General, Reattach 356
ØYØ*	Anatomical Regions, Lwr Extremities, Alter 357
ØY3*	Anatomical Regions, Lwr Extremities, Control 92, 158, 357
ØY6*	Anatomical Regions, Lwr Extremities, Detach 357
ØYM*	Anatomical Regions, Lwr Extremities, Reattach 357
ØXØ*	Anatomical Regions, Upr Extremities, Alter 356
ØX3*	Anatomical Regions, Upr Extremities, Control 91, 158, 356
ØX6*	Anatomical Regions, Upr Extremities, Detach 87
ØXQ*	Anatomical Regions, Upr Extremities, Repair 356
ØXR*	Anatomical Regions, Upr Extremities, Replace 29
ØXX*	Anatomical Regions, Upr Extremities, Transfer 29
5AØ221D	Assist with Cardiac Output using Impeller Pump, Continuous 72
5AØ211D	Assist with Cardiac Output using Impeller Pump, Intermittent 72
5AØ2116	Assist with Cardiac Output using Oth Pump, Intermittent 72
5AØ2216	Assistance with Cardiac Output using Oth Pump, Continuous 72
5AØ2[1,2]1[6,D]	Assistance/Cardiac, [Intermittent, Continuous], Output, [Oth Pump, Impeller Pump] 71
5AØ2[1,2]1Ø	Assistance/Cardiac, [Intermittent, Continuous], Output, Balloon Pump 98
ØMM*	Bursa & Lgmt, Reattach 153
ØMX*	Bursa & Lgmt, Transfer 144
Ø31[5,6]ØZD	Bypass [Rt, Lt] Axillary Artery to Upr Arm Vein, Opn Appr 110
Ø31[7,8]ØZD	Bypass [Rt, Lt] Brachial Artery to Upr Arm Vein, Opn Appr 110
Ø31[3,4]ØZD	Bypass [Rt, Lt] Subclavian Artery to Upr Arm Vein, Opn Appr 110
Ø41Ø4AØ	Bypass Abd Aorta to Abd Aorta w Autol Art, Perc Endo 95
Ø41Ø49Ø	Bypass Abd Aorta to Abd Aorta w Autol Vn, Perc Endo 95
Ø41Ø4KØ	Bypass Abd Aorta to Abd Aorta w Nonaut Sub, Perc Endo 95
Ø41Ø4JØ	Bypass Abd Aorta to Abd Aorta w Synth Sub, Perc Endo 95
Ø41ØØAØ	Bypass Abd Aorta to Abd Aorta with Autol Art, Opn Appr 94
Ø41ØØ9Ø	Bypass Abd Aorta to Abd Aorta with Autol Vn, Opn Appr 94
Ø41ØØKØ	Bypass Abd Aorta to Abd Aorta with Nonaut Sub, Opn Appr 94
Ø41ØØJØ	Bypass Abd Aorta to Abd Aorta with Synth Sub, Opn Appr 94
Ø41ØØZØ	Bypass Abd Aorta to Abd Aorta, Opn Appr 94
Ø41Ø4ZØ	Bypass Abd Aorta to Abd Aorta, Perc Endo Appr 95
Ø41Ø4A8	Bypass Abd Aorta to Bilat Com Ilia w Autol Art, Perc Endo 95
Ø41Ø498	Bypass Abd Aorta to Bilat Com Ilia w Autol Vn, Perc Endo 95
Ø41ØØK8	Bypass Abd Aorta to Bilat Com Ilia w Nonaut Sub, Opn 94
Ø41Ø4K8	Bypass Abd Aorta to Bilat Com Ilia w Nonaut Sub, Perc Endo 95
Ø41Ø4J8	Bypass Abd Aorta to Bilat Com Ilia w Synth Sub, Perc Endo 95
Ø41ØØA8	Bypass Abd Aorta to Bilat Com Ilia with Autol Art, Opn Appr 94
Ø41ØØ98	Bypass Abd Aorta to Bilat Com Ilia with Autol Vn, Opn Appr 94
Ø41ØØJ8	Bypass Abd Aorta to Bilat Com Ilia with Synth Sub, Opn Appr 94
Ø41ØØZ8	Bypass Abd Aorta to Bilat Com Ilia, Opn Appr 94
Ø41Ø4Z8	Bypass Abd Aorta to Bilat Com Ilia, Perc Endo Appr 95
Ø41Ø4AG	Bypass Abd Aorta to Bilat Ext Ilia w Autol Art, Perc Endo 95
Ø41Ø49G	Bypass Abd Aorta to Bilat Ext Ilia w Autol Vn, Perc Endo 95
Ø41ØØKG	Bypass Abd Aorta to Bilat Ext Ilia w Nonaut Sub, Opn 94
Ø41Ø4KG	Bypass Abd Aorta to Bilat Ext Ilia w Nonaut Sub, Perc Endo 95
Ø41Ø4JG	Bypass Abd Aorta to Bilat Ext Ilia w Synth Sub, Perc Endo 95
Ø41ØØAG	Bypass Abd Aorta to Bilat Ext Ilia with Autol Art, Opn Appr 94
Ø41ØØ9G	Bypass Abd Aorta to Bilat Ext Ilia with Autol Vn, Opn Appr 94
Ø41ØØJG	Bypass Abd Aorta to Bilat Ext Ilia with Synth Sub, Opn Appr 94
Ø41ØØZG	Bypass Abd Aorta to Bilat Ext Ilia, Opn Appr 95
Ø41Ø4ZG	Bypass Abd Aorta to Bilat Ext Ilia, Perc Endo Appr 95
Ø41Ø4AK	Bypass Abd Aorta to Bilat Femor A w Autol Art, Perc Endo 95
Ø41Ø49K	Bypass Abd Aorta to Bilat Femor A w Autol Vn, Perc Endo 95
Ø41Ø4KK	Bypass Abd Aorta to Bilat Femor A w Nonaut Sub, Perc Endo 95
Ø41Ø4JK	Bypass Abd Aorta to Bilat Femor A w Synth Sub, Perc Endo 95
Ø41ØØAK	Bypass Abd Aorta to Bilat Femor A with Autol Art, Opn Appr 94
Ø41ØØ9K	Bypass Abd Aorta to Bilat Femor A with Autol Vn, Opn Appr 94
Ø41ØØKK	Bypass Abd Aorta to Bilat Femor A with Nonaut Sub, Opn Appr 94
Ø41ØØJK	Bypass Abd Aorta to Bilat Femor A with Synth Sub, Opn Appr 94
Ø41ØØZK	Bypass Abd Aorta to Bilat Femor A, Opn Appr 95
Ø41Ø4ZK	Bypass Abd Aorta to Bilat Femor A, Perc Endo Appr 95
Ø41Ø4AC	Bypass Abd Aorta to Bilat Int Ilia w Autol Art, Perc Endo 95
Ø41Ø49C	Bypass Abd Aorta to Bilat Int Ilia w Autol Vn, Perc Endo 95
Ø41ØØKC	Bypass Abd Aorta to Bilat Int Ilia w Nonaut Sub, Opn 94
Ø41Ø4KC	Bypass Abd Aorta to Bilat Int Ilia w Nonaut Sub, Perc Endo 95
Ø41Ø4JC	Bypass Abd Aorta to Bilat Int Ilia w Synth Sub, Perc Endo 95
Ø41ØØAC	Bypass Abd Aorta to Bilat Int Ilia with Autol Art, Opn Appr 94
Ø41ØØ9C	Bypass Abd Aorta to Bilat Int Ilia with Autol Vn, Opn Appr 94
Ø41ØØJC	Bypass Abd Aorta to Bilat Int Ilia with Synth Sub, Opn Appr 94
Ø41ØØZC	Bypass Abd Aorta to Bilat Int Ilia, Opn Appr 95
Ø41Ø4ZC	Bypass Abd Aorta to Bilat Int Ilia, Perc Endo Appr 95
Ø41ØØ[9,A,J,K,Z]5	Bypass Abd Aorta to Bilat Renal Artery w/ [Auto Venous Tissue, Auto Arterial Tissue, Synth Sub, Nonauto Tissue Sub, No Dev], Opn 92
Ø41Ø4[9,A,J,K,Z]5	Bypass Abd Aorta to Bilat Renal Artery w/ [Auto Venous Tissue, Auto Arterial Tissue, Synth Sub, Nonauto Tissue Sub, No Dev], Perc Endo 92
Ø41Ø4A1	Bypass Abd Aorta to Celiac Art w Autol Art, Perc Endo 95
Ø41Ø491	Bypass Abd Aorta to Celiac Art w Autol Vn, Perc Endo 95
Ø41ØØK1	Bypass Abd Aorta to Celiac Art w Nonaut Sub, Opn 94
Ø41Ø4K1	Bypass Abd Aorta to Celiac Art w Nonaut Sub, Perc Endo 95
Ø41Ø4J1	Bypass Abd Aorta to Celiac Art w Synth Sub, Perc Endo 95
Ø41ØØA1	Bypass Abd Aorta to Celiac Art with Autol Art, Opn Appr 94
Ø41ØØ91	Bypass Abd Aorta to Celiac Art with Autol Vn, Opn Appr 94
Ø41ØØJ1	Bypass Abd Aorta to Celiac Art with Synth Sub, Opn Appr 94
Ø41ØØZ1	Bypass Abd Aorta to Celiac Artery, Opn Appr 94
Ø41Ø4Z1	Bypass Abd Aorta to Celiac Artery, Perc Endo Appr 95
Ø41Ø4AR	Bypass Abd Aorta to Low Art w Autol Art, Perc Endo 95
Ø41Ø49R	Bypass Abd Aorta to Low Art w Autol Vn, Perc Endo 95
Ø41Ø4KR	Bypass Abd Aorta to Low Art w Nonaut Sub, Perc Endo 95
Ø41Ø4JR	Bypass Abd Aorta to Low Art w Synth Sub, Perc Endo 95
Ø41ØØAR	Bypass Abd Aorta to Low Art with Autol Art, Opn Appr 94
Ø41ØØ9R	Bypass Abd Aorta to Low Art with Autol Vn, Opn Appr 94
Ø41ØØKR	Bypass Abd Aorta to Low Art with Nonaut Sub, Opn Appr 94
Ø41ØØJR	Bypass Abd Aorta to Low Art with Synth Sub, Opn Appr 94
Ø41Ø4AQ	Bypass Abd Aorta to Low Ex Art w Autol Art, Perc Endo 95
Ø41Ø49Q	Bypass Abd Aorta to Low Ex Art w Autol Vn, Perc Endo 95
Ø41ØØKQ	Bypass Abd Aorta to Low Ex Art w Nonaut Sub, Opn 94
Ø41Ø4KQ	Bypass Abd Aorta to Low Ex Art w Nonaut Sub, Perc Endo 95
Ø41Ø4JQ	Bypass Abd Aorta to Low Ex Art w Synth Sub, Perc Endo 95
Ø41ØØAQ	Bypass Abd Aorta to Low Ex Art with Autol Art, Opn Appr 94
Ø41ØØ9Q	Bypass Abd Aorta to Low Ex Art with Autol Vn, Opn Appr 94
Ø41ØØJQ	Bypass Abd Aorta to Low Ex Art with Synth Sub, Opn Appr 94
Ø41ØØZQ	Bypass Abd Aorta to Low Ex Art, Opn Appr 95
Ø41Ø4ZQ	Bypass Abd Aorta to Low Ex Art, Perc Endo Appr 95
Ø41Ø4A7	Bypass Abd Aorta to Lt Com Ilia w Autol Art, Perc Endo 95
Ø41Ø497	Bypass Abd Aorta to Lt Com Ilia w Autol Vn, Perc Endo 95
Ø41ØØK7	Bypass Abd Aorta to Lt Com Ilia w Nonaut Sub, Opn 94
Ø41Ø4K7	Bypass Abd Aorta to Lt Com Ilia w Nonaut Sub, Perc Endo 95
Ø41Ø4J7	Bypass Abd Aorta to Lt Com Ilia w Synth Sub, Perc Endo 95
Ø41ØØA7	Bypass Abd Aorta to Lt Com Ilia with Autol Art, Opn Appr 94
Ø41ØØ97	Bypass Abd Aorta to Lt Com Ilia with Autol Vn, Opn Appr 94
Ø41ØØJ7	Bypass Abd Aorta to Lt Com Ilia with Synth Sub, Opn Appr 94
Ø41ØØZ7	Bypass Abd Aorta to Lt Com Ilia, Opn Appr 94
Ø41Ø4Z7	Bypass Abd Aorta to Lt Com Ilia, Perc Endo Appr 95
Ø41Ø4AF	Bypass Abd Aorta to Lt Ext Ilia w Autol Art, Perc Endo 95
Ø41Ø49F	Bypass Abd Aorta to Lt Ext Ilia w Autol Vn, Perc Endo 95
Ø41ØØKF	Bypass Abd Aorta to Lt Ext Ilia w Nonaut Sub, Opn 94
Ø41Ø4KF	Bypass Abd Aorta to Lt Ext Ilia w Nonaut Sub, Perc Endo 95
Ø41Ø4JF	Bypass Abd Aorta to Lt Ext Ilia w Synth Sub, Perc Endo 95

04100AF	Bypass Abd Aorta to Lt Ext Ilia with Autol Art, Opn Appr 94
041009F	Bypass Abd Aorta to Lt Ext Ilia with Autol Vn, Opn Appr 94
04100JF	Bypass Abd Aorta to Lt Ext Ilia with Synth Sub, Opn Appr 94
04100ZF	Bypass Abd Aorta to Lt Ext Ilia, Opn Appr 95
04104ZF	Bypass Abd Aorta to Lt Ext Ilia, Perc Endo Appr 95
04104AJ	Bypass Abd Aorta to Lt Femor A w Autol Art, Perc Endo 95
041049J	Bypass Abd Aorta to Lt Femor A w Autol Vn, Perc Endo 95
04104KJ	Bypass Abd Aorta to Lt Femor A w Nonaut Sub, Perc Endo 95
04104JJ	Bypass Abd Aorta to Lt Femor A w Synth Sub, Perc Endo 95
04100AJ	Bypass Abd Aorta to Lt Femor A with Autol Art, Opn Appr 94
041009J	Bypass Abd Aorta to Lt Femor A with Autol Vn, Opn Appr 94
04100KJ	Bypass Abd Aorta to Lt Femor A with Nonaut Sub, Opn Appr 94
04100JJ	Bypass Abd Aorta to Lt Femor A with Synth Sub, Opn Appr 94
04104ZJ	Bypass Abd Aorta to Lt Femor A, Perc Endo Appr 95
04100ZJ	Bypass Abd Aorta to Lt Femor Artery, Opn Appr 95
04104AB	Bypass Abd Aorta to Lt Int Ilia w Autol Art, Perc Endo 95
041049B	Bypass Abd Aorta to Lt Int Ilia w Autol Vn, Perc Endo 95
04100KB	Bypass Abd Aorta to Lt Int Ilia w Nonaut Sub, Opn 94
04104KB	Bypass Abd Aorta to Lt Int Ilia w Nonaut Sub, Perc Endo 95
04104JB	Bypass Abd Aorta to Lt Int Ilia w Synth Sub, Perc Endo 95
04100AB	Bypass Abd Aorta to Lt Int Ilia with Autol Art, Opn Appr 94
041009B	Bypass Abd Aorta to Lt Int Ilia with Autol Vn, Opn Appr 94
04100JB	Bypass Abd Aorta to Lt Int Ilia with Synth Sub, Opn Appr 94
04100ZB	Bypass Abd Aorta to Lt Int Ilia, Opn Appr 95
04104ZB	Bypass Abd Aorta to Lt Int Ilia, Perc Endo Appr 95
04100[9,A,J,K,Z]4	Bypass Abd Aorta to Lt Renal Artery w/ [Auto Venous Tissue, Auto Arterial Tissue, Synth Sub, Nonauto Tissue Sub, No Dev], Opn 92
04104[9,A,J,K,Z]4	Bypass Abd Aorta to Lt Renal Artery w/ [Auto Venous Tissue, Auto Arterial Tissue, Synth Sub, Nonauto Tissue Sub, No Dev], Perc Endo 92
04100ZR	Bypass Abd Aorta to Lwr Artery, Opn Appr 95
04104ZR	Bypass Abd Aorta to Lwr Artery, Perc Endo Appr 95
04104A2	Bypass Abd Aorta to Mesent Art w Autol Art, Perc Endo 95
0410492	Bypass Abd Aorta to Mesent Art w Autol Vn, Perc Endo 95
04100K2	Bypass Abd Aorta to Mesent Art w Nonaut Sub, Opn 94
04104K2	Bypass Abd Aorta to Mesent Art w Nonaut Sub, Perc Endo 95
04104J2	Bypass Abd Aorta to Mesent Art w Synth Sub, Perc Endo 95
04100A2	Bypass Abd Aorta to Mesent Art with Autol Art, Opn Appr 94
0410092	Bypass Abd Aorta to Mesent Art with Autol Vn, Opn Appr 94
04100J2	Bypass Abd Aorta to Mesent Art with Synth Sub, Opn Appr 94
04104Z2	Bypass Abd Aorta to Mesent Art, Perc Endo Appr 95
04100Z2	Bypass Abd Aorta to Mesenteric Artery, Opn Appr 94
04104A6	Bypass Abd Aorta to Rt Com Ilia w Autol Art, Perc Endo 95
0410496	Bypass Abd Aorta to Rt Com Ilia w Autol Vn, Perc Endo 95
04100K6	Bypass Abd Aorta to Rt Com Ilia w Nonaut Sub, Opn 94
04104K6	Bypass Abd Aorta to Rt Com Ilia w Nonaut Sub, Perc Endo 95
04104J6	Bypass Abd Aorta to Rt Com Ilia w Synth Sub, Perc Endo 95
04100A6	Bypass Abd Aorta to Rt Com Ilia with Autol Art, Opn Appr 94
0410096	Bypass Abd Aorta to Rt Com Ilia with Autol Vn, Opn Appr 94
04100J6	Bypass Abd Aorta to Rt Com Ilia with Synth Sub, Opn Appr 94
04100Z6	Bypass Abd Aorta to Rt Com Ilia, Opn Appr 94
04104Z6	Bypass Abd Aorta to Rt Com Ilia, Perc Endo Appr 95
04104AD	Bypass Abd Aorta to Rt Ext Ilia w Autol Art, Perc Endo 95
041049D	Bypass Abd Aorta to Rt Ext Ilia w Autol Vn, Perc Endo 95
04100KD	Bypass Abd Aorta to Rt Ext Ilia w Nonaut Sub, Opn 94
04104KD	Bypass Abd Aorta to Rt Ext Ilia w Nonaut Sub, Perc Endo 95
04104JD	Bypass Abd Aorta to Rt Ext Ilia w Synth Sub, Perc Endo 95
04100AD	Bypass Abd Aorta to Rt Ext Ilia with Autol Art, Opn Appr 94
041009D	Bypass Abd Aorta to Rt Ext Ilia with Autol Vn, Opn Appr 94
04100JD	Bypass Abd Aorta to Rt Ext Ilia with Synth Sub, Opn Appr 94
04100ZD	Bypass Abd Aorta to Rt Ext Ilia, Opn Appr 95
04104ZD	Bypass Abd Aorta to Rt Ext Ilia, Perc Endo Appr 95
04104AH	Bypass Abd Aorta to Rt Femor A w Autol Art, Perc Endo 95
041049H	Bypass Abd Aorta to Rt Femor A w Autol Vn, Perc Endo 95
04104KH	Bypass Abd Aorta to Rt Femor A w Nonaut Sub, Perc Endo 95
04104JH	Bypass Abd Aorta to Rt Femor A w Synth Sub, Perc Endo 95
04100AH	Bypass Abd Aorta to Rt Femor A with Autol Art, Opn Appr 94
041009H	Bypass Abd Aorta to Rt Femor A with Autol Vn, Opn Appr 94
04100KH	Bypass Abd Aorta to Rt Femor A with Nonaut Sub, Opn Appr 94
04100JH	Bypass Abd Aorta to Rt Femor A with Synth Sub, Opn Appr 94
04100ZH	Bypass Abd Aorta to Rt Femor A, Opn Appr 95
04104ZH	Bypass Abd Aorta to Rt Femor A, Perc Endo Appr 95
04104A9	Bypass Abd Aorta to Rt Int Ilia w Autol Art, Perc Endo 95
0410499	Bypass Abd Aorta to Rt Int Ilia w Autol Vn, Perc Endo 95
04100K9	Bypass Abd Aorta to Rt Int Ilia w Nonaut Sub, Opn 94
04104K9	Bypass Abd Aorta to Rt Int Ilia w Nonaut Sub, Perc Endo 95
04104J9	Bypass Abd Aorta to Rt Int Ilia w Synth Sub, Perc Endo 95
04100A9	Bypass Abd Aorta to Rt Int Ilia with Autol Art, Opn Appr 94
0410099	Bypass Abd Aorta to Rt Int Ilia with Autol Vn, Opn Appr 94
04100J9	Bypass Abd Aorta to Rt Int Ilia with Synth Sub, Opn Appr 94
04100Z9	Bypass Abd Aorta to Rt Int Ilia, Opn Appr 94
04104Z9	Bypass Abd Aorta to Rt Int Ilia, Perc Endo Appr 95
04100[9,A,J,K,Z]3	Bypass Abd Aorta to Rt Renal Artery w/ [Auto Venous Tissue, Auto Arterial Tissue, Synth Sub, Nonauto Tissue Sub, No Dev], Opn 92
04104[9,A,J,K,Z]3	Bypass Abd Aorta to Rt Renal Artery w/ [Auto Venous Tissue, Auto Arterial Tissue, Synth Sub, Nonauto Tissue Sub, No Dev], Perc Endo 92
0D1K3J4	Bypass Asc Colon to Cutan with Synth Sub, Perc Appr 299
0T183JD	Bypass Bi Ureter to Cutan with Synth Sub, Perc Appr 259, 268, 302
0T1B3JD	Bypass Bladder to Cutaneous with Synth Sub, Perc Appr 248, 302
0D1H3J4	Bypass Cecum to Cutaneous with Synth Sub, Perc Appr 299
0D1M3J4	Bypass Descend Colon to Cutan with Synth Sub, Perc Appr 299
0D193J4	Bypass Duodenum to Cutaneous with Synth Sub, Perc Appr 299
0D153J4	Bypass Esophagus to Cutaneous with Synth Sub, Perc Appr 299
0D1B8ZH	Bypass Ileum to Cecum, Endo 235
0D1B3J4	Bypass Ileum to Cutaneous with Synth Sub, Perc Appr 299
0D1A8ZH	Bypass Jejunum to Cecum, Endo 235
0D1A3J4	Bypass Jejunum to Cutaneous with Synth Sub, Perc Appr 299
0D133J4	Bypass Low Esophag to Cutan with Synth Sub, Perc Appr 53, 299, 332
08133Z4	Bypass Lt Ant Chamber to Sclera, Perc Appr 241
03160ZD	Bypass Lt Axillary Artery to Upr Arm Vein, Opn Appr 238, 251, 320
031C0ZF	Bypass Lt Radial Artery to Lwr Arm Vein, Opn Appr 110
03140ZD	Bypass Lt Subclavian Artery to Up Arm Vein, Opn Appr 238, 251, 320
031A0ZF	Bypass Lt Ulnar Artery to Lwr Arm Vein, Opn Appr 110
0T173JD	Bypass Lt Ureter to Cutan with Synth Sub, Perc Appr 259, 268, 302
0D123J4	Bypass Mid Esophag to Cutan with Synth Sub, Perc Appr 53, 299, 332
08123Z4	Bypass Rt Ant Chamber to Sclera, Perc Appr 241
03150ZD	Bypass Rt Axillary Artery to Up Arm Vein, Opn Appr 238, 251, 320
031B0ZF	Bypass Rt Radial Artery to Lwr Arm Vein, Opn Appr 110
03130ZD	Bypass Rt Subclavian Artery to Up Arm Vein, Opn Appr 238, 251, 320
03190ZF	Bypass Rt Ulnar Artery to Lwr Arm Vein, Opn Appr 110
0T163JD	Bypass Rt Ureter to Cutan with Synth Sub, Perc Appr 259, 268, 302
0D1N3J4	Bypass Sigmoid Colon to Cutan with Synth Sub, Perc Appr 299, 332
0D1L3J4	Bypass Trans Colon to Cutan with Synth Sub, Perc Appr 299
0D113J4	Bypass Up Esophag to Cutan with Synth Sub, Perc Appr 53, 299, 332
0410[0,4][9,A,J,K,Z] [6,7,8,9,B,C,D,F,G,H, J,K,Q,R]	Bypass/Abd Aorta, [Opn, Perc Endo], [Auto Venous Tissue, Auto Arterial Tissue, Synth Sub, Nonauto Tissue Sub, No Dev], [Common Iliac Artery, Rt, Common Iliac Artery, Lt, Common Iliac Arteries, Bilat, Int Iliac Artery, Rt, Int Iliac Artery, Lt, Int Iliac Arteries, Bilat, Ext Iliac Artery, Rt, Ext Iliac Artery, Lt, Ext Iliac Arteries, Bilat, Femor Artery, Rt, Femor Artery, Lt, Femor Arteries, Bilat, Lwr Extr Artery, Lwr Artery] 208, 322
0410[0,4][9,A,J,K,Z] [3,4,5]	Bypass/Abd Aorta, [Opn, Perc Endo], [Auto Venous Tissue, Auto Arterial Tissue, Synth Sub, Nonauto Tissue Sub, No Dev], [Renal Artery, Rt, Renal Artery, Lt, Renal Artery, Bilat] 322

Ø61C*	Bypass/Common Iliac Vein, Rt 86
Ø213[Ø,4][9,A,J,K,Z] [3,8,9,C,F]	Bypass/Coronary Artery, Four or More Sites, [Opn, Perc Endo], [Auto Venous Tissue, Auto Arterial Tissue, Synth Sub, Nonauto Tissue Sub, No Dev], [Coronary Artery, Int Mammary, Rt, Int Mammary, Lt, Thoracic Artery, Abd Artery] 75, 76
Ø213[Ø,4][9,A,J,K]W	Bypass/Coronary Artery, Four or More Sites, [Opn, Perc Endo], [Auto Venous Tissue, Auto Arterial Tissue, Synth Sub, Nonauto Tissue Sub], Aorta 75, 76, 76
Ø21Ø[Ø,4][9,A,J,K,Z] [3,8,9,C,F]	Bypass/Coronary Artery, One Site, [Opn, Perc Endo], [Auto Venous Tissue, Auto Arterial Tissue, Synth Sub, Nonauto Tissue Sub, No Dev], [Coronary Artery, Int Mammary, Rt, Int Mammary, Lt, Thoracic Artery, Abd Artery] 75, 76
Ø21Ø[Ø,4][9,A,J,K]W	Bypass/Coronary Artery, One Site, [Opn, Perc Endo], [Auto Venous Tissue, Auto Arterial Tissue, Synth Sub, Nonauto Tissue Sub], Aorta 75, 76, 76
Ø212[Ø,4][9,A,J,K,Z] [3,8,9,C,F]	Bypass/Coronary Artery, Three Sites, [Opn, Perc Endo], [Auto Venous Tissue, Auto Arterial Tissue, Synth Sub, Nonauto Tissue Sub, No Dev], [Coronary Artery, Int Mammary, Lt, Thoracic Artery, Abd Artery] 75, 76
Ø212[Ø,4][9,A,J,K]W	Bypass/Coronary Artery, Three Sites, [Opn, Perc Endo], [Auto Venous Tissue, Auto Arterial Tissue, Synth Sub, Nonauto Tissue Sub], Aorta 75, 76, 76
Ø211[Ø,4][9,A,J,K,Z] [3,8,9,C,F]	Bypass/Coronary Artery, Two Sites, [Opn, Perc Endo], [Auto Venous Tissue, Auto Arterial Tissue, Synth Sub, Nonauto Tissue Sub, No Dev], [Coronary Artery, Int Mammary, Rt, Int Mammary, Lt, Thoracic Artery, Abd Artery] 75, 76, 76
Ø211[Ø,4][9,A,J,K]W	Bypass/Coronary Artery, Two Sites, [Opn, Perc Endo], [Auto Venous Tissue, Auto Arterial Tissue, Synth Sub, Nonauto Tissue Sub], Aorta 75, 76
ØW11*	Bypass/Cranial Cavity 20, 355
ØW11ØJ[9,B,G,J]	Bypass/Cranial Cavity, Opn, Synth Sub, [Pleural Cavity, Rt, Pleural Cavity, Lt, Peritoneal Cavity, Pelvic Cavity] 302
ØF18*	Bypass/Cystic Duct 119
ØF18[Ø,4][D,Z][3,B]	Bypass/Cystic Duct, [Opn, Perc Endo], [Intralum Dev, No Dev], [Duodenum, Sm Intestine] 112
ØF18[Ø,4][D,Z] [3,4,5,6,7,8,9,B]	Bypass/Cystic Duct, [Opn, Perc Endo], [Intralum Dev, No Dev], [Duodenum, Stomach, Hepatic Duct, Rt, Hepatic Duct, Lt, Hepatic Duct, Caudate, Cystic Duct, Common Bile Duct, Sm Intestine] 301
ØD1M*	Bypass/Descending Colon 106, 332
ØD1M[Ø,4,8][7,J,K,Z] [M,N,P]	Bypass/Descending Colon, [Opn, Perc Endo, Via Natrl or Artfcl Opng Endo], [Auto Tissue Sub, Synth Sub, Nonauto Tissue Sub, No Dev], [Descending Colon, Sigmoid Colon, Rectum] 242
ØD1M[Ø,4,8][7,J,K,Z] 4	Bypass/Descending Colon, [Opn, Perc Endo, Via Natrl or Artfcl Opng Endo], [Auto Tissue Sub, Synth Sub, Nonauto Tissue Sub, No Dev], Cutaneous 299
ØD19*	Bypass/Duodenum 106, 332
ØD19[Ø,4,8][7,J,K,Z] [4,9,A,B,L]	Bypass/Duodenum, [Opn, Perc Endo, Via Natrl or Artfcl Opng Endo], [Auto Tissue Sub, Synth Sub, Nonauto Tissue Sub, No Dev], [Cutaneous, Duodenum, Jejunum, Ileum, Transv Colon] 299
ØD19[Ø,4,8][7,J,K,Z] [9,A,B]	Bypass/Duodenum, [Opn, Perc Endo, Via Natrl or Artfcl Opng Endo], [Auto Tissue Sub, Synth Sub, Nonauto Tissue Sub, No Dev], [Duodenum, Jejunum, Ileum] 235
ØD19[Ø,4,8][7,J,K,Z]L	Bypass/Duodenum, [Opn, Perc Endo, Via Natrl or Artfcl Opng Endo], [Auto Tissue Sub, Synth Sub, Nonauto Tissue Sub, No Dev], Transv Colon 241
Ø613*	Bypass/Esophageal Vein 86
ØD15*	Bypass/Esophagus 53, 105, 332
ØD15[Ø,4,8][7,J,K,Z] [4,6,9,A,B]	Bypass/Esophagus, [Opn, Perc Endo, Via Natrl or Artfcl Opng Endo], [Auto Tissue Sub, Synth Sub, Nonauto Tissue Sub, No Dev], [Cutaneous, Stomach, Duodenum, Jejunum, Ileum] 299
ØD13*	Bypass/Esophagus, Lwr 105
ØD13[Ø,4,8][7,J,K,Z] [4,6]	Bypass/Esophagus, Lwr, [Opn, Perc Endo, Via Natrl or Artfcl Opng Endo], [Auto Tissue Sub, Synth Sub, Nonauto Tissue Sub, No Dev], [Cutaneous, Stomach] 53, 299, 332
ØD12*	Bypass/Esophagus, Mid 105
ØD12[Ø,4,8][7,J,K,Z] [4,6]	Bypass/Esophagus, Mid, [Opn, Perc Endo, Via Natrl or Artfcl Opng Endo], [Auto Tissue Sub, Synth Sub, Nonauto Tissue Sub, No Dev], [Cutaneous, Stomach] 53, 299, 332
ØD11*	Bypass/Esophagus, Upr 105
ØD11[Ø,4,8][7,J,K,Z] [4,6]	Bypass/Esophagus, Upr, [Opn, Perc Endo, Via Natrl or Artfcl Opng Endo], [Auto Tissue Sub, Synth Sub, Nonauto Tissue Sub, No Dev], [Cutaneous, Stomach] 53, 299, 332
Ø31N*	Bypass/Ext Carotid Artery, Lt 320
Ø31NØ[9,A,J,K,Z]K	Bypass/Ext Carotid Artery, Lt, Opn, [Auto Venous Tissue, Auto Arterial Tissue, Synth Sub, Nonauto Tissue Sub, No Dev], Extracranial Artery, Lt 21, 63, 81, 122, 208, 238
Ø31M*	Bypass/Ext Carotid Artery, Rt 320
Ø31MØ[9,A,J,K,Z]J	Bypass/Ext Carotid Artery, Rt, Opn, [Auto Venous Tissue, Auto Arterial Tissue, Synth Sub, Nonauto Tissue Sub, No Dev], Extracranial Artery, Rt 21, 63, 80, 122, 208, 238
Ø41J*	Bypass/Ext Iliac Artery, Lt 95
Ø41J[Ø,4][9,A,J,K,Z] [H,J,K]	Bypass/Ext Iliac Artery, Lt, [Opn, Perc Endo], [Auto Venous Tissue, Auto Arterial Tissue, Synth Sub, Nonauto Tissue Sub, No Dev], [Femor Artery, Rt, Femor Artery, Lt, Femor Arteries, Bilat] 208, 322
Ø41H*	Bypass/Ext Iliac Artery, Rt 95
Ø41H[Ø,4][9,A,J,K,Z] [H,J,K]	Bypass/Ext Iliac Artery, Rt, [Opn, Perc Endo], [Auto Venous Tissue, Auto Arterial Tissue, Synth Sub, Nonauto Tissue Sub, No Dev], [Femor Artery, Rt, Femor Artery, Lt, Femor Arteries, Bilat] 208, 322
Ø61G*	Bypass/Ext Iliac Vein, Lt 86
Ø61F*	Bypass/Ext Iliac Vein, Rt 86
Ø51Q*	Bypass/Ext Jugular Vein, Lt 85
Ø51P*	Bypass/Ext Jugular Vein, Rt 85
Ø51V*	Bypass/Face Vein, Lt 85
Ø51T*	Bypass/Face Vein, Rt 85
Ø41L*	Bypass/Femor Artery, Lt 82
Ø41L[Ø,4][9,A,J,K,Z] [H,J,K,L]	Bypass/Femor Artery, Lt, [Opn, Perc Endo], [Auto Venous Tissue, Auto Arterial Tissue, Synth Sub, Nonauto Tissue Sub, No Dev], [Femor Artery, Rt, Femor Artery, Lt, Femor Arteries, Bilat, Popliteal Artery] 22, 63, 122, 208, 239, 322
Ø41K*	Bypass/Femor Artery, Rt 82
Ø41K[Ø,4][9,A,J,K,Z] [H,J,K,L]	Bypass/Femor Artery, Rt, [Opn, Perc Endo], [Auto Venous Tissue, Auto Arterial Tissue, Synth Sub, Nonauto Tissue Sub, No Dev], [Femor Artery, Rt, Femor Artery, Lt, Femor Arteries, Bilat, Popliteal Artery] 22, 63, 122, 208, 239, 322
Ø61N*	Bypass/Femor Vein, Lt 86
Ø61M*	Bypass/Femor Vein, Rt 86
Ø61V*	Bypass/Foot Vein, Lt 86
Ø61T*	Bypass/Foot Vein, Rt 86
ØF14*	Bypass/Gallbladder 119
ØF14[Ø,4][D,Z][3,B]	Bypass/Gallbladder, [Opn, Perc Endo], [Intralum Dev, No Dev], [Duodenum, Sm Intestine] 112
ØF14[Ø,4][D,Z] [3,4,5,6,7,8,9,B]	Bypass/Gallbladder, [Opn, Perc Endo], [Intralum Dev, No Dev], [Duodenum, Stomach, Hepatic Duct, Rt, Hepatic Duct, Lt, Hepatic Duct, Caudate, Cystic Duct, Common Bile Duct, Sm Intestine] 301
Ø612*	Bypass/Gastric Vein 97
Ø61Q*	Bypass/Greater Saphenous Vein, Lt 86
Ø61P*	Bypass/Greater Saphenous Vein, Rt 86
Ø51H*	Bypass/Hand Vein, Lt 85
Ø51G*	Bypass/Hand Vein, Rt 85
Ø511*	Bypass/Hemiazygos Vein 325
Ø511[Ø,4] [7,9,A,J,K,Z]Y	Bypass/Hemiazygos Vein, [Opn, Perc Endo], [Auto Tissue Sub, Auto Venous Tissue, Auto Arterial Tissue, Synth Sub, Nonauto Tissue Sub, No Dev], Upr Vein 96
ØF16*	Bypass/Hepatic Duct, Lt 119
ØF16[Ø,4][D,Z] [3,4,5,6,7,8,9,B]	Bypass/Hepatic Duct, Lt, [Opn, Perc Endo], [Intralum Dev, No Dev], [Duodenum, Stomach, Hepatic Duct, Rt, Hepatic Duct, Lt, Hepatic Duct, Caudate, Cystic Duct, Common Bile Duct, Sm Intestine] 301
ØF16[Ø,4][D,Z][3,4,B]	Bypass/Hepatic Duct, Lt, [Opn, Perc Endo], [Intralum Dev, No Dev], [Duodenum, Stomach, Sm Intestine] 112
ØF15*	Bypass/Hepatic Duct, Rt 119
ØF15[Ø,4][D,Z] [3,4,5,6,7,8,9,B]	Bypass/Hepatic Duct, Rt, [Opn, Perc Endo], [Intralum Dev, No Dev], [Duodenum, Stomach, Hepatic Duct, Rt, Hepatic Duct, Lt, Hepatic Duct, Caudate, Cystic Duct, Common Bile Duct, Sm Intestine] 301
ØF15[Ø,4][D,Z][3,4,B]	Bypass/Hepatic Duct, Rt, [Opn, Perc Endo], [Intralum Dev, No Dev], [Duodenum, Stomach, Sm Intestine] 112
Ø614*	Bypass/Hepatic Vein 97
Ø61J*	Bypass/Hypogastric Vein, Lt 97
Ø61H*	Bypass/Hypogastric Vein, Rt 86
ØD1B*	Bypass/Ileum 106, 332
ØD1B[Ø,4,8][7,J,K,Z] [K,L,M,N]	Bypass/Ileum, [Opn, Perc Endo, Via Natrl or Artfcl Opng Endo], [Auto Tissue Sub, Synth Sub, Nonauto Tissue Sub, No Dev], [Ascending Colon, Transv Colon, Descending Colon, Sigmoid Colon] 241

ØD1B[0,4,8][7,J,K,Z] [4,B,H,K,L,M,N,P,Q] — Bypass/Ileum, [Opn, Perc Endo, Via Natrl or Artfcl Opng Endo], [Auto Tissue Sub, Synth Sub, Nonauto Tissue Sub, No Dev], [Cutaneous, Ileum, Cecum, Ascending Colon, Transv Colon, Descending Colon, Sigmoid Colon, Rectum, Anus] 299

ØD1B[0,4,8][7,J,K,Z]B — Bypass/Ileum, [Opn, Perc Endo, Via Natrl or Artfcl Opng Endo], [Auto Tissue Sub, Synth Sub, Nonauto Tissue Sub, No Dev], Ileum 235

ØD1B[0,4,8][7,J,K]H — Bypass/Ileum, [Opn, Perc Endo, Via Natrl or Artfcl Opng Endo], [Auto Tissue Sub, Synth Sub, Nonauto Tissue Sub], Cecum 241

ØD1B[0,4]ZH — Bypass/Ileum, [Opn, Perc Endo], No Dev, Cecum 241

ØD1B8[7,J,K]H — Bypass/Ileum, Via Natrl or Artfcl Opng Endo, [Auto Tissue Sub, Synth Sub, Nonauto Tissue Sub], Cecum 90

Ø616* — Bypass/Inferior Mesenteric Vein 97

Ø61Ø* — Bypass/Inferior Vena Cava 97

Ø61Ø[0,4][J,Z][5,6,Y] — Bypass/Inferior Vena Cava, [Opn, Perc Endo], [Synth Sub, No Dev], [Superior Mesenteric Vein, Inferior Mesenteric Vein, Lwr Vein] 105, 119

Ø312* — Bypass/Innominate Artery 80

Ø514* — Bypass/Innominate Vein, Lt 325

Ø514[0,4][7,9,A,J,K,Z]Y — Bypass/Innominate Vein, Lt, [Opn, Perc Endo], [Auto Tissue Sub, Auto Venous Tissue, Auto Arterial Tissue, Synth Sub, Nonauto Tissue Sub, No Dev], Upr Vein 96

Ø513* — Bypass/Innominate Vein, Rt 325

Ø513[0,4][7,9,A,J,K,Z]Y — Bypass/Innominate Vein, Rt, [Opn, Perc Endo], [Auto Tissue Sub, Auto Venous Tissue, Auto Arterial Tissue, Synth Sub, Nonauto Tissue Sub, No Dev], Upr Vein 96

Ø31L* — Bypass/Int Carotid Artery, Lt 320

Ø31LØ[9,A,J,K,Z]K — Bypass/Int Carotid Artery, Lt, Opn, [Auto Venous Tissue, Auto Arterial Tissue, Synth Sub, Nonauto Tissue Sub, No Dev], Extracranial Artery, Lt 21, 63, 80, 122, 207, 238

Ø31K* — Bypass/Int Carotid Artery, Rt 320

Ø31KØ[9,A,J,K,Z]J — Bypass/Int Carotid Artery, Rt, Opn, [Auto Venous Tissue, Auto Arterial Tissue, Synth Sub, Nonauto Tissue Sub, No Dev], Extracranial Artery, Rt 21, 63, 80, 122, 207, 238

Ø41F* — Bypass/Int Iliac Artery, Lt 95

Ø41F[0,4][9,A,J,K,Z] [H,J,K] — Bypass/Int Iliac Artery, Lt, [Opn, Perc Endo], [Auto Venous Tissue, Auto Arterial Tissue, Synth Sub, Nonauto Tissue Sub, No Dev], [Femor Artery, Rt, Femor Artery, Lt, Femor Arteries, Bilat] 208, 322

Ø41E* — Bypass/Int Iliac Artery, Rt 95

Ø41E[0,4][9,A,J,K,Z] [H,J,K] — Bypass/Int Iliac Artery, Rt, [Opn, Perc Endo], [Auto Venous Tissue, Auto Arterial Tissue, Synth Sub, Nonauto Tissue Sub, No Dev], [Femor Artery, Rt, Femor Artery, Lt, Femor Arteries, Bilat] 208, 322

Ø51N* — Bypass/Int Jugular Vein, Lt 85

Ø51M* — Bypass/Int Jugular Vein, Rt 85

Ø31G* — Bypass/Intracranial Artery 80

Ø51L* — Bypass/Intracranial Vein 85

ØD1A* — Bypass/Jejunum 106, 332

ØD1A[0,4,8][7,J,K,Z] [K,L,M,N] — Bypass/Jejunum, [Opn, Perc Endo, Via Natrl or Artfcl Opng Endo], [Auto Tissue Sub, Synth Sub, Nonauto Tissue Sub, No Dev], [Ascending Colon, Transv Colon, Descending Colon, Sigmoid Colon] 241

ØD1A[0,4,8][7,J,K,Z] [4,A,B,H,K,L,M,N,P,Q] — Bypass/Jejunum, [Opn, Perc Endo, Via Natrl or Artfcl Opng Endo], [Auto Tissue Sub, Synth Sub, Nonauto Tissue Sub, No Dev], [Cutaneous, Jejunum, Ileum, Cecum, Ascending Colon, Transv Colon, Descending Colon, Sigmoid Colon, Rectum, Anus] 299

ØD1A[0,4,8][7,J,K,Z] [A,B] — Bypass/Jejunum, [Opn, Perc Endo, Via Natrl or Artfcl Opng Endo], [Auto Tissue Sub, Synth Sub, Nonauto Tissue Sub, No Dev], [Jejunum, Ileum] 235

ØD1A[0,4,8][7,J,K]H — Bypass/Jejunum, [Opn, Perc Endo, Via Natrl or Artfcl Opng Endo], [Auto Tissue Sub, Synth Sub, Nonauto Tissue Sub], Cecum 241

ØD1A[0,4]ZH — Bypass/Jejunum, [Opn, Perc Endo], No Dev, Cecum 241

ØD1A8[7,J,K]H — Bypass/Jejunum, Via Natrl or Artfcl Opng Endo, [Auto Tissue Sub, Synth Sub, Nonauto Tissue Sub], Cecum 90

ØT14* — Bypass/Kidney Pelvis, Lt 248

ØT14[0,4][7,J,K,Z]B — Bypass/Kidney Pelvis, Lt, [Opn, Perc Endo], [Auto Tissue Sub, Synth Sub, Nonauto Tissue Sub, No Dev], Bladder 259, 268, 302, 353

ØT13* — Bypass/Kidney Pelvis, Rt 248

ØT13[0,4][7,J,K,Z]B — Bypass/Kidney Pelvis, Rt, [Opn, Perc Endo], [Auto Tissue Sub, Synth Sub, Nonauto Tissue Sub, No Dev], Bladder 259, 268, 302, 353

Ø81Y* — Bypass/Lacrimal Duct, Lt 42, 51

Ø81Y[0,3][J,K,Z]3 — Bypass/Lacrimal Duct, Lt, [Opn, Perc], [Synth Sub, Nonauto Tissue Sub, No Dev], Nasal Cavity 443

Ø81X* — Bypass/Lacrimal Duct, Rt 42, 51

Ø81X[0,3][J,K,Z]3 — Bypass/Lacrimal Duct, Rt, [Opn, Perc], [Synth Sub, Nonauto Tissue Sub, No Dev], Nasal Cavity 443

Ø61S* — Bypass/Lesser Saphenous Vein, Lt 86

Ø61R* — Bypass/Lesser Saphenous Vein, Rt 86

ØF1G* — Bypass/Pancreas 119

ØF1D* — Bypass/Pancreatic Duct 119

ØF1F* — Bypass/Pancreatic Duct, Accessory 119

ØW1J[0,4]J[9,B,G,J] — Bypass/Pelvic Cavity, [Opn, Perc Endo], Synth Sub, [Pleural Cavity, Rt, Pleural Cavity, Lt, Peritoneal Cavity, Pelvic Cavity] 269

ØW1G[0,4]JY — Bypass/Peritoneal Cavity, [Opn, Perc Endo], Synth Sub, Lwr Vein 113, 119, 302

ØW1G[0,3,4]J4 — Bypass/Peritoneal Cavity, [Opn, Perc, Perc Endo], Synth Sub, Cutaneous 91, 113, 123, 254, 302, 355

ØW1B[0,4]J[9,B,J] — Bypass/Pleural Cavity, Lt, [Opn, Perc Endo], Synth Sub, [Pleural Cavity, Rt, Pleural Cavity, Lt, Pelvic Cavity] 66, 355

ØW19[0,4]J[9,B,J] — Bypass/Pleural Cavity, Rt, [Opn, Perc Endo], Synth Sub, [Pleural Cavity, Rt, Pleural Cavity, Lt, Pelvic Cavity] 66, 355

Ø41N* — Bypass/Popliteal Artery, Lt 82

Ø41M* — Bypass/Popliteal Artery, Rt 82

Ø618* — Bypass/Portal Vein 97

Ø618[0,4][J,Z][9,B,Y] — Bypass/Portal Vein, [Opn, Perc Endo], [Synth Sub, No Dev], [Renal Vein, Rt, Renal Vein, Lt, Lwr Vein] 105, 119

Ø31CØ[9,A,J,K,Z]4 — Bypass/Radial Artery, Lt, Opn, [Auto Venous Tissue, Auto Arterial Tissue, Synth Sub, Nonauto Tissue Sub, No Dev], Lwr Arm Artery, Lt 80

Ø31CØ[9,A,J,K,Z]F — Bypass/Radial Artery, Lt, Opn, [Auto Venous Tissue, Auto Arterial Tissue, Synth Sub, Nonauto Tissue Sub, No Dev], Lwr Arm Vein 89, 238, 251, 320

Ø31BØ[9,A,J,K,Z]3 — Bypass/Radial Artery, Rt, Opn, [Auto Venous Tissue, Auto Arterial Tissue, Synth Sub, Nonauto Tissue Sub, No Dev], Lwr Arm Artery, Rt 80

Ø31BØ[9,A,J,K,Z]F — Bypass/Radial Artery, Rt, Opn, [Auto Venous Tissue, Auto Arterial Tissue, Synth Sub, Nonauto Tissue Sub, No Dev], Lwr Arm Vein 89, 238, 251, 320

Ø61B* — Bypass/Renal Vein, Lt 97

Ø619* — Bypass/Renal Vein, Rt 97

ØD1N* — Bypass/Sigmoid Colon 106

ØD1N[0,4,8][7,J,K,Z] [N,P] — Bypass/Sigmoid Colon, [Opn, Perc Endo, Via Natrl or Artfcl Opng Endo], [Auto Tissue Sub, Synth Sub, Nonauto Tissue Sub, No Dev], [Sigmoid Colon, Rectum] 242, 332

ØD1N[0,4,8][7,J,K] 4 — Bypass/Sigmoid Colon, [Opn, Perc Endo, Via Natrl or Artfcl Opng Endo], [Auto Tissue Sub, Synth Sub, Nonauto Tissue Sub], Cutaneous 299

ØD1N[0,4,8][7,J,K]4 — Bypass/Sigmoid Colon, [Opn, Perc Endo, Via Natrl or Artfcl Opng Endo], [Auto Tissue Sub, Synth Sub, Nonauto Tissue Sub], Cutaneous 332

ØD1N[4,8]Z4 — Bypass/Sigmoid Colon, [Perc Endo, Via Natrl or Artfcl Opng Endo], No Dev, Cutaneous 299, 332

ØØ1U[0,3][7,J,K] [4,6,7,9] — Bypass/Spinal Canal, [Opn, Perc], [Auto Tissue Sub, Synth Sub, Nonauto Tissue Sub], [Pleural Cavity, Peritoneal Cavity, Urinary Tract, Fallopian Tube] 19

Ø414[0,4][9,A,J,K,Z] [3,4,5] — Bypass/Splenic Artery, [Opn, Perc Endo], [Auto Venous Tissue, Auto Arterial Tissue, Synth Sub, Nonauto Tissue Sub, No Dev], [Renal Artery, Rt, Renal Artery, Lt, Renal Artery, Bilat] 95

Ø611* — Bypass/Splenic Vein 97

Ø611[0,4][J,Z][9,B,Y] — Bypass/Splenic Vein, [Opn, Perc Endo], [Synth Sub, No Dev], [Renal Vein, Rt, Renal Vein, Lt, Lwr Vein] 105, 119

ØD16[0,4,8][7,J,K,Z] [9,A,B,L] — Bypass/Stomach, [Opn, Perc Endo, Via Natrl or Artfcl Opng Endo], [Auto Tissue Sub, Synth Sub, Nonauto Tissue Sub, No Dev], [Duodenum, Jejunum, Ileum, Transv Colon] 90, 105, 122, 235, 299

Ø3140[9,A,J,K,Z] [M,N] — Bypass/Subclavian Artery, Lt, Opn, [Auto Venous Tissue, Auto Arterial Tissue, Synth Sub, Nonauto Tissue Sub, No Dev], [Pulmn Artery, Rt, Pulmn Artery, Lt] 93

Ø314Ø[9,A,J,K,Z] [Ø,1,2,3,4,5,6,7,8,9, B,C,D,F,J,K]	Bypass/Subclavian Artery, Lt, Opn, [Auto Venous Tissue, Auto Arterial Tissue, Synth Sub, Nonauto Tissue Sub, No Dev], [Upr Arm Artery, Rt, Upr Arm Artery, Lt, Upr Arm Artery, Bilat, Lwr Arm Artery, Rt, Lwr Arm Artery, Lt, Lwr Arm Artery, Bilat, Upr Leg Artery, Rt, Upr Leg Artery, Lt, Upr Leg Artery, Bilat, Lwr Leg Artery, Rt, Lwr Leg Artery, Lt, Lwr Leg Artery, Bilat, Upr Arm Vein, Lwr Arm Vein, Extracranial Artery, Rt, Extracranial Artery, Lt] 80
Ø313Ø[9,A,J,K,Z] [M,N]	Bypass/Subclavian Artery, Rt, Opn, [Auto Venous Tissue, Auto Arterial Tissue, Synth Sub, Nonauto Tissue Sub, No Dev], [Pulmn Artery, Rt, Pulmn Artery, Lt] 93
Ø313Ø[9,A,J,K,Z] [Ø,1,2,3,4,5,6,7,8,9, B,C,D,F,J,K]	Bypass/Subclavian Artery, Rt, Opn, [Auto Venous Tissue, Auto Arterial Tissue, Synth Sub, Nonauto Tissue Sub, No Dev], [Rt Upr Arm Artery, Lt Upr Arm Artery, Bilat Upr Arm Artery, Rt Lwr Arm Artery, Lt Lwr Arm Artery, Bilat Lwr Arm Artery, Rt Upr Leg Artery, Lt Upr Leg Artery, Bilat Upr Leg Artery, Rt Lwr Leg Artery, Lt Lwr Leg Artery, Bilat Lwr Leg Artery, Upr Arm Vein, Lwr Arm Vein, Rt Extracranial Artery, Lt Extracranial Artery] 80
Ø516*	Bypass/Subclavian Vein, Lt 325
Ø516[Ø,4][7,9,A,J,K,Z] Y	Bypass/Subclavian Vein, Lt, [Opn, Perc Endo], [Auto Tissue Sub, Auto Venous Tissue, Auto Arterial Tissue, Synth Sub, Nonauto Tissue Sub, No Dev], Upr Vein 96
Ø515*	Bypass/Subclavian Vein, Rt 325
Ø515[Ø,4][7,9,A,J,K,Z] Y	Bypass/Subclavian Vein, Rt, [Opn, Perc Endo], [Auto Tissue Sub, Auto Venous Tissue, Auto Arterial Tissue, Synth Sub, Nonauto Tissue Sub, No Dev], Upr Vein 96
Ø615*	Bypass/Superior Mesenteric Vein 97
Ø21V[Ø,4][9,A,J,K,Z] [P,Q,R]	Bypass/Superior Vena Cava, [Opn, Perc Endo], [Auto Venous Tissue, Auto Arterial Tissue, Synth Sub, Nonauto Tissue Sub, No Dev], [Pulmn Trunk, Pulmn Artery, Rt, Pulmn Artery, Lt] 92
Ø31T*	Bypass/Temporal Artery, Lt 320
Ø31TØ[9,A,J,K,Z]G	Bypass/Temporal Artery, Lt, Opn, [Auto Venous Tissue, Auto Arterial Tissue, Synth Sub, Nonauto Tissue Sub, No Dev], Intracranial Artery 7, 8, 13, 17
Ø31S*	Bypass/Temporal Artery, Rt 320
Ø31SØ[9,A,J,K,Z]G	Bypass/Temporal Artery, Rt, Opn, [Auto Venous Tissue, Auto Arterial Tissue, Synth Sub, Nonauto Tissue Sub, No Dev], Intracranial Artery 7, 8, 13, 17
Ø21W[Ø,4][9,A,J,K,Z] [B,D,P,Q,R]	Bypass/Thoracic Aorta, [Opn, Perc Endo], [Auto Venous Tissue, Auto Arterial Tissue, Synth Sub, Nonauto Tissue Sub, No Dev], [Subclavian, Carotid, Pulmn Trunk, Pulmn Artery, Rt, Pulmn Artery, Lt] 92
Ø21W[Ø,4][9,A,J,K,Z] [B,D]	Bypass/Thoracic Aorta, [Opn, Perc Endo], [Auto Venous Tissue, Auto Arterial Tissue, Synth Sub, Nonauto Tissue Sub, No Dev], [Subclavian, Carotid] 21, 319
ØB11[Ø,4][F,Z]4	Bypass/Trachea, [Opn, Perc Endo], [Tracheostomy Dev, No Dev], Cutaneous 1, 6
ØB113[F,Z]4	Bypass/Trachea, Perc, [Tracheostomy Dev, No Dev], Cutaneous 1, 6
ØD1L*	Bypass/Transv Colon 106, 332
ØD1L[Ø,4,8][7,J,K,Z] [L,M,N,P]	Bypass/Transv Colon, [Opn, Perc Endo, Via Natrl or Artfcl Opng Endo], [Auto Tissue Sub, Synth Sub, Nonauto Tissue Sub, No Dev], [Transv Colon, Descending Colon, Sigmoid Colon, Rectum] 242
ØD1L[Ø,4,8][7,J,K,Z]4	Bypass/Transv Colon, [Opn, Perc Endo, Via Natrl or Artfcl Opng Endo], [Auto Tissue Sub, Synth Sub, Nonauto Tissue Sub, No Dev], Cutaneous 299
ØD1L[Ø,4,8]Z4	Bypass/Transv Colon, [Opn, Perc Endo, Via Natrl or Artfcl Opng Endo], No Dev, Cutaneous 90
Ø31AØ[9,A,J,K,Z]4	Bypass/Ulnar Artery, Lt, Opn, [Auto Venous Tissue, Auto Arterial Tissue, Synth Sub, Nonauto Tissue Sub, No Dev], Lwr Arm Artery, Lt 80
Ø31AØ[9,A,J,K,Z]F	Bypass/Ulnar Artery, Lt, Opn, [Auto Venous Tissue, Auto Arterial Tissue, Synth Sub, Nonauto Tissue Sub, No Dev], Lwr Arm Vein 89, 238, 251, 320
Ø319Ø[9,A,J,K,Z]3	Bypass/Ulnar Artery, Rt, Opn, [Auto Venous Tissue, Auto Arterial Tissue, Synth Sub, Nonauto Tissue Sub, No Dev], Lwr Arm Artery, Rt 80
Ø319Ø[9,A,J,K,Z]F	Bypass/Ulnar Artery, Rt, Opn, [Auto Venous Tissue, Auto Arterial Tissue, Synth Sub, Nonauto Tissue Sub, No Dev], Lwr Arm Vein 89, 238, 251, 320
ØT17*	Bypass/Ureter, Lt 248, 353
ØT17[Ø,4][7,J,K,Z] [6,7,8,9,A,C,D]	Bypass/Ureter, Lt, [Opn, Perc Endo], [Auto Tissue Sub, Synth Sub, Nonauto Tissue Sub, No Dev], [Ureter, Rt, Ureter, Lt, Colon, Colocutaneous, Ileum, Ileocutaneous, Cutaneous] 259, 268, 302
ØT16*	Bypass/Ureter, Rt 248, 353
ØT16[Ø,4][7,J,K,Z] [6,7,8,9,A,C,D]	Bypass/Ureter, Rt, [Opn, Perc Endo], [Auto Tissue Sub, Synth Sub, Nonauto Tissue Sub, No Dev], [Ureter, Rt, Ureter, Lt, Colon, Colocutaneous, Ileum, Ileocutaneous, Cutaneous] 259, 268, 302
ØT18*	Bypass/Ureters, Bilat 248, 353
ØT18[Ø,4][7,J,K,Z] [6,7,8,9,A,C,D]	Bypass/Ureters, Bilat, [Opn, Perc Endo], [Auto Tissue Sub, Synth Sub, Nonauto Tissue Sub, No Dev], [Ureter, Rt, Ureter, Lt, Colon, Colocutaneous, Ileum, Ileocutaneous, Cutaneous] 259, 268, 302
Ø21LØA[P,Q,R]	Bypass/Ventricle, Lt, Opn, Auto Arterial Tissue, [Pulmn Trunk, Pulmn Artery, Rt, Pulmn Artery, Lt] 74
Ø21LØ9[P,Q,R]	Bypass/Ventricle, Lt, Opn, Auto Venous Tissue, [Pulmn Trunk, Pulmn Artery, Rt, Pulmn Artery, Lt] 74
Ø21LØZ[5,8,9,C,F,P,Q, R,W]	Bypass/Ventricle, Lt, Opn, No Dev, [Coronary Circulation, Int Mammary, Rt, Int Mammary, Lt, Thoracic Artery, Abd Artery, Pulmn Trunk, Pulmn Artery, Rt, Pulmn Artery, Lt, Aorta] 74
Ø21LØK[P,Q,R]	Bypass/Ventricle, Lt, Opn, Nonauto Tissue Sub, [Pulmn Trunk, Pulmn Artery, Rt, Pulmn Artery, Lt] 74
Ø21LØJ[P,Q,R]	Bypass/Ventricle, Lt, Opn, Synth Sub, [Pulmn Trunk, Pulmn Artery, Rt, Pulmn Artery, Lt] 74
Ø21L4A[P,Q,R]	Bypass/Ventricle, Lt, Perc Endo, Auto Arterial Tissue, [Pulmn Trunk, Pulmn Artery, Rt, Pulmn Artery, Lt] 74
Ø21L49[P,Q,R]	Bypass/Ventricle, Lt, Perc Endo, Auto Venous Tissue, [Pulmn Trunk, Pulmn Artery, Rt, Pulmn Artery, Lt] 74
Ø21L4Z[5,8,9,C,F,P,Q, R,W]	Bypass/Ventricle, Lt, Perc Endo, No Dev, [Coronary Circulation, Int Mammary, Rt, Int Mammary, Lt, Thoracic Artery, Abd Artery, Pulmn Trunk, Pulmn Artery, Rt, Pulmn Artery, Lt, Aorta] 74
Ø21L4K[P,Q,R]	Bypass/Ventricle, Lt, Perc Endo, Nonauto Tissue Sub, [Pulmn Trunk, Pulmn Artery, Rt, Pulmn Artery, Lt] 74
Ø21L4J[P,Q,R]	Bypass/Ventricle, Lt, Perc Endo, Synth Sub, [Pulmn Trunk, Pulmn Artery, Rt, Pulmn Artery, Lt] 74
Ø21KØA[P,Q,R]	Bypass/Ventricle, Rt, Opn, Auto Arterial Tissue, [Pulmn Trunk, Pulmn Artery, Rt, Pulmn Artery, Lt] 74
Ø21KØ9[P,Q,R]	Bypass/Ventricle, Rt, Opn, Auto Venous Tissue, [Pulmn Trunk, Pulmn Artery, Rt, Pulmn Artery, Lt] 74
Ø21KØZ[5,8,9,C,F, P,Q,R,W]	Bypass/Ventricle, Rt, Opn, No Dev, [Coronary Circulation, Int Mammary, Rt, Int Mammary, Lt, Thoracic Artery, Abd Artery, Pulmn Trunk, Pulmn Artery, Rt, Pulmn Artery, Lt, Aorta] 74
Ø21KØK[P,Q,R]	Bypass/Ventricle, Rt, Opn, Nonauto Tissue Sub, [Pulmn Trunk, Pulmn Artery, Rt, Pulmn Artery, Lt] 74
Ø21KØJ[P,Q,R]	Bypass/Ventricle, Rt, Opn, Synth Sub, [Pulmn Trunk, Pulmn Artery, Rt, Pulmn Artery, Lt] 74
Ø21K4A[P,Q,R]	Bypass/Ventricle, Rt, Perc Endo, Auto Arterial Tissue, [Pulmn Trunk, Pulmn Artery, Rt, Pulmn Artery, Lt] 74
Ø21K49[P,Q,R]	Bypass/Ventricle, Rt, Perc Endo, Auto Venous Tissue, [Pulmn Trunk, Pulmn Artery, Rt, Pulmn Artery, Lt] 74
Ø21K4Z[5,8,9,C,F,P, Q,R,W]	Bypass/Ventricle, Rt, Perc Endo, No Dev, [Coronary Circulation, Int Mammary, Rt, Int Mammary, Lt, Thoracic Artery, Abd Artery, Pulmn Trunk, Pulmn Artery, Rt, Pulmn Artery, Lt, Aorta] 74
Ø21K4K[P,Q,R]	Bypass/Ventricle, Rt, Perc Endo, Nonauto Tissue Sub, [Pulmn Trunk, Pulmn Artery, Rt, Pulmn Artery, Lt] 74
Ø21K4J[P,Q,R]	Bypass/Ventricle, Rt, Perc Endo, Synth Sub, [Pulmn Trunk, Pulmn Artery, Rt, Pulmn Artery, Lt] 74
Ø51S*	Bypass/Vert Vein, Lt 85
Ø51R*	Bypass/Vert Vein, Rt 85
ØØ1*	Central Nervous Sys, Bypass 295
ØØK*	Central Nervous Sys, Map 318
ØØQ*	Central Nervous Sys, Repair 318
ØØT*	Central Nervous Sys, Resect 318, 414
ØØN*	Central Nervous Sys, Rls 318
ØØU*	Central Nervous Sys, Supl 318
ØØX*	Central Nervous Sys, Transfer 24, 318
ØW3PØZZ	Control Bleeding in Gastrointestinal Tract, Opn Appr 269
ØW3P7ZZ	Control Bleeding in Gastrointestinal Tract, Via Opng 110
ØW3G3ZZ	Control Bleeding in Peritoneal Cavity, Perc Appr 91
ØW3G4ZZ	Control Bleeding in Peritoneal Cavity, Perc Endo Appr 91
ØW3HØZZ	Control Bleeding in Retroperitoneum, Opn Appr 269
ØW3F*	Control/Abd Wall 91, 113, 123, 158, 254, 355
ØW3F[Ø,3,4]ZZ	Control/Abd Wall, [Opn, Perc, Perc Endo] 217, 302
ØY3L[Ø,3,4]ZZ	Control/Ankle Rgn, Lt, [Opn, Perc, Perc Endo] 219, 303
ØY3K[Ø,3,4]ZZ	Control/Ankle Rgn, Rt, [Opn, Perc, Perc Endo] 219, 303
ØX35[Ø,3,4]ZZ	Control/Axilla, Lt, [Opn, Perc, Perc Endo] 218, 303

085G3ZZ	Destr of Rt Retinal Vessel, Perc Appr 329, 444
0856XZZ	Destr of Rt Sclera, Ext Appr 329, 443
025K3ZZ	Destr of Rt Ventricle, Perc Appr 98
08543ZZ	Destr of Rt Vitreous, Perc Appr 329, 443
0R590ZZ	Destr of Thoracic Vert Disc, Opn Appr 349
0R5B0ZZ	Destr of Thoracolumbar Vert Disc, Opn Appr 349
0H5RXZZ	Destr of Toe Nail, Ext Appr 219
025J3ZZ	Destr of Tricuspid Valve, Perc Appr 98
025M3ZZ	Destr of Ventricular Septum, Perc Appr 98
0450*	Destr/Abd Aorta 110, 322
0450[0,3,4]ZZ	Destr/Abd Aorta, [Opn, Perc, Perc Endo] 92
0M5J*	Destr/Abd Bursa & Lgmt, Lt 133, 342
0M5H*	Destr/Abd Bursa & Lgmt, Rt 133, 342
0K5L*	Destr/Abd Muscle, Lt 138, 338
0K5L[0,3,4]ZZ	Destr/Abd Muscle, Lt, [Opn, Perc, Perc Endo] 213, 451
0K5K*	Destr/Abd Muscle, Rt 138, 338
0K5K[0,3,4]ZZ	Destr/Abd Muscle, Rt, [Opn, Perc, Perc Endo] 213, 451
015M*	Destr/Abd Sympathetic Nerve 24, 89
0L5G*	Destr/Abd Tndn, Lt 141, 340
0L5F*	Destr/Abd Tndn, Rt 141, 340
095P*	Destr/Accessory Sinus 55
0Q55[0,3,4]ZZ	Destr/Acetab, Lt, [Opn, Perc, Perc Endo] 456
0Q54[0,3,4]ZZ	Destr/Acetab, Rt, [Opn, Perc, Perc Endo] 456
0Q55*	Destr/Acetabulum, Lt 135
0Q54*	Destr/Acetabulum, Rt 135
0R5H*	Destr/Acromioclavicular Jt, Lt 136, 349
0R5G*	Destr/Acromioclavicular Jt, Rt 136, 349
0C5Q*	Destr/Adenoids 52
0G52*	Destr/Adrenal Gland, Lt 235
0G53*	Destr/Adrenal Gland, Rt 235
0G54*	Destr/Adrenal Glands, Bilat 235
0F5C[0,3,7]ZZ	Destr/Ampulla of Vater, [Opn, Perc, Via Natrl or Artfcl Opng] 112, 120
0D5R[0,3]ZZ	Destr/Anal Sphincter, [Opn, Perc] 109, 211, 448
0M5R*	Destr/Ankle Bursa & Lgmt, Lt 132, 342
0M5Q*	Destr/Ankle Bursa & Lgmt, Rt 132, 342
0S5G*	Destr/Ankle Jt, Lt 133
0S5F*	Destr/Ankle Jt, Rt 133
0L5T*	Destr/Ankle Tndn, Lt 141, 340
0L5S*	Destr/Ankle Tndn, Rt 141, 340
045Q*	Destr/Ant Tibial Artery, Lt 82, 239, 323
045P*	Destr/Ant Tibial Artery, Rt 82, 239, 323
0D5Q[0,3,7,X]ZZ	Destr/Anus, [Opn, Perc, Via Natrl or Artfcl Opng, Ext] 109, 211, 448
025F[0,4]ZZ	Destr/Aortic Valve, [Opn, Perc Endo] 74
0D5J*	Destr/Appendix 108
0D5K[0,3,7]ZZ	Destr/Ascending Colon, [Opn, Perc, Via Natrl or Artfcl Opng] 108, 299, 448
0255[0,4]ZZ	Destr/Atrial Septum, [Opn, Perc Endo] 74
0257[0,4]ZZ	Destr/Atrium, Lt, [Opn, Perc Endo] 74
0256[0,4]ZZ	Destr/Atrium, Rt, [Opn, Perc Endo] 74
0356*	Destr/Axillary Artery, Lt 81, 239, 320
0355*	Destr/Axillary Artery, Rt 81, 239, 320
0558*	Destr/Axillary Vein, Lt 85, 240, 325
0557*	Destr/Axillary Vein, Rt 85, 240, 325
0550*	Destr/Azygos Vein 60
0550[0,3,4]ZZ	Destr/Azygos Vein, [Opn, Perc, Perc Endo] 96
0058*	Destr/Basal Ganglia 7, 414
0058[0,3,4]ZZ	Destr/Basal Ganglia, [Opn, Perc, Perc Endo] 12, 16, 295
055C*	Destr/Basilic Vein, Lt 85, 240, 325
055B*	Destr/Basilic Vein, Rt 85, 240, 325
0T5B*	Destr/Bladder 259
0T5C*	Destr/Bladder Neck 259
0T5C[0,3,4,7,8]ZZ	Destr/Bladder Neck, [Opn, Perc, Perc Endo, Via Natrl or Artfcl Opng, Via Natrl or Artfcl Opng Endo] 458
0T5C[0,3,4]ZZ	Destr/Bladder Neck, [Opn, Perc, Perc Endo] 249, 268, 302
0T5C[7,8]ZZ	Destr/Bladder Neck, [Via Natrl or Artfcl Opng, Via Natrl or Artfcl Opng Endo] 250
0T5B[0,3,4,7,8]ZZ	Destr/Bladder, [Opn, Perc, Perc Endo, Via Natrl or Artfcl Opng, Via Natrl or Artfcl Opng Endo] 458
0T5B[0,3,4]ZZ	Destr/Bladder, [Opn, Perc, Perc Endo] 249, 268, 302
0T5B[7,8]ZZ	Destr/Bladder, [Via Natrl or Artfcl Opng, Via Natrl or Artfcl Opng Endo] 250
0358*	Destr/Brachial Artery, Lt 81, 239, 320
0357*	Destr/Brachial Artery, Rt 81, 239, 320
055A*	Destr/Brachial Vein, Lt 85, 240, 325
0559*	Destr/Brachial Vein, Rt 85, 240, 325
0050*	Destr/Brain 7, 317, 414
0050[0,3,4]ZZ	Destr/Brain, [Opn, Perc, Perc Endo] 12, 16, 295
0H5V*	Destr/Breast, Bilat 222, 336
0H5V[0,3,7,8,X]ZZ	Destr/Breast, Bilat, [Opn, Perc, Via Natrl or Artfcl Opng, Via Natrl or Artfcl Opng Endo, Ext] 449
0H5U*	Destr/Breast, Lt 222, 336
0H5U[0,3,7,8,X]ZZ	Destr/Breast, Lt, [Opn, Perc, Via Natrl or Artfcl Opng, Via Natrl or Artfcl Opng Endo, Ext] 449
0H5T*	Destr/Breast, Rt 222, 336
0H5T[0,3,7,8,X]ZZ	Destr/Breast, Rt, [Opn, Perc, Via Natrl or Artfcl Opng, Via Natrl or Artfcl Opng Endo, Ext] 449
0C54*	Destr/Buccal Mucosa 56, 331
0C54[0,3,X]ZZ	Destr/Buccal Mucosa, [Opn, Perc, Ext] 447
0B52*	Destr/Carina 52, 64
0R5R*	Destr/Carpal Jt, Lt 150
0R5R[0,3,4]ZZ	Destr/Carpal Jt, Lt, [Opn, Perc, Perc Endo] 315
0R5Q*	Destr/Carpal Jt, Rt 150
0R5Q[0,3,4]ZZ	Destr/Carpal Jt, Rt, [Opn, Perc, Perc Endo] 315
0P5N*	Destr/Carpal, Lt 150
0P5N[0,3,4]ZZ	Destr/Carpal, Lt, [Opn, Perc, Perc Endo] 315, 455
0P5M*	Destr/Carpal, Rt 150
0P5M[0,3,4]ZZ	Destr/Carpal, Rt, [Opn, Perc, Perc Endo] 315, 455
0D5H[0,3,7]	Destr/Cecum, [Opn, Perc, Via Natrl or Artfcl Opng] 108, 299, 448
0451[0,3,4]ZZ	Destr/Celiac Artery, [Opn, Perc, Perc Endo] 95
055F*	Destr/Cephalic Vein, Lt 85, 240, 325
055D*	Destr/Cephalic Vein, Rt 85, 240, 325
005C*	Destr/Cerebellum 8, 317, 414
005C[0,3,4]ZZ	Destr/Cerebellum, [Opn, Perc, Perc Endo] 12, 16, 295
0057*	Destr/Cerebral Hemisphere 7, 317, 414
0057[0,3,4]ZZ	Destr/Cerebral Hemisphere, [Opn, Perc, Perc Endo] 12, 16, 295
0051*	Destr/Cerebral Meninges 7, 414
0051[0,3,4]ZZ	Destr/Cerebral Meninges, [Opn, Perc, Perc Endo] 12, 16, 295
0056*	Destr/Cerebral Ventricle 7, 414
0056[0,3,4]ZZ	Destr/Cerebral Ventricle, [Opn, Perc, Perc Endo] 12, 16
0151[0,4]ZZ	Destr/Cervical Nerve, [Opn, Perc, Perc Endo] 19, 159, 160, 296, 318
005W*	Destr/Cervical Spinal Cord 159, 160
005W[0,3,4]ZZ	Destr/Cervical Spinal Cord, [Opn, Perc, Perc Endo] 19, 295
0R51*	Destr/Cervical Vert Jt 136, 349
0P53*	Destr/Cervical Vertebra 54, 345
0P53[0,3,4]ZZ	Destr/Cervical Vertebra, [Opn, Perc, Perc Endo] 455
0R54*	Destr/Cervicothoracic Vert Jt 136, 349
0U5C*	Destr/Cervix 267, 271
0U5C[0,3,4,7,8]ZZ	Destr/Cervix, [Opn, Perc, Perc Endo, Via Natrl or Artfcl Opng, Via Natrl or Artfcl Opng Endo] 458
0259[0,4]ZZ	Destr/Chordae Tendineae, [Opn, Perc Endo] 74
085B*	Destr/Choroid, Lt 44, 329
085B[0,3]	Destr/Choroid, Lt, [Opn, Perc] 443
085A*	Destr/Choroid, Rt 44, 329
085A[0,3]	Destr/Choroid, Rt, [Opn, Perc] 443
075L*	Destr/Cisterna Chyli 60
0P5B*	Destr/Clavicle, Lt 65, 134, 243, 345
0P5B[0,3,4]ZZ	Destr/Clavicle, Lt, [Opn, Perc, Perc Endo] 455
0P59*	Destr/Clavicle, Rt 65, 134, 243, 345
0P59[0,3,4]ZZ	Destr/Clavicle, Rt, [Opn, Perc, Perc Endo] 455
0U5J*	Destr/Clitoris 267
0U5J[0,X]ZZ	Destr/Clitoris, [Opn, Ext] 458
0S56*	Destr/Coccygeal Jt 136
0Q5S*	Destr/Coccyx 135
0Q5S[0,3,4]ZZ	Destr/Coccyx, [Opn, Perc, Perc Endo] 456
0457[0,3,4]ZZ	Destr/Colic Artery, Lt, [Opn, Perc, Perc Endo] 95
0458[0,3,4]ZZ	Destr/Colic Artery, Mid, [Opn, Perc, Perc Endo] 95
0456[0,3,4]ZZ	Destr/Colic Artery, Rt, [Opn, Perc, Perc Endo] 95

Ø657[Ø,3,4]ZZ	Destr/Colic Vein, [Opn, Perc, Perc Endo] 97
ØF59[Ø,3,7]ZZ	Destr/Common Bile Duct, [Opn, Perc, Via Natrl or Artfcl Opng] 112, 120
Ø35J*	Destr/Common Carotid Artery, Lt 21, 81, 320
Ø35H*	Destr/Common Carotid Artery, Rt 21, 81, 320
Ø45D[Ø,3,4]ZZ	Destr/Common Iliac Artery, Lt, [Opn, Perc, Perc Endo] 95
Ø45C[Ø,3,4]ZZ	Destr/Common Iliac Artery, Rt, [Opn, Perc, Perc Endo] 95
Ø65D[Ø,3,4]ZZ	Destr/Common Iliac Vein, Lt, [Opn, Perc, Perc Endo] 97
Ø65C[Ø,3,4]ZZ	Destr/Common Iliac Vein, Rt, [Opn, Perc, Perc Endo] 97
Ø258[Ø,4]ZZ	Destr/Conduction Mech, [Opn, Perc Endo] 74
Ø254[Ø,4]ZZ	Destr/Coronary Vein, [Opn, Perc, Perc Endo] 74
ØU5F*	Destr/Cul-de-sac 267, 271
ØU5F[Ø,3,4,7,8]ZZ	Destr/Cul-de-sac, [Opn, Perc, Perc Endo, Via Natrl or Artfcl Opng, Via Natrl or Artfcl Opng Endo] 458
ØF58[Ø,3,7]ZZ	Destr/Cystic Duct, [Opn, Perc, Via Natrl or Artfcl Opng] 112, 120
ØD5M[Ø,3,7]ZZ	Destr/Descending Colon, [Opn, Perc, Via Natrl or Artfcl Opng] 108, 299, 448
ØB5S*	Destr/Diaphragm, Lt 61, 153
ØB5R*	Destr/Diaphragm, Rt 61, 153
ØD59[Ø,3,7]ZZ	Destr/Duodenum, [Opn, Perc, Via Natrl or Artfcl Opng] 105, 122, 299, 448
ØØ52*	Destr/Dura Mater 7, 414
ØØ52[Ø,3,4]ZZ	Destr/Dura Mater, [Opn, Perc, Perc Endo] 12, 16, 295
ØM54*	Destr/Elbow Bursa & Lgmt, Lt 133, 243, 342
ØM53*	Destr/Elbow Bursa & Lgmt, Rt 133, 243, 342
ØR5M*	Destr/Elbow Jt, Lt 136, 244, 349
ØR5L*	Destr/Elbow Jt, Rt 136, 244, 349
ØU5B*	Destr/Endometrium 262, 263, 265
ØV5L*	Destr/Epididymis, Bilat 257
ØV5L[Ø,3,4]ZZ	Destr/Epididymis, Bilat, [Opn, Perc, Perc Endo] 459
ØV5K*	Destr/Epididymis, Lt 257
ØV5K[Ø,3,4]ZZ	Destr/Epididymis, Lt, [Opn, Perc, Perc Endo] 459
ØV5J*	Destr/Epididymis, Rt 257
ØV5J[Ø,3,4]ZZ	Destr/Epididymis, Rt, [Opn, Perc, Perc Endo] 459
ØC5R*	Destr/Epiglottis 52, 65, 331
Ø653*	Destr/Esophageal Vein 22, 86, 327
ØD54[Ø,3,7]ZZ	Destr/Esophagogastric Junction, [Opn, Perc, Via Natrl or Artfcl Opng] 53, 105, 299
ØD55[Ø,3,7]ZZ	Destr/Esophagus, [Opn, Perc, Via Natrl or Artfcl Opng] 53, 105, 299
ØD53[Ø,3,7]ZZ	Destr/Esophagus, Lwr, [Opn, Perc, Via Natrl or Artfcl Opng] 53, 105, 299
ØD52[Ø,3,7]ZZ	Destr/Esophagus, Mid, [Opn, Perc, Via Natrl or Artfcl Opng] 53, 105, 299
ØD51[Ø,3,7]ZZ	Destr/Esophagus, Upr, [Opn, Perc, Via Natrl or Artfcl Opng] 53, 105, 299
ØN5G*	Destr/Ethmoid Bone, Lt 134
ØN5G[Ø,3,4]ZZ	Destr/Ethmoid Bone, Lt, [Opn, Perc, Perc Endo] 454
ØN5F*	Destr/Ethmoid Bone, Rt 134
ØN5F[Ø,3,4]ZZ	Destr/Ethmoid Bone, Rt, [Opn, Perc, Perc Endo] 454
Ø95V*	Destr/Ethmoid Sinus, Lt 55
Ø95V[Ø,3,4]ZZ	Destr/Ethmoid Sinus, Lt, [Opn, Perc, Perc Endo] 446
Ø95U*	Destr/Ethmoid Sinus, Rt 55
Ø95U[Ø,3,4]ZZ	Destr/Ethmoid Sinus, Rt, [Opn, Perc, Perc Endo] 446
Ø35N*	Destr/Ext Carotid Artery, Lt 21, 81, 320
Ø35M*	Destr/Ext Carotid Artery, Rt 21, 81, 320
Ø45J[Ø,3,4]ZZ	Destr/Ext Iliac Artery, Lt, [Opn, Perc, Perc Endo] 95
Ø45H[Ø,3,4]ZZ	Destr/Ext Iliac Artery, Rt, [Opn, Perc, Perc Endo] 95
Ø65G[Ø,3,4]ZZ	Destr/Ext Iliac Vein, Lt, [Opn, Perc, Perc Endo] 97
Ø65F[Ø,3,4]ZZ	Destr/Ext Iliac Vein, Rt, [Opn, Perc, Perc Endo] 97
Ø55Q*	Destr/Ext Jugular Vein, Lt 22, 85, 325
Ø55P*	Destr/Ext Jugular Vein, Rt 22, 85, 325
Ø85M*	Destr/Extraocular Muscle, Lt 42, 329
Ø85M[Ø,3]ZZ	Destr/Extraocular Muscle, Lt, [Opn, Perc] 444
Ø85L*	Destr/Extraocular Muscle, Rt 42, 329
Ø85L[Ø,3]ZZ	Destr/Extraocular Muscle, Rt, [Opn, Perc] 444
Ø35R*	Destr/Face Artery 21, 81, 320
Ø55V*	Destr/Face Vein, Lt 22, 85, 325
Ø55T*	Destr/Face Vein, Rt 22, 85, 325
ØK51*	Destr/Facial Muscle 138, 338

ØK51[Ø,3,4]ZZ	Destr/Facial Muscle, [Opn, Perc, Perc Endo] 213, 451
ØU56*	Destr/Fallopian Tube, Lt 262, 263, 265
ØU55*	Destr/Fallopian Tube, Rt 262, 263, 265
ØU57*	Destr/Fallopian Tubes, Bilat 266
ØU57[Ø,3,4,7,8]ZZ	Destr/Fallopian Tubes, Bilat, [Opn, Perc, Perc Endo, Via Natrl or Artfcl Opng, Via Natrl or Artfcl Opng Endo] 271, 458
Ø45L*	Destr/Femor Artery, Lt 82, 239, 322
Ø45K*	Destr/Femor Artery, Rt 82, 239, 322
ØQ59*	Destr/Femor Shaft, Lt 137
ØQ59[Ø,3,4]ZZ	Destr/Femor Shaft, Lt, [Opn, Perc, Perc Endo] 456
ØQ58*	Destr/Femor Shaft, Rt 137
ØQ58[Ø,3,4]ZZ	Destr/Femor Shaft, Rt, [Opn, Perc, Perc Endo] 456
Ø65N*	Destr/Femor Vein, Lt 88, 327
Ø65M*	Destr/Femor Vein, Rt 88, 327
ØQ5K*	Destr/Fibula, Lt 135
ØQ5K[Ø,3,4]ZZ	Destr/Fibula, Lt, [Opn, Perc, Perc Endo] 456
ØQ5J*	Destr/Fibula, Rt 135
ØQ5J[Ø,3,4]ZZ	Destr/Fibula, Rt, [Opn, Perc, Perc Endo] 456
ØR5X*	Destr/Finger Phalangeal Jt, Lt 150
ØR5X[Ø,3,4]ZZ	Destr/Finger Phalangeal Jt, Lt, [Opn, Perc, Perc Endo] 315
ØR5W*	Destr/Finger Phalangeal Jt, Rt 150
ØR5W[Ø,3,4]ZZ	Destr/Finger Phalangeal Jt, Rt, [Opn, Perc, Perc Endo] 315
ØP5V*	Destr/Finger Phalanx, Lt 134, 345
ØP5V[Ø,3,4]ZZ	Destr/Finger Phalanx, Lt, [Opn, Perc, Perc Endo] 455
ØP5T*	Destr/Finger Phalanx, Rt 134, 345
ØP5T[Ø,3,4]ZZ	Destr/Finger Phalanx, Rt, [Opn, Perc, Perc Endo] 455
Ø45W*	Destr/Foot Artery, Lt 82, 239, 323
Ø45V*	Destr/Foot Artery, Rt 82, 239, 323
ØM5T*	Destr/Foot Bursa & Lgmt, Lt 145, 243, 342
ØM5T[Ø,3,4]ZZ	Destr/Foot Bursa & Lgmt, Lt, [Opn, Perc, Perc Endo] 453
ØM5S*	Destr/Foot Bursa & Lgmt, Rt 145, 243, 342
ØM5S[Ø,3,4]ZZ	Destr/Foot Bursa & Lgmt, Rt, [Opn, Perc, Perc Endo] 453
ØK5W*	Destr/Foot Muscle, Lt 138, 338
ØK5W[Ø,3,4]ZZ	Destr/Foot Muscle, Lt, [Opn, Perc, Perc Endo] 213, 451
ØK5V*	Destr/Foot Muscle, Rt 138, 338
ØK5V[Ø,3,4]ZZ	Destr/Foot Muscle, Rt, [Opn, Perc, Perc Endo] 213, 451
ØL5W*	Destr/Foot Tndn, Lt 141, 340
ØL5V*	Destr/Foot Tndn, Rt 141, 340
Ø65V*	Destr/Foot Vein, Lt 88, 327
Ø65T*	Destr/Foot Vein, Rt 88, 327
ØN52*	Destr/Frontal Bone, Lt 154, 414
ØN52[Ø,3,4]ZZ	Destr/Frontal Bone, Lt, [Opn, Perc, Perc Endo] 9, 13, 17, 301
ØN51*	Destr/Frontal Bone, Rt 154, 414
ØN51[Ø,3,4]ZZ	Destr/Frontal Bone, Rt, [Opn, Perc, Perc Endo] 9, 13, 17, 301
Ø95T*	Destr/Frontal Sinus, Lt 55
Ø95S*	Destr/Frontal Sinus, Rt 55
ØF54*	Destr/Gallbladder 120, 335
ØF54[Ø,3,4]ZZ	Destr/Gallbladder, [Opn, Perc, Perc Endo] 301
ØF54[Ø,3]ZZ	Destr/Gallbladder, [Opn, Perc] 121
Ø452[Ø,3,4]ZZ	Destr/Gastric Artery, [Opn, Perc, Perc Endo] 95
Ø652[Ø,3,4]ZZ	Destr/Gastric Vein, [Opn, Perc, Perc Endo] 97
ØP58*	Destr/Glenoid Cavity, Lt 65, 134, 243, 345
ØP58[Ø,3,4]ZZ	Destr/Glenoid Cavity, Lt, [Opn, Perc, Perc Endo] 455
ØP57*	Destr/Glenoid Cavity, Rt 65, 134, 243, 345
ØP57[Ø,3,4]ZZ	Destr/Glenoid Cavity, Rt, [Opn, Perc, Perc Endo] 455
ØD5S*	Destr/Greater Omentum 112, 122, 242, 268
ØD5S[Ø,3,4]ZZ	Destr/Greater Omentum, [Opn, Perc, Perc Endo] 299, 448
Ø65Q*	Destr/Greater Saphenous Vein, Lt 88, 327
Ø65P*	Destr/Greater Saphenous Vein, Rt 88, 327
Ø35F*	Destr/Hand Artery, Lt 81, 239, 320
Ø35D*	Destr/Hand Artery, Rt 81, 239, 320
ØM58*	Destr/Hand Bursa & Lgmt, Lt 150
ØM58[Ø,3,4]ZZ	Destr/Hand Bursa & Lgmt, Lt, [Opn, Perc, Perc Endo] 315
ØM57*	Destr/Hand Bursa & Lgmt, Rt 150
ØM57[Ø,3,4]ZZ	Destr/Hand Bursa & Lgmt, Rt, [Opn, Perc, Perc Endo] 315
ØK5D*	Destr/Hand Muscle, Lt 149
ØK5D[Ø,3,4]ZZ	Destr/Hand Muscle, Lt, [Opn, Perc, Perc Endo] 314
ØK5C*	Destr/Hand Muscle, Rt 149
ØK5C[Ø,3,4]ZZ	Destr/Hand Muscle, Rt, [Opn, Perc, Perc Endo] 314
ØL58*	Destr/Hand Tndn, Lt 149

0L58[0,3,4]ZZ	Destr/Hand Tndn, Lt, [Opn, Perc, Perc Endo] 215, 314, 452	
0L57*	Destr/Hand Tndn, Rt 149	
0L57[0,3,4]ZZ	Destr/Hand Tndn, Rt, [Opn, Perc, Perc Endo] 215, 314, 452	
055H*	Destr/Hand Vein, Lt 85, 240, 325	
055G*	Destr/Hand Vein, Rt 85, 240, 325	
0C52*	Destr/Hard Palate 56	
0C52[0,3,X]ZZ	Destr/Hard Palate, [Opn, Perc, Ext] 447	
0M50*	Destr/Head and Neck Bursa & Lgmt 133, 342	
015K*	Destr/Head and Neck Sympathetic Nerve 24, 50, 89	
0L50*	Destr/Head and Neck Tndn 141, 340	
0K50*	Destr/Head Muscle 138, 338	
0K50[0,3,4]ZZ	Destr/Head Muscle, [Opn, Perc, Perc Endo] 213, 451	
0551*	Destr/Hemiazygos Vein 60	
0551[0,3,4]ZZ	Destr/Hemiazygos Vein, [Opn, Perc, Perc Endo] 96	
0453[0,3,4]ZZ	Destr/Hepatic Artery, [Opn, Perc, Perc Endo] 95	
0F56[0,3,7]ZZ	Destr/Hepatic Duct, Lt, [Opn, Perc, Via Natrl or Artfcl Opng] 112, 120	
0F55[0,3,7]ZZ	Destr/Hepatic Duct, Rt, [Opn, Perc, Via Natrl or Artfcl Opng] 112, 120	
0654[0,3,4]ZZ	Destr/Hepatic Vein, [Opn, Perc, Perc Endo] 97	
0M5M*	Destr/Hip Bursa & Lgmt, Lt 137, 342	
0M5L*	Destr/Hip Bursa & Lgmt, Rt 137, 342	
0S5B*	Destr/Hip Jt, Lt 137	
0S59*	Destr/Hip Jt, Rt 137	
0K5P*	Destr/Hip Muscle, Lt 138, 338	
0K5P[0,3,4]ZZ	Destr/Hip Muscle, Lt, [Opn, Perc, Perc Endo] 213, 451	
0K5N*	Destr/Hip Muscle, Rt 138, 338	
0K5N[0,3,4]ZZ	Destr/Hip Muscle, Rt, [Opn, Perc, Perc Endo] 213, 451	
0L5K*	Destr/Hip Tndn, Lt 141, 340	
0L5J*	Destr/Hip Tndn, Rt 141, 340	
0P5D*	Destr/Humeral Head, Lt 134, 345	
0P5D[0,3,4]ZZ	Destr/Humeral Head, Lt, [Opn, Perc, Perc Endo] 455	
0P5C*	Destr/Humeral Head, Rt 134, 345	
0P5C[0,3,4]ZZ	Destr/Humeral Head, Rt, [Opn, Perc, Perc Endo] 455	
0P5G*	Destr/Humeral Shaft, Lt 134, 345	
0P5G[0,3,4]ZZ	Destr/Humeral Shaft, Lt, [Opn, Perc, Perc Endo] 455	
0P5F*	Destr/Humeral Shaft, Rt 134, 345	
0P5F[0,3,4]ZZ	Destr/Humeral Shaft, Rt, [Opn, Perc, Perc Endo] 455	
0U5K*	Destr/Hymen 267, 274	
0U5K[0,3,4,7,8]ZZ	Destr/Hymen, [Opn, Perc, Perc Endo, Via Natrl or Artfcl Opng, Via Natrl or Artfcl Opng Endo] 458	
0N5X*	Destr/Hyoid Bone 134	
0N5X[0,3,4]ZZ	Destr/Hyoid Bone, [Opn, Perc, Perc Endo] 454	
065J[0,3,4]ZZ	Destr/Hypogastric Vein, Lt, [Opn, Perc, Perc Endo] 97	
065H[0,3,4]ZZ	Destr/Hypogastric Vein, Rt, [Opn, Perc, Perc Endo] 97	
005A*	Destr/Hypothalamus 7, 317, 414	
005A[0,3,4]ZZ	Destr/Hypothalamus, [Opn, Perc, Perc Endo] 12, 16, 295	
0D5C*	Destr/Ileocecal Valve 108	
0D5C[0,3,4,7,8]ZZ	Destr/Ileocecal Valve, [Opn, Perc, Perc Endo, Via Natrl or Artfcl Opng, Via Natrl or Artfcl Opng Endo] 299, 448	
0D5B*	Destr/Ileum 108	
0D5B[0,3,4,7,8]ZZ	Destr/Ileum, [Opn, Perc, Perc Endo, Via Natrl or Artfcl Opng, Via Natrl or Artfcl Opng Endo] 299, 448	
045B[0,3,4]ZZ	Destr/Inferior Mesenteric Artery, [Opn, Perc, Perc Endo] 95	
0656[0,3,4]ZZ	Destr/Inferior Mesenteric Vein, [Opn, Perc, Perc Endo] 97	
0G5P*	Destr/Inferior Parathyroid Gland, Lt 237, 253	
0G5N*	Destr/Inferior Parathyroid Gland, Rt 237, 253	
0650[0,3,4]ZZ	Destr/Inferior Vena Cava, [Opn, Perc, Perc Endo] 97	
0352*	Destr/Innominate Artery 60	
0352[0,3,4]ZZ	Destr/Innominate Artery, [Opn, Perc, Perc Endo] 93	
0554*	Destr/Innominate Vein, Lt 60	
0554[0,3,4]ZZ	Destr/Innominate Vein, Lt, [Opn, Perc, Perc Endo] 96	
0553*	Destr/Innominate Vein, Rt 60	
0553[0,3,4]ZZ	Destr/Innominate Vein, Rt, [Opn, Perc, Perc Endo] 96	
035L*	Destr/Int Carotid Artery, Lt 21, 81, 320	
035K*	Destr/Int Carotid Artery, Rt 21, 81, 320	
045F[0,3,4]ZZ	Destr/Int Iliac Artery, Lt, [Opn, Perc, Perc Endo] 95	
045E[0,3,4]ZZ	Destr/Int Iliac Artery, Rt, [Opn, Perc, Perc Endo] 95	
055N*	Destr/Int Jugular Vein, Lt 22, 85, 325	
055M*	Destr/Int Jugular Vein, Rt 22, 85, 325	
0351*	Destr/Int Mammary Artery, Lt 60	
0351[0,3,4]ZZ	Destr/Int Mammary Artery, Lt, [Opn, Perc, Perc Endo] 93	
0350*	Destr/Int Mammary Artery, Rt 60	
0350[0,3,4]ZZ	Destr/Int Mammary Artery, Rt, [Opn, Perc, Perc Endo] 93	
035G*	Destr/Intracranial Artery 320	
035G[0,3,4]ZZ	Destr/Intracranial Artery, [Opn, Perc, Perc Endo] 7, 8, 13, 17	
055L*	Destr/Intracranial Vein 325	
055L[0,3,4]ZZ	Destr/Intracranial Vein, [Opn, Perc, Perc Endo] 7, 9, 13, 17	
0D5A*	Destr/Jejunum 108	
0D5A[0,3,4,7,8]ZZ	Destr/Jejunum, [Opn, Perc, Perc Endo, Via Natrl or Artfcl Opng, Via Natrl or Artfcl Opng Endo] 299, 448	
0T54*	Destr/Kidney Pelvis, Lt 248	
0T53*	Destr/Kidney Pelvis, Rt 248	
0T51*	Destr/Kidney, Lt 248	
0T50*	Destr/Kidney, Rt 248	
0M5P*	Destr/Knee Bursa & Lgmt, Lt 134, 342	
0M5P[0,3,4]ZZ	Destr/Knee Bursa & Lgmt, Lt, [Opn, Perc, Perc Endo] 453	
0M5N*	Destr/Knee Bursa & Lgmt, Rt 134, 342	
0M5N[0,3,4]ZZ	Destr/Knee Bursa & Lgmt, Rt, [Opn, Perc, Perc Endo] 453	
0S5D*	Destr/Knee Jt, Lt 136	
0S5D[0,3,4]ZZ	Destr/Knee Jt, Lt, [Opn, Perc, Perc Endo] 457	
0S5C*	Destr/Knee Jt, Rt 136	
0S5C[0,3,4]ZZ	Destr/Knee Jt, Rt, [Opn, Perc, Perc Endo] 457	
0L5R*	Destr/Knee Tndn, Lt 141, 340	
0L5Q*	Destr/Knee Tndn, Rt 141, 340	
0N5J*	Destr/Lacrimal Bone, Lt 134	
0N5J[0,3,4]ZZ	Destr/Lacrimal Bone, Lt, [Opn, Perc, Perc Endo] 454	
0N5H*	Destr/Lacrimal Bone, Rt 134	
0N5H[0,3,4]ZZ	Destr/Lacrimal Bone, Rt, [Opn, Perc, Perc Endo] 454	
085Y*	Destr/Lacrimal Duct, Lt 42, 329	
085Y[0,3,7,8]ZZ	Destr/Lacrimal Duct, Lt, [Opn, Perc, Via Natrl or Artfcl Opng, Via Natrl or Artfcl Opng Endo] 444	
085X*	Destr/Lacrimal Duct, Rt 42, 329	
085X[0,3,7,8]ZZ	Destr/Lacrimal Duct, Rt, [Opn, Perc, Via Natrl or Artfcl Opng, Via Natrl or Artfcl Opng Endo] 444	
085W*	Destr/Lacrimal Gland, Lt 42, 329	
085W[0,3]ZZ	Destr/Lacrimal Gland, Lt, [Opn, Perc] 444	
085V*	Destr/Lacrimal Gland, Rt 42, 329	
085V[0,3]ZZ	Destr/Lacrimal Gland, Rt, [Opn, Perc] 444	
0C5S*	Destr/Larynx 52, 65	
0C5S[0,3,4,7,8]ZZ	Destr/Larynx, [Opn, Perc, Perc Endo, Via Natrl or Artfcl Opng, Via Natrl or Artfcl Opng Endo] 448	
0D5T*	Destr/Lesser Omentum 112, 122, 242, 268	
0D5T[0,3,4]ZZ	Destr/Lesser Omentum, [Opn, Perc, Perc Endo] 300, 448	
065S*	Destr/Lesser Saphenous Vein, Lt 88, 327	
065R*	Destr/Lesser Saphenous Vein, Rt 88, 327	
0D5E[0,3,7]ZZ	Destr/Lg Intestine, [Opn, Perc, Via Natrl or Artfcl Opng] 108, 299, 448	
0D5G[0,3,7]ZZ	Destr/Lg Intestine, Lt, [Opn, Perc, Via Natrl or Artfcl Opng] 108, 299, 448	
0D5F[0,3,7]ZZ	Destr/Lg Intestine, Rt, [Opn, Perc, Via Natrl or Artfcl Opng] 108, 299, 448	
0B59[0,3,7,8]ZZ	Destr/Lingula Bronchus, [Opn, Perc, Via Natrl or Artfcl Opng, Via Natrl or Artfcl Opng Endo] 61	
0F50*	Destr/Liver 112, 119	
0F52*	Destr/Liver, Lt Lobe 112, 119	
0F51*	Destr/Liver, Rt Lobe 112, 119	
015B[0,4]ZZ	Destr/Lumbar Nerve, [Opn, Perc Endo] 19, 159, 160, 296, 318	
005Y*	Destr/Lumbar Spinal Cord 159, 160	
005Y[0,3,4]ZZ	Destr/Lumbar Spinal Cord, [Opn, Perc, Perc Endo] 19, 295	
015N*	Destr/Lumbar Sympathetic Nerve 24, 89	
015N[0,3,4]ZZ	Destr/Lumbar Sympathetic Nerve, [Opn, Perc, Perc Endo] 440	
0S52*	Destr/Lumbar Vert Disc 159, 161	
0S52[0,3,4]ZZ	Destr/Lumbar Vert Disc, [Opn, Perc, Perc Endo] 20	
0S50*	Destr/Lumbar Vert Jt 136	
0Q50*	Destr/Lumbar Vertebra 135	
0Q50[0,3,4]ZZ	Destr/Lumbar Vertebra, [Opn, Perc, Perc Endo] 456	
0S54*	Destr/Lumbosacral Disc 159, 161	
0S54[0,3,4]ZZ	Destr/Lumbosacral Disc, [Opn, Perc, Perc Endo] 20	
0S53*	Destr/Lumbosacral Jt 136	

ØB5H[Ø,4,7]ZZ	Destr/Lung Lingula, [Opn, Perc Endo, Via Natrl or Artfcl Opng] 61
ØB5H[Ø,4]ZZ	Destr/Lung Lingula, [Opn, Perc Endo] 299
ØB5L[Ø,4,7]ZZ	Destr/Lung, Lt, [Opn, Perc Endo, Via Natrl or Artfcl Opng] 61
ØB5L[Ø,4]ZZ	Destr/Lung, Lt, [Opn, Perc Endo] 299
ØB5L[Ø,7]ZZ	Destr/Lung, Lt, [Opn, Via Natrl or Artfcl Opng] 331
ØB5K[Ø,4,7]ZZ	Destr/Lung, Rt, [Opn, Perc Endo, Via Natrl or Artfcl Opng] 61
ØB5K[Ø,4]ZZ	Destr/Lung, Rt, [Opn, Perc Endo] 299
ØB5K[Ø,7]ZZ	Destr/Lung, Rt, [Opn, Via Natrl or Artfcl Opng] 331
ØB5M[Ø,4,7]ZZ	Destr/Lungs, Bilat, [Opn, Perc Endo, Via Natrl or Artfcl Opng] 61
ØB5M[Ø,4]ZZ	Destr/Lungs, Bilat, [Opn, Perc Endo] 299
ØB5M[Ø,7]ZZ	Destr/Lungs, Bilat, [Opn, Via Natrl or Artfcl Opng] 331
ØK5B*	Destr/Lwr Arm and Wrist Muscle, Lt 138, 338
ØK5B[Ø,3,4]ZZ	Destr/Lwr Arm and Wrist Muscle, Lt, [Opn, Perc, Perc Endo] 213, 451
ØK59*	Destr/Lwr Arm and Wrist Muscle, Rt 138, 338
ØK59[Ø,3,4]ZZ	Destr/Lwr Arm and Wrist Muscle, Rt, [Opn, Perc, Perc Endo] 213, 451
ØL56*	Destr/Lwr Arm and Wrist Tndn, Lt 141, 340
ØL55*	Destr/Lwr Arm and Wrist Tndn, Rt 141, 340
Ø45Y*	Destr/Lwr Artery 82, 239, 323
ØM5W*	Destr/Lwr Extr Bursa & Lgmt, Lt 134
ØM5V*	Destr/Lwr Extr Bursa & Lgmt, Rt 134
Ø85R*	Destr/Lwr Eyelid, Lt 42, 329
Ø85R[Ø,3,X]ZZ	Destr/Lwr Eyelid, Lt, [Opn, Perc, Ext] 210, 444
Ø85Q*	Destr/Lwr Eyelid, Rt 42, 329
Ø85Q[Ø,3,X]ZZ	Destr/Lwr Eyelid, Rt, [Opn, Perc, Ext] 210, 444
ØQ5C*	Destr/Lwr Femur, Lt 137
ØQ5C[Ø,3,4]ZZ	Destr/Lwr Femur, Lt, [Opn, Perc, Perc Endo] 456
ØQ5B*	Destr/Lwr Femur, Rt 137
ØQ5B[Ø,3,4]ZZ	Destr/Lwr Femur, Rt, [Opn, Perc, Perc Endo] 456
ØK5T*	Destr/Lwr Leg Muscle, Lt 138, 338
ØK5T[Ø,3,4]ZZ	Destr/Lwr Leg Muscle, Lt, [Opn, Perc, Perc Endo] 213, 451
ØK5S*	Destr/Lwr Leg Muscle, Rt 138, 338
ØK5S[Ø,3,4]ZZ	Destr/Lwr Leg Muscle, Rt, [Opn, Perc, Perc Endo] 213, 451
ØL5P*	Destr/Lwr Leg Tndn, Lt 141, 340
ØL5N*	Destr/Lwr Leg Tndn, Rt 141, 340
ØC51*	Destr/Lwr Lip 56
ØC51[Ø,3,X]ZZ	Destr/Lwr Lip, [Opn, Perc, Ext] 210, 447
ØB5B[Ø,3,7,8]ZZ	Destr/Lwr Lobe Bronchus, Lt, [Opn, Perc, Via Natrl or Artfcl Opng, Via Natrl or Artfcl Opng Endo] 61
ØB56[Ø,3,7,8]ZZ	Destr/Lwr Lobe Bronchus, Rt, [Opn, Perc, Via Natrl or Artfcl Opng, Via Natrl or Artfcl Opng Endo] 60
ØB5J[Ø,4,7]ZZ	Destr/Lwr Lung Lobe, Lt, [Opn, Perc Endo, Via Natrl or Artfcl Opng] 61
ØB5J[Ø,4]ZZ	Destr/Lwr Lung Lobe, Lt, [Opn, Perc Endo] 299
ØB5F[Ø,4,7]ZZ	Destr/Lwr Lung Lobe, Rt, [Opn, Perc Endo, Via Natrl or Artfcl Opng] 61
ØB5F[Ø,4]ZZ	Destr/Lwr Lung Lobe, Rt, [Opn, Perc Endo] 299
Ø65Y[Ø,3,4]ZZ	Destr/Lwr Vein, [Opn, Perc, Perc Endo] 88, 327
Ø65Y[Ø,3,4]ZC	Destr/Lwr Vein, [Opn, Perc, Perc Endo], No Dev, Hemorrhoidal Plexus 109, 442
Ø75D*	Destr/Lymphatic, Aortic 290, 328
Ø75D[Ø,3,4]ZZ	Destr/Lymphatic, Aortic, [Opn, Perc, Perc Endo] 297
Ø75Ø*	Destr/Lymphatic, Head 290, 328
Ø75Ø[Ø,3,4]ZZ	Destr/Lymphatic, Head, [Opn, Perc, Perc Endo] 297
Ø759*	Destr/Lymphatic, Int Mammary, Lt 290, 328
Ø759[Ø,3,4]ZZ	Destr/Lymphatic, Int Mammary, Lt, [Opn, Perc, Perc Endo] 297
Ø758*	Destr/Lymphatic, Int Mammary, Rt 290, 328
Ø758[Ø,3,4]ZZ	Destr/Lymphatic, Int Mammary, Rt, [Opn, Perc, Perc Endo] 297
Ø756*	Destr/Lymphatic, Lt Axillary 290, 328
Ø756[Ø,3,4]ZZ	Destr/Lymphatic, Lt Axillary, [Opn, Perc, Perc Endo] 297
Ø75J*	Destr/Lymphatic, Lt Inguinal 290, 328
Ø75J[Ø,3,4]ZZ	Destr/Lymphatic, Lt Inguinal, [Opn, Perc, Perc Endo] 297
Ø75G*	Destr/Lymphatic, Lt Lwr Extr 290, 328
Ø75G[Ø,3,4]ZZ	Destr/Lymphatic, Lt Lwr Extr, [Opn, Perc, Perc Endo] 297
Ø752*	Destr/Lymphatic, Lt Neck 290, 328
Ø752[Ø,3,4]ZZ	Destr/Lymphatic, Lt Neck, [Opn, Perc, Perc Endo] 297
Ø754*	Destr/Lymphatic, Lt Upr Extr 290, 328
Ø754[Ø,3,4]ZZ	Destr/Lymphatic, Lt Upr Extr, [Opn, Perc, Perc Endo] 297

Ø75B*	Destr/Lymphatic, Mesenteric 290, 328
Ø75B[Ø,3,4]ZZ	Destr/Lymphatic, Mesenteric, [Opn, Perc, Perc Endo] 297
Ø75C*	Destr/Lymphatic, Pelvis 290, 328
Ø75C[Ø,3,4]ZZ	Destr/Lymphatic, Pelvis, [Opn, Perc, Perc Endo] 297
Ø755*	Destr/Lymphatic, Rt Axillary 290, 328
Ø755[Ø,3,4]ZZ	Destr/Lymphatic, Rt Axillary, [Opn, Perc, Perc Endo] 297
Ø75H*	Destr/Lymphatic, Rt Inguinal 290, 328
Ø75H[Ø,3,4]ZZ	Destr/Lymphatic, Rt Inguinal, [Opn, Perc, Perc Endo] 297
Ø75F*	Destr/Lymphatic, Rt Lwr Extr 290, 328
Ø75F[Ø,3,4]ZZ	Destr/Lymphatic, Rt Lwr Extr, [Opn, Perc, Perc Endo] 297
Ø751*	Destr/Lymphatic, Rt Neck 290, 328
Ø751[Ø,3,4]ZZ	Destr/Lymphatic, Rt Neck, [Opn, Perc, Perc Endo] 297
Ø753*	Destr/Lymphatic, Rt Upr Extr 290, 328
Ø753[Ø,3,4]ZZ	Destr/Lymphatic, Rt Upr Extr, [Opn, Perc, Perc Endo] 297
Ø757*	Destr/Lymphatic, Thorax 290, 328
Ø757[Ø,3,4]ZZ	Destr/Lymphatic, Thorax, [Opn, Perc, Perc Endo] 297
ØB57[Ø,3,7,8]ZZ	Destr/Main Bronchus, Lt, [Opn, Perc, Via Natrl or Artfcl Opng, Via Natrl or Artfcl Opng Endo] 60
ØB53[Ø,3,7,8]ZZ	Destr/Main Bronchus, Rt, [Opn, Perc, Via Natrl or Artfcl Opng, Via Natrl or Artfcl Opng Endo] 60
ØN5V*	Destr/Mandible, Lt 134
ØN5V[Ø,3,4]ZZ	Destr/Mandible, Lt, [Opn, Perc, Perc Endo] 454
ØN5T*	Destr/Mandible, Rt 134
ØN5T[Ø,3,4]ZZ	Destr/Mandible, Rt, [Opn, Perc, Perc Endo] 454
Ø95C*	Destr/Mastoid Sinus, Lt 55
Ø95B*	Destr/Mastoid Sinus, Rt 55
ØN5S*	Destr/Maxilla, Lt 134
ØN5S[Ø,3,4]ZZ	Destr/Maxilla, Lt, [Opn, Perc, Perc Endo] 454
ØN5R*	Destr/Maxilla, Rt 134
ØN5R[Ø,3,4]ZZ	Destr/Maxilla, Rt, [Opn, Perc, Perc Endo] 454
Ø95R*	Destr/Maxillary Sinus, Lt 55
Ø95Q*	Destr/Maxillary Sinus, Rt 55
ØØ5D*	Destr/Medulla Oblongata 8, 317, 414
ØØ5D[Ø,3,4]ZZ	Destr/Medulla Oblongata, [Opn, Perc, Perc Endo] 12, 16, 295
ØD5V*	Destr/Mesentery 112, 122, 242, 268
ØD5V[Ø,3,4]ZZ	Destr/Mesentery, [Opn, Perc, Perc Endo] 300, 449
ØP5Q*	Destr/Metacarpal, Lt 150
ØP5Q[Ø,3,4]ZZ	Destr/Metacarpal, Lt, [Opn, Perc, Perc Endo] 315, 455
ØP5P*	Destr/Metacarpal, Rt 150
ØP5P[Ø,3,4]ZZ	Destr/Metacarpal, Rt, [Opn, Perc, Perc Endo] 315, 455
ØR5T*	Destr/Metacarpocarpal Jt, Lt 150
ØR5T[Ø,3,4]ZZ	Destr/Metacarpocarpal Jt, Lt, [Opn, Perc, Perc Endo] 315
ØR5S*	Destr/Metacarpocarpal Jt, Rt 150
ØR5S[Ø,3,4]ZZ	Destr/Metacarpocarpal Jt, Rt, [Opn, Perc, Perc Endo] 315
ØR5V*	Destr/Metacarpophalangeal Jt, Lt 150
ØR5V[Ø,3,4]ZZ	Destr/Metacarpophalangeal Jt, Lt, [Opn, Perc, Perc Endo] 315
ØR5U*	Destr/Metacarpophalangeal Jt, Rt 150
ØR5U[Ø,3,4]ZZ	Destr/Metacarpophalangeal Jt, Rt, [Opn, Perc, Perc Endo] 315
ØS5N*	Destr/Metatarsal-Phalangeal Jt, Lt 145, 244
ØS5N[Ø,3,4]ZZ	Destr/Metatarsal-Phalangeal Jt, Lt, [Opn, Perc, Perc Endo] 457
ØS5M*	Destr/Metatarsal-Phalangeal Jt, Rt 145, 244
ØS5M[Ø,3,4]ZZ	Destr/Metatarsal-Phalangeal Jt, Rt, [Opn, Perc, Perc Endo] 457
ØS5L*	Destr/Metatarsal-Tarsal Jt, Lt 145, 244
ØS5L[Ø,3,4]ZZ	Destr/Metatarsal-Tarsal Jt, Lt, [Opn, Perc, Perc Endo] 457
ØS5K*	Destr/Metatarsal-Tarsal Jt, Rt 145, 244
ØS5K[Ø,3,4]ZZ	Destr/Metatarsal-Tarsal Jt, Rt, [Opn, Perc, Perc Endo] 457
ØQ5P*	Destr/Metatarsal, Lt 145, 244
ØQ5P[Ø,3,4]ZZ	Destr/Metatarsal, Lt, [Opn, Perc, Perc Endo] 456
ØQ5N*	Destr/Metatarsal, Rt 145, 244
ØQ5N[Ø,3,4]ZZ	Destr/Metatarsal, Rt, [Opn, Perc, Perc Endo] 456
ØB55[Ø,3,7,8]ZZ	Destr/Mid Lobe Bronchus, Rt, [Opn, Perc, Via Natrl or Artfcl Opng, Via Natrl or Artfcl Opng Endo] 60
ØB5D[Ø,4,7]ZZ	Destr/Mid Lung Lobe, Rt, [Opn, Perc Endo, Via Natrl or Artfcl Opng] 61
ØB5D[Ø,4]ZZ	Destr/Mid Lung Lobe, Rt, [Opn, Perc Endo] 299
ØC5J*	Destr/Minor Salivary Gland 56
ØC5J[Ø,3]ZZ	Destr/Minor Salivary Gland, [Opn, Perc] 448
Ø25G[Ø,4]ZZ	Destr/Mitral Valve, [Opn, Perc Endo] 74
ØN5B*	Destr/Nasal Bone 134
ØN5B[Ø,3,4]ZZ	Destr/Nasal Bone, [Opn, Perc, Perc Endo] 454

095L*	Destr/Nasal Turbinate 51	
095N*	Destr/Nasopharynx 51, 105	
0K53*	Destr/Neck Muscle, Lt 138, 338	
0K53[0,3,4]ZZ	Destr/Neck Muscle, Lt, [Opn, Perc, Perc Endo] 213, 451	
0K52*	Destr/Neck Muscle, Rt 138, 338	
0K52[0,3,4]ZZ	Destr/Neck Muscle, Rt, [Opn, Perc, Perc Endo] 213, 451	
0H5X*	Destr/Nipple, Lt 222, 336	
0H5W*	Destr/Nipple, Rt 222, 336	
0N58*	Destr/Occipital Bone, Lt 154, 414	
0N58[0,3,4]ZZ	Destr/Occipital Bone, Lt, [Opn, Perc, Perc Endo] 9, 13, 17, 301	
0N57*	Destr/Occipital Bone, Rt 154, 414	
0N57[0,3,4]ZZ	Destr/Occipital Bone, Rt, [Opn, Perc, Perc Endo] 9, 13, 17, 301	
0R50*	Destr/Occipital-cervical Jt 136, 349	
0N5Q*	Destr/Orbit, Lt 134	
0N5Q[0,3,4]ZZ	Destr/Orbit, Lt, [Opn, Perc, Perc Endo] 454	
0N5P*	Destr/Orbit, Rt 134	
0N5P[0,3,4]ZZ	Destr/Orbit, Rt, [Opn, Perc, Perc Endo] 454	
0U52*	Destr/Ovaries, Bilat 262, 263, 265	
0U51*	Destr/Ovary, Lt 262, 263, 265	
0U50*	Destr/Ovary, Rt 262, 263, 265	
0N5L*	Destr/Palatine Bone, Lt 134	
0N5L[0,3,4]ZZ	Destr/Palatine Bone, Lt, [Opn, Perc, Perc Endo] 454	
0N5K*	Destr/Palatine Bone, Rt 134	
0N5K[0,3,4]ZZ	Destr/Palatine Bone, Rt, [Opn, Perc, Perc Endo] 454	
0F5G[0,3]ZZ	Destr/Pancreas, [Opn, Perc] 119, 242	
0F5D[0,3,7]ZZ	Destr/Pancreatic Duct, [Opn, Perc, Via Natrl or Artfcl Opng] 119, 242	
0F5F[0,3,7]ZZ	Destr/Pancreatic Duct, Accessory, [Opn, Perc, Via Natrl or Artfcl Opng] 119, 242	
025D[0,3,4]ZZ	Destr/Papillary Muscle, [Opn, Perc, Perc Endo] 74	
0G5R*	Destr/Parathyroid Gland 237, 253	
0G5Q*	Destr/Parathyroid Glands, Multi 237, 253	
0N54*	Destr/Parietal Bone, Lt 154, 414	
0N54[0,3,4]ZZ	Destr/Parietal Bone, Lt, [Opn, Perc, Perc Endo] 9, 13, 17, 301	
0N53*	Destr/Parietal Bone, Rt 154, 414	
0N53[0,3,4]ZZ	Destr/Parietal Bone, Rt, [Opn, Perc, Perc Endo] 9, 13, 17, 301	
0C5C*	Destr/Parotid Duct, Lt 56	
0C5C[0,3]ZZ	Destr/Parotid Duct, Lt, [Opn, Perc] 448	
0C5B*	Destr/Parotid Duct, Rt 56	
0C5B[0,3]ZZ	Destr/Parotid Duct, Rt, [Opn, Perc] 447	
0C59*	Destr/Parotid Gland, Lt 56	
0C59[0,3]ZZ	Destr/Parotid Gland, Lt, [Opn, Perc] 447	
0C58*	Destr/Parotid Gland, Rt 56	
0C58[0,3]ZZ	Destr/Parotid Gland, Rt, [Opn, Perc] 447	
0Q5F*	Destr/Patella, Lt 135	
0Q5F[0,3,4]ZZ	Destr/Patella, Lt, [Opn, Perc, Perc Endo] 456	
0Q5D*	Destr/Patella, Rt 135	
0Q5D[0,3,4]ZZ	Destr/Patella, Rt, [Opn, Perc, Perc Endo] 456	
0Q53*	Destr/Pelvic Bone, Lt 135	
0Q53[0,3,4]ZZ	Destr/Pelvic Bone, Lt, [Opn, Perc, Perc Endo] 456	
0Q52*	Destr/Pelvic Bone, Rt 135	
0Q52[0,3,4]ZZ	Destr/Pelvic Bone, Rt, [Opn, Perc, Perc Endo] 456	
0V5S*	Destr/Penis 257	
0V5S[0,3,4,X]ZZ	Destr/Penis, [Opn, Perc, Perc Endo, Ext] 217, 459	
025N*	Destr/Pericardium 60, 319	
025N[0,3,4]ZZ	Destr/Pericardium, [Opn, Perc, Perc Endo] 92, 296	
0M5K*	Destr/Perineum Bursa & Lgmt 133, 342	
0K5M*	Destr/Perineum Muscle 138, 338	
0K5M[0,3,4]ZZ	Destr/Perineum Muscle, [Opn, Perc, Perc Endo] 213, 451	
0L5H*	Destr/Perineum Tndn 141, 340	
0D5W*	Destr/Peritoneum 112, 122, 242, 268	
0D5W[0,3,4]ZZ	Destr/Peritoneum, [Opn, Perc, Perc Endo] 300, 449	
045U*	Destr/Peroneal Artery, Lt 82, 239, 323	
045T*	Destr/Peroneal Artery, Rt 82, 239, 323	
0C5M*	Destr/Pharynx 52, 105	
0G51*	Destr/Pineal Body 235	
0G51[0,3,4]ZZ	Destr/Pineal Body, [Opn, Perc, Perc Endo] 9, 13, 17	
0G50*	Destr/Pituitary Gland 235	
0G50[0,3,4]ZZ	Destr/Pituitary Gland, [Opn, Perc, Perc Endo] 9, 13, 17, 211	
0B5P*	Destr/Pleura, Lt 61, 331	
0B5P[0,3,4]ZZ	Destr/Pleura, Lt, [Opn, Perc, Perc Endo] 299	
0B5N*	Destr/Pleura, Rt 61, 331	
0B5N[0,3,4]ZZ	Destr/Pleura, Rt, [Opn, Perc, Perc Endo] 299	
005B*	Destr/Pons 7, 317, 414	
005B[0,3,4]ZZ	Destr/Pons, [Opn, Perc, Perc Endo] 12, 16, 295	
045N*	Destr/Popliteal Artery, Lt 82, 239, 323	
045M*	Destr/Popliteal Artery, Rt 82, 239, 323	
0658[0,3,4]ZZ	Destr/Portal Vein, [Opn, Perc, Perc Endo] 97	
045S*	Destr/Posterior Tibial Artery, Lt 82, 239, 323	
045R*	Destr/Posterior Tibial Artery, Rt 82, 239, 323	
0V5T*	Destr/Prepuce 257	
0V5T[0,3,4,X]ZZ	Destr/Prepuce, [Opn, Perc, Perc Endo, Ext] 217, 459	
0V50*	Destr/Prostate 250	
0V50[0,3,4]ZZ	Destr/Prostate, [Opn, Perc, Perc Endo] 257	
0V50[7,8]ZZ	Destr/Prostate, [Via Natrl or Artfcl Opng, Via Natrl or Artfcl Opng Endo] 258, 440	
025R*	Destr/Pulmn Artery, Lt 60	
025R[0,3,4]ZZ	Destr/Pulmn Artery, Lt, [Opn, Perc, Perc Endo] 92	
025Q*	Destr/Pulmn Artery, Rt 60	
025Q[0,3,4]ZZ	Destr/Pulmn Artery, Rt, [Opn, Perc, Perc Endo] 92	
025P*	Destr/Pulmn Trunk 60	
025P[0,3,4]ZZ	Destr/Pulmn Trunk, [Opn, Perc, Perc Endo] 92	
025H[0,4]ZZ	Destr/Pulmn Valve, [Opn, Perc Endo] 74	
025T*	Destr/Pulmn Vein, Lt 60	
025T[0,3,4]ZZ	Destr/Pulmn Vein, Lt, [Opn, Perc, Perc Endo] 93	
025S*	Destr/Pulmn Vein, Rt 60	
025S[0,3,4]ZZ	Destr/Pulmn Vein, Rt, [Opn, Perc, Perc Endo] 93	
035C*	Destr/Radial Artery, Lt 81, 239, 320	
035B*	Destr/Radial Artery, Rt 81, 239, 320	
0P5J*	Destr/Radius, Lt 134, 345	
0P5J[0,3,4]ZZ	Destr/Radius, Lt, [Opn, Perc, Perc Endo] 455	
0P5H*	Destr/Radius, Rt 134, 345	
0P5H[0,3,4]ZZ	Destr/Radius, Rt, [Opn, Perc, Perc Endo] 455	
045A*	Destr/Renal Artery, Lt 251	
045A[0,3,4]ZZ	Destr/Renal Artery, Lt, [Opn, Perc, Perc Endo] 95	
0459*	Destr/Renal Artery, Rt 251	
0459[0,3,4]ZZ	Destr/Renal Artery, Rt, [Opn, Perc, Perc Endo] 95	
065B[0,3,4]ZZ	Destr/Renal Vein, Lt, [Opn, Perc, Perc Endo] 97	
0659[0,3,4]ZZ	Destr/Renal Vein, Rt, [Opn, Perc, Perc Endo] 97	
0P52*	Destr/Rib, Lt 65, 134, 243, 345	
0P52[0,3,4]ZZ	Destr/Rib, Lt, [Opn, Perc, Perc Endo] 455	
0P51*	Destr/Rib, Rt 65, 134, 243, 345	
0P51[0,3,4]ZZ	Destr/Rib, Rt, [Opn, Perc, Perc Endo] 455	
015R[0,4]ZZ	Destr/Sacral Nerve, [Opn, Perc Endo] 19, 159, 160, 296, 318	
015P*	Destr/Sacral Sympathetic Nerve 24, 89, 262, 263, 265	
0S55*	Destr/Sacrococcygeal Jt 136	
0S58*	Destr/Sacroiliac Jt, Lt 136	
0S57*	Destr/Sacroiliac Jt, Rt 136	
0Q51*	Destr/Sacrum 135	
0Q51[0,3,4]ZZ	Destr/Sacrum, [Opn, Perc, Perc Endo] 456	
0P56*	Destr/Scapula, Lt 65, 134, 243, 345	
0P56[0,3,4]ZZ	Destr/Scapula, Lt, [Opn, Perc, Perc Endo] 455	
0P55*	Destr/Scapula, Rt 65, 134, 243, 345	
0P55[0,3,4]ZZ	Destr/Scapula, Rt, [Opn, Perc, Perc Endo] 455	
0V52*	Destr/Seminal Vesicle, Lt 260	
0V51*	Destr/Seminal Vesicle, Rt 260	
0V53*	Destr/Seminal Vesicles, Bilat 260	
0M52*	Destr/Shldr Bursa & Lgmt, Lt 133, 342	
0M51*	Destr/Shldr Bursa & Lgmt, Rt 133, 342	
0R5K*	Destr/Shldr Jt, Lt 136, 349	
0R5J*	Destr/Shldr Jt, Rt 136, 349	
0K56*	Destr/Shldr Muscle, Lt 138, 338	
0K56[0,3,4]ZZ	Destr/Shldr Muscle, Lt, [Opn, Perc, Perc Endo] 213, 451	
0K55*	Destr/Shldr Muscle, Rt 138, 338	
0K55[0,3,4]ZZ	Destr/Shldr Muscle, Rt, [Opn, Perc, Perc Endo] 213, 451	
0L52*	Destr/Shldr Tndn, Lt 141, 340	
0L51*	Destr/Shldr Tndn, Rt 141, 340	
0D5N[0,3,7]ZZ	Destr/Sigmoid Colon, [Opn, Perc, Via Natrl or Artfcl Opng] 108, 299, 448	
0H57XZ[D,Z]	Destr/Skin, Abd, Ext, No Dev, [Multi, NQ] 219	

ØH56XZ[D,Z]	Destr/Skin, Back, Ext, No Dev, [Multi, NQ] 219	
ØH58XZ[D,Z]	Destr/Skin, Buttock, Ext, No Dev, [Multi, NQ] 219	
ØH55XZ[D,Z]	Destr/Skin, Chest, Ext, No Dev, [Multi, NQ] 219	
ØH51XZ[D,Z]	Destr/Skin, Face, Ext, No Dev, [Multi, NQ] 219	
ØH5AXZ[D,Z]	Destr/Skin, Genitalia, Ext, No Dev, [Multi, NQ] 219	
ØH5NXZ[D,Z]	Destr/Skin, Lt Foot, Ext, No Dev, [Multi, NQ] 219	
ØH5GXZ[D,Z]	Destr/Skin, Lt Hand, Ext, No Dev, [Multi, NQ] 219	
ØH5EXZ[D,Z]	Destr/Skin, Lt Lwr Arm, Ext, No Dev, [Multi, NQ] 219	
ØH5LXZ[D,Z]	Destr/Skin, Lt Lwr Leg, Ext, No Dev, [Multi, NQ] 219	
ØH5CXZ[D,Z]	Destr/Skin, Lt Upr Arm, Ext, No Dev, [Multi, NQ] 219	
ØH5JXZ[D,Z]	Destr/Skin, Lt Upr Leg, Ext, No Dev, [Multi, NQ] 219	
ØH54XZ[D,Z]	Destr/Skin, Neck, Ext, No Dev, [Multi, NQ] 219	
ØH59XZ[D,Z]	Destr/Skin, Perineum, Ext, No Dev, [Multi, NQ] 219	
ØH5MXZ[D,Z]	Destr/Skin, Rt Foot, Ext, No Dev, [Multi, NQ] 219	
ØH5FXZ[D,Z]	Destr/Skin, Rt Hand, Ext, No Dev, [Multi, NQ] 219	
ØH5DXZ[D,Z]	Destr/Skin, Rt Lwr Arm, Ext, No Dev, [Multi, NQ] 219	
ØH5KXZ[D,Z]	Destr/Skin, Rt Lwr Leg, Ext, No Dev, [Multi, NQ] 219	
ØH5BXZ[D,Z]	Destr/Skin, Rt Upr Arm, Ext, No Dev, [Multi, NQ] 219	
ØH5HXZ[D,Z]	Destr/Skin, Rt Upr Leg, Ext, No Dev, [Multi, NQ] 219	
ØH5ØXZ[D,Z]	Destr/Skin, Scalp, Ext, No Dev, [Multi, NQ] 219	
ØN5Ø*	Destr/Skull 154, 414	
ØN5Ø[Ø,3,4]ZZ	Destr/Skull, [Opn, Perc, Perc Endo] 9, 13, 17, 301	
ØD58*	Destr/Sm Intestine 108	
ØD58[Ø,3,4,7,8]ZZ	Destr/Sm Intestine, [Opn, Perc, Perc Endo, Via Natrl or Artfcl Opng, Via Natrl or Artfcl Opng Endo] 299, 448	
ØC53*	Destr/Soft Palate 56, 331	
ØC53[Ø,3,X]ZZ	Destr/Soft Palate, [Opn, Perc, Ext] 447	
ØV5G*	Destr/Spermatic Cord, Lt 257	
ØV5G[Ø,3,4]ZZ	Destr/Spermatic Cord, Lt, [Opn, Perc, Perc Endo] 459	
ØV5F*	Destr/Spermatic Cord, Rt 257	
ØV5F[Ø,3,4]ZZ	Destr/Spermatic Cord, Rt, [Opn, Perc, Perc Endo] 459	
ØV5H*	Destr/Spermatic Cords, Bilat 257	
ØV5H[Ø,3,4]ZZ	Destr/Spermatic Cords, Bilat, [Opn, Perc, Perc Endo] 459	
ØN5D*	Destr/Sphenoid Bone, Lt 134	
ØN5D[Ø,3,4]ZZ	Destr/Sphenoid Bone, Lt, [Opn, Perc, Perc Endo] 454	
ØN5C*	Destr/Sphenoid Bone, Rt 134	
ØN5C[Ø,3,4]ZZ	Destr/Sphenoid Bone, Rt, [Opn, Perc, Perc Endo] 454	
Ø95X*	Destr/Sphenoid Sinus, Lt 55	
Ø95W*	Destr/Sphenoid Sinus, Rt 55	
ØØ5T*	Destr/Spinal Meninges 159, 160	
ØØ5T[Ø,3,4]ZZ	Destr/Spinal Meninges, [Opn, Perc, Perc Endo] 19, 295	
Ø75P*	Destr/Spleen 290, 328	
Ø75P[Ø,3,4]ZZ	Destr/Spleen, [Opn, Perc, Perc Endo] 297	
Ø454[Ø,3,4]ZZ	Destr/Splenic Artery, [Opn, Perc, Perc Endo] 95	
Ø651[Ø,3,4]ZZ	Destr/Splenic Vein, [Opn, Perc, Perc Endo] 97	
ØJ58[Ø,3]ZZ	Destr/SQ Tissue & Fascia, Abd, [Opn, Perc] 219	
ØJ54[Ø,3]ZZ	Destr/SQ Tissue & Fascia, Ant Neck, [Opn, Perc] 219	
ØJ57[Ø,3]ZZ	Destr/SQ Tissue & Fascia, Back, [Opn, Perc] 219	
ØJ59[Ø,3]ZZ	Destr/SQ Tissue & Fascia, Buttock, [Opn, Perc] 219	
ØJ56[Ø,3]ZZ	Destr/SQ Tissue & Fascia, Chest, [Opn, Perc] 219	
ØJ51[Ø,3]ZZ	Destr/SQ Tissue & Fascia, Face, [Opn, Perc] 219	
ØJ5C[Ø,3]ZZ	Destr/SQ Tissue & Fascia, Genitalia, [Opn, Perc] 219	
ØJ5R[Ø,3]ZZ	Destr/SQ Tissue & Fascia, Lt Foot, [Opn, Perc] 220	
ØJ5K[Ø,3]ZZ	Destr/SQ Tissue & Fascia, Lt Hand, [Opn, Perc] 220	
ØJ5H[Ø,3]ZZ	Destr/SQ Tissue & Fascia, Lt Lwr Arm, [Opn, Perc] 220	
ØJ5P[Ø,3]ZZ	Destr/SQ Tissue & Fascia, Lt Lwr Leg, [Opn, Perc] 220	
ØJ5F[Ø,3]ZZ	Destr/SQ Tissue & Fascia, Lt Upr Arm, [Opn, Perc] 219	
ØJ5M[Ø,3]ZZ	Destr/SQ Tissue & Fascia, Lt Upr Leg, [Opn, Perc] 220	
ØJ5B[Ø,3]ZZ	Destr/SQ Tissue & Fascia, Perineum, [Opn, Perc] 219	
ØJ55[Ø,3]ZZ	Destr/SQ Tissue & Fascia, Post Neck, [Opn, Perc] 219	
ØJ5Q[Ø,3]ZZ	Destr/SQ Tissue & Fascia, Rt Foot, [Opn, Perc] 220	
ØJ5J[Ø,3]ZZ	Destr/SQ Tissue & Fascia, Rt Hand, [Opn, Perc] 220	
ØJ5G[Ø,3]ZZ	Destr/SQ Tissue & Fascia, Rt Lwr Arm, [Opn, Perc] 219	
ØJ5N[Ø,3]ZZ	Destr/SQ Tissue & Fascia, Rt Lwr Leg, [Opn, Perc] 220	
ØJ5D[Ø,3]ZZ	Destr/SQ Tissue & Fascia, Rt Upr Arm, [Opn, Perc] 219	
ØJ5L[Ø,3]ZZ	Destr/SQ Tissue & Fascia, Rt Upr Leg, [Opn, Perc] 220	
ØJ5Ø[Ø,3]ZZ	Destr/SQ Tissue & Fascia, Scalp, [Opn, Perc] 219	
ØR5F*	Destr/Sternoclavicular Jt, Lt 136, 349	
ØR5E*	Destr/Sternoclavicular Jt, Rt 136, 349	
ØP5Ø*	Destr/Sternum 65, 134, 243, 344	
ØP5Ø[Ø,3,4]ZZ	Destr/Sternum, [Opn, Perc, Perc Endo] 455	
ØD56[Ø,3,7]ZZ	Destr/Stomach, [Opn, Perc, Via Natrl or Artfcl Opng] 105, 448	
ØD57[Ø,3,7]ZZ	Destr/Stomach, Pylorus, [Opn, Perc, Via Natrl or Artfcl Opng] 105, 448	
Ø354*	Destr/Subclavian Artery, Lt 60	
Ø354[Ø,3,4]ZZ	Destr/Subclavian Artery, Lt, [Opn, Perc, Perc Endo] 93	
Ø353*	Destr/Subclavian Artery, Rt 60	
Ø353[Ø,3,4]ZZ	Destr/Subclavian Artery, Rt, [Opn, Perc, Perc Endo] 93	
Ø556*	Destr/Subclavian Vein, Lt 60	
Ø556[Ø,3,4]ZZ	Destr/Subclavian Vein, Lt, [Opn, Perc, Perc Endo] 96	
Ø555*	Destr/Subclavian Vein, Rt 60	
Ø555[Ø,3,4]ZZ	Destr/Subclavian Vein, Rt, [Opn, Perc, Perc Endo] 96	
ØC5F*	Destr/Sublingual Gland, Lt 56	
ØC5F[Ø,3]ZZ	Destr/Sublingual Gland, Lt, [Opn, Perc] 448	
ØC5D*	Destr/Sublingual Gland, Rt 56	
ØC5D[Ø,3]ZZ	Destr/Sublingual Gland, Rt, [Opn, Perc] 448	
ØC5H*	Destr/Submaxillary Gland, Lt 56	
ØC5H[Ø,3]ZZ	Destr/Submaxillary Gland, Lt, [Opn, Perc] 448	
ØC5G*	Destr/Submaxillary Gland, Rt 56	
ØC5G[Ø,3]ZZ	Destr/Submaxillary Gland, Rt, [Opn, Perc] 448	
Ø455[Ø,3,4]ZZ	Destr/Superior Mesenteric Artery, [Opn, Perc, Perc Endo] 95	
Ø655[Ø,3,4]ZZ	Destr/Superior Mesenteric Vein, [Opn, Perc, Perc Endo] 97	
ØG5M*	Destr/Superior Parathyroid Gland, Lt 237, 253	
ØG5L*	Destr/Superior Parathyroid Gland, Rt 237, 253	
Ø25V*	Destr/Superior Vena Cava 60	
Ø25V[Ø,3,4]ZZ	Destr/Superior Vena Cava, [Opn, Perc, Perc Endo] 93	
ØS5J*	Destr/Tarsal Jt, Lt 145, 244	
ØS5J[Ø,3,4]ZZ	Destr/Tarsal Jt, Lt, [Opn, Perc, Perc Endo] 457	
ØS5H*	Destr/Tarsal Jt, Rt 145, 244	
ØS5H[Ø,3,4]ZZ	Destr/Tarsal Jt, Rt, [Opn, Perc, Perc Endo] 457	
ØQ5M*	Destr/Tarsal, Lt 145, 244	
ØQ5M[Ø,3,4]ZZ	Destr/Tarsal, Lt, [Opn, Perc, Perc Endo] 456	
ØQ5L*	Destr/Tarsal, Rt 145, 244	
ØQ5L[Ø,3,4]ZZ	Destr/Tarsal, Rt, [Opn, Perc, Perc Endo] 456	
Ø35T*	Destr/Temporal Artery, Lt 21, 81, 320	
Ø35S*	Destr/Temporal Artery, Rt 21, 81, 320	
ØN56*	Destr/Temporal Bone, Lt 154, 414	
ØN56[Ø,3,4]ZZ	Destr/Temporal Bone, Lt, [Opn, Perc, Perc Endo] 9, 13, 17, 301	
ØN55*	Destr/Temporal Bone, Rt 154, 414	
ØN55[Ø,3,4]ZZ	Destr/Temporal Bone, Rt, [Opn, Perc, Perc Endo] 9, 13, 17, 301	
ØR5D*	Destr/Temporomandibular Jt, Lt 49, 136, 349	
ØR5D[Ø,3,4]ZZ	Destr/Temporomandibular Jt, Lt, [Opn, Perc, Perc Endo] 457	
ØR5C*	Destr/Temporomandibular Jt, Rt 49, 136, 349	
ØR5C[Ø,3,4]ZZ	Destr/Temporomandibular Jt, Rt, [Opn, Perc, Perc Endo] 457	
ØV5C*	Destr/Testes, Bilat 257	
ØV5B*	Destr/Testis, Lt 257	
ØV59*	Destr/Testis, Rt 257	
ØØ59*	Destr/Thalamus 7, 317, 414	
ØØ59[Ø,3,4]ZZ	Destr/Thalamus, [Opn, Perc, Perc Endo] 12, 16, 295	
Ø25W*	Destr/Thoracic Aorta 60	
Ø25W[Ø,3,4]ZZ	Destr/Thoracic Aorta, [Opn, Perc, Perc Endo] 93	
Ø75K*	Destr/Thoracic Duct 60	
Ø158[Ø,4]ZZ	Destr/Thoracic Nerve, [Opn, Perc Endo] 19, 159, 160, 296, 318	
ØØ5X*	Destr/Thoracic Spinal Cord 159, 160	
ØØ5X[Ø,3,4]ZZ	Destr/Thoracic Spinal Cord, [Opn, Perc, Perc Endo] 19, 295	
Ø15L*	Destr/Thoracic Sympathetic Nerve 24, 89	
ØR56*	Destr/Thoracic Vert Jt 136, 349	
ØP54*	Destr/Thoracic Vertebra 134, 345	
ØP54[Ø,3,4]ZZ	Destr/Thoracic Vertebra, [Opn, Perc, Perc Endo] 455	
ØR5A*	Destr/Thoracolumbar Vert Jt 136, 349	
ØM5G*	Destr/Thorax Bursa & Lgmt, Lt 133, 342	
ØM5F*	Destr/Thorax Bursa & Lgmt, Rt 133, 342	
ØK5J*	Destr/Thorax Muscle, Lt 138, 338	
ØK5J[Ø,3,4]ZZ	Destr/Thorax Muscle, Lt, [Opn, Perc, Perc Endo] 213, 451	
ØK5H*	Destr/Thorax Muscle, Rt 138, 338	
ØK5H[Ø,3,4]ZZ	Destr/Thorax Muscle, Rt, [Opn, Perc, Perc Endo] 213, 451	
ØL5D*	Destr/Thorax Tndn, Lt 141, 340	
ØL5C*	Destr/Thorax Tndn, Rt 141, 340	
ØP5S*	Destr/Thumb Phalanx, Lt 134, 345	
ØP5S[Ø,3,4]ZZ	Destr/Thumb Phalanx, Lt, [Opn, Perc, Perc Endo] 455	

0P5R*	Destr/Thumb Phalanx, Rt 134, 345
0P5R[0,3,4]ZZ	Destr/Thumb Phalanx, Rt, [Opn, Perc, Perc Endo] 455
075M*	Destr/Thymus 25, 60, 241, 290, 328
075M[0,3,4]ZZ	Destr/Thymus, [Opn, Perc, Perc Endo] 297
035V*	Destr/Thyroid Artery, Lt 21, 81, 320
035U*	Destr/Thyroid Artery, Rt 21, 81, 320
0G5K*	Destr/Thyroid Gland 237
0G5G*	Destr/Thyroid Gland Lobe, Lt 237
0G5H*	Destr/Thyroid Gland Lobe, Rt 237
0Q5H*	Destr/Tibia, Lt 135
0Q5H[0,3,4]ZZ	Destr/Tibia, Lt, [Opn, Perc, Perc Endo] 456
0Q5G*	Destr/Tibia, Rt 135
0Q5G[0,3,4]ZZ	Destr/Tibia, Rt, [Opn, Perc, Perc Endo] 456
0S5Q*	Destr/Toe Phalangeal Jt, Lt 145, 244
0S5Q[0,3,4]ZZ	Destr/Toe Phalangeal Jt, Lt, [Opn, Perc, Perc Endo] 457
0S5P*	Destr/Toe Phalangeal Jt, Rt 145, 244
0S5P[0,3,4]ZZ	Destr/Toe Phalangeal Jt, Rt, [Opn, Perc, Perc Endo] 457
0Q5R*	Destr/Toe Phalanx, Lt 135
0Q5R[0,3,4]ZZ	Destr/Toe Phalanx, Lt, [Opn, Perc, Perc Endo] 456
0Q5Q*	Destr/Toe Phalanx, Rt 135
0Q5Q[0,3,4]ZZ	Destr/Toe Phalanx, Rt, [Opn, Perc, Perc Endo] 456
0C57*	Destr/Tongue 56, 90
0C57[0,3,X]ZZ	Destr/Tongue, [Opn, Perc, Ext] 447
0K54*	Destr/Tongue, Palate, Pharynx Muscle 138, 338
0K54[0,3,4]ZZ	Destr/Tongue, Palate, Pharynx Muscle, [Opn, Perc, Perc Endo] 213, 451
0C5P*	Destr/Tonsils 52
0B51*	Destr/Trachea 52, 64
0D5L[0,3,7]ZZ	Destr/Transv Colon, [Opn, Perc, Via Natrl or Artfcl Opng] 108, 299, 448
025J[0,4]ZZ	Destr/Tricuspid Valve, [Opn, Perc Endo] 74
0M5D*	Destr/Trunk Bursa & Lgmt, Lt 133, 342
0M5C*	Destr/Trunk Bursa & Lgmt, Rt 133, 342
0K5G*	Destr/Trunk Muscle, Lt 138, 338
0K5G[0,3,4]ZZ	Destr/Trunk Muscle, Lt, [Opn, Perc, Perc Endo] 213, 451
0K5F*	Destr/Trunk Muscle, Rt 138, 338
0K5F[0,3,4]ZZ	Destr/Trunk Muscle, Rt, [Opn, Perc, Perc Endo] 213, 451
0L5B*	Destr/Trunk Tndn, Lt 141, 340
0L59*	Destr/Trunk Tndn, Rt 141, 340
0V57*	Destr/Tunica Vaginalis, Lt 257
0V56*	Destr/Tunica Vaginalis, Rt 257
0958*	Destr/Tympanic Membrane, Lt 51
0957*	Destr/Tympanic Membrane, Rt 51
0P5L*	Destr/Ulna, Lt 134, 345
0P5L[0,3,4]ZZ	Destr/Ulna, Lt, [Opn, Perc, Perc Endo] 455
0P5K*	Destr/Ulna, Rt 134, 345
0P5K[0,3,4]ZZ	Destr/Ulna, Rt, [Opn, Perc, Perc Endo] 455
035A*	Destr/Ulnar Artery, Lt 81, 239, 320
0359*	Destr/Ulnar Artery, Rt 81, 239, 320
0K58*	Destr/Upr Arm Muscle, Lt 138, 338
0K58[0,3,4]ZZ	Destr/Upr Arm Muscle, Lt, [Opn, Perc, Perc Endo] 213, 451
0K57*	Destr/Upr Arm Muscle, Rt 138, 338
0K57[0,3,4]ZZ	Destr/Upr Arm Muscle, Rt, [Opn, Perc, Perc Endo] 213, 451
0L54*	Destr/Upr Arm Tndn, Lt 141, 340
0L53*	Destr/Upr Arm Tndn, Rt 141, 340
035Y*	Destr/Upr Artery 81, 239, 320
0M5B*	Destr/Upr Extr Bursa & Lgmt, Lt 133, 342
0M59*	Destr/Upr Extr Bursa & Lgmt, Rt 133, 342
085P*	Destr/Upr Eyelid, Lt 42, 329
085P[0,3,X]ZZ	Destr/Upr Eyelid, Lt, [Opn, Perc, Ext] 210, 444
085N*	Destr/Upr Eyelid, Rt 42, 329
085N[0,3,X]ZZ	Destr/Upr Eyelid, Rt, [Opn, Perc, Ext] 210, 444
0Q57*	Destr/Upr Femur, Lt 137
0Q57[0,3,4]ZZ	Destr/Upr Femur, Lt, [Opn, Perc, Perc Endo] 456
0Q56*	Destr/Upr Femur, Rt 137
0Q56[0,3,4]ZZ	Destr/Upr Femur, Rt, [Opn, Perc, Perc Endo] 456
0K5R*	Destr/Upr Leg Muscle, Lt 138, 338
0K5R[0,3,4]ZZ	Destr/Upr Leg Muscle, Lt, [Opn, Perc, Perc Endo] 213, 451
0K5Q*	Destr/Upr Leg Muscle, Rt 138, 338
0K5Q[0,3,4]ZZ	Destr/Upr Leg Muscle, Rt, [Opn, Perc, Perc Endo] 213, 451

0L5M*	Destr/Upr Leg Tndn, Lt 141, 340
0L5L*	Destr/Upr Leg Tndn, Rt 141, 340
0C50*	Destr/Upr Lip 56
0C50[0,3,X]ZZ	Destr/Upr Lip, [Opn, Perc, Ext] 210, 447
0B58[0,3,7,8]ZZ	Destr/Upr Lobe Bronchus, Lt, [Opn, Perc, Via Natrl or Artfcl Opng, Via Natrl or Artfcl Opng Endo] 61
0B54[0,3,7,8]ZZ	Destr/Upr Lobe Bronchus, Rt, [Opn, Perc, Via Natrl or Artfcl Opng, Via Natrl or Artfcl Opng Endo] 60
0B5G[0,4,7]ZZ	Destr/Upr Lung Lobe, Lt, [Opn, Perc Endo, Via Natrl or Artfcl Opng] 61
0B5G[0,4]ZZ	Destr/Upr Lung Lobe, Lt, [Opn, Perc Endo] 299
0B5C[0,4,7]ZZ	Destr/Upr Lung Lobe, Rt, [Opn, Perc Endo, Via Natrl or Artfcl Opng] 61
0B5C[0,4]ZZ	Destr/Upr Lung Lobe, Rt, [Opn, Perc Endo] 299
055Y*	Destr/Upr Vein 85, 240, 325
0T57*	Destr/Ureter, Lt 248, 259, 268, 353
0T56*	Destr/Ureter, Rt 248, 259, 268, 353
0U54*	Destr/Uterine Supporting Structure 262, 263, 265
0U59*	Destr/Uterus 262, 263, 265
0U59[0,3,4,7,8]ZZ	Destr/Uterus, [Opn, Perc, Perc Endo, Via Natrl or Artfcl Opng, Via Natrl or Artfcl Opng Endo] 458
0C5N*	• Destr/Uvula 56
0C5N[0,3,X]ZZ	Destr/Uvula, [Opn, Perc, Ext] 448
0U5G*	Destr/Vagina 267, 274
0U5G[0,3,4,7,8,X]ZZ	Destr/Vagina, [Opn, Perc, Perc Endo, Via Natrl or Artfcl Opng Endo, Via Natrl or Artfcl Opng Endo, Ext] 217, 458
025L[0,4]ZZ	Destr/Ventricle, Lt, [Opn, Perc Endo] 74
025K[0,4]ZZ	Destr/Ventricle, Rt, [Opn, Perc Endo] 74
025M[0,4]ZZ	Destr/Ventricular Septum, [Opn, Perc Endo] 74
035Q*	Destr/Vert Artery, Lt 21, 81, 320
035P*	Destr/Vert Artery, Rt 21, 81, 320
055S*	Destr/Vert Vein, Lt 22, 85, 325
055R*	Destr/Vert Vein, Rt 22, 85, 325
0U5L*	Destr/Vestibular Gland 267, 271
0U5L[0,X]ZZ	Destr/Vestibular Gland, [Opn, Ext] 217, 458
0C5V*	Destr/Vocal Cord, Lt 52, 65
0C5V[0,3,4,7,8]ZZ	Destr/Vocal Cord, Lt, [Opn, Perc, Perc Endo, Via Natrl or Artfcl Opng, Via Natrl or Artfcl Opng Endo] 448
0C5T*	Destr/Vocal Cord, Rt 52, 65
0C5T[0,3,4,7,8]ZZ	Destr/Vocal Cord, Rt, [Opn, Perc, Perc Endo, Via Natrl or Artfcl Opng, Via Natrl or Artfcl Opng Endo] 448
0U5M*	Destr/Vulva 267, 275
0U5M[0,X]ZZ	Destr/Vulva, [Opn, Ext] 217, 458
0M56*	Destr/Wrist Bursa & Lgmt, Lt 150
0M56[0,3,4]ZZ	Destr/Wrist Bursa & Lgmt, Lt, [Opn, Perc, Perc Endo] 216, 315
0M55*	Destr/Wrist Bursa & Lgmt, Rt 150
0M55[0,3,4]ZZ	Destr/Wrist Bursa & Lgmt, Rt, [Opn, Perc, Perc Endo] 216, 315
0R5P*	Destr/Wrist Jt, Lt 150
0R5P[0,3,4]ZZ	Destr/Wrist Jt, Lt, [Opn, Perc, Perc Endo] 217, 315
0R5N*	Destr/Wrist Jt, Rt 150
0R5N[0,3,4]ZZ	Destr/Wrist Jt, Rt, [Opn, Perc, Perc Endo] 217, 315
0N5N*	Destr/Zygomatic Bone, Lt 134
0N5N[0,3,4]ZZ	Destr/Zygomatic Bone, Lt, [Opn, Perc, Perc Endo] 454
0N5M*	Destr/Zygomatic Bone, Rt 134
0N5M[0,3,4]ZZ	Destr/Zygomatic Bone, Rt, [Opn, Perc, Perc Endo] 454
0Y6[2,3,4]0ZZ	Detach at [Rt, Lt, Bilat] Hindquarter, Opn Appr 129
0X6[B,C]0ZZ	Detach at [Rt, Lt] Elbow Rgn, Opn Appr 129
0Y6[7,8]0ZZ	Detach at [Rt, Lt] Femor Rgn, Opn Appr 129
0X6[0,1]0ZZ	Detach at [Rt, Lt] Forequarter, Opn Appr 129
0Y6[F,G]0ZZ	Detach at [Rt, Lt] Knee Rgn, Opn Appr 129
0X6[2,3]0ZZ	Detach at [Rt, Lt] Shldr Rgn, Opn Appr 129
0Y640ZZ	Detach at Bilat Hindquarter, Opn Appr 76, 219
0X6C0ZZ	Detach at Lt Elbow Region, Opn Appr 218, 356
0Y680ZZ	Detach at Lt Femor Region, Opn Appr 76, 219
0X610ZZ	Detach at Lt Forequarter, Opn Appr 218, 356
0Y630ZZ	Detach at Lt Hindquarter, Opn Appr 76, 219
0Y6G0ZZ	Detach at Lt Knee Region, Opn Appr 29, 76, 219, 235
0X630ZZ	Detach at Lt Shldr Region, Opn Appr 218, 356
0X6B0ZZ	Detach at Rt Elbow Region, Opn Appr 218, 356
0Y670ZZ	Detach at Rt Femor Region, Opn Appr 76, 219
0X600ZZ	Detach at Rt Forequarter, Opn Appr 218, 356

ØY62ØZZ	Detach at Rt Hindquarter, Opn Appr 76, 219
ØY6FØZZ	Detach at Rt Knee Region, Opn Appr 29, 76, 219, 235
ØX62ØZZ	Detach at Rt Shldr Region, Opn Appr 218, 356
ØY6Q*	Detach/1st Toe, Lt 29, 87, 146, 235
ØY6QØZ[Ø,1,2,3]	Detach/1st Toe, Lt, Opn, No Dev, [Complete, High, Mid, Low] 219
ØY6P*	Detach/1st Toe, Rt 29, 87, 146, 235
ØY6PØZ[Ø,1,2,3]	Detach/1st Toe, Rt, Opn, No Dev, [Complete, High, Mid, Low] 219
ØY6S*	Detach/2nd Toe, Lt 29, 87, 146, 235
ØY6SØZ[Ø,1,2,3]	Detach/2nd Toe, Lt, Opn, No Dev, [Complete, High, Mid, Low] 219
ØY6R*	Detach/2nd Toe, Rt 29, 87, 146, 235
ØY6RØZ[Ø,1,2,3]	Detach/2nd Toe, Rt, Opn, No Dev, [Complete, High, Mid, Low] 219
ØY6U*	Detach/3rd Toe, Lt 29, 87, 146, 235
ØY6UØZ[Ø,1,2,3]	Detach/3rd Toe, Lt, Opn, No Dev, [Complete, High, Mid, Low] 219
ØY6T*	Detach/3rd Toe, Rt 29, 87, 146, 235
ØY6TØZ[Ø,1,2,3]	Detach/3rd Toe, Rt, Opn, No Dev, [Complete, High, Mid, Low] 219
ØY6W*	Detach/4th Toe, Lt 29, 87, 146, 235
ØY6WØZ[Ø,1,2,3]	Detach/4th Toe, Lt, Opn, No Dev, [Complete, High, Mid, Low] 219
ØY6V*	Detach/4th Toe, Rt 29, 87, 146, 235
ØY6VØZ[Ø,1,2,3]	Detach/4th Toe, Rt, Opn, No Dev, [Complete, High, Mid, Low] 219
ØY6Y*	Detach/5th Toe, Lt 29, 87, 146, 235
ØY6YØZ[Ø,1,2,3]	Detach/5th Toe, Lt, Opn, No Dev, [Complete, High, Mid, Low] 219
ØY6X*	Detach/5th Toe, Rt 29, 87, 146, 235
ØY6XØZ[Ø,1,2,3]	Detach/5th Toe, Rt, Opn, No Dev, [Complete, High, Mid, Low] 219
ØY6N*	Detach/Foot, Lt 29, 76, 129, 235
ØY6NØZ[Ø,4,5,6,7,8,9, B,C,D,F]	Detach/Foot, Lt, Opn, No Dev, [Complete, Complete 1st Ray, Complete 2nd Ray, Complete 3rd Ray, Complete 4th Ray, Complete 5th Ray, Partial 1st Ray, Partial 2nd Ray, Partial 3rd Ray, Partial 4th Ray, Partial 5th Ray] 219
ØY6M*	Detach/Foot, Rt 29, 76, 129, 235
ØY6MØZ[Ø,4,5,6,7,8, 9,B,C,D,F]	Detach/Foot, Rt, Opn, No Dev, [Complete, Complete 1st Ray, Complete 2nd Ray, Complete 3rd Ray, Complete 4th Ray, Complete 5th Ray, Partial 1st Ray, Partial 2nd Ray, Partial 3rd Ray, Partial 4th Ray, Partial 5th Ray] 219
ØX6K*	Detach/Hand, Lt 129, 356
ØX6KØZ[Ø,4,5,6,7,8,9, B,C,D,F]	Detach/Hand, Lt, Opn, No Dev, [Complete, Complete 1st Ray, Complete 2nd Ray, Complete 3rd Ray, Complete 4th Ray, Complete 5th Ray, Partial 1st Ray, Partial 2nd Ray, Partial 3rd Ray, Partial 4th Ray, Partial 5th Ray] 218
ØX6J*	Detach/Hand, Rt 129, 356
ØX6JØZ[Ø,4,5,6,7,8,9, B,C,D,F]	Detach/Hand, Rt, Opn, No Dev, [Complete, Complete 1st Ray, Complete 2nd Ray, Complete 3rd Ray, Complete 4th Ray, Complete 5th Ray, Partial 1st Ray, Partial 2nd Ray, Partial 3rd Ray, Partial 4th Ray, Partial 5th Ray] 218
ØX6P*	Detach/Index Finger, Lt 151
ØX6PØZ[Ø,1,2,3]	Detach/Index Finger, Lt, Opn, No Dev, [Complete, High, Mid, Low] 218, 317, 460
ØX6N*	Detach/Index Finger, Rt 151
ØX6NØZ[Ø,1,2,3]	Detach/Index Finger, Rt, Opn, No Dev, [Complete, High, Mid, Low] 218, 317, 460
ØX6W*	Detach/Little Finger, Lt 151
ØX6WØZ[Ø,1,2,3]	Detach/Little Finger, Lt, Opn, No Dev, [Compl, High, Mid, Low] 218, 317, 461
ØX6V*	Detach/Little Finger, Rt 151
ØX6VØZ[Ø,1,2,3]	Detach/Little Finger, Rt, Opn, No Dev, [Compl, High, Mid, Low] 218, 317, 461
ØX6F*	Detach/Lwr Arm, Lt 129, 356
ØX6FØZ[1,2,3]	Detach/Lwr Arm, Lt, Opn, No Dev, [High, Mid, Low] 218
ØX6D*	Detach/Lwr Arm, Rt 129, 356
ØX6DØZ[1,2,3]	Detach/Lwr Arm, Rt, Opn, No Dev, [High, Mid, Low] 218
ØY6J*	Detach/Lwr Leg, Lt 29, 76, 129, 235
ØY6JØZ[1,2,3]	Detach/Lwr Leg, Lt, Opn, No Dev, [High, Mid, Low] 219
ØY6H*	Detach/Lwr Leg, Rt 29, 76, 129, 235
ØY6HØZ[1,2,3]	Detach/Lwr Leg, Rt, Opn, No Dev, [High, Mid, Low] 219
ØX6R*	Detach/Mid Finger, Lt 151

ØX6RØZ[Ø,1,2,3]	Detach/Mid Finger, Lt, Opn, No Dev, [Compl, High, Mid, Low] 218, 317, 460
ØX6Q*	Detach/Mid Finger, Rt 151
ØX6QØZ[Ø,1,2,3]	Detach/Mid Finger, Rt, Opn, No Dev, [Compl, High, Mid, Low] 218, 317, 460
ØX6T*	Detach/Ring Finger, Lt 151
ØX6TØZ[Ø,1,2,3]	Detach/Ring Finger, Lt, Opn, No Dev, [Compl, High, Mid, Low] 218, 317, 461
ØX6S*	Detach/Ring Finger, Rt 151
ØX6SØZ[Ø,1,2,3]	Detach/Ring Finger, Rt, Opn, No Dev, [Compl, High, Mid, Low] 218, 317, 460
ØX6M*	Detach/Thumb, Lt 151
ØX6MØZ[Ø,1,2,3]	Detach/Thumb, Lt, Opn, No Dev, [Complete, High, Mid, Low] 218, 317
ØX6L*	Detach/Thumb, Rt 151
ØX6LØZ[Ø,1,2,3]	Detach/Thumb, Rt, Opn, No Dev, [Complete, High, Mid, Low] 218, 317
ØX69*	Detach/Upr Arm, Lt 129, 356
ØX69ØZ[1,2,3]	Detach/Upr Arm, Lt, Opn, No Dev, [High, Mid, Low] 218
ØX68*	Detach/Upr Arm, Rt 129, 356
ØX68ØZ[1,2,3]	Detach/Upr Arm, Rt, Opn, No Dev, [High, Mid, Low] 218
ØY6D*	Detach/Upr Leg, Lt 29, 76, 129, 235
ØY6DØZ[1,2,3]	Detach/Upr Leg, Lt, Opn, No Dev, [High, Mid, Low] 219
ØY6C*	Detach/Upr Leg, Rt 29, 76, 129, 235
ØY6CØZ[1,2,3]	Detach/Upr Leg, Rt, Opn, No Dev, [High, Mid, Low] 219
047L041	Dilation Lt Fem Art w Drug-elut Intralum, Drug Blln, Opn 22, 63, 83, 111, 122, 152, 208, 240, 252, 323
047L341	Dilation Lt Fem Art w Drug-elut Intralum, Drug Blln, Perc 22, 63, 83, 111, 122, 152, 208, 240, 252, 323
047L441	Dilation Lt Fem Art w Drug-elut Intralum, Drug Blln, Perc Endo 22, 63, 83, 111, 122, 152, 208, 240, 252, 323
047LØD1	Dilation Lt Fem Art w Intralum Dev, Drug Blln, Opn 22, 63, 83, 111, 122, 152, 208, 240, 252, 323
047L3D1	Dilation Lt Fem Art w Intralum Dev, Drug Blln, Perc 22, 63, 83, 111, 122, 152, 208, 240, 252, 323
047L4D1	Dilation Lt Fem Art w Intralum Dev, Drug Blln, Perc Endo 22, 63, 83, 111, 122, 152, 208, 240, 252, 323
047N041	Dilation Lt Popl Art w Drug-elut Intralum, Drug Blln, Opn 22, 64, 83, 111, 122, 152, 208, 240, 252, 323
047N341	Dilation Lt Popl Art w Drug-elut Intralum, Drug Blln, Perc 22, 64, 83, 111, 122, 152, 208, 240, 252, 323
047N441	Dilation Lt Popl Art w Drug-elut Intralum, Drug Blln, Perc Endo 22, 64, 83, 111, 122, 152, 208, 240, 252, 323
047NØD1	Dilation Lt Popl Art w Intralum Dev, Drug Blln, Opn 22, 64, 83, 111, 122, 152, 208, 240, 252, 323
047N3D1	Dilation Lt Popl Art w Intralum Dev, Drug Blln, Perc 22, 64, 83, 111, 122, 152, 208, 240, 252, 323
047N4D1	Dilation Lt Popl Art w Intralum Dev, Drug Blln, Perc Endo 22, 64, 83, 111, 122, 152, 208, 240, 252, 323
ØF79ØDZ	Dilation of Com Bile Duct with Intralum Dev, Opn Appr 120, 335
ØF78ØDZ	Dilation of Cystic Duct with Intralum Dev, Opn Appr 120, 335
047LØZ1	Dilation of Lt Fem Art using Drug Blln, Opn Appr 22, 63, 83, 111, 122, 152, 208, 240, 252, 323
047L3Z1	Dilation of Lt Fem Art using Drug Blln, Perc Appr 22, 63, 83, 111, 122, 152, 208, 240, 252, 323
047L4Z1	Dilation of Lt Fem Art using Drug Blln, Perc Endo Appr 22, 63, 83, 111, 122, 152, 208, 240, 252, 323
ØF76ØDZ	Dilation of Lt Hepatic Duct with Intralum Dev, Opn Appr 120, 335
047NØZ1	Dilation of Lt Popl Art using Drug Blln, Opn Appr 22, 64, 83, 111, 122, 152, 208, 240, 252, 323
047N3Z1	Dilation of Lt Popl Art using Drug Blln, Perc Appr 22, 64, 83, 111, 122, 152, 208, 240, 252, 323
047N4Z1	Dilation of Lt Popl Art using Drug Blln, Perc Endo Appr 22, 64, 83, 111, 122, 152, 208, 240, 252, 323
047KØZ1	Dilation of Rt Fem Art using Drug Blln, Opn Appr 22, 63, 83, 111, 122, 152, 208, 239, 252, 323
047K3Z1	Dilation of Rt Fem Art using Drug Blln, Perc Appr 22, 63, 83, 111, 122, 152, 208, 239, 252, 323
047K4Z1	Dilation of Rt Fem Art using Drug Blln, Perc Endo Appr 22, 63, 83, 111, 122, 152, 208, 240, 252, 323
ØF75ØDZ	Dilation of Rt Hepatic Duct with Intralum Dev, Opn Appr 120, 335

Alphabetic Index to Procedures

047MØZ1	Dilation of Rt Popl Art using Drug Blln, Opn Appr 22, 63, 83, 111, 122, 152, 208, 240, 252, 323
047M3Z1	Dilation of Rt Popl Art using Drug Blln, Perc Appr 22, 64, 83, 111, 122, 152, 208, 240, 252, 323
047M4Z1	Dilation of Rt Popl Art using Drug Blln, Perc Endo Appr 22, 64, 83, 111, 122, 152, 208, 240, 252, 323
ØD77ØZZ	Dilation of Stomach, Pylorus, Opn Appr 105
ØD773ZZ	Dilation of Stomach, Pylorus, Perc Appr 105
ØD774ZZ	Dilation of Stomach, Pylorus, Perc Endo Appr 105
ØD777ZZ	Dilation of Stomach, Pylorus, Via Opng 105
ØU7G4DZ	Dilation of Vagina with Intralum Dev, Perc Endo Appr 274
ØU7GØDZ	Dilation of Vagina with Intralum Device, Opn Appr 274
ØU7G3DZ	Dilation of Vagina with Intralum Device, Perc Appr 274
ØU7GØZZ	Dilation of Vagina, Opn Appr 274
ØU7G3ZZ	Dilation of Vagina, Perc Appr 274
ØU7G4ZZ	Dilation of Vagina, Perc Endo Appr 274
047KØ41	Dilation Rt Fem Art w Drug-elut Intralum, Drug Blln, Opn 22, 63, 83, 110, 122, 152, 208, 239, 252, 323
047K341	Dilation Rt Fem Art w Drug-elut Intralum, Drug Blln, Perc 22, 63, 83, 111, 122, 152, 208, 239, 252, 323
047K441	Dilation Rt Fem Art w Drug-elut Intralum, Drug Blln, Perc Endo 22, 63, 83, 111, 122, 152, 208, 240, 252, 323
047KØD1	Dilation Rt Fem Art w Intralum Dev, Drug Blln, Opn 22, 63, 83, 110, 122, 152, 208, 239, 252, 323
047K3D1	Dilation Rt Fem Art w Intralum Dev, Drug Blln, Perc 22, 63, 83, 111, 122, 152, 208, 239, 252, 323
047K4D1	Dilation Rt Fem Art w Intralum Dev, Drug Blln, Perc Endo 22, 63, 83, 111, 122, 152, 208, 240, 252, 323
047MØ41	Dilation Rt Popl Art w Drug-elut Intralum, Drug Blln, Opn 22, 63, 83, 111, 122, 152, 208, 240, 252, 323
047M341	Dilation Rt Popl Art w Drug-elut Intralum, Drug Blln, Perc 22, 63, 83, 111, 122, 152, 208, 240, 252, 323
047M441	Dilation Rt Popl Art w Drug-elut Intralum, Drug Blln, Perc Endo 22, 64, 83, 111, 122, 152, 208, 240, 252, 323
047MØD1	Dilation Rt Popl Art w Intralum Dev, Drug Blln, Opn 22, 63, 83, 111, 122, 152, 208, 240, 252, 323
047M3D1	Dilation Rt Popl Art w Intralum Dev, Drug Blln, Perc 22, 63, 83, 111, 122, 152, 208, 240, 252, 323
047M4D1	Dilation Rt Popl Art w Intralum Dev, Drug Blln, Perc Endo 22, 64, 83, 111, 122, 152, 208, 240, 252, 323
047Ø3[4,D,Z]Z	Dilation/Abd Aorta, Perc, [Drug-eluting Intralum Dev, Intralum Dev, No Dev], NQ 22, 63, 110, 122, 152, 208, 239, 251, 323
ØF7C[Ø,3,4,7][D,Z]Z	Dilation/Ampulla of Vater, [Opn, Perc, Perc Endo, Via Natrl or Artfcl Opng], [Intralum Dev, No Dev], NQ 112, 120, 335
ØD7Q[Ø,3,4][D,Z]Z	Dilation/Anus, [Opn, Perc, Perc Endo], [Intralum Dev, No Dev], NQ 109, 332
027F[3,4][4,D,Z]Z	Dilation/Aortic Valve, [Perc, Perc Endo], [Drug-eluting Intralum Dev, Intralum Dev, No Dev], NQ 75, 98
027FØ[4,D,Z]Z	Dilation/Aortic Valve, Opn, [Drug-eluting Intralum Dev, Intralum Dev, No Dev], NQ 71, 72
ØD7K[Ø,3,4]ZZ	Dilation/Ascending Colon, [Opn, Perc, Perc Endo] 106
057C3[D,Z]Z	Dilation/Basilic Vein, Lt, Perc, [Intralum Dev, No Dev], NQ 22, 64, 111, 122, 152, 209, 240, 252, 325
057B3[D,Z]Z	Dilation/Basilic Vein, Rt, Perc, [Intralum Dev, No Dev], NQ 22, 64, 111, 122, 152, 209, 240, 252, 325
ØT7B*	Dilation/Bladder 248, 268, 353
03783[4,D,Z]Z	Dilation/Brachial Artery, Lt, Perc, [Drug-eluting Intralum Dev, Intralum Dev, No Dev], NQ 21, 63, 110, 122, 152, 208, 239, 251, 320
03773[4,D,Z]Z	Dilation/Brachial Artery, Rt, Perc, [Drug-eluting Intralum Dev, Intralum Dev, No Dev], NQ 21, 63, 110, 122, 152, 208, 239, 251, 320
057A3[D,Z]Z	Dilation/Brachial Vein, Lt, Perc, [Intralum Dev, No Dev], NQ 22, 64, 111, 122, 152, 209, 240, 252, 325
05793[D,Z]Z	Dilation/Brachial Vein, Rt, Perc, [Intralum Dev, No Dev], NQ 22, 64, 111, 122, 152, 209, 240, 252, 325
ØB72*	Dilation/Carina 52, 64, 331
ØD7H[Ø,3,4]ZZ	Dilation/Cecum, [Opn, Perc, Perc Endo] 106
04713[4,D,Z]Z	Dilation/Celiac Artery, Perc, [Drug-eluting Intralum Dev, Intralum Dev, No Dev], NQ 22, 63, 110, 122, 152, 208, 239, 251, 323
057F3[D,Z]Z	Dilation/Cephalic Vein, Lt, Perc, [Intralum Dev, No Dev], NQ 22, 64, 111, 122, 152, 209, 240, 252, 325
057D3[D,Z]Z	Dilation/Cephalic Vein, Rt, Perc, [Intralum Dev, No Dev], NQ 22, 64, 111, 122, 152, 209, 240, 252, 325
04773[4,D,Z]Z	Dilation/Colic Artery, Lt, Perc, [Drug-eluting Intralum Dev, Intralum Dev, No Dev], NQ 22, 63, 110, 122, 152, 208, 239, 251, 323
04783[4,D,Z]Z	Dilation/Colic Artery, Mid, Perc, [Drug-eluting Intralum Dev, Intralum Dev, No Dev], NQ 22, 63, 110, 122, 152, 208, 239, 251, 323
04763[4,D,Z]Z	Dilation/Colic Artery, Rt, Perc, [Drug-eluting Intralum Dev, Intralum Dev, No Dev], NQ 22, 63, 110, 122, 152, 208, 239, 251, 323
ØF79[Ø,7]ZZ	Dilation/Common Bile Duct, [Opn, Via Natrl or Artfcl Opng] 120, 335
037J[3,4][4,D,Z]Z	Dilation/Common Carotid Artery, Lt, [Perc, Perc Endo], [Drug-eluting Intralum Dev, Intralum Dev, No Dev], NQ 20, 21, 320
037J[3,4]DZ	Dilation/Common Carotid Artery, Lt, [Perc, Perc Endo], Intralum Dev, NQ 21
037H[3,4][4,D,Z]Z	Dilation/Common Carotid Artery, Rt, [Perc, Perc Endo], [Drug-eluting Intralum Dev, Intralum Dev, No Dev], NQ 20, 21, 320
037H[3,4]DZ	Dilation/Common Carotid Artery, Rt, [Perc, Perc Endo], Intralum Dev, NQ 21
047D3[4,D,Z]Z	Dilation/Common Iliac Artery, Lt, Perc, [Drug-eluting Intralum Dev, Intralum Dev, No Dev], NQ 22, 63, 110, 122, 152, 208, 239, 251, 323
047C3[4,D,Z]Z	Dilation/Common Iliac Artery, Rt, Perc, [Drug-eluting Intralum Dev, Intralum Dev, No Dev], NQ 22, 63, 110, 122, 152, 208, 239, 251, 323
0273[Ø,3,4][4,D,T][6,Z]	Dilation/Coronary Artery, Four or More Sites, [Opn, Perc, Perc Endo], [Drug-eluting Intralum Dev, Intralum Dev, Radioact Intralum Dev], [Bifurcation, NQ] 78, 79
0273[Ø,3,4][D,T][6,Z]	Dilation/Coronary Artery, Four or More Sites, [Opn, Perc, Perc Endo], [Intralum Dev, Radioact Intralum Dev], [Bifurcation, NQ] 79, 79
0273[Ø,3,4]4[6,Z]	Dilation/Coronary Artery, Four or More Sites, [Opn, Perc, Perc Endo], Drug-eluting Intralum Dev, [Bifurcation, NQ] 78, 79
0273[3,4][4,D,T,Z][6,Z]	Dilation/Coronary Artery, Four or More Sites, [Perc, Perc Endo], [Drug-eluting Intralum Dev, Intralum Dev, Radioact Intralum Dev, No Dev], [Bifurcation, NQ] 75
0273[3,4][4,D,T][6,Z]	Dilation/Coronary Artery, Four or More Sites, [Perc, Perc Endo], [Drug-eluting Intralum Dev, Intralum Dev, Radioact Intralum Dev], [Bifurcation, NQ] 78, 79
0273[3,4]Z[6,Z]	Dilation/Coronary Artery, Four or More Sites, [Perc, Perc Endo], No Dev, [Bifurcation, NQ] 80
0273Ø[4,D,T,Z][6,Z]	Dilation/Coronary Artery, Four or More Sites, Opn, [Drug-eluting Intralum Dev, Intralum Dev, Radioact Intralum Dev, No Dev], [Bifurcation, NQ] 74
027Ø[Ø,3,4][4,D,T][6,Z]	Dilation/Coronary Artery, One Site, [Opn, Perc, Perc Endo], [Drug-eluting Intralum Dev, Intralum Dev, Radioact Intralum Dev], [Bifurcation, NQ] 78, 79
027Ø[Ø,3,4][D,T][6,Z]	Dilation/Coronary Artery, One Site, [Opn, Perc, Perc Endo], [Intralum Dev, Radioact Intralum Dev], [Bifurcation, NQ] 79, 79
027Ø[Ø,3,4]4[6,Z]	Dilation/Coronary Artery, One Site, [Opn, Perc, Perc Endo], Drug-eluting Intralum Dev, [Bifurcation, NQ] 78, 79
027Ø[3,4][4,D,T,Z][6,Z]	Dilation/Coronary Artery, One Site, [Perc, Perc Endo], [Drug-eluting Intralum Dev, Intralum Dev, Radioact Intralum Dev, No Dev], [Bifurcation, NQ] 75
027Ø[3,4][4,D,T][6,Z]	Dilation/Coronary Artery, One Site, [Perc, Perc Endo], [Drug-eluting Intralum Dev, Intralum Dev, Radioact Intralum Dev], [Bifurcation, NQ] 78, 79
027Ø[3,4]Z[6,Z]	Dilation/Coronary Artery, One Site, [Perc, Perc Endo], No Dev, [Bifurcation, NQ] 80
027ØØ[4,D,T,Z][6,Z]	Dilation/Coronary Artery, One Site, Opn, [Drug-eluting Intralum Dev, Intralum Dev, Radioact Intralum Dev, No Dev], [Bifurcation, NQ] 74
0272[Ø,3,4][4,D,T][6,Z]	Dilation/Coronary Artery, Three Sites, [Opn, Perc, Perc Endo], [Drug-eluting Intralum Dev, Intralum Dev, Radioact Intralum Dev], [Bifurcation, NQ] 78, 79, 80
0272[Ø,3,4][D,T][6,Z]	Dilation/Coronary Artery, Three Sites, [Opn, Perc, Perc Endo], [Intralum Dev, Radioact Intralum Dev], [Bifurcation, NQ] 79
0272[Ø,3,4]4[6,Z]	Dilation/Coronary Artery, Three Sites, [Opn, Perc, Perc Endo], Drug-eluting Intralum Dev, [Bifurcation, NQ] 78, 79
0272[3,4][4,D,T,Z][6,Z]	Dilation/Coronary Artery, Three Sites, [Perc, Perc Endo], [Drug-eluting Intralum Dev, Intralum Dev, Radioact Intralum Dev, No Dev], [Bifurcation, NQ] 75

0272[3,4][4,D,T][6,Z]	Dilation/Coronary Artery, Three Sites, [Perc, Perc Endo], [Drug-eluting Intralum Dev, Intralum Dev, Radioact Intralum Dev], [Bifurcation, NQ] 78, 79
0272[3,4]Z[6,Z]	Dilation/Coronary Artery, Three Sites, [Perc, Perc Endo], No Dev, [Bifurcation, NQ] 80
02720[4,D,T,Z][6,Z]	Dilation/Coronary Artery, Three Sites, Opn, [Drug-eluting Intralum Dev, Intralum Dev, Radioact Intralum Dev, No Dev], [Bifurcation, NQ] 74
0271[0,3,4][4,D,T][6,Z]	Dilation/Coronary Artery, Two Sites, [Opn, Perc, Perc Endo], [Drug-eluting Intralum Dev, Intralum Dev, Radioact Intralum Dev], [Bifurcation, NQ] 78, 79, 80
0271[0,3,4][D,T][6,Z]	Dilation/Coronary Artery, Two Sites, [Opn, Perc, Perc Endo], [Intralum Dev, Radioact Intralum Dev], [Bifurcation, NQ] 79, 79
0271[0,3,4]4[6,Z]	Dilation/Coronary Artery, Two Sites, [Opn, Perc, Perc Endo], Drug-eluting Intralum Dev, [Bifurcation, NQ] 78, 79
0271[3,4][4,D,T,Z][6,Z]	Dilation/Coronary Artery, Two Sites, [Perc, Perc Endo], [Drug-eluting Intralum Dev, Intralum Dev, Radioact Intralum Dev, No Dev], [Bifurcation, NQ] 75
0271[3,4][4,D,T][6,Z]	Dilation/Coronary Artery, Two Sites, [Perc, Perc Endo], [Drug-eluting Intralum Dev, Intralum Dev, Radioact Intralum Dev], [Bifurcation, NQ] 78, 79
0271[3,4]Z[6,Z]	Dilation/Coronary Artery, Two Sites, [Perc, Perc Endo], No Dev, [Bifurcation, NQ] 80
02710[4,D,T,Z][6,Z]	Dilation/Coronary Artery, Two Sites, Opn, [Drug-eluting Intralum Dev, Intralum Dev, Radioact Intralum Dev, No Dev], [Bifurcation, NQ] 74
0F78[0,7]ZZ	Dilation/Cystic Duct, [Opn, Via Natrl or Artfcl Opng] 120, 335
0D7M[0,3,4]ZZ	Dilation/Descending Colon, [Opn, Perc, Perc Endo] 106
0D79[0,3,4]ZZ	Dilation/Duodenum, [Opn, Perc, Perc Endo] 106
0D74[0,3,4][D,Z]Z	Dilation/Esophagogastric Junction, [Opn, Perc, Perc Endo], [Intralum Dev, No Dev], NQ 105, 300, 332
0D75[0,3,4][D,Z]Z	Dilation/Esophagus, [Opn, Perc, Perc Endo], [Intralum Dev, No Dev], NQ 105, 300, 332
0D73[0,3,4][D,Z]Z	Dilation/Esophagus, Lwr, [Opn, Perc, Perc Endo], [Intralum Dev, No Dev], NQ 105, 300, 332
0D72[0,3,4][D,Z]Z	Dilation/Esophagus, Mid, [Opn, Perc, Perc Endo], [Intralum Dev, No Dev], NQ 105, 300, 332
0D71[0,3,4][D,Z]Z	Dilation/Esophagus, Upr, [Opn, Perc, Perc Endo], [Intralum Dev, No Dev], NQ 105, 300, 332
037N[3,4][4,D,Z]Z	Dilation/Ext Carotid Artery, Lt, [Perc, Perc Endo], [Drug-eluting Intralum Dev, Intralum Dev, No Dev], NQ 21, 321
037N[3,4]DZ	Dilation/Ext Carotid Artery, Lt, [Perc, Perc Endo], Intralum Dev, NQ 21
037M[3,4][4,D,Z]Z	Dilation/Ext Carotid Artery, Rt, [Perc, Perc Endo], [Drug-eluting Intralum Dev, Intralum Dev, No Dev], NQ 21, 321
037M[3,4]DZ	Dilation/Ext Carotid Artery, Rt, [Perc, Perc Endo], Intralum Dev, NQ 21
047J3[4,D,Z]Z	Dilation/Ext Iliac Artery, Lt, Perc, [Drug-eluting Intralum Dev, Intralum Dev, No Dev], NQ 22, 63, 110, 122, 152, 208, 239, 252, 323
047H3[4,D,Z]Z	Dilation/Ext Iliac Artery, Rt, Perc, [Drug-eluting Intralum Dev, Intralum Dev, No Dev], NQ 22, 63, 110, 122, 152, 208, 239, 252, 323
057Q[3,4]DZ	Dilation/Ext Jugular Vein, Lt, [Perc, Perc Endo], Intralum Dev, NQ 21, 22, 325
057P[3,4]DZ	Dilation/Ext Jugular Vein, Rt, [Perc, Perc Endo], Intralum Dev, NQ 21, 22, 325
057T[3,4]DZ	Dilation/Face Vein, Rt, [Perc, Perc Endo], Intralum Dev, NQ 21, 22, 325
0U76*	Dilation/Fallopian Tube, Lt 262, 263, 265
0U75*	Dilation/Fallopian Tube, Rt 262, 263, 265
0U77*	Dilation/Fallopian Tubes, Bilat 262, 263, 265
047L3[4,D,Z]Z	Dilation/Femor Artery, Lt, Perc, [Drug-eluting Intralum Dev, Intralum Dev, No Dev], NQ 22, 63, 111, 122, 152, 208, 240, 252, 323
047K3[4,D,Z]Z	Dilation/Femor Artery, Rt, Perc, [Drug-eluting Intralum Dev, Intralum Dev, No Dev], NQ 22, 63, 111, 122, 152, 208, 239, 252, 323
04723[4,D,Z]Z	Dilation/Gastric Artery, Perc, [Drug-eluting Intralum Dev, Intralum Dev, No Dev], NQ 22, 63, 110, 122, 152, 208, 239, 251, 323
04733[4,D,Z]Z	Dilation/Hepatic Artery, Perc, [Drug-eluting Intralum Dev, Intralum Dev, No Dev], NQ 22, 63, 110, 122, 152, 208, 239, 251, 323
0F76[0,7]ZZ	Dilation/Hepatic Duct, Lt, [Opn, Via Natrl or Artfcl Opng] 120, 335

0F75[0,7]ZZ	Dilation/Hepatic Duct, Rt, [Opn, Via Natrl or Artfcl Opng] 120, 335
0U7K*	Dilation/Hymen 267, 354
0D7C[0,3,4]ZZ	Dilation/Ileocecal Valve, [Opn, Perc, Perc Endo] 106
0D7B[0,3,4]ZZ	Dilation/Ileum, [Opn, Perc, Perc Endo] 106
047B3[4,D,Z]Z	Dilation/Inferior Mesenteric Artery, Perc, [Drug-eluting Intralum Dev, Intralum Dev, No Dev], NQ 22, 63, 110, 122, 152, 208, 239, 251, 323
06703[D,Z]Z	Dilation/Inferior Vena Cava, Perc, [Intralum Dev, No Dev], NQ 22, 64, 111, 122, 152, 209, 241, 252, 327
037L[3,4][4,D,Z]Z	Dilation/Int Carotid Artery, Lt, [Perc, Perc Endo], [Drug-eluting Intralum Dev, Intralum Dev, No Dev], NQ 21, 321
037L[3,4]DZ	Dilation/Int Carotid Artery, Lt, [Perc, Perc Endo], Intralum Dev, NQ 21
037K[3,4][4,D,Z]Z	Dilation/Int Carotid Artery, Rt, [Perc, Perc Endo], [Drug-eluting Intralum Dev, Intralum Dev, No Dev], NQ 20, 21, 320
037K[3,4]DZ	Dilation/Int Carotid Artery, Rt, [Perc, Perc Endo], Intralum Dev, NQ 21
047F3[4,D,Z]Z	Dilation/Int Iliac Artery, Lt, Perc, [Drug-eluting Intralum Dev, Intralum Dev, No Dev], NQ 22, 63, 110, 122, 152, 208, 239, 251, 323
047E3[4,D,Z]Z	Dilation/Int Iliac Artery, Rt, Perc, [Drug-eluting Intralum Dev, Intralum Dev, No Dev], NQ 22, 63, 110, 122, 152, 208, 239, 251, 323
057N[3,4]DZ	Dilation/Int Jugular Vein, Lt, [Perc, Perc Endo], Intralum Dev, NQ 21, 22, 325
057M[3,4]DZ	Dilation/Int Jugular Vein, Rt, [Perc, Perc Endo], Intralum Dev, NQ 21, 22, 325
037G[3,4][4,D,Z]Z	Dilation/Intracranial Artery, [Perc, Perc Endo], [Drug-eluting Intralum Dev, Intralum Dev, No Dev], NQ 8, 13, 17, 320
057L[3,4]DZ	Dilation/Intracranial Vein, [Perc, Perc Endo], Intralum Dev, NQ 9, 13, 17, 325
0D7A[0,3,4]ZZ	Dilation/Jejunum, [Opn, Perc, Perc Endo] 106
0T74*	Dilation/Kidney Pelvis, Lt 248
0T73*	Dilation/Kidney Pelvis, Rt 248
087Y[0,3,7,8][D,Z]Z	Dilation/Lacrimal Duct, Lt, [Opn, Perc, Via Natrl or Artfcl Opng, Via Natrl or Artfcl Opng Endo], [Intralum Dev, No Dev], NQ 444
087Y[0,3,7,8]DZ	Dilation/Lacrimal Duct, Lt, [Opn, Perc, Via Natrl or Artfcl Opng, Via Natrl or Artfcl Opng Endo], Intralum Dev, NQ 329
087X[0,3,7,8][D,Z]Z	Dilation/Lacrimal Duct, Rt, [Opn, Perc, Via Natrl or Artfcl Opng, Via Natrl or Artfcl Opng Endo], [Intralum Dev, No Dev], NQ 444
087X[0,3,7,8]DZ	Dilation/Lacrimal Duct, Rt, [Opn, Perc, Via Natrl or Artfcl Opng, Via Natrl or Artfcl Opng Endo], Intralum Dev, NQ 329
0C7S*	Dilation/Larynx 52, 65
0C7S[0,3,4,7,8][D,Z]Z	Dilation/Larynx, [Opn, Perc, Perc Endo, Via Natrl or Artfcl Opng, Via Natrl or Artfcl Opng Endo], [Intralum Dev, No Dev], NQ 448
0D7E[0,3,4]ZZ	Dilation/Lg Intestine, [Opn, Perc, Perc Endo] 106
0D7G[0,3,4]ZZ	Dilation/Lg Intestine, Lt, [Opn, Perc, Perc Endo] 106
0D7F[0,3,4]ZZ	Dilation/Lg Intestine, Rt, [Opn, Perc, Perc Endo] 106
047Y3[4,D,Z]Z	Dilation/Lwr Artery, Perc, [Drug-eluting Intralum Dev, Intralum Dev, No Dev], NQ 22, 64, 111, 122, 152, 208, 240, 252, 323
027G[3,4][4,D,Z]Z	Dilation/Mitral Valve, [Perc, Perc Endo], [Drug-eluting Intralum Dev, Intralum Dev, No Dev], NQ 75, 98
027G0[4,D,Z]Z	Dilation/Mitral Valve, Opn, [Drug-eluting Intralum Dev, Intralum Dev, No Dev], NQ 71, 72
0F7D[0,3,7][D,Z]Z	Dilation/Pancreatic Duct, [Opn, Perc, Via Natrl or Artfcl Opng], [Intralum Dev, No Dev], NQ 119, 335
0F7D[0,3,7]DZ	Dilation/Pancreatic Duct, [Opn, Perc, Via Natrl or Artfcl Opng], Intralum Dev, NQ 112, 301
0F7D[0,3]ZZ	Dilation/Pancreatic Duct, [Opn, Perc] 112
0F7F[0,3,7][D,Z]Z	Dilation/Pancreatic Duct, Accessory, [Opn, Perc, Via Natrl or Artfcl Opng], [Intralum Dev, No Dev], NQ 119, 335
0F7F[0,3,7]DZ	Dilation/Pancreatic Duct, Accessory, [Opn, Perc, Via Natrl or Artfcl Opng], Intralum Dev, NQ 112, 301
0F7F[0,3]ZZ	Dilation/Pancreatic Duct, Accessory, [Opn, Perc] 112
027R[0,3,4][4,D,Z]T	Dilation/Pulmn Artery, Lt, [Opn, Perc, Perc Endo], [Drug-eluting Intralum Dev, Intralum Dev, No Dev], Ductus Arteriosus 93, 319
027R[0,3,4][4,D,Z]Z	Dilation/Pulmn Artery, Lt, [Opn, Perc, Perc Endo], [Drug-eluting Intralum Dev, Intralum Dev, No Dev], NQ 80
027Q*	Dilation/Pulmn Artery, Rt 80
027P*	Dilation/Pulmn Trunk 80

027H[3,4][4,D,Z]Z	Dilation/Pulmn Valve, [Perc, Perc Endo], [Drug-eluting Intralum Dev, Intralum Dev, No Dev], NQ 75, 98
027H0[4,D,Z]Z	Dilation/Pulmn Valve, Opn, [Drug-eluting Intralum Dev, Intralum Dev, No Dev], NQ 71, 72
027T*	Dilation/Pulmn Vein, Lt 80
027S*	Dilation/Pulmn Vein, Rt 80
0D7P[0,3,4][D,Z]Z	Dilation/Rectum, [Opn, Perc, Perc Endo], [Intralum Dev, No Dev], NQ 106
047A3[4,D,Z]Z	Dilation/Renal Artery, Lt, Perc, [Drug-eluting Intralum Dev, Intralum Dev, No Dev], NQ 22, 63, 110, 122, 152, 208, 239, 251, 323
04793[4,D,Z]Z	Dilation/Renal Artery, Rt, Perc, [Drug-eluting Intralum Dev, Intralum Dev, No Dev], NQ 22, 63, 110, 122, 152, 208, 239, 251, 323
0D7N[0,3,4]ZZ	Dilation/Sigmoid Colon, [Opn, Perc, Perc Endo] 106
0D78[0,3,4]ZZ	Dilation/Sm Intestine, [Opn, Perc, Perc Endo] 106
04743[4,D,Z]Z	Dilation/Splenic Artery, Perc, [Drug-eluting Intralum Dev, Intralum Dev, No Dev], NQ 22, 63, 110, 122, 208, 239, 251, 323
0D76*	Dilation/Stomach 105, 235, 332
0D77[0,3,7]DZ	Dilation/Stomach, Pylorus, [Opn, Perc, Via Natrl or Artfcl Opng], Intralum Dev, NQ 105
03743[4,D,Z]Z	Dilation/Subclavian Artery, Lt, Perc, [Drug-eluting Intralum Dev, Intralum Dev, No Dev], NQ 21, 63, 110, 122, 152, 208, 239, 251, 320
03733[4,D,Z]Z	Dilation/Subclavian Artery, Rt, Perc, [Drug-eluting Intralum Dev, Intralum Dev, No Dev], NQ 21, 63, 110, 122, 152, 208, 239, 251, 320
04753[4,D,Z]Z	Dilation/Superior Mesenteric Artery, Perc, [Drug-eluting Intralum Dev, Intralum Dev, No Dev], NQ 22, 63, 110, 122, 152, 208, 239, 251, 323
027V*	Dilation/Superior Vena Cava 80
027W*	Dilation/Thoracic Aorta 80
0B71*	Dilation/Trachea 52, 64, 331
0D7L[0,3,4]ZZ	Dilation/Transv Colon, [Opn, Perc, Perc Endo] 106
027J[3,4][4,D,Z]Z	Dilation/Tricuspid Valve, [Perc, Perc Endo], [Drug-eluting Intralum Dev, Intralum Dev, No Dev], NQ 75, 98
027J0[4,D,Z]Z	Dilation/Tricuspid Valve, Opn, [Drug-eluting Intralum Dev, Intralum Dev, No Dev], NQ 71, 72
037A3[4,D,Z]Z	Dilation/Ulnar Artery, Lt, Perc, [Drug-eluting Intralum Dev, Intralum Dev, No Dev], NQ 21, 63, 110, 122, 152, 208, 239, 251, 320
03793[4,D,Z]Z	Dilation/Ulnar Artery, Rt, Perc, [Drug-eluting Intralum Dev, Intralum Dev, No Dev], NQ 21, 63, 110, 122, 152, 208, 239, 251, 320
037Y3[4,D,Z]Z	Dilation/Upr Artery, Perc, [Drug-eluting Intralum Dev, Intralum Dev, No Dev], NQ 21, 63, 110, 122, 152, 208, 239, 251, 321
0T77[0,3,4,7,8]ZZ	Dilation/Ureter, Lt, [Opn, Perc, Perc Endo, Via Natrl or Artfcl Opng, Via Natrl or Artfcl Opng Endo] 248, 353, 458
0T76[0,3,4,7,8]ZZ	Dilation/Ureter, Rt, [Opn, Perc, Perc Endo, Via Natrl or Artfcl Opng, Via Natrl or Artfcl Opng Endo] 248, 353, 458
0T78[0,3,4]ZZ	Dilation/Ureters, Bilat, [Opn, Perc, Perc Endo] 248, 353
0T7D[0,3,4]ZZ	Dilation/Urethra, [Opn, Perc, Perc Endo] 250, 259, 353, 458
0U79*	Dilation/Uterus 262, 263, 265, 271, 354
0U7G[0,3,4][D,Z]Z	Dilation/Vagina, [Opn, Perc, Perc Endo], [Intralum Dev, No Dev], NQ 267, 354
027K*	Dilation/Ventricle, Rt 319
027K[0,3,4][4,D,Z]Z	Dilation/Ventricle, Rt, [Opn, Perc, Perc Endo], [Drug-eluting Intralum Dev, Intralum Dev, No Dev], NQ 93
037Q[3,4][4,D,Z]Z	Dilation/Vert Artery, Lt, [Perc, Perc Endo], [Drug-eluting Intralum Dev, Intralum Dev, No Dev], NQ 21, 321
037P[3,4][4,D,Z]Z	Dilation/Vert Artery, Rt, [Perc, Perc Endo], [Drug-eluting Intralum Dev, Intralum Dev, No Dev], NQ 21, 321
057S[3,4]DZ	Dilation/Vert Vein, Lt, [Perc, Perc Endo], Intralum Dev, NQ 21, 22, 325
057R[3,4]DZ	Dilation/Vert Vein, Rt, [Perc, Perc Endo], Intralum Dev, NQ 21, 22, 325
0H8[B,C,D,E,F,G]XZZ	Div [Rt Upr Arm, Lt Upr Arm, Rt Lwr Arm, Lt Lwr Arm, Rt Hand, Lt Hand], Ext 25
0H8[0,1,4,5,6,7,8,A]XZZ	Div [Scalp, Face, Neck, Chest, Back, Abd, Buttock, Genitalia] Skin, Ext 25, 113, 126, 206
0H8[7,8,A]XZZ	Div of [Abd, Buttock, Genitalia] Skin, Ext Appr 90
0H8[B,C,D,E]XZZ	Div of [Rt Upr Arm, Lt Upr Arm, Rt Lwr Arm, Lt Lwr Arm] Skin, Ext Appr 90, 113, 126

0H8[F,G]XZZ	Div of [Rt, Lt] Hand Skin, Ext Appr 149
0H8[0,1,4]XZZ	Div of [Scalp, Face, Neck] Skin, Ext Appr 53
0H87XZZ	Div of Abd Skin, Ext Appr 236, 313
0H86XZZ	Div of Back Skin, Ext Appr 236, 313
0H88XZZ	Div of Buttock Skin, Ext Appr 236, 313
0H85XZZ	Div of Chest Skin, Ext Appr 236, 313
0H81XZZ	Div of Face Skin, Ext Appr 236, 313, 377, 380
0H8AXZZ	Div of Genitalia Skin, Ext Appr 236, 313
0H8NXZZ	Div of Lt Foot Skin, Ext Appr 236, 313
0H8GXZZ	Div of Lt Hand Skin, Ext Appr 236, 313
0H8EXZZ	Div of Lt Lwr Arm Skin, Ext Appr 236, 313
0H8LXZZ	Div of Lt Lwr Leg Skin, Ext Appr 236, 313
0H8CXZZ	Div of Lt Upr Arm Skin, Ext Appr 236, 313
0H8JXZZ	Div of Lt Upr Leg Skin, Ext Appr 236, 313
0H84XZZ	Div of Neck Skin, Ext Appr 236, 313, 377, 380
0H89XZZ	Div of Perineum Skin, Ext Appr 110, 211, 266, 274, 336, 449
0H8MXZZ	Div of Rt Foot Skin, Ext Appr 236, 313
0H8FXZZ	Div of Rt Hand Skin, Ext Appr 236, 313
0H8DXZZ	Div of Rt Lwr Arm Skin, Ext Appr 236, 313
0H8KXZZ	Div of Rt Lwr Leg Skin, Ext Appr 236, 313
0N850ZZ	Div of Rt Temporal Bone, Opn Appr 9
0N853ZZ	Div of Rt Temporal Bone, Perc Appr 9
0N854ZZ	Div of Rt Temporal Bone, Perc Endo Appr 9
0H8BXZZ	Div of Rt Upr Arm Skin, Ext Appr 236, 313
0H8HXZZ	Div of Rt Upr Leg Skin, Ext Appr 236, 313
0H80XZZ	Div of Scalp Skin, Ext Appr 236, 313, 377, 380
0H8[B,C,D,E,F,G]XZZ	Div of Skin of [Rt Upr Arm, Lt Upr Arm, Rt Lwr Arm, Lt Lwr Arm, Rt Hand, Lt Hand], Ext 206
0H8[H,J,K,L,M,N]XZZ	Div of Skin of [Rt Upr Leg, Lt Upr Leg, Rt Lwr Leg, Lt Lwr Leg, Rt Foot, Lt Foot], Ext 25, 90, 113, 126, 206
0H8[0,1,4,5,6]XZZ	Div of Skin of [Scalp, Face, Neck, Chest, Back], Ext 90
0M8J*	Div/Abd Bursa & Lgmt, Lt 143, 342
0M8J[0,3,4]ZZ	Div/Abd Bursa & Lgmt, Lt, [Opn, Perc, Perc Endo] 453
0M8H*	Div/Abd Bursa & Lgmt, Rt 143, 342
0M8H[0,3,4]ZZ	Div/Abd Bursa & Lgmt, Rt, [Opn, Perc, Perc Endo] 453
0K8L*	Div/Abd Muscle, Lt 27, 138, 338
0K8K*	Div/Abd Muscle, Rt 27, 138, 338
018M*	Div/Abd Sympathetic Nerve 24, 89, 235
0L8G*	Div/Abd Tndn, Lt 28, 141, 243, 340
0L8G[0,3,4]ZZ	Div/Abd Tndn, Lt, [Opn, Perc, Perc Endo] 452
0L8F*	Div/Abd Tndn, Rt 28, 141, 243, 340
0L8F[0,3,4]ZZ	Div/Abd Tndn, Rt, [Opn, Perc, Perc Endo] 452
008L*	Div/Abducens Nerve 23, 50, 151, 317
008R*	Div/Accessory Nerve 23, 50, 151, 317
0Q85*	Div/Acetabulum, Lt 156
0Q84*	Div/Acetabulum, Rt 156
008N*	Div/Acoustic Nerve 23, 50, 151, 317
0D8R*	Div/Anal Sphincter 109, 274
0D8R[0,3]ZZ	Div/Anal Sphincter, [Opn, Perc] 449
0M8R*	Div/Ankle Bursa & Lgmt, Lt 143, 342
0M8R[0,3,4]ZZ	Div/Ankle Bursa & Lgmt, Lt, [Opn, Perc, Perc Endo] 453
0M8Q*	Div/Ankle Bursa & Lgmt, Rt 143, 342
0M8Q[0,3,4]ZZ	Div/Ankle Bursa & Lgmt, Rt, [Opn, Perc, Perc Endo] 453
0L8T*	Div/Ankle Tndn, Lt 28, 141, 243, 340
0L8T[0,3,4]ZZ	Div/Ankle Tndn, Lt, [Opn, Perc, Perc Endo] 452
0L8S*	Div/Ankle Tndn, Rt 28, 141, 243, 340
0L8S[0,3,4]ZZ	Div/Ankle Tndn, Rt, [Opn, Perc, Perc Endo] 452
0088*	Div/Basal Ganglia 8, 414
0088[0,3,4]ZZ	Div/Basal Ganglia, [Opn, Perc, Perc Endo] 12, 16, 295
0T8C*	Div/Bladder Neck 249
0T8C[0,3,4]ZZ	Div/Bladder Neck, [Opn, Perc, Perc Endo] 458
0183*	Div/Brachial Plexus 24, 151, 318
0080*	Div/Brain 8, 317, 414
0080[0,3,4]ZZ	Div/Brain, [Opn, Perc, Perc Endo] 12, 16, 295
0P8N*	Div/Carpal, Lt 150
0P8N[0,3,4]ZZ	Div/Carpal, Lt, [Opn, Perc, Perc Endo] 315
0P8M*	Div/Carpal, Rt 150
0P8M[0,3,4]ZZ	Div/Carpal, Rt, [Opn, Perc, Perc Endo] 315
0087*	Div/Cerebral Hemisphere 8, 317, 414
0087[0,3,4]ZZ	Div/Cerebral Hemisphere, [Opn, Perc, Perc Endo] 12, 16, 295

0181*	Div/Cervical Nerve 159, 160, 318
0181[0,3,4]ZZ	Div/Cervical Nerve, [Opn, Perc, Perc Endo] 19, 296
0180*	Div/Cervical Plexus 24, 151, 318
008W*	Div/Cervical Spinal Cord 121, 317
008W[0,3,4]ZZ	Div/Cervical Spinal Cord, [Opn, Perc, Perc Endo] 19, 295
0P83*	Div/Cervical Vertebra 155, 345
0289[0,3,4]ZZ	Div/Chordae Tendineae, [Opn, Perc, Perc Endo] 74
0P8B*	Div/Clavicle, Lt 65, 155, 345
0P89*	Div/Clavicle, Rt 65, 155, 345
0Q8S*	Div/Coccyx 156
0288[0,3,4]ZZ	Div/Conduction Mech, [Opn, Perc, Perc Endo] 93
0M84*	Div/Elbow Bursa & Lgmt, Lt 143, 342
0M84[0,3,4]ZZ	Div/Elbow Bursa & Lgmt, Lt, [Opn, Perc, Perc Endo] 453
0M83*	Div/Elbow Bursa & Lgmt, Rt 143, 342
0M83[0,3,4]ZZ	Div/Elbow Bursa & Lgmt, Rt, [Opn, Perc, Perc Endo] 453
0D84*	Div/Esophagogastric Junction 53, 105, 332
0D84[0,3,4,7,8]ZZ	Div/Esophagogastric Junction, [Opn, Perc, Perc Endo, Via Natrl or Artfcl Opng, Via Natrl or Artfcl Opng Endo] 300
0N8G*	Div/Ethmoid Bone, Lt 54
0N8F*	Div/Ethmoid Bone, Rt 54
0K81*	Div/Facial Muscle 27, 138, 338
008M*	Div/Facial Nerve 23, 50, 151, 317
018D*	Div/Femor Nerve 24, 151, 318
0Q89*	Div/Femor Shaft, Lt 130, 415
0Q88*	Div/Femor Shaft, Rt 130, 415
0Q8K*	Div/Fibula, Lt 133, 244
0Q8J*	Div/Fibula, Rt 133, 244
0P8V*	Div/Finger Phalanx, Lt 155, 345
0P8T*	Div/Finger Phalanx, Rt 155, 345
0M8T*	Div/Foot Bursa & Lgmt, Lt 143, 342
0M8T[0,3,4]ZZ	Div/Foot Bursa & Lgmt, Lt, [Opn, Perc, Perc Endo] 453
0M8S*	Div/Foot Bursa & Lgmt, Rt 143, 342
0M8S[0,3,4]ZZ	Div/Foot Bursa & Lgmt, Rt, [Opn, Perc, Perc Endo] 453
0K8W*	Div/Foot Muscle, Lt 27, 138, 338
0K8V*	Div/Foot Muscle, Rt 27, 138, 338
0L8W*	Div/Foot Tndn, Lt 28, 141, 243, 340
0L8W[0,3,4]ZZ	Div/Foot Tndn, Lt, [Opn, Perc, Perc Endo] 452
0L8V*	Div/Foot Tndn, Rt 28, 141, 243, 340
0L8V[0,3,4]ZZ	Div/Foot Tndn, Rt, [Opn, Perc, Perc Endo] 452
0N82[0,3,4]ZZ	Div/Frontal Bone, Lt, [Opn, Perc, Perc Endo] 9, 13, 17
0N81[0,3,4]ZZ	Div/Frontal Bone, Rt, [Opn, Perc, Perc Endo] 9, 13, 17
0P88*	Div/Glenoid Cavity, Lt 65, 155, 345
0P87*	Div/Glenoid Cavity, Rt 65, 155, 345
008P*	Div/Glossopharyngeal Nerve 8, 50
008P[0,3,4]ZZ	Div/Glossopharyngeal Nerve, [Opn, Perc, Perc Endo] 12, 16
0M88*	Div/Hand Bursa & Lgmt, Lt 150
0M88[0,3,4]ZZ	Div/Hand Bursa & Lgmt, Lt, [Opn, Perc, Perc Endo] 315
0M87*	Div/Hand Bursa & Lgmt, Rt 150
0M87[0,3,4]ZZ	Div/Hand Bursa & Lgmt, Rt, [Opn, Perc, Perc Endo] 315
0K8D*	Div/Hand Muscle, Lt 149
0K8D[0,3,4]ZZ	Div/Hand Muscle, Lt, [Opn, Perc, Perc Endo] 314
0K8C*	Div/Hand Muscle, Rt 149
0K8C[0,3,4]ZZ	Div/Hand Muscle, Rt, [Opn, Perc, Perc Endo] 314
0L88*	Div/Hand Tndn, Lt 149
0L88[0,3,4]ZZ	Div/Hand Tndn, Lt, [Opn, Perc, Perc Endo] 314, 452
0L87*	Div/Hand Tndn, Rt 149
0L87[0,3,4]ZZ	Div/Hand Tndn, Rt, [Opn, Perc, Perc Endo] 314, 452
0M80*	Div/Head and Neck Bursa & Lgmt 143, 342
0M80[0,3,4]ZZ	Div/Head and Neck Bursa & Lgmt, [Opn, Perc, Perc Endo] 453
018K*	Div/Head and Neck Sympathetic Nerve 24, 89
0L80*	Div/Head and Neck Tndn 28, 141, 243, 340
0L80[0,3,4]ZZ	Div/Head and Neck Tndn, [Opn, Perc, Perc Endo] 452
0K80*	Div/Head Muscle 27, 138, 338
0M8M*	Div/Hip Bursa & Lgmt, Lt 143, 342
0M8M[0,3,4]ZZ	Div/Hip Bursa & Lgmt, Lt, [Opn, Perc, Perc Endo] 453
0M8L*	Div/Hip Bursa & Lgmt, Rt 143, 342
0M8L[0,3,4]ZZ	Div/Hip Bursa & Lgmt, Rt, [Opn, Perc, Perc Endo] 453
0K8P*	Div/Hip Muscle, Lt 27, 138, 338
0K8N*	Div/Hip Muscle, Rt 27, 138, 338
0L8K*	Div/Hip Tndn, Lt 130, 340, 415
0L8J*	Div/Hip Tndn, Rt 130, 340, 415
0P8D*	Div/Humeral Head, Lt 132, 345
0P8C*	Div/Humeral Head, Rt 132, 345
0P8G*	Div/Humeral Shaft, Lt 132, 345
0P8F*	Div/Humeral Shaft, Rt 132, 345
0N8X*	Div/Hyoid Bone 54
008S*	Div/Hypoglossal Nerve 23, 50, 151, 317
0T82*	Div/Kidneys, Bilat 248
0M8P*	Div/Knee Bursa & Lgmt, Lt 143, 342
0M8P[0,3,4]ZZ	Div/Knee Bursa & Lgmt, Lt, [Opn, Perc, Perc Endo] 453
0M8N*	Div/Knee Bursa & Lgmt, Rt 143, 342
0M8N[0,3,4]ZZ	Div/Knee Bursa & Lgmt, Rt, [Opn, Perc, Perc Endo] 453
0L8R*	Div/Knee Tndn, Lt 28, 141, 243, 340
0L8R[0,3,4]ZZ	Div/Knee Tndn, Lt, [Opn, Perc, Perc Endo] 452
0L8Q*	Div/Knee Tndn, Rt 28, 141, 243, 340
0L8Q[0,3,4]ZZ	Div/Knee Tndn, Rt, [Opn, Perc, Perc Endo] 452
0N8J*	Div/Lacrimal Bone, Lt 54
0N8H*	Div/Lacrimal Bone, Rt 54
018B*	Div/Lumbar Nerve 159, 160, 318
018B[0,3,4]ZZ	Div/Lumbar Nerve, [Opn, Perc, Perc Endo] 19, 296
0189*	Div/Lumbar Plexus 24, 151, 318
008Y*	Div/Lumbar Spinal Cord 121, 317
008Y[0,3,4]ZZ	Div/Lumbar Spinal Cord, [Opn, Perc, Perc Endo] 19, 295
018N*	Div/Lumbar Sympathetic Nerve 24, 89
0Q80*	Div/Lumbar Vertebra 156
018A*	Div/Lumbosacral Plexus 24, 151, 318
0K8B*	Div/Lwr Arm and Wrist Muscle, Lt 27, 138, 338
0K89*	Div/Lwr Arm and Wrist Muscle, Rt 27, 138, 338
0L86*	Div/Lwr Arm and Wrist Tndn, Lt 28, 141, 243, 340
0L86[0,3,4]ZZ	Div/Lwr Arm and Wrist Tndn, Lt, [Opn, Perc, Perc Endo] 452
0L85*	Div/Lwr Arm and Wrist Tndn, Rt 28, 141, 243, 340
0L85[0,3,4]ZZ	Div/Lwr Arm and Wrist Tndn, Rt, [Opn, Perc, Perc Endo] 452
0M8W*	Div/Lwr Extr Bursa & Lgmt, Lt 143, 342
0M8W[0,3,4]ZZ	Div/Lwr Extr Bursa & Lgmt, Lt, [Opn, Perc, Perc Endo] 453
0M8V*	Div/Lwr Extr Bursa & Lgmt, Rt 143, 342
0M8V[0,3,4]ZZ	Div/Lwr Extr Bursa & Lgmt, Rt, [Opn, Perc, Perc Endo] 453
0Q8C*	Div/Lwr Femur, Lt 130, 415
0Q8B*	Div/Lwr Femur, Rt 130, 415
0K8T*	Div/Lwr Leg Muscle, Lt 27, 138, 338
0K8S*	Div/Lwr Leg Muscle, Rt 27, 138, 338
0L8P*	Div/Lwr Leg Tndn, Lt 145, 340
0L8N*	Div/Lwr Leg Tndn, Rt 145, 340
0N8V*	Div/Mandible, Lt 54
0N8T*	Div/Mandible, Rt 54
0N8S*	Div/Maxilla, Lt 54
0N8R*	Div/Maxilla, Rt 54
0185*	Div/Median Nerve 24, 151, 318
0P8Q*	Div/Metacarpal, Lt 150
0P8Q[0,3,4]ZZ	Div/Metacarpal, Lt, [Opn, Perc, Perc Endo] 315
0P8P*	Div/Metacarpal, Rt 150
0P8P[0,3,4]ZZ	Div/Metacarpal, Rt, [Opn, Perc, Perc Endo] 315
0Q8P*	Div/Metatarsal, Lt 145, 244
0Q8P[0,3,4]ZZ	Div/Metatarsal, Lt, [Opn, Perc, Perc Endo] 456, 462
0Q8N*	Div/Metatarsal, Rt 145, 244
0Q8N[0,3,4]ZZ	Div/Metatarsal, Rt, [Opn, Perc, Perc Endo] 456, 462
098L*	Div/Nasal Turbinate 330
098L[0,3,4,7,8]ZZ	Div/Nasal Turbinate, [Opn, Perc, Perc Endo, Via Natrl or Artfcl Opng, Via Natrl or Artfcl Opng Endo] 446
0K83*	Div/Neck Muscle, Lt 27, 138, 338
0K82*	Div/Neck Muscle, Rt 27, 138, 338
0N88[0,3,4]ZZ	Div/Occipital Bone, Lt, [Opn, Perc, Perc Endo] 9, 13, 17
0N87[0,3,4]ZZ	Div/Occipital Bone, Rt, [Opn, Perc, Perc Endo] 9, 13, 17
008H*	Div/Oculomotor Nerve 23, 50, 151, 317
008F*	Div/Olfactory Nerve 23, 50, 151, 317
008G*	Div/Optic Nerve 23, 50, 151, 317
0N8Q*	Div/Orbit, Lt 42, 48, 343
0N8Q[0,3,4]ZZ	Div/Orbit, Lt, [Opn, Perc, Perc Endo] 454
0N8P*	Div/Orbit, Rt 42, 48, 343
0N8P[0,3,4]ZZ	Div/Orbit, Rt, [Opn, Perc, Perc Endo] 454
0U82*	Div/Ovaries, Bilat 262, 263, 265

0U81*	Div/Ovary, Lt 262, 263, 265
0U80*	Div/Ovary, Rt 262, 263, 265
0N8L*	Div/Palatine Bone, Lt 54
0N8K*	Div/Palatine Bone, Rt 54
0F8G[0,3]ZZ	Div/Pancreas, [Opn, Perc] 106, 335
028D[0,3,4]ZZ	Div/Papillary Muscle, [Opn, Perc, Perc Endo] 74
0N84[0,3,4]ZZ	Div/Parietal Bone, Lt, [Opn, Perc, Perc Endo] 9, 13, 17
0N83[0,3,4]ZZ	Div/Parietal Bone, Rt, [Opn, Perc, Perc Endo] 9, 13, 17
0Q8F*	Div/Patella, Lt 132
0Q8D*	Div/Patella, Rt 132
0Q83*	Div/Pelvic Bone, Lt 156, 271
0Q82*	Div/Pelvic Bone, Rt 156, 271
0M8K*	Div/Perineum Bursa & Lgmt 143, 342
0M8K[0,3,4]ZZ	Div/Perineum Bursa & Lgmt, [Opn, Perc, Perc Endo] 453
0K8M*	Div/Perineum Muscle 27, 138, 338
0L8H*	Div/Perineum Tndn 28, 141, 243, 340
0L8H[0,3,4]ZZ	Div/Perineum Tndn, [Opn, Perc, Perc Endo] 452
018H*	Div/Peroneal Nerve 24, 151, 318
0182*	Div/Phrenic Nerve 24, 151, 318
0G80*	Div/Pituitary Gland 235
0G80[0,3,4]ZZ	Div/Pituitary Gland, [Opn, Perc, Perc Endo] 9, 13, 17
018C*	Div/Pudendal Nerve 24, 151, 318
0186*	Div/Radial Nerve 24, 151, 318
0P8J*	Div/Radius, Lt 148, 345
0P8H*	Div/Radius, Rt 148, 345
0P82*	Div/Rib, Lt 65, 155, 345
0P81*	Div/Rib, Rt 65, 155, 345
018R*	Div/Sacral Nerve 159, 160, 318
018R[0,3,4]ZZ	Div/Sacral Nerve, [Opn, Perc, Perc Endo] 19, 296
018Q*	Div/Sacral Plexus 24, 151, 318
018P*	Div/Sacral Sympathetic Nerve 24, 89
0Q81*	Div/Sacrum 156
0P86*	Div/Scapula, Lt 65, 155, 345
0P85*	Div/Scapula, Rt 65, 155, 345
018F*	Div/Sciatic Nerve 24, 151, 318
0M82*	Div/Shldr Bursa & Lgmt, Lt 143, 342
0M82[0,3,4]ZZ	Div/Shldr Bursa & Lgmt, Lt, [Opn, Perc, Perc Endo] 453
0M81*	Div/Shldr Bursa & Lgmt, Rt 143, 342
0M81[0,3,4]ZZ	Div/Shldr Bursa & Lgmt, Rt, [Opn, Perc, Perc Endo] 453
0K86*	Div/Shldr Muscle, Lt 27, 138, 338
0K85*	Div/Shldr Muscle, Rt 27, 138, 338
0L82*	Div/Shldr Tndn, Lt 28, 141, 243, 340
0L82[0,3,4]ZZ	Div/Shldr Tndn, Lt, [Opn, Perc, Perc Endo] 452
0L81*	Div/Shldr Tndn, Rt 28, 141, 243, 340
0L81[0,3,4]ZZ	Div/Shldr Tndn, Rt, [Opn, Perc, Perc Endo] 452
0N80[0,3,4]ZZ	Div/Skull, [Opn, Perc, Perc Endo] 9, 13, 17
0N8D*	Div/Sphenoid Bone, Lt 54
0N8C*	Div/Sphenoid Bone, Rt 54
0J88*	Div/SQ Tissue & Fascia, Abd 26, 137, 337
0J88[0,3]ZZ	Div/SQ Tissue & Fascia, Abd, [Opn, Perc] 212
0J84*	Div/SQ Tissue & Fascia, Ant Neck 26, 137, 337
0J84[0,3]ZZ	Div/SQ Tissue & Fascia, Ant Neck, [Opn, Perc] 212
0J87*	Div/SQ Tissue & Fascia, Back 26, 137, 337
0J87[0,3]ZZ	Div/SQ Tissue & Fascia, Back, [Opn, Perc] 212
0J89*	Div/SQ Tissue & Fascia, Buttock 26, 137, 337
0J89[0,3]ZZ	Div/SQ Tissue & Fascia, Buttock, [Opn, Perc] 212
0J86*	Div/SQ Tissue & Fascia, Chest 26, 137, 337
0J86[0,3]ZZ	Div/SQ Tissue & Fascia, Chest, [Opn, Perc] 212
0J81*	Div/SQ Tissue & Fascia, Face 42, 48, 337
0J81[0,3]ZZ	Div/SQ Tissue & Fascia, Face, [Opn, Perc] 450
0J8C[0,3]ZZ	Div/SQ Tissue & Fascia, Genitalia, [Opn, Perc] 212
0J8S*	Div/SQ Tissue & Fascia, Head and Neck 26, 137, 337
0J8S[0,3]ZZ	Div/SQ Tissue & Fascia, Head and Neck, [Opn, Perc] 212
0J8R*	Div/SQ Tissue & Fascia, Lt Foot 26, 137, 337
0J8R[0,3]ZZ	Div/SQ Tissue & Fascia, Lt Foot, [Opn, Perc] 212
0J8K*	Div/SQ Tissue & Fascia, Lt Hand 149
0J8K[0,3]ZZ	Div/SQ Tissue & Fascia, Lt Hand, [Opn, Perc] 212, 314, 450
0J8H*	Div/SQ Tissue & Fascia, Lt Lwr Arm 26, 137, 337
0J8H[0,3]ZZ	Div/SQ Tissue & Fascia, Lt Lwr Arm, [Opn, Perc] 212
0J8P*	Div/SQ Tissue & Fascia, Lt Lwr Leg 26, 137, 337
0J8P[0,3]ZZ	Div/SQ Tissue & Fascia, Lt Lwr Leg, [Opn, Perc] 212
0J8F*	Div/SQ Tissue & Fascia, Lt Upr Arm 26, 137, 337
0J8F[0,3]ZZ	Div/SQ Tissue & Fascia, Lt Upr Arm, [Opn, Perc] 212
0J8M*	Div/SQ Tissue & Fascia, Lt Upr Leg 26, 137, 337
0J8M[0,3]ZZ	Div/SQ Tissue & Fascia, Lt Upr Leg, [Opn, Perc] 212
0J8W*	Div/SQ Tissue & Fascia, Lwr Extr 26, 137, 337
0J8W[0,3]ZZ	Div/SQ Tissue & Fascia, Lwr Extr, [Opn, Perc] 212
0J8C*	Div/SQ Tissue & Fascia, Pelvic Region 26, 137, 337
0J8B*	Div/SQ Tissue & Fascia, Perineum 26, 137, 337
0J8B[0,3]ZZ	Div/SQ Tissue & Fascia, Perineum, [Opn, Perc] 212
0J85[0,3]ZZ	Div/SQ Tissue & Fascia, Post Neck, [Opn, Perc] 212
0J85*	Div/SQ Tissue & Fascia, Posterior Neck 26, 137, 337
0J8Q*	Div/SQ Tissue & Fascia, Rt Foot 26, 137, 337
0J8Q[0,3]ZZ	Div/SQ Tissue & Fascia, Rt Foot, [Opn, Perc] 212
0J8J*	Div/SQ Tissue & Fascia, Rt Hand 149
0J8J[0,3]ZZ	Div/SQ Tissue & Fascia, Rt Hand, [Opn, Perc] 212, 314, 450
0J8G*	Div/SQ Tissue & Fascia, Rt Lwr Arm 26, 137, 337
0J8G[0,3]ZZ	Div/SQ Tissue & Fascia, Rt Lwr Arm, [Opn, Perc] 212
0J8N*	Div/SQ Tissue & Fascia, Rt Lwr Leg 26, 137, 337
0J8N[0,3]ZZ	Div/SQ Tissue & Fascia, Rt Lwr Leg, [Opn, Perc] 212
0J8D*	Div/SQ Tissue & Fascia, Rt Upr Arm 26, 137, 337
0J8D[0,3]ZZ	Div/SQ Tissue & Fascia, Rt Upr Arm, [Opn, Perc] 212
0J8L*	Div/SQ Tissue & Fascia, Rt Upr Leg 26, 137, 337
0J8L[0,3]ZZ	Div/SQ Tissue & Fascia, Rt Upr Leg, [Opn, Perc] 212
0J80*	Div/SQ Tissue & Fascia, Scalp 26, 137, 337
0J80[0,3]ZZ	Div/SQ Tissue & Fascia, Scalp, [Opn, Perc] 212
0J8T*	Div/SQ Tissue & Fascia, Trunk 26, 137, 337
0J8T[0,3]ZZ	Div/SQ Tissue & Fascia, Trunk, [Opn, Perc] 212
0J8V*	Div/SQ Tissue & Fascia, Upr Extr 26, 137, 337
0J8V[0,3]ZZ	Div/SQ Tissue & Fascia, Upr Extr, [Opn, Perc] 212
0P80*	Div/Sternum 65, 155, 345
0D87[0,3,4,7,8]ZZ	Div/Stomach, Pylorus, [Opn, Perc, Perc Endo, Via Natrl or Artfcl Opng, Via Natrl or Artfcl Opng Endo] 105
0Q8M*	Div/Tarsal, Lt 145, 244
0Q8M[0,3,4]ZZ	Div/Tarsal, Lt, [Opn, Perc, Perc Endo] 456
0Q8L*	Div/Tarsal, Rt 145, 244
0Q8L[0,3,4]ZZ	Div/Tarsal, Rt, [Opn, Perc, Perc Endo] 456
0N86[0,3,4]ZZ	Div/Temporal Bone, Lt, [Opn, Perc, Perc Endo] 9, 13, 17
0N85[0,3,4]ZZ	Div/Temporal Bone, Rt, [Opn, Perc, Perc Endo] 13, 17
0188*	Div/Thoracic Nerve 159, 160, 318
0188[0,3,4]ZZ	Div/Thoracic Nerve, [Opn, Perc, Perc Endo] 19, 296
008X*	Div/Thoracic Spinal Cord 121, 317
008X[0,3,4]ZZ	Div/Thoracic Spinal Cord, [Opn, Perc, Perc Endo] 19, 295
018L*	Div/Thoracic Sympathetic Nerve 24, 89
0P84*	Div/Thoracic Vertebra 155, 345
0M8G*	Div/Thorax Bursa & Lgmt, Lt 143, 342
0M8G[0,3,4]ZZ	Div/Thorax Bursa & Lgmt, Lt, [Opn, Perc, Perc Endo] 453
0M8F*	Div/Thorax Bursa & Lgmt, Rt 143, 342
0M8F[0,3,4]ZZ	Div/Thorax Bursa & Lgmt, Rt, [Opn, Perc, Perc Endo] 453
0K8J*	Div/Thorax Muscle, Lt 27, 138, 338
0K8H*	Div/Thorax Muscle, Rt 27, 138, 338
0L8D*	Div/Thorax Tndn, Lt 28, 141, 243, 340
0L8D[0,3,4]ZZ	Div/Thorax Tndn, Lt, [Opn, Perc, Perc Endo] 452
0L8C*	Div/Thorax Tndn, Rt 28, 141, 243, 340
0L8C[0,3,4]ZZ	Div/Thorax Tndn, Rt, [Opn, Perc, Perc Endo] 452
0P8S*	Div/Thumb Phalanx, Lt 155, 345
0P8R*	Div/Thumb Phalanx, Rt 155, 345
0G8J*	Div/Thyroid Gland Isthmus 237
0Q8H*	Div/Tibia, Lt 133, 244
0Q8G*	Div/Tibia, Rt 133, 244
018G*	Div/Tibial Nerve 24, 151, 318
0Q8R*	Div/Toe Phalanx, Lt 156
0Q8Q*	Div/Toe Phalanx, Rt 156
0K84*	Div/Tongue, Palate, Pharynx Muscle 54, 106
008K*	Div/Trigeminal Nerve 23, 50, 317
008J*	Div/Trochlear Nerve 23, 50, 151, 317
0M8D*	Div/Trunk Bursa & Lgmt, Lt 143, 342
0M8D[0,3,4]ZZ	Div/Trunk Bursa & Lgmt, Lt, [Opn, Perc, Perc Endo] 453
0M8C*	Div/Trunk Bursa & Lgmt, Rt 143, 342
0M8C[0,3,4]ZZ	Div/Trunk Bursa & Lgmt, Rt, [Opn, Perc, Perc Endo] 453

0K900ZX	Drain of Head Muscle, Opn Appr, Diagnostic **213, 292, 451**
0U9KXZX	Drain of Hymen, Ext Appr, Diagnostic **459**
009S0ZX	Drain of Hypoglossal Nerve, Opn Appr, Diagnostic **23, 318**
009A0ZX	Drain of Hypothalamus, Opn Appr, Diagnostic **8, 12, 16, 295**
0D9C0ZX	Drain of Ileocecal Valve, Opn Appr, Diagnostic **108**
0D9B0ZX	Drain of Ileum, Opn Appr, Diagnostic **108**
0D9A0ZX	Drain of Jejunum, Opn Appr, Diagnostic **108**
0D9E0ZX	Drain of Large Intestine, Opn Appr, Diagnostic **108, 449**
0C9S0ZX	Drain of Larynx, Opn Appr, Diagnostic **52**
0D9T00Z	Drain of Lesser Omentum with Drain Dev, Opn Appr **112**
0D9T0ZZ	Drain of Lesser Omentum, Opn Appr **112**
0B990ZX	Drain of Lingula Bronchus, Opn Appr, Diagnostic **61**
0F900ZX	Drain of Liver, Opn Appr, Diagnostic **65, 211, 242, 253, 268, 292, 301, 335**
0M9J0ZZ	Drain of Lt Abd Bursa & Lgmt, Opn Appr **143**
0M9J00Z	Drain of Lt Abd Bursa/Lig with Drain Dev, Opn Appr **143**
0M9J0ZX	Drain of Lt Abd Bursa/Lig, Opn Appr, Diagn **216, 453**
0K9L0ZX	Drain of Lt Abd Muscle, Opn Appr, Diagnostic **214, 292, 451**
0L9G0ZX	Drain of Lt Abd Tndn, Opn Appr, Diagnostic **215, 452**
0G920ZX	Drain of Lt Adrenal Gland, Opn Appr, Diagnostic **235**
0M9R0ZZ	Drain of Lt Ankle Bursa & Lgmt, Opn Appr **342**
0L9T0ZX	Drain of Lt Ankle Tndn, Opn Appr, Diagnostic **215, 452**
08933ZX	Drain of Lt Ant Chamber, Perc Appr, Diagn **444**
099A0ZX	Drain of Lt Auditory Ossicle, Opn Appr, Diagnostic **446**
0H9U0ZX	Drain of Lt Breast, Opn Appr, Diagnostic **222, 242, 336, 449**
089TXZX	Drain of Lt Conjunctiva, Ext Appr, Diagnostic **444**
0899XZX	Drain of Lt Cornea, Ext Appr, Diagnostic **444**
0M9400Z	Drain of Lt Elbow Bursa/Lig with Drain Dev, Opn Appr **342**
0M944ZZ	Drain of Lt Elbow Bursa/Lig, Perc Endo Appr **243**
099V0ZX	Drain of Lt Ethmoid Sinus, Opn Appr, Diagnostic **55**
0891XZX	Drain of Lt Eye, Ext Appr, Diagnostic **444**
0U960ZZ	Drain of Lt Fallopian Tube, Opn Appr **262, 263, 265**
0M9T0ZZ	Drain of Lt Foot Bursa & Lgmt, Opn Appr **342, 453**
0K9W0ZX	Drain of Lt Foot Muscle, Opn Appr, Diagnostic **214, 292, 451**
0J9R0ZZ	Drain of Lt Foot SQ/Fascia, Opn Appr **212, 337, 450**
0L9W0ZX	Drain of Lt Foot Tndn, Opn Appr, Diagnostic **215, 452**
099T0ZX	Drain of Lt Frontal Sinus, Opn Appr, Diagnostic **55**
0K9D00Z	Drain of Lt Hand Muscle with Drain Dev, Opn Appr **149**
0K9D30Z	Drain of Lt Hand Muscle with Drain Dev, Perc Appr **149**
0K9D40Z	Drain of Lt Hand Muscle with Drain Dev, Perc Endo Appr **149**
0K9D0ZZ	Drain of Lt Hand Muscle, Opn Appr **149, 314**
0K9D0ZX	Drain of Lt Hand Muscle, Opn Appr, Diagnostic **214, 292, 451**
0J9K00Z	Drain of Lt Hand SQ/Fascia with Drain Dev, Opn Appr **450**
0J9K30Z	Drain of Lt Hand SQ/Fascia with Drain Dev, Perc Appr **450**
0J9K0ZZ	Drain of Lt Hand SQ/Fascia, Opn Appr **450**
0J9K3ZZ	Drain of Lt Hand SQ/Fascia, Perc Appr **450**
0L9800Z	Drain of Lt Hand Tndn with Drain Dev, Opn Appr **149**
0L9830Z	Drain of Lt Hand Tndn with Drain Dev, Perc Appr **149**
0L9840Z	Drain of Lt Hand Tndn with Drain Dev, Perc Endo Appr **149**
0L980ZZ	Drain of Lt Hand Tndn, Opn Appr **149, 314, 452**
0L980ZX	Drain of Lt Hand Tndn, Opn Appr, Diagnostic **215, 452**
0F960ZX	Drain of Lt Hepatic Duct, Opn Appr, Diagnostic **112**
0M9M00Z	Drain of Lt Hip Bursa/Lig with Drain Dev, Opn Appr **342**
0K9P0ZX	Drain of Lt Hip Muscle, Opn Appr, Diagnostic **214, 292, 451**
0L9K0ZX	Drain of Lt Hip Tndn, Opn Appr, Diagnostic **215, 452**
099E0ZX	Drain of Lt Inner Ear, Opn Appr, Diagnostic **446**
089D3ZX	Drain of Lt Iris, Perc Appr, Diagnostic **444**
0T94[0,3,4,7,8]0Z	Drain of Lt Kidney Pelvis w/ Drain Dev, [Opn, Perc, Perc Endo, Via Natrl or Artfcl Opng, Via Natrl or Artfcl Opng Endo] **248, 353**
0T94[0,7,8]ZZ	Drain of Lt Kidney Pelvis w/ No Dev, [Opn, Via Natrl or Artfcl Opng, Via Natrl or Artfcl Opng Endo] **248, 353**
0T940ZZ	Drain of Lt Kidney Pelvis, Opn Appr **259, 268, 302**
0T940ZX	Drain of Lt Kidney Pelvis, Opn Appr, Diagnostic **248, 292, 302, 353**
0T91[0,3,4,7,8]0Z	Drain of Lt Kidney w/ Drain Dev, [Opn, Perc, Perc Endo, Via Natrl or Artfcl Opng, Via Natrl or Artfcl Opng Endo] **248, 353**
0T91[0,7,8]ZZ	Drain of Lt Kidney w/ No Dev, [Opn, Via Natrl or Artfcl Opng, Via Natrl or Artfcl Opng Endo] **248, 353**
0T910ZX	Drain of Lt Kidney, Opn Appr, Diagnostic **248, 292, 302, 353**
0M9P0ZZ	Drain of Lt Knee Bursa & Lgmt, Opn Appr **342, 453**
0L9R0ZX	Drain of Lt Knee Tndn, Opn Appr, Diagnostic **215, 452**
0D9G0ZX	Drain of Lt Large Intestine, Opn Appr, Diagnostic **108, 449**
089K3ZX	Drain of Lt Lens, Perc Appr, Diagnostic **444**
0F920ZX	Drain of Lt Lobe Liver, Opn Appr, Diagnostic **65, 211, 242, 253, 268, 292, 301, 335**
0K9B0ZX	Drain of Lt Low Arm & Wrist Muscle, Opn Appr, Diagn **214, 292, 451**
0L960ZX	Drain of Lt Low Arm & Wrist Tndn, Opn Appr, Diagn **215, 452**
0J9H0ZZ	Drain of Lt Low Arm SQ/Fascia, Opn Appr **212, 337, 450**
0M9W0ZZ	Drain of Lt Low Extrem Bursa/Lig, Opn Appr **143**
0M9W0ZX	Drain of Lt Low Extrem Bursa/Lig, Opn Appr, Diagn **216, 453**
0J9P0ZZ	Drain of Lt Low Leg SQ/Fascia, Opn Appr **212, 337, 450**
0B9L8ZX	Drain of Lt Lung, Endo, Diagn **64, 447**
0B9L0ZX	Drain of Lt Lung, Opn Appr, Diagnostic **61, 253, 299**
0K9T0ZX	Drain of Lt Lwr Leg Muscle, Opn Appr, Diagnostic **214, 292, 451**
0L9P0ZX	Drain of Lt Lwr Leg Tndn, Opn Appr, Diagnostic **215, 452**
0B9B0ZX	Drain of Lt Lwr Lobe Bronchus, Opn Appr, Diagn **61**
0B9J8ZX	Drain of Lt Lwr Lung Lobe, Endo, Diagn **64, 447**
0B9J0ZX	Drain of Lt Lwr Lung Lobe, Opn Appr, Diagnostic **61, 253, 299**
0B970ZX	Drain of Lt Main Bronchus, Opn Appr, Diagnostic **61**
099R0ZX	Drain of Lt Maxillary Sinus, Opn Appr, Diagnostic **55**
099600Z	Drain of Lt Mid Ear with Drain Dev, Opn Appr **51, 446**
09960ZX	Drain of Lt Mid Ear, Opn Appr, Diagnostic **51, 446**
0K930ZX	Drain of Lt Neck Muscle, Opn Appr, Diagnostic **214, 292, 451**
0H9X0ZX	Drain of Lt Nipple, Opn Appr, Diagnostic **222, 242, 336, 449**
0N9800Z	Drain of Lt Occipital Bone with Drain Dev, Opn Appr **9**
0N9830Z	Drain of Lt Occipital Bone with Drain Dev, Perc Appr **9**
0N9840Z	Drain of Lt Occipital Bone with Drain Dev, Perc Endo Appr **9**
0N980ZZ	Drain of Lt Occipital Bone, Opn Appr **9**
0N980ZX	Drain of Lt Occipital Bone, Opn Appr, Diagnostic **9**
0N983ZZ	Drain of Lt Occipital Bone, Perc Appr **9**
0N983ZX	Drain of Lt Occipital Bone, Perc Appr, Diagn **9**
0N984ZZ	Drain of Lt Occipital Bone, Perc Endo Appr **9**
0N984ZX	Drain of Lt Occipital Bone, Perc Endo Appr, Diagn **9**
0C9C0ZX	Drain of Lt Parotid Duct, Opn Appr, Diagnostic **448**
0C990ZZ	Drain of Lt Parotid Gland, Opn Appr, Diagnostic **448**
089F3ZX	Drain of Lt Retina, Perc Appr, Diagnostic **444**
089H3ZX	Drain of Lt Retinal Vessel, Perc Appr, Diagn **444**
0897XZX	Drain of Lt Sclera, Ext Appr, Diagnostic **444**
0V920ZX	Drain of Lt Seminal Vesicle, Opn Appr, Diagnostic **260**
0M9200Z	Drain of Lt Shldr Bursa/Lig with Drain Dev, Opn Appr **342**
0K960ZX	Drain of Lt Shldr Muscle, Opn Appr, Diagnostic **214, 292, 451**
0L920ZX	Drain of Lt Shldr Tndn, Opn Appr, Diagnostic **215, 452**
099X0ZX	Drain of Lt Sphenoid Sinus, Opn Appr, Diagnostic **55**
0C9F0ZX	Drain of Lt Sublingual Gland, Opn Appr, Diagnostic **448**
0C9H0ZX	Drain of Lt Submaxillary Gland, Opn Appr, Diagn **448**
0V9B0ZX	Drain of Lt Testis, Opn Appr, Diagnostic **257**
0K9J0ZX	Drain of Lt Thorax Muscle, Opn Appr, Diagnostic **214, 292, 451**
0L9D0ZX	Drain of Lt Thorax Tndn, Opn Appr, Diagnostic **215, 452**
0G9G00Z	Drain of Lt Thyroid Lobe with Drain Dev, Opn Appr **237**
0K9G0ZX	Drain of Lt Trunk Muscle, Opn Appr, Diagnostic **214, 292, 451**
0L9B0ZX	Drain of Lt Trunk Tndn, Opn Appr, Diagnostic **215, 452**
0J9F0ZZ	Drain of Lt Up Arm SQ/Fascia, Opn Appr **212, 337, 450**
0M9B00Z	Drain of Lt Up Extrem Bursa/Lig with Drain Dev, Opn Appr **143**
0M9B0ZZ	Drain of Lt Up Extrem Bursa/Lig, Opn Appr **143**
0M9B0ZX	Drain of Lt Up Extrem Bursa/Lig, Opn Appr, Diagn **143, 216, 453**
0M9B3ZX	Drain of Lt Up Extrem Bursa/Lig, Perc Appr, Diagn **143**
0M9B4ZX	Drain of Lt Up Extrem Bursa/Lig, Perc Endo Appr, Diagn **143**
0J9M0ZZ	Drain of Lt Up Leg SQ/Fascia, Opn Appr **212, 337, 450**
0K980ZX	Drain of Lt Upr Arm Muscle, Opn Appr, Diagnostic **214, 292, 451**
0L940ZX	Drain of Lt Upr Arm Tndn, Opn Appr, Diagnostic **215, 452**
0K9R0ZX	Drain of Lt Upr Leg Muscle, Opn Appr, Diagnostic **214, 292, 451**
0L9M0ZX	Drain of Lt Upr Leg Tndn, Opn Appr, Diagnostic **215, 452**
0B980ZX	Drain of Lt Upr Lobe Bronchus, Opn Appr, Diagn **61**
0B9G8ZX	Drain of Lt Upr Lung Lobe, Endo, Diagn **64, 447**
0B9G0ZX	Drain of Lt Upr Lung Lobe, Opn Appr, Diagnostic **61, 253, 299**

Code	Description
0T970ZX	Drain of Lt Ureter, Opn Appr, Diagnostic 248
08953ZX	Drain of Lt Vitreous, Perc Appr, Diagnostic 444
0C9V0ZX	Drain of Lt Vocal Cord, Opn Appr, Diagnostic 52
0M960ZZ	Drain of Lt Wrist Bursa & Lgmt, Opn Appr 146, 315
0M9600Z	Drain of Lt Wrist Bursa/Lig with Drain Dev, Opn Appr 146
0M9630Z	Drain of Lt Wrist Bursa/Lig with Drain Dev, Perc Appr 146
019B0ZX	Drain of Lumbar Nerve, Opn Appr, Diagnostic 24, 319
01990ZX	Drain of Lumbar Plexus, Opn Appr, Diagnostic 24, 319
019A0ZX	Drain of Lumbosacral Plexus, Opn Appr, Diagnostic 24, 319
0B9H8ZX	Drain of Lung Lingula, Endo, Diagn 64, 447
0B9H0ZX	Drain of Lung Lingula, Opn Appr, Diagnostic 61, 253, 299
0D930ZX	Drain of Lwr Esophagus, Opn Appr, Diagnostic 105, 300
01950ZX	Drain of Median Nerve, Opn Appr, Diagnostic 24, 319
0W9C0ZX	Drain of Mediastinum, Opn Appr, Diagnostic 66, 91, 244, 293, 302
009D0ZX	Drain of Medulla Oblongata, Opn Appr, Diagnostic 8, 12, 16, 295
0D9V00Z	Drain of Mesentery with Drain Device, Opn Appr 112
0D9V0ZZ	Drain of Mesentery, Opn Appr 112
0D920ZX	Drain of Mid Esophagus, Opn Appr, Diagnostic 105, 300
0C9J0ZX	Drain of Minor Salivary Gland, Opn Appr, Diagnostic 56, 448
009H0ZX	Drain of Oculomotor Nerve, Opn Appr, Diagnostic 23, 318
009F0ZX	Drain of Olfactory Nerve, Opn Appr, Diagnostic 23, 318
009G0ZX	Drain of Optic Nerve, Opn Appr, Diagnostic 23, 318
0F9G0ZX	Drain of Pancreas, Opn Appr, Diagnostic 242, 301, 335
0J9C0ZZ	Drain of Pelvic SQ/Fascia, Opn Appr 212, 337, 450
0W9D0ZX	Drain of Pericardial Cavity, Opn Appr, Diagnostic 62, 98, 302, 355
0M9K0ZZ	Drain of Perineum Bursa & Lgmt, Opn Appr 143
0M9K00Z	Drain of Perineum Bursa/Lig with Drain Dev, Opn Appr 143
0M9K0ZX	Drain of Perineum Bursa/Lig, Opn Appr, Diagn 216, 453
0K9M0ZX	Drain of Perineum Muscle, Opn Appr, Diagnostic 214, 292, 451
0J9B0ZZ	Drain of Perineum SQ/Fascia, Opn Appr 212, 337, 450
0L9H0ZX	Drain of Perineum Tndn, Opn Appr, Diagnostic 215, 452
0W9G00Z	Drain of Peritoneal Cavity with Drain Dev, Opn Appr 113, 121, 293, 302, 355
0W9G0ZZ	Drain of Peritoneal Cavity, Opn Appr 113, 121, 293, 302, 355
0D9W00Z	Drain of Peritoneum with Drain Device, Opn Appr 112
0D9W0ZZ	Drain of Peritoneum, Opn Appr 112
019H0ZX	Drain of Peroneal Nerve, Opn Appr, Diagnostic 24, 319
01920ZX	Drain of Phrenic Nerve, Opn Appr, Diagnostic 24, 319
009B0ZX	Drain of Pons, Opn Appr, Diagnostic 8, 12, 16, 295
0J950ZZ	Drain of Post Neck SQ/Fascia, Opn Appr 212, 337, 450
0V900ZX	Drain of Prostate, Opn Appr, Diagnostic 250, 260, 440
019C0ZX	Drain of Pudendal Nerve, Opn Appr, Diagnostic 24, 319
01960ZX	Drain of Radial Nerve, Opn Appr, Diagnostic 24, 319
0D9P0ZX	Drain of Rectum, Opn Appr, Diagnostic 90, 109, 449
0M9H0ZZ	Drain of Rt Abd Bursa & Lgmt, Opn Appr 143
0M9H00Z	Drain of Rt Abd Bursa/Lig with Drain Dev, Opn Appr 143
0M9H0ZX	Drain of Rt Abd Bursa/Lig, Opn Appr, Diagn 216, 453
0K9K0ZX	Drain of Rt Abd Muscle, Opn Appr, Diagnostic 214, 292, 451
0L9F0ZX	Drain of Rt Abd Tndn, Opn Appr, Diagnostic 215, 452
0G930ZX	Drain of Rt Adrenal Gland, Opn Appr, Diagnostic 235
0M9Q0ZZ	Drain of Rt Ankle Bursa & Lgmt, Opn Appr 342
0L9S0ZX	Drain of Rt Ankle Tndn, Opn Appr, Diagnostic 215, 452
08923ZX	Drain of Rt Ant Chamber, Perc Appr, Diagn 444
09990ZX	Drain of Rt Auditory Ossicle, Opn Appr, Diagn 446
0H9T0ZX	Drain of Rt Breast, Opn Appr, Diagnostic 222, 242, 336, 449
089SXZX	Drain of Rt Conjunctiva, Ext Appr, Diagnostic 444
0898XZX	Drain of Rt Cornea, Ext Appr, Diagnostic 444
0M9300Z	Drain of Rt Elbow Bursa/Lig with Drain Dev, Opn Appr 342
0M934ZZ	Drain of Rt Elbow Bursa/Lig, Perc Endo Appr 243
099U0ZX	Drain of Rt Ethmoid Sinus, Opn Appr, Diagnostic 55
0890XZX	Drain of Rt Eye, Ext Appr, Diagnostic 444
0U950ZZ	Drain of Rt Fallopian Tube, Opn Appr 262, 263, 265
0M9S0ZZ	Drain of Rt Foot Bursa & Lgmt, Opn Appr 342, 453
0K9V0ZX	Drain of Rt Foot Muscle, Opn Appr, Diagnostic 214, 292, 451
0J9Q0ZZ	Drain of Rt Foot SQ/Fascia, Opn Appr 212, 337, 450
0L9V0ZX	Drain of Rt Foot Tndn, Opn Appr, Diagnostic 215, 452
099S0ZX	Drain of Rt Frontal Sinus, Opn Appr, Diagnostic 55
0K9C00Z	Drain of Rt Hand Muscle with Drain Dev, Opn Appr 149
0K9C30Z	Drain of Rt Hand Muscle with Drain Dev, Perc Appr 149
0K9C40Z	Drain of Rt Hand Muscle with Drain Dev, Perc Endo Appr 149
0K9C0ZZ	Drain of Rt Hand Muscle, Opn Appr 149, 314
0K9C0ZX	Drain of Rt Hand Muscle, Opn Appr, Diagnostic 214, 292, 451
0J9J3ZZ	Drain of Rt Hand SQ/Fascia, Perc Appr 450
0L9700Z	Drain of Rt Hand Tndn with Drain Dev, Opn Appr 149
0L9730Z	Drain of Rt Hand Tndn with Drain Dev, Perc Appr 149
0L9740Z	Drain of Rt Hand Tndn with Drain Dev, Perc Endo Appr 149
0L970ZZ	Drain of Rt Hand Tndn, Opn Appr 149, 314, 452
0L970ZX	Drain of Rt Hand Tndn, Opn Appr, Diagnostic 215, 452
0F950ZX	Drain of Rt Hepatic Duct, Opn Appr, Diagnostic 112
0M9L00Z	Drain of Rt Hip Bursa/Lig with Drain Dev, Opn Appr 342
0K9N0ZX	Drain of Rt Hip Muscle, Opn Appr, Diagnostic 214, 292, 451
0L9J0ZX	Drain of Rt Hip Tndn, Opn Appr, Diagnostic 215, 452
099D0ZX	Drain of Rt Inner Ear, Opn Appr, Diagnostic 446
089C3ZX	Drain of Rt Iris, Perc Appr, Diagnostic 444
0T93[0,3,4,7,8]0Z	Drain of Rt Kidney Pelvis w/ Drain Dev, [Opn, Perc, Perc Endo, Via Natrl or Artfcl Opng, Via Natrl or Artfcl Opng Endo] 248, 353
0T93[0,7,8]ZZ	Drain of Rt Kidney Pelvis w/ No Dev, [Opn, Via Natrl or Artfcl Opng, Via Natrl or Artfcl Opng Endo] 248, 353
0T930ZZ	Drain of Rt Kidney Pelvis, Opn Appr 259, 268, 302
0T930ZX	Drain of Rt Kidney Pelvis, Opn Appr, Diagnostic 248, 292, 302, 353
0T90[0,3,4,7,8]0Z	Drain of Rt Kidney w/ Drain Dev, [Opn, Perc, Perc Endo, Via Natrl or Artfcl Opng, Via Natrl or Artfcl Opng Endo] 248, 353
0T90[0,7,8]ZZ	Drain of Rt Kidney w/ No Dev, [Opn, Via Natrl or Artfcl Opng, Via Natrl or Artfcl Opng Endo] 248, 353
0T900ZX	Drain of Rt Kidney, Opn Appr, Diagnostic 248, 292, 302, 353
0M9N0ZZ	Drain of Rt Knee Bursa & Lgmt, Opn Appr 342, 453
0L9Q0ZX	Drain of Rt Knee Tndn, Opn Appr, Diagnostic 215, 452
0D9F0ZX	Drain of Rt Large Intestine, Opn Appr, Diagnostic 108, 449
089J3ZX	Drain of Rt Lens, Perc Appr, Diagnostic 444
0F910ZX	Drain of Rt Lobe Liver, Opn Appr, Diagnostic 65, 211, 242, 253, 268, 292, 301, 335
0K990ZX	Drain of Rt Low Arm & Wrist Muscle, Opn Appr, Diagn 214, 292, 451
0L950ZX	Drain of Rt Low Arm & Wrist Tndn, Opn Appr, Diagn 215, 452
0J9G0ZZ	Drain of Rt Low Arm SQ/Fascia, Opn Appr 212, 337, 450
0M9V0ZZ	Drain of Rt Low Extrem Bursa/Lig, Opn Appr 143
0M9V0ZX	Drain of Rt Low Extrem Bursa/Lig, Opn Appr, Diagn 216, 453
0J9N0ZZ	Drain of Rt Low Leg SQ/Fascia, Opn Appr 212, 337, 450
0B9K8ZX	Drain of Rt Lung, Endo, Diagn 64, 447
0B9K0ZX	Drain of Rt Lung, Opn Appr, Diagnostic 61, 253, 299
0K9S0ZX	Drain of Rt Lwr Leg Muscle, Opn Appr, Diagn 214, 292, 451
0L9N0ZX	Drain of Rt Lwr Leg Tndn, Opn Appr, Diagn 215, 452
0B960ZX	Drain of Rt Lwr Lobe Bronchus, Opn Appr, Diagn 61
0B9F8ZX	Drain of Rt Lwr Lung Lobe, Endo, Diagn 64, 447
0B9F0ZX	Drain of Rt Lwr Lung Lobe, Opn Appr, Diagnostic 61, 253, 299
0B930ZX	Drain of Rt Main Bronchus, Opn Appr, Diagnostic 61
099Q0ZX	Drain of Rt Maxillary Sinus, Opn Appr, Diagnostic 55
099500Z	Drain of Rt Mid Ear with Drain Dev, Opn Appr 51, 446
09950ZX	Drain of Rt Mid Ear, Opn Appr, Diagnostic 51, 446
0B950ZX	Drain of Rt Mid Lobe Bronchus, Opn Appr, Diagn 61
0B9D8ZX	Drain of Rt Mid Lung Lobe, Endo, Diagn 64, 447
0B9D0ZX	Drain of Rt Mid Lung Lobe, Opn Appr, Diagn 61, 253, 299
0K920ZX	Drain of Rt Neck Muscle, Opn Appr, Diagnostic 213, 292, 451
0H9W0ZX	Drain of Rt Nipple, Opn Appr, Diagnostic 222, 242, 336, 449
0C9B0ZX	Drain of Rt Parotid Duct, Opn Appr, Diagnostic 448
0C980ZX	Drain of Rt Parotid Gland, Opn Appr, Diagnostic 448
089E3ZX	Drain of Rt Retina, Perc Appr, Diagnostic 444
089G3ZX	Drain of Rt Retinal Vessel, Perc Appr, Diagn 444
0896XZX	Drain of Rt Sclera, Ext Appr, Diagnostic 444
0V910ZX	Drain of Rt Seminal Vesicle, Opn Appr, Diagnostic 260
0M9100Z	Drain of Rt Shldr Bursa/Lig with Drain Dev, Opn Appr 342
0K950ZX	Drain of Rt Shldr Muscle, Opn Appr, Diagnostic 214, 292, 451
0L910ZX	Drain of Rt Shldr Tndn, Opn Appr, Diagnostic 215, 452
099W0ZX	Drain of Rt Sphenoid Sinus, Opn Appr, Diagnostic 55
0C9D0ZX	Drain of Rt Sublingual Gland, Opn Appr, Diagn 448
0C9G0ZX	Drain of Rt Submaxillary Gland, Opn Appr, Diagn 448

0V990ZX	Drain of Rt Testis, Opn Appr, Diagnostic 257
0K9H0ZX	Drain of Rt Thorax Muscle, Opn Appr, Diagnostic 214, 292, 451
0L9C0ZX	Drain of Rt Thorax Tndn, Opn Appr, Diagnostic 215, 452
0G9H00Z	Drain of Rt Thyroid Lobe with Drain Dev, Opn Appr 237
0K9F0ZX	Drain of Rt Trunk Muscle, Opn Appr, Diagnostic 214, 292, 451
0L990ZX	Drain of Rt Trunk Tndn, Opn Appr, Diagnostic 215, 452
0J9D0ZZ	Drain of Rt Up Arm SQ/Fascia, Opn Appr 212, 337, 450
0M9900Z	Drain of Rt Up Extrem Bursa/Lig with Drain Dev, Opn Appr 143
0M990ZZ	Drain of Rt Up Extrem Bursa/Lig, Opn Appr 143
0M990ZX	Drain of Rt Up Extrem Bursa/Lig, Opn Appr, Diagn 143, 216, 453
0M993ZX	Drain of Rt Up Extrem Bursa/Lig, Perc Appr, Diagn 143
0M994ZX	Drain of Rt Up Extrem Bursa/Lig, Perc Endo Appr, Diagn 143
0J9L0ZZ	Drain of Rt Up Leg SQ/Fascia, Opn Appr 212, 337, 450
0K970ZX	Drain of Rt Upr Arm Muscle, Opn Appr, Diagn 214, 292, 451
0L930ZX	Drain of Rt Upr Arm Tndn, Opn Appr, Diagn 215, 452
0K9Q0ZX	Drain of Rt Upr Leg Muscle, Opn Appr, Diagn 214, 292, 451
0L9L0ZX	Drain of Rt Upr Leg Tndn, Opn Appr, Diagn 215, 452
0B940ZX	Drain of Rt Upr Lobe Bronchus, Opn Appr, Diagn 61
0B9C8ZX	Drain of Rt Upr Lung Lobe, Endo, Diagn 64, 447
0B9C0ZX	Drain of Rt Upr Lung Lobe, Opn Appr, Diagnostic 61, 253, 299
0T960ZX	Drain of Rt Ureter, Opn Appr, Diagnostic 248
08943ZX	Drain of Rt Vitreous, Perc Appr, Diagn 444
0C9T0ZX	Drain of Rt Vocal Cord, Opn Appr, Diagnostic 52
0M950ZZ	Drain of Rt Wrist Bursa & Lgmt, Opn Appr 146, 315
0M9500Z	Drain of Rt Wrist Bursa/Lig with Drain Dev, Opn Appr 146
0M9530Z	Drain of Rt Wrist Bursa/Lig with Drain Dev, Perc Appr 146
019R0ZX	Drain of Sacral Nerve, Opn Appr, Diagnostic 24, 319
019Q0ZX	Drain of Sacral Plexus, Opn Appr, Diagnostic 24, 319
0J900ZZ	Drain of Scalp SQ/Fascia, Opn Appr 212, 337, 450
019F0ZX	Drain of Sciatic Nerve, Opn Appr, Diagnostic 24, 319
0D9N0ZX	Drain of Sigmoid Colon, Opn Appr, Diagnostic 108, 449
0D980ZX	Drain of Sm Intestine, Opn Appr, Diagnostic 108
009U00Z	Drain of Spinal Canal with Drain Device, Opn Appr 19, 159, 160, 295
009U0ZZ	Drain of Spinal Canal, Opn Appr 19, 159, 160, 295
009U0ZX	Drain of Spinal Canal, Opn Appr, Diagnostic 19, 159, 160, 295
079P0ZX	Drain of Spleen, Opn Appr, Diagnostic 290, 297
0J9[6,7,8,9,B,C]0ZZ	Drain of SQ Tissue & Fascia of [Chest, Back, Abd, Buttock, Perineum, Pelvic Rgn], Opn 137
0J9[L,M,N,P,Q,R]0ZZ	Drain of SQ Tissue & Fascia of [Rt Upr Leg, Lt Upr Leg, Rt Lwr Leg, Lt Lwr Leg, Rt Foot, Lt Foot], Opn 137
0J9[0,4,5]0ZZ	Drain of SQ Tissue & Fascia of [Scalp, Ant Neck, Post Neck], Opn 137
0D960ZX	Drain of Stomach, Opn Appr, Diagnostic 105, 449
0D970ZX	Drain of Stomach, Pylorus, Opn Appr, Diagnostic 105, 449
00950ZX	Drain of Subarachnoid Space, Opn Appr, Diagnostic 8, 12, 16, 295
00940ZX	Drain of Subdural Space, Opn Appr, Diagnostic 8, 12, 16, 295
00990ZX	Drain of Thalamus, Opn Appr, Diagnostic 8, 12, 16, 295
01980ZX	Drain of Thoracic Nerve, Opn Appr, Diagnostic 24, 319
079M4ZZ	Drain of Thymus, Perc Endo Appr 25
0G9K00Z	Drain of Thyroid Gland with Drain Dev, Opn Appr 237
019G0ZX	Drain of Tibial Nerve, Opn Appr, Diagnostic 24, 319
0C970ZX	Drain of Tongue, Opn Appr, Diagnostic 56
0K940ZX	Drain of Tongue/Palate/Phar Muscle, Opn Appr, Diagn 214, 292, 451
0B910ZX	Drain of Trachea, Opn Appr, Diagnostic 64
0D9L0ZX	Drain of Transv Colon, Opn Appr, Diagnostic 108, 449
009K0ZX	Drain of Trigeminal Nerve, Opn Appr, Diagnostic 23, 318
009J0ZX	Drain of Trochlear Nerve, Opn Appr, Diagnostic 23, 318
01940ZX	Drain of Ulnar Nerve, Opn Appr, Diagnostic 24, 319
0D910ZX	Drain of Upr Esophagus, Opn Appr, Diagnostic 105, 300
0U940ZX	Drain of Uterine Support Struct, Opn Appr, Diagn 262, 263, 265
0U990ZX	Drain of Uterus, Opn Appr, Diagnostic 262, 263, 265
009Q0ZX	Drain of Vagus Nerve, Opn Appr, Diagnostic 23, 318
0M9V00Z	Drain Rt Low Extrem Bursa/Lig w Drain Dev, Opn 143
0M9540Z	Drain Rt Wrist Bursa/Lig w Drain Dev, Perc Endo 146
0B9[J,K,L,M]0ZX	Drain, [Lt Lwr Lung Lobe, Rt Lung, Lt Lung, Bilat Lungs], Opn Appr, Dx 153
0B9[C,D,F,G,H]0ZX	Drain, [Rt Upr Lung Lobe, Rt Mid Lung Lobe, Rt Lwr Lung Lobe, Lt Upr Lung Lobe, Lung Lingula], Opn Appr, Dx 153
0V90[0,7,8]ZZ	Drain, Prostate [Opn, Via Natrl or Artfcl Opng, Via Natrl or Artfcl Opng Endo] 440
0V90[0,7,8]0Z	Drain, Prostate w/ Drain Dev [Opn, Via Natrl or Artfcl Opng, Via Natrl or Artfcl Opng Endo] 440
0490[0,3,4]ZX	Drain/Abd Aorta, [Opn, Perc, Perc Endo] 83, 441
0M9J[0,3,4]ZX	Drain/Abd Bursa & Lgmt, Lt, [Opn, Perc, Perc Endo] 143
0M9J0[0,Z]Z	Drain/Abd Bursa & Lgmt, Lt, Opn, [Drain Dev, No Dev], NQ 342, 453
0M9H[0,3,4]ZX	Drain/Abd Bursa & Lgmt, Rt, [Opn, Perc, Perc Endo] 143
0M9H0[0,Z]Z	Drain/Abd Bursa & Lgmt, Rt, Opn, [Drain Dev, No Dev], NQ 342, 453
0K9L[0,4]ZZ	Drain/Abd Muscle, Lt, [Opn, Perc Endo] 139, 214, 338, 451
0K9L[0,3,4]ZX	Drain/Abd Muscle, Lt, [Opn, Perc, Perc Endo] 139
0K9L[0,3,4]0Z	Drain/Abd Muscle, Lt, [Opn, Perc, Perc Endo], Drain Dev, NQ 139, 214, 338, 451
0K9K[0,4]ZZ	Drain/Abd Muscle, Rt, [Opn, Perc Endo] 139, 214, 338, 451
0K9K[0,3,4]ZX	Drain/Abd Muscle, Rt, [Opn, Perc, Perc Endo] 139
0K9K[0,3,4]0Z	Drain/Abd Muscle, Rt, [Opn, Perc, Perc Endo], Drain Dev, NQ 139, 214, 338, 451
019M*	Drain/Abd Sympathetic Nerve 24
019M[0,3,4][0,Z]Z	Drain/Abd Sympathetic Nerve, [Opn, Perc, Perc Endo], [Drain Dev, No Dev], NQ 89
0L9G*	Drain/Abd Tndn, Lt 141
0L9G[0,3,4][0,Z]Z	Drain/Abd Tndn, Lt, [Opn, Perc, Perc Endo], [Drain Dev, No Dev], NQ 340, 452
0L9F*	Drain/Abd Tndn, Rt 141
0L9F[0,3,4][0,Z]Z	Drain/Abd Tndn, Rt, [Opn, Perc, Perc Endo], [Drain Dev, No Dev], NQ 340, 452
0W9F[0,3,4]ZX	Drain/Abd Wall, [Opn, Perc, Perc Endo] 113, 217, 302, 355, 460
0W9F0[0,Z]Z	Drain/Abd Wall, Opn, [Drain Dev, No Dev], NQ 91, 123, 254
009L[0,3,4][0,Z]Z	Drain/Abducens Nerve, [Opn, Perc, Perc Endo], [Drain Dev, No Dev], NQ 23
009R[0,3,4][0,Z]Z	Drain/Accessory Nerve, [Opn, Perc, Perc Endo], [Drain Dev, No Dev], NQ 23
099P0[0,Z]Z	Drain/Accessory Sinus, Opn, [Drain Dev, No Dev], NQ 55
0Q95[0,3,4]ZX	Drain/Acetab, Lt, [Opn, Perc, Perc Endo] 130, 244, 253, 259, 292, 456
0Q95[0,3,4][0,Z]Z	Drain/Acetab, Lt, [Opn, Perc, Perc Endo], [Drain Dev, No Dev], NQ 135
0Q94[0,3,4]ZX	Drain/Acetab, Rt, [Opn, Perc, Perc Endo] 130, 244, 253, 259, 292, 456
0Q94[0,3,4][0,Z]Z	Drain/Acetab, Rt, [Opn, Perc, Perc Endo], [Drain Dev, No Dev], NQ 135
009N[0,3,4][0,Z]Z	Drain/Acoustic Nerve, [Opn, Perc, Perc Endo], [Drain Dev, No Dev], NQ 23
0R9H0[0,Z]Z	Drain/Acromioclavicular Jt, Lt, Opn, [Drain Dev, No Dev], NQ 147, 349
0R9G0[0,Z]Z	Drain/Acromioclavicular Jt, Rt, Opn, [Drain Dev, No Dev], NQ 147, 349
0C9Q*	Drain/Adenoids 52
0C9Q[0,3,X]ZX	Drain/Adenoids, [Opn, Perc, Ext] 448
0F9C[0,3,7][0,Z]Z	Drain/Ampulla of Vater, [Opn, Perc, Via Natrl or Artfcl Opng], [Drain Dev, No Dev], NQ 120, 335
0D9R[0,3,4][0,Z]Z	Drain/Anal Sphincter, [Opn, Perc, Perc Endo], [Drain Dev, No Dev], NQ 109, 274, 449
0M9R[0,3,4]0Z	Drain/Ankle Bursa & Lgmt, Lt, [Opn, Perc, Perc Endo], Drain Dev, NQ 342
0M9R[3,4]0Z	Drain/Ankle Bursa & Lgmt, Lt, [Perc, Perc Endo], Drain Dev, NQ 132
0M9R0[0,Z]Z	Drain/Ankle Bursa & Lgmt, Lt, Opn, [Drain Dev, No Dev], NQ 143, 453
0M9Q[0,3,4]0Z	Drain/Ankle Bursa & Lgmt, Rt, [Opn, Perc, Perc Endo], Drain Dev, NQ 342
0M9Q[3,4]0Z	Drain/Ankle Bursa & Lgmt, Rt, [Perc, Perc Endo], Drain Dev, NQ 132
0M9Q0[0,Z]Z	Drain/Ankle Bursa & Lgmt, Rt, Opn, [Drain Dev, No Dev], NQ 143, 453
0S9G0[0,Z]Z	Drain/Ankle Jt, Lt, Opn, [Drain Dev, No Dev], NQ 133, 351
0S9F0[0,Z]Z	Drain/Ankle Jt, Rt, Opn, [Drain Dev, No Dev], NQ 133, 351
0L9T*	Drain/Ankle Tndn, Lt 141
0L9T[0,3,4][0,Z]Z	Drain/Ankle Tndn, Lt, [Opn, Perc, Perc Endo], [Drain Dev, No Dev], NQ 340, 452

0L9S*	Drain/Ankle Tndn, Rt 141
0L9S[0,3,4][0,Z]Z	Drain/Ankle Tndn, Rt, [Opn, Perc, Perc Endo], [Drain Dev, No Dev], NQ 340, 452
0893*	Drain/Ant Chamber, Lt 44, 329
08933[0,Z]Z	Drain/Ant Chamber, Lt, Perc, [Drain Dev, No Dev], NQ 444
0892*	Drain/Ant Chamber, Rt 44, 329
08923[0,Z]Z	Drain/Ant Chamber, Rt, Perc, [Drain Dev, No Dev], NQ 444
049Q[0,3,4]ZX	Drain/Ant Tibial Artery, Lt, [Opn, Perc, Perc Endo] 83, 441
049P[0,3,4]ZX	Drain/Ant Tibial Artery, Rt, [Opn, Perc, Perc Endo] 83, 441
0D9Q[0,3,4,7,8,X][0,Z]Z	Drain/Anus, [Opn, Perc, Perc Endo, Via Natrl or Artfcl Opng, Via Natrl or Artfcl Opng Endo, Ext], [Drain Dev, No Dev], NQ 109, 211
0D9J*	Drain/Appendix 108
0D9K[0,3,4,7,8]ZZ	Drain/Ascending Colon, [Opn, Perc, Perc Endo, Via Natrl or Artfcl Opng, Via Natrl or Artfcl Opng Endo] 108, 333
0D9K[0,3,4]0Z	Drain/Ascending Colon, [Opn, Perc, Perc Endo], Drain Dev, NQ 108, 333
099A*	Drain/Auditory Ossicle, Lt 51
0999*	Drain/Auditory Ossicle, Rt 51
0396[0,3,4]ZX	Drain/Axillary Artery, Lt, [Opn, Perc, Perc Endo] 81, 441
0395[0,3,4]ZX	Drain/Axillary Artery, Rt, [Opn, Perc, Perc Endo] 81, 441
0598[0,3,4]ZX	Drain/Axillary Vein, Lt, [Opn, Perc, Perc Endo] 85, 442
0597[0,3,4]ZX	Drain/Axillary Vein, Rt, [Opn, Perc, Perc Endo] 85, 442
0590[0,3,4]ZX	Drain/Azygos Vein, [Opn, Perc, Perc Endo] 85, 442
0098[0,3,4][0,Z]Z	Drain/Basal Ganglia, [Opn, Perc, Perc Endo], [Drain Dev, No Dev], NQ 8, 12, 16, 295, 414
059C[0,3,4]ZX	Drain/Basilic Vein, Lt, [Opn, Perc, Perc Endo] 85, 442
059B[0,3,4]ZX	Drain/Basilic Vein, Rt, [Opn, Perc, Perc Endo] 85, 442
0G94[0,3,4][0,Z]Z	Drain/Bilat Adrenal Glands, [Opn, Perc, Perc Endo], [Drain Dev, No Dev], NQ 235
0T9C[0,3,4,7,8]ZX	Drain/Bladder Neck, [Opn, Perc, Perc Endo, Via Natrl or Artfcl Opng, Via Natrl or Artfcl Opng Endo] 259, 268
0T9C[3,4,7,8]ZX	Drain/Bladder Neck, [Perc, Perc Endo, Via Natrl or Artfcl Opng, Via Natrl or Artfcl Opng Endo] 250, 458
0T9C0[0,Z]Z	Drain/Bladder Neck, Opn, [Drain Dev, No Dev], NQ 249, 353
0T9B[0,3,4,7,8]ZX	Drain/Bladder, [Opn, Perc, Perc Endo, Via Natrl or Artfcl Opng, Via Natrl or Artfcl Opng Endo] 259, 268
0T9B[3,4,7,8]ZX	Drain/Bladder, [Perc, Perc Endo, Via Natrl or Artfcl Opng, Via Natrl or Artfcl Opng Endo] 250, 458
0T9B0[0,Z]Z	Drain/Bladder, Opn, [Drain Dev, No Dev], NQ 249, 353
0398[0,3,4]ZX	Drain/Brachial Artery, Lt, [Opn, Perc, Perc Endo] 81, 441
0397[0,3,4]ZX	Drain/Brachial Artery, Rt, [Opn, Perc, Perc Endo] 81, 441
0193[0,3,4][0,Z]Z	Drain/Brachial Plexus, [Opn, Perc, Perc Endo], [Drain Dev, No Dev], NQ 24
059A[0,3,4]ZX	Drain/Brachial Vein, Lt, [Opn, Perc, Perc Endo] 85, 442
0599[0,3,4]ZX	Drain/Brachial Vein, Rt, [Opn, Perc, Perc Endo] 85, 442
0090[0,3,4][0,Z]Z	Drain/Brain, [Opn, Perc, Perc Endo], [Drain Dev, No Dev], NQ 8, 12, 16, 317, 414
0C94[0,3,X][0,Z]Z	Drain/Buccal Mucosa, [Opn, Perc, Ext], [Drain Dev, No Dev], NQ 56, 210, 331
0B92[0,3,4,7,8][0,Z]Z	Drain/Carina, [Opn, Perc, Perc Endo, Via Natrl or Artfcl Opng, Via Natrl or Artfcl Opng Endo], [Drain Dev, No Dev], NQ 64
0R9R0[0,Z]Z	Drain/Carpal Jt, Lt, Opn, [Drain Dev, No Dev], NQ 146, 315
0R9Q0[0,Z]Z	Drain/Carpal Jt, Rt, Opn, [Drain Dev, No Dev], NQ 146, 315
0P9N*	Drain/Carpal, Lt 150
0P9N[0,3,4]ZX	Drain/Carpal, Lt, [Opn, Perc, Perc Endo] 216, 243, 253, 259, 315, 455
0P9M*	Drain/Carpal, Rt 150
0P9M[0,3,4]ZX	Drain/Carpal, Rt, [Opn, Perc, Perc Endo] 216, 243, 253, 259, 315, 455
0D9H[0,3,4,7,8]ZZ	Drain/Cecum, [Opn, Perc, Perc Endo, Via Natrl or Artfcl Opng, Via Natrl or Artfcl Opng Endo] 108, 333
0D9H[0,3,4]0Z	Drain/Cecum, [Opn, Perc, Perc Endo], Drain Dev, NQ 108, 333
0491[0,3,4]ZX	Drain/Celiac Artery, [Opn, Perc, Perc Endo] 83, 441
059F[0,3,4]ZX	Drain/Cephalic Vein, Lt, [Opn, Perc, Perc Endo] 85, 442
059D[0,3,4]ZX	Drain/Cephalic Vein, Rt, [Opn, Perc, Perc Endo] 85, 442
009C[0,3,4][0,Z]Z	Drain/Cerebellum, [Opn, Perc, Perc Endo], [Drain Dev, No Dev], NQ 8, 12, 16, 317, 414
0097[0,3,4][0,Z]Z	Drain/Cerebral Hemisphere, [Opn, Perc, Perc Endo], [Drain Dev, No Dev], NQ 8, 12, 16, 317, 414
00910[0,Z]Z	Drain/Cerebral Meninges, Opn, [Drain Dev, No Dev], NQ 8, 12, 16, 295, 317, 414
0096[0,3,4]0Z	Drain/Cerebral Ventricle, [Opn, Perc, Perc Endo], Drain Dev, NQ 8, 295, 317, 414
00960[0,Z]Z	Drain/Cerebral Ventricle, Opn, [Drain Dev, No Dev], NQ 12, 16
0191[0,3,4][0,Z]Z	Drain/Cervical Nerve, [Opn, Perc, Perc Endo], [Drain Dev, No Dev], NQ 24
0190[0,3,4][0,Z]Z	Drain/Cervical Plexus, [Opn, Perc, Perc Endo], [Drain Dev, No Dev], NQ 24
009W*	Drain/Cervical Spinal Cord 159, 160
009W[0,3,4]ZX	Drain/Cervical Spinal Cord, [Opn, Perc, Perc Endo] 19, 295
009W[0,3,4][0,Z]Z	Drain/Cervical Spinal Cord, [Opn, Perc, Perc Endo], [Drain Dev, No Dev], NQ 19, 295, 318
0R930[0,Z]Z	Drain/Cervical Vert Disc, Opn, [Drain Dev, No Dev], NQ 156
0R910[0,Z]Z	Drain/Cervical Vert Jt, Opn, [Drain Dev, No Dev], NQ 156
0P93[0,3,4]ZX	Drain/Cervical Vertebra, [Opn, Perc, Perc Endo] 54, 129, 292, 455
0P93[0,3,4][0,Z]Z	Drain/Cervical Vertebra, [Opn, Perc, Perc Endo], [Drain Dev, No Dev], NQ 134
0R950[0,Z]Z	Drain/Cervicothoracic Vert Disc, Opn, [Drain Dev, No Dev], NQ 156
0R940[0,Z]Z	Drain/Cervicothoracic Vert Jt, Opn, [Drain Dev, No Dev], NQ 156
0U9C*	Drain/Cervix 271
0U9C[0,3,4,7,8]ZX	Drain/Cervix, [Opn, Perc, Perc Endo, Via Natrl or Artfcl Opng, Via Natrl or Artfcl Opng Endo] 217, 266, 458
0U9C[0,3,4,7,8][0,Z]Z	Drain/Cervix, [Opn, Perc, Perc Endo, Via Natrl or Artfcl Opng, Via Natrl or Artfcl Opng Endo], [Drain Dev, No Dev], NQ 267, 459
089B*	Drain/Choroid, Lt 44
089B[0,3]ZX	Drain/Choroid, Lt, [Opn, Perc] 444
089B[0,3][0,Z]Z	Drain/Choroid, Lt, [Opn, Perc], [Drain Dev, No Dev], NQ 329, 444
089A*	Drain/Choroid, Rt 44
089A[0,3]ZX	Drain/Choroid, Rt, [Opn, Perc] 444
089A[0,3][0,Z]Z	Drain/Choroid, Rt, [Opn, Perc], [Drain Dev, No Dev], NQ 329, 444
079L[0,3,4]ZX	Drain/Cisterna Chyli, [Opn, Perc, Perc Endo] 25, 90, 112, 122, 153, 209, 241, 252, 290, 443
079L[0,3,4][0,Z]Z	Drain/Cisterna Chyli, [Opn, Perc, Perc Endo], [Drain Dev, No Dev], NQ 60, 328
0P9B[0,3,4]ZX	Drain/Clavicle, Lt, [Opn, Perc, Perc Endo] 65, 129, 216, 243, 253, 259, 455
0P9B[0,3,4][0,Z]Z	Drain/Clavicle, Lt, [Opn, Perc, Perc Endo], [Drain Dev, No Dev], NQ 134
0P99[0,3,4]ZX	Drain/Clavicle, Rt, [Opn, Perc, Perc Endo] 65, 129, 216, 243, 253, 259, 455
0P99[0,3,4][0,Z]Z	Drain/Clavicle, Rt, [Opn, Perc, Perc Endo], [Drain Dev, No Dev], NQ 134
0U9J*	Drain/Clitoris 267
0U9J[0,X]ZX	Drain/Clitoris, [Opn, Ext] 217, 275, 459
0U9J[0,X][0,Z]Z	Drain/Clitoris, [Opn, Ext], [Drain Dev, No Dev], NQ 459
0S960[0,Z]Z	Drain/Coccygeal Jt, Opn, [Drain Dev, No Dev], NQ 157
0Q9S[0,3,4]ZX	Drain/Coccyx, [Opn, Perc, Perc Endo] 130, 244, 253, 259, 292, 456
0Q9S[0,3,4][0,Z]Z	Drain/Coccyx, [Opn, Perc, Perc Endo], [Drain Dev, No Dev], NQ 135
0497[0,3,4]ZX	Drain/Colic Artery, Lt, [Opn, Perc, Perc Endo] 83, 441
0498[0,3,4]ZX	Drain/Colic Artery, Mid, [Opn, Perc, Perc Endo] 83, 441
0496[0,3,4]ZX	Drain/Colic Artery, Rt, [Opn, Perc, Perc Endo] 83, 441
0697[0,3,4]ZX	Drain/Colic Vein, [Opn, Perc, Perc Endo] 86, 442
0F99[0,3,4]0Z	Drain/Common Bile Duct, [Opn, Perc, Perc Endo], Drain Dev, NQ 120
039J[0,3,4]ZX	Drain/Common Carotid Artery, Lt, [Opn, Perc, Perc Endo] 81, 441
039H[0,3,4]ZX	Drain/Common Carotid Artery, Rt, [Opn, Perc, Perc Endo] 81, 441
049D[0,3,4]ZX	Drain/Common Iliac Artery, Lt, [Opn, Perc, Perc Endo] 83, 441
049C[0,3,4]ZX	Drain/Common Iliac Artery, Rt, [Opn, Perc, Perc Endo] 83, 441
069D[0,3,4]ZX	Drain/Common Iliac Vein, Lt, [Opn, Perc, Perc Endo] 86, 442
069C[0,3,4]ZX	Drain/Common Iliac Vein, Rt, [Opn, Perc, Perc Endo] 86, 442
089T*	Drain/Conjunctiva, Lt 42
089TX[0,Z]Z	Drain/Conjunctiva, Lt, Ext, [Drain Dev, No Dev], NQ 444
089S*	Drain/Conjunctiva, Rt 42
089SX[0,Z]Z	Drain/Conjunctiva, Rt, Ext, [Drain Dev, No Dev], NQ 444

Ø899*	Drain/Cornea, Lt **329**
Ø899X[Ø,Z]Z	Drain/Cornea, Lt, Ext, [Drain Dev, No Dev], NQ **44, 444**
Ø898*	Drain/Cornea, Rt **329**
Ø898X[Ø,Z]Z	Drain/Cornea, Rt, Ext, [Drain Dev, No Dev], NQ **44, 444**
ØW91Ø[Ø,Z]Z	Drain/Cranial Cavity, Opn, [Drain Dev, No Dev], NQ **10, 14, 18, 49, 302, 355, 415**
ØU9F[Ø,3,4,7,8]ZX	Drain/Cul-de-sac, [Opn, Perc, Perc Endo, Via Natrl or Artfcl Opng, Via Natrl or Artfcl Opng Endo] **267, 271, 459**
ØU9F[Ø,7,8]ZZ	Drain/Cul-de-sac, [Opn, Via Natrl or Artfcl Opng, Via Natrl or Artfcl Opng Endo] **271**
ØU9F[Ø,7,8][Ø,Z]Z	Drain/Cul-de-sac, [Opn, Via Natrl or Artfcl Opng, Via Natrl or Artfcl Opng Endo], [Drain Dev, No Dev], NQ **269**
ØU9F[Ø,7,8]ØZ	Drain/Cul-de-sac, [Opn, Via Natrl or Artfcl Opng, Via Natrl or Artfcl Opng Endo], Drain Dev, NQ **271**
ØF98[Ø,3,4,7,8][Ø,Z]Z	Drain/Cystic Duct, [Opn, Perc, Perc Endo, Via Natrl or Artfcl Opng, Via Natrl or Artfcl Opng Endo], [Drain Dev, No Dev], NQ **112**
ØF98[Ø,3,4,7,8][Ø,Z]Z	Drain/Cystic Duct, [Opn, Perc, Perc Endo, Via Natrl or Artfcl Opng, Via Natrl or Artfcl Opng Endo], [Drain Dev, No Dev], NQ **120, 335**
ØD9M[Ø,3,4,7,8]ZZ	Drain/Descending Colon, [Opn, Perc, Perc Endo, Via Natrl or Artfcl Opng, Via Natrl or Artfcl Opng Endo] **108, 333**
ØD9M[Ø,3,4]ØZ	Drain/Descending Colon, [Opn, Perc, Perc Endo], Drain Dev, NQ **108, 333**
ØB9S*	Drain/Diaphragm, Lt **61**
ØB9R*	Drain/Diaphragm, Rt **61**
ØD99[Ø,3,4,7,8]ZZ	Drain/Duodenum, [Opn, Perc, Perc Endo, Via Natrl or Artfcl Opng, Via Natrl or Artfcl Opng Endo] **105, 122, 332**
ØD99[Ø,3,4]ØZ	Drain/Duodenum, [Opn, Perc, Perc Endo], Drain Dev, NQ **105, 122, 332**
ØØ92Ø[Ø,Z]Z	Drain/Dura Mater, Opn, [Drain Dev, No Dev], NQ **8, 12, 16, 295, 317, 414**
ØM94[Ø,4]ZZ	Drain/Elbow Bursa & Lgmt, Lt, [Opn, Perc Endo] **342**
ØM94Ø[Ø,Z]Z	Drain/Elbow Bursa & Lgmt, Lt, Opn, [Drain Dev, No Dev], NQ **143, 453**
ØM93[Ø,4]ZZ	Drain/Elbow Bursa & Lgmt, Rt, [Opn, Perc Endo] **342**
ØM93Ø[Ø,Z]Z	Drain/Elbow Bursa & Lgmt, Rt, Opn, [Drain Dev, No Dev], NQ **143, 453**
ØR9MØ[Ø,Z]Z	Drain/Elbow Jt, Lt, Opn, [Drain Dev, No Dev], NQ **147, 244, 349**
ØR9LØ[Ø,Z]Z	Drain/Elbow Jt, Rt, Opn, [Drain Dev, No Dev], NQ **147, 244, 349**
ØV9L[Ø,3,4][Ø,Z]Z	Drain/Epididymis, Bilat, [Opn, Perc, Perc Endo], [Drain Dev, No Dev], NQ **257**
ØV9K[Ø,3,4][Ø,Z]Z	Drain/Epididymis, Lt, [Opn, Perc, Perc Endo], [Drain Dev, No Dev], NQ **257**
ØV9J[Ø,3,4][Ø,Z]Z	Drain/Epididymis, Rt, [Opn, Perc, Perc Endo], [Drain Dev, No Dev], NQ **257**
ØØ93[Ø,3,4][Ø,Z]Z	Drain/Epidural Space, [Opn, Perc, Perc Endo], [Drain Dev, No Dev], NQ **8, 12, 16, 317, 414**
ØC9R[Ø,3,4,7,8][Ø,Z]Z	Drain/Epiglottis, [Opn, Perc, Perc Endo, Via Natrl or Artfcl Opng, Via Natrl or Artfcl Opng Endo], [Drain Dev, No Dev], NQ **52**
Ø693*	Drain/Esophageal Vein **86**
Ø693[Ø,3,4]ZX	Drain/Esophageal Vein, [Opn, Perc, Perc Endo] **442**
Ø693[Ø,3,4][Ø,Z]Z	Drain/Esophageal Vein, [Opn, Perc, Perc Endo], [Drain Dev, No Dev], NQ **25, 51, 241, 327**
ØD94[Ø,3,4,7,8][Ø,Z]Z	Drain/Esophagogastric Junction, [Opn, Perc, Perc Endo, Via Natrl or Artfcl Opng, Via Natrl or Artfcl Opng Endo], [Drain Dev, No Dev], NQ **105, 332**
ØD95[Ø,3,4,7,8][Ø,Z]Z	Drain/Esophagus, [Opn, Perc, Perc Endo, Via Natrl or Artfcl Opng, Via Natrl or Artfcl Opng Endo], [Drain Dev, No Dev], NQ **105, 332**
ØD93[Ø,3,4,7,8][Ø,Z]Z	Drain/Esophagus, Lwr, [Opn, Perc, Perc Endo, Via Natrl or Artfcl Opng, Via Natrl or Artfcl Opng Endo], [Drain Dev, No Dev], NQ **105, 332**
ØD92[Ø,3,4,7,8][Ø,Z]Z	Drain/Esophagus, Mid, [Opn, Perc, Perc Endo, Via Natrl or Artfcl Opng, Via Natrl or Artfcl Opng Endo], [Drain Dev, No Dev], NQ **105, 332**
ØD91[Ø,3,4,7,8][Ø,Z]Z	Drain/Esophagus, Upr, [Opn, Perc, Perc Endo, Via Natrl or Artfcl Opng, Via Natrl or Artfcl Opng Endo], [Drain Dev, No Dev], NQ **105, 332**
ØN9G*	Drain/Ethmoid Bone, Lt **54**
ØN9G[Ø,3,4]ZX	Drain/Ethmoid Bone, Lt, [Opn, Perc, Perc Endo] **129, 454**
ØN9F*	Drain/Ethmoid Bone, Rt **54**
ØN9F[Ø,3,4]ZX	Drain/Ethmoid Bone, Rt, [Opn, Perc, Perc Endo] **129, 454**
Ø99VØ[Ø,Z]Z	Drain/Ethmoid Sinus, Lt, Opn, [Drain Dev, No Dev], NQ **55**
Ø99UØ[Ø,Z]Z	Drain/Ethmoid Sinus, Rt, Opn, [Drain Dev, No Dev], NQ **55**
Ø99G[Ø,3,4,7,8]ZX	Drain/Eustachian Tube, Lt, [Opn, Perc, Perc Endo, Via Natrl or Artfcl Opng, Via Natrl or Artfcl Opng Endo] **51, 446**
Ø99F[Ø,3,4,7,8]ZX	Drain/Eustachian Tube, Rt, [Opn, Perc, Perc Endo, Via Natrl or Artfcl Opng, Via Natrl or Artfcl Opng Endo] **51, 446**
Ø39N[Ø,3,4]ZX	Drain/Ext Carotid Artery, Lt, [Opn, Perc, Perc Endo] **81, 441**
Ø39M[Ø,3,4]ZX	Drain/Ext Carotid Artery, Rt, [Opn, Perc, Perc Endo] **81, 441**
Ø49J[Ø,3,4]ZX	Drain/Ext Iliac Artery, Lt, [Opn, Perc, Perc Endo] **83, 441**
Ø49H[Ø,3,4]ZX	Drain/Ext Iliac Artery, Rt, [Opn, Perc, Perc Endo] **83, 441**
Ø69G[Ø,3,4]ZX	Drain/Ext Iliac Vein, Lt, [Opn, Perc, Perc Endo] **86, 442**
Ø69F[Ø,3,4]ZX	Drain/Ext Iliac Vein, Rt, [Opn, Perc, Perc Endo] **86, 442**
Ø59Q[Ø,3,4]ZX	Drain/Ext Jugular Vein, Lt, [Opn, Perc, Perc Endo] **85, 442**
Ø59P[Ø,3,4]ZX	Drain/Ext Jugular Vein, Rt, [Opn, Perc, Perc Endo] **85, 442**
Ø89M*	Drain/Extraocular Muscle, Lt **42**
Ø89M[Ø,3]ZX	Drain/Extraocular Muscle, Lt, [Opn, Perc] **444**
Ø89M[Ø,3][Ø,Z]Z	Drain/Extraocular Muscle, Lt, [Opn, Perc], [Drain Dev, No Dev], NQ **329, 444**
Ø89L*	Drain/Extraocular Muscle, Rt **42**
Ø89L[Ø,3]ZX	Drain/Extraocular Muscle, Rt, [Opn, Perc] **444**
Ø89L[Ø,3][Ø,Z]Z	Drain/Extraocular Muscle, Rt, [Opn, Perc], [Drain Dev, No Dev], NQ **329, 444**
Ø891X[Ø,Z]Z	Drain/Eye, Lt, Ext, [Drain Dev, No Dev], NQ **42, 444**
Ø89ØX[Ø,Z]Z	Drain/Eye, Rt, Ext, [Drain Dev, No Dev], NQ **42, 444**
Ø39R[Ø,3,4]ZX	Drain/Face Artery, [Opn, Perc, Perc Endo] **81, 441**
Ø59V[Ø,3,4]ZX	Drain/Face Vein, Lt, [Opn, Perc, Perc Endo] **85, 442**
Ø59T[Ø,3,4]ZX	Drain/Face Vein, Rt, [Opn, Perc, Perc Endo] **85, 442**
ØW92[Ø,3,4][Ø,Z]Z	Drain/Face, [Opn, Perc, Perc Endo], [Drain Dev, No Dev], NQ **56, 217, 355**
ØK91[Ø,4]ZZ	Drain/Facial Muscle, [Opn, Perc Endo] **54, 138, 213, 338, 451**
ØK91[Ø,3,4]ZX	Drain/Facial Muscle, [Opn, Perc, Perc Endo] **138**
ØK91[Ø,3,4]ØZ	Drain/Facial Muscle, [Opn, Perc, Perc Endo], Drain Dev, NQ **54, 138, 213, 338, 451**
ØØ9M[Ø,3,4][Ø,Z]Z	Drain/Facial Nerve, [Opn, Perc, Perc Endo], [Drain Dev, No Dev], NQ **23**
ØU96[Ø,3,4,7,8]ZX	Drain/Fallopian Tube, Lt, [Opn, Perc, Perc Endo, Via Natrl or Artfcl Opng, Via Natrl or Artfcl Opng Endo] **262, 263, 265**
ØU96[Ø,3,4,7,8]ØZ	Drain/Fallopian Tube, Lt, [Opn, Perc, Perc Endo, Via Natrl or Artfcl Opng, Via Natrl or Artfcl Opng Endo], Drain Dev, NQ **262, 263, 265**
ØU95[Ø,3,4,7,8]ZX	Drain/Fallopian Tube, Rt, [Opn, Perc, Perc Endo, Via Natrl or Artfcl Opng, Via Natrl or Artfcl Opng Endo] **262, 263, 265**
ØU95[Ø,3,4,7,8]ØZ	Drain/Fallopian Tube, Rt, [Opn, Perc, Perc Endo, Via Natrl or Artfcl Opng, Via Natrl or Artfcl Opng Endo], Drain Dev, NQ **262, 263, 265**
ØU97[Ø,3,4,7,8]ZX	Drain/Fallopian Tubes, Bilat, [Opn, Perc, Perc Endo, Via Natrl or Artfcl Opng, Via Natrl or Artfcl Opng Endo] **262, 263, 265**
ØU97[Ø,3,4,7,8]ØZ	Drain/Fallopian Tubes, Bilat, [Opn, Perc, Perc Endo, Via Natrl or Artfcl Opng, Via Natrl or Artfcl Opng Endo], Drain Dev, NQ **262, 263, 265**
Ø49L[Ø,3,4]ZX	Drain/Femor Artery, Lt, [Opn, Perc, Perc Endo] **83, 441**
Ø49K[Ø,3,4]ZX	Drain/Femor Artery, Rt, [Opn, Perc, Perc Endo] **83, 441**
Ø19D[Ø,3,4][Ø,Z]Z	Drain/Femor Nerve, [Opn, Perc, Perc Endo], [Drain Dev, No Dev], NQ **24**
ØQ99[Ø,3,4]ZX	Drain/Femor Shaft, Lt, [Opn, Perc, Perc Endo] **130, 216, 244, 253, 259, 456**
ØQ99[Ø,3,4][Ø,Z]Z	Drain/Femor Shaft, Lt, [Opn, Perc, Perc Endo], [Drain Dev, No Dev], NQ **137**
ØQ98[Ø,3,4]ZX	Drain/Femor Shaft, Rt, [Opn, Perc, Perc Endo] **130, 216, 244, 253, 259, 456**
ØQ98[Ø,3,4][Ø,Z]Z	Drain/Femor Shaft, Rt, [Opn, Perc, Perc Endo], [Drain Dev, No Dev], NQ **137**
Ø69N[Ø,3,4]ZX	Drain/Femor Vein, Lt, [Opn, Perc, Perc Endo] **86, 442**
Ø69M[Ø,3,4]ZX	Drain/Femor Vein, Rt, [Opn, Perc, Perc Endo] **86, 442**
ØQ9K[Ø,3,4]ZX	Drain/Fibula, Lt, [Opn, Perc, Perc Endo] **130, 217, 244, 253, 259, 456**
ØQ9K[Ø,3,4][Ø,Z]Z	Drain/Fibula, Lt, [Opn, Perc, Perc Endo], [Drain Dev, No Dev], NQ **135**
ØQ9J[Ø,3,4]ZX	Drain/Fibula, Rt, [Opn, Perc, Perc Endo] **130, 217, 244, 253, 259, 456**
ØQ9J[Ø,3,4][Ø,Z]Z	Drain/Fibula, Rt, [Opn, Perc, Perc Endo], [Drain Dev, No Dev], NQ **135**
ØR9XØ[Ø,Z]Z	Drain/Finger Phalangeal Jt, Lt, Opn, [Drain Dev, No Dev], NQ **146, 316**

0R9W0[0,Z]Z	Drain/Finger Phalangeal Jt, Rt, Opn, [Drain Dev, No Dev], NQ **146, 316**
0P9V[0,3,4]ZX	Drain/Finger Phalanx, Lt, [Opn, Perc, Perc Endo] **129, 216, 292, 455**
0P9V[0,3,4][0,Z]Z	Drain/Finger Phalanx, Lt, [Opn, Perc, Perc Endo], [Drain Dev, No Dev], NQ **134**
0P9T[0,3,4]ZX	Drain/Finger Phalanx, Rt, [Opn, Perc, Perc Endo] **129, 216, 292, 455**
0P9T[0,3,4][0,Z]Z	Drain/Finger Phalanx, Rt, [Opn, Perc, Perc Endo], [Drain Dev, No Dev], NQ **134**
049W[0,3,4]ZX	Drain/Foot Artery, Lt, [Opn, Perc, Perc Endo] **83, 441**
049V[0,3,4]ZX	Drain/Foot Artery, Rt, [Opn, Perc, Perc Endo] **83, 441**
0M9T[0,3,4]0Z	Drain/Foot Bursa & Lgmt, Lt, [Opn, Perc, Perc Endo], Drain Dev, NQ **343, 453**
0M9T[3,4]0Z	Drain/Foot Bursa & Lgmt, Lt, [Perc, Perc Endo], Drain Dev, NQ **145**
0M9T0[0,Z]Z	Drain/Foot Bursa & Lgmt, Lt, Opn, [Drain Dev, No Dev], NQ **143**
0M9S[0,3,4]0Z	Drain/Foot Bursa & Lgmt, Rt, [Opn, Perc, Perc Endo], Drain Dev, NQ **342, 453**
0M9S[3,4]0Z	Drain/Foot Bursa & Lgmt, Rt, [Perc, Perc Endo], Drain Dev, NQ **145**
0M9S0[0,Z]Z	Drain/Foot Bursa & Lgmt, Rt, Opn, [Drain Dev, No Dev], NQ **143**
0K9W[0,4]ZZ	Drain/Foot Muscle, Lt, [Opn, Perc Endo] **139, 214, 339, 451**
0K9W[0,3,4]ZX	Drain/Foot Muscle, Lt, [Opn, Perc, Perc Endo] **139**
0K9W[0,3,4]0Z	Drain/Foot Muscle, Lt, [Opn, Perc, Perc Endo], Drain Dev, NQ **139, 214, 339, 451**
0K9V[0,4]ZZ	Drain/Foot Muscle, Rt, [Opn, Perc Endo] **139, 214, 339, 451**
0K9V[0,3,4]ZX	Drain/Foot Muscle, Rt, [Opn, Perc, Perc Endo] **139**
0K9V[0,3,4]0Z	Drain/Foot Muscle, Rt, [Opn, Perc, Perc Endo], Drain Dev, NQ **139, 214, 339, 451**
0L9W*	Drain/Foot Tndn, Lt **141**
0L9W[0,3,4][0,Z]Z	Drain/Foot Tndn, Lt, [Opn, Perc, Perc Endo], [Drain Dev, No Dev], NQ **340, 452**
0L9V*	Drain/Foot Tndn, Rt **141**
0L9V[0,3,4][0,Z]Z	Drain/Foot Tndn, Rt, [Opn, Perc, Perc Endo], [Drain Dev, No Dev], NQ **340, 452**
069V[0,3,4]ZX	Drain/Foot Vein, Lt, [Opn, Perc, Perc Endo] **86, 442**
069T[0,3,4]ZX	Drain/Foot Vein, Rt, [Opn, Perc, Perc Endo] **86, 442**
0N92[0,3,4]ZX	Drain/Frontal Bone, Lt, [Opn, Perc, Perc Endo] **9, 13, 18, 129, 243**
0N92[0,3,4][0,Z]Z	Drain/Frontal Bone, Lt, [Opn, Perc, Perc Endo], [Drain Dev, No Dev], NQ **9, 13, 18, 414**
0N91[0,3,4]ZX	Drain/Frontal Bone, Rt, [Opn, Perc, Perc Endo] **9, 13, 18, 129, 243**
0N91[0,3,4][0,Z]Z	Drain/Frontal Bone, Rt, [Opn, Perc, Perc Endo], [Drain Dev, No Dev], NQ **9, 13, 18, 414**
099T0[0,Z]Z	Drain/Frontal Sinus, Lt, Opn, [Drain Dev, No Dev], NQ **55**
099S0[0,Z]Z	Drain/Frontal Sinus, Rt, Opn, [Drain Dev, No Dev], NQ **55**
0F94[0,3]0Z	Drain/Gallbladder, [Opn, Perc], Drain Dev, NQ **120**
0F940Z[X,Z]	Drain/Gallbladder, Opn, No Dev, [Dx, NQ] **112**
0492[0,3,4]ZX	Drain/Gastric Artery, [Opn, Perc, Perc Endo] **83, 441**
0692[0,3,4]ZX	Drain/Gastric Vein, [Opn, Perc, Perc Endo] **86, 442**
0P98[0,3,4]ZX	Drain/Glenoid Cavity, Lt, [Opn, Perc, Perc Endo] **65, 129, 216, 243, 253, 259, 455**
0P98[0,3,4][0,Z]Z	Drain/Glenoid Cavity, Lt, [Opn, Perc, Perc Endo], [Drain Dev, No Dev], NQ **134**
0P97[0,3,4]ZX	Drain/Glenoid Cavity, Rt, [Opn, Perc, Perc Endo] **65, 129, 216, 243, 253, 259, 455**
0P97[0,3,4][0,Z]Z	Drain/Glenoid Cavity, Rt, [Opn, Perc, Perc Endo], [Drain Dev, No Dev], NQ **134**
009P[0,3,4][0,Z]Z	Drain/Glossopharyngeal Nerve, [Opn, Perc, Perc Endo], [Drain Dev, No Dev], NQ **23**
0D9S[0,3,4]ZX	Drain/Greater Omentum, [Opn, Perc, Perc Endo] **112, 121, 268, 292**
0D9S0[0,Z]Z	Drain/Greater Omentum, Opn, [Drain Dev, No Dev], NQ **333**
069Q[0,3,4]ZX	Drain/Greater Saphenous Vein, Lt, [Opn, Perc, Perc Endo] **86, 442**
069P[0,3,4]ZX	Drain/Greater Saphenous Vein, Rt, [Opn, Perc, Perc Endo] **86, 442**
039F[0,3,4]ZX	Drain/Hand Artery, Lt, [Opn, Perc, Perc Endo] **81, 441**
039D[0,3,4]ZX	Drain/Hand Artery, Rt, [Opn, Perc, Perc Endo] **81, 441**
0M980[0,Z]Z	Drain/Hand Bursa & Lgmt, Lt, Opn, [Drain Dev, No Dev], NQ **150, 315**
0M970[0,Z]Z	Drain/Hand Bursa & Lgmt, Rt, Opn, [Drain Dev, No Dev], NQ **150, 315**
0K9D[0,3,4]ZX	Drain/Hand Muscle, Lt, [Opn, Perc, Perc Endo] **139**
0K9D[0,3,4]0Z	Drain/Hand Muscle, Lt, [Opn, Perc, Perc Endo], Drain Dev, NQ **314**
0K9C[0,3,4]ZX	Drain/Hand Muscle, Rt, [Opn, Perc, Perc Endo] **139**
0K9C[0,3,4]0Z	Drain/Hand Muscle, Rt, [Opn, Perc, Perc Endo], Drain Dev, NQ **314**
0L98[0,3,4]ZX	Drain/Hand Tndn, Lt, [Opn, Perc, Perc Endo] **141**
0L98[0,3,4]0Z	Drain/Hand Tndn, Lt, [Opn, Perc, Perc Endo], Drain Dev, NQ **314, 452**
0L97[0,3,4]ZX	Drain/Hand Tndn, Rt, [Opn, Perc, Perc Endo] **141**
0L97[0,3,4]0Z	Drain/Hand Tndn, Rt, [Opn, Perc, Perc Endo], Drain Dev, NQ **314, 452**
059H[0,3,4]ZX	Drain/Hand Vein, Lt, [Opn, Perc, Perc Endo] **85, 442**
059G[0,3,4]ZX	Drain/Hand Vein, Rt, [Opn, Perc, Perc Endo] **85, 442**
0C92*	Drain/Hard Palate **56**
0C92[0,3,X]ZX	Drain/Hard Palate, [Opn, Perc, Ext] **448**
0M90[3,4]0Z	Drain/Head and Neck Bursa & Lgmt, [Perc, Perc Endo], Drain Dev, NQ **153**
0M900[0,Z]Z	Drain/Head and Neck Bursa & Lgmt, Opn, [Drain Dev, No Dev], NQ **143, 342, 453**
019K*	Drain/Head and Neck Sympathetic Nerve **24**
019K[0,3,4][0,Z]Z	Drain/Head and Neck Sympathetic Nerve, [Opn, Perc, Perc Endo], [Drain Dev, No Dev], NQ **89**
0L90*	Drain/Head and Neck Tndn **141**
0L90[0,3,4][0,Z]Z	Drain/Head and Neck Tndn, [Opn, Perc, Perc Endo], [Drain Dev, No Dev], NQ **340, 452**
0K90[0,4]ZZ	Drain/Head Muscle, [Opn, Perc Endo] **54, 138, 213, 338, 451**
0K90[0,3,4]ZX	Drain/Head Muscle, [Opn, Perc, Perc Endo] **138**
0K90[0,3,4]0Z	Drain/Head Muscle, [Opn, Perc, Perc Endo], Drain Dev, NQ **54, 138, 213, 338, 451**
0591[0,3,4]ZX	Drain/Hemiazygos Vein, [Opn, Perc, Perc Endo] **85, 442**
0493[0,3,4]ZX	Drain/Hepatic Artery, [Opn, Perc, Perc Endo] **83, 441**
0F96[0,3,4,7,8][0,Z]Z	Drain/Hepatic Duct, Lt, [Opn, Perc, Perc Endo, Via Natrl or Artfcl Opng, Via Natrl or Artfcl Opng Endo], [Drain Dev, No Dev], NQ **112, 120, 335**
0F95[0,3,4,7,8][0,Z]Z	Drain/Hepatic Duct, Rt, [Opn, Perc, Perc Endo, Via Natrl or Artfcl Opng, Via Natrl or Artfcl Opng Endo], [Drain Dev, No Dev], NQ **112, 120, 335**
0694[0,3,4]ZX	Drain/Hepatic Vein, [Opn, Perc, Perc Endo] **86, 442**
0M9M[0,4]ZZ	Drain/Hip Bursa & Lgmt, Lt, [Opn, Perc Endo] **342**
0M9M0[0,Z]Z	Drain/Hip Bursa & Lgmt, Lt, Opn, [Drain Dev, No Dev], NQ **143, 453**
0M9L[0,4]ZZ	Drain/Hip Bursa & Lgmt, Rt, [Opn, Perc Endo] **342**
0M9L0[0,Z]Z	Drain/Hip Bursa & Lgmt, Rt, Opn, [Drain Dev, No Dev], NQ **143, 453**
0S9B0[0,Z]Z	Drain/Hip Jt, Lt, Opn, [Drain Dev, No Dev], NQ **131, 351**
0S990[0,Z]Z	Drain/Hip Jt, Rt, Opn, [Drain Dev, No Dev], NQ **131, 351**
0K9P[0,4]ZZ	Drain/Hip Muscle, Lt, [Opn, Perc Endo] **139, 214, 338, 451**
0K9P[0,3,4]ZX	Drain/Hip Muscle, Lt, [Opn, Perc, Perc Endo] **139**
0K9P[0,3,4]0Z	Drain/Hip Muscle, Lt, [Opn, Perc, Perc Endo], Drain Dev, NQ **139, 214, 338, 451**
0K9N[0,4]ZZ	Drain/Hip Muscle, Rt, [Opn, Perc Endo] **139, 214, 338, 451**
0K9N[0,3,4]ZX	Drain/Hip Muscle, Rt, [Opn, Perc, Perc Endo] **139**
0K9N[0,3,4]0Z	Drain/Hip Muscle, Rt, [Opn, Perc, Perc Endo], Drain Dev, NQ **139, 214, 338, 451**
0L9K*	Drain/Hip Tndn, Lt **141**
0L9K[0,3,4][0,Z]Z	Drain/Hip Tndn, Lt, [Opn, Perc, Perc Endo], [Drain Dev, No Dev], NQ **340, 452**
0L9J*	Drain/Hip Tndn, Rt **141**
0L9J[0,3,4][0,Z]Z	Drain/Hip Tndn, Rt, [Opn, Perc, Perc Endo], [Drain Dev, No Dev], NQ **340, 452**
0P9D[0,3,4]ZX	Drain/Humeral Head, Lt, [Opn, Perc, Perc Endo] **129, 216, 243, 253, 259, 455**
0P9D[0,3,4][0,Z]Z	Drain/Humeral Head, Lt, [Opn, Perc, Perc Endo], [Drain Dev, No Dev], NQ **134**
0P9C[0,3,4]ZX	Drain/Humeral Head, Rt, [Opn, Perc, Perc Endo] **129, 216, 243, 253, 259, 455**
0P9C[0,3,4][0,Z]Z	Drain/Humeral Head, Rt, [Opn, Perc, Perc Endo], [Drain Dev, No Dev], NQ **134**
0P9G[0,3,4]ZX	Drain/Humeral Shaft, Lt, [Opn, Perc, Perc Endo] **129, 216, 243, 253, 259, 455**

ØP9G[0,3,4][0,Z]Z	Drain/Humeral Shaft, Lt, [Opn, Perc, Perc Endo], [Drain Dev, No Dev], NQ 134
ØP9F[0,3,4]ZX	Drain/Humeral Shaft, Rt, [Opn, Perc, Perc Endo] 129, 216, 243, 253, 259, 455
ØP9F[0,3,4][0,Z]Z	Drain/Humeral Shaft, Rt, [Opn, Perc, Perc Endo], [Drain Dev, No Dev], NQ 134
ØU9K[0,3,4,7,8,X]ZX	Drain/Hymen, [Opn, Perc, Perc Endo, Via Natrl or Artfcl Opng, Via Natrl or Artfcl Opng Endo, Ext] 267
ØU9K[0,3,4,7,8,X]ZZ	Drain/Hymen, [Opn, Perc, Perc Endo, Via Natrl or Artfcl Opng, Via Natrl or Artfcl Opng Endo, Ext] 271
ØU9K[0,3,4,7,8]ZX	Drain/Hymen, [Opn, Perc, Perc Endo, Via Natrl or Artfcl Opng, Via Natrl or Artfcl Opng Endo] 459
ØN9X*	Drain/Hyoid Bone 54
ØN9X[0,3,4]ZX	Drain/Hyoid Bone, [Opn, Perc, Perc Endo] 129, 454
069J[0,3,4]ZX	Drain/Hypogastric Vein, Lt, [Opn, Perc, Perc Endo] 86, 442
069H[0,3,4]ZX	Drain/Hypogastric Vein, Rt, [Opn, Perc, Perc Endo] 86, 442
009S[0,3,4][0,Z]Z	Drain/Hypoglossal Nerve, [Opn, Perc, Perc Endo], [Drain Dev, No Dev], NQ 23
009A[0,3,4][0,Z]Z	Drain/Hypothalamus, [Opn, Perc, Perc Endo], [Drain Dev, No Dev], NQ 8, 12, 16, 295, 317, 414
ØD9C[0,3,4,7,8][0,Z]Z	Drain/Ileocecal Valve, [Opn, Perc, Perc Endo, Via Natrl or Artfcl Opng, Via Natrl or Artfcl Opng Endo], [Drain Dev, No Dev], NQ 108, 300, 333
ØD9B[0,3,4,7,8]ZZ	Drain/Ileum, [Opn, Perc, Perc Endo, Via Natrl or Artfcl Opng, Via Natrl or Artfcl Opng Endo] 108, 300, 333
ØD9B[0,3,4]0Z	Drain/Ileum, [Opn, Perc, Perc Endo], Drain Dev, NQ 108, 300, 333
049B[0,3,4]ZX	Drain/Inferior Mesenteric Artery, [Opn, Perc, Perc Endo] 83, 441
0696[0,3,4]ZX	Drain/Inferior Mesenteric Vein, [Opn, Perc, Perc Endo] 86, 442
ØG9P[0,3,4]ZX	Drain/Inferior Parathyroid Gland, Lt, [Opn, Perc, Perc Endo] 153, 238
ØG9P0[0,Z]Z	Drain/Inferior Parathyroid Gland, Lt, Opn, [Drain Dev, No Dev], NQ 53, 211, 238, 336
ØG9N[0,3,4]ZX	Drain/Inferior Parathyroid Gland, Rt, [Opn, Perc, Perc Endo] 153, 238
ØG9N0[0,Z]Z	Drain/Inferior Parathyroid Gland, Rt, Opn, [Drain Dev, No Dev], NQ 53, 211, 238, 336
0690[0,3,4]ZX	Drain/Inferior Vena Cava, [Opn, Perc, Perc Endo] 86, 442
ØY96*	Drain/Inguinal Region, Lt 114, 357
ØY95*	Drain/Inguinal Region, Rt 114, 357
ØY96[0,3,4]ZX	Drain/Inguinal Rgn, Lt, [Opn, Perc, Perc Endo] 121, 269, 293, 303, 461
ØY96[0,3,4][0,Z]Z	Drain/Inguinal Rgn, Lt, [Opn, Perc, Perc Endo], [Drain Dev, No Dev], NQ 92, 123, 219, 254, 303
ØY95[0,3,4]ZX	Drain/Inguinal Rgn, Rt, [Opn, Perc, Perc Endo] 121, 269, 293, 303, 461
ØY95[0,3,4][0,Z]Z	Drain/Inguinal Rgn, Rt, [Opn, Perc, Perc Endo], [Drain Dev, No Dev], NQ 92, 123, 219, 254, 303
099E*	Drain/Inner Ear, Lt 51
099D*	Drain/Inner Ear, Rt 51
0392[0,3,4]ZX	Drain/Innominate Artery, [Opn, Perc, Perc Endo] 81, 441
0594[0,3,4]ZX	Drain/Innominate Vein, Lt, [Opn, Perc, Perc Endo] 85, 442
0593[0,3,4]ZX	Drain/Innominate Vein, Rt, [Opn, Perc, Perc Endo] 85, 442
039L[0,3,4]ZX	Drain/Int Carotid Artery, Lt, [Opn, Perc, Perc Endo] 81, 441
039K[0,3,4]ZX	Drain/Int Carotid Artery, Rt, [Opn, Perc, Perc Endo] 81, 441
049F[0,3,4]ZX	Drain/Int Iliac Artery, Lt, [Opn, Perc, Perc Endo] 83, 441
049E[0,3,4]ZX	Drain/Int Iliac Artery, Rt, [Opn, Perc, Perc Endo] 83, 441
059N[0,3,4]ZX	Drain/Int Jugular Vein, Lt, [Opn, Perc, Perc Endo] 85, 442
059M[0,3,4]ZX	Drain/Int Jugular Vein, Rt, [Opn, Perc, Perc Endo] 85, 442
0391[0,3,4]ZX	Drain/Int Mammary Artery, Lt, [Opn, Perc, Perc Endo] 81, 441
0390[0,3,4]ZX	Drain/Int Mammary Artery, Rt, [Opn, Perc, Perc Endo] 81, 441
039G[0,3,4]ZX	Drain/Intracranial Artery, [Opn, Perc, Perc Endo] 81, 441
059L[0,3,4]ZX	Drain/Intracranial Vein, [Opn, Perc, Perc Endo] 85, 442
089D*	Drain/Iris, Lt 44, 329
089D3[0,Z]Z	Drain/Iris, Lt, Perc, [Drain Dev, No Dev], NQ 444
089C*	Drain/Iris, Rt 44, 329
089C3[0,Z]Z	Drain/Iris, Rt, Perc, [Drain Dev, No Dev], NQ 444
ØD9A[0,3,4,7,8]ZZ	Drain/Jejunum, [Opn, Perc, Perc Endo, Via Natrl or Artfcl Opng, Via Natrl or Artfcl Opng Endo] 108, 300, 332
ØD9A[0,3,4]0Z	Drain/Jejunum, [Opn, Perc, Perc Endo], Drain Dev, NQ 108, 300, 332

ØT94[0,3,4]0Z	Drain/Kidney Pelvis, Lt, [Opn, Perc, Perc Endo], Drain Dev, NQ 259, 268, 302
ØT94[7,8]0Z	Drain/Kidney Pelvis, Lt, [Via Natrl or Artfcl Opng, Via Natrl or Artfcl Opng Endo], Drain Dev, NQ 458
ØT93[0,3,4]0Z	Drain/Kidney Pelvis, Rt, [Opn, Perc, Perc Endo], Drain Dev, NQ 259, 268, 302
ØT93[7,8]0Z	Drain/Kidney Pelvis, Rt, [Via Natrl or Artfcl Opng, Via Natrl or Artfcl Opng Endo], Drain Dev, NQ 458
ØM9P[0,3,4]0Z	Drain/Knee Bursa & Lgmt, Lt, [Opn, Perc, Perc Endo], Drain Dev, NQ 342, 453
ØM9P[3,4]0Z	Drain/Knee Bursa & Lgmt, Lt, [Perc, Perc Endo], Drain Dev, NQ 132, 243
ØM9P0[0,Z]Z	Drain/Knee Bursa & Lgmt, Lt, Opn, [Drain Dev, No Dev], NQ 143
ØM9N[0,3,4]0Z	Drain/Knee Bursa & Lgmt, Rt, [Opn, Perc, Perc Endo], Drain Dev, NQ 342, 453
ØM9N[3,4]0Z	Drain/Knee Bursa & Lgmt, Rt, [Perc, Perc Endo], Drain Dev, NQ 132, 243
ØM9N0[0,Z]Z	Drain/Knee Bursa & Lgmt, Rt, Opn, [Drain Dev, No Dev], NQ 143
ØS9D0[0,Z]Z	Drain/Knee Jt, Lt, Opn, [Drain Dev, No Dev], NQ 132, 244, 351, 457
ØS9C0[0,Z]Z	Drain/Knee Jt, Rt, Opn, [Drain Dev, No Dev], NQ 132, 244, 351, 457
ØL9R*	Drain/Knee Tndn, Lt 141
ØL9R[0,3,4][0,Z]Z	Drain/Knee Tndn, Lt, [Opn, Perc, Perc Endo], [Drain Dev, No Dev], NQ 340, 452
ØL9Q*	Drain/Knee Tndn, Rt 141
ØL9Q[0,3,4][0,Z]Z	Drain/Knee Tndn, Rt, [Opn, Perc, Perc Endo], [Drain Dev, No Dev], NQ 340, 452
ØN9J*	Drain/Lacrimal Bone, Lt 54
ØN9J[0,3,4]ZX	Drain/Lacrimal Bone, Lt, [Opn, Perc, Perc Endo] 129, 454
ØN9H*	Drain/Lacrimal Bone, Rt 54
ØN9H[0,3,4]ZX	Drain/Lacrimal Bone, Rt, [Opn, Perc, Perc Endo] 129, 454
089Y*	Drain/Lacrimal Duct, Lt 42
089Y[0,3,7,8]ZX	Drain/Lacrimal Duct, Lt, [Opn, Perc, Via Natrl or Artfcl Opng, Via Natrl or Artfcl Opng Endo] 51, 444
089Y[0,3,7,8][0,Z]Z	Drain/Lacrimal Duct, Lt, [Opn, Perc, Via Natrl or Artfcl Opng, Via Natrl or Artfcl Opng Endo], [Drain Dev, No Dev], NQ 444
089Y[7,8][0,Z]Z	Drain/Lacrimal Duct, Lt, [Via Natrl or Artfcl Opng, Via Natrl or Artfcl Opng Endo], [Drain Dev, No Dev], NQ 329
089X*	Drain/Lacrimal Duct, Rt 42
089X[0,3,7,8]ZX	Drain/Lacrimal Duct, Rt, [Opn, Perc, Via Natrl or Artfcl Opng, Via Natrl or Artfcl Opng Endo] 51, 444
089X[0,3,7,8][0,Z]Z	Drain/Lacrimal Duct, Rt, [Opn, Perc, Via Natrl or Artfcl Opng, Via Natrl or Artfcl Opng Endo], [Drain Dev, No Dev], NQ 444
089X[7,8][0,Z]Z	Drain/Lacrimal Duct, Rt, [Via Natrl or Artfcl Opng, Via Natrl or Artfcl Opng Endo], [Drain Dev, No Dev], NQ 329
089W*	Drain/Lacrimal Gland, Lt 42
089W[0,3]ZX	Drain/Lacrimal Gland, Lt, [Opn, Perc] 329, 444
089W[0,3][0,Z]Z	Drain/Lacrimal Gland, Lt, [Opn, Perc], [Drain Dev, No Dev], NQ 444
089V*	Drain/Lacrimal Gland, Rt 42
089V[0,3]ZX	Drain/Lacrimal Gland, Rt, [Opn, Perc] 329, 444
089V[0,3][0,Z]Z	Drain/Lacrimal Gland, Rt, [Opn, Perc], [Drain Dev, No Dev], NQ 444
ØC9S[0,3,4,7,8][0,Z]Z	Drain/Larynx, [Opn, Perc, Perc Endo, Via Natrl or Artfcl Opng, Via Natrl or Artfcl Opng Endo], [Drain Dev, No Dev], NQ 52
089K*	Drain/Lens, Lt 44, 329
089K3[0,Z]Z	Drain/Lens, Lt, Perc, [Drain Dev, No Dev], NQ 444
089J*	Drain/Lens, Rt 44, 329
089J3[0,Z]Z	Drain/Lens, Rt, Perc, [Drain Dev, No Dev], NQ 444
ØD9T[0,3,4]ZX	Drain/Lesser Omentum, [Opn, Perc, Perc Endo] 112, 121, 268, 292
ØD9T0[0,Z]Z	Drain/Lesser Omentum, Opn, [Drain Dev, No Dev], NQ 333
069S[0,3,4]ZX	Drain/Lesser Saphenous Vein, Lt, [Opn, Perc, Perc Endo] 86, 442
069R[0,3,4]ZX	Drain/Lesser Saphenous Vein, Rt, [Opn, Perc, Perc Endo] 86, 442
ØD9E[0,3,4,7,8]ZZ	Drain/Lg Intestine, [Opn, Perc, Perc Endo, Via Natrl or Artfcl Opng, Via Natrl or Artfcl Opng Endo] 108, 333
ØD9E[0,3,4]0Z	Drain/Lg Intestine, [Opn, Perc, Perc Endo], Drain Dev, NQ 108, 333

0796[0,3,4]ZX	Drain/Lymphatic, Lt Axillary, [Opn, Perc, Perc Endo] 25, 89, 153, 209, 241, 443
0796[0,3,4][0,Z]Z	Drain/Lymphatic, Lt Axillary, [Opn, Perc, Perc Endo], [Drain Dev, No Dev], NQ 209, 443
079J*	Drain/Lymphatic, Lt Inguinal 290
079J[0,3,4]ZX	Drain/Lymphatic, Lt Inguinal, [Opn, Perc, Perc Endo] 25, 90, 153, 209, 241, 258, 268, 443
079J[0,3,4][0,Z]Z	Drain/Lymphatic, Lt Inguinal, [Opn, Perc, Perc Endo], [Drain Dev, No Dev], NQ 209, 443
079G*	Drain/Lymphatic, Lt Lwr Extr 290
079G[0,3,4]ZX	Drain/Lymphatic, Lt Lwr Extr, [Opn, Perc, Perc Endo] 25, 90, 153, 209, 241, 443
079G[0,3,4][0,Z]Z	Drain/Lymphatic, Lt Lwr Extr, [Opn, Perc, Perc Endo], [Drain Dev, No Dev], NQ 209, 443
0792*	Drain/Lymphatic, Lt Neck 290
0792[0,3,4]ZX	Drain/Lymphatic, Lt Neck, [Opn, Perc, Perc Endo] 25, 51, 89, 153, 209, 241, 443
0792[0,3,4][0,Z]Z	Drain/Lymphatic, Lt Neck, [Opn, Perc, Perc Endo], [Drain Dev, No Dev], NQ 209, 443
0794*	Drain/Lymphatic, Lt Upr Extr 290
0794[0,3,4]ZX	Drain/Lymphatic, Lt Upr Extr, [Opn, Perc, Perc Endo] 25, 89, 153, 209, 241, 443
0794[0,3,4][0,Z]Z	Drain/Lymphatic, Lt Upr Extr, [Opn, Perc, Perc Endo], [Drain Dev, No Dev], NQ 209, 443
079B*	Drain/Lymphatic, Mesenteric 290
079B[0,3,4]ZX	Drain/Lymphatic, Mesenteric, [Opn, Perc, Perc Endo] 25, 89, 112, 122, 153, 209, 241, 443
079B[0,3,4][0,Z]Z	Drain/Lymphatic, Mesenteric, [Opn, Perc, Perc Endo], [Drain Dev, No Dev], NQ 209, 443
079C*	Drain/Lymphatic, Pelvis 290
079C[0,3,4]ZX	Drain/Lymphatic, Pelvis, [Opn, Perc, Perc Endo] 25, 90, 112, 122, 153, 209, 241, 252, 258, 268, 443
079C[0,3,4][0,Z]Z	Drain/Lymphatic, Pelvis, [Opn, Perc, Perc Endo], [Drain Dev, No Dev], NQ 209, 443
0795*	Drain/Lymphatic, Rt Axillary 290
0795[0,3,4]ZX	Drain/Lymphatic, Rt Axillary, [Opn, Perc, Perc Endo] 25, 89, 153, 209, 241, 443
0795[0,3,4][0,Z]Z	Drain/Lymphatic, Rt Axillary, [Opn, Perc, Perc Endo], [Drain Dev, No Dev], NQ 209, 443
079H*	Drain/Lymphatic, Rt Inguinal 290
079H[0,3,4]ZX	Drain/Lymphatic, Rt Inguinal, [Opn, Perc, Perc Endo] 25, 90, 153, 209, 241, 258, 268, 443
079H[0,3,4][0,Z]Z	Drain/Lymphatic, Rt Inguinal, [Opn, Perc, Perc Endo], [Drain Dev, No Dev], NQ 209, 443
079F*	Drain/Lymphatic, Rt Lwr Extr 290
079F[0,3,4]ZX	Drain/Lymphatic, Rt Lwr Extr, [Opn, Perc, Perc Endo] 25, 90, 153, 209, 241, 443
079F[0,3,4][0,Z]Z	Drain/Lymphatic, Rt Lwr Extr, [Opn, Perc, Perc Endo], [Drain Dev, No Dev], NQ 209, 443
0791*	Drain/Lymphatic, Rt Neck 290
0791[0,3,4]ZX	Drain/Lymphatic, Rt Neck, [Opn, Perc, Perc Endo] 25, 51, 89, 153, 209, 241, 443
0791[0,3,4][0,Z]Z	Drain/Lymphatic, Rt Neck, [Opn, Perc, Perc Endo], [Drain Dev, No Dev], NQ 209, 443
0793*	Drain/Lymphatic, Rt Upr Extr 290
0793[0,3,4]ZX	Drain/Lymphatic, Rt Upr Extr, [Opn, Perc, Perc Endo] 25, 89, 153, 209, 241, 443
0793[0,3,4][0,Z]Z	Drain/Lymphatic, Rt Upr Extr, [Opn, Perc, Perc Endo], [Drain Dev, No Dev], NQ 209, 443
0797*	Drain/Lymphatic, Thorax 290
0797[0,3,4]ZX	Drain/Lymphatic, Thorax, [Opn, Perc, Perc Endo] 25, 64, 89, 153, 209, 241, 443
0797[0,3,4][0,Z]Z	Drain/Lymphatic, Thorax, [Opn, Perc, Perc Endo], [Drain Dev, No Dev], NQ 209, 443
0B97[0,3,4,7,8][0,Z]Z	Drain/Main Bronchus, Lt, [Opn, Perc, Perc Endo, Via Natrl or Artfcl Opng, Via Natrl or Artfcl Opng Endo], [Drain Dev, No Dev], NQ 61
0B93[0,3,4,7,8][0,Z]Z	Drain/Main Bronchus, Rt, [Opn, Perc, Perc Endo, Via Natrl or Artfcl Opng, Via Natrl or Artfcl Opng Endo], [Drain Dev, No Dev], NQ 61
0N9V[0,3,4]ZX	Drain/Mandible, Lt, [Opn, Perc, Perc Endo] 54, 129, 454
0N9T[0,3,4]ZX	Drain/Mandible, Rt, [Opn, Perc, Perc Endo] 54, 129, 454
099C[0,3,4]ZX	Drain/Mastoid Sinus, Lt, [Opn, Perc, Perc Endo] 51, 446
099C[0,3,4][0,Z]Z	Drain/Mastoid Sinus, Lt, [Opn, Perc, Perc Endo], [Drain Dev, No Dev], NQ 55, 446
099B[0,3,4]ZX	Drain/Mastoid Sinus, Rt, [Opn, Perc, Perc Endo] 51, 446
099B[0,3,4][0,Z]Z	Drain/Mastoid Sinus, Rt, [Opn, Perc, Perc Endo], [Drain Dev, No Dev], NQ 55, 446
0N9S[0,3,4]ZX	Drain/Maxilla, Lt, [Opn, Perc, Perc Endo] 54, 129, 454
0N9R[0,3,4]ZX	Drain/Maxilla, Rt, [Opn, Perc, Perc Endo] 54, 129, 454
099R0[0,Z]Z	Drain/Maxillary Sinus, Lt, Opn, [Drain Dev, No Dev], NQ 55
099Q0[0,Z]Z	Drain/Maxillary Sinus, Rt, Opn, [Drain Dev, No Dev], NQ 55
0195[0,3,4][0,Z]Z	Drain/Median Nerve, [Opn, Perc, Perc Endo], [Drain Dev, No Dev], NQ 24
0W9C[0,3,4][0,Z]Z	Drain/Mediastinum, [Opn, Perc, Perc Endo], [Drain Dev, No Dev], NQ 66, 91, 355
009D[0,3,4][0,Z]Z	Drain/Medulla Oblongata, [Opn, Perc, Perc Endo], [Drain Dev, No Dev], NQ 8, 12, 16, 318, 414
0D9V[0,3,4]ZX	Drain/Mesentery, [Opn, Perc, Perc Endo] 112, 121, 268, 292
0D9V0[0,Z]Z	Drain/Mesentery, Opn, [Drain Dev, No Dev], NQ 333
0P9Q*	Drain/Metacarpal, Lt 150
0P9Q[0,3,4]ZX	Drain/Metacarpal, Lt, [Opn, Perc, Perc Endo] 216, 243, 253, 259, 315, 455
0P9P*	Drain/Metacarpal, Rt 150
0P9P[0,3,4]ZX	Drain/Metacarpal, Rt, [Opn, Perc, Perc Endo] 216, 243, 253, 259, 315, 455
0R9T0[0,Z]Z	Drain/Metacarpocarpal Jt, Lt, Opn, [Drain Dev, No Dev], NQ 146, 315
0R9S0[0,Z]Z	Drain/Metacarpocarpal Jt, Rt, Opn, [Drain Dev, No Dev], NQ 146, 315
0R9V0[0,Z]Z	Drain/Metacarpophalangeal Jt, Lt, Opn, [Drain Dev, No Dev], NQ 146, 316
0R9U0[0,Z]Z	Drain/Metacarpophalangeal Jt, Rt, Opn, [Drain Dev, No Dev], NQ 146, 315
0S9N0[0,Z]Z	Drain/Metatarsal-Phalangeal Jt, Lt, Opn, [Drain Dev, No Dev], NQ 145, 351, 457
0S9M0[0,Z]Z	Drain/Metatarsal-Phalangeal Jt, Rt, Opn, [Drain Dev, No Dev], NQ 145, 351, 457
0S9L0[0,Z]Z	Drain/Metatarsal-Tarsal Jt, Lt, Opn, [Drain Dev, No Dev], NQ 145, 351, 457
0S9K0[0,Z]Z	Drain/Metatarsal-Tarsal Jt, Rt, Opn, [Drain Dev, No Dev], NQ 145, 351, 457
0Q9P[0,3,4]ZX	Drain/Metatarsal, Lt, [Opn, Perc, Perc Endo] 130, 217, 244, 253, 259, 456
0Q9P[0,3,4][0,Z]Z	Drain/Metatarsal, Lt, [Opn, Perc, Perc Endo], [Drain Dev, No Dev], NQ 145
0Q9N[0,3,4]ZX	Drain/Metatarsal, Rt, [Opn, Perc, Perc Endo] 130, 217, 244, 253, 259, 456
0Q9N[0,3,4][0,Z]Z	Drain/Metatarsal, Rt, [Opn, Perc, Perc Endo], [Drain Dev, No Dev], NQ 145
0B95[0,3,4,7,8][0,Z]Z	Drain/Mid Lobe Bronchus, Rt, [Opn, Perc, Perc Endo, Via Natrl or Artfcl Opng, Via Natrl or Artfcl Opng Endo], [Drain Dev, No Dev], NQ 61
0B9D[0,8]ZX	Drain/Mid Lung Lobe, Rt, [Opn, Via Natrl or Artfcl Opng Endo] 90
0B9D[3,4,7,8][0,Z]Z	Drain/Mid Lung Lobe, Rt, [Perc, Perc Endo, Via Natrl or Artfcl Opng, Via Natrl or Artfcl Opng Endo], [Drain Dev, No Dev], NQ 64
0B9D0[0,Z]Z	Drain/Mid Lung Lobe, Rt, Opn, [Drain Dev, No Dev], NQ 61, 331
099N[0,3,4,7,8][0,Z]Z	Drain/Nasopharynx, [Opn, Perc, Perc Endo, Via Natrl or Artfcl Opng, Via Natrl or Artfcl Opng Endo], [Drain Dev, No Dev], NQ 51, 330
0K93[0,4]ZZ	Drain/Neck Muscle, Lt, [Opn, Perc Endo] 54, 138, 214, 338, 451
0K93[0,3,4]ZX	Drain/Neck Muscle, Lt, [Opn, Perc, Perc Endo] 138
0K93[0,3,4]0Z	Drain/Neck Muscle, Lt, [Opn, Perc, Perc Endo], Drain Dev, NQ 54, 138, 214, 338, 451
0K92[0,4]ZZ	Drain/Neck Muscle, Rt, [Opn, Perc Endo] 54, 138, 214, 338, 451
0K92[0,3,4]ZX	Drain/Neck Muscle, Rt, [Opn, Perc, Perc Endo] 138
0K92[0,3,4]0Z	Drain/Neck Muscle, Rt, [Opn, Perc, Perc Endo], Drain Dev, NQ 54, 138, 214, 338, 451
0W96[0,3,4][0,Z]Z	Drain/Neck, [Opn, Perc, Perc Endo], [Drain Dev, No Dev], NQ 55, 217, 238, 355
0N98[0,3,4]ZX	Drain/Occipital Bone, Lt, [Opn, Perc, Perc Endo] 14, 18, 129, 243
0N98[0,3,4][0,Z]Z	Drain/Occipital Bone, Lt, [Opn, Perc, Perc Endo], [Drain Dev, No Dev], NQ 14, 18, 415
0N97*	Drain/Occipital Bone, Rt 9

0N97[0,3,4]ZX	Drain/Occipital Bone, Rt, [Opn, Perc, Perc Endo] 13, 18, 129, 243
0N97[0,3,4][0,Z]Z	Drain/Occipital Bone, Rt, [Opn, Perc, Perc Endo], [Drain Dev, No Dev], NQ 13, 18, 415
0R900[0,Z]Z	Drain/Occipital-cervical Jt, Opn, [Drain Dev, No Dev], NQ 156
009H[0,3,4][0,Z]Z	Drain/Oculomotor Nerve, [Opn, Perc, Perc Endo], [Drain Dev, No Dev], NQ 23
009F[0,3,4][0,Z]Z	Drain/Olfactory Nerve, [Opn, Perc, Perc Endo], [Drain Dev, No Dev], NQ 23
009G[0,3,4][0,Z]Z	Drain/Optic Nerve, [Opn, Perc, Perc Endo], [Drain Dev, No Dev], NQ 23
0W93[0,3,4][0,Z]Z	Drain/Oral Cavity and Throat, [Opn, Perc, Perc Endo], [Drain Dev, No Dev], NQ 56, 217, 355
0N9Q[0,4]ZZ	Drain/Orbit, Lt, [Opn, Perc Endo] 42, 48, 343, 454
0N9Q[0,3,4]ZX	Drain/Orbit, Lt, [Opn, Perc, Perc Endo] 42, 454
0N9Q[0,3,4]0Z	Drain/Orbit, Lt, [Opn, Perc, Perc Endo], Drain Dev, NQ 42, 48, 343, 454
0N9P[0,4]ZZ	Drain/Orbit, Rt, [Opn, Perc Endo] 42, 48, 343, 454
0N9P[0,3,4]ZX	Drain/Orbit, Rt, [Opn, Perc, Perc Endo] 42, 454
0N9P[0,3,4]0Z	Drain/Orbit, Rt, [Opn, Perc, Perc Endo], Drain Dev, NQ 42, 48, 343, 454
0U92*	Drain/Ovaries, Bilat 262, 263, 265
0U91*	Drain/Ovary, Lt 262, 263, 265
0U90*	Drain/Ovary, Rt 262, 263, 265
0N9L*	Drain/Palatine Bone, Lt 54
0N9L[0,3,4]ZX	Drain/Palatine Bone, Lt, [Opn, Perc, Perc Endo] 129, 454
0N9K*	Drain/Palatine Bone, Rt 54
0N9K[0,3,4]ZX	Drain/Palatine Bone, Rt, [Opn, Perc, Perc Endo] 129, 454
0F9G[0,3,4][0,Z]Z	Drain/Pancreas, [Opn, Perc, Perc Endo], [Drain Dev, No Dev], NQ 119
0F9D[0,3,4,7,8]ZZ	Drain/Pancreatic Duct, [Opn, Perc, Perc Endo, Via Natrl or Artfcl Opng, Via Natrl or Artfcl Opng Endo] 119
0F9D[0,3,4,7]0Z	Drain/Pancreatic Duct, [Opn, Perc, Perc Endo, Via Natrl or Artfcl Opng], Drain Dev, NQ 119
0F9F[0,3,4,7,8]ZZ	Drain/Pancreatic Duct, Accessory, [Opn, Perc, Perc Endo, Via Natrl or Artfcl Opng, Via Natrl or Artfcl Opng Endo] 119
0F9F[0,3,4,7]0Z	Drain/Pancreatic Duct, Accessory, [Opn, Perc, Perc Endo, Via Natrl or Artfcl Opng], Drain Dev, NQ 119
0G9R[0,3,4]ZX	Drain/Parathyroid Gland, [Opn, Perc, Perc Endo] 153, 238
0G9R0[0,Z]Z	Drain/Parathyroid Gland, Opn, [Drain Dev, No Dev], NQ 53, 211, 238, 336
0G9Q[0,3,4]ZX	Drain/Parathyroid Glands, Multi, [Opn, Perc, Perc Endo] 153, 238
0G9Q0[0,Z]Z	Drain/Parathyroid Glands, Multi, Opn, [Drain Dev, No Dev], NQ 53, 211, 238, 336
0N94[0,3,4]ZX	Drain/Parietal Bone, Lt, [Opn, Perc, Perc Endo] 9, 13, 18, 129, 243
0N94[0,3,4][0,Z]Z	Drain/Parietal Bone, Lt, [Opn, Perc, Perc Endo], [Drain Dev, No Dev], NQ 9, 13, 18, 414
0N93[0,3,4]ZX	Drain/Parietal Bone, Rt, [Opn, Perc, Perc Endo] 9, 13, 18, 129, 243
0N93[0,3,4][0,Z]Z	Drain/Parietal Bone, Rt, [Opn, Perc, Perc Endo], [Drain Dev, No Dev], NQ 9, 13, 18, 414
0Q9F[0,3,4]ZX	Drain/Patella, Lt, [Opn, Perc, Perc Endo] 130, 217, 244, 253, 259, 456
0Q9F[0,3,4][0,Z]Z	Drain/Patella, Lt, [Opn, Perc, Perc Endo], [Drain Dev, No Dev], NQ 135, 347
0Q9D[0,3,4]ZX	Drain/Patella, Rt, [Opn, Perc, Perc Endo] 130, 217, 244, 253, 259, 456
0Q9D[0,3,4][0,Z]Z	Drain/Patella, Rt, [Opn, Perc, Perc Endo], [Drain Dev, No Dev], NQ 135, 347
0Q93[0,3,4]ZX	Drain/Pelvic Bone, Lt, [Opn, Perc, Perc Endo] 130, 244, 253, 259, 292, 456
0Q93[0,3,4][0,Z]Z	Drain/Pelvic Bone, Lt, [Opn, Perc, Perc Endo], [Drain Dev, No Dev], NQ 135
0Q92[0,3,4]ZX	Drain/Pelvic Bone, Rt, [Opn, Perc, Perc Endo] 130, 244, 253, 259, 292, 456
0Q92[0,3,4][0,Z]Z	Drain/Pelvic Bone, Rt, [Opn, Perc, Perc Endo], [Drain Dev, No Dev], NQ 135
0W9J[0,4]ZZ	Drain/Pelvic Cavity, [Opn, Perc Endo] 113, 355
0W9J[0,4][0,Z]Z	Drain/Pelvic Cavity, [Opn, Perc Endo], [Drain Dev, No Dev], NQ 28, 91, 123, 254
0W9J[0,4]0Z	Drain/Pelvic Cavity, [Opn, Perc Endo], Drain Dev, NQ 113, 355

0W9J[0,3,4]ZX	Drain/Pelvic Cavity, [Opn, Perc, Perc Endo] 113, 121, 269, 293, 302, 355, 460
0V9S*	Drain/Penis 257
0V9S[0,3,4,X]ZX	Drain/Penis, [Opn, Perc, Perc Endo, Ext] 217, 459
0V9S[0,3,4,X][0,Z]Z	Drain/Penis, [Opn, Perc, Perc Endo, Ext], [Drain Dev, No Dev], NQ 459
0W9D0[0,Z]Z	Drain/Pericardial Cavity, Opn, [Drain Dev, No Dev], NQ 62, 98, 302, 355
0M9K[0,3,4]ZX	Drain/Perineum Bursa & Lgmt, [Opn, Perc, Perc Endo] 143
0M9K0[0,Z]Z	Drain/Perineum Bursa & Lgmt, Opn, [Drain Dev, No Dev], NQ 342, 453
0K9M[0,4]ZZ	Drain/Perineum Muscle, [Opn, Perc Endo] 139, 214, 338, 451
0K9M[0,3,4]ZX	Drain/Perineum Muscle, [Opn, Perc, Perc Endo] 139
0K9M[0,3,4]0Z	Drain/Perineum Muscle, [Opn, Perc, Perc Endo], Drain Dev, NQ 139, 214, 338, 451
0L9H*	Drain/Perineum Tndn 141
0L9H[0,3,4][0,Z]Z	Drain/Perineum Tndn, [Opn, Perc, Perc Endo], [Drain Dev, No Dev], NQ 340, 452
0W9N[0,3,4][0,Z]Z	Drain/Perineum, Female, [Opn, Perc, Perc Endo], [Drain Dev, No Dev], NQ 217, 267, 275, 460
0W9G[0,3,4]ZX	Drain/Peritoneal Cavity, [Opn, Perc, Perc Endo] 113, 121, 269, 293, 302, 355, 460
0W9G0[0,Z]Z	Drain/Peritoneal Cavity, Opn, [Drain Dev, No Dev], NQ 91, 254, 269
0D9W[0,3,4]ZX	Drain/Peritoneum, [Opn, Perc, Perc Endo] 112, 121, 268, 292
0D9W0[0,Z]Z	Drain/Peritoneum, Opn, [Drain Dev, No Dev], NQ 333
049U[0,3,4]ZX	Drain/Peroneal Artery, Lt, [Opn, Perc, Perc Endo] 83, 441
049T[0,3,4]ZX	Drain/Peroneal Artery, Rt, [Opn, Perc, Perc Endo] 83, 441
019H[0,3,4][0,Z]Z	Drain/Peroneal Nerve, [Opn, Perc, Perc Endo], [Drain Dev, No Dev], NQ 24
0C9M[0,3,4,7,8][0,Z]Z	Drain/Pharynx, [Opn, Perc, Perc Endo, Via Natrl or Artfcl Opng, Via Natrl or Artfcl Opng Endo], [Drain Dev, No Dev], NQ 52, 331
0192[0,3,4][0,Z]Z	Drain/Phrenic Nerve, [Opn, Perc, Perc Endo], [Drain Dev, No Dev], NQ 24
0G91*	Drain/Pineal Body 235
0G91[0,3,4]ZX	Drain/Pineal Body, [Opn, Perc, Perc Endo] 9, 13, 17
0G91[0,3,4][0,Z]Z	Drain/Pineal Body, [Opn, Perc, Perc Endo], [Drain Dev, No Dev], NQ 9, 13, 17
0G90*	Drain/Pituitary Gland 235
0G90[0,3,4]ZX	Drain/Pituitary Gland, [Opn, Perc, Perc Endo] 9, 13, 17
0G90[0,3,4][0,Z]Z	Drain/Pituitary Gland, [Opn, Perc, Perc Endo], [Drain Dev, No Dev], NQ 9, 13, 17, 211
0B9P4[0,Z]Z	Drain/Pleura, Lt, Perc Endo, [Drain Dev, No Dev], NQ 64
0B9N4[0,Z]Z	Drain/Pleura, Rt, Perc Endo, [Drain Dev, No Dev], NQ 64
009B[0,3,4][0,Z]Z	Drain/Pons, [Opn, Perc, Perc Endo], [Drain Dev, No Dev], NQ 8, 12, 16, 317, 414
049N[0,3,4]ZX	Drain/Popliteal Artery, Lt, [Opn, Perc, Perc Endo] 83, 441
049M[0,3,4]ZX	Drain/Popliteal Artery, Rt, [Opn, Perc, Perc Endo] 83, 441
0698[0,3,4]ZX	Drain/Portal Vein, [Opn, Perc, Perc Endo] 86, 442
049S[0,3,4]ZX	Drain/Post Tibial Artery, Lt, [Opn, Perc, Perc Endo] 83, 441
049R[0,3,4]ZX	Drain/Post Tibial Artery, Rt, [Opn, Perc, Perc Endo] 83, 441
0V9T*	Drain/Prepuce 257
0V9T[0,3,4,X]ZX	Drain/Prepuce, [Opn, Perc, Perc Endo, Ext] 217, 459
0V9T[0,3,4,X][0,Z]Z	Drain/Prepuce, [Opn, Perc, Perc Endo, Ext], [Drain Dev, No Dev], NQ 459
0V90[0,7,8][0,Z]Z	Drain/Prostate, [Opn, Via Natrl or Artfcl Opng, Via Natrl or Artfcl Opng Endo], [Drain Dev, No Dev], NQ 260
019C[0,3,4][0,Z]Z	Drain/Pudendal Nerve, [Opn, Perc, Perc Endo], [Drain Dev, No Dev], NQ 24
039C[0,3,4]ZX	Drain/Radial Artery, Lt, [Opn, Perc, Perc Endo] 81, 441
039B[0,3,4]ZX	Drain/Radial Artery, Rt, [Opn, Perc, Perc Endo] 81, 441
0196[0,3,4][0,Z]Z	Drain/Radial Nerve, [Opn, Perc, Perc Endo], [Drain Dev, No Dev], NQ 24
0P9J[0,3,4]ZX	Drain/Radius, Lt, [Opn, Perc, Perc Endo] 129, 216, 243, 253, 259, 455
0P9J[0,3,4][0,Z]Z	Drain/Radius, Lt, [Opn, Perc, Perc Endo], [Drain Dev, No Dev], NQ 134
0P9H[0,3,4]ZX	Drain/Radius, Rt, [Opn, Perc, Perc Endo] 129, 216, 243, 253, 259, 455
0P9H[0,3,4][0,Z]Z	Drain/Radius, Rt, [Opn, Perc, Perc Endo], [Drain Dev, No Dev], NQ 134
0D9P[0,3,4,7,8]ZZ	Drain/Rectum, [Opn, Perc, Perc Endo, Via Natrl or Artfcl Opng, Via Natrl or Artfcl Opng Endo] 109, 333

ØD9P[Ø,3,4]ØZ	Drain/Rectum, [Opn, Perc, Perc Endo], Drain Dev, NQ 106, 333
Ø49A[Ø,3,4]ZX	Drain/Renal Artery, Lt, [Opn, Perc, Perc Endo] 83, 441
Ø499[Ø,3,4]ZX	Drain/Renal Artery, Rt, [Opn, Perc, Perc Endo] 83, 441
Ø69B[Ø,3,4]ZX	Drain/Renal Vein, Lt, [Opn, Perc, Perc Endo] 86, 442
Ø699[Ø,3,4]ZX	Drain/Renal Vein, Rt, [Opn, Perc, Perc Endo] 86, 442
Ø89F*	Drain/Retina, Lt 44
Ø89F3[Ø,Z]Z	Drain/Retina, Lt, Perc, [Drain Dev, No Dev], NQ 329, 444
Ø89E*	Drain/Retina, Rt 44
Ø89E3[Ø,Z]Z	Drain/Retina, Rt, Perc, [Drain Dev, No Dev], NQ 329, 444
Ø89H*	Drain/Retinal Vessel, Lt 44
Ø89H3[Ø,Z]Z	Drain/Retinal Vessel, Lt, Perc, [Drain Dev, No Dev], NQ 329, 444
Ø89G*	Drain/Retinal Vessel, Rt 44
Ø89G3[Ø,Z]Z	Drain/Retinal Vessel, Rt, Perc, [Drain Dev, No Dev], NQ 329, 444
ØW9H*	Drain/Retroperitoneum 113, 355
ØW9H[Ø,3,4]ZX	Drain/Retroperitoneum, [Opn, Perc, Perc Endo] 121, 269, 293, 302, 460
ØW9H[Ø,3,4][Ø,Z]Z	Drain/Retroperitoneum, [Opn, Perc, Perc Endo], [Drain Dev, No Dev], NQ 91, 123, 217, 254, 302
ØP92[Ø,3,4]ZX	Drain/Rib, Lt, [Opn, Perc, Perc Endo] 65, 129, 216, 243, 253, 259, 455
ØP92[Ø,3,4][Ø,Z]Z	Drain/Rib, Lt, [Opn, Perc, Perc Endo], [Drain Dev, No Dev], NQ 134
ØP91[Ø,3,4]ZX	Drain/Rib, Rt, [Opn, Perc, Perc Endo] 65, 129, 216, 243, 253, 259, 455
ØP91[Ø,3,4][Ø,Z]Z	Drain/Rib, Rt, [Opn, Perc, Perc Endo], [Drain Dev, No Dev], NQ 134
ØG93[Ø,3,4][Ø,Z]Z	Drain/Rt Adrenal Gland, [Opn, Perc, Perc Endo], [Drain Dev, No Dev], NQ 235
Ø19R[Ø,3,4][Ø,Z]Z	Drain/Sacral Nerve, [Opn, Perc, Perc Endo], [Drain Dev, No Dev], NQ 24
Ø19Q[Ø,3,4][Ø,Z]Z	Drain/Sacral Plexus, [Opn, Perc, Perc Endo], [Drain Dev, No Dev], NQ 24
Ø19P*	Drain/Sacral Sympathetic Nerve 24
Ø19P[Ø,3,4][Ø,Z]Z	Drain/Sacral Sympathetic Nerve, [Opn, Perc, Perc Endo], [Drain Dev, No Dev], NQ 89
ØS95Ø[Ø,Z]Z	Drain/Sacrococcygeal Jt, Opn, [Drain Dev, No Dev], NQ 157
ØS98Ø[Ø,Z]Z	Drain/Sacroiliac Jt, Lt, Opn, [Drain Dev, No Dev], NQ 157
ØS97Ø[Ø,Z]Z	Drain/Sacroiliac Jt, Rt, Opn, [Drain Dev, No Dev], NQ 157
ØQ91[Ø,3,4]ZX	Drain/Sacrum, [Opn, Perc, Perc Endo] 130, 244, 253, 259, 292, 456
ØQ91[Ø,3,4][Ø,Z]Z	Drain/Sacrum, [Opn, Perc, Perc Endo], [Drain Dev, No Dev], NQ 135
ØP96[Ø,3,4]ZX	Drain/Scapula, Lt, [Opn, Perc, Perc Endo] 65, 129, 216, 243, 253, 259, 455
ØP96[Ø,3,4][Ø,Z]Z	Drain/Scapula, Lt, [Opn, Perc, Perc Endo], [Drain Dev, No Dev], NQ 134
ØP95[Ø,3,4]ZX	Drain/Scapula, Rt, [Opn, Perc, Perc Endo] 65, 129, 216, 243, 253, 259, 455
ØP95[Ø,3,4][Ø,Z]Z	Drain/Scapula, Rt, [Opn, Perc, Perc Endo], [Drain Dev, No Dev], NQ 134
Ø19F[Ø,3,4][Ø,Z]Z	Drain/Sciatic Nerve, [Opn, Perc, Perc Endo], [Drain Dev, No Dev], NQ 24
Ø897*	Drain/Sclera, Lt 329
Ø897X[Ø,Z]Z	Drain/Sclera, Lt, Ext, [Drain Dev, No Dev], NQ 42, 444
Ø896*	Drain/Sclera, Rt 329
Ø896X[Ø,Z]Z	Drain/Sclera, Rt, Ext, [Drain Dev, No Dev], NQ 42, 444
ØV92Ø[Ø,Z]Z	Drain/Seminal Vesicle, Lt, Opn, [Drain Dev, No Dev], NQ 260
ØV91Ø[Ø,Z]Z	Drain/Seminal Vesicle, Rt, Opn, [Drain Dev, No Dev], NQ 260
ØV93Ø[Ø,Z]Z	Drain/Seminal Vesicles, Bilat, Opn, [Drain Dev, No Dev], NQ 260
ØM92[Ø,4]ZZ	Drain/Shldr Bursa & Lgmt, Lt, [Opn, Perc Endo] 342
ØM92Ø[Ø,Z]Z	Drain/Shldr Bursa & Lgmt, Lt, Opn, [Drain Dev, No Dev], NQ 143, 453
ØM91[Ø,4]ZZ	Drain/Shldr Bursa & Lgmt, Rt, [Opn, Perc Endo] 342
ØM91Ø[Ø,Z]Z	Drain/Shldr Bursa & Lgmt, Rt, Opn, [Drain Dev, No Dev], NQ 143, 453
ØR9KØ[Ø,Z]Z	Drain/Shldr Jt, Lt, Opn, [Drain Dev, No Dev], NQ 147, 349
ØR9JØ[Ø,Z]Z	Drain/Shldr Jt, Rt, Opn, [Drain Dev, No Dev], NQ 147, 349
ØK96[Ø,4]ZZ	Drain/Shldr Muscle, Lt, [Opn, Perc Endo] 138, 214, 338, 451
ØK96[Ø,3,4]ZX	Drain/Shldr Muscle, Lt, [Opn, Perc, Perc Endo] 138
ØK96[Ø,3,4]ØZ	Drain/Shldr Muscle, Lt, [Opn, Perc, Perc Endo], Drain Dev, NQ 138, 214, 338, 451
ØK95[Ø,4]ZZ	Drain/Shldr Muscle, Rt, [Opn, Perc Endo] 138, 214, 338, 451
ØK95[Ø,3,4]ZX	Drain/Shldr Muscle, Rt, [Opn, Perc, Perc Endo] 138
ØK95[Ø,3,4]ØZ	Drain/Shldr Muscle, Rt, [Opn, Perc, Perc Endo], Drain Dev, NQ 138, 214, 338, 451
ØL92*	Drain/Shldr Tndn, Lt 141
ØL92[Ø,3,4][Ø,Z]Z	Drain/Shldr Tndn, Lt, [Opn, Perc, Perc Endo], [Drain Dev, No Dev], NQ 340, 452
ØL91*	Drain/Shldr Tndn, Rt 141
ØL91[Ø,3,4][Ø,Z]Z	Drain/Shldr Tndn, Rt, [Opn, Perc, Perc Endo], [Drain Dev, No Dev], NQ 340, 452
ØD9N[Ø,3,4,7,8]ZZ	Drain/Sigmoid Colon, [Opn, Perc, Perc Endo, Via Natrl or Artfcl Opng, Via Natrl or Artfcl Opng Endo] 109, 333
ØD9N[Ø,3,4]ØZ	Drain/Sigmoid Colon, [Opn, Perc, Perc Endo], Drain Dev, NQ 109, 333
ØH99X[Ø,Z]Z	Drain/Skin, Perineum, Ext, [Drain Dev, No Dev], NQ 211, 266, 274, 449
ØN9Ø[Ø,3,4]ZX	Drain/Skull, [Opn, Perc, Perc Endo] 9, 13, 17, 129, 243
ØN9Ø[Ø,3,4][Ø,Z]Z	Drain/Skull, [Opn, Perc, Perc Endo], [Drain Dev, No Dev], NQ 9, 13, 17, 414
ØD98[Ø,3,4,7,8]ZZ	Drain/Sm Intestine, [Opn, Perc, Perc Endo, Via Natrl or Artfcl Opng, Via Natrl or Artfcl Opng Endo] 108, 300, 332
ØD98[Ø,3,4]ØZ	Drain/Sm Intestine, [Opn, Perc, Perc Endo], Drain Dev, NQ 108, 300, 332
ØC93*	Drain/Soft Palate 56
ØC93[Ø,3,X]ZX	Drain/Soft Palate, [Opn, Perc, Ext] 448
ØN9D*	Drain/Sphenoid Bone, Lt 54
ØN9D[Ø,3,4]ZX	Drain/Sphenoid Bone, Lt, [Opn, Perc, Perc Endo] 129, 454
ØN9C*	Drain/Sphenoid Bone, Rt 54
ØN9C[Ø,3,4]ZX	Drain/Sphenoid Bone, Rt, [Opn, Perc, Perc Endo] 129, 454
Ø99XØ[Ø,Z]Z	Drain/Sphenoid Sinus, Lt, Opn, [Drain Dev, No Dev], NQ 55
Ø99WØ[Ø,Z]Z	Drain/Sphenoid Sinus, Rt, Opn, [Drain Dev, No Dev], NQ 55
ØØ9UØ[Ø,Z]Z	Drain/Spinal Canal, Opn, [Drain Dev, No Dev], NQ 318
ØØ9T*	Drain/Spinal Meninges 159, 160
ØØ9T[Ø,3,4]ZX	Drain/Spinal Meninges, [Opn, Perc, Perc Endo] 19, 295
ØØ9T[Ø,3,4][Ø,Z]Z	Drain/Spinal Meninges, [Opn, Perc, Perc Endo], [Drain Dev, No Dev], NQ 19, 295, 318
Ø79PØ[Ø,Z]Z	Drain/Spleen, Opn, [Drain Dev, No Dev], NQ 290, 297, 328
Ø494[Ø,3,4]ZX	Drain/Splenic Artery, [Opn, Perc, Perc Endo] 83, 441
Ø691[Ø,3,4]ZX	Drain/Splenic Vein, [Opn, Perc, Perc Endo] 86, 442
ØJ9[D,F,G,H]ØZZ	Drain/SQ Tissue & Fascia, [Rt Upr Arm, Lt Upr Arm, Rt Lwr Arm, Lt Lwr Arm], Opn 137
ØJ91[Ø,3]ØZ	Drain/SQ Tissue & Fascia, Face, [Opn, Perc], Drain Dev, NQ 56, 212, 337
ØJ9K[Ø,3][Ø,Z]Z	Drain/SQ Tissue & Fascia, Lt Hand, [Opn, Perc], [Drain Dev, No Dev], NQ 149, 212, 314
ØJ9J[Ø,3]ZZ	Drain/SQ Tissue & Fascia, Rt Hand, [Opn, Perc] 450
ØJ9J[Ø,3][Ø,Z]Z	Drain/SQ Tissue & Fascia, Rt Hand, [Opn, Perc], [Drain Dev, No Dev], NQ 149, 212, 314
ØJ9J[Ø,3]ØZ	Drain/SQ Tissue & Fascia, Rt Hand, [Opn, Perc], Drain Dev, NQ 450
ØR9FØ[Ø,Z]Z	Drain/Sternoclavicular Jt, Lt, Opn, [Drain Dev, No Dev], NQ 147, 349
ØR9EØ[Ø,Z]Z	Drain/Sternoclavicular Jt, Rt, Opn, [Drain Dev, No Dev], NQ 147, 349
ØP9Ø[Ø,3,4]ZX	Drain/Sternum, [Opn, Perc, Perc Endo] 65, 129, 216, 243, 253, 259, 455
ØP9Ø[Ø,3,4][Ø,Z]Z	Drain/Sternum, [Opn, Perc, Perc Endo], [Drain Dev, No Dev], NQ 134
ØD96[Ø,3,4,7,8]ZZ	Drain/Stomach, [Opn, Perc, Perc Endo, Via Natrl or Artfcl Opng, Via Natrl or Artfcl Opng Endo] 105, 122, 332
ØD96[Ø,3,4]ØZ	Drain/Stomach, [Opn, Perc, Perc Endo], Drain Dev, NQ 105, 122, 332
ØD97[Ø,3,4,7,8]ZZ	Drain/Stomach, Pylorus, [Opn, Perc, Perc Endo, Via Natrl or Artfcl Opng, Via Natrl or Artfcl Opng Endo] 105
ØD97[Ø,3,4]ØZ	Drain/Stomach, Pylorus, [Opn, Perc, Perc Endo], Drain Dev, NQ 105
ØØ95Ø[Ø,Z]Z	Drain/Subarachnoid Space, Opn, [Drain Dev, No Dev], NQ 8, 12, 16, 295, 317, 414
Ø394[Ø,3,4]ZX	Drain/Subclavian Artery, Lt, [Opn, Perc, Perc Endo] 81, 441
Ø393[Ø,3,4]ZX	Drain/Subclavian Artery, Rt, [Opn, Perc, Perc Endo] 81, 441
Ø596[Ø,3,4]ZX	Drain/Subclavian Vein, Lt, [Opn, Perc, Perc Endo] 85, 442
Ø595[Ø,3,4]ZX	Drain/Subclavian Vein, Rt, [Opn, Perc, Perc Endo] 85, 442

00940[0,Z]Z	Drain/Subdural Space, Opn, [Drain Dev, No Dev], NQ 8, 12, 16, 295, 317, 414
0495[0,3,4]ZX	Drain/Superior Mesenteric Artery, [Opn, Perc, Perc Endo] 83, 441
0695[0,3,4]ZX	Drain/Superior Mesenteric Vein, [Opn, Perc, Perc Endo] 86, 442
0G9M[0,3,4]ZX	Drain/Superior Parathyroid Gland, Lt, [Opn, Perc, Perc Endo] 153, 238
0G9M0[0,Z]Z	Drain/Superior Parathyroid Gland, Lt, Opn, [Drain Dev, No Dev], NQ 53, 211, 238, 336
0G9L[0,3,4]ZX	Drain/Superior Parathyroid Gland, Rt, [Opn, Perc, Perc Endo] 153, 238
0G9L0[0,Z]Z	Drain/Superior Parathyroid Gland, Rt, Opn, [Drain Dev, No Dev], NQ 53, 211, 238, 336
0S9J0[0,Z]Z	Drain/Tarsal Jt, Lt, Opn, [Drain Dev, No Dev], NQ 145, 351, 457
0S9H0[0,Z]Z	Drain/Tarsal Jt, Rt, Opn, [Drain Dev, No Dev], NQ 145, 351, 457
0Q9M[0,3,4]ZX	Drain/Tarsal, Lt, [Opn, Perc, Perc Endo] 130, 217, 244, 253, 259, 456
0Q9M[0,3,4][0,Z]Z	Drain/Tarsal, Lt, [Opn, Perc, Perc Endo], [Drain Dev, No Dev], NQ 145
0Q9L[0,3,4]ZX	Drain/Tarsal, Rt, [Opn, Perc, Perc Endo] 130, 217, 244, 253, 259, 456
0Q9L[0,3,4][0,Z]Z	Drain/Tarsal, Rt, [Opn, Perc, Perc Endo], [Drain Dev, No Dev], NQ 145
039T[0,3,4]ZX	Drain/Temporal Artery, Lt, [Opn, Perc, Perc Endo] 25, 42, 50, 63, 81, 152, 239, 251, 441
039S[0,3,4]ZX	Drain/Temporal Artery, Rt, [Opn, Perc, Perc Endo] 25, 42, 50, 63, 81, 152, 239, 251, 441
0N96*	Drain/Temporal Bone, Lt 9
0N96[0,3,4]ZX	Drain/Temporal Bone, Lt, [Opn, Perc, Perc Endo] 13, 18, 129, 243
0N96[0,3,4][0,Z]Z	Drain/Temporal Bone, Lt, [Opn, Perc, Perc Endo], [Drain Dev, No Dev], NQ 13, 18, 414
0N95*	Drain/Temporal Bone, Rt 9
0N95[0,3,4]ZX	Drain/Temporal Bone, Rt, [Opn, Perc, Perc Endo] 13, 18, 129, 243
0N95[0,3,4][0,Z]Z	Drain/Temporal Bone, Rt, [Opn, Perc, Perc Endo], [Drain Dev, No Dev], NQ 13, 18, 414
0R9D*	Drain/Temporomandibular Jt, Lt 55
0R9D[0,3,4]ZX	Drain/Temporomandibular Jt, Lt, [Opn, Perc, Perc Endo] 130, 457
0R9C*	Drain/Temporomandibular Jt, Rt 55
0R9C[0,3,4]ZX	Drain/Temporomandibular Jt, Rt, [Opn, Perc, Perc Endo] 130, 457
0V9C0[0,Z]Z	Drain/Testes, Bilat, Opn, [Drain Dev, No Dev], NQ 257, 354
0V9B0[0,Z]Z	Drain/Testis, Lt, Opn, [Drain Dev, No Dev], NQ 257, 354
0V990[0,Z]Z	Drain/Testis, Rt, Opn, [Drain Dev, No Dev], NQ 257, 354
0099[0,3,4][0,Z]Z	Drain/Thalamus, [Opn, Perc, Perc Endo], [Drain Dev, No Dev], NQ 8, 12, 16, 295, 317, 414
079K[0,3,4]ZX	Drain/Thoracic Duct, [Opn, Perc, Perc Endo] 25, 64, 90, 153, 209, 241, 290, 443
079K[0,3,4][0,Z]Z	Drain/Thoracic Duct, [Opn, Perc, Perc Endo], [Drain Dev, No Dev], NQ 60, 328
0198[0,3,4][0,Z]Z	Drain/Thoracic Nerve, [Opn, Perc, Perc Endo], [Drain Dev, No Dev], NQ 24
009X*	Drain/Thoracic Spinal Cord 159, 160
009X[0,3,4]ZX	Drain/Thoracic Spinal Cord, [Opn, Perc, Perc Endo] 19, 295
009X[0,3,4][0,Z]Z	Drain/Thoracic Spinal Cord, [Opn, Perc, Perc Endo], [Drain Dev, No Dev], NQ 19, 295, 318
019L*	Drain/Thoracic Sympathetic Nerve 24
019L[0,3,4][0,Z]Z	Drain/Thoracic Sympathetic Nerve, [Opn, Perc, Perc Endo], [Drain Dev, No Dev], NQ 89
0R990[0,Z]Z	Drain/Thoracic Vert Disc, Opn, [Drain Dev, No Dev], NQ 156
0R960[0,Z]Z	Drain/Thoracic Vert Jt, Opn, [Drain Dev, No Dev], NQ 156
0P94[0,3,4]ZX	Drain/Thoracic Vertebra, [Opn, Perc, Perc Endo] 65, 129, 292, 455
0P94[0,3,4][0,Z]Z	Drain/Thoracic Vertebra, [Opn, Perc, Perc Endo], [Drain Dev, No Dev], NQ 134
0R9B0[0,Z]Z	Drain/Thoracolumbar Vert Disc, Opn, [Drain Dev, No Dev], NQ 156
0R9A0[0,Z]Z	Drain/Thoracolumbar Vert Jt, Opn, [Drain Dev, No Dev], NQ 156
0M9G0[0,Z]Z	Drain/Thorax Bursa & Lgmt, Lt, Opn, [Drain Dev, No Dev], NQ 143, 342, 453

0M9F0[0,Z]Z	Drain/Thorax Bursa & Lgmt, Rt, Opn, [Drain Dev, No Dev], NQ 143, 342, 453
0K9J[0,4]ZZ	Drain/Thorax Muscle, Lt, [Opn, Perc Endo] 139, 214, 338, 451
0K9J[0,3,4]ZX	Drain/Thorax Muscle, Lt, [Opn, Perc, Perc Endo] 139
0K9J[0,3,4]0Z	Drain/Thorax Muscle, Lt, [Opn, Perc, Perc Endo], Drain Dev, NQ 139, 214, 338, 451
0K9H[0,4]ZZ	Drain/Thorax Muscle, Rt, [Opn, Perc Endo] 139, 214, 338, 451
0K9H[0,3,4]ZX	Drain/Thorax Muscle, Rt, [Opn, Perc, Perc Endo] 139
0K9H[0,3,4]0Z	Drain/Thorax Muscle, Rt, [Opn, Perc, Perc Endo], Drain Dev, NQ 139, 214, 338, 451
0L9D*	Drain/Thorax Tndn, Lt 141
0L9D[0,3,4][0,Z]Z	Drain/Thorax Tndn, Lt, [Opn, Perc, Perc Endo], [Drain Dev, No Dev], NQ 340, 452
0L9C*	Drain/Thorax Tndn, Rt 141
0L9C[0,3,4][0,Z]Z	Drain/Thorax Tndn, Rt, [Opn, Perc, Perc Endo], [Drain Dev, No Dev], NQ 340, 452
0P9S[0,3,4]ZX	Drain/Thumb Phalanx, Lt, [Opn, Perc, Perc Endo] 129, 216, 292, 455
0P9S[0,3,4][0,Z]Z	Drain/Thumb Phalanx, Lt, [Opn, Perc, Perc Endo], [Drain Dev, No Dev], NQ 134
0P9R[0,3,4]ZX	Drain/Thumb Phalanx, Rt, [Opn, Perc, Perc Endo] 129, 216, 292, 455
0P9R[0,3,4][0,Z]Z	Drain/Thumb Phalanx, Rt, [Opn, Perc, Perc Endo], [Drain Dev, No Dev], NQ 134
079M*	Drain/Thymus 60, 241, 290
079M[0,3,4]ZX	Drain/Thymus, [Opn, Perc, Perc Endo] 297
079M[0,3,4][0,Z]Z	Drain/Thymus, [Opn, Perc, Perc Endo], [Drain Dev, No Dev], NQ 297, 328
039V[0,3,4]ZX	Drain/Thyroid Artery, Lt, [Opn, Perc, Perc Endo] 81, 441
039U[0,3,4]ZX	Drain/Thyroid Artery, Rt, [Opn, Perc, Perc Endo] 81, 441
0G9G0[0,Z]Z	Drain/Thyroid Gland Lobe, Lt, Opn, [Drain Dev, No Dev], NQ 53, 211, 336
0G9G0Z[X,Z]	Drain/Thyroid Gland Lobe, Lt, Opn, No Dev, [Dx, NQ] 237
0G9K0Z[X,Z]	Drain/Thyroid Gland Lobe, Opn, No Dev, [Dx, NQ] 237
0G9H0[0,Z]Z	Drain/Thyroid Gland Lobe, Rt, Opn, [Drain Dev, No Dev], NQ 53, 211, 336
0G9H0Z[X,Z]	Drain/Thyroid Gland Lobe, Rt, Opn, No Dev, [Dx, NQ] 237
0G9K0[0,Z]Z	Drain/Thyroid Gland, Opn, [Drain Dev, No Dev], NQ 53, 211, 336
0Q9H[0,3,4]ZX	Drain/Tibia, Lt, [Opn, Perc, Perc Endo] 130, 217, 244, 253, 259, 456
0Q9H[0,3,4][0,Z]Z	Drain/Tibia, Lt, [Opn, Perc, Perc Endo], [Drain Dev, No Dev], NQ 135
0Q9G[0,3,4]ZX	Drain/Tibia, Rt, [Opn, Perc, Perc Endo] 130, 217, 244, 253, 259, 456
0Q9G[0,3,4][0,Z]Z	Drain/Tibia, Rt, [Opn, Perc, Perc Endo], [Drain Dev, No Dev], NQ 135
019G[0,3,4][0,Z]Z	Drain/Tibial Nerve, [Opn, Perc, Perc Endo], [Drain Dev, No Dev], NQ 24
0S9Q0[0,Z]Z	Drain/Toe Phalangeal Jt, Lt, Opn, [Drain Dev, No Dev], NQ 145, 351, 457
0S9P0[0,Z]Z	Drain/Toe Phalangeal Jt, Rt, Opn, [Drain Dev, No Dev], NQ 145, 351, 457
0Q9R[0,3,4]ZX	Drain/Toe Phalanx, Lt, [Opn, Perc, Perc Endo] 130, 217, 292, 456
0Q9R[0,3,4][0,Z]Z	Drain/Toe Phalanx, Lt, [Opn, Perc, Perc Endo], [Drain Dev, No Dev], NQ 135
0Q9Q[0,3,4]ZX	Drain/Toe Phalanx, Rt, [Opn, Perc, Perc Endo] 130, 217, 292, 456
0Q9Q[0,3,4][0,Z]Z	Drain/Toe Phalanx, Rt, [Opn, Perc, Perc Endo], [Drain Dev, No Dev], NQ 135
0C97[0,3,X][0,Z]Z	Drain/Tongue, [Opn, Perc, Ext], [Drain Dev, No Dev], NQ 56
0K94[0,4]ZZ	Drain/Tongue, Palate, Pharynx Muscle, [Opn, Perc Endo] 138, 214, 338, 451
0K94[0,3,4]ZX	Drain/Tongue, Palate, Pharynx Muscle, [Opn, Perc, Perc Endo] 138
0K94[0,3,4]0Z	Drain/Tongue, Palate, Pharynx Muscle, [Opn, Perc, Perc Endo], Drain Dev, NQ 138, 214, 338, 451
0C9P*	Drain/Tonsils 52
0C9P[0,3,X]ZX	Drain/Tonsils, [Opn, Perc, Ext] 448
0B91[0,3,4,7,8][0,Z]Z	Drain/Trachea, [Opn, Perc, Perc Endo, Via Natrl or Artfcl Opng, Via Natrl or Artfcl Opng Endo], [Drain Dev, No Dev], NQ 64
0D9L[0,3,4,7,8]ZZ	Drain/Transv Colon, [Opn, Perc, Perc Endo, Via Natrl or Artfcl Opng, Via Natrl or Artfcl Opng Endo] 108, 333

0D9L[0,3,4]0Z	Drain/Transv Colon, [Opn, Perc, Perc Endo], Drain Dev, NQ 108, 333
009K[0,3,4][0,Z]Z	Drain/Trigeminal Nerve, [Opn, Perc, Perc Endo], [Drain Dev, No Dev], NQ 23
009J[0,3,4][0,Z]Z	Drain/Trochlear Nerve, [Opn, Perc, Perc Endo], [Drain Dev, No Dev], NQ 23
0M9D0[0,Z]Z	Drain/Trunk Bursa & Lgmt, Lt, Opn, [Drain Dev, No Dev], NQ 143, 342, 453
0M9C0[0,Z]Z	Drain/Trunk Bursa & Lgmt, Rt, Opn, [Drain Dev, No Dev], NQ 143, 342, 453
0K9G[0,4]ZZ	Drain/Trunk Muscle, Lt, [Opn, Perc Endo] 139, 214, 338, 451
0K9G[0,3,4]ZX	Drain/Trunk Muscle, Lt, [Opn, Perc, Perc Endo] 139
0K9G[0,3,4]0Z	Drain/Trunk Muscle, Lt, [Opn, Perc, Perc Endo], Drain Dev, NQ 139, 214, 338, 451
0K9F[0,4]ZZ	Drain/Trunk Muscle, Rt, [Opn, Perc Endo] 139, 214, 338, 451
0K9F[0,3,4]ZX	Drain/Trunk Muscle, Rt, [Opn, Perc, Perc Endo] 139
0K9F[0,3,4]0Z	Drain/Trunk Muscle, Rt, [Opn, Perc, Perc Endo], Drain Dev, NQ 139, 214, 338, 451
0L9B*	Drain/Trunk Tndn, Lt 141
0L9B[0,3,4][0,Z]Z	Drain/Trunk Tndn, Lt, [Opn, Perc, Perc Endo], [Drain Dev, No Dev], NQ 340, 452
0L99*	Drain/Trunk Tndn, Rt 141
0L99[0,3,4][0,Z]Z	Drain/Trunk Tndn, Rt, [Opn, Perc, Perc Endo], [Drain Dev, No Dev], NQ 340, 452
0998[0,3,4,7,8]ZX	Drain/Tympanic Membrane, Lt, [Opn, Perc, Perc Endo, Via Natrl or Artfcl Opng, Via Natrl or Artfcl Opng Endo] 51, 446
0998[0,3,4,7,8]0Z	Drain/Tympanic Membrane, Lt, [Opn, Perc, Perc Endo, Via Natrl or Artfcl Opng, Via Natrl or Artfcl Opng Endo], Drain Dev, NQ 51, 446
0997[0,3,4,7,8]ZX	Drain/Tympanic Membrane, Rt, [Opn, Perc, Perc Endo, Via Natrl or Artfcl Opng, Via Natrl or Artfcl Opng Endo] 51, 446
0997[0,3,4,7,8]0Z	Drain/Tympanic Membrane, Rt, [Opn, Perc, Perc Endo, Via Natrl or Artfcl Opng, Via Natrl or Artfcl Opng Endo], Drain Dev, NQ 51, 446
0P9L[0,3,4]ZX	Drain/Ulna, Lt, [Opn, Perc, Perc Endo] 129, 216, 243, 253, 259, 455
0P9L[0,3,4][0,Z]Z	Drain/Ulna, Lt, [Opn, Perc, Perc Endo], [Drain Dev, No Dev], NQ 134
0P9K[0,3,4]ZX	Drain/Ulna, Rt, [Opn, Perc, Perc Endo] 129, 216, 243, 253, 259, 455
0P9K[0,3,4][0,Z]Z	Drain/Ulna, Rt, [Opn, Perc, Perc Endo], [Drain Dev, No Dev], NQ 134
039A[0,3,4]ZX	Drain/Ulnar Artery, Lt, [Opn, Perc, Perc Endo] 81, 441
0399[0,3,4]ZX	Drain/Ulnar Artery, Rt, [Opn, Perc, Perc Endo] 81, 441
0194[0,3,4][0,Z]Z	Drain/Ulnar Nerve, [Opn, Perc, Perc Endo], [Drain Dev, No Dev], NQ 24
0K98[0,4]ZZ	Drain/Upr Arm Muscle, Lt, [Opn, Perc Endo] 139, 214, 338, 451
0K98[0,3,4]ZX	Drain/Upr Arm Muscle, Lt, [Opn, Perc, Perc Endo] 139
0K98[0,3,4]0Z	Drain/Upr Arm Muscle, Lt, [Opn, Perc, Perc Endo], Drain Dev, NQ 139, 214, 338, 451
0K97[0,4]ZZ	Drain/Upr Arm Muscle, Rt, [Opn, Perc Endo] 139, 214, 338, 451
0K97[0,3,4]ZX	Drain/Upr Arm Muscle, Rt, [Opn, Perc, Perc Endo] 139
0K97[0,3,4]0Z	Drain/Upr Arm Muscle, Rt, [Opn, Perc, Perc Endo], Drain Dev, NQ 139, 214, 338, 451
0L94*	Drain/Upr Arm Tndn, Lt 141
0L94[0,3,4][0,Z]Z	Drain/Upr Arm Tndn, Lt, [Opn, Perc, Perc Endo], [Drain Dev, No Dev], NQ 340, 452
0L93*	Drain/Upr Arm Tndn, Rt 141
0L93[0,3,4][0,Z]Z	Drain/Upr Arm Tndn, Rt, [Opn, Perc, Perc Endo], [Drain Dev, No Dev], NQ 340, 452
039Y[0,3,4]ZX	Drain/Upr Artery, [Opn, Perc, Perc Endo] 81, 441
0M9B0[0,Z]Z	Drain/Upr Extr Bursa & Lgmt, Lt, Opn, [Drain Dev, No Dev], NQ 342, 453
0M990[0,Z]Z	Drain/Upr Extr Bursa & Lgmt, Rt, Opn, [Drain Dev, No Dev], NQ 342, 453
089P[0,3,X]ZX	Drain/Upr Eyelid, Lt, [Opn, Perc, Ext] 42, 329, 444
089N[0,3,X]ZX	Drain/Upr Eyelid, Rt, [Opn, Perc, Ext] 42, 329, 444
0Q97[0,3,4]ZX	Drain/Upr Femur, Lt, [Opn, Perc, Perc Endo] 130, 216, 244, 253, 259, 456
0Q97[0,3,4][0,Z]Z	Drain/Upr Femur, Lt, [Opn, Perc, Perc Endo], [Drain Dev, No Dev], NQ 137
0Q96[0,3,4]ZX	Drain/Upr Femur, Rt, [Opn, Perc, Perc Endo] 130, 216, 244, 253, 259, 456

0Q96[0,3,4][0,Z]Z	Drain/Upr Femur, Rt, [Opn, Perc, Perc Endo], [Drain Dev, No Dev], NQ 137
0W94[0,3,4][0,Z]Z	Drain/Upr Jaw, [Opn, Perc, Perc Endo], [Drain Dev, No Dev], NQ 56, 217, 355
0K9R[0,4]ZZ	Drain/Upr Leg Muscle, Lt, [Opn, Perc Endo] 139, 214, 338, 451
0K9R[0,3,4]ZX	Drain/Upr Leg Muscle, Lt, [Opn, Perc, Perc Endo] 139
0K9R[0,3,4]0Z	Drain/Upr Leg Muscle, Lt, [Opn, Perc, Perc Endo], Drain Dev, NQ 139, 214, 338, 451
0K9Q[0,4]ZZ	Drain/Upr Leg Muscle, Rt, [Opn, Perc Endo] 139, 214, 338, 451
0K9Q[0,3,4]ZX	Drain/Upr Leg Muscle, Rt, [Opn, Perc, Perc Endo] 139
0K9Q[0,3,4]0Z	Drain/Upr Leg Muscle, Rt, [Opn, Perc, Perc Endo], Drain Dev, NQ 139, 214, 338, 451
0L9M*	Drain/Upr Leg Tndn, Lt 141
0L9M[0,3,4][0,Z]Z	Drain/Upr Leg Tndn, Lt, [Opn, Perc, Perc Endo], [Drain Dev, No Dev], NQ 340, 452
0L9L*	Drain/Upr Leg Tndn, Rt 141
0L9L[0,3,4][0,Z]Z	Drain/Upr Leg Tndn, Rt, [Opn, Perc, Perc Endo], [Drain Dev, No Dev], NQ 340, 452
0C90[0,3,X][0,Z]Z	Drain/Upr Lip, [Opn, Perc, Ext], [Drain Dev, No Dev], NQ 56, 210, 331
0B98[0,3,4,7,8][0,Z]Z	Drain/Upr Lobe Bronchus, Lt, [Opn, Perc, Perc Endo, Via Natrl or Artfcl Opng, Via Natrl or Artfcl Opng Endo], [Drain Dev, No Dev], NQ 61
0B94[0,3,4,7,8][0,Z]Z	Drain/Upr Lobe Bronchus, Rt, [Opn, Perc, Perc Endo, Via Natrl or Artfcl Opng, Via Natrl or Artfcl Opng Endo], [Drain Dev, No Dev], NQ 61
0B9G[0,8]ZX	Drain/Upr Lung Lobe, Lt, [Opn, Via Natrl or Artfcl Opng Endo] 90
0B9G[3,4,7,8][0,Z]Z	Drain/Upr Lung Lobe, Lt, [Perc, Perc Endo, Via Natrl or Artfcl Opng, Via Natrl or Artfcl Opng Endo], [Drain Dev, No Dev], NQ 64
0B9G0[0,Z]Z	Drain/Upr Lung Lobe, Lt, Opn, [Drain Dev, No Dev], NQ 61, 331
0B9C[0,8]ZX	Drain/Upr Lung Lobe, Rt, [Opn, Via Natrl or Artfcl Opng Endo] 90
0B9C[3,4,7,8][0,Z]Z	Drain/Upr Lung Lobe, Rt, [Perc, Perc Endo, Via Natrl or Artfcl Opng, Via Natrl or Artfcl Opng Endo], [Drain Dev, No Dev], NQ 64
0B9C0[0,Z]Z	Drain/Upr Lung Lobe, Rt, Opn, [Drain Dev, No Dev], NQ 61, 331
059Y[0,3,4]ZX	Drain/Upr Vein, [Opn, Perc, Perc Endo] 85, 442
0T97[0,3,4,7,8]ZZ	Drain/Ureter, Lt, [Opn, Perc, Perc Endo, Via Natrl or Artfcl Opng, Via Natrl or Artfcl Opng Endo] 248, 458
0T96[0,3,4,7,8]ZZ	Drain/Ureter, Rt, [Opn, Perc, Perc Endo, Via Natrl or Artfcl Opng, Via Natrl or Artfcl Opng Endo] 248, 458
0T98[0,3,4,7,8]ZZ	Drain/Ureters, Bilat, [Opn, Perc, Perc Endo, Via Natrl or Artfcl Opng, Via Natrl or Artfcl Opng Endo] 248, 458
0T9D[0,3,4,7,8,X][0,Z]Z	Drain/Urethra, [Opn, Perc, Perc Endo, Via Natrl or Artfcl Opng, Via Natrl or Artfcl Opng Endo, Ext], [Drain Dev, No Dev], NQ 250
0T9D[0,3,4]0Z	Drain/Urethra, [Opn, Perc, Perc Endo], Drain Dev, NQ 353, 458
0U94[0,3,4][0,Z]Z	Drain/Uterine Supporting Structure, [Opn, Perc, Perc Endo], [Drain Dev, No Dev], NQ 267
0U94[3,4]ZX	Drain/Uterine Supporting Structure, [Perc, Perc Endo] 266, 458
0U99[0,3,4,7,8][0,Z]Z	Drain/Uterus, [Opn, Perc, Perc Endo, Via Natrl or Artfcl Opng, Via Natrl or Artfcl Opng Endo], [Drain Dev, No Dev], NQ 262, 264, 265, 271, 354
0U99[3,4,7,8]ZX	Drain/Uterus, [Perc, Perc Endo, Via Natrl or Artfcl Opng, Via Natrl or Artfcl Opng Endo] 266, 458
0C9N*	Drain/Uvula 56
0C9N[0,3,X]ZX	Drain/Uvula, [Opn, Perc, Ext] 448
0C9N[0,3,X][0,Z]Z	Drain/Uvula, [Opn, Perc, Ext], [Drain Dev, No Dev], NQ 448
0U9G*	Drain/Vagina 267, 275
0U9G[0,3,4,7,8,X]ZX	Drain/Vagina, [Opn, Perc, Perc Endo, Via Natrl or Artfcl Opng, Via Natrl or Artfcl Opng Endo, Ext] 217, 459
0U9G[0,3,4,7,8,X][0,Z]Z	Drain/Vagina, [Opn, Perc, Perc Endo, Via Natrl or Artfcl Opng, Via Natrl or Artfcl Opng Endo, Ext], [Drain Dev, No Dev], NQ 459
009Q[0,3,4][0,Z]Z	Drain/Vagus Nerve, [Opn, Perc, Perc Endo], [Drain Dev, No Dev], NQ 23
039Q[0,3,4]ZX	Drain/Vert Artery, Lt, [Opn, Perc, Perc Endo] 81, 441
039P[0,3,4]ZX	Drain/Vert Artery, Rt, [Opn, Perc, Perc Endo] 81, 441
059S[0,3,4]ZX	Drain/Vert Vein, Lt, [Opn, Perc, Perc Endo] 85, 442
059R[0,3,4]ZX	Drain/Vert Vein, Rt, [Opn, Perc, Perc Endo] 85, 442
0U9L[0,X]ZX	Drain/Vestibular Gland, [Opn, Ext] 267, 271, 459

Ø895*	Drain/Vitreous, Lt 44
08953[Ø,Z]Z	Drain/Vitreous, Lt, Perc, [Drain Dev, No Dev], NQ 241, 329, 444
Ø894*	Drain/Vitreous, Rt 44
08943[Ø,Z]Z	Drain/Vitreous, Rt, Perc, [Drain Dev, No Dev], NQ 241, 329, 444
ØC9V[Ø,3,4,7,8][Ø,Z]Z	Drain/Vocal Cord, Lt, [Opn, Perc, Perc Endo, Via Natrl or Artfcl Opng, Via Natrl or Artfcl Opng Endo], [Drain Dev, No Dev], NQ 52
ØC9T[Ø,3,4,7,8][Ø,Z]Z	Drain/Vocal Cord, Rt, [Opn, Perc, Perc Endo, Via Natrl or Artfcl Opng, Via Natrl or Artfcl Opng Endo], [Drain Dev, No Dev], NQ 52
ØU9M*	Drain/Vulva 267, 275
ØU9M[Ø,X]ZX	Drain/Vulva, [Opn, Ext] 217, 459
ØU9M[Ø,X][Ø,Z]Z	Drain/Vulva, [Opn, Ext], [Drain Dev, No Dev], NQ 217, 459
ØM96[Ø,3,4]ØZ	Drain/Wrist Bursa & Lgmt, Lt, [Opn, Perc, Perc Endo], Drain Dev, NQ 315
ØM95[Ø,3,4]ØZ	Drain/Wrist Bursa & Lgmt, Rt, [Opn, Perc, Perc Endo], Drain Dev, NQ 315
ØR9PØ[Ø,Z]Z	Drain/Wrist Jt, Lt, Opn, [Drain Dev, No Dev], NQ 146, 315
ØR9NØ[Ø,Z]Z	Drain/Wrist Jt, Rt, Opn, [Drain Dev, No Dev], NQ 146, 315
ØN9N*	Drain/Zygomatic Bone, Lt 54
ØN9N[Ø,3,4]ZX	Drain/Zygomatic Bone, Lt, [Opn, Perc, Perc Endo] 129, 454
ØN9M*	Drain/Zygomatic Bone, Rt 54
ØN9M[Ø,3,4]ZX	Drain/Zygomatic Bone, Rt, [Opn, Perc, Perc Endo] 129, 454
Ø9Ø*	Ear, Nose, Sinus, Alter 51, 330
Ø91*	Ear, Nose, Sinus, Bypass 51
Ø98*	Ear, Nose, Sinus, Div 51
Ø9M*	Ear, Nose, Sinus, Reattach 51, 330
Ø9R*	Ear, Nose, Sinus, Replace 52
Ø9U*	Ear, Nose, Sinus, Supl 52
ØGH*	Endocrine Sys, Insert 53, 238, 336
ØKB[C,D]ØZX	Exc [Rt Hand, Lt Hand] Muscle, Opn 27
ØHB[Ø,1,4,5,6,7,8,A]XZZ	Exc [Scalp, Face, Neck, Chest, Back, Abd, Buttock, Genitalia] Skin, Ext 25, 123, 126, 313
ØJB[4,5,6]ØZZ	Exc of [Ant Neck, Post Neck, Chest] SQ Tissue & Fascia, Opn Appr 54
ØDB[K,L,M,N]ØZX	Exc of [Ascending, Transv, Descending, Sigmoid] Colon, Opn Appr, Dx 109
ØFB[4,5,6,8,9,C]ØZX	Exc of [Gallbladder, Rt Hepatic Duct, Lt Hepatic Duct, Cystic Duct, Common Bile Duct, Ampulla of Vater], Opn Appr, Dx 121
ØDB[S,T,V,W]ØZX	Exc of [Greater Omentum, Lesser Omentum, Mesentery, Peritoneum], Opn Appr, Dx 121
ØDB[E,F,G]ØZX	Exc of [Lg, Rt Lg, Lt Lg] Intestine, Opn Appr, Dx 109
ØFB[Ø,1,2]ØZX	Exc of [Liver, Rt Lobe Liver, Lt Lobe Liver], Opn Appr, Dx 53, 90, 153, 259
ØFB[D,F,G]ØZX	Exc of [Pancreatic Duct, Accessory Pancreatic Duct, Pancreas], Opn Appr, Dx 112, 121
ØTB[3,4]ØZX	Exc of [Rt, Lt] Kidney Pelvis, Opn Appr, Dx 158
ØTB[Ø,1]ØZX	Exc of [Rt, Lt] Kidney, Opn Appr, Dx 158
ØBB[N,P]4ZX	Exc of [Rt, Lt] Pleura, Perc Endo Appr, Dx 64
Ø2B[Q,R]3ZZ	Exc of [Rt, Lt] Pulmn Artery, Perc Appr 105
Ø2B[S,T]3ZZ	Exc of [Rt, Lt] Pulmn Vein, Perc Appr 105
Ø8B[6,7]XZZ	Exc of [Rt, Lt] Sclera, Ext Appr 43
Ø8B[6,7]XZX	Exc of [Rt, Lt] Sclera, Ext Appr, Dx 44
ØKB[H,J]ØZX	Exc of [Rt, Lt] Thorax Muscle, Opn Appr, Dx 65
ØJB[Ø,1,4,5,6,7,8,9,B,C,D,F,G,H,L,M,N,P,Q,R]ØZZ	Exc of [Scalp, Face, Ant Neck, Post Neck, Chest, Back, Abd, Buttock, Perineum, Pelvic Rgn, [Rt, Lt] Upr Arm, [Rt, Lt] Lwr Arm, [Rt, Lt] Upr Leg, [Rt, Lt] Lwr Leg, [Rt, Lt] Foot], SQ Tissue & Fascia, Opn Appr 253,259, 268
ØHB[Ø,1,4,5,6,7,8,A,B,C,D,E,F,G,H,J,K,L,M,N]XZZ	Exc of [Scalp, Face, Neck, Chest, Back, Abd, Buttock, Genitalia, Rt Upr Arm, Lt Upr Arm, Rt Lwr Arm, Lt Lwr Arm, Rt Hand, Lt Hand, Rt Upr Leg, Lt Upr Leg, Rt Lwr Leg, Lt Lwr Leg, Rt Foot, Lt Foot], Skin, Ext Appr 259,253, 268
ØDB[8,9,A,B,C]ØZX	Exc of [Sm Intestine, Duodenum, Jejunum, Ileum, Ileocecal Valve], Opn Appr, Dx 109
Ø2B[V,W]3ZZ	Exc of [Superior Vena Cava, Thoracic Aorta], Perc Appr 105
ØHB7XZZ	Exc of Abd Skin, Ext Appr 43, 113, 206, 236, 292, 377, 380
ØJB8ØZZ	Exc of Abd SQ/Fascia, Opn Appr 43, 206, 237, 292
ØJB83ZZ	Exc of Abd SQ/Fascia, Perc Appr 450
ØWBFXZZ	Exc of Abd Wall, Ext Appr 144
ØWBFØZZ	Exc of Abd Wall, Opn Appr 144
ØWBF3ZZ	Exc of Abd Wall, Perc Appr 144
ØWBF4ZZ	Exc of Abd Wall, Perc Endo Appr 144
ØWBFXZ2	Exc of Abd Wall, Stoma, Ext Appr 144, 217, 245, 302, 460

ØØBLØZX	Exc of Abducens Nerve, Opn Appr, Diagnostic 23, 50, 151, 318
ØØBRØZX	Exc of Accessory Nerve, Opn Appr, Diagnostic 23, 50, 151, 318
ØFBFØZX	Exc of Accessory Pancreatic Duct, Opn Appr, Diagn 242, 301, 335
Ø9BPØZX	Exc of Accessory Sinus, Opn Appr, Diagnostic 55
ØØBNØZZ	Exc of Acoustic Nerve, Opn Appr 8, 12, 16
ØØBNØZX	Exc of Acoustic Nerve, Opn Appr, Diagnostic 23, 50, 151, 318
ØFBCØZX	Exc of Ampulla of Vater, Opn Appr, Diagnostic 112
ØJB4ØZZ	Exc of Ant Neck SQ/Fascia, Opn Appr 43, 206, 237, 292
ØJB43ZZ	Exc of Ant Neck SQ/Fascia, Perc Appr 450
Ø2BF3ZZ	Exc of Aortic Valve, Perc Appr 98
ØDBKØZX	Exc of Ascending Colon, Opn Appr, Diagnostic 449
ØDBK7ZZ	Exc of Ascending Colon, Via Opng 109, 449
Ø2B53ZZ	Exc of Atrial Septum, Perc Appr 98
ØHB6XZZ	Exc of Back Skin, Ext Appr 43, 113, 206, 236, 292, 377, 380
ØJB7ØZZ	Exc of Back SQ/Fascia, Opn Appr 43, 206, 237, 292
ØJB73ZZ	Exc of Back SQ/Fascia, Perc Appr 450
ØØB8ØZX	Exc of Basal Ganglia, Opn Appr, Diagnostic 8, 12, 16, 295
ØGB4ØZX	Exc of Bilat Adrenal Glands, Opn Appr, Diagn 235
ØHBV[7,8,X]ZZ	Exc of Bilat Breast, [Via Natrl or Artfcl Opng, Via Natrl or Artfcl Opng Endo, Ext Appr] 242
ØHBVØZX	Exc of Bilat Breast, Opn Appr, Diagnostic 222, 242, 336, 449
ØBBMØZX	Exc of Bilat Lungs, Opn Appr, Diagnostic 61, 153, 253, 299
ØVB3ØZX	Exc of Bilat Seminal Vesicles, Opn Appr, Diagn 260
ØVBC[Ø,3,4]ZZ	Exc of Bilat Testes, [Opn, Perc, Perc Endo] 257
ØVBCØZX	Exc of Bilat Testes, Opn Appr, Diagnostic 257
ØTBCØZX	Exc of Bladder Neck, Opn Appr, Diagnostic 249, 302
ØTBBØZX	Exc of Bladder, Opn Appr, Diagnostic 249, 302
Ø1B3ØZX	Exc of Brachial Plexus, Opn Appr, Diagnostic 24, 151, 319
ØØBØØZX	Exc of Brain, Opn Appr, Diagnostic 8, 12, 16, 295
ØHB8XZZ	Exc of Buttock Skin, Ext Appr 43, 113, 206, 236, 292, 377, 380
ØJB9ØZZ	Exc of Buttock SQ/Fascia, Opn Appr 43, 206, 237, 292
ØJB93ZZ	Exc of Buttock SQ/Fascia, Perc Appr 450
ØBB2ØZX	Exc of Carina, Opn Appr, Diagnostic 52, 64
ØDBHØZX	Exc of Cecum, Opn Appr, Diagnostic 109, 449
ØDBH7ZZ	Exc of Cecum, Via Natrl or Artfcl Opng 109, 449
ØØBCØZX	Exc of Cerebellum, Opn Appr, Diagnostic 8, 12, 16, 295
ØØB7ØZX	Exc of Cerebral Hemisphere, Opn Appr, Diagnostic 8, 12, 16, 295
ØØB1ØZX	Exc of Cerebral Meninges, Opn Appr, Diagnostic 8, 12, 16, 295
ØØB6ØZX	Exc of Cerebral Ventricle, Opn Appr, Diagnostic 8, 12, 16, 295
Ø1B1ØZX	Exc of Cervical Nerve, Opn Appr, Diagnostic 24, 151, 319
Ø1BØØZX	Exc of Cervical Plexus, Opn Appr, Diagnostic 24, 151, 319
ØHB5XZZ	Exc of Chest Skin, Ext Appr 43, 113, 206, 236, 292, 377, 380
ØJB6ØZZ	Exc of Chest SQ/Fascia, Opn Appr 43, 206, 237, 292
ØJB63ZZ	Exc of Chest SQ/Fascia, Perc Appr 450
Ø2B93ZZ	Exc of Chordae Tendineae, Perc Appr 98
ØFB9ØZX	Exc of Common Bile Duct, Opn Appr, Diagnostic 112
Ø2B83ZZ	Exc of Conduction Mechanism, Perc Appr 98
ØFB8ØZX	Exc of Cystic Duct, Opn Appr, Diagnostic 112
ØDBMØZX	Exc of Descending Colon, Opn Appr, Diagnostic 449
ØDBM7ZZ	Exc of Descending Colon, Via Opng 109, 449
ØDB97ZZ	Exc of Duodenum, Via Natrl or Artfcl Opng 333
ØØB2ØZX	Exc of Dura Mater, Opn Appr, Diagnostic 8, 12, 16, 295
ØCBRØZX	Exc of Epiglottis, Opn Appr, Diagnostic 52, 65
ØDB4ØZX	Exc of Esophagogastric Junction, Opn Appr, Diagn 53, 105, 300
ØDB5ØZX	Exc of Esophagus, Opn Appr, Diagnostic 53, 105, 300
ØHB1XZZ	Exc of Face Skin, Ext Appr 43, 113, 206, 236, 292
ØJB1ØZZ	Exc of Face SQ/Fascia, Opn Appr 43, 206, 237, 292
ØJB13ZZ	Exc of Face SQ/Fascia, Perc Appr 450
ØKB1ØZX	Exc of Facial Muscle, Opn Appr, Diagnostic 27, 214, 292, 451
ØØBMØZX	Exc of Facial Nerve, Opn Appr, Diagnostic 23, 50, 151, 318
Ø1BDØZX	Exc of Femor Nerve, Opn Appr, Diagnostic 24, 151, 319
ØFB4ØZX	Exc of Gallbladder, Opn Appr, Diagnostic 112
ØFB44ZZ	Exc of Gallbladder, Perc Endo Appr 121
ØHBAXZZ	Exc of Genitalia Skin, Ext Appr 43, 113, 206, 236, 292, 377, 380
ØØBPØZX	Exc of Glossopharyngeal Nerve, Opn Appr, Diagn 23, 50, 151, 318
ØDBSØZX	Exc of Greater Omentum, Opn Appr, Diagnostic 112, 268, 292

0LB00ZX	Exc of Head and Neck Tndn, Opn Appr, Diagnostic 215, 453
0KB00ZX	Exc of Head Muscle, Opn Appr, Diagnostic 27, 214, 292, 451
0UBKXZZ	Exc of Hymen, Ext Appr 459
0UBKXZX	Exc of Hymen, Ext Appr, Diagnostic 459
00BS0ZX	Exc of Hypoglossal Nerve, Opn Appr, Diagnostic 23, 50, 151, 318
00BA0ZX	Exc of Hypothalamus, Opn Appr, Diagnostic 8, 12, 16, 295
0DBC7ZZ	Exc of Ileocecal Valve, Via Opng 300
0DBB7ZZ	Exc of Ileum, Via Natrl or Artfcl Opng 300, 333
03B23ZZ	Exc of Innominate Artery, Perc Appr 105, 321
0DBA7ZZ	Exc of Jejunum, Via Natrl or Artfcl Opng 300, 333
0DBE0ZX	Exc of Large Intestine, Opn Appr, Diagnostic 449
0DBE7ZZ	Exc of Large Intestine, Via Opng 109, 449
0CBS0ZX	Exc of Larynx, Opn Appr, Diagnostic 52, 65
0DBT0ZX	Exc of Lesser Omentum, Opn Appr, Diagnostic 112, 268, 292
0BB90ZX	Exc of Lingula Bronchus, Opn Appr, Diagnostic 61
0FB00ZX	Exc of Liver, Opn Appr, Diagnostic 65, 242, 268
0MBJ0ZX	Exc of Lt Abd Bursa/Lig, Opn Appr, Diagn 216, 453
0KBL0ZX	Exc of Lt Abd Muscle, Opn Appr, Diagnostic 27, 214, 292, 451
0LBG0ZX	Exc of Lt Abd Tndn, Opn Appr, Diagnostic 216, 453
0GB20ZX	Exc of Lt Adrenal Gland, Opn Appr, Diagnostic 235
0LBT0ZZ	Exc of Lt Ankle Tndn, Opn Appr 216
0LBT0ZX	Exc of Lt Ankle Tndn, Opn Appr, Diagnostic 216, 453
02B70ZK	Exc of Lt Atrial Appendage, Opn Appr 80
02B73ZK	Exc of Lt Atrial Appendage, Perc Appr 98
02B74ZK	Exc of Lt Atrial Appendage, Perc Endo Appr 98
02B73ZZ	Exc of Lt Atrium, Perc Appr 98
0HBU[7,8,X]ZZ	Exc of Lt Breast, [Via Natrl or Artfcl Opng, Via Natrl or Artfcl Opng Endo, Ext Appr] 242
0HBU0ZX	Exc of Lt Breast, Opn Appr, Diagnostic 222, 242, 336, 449
08BTXZZ	Exc of Lt Conjunctiva, Ext Appr 329
09BV0ZX	Exc of Lt Ethmoid Sinus, Opn Appr, Diagnostic 55
0KBW0ZX	Exc of Lt Foot Muscle, Opn Appr, Diagnostic 27, 214, 292, 451
0HBNXZZ	Exc of Lt Foot Skin, Ext Appr 43, 113, 206, 236, 292, 377, 380
0JBR0ZZ	Exc of Lt Foot SQ/Fascia, Opn Appr 44, 206, 237, 292
0JBR3ZZ	Exc of Lt Foot SQ/Fascia, Perc Appr 450
0LBW0ZX	Exc of Lt Foot Tndn, Opn Appr, Diagnostic 216, 453
09BT0ZX	Exc of Lt Frontal Sinus, Opn Appr, Diagnostic 55
0KBD0ZX	Exc of Lt Hand Muscle, Opn Appr, Diagnostic 214, 292, 451
0HBGXZZ	Exc of Lt Hand Skin, Ext Appr 43, 113, 206, 236, 292, 377, 380
0LB80ZX	Exc of Lt Hand Tndn, Opn Appr, Diagnostic 215, 453
0FB60ZX	Exc of Lt Hepatic Duct, Opn Appr, Diagnostic 112
0KBP0ZX	Exc of Lt Hip Muscle, Opn Appr, Diagnostic 27, 214, 292, 451
0LBK0ZX	Exc of Lt Hip Tndn, Opn Appr, Diagnostic 216, 453
09BE0ZX	Exc of Lt Inner Ear, Opn Appr, Diagnostic 446
03B13ZZ	Exc of Lt Int Mammary Artery, Perc Appr 105, 321
0TB4[0,3,4,7,8]ZZ	Exc of Lt Kidney Pelvis, [Opn, Perc, Perc Endo, Via Natrl or Artfcl Opng, Via Natrl or Artfcl Opng Endo] 249, 353
0TB40ZX	Exc of Lt Kidney Pelvis, Opn Appr, Diagnostic 249, 293, 302, 353
0TB1[0,3,4,7,8]ZZ	Exc of Lt Kidney, [Opn, Perc, Perc Endo, Via Natrl or Artfcl Opng, Via Natrl or Artfcl Opng Endo] 249, 353
0TB10ZX	Exc of Lt Kidney, Opn Appr, Diagnostic 249, 293, 302, 353
0LBR0ZX	Exc of Lt Knee Tndn, Opn Appr, Diagnostic 216, 453
0DBG0ZX	Exc of Lt Large Intestine, Opn Appr, Diagnostic 449
0DBG7ZZ	Exc of Lt Large Intestine, Via Opng 109, 449
08BK3ZX	Exc of Lt Lens, Perc Appr, Diagnostic 329
0FB20ZX	Exc of Lt Lobe Liver, Opn Appr, Diagnostic 65, 242, 268
0KBB0ZX	Exc of Lt Low Arm & Wrist Muscle, Opn Appr, Diagn 27, 214, 292, 451
0LB60ZX	Exc of Lt Low Arm & Wrist Tndn, Opn Appr, Diagn 215, 453
0JBH0ZZ	Exc of Lt Low Arm SQ/Fascia, Opn Appr 43, 206, 237, 292
0JBH3ZZ	Exc of Lt Low Arm SQ/Fascia, Perc Appr 450
0MBW0ZX	Exc of Lt Low Extrem Bursa/Lig, Opn Appr, Diagn 216, 454
0JBP0ZZ	Exc of Lt Low Leg SQ/Fascia, Opn Appr 43, 206, 237, 292
0JBP3ZZ	Exc of Lt Low Leg SQ/Fascia, Perc Appr 450
0BBL0ZX	Exc of Lt Lung, Opn Appr, Diagnostic 61, 299
0BBL4ZZ	Exc of Lt Lung, Perc Endo Appr 331
0HBEXZZ	Exc of Lt Lwr Arm Skin, Ext Appr 43, 113, 206, 236, 292, 377, 380
0KBT0ZX	Exc of Lt Lwr Leg Muscle, Opn Appr, Diagnostic 27, 214, 292, 451
0HBLXZZ	Exc of Lt Lwr Leg Skin, Ext Appr 43, 113, 206, 236, 292, 377, 380
0LBP0ZX	Exc of Lt Lwr Leg Tndn, Opn Appr, Diagnostic 216, 453
0BBB0ZX	Exc of Lt Lwr Lobe Bronchus, Opn Appr, Diagn 61
0BBJ0ZX	Exc of Lt Lwr Lung Lobe, Opn Appr, Diagnostic 61, 299
0BBJ4ZZ	Exc of Lt Lwr Lung Lobe, Perc Endo Appr 331
0BB70ZX	Exc of Lt Main Bronchus, Opn Appr, Diagnostic 61
09BR0ZX	Exc of Lt Maxillary Sinus, Opn Appr, Diagnostic 55
0KB30ZX	Exc of Lt Neck Muscle, Opn Appr, Diagnostic 27, 214, 292, 451
0HBX0ZX	Exc of Lt Nipple, Opn Appr, Diagnostic 222, 242, 336, 449
0CBC0ZX	Exc of Lt Parotid Duct, Opn Appr, Diagnostic 56, 448
0CB90ZX	Exc of Lt Parotid Gland, Opn Appr, Diagnostic 56, 448
02BR3ZZ	Exc of Lt Pulmn Artery, Perc Appr 319
02BT3ZZ	Exc of Lt Pulmn Vein, Perc Appr 319
0VB20ZX	Exc of Lt Seminal Vesicle, Opn Appr, Diagnostic 260
0KB60ZX	Exc of Lt Shldr Muscle, Opn Appr, Diagnostic 27, 214, 292, 451
0LB20ZX	Exc of Lt Shldr Tndn, Opn Appr, Diagnostic 215, 453
09BX0ZX	Exc of Lt Sphenoid Sinus, Opn Appr, Diagnostic 55
03B43ZZ	Exc of Lt Subclavian Artery, Perc Appr 105, 321
0CBF0ZX	Exc of Lt Sublingual Gland, Opn Appr, Diagnostic 57, 448
0CBH0ZX	Exc of Lt Submaxillary Gland, Opn Appr, Diagn 57, 448
0VBB[0,3,4]ZZ	Exc of Lt Testis, [Opn, Perc, Perc Endo] 257
0VBB0ZX	Exc of Lt Testis, Opn Appr, Diagnostic 257
0KBJ0ZX	Exc of Lt Thorax Muscle, Opn Appr, Diagnostic 27, 214, 292, 451
0LBD0ZX	Exc of Lt Thorax Tndn, Opn Appr, Diagnostic 216, 453
0GBG0ZX	Exc of Lt Thyroid Gland Lobe, Opn Appr, Diagn 238
0KBG0ZX	Exc of Lt Trunk Muscle, Opn Appr, Diagnostic 27, 214, 292, 451
0LBB0ZX	Exc of Lt Trunk Tndn, Opn Appr, Diagnostic 216, 453
0VB70ZZ	Exc of Lt Tunica Vaginalis, Opn Appr 459
0JBF0ZZ	Exc of Lt Up Arm SQ/Fascia, Opn Appr 43, 206, 237, 292
0JBF3ZZ	Exc of Lt Up Arm SQ/Fascia, Perc Appr 450
0JBM0ZZ	Exc of Lt Up Leg SQ/Fascia, Opn Appr 43, 206, 237, 292
0JBM3ZZ	Exc of Lt Up Leg SQ/Fascia, Perc Appr 450
0KB80ZX	Exc of Lt Upr Arm Muscle, Opn Appr, Diagnostic 27, 214, 292, 451
0HBCXZZ	Exc of Lt Upr Arm Skin, Ext Appr 43, 113, 206, 236, 292, 377, 380
0LB40ZX	Exc of Lt Upr Arm Tndn, Opn Appr, Diagnostic 215, 453
0KBR0ZX	Exc of Lt Upr Leg Muscle, Opn Appr, Diagnostic 27, 214, 292, 451
0HBJXZZ	Exc of Lt Upr Leg Skin, Ext Appr 43, 113, 206, 236, 292, 377, 380
0LBM0ZX	Exc of Lt Upr Leg Tndn, Opn Appr, Diagnostic 216, 453
0BB80ZX	Exc of Lt Upr Lobe Bronchus, Opn Appr, Diagn 61
0BBG0ZX	Exc of Lt Upr Lung Lobe, Opn Appr, Diagnostic 61, 299
0BBG4ZZ	Exc of Lt Upr Lung Lobe, Perc Endo Appr 331
0TB70ZX	Exc of Lt Ureter, Opn Appr, Diagnostic 249
08B53ZZ	Exc of Lt Vitreous, Perc Appr 329
0CBV0ZX	Exc of Lt Vocal Cord, Opn Appr, Diagnostic 52, 65
01BB0ZX	Exc of Lumbar Nerve, Opn Appr, Diagnostic 24, 151, 319
01B90ZX	Exc of Lumbar Plexus, Opn Appr, Diagnostic 24, 151, 319
01BA0ZX	Exc of Lumbosacral Plexus, Opn Appr, Diagnostic 24, 151, 319
0BBH0ZX	Exc of Lung Lingula, Opn Appr, Diagnostic 61, 299
0BBH4ZZ	Exc of Lung Lingula, Perc Endo Appr 331
0DB30ZX	Exc of Lwr Esophagus, Opn Appr, Diagnostic 53, 105, 300
01B50ZX	Exc of Median Nerve, Opn Appr, Diagnostic 24, 151, 319
0WBC0ZX	Exc of Mediastinum, Opn Appr, Diagnostic 66, 91, 244, 293, 302
00BD0ZX	Exc of Medulla Oblongata, Opn Appr, Diagnostic 8, 12, 16, 295
0DBV0ZX	Exc of Mesentery, Opn Appr, Diagnostic 112, 268, 292
0DB20ZX	Exc of Mid Esophagus, Opn Appr, Diagnostic 53, 105, 300
0CBJ0ZX	Exc of Minor Salivary Gland, Opn Appr, Diagnostic 57, 448
02BG3ZZ	Exc of Mitral Valve, Perc Appr 98
0HB4XZZ	Exc of Neck Skin, Ext Appr 43, 113, 206, 236, 292
0WB6XZ2	Exc of Neck, Stoma, Ext Appr 55, 66, 91, 217, 355
00BH0ZX	Exc of Oculomotor Nerve, Opn Appr, Diagnostic 23, 50, 151, 318
00BF0ZX	Exc of Olfactory Nerve, Opn Appr, Diagnostic 23, 50, 151, 318
00BG0ZX	Exc of Optic Nerve, Opn Appr, Diagnostic 23, 50, 151, 318

0FBG0ZX	Exc of Pancreas, Opn Appr, Diagnostic 242, 301, 335
0FBD0ZX	Exc of Pancreatic Duct, Opn Appr, Diagnostic 242, 301, 335
0JBC0ZZ	Exc of Pelvic SQ/Fascia, Opn Appr 43, 206, 237, 292
0JBC3ZZ	Exc of Pelvic SQ/Fascia, Perc Appr 450
0MBK0ZX	Exc of Perineum Bursa/Lig, Opn Appr, Diagn 216, 453
0KBM0ZX	Exc of Perineum Muscle, Opn Appr, Diagnostic 27, 214, 292, 451
0HB9XZZ	Exc of Perineum Skin, Ext Appr 219
0JBB0ZZ	Exc of Perineum SQ/Fascia, Opn Appr 43, 206, 237, 292
0JBB3ZZ	Exc of Perineum SQ/Fascia, Perc Appr 450
0LBN0ZX	Exc of Perineum Tndn, Opn Appr, Diagnostic 216, 453
0DBW0ZX	Exc of Peritoneum, Opn Appr, Diagnostic 112, 268, 292
01BH0ZX	Exc of Peroneal Nerve, Opn Appr, Diagnostic 24, 151, 319
01B20ZX	Exc of Phrenic Nerve, Opn Appr, Diagnostic 24, 151, 319
00BB0ZX	Exc of Pons, Opn Appr, Diagnostic 8, 12, 16, 295
0JB50ZZ	Exc of Post Neck SQ/Fascia, Opn Appr 43, 206, 237, 292
0JB53ZZ	Exc of Post Neck SQ/Fascia, Perc Appr 450
0VB00ZX	Exc of Prostate, Opn Appr, Diagnostic 250, 260, 440
01BC0ZX	Exc of Pudendal Nerve, Opn Appr, Diagnostic 24, 151, 319
02BP3ZZ	Exc of Pulmn Trunk, Perc Appr 105, 319
02BH3ZZ	Exc of Pulmn Valve, Perc Appr 98
01B60ZX	Exc of Radial Nerve, Opn Appr, Diagnostic 24, 151, 319
0DBP0ZX	Exc of Rectum, Opn Appr, Diagnostic 90, 109, 449
0WBH0ZX	Exc of Retroperitoneum, Opn Appr, Diagnostic 113, 121, 269, 293
0MBH0ZX	Exc of Rt Abd Bursa/Lig, Opn Appr, Diagn 216, 453
0KBK0ZX	Exc of Rt Abd Muscle, Opn Appr, Diagnostic 27, 214, 292, 451
0LBF0ZX	Exc of Rt Abd Tndn, Opn Appr, Diagnostic 216, 453
0GB30ZX	Exc of Rt Adrenal Gland, Opn Appr, Diagnostic 235
0LBS0ZZ	Exc of Rt Ankle Tndn, Opn Appr 216
0LBS0ZX	Exc of Rt Ankle Tndn, Opn Appr, Diagnostic 216, 453
02B63ZZ	Exc of Rt Atrium, Perc Appr 98
0HBT[7,8,X]ZZ	Exc of Rt Breast, [Via Natrl or Artfcl Opng, Via Natrl or Artfcl Opng Endo, Ext Appr] 242
0HBT0ZX	Exc of Rt Breast, Opn Appr, Diagnostic 222, 242, 336, 449
08BSXZZ	Exc of Rt Conjunctiva, Ext Appr 329
09BU0ZX	Exc of Rt Ethmoid Sinus, Opn Appr, Diagnostic 55
0KBV0ZX	Exc of Rt Foot Muscle, Opn Appr, Diagnostic 27, 214, 292, 451
0HBMXZZ	Exc of Rt Foot Skin, Ext Appr 43, 113, 206, 236, 292, 377, 380
0JBQ0ZZ	Exc of Rt Foot SQ/Fascia, Opn Appr 43, 206, 237, 292
0JBQ3ZZ	Exc of Rt Foot SQ/Fascia, Perc Appr 450
0LBV0ZX	Exc of Rt Foot Tndn, Opn Appr, Diagnostic 216, 453
09BS0ZX	Exc of Rt Frontal Sinus, Opn Appr, Diagnostic 55
0KBC0ZX	Exc of Rt Hand Muscle, Opn Appr, Diagnostic 214, 292, 451
0HBFXZZ	Exc of Rt Hand Skin, Ext Appr 43, 113, 206, 236, 292, 377, 380
0LB70ZX	Exc of Rt Hand Tndn, Opn Appr, Diagnostic 215, 453
0FB50ZX	Exc of Rt Hepatic Duct, Opn Appr, Diagnostic 112
0KBN0ZX	Exc of Rt Hip Muscle, Opn Appr, Diagnostic 27, 214, 292, 451
0LBJ0ZX	Exc of Rt Hip Tndn, Opn Appr, Diagnostic 216, 453
09BD0ZX	Exc of Rt Inner Ear, Opn Appr, Diagnostic 446
03B03ZZ	Exc of Rt Int Mammary Artery, Perc Appr 105, 321
0TB3[0,3,4,7,8]ZZ	Exc of Rt Kidney Pelvis, [Opn, Perc, Perc Endo, Via Natrl or Artfcl Opng, Via Natrl or Artfcl Opng Endo] 249, 353
0TB30ZX	Exc of Rt Kidney Pelvis, Opn Appr, Diagnostic 249, 293, 302, 353
0TB0[0,3,4,7,8]ZZ	Exc of Rt Kidney, [Opn, Perc, Perc Endo, Via Natrl or Artfcl Opng, Via Natrl or Artfcl Opng Endo] 249, 353
0TB00ZX	Exc of Rt Kidney, Opn Appr, Diagnostic 248, 293, 302, 353
0LBQ0ZX	Exc of Rt Knee Tndn, Opn Appr, Diagnostic 216, 453
0DBF0ZX	Exc of Rt Large Intestine, Opn Appr, Diagnostic 449
0DBF7ZZ	Exc of Rt Large Intestine, Via Opng 109, 449
08BJ3ZX	Exc of Rt Lens, Perc Appr, Diagnostic 329
0FB10ZX	Exc of Rt Lobe Liver, Opn Appr, Diagnostic 65, 242, 268
0KB90ZX	Exc of Rt Low Arm & Wrist Muscle, Opn Appr, Diagn 27, 214, 292, 451
0LB50ZX	Exc of Rt Low Arm & Wrist Tndn, Opn Appr, Diagn 215, 453
0JBG0ZZ	Exc of Rt Low Arm SQ/Fascia, Opn Appr 43, 206, 237, 292
0JBG3ZZ	Exc of Rt Low Arm SQ/Fascia, Perc Appr 450
0MBV0ZX	Exc of Rt Low Extrem Bursa/Lig, Opn Appr, Diagn 216, 454
0JBN0ZZ	Exc of Rt Low Leg SQ/Fascia, Opn Appr 43, 206, 237, 292
0JBN3ZZ	Exc of Rt Low Leg SQ/Fascia, Perc Appr 450

0BBK0ZX	Exc of Rt Lung, Opn Appr, Diagnostic 61, 299
0BBK4ZZ	Exc of Rt Lung, Perc Endo Appr 331
0HBDXZZ	Exc of Rt Lwr Arm Skin, Ext Appr 43, 113, 206, 236, 292, 377, 380
0KBS0ZX	Exc of Rt Lwr Leg Muscle, Opn Appr, Diagn 27, 214, 292, 451
0HBKXZZ	Exc of Rt Lwr Leg Skin, Ext Appr 43, 113, 206, 236, 292, 377, 380
0LBN0ZX	Exc of Rt Lwr Leg Tndn, Opn Appr, Diagn 216, 453
0BB60ZX	Exc of Rt Lwr Lobe Bronchus, Opn Appr, Diagn 61
0BBF0ZX	Exc of Rt Lwr Lung Lobe, Opn Appr, Diagnostic 61, 299
0BBF4ZZ	Exc of Rt Lwr Lung Lobe, Perc Endo Appr 331
0BB30ZX	Exc of Rt Main Bronchus, Opn Appr, Diagnostic 61
09BQ0ZX	Exc of Rt Maxillary Sinus, Opn Appr, Diagnostic 55
0BB50ZX	Exc of Rt Mid Lobe Bronchus, Opn Appr, Diagn 61
0BBD0ZX	Exc of Rt Mid Lung Lobe, Opn Appr, Diagn 61, 299
0BBD4ZZ	Exc of Rt Mid Lung Lobe, Perc Endo Appr 331
0KB20ZX	Exc of Rt Neck Muscle, Opn Appr, Diagnostic 27, 214, 292, 451
0HBW0ZX	Exc of Rt Nipple, Opn Appr, Diagnostic 222, 242, 336, 449
0CBB0ZX	Exc of Rt Parotid Duct, Opn Appr, Diagnostic 56, 448
0CB80ZX	Exc of Rt Parotid Gland, Opn Appr, Diagnostic 56, 448
02BQ3ZZ	Exc of Rt Pulmn Artery, Perc Appr 319
02BS3ZZ	Exc of Rt Pulmn Vein, Perc Appr 319
0VB10ZX	Exc of Rt Seminal Vesicle, Opn Appr, Diagnostic 260
0KB50ZX	Exc of Rt Shldr Muscle, Opn Appr, Diagnostic 27, 214, 292, 451
0LB10ZX	Exc of Rt Shldr Tndn, Opn Appr, Diagnostic 215, 453
09BW0ZX	Exc of Rt Sphenoid Sinus, Opn Appr, Diagnostic 55
03B33ZZ	Exc of Rt Subclavian Artery, Perc Appr 105, 321
0CBD0ZX	Exc of Rt Sublingual Gland, Opn Appr, Diagn 56, 448
0CBG0ZX	Exc of Rt Submaxillary Gland, Opn Appr, Diagn 57, 448
0VB9[0,3,4]ZZ	Exc of Rt Testis, [Opn, Perc, Perc Endo] 257
0VB90ZX	Exc of Rt Testis, Opn Appr, Diagnostic 257
0KBH0ZX	Exc of Rt Thorax Muscle, Opn Appr, Diagnostic 27, 214, 292, 451
0LBC0ZX	Exc of Rt Thorax Tndn, Opn Appr, Diagnostic 216, 453
0GBH0ZX	Exc of Rt Thyroid Gland Lobe, Opn Appr, Diagn 238
0KBF0ZX	Exc of Rt Trunk Muscle, Opn Appr, Diagnostic 27, 214, 292, 451
0LB90ZX	Exc of Rt Trunk Tndn, Opn Appr, Diagnostic 215, 453
0VB60ZZ	Exc of Rt Tunica Vaginalis, Opn Appr 459
0JBD0ZZ	Exc of Rt Up Arm SQ/Fascia, Opn Appr 43, 206, 237, 292
0JBD3ZZ	Exc of Rt Up Arm SQ/Fascia, Perc Appr 450
0MB90ZZ	Exc of Rt Up Extrem Bursa/Lig, Opn Appr 143
0MB90ZX	Exc of Rt Up Extrem Bursa/Lig, Opn Appr, Diagn 143, 216, 453
0MB93ZZ	Exc of Rt Up Extrem Bursa/Lig, Perc Appr 143
0MB93ZX	Exc of Rt Up Extrem Bursa/Lig, Perc Appr, Diagn 143
0MB94ZZ	Exc of Rt Up Extrem Bursa/Lig, Perc Endo Appr 143
0JBL0ZZ	Exc of Rt Up Leg SQ/Fascia, Opn Appr 43, 206, 237, 292
0JBL3ZZ	Exc of Rt Up Leg SQ/Fascia, Perc Appr 450
0KB70ZX	Exc of Rt Upr Arm Muscle, Opn Appr, Diagn 27, 214, 292, 451
0HBBXZZ	Exc of Rt Upr Arm Skin, Ext Appr 43, 113, 206, 236, 292, 377, 380
0LB30ZX	Exc of Rt Upr Arm Tndn, Opn Appr, Diagn 215, 453
0KBQ0ZX	Exc of Rt Upr Leg Muscle, Opn Appr, Diagn 27, 214, 292, 451
0HBHXZZ	Exc of Rt Upr Leg Skin, Ext Appr 43, 113, 206, 236, 292, 377, 380
0LBL0ZX	Exc of Rt Upr Leg Tndn, Opn Appr, Diagn 216, 453
0BB40ZX	Exc of Rt Upr Lobe Bronchus, Opn Appr, Diagn 61
0BBC0ZX	Exc of Rt Upr Lung Lobe, Opn Appr, Diagnostic 61, 299
0BBC4ZZ	Exc of Rt Upr Lung Lobe, Perc Endo Appr 331
0TB60ZX	Exc of Rt Ureter, Opn Appr, Diagnostic 249
08B43ZZ	Exc of Rt Vitreous, Perc Appr 329
0CBT0ZX	Exc of Rt Vocal Cord, Opn Appr, Diagnostic 52, 65
01BR0ZX	Exc of Sacral Nerve, Opn Appr, Diagnostic 24, 151, 319
01BQ0ZX	Exc of Sacral Plexus, Opn Appr, Diagnostic 24, 151, 319
0HB0XZZ	Exc of Scalp Skin, Ext Appr 43, 113, 206, 236, 292
0JB00ZZ	Exc of Scalp SQ/Fascia, Opn Appr 43, 53, 206, 237, 292
0JB03ZZ	Exc of Scalp SQ/Fascia, Perc Appr 450
01BF0ZX	Exc of Sciatic Nerve, Opn Appr, Diagnostic 24, 151, 319
0DBN0ZX	Exc of Sigmoid Colon, Opn Appr, Diagnostic 449
0DBN7ZZ	Exc of Sigmoid Colon, Via Natrl or Artfcl Opng 109, 449
0HB[6,7,8,A]XZZ	Exc of Skin of [Back, Abd, Buttock, Genitalia], Ext 53, 65, 90

Code	Description
ØHB[B,C,D,E,F,G]XZZ	Exc of Skin of [Rt Upr Arm, Lt Upr Arm, Rt Lwr Arm, Lt Lwr Arm, Rt Hand, Lt Hand], Ext 25, 53, 65, 90, 123, 126, 313
ØHB[H,J,K,L,M,N]XZZ	Exc of Skin of [Rt Upr Leg, Lt Upr Leg, Rt Lwr Leg, Lt Lwr Leg, Rt Foot, Lt Foot], Ext 25, 53, 65, 90, 123, 126, 313
ØHB[Ø,1,4,5]XZZ	Exc of Skin of [Scalp, Face, Neck, Chest], Ext 53, 65, 90
07BPØZX	Exc of Spleen, Opn Appr, Diagnostic 290, 297
ØJB[7,8,9,B,C]ØZZ	Exc of SQ Tissue & Fascia of [Back, Abd, Buttock, Perineum, Pelvic Rgn], Opn 26, 54, 65, 91, 113, 123, 126, 313
ØJB[D,F,G,H]ØZZ	Exc of SQ Tissue & Fascia of [Rt Upr Arm, Lt Upr Arm, Rt Lwr Arm, Lt Lwr Arm], Opn 26, 54, 65, 91, 113, 123, 127, 313
ØJB[L,M,N,P,Q,R]ØZZ	Exc of SQ Tissue & Fascia of [Rt Upr Leg, Lt Upr Leg, Rt Lwr Leg, Lt Lwr Leg, Rt Foot, Lt Foot], Opn 26, 54, 65, 91, 123, 127, 313
ØJB[Ø,1,4,5,6]ØZZ	Exc of SQ Tissue & Fascia of [Scalp, Face, Ant Neck, Post Neck, Chest], Opn 26, 65, 90, 113, 123, 126, 313
ØDB6ØZX	Exc of Stomach, Opn Appr, Diagnostic 105, 449
ØDB7ØZX	Exc of Stomach, Pylorus, Opn Appr, Diagnostic 105, 449
02BV3ZZ	Exc of Superior Vena Cava, Perc Appr 319
ØHBYØZX	Exc of Supernumerary Breast, Opn Appr, Diagnostic 222, 242, 336, 449
00B9ØZX	Exc of Thalamus, Opn Appr, Diagnostic 8, 12, 16, 295
02BW3ZZ	Exc of Thoracic Aorta, Perc Appr 60, 93
01B8ØZX	Exc of Thoracic Nerve, Opn Appr, Diagnostic 24, 151, 319
01BGØZX	Exc of Tibial Nerve, Opn Appr, Diagnostic 24, 151, 319
ØCB7ØZX	Exc of Tongue, Opn Appr, Diagnostic 56
ØKB4ØZX	Exc of Tongue/Palate/Phar Muscle, Opn Appr, Diagn 27, 214, 292, 451
ØBB1ØZX	Exc of Trachea, Opn Appr, Diagnostic 52, 64
ØDBLØZX	Exc of Transv Colon, Opn Appr, Diagnostic 449
ØDBL7ZX	Exc of Transv Colon, Via Opng 109, 449
02BJ3ZZ	Exc of Tricuspid Valve, Perc Appr 98
00BKØZX	Exc of Trigeminal Nerve, Opn Appr, Diagnostic 23, 50, 151, 318
00BJØZX	Exc of Trochlear Nerve, Opn Appr, Diagnostic 23, 50, 151, 318
01B4ØZX	Exc of Ulnar Nerve, Opn Appr, Diagnostic 24, 151, 319
ØDB1ØZX	Exc of Upr Esophagus, Opn Appr, Diagnostic 53, 105, 300
ØUB4ØZX	Exc of Uterine Support Struct, Opn Appr, Diagn 262, 264, 266
ØUB9ØZX	Exc of Uterus, Opn Appr, Diagnostic 262, 264, 266
00BQØZX	Exc of Vagus Nerve, Opn Appr, Diagnostic 23, 50, 151, 318
02BM3ZZ	Exc of Ventricular Septum, Perc Appr 98
ØUBMXZZ	Exc of Vulva, Ext Appr 274
ØUBMXZX	Exc of Vulva, Ext Appr, Diagnostic 267
ØUBMØZZ	Exc of Vulva, Opn Appr 267
ØUBMØZX	Exc of Vulva, Opn Appr, Diagnostic 267
04BØ[Ø,3,4]ZX	Exc/Abd Aorta, [Opn, Perc, Perc Endo] 83, 441
04BØ[Ø,3,4]ZZ	Exc/Abd Aorta, [Opn, Perc, Perc Endo] 92, 111, 323
ØMBJ*	Exc/Abd Bursa & Lgmt, Lt 143
ØMBJ[Ø,3,4]ZZ	Exc/Abd Bursa & Lgmt, Lt, [Opn, Perc, Perc Endo] 343, 453
ØMBH*	Exc/Abd Bursa & Lgmt, Rt 143
ØMBH[Ø,3,4]ZZ	Exc/Abd Bursa & Lgmt, Rt, [Opn, Perc, Perc Endo] 343, 453
ØKBL*	Exc/Abd Muscle, Lt 139
ØKBL[Ø,3,4]ZZ	Exc/Abd Muscle, Lt, [Opn, Perc, Perc Endo] 27, 214, 339
ØKBK*	Exc/Abd Muscle, Rt 139
ØKBK[Ø,3,4]ZZ	Exc/Abd Muscle, Rt, [Opn, Perc, Perc Endo] 27, 214, 339
01BM*	Exc/Abd Sympathetic Nerve 24
01BM[Ø,3,4]ZZ	Exc/Abd Sympathetic Nerve, [Opn, Perc, Perc Endo] 89
ØLBG*	Exc/Abd Tndn, Lt 141
ØLBG[Ø,3,4]ZZ	Exc/Abd Tndn, Lt, [Opn, Perc, Perc Endo] 28, 341
ØLBF*	Exc/Abd Tndn, Rt 141
ØLBF[Ø,3,4]ZZ	Exc/Abd Tndn, Rt, [Opn, Perc, Perc Endo] 28, 341
ØWBF*	Exc/Abd Wall 113
ØWBF[Ø,3,4,X]ZZ	Exc/Abd Wall, [Opn, Perc, Perc Endo, Ext] 245
ØWBF[Ø,3,4,X]ZX	Exc/Abd Wall, [Opn, Perc, Perc Endo, Ext] 355
ØWBF[Ø,3,4,X]Z[X,Z]	Exc/Abd Wall, [Opn, Perc, Perc Endo, Ext], No Dev, [Dx, NQ] 217, 302, 460
00BL[Ø,3,4]ZZ	Exc/Abducens Nerve, [Opn, Perc, Perc Endo] 23, 50, 151, 318, 440
00BR[Ø,3,4]ZZ	Exc/Accessory Nerve, [Opn, Perc, Perc Endo] 23, 50, 151, 318, 440
09BP[Ø,3,4]ZZ	Exc/Accessory Sinus, [Opn, Perc, Perc Endo] 55
ØQB5[Ø,3,4]ZX	Exc/Acetab, Lt, [Opn, Perc, Perc Endo] 130, 254, 259, 292, 456
ØQB5[Ø,3,4]ZZ	Exc/Acetab, Lt, [Opn, Perc, Perc Endo] 54, 156, 347
ØQB4[Ø,3,4]ZX	Exc/Acetab, Rt, [Opn, Perc, Perc Endo] 130, 254, 259, 292, 456
ØQB4[Ø,3,4]ZZ	Exc/Acetab, Rt, [Opn, Perc, Perc Endo] 54, 156, 347
ØQB5*	Exc/Acetabulum, Lt 244
ØQB4*	Exc/Acetabulum, Rt 244
00BN[Ø,3,4]ZZ	Exc/Acoustic Nerve, [Opn, Perc, Perc Endo] 50
00BN[3,4]ZZ	Exc/Acoustic Nerve, [Perc, Perc Endo] 23, 151, 318, 440
ØRBH[Ø,3,4]ZZ	Exc/Acromioclavicular Jt, Lt, [Opn, Perc, Perc Endo] 149, 349, 457
ØRBG[Ø,3,4]ZZ	Exc/Acromioclavicular Jt, Rt, [Opn, Perc, Perc Endo] 149, 349, 457
ØCBQ*	Exc/Adenoids 52
ØCBQ[Ø,3,X]ZX	Exc/Adenoids, [Opn, Perc, Ext] 448
ØFBC[Ø,3,7]ZZ	Exc/Ampulla of Vater, [Opn, Perc, Via Natrl or Artfcl Opng] 112, 120
ØDBR[Ø,3,4]ZZ	Exc/Anal Sphincter, [Opn, Perc, Perc Endo] 109, 449
ØMBR[Ø,3,4]ZZ	Exc/Ankle Bursa & Lgmt, Lt, [Opn, Perc, Perc Endo] 143, 343, 454
ØMBQ[Ø,3,4]ZZ	Exc/Ankle Bursa & Lgmt, Rt, [Opn, Perc, Perc Endo] 143, 343, 454
ØSBG[Ø,3,4]ZZ	Exc/Ankle Jt, Lt, [Opn, Perc, Perc Endo] 133, 351, 457
ØSBF[Ø,3,4]ZZ	Exc/Ankle Jt, Rt, [Opn, Perc, Perc Endo] 133, 351, 457
ØYBL[Ø,3,4]ZZ	Exc/Ankle Rgn, Lt, [Opn, Perc, Perc Endo] 29, 92, 144, 207, 357, 461
ØYBK[Ø,3,4]ZZ	Exc/Ankle Rgn, Rt, [Opn, Perc, Perc Endo] 29, 92, 144, 207, 357, 461
ØLBT*	Exc/Ankle Tndn, Lt 141
ØLBT[Ø,3,4]ZZ	Exc/Ankle Tndn, Lt, [Opn, Perc, Perc Endo] 28, 341
ØLBS*	Exc/Ankle Tndn, Rt 141
ØLBS[Ø,3,4]ZZ	Exc/Ankle Tndn, Rt, [Opn, Perc, Perc Endo] 28, 341
04BQ*	Exc/Ant Tibial Artery, Lt 83
04BQ[Ø,3,4]ZZ	Exc/Ant Tibial Artery, Lt, [Opn, Perc, Perc Endo] 240, 323
04BQ[Ø,3,4]ZX	Exc/Ant Tibial Artery, Lt, [Opn, Perc, Perc Endo] 442
04BP*	Exc/Ant Tibial Artery, Rt 83
04BP[Ø,3,4]ZZ	Exc/Ant Tibial Artery, Rt, [Opn, Perc, Perc Endo] 240, 323
04BP[Ø,3,4]ZX	Exc/Ant Tibial Artery, Rt, [Opn, Perc, Perc Endo] 442
ØDBQ[Ø,3,4,7,8,X]ZZ	Exc/Anus, [Opn, Perc, Perc Endo, Via Natrl or Artfcl Opng, Via Natrl or Artfcl Opng Endo, Ext] 109, 449
ØDBQ[Ø,3,4]ZZ	Exc/Anus, [Opn, Perc, Perc Endo] 211, 333
02BF[Ø,4]ZZ	Exc/Aortic Valve, [Opn, Perc Endo] 74
ØDBJ*	Exc/Appendix 108
ØDBK[Ø,3,4]ZZ	Exc/Ascending Colon, [Opn, Perc, Perc Endo] 90, 106, 300, 333
ØDBK[Ø,3,7]ZZ	Exc/Ascending Colon, [Opn, Perc, Via Natrl or Artfcl Opng] 242
02B5[Ø,4]ZZ	Exc/Atrial Septum, [Opn, Perc Endo] 74
02B7[Ø,4]ZZ	Exc/Atrium, Lt, [Opn, Perc Endo] 74
02B6[Ø,4]ZZ	Exc/Atrium, Rt, [Opn, Perc Endo] 74
09BA*	Exc/Auditory Ossicle, Lt 51
09BAØZ[X,Z]	Exc/Auditory Ossicle, Lt, Opn, No Dev, [Dx, NQ] 446
09B9*	Exc/Auditory Ossicle, Rt 51
09B9ØZ[X,Z]	Exc/Auditory Ossicle, Rt, Opn, No Dev, [Dx, NQ] 446
ØXB5[Ø,3,4]ZZ	Exc/Axilla, Lt, [Opn, Perc, Perc Endo] 28, 91, 144, 207, 356, 461
ØXB4[Ø,3,4]ZZ	Exc/Axilla, Rt, [Opn, Perc, Perc Endo] 28, 91, 144, 207, 356, 461
03B6*	Exc/Axillary Artery, Lt 81
03B6[Ø,3,4]ZZ	Exc/Axillary Artery, Lt, [Opn, Perc, Perc Endo] 239, 321
03B6[Ø,3,4]ZX	Exc/Axillary Artery, Lt, [Opn, Perc, Perc Endo] 441
03B5*	Exc/Axillary Artery, Rt 81
03B5[Ø,3,4]ZZ	Exc/Axillary Artery, Rt, [Opn, Perc, Perc Endo] 239, 321
03B5[Ø,3,4]ZX	Exc/Axillary Artery, Rt, [Opn, Perc, Perc Endo] 441
05B8*	Exc/Axillary Vein, Lt 85
05B8[Ø,3,4]ZZ	Exc/Axillary Vein, Lt, [Opn, Perc, Perc Endo] 240, 325
05B8[Ø,3,4]ZX	Exc/Axillary Vein, Lt, [Opn, Perc, Perc Endo] 442
05B7*	Exc/Axillary Vein, Rt 85
05B7[Ø,3,4]ZZ	Exc/Axillary Vein, Rt, [Opn, Perc, Perc Endo] 240, 325
05B7[Ø,3,4]ZX	Exc/Axillary Vein, Rt, [Opn, Perc, Perc Endo] 442
05BØ[Ø,3,4]ZZ	Exc/Azygos Vein, [Opn, Perc, Perc Endo] 60, 96
05BØ[Ø,3,4]ZX	Exc/Azygos Vein, [Opn, Perc, Perc Endo] 85, 442
00B8[Ø,3,4]ZZ	Exc/Basal Ganglia, [Opn, Perc, Perc Endo] 8, 12, 16, 295, 414
05BC*	Exc/Basilic Vein, Lt 85
05BC[Ø,3,4]ZZ	Exc/Basilic Vein, Lt, [Opn, Perc, Perc Endo] 240, 325
05BC[Ø,3,4]ZX	Exc/Basilic Vein, Lt, [Opn, Perc, Perc Endo] 442
05BB*	Exc/Basilic Vein, Rt 85
05BB[Ø,3,4]ZZ	Exc/Basilic Vein, Rt, [Opn, Perc, Perc Endo] 240, 325

05BB[0,3,4]ZX	Exc/Basilic Vein, Rt, [Opn, Perc, Perc Endo] 442
0GB4[0,3,4]ZZ	Exc/Bilat Adrenal Glands, [Opn, Perc, Perc Endo] 235
0TBC[0,3,4,7,8]ZX	Exc/Bladder Neck, [Opn, Perc, Perc Endo, Via Natrl or Artfcl Opng, Via Natrl or Artfcl Opng Endo] 259, 268
0TBC[0,3,4]ZZ	Exc/Bladder Neck, [Opn, Perc, Perc Endo] 248, 257, 268, 302, 353
0TBC[3,4,7,8]ZX	Exc/Bladder Neck, [Perc, Perc Endo, Via Natrl or Artfcl Opng, Via Natrl or Artfcl Opng Endo] 250, 458
0TBC[7,8]ZZ	Exc/Bladder Neck, [Via Natrl or Artfcl Opng, Via Natrl or Artfcl Opng Endo] 250, 260, 458
0TBB[0,3,4,7,8]ZX	Exc/Bladder, [Opn, Perc, Perc Endo, Via Natrl or Artfcl Opng, Via Natrl or Artfcl Opng Endo] 259, 268
0TBB[0,3,4]ZZ	Exc/Bladder, [Opn, Perc, Perc Endo] 248, 257, 268, 302, 353
0TBB[3,4,7,8]ZX	Exc/Bladder, [Perc, Perc Endo, Via Natrl or Artfcl Opng, Via Natrl or Artfcl Opng Endo] 250, 458
0TBB[7,8]ZZ	Exc/Bladder, [Via Natrl or Artfcl Opng, Via Natrl or Artfcl Opng Endo] 250, 259, 458
03B8*	Exc/Brachial Artery, Lt 81
03B8[0,3,4]ZZ	Exc/Brachial Artery, Lt, [Opn, Perc, Perc Endo] 239, 321
03B8[0,3,4]ZX	Exc/Brachial Artery, Lt, [Opn, Perc, Perc Endo] 441
03B7*	Exc/Brachial Artery, Rt 81
03B7[0,3,4]ZZ	Exc/Brachial Artery, Rt, [Opn, Perc, Perc Endo] 239, 321
03B7[0,3,4]ZX	Exc/Brachial Artery, Rt, [Opn, Perc, Perc Endo] 441
01B3[0,3,4]ZZ	Exc/Brachial Plexus, [Opn, Perc, Perc Endo] 24, 151, 319, 440
05BA*	Exc/Brachial Vein, Lt 85
05BA[0,3,4]ZZ	Exc/Brachial Vein, Lt, [Opn, Perc, Perc Endo] 240, 325
05BA[0,3,4]ZX	Exc/Brachial Vein, Lt, [Opn, Perc, Perc Endo] 442
05B9*	Exc/Brachial Vein, Rt 85
05B9[0,3,4]ZZ	Exc/Brachial Vein, Rt, [Opn, Perc, Perc Endo] 240, 325
05B9[0,3,4]ZX	Exc/Brachial Vein, Rt, [Opn, Perc, Perc Endo] 442
00B0[0,3,4]ZZ	Exc/Brain, [Opn, Perc, Perc Endo] 8, 12, 16, 295, 318, 414
0HBV[0,3,7,8,X]ZZ	Exc/Breast, Bilat, [Opn, Perc, Via Natrl or Artfcl Opng, Via Natrl or Artfcl Opng Endo, Ext] 222, 336, 449
0HBV[0,3]ZZ	Exc/Breast, Bilat, [Opn, Perc] 221, 236
0HBU[0,3,7,8,X]ZZ	Exc/Breast, Lt, [Opn, Perc, Via Natrl or Artfcl Opng, Via Natrl or Artfcl Opng Endo, Ext] 222, 449, 336
0HBU[0,3]ZZ	Exc/Breast, Lt, [Opn, Perc] 221, 236
0HBT[0,3,7,8,X]ZZ	Exc/Breast, Rt, [Opn, Perc, Via Natrl or Artfcl Opng, Via Natrl or Artfcl Opng Endo, Ext] 222, 336, 449
0HBT[0,3]ZZ	Exc/Breast, Rt, [Opn, Perc] 221, 236
0CB4[0,3,X]ZZ	Exc/Buccal Mucosa, [Opn, Perc, Ext] 56, 331, 448
0YB1[0,3,4]ZZ	Exc/Buttock, Lt, [Opn, Perc, Perc Endo] 29, 92, 144, 207, 357, 461
0YB0[0,3,4]ZZ	Exc/Buttock, Rt, [Opn, Perc, Perc Endo] 29, 92, 144, 207, 357, 461
0BB2[0,3,4,7,8]ZZ	Exc/Carina, [Opn, Perc, Perc Endo, Via Natrl or Artfcl Opng, Via Natrl or Artfcl Opng Endo] 52, 64
0RBR[0,3,4]ZZ	Exc/Carpal Jt, Lt, [Opn, Perc, Perc Endo] 150, 316, 457
0RBQ[0,3,4]ZZ	Exc/Carpal Jt, Rt, [Opn, Perc, Perc Endo] 150, 316, 457
0PBN*	Exc/Carpal, Lt 150
0PBN[0,3,4]ZX	Exc/Carpal, Lt, [Opn, Perc, Perc Endo] 216, 243, 253, 259, 455
0PBN[0,3,4]Z[X,Z]	Exc/Carpal, Lt, [Opn, Perc, Perc Endo], No Dev, [Dx, NQ] 315
0PBM*	Exc/Carpal, Rt 150
0PBM[0,3,4]ZX	Exc/Carpal, Rt, [Opn, Perc, Perc Endo] 216, 243, 253, 259, 455
0PBM[0,3,4]Z[X,Z]	Exc/Carpal, Rt, [Opn, Perc, Perc Endo], No Dev, [Dx, NQ] 315
0DBH[0,3,4]ZZ	Exc/Cecum, [Opn, Perc, Perc Endo] 90, 106, 300, 333
0DBH[0,3,7]ZZ	Exc/Cecum, [Opn, Perc, Via Natrl or Artfcl Opng] 242
04B1[0,3,4]ZX	Exc/Celiac Artery, [Opn, Perc, Perc Endo] 83, 441
04B1[0,3,4]ZZ	Exc/Celiac Artery, [Opn, Perc, Perc Endo] 95
05BF*	Exc/Cephalic Vein, Lt 85
05BF[0,3,4]ZZ	Exc/Cephalic Vein, Lt, [Opn, Perc, Perc Endo] 240, 325
05BF[0,3,4]ZX	Exc/Cephalic Vein, Lt, [Opn, Perc, Perc Endo] 442
05BD*	Exc/Cephalic Vein, Rt 85
05BD[0,3,4]ZZ	Exc/Cephalic Vein, Rt, [Opn, Perc, Perc Endo] 240, 325
05BD[0,3,4]ZX	Exc/Cephalic Vein, Rt, [Opn, Perc, Perc Endo] 442
00BC[0,3,4]ZZ	Exc/Cerebellum, [Opn, Perc, Perc Endo] 8, 12, 16, 295, 318, 414
00B7[0,3,4]ZZ	Exc/Cerebral Hemisphere, [Opn, Perc, Perc Endo] 8, 12, 16, 295, 318, 414
00B1[0,3,4]ZZ	Exc/Cerebral Meninges, [Opn, Perc, Perc Endo] 8, 12, 16, 295, 414
00B6[0,3,4]ZZ	Exc/Cerebral Ventricle, [Opn, Perc, Perc Endo] 8, 12, 16, 295, 318, 414
01B1[0,3,4]ZZ	Exc/Cervical Nerve, [Opn, Perc, Perc Endo] 24, 151, 319, 440
01B0[0,3,4]ZZ	Exc/Cervical Plexus, [Opn, Perc, Perc Endo] 24, 151, 319, 440
00BW*	Exc/Cervical Spinal Cord 159, 160
00BW[0,3,4]Z[X,Z]	Exc/Cervical Spinal Cord, [Opn, Perc, Perc Endo], No Dev, [Dx, NQ] 19, 295
0RB3[0,3,4]ZZ	Exc/Cervical Vert Disc, [Opn, Perc, Perc Endo] 19, 159, 160, 349
0RB1[0,3,4]ZZ	Exc/Cervical Vert Jt, [Opn, Perc, Perc Endo] 19, 159, 160, 301, 349
0PB3*	Exc/Cervical Vertebra 54
0PB3[0,3,4]ZX	Exc/Cervical Vertebra, [Opn, Perc, Perc Endo] 129, 292, 455
0PB3[0,3,4]ZZ	Exc/Cervical Vertebra, [Opn, Perc, Perc Endo] 155, 243, 345
0RB5[0,3,4]ZZ	Exc/Cervicothoracic Vert Disc, [Opn, Perc, Perc Endo] 19, 159, 160, 349
0RB4[0,3,4]ZZ	Exc/Cervicothoracic Vert Jt, [Opn, Perc, Perc Endo] 19, 159, 160, 301, 349
0UBC*	Exc/Cervix 271
0UBC[0,3,4,7,8]ZX	Exc/Cervix, [Opn, Perc, Perc Endo, Via Natrl or Artfcl Opng, Via Natrl or Artfcl Opng Endo] 266
0UBC[0,3,4,7,8]ZZ	Exc/Cervix, [Opn, Perc, Perc Endo, Via Natrl or Artfcl Opng, Via Natrl or Artfcl Opng Endo] 267
0UBC[0,3,4,7,8]Z[X,Z]	Exc/Cervix, [Opn, Perc, Perc Endo, Via Natrl or Artfcl Opng, Via Natrl or Artfcl Opng Endo], No Dev, [Dx, NQ] 217, 459
0WB8[0,3,4,X]ZZ	Exc/Chest Wall, [Opn, Perc, Perc Endo, Ext] 66, 136, 217, 244, 302, 460
02B9[0,4]ZZ	Exc/Chordae Tendineae, [Opn, Perc Endo] 74
08BB*	Exc/Choroid, Lt 44
08BB[0,3]ZZ	Exc/Choroid, Lt, [Opn, Perc] 329
08BB[0,3]Z[X,Z]	Exc/Choroid, Lt, [Opn, Perc], No Dev, [Dx, NQ] 444
08BA*	Exc/Choroid, Rt 44
08BA[0,3]ZZ	Exc/Choroid, Rt, [Opn, Perc] 329
08BA[0,3]Z[X,Z]	Exc/Choroid, Rt, [Opn, Perc], No Dev, [Dx, NQ] 444
07BL[0,3,4]ZX	Exc/Cisterna Chyli, [Opn, Perc, Perc Endo] 25, 90, 112, 122, 153, 209, 241, 252, 290, 443
07BL[0,3,4]ZZ	Exc/Cisterna Chyli, [Opn, Perc, Perc Endo] 60
0PBB*	Exc/Clavicle, Lt 65
0PBB[0,3,4]ZX	Exc/Clavicle, Lt, [Opn, Perc, Perc Endo] 129, 216, 243, 253, 259, 455
0PBB[0,3,4]ZZ	Exc/Clavicle, Lt, [Opn, Perc, Perc Endo] 19, 155, 345
0PB9*	Exc/Clavicle, Rt 65
0PB9[0,3,4]ZX	Exc/Clavicle, Rt, [Opn, Perc, Perc Endo] 129, 216, 243, 253, 259, 455
0PB9[0,3,4]ZZ	Exc/Clavicle, Rt, [Opn, Perc, Perc Endo] 19, 155, 345
0UBJ*	Exc/Clitoris 267
0UBJ[0,X]Z[X,Z]	Exc/Clitoris, [Opn, Ext], No Dev, [Dx, NQ] 459
0SB6[0,3,4]ZZ	Exc/Coccygeal Jt, [Opn, Perc, Perc Endo] 20, 159, 161, 302, 351
0QBS*	Exc/Coccyx 244
0QBS[0,3,4]ZX	Exc/Coccyx, [Opn, Perc, Perc Endo] 130, 254, 259, 292, 456
0QBS[0,3,4]ZZ	Exc/Coccyx, [Opn, Perc, Perc Endo] 54, 156, 347
04B7[0,3,4]ZX	Exc/Colic Artery, Lt, [Opn, Perc, Perc Endo] 83, 441
04B7[0,3,4]ZZ	Exc/Colic Artery, Lt, [Opn, Perc, Perc Endo] 95
04B8[0,3,4]ZX	Exc/Colic Artery, Mid, [Opn, Perc, Perc Endo] 83, 441
04B8[0,3,4]ZZ	Exc/Colic Artery, Mid, [Opn, Perc, Perc Endo] 95
04B6[0,3,4]ZX	Exc/Colic Artery, Rt, [Opn, Perc, Perc Endo] 83, 441
04B6[0,3,4]ZZ	Exc/Colic Artery, Rt, [Opn, Perc, Perc Endo] 95
06B7[0,3,4]ZX	Exc/Colic Vein, [Opn, Perc, Perc Endo] 86, 442
06B7[0,3,4]ZZ	Exc/Colic Vein, [Opn, Perc, Perc Endo] 97
0FB9[0,3,7]ZZ	Exc/Common Bile Duct, [Opn, Perc, Via Natrl or Artfcl Opng] 112, 120
03BJ*	Exc/Common Carotid Artery, Lt 81
03BJ[0,3,4]ZZ	Exc/Common Carotid Artery, Lt, [Opn, Perc, Perc Endo] 21, 50, 321
03BJ[0,3,4]ZX	Exc/Common Carotid Artery, Lt, [Opn, Perc, Perc Endo] 441
03BH*	Exc/Common Carotid Artery, Rt 81
03BH[0,3,4]ZZ	Exc/Common Carotid Artery, Rt, [Opn, Perc, Perc Endo] 21, 50, 321
03BH[0,3,4]ZX	Exc/Common Carotid Artery, Rt, [Opn, Perc, Perc Endo] 441
04BD[0,3,4]ZX	Exc/Common Iliac Artery, Lt, [Opn, Perc, Perc Endo] 83, 441
04BD[0,3,4]ZZ	Exc/Common Iliac Artery, Lt, [Opn, Perc, Perc Endo] 95
04BC[0,3,4]ZX	Exc/Common Iliac Artery, Rt, [Opn, Perc, Perc Endo] 83, 441
04BC[0,3,4]ZZ	Exc/Common Iliac Artery, Rt, [Opn, Perc, Perc Endo] 95
06BD[0,3,4]ZX	Exc/Common Iliac Vein, Lt, [Opn, Perc, Perc Endo] 86, 442
06BD[0,3,4]ZZ	Exc/Common Iliac Vein, Lt, [Opn, Perc, Perc Endo] 97

06BC[0,3,4]ZX	Exc/Common Iliac Vein, Rt, [Opn, Perc, Perc Endo] 86, 442
06BC[0,3,4]ZZ	Exc/Common Iliac Vein, Rt, [Opn, Perc, Perc Endo] 97
02B8[0,4]ZZ	Exc/Conduction Mech, [Opn, Perc Endo] 74
08BT*	Exc/Conjunctiva, Lt 43
08BTXZ[X,Z]	Exc/Conjunctiva, Lt, Ext, No Dev, [Dx, NQ] 444
08BS*	Exc/Conjunctiva, Rt 43
08BSXZ[X,Z]	Exc/Conjunctiva, Rt, Ext, No Dev, [Dx, NQ] 444
08B9*	Exc/Cornea, Lt 42, 329
08B9XZ[X,Z]	Exc/Cornea, Lt, Ext, No Dev, [Dx, NQ] 444
08B8*	Exc/Cornea, Rt 42, 329
08B8XZ[X,Z]	Exc/Cornea, Rt, Ext, No Dev, [Dx, NQ] 444
02B4[0,3,4]ZZ	Exc/Coronary Vein, [Opn, Perc, Perc Endo] 74
0UBF*	Exc/Cul-de-sac 267, 271
0UBF[0,3,4,7,8]Z[X,Z]	Exc/Cul-de-sac, [Opn, Perc, Perc Endo, Via Natrl or Artfcl Opng, Via Natrl or Artfcl Opng Endo, No Dev, [Dx, NQ] 459
0FB8[0,3,7]ZZ	Exc/Cystic Duct, [Opn, Perc, Via Natrl or Artfcl Opng] 120, 335
0DBM[0,3,4]ZZ	Exc/Descending Colon, [Opn, Perc, Perc Endo] 90, 106, 300, 333
0DBM[0,3,7]ZZ	Exc/Descending Colon, [Opn, Perc, Via Natrl or Artfcl Opng] 242
0BBS*	Exc/Diaphragm, Lt 61
0BBS[0,3,4]ZZ	Exc/Diaphragm, Lt, [Opn, Perc, Perc Endo] 153
0BBR*	Exc/Diaphragm, Rt 61
0BBR[0,3,4]ZZ	Exc/Diaphragm, Rt, [Opn, Perc, Perc Endo] 153
0DB9[0,3]ZZ	Exc/Duodenum, [Opn, Perc] 105, 122, 300, 449
00B2[0,3,4]ZZ	Exc/Dura Mater, [Opn, Perc, Perc Endo] 8, 12, 16, 295, 414
0MB4[0,3,4]ZZ	Exc/Elbow Bursa & Lgmt, Lt, [Opn, Perc, Perc Endo] 143, 343, 453
0MB3[0,3,4]ZZ	Exc/Elbow Bursa & Lgmt, Rt, [Opn, Perc, Perc Endo] 143, 343, 453
0RBM[0,3,4]ZZ	Exc/Elbow Jt, Lt, [Opn, Perc, Perc Endo] 149, 349, 457
0RBL[0,3,4]ZZ	Exc/Elbow Jt, Rt, [Opn, Perc, Perc Endo] 149, 349, 457
0XBC[0,3,4]ZZ	Exc/Elbow Rgn, Lt, [Opn, Perc, Perc Endo] 28, 91, 144, 207, 356, 461
0XBB[0,3,4]ZZ	Exc/Elbow Rgn, Rt, [Opn, Perc, Perc Endo] 28, 91, 144, 207, 356, 461
0VBL[0,3,4]ZZ	Exc/Epididymis, Bilat, [Opn, Perc, Perc Endo] 257, 459
0VBK[0,3,4]ZZ	Exc/Epididymis, Lt, [Opn, Perc, Perc Endo] 257, 459
0VBJ[0,3,4]ZZ	Exc/Epididymis, Rt, [Opn, Perc, Perc Endo] 257, 459
0CBR[0,3,4,7,8]ZZ	Exc/Epiglottis, [Opn, Perc, Perc Endo, Via Natrl or Artfcl Opng, Via Natrl or Artfcl Opng Endo] 52, 65, 331
06B3*	Exc/Esophageal Vein 86
06B3[0,3,4]ZZ	Exc/Esophageal Vein, [Opn, Perc, Perc Endo] 22, 327
06B3[0,3,4]ZX	Exc/Esophageal Vein, [Opn, Perc, Perc Endo] 442
0DB4[0,3,4,7]ZZ	Exc/Esophagogastric Junction, [Opn, Perc, Perc Endo, Via Natrl or Artfcl Opng] 105, 300, 333
0DB5[0,3,7]ZZ	Exc/Esophagus, [Opn, Perc, Via Natrl or Artfcl Opng] 53, 105, 300, 333
0DB3[0,3,7]ZZ	Exc/Esophagus, Lwr, [Opn, Perc, Via Natrl or Artfcl Opng] 53, 105, 300, 333
0DB2[0,3,7]ZZ	Exc/Esophagus, Mid, [Opn, Perc, Via Natrl or Artfcl Opng] 53, 105, 300, 333
0DB1[0,3,7]ZZ	Exc/Esophagus, Upr, [Opn, Perc, Via Natrl or Artfcl Opng] 53, 105, 300, 333
0NBG[0,3,4]ZZ	Exc/Ethmoid Bone, Lt, [Opn, Perc, Perc Endo] 48, 154, 343
0NBG[0,3,4]ZX	Exc/Ethmoid Bone, Lt, [Opn, Perc, Perc Endo] 54, 129, 454
0NBF[0,3,4]ZZ	Exc/Ethmoid Bone, Rt, [Opn, Perc, Perc Endo] 48, 154, 343
0NBF[0,3,4]ZX	Exc/Ethmoid Bone, Rt, [Opn, Perc, Perc Endo] 54, 129, 454
09BV[0,3,4]ZZ	Exc/Ethmoid Sinus, Lt, [Opn, Perc, Perc Endo] 55, 446
09BU[0,3,4]ZZ	Exc/Ethmoid Sinus, Rt, [Opn, Perc, Perc Endo] 55, 446
03BN*	Exc/Ext Carotid Artery, Lt 81
03BN[0,3,4]ZZ	Exc/Ext Carotid Artery, Lt, [Opn, Perc, Perc Endo] 21, 50, 321
03BN[0,3,4]ZX	Exc/Ext Carotid Artery, Lt, [Opn, Perc, Perc Endo] 441
03BM*	Exc/Ext Carotid Artery, Rt 81
03BM[0,3,4]ZZ	Exc/Ext Carotid Artery, Rt, [Opn, Perc, Perc Endo] 21, 50, 321
03BM[0,3,4]ZX	Exc/Ext Carotid Artery, Rt, [Opn, Perc, Perc Endo] 441
04BJ[0,3,4]ZX	Exc/Ext Iliac Artery, Lt, [Opn, Perc, Perc Endo] 83, 441
04BJ[0,3,4]ZZ	Exc/Ext Iliac Artery, Lt, [Opn, Perc, Perc Endo] 95
04BH[0,3,4]ZX	Exc/Ext Iliac Artery, Rt, [Opn, Perc, Perc Endo] 83, 441
04BH[0,3,4]ZZ	Exc/Ext Iliac Artery, Rt, [Opn, Perc, Perc Endo] 95
06BG[0,3,4]ZX	Exc/Ext Iliac Vein, Lt, [Opn, Perc, Perc Endo] 86, 442
06BG[0,3,4]ZZ	Exc/Ext Iliac Vein, Lt, [Opn, Perc, Perc Endo] 97

06BF[0,3,4]ZX	Exc/Ext Iliac Vein, Rt, [Opn, Perc, Perc Endo] 86, 442
06BF[0,3,4]ZZ	Exc/Ext Iliac Vein, Rt, [Opn, Perc, Perc Endo] 97
05BQ*	Exc/Ext Jugular Vein, Lt 85
05BQ[0,4]ZZ	Exc/Ext Jugular Vein, Lt, [Opn, Perc Endo] 51
05BQ[0,3,4]ZZ	Exc/Ext Jugular Vein, Lt, [Opn, Perc, Perc Endo] 22, 325
05BQ[0,3,4]ZX	Exc/Ext Jugular Vein, Lt, [Opn, Perc, Perc Endo] 442
05BP*	Exc/Ext Jugular Vein, Rt 85
05BP[0,4]ZZ	Exc/Ext Jugular Vein, Rt, [Opn, Perc Endo] 51
05BP[0,3,4]ZZ	Exc/Ext Jugular Vein, Rt, [Opn, Perc, Perc Endo] 22, 325
05BP[0,3,4]ZX	Exc/Ext Jugular Vein, Rt, [Opn, Perc, Perc Endo] 442
08BM*	Exc/Extraocular Muscle, Lt 42
08BM[0,3]Z[X,Z]	Exc/Extraocular Muscle, Lt, [Opn, Perc], No Dev, [Dx, NQ] 444
08BL*	Exc/Extraocular Muscle, Rt 42
08BL[0,3]Z[X,Z]	Exc/Extraocular Muscle, Rt, [Opn, Perc], No Dev, [Dx, NQ] 444
08B1[0,3,X]ZX	Exc/Eye, Lt, [Opn, Perc, Ext] 42
08B1[0,3,X]ZZ	Exc/Eye, Lt, [Opn, Perc, Ext] 42, 210, 329
08B1[0,3,X]Z[X,Z]	Exc/Eye, Lt, [Opn, Perc, Ext], No Dev, [Dx, NQ] 444
08B0[0,3,X]ZX	Exc/Eye, Rt, [Opn, Perc, Ext] 42
08B0[0,3,X]ZZ	Exc/Eye, Rt, [Opn, Perc, Ext] 42, 210, 329
08B0[0,3,X]Z[X,Z]	Exc/Eye, Rt, [Opn, Perc, Ext], No Dev, [Dx, NQ] 444
03BR*	Exc/Face Artery 81
03BR[0,3,4]ZZ	Exc/Face Artery, [Opn, Perc, Perc Endo] 21, 50, 321
03BR[0,3,4]ZX	Exc/Face Artery, [Opn, Perc, Perc Endo] 441
05BV*	Exc/Face Vein, Lt 85
05BV[0,4]ZZ	Exc/Face Vein, Lt, [Opn, Perc Endo] 51
05BV[0,3,4]ZZ	Exc/Face Vein, Lt, [Opn, Perc, Perc Endo] 22, 325
05BV[0,3,4]ZX	Exc/Face Vein, Lt, [Opn, Perc, Perc Endo] 442
05BT*	Exc/Face Vein, Rt 85
05BT[0,4]ZZ	Exc/Face Vein, Rt, [Opn, Perc Endo] 51
05BT[0,3,4]ZZ	Exc/Face Vein, Rt, [Opn, Perc, Perc Endo] 22, 325
05BT[0,3,4]ZX	Exc/Face Vein, Rt, [Opn, Perc, Perc Endo] 442
0WB2[0,3,4,X]ZZ	Exc/Face, [Opn, Perc, Perc Endo, Ext] 28, 44, 55, 91, 144, 207, 355, 460
0KB1*	Exc/Facial Muscle 139
0KB1[0,3,4]ZZ	Exc/Facial Muscle, [Opn, Perc, Perc Endo] 27, 214, 339
00BM[0,3,4]ZZ	Exc/Facial Nerve, [Opn, Perc, Perc Endo] 23, 50, 151, 318, 440
0UB6*	Exc/Fallopian Tube, Lt 262, 264, 266
0UB6[0,3,4,7,8]ZZ	Exc/Fallopian Tube, Lt, [Opn, Perc, Perc Endo, Via Natrl or Artfcl Opng, Via Natrl or Artfcl Opng Endo] 271
0UB5*	Exc/Fallopian Tube, Rt 262, 264, 266
0UB5[0,3,4,7,8]ZZ	Exc/Fallopian Tube, Rt, [Opn, Perc, Perc Endo, Via Natrl or Artfcl Opng, Via Natrl or Artfcl Opng Endo] 271
0UB7[0,3,4,7,8]ZX	Exc/Fallopian Tubes, Bilat, [Opn, Perc, Perc Endo, Via Natrl or Artfcl Opng, Via Natrl or Artfcl Opng Endo] 262, 264, 266
0UB7[0,3,4,7,8]ZZ	Exc/Fallopian Tubes, Bilat, [Opn, Perc, Perc Endo, Via Natrl or Artfcl Opng, Via Natrl or Artfcl Opng Endo] 266, 271
04BL*	Exc/Femor Artery, Lt 83
04BL[0,3,4]ZZ	Exc/Femor Artery, Lt, [Opn, Perc, Perc Endo] 240, 323
04BL[0,3,4]ZX	Exc/Femor Artery, Lt, [Opn, Perc, Perc Endo] 442
04BK*	Exc/Femor Artery, Rt 83
04BK[0,3,4]ZZ	Exc/Femor Artery, Rt, [Opn, Perc, Perc Endo] 240, 323
04BK[0,3,4]ZX	Exc/Femor Artery, Rt, [Opn, Perc, Perc Endo] 441
01BD[0,3,4]ZZ	Exc/Femor Nerve, [Opn, Perc, Perc Endo] 24, 151, 319, 440
0YB8*	Exc/Femor Region, Lt 114
0YB7*	Exc/Femor Region, Rt 114
0YB8[0,3,4]ZX	Exc/Femor Rgn, Lt, [Opn, Perc, Perc Endo] 121, 269, 293, 357
0YB8[0,3,4]ZZ	Exc/Femor Rgn, Lt, [Opn, Perc, Perc Endo] 144, 219, 245
0YB8[0,3,4]Z[X,Z]	Exc/Femor Rgn, Lt, [Opn, Perc, Perc Endo], No Dev, [Dx, NQ] 303, 461
0YB7[0,3,4]ZX	Exc/Femor Rgn, Rt, [Opn, Perc, Perc Endo] 121, 269, 293, 357
0YB7[0,3,4]ZZ	Exc/Femor Rgn, Rt, [Opn, Perc, Perc Endo] 144, 219, 245
0YB7[0,3,4]Z[X,Z]	Exc/Femor Rgn, Rt, [Opn, Perc, Perc Endo], No Dev, [Dx, NQ] 303, 461
0QB9[0,3,4]ZX	Exc/Femor Shaft, Lt, [Opn, Perc, Perc Endo] 130, 217, 244, 254, 259, 456
0QB9[0,3,4]ZZ	Exc/Femor Shaft, Lt, [Opn, Perc, Perc Endo] 137, 347
0QB8[0,3,4]ZX	Exc/Femor Shaft, Rt, [Opn, Perc, Perc Endo] 130, 217, 244, 254, 259, 456
0QB8[0,3,4]ZZ	Exc/Femor Shaft, Rt, [Opn, Perc, Perc Endo] 137, 347
06BN[0,3,4]ZX	Exc/Femor Vein, Lt, [Opn, Perc, Perc Endo] 86, 442
06BN[0,3,4]ZZ	Exc/Femor Vein, Lt, [Opn, Perc, Perc Endo] 88, 327

Ø6BM[Ø,3,4]ZX	Exc/Femor Vein, Rt, [Opn, Perc, Perc Endo] 86, 442
Ø6BM[Ø,3,4]ZZ	Exc/Femor Vein, Rt, [Opn, Perc, Perc Endo] 88, 327
ØQBK[Ø,3,4]ZX	Exc/Fibula, Lt, [Opn, Perc, Perc Endo] 130, 217, 244, 254, 259, 456
ØQBK[Ø,3,4]ZZ	Exc/Fibula, Lt, [Opn, Perc, Perc Endo] 133, 347
ØQBJ[Ø,3,4]ZX	Exc/Fibula, Rt, [Opn, Perc, Perc Endo] 130, 217, 244, 254, 259, 456
ØQBJ[Ø,3,4]ZZ	Exc/Fibula, Rt, [Opn, Perc, Perc Endo] 133, 347
ØRBX[Ø,3,4]ZZ	Exc/Finger Phalangeal Jt, Lt, [Opn, Perc, Perc Endo] 150, 316, 457
ØRBW[Ø,3,4]ZZ	Exc/Finger Phalangeal Jt, Rt, [Opn, Perc, Perc Endo] 150, 316, 457
ØPBV[Ø,3,4]ZX	Exc/Finger Phalanx, Lt, [Opn, Perc, Perc Endo] 130, 216, 292, 455
ØPBV[Ø,3,4]ZZ	Exc/Finger Phalanx, Lt, [Opn, Perc, Perc Endo] 54, 155, 244, 345
ØPBT[Ø,3,4]ZX	Exc/Finger Phalanx, Rt, [Opn, Perc, Perc Endo] 130, 216, 292, 455
ØPBT[Ø,3,4]ZZ	Exc/Finger Phalanx, Rt, [Opn, Perc, Perc Endo] 54, 155, 244, 345
Ø4BW*	Exc/Foot Artery, Lt 83
Ø4BW[Ø,3,4]ZZ	Exc/Foot Artery, Lt, [Opn, Perc, Perc Endo] 240, 323
Ø4BW[Ø,3,4]ZX	Exc/Foot Artery, Lt, [Opn, Perc, Perc Endo] 442
Ø4BV*	Exc/Foot Artery, Rt 83
Ø4BV[Ø,3,4]ZZ	Exc/Foot Artery, Rt, [Opn, Perc, Perc Endo] 240, 323
Ø4BV[Ø,3,4]ZX	Exc/Foot Artery, Rt, [Opn, Perc, Perc Endo] 442
ØMBT[Ø,3,4]ZZ	Exc/Foot Bursa & Lgmt, Lt, [Opn, Perc, Perc Endo] 143, 343, 454
ØMBS[Ø,3,4]ZZ	Exc/Foot Bursa & Lgmt, Rt, [Opn, Perc, Perc Endo] 143, 343, 454
ØKBW*	Exc/Foot Muscle, Lt 139
ØKBW[Ø,3,4]ZZ	Exc/Foot Muscle, Lt, [Opn, Perc, Perc Endo] 27, 214, 339
ØKBV*	Exc/Foot Muscle, Rt 139
ØKBV[Ø,3,4]ZZ	Exc/Foot Muscle, Rt, [Opn, Perc, Perc Endo] 27, 214, 339
ØLBW*	Exc/Foot Tndn, Lt 141
ØLBW[Ø,3,4]ZZ	Exc/Foot Tndn, Lt, [Opn, Perc, Perc Endo] 28, 341
ØLBV*	Exc/Foot Tndn, Rt 141
ØLBV[Ø,3,4]ZZ	Exc/Foot Tndn, Rt, [Opn, Perc, Perc Endo] 28, 341
Ø6BV[Ø,3,4]ZX	Exc/Foot Vein, Lt, [Opn, Perc, Perc Endo] 87, 442
Ø6BV[Ø,3,4]ZZ	Exc/Foot Vein, Lt, [Opn, Perc, Perc Endo] 88, 327
Ø6BT[Ø,3,4]ZX	Exc/Foot Vein, Rt, [Opn, Perc, Perc Endo] 87, 442
Ø6BT[Ø,3,4]ZZ	Exc/Foot Vein, Rt, [Opn, Perc, Perc Endo] 88, 327
ØYBN[Ø,3,4]ZZ	Exc/Foot, Lt, [Opn, Perc, Perc Endo] 29, 92, 144, 207, 357, 461
ØYBM[Ø,3,4]ZZ	Exc/Foot, Rt, [Opn, Perc, Perc Endo] 29, 92, 144, 207, 357, 461
ØNB2*	Exc/Frontal Bone, Lt 9
ØNB2[Ø,3,4]ZX	Exc/Frontal Bone, Lt, [Opn, Perc, Perc Endo] 129, 243
ØNB2[Ø,3,4]ZZ	Exc/Frontal Bone, Lt, [Opn, Perc, Perc Endo] 48, 154, 301, 343, 415
ØNB2[Ø,3,4]Z[X,Z]	Exc/Frontal Bone, Lt, [Opn, Perc, Perc Endo], No Dev, [Dx, NQ] 14, 18
ØNB1*	Exc/Frontal Bone, Rt 9
ØNB1[Ø,3,4]ZX	Exc/Frontal Bone, Rt, [Opn, Perc, Perc Endo] 129, 243
ØNB1[Ø,3,4]ZZ	Exc/Frontal Bone, Rt, [Opn, Perc, Perc Endo] 48, 154, 301, 343, 415
ØNB1[Ø,3,4]Z[X,Z]	Exc/Frontal Bone, Rt, [Opn, Perc, Perc Endo], No Dev, [Dx, NQ] 14, 18
Ø9BT[Ø,3,4]ZZ	Exc/Frontal Sinus, Lt, [Opn, Perc, Perc Endo] 55
Ø9BS[Ø,3,4]ZZ	Exc/Frontal Sinus, Rt, [Opn, Perc, Perc Endo] 55
ØFB4[Ø,3,4]ZZ	Exc/Gallbladder, [Opn, Perc, Perc Endo] 120, 301, 335
ØFB4[Ø,3]ZZ	Exc/Gallbladder, [Opn, Perc] 121
Ø4B2[Ø,3,4]ZX	Exc/Gastric Artery, [Opn, Perc, Perc Endo] 83, 441
Ø4B2[Ø,3,4]ZZ	Exc/Gastric Artery, [Opn, Perc, Perc Endo] 95
Ø6B2[Ø,3,4]ZX	Exc/Gastric Vein, [Opn, Perc, Perc Endo] 86, 442
Ø6B2[Ø,3,4]ZZ	Exc/Gastric Vein, [Opn, Perc, Perc Endo] 97
ØPB8*	Exc/Glenoid Cavity, Lt 65
ØPB8[Ø,3,4]ZX	Exc/Glenoid Cavity, Lt, [Opn, Perc, Perc Endo] 129, 216, 243, 253, 259, 455
ØPB8[Ø,3,4]ZZ	Exc/Glenoid Cavity, Lt, [Opn, Perc, Perc Endo] 19, 155, 345
ØPB7*	Exc/Glenoid Cavity, Rt 65
ØPB7[Ø,3,4]ZX	Exc/Glenoid Cavity, Rt, [Opn, Perc, Perc Endo] 129, 216, 243, 253, 259, 455
ØPB7[Ø,3,4]ZZ	Exc/Glenoid Cavity, Rt, [Opn, Perc, Perc Endo] 19, 155, 345
ØØBP[Ø,3,4]ZZ	Exc/Glossopharyngeal Nerve, [Opn, Perc, Perc Endo] 23, 50, 151, 318, 440
ØDBS[Ø,3,4]ZZ	Exc/Greater Omentum, [Opn, Perc, Perc Endo] 112, 123, 242, 268, 300, 449
Ø6BQ[Ø,3,4]ZX	Exc/Greater Saphenous Vein, Lt, [Opn, Perc, Perc Endo] 86, 442
Ø6BQ[Ø,3,4]ZZ	Exc/Greater Saphenous Vein, Lt, [Opn, Perc, Perc Endo] 88, 327
Ø6BP[Ø,3,4]ZX	Exc/Greater Saphenous Vein, Rt, [Opn, Perc, Perc Endo] 86, 442
Ø6BP[Ø,3,4]ZZ	Exc/Greater Saphenous Vein, Rt, [Opn, Perc, Perc Endo] 88, 327
Ø3BF*	Exc/Hand Artery, Lt 81
Ø3BF[Ø,3,4]ZZ	Exc/Hand Artery, Lt, [Opn, Perc, Perc Endo] 239, 321
Ø3BF[Ø,3,4]ZX	Exc/Hand Artery, Lt, [Opn, Perc, Perc Endo] 441
Ø3BD*	Exc/Hand Artery, Rt 81
Ø3BD[Ø,3,4]ZZ	Exc/Hand Artery, Rt, [Opn, Perc, Perc Endo] 239, 321
Ø3BD[Ø,3,4]ZX	Exc/Hand Artery, Rt, [Opn, Perc, Perc Endo] 441
ØMB8[Ø,3,4]ZZ	Exc/Hand Bursa & Lgmt, Lt, [Opn, Perc, Perc Endo] 150, 315
ØMB7[Ø,3,4]ZZ	Exc/Hand Bursa & Lgmt, Rt, [Opn, Perc, Perc Endo] 150, 315
ØKBD[Ø,3,4]ZX	Exc/Hand Muscle, Lt, [Opn, Perc, Perc Endo] 139
ØKBD[Ø,3,4]ZZ	Exc/Hand Muscle, Lt, [Opn, Perc, Perc Endo] 149, 314
ØKBC[Ø,3,4]ZX	Exc/Hand Muscle, Rt, [Opn, Perc, Perc Endo] 139
ØKBC[Ø,3,4]ZZ	Exc/Hand Muscle, Rt, [Opn, Perc, Perc Endo] 149, 314
ØLB8[Ø,3,4]ZX	Exc/Hand Tndn, Lt, [Opn, Perc, Perc Endo] 141
ØLB8[Ø,3,4]ZZ	Exc/Hand Tndn, Lt, [Opn, Perc, Perc Endo] 149, 243, 315
ØLB7[Ø,3,4]ZX	Exc/Hand Tndn, Rt, [Opn, Perc, Perc Endo] 141
ØLB7[Ø,3,4]ZZ	Exc/Hand Tndn, Rt, [Opn, Perc, Perc Endo] 149, 243, 315
Ø5BH*	Exc/Hand Vein, Lt 85
Ø5BH[Ø,3,4]ZZ	Exc/Hand Vein, Lt, [Opn, Perc, Perc Endo] 240, 325
Ø5BH[Ø,3,4]ZX	Exc/Hand Vein, Lt, [Opn, Perc, Perc Endo] 442
Ø5BG*	Exc/Hand Vein, Rt 85
Ø5BG[Ø,3,4]ZZ	Exc/Hand Vein, Rt, [Opn, Perc, Perc Endo] 240, 325
Ø5BG[Ø,3,4]ZX	Exc/Hand Vein, Rt, [Opn, Perc, Perc Endo] 442
ØXBK[Ø,3,4]ZZ	Exc/Hand, Lt, [Opn, Perc, Perc Endo] 29, 92, 144, 207, 356, 461
ØXBJ[Ø,3,4]ZZ	Exc/Hand, Rt, [Opn, Perc, Perc Endo] 29, 92, 144, 207, 356, 461
ØCB2*	Exc/Hard Palate 56
ØCB2[Ø,3,X]Z[X,Z]	Exc/Hard Palate, [Opn, Perc, Ext], No Dev, [Dx, NQ] 448
ØMBØ[Ø,3,4]ZZ	Exc/Head and Neck Bursa & Lgmt, [Opn, Perc, Perc Endo] 143, 343, 453
Ø1BK*	Exc/Head and Neck Sympathetic Nerve 24
Ø1BK[Ø,3,4]ZZ	Exc/Head and Neck Sympathetic Nerve, [Opn, Perc, Perc Endo] 50, 89
ØLBØ*	Exc/Head and Neck Tndn 141
ØLBØ[Ø,3,4]ZZ	Exc/Head and Neck Tndn, [Opn, Perc, Perc Endo] 28, 340
ØKBØ*	Exc/Head Muscle 139
ØKBØ[Ø,3,4]ZZ	Exc/Head Muscle, [Opn, Perc, Perc Endo] 27, 214, 339
ØWBØ[Ø,3,4,X]ZZ	Exc/Head, [Opn, Perc, Perc Endo, Ext] 28, 44, 55, 91, 144, 207, 355, 460
Ø5B1[Ø,3,4]ZZ	Exc/Hemiazygos Vein, [Opn, Perc, Perc Endo] 60, 96
Ø5B1[Ø,3,4]ZX	Exc/Hemiazygos Vein, [Opn, Perc, Perc Endo] 85, 442
Ø4B3[Ø,3,4]ZX	Exc/Hepatic Artery, [Opn, Perc, Perc Endo] 83, 441
Ø4B3[Ø,3,4]ZZ	Exc/Hepatic Artery, [Opn, Perc, Perc Endo] 95
ØFB6[Ø,3,7]ZZ	Exc/Hepatic Duct, Lt, [Opn, Perc, Via Natrl or Artfcl Opng] 112, 120
ØFB5[Ø,3,7]ZZ	Exc/Hepatic Duct, Rt, [Opn, Perc, Via Natrl or Artfcl Opng] 112, 120
Ø6B4[Ø,3,4]ZX	Exc/Hepatic Vein, [Opn, Perc, Perc Endo] 86, 442
Ø6B4[Ø,3,4]ZZ	Exc/Hepatic Vein, [Opn, Perc, Perc Endo] 97
ØMBM[Ø,3,4]ZZ	Exc/Hip Bursa & Lgmt, Lt, [Opn, Perc, Perc Endo] 143, 343, 454
ØMBL[Ø,3,4]ZZ	Exc/Hip Bursa & Lgmt, Rt, [Opn, Perc, Perc Endo] 143, 343, 454
ØSBB[Ø,3,4]ZZ	Exc/Hip Jt, Lt, [Opn, Perc, Perc Endo] 131, 351, 416
ØSB9[Ø,3,4]ZZ	Exc/Hip Jt, Rt, [Opn, Perc, Perc Endo] 131, 351, 416
ØKBP*	Exc/Hip Muscle, Lt 139
ØKBP[Ø,3,4]ZZ	Exc/Hip Muscle, Lt, [Opn, Perc, Perc Endo] 27, 214, 339
ØKBN*	Exc/Hip Muscle, Rt 139
ØKBN[Ø,3,4]ZZ	Exc/Hip Muscle, Rt, [Opn, Perc, Perc Endo] 27, 214, 339
ØLBK*	Exc/Hip Tndn, Lt 141
ØLBK[Ø,3,4]ZZ	Exc/Hip Tndn, Lt, [Opn, Perc, Perc Endo] 28, 341
ØLBJ*	Exc/Hip Tndn, Rt 141
ØLBJ[Ø,3,4]ZZ	Exc/Hip Tndn, Rt, [Opn, Perc, Perc Endo] 28, 341
ØPBD[Ø,3,4]ZX	Exc/Humeral Head, Lt, [Opn, Perc, Perc Endo] 129, 216, 243, 253, 259, 455

ØPBD[Ø,3,4]ZZ	Exc/Humeral Head, Lt, [Opn, Perc, Perc Endo] 132, 345
ØPBC[Ø,3,4]ZX	Exc/Humeral Head, Rt, [Opn, Perc, Perc Endo] 129, 216, 243, 253, 259, 455
ØPBC[Ø,3,4]ZZ	Exc/Humeral Head, Rt, [Opn, Perc, Perc Endo] 132, 345
ØPBG[Ø,3,4]ZX	Exc/Humeral Shaft, Lt, [Opn, Perc, Perc Endo] 129, 216, 243, 253, 259, 455
ØPBG[Ø,3,4]ZZ	Exc/Humeral Shaft, Lt, [Opn, Perc, Perc Endo] 132, 345
ØPBF[Ø,3,4]ZX	Exc/Humeral Shaft, Rt, [Opn, Perc, Perc Endo] 129, 216, 243, 253, 259, 455
ØPBF[Ø,3,4]ZZ	Exc/Humeral Shaft, Rt, [Opn, Perc, Perc Endo] 132, 345
ØUBK*	Exc/Hymen 267
ØUBK[Ø,3,4,7,8,X]ZX	Exc/Hymen, [Opn, Perc, Perc Endo, Via Natrl or Artfcl Opng, Via Natrl or Artfcl Opng Endo, Ext] 271
ØUBK[Ø,3,4,7,8,X]ZZ	Exc/Hymen, [Opn, Perc, Perc Endo, Via Natrl or Artfcl Opng, Via Natrl or Artfcl Opng Endo, Ext] 275
ØUBK[Ø,3,4,7,8]Z[X,Z]	Exc/Hymen, [Opn, Perc, Perc Endo, Via Natrl or Artfcl Opng, Via Natrl or Artfcl Opng Endo], No Dev, [Dx, NQ] 459
ØNBX[Ø,3,4]ZZ	Exc/Hyoid Bone, [Opn, Perc, Perc Endo] 48, 154, 344
ØNBX[Ø,3,4]ZX	Exc/Hyoid Bone, [Opn, Perc, Perc Endo] 54, 129, 454
Ø6BJ[Ø,3,4]ZX	Exc/Hypogastric Vein, Lt, [Opn, Perc, Perc Endo] 86, 442
Ø6BJ[Ø,3,4]ZZ	Exc/Hypogastric Vein, Lt, [Opn, Perc, Perc Endo] 97
Ø6BH[Ø,3,4]ZX	Exc/Hypogastric Vein, Rt, [Opn, Perc, Perc Endo] 86, 442
Ø6BH[Ø,3,4]ZZ	Exc/Hypogastric Vein, Rt, [Opn, Perc, Perc Endo] 97
ØØBS[Ø,3,4]ZZ	Exc/Hypoglossal Nerve, [Opn, Perc, Perc Endo] 23, 50, 151, 318, 440
ØØBA[Ø,3,4]ZZ	Exc/Hypothalamus, [Opn, Perc, Perc Endo] 8, 12, 16, 295, 318, 414
ØDBC[Ø,3,4,7,8]ZZ	Exc/Ileocecal Valve, [Opn, Perc, Perc Endo, Via Natrl or Artfcl Opng, Via Natrl or Artfcl Opng Endo] 109, 449
ØDBB[Ø,3,4,7,8]ZZ	Exc/Ileum, [Opn, Perc, Perc Endo, Via Natrl or Artfcl Opng, Via Natrl or Artfcl Opng Endo] 109, 449
Ø4BB[Ø,3,4]ZX	Exc/Inferior Mesenteric Artery, [Opn, Perc, Perc Endo] 83, 441
Ø4BB[Ø,3,4]ZZ	Exc/Inferior Mesenteric Artery, [Opn, Perc, Perc Endo] 95
Ø6B6[Ø,3,4]ZX	Exc/Inferior Mesenteric Vein, [Opn, Perc, Perc Endo] 86, 442
Ø6B6[Ø,3,4]ZZ	Exc/Inferior Mesenteric Vein, [Opn, Perc, Perc Endo] 97
ØGBP*	Exc/Inferior Parathyroid Gland, Lt 238
ØGBP[Ø,3,4]ZX	Exc/Inferior Parathyroid Gland, Lt, [Opn, Perc, Perc Endo] 153
ØGBP[Ø,3,4]ZZ	Exc/Inferior Parathyroid Gland, Lt, [Opn, Perc, Perc Endo] 253
ØGBN*	Exc/Inferior Parathyroid Gland, Rt 238
ØGBN[Ø,3,4]ZX	Exc/Inferior Parathyroid Gland, Rt, [Opn, Perc, Perc Endo] 153
ØGBN[Ø,3,4]ZZ	Exc/Inferior Parathyroid Gland, Rt, [Opn, Perc, Perc Endo] 253
Ø6BØ[Ø,3,4]ZX	Exc/Inferior Vena Cava, [Opn, Perc, Perc Endo] 86, 442
Ø6BØ[Ø,3,4]ZZ	Exc/Inferior Vena Cava, [Opn, Perc, Perc Endo] 97
ØYB6*	Exc/Inguinal Region, Lt 114
ØYB5*	Exc/Inguinal Region, Rt 114
ØYB6[Ø,3,4]ZX	Exc/Inguinal Rgn, Lt, [Opn, Perc, Perc Endo] 121, 269, 293, 357
ØYB6[Ø,3,4]ZZ	Exc/Inguinal Rgn, Lt, [Opn, Perc, Perc Endo] 144, 219, 245
ØYB6[Ø,3,4]Z[X,Z]	Exc/Inguinal Rgn, Lt, [Opn, Perc, Perc Endo], No Dev, [Dx, NQ] 303, 461
ØYB5[Ø,3,4]ZX	Exc/Inguinal Rgn, Rt, [Opn, Perc, Perc Endo] 121, 269, 293, 357
ØYB5[Ø,3,4]ZZ	Exc/Inguinal Rgn, Rt, [Opn, Perc, Perc Endo] 144, 219, 245
ØYB5[Ø,3,4]Z[X,Z]	Exc/Inguinal Rgn, Rt, [Opn, Perc, Perc Endo], No Dev, [Dx, NQ] 303, 461
Ø9BE*	Exc/Inner Ear, Lt 51
Ø9BD*	Exc/Inner Ear, Rt 51
Ø3B2[Ø,3,4]ZZ	Exc/Innominate Artery, [Opn, Perc, Perc Endo] 60, 93
Ø3B2[Ø,3,4]ZX	Exc/Innominate Artery, [Opn, Perc, Perc Endo] 81, 441
Ø5B4[Ø,3,4]ZZ	Exc/Innominate Vein, Lt, [Opn, Perc, Perc Endo] 60, 96
Ø5B4[Ø,3,4]ZX	Exc/Innominate Vein, Lt, [Opn, Perc, Perc Endo] 85, 442
Ø5B3[Ø,3,4]ZZ	Exc/Innominate Vein, Rt, [Opn, Perc, Perc Endo] 60, 96
Ø5B3[Ø,3,4]ZX	Exc/Innominate Vein, Rt, [Opn, Perc, Perc Endo] 85, 442
Ø3BL*	Exc/Int Carotid Artery, Lt 81
Ø3BL[Ø,3,4]ZZ	Exc/Int Carotid Artery, Lt, [Opn, Perc, Perc Endo] 21, 50, 321
Ø3BL[Ø,3,4]ZX	Exc/Int Carotid Artery, Lt, [Opn, Perc, Perc Endo] 441
Ø3BK*	Exc/Int Carotid Artery, Rt 81
Ø3BK[Ø,3,4]ZZ	Exc/Int Carotid Artery, Rt, [Opn, Perc, Perc Endo] 21, 50, 321
Ø3BK[Ø,3,4]ZX	Exc/Int Carotid Artery, Rt, [Opn, Perc, Perc Endo] 441
Ø4BF[Ø,3,4]ZX	Exc/Int Iliac Artery, Lt, [Opn, Perc, Perc Endo] 83, 441
Ø4BF[Ø,3,4]ZZ	Exc/Int Iliac Artery, Lt, [Opn, Perc, Perc Endo] 95
Ø4BE[Ø,3,4]ZX	Exc/Int Iliac Artery, Rt, [Opn, Perc, Perc Endo] 83, 441
Ø4BE[Ø,3,4]ZZ	Exc/Int Iliac Artery, Rt, [Opn, Perc, Perc Endo] 95
Ø5BN*	Exc/Int Jugular Vein, Lt 85
Ø5BN[Ø,4]ZZ	Exc/Int Jugular Vein, Lt, [Opn, Perc Endo] 51
Ø5BN[Ø,3,4]ZZ	Exc/Int Jugular Vein, Lt, [Opn, Perc, Perc Endo] 22, 325
Ø5BN[Ø,3,4]ZX	Exc/Int Jugular Vein, Lt, [Opn, Perc, Perc Endo] 442
Ø5BM*	Exc/Int Jugular Vein, Rt 85
Ø5BM[Ø,4]ZZ	Exc/Int Jugular Vein, Rt, [Opn, Perc Endo] 51
Ø5BM[Ø,3,4]ZZ	Exc/Int Jugular Vein, Rt, [Opn, Perc, Perc Endo] 22, 325
Ø5BM[Ø,3,4]ZX	Exc/Int Jugular Vein, Rt, [Opn, Perc, Perc Endo] 442
Ø3B1[Ø,3,4]ZZ	Exc/Int Mammary Artery, Lt, [Opn, Perc, Perc Endo] 60, 93
Ø3B1[Ø,3,4]ZX	Exc/Int Mammary Artery, Lt, [Opn, Perc, Perc Endo] 81, 441
Ø3BØ[Ø,3,4]ZZ	Exc/Int Mammary Artery, Rt, [Opn, Perc, Perc Endo] 60, 93
Ø3BØ[Ø,3,4]ZX	Exc/Int Mammary Artery, Rt, [Opn, Perc, Perc Endo] 81, 441
Ø3BG[Ø,3,4]ZZ	Exc/Intracranial Artery, [Opn, Perc, Perc Endo] 7, 8, 13, 17, 321
Ø3BG[Ø,3,4]ZX	Exc/Intracranial Artery, [Opn, Perc, Perc Endo] 81, 441
Ø5BL[Ø,3,4]ZZ	Exc/Intracranial Vein, [Opn, Perc, Perc Endo] 7, 9, 13, 17, 325
Ø5BL[Ø,3,4]ZX	Exc/Intracranial Vein, [Opn, Perc, Perc Endo] 85, 442
Ø8BD*	Exc/Iris, Lt 44, 329
Ø8BD3Z[X,Z]	Exc/Iris, Lt, Perc, No Dev, [Dx, NQ] 444
Ø8BC*	Exc/Iris, Rt 44, 329
Ø8BC3Z[X,Z]	Exc/Iris, Rt, Perc, No Dev, [Dx, NQ] 444
ØDBA[Ø,3,4,7,8]ZZ	Exc/Jejunum, [Opn, Perc, Perc Endo, Via Natrl or Artfcl Opng, Via Natrl or Artfcl Opng Endo] 109, 449
ØTB4[Ø,3,4]ZZ	Exc/Kidney Pelvis, Lt, [Opn, Perc, Perc Endo] 259, 302
ØTB3[Ø,3,4]ZZ	Exc/Kidney Pelvis, Rt, [Opn, Perc, Perc Endo] 259, 302
ØTB1[Ø,3,4]ZZ	Exc/Kidney, Lt, [Opn, Perc, Perc Endo] 259, 302
ØTBØ[Ø,3,4]ZZ	Exc/Kidney, Rt, [Opn, Perc, Perc Endo] 259, 302
ØMBP[Ø,3,4]ZZ	Exc/Knee Bursa & Lgmt, Lt, [Opn, Perc, Perc Endo] 143, 343, 454
ØMBN[Ø,3,4]ZZ	Exc/Knee Bursa & Lgmt, Rt, [Opn, Perc, Perc Endo] 143, 343, 454
ØSBD[Ø,3,4]ZZ	Exc/Knee Jt, Lt, [Opn, Perc, Perc Endo] 132, 244, 351, 457
ØSBC[Ø,3,4]ZZ	Exc/Knee Jt, Rt, [Opn, Perc, Perc Endo] 132, 244, 351, 457
ØYBG[Ø,3,4]ZZ	Exc/Knee Rgn, Lt, [Opn, Perc, Perc Endo] 29, 92, 144, 207, 357, 461
ØYBF[Ø,3,4]ZZ	Exc/Knee Rgn, Rt, [Opn, Perc, Perc Endo] 29, 92, 144, 207, 357, 461
ØLBR*	Exc/Knee Tndn, Lt 141
ØLBR[Ø,3,4]ZZ	Exc/Knee Tndn, Lt, [Opn, Perc, Perc Endo] 28, 341
ØLBQ*	Exc/Knee Tndn, Rt 141
ØLBQ[Ø,3,4]ZZ	Exc/Knee Tndn, Rt, [Opn, Perc, Perc Endo] 28, 341
ØNBJ[Ø,3,4]ZZ	Exc/Lacrimal Bone, Lt, [Opn, Perc, Perc Endo] 48, 154, 343
ØNBJ[Ø,3,4]ZX	Exc/Lacrimal Bone, Lt, [Opn, Perc, Perc Endo] 54, 129, 454
ØNBH[Ø,3,4]ZZ	Exc/Lacrimal Bone, Rt, [Opn, Perc, Perc Endo] 48, 154, 343
ØNBH[Ø,3,4]ZX	Exc/Lacrimal Bone, Rt, [Opn, Perc, Perc Endo] 54, 129, 454
Ø8BY*	Exc/Lacrimal Duct, Lt 43
Ø8BY[Ø,3,7,8]ZZ	Exc/Lacrimal Duct, Lt, [Opn, Perc, Via Natrl or Artfcl Opng, Via Natrl or Artfcl Opng Endo] 329
Ø8BY[Ø,3,7,8]ZX	Exc/Lacrimal Duct, Lt, [Opn, Perc, Via Natrl or Artfcl Opng, Via Natrl or Artfcl Opng Endo] 51
Ø8BY[Ø,3,7,8]Z[X,Z]	Exc/Lacrimal Duct, Lt, [Opn, Perc, Via Natrl or Artfcl Opng, Via Natrl or Artfcl Opng Endo], No Dev, [Dx, NQ] 444
Ø8BX*	Exc/Lacrimal Duct, Rt 43
Ø8BX[Ø,3,7,8]ZZ	Exc/Lacrimal Duct, Rt, [Opn, Perc, Via Natrl or Artfcl Opng, Via Natrl or Artfcl Opng Endo] 329
Ø8BX[Ø,3,7,8]ZX	Exc/Lacrimal Duct, Rt, [Opn, Perc, Via Natrl or Artfcl Opng, Via Natrl or Artfcl Opng Endo] 51
Ø8BX[Ø,3,7,8]Z[X,Z]	Exc/Lacrimal Duct, Rt, [Opn, Perc, Via Natrl or Artfcl Opng, Via Natrl or Artfcl Opng Endo], No Dev, [Dx, NQ] 444
Ø8BW*	Exc/Lacrimal Gland, Lt 43, 329
Ø8BW[Ø,3]Z[X,Z]	Exc/Lacrimal Gland, Lt, [Opn, Perc], No Dev, [Dx, NQ] 444
Ø8BV*	Exc/Lacrimal Gland, Rt 43, 329
Ø8BV[Ø,3]Z[X,Z]	Exc/Lacrimal Gland, Rt, [Opn, Perc], No Dev, [Dx, NQ] 444
ØCBS[Ø,3,4,7,8]ZZ	Exc/Larynx, [Opn, Perc, Perc Endo, Via Natrl or Artfcl Opng, Via Natrl or Artfcl Opng Endo] 48, 65, 331
Ø8BK*	Exc/Lens, Lt 44
Ø8BK3Z[X,Z]	Exc/Lens, Lt, Perc, No Dev, [Dx, NQ] 444
Ø8BJ*	Exc/Lens, Rt 44
Ø8BJ3Z[X,Z]	Exc/Lens, Rt, Perc, No Dev, [Dx, NQ] 444
ØDBT[Ø,3,4]ZZ	Exc/Lesser Omentum, [Opn, Perc, Perc Endo] 112, 123, 242, 268, 300, 449
Ø6BS[Ø,3,4]ZX	Exc/Lesser Saphenous Vein, Lt, [Opn, Perc, Perc Endo] 87, 442
Ø6BS[Ø,3,4]ZZ	Exc/Lesser Saphenous Vein, Lt, [Opn, Perc, Perc Endo] 88, 327

Code	Description
06BR[0,3,4]ZX	Exc/Lesser Saphenous Vein, Rt, [Opn, Perc, Perc Endo] 87, 442
06BR[0,3,4]ZZ	Exc/Lesser Saphenous Vein, Rt, [Opn, Perc, Perc Endo] 88, 327
0DBE[0,3,4]ZZ	Exc/Lg Intestine, [Opn, Perc, Perc Endo] 90, 106, 300, 333
0DBE[0,3,7]ZZ	Exc/Lg Intestine, [Opn, Perc, Via Natrl or Artfcl Opng] 242
0DBG[0,3,4]ZZ	Exc/Lg Intestine, Lt, [Opn, Perc, Perc Endo] 90, 106, 300, 333
0DBG[0,3,7]ZZ	Exc/Lg Intestine, Lt, [Opn, Perc, Via Natrl or Artfcl Opng] 242
0DBF[0,3,4]ZZ	Exc/Lg Intestine, Rt, [Opn, Perc, Perc Endo] 90, 106, 300, 333
0DBF[0,3,7]ZZ	Exc/Lg Intestine, Rt, [Opn, Perc, Via Natrl or Artfcl Opng] 242
0BB9[0,3,7]ZZ	Exc/Lingula Bronchus, [Opn, Perc, Via Natrl or Artfcl Opng] 61
0FB0[0,4]ZX	Exc/Liver, [Opn, Perc Endo] 112, 121, 211, 253, 292, 301, 335
0FB0[0,3,4]ZZ	Exc/Liver, [Opn, Perc, Perc Endo] 119, 335
0FB2[0,4]ZX	Exc/Liver, Lt Lobe, [Opn, Perc Endo] 112, 121, 211, 253, 292, 301, 335
0FB2[0,3,4]ZZ	Exc/Liver, Lt Lobe, [Opn, Perc, Perc Endo] 119, 335
0FB1[0,4]ZX	Exc/Liver, Rt Lobe, [Opn, Perc Endo] 112, 121, 211, 253, 292, 301, 335
0FB1[0,3,4]ZZ	Exc/Liver, Rt Lobe, [Opn, Perc, Perc Endo] 119, 335
0GB2[0,3,4]ZZ	Exc/Lt Adrenal Gland, [Opn, Perc, Perc Endo] 235
01BB[0,3,4]ZZ	Exc/Lumbar Nerve, [Opn, Perc, Perc Endo] 24, 151, 319, 440
01B9[0,3,4]ZZ	Exc/Lumbar Plexus, [Opn, Perc, Perc Endo] 24, 151, 319, 440
00BY*	Exc/Lumbar Spinal Cord 159, 160
00BY[0,3,4]Z[X,Z]	Exc/Lumbar Spinal Cord, [Opn, Perc, Perc Endo], No Dev, [Dx, NQ] 19, 295
01BN*	Exc/Lumbar Sympathetic Nerve 24
01BN[0,3,4]ZZ	Exc/Lumbar Sympathetic Nerve, [Opn, Perc, Perc Endo] 89, 441
0SB2[0,3,4]ZZ	Exc/Lumbar Vert Disc, [Opn, Perc, Perc Endo] 20, 159, 161, 351
0SB0[0,3,4]ZZ	Exc/Lumbar Vert Jt, [Opn, Perc, Perc Endo] 20, 159, 161, 302, 351
0QB0*	Exc/Lumbar Vertebra 244
0QB0[0,3,4]ZX	Exc/Lumbar Vertebra, [Opn, Perc, Perc Endo] 130, 253, 259, 292, 456
0QB0[0,3,4]ZZ	Exc/Lumbar Vertebra, [Opn, Perc, Perc Endo] 54, 156, 347
0SB4[0,3,4]ZZ	Exc/Lumbosacral Disc, [Opn, Perc, Perc Endo] 20, 159, 161, 351
0SB3[0,3,4]ZZ	Exc/Lumbosacral Jt, [Opn, Perc, Perc Endo] 20, 159, 161, 302, 351
01BA[0,3,4]ZZ	Exc/Lumbosacral Plexus, [Opn, Perc, Perc Endo] 24, 151, 319, 440
0BBH[0,4,7,8]ZX	Exc/Lung Lingula, [Opn, Perc Endo, Via Natrl or Artfcl Opng, Via Natrl or Artfcl Opng Endo] 90
0BBH[0,4]ZX	Exc/Lung Lingula, [Opn, Perc Endo] 153, 253
0BBH[0,3,4,7]ZZ	Exc/Lung Lingula, [Opn, Perc, Perc Endo, Via Natrl or Artfcl Opng] 61, 299
0BBH[4,7,8]ZX	Exc/Lung Lingula, [Perc Endo, Via Natrl or Artfcl Opng, Via Natrl or Artfcl Opng Endo] 64
0BBH[7,8]ZX	Exc/Lung Lingula, [Via Natrl or Artfcl Opng, Via Natrl or Artfcl Opng Endo] 447
0BBL[0,4,7,8]ZX	Exc/Lung, Lt, [Opn, Perc Endo, Via Natrl or Artfcl Opng, Via Natrl or Artfcl Opng Endo] 90
0BBL[0,4]ZX	Exc/Lung, Lt, [Opn, Perc Endo] 153, 253
0BBL[0,3,4,7]ZZ	Exc/Lung, Lt, [Opn, Perc, Perc Endo, Via Natrl or Artfcl Opng] 61, 299
0BBL[4,7,8]ZX	Exc/Lung, Lt, [Perc Endo, Via Natrl or Artfcl Opng, Via Natrl or Artfcl Opng Endo] 64
0BBL[7,8]ZX	Exc/Lung, Lt, [Via Natrl or Artfcl Opng, Via Natrl or Artfcl Opng Endo] 447
0BBK[0,4,7,8]ZX	Exc/Lung, Rt, [Opn, Perc Endo, Via Natrl or Artfcl Opng, Via Natrl or Artfcl Opng Endo] 90
0BBK[0,4]ZX	Exc/Lung, Rt, [Opn, Perc Endo] 153, 253
0BBK[0,3,4,7]ZZ	Exc/Lung, Rt, [Opn, Perc, Perc Endo, Via Natrl or Artfcl Opng] 61, 299
0BBK[4,7,8]ZX	Exc/Lung, Rt, [Perc Endo, Via Natrl or Artfcl Opng, Via Natrl or Artfcl Opng Endo] 64
0BBK[7,8]ZX	Exc/Lung, Rt, [Via Natrl or Artfcl Opng, Via Natrl or Artfcl Opng Endo] 447
0BBM[0,4,7,8]ZX	Exc/Lungs, Bilat, [Opn, Perc Endo, Via Natrl or Artfcl Opng, Via Natrl or Artfcl Opng Endo] 90
0BBM[0,3,7]ZZ	Exc/Lungs, Bilat, [Opn, Perc, Via Natrl or Artfcl Opng] 61, 299, 331
0BBM[4,7,8]ZX	Exc/Lungs, Bilat, [Perc Endo, Via Natrl or Artfcl Opng, Via Natrl or Artfcl Opng Endo] 64, 447
0KBB*	Exc/Lwr Arm and Wrist Muscle, Lt 139
0KBB[0,3,4]ZZ	Exc/Lwr Arm and Wrist Muscle, Lt, [Opn, Perc, Perc Endo] 27, 214, 339
0KB9*	Exc/Lwr Arm and Wrist Muscle, Rt 139
0KB9[0,3,4]ZZ	Exc/Lwr Arm and Wrist Muscle, Rt, [Opn, Perc, Perc Endo] 27, 214, 339
0LB6*	Exc/Lwr Arm and Wrist Tndn, Lt 141
0LB6[0,3,4]ZZ	Exc/Lwr Arm and Wrist Tndn, Lt, [Opn, Perc, Perc Endo] 28, 340
0LB5*	Exc/Lwr Arm and Wrist Tndn, Rt 141
0LB5[0,3,4]ZZ	Exc/Lwr Arm and Wrist Tndn, Rt, [Opn, Perc, Perc Endo] 28, 340
0XBF[0,3,4]ZZ	Exc/Lwr Arm, Lt, [Opn, Perc, Perc Endo] 29, 92, 144, 207, 356, 461
0XBD[0,3,4]ZZ	Exc/Lwr Arm, Rt, [Opn, Perc, Perc Endo] 29, 91, 144, 207, 356, 461
04BY*	Exc/Lwr Artery 83
04BY[0,3,4]ZZ	Exc/Lwr Artery, [Opn, Perc, Perc Endo] 240, 323
04BY[0,3,4]ZX	Exc/Lwr Artery, [Opn, Perc, Perc Endo] 442
0WBL[0,3,4,X]ZZ	Exc/Lwr Back, [Opn, Perc, Perc Endo, Ext] 28, 91, 144, 207, 355, 460
0MBW*	Exc/Lwr Extr Bursa & Lgmt, Lt 143
0MBW[0,3,4]ZZ	Exc/Lwr Extr Bursa & Lgmt, Lt, [Opn, Perc, Perc Endo] 343, 454
0MBV*	Exc/Lwr Extr Bursa & Lgmt, Rt 143
0MBV[0,3,4]ZZ	Exc/Lwr Extr Bursa & Lgmt, Rt, [Opn, Perc, Perc Endo] 343, 454
0YBB[0,3,4]ZZ	Exc/Lwr Extr, Lt, [Opn, Perc, Perc Endo] 29, 92, 144, 207, 357, 461
0YB9[0,3,4]ZZ	Exc/Lwr Extr, Rt, [Opn, Perc, Perc Endo] 29, 92, 144, 207, 357, 461
08BR*	Exc/Lwr Eyelid, Lt 42, 329
08BR[0,3,X]ZZ	Exc/Lwr Eyelid, Lt, [Opn, Perc, Ext] 210, 241
08BR[0,3,X]Z[X,Z]	Exc/Lwr Eyelid, Lt, [Opn, Perc, Ext], No Dev, [Dx, NQ] 444
08BQ*	Exc/Lwr Eyelid, Rt 42, 329
08BQ[0,3,X]ZZ	Exc/Lwr Eyelid, Rt, [Opn, Perc, Ext] 210, 241
08BQ[0,3,X]Z[X,Z]	Exc/Lwr Eyelid, Rt, [Opn, Perc, Ext], No Dev, [Dx, NQ] 444
0QBC[0,3,4]ZX	Exc/Lwr Femur, Lt, [Opn, Perc, Perc Endo] 130, 217, 244, 254, 259, 456
0QBC[0,3,4]ZZ	Exc/Lwr Femur, Lt, [Opn, Perc, Perc Endo] 137, 347
0QBB[0,3,4]ZX	Exc/Lwr Femur, Rt, [Opn, Perc, Perc Endo] 130, 217, 244, 254, 259, 456
0QBB[0,3,4]ZZ	Exc/Lwr Femur, Rt, [Opn, Perc, Perc Endo] 137, 347
0WB5[0,3,4,X]ZZ	Exc/Lwr Jaw, [Opn, Perc, Perc Endo, Ext] 28, 55, 91, 144, 207, 355, 460
0KBT*	Exc/Lwr Leg Muscle, Lt 139
0KBT[0,3,4]ZZ	Exc/Lwr Leg Muscle, Lt, [Opn, Perc, Perc Endo] 27, 214, 339
0KBS*	Exc/Lwr Leg Muscle, Rt 139
0KBS[0,3,4]ZZ	Exc/Lwr Leg Muscle, Rt, [Opn, Perc, Perc Endo] 27, 214, 339
0LBP*	Exc/Lwr Leg Tndn, Lt 141
0LBP[0,3,4]ZZ	Exc/Lwr Leg Tndn, Lt, [Opn, Perc, Perc Endo] 28, 341
0LBN*	Exc/Lwr Leg Tndn, Rt 141
0LBN[0,3,4]ZZ	Exc/Lwr Leg Tndn, Rt, [Opn, Perc, Perc Endo] 28, 341
0YBJ[0,3,4]ZZ	Exc/Lwr Leg, Lt, [Opn, Perc, Perc Endo] 29, 92, 144, 207, 357, 461
0YBH[0,3,4]ZZ	Exc/Lwr Leg, Rt, [Opn, Perc, Perc Endo] 29, 92, 144, 207, 357, 461
0CB1[0,3,X]ZZ	Exc/Lwr Lip, [Opn, Perc, Ext] 56, 211, 448
0BBB[0,3,7]ZZ	Exc/Lwr Lobe Bronchus, Lt, [Opn, Perc, Via Natrl or Artfcl Opng] 61
0BB6[0,3,7]ZZ	Exc/Lwr Lobe Bronchus, Rt, [Opn, Perc, Via Natrl or Artfcl Opng] 61
0BBJ[0,4,7,8]ZX	Exc/Lwr Lung Lobe, Lt, [Opn, Perc Endo, Via Natrl or Artfcl Opng, Via Natrl or Artfcl Opng Endo] 90
0BBJ[0,4]ZX	Exc/Lwr Lung Lobe, Lt, [Opn, Perc Endo] 153, 253
0BBJ[0,3,4,7]ZZ	Exc/Lwr Lung Lobe, Lt, [Opn, Perc, Perc Endo, Via Natrl or Artfcl Opng] 61, 299
0BBJ[4,7,8]ZX	Exc/Lwr Lung Lobe, Lt, [Perc Endo, Via Natrl or Artfcl Opng, Via Natrl or Artfcl Opng Endo] 64
0BBJ[7,8]ZX	Exc/Lwr Lung Lobe, Lt, [Via Natrl or Artfcl Opng, Via Natrl or Artfcl Opng Endo] 447
0BBF[0,4,7,8]ZX	Exc/Lwr Lung Lobe, Rt, [Opn, Perc Endo, Via Natrl or Artfcl Opng, Via Natrl or Artfcl Opng Endo] 90
0BBF[0,4]ZX	Exc/Lwr Lung Lobe, Rt, [Opn, Perc Endo] 153, 253
0BBF[0,3,4,7]ZZ	Exc/Lwr Lung Lobe, Rt, [Opn, Perc, Perc Endo, Via Natrl or Artfcl Opng] 61, 299
0BBF[4,7,8]ZX	Exc/Lwr Lung Lobe, Rt, [Perc Endo, Via Natrl or Artfcl Opng, Via Natrl or Artfcl Opng Endo] 64

ØBBF[7,8]ZX	Exc/Lwr Lung Lobe, Rt, [Via Natrl or Artfcl Opng, Via Natrl or Artfcl Opng Endo] 447
06BY[0,3,4]ZZ	Exc/Lwr Vein, [Opn, Perc, Perc Endo] 241, 327
06BY[0,3,4]Z[X,Z]	Exc/Lwr Vein, [Opn, Perc, Perc Endo], No Dev, [Dx, NQ] 87
06BY[0,3,4]Z[C,X]	Exc/Lwr Vein, [Opn, Perc, Perc Endo], No Dev, [Hemorrhoidal Plexus, Dx] 443
06BY[0,3,4]ZC	Exc/Lwr Vein, [Opn, Perc, Perc Endo], No Dev, Hemorrhoidal Plexus 109, 271
07BD*	Exc/Lymphatic, Aortic 112, 290
07BD[0,3,4]ZX	Exc/Lymphatic, Aortic, [Opn, Perc, Perc Endo] 25, 90, 122, 153, 241, 252
07BD[0,3,4]Z[X,Z]	Exc/Lymphatic, Aortic, [Opn, Perc, Perc Endo], No Dev, [Dx, NQ] 209, 443
07B0*	Exc/Lymphatic, Head 290
07B0[0,4]ZZ	Exc/Lymphatic, Head, [Opn, Perc Endo] 51, 297
07B0[0,3,4]ZX	Exc/Lymphatic, Head, [Opn, Perc, Perc Endo] 25, 51, 90, 153, 241
07B0[0,3,4]Z[X,Z]	Exc/Lymphatic, Head, [Opn, Perc, Perc Endo], No Dev, [Dx, NQ] 209, 443
07B9*	Exc/Lymphatic, Int Mammary, Lt 290
07B9[0,3,4]ZX	Exc/Lymphatic, Int Mammary, Lt, [Opn, Perc, Perc Endo] 25, 90, 153, 241, 443
07B9[0,3,4]ZZ	Exc/Lymphatic, Int Mammary, Lt, [Opn, Perc, Perc Endo] 60
07B9[0,3,4]Z[X,Z]	Exc/Lymphatic, Int Mammary, Lt, [Opn, Perc, Perc Endo], No Dev, [Dx, NQ] 209
07B8*	Exc/Lymphatic, Int Mammary, Rt 290
07B8[0,3,4]ZX	Exc/Lymphatic, Int Mammary, Rt, [Opn, Perc, Perc Endo] 25, 90, 153, 241, 443
07B8[0,3,4]ZZ	Exc/Lymphatic, Int Mammary, Rt, [Opn, Perc, Perc Endo] 60
07B8[0,3,4]Z[X,Z]	Exc/Lymphatic, Int Mammary, Rt, [Opn, Perc, Perc Endo], No Dev, [Dx, NQ] 209
07B6*	Exc/Lymphatic, Lt Axillary 90, 153, 290
07B6[0,3,4]ZX	Exc/Lymphatic, Lt Axillary, [Opn, Perc, Perc Endo] 25, 241
07B6[0,3,4]ZZ	Exc/Lymphatic, Lt Axillary, [Opn, Perc, Perc Endo] 51, 64, 112
07B6[0,3,4]Z[X,Z]	Exc/Lymphatic, Lt Axillary, [Opn, Perc, Perc Endo], No Dev, [Dx, NQ] 209, 443
07BJ*	Exc/Lymphatic, Lt Inguinal 90, 153, 258, 268, 290
07BJ[0,4]ZZ	Exc/Lymphatic, Lt Inguinal, [Opn, Perc Endo] 262
07BJ[0,3,4]ZX	Exc/Lymphatic, Lt Inguinal, [Opn, Perc, Perc Endo] 25, 241
07BJ[0,3,4]ZZ	Exc/Lymphatic, Lt Inguinal, [Opn, Perc, Perc Endo] 64, 112, 252, 271
07BJ[0,3,4]Z[X,Z]	Exc/Lymphatic, Lt Inguinal, [Opn, Perc, Perc Endo], No Dev, [Dx, NQ] 209, 443
07BG*	Exc/Lymphatic, Lt Lwr Extr 290
07BG[0,4]ZZ	Exc/Lymphatic, Lt Lwr Extr, [Opn, Perc Endo] 90, 153, 241, 297
07BG[0,3,4]ZX	Exc/Lymphatic, Lt Lwr Extr, [Opn, Perc, Perc Endo] 25, 90, 153, 241
07BG[0,3,4]Z[X,Z]	Exc/Lymphatic, Lt Lwr Extr, [Opn, Perc, Perc Endo], No Dev, [Dx, NQ] 209, 443
07B2*	Exc/Lymphatic, Lt Neck 51, 90, 153, 241, 290
07B2[0,3,4]ZX	Exc/Lymphatic, Lt Neck, [Opn, Perc, Perc Endo] 25
07B2[0,3,4]ZZ	Exc/Lymphatic, Lt Neck, [Opn, Perc, Perc Endo] 64, 112
07B2[0,3,4]Z[X,Z]	Exc/Lymphatic, Lt Neck, [Opn, Perc, Perc Endo], No Dev, [Dx, NQ] 209, 443
07B4*	Exc/Lymphatic, Lt Upr Extr 290
07B4[0,4]ZZ	Exc/Lymphatic, Lt Upr Extr, [Opn, Perc Endo] 90, 153, 241, 297
07B4[0,3,4]ZX	Exc/Lymphatic, Lt Upr Extr, [Opn, Perc, Perc Endo] 25, 90, 153, 241
07B4[0,3,4]Z[X,Z]	Exc/Lymphatic, Lt Upr Extr, [Opn, Perc, Perc Endo], No Dev, [Dx, NQ] 209, 443
07BB*	Exc/Lymphatic, Mesenteric 112, 290
07BB[0,4]ZZ	Exc/Lymphatic, Mesenteric, [Opn, Perc Endo] 241, 297
07BB[0,3,4]ZX	Exc/Lymphatic, Mesenteric, [Opn, Perc, Perc Endo] 25, 90, 122, 153, 241
07BB[0,3,4]Z[X,Z]	Exc/Lymphatic, Mesenteric, [Opn, Perc, Perc Endo], No Dev, [Dx, NQ] 209, 443
07BC*	Exc/Lymphatic, Pelvis 112, 290
07BC[0,3,4]ZX	Exc/Lymphatic, Pelvis, [Opn, Perc, Perc Endo] 25, 90, 122, 153, 241, 252, 258, 268
07BC[0,3,4]Z[X,Z]	Exc/Lymphatic, Pelvis, [Opn, Perc, Perc Endo], No Dev, [Dx, NQ] 209, 443
07B5*	Exc/Lymphatic, Rt Axillary 90, 153, 290
07B5[0,3,4]ZX	Exc/Lymphatic, Rt Axillary, [Opn, Perc, Perc Endo] 25, 241

07B5[0,3,4]ZZ	Exc/Lymphatic, Rt Axillary, [Opn, Perc, Perc Endo] 51, 64, 112
07B5[0,3,4]Z[X,Z]	Exc/Lymphatic, Rt Axillary, [Opn, Perc, Perc Endo], No Dev, [Dx, NQ] 209, 443
07BH*	Exc/Lymphatic, Rt Inguinal 90, 153, 258, 268, 290
07BH[0,4]ZZ	Exc/Lymphatic, Rt Inguinal, [Opn, Perc Endo] 262
07BH[0,3,4]ZX	Exc/Lymphatic, Rt Inguinal, [Opn, Perc, Perc Endo] 25, 241
07BH[0,3,4]ZZ	Exc/Lymphatic, Rt Inguinal, [Opn, Perc, Perc Endo] 64, 112, 252, 271
07BH[0,3,4]Z[X,Z]	Exc/Lymphatic, Rt Inguinal, [Opn, Perc, Perc Endo], No Dev, [Dx, NQ] 209, 443
07BF*	Exc/Lymphatic, Rt Lwr Extr 290
07BF[0,4]ZZ	Exc/Lymphatic, Rt Lwr Extr, [Opn, Perc Endo] 90, 153, 241, 297
07BF[0,3,4]ZX	Exc/Lymphatic, Rt Lwr Extr, [Opn, Perc, Perc Endo] 25, 90, 153, 241
07BF[0,3,4]Z[X,Z]	Exc/Lymphatic, Rt Lwr Extr, [Opn, Perc, Perc Endo], No Dev, [Dx, NQ] 209, 443
07B1*	Exc/Lymphatic, Rt Neck 51, 90, 153, 241, 290
07B1[0,3,4]ZX	Exc/Lymphatic, Rt Neck, [Opn, Perc, Perc Endo] 25
07B1[0,3,4]ZZ	Exc/Lymphatic, Rt Neck, [Opn, Perc, Perc Endo] 64, 112
07B1[0,3,4]Z[X,Z]	Exc/Lymphatic, Rt Neck, [Opn, Perc, Perc Endo], No Dev, [Dx, NQ] 209, 443
07B3*	Exc/Lymphatic, Rt Upr Extr 290
07B3[0,4]ZZ	Exc/Lymphatic, Rt Upr Extr, [Opn, Perc Endo] 90, 153, 241, 297
07B3[0,3,4]ZX	Exc/Lymphatic, Rt Upr Extr, [Opn, Perc, Perc Endo] 25, 90, 153, 241
07B3[0,3,4]Z[X,Z]	Exc/Lymphatic, Rt Upr Extr, [Opn, Perc, Perc Endo], No Dev, [Dx, NQ] 209, 443
07B7*	Exc/Lymphatic, Thorax 290
07B7[0,4]ZZ	Exc/Lymphatic, Thorax, [Opn, Perc Endo] 64, 90, 153, 241, 297
07B7[0,3,4]ZX	Exc/Lymphatic, Thorax, [Opn, Perc, Perc Endo] 25, 90, 153, 241
07B7[0,3,4]Z[X,Z]	Exc/Lymphatic, Thorax, [Opn, Perc, Perc Endo], No Dev, [Dx, NQ] 209, 443
0BB7[0,3,7]ZZ	Exc/Main Bronchus, Lt, [Opn, Perc, Via Natrl or Artfcl Opng] 61
0BB3[0,3,7]ZZ	Exc/Main Bronchus, Rt, [Opn, Perc, Via Natrl or Artfcl Opng] 61
0NBV[0,3,4]ZZ	Exc/Mandible, Lt, [Opn, Perc, Perc Endo] 48, 154, 344
0NBT[0,3,4]ZZ	Exc/Mandible, Rt, [Opn, Perc, Perc Endo] 48, 154, 343
09BC[0,3,4]ZX	Exc/Mastoid Sinus, Lt, [Opn, Perc, Perc Endo] 51, 446
09BC[0,3,4]ZZ	Exc/Mastoid Sinus, Lt, [Opn, Perc, Perc Endo] 55
09BB[0,3,4]ZX	Exc/Mastoid Sinus, Rt, [Opn, Perc, Perc Endo] 51, 446
09BB[0,3,4]ZZ	Exc/Mastoid Sinus, Rt, [Opn, Perc, Perc Endo] 55
0NBS[0,3,4]ZZ	Exc/Maxilla, Lt, [Opn, Perc, Perc Endo] 48, 154, 343
0NBR[0,3,4]ZZ	Exc/Maxilla, Rt, [Opn, Perc, Perc Endo] 48, 154, 343
09BR[0,3,4]ZZ	Exc/Maxillary Sinus, Lt, [Opn, Perc, Perc Endo] 55, 153
09BQ[0,3,4]ZZ	Exc/Maxillary Sinus, Rt, [Opn, Perc, Perc Endo] 55, 153
01B5[0,3,4]ZZ	Exc/Median Nerve, [Opn, Perc, Perc Endo] 24, 151, 319, 440
0WBC[0,3,4]ZZ	Exc/Mediastinum, [Opn, Perc, Perc Endo] 62, 245, 302, 460
00BD[0,3,4]ZZ	Exc/Medulla Oblongata, [Opn, Perc, Perc Endo] 8, 12, 16, 295, 318, 414
0DBV[0,3,4]ZZ	Exc/Mesentery, [Opn, Perc, Perc Endo] 112, 123, 242, 268, 300, 449
0PBQ*	Exc/Metacarpal, Lt 150
0PBQ[0,3,4]ZX	Exc/Metacarpal, Lt, [Opn, Perc, Perc Endo] 216, 243, 253, 259, 455
0PBQ[0,3,4]Z[X,Z]	Exc/Metacarpal, Lt, [Opn, Perc, Perc Endo], No Dev, [Dx, NQ] 315
0PBP*	Exc/Metacarpal, Rt 150
0PBP[0,3,4]ZX	Exc/Metacarpal, Rt, [Opn, Perc, Perc Endo] 216, 243, 253, 259, 455
0PBP[0,3,4]Z[X,Z]	Exc/Metacarpal, Rt, [Opn, Perc, Perc Endo], No Dev, [Dx, NQ] 315
0RBT[0,3,4]ZZ	Exc/Metacarpocarpal Jt, Lt, [Opn, Perc, Perc Endo] 150, 316, 457
0RBS[0,3,4]ZZ	Exc/Metacarpocarpal Jt, Rt, [Opn, Perc, Perc Endo] 150, 316, 457
0RBV[0,3,4]ZZ	Exc/Metacarpophalangeal Jt, Lt, [Opn, Perc, Perc Endo] 150, 316, 457
0RBU[0,3,4]ZZ	Exc/Metacarpophalangeal Jt, Rt, [Opn, Perc, Perc Endo] 150, 316, 457
0SBN[0,3,4]ZZ	Exc/Metatarsal-Phalangeal Jt, Lt, [Opn, Perc, Perc Endo] 145, 351, 457
0SBM[0,3,4]ZZ	Exc/Metatarsal-Phalangeal Jt, Rt, [Opn, Perc, Perc Endo] 145, 351, 457

0SBL[0,3,4]ZZ	Exc/Metatarsal-Tarsal Jt, Lt, [Opn, Perc, Perc Endo] 145, 351, 457
0SBK[0,3,4]ZZ	Exc/Metatarsal-Tarsal Jt, Rt, [Opn, Perc, Perc Endo] 145, 351, 457
0QBP*	Exc/Metatarsal, Lt 244
0QBP[0,3,4]ZX	Exc/Metatarsal, Lt, [Opn, Perc, Perc Endo] 130, 217, 254, 259
0QBP[0,3,4]ZZ	Exc/Metatarsal, Lt, [Opn, Perc, Perc Endo] 145, 347, 462
0QBP[0,3,4]Z[X,Z]	Exc/Metatarsal, Lt, [Opn, Perc, Perc Endo], No Dev, [Dx, NQ] 456
0QBN*	Exc/Metatarsal, Rt 244
0QBN[0,3,4]ZX	Exc/Metatarsal, Rt, [Opn, Perc, Perc Endo] 130, 217, 254, 259
0QBN[0,3,4]ZZ	Exc/Metatarsal, Rt, [Opn, Perc, Perc Endo] 145, 347, 462
0QBN[0,3,4]Z[X,Z]	Exc/Metatarsal, Rt, [Opn, Perc, Perc Endo], No Dev, [Dx, NQ] 456
09B6*	Exc/Mid Ear, Lt 51
09B60Z[X,Z]	Exc/Mid Ear, Lt, Opn, No Dev, [Dx, NQ] 446
09B5*	Exc/Mid Ear, Rt 51
09B50Z[X,Z]	Exc/Mid Ear, Rt, Opn, No Dev, [Dx, NQ] 446
0BB5[0,3,7]ZZ	Exc/Mid Lobe Bronchus, Rt, [Opn, Perc, Via Natrl or Artfcl Opng] 61
0BBD[0,4,7,8]ZX	Exc/Mid Lung Lobe, Rt, [Opn, Perc Endo, Via Natrl or Artfcl Opng, Via Natrl or Artfcl Opng Endo] 90
0BBD[0,4]ZX	Exc/Mid Lung Lobe, Rt, [Opn, Perc Endo] 153, 253
0BBD[0,3,4,7]ZZ	Exc/Mid Lung Lobe, Rt, [Opn, Perc, Perc Endo, Via Natrl or Artfcl Opng] 61, 299
0BBD[4,7,8]ZX	Exc/Mid Lung Lobe, Rt, [Perc Endo, Via Natrl or Artfcl Opng, Via Natrl or Artfcl Opng Endo] 64
0BBD[7,8]ZX	Exc/Mid Lung Lobe, Rt, [Via Natrl or Artfcl Opng, Via Natrl or Artfcl Opng Endo] 447
0CBJ[0,3]ZZ	Exc/Minor Salivary Gland, [Opn, Perc] 57, 448
02BG[0,4]ZZ	Exc/Mitral Valve, [Opn, Perc Endo] 74
0NBB[0,3,4]ZZ	Exc/Nasal Bone, [Opn, Perc, Perc Endo] 48, 154, 343
09BM[0,3,4]ZZ	Exc/Nasal Septum, [Opn, Perc, Perc Endo] 51, 330, 446
09BL[0,3,4,7,8]ZZ	Exc/Nasal Turbinate, [Opn, Perc, Perc Endo, Via Natrl or Artfcl Opng, Via Natrl or Artfcl Opng Endo] 51, 330, 446
09BN[0,3,4,7,8]ZZ	Exc/Nasopharynx, [Opn, Perc, Perc Endo, Via Natrl or Artfcl Opng, Via Natrl or Artfcl Opng Endo] 51, 105
0KB3*	Exc/Neck Muscle, Lt 139
0KB3[0,3,4]ZZ	Exc/Neck Muscle, Lt, [Opn, Perc, Perc Endo] 27, 214, 339
0KB2*	Exc/Neck Muscle, Rt 139
0KB2[0,3,4]ZZ	Exc/Neck Muscle, Rt, [Opn, Perc, Perc Endo] 27, 214, 339
0WB6[0,3,4,X]ZZ	Exc/Neck, [Opn, Perc, Perc Endo, Ext] 28, 55, 91, 144, 207, 355, 460
0HBX[0,3,7,8,X]ZZ	Exc/Nipple, Lt, [Opn, Perc, Via Natrl or Artfcl Opng, Via Natrl or Artfcl Opng Endo, Ext] 222, 336
0HBW[0,3,7,8,X]ZZ	Exc/Nipple, Rt, [Opn, Perc, Via Natrl or Artfcl Opng, Via Natrl or Artfcl Opng Endo, Ext] 222, 336
0NB8*	Exc/Occipital Bone, Lt 9
0NB8[0,3,4]ZX	Exc/Occipital Bone, Lt, [Opn, Perc, Perc Endo] 129, 243
0NB8[0,3,4]ZZ	Exc/Occipital Bone, Lt, [Opn, Perc, Perc Endo] 48, 154, 301, 343, 415
0NB8[0,3,4]Z[X,Z]	Exc/Occipital Bone, Lt, [Opn, Perc, Perc Endo], No Dev, [Dx, NQ] 14, 18
0NB7*	Exc/Occipital Bone, Rt 9
0NB7[0,3,4]ZX	Exc/Occipital Bone, Rt, [Opn, Perc, Perc Endo] 129, 243
0NB7[0,3,4]ZZ	Exc/Occipital Bone, Rt, [Opn, Perc, Perc Endo] 48, 154, 301, 343, 415
0NB7[0,3,4]Z[X,Z]	Exc/Occipital Bone, Rt, [Opn, Perc, Perc Endo], No Dev, [Dx, NQ] 14, 18
0RB0[0,3,4]ZZ	Exc/Occipital-cervical Jt, [Opn, Perc, Perc Endo] 19, 159, 160, 301, 349
00BH[0,3,4]ZZ	Exc/Oculomotor Nerve, [Opn, Perc, Perc Endo] 23, 50, 151, 318, 440
00BF[0,3,4]ZZ	Exc/Olfactory Nerve, [Opn, Perc, Perc Endo] 23, 50, 151, 318, 440
00BG[0,3,4]ZZ	Exc/Optic Nerve, [Opn, Perc, Perc Endo] 23, 50, 151, 318, 440
0NBQ*	Exc/Orbit, Lt 42
0NBQ[0,3,4]ZZ	Exc/Orbit, Lt, [Opn, Perc, Perc Endo] 48, 343
0NBQ[0,3,4]Z[X,Z]	Exc/Orbit, Lt, [Opn, Perc, Perc Endo], No Dev, [Dx, NQ] 454
0NBP*	Exc/Orbit, Rt 42
0NBP[0,3,4]ZZ	Exc/Orbit, Rt, [Opn, Perc, Perc Endo] 48, 343
0NBP[0,3,4]Z[X,Z]	Exc/Orbit, Rt, [Opn, Perc, Perc Endo], No Dev, [Dx, NQ] 454
0UB2*	Exc/Ovaries, Bilat 262, 264, 266
0UB2[0,3,4,7,8]ZZ	Exc/Ovaries, Bilat, [Opn, Perc, Perc Endo, Via Natrl or Artfcl Opng, Via Natrl or Artfcl Opng Endo] 244
0UB1*	Exc/Ovary, Lt 262, 264, 266
0UB1[0,3,4,7,8]ZZ	Exc/Ovary, Lt, [Opn, Perc, Perc Endo, Via Natrl or Artfcl Opng, Via Natrl or Artfcl Opng Endo] 244
0UB0*	Exc/Ovary, Rt 262, 264, 266
0UB0[0,3,4,7,8]ZZ	Exc/Ovary, Rt, [Opn, Perc, Perc Endo, Via Natrl or Artfcl Opng, Via Natrl or Artfcl Opng Endo] 244
0NBL[0,3,4]ZZ	Exc/Palatine Bone, Lt, [Opn, Perc, Perc Endo] 48, 154, 343
0NBL[0,3,4]ZX	Exc/Palatine Bone, Lt, [Opn, Perc, Perc Endo] 54, 129, 454
0NBK[0,3,4]ZZ	Exc/Palatine Bone, Rt, [Opn, Perc, Perc Endo] 48, 154, 343
0NBK[0,3,4]ZX	Exc/Palatine Bone, Rt, [Opn, Perc, Perc Endo] 54, 129, 454
0FBG[0,3,4]ZZ	Exc/Pancreas, [Opn, Perc, Perc Endo] 119, 242, 335
0FBD[0,3,7]ZZ	Exc/Pancreatic Duct, [Opn, Perc, Via Natrl or Artfcl Opng] 119, 242
0FBF[0,3,7]ZZ	Exc/Pancreatic Duct, Accessory, [Opn, Perc, Via Natrl or Artfcl Opng] 119, 242
02BD[0,3,4]ZZ	Exc/Papillary Muscle, [Opn, Perc, Perc Endo] 74
0GBR*	Exc/Parathyroid Gland 238
0GBR[0,3,4]ZX	Exc/Parathyroid Gland, [Opn, Perc, Perc Endo] 153
0GBR[0,3,4]ZZ	Exc/Parathyroid Gland, [Opn, Perc, Perc Endo] 253
0GBQ*	Exc/Parathyroid Glands, Multi 238
0GBQ[0,3,4]ZX	Exc/Parathyroid Glands, Multi, [Opn, Perc, Perc Endo] 153
0GBQ[0,3,4]ZZ	Exc/Parathyroid Glands, Multi, [Opn, Perc, Perc Endo] 253
0NB4*	Exc/Parietal Bone, Lt 9
0NB4[0,3,4]ZX	Exc/Parietal Bone, Lt, [Opn, Perc, Perc Endo] 129, 243
0NB4[0,3,4]ZZ	Exc/Parietal Bone, Lt, [Opn, Perc, Perc Endo] 48, 154, 301, 343, 415
0NB4[0,3,4]Z[X,Z]	Exc/Parietal Bone, Lt, [Opn, Perc, Perc Endo], No Dev, [Dx, NQ] 14, 18
0NB3*	Exc/Parietal Bone, Rt 9
0NB3[0,3,4]ZX	Exc/Parietal Bone, Rt, [Opn, Perc, Perc Endo] 129, 243
0NB3[0,3,4]ZZ	Exc/Parietal Bone, Rt, [Opn, Perc, Perc Endo] 48, 154, 301, 415
0NB3[0,3,4]Z[X,Z]	Exc/Parietal Bone, Rt, [Opn, Perc, Perc Endo], No Dev, [Dx, NQ] 14, 18
0CBC[0,3]ZZ	Exc/Parotid Duct, Lt, [Opn, Perc] 56, 448
0CBB[0,3]ZZ	Exc/Parotid Duct, Rt, [Opn, Perc] 56, 448
0CB9[0,3]ZZ	Exc/Parotid Gland, Lt, [Opn, Perc] 56, 448
0CB8[0,3]ZZ	Exc/Parotid Gland, Rt, [Opn, Perc] 56, 448
0QBF[0,3,4]ZX	Exc/Patella, Lt, [Opn, Perc, Perc Endo] 130, 217, 244, 254, 259, 456
0QBF[0,3,4]ZZ	Exc/Patella, Lt, [Opn, Perc, Perc Endo] 132, 347
0QBD[0,3,4]ZX	Exc/Patella, Rt, [Opn, Perc, Perc Endo] 130, 217, 244, 254, 259, 456
0QBD[0,3,4]ZZ	Exc/Patella, Rt, [Opn, Perc, Perc Endo] 132, 347
0QB3*	Exc/Pelvic Bone, Lt 244
0QB3[0,3,4]ZX	Exc/Pelvic Bone, Lt, [Opn, Perc, Perc Endo] 130, 254, 259, 292, 456
0QB3[0,3,4]ZZ	Exc/Pelvic Bone, Lt, [Opn, Perc, Perc Endo] 54, 156, 347
0QB2*	Exc/Pelvic Bone, Rt 244
0QB2[0,3,4]ZX	Exc/Pelvic Bone, Rt, [Opn, Perc, Perc Endo] 130, 253, 259, 292, 456
0QB2[0,3,4]ZZ	Exc/Pelvic Bone, Rt, [Opn, Perc, Perc Endo] 54, 156, 347
0VBS*	Exc/Penis 257
0VBS[0,3,4,X]Z[X,Z]	Exc/Penis, [Opn, Perc, Perc Endo, Ext], No Dev, [Dx, NQ] 217, 459
02BN*	Exc/Pericardium 60
02BN[0,3,4]ZZ	Exc/Pericardium, [Opn, Perc, Perc Endo] 319
02BN[0,3,4]Z[X,Z]	Exc/Pericardium, [Opn, Perc, Perc Endo], No Dev, [Dx, NQ] 93, 296
0MBK*	Exc/Perineum Bursa & Lgmt 143
0MBK[0,3,4]ZZ	Exc/Perineum Bursa & Lgmt, [Opn, Perc, Perc Endo] 343, 454
0KBM*	Exc/Perineum Muscle 139
0KBM[0,3,4]ZZ	Exc/Perineum Muscle, [Opn, Perc, Perc Endo] 27, 214, 339
0LBH*	Exc/Perineum Tndn 141
0LBH[0,3,4]ZZ	Exc/Perineum Tndn, [Opn, Perc, Perc Endo] 28, 341
0WBN*	Exc/Perineum, Female 267, 275
0WBN[0,3,4,X]Z[X,Z]	Exc/Perineum, Female, [Opn, Perc, Perc Endo, Ext], No Dev, [Dx, NQ] 217, 460
0WBM[0,3,4,X]ZZ	Exc/Perineum, Male, [Opn, Perc, Perc Endo, Ext] 28, 91, 144, 207, 355, 460

ØDBW[Ø,3,4]ZZ	Exc/Peritoneum, [Opn, Perc, Perc Endo] 112, 123, 242, 268, 300, 449
04BU*	Exc/Peroneal Artery, Lt 83
04BU[Ø,3,4]ZZ	Exc/Peroneal Artery, Lt, [Opn, Perc, Perc Endo] 240, 323
04BU[Ø,3,4]ZX	Exc/Peroneal Artery, Lt, [Opn, Perc, Perc Endo] 442
04BT*	Exc/Peroneal Artery, Rt 83
04BT[Ø,3,4]ZZ	Exc/Peroneal Artery, Rt, [Opn, Perc, Perc Endo] 240, 323
04BT[Ø,3,4]ZX	Exc/Peroneal Artery, Rt, [Opn, Perc, Perc Endo] 442
01BH[Ø,3,4]ZZ	Exc/Peroneal Nerve, [Opn, Perc, Perc Endo] 24, 151, 319, 441
ØCBM[Ø,3,4,7,8]ZZ	Exc/Pharynx, [Opn, Perc, Perc Endo, Via Natrl or Artfcl Opng, Via Natrl or Artfcl Opng Endo] 52, 105
01B2[Ø,3,4]ZZ	Exc/Phrenic Nerve, [Opn, Perc, Perc Endo] 24, 151, 319, 440
ØGB1*	Exc/Pineal Body 235
ØGB1[Ø,3,4]Z[X,Z]	Exc/Pineal Body, [Opn, Perc, Perc Endo], No Dev, [Dx, NQ] 9, 13, 17
ØGBØ*	Exc/Pituitary Gland 235
ØGBØ[Ø,3,4]ZZ	Exc/Pituitary Gland, [Opn, Perc, Perc Endo] 211
ØGBØ[Ø,3,4]Z[X,Z]	Exc/Pituitary Gland, [Opn, Perc, Perc Endo], No Dev, [Dx, NQ] 9, 13, 17
ØBBP[Ø,3,4]ZZ	Exc/Pleura, Lt, [Opn, Perc, Perc Endo] 61, 331
ØBBN[Ø,3,4]ZZ	Exc/Pleura, Rt, [Opn, Perc, Perc Endo] 61, 331
ØØBB[Ø,3,4]ZZ	Exc/Pons, [Opn, Perc, Perc Endo] 8, 12, 16, 295, 318, 414
04BN*	Exc/Popliteal Artery, Lt 83
04BN[Ø,3,4]ZZ	Exc/Popliteal Artery, Lt, [Opn, Perc, Perc Endo] 240, 323
04BN[Ø,3,4]ZX	Exc/Popliteal Artery, Lt, [Opn, Perc, Perc Endo] 442
04BM*	Exc/Popliteal Artery, Rt 83
04BM[Ø,3,4]ZZ	Exc/Popliteal Artery, Rt, [Opn, Perc, Perc Endo] 240, 323
04BM[Ø,3,4]ZX	Exc/Popliteal Artery, Rt, [Opn, Perc, Perc Endo] 442
06B8[Ø,3,4]ZX	Exc/Portal Vein, [Opn, Perc, Perc Endo] 86, 442
06B8[Ø,3,4]ZZ	Exc/Portal Vein, [Opn, Perc, Perc Endo] 97
04BS[Ø,3,4]ZZ	Exc/Post Tibial Artery, Lt, [Opn, Perc, Perc Endo] 240, 323
04BS[Ø,3,4]ZX	Exc/Post Tibial Artery, Lt, [Opn, Perc, Perc Endo] 442
04BR[Ø,3,4]ZZ	Exc/Post Tibial Artery, Rt, [Opn, Perc, Perc Endo] 240, 323
04BR[Ø,3,4]ZX	Exc/Post Tibial Artery, Rt, [Opn, Perc, Perc Endo] 442
04BS*	Exc/Posterior Tibial Artery, Lt 83
04BR*	Exc/Posterior Tibial Artery, Rt 83
ØVBT*	Exc/Prepuce 257
ØVBT[Ø,3,4,X]Z[X,Z]	Exc/Prepuce, [Opn, Perc, Perc Endo, Ext], No Dev, [Dx, NQ] 217, 459
ØVBØ[Ø,3,4,7,8]ZZ	Exc/Prostate, [Opn, Perc, Perc Endo, Via Natrl or Artfcl Opng, Via Natrl or Artfcl Opng Endo] 440
ØVBØ[Ø,3,4]ZZ	Exc/Prostate, [Opn, Perc, Perc Endo] 260
ØVBØ[7,8]ZZ	Exc/Prostate, [Via Natrl or Artfcl Opng, Via Natrl or Artfcl Opng Endo] 250, 258
01BC[Ø,3,4]ZZ	Exc/Pudendal Nerve, [Opn, Perc, Perc Endo] 24, 151, 319, 440
02BR[Ø,3,4]ZZ	Exc/Pulmn Artery, Lt, [Opn, Perc, Perc Endo] 60, 93
02BR[Ø,3,4]ZX	Exc/Pulmn Artery, Lt, [Opn, Perc, Perc Endo] 80, 441
02BQ[Ø,3,4]ZZ	Exc/Pulmn Artery, Rt, [Opn, Perc, Perc Endo] 60, 93
02BQ[Ø,3,4]ZX	Exc/Pulmn Artery, Rt, [Opn, Perc, Perc Endo] 80, 441
02BP[Ø,3,4]ZZ	Exc/Pulmn Trunk, [Opn, Perc, Perc Endo] 60, 93
02BP[Ø,3,4]ZX	Exc/Pulmn Trunk, [Opn, Perc, Perc Endo] 80, 441
02BH[Ø,4]ZZ	Exc/Pulmn Valve, [Opn, Perc Endo] 74
02BT[Ø,3,4]ZZ	Exc/Pulmn Vein, Lt, [Opn, Perc, Perc Endo] 60, 93
02BT[Ø,3,4]ZX	Exc/Pulmn Vein, Lt, [Opn, Perc, Perc Endo] 80, 441
02BS[Ø,3,4]ZZ	Exc/Pulmn Vein, Rt, [Opn, Perc, Perc Endo] 60, 93
02BS[Ø,3,4]ZX	Exc/Pulmn Vein, Rt, [Opn, Perc, Perc Endo] 80, 441
03BC*	Exc/Radial Artery, Lt 81
03BC[Ø,3,4]ZZ	Exc/Radial Artery, Lt, [Opn, Perc, Perc Endo] 239, 321
03BC[Ø,3,4]ZX	Exc/Radial Artery, Lt, [Opn, Perc, Perc Endo] 441
03BB*	Exc/Radial Artery, Rt 81
03BB[Ø,3,4]ZZ	Exc/Radial Artery, Rt, [Opn, Perc, Perc Endo] 239, 321
03BB[Ø,3,4]ZX	Exc/Radial Artery, Rt, [Opn, Perc, Perc Endo] 441
01B6[Ø,3,4]ZZ	Exc/Radial Nerve, [Opn, Perc, Perc Endo] 24, 151, 319, 440
ØPBJ[Ø,3,4]ZX	Exc/Radius, Lt, [Opn, Perc, Perc Endo] 129, 216, 243, 253, 259, 455
ØPBJ[Ø,3,4]ZZ	Exc/Radius, Lt, [Opn, Perc, Perc Endo] 148, 345
ØPBH[Ø,3,4]ZX	Exc/Radius, Rt, [Opn, Perc, Perc Endo] 129, 216, 243, 253, 259, 455
ØPBH[Ø,3,4]ZZ	Exc/Radius, Rt, [Opn, Perc, Perc Endo] 148, 345
ØDBP[Ø,4]ZZ	Exc/Rectum, [Opn, Perc Endo] 107, 257, 300
ØDBP[Ø,3,4,7]ZZ	Exc/Rectum, [Opn, Perc, Perc Endo, Via Natrl or Artfcl Opng] 90, 333
ØDBP[3,7]ZZ	Exc/Rectum, [Perc, Via Natrl or Artfcl Opng] 109, 211, 449
04BA[Ø,3,4]ZX	Exc/Renal Artery, Lt, [Opn, Perc, Perc Endo] 83, 441
04BA[Ø,3,4]ZZ	Exc/Renal Artery, Lt, [Opn, Perc, Perc Endo] 95
04B9[Ø,3,4]ZX	Exc/Renal Artery, Rt, [Opn, Perc, Perc Endo] 83, 441
04B9[Ø,3,4]ZZ	Exc/Renal Artery, Rt, [Opn, Perc, Perc Endo] 95
06BB[Ø,3,4]ZX	Exc/Renal Vein, Lt, [Opn, Perc, Perc Endo] 86, 442
06BB[Ø,3,4]ZZ	Exc/Renal Vein, Lt, [Opn, Perc, Perc Endo] 97
06B9[Ø,3,4]ZX	Exc/Renal Vein, Rt, [Opn, Perc, Perc Endo] 86, 442
06B9[Ø,3,4]ZZ	Exc/Renal Vein, Rt, [Opn, Perc, Perc Endo] 97
08BF*	Exc/Retina, Lt 44
08BF3Z[X,Z]	Exc/Retina, Lt, Perc, No Dev, [Dx, NQ] 444
08BE*	Exc/Retina, Rt 44
08BE3Z[X,Z]	Exc/Retina, Rt, Perc, No Dev, [Dx, NQ] 444
ØWBH[Ø,3,4]ZZ	Exc/Retroperitoneum, [Opn, Perc, Perc Endo] 158, 217, 249, 257, 269, 302
ØPB2*	Exc/Rib, Lt 65
ØPB2[Ø,3,4]ZX	Exc/Rib, Lt, [Opn, Perc, Perc Endo] 129, 216, 243, 253, 259, 455
ØPB2[Ø,3,4]ZZ	Exc/Rib, Lt, [Opn, Perc, Perc Endo] 19, 155, 345
ØPB1*	Exc/Rib, Rt 65
ØPB1[Ø,3,4]ZX	Exc/Rib, Rt, [Opn, Perc, Perc Endo] 129, 216, 243, 253, 259, 455
ØPB1[Ø,3,4]ZZ	Exc/Rib, Rt, [Opn, Perc, Perc Endo] 19, 155, 345
ØGB3[Ø,3,4]ZZ	Exc/Rt Adrenal Gland, [Opn, Perc, Perc Endo] 235
01BR[Ø,3,4]ZZ	Exc/Sacral Nerve, [Opn, Perc, Perc Endo] 24, 151, 319, 441
01BQ[Ø,3,4]ZZ	Exc/Sacral Plexus, [Opn, Perc, Perc Endo] 24, 151, 319, 441
01BP*	Exc/Sacral Sympathetic Nerve 24
01BP[Ø,3,4]ZZ	Exc/Sacral Sympathetic Nerve, [Opn, Perc, Perc Endo] 89, 267
ØSB5[Ø,3,4]ZZ	Exc/Sacrococcygeal Jt, [Opn, Perc, Perc Endo] 20, 159, 161, 302, 351
ØSB8[Ø,3,4]ZZ	Exc/Sacroiliac Jt, Lt, [Opn, Perc, Perc Endo] 20, 159, 161, 302, 351
ØSB7[Ø,3,4]ZZ	Exc/Sacroiliac Jt, Rt, [Opn, Perc, Perc Endo] 20, 159; 161, 302, 351
ØQB1*	Exc/Sacrum 244
ØQB1[Ø,3,4]ZX	Exc/Sacrum, [Opn, Perc, Perc Endo] 130, 253, 259, 292, 456
ØQB1[Ø,3,4]ZZ	Exc/Sacrum, [Opn, Perc, Perc Endo] 54, 156, 347
ØPB6*	Exc/Scapula, Lt 65
ØPB6[Ø,3,4]ZX	Exc/Scapula, Lt, [Opn, Perc, Perc Endo] 129, 216, 243, 253, 259, 455
ØPB6[Ø,3,4]ZZ	Exc/Scapula, Lt, [Opn, Perc, Perc Endo] 19, 155, 345
ØPB5*	Exc/Scapula, Rt 65
ØPB5[Ø,3,4]ZX	Exc/Scapula, Rt, [Opn, Perc, Perc Endo] 129, 216, 243, 253, 259, 455
ØPB5[Ø,3,4]ZZ	Exc/Scapula, Rt, [Opn, Perc, Perc Endo] 19, 155, 345
01BF[Ø,3,4]ZZ	Exc/Sciatic Nerve, [Opn, Perc, Perc Endo] 24, 151, 319, 440
08B7*	Exc/Sclera, Lt 329
08B7XZ[X,Z]	Exc/Sclera, Lt, Ext, No Dev, [Dx, NQ] 444
08B6*	Exc/Sclera, Rt 329
08B6XZ[X,Z]	Exc/Sclera, Rt, Ext, No Dev, [Dx, NQ] 444
ØVB2[Ø,3,4]ZZ	Exc/Seminal Vesicle, Lt, [Opn, Perc, Perc Endo] 260
ØVB1[Ø,3,4]ZZ	Exc/Seminal Vesicle, Rt, [Opn, Perc, Perc Endo] 260
ØVB3[Ø,3,4]ZZ	Exc/Seminal Vesicles, Bilat, [Opn, Perc, Perc Endo] 260
ØMB2[Ø,3,4]ZZ	Exc/Shldr Bursa & Lgmt, Lt, [Opn, Perc, Perc Endo] 143, 343, 453
ØMB1[Ø,3,4]ZZ	Exc/Shldr Bursa & Lgmt, Rt, [Opn, Perc, Perc Endo] 143, 343, 453
ØRBK[Ø,3,4]ZZ	Exc/Shldr Jt, Lt, [Opn, Perc, Perc Endo] 149, 349, 457
ØRBJ[Ø,3,4]ZZ	Exc/Shldr Jt, Rt, [Opn, Perc, Perc Endo] 149, 349, 457
ØKB6*	Exc/Shldr Muscle, Lt 139
ØKB6[Ø,3,4]ZZ	Exc/Shldr Muscle, Lt, [Opn, Perc, Perc Endo] 27, 214, 339
ØKB5*	Exc/Shldr Muscle, Rt 139
ØKB5[Ø,3,4]ZZ	Exc/Shldr Muscle, Rt, [Opn, Perc, Perc Endo] 27, 214, 339
ØXB3[Ø,3,4]ZZ	Exc/Shldr Rgn, Lt, [Opn, Perc, Perc Endo] 28, 91, 144, 207, 356, 461
ØXB2[Ø,3,4]ZZ	Exc/Shldr Rgn, Rt, [Opn, Perc, Perc Endo] 28, 91, 144, 207, 356, 461
ØLB2*	Exc/Shldr Tndn, Lt 141
ØLB2[Ø,3,4]ZZ	Exc/Shldr Tndn, Lt, [Opn, Perc, Perc Endo] 28, 340
ØLB1*	Exc/Shldr Tndn, Rt 141
ØLB1[Ø,3,4]ZZ	Exc/Shldr Tndn, Rt, [Opn, Perc, Perc Endo] 28, 340

0DBN[0,3,4]ZZ	Exc/Sigmoid Colon, [Opn, Perc, Perc Endo] 90, 106, 300, 333
0DBN[0,3,7]ZZ	Exc/Sigmoid Colon, [Opn, Perc, Via Natrl or Artfcl Opng] 242
0NB0*	Exc/Skull 9
0NB0[0,3,4]ZX	Exc/Skull, [Opn, Perc, Perc Endo] 129, 243
0NB0[0,3,4]ZZ	Exc/Skull, [Opn, Perc, Perc Endo] 48, 154, 301, 343, 415
0NB0[0,3,4]Z[X,Z]	Exc/Skull, [Opn, Perc, Perc Endo], No Dev, [Dx, NQ] 14, 18
0DB8[0,4,7]ZZ	Exc/Sm Intestine, [Opn, Perc Endo, Via Natrl or Artfcl Opng] 333
0DB8[0,4]ZZ	Exc/Sm Intestine, [Opn, Perc Endo] 90, 106, 242
0DB8[0,3,4,7,8]ZZ	Exc/Sm Intestine, [Opn, Perc, Perc Endo, Via Natrl or Artfcl Opng, Via Natrl or Artfcl Opng Endo] 300
0DB8[3,7,8]ZZ	Exc/Sm Intestine, [Perc, Via Natrl or Artfcl Opng, Via Natrl or Artfcl Opng Endo] 109, 449
0CB3*	Exc/Soft Palate 56
0CB3[0,3,X]ZZ	Exc/Soft Palate, [Opn, Perc, Ext] 331
0CB3[0,3,X]Z[X,Z]	Exc/Soft Palate, [Opn, Perc, Ext], No Dev, [Dx, NQ] 448
0VBG[0,3,4]ZZ	Exc/Spermatic Cord, Lt, [Opn, Perc, Perc Endo] 257, 459
0VBF[0,3,4]ZZ	Exc/Spermatic Cord, Rt, [Opn, Perc, Perc Endo] 257, 459
0VBH[0,3,4]ZZ	Exc/Spermatic Cords, Bilat, [Opn, Perc, Perc Endo] 257, 459
0NBD[0,3,4]ZZ	Exc/Sphenoid Bone, Lt, [Opn, Perc, Perc Endo] 48, 154, 343
0NBD[0,3,4]ZX	Exc/Sphenoid Bone, Lt, [Opn, Perc, Perc Endo] 54, 129, 454
0NBC[0,3,4]ZZ	Exc/Sphenoid Bone, Rt, [Opn, Perc, Perc Endo] 48, 154, 343
0NBC[0,3,4]ZX	Exc/Sphenoid Bone, Rt, [Opn, Perc, Perc Endo] 54, 129, 454
09BX[0,3,4]ZZ	Exc/Sphenoid Sinus, Lt, [Opn, Perc, Perc Endo] 55
09BW[0,3,4]ZZ	Exc/Sphenoid Sinus, Rt, [Opn, Perc, Perc Endo] 55
00BT*	Exc/Spinal Meninges 159, 160
00BT[0,3,4]Z[X,Z]	Exc/Spinal Meninges, [Opn, Perc, Perc Endo], No Dev, [Dx, NQ] 19, 295
07BP[0,3,4]ZZ	Exc/Spleen, [Opn, Perc, Perc Endo] 153, 290, 298, 328
04B4[0,3,4]ZX	Exc/Splenic Artery, [Opn, Perc, Perc Endo] 83, 441
04B4[0,3,4]ZZ	Exc/Splenic Artery, [Opn, Perc, Perc Endo] 95
06B1[0,3,4]ZX	Exc/Splenic Vein, [Opn, Perc, Perc Endo] 86, 442
06B1[0,3,4]ZZ	Exc/Splenic Vein, [Opn, Perc, Perc Endo] 97
0JB1[0,3]ZZ	Exc/SQ Tissue & Fascia, Face, [Opn, Perc] 53
0JBK[0,3]ZZ	Exc/SQ Tissue & Fascia, Lt Hand, [Opn, Perc] 149, 212, 314, 450
0JBJ[0,3]ZZ	Exc/SQ Tissue & Fascia, Rt Hand, [Opn, Perc] 149, 212, 314, 450
0RBF[0,3,4]ZZ	Exc/Sternoclavicular Jt, Lt, [Opn, Perc, Perc Endo] 149, 349, 457
0RBE[0,3,4]ZZ	Exc/Sternoclavicular Jt, Rt, [Opn, Perc, Perc Endo] 149, 349, 457
0PB0*	Exc/Sternum 65
0PB0[0,3,4]ZX	Exc/Sternum, [Opn, Perc, Perc Endo] 129, 216, 243, 253, 259, 455
0PB0[0,3,4]ZZ	Exc/Sternum, [Opn, Perc, Perc Endo] 19, 155, 345
0DB6[0,3,4,7,8]Z3	Exc/Stomach, [Opn, Perc, Perc Endo, Via Natrl or Artfcl Opng, Via Natrl or Artfcl Opng Endo], No Dev, Vertical 90, 105, 235, 300, 333
0DB6[0,3,7]ZZ	Exc/Stomach, [Opn, Perc, Via Natrl or Artfcl Opng] 90, 105, 235, 300, 333
0DB7[0,3,7]ZZ	Exc/Stomach, Pylorus, [Opn, Perc, Via Natrl or Artfcl Opng] 105, 122, 242
03B4[0,3,4]ZZ	Exc/Subclavian Artery, Lt, [Opn, Perc, Perc Endo] 60, 93
03B4[0,3,4]ZX	Exc/Subclavian Artery, Lt, [Opn, Perc, Perc Endo] 81, 441
03B3[0,3,4]ZZ	Exc/Subclavian Artery, Rt, [Opn, Perc, Perc Endo] 60, 93
03B3[0,3,4]ZX	Exc/Subclavian Artery, Rt, [Opn, Perc, Perc Endo] 81, 441
05B6[0,3,4]ZZ	Exc/Subclavian Vein, Lt, [Opn, Perc, Perc Endo] 60, 96
05B6[0,3,4]ZX	Exc/Subclavian Vein, Lt, [Opn, Perc, Perc Endo] 85, 442
05B5[0,3,4]ZZ	Exc/Subclavian Vein, Rt, [Opn, Perc, Perc Endo] 60, 96
05B5[0,3,4]ZX	Exc/Subclavian Vein, Rt, [Opn, Perc, Perc Endo] 85, 442
0CBF[0,3]ZZ	Exc/Sublingual Gland, Lt, [Opn, Perc] 57, 448
0CBD[0,3]ZZ	Exc/Sublingual Gland, Rt, [Opn, Perc] 57, 448
0CBH[0,3]ZZ	Exc/Submaxillary Gland, Lt, [Opn, Perc] 57, 448
0CBG[0,3]ZZ	Exc/Submaxillary Gland, Rt, [Opn, Perc] 57, 448
04B5[0,3,4]ZX	Exc/Superior Mesenteric Artery, [Opn, Perc, Perc Endo] 83, 441
04B5[0,3,4]ZZ	Exc/Superior Mesenteric Artery, [Opn, Perc, Perc Endo] 95
06B5[0,3,4]ZX	Exc/Superior Mesenteric Vein, [Opn, Perc, Perc Endo] 86, 442
06B5[0,3,4]ZZ	Exc/Superior Mesenteric Vein, [Opn, Perc, Perc Endo] 97
0GBM*	Exc/Superior Parathyroid Gland, Lt 238
0GBM[0,3,4]ZX	Exc/Superior Parathyroid Gland, Lt, [Opn, Perc, Perc Endo] 153
0GBM[0,3,4]ZZ	Exc/Superior Parathyroid Gland, Lt, [Opn, Perc, Perc Endo] 253
0GBL*	Exc/Superior Parathyroid Gland, Rt 238
0GBL[0,3,4]ZX	Exc/Superior Parathyroid Gland, Rt, [Opn, Perc, Perc Endo] 153
0GBL[0,3,4]ZZ	Exc/Superior Parathyroid Gland, Rt, [Opn, Perc, Perc Endo] 253
02BV[0,3,4]ZZ	Exc/Superior Vena Cava, [Opn, Perc, Perc Endo] 60, 93
02BV[0,3,4]ZX	Exc/Superior Vena Cava, [Opn, Perc, Perc Endo] 80, 441
0HBY[0,3,7,8,X]ZZ	Exc/Supernumerary Breast, [Opn, Perc, Via Natrl or Artfcl Opng, Via Natrl or Artfcl Opng Endo, Ext] 222, 336
0SBJ[0,3,4]ZZ	Exc/Tarsal Jt, Lt, [Opn, Perc, Perc Endo] 145, 351, 457
0SBH[0,3,4]ZZ	Exc/Tarsal Jt, Rt, [Opn, Perc, Perc Endo] 145, 351, 457
0QBM*	Exc/Tarsal, Lt 244
0QBM[0,3,4]ZX	Exc/Tarsal, Lt, [Opn, Perc, Perc Endo] 130, 217, 254, 259
0QBM[0,3,4]ZZ	Exc/Tarsal, Lt, [Opn, Perc, Perc Endo] 145, 347
0QBM[0,3,4]Z[X,Z]	Exc/Tarsal, Lt, [Opn, Perc, Perc Endo], No Dev, [Dx, NQ] 456
0QBL*	Exc/Tarsal, Rt 244
0QBL[0,3,4]ZX	Exc/Tarsal, Rt, [Opn, Perc, Perc Endo] 130, 217, 254, 259
0QBL[0,3,4]ZZ	Exc/Tarsal, Rt, [Opn, Perc, Perc Endo] 145, 347
0QBL[0,3,4]Z[X,Z]	Exc/Tarsal, Rt, [Opn, Perc, Perc Endo], No Dev, [Dx, NQ] 456
03BT*	Exc/Temporal Artery, Lt 50, 81
03BT[0,3,4]ZZ	Exc/Temporal Artery, Lt, [Opn, Perc, Perc Endo] 21, 321
03BT[0,3,4]ZX	Exc/Temporal Artery, Lt, [Opn, Perc, Perc Endo] 25, 42, 63, 152, 239, 251, 441
03BS*	Exc/Temporal Artery, Rt 50, 81
03BS[0,3,4]ZZ	Exc/Temporal Artery, Rt, [Opn, Perc, Perc Endo] 21, 321
03BS[0,3,4]ZX	Exc/Temporal Artery, Rt, [Opn, Perc, Perc Endo] 25, 42, 63, 152, 239, 251, 441
0NB6*	Exc/Temporal Bone, Lt 9
0NB6[0,3,4]ZX	Exc/Temporal Bone, Lt, [Opn, Perc, Perc Endo] 129, 243
0NB6[0,3,4]ZZ	Exc/Temporal Bone, Lt, [Opn, Perc, Perc Endo] 48, 154, 301, 343, 415
0NB6[0,3,4]Z[X,Z]	Exc/Temporal Bone, Lt, [Opn, Perc, Perc Endo], No Dev, [Dx, NQ] 14, 18
0NB5*	Exc/Temporal Bone, Rt 9
0NB5[0,3,4]ZX	Exc/Temporal Bone, Rt, [Opn, Perc, Perc Endo] 129, 243
0NB5[0,3,4]ZZ	Exc/Temporal Bone, Rt, [Opn, Perc, Perc Endo] 48, 154, 301, 343, 415
0NB5[0,3,4]Z[X,Z]	Exc/Temporal Bone, Rt, [Opn, Perc, Perc Endo], No Dev, [Dx, NQ] 14, 18
0RBD[0,3,4]ZZ	Exc/Temporomandibular Jt, Lt, [Opn, Perc, Perc Endo] 49, 136, 349
0RBD[0,3,4]ZX	Exc/Temporomandibular Jt, Lt, [Opn, Perc, Perc Endo] 55, 130
0RBD[0,3,4]Z[X,Z]	Exc/Temporomandibular Jt, Lt, [Opn, Perc, Perc Endo], No Dev, [Dx, NQ] 457
0RBC[0,3,4]ZZ	Exc/Temporomandibular Jt, Rt, [Opn, Perc, Perc Endo] 49, 136, 349
0RBC[0,3,4]ZX	Exc/Temporomandibular Jt, Rt, [Opn, Perc, Perc Endo] 55, 130
0RBC[0,3,4]Z[X,Z]	Exc/Temporomandibular Jt, Rt, [Opn, Perc, Perc Endo], No Dev, [Dx, NQ] 457
00B9[0,3,4]ZZ	Exc/Thalamus, [Opn, Perc, Perc Endo] 8, 12, 16, 295, 318, 414
02BW[0,4]ZZ	Exc/Thoracic Aorta, [Opn, Perc Endo] 92, 110
02BW[0,3,4]ZZ	Exc/Thoracic Aorta, [Opn, Perc, Perc Endo] 319
02BW[0,3,4]ZX	Exc/Thoracic Aorta, [Opn, Perc, Perc Endo] 80, 441
07BK[0,3,4]ZX	Exc/Thoracic Duct, [Opn, Perc, Perc Endo] 25, 64, 90, 153, 209, 241, 290, 443
07BK[0,3,4]ZZ	Exc/Thoracic Duct, [Opn, Perc, Perc Endo] 60
01B8[0,3,4]ZZ	Exc/Thoracic Nerve, [Opn, Perc, Perc Endo] 24, 151, 319, 440
00BX*	Exc/Thoracic Spinal Cord 159, 160
00BX[0,3,4]Z[X,Z]	Exc/Thoracic Spinal Cord, [Opn, Perc, Perc Endo], No Dev, [Dx, NQ] 19, 295
01BL*	Exc/Thoracic Sympathetic Nerve 24
01BL[0,3,4]ZZ	Exc/Thoracic Sympathetic Nerve, [Opn, Perc, Perc Endo] 89
0RB9[0,3,4]ZZ	Exc/Thoracic Vert Disc, [Opn, Perc, Perc Endo] 19, 159, 160, 349
0RB6[0,3,4]ZZ	Exc/Thoracic Vert Jt, [Opn, Perc, Perc Endo] 19, 159, 160, 301, 349
0PB4[0,3,4]ZZ	Exc/Thoracic Vertebra, [Opn, Perc, Perc Endo] 54, 155, 243, 345
0PB4[0,3,4]ZX	Exc/Thoracic Vertebra, [Opn, Perc, Perc Endo] 65, 129, 292, 455
0RBB[0,3,4]ZZ	Exc/Thoracolumbar Vert Disc, [Opn, Perc, Perc Endo] 19, 159, 160, 349
0RBA[0,3,4]ZZ	Exc/Thoracolumbar Vert Jt, [Opn, Perc, Perc Endo] 19, 159, 160, 301, 349
0MBG[0,3,4]ZZ	Exc/Thorax Bursa & Lgmt, Lt, [Opn, Perc, Perc Endo] 143, 343, 453

Alphabetic Index to Procedures (sidebar)

ØMBF[Ø,3,4]ZZ	Exc/Thorax Bursa & Lgmt, Rt, [Opn, Perc, Perc Endo] 143, 343, 453
ØKBJ*	Exc/Thorax Muscle, Lt 139
ØKBJ[Ø,3,4]ZZ	Exc/Thorax Muscle, Lt, [Opn, Perc, Perc Endo] 27, 214, 339
ØKBH*	Exc/Thorax Muscle, Rt 139
ØKBH[Ø,3,4]ZZ	Exc/Thorax Muscle, Rt, [Opn, Perc, Perc Endo] 27, 214, 339
ØLBD*	Exc/Thorax Tndn, Lt 141
ØLBD[Ø,3,4]ZZ	Exc/Thorax Tndn, Lt, [Opn, Perc, Perc Endo] 28, 341
ØLBC*	Exc/Thorax Tndn, Rt 141
ØLBC[Ø,3,4]ZZ	Exc/Thorax Tndn, Rt, [Opn, Perc, Perc Endo] 28, 341
ØPBS[Ø,3,4]ZX	Exc/Thumb Phalanx, Lt, [Opn, Perc, Perc Endo] 130, 216, 292, 455
ØPBS[Ø,3,4]ZZ	Exc/Thumb Phalanx, Lt, [Opn, Perc, Perc Endo] 54, 155, 243, 345
ØPBR[Ø,3,4]ZX	Exc/Thumb Phalanx, Rt, [Opn, Perc, Perc Endo] 130, 216, 292, 455
ØPBR[Ø,3,4]ZZ	Exc/Thumb Phalanx, Rt, [Opn, Perc, Perc Endo] 54, 155, 243, 345
Ø7BM*	Exc/Thymus 60, 241
Ø7BM[Ø,3,4]ZZ	Exc/Thymus, [Opn, Perc, Perc Endo] 25, 328
Ø7BM[Ø,3,4]Z[X,Z]	Exc/Thymus, [Opn, Perc, Perc Endo], No Dev, [Dx, NQ] 290, 297
Ø3BV*	Exc/Thyroid Artery, Lt 81
Ø3BV[Ø,3,4]ZZ	Exc/Thyroid Artery, Lt, [Opn, Perc, Perc Endo] 21, 50, 321
Ø3BV[Ø,3,4]ZX	Exc/Thyroid Artery, Lt, [Opn, Perc, Perc Endo] 441
Ø3BU*	Exc/Thyroid Artery, Rt 81
Ø3BU[Ø,3,4]ZZ	Exc/Thyroid Artery, Rt, [Opn, Perc, Perc Endo] 21, 50, 321
Ø3BU[Ø,3,4]ZX	Exc/Thyroid Artery, Rt, [Opn, Perc, Perc Endo] 441
ØGBG[Ø,3,4]ZZ	Exc/Thyroid Gland Lobe, Lt, [Opn, Perc, Perc Endo] 238
ØGBH[Ø,3,4]ZZ	Exc/Thyroid Gland Lobe, Rt, [Opn, Perc, Perc Endo] 238
ØQBH[Ø,3,4]ZX	Exc/Tibia, Lt, [Opn, Perc, Perc Endo] 130, 217, 244, 254, 259, 456
ØQBH[Ø,3,4]ZZ	Exc/Tibia, Lt, [Opn, Perc, Perc Endo] 133, 347
ØQBG[Ø,3,4]ZX	Exc/Tibia, Rt, [Opn, Perc, Perc Endo] 130, 217, 244, 254, 259, 456
ØQBG[Ø,3,4]ZZ	Exc/Tibia, Rt, [Opn, Perc, Perc Endo] 133, 347
Ø1BG[Ø,3,4]ZZ	Exc/Tibial Nerve, [Opn, Perc, Perc Endo] 24, 151, 319, 440
ØSBQ[Ø,3,4]ZZ	Exc/Toe Phalangeal Jt, Lt, [Opn, Perc, Perc Endo] 145, 351, 457
ØSBP[Ø,3,4]ZZ	Exc/Toe Phalangeal Jt, Rt, [Opn, Perc, Perc Endo] 145, 351, 457
ØQBR[Ø,3,4]ZX	Exc/Toe Phalanx, Lt, [Opn, Perc, Perc Endo] 130, 217, 292, 456
ØQBR[Ø,3,4]ZZ	Exc/Toe Phalanx, Lt, [Opn, Perc, Perc Endo] 54, 156, 244, 347
ØQBQ[Ø,3,4]ZX	Exc/Toe Phalanx, Rt, [Opn, Perc, Perc Endo] 130, 217, 292, 456
ØQBQ[Ø,3,4]ZZ	Exc/Toe Phalanx, Rt, [Opn, Perc, Perc Endo] 54, 156, 244, 347
ØCB7[Ø,3,X]ZZ	Exc/Tongue, [Opn, Perc, Ext] 56, 237
ØKB4*	Exc/Tongue, Palate, Pharynx Muscle 139
ØKB4[Ø,3,4]ZZ	Exc/Tongue, Palate, Pharynx Muscle, [Opn, Perc, Perc Endo] 27, 214, 339
ØCBP*	Exc/Tonsils 52
ØCBP[Ø,3,X]ZX	Exc/Tonsils, [Opn, Perc, Ext] 448
ØBB1[Ø,3,4,7,8]ZZ	Exc/Trachea, [Opn, Perc, Perc Endo, Via Natrl or Artfcl Opng, Via Natrl or Artfcl Opng Endo] 52, 64
ØDBL[Ø,3,4]ZZ	Exc/Transv Colon, [Opn, Perc, Perc Endo] 90, 106, 300, 333
ØDBL[Ø,3,7]ZZ	Exc/Transv Colon, [Opn, Perc, Via Natrl or Artfcl Opng] 242
Ø2BJ[Ø,4]ZZ	Exc/Tricuspid Valve, [Opn, Perc Endo] 74
ØØBK[Ø,3,4]ZZ	Exc/Trigeminal Nerve, [Opn, Perc, Perc Endo] 23, 50, 151, 318, 440
ØØBJ[Ø,3,4]ZZ	Exc/Trochlear Nerve, [Opn, Perc, Perc Endo] 23, 50, 151, 318, 440
ØMBD[Ø,3,4]ZZ	Exc/Trunk Bursa & Lgmt, Lt, [Opn, Perc, Perc Endo] 143, 343, 453
ØMBC[Ø,3,4]ZZ	Exc/Trunk Bursa & Lgmt, Rt, [Opn, Perc, Perc Endo] 143, 343, 453
ØKBG*	Exc/Trunk Muscle, Lt 139
ØKBG[Ø,3,4]ZZ	Exc/Trunk Muscle, Lt, [Opn, Perc, Perc Endo] 27, 214, 339
ØKBF*	Exc/Trunk Muscle, Rt 139
ØKBF[Ø,3,4]ZZ	Exc/Trunk Muscle, Rt, [Opn, Perc, Perc Endo] 27, 214, 339
ØLBB*	Exc/Trunk Tndn, Lt 141
ØLBB[Ø,3,4]ZZ	Exc/Trunk Tndn, Lt, [Opn, Perc, Perc Endo] 28, 341
ØLB9*	Exc/Trunk Tndn, Rt 141
ØLB9[Ø,3,4]ZZ	Exc/Trunk Tndn, Rt, [Opn, Perc, Perc Endo] 28, 340
ØVB7[Ø,3,4]ZZ	Exc/Tunica Vaginalis, Lt, [Opn, Perc, Perc Endo] 257
ØVB6[Ø,3,4]ZZ	Exc/Tunica Vaginalis, Rt, [Opn, Perc, Perc Endo] 257
Ø9B8*	Exc/Tympanic Membrane, Lt 51

Ø9B8[Ø,3,4,7,8]Z[X,Z]	Exc/Tympanic Membrane, Lt, [Opn, Perc, Perc Endo, Via Natrl or Artfcl Opng, Via Natrl or Artfcl Opng Endo], No Dev, [Dx, NQ] 446
Ø9B7*	Exc/Tympanic Membrane, Rt 51
Ø9B7[Ø,3,4,7,8]Z[X,Z]	Exc/Tympanic Membrane, Rt, [Opn, Perc, Perc Endo, Via Natrl or Artfcl Opng, Via Natrl or Artfcl Opng Endo], No Dev, [Dx, NQ] 446
ØPBL[Ø,3,4]ZX	Exc/Ulna, Lt, [Opn, Perc, Perc Endo] 130, 216, 243, 253, 259, 455
ØPBL[Ø,3,4]ZZ	Exc/Ulna, Lt, [Opn, Perc, Perc Endo] 148, 345
ØPBK[Ø,3,4]ZX	Exc/Ulna, Rt, [Opn, Perc, Perc Endo] 129, 216, 243, 253, 259, 455
ØPBK[Ø,3,4]ZZ	Exc/Ulna, Rt, [Opn, Perc, Perc Endo] 148, 345
Ø3BA*	Exc/Ulnar Artery, Lt 81
Ø3BA[Ø,3,4]ZZ	Exc/Ulnar Artery, Lt, [Opn, Perc, Perc Endo] 239, 321
Ø3BA[Ø,3,4]ZX	Exc/Ulnar Artery, Lt, [Opn, Perc, Perc Endo] 441
Ø3B9*	Exc/Ulnar Artery, Rt 81
Ø3B9[Ø,3,4]ZZ	Exc/Ulnar Artery, Rt, [Opn, Perc, Perc Endo] 239, 321
Ø3B9[Ø,3,4]ZX	Exc/Ulnar Artery, Rt, [Opn, Perc, Perc Endo] 441
Ø1B4[Ø,3,4]ZZ	Exc/Ulnar Nerve, [Opn, Perc, Perc Endo] 24, 151, 319, 440
ØKB8*	Exc/Upr Arm Muscle, Lt 139
ØKB8[Ø,3,4]ZZ	Exc/Upr Arm Muscle, Lt, [Opn, Perc, Perc Endo] 27, 214, 339
ØKB7*	Exc/Upr Arm Muscle, Rt 139
ØKB7[Ø,3,4]ZZ	Exc/Upr Arm Muscle, Rt, [Opn, Perc, Perc Endo] 27, 214, 339
ØLB4*	Exc/Upr Arm Tndn, Lt 141
ØLB4[Ø,3,4]ZZ	Exc/Upr Arm Tndn, Lt, [Opn, Perc, Perc Endo] 28, 340
ØLB3*	Exc/Upr Arm Tndn, Rt 141
ØLB3[Ø,3,4]ZZ	Exc/Upr Arm Tndn, Rt, [Opn, Perc, Perc Endo] 28, 340
ØXB9[Ø,3,4]ZZ	Exc/Upr Arm, Lt, [Opn, Perc, Perc Endo] 28, 91, 144, 207, 356, 461
ØXB8[Ø,3,4]ZZ	Exc/Upr Arm, Rt, [Opn, Perc, Perc Endo] 28, 91, 144, 207, 356, 461
Ø3BY*	Exc/Upr Artery 81
Ø3BY[Ø,3,4]ZZ	Exc/Upr Artery, [Opn, Perc, Perc Endo] 239, 321
Ø3BY[Ø,3,4]ZX	Exc/Upr Artery, [Opn, Perc, Perc Endo] 441
ØWBK[Ø,3,4,X]ZZ	Exc/Upr Back, [Opn, Perc, Perc Endo, Ext] 28, 91, 144, 207, 355, 460
ØMBB[Ø,3,4]ZZ	Exc/Upr Extr Bursa & Lgmt, Lt, [Opn, Perc, Perc Endo] 143, 343, 453
ØMB9[Ø,3,4]ZZ	Exc/Upr Extr Bursa & Lgmt, Rt, [Opn, Perc, Perc Endo] 343, 453
ØXB7[Ø,3,4]ZZ	Exc/Upr Extr, Lt, [Opn, Perc, Perc Endo] 28, 91, 144, 207, 356, 461
ØXB6[Ø,3,4]ZZ	Exc/Upr Extr, Rt, [Opn, Perc, Perc Endo] 28, 91, 144, 207, 356, 461
Ø8BP*	Exc/Upr Eyelid, Lt 42, 329
Ø8BP[Ø,3,X]ZZ	Exc/Upr Eyelid, Lt, [Opn, Perc, Ext] 210, 241
Ø8BP[Ø,3,X]Z[X,Z]	Exc/Upr Eyelid, Lt, [Opn, Perc, Ext], No Dev, [Dx, NQ] 444
Ø8BN*	Exc/Upr Eyelid, Rt 42, 329
Ø8BN[Ø,3,X]ZZ	Exc/Upr Eyelid, Rt, [Opn, Perc, Ext] 210, 241
Ø8BN[Ø,3,X]Z[X,Z]	Exc/Upr Eyelid, Rt, [Opn, Perc, Ext], No Dev, [Dx, NQ] 444
ØQB7[Ø,3,4]ZX	Exc/Upr Femur, Lt, [Opn, Perc, Perc Endo] 130, 217, 244, 254, 259, 456
ØQB7[Ø,3,4]ZZ	Exc/Upr Femur, Lt, [Opn, Perc, Perc Endo] 137, 347
ØQB6[Ø,3,4]ZX	Exc/Upr Femur, Rt, [Opn, Perc, Perc Endo] 130, 217, 244, 254, 259, 456
ØQB6[Ø,3,4]ZZ	Exc/Upr Femur, Rt, [Opn, Perc, Perc Endo] 137, 347
ØWB4[Ø,3,4,X]ZZ	Exc/Upr Jaw, [Opn, Perc, Perc Endo, Ext] 28, 55, 91, 144, 207, 355, 460
ØKBR*	Exc/Upr Leg Muscle, Lt 139
ØKBR[Ø,3,4]ZZ	Exc/Upr Leg Muscle, Lt, [Opn, Perc, Perc Endo] 27, 214, 339
ØKBQ*	Exc/Upr Leg Muscle, Rt 139
ØKBQ[Ø,3,4]ZZ	Exc/Upr Leg Muscle, Rt, [Opn, Perc, Perc Endo] 27, 214, 339
ØLBM*	Exc/Upr Leg Tndn, Lt 141
ØLBM[Ø,3,4]ZZ	Exc/Upr Leg Tndn, Lt, [Opn, Perc, Perc Endo] 28, 341
ØLBL*	Exc/Upr Leg Tndn, Rt 141
ØLBL[Ø,3,4]ZZ	Exc/Upr Leg Tndn, Rt, [Opn, Perc, Perc Endo] 28, 341
ØYBD[Ø,3,4]ZZ	Exc/Upr Leg, Lt, [Opn, Perc, Perc Endo] 29, 92, 144, 207, 357, 461
ØYBC[Ø,3,4]ZZ	Exc/Upr Leg, Rt, [Opn, Perc, Perc Endo] 29, 92, 144, 207, 357, 461
ØCBØ[Ø,3,X]ZZ	Exc/Upr Lip, [Opn, Perc, Ext] 56, 210, 448

0BB8[0,3,7]ZZ	Exc/Upr Lobe Bronchus, Lt, [Opn, Perc, Via Natrl or Artfcl Opng] 61
0BB4[0,3,7]ZZ	Exc/Upr Lobe Bronchus, Rt, [Opn, Perc, Via Natrl or Artfcl Opng] 61
0BBG[0,4,7,8]ZX	Exc/Upr Lung Lobe, Lt, [Opn, Perc Endo, Via Natrl or Artfcl Opng, Via Natrl or Artfcl Opng Endo] 90
0BBG[0,4]ZX	Exc/Upr Lung Lobe, Lt, [Opn, Perc Endo] 153, 253
0BBG[0,3,4,7]ZZ	Exc/Upr Lung Lobe, Lt, [Opn, Perc, Perc Endo, Via Natrl or Artfcl Opng] 61, 299
0BBG[4,7,8]ZX	Exc/Upr Lung Lobe, Lt, [Perc Endo, Via Natrl or Artfcl Opng, Via Natrl or Artfcl Opng Endo] 64
0BBG[7,8]ZX	Exc/Upr Lung Lobe, Lt, [Via Natrl or Artfcl Opng, Via Natrl or Artfcl Opng Endo] 447
0BBC[0,4,7,8]ZX	Exc/Upr Lung Lobe, Rt, [Opn, Perc Endo, Via Natrl or Artfcl Opng, Via Natrl or Artfcl Opng Endo] 90
0BBC[0,4]ZX	Exc/Upr Lung Lobe, Rt, [Opn, Perc Endo] 153, 253
0BBC[0,3,4,7]ZZ	Exc/Upr Lung Lobe, Rt, [Opn, Perc, Perc Endo, Via Natrl or Artfcl Opng] 61, 299
0BBC[4,7,8]ZX	Exc/Upr Lung Lobe, Rt, [Perc Endo, Via Natrl or Artfcl Opng, Via Natrl or Artfcl Opng Endo] 64
0BBC[7,8]ZX	Exc/Upr Lung Lobe, Rt, [Via Natrl or Artfcl Opng, Via Natrl or Artfcl Opng Endo] 447
05BY*	Exc/Upr Vein 85
05BY[0,3,4]ZZ	Exc/Upr Vein, [Opn, Perc, Perc Endo] 240, 325
05BY[0,3,4]ZX	Exc/Upr Vein, [Opn, Perc, Perc Endo] 442
0TB7[0,3,4,7,8]ZZ	Exc/Ureter, Lt, [Opn, Perc, Perc Endo, Via Natrl or Artfcl Opng, Via Natrl or Artfcl Opng Endo] 249, 259, 268, 353
0TB6[0,3,4,7,8]ZZ	Exc/Ureter, Rt, [Opn, Perc, Perc Endo, Via Natrl or Artfcl Opng, Via Natrl or Artfcl Opng Endo] 249, 259, 268, 353
0TBD[0,3,4,7,8,X]ZZ	Exc/Urethra, [Opn, Perc, Perc Endo, Via Natrl or Artfcl Opng, Via Natrl or Artfcl Opng Endo, Ext] 250
0UB4[0,3,4,7,8]ZZ	Exc/Uterine Supporting Structure, [Opn, Perc, Perc Endo, Via Natrl or Artfcl Opng, Via Natrl or Artfcl Opng Endo] 262, 264, 266
0UB4[3,4,7,8]ZX	Exc/Uterine Supporting Structure, [Perc, Perc Endo, Via Natrl or Artfcl Opng, Via Natrl or Artfcl Opng Endo] 266, 459
0UB9[0,3,4,7,8]ZZ	Exc/Uterus, [Opn, Perc, Perc Endo, Via Natrl or Artfcl Opng, Via Natrl or Artfcl Opng Endo] 262, 264, 266, 459
0UB9[3,4,7,8]ZX	Exc/Uterus, [Perc, Perc Endo, Via Natrl or Artfcl Opng, Via Natrl or Artfcl Opng Endo] 266, 459
0CBN*	Exc/Uvula 56
0CBN[0,3,X]Z[X,Z]	Exc/Uvula, [Opn, Perc, Ext], No Dev, [Dx, NQ] 448
0UBG*	Exc/Vagina 267, 275
0UBG[0,3,4,7,8,X]Z[X,Z]	Exc/Vagina, [Opn, Perc, Perc Endo, Via Natrl or Artfcl Opng, Via Natrl or Artfcl Opng Endo, Ext], No Dev, [Dx, NQ] 217, 459
00BQ[0,3,4]ZZ	Exc/Vagus Nerve, [Opn, Perc, Perc Endo] 23, 50, 151, 318, 440
02BL[0,3,4]ZZ	Exc/Ventricle, Lt, [Opn, Perc, Perc Endo] 74
02BK[0,3,4]ZZ	Exc/Ventricle, Rt, [Opn, Perc, Perc Endo] 74
02BM[0,4]ZZ	Exc/Ventricular Septum, [Opn, Perc Endo] 74
03BQ*	Exc/Vert Artery, Lt 81
03BQ[0,3,4]ZZ	Exc/Vert Artery, Lt, [Opn, Perc, Perc Endo] 21, 50, 321
03BQ[0,3,4]ZX	Exc/Vert Artery, Lt, [Opn, Perc, Perc Endo] 441
03BP*	Exc/Vert Artery, Rt 81
03BP[0,3,4]ZZ	Exc/Vert Artery, Rt, [Opn, Perc, Perc Endo] 21, 50, 321
03BP[0,3,4]ZX	Exc/Vert Artery, Rt, [Opn, Perc, Perc Endo] 441
05BS*	Exc/Vert Vein, Lt 85
05BS[0,4]ZZ	Exc/Vert Vein, Lt, [Opn, Perc Endo] 51
05BS[0,3,4]ZZ	Exc/Vert Vein, Lt, [Opn, Perc, Perc Endo] 22, 325
05BS[0,3,4]ZX	Exc/Vert Vein, Lt, [Opn, Perc, Perc Endo] 442
05BR*	Exc/Vert Vein, Rt 85
05BR[0,4]ZZ	Exc/Vert Vein, Rt, [Opn, Perc Endo] 51
05BR[0,3,4]ZZ	Exc/Vert Vein, Rt, [Opn, Perc, Perc Endo] 22, 325
05BR[0,3,4]ZX	Exc/Vert Vein, Rt, [Opn, Perc, Perc Endo] 442
0UBL*	Exc/Vestibular Gland 267, 272
0UBL[0,X]ZZ	Exc/Vestibular Gland, [Opn, Ext] 217
0UBL[0,X]Z[X,Z]	Exc/Vestibular Gland, [Opn, Ext], No Dev, [Dx, NQ] 459
08B5*	Exc/Vitreous, Lt 44
08B53Z[X,Z]	Exc/Vitreous, Lt, Perc, No Dev, [Dx, NQ] 444
08B4*	Exc/Vitreous, Rt 44
08B43Z[X,Z]	Exc/Vitreous, Rt, Perc, No Dev, [Dx, NQ] 444
0CBV[0,3,4,7,8]ZZ	Exc/Vocal Cord, Lt, [Opn, Perc, Perc Endo, Via Natrl or Artfcl Opng, Via Natrl or Artfcl Opng Endo] 52, 65, 331
0CBT[0,3,4,7,8]ZZ	Exc/Vocal Cord, Rt, [Opn, Perc, Perc Endo, Via Natrl or Artfcl Opng, Via Natrl or Artfcl Opng Endo] 52, 65, 331
0UBM[0,X]ZX	Exc/Vulva, [Opn, Ext] 217, 275, 459
0MB6[0,3,4]ZZ	Exc/Wrist Bursa & Lgmt, Lt, [Opn, Perc, Perc Endo] 143, 343, 453
0MB5[0,3,4]ZZ	Exc/Wrist Bursa & Lgmt, Rt, [Opn, Perc, Perc Endo] 143, 343, 453
0RBP[0,3,4]ZZ	Exc/Wrist Jt, Lt, [Opn, Perc, Perc Endo] 150, 316, 457
0RBN[0,3,4]ZZ	Exc/Wrist Jt, Rt, [Opn, Perc, Perc Endo] 150, 316, 457
0XBH[0,3,4]ZZ	Exc/Wrist Rgn, Lt, [Opn, Perc, Perc Endo] 29, 92, 144, 207, 356, 461
0XBG[0,3,4]ZZ	Exc/Wrist Rgn, Rt, [Opn, Perc, Perc Endo] 29, 92, 144, 207, 356, 461
0NBN[0,3,4]ZZ	Exc/Zygomatic Bone, Lt, [Opn, Perc, Perc Endo] 48, 154, 343
0NBN[0,3,4]ZX	Exc/Zygomatic Bone, Lt, [Opn, Perc, Perc Endo] 54, 129, 454
0NBM[0,3,4]ZZ	Exc/Zygomatic Bone, Rt, [Opn, Perc, Perc Endo] 48, 154, 343
0NBM[0,3,4]ZX	Exc/Zygomatic Bone, Rt, [Opn, Perc, Perc Endo] 54, 129, 454
03C[H,J,K,L,M,N]0ZZ	Extir [Rt Common Carotid, Lt Common Carotid, Rt Int Carotid, Lt Int Carotid, Rt Ext Carotid, Lt Ext Carotid] Artery, Opn 21, 50
03C[P,Q,R,S,T,U,V]0ZZ	Extir [Rt Vert, Lt Vert, Face, Rt Temporal, Lt Temporal, Rt Thyroid, Lt Thyroid] Artery, Opn 21, 50
0WC[J,P,R]0ZZ	Extir of Matter from [Pelvic Cavity, Gastrointestinal Tract, Genitourinary Tract], Opn Appr 121
09C[5,6,9,A,D,E]0ZZ	Extir of Matter from [Rt Mid Ear, Lt Mid Ear, Rt Auditory Ossicle, Lt Auditory Ossicle, Rt Inner Ear, Lt Inner Ear], Opn Appr 51
08C[2,3]3ZZ	Extir of Matter from [Rt, Lt] Ant Chamber, Perc Appr 44
03C[H,J]0ZZ	Extir of Matter from [Rt, Lt] Common Carotid Artery, Opn Appr 81
08C[S,T]XZZ	Extir of Matter from [Rt, Lt] Conjunctiva, Ext Appr 43
08C[8,9]XZZ	Extir of Matter from [Rt, Lt] Cornea, Ext Appr 43
03C[M,N]0ZZ	Extir of Matter from [Rt, Lt] Ext Carotid Artery, Opn Appr 81
08C[L,M]XZZ	Extir of Matter from [Rt, Lt] Extraocular Muscle, Ext Appr 44
08C[0,1]XZZ	Extir of Matter from [Rt, Lt] Eye, Ext Appr 44
0FC[5,6]0ZZ	Extir of Matter from [Rt, Lt] Hepatic Duct, Opn Appr 120
03C[K,L]0ZZ	Extir of Matter from [Rt, Lt] Int Carotid Artery, Opn Appr 81
08C[V,W]XZZ	Extir of Matter from [Rt, Lt] Lacrimal Gland, Ext Appr 44
03C[S,T]0ZZ	Extir of Matter from [Rt, Lt] Temporal Artery, Opn Appr 81
03C[U,V]0ZZ	Extir of Matter from [Rt, Lt] Thyroid Artery, Opn Appr 81
03C[P,Q]0ZZ	Extir of Matter from [Rt, Lt] Vert Artery, Opn Appr 81
02C00ZZ	Extir of Matter from 1 Cor Art, Opn Appr 74
02C03ZZ	Extir of Matter from 1 Cor Art, Perc Appr 75
02C10ZZ	Extir of Matter from 2 Cor Art, Opn Appr 74
02C13ZZ	Extir of Matter from 2 Cor Art, Perc Appr 75
02C20ZZ	Extir of Matter from 3 Cor Art, Opn Appr 74
02C23ZZ	Extir of Matter from 3 Cor Art, Perc Appr 75
02C30ZZ	Extir of Matter from 4+ Cor Art, Opn Appr 74
02C33ZZ	Extir of Matter from 4+ Cor Art, Perc Appr 75
0CCQ0ZZ	Extir of Matter from Adenoids, Opn Appr 52
0CCQ3ZZ	Extir of Matter from Adenoids, Perc Appr 52
0FCC0ZZ	Extir of Matter from Ampulla of Vater, Opn Appr 106, 119
02CF0ZZ	Extir of Matter from Aortic Valve, Opn Appr 74
0FC90ZZ	Extir of Matter from Common Bile Duct, Opn Appr 120, 301, 335
0FC80ZZ	Extir of Matter from Cystic Duct, Opn Appr 120, 301
03CR0ZZ	Extir of Matter from Face Artery, Opn Appr 81, 239
03CG3ZZ	Extir of Matter from Intracran Art, Perc Appr 81
05CL3ZZ	Extir of Matter from Intracranial Vein, Perc Appr 85
08C33ZZ	Extir of Matter from Lt Ant Chamber, Perc Appr 329, 444
03CJ0ZZ	Extir of Matter from Lt Com Carotid, Opn Appr 239
08CTXZZ	Extir of Matter from Lt Conjunctiva, Extern Appr 329, 444
08C9XZZ	Extir of Matter from Lt Cornea, Ext Appr 329, 444
03CN0ZZ	Extir of Matter from Lt Ext Carotid, Opn Appr 239
08C1XZZ	Extir of Matter from Lt Eye, Ext Appr 329, 444
0FC60ZZ	Extir of Matter from Lt Hepatic Duct, Opn Appr 301
03CL0ZZ	Extir of Matter from Lt Int Carotid, Opn Appr 239
09C60ZZ	Extir of Matter from Lt Mid Ear, Opn Appr 446
03CT0ZZ	Extir of Matter from Lt Temporal Art, Opn Appr 239
03CV0ZZ	Extir of Matter from Lt Thyroid Art, Opn Appr 239
03CQ0ZZ	Extir of Matter from Lt Verteb Art, Opn Appr 239
02CG0ZZ	Extir of Matter from Mitral Valve, Opn Appr 74
02CH0ZZ	Extir of Matter from Pulmn Valve, Opn Appr 74

04CD[0,3,4]ZZ	Extir/Common Iliac Artery, Lt, [Opn, Perc, Perc Endo] 95
04CC*	Extir/Common Iliac Artery, Rt 111, 252
04CC[0,3,4]ZZ	Extir/Common Iliac Artery, Rt, [Opn, Perc, Perc Endo] 95
06CD[0,3,4]ZZ	Extir/Common Iliac Vein, Lt, [Opn, Perc, Perc Endo] 97
06CC[0,3,4]ZZ	Extir/Common Iliac Vein, Rt, [Opn, Perc, Perc Endo] 97
02C8[0,3,4]ZZ	Extir/Conduction Mech, [Opn, Perc, Perc Endo] 74
02C3[3,4]ZZ	Extir/Coronary Artery, Four or More Sites, [Perc, Perc Endo] 78, 79, 80
02C0[3,4]ZZ	Extir/Coronary Artery, One Site, [Perc, Perc Endo] 78, 79, 80
02C2[3,4]ZZ	Extir/Coronary Artery, Three Sites, [Perc, Perc Endo] 78, 79, 80
02C1[3,4]ZZ	Extir/Coronary Artery, Two Sites, [Perc, Perc Endo] 78, 79, 80
02C4[0,3,4]ZZ	Extir/Coronary Vein, [Opn, Perc, Perc Endo] 74
0WC1[0,3,4]ZZ	Extir/Cranial Cavity, [Opn, Perc, Perc Endo] 10, 14, 18, 49, 302, 355, 415
0UCF*	Extir/Cul-de-sac 269, 272
0DCM[0,3,4]ZZ	Extir/Descending Colon, [Opn, Perc, Perc Endo] 109, 333
0BCS*	Extir/Diaphragm, Lt 61
0BCR*	Extir/Diaphragm, Rt 61
0DC9[0,3,4]ZZ	Extir/Duodenum, [Opn, Perc, Perc Endo] 105, 123, 333
00C2*	Extir/Dura Mater 318, 414
00C2[0,3,4]ZZ	Extir/Dura Mater, [Opn, Perc, Perc Endo] 8, 12, 16, 295
0MC4*	Extir/Elbow Bursa & Lgmt, Lt 143, 343
0MC4[0,3,4]ZZ	Extir/Elbow Bursa & Lgmt, Lt, [Opn, Perc, Perc Endo] 454
0MC3*	Extir/Elbow Bursa & Lgmt, Rt 143, 343
0MC3[0,3,4]ZZ	Extir/Elbow Bursa & Lgmt, Rt, [Opn, Perc, Perc Endo] 454
0RCM*	Extir/Elbow Jt, Lt 147, 244, 349
0RCL*	Extir/Elbow Jt, Rt 147, 244, 349
0UCB*	Extir/Endometrium 269
0VCL*	Extir/Epididymis, Bilat 258
0VCK*	Extir/Epididymis, Lt 257
0VCJ*	Extir/Epididymis, Rt 257
00C3*	Extir/Epidural Space 318
00C3[0,3,4]ZZ	Extir/Epidural Space, [Opn, Perc, Perc Endo] 8, 12, 16
0CCR*	Extir/Epiglottis 52
06C3*	Extir/Esophageal Vein 25, 51, 87, 241, 327
0DC4[0,3,4]ZZ	Extir/Esophagogastric Junction, [Opn, Perc, Perc Endo] 105, 333
0DC5[0,3,4]ZZ	Extir/Esophagus, [Opn, Perc, Perc Endo] 105, 333
0DC3[0,3,4]ZZ	Extir/Esophagus, Lwr, [Opn, Perc, Perc Endo] 105, 333
0DC2[0,3,4]ZZ	Extir/Esophagus, Mid, [Opn, Perc, Perc Endo] 105, 333
0DC1[0,3,4]ZZ	Extir/Esophagus, Upr, [Opn, Perc, Perc Endo] 105, 333
0NCG*	Extir/Ethmoid Bone, Lt 54
0NCF*	Extir/Ethmoid Bone, Rt 54
09CV*	Extir/Ethmoid Sinus, Lt 55
09CU*	Extir/Ethmoid Sinus, Rt 55
03CN[3,4]ZZ	Extir/Ext Carotid Artery, Lt, [Perc, Perc Endo] 9, 13, 17
03CM[3,4]ZZ	Extir/Ext Carotid Artery, Rt, [Perc, Perc Endo] 8, 13, 17
04CJ*	Extir/Ext Iliac Artery, Lt 111, 252
04CJ[0,3,4]ZZ	Extir/Ext Iliac Artery, Lt, [Opn, Perc, Perc Endo] 95
04CH*	Extir/Ext Iliac Artery, Rt 111, 252
04CH[0,3,4]ZZ	Extir/Ext Iliac Artery, Rt, [Opn, Perc, Perc Endo] 95
06CG[0,3,4]ZZ	Extir/Ext Iliac Vein, Lt, [Opn, Perc, Perc Endo] 97
06CF[0,3,4]ZZ	Extir/Ext Iliac Vein, Rt, [Opn, Perc, Perc Endo] 97
05CQ*	Extir/Ext Jugular Vein, Lt 25, 51, 85, 240, 325
05CP*	Extir/Ext Jugular Vein, Rt 25, 51, 85, 240, 325
08CM*	Extir/Extraocular Muscle, Lt 329
08CM[0,3,X]ZZ	Extir/Extraocular Muscle, Lt, [Opn, Perc, Ext] 444
08CM[0,3]ZZ	Extir/Extraocular Muscle, Lt, [Opn, Perc] 43
08CL*	Extir/Extraocular Muscle, Rt 329
08CL[0,3,X]ZZ	Extir/Extraocular Muscle, Rt, [Opn, Perc, Ext] 444
08CL[0,3]ZZ	Extir/Extraocular Muscle, Rt, [Opn, Perc] 43
03CR[3,4]ZZ	Extir/Face Artery, [Perc, Perc Endo] 9, 13, 17
05CV*	Extir/Face Vein, Lt 25, 51, 85, 240, 325
05CT*	Extir/Face Vein, Rt 25, 51, 85, 240, 325
0KC1*	Extir/Facial Muscle 54, 139, 339
0KC1[0,3,4]ZZ	Extir/Facial Muscle, [Opn, Perc, Perc Endo] 214, 451
00CM*	Extir/Facial Nerve 23
0UC6*	Extir/Fallopian Tube, Lt 263, 264, 266
0UC5*	Extir/Fallopian Tube, Rt 263, 264, 266
0UC7*	Extir/Fallopian Tubes, Bilat 263, 264, 266
04CL*	Extir/Femor Artery, Lt 83, 240
04CL[0,3,4]ZZ	Extir/Femor Artery, Lt, [Opn, Perc, Perc Endo] 296
04CK*	Extir/Femor Artery, Rt 83, 240
04CK[0,3,4]ZZ	Extir/Femor Artery, Rt, [Opn, Perc, Perc Endo] 296
0QC9*	Extir/Femor Shaft, Lt 130, 415
0QC8*	Extir/Femor Shaft, Rt 130, 415
06CN*	Extir/Femor Vein, Lt 88, 327
06CN[0,3,4]ZZ	Extir/Femor Vein, Lt, [Opn, Perc, Perc Endo] 443
06CM*	Extir/Femor Vein, Rt 88, 327
06CM[0,3,4]ZZ	Extir/Femor Vein, Rt, [Opn, Perc, Perc Endo] 443
0QCK*	Extir/Fibula, Lt 133
0QCJ*	Extir/Fibula, Rt 133
0RCX*	Extir/Finger Phalangeal Jt, Lt 146
0RCX[0,3,4]ZZ	Extir/Finger Phalangeal Jt, Lt, [Opn, Perc, Perc Endo] 316
0RCW*	Extir/Finger Phalangeal Jt, Rt 146
0RCW[0,3,4]ZZ	Extir/Finger Phalangeal Jt, Rt, [Opn, Perc, Perc Endo] 316
0PCV*	Extir/Finger Phalanx, Lt 155, 345
0PCT*	Extir/Finger Phalanx, Rt 155, 345
04CW*	Extir/Foot Artery, Lt 83, 240
04CW[0,3,4]ZZ	Extir/Foot Artery, Lt, [Opn, Perc, Perc Endo] 296
04CV*	Extir/Foot Artery, Rt 83, 240
04CV[0,3,4]ZZ	Extir/Foot Artery, Rt, [Opn, Perc, Perc Endo] 296
0MCT*	Extir/Foot Bursa & Lgmt, Lt 143, 343
0MCT[0,3,4]ZZ	Extir/Foot Bursa & Lgmt, Lt, [Opn, Perc, Perc Endo] 454
0MCS*	Extir/Foot Bursa & Lgmt, Rt 143, 343
0MCS[0,3,4]ZZ	Extir/Foot Bursa & Lgmt, Rt, [Opn, Perc, Perc Endo] 454
0KCW*	Extir/Foot Muscle, Lt 139, 339
0KCW[0,3,4]ZZ	Extir/Foot Muscle, Lt, [Opn, Perc, Perc Endo] 215, 452
0KCV*	Extir/Foot Muscle, Rt 139, 339
0KCV[0,3,4]ZZ	Extir/Foot Muscle, Rt, [Opn, Perc, Perc Endo] 215, 452
0LCW*	Extir/Foot Tndn, Lt 141, 341
0LCW[0,3,4]ZZ	Extir/Foot Tndn, Lt, [Opn, Perc, Perc Endo] 453
0LCV*	Extir/Foot Tndn, Rt 141, 341
0LCV[0,3,4]ZZ	Extir/Foot Tndn, Rt, [Opn, Perc, Perc Endo] 453
06CV*	Extir/Foot Vein, Lt 89, 327
06CV[0,3,4]ZZ	Extir/Foot Vein, Lt, [Opn, Perc, Perc Endo] 443
06CT*	Extir/Foot Vein, Rt 89, 327
06CT[0,3,4]ZZ	Extir/Foot Vein, Rt, [Opn, Perc, Perc Endo] 443
0NC2*	Extir/Frontal Bone, Lt 9, 48, 344, 415
0NC2[0,3,4]ZZ	Extir/Frontal Bone, Lt, [Opn, Perc, Perc Endo] 14, 18, 301
0NC1*	Extir/Frontal Bone, Rt 9, 48, 344, 415
0NC1[0,3,4]ZZ	Extir/Frontal Bone, Rt, [Opn, Perc, Perc Endo] 14, 18, 301
09CT*	Extir/Frontal Sinus, Lt 55
09CS*	Extir/Frontal Sinus, Rt 55
0FC4*	Extir/Gallbladder 120
04C2*	Extir/Gastric Artery 111, 252
04C2[0,3,4]ZZ	Extir/Gastric Artery, [Opn, Perc, Perc Endo] 95
06C2[0,3,4]ZZ	Extir/Gastric Vein, [Opn, Perc, Perc Endo] 97
0WCP[0,3,4]ZZ	Extir/Gastrointestinal Tract, [Opn, Perc, Perc Endo] 91, 113, 254, 302, 355
0WCP[3,4]ZZ	Extir/Gastrointestinal Tract, [Perc, Perc Endo] 123, 217
0WCR[0,3,4]ZZ	Extir/Genitourinary Tract, [Opn, Perc, Perc Endo] 91, 113, 254, 302, 355
0WCR[3,4]ZZ	Extir/Genitourinary Tract, [Perc, Perc Endo] 123, 217
0PC8*	Extir/Glenoid Cavity, Lt 65, 155, 345
0PC7*	Extir/Glenoid Cavity, Rt 65, 155, 345
00CP*	Extir/Glossopharyngeal Nerve 23
0DCQ*	Extir/Greater Omentum 112, 253, 333
06CQ*	Extir/Greater Saphenous Vein, Lt 89, 327
06CQ[0,3,4]ZZ	Extir/Greater Saphenous Vein, Lt, [Opn, Perc, Perc Endo] 443
06CP*	Extir/Greater Saphenous Vein, Rt 89, 327
06CP[0,3,4]ZZ	Extir/Greater Saphenous Vein, Rt, [Opn, Perc, Perc Endo] 443
03CF*	Extir/Hand Artery, Lt 81, 239
03CD*	Extir/Hand Artery, Rt 81, 239
0MC8*	Extir/Hand Bursa & Lgmt, Lt 150
0MC8[0,3,4]ZZ	Extir/Hand Bursa & Lgmt, Lt, [Opn, Perc, Perc Endo] 315
0MC7*	Extir/Hand Bursa & Lgmt, Rt 150
0MC7[0,3,4]ZZ	Extir/Hand Bursa & Lgmt, Rt, [Opn, Perc, Perc Endo] 315
0KCD*	Extir/Hand Muscle, Lt 149
0KCD[0,3,4]ZZ	Extir/Hand Muscle, Lt, [Opn, Perc, Perc Endo] 314

0KCC*	Extir/Hand Muscle, Rt 149
0KCC[0,3,4]ZZ	Extir/Hand Muscle, Rt, [Opn, Perc, Perc Endo] 314
0LC8*	Extir/Hand Tndn, Lt 149
0LC8[0,3,4]ZZ	Extir/Hand Tndn, Lt, [Opn, Perc, Perc Endo] 315, 453
0LC7*	Extir/Hand Tndn, Rt 149
0LC7[0,3,4]ZZ	Extir/Hand Tndn, Rt, [Opn, Perc, Perc Endo] 315, 453
05CH*	Extir/Hand Vein, Lt 85, 240, 325
05CG*	Extir/Hand Vein, Rt 85, 240, 325
0CC2[0,3]ZZ	Extir/Hard Palate, [Opn, Perc] 56
0MC0*	Extir/Head and Neck Bursa & Lgmt 143, 343
0MC0[0,3,4]ZZ	Extir/Head and Neck Bursa & Lgmt, [Opn, Perc, Perc Endo] 454
01CK*	Extir/Head and Neck Sympathetic Nerve 89
0LC0*	Extir/Head and Neck Tndn 141, 341
0LC0[0,3,4]ZZ	Extir/Head and Neck Tndn, [Opn, Perc, Perc Endo] 453
0KC0*	Extir/Head Muscle 54, 139, 339
0KC0[0,3,4]ZZ	Extir/Head Muscle, [Opn, Perc, Perc Endo] 214, 451
05C1*	Extir/Hemiazygos Vein 60
05C1[0,3,4]ZZ	Extir/Hemiazygos Vein, [Opn, Perc, Perc Endo] 96
04C3*	Extir/Hepatic Artery 111, 252
04C3[0,3,4]ZZ	Extir/Hepatic Artery, [Opn, Perc, Perc Endo] 95
06C4[0,3,4]ZZ	Extir/Hepatic Vein, [Opn, Perc, Perc Endo] 97
0MCM*	Extir/Hip Bursa & Lgmt, Lt 143, 343
0MCM[0,3,4]ZZ	Extir/Hip Bursa & Lgmt, Lt, [Opn, Perc, Perc Endo] 454
0MCL*	Extir/Hip Bursa & Lgmt, Rt 143, 343
0MCL[0,3,4]ZZ	Extir/Hip Bursa & Lgmt, Rt, [Opn, Perc, Perc Endo] 454
0SCB*	Extir/Hip Jt, Lt 131, 351
0SC9*	Extir/Hip Jt, Rt 131, 351
0KCP*	Extir/Hip Muscle, Lt 139, 339
0KCP[0,3,4]ZZ	Extir/Hip Muscle, Lt, [Opn, Perc, Perc Endo] 214, 452
0KCN*	Extir/Hip Muscle, Rt 139, 339
0KCN[0,3,4]ZZ	Extir/Hip Muscle, Rt, [Opn, Perc, Perc Endo] 214, 452
0LCK*	Extir/Hip Tndn, Lt 141, 341
0LCK[0,3,4]ZZ	Extir/Hip Tndn, Lt, [Opn, Perc, Perc Endo] 453
0LCJ*	Extir/Hip Tndn, Rt 141, 341
0LCJ[0,3,4]ZZ	Extir/Hip Tndn, Rt, [Opn, Perc, Perc Endo] 453
0PCD*	Extir/Humeral Head, Lt 132, 345
0PCC*	Extir/Humeral Head, Rt 132, 345
0PCG*	Extir/Humeral Shaft, Lt 132, 345
0PCF*	Extir/Humeral Shaft, Rt 132, 345
0NCX*	Extir/Hyoid Bone 54
06CJ[0,3,4]ZZ	Extir/Hypogastric Vein, Lt, [Opn, Perc, Perc Endo] 97
06CH[0,3,4]ZZ	Extir/Hypogastric Vein, Rt, [Opn, Perc, Perc Endo] 97
00CS*	Extir/Hypoglossal Nerve 23
00CA*	Extir/Hypothalamus 318, 414
00CA[0,3,4]ZZ	Extir/Hypothalamus, [Opn, Perc, Perc Endo] 8, 12, 16, 295
0DCC[0,3,4]ZZ	Extir/Ileocecal Valve, [Opn, Perc, Perc Endo] 109, 300, 333
0DCB[0,3,4]ZZ	Extir/Ileum, [Opn, Perc, Perc Endo] 109, 300, 333
04CB*	Extir/Inferior Mesenteric Artery 111, 252
04CB[0,3,4]ZZ	Extir/Inferior Mesenteric Artery, [Opn, Perc, Perc Endo] 95
06C6[0,3,4]ZZ	Extir/Inferior Mesenteric Vein, [Opn, Perc, Perc Endo] 97
0GCP*	Extir/Inferior Parathyroid Gland, Lt 53, 238, 336
0GCP[0,3,4]ZZ	Extir/Inferior Parathyroid Gland, Lt, [Opn, Perc, Perc Endo] 211
0GCN*	Extir/Inferior Parathyroid Gland, Rt 53, 238, 336
0GCN[0,3,4]ZZ	Extir/Inferior Parathyroid Gland, Rt, [Opn, Perc, Perc Endo] 211
06C0[0,3,4]ZZ	Extir/Inferior Vena Cava, [Opn, Perc, Perc Endo] 97
03C2*	Extir/Innominate Artery 60
03C2[0,3,4]ZZ	Extir/Innominate Artery, [Opn, Perc, Perc Endo] 93
05C4*	Extir/Innominate Vein, Lt 60
05C4[0,3,4]ZZ	Extir/Innominate Vein, Lt, [Opn, Perc, Perc Endo] 97
05C3*	Extir/Innominate Vein, Rt 60
05C3[0,3,4]ZZ	Extir/Innominate Vein, Rt, [Opn, Perc, Perc Endo] 97
03CL[3,X]ZZ	Extir/Int Carotid Artery, Lt, [Perc, Perc Endo] 8, 13, 17
03CK[3,X]ZZ	Extir/Int Carotid Artery, Rt, [Perc, Perc Endo] 8, 13, 17
04CF*	Extir/Int Iliac Artery, Lt 111, 252
04CF[0,3,4]ZZ	Extir/Int Iliac Artery, Lt, [Opn, Perc, Perc Endo] 95
04CE*	Extir/Int Iliac Artery, Rt 111, 252
04CE[0,3,4]ZZ	Extir/Int Iliac Artery, Rt, [Opn, Perc, Perc Endo] 95
05CN*	Extir/Int Jugular Vein, Lt 25, 51, 85, 240, 325
05CM*	Extir/Int Jugular Vein, Rt 25, 51, 85, 240, 325
03C1*	Extir/Int Mammary Artery, Lt 60
03C1[0,3,4]ZZ	Extir/Int Mammary Artery, Lt, [Opn, Perc, Perc Endo] 93
03C0*	Extir/Int Mammary Artery, Rt 60
03C0[0,3,4]ZZ	Extir/Int Mammary Artery, Rt, [Opn, Perc, Perc Endo] 93
03CG[0,4]ZZ	Extir/Intracranial Artery, [Opn, Perc Endo] 7
03CG[0,3,4]ZZ	Extir/Intracranial Artery, [Opn, Perc, Perc Endo] 8, 13, 17
05CL*	Extir/Intracranial Vein 325
05CL[0,4]ZZ	Extir/Intracranial Vein, [Opn, Perc Endo] 7
05CL[0,3,4]ZZ	Extir/Intracranial Vein, [Opn, Perc, Perc Endo] 9, 13, 17
08CD*	Extir/Iris, Lt 44, 329
08CD[3,X]ZZ	Extir/Iris, Lt, [Perc, Ext] 444
08CC*	Extir/Iris, Rt 44, 329
08CC[3,X]ZZ	Extir/Iris, Rt, [Perc, Ext] 444
0DCA[0,3,4]ZZ	Extir/Jejunum, [Opn, Perc, Perc Endo] 109, 300, 333
0TC4*	Extir/Kidney Pelvis, Lt 353
0TC4[0,3,4]ZZ	Extir/Kidney Pelvis, Lt, [Opn, Perc, Perc Endo] 249
0TC4[7,8]ZZ	Extir/Kidney Pelvis, Lt, [Via Natrl or Artfcl Opng, Via Natrl or Artfcl Opng Endo] 250, 458
0TC3*	Extir/Kidney Pelvis, Rt 353
0TC3[0,3,4]ZZ	Extir/Kidney Pelvis, Rt, [Opn, Perc, Perc Endo] 249
0TC3[7,8]ZZ	Extir/Kidney Pelvis, Rt, [Via Natrl or Artfcl Opng, Via Natrl or Artfcl Opng Endo] 250, 458
0TC1*	Extir/Kidney, Lt 249, 353
0TC0*	Extir/Kidney, Rt 249, 353
0MCP*	Extir/Knee Bursa & Lgmt, Lt 143, 343
0MCP[0,3,4]ZZ	Extir/Knee Bursa & Lgmt, Lt, [Opn, Perc, Perc Endo] 454
0MCN*	Extir/Knee Bursa & Lgmt, Rt 143, 343
0MCN[0,3,4]ZZ	Extir/Knee Bursa & Lgmt, Rt, [Opn, Perc, Perc Endo] 454
0SCD*	Extir/Knee Jt, Lt 132, 244, 351
0SCD[0,3,4]ZZ	Extir/Knee Jt, Lt, [Opn, Perc, Perc Endo] 457
0SCC*	Extir/Knee Jt, Rt 132, 244, 351
0SCC[0,3,4]ZZ	Extir/Knee Jt, Rt, [Opn, Perc, Perc Endo] 457
0LCR*	Extir/Knee Tndn, Lt 141, 341
0LCR[0,3,4]ZZ	Extir/Knee Tndn, Lt, [Opn, Perc, Perc Endo] 453
0LCQ*	Extir/Knee Tndn, Rt 141, 341
0LCQ[0,3,4]ZZ	Extir/Knee Tndn, Rt, [Opn, Perc, Perc Endo] 453
0NCJ*	Extir/Lacrimal Bone, Lt 54
0NCH*	Extir/Lacrimal Bone, Rt 54
08CY*	Extir/Lacrimal Duct, Lt 43
08CY[0,3,7,8]ZZ	Extir/Lacrimal Duct, Lt, [Opn, Perc, Via Natrl or Artfcl Opng, Via Natrl or Artfcl Opng Endo] 444
08CX*	Extir/Lacrimal Duct, Rt 43
08CX[0,3,7,8]ZZ	Extir/Lacrimal Duct, Rt, [Opn, Perc, Via Natrl or Artfcl Opng, Via Natrl or Artfcl Opng Endo] 444
08CW[0,3,X]ZZ	Extir/Lacrimal Gland, Lt, [Opn, Perc, Ext] 444
08CW[0,3]ZZ	Extir/Lacrimal Gland, Lt, [Opn, Perc] 43
08CW[3,X]ZZ	Extir/Lacrimal Gland, Lt, [Perc, Ext] 330
08CV[0,3,X]ZZ	Extir/Lacrimal Gland, Rt, [Opn, Perc, Ext] 444
08CV[0,3]ZZ	Extir/Lacrimal Gland, Rt, [Opn, Perc] 43
08CV[3,X]ZZ	Extir/Lacrimal Gland, Rt, [Perc, Ext] 329
0CCS[0,3,4]ZZ	Extir/Larynx, [Opn, Perc, Perc Endo] 52
08CK*	Extir/Lens, Lt 44, 329
08CK[3,X]ZZ	Extir/Lens, Lt, [Perc, Ext] 444
08CJ*	Extir/Lens, Rt 44, 329
08CJ[3,X]ZZ	Extir/Lens, Rt, [Perc, Ext] 444
0DCT*	Extir/Lesser Omentum 112, 253, 333
06CS*	Extir/Lesser Saphenous Vein, Lt 89, 327
06CS[0,3,4]ZZ	Extir/Lesser Saphenous Vein, Lt, [Opn, Perc, Perc Endo] 443
06CR*	Extir/Lesser Saphenous Vein, Rt 89, 327
06CR[0,3,4]ZZ	Extir/Lesser Saphenous Vein, Rt, [Opn, Perc, Perc Endo] 443
0DCE[0,3,4]ZZ	Extir/Lg Intestine, [Opn, Perc, Perc Endo] 109, 333
0DCG[0,3,4]ZZ	Extir/Lg Intestine, Lt, [Opn, Perc, Perc Endo] 109, 333
0DCF[0,3,4]ZZ	Extir/Lg Intestine, Rt, [Opn, Perc, Perc Endo] 109, 333
0BC9[0,3,4]ZZ	Extir/Lingula Bronchus, [Opn, Perc, Perc Endo] 61
0FC0*	Extir/Liver 119, 335
0FC2*	Extir/Liver, Lt Lobe 119, 335
0FC1*	Extir/Liver, Rt Lobe 119, 335
00CY*	Extir/Lumbar Spinal Cord 318
00CY[0,3,4]ZZ	Extir/Lumbar Spinal Cord, [Opn, Perc, Perc Endo] 19
01CN*	Extir/Lumbar Sympathetic Nerve 89
0SC2*	Extir/Lumbar Vert Disc 157

0SC0*	Extir/Lumbar Vert Jt 157
0QC0*	Extir/Lumbar Vertebra 156
0SC4*	Extir/Lumbosacral Disc 157
0SC3*	Extir/Lumbosacral Jt 157
0BCH*	Extir/Lung Lingula 61, 331
0BCL*	Extir/Lung, Lt 61, 331
0BCK*	Extir/Lung, Rt 61, 331
0BCM*	Extir/Lungs, Bilat 61, 331
0KCB*	Extir/Lwr Arm and Wrist Muscle, Lt 139, 339
0KCB[0,3,4]ZZ	Extir/Lwr Arm and Wrist Muscle, Lt, [Opn, Perc, Perc Endo] 214, 451
0KC9*	Extir/Lwr Arm and Wrist Muscle, Rt 139, 339
0KC9[0,3,4]ZZ	Extir/Lwr Arm and Wrist Muscle, Rt, [Opn, Perc, Perc Endo] 214, 451
0LC6*	Extir/Lwr Arm and Wrist Tndn, Lt 141, 341
0LC6[0,3,4]ZZ	Extir/Lwr Arm and Wrist Tndn, Lt, [Opn, Perc, Perc Endo] 453
0LC5*	Extir/Lwr Arm and Wrist Tndn, Rt 141, 341
0LC5[0,3,4]ZZ	Extir/Lwr Arm and Wrist Tndn, Rt, [Opn, Perc, Perc Endo] 453
04CY*	Extir/Lwr Artery 22, 83, 111, 122, 240, 252
04CY[0,3,4]ZZ	Extir/Lwr Artery, [Opn, Perc, Perc Endo] 296
0MCW*	Extir/Lwr Extr Bursa & Lgmt, Lt 143, 343
0MCW[0,3,4]ZZ	Extir/Lwr Extr Bursa & Lgmt, Lt, [Opn, Perc, Perc Endo] 454
0MCV*	Extir/Lwr Extr Bursa & Lgmt, Rt 143, 343
0MCV[0,3,4]ZZ	Extir/Lwr Extr Bursa & Lgmt, Rt, [Opn, Perc, Perc Endo] 454
0QCC*	Extir/Lwr Femur, Lt 130, 415
0QCB*	Extir/Lwr Femur, Rt 130, 415
0KCT*	Extir/Lwr Leg Muscle, Lt 139, 339
0KCT[0,3,4]ZZ	Extir/Lwr Leg Muscle, Lt, [Opn, Perc, Perc Endo] 214, 452
0KCS*	Extir/Lwr Leg Muscle, Rt 139, 339
0KCS[0,3,4]ZZ	Extir/Lwr Leg Muscle, Rt, [Opn, Perc, Perc Endo] 214, 452
0LCP*	Extir/Lwr Leg Tndn, Lt 141, 341
0LCP[0,3,4]ZZ	Extir/Lwr Leg Tndn, Lt, [Opn, Perc, Perc Endo] 453
0LCN*	Extir/Lwr Leg Tndn, Rt 141, 341
0LCN[0,3,4]ZZ	Extir/Lwr Leg Tndn, Rt, [Opn, Perc, Perc Endo] 453
0CC1[0,3]ZZ	Extir/Lwr Lip, [Opn, Perc] 56, 211, 331, 448
0BCB[0,3,4]ZZ	Extir/Lwr Lobe Bronchus, Lt, [Opn, Perc, Perc Endo] 61
0BC6[0,3,4]ZZ	Extir/Lwr Lobe Bronchus, Rt, [Opn, Perc, Perc Endo] 61
0BCJ*	Extir/Lwr Lung Lobe, Lt 61, 331
0BCF*	Extir/Lwr Lung Lobe, Rt 61, 331
06CY*	Extir/Lwr Vein 87, 111, 122, 241, 252, 327
07CD[0,3,4]ZZ	Extir/Lymphatic, Aortic, [Opn, Perc, Perc Endo] 209, 290, 443
07C0[0,3,4]ZZ	Extir/Lymphatic, Head, [Opn, Perc, Perc Endo] 209, 290, 443
07C9[0,3,4]ZZ	Extir/Lymphatic, Int Mammary, Lt, [Opn, Perc, Perc Endo] 209, 290, 443
07C8[0,3,4]ZZ	Extir/Lymphatic, Int Mammary, Rt, [Opn, Perc, Perc Endo] 209, 290, 443
07C6[0,3,4]ZZ	Extir/Lymphatic, Lt Axillary, [Opn, Perc, Perc Endo] 209, 290, 443
07CJ[0,3,4]ZZ	Extir/Lymphatic, Lt Inguinal, [Opn, Perc, Perc Endo] 209, 290, 443
07CG[0,3,4]ZZ	Extir/Lymphatic, Lt Lwr Extr, [Opn, Perc, Perc Endo] 209, 290, 443
07C2[0,3,4]ZZ	Extir/Lymphatic, Lt Neck, [Opn, Perc, Perc Endo] 209, 290, 443
07C4[0,3,4]ZZ	Extir/Lymphatic, Lt Upr Extr, [Opn, Perc, Perc Endo] 209, 290, 443
07CB[0,3,4]ZZ	Extir/Lymphatic, Mesenteric, [Opn, Perc, Perc Endo] 209, 290, 443
07CC[0,3,4]ZZ	Extir/Lymphatic, Pelvis, [Opn, Perc, Perc Endo] 209, 290, 443
07C5[0,3,4]ZZ	Extir/Lymphatic, Rt Axillary, [Opn, Perc, Perc Endo] 209, 290, 443
07CH[0,3,4]ZZ	Extir/Lymphatic, Rt Inguinal, [Opn, Perc, Perc Endo] 209, 290, 443
07CF[0,3,4]ZZ	Extir/Lymphatic, Rt Lwr Extr, [Opn, Perc, Perc Endo] 209, 290, 443
07C1[0,3,4]ZZ	Extir/Lymphatic, Rt Neck, [Opn, Perc, Perc Endo] 209, 290, 443
07C3[0,3,4]ZZ	Extir/Lymphatic, Rt Upr Extr, [Opn, Perc, Perc Endo] 209, 290, 443
07C7[0,3,4]ZZ	Extir/Lymphatic, Thorax, [Opn, Perc, Perc Endo] 209, 290, 443
0BC7[0,3,4]ZZ	Extir/Main Bronchus, Lt, [Opn, Perc, Perc Endo] 61
0BC3[0,3,4]ZZ	Extir/Main Bronchus, Rt, [Opn, Perc, Perc Endo] 61
09CC*	Extir/Mastoid Sinus, Lt 55
09CC[0,3,4]ZZ	Extir/Mastoid Sinus, Lt, [Opn, Perc, Perc Endo] 446
09CB*	Extir/Mastoid Sinus, Rt 55
09CB[0,3,4]ZZ	Extir/Mastoid Sinus, Rt, [Opn, Perc, Perc Endo] 446
09CR*	Extir/Maxillary Sinus, Lt 55
09CQ*	Extir/Maxillary Sinus, Rt 55
0WCC[0,3,4]ZZ	Extir/Mediastinum, [Opn, Perc, Perc Endo] 66, 91, 355
00CD*	Extir/Medulla Oblongata 318, 414
00CD[0,3,4]ZZ	Extir/Medulla Oblongata, [Opn, Perc, Perc Endo] 8, 12, 16
0DCV*	Extir/Mesentery 112, 253, 333
0PCQ*	Extir/Metacarpal, Lt 150
0PCQ[0,3,4]ZZ	Extir/Metacarpal, Lt, [Opn, Perc, Perc Endo] 315
0PCP*	Extir/Metacarpal, Rt 150
0PCP[0,3,4]ZZ	Extir/Metacarpal, Rt, [Opn, Perc, Perc Endo] 315
0RCT*	Extir/Metacarpocarpal Jt, Lt 146
0RCT[0,3,4]ZZ	Extir/Metacarpocarpal Jt, Lt, [Opn, Perc, Perc Endo] 316
0RCS*	Extir/Metacarpocarpal Jt, Rt 146
0RCS[0,3,4]ZZ	Extir/Metacarpocarpal Jt, Rt, [Opn, Perc, Perc Endo] 316
0RCV*	Extir/Metacarpophalangeal Jt, Lt 146
0RCV[0,3,4]ZZ	Extir/Metacarpophalangeal Jt, Lt, [Opn, Perc, Perc Endo] 316
0RCU*	Extir/Metacarpophalangeal Jt, Rt 146
0RCU[0,3,4]ZZ	Extir/Metacarpophalangeal Jt, Rt, [Opn, Perc, Perc Endo] 316
0SCN*	Extir/Metatarsal-Phalangeal Jt, Lt 145, 351
0SCN[0,3,4]ZZ	Extir/Metatarsal-Phalangeal Jt, Lt, [Opn, Perc, Perc Endo] 457
0SCM*	Extir/Metatarsal-Phalangeal Jt, Rt 145, 351
0SCM[0,3,4]ZZ	Extir/Metatarsal-Phalangeal Jt, Rt, [Opn, Perc, Perc Endo] 457
0SCL*	Extir/Metatarsal-Tarsal Jt, Lt 145, 351
0SCL[0,3,4]ZZ	Extir/Metatarsal-Tarsal Jt, Lt, [Opn, Perc, Perc Endo] 457
0SCK*	Extir/Metatarsal-Tarsal Jt, Rt 145, 351
0SCK[0,3,4]ZZ	Extir/Metatarsal-Tarsal Jt, Rt, [Opn, Perc, Perc Endo] 457
0QCP*	Extir/Metatarsal, Lt 145
0QCN*	Extir/Metatarsal, Rt 145
0BC5[0,3,4]ZZ	Extir/Mid Lobe Bronchus, Rt, [Opn, Perc, Perc Endo] 61
0BCD*	Extir/Mid Lung Lobe, Rt 61, 331
02CG[3,4]ZZ	Extir/Mitral Valve, [Perc, Perc Endo] 93
09CN*	Extir/Nasopharynx 51, 330
0KC3*	Extir/Neck Muscle, Lt 54, 139, 339
0KC3[0,3,4]ZZ	Extir/Neck Muscle, Lt, [Opn, Perc, Perc Endo] 214, 451
0KC2*	Extir/Neck Muscle, Rt 54, 139, 339
0KC2[0,3,4]ZZ	Extir/Neck Muscle, Rt, [Opn, Perc, Perc Endo] 214, 451
0NC8*	Extir/Occipital Bone, Lt 10, 48, 344, 415
0NC8[0,3,4]ZZ	Extir/Occipital Bone, Lt, [Opn, Perc, Perc Endo] 14, 18, 301
0NC7*	Extir/Occipital Bone, Rt 10, 48, 344, 415
0NC7[0,3,4]ZZ	Extir/Occipital Bone, Rt, [Opn, Perc, Perc Endo] 14, 18, 301
0RC0*	Extir/Occipital-cervical Jt 156
00CH*	Extir/Oculomotor Nerve 23
00CF*	Extir/Olfactory Nerve 23
00CG*	Extir/Optic Nerve 23
0WC3[0,3,4]ZZ	Extir/Oral Cavity and Throat, [Opn, Perc, Perc Endo] 56, 217, 355, 460
0NCQ*	Extir/Orbit, Lt 54
0NCP*	Extir/Orbit, Rt 54
0UC2*	Extir/Ovaries, Bilat 263, 264, 266
0UC1*	Extir/Ovary, Lt 263, 264, 266
0UC0*	Extir/Ovary, Rt 263, 264, 266
0NCL*	Extir/Palatine Bone, Lt 54
0NCK*	Extir/Palatine Bone, Rt 54
0FCG*	Extir/Pancreas 119
0FCD[0,7]ZZ	Extir/Pancreatic Duct, [Opn, Via Natrl or Artfcl Opng] 119
0FCF[0,7]ZZ	Extir/Pancreatic Duct, Accessory, [Opn, Via Natrl or Artfcl Opng] 119
02CD[0,3,4]ZZ	Extir/Papillary Muscle, [Opn, Perc, Perc Endo] 74
0GCR*	Extir/Parathyroid Gland 53, 238, 336
0GCR[0,3,4]ZZ	Extir/Parathyroid Gland, [Opn, Perc, Perc Endo] 211
0GCQ*	Extir/Parathyroid Glands, Multi 53, 238, 336
0GCQ[0,3,4]ZZ	Extir/Parathyroid Glands, Multi, [Opn, Perc, Perc Endo] 211
0NC4*	Extir/Parietal Bone, Lt 9, 48, 344, 415
0NC4[0,3,4]ZZ	Extir/Parietal Bone, Lt, [Opn, Perc, Perc Endo] 14, 18, 301
0NC3*	Extir/Parietal Bone, Rt 9, 48, 344, 415
0NC3[0,3,4]ZZ	Extir/Parietal Bone, Rt, [Opn, Perc, Perc Endo] 14, 18, 301
0QCF*	Extir/Patella, Lt 132
0QCD*	Extir/Patella, Rt 132

0QC3*	Extir/Pelvic Bone, Lt 156
0QC2*	Extir/Pelvic Bone, Rt 156
0WCJ[0,3,4]ZZ	Extir/Pelvic Cavity, [Opn, Perc, Perc Endo] 91, 113, 254, 302, 355
0WCJ[3,4]ZZ	Extir/Pelvic Cavity, [Perc, Perc Endo] 123, 217
0VCS[0,3,4]ZZ	Extir/Penis, [Opn, Perc, Perc Endo] 257, 459
0WCD[0,3,4]ZZ	Extir/Pericardial Cavity, [Opn, Perc, Perc Endo] 62, 98, 302, 355
02CN*	Extir/Pericardium 60, 319
02CN[0,3,4]ZZ	Extir/Pericardium, [Opn, Perc, Perc Endo] 93, 296
0MCK*	Extir/Perineum Bursa & Lgmt 143, 343
0MCK[0,3,4]ZZ	Extir/Perineum Bursa & Lgmt, [Opn, Perc, Perc Endo] 454
0KCM*	Extir/Perineum Muscle 139, 339
0KCM[0,3,4]ZZ	Extir/Perineum Muscle, [Opn, Perc, Perc Endo] 214, 452
0LCH*	Extir/Perineum Tndn 141, 341
0LCH[0,3,4]ZZ	Extir/Perineum Tndn, [Opn, Perc, Perc Endo] 453
0WCG[0,3,4]ZZ	Extir/Peritoneal Cavity, [Opn, Perc, Perc Endo] 113, 254, 355
0DCW*	Extir/Peritoneum 112, 253, 333
04CU*	Extir/Peroneal Artery, Lt 83, 240
04CU[0,3,4]ZZ	Extir/Peroneal Artery, Lt, [Opn, Perc, Perc Endo] 296
04CT*	Extir/Peroneal Artery, Rt 83, 240
04CT[0,3,4]ZZ	Extir/Peroneal Artery, Rt, [Opn, Perc, Perc Endo] 296
0CCM[0,3,4]ZZ	Extir/Pharynx, [Opn, Perc, Perc Endo] 52, 331
0GC1*	Extir/Pineal Body 235
0GC1[0,3,4]ZZ	Extir/Pineal Body, [Opn, Perc, Perc Endo] 9, 13, 17
0GC0*	Extir/Pituitary Gland 235
0GC0[0,3,4]ZZ	Extir/Pituitary Gland, [Opn, Perc, Perc Endo] 9, 13, 17, 211
00CB*	Extir/Pons 318, 414
00CB[0,3,4]ZZ	Extir/Pons, [Opn, Perc, Perc Endo] 8, 12, 16
04CN*	Extir/Popliteal Artery, Lt 83, 240
04CN[0,3,4]ZZ	Extir/Popliteal Artery, Lt, [Opn, Perc, Perc Endo] 296
04CM*	Extir/Popliteal Artery, Rt 83, 240
04CM[0,3,4]ZZ	Extir/Popliteal Artery, Rt, [Opn, Perc, Perc Endo] 296
06C8[0,3,4]ZZ	Extir/Portal Vein, [Opn, Perc, Perc Endo] 97
04CS[0,3,4]ZZ	Extir/Post Tibial Artery, Lt, [Opn, Perc, Perc Endo] 296
04CR[0,3,4]ZZ	Extir/Post Tibial Artery, Rt, [Opn, Perc, Perc Endo] 296
04CS*	Extir/Posterior Tibial Artery, Lt 83, 240
04CR*	Extir/Posterior Tibial Artery, Rt 83, 240
0VCT*	Extir/Prepuce 257
0VCT[0,3,4,X]ZZ	Extir/Prepuce, [Opn, Perc, Perc Endo, Ext] 459
0VC0*	Extir/Prostate 260, 440
02CR*	Extir/Pulmn Artery, Lt 60, 319
02CR[0,3,4]ZZ	Extir/Pulmn Artery, Lt, [Opn, Perc, Perc Endo] 93
02CQ*	Extir/Pulmn Artery, Rt 60, 319
02CQ[0,3,4]ZZ	Extir/Pulmn Artery, Rt, [Opn, Perc, Perc Endo] 93
02CP*	Extir/Pulmn Trunk 60, 319
02CP[0,3,4]ZZ	Extir/Pulmn Trunk, [Opn, Perc, Perc Endo] 93
02CH[3,4]ZZ	Extir/Pulmn Valve, [Perc, Perc Endo] 93
02CT*	Extir/Pulmn Vein, Lt 60, 319
02CT[0,3,4]ZZ	Extir/Pulmn Vein, Lt, [Opn, Perc, Perc Endo] 93
02CS*	Extir/Pulmn Vein, Rt 60, 319
02CS[0,3,4]ZZ	Extir/Pulmn Vein, Rt, [Opn, Perc, Perc Endo] 93
03CC*	Extir/Radial Artery, Lt 81, 239
03CB*	Extir/Radial Artery, Rt 81, 239
0PCJ*	Extir/Radius, Lt 148, 345
0PCH*	Extir/Radius, Rt 148, 345
0DCP[0,3,4]ZZ	Extir/Rectum, [Opn, Perc, Perc Endo] 109, 333
04CA*	Extir/Renal Artery, Lt 111, 252
04CA[0,3,4]ZZ	Extir/Renal Artery, Lt, [Opn, Perc, Perc Endo] 95
04C9*	Extir/Renal Artery, Rt 111, 252
04C9[0,3,4]ZZ	Extir/Renal Artery, Rt, [Opn, Perc, Perc Endo] 95
06CB*	Extir/Renal Vein, Lt 252
06CB[0,3,4]ZZ	Extir/Renal Vein, Lt, [Opn, Perc, Perc Endo] 97
06C9*	Extir/Renal Vein, Rt 252
06C9[0,3,4]ZZ	Extir/Renal Vein, Rt, [Opn, Perc, Perc Endo] 97
0WCQ[7,8]ZZ	Extir/Respiratory Tract, [Via Natrl or Artfcl Opng, Via Natrl or Artfcl Opng Endo] 66, 355
08CF*	Extir/Retina, Lt 44, 329
08CF[3,X]ZZ	Extir/Retina, Lt, [Perc, Ext] 444
08CE*	Extir/Retina, Rt 44, 329
08CE[3,X]ZZ	Extir/Retina, Rt, [Perc, Ext] 444

08CH*	Extir/Retinal Vessel, Lt 44, 329
08CH[3,X]ZZ	Extir/Retinal Vessel, Lt, [Perc, Ext] 444
08CG*	Extir/Retinal Vessel, Rt 44, 329
08CG[3,X]ZZ	Extir/Retinal Vessel, Rt, [Perc, Ext] 444
0PC2*	Extir/Rib, Lt 65, 155, 345
0PC1*	Extir/Rib, Rt 65, 155, 345
01CP*	Extir/Sacral Sympathetic Nerve 89
0SC5*	Extir/Sacrococcygeal Jt 157
0SC8*	Extir/Sacroiliac Jt, Lt 157
0SC7*	Extir/Sacroiliac Jt, Rt 157
0QC1*	Extir/Sacrum 156
0PC6*	Extir/Scapula, Lt 65, 155, 345
0PC5*	Extir/Scapula, Rt 65, 155, 345
0VC2*	Extir/Seminal Vesicle, Lt 260
0VC1*	Extir/Seminal Vesicle, Rt 260
0VC3*	Extir/Seminal Vesicles, Bilat 260
0MC2*	Extir/Shldr Bursa & Lgmt, Lt 143, 343
0MC2[0,3,4]ZZ	Extir/Shldr Bursa & Lgmt, Lt, [Opn, Perc, Perc Endo] 454
0MC1*	Extir/Shldr Bursa & Lgmt, Rt 143, 343
0MC1[0,3,4]ZZ	Extir/Shldr Bursa & Lgmt, Rt, [Opn, Perc, Perc Endo] 454
0RCK*	Extir/Shldr Jt, Lt 147, 349
0RCJ*	Extir/Shldr Jt, Rt 147, 349
0KC6*	Extir/Shldr Muscle, Lt 139, 339
0KC6[0,3,4]ZZ	Extir/Shldr Muscle, Lt, [Opn, Perc, Perc Endo] 214, 451
0KC5*	Extir/Shldr Muscle, Rt 139, 339
0KC5[0,3,4]ZZ	Extir/Shldr Muscle, Rt, [Opn, Perc, Perc Endo] 214, 451
0LC2*	Extir/Shldr Tndn, Lt 141, 341
0LC2[0,3,4]ZZ	Extir/Shldr Tndn, Lt, [Opn, Perc, Perc Endo] 453
0LC1*	Extir/Shldr Tndn, Rt 141, 341
0LC1[0,3,4]ZZ	Extir/Shldr Tndn, Rt, [Opn, Perc, Perc Endo] 453
0DCN[0,3,4]ZZ	Extir/Sigmoid Colon, [Opn, Perc, Perc Endo] 109, 333
0DC8[0,3,4]ZZ	Extir/Sm Intestine, [Opn, Perc, Perc Endo] 109, 300, 333
0CC3[0,3]ZZ	Extir/Soft Palate, [Opn, Perc] 56
0VCG*	Extir/Spermatic Cord, Lt 257
0VCF*	Extir/Spermatic Cord, Rt 257
0VCH*	Extir/Spermatic Cords, Bilat 257
0NCD*	Extir/Sphenoid Bone, Lt 54
0NCC*	Extir/Sphenoid Bone, Rt 54
09CX*	Extir/Sphenoid Sinus, Lt 55
09CW*	Extir/Sphenoid Sinus, Rt 55
00CT*	Extir/Spinal Meninges 318
00CT[0,3,4]ZZ	Extir/Spinal Meninges, [Opn, Perc, Perc Endo] 19
04C4*	Extir/Splenic Artery 111, 252
04C4[0,3,4]ZZ	Extir/Splenic Artery, [Opn, Perc, Perc Endo] 95
06C1[0,3,4]ZZ	Extir/Splenic Vein, [Opn, Perc, Perc Endo] 97
0RCF*	Extir/Sternoclavicular Jt, Lt 147, 349
0RCE*	Extir/Sternoclavicular Jt, Rt 147, 349
0PC0*	Extir/Sternum 65, 155, 345
0DC6[0,3,4]ZZ	Extir/Stomach, [Opn, Perc, Perc Endo] 105, 123, 333
0DC7[0,3,4]ZZ	Extir/Stomach, Pylorus, [Opn, Perc, Perc Endo] 105
00C5*	Extir/Subarachnoid Space 318, 414
00C5[0,3,4]ZZ	Extir/Subarachnoid Space, [Opn, Perc, Perc Endo] 8, 12, 16, 295
03C4*	Extir/Subclavian Artery, Lt 60
03C4[0,3,4]ZZ	Extir/Subclavian Artery, Lt, [Opn, Perc, Perc Endo] 93
03C3*	Extir/Subclavian Artery, Rt 60
03C3[0,3,4]ZZ	Extir/Subclavian Artery, Rt, [Opn, Perc, Perc Endo] 93
05C6*	Extir/Subclavian Vein, Lt 60
05C6[0,3,4]ZZ	Extir/Subclavian Vein, Lt, [Opn, Perc, Perc Endo] 97
05C5*	Extir/Subclavian Vein, Rt 60
05C5[0,3,4]ZZ	Extir/Subclavian Vein, Rt, [Opn, Perc, Perc Endo] 97
00C4*	Extir/Subdural Space 318, 414
00C4[0,3,4]ZZ	Extir/Subdural Space, [Opn, Perc, Perc Endo] 8, 12, 16, 295
04C5*	Extir/Superior Mesenteric Artery 111, 252
04C5[0,3,4]ZZ	Extir/Superior Mesenteric Artery, [Opn, Perc, Perc Endo] 95
06C5[0,3,4]ZZ	Extir/Superior Mesenteric Vein, [Opn, Perc, Perc Endo] 97
0GCM*	Extir/Superior Parathyroid Gland, Lt 53, 238, 336
0GCM[0,3,4]ZZ	Extir/Superior Parathyroid Gland, Lt, [Opn, Perc, Perc Endo] 211
0GCL*	Extir/Superior Parathyroid Gland, Rt 53, 238, 336

ØGCL[Ø,3,4]ZZ	Extir/Superior Parathyroid Gland, Rt, [Opn, Perc, Perc Endo] 211
Ø2CV*	Extir/Superior Vena Cava 60, 319
Ø2CV[Ø,3,4]ZZ	Extir/Superior Vena Cava, [Opn, Perc, Perc Endo] 93
ØSCJ*	Extir/Tarsal Jt, Lt 145, 351
ØSCJ[Ø,3,4]ZZ	Extir/Tarsal Jt, Lt, [Opn, Perc, Perc Endo] 457
ØSCH*	Extir/Tarsal Jt, Rt 145, 351
ØSCH[Ø,3,4]ZZ	Extir/Tarsal Jt, Rt, [Opn, Perc, Perc Endo] 457
ØQCM*	Extir/Tarsal, Lt 145
ØQCL*	Extir/Tarsal, Rt 145
Ø3CT[3,4]ZZ	Extir/Temporal Artery, Lt, [Perc, Perc Endo] 9, 13, 17
Ø3CS[3,4]ZZ	Extir/Temporal Artery, Rt, [Perc, Perc Endo] 9, 13, 17
ØNC6*	Extir/Temporal Bone, Lt 9, 48, 344, 415
ØNC6[Ø,3,4]ZZ	Extir/Temporal Bone, Lt, [Opn, Perc, Perc Endo] 14, 18, 301
ØNC5*	Extir/Temporal Bone, Rt 9, 48, 344, 415
ØNC5[Ø,3,4]ZZ	Extir/Temporal Bone, Rt, [Opn, Perc, Perc Endo] 14, 18, 301
ØRCD*	Extir/Temporomandibular Jt, Lt 49, 156, 349
ØRCC*	Extir/Temporomandibular Jt, Rt 49, 156, 349
ØVCC*	Extir/Testes, Bilat 257, 354
ØVCB*	Extir/Testis, Lt 257, 354
ØVC9*	Extir/Testis, Rt 257, 354
ØØC9*	Extir/Thalamus 318, 414
ØØC9[Ø,3,4]ZZ	Extir/Thalamus, [Opn, Perc, Perc Endo] 8, 12, 16, 295
Ø2CW*	Extir/Thoracic Aorta 110, 319
Ø2CW[Ø,3,4]ZZ	Extir/Thoracic Aorta, [Opn, Perc, Perc Endo] 92
Ø7CK[Ø,3,4]ZZ	Extir/Thoracic Duct, [Opn, Perc, Perc Endo] 209, 290, 443
ØØCX*	Extir/Thoracic Spinal Cord 318
ØØCX[Ø,3,4]ZZ	Extir/Thoracic Spinal Cord, [Opn, Perc, Perc Endo] 19
Ø1CL*	Extir/Thoracic Sympathetic Nerve 89
ØRC9*	Extir/Thoracic Vert Disc 156
ØRC6*	Extir/Thoracic Vert Jt 156
ØPC4*	Extir/Thoracic Vertebra 155, 345
ØRCB*	Extir/Thoracolumbar Vert Disc 156
ØRCA*	Extir/Thoracolumbar Vert Jt 156
ØMCG*	Extir/Thorax Bursa & Lgmt, Lt 143, 343
ØMCG[Ø,3,4]ZZ	Extir/Thorax Bursa & Lgmt, Lt, [Opn, Perc, Perc Endo] 454
ØMCF*	Extir/Thorax Bursa & Lgmt, Rt 143, 343
ØMCF[Ø,3,4]ZZ	Extir/Thorax Bursa & Lgmt, Rt, [Opn, Perc, Perc Endo] 454
ØKCJ*	Extir/Thorax Muscle, Lt 139, 339
ØKCJ[Ø,3,4]ZZ	Extir/Thorax Muscle, Lt, [Opn, Perc, Perc Endo] 214, 452
ØKCH*	Extir/Thorax Muscle, Rt 139, 339
ØKCH[Ø,3,4]ZZ	Extir/Thorax Muscle, Rt, [Opn, Perc, Perc Endo] 214, 452
ØLCD*	Extir/Thorax Tndn, Lt 141, 341
ØLCD[Ø,3,4]ZZ	Extir/Thorax Tndn, Lt, [Opn, Perc, Perc Endo] 453
ØLCC*	Extir/Thorax Tndn, Rt 141, 341
ØLCC[Ø,3,4]ZZ	Extir/Thorax Tndn, Rt, [Opn, Perc, Perc Endo] 453
ØPCS*	Extir/Thumb Phalanx, Lt 155, 345
ØPCR*	Extir/Thumb Phalanx, Rt 155, 345
Ø7CM*	Extir/Thymus 60, 241, 328
Ø7CM[Ø,3,4]ZZ	Extir/Thymus, [Opn, Perc, Perc Endo] 290, 298
Ø3CV[3,4]ZZ	Extir/Thyroid Artery, Lt, [Perc, Perc Endo] 9, 13, 17
Ø3CU[3,4]ZZ	Extir/Thyroid Artery, Rt, [Perc, Perc Endo] 9, 13, 17
ØGCK*	Extir/Thyroid Gland 53, 238, 336
ØGCG*	Extir/Thyroid Gland Lobe, Lt 53, 238, 336
ØGCG[Ø,3,4]ZZ	Extir/Thyroid Gland Lobe, Lt, [Opn, Perc, Perc Endo] 211
ØGCH*	Extir/Thyroid Gland Lobe, Rt 53, 238, 336
ØGCH[Ø,3,4]ZZ	Extir/Thyroid Gland Lobe, Rt, [Opn, Perc, Perc Endo] 211
ØGCK[Ø,3,4]ZZ	Extir/Thyroid Gland, [Opn, Perc, Perc Endo] 211
ØQCH*	Extir/Tibia, Lt 133
ØQCG*	Extir/Tibia, Rt 133
ØSCQ*	Extir/Toe Phalangeal Jt, Lt 145, 351
ØSCQ[Ø,3,4]ZZ	Extir/Toe Phalangeal Jt, Lt, [Opn, Perc, Perc Endo] 457
ØSCP*	Extir/Toe Phalangeal Jt, Rt 145, 351
ØSCP[Ø,3,4]ZZ	Extir/Toe Phalangeal Jt, Rt, [Opn, Perc, Perc Endo] 457
ØQCR*	Extir/Toe Phalanx, Lt 156
ØQCQ*	Extir/Toe Phalanx, Rt 156
ØCC7[Ø,3]ZZ	Extir/Tongue, [Opn, Perc] 56
ØKC4*	Extir/Tongue, Palate, Pharynx Muscle 139, 339
ØKC4[Ø,3,4]ZZ	Extir/Tongue, Palate, Pharynx Muscle, [Opn, Perc, Perc Endo] 214, 451
ØCCP[Ø,3]ZZ	Extir/Tonsils, [Opn, Perc] 52, 331
ØBC1[Ø,3,4]ZZ	Extir/Trachea, [Opn, Perc, Perc Endo] 64
ØDCL[Ø,3,4]ZZ	Extir/Transv Colon, [Opn, Perc, Perc Endo] 109, 333
Ø2CJ[3,4]ZZ	Extir/Tricuspid Valve, [Perc, Perc Endo] 93
ØØCK*	Extir/Trigeminal Nerve 23
ØØCJ*	Extir/Trochlear Nerve 23
ØMCD*	Extir/Trunk Bursa & Lgmt, Lt 143, 343
ØMCD[Ø,3,4]ZZ	Extir/Trunk Bursa & Lgmt, Lt, [Opn, Perc, Perc Endo] 454
ØMCC*	Extir/Trunk Bursa & Lgmt, Rt 143, 343
ØMCC[Ø,3,4]ZZ	Extir/Trunk Bursa & Lgmt, Rt, [Opn, Perc, Perc Endo] 454
ØKCG*	Extir/Trunk Muscle, Lt 139, 339
ØKCG[Ø,3,4]ZZ	Extir/Trunk Muscle, Lt, [Opn, Perc, Perc Endo] 214, 452
ØKCF*	Extir/Trunk Muscle, Rt 139, 339
ØKCF[Ø,3,4]ZZ	Extir/Trunk Muscle, Rt, [Opn, Perc, Perc Endo] 214, 451
ØLCB*	Extir/Trunk Tndn, Lt 141, 341
ØLCB[Ø,3,4]ZZ	Extir/Trunk Tndn, Lt, [Opn, Perc, Perc Endo] 453
ØLC9*	Extir/Trunk Tndn, Rt 141, 341
ØLC9[Ø,3,4]ZZ	Extir/Trunk Tndn, Rt, [Opn, Perc, Perc Endo] 453
ØPCL*	Extir/Ulna, Lt 148, 345
ØPCK*	Extir/Ulna, Rt 148, 345
Ø3CA*	Extir/Ulnar Artery, Lt 81, 239
Ø3C9*	Extir/Ulnar Artery, Rt 81, 239
ØKC8*	Extir/Upr Arm Muscle, Lt 139, 339
ØKC8[Ø,3,4]ZZ	Extir/Upr Arm Muscle, Lt, [Opn, Perc, Perc Endo] 214, 451
ØKC7*	Extir/Upr Arm Muscle, Rt 139, 339
ØKC7[Ø,3,4]ZZ	Extir/Upr Arm Muscle, Rt, [Opn, Perc, Perc Endo] 214, 451
ØLC4*	Extir/Upr Arm Tndn, Lt 141, 341
ØLC4[Ø,3,4]ZZ	Extir/Upr Arm Tndn, Lt, [Opn, Perc, Perc Endo] 453
ØLC3*	Extir/Upr Arm Tndn, Rt 141, 341
ØLC3[Ø,3,4]ZZ	Extir/Upr Arm Tndn, Rt, [Opn, Perc, Perc Endo] 453
Ø3CY*	Extir/Upr Artery 21, 81, 110, 122, 239, 251
ØMCB*	Extir/Upr Extr Bursa & Lgmt, Lt 143, 343
ØMCB[Ø,3,4]ZZ	Extir/Upr Extr Bursa & Lgmt, Lt, [Opn, Perc, Perc Endo] 454
ØMC9*	Extir/Upr Extr Bursa & Lgmt, Rt 143, 343
ØMC9[Ø,3,4]ZZ	Extir/Upr Extr Bursa & Lgmt, Rt, [Opn, Perc, Perc Endo] 454
ØQC7*	Extir/Upr Femur, Lt 130, 415
ØQC6*	Extir/Upr Femur, Rt 130, 415
ØKCR*	Extir/Upr Leg Muscle, Lt 139, 339
ØKCR[Ø,3,4]ZZ	Extir/Upr Leg Muscle, Lt, [Opn, Perc, Perc Endo] 214, 452
ØKCQ*	Extir/Upr Leg Muscle, Rt 139, 339
ØKCQ[Ø,3,4]ZZ	Extir/Upr Leg Muscle, Rt, [Opn, Perc, Perc Endo] 214, 452
ØLCM*	Extir/Upr Leg Tndn, Lt 141, 341
ØLCM[Ø,3,4]ZZ	Extir/Upr Leg Tndn, Lt, [Opn, Perc, Perc Endo] 453
ØLCL*	Extir/Upr Leg Tndn, Rt 141, 341
ØLCL[Ø,3,4]ZZ	Extir/Upr Leg Tndn, Rt, [Opn, Perc, Perc Endo] 453
ØCCØ[Ø,3]ZZ	Extir/Upr Lip, [Opn, Perc] 56, 211, 331, 448
ØBC8[Ø,3,4]ZZ	Extir/Upr Lobe Bronchus, Lt, [Opn, Perc, Perc Endo] 61
ØBC4[Ø,3,4]ZZ	Extir/Upr Lobe Bronchus, Rt, [Opn, Perc, Perc Endo] 61
ØBCG*	Extir/Upr Lung Lobe, Lt 61, 331
ØBCC*	Extir/Upr Lung Lobe, Rt 61, 331
Ø5CY*	Extir/Upr Vein 85, 111, 122, 240, 252, 325
ØTC7[Ø,3,4,7,8]ZZ	Extir/Ureter, Lt, [Opn, Perc, Perc Endo, Via Natrl or Artfcl Opng, Via Natrl or Artfcl Opng Endo] 458
ØTC7[Ø,3,4]ZZ	Extir/Ureter, Lt, [Opn, Perc, Perc Endo] 249
ØTC7[7,8]ZZ	Extir/Ureter, Lt, [Via Natrl or Artfcl Opng, Via Natrl or Artfcl Opng Endo] 250, 353
ØTC6[Ø,3,4,7,8]ZZ	Extir/Ureter, Rt, [Opn, Perc, Perc Endo, Via Natrl or Artfcl Opng, Via Natrl or Artfcl Opng Endo] 458
ØTC6[Ø,3,4]ZZ	Extir/Ureter, Rt, [Opn, Perc, Perc Endo] 249
ØTC6[7,8]ZZ	Extir/Ureter, Rt, [Via Natrl or Artfcl Opng, Via Natrl or Artfcl Opng Endo] 250, 353
ØTCD[Ø,3,4]ZZ	Extir/Urethra, [Opn, Perc, Perc Endo] 250, 353, 458
ØUC4*	Extir/Uterine Supporting Structure 267
ØUC9[Ø,3,4]ZZ	Extir/Uterus, [Opn, Perc, Perc Endo] 263, 264, 266, 272, 354
ØCCN[Ø,3]ZZ	Extir/Uvula, [Opn, Perc] 56, 448
ØUCG[Ø,3,4]ZZ	Extir/Vagina, [Opn, Perc, Perc Endo] 267, 275, 459
ØØCQ*	Extir/Vagus Nerve 23
Ø2CL[Ø,3,4]ZZ	Extir/Ventricle, Lt, [Opn, Perc, Perc Endo] 74
Ø2CK[Ø,3,4]ZZ	Extir/Ventricle, Rt, [Opn, Perc, Perc Endo] 74
Ø2CM[Ø,3,4]ZZ	Extir/Ventricular Septum, [Opn, Perc, Perc Endo] 74

Ø3CQ[3,4]ZZ	Extir/Vert Artery, Lt, [Perc, Perc Endo] 9, 13, 17
Ø3CP[3,4]ZZ	Extir/Vert Artery, Rt, [Perc, Perc Endo] 9, 13, 17
Ø5CS*	Extir/Vert Vein, Lt 25, 51, 85, 240, 325
Ø5CR*	Extir/Vert Vein, Rt 25, 51, 85, 240, 325
ØUCL*	Extir/Vestibular Gland 267, 272
ØUCL[Ø,X]ZZ	Extir/Vestibular Gland, [Opn, Ext] 459
Ø8C5*	Extir/Vitreous, Lt 44, 329
Ø8C5[3,X]ZZ	Extir/Vitreous, Lt, [Perc, Ext] 444
Ø8C4*	Extir/Vitreous, Rt 44, 329
Ø8C4[3,X]ZZ	Extir/Vitreous, Rt, [Perc, Ext] 444
ØCCV*	Extir/Vocal Cord, Lt 52
ØCCT*	Extir/Vocal Cord, Rt 52
ØMC6*	Extir/Wrist Bursa & Lgmt, Lt 146
ØMC6[Ø,3,4]ZZ	Extir/Wrist Bursa & Lgmt, Lt, [Opn, Perc, Perc Endo] 315
ØMC5*	Extir/Wrist Bursa & Lgmt, Rt 146
ØMC5[Ø,3,4]ZZ	Extir/Wrist Bursa & Lgmt, Rt, [Opn, Perc, Perc Endo] 315
ØRCP*	Extir/Wrist Jt, Lt 146
ØRCP[Ø,3,4]ZZ	Extir/Wrist Jt, Lt, [Opn, Perc, Perc Endo] 316
ØRCN*	Extir/Wrist Jt, Rt 146
ØRCN[Ø,3,4]ZZ	Extir/Wrist Jt, Rt, [Opn, Perc, Perc Endo] 316
ØNCN*	Extir/Zygomatic Bone, Lt 54
ØNCM*	Extir/Zygomatic Bone, Rt 54
X2CØ361	Extirpate matter from 1 Cor Art, Orbit Athrect, New Tech 1 75, 78, 79, 80
X2C1361	Extirpate matter from 2 Cor Art, Orbit Athrect, New Tech 1 75, 78, 79, 80
X2C2361	Extirpate matter from 3 Cor Art, Orbit Athrect, New Tech 1 75, 78, 79, 80
X2C3361	Extirpate matter from 4+ Cor Art, Orbit Athrect, New Tech 1 75, 78, 79, 80
5A15223	Extracorporeal Membrane Oxygenation, Continuous 1
Ø8D[J,K]3ZZ	Extract of [Rt, Lt] Lens, Perc Appr 44
ØJD83ZZ	Extract of Abd SQ/Fascia, Perc Appr 223
ØJD73ZZ	Extract of Back SQ/Fascia, Perc Appr 223
ØJD93ZZ	Extract of Buttock SQ/Fascia, Perc Appr 223
ØJD63ZZ	Extract of Chest SQ/Fascia, Perc Appr 223
Ø9DAØZZ	Extract of Lt Auditory Ossicle, Opn Appr 446
Ø8DK3ZZ	Extract of Lt Lens, Perc Appr 241, 444
ØJDM3ZZ	Extract of Lt Up Leg SQ/Fascia, Perc Appr 223
Ø9D9ØZZ	Extract of Rt Auditory Ossicle, Opn Appr 446
Ø8DJ3ZZ	Extract of Rt Lens, Perc Appr 241, 444
ØJDL3ZZ	Extract of Rt Up Leg SQ/Fascia, Perc Appr 223
Ø9D[9,A]ØZZ	Extract, [Rt Auditory Ossicle, Lt Auditory Ossicle], Opn 51
ØMDJ*	Extract/Abd Bursa & Lgmt, Lt 144, 343
ØMDJ[Ø,3,4]ZZ	Extract/Abd Bursa & Lgmt, Lt, [Opn, Perc, Perc Endo] 454
ØMDH*	Extract/Abd Bursa & Lgmt, Rt 144, 343
ØMDH[Ø,3,4]ZZ	Extract/Abd Bursa & Lgmt, Rt, [Opn, Perc, Perc Endo] 454
Ø1DM*	Extract/Abd Sympathetic Nerve 89
ØØDL*	Extract/Abducens Nerve 23, 50, 151, 318
ØØDL[Ø,3,4]ZZ	Extract/Abducens Nerve, [Opn, Perc, Perc Endo] 440
ØØDR*	Extract/Accessory Nerve 23, 50, 151, 318
ØØDR[Ø,3,4]ZZ	Extract/Accessory Nerve, [Opn, Perc, Perc Endo] 440
Ø9DP*	Extract/Accessory Sinus 55
ØØDN*	Extract/Acoustic Nerve 23, 50, 151, 318
ØØDN[Ø,3,4]ZZ	Extract/Acoustic Nerve, [Opn, Perc, Perc Endo] 440
ØMDR*	Extract/Ankle Bursa & Lgmt, Lt 144, 343
ØMDR[Ø,3,4]ZZ	Extract/Ankle Bursa & Lgmt, Lt, [Opn, Perc, Perc Endo] 454
ØMDQ*	Extract/Ankle Bursa & Lgmt, Rt 144, 343
ØMDQ[Ø,3,4]ZZ	Extract/Ankle Bursa & Lgmt, Rt, [Opn, Perc, Perc Endo] 454
Ø1D3*	Extract/Brachial Plexus 152, 319
Ø1D3[Ø,3,4]ZZ	Extract/Brachial Plexus, [Opn, Perc, Perc Endo] 441
ØØD1*	Extract/Cerebral Meninges 414
ØØD1[Ø,3,4]ZZ	Extract/Cerebral Meninges, [Opn, Perc, Perc Endo] 8, 12, 16, 295
Ø1D1*	Extract/Cervical Nerve 151, 319
Ø1D1[Ø,3,4]ZZ	Extract/Cervical Nerve, [Opn, Perc, Perc Endo] 441
Ø1DØ*	Extract/Cervical Plexus 151, 319
Ø1DØ[Ø,3,4]ZZ	Extract/Cervical Plexus, [Opn, Perc, Perc Endo] 441
Ø8D9*	Extract/Cornea, Lt 43
Ø8D9XZ[X,Z]	Extract/Cornea, Lt, Ext, No Dev, [Dx, NQ] 444
Ø8D8*	Extract/Cornea, Rt 43
Ø8D8XZ[X,Z]	Extract/Cornea, Rt, Ext, No Dev, [Dx, NQ] 444
ØØD2*	Extract/Dura Mater 414
ØØD2[Ø,3,4]ZZ	Extract/Dura Mater, [Opn, Perc, Perc Endo] 8, 12, 16, 295
ØMD4*	Extract/Elbow Bursa & Lgmt, Lt 143, 343
ØMD4[Ø,3,4]ZZ	Extract/Elbow Bursa & Lgmt, Lt, [Opn, Perc, Perc Endo] 454
ØMD3*	Extract/Elbow Bursa & Lgmt, Rt 143, 343
ØMD3[Ø,3,4]ZZ	Extract/Elbow Bursa & Lgmt, Rt, [Opn, Perc, Perc Endo] 454
ØUDB*	Extract/Endometrium 266, 272
ØUDB[7,8]Z[X,Z]	Extract/Endometrium, [Via Natrl or Artfcl Opng, Via Natrl or Artfcl Opng Endo], No Dev, [Dx, NQ] 271, 459
Ø9DV*	Extract/Ethmoid Sinus, Lt 55
Ø9DV[Ø,3,4]ZZ	Extract/Ethmoid Sinus, Lt, [Opn, Perc, Perc Endo] 447
Ø9DU*	Extract/Ethmoid Sinus, Rt 55
Ø9DU[Ø,3,4]ZZ	Extract/Ethmoid Sinus, Rt, [Opn, Perc, Perc Endo] 447
ØØDM*	Extract/Facial Nerve 23, 50, 151, 318
ØØDM[Ø,3,4]ZZ	Extract/Facial Nerve, [Opn, Perc, Perc Endo] 440
Ø1DD*	Extract/Femor Nerve 152, 319
Ø1DD[Ø,3,4]ZZ	Extract/Femor Nerve, [Opn, Perc, Perc Endo] 441
Ø6DN[Ø,3,4]ZZ	Extract/Femor Vein, Lt, [Opn, Perc, Perc Endo] 443
Ø6DM[Ø,3,4]ZZ	Extract/Femor Vein, Rt, [Opn, Perc, Perc Endo] 443
ØMDT*	Extract/Foot Bursa & Lgmt, Lt 144, 343
ØMDT[Ø,3,4]ZZ	Extract/Foot Bursa & Lgmt, Lt, [Opn, Perc, Perc Endo] 454
ØMDS*	Extract/Foot Bursa & Lgmt, Rt 144, 343
ØMDS[Ø,3,4]ZZ	Extract/Foot Bursa & Lgmt, Rt, [Opn, Perc, Perc Endo] 454
Ø6DV[Ø,3,4]ZZ	Extract/Foot Vein, Lt, [Opn, Perc, Perc Endo] 443
Ø6DT[Ø,3,4]ZZ	Extract/Foot Vein, Rt, [Opn, Perc, Perc Endo] 443
Ø9DT*	Extract/Frontal Sinus, Lt 55
Ø9DS*	Extract/Frontal Sinus, Rt 55
ØØDP*	Extract/Glossopharyngeal Nerve 23, 50, 151, 318
ØØDP[Ø,3,4]ZZ	Extract/Glossopharyngeal Nerve, [Opn, Perc, Perc Endo] 440
Ø6DQ[Ø,3,4]ZZ	Extract/Greater Saphenous Vein, Lt, [Opn, Perc, Perc Endo] 443
Ø6DP[Ø,3,4]ZZ	Extract/Greater Saphenous Vein, Rt, [Opn, Perc, Perc Endo] 443
ØMD8*	Extract/Hand Bursa & Lgmt, Lt 150
ØMD8[Ø,3,4]ZZ	Extract/Hand Bursa & Lgmt, Lt, [Opn, Perc, Perc Endo] 315
ØMD7*	Extract/Hand Bursa & Lgmt, Rt 150
ØMD7[Ø,3,4]ZZ	Extract/Hand Bursa & Lgmt, Rt, [Opn, Perc, Perc Endo] 315
ØMDØ*	Extract/Head and Neck Bursa & Lgmt 143, 343
ØMDØ[Ø,3,4]ZZ	Extract/Head and Neck Bursa & Lgmt, [Opn, Perc, Perc Endo] 454
Ø1DK*	Extract/Head and Neck Sympathetic Nerve 50, 89
ØMDM*	Extract/Hip Bursa & Lgmt, Lt 144, 343
ØMDM[Ø,3,4]ZZ	Extract/Hip Bursa & Lgmt, Lt, [Opn, Perc, Perc Endo] 454
ØMDL*	Extract/Hip Bursa & Lgmt, Rt 144, 343
ØMDL[Ø,3,4]ZZ	Extract/Hip Bursa & Lgmt, Rt, [Opn, Perc, Perc Endo] 454
ØØDS*	Extract/Hypoglossal Nerve 23, 50, 151, 318
ØØDS[Ø,3,4]ZZ	Extract/Hypoglossal Nerve, [Opn, Perc, Perc Endo] 440
ØTD1*	Extract/Kidney, Lt 249
ØTDØ*	Extract/Kidney, Rt 249
ØMDP*	Extract/Knee Bursa & Lgmt, Lt 144, 343
ØMDP[Ø,3,4]ZZ	Extract/Knee Bursa & Lgmt, Lt, [Opn, Perc, Perc Endo] 454
ØMDN*	Extract/Knee Bursa & Lgmt, Rt 144, 343
ØMDN[Ø,3,4]ZZ	Extract/Knee Bursa & Lgmt, Rt, [Opn, Perc, Perc Endo] 454
Ø6DS[Ø,3,4]ZZ	Extract/Lesser Saphenous Vein, Lt, [Opn, Perc, Perc Endo] 443
Ø6DR[Ø,3,4]ZZ	Extract/Lesser Saphenous Vein, Rt, [Opn, Perc, Perc Endo] 443
Ø1DB*	Extract/Lumbar Nerve 152, 319
Ø1DB[Ø,3,4]ZZ	Extract/Lumbar Nerve, [Opn, Perc, Perc Endo] 441
Ø1D9*	Extract/Lumbar Plexus 152, 319
Ø1D9[Ø,3,4]ZZ	Extract/Lumbar Plexus, [Opn, Perc, Perc Endo] 441
Ø1DN*	Extract/Lumbar Sympathetic Nerve 89
Ø1DN[Ø,3,4]ZZ	Extract/Lumbar Sympathetic Nerve, [Opn, Perc, Perc Endo] 441
Ø1DA*	Extract/Lumbosacral Plexus 152, 319
Ø1DA[Ø,3,4]ZZ	Extract/Lumbosacral Plexus, [Opn, Perc, Perc Endo] 441
ØMDW*	Extract/Lwr Extr Bursa & Lgmt, Lt 144, 343
ØMDW[Ø,3,4]ZZ	Extract/Lwr Extr Bursa & Lgmt, Lt, [Opn, Perc, Perc Endo] 454
ØMDV*	Extract/Lwr Extr Bursa & Lgmt, Rt 144, 343
ØMDV[Ø,3,4]ZZ	Extract/Lwr Extr Bursa & Lgmt, Rt, [Opn, Perc, Perc Endo] 454

Code	Description
06DY[0,3,4]ZZ	Extract/Lwr Vein, [Opn, Perc, Perc Endo] 443
09DC*	Extract/Mastoid Sinus, Lt 55
09DB*	Extract/Mastoid Sinus, Rt 55
09DR*	Extract/Maxillary Sinus, Lt 55
09DQ*	Extract/Maxillary Sinus, Rt 55
01D5*	Extract/Median Nerve 152, 319
01D5[0,3,4]ZZ	Extract/Median Nerve, [Opn, Perc, Perc Endo] 441
09DM*	Extract/Nasal Septum 51, 330
09DM[0,3,4]ZZ	Extract/Nasal Septum, [Opn, Perc, Perc Endo] 210, 447
09DL*	Extract/Nasal Turbinate 51, 330
09DL[0,3,4,7,8]ZZ	Extract/Nasal Turbinate, [Opn, Perc, Perc Endo, Via Natrl or Artfcl Opng, Via Natrl or Artfcl Opng Endo] 447
00DH*	Extract/Oculomotor Nerve 23, 50, 151, 318
00DH[0,3,4]ZZ	Extract/Oculomotor Nerve, [Opn, Perc, Perc Endo] 440
00DF*	Extract/Olfactory Nerve 23, 50, 151, 318
00DF[0,3,4]ZZ	Extract/Olfactory Nerve, [Opn, Perc, Perc Endo] 440
00DG*	Extract/Optic Nerve 23, 50, 151, 318
00DG[0,3,4]ZZ	Extract/Optic Nerve, [Opn, Perc, Perc Endo] 440
0UDN*	Extract/Ova 263, 264, 266
0MDK*	Extract/Perineum Bursa & Lgmt 144, 343
0MDK[0,3,4]ZZ	Extract/Perineum Bursa & Lgmt, [Opn, Perc, Perc Endo] 454
01DH*	Extract/Peroneal Nerve 152, 319
01DH[0,3,4]ZZ	Extract/Peroneal Nerve, [Opn, Perc, Perc Endo] 441
01D2*	Extract/Phrenic Nerve 151, 319
01D2[0,3,4]ZZ	Extract/Phrenic Nerve, [Opn, Perc, Perc Endo] 441
0BDP[0,3,4]Z[X,Z]	Extract/Pleura, Lt, [Opn, Perc, Perc Endo], No Dev, [Dx, NQ] 299
0BDN[0,3,4]Z[X,Z]	Extract/Pleura, Rt, [Opn, Perc, Perc Endo], No Dev, [Dx, NQ] 299
10D2*	Extract/Products of Conception, Ectopic 263, 264, 266
10D00Z[0,1,2]	Extract/Products of Conception, Opn, No Dev, [Classical, Low Cervical, Extraperitoneal] 271
10D1*	Extract/Products of Conception, Retained 272
10D1[7,8]ZZ	Extract/Products of Conception, Retained, [Via Natrl or Artfcl Opng, Via Natrl or Artfcl Opng Endo] 271
10D07Z[3,4,5,6,7,8]	Extract/Products of Conception, Via Natrl or Artfcl Opng, No Dev, [Low Forceps, Mid Forceps, High Forceps, Vacuum, Int Version, Oth] 271,271, 273, 275
01DC*	Extract/Pudendal Nerve 152, 319
01DC[0,3,4]ZZ	Extract/Pudendal Nerve, [Opn, Perc, Perc Endo] 441
01D6*	Extract/Radial Nerve 152, 319
01D6[0,3,4]ZZ	Extract/Radial Nerve, [Opn, Perc, Perc Endo] 441
01DR*	Extract/Sacral Nerve 152, 319
01DR[0,3,4]ZZ	Extract/Sacral Nerve, [Opn, Perc, Perc Endo] 441
01DQ*	Extract/Sacral Plexus 152, 319
01DQ[0,3,4]ZZ	Extract/Sacral Plexus, [Opn, Perc, Perc Endo] 441
01DP*	Extract/Sacral Sympathetic Nerve 89, 267
01DF*	Extract/Sciatic Nerve 152, 319
01DF[0,3,4]ZZ	Extract/Sciatic Nerve, [Opn, Perc, Perc Endo] 441
0MD2*	Extract/Shldr Bursa & Lgmt, Lt 143, 343
0MD2[0,3,4]ZZ	Extract/Shldr Bursa & Lgmt, Lt, [Opn, Perc, Perc Endo] 454
0MD1*	Extract/Shldr Bursa & Lgmt, Rt 143, 343
0MD1[0,3,4]ZZ	Extract/Shldr Bursa & Lgmt, Rt, [Opn, Perc, Perc Endo] 454
09DX*	Extract/Sphenoid Sinus, Lt 55
09DW*	Extract/Sphenoid Sinus, Rt 55
00DT*	Extract/Spinal Meninges 159, 160, 318
00DT[0,3,4]ZZ	Extract/Spinal Meninges, [Opn, Perc, Perc Endo] 19, 295
0JD8*	Extract/SQ Tissue & Fascia, Abd 26, 137, 337
0JD8[0,3]ZZ	Extract/SQ Tissue & Fascia, Abd, [Opn, Perc] 212
0JD4*	Extract/SQ Tissue & Fascia, Ant Neck 26, 137, 337
0JD4[0,3]ZZ	Extract/SQ Tissue & Fascia, Ant Neck, [Opn, Perc] 212
0JD7*	Extract/SQ Tissue & Fascia, Back 26, 137, 337
0JD7[0,3]ZZ	Extract/SQ Tissue & Fascia, Back, [Opn, Perc] 212
0JD9*	Extract/SQ Tissue & Fascia, Buttock 26, 137, 337
0JD9[0,3]ZZ	Extract/SQ Tissue & Fascia, Buttock, [Opn, Perc] 212
0JD6*	Extract/SQ Tissue & Fascia, Chest 26, 137, 337
0JD6[0,3]ZZ	Extract/SQ Tissue & Fascia, Chest, [Opn, Perc] 212
0JD1*	Extract/SQ Tissue & Fascia, Face 26, 137, 337
0JD1[0,3]ZZ	Extract/SQ Tissue & Fascia, Face, [Opn, Perc] 212
0JDC[0,3]ZZ	Extract/SQ Tissue & Fascia, Genitalia, [Opn, Perc] 212
0JDR*	Extract/SQ Tissue & Fascia, Lt Foot 26, 137, 337
0JDR[0,3]ZZ	Extract/SQ Tissue & Fascia, Lt Foot, [Opn, Perc] 212

Code	Description
0JDK*	Extract/SQ Tissue & Fascia, Lt Hand 149
0JDK[0,3]ZZ	Extract/SQ Tissue & Fascia, Lt Hand, [Opn, Perc] 314
0JDH*	Extract/SQ Tissue & Fascia, Lt Lwr Arm 26, 137, 337
0JDH[0,3]ZZ	Extract/SQ Tissue & Fascia, Lt Lwr Arm, [Opn, Perc] 212
0JDP*	Extract/SQ Tissue & Fascia, Lt Lwr Leg 26, 137, 337
0JDP[0,3]ZZ	Extract/SQ Tissue & Fascia, Lt Lwr Leg, [Opn, Perc] 212
0JDF*	Extract/SQ Tissue & Fascia, Lt Upr Arm 26, 137, 337
0JDF[0,3]ZZ	Extract/SQ Tissue & Fascia, Lt Upr Arm, [Opn, Perc] 212
0JDM*	Extract/SQ Tissue & Fascia, Lt Upr Leg 26, 137, 337
0JDM[0,3]ZZ	Extract/SQ Tissue & Fascia, Lt Upr Leg, [Opn, Perc] 212
0JDC*	Extract/SQ Tissue & Fascia, Pelvic Region 26, 137, 337
0JDB*	Extract/SQ Tissue & Fascia, Perineum 26, 137, 337
0JDB[0,3]ZZ	Extract/SQ Tissue & Fascia, Perineum, [Opn, Perc] 212
0JD5[0,3]ZZ	Extract/SQ Tissue & Fascia, Post Neck, [Opn, Perc] 212
0JD5*	Extract/SQ Tissue & Fascia, Posterior Neck 26, 137, 337
0JDQ*	Extract/SQ Tissue & Fascia, Rt Foot 26, 137, 337
0JDQ[0,3]ZZ	Extract/SQ Tissue [Opn, Perc] 212
0JDJ*	Extract/SQ Tissue & Fascia, Rt Hand 149
0JDJ[0,3]ZZ	Extract/SQ Tissue & Fascia, Rt Hand, [Opn, Perc] 314
0JDG*	Extract/SQ Tissue & Fascia, Rt Lwr Arm 26, 137, 337
0JDG[0,3]ZZ	Extract/SQ Tissue & Fascia, Rt Lwr Arm, [Opn, Perc] 212
0JDN*	Extract/SQ Tissue & Fascia, Rt Lwr Leg 26, 137, 337
0JDN[0,3]ZZ	Extract/SQ Tissue & Fascia, Rt Lwr Leg, [Opn, Perc] 212
0JDD*	Extract/SQ Tissue & Fascia, Rt Upr Arm 26, 137, 337
0JDD[0,3]ZZ	Extract/SQ Tissue & Fascia, Rt Upr Arm, [Opn, Perc] 212
0JDL*	Extract/SQ Tissue & Fascia, Rt Upr Leg 26, 137, 337
0JDL[0,3]ZZ	Extract/SQ Tissue & Fascia, Rt Upr Leg, [Opn, Perc] 212
0JD0*	Extract/SQ Tissue & Fascia, Scalp 26, 137, 337
0JD0[0,3]ZZ	Extract/SQ Tissue & Fascia, Scalp, [Opn, Perc] 212
01D8*	Extract/Thoracic Nerve 152, 319
01D8[0,3,4]ZZ	Extract/Thoracic Nerve, [Opn, Perc, Perc Endo] 441
01DL*	Extract/Thoracic Sympathetic Nerve 89
0MDG*	Extract/Thorax Bursa & Lgmt, Lt 144, 343
0MDG[0,3,4]ZZ	Extract/Thorax Bursa & Lgmt, Lt, [Opn, Perc, Perc Endo] 454
0MDF*	Extract/Thorax Bursa & Lgmt, Rt 144, 343
0MDF[0,3,4]ZZ	Extract/Thorax Bursa & Lgmt, Rt, [Opn, Perc, Perc Endo] 454
01DG*	Extract/Tibial Nerve 152, 319
01DG[0,3,4]ZZ	Extract/Tibial Nerve, [Opn, Perc, Perc Endo] 441
00DK*	Extract/Trigeminal Nerve 23, 50, 151, 318
00DK[0,3,4]ZZ	Extract/Trigeminal Nerve, [Opn, Perc, Perc Endo] 440
00DJ*	Extract/Trochlear Nerve 23, 50, 151, 318
00DJ[0,3,4]ZZ	Extract/Trochlear Nerve, [Opn, Perc, Perc Endo] 440
0MDD*	Extract/Trunk Bursa & Lgmt, Lt 144, 343
0MDD[0,3,4]ZZ	Extract/Trunk Bursa & Lgmt, Lt, [Opn, Perc, Perc Endo] 454
0MDC*	Extract/Trunk Bursa & Lgmt, Rt 144, 343
0MDC[0,3,4]ZZ	Extract/Trunk Bursa & Lgmt, Rt, [Opn, Perc, Perc Endo] 454
09D8*	Extract/Tympanic Membrane, Lt 51
09D7*	Extract/Tympanic Membrane, Rt 51
01D4*	Extract/Ulnar Nerve 152, 319
01D4[0,3,4]ZZ	Extract/Ulnar Nerve, [Opn, Perc, Perc Endo] 441
0MDB*	Extract/Upr Extr Bursa & Lgmt, Lt 143, 343
0MDB[0,3,4]ZZ	Extract/Upr Extr Bursa & Lgmt, Lt, [Opn, Perc, Perc Endo] 454
0MD9*	Extract/Upr Extr Bursa & Lgmt, Rt 143, 343
0MD9[0,3,4]ZZ	Extract/Upr Extr Bursa & Lgmt, Rt, [Opn, Perc, Perc Endo] 454
00DQ*	Extract/Vagus Nerve 23, 50, 151, 318
00DQ[0,3,4]ZZ	Extract/Vagus Nerve, [Opn, Perc, Perc Endo] 440
0CDV*	Extract/Vocal Cord, Lt 52, 65
0CDV[0,3,4,7,8]ZZ	Extract/Vocal Cord, Lt, [Opn, Perc, Perc Endo, Via Natrl or Artfcl Opng, Via Natrl or Artfcl Opng Endo] 448
0CDT*	Extract/Vocal Cord, Rt 52, 65
0CDT[0,3,4,7,8]ZZ	Extract/Vocal Cord, Rt, [Opn, Perc, Perc Endo, Via Natrl or Artfcl Opng, Via Natrl or Artfcl Opng Endo] 448
0MD6*	Extract/Wrist Bursa & Lgmt, Lt 143, 343
0MD6[0,3,4]ZZ	Extract/Wrist Bursa & Lgmt, Lt, [Opn, Perc, Perc Endo] 454
0MD5*	Extract/Wrist Bursa & Lgmt, Rt 143, 343
0MD5[0,3,4]ZZ	Extract/Wrist Bursa & Lgmt, Rt, [Opn, Perc, Perc Endo] 454
081*	Eye, Bypass 329
087*	Eye, Dilation 42, 51
08L*	Eye, Occlsn 43, 330
08M*	Eye, Reattach 43, 330

Ø8R*	Eye, Replace 330
Ø8V*	Eye, Restrict 43, 51, 330
Ø8X*	Eye, Transfer 43
ØSGQ[Ø,3,4] [4,5,7,J,K,Z]Z	Fusion/Toe Phalangeal Jt, Lt, [Opn, Perc, Perc Endo], [Int Fix Dev, Ext Fix Dev, Auto Tissue Sub, Synth Sub, Nonauto Tissue Sub, No Dev], NQ 457
ØU1*	Female Reproductive Sys, Bypass 262, 263, 265
ØUV*	Female Reproductive Sys, Restrict 267, 354
ØUY*	Female Reproductive Sys, Transplantation 263, 264, 266
B21F*	Fluoroscopy/Bypass Graft, Oth 71, 73, 76, 99
B211[Ø,1,Y]ZZ	Fluoroscopy/Coronary Arteries, Multi, [High Osmolar, Low Osmolar, Oth Contrast], None, None 71, 73, 76, 99
B212[Ø,1,Y]ZZ	Fluoroscopy/Coronary Artery Bypass Graft, Single, [High Osmolar, Low Osmolar, Oth Contrast], None, None 71, 73, 76, 99
B213[Ø,1,Y]ZZ	Fluoroscopy/Coronary Artery Bypass Grafts, Multi, [High Osmolar, Low Osmolar, Oth Contrast], None, None 71, 73, 76, 99
B21Ø[Ø,1,Y]ZZ	Fluoroscopy/Coronary Artery, Single, [High Osmolar, Low Osmolar, Oth Contrast], None, None 71, 73, 76, 99
B215*	Fluoroscopy/Heart, Lt 71, 73, 76, 99
B214*	Fluoroscopy/Heart, Rt 71, 73, 76, 99
B216*	Fluoroscopy/Heart, Rt and Lt 71, 73, 76, 99
B218*	Fluoroscopy/Int Mammary Bypass Graft, Lt 71, 73, 76, 99
B217*	Fluoroscopy/Int Mammary Bypass Graft, Rt 71, 73, 76, 99
Ø8F[4,5]3ZZ	Fragmn in [Rt, Lt] Vitreous, Perc Appr 44
ØTFCXZZ	Fragmn in Bladder Neck, Ext Appr 255
ØTFBXZZ	Fragmn in Bladder, Ext Appr 255
ØWFRXZZ	Fragmn in Genitourinary Tract, Ext Appr 255
ØTF4XZZ	Fragmn in Lt Kidney Pelvis, Ext Appr 255
ØTF7XZZ	Fragmn in Lt Ureter, Ext Appr 255
Ø8F53ZZ	Fragmn in Lt Vitreous, Perc Appr 330, 444
ØTF3XZZ	Fragmn in Rt Kidney Pelvis, Ext Appr 255
ØTF6XZZ	Fragmn in Rt Ureter, Ext Appr 255
Ø8F43ZZ	Fragmn in Rt Vitreous, Perc Appr 330, 444
ØFFC[Ø,3,4,7]ZZ	Fragmn/Ampulla of Vater, [Opn, Perc, Perc Endo, Via Natrl or Artfcl Opng] 120, 301
ØDFQ[Ø,3,4,7,8]ZZ	Fragmn/Anus, [Opn, Perc, Perc Endo, Via Natrl or Artfcl Opng, Via Natrl or Artfcl Opng Endo] 109, 333
ØDFJ[Ø,3,4,7,8]ZZ	Fragmn/Appendix, [Opn, Perc, Perc Endo, Via Natrl or Artfcl Opng, Via Natrl or Artfcl Opng Endo] 108
ØDFK[Ø,3,4,7,8]ZZ	Fragmn/Ascending Colon, [Opn, Perc, Perc Endo, Via Natrl or Artfcl Opng, Via Natrl or Artfcl Opng Endo] 107, 333
ØBF2[Ø,3,4,7,8]ZZ	Fragmn/Carina, [Opn, Perc, Perc Endo, Via Natrl or Artfcl Opng, Via Natrl or Artfcl Opng Endo] 52, 61, 331
ØDFH[Ø,3,4,7,8]ZZ	Fragmn/Cecum, [Opn, Perc, Perc Endo, Via Natrl or Artfcl Opng, Via Natrl or Artfcl Opng Endo] 107, 333
ØØF6[Ø,3,4]ZZ	Fragmn/Cerebral Ventricle, [Opn, Perc, Perc Endo] 8, 12, 16, 318, 414
ØFF9[Ø,3,4,7]ZZ	Fragmn/Common Bile Duct, [Opn, Perc, Perc Endo, Via Natrl or Artfcl Opng] 120, 301
ØWF1[Ø,3,4]ZZ	Fragmn/Cranial Cavity, [Opn, Perc, Perc Endo] 10, 14, 18, 355, 415
ØFF8[Ø,3,4,7]ZZ	Fragmn/Cystic Duct, [Opn, Perc, Perc Endo, Via Natrl or Artfcl Opng] 120, 301
ØDFM[Ø,3,4,7,8]ZZ	Fragmn/Descending Colon, [Opn, Perc, Perc Endo, Via Natrl or Artfcl Opng, Via Natrl or Artfcl Opng Endo] 107, 333
ØDF9[Ø,3,4,7,8]ZZ	Fragmn/Duodenum, [Opn, Perc, Perc Endo, Via Natrl or Artfcl Opng, Via Natrl or Artfcl Opng Endo] 106, 333
ØØF3[Ø,3,4]ZZ	Fragmn/Epidural Space, [Opn, Perc, Perc Endo] 8, 12, 16, 318, 414
ØDF5[Ø,3,4,7,8]ZZ	Fragmn/Esophagus, [Opn, Perc, Perc Endo, Via Natrl or Artfcl Opng, Via Natrl or Artfcl Opng Endo] 105, 333
ØUF6[Ø,3,4,7,8]ZZ	Fragmn/Fallopian Tube, Lt, [Opn, Perc, Perc Endo, Via Natrl or Artfcl Opng, Via Natrl or Artfcl Opng Endo] 263, 264, 266, 354
ØUF5[Ø,3,4,7,8]ZZ	Fragmn/Fallopian Tube, Rt, [Opn, Perc, Perc Endo, Via Natrl or Artfcl Opng, Via Natrl or Artfcl Opng Endo] 263, 264, 266, 354
ØUF7[Ø,3,4,7,8]ZZ	Fragmn/Fallopian Tubes, Bilat, [Opn, Perc, Perc Endo, Via Natrl or Artfcl Opng, Via Natrl or Artfcl Opng Endo] 263, 264, 266, 354
ØFF4[Ø,3,4,7]ZZ	Fragmn/Gallbladder, [Opn, Perc, Perc Endo, Via Natrl or Artfcl Opng] 120
ØFF6[Ø,3,4,7]ZZ	Fragmn/Hepatic Duct, Lt, [Opn, Perc, Perc Endo, Via Natrl or Artfcl Opng] 120, 301
ØFF5[Ø,3,4,7]ZZ	Fragmn/Hepatic Duct, Rt, [Opn, Perc, Perc Endo, Via Natrl or Artfcl Opng] 120, 301
ØDFB[Ø,3,4,7,8]ZZ	Fragmn/Ileum, [Opn, Perc, Perc Endo, Via Natrl or Artfcl Opng, Via Natrl or Artfcl Opng Endo] 106, 333
ØDFA[Ø,3,4,7,8]ZZ	Fragmn/Jejunum, [Opn, Perc, Perc Endo, Via Natrl or Artfcl Opng, Via Natrl or Artfcl Opng Endo] 106, 333
ØTF4[3,4]ZZ	Fragmn/Kidney Pelvis, Lt, [Perc, Perc Endo] 249, 353
ØTF3[3,4]ZZ	Fragmn/Kidney Pelvis, Rt, [Perc, Perc Endo] 249, 353
ØDFE[Ø,3,4,7,8]ZZ	Fragmn/Lg Intestine, [Opn, Perc, Perc Endo, Via Natrl or Artfcl Opng, Via Natrl or Artfcl Opng Endo] 106, 333
ØDFG[Ø,3,4,7,8]ZZ	Fragmn/Lg Intestine, Lt, [Opn, Perc, Perc Endo, Via Natrl or Artfcl Opng, Via Natrl or Artfcl Opng Endo] 107, 333
ØDFF[Ø,3,4,7,8]ZZ	Fragmn/Lg Intestine, Rt, [Opn, Perc, Perc Endo, Via Natrl or Artfcl Opng, Via Natrl or Artfcl Opng Endo] 107, 333
ØBF9[Ø,3,4,7,8]ZZ	Fragmn/Lingula Bronchus, [Opn, Perc, Perc Endo, Via Natrl or Artfcl Opng, Via Natrl or Artfcl Opng Endo] 62
ØBFB[Ø,3,4,7,8]ZZ	Fragmn/Lwr Lobe Bronchus, Lt, [Opn, Perc, Perc Endo, Via Natrl or Artfcl Opng, Via Natrl or Artfcl Opng Endo] 62
ØBF6[Ø,3,4,7,8]ZZ	Fragmn/Lwr Lobe Bronchus, Rt, [Opn, Perc, Perc Endo, Via Natrl or Artfcl Opng, Via Natrl or Artfcl Opng Endo] 61
ØBF7[Ø,3,4,7,8]ZZ	Fragmn/Main Bronchus, Lt, [Opn, Perc, Perc Endo, Via Natrl or Artfcl Opng, Via Natrl or Artfcl Opng Endo] 61
ØBF3[Ø,3,4,7,8]ZZ	Fragmn/Main Bronchus, Rt, [Opn, Perc, Perc Endo, Via Natrl or Artfcl Opng, Via Natrl or Artfcl Opng Endo] 61
ØWFC[Ø,3,4]ZZ	Fragmn/Mediastinum, [Opn, Perc, Perc Endo] 66, 355
ØBF5[Ø,3,4,7,8]ZZ	Fragmn/Mid Lobe Bronchus, Rt, [Opn, Perc, Perc Endo, Via Natrl or Artfcl Opng, Via Natrl or Artfcl Opng Endo] 61
ØWF3[Ø,3,4]ZZ	Fragmn/Oral Cavity and Throat, [Opn, Perc, Perc Endo] 56, 217, 355, 460
ØFFD[Ø,3,4,7,8]ZZ	Fragmn/Pancreatic Duct, [Opn, Perc, Perc Endo, Via Natrl or Artfcl Opng, Via Natrl or Artfcl Opng Endo] 119
ØFFF[Ø,3,4,7,8]ZZ	Fragmn/Pancreatic Duct, Accessory, [Opn, Perc, Perc Endo, Via Natrl or Artfcl Opng, Via Natrl or Artfcl Opng Endo] 119
ØWFD*	Fragmn/Pericardial Cavity 355
ØWFD[Ø,3,4,X]ZZ	Fragmn/Pericardial Cavity, [Opn, Perc, Perc Endo, Ext] 98
Ø2FN[Ø,3,4]ZZ	Fragmn/Pericardium, [Opn, Perc, Perc Endo] 93, 319
ØWFG[Ø,3,4]ZZ	Fragmn/Peritoneal Cavity, [Opn, Perc, Perc Endo] 113, 123, 302, 355
ØWFB[Ø,3,4]ZZ	Fragmn/Pleural Cavity, Lt, [Opn, Perc, Perc Endo] 66, 355
ØWF9[Ø,3,4]ZZ	Fragmn/Pleural Cavity, Rt, [Opn, Perc, Perc Endo] 66, 355
ØDFP[Ø,3,4,7,8]ZZ	Fragmn/Rectum, [Opn, Perc, Perc Endo, Via Natrl or Artfcl Opng, Via Natrl or Artfcl Opng Endo] 109, 271, 333
ØWFQ[Ø,3,4]ZZ	Fragmn/Respiratory Tract, [Opn, Perc, Perc Endo, Via Natrl or Artfcl Opng, Via Natrl or Artfcl Opng Endo] 66, 355
ØDFN[Ø,3,4,7,8]ZZ	Fragmn/Sigmoid Colon, [Opn, Perc, Perc Endo, Via Natrl or Artfcl Opng, Via Natrl or Artfcl Opng Endo] 107, 333
ØDF8[Ø,3,4,7,8]ZZ	Fragmn/Sm Intestine, [Opn, Perc, Perc Endo, Via Natrl or Artfcl Opng, Via Natrl or Artfcl Opng Endo] 106, 333
ØØFU*	Fragmn/Spinal Canal 159, 160, 318
ØØFU[Ø,3,4,X]ZZ	Fragmn/Spinal Canal, [Opn, Perc, Perc Endo, Ext] 19, 296
ØDF6[Ø,3,4,7,8]ZZ	Fragmn/Stomach, [Opn, Perc, Perc Endo, Via Natrl or Artfcl Opng, Via Natrl or Artfcl Opng Endo] 105, 235, 333
ØØF5[Ø,3,4]ZZ	Fragmn/Subarachnoid Space, [Opn, Perc, Perc Endo] 8, 12, 16, 318, 414
ØØF4[Ø,3,4]ZZ	Fragmn/Subdural Space, [Opn, Perc, Perc Endo] 8, 12, 16, 318, 414
ØBF1[Ø,3,4,7,8]ZZ	Fragmn/Trachea, [Opn, Perc, Perc Endo, Via Natrl or Artfcl Opng, Via Natrl or Artfcl Opng Endo] 52, 61, 331
ØDFL[Ø,3,4,7,8]ZZ	Fragmn/Transv Colon, [Opn, Perc, Perc Endo, Via Natrl or Artfcl Opng, Via Natrl or Artfcl Opng Endo] 107, 333
ØBF8[Ø,3,4,7,8]ZZ	Fragmn/Upr Lobe Bronchus, Lt, [Opn, Perc, Perc Endo, Via Natrl or Artfcl Opng, Via Natrl or Artfcl Opng Endo] 62
ØBF4[Ø,3,4,7,8]ZZ	Fragmn/Upr Lobe Bronchus, Rt, [Opn, Perc, Perc Endo, Via Natrl or Artfcl Opng, Via Natrl or Artfcl Opng Endo] 61
ØUF9[Ø,3,4,7,8]ZZ	Fragmn/Uterus, [Opn, Perc, Perc Endo, Via Natrl or Artfcl Opng, Via Natrl or Artfcl Opng Endo] 269
ØSGNØZZ	Fusion of Lt Metatarsal-Phalangeal Jt, Opn Appr 462
ØSGN3ZZ	Fusion of Lt Metatarsal-Phalangeal Jt, Perc Appr 462
ØSGN4ZZ	Fusion of Lt Metatarsophal Jt, Perc Endo Appr 462
ØSGMØZZ	Fusion of Rt Metatarsal-Phalangeal Jt, Opn Appr 462
ØSGM3ZZ	Fusion of Rt Metatarsal-Phalangeal Jt, Perc Appr 462
ØSGM4ZZ	Fusion of Rt Metatarsophal Jt, Perc Endo Appr 462

ØRG1[Ø,3,4] [7,A,J,K,Z][Ø,1,J]	Fusion/ Cervical Vert Jt, [Opn, Perc, Perc Endo], [Auto Tissue Sub, Interbody Fusion Dev, Synth Sub, Nonauto Tissue Sub, No Dev], [Ant Appr, Ant Column, Post Appr, Post Column, Post Appr, Ant Column] 19
ØRGH*	Fusion/Acromioclavicular Jt, Lt 147
ØRGG*	Fusion/Acromioclavicular Jt, Rt 147
ØSGG*	Fusion/Ankle Jt, Lt 133, 244, 351
ØSGF*	Fusion/Ankle Jt, Rt 133, 244, 351
ØRGR*	Fusion/Carpal Jt, Lt 150
ØRGR[Ø,3,4] [4,5,7,J,K,Z]Z	Fusion/Carpal Jt, Lt, [Opn, Perc, Perc Endo], [Int Fix Dev, Ext Fix Dev, Auto Tissue Sub, Synth Sub, Nonauto Tissue Sub, No Dev] , NQ 316
ØRGQ*	Fusion/Carpal Jt, Rt 150
ØRGQ[Ø,3,4] [4,5,7,J,K,Z]Z	Fusion/Carpal Jt, Rt, [Opn, Perc, Perc Endo], [Int Fix Dev, Ext Fix Dev, Auto Tissue Sub, Synth Sub, Nonauto Tissue Sub, No Dev] , NQ 316
ØRG1*	Fusion/Cervical Vert Jt 129, 349
ØRG1[Ø,3,4] [7,A,J,K,Z][1,J]	Fusion/Cervical Vert Jt, [Opn, Perc, Perc Endo], [Auto Tissue Sub, Interbody Fusion Dev, Synth Sub, Nonauto Tissue Sub, No Dev], [Post Appr, Post Column, Post Appr, Ant Column] 125
ØRG1[Ø,3,4] [7,A,J,K,Z]Ø	Fusion/Cervical Vert Jt, [Opn, Perc, Perc Endo], [Auto Tissue Sub, Interbody Fusion Dev, Synth Sub, Nonauto Tissue Sub, No Dev], Ant Appr, Ant Column 125
ØRG2*	Fusion/Cervical Vert Jts, 2 or more 129, 349
ØRG2[Ø,3,4] [7,A,J,K,Z][Ø,1,J]	Fusion/Cervical Vert Jts, 2 or more, [Opn, Perc, Perc Endo], [Auto Tissue Sub, Interbody Fusion Dev, Synth Sub, Nonauto Tissue Sub, No Dev], [Ant Appr, Ant Column, Post Appr, Post Column, Post Appr, Ant Column] 19
ØRG2[Ø,3,4] [7,A,J,K,Z][1,J]	Fusion/Cervical Vert Jts, 2 or more, [Opn, Perc, Perc Endo], [Auto Tissue Sub, Interbody Fusion Dev, Synth Sub, Nonauto Tissue Sub, No Dev], [Post Appr, Post Column, Post Appr, Ant Column] 125
ØRG2[Ø,3,4] [7,A,J,K,Z]Ø	Fusion/Cervical Vert Jts, 2 or more, [Opn, Perc, Perc Endo], [Auto Tissue Sub, Interbody Fusion Dev, Synth Sub, Nonauto Tissue Sub, No Dev], Ant Appr, Ant Column 125
ØRG4*	Fusion/Cervicothoracic Vert Jt 129, 349
ØRG4[Ø,3,4] [7,A,J,K,Z][Ø,1,J]	Fusion/Cervicothoracic Vert Jt, [Opn, Perc, Perc Endo], [Auto Tissue Sub, Interbody Fusion Dev, Synth Sub, Nonauto Tissue Sub, No Dev], [Ant Appr, Ant Column, Post Appr, Post Column, Post Appr, Ant Column] 19
ØRG4[Ø,3,4] [7,A,J,K,Z][1,J]	Fusion/Cervicothoracic Vert Jt, [Opn, Perc, Perc Endo], [Auto Tissue Sub, Interbody Fusion Dev, Synth Sub, Nonauto Tissue Sub, No Dev], [Post Appr, Post Column, Post Appr, Ant Column] 125
ØRG4[Ø,3,4] [7,A,J,K,Z]Ø	Fusion/Cervicothoracic Vert Jt, [Opn, Perc, Perc Endo], [Auto Tissue Sub, Interbody Fusion Dev, Synth Sub, Nonauto Tissue Sub, No Dev], Ant Appr, Ant Column 125
ØSG6*	Fusion/Coccygeal Jt 20, 126, 351
ØRGM*	Fusion/Elbow Jt, Lt 147, 349
ØRGL*	Fusion/Elbow Jt, Rt 147, 349
ØRGX*	Fusion/Finger Phalangeal Jt, Lt 150
ØRGX[Ø,3,4] [4,5,7,J,K,Z]Z	Fusion/Finger Phalangeal Jt, Lt, [Opn, Perc, Perc Endo], [Int Fix Dev, Ext Fix Dev, Auto Tissue Sub, Synth Sub, Nonauto Tissue Sub, No Dev], NQ 316
ØRGW*	Fusion/Finger Phalangeal Jt, Rt 150
ØRGW[Ø,3,4] [4,5,7,J,K,Z]Z	Fusion/Finger Phalangeal Jt, Rt, [Opn, Perc, Perc Endo], [Int Fix Dev, Ext Fix Dev, Auto Tissue Sub, Synth Sub, Nonauto Tissue Sub, No Dev], NQ 316
ØSGB*	Fusion/Hip Jt, Lt 131, 351, 416
ØSG9*	Fusion/Hip Jt, Rt 131, 351, 416
ØSGD*	Fusion/Knee Jt, Lt 132, 351
ØSGC*	Fusion/Knee Jt, Rt 132, 351
ØSGØ*	Fusion/Lumbar Vert Jt 20, 126, 351
ØSGØ[Ø,3,4] [7,A,J,K,Z][1,J]	Fusion/Lumbar Vert Jt, [Opn, Perc, Perc Endo], [Auto Tissue Sub, Interbody Fusion Dev, Synth Sub, Nonauto Tissue Sub, No Dev], [Post Appr, Post Column, Post Appr, Ant Column] 125
ØSGØ[Ø,3,4] [7,A,J,K,Z]Ø	Fusion/Lumbar Vert Jt, [Opn, Perc, Perc Endo], [Auto Tissue Sub, Interbody Fusion Dev, Synth Sub, Nonauto Tissue Sub, No Dev], Ant Appr, Ant Column 125
ØSG1*	Fusion/Lumbar Vert Jts, 2 or more 20, 126, 351
ØSG1[Ø,3,4] [7,A,J,K,Z][1,J]	Fusion/Lumbar Vert Jts, 2 or more, [Opn, Perc, Perc Endo], [Auto Tissue Sub, Interbody Fusion Dev, Synth Sub, Nonauto Tissue Sub, No Dev], [Post Appr, Post Column, Post Appr, Ant Column] 125
ØSG1[Ø,3,4] [7,A,J,K,Z]Ø	Fusion/Lumbar Vert Jts, 2 or more, [Opn, Perc, Perc Endo], [Auto Tissue Sub, Interbody Fusion Dev, Synth Sub, Nonauto Tissue Sub, No Dev], Ant Appr, Ant Column 125
ØSG3*	Fusion/Lumbosacral Jt 20, 126, 351
ØSG3[Ø,3,4] [7,A,J,K,Z][1,J]	Fusion/Lumbosacral Jt, [Opn, Perc, Perc Endo], [Auto Tissue Sub, Interbody Fusion Dev, Synth Sub, Nonauto Tissue Sub, No Dev], [Post Appr, Post Column, Post Appr, Ant Column] 125
ØSG3[Ø,3,4] [7,A,J,K,Z]Ø	Fusion/Lumbosacral Jt, [Opn, Perc, Perc Endo], [Auto Tissue Sub, Interbody Fusion Dev, Synth Sub, Nonauto Tissue Sub, No Dev], Ant Appr, Ant Column 125
ØRGT*	Fusion/Metacarpocarpal Jt, Lt 150
ØRGT[Ø,3,4] [4,5,7,J,K,Z]Z	Fusion/Metacarpocarpal Jt, Lt, [Opn, Perc, Perc Endo], [Int Fix Dev, Ext Fix Dev, Auto Tissue Sub, Synth Sub, Nonauto Tissue Sub, No Dev], NQ 316
ØRGS*	Fusion/Metacarpocarpal Jt, Rt 150
ØRGS[Ø,3,4] [4,5,7,J,K,Z]Z	Fusion/Metacarpocarpal Jt, Rt, [Opn, Perc, Perc Endo], [Int Fix Dev, Ext Fix Dev, Auto Tissue Sub, Synth Sub, Nonauto Tissue Sub, No Dev], NQ 316
ØRGV*	Fusion/Metacarpophalangeal Jt, Lt 150
ØRGV[Ø,3,4] [4,5,7,J,K,Z]Z	Fusion/Metacarpophalangeal Jt, Lt, [Opn, Perc, Perc Endo], [Int Fix Dev, Ext Fix Dev, Auto Tissue Sub, Synth Sub, Nonauto Tissue Sub, No Dev], NQ 316
ØRGU*	Fusion/Metacarpophalangeal Jt, Rt 150
ØRGU[Ø,3,4] [4,5,7,J,K,Z]Z	Fusion/Metacarpophalangeal Jt, Rt, [Opn, Perc, Perc Endo], [Int Fix Dev, Ext Fix Dev, Auto Tissue Sub, Synth Sub, Nonauto Tissue Sub, No Dev], NQ 316
ØSGN*	Fusion/Metatarsal-Phalangeal Jt, Lt 145, 351
ØSGM*	Fusion/Metatarsal-Phalangeal Jt, Rt 145, 351
ØSGL*	Fusion/Metatarsal-Tarsal Jt, Lt 145, 351
ØSGK*	Fusion/Metatarsal-Tarsal Jt, Rt 145, 351
ØRGØ*	Fusion/Occipital-cervical Jt 129, 349
ØRGØ[Ø,3,4] [7,A,J,K,Z][Ø,1,J]	Fusion/Occipital-cervical Jt, [Opn, Perc, Perc Endo], [Auto Tissue Sub, Interbody Fusion Dev, Synth Sub, Nonauto Tissue Sub, No Dev], [Ant Appr, Ant Column, Post Appr, Post Column, Post Appr, Ant Column] 19
ØSG5*	Fusion/Sacrococcygeal Jt 20, 126, 351
ØSG8*	Fusion/Sacroiliac Jt, Lt 20, 125, 126, 351
ØSG7*	Fusion/Sacroiliac Jt, Rt 20, 125, 126, 351
ØRGK*	Fusion/Shldr Jt, Lt 147
ØRGJ*	Fusion/Shldr Jt, Rt 147
ØRGF*	Fusion/Sternoclavicular Jt, Lt 147
ØRGE*	Fusion/Sternoclavicular Jt, Rt 147
ØSGJ*	Fusion/Tarsal Jt, Lt 145, 351
ØSGH*	Fusion/Tarsal Jt, Rt 145, 351
ØRGD*	Fusion/Temporomandibular Jt, Lt 49, 156, 349
ØRGC*	Fusion/Temporomandibular Jt, Rt 49, 156, 349
ØRG6*	Fusion/Thoracic Vert Jt 126, 349
ØRG6[Ø,3,4] [7,A,J,K,Z][Ø,1,J]	Fusion/Thoracic Vert Jt, [Opn, Perc, Perc Endo], [Auto Tissue Sub, Interbody Fusion Dev, Synth Sub, Nonauto Tissue Sub, No Dev], [Ant Appr, Ant Column, Post Appr, Post Column, Post Appr, Ant Column] 19
ØRG6[Ø,3,4] [7,A,J,K,Z][1,J]	Fusion/Thoracic Vert Jt, [Opn, Perc, Perc Endo], [Auto Tissue Sub, Interbody Fusion Dev, Synth Sub, Nonauto Tissue Sub, No Dev], [Post Appr, Post Column, Post Appr, Ant Column] 125
ØRG6[Ø,3,4] [7,A,J,K,Z]Ø	Fusion/Thoracic Vert Jt, [Opn, Perc, Perc Endo], [Auto Tissue Sub, Interbody Fusion Dev, Synth Sub, Nonauto Tissue Sub, No Dev], Ant Appr, Ant Column 125
ØRG7*	Fusion/Thoracic Vert Jts, 2 to 7 126, 349
ØRG7[Ø,3,4] [7,A,J,K,Z][Ø,1,J]	Fusion/Thoracic Vert Jts, 2 to 7, [Opn, Perc, Perc Endo], [Auto Tissue Sub, Interbody Fusion Dev, Synth Sub, Nonauto Tissue Sub, No Dev], [Ant Appr, Ant Column, Post Appr, Post Column, Post Appr, Ant Column] 20
ØRG7[Ø,3,4] [7,A,J,K,Z][1,J]	Fusion/Thoracic Vert Jts, 2 to 7, [Opn, Perc, Perc Endo], [Auto Tissue Sub, Interbody Fusion Dev, Synth Sub, Nonauto Tissue Sub, No Dev], [Post Appr, Post Column, Post Appr, Ant Column] 125
ØRG7[Ø,3,4] [7,A,J,K,Z]Ø	Fusion/Thoracic Vert Jts, 2 to 7, [Opn, Perc, Perc Endo], [Auto Tissue Sub, Interbody Fusion Dev, Synth Sub, Nonauto Tissue Sub, No Dev], Ant Appr, Ant Column 125
ØRG8*	Fusion/Thoracic Vert Jts, 8 or more 126, 349
ØRG8[Ø,3,4] [7,A,J,K,Z][Ø,1,J]	Fusion/Thoracic Vert Jts, 8 or more, [Opn, Perc, Perc Endo], [Auto Tissue Sub, Interbody Fusion Dev, Synth Sub, Nonauto Tissue Sub, No Dev], [Ant Appr, Ant Column, Post Appr, Post Column, Post Appr, Ant Column] 20

ØRG8[0,3,4] [7,A,J,K,Z][1,J]	Fusion/Thoracic Vert Jts, 8 or more, [Opn, Perc, Perc Endo], [Auto Tissue Sub, Interbody Fusion Dev, Synth Sub, Nonauto Tissue Sub, No Dev], [Post Appr, Post Column, Post Appr, Ant Column] 125
ØRG8[0,3,4] [7,A,J,K,Z]0	Fusion/Thoracic Vert Jts, 8 or more, [Opn, Perc, Perc Endo], [Auto Tissue Sub, Interbody Fusion Dev, Synth Sub, Nonauto Tissue Sub, No Dev], Ant Appr, Ant Column 125
ØRGA*	Fusion/Thoracolumbar Vert Jt 126, 349
ØRGA[0,3,4] [7,A,J,K,Z][0,1,J]	Fusion/Thoracolumbar Vert Jt, [Opn, Perc, Perc Endo], [Auto Tissue Sub, Interbody Fusion Dev, Synth Sub, Nonauto Tissue Sub, No Dev], [Ant Appr, Ant Column, Post Appr, Post Column, Post Appr, Ant Column] 20
ØRGA[0,3,4] [7,A,J,K,Z][1,J]	Fusion/Thoracolumbar Vert Jt, [Opn, Perc, Perc Endo], [Auto Tissue Sub, Interbody Fusion Dev, Synth Sub, Nonauto Tissue Sub, No Dev], [Post Appr, Post Column, Post Appr, Ant Column] 125
ØRGA[0,3,4] [7,A,J,K,Z]0	Fusion/Thoracolumbar Vert Jt, [Opn, Perc, Perc Endo], [Auto Tissue Sub, Interbody Fusion Dev, Synth Sub, Nonauto Tissue Sub, No Dev], Ant Appr, Ant Column 125
ØSGQ*	Fusion/Toe Phalangeal Jt, Lt 145
ØSGP*	Fusion/Toe Phalangeal Jt, Rt 145
ØSGP[0,3,4] [4,5,7,J,K,Z]Z	Fusion/Toe Phalangeal Jt, Rt, [Opn, Perc, Perc Endo], [Int Fix Dev, Ext Fix Dev, Auto Tissue Sub, Synth Sub, Nonauto Tissue Sub, No Dev], NQ 457
ØRGP*	Fusion/Wrist Jt, Lt 150
ØRGP[0,3,4] [4,5,7,J,K,Z]Z	Fusion/Wrist Jt, Lt, [Opn, Perc, Perc Endo], [Int Fix Dev, Ext Fix Dev, Auto Tissue Sub, Synth Sub, Nonauto Tissue Sub, No Dev], NQ 316
ØRGN*	Fusion/Wrist Jt, Rt 150
ØRGN[0,3,4] [4,5,7,J,K,Z]Z	Fusion/Wrist Jt, Rt, [Opn, Perc, Perc Endo], [Int Fix Dev, Ext Fix Dev, Auto Tissue Sub, Synth Sub, Nonauto Tissue Sub, No Dev], NQ 316
ØDM*	Gastrointestinal Sys, Reattach 333
ØDR*	Gastrointestinal Sys, Replace 334
ØDX*	Gastrointestinal Sys, Transfer 53, 106, 335
HZ48ZZZ	Group Counsel for Substance Abuse Tx, Confrontational 312
HZ49ZZZ	Group Counsel for Substance Abuse Tx, Continuing Care 312
HZ44ZZZ	Group Counsel for Substance Abuse Tx, Interpersonal 312
HZ46ZZZ	Group Counsel for Substance Abuse Tx, Psychoeducation 312
HZ42ZZZ	Group Counsel for Substance Abuse, Cognitive Behavioral 312
HZ47ZZZ	Group Counsel for Substance Abuse, Motivational Enhance 312
HZ43ZZZ	Group Counseling for Substance Abuse Tx, 12-Step 312
HZ41ZZZ	Group Counseling for Substance Abuse Tx, Behavioral 312
HZ40ZZZ	Group Counseling for Substance Abuse Tx, Cognitive 312
HZ4BZZZ	Group Counseling for Substance Abuse Tx, Spiritual 312
HZ45ZZZ	Group Counseling for Substance Abuse Tx, Vocational 312
ØN5*	Head and Facial Bones, Destr 48, 343
ØNQ*	Head and Facial Bones, Repair 344
ØNT*	Head and Facial Bones, Resect 154, 344
Ø2S*	Heart and Great Vessels, Repos 80, 320
ØF1*	Hepatobiliary Sys and Pancreas, Bypass 335
ØF8*	Hepatobiliary Sys and Pancreas, Div 119
ØFQ*	Hepatobiliary Sys and Pancreas, Repair 335
ØFR*	Hepatobiliary Sys and Pancreas, Replace 335
ØFN*	Hepatobiliary Sys and Pancreas, Rls 108, 123, 253, 335
ØFU*	Hepatobiliary Sys and Pancreas, Supl 335
B2Ø*	Imaging, Heart, Plain Radiography 71, 73, 76, 99
HZ31ZZZ	Indiv Counsel for Substance Abuse Tx, Behavioral 312
HZ30ZZZ	Indiv Counsel for Substance Abuse Tx, Cognitive 312
HZ38ZZZ	Indiv Counsel for Substance Abuse Tx, Confrontational 312
HZ39ZZZ	Indiv Counsel for Substance Abuse Tx, Continuing Care 312
HZ34ZZZ	Indiv Counsel for Substance Abuse Tx, Interpersonal 312
HZ36ZZZ	Indiv Counsel for Substance Abuse Tx, Psychoeducation 312
HZ3BZZZ	Indiv Counsel for Substance Abuse Tx, Spiritual 312
HZ35ZZZ	Indiv Counsel for Substance Abuse Tx, Vocational 312
HZ32ZZZ	Indiv Counsel for Substance Abuse, Cognitive Behavioral 312
HZ37ZZZ	Indiv Counsel for Substance Abuse, Motivational Enhance 312
HZ53ZZZ	Indiv Psychotherapy for Substance Abuse Tx, 12 Step 312
HZ50ZZZ	Indiv Psychotherapy for Substance Abuse Tx, Cognitive 312
HZ59ZZZ	Indiv Psychotherapy for Substance Abuse Tx, Support 312
HZ51ZZZ	Indiv Psychotherapy for Substance Abuse, Behavioral 312
HZ52ZZZ	Indiv Psychotherapy for Substance Abuse, Cognitiv Behavioral 312
HZ58ZZZ	Indiv Psychotherapy for Substance Abuse, Confrontational 312
HZ55ZZZ	Indiv Psychotherapy for Substance Abuse, Interactive 312
HZ54ZZZ	Indiv Psychotherapy for Substance Abuse, Interpersonal 312
HZ57ZZZ	Indiv Psychotherapy for Substance Abuse, Motivation Enhance 312
HZ5BZZZ	Indiv Psychotherapy for Substance Abuse, Psychoanalysis 312
HZ5CZZZ	Indiv Psychotherapy for Substance Abuse, Psychodynamic 312
HZ56ZZZ	Indiv Psychotherapy for Substance Abuse, Psychoeducation 312
HZ5DZZZ	Indiv Psychotherapy for Substance Abuse, Psychophys 312
HZ33ZZZ	Individual Counseling for Substance Abuse Tx, 12-Step 312
Ø2HA4RS	Insert Bivent Ext Heart Assist in Heart, Perc Endo 1, 71
ØJHN3HZ	Insert Contracept Dev in Rt Low Leg SQ/Fascia, Perc 220
Ø2HAØRS	Insert of Bivent Ext Heart Assist into Heart, Opn Appr 1, 71
Ø2HA3RS	Insert of Bivent Ext Heart Assist into Heart, Perc Appr 1, 71
Ø2H73MZ	Insert of Cardiac Lead into Lt Atrium, Perc Appr 30, 77, 88, 358
Ø2H63MZ	Insert of Cardiac Lead into Rt Atrium, Perc Appr 30, 77, 88, 358
Ø2H64MZ	Insert of Cardiac Lead into Rt Atrium, Perc Endo Appr 29, 77, 358
Ø2H44KZ	Insert of Defib Lead into Cor Vein, Perc Endo Appr 73, 92
Ø2H40KZ	Insert of Defibrillator Lead into Cor Vein, Opn Appr 73, 92
Ø2H43KZ	Insert of Defibrillator Lead into Cor Vein, Perc Appr 78
Ø2HAØRZ	Insert of Ext Heart Assist into Heart, Opn Appr 1, 71
Ø2HA3RZ	Insert of Ext Heart Assist into Heart, Perc Appr 71
Ø2HA4RZ	Insert of Ext Heart Assist into Heart, Perc Endo Appr 1, 71
ØDH6ØUZ	Insert of Feeding Device into Stomach, Opn Appr 106, 333
ØDH543Z	Insert of Inf Dev into Esophag, Perc Endo Appr 105
Ø2H643Z	Insert of Inf Dev into Rt Atrium, Perc Endo Appr 74
Ø2HK43Z	Insert of Inf Dev into Rt Ventricle, Perc Endo Appr 74
ØØHØ33Z	Insert of Inf Device into Brain, Perc Appr 296
ØDH583Z	Insert of Inf Device into Esophagus, Endo 106
ØDH5Ø3Z	Insert of Inf Device into Esophagus, Opn Appr 105
ØDH533Z	Insert of Inf Device into Esophagus, Perc Appr 105
ØDH573Z	Insert of Inf Device into Esophagus, Via Opng 105
ØWHPØ3Z	Insert of Inf Device into GI Tract, Opn Appr 113
Ø2H6Ø3Z	Insert of Inf Device into Rt Atrium, Opn Appr 74
Ø2HKØ3Z	Insert of Inf Device into Rt Ventricle, Opn Appr 74
Ø2H6ØDZ	Insert of Intralum Dev into Rt Atrium, Opn Appr 74
Ø2H63DZ	Insert of Intralum Dev into Rt Atrium, Perc Appr 74
Ø2H64DZ	Insert of Intralum Dev into Rt Atrium, Perc Endo Appr 74
Ø2HKØDZ	Insert of Intralum Dev into Rt Ventricle, Opn Appr 74
Ø2HK3DZ	Insert of Intralum Dev into Rt Ventricle, Perc Appr 74
Ø2HK4DZ	Insert of Intralum Dev into Rt Ventricle, Perc Endo Appr 74
ØDH542Z	Insert of Monitor Dev into Esophag, Perc Endo Appr 105
Ø2H742Z	Insert of Monitor Dev into Lt Atrium, Perc Endo Appr 319
Ø2H642Z	Insert of Monitor Dev into Rt Atrium, Perc Endo Appr 319
Ø2HVØ2Z	Insert of Monitor Dev into Sup Vena Cava, Opn Appr 271
Ø2H6[0,3,4]2Z	Insert of Monitoring Dev into Rt Atrium, [Opn, Perc, Perc Endo] 74
ØDH582Z	Insert of Monitoring Device into Esophagus, Endo 106
ØDH5Ø2Z	Insert of Monitoring Device into Esophagus, Opn Appr 105
ØDH532Z	Insert of Monitoring Device into Esophagus, Perc Appr 105
ØDH572Z	Insert of Monitoring Device into Esophagus, Via Opng 105
Ø2H7Ø2Z	Insert of Monitoring Device into Lt Atrium, Opn Appr 319
Ø2H6Ø2Z	Insert of Monitoring Device into Rt Atrium, Opn Appr 319
ØJH8[0,3][D,E]Z	Insert of Multi Array [Stimulator Generator, Rechargeable Stimulator Generator] into Abd SQ Tissue & Fascia, [Opn, Perc] Appr 11, 16
ØJH7[0,3][D,E]Z	Insert of Multi Array [Stimulator Generator, Rechargeable Stimulator Generator] into Back SQ Tissue & Fascia, [Opn, Perc] Appr 11, 16
ØJH6[0,3][D,E]Z	Insert of Multi Array [Stimulator Generator, Rechargeable Stimulator Generator] into Chest SQ Tissue & Fascia, [Opn, Perc] Appr 11, 16
ØNHØØNZ	Insert of Neurostim into Skull, Opn Appr 11, 16, 28
Ø2H73JZ	Insert of Pacemaker Lead into Lt Atrium, Perc Appr 30, 77, 78, 88, 358

02HL3JZ	Insert of Pacemaker Lead into Lt Ventricle, Perc Appr **24, 29, 30, 77, 78, 88, 319, 358**
02H63JZ	Insert of Pacemaker Lead into Rt Atrium, Perc Appr **30, 77, 78, 88, 358**
02HK3JZ	Insert of Pacemaker Lead into Rt Ventricle, Perc Appr **24, 29, 30, 77, 78, 88, 319, 358**
02HR00Z	Insert of Pressure Sens into Lt Pulm Art, Opn Appr **89**
02HR30Z	Insert of Pressure Sens into Lt Pulm Art, Perc Appr **89**
02HR40Z	Insert of Pressure Sens into Lt Pulm Art, Perc Endo Appr **89**
02HQ00Z	Insert of Pressure Sens into Rt Pulm Art, Opn Appr **89**
02HQ30Z	Insert of Pressure Sens into Rt Pulm Art, Perc Appr **89**
02HQ40Z	Insert of Pressure Sens into Rt Pulm Art, Perc Endo Appr **89**
0WHC01Z	Insert of Radioact Elem into Mediastinum, Opn Appr **78, 79**
0WHC31Z	Insert of Radioact Elem into Mediastinum, Perc Appr **78, 79**
0WHC41Z	Insert of Radioact Elem into Mediastinum, Perc Endo Appr **78, 79**
0WHD01Z	Insert of Radioact Elem into Pericard Cav, Opn Appr **78, 79**
0WHD31Z	Insert of Radioact Elem into Pericard Cav, Perc Appr **78, 79**
0WHD41Z	Insert Radioact Elem in Pericard Cav, Perc Endo **78, 79**
04H0[0,3,4]DZ	Insert/Abd Aorta, [Opn, Perc, Perc Endo], Intralum Dev, NQ **83, 111, 296, 323**
0WHF*	Insert/Abd Wall **113, 355**
0WHF[0,3,4]1Z	Insert/Abd Wall, [Opn, Perc, Perc Endo], Radioact Elmt, NQ **460**
0QH5*	Insert/Acetabulum, Lt **156, 347**
0QH4*	Insert/Acetabulum, Rt **156, 347**
0RHH[0,3,4]4Z	Insert/Acromioclavicular Jt, Lt, [Opn, Perc, Perc Endo], Int Fix Dev, NQ **147, 349**
0RHG[0,3,4]4Z	Insert/Acromioclavicular Jt, Rt, [Opn, Perc, Perc Endo], Int Fix Dev, NQ **147, 349**
0DHR*	Insert/Anal Sphincter **109**
0SHG[0,3,4][4,5]Z	Insert/Ankle Jt, Lt, [Opn, Perc, Perc Endo], [Int Fix Dev, Ext Fix Dev], NQ **133, 351**
0SHF[0,3,4][4,5]Z	Insert/Ankle Jt, Rt, [Opn, Perc, Perc Endo], [Int Fix Dev, Ext Fix Dev], NQ **133, 351**
0YHL[0,3,4][3,Y]Z	Insert/Ankle Rgn, Lt, [Opn, Perc, Perc Endo], [Inf Dev, Oth Dev] , NQ **220**
0YHL[0,3,4]1Z	Insert/Ankle Rgn, Lt, [Opn, Perc, Perc Endo], Radioact Elmt, NQ **357, 461**
0YHK[0,3,4][3,Y]Z	Insert/Ankle Rgn, Rt, [Opn, Perc, Perc Endo], [Inf Dev, Oth Dev], NQ **220**
0YHK[0,3,4]1Z	Insert/Ankle Rgn, Rt, [Opn, Perc, Perc Endo], Radioact Elmt, NQ **357, 461**
04HQ[0,3,4]DZ	Insert/Ant Tibial Artery, Lt, [Opn, Perc, Perc Endo], Intralum Dev, NQ **83, 297, 323**
04HP[0,3,4]DZ	Insert/Ant Tibial Artery, Rt, [Opn, Perc, Perc Endo], Intralum Dev, NQ **83, 297, 323**
0DHQ*	Insert/Anus **333**
0DHQ[0,3,4,7,8]DZ	Insert/Anus, [Opn, Perc, Perc Endo, Via Natrl or Artfcl Opng, Via Natrl or Artfcl Opng Endo], Intralum Dev, NQ **109**
0DHQ[0,3,4]LZ	Insert/Anus, [Opn, Perc, Perc Endo], Artfcl Sphincter, NQ **107, 211**
02H7[0,4]MZ	Insert/Atrium, Lt, [Opn, Perc, Perc Endo], Cardiac Lead, NQ **29, 77, 78, 357, 358**
02H7[0,3,4][2,3,D]Z	Insert/Atrium, Lt, [Opn, Perc, Perc Endo], [Monitoring Dev, Inf Dev, Intralum Dev], NQ **74**
02H7[0,3,4]KZ	Insert/Atrium, Lt, [Opn, Perc, Perc Endo], Cardiac Lead, Defibrillator, NQ **73, 74, 92**
02H7[0,3,4]JZ	Insert/Atrium, Lt, [Opn, Perc, Perc Endo], Cardiac Lead, Pacemaker, NQ **29, 77, 78, 357, 358**
02H7[0,3,4]0Z	Insert/Atrium, Lt, [Opn, Perc, Perc Endo], Monitoring Dev, Pressure Sensor, NQ **89**
02H73[J,M]Z	Insert/Atrium, Lt, Perc, [Cardiac Lead, Pacemaker, Cardiac Lead], NQ **24**
02H73[2,J,M]Z	Insert/Atrium, Lt, Perc, [Monitoring Dev, Cardiac Lead, Pacemaker, Cardiac Lead], NQ **319**
02H6[0,4]MZ	Insert/Atrium, Rt, [Opn, Perc Endo], Cardiac Lead, NQ **29, 77, 78, 357, 358**
02H6[0,3,4]KZ	Insert/Atrium, Rt, [Opn, Perc, Perc Endo], Cardiac Lead, Defibrillator, NQ **73, 74, 92**
02H6[0,3,4]JZ	Insert/Atrium, Rt, [Opn, Perc, Perc Endo], Cardiac Lead, Pacemaker, NQ **29, 77, 78, 357, 358**
02H6[0,3,4]0Z	Insert/Atrium, Rt, [Opn, Perc, Perc Endo], Monitoring Dev, Pressure Sensor, NQ **89**
02H6[3,4]JZ	Insert/Atrium, Rt, [Perc, Perc Endo], Cardiac Lead, Pacemaker, NQ **29, 77, 358**
02H63[J,M]Z	Insert/Atrium, Rt, Perc, [Cardiac Lead, Pacemaker, Cardiac Lead], NQ **24**
02H63[2,J,M]Z	Insert/Atrium, Rt, Perc, [Monitoring Dev, Cardiac Lead, Pacemaker, Cardiac Lead], NQ **319**
0XH5[0,3,4][3,Y]Z	Insert/Axilla, Lt, [Opn, Perc, Perc Endo], [Inf Dev, Oth Dev], NQ **220**
0XH5[0,3,4]1Z	Insert/Axilla, Lt, [Opn, Perc, Perc Endo], Radioact Elmt, NQ **356, 461**
0XH4[0,3,4][3,Y]Z	Insert/Axilla, Rt, [Opn, Perc, Perc Endo], [Inf Dev, Oth Dev], NQ **220**
0XH4[0,3,4]1Z	Insert/Axilla, Rt, [Opn, Perc, Perc Endo], Radioact Elmt, NQ **356, 461**
03H6[0,3,4]DZ	Insert/Axillary Artery, Lt, [Opn, Perc, Perc Endo], Intralum Dev, NQ **63, 81, 296, 321**
03H5[0,3,4]DZ	Insert/Axillary Artery, Rt, [Opn, Perc, Perc Endo], Intralum Dev, NQ **63, 81, 296, 321**
05H8[0,3,4]DZ	Insert/Axillary Vein, Lt, [Opn, Perc, Perc Endo], Intralum Dev, NQ **85, 297, 326**
05H7[0,3,4]DZ	Insert/Axillary Vein, Rt, [Opn, Perc, Perc Endo], Intralum Dev, NQ **85, 297, 326**
05H0[0,3,4]DZ	Insert/Azygos Vein, [Opn, Perc, Perc Endo], Intralum Dev, NQ **64, 85, 297, 325**
05HC[0,3,4]DZ	Insert/Basilic Vein, Lt, [Opn, Perc, Perc Endo], Intralum Dev, NQ **85, 297, 326**
05HB[0,3,4]DZ	Insert/Basilic Vein, Rt, [Opn, Perc, Perc Endo], Intralum Dev, NQ **85, 297, 326**
0THC*	Insert/Bladder Neck **249, 353**
0THB[0,3,4,7,8][2,L,M]Z	Insert/Bladder, [Opn, Perc, Perc Endo, Via Natrl or Artfcl Opng, Via Natrl or Artfcl Opng Endo], [Monitoring Dev, Artfcl Sphincter, Stimulator Lead], NQ **249**
0THB[0,3,4,7,8][2,L]Z	Insert/Bladder, [Opn, Perc, Perc Endo, Via Natrl or Artfcl Opng, Via Natrl or Artfcl Opng Endo], [Monitoring Dev, Artfcl Sphincter], NQ **353**
03H8[0,3,4]DZ	Insert/Brachial Artery, Lt, [Opn, Perc, Perc Endo], Intralum Dev, NQ **81, 296, 321**
03H7[0,3,4]DZ	Insert/Brachial Artery, Rt, [Opn, Perc, Perc Endo], Intralum Dev, NQ **81, 296, 321**
05HA[0,3,4]DZ	Insert/Brachial Vein, Lt, [Opn, Perc, Perc Endo], Intralum Dev, NQ **85, 297, 326**
05H9[0,3,4]DZ	Insert/Brachial Vein, Rt, [Opn, Perc, Perc Endo], Intralum Dev, NQ **85, 297, 326**
00H0*	Insert/Brain **318**
00H0[0,3,4][2,3,M]Z	Insert/Brain, [Opn, Perc, Perc Endo], [Monitoring Dev, Inf Dev, Neurostimulator Lead], NQ **8, 12, 16**
00H0[0,3,4][2,3]Z	Insert/Brain, [Opn, Perc, Perc Endo], [Monitoring Dev, Inf Dev] , NQ **414**
00H0[0,3,4]MZ	Insert/Brain, [Opn, Perc, Perc Endo], Neurostimulator Lead, NQ **11, 16, 296**
0HHV[0,3,7,8,X]1Z	Insert/Breast, Bilat, [Opn, Perc, Via Natrl or Artfcl Opng, Via Natrl or Artfcl Opng Endo, Ext], Radioact Elmt, NQ **211, 449**
0HHV[0,3,7,8]NZ	Insert/Breast, Bilat, [Opn, Perc, Via Natrl or Artfcl Opng, Via Natrl or Artfcl Opng Endo], Tissue Expander, NQ **222, 449**
0HHU[0,3,7,8,X]1Z	Insert/Breast, Lt, [Opn, Perc, Via Natrl or Artfcl Opng, Via Natrl or Artfcl Opng Endo, Ext], Radioact Elmt, NQ **211, 449**
0HHU[0,3,7,8]NZ	Insert/Breast, Lt, [Opn, Perc, Via Natrl or Artfcl Opng, Via Natrl or Artfcl Opng Endo], Tissue Expander, NQ **222, 449**
0HHT[0,3,7,8,X]1Z	Insert/Breast, Rt, [Opn, Perc, Via Natrl or Artfcl Opng, Via Natrl or Artfcl Opng Endo, Ext], Radioact Elmt, NQ **211, 449**
0HHT[0,3,7,8]NZ	Insert/Breast, Rt, [Opn, Perc, Via Natrl or Artfcl Opng, Via Natrl or Artfcl Opng Endo], Tissue Expander, NQ **222, 449**
0YH1[0,3,4][3,Y]Z	Insert/Buttock, Lt, [Opn, Perc, Perc Endo], [Inf Dev, Oth Dev], NQ **220**
0YH1[0,3,4]1Z	Insert/Buttock, Lt, [Opn, Perc, Perc Endo], Radioact Elmt, NQ **357, 461**
0YH0[0,3,4][3,Y]Z	Insert/Buttock, Rt, [Opn, Perc, Perc Endo], [Inf Dev, Oth Dev], NQ **220**
0YH0[0,3,4]1Z	Insert/Buttock, Rt, [Opn, Perc, Perc Endo], Radioact Elmt, NQ **357, 461**
0RHR[0,3,4][4,5]Z	Insert/Carpal Jt, Lt, [Opn, Perc, Perc Endo], [Int Fix Dev, Ext Fix Dev], NQ **146, 316**
0RHQ[0,3,4][4,5]Z	Insert/Carpal Jt, Rt, [Opn, Perc, Perc Endo], [Int Fix Dev, Ext Fix Dev], NQ **146, 316**
0PHN*	Insert/Carpal, Lt **150**

Code	Description
0PHN[0,3,4][4,5]Z	Insert/Carpal, Lt, [Opn, Perc, Perc Endo], [Int Fix Dev, Ext Fix Dev], NQ **315**
0PHM*	Insert/Carpal, Rt **150**
0PHM[0,3,4][4,5]Z	Insert/Carpal, Rt, [Opn, Perc, Perc Endo], [Int Fix Dev, Ext Fix Dev], NQ **315**
04H1[0,3,4]DZ	Insert/Celiac Artery, [Opn, Perc, Perc Endo], Intralum Dev, NQ **83, 296, 323**
05HF[0,3,4]DZ	Insert/Cephalic Vein, Lt, [Opn, Perc, Perc Endo], Intralum Dev, NQ **85, 297, 326**
05HD[0,3,4]DZ	Insert/Cephalic Vein, Rt, [Opn, Perc, Perc Endo], Intralum Dev, NQ **85, 297, 326**
00H6*	Insert/Cerebral Ventricle **318**
00H6[0,3,4][2,3,M]Z	Insert/Cerebral Ventricle, [Opn, Perc, Perc Endo], [Monitoring Dev, Inf Dev, Neurostimulator Lead], NQ **8, 12, 16**
00H6[0,3,4][2,3]Z	Insert/Cerebral Ventricle, [Opn, Perc, Perc Endo], [Monitoring Dev, Inf Dev], NQ **414**
00H6[0,3,4]MZ	Insert/Cerebral Ventricle, [Opn, Perc, Perc Endo], Neurostimulator Lead, NQ **11, 16, 296**
0RH1[0,3,4][B,C,D]Z	Insert/Cervical Vert Jt, [Opn, Perc, Perc Endo], [Spinal Stabliz Dev, Interspinous Process, Spinal Stabliz Dev, Pedicle-Based, Spinal Stabliz Dev, Facet Replace], NQ **20, 159, 160, 161, 349**
0RH1[0,3,4]4Z	Insert/Cervical Vert Jt, [Opn, Perc, Perc Endo], Int Fix Dev, NQ **156**
0PH3*	Insert/Cervical Vertebra **155, 345**
0RH4[0,3,4][B,C,D]Z	Insert/Cervicothoracic Vert Jt, [Opn, Perc, Perc Endo], [Spinal Stabliz Dev, Interspinous Process, Spinal Stabliz Dev, Pedicle-Based, Spinal Stabliz Dev, Facet Replace], NQ **20, 159, 160, 161, 349**
0RH4[0,3,4]4Z	Insert/Cervicothoracic Vert Jt, [Opn, Perc, Perc Endo], Int Fix Dev, NQ **156**
0UHC[0,3,4,7,8]1Z	Insert/Cervix, [Opn, Perc, Perc Endo, Via Natrl or Artfcl Opng, Via Natrl or Artfcl Opng Endo], Radioact Elmt, NQ **266, 354, 459**
0WH8[0,3,4]1Z	Insert/Chest Wall, [Opn, Perc, Perc Endo], Radioact Elmt, NQ **66, 355, 460**
0PHB*	Insert/Clavicle, Lt **65, 155, 345**
0PH9*	Insert/Clavicle, Rt **65, 155, 345**
0SH6[0,3,4]4Z	Insert/Coccygeal Jt, [Opn, Perc, Perc Endo], Int Fix Dev, NQ **157**
0QHS*	Insert/Coccyx **156, 347**
04H7[0,3,4]DZ	Insert/Colic Artery, Lt, [Opn, Perc, Perc Endo], Intralum Dev, NQ **83, 296, 323**
04H8[0,3,4]DZ	Insert/Colic Artery, Mid, [Opn, Perc, Perc Endo], Intralum Dev, NQ **83, 296, 323**
04H6[0,3,4]DZ	Insert/Colic Artery, Rt, [Opn, Perc, Perc Endo], Intralum Dev, NQ **83, 296, 323**
06H7[0,3,4]DZ	Insert/Colic Vein, [Opn, Perc, Perc Endo], Intralum Dev, NQ **87, 111, 297, 327**
03HJ[0,3,4]DZ	Insert/Common Carotid Artery, Lt, [Opn, Perc, Perc Endo], Intralum Dev, NQ **50, 81, 296, 321**
03HH[0,3,4]DZ	Insert/Common Carotid Artery, Rt, [Opn, Perc, Perc Endo], Intralum Dev, NQ **81, 296, 321**
04HD[0,3,4]DZ	Insert/Common Iliac Artery, Lt, [Opn, Perc, Perc Endo], Intralum Dev, NQ **83, 297, 323**
04HC[0,3,4]DZ	Insert/Common Iliac Artery, Rt, [Opn, Perc, Perc Endo], Intralum Dev, NQ **83, 297, 323**
06HD[0,3,4]DZ	Insert/Common Iliac Vein, Lt, [Opn, Perc, Perc Endo], Intralum Dev, NQ **87, 271, 297, 327**
06HC[0,3,4]DZ	Insert/Common Iliac Vein, Rt, [Opn, Perc, Perc Endo], Intralum Dev, NQ **87, 271, 297, 327**
02H4[0,4][J,M]Z	Insert/Coronary Vein, [Opn, Perc Endo], [Cardiac Lead, Pacemaker, Cardiac Lead], NQ **29, 77, 357, 358**
02H4[0,4]KZ	Insert/Coronary Vein, [Opn, Perc Endo], Cardiac Lead, Defibrillator, NQ **73, 74**
02H4[0,3,4][J,M]Z	Insert/Coronary Vein, [Opn, Perc, Perc Endo], [Cardiac Lead, Pacemaker, Cardiac Lead], NQ **78**
02H4[0,3,4][2,3,D]Z	Insert/Coronary Vein, [Opn, Perc, Perc Endo], [Monitoring Dev, Inf Dev, Intralum Dev], NQ **74**
02H4[0,3,4]0Z	Insert/Coronary Vein, [Opn, Perc, Perc Endo], Monitoring Dev, Pressure Sensor, NQ **89**
02H43[J,K,M]Z	Insert/Coronary Vein, Perc, [Cardiac Lead, Pacemaker, Cardiac Lead, Defibrillator, Cardiac Lead], NQ **73, 92**
0WH1[0,3,4]YZ	Insert/Cranial Cavity, [Opn, Perc, Perc Endo], Oth Dev, NQ **10, 14, 18**
0WH1[0,3,4]1Z	Insert/Cranial Cavity, [Opn, Perc, Perc Endo], Radioact Elmt, NQ **28, 355, 460**
00HE*	Insert/Cranial Nerve **23**
00HE[0,3,4]MZ	Insert/Cranial Nerve, [Opn, Perc, Perc Endo], Neurostimulator Lead, NQ **31, 50, 80, 151, 251, 258, 267, 318**
0BHS*	Insert/Diaphragm, Lt **62**
0BHS[0,3,4]MZ	Insert/Diaphragm, Lt, [Opn, Perc, Perc Endo], Diaphragmatic Pacemaker Lead, NQ **331**
0BHR*	Insert/Diaphragm, Rt **62**
0BHR[0,3,4]MZ	Insert/Diaphragm, Rt, [Opn, Perc, Perc Endo], Diaphragmatic Pacemaker Lead, NQ **331**
0DH9[0,3,4,7,8][2,3]Z	Insert/Duodenum, [Opn, Perc, Perc Endo, Via Natrl or Artfcl Opng, Via Natrl or Artfcl Opng Endo], [Monitoring Dev, Inf Dev], NQ **106, 123, 333**
0RHM[0,3,4][4,5]Z	Insert/Elbow Jt, Lt, [Opn, Perc, Perc Endo], [Int Fix Dev, Ext Fix Dev], NQ **147, 349**
0RHL[0,3,4][4,5]Z	Insert/Elbow Jt, Rt, [Opn, Perc, Perc Endo], [Int Fix Dev, Ext Fix Dev], NQ **147, 349**
0XHC[0,3,4][3,Y]Z	Insert/Elbow Rgn, Lt, [Opn, Perc, Perc Endo], [Inf Dev, Oth Dev], NQ **220**
0XHC[0,3,4]1Z	Insert/Elbow Rgn, Lt, [Opn, Perc, Perc Endo], Radioact Elmt, NQ **356, 461**
0XHB[0,3,4][3,Y]Z	Insert/Elbow Rgn, Rt, [Opn, Perc, Perc Endo], [Inf Dev, Oth Dev], NQ **220**
0XHB[0,3,4]1Z	Insert/Elbow Rgn, Rt, [Opn, Perc, Perc Endo], Radioact Elmt, NQ **356, 461**
0GHS[0,3,4][2,3]Z	Insert/Endocrine Gland, [Opn, Perc, Perc Endo], [Monitoring Dev, Inf Dev], NQ **211**
06H3[0,3,4]DZ	Insert/Esophageal Vein, [Opn, Perc, Perc Endo], Intralum Dev, NQ **51, 87, 111, 297, 327**
0DH5[0,3,4,7,8][1,2,3]Z	Insert/Esophagus, [Opn, Perc, Perc Endo, Via Natrl or Artfcl Opng, Via Natrl or Artfcl Opng Endo], [Radioact Elmt, Monitoring Dev, Inf Dev], NQ **333**
0DH5[0,3,4,7,8]1Z	Insert/Esophagus, [Opn, Perc, Perc Endo, Via Natrl or Artfcl Opng, Via Natrl or Artfcl Opng Endo], Radioact Elmt, NQ **112, 449**
0NHG*	Insert/Ethmoid Bone, Lt **54**
0NHF*	Insert/Ethmoid Bone, Rt **54**
03HN[0,3,4]DZ	Insert/Ext Carotid Artery, Lt, [Opn, Perc, Perc Endo], Intralum Dev, NQ **50, 81, 296, 321**
03HM[0,3,4]DZ	Insert/Ext Carotid Artery, Rt, [Opn, Perc, Perc Endo], Intralum Dev, NQ **50, 81, 296, 321**
04HJ[0,3,4]DZ	Insert/Ext Iliac Artery, Lt, [Opn, Perc, Perc Endo], Intralum Dev, NQ **83, 297, 323**
04HH[0,3,4]DZ	Insert/Ext Iliac Artery, Rt, [Opn, Perc, Perc Endo], Intralum Dev, NQ **83, 297, 323**
06HG[0,3,4]DZ	Insert/Ext Iliac Vein, Lt, [Opn, Perc, Perc Endo], Intralum Dev, NQ **87, 271, 297, 327**
06HF[0,3,4]DZ	Insert/Ext Iliac Vein, Rt, [Opn, Perc, Perc Endo], Intralum Dev, NQ **87, 271, 297, 327**
05HQ[0,3,4]DZ	Insert/Ext Jugular Vein, Lt, [Opn, Perc, Perc Endo], Intralum Dev, NQ **51, 85, 297, 326**
05HP[0,3,4]DZ	Insert/Ext Jugular Vein, Rt, [Opn, Perc, Perc Endo], Intralum Dev, NQ **51, 85, 297, 326**
08H[0,1]05Z	Insert/Eye, [Rt, Lt], Opn, Epiretinal Visual Prosthesis, NQ **44, 330**
08H1[3,X][1,3]Z	Insert/Eye, Lt, [Perc, Ext], [Radioact Elmt, Inf Dev], NQ **444**
08H1[3,X]3Z	Insert/Eye, Lt, [Perc, Ext], Inf Dev, NQ **43**
08H1[3,X]1Z	Insert/Eye, Lt, [Perc, Ext], Radioact Elmt, NQ **25, 44, 330**
08H0[3,X][1,3]Z	Insert/Eye, Rt, [Perc, Ext], [Radioact Elmt, Inf Dev], NQ **444**
08H0[3,X]3Z	Insert/Eye, Rt, [Perc, Ext], Inf Dev, NQ **43**
08H0[3,X]1Z	Insert/Eye, Rt, [Perc, Ext], Radioact Elmt, NQ **25, 44, 330**
03HR[0,3,4]DZ	Insert/Face Artery, [Opn, Perc, Perc Endo], Intralum Dev, NQ **50, 81, 296, 321**
05HV[0,3,4]DZ	Insert/Face Vein, Lt, [Opn, Perc, Perc Endo], Intralum Dev, NQ **51, 85, 297, 326**
05HT[0,3,4]DZ	Insert/Face Vein, Rt, [Opn, Perc, Perc Endo], Intralum Dev, NQ **51, 85, 297, 326**
0WH2[0,3,4][3,Y]Z	Insert/Face, [Opn, Perc, Perc Endo], [Inf Dev, Oth Dev], NQ **220**
0WH2[0,3,4]1Z	Insert/Face, [Opn, Perc, Perc Endo], Radioact Elmt, NQ **28, 355, 460**
0NHW*	Insert/Facial Bone **54**
04HL[0,3,4]DZ	Insert/Femor Artery, Lt, [Opn, Perc, Perc Endo], Intralum Dev, NQ **83, 297, 323**
04HK[0,3,4]DZ	Insert/Femor Artery, Rt, [Opn, Perc, Perc Endo], Intralum Dev, NQ **83, 297, 323**
0YH8[0,3,4][3,Y]Z	Insert/Femor Rgn, Lt, [Opn, Perc, Perc Endo], [Inf Dev, Oth Dev], NQ **220**

Code	Description
0YH8[0,3,4]1Z	Insert/Femor Rgn, Lt, [Opn, Perc, Perc Endo], Radioact Elmt, NQ 357, 461
0YH7[0,3,4][3,Y]Z	Insert/Femor Rgn, Rt, [Opn, Perc, Perc Endo], [Inf Dev, Oth Dev], NQ 220
0YH7[0,3,4]1Z	Insert/Femor Rgn, Rt, [Opn, Perc, Perc Endo], Radioact Elmt, NQ 357, 461
0QH9[0,3,4] [4,5,6,B,C,D]Z	Insert/Femor Shaft, Lt, [Opn, Perc, Perc Endo], [Int Fix Dev, Ext Fix Dev, Int Fix Dev, Intramedullary Int Fix Dev, Ext Fix Dev, Monop, Ext Fix Dev, Ring, Ext Fix Dev, Hybrid], NQ 130, 347, 415
0QH8[0,3,4] [4,5,6,B,C,D]Z	Insert/Femor Shaft, Rt, [Opn, Perc, Perc Endo], [Int Fix Dev, Ext Fix Dev, Int Fix Dev, Intramedullary Int Fix Dev, Ext Fix Dev, Monop, Ext Fix Dev, Ring, Ext Fix Dev, Hybrid], NQ 130, 347, 415
06HN[0,3,4]DZ	Insert/Femor Vein, Lt, [Opn, Perc, Perc Endo], Intralum Dev, NQ 87, 297, 327
06HM[0,3,4]DZ	Insert/Femor Vein, Rt, [Opn, Perc, Perc Endo], Intralum Dev, NQ 87, 297, 327
0QHK[0,3,4] [4,5,6,B,C,D]Z	Insert/Fibula, Lt, [Opn, Perc, Perc Endo], [Int Fix Dev, Ext Fix Dev, Int Fix Dev, Intramedullary Int Fix Dev, Ext Fix Dev, Monop, Ext Fix Dev, Ring, Ext Fix Dev, Hybrid], NQ 133, 347
0QHJ[0,3,4] [4,5,6,B,C,D]Z	Insert/Fibula, Rt, [Opn, Perc, Perc Endo], [Int Fix Dev, Ext Fix Dev, Int Fix Dev, Intramedullary Int Fix Dev, Ext Fix Dev, Monop, Ext Fix Dev, Ring, Ext Fix Dev, Hybrid], NQ 133, 347
0RHX[0,3,4][4,5]Z	Insert/Finger Phalangeal Jt, Lt, [Opn, Perc, Perc Endo], [Int Fix Dev, Ext Fix Dev], NQ 147, 316
0RHW[0,3,4][4,5]Z	Insert/Finger Phalangeal Jt, Rt, [Opn, Perc, Perc Endo], [Int Fix Dev, Ext Fix Dev], NQ 147, 316
0PHV*	Insert/Finger Phalanx, Lt 155, 345
0PHT*	Insert/Finger Phalanx, Rt 155, 345
04HW[0,3,4]DZ	Insert/Foot Artery, Lt, [Opn, Perc, Perc Endo], Intralum Dev, NQ 84, 297, 323
04HV[0,3,4]DZ	Insert/Foot Artery, Rt, [Opn, Perc, Perc Endo], Intralum Dev, NQ 84, 297, 323
06HV[0,3,4]DZ	Insert/Foot Vein, Lt, [Opn, Perc, Perc Endo], Intralum Dev, NQ 87, 297, 327
06HT[0,3,4]DZ	Insert/Foot Vein, Rt, [Opn, Perc, Perc Endo], Intralum Dev, NQ 87, 297, 327
0YHN[0,3,4][3,Y]Z	Insert/Foot, Lt, [Opn, Perc, Perc Endo], [Inf Dev, Oth Dev], NQ 220
0YHN[0,3,4]1Z	Insert/Foot, Lt, [Opn, Perc, Perc Endo], Radioact Elmt, NQ 357, 461
0YHM[0,3,4][3,Y]Z	Insert/Foot, Rt, [Opn, Perc, Perc Endo], [Inf Dev, Oth Dev], NQ 220
0YHM[0,3,4]1Z	Insert/Foot, Rt, [Opn, Perc, Perc Endo], Radioact Elmt, NQ 357, 461
0NH2*	Insert/Frontal Bone, Lt 10, 48, 154, 344, 415
0NH2[0,3,4]4Z	Insert/Frontal Bone, Lt, [Opn, Perc, Perc Endo], Int Fix Dev, NQ 14, 18
0NH1*	Insert/Frontal Bone, Rt 10, 48, 154, 344, 415
0NH1[0,3,4]4Z	Insert/Frontal Bone, Rt, [Opn, Perc, Perc Endo], Int Fix Dev, NQ 14, 18
0FH4[0,3,4]2Z	Insert/Gallbladder, [Opn, Perc, Perc Endo], Monitoring Dev, NQ 120
04H2[0,3,4]DZ	Insert/Gastric Artery, [Opn, Perc, Perc Endo], Intralum Dev, NQ 83, 296, 323
06H2[0,3,4]DZ	Insert/Gastric Vein, [Opn, Perc, Perc Endo], Intralum Dev, NQ 87, 111, 297, 327
0WHP[0,3,4,7,8]1Z	Insert/Gastrointestinal Tract, [Opn, Perc, Perc Endo, Via Natrl or Artfcl Opng, Via Natrl or Artfcl Opng Endo], Radioact Elmt, NQ 113, 355, 460
0WHR[0,3,4,7,8]1Z	Insert/Genitourinary Tract, [Opn, Perc, Perc Endo, Via Natrl or Artfcl Opng, Via Natrl or Artfcl Opng Endo], Radioact Elmt, NQ 254, 260, 266, 356, 460
0PH8*	Insert/Glenoid Cavity, Lt 65, 155, 345
0PH7*	Insert/Glenoid Cavity, Rt 65, 155, 345
06HQ[0,3,4]DZ	Insert/Greater Saphenous Vein, Lt, [Opn, Perc, Perc Endo], Intralum Dev, NQ 87, 297, 327
06HP[0,3,4]DZ	Insert/Greater Saphenous Vein, Rt, [Opn, Perc, Perc Endo], Intralum Dev, NQ 87, 297, 327
03HF[0,3,4]DZ	Insert/Hand Artery, Lt, [Opn, Perc, Perc Endo], Intralum Dev, NQ 81, 296, 321
03HD[0,3,4]DZ	Insert/Hand Artery, Rt, [Opn, Perc, Perc Endo], Intralum Dev, NQ 81, 296, 321
05HH[0,3,4]DZ	Insert/Hand Vein, Lt, [Opn, Perc, Perc Endo], Intralum Dev, NQ 85, 297, 326
05HG[0,3,4]DZ	Insert/Hand Vein, Rt, [Opn, Perc, Perc Endo], Intralum Dev, NQ 85, 297, 326
0XHK[0,3,4][3,Y]Z	Insert/Hand, Lt, [Opn, Perc, Perc Endo], [Inf Dev, Oth Dev], NQ 220
0XHK[0,3,4]1Z	Insert/Hand, Lt, [Opn, Perc, Perc Endo], Radioact Elmt, NQ 356, 461
0XHJ[0,3,4][3,Y]Z	Insert/Hand, Rt, [Opn, Perc, Perc Endo], [Inf Dev, Oth Dev], NQ 220
0XHJ[0,3,4]1Z	Insert/Hand, Rt, [Opn, Perc, Perc Endo], Radioact Elmt, NQ 356, 461
0WH0[0,3,4][3,Y]Z	Insert/Head, [Opn, Perc, Perc Endo], [Inf Dev, Oth Dev], NQ 220
0WH0[0,3,4]1Z	Insert/Head, [Opn, Perc, Perc Endo], Radioact Elmt, NQ 28, 355, 460
02HA[0,3,4]QZ	Insert/Heart, [Opn, Perc, Perc Endo], Implantable Heart Assist Sys, NQ 1
05H1[0,3,4]DZ	Insert/Hemiazygos Vein, [Opn, Perc, Perc Endo], Intralum Dev, NQ 64, 85, 297, 325
04H3[0,3,4]DZ	Insert/Hepatic Artery, [Opn, Perc, Perc Endo], Intralum Dev, NQ 83, 296, 323
06H4[0,3,4]DZ	Insert/Hepatic Vein, [Opn, Perc, Perc Endo], Intralum Dev, NQ 87, 111, 297, 327
0FHB[0,3,4,7,8][1,2]Z	Insert/Hepatobiliary Duct, [Opn, Perc, Perc Endo, Via Natrl or Artfcl Opng, Via Natrl or Artfcl Opng Endo], [Radioact Elmt, Monitoring Dev], NQ 335
0FHB[0,3,4,7,8]2Z	Insert/Hepatobiliary Duct, [Opn, Perc, Perc Endo, Via Natrl or Artfcl Opng, Via Natrl or Artfcl Opng Endo], Monitoring Dev, NQ 120
0FHB[0,3,4,7,8]1Z	Insert/Hepatobiliary Duct, [Opn, Perc, Perc Endo, Via Natrl or Artfcl Opng, Via Natrl or Artfcl Opng Endo], Radioact Elmt, NQ 449
0FHB[0,3,7]DZ	Insert/Hepatobiliary Duct, [Opn, Perc, Via Natrl or Artfcl Opng] , Intralum Dev, NQ 113, 120, 301, 335
0SHB[0,3,4][4,5]Z	Insert/Hip Jt, Lt, [Opn, Perc, Perc Endo], [Int Fix Dev, Ext Fix Dev], NQ 131, 351
0SH9[0,3,4][4,5]Z	Insert/Hip Jt, Rt, [Opn, Perc, Perc Endo], [Int Fix Dev, Ext Fix Dev], NQ 131, 351
0PHD[0,3,4] [4,5,6,B,C,D]Z	Insert/Humeral Head, Lt, [Opn, Perc, Perc Endo], [Int Fix Dev, Ext Fix Dev, Int Fix Dev, Intramedullary Int Fix Dev, Ext Fix Dev, Monop, Ext Fix Dev, Ring, Ext Fix Dev, Hybrid], NQ 132, 345
0PHC[0,3,4] [4,5,6,B,C,D]Z	Insert/Humeral Head, Rt, [Opn, Perc, Perc Endo], [Int Fix Dev, Ext Fix Dev, Int Fix Dev, Intramedullary Int Fix Dev, Ext Fix Dev, Monop, Ext Fix Dev, Ring, Ext Fix Dev, Hybrid], NQ 132, 345
0PHG[0,3,4] [4,5,6,B,C,D]Z	Insert/Humeral Shaft, Lt, [Opn, Perc, Perc Endo], [Int Fix Dev, Ext Fix Dev, Int Fix Dev, Intramedullary Int Fix Dev, Ext Fix Dev, Monop, Ext Fix Dev, Ring, Ext Fix Dev, Hybrid], NQ 132, 345
0PHF[0,3,4] [4,5,6,B,C,D]Z	Insert/Humeral Shaft, Rt, [Opn, Perc, Perc Endo], [Int Fix Dev, Ext Fix Dev, Int Fix Dev, Intramedullary Int Fix Dev, Ext Fix Dev, Monop, Ext Fix Dev, Ring, Ext Fix Dev, Hybrid], NQ 132, 345
0NHX*	Insert/Hyoid Bone 54
06HJ[0,3,4]DZ	Insert/Hypogastric Vein, Lt, [Opn, Perc, Perc Endo], Intralum Dev, NQ 87, 271, 297, 327
06HH[0,3,4]DZ	Insert/Hypogastric Vein, Rt, [Opn, Perc, Perc Endo], Intralum Dev, NQ 87, 271, 297, 327
0DHB[0,3,4,7,8][2,3]Z	Insert/Ileum, [Opn, Perc, Perc Endo, Via Natrl or Artfcl Opng, Via Natrl or Artfcl Opng Endo], [Monitoring Dev, Inf Dev], NQ 109, 333
04HB[0,3,4]DZ	Insert/Inferior Mesenteric Artery, [Opn, Perc, Perc Endo], Intralum Dev, NQ 83, 297, 323
06H6[0,3,4]DZ	Insert/Inferior Mesenteric Vein, [Opn, Perc, Perc Endo], Intralum Dev, NQ 87, 111, 297, 327
06H0[0,3,4]DZ	Insert/Inferior Vena Cava, [Opn, Perc, Perc Endo], Intralum Dev, NQ 25, 64, 87, 111, 122, 153, 241, 252, 258, 268, 271, 290, 327
0YH6[0,3,4][3,Y]Z	Insert/Inguinal Rgn, Lt, [Opn, Perc, Perc Endo], [Inf Dev, Oth Dev], NQ 220
0YH6[0,3,4]1Z	Insert/Inguinal Rgn, Lt, [Opn, Perc, Perc Endo], Radioact Elmt, NQ 357, 461
0YH5[0,3,4][3,Y]Z	Insert/Inguinal Rgn, Rt, [Opn, Perc, Perc Endo], [Inf Dev, Oth Dev], NQ 220
0YH5[0,3,4]1Z	Insert/Inguinal Rgn, Rt, [Opn, Perc, Perc Endo], Radioact Elmt, NQ 357, 461
09HE[0,3,4][5,6,S]Z	Insert/Inner Ear, Lt, [Opn, Perc, Perc Endo], [Hearing Dev, Single Channel Cochlear Prosthesis, Hearing Dev, Multi Channel Cochlear Prosthesis, Hearing Dev], NQ 48, 48
09HE[0,3,4]4Z	Insert/Inner Ear, Lt, [Opn, Perc, Perc Endo], Hearing Dev, Bone Conduction, NQ 51

09HD[0,3,4][5,6,S]Z	Insert/Inner Ear, Rt, [Opn, Perc, Perc Endo], [Hearing Dev, Single Channel Cochlear Prosthesis, Hearing Dev, Multi Channel Cochlear Prosthesis, Hearing Dev], NQ 48
09HD[0,3,4]4Z	Insert/Inner Ear, Rt, [Opn, Perc, Perc Endo], Hearing Dev, Bone Conduction, NQ 51
03H2[0,3,4]DZ	Insert/Innominate Artery, [Opn, Perc, Perc Endo], Intralum Dev, NQ 50, 81, 296, 321
05H4[0,3,4]DZ	Insert/Innominate Vein, Lt, [Opn, Perc, Perc Endo], Intralum Dev, NQ 64, 85, 297, 325
05H3[0,3,4]DZ	Insert/Innominate Vein, Rt, [Opn, Perc, Perc Endo], Intralum Dev, NQ 64, 85, 297, 325
03HL[0,3,4][D,M]Z	Insert/Int Carotid Artery, Lt, [Opn, Perc, Perc Endo], [Intralum Dev, Stimulator Lead], NQ 81
03HL[0,3,4]DZ	Insert/Int Carotid Artery, Lt, [Opn, Perc, Perc Endo], Intralum Dev, NQ 296, 321
03HK[0,3,4][D,M]Z	Insert/Int Carotid Artery, Rt, [Opn, Perc, Perc Endo], [Intralum Dev, Stimulator Lead], NQ 81
03HK[0,3,4]DZ	Insert/Int Carotid Artery, Rt, [Opn, Perc, Perc Endo], Intralum Dev, NQ 50, 296, 321
04HF[0,3,4]DZ	Insert/Int Iliac Artery, Lt, [Opn, Perc, Perc Endo], Intralum Dev, NQ 83, 297, 323
04HE[0,3,4]DZ	Insert/Int Iliac Artery, Rt, [Opn, Perc, Perc Endo], Intralum Dev, NQ 83, 297, 323
05HN[0,3,4]DZ	Insert/Int Jugular Vein, Lt, [Opn, Perc, Perc Endo], Intralum Dev, NQ 51, 85, 297, 326
05HM[0,3,4]DZ	Insert/Int Jugular Vein, Rt, [Opn, Perc, Perc Endo], Intralum Dev, NQ 51, 85, 297, 326
03H1[0,3,4]DZ	Insert/Int Mammary Artery, Lt, [Opn, Perc, Perc Endo], Intralum Dev, NQ 63, 81, 296, 321
03H0[0,3,4]DZ	Insert/Int Mammary Artery, Rt, [Opn, Perc, Perc Endo], Intralum Dev, NQ 63, 81, 296, 321
03HG[0,3,4]DZ	Insert/Intracranial Artery, [Opn, Perc, Perc Endo], Intralum Dev, NQ 81, 296, 321
05HL[0,3,4]DZ	Insert/Intracranial Vein, [Opn, Perc, Perc Endo], Intralum Dev, NQ 85, 297, 326
0DHA[0,3,4,7,8][2,3]Z	Insert/Jejunum, [Opn, Perc, Perc Endo, Via Natrl or Artfcl Opng, Via Natrl or Artfcl Opng Endo], [Monitoring Dev, Inf Dev], NQ 109, 333
0TH5[0,3,4,7,8]2Z	Insert/Kidney, [Opn, Perc, Perc Endo, Via Natrl or Artfcl Opng, Via Natrl or Artfcl Opng Endo], Monitoring Dev, NQ 249, 353
0SHD[0,3,4][4,5]Z	Insert/Knee Jt, Lt, [Opn, Perc, Perc Endo], [Int Fix Dev, Ext Fix Dev], NQ 132, 351, 457
0SHC[0,3,4][4,5]Z	Insert/Knee Jt, Rt, [Opn, Perc, Perc Endo], [Int Fix Dev, Ext Fix Dev], NQ 132, 351, 457
0YHG[0,3,4][3,Y]Z	Insert/Knee Rgn, Lt, [Opn, Perc, Perc Endo], [Inf Dev, Oth Dev], NQ 220
0YHG[0,3,4]1Z	Insert/Knee Rgn, Lt, [Opn, Perc, Perc Endo], Radioact Elmt, NQ 357, 461
0YHF[0,3,4][3,Y]Z	Insert/Knee Rgn, Rt, [Opn, Perc, Perc Endo], [Inf Dev, Oth Dev], NQ 220
0YHF[0,3,4]1Z	Insert/Knee Rgn, Rt, [Opn, Perc, Perc Endo], Radioact Elmt, NQ 357, 461
0NHJ*	Insert/Lacrimal Bone, Lt 54
0NHH*	Insert/Lacrimal Bone, Rt 54
06HS[0,3,4]DZ	Insert/Lesser Saphenous Vein, Lt, [Opn, Perc, Perc Endo], Intralum Dev, NQ 87, 297, 327
06HR[0,3,4]DZ	Insert/Lesser Saphenous Vein, Rt, [Opn, Perc, Perc Endo], Intralum Dev, NQ 87, 297, 327
0BH9[0,3,4,7]GZ	Insert/Lingula Bronchus, [Opn, Perc, Perc Endo, Via Natrl or Artfcl Opng], Endobronchial Valve, NQ 62
0FH0[0,3,4]2Z	Insert/Liver, [Opn, Perc, Perc Endo], Monitoring Dev, NQ 119, 335
0FH2[0,3,4]2Z	Insert/Liver, Lt Lobe, [Opn, Perc, Perc Endo], Monitoring Dev, NQ 119, 335
0FH1[0,3,4]2Z	Insert/Liver, Rt Lobe, [Opn, Perc, Perc Endo], Monitoring Dev, NQ 119, 335
0SH0[0,3,4][B,C,D]Z	Insert/Lumbar Vert Jt, [Opn, Perc, Perc Endo], [Spinal Stabliz Dev, Interspinous Process, Spinal Stabliz Dev, Pedicle-Based, Spinal Stabliz Dev, Facet Replace], NQ 20, 159, 160, 161, 351
0SH0[0,3,4]4Z	Insert/Lumbar Vert Jt, [Opn, Perc, Perc Endo], Int Fix Dev, NQ 157
0QH0*	Insert/Lumbar Vertebra 156, 347
0SH3[0,3,4][B,C,D]Z	Insert/Lumbosacral Jt, [Opn, Perc, Perc Endo], [Spinal Stabliz Dev, Interspinous Process, Spinal Stabliz Dev, Pedicle-Based, Spinal Stabliz Dev, Facet Replace], NQ 20, 159, 160, 161, 351
0SH3[0,3,4]4Z	Insert/Lumbosacral Jt, [Opn, Perc, Perc Endo], Int Fix Dev, NQ 157
0BHL*	Insert/Lung, Lt 331
0BHL[0,3,4,7,8][2,3]Z	Insert/Lung, Lt, [Opn, Perc, Perc Endo, Via Natrl or Artfcl Opng, Via Natrl or Artfcl Opng Endo], [Monitoring Dev, Inf Dev], NQ 62
0BHL[0,3,4,7,8]1Z	Insert/Lung, Lt, [Opn, Perc, Perc Endo, Via Natrl or Artfcl Opng, Via Natrl or Artfcl Opng Endo], Radioact Elmt, NQ 64, 447
0BHK*	Insert/Lung, Rt 331
0BHK[0,3,4,7,8][2,3]Z	Insert/Lung, Rt, [Opn, Perc, Perc Endo, Via Natrl or Artfcl Opng, Via Natrl or Artfcl Opng Endo], [Monitoring Dev, Inf Dev], NQ 62
0BHK[0,3,4,7,8]1Z	Insert/Lung, Rt, [Opn, Perc, Perc Endo, Via Natrl or Artfcl Opng, Via Natrl or Artfcl Opng Endo], Radioact Elmt, NQ 64, 447
0XHF[0,3,4][3,Y]Z	Insert/Lwr Arm, Lt, [Opn, Perc, Perc Endo], [Inf Dev, Oth Dev], NQ 220
0XHF[0,3,4]1Z	Insert/Lwr Arm, Lt, [Opn, Perc, Perc Endo], Radioact Elmt, NQ 356, 461
0XHD[0,3,4][3,Y]Z	Insert/Lwr Arm, Rt, [Opn, Perc, Perc Endo], [Inf Dev, Oth Dev], NQ 220
0XHD[0,3,4]1Z	Insert/Lwr Arm, Rt, [Opn, Perc, Perc Endo], Radioact Elmt, NQ 356, 461
04HY[0,3,4][2,D]Z	Insert/Lwr Artery, [Opn, Perc, Perc Endo], [Monitoring Dev, Intralum Dev], NQ 84, 297, 324
04HY[0,3,4]2Z	Insert/Lwr Artery, [Opn, Perc, Perc Endo], Monitoring Dev, NQ 240
0WHL[0,3,4][3,Y]Z	Insert/Lwr Back, [Opn, Perc, Perc Endo], [Inf Dev, Oth Dev], NQ 220
0WHL[0,3,4]1Z	Insert/Lwr Back, [Opn, Perc, Perc Endo], Radioact Elmt, NQ 355, 460
0QHY*	Insert/Lwr Bone 156, 347
0YHB[0,3,4][3,Y]Z	Insert/Lwr Extr, Lt, [Opn, Perc, Perc Endo], [Inf Dev, Oth Dev], NQ 220
0YHB[0,3,4]1Z	Insert/Lwr Extr, Lt, [Opn, Perc, Perc Endo], Radioact Elmt, NQ 357, 461
0YH9[0,3,4][3,Y]Z	Insert/Lwr Extr, Rt, [Opn, Perc, Perc Endo], [Inf Dev, Oth Dev], NQ 220
0YH9[0,3,4]1Z	Insert/Lwr Extr, Rt, [Opn, Perc, Perc Endo], Radioact Elmt, NQ 357, 461
0QHC[0,3,4][4,5,6,B,C,D]Z	Insert/Lwr Femur, Lt, [Opn, Perc, Perc Endo], [Int Fix Dev, Ext Fix Dev, Int Fix Dev, Intramedullary Int Fix Dev, Ext Fix Dev, Monop, Ext Fix Dev, Ring, Ext Fix Dev, Hybrid], NQ 130, 347, 415
0QHB[0,3,4][4,5,6,B,C,D]Z	Insert/Lwr Femur, Rt, [Opn, Perc, Perc Endo], [Int Fix Dev, Ext Fix Dev, Int Fix Dev, Intramedullary Int Fix Dev, Ext Fix Dev, Monop, Ext Fix Dev, Ring, Ext Fix Dev, Hybrid], NQ 130, 347, 415
0WH5[0,3,4][3,Y]Z	Insert/Lwr Jaw, [Opn, Perc, Perc Endo], [Inf Dev, Oth Dev], NQ 220
0WH5[0,3,4]1Z	Insert/Lwr Jaw, [Opn, Perc, Perc Endo], Radioact Elmt, NQ 55, 355, 460
0YHJ[0,3,4][3,Y]Z	Insert/Lwr Leg, Lt, [Opn, Perc, Perc Endo], [Inf Dev, Oth Dev], NQ 220
0YHJ[0,3,4]1Z	Insert/Lwr Leg, Lt, [Opn, Perc, Perc Endo], Radioact Elmt, NQ 357, 461
0YHH[0,3,4][3,Y]Z	Insert/Lwr Leg, Rt, [Opn, Perc, Perc Endo], [Inf Dev, Oth Dev], NQ 220
0YHH[0,3,4]1Z	Insert/Lwr Leg, Rt, [Opn, Perc, Perc Endo], Radioact Elmt, NQ 357, 461
0BHB[0,3,4,7]GZ	Insert/Lwr Lobe Bronchus, Lt, [Opn, Perc, Perc Endo, Via Natrl or Artfcl Opng], Endobronchial Valve, NQ 62
0BH6[0,3,4,7]GZ	Insert/Lwr Lobe Bronchus, Rt, [Opn, Perc, Perc Endo, Via Natrl or Artfcl Opng], Endobronchial Valve, NQ 62
06HY[0,3,4][2,D]Z	Insert/Lwr Vein, [Opn, Perc, Perc Endo], [Monitoring Dev, Intralum Dev], NQ 327
06HY[0,3,4]DZ	Insert/Lwr Vein, [Opn, Perc, Perc Endo], Intralum Dev, NQ 51, 64, 87, 111, 271, 297
06HY[0,3,4]2Z	Insert/Lwr Vein, [Opn, Perc, Perc Endo], Monitoring Dev, NQ 89, 443
0BH7[0,3,4,7]GZ	Insert/Main Bronchus, Lt, [Opn, Perc, Perc Endo, Via Natrl or Artfcl Opng], Endobronchial Valve, NQ 62
0BH3[0,3,4,7]GZ	Insert/Main Bronchus, Rt, [Opn, Perc, Perc Endo, Via Natrl or Artfcl Opng], Endobronchial Valve, NQ 62
0NHV*	Insert/Mandible, Lt 54
0NHT*	Insert/Mandible, Rt 54

ØNHS*	Insert/Maxilla, Lt 54
ØNHR*	Insert/Maxilla, Rt 54
ØWHC*	Insert/Mediastinum 91, 355
ØWHC[Ø,3,4][3,Y]Z	Insert/Mediastinum, [Opn, Perc, Perc Endo], [Inf Dev, Oth Dev], NQ 66
ØWHC[Ø,3,4]1Z	Insert/Mediastinum, [Opn, Perc, Perc Endo], Radioact Elmt, NQ 79, 460
ØPHQ*	Insert/Metacarpal, Lt 150
ØPHQ[Ø,3,4][4,5]Z	Insert/Metacarpal, Lt, [Opn, Perc, Perc Endo], [Int Fix Dev, Ext Fix Dev], NQ 315
ØPHP*	Insert/Metacarpal, Rt 150
ØPHP[Ø,3,4][4,5]Z	Insert/Metacarpal, Rt, [Opn, Perc, Perc Endo], [Int Fix Dev, Ext Fix Dev], NQ 315
ØRHT[Ø,3,4][4,5]Z	Insert/Metacarpocarpal Jt, Lt, [Opn, Perc, Perc Endo], [Int Fix Dev, Ext Fix Dev], NQ 146, 316
ØRHS[Ø,3,4][4,5]Z	Insert/Metacarpocarpal Jt, Rt, [Opn, Perc, Perc Endo], [Int Fix Dev, Ext Fix Dev], NQ 146, 316
ØRHV[Ø,3,4][4,5]Z	Insert/Metacarpophalangeal Jt, Lt, [Opn, Perc, Perc Endo], [Int Fix Dev, Ext Fix Dev], NQ 147, 316
ØRHU[Ø,3,4][4,5]Z	Insert/Metacarpophalangeal Jt, Rt, [Opn, Perc, Perc Endo], [Int Fix Dev, Ext Fix Dev], NQ 146, 316
ØSHN[Ø,3,4][4,5]Z	Insert/Metatarsal-Phalangeal Jt, Lt, [Opn, Perc, Perc Endo], [Int Fix Dev, Ext Fix Dev], NQ 145, 351, 457
ØSHM[Ø,3,4][4,5]Z	Insert/Metatarsal-Phalangeal Jt, Rt, [Opn, Perc, Perc Endo], [Int Fix Dev, Ext Fix Dev], NQ 145, 351, 457
ØSHL[Ø,3,4][4,5]Z	Insert/Metatarsal-Tarsal Jt, Lt, [Opn, Perc, Perc Endo], [Int Fix Dev, Ext Fix Dev], NQ 145, 351, 457
ØSHK[Ø,3,4][4,5]Z	Insert/Metatarsal-Tarsal Jt, Rt, [Opn, Perc, Perc Endo], [Int Fix Dev, Ext Fix Dev], NQ 145, 351, 457
ØQHP*	Insert/Metatarsal, Lt 145, 347
ØQHN*	Insert/Metatarsal, Rt 145, 347
ØBH5[Ø,3,4,7]GZ	Insert/Mid Lobe Bronchus, Rt, [Opn, Perc, Perc Endo, Via Natrl or Artfcl Opng], Endobronchial Valve, NQ 62
ØWH6[Ø,3,4][3,Y]Z	Insert/Neck, [Opn, Perc, Perc Endo], [Inf Dev, Oth Dev], NQ 220
ØWH6[Ø,3,4]1Z	Insert/Neck, [Opn, Perc, Perc Endo], Radioact Elmt, NQ 55, 245, 355, 460
ØHHX[Ø,3,7,8,X]1Z	Insert/Nipple, Lt, [Opn, Perc, Via Natrl or Artfcl Opng, Via Natrl or Artfcl Opng Endo, Ext], Radioact Elmt, NQ 211
ØHHX[Ø,3,7,8,X]1Z	Insert/Nipple, Lt, [Opn, Perc, Via Natrl or Artfcl Opng, Via Natrl or Artfcl Opng Endo, Ext], Radioact Elmt, NQ 450
ØHHX[Ø,3,7,8]NZ	Insert/Nipple, Lt, [Opn, Perc, Via Natrl or Artfcl Opng, Via Natrl or Artfcl Opng Endo], Tissue Expander, NQ 222, 450
ØHHW[Ø,3,7,8,X]1Z	Insert/Nipple, Rt, [Opn, Perc, Via Natrl or Artfcl Opng, Via Natrl or Artfcl Opng Endo, Ext], Radioact Elmt, NQ 211, 449
ØHHW[Ø,3,7,8]NZ	Insert/Nipple, Rt, [Opn, Perc, Via Natrl or Artfcl Opng, Via Natrl or Artfcl Opng Endo], Tissue Expander, NQ 222, 449
ØNH8*	Insert/Occipital Bone, Lt 10, 48, 154, 344, 415
ØNH8[Ø,3,4]4Z	Insert/Occipital Bone, Lt, [Opn, Perc, Perc Endo], Int Fix Dev, NQ 14, 18
ØNH7*	Insert/Occipital Bone, Rt 10, 48, 154, 344, 415
ØNH7[Ø,3,4]4Z	Insert/Occipital Bone, Rt, [Opn, Perc, Perc Endo], Int Fix Dev, NQ 14, 18
ØRHØ[Ø,3,4][B,C,D]Z	Insert/Occipital-cervical Jt, [Opn, Perc, Perc Endo], [Spinal Stabliz Dev, Interspinous Process, Spinal Stabliz Dev, Pedicle-Based, Spinal Stabliz Dev, Facet Replace], NQ 20, 159, 160, 160, 349
ØRHØ[Ø,3,4]4Z	Insert/Occipital-cervical Jt, [Opn, Perc, Perc Endo], Int Fix Dev, NQ 156
ØWH3*	Insert/Oral Cavity and Throat 355
ØWH3[Ø,3,4][3,Y]Z	Insert/Oral Cavity and Throat, [Opn, Perc, Perc Endo], [Inf Dev, Oth Dev], NQ 56, 217
ØWH3[Ø,3,4][1,3,Y]Z	Insert/Oral Cavity and Throat, [Opn, Perc, Perc Endo], [Radioact Elmt, Inf Dev, Oth Dev], NQ 460
ØWH3[Ø,3,4]1Z	Insert/Oral Cavity and Throat, [Opn, Perc, Perc Endo], Radioact Elmt, NQ 55
ØNHQ*	Insert/Orbit, Lt 54
ØNHP*	Insert/Orbit, Rt 54
ØNHL*	Insert/Palatine Bone, Lt 54
ØNHK*	Insert/Palatine Bone, Rt 54
ØFHG[Ø,3,4]2Z	Insert/Pancreas, [Opn, Perc, Perc Endo], Monitoring Dev, NQ 119
ØFHD[Ø,3,4,7,8]2Z	Insert/Pancreatic Duct, [Opn, Perc, Perc Endo, Via Natrl or Artfcl Opng, Via Natrl or Artfcl Opng Endo], Monitoring Dev, NQ 119

ØFHD[Ø,3,4,7,8]1Z	Insert/Pancreatic Duct, [Opn, Perc, Perc Endo, Via Natrl or Artfcl Opng, Via Natrl or Artfcl Opng Endo], Radioact Elmt, NQ 335, 449
ØFHD[Ø,3,7]DZ	Insert/Pancreatic Duct, [Opn, Perc, Via Natrl or Artfcl Opng], Intralum Dev, NQ 113, 119, 301, 335
ØNH4*	Insert/Parietal Bone, Lt 10, 48, 154, 344, 415
ØNH4[Ø,3,4]4Z	Insert/Parietal Bone, Lt, [Opn, Perc, Perc Endo], Int Fix Dev, NQ 14, 18
ØNH3*	Insert/Parietal Bone, Rt 10, 48, 154, 344, 415
ØNH3[Ø,3,4]4Z	Insert/Parietal Bone, Rt, [Opn, Perc, Perc Endo], Int Fix Dev, NQ 14, 18
ØQHF*	Insert/Patella, Lt 132, 347
ØQHD*	Insert/Patella, Rt 132, 347
ØQH3*	Insert/Pelvic Bone, Lt 156, 347
ØQH2*	Insert/Pelvic Bone, Rt 156, 347
ØWHJ[Ø,3,4][3,Y]Z	Insert/Pelvic Cavity, [Opn, Perc, Perc Endo], [Inf Dev, Oth Dev], NQ 113
ØWHJ[Ø,3,4]1Z	Insert/Pelvic Cavity, [Opn, Perc, Perc Endo], Radioact Elmt, NQ 260, 266, 355, 460
ØWHD*	Insert/Pericardial Cavity 355
ØWHD[Ø,3,4][3,Y]Z	Insert/Pericardial Cavity, [Opn, Perc, Perc Endo], [Inf Dev, Oth Dev], NQ 62, 98, 302
ØWHD[Ø,3,4]1Z	Insert/Pericardial Cavity, [Opn, Perc, Perc Endo], Radioact Elmt, NQ 79, 91, 460
02HN[Ø,3,4][J,K,M]Z	Insert/Pericardium, [Opn, Perc, Perc Endo], [Cardiac Lead, Pacemaker, Cardiac Lead, Defibrillator, Cardiac Lead], NQ 73, 73, 74
02HN[Ø,3,4][J,M]Z	Insert/Pericardium, [Opn, Perc, Perc Endo], [Cardiac Lead, Pacemaker, Cardiac Lead], NQ 24, 29, 30, 77, 88, 358
02HN[Ø,3,4][Ø,2,J,M]Z	Insert/Pericardium, [Opn, Perc, Perc Endo], [Monitoring Dev, Pressure Sensor, Monitoring Dev, Cardiac Lead, Pacemaker, Cardiac Lead], NQ 319
02HN[Ø,3,4][Ø,2]Z	Insert/Pericardium, [Opn, Perc, Perc Endo], [Monitoring Dev, Pressure Sensor, Monitoring Dev], NQ 60, 93, 296
02HN[Ø,3,4]KZ	Insert/Pericardium, [Opn, Perc, Perc Endo], Cardiac Lead, Defibrillator, NQ 92
ØWHN[Ø,3,4][3,Y]Z	Insert/Perineum, Female, [Opn, Perc, Perc Endo], [Inf Dev, Oth Dev], NQ 217, 267, 275
ØWHN[Ø,3,4][1,3,Y]Z	Insert/Perineum, Female, [Opn, Perc, Perc Endo], [Radioact Elmt, Inf Dev, Oth Dev], NQ 460
ØWHN[Ø,3,4]1Z	Insert/Perineum, Female, [Opn, Perc, Perc Endo], Radioact Elmt, NQ 266, 355
ØWHM[Ø,3,4][3,Y]Z	Insert/Perineum, Male, [Opn, Perc, Perc Endo], [Inf Dev, Oth Dev], NQ 220
ØWHM[Ø,3,4]1Z	Insert/Perineum, Male, [Opn, Perc, Perc Endo], Radioact Elmt, NQ 260, 355, 460
01HY[Ø,3,4]MZ	Insert/Peripheral Nerve, [Opn, Perc, Perc Endo], Neurostimulator Lead, NQ 31, 50, 80, 152, 251, 258, 267, 319
ØWHG*	Insert/Peritoneal Cavity 113
ØWHG[Ø,3,4]1Z	Insert/Peritoneal Cavity, [Opn, Perc, Perc Endo], Radioact Elmt, NQ 245, 355, 460
04HU[Ø,3,4]DZ	Insert/Peroneal Artery, Lt, [Opn, Perc, Perc Endo], Intralum Dev, NQ 84, 297, 323
04HT[Ø,3,4]DZ	Insert/Peroneal Artery, Rt, [Opn, Perc, Perc Endo], Intralum Dev, NQ 84, 297, 323
ØWHB[Ø,3,4]1Z	Insert/Pleural Cavity, Lt, [Opn, Perc, Perc Endo], Radioact Elmt, NQ 66, 355, 460
ØWH9[Ø,3,4]1Z	Insert/Pleural Cavity, Rt, [Opn, Perc, Perc Endo], Radioact Elmt, NQ 66, 355, 460
04HN[Ø,3,4]DZ	Insert/Popliteal Artery, Lt, [Opn, Perc, Perc Endo], Intralum Dev, NQ 83, 297, 323
04HM[Ø,3,4]DZ	Insert/Popliteal Artery, Rt, [Opn, Perc, Perc Endo], Intralum Dev, NQ 83, 297, 323
06H8[Ø,3,4]DZ	Insert/Portal Vein, [Opn, Perc, Perc Endo], Intralum Dev, NQ 87, 111, 297, 327
04HS[Ø,3,4]DZ	Insert/Post Tibial Artery, Lt, [Opn, Perc, Perc Endo], Intralum Dev, NQ 83, 297, 323
04HR[Ø,3,4]DZ	Insert/Post Tibial Artery, Rt, [Opn, Perc, Perc Endo], Intralum Dev, NQ 83, 297, 323
10H00[3,Y]Z	Insert/Products of Conception, Opn, [Monitoring Electrode, Oth Dev], NQ 272
ØVHØ*	Insert/Prostate 260, 354
ØVHØ[Ø,3,4,7,8]1Z	Insert/Prostate, [Opn, Perc, Perc Endo, Via Natrl or Artfcl Opng, Via Natrl or Artfcl Opng Endo], Radioact Elmt, NQ 459

02HR[0,3,4]DZ	Insert/Pulmn Artery, Lt, [Opn, Perc, Perc Endo], Intralum Dev, NQ 93
02HQ[0,3,4]DZ	Insert/Pulmn Artery, Rt, [Opn, Perc, Perc Endo], Intralum Dev, NQ 93
02HP[0,3,4]DZ	Insert/Pulmn Trunk, [Opn, Perc, Perc Endo], Intralum Dev, NQ 93
02HT[0,3,4][2,D]Z	Insert/Pulmn Vein, Lt, [Opn, Perc, Perc Endo], [Monitoring Dev, Intralum Dev], NQ 93
02HT[0,3,4]0Z	Insert/Pulmn Vein, Lt, [Opn, Perc, Perc Endo], Monitoring Dev, Pressure Sensor, NQ 89
02HS[0,3,4][2,D]Z	Insert/Pulmn Vein, Rt, [Opn, Perc, Perc Endo], [Monitoring Dev, Intralum Dev], NQ 93
02HS[0,3,4]0Z	Insert/Pulmn Vein, Rt, [Opn, Perc, Perc Endo], Monitoring Dev, Pressure Sensor, NQ 89
03HC[0,3,4]DZ	Insert/Radial Artery, Lt, [Opn, Perc, Perc Endo], Intralum Dev, NQ 81, 296, 321
03HB[0,3,4]DZ	Insert/Radial Artery, Rt, [Opn, Perc, Perc Endo], Intralum Dev, NQ 81, 296, 321
0PHJ[0,3,4] [4,5,6,B,C,D]Z	Insert/Radius, Lt, [Opn, Perc, Perc Endo], [Int Fix Dev, Ext Fix Dev, Int Fix Dev, Intramedullary Int Fix Dev, Ext Fix Dev, Monop, Ext Fix Dev, Ring, Ext Fix Dev, Hybrid], NQ 148, 345
0PHH[0,3,4] [4,5,6,B,C,D]Z	Insert/Radius, Rt, [Opn, Perc, Perc Endo], [Int Fix Dev, Ext Fix Dev, Int Fix Dev, Intramedullary Int Fix Dev, Ext Fix Dev, Monop, Ext Fix Dev, Ring, Ext Fix Dev, Hybrid], NQ 148, 345
0DHP[0,3,4,7,8]1Z	Insert/Rectum, [Opn, Perc, Perc Endo, Via Natrl or Artfcl Opng, Via Natrl or Artfcl Opng Endo], Radioact Elmt, NQ 112, 333, 449
04HA[0,3,4]DZ	Insert/Renal Artery, Lt, [Opn, Perc, Perc Endo], Intralum Dev, NQ 83, 297, 323
04H9[0,3,4]DZ	Insert/Renal Artery, Rt, [Opn, Perc, Perc Endo], Intralum Dev, NQ 83, 297, 323
06HB[0,3,4]DZ	Insert/Renal Vein, Lt, [Opn, Perc, Perc Endo], Intralum Dev, NQ 87, 297, 327
06H9[0,3,4]DZ	Insert/Renal Vein, Rt, [Opn, Perc, Perc Endo], Intralum Dev, NQ 87, 297, 327
0WHQ[0,3,4,7,8]1Z	Insert/Respiratory Tract, [Opn, Perc, Perc Endo, Via Natrl or Artfcl Opng, Via Natrl or Artfcl Opng Endo], Radioact Elmt, NQ 66, 356, 460
0WHQ[3,4]3Z	Insert/Respiratory Tract, [Perc, Perc Endo], Inf Dev, NQ 66, 356
0WHQ[3,4]YZ	Insert/Respiratory Tract, [Perc, Perc Endo], Oth Dev, NQ 66, 356
0WHH[0,3,4][3,Y]Z	Insert/Retroperitoneum, [Opn, Perc, Perc Endo], [Inf Dev, Oth Dev], NQ 113
0WHH[0,3,4]1Z	Insert/Retroperitoneum, [Opn, Perc, Perc Endo], Radioact Elmt, NQ 245, 254, 355, 460
0PH2*	Insert/Rib, Lt 65, 155, 345
0PH1*	Insert/Rib, Rt 65, 155, 345
0SH5[0,3,4]4Z	Insert/Sacrococcygeal Jt, [Opn, Perc, Perc Endo], Int Fix Dev, NQ 157
0SH8[0,3,4]4Z	Insert/Sacroiliac Jt, Lt, [Opn, Perc, Perc Endo], Int Fix Dev, NQ 157
0SH7[0,3,4]4Z	Insert/Sacroiliac Jt, Rt, [Opn, Perc, Perc Endo], Int Fix Dev, NQ 157
0QH1*	Insert/Sacrum 156, 347
0PH6*	Insert/Scapula, Lt 65, 155, 345
0PH5*	Insert/Scapula, Rt 65, 155, 345
0RHK[0,3,4]4Z	Insert/Shldr Jt, Lt, [Opn, Perc, Perc Endo], Int Fix Dev, NQ 147, 349
0RHJ[0,3,4]4Z	Insert/Shldr Jt, Rt, [Opn, Perc, Perc Endo], Int Fix Dev, NQ 147, 349
0XH3[0,3,4][3,Y]Z	Insert/Shldr Rgn, Lt, [Opn, Perc, Perc Endo], [Inf Dev, Oth Dev], NQ 220
0XH3[0,3,4]1Z	Insert/Shldr Rgn, Lt, [Opn, Perc, Perc Endo], Radioact Elmt, NQ 356, 461
0XH2[0,3,4][3,Y]Z	Insert/Shldr Rgn, Rt, [Opn, Perc, Perc Endo], [Inf Dev, Oth Dev], NQ 220
0XH2[0,3,4]1Z	Insert/Shldr Rgn, Rt, [Opn, Perc, Perc Endo], Radioact Elmt, NQ 356, 461
0NH0[0,3,4][4,M]Z	Insert/Skull, [Opn, Perc, Perc Endo], [Int Fix Dev, Bone Growth Stimulator], NQ 10, 14, 18
0NH0[0,3,4]4Z	Insert/Skull, [Opn, Perc, Perc Endo], Int Fix Dev, NQ 154, 344, 415
0DH8[0,3,4,7,8][2,3]Z	Insert/Sm Intestine, [Opn, Perc, Perc Endo, Via Natrl or Artfcl Opng, Via Natrl or Artfcl Opng Endo], [Monitoring Dev, Inf Dev], NQ 109, 333
0NHD*	Insert/Sphenoid Bone, Lt 54
0NHC*	Insert/Sphenoid Bone, Rt 54
00HU[0,3,4][2,M]Z	Insert/Spinal Canal, [Opn, Perc, Perc Endo], [Monitoring Dev, Neurostimulator Lead], NQ 19, 159, 160, 296, 318
00HU[0,3,4]MZ	Insert/Spinal Canal, [Opn, Perc, Perc Endo], Neurostimulator Lead, NQ 20, 160, 251, 258, 267
00HV[0,3,4][2,M]Z	Insert/Spinal Cord, [Opn, Perc, Perc Endo], [Monitoring Dev, Neurostimulator Lead], NQ 19, 159, 160, 296, 318
00HV[0,3,4]MZ	Insert/Spinal Cord, [Opn, Perc, Perc Endo], Neurostimulator Lead, NQ 20, 160, 251, 258, 267
04H4[0,3,4]DZ	Insert/Splenic Artery, [Opn, Perc, Perc Endo], Intralum Dev, NQ 83, 296, 323
06H1[0,3,4]DZ	Insert/Splenic Vein, [Opn, Perc, Perc Endo], Intralum Dev, NQ 87, 111, 297, 327
0JH8[0,3][7,P]Z	Insert/SQ Tissue & Fascia, Abd, [Opn, Perc], [Cardiac Resynchronization Pacemaker Pulse Generator, Cardiac Rhythm Related Dev], NQ 77, 88
0JH8[0,3][P,V]Z	Insert/SQ Tissue & Fascia, Abd, [Opn, Perc], [Cardiac Rhythm Related Dev, Inf Pump], NQ 337
0JH8[0,3][8,9,A]Z	Insert/SQ Tissue & Fascia, Abd, [Opn, Perc], [Defibrillator Generator, Cardiac Resynchronization Defibrillator Pulse Generator, Contractility Modulation Dev], NQ 78
0JH8[0,3][2,H,W,X]Z	Insert/SQ Tissue & Fascia, Abd, [Opn, Perc], [Monitoring Dev, Contraceptive Dev, Reservoir, Vascular Access Dev], NQ 220
0JH8[0,3][6,7,P]Z	Insert/SQ Tissue & Fascia, Abd, [Opn, Perc], [Pacemaker, Dual Chamber, Cardiac Resynchronization Pacemaker Pulse Generator, Cardiac Rhythm Related Dev], NQ 77
0JH8[0,3][6,P]Z	Insert/SQ Tissue & Fascia, Abd, [Opn, Perc], [Pacemaker, Dual Chamber, Cardiac Rhythm Related Dev], NQ 29, 358
0JH8[0,3][4,5,P]Z	Insert/SQ Tissue & Fascia, Abd, [Opn, Perc], [Pacemaker, Single Chamber, Pacemaker, Single Chamber Rate Responsive, Cardiac Rhythm Related Dev], NQ 29, 77, 357
0JH8[0,3][4,5,6,7,P]Z	Insert/SQ Tissue & Fascia, Abd, [Opn, Perc], [Pacemaker, Single Chamber, Pacemaker, Single Chamber Rate Responsive, Pacemaker, Dual Chamber, Cardiac Resynchronization Pacemaker Pulse Generator, Cardiac Rhythm Related Dev], NQ 77
0JH8[0,3][4,5,6,P]Z	Insert/SQ Tissue & Fascia, Abd, [Opn, Perc], [Pacemaker, Single Chamber, Pacemaker, Single Chamber Rate Responsive, Pacemaker, Dual Chamber, Cardiac Resynchronization Pacemaker Pulse Generator, Cardiac Rhythm Related Dev], NQ 30, 358
0JH8[0,3][4,5,6]Z	Insert/SQ Tissue & Fascia, Abd, [Opn, Perc], [Pacemaker, Single Chamber, Pacemaker, Single Chamber Rate Responsive, Pacemaker, Dual Chamber], NQ 29, 30, 77, 78, 358
0JH8[0,3][W,X]Z	Insert/SQ Tissue & Fascia, Abd, [Opn, Perc], [Reservoir, Vascular Access Dev], NQ 254
0JH8[0,3][B,C,D,E,M,N,P,V]Z	Insert/SQ Tissue & Fascia, Abd, [Opn, Perc], [Stimulator Generator, Single Array, Stimulator Generator, Single Array Rechargeable, Stimulator Generator, Multi Array, Stimulator Generator, Multi Array Rechargeable, Stimulator Generator, Tissue Expander, Cardiac Rhythm Related Dev, Inf Dev, Pump], NQ 26
0JH8[0,3][B,C,D,E]Z	Insert/SQ Tissue & Fascia, Abd, [Opn, Perc], [Stimulator Generator, Single Array, Stimulator Generator, Single Array Rechargeable, Stimulator Generator, Multi Array, Stimulator Generator, Multi Array Rechargeable], NQ 20, 31, 160
0JH8[0,3][N,V]Z	Insert/SQ Tissue & Fascia, Abd, [Opn, Perc], [Tissue Expander, Inf Pump], NQ 91, 113
0JH8[0,3]9Z	Insert/SQ Tissue & Fascia, Abd, [Opn, Perc], Cardiac Resynchronization Defibrillator Pulse Generator, NQ 72, 73
0JH8[0,3]7Z	Insert/SQ Tissue & Fascia, Abd, [Opn, Perc], Cardiac Resynchronization Pacemaker Pulse Generator, NQ 76, 78
0JH8[0,3]PZ	Insert/SQ Tissue & Fascia, Abd, [Opn, Perc], Cardiac Rhythm Related Dev, NQ 30, 358
0JH8[0,3]AZ	Insert/SQ Tissue & Fascia, Abd, [Opn, Perc], Contractility Modulation Dev, NQ 72, 73
0JH8[0,3]8Z	Insert/SQ Tissue & Fascia, Abd, [Opn, Perc], Defibrillator Generator, NQ 73, 74
0JH8[0,3]VZ	Insert/SQ Tissue & Fascia, Abd, [Opn, Perc], Inf Pump, NQ 65, 123, 153, 212, 242, 253, 259, 268, 292
0JH8[0,3]0Z	Insert/SQ Tissue & Fascia, Abd, [Opn, Perc], Monitoring Dev, Hemodynamic, NQ 88, 92
0JH8[0,3]6Z	Insert/SQ Tissue & Fascia, Abd, [Opn, Perc], Pacemaker, Dual Chamber, NQ 88
0JH8[0,3]5Z	Insert/SQ Tissue & Fascia, Abd, [Opn, Perc], Pacemaker, Single Chamber Rate Responsive, NQ 88
0JH8[0,3]4Z	Insert/SQ Tissue & Fascia, Abd, [Opn, Perc], Pacemaker, Single Chamber, NQ 88

Alphabetic Index to Procedures

ØJH8[Ø,3]MZ	Insert/SQ Tissue & Fascia, Abd, [Opn, Perc], Stimulator Generator, NQ **87**
ØJH8[Ø,3]NZ	Insert/SQ Tissue & Fascia, Abd, [Opn, Perc], Tissue Expander, NQ **127, 206, 237, 314, 378, 380**
ØJH4*	Insert/SQ Tissue & Fascia, Ant Neck **26, 54, 91, 113, 127, 206, 237, 380**
ØJH4[Ø,3]NZ	Insert/SQ Tissue & Fascia, Ant Neck, [Opn, Perc], Tissue Expander, NQ **314, 378**
ØJH7*	Insert/SQ Tissue & Fascia, Back **26**
ØJH7[Ø,3][B,C,D,E]Z	Insert/SQ Tissue & Fascia, Back, [Opn, Perc], [Stimulator Generator, Single Array, Stimulator Generator, Single Array Rechargeable, Stimulator Generator, Multi Array, Stimulator Generator, Multi Array Rechargeable], NQ **20, 31, 160**
ØJH7[Ø,3][N,V]Z	Insert/SQ Tissue & Fascia, Back, [Opn, Perc], [Tissue Expander, Inf Pump], NQ **91, 113**
ØJH7[Ø,3]VZ	Insert/SQ Tissue & Fascia, Back, [Opn, Perc], Inf Pump, NQ **65, 123, 153, 212, 242, 253, 259, 268, 292, 337**
ØJH7[Ø,3]MZ	Insert/SQ Tissue & Fascia, Back, [Opn, Perc], Stimulator Generator, NQ **87**
ØJH7[Ø,3]NZ	Insert/SQ Tissue & Fascia, Back, [Opn, Perc], Tissue Expander, NQ **127, 206, 237, 314, 378, 380**
ØJH9*	Insert/SQ Tissue & Fascia, Buttock **26, 91, 127, 206, 237, 380**
ØJH9[Ø,3]NZ	Insert/SQ Tissue & Fascia, Buttock, [Opn, Perc], Tissue Expander, NQ **314, 378**
ØJH6[Ø,3][7,P]Z	Insert/SQ Tissue & Fascia, Chest, [Opn, Perc], [Cardiac Resynchronization Pacemaker Pulse Generator, Cardiac Rhythm Related Dev], NQ **77, 88**
ØJH6[Ø,3][P,V]Z	Insert/SQ Tissue & Fascia, Chest, [Opn, Perc], [Cardiac Rhythm Related Dev, Inf Pump], NQ **337**
ØJH6[Ø,3][8,9,A]Z	Insert/SQ Tissue & Fascia, Chest, [Opn, Perc], [Defibrillator Generator, Cardiac Resynchronization Defibrillator Pulse Generator, Contractility Modulation Dev], NQ **78**
ØJH6[Ø,3][2,H,W,X]Z	Insert/SQ Tissue & Fascia, Chest, [Opn, Perc], [Monitoring Dev, Contraceptive Dev, Reservoir, Vascular Access Dev], NQ **220**
ØJH6[Ø,3][6,7,P]Z	Insert/SQ Tissue & Fascia, Chest, [Opn, Perc], [Pacemaker, Dual Chamber, Cardiac Resynchronization Pacemaker Pulse Generator, Cardiac Rhythm Related Dev], NQ **77**
ØJH6[Ø,3][6,P]Z	Insert/SQ Tissue & Fascia, Chest, [Opn, Perc], [Pacemaker, Dual Chamber, Cardiac Rhythm Related Dev], NQ **29, 358**
ØJH6[Ø,3][4,5,P]Z	Insert/SQ Tissue & Fascia, Chest, [Opn, Perc], [Pacemaker, Single Chamber, Pacemaker, Single Chamber Rate Responsive, Cardiac Rhythm Related Dev], NQ **29, 77, 357**
ØJH6[Ø,3][4,5,6,7,P]Z	Insert/SQ Tissue & Fascia, Chest, [Opn, Perc], [Pacemaker, Single Chamber, Pacemaker, Single Chamber Rate Responsive, Pacemaker, Dual Chamber, Cardiac Resynchronization Pacemaker Pulse Generator, Cardiac Rhythm Related Dev], NQ **77**
ØJH6[Ø,3][4,5,6,P]Z	Insert/SQ Tissue & Fascia, Chest, [Opn, Perc], [Pacemaker, Single Chamber, Pacemaker, Single Chamber Rate Responsive, Pacemaker, Dual Chamber, Cardiac Rhythm Related Dev], NQ **30, 358**
ØJH6[Ø,3][4,5,6]Z	Insert/SQ Tissue & Fascia, Chest, [Opn, Perc], [Pacemaker, Single Chamber, Pacemaker, Single Chamber Rate Responsive, Pacemaker, Dual Chamber], NQ **29, 30, 77, 358**
ØJH6[Ø,3][W,X]Z	Insert/SQ Tissue & Fascia, Chest, [Opn, Perc], [Reservoir, Vascular Access Dev], NQ **254**
ØJH6[Ø,3][B,C,D,E,M,N,P,V]Z	Insert/SQ Tissue & Fascia, Chest, [Opn, Perc], [Stimulator Generator, Single Array, Stimulator Generator, Single Array Rechargeable, Stimulator Generator, Multi Array, Stimulator Generator, Multi Array Rechargeable, Stimulator Generator, Tissue Expander, Cardiac Rhythm Related Dev, Inf Dev, Pump], NQ **26**
ØJH6[Ø,3][B,C,D,E]Z	Insert/SQ Tissue & Fascia, Chest, [Opn, Perc], [Stimulator Generator, Single Array, Stimulator Generator, Single Array Rechargeable, Stimulator Generator, Multi Array, Stimulator Generator, Multi Array Rechargeable], NQ **20, 31, 160**
ØJH6[Ø,3][N,V]Z	Insert/SQ Tissue & Fascia, Chest, [Opn, Perc], [Tissue Expander, Inf Pump], NQ **91, 113**
ØJH6[Ø,3]9Z	Insert/SQ Tissue & Fascia, Chest, [Opn, Perc], Cardiac Resynchronization Defibrillator Pulse Generator, NQ **72, 73**
ØJH6[Ø,3]7Z	Insert/SQ Tissue & Fascia, Chest, [Opn, Perc], Cardiac Resynchronization Pacemaker Pulse Generator, NQ **76, 78**
ØJH6[Ø,3]PZ	Insert/SQ Tissue & Fascia, Chest, [Opn, Perc], Cardiac Rhythm Related Dev, NQ **30, 358**
ØJH6[Ø,3]AZ	Insert/SQ Tissue & Fascia, Chest, [Opn, Perc], Contractility Modulation Dev, NQ **72, 73**
ØJH6[Ø,3]8Z	Insert/SQ Tissue & Fascia, Chest, [Opn, Perc], Defibrillator Generator, NQ **72, 73, 74**
ØJH6[Ø,3]VZ	Insert/SQ Tissue & Fascia, Chest, [Opn, Perc], Inf Pump, NQ **65, 123, 153, 212, 242, 253, 259, 268, 292**
ØJH6[Ø,3]ØZ	Insert/SQ Tissue & Fascia, Chest, [Opn, Perc], Monitoring Dev, Hemodynamic, NQ **88, 92**
ØJH6[Ø,3]6Z	Insert/SQ Tissue & Fascia, Chest, [Opn, Perc], Pacemaker, Dual Chamber, NQ **88**
ØJH6[Ø,3]5Z	Insert/SQ Tissue & Fascia, Chest, [Opn, Perc], Pacemaker, Single Chamber Rate Responsive, NQ **88**
ØJH6[Ø,3]4Z	Insert/SQ Tissue & Fascia, Chest, [Opn, Perc], Pacemaker, Single Chamber, NQ **88**
ØJH6[Ø,3]MZ	Insert/SQ Tissue & Fascia, Chest, [Opn, Perc], Stimulator Generator, NQ **87**
ØJH6[Ø,3]NZ	Insert/SQ Tissue & Fascia, Chest, [Opn, Perc], Tissue Expander, NQ **127, 206, 237, 314, 378, 380**
ØJH1*	Insert/SQ Tissue & Fascia, Face **26, 54, 91, 113, 127, 206, 237, 380**
ØJH1[Ø,3]NZ	Insert/SQ Tissue & Fascia, Face, [Opn, Perc], Tissue Expander, NQ **313, 378**
ØJHC[Ø,3]NZ	Insert/SQ Tissue & Fascia, Genitalia, [Opn, Perc], Tissue Expander, NQ **314, 378**
ØJHS[Ø,3]1Z	Insert/SQ Tissue & Fascia, Head and Neck, [Opn, Perc], Radioact Elmt, NQ **212, 337, 450**
ØJHR*	Insert/SQ Tissue & Fascia, Lt Foot **26, 91, 127, 207, 237, 380**
ØJHR[Ø,3]NZ	Insert/SQ Tissue & Fascia, Lt Foot, [Opn, Perc], Tissue Expander, NQ **314, 378**
ØJHK*	Insert/SQ Tissue & Fascia, Lt Hand **26, 149, 207, 237, 380**
ØJHK[Ø,3]NZ	Insert/SQ Tissue & Fascia, Lt Hand, [Opn, Perc], Tissue Expander, NQ **314, 378**
ØJHH[Ø,3][W,X]Z	Insert/SQ Tissue & Fascia, Lt Lwr Arm, [Opn, Perc], [Reservoir, Vascular Access Dev], NQ **220, 254**
ØJHH[Ø,3]NZ	Insert/SQ Tissue & Fascia, Lt Lwr Arm, [Opn, Perc], Tissue Expander, NQ **26, 91, 127, 206, 237, 314, 378, 380**
ØJHP[Ø,3][H,W,X]Z	Insert/SQ Tissue & Fascia, Lt Lwr Leg, [Opn, Perc], [Contraceptive Dev, Reservoir, Vascular Access Dev], NQ **220**
ØJHP[Ø,3][W,X]Z	Insert/SQ Tissue & Fascia, Lt Lwr Leg, [Opn, Perc], [Reservoir, Vascular Access Dev], NQ **254**
ØJHP[Ø,3]NZ	Insert/SQ Tissue & Fascia, Lt Lwr Leg, [Opn, Perc], Tissue Expander, NQ **26, 91, 127, 207, 237, 314, 378, 380**
ØJHF[Ø,3][W,X]Z	Insert/SQ Tissue & Fascia, Lt Upr Arm, [Opn, Perc], [Reservoir, Vascular Access Dev], NQ **220, 254**
ØJHF[Ø,3]NZ	Insert/SQ Tissue & Fascia, Lt Upr Arm, [Opn, Perc], Tissue Expander, NQ **26, 91, 127, 206, 237, 314, 378, 380**
ØJHM[Ø,3][W,X]Z	Insert/SQ Tissue & Fascia, Lt Upr Leg, [Opn, Perc], [Reservoir, Vascular Access Dev], NQ **220, 254**
ØJHM[Ø,3]NZ	Insert/SQ Tissue & Fascia, Lt Upr Leg, [Opn, Perc], Tissue Expander, NQ **26, 91, 127, 207, 237, 314, 378, 380**
ØJHW[Ø,3]1Z	Insert/SQ Tissue & Fascia, Lwr Extr, [Opn, Perc], Radioact Elmt, NQ **212, 337, 450**
ØJHC*	Insert/SQ Tissue & Fascia, Pelvic Region **26, 91, 127, 206, 237, 380**
ØJHB*	Insert/SQ Tissue & Fascia, Perineum **26, 91, 127, 206, 237, 380**
ØJHB[Ø,3]NZ	Insert/SQ Tissue & Fascia, Perineum, [Opn, Perc], Tissue Expander, NQ **314, 378**
ØJH5[Ø,3]NZ	Insert/SQ Tissue & Fascia, Post Neck, [Opn, Perc], Tissue Expander, NQ **314, 378**
ØJH5*	Insert/SQ Tissue & Fascia, Posterior Neck **26, 54, 91, 113, 127, 206, 237, 380**
ØJHQ*	Insert/SQ Tissue & Fascia, Rt Foot **26, 91, 127, 207, 237, 380**
ØJHQ[Ø,3]NZ	Insert/SQ Tissue & Fascia, Rt Foot, [Opn, Perc], Tissue Expander, NQ **314, 378**
ØJHJ*	Insert/SQ Tissue & Fascia, Rt Hand **26, 149, 206, 237, 380**
ØJHJ[Ø,3]NZ	Insert/SQ Tissue & Fascia, Rt Hand, [Opn, Perc], Tissue Expander, NQ **314, 378**
ØJHG[Ø,3][W,X]Z	Insert/SQ Tissue & Fascia, Rt Lwr Arm, [Opn, Perc], [Reservoir, Vascular Access Dev], NQ **220, 254**
ØJHG[Ø,3]NZ	Insert/SQ Tissue & Fascia, Rt Lwr Arm, [Opn, Perc], Tissue Expander, NQ **26, 91, 127, 206, 237, 314, 378, 380**
ØJHN[Ø,3][W,X]Z	Insert/SQ Tissue & Fascia, Rt Lwr Leg, [Opn, Perc], [Reservoir, Vascular Access Dev], NQ **220, 254**
ØJHN[Ø,3]NZ	Insert/SQ Tissue & Fascia, Rt Lwr Leg, [Opn, Perc], Tissue Expander, NQ **26, 91, 127, 207, 237, 314, 378, 380**
ØJHD[Ø,3][W,X]Z	Insert/SQ Tissue & Fascia, Rt Upr Arm, [Opn, Perc], [Reservoir, Vascular Access Dev], NQ **220, 254**

Code	Description
0JHD[0,3]NZ	Insert/SQ Tissue & Fascia, Rt Upr Arm, [Opn, Perc], Tissue Expander, NQ 26, 91, 127, 206, 237, 314, 378, 380
0JHL[0,3][W,X]Z	Insert/SQ Tissue & Fascia, Rt Upr Leg, [Opn, Perc], [Reservoir, Vascular Access Dev], NQ 220, 254
0JHL[0,3]NZ	Insert/SQ Tissue & Fascia, Rt Upr Leg, [Opn, Perc], Tissue Expander, NQ 26, 91, 127, 207, 237, 314, 378, 380
0JH0*	Insert/SQ Tissue & Fascia, Scalp 26, 54, 91, 113, 127, 206, 237, 380
0JH0[0,3]NZ	Insert/SQ Tissue & Fascia, Scalp, [Opn, Perc], Tissue Expander, NQ 313, 378
0JHT[0,3][1,V]Z	Insert/SQ Tissue & Fascia, Trunk, [Opn, Perc], [Radioact Elmt, Inf Pump], NQ 212, 337
0JHT[0,3]VZ	Insert/SQ Tissue & Fascia, Trunk, [Opn, Perc], Inf Pump, NQ 26, 65, 91, 113, 123, 153, 242, 253, 259, 268, 292
0JHT[0,3]1Z	Insert/SQ Tissue & Fascia, Trunk, [Opn, Perc], Radioact Elmt, NQ 450
0JHV[0,3]1Z	Insert/SQ Tissue & Fascia, Upr Extr, [Opn, Perc], Radioact Elmt, NQ 212, 337, 450
0RHF[0,3,4]4Z	Insert/Sternoclavicular Jt, Lt, [Opn, Perc, Perc Endo], Int Fix Dev, NQ 147, 349
0RHE[0,3,4]4Z	Insert/Sternoclavicular Jt, Rt, [Opn, Perc, Perc Endo], Int Fix Dev, NQ 147, 349
0PH0*	Insert/Sternum 65, 155, 345
0PH0[0,3,4]0Z	Insert/Sternum, [Opn, Perc, Perc Endo], Int Fix Dev, Rigid Plate, NQ 91
0DH6[0,3,4,7,8][2,3,D]Z	Insert/Stomach, [Opn, Perc, Perc Endo, Via Natrl or Artfcl Opng, Via Natrl or Artfcl Opng Endo], [Monitoring Dev, Inf Dev, Intralum Dev], NQ 106, 333
0DH6[0,3,4,7,8]DZ	Insert/Stomach, [Opn, Perc, Perc Endo, Via Natrl or Artfcl Opng, Via Natrl or Artfcl Opng Endo], Intralum Dev, NQ 235
0DH6[0,3,4]MZ	Insert/Stomach, [Opn, Perc, Perc Endo], Stimulator Lead, NQ 25, 31, 53, 87, 153, 253, 259, 268, 333
03H4[0,3,4]DZ	Insert/Subclavian Artery, Lt, [Opn, Perc, Perc Endo], Intralum Dev, NQ 63, 81, 296, 321
03H3[0,3,4]DZ	Insert/Subclavian Artery, Rt, [Opn, Perc, Perc Endo], Intralum Dev, NQ 63, 81, 296, 321
05H6[0,3,4]DZ	Insert/Subclavian Vein, Lt, [Opn, Perc, Perc Endo], Intralum Dev, NQ 64, 85, 297, 326
05H5[0,3,4]DZ	Insert/Subclavian Vein, Rt, [Opn, Perc, Perc Endo], Intralum Dev, NQ 64, 85, 297, 325
04H5[0,3,4]DZ	Insert/Superior Mesenteric Artery, [Opn, Perc, Perc Endo], Intralum Dev, NQ 83, 296, 323
06H5[0,3,4]DZ	Insert/Superior Mesenteric Vein, [Opn, Perc, Perc Endo], Intralum Dev, NQ 87, 111, 297, 327
02HV[0,3,4][2,D]Z	Insert/Superior Vena Cava, [Opn, Perc, Perc Endo], [Monitoring Dev, Intralum Dev], NQ 24, 63, 80, 110, 121, 152, 238, 251, 258, 268, 290, 319
02HV[0,3,4]DZ	Insert/Superior Vena Cava, [Opn, Perc, Perc Endo], Intralum Dev, NQ 271
02HV[0,3,4]0Z	Insert/Superior Vena Cava, [Opn, Perc, Perc Endo], Monitoring Dev, Pressure Sensor, NQ 89
02HV[3,4]2Z	Insert/Superior Vena Cava, [Perc, Perc Endo], Monitoring Dev, NQ 271
0SHJ[0,3,4][4,5]Z	Insert/Tarsal Jt, Lt, [Opn, Perc, Perc Endo], [Int Fix Dev, Ext Fix Dev], NQ 145, 351, 457
0SHH[0,3,4][4,5]Z	Insert/Tarsal Jt, Rt, [Opn, Perc, Perc Endo], [Int Fix Dev, Ext Fix Dev], NQ 145, 351, 457
0QHM*	Insert/Tarsal, Lt 145, 347
0QHL*	Insert/Tarsal, Rt 145, 347
03HT[0,3,4]DZ	Insert/Temporal Artery, Lt, [Opn, Perc, Perc Endo], Intralum Dev, NQ 50, 81, 296, 321
03HS[0,3,4]DZ	Insert/Temporal Artery, Rt, [Opn, Perc, Perc Endo], Intralum Dev, NQ 50, 81, 296, 321
0NH6[0,3,4]SZ	Insert/Temporal Bone, Lt, [Opn, Perc, Perc Endo], Bone Conduction Hearing Dev, NQ 54
0NH6[0,3,4]4Z	Insert/Temporal Bone, Lt, [Opn, Perc, Perc Endo], Int Fix Dev, NQ 10, 14, 18, 48, 154, 344, 415
0NH5[0,3,4]SZ	Insert/Temporal Bone, Rt, [Opn, Perc, Perc Endo], Bone Conduction Hearing Dev, NQ 54
0NH5[0,3,4]4Z	Insert/Temporal Bone, Rt, [Opn, Perc, Perc Endo], Int Fix Dev, NQ 10, 14, 18, 48, 154, 344, 415
0RHD[0,3,4][3,4]Z	Insert/Temporomandibular Jt, Lt, [Opn, Perc, Perc Endo], [Inf Dev, Int Fix Dev], NQ 55
0RHC[0,3,4][3,4]Z	Insert/Temporomandibular Jt, Rt, [Opn, Perc, Perc Endo], [Inf Dev, Int Fix Dev], NQ 55
02HW[0,3,4][2,D]Z	Insert/Thoracic Aorta, [Opn, Perc, Perc Endo], [Monitoring Dev, Intralum Dev], NQ 93
0RH6[0,3,4][B,C,D]Z	Insert/Thoracic Vert Jt, [Opn, Perc, Perc Endo], [Spinal Stabliz Dev, Interspinous Process, Spinal Stabliz Dev, Pedicle-Based, Spinal Stabliz Dev, Facet Replace], NQ 20, 159, 160, 161, 349
0RH6[0,3,4]4Z	Insert/Thoracic Vert Jt, [Opn, Perc, Perc Endo], Int Fix Dev, NQ 156
0PH4*	Insert/Thoracic Vertebra 155, 345
0RHA[0,3,4][B,C,D]Z	Insert/Thoracolumbar Vert Jt, [Opn, Perc, Perc Endo], [Spinal Stabliz Dev, Interspinous Process, Spinal Stabliz Dev, Pedicle-Based, Spinal Stabliz Dev, Facet Replace], NQ 20, 159, 160, 161, 349
0RHA[0,3,4]4Z	Insert/Thoracolumbar Vert Jt, [Opn, Perc, Perc Endo], Int Fix Dev, NQ 156
0PHS*	Insert/Thumb Phalanx, Lt 155, 345
0PHR*	Insert/Thumb Phalanx, Rt 155, 345
03HV[0,3,4]DZ	Insert/Thyroid Artery, Lt, [Opn, Perc, Perc Endo], Intralum Dev, NQ 50, 82, 296, 321
03HU[0,3,4]DZ	Insert/Thyroid Artery, Rt, [Opn, Perc, Perc Endo], Intralum Dev, NQ 50, 81, 296, 321
0QHH[0,3,4][4,5,6,B,C,D]Z	Insert/Tibia, Lt, [Opn, Perc, Perc Endo], [Int Fix Dev, Ext Fix Dev, Int Fix Dev, Intramedullary Int Fix Dev, Ext Fix Dev, Monop, Ext Fix Dev, Ring, Ext Fix Dev, Hybrid], NQ 133, 347
0QHG[0,3,4][4,5,6,B,C,D]Z	Insert/Tibia, Rt, [Opn, Perc, Perc Endo], [Int Fix Dev, Ext Fix Dev, Int Fix Dev, Intramedullary Int Fix Dev, Ext Fix Dev, Monop, Ext Fix Dev, Ring, Ext Fix Dev, Hybrid], NQ 133, 347
0SHQ[0,3,4][4,5]Z	Insert/Toe Phalangeal Jt, Lt, [Opn, Perc, Perc Endo], [Int Fix Dev, Ext Fix Dev], NQ 145, 351, 457
0SHP[0,3,4][4,5]Z	Insert/Toe Phalangeal Jt, Rt, [Opn, Perc, Perc Endo], [Int Fix Dev, Ext Fix Dev], NQ 145, 351, 457
0QHR*	Insert/Toe Phalanx, Lt 156, 347
0QHQ*	Insert/Toe Phalanx, Rt 156, 347
0CH7*	Insert/Tongue 52, 331
0CH7[0,3,X]1Z	Insert/Tongue, [Opn, Perc, Ext], Radioact Elmt, NQ 448
0BH1[0,3,4,7,8]DZ	Insert/Trachea, [Opn, Perc, Perc Endo, Via Natrl or Artfcl Opng, Via Natrl or Artfcl Opng Endo], Intralum Dev, NQ 64
0BH1[0,7,8]2Z	Insert/Trachea, [Opn, Via Natrl or Artfcl Opng, Via Natrl or Artfcl Opng Endo], Monitoring Dev, NQ 64
0BH0[0,3,4,7,8]1Z	Insert/Tracheobronchial Tree, [Opn, Perc, Perc Endo, Via Natrl or Artfcl Opng, Via Natrl or Artfcl Opng Endo], Radioact Elmt, NQ 64, 331, 447
0BH0[0,3,4][2,3,D]Z	Insert/Tracheobronchial Tree, [Opn, Perc, Perc Endo], [Monitoring Dev, Inf Dev, Intralum Dev], NQ 62
0PHL[0,3,4][4,5,6,B,C,D]Z	Insert/Ulna, Lt, [Opn, Perc, Perc Endo], [Int Fix Dev, Ext Fix Dev, Int Fix Dev, Intramedullary Int Fix Dev, Ext Fix Dev, Monop, Ext Fix Dev, Ring, Ext Fix Dev, Hybrid], NQ 148, 345
0PHK[0,3,4][4,5,6,B,C,D]Z	Insert/Ulna, Rt, [Opn, Perc, Perc Endo], [Int Fix Dev, Ext Fix Dev, Int Fix Dev, Intramedullary Int Fix Dev, Ext Fix Dev, Monop, Ext Fix Dev, Ring, Ext Fix Dev, Hybrid], NQ 148, 345
03HA[0,3,4]DZ	Insert/Ulnar Artery, Lt, [Opn, Perc, Perc Endo], Intralum Dev, NQ 81, 296, 321
03H9[0,3,4]DZ	Insert/Ulnar Artery, Rt, [Opn, Perc, Perc Endo], Intralum Dev, NQ 81, 296, 321
0XH9[0,3,4][3,Y]Z	Insert/Upr Arm, Lt, [Opn, Perc, Perc Endo], [Inf Dev, Oth Dev], NQ 220
0XH9[0,3,4]1Z	Insert/Upr Arm, Lt, [Opn, Perc, Perc Endo], Radioact Elmt, NQ 356, 461
0XH8[0,3,4][3,Y]Z	Insert/Upr Arm, Rt, [Opn, Perc, Perc Endo], [Inf Dev, Oth Dev], NQ 220
0XH8[0,3,4]1Z	Insert/Upr Arm, Rt, [Opn, Perc, Perc Endo], Radioact Elmt, NQ 356, 461
03HY[0,3,4][2,D]Z	Insert/Upr Artery, [Opn, Perc, Perc Endo], [Monitoring Dev, Intralum Dev], NQ 82
03HY[0,3,4]DZ	Insert/Upr Artery, [Opn, Perc, Perc Endo], Intralum Dev, NQ 50, 296, 321
0WHK[0,3,4][3,Y]Z	Insert/Upr Back, [Opn, Perc, Perc Endo], [Inf Dev, Oth Dev], NQ 220
0WHK[0,3,4]1Z	Insert/Upr Back, [Opn, Perc, Perc Endo], Radioact Elmt, NQ 355, 460
0PHY*	Insert/Upr Bone 65, 155, 345
0XH7[0,3,4][3,Y]Z	Insert/Upr Extr, Lt, [Opn, Perc, Perc Endo], [Inf Dev, Oth Dev], NQ 220
0XH7[0,3,4]1Z	Insert/Upr Extr, Lt, [Opn, Perc, Perc Endo], Radioact Elmt, NQ 356, 461

Alphabetic Index to Procedures

ØXH6[Ø,3,4][3,Y]Z	Insert/Upr Extr, Rt, [Opn, Perc, Perc Endo], [Inf Dev, Oth Dev], NQ **220**
ØXH6[Ø,3,4]1Z	Insert/Upr Extr, Rt, [Opn, Perc, Perc Endo], Radioact Elmt, NQ **356, 461**
ØQH7[Ø,3,4][4,5,6,B,C,D]Z	Insert/Upr Femur, Lt, [Opn, Perc, Perc Endo], [Int Fix Dev, Ext Fix Dev, Int Fix Dev, Intramedullary Int Fix Dev, Ext Fix Dev, Monop, Ext Fix Dev, Ring, Ext Fix Dev, Hybrid], NQ **130, 347, 415**
ØQH6[Ø,3,4][4,5,6,B,C,D]Z	Insert/Upr Femur, Rt, [Opn, Perc, Perc Endo], [Int Fix Dev, Ext Fix Dev, Int Fix Dev, Intramedullary Int Fix Dev, Ext Fix Dev, Monop, Ext Fix Dev, Ring, Ext Fix Dev, Hybrid], NQ **130, 347, 415**
ØWH4[Ø,3,4][3,Y]Z	Insert/Upr Jaw, [Opn, Perc, Perc Endo], [Inf Dev, Oth Dev], NQ **220**
ØWH4[Ø,3,4]1Z	Insert/Upr Jaw, [Opn, Perc, Perc Endo], Radioact Elmt, NQ **55, 355, 460**
ØYHD[Ø,3,4][3,Y]Z	Insert/Upr Leg, Lt, [Opn, Perc, Perc Endo], [Inf Dev, Oth Dev], NQ **220**
ØYHD[Ø,3,4]1Z	Insert/Upr Leg, Lt, [Opn, Perc, Perc Endo], Radioact Elmt, NQ **357, 461**
ØYHC[Ø,3,4][3,Y]Z	Insert/Upr Leg, Rt, [Opn, Perc, Perc Endo], [Inf Dev, Oth Dev], NQ **220**
ØYHC[Ø,3,4]1Z	Insert/Upr Leg, Rt, [Opn, Perc, Perc Endo], Radioact Elmt, NQ **357, 461**
ØBH8[Ø,3,4,7]GZ	Insert/Upr Lobe Bronchus, Lt, [Opn, Perc, Perc Endo, Via Natrl or Artfcl Opng], Endobronchial Valve, NQ **62**
ØBH4[Ø,3,4,7]GZ	Insert/Upr Lobe Bronchus, Rt, [Opn, Perc, Perc Endo, Via Natrl or Artfcl Opng], Endobronchial Valve, NQ **62**
Ø5HY[Ø,3,4][2,D]Z	Insert/Upr Vein, [Opn, Perc, Perc Endo], [Monitoring Dev, Intralum Dev], NQ **51, 85, 326**
Ø5HY[Ø,3,4]DZ	Insert/Upr Vein, [Opn, Perc, Perc Endo], Intralum Dev, NQ **64, 111, 271, 297**
Ø5HY[Ø,3,4]2Z	Insert/Upr Vein, [Opn, Perc, Perc Endo], Monitoring Dev, NQ **25, 240**
ØTH9[Ø,3,4,7,8][2,M]Z	Insert/Ureter, [Opn, Perc, Perc Endo, Via Natrl or Artfcl Opng, Via Natrl or Artfcl Opng Endo], [Monitoring Dev, Stimulator Lead], NQ **249**
ØTH9[Ø,3,4,7,8]2Z	Insert/Ureter, [Opn, Perc, Perc Endo, Via Natrl or Artfcl Opng, Via Natrl or Artfcl Opng Endo], Monitoring Dev, NQ **458**
ØTHD[Ø,3,4,7,8,X][2,L]Z	Insert/Urethra, [Opn, Perc, Perc Endo, Via Natrl or Artfcl Opng, Via Natrl or Artfcl Opng Endo, Ext], [Monitoring Dev, Artfcl Sphincter], NQ **353**
ØTHD[Ø,3,4,7,8,X]LZ	Insert/Urethra, [Opn, Perc, Perc Endo, Via Natrl or Artfcl Opng, Via Natrl or Artfcl Opng Endo, Ext], Artfcl Sphincter, NQ **249**
ØTHD[Ø,3,4,7,8,X]2 Z	Insert/Urethra, [Opn, Perc, Perc Endo, Via Natrl or Artfcl Opng, Via Natrl or Artfcl Opng Endo, Ext], Monitoring Dev, NQ **250**
ØTHD[Ø,3,4,7,8,X]2Z	Insert/Urethra, [Opn, Perc, Perc Endo, Via Natrl or Artfcl Opng, Via Natrl or Artfcl Opng Endo, Ext], Monitoring Dev, NQ **458**
ØUHH*	Insert/Vagina and Cul-de-sac **267, 275**
ØUHH[Ø,3,4,7,8]3Z	Insert/Vagina and Cul-de-sac, [Opn, Perc, Perc Endo, Via Natrl or Artfcl Opng, Via Natrl or Artfcl Opng Endo], Inf Dev, NQ **459**
ØUHG[Ø,3,4,7,8,X]1Z	Insert/Vagina, [Opn, Perc, Perc Endo, Via Natrl or Artfcl Opng, Via Natrl or Artfcl Opng Endo, Ext], Radioact Elmt, NQ **266, 354, 459**
Ø2HL[Ø,3,4][J,M]Z	Insert/Ventricle, Lt, [Opn, Perc, Perc Endo], [Cardiac Lead, Pacemaker, Cardiac Lead], NQ **29, 77, 78, 357, 358**
Ø2HL[Ø,3,4][2,3,D]Z	Insert/Ventricle, Lt, [Opn, Perc, Perc Endo], [Monitoring Dev, Inf Dev, Intralum Dev], NQ **75**
Ø2HL[Ø,3,4]KZ	Insert/Ventricle, Lt, [Opn, Perc, Perc Endo], Cardiac Lead, Defibrillator, NQ **72, 73, 74, 92**
Ø2HL[Ø,3,4]MZ	Insert/Ventricle, Lt, [Opn, Perc, Perc Endo], Cardiac Lead, NQ **72, 73**
Ø2HL[Ø,3,4]JZ	Insert/Ventricle, Lt, [Opn, Perc, Perc Endo], Cardiac Lead, Pacemaker, NQ **76**
Ø2HL[Ø,3,4]2Z	Insert/Ventricle, Lt, [Opn, Perc, Perc Endo], Monitoring Dev, NQ **319**
Ø2HL[Ø,3,4]ØZ	Insert/Ventricle, Lt, [Opn, Perc, Perc Endo], Monitoring Dev, Pressure Sensor, NQ **89**
Ø2HK[Ø,3,4][J,M]Z	Insert/Ventricle, Rt, [Opn, Perc, Perc Endo], [Cardiac Lead, Pacemaker, Cardiac Lead], NQ **29, 77, 78, 357, 358**
Ø2HK[Ø,3,4][Ø,2]Z	Insert/Ventricle, Rt, [Opn, Perc, Perc Endo], [Monitoring Dev, Pressure Sensor, Monitoring Dev], NQ **88, 92**
Ø2HK[Ø,3,4]KZ	Insert/Ventricle, Rt, [Opn, Perc, Perc Endo], Cardiac Lead, Defibrillator, NQ **72, 73, 74, 92**
Ø2HK[Ø,3,4]JZ	Insert/Ventricle, Rt, [Opn, Perc, Perc Endo], Cardiac Lead, Pacemaker, NQ **76**
Ø2HK[3,4][J,M]Z	Insert/Ventricle, Rt, [Perc, Perc Endo], [Cardiac Lead, Pacemaker, Cardiac Lead], NQ **29, 77, 358**
Ø3HQ[Ø,3,4]DZ	Insert/Vert Artery, Lt, [Opn, Perc, Perc Endo], Intralum Dev, NQ **50, 81, 296, 321**
Ø3HP[Ø,3,4]DZ	Insert/Vert Artery, Rt, [Opn, Perc, Perc Endo], Intralum Dev, NQ **50, 81, 296, 321**
Ø5HS[Ø,3,4]DZ	Insert/Vert Vein, Lt, [Opn, Perc, Perc Endo], Intralum Dev, NQ **51, 85, 297, 326**
Ø5HR[Ø,3,4]DZ	Insert/Vert Vein, Rt, [Opn, Perc, Perc Endo], Intralum Dev, NQ **51, 85, 297, 326**
ØRHP[Ø,3,4][4,5]Z	Insert/Wrist Jt, Lt, [Opn, Perc, Perc Endo], [Int Fix Dev, Ext Fix Dev], NQ **146, 316**
ØRHN[Ø,3,4][4,5]Z	Insert/Wrist Jt, Rt, [Opn, Perc, Perc Endo], [Int Fix Dev, Ext Fix Dev], NQ **146, 316**
ØXHH[Ø,3,4][3,Y]Z	Insert/Wrist Rgn, Lt, [Opn, Perc, Perc Endo], [Inf Dev, Oth Dev], NQ **220**
ØXHH[Ø,3,4]1Z	Insert/Wrist Rgn, Lt, [Opn, Perc, Perc Endo], Radioact Elmt, NQ **356, 461**
ØXHG[Ø,3,4][3,Y]Z	Insert/Wrist Rgn, Rt, [Opn, Perc, Perc Endo], [Inf Dev, Oth Dev], NQ **220**
ØXHG[Ø,3,4]1Z	Insert/Wrist Rgn, Rt, [Opn, Perc, Perc Endo], Radioact Elmt, NQ **356, 461**
ØNHN*	Insert/Zygomatic Bone, Lt **54**
ØNHM*	Insert/Zygomatic Bone, Rt **54**
ØWJ[F,G,H,J,P]ØZZ	Inspect of [Abd Wall, Peritoneal Cavity, Retroperitoneum, Pelvic Cavity, Gastrointestinal Tract], Perc Endo Appr **91**
ØWJ[F,H]ØZZ	Inspect of [Abd Wall, Retroperitoneum], Opn Appr **123**
ØRJ[4,5,6,9]3ZZ	Inspect of [Cervicothoracic Vert Jt, Cervicothoracic Vert Disc, Thoracic Vert Jt, Thoracic Vert Disc], Perc Appr **130**
ØRJ[4,5,6,9]4ZZ	Inspect of [Cervicothoracic Vert Jt, Cervicothoracic Vert Disc, Thoracic Vert Jt, Thoracic Vert Disc], Perc Endo **148**
Ø2J[A,Y]4ZZ	Inspect of [Heart, Great Vessel], Perc Endo Appr **50, 63, 290**
Ø5SJ[Ø,3,5,6]4ZZ	Inspect of [Lumbar Vert, Lumbosacral, Sacrococcygeal, Coccygeal] Jt, Perc Endo **148**
ØWJ[C,D]4ZZ	Inspect of [Mediastinum Pericardial Cavity], Perc Endo Appr **55**
ØRJ[Ø,1,3]3ZZ	Inspect of [Occipital-cervical Jt, Cervical Vert Jt, Cervical Vert Disc], Perc Appr **130**
ØRJ[Ø,1,3]4ZZ	Inspect of [Occipital-cervical Jt, Cervical Vert Jt, Cervical Vert Disc], Perc Endo **148**
ØRJ[G,H]ØZZ	Inspect of [Rt Acromioclavicular Jt, Lt Acromioclavicular Jt], Opn Appr **148**
ØRJ[G,H]3ZZ	Inspect of [Rt Acromioclavicular Jt, Lt Acromioclavicular Jt], Perc Appr **130**
ØRJ[G,H]4ZZ	Inspect of [Rt Acromioclavicular Jt, Lt Acromioclavicular Jt], Perc Endo **148**
ØRJ[W,X]ØZZ	Inspect of [Rt Finger Phalangeal Jt, Lt Finger Phalangeal Jt], Opn Appr **147**
ØRJ[W,X]3ZZ	Inspect of [Rt Finger Phalangeal Jt, Lt Finger Phalangeal Jt], Perc Appr **130**
ØRJ[W,X]4ZZ	Inspect of [Rt Finger Phalangeal Jt, Lt Finger Phalangeal Jt], Perc Endo **148**
Ø5SJ[C,D,F,G,H,J]3ZZ	Inspect of [Rt Knee, Lt Knee, Rt Ankle, Lt Ankle, Rt Tarsal, Lt Tarsal] Jt, Perc Appr **130**
Ø5SJ[C,D,F,G,H,J]4ZZ	Inspect of [Rt Knee, Lt Knee, Rt Ankle, Lt Ankle, Rt Tarsal, Lt Tarsal] Jt, Perc Endo **148**
ØRJ[S,T]ØZZ	Inspect of [Rt Metacarpocarpal Jt, Lt Metacarpocarpal Jt], Opn Appr **147**
ØRJ[S,T]3ZZ	Inspect of [Rt Metacarpocarpal Jt, Lt Metacarpocarpal Jt], Perc Appr **130**
ØRJ[S,T]4ZZ	Inspect of [Rt Metacarpocarpal Jt, Lt Metacarpocarpal Jt], Perc Endo **148**
ØRJ[U,V]ØZZ	Inspect of [Rt Metacarpophalangeal Jt, Lt Metacarpophalangeal Jt], Opn Appr **147**
ØRJ[U,V]3ZZ	Inspect of [Rt Metacarpophalangeal Jt, Lt Metacarpophalangeal Jt], Perc Appr **130**
ØRJ[U,V]4ZZ	Inspect of [Rt Metacarpophalangeal Jt, Lt Metacarpophalangeal Jt], Perc Endo **148**
Ø5SJ[M,N]3ZZ	Inspect of [Rt Metatarsal-Phalangeal, Lt Metatarsal-Phalangeal] Jt, Perc Appr **130**
Ø5SJ[M,N]4ZZ	Inspect of [Rt Metatarsal-Phalangeal, Lt Metatarsal-Phalangeal] Jt, Perc Endo **148**
Ø5SJ[K,L]3ZZ	Inspect of [Rt Metatarsal-Tarsal, Lt Metatarsal-Tarsal] Jt, Perc Appr **130**

ØSJ[K,L]4ZZ	Inspect of [Rt Metatarsal-Tarsal, Lt Metatarsal-Tarsal] Jt, Perc Endo 148
ØSJ[7,8,9,B]3ZZ	Inspect of [Rt Sacroiliac, Lt Sacroiliac, Rt Hip Jt, Lt Hip] Jt, Perc Appr 130
ØSJ[7,8,9,B]4ZZ	Inspect of [Rt Sacroiliac, Lt Sacroiliac, Rt Hip Jt, Lt Hip] Jt, Perc Endo 148
ØRJ[J,K,L,M]ØZZ	Inspect of [Rt Shldr Jt, Lt Shldr Jt, Rt Elbow Jt, Lt Elbow Jt], Opn Appr 148
ØRJ[J,K,L,M]3ZZ	Inspect of [Rt Shldr Jt, Lt Shldr Jt, Rt Elbow Jt, Lt Elbow Jt], Perc Appr 130
ØRJ[J,K,L,M]4ZZ	Inspect of [Rt Shldr Jt, Lt Shldr Jt, Rt Elbow Jt, Lt Elbow Jt], Perc Endo 148
ØRJ[E,F]ØZZ	Inspect of [Rt Sternoclavicular Jt, Lt Sternoclavicular Jt], Opn Appr 148
ØRJ[E,F]3ZZ	Inspect of [Rt Sternoclavicular Jt, Lt Sternoclavicular Jt], Perc Appr 130
ØRJ[E,F]4ZZ	Inspect of [Rt Sternoclavicular Jt, Lt Sternoclavicular Jt], Perc Endo 148
ØSJ[P,Q]3ZZ	Inspect of [Rt Toe Phalangeal, Lt Toe Phalangeal] Jt, Perc Appr 130
ØSJ[P,Q]4ZZ	Inspect of [Rt Toe Phalangeal, Lt Toe Phalangeal] Jt, Perc Endo 148
ØRJ[N,P,Q,R]ØZZ	Inspect of [Rt Wrist Jt, Lt Wrist Jt, Rt Carpal Jt, Lt Carpal Jt], Opn Appr 147
ØRJ[N,P,Q,R]3ZZ	Inspect of [Rt Wrist Jt, Lt Wrist Jt, Rt Carpal Jt, Lt Carpal Jt], Perc Appr 130
ØRJ[N,P,Q,R]4ZZ	Inspect of [Rt Wrist Jt, Lt Wrist Jt, Rt Carpal Jt, Lt Carpal Jt], Perc Endo 148
ØSJ[F,G]ØZZ	Inspect of [Rt, Lt] Ankle Jt, Opn Appr 133
Ø8J[Ø,1]XZZ	Inspect of [Rt, Lt] Eye, Ext Appr 43, 51
ØSJ[9,B]ØZZ	Inspect of [Rt, Lt] Hip Jt, Opn Appr 131
ØSJ[C,D]ØZZ	Inspect of [Rt, Lt] Knee Jt, Opn Appr 132
Ø8J[J,K]XZZ	Inspect of [Rt, Lt] Lens, Ext Appr 42
ØSJ[M,N]ØZZ	Inspect of [Rt, Lt] Metatarsal-Phalangeal Jt, Opn Appr 145
ØSJ[K,L]ØZZ	Inspect of [Rt, Lt] Metatarsal-Tarsal Jt, Opn Appr 145
ØSJ[7,8]ØZZ	Inspect of [Rt, Lt] Sacroiliac Jt, Opn Appr 157
ØSJ[H,J]ØZZ	Inspect of [Rt, Lt] Tarsal Jt, Opn Appr 145
ØSJ[P,Q]ØZZ	Inspect of [Rt, Lt] Toe Phalangeal Jt, Opn Appr 145
ØSJ[5,6]ØZZ	Inspect of [Sacrococcygeal, Coccygeal] Jt, Opn Appr 157
ØSJ[5,6]3ZZ	Inspect of [Sacrococcygeal, Coccygeal] Jt, Perc Appr 130
ØRJ[A,B]3ZZ	Inspect of [Thoracolumbar Vert Jt, Thoracolumbar Vert Disc], Perc Appr 130
ØRJ[A,B]4ZZ	Inspect of [Thoracolumbar Vert Jt, Thoracolumbar Vert Disc], Perc Endo 148
ØGJ[K,R,S]ØZZ	Inspect of [Thyroid Gland, Parathyroid Gland, Endocrine Gland], Opn 53
ØBJ[Ø,K,L]4ZZ	Inspect of [Tracheobronchial Tree, Rt Lung, Lt Lung], Perc Endo 90
ØDJ[Ø,6,D,U,V,W]ØZZ	Inspect of [Upr Intestinal Tract, Stomach, Lwr Intestinal Tract, Omentum, Mesentery, Peritoneum], Opn Appr 65, 90
ØDJ[Ø,6,D]ØZZ	Inspect of [Upr Intestinal Tract, Stomach, Lwr Intestinal Tract], Opn Appr 112
ØDJ[Ø,6]4ZZ	Inspect of [Upr Intestinal Tract, Stomach], Perc Endo Appr 106
ØWJF3ZZ	Inspect of Abd Wall, Perc Appr 269
ØWJF4ZZ	Inspect of Abd Wall, Perc Endo Appr 266, 272
ØYJEØZZ	Inspect of Bilat Femor Region, Opn Appr 221
ØYJAØZZ	Inspect of Bilat Inguinal Region, Opn Appr 92, 123, 219, 254
ØØJØØZZ	Inspect of Brain, Opn Appr 48, 414
ØRJ54ZZ	Inspect of C-thor Disc, Perc Endo Appr 349
ØRJ44ZZ	Inspect of C-thor Jt, Perc Endo Appr 349
ØRJ[1,3]ØZZ	Inspect of Cervical Vert [Jt, Disc], Opn Appr 156
ØRJ34ZZ	Inspect of Cervical Vert Disc, Perc Endo Appr 349
ØRJ14ZZ	Inspect of Cervical Vert Jt, Perc Endo Appr 349
ØRJ[4,5]ØZZ	Inspect of Cervicothoracic Vert [Jt, Disc], Opn Appr 156
ØSJ64ZZ	Inspect of Coccygeal Jt, Perc Endo Appr 351
ØWJ1ØZZ	Inspect of Cranial Cavity, Opn Appr 49, 415
ØGJSØZZ	Inspect of Endocrine Gland, Opn Appr 211, 336
ØGJS3ZZ	Inspect of Endocrine Gland, Perc Appr 153
ØGJS4ZZ	Inspect of Endocrine Gland, Perc Endo Appr 153
ØWJ2ØZZ	Inspect of Face, Opn Appr 220
ØFJ44ZZ	Inspect of Gallbladder, Perc Endo Appr 211, 253, 266, 271, 292, 335, 449
ØWJPØZZ	Inspect of Gastrointestinal Tract, Opn Appr 66, 245, 257
ØWJP4ZZ	Inspect of Gastrointestinal Tract, Perc Endo Appr 266
ØWJRØZZ	Inspect of Genitourinary Tract, Opn Appr 66, 91, 245, 257
ØWJR4ZZ	Inspect of Genitourinary Tract, Perc Endo Appr 266
Ø2JYØZZ	Inspect of Great Vessel, Opn Appr 60, 89, 251, 319
Ø2JY4ZZ	Inspect of Great Vessel, Perc Endo Appr 89
ØWJØØZZ	Inspect of Head, Opn Appr 220
Ø2JAØZZ	Inspect of Heart, Opn Appr 60, 251, 319
ØFJØØZZ	Inspect of Liver, Opn Appr 65, 90, 242, 257, 268
ØFJØ4ZZ	Inspect of Liver, Perc Endo Appr 266, 449
ØYJLØZZ	Inspect of Lt Ankle Region, Opn Appr 221
ØXJ5ØZZ	Inspect of Lt Axilla, Opn Appr 220
ØYJ1ØZZ	Inspect of Lt Buttock, Opn Appr 220
ØRJRØZZ	Inspect of Lt Carpal Jt, Opn Appr 316
ØRJR4ZZ	Inspect of Lt Carpal Jt, Perc Endo Appr 349
ØXJCØZZ	Inspect of Lt Elbow Region, Opn Appr 220
Ø8J1XZZ	Inspect of Lt Eye, Ext Appr 330, 445
ØYJ8ØZZ	Inspect of Lt Femor Region, Opn Appr 220
ØRJXØZZ	Inspect of Lt Finger Phalangeal Jt, Opn Appr 316
ØRJX4ZZ	Inspect of Lt Finger Phalanx Jt, Perc Endo Appr 349
ØYJNØZZ	Inspect of Lt Foot, Opn Appr 221
ØXJKØZZ	Inspect of Lt Hand, Opn Appr 220
ØYJ6ØZZ	Inspect of Lt Inguinal Region, Opn Appr 92, 123, 219, 254
ØSJD4ZZ	Inspect of Lt Knee Jt, Perc Endo Appr 244
ØYJGØZZ	Inspect of Lt Knee Region, Opn Appr 221
Ø8JKXZZ	Inspect of Lt Lens, Ext Appr 445
ØBJL4ZZ	Inspect of Lt Lung, Perc Endo Appr 331
ØXJFØZZ	Inspect of Lt Lwr Arm, Opn Appr 220
ØYJBØZZ	Inspect of Lt Lwr Extr, Opn Appr 220
ØYJJØZZ	Inspect of Lt Lwr Leg, Opn Appr 221
ØRJTØZZ	Inspect of Lt Metacarpocarpal Jt, Opn Appr 316
ØRJT4ZZ	Inspect of Lt Metacarpocarpal Jt, Perc Endo Appr 349
ØRJV4ZZ	Inspect of Lt Metacarpophal Jt, Perc Endo Appr 349
ØRJVØZZ	Inspect of Lt Metacarpophalangeal Jt, Opn Appr 316
ØSJLØZZ	Inspect of Lt Metatarsal-Tarsal Jt, Opn Appr 457
ØSJNØZZ	Inspect of Lt Metatarsophal Jt, Opn Appr 457
ØWJBØZZ	Inspect of Lt Pleural Cavity, Opn Appr 62, 254, 302
ØSJ84ZZ	Inspect of Lt Sacroiliac Jt, Perc Endo Appr 351
ØXJ3ØZZ	Inspect of Lt Shldr Region, Opn Appr 220
ØSJJØZZ	Inspect of Lt Tarsal Jt, Opn Appr 457
ØSJQØZZ	Inspect of Lt Toe Phalangeal Jt, Opn Appr 457
ØXJ9ØZZ	Inspect of Lt Upr Arm, Opn Appr 220
ØXJ7ØZZ	Inspect of Lt Upr Extr, Opn Appr 220
ØYJDØZZ	Inspect of Lt Upr Leg, Opn Appr 221
ØRJPØZZ	Inspect of Lt Wrist Jt, Opn Appr 316
ØRJP4ZZ	Inspect of Lt Wrist Jt, Perc Endo Appr 349
ØXJHØZZ	Inspect of Lt Wrist Region, Opn Appr 220
ØSJ[Ø,2]ØZZ	Inspect of Lumbar Vert [Jt, Disc], Opn Appr 157
ØSJØ3ZZ	Inspect of Lumbar Vert Jt, Perc Appr 130
ØSJØ4ZZ	Inspect of Lumbar Vert Jt, Perc Endo Appr 351
ØSJ[3,4]ØZZ	Inspect of Lumbosacral [Jt, Disc], Opn Appr 157
ØSJ33ZZ	Inspect of Lumbosacral Jt, Perc Appr 130
ØSJ34ZZ	Inspect of Lumbosacral Jt, Perc Endo Appr 351
ØWJLØZZ	Inspect of Lwr Back, Opn Appr 220
ØQJYØZZ	Inspect of Lwr Bone, Opn Appr 130
ØQJY3ZZ	Inspect of Lwr Bone, Perc Appr 130
ØQJY4ZZ	Inspect of Lwr Bone, Perc Endo Appr 130
ØDJDØZZ	Inspect of Lwr Intestinal Tract, Opn Appr 121, 211, 242, 253, 257, 268, 271, 292
ØDJD4ZZ	Inspect of Lwr Intestinal Tract, Perc Endo Appr 109, 449
ØWJ5ØZZ	Inspect of Lwr Jaw, Opn Appr 220
ØLJYØZZ	Inspect of Lwr Tndn, Opn Appr 141
ØLJY3ZZ	Inspect of Lwr Tndn, Perc Appr 141
ØLJY4ZZ	Inspect of Lwr Tndn, Perc Endo Appr 141
ØWJCØZZ	Inspect of Mediastinum, Opn Appr 62, 254, 356
ØWJC4ZZ	Inspect of Mediastinum, Perc Endo Appr 293
ØDJVØZZ	Inspect of Mesentery, Opn Appr 242, 257
ØDJV4ZZ	Inspect of Mesentery, Perc Endo Appr 266
ØWJ6ØZZ	Inspect of Neck, Opn Appr 55, 217
ØRJØØZZ	Inspect of Occipital-cervical Jt, Opn Appr 156
ØRJØ4ZZ	Inspect of Occipital-cervical Jt, Perc Endo Appr 349

0DJU0ZZ	Inspect of Omentum, Opn Appr 242, 257
0DJU4ZZ	Inspect of Omentum, Perc Endo Appr 266
0FJG4ZZ	Inspect of Pancreas, Perc Endo Appr 211, 253, 266, 271, 292, 449
0FJD4ZZ	Inspect of Pancreatic Duct, Perc Endo Appr 211, 253, 266, 271, 292, 449
0GJR0ZZ	Inspect of Parathyroid Gland, Opn Appr 211, 336
0WJJ0ZZ	Inspect of Pelvic Cavity, Opn Appr 66, 245, 257
0WJJ4ZZ	Inspect of Pelvic Cavity, Perc Endo Appr 266
0WJD4ZZ	Inspect of Pericardial Cavity, Perc Endo Appr 66, 91, 293, 302
0WJG0ZZ	Inspect of Peritoneal Cavity, Opn Appr 66, 245, 257
0WJG4ZZ	Inspect of Peritoneal Cavity, Perc Endo Appr 266
0DJW0ZZ	Inspect of Peritoneum, Opn Appr 242, 257
0DJW4ZZ	Inspect of Peritoneum, Perc Endo Appr 266
0WJQ0ZZ	Inspect of Respiratory Tract, Opn Appr 62, 91, 254, 303
0WJQ4ZZ	Inspect of Respiratory Tract, Perc Endo Appr 91
0WJH0ZZ	Inspect of Retroperitoneum, Opn Appr 217, 254
0YJK0ZZ	Inspect of Rt Ankle Region, Opn Appr 221
0XJ40ZZ	Inspect of Rt Axilla, Opn Appr 220
0YJ00ZZ	Inspect of Rt Buttock, Opn Appr 220
0RJQ0ZZ	Inspect of Rt Carpal Jt, Opn Appr 316
0RJQ4ZZ	Inspect of Rt Carpal Jt, Perc Endo Appr 349
0XJB0ZZ	Inspect of Rt Elbow Region, Opn Appr 220
08J0XZZ	Inspect of Rt Eye, Ext Appr 330, 444
0YJ70ZZ	Inspect of Rt Femor Region, Opn Appr 92, 123, 219, 254
0RJW0ZZ	Inspect of Rt Finger Phalangeal Jt, Opn Appr 316
0RJW4ZZ	Inspect of Rt Finger Phalanx Jt, Perc Endo Appr 349
0YJM0ZZ	Inspect of Rt Foot, Opn Appr 221
0XJJ0ZZ	Inspect of Rt Hand, Opn Appr 220
0YJ50ZZ	Inspect of Rt Inguinal Region, Opn Appr 92, 123, 219, 254
0SJC4ZZ	Inspect of Rt Knee Jt, Perc Endo Appr 244
0YJF0ZZ	Inspect of Rt Knee Region, Opn Appr 221
08JJXZZ	Inspect of Rt Lens, Ext Appr 445
0BJK4ZZ	Inspect of Rt Lung, Perc Endo Appr 331
0XJD0ZZ	Inspect of Rt Lwr Arm, Opn Appr 220
0YJ90ZZ	Inspect of Rt Lwr Extr, Opn Appr 220
0YJH0ZZ	Inspect of Rt Lwr Leg, Opn Appr 221
0RJS4ZZ	Inspect of Rt Metacarpocarp Jt, Perc Endo Appr 349
0RJS0ZZ	Inspect of Rt Metacarpocarpal Jt, Opn Appr 316
0RJU4ZZ	Inspect of Rt Metacarpophal Jt, Perc Endo Appr 349
0RJU0ZZ	Inspect of Rt Metacarpophalangeal Jt, Opn Appr 316
0SJK0ZZ	Inspect of Rt Metatarsal-Tarsal Jt, Opn Appr 457
0SJM0ZZ	Inspect of Rt Metatarsophal Jt, Opn Appr 457
0WJ90ZZ	Inspect of Rt Pleural Cavity, Opn Appr 62, 254, 302
0SJ74ZZ	Inspect of Rt Sacroiliac Jt, Perc Endo Appr 351
0XJ20ZZ	Inspect of Rt Shldr Region, Opn Appr 220
0SJH0ZZ	Inspect of Rt Tarsal Jt, Opn Appr 457
0SJP0ZZ	Inspect of Rt Toe Phalangeal Jt, Opn Appr 457
0XJ80ZZ	Inspect of Rt Upr Arm, Opn Appr 220
0XJ60ZZ	Inspect of Rt Upr Extr, Opn Appr 220
0YJC0ZZ	Inspect of Rt Upr Leg, Opn Appr 221
0RJN0ZZ	Inspect of Rt Wrist Jt, Opn Appr 316
0RJN4ZZ	Inspect of Rt Wrist Jt, Perc Endo Appr 349
0XJG0ZZ	Inspect of Rt Wrist Region, Opn Appr 220
0SJ54ZZ	Inspect of Sacrococcygeal Jt, Perc Endo Appr 351
00JU0ZZ	Inspect of Spinal Canal, Opn Appr 318
00JV0ZZ	Inspect of Spinal Cord, Opn Appr 318
07JP0ZZ	Inspect of Spleen, Opn Appr 64, 90, 112, 121, 210, 241, 252, 257, 268, 271, 290, 298, 328
0DJ60ZZ	Inspect of Stomach, Opn Appr 211, 242, 253, 257, 268, 271, 292
0RJB4ZZ	Inspect of T-lum Disc, Perc Endo Appr 349
0RJA4ZZ	Inspect of T-lum Jt, Perc Endo Appr 349
0RJ[6,9]0ZZ	Inspect of Thoracic Vert [Jt, Disc], Opn Appr 156
0RJ94ZZ	Inspect of Thoracic Vert Disc, Perc Endo Appr 349
0RJ64ZZ	Inspect of Thoracic Vert Jt, Perc Endo Appr 349
0RJ[A,B]0ZZ	Inspect of Thoracolumbar Vert [Jt, Disc], Opn Appr 156
07JM3ZZ	Inspect of Thymus, Perc Appr 235
0GJK0ZZ	Inspect of Thyroid Gland, Opn Appr 211, 336
0BJ10ZZ	Inspect of Trachea, Opn Appr 64
0BJ04ZZ	Inspect of Tracheobronchial Tree, Perc Endo Appr 331
0WJK0ZZ	Inspect of Upr Back, Opn Appr 220
0DJ00ZZ	Inspect of Upr Intestinal Tract, Opn Appr 121, 211, 242, 253, 257, 268, 271, 292
0DJ04ZZ	Inspect of Upr Intestinal Tract, Perc Endo Appr 53
0WJ40ZZ	Inspect of Upr Jaw, Opn Appr 220
0LJX0ZZ	Inspect of Upr Tndn, Opn Appr 149
0LJX3ZZ	Inspect of Upr Tndn, Perc Appr 149
0LJX4ZZ	Inspect of Upr Tndn, Perc Endo Appr 149
0TJD0ZZ	Inspect of Urethra, Opn Appr 250, 268, 353, 458
0UJM0ZZ	Inspect of Vulva, Opn Appr 217, 267, 275, 459
0WJF[0,4]ZZ	Inspect/Abd Wall, [Opn, Perc Endo] 217, 254
0WJF[0,3,4]ZZ	Inspect/Abd Wall, [Opn, Perc, Perc Endo] 113, 356
0WJF[0,3]ZZ	Inspect/Abd Wall, [Opn, Perc] 303
0WJF[3,4]ZZ	Inspect/Abd Wall, [Perc, Perc Endo] 121, 293, 460
0RJH[0,4]ZZ	Inspect/Acromioclavicular Jt, Lt, [Opn, Perc Endo] 349
0RJG[0,4]ZZ	Inspect/Acromioclavicular Jt, Rt, [Opn, Perc Endo] 349
0GJ5*	Inspect/Adrenal Gland 235
0SJG[0,4]ZZ	Inspect/Ankle Jt, Lt, [Opn, Perc Endo] 351
0SJF[0,4]ZZ	Inspect/Ankle Jt, Rt, [Opn, Perc Endo] 351
0TJB[0,3,4,7]ZZ	Inspect/Bladder, [Opn, Perc, Perc Endo, Via Natrl or Artfcl Opng] 250, 353
0TJB[3,4,7]ZZ	Inspect/Bladder, [Perc, Perc Endo, Via Natrl or Artfcl Opng] 260, 302
0TJB[3,4]ZZ	Inspect/Bladder, [Perc, Perc Endo] 458
00J0*	Inspect/Brain 318
00J0[0,3,4]ZZ	Inspect/Brain, [Opn, Perc, Perc Endo] 8, 12, 16, 296
0WJ8[0,3,4]ZZ	Inspect/Chest Wall, [Opn, Perc, Perc Endo] 66
07JL[0,3,4]ZZ	Inspect/Cisterna Chyli, [Opn, Perc, Perc Endo] 210, 290, 443
0WJ1*	Inspect/Cranial Cavity 10, 356
0WJ1[0,3,4]ZZ	Inspect/Cranial Cavity, [Opn, Perc, Perc Endo] 14, 18, 302
00JE*	Inspect/Cranial Nerve 23
0BJT*	Inspect/Diaphragm 64
0RJM[0,4]ZZ	Inspect/Elbow Jt, Lt, [Opn, Perc Endo] 349
0RJL[0,4]ZZ	Inspect/Elbow Jt, Rt, [Opn, Perc Endo] 349
0GJS*	Inspect/Endocrine Gland 238
0VJM[0,3,4]ZZ	Inspect/Epididymis and Spermatic Cord, [Opn, Perc, Perc Endo] 258, 459
08JM*	Inspect/Extraocular Muscle, Lt 43
08JM[0,X]ZZ	Inspect/Extraocular Muscle, Lt, [Opn, Ext] 445
08JL*	Inspect/Extraocular Muscle, Rt 43
08JL[0,X]ZZ	Inspect/Extraocular Muscle, Rt, [Opn, Ext] 445
0NJW[0,3,4]ZZ	Inspect/Facial Bone, [Opn, Perc, Perc Endo] 48, 129, 344
0UJ8[0,3,4,7,8]ZZ	Inspect/Fallopian Tube, [Opn, Perc, Perc Endo, Via Natrl or Artfcl Opng, Via Natrl or Artfcl Opng Endo] 263, 264, 266
0YJE[3,4]ZZ	Inspect/Femor Rgn, Bilat, [Perc, Perc Endo] 114, 121, 269, 293, 303, 357, 462
0YJ8[3,4]ZZ	Inspect/Femor Rgn, Lt, [Perc, Perc Endo] 114, 121, 269, 293, 303, 357, 462
0YJ7[0,3,4]ZZ	Inspect/Femor Rgn, Rt, [Opn, Perc, Perc Endo] 114, 303, 357
0YJ7[3,4]ZZ	Inspect/Femor Rgn, Rt, [Perc, Perc Endo] 121, 269, 293, 462
0FJ4[0,3,4]ZZ	Inspect/Gallbladder, [Opn, Perc, Perc Endo] 113, 121
0WJP*	Inspect/Gastrointestinal Tract 114, 121, 356
0WJP[0,4]ZZ	Inspect/Gastrointestinal Tract, [Opn, Perc Endo] 217, 254, 272
0WJP[0,3,4,7,8]ZZ	Inspect/Gastrointestinal Tract, [Opn, Perc, Perc Endo, Via Natrl or Artfcl Opng, Via Natrl or Artfcl Opng Endo] 293
0WJP[0,3,7,8]ZZ	Inspect/Gastrointestinal Tract, [Opn, Perc, Via Natrl or Artfcl Opng, Via Natrl or Artfcl Opng Endo] 269, 303
0WJP[3,4,7,8]ZZ	Inspect/Gastrointestinal Tract, [Perc, Perc Endo, Via Natrl or Artfcl Opng, Via Natrl or Artfcl Opng Endo] 460
0WJR*	Inspect/Genitourinary Tract 114, 121, 356
0WJR[0,4]ZZ	Inspect/Genitourinary Tract, [Opn, Perc Endo] 217, 254, 272
0WJR[0,3,4,7,8]ZZ	Inspect/Genitourinary Tract, [Opn, Perc, Perc Endo, Via Natrl or Artfcl Opng, Via Natrl or Artfcl Opng Endo] 293
0WJR[0,3,7,8]ZZ	Inspect/Genitourinary Tract, [Opn, Perc, Via Natrl or Artfcl Opng, Via Natrl or Artfcl Opng Endo] 269, 303
0WJR[3,4,7,8]ZZ	Inspect/Genitourinary Tract, [Perc, Perc Endo, Via Natrl or Artfcl Opng, Via Natrl or Artfcl Opng Endo] 460
02JY[0,4]ZZ	Inspect/Great Vessel, [Opn, Perc Endo] 296
0XJK[3,4]ZZ	Inspect/Hand, Lt, [Perc, Perc Endo] 144
0XJJ[3,4]ZZ	Inspect/Hand, Rt, [Perc, Perc Endo] 144
02JA[0,4]ZZ	Inspect/Heart, [Opn, Perc Endo] 89, 296

ØFJB*	Inspect/Hepatobiliary Duct 120
ØSJB[Ø,4]ZZ	Inspect/Hip Jt, Lt, [Opn, Perc Endo] 351
ØSJ9[Ø,4]ZZ	Inspect/Hip Jt, Rt, [Opn, Perc Endo] 351
ØYJA[Ø,3,4]ZZ	Inspect/Inguinal Rgn, Bilat, [Opn, Perc, Perc Endo] 114, 303, 357
ØYJA[3,4]ZZ	Inspect/Inguinal Rgn, Bilat, [Perc, Perc Endo] 121, 269, 293, 462
ØYJ6[Ø,3,4]ZZ	Inspect/Inguinal Rgn, Lt, [Opn, Perc, Perc Endo] 114, 303, 357
ØYJ6[3,4]ZZ	Inspect/Inguinal Rgn, Lt, [Perc, Perc Endo] 121, 269, 293, 461
ØYJ5[Ø,3,4]ZZ	Inspect/Inguinal Rgn, Rt, [Opn, Perc, Perc Endo] 114, 303, 357
ØYJ5[3,4]ZZ	Inspect/Inguinal Rgn, Rt, [Perc, Perc Endo] 121, 269, 293, 461
Ø9JE*	Inspect/Inner Ear, Lt 51
Ø9JE[Ø,3,4,X]ZZ	Inspect/Inner Ear, Lt, [Opn, Perc, Perc Endo, Ext] 447
Ø9JD*	Inspect/Inner Ear, Rt 51
Ø9JD[Ø,3,4,X]ZZ	Inspect/Inner Ear, Rt, [Opn, Perc, Perc Endo, Ext] 447
ØTJ5[Ø,3,7]ZZ	Inspect/Kidney, [Opn, Perc, Via Natrl or Artfcl Opng] 249, 353
ØTJ5[3,7]ZZ	Inspect/Kidney, [Perc, Via Natrl or Artfcl Opng] 293, 302
ØSJD[Ø,4]ZZ	Inspect/Knee Jt, Lt, [Opn, Perc Endo] 351, 457
ØSJC[Ø,4]ZZ	Inspect/Knee Jt, Rt, [Opn, Perc Endo] 351, 457
ØFJØ[Ø,4]ZZ	Inspect/Liver, [Opn, Perc Endo] 271
ØFJØ[Ø,3,4]ZZ	Inspect/Liver, [Opn, Perc, Perc Endo] 113, 121, 211, 253, 292, 335
ØFJØ[Ø,3]ZZ	Inspect/Liver, [Opn, Perc] 301
ØSJ2[3,4]ZZ	Inspect/Lumbar Vert Disc, [Perc, Perc Endo] 130
ØSJ4[3,4]ZZ	Inspect/Lumbosacral Disc, [Perc, Perc Endo] 130
ØBJL[Ø,3,4,7,X]ZZ	Inspect/Lung, Lt, [Opn, Perc, Perc Endo, Via Natrl or Artfcl Opng, Ext] 64
ØBJK[Ø,3,4,7,X]ZZ	Inspect/Lung, Rt, [Opn, Perc, Perc Endo, Via Natrl or Artfcl Opng, Ext] 64
Ø4JY[Ø,3]ZZ	Inspect/Lwr Artery, [Opn, Perc] 84
ØMJY[Ø,3,4]ZZ	Inspect/Lwr Bursa & Lgmt, [Opn, Perc, Perc Endo] 129
ØDJD[Ø,4]ZZ	Inspect/Lwr Intestinal Tract, [Opn, Perc Endo] 300, 333
ØKJY[Ø,3,4]ZZ	Inspect/Lwr Muscle, [Opn, Perc, Perc Endo] 139
Ø6JY[Ø,3,4]ZZ	Inspect/Lwr Vein, [Opn, Perc, Perc Endo] 87
Ø7JN[Ø,3,4]ZZ	Inspect/Lymphatic, [Opn, Perc, Perc Endo] 112, 210, 290, 443
ØWJC*	Inspect/Mediastinum 91
ØWJC[Ø,4]ZZ	Inspect/Mediastinum, [Opn, Perc Endo] 302
ØWJC[3,4]ZZ	Inspect/Mediastinum, [Perc, Perc Endo] 66
ØDJV[Ø,4]ZZ	Inspect/Mesentery, [Opn, Perc Endo] 211, 253, 271
ØDJV[Ø,3,4]ZZ	Inspect/Mesentery, [Opn, Perc, Perc Endo] 112, 121, 292, 333
ØDJV[Ø,3]ZZ	Inspect/Mesentery, [Opn, Perc] 268, 300
ØDJV[3,4]ZZ	Inspect/Mesentery, [Perc, Perc Endo] 449
ØSJN[Ø,4]ZZ	Inspect/Metatarsal-Phalangeal Jt, Lt, [Opn, Perc Endo] 351
ØSJM[Ø,4]ZZ	Inspect/Metatarsal-Phalangeal Jt, Rt, [Opn, Perc Endo] 351
ØSJL[Ø,4]ZZ	Inspect/Metatarsal-Tarsal Jt, Lt, [Opn, Perc Endo] 351
ØSJK[Ø,4]ZZ	Inspect/Metatarsal-Tarsal Jt, Rt, [Opn, Perc Endo] 351
ØNJB[Ø,3,4]ZZ	Inspect/Nasal Bone, [Opn, Perc, Perc Endo] 48, 129, 344
ØWJ6[Ø,3,4]ZZ	Inspect/Neck, [Opn, Perc, Perc Endo] 238, 356
ØWJ6[3,4]ZZ	Inspect/Neck, [Perc, Perc Endo] 158
ØDJU[Ø,4]ZZ	Inspect/Omentum, [Opn, Perc Endo] 211, 253, 271
ØDJU[Ø,3,4]ZZ	Inspect/Omentum, [Opn, Perc, Perc Endo] 112, 121, 292, 333
ØDJU[Ø,3]ZZ	Inspect/Omentum, [Opn, Perc] 268, 300
ØDJU[3,4]ZZ	Inspect/Omentum, [Perc, Perc Endo] 449
ØUJ3[Ø,3,4]ZZ	Inspect/Ovary, [Opn, Perc, Perc Endo] 263, 264, 266
ØFJG[Ø,3,4]ZZ	Inspect/Pancreas, [Opn, Perc, Perc Endo] 113, 121, 335
ØFJG[Ø,3]ZZ	Inspect/Pancreas, [Opn, Perc] 242, 301
ØFJD*	Inspect/Pancreatic Duct 113, 121, 335
ØFJD[Ø,3,7,8]ZZ	Inspect/Pancreatic Duct, [Opn, Perc, Via Natrl or Artfcl Opng, Via Natrl or Artfcl Opng Endo] 242, 301
ØGJR*	Inspect/Parathyroid Gland 238
ØGJR[3,4]ZZ	Inspect/Parathyroid Gland, [Perc, Perc Endo] 153
ØWJJ*	Inspect/Pelvic Cavity 113, 121, 356
ØWJJ[Ø,4]ZZ	Inspect/Pelvic Cavity, [Opn, Perc Endo] 217, 254, 272
ØWJJ[Ø,3,4]ZZ	Inspect/Pelvic Cavity, [Opn, Perc, Perc Endo] 293
ØWJJ[Ø,3]ZZ	Inspect/Pelvic Cavity, [Opn, Perc] 269, 303
ØWJJ[3,4]ZZ	Inspect/Pelvic Cavity, [Perc, Perc Endo] 460
ØWJN[Ø,3,4]ZZ	Inspect/Perineum, Female, [Opn, Perc, Perc Endo] 269
ØWJM[Ø,4]ZZ	Inspect/Perineum, Male, [Opn, Perc Endo] 220
ØWJG*	Inspect/Peritoneal Cavity 113, 121, 356
ØWJG[Ø,4]ZZ	Inspect/Peritoneal Cavity, [Opn, Perc Endo] 217, 254, 272
ØWJG[Ø,3,4]ZZ	Inspect/Peritoneal Cavity, [Opn, Perc, Perc Endo] 293
ØWJG[Ø,3]ZZ	Inspect/Peritoneal Cavity, [Opn, Perc] 269, 303
ØWJG[3,4]ZZ	Inspect/Peritoneal Cavity, [Perc, Perc Endo] 460
ØDJW[Ø,4]ZZ	Inspect/Peritoneum, [Opn, Perc Endo] 211, 253, 271
ØDJW[Ø,3,4]ZZ	Inspect/Peritoneum, [Opn, Perc, Perc Endo] 112, 121, 292, 333
ØDJW[Ø,3]ZZ	Inspect/Peritoneum, [Opn, Perc] 268, 300
ØDJW[3,4]ZZ	Inspect/Peritoneum, [Perc, Perc Endo] 449
ØGJ1*	Inspect/Pineal Body 235
ØGJ1[Ø,3,4]ZZ	Inspect/Pineal Body, [Opn, Perc, Perc Endo] 9, 13, 17
ØGJØ*	Inspect/Pituitary Gland 235
ØGJØ[Ø,3,4]ZZ	Inspect/Pituitary Gland, [Opn, Perc, Perc Endo] 9, 13, 17
ØBJQ*	Inspect/Pleura 64
ØWJB[Ø,4]ZZ	Inspect/Pleural Cavity, Lt, [Opn, Perc Endo] 91, 356
ØWJB[3,4]ZZ	Inspect/Pleural Cavity, Lt, [Perc, Perc Endo] 66
ØWJ9[Ø,4]ZZ	Inspect/Pleural Cavity, Rt, [Opn, Perc Endo] 91, 356
ØWJ9[3,4]ZZ	Inspect/Pleural Cavity, Rt, [Perc, Perc Endo] 66
ØVJ4[Ø,3,4]ZZ	Inspect/Prostate and Seminal Vesicles, [Opn, Perc, Perc Endo] 260, 440
ØWJQ[Ø,4]ZZ	Inspect/Respiratory Tract, [Opn, Perc Endo] 356
ØWJQ[3,4,7,8]ZZ	Inspect/Respiratory Tract, [Perc, Perc Endo, Via Natrl or Artfcl Opng, Via Natrl or Artfcl Opng Endo] 66
ØWJH*	Inspect/Retroperitoneum 113, 356
ØWJH[Ø,3,4]ZZ	Inspect/Retroperitoneum, [Opn, Perc, Perc Endo] 303
ØWJH[3,4]ZZ	Inspect/Retroperitoneum, [Perc, Perc Endo] 121, 269, 293, 460
ØRJK[Ø,4]ZZ	Inspect/Shldr Jt, Lt, [Opn, Perc Endo] 349
ØRJJ[Ø,4]ZZ	Inspect/Shldr Jt, Rt, [Opn, Perc Endo] 349
ØNJØ[Ø,3,4]ZZ	Inspect/Skull, [Opn, Perc, Perc Endo] 10, 14, 18, 129, 344
ØØJU*	Inspect/Spinal Canal 159, 160
ØØJU[Ø,3,4]ZZ	Inspect/Spinal Canal, [Opn, Perc, Perc Endo] 19, 296
ØØJV*	Inspect/Spinal Cord 159, 160
ØØJV[Ø,3,4]ZZ	Inspect/Spinal Cord, [Opn, Perc, Perc Endo] 19, 296
ØRJF[Ø,4]ZZ	Inspect/Sternoclavicular Jt, Lt, [Opn, Perc Endo] 349
ØRJE[Ø,4]ZZ	Inspect/Sternoclavicular Jt, Rt, [Opn, Perc Endo] 349
ØDJ6[Ø,4]ZZ	Inspect/Stomach, [Opn, Perc Endo] 121, 300, 333
ØSJJ[Ø,4]ZZ	Inspect/Tarsal Jt, Lt, [Opn, Perc Endo] 351
ØSJH[Ø,4]ZZ	Inspect/Tarsal Jt, Rt, [Opn, Perc Endo] 351
ØRJD[Ø,3,4]ZZ	Inspect/Temporomandibular Jt, Lt, [Opn, Perc, Perc Endo] 49, 130, 349
ØRJC[Ø,3,4]ZZ	Inspect/Temporomandibular Jt, Rt, [Opn, Perc, Perc Endo] 49, 130, 349
ØVJD[Ø,3,4]ZZ	Inspect/Testis, [Opn, Perc, Perc Endo] 258
Ø7JK[Ø,3,4]ZZ	Inspect/Thoracic Duct, [Opn, Perc, Perc Endo] 210, 290, 443
Ø7JM[Ø,4]ZZ	Inspect/Thymus, [Opn, Perc Endo] 60, 241, 290, 298, 328
Ø7JM[3,4]ZZ	Inspect/Thymus, [Perc, Perc Endo] 25
ØGJK*	Inspect/Thyroid Gland 238
ØGJK[3,4]ZZ	Inspect/Thyroid Gland, [Perc, Perc Endo] 153
ØSJQ[Ø,4]ZZ	Inspect/Toe Phalangeal Jt, Lt, [Opn, Perc Endo] 351
ØSJP[Ø,4]ZZ	Inspect/Toe Phalangeal Jt, Rt, [Opn, Perc Endo] 351
ØBJØ[Ø,3,4,7,X]ZZ	Inspect/Tracheobronchial Tree, [Opn, Perc, Perc Endo, Via Natrl or Artfcl Opng, Ext] 64
Ø9J8[Ø,3,4,7,X]ZZ	Inspect/Tympanic Membrane, Lt, [Opn, Perc, Perc Endo, Via Natrl or Artfcl Opng, Ext] 51, 447
Ø9J7[Ø,3,4,7,X]ZZ	Inspect/Tympanic Membrane, Rt, [Opn, Perc, Perc Endo, Via Natrl or Artfcl Opng, Ext] 51, 447
Ø3JY[Ø,3]ZZ	Inspect/Upr Artery, [Opn, Perc] 82
ØPJY[Ø,3,4]ZZ	Inspect/Upr Bone, [Opn, Perc, Perc Endo] 65, 130
ØMJX[Ø,3,4]ZZ	Inspect/Upr Bursa & Lgmt, [Opn, Perc, Perc Endo] 129
ØDJØ[Ø,4]ZZ	Inspect/Upr Intestinal Tract, [Opn, Perc Endo] 300, 333
ØKJX[Ø,3,4]ZZ	Inspect/Upr Muscle, [Opn, Perc, Perc Endo] 139
ØLJX[Ø,3,4]ZZ	Inspect/Upr Tndn, [Opn, Perc, Perc Endo] 315, 453
Ø5JY[Ø,3,4]ZZ	Inspect/Upr Vein, [Opn, Perc, Perc Endo] 85
ØTJ9[Ø,3,7]ZZ	Inspect/Ureter, [Opn, Perc, Via Natrl or Artfcl Opng] 249, 458
ØUJD[Ø,3,4]ZZ	Inspect/Uterus and Cervix, [Opn, Perc, Perc Endo] 263, 264, 266
ØUJH[Ø,3,4,7]ZZ	Inspect/Vagina and Cul-de-sac, [Opn, Perc, Perc Endo, Via Natrl or Artfcl Opng] 267, 272, 459
ØVJR[Ø,3,4]ZZ	Inspect/Vas Deferens, [Opn, Perc, Perc Endo] 258, 459
3EØP3QØ	Introduce Autol Fertilized Ovum in Fem Reprod, Perc 269
3EØP7QØ	Introduce Autol Fertilized Ovum in Fem Reprod, Via Opng 269
3EØS3Ø2	Introduce High dose IL-2 in Epidural Space, Perc 305
3EØP3Q1	Introduce Nonaut Fertilized Ovum in Fem Reprod, Perc 269

3E0P7Q1	Introduce Nonaut Fertilized Ovum in Fem Reprod, Via Opng 269
3E0R302	Introduce of High dose IL-2 into Spinal Canal, Perc Appr 305
3E0P73Z	Introduction of Anti-inflam into Fem Reprod, Via Opng 269
3E0C3BZ	Introduction of Local Anesthetic into Eye, Perc Appr 44
3E0CX29	Introduction of Oth Anti-infect into Eye, Extern Appr 44, 462
3E0C729	Introduction of Oth Anti-infective into Eye, Via Opng 44, 462
3E0CXSF	Introduction of Oth Gas into Eye, Ext Appr 245, 462
3E0C3SF	Introduction of Oth Gas into Eye, Perc Appr 462
3E0C7SF	Introduction of Oth Gas into Eye, Via Opng 44, 462
3E0CXGC	Introduction of Oth Therap Subst into Eye, Extern Appr 44, 462
3E0C3GC	Introduction of Oth Therap Subst into Eye, Perc Appr 44, 357, 462
3E0C7GC	Introduction of Oth Therap Subst into Eye, Via Opng 44, 462
3E0G3GC	Introduction of Oth Therap Subst into Up GI, Perc Appr 236, 462
3E0J[3,7,8]U[0,1]	Introduction/Biliary and Pancreatic Tract, [Perc, Via Natrl or Artfcl Opng, Via Natrl or Artfcl Opng Endo], Pancreatic Islet Cells, [Auto, Nonauto] 254
3E06[0,3]02	Introduction/Central Artery, [Opn, Perc], Antineoplastic, High-dose Interleukin-2 305
3E06[0,3]17	Introduction/Central Artery, [Opn, Perc], Thrombolytic, Oth Thrombolytic 33
3E04[0,3]02	Introduction/Central Vein, [Opn, Perc], Antineoplastic, High-dose Interleukin-2 305
3E04[0,3]TZ	Introduction/Central Vein, [Opn, Perc], Destr Agent, NQ 22, 89
3E04[0,3]17	Introduction/Central Vein, [Opn, Perc], Thrombolytic, Oth Thrombolytic 33
3E0Q[3,7]05	Introduction/Cranial Cavity and Brain, [Perc, Via Natrl or Artfcl Opng], Antineoplastic, Oth Antineoplastic 11
3E0B[3,7,X] [3,B,H,K,T]Z	Introduction/Ear, [Perc, Via Natrl or Artfcl Opng, Ext], [Anti-inflam, Local Anesthetic, Radioact Substance, Oth Dx Substance, Destr Agent], NQ 55
3E0B[3,7,X]29	Introduction/Ear, [Perc, Via Natrl or Artfcl Opng, Ext], Anti-infective, Oth Anti-infective 55
3E0B[3,7,X]GC	Introduction/Ear, [Perc, Via Natrl or Artfcl Opng, Ext], Oth Therapeutic Substance, Oth Substance 55
3E0C[3,X]SF	Introduction/Eye, [Perc, Ext], Gas, Oth Gas 44, 357
3E0C[3,7,X]MZ	Introduction/Eye, [Perc, Via Natrl or Artfcl Opng, Ext], Pigment, NQ 357
3E0CX[3,B,H,K,M,T]Z	Introduction/Eye, Ext, [Anti-inflam, Local Anesthetic, Radioact Substance, Oth Dx Substance, Pigment, Destr Agent], NQ 44
3E0CX[3,B,H,K,M,T]Z	Introduction/Eye, Ext, [Anti-inflam, Local Anesthetic, Radioact Substance, Oth Dx Substance, Pigment, Destr Agent], NQ 462
3E0C3[3,B,H,K,M,T]Z	Introduction/Eye, Perc, [Anti-inflam, Local Anesthetic, Radioact Substance, Oth Dx Substance, Pigment, Destr Agent], NQ 462
3E0C3[3,H,K,M,T]Z	Introduction/Eye, Perc, [Anti-inflam, Radioact Substance, Oth Dx Substance, Pigment, Destr Agent], NQ 44
3E0C7[3,B,H,K,M,T]Z	Introduction/Eye, Via Natrl or Artfcl Opng, [Anti-inflam, Local Anesthetic, Radioact Substance, Oth Dx Substance, Pigment, Destr Agent], NQ 44, 462
3E08[0,3]17	Introduction/Heart, [Opn, Perc], Thrombolytic, Oth Thrombolytic 33
3E05[0,3]02	Introduction/Peripheral Artery, [Opn, Perc], Antineoplastic, High-dose Interleukin-2 305
3E05[0,3]17	Introduction/Peripheral Artery, [Opn, Perc], Thrombolytic, Oth Thrombolytic 33
3E03[0,3]02	Introduction/Peripheral Vein, [Opn, Perc], Antineoplastic, High-dose Interleukin-2 305
3E03[0,3]TZ	Introduction/Peripheral Vein, [Opn, Perc], Destr Agent, NQ 22, 89
3E03[0,3]U[0,1]	Introduction/Peripheral Vein, [Opn, Perc], Pancreatic Islet Cells, [Auto, Nonauto] 254
3E03[0,3]17	Introduction/Peripheral Vein, [Opn, Perc], Thrombolytic, Oth Thrombolytic 33
3E1N*	Irrigation/Male Reproductive 257
3E1N[3,7,8]8[X,Z]	Irrigation/Male Reproductive, [Perc, Via Natrl or Artfcl Opng, Via Natrl or Artfcl Opng Endo], Irrigating Substance, [Dx, NQ] 462
DFY[1,2,3]KZZ	Laser Interstitial Thermal Therapy of [Gallbladder, Bile Ducts, Pancreas] 260, 303
DGY[0,1,4,5]KZZ	Laser Interstitial Thermal Therapy of [Pituitary Gland, Pineal Body, Parathyroid Glands, Thyroid] 238

DGY2KZZ	Laser Interstitial Thermal Therapy of Adrenal Glands 63, 260, 303
DDY8KZZ	Laser Interstitial Thermal Therapy of Anus 62
DFY2KZZ	Laser Interstitial Thermal Therapy of Bile Ducts 62
D0Y0KZZ	Laser Interstitial Thermal Therapy of Brain 10, 14, 19
D0Y1KZZ	Laser Interstitial Thermal Therapy of Brain Stem 10, 14, 19
DBY1KZZ	Laser Interstitial Thermal Therapy of Bronchus 62, 223, 260, 303
DBY7KZZ	Laser Interstitial Thermal Therapy of Chest Wall 62, 223, 260, 303
DDY5KZZ	Laser Interstitial Thermal Therapy of Colon 62
DBY8KZZ	Laser Interstitial Thermal Therapy of Diaphragm 62, 223, 260, 303
DDY2KZZ	Laser Interstitial Thermal Therapy of Duodenum 62
DDY0KZZ	Laser Interstitial Thermal Therapy of Esophagus 62
DFY1KZZ	Laser Interstitial Thermal Therapy of Gallbladder 62
DDY4KZZ	Laser Interstitial Thermal Therapy of Ileum 62
DDY3KZZ	Laser Interstitial Thermal Therapy of Jejunum 62
DFY0KZZ	Laser Interstitial Thermal Therapy of Liver 114, 119
DMY0KZZ	Laser Interstitial Thermal Therapy of Lt Breast 63, 223, 260, 303
DBY2KZZ	Laser Interstitial Thermal Therapy of Lung 62, 223, 260, 303
DBY6KZZ	Laser Interstitial Thermal Therapy of Mediastinum 62, 223, 260, 303
DFY3KZZ	Laser Interstitial Thermal Therapy of Pancreas 62
DGY4KZZ	Laser Interstitial Thermal Therapy of Parathyroid Glands 303
D0Y7KZZ	Laser Interstitial Thermal Therapy of Peripheral Nerve 62, 260, 303
DGY1KZZ	Laser Interstitial Thermal Therapy of Pineal Body 303
DGY0KZZ	Laser Interstitial Thermal Therapy of Pituitary Gland 303
DBY5KZZ	Laser Interstitial Thermal Therapy of Pleura 62, 223, 260, 303
DVY0KZZ	Laser Interstitial Thermal Therapy of Prostate 63, 223, 260, 303
DDY7KZZ	Laser Interstitial Thermal Therapy of Rectum 62
DMY1KZZ	Laser Interstitial Thermal Therapy of Rt Breast 63, 223, 260, 303
D0Y6KZZ	Laser Interstitial Thermal Therapy of Spinal Cord 62, 260, 303
DDY1KZZ	Laser Interstitial Thermal Therapy of Stomach 62
DGY5KZZ	Laser Interstitial Thermal Therapy of Thyroid 303
DBY0KZZ	Laser Interstitial Thermal Therapy of Trachea 62, 223, 260, 303
DDY[0,1,2,3,4,5,7,8]KZZ	Laser Interstitial Thermal Therapy of [Esophagus, Stomach, Duodenum, Jejunum, Ileum, Colon, Rectum, Anus] 260, 303
047*	Lwr Arteries, Dilation 82
04C*	Lwr Arteries, Extir 323
04Q*	Lwr Arteries, Repair 84, 324
04S*	Lwr Arteries, Repos 84
04N*	Lwr Arteries, Rls 84
0Q5*	Lwr Bones, Destr 347
0Q8*	Lwr Bones, Div 347
0QC*	Lwr Bones, Extir 347
0QT*	Lwr Bones, Resect 348
0S5*	Lwr Jts, Destr 351
0ST*	Lwr Jts, Resect 352
067*	Lwr Veins, Dilation 86
06D*	Lwr Veins, Extract 89
06Q*	Lwr Veins, Repair 327
06S*	Lwr Veins, Repos 87
06N*	Lwr Veins, Rls 87
06U*	Lwr Veins, Supl 87
07L*	Lymphatic and Hemic Systems, Occlsn 328
07S*	Lymphatic and Hemic Systems, Repos 329
0V1*	Male Reproductive Sys, Bypass 257
0V7*	Male Reproductive Sys, Dilation 257, 354
0VM*	Male Reproductive Sys, Reattach 354
0VR*	Male Reproductive Sys, Replace 244, 258
0VS*	Male Reproductive Sys, Repos 258
02K80ZZ	Map Conduction Mechanism, Opn Appr 78, 79, 80
02K83ZZ	Map Conduction Mechanism, Perc Appr 98
02K84ZZ	Map Conduction Mechanism, Perc Endo Appr 98
00K8[0,3,4]ZZ	Map/Basal Ganglia, [Opn, Perc, Perc Endo] 8, 12, 16, 296
00K0[0,3,4]ZZ	Map/Brain, [Opn, Perc, Perc Endo] 8, 12, 16, 296
00KC[0,3,4]ZZ	Map/Cerebellum, [Opn, Perc, Perc Endo] 8, 12, 16, 296

00K7[0,3,4]ZZ	Map/Cerebral Hemisphere, [Opn, Perc, Perc Endo] 8, 12, 16, 296
00KA[0,3,4]ZZ	Map/Hypothalamus, [Opn, Perc, Perc Endo] 8, 12, 16, 296
00KD[0,3,4]ZZ	Map/Medulla Oblongata, [Opn, Perc, Perc Endo] 8, 12, 16, 296
00KB[0,3,4]ZZ	Map/Pons, [Opn, Perc, Perc Endo] 8, 12, 16, 296
00K9[0,3,4]ZZ	Map/Thalamus, [Opn, Perc, Perc Endo] 8, 12, 16, 296
4A023FZ	Measurement of Cardiac Rhythm, Perc Appr 71, 98
4A0C[3,4,7,8]5Z	Measurement/Biliary, [Perc, Perc Endo, Via Natrl or Artfcl Opng, Via Natrl or Artfcl Opng Endo], Flow, NQ 114, 121
4A0C[3,4,7]BZ	Measurement/Biliary, [Perc, Perc Endo, Via Natrl or Artfcl Opng], Pressure, NQ 114, 121
4A02[0,3]N[6,7,8]	Measurement/Cardiac, [Opn, Perc], Sampling and Pressure, [Rt Heart, Lt Heart, Bilat] 71, 73, 76, 99
4A06*	Measurement/Lymphatic 219
4A06[0,3][5,B]Z	Measurement/Lymphatic, [Opn, Perc], [Flow, Pressure], NQ 293, 462
XR2H021	Monitor Lt Knee Jt w Intraop Knee Sens, Opn, New Tech 1 132, 462
XR2G021	Monitor Rt Knee Jt w Intraop Knee Sens, Opn, New Tech 1 132, 462
4A16*	Monitoring/Lymphatic 219
4A16[0,3][5,B]Z	Monitoring/Lymphatic, [Opn, Perc], [Flow, Pressure], NQ 293, 462
0C0*	Mouth and Throat, Alter 56, 331
0CL*	Mouth and Throat, Occlsn 57
0CV*	Mouth and Throat, Restrict 57
0CX*	Mouth and Throat, Transfer 56, 332
0KH*	Muscles, Insert 27, 139, 339
0KM*	Muscles, Reattach 27
0KS*	Muscles, Repos 27
0KU*	Muscles, Supl 27
10T*	Obstetrics, Preg, Resect 263, 264, 266, 272
10P*	Obstetrics, Preg, Rmvl 272
02L70CK	Occlsn of LAA with Extralum Dev, Opn Appr 80
02L73CK	Occlsn of LAA with Extralum Dev, Perc Appr 98
02L74CK	Occlsn of LAA with Extralum Dev, Perc Endo Appr 98
02L70DK	Occlsn of LAA with Intralum Dev, Opn Appr 80
02L73DK	Occlsn of LAA with Intralum Dev, Perc Appr 98
02L74DK	Occlsn of LAA with Intralum Dev, Perc Endo Appr 98
02L70ZK	Occlsn of Lt Atrial Appendage, Opn Appr 80
02L73ZK	Occlsn of Lt Atrial Appendage, Perc Appr 98
02L74ZK	Occlsn of Lt Atrial Appendage, Perc Endo Appr 98
04L0*	Occlsn/Abd Aorta 111, 324
04L0[0,3,4][C,D,Z]Z	Occlsn/Abd Aorta, [Opn, Perc, Perc Endo], [Extralum Dev, Intralum Dev, No Dev], NQ 92
0FLC*	Occlsn/Ampulla of Vater 120, 335
04LQ*	Occlsn/Ant Tibial Artery, Lt 324
04LQ[0,3,4][C,D,Z]Z	Occlsn/Ant Tibial Artery, Lt, [Opn, Perc, Perc Endo], [Extralum Dev, Intralum Dev, No Dev], NQ 84
04LP*	Occlsn/Ant Tibial Artery, Rt 324
04LP[0,3,4][C,D,Z]Z	Occlsn/Ant Tibial Artery, Rt, [Opn, Perc, Perc Endo], [Extralum Dev, Intralum Dev, No Dev], NQ 84
0DLQ*	Occlsn/Anus 109, 333
0DLK*	Occlsn/Ascending Colon 107
03L6*	Occlsn/Axillary Artery, Lt 321
03L6[0,3,4][C,D,Z]Z	Occlsn/Axillary Artery, Lt, [Opn, Perc, Perc Endo], [Extralum Dev, Intralum Dev, No Dev], NQ 82
03L6[0,3,4][C,Z]Z	Occlsn/Axillary Artery, Lt, [Opn, Perc, Perc Endo], [Extralum Dev, No Dev], NQ 239
03L5*	Occlsn/Axillary Artery, Rt 321
03L5[0,3,4][C,D,Z]Z	Occlsn/Axillary Artery, Rt, [Opn, Perc, Perc Endo], [Extralum Dev, Intralum Dev, No Dev], NQ 82
03L5[0,3,4][C,Z]Z	Occlsn/Axillary Artery, Rt, [Opn, Perc, Perc Endo], [Extralum Dev, No Dev], NQ 239
05L8[0,3,4][C,D,Z]Z	Occlsn/Axillary Vein, Lt, [Opn, Perc, Perc Endo], [Extralum Dev, Intralum Dev, No Dev], NQ 85
05L8[0,3,4][C,Z]Z	Occlsn/Axillary Vein, Lt, [Opn, Perc, Perc Endo], [Extralum Dev, No Dev], NQ 240
05L7[0,3,4][C,D,Z]Z	Occlsn/Axillary Vein, Rt, [Opn, Perc, Perc Endo], [Extralum Dev, Intralum Dev, No Dev], NQ 85
05L7[0,3,4][C,Z]Z	Occlsn/Axillary Vein, Rt, [Opn, Perc, Perc Endo], [Extralum Dev, No Dev], NQ 240
05L0[0,3,4][C,D,Z]Z	Occlsn/Azygos Vein, [Opn, Perc, Perc Endo], [Extralum Dev, Intralum Dev, No Dev], NQ 97
05LC[0,3,4][C,D,Z]Z	Occlsn/Basilic Vein, Lt, [Opn, Perc, Perc Endo], [Extralum Dev, Intralum Dev, No Dev], NQ 85
05LC[0,3,4][C,Z]Z	Occlsn/Basilic Vein, Lt, [Opn, Perc, Perc Endo], [Extralum Dev, No Dev], NQ 241
05LB[0,3,4][C,D,Z]Z	Occlsn/Basilic Vein, Rt, [Opn, Perc, Perc Endo], [Extralum Dev, Intralum Dev, No Dev], NQ 85
05LB[0,3,4][C,Z]Z	Occlsn/Basilic Vein, Rt, [Opn, Perc, Perc Endo], [Extralum Dev, No Dev], NQ 241
0TLB*	Occlsn/Bladder 250, 353
0TLC*	Occlsn/Bladder Neck 250, 353
03L8*	Occlsn/Brachial Artery, Lt 321
03L8[0,3,4][C,D,Z]Z	Occlsn/Brachial Artery, Lt, [Opn, Perc, Perc Endo], [Extralum Dev, Intralum Dev, No Dev], NQ 82
03L8[0,3,4][C,Z]Z	Occlsn/Brachial Artery, Lt, [Opn, Perc, Perc Endo], [Extralum Dev, No Dev], NQ 239
03L7*	Occlsn/Brachial Artery, Rt 321
03L7[0,3,4][C,D,Z]Z	Occlsn/Brachial Artery, Rt, [Opn, Perc, Perc Endo], [Extralum Dev, Intralum Dev, No Dev], NQ 82
03L7[0,3,4][C,Z]Z	Occlsn/Brachial Artery, Rt, [Opn, Perc, Perc Endo], [Extralum Dev, No Dev], NQ 239
05LA[0,3,4][C,D,Z]Z	Occlsn/Brachial Vein, Lt, [Opn, Perc, Perc Endo], [Extralum Dev, Intralum Dev, No Dev], NQ 85
05LA[0,3,4][C,Z]Z	Occlsn/Brachial Vein, Lt, [Opn, Perc, Perc Endo], [Extralum Dev, No Dev], NQ 241
05L9[0,3,4][C,D,Z]Z	Occlsn/Brachial Vein, Rt, [Opn, Perc, Perc Endo], [Extralum Dev, Intralum Dev, No Dev], NQ 85
05L9[0,3,4][C,Z]Z	Occlsn/Brachial Vein, Rt, [Opn, Perc, Perc Endo], [Extralum Dev, No Dev], NQ 241
0BL2*	Occlsn/Carina 52, 64, 331
0DLH*	Occlsn/Cecum 107
04L1*	Occlsn/Celiac Artery 111, 324
04L1[0,3,4][C,D,Z]Z	Occlsn/Celiac Artery, [Opn, Perc, Perc Endo], [Extralum Dev, Intralum Dev, No Dev], NQ 95, 442
05LF[0,3,4][C,D,Z]Z	Occlsn/Cephalic Vein, Lt, [Opn, Perc, Perc Endo], [Extralum Dev, Intralum Dev, No Dev], NQ 86
05LF[0,3,4][C,Z]Z	Occlsn/Cephalic Vein, Lt, [Opn, Perc, Perc Endo], [Extralum Dev, No Dev], NQ 241
05LD[0,3,4][C,D,Z]Z	Occlsn/Cephalic Vein, Rt, [Opn, Perc, Perc Endo], [Extralum Dev, Intralum Dev, No Dev], NQ 86
05LD[0,3,4][C,Z]Z	Occlsn/Cephalic Vein, Rt, [Opn, Perc, Perc Endo], [Extralum Dev, No Dev], NQ 241
07LL*	Occlsn/Cisterna Chyli 60
04L7*	Occlsn/Colic Artery, Lt 111, 324
04L7[0,3,4][C,D,Z]Z	Occlsn/Colic Artery, Lt, [Opn, Perc, Perc Endo], [Extralum Dev, Intralum Dev, No Dev], NQ 96, 442
04L8*	Occlsn/Colic Artery, Mid 111, 324
04L8[0,3,4][C,D,Z]Z	Occlsn/Colic Artery, Mid, [Opn, Perc, Perc Endo], [Extralum Dev, Intralum Dev, No Dev], NQ 96, 442
04L6*	Occlsn/Colic Artery, Rt 111, 324
04L6[0,3,4][C,D,Z]Z	Occlsn/Colic Artery, Rt, [Opn, Perc, Perc Endo], [Extralum Dev, Intralum Dev, No Dev], NQ 96, 442
06L7*	Occlsn/Colic Vein 111, 327
06L7[0,3,4][C,D,Z]Z	Occlsn/Colic Vein, [Opn, Perc, Perc Endo], [Extralum Dev, Intralum Dev, No Dev], NQ 97
0FL90[C,D,Z]Z	Occlsn/Common Bile Duct, Opn, [Extralum Dev, Intralum Dev, No Dev], NQ 120, 301, 335, 449
03LJ*	Occlsn/Common Carotid Artery, Lt 321
03LJ[0,3,4][B,D]Z	Occlsn/Common Carotid Artery, Lt, [Opn, Perc, Perc Endo], [Bioactive Intralum Dev, Intralum Dev], NQ 7, 9, 13, 17, 94, 251
03LJ[0,3,4][C,Z]Z	Occlsn/Common Carotid Artery, Lt, [Opn, Perc, Perc Endo], [Extralum Dev, No Dev], NQ 25, 50, 82
03LH*	Occlsn/Common Carotid Artery, Rt 321
03LH[0,3,4][B,D]Z	Occlsn/Common Carotid Artery, Rt, [Opn, Perc, Perc Endo], [Bioactive Intralum Dev, Intralum Dev], NQ 7, 9, 13, 17, 94, 251
03LH[0,3,4][C,Z]Z	Occlsn/Common Carotid Artery, Rt, [Opn, Perc, Perc Endo], [Extralum Dev, No Dev], NQ 25, 50, 82
04LD*	Occlsn/Common Iliac Artery, Lt 324
04LD[0,3,4][C,D,Z]Z	Occlsn/Common Iliac Artery, Lt, [Opn, Perc, Perc Endo], [Extralum Dev, Intralum Dev, No Dev], NQ 96
04LD[0,3,4][C,Z]Z	Occlsn/Common Iliac Artery, Lt, [Opn, Perc, Perc Endo], [Extralum Dev, No Dev], NQ 111, 442
04LC*	Occlsn/Common Iliac Artery, Rt 324

04LC[0,3,4][C,D,Z]Z	Occlsn/Common Iliac Artery, Rt, [Opn, Perc, Perc Endo], [Extralum Dev, Intralum Dev, No Dev], NQ 96
04LC[0,3,4][C,Z]Z	Occlsn/Common Iliac Artery, Rt, [Opn, Perc, Perc Endo], [Extralum Dev, No Dev], NQ 111, 442
06LD*	Occlsn/Common Iliac Vein, Lt 327
06LD[0,3,4][C,D,Z]Z	Occlsn/Common Iliac Vein, Lt, [Opn, Perc, Perc Endo], [Extralum Dev, Intralum Dev, No Dev], NQ 97
06LD[0,3,4][C,Z]Z	Occlsn/Common Iliac Vein, Lt, [Opn, Perc, Perc Endo], [Extralum Dev, No Dev], NQ 111
06LC*	Occlsn/Common Iliac Vein, Rt 327
06LC[0,3,4][C,D,Z]Z	Occlsn/Common Iliac Vein, Rt, [Opn, Perc, Perc Endo], [Extralum Dev, Intralum Dev, No Dev], NQ 97
06LC[0,3,4][C,Z]Z	Occlsn/Common Iliac Vein, Rt, [Opn, Perc, Perc Endo], [Extralum Dev, No Dev], NQ 111
0ULF*	Occlsn/Cul-de-sac 267
0FL80[C,D,Z]Z	Occlsn/Cystic Duct, Opn, [Extralum Dev, Intralum Dev, No Dev], NQ 120, 301, 335, 449
0DLM*	Occlsn/Descending Colon 107
0DL9*	Occlsn/Duodenum 107, 123
06L3*	Occlsn/Esophageal Vein 327
06L3[0,3,4]ZZ	Occlsn/Esophageal Vein, [Opn, Perc, Perc Endo] 105, 122
06L3[0,3,4][C,D,Z]Z	Occlsn/Esophageal Vein, [Opn, Perc, Perc Endo], [Extralum Dev, Intralum Dev, No Dev], NQ 97
06L3[0,3,4][C,D]Z	Occlsn/Esophageal Vein, [Opn, Perc, Perc Endo], [Extralum Dev, Intralum Dev], NQ 111
03LN*	Occlsn/Ext Carotid Artery, Lt 321
03LN[0,3,4][B,D]Z	Occlsn/Ext Carotid Artery, Lt, [Opn, Perc, Perc Endo], [Bioactive Intralum Dev, Intralum Dev], NQ 7, 9, 13, 17, 94, 251
03LN[0,3,4][C,Z]Z	Occlsn/Ext Carotid Artery, Lt, [Opn, Perc, Perc Endo], [Extralum Dev, No Dev], NQ 25, 50, 82
03LM*	Occlsn/Ext Carotid Artery, Rt 321
03LM[0,3,4][B,D]Z	Occlsn/Ext Carotid Artery, Rt, [Opn, Perc, Perc Endo], [Bioactive Intralum Dev, Intralum Dev], NQ 7, 9, 13, 17, 94, 251
03LM[0,3,4][C,Z]Z	Occlsn/Ext Carotid Artery, Rt, [Opn, Perc, Perc Endo], [Extralum Dev, No Dev], NQ 25, 50, 82
04LJ*	Occlsn/Ext Iliac Artery, Lt 324
04LJ[0,3,4][C,D,Z]Z	Occlsn/Ext Iliac Artery, Lt, [Opn, Perc, Perc Endo], [Extralum Dev, Intralum Dev, No Dev], NQ 96
04LJ[0,3,4][C,Z]Z	Occlsn/Ext Iliac Artery, Lt, [Opn, Perc, Perc Endo], [Extralum Dev, No Dev], NQ 111, 442
04LH*	Occlsn/Ext Iliac Artery, Rt 324
04LH[0,3,4][C,D,Z]Z	Occlsn/Ext Iliac Artery, Rt, [Opn, Perc, Perc Endo], [Extralum Dev, Intralum Dev, No Dev], NQ 96
04LH[0,3,4][C,Z]Z	Occlsn/Ext Iliac Artery, Rt, [Opn, Perc, Perc Endo], [Extralum Dev, No Dev], NQ 111, 442
06LG*	Occlsn/Ext Iliac Vein, Lt 327
06LG[0,3,4][C,D,Z]Z	Occlsn/Ext Iliac Vein, Lt, [Opn, Perc, Perc Endo], [Extralum Dev, Intralum Dev, No Dev], NQ 97
06LG[0,3,4][C,Z]Z	Occlsn/Ext Iliac Vein, Lt, [Opn, Perc, Perc Endo], [Extralum Dev, No Dev], NQ 111
06LF*	Occlsn/Ext Iliac Vein, Rt 327
06LF[0,3,4][C,D,Z]Z	Occlsn/Ext Iliac Vein, Rt, [Opn, Perc, Perc Endo], [Extralum Dev, Intralum Dev, No Dev], NQ 97
06LF[0,3,4][C,Z]Z	Occlsn/Ext Iliac Vein, Rt, [Opn, Perc, Perc Endo], [Extralum Dev, No Dev], NQ 111
05LQ*	Occlsn/Ext Jugular Vein, Lt 25, 51, 86
05LP*	Occlsn/Ext Jugular Vein, Rt 25, 51, 86
03LR*	Occlsn/Face Artery 321
03LR[0,3,4][C,Z]Z	Occlsn/Face Artery, [Opn, Perc, Perc Endo], [Extralum Dev, No Dev], NQ 25, 51, 82
03LR[0,3,4]DZ	Occlsn/Face Artery, [Opn, Perc, Perc Endo], Intralum Dev, NQ 7, 9, 13, 17, 94, 251
05LV*	Occlsn/Face Vein, Lt 25, 51, 86
05LT*	Occlsn/Face Vein, Rt 25, 51, 86
0UL6*	Occlsn/Fallopian Tube, Lt 263, 264, 266
0UL6[0,3,4,7,8][D,Z]Z	Occlsn/Fallopian Tube, Lt, [Opn, Perc, Perc Endo, Via Natrl or Artfcl Opng, Via Natrl or Artfcl Opng Endo], [Intralum Dev, No Dev], NQ 271, 459
0UL6[0,3,4]CZ	Occlsn/Fallopian Tube, Lt, [Opn, Perc, Perc Endo], Extralum Dev, NQ 271, 459
0UL5*	Occlsn/Fallopian Tube, Rt 263, 264, 266
0UL5[0,3,4,7,8][D,Z]Z	Occlsn/Fallopian Tube, Rt, [Opn, Perc, Perc Endo, Via Natrl or Artfcl Opng, Via Natrl or Artfcl Opng Endo], [Intralum Dev, No Dev], NQ 271, 459
0UL5[0,3,4]CZ	Occlsn/Fallopian Tube, Rt, [Opn, Perc, Perc Endo], Extralum Dev, NQ 271, 459
0UL7*	Occlsn/Fallopian Tubes, Bilat 266
0UL7[0,3,4,7,8][D,Z]Z	Occlsn/Fallopian Tubes, Bilat, [Opn, Perc, Perc Endo, Via Natrl or Artfcl Opng, Via Natrl or Artfcl Opng Endo], [Intralum Dev, No Dev], NQ 271, 459
0UL7[0,3,4]CZ	Occlsn/Fallopian Tubes, Bilat, [Opn, Perc, Perc Endo], Extralum Dev, NQ 271, 459
04LL*	Occlsn/Femor Artery, Lt 324
04LL[0,3,4][C,D,Z]Z	Occlsn/Femor Artery, Lt, [Opn, Perc, Perc Endo], [Extralum Dev, Intralum Dev, No Dev], NQ 84
04LK*	Occlsn/Femor Artery, Rt 324
04LK[0,3,4][C,D,Z]Z	Occlsn/Femor Artery, Rt, [Opn, Perc, Perc Endo], [Extralum Dev, Intralum Dev, No Dev], NQ 84
06LN*	Occlsn/Femor Vein, Lt 327
06LN[0,3,4][C,D,Z]Z	Occlsn/Femor Vein, Lt, [Opn, Perc, Perc Endo], [Extralum Dev, Intralum Dev, No Dev], NQ 89
06LM*	Occlsn/Femor Vein, Rt 327
06LM[0,3,4][C,D,Z]Z	Occlsn/Femor Vein, Rt, [Opn, Perc, Perc Endo], [Extralum Dev, Intralum Dev, No Dev], NQ 89
04LW*	Occlsn/Foot Artery, Lt 324
04LW[0,3,4][C,D,Z]Z	Occlsn/Foot Artery, Lt, [Opn, Perc, Perc Endo], [Extralum Dev, Intralum Dev, No Dev], NQ 84
04LV*	Occlsn/Foot Artery, Rt 324
04LV[0,3,4][C,D,Z]Z	Occlsn/Foot Artery, Rt, [Opn, Perc, Perc Endo], [Extralum Dev, Intralum Dev, No Dev], NQ 84
06LV*	Occlsn/Foot Vein, Lt 327
06LV[0,3,4][C,D,Z]Z	Occlsn/Foot Vein, Lt, [Opn, Perc, Perc Endo], [Extralum Dev, Intralum Dev, No Dev], NQ 89
06LT*	Occlsn/Foot Vein, Rt 327
06LT[0,3,4][C,D,Z]Z	Occlsn/Foot Vein, Rt, [Opn, Perc, Perc Endo], [Extralum Dev, Intralum Dev, No Dev], NQ 89
04L2[0,4]DZ	Occlsn/Gastric Artery, [Opn, Perc Endo], Intralum Dev, NQ 95, 111, 324, 442
04L2[0,3,4][C,Z]Z	Occlsn/Gastric Artery, [Opn, Perc, Perc Endo], [Extralum Dev, No Dev], NQ 95, 111, 324, 442
06L2*	Occlsn/Gastric Vein 327
06L2[0,3,4]ZZ	Occlsn/Gastric Vein, [Opn, Perc, Perc Endo] 105, 122
06L2[0,3,4][C,D,Z]Z	Occlsn/Gastric Vein, [Opn, Perc, Perc Endo], [Extralum Dev, Intralum Dev, No Dev], NQ 97
06L2[0,3,4][C,D]Z	Occlsn/Gastric Vein, [Opn, Perc, Perc Endo], [Extralum Dev, Intralum Dev], NQ 111
06LQ*	Occlsn/Greater Saphenous Vein, Lt 327
06LQ[0,3,4][C,D,Z]Z	Occlsn/Greater Saphenous Vein, Lt, [Opn, Perc, Perc Endo], [Extralum Dev, Intralum Dev, No Dev], NQ 89
06LP*	Occlsn/Greater Saphenous Vein, Rt 327
06LP[0,3,4][C,D,Z]Z	Occlsn/Greater Saphenous Vein, Rt, [Opn, Perc, Perc Endo], [Extralum Dev, Intralum Dev, No Dev], NQ 89
03LF*	Occlsn/Hand Artery, Lt 321
03LF[0,3,4][C,D,Z]Z	Occlsn/Hand Artery, Lt, [Opn, Perc, Perc Endo], [Extralum Dev, Intralum Dev, No Dev], NQ 82
03LF[0,3,4][C,Z]Z	Occlsn/Hand Artery, Lt, [Opn, Perc, Perc Endo], [Extralum Dev, No Dev], NQ 239
03LD*	Occlsn/Hand Artery, Rt 321
03LD[0,3,4][C,D,Z]Z	Occlsn/Hand Artery, Rt, [Opn, Perc, Perc Endo], [Extralum Dev, Intralum Dev, No Dev], NQ 82
03LD[0,3,4][C,Z]Z	Occlsn/Hand Artery, Rt, [Opn, Perc, Perc Endo], [Extralum Dev, No Dev], NQ 239
05LH[0,3,4][C,D,Z]Z	Occlsn/Hand Vein, Lt, [Opn, Perc, Perc Endo], [Extralum Dev, Intralum Dev, No Dev], NQ 86
05LH[0,3,4][C,Z]Z	Occlsn/Hand Vein, Lt, [Opn, Perc, Perc Endo], [Extralum Dev, No Dev], NQ 241
05LG[0,3,4][C,D,Z]Z	Occlsn/Hand Vein, Rt, [Opn, Perc, Perc Endo], [Extralum Dev, Intralum Dev, No Dev], NQ 86
05LG[0,3,4][C,Z]Z	Occlsn/Hand Vein, Rt, [Opn, Perc, Perc Endo], [Extralum Dev, No Dev], NQ 241
05L1[0,3,4][C,D,Z]Z	Occlsn/Hemiazygos Vein, [Opn, Perc, Perc Endo], [Extralum Dev, Intralum Dev, No Dev], NQ 97
04L3*	Occlsn/Hepatic Artery 111, 324
04L3[0,3,4][C,D,Z]Z	Occlsn/Hepatic Artery, [Opn, Perc, Perc Endo], [Extralum Dev, Intralum Dev, No Dev], NQ 96, 442
0FL60[C,D,Z]Z	Occlsn/Hepatic Duct, Lt, Opn, [Extralum Dev, Intralum Dev, No Dev], NQ 120, 301, 335, 449

ØFL5Ø[C,D,Z]Z	Occlsn/Hepatic Duct, Rt, Opn, [Extralum Dev, Intralum Dev, No Dev], NQ 120, 301, 335, 449
06L4*	Occlsn/Hepatic Vein 111, 327
06L4[Ø,3,4][C,D,Z]Z	Occlsn/Hepatic Vein, [Opn, Perc, Perc Endo], [Extralum Dev, Intralum Dev, No Dev], NQ 97
06LJ*	Occlsn/Hypogastric Vein, Lt 111, 327
06LJ[Ø,3,4][C,D,Z]Z	Occlsn/Hypogastric Vein, Lt, [Opn, Perc, Perc Endo], [Extralum Dev, Intralum Dev, No Dev], NQ 97
06LH*	Occlsn/Hypogastric Vein, Rt 111, 327
06LH[Ø,3,4][C,D,Z]Z	Occlsn/Hypogastric Vein, Rt, [Opn, Perc, Perc Endo], [Extralum Dev, Intralum Dev, No Dev], NQ 97
ØDLC*	Occlsn/Ileocecal Valve 107
ØDLB*	Occlsn/Ileum 107
04LB*	Occlsn/Inferior Mesenteric Artery 111, 324
04LB[Ø,3,4][C,D,Z]Z	Occlsn/Inferior Mesenteric Artery, [Opn, Perc, Perc Endo], [Extralum Dev, Intralum Dev, No Dev], NQ
04LB[Ø,3,4][C,D,Z]Z	Occlsn/Inferior Mesenteric Artery, [Opn, Perc, Perc Endo], [Extralum Dev, Intralum Dev, No Dev], NQ 96, 442
06L6*	Occlsn/Inferior Mesenteric Vein 111, 327
06L6[Ø,3,4][C,D,Z]Z	Occlsn/Inferior Mesenteric Vein, [Opn, Perc, Perc Endo], [Extralum Dev, Intralum Dev, No Dev], NQ 97
06LØ*	Occlsn/Inferior Vena Cava 25, 64, 87, 111, 122, 153, 241, 252, 258, 268, 271, 290, 327
03L2*	Occlsn/Innominate Artery 60, 105, 321
03L2[Ø,3,4][C,D,Z]Z	Occlsn/Innominate Artery, [Opn, Perc, Perc Endo], [Extralum Dev, Intralum Dev, No Dev], NQ 93
05L4*	Occlsn/Innominate Vein, Lt 60, 105
05L4[Ø,3,4][C,D,Z]Z	Occlsn/Innominate Vein, Lt, [Opn, Perc, Perc Endo], [Extralum Dev, Intralum Dev, No Dev], NQ 97
05L3*	Occlsn/Innominate Vein, Rt 60, 105
05L3[Ø,3,4][C,D,Z]Z	Occlsn/Innominate Vein, Rt, [Opn, Perc, Perc Endo], [Extralum Dev, Intralum Dev, No Dev], NQ 97
03LL[Ø,3,4][B,C,D,Z]Z	Occlsn/Int Carotid Artery, Lt, [Opn, Perc, Perc Endo], [Bioactive Intralum Dev, Extralum Dev, Intralum Dev, No Dev], NQ 7, 9, 13, 17
03LL[Ø,3,4][B,D]Z	Occlsn/Int Carotid Artery, Lt, [Opn, Perc, Perc Endo], [Bioactive Intralum Dev, Intralum Dev], NQ 94, 251, 321
03LL[Ø,3,4][C,Z]Z	Occlsn/Int Carotid Artery, Lt, [Opn, Perc, Perc Endo], [Extralum Dev, No Dev], NQ 82
03LK[Ø,3,4][B,C,D,Z]Z	Occlsn/Int Carotid Artery, Rt, [Opn, Perc, Perc Endo], [Bioactive Intralum Dev, Extralum Dev, Intralum Dev, No Dev], NQ 7, 9, 13, 17
03LK[Ø,3,4][B,D]Z	Occlsn/Int Carotid Artery, Rt, [Opn, Perc, Perc Endo], [Bioactive Intralum Dev, Intralum Dev], NQ 94, 251, 321
03LK[Ø,3,4][C,Z]Z	Occlsn/Int Carotid Artery, Rt, [Opn, Perc, Perc Endo], [Extralum Dev, No Dev], NQ 82
04LF[Ø,3,4][C,D,Z]Z	Occlsn/Int Iliac Artery, Lt, [Opn, Perc, Perc Endo], [Extralum Dev, Intralum Dev, No Dev], NQ 96, 324
04LF[Ø,3,4][C,D,Z]U	Occlsn/Int Iliac Artery, Lt, [Opn, Perc, Perc Endo], [Extralum Dev, Intralum Dev, No Dev], Uterine Artery, Lt 268
04LF[Ø,3,4][C,Z]Z	Occlsn/Int Iliac Artery, Lt, [Opn, Perc, Perc Endo], [Extralum Dev, No Dev], NQ 111, 442
04LE[Ø,3,4][C,D,Z]Z	Occlsn/Int Iliac Artery, Rt, [Opn, Perc, Perc Endo], [Extralum Dev, Intralum Dev, No Dev], NQ 96, 324
04LE[Ø,3,4][C,D,Z]T	Occlsn/Int Iliac Artery, Rt, [Opn, Perc, Perc Endo], [Extralum Dev, Intralum Dev, No Dev], Uterine Artery, Rt 268
04LE[Ø,3,4][C,Z]Z	Occlsn/Int Iliac Artery, Rt, [Opn, Perc, Perc Endo], [Extralum Dev, No Dev], NQ 111, 442
Ø5LN*	Occlsn/Int Jugular Vein, Lt 25, 51, 86
Ø5LM*	Occlsn/Int Jugular Vein, Rt 25, 51, 86
03L1*	Occlsn/Int Mammary Artery, Lt 321
03L1[Ø,3,4][C,D,Z]Z	Occlsn/Int Mammary Artery, Lt, [Opn, Perc, Perc Endo], [Extralum Dev, Intralum Dev, No Dev], NQ 93
03LØ*	Occlsn/Int Mammary Artery, Rt 321
03LØ[Ø,3,4][C,D,Z]Z	Occlsn/Int Mammary Artery, Rt, [Opn, Perc, Perc Endo], [Extralum Dev, Intralum Dev, No Dev], NQ 93
03LG*	Occlsn/Intracranial Artery 321
03LG[Ø,3,4][B,C,D,Z]Z	Occlsn/Intracranial Artery, [Opn, Perc, Perc Endo], [Bioactive Intralum Dev, Extralum Dev, Intralum Dev, No Dev], NQ 7, 9, 13, 17
03LG[Ø,3,4][B,D]Z	Occlsn/Intracranial Artery, [Opn, Perc, Perc Endo], [Bioactive Intralum Dev, Intralum Dev], NQ 94, 251
03LG[Ø,3,4][C,Z]Z	Occlsn/Intracranial Artery, [Opn, Perc, Perc Endo], [Extralum Dev, No Dev], NQ 414
Ø5LL*	Occlsn/Intracranial Vein 414
Ø5LL[Ø,3,4][C,D,Z]Z	Occlsn/Intracranial Vein, [Opn, Perc, Perc Endo], [Extralum Dev, Intralum Dev, No Dev], NQ 7, 9, 13, 17
ØDLA*	Occlsn/Jejunum 107
ØTL4*	Occlsn/Kidney Pelvis, Lt 249, 353
ØTL3*	Occlsn/Kidney Pelvis, Rt 249, 353
08LY[Ø,3,7,8][D,Z]Z	Occlsn/Lacrimal Duct, Lt, [Opn, Perc, Via Natrl or Artfcl Opng, Via Natrl or Artfcl Opng Endo], [Intralum Dev, No Dev], NQ 445
08LY[Ø,3]CZ	Occlsn/Lacrimal Duct, Lt, [Opn, Perc], Extralum Dev, NQ 445
08LX[Ø,3,7,8][D,Z]Z	Occlsn/Lacrimal Duct, Rt, [Opn, Perc, Via Natrl or Artfcl Opng, Via Natrl or Artfcl Opng Endo], [Intralum Dev, No Dev], NQ 445
08LX[Ø,3]CZ	Occlsn/Lacrimal Duct, Rt, [Opn, Perc], Extralum Dev, NQ 445
ØDLE*	Occlsn/Large Intestine 107
ØDLG*	Occlsn/Large Intestine, Lt 107
ØDLF*	Occlsn/Large Intestine, Rt 107
06LS*	Occlsn/Lesser Saphenous Vein, Lt 327
06LS[Ø,3,4][C,D,Z]Z	Occlsn/Lesser Saphenous Vein, Lt, [Opn, Perc, Perc Endo], [Extralum Dev, Intralum Dev, No Dev], NQ 89
06LR*	Occlsn/Lesser Saphenous Vein, Rt 327
06LR[Ø,3,4][C,D,Z]Z	Occlsn/Lesser Saphenous Vein, Rt, [Opn, Perc, Perc Endo], [Extralum Dev, Intralum Dev, No Dev], NQ 89
ØBL9*	Occlsn/Lingula Bronchus 62
04LY*	Occlsn/Lwr Artery 324
04LY[Ø,3,4][C,D,Z]Z	Occlsn/Lwr Artery, [Opn, Perc, Perc Endo], [Extralum Dev, Intralum Dev, No Dev], NQ 84
ØBLB*	Occlsn/Lwr Lobe Bronchus, Lt 62
ØBL6*	Occlsn/Lwr Lobe Bronchus, Rt 62
06LY[Ø,3,4][C,D,Z]C	Occlsn/Lwr Vein, [Opn, Perc, Perc Endo], [Extralum Dev, Intralum Dev, No Dev], Hemorrhoidal Plexus 109
06LY[Ø,3,4][C,D,Z]C	Occlsn/Lwr Vein, [Opn, Perc, Perc Endo], [Extralum Dev, Intralum Dev, No Dev], Hemorrhoidal Plexus 443
06LY[Ø,3,4][C,D,Z]Z	Occlsn/Lwr Vein, [Opn, Perc, Perc Endo], [Extralum Dev, Intralum Dev, No Dev], NQ 327
06LY[Ø,3,4][C,Z]Z	Occlsn/Lwr Vein, [Opn, Perc, Perc Endo], [Extralum Dev, No Dev], NQ 87
06LY[Ø,3,4]DZ	Occlsn/Lwr Vein, [Opn, Perc, Perc Endo], Intralum Dev, NQ 89
07LD[Ø,3,4][C,D,Z]Z	Occlsn/Lymphatic, Aortic, [Opn, Perc, Perc Endo], [Extralum Dev, Intralum Dev, No Dev], NQ 291, 298
07LØ[Ø,3,4][C,D,Z]Z	Occlsn/Lymphatic, Head, [Opn, Perc, Perc Endo], [Extralum Dev, Intralum Dev, No Dev], NQ 290, 298
07L9[Ø,3,4][C,D,Z]Z	Occlsn/Lymphatic, Int Mammary, Lt, [Opn, Perc, Perc Endo], [Extralum Dev, Intralum Dev, No Dev], NQ 291, 298
07L8[Ø,3,4][C,D,Z]Z	Occlsn/Lymphatic, Int Mammary, Rt, [Opn, Perc, Perc Endo], [Extralum Dev, Intralum Dev, No Dev], NQ 291, 298
07L6[Ø,3,4][C,D,Z]Z	Occlsn/Lymphatic, Lt Axillary, [Opn, Perc, Perc Endo], [Extralum Dev, Intralum Dev, No Dev], NQ 290, 298
07LJ[Ø,3,4][C,D,Z]Z	Occlsn/Lymphatic, Lt Inguinal, [Opn, Perc, Perc Endo], [Extralum Dev, Intralum Dev, No Dev], NQ 291, 298
07LG[Ø,3,4][C,D,Z]Z	Occlsn/Lymphatic, Lt Lwr Extr, [Opn, Perc, Perc Endo], [Extralum Dev, Intralum Dev, No Dev], NQ 291, 298
07L2[Ø,3,4][C,D,Z]Z	Occlsn/Lymphatic, Lt Neck, [Opn, Perc, Perc Endo], [Extralum Dev, Intralum Dev, No Dev], NQ 290, 298
07L4[Ø,3,4][C,D,Z]Z	Occlsn/Lymphatic, Lt Upr Extr, [Opn, Perc, Perc Endo], [Extralum Dev, Intralum Dev, No Dev], NQ 290, 298
07LB[Ø,3,4][C,D,Z]Z	Occlsn/Lymphatic, Mesenteric, [Opn, Perc, Perc Endo], [Extralum Dev, Intralum Dev, No Dev], NQ 291, 298
07LC[Ø,3,4][C,D,Z]Z	Occlsn/Lymphatic, Pelvis, [Opn, Perc, Perc Endo], [Extralum Dev, Intralum Dev, No Dev], NQ 291, 298
07L5[Ø,3,4][C,D,Z]Z	Occlsn/Lymphatic, Rt Axillary, [Opn, Perc, Perc Endo], [Extralum Dev, Intralum Dev, No Dev], NQ 290, 298
07LH[Ø,3,4][C,D,Z]Z	Occlsn/Lymphatic, Rt Inguinal, [Opn, Perc, Perc Endo], [Extralum Dev, Intralum Dev, No Dev], NQ 291, 298
07LF[Ø,3,4][C,D,Z]Z	Occlsn/Lymphatic, Rt Lwr Extr, [Opn, Perc, Perc Endo], [Extralum Dev, Intralum Dev, No Dev], NQ 291, 298
07L1[Ø,3,4][C,D,Z]Z	Occlsn/Lymphatic, Rt Neck, [Opn, Perc, Perc Endo], [Extralum Dev, Intralum Dev, No Dev], NQ 290, 298
07L3[Ø,3,4][C,D,Z]Z	Occlsn/Lymphatic, Rt Upr Extr, [Opn, Perc, Perc Endo], [Extralum Dev, Intralum Dev, No Dev], NQ 290, 298
07L7[Ø,3,4][C,D,Z]Z	Occlsn/Lymphatic, Thorax, [Opn, Perc, Perc Endo], [Extralum Dev, Intralum Dev, No Dev], NQ 291, 298
ØBL7*	Occlsn/Main Bronchus, Lt 62
ØBL3*	Occlsn/Main Bronchus, Rt 62
ØBL5*	Occlsn/Mid Lobe Bronchus, Rt 62
ØFLD*	Occlsn/Pancreatic Duct 113, 119, 335

05LR*	Occlsn/Vert Vein, Rt 25, 51, 86	ØXM[J,K]ØZZ	Reattach of [Rt, Lt] Hand, Opn Appr 131
01C*	Peripheral Nervous Sys, Extir 24	ØXM[N,P]ØZZ	Reattach of [Rt, Lt] Index Finger, Opn Appr 151
01D*	Peripheral Nervous Sys, Extract 24	ØYM[5,6]ØZZ	Reattach of [Rt, Lt] Inguinal Rgn, Opn Appr 158
01H*	Peripheral Nervous Sys, Insert 24	ØYM[F,G]ØZZ	Reattach of [Rt, Lt] Knee Rgn, Opn Appr 128
01J*	Peripheral Nervous Sys, Inspect 24	ØXM[V,W]ØZZ	Reattach of [Rt, Lt] Little Finger, Opn Appr 151
01Q*	Peripheral Nervous Sys, Repair 24	ØXM[D,F]ØZZ	Reattach of [Rt, Lt] Lwr Arm, Opn Appr 131
01S*	Peripheral Nervous Sys, Repos 24	ØYM[9,B]ØZZ	Reattach of [Rt, Lt] Lwr Extr, Opn Appr 158
01N*	Peripheral Nervous Sys, Rls 24	ØYM[H,J]ØZZ	Reattach of [Rt, Lt] Lwr Leg, Opn Appr 128
01U*	Peripheral Nervous Sys, Supl 24, 319	ØXM[Q,R]ØZZ	Reattach of [Rt, Lt] Mid Finger, Opn Appr 151
01X*	Peripheral Nervous Sys, Transfer 24	ØXM[S,T]ØZZ	Reattach of [Rt, Lt] Ring Finger, Opn Appr 151
F02*	Phys Rehab & Diag Audiology, Rehab, ADL Assess 385	ØXM[2,3]ØZZ	Reattach of [Rt, Lt] Shldr Rgn, Opn Appr 131
F08*	Phys Rehab & Diag Audiology, Rehab, ADL Trmt 385	ØXM[L,M]ØZZ	Reattach of [Rt, Lt] Thumb, Opn Appr 151
F0F*	Phys Rehab & Diag Audiology, Rehab, Caregiver Train 385	ØXM[8,9]ØZZ	Reattach of [Rt, Lt] Upr Arm, Opn Appr 131
F0B*	Phys Rehab & Diag Audiology, Rehab, Cochlear Impl Trmt 385	ØXM[6,7]ØZZ	Reattach of [Rt, Lt] Upr Extr, Opn Appr 131
F0D*	Phys Rehab & Diag Audiology, Rehab, Device Fit 385	ØYM[C,D]ØZZ	Reattach of [Rt, Lt] Upr Leg, Opn Appr 128
F09*	Phys Rehab & Diag Audiology, Rehab, Hear Trmt 385	ØXM[G,H]ØZZ	Reattach of [Rt, Lt] Wrist Rgn, Opn Appr 131
F07*	Phys Rehab & Diag Audiology, Rehab, Motor Trmt 385	ØBM[1,2]ØZZ	Reattach of [Trachea, Carina], Opn Appr 52
F01*	Phys Rehab & Diag Audiology, Rehab, Motor/Nrv Assess 385	ØCM[0,1,3,7,N]ØZZ	Reattach of [Upr Lip, Lwr Lip, Soft Palate, Tongue, Uvula], Opn Appr 56
F00*	Phys Rehab & Diag Audiology, Rehab, Speech Assess 385		
F06*	Phys Rehab & Diag Audiology, Rehab, Speech Trmt 385	ØHM7XZZ	Reattach of Abd Skin, Ext Appr 212, 236, 336, 450
F0C*	Phys Rehab & Diag Audiology, Rehab, Vestib Trmt 385	ØWMF0ZZ	Reattach of Abd Wall, Opn Appr 110, 123, 217, 303
BF0C0ZZ	Plain Radiography of Hepatobil Sys, All using H Osm Contrast 462	ØHM6XZZ	Reattach of Back Skin, Ext Appr 211, 336, 450
		ØHMVXZZ	Reattach of Bilat Breast, Ext Appr 222
BF0C1ZZ	Plain Radiography of Hepatobil Sys, All using Lt Osm Contrast 462	ØHM8XZZ	Reattach of Buttock Skin, Ext Appr 212, 336, 450
		ØBM2ØZZ	Reattach of Carina, Opn Appr 331
BF0CYZZ	Plain Radiography of Hepatobil Sys, All using Oth Contrast 462	ØHM5XZZ	Reattach of Chest Skin, Ext Appr 211, 336, 450
BF0C[0,1,Y]ZZ	Plain Radiography of Hepatobiliary Sys, All using [High Osmolar, Low Osmolar, Oth] Contrast 121	ØWM8ØZZ	Reattach of Chest Wall, Opn Appr 66, 158, 217
		ØUMJXZZ	Reattach of Clitoris, Ext Appr 267, 459
BF03[0,1,Y]ZZ	Plain Radiography/Gallbladder and Bile Ducts, [High Osmolar, Low Osmolar, Oth Contrast], None, None 121	ØFM9ØZZ	Reattach of Common Bile Duct, Opn Appr 120, 335
		ØFM8ØZZ	Reattach of Cystic Duct, Opn Appr 120, 335
F0DZ8ZZ	Prosthesis Device Fitting 158, 357	ØHM1XZZ	Reattach of Face Skin, Ext Appr 211, 336, 450
DW2*	Radiation Therapy, Anatomical Regions, Stereo Radiosurg 246, 304	ØWM2ØZZ	Reattach of Face, Opn Appr 217, 460
		ØWMNØZZ	Reattach of Female Perineum, Opn Appr 267, 275, 460
DM2*	Radiation Therapy, Breast, Stereotactic Radiosurgery 246, 304	ØFM4ØZZ	Reattach of Gallbladder, Opn Appr 120, 301, 335, 449
D02*	Radiation Therapy, Central Periph Nerv Sys, Stereo Radiosurg 246, 304	ØHMAXZZ	Reattach of Genitalia Skin, Ext Appr 212, 336, 450
		ØUMKXZZ	Reattach of Hymen, Ext Appr 459
DG2*	Radiation Therapy, Endocrine Sys, Stereo Radiosurg 246, 304	ØYMLØZZ	Reattach of Lt Ankle Region, Opn Appr 416
D92*	Radiation Therapy, ENT & Mouth, Stereo Radiosurg 246, 304	ØXM5ØZZ	Reattach of Lt Axilla, Opn Appr 356, 416
		ØHMUXZZ	Reattach of Lt Breast, Ext Appr 222
D82*	Radiation Therapy, Eye, Stereotactic Radiosurgery 246, 304	ØYM1ØZZ	Reattach of Lt Buttock, Opn Appr 219, 462
DU2*	Radiation Therapy, Fem Reprod Sys, Stereo Radiosurg 246, 304	ØHM3XZZ	Reattach of Lt Ear Skin, Ext Appr 211, 336, 450
		ØXMCØZZ	Reattach of Lt Elbow Region, Opn Appr 356, 416
DD2*	Radiation Therapy, GI Sys, Stereo Radiosurg 246, 304	09M1XZZ	Reattach of Lt Ext Ear, Ext Appr 447
DF2*	Radiation Therapy, Hepatobil Pancreas, Stereo Radiosurg 246, 304	ØYM8ØZZ	Reattach of Lt Femor Region, Opn Appr 416
		ØHMNXZZ	Reattach of Lt Foot Skin, Ext Appr 212, 336, 450
D72*	Radiation Therapy, Lymph & Hemat Sys, Stereo Radiosurg 246, 304	ØYMNØZZ	Reattach of Lt Foot, Opn Appr 416
		ØXM1ØZZ	Reattach of Lt Forequarter, Opn Appr 356, 416
DV2*	Radiation Therapy, Male Reprod Sys, Stereo Radiosurg 246, 304	ØHMGXZZ	Reattach of Lt Hand Skin, Ext Appr 212, 336, 450
		ØXMKØZZ	Reattach of Lt Hand, Opn Appr 356, 416
DB2*	Radiation Therapy, Resp Sys, Stereo Radiosurg 246, 304	ØFM6ØZZ	Reattach of Lt Hepatic Duct, Opn Appr 120, 335
DT2*	Radiation Therapy, Urinary Sys, Stereotactic Radiosurgery 246, 304	ØXMPØZZ	Reattach of Lt Index Finger, Opn Appr 317
		ØYMGØZZ	Reattach of Lt Knee Region, Opn Appr 416
BF030ZZ	Radiography of Gallbladder & Bile Duct using H Osm Contrast 462	ØXMWØZZ	Reattach of Lt Little Finger, Opn Appr 317
		ØHMEXZZ	Reattach of Lt Lwr Arm Skin, Ext Appr 212, 336, 450
BF031ZZ	Radiography of Gallbladder & Bile Duct using Lt Osm Contrast 462	ØXMFØZZ	Reattach of Lt Lwr Arm, Opn Appr 356, 416
		08MRXZZ	Reattach of Lt Lwr Eyelid, Ext Appr 210, 445
BF03YZZ	Radiography of Gallbladder & Bile Duct using Oth Contrast 462	ØHMLXZZ	Reattach of Lt Lwr Leg Skin, Ext Appr 212, 336, 450
		ØYMJØZZ	Reattach of Lt Lwr Leg, Opn Appr 416
ØHM[1,2,3,4,9]XZZ	Reattach of [Face, Rt Ear, Lt Ear, Neck, Perineum] Skin, Ext Appr 53	ØXMRØZZ	Reattach of Lt Mid Finger, Opn Appr 317
		ØHMXXZZ	Reattach of Lt Nipple, Ext Appr 222, 336
ØWM[2,4,5,6]ØZZ	Reattach of [Face, Upr Jaw, Lwr Jaw, Neck], Opn Appr 55	ØXMTØZZ	Reattach of Lt Ring Finger, Opn Appr 317
ØYM[2,3,4]ØZZ	Reattach of [Rt, Lt, Bilat] Hindquarter, Opn Appr 158	ØXM3ØZZ	Reattach of Lt Shldr Region, Opn Appr 356, 416
ØYM[P,Q]ØZZ	Reattach of [Rt, Lt] 1st Toe, Opn Appr 146	ØXMMØZZ	Reattach of Lt Thumb, Opn Appr 317
ØYM[R,S]ØZZ	Reattach of [Rt, Lt] 2nd Toe, Opn Appr 146	ØHMCXZZ	Reattach of Lt Upr Arm Skin, Ext Appr 212, 336, 450
ØYM[T,U]ØZZ	Reattach of [Rt, Lt] 3rd Toe, Opn Appr 146	ØXM9ØZZ	Reattach of Lt Upr Arm, Opn Appr 356, 416
ØYM[V,W]ØZZ	Reattach of [Rt, Lt] 4th Toe, Opn Appr 146	ØXM7ØZZ	Reattach of Lt Upr Extr, Opn Appr 356, 416
ØYM[X,Y]ØZZ	Reattach of [Rt, Lt] 5th Toe, Opn Appr 146	08MPXZZ	Reattach of Lt Upr Eyelid, Ext Appr 210, 445
ØYM[K,L]ØZZ	Reattach of [Rt, Lt] Ankle Rgn, Opn Appr 128	ØHMJXZZ	Reattach of Lt Upr Leg Skin, Ext Appr 212, 336, 450
ØXM[4,5]ØZZ	Reattach of [Rt, Lt] Axilla, Opn Appr 131	ØYMDØZZ	Reattach of Lt Upr Leg, Opn Appr 416
ØXM[B,C]ØZZ	Reattach of [Rt, Lt] Elbow Rgn, Opn Appr 131	ØXMHØZZ	Reattach of Lt Wrist Region, Opn Appr 356, 416
ØYM[7,8]ØZZ	Reattach of [Rt, Lt] Femor Rgn, Opn Appr 128		
ØYM[M,N]ØZZ	Reattach of [Rt, Lt] Foot, Opn Appr 128		
ØXM[0,1]ØZZ	Reattach of [Rt, Lt] Forequarter, Opn Appr 131		

ØVMG*	Reattach/Spermatic Cord, Lt 258
ØVMF*	Reattach/Spermatic Cord, Rt 258
ØVMH*	Reattach/Spermatic Cords, Bilat 258
ØDM6*	Reattach/Stomach 106, 235
ØGMM*	Reattach/Superior Parathyroid Gland, Lt 238
ØGML*	Reattach/Superior Parathyroid Gland, Rt 238
ØVMC*	Reattach/Testes, Bilat 258
ØVMB*	Reattach/Testis, Lt 258
ØVM9*	Reattach/Testis, Rt 258
ØKMJ*	Reattach/Thorax Muscle, Lt 139, 339
ØKMH*	Reattach/Thorax Muscle, Rt 139, 339
ØLMD*	Reattach/Thorax Tndn, Lt 141, 341
ØLMC*	Reattach/Thorax Tndn, Rt 141, 341
ØGMG*	Reattach/Thyroid Gland Lobe, Lt 238
ØGMH*	Reattach/Thyroid Gland Lobe, Rt 238
ØKM4*	Reattach/Tongue, Palate, Pharynx Muscle 139, 339
ØDML*	Reattach/Transv Colon 107
ØKMG*	Reattach/Trunk Muscle, Lt 139, 339
ØKMF*	Reattach/Trunk Muscle, Rt 139, 339
ØLMB*	Reattach/Trunk Tndn, Lt 141, 341
ØLM9*	Reattach/Trunk Tndn, Rt 141, 341
ØVM7*	Reattach/Tunica Vaginalis, Lt 258
ØVM6*	Reattach/Tunica Vaginalis, Rt 258
ØKM8*	Reattach/Upr Arm Muscle, Lt 139, 339
ØKM7*	Reattach/Upr Arm Muscle, Rt 139, 339
ØLM4*	Reattach/Upr Arm Tndn, Lt 141, 341
ØLM3*	Reattach/Upr Arm Tndn, Rt 141, 341
ØKMR*	Reattach/Upr Leg Muscle, Lt 139, 339
ØKMQ*	Reattach/Upr Leg Muscle, Rt 139, 339
ØLMM*	Reattach/Upr Leg Tndn, Lt 141, 341
ØLML*	Reattach/Upr Leg Tndn, Rt 141, 341
ØTM7*	Reattach/Ureter, Lt 249, 353
ØTM6*	Reattach/Ureter, Rt 249, 353
ØTM8*	Reattach/Ureters, Bilat 249, 353
ØTMD*	Reattach/Urethra 250, 257, 268, 353
ØUM4*	Reattach/Uterine Supporting Structure 267, 354
ØUM9*	Reattach/Uterus 269
ØUMG*	Reattach/Vagina 267, 354
ØRPD47Z	Remove Autol Sub from Lt Temporomandib Jt, Perc Endo 136
ØRPC47Z	Remove Autol Sub from Rt Temporomandib Jt, Perc Endo 136
ØRPD40Z	Remove Drain Dev from Lt Temporomandib Jt, Perc Endo 136
ØRPC40Z	Remove Drain Dev from Rt Temporomandib Jt, Perc Endo 136
ØRPD03Z	Remove Inf Dev from Lt Temporomandib Jt, Opn 136
ØRPD33Z	Remove Inf Dev from Lt Temporomandib Jt, Perc 136
ØRPD43Z	Remove Inf Dev from Lt Temporomandib Jt, Perc Endo 136
ØRPC03Z	Remove Inf Dev from Rt Temporomandib Jt, Opn 136
ØRPC33Z	Remove Inf Dev from Rt Temporomandib Jt, Perc 136
ØRPC43Z	Remove Inf Dev from Rt Temporomandib Jt, Perc Endo 136
ØRPD44Z	Remove Int Fix from Lt Temporomandib Jt, Perc Endo 136
ØRPC44Z	Remove Int Fix from Rt Temporomandib Jt, Perc Endo 136
ØRPD4KZ	Remove Nonaut Sub from Lt Temporomandib Jt, Perc Endo 136
ØRPC4KZ	Remove Nonaut Sub from Rt Temporomandib Jt, Perc Endo 136
ØRPD4JZ	Remove Synth Sub from Lt Temporomandib Jt, Perc Endo 136
ØRPC4JZ	Remove Synth Sub from Rt Temporomandib Jt, Perc Endo 136
ØWQFØZZ	Repair Abd Wall, Opn Appr 460
ØWQFXZ2	Repair Abd Wall, Stoma, Ext Appr 109, 110, 260, 303, 460
ØDQQXZZ	Repair Anus, Ext Appr 272
ØDQKØZZ	Repair Ascending Colon, Opn Appr 109
ØTQBØZZ	Repair Bladder, Opn Appr 274
ØTQB3ZZ	Repair Bladder, Perc Appr 274
ØTQB4ZZ	Repair Bladder, Perc Endo Appr 274
ØTQB7ZZ	Repair Bladder, Via Natrl or Artfcl Opng 274
ØTQB8ZZ	Repair Bladder, Via Natrl or Artfcl Opng Endo 274
ØDQHØZZ	Repair Cecum, Opn Appr 109
ØRQ3ØZZ	Repair Cervical Vert Disc, Opn Appr 301, 350
ØUQCØZZ	Repair Cervix, Opn Appr 274
ØUQC3ZZ	Repair Cervix, Perc Appr 274
ØUQC4ZZ	Repair Cervix, Perc Endo Appr 274

ØUQC7ZZ	Repair Cervix, Via Natrl or Artfcl Opng 274
ØUQC8ZZ	Repair Cervix, Via Natrl or Artfcl Opng Endo 274
ØDQMØZZ	Repair Descending Colon, Opn Appr 109
ØDQ9ØZZ	Repair Duodenum, Opn Appr 109
ØWQ2XZZ	Repair Face, Ext Appr 42
ØHQQXZZ	Repair Finger Nail, Ext Appr 212, 336
Ø2QAØZZ	Repair Heart, Opn Appr 60, 296
ØUQKXZZ	Repair Hymen, Ext Appr 459
ØDQBØZZ	Repair Ileum, Opn Appr 109
ØDQAØZZ	Repair Jejunum, Opn Appr 109
ØDQEØZZ	Repair Large Intestine, Opn Appr 109
08Q33ZZ	Repair Lt Ant Chamber, Perc Appr 44, 330, 445
08QTXZZ	Repair Lt Conjunctiva, Ext Appr 330, 445
08Q9XZZ	Repair Lt Cornea, Ext Appr 44, 330, 445
08Q1XZZ	Repair Lt Eye, Ext Appr 330, 445
08QD3ZZ	Repair Lt Iris, Perc Appr 241, 330, 445
ØDQGØZZ	Repair Lt Large Intestine, Opn Appr 109
08QK3ZZ	Repair Lt Lens, Perc Appr 330, 445
09Q6ØZZ	Repair Lt Mid Ear, Opn Appr 447
08QF3ZZ	Repair Lt Retina, Perc Appr 241, 330, 445
08QH3ZZ	Repair Lt Retinal Vessel, Perc Appr 330, 445
08Q7XZZ	Repair Lt Sclera, Ext Appr 44, 330, 445
08Q53ZZ	Repair Lt Vitreous, Perc Appr 44, 330, 445
ØSQ2ØZZ	Repair Lumbar Vert Disc, Opn Appr 302, 352
ØSQ4ØZZ	Repair Lumbosacral Disc, Opn Appr 302, 352
ØWQ6XZ2	Repair Neck, Stoma, Ext Appr 66, 91, 106, 217, 303
09QKXZZ	Repair Nose, Ext Appr 90
ØHQ9XZZ	Repair Perineum Skin, Ext Appr 266, 272, 274
ØJQBØZZ	Repair Perineum SQ/Fascia, Opn Appr 272
ØDQPØZZ	Repair Rectum, Opn Appr 274
ØDQP3ZZ	Repair Rectum, Perc Appr 274
ØDQP4ZZ	Repair Rectum, Perc Endo Appr 274
ØDQP7ZZ	Repair Rectum, Via Natrl or Artfcl Opng 271, 272, 273, 274, 275
ØDQP8ZZ	Repair Rectum, Via Natrl or Artfcl Opng Endo 274
08Q23ZZ	Repair Rt Ant Chamber, Perc Appr 44, 330, 445
08QSXZZ	Repair Rt Conjunctiva, Ext Appr 330, 445
08Q8XZZ	Repair Rt Cornea, Ext Appr 44, 330, 445
08QØXZZ	Repair Rt Eye, Ext Appr 330, 445
08QC3ZZ	Repair Rt Iris, Perc Appr 241, 330, 445
08QVØZZ	Repair Rt Lacrimal Gland, Opn Appr 43
08QV3ZZ	Repair Rt Lacrimal Gland, Perc Appr 43
ØDQFØZZ	Repair Rt Large Intestine, Opn Appr 109
08QJ3ZZ	Repair Rt Lens, Perc Appr 330, 445
09Q5ØZZ	Repair Rt Mid Ear, Opn Appr 447
08QE3ZZ	Repair Rt Retina, Perc Appr 241, 330, 445
08QG3ZZ	Repair Rt Retinal Vessel, Perc Appr 330, 445
08Q6XZZ	Repair Rt Sclera, Ext Appr 44, 330, 445
08Q43ZZ	Repair Rt Vitreous, Perc Appr 44, 330, 445
ØDQNØZZ	Repair Sigmoid Colon, Opn Appr 109
ØNQØXZZ	Repair Skull, Ext Appr 301
ØDQ8ØZZ	Repair Sm Intestine, Opn Appr 109
ØDQ64ZZ	Repair Stomach, Perc Endo Appr 449
ØRQ9ØZZ	Repair Thoracic Vert Disc, Opn Appr 301, 350
ØRQBØZZ	Repair Thoracolumbar Vert Disc, Opn Appr 301, 350
07QM4ZZ	Repair Thymus, Perc Endo Appr 25
ØHQRXZZ	Repair Toe Nail, Ext Appr 212, 336
ØDQLØZZ	Repair Transv Colon, Opn Appr 109
ØTQDXZZ	Repair Urethra, Ext Appr 274
ØTQDØZZ	Repair Urethra, Opn Appr 274
ØTQD3ZZ	Repair Urethra, Perc Appr 274
ØTQD4ZZ	Repair Urethra, Perc Endo Appr 274
ØTQD7ZZ	Repair Urethra, Via Natrl or Artfcl Opng 274
ØTQD8ZZ	Repair Urethra, Via Natrl or Artfcl Opng Endo 274
ØYQQ*	Repair/1st Toe, Lt 357
ØYQP*	Repair/1st Toe, Rt 357
ØYQS*	Repair/2nd Toe, Lt 357
ØYQR*	Repair/2nd Toe, Rt 357
ØYQU*	Repair/3rd Toe, Lt 357
ØYQT*	Repair/3rd Toe, Rt 357
ØYQW*	Repair/4th Toe, Lt 357

ØYQV*	Repair/4th Toe, Rt 357	
ØYQY*	Repair/5th Toe, Lt 357	
ØYQX*	Repair/5th Toe, Rt 357	
ØMQJ*	Repair/Abd Bursa & Lgmt, Lt 144	
ØMQH*	Repair/Abd Bursa & Lgmt, Rt 144	
ØKQL*	Repair/Abd Muscle, Lt 27, 140, 339	
ØKQK*	Repair/Abd Muscle, Rt 27, 140, 339	
ØLQG*	Repair/Abd Tndn, Lt 28, 142, 341	
ØLQF*	Repair/Abd Tndn, Rt 28, 142, 341	
ØWQF*	Repair/Abd Wall 269, 356	
ØØQL*	Repair/Abducens Nerve 23, 50	
ØØQR*	Repair/Accessory Nerve 23, 50	
Ø9QP*	Repair/Accessory Sinus 56	
ØQQ5*	Repair/Acetabulum, Lt 156	
ØQQ4*	Repair/Acetabulum, Rt 156	
ØØQN*	Repair/Acoustic Nerve 23, 50	
ØRQH*	Repair/Acromioclavicular Jt, Lt 148, 350	
ØRQG*	Repair/Acromioclavicular Jt, Rt 148, 350	
ØCQQ*	Repair/Adenoids 53	
ØGQ2*	Repair/Adrenal Gland, Lt 235, 336	
ØGQ3*	Repair/Adrenal Gland, Rt 235, 336	
ØGQ4*	Repair/Adrenal Glands, Bilat 235, 336	
ØFQC*	Repair/Ampulla of Vater 106, 119	
ØDQR*	Repair/Anal Sphincter 109, 334	
ØMQR*	Repair/Ankle Bursa & Lgmt, Lt 144, 343	
ØMQQ*	Repair/Ankle Bursa & Lgmt, Rt 144, 343	
ØSQG*	Repair/Ankle Jt, Lt 133, 352	
ØSQF*	Repair/Ankle Jt, Rt 133, 352	
ØYQL*	Repair/Ankle Region, Lt 357	
ØYQK*	Repair/Ankle Region, Rt 357	
ØLQT*	Repair/Ankle Tndn, Lt 142, 341	
ØLQS*	Repair/Ankle Tndn, Rt 142, 341	
Ø4QQ*	Repair/Ant Tibial Artery, Lt 240	
Ø4QP*	Repair/Ant Tibial Artery, Rt 240	
ØDQQ*	Repair/Anus 109, 334	
Ø2QF*	Repair/Aortic Valve 71, 72	
ØDQJ*	Repair/Appendix 108, 334	
ØDQK*	Repair/Ascending Colon 107, 334	
Ø2Q7*	Repair/Atrium, Lt 320	
Ø2Q6*	Repair/Atrium, Rt 320	
Ø3Q6*	Repair/Axillary Artery, Lt 239	
Ø3Q5*	Repair/Axillary Artery, Rt 239	
Ø5Q8*	Repair/Axillary Vein, Lt 88	
Ø5Q7*	Repair/Axillary Vein, Rt 88	
Ø5QØ*	Repair/Azygos Vein 88	
ØØQ8*	Repair/Basal Ganglia 414	
Ø5QC*	Repair/Basilic Vein, Lt 88	
Ø5QB*	Repair/Basilic Vein, Rt 88	
ØTQB*	Repair/Bladder 109, 248, 260, 268, 354	
Ø3Q8*	Repair/Brachial Artery, Lt 239	
Ø3Q7*	Repair/Brachial Artery, Rt 239	
Ø1Q3*	Repair/Brachial Plexus 152, 319	
Ø5QA*	Repair/Brachial Vein, Lt 88	
Ø5Q9*	Repair/Brachial Vein, Rt 88	
ØØQØ*	Repair/Brain 414	
ØCQ4*	Repair/Buccal Mucosa 56, 332	
ØYQ1*	Repair/Buttock, Lt 357	
ØYQØ*	Repair/Buttock, Rt 357	
ØBQ2*	Repair/Carina 52, 331	
ØRQR*	Repair/Carpal Jt, Lt 28, 147	
ØRQQ*	Repair/Carpal Jt, Rt 28, 147	
ØPQN*	Repair/Carpal, Lt 150	
ØPQM*	Repair/Carpal, Rt 150	
ØDQH*	Repair/Cecum 107, 334	
Ø5QF*	Repair/Cephalic Vein, Lt 88	
Ø5QD*	Repair/Cephalic Vein, Rt 88	
ØØQC*	Repair/Cerebellum 414	
ØØQ7*	Repair/Cerebral Hemisphere 414	
ØØQ1*	Repair/Cerebral Meninges 414	
ØØQ6*	Repair/Cerebral Ventricle 414	
Ø1Q1*	Repair/Cervical Nerve 152, 319	
Ø1QØ*	Repair/Cervical Plexus 152, 319	
ØØQW*	Repair/Cervical Spinal Cord 159, 160	
ØRQ1*	Repair/Cervical Vert Jt 157	
ØPQ3*	Repair/Cervical Vertebra 155	
ØRQ5*	Repair/Cervicothoracic Vert Disc 157	
ØRQ4*	Repair/Cervicothoracic Vert Jt 157	
ØUQC*	Repair/Cervix 267, 354	
ØWQ8*	Repair/Chest Wall 66, 158, 356	
Ø8QB*	Repair/Choroid, Lt 44, 330	
Ø8QA*	Repair/Choroid, Rt 44, 330	
Ø7QL*	Repair/Cisterna Chyli 60	
ØPQB*	Repair/Clavicle, Lt 66, 155, 346	
ØPQ9*	Repair/Clavicle, Rt 66, 155, 346	
ØUQJ*	Repair/Clitoris 267	
ØSQ6*	Repair/Coccygeal Jt 157	
ØQQS*	Repair/Coccyx 156	
Ø6Q7*	Repair/Colic Vein 89	
ØFQ9*	Repair/Common Bile Duct 120	
Ø3QJ*	Repair/Common Carotid Artery, Lt 21	
Ø3QH*	Repair/Common Carotid Artery, Rt 21	
Ø4QD*	Repair/Common Iliac Artery, Lt 240	
Ø4QC*	Repair/Common Iliac Artery, Rt 240	
Ø6QD*	Repair/Common Iliac Vein, Lt 89	
Ø6QC*	Repair/Common Iliac Vein, Rt 89	
Ø2Q8*	Repair/Conduction Mechanism 320	
ØUQF*	Repair/Cul-de-sac 267	
ØFQ8*	Repair/Cystic Duct 120	
ØBQS*	Repair/Diaphragm, Lt 105, 331	
ØBQR*	Repair/Diaphragm, Rt 105, 331	
ØDQ9*	Repair/Duodenum 106, 334	
ØØQ2*	Repair/Dura Mater 414	
ØMQ4*	Repair/Elbow Bursa & Lgmt, Lt 144, 343	
ØMQ3*	Repair/Elbow Bursa & Lgmt, Rt 144, 343	
ØRQM*	Repair/Elbow Jt, Lt 148, 350	
ØRQL*	Repair/Elbow Jt, Rt 148, 350	
ØVQL*	Repair/Epididymis, Bilat 258, 355	
ØVQK*	Repair/Epididymis, Lt 258, 355	
ØVQJ*	Repair/Epididymis, Rt 258, 355	
ØCQR*	Repair/Epiglottis 53, 65, 332	
Ø6Q3*	Repair/Esophageal Vein 89	
ØDQ4*	Repair/Esophagogastric Junction 106, 334	
ØDQ5*	Repair/Esophagus 53, 62, 106, 334	
ØDQ3*	Repair/Esophagus, Lwr 106, 334	
ØDQ2*	Repair/Esophagus, Mid 106, 334	
ØDQ1*	Repair/Esophagus, Upr 106, 334	
ØNQG*	Repair/Ethmoid Bone, Lt 49	
ØNQF*	Repair/Ethmoid Bone, Rt 49	
Ø9QV*	Repair/Ethmoid Sinus, Lt 56	
Ø9QU*	Repair/Ethmoid Sinus, Rt 56	
Ø3QN*	Repair/Ext Carotid Artery, Lt 21	
Ø3QM*	Repair/Ext Carotid Artery, Rt 21	
Ø4QJ*	Repair/Ext Iliac Artery, Lt 240	
Ø4QH*	Repair/Ext Iliac Artery, Rt 240	
Ø6QG*	Repair/Ext Iliac Vein, Lt 89	
Ø6QF*	Repair/Ext Iliac Vein, Rt 89	
Ø5QQ*	Repair/Ext Jugular Vein, Lt 88	
Ø5QP*	Repair/Ext Jugular Vein, Rt 88	
Ø8QM*	Repair/Extraocular Muscle, Lt 43, 330	
Ø8QL*	Repair/Extraocular Muscle, Rt 43, 330	
ØWQ2*	Repair/Face 55, 356	
Ø3QR*	Repair/Face Artery 21	
Ø5QV*	Repair/Face Vein, Lt 88	
Ø5QT*	Repair/Face Vein, Rt 88	
ØKQ1*	Repair/Facial Muscle 27, 140, 339	
ØØQM*	Repair/Facial Nerve 23, 50	
ØUQ6*	Repair/Fallopian Tube, Lt 263, 264, 266, 354	
ØUQ5*	Repair/Fallopian Tube, Rt 263, 264, 266, 354	
ØUQ7*	Repair/Fallopian Tubes, Bilat 263, 264, 266, 354	
Ø4QL*	Repair/Femor Artery, Lt 240	

04QK*	Repair/Femor Artery, Rt 240	
01QD*	Repair/Femor Nerve 152, 319	
0QQ9*	Repair/Femor Shaft, Lt 131, 348, 416	
0QQ8*	Repair/Femor Shaft, Rt 131, 348, 416	
06QN*	Repair/Femor Vein, Lt 89	
06QM*	Repair/Femor Vein, Rt 89	
0QQK*	Repair/Fibula, Lt 133, 348	
0QQJ*	Repair/Fibula, Rt 133, 348	
0RQX*	Repair/Finger Phalangeal Jt, Lt 28, 147	
0RQW*	Repair/Finger Phalangeal Jt, Rt 28, 147	
0PQV*	Repair/Finger Phalanx, Lt 155	
0PQT*	Repair/Finger Phalanx, Rt 155	
04QW*	Repair/Foot Artery, Lt 240	
04QV*	Repair/Foot Artery, Rt 240	
0MQT*	Repair/Foot Bursa & Lgmt, Lt 145, 343	
0MQS*	Repair/Foot Bursa & Lgmt, Rt 145, 343	
0KQW*	Repair/Foot Muscle, Lt 27, 140, 242, 339	
0KQV*	Repair/Foot Muscle, Rt 27, 140, 242, 339	
0LQW*	Repair/Foot Tndn, Lt 28, 142, 341	
0LQV*	Repair/Foot Tndn, Rt 28, 142, 341	
06QV*	Repair/Foot Vein, Lt 89	
06QT*	Repair/Foot Vein, Rt 89	
0YQN*	Repair/Foot, Lt 357	
0YQM*	Repair/Foot, Rt 357	
0NQ2*	Repair/Frontal Bone, Lt 10, 49, 154, 415	
0NQ1*	Repair/Frontal Bone, Rt 10, 49, 154, 415	
09QT*	Repair/Frontal Sinus, Lt 56	
09QS*	Repair/Frontal Sinus, Rt 56	
0FQ4*	Repair/Gallbladder 120	
06Q2*	Repair/Gastric Vein 89	
0PQ8*	Repair/Glenoid Cavity, Lt 66, 155, 346	
0PQ7*	Repair/Glenoid Cavity, Rt 66, 155, 346	
00QP*	Repair/Glossopharyngeal Nerve 23, 50	
0DQS*	Repair/Greater Omentum 110	
06QQ*	Repair/Greater Saphenous Vein, Lt 89	
06QP*	Repair/Greater Saphenous Vein, Rt 89	
03QF*	Repair/Hand Artery, Lt 239	
03QD*	Repair/Hand Artery, Rt 239	
0MQ8*	Repair/Hand Bursa & Lgmt, Lt 144, 343	
0MQ7*	Repair/Hand Bursa & Lgmt, Rt 144, 343	
0KQD*	Repair/Hand Muscle, Lt 149	
0KQC*	Repair/Hand Muscle, Rt 149	
0LQ8*	Repair/Hand Tndn, Lt 28, 149	
0LQ7*	Repair/Hand Tndn, Rt 28, 149	
05QH*	Repair/Hand Vein, Lt 88	
05QG*	Repair/Hand Vein, Rt 88	
0XQK*	Repair/Hand, Lt 29	
0XQJ*	Repair/Hand, Rt 29	
0CQ2*	Repair/Hard Palate 25, 53, 332	
0WQ0*	Repair/Head 356	
0MQ0*	Repair/Head and Neck Bursa & Lgmt 144	
0LQ0*	Repair/Head and Neck Tndn 28, 142, 341	
0KQ0*	Repair/Head Muscle 27, 140, 339	
02QA*	Repair/Heart 320	
05Q1*	Repair/Hemiazygos Vein 88	
0FQ6*	Repair/Hepatic Duct, Lt 120	
0FQ5*	Repair/Hepatic Duct, Rt 120	
06Q4*	Repair/Hepatic Vein 89	
0MQM*	Repair/Hip Bursa & Lgmt, Lt 144	
0MQL*	Repair/Hip Bursa & Lgmt, Rt 144	
0SQB*	Repair/Hip Jt, Lt 131, 352, 416	
0SQ9*	Repair/Hip Jt, Rt 131, 352, 416	
0KQP*	Repair/Hip Muscle, Lt 27, 140, 242, 339	
0KQN*	Repair/Hip Muscle, Rt 27, 140, 242, 339	
0LQK*	Repair/Hip Tndn, Lt 28, 142, 341	
0LQJ*	Repair/Hip Tndn, Rt 28, 142, 341	
0PQD*	Repair/Humeral Head, Lt 133, 346	
0PQC*	Repair/Humeral Head, Rt 133, 346	
0PQG*	Repair/Humeral Shaft, Lt 133, 346	
0PQF*	Repair/Humeral Shaft, Rt 133, 346	
0UQK*	Repair/Hymen 267	
0NQX*	Repair/Hyoid Bone 49	
06QJ*	Repair/Hypogastric Vein, Lt 89	
06QH*	Repair/Hypogastric Vein, Rt 89	
00QS*	Repair/Hypoglossal Nerve 23, 50	
00QA*	Repair/Hypothalamus 414	
0DQC*	Repair/Ileocecal Valve 107, 334	
0DQB*	Repair/Ileum 107, 334	
0XQP*	Repair/Index Finger, Lt 29	
0XQN*	Repair/Index Finger, Rt 29	
06Q6*	Repair/Inferior Mesenteric Vein 89	
0GQP*	Repair/Inferior Parathyroid Gland, Lt 238	
0GQN*	Repair/Inferior Parathyroid Gland, Rt 238	
06Q0*	Repair/Inferior Vena Cava 89	
03Q2*	Repair/Innominate Artery 63	
05Q4*	Repair/Innominate Vein, Lt 88	
05Q3*	Repair/Innominate Vein, Rt 88	
03QL*	Repair/Int Carotid Artery, Lt 21	
03QK*	Repair/Int Carotid Artery, Rt 21	
04QF*	Repair/Int Iliac Artery, Lt 240	
04QE*	Repair/Int Iliac Artery, Rt 240	
05QN*	Repair/Int Jugular Vein, Lt 88	
05QM*	Repair/Int Jugular Vein, Rt 88	
03Q1*	Repair/Int Mammary Artery, Lt 63	
03Q0*	Repair/Int Mammary Artery, Rt 63	
05QL*	Repair/Intracranial Vein 88	
0DQA*	Repair/Jejunum 107, 334	
0TQ4*	Repair/Kidney Pelvis, Lt 249, 354	
0TQ3*	Repair/Kidney Pelvis, Rt 249, 354	
0TQ1*	Repair/Kidney, Lt 249, 260	
0TQ0*	Repair/Kidney, Rt 249, 260	
0MQP*	Repair/Knee Bursa & Lgmt, Lt 132, 343	
0MQN*	Repair/Knee Bursa & Lgmt, Rt 132, 343	
0SQD*	Repair/Knee Jt, Lt 132, 352	
0SQC*	Repair/Knee Jt, Rt 132, 352	
0YQG*	Repair/Knee Region, Lt 357	
0YQF*	Repair/Knee Region, Rt 357	
0LQR*	Repair/Knee Tndn, Lt 142, 341	
0LQQ*	Repair/Knee Tndn, Rt 142, 341	
0NQJ*	Repair/Lacrimal Bone, Lt 49	
0NQH*	Repair/Lacrimal Bone, Rt 49	
08QY*	Repair/Lacrimal Duct, Lt 43, 330	
08QX*	Repair/Lacrimal Duct, Rt 43, 330	
08QW*	Repair/Lacrimal Gland, Lt 43, 330	
08QV*	Repair/Lacrimal Gland, Rt 330	
0DQE*	Repair/Large Intestine 107, 334	
0CQS*	Repair/Larynx 53, 65, 332	
0DQT*	Repair/Lesser Omentum 110	
06QS*	Repair/Lesser Saphenous Vein, Lt 89	
06QR*	Repair/Lesser Saphenous Vein, Rt 89	
0BQ9*	Repair/Lingula Bronchus 331	
0XQW*	Repair/Little Finger, Lt 29	
0XQV*	Repair/Little Finger, Rt 29	
0FQ0*	Repair/Liver 119	
0FQ2*	Repair/Liver, Lt Lobe 119	
0FQ1*	Repair/Liver, Rt Lobe 119	
01QB*	Repair/Lumbar Nerve 152, 319	
01Q9*	Repair/Lumbar Plexus 152, 319	
00QY*	Repair/Lumbar Spinal Cord 159, 160	
0SQ0*	Repair/Lumbar Vert Jt 157	
0QQ0*	Repair/Lumbar Vertebra 156	
0SQ3*	Repair/Lumbosacral Jt 157	
01QA*	Repair/Lumbosacral Plexus 152, 319	
0BQL*	Repair/Lung, Lt 331	
0BQK*	Repair/Lung, Rt 331	
0BQM*	Repair/Lungs, Bilat 331	
0KQB*	Repair/Lwr Arm and Wrist Muscle, Lt 27, 140, 242, 339	
0KQ9*	Repair/Lwr Arm and Wrist Muscle, Rt 27, 140, 242, 339	
0LQ6*	Repair/Lwr Arm and Wrist Tndn, Lt 28, 142, 341	
0LQ5*	Repair/Lwr Arm and Wrist Tndn, Rt 28, 142, 341	

04QY*	Repair/Lwr Artery 111, 122, 240, 252
0WQL*	Repair/Lwr Back 356
0MQW*	Repair/Lwr Extr Bursa & Lgmt, Lt 144
0MQV*	Repair/Lwr Extr Bursa & Lgmt, Rt 144
0YQB*	Repair/Lwr Extr, Lt 357
0YQ9*	Repair/Lwr Extr, Rt 357
0QQC*	Repair/Lwr Femur, Lt 131, 348, 416
0QQB*	Repair/Lwr Femur, Rt 131, 348, 416
0WQ5*	Repair/Lwr Jaw 55, 356
0KQT*	Repair/Lwr Leg Muscle, Lt 27, 140, 242, 339
0KQS*	Repair/Lwr Leg Muscle, Rt 27, 140, 242, 339
0LQP*	Repair/Lwr Leg Tndn, Lt 28, 142, 341
0LQN*	Repair/Lwr Leg Tndn, Rt 28, 142, 341
0YQJ*	Repair/Lwr Leg, Lt 357
0YQH*	Repair/Lwr Leg, Rt 357
0BQB*	Repair/Lwr Lobe Bronchus, Lt 331
0BQ6*	Repair/Lwr Lobe Bronchus, Rt 331
06QY*	Repair/Lwr Vein 87, 112, 122, 241, 252
07QD*	Repair/Lymphatic, Aortic 328
07Q0*	Repair/Lymphatic, Head 328
07Q9*	Repair/Lymphatic, Int Mammary, Lt 328
07Q8*	Repair/Lymphatic, Int Mammary, Rt 328
07Q6*	Repair/Lymphatic, Lt Axillary 328
07QJ*	Repair/Lymphatic, Lt Inguinal 328
07QG*	Repair/Lymphatic, Lt Lwr Extr 328
07Q2*	Repair/Lymphatic, Lt Neck 328
07Q4*	Repair/Lymphatic, Lt Upr Extr 328
07QB*	Repair/Lymphatic, Mesenteric 328
07QC*	Repair/Lymphatic, Pelvis 328
07Q5*	Repair/Lymphatic, Rt Axillary 328
07QH*	Repair/Lymphatic, Rt Inguinal 328
07QF*	Repair/Lymphatic, Rt Lwr Extr 328
07Q1*	Repair/Lymphatic, Rt Neck 328
07Q3*	Repair/Lymphatic, Rt Upr Extr 328
07Q7*	Repair/Lymphatic, Thorax 328
0BQ7*	Repair/Main Bronchus, Lt 331
0BQ3*	Repair/Main Bronchus, Rt 331
0NQV*	Repair/Mandible, Lt 49, 154
0NQT*	Repair/Mandible, Rt 49, 154
09QC*	Repair/Mastoid Sinus, Lt 56
09QB*	Repair/Mastoid Sinus, Rt 56
0NQS*	Repair/Maxilla, Lt 49, 154
0NQR*	Repair/Maxilla, Rt 49, 154
09QR*	Repair/Maxillary Sinus, Lt 56
09QQ*	Repair/Maxillary Sinus, Rt 56
01Q5*	Repair/Median Nerve 152, 319
0WQC*	Repair/Mediastinum 66, 356
00QD*	Repair/Medulla Oblongata 414
0DQV*	Repair/Mesentery 112, 123, 334
0PQQ*	Repair/Metacarpal, Lt 150
0PQP*	Repair/Metacarpal, Rt 150
0RQT*	Repair/Metacarpocarpal Jt, Lt 28, 147
0RQS*	Repair/Metacarpocarpal Jt, Rt 28, 147
0RQV*	Repair/Metacarpophalangeal Jt, Lt 28, 147
0RQU*	Repair/Metacarpophalangeal Jt, Rt 28, 147
0SQN*	Repair/Metatarsal-Phalangeal Jt, Lt 158
0SQM*	Repair/Metatarsal-Phalangeal Jt, Rt 158
0SQL*	Repair/Metatarsal-Tarsal Jt, Lt 158
0SQK*	Repair/Metatarsal-Tarsal Jt, Rt 158
0QQP*	Repair/Metatarsal, Lt 145, 348
0QQN*	Repair/Metatarsal, Rt 145, 348
0XQR*	Repair/Mid Finger, Lt 29
0XQQ*	Repair/Mid Finger, Rt 29
0BQ5*	Repair/Mid Lobe Bronchus, Rt 331
0CQJ*	Repair/Minor Salivary Gland 57, 332
02QG*	Repair/Mitral Valve 71, 72
0NQB*	Repair/Nasal Bone 54, 154
09QM*	Repair/Nasal Septum 52, 153, 330
09QL*	Repair/Nasal Turbinate 52, 330
09QN*	Repair/Nasopharynx 25, 52, 330

0WQ6*	Repair/Neck 55, 356
0KQ3*	Repair/Neck Muscle, Lt 27, 140, 339
0KQ2*	Repair/Neck Muscle, Rt 27, 140, 339
0HQX*	Repair/Nipple, Lt 222, 336
0HQW*	Repair/Nipple, Rt 222, 336
09QK*	Repair/Nose 52, 153, 330
0NQ8*	Repair/Occipital Bone, Lt 10, 49, 154, 415
0NQ7*	Repair/Occipital Bone, Rt 10, 49, 154, 415
0RQ0*	Repair/Occipital-cervical Jt 157
00QH*	Repair/Oculomotor Nerve 23, 50
00QF*	Repair/Olfactory Nerve 23, 50
00QG*	Repair/Optic Nerve 23, 50
0NQQ*	Repair/Orbit, Lt 42, 49
0NQP*	Repair/Orbit, Rt 42, 49
0UQ2*	Repair/Ovaries, Bilat 263, 264, 266, 354
0UQ1*	Repair/Ovary, Lt 263, 264, 266, 354
0UQ0*	Repair/Ovary, Rt 263, 264, 266, 354
0NQL*	Repair/Palatine Bone, Lt 49
0NQK*	Repair/Palatine Bone, Rt 49
0FQG*	Repair/Pancreas 119
0FQD*	Repair/Pancreatic Duct 119
0FQF*	Repair/Pancreatic Duct, Accessory 119
0GQR*	Repair/Parathyroid Gland 238
0GQQ*	Repair/Parathyroid Glands, Multi 238
0NQ4*	Repair/Parietal Bone, Lt 10, 49, 154, 415
0NQ3*	Repair/Parietal Bone, Rt 10, 49, 154, 415
0CQC*	Repair/Parotid Duct, Lt 57, 332
0CQB*	Repair/Parotid Duct, Rt 57, 332
0CQ9*	Repair/Parotid Gland, Lt 57, 332
0CQ8*	Repair/Parotid Gland, Rt 57, 332
0QQ3*	Repair/Pelvic Bone, Lt 156
0QQ2*	Repair/Pelvic Bone, Rt 156
0VQS*	Repair/Penis 257, 355
02QN*	Repair/Pericardium 320
0MQK*	Repair/Perineum Bursa & Lgmt 144
0KQM*	Repair/Perineum Muscle 27, 140, 339
0LQH*	Repair/Perineum Tndn 28, 142, 341
0WQM*	Repair/Perineum, Male 356
0DQW*	Repair/Peritoneum 112, 123, 334
04QU*	Repair/Peroneal Artery, Lt 240
04QT*	Repair/Peroneal Artery, Rt 240
01QH*	Repair/Peroneal Nerve 152, 319
0CQM*	Repair/Pharynx 25, 53, 332
01Q2*	Repair/Phrenic Nerve 152, 319
0GQ1*	Repair/Pineal Body 235
0GQ0*	Repair/Pituitary Gland 235
0BQP*	Repair/Pleura, Lt 331
0BQN*	Repair/Pleura, Rt 331
00QB*	Repair/Pons 414
04QN*	Repair/Popliteal Artery, Lt 240
04QM*	Repair/Popliteal Artery, Rt 240
06Q8*	Repair/Portal Vein 89
04QS*	Repair/Posterior Tibial Artery, Lt 240
04QR*	Repair/Posterior Tibial Artery, Rt 240
0VQT*	Repair/Prepuce 257, 355
0VQ0*	Repair/Prostate 260, 355, 440
01QC*	Repair/Pudendal Nerve 152, 319
02QR*	Repair/Pulmn Artery, Lt 63, 80, 320
02QQ*	Repair/Pulmn Artery, Rt 63, 80, 320
02QP*	Repair/Pulmn Trunk 63, 80, 320
02QH*	Repair/Pulmn Valve 71, 72
02QT*	Repair/Pulmn Vein, Lt 88, 320
02QS*	Repair/Pulmn Vein, Rt 88, 320
03QC*	Repair/Radial Artery, Lt 239
03QB*	Repair/Radial Artery, Rt 239
01Q6*	Repair/Radial Nerve 152, 319
0PQJ*	Repair/Radius, Lt 148, 346
0PQH*	Repair/Radius, Rt 148, 346
0DQP*	Repair/Rectum 107, 334
06QB*	Repair/Renal Vein, Lt 89

Ø6Q9*	Repair/Renal Vein, Rt 89
ØPQ2*	Repair/Rib, Lt 66, 155, 346
ØPQ1*	Repair/Rib, Rt 66, 155, 346
ØXQT*	Repair/Ring Finger, Lt 29
ØXQS*	Repair/Ring Finger, Rt 29
Ø1QR*	Repair/Sacral Nerve 319
Ø1QQ*	Repair/Sacral Plexus 152, 319
ØSQ5*	Repair/Sacrococcygeal Jt 157
ØSQ8*	Repair/Sacroiliac Jt, Lt 157
ØSQ7*	Repair/Sacroiliac Jt, Rt 157
ØQQ1*	Repair/Sacrum 156
ØPQ6*	Repair/Scapula, Lt 66, 155, 346
ØPQ5*	Repair/Scapula, Rt 66, 155, 346
Ø1QF*	Repair/Sciatic Nerve 152, 319
ØVQ2*	Repair/Seminal Vesicle, Lt 260
ØVQ1*	Repair/Seminal Vesicle, Rt 260
ØVQ3*	Repair/Seminal Vesicles, Bilat 260
ØMQ2*	Repair/Shldr Bursa & Lgmt, Lt 144, 343
ØMQ1*	Repair/Shldr Bursa & Lgmt, Rt 144, 343
ØRQK*	Repair/Shldr Jt, Lt 148, 350
ØRQJ*	Repair/Shldr Jt, Rt 148, 350
ØKQ6*	Repair/Shldr Muscle, Lt 27, 140, 242, 339
ØKQ5*	Repair/Shldr Muscle, Rt 27, 140, 242, 339
ØLQ2*	Repair/Shldr Tndn, Lt 148, 341
ØLQ1*	Repair/Shldr Tndn, Rt 148, 341
ØDQN*	Repair/Sigmoid Colon 107, 334
ØNQØ*	Repair/Skull 10, 49, 154, 415
ØDQ8*	Repair/Sm Intestine 107, 334
ØCQ3*	Repair/Soft Palate 25, 53, 332
ØVQG*	Repair/Spermatic Cord, Lt 258, 355
ØVQF*	Repair/Spermatic Cord, Rt 258, 355
ØVQH*	Repair/Spermatic Cords, Bilat 258, 355
ØNQD*	Repair/Sphenoid Bone, Lt 49
ØNQC*	Repair/Sphenoid Bone, Rt 49
Ø9QX*	Repair/Sphenoid Sinus, Lt 56
Ø9QW*	Repair/Sphenoid Sinus, Rt 56
ØØQT*	Repair/Spinal Meninges 159, 160
Ø7QP*	Repair/Spleen 290, 329
Ø6Q1*	Repair/Splenic Vein 89
ØJQ8*	Repair/SQ Tissue & Fascia, Abd 138, 337
ØJQ4*	Repair/SQ Tissue & Fascia, Ant Neck 138, 337
ØJQ7*	Repair/SQ Tissue & Fascia, Back 138, 337
ØJQ9*	Repair/SQ Tissue & Fascia, Buttock 138, 337
ØJQ6*	Repair/SQ Tissue & Fascia, Chest 138, 337
ØJQ1*	Repair/SQ Tissue & Fascia, Face 138, 337
ØJQR*	Repair/SQ Tissue & Fascia, Lt Foot 138, 242, 337
ØJQK*	Repair/SQ Tissue & Fascia, Lt Hand 26, 149
ØJQH*	Repair/SQ Tissue & Fascia, Lt Lwr Arm 138, 242, 337
ØJQP*	Repair/SQ Tissue & Fascia, Lt Lwr Leg 138, 242, 337
ØJQF*	Repair/SQ Tissue & Fascia, Lt Upr Arm 138, 242, 337
ØJQM*	Repair/SQ Tissue & Fascia, Lt Upr Leg 138, 242, 337
ØJQC*	Repair/SQ Tissue & Fascia, Pelvic Region 107, 138, 249, 267, 337
ØJQB*	Repair/SQ Tissue & Fascia, Perineum 138, 242, 337
ØJQ5*	Repair/SQ Tissue & Fascia, Posterior Neck 138, 337
ØJQQ*	Repair/SQ Tissue & Fascia, Rt Foot 138, 242, 337
ØJQJ*	Repair/SQ Tissue & Fascia, Rt Hand 26, 149
ØJQG*	Repair/SQ Tissue & Fascia, Rt Lwr Arm 138, 242, 337
ØJQN*	Repair/SQ Tissue & Fascia, Rt Lwr Leg 138, 242, 337
ØJQD*	Repair/SQ Tissue & Fascia, Rt Upr Arm 138, 242, 337
ØJQL*	Repair/SQ Tissue & Fascia, Rt Upr Leg 138, 242, 337
ØJQØ*	Repair/SQ Tissue & Fascia, Scalp 26, 138, 337
ØRQF*	Repair/Sternoclavicular Jt, Lt 148, 350
ØRQE*	Repair/Sternoclavicular Jt, Rt 148, 350
ØPQØ*	Repair/Sternum 66, 155, 346
ØDQ6*	Repair/Stomach 106, 236, 334
ØDQ7*	Repair/Stomach, Pylorus 106
Ø3Q4*	Repair/Subclavian Artery, Lt 63
Ø3Q3*	Repair/Subclavian Artery, Rt 63
Ø5Q6*	Repair/Subclavian Vein, Lt 88
Ø5Q5*	Repair/Subclavian Vein, Rt 88
ØCQF*	Repair/Sublingual Gland, Lt 57, 332
ØCQD*	Repair/Sublingual Gland, Rt 57, 332
ØCQH*	Repair/Submaxillary Gland, Lt 57, 332
ØCQG*	Repair/Submaxillary Gland, Rt 57, 332
Ø6Q5*	Repair/Superior Mesenteric Vein 89
ØGQM*	Repair/Superior Parathyroid Gland, Lt 238
ØGQL*	Repair/Superior Parathyroid Gland, Rt 238
Ø2QV*	Repair/Superior Vena Cava 88, 320
ØSQJ*	Repair/Tarsal Jt, Lt 157
ØSQH*	Repair/Tarsal Jt, Rt 157
ØQQM*	Repair/Tarsal, Lt 145, 348
ØQQL*	Repair/Tarsal, Rt 145, 348
Ø3QT*	Repair/Temporal Artery, Lt 21
Ø3QS*	Repair/Temporal Artery, Rt 21
ØNQ6*	Repair/Temporal Bone, Lt 10, 49, 154, 415
ØNQ5*	Repair/Temporal Bone, Rt 10, 49, 154, 415
ØVQC*	Repair/Testes, Bilat 258, 355
ØVQB*	Repair/Testis, Lt 258, 355
ØVQ9*	Repair/Testis, Rt 258, 355
ØØQ9*	Repair/Thalamus 414
Ø2QW*	Repair/Thoracic Aorta 63, 320
Ø7QK*	Repair/Thoracic Duct 60, 329
Ø1Q8*	Repair/Thoracic Nerve 152, 319
ØØQX*	Repair/Thoracic Spinal Cord 159, 160
ØRQ6*	Repair/Thoracic Vert Jt 157
ØPQ4*	Repair/Thoracic Vertebra 155
ØRQA*	Repair/Thoracolumbar Vert Jt 157
ØMQG*	Repair/Thorax Bursa & Lgmt, Lt 144
ØMQF*	Repair/Thorax Bursa & Lgmt, Rt 144
ØKQJ*	Repair/Thorax Muscle, Lt 27, 140, 339
ØKQH*	Repair/Thorax Muscle, Rt 27, 140, 339
ØLQD*	Repair/Thorax Tndn, Lt 28, 142, 341
ØLQC*	Repair/Thorax Tndn, Rt 28, 142, 341
ØPQS*	Repair/Thumb Phalanx, Lt 155
ØPQR*	Repair/Thumb Phalanx, Rt 155
ØXQM*	Repair/Thumb, Lt 29
ØXQL*	Repair/Thumb, Rt 29
Ø7QM*	Repair/Thymus 60, 241, 329
ØGQK*	Repair/Thyroid Gland 238, 336
ØGQJ*	Repair/Thyroid Gland Isthmus 238, 336
ØGQG*	Repair/Thyroid Gland Lobe, Lt 238, 336
ØGQH*	Repair/Thyroid Gland Lobe, Rt 238, 336
ØQQH*	Repair/Tibia, Lt 133, 348
ØQQG*	Repair/Tibia, Rt 133, 348
Ø1QG*	Repair/Tibial Nerve 152, 319
ØSQQ*	Repair/Toe Phalangeal Jt, Lt 158
ØSQP*	Repair/Toe Phalangeal Jt, Rt 158
ØQQR*	Repair/Toe Phalanx, Lt 156, 348
ØQQQ*	Repair/Toe Phalanx, Rt 156, 348
ØCQ7*	Repair/Tongue 56
ØKQ4*	Repair/Tongue, Palate, Pharynx Muscle 27, 140, 339
ØCQP*	Repair/Tonsils 53
ØBQ1*	Repair/Trachea 52, 90, 331
Ø2QJ*	Repair/Tricuspid Valve 71, 72
ØØQK*	Repair/Trigeminal Nerve 23, 50
ØØQJ*	Repair/Trochlear Nerve 23, 50
ØMQD*	Repair/Trunk Bursa & Lgmt, Lt 144
ØMQC*	Repair/Trunk Bursa & Lgmt, Rt 144
ØKQG*	Repair/Trunk Muscle, Lt 27, 140, 339
ØKQF*	Repair/Trunk Muscle, Rt 27, 140, 339
ØLQB*	Repair/Trunk Tndn, Lt 28, 142, 341
ØLQ9*	Repair/Trunk Tndn, Rt 28, 142, 341
Ø9Q8*	Repair/Tympanic Membrane, Lt 52
Ø9Q7*	Repair/Tympanic Membrane, Rt 52
ØPQL*	Repair/Ulna, Lt 148, 346
ØPQK*	Repair/Ulna, Rt 148, 346
Ø3QA*	Repair/Ulnar Artery, Lt 239
Ø3Q9*	Repair/Ulnar Artery, Rt 239
Ø1Q4*	Repair/Ulnar Nerve 152, 319

ØKQ8*	Repair/Upr Arm Muscle, Lt 27, 140, 242, 339
ØKQ7*	Repair/Upr Arm Muscle, Rt 27, 140, 242, 339
ØLQ4*	Repair/Upr Arm Tndn, Lt 28, 142, 341
ØLQ3*	Repair/Upr Arm Tndn, Rt 28, 142, 341
Ø3QY*	Repair/Upr Artery 110, 122, 239, 251
ØWQK*	Repair/Upr Back 356
ØMQB*	Repair/Upr Extr Bursa & Lgmt, Lt 144
ØMQ9*	Repair/Upr Extr Bursa & Lgmt, Rt 144
ØQQ7*	Repair/Upr Femur, Lt 130, 348, 415
ØQQ6*	Repair/Upr Femur, Rt 130, 348, 415
ØWQ4*	Repair/Upr Jaw 55, 356
ØKQR*	Repair/Upr Leg Muscle, Lt 140, 339
ØKQQ*	Repair/Upr Leg Muscle, Rt 140, 339
ØLQM*	Repair/Upr Leg Tndn, Lt 28, 142, 341
ØLQL*	Repair/Upr Leg Tndn, Rt 28, 142, 341
ØYQD*	Repair/Upr Leg, Lt 357
ØYQC*	Repair/Upr Leg, Rt 357
ØBQ8*	Repair/Upr Lobe Bronchus, Lt 331
ØBQ4*	Repair/Upr Lobe Bronchus, Rt 331
Ø5QY*	Repair/Upr Vein 86, 111, 122, 241, 252
ØTQ7*	Repair/Ureter, Lt 109, 249, 260, 268, 354
ØTQ6*	Repair/Ureter, Rt 109, 249, 354
ØTQD*	Repair/Urethra 257, 354
ØUQ4*	Repair/Uterine Supporting Structure 267, 354
ØUQ9*	Repair/Uterus 109, 263, 264, 266, 272, 354
ØCQN*	Repair/Uvula 56
ØUQG*	Repair/Vagina 354
ØØQQ*	Repair/Vagus Nerve 23, 50
ØVQQ*	Repair/Vas Deferens, Bilat 258, 355
ØVQP*	Repair/Vas Deferens, Lt 258, 355
ØVQN*	Repair/Vas Deferens, Rt 258, 355
Ø2QL*	Repair/Ventricle, Lt 320
Ø2QK*	Repair/Ventricle, Rt 320
Ø3QQ*	Repair/Vert Artery, Lt 21
Ø3QP*	Repair/Vert Artery, Rt 21
Ø5QS*	Repair/Vert Vein, Lt 22, 88
Ø5QR*	Repair/Vert Vein, Rt 22, 88
ØUQL*	Repair/Vestibular Gland 267, 272
ØCQV*	Repair/Vocal Cord, Lt 53, 65, 332
ØCQT*	Repair/Vocal Cord, Rt 53, 65, 332
ØUQM*	Repair/Vulva 109, 267, 354
ØMQ6*	Repair/Wrist Bursa & Lgmt, Lt 144, 343
ØMQ5*	Repair/Wrist Bursa & Lgmt, Rt 144, 343
ØRQP*	Repair/Wrist Jt, Lt 28, 147
ØRQN*	Repair/Wrist Jt, Rt 28, 147
ØNQN*	Repair/Zygomatic Bone, Lt 49
ØNQM*	Repair/Zygomatic Bone, Rt 49
ØJR437Z	Replace Ant Neck SQ/Fascia w Autol Sub, Perc 236
ØHR8X73	Replace Buttock Skin w Autol Sub, Full Thick, Extern 113
ØJR937Z	Replace Buttock SQ/Fascia w Autol Sub, Perc 236
ØHRGX74	Replace Lt Hand Skin w Autol Sub, Part Thick, Extern 450
ØJRKØKZ	Replace Lt Hand SQ/Fascia w Nonaut Sub, Opn 149
ØJRK3KZ	Replace Lt Hand SQ/Fascia w Nonaut Sub, Perc 149
ØSRUØJ9	Replace Lt Knee Jt, Femor w Synth Sub, Cement, Opn 128, 245
ØSRUØJA	Replace Lt Knee Jt, Femor w Synth Sub, Uncement, Opn 128, 245
ØJRH37Z	Replace Lt Low Arm SQ/Fascia w Autol Sub, Perc 236
ØJRP37Z	Replace Lt Low Leg SQ/Fascia w Autol Sub, Perc 236
ØJRF37Z	Replace Lt Up Arm SQ/Fascia w Autol Sub, Perc 236
ØJRM37Z	Replace Lt Up Leg SQ/Fascia w Autol Sub, Perc 236
ØJR[7,8,9,B,C]37Z	Replace of [Back, Abd, Buttock, Perineum, Pelvic Rgn] SQ Tissue & Fascia w/ Auto Tissue Sub, Perc Appr 54
ØHR[5,6,7]X74	Replace of [Chest, Back, Abd] Skin w/ Auto Tissue Sub, Partial Thickness, Ext Appr 65
ØJR[D,F,G,H,J,K]37Z	Replace of [Rt Upr Arm, Lt Upr Arm, Rt Lwr Arm, Lt Lwr Arm, Rt Hand, Lt Hand] SQ Tissue & Fascia w/ Auto Tissue Sub, Perc Appr 54
Ø8R[8,9]X7Z	Replace of [Rt, Lt] Cornea w/ Auto Tissue Sub, Ext Appr 43
ØJR[Ø,1,4,5,6]37Z	Replace of [Scalp, Face, Ant Neck, Post Neck, Chest] SQ Tissue & Fascia w/ Auto Tissue Sub, Perc Appr 54
ØHR7XJZ	Replace of Abd Skin with Synth Sub, Extern Appr 113, 236, 313, 377
ØJR837Z	Replace of Abd SQ/Fascia with Autol Sub, Perc Appr 236
Ø2RFØ7Z	Replace of Aortic Valve with Autol Sub, Opn Appr 71, 72
Ø2RF47Z	Replace of Aortic Valve with Autol Sub, Perc Endo Appr 71, 72
Ø2RFØKZ	Replace of Aortic Valve with Nonaut Sub, Opn Appr 71, 72
Ø2RF4KZ	Replace of Aortic Valve with Nonaut Sub, Perc Endo Appr 71, 72
Ø2RFØJZ	Replace of Aortic Valve with Synth Sub, Opn Appr 71, 72
Ø2RF4JZ	Replace of Aortic Valve with Synth Sub, Perc Endo Appr 71, 72
Ø2RFØ8Z	Replace of Aortic Valve with Zooplastic, Opn Appr 71, 72
Ø2RF48Z	Replace of Aortic Valve with Zooplastic, Perc Endo Appr 71, 72
ØHR6XJZ	Replace of Back Skin with Synth Sub, Extern Appr 113, 236, 313, 377
ØJR737Z	Replace of Back SQ/Fascia with Autol Sub, Perc Appr 236
ØHRV37Z	Replace of Bi Breast with Autol Sub, Perc Appr 223
ØHRVØKZ	Replace of Bi Breast with Nonaut Sub, Opn Appr 222
ØHRVXJZ	Replace of Bi Breast with Synth Sub, Extern Appr 222
ØHRVØJZ	Replace of Bi Breast with Synth Sub, Opn Appr 221, 222, 337
ØHRV3JZ	Replace of Bi Breast with Synth Sub, Perc Appr 221, 337
ØHR8XJZ	Replace of Buttock Skin with Synth Sub, Extern Appr 236, 313, 377
ØRR5ØJZ	Replace of C-thor Disc with Synth Sub, Opn Appr 20, 159, 160, 161, 350
ØRR3ØJZ	Replace of Cerv Disc with Synth Sub, Opn Appr 20, 159, 160, 161, 350
ØHR5XJZ	Replace of Chest Skin with Synth Sub, Extern Appr 113, 236, 313, 377
ØJR637Z	Replace of Chest SQ/Fascia with Autol Sub, Perc Appr 236
ØHR1XJZ	Replace of Face Skin with Synth Sub, Extern Appr 236, 313, 377
ØJR1Ø7Z	Replace of Face SQ/Fascia with Autol Sub, Opn Appr 48
ØJR137Z	Replace of Face SQ/Fascia with Autol Sub, Perc Appr 236
ØHRAXJZ	Replace of Genitalia Skin with Synth Sub, Extern Appr 236, 313, 378
ØHRU37Z	Replace of Lt Breast with Autol Sub, Perc Appr 223
ØHRUØKZ	Replace of Lt Breast with Nonaut Sub, Opn Appr 221, 222, 337
ØHRUXJZ	Replace of Lt Breast with Synth Sub, Extern Appr 222
ØHRUØJZ	Replace of Lt Breast with Synth Sub, Opn Appr 221, 222, 337
ØHRU3JZ	Replace of Lt Breast with Synth Sub, Perc Appr 221, 337
Ø8R937Z	Replace of Lt Cornea with Autol Sub, Perc Appr 44
ØHR3XJZ	Replace of Lt Ear Skin with Synth Sub, Extern Appr 212, 450
Ø8R1ØKZ	Replace of Lt Eye with Nonaut Sub, Opn Appr 43, 241
Ø8R13JZ	Replace of Lt Eye with Synth Sub, Perc Appr 43, 241
ØHRNXJZ	Replace of Lt Foot Skin with Synth Sub, Extern Appr 237, 313, 378
ØJRR37Z	Replace of Lt Foot SQ/Fascia with Autol Sub, Perc Appr 236
ØHRGXJZ	Replace of Lt Hand Skin with Synth Sub, Extern Appr 313, 378
ØJRKØ7Z	Replace of Lt Hand SQ/Fascia with Autol Sub, Opn Appr 26, 149, 314
ØJRK37Z	Replace of Lt Hand SQ/Fascia with Autol Sub, Perc Appr 236, 338
ØJRKØJZ	Replace of Lt Hand SQ/Fascia with Synth Sub, Opn Appr 149
ØJRK3JZ	Replace of Lt Hand SQ/Fascia with Synth Sub, Perc Appr 149
Ø8RK3ØZ	Replace of Lt Lens with Intraoc Telescp, Perc Appr 445
ØHREXJZ	Replace of Lt Low Arm Skin with Synth Sub, Extern Appr 236, 313, 378
ØHRLXJZ	Replace of Lt Low Leg Skin with Synth Sub, Extern Appr 236, 313, 378
ØXRMØ7P	Replace of Lt Thumb with Lt Toe, Autol Sub, Opn Appr 147
ØXRM47P	Replace of Lt Thumb with Lt Toe, Autol Sub, Perc Endo Appr 147
ØXRMØ7N	Replace of Lt Thumb with Rt Toe, Autol Sub, Opn Appr 147
ØXRM47N	Replace of Lt Thumb with Rt Toe, Autol Sub, Perc Endo Appr 147
ØHRCXJZ	Replace of Lt Up Arm Skin with Synth Sub, Extern Appr 236, 313, 378
ØHRJXJZ	Replace of Lt Up Leg Skin with Synth Sub, Extern Appr 236, 313, 378
ØCRV87Z	Replace of Lt Vocal Cord with Autol Sub, Endo 448
ØSR2ØJZ	Replace of Lum Disc with Synth Sub, Opn Appr 20, 159, 160, 161, 352

0SR40JZ	Replace of Lumsac Disc with Synth Sub, Opn Appr **20, 160, 161, 352**
0HR4XJZ	Replace of Neck Skin with Synth Sub, Extern Appr **236, 313, 377**
09RK07Z	Replace of Nose with Autol Sub, Opn Appr **90**
0JRC37Z	Replace of Pelvic SQ/Fascia with Autol Sub, Perc Appr **236**
0HR9XJZ	Replace of Perineum Skin with Synth Sub, Extern Appr **450**
02RH47Z	Replace of Pulm Valve with Autol Sub, Perc Endo Appr **71, 72**
02RH0KZ	Replace of Pulm Valve with Nonaut Sub, Opn Appr **71, 72**
02RH4KZ	Replace of Pulm Valve with Nonaut Sub, Perc Endo Appr **71, 72**
02RH4JZ	Replace of Pulm Valve with Synth Sub, Perc Endo Appr **71, 72**
02RH08Z	Replace of Pulm Valve with Zooplastic, Opn Appr **71, 72**
02RH48Z	Replace of Pulm Valve with Zooplastic, Perc Endo Appr **71, 72**
02RH07Z	Replace of Pulmn Valve with Autol Sub, Opn Appr **71, 72**
02RH0JZ	Replace of Pulmn Valve with Synth Sub, Opn Appr **71, 72**
0HRT37Z	Replace of Rt Breast with Autol Sub, Perc Appr **223**
0HRT0KZ	Replace of Rt Breast with Nonaut Sub, Opn Appr **221, 222, 337**
0HRTXJZ	Replace of Rt Breast with Synth Sub, Extern Appr **222**
0HRT0JZ	Replace of Rt Breast with Synth Sub, Opn Appr **221, 222, 337**
0HRT3JZ	Replace of Rt Breast with Synth Sub, Perc Appr **221, 337**
08R837Z	Replace of Rt Cornea with Autol Sub, Perc Appr **44**
0HR2XJZ	Replace of Rt Ear Skin with Synth Sub, Extern Appr **212, 450**
08R00KZ	Replace of Rt Eye with Nonaut Sub, Opn Appr **43, 241**
08R03JZ	Replace of Rt Eye with Synth Sub, Perc Appr **43, 241**
0HRMXJZ	Replace of Rt Foot Skin with Synth Sub, Extern Appr **237, 313, 378**
0JRQ37Z	Replace of Rt Foot SQ/Fascia with Autol Sub, Perc Appr **236**
0HRFXJZ	Replace of Rt Hand Skin with Synth Sub, Extern Appr **313, 378**
0JRJ07Z	Replace of Rt Hand SQ/Fascia with Autol Sub, Opn Appr **26, 149, 314**
0JRJ37Z	Replace of Rt Hand SQ/Fascia with Autol Sub, Perc Appr **236, 338**
0JRJ0JZ	Replace of Rt Hand SQ/Fascia with Synth Sub, Opn Appr **149**
0JRJ3JZ	Replace of Rt Hand SQ/Fascia with Synth Sub, Perc Appr **149**
08RJ30Z	Replace of Rt Lens with Intraoc Telescp, Perc Appr **445**
0HRDXJZ	Replace of Rt Low Arm Skin with Synth Sub, Extern Appr **236, 313, 378**
0HRKXJZ	Replace of Rt Low Leg Skin with Synth Sub, Extern Appr **236, 313, 378**
0XRL07P	Replace of Rt Thumb with Lt Toe, Autol Sub, Opn Appr **147**
0XRL47P	Replace of Rt Thumb with Lt Toe, Autol Sub, Perc Endo Appr **147**
0XRL07N	Replace of Rt Thumb with Rt Toe, Autol Sub, Opn Appr **147**
0XRL47N	Replace of Rt Thumb with Rt Toe, Autol Sub, Perc Endo Appr **147**
0HRBXJZ	Replace of Rt Up Arm Skin with Synth Sub, Extern Appr **236, 313, 378**
0HRHXJZ	Replace of Rt Up Leg Skin with Synth Sub, Extern Appr **236, 313, 378**
0HR0XJZ	Replace of Scalp Skin with Synth Sub, Extern Appr **236, 313, 377**
0JR037Z	Replace of Scalp SQ/Fascia with Autol Sub, Perc Appr **236**
0JR[L,M,N,P,Q,R]37Z	Replace of SQ Tissue & Fascia of [Rt Upr Leg, Lt Upr Leg, Rt Lwr Leg, Lt Lwr Leg, Rt Foot, Lt Foot] w/ Auto Tissue Sub, Perc **54**
0RRB0JZ	Replace of T-lum Disc with Synth Sub, Opn Appr **20, 159, 161, 350**
0RR90JZ	Replace of Thor Disc with Synth Sub, Opn Appr **20, 159, 161, 350**
0JRB37Z	Replace Perineum SQ/Fascia w Autol Sub, Perc **236**
0JR537Z	Replace Post Neck SQ/Fascia w Autol Sub, Perc **236**
0HRFX74	Replace Rt Hand Skin w Autol Sub, Part Thick, Extern **450**
0JRJ0KZ	Replace Rt Hand SQ/Fascia w Nonaut Sub, Opn **149**
0JRJ3KZ	Replace Rt Hand SQ/Fascia w Nonaut Sub, Perc **149**
0SRT0J9	Replace Rt Knee Jt, Femor w Synth Sub, Cement, Opn **128, 245**
0SRT0JA	Replace Rt Knee Jt, Femor w Synth Sub, Uncement, Opn **128, 245**
0SRV0J9	Replace Rt Knee Jt, Tibial w Synth Sub, Cement, Opn **128, 245**
0SRV0JA	Replace Rt Knee Jt, Tibial w Synth Sub, Uncement, Opn **128, 245**
0JRG37Z	Replace Rt Low Arm SQ/Fascia w Autol Sub, Perc **236**
0JRN37Z	Replace Rt Low Leg SQ/Fascia w Autol Sub, Perc **236**
0JRD37Z	Replace Rt Up Arm SQ/Fascia w Autol Sub, Perc **236**

0JRL37Z	Replace Rt Up Leg SQ/Fascia w Autol Sub, Perc **236**
04R0*	Replace/Abd Aorta **324**
04R0[0,4][7,J,K]Z	Replace/Abd Aorta, [Opn Perc Endo], [Auto Tissue Sub, Synth Sub, Nonauto Tissue Sub], NQ **92**
0LRG*	Replace/Abd Tndn, Lt **142, 341**
0LRF*	Replace/Abd Tndn, Rt **142, 341**
0QR5[0,3,4]JZ	Replace/Acetab, Lt, [Opn, Perc, Perc Endo], Synth Sub, NQ **348**
0QR4[0,3,4]JZ	Replace/Acetab, Rt, [Opn, Perc, Perc Endo], Synth Sub, NQ **348**
0QR5*	Replace/Acetabulum, Lt **156**
0QR4*	Replace/Acetabulum, Rt **156**
0RRH*	Replace/Acromioclavicular Jt, Lt **131, 350**
0RRG*	Replace/Acromioclavicular Jt, Rt **131, 350**
0FRC*	Replace/Ampulla of Vater **120**
0DRR*	Replace/Anal Sphincter **110**
0DRR[0,4][7,J,K]Z	Replace/Anal Sphincter, [Opn, Perc Endo], [Auto Tissue Sub, Synth Sub, Nonauto Tissue Sub], NQ **211, 449**
0SRG*	Replace/Ankle Jt, Lt **126, 128, 352**
0SRF*	Replace/Ankle Jt, Rt **126, 128, 352**
0LRT*	Replace/Ankle Tndn, Lt **142, 341**
0LRS*	Replace/Ankle Tndn, Rt **142, 341**
04RQ*	Replace/Ant Tibial Artery, Lt **84, 240, 324**
04RP*	Replace/Ant Tibial Artery, Rt **84, 240, 324**
02RF3[7,8,J,K]Z	Replace/Aortic Valve, [Opn, Perc, Perc Endo], [Auto Tissue Sub, Zooplastic Tissue, Synth Sub, Nonauto Tissue Sub], NQ **92**
02RF3[7,8,J,K]H	Replace/Aortic Valve, Perc, [Auto Tissue Sub, Zooplastic Tissue, Synth Sub, Nonauto Tissue Sub], Transapical **92**
02R5*	Replace/Atrial Septum **320**
02R5[0,4][7,8,J,K]Z	Replace/Atrial Septum, [Opn, Perc Endo], [Auto Tissue Sub, Zooplastic Tissue, Synth Sub, Nonauto Tissue Sub], NQ **93**
02R7*	Replace/Atrium, Lt **320**
02R7[0,4][7,8,J,K]Z	Replace/Atrium, Lt, [Opn, Perc Endo], [Auto Tissue Sub, Zooplastic Tissue, Synth Sub, Nonauto Tissue Sub], NQ **93**
02R6*	Replace/Atrium, Rt **320**
02R6[0,4][7,8,J,K]Z	Replace/Atrium, Rt, [Opn, Perc Endo], [Auto Tissue Sub, Zooplastic Tissue, Synth Sub, Nonauto Tissue Sub], NQ **93**
09RA0[7,J,K]Z	Replace/Auditory Ossicle, Lt, Opn, [Auto Tissue Sub, Synth Sub, Nonauto Tissue Sub], NQ **447**
09R90[7,J,K]Z	Replace/Auditory Ossicle, Rt, Opn, [Auto Tissue Sub, Synth Sub, Nonauto Tissue Sub], NQ **447**
03R6*	Replace/Axillary Artery, Lt **82, 321**
03R5*	Replace/Axillary Artery, Rt **82, 321**
05R8*	Replace/Axillary Vein, Lt **86, 326**
05R7*	Replace/Axillary Vein, Rt **86, 326**
05R0*	Replace/Azygos Vein **60, 326**
05R0[0,4][7,J,K]Z	Replace/Azygos Vein, [Opn, Perc Endo], [Auto Tissue Sub, Synth Sub, Nonauto Tissue Sub], NQ **71, 72**
05RC*	Replace/Basilic Vein, Lt **86, 326**
05RB*	Replace/Basilic Vein, Rt **86, 326**
0TRB*	Replace/Bladder **248, 354**
0TRC*	Replace/Bladder Neck **248, 354**
03R8*	Replace/Brachial Artery, Lt **82, 321**
03R7*	Replace/Brachial Artery, Rt **82, 321**
05RA*	Replace/Brachial Vein, Lt **86, 326**
05R9*	Replace/Brachial Vein, Rt **86, 326**
0HRVX[7,K]Z	Replace/Breast, Bilat, Ext, [Auto Tissue Sub, Nonauto Tissue Sub], NQ **206, 313, 378, 380**
0HRV07[5,6,7,8,9,Z]	Replace/Breast, Bilat, Opn, Auto Tissue Sub, [Latissimus Dorsi Myocutaneous Flap, Transv Rectus Abdominis Myocutaneous Flap, Deep Inferior Epigastric Artery Perforator Flap, Superf Inferior Epigastric Artery Flap, Gluteal Artery Perforator Flap, NQ] **222**
0HRV07[5,6,7,8,9]	Replace/Breast, Bilat, Opn, Auto Tissue Sub, [Latissimus Dorsi Myocutaneous Flap, Transv Rectus Abdominis Myocutaneous Flap, Deep Inferior Epigastric Artery Perforator Flap, Superf Inferior Epigastric Artery Flap, Gluteal Artery Perforator Flap] **221, 337**
0HRV3[7,J,K]Z	Replace/Breast, Bilat, Perc, [Auto Tissue Sub, Synth Sub, Nonauto Tissue Sub], NQ **222**
0HRUX[7,K]Z	Replace/Breast, Lt, Ext, [Auto Tissue Sub, Nonauto Tissue Sub], NQ **206, 313, 378, 380**

08RRØ[Ø,3][7,J,K]Z	Replace/Eye, Rt, [Opn, Perc], [Auto Tissue Sub, Synth Sub, Nonauto Tissue Sub], NQ 445
08RRØØ[7,J]Z	Replace/Eye, Rt, Opn, [Auto Tissue Sub, Synth Sub], NQ 42
08RRØ3[7,K]Z	Replace/Eye, Rt, Perc, [Auto Tissue Sub, Nonauto Tissue Sub], NQ 42
03RR*	Replace/Face Artery 25, 82
05RV*	Replace/Face Vein, Lt 25, 86
05RT*	Replace/Face Vein, Rt 25, 86
04RL*	Replace/Femor Artery, Lt 84, 240, 324
04RK*	Replace/Femor Artery, Rt 84, 240, 324
0QR9*	Replace/Femor Shaft, Lt 131, 348, 416
0QR8*	Replace/Femor Shaft, Rt 131, 348, 416
06RN*	Replace/Femor Vein, Lt 89, 327
06RM*	Replace/Femor Vein, Rt 89, 327
0QRK*	Replace/Fibula, Lt 133, 348
0QRJ*	Replace/Fibula, Rt 133, 348
0HRQ*	Replace/Finger Nail 336
0HRQX[7,J,K]Z	Replace/Finger Nail, Ext, [Auto Tissue Sub, Synth Sub, Nonauto Tissue Sub], NQ 212, 337
0RRX*	Replace/Finger Phalangeal Jt, Lt 28, 147
0RRXØ[7,J,K]Z	Replace/Finger Phalangeal Jt, Lt, Opn, [Auto Tissue Sub, Synth Sub, Nonauto Tissue Sub], NQ 316
0RRW*	Replace/Finger Phalangeal Jt, Rt 28, 147
0RRWØ[7,J,K]Z	Replace/Finger Phalangeal Jt, Rt, Opn, [Auto Tissue Sub, Synth Sub, Nonauto Tissue Sub], NQ 316
0PRV*	Replace/Finger Phalanx, Lt 155
0PRT*	Replace/Finger Phalanx, Rt 155
04RW*	Replace/Foot Artery, Lt 84, 240, 324
04RV*	Replace/Foot Artery, Rt 84, 240, 324
0LRW*	Replace/Foot Tndn, Lt 142, 341
0LRV*	Replace/Foot Tndn, Rt 142, 341
06RV*	Replace/Foot Vein, Lt 89, 327
06RT*	Replace/Foot Vein, Rt 89, 327
0NR2*	Replace/Frontal Bone, Lt 10, 49, 154
0NR2[Ø,3,4][7,J,K]Z	Replace/Frontal Bone, Lt, [Opn, Perc, Perc Endo], [Auto Tissue Sub, Synth Sub, Nonauto Tissue Sub], NQ 14, 18
0NR2[Ø,3,4]JZ	Replace/Frontal Bone, Lt, [Opn, Perc, Perc Endo], Synth Sub, NQ 344, 415
0NR1*	Replace/Frontal Bone, Rt 10, 49, 154
0NR1[Ø,3,4][7,J,K]Z	Replace/Frontal Bone, Rt, [Opn, Perc, Perc Endo], [Auto Tissue Sub, Synth Sub, Nonauto Tissue Sub], NQ 14, 18
0NR1[Ø,3,4]JZ	Replace/Frontal Bone, Rt, [Opn, Perc, Perc Endo], Synth Sub, NQ 344, 415
04R2*	Replace/Gastric Artery 324
04R2[Ø,4][7,J,K]Z	Replace/Gastric Artery, [Opn, Perc Endo], [Auto Tissue Sub, Synth Sub, Nonauto Tissue Sub], NQ 96
06R2[Ø,4][7,J,K]Z	Replace/Gastric Vein, [Opn, Perc Endo], [Auto Tissue Sub, Synth Sub, Nonauto Tissue Sub], NQ 98
0PR8*	Replace/Glenoid Cavity, Lt 155
0PR8[Ø,3,4]JZ	Replace/Glenoid Cavity, Lt, [Opn, Perc, Perc Endo], Synth Sub, NQ 66, 346
0PR7*	Replace/Glenoid Cavity, Rt 155
0PR7[Ø,3,4]JZ	Replace/Glenoid Cavity, Rt, [Opn, Perc, Perc Endo], Synth Sub, NQ 66, 346
0DRS*	Replace/Greater Omentum 112, 123
0DRS[Ø,4][7,J,K]Z	Replace/Greater Omentum, [Opn, Perc Endo], [Auto Tissue Sub, Synth Sub, Nonauto Tissue Sub], NQ 300
06RQ*	Replace/Greater Saphenous Vein, Lt 89, 327
06RP*	Replace/Greater Saphenous Vein, Rt 89, 327
0HRSX[J,K]Z	Replace/Hair, Ext, [Synth Sub, Nonauto Tissue Sub], NQ 212, 337, 450
03RF*	Replace/Hand Artery, Lt 82, 321
03RD*	Replace/Hand Artery, Rt 82, 321
0LR8*	Replace/Hand Tndn, Lt 28, 150
0LR8[Ø,4][7,J,K]Z	Replace/Hand Tndn, Lt, [Opn, Perc Endo], [Auto Tissue Sub, Synth Sub, Nonauto Tissue Sub], NQ 216, 315
0LR7*	Replace/Hand Tndn, Rt 28, 149
0LR7[Ø,4][7,J,K]Z	Replace/Hand Tndn, Rt, [Opn, Perc Endo], [Auto Tissue Sub, Synth Sub, Nonauto Tissue Sub], NQ 216, 315
05RH*	Replace/Hand Vein, Lt 86, 326
05RG*	Replace/Hand Vein, Rt 86, 326
0CR2*	Replace/Hard Palate 25, 53

0CR2[Ø,3,X][7,J,K]Z	Replace/Hard Palate, [Opn, Perc, Ext], [Auto Tissue Sub, Synth Sub, Nonauto Tissue Sub], NQ 211
0LRØ*	Replace/Head and Neck Tndn 142, 341
05R1*	Replace/Hemiazygos Vein 60, 326
05R1[Ø,4][7,J,K]Z	Replace/Hemiazygos Vein, [Opn, Perc Endo], [Auto Tissue Sub, Synth Sub, Nonauto Tissue Sub], NQ 71, 72
04R3*	Replace/Hepatic Artery 324
04R3[Ø,4][7,J,K]Z	Replace/Hepatic Artery, [Opn, Perc Endo], [Auto Tissue Sub, Synth Sub, Nonauto Tissue Sub], NQ 96
0FR6*	Replace/Hepatic Duct, Lt 120
0FR6[Ø,4]JZ	Replace/Hepatic Duct, Lt, [Opn, Perc Endo], Synth Sub, NQ 301, 449
0FR5*	Replace/Hepatic Duct, Rt 120
0FR5[Ø,4]JZ	Replace/Hepatic Duct, Rt, [Opn, Perc Endo], Synth Sub, NQ 301, 449
06R4[Ø,4][7,J,K]Z	Replace/Hepatic Vein, [Opn, Perc Endo], [Auto Tissue Sub, Synth Sub, Nonauto Tissue Sub], NQ 98
0SRE*	Replace/Hip Jt, Acetabular Surface, Lt 126, 128, 244, 352, 416
0SREØ[Ø,1,3,J][9,A,Z]	Replace/Hip Jt, Acetabular Surface, Lt, Opn, [Synth Sub, Polyethylene, Synth Sub, Metal, Synth Sub, Ceramic, Synth Sub], [Cemented, Uncemented, NQ] 128
0SREØ[Ø,1,3,J][9,A,Z]	Replace/Hip Jt, Acetabular Surface, Lt, Opn, [Synth Sub, Polyethylene, Synth Sub, Metal, Synth Sub, Ceramic, Synth Sub], [Cemented, Uncemented, NQ] 245
0SRA*	Replace/Hip Jt, Acetabular Surface, Rt 126, 128, 244, 352, 416
0SRAØ[Ø,1,3,J][9,A,Z]	Replace/Hip Jt, Acetabular Surface, Rt, Opn, [Synth Sub, Polyethylene, Synth Sub, Metal, Synth Sub, Ceramic, Synth Sub], [Cemented, Uncemented, NQ] 127, 245
0SRS*	Replace/Hip Jt, Femor Surface, Lt 126, 128, 244, 352, 416
0SRSØ[1,3,J][9,A,Z]	Replace/Hip Jt, Femor Surface, Lt, Opn, [Synth Sub, Metal, Synth Sub, Ceramic, Synth Sub], [Cemented, Uncemented, NQ] 128, 245
0SRR*	Replace/Hip Jt, Femor Surface, Rt 126, 128, 244, 352, 416
0SRRØ[1,3,J][9,A,Z]	Replace/Hip Jt, Femor Surface, Rt, Opn, [Synth Sub, Metal, Synth Sub, Ceramic, Synth Sub], [Cemented, Uncemented, NQ] 127, 245
0SRB*	Replace/Hip Jt, Lt 126, 128, 352, 416
0SRBØ[1,2,3,4,J][9,A,Z]	Replace/Hip Jt, Lt, Opn, [Synth Sub, Metal, Synth Sub, Metal on Polyethylene, Synth Sub, Ceramic, Synth Sub, Ceramic on Polyethylene, Synth Sub], [Cemented, Uncemented, NQ] 128, 245
0SR9*	Replace/Hip Jt, Rt 126, 128, 352, 416
0SR9Ø[1,2,3,4,J][9,A,Z]	Replace/Hip Jt, Rt, Opn, [Synth Sub, Metal, Synth Sub, Metal on Polyethylene, Synth Sub, Ceramic, Synth Sub, Ceramic on Polyethylene, Synth Sub], [Cemented, Uncemented, NQ] 127, 245
0LRK*	Replace/Hip Tndn, Lt 142, 341
0LRJ*	Replace/Hip Tndn, Rt 142, 341
0PRD[Ø,3,4][7,J,K]Z	Replace/Humeral Head, Lt, [Opn, Perc, Perc Endo], [Auto Tissue Sub, Nonauto Tissue Sub], NQ 133, 346
0PRD[3,4]JZ	Replace/Humeral Head, Lt, [Perc, Perc Endo], Synth Sub, NQ 133, 346
0PRC[Ø,3,4][7,J,K]Z	Replace/Humeral Head, Rt, [Opn, Perc, Perc Endo], [Auto Tissue Sub, Nonauto Tissue Sub], NQ 133, 346
0PRC[3,4]JZ	Replace/Humeral Head, Rt, [Perc, Perc Endo], Synth Sub, NQ 133, 346
0PRG*	Replace/Humeral Shaft, Lt 133, 346
0PRF*	Replace/Humeral Shaft, Rt 133, 346
0NRX*	Replace/Hyoid Bone 49
0NRX[Ø,3,4]JZ	Replace/Hyoid Bone, [Opn, Perc, Perc Endo], Synth Sub, NQ 42, 154, 344
06RJ[Ø,4][7,J,K]Z	Replace/Hypogastric Vein, Lt, [Opn, Perc Endo], [Auto Tissue Sub, Synth Sub, Nonauto Tissue Sub], NQ 98
06RH[Ø,4][7,J,K]Z	Replace/Hypogastric Vein, Rt, [Opn, Perc Endo], [Auto Tissue Sub, Synth Sub, Nonauto Tissue Sub], NQ 98
04RB*	Replace/Inferior Mesenteric Artery 324
04RB[Ø,4][7,J,K]Z	Replace/Inferior Mesenteric Artery, [Opn, Perc Endo], [Auto Tissue Sub, Synth Sub, Nonauto Tissue Sub], NQ 96
06R6[Ø,4][7,J,K]Z	Replace/Inferior Mesenteric Vein, [Opn, Perc Endo], [Auto Tissue Sub, Synth Sub, Nonauto Tissue Sub], NQ 98
06RØ[Ø,4][7,J,K]Z	Replace/Inferior Vena Cava, [Opn, Perc Endo], [Auto Tissue Sub, Synth Sub, Nonauto Tissue Sub], NQ 98
03R2*	Replace/Innominate Artery 60, 321
03R2[Ø,4][7,J,K]Z	Replace/Innominate Artery, [Opn, Perc Endo], [Auto Tissue Sub, Synth Sub, Nonauto Tissue Sub], NQ 71, 72

05R4*	Replace/Innominate Vein, Lt 60, 326
05R4[0,4][7,J,K]Z	Replace/Innominate Vein, Lt, [Opn, Perc Endo], [Auto Tissue Sub, Synth Sub, Nonauto Tissue Sub], NQ 71, 72
05R3*	Replace/Innominate Vein, Rt 60, 326
05R3[0,4][7,J,K]Z	Replace/Innominate Vein, Rt, [Opn, Perc Endo], [Auto Tissue Sub, Synth Sub, Nonauto Tissue Sub], NQ 71, 72
03RL*	Replace/Int Carotid Artery, Lt 25, 82
03RK*	Replace/Int Carotid Artery, Rt 25, 82
04RF*	Replace/Int Iliac Artery, Lt 324
04RF[0,4][7,J,K]Z	Replace/Int Iliac Artery, Lt, [Opn, Perc Endo], [Auto Tissue Sub, Synth Sub, Nonauto Tissue Sub], NQ 96
04RE*	Replace/Int Iliac Artery, Rt 324
04RE[0,4][7,J,K]Z	Replace/Int Iliac Artery, Rt, [Opn, Perc Endo], [Auto Tissue Sub, Synth Sub, Nonauto Tissue Sub], NQ 96
05RN*	Replace/Int Jugular Vein, Lt 25, 86
05RM*	Replace/Int Jugular Vein, Rt 25, 86
03R1*	Replace/Int Mammary Artery, Lt 60, 321
03R1[0,4][7,J,K]Z	Replace/Int Mammary Artery, Lt, [Opn, Perc Endo], [Auto Tissue Sub, Synth Sub, Nonauto Tissue Sub], NQ 71, 72
03R0*	Replace/Int Mammary Artery, Rt 60, 321
03R0[0,4][7,J,K]Z	Replace/Int Mammary Artery, Rt, [Opn, Perc Endo], [Auto Tissue Sub, Synth Sub, Nonauto Tissue Sub], NQ 71, 72
03RG*	Replace/Intracranial Artery 321
03RG[0,4][7,J,K]Z	Replace/Intracranial Artery, [Opn, Perc Endo], [Auto Tissue Sub, Synth Sub, Nonauto Tissue Sub], NQ 7, 9, 13, 17
05RL*	Replace/Intracranial Vein 326
05RL[0,4][7,J,K]Z	Replace/Intracranial Vein, [Opn, Perc Endo], [Auto Tissue Sub, Synth Sub, Nonauto Tissue Sub], NQ 7, 9, 13, 17
08RD*	Replace/Iris, Lt 44
08RD3[7,J,K]Z	Replace/Iris, Lt, Perc, [Auto Tissue Sub, Synth Sub, Nonauto Tissue Sub], NQ 445
08RC*	Replace/Iris, Rt 44
08RC3[7,J,K]Z	Replace/Iris, Rt, Perc, [Auto Tissue Sub, Synth Sub, Nonauto Tissue Sub], NQ 445
0TR4*	Replace/Kidney Pelvis, Lt 249
0TR3*	Replace/Kidney Pelvis, Rt 249
0SRU*	Replace/Knee Jt, Femor Surface, Lt 126, 128, 352
0SRU0J[9,A,Z]	Replace/Knee Jt, Femor Surface, Lt, Opn, Synth Sub, [Cemented, Uncemented, NQ] 128, 245
0SRT*	Replace/Knee Jt, Femor Surface, Rt 126, 128, 352
0SRT0J[9,A,Z]	Replace/Knee Jt, Femor Surface, Rt, Opn, Synth Sub, [Cemented, Uncemented, NQ] 128, 245
0SRD*	Replace/Knee Jt, Lt 126, 128, 352
0SRD0J[9,A,Z]	Replace/Knee Jt, Lt, Opn, Synth Sub, [Cemented, Uncemented, NQ] 128, 245
0SRC*	Replace/Knee Jt, Rt 126, 128, 352
0SRC0J[9,A,Z]	Replace/Knee Jt, Rt, Opn, Synth Sub, [Cemented, Uncemented, NQ] 128, 245
0SRW*	Replace/Knee Jt, Tibial Surface, Lt 126, 128, 352
0SRW0J[9,A,Z]	Replace/Knee Jt, Tibial Surface, Lt, Opn, Synth Sub, [Cemented, Uncemented, NQ] 128, 245
0SRV*	Replace/Knee Jt, Tibial Surface, Rt 126, 128, 352
0SRV0J[9,A,Z]	Replace/Knee Jt, Tibial Surface, Rt, Opn, Synth Sub, [Cemented, Uncemented, NQ] 128, 245
0LRR*	Replace/Knee Tndn, Lt 142, 341
0LRQ*	Replace/Knee Tndn, Rt 142, 341
0NRJ*	Replace/Lacrimal Bone, Lt 49
0NRJ[0,3,4]JZ	Replace/Lacrimal Bone, Lt, [Opn, Perc, Perc Endo], Synth Sub, NQ 42, 154, 344
0NRH*	Replace/Lacrimal Bone, Rt 49
0NRH[0,3,4]JZ	Replace/Lacrimal Bone, Rt, [Opn, Perc, Perc Endo], Synth Sub, NQ 42, 154, 344
08RY*	Replace/Lacrimal Duct, Lt 43
08RY[0,3,7,8][7,J,K]Z	Replace/Lacrimal Duct, Lt, [Opn, Perc, Via Natrl or Artfcl Opng, Via Natrl or Artfcl Opng Endo], [Auto Tissue Sub, Synth Sub, Nonauto Tissue Sub], NQ 210, 445
08RX*	Replace/Lacrimal Duct, Rt 43
08RX[0,3,7,8][7,J,K]Z	Replace/Lacrimal Duct, Rt, [Opn, Perc, Via Natrl or Artfcl Opng, Via Natrl or Artfcl Opng Endo], [Auto Tissue Sub, Synth Sub, Nonauto Tissue Sub], NQ 210, 445
0CRS*	Replace/Larynx 53, 65, 332
08RK*	Replace/Lens, Lt 44
08RK3[7,J,K]Z	Replace/Lens, Lt, Perc, [Auto Tissue Sub, Synth Sub, Nonauto Tissue Sub], NQ 445
08RJ*	Replace/Lens, Rt 44
08RJ3[7,J,K]Z	Replace/Lens, Rt, Perc, [Auto Tissue Sub, Synth Sub, Nonauto Tissue Sub], NQ 445
0DRT*	Replace/Lesser Omentum 112, 123
0DRT[0,4][7,J,K]Z	Replace/Lesser Omentum, [Opn, Perc Endo], [Auto Tissue Sub, Synth Sub, Nonauto Tissue Sub], NQ 300
06RS*	Replace/Lesser Saphenous Vein, Lt 89, 327
06RR*	Replace/Lesser Saphenous Vein, Rt 89, 327
0SR20[7,K]Z	Replace/Lumbar Vert Disc, Opn, [Auto Tissue Sub, Nonauto Tissue Sub], NQ 158
0SR00[7,J,K]Z	Replace/Lumbar Vert Jt, Opn, [Auto Tissue Sub, Synth Sub, Nonauto Tissue Sub], NQ 158
0QR0*	Replace/Lumbar Vertebra 156
0SR40[7,K]Z	Replace/Lumbosacral Disc, Opn, [Auto Tissue Sub, Nonauto Tissue Sub], NQ 158
0SR30[7,J,K]Z	Replace/Lumbosacral Jt, Opn, [Auto Tissue Sub, Synth Sub, Nonauto Tissue Sub], NQ 158
0LR6*	Replace/Lwr Arm and Wrist Tndn, Lt 142, 341
0LR5*	Replace/Lwr Arm and Wrist Tndn, Rt 142, 341
04RY*	Replace/Lwr Artery 84, 240, 324
08RR*	Replace/Lwr Eyelid, Lt 43
08RR[0,3,X][7,J,K]Z	Replace/Lwr Eyelid, Lt, [Opn, Perc, Ext], [Auto Tissue Sub, Synth Sub, Nonauto Tissue Sub], NQ 210, 445
08RR[0,3,X]JZ	Replace/Lwr Eyelid, Lt, [Opn, Perc, Ext], Synth Sub, NQ 241
08RQ*	Replace/Lwr Eyelid, Rt 43
08RQ[0,3,X][7,J,K]Z	Replace/Lwr Eyelid, Rt, [Opn, Perc, Ext], [Auto Tissue Sub, Synth Sub, Nonauto Tissue Sub], NQ 210, 445
08RQ[0,3,X]JZ	Replace/Lwr Eyelid, Rt, [Opn, Perc, Ext], Synth Sub, NQ 241
0QRC*	Replace/Lwr Femur, Lt 131, 348, 416
0QRB*	Replace/Lwr Femur, Rt 131, 348, 416
0CR6*	Replace/Lwr Gingiva 56, 332
0LRP*	Replace/Lwr Leg Tndn, Lt 142, 341
0LRN*	Replace/Lwr Leg Tndn, Rt 142, 341
0CR1*	Replace/Lwr Lip 56, 332
0CR1[0,3,X][7,J,K]Z	Replace/Lwr Lip, [Opn, Perc, Ext], [Auto Tissue Sub, Synth Sub, Nonauto Tissue Sub], NQ 211, 448
06RY*	Replace/Lwr Vein 89, 327
0NRV*	Replace/Mandible, Lt 48, 154, 344
0NRT*	Replace/Mandible, Rt 48, 154, 344
0NRS*	Replace/Maxilla, Lt 49, 344
0NRR*	Replace/Maxilla, Rt 49, 344
0DRV*	Replace/Mesentery 112, 123
0DRV[0,4][7,J,K]Z	Replace/Mesentery, [Opn, Perc Endo], [Auto Tissue Sub, Synth Sub, Nonauto Tissue Sub], NQ 300
0PRQ*	Replace/Metacarpal, Lt 150
0PRQ[0,3,4][7,J,K]Z	Replace/Metacarpal, Lt, [Opn, Perc, Perc Endo], [Auto Tissue Sub, Synth Sub, Nonauto Tissue Sub], NQ 315
0PRP*	Replace/Metacarpal, Rt 150
0PRP[0,3,4][7,J,K]Z	Replace/Metacarpal, Rt, [Opn, Perc, Perc Endo], [Auto Tissue Sub, Synth Sub, Nonauto Tissue Sub], NQ 315
0RRT*	Replace/Metacarpocarpal Jt, Lt 28, 147
0RRT0[7,J,K]Z	Replace/Metacarpocarpal Jt, Lt, Opn, [Auto Tissue Sub, Synth Sub, Nonauto Tissue Sub], NQ 316
0RRS*	Replace/Metacarpocarpal Jt, Rt 28, 147
0RRS0[7,J,K]Z	Replace/Metacarpocarpal Jt, Rt, Opn, [Auto Tissue Sub, Synth Sub, Nonauto Tissue Sub], NQ 316
0RRV*	Replace/Metacarpophalangeal Jt, Lt 28, 147
0RRV0[7,J,K]Z	Replace/Metacarpophalangeal Jt, Lt, Opn, [Auto Tissue Sub, Synth Sub, Nonauto Tissue Sub], NQ 316
0RRU*	Replace/Metacarpophalangeal Jt, Rt 28, 147
0RRU0[7,J,K]Z	Replace/Metacarpophalangeal Jt, Rt, Opn, [Auto Tissue Sub, Synth Sub, Nonauto Tissue Sub], NQ 316
0SRN*	Replace/Metatarsal-Phalangeal Jt, Lt 146, 352
0SRN0[7,J,K]Z	Replace/Metatarsal-Phalangeal Jt, Lt, Opn, [Auto Tissue Sub, Synth Sub, Nonauto Tissue Sub], NQ 458
0SRM*	Replace/Metatarsal-Phalangeal Jt, Rt 146, 352
0SRM0[7,J,K]Z	Replace/Metatarsal-Phalangeal Jt, Rt, Opn, [Auto Tissue Sub, Synth Sub, Nonauto Tissue Sub], NQ 458
0SRL*	Replace/Metatarsal-Tarsal Jt, Lt 146, 352
0SRL0[7,J,K]Z	Replace/Metatarsal-Tarsal Jt, Lt, Opn, [Auto Tissue Sub, Synth Sub, Nonauto Tissue Sub], NQ 458

ØSRK*	Replace/Metatarsal-Tarsal Jt, Rt 146, 352
ØSRKØ[7,J,K]Z	Replace/Metatarsal-Tarsal Jt, Rt, Opn, [Auto Tissue Sub, Synth Sub, Nonauto Tissue Sub], NQ 458
ØQRP*	Replace/Metatarsal, Lt 145, 348
ØQRN*	Replace/Metatarsal, Rt 145, 348
Ø9R6Ø[7,J,K]Z	Replace/Mid Ear, Lt, Opn, [Auto Tissue Sub, Synth Sub, Nonauto Tissue Sub], NQ 447
Ø9R5Ø[7,J,K]Z	Replace/Mid Ear, Rt, Opn, [Auto Tissue Sub, Synth Sub, Nonauto Tissue Sub], NQ 447
Ø2RG[Ø,3,4][7,8,J,K]Z	Replace/Mitral Valve, [Opn, Perc, Perc Endo], [Auto Tissue Sub, Zooplastic Tissue, Synth Sub, Nonauto Tissue Sub], NQ 71, 72
Ø2RG3[7,8,J,K]H	Replace/Mitral Valve, Perc, [Auto Tissue Sub, Zooplastic Tissue, Synth Sub, Nonauto Tissue Sub], Transapical 92
ØNRB*	Replace/Nasal Bone 54, 154, 344
ØNRB[Ø,3,4][7,J,K]Z	Replace/Nasal Bone, [Opn, Perc, Perc Endo], [Auto Tissue Sub, Synth Sub, Nonauto Tissue Sub], NQ 216, 454
Ø9RM*	Replace/Nasal Septum 153, 331
Ø9RM[Ø,3,4][7,J,K]Z	Replace/Nasal Septum, [Opn, Perc, Perc Endo], [Auto Tissue Sub, Synth Sub, Nonauto Tissue Sub], NQ 210, 447
Ø9RL*	Replace/Nasal Turbinate 331
Ø9RL[Ø,3,4,7,8][7,J,K]Z	Replace/Nasal Turbinate, [Opn, Perc, Perc Endo, Via Natrl or Artfcl Opng, Via Natrl or Artfcl Opng Endo], [Auto Tissue Sub, Synth Sub, Nonauto Tissue Sub], NQ 210, 447
Ø9RN*	Replace/Nasopharynx 25, 331
Ø9RN[Ø,7,8][7,J,K]Z	Replace/Nasopharynx, [Opn, Via Natrl or Artfcl Opng, Via Natrl or Artfcl Opng Endo], [Auto Tissue Sub, Synth Sub, Nonauto Tissue Sub], NQ 447
ØHRX*	Replace/Nipple, Lt 222, 337
ØHRW*	Replace/Nipple, Rt 222, 337
Ø9RK*	Replace/Nose 153, 331
Ø9RK[Ø,X][7,J,K]Z	Replace/Nose, [Opn, Ext], [Auto Tissue Sub, Synth Sub, Nonauto Tissue Sub], NQ 210, 447
ØNR8*	Replace/Occipital Bone, Lt 10, 49, 154
ØNR8[Ø,3,4][7,J,K]Z	Replace/Occipital Bone, Lt, [Opn, Perc, Perc Endo], [Auto Tissue Sub, Synth Sub, Nonauto Tissue Sub], NQ 14, 18
ØNR8[Ø,3,4]JZ	Replace/Occipital Bone, Lt, [Opn, Perc, Perc Endo], Synth Sub, NQ 344, 415
ØNR7*	Replace/Occipital Bone, Rt 10, 49, 154
ØNR7[Ø,3,4][7,J,K]Z	Replace/Occipital Bone, Rt, [Opn, Perc, Perc Endo], [Auto Tissue Sub, Synth Sub, Nonauto Tissue Sub], NQ 14, 18
ØNR7[Ø,3,4]JZ	Replace/Occipital Bone, Rt, [Opn, Perc, Perc Endo], Synth Sub, NQ 344, 415
ØRRØØ[7,K]Z	Replace/Occipital-cervical Jt, Opn, [Auto Tissue Sub, Synth Sub, Nonauto Tissue Sub], NQ 157
ØNRQ*	Replace/Orbit, Lt 49
ØNRQ[Ø,3,4][7,J]Z	Replace/Orbit, Lt, [Opn, Perc, Perc Endo], [Auto Tissue Sub, Synth Sub], NQ 42, 344, 455
ØNRP*	Replace/Orbit, Rt 49
ØNRP[Ø,3,4][7,J]Z	Replace/Orbit, Rt, [Opn, Perc, Perc Endo], [Auto Tissue Sub, Synth Sub], NQ 42, 344, 454
ØNRL*	Replace/Palatine Bone, Lt 49
ØNRL[Ø,3,4]JZ	Replace/Palatine Bone, Lt, [Opn, Perc, Perc Endo], Synth Sub, NQ 42, 154, 344
ØNRK*	Replace/Palatine Bone, Rt 49
ØNRK[Ø,3,4]JZ	Replace/Palatine Bone, Rt, [Opn, Perc, Perc Endo], Synth Sub, NQ 42, 154, 344
ØFRD*	Replace/Pancreatic Duct 119
ØFRF*	Replace/Pancreatic Duct, Accessory 119
Ø2RD[Ø,4][7,8,J,K]Z	Replace/Papillary Muscle, [Opn, Perc Endo], [Auto Tissue Sub, Zooplastic Tissue, Synth Sub, Nonauto Tissue Sub], NQ 75
ØNR4*	Replace/Parietal Bone, Lt 10, 49, 154
ØNR4[Ø,3,4][7,J,K]Z	Replace/Parietal Bone, Lt, [Opn, Perc, Perc Endo], [Auto Tissue Sub, Synth Sub, Nonauto Tissue Sub], NQ 14, 18
ØNR4[Ø,3,4]JZ	Replace/Parietal Bone, Lt, [Opn, Perc, Perc Endo], Synth Sub, NQ 344, 415
ØNR3*	Replace/Parietal Bone, Rt 10, 49, 154
ØNR3[Ø,3,4][7,J,K]Z	Replace/Parietal Bone, Rt, [Opn, Perc, Perc Endo], [Auto Tissue Sub, Synth Sub, Nonauto Tissue Sub], NQ 14, 18
ØNR3[Ø,3,4]JZ	Replace/Parietal Bone, Rt, [Opn, Perc, Perc Endo], Synth Sub, NQ 344, 415
ØCRC*	Replace/Parotid Duct, Lt 57, 332
ØCRB*	Replace/Parotid Duct, Rt 57, 332
ØQRF*	Replace/Patella, Lt 132, 348
ØQRD*	Replace/Patella, Rt 132, 348

ØQR3*	Replace/Pelvic Bone, Lt 156
ØQR2*	Replace/Pelvic Bone, Rt 156
Ø2RN*	Replace/Pericardium 320
Ø2RN[Ø,4][7,8,J,K]Z	Replace/Pericardium, [Opn, Perc Endo], [Auto Tissue Sub, Zooplastic Tissue, Synth Sub, Nonauto Tissue Sub], NQ 93
ØLRH*	Replace/Perineum Tndn 142, 341
ØDRW*	Replace/Peritoneum 112, 123
ØDRW[Ø,4][7,J,K]Z	Replace/Peritoneum, [Opn, Perc Endo], [Auto Tissue Sub, Synth Sub, Nonauto Tissue Sub], NQ 300
Ø4RU*	Replace/Peroneal Artery, Lt 84, 240, 324
Ø4RT*	Replace/Peroneal Artery, Rt 84, 240, 324
ØCRM*	Replace/Pharynx 25, 53, 332
ØCRM[Ø,7,8][7,J,K]Z	Replace/Pharynx, [Opn, Via Natrl or Artfcl Opng, Via Natrl or Artfcl Opng Endo], [Auto Tissue Sub, Synth Sub, Nonauto Tissue Sub], NQ 448
Ø4RN*	Replace/Popliteal Artery, Lt 84, 240, 324
Ø4RM*	Replace/Popliteal Artery, Rt 84, 240, 324
Ø6R8[Ø,4][7,J,K]Z	Replace/Portal Vein, [Opn, Perc Endo], [Auto Tissue Sub, Synth Sub, Nonauto Tissue Sub], NQ 98
Ø4RS*	Replace/Posterior Tibial Artery, Lt 84, 240, 324
Ø4RR*	Replace/Posterior Tibial Artery, Rt 84, 240, 324
Ø2RR*	Replace/Pulmn Artery, Lt 60, 320
Ø2RR[Ø,4][7,8,J,K]Z	Replace/Pulmn Artery, Lt, [Opn, Perc Endo], [Auto Tissue Sub, Zooplastic Tissue, Synth Sub, Nonauto Tissue Sub], NQ 71, 72
Ø2RQ*	Replace/Pulmn Artery, Rt 60, 320
Ø2RQ[Ø,4][7,8,J,K]Z	Replace/Pulmn Artery, Rt, [Opn, Perc Endo], [Auto Tissue Sub, Zooplastic Tissue, Synth Sub, Nonauto Tissue Sub], NQ 71, 72
Ø2RP*	Replace/Pulmn Trunk 60, 320
Ø2RP[Ø,4][7,8,J,K]Z	Replace/Pulmn Trunk, [Opn, Perc Endo], [Auto Tissue Sub, Zooplastic Tissue, Synth Sub, Nonauto Tissue Sub], NQ 71, 72
Ø2RH3[7,8,J,K]Z	Replace/Pulmn Valve, [Opn, Perc, Perc Endo], [Auto Tissue Sub, Zooplastic Tissue, Synth Sub, Nonauto Tissue Sub], NQ 92
Ø2RH3[7,8,J,K]H	Replace/Pulmn Valve, Perc, [Auto Tissue Sub, Zooplastic Tissue, Synth Sub, Nonauto Tissue Sub], Transapical 92
Ø2RT*	Replace/Pulmn Vein, Lt 60, 320
Ø2RT[Ø,4][7,8,J,K]Z	Replace/Pulmn Vein, Lt, [Opn, Perc Endo], [Auto Tissue Sub, Zooplastic Tissue, Synth Sub, Nonauto Tissue Sub], NQ 71, 72
Ø2RS*	Replace/Pulmn Vein, Rt 60, 320
Ø2RS[Ø,4][7,8,J,K]Z	Replace/Pulmn Vein, Rt, [Opn, Perc Endo], [Auto Tissue Sub, Zooplastic Tissue, Synth Sub, Nonauto Tissue Sub], NQ 71, 72
Ø3RC*	Replace/Radial Artery, Lt 82, 321
Ø3RB*	Replace/Radial Artery, Rt 82, 321
ØPRJ*	Replace/Radius, Lt 148, 346
ØPRJ[Ø,3,4][7,K]Z	Replace/Radius, Lt, [Opn, Perc, Perc Endo], [Auto Tissue Sub, Nonauto Tissue Sub], NQ 455
ØPRH*	Replace/Radius, Rt 148, 346
ØPRH[Ø,3,4][7,K]Z	Replace/Radius, Rt, [Opn, Perc, Perc Endo], [Auto Tissue Sub, Nonauto Tissue Sub], NQ 455
Ø4RA*	Replace/Renal Artery, Lt 252
Ø4RA[Ø,4][7,J,K]Z	Replace/Renal Artery, Lt, [Opn, Perc Endo], [Auto Tissue Sub, Synth Sub, Nonauto Tissue Sub], NQ 96
Ø4R9*	Replace/Renal Artery, Rt 252
Ø4R9[Ø,4][7,J,K]Z	Replace/Renal Artery, Rt, [Opn, Perc Endo], [Auto Tissue Sub, Synth Sub, Nonauto Tissue Sub], NQ 96
Ø6RB[Ø,4][7,J,K]Z	Replace/Renal Vein, Lt, [Opn, Perc Endo], [Auto Tissue Sub, Synth Sub, Nonauto Tissue Sub], NQ 98
Ø6R9[Ø,4][7,J,K]Z	Replace/Renal Vein, Rt, [Opn, Perc Endo], [Auto Tissue Sub, Synth Sub, Nonauto Tissue Sub], NQ 98
Ø8RH*	Replace/Retinal Vessel, Lt 44
Ø8RH3[7,K]Z	Replace/Retinal Vessel, Lt, Perc, [Auto Tissue Sub, Synth Sub, Nonauto Tissue Sub], NQ 445
Ø8RG*	Replace/Retinal Vessel, Rt 44
Ø8RG3[7,K]Z	Replace/Retinal Vessel, Rt, Perc, [Auto Tissue Sub, Synth Sub, Nonauto Tissue Sub], NQ 445
ØPR2*	Replace/Rib, Lt 155
ØPR2[Ø,3,4]JZ	Replace/Rib, Lt, [Opn, Perc, Perc Endo], Synth Sub, NQ 66, 346
ØPR1*	Replace/Rib, Rt 155
ØPR1[Ø,3,4]JZ	Replace/Rib, Rt, [Opn, Perc, Perc Endo], Synth Sub, NQ 66, 346
ØSR5*	Replace/Sacrococcygeal Jt 158
ØSR8*	Replace/Sacroiliac Jt, Lt 158
ØSR7*	Replace/Sacroiliac Jt, Rt 158
ØQR1*	Replace/Sacrum 156
ØPR6*	Replace/Scapula, Lt 155

ØPR6[0,3,4]JZ	Replace/Scapula, Lt, [Opn, Perc, Perc Endo], Synth Sub, NQ **66, 346**
ØPR5*	Replace/Scapula, Rt **155**
ØPR5[0,3,4]JZ	Replace/Scapula, Rt, [Opn, Perc, Perc Endo], Synth Sub, NQ **66, 346**
Ø8R7*	Replace/Sclera, Lt **43**
Ø8R7X[7,J,K]Z	Replace/Sclera, Lt, Ext, [Auto Tissue Sub, Synth Sub, Nonauto Tissue Sub], NQ **445**
Ø8R6*	Replace/Sclera, Rt **43**
Ø8R6X[7,J,K]Z	Replace/Sclera, Rt, Ext, [Auto Tissue Sub, Synth Sub, Nonauto Tissue Sub], NQ **445**
ØRRK*	Replace/Shldr Jt, Lt **131, 350**
ØRRJ*	Replace/Shldr Jt, Rt **131, 350**
ØLR2*	Replace/Shldr Tndn, Lt **142, 341**
ØLR1*	Replace/Shldr Tndn, Rt **142, 341**
ØHR7*	Replace/Skin, Abd **26, 90, 126, 206, 380**
ØHR7X[7,J,K][3,4]	Replace/Skin, Abd, Ext, [Auto Tissue Sub, Synth Sub, Nonauto Tissue Sub], [Full Thickness, Partial Thickness] **236, 313, 377**
ØHR7X[7,J][3,4]	Replace/Skin, Abd, Ext, [Auto Tissue Sub, Synth Sub], [Full Thickness, Partial Thickness] **113**
ØHR7XK[3,4]	Replace/Skin, Abd, Ext, Nonauto Tissue Sub, [Full Thickness, Partial Thickness] **53**
ØHR6*	Replace/Skin, Back **26, 90, 126, 206, 380**
ØHR6X[7,J,K][3,4]	Replace/Skin, Back, Ext, [Auto Tissue Sub, Synth Sub, Nonauto Tissue Sub], [Full Thickness, Partial Thickness] **236, 313, 377**
ØHR6X[7,J][3,4]	Replace/Skin, Back, Ext, [Auto Tissue Sub, Synth Sub], [Full Thickness, Partial Thickness] **113**
ØHR6XK[3,4]	Replace/Skin, Back, Ext, Nonauto Tissue Sub, [Full Thickness, Partial Thickness] **53**
ØHR8*	Replace/Skin, Buttock **26, 90, 126, 206, 380**
ØHR8X[7,J,K][3,4]	Replace/Skin, Buttock, Ext, [Auto Tissue Sub, Synth Sub, Nonauto Tissue Sub], [Full Thickness, Partial Thickness] **236, 313, 377**
ØHR8XK[3,4]	Replace/Skin, Buttock, Ext, Nonauto Tissue Sub, [Full Thickness, Partial Thickness] **53**
ØHR8XJ[3,4,Z]	Replace/Skin, Buttock, Ext, Synth Sub, [Full Thickness, Partial Thickness, NQ] **113**
ØHR5*	Replace/Skin, Chest **25, 90, 126, 206, 380**
ØHR5X[7,J,K][3,4]	Replace/Skin, Chest, Ext, [Auto Tissue Sub, Synth Sub, Nonauto Tissue Sub], [Full Thickness, Partial Thickness] **236, 313, 377**
ØHR5X[7,J][3,4]	Replace/Skin, Chest, Ext, [Auto Tissue Sub, Synth Sub], [Full Thickness, Partial Thickness] **113**
ØHR5XK[3,4]	Replace/Skin, Chest, Ext, Nonauto Tissue Sub, [Full Thickness, Partial Thickness] **53**
ØHR1*	Replace/Skin, Face **25, 53, 126, 206, 380**
ØHR1X[7,J,K][3,4]	Replace/Skin, Face, Ext, [Auto Tissue Sub, Synth Sub, Nonauto Tissue Sub], [Full Thickness, Partial Thickness] **236, 313, 377**
ØHR1XK[3,4]	Replace/Skin, Face, Ext, Nonauto Tissue Sub, [Full Thickness, Partial Thickness] **90**
ØHRA*	Replace/Skin, Genitalia **26, 90, 126, 206, 380**
ØHRAX[7,J,K][3,4]	Replace/Skin, Genitalia, Ext, [Auto Tissue Sub, Synth Sub, Nonauto Tissue Sub], [Full Thickness, Partial Thickness] **313, 378**
ØHRAX[7,J][3,4]	Replace/Skin, Genitalia, Ext, [Auto Tissue Sub, Synth Sub], [Full Thickness, Partial Thickness] **236**
ØHR3*	Replace/Skin, Lt Ear **53, 336**
ØHR3X[7,J,K][3,4]	Replace/Skin, Lt Ear, Ext, [Auto Tissue Sub, Synth Sub, Nonauto Tissue Sub], [Full Thickness, Partial Thickness] **212, 450**
ØHRN*	Replace/Skin, Lt Foot **26, 90, 126, 206, 380**
ØHRNX[7,J,K][3,4]	Replace/Skin, Lt Foot, Ext, [Auto Tissue Sub, Synth Sub, Nonauto Tissue Sub], [Full Thickness, Partial Thickness] **313, 378**
ØHRNX[7,J][3,4]	Replace/Skin, Lt Foot, Ext, [Auto Tissue Sub, Synth Sub], [Full Thickness, Partial Thickness] **237**
ØHRG*	Replace/Skin, Lt Hand **26, 90, 149, 206, 380**
ØHRGX[7,J,K][3,4]	Replace/Skin, Lt Hand, Ext, [Auto Tissue Sub, Synth Sub, Nonauto Tissue Sub], [Full Thickness, Partial Thickness] **378**
ØHRGX[J,K][3,4]	Replace/Skin, Lt Hand, Ext, [Synth Sub, Nonauto Tissue Sub], [Full Thickness, Partial Thickness] **313**
ØHRGX7[3,4]	Replace/Skin, Lt Hand, Ext, Auto Tissue Sub, [Full Thickness, Partial Thickness] **314**
ØHRGXJ[3,4,Z]	Replace/Skin, Lt Hand, Ext, Synth Sub, [Full Thickness, Partial Thickness, NQ] **236**
ØHRE*	Replace/Skin, Lt Lwr Arm **26, 90, 126, 206, 380**
ØHREX[7,J,K][3,4]	Replace/Skin, Lt Lwr Arm, Ext, [Auto Tissue Sub, Synth Sub, Nonauto Tissue Sub], [Full Thickness, Partial Thickness] **313, 378**
ØHREX[7,J][3,4]	Replace/Skin, Lt Lwr Arm, Ext, [Auto Tissue Sub, Synth Sub], [Full Thickness, Partial Thickness] **236**
ØHRL*	Replace/Skin, Lt Lwr Leg **26, 90, 126, 206, 380**
ØHRLX[7,J,K][3,4]	Replace/Skin, Lt Lwr Leg, Ext, [Auto Tissue Sub, Synth Sub, Nonauto Tissue Sub], [Full Thickness, Partial Thickness] **313, 378**
ØHRLX[7,J][3,4]	Replace/Skin, Lt Lwr Leg, Ext, [Auto Tissue Sub, Synth Sub], [Full Thickness, Partial Thickness] **237**
ØHRC*	Replace/Skin, Lt Upr Arm **26, 90, 126, 206, 380**
ØHRCX[7,J,K][3,4]	Replace/Skin, Lt Upr Arm, Ext, [Auto Tissue Sub, Synth Sub, Nonauto Tissue Sub], [Full Thickness, Partial Thickness] **313, 378**
ØHRCX[7,J][3,4]	Replace/Skin, Lt Upr Arm, Ext, [Auto Tissue Sub, Synth Sub], [Full Thickness, Partial Thickness] **236**
ØHRJ*	Replace/Skin, Lt Upr Leg **26, 90, 126, 206, 380**
ØHRJX[7,J,K][3,4]	Replace/Skin, Lt Upr Leg, Ext, [Auto Tissue Sub, Synth Sub, Nonauto Tissue Sub], [Full Thickness, Partial Thickness] **313, 378**
ØHRJX[7,J][3,4]	Replace/Skin, Lt Upr Leg, Ext, [Auto Tissue Sub, Synth Sub], [Full Thickness, Partial Thickness] **236**
ØHR4*	Replace/Skin, Neck **25, 53, 126, 206, 380**
ØHR4X[7,J,K][3,4]	Replace/Skin, Neck, Ext, [Auto Tissue Sub, Synth Sub, Nonauto Tissue Sub], [Full Thickness, Partial Thickness] **236, 313, 377**
ØHR4XK[3,4]	Replace/Skin, Neck, Ext, Nonauto Tissue Sub, [Full Thickness, Partial Thickness] **90**
ØHR9*	Replace/Skin, Perineum **266, 274, 336**
ØHR9X[7,J,K][3,4]	Replace/Skin, Perineum, Ext, [Auto Tissue Sub, Synth Sub, Nonauto Tissue Sub], [Full Thickness, Partial Thickness] **336, 450**
ØHR2*	Replace/Skin, Rt Ear **53, 336**
ØHR2X[7,J,K][3,4]	Replace/Skin, Rt Ear, Ext, [Auto Tissue Sub, Synth Sub, Nonauto Tissue Sub], [Full Thickness, Partial Thickness] **212, 450**
ØHRM*	Replace/Skin, Rt Foot **26, 90, 126, 206, 380**
ØHRMX[7,J,K][3,4]	Replace/Skin, Rt Foot, Ext, [Auto Tissue Sub, Synth Sub, Nonauto Tissue Sub], [Full Thickness, Partial Thickness] **313, 378**
ØHRMX[7,J][3,4]	Replace/Skin, Rt Foot, Ext, [Auto Tissue Sub, Synth Sub], [Full Thickness, Partial Thickness] **237**
ØHRF*	Replace/Skin, Rt Hand **26, 90, 149, 206, 380**
ØHRFX[7,J,K][3,4]	Replace/Skin, Rt Hand, Ext, [Auto Tissue Sub, Synth Sub, Nonauto Tissue Sub], [Full Thickness, Partial Thickness] **378**
ØHRFX[J,K][3,4]	Replace/Skin, Rt Hand, Ext, [Synth Sub, Nonauto Tissue Sub], [Full Thickness, Partial Thickness] **313**
ØHRFX7[3,4]	Replace/Skin, Rt Hand, Ext, Auto Tissue Sub, [Full Thickness, Partial Thickness] **314**
ØHRFXJ[3,4,Z]	Replace/Skin, Rt Hand, Ext, Synth Sub, [Full Thickness, Partial Thickness, NQ] **236**
ØHRD*	Replace/Skin, Rt Lwr Arm **26, 90, 126, 206, 380**
ØHRDX[7,J,K][3,4]	Replace/Skin, Rt Lwr Arm, Ext, [Auto Tissue Sub, Synth Sub, Nonauto Tissue Sub], [Full Thickness, Partial Thickness] **313, 378**
ØHRDX[7,J][3,4]	Replace/Skin, Rt Lwr Arm, Ext, [Auto Tissue Sub, Synth Sub], [Full Thickness, Partial Thickness] **236**
ØHRK*	Replace/Skin, Rt Lwr Leg **26, 90, 126, 206, 380**
ØHRKX[7,J,K][3,4]	Replace/Skin, Rt Lwr Leg, Ext, [Auto Tissue Sub, Synth Sub, Nonauto Tissue Sub], [Full Thickness, Partial Thickness] **313, 378**
ØHRKX[7,J][3,4]	Replace/Skin, Rt Lwr Leg, Ext, [Auto Tissue Sub, Synth Sub], [Full Thickness, Partial Thickness] **236**
ØHRB*	Replace/Skin, Rt Upr Arm **26, 90, 126, 206, 380**
ØHRBX[7,J,K][3,4]	Replace/Skin, Rt Upr Arm, Ext, [Auto Tissue Sub, Synth Sub, Nonauto Tissue Sub], [Full Thickness, Partial Thickness] **313, 378**
ØHRBX[7,J][3,4]	Replace/Skin, Rt Upr Arm, Ext, [Auto Tissue Sub, Synth Sub], [Full Thickness, Partial Thickness] **236**
ØHRH*	Replace/Skin, Rt Upr Leg **26, 90, 126, 206, 380**

ØHRHX[7,J,K][3,4]	Replace/Skin, Rt Upr Leg, Ext, [Auto Tissue Sub, Synth Sub, Nonauto Tissue Sub], [Full Thickness, Partial Thickness] 313, 378
ØHRHX[7,J][3,4]	Replace/Skin, Rt Upr Leg, Ext, [Auto Tissue Sub, Synth Sub], [Full Thickness, Partial Thickness] 236
ØHRØ*	Replace/Skin, Scalp 25, 53, 126, 206, 380
ØHRØX[7,J,K][3,4]	Replace/Skin, Scalp, Ext, [Auto Tissue Sub, Synth Sub, Nonauto Tissue Sub], [Full Thickness, Partial Thickness] 236, 313, 377
ØHRØXK[3,4]	Replace/Skin, Scalp, Ext, Nonauto Tissue Sub, [Full Thickness, Partial Thickness] 90
ØNRØ*	Replace/Skull 10, 49, 154, 344, 415
ØNRØ[0,3,4][7,J,K]Z	Replace/Skull, [Opn, Perc, Perc Endo], [Auto Tissue Sub, Synth Sub, Nonauto Tissue Sub], NQ 14, 18
ØCR3*	Replace/Soft Palate 25, 53
ØCR3[0,3,X][7,J,K]Z	Replace/Soft Palate, [Opn, Perc, Ext], [Auto Tissue Sub, Synth Sub, Nonauto Tissue Sub], NQ 211
ØNRD*	Replace/Sphenoid Bone, Lt 49
ØNRD[0,3,4]JZ	Replace/Sphenoid Bone, Lt, [Opn, Perc, Perc Endo], Synth Sub, NQ 42, 154, 344
ØNRC*	Replace/Sphenoid Bone, Rt 49
ØNRC[0,3,4]JZ	Replace/Sphenoid Bone, Rt, [Opn, Perc, Perc Endo], Synth Sub, NQ 42, 154, 344
04R4*	Replace/Splenic Artery 324
04R4[0,4][7,J,K]Z	Replace/Splenic Artery, [Opn, Perc Endo], [Auto Tissue Sub, Synth Sub, Nonauto Tissue Sub], NQ 96
06R1[0,4][7,J,K]Z	Replace/Splenic Vein, [Opn, Perc Endo], [Auto Tissue Sub, Synth Sub, Nonauto Tissue Sub], NQ 98
ØJR8*	Replace/SQ Tissue & Fascia, Abd 138, 337
ØJR8[0,3][7,J,K]Z	Replace/SQ Tissue & Fascia, Abd, [Opn, Perc], [Auto Tissue Sub, Synth Sub, Nonauto Tissue Sub], NQ 213
ØJR4*	Replace/SQ Tissue & Fascia, Ant Neck 138, 337
ØJR4[0,3][7,J,K]Z	Replace/SQ Tissue & Fascia, Ant Neck, [Opn, Perc], [Auto Tissue Sub, Synth Sub, Nonauto Tissue Sub], NQ 213
ØJR7*	Replace/SQ Tissue & Fascia, Back 138, 337
ØJR7[0,3][7,J,K]Z	Replace/SQ Tissue & Fascia, Back, [Opn, Perc], [Auto Tissue Sub, Synth Sub, Nonauto Tissue Sub], NQ 213
ØJR9*	Replace/SQ Tissue & Fascia, Buttock 138, 337
ØJR9[0,3][7,J,K]Z	Replace/SQ Tissue & Fascia, Buttock, [Opn, Perc], [Auto Tissue Sub, Synth Sub, Nonauto Tissue Sub], NQ 213
ØJR6*	Replace/SQ Tissue & Fascia, Chest 138, 337
ØJR6[0,3][7,J,K]Z	Replace/SQ Tissue & Fascia, Chest, [Opn, Perc], [Auto Tissue Sub, Synth Sub, Nonauto Tissue Sub], NQ 213
ØJR1*	Replace/SQ Tissue & Fascia, Face 138, 337
ØJR1[0,3][7,J,K]Z	Replace/SQ Tissue & Fascia, Face, [Opn, Perc], [Auto Tissue Sub, Nonauto Tissue Sub], NQ 42
ØJR1[0,3][7,J,K]Z	Replace/SQ Tissue & Fascia, Face, [Opn, Perc], [Auto Tissue Sub, Synth Sub, Nonauto Tissue Sub], NQ 213
ØJR1[0,3]KZ	Replace/SQ Tissue & Fascia, Face, [Opn, Perc], Nonauto Tissue Sub, NQ 48
ØJRC[0,3][7,J,K]Z	Replace/SQ Tissue & Fascia, Genitalia, [Opn, Perc], [Auto Tissue Sub, Synth Sub, Nonauto Tissue Sub], NQ 213
ØJRR*	Replace/SQ Tissue & Fascia, Lt Foot 138, 338
ØJRR[0,3][7,J,K]Z	Replace/SQ Tissue & Fascia, Lt Foot, [Opn, Perc], [Auto Tissue Sub, Synth Sub, Nonauto Tissue Sub], NQ 213
ØJRK[0,3][7,J,K]Z	Replace/SQ Tissue & Fascia, Lt Hand, [Opn, Perc], [Auto Tissue Sub, Synth Sub, Nonauto Tissue Sub], NQ 213
ØJRK[0,3][J,K]Z	Replace/SQ Tissue & Fascia, Lt Hand, [Opn, Perc], [Synth Sub, Nonauto Tissue Sub], NQ 26, 314
ØJRH*	Replace/SQ Tissue & Fascia, Lt Lwr Arm 138, 338
ØJRH[0,3][7,J,K]Z	Replace/SQ Tissue & Fascia, Lt Lwr Arm, [Opn, Perc], [Auto Tissue Sub, Synth Sub, Nonauto Tissue Sub], NQ 213
ØJRP*	Replace/SQ Tissue & Fascia, Lt Lwr Leg 138, 338
ØJRP[0,3][7,J,K]Z	Replace/SQ Tissue & Fascia, Lt Lwr Leg, [Opn, Perc], [Auto Tissue Sub, Synth Sub, Nonauto Tissue Sub], NQ 213
ØJRF*	Replace/SQ Tissue & Fascia, Lt Upr Arm 138, 337
ØJRF[0,3][7,J,K]Z	Replace/SQ Tissue & Fascia, Lt Upr Arm, [Opn, Perc], [Auto Tissue Sub, Synth Sub, Nonauto Tissue Sub], NQ 213
ØJRM*	Replace/SQ Tissue & Fascia, Lt Upr Leg 138, 338
ØJRM[0,3][7,J,K]Z	Replace/SQ Tissue & Fascia, Lt Upr Leg, [Opn, Perc], [Auto Tissue Sub, Synth Sub, Nonauto Tissue Sub], NQ 213
ØJRC*	Replace/SQ Tissue & Fascia, Pelvic Region 138, 337
ØJRB*	Replace/SQ Tissue & Fascia, Perineum 138, 337
ØJRB[0,3][7,J,K]Z	Replace/SQ Tissue & Fascia, Perineum, [Opn, Perc], [Auto Tissue Sub, Synth Sub, Nonauto Tissue Sub], NQ 213
ØJR5[0,3][7,J,K]Z	Replace/SQ Tissue & Fascia, Post Neck, [Opn, Perc], [Auto Tissue Sub, Synth Sub, Nonauto Tissue Sub], NQ 213
ØJR5*	Replace/SQ Tissue & Fascia, Posterior Neck 138, 337
ØJRQ*	Replace/SQ Tissue & Fascia, Rt Foot 138, 338
ØJRQ[0,3][7,J,K]Z	Replace/SQ Tissue & Fascia, Rt Foot, [Opn, Perc], [Auto Tissue Sub, Synth Sub, Nonauto Tissue Sub], NQ 213
ØJRJ[0,3][7,J,K]Z	Replace/SQ Tissue & Fascia, Rt Hand, [Opn, Perc], [Auto Tissue Sub, Synth Sub, Nonauto Tissue Sub], NQ 213
ØJRJ[0,3][J,K]Z	Replace/SQ Tissue & Fascia, Rt Hand, [Opn, Perc], [Synth Sub, Nonauto Tissue Sub], NQ 26, 314
ØJRG*	Replace/SQ Tissue & Fascia, Rt Lwr Arm 138, 338
ØJRG[0,3][7,J,K]Z	Replace/SQ Tissue & Fascia, Rt Lwr Arm, [Opn, Perc], [Auto Tissue Sub, Synth Sub, Nonauto Tissue Sub], NQ 213
ØJRN*	Replace/SQ Tissue & Fascia, Rt Lwr Leg 138, 338
ØJRN[0,3][7,J,K]Z	Replace/SQ Tissue & Fascia, Rt Lwr Leg, [Opn, Perc], [Auto Tissue Sub, Synth Sub, Nonauto Tissue Sub], NQ 213
ØJRD*	Replace/SQ Tissue & Fascia, Rt Upr Arm 138, 337
ØJRD[0,3][7,J,K]Z	Replace/SQ Tissue & Fascia, Rt Upr Arm, [Opn, Perc], [Auto Tissue Sub, Synth Sub, Nonauto Tissue Sub], NQ 213
ØJRL*	Replace/SQ Tissue & Fascia, Rt Upr Leg 138, 338
ØJRL[0,3][7,J,K]Z	Replace/SQ Tissue & Fascia, Rt Upr Leg, [Opn, Perc], [Auto Tissue Sub, Synth Sub, Nonauto Tissue Sub], NQ 213
ØJRØ*	Replace/SQ Tissue & Fascia, Scalp 138, 337
ØJRØ[0,3][7,J,K]Z	Replace/SQ Tissue & Fascia, Scalp, [Opn, Perc], [Auto Tissue Sub, Synth Sub, Nonauto Tissue Sub], NQ 213
ØRRF*	Replace/Sternoclavicular Jt, Lt 131, 350
ØRRE*	Replace/Sternoclavicular Jt, Rt 131, 350
ØPRØ*	Replace/Sternum 155
ØPRØ[0,3,4]JZ	Replace/Sternum, [Opn, Perc, Perc Endo], Synth Sub, NQ 66, 346
03R4*	Replace/Subclavian Artery, Lt 60, 321
03R4[0,4][7,J,K]Z	Replace/Subclavian Artery, Lt, [Opn, Perc Endo], [Auto Tissue Sub, Synth Sub, Nonauto Tissue Sub], NQ 71, 72
03R3*	Replace/Subclavian Artery, Rt 60, 321
03R3[0,4][7,J,K]Z	Replace/Subclavian Artery, Rt, [Opn, Perc Endo], [Auto Tissue Sub, Synth Sub, Nonauto Tissue Sub], NQ 71, 72
05R6*	Replace/Subclavian Vein, Lt 60, 326
05R6[0,4][7,J,K]Z	Replace/Subclavian Vein, Lt, [Opn, Perc Endo], [Auto Tissue Sub, Synth Sub, Nonauto Tissue Sub], NQ 71, 72
05R5*	Replace/Subclavian Vein, Rt 60, 326
05R5[0,4][7,J,K]Z	Replace/Subclavian Vein, Rt, [Opn, Perc Endo], [Auto Tissue Sub, Synth Sub, Nonauto Tissue Sub], NQ 71, 72
04R5*	Replace/Superior Mesenteric Artery 324
04R5[0,4][7,J,K]Z	Replace/Superior Mesenteric Artery, [Opn, Perc Endo], [Auto Tissue Sub, Synth Sub, Nonauto Tissue Sub], NQ 96
06R5[0,4][7,J,K]Z	Replace/Superior Mesenteric Vein, [Opn, Perc Endo], [Auto Tissue Sub, Synth Sub, Nonauto Tissue Sub], NQ 98
02RV*	Replace/Superior Vena Cava 60, 320
02RV[0,4][7,8,J,K]Z	Replace/Superior Vena Cava, [Opn, Perc Endo], [Auto Tissue Sub, Zooplastic Tissue, Synth Sub, Nonauto Tissue Sub], NQ 71, 72
ØSRJ*	Replace/Tarsal Jt, Lt 146, 352
ØSRJØ[7,J,K]Z	Replace/Tarsal Jt, Lt, Opn, [Auto Tissue Sub, Synth Sub, Nonauto Tissue Sub], NQ 458
ØSRH*	Replace/Tarsal Jt, Rt 146, 352
ØSRHØ[7,J,K]Z	Replace/Tarsal Jt, Rt, Opn, [Auto Tissue Sub, Synth Sub, Nonauto Tissue Sub], NQ 458
ØQRM*	Replace/Tarsal, Lt 145, 348
ØQRL*	Replace/Tarsal, Rt 145, 348
03RT*	Replace/Temporal Artery, Lt 25, 82
03RS*	Replace/Temporal Artery, Rt 25, 82
ØNR6*	Replace/Temporal Bone, Lt 10, 49, 154
ØNR6[0,3,4][7,J,K]Z	Replace/Temporal Bone, Lt, [Opn, Perc, Perc Endo], [Auto Tissue Sub, Synth Sub, Nonauto Tissue Sub], NQ 14, 18
ØNR6[0,3,4]JZ	Replace/Temporal Bone, Lt, [Opn, Perc, Perc Endo], Synth Sub, NQ 344, 415
ØNR5*	Replace/Temporal Bone, Rt 10, 49, 154
ØNR5[0,3,4][7,J,K]Z	Replace/Temporal Bone, Rt, [Opn, Perc, Perc Endo], [Auto Tissue Sub, Synth Sub, Nonauto Tissue Sub], NQ 14, 18
ØNR5[0,3,4]JZ	Replace/Temporal Bone, Rt, [Opn, Perc, Perc Endo], Synth Sub, NQ 344, 415
ØRRD*	Replace/Temporomandibular Jt, Lt 55, 157, 350
ØRRC*	Replace/Temporomandibular Jt, Rt 55, 157, 350

Code	Description
Ø2RW*	Replace/Thoracic Aorta **60, 320**
Ø2RW[Ø,4][7,8,J,K]Z	Replace/Thoracic Aorta, [Opn, Perc Endo], [Auto Tissue Sub, Zooplastic Tissue, Synth Sub, Nonauto Tissue Sub], NQ **71, 72**
ØRR9Ø[7,K]Z	Replace/Thoracic Vert Disc, Opn, [Auto Tissue Sub, Nonauto Tissue Sub], NQ **157**
ØRR6Ø[7,J,K]Z	Replace/Thoracic Vert Jt, Opn, [Auto Tissue Sub, Synth Sub, Nonauto Tissue Sub], NQ **157**
ØPR4*	Replace/Thoracic Vertebra **155**
ØRRBØ[7,K]Z	Replace/Thoracolumbar Vert Disc, Opn, [Auto Tissue Sub, Nonauto Tissue Sub], NQ **157**
ØRRAØ[7,J,K]Z	Replace/Thoracolumbar Vert Jt, Opn, [Auto Tissue Sub, Synth Sub, Nonauto Tissue Sub], NQ **157**
ØLRD*	Replace/Thorax Tndn, Lt **142, 341**
ØLRC*	Replace/Thorax Tndn, Rt **142, 341**
ØPRS*	Replace/Thumb Phalanx, Lt **155**
ØPRR*	Replace/Thumb Phalanx, Rt **155**
ØXRM[Ø,4]7[N,P]	Replace/Thumb, Lt, [Opn, Perc Endo], Auto Tissue Sub, [Toe, Rt, Toe, Lt] **317**
ØXRL[Ø,4]7[N,P]	Replace/Thumb, Rt, [Opn, Perc Endo], Auto Tissue Sub, [Toe, Rt, Toe, Lt] **317**
Ø3RV*	Replace/Thyroid Artery, Lt **25, 82**
Ø3RU*	Replace/Thyroid Artery, Rt **25, 82**
ØQRH*	Replace/Tibia, Lt **133, 348**
ØQRG*	Replace/Tibia, Rt **133, 348**
ØHRR*	Replace/Toe Nail **337**
ØHRRX[7,J,K]Z	Replace/Toe Nail, Ext, [Auto Tissue Sub, Synth Sub, Nonauto Tissue Sub], NQ **212, 337**
ØSRQ*	Replace/Toe Phalangeal Jt, Lt **146, 352**
ØSRQØ[7,J,K]Z	Replace/Toe Phalangeal Jt, Lt, Opn, [Auto Tissue Sub, Synth Sub, Nonauto Tissue Sub], NQ **458**
ØSRP*	Replace/Toe Phalangeal Jt, Rt **146, 352**
ØSRPØ[7,J,K]Z	Replace/Toe Phalangeal Jt, Rt, Opn, [Auto Tissue Sub, Synth Sub, Nonauto Tissue Sub], NQ **458**
ØQRR*	Replace/Toe Phalanx, Lt **156**
ØQRQ*	Replace/Toe Phalanx, Rt **156**
ØCR7*	Replace/Tongue **56, 332**
Ø2RJ*	Replace/Tricuspid Valve **71, 72**
ØLRB*	Replace/Trunk Tndn, Lt **142, 341**
ØLR9*	Replace/Trunk Tndn, Rt **142, 341**
ØPRL*	Replace/Ulna, Lt **148, 346**
ØPRL[Ø,3,4][7,K]Z	Replace/Ulna, Lt, [Opn, Perc, Perc Endo], [Auto Tissue Sub, Nonauto Tissue Sub], NQ **456**
ØPRK*	Replace/Ulna, Rt **148, 346**
ØPRK[Ø,3,4][7,K]Z	Replace/Ulna, Rt, [Opn, Perc, Perc Endo], [Auto Tissue Sub, Nonauto Tissue Sub], NQ **455**
Ø3RA*	Replace/Ulnar Artery, Lt **82, 321**
Ø3R9*	Replace/Ulnar Artery, Rt **82, 321**
ØLR4*	Replace/Upr Arm Tndn, Lt **142, 341**
ØLR3*	Replace/Upr Arm Tndn, Rt **142, 341**
Ø3RY*	Replace/Upr Artery **82, 321**
Ø8RP*	Replace/Upr Eyelid, Lt **43**
Ø8RP[Ø,3,X][7,J,K]Z	Replace/Upr Eyelid, Lt, [Opn, Perc, Ext], [Auto Tissue Sub, Synth Sub, Nonauto Tissue Sub], NQ **210, 445**
Ø8RP[Ø,3,X]JZ	Replace/Upr Eyelid, Lt, [Opn, Perc, Ext], Synth Sub, NQ **241**
Ø8RN*	Replace/Upr Eyelid, Rt **43**
Ø8RN[Ø,3,X][7,J,K]Z	Replace/Upr Eyelid, Rt, [Opn, Perc, Ext], [Auto Tissue Sub, Synth Sub, Nonauto Tissue Sub], NQ **210, 445**
Ø8RN[Ø,3,X]JZ	Replace/Upr Eyelid, Rt, [Opn, Perc, Ext], Synth Sub, NQ **241**
ØQR7*	Replace/Upr Femur, Lt **131, 348, 416**
ØQR6*	Replace/Upr Femur, Rt **131, 348, 416**
ØCR5*	Replace/Upr Gingiva **56, 332**
ØLRM*	Replace/Upr Leg Tndn, Lt **142, 341**
ØLRL*	Replace/Upr Leg Tndn, Rt **142, 341**
ØCRØ*	Replace/Upr Lip **56, 332**
ØCRØ[Ø,3,X][7,J,K]Z	Replace/Upr Lip, [Opn, Perc, Ext], [Auto Tissue Sub, Synth Sub, Nonauto Tissue Sub], NQ **211, 448**
Ø5RY*	Replace/Upr Vein **86, 326**
ØTR7*	Replace/Ureter, Lt **249, 354**
ØTR6*	Replace/Ureter, Rt **249, 354**
ØTRD*	Replace/Urethra **250, 257, 354**
ØCRN*	Replace/Uvula **56**
ØCRN[Ø,3,X][7,J,K]Z	Replace/Uvula, [Opn, Perc, Ext], [Auto Tissue Sub, Synth Sub, Nonauto Tissue Sub], NQ **448**
Ø2RL[Ø,4][7,K]Z	Replace/Ventricle, Lt, [Opn, Perc Endo], [Auto Tissue Sub, Nonauto Tissue Sub], NQ **75**
Ø2RL[Ø,4][8,J]Z	Replace/Ventricle, Lt, [Opn, Perc Endo], [Zooplastic Tissue, Synth Sub], NQ **93, 320**
Ø2RK[Ø,4][7,K]Z	Replace/Ventricle, Rt, [Opn, Perc Endo], [Auto Tissue Sub, Nonauto Tissue Sub], NQ **75**
Ø2RK[Ø,4][8,J]Z	Replace/Ventricle, Rt, [Opn, Perc Endo], [Zooplastic Tissue, Synth Sub], NQ **93, 320**
Ø2RM[Ø,4][7,J,K]Z	Replace/Ventricular Septum, [Opn, Perc Endo], [Auto Tissue Sub, Synth Sub, Nonauto Tissue Sub], NQ **75**
Ø2RM[Ø,4]8Z	Replace/Ventricular Septum, [Opn, Perc Endo], Zooplastic Tissue, NQ **93, 320**
Ø3RQ*	Replace/Vert Artery, Lt **25, 82**
Ø3RP*	Replace/Vert Artery, Rt **25, 82**
Ø5RS*	Replace/Vert Vein, Lt **25, 86**
Ø5RR*	Replace/Vert Vein, Rt **25, 86**
Ø8R5*	Replace/Vitreous, Lt **44, 241**
Ø8R53[7,J,K]Z	Replace/Vitreous, Lt, Perc, [Auto Tissue Sub, Synth Sub, Nonauto Tissue Sub], NQ **445**
Ø8R4*	Replace/Vitreous, Rt **44, 241**
Ø8R43[7,J,K]Z	Replace/Vitreous, Rt, Perc, [Auto Tissue Sub, Synth Sub, Nonauto Tissue Sub], NQ **445**
ØCRV*	Replace/Vocal Cord, Lt **53, 65**
ØCRV[Ø,7][7,K]Z	Replace/Vocal Cord, Lt, [Opn, Via Natrl or Artfcl Opng], [Auto Tissue Sub, Nonauto Tissue Sub], NQ **332**
ØCRV[Ø,7]JZ	Replace/Vocal Cord, Lt, [Opn, Via Natrl or Artfcl Opng], Synth Sub, NQ **448**
ØCRV8[J,K]Z	Replace/Vocal Cord, Lt, Via Natrl or Artfcl Opng Endo, [Synth Sub, Nonauto Tissue Sub], NQ **332**
ØCRT*	Replace/Vocal Cord, Rt **53, 65**
ØCRT[Ø,7,8][7,K]Z	Replace/Vocal Cord, Rt, [Opn, Via Natrl or Artfcl Opng, Via Natrl or Artfcl Opng Endo], [Auto Tissue Sub, Nonauto Tissue Sub], NQ **332**
ØCRT[Ø,7,8]JZ	Replace/Vocal Cord, Rt, [Opn, Via Natrl or Artfcl Opng, Via Natrl or Artfcl Opng Endo], Synth Sub, NQ **448**
ØRRP*	Replace/Wrist Jt, Lt **131, 350**
ØRRN*	Replace/Wrist Jt, Rt **131, 350**
ØNRN*	Replace/Zygomatic Bone, Lt **49**
ØNRN[Ø,3,4]JZ	Replace/Zygomatic Bone, Lt, [Opn, Perc, Perc Endo], Synth Sub, NQ **42, 154, 344**
ØNRM*	Replace/Zygomatic Bone, Rt **49**
ØNRM[Ø,3,4]JZ	Replace/Zygomatic Bone, Rt, [Opn, Perc, Perc Endo], Synth Sub, NQ **42, 154, 344**
Ø8S[C,D,G,H,J,K]3ZZ	Repos [Rt Iris, Lt Iris, Rt Retinal Vessel, Lt Retinal Vessel, Rt Lens, Lt Lens], Perc **44**
ØBS[1,2]ØZZ	Repos [Trachea, Carina], Opn Appr **52**
ØHSVØZZ	Repos Bilat Breast, Opn Appr **222, 337**
ØBS2ØZZ	Repos Carina, Opn Appr **331**
ØPS3XZZ	Repos Cervical Vertebra, Ext Appr **19, 159, 160, 301, 346**
ØPS33ZZ	Repos Cervical Vertebra, Perc Appr **155, 158**
ØQSS3ZZ	Repos Coccyx, Perc Appr **158**
ØQS5ØZZ	Repos Lt Acetabulum, Opn Appr **156, 348**
ØHSUØZZ	Repos Lt Breast, Opn Appr **222, 337**
ØPSNØZZ	Repos Lt Carpal, Opn Appr **150, 315**
ØPSBØZZ	Repos Lt Clavicle, Opn Appr **155, 346**
ØQS9ØZZ	Repos Lt Femor Shaft, Opn Appr **131, 348, 416**
ØQSKØZZ	Repos Lt Fibula, Opn Appr **133, 348**
ØPSVØZZ	Repos Lt Finger Phalanx, Opn Appr **150, 315**
ØPS8ØZZ	Repos Lt Glenoid Cavity, Opn Appr **155, 346**
ØPSDØZZ	Repos Lt Humeral Head, Opn Appr **133, 346**
ØPSGØZZ	Repos Lt Humeral Shaft, Opn Appr **133, 346**
Ø8SD3ZZ	Repos Lt Iris, Perc Appr **330, 445**
Ø8SK3ZZ	Repos Lt Lens, Perc Appr **330, 445**
ØQSCØZZ	Repos Lt Lwr Femur, Opn Appr **131, 348, 416**
ØPSQØZZ	Repos Lt Metacarpal, Opn Appr **150, 315**
ØQSPØZZ	Repos Lt Metatarsal, Opn Appr **145, 348**
ØHSXXZZ	Repos Lt Nipple, Ext Appr **222, 337**
ØQSFØZZ	Repos Lt Patella, Opn Appr **156, 348**
ØQS3ØZZ	Repos Lt Pelvic Bone, Opn Appr **156, 348**
ØPSJØZZ	Repos Lt Radius, Opn Appr **149, 346**

Ø8SH3ZZ	Repos Lt Retinal Vessel, Perc Appr 330, 445
ØPS2ØZZ	Repos Lt Rib, Opn Appr 155, 346
ØPS6ØZZ	Repos Lt Scapula, Opn Appr 155, 346
ØQSMØZZ	Repos Lt Tarsal, Opn Appr 145, 348
ØPSSØZZ	Repos Lt Thumb Phalanx, Opn Appr 150, 315
ØQSHØZZ	Repos Lt Tibia, Opn Appr 133, 348
ØQSRØZZ	Repos Lt Toe Phalanx, Opn Appr 145, 348
ØPSLØZZ	Repos Lt Ulna, Opn Appr 149, 346
ØQS7ØZZ	Repos Lt Upr Femur, Opn Appr 131, 348, 416
ØQSØØ4Z	Repos Lumbar Vertebra with Int Fix, Opn Appr 159
ØQSØ34Z	Repos Lumbar Vertebra with Int Fix, Perc Appr 159
ØQSØ44Z	Repos Lumbar Vertebra with Int Fix, Perc Endo Appr 159
ØQSØXZZ	Repos Lumbar Vertebra, Ext Appr 19, 159, 160, 301, 348
ØQSØØZZ	Repos Lumbar Vertebra, Opn Appr 159
ØQSØ3ZZ	Repos Lumbar Vertebra, Perc Appr 158
ØQSØ4ZZ	Repos Lumbar Vertebra, Perc Endo Appr 159
1ØSØ7ZZ	Repos Products of Conception, Via Opng 271, 273, 275
ØQS4ØZZ	Repos Rt Acetabulum, Opn Appr 156, 348
ØHSTØZZ	Repos Rt Breast, Opn Appr 222, 337
ØPSMØZZ	Repos Rt Carpal, Opn Appr 150, 315
ØPS9ØZZ	Repos Rt Clavicle, Opn Appr 155, 346
ØQS8ØZZ	Repos Rt Femor Shaft, Opn Appr 131, 348, 416
ØQSJØZZ	Repos Rt Fibula, Opn Appr 133, 348
ØPSTØZZ	Repos Rt Finger Phalanx, Opn Appr 150, 315
ØPS7ØZZ	Repos Rt Glenoid Cavity, Opn Appr 155, 346
ØPSCØZZ	Repos Rt Humeral Head, Opn Appr 133, 346
ØPSFØZZ	Repos Rt Humeral Shaft, Opn Appr 133, 346
Ø8SC3ZZ	Repos Rt Iris, Perc Appr 330, 445
Ø8SJ3ZZ	Repos Rt Lens, Perc Appr 330, 445
ØQSBØZZ	Repos Rt Lwr Femur, Opn Appr 131, 348, 416
ØPSPØZZ	Repos Rt Metacarpal, Opn Appr 150, 315
ØQSNØZZ	Repos Rt Metatarsal, Opn Appr 145, 348
ØHSWXZZ	Repos Rt Nipple, Ext Appr 222, 337
ØQSDØZZ	Repos Rt Patella, Opn Appr 156, 348
ØQS2ØZZ	Repos Rt Pelvic Bone, Opn Appr 156, 348
ØPSHØZZ	Repos Rt Radius, Opn Appr 149, 346
Ø8SG3ZZ	Repos Rt Retinal Vessel, Perc Appr 330, 445
ØPS1ØZZ	Repos Rt Rib, Opn Appr 155, 346
ØPS5ØZZ	Repos Rt Scapula, Opn Appr 155, 346
ØQSLØZZ	Repos Rt Tarsal, Opn Appr 145, 348
ØPSRØZZ	Repos Rt Thumb Phalanx, Opn Appr 150, 315
ØQSGØZZ	Repos Rt Tibia, Opn Appr 133, 348
ØQSQØZZ	Repos Rt Toe Phalanx, Opn Appr 145, 348
ØPSKØZZ	Repos Rt Ulna, Opn Appr 149, 346
ØQS6ØZZ	Repos Rt Upr Femur, Opn Appr 131, 348, 416
ØQS1XZZ	Repos Sacrum, Ext Appr 19, 159, 160, 301, 348
ØQS13ZZ	Repos Sacrum, Perc Appr 158
ØNSØXZZ	Repos Skull, Ext Appr 14, 18
Ø7SPØZZ	Repos Spleen, Opn Appr 290, 298
ØPSØØZZ	Repos Sternum, Opn Appr 155, 346
ØDS68ZZ	Repos Stomach, Endo 106, 334
ØDS6ØZZ	Repos Stomach, Opn Appr 106, 334
ØDS64ZZ	Repos Stomach, Perc Endo Appr 106, 334
ØDS67ZZ	Repos Stomach, Via Natrl or Artfcl Opng 106, 334
ØPS4XZZ	Repos Thoracic Vertebra, Ext Appr 19, 159, 160, 301, 346
ØPS43ZZ	Repos Thoracic Vertebra, Perc Appr 158
Ø7SMØZZ	Repos Thymus, Opn Appr 60, 241, 291, 298
ØBS1ØZZ	Repos Trachea, Opn Appr 331
Ø4SØ*	Repos/Abd Aorta 240, 252, 324
ØMSJ*	Repos/Abd Bursa & Lgmt, Lt 153
ØMSH*	Repos/Abd Bursa & Lgmt, Rt 153
ØKSL*	Repos/Abd Muscle, Lt 140, 243, 339
ØKSK*	Repos/Abd Muscle, Rt 140, 243, 339
ØLSG*	Repos/Abd Tndn, Lt 142, 341
ØLSG[Ø,4]ZZ	Repos/Abd Tndn, Lt, [Opn, Perc Endo] 216
ØLSF*	Repos/Abd Tndn, Rt 142, 341
ØLSF[Ø,4]ZZ	Repos/Abd Tndn, Rt, [Opn, Perc Endo] 216
ØØSL*	Repos/Abducens Nerve 23
ØØSR*	Repos/Accessory Nerve 23

ØQS5[Ø,3,4]4Z	Repos/Acetab, Lt, [Opn, Perc, Perc Endo], Int Fix Dev, NQ 156, 348
ØQS5Ø[4,Z]Z	Repos/Acetab, Lt, Opn, [Int Fix Dev, No Dev], NQ 54
ØQS4[Ø,3,4]4Z	Repos/Acetab, Rt, [Opn, Perc, Perc Endo], Int Fix Dev, NQ 156, 348
ØQS4Ø[4,Z]Z	Repos/Acetab, Rt, Opn, [Int Fix Dev, No Dev], NQ 54
ØØSN*	Repos/Acoustic Nerve 23
ØRSHØ[4,Z]Z	Repos/Acromioclavicular Jt, Lt, Opn, [Int Fix Dev, No Dev], NQ 149, 350
ØRSGØ[4,Z]Z	Repos/Acromioclavicular Jt, Rt, Opn, [Int Fix Dev, No Dev], NQ 149, 350
ØGS2*	Repos/Adrenal Gland, Lt 235, 336
ØGS3*	Repos/Adrenal Gland, Rt 235, 336
ØFSC*	Repos/Ampulla of Vater 120, 335
ØMSR*	Repos/Ankle Bursa & Lgmt, Lt 153
ØMSQ*	Repos/Ankle Bursa & Lgmt, Rt 153
ØSSGØ[4,5,Z]Z	Repos/Ankle Jt, Lt, Opn, [Int Fix Dev, Ext Fix Dev, No Dev], NQ 133, 352
ØSSFØ[4,5,Z]Z	Repos/Ankle Jt, Rt, Opn, [Int Fix Dev, Ext Fix Dev, No Dev], NQ 133, 352
ØLST*	Repos/Ankle Tndn, Lt 142, 341
ØLST[Ø,4]ZZ	Repos/Ankle Tndn, Lt, [Opn, Perc Endo] 216
ØLSS*	Repos/Ankle Tndn, Rt 142, 341
ØLSS[Ø,4]ZZ	Repos/Ankle Tndn, Rt, [Opn, Perc Endo] 216
Ø4SQ*	Repos/Ant Tibial Artery, Lt 324
Ø4SQ[Ø,3,4]ZZ	Repos/Ant Tibial Artery, Lt, [Opn, Perc, Perc Endo] 209
Ø4SP*	Repos/Ant Tibial Artery, Rt 324
Ø4SP[Ø,3,4]ZZ	Repos/Ant Tibial Artery, Rt, [Opn, Perc, Perc Endo] 209
ØDSQ*	Repos/Anus 110
ØDSK[Ø,4,7,8]ZZ	Repos/Ascending Colon, [Opn, Perc Endo, Via Natrl or Artfcl Opng, Via Natrl or Artfcl Opng Endo] 109
Ø9SA*	Repos/Auditory Ossicle, Lt 52
Ø9S9*	Repos/Auditory Ossicle, Rt 52
Ø3S6[Ø,3,4]ZZ	Repos/Axillary Artery, Lt, [Opn, Perc, Perc Endo] 208
Ø3S5[Ø,3,4]ZZ	Repos/Axillary Artery, Rt, [Opn, Perc, Perc Endo] 208
Ø5S8[Ø,3,4]ZZ	Repos/Axillary Vein, Lt, [Opn, Perc, Perc Endo] 209
Ø5S7[Ø,3,4]ZZ	Repos/Axillary Vein, Rt, [Opn, Perc, Perc Endo] 209
Ø5SC[Ø,3,4]ZZ	Repos/Basilic Vein, Lt, [Opn, Perc, Perc Endo] 209
Ø5SB[Ø,3,4]ZZ	Repos/Basilic Vein, Rt, [Opn, Perc, Perc Endo] 209
ØTSB*	Repos/Bladder 248
ØTSC*	Repos/Bladder Neck 250, 267
Ø3S8[Ø,3,4]ZZ	Repos/Brachial Artery, Lt, [Opn, Perc, Perc Endo] 208
Ø3S7[Ø,3,4]ZZ	Repos/Brachial Artery, Rt, [Opn, Perc, Perc Endo] 208
Ø5SA[Ø,3,4]ZZ	Repos/Brachial Vein, Lt, [Opn, Perc, Perc Endo] 209
Ø5S9[Ø,3,4]ZZ	Repos/Brachial Vein, Rt, [Opn, Perc, Perc Endo] 209
ØRSRØ[4,5,Z]Z	Repos/Carpal Jt, Lt, Opn, [Int Fix Dev, Ext Fix Dev, No Dev], NQ 150, 316
ØRSQØ[4,5,Z]Z	Repos/Carpal Jt, Rt, Opn, [Int Fix Dev, Ext Fix Dev, No Dev], NQ 150, 316
ØPSN[Ø,3,4][4,5]Z	Repos/Carpal, Lt, [Opn, Perc, Perc Endo], [Int Fix Dev, Ext Fix Dev], NQ 150, 315
ØPSM[Ø,3,4][4,5]Z	Repos/Carpal, Rt, [Opn, Perc, Perc Endo], [Int Fix Dev, Ext Fix Dev], NQ 150, 315
ØDSH[Ø,4,7,8]ZZ	Repos/Cecum, [Opn, Perc Endo, Via Natrl or Artfcl Opng, Via Natrl or Artfcl Opng Endo] 107, 123, 300, 334
Ø4S1*	Repos/Celiac Artery 240, 252, 324
Ø5SF[Ø,3,4]ZZ	Repos/Cephalic Vein, Lt, [Opn, Perc, Perc Endo] 209
Ø5SD[Ø,3,4]ZZ	Repos/Cephalic Vein, Rt, [Opn, Perc, Perc Endo] 209
ØØSW*	Repos/Cervical Spinal Cord 159, 160, 318
ØØSW[Ø,3,4]ZZ	Repos/Cervical Spinal Cord, [Opn, Perc, Perc Endo] 19, 296
ØRS1Ø[4,Z]Z	Repos/Cervical Vert Jt, Opn, [Int Fix Dev, No Dev], NQ 157, 350
ØPS3[Ø,4]ZZ	Repos/Cervical Vertebra, [Opn, Perc Endo] 19, 159, 160, 301, 346
ØPS3[Ø,3,4]4Z	Repos/Cervical Vertebra, [Opn, Perc, Perc Endo], Int Fix Dev, NQ 19, 159, 160, 301, 346
ØRS4Ø[4,Z]Z	Repos/Cervicothoracic Vert Jt, Opn, [Int Fix Dev, No Dev], NQ 157, 350
ØUSC*	Repos/Cervix 263, 264, 266, 272, 354
ØPSB[Ø,3,4]4Z	Repos/Clavicle, Lt, [Opn, Perc, Perc Endo], Int Fix Dev, NQ 155, 346
ØPSBØ[4,Z]Z	Repos/Clavicle, Lt, Opn, [Int Fix Dev, No Dev], NQ 54

ØPS9[Ø,3,4]4Z	Repos/Clavicle, Rt, [Opn, Perc Endo], Int Fix Dev, NQ 155, 346
ØPS9Ø[4,Z]Z	Repos/Clavicle, Rt, Opn, [Int Fix Dev, No Dev], NQ 54
ØSS6Ø[4,Z]Z	Repos/Coccygeal Jt, Opn, [Int Fix Dev, No Dev], NQ 158, 352
ØQSS*	Repos/Coccyx 159, 160, 348
ØQSS[Ø,3,4,X]ZZ	Repos/Coccyx, [Opn, Perc, Perc Endo, Ext] 19, 301
ØQSS[Ø,3,4]4Z	Repos/Coccyx, [Opn, Perc, Perc Endo], Int Fix Dev, NQ 19, 301
04S7*	Repos/Colic Artery, Lt 240, 252, 324
04S8*	Repos/Colic Artery, Mid 240, 252, 324
04S6*	Repos/Colic Artery, Rt 240, 252, 324
06S7*	Repos/Colic Vein 241, 252, 327
ØFS9*	Repos/Common Bile Duct 120, 335
03SJ*	Repos/Common Carotid Artery, Lt 21
03SH*	Repos/Common Carotid Artery, Rt 21
04SD*	Repos/Common Iliac Artery, Lt 324
04SC*	Repos/Common Iliac Artery, Rt 324
06SD*	Repos/Common Iliac Vein, Lt 327
06SC*	Repos/Common Iliac Vein, Rt 327
ØUSF*	Repos/Cul-de-sac 267
ØFS8*	Repos/Cystic Duct 120, 335
ØDSM[Ø,4,7,8]ZZ	Repos/Descending Colon, [Opn, Perc Endo, Via Natrl or Artfcl Opng, Via Natrl or Artfcl Opng Endo] 109
ØDS9[Ø,4,7,8]ZZ	Repos/Duodenum, [Opn, Perc Endo, Via Natrl or Artfcl Opng, Via Natrl or Artfcl Opng Endo] 109
ØMS4*	Repos/Elbow Bursa & Lgmt, Lt 153
ØMS3*	Repos/Elbow Bursa & Lgmt, Rt 153
ØRSM[4,5,Z]Z	Repos/Elbow Jt, Lt, Opn, [Int Fix Dev, Ext Fix Dev, No Dev], NQ 149, 350
ØRSL[4,5,Z]Z	Repos/Elbow Jt, Rt, Opn, [Int Fix Dev, Ext Fix Dev, No Dev], NQ 149, 350
ØCSR*	Repos/Epiglottis 53, 65, 332
06S3*	Repos/Esophageal Vein 241, 252, 327
ØDS5*	Repos/Esophagus 106, 334
ØNSG[4,Z]Z	Repos/Ethmoid Bone, Lt, Opn, [Int Fix Dev, No Dev], NQ 42, 49, 154, 344
ØNSF[4,Z]Z	Repos/Ethmoid Bone, Rt, Opn, [Int Fix Dev, No Dev], NQ 42, 49, 154, 344
03SN*	Repos/Ext Carotid Artery, Lt 22
03SM*	Repos/Ext Carotid Artery, Rt 22
09S2*	Repos/Ext Ear, Bilat 52, 331
09S2[Ø,4,X]ZZ	Repos/Ext Ear, Bilat, [Opn, Perc Endo, Ext] 210, 447
09S1*	Repos/Ext Ear, Lt 52, 331
09S1[Ø,4,X]ZZ	Repos/Ext Ear, Lt, [Opn, Perc Endo, Ext] 210, 447
09SØ*	Repos/Ext Ear, Rt 52, 331
09SØ[Ø,4,X]ZZ	Repos/Ext Ear, Rt, [Opn, Perc Endo, Ext] 210, 447
04SJ*	Repos/Ext Iliac Artery, Lt 324
04SH*	Repos/Ext Iliac Artery, Rt 324
06SG*	Repos/Ext Iliac Vein, Lt 327
06SF*	Repos/Ext Iliac Vein, Rt 327
08SM*	Repos/Extraocular Muscle, Lt 43
08SM[Ø,3]ZZ	Repos/Extraocular Muscle, Lt, [Opn, Perc] 445
08SL*	Repos/Extraocular Muscle, Rt 43
08SL[Ø,3]ZZ	Repos/Extraocular Muscle, Rt, [Opn, Perc] 445
03SR*	Repos/Face Artery 22
ØKS1*	Repos/Facial Muscle 44, 140, 243, 339
ØØSM*	Repos/Facial Nerve 23
ØUS6*	Repos/Fallopian Tube, Lt 263, 264, 266, 354
ØUS5*	Repos/Fallopian Tube, Rt 263, 264, 266, 354
ØUS7*	Repos/Fallopian Tubes, Bilat 263, 264, 266, 354
04SL*	Repos/Femor Artery, Lt 324
04SL[Ø,3,4]ZZ	Repos/Femor Artery, Lt, [Opn, Perc, Perc Endo] 209
04SK*	Repos/Femor Artery, Rt 324
04SK[Ø,3,4]ZZ	Repos/Femor Artery, Rt, [Opn, Perc, Perc Endo] 209
ØQS9[Ø,3,4] [4,5,6,B,C,D]Z	Repos/Femor Shaft, Lt, [Opn, Perc, Perc Endo], [Int Fix Dev, Ext Fix Dev, Int Fix Dev, Intramedullary Int Fix Dev, Ext Fix Dev, Monop, Ext Fix Dev, Ring, Ext Fix Dev, Hybrid], NQ 131, 348, 416
ØQS9Ø[4,6]Z	Repos/Femor Shaft, Lt, Opn, [Int Fix Dev, Intramedullary Int Fix Dev], NQ 244
ØQS8[Ø,3,4] [4,5,6,B,C,D]Z	Repos/Femor Shaft, Rt, [Opn, Perc, Perc Endo], [Int Fix Dev, Ext Fix Dev, Int Fix Dev, Intramedullary Int Fix Dev, Ext Fix Dev, Monop, Ext Fix Dev, Ring, Ext Fix Dev, Hybrid], NQ

ØQS8[Ø,3,4] [4,5,6,B,C,D]Z	Repos/Femor Shaft, Rt, [Opn, Perc, Perc Endo], [Int Fix Dev, Ext Fix Dev, Int Fix Dev, Intramedullary Int Fix Dev, Ext Fix Dev, Monop, Ext Fix Dev, Ring, Ext Fix Dev, Hybrid], NQ 131, 348, 416
ØQS8Ø[4,6]Z	Repos/Femor Shaft, Rt, Opn, [Int Fix Dev, Intramedullary Int Fix Dev], NQ 244
06SN*	Repos/Femor Vein, Lt 327
06SN[Ø,3,4]ZZ	Repos/Femor Vein, Lt, [Opn, Perc, Perc Endo] 209
06SM*	Repos/Femor Vein, Rt 327
06SM[Ø,3,4]ZZ	Repos/Femor Vein, Rt, [Opn, Perc, Perc Endo] 209
ØQSK[Ø,3,4] [4,5,6,B,C,D]Z	Repos/Fibula, Lt, [Opn, Perc, Perc Endo], [Int Fix Dev, Ext Fix Dev, Int Fix Dev, Intramedullary Int Fix Dev, Ext Fix Dev, Monop, Ext Fix Dev, Ring, Ext Fix Dev, Hybrid], NQ 133, 348
ØQSJ[Ø,3,4] [4,5,6,B,C,D]Z	Repos/Fibula, Rt, [Opn, Perc, Perc Endo], [Int Fix Dev, Ext Fix Dev, Int Fix Dev, Intramedullary Int Fix Dev, Ext Fix Dev, Monop, Ext Fix Dev, Ring, Ext Fix Dev, Hybrid], NQ 133, 348
ØRSXØ[4,5,Z]Z	Repos/Finger Phalangeal Jt, Lt, Opn, [Int Fix Dev, Ext Fix Dev, No Dev], NQ 150, 317
ØRSWØ[4,5,Z]Z	Repos/Finger Phalangeal Jt, Rt, Opn, [Int Fix Dev, Ext Fix Dev, No Dev], NQ 150, 317
ØPSV[Ø,3,4]5Z	Repos/Finger Phalanx, Lt, [Opn, Perc, Perc Endo], Ext Fix Dev, NQ 155, 346
ØPSV[Ø,3,4]4Z	Repos/Finger Phalanx, Lt, [Opn, Perc, Perc Endo], Int Fix Dev, NQ 150, 315
ØPST[Ø,3,4]5Z	Repos/Finger Phalanx, Rt, [Opn, Perc, Perc Endo], Ext Fix Dev, NQ 155, 346
ØPST[Ø,3,4]4Z	Repos/Finger Phalanx, Rt, [Opn, Perc, Perc Endo], Int Fix Dev, NQ 150, 315
04SW*	Repos/Foot Artery, Lt 324
04SW[Ø,3,4]ZZ	Repos/Foot Artery, Lt, [Opn, Perc, Perc Endo] 209
04SV*	Repos/Foot Artery, Rt 324
04SV[Ø,3,4]ZZ	Repos/Foot Artery, Rt, [Opn, Perc, Perc Endo] 209
ØMST*	Repos/Foot Bursa & Lgmt, Lt 153
ØMSS*	Repos/Foot Bursa & Lgmt, Rt 153
ØKSW*	Repos/Foot Muscle, Lt 140, 243, 339
ØKSV*	Repos/Foot Muscle, Rt 140, 243, 339
ØLSW*	Repos/Foot Tndn, Lt 142, 341
ØLSW[Ø,4]ZZ	Repos/Foot Tndn, Lt, [Opn, Perc Endo] 216
ØLSV*	Repos/Foot Tndn, Rt 142, 341
ØLSV[Ø,4]ZZ	Repos/Foot Tndn, Rt, [Opn, Perc Endo] 216
06SV*	Repos/Foot Vein, Lt 327
06SV[Ø,3,4]ZZ	Repos/Foot Vein, Lt, [Opn, Perc, Perc Endo] 209
06ST*	Repos/Foot Vein, Rt 327
06ST[Ø,3,4]ZZ	Repos/Foot Vein, Rt, [Opn, Perc, Perc Endo] 209
ØNS2*	Repos/Frontal Bone, Lt 10, 49, 154, 344, 415
ØNS2[Ø,3,4,X]ZZ	Repos/Frontal Bone, Lt, [Opn, Perc, Perc Endo, Ext] 14, 18
ØNS2[Ø,3,4]4Z	Repos/Frontal Bone, Lt, [Opn, Perc, Perc Endo], Int Fix Dev, NQ 14, 18
ØNS1*	Repos/Frontal Bone, Rt 10, 49, 154, 344, 415
ØNS1[Ø,3,4,X]ZZ	Repos/Frontal Bone, Rt, [Opn, Perc, Perc Endo, Ext] 14, 18
ØNS1[Ø,3,4]4Z	Repos/Frontal Bone, Rt, [Opn, Perc, Perc Endo], Int Fix Dev, NQ 14, 18
ØFS4*	Repos/Gallbladder 120, 335
ØFS4[Ø,4]ZZ	Repos/Gallbladder, [Opn, Perc Endo] 301, 449
04S2*	Repos/Gastric Artery 240, 252, 324
06S2*	Repos/Gastric Vein 241, 252, 327
ØPS8[Ø,3,4]4Z	Repos/Glenoid Cavity, Lt, [Opn, Perc, Perc Endo], Int Fix Dev, NQ 155, 346
ØPS8Ø[4,Z]Z	Repos/Glenoid Cavity, Lt, Opn, [Int Fix Dev, No Dev], NQ 54
ØPS7[Ø,3,4]4Z	Repos/Glenoid Cavity, Rt, [Opn, Perc, Perc Endo], Int Fix Dev, NQ 155, 346
ØPS7Ø[4,Z]Z	Repos/Glenoid Cavity, Rt, Opn, [Int Fix Dev, No Dev], NQ 54
ØØSP*	Repos/Glossopharyngeal Nerve 23
06SQ*	Repos/Greater Saphenous Vein, Lt 327
06SQ[Ø,3,4]ZZ	Repos/Greater Saphenous Vein, Lt, [Opn, Perc, Perc Endo] 209
06SP*	Repos/Greater Saphenous Vein, Rt 327
06SP[Ø,3,4]ZZ	Repos/Greater Saphenous Vein, Rt, [Opn, Perc, Perc Endo] 209
03SF[Ø,3,4]ZZ	Repos/Hand Artery, Lt, [Opn, Perc, Perc Endo] 208
03SD[Ø,3,4]ZZ	Repos/Hand Artery, Rt, [Opn, Perc, Perc Endo] 208
ØMS8*	Repos/Hand Bursa & Lgmt, Lt 153
ØMS7*	Repos/Hand Bursa & Lgmt, Rt 153
ØKSD*	Repos/Hand Muscle, Lt 149

ØKSD[Ø,4]ZZ	Repos/Hand Muscle, Lt, [Opn, Perc Endo] 314	
ØKSC*	Repos/Hand Muscle, Rt 149	
ØKSC[Ø,4]ZZ	Repos/Hand Muscle, Rt, [Opn, Perc Endo] 314	
ØLS8*	Repos/Hand Tndn, Lt 150	
ØLS8[Ø,4]ZZ	Repos/Hand Tndn, Lt, [Opn, Perc Endo] 315	
ØLS7*	Repos/Hand Tndn, Rt 150	
ØLS7[Ø,4]ZZ	Repos/Hand Tndn, Rt, [Opn, Perc Endo] 315	
05SH[Ø,3,4]ZZ	Repos/Hand Vein, Lt, [Opn, Perc, Perc Endo] 209	
05SG[Ø,3,4]ZZ	Repos/Hand Vein, Rt, [Opn, Perc, Perc Endo] 209	
ØCS2*	Repos/Hard Palate 25, 53	
ØCS2[Ø,X]ZZ	Repos/Hard Palate, [Opn, Ext] 211	
ØMSØ*	Repos/Head and Neck Bursa & Lgmt 153	
ØLSØ*	Repos/Head and Neck Tndn 142, 341	
ØLSØ[Ø,4]ZZ	Repos/Head and Neck Tndn, [Opn, Perc Endo] 216	
ØKSØ*	Repos/Head Muscle 140, 243, 339	
04S3*	Repos/Hepatic Artery 240, 252, 324	
ØFS6*	Repos/Hepatic Duct, Lt 120, 335	
ØFS5*	Repos/Hepatic Duct, Rt 120, 335	
06S4*	Repos/Hepatic Vein 241, 252, 327	
ØMSM*	Repos/Hip Bursa & Lgmt, Lt 153	
ØMSL*	Repos/Hip Bursa & Lgmt, Rt 153	
ØSSBØ[4,5,Z]Z	Repos/Hip Jt, Lt, Opn, [Int Fix Dev, Ext Fix Dev, No Dev], NQ 131, 352, 416	
ØSS9Ø[4,5,Z]Z	Repos/Hip Jt, Rt, Opn, [Int Fix Dev, Ext Fix Dev, No Dev], NQ 131, 352, 416	
ØKSP*	Repos/Hip Muscle, Lt 140, 243, 339	
ØKSN*	Repos/Hip Muscle, Rt 140, 243, 339	
ØLSK*	Repos/Hip Tndn, Lt 142, 341	
ØLSK[Ø,4]ZZ	Repos/Hip Tndn, Lt, [Opn, Perc Endo] 216	
ØLSJ*	Repos/Hip Tndn, Rt 142, 341	
ØLSJ[Ø,4]ZZ	Repos/Hip Tndn, Rt, [Opn, Perc Endo] 216	
ØPSD[Ø,3,4][4,5,6,B,C,D]Z	Repos/Humeral Head, Lt, [Opn, Perc, Perc Endo], [Int Fix Dev, Ext Fix Dev, Int Fix Dev, Intramedullary Int Fix Dev, Ext Fix Dev, Monop, Ext Fix Dev, Ring, Ext Fix Dev, Hybrid], NQ 133, 346	
ØPSC[Ø,3,4][4,5,6,B,C,D]Z	Repos/Humeral Head, Rt, [Opn, Perc, Perc Endo], [Int Fix Dev, Ext Fix Dev, Int Fix Dev, Intramedullary Int Fix Dev, Ext Fix Dev, Monop, Ext Fix Dev, Ring, Ext Fix Dev, Hybrid], NQ 133, 346	
ØPSG[Ø,3,4][4,5,6,B,C,D]Z	Repos/Humeral Shaft, Lt, [Opn, Perc, Perc Endo], [Int Fix Dev, Ext Fix Dev, Int Fix Dev, Intramedullary Int Fix Dev, Ext Fix Dev, Monop, Ext Fix Dev, Ring, Ext Fix Dev, Hybrid], NQ 133, 346	
ØPSF[Ø,3,4][4,5,6,B,C,D]Z	Repos/Humeral Shaft, Rt, [Opn, Perc, Perc Endo], [Int Fix Dev, Ext Fix Dev, Int Fix Dev, Intramedullary Int Fix Dev, Ext Fix Dev, Monop, Ext Fix Dev, Ring, Ext Fix Dev, Hybrid], NQ 133, 346	
ØNSXØ[4,Z]Z	Repos/Hyoid Bone, Opn, [Int Fix Dev, No Dev], NQ 42, 49, 154, 344	
06SJ*	Repos/Hypogastric Vein, Lt 327	
06SH*	Repos/Hypogastric Vein, Rt 327	
00SS*	Repos/Hypoglossal Nerve 23	
ØDSB[Ø,4,7,8]ZZ	Repos/Ileum, [Opn, Perc Endo, Via Natrl or Artfcl Opng, Via Natrl or Artfcl Opng Endo] 107, 123, 300, 334	
04SB*	Repos/Inferior Mesenteric Artery 240, 252, 324	
06S6*	Repos/Inferior Mesenteric Vein 241, 252, 327	
ØGSP*	Repos/Inferior Parathyroid Gland, Lt 238	
ØGSN*	Repos/Inferior Parathyroid Gland, Rt 238	
06SØ*	Repos/Inferior Vena Cava 241, 252, 327	
03SL*	Repos/Int Carotid Artery, Lt 21	
03SK*	Repos/Int Carotid Artery, Rt 21	
04SF*	Repos/Int Iliac Artery, Lt 324	
04SE*	Repos/Int Iliac Artery, Rt 324	
ØDSA[Ø,4,7,8]ZZ	Repos/Jejunum, [Opn, Perc Endo, Via Natrl or Artfcl Opng, Via Natrl or Artfcl Opng Endo] 109	
ØTS4*	Repos/Kidney Pelvis, Lt 249	
ØTS3*	Repos/Kidney Pelvis, Rt 249	
ØTS1*	Repos/Kidney, Lt 249, 354	
ØTSØ*	Repos/Kidney, Rt 249, 354	
ØTS2*	Repos/Kidneys, Bilat 249, 354	
ØMSP*	Repos/Knee Bursa & Lgmt, Lt 153	
ØMSN*	Repos/Knee Bursa & Lgmt, Rt 153	
ØSSDØ[4,5,Z]Z	Repos/Knee Jt, Lt, Opn, [Int Fix Dev, Ext Fix Dev, No Dev], NQ 132, 352	
ØSSCØ[4,5,Z]Z	Repos/Knee Jt, Rt, Opn, [Int Fix Dev, Ext Fix Dev, No Dev], NQ 132, 352	
ØLSR*	Repos/Knee Tndn, Lt 142, 341	
ØLSR[Ø,4]ZZ	Repos/Knee Tndn, Lt, [Opn, Perc Endo] 216	
ØLSQ*	Repos/Knee Tndn, Rt 142, 341	
ØLSQ[Ø,4]ZZ	Repos/Knee Tndn, Rt, [Opn, Perc Endo] 216	
ØNSJØ[4,Z]Z	Repos/Lacrimal Bone, Lt, Opn, [Int Fix Dev, No Dev], NQ 42, 49, 154, 344	
ØNSHØ[4,Z]Z	Repos/Lacrimal Bone, Rt, Opn, [Int Fix Dev, No Dev], NQ 42, 49, 154, 344	
08SY*	Repos/Lacrimal Duct, Lt 43, 51, 330	
08SY[Ø,3,7,8]ZZ	Repos/Lacrimal Duct, Lt, [Opn, Perc, Via Natrl or Artfcl Opng, Via Natrl or Artfcl Opng Endo] 446	
08SX*	Repos/Lacrimal Duct, Rt 43, 51, 330	
08SX[Ø,3,7,8]ZZ	Repos/Lacrimal Duct, Rt, [Opn, Perc, Via Natrl or Artfcl Opng, Via Natrl or Artfcl Opng Endo] 446	
08SW*	Repos/Lacrimal Gland, Lt 43, 330	
08SW[Ø,3]ZZ	Repos/Lacrimal Gland, Lt, [Opn, Perc] 446	
08SV*	Repos/Lacrimal Gland, Rt 43, 330	
08SV[Ø,3]ZZ	Repos/Lacrimal Gland, Rt, [Opn, Perc] 446	
06SS*	Repos/Lesser Saphenous Vein, Lt 327	
06SS[Ø,3,4]ZZ	Repos/Lesser Saphenous Vein, Lt, [Opn, Perc, Perc Endo] 209	
06SR*	Repos/Lesser Saphenous Vein, Rt 327	
06SR[Ø,3,4]ZZ	Repos/Lesser Saphenous Vein, Rt, [Opn, Perc, Perc Endo] 209	
ØFSØ*	Repos/Liver 119, 335	
00SY*	Repos/Lumbar Spinal Cord 159, 160, 318	
00SY[Ø,3,4]ZZ	Repos/Lumbar Spinal Cord, [Opn, Perc, Perc Endo] 19, 296	
ØSS00[4,Z]Z	Repos/Lumbar Vert Jt, Opn, [Int Fix Dev, No Dev], NQ 158, 352	
ØQSØ[Ø,4]ZZ	Repos/Lumbar Vertebra, [Opn, Perc Endo] 19, 160, 301, 348	
ØQSØ[Ø,3,4]4Z	Repos/Lumbar Vertebra, [Opn, Perc Endo], Int Fix Dev, NQ 19, 160, 301, 348	
ØSS30[4,Z]Z	Repos/Lumbosacral Jt, Opn, [Int Fix Dev, No Dev], NQ 158, 352	
ØKSB*	Repos/Lwr Arm and Wrist Muscle, Lt 140, 243, 339	
ØKS9*	Repos/Lwr Arm and Wrist Muscle, Rt 140, 243, 339	
ØLS6*	Repos/Lwr Arm and Wrist Tndn, Lt 142, 341	
ØLS6[Ø,4]ZZ	Repos/Lwr Arm and Wrist Tndn, Lt, [Opn, Perc Endo] 216	
ØLS5*	Repos/Lwr Arm and Wrist Tndn, Rt 142, 341	
ØLS5[Ø,4]ZZ	Repos/Lwr Arm and Wrist Tndn, Rt, [Opn, Perc Endo] 216	
04SY*	Repos/Lwr Artery 324	
04SY[Ø,3,4]ZZ	Repos/Lwr Artery, [Opn, Perc, Perc Endo] 209	
ØMSW*	Repos/Lwr Extr Bursa & Lgmt, Lt 144	
ØMSV*	Repos/Lwr Extr Bursa & Lgmt, Rt 144	
08SR*	Repos/Lwr Eyelid, Lt 25, 43, 241, 330	
08SR[Ø,3,X]ZZ	Repos/Lwr Eyelid, Lt, [Opn, Perc, Ext] 210, 446	
08SQ*	Repos/Lwr Eyelid, Rt 25, 43, 241, 330	
08SQ[Ø,3,X]ZZ	Repos/Lwr Eyelid, Rt, [Opn, Perc, Ext] 210, 445	
ØQSC[Ø,3,4][4,5,6,B,C,D]Z	Repos/Lwr Femur, Lt, [Opn, Perc, Perc Endo], [Int Fix Dev, Ext Fix Dev, Int Fix Dev, Intramedullary Int Fix Dev, Ext Fix Dev, Monop, Ext Fix Dev, Ring, Ext Fix Dev, Hybrid], NQ 131, 348, 416	
ØQSCØ[4,6]Z	Repos/Lwr Femur, Lt, Opn, [Int Fix Dev, Intramedullary Int Fix Dev], NQ 244	
ØQSB[Ø,3,4][4,5,6,B,C,D]Z	Repos/Lwr Femur, Rt, [Opn, Perc, Perc Endo], [Int Fix Dev, Ext Fix Dev, Int Fix Dev, Intramedullary Int Fix Dev, Ext Fix Dev, Monop, Ext Fix Dev, Ring, Ext Fix Dev, Hybrid], NQ 131, 348, 416	
ØQSBØ[4,6]Z	Repos/Lwr Femur, Rt, Opn, [Int Fix Dev, Intramedullary Int Fix Dev], NQ 244	
ØKST*	Repos/Lwr Leg Muscle, Lt 140, 243, 339	
ØKSS*	Repos/Lwr Leg Muscle, Rt 140, 243, 339	
ØLSP*	Repos/Lwr Leg Tndn, Lt 142, 341	
ØLSP[Ø,4]ZZ	Repos/Lwr Leg Tndn, Lt, [Opn, Perc Endo] 216	
ØLSN*	Repos/Lwr Leg Tndn, Rt 142, 341	
ØLSN[Ø,4]ZZ	Repos/Lwr Leg Tndn, Rt, [Opn, Perc Endo] 216	
ØCS1*	Repos/Lwr Lip 56, 332	
ØCS1[Ø,X]ZZ	Repos/Lwr Lip, [Opn, Ext] 211, 448	
06SY*	Repos/Lwr Vein 327	
06SY[Ø,3,4]ZZ	Repos/Lwr Vein, [Opn, Perc, Perc Endo] 209	
ØNSVØ[4,5,Z]Z	Repos/Mandible, Lt, Opn, [Int Fix Dev, Ext Fix Dev, No Dev], NQ 49, 154, 344	
ØNSTØ[4,5,Z]Z	Repos/Mandible, Rt, Opn, [Int Fix Dev, Ext Fix Dev, No Dev], NQ 49, 154, 344	
ØNSSØ[4,5,Z]Z	Repos/Maxilla, Lt, Opn, [Int Fix Dev, Ext Fix Dev, No Dev], NQ 49, 154, 344	

ØNSRØ[4,5,Z]Z	Repos/Maxilla, Rt, Opn, [Int Fix Dev, Ext Fix Dev, No Dev], NQ 49, 154, 344
ØPSQ[Ø,3,4][4,5]Z	Repos/Metacarpal, Lt, [Opn, Perc, Perc Endo], [Int Fix Dev, Ext Fix Dev], NQ 150, 315
ØPSP[Ø,3,4][4,5]Z	Repos/Metacarpal, Rt, [Opn, Perc, Perc Endo], [Int Fix Dev, Ext Fix Dev], NQ 150, 315
ØRSTØ[4,5,Z]Z	Repos/Metacarpocarpal Jt, Lt, Opn, [Int Fix Dev, No Dev], NQ 150, 316
ØRSSØ[4,5,Z]Z	Repos/Metacarpocarpal Jt, Rt, Opn, [Int Fix Dev, Ext Fix Dev, No Dev], NQ 150, 316
ØRSVØ[4,5,Z]Z	Repos/Metacarpophalangeal Jt, Lt, Opn, [Int Fix Dev, Ext Fix Dev, No Dev], NQ 150, 317
ØRSUØ[4,5,Z]Z	Repos/Metacarpophalangeal Jt, Rt, Opn, [Int Fix Dev, Ext Fix Dev, No Dev], NQ 150, 316
ØSSNØ[4,5,Z]Z	Repos/Metatarsal-Phalangeal Jt, Lt, Opn, [Int Fix Dev, Ext Fix Dev, No Dev], NQ 146, 352
ØSSMØ[4,5,Z]Z	Repos/Metatarsal-Phalangeal Jt, Rt, Opn, [Int Fix Dev, Ext Fix Dev, No Dev], NQ 146, 352
ØSSLØ[4,5,Z]Z	Repos/Metatarsal-Tarsal Jt, Lt, Opn, [Int Fix Dev, Ext Fix Dev, No Dev], NQ 146, 352
ØSSKØ[4,5,Z]Z	Repos/Metatarsal-Tarsal Jt, Rt, Opn, [Int Fix Dev, Ext Fix Dev, No Dev], NQ 146, 352
ØQSP[Ø,3,4][4,5]Z	Repos/Metatarsal, Lt, [Opn, Perc, Perc Endo], [Int Fix Dev, Ext Fix Dev], NQ 145, 348
ØQSN[Ø,3,4][4,5]Z	Repos/Metatarsal, Rt, [Opn, Perc, Perc Endo], [Int Fix Dev, Ext Fix Dev], NQ 145, 348
ØNSBØ[4,Z]Z	Repos/Nasal Bone, Opn, [Int Fix Dev, No Dev], NQ 49, 154, 216, 344, 455
Ø9SM*	Repos/Nasal Septum 52, 153, 331
Ø9SM[Ø,4]ZZ	Repos/Nasal Septum, [Opn, Perc Endo] 210, 447
Ø9SL*	Repos/Nasal Turbinate 52, 331
Ø9SL[Ø,4,7,8]ZZ	Repos/Nasal Turbinate, [Opn, Perc Endo, Via Natrl or Artfcl Opng, Via Natrl or Artfcl Opng Endo] 447
ØKS3*	Repos/Neck Muscle, Lt 140, 243, 339
ØKS2*	Repos/Neck Muscle, Rt 140, 243, 339
Ø9SK*	Repos/Nose 52, 153, 331
Ø9SK[Ø,4,X]ZZ	Repos/Nose, [Opn, Perc Endo, Ext] 210, 447
ØNS8*	Repos/Occipital Bone, Lt 10, 49, 154, 344, 415
ØNS8[Ø,3,4,X]ZZ	Repos/Occipital Bone, Lt, [Opn, Perc, Perc Endo, Ext] 14, 18
ØNS8[Ø,3,4]4Z	Repos/Occipital Bone, Lt, [Opn, Perc, Perc Endo], Int Fix Dev, NQ 14, 18
ØNS7*	Repos/Occipital Bone, Rt 10, 49, 154, 344, 415
ØNS7[Ø,3,4,X]ZZ	Repos/Occipital Bone, Rt, [Opn, Perc, Perc Endo, Ext] 14, 18
ØNS7[Ø,3,4]4Z	Repos/Occipital Bone, Rt, [Opn, Perc, Perc Endo], Int Fix Dev, NQ 14, 18
ØRSØØ[4,Z]Z	Repos/Occipital-cervical Jt, Opn, [Int Fix Dev, No Dev], NQ 157, 350
ØØSH*	Repos/Oculomotor Nerve 23
ØØSF*	Repos/Olfactory Nerve 23
ØØSG*	Repos/Optic Nerve 23
ØNSQØ[4,Z]Z	Repos/Orbit, Lt, Opn, [Int Fix Dev, No Dev], NQ 42, 49, 154, 344
ØNSPØ[4,Z]Z	Repos/Orbit, Rt, Opn, [Int Fix Dev, No Dev], NQ 42, 49, 154, 344
ØUS2*	Repos/Ovaries, Bilat 263, 264, 266, 354
ØUS1*	Repos/Ovary, Lt 263, 264, 266, 354
ØUSØ*	Repos/Ovary, Rt 263, 264, 266, 354
ØNSLØ[4,Z]Z	Repos/Palatine Bone, Lt, Opn, [Int Fix Dev, No Dev], NQ 42, 49, 154, 344
ØNSKØ[4,Z]Z	Repos/Palatine Bone, Rt, Opn, [Int Fix Dev, No Dev], NQ 42, 49, 154, 344
ØFSG*	Repos/Pancreas 119
ØFSD*	Repos/Pancreatic Duct 119, 335
ØFSF*	Repos/Pancreatic Duct, Accessory 119, 335
ØGSR*	Repos/Parathyroid Gland 238
ØGSQ*	Repos/Parathyroid Glands, Multi 238
ØNS4*	Repos/Parietal Bone, Lt 10, 49, 154, 344, 415
ØNS4[Ø,3,4,X]ZZ	Repos/Parietal Bone, Lt, [Opn, Perc, Perc Endo, Ext] 14, 18
ØNS4[Ø,3,4]4Z	Repos/Parietal Bone, Lt, [Opn, Perc, Perc Endo], Int Fix Dev, NQ 14, 18
ØNS3*	Repos/Parietal Bone, Rt 10, 49, 154, 344, 415
ØNS3[Ø,3,4,X]ZZ	Repos/Parietal Bone, Rt, [Opn, Perc, Perc Endo, Ext] 14, 18
ØNS3[Ø,3,4]4Z	Repos/Parietal Bone, Rt, [Opn, Perc, Perc Endo], Int Fix Dev, NQ 14, 18
ØCSC*	Repos/Parotid Duct, Lt 57, 332
ØCSB*	Repos/Parotid Duct, Rt 57, 332
ØQSF[Ø,3,4][4,5]Z	Repos/Patella, Lt, [Opn, Perc, Perc Endo], [Int Fix Dev, Ext Fix Dev], NQ 348
ØQSF[Ø,3,4]5Z	Repos/Patella, Lt, [Opn, Perc, Perc Endo], Ext Fix Dev, NQ 132
ØQSF[Ø,3,4]4Z	Repos/Patella, Lt, [Opn, Perc, Perc Endo], Int Fix Dev, NQ 156
ØQSFØ[4,Z]Z	Repos/Patella, Lt, Opn, [Int Fix Dev, No Dev], NQ 55
ØQSD[Ø,3,4][4,5]Z	Repos/Patella, Rt, [Opn, Perc, Perc Endo], [Int Fix Dev, Ext Fix Dev], NQ 348
ØQSD[Ø,3,4]5Z	Repos/Patella, Rt, [Opn, Perc, Perc Endo], Ext Fix Dev, NQ 132
ØQSD[Ø,3,4]4Z	Repos/Patella, Rt, [Opn, Perc, Perc Endo], Int Fix Dev, NQ 156
ØQSDØ[4,Z]Z	Repos/Patella, Rt, Opn, [Int Fix Dev, No Dev], NQ 55
ØQS3[Ø,3,4][4,5]Z	Repos/Pelvic Bone, Lt, [Opn, Perc, Perc Endo], [Int Fix Dev, Ext Fix Dev], NQ 156, 348
ØQS3Ø[4,Z]Z	Repos/Pelvic Bone, Lt, Opn, [Int Fix Dev, No Dev], NQ 54
ØQS2[Ø,3,4][4,5]Z	Repos/Pelvic Bone, Rt, [Opn, Perc, Perc Endo], [Int Fix Dev, Ext Fix Dev], NQ 156, 348
ØQS2Ø[4,Z]Z	Repos/Pelvic Bone, Rt, Opn, [Int Fix Dev, No Dev], NQ 54
ØMSK*	Repos/Perineum Bursa & Lgmt 153
ØKSM*	Repos/Perineum Muscle 140, 243, 339
ØLSH*	Repos/Perineum Tndn 142, 341
ØLSH[Ø,4]ZZ	Repos/Perineum Tndn, [Opn, Perc Endo] 216
Ø4SU*	Repos/Peroneal Artery, Lt 324
Ø4SU[Ø,3,4]ZZ	Repos/Peroneal Artery, Lt, [Opn, Perc, Perc Endo] 209
Ø4ST*	Repos/Peroneal Artery, Rt 324
Ø4ST[Ø,3,4]ZZ	Repos/Peroneal Artery, Rt, [Opn, Perc, Perc Endo] 209
Ø4SN*	Repos/Popliteal Artery, Lt 324
Ø4SN[Ø,3,4]ZZ	Repos/Popliteal Artery, Lt, [Opn, Perc, Perc Endo] 209
Ø4SM*	Repos/Popliteal Artery, Rt 324
Ø4SM[Ø,3,4]ZZ	Repos/Popliteal Artery, Rt, [Opn, Perc, Perc Endo] 209
Ø6S8*	Repos/Portal Vein 241, 252, 327
Ø4SS[Ø,3,4]ZZ	Repos/Post Tibial Artery, Lt, [Opn, Perc, Perc Endo] 209
Ø4SR[Ø,3,4]ZZ	Repos/Post Tibial Artery, Rt, [Opn, Perc, Perc Endo] 209
Ø4SS*	Repos/Posterior Tibial Artery, Lt 324
Ø4SR*	Repos/Posterior Tibial Artery, Rt 324
1ØS2*	Repos/Products of Conception, Ectopic 269
Ø3SC[Ø,3,4]ZZ	Repos/Radial Artery, Lt, [Opn, Perc, Perc Endo] 208
Ø3SB[Ø,3,4]ZZ	Repos/Radial Artery, Rt, [Opn, Perc, Perc Endo] 208
ØPSJ[Ø,3,4] [4,5,6,B,C,D]Z	Repos/Radius, Lt, [Opn, Perc, Perc Endo], [Int Fix Dev, Ext Fix Dev, Int Fix Dev, Intramedullary Int Fix Dev, Ext Fix Dev, Monop, Ext Fix Dev, Ring, Ext Fix Dev, Hybrid], NQ 149, 346
ØPSJ[3,4][4,6]Z	Repos/Radius, Lt, [Perc, Perc Endo], [Int Fix Dev, Intramedullary Int Fix Dev], NQ 456
ØPSH[Ø,3,4] [4,5,6,B,C,D]Z	Repos/Radius, Rt, [Opn, Perc, Perc Endo], [Int Fix Dev, Ext Fix Dev, Int Fix Dev, Intramedullary Int Fix Dev, Ext Fix Dev, Monop, Ext Fix Dev, Ring, Ext Fix Dev, Hybrid], NQ 149, 346
ØPSH[3,4][4,6]Z	Repos/Radius, Rt, [Perc, Perc Endo], [Int Fix Dev, Intramedullary Int Fix Dev], NQ 456
ØDSP[Ø,4,7,8]ZZ	Repos/Rectum, [Opn, Perc Endo, Via Natrl or Artfcl Opng, Via Natrl or Artfcl Opng Endo] 107, 334
Ø4SA*	Repos/Renal Artery, Lt 248
Ø4S9*	Repos/Renal Artery, Rt 248
Ø6SB*	Repos/Renal Vein, Lt 248
Ø6S9*	Repos/Renal Vein, Rt 248
ØPS2[Ø,3,4]4Z	Repos/Rib, Lt, [Opn, Perc, Perc Endo], Int Fix Dev, NQ 155, 346
ØPS2Ø[4,Z]Z	Repos/Rib, Lt, Opn, [Int Fix Dev, No Dev], NQ 54
ØPS1[Ø,3,4]4Z	Repos/Rib, Rt, [Opn, Perc, Perc Endo], Int Fix Dev, NQ 155, 346
ØPS1Ø[4,Z]Z	Repos/Rib, Rt, Opn, [Int Fix Dev, No Dev], NQ 54
ØSS5Ø[4,Z]Z	Repos/Sacrococcygeal Jt, Opn, [Int Fix Dev, No Dev], NQ 158, 352
ØSS8Ø[4,Z]Z	Repos/Sacroiliac Jt, Lt, Opn, [Int Fix Dev, No Dev], NQ 158, 352
ØSS7Ø[4,Z]Z	Repos/Sacroiliac Jt, Rt, Opn, [Int Fix Dev, No Dev], NQ 158, 352
ØQS1[Ø,4]ZZ	Repos/Sacrum, [Opn, Perc Endo] 19, 159, 160, 301, 348
ØQS1[Ø,3,4]4Z	Repos/Sacrum, [Opn, Perc, Perc Endo], Int Fix Dev, NQ 19, 159, 160, 301, 348
ØPS6[Ø,3,4]4Z	Repos/Scapula, Lt, [Opn, Perc, Perc Endo], Int Fix Dev, NQ 155, 346
ØPS6Ø[4,Z]Z	Repos/Scapula, Lt, Opn, [Int Fix Dev, No Dev], NQ 54
ØPS5[Ø,3,4]4Z	Repos/Scapula, Rt, [Opn, Perc, Perc Endo], Int Fix Dev, NQ 155, 346
ØPS5Ø[4,Z]Z	Repos/Scapula, Rt, Opn, [Int Fix Dev, No Dev], NQ 54
ØMS2*	Repos/Shldr Bursa & Lgmt, Lt 153
ØMS1*	Repos/Shldr Bursa & Lgmt, Rt 153

0RSK0[4,Z]Z	Repos/Shldr Jt, Lt, Opn, [Int Fix Dev, No Dev], NQ 149, 350
0RSJ0[4,Z]Z	Repos/Shldr Jt, Rt, Opn, [Int Fix Dev, No Dev], NQ 149, 350
0KS6*	Repos/Shldr Muscle, Lt 140, 243, 339
0KS5*	Repos/Shldr Muscle, Rt 140, 243, 339
0LS2*	Repos/Shldr Tndn, Lt 142, 341
0LS2[0,4]ZZ	Repos/Shldr Tndn, Lt, [Opn, Perc Endo] 216
0LS1*	Repos/Shldr Tndn, Rt 142, 341
0LS1[0,4]ZZ	Repos/Shldr Tndn, Rt, [Opn, Perc Endo] 216
0DSN[0,4,7,8]ZZ	Repos/Sigmoid Colon, [Opn, Perc Endo, Via Natrl or Artfcl Opng, Via Natrl or Artfcl Opng Endo] 109
0NS0*	Repos/Skull 10, 49, 154, 344, 415
0NS0[0,3,4][4,5,Z]Z	Repos/Skull, [Opn, Perc, Perc Endo], [Int Fix Dev, Ext Fix Dev, No Dev], NQ 14, 18
0CS3*	Repos/Soft Palate 25, 53
0CS3[0,X]ZZ	Repos/Soft Palate, [Opn, Ext] 211
0VSG*	Repos/Spermatic Cord, Lt 355
0VSF*	Repos/Spermatic Cord, Rt 355
0VSH*	Repos/Spermatic Cords, Bilat 355
0NSD0[4,Z]Z	Repos/Sphenoid Bone, Lt, Opn, [Int Fix Dev, No Dev], NQ 42, 49, 154, 344
0NSC0[4,Z]Z	Repos/Sphenoid Bone, Rt, Opn, [Int Fix Dev, No Dev], NQ 42, 49, 154, 344
04S4*	Repos/Splenic Artery 240, 252, 324
06S1*	Repos/Splenic Vein 241, 252, 327
0RSF0[4,Z]Z	Repos/Sternoclavicular Jt, Lt, Opn, [Int Fix Dev, No Dev], NQ 149, 350
0RSE0[4,Z]Z	Repos/Sternoclavicular Jt, Rt, Opn, [Int Fix Dev, No Dev], NQ 149, 350
0PS0[0,3,4][0,4]Z	Repos/Sternum, [Opn, Perc, Perc Endo], [Int Fix Dev, Rigid Plate, Int Fix Dev], NQ 155, 346
0PS0[0,3,4]0Z	Repos/Sternum, [Opn, Perc, Perc Endo], Int Fix Dev, Rigid Plate, NQ 66, 91
0PS00[4,Z]Z	Repos/Sternum, Opn, [Int Fix Dev, No Dev], NQ 54
0DS6[7,8]ZZ	Repos/Stomach, [Via Natrl or Artfcl Opng, Via Natrl or Artfcl Opng Endo] 123, 242
04S5*	Repos/Superior Mesenteric Artery 240, 252, 324
06S5*	Repos/Superior Mesenteric Vein 241, 252, 327
0GSM*	Repos/Superior Parathyroid Gland, Lt 238
0GSL*	Repos/Superior Parathyroid Gland, Rt 238
0SSJ0[4,5,Z]Z	Repos/Tarsal Jt, Lt, Opn, [Int Fix Dev, Ext Fix Dev, No Dev], NQ 146, 352
0SSH0[4,5,Z]Z	Repos/Tarsal Jt, Rt, Opn, [Int Fix Dev, Ext Fix Dev, No Dev], NQ 146, 352
0QSM[0,3,4][4,5]Z	Repos/Tarsal, Lt, [Opn, Perc, Perc Endo], [Int Fix Dev, Ext Fix Dev], NQ 145, 348
0QSL[0,3,4][4,5]Z	Repos/Tarsal, Rt, [Opn, Perc, Perc Endo], [Int Fix Dev, Ext Fix Dev], NQ 145, 348
03ST*	Repos/Temporal Artery, Lt 22
03SS*	Repos/Temporal Artery, Rt 22
0NS6*	Repos/Temporal Bone, Lt 10, 49, 154, 344, 415
0NS6[0,3,4,X]ZZ	Repos/Temporal Bone, Lt, [Opn, Perc, Perc Endo, Ext] 14, 18
0NS6[0,3,4]4Z	Repos/Temporal Bone, Lt, [Opn, Perc, Perc Endo], Int Fix Dev, NQ 14, 18
0NS5*	Repos/Temporal Bone, Rt 10, 49, 154, 344, 415
0NS5[0,3,4,X]ZZ	Repos/Temporal Bone, Rt, [Opn, Perc, Perc Endo, Ext] 14, 18
0NS5[0,3,4]4Z	Repos/Temporal Bone, Rt, [Opn, Perc, Perc Endo], Int Fix Dev, NQ 14, 18
0RSD0[4,Z]Z	Repos/Temporomandibular Jt, Lt, Opn, [Int Fix Dev, No Dev], NQ 49, 157, 350
0RSC0[4,Z]Z	Repos/Temporomandibular Jt, Rt, Opn, [Int Fix Dev, No Dev], NQ 49, 157, 350
00SX*	Repos/Thoracic Spinal Cord 159, 160, 318
00SX[0,3,4]ZZ	Repos/Thoracic Spinal Cord, [Opn, Perc, Perc Endo] 19, 296
0RS60[4,Z]Z	Repos/Thoracic Vert Jt, Opn, [Int Fix Dev, No Dev], NQ 157, 350
0PS4[0,4]ZZ	Repos/Thoracic Vertebra, [Opn, Perc Endo] 19, 159, 160, 301, 346
0PS4[0,3,4]4Z	Repos/Thoracic Vertebra, [Opn, Perc, Perc Endo], Int Fix Dev, NQ 19, 159, 160, 301, 346
0RSA0[4,Z]Z	Repos/Thoracolumbar Vert Jt, Opn, [Int Fix Dev, No Dev], NQ 157, 350
0MSG*	Repos/Thorax Bursa & Lgmt, Lt 153
0MSF*	Repos/Thorax Bursa & Lgmt, Rt 153
0KSJ*	Repos/Thorax Muscle, Lt 140, 243, 339
0KSH*	Repos/Thorax Muscle, Rt 140, 243, 339
0LSD*	Repos/Thorax Tndn, Lt 142, 341
0LSD[0,4]ZZ	Repos/Thorax Tndn, Lt, [Opn, Perc Endo] 216
0LSC*	Repos/Thorax Tndn, Rt 142, 341
0LSC[0,4]ZZ	Repos/Thorax Tndn, Rt, [Opn, Perc Endo] 216
0PSS[0,3,4]5Z	Repos/Thumb Phalanx, Lt, [Opn, Perc, Perc Endo], Ext Fix Dev, NQ 155, 346
0PSS[0,3,4]4Z	Repos/Thumb Phalanx, Lt, [Opn, Perc, Perc Endo], Int Fix Dev, NQ 150, 315
0PSR[0,3,4]5Z	Repos/Thumb Phalanx, Rt, [Opn, Perc, Perc Endo], Ext Fix Dev, NQ 155, 346
0PSR[0,3,4]4Z	Repos/Thumb Phalanx, Rt, [Opn, Perc, Perc Endo], Int Fix Dev, NQ 150, 315
0GSG*	Repos/Thyroid Gland Lobe, Lt 238
0GSH*	Repos/Thyroid Gland Lobe, Rt 238
0QSH[0,3,4][4,5,6,B,C,D]Z	Repos/Tibia, Lt, [Opn, Perc, Perc Endo], [Int Fix Dev, Ext Fix Dev, Int Fix Dev, Intramedullary Int Fix Dev, Ext Fix Dev, Monop, Ext Fix Dev, Ring, Ext Fix Dev, Hybrid], NQ 133, 348
0QSG[0,3,4][4,5,6,B,C,D]Z	Repos/Tibia, Rt, [Opn, Perc, Perc Endo], [Int Fix Dev, Ext Fix Dev, Int Fix Dev, Intramedullary Int Fix Dev, Ext Fix Dev, Monop, Ext Fix Dev, Ring, Ext Fix Dev, Hybrid], NQ 133, 348
0SSQ0[4,5,Z]Z	Repos/Toe Phalangeal Jt, Lt, Opn, [Int Fix Dev, Ext Fix Dev, No Dev], NQ 146, 352
0SSP0[4,5,Z]Z	Repos/Toe Phalangeal Jt, Rt, Opn, [Int Fix Dev, Ext Fix Dev, No Dev], NQ 146, 352
0QSR[0,3,4][4,5]Z	Repos/Toe Phalanx, Lt, [Opn, Perc, Perc Endo], [Int Fix Dev, Ext Fix Dev], NQ 348
0QSR[0,3,4]5Z	Repos/Toe Phalanx, Lt, [Opn, Perc, Perc Endo], Ext Fix Dev, NQ 156
0QSR[0,3,4]4Z	Repos/Toe Phalanx, Lt, [Opn, Perc, Perc Endo], Int Fix Dev, NQ 145
0QSQ[0,3,4][4,5]Z	Repos/Toe Phalanx, Rt, [Opn, Perc, Perc Endo], [Int Fix Dev, Ext Fix Dev], NQ 348
0QSQ[0,3,4]5Z	Repos/Toe Phalanx, Rt, [Opn, Perc, Perc Endo], Ext Fix Dev, NQ 156
0QSQ[0,3,4]4Z	Repos/Toe Phalanx, Rt, [Opn, Perc, Perc Endo], Int Fix Dev, NQ 145
0CS7*	Repos/Tongue 56, 332
0KS4*	Repos/Tongue, Palate, Pharynx Muscle 140, 243, 339
0DSL[0,4,7,8]ZZ	Repos/Transv Colon, [Opn, Perc Endo, Via Natrl or Artfcl Opng, Via Natrl or Artfcl Opng Endo] 109
00SK*	Repos/Trigeminal Nerve 23
00SJ*	Repos/Trochlear Nerve 23
0MSD*	Repos/Trunk Bursa & Lgmt, Lt 153
0MSC*	Repos/Trunk Bursa & Lgmt, Rt 153
0KSG*	Repos/Trunk Muscle, Lt 140, 243, 339
0KSF*	Repos/Trunk Muscle, Rt 140, 243, 339
0LSB*	Repos/Trunk Tndn, Lt 142, 341
0LSB[0,4]ZZ	Repos/Trunk Tndn, Lt, [Opn, Perc Endo] 216
0LS9*	Repos/Trunk Tndn, Rt 142, 341
0LS9[0,4]ZZ	Repos/Trunk Tndn, Rt, [Opn, Perc Endo] 216
09S8*	Repos/Tympanic Membrane, Lt 52
09S8[0,4,7,8]ZZ	Repos/Tympanic Membrane, Lt, [Opn, Perc Endo, Via Natrl or Artfcl Opng, Via Natrl or Artfcl Opng Endo] 447
09S7*	Repos/Tympanic Membrane, Rt 52
09S7[0,4,7,8]ZZ	Repos/Tympanic Membrane, Rt, [Opn, Perc Endo, Via Natrl or Artfcl Opng, Via Natrl or Artfcl Opng Endo] 447
0PSL[0,3,4][4,5,6,B,C,D]Z	Repos/Ulna, Lt, [Opn, Perc, Perc Endo], [Int Fix Dev, Ext Fix Dev, Int Fix Dev, Intramedullary Int Fix Dev, Ext Fix Dev, Monop, Ext Fix Dev, Ring, Ext Fix Dev, Hybrid], NQ 149, 346
0PSL[3,4][4,6]Z	Repos/Ulna, Lt, [Perc, Perc Endo], [Int Fix Dev, Intramedullary Int Fix Dev], NQ 456
0PSK[0,3,4][4,5,6,B,C,D]Z	Repos/Ulna, Rt, [Opn, Perc, Perc Endo], [Int Fix Dev, Ext Fix Dev, Int Fix Dev, Intramedullary Int Fix Dev, Ext Fix Dev, Monop, Ext Fix Dev, Ring, Ext Fix Dev, Hybrid], NQ 149, 346
0PSK[3,4][4,6]Z	Repos/Ulna, Rt, [Perc, Perc Endo], [Int Fix Dev, Intramedullary Int Fix Dev], NQ 456
03SA[0,3,4]ZZ	Repos/Ulnar Artery, Lt, [Opn, Perc, Perc Endo] 208
03S9[0,3,4]ZZ	Repos/Ulnar Artery, Rt, [Opn, Perc, Perc Endo] 208
0KS8*	Repos/Upr Arm Muscle, Lt 140, 243, 339
0KS7*	Repos/Upr Arm Muscle, Rt 140, 243, 339
0LS4*	Repos/Upr Arm Tndn, Lt 142, 341
0LS4[0,4]ZZ	Repos/Upr Arm Tndn, Lt, [Opn, Perc Endo] 216

ØLS3*	Repos/Upr Arm Tndn, Rt 142, 341
ØLS3[Ø,4]ZZ	Repos/Upr Arm Tndn, Rt, [Opn, Perc Endo] 216
ØMSB*	Repos/Upr Extr Bursa & Lgmt, Lt 144
ØMS9*	Repos/Upr Extr Bursa & Lgmt, Rt 144
Ø8SP*	Repos/Upr Eyelid, Lt 25, 43, 241, 330
Ø8SP[Ø,3,X]ZZ	Repos/Upr Eyelid, Lt, [Opn, Perc, Ext] 210, 445
Ø8SN*	Repos/Upr Eyelid, Rt 25, 43, 241, 330
Ø8SN[Ø,3,X]ZZ	Repos/Upr Eyelid, Rt, [Opn, Perc, Ext] 210, 445
ØQS7[Ø,3,4] [4,5,6,B,C,D]Z	Repos/Upr Femur, Lt, [Opn, Perc, Perc Endo], [Int Fix Dev, Ext Fix Dev, Int Fix Dev, Intramedullary Int Fix Dev, Ext Fix Dev, Monop, Ext Fix Dev, Ring, Ext Fix Dev, Hybrid], NQ 131, 348, 416
ØQS7Ø[4,6]Z	Repos/Upr Femur, Lt, Opn, [Int Fix Dev, Intramedullary Int Fix Dev], NQ 244
ØQS6[Ø,3,4] [4,5,6,B,C,D]Z	Repos/Upr Femur, Rt, [Opn, Perc, Perc Endo], [Int Fix Dev, Ext Fix Dev, Int Fix Dev, Intramedullary Int Fix Dev, Ext Fix Dev, Monop, Ext Fix Dev, Ring, Ext Fix Dev, Hybrid], NQ 131, 348, 416
ØQS6Ø[4,6]Z	Repos/Upr Femur, Rt, Opn, [Int Fix Dev, Intramedullary Fix Dev], NQ 244
ØKSR*	Repos/Upr Leg Muscle, Lt 140, 243, 339
ØKSQ*	Repos/Upr Leg Muscle, Rt 140, 243, 339
ØLSM*	Repos/Upr Leg Tndn, Lt 142, 341
ØLSM[Ø,4]ZZ	Repos/Upr Leg Tndn, Lt, [Opn, Perc Endo] 216
ØLSL*	Repos/Upr Leg Tndn, Rt 142, 341
ØLSL[Ø,4]ZZ	Repos/Upr Leg Tndn, Rt, [Opn, Perc Endo] 216
ØCSØ*	Repos/Upr Lip 56, 332
ØCSØ[Ø,X]ZZ	Repos/Upr Lip, [Opn, Ext] 211, 448
ØTS7*	Repos/Ureter, Lt 249
ØTS6*	Repos/Ureter, Rt 249
ØTS8*	Repos/Ureters, Bilat 249
ØTSD*	Repos/Urethra 250, 257, 267
ØUS4*	Repos/Uterine Supporting Structure 267, 354
ØUS9[Ø,4]ZZ	Repos/Uterus, [Opn, Perc Endo] 267, 272
ØCSN*	Repos/Uvula 56
ØCSN[Ø,X]ZZ	Repos/Uvula, [Opn, Ext] 448
ØUSG*	Repos/Vagina 250, 267
ØØSQ*	Repos/Vagus Nerve 23
Ø3SQ*	Repos/Vert Artery, Lt 22
Ø3SP*	Repos/Vert Artery, Rt 22
ØCSV*	Repos/Vocal Cord, Lt 53, 65, 332
ØCST*	Repos/Vocal Cord, Rt 53, 65, 332
ØMS6*	Repos/Wrist Bursa & Lgmt, Lt 153
ØMS5*	Repos/Wrist Bursa & Lgmt, Rt 153
ØRSP[4,5,Z]Z	Repos/Wrist Jt, Lt, Opn, [Int Fix Dev, Ext Fix Dev, No Dev], NQ 150, 316
ØRSN[4,5,Z]Z	Repos/Wrist Jt, Rt, Opn, [Int Fix Dev, Ext Fix Dev, No Dev], NQ 150, 316
ØNSN[4,Z]Z	Repos/Zygomatic Bone, Lt, Opn, [Int Fix Dev, No Dev], NQ 49, 154, 344
ØNSM[4,Z]Z	Repos/Zygomatic Bone, Rt, Opn, [Int Fix Dev, No Dev], NQ 49, 154, 344
ØRT[3,4,5,9,B]ØZZ	Resect [Cervical Vert Disc, Cervicothoracic Vert Jt, Cervicothoracic Vert Disc, Thoracic Vert Disc, Thoracolumbar Vert Disc], Opn 20, 159, 161
ØST[2,4]ØZZ	Resect [Lumbar Vert Disc, Lumbosacral Disc], Opn 20, 160, 161
ØPT[Ø,1,2,5,6,7,8,9,B] ØZZ	Resect [Sternum, Rt rib, Lt rib, Rt scapula, Lt scapula, Rt glenoid cavity, Lt glenoid cavity, Rt clavicle, Lt clavicle], Opn 19
Ø9T[9,A,D,E]ØZZ	Resect of [Rt Auditory Ossicle, Lt Auditory Ossicle, Rt Inner Ear, Lt Inner Ear], Opn Appr 52
ØPT[M,N,P,Q]ØZZ	Resect of [Rt Carpal, Lt Carpal, Rt Metacarpal, Lt Metacarpal], Opn Appr 150
ØPT[7,8,9,B]ØZZ	Resect of [Rt Glenoid Cavity, Lt Glenoid Cavity, Rt Clavicle, Lt Clavicle], Opn Appr 66, 155
ØST[M,N]ØZZ	Resect of [Rt Metatarsal-Phalangeal Jt, Rt Metatarsal-Phalangeal Jt], Opn 146
ØST[K,L]ØZZ	Resect of [Rt Metatarsal-Tarsal Jt, Lt Metatarsal-Tarsal Jt], Opn 146
ØQT[2,3,4,5]ØZZ	Resect of [Rt Pelvic Bone, Lt Pelvic Bone, Rt Acetab, Lt Acetab], Opn Appr 55, 156
ØPT[H,J,K,L]ØZZ	Resect of [Rt Radius, Lt Radius, Rt Ulna, Lt Ulna], Opn Appr 149

ØRT[J,K,L,M]ØZZ	Resect of [Rt Shldr, Lt Shldr, Rt Elbow, Lt Elbow] Jt, Opn Appr 149
ØPT[R,S,T,V]ØZZ	Resect of [Rt Thumb, Lt Thumb, Rt Finger, Lt Finger] Phalanx, Opn Appr 54, 155
ØQT[G,H,J,K]ØZZ	Resect of [Rt Tibia, Lt Tibia, Rt Fibula, Lt Fibula], Opn Appr 133
ØST[P,Q]ØZZ	Resect of [Rt Toe Phalangeal Jt, Lt Toe Phalangeal Jt], Opn 146
ØQT[Q,R,S]ØZZ	Resect of [Rt Toe Phalanx, Lt Toe Phalanx, Coccyx], Opn Appr 55, 156
ØRT[G,H]ØZZ	Resect of [Rt, Lt] Acromioclavicular Jt, Opn Appr 149
ØST[F,G]ØZZ	Resect of [Rt, Lt] Ankle Jt, Opn Appr 133
ØRT[Q,R]ØZZ	Resect of [Rt, Lt] Carpal Jt, Opn Appr 151
ØNT[F,G]ØZZ	Resect of [Rt, Lt] Ethmoid Bone, Opn Appr 49
Ø8T[Ø,1]XZZ	Resect of [Rt, Lt] Eye, Ext Appr 42, 48, 153
ØQT[8,9]ØZZ	Resect of [Rt, Lt] Femor Shaft, Opn Appr 131
ØRT[W,X]ØZZ	Resect of [Rt, Lt] Finger Phalangeal Jt, Opn Appr 151
ØNT[1,2]ØZZ	Resect of [Rt, Lt] Frontal Bone, Opn Appr 49
ØST[9,B]ØZZ	Resect of [Rt, Lt] Hip Jt, Opn Appr 131
ØPT[C,D]ØZZ	Resect of [Rt, Lt] Humeral Head, Opn Appr 133
ØPT[F,G]ØZZ	Resect of [Rt, Lt] Humeral Shaft, Opn Appr 133
ØST[C,D]ØZZ	Resect of [Rt, Lt] Knee Jt, Opn Appr 132
ØNT[H,J]ØZZ	Resect of [Rt, Lt] Lacrimal Bone, Opn Appr 49
ØQT[B,C]ØZZ	Resect of [Rt, Lt] Lwr Femur, Opn Appr 131
ØNT[T,V]ØZZ	Resect of [Rt, Lt] Mandible, Opn Appr 48
ØNT[R,S]ØZZ	Resect of [Rt, Lt] Maxilla, Opn Appr 49
ØRT[S,T]ØZZ	Resect of [Rt, Lt] Metacarpocarpal Jt, Opn Appr 151
ØRT[U,V]ØZZ	Resect of [Rt, Lt] Metacarpophalangeal Jt, Opn Appr 151
ØQT[N,P]ØZZ	Resect of [Rt, Lt] Metatarsal, Opn Appr 145
Ø9T[5,6]ØZZ	Resect of [Rt, Lt] Mid Ear, Opn Appr 52
ØNT[7,8]ØZZ	Resect of [Rt, Lt] Occipital Bone, Opn Appr 49
ØNT[P,Q]ØZZ	Resect of [Rt, Lt] Orbit, Opn Appr 49
ØNT[K,L]ØZZ	Resect of [Rt, Lt] Palatine Bone, Opn Appr 49
ØNT[3,4]ØZZ	Resect of [Rt, Lt] Parietal Bone, Opn Appr 49
ØCT[B,C]ØZZ	Resect of [Rt, Lt] Parotid Duct, Opn Appr 57
ØCT[8,9]ØZZ	Resect of [Rt, Lt] Parotid Gland, Opn Appr 57
ØQT[D,F]ØZZ	Resect of [Rt, Lt] Patella, Opn Appr 132
ØST[7,8]ØZZ	Resect of [Rt, Lt] Sacroiliac Jt, Opn Appr 158
ØNT[C,D]ØZZ	Resect of [Rt, Lt] Sphenoid Bone, Opn Appr 49
ØRT[E,F]ØZZ	Resect of [Rt, Lt] Sternoclavicular Jt, Opn Appr 149
ØCT[D,F]ØZZ	Resect of [Rt, Lt] Sublingual Gland, Opn Appr 57
ØCT[G,H]ØZZ	Resect of [Rt, Lt] Submaxillary Gland, Opn Appr 57
ØST[H,J]ØZZ	Resect of [Rt, Lt] Tarsal Jt, Opn Appr 146
ØQT[L,M]ØZZ	Resect of [Rt, Lt] Tarsal, Opn Appr 145
ØNT[5,6]ØZZ	Resect of [Rt, Lt] Temporal Bone, Opn Appr 49
ØRT[C,D]ØZZ	Resect of [Rt, Lt] Temporomandibular Jt, Opn Appr 49, 157
ØQT[6,7]ØZZ	Resect of [Rt, Lt] Upr Femur, Opn Appr 131
ØRT[N,P]ØZZ	Resect of [Rt, Lt] Wrist Jt, Opn Appr 151
ØNT[M,N]ØZZ	Resect of [Rt, Lt] Zygomatic Bone, Opn Appr 49
ØST[5,6]ØZZ	Resect of [Sacrococcygeal, Coccygeal] Jt, Opn Appr 158
ØPT[Ø,1,2,5,6]ØZZ	Resect of [Sternum, Rt Rib, Lt Rib, Rt Scapula, Lt Scapula], Opn Appr 66, 155
ØHTVØZZ	Resect of Bilat Breast, Opn Appr 221, 222, 223, 337
ØUT7ØZZ	Resect of Bilat Fallopian Tubes, Opn Appr 107, 262, 462
ØUT2ØZZ	Resect of Bilat Ovaries, Opn Appr 107, 262, 462
ØTTBØZZ	Resect of Bladder, Opn Appr 107, 262
ØRT3ØZZ	Resect of Cervical Vert Disc, Opn Appr 350
ØRT5ØZZ	Resect of Cervicothoracic Vert Disc, Opn Appr 350
ØRT4ØZZ	Resect of Cervicothoracic Vert Jt, Opn Appr 350
ØUTCØZZ	Resect of Cervix, Opn Appr 107, 262
ØUTC4ZZ	Resect of Cervix, Perc Endo Appr 262
Ø2T83ZZ	Resect of Conduction Mechanism, Perc Appr 98
ØDT9ØZZ	Resect of Duodenum, Opn Appr 106
ØFT4ØZZ	Resect of Gallbladder, Opn Appr 121
ØFT44ZZ	Resect of Gallbladder, Perc Endo Appr 121, 449
ØUTKXZZ	Resect of Hymen, Ext Appr 459
ØNTXØZZ	Resect of Hyoid Bone, Opn Appr 49
ØQT5ØZZ	Resect of Lt Acetabulum, Opn Appr 244
ØRTHØZZ	Resect of Lt Acromioclavicular Jt, Opn Appr 350
Ø9TAØZZ	Resect of Lt Auditory Ossicle, Opn Appr 447
Ø7T6ØZZ	Resect of Lt Axillary Lymphatic, Opn Appr 221, 222, 223
ØHTUØZZ	Resect of Lt Breast, Opn Appr 221, 222, 223, 337

ØRTRØZZ	Resect of Lt Carpal Jt, Opn Appr 317
ØPTNØZZ	Resect of Lt Carpal, Opn Appr 315
ØPTBØZZ	Resect of Lt Clavicle, Opn Appr 347
08T9XZZ	Resect of Lt Cornea, Ext Appr 44, 330, 446
ØRTMØZZ	Resect of Lt Elbow Jt, Opn Appr 350
08T1XZZ	Resect of Lt Eye, Ext Appr 330, 446
ØQT90ZZ	Resect of Lt Femor Shaft, Opn Appr 416
ØRTXØZZ	Resect of Lt Finger Phalangeal Jt, Opn Appr 317
ØPTVØZZ	Resect of Lt Finger Phalanx, Opn Appr 347
ØNT20ZZ	Resect of Lt Frontal Bone, Opn Appr 10, 14, 18, 301, 415
ØPT80ZZ	Resect of Lt Glenoid Cavity, Opn Appr 346
ØSTBØZZ	Resect of Lt Hip Jt, Opn Appr 416
ØPTDØZZ	Resect of Lt Humeral Head, Opn Appr 347
ØPTGØZZ	Resect of Lt Humeral Shaft, Opn Appr 347
07T90ZZ	Resect of Lt Int Mammary Lymphatic, Opn Appr 221, 222, 223
08TD3ZZ	Resect of Lt Iris, Perc Appr 44, 330, 446
08TK3ZZ	Resect of Lt Lens, Perc Appr 44, 330, 446
ØQTCØZZ	Resect of Lt Lwr Femur, Opn Appr 416
ØPTQØZZ	Resect of Lt Metacarpal, Opn Appr 315
ØRTTØZZ	Resect of Lt Metacarpocarpal Jt, Opn Appr 317
ØRTVØZZ	Resect of Lt Metacarpophalangeal Jt, Opn Appr 317
ØSTNØZZ	Resect of Lt Metatarsal-Phalangeal Jt, Opn Appr 244, 458
ØSTLØZZ	Resect of Lt Metatarsal-Tarsal Jt, Opn Appr 244, 458
ØQTPØZZ	Resect of Lt Metatarsal, Opn Appr 457
ØHTXXZZ	Resect of Lt Nipple, Ext Appr 222, 337
ØNT80ZZ	Resect of Lt Occipital Bone, Opn Appr 10, 14, 18, 301, 415
ØNT40ZZ	Resect of Lt Parietal Bone, Opn Appr 10, 14, 18, 301, 415
ØCTCØZZ	Resect of Lt Parotid Duct, Opn Appr 448
ØCT90ZZ	Resect of Lt Parotid Gland, Opn Appr 448
ØPTJØZZ	Resect of Lt Radius, Opn Appr 347
ØPT20ZZ	Resect of Lt Rib, Opn Appr 346
ØPT60ZZ	Resect of Lt Scapula, Opn Appr 346
ØRTKØZZ	Resect of Lt Shldr Jt, Opn Appr 350
ØRTFØZZ	Resect of Lt Sternoclavicular Jt, Opn Appr 350
ØCTFØZZ	Resect of Lt Sublingual Gland, Opn Appr 448
ØCTHØZZ	Resect of Lt Submaxillary Gland, Opn Appr 448
ØSTJØZZ	Resect of Lt Tarsal Jt, Opn Appr 244, 458
ØQTMØZZ	Resect of Lt Tarsal, Opn Appr 457
ØNT60ZZ	Resect of Lt Temporal Bone, Opn Appr 10, 14, 18, 301, 415
ØRTDØZZ	Resect of Lt Temporomandibular Jt, Opn Appr 350
ØKTJØZZ	Resect of Lt Thorax Muscle, Opn Appr 221, 222, 223
ØPTSØZZ	Resect of Lt Thumb Phalanx, Opn Appr 347
ØSTQØZZ	Resect of Lt Toe Phalangeal Jt, Opn Appr 244, 458
ØPTLØZZ	Resect of Lt Ulna, Opn Appr 347
ØQT70ZZ	Resect of Lt Upr Femur, Opn Appr 416
08T53ZZ	Resect of Lt Vitreous, Perc Appr 44, 330, 446
ØRTPØZZ	Resect of Lt Wrist Jt, Opn Appr 317
ØCTJØZZ	Resect of Minor Salivary Gland, Opn Appr 57, 448
ØNTBØZZ	Resect of Nasal Bone, Opn Appr 49
ØFTGØZZ	Resect of Pancreas, Opn Appr 106
ØQT40ZZ	Resect of Rt Acetabulum, Opn Appr 244
ØRTGØZZ	Resect of Rt Acromioclavicular Jt, Opn Appr 350
09T90ZZ	Resect of Rt Auditory Ossicle, Opn Appr 447
07T50ZZ	Resect of Rt Axillary Lymphatic, Opn Appr 221, 222, 223
ØHTTØZZ	Resect of Rt Breast, Opn Appr 221, 222, 223, 337
ØRTQØZZ	Resect of Rt Carpal Jt, Opn Appr 317
ØPTMØZZ	Resect of Rt Carpal, Opn Appr 315
ØPT90ZZ	Resect of Rt Clavicle, Opn Appr 347
08T8XZZ	Resect of Rt Cornea, Ext Appr 44, 330, 446
ØRTLØZZ	Resect of Rt Elbow Jt, Opn Appr 350
08T0XZZ	Resect of Rt Eye, Ext Appr 330, 446
ØQT80ZZ	Resect of Rt Femor Shaft, Opn Appr 416
ØRTWØZZ	Resect of Rt Finger Phalangeal Jt, Opn Appr 317
ØPTTØZZ	Resect of Rt Finger Phalanx, Opn Appr 347
ØNT10ZZ	Resect of Rt Frontal Bone, Opn Appr 10, 14, 18, 301, 415
ØPT70ZZ	Resect of Rt Glenoid Cavity, Opn Appr 346
ØST90ZZ	Resect of Rt Hip Jt, Opn Appr 416
ØPTCØZZ	Resect of Rt Humeral Head, Opn Appr 347
ØPTFØZZ	Resect of Rt Humeral Shaft, Opn Appr 347
07T80ZZ	Resect of Rt Int Mammary Lymphatic, Opn Appr 221, 222, 223
08TC3ZZ	Resect of Rt Iris, Perc Appr 44, 330, 446
08TJ3ZZ	Resect of Rt Lens, Perc Appr 44, 330, 446
ØQTBØZZ	Resect of Rt Lwr Femur, Opn Appr 416
ØPTPØZZ	Resect of Rt Metacarpal, Opn Appr 315
ØRTSØZZ	Resect of Rt Metacarpocarpal Jt, Opn Appr 317
ØRTUØZZ	Resect of Rt Metacarpophalangeal Jt, Opn Appr 317
ØSTKØZZ	Resect of Rt Metatarsal-Tarsal Jt, Opn Appr 244, 458
ØQTNØZZ	Resect of Rt Metatarsal, Opn Appr 457
ØSTMØZZ	Resect of Rt Metatarsophal Jt, Opn Appr 244, 458
ØHTWXZZ	Resect of Rt Nipple, Ext Appr 222, 337
ØNT70ZZ	Resect of Rt Occipital Bone, Opn Appr 10, 14, 18, 301, 415
ØNT30ZZ	Resect of Rt Parietal Bone, Opn Appr 10, 14, 18, 301, 415
ØCTBØZZ	Resect of Rt Parotid Duct, Opn Appr 448
ØCT80ZZ	Resect of Rt Parotid Gland, Opn Appr 448
ØPTHØZZ	Resect of Rt Radius, Opn Appr 347
ØPT10ZZ	Resect of Rt Rib, Opn Appr 346
ØPT50ZZ	Resect of Rt Scapula, Opn Appr 346
ØRTJØZZ	Resect of Rt Shldr Jt, Opn Appr 350
ØRTEØZZ	Resect of Rt Sternoclavicular Jt, Opn Appr 350
ØCTDØZZ	Resect of Rt Sublingual Gland, Opn Appr 448
ØCTGØZZ	Resect of Rt Submaxillary Gland, Opn Appr 448
ØSTHØZZ	Resect of Rt Tarsal Jt, Opn Appr 244, 458
ØQTLØZZ	Resect of Rt Tarsal, Opn Appr 457
ØNT50ZZ	Resect of Rt Temporal Bone, Opn Appr 10, 14, 18, 301, 415
ØRTCØZZ	Resect of Rt Temporomandibular Jt, Opn Appr 350
ØKTHØZZ	Resect of Rt Thorax Muscle, Opn Appr 221, 222, 223
ØPTRØZZ	Resect of Rt Thumb Phalanx, Opn Appr 347
ØSTPØZZ	Resect of Rt Toe Phalangeal Jt, Opn Appr 244, 458
ØPTKØZZ	Resect of Rt Ulna, Opn Appr 347
ØQT60ZZ	Resect of Rt Upr Femur, Opn Appr 416
08T43ZZ	Resect of Rt Vitreous, Perc Appr 44, 330, 446
ØRTNØZZ	Resect of Rt Wrist Jt, Opn Appr 317
ØPT00ZZ	Resect of Sternum, Opn Appr 346
ØHTYØZZ	Resect of Supernumerary Breast, Opn Appr 222, 337
ØRT90ZZ	Resect of Thoracic Vert Disc, Opn Appr 350
ØRTBØZZ	Resect of Thoracolumbar Vert Disc, Opn Appr 350
07T70ZZ	Resect of Thorax Lymphatic, Opn Appr 221, 222, 223
ØTTDØZZ	Resect of Urethra, Opn Appr 107, 262
ØUT44ZZ	Resect of Uterine Support Struct, Perc Endo Appr 262
ØUT40ZZ	Resect of Uterine Supporting Structure, Opn Appr 262
ØUT90ZZ	Resect of Uterus, Opn Appr 107, 262
ØUT94ZZ	Resect of Uterus, Perc Endo Appr 262
ØUT9FZZ	Resect of Uterus, Via Opng w Perc Endo 262
ØUTGØZZ	Resect of Vagina, Opn Appr 107, 262
ØMTJ*	Resect/Abd Bursa & Lgmt, Lt 144, 343
ØMTJ[0,4]ZZ	Resect/Abd Bursa & Lgmt, Lt, [Opn, Perc Endo] 454
ØMTH*	Resect/Abd Bursa & Lgmt, Rt 144, 343
ØMTH[0,4]ZZ	Resect/Abd Bursa & Lgmt, Rt, [Opn, Perc Endo] 454
ØKTL*	Resect/Abd Muscle, Lt 27, 140, 340
ØKTL[0,4]ZZ	Resect/Abd Muscle, Lt, [Opn, Perc Endo] 215
ØKTK*	Resect/Abd Muscle, Rt 27, 140, 339
ØKTK[0,4]ZZ	Resect/Abd Muscle, Rt, [Opn, Perc Endo] 215
ØLTG*	Resect/Abd Tndn, Lt 142, 342
ØLTF*	Resect/Abd Tndn, Rt 142, 342
09TP*	Resect/Accessory Sinus 56
ØCTQ*	Resect/Adenoids 53
ØGT2*	Resect/Adrenal Gland, Lt 235
ØGT2[0,4]ZZ	Resect/Adrenal Gland, Lt, [Opn, Perc Endo] 211
ØGT3*	Resect/Adrenal Gland, Rt 235
ØGT3[0,4]ZZ	Resect/Adrenal Gland, Rt, [Opn, Perc Endo] 211
ØGT4*	Resect/Adrenal Glands, Bilat 235
ØGT4[0,4]ZZ	Resect/Adrenal Glands, Bilat, [Opn, Perc Endo] 211
ØFTC*	Resect/Ampulla of Vater 113, 120
ØDTR*	Resect/Anal Sphincter 110
ØDTR[0,4]ZZ	Resect/Anal Sphincter, [Opn, Perc Endo] 449
ØMTR*	Resect/Ankle Bursa & Lgmt, Lt 144, 343
ØMTR[0,4]ZZ	Resect/Ankle Bursa & Lgmt, Lt, [Opn, Perc Endo] 454
ØMTQ*	Resect/Ankle Bursa & Lgmt, Rt 144, 343
ØMTQ[0,4]ZZ	Resect/Ankle Bursa & Lgmt, Rt, [Opn, Perc Endo] 454
ØLTT*	Resect/Ankle Tndn, Lt 142, 342

Alphabetic Index to Procedures

ØLTS*	Resect/Ankle Tndn, Rt 142, 342
ØDTQ*	Resect/Anus 110
ØDTQ[Ø,4,7,8]ZZ	Resect/Anus, [Opn, Perc Endo, Via Natrl or Artfcl Opng, Via Natrl or Artfcl Opng Endo] 449
ØDTJ*	Resect/Appendix 108, 268, 334
ØDTJ[Ø,7,8]ZZ	Resect/Appendix, [Opn, Via Natrl or Artfcl Opng, Via Natrl or Artfcl Opng Endo] 90
ØDTK*	Resect/Ascending Colon 90, 107, 334
ØDTK[Ø,4,7,8]ZZ	Resect/Ascending Colon, [Opn, Perc Endo, Via Natrl or Artfcl Opng, Via Natrl or Artfcl Opng Endo] 300
02T5[Ø,3,4]ZZ	Resect/Atrial Septum, [Opn, Perc, Perc Endo] 75
ØTTB*	Resect/Bladder 248, 257, 268, 354
ØTTC*	Resect/Bladder Neck 248, 257, 268, 354
ØTTC[Ø,4,7,8]ZZ	Resect/Bladder Neck, [Opn, Perc Endo, Via Natrl or Artfcl Opng, Via Natrl or Artfcl Opng Endo] 302
ØTTB[Ø,4,7,8]ZZ	Resect/Bladder, [Opn, Perc Endo, Via Natrl or Artfcl Opng, Via Natrl or Artfcl Opng Endo] 302
ØBT2*	Resect/Carina 52, 62
ØDTH*	Resect/Cecum 90, 107, 334
00T7[Ø,3,4]ZZ	Resect/Cerebral Hemisphere, [Opn, Perc, Perc Endo] 8, 12, 17, 296
ØUTC*	Resect/Cervix 267
ØUTC[7,8]ZZ	Resect/Cervix, [Via Natrl or Artfcl Opng, Via Natrl or Artfcl Opng Endo] 262
02T9[Ø,3,4]ZZ	Resect/Chordae Tendineae, [Opn, Perc, Perc Endo] 75
07TL*	Resect/Cisterna Chyli 60
ØUTJ*	Resect/Clitoris 267
ØUTJ[Ø,X]ZZ	Resect/Clitoris, [Opn, Ext] 459
ØFT9*	Resect/Common Bile Duct 113, 120
02T8[Ø,4]ZZ	Resect/Conduction Mech, [Opn, Perc Endo] 75
ØUTF*	Resect/Cul-de-sac 267
ØFT8*	Resect/Cystic Duct 113, 120
ØDTM*	Resect/Descending Colon 90, 107, 334
ØDTM[Ø,4,7,8]ZZ	Resect/Descending Colon, [Opn, Perc Endo, Via Natrl or Artfcl Opng, Via Natrl or Artfcl Opng Endo] 300
ØBTS*	Resect/Diaphragm, Lt 65
ØBTR*	Resect/Diaphragm, Rt 65
ØDT9*	Resect/Duodenum 90, 107, 242, 334
ØDT9[Ø,4,7,8]ZZ	Resect/Duodenum, [Opn, Perc Endo, Via Natrl or Artfcl Opng, Via Natrl or Artfcl Opng Endo] 300
ØMT4*	Resect/Elbow Bursa & Lgmt, Lt 144, 343
ØMT4[Ø,4]ZZ	Resect/Elbow Bursa & Lgmt, Lt, [Opn, Perc Endo] 454
ØMT3*	Resect/Elbow Bursa & Lgmt, Rt 144, 343
ØMT3[Ø,4]ZZ	Resect/Elbow Bursa & Lgmt, Rt, [Opn, Perc Endo] 454
ØVTL*	Resect/Epididymis, Bilat 258
ØVTK*	Resect/Epididymis, Lt 258
ØVTJ*	Resect/Epididymis, Rt 258
ØCTR*	Resect/Epiglottis 53, 65, 332
ØDT4*	Resect/Esophagogastric Junction 106, 334
ØDT4[Ø,4,7,8]ZZ	Resect/Esophagogastric Junction, [Opn, Perc Endo, Via Natrl or Artfcl Opng, Via Natrl or Artfcl Opng Endo] 300
ØDT5*	Resect/Esophagus 53, 106, 334
ØDT5[Ø,4,7,8]ZZ	Resect/Esophagus, [Opn, Perc Endo, Via Natrl or Artfcl Opng, Via Natrl or Artfcl Opng Endo] 300
ØDT3*	Resect/Esophagus, Lwr 53, 106, 334
ØDT3[Ø,4,7,8]ZZ	Resect/Esophagus, Lwr, [Opn, Perc Endo, Via Natrl or Artfcl Opng, Via Natrl or Artfcl Opng Endo] 300
ØDT2*	Resect/Esophagus, Mid 53, 106, 334
ØDT2[Ø,4,7,8]ZZ	Resect/Esophagus, Mid, [Opn, Perc Endo, Via Natrl or Artfcl Opng, Via Natrl or Artfcl Opng Endo] 300
ØDT1*	Resect/Esophagus, Upr 53, 106, 334
ØDT1[Ø,4,7,8]ZZ	Resect/Esophagus, Upr, [Opn, Perc Endo, Via Natrl or Artfcl Opng, Via Natrl or Artfcl Opng Endo] 300
09TV*	Resect/Ethmoid Sinus, Lt 56
09TV[Ø,4]ZZ	Resect/Ethmoid Sinus, Lt, [Opn, Perc Endo] 447
09TU*	Resect/Ethmoid Sinus, Rt 56
09TU[Ø,4]ZZ	Resect/Ethmoid Sinus, Rt, [Opn, Perc Endo] 447
09T1*	Resect/Ext Ear, Lt 52, 331
09T1[Ø,4,X]ZZ	Resect/Ext Ear, Lt, [Opn, Perc Endo, Ext] 210, 447
09TØ*	Resect/Ext Ear, Rt 52, 331
09TØ[Ø,4,X]ZZ	Resect/Ext Ear, Rt, [Opn, Perc Endo, Ext] 210, 447
08TM*	Resect/Extraocular Muscle, Lt 43

08TM[Ø,3]ZZ	Resect/Extraocular Muscle, Lt, [Opn, Perc] 446
08TL*	Resect/Extraocular Muscle, Rt 43
08TL[Ø,3]ZZ	Resect/Extraocular Muscle, Rt, [Opn, Perc] 446
ØKT1*	Resect/Facial Muscle 27, 140, 339
ØKT1[Ø,4]ZZ	Resect/Facial Muscle, [Opn, Perc Endo] 215
ØUT6*	Resect/Fallopian Tube, Lt 263, 264, 266
ØUT6[Ø,4,7,8,F]ZZ	Resect/Fallopian Tube, Lt, [Opn, Perc Endo, Via Natrl or Artfcl Opng, Via Natrl or Artfcl Opng Endo, Via Natrl or Artfcl Opng w/ Perc Endo Assistance] 271
ØUT5*	Resect/Fallopian Tube, Rt 263, 264, 266
ØUT5[Ø,4,7,8,F]ZZ	Resect/Fallopian Tube, Rt, [Opn, Perc Endo, Via Natrl or Artfcl Opng, Via Natrl or Artfcl Opng Endo, Via Natrl or Artfcl Opng w/ Perc Endo Assistance] 271
ØUT7*	Resect/Fallopian Tubes, Bilat 263, 264, 266
ØUT7[Ø,4,7,8,F]ZZ	Resect/Fallopian Tubes, Bilat, [Opn, Perc Endo, Via Natrl or Artfcl Opng, Via Natrl or Artfcl Opng Endo, Via Natrl or Artfcl Opng w/ Perc Endo Assistance] 271
ØMTT*	Resect/Foot Bursa & Lgmt, Lt 144, 343
ØMTT[Ø,4]ZZ	Resect/Foot Bursa & Lgmt, Lt, [Opn, Perc Endo] 454
ØMTS*	Resect/Foot Bursa & Lgmt, Rt 144, 343
ØMTS[Ø,4]ZZ	Resect/Foot Bursa & Lgmt, Rt, [Opn, Perc Endo] 454
ØKTW*	Resect/Foot Muscle, Lt 27, 140, 340
ØKTW[Ø,4]ZZ	Resect/Foot Muscle, Lt, [Opn, Perc Endo] 215
ØKTV*	Resect/Foot Muscle, Rt 27, 140, 340
ØKTV[Ø,4]ZZ	Resect/Foot Muscle, Rt, [Opn, Perc Endo] 215
ØLTW*	Resect/Foot Tndn, Lt 142, 342
ØLTV*	Resect/Foot Tndn, Rt 142, 342
09TT*	Resect/Frontal Sinus, Lt 56
09TS*	Resect/Frontal Sinus, Rt 56
ØFT4*	Resect/Gallbladder 113, 120, 335
ØFT4[Ø,4]ZZ	Resect/Gallbladder, [Opn, Perc Endo] 301
ØDTS*	Resect/Greater Omentum 112, 123, 242, 268
ØDTS[Ø,4]ZZ	Resect/Greater Omentum, [Opn, Perc Endo] 300, 449
ØMT8*	Resect/Hand Bursa & Lgmt, Lt 150
ØMT8[Ø,4]ZZ	Resect/Hand Bursa & Lgmt, Lt, [Opn, Perc Endo] 315
ØMT7*	Resect/Hand Bursa & Lgmt, Rt 150
ØMT7[Ø,4]ZZ	Resect/Hand Bursa & Lgmt, Rt, [Opn, Perc Endo] 315
ØKTD*	Resect/Hand Muscle, Lt 149
ØKTD[Ø,4]ZZ	Resect/Hand Muscle, Lt, [Opn, Perc Endo] 314
ØKTC*	Resect/Hand Muscle, Rt 149
ØKTC[Ø,4]ZZ	Resect/Hand Muscle, Rt, [Opn, Perc Endo] 314
ØLT8*	Resect/Hand Tndn, Lt 150, 243
ØLT8[Ø,4]ZZ	Resect/Hand Tndn, Lt, [Opn, Perc Endo] 315
ØLT7*	Resect/Hand Tndn, Rt 150, 243
ØLT7[Ø,4]ZZ	Resect/Hand Tndn, Rt, [Opn, Perc Endo] 315
ØCT2*	Resect/Hard Palate 48
ØCT2[Ø,X]ZZ	Resect/Hard Palate, [Opn, Ext] 448
ØMTØ*	Resect/Head and Neck Bursa & Lgmt 144, 343
ØMTØ[Ø,4]ZZ	Resect/Head and Neck Bursa & Lgmt, [Opn, Perc Endo] 454
ØLTØ*	Resect/Head and Neck Tndn 142, 341
ØKTØ*	Resect/Head Muscle 27, 140, 339
ØKTØ[Ø,4]ZZ	Resect/Head Muscle, [Opn, Perc Endo] 215
ØFT6*	Resect/Hepatic Duct, Lt 113, 120
ØFT5*	Resect/Hepatic Duct, Rt 113, 120
ØMTM*	Resect/Hip Bursa & Lgmt, Lt 144, 343
ØMTM[Ø,4]ZZ	Resect/Hip Bursa & Lgmt, Lt, [Opn, Perc Endo] 454
ØMTL*	Resect/Hip Bursa & Lgmt, Rt 144, 343
ØMTL[Ø,4]ZZ	Resect/Hip Bursa & Lgmt, Rt, [Opn, Perc Endo] 454
ØKTP*	Resect/Hip Muscle, Lt 27, 140, 340
ØKTP[Ø,4]ZZ	Resect/Hip Muscle, Lt, [Opn, Perc Endo] 215
ØKTN*	Resect/Hip Muscle, Rt 27, 140, 340
ØKTN[Ø,4]ZZ	Resect/Hip Muscle, Rt, [Opn, Perc Endo] 215
ØLTK*	Resect/Hip Tndn, Lt 142, 342
ØLTJ*	Resect/Hip Tndn, Rt 142, 342
ØUTK*	Resect/Hymen 267, 275
ØUTK[Ø,4,7,8]ZZ	Resect/Hymen, [Opn, Perc Endo, Via Natrl or Artfcl Opng, Via Natrl or Artfcl Opng Endo] 459
ØDTC*	Resect/Ileocecal Valve 90, 107, 242, 334
ØDTC[Ø,4,7,8]ZZ	Resect/Ileocecal Valve, [Opn, Perc Endo, Via Natrl or Artfcl Opng, Via Natrl or Artfcl Opng Endo] 300
ØDTB*	Resect/Ileum 90, 107, 242, 334

ØDTB[Ø,4,7,8]ZZ	Resect/Ileum, [Opn, Perc Endo, Via Natrl or Artfcl Opng, Via Natrl or Artfcl Opng Endo] **300**
ØGTP*	Resect/Inferior Parathyroid Gland, Lt **238, 253**
ØGTN*	Resect/Inferior Parathyroid Gland, Rt **238, 253**
ØDTA*	Resect/Jejunum **90, 107, 242, 334**
ØDTA[Ø,4,7,8]ZZ	Resect/Jejunum, [Opn, Perc Endo, Via Natrl or Artfcl Opng, Via Natrl or Artfcl Opng Endo] **300**
ØTT4*	Resect/Kidney Pelvis, Lt **249, 354**
ØTT3*	Resect/Kidney Pelvis, Rt **249, 354**
ØTT1*	Resect/Kidney, Lt **249, 354**
ØTTØ*	Resect/Kidney, Rt **249, 354**
ØTT2*	Resect/Kidneys, Bilat **249, 354**
ØMTP*	Resect/Knee Bursa & Lgmt, Lt **144, 343**
ØMTP[Ø,4]ZZ	Resect/Knee Bursa & Lgmt, Lt, [Opn, Perc Endo] **454**
ØMTN*	Resect/Knee Bursa & Lgmt, Rt **144, 343**
ØMTN[Ø,4]ZZ	Resect/Knee Bursa & Lgmt, Rt, [Opn, Perc Endo] **454**
ØLTR*	Resect/Knee Tndn, Lt **142, 342**
ØLTQ*	Resect/Knee Tndn, Rt **142, 342**
Ø8TY*	Resect/Lacrimal Duct, Lt **43, 51, 330**
Ø8TY[Ø,3,7,8]ZZ	Resect/Lacrimal Duct, Lt, [Opn, Perc, Via Natrl or Artfcl Opng, Via Natrl or Artfcl Opng Endo] **446**
Ø8TX*	Resect/Lacrimal Duct, Rt **43, 51, 330**
Ø8TX[Ø,3,7,8]ZZ	Resect/Lacrimal Duct, Rt, [Opn, Perc, Via Natrl or Artfcl Opng, Via Natrl or Artfcl Opng Endo] **446**
Ø8TW*	Resect/Lacrimal Gland, Lt **43, 330**
Ø8TW[Ø,3]ZZ	Resect/Lacrimal Gland, Lt, [Opn, Perc] **446**
Ø8TV*	Resect/Lacrimal Gland, Rt **43, 330**
Ø8TV[Ø,3]ZZ	Resect/Lacrimal Gland, Rt, [Opn, Perc] **446**
ØDTE*	Resect/Large Intestine **90, 107, 334**
ØDTG*	Resect/Large Intestine, Lt **90, 107, 242, 334**
ØDTF*	Resect/Large Intestine, Rt **90, 107, 334**
ØCTS[Ø,4,7,8]ZZ	Resect/Larynx, [Opn, Perc Endo, Via Natrl or Artfcl Opng, Via Natrl or Artfcl Opng Endo] **2**
ØDTT*	Resect/Lesser Omentum **112, 123, 242, 268**
ØDTT[Ø,4]ZZ	Resect/Lesser Omentum, [Opn, Perc Endo] **300, 449**
ØDTE[Ø,4,7,8]ZZ	Resect/Lg Intestine, [Opn, Perc Endo, Via Natrl or Artfcl Opng, Via Natrl or Artfcl Opng Endo] **300**
ØDTG[Ø,4,7,8]ZZ	Resect/Lg Intestine, Lt, [Opn, Perc Endo, Via Natrl or Artfcl Opng, Via Natrl or Artfcl Opng Endo] **300**
ØDTF[Ø,4,7,8]ZZ	Resect/Lg Intestine, Rt, [Opn, Perc Endo, Via Natrl or Artfcl Opng, Via Natrl or Artfcl Opng Endo] **300**
ØBT9*	Resect/Lingula Bronchus **62**
ØFTØ*	Resect/Liver **119, 335**
ØFT2*	Resect/Liver, Lt Lobe **119, 335**
ØFT1*	Resect/Liver, Rt Lobe **119, 335**
ØBTH*	Resect/Lung Lingula **62**
ØBTH[Ø,4]ZZ	Resect/Lung Lingula, [Opn, Perc Endo] **299**
ØBTL*	Resect/Lung, Lt **62**
ØBTK*	Resect/Lung, Rt **62**
ØBTM*	Resect/Lungs, Bilat **62**
ØKTB*	Resect/Lwr Arm and Wrist Muscle, Lt **27, 140, 339**
ØKTB[Ø,4]ZZ	Resect/Lwr Arm and Wrist Muscle, Lt, [Opn, Perc Endo] **215**
ØKT9*	Resect/Lwr Arm and Wrist Muscle, Rt **27, 140, 339**
ØKT9[Ø,4]ZZ	Resect/Lwr Arm and Wrist Muscle, Rt, [Opn, Perc Endo] **215**
ØLT6*	Resect/Lwr Arm and Wrist Tndn, Lt **142, 341**
ØLT5*	Resect/Lwr Arm and Wrist Tndn, Rt **142, 341**
ØMTW*	Resect/Lwr Extr Bursa & Lgmt, Lt **144, 343**
ØMTW[Ø,4]ZZ	Resect/Lwr Extr Bursa & Lgmt, Lt, [Opn, Perc Endo] **454**
ØMTV*	Resect/Lwr Extr Bursa & Lgmt, Rt **144, 343**
ØMTV[Ø,4]ZZ	Resect/Lwr Extr Bursa & Lgmt, Rt, [Opn, Perc Endo] **454**
Ø8TR*	Resect/Lwr Eyelid, Lt **43, 330**
Ø8TR[Ø,X]ZZ	Resect/Lwr Eyelid, Lt, [Opn, Ext] **210, 446**
Ø8TQ*	Resect/Lwr Eyelid, Rt **43, 330**
Ø8TQ[Ø,X]ZZ	Resect/Lwr Eyelid, Rt, [Opn, Ext] **210, 446**
ØKTT*	Resect/Lwr Leg Muscle, Lt **27, 140, 340**
ØKTT[Ø,4]ZZ	Resect/Lwr Leg Muscle, Lt, [Opn, Perc Endo] **215**
ØKTS*	Resect/Lwr Leg Muscle, Rt **27, 140, 340**
ØKTS[Ø,4]ZZ	Resect/Lwr Leg Muscle, Rt, [Opn, Perc Endo] **215**
ØLTP*	Resect/Lwr Leg Tndn, Lt **142, 342**
ØLTN*	Resect/Lwr Leg Tndn, Rt **142, 342**
ØCT1*	Resect/Lwr Lip **56, 332**

ØCT1[Ø,X]ZZ	Resect/Lwr Lip, [Opn, Ext] **448**
ØBTB*	Resect/Lwr Lobe Bronchus, Lt **62**
ØBT6*	Resect/Lwr Lobe Bronchus, Rt **62**
ØBTJ*	Resect/Lwr Lung Lobe, Lt **62**
ØBTF*	Resect/Lwr Lung Lobe, Rt **62**
Ø7TD*	Resect/Lymphatic, Aortic **60, 112, 153, 241, 248, 257, 262**
Ø7TD[Ø,4]ZZ	Resect/Lymphatic, Aortic, [Opn, Perc Endo] **210, 291, 298**
Ø7TØ*	Resect/Lymphatic, Head **48, 64, 112, 252, 259, 262**
Ø7TØ[Ø,4]ZZ	Resect/Lymphatic, Head, [Opn, Perc Endo] **210, 291, 298**
Ø7T9*	Resect/Lymphatic, Int Mammary, Lt **48, 64, 112, 153, 248, 257, 262**
Ø7T9[Ø,4]ZZ	Resect/Lymphatic, Int Mammary, Lt, [Opn, Perc Endo] **210, 291, 298**
Ø7T8*	Resect/Lymphatic, Int Mammary, Rt **48, 64, 112, 153, 248, 257, 262**
Ø7T8[Ø,4]ZZ	Resect/Lymphatic, Int Mammary, Rt, [Opn, Perc Endo] **210, 291, 298**
Ø7T6*	Resect/Lymphatic, Lt Axillary **112, 153**
Ø7T6[Ø,4]ZZ	Resect/Lymphatic, Lt Axillary, [Opn, Perc Endo] **210, 291, 298**
Ø7TJ*	Resect/Lymphatic, Lt Inguinal **112, 153, 248, 257, 262**
Ø7TJ[Ø,4]ZZ	Resect/Lymphatic, Lt Inguinal, [Opn, Perc Endo] **210, 291, 298**
Ø7TG*	Resect/Lymphatic, Lt Lwr Extr **48, 64, 112, 253, 259, 262**
Ø7TG[Ø,4]ZZ	Resect/Lymphatic, Lt Lwr Extr, [Opn, Perc Endo] **210, 291, 298**
Ø7T2*	Resect/Lymphatic, Lt Neck **48, 64, 241**
Ø7T2[Ø,4]ZZ	Resect/Lymphatic, Lt Neck, [Opn, Perc Endo] **210, 291, 298**
Ø7T4*	Resect/Lymphatic, Lt Upr Extr **48, 64, 112, 252, 259, 262**
Ø7T4[Ø,4]ZZ	Resect/Lymphatic, Lt Upr Extr, [Opn, Perc Endo] **210, 291, 298**
Ø7TB*	Resect/Lymphatic, Mesenteric **48, 64, 112, 252, 259, 262**
Ø7TB[Ø,4]ZZ	Resect/Lymphatic, Mesenteric, [Opn, Perc Endo] **210, 291, 298**
Ø7TC*	Resect/Lymphatic, Pelvis **112, 153, 241, 248, 257, 262**
Ø7TC[Ø,4]ZZ	Resect/Lymphatic, Pelvis, [Opn, Perc Endo] **210, 291, 298**
Ø7T5*	Resect/Lymphatic, Rt Axillary **112, 153**
Ø7T5[Ø,4]ZZ	Resect/Lymphatic, Rt Axillary, [Opn, Perc Endo] **210, 291, 298**
Ø7TH*	Resect/Lymphatic, Rt Inguinal **112, 153, 248, 257, 262**
Ø7TH[Ø,4]ZZ	Resect/Lymphatic, Rt Inguinal, [Opn, Perc Endo] **210, 291, 298**
Ø7TF*	Resect/Lymphatic, Rt Lwr Extr **48, 64, 112, 252, 259, 262**
Ø7TF[Ø,4]ZZ	Resect/Lymphatic, Rt Lwr Extr, [Opn, Perc Endo] **210, 291, 298**
Ø7T1*	Resect/Lymphatic, Rt Neck **48, 64, 241**
Ø7T1[Ø,4]ZZ	Resect/Lymphatic, Rt Neck, [Opn, Perc Endo] **210, 291, 298**
Ø7T3*	Resect/Lymphatic, Rt Upr Extr **48, 64, 112, 252, 259, 262**
Ø7T3[Ø,4]ZZ	Resect/Lymphatic, Rt Upr Extr, [Opn, Perc Endo] **210, 291, 298**
Ø7T7*	Resect/Lymphatic, Thorax **48, 64, 112, 252, 259, 262**
Ø7T7[Ø,4]ZZ	Resect/Lymphatic, Thorax, [Opn, Perc Endo] **210, 291, 298**
ØBT7*	Resect/Main Bronchus, Lt **62**
ØBT3*	Resect/Main Bronchus, Rt **62**
Ø9TC*	Resect/Mastoid Sinus, Lt **56**
Ø9TB*	Resect/Mastoid Sinus, Rt **56**
Ø9TR*	Resect/Maxillary Sinus, Lt **56, 153**
Ø9TQ*	Resect/Maxillary Sinus, Rt **56, 153**
ØBT5*	Resect/Mid Lobe Bronchus, Rt **62**
ØBTD*	Resect/Mid Lung Lobe, Rt **62**
Ø9TM*	Resect/Nasal Septum **52, 331**
Ø9TM[Ø,4]ZZ	Resect/Nasal Septum, [Opn, Perc Endo] **447**
Ø9TL*	Resect/Nasal Turbinate **52, 331**
Ø9TL[Ø,4,7,8]ZZ	Resect/Nasal Turbinate, [Opn, Perc Endo, Via Natrl or Artfcl Opng, Via Natrl or Artfcl Opng Endo] **447**
Ø9TN*	Resect/Nasopharynx **52, 105**
ØKT3*	Resect/Neck Muscle, Lt **27, 140, 339**
ØKT3[Ø,4]ZZ	Resect/Neck Muscle, Lt, [Opn, Perc Endo] **215**
ØKT2*	Resect/Neck Muscle, Rt **27, 140, 339**
ØKT2[Ø,4]ZZ	Resect/Neck Muscle, Rt, [Opn, Perc Endo] **215**
Ø9TK*	Resect/Nose **48, 331**
Ø9TK[Ø,4,X]ZZ	Resect/Nose, [Opn, Perc Endo, Ext] **210**
ØUT2*	Resect/Ovaries, Bilat **263, 264, 266**
ØUT2[Ø,4,7,8,F]ZZ	Resect/Ovaries, Bilat, [Opn, Perc Endo, Via Natrl or Artfcl Opng, Via Natrl or Artfcl Opng Endo, Via Natrl or Artfcl Opng w/ Perc Endo Assistance] **217**
ØUT1*	Resect/Ovary, Lt **263, 264, 266**
ØUT1[Ø,4,7,8,F]ZZ	Resect/Ovary, Lt, [Opn, Perc Endo, Via Natrl or Artfcl Opng, Via Natrl or Artfcl Opng Endo, Via Natrl or Artfcl Opng w/ Perc Endo Assistance] **217**

0UT0*	Resect/Ovary, Rt 263, 264, 266
0UT0[0,4,7,8,F]ZZ	Resect/Ovary, Rt, [Opn, Perc Endo, Via Natrl or Artfcl Opng, Via Natrl or Artfcl Opng Endo, Via Natrl or Artfcl Opng w/ Perc Endo Assistance] 217
0FTG*	Resect/Pancreas 119, 335
0FTD[0,7]ZZ	Resect/Pancreatic Duct, [Opn, Via Natrl or Artfcl Opng] 119, 242
0FTF[0,7]ZZ	Resect/Pancreatic Duct, Accessory, [Opn, Via Natrl or Artfcl Opng] 119, 242
02TD[0,3,4]ZZ	Resect/Papillary Muscle, [Opn, Perc, Perc Endo] 75
0GTR*	Resect/Parathyroid Gland 238, 253
0GTQ*	Resect/Parathyroid Glands, Multi 238, 253
0VTS*	Resect/Penis 257
02TN*	Resect/Pericardium 60, 320
02TN[0,3,4]ZZ	Resect/Pericardium, [Opn, Perc, Perc Endo] 93, 296
0MTK*	Resect/Perineum Bursa & Lgmt 144, 343
0MTK[0,4]ZZ	Resect/Perineum Bursa & Lgmt, [Opn, Perc Endo] 454
0KTM*	Resect/Perineum Muscle 27, 140, 340
0KTM[0,4]ZZ	Resect/Perineum Muscle, [Opn, Perc Endo] 215
0LTH*	Resect/Perineum Tndn 142, 342
0CTM*	Resect/Pharynx 53, 105
0GT1*	Resect/Pineal Body 235
0GT1[0,4]ZZ	Resect/Pineal Body, [Opn, Perc Endo] 9, 13, 17
0GT0*	Resect/Pituitary Gland 235
0GT0[0,4]ZZ	Resect/Pituitary Gland, [Opn, Perc Endo] 9, 13, 17, 211
0VT0*	Resect/Prostate 250, 257
0VT0[0,4]ZZ	Resect/Prostate, [Opn, Perc Endo] 257
0VT0[4,7,8]ZZ	Resect/Prostate, [Perc Endo, Via Natrl or Artfcl Opng, Via Natrl or Artfcl Opng Endo] 440
0VT0[7,8]ZZ	Resect/Prostate, [Via Natrl or Artfcl Opng, Via Natrl or Artfcl Opng Endo] 258
02TH[0,3,4]ZZ	Resect/Pulmn Valve, [Opn, Perc, Perc Endo] 75
0DTP*	Resect/Rectum 107
0DTP[0,4,7,8]ZZ	Resect/Rectum, [Opn, Perc Endo, Via Natrl or Artfcl Opng, Via Natrl or Artfcl Opng Endo] 300
0DTP[0,4]ZZ	Resect/Rectum, [Opn, Perc Endo] 90, 334
0VT2*	Resect/Seminal Vesicle, Lt 260
0VT1*	Resect/Seminal Vesicle, Rt 260
0VT3*	Resect/Seminal Vesicles, Bilat 250, 257, 260
0MT2*	Resect/Shldr Bursa & Lgmt, Lt 144, 343
0MT2[0,4]ZZ	Resect/Shldr Bursa & Lgmt, Lt, [Opn, Perc Endo] 454
0MT1*	Resect/Shldr Bursa & Lgmt, Rt 144, 343
0MT1[0,4]ZZ	Resect/Shldr Bursa & Lgmt, Rt, [Opn, Perc Endo] 454
0KT6*	Resect/Shldr Muscle, Lt 27, 140, 339
0KT6[0,4]ZZ	Resect/Shldr Muscle, Lt, [Opn, Perc Endo] 215
0KT5*	Resect/Shldr Muscle, Rt 27, 140, 339
0KT5[0,4]ZZ	Resect/Shldr Muscle, Rt, [Opn, Perc Endo] 215
0LT2*	Resect/Shldr Tndn, Lt 142, 341
0LT1*	Resect/Shldr Tndn, Rt 142, 341
0DTN*	Resect/Sigmoid Colon 107, 334
0DTN[0,4,7,8]ZZ	Resect/Sigmoid Colon, [Opn, Perc Endo, Via Natrl or Artfcl Opng, Via Natrl or Artfcl Opng Endo] 300
0DT8*	Resect/Sm Intestine 107, 334
0DT8[0,4,7,8]ZZ	Resect/Sm Intestine, [Opn, Perc Endo, Via Natrl or Artfcl Opng, Via Natrl or Artfcl Opng Endo] 300
0CT3*	Resect/Soft Palate 56, 332
0CT3[0,X]ZZ	Resect/Soft Palate, [Opn, Ext] 448
0VTG*	Resect/Spermatic Cord, Lt 258
0VTG[0,4]ZZ	Resect/Spermatic Cord, Lt, [Opn, Perc Endo] 459
0VTF*	Resect/Spermatic Cord, Rt 258
0VTF[0,4]ZZ	Resect/Spermatic Cord, Rt, [Opn, Perc Endo] 459
0VTH*	Resect/Spermatic Cords, Bilat 258
0VTH[0,4]ZZ	Resect/Spermatic Cords, Bilat, [Opn, Perc Endo] 459
09TX*	Resect/Sphenoid Sinus, Lt 56
09TW*	Resect/Sphenoid Sinus, Rt 56
07TP*	Resect/Spleen 90, 112, 153, 290, 329
07TP[0,4]ZZ	Resect/Spleen, [Opn, Perc Endo] 298
0DT6*	Resect/Stomach 90, 106, 334
0DT6[0,4,7,8]ZZ	Resect/Stomach, [Opn, Perc Endo, Via Natrl or Artfcl Opng, Via Natrl or Artfcl Opng Endo] 300
0DT7*	Resect/Stomach, Pylorus 90, 106, 334
0DT7[0,4,7,8]ZZ	Resect/Stomach, Pylorus, [Opn, Perc Endo, Via Natrl or Artfcl Opng, Via Natrl or Artfcl Opng Endo] 300
0GTM*	Resect/Superior Parathyroid Gland, Lt 238, 253
0GTL*	Resect/Superior Parathyroid Gland, Rt 238, 253
0VTC*	Resect/Testes, Bilat 158, 258, 355
0VTB*	Resect/Testis, Lt 258, 355
0VT9*	Resect/Testis, Rt 258, 355
07TK*	Resect/Thoracic Duct 60
0MTG*	Resect/Thorax Bursa & Lgmt, Lt 144, 343
0MTG[0,4]ZZ	Resect/Thorax Bursa & Lgmt, Lt, [Opn, Perc Endo] 454
0MTF*	Resect/Thorax Bursa & Lgmt, Rt 144, 343
0MTF[0,4]ZZ	Resect/Thorax Bursa & Lgmt, Rt, [Opn, Perc Endo] 454
0KTJ*	Resect/Thorax Muscle, Lt 27, 140, 339
0KTJ[0,4]ZZ	Resect/Thorax Muscle, Lt, [Opn, Perc Endo] 215
0KTH*	Resect/Thorax Muscle, Rt 27, 140, 339
0KTH[0,4]ZZ	Resect/Thorax Muscle, Rt, [Opn, Perc Endo] 215
0LTD*	Resect/Thorax Tndn, Lt 142, 342
0LTC*	Resect/Thorax Tndn, Rt 142, 342
07TM*	Resect/Thymus 25, 60, 241, 329
07TM[0,4]ZZ	Resect/Thymus, [Opn, Perc Endo] 291, 298
0GTK*	Resect/Thyroid Gland 238
0GTG*	Resect/Thyroid Gland Lobe, Lt 238
0GTH*	Resect/Thyroid Gland Lobe, Rt 238
0CT7*	Resect/Tongue 48
0KT4*	Resect/Tongue, Palate, Pharynx Muscle 27, 140, 339
0KT4[0,4]ZZ	Resect/Tongue, Palate, Pharynx Muscle, [Opn, Perc Endo] 215
0CTP*	Resect/Tonsils 53
0CTP[0,X]ZZ	Resect/Tonsils, [Opn, Ext] 448
0BT1*	Resect/Trachea 52, 62
0DTL*	Resect/Transv Colon 90, 107, 334
0DTL[0,4,7,8]ZZ	Resect/Transv Colon, [Opn, Perc Endo, Via Natrl or Artfcl Opng, Via Natrl or Artfcl Opng Endo] 300
0MTD*	Resect/Trunk Bursa & Lgmt, Lt 144, 343
0MTD[0,4]ZZ	Resect/Trunk Bursa & Lgmt, Lt, [Opn, Perc Endo] 454
0MTC*	Resect/Trunk Bursa & Lgmt, Rt 144, 343
0MTC[0,4]ZZ	Resect/Trunk Bursa & Lgmt, Rt, [Opn, Perc Endo] 454
0KTG*	Resect/Trunk Muscle, Lt 27, 140, 339
0KTG[0,4]ZZ	Resect/Trunk Muscle, Lt, [Opn, Perc Endo] 215
0KTF*	Resect/Trunk Muscle, Rt 27, 140, 339
0KTF[0,4]ZZ	Resect/Trunk Muscle, Rt, [Opn, Perc Endo] 215
0LTB*	Resect/Trunk Tndn, Lt 142, 342
0LT9*	Resect/Trunk Tndn, Rt 142, 341
0VT7*	Resect/Tunica Vaginalis, Lt 258
0VT6*	Resect/Tunica Vaginalis, Rt 258
09T8*	Resect/Tympanic Membrane, Lt 52
09T7*	Resect/Tympanic Membrane, Rt 52
0KT8*	Resect/Upr Arm Muscle, Lt 27, 140, 339
0KT8[0,4]ZZ	Resect/Upr Arm Muscle, Lt, [Opn, Perc Endo] 215
0KT7*	Resect/Upr Arm Muscle, Rt 27, 140, 339
0KT7[0,4]ZZ	Resect/Upr Arm Muscle, Rt, [Opn, Perc Endo] 215
0LT4*	Resect/Upr Arm Tndn, Lt 142, 341
0LT3*	Resect/Upr Arm Tndn, Rt 142, 341
0MTB*	Resect/Upr Extr Bursa & Lgmt, Lt 144, 343
0MTB[0,4]ZZ	Resect/Upr Extr Bursa & Lgmt, Lt, [Opn, Perc Endo] 454
0MT9*	Resect/Upr Extr Bursa & Lgmt, Rt 144, 343
0MT9[0,4]ZZ	Resect/Upr Extr Bursa & Lgmt, Rt, [Opn, Perc Endo] 454
08TP*	Resect/Upr Eyelid, Lt 43, 330
08TP[0,X]ZZ	Resect/Upr Eyelid, Lt, [Opn, Ext] 210, 446
08TN*	Resect/Upr Eyelid, Rt 43, 330
08TN[0,X]ZZ	Resect/Upr Eyelid, Rt, [Opn, Ext] 210, 446
0KTR*	Resect/Upr Leg Muscle, Lt 27, 140, 340
0KTR[0,4]ZZ	Resect/Upr Leg Muscle, Lt, [Opn, Perc Endo] 215
0KTQ*	Resect/Upr Leg Muscle, Rt 27, 140, 340
0KTQ[0,4]ZZ	Resect/Upr Leg Muscle, Rt, [Opn, Perc Endo] 215
0LTM*	Resect/Upr Leg Tndn, Lt 142, 342
0LTL*	Resect/Upr Leg Tndn, Rt 142, 342
0CT0*	Resect/Upr Lip 56, 332
0CT0[0,X]ZZ	Resect/Upr Lip, [Opn, Ext] 448
0BT8*	Resect/Upr Lobe Bronchus, Lt 62
0BT4*	Resect/Upr Lobe Bronchus, Rt 62

ØBTG*	Resect/Upr Lung Lobe, Lt **62**
ØBTC*	Resect/Upr Lung Lobe, Rt **62**
ØTT7*	Resect/Ureter, Lt **249, 354**
ØTT6*	Resect/Ureter, Rt **249, 354**
ØUT4*	Resect/Uterine Supporting Structure **267**
ØUT4[7,8]ZZ	Resect/Uterine Supporting Structure, [Via Natrl or Artfcl Opng, Via Natrl or Artfcl Opng Endo] **262**
ØUT9*	Resect/Uterus **263, 264, 266, 272**
ØUT9[7,8,F]ZZ	Resect/Uterus, [Via Natrl or Artfcl Opng, Via Natrl or Artfcl Opng Endo, Via Natrl or Artfcl Opng w/ Perc Endo Assistance] **459**
ØUT9[7,8]ZZ	Resect/Uterus, [Via Natrl or Artfcl Opng, Via Natrl or Artfcl Opng Endo] **262**
ØCTN*	Resect/Uvula **56**
ØCTN[Ø,X]ZZ	Resect/Uvula, [Opn, Ext] **448**
ØUTG*	Resect/Vagina **267**
Ø2TM[Ø,3,4]ZZ	Resect/Ventricular Septum, [Opn, Perc, Perc Endo] **75**
ØUTL*	Resect/Vestibular Gland **267, 272**
ØUTL[Ø,X]ZZ	Resect/Vestibular Gland, [Opn, Ext] **217, 459**
ØCTV*	Resect/Vocal Cord, Lt **53, 65, 332**
ØCTT*	Resect/Vocal Cord, Rt **53, 65, 332**
ØUTM*	Resect/Vulva **262, 267**
ØUTM[Ø,X]ZZ	Resect/Vulva, [Opn, Ext] **217**
ØMT6*	Resect/Wrist Bursa & Lgmt, Lt **144, 343**
ØMT6[Ø,4]ZZ	Resect/Wrist Bursa & Lgmt, Lt, [Opn, Perc Endo] **454**
ØMT5*	Resect/Wrist Bursa & Lgmt, Rt **144, 343**
ØMT5[Ø,4]ZZ	Resect/Wrist Bursa & Lgmt, Rt, [Opn, Perc Endo] **454**
ØBD*	Respiratory Sys, Extract **61, 331**
ØBM*	Respiratory Sys, Reattach **62**
ØBQ*	Respiratory Sys, Repair **62**
ØBS*	Respiratory Sys, Repos **62**
ØBT*	Respiratory Sys, Resect **331**
ØBV*	Respiratory Sys, Restrict **62**
ØBU*	Respiratory Sys, Supl **62**
5A1955Z	Respiratory Ventilation, > 96 Consecutive Hrs **1, 70, 309, 377, 382**
5A1945Z	Respiratory Ventilation, 24-96 Consecutive Hrs **70**
5A1935Z	Respiratory Ventilation, < 24 Consecutive Hrs **70**
Ø2VR4CT	Restrict Ductus Arterio w Extralum Dev, Perc Endo **80**
Ø2VR4DT	Restrict Ductus Arterio w Intralum Dev, Perc Endo **93**
Ø4VØØDZ	Restrict of Abd Aorta with Intralum Dev, Opn Appr **96**
Ø4VØ3DZ	Restrict of Abd Aorta with Intralum Dev, Perc Appr **92**
Ø4VØ4DZ	Restrict of Abd Aorta with Intralum Dev, Perc Endo Appr **92**
Ø4VØØZZ	Restrict of Abd Aorta, Opn Appr **96**
Ø4VØ3ZZ	Restrict of Abd Aorta, Perc Appr **96**
Ø4VØ4ZZ	Restrict of Abd Aorta, Perc Endo Appr **96**
ØUVCØCZ	Restrict of Cervix with Extralum Dev, Opn Appr **274**
ØUVC3CZ	Restrict of Cervix with Extralum Dev, Perc Appr **274**
ØUVC4CZ	Restrict of Cervix with Extralum Dev, Perc Endo Appr **274**
ØUVCØDZ	Restrict of Cervix with Intralum Dev, Opn Appr **274**
ØUVC3DZ	Restrict of Cervix with Intralum Dev, Perc Appr **274**
ØUVC4DZ	Restrict of Cervix with Intralum Dev, Perc Endo Appr **274**
ØUVC8DZ	Restrict of Cervix with Intralum Device, Endo **274**
ØUVC7DZ	Restrict of Cervix with Intralum Device, Via Opng **274**
ØUVC8ZZ	Restrict of Cervix, Endo **274**
ØUVCØZZ	Restrict of Cervix, Opn Appr **274**
ØUVC3ZZ	Restrict of Cervix, Perc Appr **274**
ØUVC4ZZ	Restrict of Cervix, Perc Endo Appr **274**
ØUVC7ZZ	Restrict of Cervix, Via Natrl or Artfcl Opng **274**
Ø2VRØCT	Restrict of Ductus Arterio with Extralum Dev, Opn Appr **80**
Ø2VR3CT	Restrict of Ductus Arterio with Extralum Dev, Perc Appr **80**
Ø2VRØDT	Restrict of Ductus Arterio with Intralum Dev, Opn Appr **93**
Ø2VR3DT	Restrict of Ductus Arterio with Intralum Dev, Perc Appr **93**
Ø2VRØZT	Restrict of Ductus Arteriosus, Opn Appr **93**
Ø2VR3ZT	Restrict of Ductus Arteriosus, Perc Appr **93**
Ø2VR4ZT	Restrict of Ductus Arteriosus, Perc Endo Appr **93**
Ø2VRØCZ	Restrict of Lt Pulm Art with Extralum Dev, Opn Appr **93**
Ø2VR3CZ	Restrict of Lt Pulm Art with Extralum Dev, Perc Appr **93**
Ø2VR4CZ	Restrict of Lt Pulm Art with Extralum Dev, Perc Endo Appr **93**
Ø2VRØDZ	Restrict of Lt Pulm Art with Intralum Dev, Opn Appr **93**

Ø2VR3DZ	Restrict of Lt Pulm Art with Intralum Dev, Perc Appr **93**
Ø2VR4DZ	Restrict of Lt Pulm Art with Intralum Dev, Perc Endo Appr **93**
Ø2VRØZZ	Restrict of Lt Pulmn Artery, Opn Appr **93**
Ø2VR3ZZ	Restrict of Lt Pulmn Artery, Perc Appr **93**
Ø2VR4ZZ	Restrict of Lt Pulmn Artery, Perc Endo Appr **93**
ØDV64CZ	Restrict of Stomach with Extralum Dev, Perc Endo Appr **449**
ØDV68ZZ	Restrict of Stomach, Endo **106, 334**
ØDV67ZZ	Restrict of Stomach, Via Natrl or Artfcl Opng **106, 334**
Ø4VØ[Ø,3,4][D,Z]Z	Restrict/Abd Aorta, [Opn, Perc, Perc Endo], [Intralum Dev, No Dev], NQ **252, 325**
Ø4VØ[Ø,3,4]CZ	Restrict/Abd Aorta, [Opn, Perc, Perc Endo], Extralum Dev, NQ **84**
Ø4VØ[Ø,3,4]DJ	Restrict/Abd Aorta, [Opn, Perc, Perc Endo], Intralum Dev, Temporary **22, 84, 325**
ØFVC*	Restrict/Ampulla of Vater **120, 335**
Ø4VQ[Ø,3,4][D,Z]Z	Restrict/Ant Tibial Artery, Lt, [Opn, Perc, Perc Endo], [Intralum Dev, No Dev], NQ **96, 325**
Ø4VQ[Ø,3,4]CZ	Restrict/Ant Tibial Artery, Lt, [Opn, Perc, Perc Endo], Extralum Dev, NQ **84**
Ø4VP[Ø,3,4][D,Z]Z	Restrict/Ant Tibial Artery, Rt, [Opn, Perc, Perc Endo], [Intralum Dev, No Dev], NQ **96, 325**
Ø4VP[Ø,3,4]CZ	Restrict/Ant Tibial Artery, Rt, [Opn, Perc, Perc Endo], Extralum Dev, NQ **84**
ØDVQ*	Restrict/Anus **110**
ØDVQ[Ø,3,4,X]CZ	Restrict/Anus, [Opn, Perc, Perc Endo, Ext], Extralum Dev, NQ **211**
ØDVQ[Ø,3,4,7,8,X][D,Z]Z	Restrict/Anus, [Opn, Perc, Perc Endo, Via Natrl or Artfcl Opng, Via Natrl or Artfcl Opng Endo, Ext], [Intralum Dev, No Dev], NQ **211**
ØDVK*	Restrict/Ascending Colon **107, 334**
Ø3V6[Ø,3,4][D,Z]Z	Restrict/Axillary Artery, Lt, [Opn, Perc, Perc Endo], [Intralum Dev, No Dev], NQ **94, 322**
Ø3V6[Ø,3,4]CZ	Restrict/Axillary Artery, Lt, [Opn, Perc, Perc Endo], Extralum Dev, NQ **82**
Ø3V5[Ø,3,4][D,Z]Z	Restrict/Axillary Artery, Rt, [Opn, Perc, Perc Endo], [Intralum Dev, No Dev], NQ **94, 322**
Ø3V5[Ø,3,4]CZ	Restrict/Axillary Artery, Rt, [Opn, Perc, Perc Endo], Extralum Dev, NQ **82**
Ø5V8[Ø,3,4][D,Z]Z	Restrict/Axillary Vein, Lt, [Opn, Perc, Perc Endo], [Intralum Dev, No Dev], NQ **97, 326**
Ø5V8[Ø,3,4]CZ	Restrict/Axillary Vein, Lt, [Opn, Perc, Perc Endo], Extralum Dev, NQ **86**
Ø5V7[Ø,3,4][D,Z]Z	Restrict/Axillary Vein, Rt, [Opn, Perc, Perc Endo], [Intralum Dev, No Dev], NQ **97, 326**
Ø5V7[Ø,3,4]CZ	Restrict/Axillary Vein, Rt, [Opn, Perc, Perc Endo], Extralum Dev, NQ **86**
Ø5VØ[Ø,3,4][D,Z]Z	Restrict/Azygos Vein, [Opn, Perc, Perc Endo], [Intralum Dev, No Dev], NQ **97, 326**
Ø5VØ[Ø,3,4]CZ	Restrict/Azygos Vein, [Opn, Perc, Perc Endo], Extralum Dev, NQ **86**
Ø5VC[Ø,3,4][D,Z]Z	Restrict/Basilic Vein, Lt, [Opn, Perc, Perc Endo], [Intralum Dev, No Dev], NQ **97, 326**
Ø5VC[Ø,3,4]CZ	Restrict/Basilic Vein, Lt, [Opn, Perc, Perc Endo], Extralum Dev, NQ **86**
Ø5VB[Ø,3,4][D,Z]Z	Restrict/Basilic Vein, Rt, [Opn, Perc, Perc Endo], [Intralum Dev, No Dev], NQ **97, 326**
Ø5VB[Ø,3,4]CZ	Restrict/Basilic Vein, Rt, [Opn, Perc, Perc Endo], Extralum Dev, NQ **86**
ØTVB*	Restrict/Bladder **248, 268, 354**
ØTVC*	Restrict/Bladder Neck **248, 267**
Ø3V8[Ø,3,4][D,Z]Z	Restrict/Brachial Artery, Lt, [Opn, Perc, Perc Endo], [Intralum Dev, No Dev], NQ **94, 322**
Ø3V8[Ø,3,4]CZ	Restrict/Brachial Artery, Lt, [Opn, Perc, Perc Endo], Extralum Dev, NQ **82**
Ø3V7[Ø,3,4][D,Z]Z	Restrict/Brachial Artery, Rt, [Opn, Perc, Perc Endo], [Intralum Dev, No Dev], NQ **94, 322**
Ø3V7[Ø,3,4]CZ	Restrict/Brachial Artery, Rt, [Opn, Perc, Perc Endo], Extralum Dev, NQ **82**
Ø5VA[Ø,3,4][D,Z]Z	Restrict/Brachial Vein, Lt, [Opn, Perc, Perc Endo], [Intralum Dev, No Dev], NQ **97, 326**
Ø5VA[Ø,3,4]CZ	Restrict/Brachial Vein, Lt, [Opn, Perc, Perc Endo], Extralum Dev, NQ **86**
Ø5V9[Ø,3,4][D,Z]Z	Restrict/Brachial Vein, Rt, [Opn, Perc, Perc Endo], [Intralum Dev, No Dev], NQ **97, 326**

05V9[Ø,3,4]CZ	Restrict/Brachial Vein, Rt, [Opn, Perc, Perc Endo], Extralum Dev, NQ 86
ØBV2*	Restrict/Carina 52, 331
ØDVH*	Restrict/Cecum 107, 334
04V1[Ø,3,4]ZZ	Restrict/Celiac Artery, [Opn, Perc, Perc Endo] 252
04V1[Ø,3,4][D,Z]Z	Restrict/Celiac Artery, [Opn, Perc, Perc Endo], [Intralum Dev, No Dev], NQ 96, 325
04V1[Ø,3,4]CZ	Restrict/Celiac Artery, [Opn, Perc, Perc Endo], Extralum Dev, NQ 84
05VF[Ø,3,4][D,Z]Z	Restrict/Cephalic Vein, Lt, [Opn, Perc, Perc Endo], [Intralum Dev, No Dev], NQ 97, 326
05VF[Ø,3,4]CZ	Restrict/Cephalic Vein, Lt, [Opn, Perc, Perc Endo], Extralum Dev, NQ 86
05VD[Ø,3,4][D,Z]Z	Restrict/Cephalic Vein, Rt, [Opn, Perc, Perc Endo], [Intralum Dev, No Dev], NQ 97, 326
05VD[Ø,3,4]CZ	Restrict/Cephalic Vein, Rt, [Opn, Perc, Perc Endo], Extralum Dev, NQ 86
07VL*	Restrict/Cisterna Chyli 60
04V7[Ø,3,4]ZZ	Restrict/Colic Artery, Lt, [Opn, Perc, Perc Endo] 252
04V7[Ø,3,4][D,Z]Z	Restrict/Colic Artery, Lt, [Opn, Perc, Perc Endo], [Intralum Dev, No Dev], NQ 96, 325
04V7[Ø,3,4]CZ	Restrict/Colic Artery, Lt, [Opn, Perc, Perc Endo], Extralum Dev, NQ 84
04V8[Ø,3,4]ZZ	Restrict/Colic Artery, Mid, [Opn, Perc, Perc Endo] 252
04V8[Ø,3,4][D,Z]Z	Restrict/Colic Artery, Mid, [Opn, Perc, Perc Endo], [Intralum Dev, No Dev], NQ 96, 325
04V8[Ø,3,4]CZ	Restrict/Colic Artery, Mid, [Opn, Perc, Perc Endo], Extralum Dev, NQ 84
04V6[Ø,3,4]ZZ	Restrict/Colic Artery, Rt, [Opn, Perc, Perc Endo] 252
04V6[Ø,3,4][D,Z]Z	Restrict/Colic Artery, Rt, [Opn, Perc, Perc Endo], [Intralum Dev, No Dev], NQ 96, 325
04V6[Ø,3,4]CZ	Restrict/Colic Artery, Rt, [Opn, Perc, Perc Endo], Extralum Dev, NQ 84
06V7[Ø,3,4]ZZ	Restrict/Colic Vein, [Opn, Perc, Perc Endo] 252
06V7[Ø,3,4][D,Z]Z	Restrict/Colic Vein, [Opn, Perc, Perc Endo], [Intralum Dev, No Dev], NQ 98, 328
06V7[Ø,3,4]CZ	Restrict/Colic Vein, [Opn, Perc, Perc Endo], Extralum Dev, NQ 87
ØFV9Ø[C,D,Z]Z	Restrict/Common Bile Duct, Opn, [Extralum Dev, Intralum Dev, No Dev], NQ 120, 301, 335, 449
03VJ[Ø,3,4][B,D,Z]Z	Restrict/Common Carotid Artery, Lt, [Opn, Perc, Perc Endo], [Bioactive Intralum Dev, Intralum Dev, No Dev], NQ 94, 322
03VJ[Ø,3,4][B,D]Z	Restrict/Common Carotid Artery, Lt, [Opn, Perc, Perc Endo], [Bioactive Intralum Dev, Intralum Dev], NQ 7, 9, 13, 17, 251
03VJ[Ø,3,4]CZ	Restrict/Common Carotid Artery, Lt, [Opn, Perc, Perc Endo], Extralum Dev, NQ 82
03VH[Ø,3,4][B,D,Z]Z	Restrict/Common Carotid Artery, Rt, [Opn, Perc, Perc Endo], [Bioactive Intralum Dev, Intralum Dev, No Dev], NQ 94, 322
03VH[Ø,3,4][B,D]Z	Restrict/Common Carotid Artery, Rt, [Opn, Perc, Perc Endo], [Bioactive Intralum Dev, Intralum Dev], NQ 7, 9, 13, 17, 251
03VH[Ø,3,4]CZ	Restrict/Common Carotid Artery, Rt, [Opn, Perc, Perc Endo], Extralum Dev, NQ 82
04VD[Ø,3,4][D,Z]Z	Restrict/Common Iliac Artery, Lt, [Opn, Perc, Perc Endo], [Intralum Dev, No Dev], NQ 96, 325
04VD[Ø,3,4]CZ	Restrict/Common Iliac Artery, Lt, [Opn, Perc, Perc Endo], Extralum Dev, NQ 84
04VC[Ø,3,4][D,Z]Z	Restrict/Common Iliac Artery, Rt, [Opn, Perc, Perc Endo], [Intralum Dev, No Dev], NQ 96, 325
04VC[Ø,3,4]CZ	Restrict/Common Iliac Artery, Rt, [Opn, Perc, Perc Endo], Extralum Dev, NQ 84
06VD[Ø,3,4][D,Z]Z	Restrict/Common Iliac Vein, Lt, [Opn, Perc, Perc Endo], [Intralum Dev, No Dev], NQ 98, 328
06VD[Ø,3,4]CZ	Restrict/Common Iliac Vein, Lt, [Opn, Perc, Perc Endo], Extralum Dev, NQ 87
06VC[Ø,3,4][D,Z]Z	Restrict/Common Iliac Vein, Rt, [Opn, Perc, Perc Endo], [Intralum Dev, No Dev], NQ 98, 328
06VC[Ø,3,4]CZ	Restrict/Common Iliac Vein, Rt, [Opn, Perc, Perc Endo], Extralum Dev, NQ 87
ØFV8Ø[C,D,Z]Z	Restrict/Cystic Duct, Opn, [Extralum Dev, Intralum Dev, No Dev], NQ 120, 301, 335, 449
ØDVM*	Restrict/Descending Colon 107, 334
ØDV9*	Restrict/Duodenum 107, 334
06V3[Ø,3,4]ZZ	Restrict/Esophageal Vein, [Opn, Perc, Perc Endo] 252
06V3[Ø,3,4][D,Z]Z	Restrict/Esophageal Vein, [Opn, Perc, Perc Endo], [Intralum Dev, No Dev], NQ 98, 328
06V3[Ø,3,4]CZ	Restrict/Esophageal Vein, [Opn, Perc, Perc Endo], Extralum Dev, NQ 87
ØDV4*	Restrict/Esophagogastric Junction 106, 334
ØDV44[C,D,Z]Z	Restrict/Esophagogastric Junction, Perc Endo, [Extralum Dev, Intralum Dev, No Dev], NQ 449
ØDV5*	Restrict/Esophagus 106, 334
ØDV3*	Restrict/Esophagus, Lwr 106, 334
ØDV2*	Restrict/Esophagus, Mid 106, 334
ØDV1*	Restrict/Esophagus, Upr 106, 334
03VN[Ø,3,4][B,D,Z]Z	Restrict/Ext Carotid Artery, Lt, [Opn, Perc, Perc Endo], [Bioactive Intralum Dev, Intralum Dev, No Dev], NQ 94, 322
03VN[Ø,3,4][B,D]Z	Restrict/Ext Carotid Artery, Lt, [Opn, Perc, Perc Endo], [Bioactive Intralum Dev, Intralum Dev], NQ 7, 9, 13, 17, 251
03VN[Ø,3,4]CZ	Restrict/Ext Carotid Artery, Lt, [Opn, Perc, Perc Endo], Extralum Dev, NQ 82
03VM[Ø,3,4][B,D,Z]Z	Restrict/Ext Carotid Artery, Rt, [Opn, Perc, Perc Endo], [Bioactive Intralum Dev, Intralum Dev, No Dev], NQ 94, 322
03VM[Ø,3,4][B,D]Z	Restrict/Ext Carotid Artery, Rt, [Opn, Perc, Perc Endo], [Bioactive Intralum Dev, Intralum Dev], NQ 7, 9, 13, 17, 251
03VM[Ø,3,4]CZ	Restrict/Ext Carotid Artery, Rt, [Opn, Perc, Perc Endo], Extralum Dev, NQ 82
04VJ[Ø,3,4][D,Z]Z	Restrict/Ext Iliac Artery, Lt, [Opn, Perc, Perc Endo], [Intralum Dev, No Dev], NQ 96, 325
04VJ[Ø,3,4]CZ	Restrict/Ext Iliac Artery, Lt, [Opn, Perc, Perc Endo], Extralum Dev, NQ 84
04VH[Ø,3,4][D,Z]Z	Restrict/Ext Iliac Artery, Rt, [Opn, Perc, Perc Endo], [Intralum Dev, No Dev], NQ 96, 325
04VH[Ø,3,4]CZ	Restrict/Ext Iliac Artery, Rt, [Opn, Perc, Perc Endo], Extralum Dev, NQ 84
06VG[Ø,3,4][D,Z]Z	Restrict/Ext Iliac Vein, Lt, [Opn, Perc, Perc Endo], [Intralum Dev, No Dev], NQ 98, 328
06VG[Ø,3,4]CZ	Restrict/Ext Iliac Vein, Lt, [Opn, Perc, Perc Endo], Extralum Dev, NQ 87
06VF[Ø,3,4][D,Z]Z	Restrict/Ext Iliac Vein, Rt, [Opn, Perc, Perc Endo], [Intralum Dev, No Dev], NQ 98, 328
06VF[Ø,3,4]CZ	Restrict/Ext Iliac Vein, Rt, [Opn, Perc, Perc Endo], Extralum Dev, NQ 87
05VQ[Ø,3,4][D,Z]Z	Restrict/Ext Jugular Vein, Lt, [Opn, Perc, Perc Endo], [Intralum Dev, No Dev], NQ 97, 326
05VQ[Ø,3,4]CZ	Restrict/Ext Jugular Vein, Lt, [Opn, Perc, Perc Endo], Extralum Dev, NQ 86
05VP[Ø,3,4][D,Z]Z	Restrict/Ext Jugular Vein, Rt, [Opn, Perc, Perc Endo], [Intralum Dev, No Dev], NQ 97, 326
05VP[Ø,3,4]CZ	Restrict/Ext Jugular Vein, Rt, [Opn, Perc, Perc Endo], Extralum Dev, NQ 86
03VR[Ø,3,4][D,Z]Z	Restrict/Face Artery, [Opn, Perc, Perc Endo], [Intralum Dev, No Dev], NQ 94, 322
03VR[Ø,3,4]CZ	Restrict/Face Artery, [Opn, Perc, Perc Endo], Extralum Dev, NQ 82
03VR[Ø,3,4]DZ	Restrict/Face Artery, [Opn, Perc, Perc Endo], Intralum Dev, NQ 7, 9, 13, 17, 251
05VV[Ø,3,4][D,Z]Z	Restrict/Face Vein, Lt, [Opn, Perc, Perc Endo], [Intralum Dev, No Dev], NQ 97, 326
05VV[Ø,3,4]CZ	Restrict/Face Vein, Lt, [Opn, Perc, Perc Endo], Extralum Dev, NQ 86
05VT[Ø,3,4][D,Z]Z	Restrict/Face Vein, Rt, [Opn, Perc, Perc Endo], [Intralum Dev, No Dev], NQ 97, 326
05VT[Ø,3,4]CZ	Restrict/Face Vein, Rt, [Opn, Perc, Perc Endo], Extralum Dev, NQ 86
04VL[Ø,3,4][D,Z]Z	Restrict/Femor Artery, Lt, [Opn, Perc, Perc Endo], [Intralum Dev, No Dev], NQ 96, 325
04VL[Ø,3,4]CZ	Restrict/Femor Artery, Lt, [Opn, Perc, Perc Endo], Extralum Dev, NQ 84
04VK[Ø,3,4][D,Z]Z	Restrict/Femor Artery, Rt, [Opn, Perc, Perc Endo], [Intralum Dev, No Dev], NQ 96, 325
04VK[Ø,3,4]CZ	Restrict/Femor Artery, Rt, [Opn, Perc, Perc Endo], Extralum Dev, NQ 84
06VN[Ø,3,4][D,Z]Z	Restrict/Femor Vein, Lt, [Opn, Perc, Perc Endo], [Intralum Dev, No Dev], NQ 98, 328
06VN[Ø,3,4]CZ	Restrict/Femor Vein, Lt, [Opn, Perc, Perc Endo], Extralum Dev, NQ 87
06VM[Ø,3,4][D,Z]Z	Restrict/Femor Vein, Rt, [Opn, Perc, Perc Endo], [Intralum Dev, No Dev], NQ 98, 328

06VM[0,3,4]CZ	Restrict/Femor Vein, Rt, [Opn, Perc, Perc Endo], Extralum Dev, NQ **87**
04VW[0,3,4][D,Z]Z	Restrict/Foot Artery, Lt, [Opn, Perc, Perc Endo], [Intralum Dev, No Dev], NQ **96, 325**
04VW[0,3,4]CZ	Restrict/Foot Artery, Lt, [Opn, Perc, Perc Endo], Extralum Dev, NQ **84**
04VV[0,3,4][D,Z]Z	Restrict/Foot Artery, Rt, [Opn, Perc, Perc Endo], [Intralum Dev, No Dev], NQ **96, 325**
04VV[0,3,4]CZ	Restrict/Foot Artery, Rt, [Opn, Perc, Perc Endo], Extralum Dev, NQ **84**
06VV[0,3,4][D,Z]Z	Restrict/Foot Vein, Lt, [Opn, Perc, Perc Endo], [Intralum Dev, No Dev], NQ **98, 328**
06VV[0,3,4]CZ	Restrict/Foot Vein, Lt, [Opn, Perc, Perc Endo], Extralum Dev, NQ **87**
06VT[0,3,4][D,Z]Z	Restrict/Foot Vein, Rt, [Opn, Perc, Perc Endo], [Intralum Dev, No Dev], NQ **98, 328**
06VT[0,3,4]CZ	Restrict/Foot Vein, Rt, [Opn, Perc, Perc Endo], Extralum Dev, NQ **87**
04V2[0,3,4]ZZ	Restrict/Gastric Artery, [Opn, Perc, Perc Endo] **252**
04V2[0,3,4][D,Z]Z	Restrict/Gastric Artery, [Opn, Perc, Perc Endo], [Intralum Dev, No Dev], NQ **96, 325**
04V2[0,3,4]CZ	Restrict/Gastric Artery, [Opn, Perc, Perc Endo], Extralum Dev, NQ **84**
06V2[0,3,4]ZZ	Restrict/Gastric Vein, [Opn, Perc, Perc Endo] **252**
06V2[0,3,4][D,Z]Z	Restrict/Gastric Vein, [Opn, Perc, Perc Endo], [Intralum Dev, No Dev], NQ **98, 328**
06V2[0,3,4]CZ	Restrict/Gastric Vein, [Opn, Perc, Perc Endo], Extralum Dev, NQ **87**
06VQ[0,3,4][D,Z]Z	Restrict/Greater Saphenous Vein, Lt, [Opn, Perc, Perc Endo], [Intralum Dev, No Dev], NQ **98, 328**
06VQ[0,3,4]CZ	Restrict/Greater Saphenous Vein, Lt, [Opn, Perc, Perc Endo], Extralum Dev, NQ **87**
06VP[0,3,4][D,Z]Z	Restrict/Greater Saphenous Vein, Rt, [Opn, Perc, Perc Endo], [Intralum Dev, No Dev], NQ **98, 328**
06VP[0,3,4]CZ	Restrict/Greater Saphenous Vein, Rt, [Opn, Perc, Perc Endo], Extralum Dev, NQ **87**
03VF[0,3,4][D,Z]Z	Restrict/Hand Artery, Lt, [Opn, Perc, Perc Endo], [Intralum Dev, No Dev], NQ **94, 322**
03VF[0,3,4]CZ	Restrict/Hand Artery, Lt, [Opn, Perc, Perc Endo], Extralum Dev, NQ **82**
03VD[0,3,4][D,Z]Z	Restrict/Hand Artery, Rt, [Opn, Perc, Perc Endo], [Intralum Dev, No Dev], NQ **94, 322**
03VD[0,3,4]CZ	Restrict/Hand Artery, Rt, [Opn, Perc, Perc Endo], Extralum Dev, NQ **82**
05VH[0,3,4][D,Z]Z	Restrict/Hand Vein, Lt, [Opn, Perc, Perc Endo], [Intralum Dev, No Dev], NQ **97, 326**
05VH[0,3,4]CZ	Restrict/Hand Vein, Lt, [Opn, Perc, Perc Endo], Extralum Dev, NQ **86**
05VG[0,3,4][D,Z]Z	Restrict/Hand Vein, Rt, [Opn, Perc, Perc Endo], [Intralum Dev, No Dev], NQ **97, 326**
05VG[0,3,4]CZ	Restrict/Hand Vein, Rt, [Opn, Perc, Perc Endo], Extralum Dev, NQ **86**
02VA*	Restrict/Heart **320**
02VA[0,3,4][C,Z]Z	Restrict/Heart, [Opn, Perc, Perc Endo], [Extralum Dev, No Dev], NQ **93**
05V1[0,3,4][D,Z]Z	Restrict/Hemiazygos Vein, [Opn, Perc, Perc Endo], [Intralum Dev, No Dev], NQ **97, 326**
05V1[0,3,4]CZ	Restrict/Hemiazygos Vein, [Opn, Perc, Perc Endo], Extralum Dev, NQ **86**
04V3[0,3,4]ZZ	Restrict/Hepatic Artery, [Opn, Perc, Perc Endo] **252**
04V3[0,3,4][D,Z]Z	Restrict/Hepatic Artery, [Opn, Perc, Perc Endo], [Intralum Dev, No Dev], NQ **96, 325**
04V3[0,3,4]CZ	Restrict/Hepatic Artery, [Opn, Perc, Perc Endo], Extralum Dev, NQ **84**
0FV60[C,D,Z]Z	Restrict/Hepatic Duct, Lt, Opn, [Extralum Dev, Intralum Dev, No Dev], NQ **120, 301, 335, 449**
0FV50[C,D,Z]Z	Restrict/Hepatic Duct, Rt, Opn, [Extralum Dev, Intralum Dev, No Dev], NQ **120, 301, 335, 449**
06V4[0,3,4]ZZ	Restrict/Hepatic Vein, [Opn, Perc, Perc Endo] **252**
06V4[0,3,4][D,Z]Z	Restrict/Hepatic Vein, [Opn, Perc, Perc Endo], [Intralum Dev, No Dev], NQ **98, 328**
06V4[0,3,4]CZ	Restrict/Hepatic Vein, [Opn, Perc, Perc Endo], Extralum Dev, NQ **87**
06VJ[0,3,4][D,Z]Z	Restrict/Hypogastric Vein, Lt, [Opn, Perc, Perc Endo], [Intralum Dev, No Dev], NQ **98, 328**
06VJ[0,3,4]CZ	Restrict/Hypogastric Vein, Lt, [Opn, Perc, Perc Endo], Extralum Dev, NQ **87**
06VH[0,3,4][D,Z]Z	Restrict/Hypogastric Vein, Rt, [Opn, Perc, Perc Endo], [Intralum Dev, No Dev], NQ **98, 328**
06VH[0,3,4]CZ	Restrict/Hypogastric Vein, Rt, [Opn, Perc, Perc Endo], Extralum Dev, NQ **87**
0DVC*	Restrict/Ileocecal Valve **107, 334**
0DVB*	Restrict/Ileum **107, 334**
04VB[0,3,4]ZZ	Restrict/Inferior Mesenteric Artery, [Opn, Perc, Perc Endo] **252**
04VB[0,3,4][D,Z]Z	Restrict/Inferior Mesenteric Artery, [Opn, Perc, Perc Endo], [Intralum Dev, No Dev], NQ **96, 325**
04VB[0,3,4]CZ	Restrict/Inferior Mesenteric Artery, [Opn, Perc, Perc Endo], Extralum Dev, NQ **84**
06V6[0,3,4]ZZ	Restrict/Inferior Mesenteric Vein, [Opn, Perc, Perc Endo] **252**
06V6[0,3,4][D,Z]Z	Restrict/Inferior Mesenteric Vein, [Opn, Perc, Perc Endo], [Intralum Dev, No Dev], NQ **98, 328**
06V6[0,3,4]CZ	Restrict/Inferior Mesenteric Vein, [Opn, Perc, Perc Endo], Extralum Dev, NQ **87**
06V0*	Restrict/Inferior Vena Cava **25, 64, 87, 112, 122, 153, 241, 252, 258, 268, 271, 290, 328**
03V2[0,3,4][D,Z]Z	Restrict/Innominate Artery, [Opn, Perc, Perc Endo], [Intralum Dev, No Dev], NQ **94, 322**
03V2[0,3,4]CZ	Restrict/Innominate Artery, [Opn, Perc, Perc Endo], Extralum Dev, NQ **82**
05V4[0,3,4][D,Z]Z	Restrict/Innominate Vein, Lt, [Opn, Perc, Perc Endo], [Intralum Dev, No Dev], NQ **97, 326**
05V4[0,3,4]CZ	Restrict/Innominate Vein, Lt, [Opn, Perc, Perc Endo], Extralum Dev, NQ **86**
05V3[0,3,4][D,Z]Z	Restrict/Innominate Vein, Rt, [Opn, Perc, Perc Endo], [Intralum Dev, No Dev], NQ **97, 326**
05V3[0,3,4]CZ	Restrict/Innominate Vein, Rt, [Opn, Perc, Perc Endo], Extralum Dev, NQ **86**
03VL[0,3,4][B,C,D]Z	Restrict/Int Carotid Artery, Lt, [Opn, Perc, Perc Endo], [Bioactive Intralum Dev, Extralum Dev, Intralum Dev], NQ **7, 9, 13, 17**
03VL[0,3,4][B,D,Z]Z	Restrict/Int Carotid Artery, Lt, [Opn, Perc, Perc Endo], [Bioactive Intralum Dev, Intralum Dev, No Dev], NQ **94, 322**
03VL[0,3,4][B,D]Z	Restrict/Int Carotid Artery, Lt, [Opn, Perc, Perc Endo], [Bioactive Intralum Dev, Intralum Dev], NQ **251**
03VL[0,3,4]CZ	Restrict/Int Carotid Artery, Lt, [Opn, Perc, Perc Endo], Extralum Dev, NQ **82**
03VK[0,3,4][B,C,D]Z	Restrict/Int Carotid Artery, Rt, [Opn, Perc, Perc Endo], [Bioactive Intralum Dev, Extralum Dev, Intralum Dev], NQ **7, 9, 13, 17**
03VK[0,3,4][B,D,Z]Z	Restrict/Int Carotid Artery, Rt, [Opn, Perc, Perc Endo], [Bioactive Intralum Dev, Intralum Dev, No Dev], NQ **94, 322**
03VK[0,3,4][B,D]Z	Restrict/Int Carotid Artery, Rt, [Opn, Perc, Perc Endo], [Bioactive Intralum Dev, Intralum Dev], NQ **251**
03VK[0,3,4]CZ	Restrict/Int Carotid Artery, Rt, [Opn, Perc, Perc Endo], Extralum Dev, NQ **82**
04VF[0,3,4][D,Z]Z	Restrict/Int Iliac Artery, Lt, [Opn, Perc, Perc Endo], [Intralum Dev, No Dev], NQ **96, 325**
04VF[0,3,4]CZ	Restrict/Int Iliac Artery, Lt, [Opn, Perc, Perc Endo], Extralum Dev, NQ **84**
04VE[0,3,4][D,Z]Z	Restrict/Int Iliac Artery, Rt, [Opn, Perc, Perc Endo], [Intralum Dev, No Dev], NQ **96, 325**
04VE[0,3,4]CZ	Restrict/Int Iliac Artery, Rt, [Opn, Perc, Perc Endo], Extralum Dev, NQ **84**
05VN[0,3,4][D,Z]Z	Restrict/Int Jugular Vein, Lt, [Opn, Perc, Perc Endo], [Intralum Dev, No Dev], NQ **97, 326**
05VN[0,3,4]CZ	Restrict/Int Jugular Vein, Lt, [Opn, Perc, Perc Endo], Extralum Dev, NQ **86**
05VM[0,3,4][D,Z]Z	Restrict/Int Jugular Vein, Rt, [Opn, Perc, Perc Endo], [Intralum Dev, No Dev], NQ **97, 326**
05VM[0,3,4]CZ	Restrict/Int Jugular Vein, Rt, [Opn, Perc, Perc Endo], Extralum Dev, NQ **86**
03V1[0,3,4][D,Z]Z	Restrict/Int Mammary Artery, Lt, [Opn, Perc, Perc Endo], [Intralum Dev, No Dev], NQ **94, 322**
03V1[0,3,4]CZ	Restrict/Int Mammary Artery, Lt, [Opn, Perc, Perc Endo], Extralum Dev, NQ **82**
03V0[0,3,4][D,Z]Z	Restrict/Int Mammary Artery, Rt, [Opn, Perc, Perc Endo], [Intralum Dev, No Dev], NQ **94, 322**
03V0[0,3,4]CZ	Restrict/Int Mammary Artery, Rt, [Opn, Perc, Perc Endo], Extralum Dev, NQ **82**

Alphabetic Index to Procedures

Code	Description
03VG[0,3,4][B,C,D,Z]Z	Restrict/Intracranial Artery, [Opn, Perc, Perc Endo], [Bioactive Intralum Dev, Extralum Dev, Intralum Dev, No Dev], NQ 7, 9, 13, 17
03VG[0,3,4][B,D,Z]Z	Restrict/Intracranial Artery, [Opn, Perc, Perc Endo], [Bioactive Intralum Dev, Intralum Dev, No Dev], NQ 94, 322
03VG[0,3,4][B,D]Z	Restrict/Intracranial Artery, [Opn, Perc, Perc Endo], [Bioactive Intralum Dev, Intralum Dev], NQ 251
03VG[0,3,4]CZ	Restrict/Intracranial Artery, [Opn, Perc, Perc Endo], Extralum Dev, NQ 82
05VL[0,3,4][C,D,Z]Z	Restrict/Intracranial Vein, [Opn, Perc, Perc Endo], [Extralum Dev, Intralum Dev, No Dev], NQ 7, 9, 13, 17
05VL[0,3,4][D,Z]Z	Restrict/Intracranial Vein, [Opn, Perc, Perc Endo], [Intralum Dev, No Dev], NQ 97, 326
05VL[0,3,4]CZ	Restrict/Intracranial Vein, [Opn, Perc, Perc Endo], Extralum Dev, NQ 86
0DVA*	Restrict/Jejunum 107, 334
0TV4*	Restrict/Kidney Pelvis, Lt 249
0TV3*	Restrict/Kidney Pelvis, Rt 249
08VY[0,3,7,8][D,Z]Z	Restrict/Lacrimal Duct, Lt, [Opn, Perc, Via Natrl or Artfcl Opng, Via Natrl or Artfcl Opng Endo], [Intralum Dev, No Dev], NQ 446
08VY[0,3]CZ	Restrict/Lacrimal Duct, Lt, [Opn, Perc], Extralum Dev, NQ 446
08VX[0,3,7,8][D,Z]Z	Restrict/Lacrimal Duct, Rt, [Opn, Perc, Via Natrl or Artfcl Opng, Via Natrl or Artfcl Opng Endo], [Intralum Dev, No Dev], NQ 446
08VX[0,3]CZ	Restrict/Lacrimal Duct, Rt, [Opn, Perc], Extralum Dev, NQ 446
0DVE*	Restrict/Large Intestine 107, 334
0DVG*	Restrict/Large Intestine, Lt 107, 334
0DVF*	Restrict/Large Intestine, Rt 107, 334
06VS[0,3,4][D,Z]Z	Restrict/Lesser Saphenous Vein, Lt, [Opn, Perc, Perc Endo], [Intralum Dev, No Dev], NQ 98, 328
06VS[0,3,4]CZ	Restrict/Lesser Saphenous Vein, Lt, [Opn, Perc, Perc Endo], Extralum Dev, NQ 87
06VR[0,3,4][D,Z]Z	Restrict/Lesser Saphenous Vein, Rt, [Opn, Perc, Perc Endo], [Intralum Dev, No Dev], NQ 98, 328
06VR[0,3,4]CZ	Restrict/Lesser Saphenous Vein, Rt, [Opn, Perc, Perc Endo], Extralum Dev, NQ 87
04VY[0,3,4][D,Z]Z	Restrict/Lwr Artery, [Opn, Perc, Perc Endo], [Intralum Dev, No Dev], NQ 96, 325
04VY[0,3,4]CZ	Restrict/Lwr Artery, [Opn, Perc, Perc Endo], Extralum Dev, NQ 84
06VY[0,3,4][D,Z]Z	Restrict/Lwr Vein, [Opn, Perc, Perc Endo], [Intralum Dev, No Dev], NQ 98, 328
06VY[0,3,4]CZ	Restrict/Lwr Vein, [Opn, Perc, Perc Endo], Extralum Dev, NQ 87
07VD*	Restrict/Lymphatic, Aortic 329
07VD[0,3,4][C,D,Z]Z	Restrict/Lymphatic, Aortic, [Opn, Perc, Perc Endo], [Extralum Dev, Intralum Dev, No Dev], NQ 291, 299
07V0*	Restrict/Lymphatic, Head 329
07V0[0,3,4][C,D,Z]Z	Restrict/Lymphatic, Head, [Opn, Perc, Perc Endo], [Extralum Dev, Intralum Dev, No Dev], NQ 291, 298
07V9*	Restrict/Lymphatic, Int Mammary, Lt 329
07V9[0,3,4][C,D,Z]Z	Restrict/Lymphatic, Int Mammary, Lt, [Opn, Perc, Perc Endo], [Extralum Dev, Intralum Dev, No Dev], NQ 291, 298
07V8*	Restrict/Lymphatic, Int Mammary, Rt 329
07V8[0,3,4][C,D,Z]Z	Restrict/Lymphatic, Int Mammary, Rt, [Opn, Perc, Perc Endo], [Extralum Dev, Intralum Dev, No Dev], NQ 291, 298
07V6*	Restrict/Lymphatic, Lt Axillary 329
07V6[0,3,4][C,D,Z]Z	Restrict/Lymphatic, Lt Axillary, [Opn, Perc, Perc Endo], [Extralum Dev, Intralum Dev, No Dev], NQ 291, 298
07VJ*	Restrict/Lymphatic, Lt Inguinal 329
07VJ[0,3,4][C,D,Z]Z	Restrict/Lymphatic, Lt Inguinal, [Opn, Perc, Perc Endo], [Extralum Dev, Intralum Dev, No Dev], NQ 291, 299
07VG*	Restrict/Lymphatic, Lt Lwr Extr 329
07VG[0,3,4][C,D,Z]Z	Restrict/Lymphatic, Lt Lwr Extr, [Opn, Perc, Perc Endo], [Extralum Dev, Intralum Dev, No Dev], NQ 291, 299
07V2*	Restrict/Lymphatic, Lt Neck 329
07V2[0,3,4][C,D,Z]Z	Restrict/Lymphatic, Lt Neck, [Opn, Perc, Perc Endo], [Extralum Dev, Intralum Dev, No Dev], NQ 291, 298
07V4*	Restrict/Lymphatic, Lt Upr Extr 329
07V4[0,3,4][C,D,Z]Z	Restrict/Lymphatic, Lt Upr Extr, [Opn, Perc, Perc Endo], [Extralum Dev, Intralum Dev, No Dev], NQ 291, 298
07VB*	Restrict/Lymphatic, Mesenteric 329
07VB[0,3,4][C,D,Z]Z	Restrict/Lymphatic, Mesenteric, [Opn, Perc, Perc Endo], [Extralum Dev, Intralum Dev, No Dev], NQ 291, 299
07VC*	Restrict/Lymphatic, Pelvis 329
07VC[0,3,4][C,D,Z]Z	Restrict/Lymphatic, Pelvis, [Opn, Perc, Perc Endo], [Extralum Dev, Intralum Dev, No Dev], NQ 291, 299
07V5*	Restrict/Lymphatic, Rt Axillary 329
07V5[0,3,4][C,D,Z]Z	Restrict/Lymphatic, Rt Axillary, [Opn, Perc, Perc Endo], [Extralum Dev, Intralum Dev, No Dev], NQ 291, 298
07VH*	Restrict/Lymphatic, Rt Inguinal 329
07VH[0,3,4][C,D,Z]Z	Restrict/Lymphatic, Rt Inguinal, [Opn, Perc, Perc Endo], [Extralum Dev, Intralum Dev, No Dev], NQ 291, 299
07VF*	Restrict/Lymphatic, Rt Lwr Extr 329
07VF[0,3,4][C,D,Z]Z	Restrict/Lymphatic, Rt Lwr Extr, [Opn, Perc, Perc Endo], [Extralum Dev, Intralum Dev, No Dev], NQ 291, 299
07V1*	Restrict/Lymphatic, Rt Neck 329
07V1[0,3,4][C,D,Z]Z	Restrict/Lymphatic, Rt Neck, [Opn, Perc, Perc Endo], [Extralum Dev, Intralum Dev, No Dev], NQ 291, 298
07V3*	Restrict/Lymphatic, Rt Upr Extr 329
07V3[0,3,4][C,D,Z]Z	Restrict/Lymphatic, Rt Upr Extr, [Opn, Perc, Perc Endo], [Extralum Dev, Intralum Dev, No Dev], NQ 291, 298
07V7*	Restrict/Lymphatic, Thorax 329
07V7[0,3,4][C,D,Z]Z	Restrict/Lymphatic, Thorax, [Opn, Perc, Perc Endo], [Extralum Dev, Intralum Dev, No Dev], NQ 291, 298
0FVD*	Restrict/Pancreatic Duct 119, 335
0FVF*	Restrict/Pancreatic Duct, Accessory 119, 335
0CVC[7,8][D,Z]Z	Restrict/Parotid Duct, Lt, [Via Natrl or Artfcl Opng, Via Natrl or Artfcl Opng Endo], [Intralum Dev, No Dev], NQ 332
0CVB[7,8][D,Z]Z	Restrict/Parotid Duct, Rt, [Via Natrl or Artfcl Opng, Via Natrl or Artfcl Opng Endo], [Intralum Dev, No Dev], NQ 332
04VU[0,3,4][D,Z]Z	Restrict/Peroneal Artery, Lt, [Opn, Perc, Perc Endo], [Intralum Dev, No Dev], NQ 96, 325
04VU[0,3,4]CZ	Restrict/Peroneal Artery, Lt, [Opn, Perc, Perc Endo], Extralum Dev, NQ 84
04VT[0,3,4][D,Z]Z	Restrict/Peroneal Artery, Rt, [Opn, Perc, Perc Endo], [Intralum Dev, No Dev], NQ 96, 325
04VT[0,3,4]CZ	Restrict/Peroneal Artery, Rt, [Opn, Perc, Perc Endo], Extralum Dev, NQ 84
04VN[0,3,4][D,Z]Z	Restrict/Popliteal Artery, Lt, [Opn, Perc, Perc Endo], [Intralum Dev, No Dev], NQ 96, 325
04VN[0,3,4]CZ	Restrict/Popliteal Artery, Lt, [Opn, Perc, Perc Endo], Extralum Dev, NQ 84
04VM[0,3,4][D,Z]Z	Restrict/Popliteal Artery, Rt, [Opn, Perc, Perc Endo], [Intralum Dev, No Dev], NQ 96, 325
04VM[0,3,4]CZ	Restrict/Popliteal Artery, Rt, [Opn, Perc, Perc Endo], Extralum Dev, NQ 84
06V8[0,3,4]ZZ	Restrict/Portal Vein, [Opn, Perc, Perc Endo] 252
06V8[0,3,4][D,Z]Z	Restrict/Portal Vein, [Opn, Perc, Perc Endo], [Intralum Dev, No Dev], NQ 98, 328
06V8[0,3,4]CZ	Restrict/Portal Vein, [Opn, Perc, Perc Endo], Extralum Dev, NQ 87
04VS[0,3,4][D,Z]Z	Restrict/Post Tibial Artery, Lt, [Opn, Perc, Perc Endo], [Intralum Dev, No Dev], NQ 96, 325
04VS[0,3,4]CZ	Restrict/Post Tibial Artery, Lt, [Opn, Perc, Perc Endo], Extralum Dev, NQ 84
04VR[0,3,4][D,Z]Z	Restrict/Post Tibial Artery, Rt, [Opn, Perc, Perc Endo], [Intralum Dev, No Dev], NQ 96, 325
04VR[0,3,4]CZ	Restrict/Post Tibial Artery, Rt, [Opn, Perc, Perc Endo], Extralum Dev, NQ 84
02VR[0,3,4][D,Z][T,Z]	Restrict/Pulmn Artery, Lt, [Opn, Perc, Perc Endo], [Intralum Dev, No Dev], [Ductus Arteriosus, NQ] 320
02VQ[0,3,4][D,Z]Z	Restrict/Pulmn Artery, Rt, [Opn, Perc, Perc Endo], [Intralum Dev, No Dev], NQ 93, 320
02VQ[0,3,4]CZ	Restrict/Pulmn Artery, Rt, [Opn, Perc, Perc Endo], Extralum Dev, NQ 93
02VP[0,3,4][D,Z]Z	Restrict/Pulmn Trunk, [Opn, Perc, Perc Endo], [Intralum Dev, No Dev], NQ 93, 320
02VP[0,3,4]CZ	Restrict/Pulmn Trunk, [Opn, Perc, Perc Endo], Extralum Dev, NQ 80
02VT[0,3,4][D,Z]Z	Restrict/Pulmn Vein, Lt, [Opn, Perc, Perc Endo], [Intralum Dev, No Dev], NQ 93, 320
02VT[0,3,4]CZ	Restrict/Pulmn Vein, Lt, [Opn, Perc, Perc Endo], Extralum Dev, NQ 80
02VS[0,3,4][D,Z]Z	Restrict/Pulmn Vein, Rt, [Opn, Perc, Perc Endo], [Intralum Dev, No Dev], NQ 93, 320
02VS[0,3,4]CZ	Restrict/Pulmn Vein, Rt, [Opn, Perc, Perc Endo], Extralum Dev, NQ 80
03VC[0,3,4][D,Z]Z	Restrict/Radial Artery, Lt, [Opn, Perc, Perc Endo], [Intralum Dev, No Dev], NQ 94, 322

Code	Description
03VC[0,3,4]CZ	Restrict/Radial Artery, Lt, [Opn, Perc, Perc Endo], Extralum Dev, NQ **82**
03VB[0,3,4][D,Z]Z	Restrict/Radial Artery, Rt, [Opn, Perc, Perc Endo], [Intralum Dev, No Dev], NQ **94, 322**
03VB[0,3,4]CZ	Restrict/Radial Artery, Rt, [Opn, Perc, Perc Endo], Extralum Dev, NQ **82**
0DVP*	Restrict/Rectum **110, 271, 334**
04VA[0,3,4][D,Z]Z	Restrict/Renal Artery, Lt, [Opn, Perc, Perc Endo], [Intralum Dev, No Dev], NQ **96, 252, 325**
04VA[0,3,4]CZ	Restrict/Renal Artery, Lt, [Opn, Perc, Perc Endo], Extralum Dev, NQ **84**
04V9[0,3,4][D,Z]Z	Restrict/Renal Artery, Rt, [Opn, Perc, Perc Endo], [Intralum Dev, No Dev], NQ **96, 252, 325**
04V9[0,3,4]CZ	Restrict/Renal Artery, Rt, [Opn, Perc, Perc Endo], Extralum Dev, NQ **84**
06VB[0,3,4][D,Z]Z	Restrict/Renal Vein, Lt, [Opn, Perc, Perc Endo], [Intralum Dev, No Dev], NQ **98, 252, 328**
06VB[0,3,4]CZ	Restrict/Renal Vein, Lt, [Opn, Perc, Perc Endo], Extralum Dev, NQ **87**
06V9[0,3,4][D,Z]Z	Restrict/Renal Vein, Rt, [Opn, Perc, Perc Endo], [Intralum Dev, No Dev], NQ **98, 252, 328**
06V9[0,3,4]CZ	Restrict/Renal Vein, Rt, [Opn, Perc, Perc Endo], Extralum Dev, NQ **87**
0DVN*	Restrict/Sigmoid Colon **107, 334**
0DV8*	Restrict/Sm Intestine **107, 334**
04V4[0,3,4]ZZ	Restrict/Splenic Artery, [Opn, Perc, Perc Endo] **252**
04V4[0,3,4][D,Z]Z	Restrict/Splenic Artery, [Opn, Perc, Perc Endo], [Intralum Dev, No Dev], NQ **96, 325**
04V4[0,3,4]CZ	Restrict/Splenic Artery, [Opn, Perc, Perc Endo], Extralum Dev, NQ **84**
06V1[0,3,4]ZZ	Restrict/Splenic Vein, [Opn, Perc, Perc Endo] **252**
06V1[0,3,4][D,Z]Z	Restrict/Splenic Vein, [Opn, Perc, Perc Endo], [Intralum Dev, No Dev], NQ **98, 328**
06V1[0,3,4]CZ	Restrict/Splenic Vein, [Opn, Perc, Perc Endo], Extralum Dev, NQ **87**
0DV6[0,3,4][C,D,Z]Z	Restrict/Stomach, [Opn, Perc, Perc Endo], [Extralum Dev, Intralum Dev, No Dev], NQ **106, 236, 334**
0DV6[7,8]ZZ	Restrict/Stomach, [Via Natrl or Artfcl Opng, Via Natrl or Artfcl Opng Endo] **236**
0DV7*	Restrict/Stomach, Pylorus **106**
03V4[0,3,4][D,Z]Z	Restrict/Subclavian Artery, Lt, [Opn, Perc, Perc Endo], [Intralum Dev, No Dev], NQ **94, 322**
03V4[0,3,4]CZ	Restrict/Subclavian Artery, Lt, [Opn, Perc, Perc Endo], Extralum Dev, NQ **82**
03V3[0,3,4][D,Z]Z	Restrict/Subclavian Artery, Rt, [Opn, Perc, Perc Endo], [Intralum Dev, No Dev], NQ **94, 322**
03V3[0,3,4]CZ	Restrict/Subclavian Artery, Rt, [Opn, Perc, Perc Endo], Extralum Dev, NQ **82**
05V6[0,3,4][D,Z]Z	Restrict/Subclavian Vein, Lt, [Opn, Perc, Perc Endo], [Intralum Dev, No Dev], NQ **97, 326**
05V6[0,3,4]CZ	Restrict/Subclavian Vein, Lt, [Opn, Perc, Perc Endo], Extralum Dev, NQ **86**
05V5[0,3,4][D,Z]Z	Restrict/Subclavian Vein, Rt, [Opn, Perc, Perc Endo], [Intralum Dev, No Dev], NQ **97, 326**
05V5[0,3,4]CZ	Restrict/Subclavian Vein, Rt, [Opn, Perc, Perc Endo], Extralum Dev, NQ **86**
04V5[0,3,4]ZZ	Restrict/Superior Mesenteric Artery, [Opn, Perc, Perc Endo] **252**
04V5[0,3,4][D,Z]Z	Restrict/Superior Mesenteric Artery, [Opn, Perc, Perc Endo], [Intralum Dev, No Dev], NQ **96, 325**
04V5[0,3,4]CZ	Restrict/Superior Mesenteric Artery, [Opn, Perc, Perc Endo], Extralum Dev, NQ **84**
06V5[0,3,4]ZZ	Restrict/Superior Mesenteric Vein, [Opn, Perc, Perc Endo] **252**
06V5[0,3,4][D,Z]Z	Restrict/Superior Mesenteric Vein, [Opn, Perc, Perc Endo], [Intralum Dev, No Dev], NQ **98, 328**
06V5[0,3,4]CZ	Restrict/Superior Mesenteric Vein, [Opn, Perc, Perc Endo], Extralum Dev, NQ **87**
02VV*	Restrict/Superior Vena Cava **24, 63, 80, 110, 121, 152, 238, 251, 258, 268, 271, 290, 320**
03VT[0,3,4][D,Z]Z	Restrict/Temporal Artery, Lt, [Opn, Perc, Perc Endo], [Intralum Dev, No Dev], NQ **94, 322**
03VT[0,3,4]CZ	Restrict/Temporal Artery, Lt, [Opn, Perc, Perc Endo], Extralum Dev, NQ **82**
03VT[0,3,4]DZ	Restrict/Temporal Artery, Lt, [Opn, Perc, Perc Endo], Intralum Dev, NQ **7, 9, 13, 17, 251**
03VS[0,3,4][D,Z]Z	Restrict/Temporal Artery, Rt, [Opn, Perc, Perc Endo], [Intralum Dev, No Dev], NQ **94, 322**
03VS[0,3,4]CZ	Restrict/Temporal Artery, Rt, [Opn, Perc, Perc Endo], Extralum Dev, NQ **82**
03VS[0,3,4]DZ	Restrict/Temporal Artery, Rt, [Opn, Perc, Perc Endo], Intralum Dev, NQ **7, 9, 13, 17, 251**
02VW[0,3,4]ZZ	Restrict/Thoracic Aorta, [Opn, Perc, Perc Endo] **93**
02VW[0,3,4][D,Z]Z	Restrict/Thoracic Aorta, [Opn, Perc, Perc Endo], [Intralum Dev, No Dev], NQ **320**
02VW[0,3,4]CZ	Restrict/Thoracic Aorta, [Opn, Perc, Perc Endo], Extralum Dev, NQ **80**
02VW[0,3,4]DZ	Restrict/Thoracic Aorta, [Opn, Perc, Perc Endo], Intralum Dev, NQ **71, 72, 251**
07VK*	Restrict/Thoracic Duct **60**
03VV[0,3,4][D,Z]Z	Restrict/Thyroid Artery, Lt, [Opn, Perc, Perc Endo], [Intralum Dev, No Dev], NQ **94, 322**
03VV[0,3,4]CZ	Restrict/Thyroid Artery, Lt, [Opn, Perc, Perc Endo], Extralum Dev, NQ **82**
03VV[0,3,4]DZ	Restrict/Thyroid Artery, Lt, [Opn, Perc, Perc Endo], Intralum Dev, NQ **7, 9, 13, 17, 251**
03VU[0,3,4][D,Z]Z	Restrict/Thyroid Artery, Rt, [Opn, Perc, Perc Endo], [Intralum Dev, No Dev], NQ **94, 322**
03VU[0,3,4]CZ	Restrict/Thyroid Artery, Rt, [Opn, Perc, Perc Endo], Extralum Dev, NQ **82**
03VU[0,3,4]DZ	Restrict/Thyroid Artery, Rt, [Opn, Perc, Perc Endo], Intralum Dev, NQ **7, 9, 13, 17, 251**
0BV1*	Restrict/Trachea **52, 331**
0DVL*	Restrict/Transv Colon **107, 334**
03VA[0,3,4][D,Z]Z	Restrict/Ulnar Artery, Lt, [Opn, Perc, Perc Endo], [Intralum Dev, No Dev], NQ **94, 322**
03VA[0,3,4]CZ	Restrict/Ulnar Artery, Lt, [Opn, Perc, Perc Endo], Extralum Dev, NQ **82**
03V9[0,3,4][D,Z]Z	Restrict/Ulnar Artery, Rt, [Opn, Perc, Perc Endo], [Intralum Dev, No Dev], NQ **94, 322**
03V9[0,3,4]CZ	Restrict/Ulnar Artery, Rt, [Opn, Perc, Perc Endo], Extralum Dev, NQ **82**
03VY[0,3,4][D,Z]Z	Restrict/Upr Artery, [Opn, Perc, Perc Endo], [Intralum Dev, No Dev], NQ **94, 322**
03VY[0,3,4]CZ	Restrict/Upr Artery, [Opn, Perc, Perc Endo], Extralum Dev, NQ **82**
05VY[0,3,4][D,Z]Z	Restrict/Upr Vein, [Opn, Perc, Perc Endo], [Intralum Dev, No Dev], NQ **97, 326**
05VY[0,3,4]CZ	Restrict/Upr Vein, [Opn, Perc, Perc Endo], Extralum Dev, NQ **86**
0TV7*	Restrict/Ureter, Lt **249, 354**
0TV6*	Restrict/Ureter, Rt **249, 354**
0TVD*	Restrict/Urethra **250, 257, 268, 354**
03VQ[0,3,4][B,D,Z]Z	Restrict/Vert Artery, Lt, [Opn, Perc, Perc Endo], [Bioactive Intralum Dev, Intralum Dev, No Dev], NQ **94, 322**
03VQ[0,3,4][B,D]Z	Restrict/Vert Artery, Lt, [Opn, Perc, Perc Endo], [Bioactive Intralum Dev, Intralum Dev], NQ **7, 9, 13, 17, 251**
03VQ[0,3,4]CZ	Restrict/Vert Artery, Lt, [Opn, Perc, Perc Endo], Extralum Dev, NQ **82**
03VP[0,3,4][B,D,Z]Z	Restrict/Vert Artery, Rt, [Opn, Perc, Perc Endo], [Bioactive Intralum Dev, Intralum Dev, No Dev], NQ **94, 322**
03VP[0,3,4][B,D]Z	Restrict/Vert Artery, Rt, [Opn, Perc, Perc Endo], [Bioactive Intralum Dev, Intralum Dev], NQ **7, 9, 13, 17, 251**
03VP[0,3,4]CZ	Restrict/Vert Artery, Rt, [Opn, Perc, Perc Endo], Extralum Dev, NQ **82**
05VS[0,3,4][D,Z]Z	Restrict/Vert Vein, Lt, [Opn, Perc, Perc Endo], [Intralum Dev, No Dev], NQ **97, 326**
05VS[0,3,4]CZ	Restrict/Vert Vein, Lt, [Opn, Perc, Perc Endo], Extralum Dev, NQ **86**
05VR[0,3,4][D,Z]Z	Restrict/Vert Vein, Rt, [Opn, Perc, Perc Endo], [Intralum Dev, No Dev], NQ **97, 326**
05VR[0,3,4]CZ	Restrict/Vert Vein, Rt, [Opn, Perc, Perc Endo], Extralum Dev, NQ **86**
0VW40[0,3,7,J,K]Z	Rev of [Drain Dev, Inf Dev, Auto Tissue Sub, Synth Sub, Nonauto Tissue Sub] in Prostate and Seminal Vesicles, Opn **440**
0VW43[0,3,7,J,K]Z	Rev of [Drain Dev, Inf Dev, Auto Tissue Sub, Synth Sub, Nonauto Tissue Sub] in Prostate and Seminal Vesicles, Perc **440**
0VW44[0,3,7,J,K]Z	Rev of [Drain Dev, Inf Dev, Auto Tissue Sub, Synth Sub, Nonauto Tissue Sub] in Prostate and Seminal Vesicles, Perc Endo **440**

0VW47[0,3,7,J,K]Z	Rev of [Drain Dev, Inf Dev, Auto Tissue Sub, Synth Sub, Nonauto Tissue Sub] in Prostate and Seminal Vesicles, Via Natrl or Artfcl Opng **440**
0VW48[0,3,7,J,K]Z	Rev of [Drain Dev, Inf Dev, Auto Tissue Sub, Synth Sub, Nonauto Tissue Sub] in Prostate and Seminal Vesicles, Via Natrl or Artfcl Opng Endo **440**
0CWY37Z	Rev of Autol Sub in Mouth/Throat, Perc Appr **56, 211, 448**
0NW007Z	Rev of Autol Sub in Skull, Opn Appr **10**
0NW037Z	Rev of Autol Sub in Skull, Perc Appr **10**
0NW047Z	Rev of Autol Sub in Skull, Perc Endo Appr **10**
0NW00MZ	Rev of Bone Growth Stimulator in Skull, Opn Appr **10**
0NW03MZ	Rev of Bone Growth Stimulator in Skull, Perc Appr **10**
0NW04MZ	Rev of Bone Stim in Skull, Perc Endo Appr **10**
0NW000Z	Rev of Drain Device in Skull, Opn Appr **10**
0NW030Z	Rev of Drain Device in Skull, Perc Appr **10**
0NW040Z	Rev of Drain Device in Skull, Perc Endo Appr **10**
0NW005Z	Rev of Ext Fix Device in Skull, Opn Appr **10**
0NW035Z	Rev of Ext Fix Device in Skull, Perc Appr **10**
0NW045Z	Rev of Ext Fix in Skull, Perc Endo Appr **10**
02WA0RZ	Rev of Ext Heart Assist in Heart, Opn Appr **71**
02WA3RZ	Rev of Ext Heart Assist in Heart, Perc Appr **71**
02WA4RZ	Rev of Ext Heart Assist in Heart, Perc Endo Appr **71**
0NW00SZ	Rev of Hearing Device in Skull, Opn Appr **10**
0NW03SZ	Rev of Hearing Device in Skull, Perc Appr **10**
0NW04SZ	Rev of Hearing Device in Skull, Perc Endo Appr **10**
02WA0QZ	Rev of Implant Heart Assist in Heart, Opn Appr **71**
02WA3QZ	Rev of Implant Heart Assist in Heart, Perc Appr **71**
0NW004Z	Rev of Int Fix Device in Skull, Opn Appr **10**
0NW034Z	Rev of Int Fix Device in Skull, Perc Appr **10**
0NW044Z	Rev of Int Fix in Skull, Perc Endo Appr **10**
0SWD09Z	Rev of Liner in Lt Knee Jt, Opn Appr **132, 353, 458**
0SWC09Z	Rev of Liner in Rt Knee Jt, Opn Appr **132, 353, 458**
0NW00NZ	Rev of Neurostim in Skull, Opn Appr **10, 14, 18**
0NW00KZ	Rev of Nonaut Sub in Skull, Opn Appr **10**
0NW03KZ	Rev of Nonaut Sub in Skull, Perc Appr **10**
0NW04KZ	Rev of Nonaut Sub in Skull, Perc Endo Appr **10**
08W[J,K]3JZ	Rev of Synth Sub in [Rt, Lt] Lens, Perc Appr **44**
02WA0JZ	Rev of Synth Sub in Heart, Opn Appr **71**
08WK3JZ	Rev of Synth Sub in Lt Lens, Perc Appr **330, 446**
08WJ3JZ	Rev of Synth Sub in Rt Lens, Perc Appr **330, 446**
0NW00JZ	Rev of Synth Sub in Skull, Opn Appr **10**
0NW03JZ	Rev of Synth Sub in Skull, Perc Appr **10**
0NW04JZ	Rev of Synth Sub in Skull, Perc Endo Appr **10**
0WWF[0,3,4] [0,1,3,7,J,K,Y]Z	Rev/Abd Wall, [Opn, Perc, Perc Endo], [Drain Dev, Radioact Elmt, Inf Dev, Auto Tissue Sub, Synth Sub, Nonauto Tissue Sub, Oth Dev], NQ **114, 356**
0QW5[0,3,4][4,7,J,K]Z	Rev/Acetab, Lt, [Opn, Perc, Perc Endo], [Int Fix Dev, Auto Tissue Sub, Synth Sub, Nonauto Tissue Sub], NQ **136**
0QW4[0,3,4][4,7,J,K]Z	Rev/Acetab, Rt, [Opn, Perc, Perc Endo], [Int Fix Dev, Auto Tissue Sub, Synth Sub, Nonauto Tissue Sub], NQ **136**
0RWH[0,3,4] [0,3,4,7,8,K]Z	Rev/Acromioclavicular Jt, Lt, [Opn, Perc, Perc Endo], [Drain Dev, Inf Dev, Int Fix Dev, Auto Tissue Sub, Spacer, Nonauto Tissue Sub], NQ **148**
0RWH[0,3,4] [0,3,4,7,8,J,K]Z	Rev/Acromioclavicular Jt, Lt, [Opn, Perc, Perc Endo], [Drain Dev, Inf Dev, Int Fix Dev, Auto Tissue Sub, Spacer, Synth Sub, Nonauto Tissue Sub], NQ **350**
0RWH[0,3,4]JZ	Rev/Acromioclavicular Jt, Lt, [Opn, Perc, Perc Endo], Synth Sub, NQ **157**
0RWG[0,3,4] [0,3,4,7,8,K]Z	Rev/Acromioclavicular Jt, Rt, [Opn, Perc, Perc Endo], [Drain Dev, Inf Dev, Int Fix Dev, Auto Tissue Sub, Spacer, Nonauto Tissue Sub], NQ **148**
0RWG[0,3,4] [0,3,4,7,8,J,K]Z	Rev/Acromioclavicular Jt, Rt, [Opn, Perc, Perc Endo], [Drain Dev, Inf Dev, Int Fix Dev, Auto Tissue Sub, Spacer, Synth Sub, Nonauto Tissue Sub], NQ **350**
0RWG[0,3,4]JZ	Rev/Acromioclavicular Jt, Rt, [Opn, Perc, Perc Endo], Synth Sub, NQ **157**
0GW5[0,3,4]0Z	Rev/Adrenal Gland, [Opn, Perc, Perc Endo], Drain Dev, NQ **235**
0DWR*	Rev/Anal Sphincter **110**
0SWG[0,3,4] [0,3,4,5,7,8,K]Z	Rev/Ankle Jt, Lt, [Opn, Perc, Perc Endo], [Drain Dev, Inf Dev, Int Fix Dev, Ext Fix Dev, Auto Tissue Sub, Spacer, Nonauto Tissue Sub], NQ **133**
0SWG[0,3,4] [0,3,4,5,7,8,J,K]Z	Rev/Ankle Jt, Lt, [Opn, Perc, Perc Endo], [Drain Dev, Inf Dev, Int Fix Dev, Ext Fix Dev, Auto Tissue Sub, Spacer, Synth Sub, Nonauto Tissue Sub], NQ **353**
0SWG[0,3,4]JZ	Rev/Ankle Jt, Lt, [Opn, Perc, Perc Endo], Synth Sub, NQ **158**
0SWF[0,3,4] [0,3,4,5,7,8,K]Z	Rev/Ankle Jt, Rt, [Opn, Perc, Perc Endo], [Drain Dev, Inf Dev, Int Fix Dev, Ext Fix Dev, Auto Tissue Sub, Spacer, Nonauto Tissue Sub], NQ **133**
0SWF[0,3,4] [0,3,4,5,7,8,J,K]Z	Rev/Ankle Jt, Rt, [Opn, Perc, Perc Endo], [Drain Dev, Inf Dev, Int Fix Dev, Ext Fix Dev, Auto Tissue Sub, Spacer, Synth Sub, Nonauto Tissue Sub], NQ **353**
0SWF[0,3,4]JZ	Rev/Ankle Jt, Rt, [Opn, Perc, Perc Endo], Synth Sub, NQ **158**
0DWQ*	Rev/Anus **107, 335**
0DWQ[0,3,4,7,8]LZ	Rev/Anus, [Opn, Perc, Perc Endo, Via Natrl or Artfcl Opng, Via Natrl or Artfcl Opng Endo], Artfcl Sphincter, NQ **211**
02WF[0,4][7,8,J,K]Z	Rev/Aortic Valve, [Opn, Perc Endo], [Auto Tissue Sub, Zooplastic Tissue, Synth Sub, Nonauto Tissue Sub], NQ **75**
02W5[0,4]JZ	Rev/Atrial Septum, [Opn, Perc Endo], Synth Sub, NQ **75**
09WA*	Rev/Auditory Ossicle, Lt **52**
09W9*	Rev/Auditory Ossicle, Rt **52**
0TWB[0,3,4,7,8] [0,2,3,7,C,D,J,K,L,M]Z	Rev/Bladder, [Opn, Perc, Perc Endo, Via Natrl or Artfcl Opng, Via Natrl or Artfcl Opng Endo], [Drain Dev, Monitoring Dev, Inf Dev, Auto Tissue Sub, Extralum Dev, Intralum Dev, Synth Sub, Nonauto Tissue Sub, Artfcl Sphincter, Stimulator Lead], NQ **250, 354**
00W0[0,3,4] [0,2,3,7,J,K,M]Z	Rev/Brain, [Opn, Perc, Perc Endo], [Drain Dev, Monitoring Dev, Inf Dev, Auto Tissue Sub, Synth Sub, Nonauto Tissue Sub, Neurostimulator Lead], NQ **8, 12, 17**
00W0[3,4] [0,2,3,7,J,K,M]Z	Rev/Brain, [Perc, Perc Endo], [Drain Dev, Monitoring Dev, Inf Dev, Auto Tissue Sub, Synth Sub, Nonauto Tissue Sub, Neurostimulator Lead], NQ **318, 414**
00W00[0,2,3,7,M]Z	Rev/Brain, Opn, [Drain Dev, Monitoring Dev, Inf Dev, Auto Tissue Sub, Neurostimulator Lead], NQ **318, 414**
0HWU[0,3]JZ	Rev/Breast, Lt, [Opn, Perc], Synth Sub, NQ **222, 337, 450**
0HWT[0,3]JZ	Rev/Breast, Rt, [Opn, Perc], Synth Sub, NQ **222, 337, 450**
0RWR[0,3,4] [0,3,4,5,7,8,K]Z	Rev/Carpal Jt, Lt, [Opn, Perc, Perc Endo], [Drain Dev, Inf Dev, Int Fix Dev, Ext Fix Dev, Auto Tissue Sub, Spacer, Nonauto Tissue Sub], NQ **147, 317**
0RWR[0,3,4]JZ	Rev/Carpal Jt, Lt, [Opn, Perc, Perc Endo], Synth Sub, NQ **157, 351**
0RWQ[0,3,4] [0,3,4,5,7,8,K]Z	Rev/Carpal Jt, Rt, [Opn, Perc, Perc Endo], [Drain Dev, Inf Dev, Int Fix Dev, Ext Fix Dev, Auto Tissue Sub, Spacer, Nonauto Tissue Sub], NQ **147, 317**
0RWQ[0,3,4]JZ	Rev/Carpal Jt, Rt, [Opn, Perc, Perc Endo], Synth Sub, NQ **157, 351**
0PWN[0,3,4] [4,5,7,J,K]Z	Rev/Carpal, Lt, [Opn, Perc, Perc Endo], [Int Fix Dev, Ext Fix Dev, Auto Tissue Sub, Synth Sub, Nonauto Tissue Sub], NQ **150**
0PWM[0,3,4] [4,5,7,J,K]Z	Rev/Carpal, Rt, [Opn, Perc, Perc Endo], [Int Fix Dev, Ext Fix Dev, Auto Tissue Sub, Synth Sub, Nonauto Tissue Sub], NQ **150**
00W6[0,3,4][0,2,3,M]Z	Rev/Cerebral Ventricle, [Opn, Perc, Perc Endo], [Drain Dev, Monitoring Dev, Inf Dev, Neurostimulator Lead], NQ **8, 12, 17, 414**
00W6[0,3,4] [0,2,3,J,M]Z	Rev/Cerebral Ventricle, [Opn, Perc, Perc Endo], [Drain Dev, Monitoring Dev, Inf Dev, Synth Sub, Neurostimulator Lead], NQ **318**
00W6[0,3,4]JZ	Rev/Cerebral Ventricle, [Opn, Perc, Perc Endo], Synth Sub, NQ **20, 296**
0RW3[0,3,4][0,3,7,K]Z	Rev/Cervical Vert Disc, [Opn, Perc, Perc Endo], [Drain Dev, Inf Dev, Auto Tissue Sub, Nonauto Tissue Sub], NQ **157**
0RW3[0,3,4]JZ	Rev/Cervical Vert Disc, [Opn, Perc, Perc Endo], Synth Sub, NQ **20, 159, 161, 350**
0RW1[0,3,4] [0,3,4,7,8,A,J,K]Z	Rev/Cervical Vert Jt, [Opn, Perc, Perc Endo], [Drain Dev, Inf Dev, Int Fix Dev, Auto Tissue Sub, Spacer, Interbody Fusion Dev, Synth Sub, Nonauto Tissue Sub], NQ **157**
0RW1[0,3,4][4,J]Z	Rev/Cervical Vert Jt, [Opn, Perc, Perc Endo], [Int Fix Dev, Synth Sub], NQ **350**
0PW3[0,3,4][4,7,J,K]Z	Rev/Cervical Vertebra, [Opn, Perc, Perc Endo], [Int Fix Dev, Auto Tissue Sub, Synth Sub, Nonauto Tissue Sub], NQ **135**
0RW5[0,3,4][0,3,7,K]Z	Rev/Cervicothoracic Vert Disc, [Opn, Perc, Perc Endo], [Drain Dev, Inf Dev, Auto Tissue Sub, Nonauto Tissue Sub], NQ **157**
0RW5[0,3,4]JZ	Rev/Cervicothoracic Vert Disc, [Opn, Perc, Perc Endo], Synth Sub, NQ **20, 159, 161, 350**
0RW4[0,3,4] [0,3,4,7,8,A,J,K]Z	Rev/Cervicothoracic Vert Jt, [Opn, Perc, Perc Endo], [Drain Dev, Inf Dev, Int Fix Dev, Auto Tissue Sub, Spacer, Interbody Fusion Dev, Synth Sub, Nonauto Tissue Sub], NQ **157**
0RW4[0,3,4][4,J]Z	Rev/Cervicothoracic Vert Jt, [Opn, Perc, Perc Endo], [Int Fix Dev, Synth Sub], NQ **350**

07WL[0,3,4][7,J,K]Z Rev/Cisterna Chyli, [Opn, Perc, Perc Endo], [Auto Tissue Sub, Synth Sub, Nonauto Tissue Sub], NQ 291, 299, 329

07WL[0,3,4][0,3,C,D]Z Rev/Cisterna Chyli, [Opn, Perc, Perc Endo], [Drain Dev, Inf Dev, Extralum Dev, Intralum Dev], NQ 60

0PWB[0,3,4][4,7,J,K]Z Rev/Clavicle, Lt, [Opn, Perc, Perc Endo], [Int Fix Dev, Auto Tissue Sub, Synth Sub, Nonauto Tissue Sub], NQ 135

0PW9[0,3,4][4,7,J,K]Z Rev/Clavicle, Rt, [Opn, Perc, Perc Endo], [Int Fix Dev, Auto Tissue Sub, Synth Sub, Nonauto Tissue Sub], NQ 135

0SW6[0,3,4][0,3,4,7,8,J,K]Z Rev/Coccygeal Jt, [Opn, Perc, Perc Endo], [Drain Dev, Inf Dev, Int Fix Dev, Auto Tissue Sub, Spacer, Synth Sub, Nonauto Tissue Sub], NQ 158

0QWS[0,3,4][4,7,J,K]Z Rev/Coccyx, [Opn, Perc, Perc Endo], [Int Fix Dev, Auto Tissue Sub, Synth Sub, Nonauto Tissue Sub], NQ 136

0WW1[0,3,4][0,1,3,J,Y]Z Rev/Cranial Cavity, [Opn, Perc, Perc Endo], [Drain Dev, Radioact Elmt, Inf Dev, Synth Sub, Oth Dev], NQ 10, 14

0WW1[0,3,4][0,1,3,J,Y]Z Rev/Cranial Cavity, [Opn, Perc, Perc Endo], [Drain Dev, Radioact Elmt, Inf Dev, Synth Sub, Oth Dev], NQ 19

00WE[0,3,4][0,2,3,7,M]Z Rev/Cranial Nerve, [Opn, Perc, Perc Endo], [Drain Dev, Monitoring Dev, Inf Dev, Auto Tissue Sub, Neurostimulator Lead], NQ 24

0BWT[0,3,4,7,8][0,2,7,J,K,M]Z Rev/Diaphragm, [Opn, Perc, Perc Endo, Via Natrl or Artfcl Opng, Via Natrl or Artfcl Opng Endo], [Drain Dev, Monitoring Dev, Auto Tissue Sub, Synth Sub, Nonauto Tissue Sub, Diaphragmatic Pacemaker Lead], NQ 62

09WJ[0,3,4]DZ Rev/Ear, Lt, [Opn, Perc, Perc Endo], Intralum Dev, NQ 52

09WJ[0,7,8][0,7,J,K]Z Rev/Ear, Lt, [Opn, Via Natrl or Artfcl Opng, Via Natrl or Artfcl Opng Endo], [Drain Dev, Auto Tissue Sub, Synth Sub, Nonauto Tissue Sub], NQ 52

09WJ4[0,7]Z Rev/Ear, Lt, Perc Endo, [Drain Dev, Auto Tissue Sub], NQ 52

09WJ3[0,7]Z Rev/Ear, Lt, Perc, [Drain Dev, Auto Tissue Sub], NQ 52

09WH[0,3,4]DZ Rev/Ear, Rt, [Opn, Perc, Perc Endo], Intralum Dev, NQ 52

09WH[0,7,8][0,7,J,K]Z Rev/Ear, Rt, [Opn, Via Natrl or Artfcl Opng, Via Natrl or Artfcl Opng Endo], [Drain Dev, Auto Tissue Sub, Synth Sub, Nonauto Tissue Sub], NQ 52

09WH4[0,7]Z Rev/Ear, Rt, Perc Endo, [Drain Dev, Auto Tissue Sub], NQ 52

09WH3[0,7]Z Rev/Ear, Rt, Perc, [Drain Dev, Auto Tissue Sub], NQ 52

0RWM[0,3,4][0,3,4,5,7,8,K]Z Rev/Elbow Jt, Lt, [Opn, Perc, Perc Endo], [Drain Dev, Inf Dev, Int Fix Dev, Ext Fix Dev, Auto Tissue Sub, Spacer, Nonauto Tissue Sub], NQ 148

0RWM[0,3,4][0,3,4,5,7,8,J,K]Z Rev/Elbow Jt, Lt, [Opn, Perc, Perc Endo], [Drain Dev, Inf Dev, Int Fix Dev, Ext Fix Dev, Auto Tissue Sub, Spacer, Synth Sub, Nonauto Tissue Sub], NQ 351

0RWM[0,3,4]JZ Rev/Elbow Jt, Lt, [Opn, Perc, Perc Endo], Synth Sub, NQ 157

0RWL[0,3,4][0,3,4,5,7,8,K]Z Rev/Elbow Jt, Rt, [Opn, Perc, Perc Endo], [Drain Dev, Inf Dev, Int Fix Dev, Ext Fix Dev, Auto Tissue Sub, Spacer, Nonauto Tissue Sub], NQ 148

0RWL[0,3,4][0,3,4,5,7,8,J,K]Z Rev/Elbow Jt, Rt, [Opn, Perc, Perc Endo], [Drain Dev, Inf Dev, Int Fix Dev, Ext Fix Dev, Auto Tissue Sub, Spacer, Synth Sub, Nonauto Tissue Sub], NQ 351

0RWL[0,3,4]JZ Rev/Elbow Jt, Rt, [Opn, Perc, Perc Endo], Synth Sub, NQ 157

0VWM[0,3,4,7,8][0,3,7,C,J,K]Z Rev/Epididymis and Spermatic Cord, [Opn, Perc, Perc Endo, Via Natrl or Artfcl Opng, Via Natrl or Artfcl Opng Endo], [Drain Dev, Inf Dev, Auto Tissue Sub, Extralum Dev, Synth Sub, Nonauto Tissue Sub], NQ 258

0DW5[7,8]DZ Rev/Esophagus, [Via Natrl or Artfcl Opng, Via Natrl or Artfcl Opng Endo], Intralum Dev, NQ 106, 335

08WM* Rev/Extraocular Muscle, Lt 43

08WM[0,3][0,7,J,K]Z Rev/Extraocular Muscle, Lt, [Opn, Perc], [Drain Dev, Auto Tissue Sub, Synth Sub, Nonauto Tissue Sub], NQ 446

08WM[0,3]0Z Rev/Extraocular Muscle, Lt, [Opn, Perc], Drain Dev, NQ 330

08WL* Rev/Extraocular Muscle, Rt 43

08WL[0,3][0,7,J,K]Z Rev/Extraocular Muscle, Rt, [Opn, Perc], [Drain Dev, Auto Tissue Sub, Synth Sub, Nonauto Tissue Sub], NQ 446

08WL[0,3]0Z Rev/Extraocular Muscle, Rt, [Opn, Perc], Drain Dev, NQ 330

08W1[0,3,7,8][0,3,7,C,D,K]Z Rev/Eye, Lt, [Opn, Perc, Via Natrl or Artfcl Opng, Via Natrl or Artfcl Opng Endo], [Drain Dev, Inf Dev, Auto Tissue Sub, Extralum Dev, Intralum Dev, Nonauto Tissue Sub], NQ 43

08W1[0,3,7,8][0,3,7,C,D,J,K]Z Rev/Eye, Lt, [Opn, Perc, Via Natrl or Artfcl Opng, Via Natrl or Artfcl Opng Endo], [Drain Dev, Inf Dev, Auto Tissue Sub, Extralum Dev, Intralum Dev, Synth Sub, Nonauto Tissue Sub], NQ 446

08W1[0,3]JZ Rev/Eye, Lt, [Opn, Perc], Synth Sub, NQ 42, 330

08W1[7,8]JZ Rev/Eye, Lt, [Via Natrl or Artfcl Opng, Via Natrl or Artfcl Opng Endo], Synth Sub, NQ 43

08W0[0,3,7,8][0,3,7,C,D,K]Z Rev/Eye, Rt, [Opn, Perc, Via Natrl or Artfcl Opng, Via Natrl or Artfcl Opng Endo], [Drain Dev, Inf Dev, Auto Tissue Sub, Extralum Dev, Intralum Dev, Nonauto Tissue Sub], NQ 43

08W0[0,3,7,8][0,3,7,C,D,J,K]Z Rev/Eye, Rt, [Opn, Perc, Via Natrl or Artfcl Opng, Via Natrl or Artfcl Opng Endo], [Drain Dev, Inf Dev, Auto Tissue Sub, Extralum Dev, Intralum Dev, Synth Sub, Nonauto Tissue Sub], NQ 446

08W0[0,3]JZ Rev/Eye, Rt, [Opn, Perc], Synth Sub, NQ 42, 330

08W0[7,8]JZ Rev/Eye, Rt, [Via Natrl or Artfcl Opng, Via Natrl or Artfcl Opng Endo], Synth Sub, NQ 43

0WW2[0,3,4][0,1,3,7,J,K,Y]Z Rev/Face, [Opn, Perc, Perc Endo], [Drain Dev, Radioact Elmt, Inf Dev, Auto Tissue Sub, Synth Sub, Nonauto Tissue Sub, Oth Dev], NQ 220

0NWW[0,3,4][0,4,7,J,K,M]Z Rev/Facial Bone, [Opn, Perc, Perc Endo], [Drain Dev, Int Fix Dev, Auto Tissue Sub, Synth Sub, Nonauto Tissue Sub, Bone Growth Stimulator], NQ 54

0UW8[0,3,4,7,8][0,3,7,C,D,J,K]Z Rev/Fallopian Tube, [Opn, Perc, Perc Endo, Via Natrl or Artfcl Opng, Via Natrl or Artfcl Opng Endo], [Drain Dev, Inf Dev, Auto Tissue Sub, Extralum Dev, Intralum Dev, Synth Sub, Nonauto Tissue Sub], NQ 263, 264, 266

0QW9[0,3,4][4,5,7,J,K]Z Rev/Femur Shaft, Lt, [Opn, Perc, Perc Endo], [Int Fix Dev, Ext Fix Dev, Auto Tissue Sub, Synth Sub, Nonauto Tissue Sub], NQ 137

0QW8[0,3,4][4,5,7,J,K]Z Rev/Femur Shaft, Rt, [Opn, Perc, Perc Endo], [Int Fix Dev, Ext Fix Dev, Auto Tissue Sub, Synth Sub, Nonauto Tissue Sub], NQ 137

0QWK[0,3,4][4,5,7,J,K]Z Rev/Fibula, Lt, [Opn, Perc, Perc Endo], [Int Fix Dev, Ext Fix Dev, Auto Tissue Sub, Synth Sub, Nonauto Tissue Sub], NQ 136

0QWJ[0,3,4][4,5,7,J,K]Z Rev/Fibula, Rt, [Opn, Perc, Perc Endo], [Int Fix Dev, Ext Fix Dev, Auto Tissue Sub, Synth Sub, Nonauto Tissue Sub], NQ 136

0RWX[0,3,4][0,3,4,5,7,8,K]Z Rev/Finger Phalangeal Jt, Lt, [Opn, Perc, Perc Endo], [Drain Dev, Inf Dev, Int Fix Dev, Ext Fix Dev, Auto Tissue Sub, Spacer, Nonauto Tissue Sub], NQ 147, 317

0RWX[0,3,4]JZ Rev/Finger Phalangeal Jt, Lt, [Opn, Perc, Perc Endo], Synth Sub, NQ 157, 351

0RWW[0,3,4][0,3,4,5,7,8,K]Z Rev/Finger Phalangeal Jt, Rt, [Opn, Perc, Perc Endo], [Drain Dev, Inf Dev, Int Fix Dev, Ext Fix Dev, Auto Tissue Sub, Spacer, Nonauto Tissue Sub], NQ 147, 317

0RWW[0,3,4]JZ Rev/Finger Phalangeal Jt, Rt, [Opn, Perc, Perc Endo], Synth Sub, NQ 157, 351

0PWV[0,3,4][4,5,7,J,K]Z Rev/Finger Phalanx, Lt, [Opn, Perc, Perc Endo], [Int Fix Dev, Ext Fix Dev, Auto Tissue Sub, Synth Sub, Nonauto Tissue Sub], NQ 135

0PWT[0,3,4][4,5,7,J,K]Z Rev/Finger Phalanx, Rt, [Opn, Perc, Perc Endo], [Int Fix Dev, Ext Fix Dev, Auto Tissue Sub, Synth Sub, Nonauto Tissue Sub], NQ 135

0FW4[0,3,4][0,2,3,D]Z Rev/Gallbladder, [Opn, Perc, Perc Endo], [Drain Dev, Monitoring Dev, Inf Dev, Intralum Dev], NQ 120

0WWP0[1,3,Y]Z Rev/Gastrointestinal Tract, Opn, [Radioact Elmt, Inf Dev, Oth Dev], NQ 114

0PW8[0,3,4][4,7,J,K]Z Rev/Glenoid Cavity, Lt, [Opn, Perc, Perc Endo], [Int Fix Dev, Auto Tissue Sub, Synth Sub, Nonauto Tissue Sub], NQ 135

0PW7[0,3,4][4,7,J,K]Z Rev/Glenoid Cavity, Rt, [Opn, Perc, Perc Endo], [Int Fix Dev, Auto Tissue Sub, Synth Sub, Nonauto Tissue Sub], NQ 135

02WY[0,3,4][2,3,7,8,C,D,J,K]Z Rev/Great Vessel, [Opn, Perc, Perc Endo], [Monitoring Dev, Inf Dev, Auto Tissue Sub, Zooplastic Tissue, Extralum Dev, Intralum Dev, Synth Sub, Nonauto Tissue Sub], NQ 93

0WW0[0,3,4][0,1,3,7,J,K,Y]Z Rev/Head, [Opn, Perc, Perc Endo], [Drain Dev, Radioact Elmt, Inf Dev, Auto Tissue Sub, Synth Sub, Nonauto Tissue Sub, Oth Dev], NQ 220

02WA[0,3,4][Q,R]Z Rev/Heart, [Opn, Perc, Perc Endo], [Implantable Heart Assist Sys, Ext Heart Assist Sys], NQ 1

02WA[0,3,4][2,3,7,8,C,D,K]Z Rev/Heart, [Opn, Perc, Perc Endo], [Monitoring Dev, Inf Dev, Auto Tissue Sub, Zooplastic Tissue, Extralum Dev, Intralum Dev, Nonauto Tissue Sub], NQ 75

02WA[0,3,4][K,M]Z Rev/Heart, [Opn, Perc, Perc Endo], [Nonauto Tissue Sub, Cardiac Lead], NQ 320

02WA[0,3,4]MZ Rev/Heart, [Opn, Perc, Perc Endo], Cardiac Lead, NQ 24, 88

02WA[3,4]JZ Rev/Heart, [Perc, Perc Endo], Synth Sub, NQ 75, 320

0FWB[0,3,4,7,8][0,2,3,7,C,D,J,K]Z Rev/Hepatobiliary Duct, [Opn, Perc, Perc Endo, Via Natrl or Artfcl Opng, Via Natrl or Artfcl Opng Endo], [Drain Dev, Monitoring Dev, Inf Dev, Auto Tissue Sub, Extralum Dev, Intralum Dev, Synth Sub, Nonauto Tissue Sub], NQ 120, 336

0SWB[0,3,4]JZ Rev/Hip Jt, Lt, [Opn, Perc, Perc Endo], Synth Sub, NQ 127, 244, 416

0SWB0[0,3,4,5,7,8,9,B,K]Z Rev/Hip Jt, Lt, Opn, [Drain Dev, Inf Dev, Int Fix Dev, Ext Fix Dev, Auto Tissue Sub, Spacer, Liner, Resurfacing Dev, Nonauto Tissue Sub], NQ 131

ØSWBØ[Ø,3,4,5,7,8,9, B,J,K]Z	Rev/Hip Jt, Lt, Opn, [Drain Dev, Inf Dev, Int Fix Dev, Ext Fix Dev, Auto Tissue Sub, Spacer, Liner, Resurfacing Dev, Synth Sub, Nonauto Tissue Sub], NQ 353
ØSWB4[Ø,3,4,5,7,8,K] Z	Rev/Hip Jt, Lt, Perc Endo, [Drain Dev, Inf Dev, Int Fix Dev, Ext Fix Dev, Auto Tissue Sub, Spacer, Nonauto Tissue Sub], NQ 131
ØSWB4[Ø,3,4,5,7,8,J, K]Z	Rev/Hip Jt, Lt, Perc Endo, [Drain Dev, Inf Dev, Int Fix Dev, Ext Fix Dev, Auto Tissue Sub, Spacer, Synth Sub, Nonauto Tissue Sub], NQ 353
ØSWB3[Ø,3,4,5,7,8,K] Z	Rev/Hip Jt, Lt, Perc, [Drain Dev, Inf Dev, Int Fix Dev, Ext Fix Dev, Auto Tissue Sub, Spacer, Nonauto Tissue Sub], NQ 131
ØSWB3[Ø,3,4,5,7,8,J, K]Z	Rev/Hip Jt, Lt, Perc, [Drain Dev, Inf Dev, Int Fix Dev, Ext Fix Dev, Auto Tissue Sub, Spacer, Synth Sub, Nonauto Tissue Sub], NQ 353
ØSW9[Ø,3,4]JZ	Rev/Hip Jt, Rt, [Opn, Perc, Perc Endo], Synth Sub, NQ 127, 244, 416
ØSW9Ø[Ø,3,4,5,7,8,9, B,K]Z	Rev/Hip Jt, Rt, Opn, [Drain Dev, Inf Dev, Int Fix Dev, Ext Fix Dev, Auto Tissue Sub, Spacer, Liner, Resurfacing Dev, Nonauto Tissue Sub], NQ 131
ØSW9Ø[Ø,3,4,5,7,8,9, B,J,K]Z	Rev/Hip Jt, Rt, Opn, [Drain Dev, Inf Dev, Int Fix Dev, Ext Fix Dev, Auto Tissue Sub, Spacer, Liner, Resurfacing Dev, Synth Sub, Nonauto Tissue Sub], NQ 352
ØSW94[Ø,3,4,5,7,8,K] Z	Rev/Hip Jt, Rt, Perc Endo, [Drain Dev, Inf Dev, Int Fix Dev, Ext Fix Dev, Auto Tissue Sub, Spacer, Nonauto Tissue Sub], NQ 131
ØSW94[Ø,3,4,5,7,8,J, K]Z	Rev/Hip Jt, Rt, Perc Endo, [Drain Dev, Inf Dev, Int Fix Dev, Ext Fix Dev, Auto Tissue Sub, Spacer, Synth Sub, Nonauto Tissue Sub], NQ 353
ØSW93[Ø,3,4,5,7,8,K] Z	Rev/Hip Jt, Rt, Perc, [Drain Dev, Inf Dev, Int Fix Dev, Ext Fix Dev, Auto Tissue Sub, Spacer, Nonauto Tissue Sub], NQ 131
ØSW93[Ø,3,4,5,7,8,J, K]Z	Rev/Hip Jt, Rt, Perc, [Drain Dev, Inf Dev, Int Fix Dev, Ext Fix Dev, Auto Tissue Sub, Spacer, Synth Sub, Nonauto Tissue Sub], NQ 353
ØPWD[Ø,3,4] [4,5,7,J,K]Z	Rev/Humeral Head, Lt, [Opn, Perc, Perc Endo], [Int Fix Dev, Ext Fix Dev, Auto Tissue Sub, Synth Sub, Nonauto Tissue Sub], NQ 135
ØPWC[Ø,3,4] [4,5,7,J,K]Z	Rev/Humeral Head, Rt, [Opn, Perc, Perc Endo], [Int Fix Dev, Ext Fix Dev, Auto Tissue Sub, Synth Sub, Nonauto Tissue Sub], NQ 135
ØPWG[Ø,3,4] [4,5,7,J,K]Z	Rev/Humeral Shaft, Lt, [Opn, Perc, Perc Endo], [Int Fix Dev, Ext Fix Dev, Auto Tissue Sub, Synth Sub, Nonauto Tissue Sub], NQ 135
ØPWF[Ø,3,4] [4,5,7,J,K]Z	Rev/Humeral Shaft, Rt, [Opn, Perc, Perc Endo], [Int Fix Dev, Ext Fix Dev, Auto Tissue Sub, Synth Sub, Nonauto Tissue Sub], NQ 135
Ø9WE*	Rev/Inner Ear, Lt 52
Ø9WD*	Rev/Inner Ear, Rt 52
ØTW5[Ø,3,4,7,8] [Ø,2,3,7,C,D,J,K]Z	Rev/Kidney, [Opn, Perc, Perc Endo, Via Natrl or Artfcl Opng, Via Natrl or Artfcl Opng Endo], [Drain Dev, Monitoring Dev, Inf Dev, Auto Tissue Sub, Extralum Dev, Intralum Dev, Synth Sub, Nonauto Tissue Sub], NQ 249, 354
ØSWD[Ø,3,4] [Ø,3,4,5,7,8,K]Z	Rev/Knee Jt, Lt, [Opn, Perc, Perc Endo], [Drain Dev, Inf Dev, Int Fix Dev, Ext Fix Dev, Auto Tissue Sub, Spacer, Nonauto Tissue Sub], NQ 132, 458
ØSWD[Ø,3,4,5,7,8,J,K]Z	Rev/Knee Jt, Lt, [Opn, Perc, Perc Endo], [Drain Dev, Inf Dev, Int Fix Dev, Ext Fix Dev, Auto Tissue Sub, Spacer, Synth Sub, Nonauto Tissue Sub], NQ 353
ØSWD[Ø,3,4]JZ	Rev/Knee Jt, Lt, [Opn, Perc, Perc Endo], Synth Sub, NQ 127
ØSWC[Ø,3,4] [Ø,3,4,5,7,8,K]Z	Rev/Knee Jt, Rt, [Opn, Perc, Perc Endo], [Drain Dev, Inf Dev, Int Fix Dev, Ext Fix Dev, Auto Tissue Sub, Spacer, Nonauto Tissue Sub], NQ 132, 458
ØSWC[Ø,3,4] [Ø,3,4,5,7,8,J,K]Z	Rev/Knee Jt, Rt, [Opn, Perc, Perc Endo], [Drain Dev, Inf Dev, Int Fix Dev, Ext Fix Dev, Auto Tissue Sub, Spacer, Synth Sub, Nonauto Tissue Sub], NQ 353
ØSWC[Ø,3,4]JZ	Rev/Knee Jt, Rt, [Opn, Perc, Perc Endo], Synth Sub, NQ 127
ØDWE*	Rev/Large Intestine 107, 335
ØCWS[Ø,3,7,8] [Ø,7,D,J,K]Z	Rev/Larynx, [Opn, Perc, Via Natrl or Artfcl Opng, Via Natrl or Artfcl Opng Endo], [Drain Dev, Auto Tissue Sub, Intralum Dev, Synth Sub, Nonauto Tissue Sub], NQ 53
ØFWØ[Ø,3,4][Ø,2,3]Z	Rev/Liver, [Opn, Perc, Perc Endo], [Drain Dev, Monitoring Dev, Inf Dev], NQ 119, 335
ØSW2[Ø,3,4][Ø,3,7,K] Z	Rev/Lumbar Vert Disc, [Opn, Perc, Perc Endo], [Drain Dev, Inf Dev, Auto Tissue Sub, Nonauto Tissue Sub], NQ 158
ØSW2[Ø,3,4]JZ	Rev/Lumbar Vert Disc, [Opn, Perc, Perc Endo], Synth Sub, NQ 20, 160, 161, 352
ØSWØ[Ø,3,4] [Ø,3,4,7,8,A,J,K]Z	Rev/Lumbar Vert Jt, [Opn, Perc, Perc Endo], [Drain Dev, Inf Dev, Int Fix Dev, Auto Tissue Sub, Spacer, Interbody Fusion Dev, Synth Sub, Nonauto Tissue Sub], NQ 158
ØSWØ[Ø,3,4][4,J]Z	Rev/Lumbar Vert Jt, [Opn, Perc, Perc Endo], [Int Fix Dev, Synth Sub], NQ 352
ØQWØ[Ø,3,4][4,7,J,K] Z	Rev/Lumbar Vertebra, [Opn, Perc, Perc Endo], [Int Fix Dev, Auto Tissue Sub, Synth Sub, Nonauto Tissue Sub], NQ 135
ØSW4[Ø,3,4][Ø,3,7,K] Z	Rev/Lumbosacral Disc, [Opn, Perc, Perc Endo], [Drain Dev, Inf Dev, Auto Tissue Sub, Nonauto Tissue Sub], NQ 158
ØSW4[Ø,3,4]JZ	Rev/Lumbosacral Disc, [Opn, Perc, Perc Endo], Synth Sub, NQ 20, 160, 161, 352
ØSW3[Ø,3,4] [Ø,3,4,7,8,A,J,K]Z	Rev/Lumbosacral Jt, [Opn, Perc, Perc Endo], [Drain Dev, Inf Dev, Int Fix Dev, Auto Tissue Sub, Spacer, Interbody Fusion Dev, Synth Sub, Nonauto Tissue Sub], NQ 158
ØSW3[Ø,3,4][4,J]Z	Rev/Lumbosacral Jt, [Opn, Perc, Perc Endo], [Int Fix Dev, Synth Sub], NQ 352
ØBWL[Ø,3,4,7,8] [Ø,2,3]Z	Rev/Lung, Lt, [Opn, Perc, Perc Endo, Via Natrl or Artfcl Opng, Via Natrl or Artfcl Opng Endo], [Drain Dev, Monitoring Dev, Inf Dev], NQ 62, 331
ØBWK[Ø,3,4,7,8] [Ø,2,3]Z	Rev/Lung, Rt, [Opn, Perc, Perc Endo, Via Natrl or Artfcl Opng, Via Natrl or Artfcl Opng Endo], [Drain Dev, Monitoring Dev, Inf Dev], NQ 62, 331
Ø4WY[Ø,3,4][7,J,K]Z	Rev/Lwr Artery, [Opn, Perc, Perc Endo], [Auto Tissue Sub, Synth Sub, Nonauto Tissue Sub], NQ 442
Ø4WY[Ø,3,4] [Ø,2,3,7,C,D,J,K]Z	Rev/Lwr Artery, [Opn, Perc, Perc Endo], [Drain Dev, Monitoring Dev, Inf Dev, Auto Tissue Sub, Extralum Dev, Intralum Dev, Synth Sub, Nonauto Tissue Sub], NQ 84
Ø4WY[Ø,3,4] [Ø,2,3,C,D]Z	Rev/Lwr Artery, [Opn, Perc, Perc Endo], [Drain Dev, Monitoring Dev, Inf Dev, Extralum Dev, Intralum Dev], NQ 240, 297, 325
ØWWL[Ø,3,4] [Ø,1,3,7,J,K,Y]Z	Rev/Lwr Back, [Opn, Perc, Perc Endo], [Drain Dev, Radioact Elmt, Inf Dev, Auto Tissue Sub, Synth Sub, Nonauto Tissue Sub, Oth Dev], NQ 220
ØQWY[Ø,3,4][Ø,M]Z	Rev/Lwr Bone, [Opn, Perc, Perc Endo], [Drain Dev, Bone Growth Stimulator], NQ 136
ØMWY[Ø,3,4][Ø,7,J,K] Z	Rev/Lwr Bursa & Lgmt, [Opn, Perc, Perc Endo], [Drain Dev, Auto Tissue Sub, Synth Sub, Nonauto Tissue Sub], NQ 144, 343, 454
ØYWB[Ø,3,4] [Ø,3,7,J,K,Y]Z	Rev/Lwr Extr, Lt, [Opn, Perc, Perc Endo], [Drain Dev, Inf Dev, Auto Tissue Sub, Synth Sub, Nonauto Tissue Sub, Oth Dev], NQ 221
ØYW9[Ø,3,4] [Ø,3,7,J,K,Y]Z	Rev/Lwr Extr, Rt, [Opn, Perc, Perc Endo], [Drain Dev, Inf Dev, Auto Tissue Sub, Synth Sub, Nonauto Tissue Sub, Oth Dev], NQ 221
ØQWC[Ø,3,4] [4,5,7,J,K]Z	Rev/Lwr Femur, Lt, [Opn, Perc, Perc Endo], [Int Fix Dev, Ext Fix Dev, Auto Tissue Sub, Synth Sub, Nonauto Tissue Sub], NQ 137
ØQWB[Ø,3,4] [4,5,7,J,K]Z	Rev/Lwr Femur, Rt, [Opn, Perc, Perc Endo], [Int Fix Dev, Ext Fix Dev, Auto Tissue Sub, Synth Sub, Nonauto Tissue Sub], NQ 137
ØDWD[Ø,3,4,7,8] [Ø,2,3,7,C,D,J,K,U]Z	Rev/Lwr Intestinal Tract, [Opn, Perc, Perc Endo, Via Natrl or Artfcl Opng, Via Natrl or Artfcl Opng Endo], [Drain Dev, Monitoring Dev, Inf Dev, Auto Tissue Sub, Extralum Dev, Intralum Dev, Synth Sub, Nonauto Tissue Sub, Feeding Dev], NQ 109, 335
ØWW5[Ø,3,4] [Ø,1,3,7,J,K,Y]Z	Rev/Lwr Jaw, [Opn, Perc, Perc Endo], [Drain Dev, Radioact Elmt, Inf Dev, Auto Tissue Sub, Synth Sub, Nonauto Tissue Sub, Oth Dev], NQ 220
ØKWY[Ø,3,4] [Ø,7,J,K,M]Z	Rev/Lwr Muscle, [Opn, Perc, Perc Endo], [Drain Dev, Auto Tissue Sub, Synth Sub, Nonauto Tissue Sub, Stimulator Lead], NQ 140, 215, 340, 452
ØLWY[Ø,3,4][Ø,7,J,K]Z	Rev/Lwr Tndn, [Opn, Perc, Perc Endo], [Drain Dev, Auto Tissue Sub, Synth Sub, Nonauto Tissue Sub], NQ 143, 342
ØLWY[Ø,3,4][Ø,7,J,K]Z	Rev/Lwr Tndn, [Opn, Perc, Perc Endo], [Drain Dev, Auto Tissue Sub, Synth Sub, Nonauto Tissue Sub], NQ 453
Ø6WY[Ø,3,4][7,J,K]Z	Rev/Lwr Vein, [Opn, Perc, Perc Endo], [Auto Tissue Sub, Synth Sub, Nonauto Tissue Sub], NQ 87
Ø6WY[Ø,3,4] [Ø,2,3,7,C,D,J,K]Z	Rev/Lwr Vein, [Opn, Perc, Perc Endo], [Drain Dev, Monitoring Dev, Inf Dev, Auto Tissue Sub, Extralum Dev, Intralum Dev, Synth Sub, Nonauto Tissue Sub], NQ 443
Ø6WY[Ø,3,4] [Ø,2,3,C,D]Z	Rev/Lwr Vein, [Opn, Perc, Perc Endo], [Drain Dev, Monitoring Dev, Inf Dev, Extralum Dev, Intralum Dev], NQ 89, 328
Ø7WN[Ø,3,4][7,J,K]Z	Rev/Lymphatic, [Opn, Perc, Perc Endo], [Auto Tissue Sub, Synth Sub, Nonauto Tissue Sub], NQ 299, 329
Ø7WN[Ø,3,4] [Ø,3,7,C,D,J,K]Z	Rev/Lymphatic, [Opn, Perc, Perc Endo], [Drain Dev, Inf Dev, Auto Tissue Sub, Extralum Dev, Intralum Dev, Synth Sub, Nonauto Tissue Sub], NQ 291
Ø7WN[Ø,3,4][Ø,3,C,D] Z	Rev/Lymphatic, [Opn, Perc, Perc Endo], [Drain Dev, Inf Dev, Extralum Dev, Intralum Dev], NQ 210, 443
ØWWC[Ø,3,4] [Ø,1,3,7,J,K,Y]Z	Rev/Mediastinum, [Opn, Perc, Perc Endo], [Drain Dev, Radioact Elmt, Inf Dev, Auto Tissue Sub, Synth Sub, Nonauto Tissue Sub, Oth Dev], NQ 66, 91, 356

ØDWV[Ø,3,4][7,J,K]Z	Rev/Mesentery, [Opn, Perc, Perc Endo], [Auto Tissue Sub, Synth Sub, Nonauto Tissue Sub], NQ 112
ØPWQ[Ø,3,4] [4,5,7,J,K]Z	Rev/Metacarpal, Lt, [Opn, Perc, Perc Endo], [Int Fix Dev, Ext Fix Dev, Auto Tissue Sub, Synth Sub, Nonauto Tissue Sub], NQ 150
ØPWP[Ø,3,4] [4,5,7,J,K]Z	Rev/Metacarpal, Rt, [Opn, Perc, Perc Endo], [Int Fix Dev, Ext Fix Dev, Auto Tissue Sub, Synth Sub, Nonauto Tissue Sub], NQ 150
ØRWT[Ø,3,4] [Ø,3,4,5,7,8,K]Z	Rev/Metacarpocarpal Jt, Lt, [Opn, Perc, Perc Endo], [Drain Dev, Inf Dev, Int Fix Dev, Ext Fix Dev, Auto Tissue Sub, Spacer, Nonauto Tissue Sub], NQ 147, 317
ØRWT[Ø,3,4]JZ	Rev/Metacarpocarpal Jt, Lt, [Opn, Perc, Perc Endo], Synth Sub, NQ 157, 351
ØRWS[Ø,3,4] [Ø,3,4,5,7,8,K]Z	Rev/Metacarpocarpal Jt, Rt, [Opn, Perc, Perc Endo], [Drain Dev, Inf Dev, Int Fix Dev, Ext Fix Dev, Auto Tissue Sub, Spacer, Nonauto Tissue Sub], NQ 147, 317
ØRWS[Ø,3,4]JZ	Rev/Metacarpocarpal Jt, Rt, [Opn, Perc, Perc Endo], Synth Sub, NQ 157, 351
ØRWV[Ø,3,4] [Ø,3,4,5,7,8,K]Z	Rev/Metacarpophalangeal Jt, Lt, [Opn, Perc, Perc Endo], [Drain Dev, Inf Dev, Int Fix Dev, Ext Fix Dev, Auto Tissue Sub, Spacer, Nonauto Tissue Sub], NQ 147, 317
ØRWV[Ø,3,4]JZ	Rev/Metacarpophalangeal Jt, Lt, [Opn, Perc, Perc Endo], Synth Sub, NQ 157, 351
ØRWU[Ø,3,4] [Ø,3,4,5,7,8,K]Z	Rev/Metacarpophalangeal Jt, Rt, [Opn, Perc, Perc Endo], [Drain Dev, Inf Dev, Int Fix Dev, Ext Fix Dev, Auto Tissue Sub, Spacer, Nonauto Tissue Sub], NQ 147, 317
ØRWU[Ø,3,4]JZ	Rev/Metacarpophalangeal Jt, Rt, [Opn, Perc, Perc Endo], Synth Sub, NQ 157, 351
ØSWN[Ø,3,4] [Ø,3,4,5,7,8,K]Z	Rev/Metatarsal-Phalangeal Jt, Lt, [Opn, Perc, Perc Endo], [Drain Dev, Inf Dev, Int Fix Dev, Ext Fix Dev, Auto Tissue Sub, Spacer, Nonauto Tissue Sub], NQ 146, 458
ØSWN[Ø,3,4] [Ø,3,4,5,7,8,J,K]Z	Rev/Metatarsal-Phalangeal Jt, Lt, [Opn, Perc, Perc Endo], [Drain Dev, Inf Dev, Int Fix Dev, Ext Fix Dev, Auto Tissue Sub, Spacer, Synth Sub, Nonauto Tissue Sub], NQ 353
ØSWN[Ø,3,4]JZ	Rev/Metatarsal-Phalangeal Jt, Lt, [Opn, Perc, Perc Endo], Synth Sub, NQ 158
ØSWM[Ø,3,4] [Ø,3,4,5,7,8,K]Z	Rev/Metatarsal-Phalangeal Jt, Rt, [Opn, Perc, Perc Endo], [Drain Dev, Inf Dev, Int Fix Dev, Ext Fix Dev, Auto Tissue Sub, Spacer, Nonauto Tissue Sub], NQ 146, 458
ØSWM[Ø,3,4] [Ø,3,4,5,7,8,J,K]Z	Rev/Metatarsal-Phalangeal Jt, Rt, [Opn, Perc, Perc Endo], [Drain Dev, Inf Dev, Int Fix Dev, Ext Fix Dev, Auto Tissue Sub, Spacer, Synth Sub, Nonauto Tissue Sub], NQ 353
ØSWM[Ø,3,4]JZ	Rev/Metatarsal-Phalangeal Jt, Rt, [Opn, Perc, Perc Endo], Synth Sub, NQ 158
ØSWL[Ø,3,4] [Ø,3,4,5,7,8,K]Z	Rev/Metatarsal-Tarsal Jt, Lt, [Opn, Perc, Perc Endo], [Drain Dev, Inf Dev, Int Fix Dev, Ext Fix Dev, Auto Tissue Sub, Spacer, Nonauto Tissue Sub], NQ 146, 458
ØSWL[Ø,3,4] [Ø,3,4,5,7,8,J,K]Z	Rev/Metatarsal-Tarsal Jt, Lt, [Opn, Perc, Perc Endo], [Drain Dev, Inf Dev, Int Fix Dev, Ext Fix Dev, Auto Tissue Sub, Spacer, Synth Sub, Nonauto Tissue Sub], NQ 353
ØSWL[Ø,3,4]JZ	Rev/Metatarsal-Tarsal Jt, Lt, [Opn, Perc, Perc Endo], Synth Sub, NQ 158
ØSWK[Ø,3,4] [Ø,3,4,5,7,8,K]Z	Rev/Metatarsal-Tarsal Jt, Rt, [Opn, Perc, Perc Endo], [Drain Dev, Inf Dev, Int Fix Dev, Ext Fix Dev, Auto Tissue Sub, Spacer, Nonauto Tissue Sub], NQ 146, 458
ØSWK[Ø,3,4] [Ø,3,4,5,7,8,J,K]Z	Rev/Metatarsal-Tarsal Jt, Rt, [Opn, Perc, Perc Endo], [Drain Dev, Inf Dev, Int Fix Dev, Ext Fix Dev, Auto Tissue Sub, Spacer, Synth Sub, Nonauto Tissue Sub], NQ 353
ØSWK[Ø,3,4]JZ	Rev/Metatarsal-Tarsal Jt, Rt, [Opn, Perc, Perc Endo], Synth Sub, NQ 158
ØQWP[Ø,3,4] [4,5,7,J,K]Z	Rev/Metatarsal, Lt, [Opn, Perc, Perc Endo], [Int Fix Dev, Ext Fix Dev, Auto Tissue Sub, Synth Sub, Nonauto Tissue Sub], NQ 145
ØQWN[Ø,3,4] [4,5,7,J,K]Z	Rev/Metatarsal, Rt, [Opn, Perc, Perc Endo], [Int Fix Dev, Ext Fix Dev, Auto Tissue Sub, Synth Sub, Nonauto Tissue Sub], NQ 145
Ø2WG[Ø,4][7,8,J,K]Z	Rev/Mitral Valve, [Opn, Perc Endo], [Auto Tissue Sub, Zooplastic Tissue, Synth Sub, Nonauto Tissue Sub], NQ 75
ØCWY[Ø,3,7,8] [Ø,1,D,J,K]Z	Rev/Mouth and Throat, [Opn, Perc, Via Natrl or Artfcl Opng, Via Natrl or Artfcl Opng Endo], [Drain Dev, Radioact Elmt, Intralum Dev, Synth Sub, Nonauto Tissue Sub], NQ 332
ØCWY[Ø,3][Ø,1,D,J,K]Z	Rev/Mouth and Throat, [Opn, Perc], [Drain Dev, Radioact Elmt, Intralum Dev, Synth Sub, Nonauto Tissue Sub], NQ 56, 211, 448
ØCWY[3,7,8]7Z	Rev/Mouth and Throat, [Perc, Via Natrl or Artfcl Opng, Via Natrl or Artfcl Opng Endo], Auto Tissue Sub, NQ 332
ØCWY[7,8] [Ø,1,7,D,J,K]Z	Rev/Mouth and Throat, [Via Natrl or Artfcl Opng, Via Natrl or Artfcl Opng Endo], [Drain Dev, Radioact Elmt, Auto Tissue Sub, Intralum Dev, Synth Sub, Nonauto Tissue Sub], NQ 53
ØWW6[Ø,3,4] [Ø,1,3,7,J,K,Y]Z	Rev/Neck, [Opn, Perc, Perc Endo], [Drain Dev, Radioact Elmt, Inf Dev, Auto Tissue Sub, Synth Sub, Nonauto Tissue Sub, Oth Dev], NQ 220
ØRWØ[Ø,3,4] [Ø,3,4,7,8,A,J,K]Z	Rev/Occipital-cervical Jt, [Opn, Perc, Perc Endo], [Drain Dev, Inf Dev, Int Fix Dev, Auto Tissue Sub, Spacer, Interbody Fusion Dev, Synth Sub, Nonauto Tissue Sub], NQ 157
ØRWØ[Ø,3,4][4,J]Z	Rev/Occipital-cervical Jt, [Opn, Perc, Perc Endo], [Int Fix Dev, Synth Sub], NQ 350
ØDWU[Ø,3,4][7,J,K]Z	Rev/Omentum, [Opn, Perc, Perc Endo], [Auto Tissue Sub, Synth Sub, Nonauto Tissue Sub], NQ 112
ØUW3[Ø,3,4][Ø,3]Z	Rev/Ovary, [Opn, Perc, Perc Endo], [Drain Dev, Inf Dev], NQ 263, 264, 266
ØFWG[Ø,3,4][Ø,2,3,D]Z	Rev/Pancreas, [Opn, Perc, Perc Endo], [Drain Dev, Monitoring Dev, Inf Dev, Intralum Dev], NQ 119
ØFWD[Ø,3,4,7,8] [Ø,2,3,7,C,D,J,K]Z	Rev/Pancreatic Duct, [Opn, Perc, Perc Endo, Via Natrl or Artfcl Opng, Via Natrl or Artfcl Opng Endo], [Drain Dev, Monitoring Dev, Inf Dev, Auto Tissue Sub, Extralum Dev, Intralum Dev, Synth Sub, Nonauto Tissue Sub], NQ 119
ØGWR[Ø,3,4]ØZ	Rev/Parathyroid Gland, [Opn, Perc, Perc Endo], Drain Dev, NQ 53, 211, 238, 336
ØQWF[Ø,3,4] [4,5,7,J,K]Z	Rev/Patella, Lt, [Opn, Perc, Perc Endo], [Int Fix Dev, Ext Fix Dev, Auto Tissue Sub, Synth Sub, Nonauto Tissue Sub], NQ 136, 349
ØQWD[Ø,3,4] [4,5,7,J,K]Z	Rev/Patella, Rt, [Opn, Perc, Perc Endo], [Int Fix Dev, Ext Fix Dev, Auto Tissue Sub, Synth Sub, Nonauto Tissue Sub], NQ 136, 349
ØQW3[Ø,3,4] [4,5,7,J,K]Z	Rev/Pelvic Bone, Lt, [Opn, Perc, Perc Endo], [Int Fix Dev, Ext Fix Dev, Auto Tissue Sub, Synth Sub, Nonauto Tissue Sub], NQ 136
ØQW2[Ø,3,4] [4,5,7,J,K]Z	Rev/Pelvic Bone, Rt, [Opn, Perc, Perc Endo], [Int Fix Dev, Ext Fix Dev, Auto Tissue Sub, Synth Sub, Nonauto Tissue Sub], NQ 135
ØWWJ[Ø,3,4] [Ø,1,3,J,Y]Z	Rev/Pelvic Cavity, [Opn, Perc, Perc Endo], [Drain Dev, Radioact Elmt, Inf Dev, Synth Sub, Oth Dev], NQ 114
ØVWS[Ø,3,4,7,8] [Ø,3,7,J,K]Z	Rev/Penis, [Opn, Perc, Perc Endo, Via Natrl or Artfcl Opng, Via Natrl or Artfcl Opng Endo], [Drain Dev, Inf Dev, Auto Tissue Sub, Synth Sub, Nonauto Tissue Sub], NQ 257, 459
ØWWD[Ø,3,4] [Ø,1,3,Y]Z	Rev/Pericardial Cavity, [Opn, Perc, Perc Endo], [Drain Dev, Radioact Elmt, Inf Dev, Oth Dev], NQ 62, 98, 303, 356
ØWWN[Ø,3,4] [Ø,1,3,7,J,K,Y]Z	Rev/Perineum, Female, [Opn, Perc, Perc Endo], [Drain Dev, Radioact Elmt, Inf Dev, Auto Tissue Sub, Synth Sub, Nonauto Tissue Sub, Oth Dev], NQ 218, 267, 275, 460
ØWWM[Ø,3,4][7,K]Z	Rev/Perineum, Male, [Opn, Perc, Perc Endo], [Auto Tissue Sub, Nonauto Tissue Sub], NQ 257, 460
ØWWM[Ø,3,4] [Ø,1,3,J,Y]Z	Rev/Perineum, Male, [Opn, Perc, Perc Endo], [Drain Dev, Radioact Elmt, Inf Dev, Synth Sub, Oth Dev], NQ 220
Ø1WY[Ø,3,4][Ø,2,7,M]Z	Rev/Peripheral Nerve, [Opn, Perc, Perc Endo], [Drain Dev, Monitoring Dev, Auto Tissue Sub, Neurostimulator Lead], NQ 24
ØWWG[Ø,3,4] [Ø,1,3,J,Y]Z	Rev/Peritoneal Cavity, [Opn, Perc, Perc Endo], [Drain Dev, Radioact Elmt, Inf Dev, Synth Sub, Oth Dev], NQ 114
ØDWW[Ø,3,4][7,J,K]Z	Rev/Peritoneum, [Opn, Perc, Perc Endo], [Auto Tissue Sub, Synth Sub, Nonauto Tissue Sub], NQ 112
ØDWW[Ø,3,4]JZ	Rev/Peritoneum, [Opn, Perc, Perc Endo], Synth Sub, NQ 25, 90, 123, 253, 335
ØGW1[Ø,3,4]ØZ	Rev/Pineal Body, [Opn, Perc, Perc Endo], Drain Dev, NQ 9, 13, 17, 235
ØGWØ[Ø,3,4]ØZ	Rev/Pituitary Gland, [Opn, Perc, Perc Endo], Drain Dev, NQ 9, 13, 17, 211, 235
ØVW4[Ø,3,4,7,8] [Ø,3,7,J,K]Z	Rev/Prostate and Seminal Vesicles, [Opn, Perc, Perc Endo, Via Natrl or Artfcl Opng, Via Natrl or Artfcl Opng Endo], [Drain Dev, Inf Dev, Auto Tissue Sub, Synth Sub, Nonauto Tissue Sub], NQ 260
Ø2WH[Ø,4][7,8,J,K]Z	Rev/Pulmn Valve, [Opn, Perc Endo], [Auto Tissue Sub, Zooplastic Tissue, Synth Sub, Nonauto Tissue Sub], NQ 75
ØPWJ[Ø,3,4] [4,5,7,J,K]Z	Rev/Radius, Lt, [Opn, Perc, Perc Endo], [Int Fix Dev, Ext Fix Dev, Auto Tissue Sub, Synth Sub, Nonauto Tissue Sub], NQ 135
ØPWH[Ø,3,4] [4,5,7,J,K]Z	Rev/Radius, Rt, [Opn, Perc, Perc Endo], [Int Fix Dev, Ext Fix Dev, Auto Tissue Sub, Synth Sub, Nonauto Tissue Sub], NQ 135
ØWWQ[3,4,7,8][1,3,Y]Z	Rev/Respiratory Tract, [Perc, Perc Endo, Via Natrl or Artfcl Opng, Via Natrl or Artfcl Opng Endo], [Radioact Elmt, Inf Dev, Oth Dev], NQ 66, 356
ØWWH[Ø,3,4][Ø,1,3,Y]Z	Rev/Retroperitoneum, [Opn, Perc, Perc Endo], [Drain Dev, Radioact Elmt, Inf Dev, Oth Dev], NQ 114
ØPW2[Ø,3,4][4,7,J,K]Z	Rev/Rib, Lt, [Opn, Perc, Perc Endo], [Int Fix Dev, Auto Tissue Sub, Synth Sub, Nonauto Tissue Sub], NQ 135
ØPW1[Ø,3,4][4,7,J,K]Z	Rev/Rib, Rt, [Opn, Perc, Perc Endo], [Int Fix Dev, Auto Tissue Sub, Synth Sub, Nonauto Tissue Sub], NQ 135

0SWQ[0,3,4] [0,3,4,5,7,8,K]Z	Rev/Toe Phalangeal Jt, Lt, [Opn, Perc, Perc Endo], [Drain Dev, Inf Dev, Int Fix Dev, Ext Fix Dev, Auto Tissue Sub, Spacer, Nonauto Tissue Sub], NQ 146, 458
0SWQ[0,3,4] [0,3,4,5,7,8,J,K]Z	Rev/Toe Phalangeal Jt, Lt, [Opn, Perc, Perc Endo], [Drain Dev, Inf Dev, Int Fix Dev, Ext Fix Dev, Auto Tissue Sub, Spacer, Synth Sub, Nonauto Tissue Sub], NQ 353
0SWQ[0,3,4]JZ	Rev/Toe Phalangeal Jt, Lt, [Opn, Perc, Perc Endo], Synth Sub, NQ 158
0SWP[0,3,4] [0,3,4,5,7,8,K]Z	Rev/Toe Phalangeal Jt, Rt, [Opn, Perc, Perc Endo], [Drain Dev, Inf Dev, Int Fix Dev, Ext Fix Dev, Auto Tissue Sub, Spacer, Nonauto Tissue Sub], NQ 146, 458
0SWP[0,3,4] [0,3,4,5,7,8,J,K]Z	Rev/Toe Phalangeal Jt, Rt, [Opn, Perc, Perc Endo], [Drain Dev, Inf Dev, Int Fix Dev, Ext Fix Dev, Auto Tissue Sub, Spacer, Synth Sub, Nonauto Tissue Sub], NQ 353
0SWP[0,3,4]JZ	Rev/Toe Phalangeal Jt, Rt, [Opn, Perc, Perc Endo], Synth Sub, NQ 158
0QWR[0,3,4] [4,5,7,J,K]Z	Rev/Toe Phalanx, Lt, [Opn, Perc, Perc Endo], [Int Fix Dev, Ext Fix Dev, Auto Tissue Sub, Synth Sub, Nonauto Tissue Sub], NQ 136
0QWQ[0,3,4] [4,5,7,J,K]Z	Rev/Toe Phalanx, Rt, [Opn, Perc, Perc Endo], [Int Fix Dev, Ext Fix Dev, Auto Tissue Sub, Synth Sub, Nonauto Tissue Sub], NQ 136
0BW1[0,3,4,7,8] [0,2,7,C,D,F,J,K]Z	Rev/Trachea, [Opn, Perc, Perc Endo, Via Natrl or Artfcl Opng, Via Natrl or Artfcl Opng Endo], [Drain Dev, Monitoring Dev, Auto Tissue Sub, Extralum Dev, Intralum Dev, Tracheostomy Dev, Synth Sub, Nonauto Tissue Sub], NQ 65
0BW1[0,3,4]FZ	Rev/Trachea, [Opn, Perc, Perc Endo], Tracheostomy Dev, NQ 52, 90, 210, 331
0BW0[0,3,4] [0,2,C,D,J,K]Z	Rev/Tracheobronchial Tree, [Opn, Perc, Perc Endo], [Drain Dev, Monitoring Dev, Extralum Dev, Intralum Dev, Synth Sub, Nonauto Tissue Sub], NQ 62
0BW0[7,8][3,7,C,J,K]Z	Rev/Tracheobronchial Tree, [Via Natrl or Artfcl Opng, Via Natrl or Artfcl Opng Endo], [Inf Dev, Auto Tissue Sub, Extralum Dev, Synth Sub, Nonauto Tissue Sub], NQ 65
0BW00[3,7]Z	Rev/Tracheobronchial Tree, Opn, [Inf Dev, Auto Tissue Sub], NQ 65
0BW04[3,7]Z	Rev/Tracheobronchial Tree, Perc Endo, [Inf Dev, Auto Tissue Sub], NQ 65
0BW03[3,7]Z	Rev/Tracheobronchial Tree, Perc, [Inf Dev, Auto Tissue Sub], NQ 65
0BW08[0,2,D]Z	Rev/Tracheobronchial Tree, Via Natrl or Artfcl Opng Endo, [Drain Dev, Monitoring Dev, Intralum Dev], NQ 62
0BW07[0,2,D]Z	Rev/Tracheobronchial Tree, Via Natrl or Artfcl Opng, [Drain Dev, Monitoring Dev, Intralum Dev], NQ 62
02WJ[0,4][7,8,J,K]Z	Rev/Tricuspid Valve, [Opn, Perc Endo], [Auto Tissue Sub, Zooplastic Tissue, Synth Sub, Nonauto Tissue Sub], NQ 75
09W8*	Rev/Tympanic Membrane, Lt 52
09W7*	Rev/Tympanic Membrane, Rt 52
0PWL[0,3,4] [4,5,7,J,K]Z	Rev/Ulna, Lt, [Opn, Perc, Perc Endo], [Int Fix Dev, Ext Fix Dev, Auto Tissue Sub, Synth Sub, Nonauto Tissue Sub], NQ 135
0PWK[0,3,4] [4,5,7,J,K]Z	Rev/Ulna, Rt, [Opn, Perc, Perc Endo], [Int Fix Dev, Ext Fix Dev, Auto Tissue Sub, Synth Sub, Nonauto Tissue Sub], NQ 135
03WY[0,3,4][7,K]Z	Rev/Upr Artery, [Opn, Perc, Perc Endo], [Auto Tissue Sub, Nonauto Tissue Sub], NQ 441
03WY[0,3,4] [0,2,3,7,C,D,J,K,M]Z	Rev/Upr Artery, [Opn, Perc, Perc Endo], [Drain Dev, Monitoring Dev, Inf Dev, Auto Tissue Sub, Extralum Dev, Intralum Dev, Synth Sub, Nonauto Tissue Sub, Stimulator Lead], NQ 82
03WY[0,3,4]JZ	Rev/Upr Artery, [Opn, Perc, Perc Endo], Synth Sub, NQ 251
0WWK[0,3,4] [0,1,3,7,J,K,Y]Z	Rev/Upr Back, [Opn, Perc, Perc Endo], [Drain Dev, Radioact Elmt, Inf Dev, Auto Tissue Sub, Synth Sub, Nonauto Tissue Sub, Oth Dev], NQ 220
0PWY[0,3,4][0,M]Z	Rev/Upr Bone, [Opn, Perc, Perc Endo], [Drain Dev, Bone Growth Stimulator], NQ 135
0MWX[0,3,4] [0,7,J,K]Z	Rev/Upr Bursa & Lgmt, [Opn, Perc, Perc Endo], [Drain Dev, Auto Tissue Sub, Synth Sub, Nonauto Tissue Sub], NQ 144, 343, 454
0XW7[0,3,4] [0,3,7,J,K,Y]Z	Rev/Upr Extr, Lt, [Opn, Perc, Perc Endo], [Drain Dev, Inf Dev, Auto Tissue Sub, Synth Sub, Nonauto Tissue Sub, Oth Dev], NQ 220
0XW6[0,3,4] [0,3,7,J,K,Y]Z	Rev/Upr Extr, Rt, [Opn, Perc, Perc Endo], [Drain Dev, Inf Dev, Auto Tissue Sub, Synth Sub, Nonauto Tissue Sub, Oth Dev], NQ 220
0QW7[0,3,4] [4,5,7,J,K]Z	Rev/Upr Femur, Lt, [Opn, Perc, Perc Endo], [Int Fix Dev, Ext Fix Dev, Auto Tissue Sub, Synth Sub, Nonauto Tissue Sub], NQ 137
0QW6[0,3,4] [4,5,7,J,K]Z	Rev/Upr Femur, Rt, [Opn, Perc, Perc Endo], [Int Fix Dev, Ext Fix Dev, Auto Tissue Sub, Synth Sub, Nonauto Tissue Sub], NQ 137

0DW0[0,3,4,7,8] [0,2,3,7,C,D,J,K]Z	Rev/Upr Intestinal Tract, [Opn, Perc, Perc Endo, Via Natrl or Artfcl Opng, Via Natrl or Artfcl Opng Endo], [Drain Dev, Monitoring Dev, Inf Dev, Auto Tissue Sub, Extralum Dev, Intralum Dev, Synth Sub, Nonauto Tissue Sub], NQ 109, 335
0DW0[0,3,7,8]UZ	Rev/Upr Intestinal Tract, [Opn, Perc, Via Natrl or Artfcl Opng, Via Natrl or Artfcl Opng Endo], Feeding Dev, NQ 109, 335
0WW4[0,3,4] [0,1,3,7,J,K,Y]Z	Rev/Upr Jaw, [Opn, Perc, Perc Endo], [Drain Dev, Radioact Elmt, Inf Dev, Auto Tissue Sub, Synth Sub, Nonauto Tissue Sub, Oth Dev], NQ 220
0KWX[0,3,4] [0,7,J,K,M]Z	Rev/Upr Muscle, [Opn, Perc, Perc Endo], [Drain Dev, Auto Tissue Sub, Synth Sub, Nonauto Tissue Sub, Stimulator Lead], NQ 140, 215, 340, 452
0LWX[0,3,4][0,7,J,K]Z	Rev/Upr Tndn, [Opn, Perc, Perc Endo], [Drain Dev, Auto Tissue Sub, Synth Sub, Nonauto Tissue Sub], NQ 143, 453
0LWX[0,3,4][0,7,J,K]Z	Rev/Upr Tndn, [Opn, Perc, Perc Endo], [Drain Dev, Auto Tissue Sub, Synth Sub, Nonauto Tissue Sub], NQ 342
05WY[0,3,4][7,J,K]Z	Rev/Upr Vein, [Opn, Perc, Perc Endo], [Auto Tissue Sub, Synth Sub, Nonauto Tissue Sub], NQ 442
05WY[0,3,4] [0,2,3,7,C,D,J,K]Z	Rev/Upr Vein, [Opn, Perc, Perc Endo], [Drain Dev, Monitoring Dev, Inf Dev, Auto Tissue Sub, Extralum Dev, Intralum Dev, Synth Sub, Nonauto Tissue Sub], NQ 86
0TW9[0,3,4,7,8] [0,2,3,7,C,D,J,K,M]Z	Rev/Ureter, [Opn, Perc, Perc Endo, Via Natrl or Artfcl Opng, Via Natrl or Artfcl Opng Endo], [Drain Dev, Monitoring Dev, Inf Dev, Auto Tissue Sub, Extralum Dev, Intralum Dev, Synth Sub, Nonauto Tissue Sub, Stimulator Lead], NQ 249, 458
0TWD[0,3,4,7,8] [0,2,3,7,C,D,J,K,L]Z	Rev/Urethra, [Opn, Perc, Perc Endo, Via Natrl or Artfcl Opng, Via Natrl or Artfcl Opng Endo], [Drain Dev, Monitoring Dev, Inf Dev, Auto Tissue Sub, Extralum Dev, Intralum Dev, Synth Sub, Nonauto Tissue Sub, Artfcl Sphincter], NQ 250, 458
0TWD[0,3,4,7,8] [0,2,3,7,C,D,J,K]Z	Rev/Urethra, [Opn, Perc, Perc Endo, Via Natrl or Artfcl Opng, Via Natrl or Artfcl Opng Endo], [Drain Dev, Monitoring Dev, Inf Dev, Auto Tissue Sub, Extralum Dev, Intralum Dev, Synth Sub, Nonauto Tissue Sub], NQ 354
0TWD[0,3,4,7,8]LZ	Rev/Urethra, [Opn, Perc, Perc Endo, Via Natrl or Artfcl Opng, Via Natrl or Artfcl Opng Endo], Artfcl Sphincter, NQ 260, 269
0UWD[0,3,4,7,8] [0,1,3,7,C,D,H,J,K]Z	Rev/Uterus and Cervix, [Opn, Perc, Perc Endo, Via Natrl or Artfcl Opng, Via Natrl or Artfcl Opng Endo], [Drain Dev, Radioact Elmt, Inf Dev, Auto Tissue Sub, Extralum Dev, Intralum Dev, Contraceptive Dev, Synth Sub, Nonauto Tissue Sub], NQ 272
0UWD[0,3,4,7,8] [0,1,3,7,D,H,J,K]Z	Rev/Uterus and Cervix, [Opn, Perc, Perc Endo, Via Natrl or Artfcl Opng, Via Natrl or Artfcl Opng Endo], [Drain Dev, Radioact Elmt, Inf Dev, Auto Tissue Sub, Intralum Dev, Contraceptive Dev, Synth Sub, Nonauto Tissue Sub], NQ 263, 264, 266, 354
0UWD[0,3,4,7,8]CZ	Rev/Uterus and Cervix, [Opn, Perc, Perc Endo, Via Natrl or Artfcl Opng, Via Natrl or Artfcl Opng Endo], Extralum Dev, NQ 267, 459
0UWH[0,3,4,7,8] [0,1,3,7,D,J,K]Z	Rev/Vagina and Cul-de-sac, [Opn, Perc, Perc Endo, Via Natrl or Artfcl Opng, Via Natrl or Artfcl Opng Endo], [Drain Dev, Radioact Elmt, Inf Dev, Auto Tissue Sub, Intralum Dev, Synth Sub, Nonauto Tissue Sub], NQ 267, 275, 459
02WM[0,4]JZ	Rev/Ventricular Septum, [Opn, Perc Endo], Synth Sub, NQ 75
0UWM0[0,7,J,K]Z	Rev/Vulva, Opn, [Drain Dev, Auto Tissue Sub, Synth Sub, Nonauto Tissue Sub], NQ 217, 267, 275, 459
0RWP[0,3,4] [0,3,4,5,7,8,K]Z	Rev/Wrist Jt, Lt, [Opn, Perc, Perc Endo], [Drain Dev, Inf Dev, Int Fix Dev, Ext Fix Dev, Auto Tissue Sub, Spacer, Nonauto Tissue Sub], NQ 147, 317
0RWP[0,3,4]JZ	Rev/Wrist Jt, Lt, [Opn, Perc, Perc Endo], Synth Sub, NQ 157, 351
0RWN[0,3,4] [0,3,4,5,7,8,K]Z	Rev/Wrist Jt, Rt, [Opn, Perc, Perc Endo], [Drain Dev, Inf Dev, Int Fix Dev, Ext Fix Dev, Auto Tissue Sub, Spacer, Nonauto Tissue Sub], NQ 147, 317
0RWN[0,3,4]JZ	Rev/Wrist Jt, Rt, [Opn, Perc, Perc Endo], Synth Sub, NQ 157, 351
0DW04UZ	Revise of Feeding Dev in Up Intest Tract, Perc Endo Appr 106, 123, 236, 300
02WA4QZ	Revise of Implant Heart Assist in Heart, Perc Endo Appr 71
08N[0,1,6,7]XZZ	Rls [Rt Eye, Lt Eye, Rt Sclera, Lt Sclera], Ext Appr 43
08N[C,D,E,F,G,H,J,K]3ZZ	Rls [Rt Iris, Lt Iris, Rt Retina, Lt Retina, Rt Retinal Vessel, Lt Retinal Vessel, Rt Lens, Lt Lens], Perc Appr 44
09N[9,A]0ZZ	Rls [Rt, Lt] Auditory Ossicle, Opn Appr 52
08N[S,T]XZZ	Rls [Rt, Lt] Conjunctiva, Ext Appr 43
09N[D,E]0ZZ	Rls [Rt, Lt] Inner Ear, Opn Appr 52
0HN7XZZ	Rls Abd Skin, Ext Appr 212, 336, 450
02NF0ZZ	Rls Aortic Valve, Opn Appr 71, 72
0HN6XZZ	Rls Back Skin, Ext Appr 212, 336, 450

0HN8XZZ	Rls Buttock Skin, Ext Appr 212, 336, 450
0HN5XZZ	Rls Chest Skin, Ext Appr 212, 336, 450
0HN1XZZ	Rls Face Skin, Ext Appr 212, 336, 450
0HNQXZZ	Rls Finger Nail, Ext Appr 212, 336, 450
0HNAXZZ	Rls Genitalia Skin, Ext Appr 212, 336, 450
0UNKXZZ	Rls Hymen, Ext Appr 459
08N33ZZ	Rls Lt Ant Chamber, Perc Appr 44, 330, 445
08NTXZZ	Rls Lt Conjunctiva, Ext Appr 445
08N9XZZ	Rls Lt Cornea, Ext Appr 44, 330, 445
0HN3XZZ	Rls Lt Ear Skin, Ext Appr 212, 336, 450
08N1XZZ	Rls Lt Eye, Ext Appr 445
0HNNXZZ	Rls Lt Foot Skin, Ext Appr 212, 336, 450
0HNGXZZ	Rls Lt Hand Skin, Ext Appr 212, 336, 450
08ND3ZZ	Rls Lt Iris, Perc Appr 330, 445
08NK3ZZ	Rls Lt Lens, Perc Appr 330, 445
0HNEXZZ	Rls Lt Lwr Arm Skin, Ext Appr 212, 336, 450
0HNLXZZ	Rls Lt Lwr Leg Skin, Ext Appr 212, 336, 450
09N60ZZ	Rls Lt Mid Ear, Opn Appr 447
08NF3ZZ	Rls Lt Retina, Perc Appr 330, 445
08NH3ZZ	Rls Lt Retinal Vessel, Perc Appr 330, 445
08N7XZZ	Rls Lt Sclera, Ext Appr 330, 445
0HNCXZZ	Rls Lt Upr Arm Skin, Ext Appr 212, 336, 450
0HNJXZZ	Rls Lt Upr Leg Skin, Ext Appr 212, 336, 450
08N53ZZ	Rls Lt Vitreous, Perc Appr 44, 330, 445
02NG0ZZ	Rls Mitral Valve, Opn Appr 71, 72
0HN4XZZ	Rls Neck Skin, Ext Appr 212, 336, 450
0HN[0,1,2,3,4]XZZ	Rls of Skin of [Scalp, Face, Rt Ear, Lt Ear, Neck], Ext 53
0HN9XZZ	Rls Perineum Skin, Ext Appr 212, 336, 450
02NH0ZZ	Rls Pulmn Valve, Opn Appr 71, 72
08N23ZZ	Rls Rt Ant Chamber, Perc Appr 44, 330, 445
08NSXZZ	Rls Rt Conjunctiva, Ext Appr 445
08N8XZZ	Rls Rt Cornea, Ext Appr 44, 330, 445
0HN2XZZ	Rls Rt Ear Skin, Ext Appr 212, 336, 450
08N0XZZ	Rls Rt Eye, Ext Appr 445
0HNMXZZ	Rls Rt Foot Skin, Ext Appr 212, 336, 450
0HNFXZZ	Rls Rt Hand Skin, Ext Appr 212, 336, 450
08NC3ZZ	Rls Rt Iris, Perc Appr 330, 445
08NJ3ZZ	Rls Rt Lens, Perc Appr 330, 445
0HNDXZZ	Rls Rt Lwr Arm Skin, Ext Appr 212, 336, 450
0HNKXZZ	Rls Rt Lwr Leg Skin, Ext Appr 212, 336, 450
09N50ZZ	Rls Rt Mid Ear, Opn Appr 447
08NE3ZZ	Rls Rt Retina, Perc Appr 330, 445
08NG3ZZ	Rls Rt Retinal Vessel, Perc Appr 330, 445
08N6XZZ	Rls Rt Sclera, Ext Appr 330, 445
0HNBXZZ	Rls Rt Upr Arm Skin, Ext Appr 212, 336, 450
0HNHXZZ	Rls Rt Upr Leg Skin, Ext Appr 212, 336, 450
08N43ZZ	Rls Rt Vitreous, Perc Appr 44, 330, 445
0HN0XZZ	Rls Scalp Skin, Ext Appr 212, 336, 450
07NM4ZZ	Rls Thymus, Perc Endo Appr 25
0HNRXZZ	Rls Toe Nail, Ext Appr 212, 336, 450
02NJ0ZZ	Rls Tricuspid Valve, Opn Appr 71, 72
0UNGXZZ	Rls Vagina, Ext Appr 274
0UNG0ZZ	Rls Vagina, Opn Appr 274
0UNG3ZZ	Rls Vagina, Perc Appr 274
0UNG4ZZ	Rls Vagina, Perc Endo Appr 274
0UNG7ZZ	Rls Vagina, Via Natrl or Artfcl Opng 274
0UNG8ZZ	Rls Vagina, Via Natrl or Artfcl Opng Endo 274
0UNMXZZ	Rls Vulva, Ext Appr 274
0UNM0ZZ	Rls Vulva, Opn Appr 274
09N[5,6]0ZZ	Rls, [Rt Mid Ear, Lt Mid Ear], Opn 51
04N0[0,4]ZZ	Rls/Abd Aorta, [Opn, Perc Endo] 111
0MNJ*	Rls/Abd Bursa & Lgmt, Lt 144
0MNH*	Rls/Abd Bursa & Lgmt, Rt 144
0KNL[0,3,4]ZZ	Rls/Abd Muscle, Lt, [Opn, Perc, Perc Endo] 140
0KNK[0,3,4]ZZ	Rls/Abd Muscle, Rt, [Opn, Perc, Perc Endo] 140
0LNG[0,3,4]ZZ	Rls/Abd Tndn, Lt, [Opn, Perc, Perc Endo] 142
0LNF[0,3,4]ZZ	Rls/Abd Tndn, Rt, [Opn, Perc, Perc Endo] 142
00NL*	Rls/Abducens Nerve 23, 50
00NL[0,3,4]ZZ	Rls/Abducens Nerve, [Opn, Perc, Perc Endo] 440
00NR*	Rls/Accessory Nerve 23, 50

00NR[0,3,4]ZZ	Rls/Accessory Nerve, [Opn, Perc, Perc Endo] 440
09NP*	Rls/Accessory Sinus 55
0QN5*	Rls/Acetabulum, Lt 156
0QN4*	Rls/Acetabulum, Rt 156
00NN*	Rls/Acoustic Nerve 23, 50
00NN[0,3,4]ZZ	Rls/Acoustic Nerve, [Opn, Perc, Perc Endo] 440
0RNH[0,3,4]ZZ	Rls/Acromioclavicular Jt, Lt, [Opn, Perc, Perc Endo] 149, 349
0RNG[0,3,4]ZZ	Rls/Acromioclavicular Jt, Rt, [Opn, Perc, Perc Endo] 149, 349
0CNQ*	Rls/Adenoids 53
0GN2*	Rls/Adrenal Gland, Lt 235, 336
0GN3*	Rls/Adrenal Gland, Rt 235, 336
0GN4*	Rls/Adrenal Glands, Bilat 235, 336
0FNC*	Rls/Ampulla of Vater 268
0FNC[0,3,7,8]ZZ	Rls/Ampulla of Vater, [Opn, Perc, Via Natrl or Artfcl Opng, Via Natrl or Artfcl Opng Endo] 242
0DNR*	Rls/Anal Sphincter 109, 334
0DNR[0,3,4]ZZ	Rls/Anal Sphincter, [Opn, Perc, Perc Endo] 211, 449
0MNR*	Rls/Ankle Bursa & Lgmt, Lt 144
0MNQ*	Rls/Ankle Bursa & Lgmt, Rt 144
0SNG[0,3,4]ZZ	Rls/Ankle Jt, Lt, [Opn, Perc, Perc Endo] 133, 352
0SNF[0,3,4]ZZ	Rls/Ankle Jt, Rt, [Opn, Perc, Perc Endo] 133, 352
0LNT[0,3,4]ZZ	Rls/Ankle Tndn, Lt, [Opn, Perc, Perc Endo] 142
0LNS[0,3,4]ZZ	Rls/Ankle Tndn, Rt, [Opn, Perc, Perc Endo] 142
0DNQ*	Rls/Anus 109
02NF[3,4]ZZ	Rls/Aortic Valve, [Perc, Perc Endo] 93
0DNJ[0,3,4]ZZ	Rls/Appendix, [Opn, Perc, Perc Endo] 108, 123, 253, 268, 334
0DNJ[0,3]ZZ	Rls/Appendix, [Opn, Perc] 242
0DNJ[7,8]ZZ	Rls/Appendix, [Via Natrl or Artfcl Opng, Via Natrl or Artfcl Opng Endo] 108
0DNK[0,3,4]ZZ	Rls/Ascending Colon, [Opn, Perc, Perc Endo] 108, 123, 253, 268, 334
0DNK[0,3]ZZ	Rls/Ascending Colon, [Opn, Perc] 242
02N5[0,3,4]ZZ	Rls/Atrial Septum, [Opn, Perc, Perc Endo] 75
02N7[0,3,4]ZZ	Rls/Atrium, Lt, [Opn, Perc, Perc Endo] 75
02N6[0,3,4]ZZ	Rls/Atrium, Rt, [Opn, Perc, Perc Endo] 75
00N8*	Rls/Basal Ganglia 414
00N8[0,3,4]ZZ	Rls/Basal Ganglia, [Opn, Perc, Perc Endo] 8, 12, 16
0TNC[0,3,4]ZZ	Rls/Bladder Neck, [Opn, Perc, Perc Endo] 250, 353
0TNC[3,4]ZZ	Rls/Bladder Neck, [Perc, Perc Endo] 260, 268, 302
0TNC[7,8]ZZ	Rls/Bladder Neck, [Via Natrl or Artfcl Opng, Via Natrl or Artfcl Opng Endo] 250
0TNB[0,3,4]ZZ	Rls/Bladder, [Opn, Perc, Perc Endo] 250, 353
0TNB[3,4]ZZ	Rls/Bladder, [Perc, Perc Endo] 260, 268, 302
0TNB[7,8]ZZ	Rls/Bladder, [Via Natrl or Artfcl Opng, Via Natrl or Artfcl Opng Endo] 250
01N3*	Rls/Brachial Plexus 152, 319
01N3[0,3,4]ZZ	Rls/Brachial Plexus, [Opn, Perc, Perc Endo] 441
00N0[0,3,4]ZZ	Rls/Brain, [Opn, Perc, Perc Endo] 8, 12, 16, 296
0HNV*	Rls/Breast, Bilat 222
0HNU*	Rls/Breast, Lt 222
0HNT*	Rls/Breast, Rt 222
0CN4*	Rls/Buccal Mucosa 56, 331
0CN4[0,3,X]ZZ	Rls/Buccal Mucosa, [Opn, Perc, Ext] 211, 448
0BN2*	Rls/Carina 52, 64, 331
0RNR[0,3,4]ZZ	Rls/Carpal Jt, Lt, [Opn, Perc, Perc Endo] 150, 316
0RNQ[0,3,4]ZZ	Rls/Carpal Jt, Rt, [Opn, Perc, Perc Endo] 150, 316
0PNN*	Rls/Carpal, Lt 150
0PNN[0,3,4]ZZ	Rls/Carpal, Lt, [Opn, Perc, Perc Endo] 315
0PNM*	Rls/Carpal, Rt 150
0PNM[0,3,4]ZZ	Rls/Carpal, Rt, [Opn, Perc, Perc Endo] 315
0DNH[0,3,4]ZZ	Rls/Cecum, [Opn, Perc, Perc Endo] 108, 123, 253, 268, 334
0DNH[0,3]ZZ	Rls/Cecum, [Opn, Perc] 242
04N1[0,4]ZZ	Rls/Celiac Artery, [Opn, Perc Endo] 111
00NC*	Rls/Cerebellum 414
00NC[0,3,4]ZZ	Rls/Cerebellum, [Opn, Perc, Perc Endo] 8, 12, 16
00N7[0,3,4]ZZ	Rls/Cerebral Hemisphere, [Opn, Perc, Perc Endo] 8, 12, 16, 296
00N1[0,3,4]ZZ	Rls/Cerebral Meninges, [Opn, Perc, Perc Endo] 8, 12, 16, 296
00N6*	Rls/Cerebral Ventricle 414
00N6[0,3,4]ZZ	Rls/Cerebral Ventricle, [Opn, Perc, Perc Endo] 8, 12, 16
01N1*	Rls/Cervical Nerve 152, 319

01N1[0,3,4]ZZ	Rls/Cervical Nerve, [Opn, Perc, Perc Endo] 441	
01N0*	Rls/Cervical Plexus 152, 319	
01N0[0,3,4]ZZ	Rls/Cervical Plexus, [Opn, Perc, Perc Endo] 441	
00NW*	Rls/Cervical Spinal Cord 159, 160	
00NW[0,3,4]ZZ	Rls/Cervical Spinal Cord, [Opn, Perc, Perc Endo] 19, 296	
0RN3[0,3,4]ZZ	Rls/Cervical Vert Disc, [Opn, Perc, Perc Endo] 349	
0RN1[0,3,4]ZZ	Rls/Cervical Vert Jt, [Opn, Perc, Perc Endo] 349	
0PN3*	Rls/Cervical Vertebra 155	
0RN5[0,3,4]ZZ	Rls/Cervicothoracic Vert Disc, [Opn, Perc, Perc Endo] 349	
0RN4[0,3,4]ZZ	Rls/Cervicothoracic Vert Jt, [Opn, Perc, Perc Endo] 349	
0UNC*	Rls/Cervix 269	
02N9[0,3,4]ZZ	Rls/Chordae Tendineae, [Opn, Perc, Perc Endo] 75	
08NB*	Rls/Choroid, Lt 44, 330	
08NB[0,3]ZZ	Rls/Choroid, Lt, [Opn, Perc] 445	
08NA*	Rls/Choroid, Rt 44, 330	
08NA[0,3]ZZ	Rls/Choroid, Rt, [Opn, Perc] 445	
07NL*	Rls/Cisterna Chyli 60	
0PNB*	Rls/Clavicle, Lt 66, 155, 345	
0PN9*	Rls/Clavicle, Rt 66, 155, 345	
0UNJ*	Rls/Clitoris 267	
0UNJ[0,X]ZZ	Rls/Clitoris, [Opn, Ext] 459	
0SN6[0,3,4]ZZ	Rls/Coccygeal Jt, [Opn, Perc, Perc Endo] 351	
0QNS*	Rls/Coccyx 156	
04N7[0,4]ZZ	Rls/Colic Artery, Lt, [Opn, Perc Endo] 111	
04N8[0,4]ZZ	Rls/Colic Artery, Mid, [Opn, Perc Endo] 111	
04N6[0,4]ZZ	Rls/Colic Artery, Rt, [Opn, Perc Endo] 111	
06N7[0,4]ZZ	Rls/Colic Vein, [Opn, Perc Endo] 112	
0FN9*	Rls/Common Bile Duct 268	
0FN9[0,3,7,8]ZZ	Rls/Common Bile Duct, [Opn, Perc, Via Natrl or Artfcl Opng, Via Natrl or Artfcl Opng Endo] 242	
04ND[0,4]ZZ	Rls/Common Iliac Artery, Lt, [Opn, Perc Endo] 111	
04NC[0,4]ZZ	Rls/Common Iliac Artery, Rt, [Opn, Perc Endo] 111	
06ND[0,4]ZZ	Rls/Common Iliac Vein, Lt, [Opn, Perc Endo] 112	
06NC[0,4]ZZ	Rls/Common Iliac Vein, Rt, [Opn, Perc Endo] 112	
02N8[0,3,4]ZZ	Rls/Conduction Mech, [Opn, Perc, Perc Endo] 93	
02N8*	Rls/Conduction Mechanism 320	
02N4*	Rls/Coronary Vein 320	
02N4[0,3,4]ZZ	Rls/Coronary Vein, [Opn, Perc, Perc Endo] 93	
0UNF*	Rls/Cul-de-sac 267	
0FN8*	Rls/Cystic Duct 268	
0FN8[0,3,7,8]ZZ	Rls/Cystic Duct, [Opn, Perc, Via Natrl or Artfcl Opng, Via Natrl or Artfcl Opng Endo] 242	
0DNM[0,3,4]ZZ	Rls/Descending Colon, [Opn, Perc, Perc Endo] 108, 123, 253, 268, 334	
0DNM[0,3]ZZ	Rls/Descending Colon, [Opn, Perc] 242	
0BNS*	Rls/Diaphragm, Lt 62	
0BNR*	Rls/Diaphragm, Rt 62	
0DN9[0,3,4]ZZ	Rls/Duodenum, [Opn, Perc, Perc Endo] 107, 123, 253, 268, 333	
0DN9[0,3]ZZ	Rls/Duodenum, [Opn, Perc] 242	
00N2[0,3,4]ZZ	Rls/Dura Mater, [Opn, Perc, Perc Endo] 8, 12, 16, 296	
0MN4*	Rls/Elbow Bursa & Lgmt, Lt 144	
0MN3*	Rls/Elbow Bursa & Lgmt, Rt 144	
0RNM[0,3,4]ZZ	Rls/Elbow Jt, Lt, [Opn, Perc, Perc Endo] 149, 350	
0RNL[0,3,4]ZZ	Rls/Elbow Jt, Rt, [Opn, Perc, Perc Endo] 149, 349	
0VNL*	Rls/Epididymis, Bilat 258, 354	
0VNK*	Rls/Epididymis, Lt 258, 354	
0VNJ*	Rls/Epididymis, Rt 258, 354	
0CNR*	Rls/Epiglottis 53, 65, 332	
06N3[0,4]ZZ	Rls/Esophageal Vein, [Opn, Perc Endo] 111	
0DN4*	Rls/Esophagogastric Junction 106, 333	
0DN5*	Rls/Esophagus 53, 106, 333	
0DN3*	Rls/Esophagus, Lwr 106, 333	
0DN2*	Rls/Esophagus, Mid 106, 333	
0DN1*	Rls/Esophagus, Upr 106, 333	
0NNG*	Rls/Ethmoid Bone, Lt 49, 344	
0NNF*	Rls/Ethmoid Bone, Rt 48, 344	
09NV*	Rls/Ethmoid Sinus, Lt 56	
09NU*	Rls/Ethmoid Sinus, Rt 56	
09N4*	Rls/Ext Auditory Canal, Lt 51, 330	
09N4[0,3,4,7,8,X]ZZ	Rls/Ext Auditory Canal, Lt, [Opn, Perc, Perc Endo, Via Natrl or Artfcl Opng, Via Natrl or Artfcl Opng Endo, Ext] 210, 447	
09N3*	Rls/Ext Auditory Canal, Rt 51, 330	
09N3[0,3,4,7,8,X]ZZ	Rls/Ext Auditory Canal, Rt, [Opn, Perc, Perc Endo, Via Natrl or Artfcl Opng, Via Natrl or Artfcl Opng Endo, Ext] 210, 447	
09N1*	Rls/Ext Ear, Lt 51, 330	
09N1[0,3,4,X]ZZ	Rls/Ext Ear, Lt, [Opn, Perc, Perc Endo, Ext] 210, 447	
09N0*	Rls/Ext Ear, Rt 51, 330	
09N0[0,3,4,X]ZZ	Rls/Ext Ear, Rt, [Opn, Perc, Perc Endo, Ext] 210, 447	
04NJ[0,4]ZZ	Rls/Ext Iliac Artery, Lt, [Opn, Perc Endo] 111	
04NH[0,4]ZZ	Rls/Ext Iliac Artery, Rt, [Opn, Perc Endo] 111	
06NG[0,4]ZZ	Rls/Ext Iliac Vein, Lt, [Opn, Perc Endo] 112	
06NF[0,4]ZZ	Rls/Ext Iliac Vein, Rt, [Opn, Perc Endo] 112	
08NM*	Rls/Extraocular Muscle, Lt 43, 330	
08NM[0,3]ZZ	Rls/Extraocular Muscle, Lt, [Opn, Perc] 445	
08NL*	Rls/Extraocular Muscle, Rt 43, 330	
08NL[0,3]ZZ	Rls/Extraocular Muscle, Rt, [Opn, Perc] 445	
0KN1[0,3,4]ZZ	Rls/Facial Muscle, [Opn, Perc, Perc Endo] 139	
00NM*	Rls/Facial Nerve 23, 50	
00NM[0,3,4]ZZ	Rls/Facial Nerve, [Opn, Perc, Perc Endo] 440	
0UN6*	Rls/Fallopian Tube, Lt 263, 264, 266, 354	
0UN5*	Rls/Fallopian Tube, Rt 263, 264, 266, 354	
0UN7*	Rls/Fallopian Tubes, Bilat 263, 264, 266, 354	
01ND*	Rls/Femor Nerve 152, 319	
01ND[0,3,4]ZZ	Rls/Femor Nerve, [Opn, Perc, Perc Endo] 441	
0QN9*	Rls/Femor Shaft, Lt 130, 347, 415	
0QN8*	Rls/Femor Shaft, Rt 130, 347, 415	
0QNK*	Rls/Fibula, Lt 133, 347	
0QNJ*	Rls/Fibula, Rt 133, 347	
0RNX[0,3,4]ZZ	Rls/Finger Phalangeal Jt, Lt, [Opn, Perc, Perc Endo] 150, 316	
0RNW[0,3,4]ZZ	Rls/Finger Phalangeal Jt, Rt, [Opn, Perc, Perc Endo] 150, 316	
0PNV*	Rls/Finger Phalanx, Lt 155	
0PNT*	Rls/Finger Phalanx, Rt 155	
0MNT*	Rls/Foot Bursa & Lgmt, Lt 144	
0MNS*	Rls/Foot Bursa & Lgmt, Rt 144	
0KNW[0,3,4]ZZ	Rls/Foot Muscle, Lt, [Opn, Perc, Perc Endo] 140	
0KNV[0,3,4]ZZ	Rls/Foot Muscle, Rt, [Opn, Perc, Perc Endo] 140	
0LNW[0,3,4]ZZ	Rls/Foot Tndn, Lt, [Opn, Perc, Perc Endo] 142	
0LNV[0,3,4]ZZ	Rls/Foot Tndn, Rt, [Opn, Perc, Perc Endo] 142	
0NN2*	Rls/Frontal Bone, Lt 10, 48, 154, 344, 415	
0NN2[0,3,4]ZZ	Rls/Frontal Bone, Lt, [Opn, Perc, Perc Endo] 14, 18	
0NN1*	Rls/Frontal Bone, Rt 10, 48, 154, 344, 415	
0NN1[0,3,4]ZZ	Rls/Frontal Bone, Rt, [Opn, Perc, Perc Endo] 14, 18	
09NT*	Rls/Frontal Sinus, Lt 56	
09NS*	Rls/Frontal Sinus, Rt 56	
0FN4*	Rls/Gallbladder 268	
0FN4[0,3]ZZ	Rls/Gallbladder, [Opn, Perc] 242	
04N2[0,4]ZZ	Rls/Gastric Artery, [Opn, Perc Endo] 111	
06N2[0,4]ZZ	Rls/Gastric Vein, [Opn, Perc Endo] 111	
0PN8*	Rls/Glenoid Cavity, Lt 66, 155, 345	
0PN7*	Rls/Glenoid Cavity, Rt 66, 155, 345	
00NP*	Rls/Glossopharyngeal Nerve 23, 50	
00NP[0,3,4]ZZ	Rls/Glossopharyngeal Nerve, [Opn, Perc, Perc Endo] 440	
0DNS*	Rls/Greater Omentum 108, 123, 253, 268, 334	
0DNS[0,3]ZZ	Rls/Greater Omentum, [Opn, Perc] 242	
0MN8*	Rls/Hand Bursa & Lgmt, Lt 150	
0MN8[0,3,4,X]ZZ	Rls/Hand Bursa & Lgmt, Lt, [Opn, Perc, Perc Endo, Ext] 216, 315	
0MN7*	Rls/Hand Bursa & Lgmt, Rt 150	
0MN7[0,3,4,X]ZZ	Rls/Hand Bursa & Lgmt, Rt, [Opn, Perc, Perc Endo, Ext] 216, 315	
0KND[0,3,4]ZZ	Rls/Hand Muscle, Lt, [Opn, Perc, Perc Endo] 149, 215, 314	
0KNC[0,3,4]ZZ	Rls/Hand Muscle, Rt, [Opn, Perc, Perc Endo] 149, 215, 314	
0LN8[0,3,4]ZZ	Rls/Hand Tndn, Lt, [Opn, Perc, Perc Endo] 149, 216, 315	
0LN7[0,3,4]ZZ	Rls/Hand Tndn, Rt, [Opn, Perc, Perc Endo] 149, 216, 315	
0CN2*	Rls/Hard Palate 56, 331	
0CN2[0,3,X]ZZ	Rls/Hard Palate, [Opn, Perc, Ext] 211, 448	
0MN0*	Rls/Head and Neck Bursa & Lgmt 144	
0LN0[0,3,4]ZZ	Rls/Head and Neck Tndn, [Opn, Perc, Perc Endo] 142	
0KN0[0,3,4]ZZ	Rls/Head Muscle, [Opn, Perc, Perc Endo] 139	
04N3[0,4]ZZ	Rls/Hepatic Artery, [Opn, Perc Endo] 111	
0FN6*	Rls/Hepatic Duct, Lt 268	

Code	Description
0FN6[0,3,7,8]ZZ	Rls/Hepatic Duct, Lt, [Opn, Perc, Via Natrl or Artfcl Opng, Via Natrl or Artfcl Opng Endo] 242
0FN5*	Rls/Hepatic Duct, Rt 268
0FN5[0,3,7,8]ZZ	Rls/Hepatic Duct, Rt, [Opn, Perc, Via Natrl or Artfcl Opng, Via Natrl or Artfcl Opng Endo] 242
06N4[0,4]ZZ	Rls/Hepatic Vein, [Opn, Perc Endo] 111
0MNM*	Rls/Hip Bursa & Lgmt, Lt 144
0MNL*	Rls/Hip Bursa & Lgmt, Rt 144
0SNB[0,3,4]ZZ	Rls/Hip Jt, Lt, [Opn, Perc, Perc Endo] 131, 352, 416
0SN9[0,3,4]ZZ	Rls/Hip Jt, Rt, [Opn, Perc, Perc Endo] 131, 351, 416
0KNP[0,3,4]ZZ	Rls/Hip Muscle, Lt, [Opn, Perc, Perc Endo] 140
0KNN[0,3,4]ZZ	Rls/Hip Muscle, Rt, [Opn, Perc, Perc Endo] 140
0LNK[0,3,4]ZZ	Rls/Hip Tndn, Lt, [Opn, Perc, Perc Endo] 142
0LNJ[0,3,4]ZZ	Rls/Hip Tndn, Rt, [Opn, Perc, Perc Endo] 142
0PND*	Rls/Humeral Head, Lt 132, 345
0PNC*	Rls/Humeral Head, Rt 132, 345
0PNG*	Rls/Humeral Shaft, Lt 132, 345
0PNF*	Rls/Humeral Shaft, Rt 132, 345
0UNK*	Rls/Hymen 267
0UNK[0,3,4,7,8]ZZ	Rls/Hymen, [Opn, Perc, Perc Endo, Via Natrl or Artfcl Opng, Via Natrl or Artfcl Opng Endo] 459
0NNX*	Rls/Hyoid Bone 56, 344
0NNX[0,3,4]ZZ	Rls/Hyoid Bone, [Opn, Perc, Perc Endo] 216, 454
06NJ[0,4]ZZ	Rls/Hypogastric Vein, Lt, [Opn, Perc Endo] 112
06NH[0,4]ZZ	Rls/Hypogastric Vein, Rt, [Opn, Perc Endo] 112
00NS*	Rls/Hypoglossal Nerve 23, 50
00NS[0,3,4]ZZ	Rls/Hypoglossal Nerve, [Opn, Perc, Perc Endo] 440
00NA*	Rls/Hypothalamus 414
00NA[0,3,4]ZZ	Rls/Hypothalamus, [Opn, Perc, Perc Endo] 8, 12, 16, 296
0DNC*	Rls/Ileocecal Valve 334
0DNC[0,3,4]ZZ	Rls/Ileocecal Valve, [Opn, Perc, Perc Endo] 108, 123, 253, 268
0DNC[0,3]ZZ	Rls/Ileocecal Valve, [Opn, Perc] 242
0DNC[7,8]ZZ	Rls/Ileocecal Valve, [Via Natrl or Artfcl Opng, Via Natrl or Artfcl Opng Endo] 107
0DNB[0,3,4]ZZ	Rls/Ileum, [Opn, Perc, Perc Endo] 108, 123, 253, 268, 333
0DNB[0,3]ZZ	Rls/Ileum, [Opn, Perc] 242
04NB[0,4]ZZ	Rls/Inferior Mesenteric Artery, [Opn, Perc Endo] 111
06N6[0,4]ZZ	Rls/Inferior Mesenteric Vein, [Opn, Perc Endo] 112
0GNP*	Rls/Inferior Parathyroid Gland, Lt 238
0GNN*	Rls/Inferior Parathyroid Gland, Rt 238
06N0[0,4]ZZ	Rls/Inferior Vena Cava, [Opn, Perc Endo] 111
04NF[0,4]ZZ	Rls/Int Iliac Artery, Lt, [Opn, Perc Endo] 111
04NE[0,4]ZZ	Rls/Int Iliac Artery, Rt, [Opn, Perc Endo] 111
0DNA[0,3,4]ZZ	Rls/Jejunum, [Opn, Perc, Perc Endo] 108, 123, 253, 268, 333
0DNA[0,3]ZZ	Rls/Jejunum, [Opn, Perc] 242
0TN4*	Rls/Kidney Pelvis, Lt 249, 260, 268, 353
0TN4[0,3,4,7,8]ZZ	Rls/Kidney Pelvis, Lt, [Opn, Perc, Perc Endo, Via Natrl or Artfcl Opng, Via Natrl or Artfcl Opng Endo] 302
0TN3*	Rls/Kidney Pelvis, Rt 249, 260, 268, 353
0TN3[0,3,4,7,8]ZZ	Rls/Kidney Pelvis, Rt, [Opn, Perc, Perc Endo, Via Natrl or Artfcl Opng, Via Natrl or Artfcl Opng Endo] 302
0TN1*	Rls/Kidney, Lt 249, 260, 268, 353
0TN1[0,3,4,7,8]ZZ	Rls/Kidney, Lt, [Opn, Perc, Perc Endo, Via Natrl or Artfcl Opng, Via Natrl or Artfcl Opng Endo] 302
0TN0*	Rls/Kidney, Rt 249, 260, 268, 353
0TN0[0,3,4,7,8]ZZ	Rls/Kidney, Rt, [Opn, Perc, Perc Endo, Via Natrl or Artfcl Opng, Via Natrl or Artfcl Opng Endo] 302
0MNP*	Rls/Knee Bursa & Lgmt, Lt 144
0MNN*	Rls/Knee Bursa & Lgmt, Rt 144
0SND[0,3,4]ZZ	Rls/Knee Jt, Lt, [Opn, Perc, Perc Endo] 132, 352, 457
0SNC[0,3,4]ZZ	Rls/Knee Jt, Rt, [Opn, Perc, Perc Endo] 132, 352, 457
0LNR[0,3,4]ZZ	Rls/Knee Tndn, Lt, [Opn, Perc, Perc Endo] 142
0LNQ[0,3,4]ZZ	Rls/Knee Tndn, Rt, [Opn, Perc, Perc Endo] 142
0NNJ*	Rls/Lacrimal Bone, Lt 49, 344
0NNH*	Rls/Lacrimal Bone, Rt 49, 344
08NY*	Rls/Lacrimal Duct, Lt 43, 51, 330
08NY[0,3,7,8]ZZ	Rls/Lacrimal Duct, Lt, [Opn, Perc, Via Natrl or Artfcl Opng, Via Natrl or Artfcl Opng Endo] 445
08NX*	Rls/Lacrimal Duct, Rt 43, 51, 330
08NX[0,3,7,8]ZZ	Rls/Lacrimal Duct, Rt, [Opn, Perc, Via Natrl or Artfcl Opng, Via Natrl or Artfcl Opng Endo] 445
08NW*	Rls/Lacrimal Gland, Lt 43, 330
08NW[0,3]ZZ	Rls/Lacrimal Gland, Lt, [Opn, Perc] 445
08NV*	Rls/Lacrimal Gland, Rt 43, 330
08NV[0,3]ZZ	Rls/Lacrimal Gland, Rt, [Opn, Perc] 445
0CNS*	Rls/Larynx 53, 65, 332
0DNT*	Rls/Lesser Omentum 108, 123, 253, 268, 334
0DNT[0,3]ZZ	Rls/Lesser Omentum, [Opn, Perc] 242
0DNE[0,3,4]ZZ	Rls/Lg Intestine, [Opn, Perc, Perc Endo] 108, 123, 253, 268, 334
0DNE[0,3]ZZ	Rls/Lg Intestine, [Opn, Perc] 242
0DNG[0,3,4]ZZ	Rls/Lg Intestine, Lt, [Opn, Perc, Perc Endo] 108, 123, 253, 268, 334
0DNG[0,3]ZZ	Rls/Lg Intestine, Lt, [Opn, Perc] 242
0DNF[0,3,4]ZZ	Rls/Lg Intestine, Rt, [Opn, Perc, Perc Endo] 108, 123, 253, 268, 334
0DNF[0,3]ZZ	Rls/Lg Intestine, Rt, [Opn, Perc] 242
0BN9*	Rls/Lingula Bronchus 62
0FN0*	Rls/Liver 268
0FN0[0,3]ZZ	Rls/Liver, [Opn, Perc] 242
0FN2*	Rls/Liver, Lt Lobe 268
0FN2[0,3]ZZ	Rls/Liver, Lt Lobe, [Opn, Perc] 242
0FN1*	Rls/Liver, Rt Lobe 268
0FN1[0,3]ZZ	Rls/Liver, Rt Lobe, [Opn, Perc] 242
01NB*	Rls/Lumbar Nerve 152, 319
01NB[0,3,4]ZZ	Rls/Lumbar Nerve, [Opn, Perc, Perc Endo] 441
01N9*	Rls/Lumbar Plexus 152, 319
01N9[0,3,4]ZZ	Rls/Lumbar Plexus, [Opn, Perc, Perc Endo] 441
00NY*	Rls/Lumbar Spinal Cord 159, 160
00NY[0,3,4]ZZ	Rls/Lumbar Spinal Cord, [Opn, Perc, Perc Endo] 19, 296
0SN2[0,3,4]ZZ	Rls/Lumbar Vert Disc, [Opn, Perc, Perc Endo] 351
0SN0[0,3,4]ZZ	Rls/Lumbar Vert Jt, [Opn, Perc, Perc Endo] 351
0QN0*	Rls/Lumbar Vertebra 156
0SN4[0,3,4]ZZ	Rls/Lumbosacral Disc, [Opn, Perc, Perc Endo] 351
0SN3[0,3,4]ZZ	Rls/Lumbosacral Jt, [Opn, Perc, Perc Endo] 351
01NA*	Rls/Lumbosacral Plexus 152, 319
01NA[0,3,4]ZZ	Rls/Lumbosacral Plexus, [Opn, Perc, Perc Endo] 441
0BNH*	Rls/Lung Lingula 62
0BNL*	Rls/Lung, Lt 62
0BNK*	Rls/Lung, Rt 62
0BNM*	Rls/Lungs, Bilat 62
0KNB[0,3,4]ZZ	Rls/Lwr Arm and Wrist Muscle, Lt, [Opn, Perc, Perc Endo] 140
0KN9[0,3,4]ZZ	Rls/Lwr Arm and Wrist Muscle, Rt, [Opn, Perc, Perc Endo] 139
0LN6[0,3,4]ZZ	Rls/Lwr Arm and Wrist Tndn, Lt, [Opn, Perc, Perc Endo] 142
0LN5[0,3,4]ZZ	Rls/Lwr Arm and Wrist Tndn, Rt, [Opn, Perc, Perc Endo] 142
0MNW*	Rls/Lwr Extr Bursa & Lgmt, Lt 144
0MNV*	Rls/Lwr Extr Bursa & Lgmt, Rt 144
08NR*	Rls/Lwr Eyelid, Lt 25, 43, 330
08NR[0,3,X]ZZ	Rls/Lwr Eyelid, Lt, [Opn, Perc, Ext] 210, 445
08NQ*	Rls/Lwr Eyelid, Rt 25, 43, 330
08NQ[0,3,X]ZZ	Rls/Lwr Eyelid, Rt, [Opn, Perc, Ext] 210, 445
0QNC*	Rls/Lwr Femur, Lt 130, 347, 415
0QNB*	Rls/Lwr Femur, Rt 130, 347, 415
0KNT[0,3,4]ZZ	Rls/Lwr Leg Muscle, Lt, [Opn, Perc, Perc Endo] 140
0KNS[0,3,4]ZZ	Rls/Lwr Leg Muscle, Rt, [Opn, Perc, Perc Endo] 140
0LNP[0,3,4]ZZ	Rls/Lwr Leg Tndn, Lt, [Opn, Perc, Perc Endo] 142
0LNN[0,3,4]ZZ	Rls/Lwr Leg Tndn, Rt, [Opn, Perc, Perc Endo] 142
0BNB*	Rls/Lwr Lobe Bronchus, Lt 62
0BN6*	Rls/Lwr Lobe Bronchus, Rt 62
0BNJ*	Rls/Lwr Lung Lobe, Lt 62
0BNF*	Rls/Lwr Lung Lobe, Rt 62
07ND*	Rls/Lymphatic, Aortic 328
07ND[0,3,4]ZZ	Rls/Lymphatic, Aortic, [Opn, Perc, Perc Endo] 291, 298
07N0*	Rls/Lymphatic, Head 328
07N0[0,3,4]ZZ	Rls/Lymphatic, Head, [Opn, Perc, Perc Endo] 291, 298
07N9*	Rls/Lymphatic, Int Mammary, Lt 328
07N9[0,3,4]ZZ	Rls/Lymphatic, Int Mammary, Lt, [Opn, Perc, Perc Endo] 291, 298
07N8*	Rls/Lymphatic, Int Mammary, Rt 328
07N8[0,3,4]ZZ	Rls/Lymphatic, Int Mammary, Rt, [Opn, Perc, Perc Endo] 291, 298
07N6*	Rls/Lymphatic, Lt Axillary 328

07N6[0,3,4]ZZ	Rls/Lymphatic, Lt Axillary, [Opn, Perc, Perc Endo] **291, 298**
07NJ*	Rls/Lymphatic, Lt Inguinal **328**
07NJ[0,3,4]ZZ	Rls/Lymphatic, Lt Inguinal, [Opn, Perc, Perc Endo] **291, 298**
07NG*	Rls/Lymphatic, Lt Lwr Extr **328**
07NG[0,3,4]ZZ	Rls/Lymphatic, Lt Lwr Extr, [Opn, Perc, Perc Endo] **291, 298**
07N2*	Rls/Lymphatic, Lt Neck **328**
07N2[0,3,4]ZZ	Rls/Lymphatic, Lt Neck, [Opn, Perc, Perc Endo] **291, 298**
07N4*	Rls/Lymphatic, Lt Upr Extr **328**
07N4[0,3,4]ZZ	Rls/Lymphatic, Lt Upr Extr, [Opn, Perc, Perc Endo] **291, 298**
07NB*	Rls/Lymphatic, Mesenteric **328**
07NB[0,3,4]ZZ	Rls/Lymphatic, Mesenteric, [Opn, Perc, Perc Endo] **291, 298**
07NC*	Rls/Lymphatic, Pelvis **328**
07NC[0,3,4]ZZ	Rls/Lymphatic, Pelvis, [Opn, Perc, Perc Endo] **291, 298**
07N5*	Rls/Lymphatic, Rt Axillary **328**
07N5[0,3,4]ZZ	Rls/Lymphatic, Rt Axillary, [Opn, Perc, Perc Endo] **291, 298**
07NH*	Rls/Lymphatic, Rt Inguinal **328**
07NH[0,3,4]ZZ	Rls/Lymphatic, Rt Inguinal, [Opn, Perc, Perc Endo] **291, 298**
07NF*	Rls/Lymphatic, Rt Lwr Extr **328**
07NF[0,3,4]ZZ	Rls/Lymphatic, Rt Lwr Extr, [Opn, Perc, Perc Endo] **291, 298**
07N1*	Rls/Lymphatic, Rt Neck **328**
07N1[0,3,4]ZZ	Rls/Lymphatic, Rt Neck, [Opn, Perc, Perc Endo] **291, 298**
07N3*	Rls/Lymphatic, Rt Upr Extr **328**
07N3[0,3,4]ZZ	Rls/Lymphatic, Rt Upr Extr, [Opn, Perc, Perc Endo] **291, 298**
07N7*	Rls/Lymphatic, Thorax **328**
07N7[0,3,4]ZZ	Rls/Lymphatic, Thorax, [Opn, Perc, Perc Endo] **291, 298**
0BN7*	Rls/Main Bronchus, Lt **62**
0BN3*	Rls/Main Bronchus, Rt **62**
0NNV*	Rls/Mandible, Lt **49, 344**
0NNT*	Rls/Mandible, Rt **49, 344**
09NC*	Rls/Mastoid Sinus, Lt **51**
09NB*	Rls/Mastoid Sinus, Rt **51**
0NNS*	Rls/Maxilla, Lt **49, 344**
0NNR*	Rls/Maxilla, Rt **49, 344**
09NR*	Rls/Maxillary Sinus, Lt **56**
09NQ*	Rls/Maxillary Sinus, Rt **56**
01N5*	Rls/Median Nerve **149**
01N5[0,3,4]ZZ	Rls/Median Nerve, [Opn, Perc, Perc Endo] **314, 441**
00ND*	Rls/Medulla Oblongata **414**
00ND[0,3,4]ZZ	Rls/Medulla Oblongata, [Opn, Perc, Perc Endo] **8, 12, 16**
0DNV*	Rls/Mesentery **108, 123, 253, 268, 334**
0DNV[0,3]ZZ	Rls/Mesentery, [Opn, Perc] **242**
0PNQ*	Rls/Metacarpal, Lt **150**
0PNQ[0,3,4]ZZ	Rls/Metacarpal, Lt, [Opn, Perc, Perc Endo] **315**
0PNP*	Rls/Metacarpal, Rt **150**
0PNP[0,3,4]ZZ	Rls/Metacarpal, Rt, [Opn, Perc, Perc Endo] **315**
0RNT[0,3,4]ZZ	Rls/Metacarpocarpal Jt, Lt, [Opn, Perc, Perc Endo] **150, 316**
0RNS[0,3,4]ZZ	Rls/Metacarpocarpal Jt, Rt, [Opn, Perc, Perc Endo] **150, 316**
0RNV[0,3,4]ZZ	Rls/Metacarpophalangeal Jt, Lt, [Opn, Perc, Perc Endo] **150, 316**
0RNU[0,3,4]ZZ	Rls/Metacarpophalangeal Jt, Rt, [Opn, Perc, Perc Endo] **150, 316**
0SNN[0,3,4]ZZ	Rls/Metatarsal-Phalangeal Jt, Lt, [Opn, Perc, Perc Endo] **146, 352**
0SNM[0,3,4]ZZ	Rls/Metatarsal-Phalangeal Jt, Rt, [Opn, Perc, Perc Endo] **146, 352**
0SNL[0,3,4]ZZ	Rls/Metatarsal-Tarsal Jt, Lt, [Opn, Perc, Perc Endo] **146, 352**
0SNK[0,3,4]ZZ	Rls/Metatarsal-Tarsal Jt, Rt, [Opn, Perc, Perc Endo] **146, 352**
0QNP*	Rls/Metatarsal, Lt **145, 347**
0QNN*	Rls/Metatarsal, Rt **145, 347**
0BN5*	Rls/Mid Lobe Bronchus, Rt **62**
0BND*	Rls/Mid Lung Lobe, Rt **62**
0CNJ*	Rls/Minor Salivary Gland **57, 332**
02NG[3,4]ZZ	Rls/Mitral Valve, [Perc, Perc Endo] **93**
09NN*	Rls/Nasopharynx **51**
0KN3[0,3,4]ZZ	Rls/Neck Muscle, Lt, [Opn, Perc, Perc Endo] **139**
0KN2[0,3,4]ZZ	Rls/Neck Muscle, Rt, [Opn, Perc, Perc Endo] **139**
0HNX*	Rls/Nipple, Lt **222**
0HNW*	Rls/Nipple, Rt **222**
0NN8*	Rls/Occipital Bone, Lt **10, 48, 154, 344, 415**
0NN8[0,3,4]ZZ	Rls/Occipital Bone, Lt, [Opn, Perc, Perc Endo] **14, 18**

0NN7*	Rls/Occipital Bone, Rt **10, 48, 154, 344, 415**
0NN7[0,3,4]ZZ	Rls/Occipital Bone, Rt, [Opn, Perc, Perc Endo] **14, 18**
0RN0[0,3,4]ZZ	Rls/Occipital-cervical Jt, [Opn, Perc, Perc Endo] **349**
00NH*	Rls/Oculomotor Nerve **23, 50**
00NH[0,3,4]ZZ	Rls/Oculomotor Nerve, [Opn, Perc, Perc Endo] **440**
00NF*	Rls/Olfactory Nerve **23, 50**
00NF[0,3,4]ZZ	Rls/Olfactory Nerve, [Opn, Perc, Perc Endo] **440**
00NG*	Rls/Optic Nerve **23, 50**
00NG[0,3,4]ZZ	Rls/Optic Nerve, [Opn, Perc, Perc Endo] **440**
0NNQ*	Rls/Orbit, Lt **49, 344**
0NNP*	Rls/Orbit, Rt **49, 344**
0UN2*	Rls/Ovaries, Bilat **263, 264, 266, 354**
0UN1*	Rls/Ovary, Lt **263, 264, 266, 354**
0UN0*	Rls/Ovary, Rt **263, 264, 266, 354**
0NNL*	Rls/Palatine Bone, Lt **49, 344**
0NNK*	Rls/Palatine Bone, Rt **49, 344**
0FNG*	Rls/Pancreas **268**
0FNG[0,3]ZZ	Rls/Pancreas, [Opn, Perc] **242**
0FND*	Rls/Pancreatic Duct **268**
0FND[0,3,7,8]ZZ	Rls/Pancreatic Duct, [Opn, Perc, Via Natrl or Artfcl Opng, Via Natrl or Artfcl Opng Endo] **242**
0FNF*	Rls/Pancreatic Duct, Accessory **268**
0FNF[0,3,7,8]ZZ	Rls/Pancreatic Duct, Accessory, [Opn, Perc, Via Natrl or Artfcl Opng, Via Natrl or Artfcl Opng Endo] **242**
02ND[0,3,4]ZZ	Rls/Papillary Muscle, [Opn, Perc, Perc Endo] **75**
0GNR*	Rls/Parathyroid Gland **238**
0GNQ*	Rls/Parathyroid Glands, Multi **238**
0NN4*	Rls/Parietal Bone, Lt **10, 48, 154, 344, 415**
0NN4[0,3,4]ZZ	Rls/Parietal Bone, Lt, [Opn, Perc, Perc Endo] **14, 18**
0NN3*	Rls/Parietal Bone, Rt **10, 48, 154, 344, 415**
0NN3[0,3,4]ZZ	Rls/Parietal Bone, Rt, [Opn, Perc, Perc Endo] **14, 18**
0CNC*	Rls/Parotid Duct, Lt **57, 332**
0CNB*	Rls/Parotid Duct, Rt **57, 331**
0CN9*	Rls/Parotid Gland, Lt **57, 331**
0CN8*	Rls/Parotid Gland, Rt **57, 331**
0QNF*	Rls/Patella, Lt **132, 347**
0QND*	Rls/Patella, Rt **132, 347**
0QN3*	Rls/Pelvic Bone, Lt **156**
0QN2*	Rls/Pelvic Bone, Rt **156**
0VNS*	Rls/Penis **257**
0VNS[0,3,4]ZZ	Rls/Penis, [Opn, Perc, Perc Endo] **459**
02NN*	Rls/Pericardium **60, 320**
02NN[0,3,4]ZZ	Rls/Pericardium, [Opn, Perc, Perc Endo] **93, 296**
0MNK*	Rls/Perineum Bursa & Lgmt **144**
0KNM[0,3,4]ZZ	Rls/Perineum Muscle, [Opn, Perc, Perc Endo] **140**
0LNH[0,3,4]ZZ	Rls/Perineum Tndn, [Opn, Perc, Perc Endo] **142**
0DNW*	Rls/Peritoneum **108, 123, 253, 268, 334**
0DNW[0,3]ZZ	Rls/Peritoneum, [Opn, Perc] **242**
01NH*	Rls/Peroneal Nerve **152, 319**
01NH[0,3,4]ZZ	Rls/Peroneal Nerve, [Opn, Perc, Perc Endo] **441**
0CNM*	Rls/Pharynx **52**
01N2*	Rls/Phrenic Nerve **152, 319**
01N2[0,3,4]ZZ	Rls/Phrenic Nerve, [Opn, Perc, Perc Endo] **441**
0GN1*	Rls/Pineal Body **235**
0GN1[0,3,4]ZZ	Rls/Pineal Body, [Opn, Perc, Perc Endo] **9, 13, 17**
0GN0*	Rls/Pituitary Gland **235**
0GN0[0,3,4]ZZ	Rls/Pituitary Gland, [Opn, Perc, Perc Endo] **9, 13, 17, 211**
0BNP*	Rls/Pleura, Lt **64, 331**
0BNN*	Rls/Pleura, Rt **64, 331**
00NB*	Rls/Pons **414**
00NB[0,3,4]ZZ	Rls/Pons, [Opn, Perc, Perc Endo] **8, 12, 16**
06N8[0,4]ZZ	Rls/Portal Vein, [Opn, Perc Endo] **112**
0VN0*	Rls/Prostate **260, 354, 440**
01NC*	Rls/Pudendal Nerve **152, 319**
01NC[0,3,4]ZZ	Rls/Pudendal Nerve, [Opn, Perc, Perc Endo] **441**
02NR*	Rls/Pulmn Artery, Lt **80**
02NQ*	Rls/Pulmn Artery, Rt **80**
02NP*	Rls/Pulmn Trunk **80**
02NH[3,4]ZZ	Rls/Pulmn Valve, [Perc, Perc Endo] **93**
02NT*	Rls/Pulmn Vein, Lt **80**

0DP57DZ	Rmvl of Intralum Device from Esophagus, Via Opng **106, 334**
09PJ0DZ	Rmvl of Intralum Device from Lt Ear, Opn Appr **52**
09PJ3DZ	Rmvl of Intralum Device from Lt Ear, Perc Appr **52**
09PH0DZ	Rmvl of Intralum Device from Rt Ear, Opn Appr **52**
09PH3DZ	Rmvl of Intralum Device from Rt Ear, Perc Appr **52**
0SPB09Z	Rmvl of Liner from Lt Hip Jt, Opn Appr **127, 128, 245, 416**
0SPD09Z	Rmvl of Liner from Lt Knee Jt, Opn Appr **127, 128, 132, 245, 352**
0SP909Z	Rmvl of Liner from Rt Hip Jt, Opn Appr **127, 128, 245, 416**
0SPC09Z	Rmvl of Liner from Rt Knee Jt, Opn Appr **127, 128, 132, 245, 352**
00P6X2Z	Rmvl of Monitor Dev from Cereb Ventricle, Extern Appr **318, 414**
00PEXMZ	Rmvl of Neuro Lead from Cranial Nrv, Extern Appr **23**
01PYXMZ	Rmvl of Neuro Lead from Periph Nrv, Extern Appr **24**
0NP00NZ	Rmvl of Neurostim from Skull, Opn Appr **28**
0NPW0KZ	Rmvl of Nonaut Sub from Facial Bone, Opn Appr **134**
0NPW3KZ	Rmvl of Nonaut Sub from Facial Bone, Perc Appr **134**
0NPW4KZ	Rmvl of Nonaut Sub from Facial Bone, Perc Endo Appr **134**
0RPD0KZ	Rmvl of Nonaut Sub from Lt Temporomandib Jt, Opn Appr **136**
0RPD3KZ	Rmvl of Nonaut Sub from Lt Temporomandib Jt, Perc Appr **136**
0WPMXKZ	Rmvl of Nonaut Sub from Male Perineum, Extern Appr **257**
0RPC0KZ	Rmvl of Nonaut Sub from Rt Temporomandib Jt, Opn Appr **136**
0RPC3KZ	Rmvl of Nonaut Sub from Rt Temporomandib Jt, Perc Appr **136**
0WPQ81Z	Rmvl of Radioact Elmt from Respiratory Tract, Endo **66, 356**
0SPB0BZ	Rmvl of Resurfacing Device from Lt Hip Jt, Opn Appr **128, 131, 245**
0SP90BZ	Rmvl of Resurfacing Device from Rt Hip Jt, Opn Appr **127, 128, 131, 245**
0SPB08Z	Rmvl of Spacer from Lt Hip Jt, Opn Appr **128, 245**
0SPB48Z	Rmvl of Spacer from Lt Hip Jt, Perc Endo Appr **128, 245**
0SP908Z	Rmvl of Spacer from Rt Hip Jt, Opn Appr **127, 128, 245**
0SP948Z	Rmvl of Spacer from Rt Hip Jt, Perc Endo Appr **127, 128, 245**
0TPBXMZ	Rmvl of Stimulator Lead from Bladder, Ext Appr **250**
0TP9XMZ	Rmvl of Stimulator Lead from Ureter, Ext Appr **249**
08P[0,1]XJZ	Rmvl of Synth Sub from [Rt, Lt] Eye, Ext Appr **44**
08P[J,K]3JZ	Rmvl of Synth Sub from [Rt, Lt] Lens, Perc Appr **44**
08P13JZ	Rmvl of Synth Sub from Lt Eye, Perc Appr **241**
0SPB0JZ	Rmvl of Synth Sub from Lt Hip Jt, Opn Appr **128, 245**
0SPB4JZ	Rmvl of Synth Sub from Lt Hip Jt, Perc Endo Appr **128, 245**
0SPD0JZ	Rmvl of Synth Sub from Lt Knee Jt, Opn Appr **128, 245, 246**
0SPD4JZ	Rmvl of Synth Sub from Lt Knee Jt, Perc Endo Appr **128, 245, 246**
08PK3JZ	Rmvl of Synth Sub from Lt Lens, Perc Appr **330, 445**
0RPD0JZ	Rmvl of Synth Sub from Lt Temporomandib Jt, Opn Appr **136**
0RPD3JZ	Rmvl of Synth Sub from Lt Temporomandib Jt, Perc Appr **136**
0WPMXJZ	Rmvl of Synth Sub from Male Perineum, Extern Appr **257, 460**
08P03JZ	Rmvl of Synth Sub from Rt Eye, Perc Appr **241**
0SP90JZ	Rmvl of Synth Sub from Rt Hip Jt, Opn Appr **127, 245**
0SP94JZ	Rmvl of Synth Sub from Rt Hip Jt, Perc Endo Appr **127, 128, 245**
0SPC0JZ	Rmvl of Synth Sub from Rt Knee Jt, Opn Appr **128, 245**
0SPC4JZ	Rmvl of Synth Sub from Rt Knee Jt, Perc Endo Appr **128, 245**
08PJ3JZ	Rmvl of Synth Sub from Rt Lens, Perc Appr **330, 445**
0RPC0JZ	Rmvl of Synth Sub from Rt Temporomandib Jt, Opn Appr **136**
0RPC3JZ	Rmvl of Synth Sub from Rt Temporomandib Jt, Perc Appr **136**
0WPF[0,3,4] [0,1,3,7,J,K,Y]Z	Rmvl/Abd Wall, [Opn, Perc, Perc Endo], [Drain Dev, Radioact Elmt, Inf Dev, Auto Tissue Sub, Synth Sub, Nonauto Tissue Sub, Oth Dev], NQ **114, 356**
0QP5[0,3,4][4,7,J,K]Z	Rmvl/Acetab, Lt, [Opn, Perc, Perc Endo], [Int Fix Dev, Auto Tissue Sub, Synth Sub, Nonauto Tissue Sub], NQ **135, 347, 456**
0QP4[0,3,4][4,7,J,K]Z	Rmvl/Acetab, Rt, [Opn, Perc, Perc Endo], [Int Fix Dev, Auto Tissue Sub, Synth Sub, Nonauto Tissue Sub], NQ **135, 347, 456**
0RPH[0,3,4] [0,3,4,7,K]Z	Rmvl/Acromioclavicular Jt, Lt, [Opn, Perc, Perc Endo], [Drain Dev, Inf Dev, Int Fix Dev, Auto Tissue Sub, Nonauto Tissue Sub], NQ **148**
0RPH[0,3,4] [0,3,4,7,J,K]Z	Rmvl/Acromioclavicular Jt, Lt, [Opn, Perc, Perc Endo], [Drain Dev, Inf Dev, Int Fix Dev, Auto Tissue Sub, Synth Sub, Nonauto Tissue Sub], NQ **350**
0RPH[0,3,4]JZ	Rmvl/Acromioclavicular Jt, Lt, [Opn, Perc, Perc Endo], Synth Sub, NQ **136**
0RPG[0,3,4] [0,3,4,7,K]Z	Rmvl/Acromioclavicular Jt, Rt, [Opn, Perc, Perc Endo], [Drain Dev, Inf Dev, Int Fix Dev, Auto Tissue Sub, Nonauto Tissue Sub], NQ **148**
0RPG[0,3,4] [0,3,4,7,J,K]Z	Rmvl/Acromioclavicular Jt, Rt, [Opn, Perc, Perc Endo], [Drain Dev, Inf Dev, Int Fix Dev, Auto Tissue Sub, Synth Sub, Nonauto Tissue Sub], NQ **350**
0RPG[0,3,4]JZ	Rmvl/Acromioclavicular Jt, Rt, [Opn, Perc, Perc Endo], Synth Sub, NQ **136**
0GP5[0,3,4]0Z	Rmvl/Adrenal Gland, [Opn, Perc, Perc Endo], Drain Dev, NQ **235**
0DPR*	Rmvl/Anal Sphincter **25, 53, 153, 259, 268, 334**
0SPG[0,3,4] [0,3,4,5,7,K]Z	Rmvl/Ankle Jt, Lt, [Opn, Perc, Perc Endo], [Drain Dev, Inf Dev, Int Fix Dev, Ext Fix Dev, Auto Tissue Sub, Nonauto Tissue Sub], NQ **133**
0SPG[0,3,4] [0,3,4,5,7,J,K]Z	Rmvl/Ankle Jt, Lt, [Opn, Perc, Perc Endo], [Drain Dev, Inf Dev, Int Fix Dev, Ext Fix Dev, Auto Tissue Sub, Synth Sub, Nonauto Tissue Sub], NQ **352**
0SPG[0,3,4]JZ	Rmvl/Ankle Jt, Lt, [Opn, Perc, Perc Endo], Synth Sub, NQ **136**
0SPF[0,3,4] [0,3,4,5,7,K]Z	Rmvl/Ankle Jt, Rt, [Opn, Perc, Perc Endo], [Drain Dev, Inf Dev, Int Fix Dev, Ext Fix Dev, Auto Tissue Sub, Nonauto Tissue Sub], NQ **133**
0SPF[0,3,4] [0,3,4,5,7,J,K]Z	Rmvl/Ankle Jt, Rt, [Opn, Perc, Perc Endo], [Drain Dev, Inf Dev, Int Fix Dev, Ext Fix Dev, Auto Tissue Sub, Synth Sub, Nonauto Tissue Sub], NQ **352**
0SPF[0,3,4]JZ	Rmvl/Ankle Jt, Rt, [Opn, Perc, Perc Endo], Synth Sub, NQ **136**
0DPQ*	Rmvl/Anus **107, 334**
0DPQ[0,3,4,7,8]LZ	Rmvl/Anus, [Opn, Perc, Perc Endo, Via Natrl or Artfcl Opng, Via Natrl or Artfcl Opng Endo], Artfcl Sphincter, NQ **211**
0TPB[0,3,4,7,8,X]MZ	Rmvl/Bladder, [Opn, Perc, Perc Endo, Via Natrl or Artfcl Opng, Via Natrl or Artfcl Opng Endo, Ext], Stimulator Lead, NQ **458**
0TPB[0,3,4,7,8] [0,2,3,7,C,D,J,K,L,M] Z	Rmvl/Bladder, [Opn, Perc, Perc Endo, Via Natrl or Artfcl Opng, Via Natrl or Artfcl Opng Endo], [Drain Dev, Monitoring Dev, Inf Dev, Auto Tissue Sub, Extralum Dev, Intralum Dev, Synth Sub, Nonauto Tissue Sub, Artfcl Sphincter, Stimulator Lead], NQ **250**
0TPB[0,3,4,7,8] [0,2,3,7,C,D,J,K,L]Z	Rmvl/Bladder, [Opn, Perc, Perc Endo, Via Natrl or Artfcl Opng, Via Natrl or Artfcl Opng Endo], [Drain Dev, Monitoring Dev, Inf Dev, Auto Tissue Sub, Extralum Dev, Intralum Dev, Synth Sub, Nonauto Tissue Sub, Artfcl Sphincter], NQ **354**
00P0[0,3,4] [0,2,3,7,J,K,M]Z	Rmvl/Brain, [Opn, Perc, Perc Endo], [Drain Dev, Monitoring Dev, Inf Dev, Auto Tissue Sub, Synth Sub, Nonauto Tissue Sub, Neurostimulator Lead], NQ **8, 12, 16**
00P0[0,3,4] [0,2,3,7,J,K]Z	Rmvl/Brain, [Opn, Perc, Perc Endo], [Drain Dev, Monitoring Dev, Inf Dev, Auto Tissue Sub, Synth Sub, Nonauto Tissue Sub], NQ **318, 414**
00P0[0,3,4]MZ	Rmvl/Brain, [Opn, Perc, Perc Endo], Neurostimulator Lead, NQ **296**
0HPU[0,3][J,N]Z	Rmvl/Breast, Lt, [Opn, Perc], [Synth Sub, Tissue Expander], NQ **222, 336, 450**
0HPT[0,3][J,N]Z	Rmvl/Breast, Rt, [Opn, Perc], [Synth Sub, Tissue Expander], NQ **222, 336, 450**
0RPR[0,3,4] [0,3,4,5,7,K]Z	Rmvl/Carpal Jt, Lt, [Opn, Perc, Perc Endo], [Drain Dev, Inf Dev, Int Fix Dev, Ext Fix Dev, Auto Tissue Sub, Nonauto Tissue Sub], NQ **147**
0RPR[0,3,4] [0,3,4,5,7,J,K]Z	Rmvl/Carpal Jt, Lt, [Opn, Perc, Perc Endo], [Drain Dev, Inf Dev, Int Fix Dev, Ext Fix Dev, Auto Tissue Sub, Synth Sub, Nonauto Tissue Sub], NQ **316**
0RPR[0,3,4]JZ	Rmvl/Carpal Jt, Lt, [Opn, Perc, Perc Endo], Synth Sub, NQ **136**
0RPQ[0,3,4] [0,3,4,5,7,K]Z	Rmvl/Carpal Jt, Rt, [Opn, Perc, Perc Endo], [Drain Dev, Inf Dev, Int Fix Dev, Ext Fix Dev, Auto Tissue Sub, Nonauto Tissue Sub], NQ **147**
0RPQ[0,3,4] [0,3,4,5,7,J,K]Z	Rmvl/Carpal Jt, Rt, [Opn, Perc, Perc Endo], [Drain Dev, Inf Dev, Int Fix Dev, Ext Fix Dev, Auto Tissue Sub, Synth Sub, Nonauto Tissue Sub], NQ **316**
0RPQ[0,3,4]JZ	Rmvl/Carpal Jt, Rt, [Opn, Perc, Perc Endo], Synth Sub, NQ **136**
0PPN[0,3,4] [4,5,7,J,K]Z	Rmvl/Carpal, Lt, [Opn, Perc, Perc Endo], [Int Fix Dev, Ext Fix Dev, Auto Tissue Sub, Synth Sub, Nonauto Tissue Sub], NQ **134, 315, 455**
0PPM[0,3,4] [4,5,7,J,K]Z	Rmvl/Carpal, Rt, [Opn, Perc, Perc Endo], [Int Fix Dev, Ext Fix Dev, Auto Tissue Sub, Synth Sub, Nonauto Tissue Sub], NQ **134, 315, 455**
00P6[0,3,4,X]MZ	Rmvl/Cerebral Ventricle, [Opn, Perc, Perc Endo, Ext], Neurostimulator Lead, NQ **296**

00P6[0,3,4][0,2,3,M]Z	Rmvl/Cerebral Ventricle, [Opn, Perc, Perc Endo], [Drain Dev, Monitoring Dev, Inf Dev, Neurostimulator Lead], NQ 8, 12, 16
00P6[0,3,4][0,2,3,J]Z	Rmvl/Cerebral Ventricle, [Opn, Perc, Perc Endo], [Drain Dev, Monitoring Dev, Inf Dev, Synth Sub], NQ 318
00P6[0,3,4][0,2,3]Z	Rmvl/Cerebral Ventricle, [Opn, Perc, Perc Endo], [Drain Dev, Monitoring Dev, Inf Dev], NQ 414
00P6[0,3,4]JZ	Rmvl/Cerebral Ventricle, [Opn, Perc, Perc Endo], Synth Sub, NQ 20
00P6X[2,M]Z	Rmvl/Cerebral Ventricle, Ext, [Monitoring Dev, Neurostimulator Lead], NQ 8, 12, 16
0RP3[0,3,4][0,3,7,K]Z	Rmvl/Cervical Vert Disc, [Opn, Perc, Perc Endo], [Drain Dev, Inf Dev, Auto Tissue Sub, Nonauto Tissue Sub], NQ 156
0RP3[0,3,4]JZ	Rmvl/Cervical Vert Disc, [Opn, Perc, Perc Endo], Synth Sub, NQ 136, 350
0RP1[0,3,4][0,3,4,7,A,K]Z	Rmvl/Cervical Vert Jt, [Opn, Perc, Perc Endo], [Drain Dev, Inf Dev, Int Fix Dev, Auto Tissue Sub, Interbody Fusion Dev, Nonauto Tissue Sub], NQ 156
0RP1[0,3,4]JZ	Rmvl/Cervical Vert Jt, [Opn, Perc, Perc Endo], Synth Sub, NQ 136, 350
0PP3[0,3,4][4,7,J,K]Z	Rmvl/Cervical Vertebra, [Opn, Perc, Perc Endo], [Int Fix Dev, Auto Tissue Sub, Synth Sub, Nonauto Tissue Sub], NQ 134, 345, 455
0RP5[0,3,4][0,3,7,K]Z	Rmvl/Cervicothoracic Vert Disc, [Opn, Perc, Perc Endo], [Drain Dev, Inf Dev, Auto Tissue Sub, Nonauto Tissue Sub], NQ 156
0RP5[0,3,4]JZ	Rmvl/Cervicothoracic Vert Disc, [Opn, Perc, Perc Endo], Synth Sub, NQ 136, 350
0RP4[0,3,4][0,3,4,7,A,K]Z	Rmvl/Cervicothoracic Vert Jt, [Opn, Perc, Perc Endo], [Drain Dev, Inf Dev, Int Fix Dev, Auto Tissue Sub, Interbody Fusion Dev, Nonauto Tissue Sub], NQ 156
0RP4[0,3,4]JZ	Rmvl/Cervicothoracic Vert Jt, [Opn, Perc, Perc Endo], Synth Sub, NQ 136, 350
07PL[0,3,4][7,J,K]Z	Rmvl/Cisterna Chyli, [Opn, Perc, Perc Endo], [Auto Tissue Sub, Synth Sub, Nonauto Tissue Sub], NQ 291, 298, 328
07PL[0,3,4][0,3,C,D]Z	Rmvl/Cisterna Chyli, [Opn, Perc, Perc Endo], [Drain Dev, Inf Dev, Extralum Dev, Intralum Dev], NQ 60
0PPB[0,3,4][4,7,J,K]Z	Rmvl/Clavicle, Lt, [Opn, Perc, Perc Endo], [Int Fix Dev, Auto Tissue Sub, Synth Sub, Nonauto Tissue Sub], NQ 134, 346, 455
0PP9[0,3,4][4,7,J,K]Z	Rmvl/Clavicle, Rt, [Opn, Perc, Perc Endo], [Int Fix Dev, Auto Tissue Sub, Synth Sub, Nonauto Tissue Sub], NQ 134, 346, 455
0SP6[0,3,4][0,3,4,7,K]Z	Rmvl/Coccygeal Jt, [Opn, Perc, Perc Endo], [Drain Dev, Inf Dev, Int Fix Dev, Auto Tissue Sub, Nonauto Tissue Sub], NQ 157
0SP6[0,3,4]JZ	Rmvl/Coccygeal Jt, [Opn, Perc, Perc Endo], Synth Sub, NQ 136, 352
0QPS[0,3,4][4,7,J,K]Z	Rmvl/Coccyx, [Opn, Perc, Perc Endo], [Int Fix Dev, Auto Tissue Sub, Synth Sub, Nonauto Tissue Sub], NQ 135, 348, 456
0WP1[0,3,4][0,1,J,Y]Z	Rmvl/Cranial Cavity, [Opn, Perc, Perc Endo], [Drain Dev, Radioact Elmt, Synth Sub, Oth Dev], NQ 10, 14, 19
00PE[0,3,4,X]MZ	Rmvl/Cranial Nerve, [Opn, Perc, Perc Endo, Ext], Neurostimulator Lead, NQ 50, 151, 258, 267, 318
00PE[0,3,4][0,2,3,7,M]Z	Rmvl/Cranial Nerve, [Opn, Perc, Perc Endo], [Drain Dev, Monitoring Dev, Inf Dev, Auto Tissue Sub, Neurostimulator Lead], NQ 23
0BPT[0,3,4,7,8][0,2,7,J,K,M]Z	Rmvl/Diaphragm, [Opn, Perc, Perc Endo, Via Natrl or Artfcl Opng, Via Natrl or Artfcl Opng Endo], [Drain Dev, Monitoring Dev, Auto Tissue Sub, Synth Sub, Nonauto Tissue Sub, Diaphragmatic Pacemaker Lead], NQ 62
09PJ[0,7,8][7,J,K]Z	Rmvl/Ear, Lt, [Opn, Via Natrl or Artfcl Opng, Via Natrl or Artfcl Opng Endo], [Auto Tissue Sub, Synth Sub, Nonauto Tissue Sub], NQ 52
09PH[0,7,8][7,J,K]Z	Rmvl/Ear, Rt, [Opn, Via Natrl or Artfcl Opng, Via Natrl or Artfcl Opng Endo], [Auto Tissue Sub, Synth Sub, Nonauto Tissue Sub], NQ 52
0RPM[0,3,4][0,3,4,5,7,K]Z	Rmvl/Elbow Jt, Lt, [Opn, Perc, Perc Endo], [Drain Dev, Inf Dev, Int Fix Dev, Ext Fix Dev, Auto Tissue Sub, Nonauto Tissue Sub], NQ 148
0RPM[0,3,4][0,3,4,5,7,J,K]Z	Rmvl/Elbow Jt, Lt, [Opn, Perc, Perc Endo], [Drain Dev, Inf Dev, Int Fix Dev, Ext Fix Dev, Auto Tissue Sub, Synth Sub, Nonauto Tissue Sub], NQ 350
0RPM[0,3,4]JZ	Rmvl/Elbow Jt, Lt, [Opn, Perc, Perc Endo], Synth Sub, NQ 136
0RPL[0,3,4][0,3,4,5,7,K]Z	Rmvl/Elbow Jt, Rt, [Opn, Perc, Perc Endo], [Drain Dev, Inf Dev, Int Fix Dev, Ext Fix Dev, Auto Tissue Sub, Nonauto Tissue Sub], NQ 148
0RPL[0,3,4][0,3,4,5,7,J,K]Z	Rmvl/Elbow Jt, Rt, [Opn, Perc, Perc Endo], [Drain Dev, Inf Dev, Int Fix Dev, Ext Fix Dev, Auto Tissue Sub, Synth Sub, Nonauto Tissue Sub], NQ 350
0RPL[0,3,4]JZ	Rmvl/Elbow Jt, Rt, [Opn, Perc, Perc Endo], Synth Sub, NQ 136
0VPM[0,3,4,7,8][0,3,7,C,J,K]Z	Rmvl/Epididymis and Spermatic Cord, [Opn, Perc, Perc Endo, Via Natrl or Artfcl Opng, Via Natrl or Artfcl Opng Endo], [Drain Dev, Inf Dev, Auto Tissue Sub, Extralum Dev, Synth Sub, Nonauto Tissue Sub], NQ 258
0DP5[0,3,4][1,2,3,U]Z	Rmvl/Esophagus, [Opn, Perc, Perc Endo], [Radioact Elmt, Monitoring Dev, Inf Dev, Feeding Dev], NQ 106, 334
08PM*	Rmvl/Extraocular Muscle, Lt 43
08PM[0,3][0,7,J,K]Z	Rmvl/Extraocular Muscle, Lt, [Opn, Perc], [Drain Dev, Auto Tissue Sub, Synth Sub, Nonauto Tissue Sub], NQ 445
08PM[0,3]0Z	Rmvl/Extraocular Muscle, Lt, [Opn, Perc], Drain Dev, NQ 330
08PL*	Rmvl/Extraocular Muscle, Rt 43
08PL[0,3][0,7,J,K]Z	Rmvl/Extraocular Muscle, Rt, [Opn, Perc], [Drain Dev, Auto Tissue Sub, Synth Sub, Nonauto Tissue Sub], NQ 445
08PL[0,3]0Z	Rmvl/Extraocular Muscle, Rt, [Opn, Perc], Drain Dev, NQ 330
08P1[0,3,X]JZ	Rmvl/Eye, Lt, [Opn, Perc, Ext], Synth Sub, NQ 330
08P1[0,3,7,8][0,1,3,7,C,D,J,K]Z	Rmvl/Eye, Lt, [Opn, Perc, Via Natrl or Artfcl Opng, Via Natrl or Artfcl Opng Endo], [Drain Dev, Radioact Elmt, Inf Dev, Auto Tissue Sub, Extralum Dev, Intralum Dev, Synth Sub, Nonauto Tissue Sub], NQ 445
08P1[3,7,8][0,1,3,7,C,D,J,K]Z	Rmvl/Eye, Lt, [Perc, Via Natrl or Artfcl Opng, Via Natrl or Artfcl Opng Endo], [Drain Dev, Radioact Elmt, Inf Dev, Auto Tissue Sub, Extralum Dev, Intralum Dev, Synth Sub, Nonauto Tissue Sub], NQ 43
08P1X[7,K]Z	Rmvl/Eye, Lt, Ext, [Auto Tissue Sub, Nonauto Tissue Sub], NQ 43
08P1X[7,J,K]Z	Rmvl/Eye, Lt, Ext, [Auto Tissue Sub, Synth Sub, Nonauto Tissue Sub], NQ 445
08P10[0,1,7,C,D,K]Z	Rmvl/Eye, Lt, Opn, [Drain Dev, Radioact Elmt, Auto Tissue Sub, Extralum Dev, Intralum Dev, Nonauto Tissue Sub], NQ 43
08P10[3,J]Z	Rmvl/Eye, Lt, Opn, [Inf Dev, Synth Sub], NQ 42
08P0[0,3,X]JZ	Rmvl/Eye, Rt, [Opn, Perc, Ext], Synth Sub, NQ 330
08P0[0,3,7,8][0,1,3,7,C,D,J,K]Z	Rmvl/Eye, Rt, [Opn, Perc, Via Natrl or Artfcl Opng, Via Natrl or Artfcl Opng Endo], [Drain Dev, Radioact Elmt, Inf Dev, Auto Tissue Sub, Extralum Dev, Intralum Dev, Synth Sub, Nonauto Tissue Sub], NQ 445
08P0[3,7,8][0,1,3,7,C,D,J,K]Z	Rmvl/Eye, Rt, [Perc, Via Natrl or Artfcl Opng, Via Natrl or Artfcl Opng Endo], [Drain Dev, Radioact Elmt, Inf Dev, Auto Tissue Sub, Extralum Dev, Intralum Dev, Synth Sub, Nonauto Tissue Sub], NQ 43
08P0X[1,7,K]Z	Rmvl/Eye, Rt, Ext, [Radioact Elmt, Auto Tissue Sub, Nonauto Tissue Sub], NQ 43
08P0X[1,7,J,K]Z	Rmvl/Eye, Rt, Ext, [Radioact Elmt, Auto Tissue Sub, Synth Sub, Nonauto Tissue Sub], NQ 445
08P00[0,1,7,C,D,K]Z	Rmvl/Eye, Rt, Opn, [Drain Dev, Radioact Elmt, Auto Tissue Sub, Extralum Dev, Intralum Dev, Nonauto Tissue Sub], NQ 43
08P00[3,J]Z	Rmvl/Eye, Rt, Opn, [Inf Dev, Synth Sub], NQ 42
0NPW[0,3,4,X]4Z	Rmvl/Facial Bone, [Opn, Perc, Perc Endo, Ext], Int Fix Dev, NQ 49, 344
0NPW[0,3,4][0,7,K,M]Z	Rmvl/Facial Bone, [Opn, Perc, Perc Endo], [Drain Dev, Auto Tissue Sub, Nonauto Tissue Sub, Bone Growth Stimulator], NQ 54
0NPW[0,3,4]JZ	Rmvl/Facial Bone, [Opn, Perc, Perc Endo], Synth Sub, NQ 42, 344, 454
0UP8[0,3,4,7,8][0,3,7,C,D,J,K]Z	Rmvl/Fallopian Tube, [Opn, Perc, Perc Endo, Via Natrl or Artfcl Opng, Via Natrl or Artfcl Opng Endo], [Drain Dev, Inf Dev, Auto Tissue Sub, Extralum Dev, Intralum Dev, Synth Sub, Nonauto Tissue Sub], NQ 263, 264, 266
0QP9[0,3,4][4,5,7,J,K]Z	Rmvl/Femor Shaft, Lt, [Opn, Perc, Perc Endo], [Int Fix Dev, Ext Fix Dev, Auto Tissue Sub, Synth Sub, Nonauto Tissue Sub], NQ 137, 244, 347, 456
0QP8[0,3,4][4,5,7,J,K]Z	Rmvl/Femor Shaft, Rt, [Opn, Perc, Perc Endo], [Int Fix Dev, Ext Fix Dev, Auto Tissue Sub, Synth Sub, Nonauto Tissue Sub], NQ 137, 244, 347, 456
0QPK[0,3,4][4,5,7,J,K]Z	Rmvl/Fibula, Lt, [Opn, Perc, Perc Endo], [Int Fix Dev, Ext Fix Dev, Auto Tissue Sub, Synth Sub, Nonauto Tissue Sub], NQ 135, 348, 456
0QPJ[0,3,4][4,5,7,J,K]Z	Rmvl/Fibula, Rt, [Opn, Perc, Perc Endo], [Int Fix Dev, Ext Fix Dev, Auto Tissue Sub, Synth Sub, Nonauto Tissue Sub], NQ 135, 348, 456
0RPX[0,3,4][0,3,4,5,7,K]Z	Rmvl/Finger Phalangeal Jt, Lt, [Opn, Perc, Perc Endo], [Drain Dev, Inf Dev, Int Fix Dev, Ext Fix Dev, Auto Tissue Sub, Nonauto Tissue Sub], NQ 147
0RPX[0,3,4][0,3,4,5,7,J,K]Z	Rmvl/Finger Phalangeal Jt, Lt, [Opn, Perc, Perc Endo], [Drain Dev, Inf Dev, Int Fix Dev, Ext Fix Dev, Auto Tissue Sub, Synth Sub, Nonauto Tissue Sub], NQ 316

ØRPX[Ø,3,4]JZ	Rmvl/Finger Phalangeal Jt, Lt, [Opn, Perc, Perc Endo], Synth Sub, NQ 136
ØRPW[Ø,3,4] [Ø,3,4,5,7,K]Z	Rmvl/Finger Phalangeal Jt, Rt, [Opn, Perc, Perc Endo], [Drain Dev, Inf Dev, Int Fix Dev, Ext Fix Dev, Auto Tissue Sub, Nonauto Tissue Sub], NQ 147
ØRPW[Ø,3,4] [Ø,3,4,5,7,J,K]Z	Rmvl/Finger Phalangeal Jt, Rt, [Opn, Perc, Perc Endo], [Drain Dev, Inf Dev, Int Fix Dev, Ext Fix Dev, Auto Tissue Sub, Synth Sub, Nonauto Tissue Sub], NQ 316
ØRPW[Ø,3,4]JZ	Rmvl/Finger Phalangeal Jt, Rt, [Opn, Perc, Perc Endo], Synth Sub, NQ 136
ØPPV[Ø,3,4][4,5,7,J,K]Z	Rmvl/Finger Phalanx, Lt, [Opn, Perc, Perc Endo], [Int Fix Dev, Ext Fix Dev, Auto Tissue Sub, Synth Sub, Nonauto Tissue Sub], NQ 135, 346, 455
ØPPT[Ø,3,4][4,5,7,J,K]Z	Rmvl/Finger Phalanx, Rt, [Opn, Perc, Perc Endo], [Int Fix Dev, Ext Fix Dev, Auto Tissue Sub, Synth Sub, Nonauto Tissue Sub], NQ 135, 346, 455
ØFP4[Ø,3,4][Ø,2,3,D]Z	Rmvl/Gallbladder, [Opn, Perc, Perc Endo], [Drain Dev, Monitoring Dev, Inf Dev, Intralum Dev], NQ 120
ØFP4[Ø,3,4]DZ	Rmvl/Gallbladder, [Opn, Perc, Perc Endo], Intralum Dev, NQ 301, 335
ØWPPØ[1,3,Y]Z	Rmvl/Gastrointestinal Tract, Opn, [Radioact Elmt, Inf Dev, Oth Dev], NQ 114
ØPP8[Ø,3,4][4,7,J,K]Z	Rmvl/Glenoid Cavity, Lt, [Opn, Perc, Perc Endo], [Int Fix Dev, Auto Tissue Sub, Synth Sub, Nonauto Tissue Sub], NQ 134, 346, 455
ØPP7[Ø,3,4][4,7,J,K]Z	Rmvl/Glenoid Cavity, Rt, [Opn, Perc, Perc Endo], [Int Fix Dev, Auto Tissue Sub, Synth Sub, Nonauto Tissue Sub], NQ 134, 346
ØPP7[Ø,3,4][4,7,J,K]Z	Rmvl/Glenoid Cavity, Rt, [Opn, Perc, Perc Endo], [Int Fix Dev, Auto Tissue Sub, Synth Sub, Nonauto Tissue Sub], NQ 455
Ø2PY[Ø,3,4] [2,3,7,8,C,D,J,K]Z	Rmvl/Great Vessel, [Opn, Perc, Perc Endo], [Monitoring Dev, Inf Dev, Auto Tissue Sub, Zooplastic Tissue, Extralum Dev, Synth Sub, Nonauto Tissue Sub], NQ 93
Ø2PA[Ø,3,4,X]MZ	Rmvl/Heart, [Opn, Perc, Perc Endo, Ext], Cardiac Lead, NQ 24, 30, 77, 78, 88, 320, 358
Ø2PA[Ø,3,4][Q,R]Z	Rmvl/Heart, [Opn, Perc, Perc Endo], [Implantable Heart Assist Sys, Ext Heart Assist Sys], NQ 92
Ø2PA[Ø,3,4] [2,3,7,8,C,D,J,K]Z	Rmvl/Heart, [Opn, Perc, Perc Endo], [Monitoring Dev, Inf Dev, Auto Tissue Sub, Zooplastic Tissue, Extralum Dev, Intralum Dev, Synth Sub, Nonauto Tissue Sub], NQ 75
Ø2PA[Ø,3,4]RZ	Rmvl/Heart, [Opn, Perc, Perc Endo], Ext Heart Assist Sys, NQ 1
ØFPB[Ø,3,4,7,8] [Ø,1,2,3,7,C,D,J,K]Z	Rmvl/Hepatobiliary Duct, [Opn, Perc, Perc Endo, Via Natrl or Artfcl Opng, Via Natrl or Artfcl Opng Endo], [Drain Dev, Radioact Elmt, Monitoring Dev, Inf Dev, Auto Tissue Sub, Extralum Dev, Intralum Dev, Synth Sub, Nonauto Tissue Sub], NQ 120, 335
ØSPB[Ø,3,4] [Ø,3,4,5,7,K]Z	Rmvl/Hip Jt, Lt, [Opn, Perc, Perc Endo], [Drain Dev, Inf Dev, Int Fix Dev, Ext Fix Dev, Auto Tissue Sub, Nonauto Tissue Sub], NQ 131
ØSPB[Ø,3,4]JZ	Rmvl/Hip Jt, Lt, [Opn, Perc, Perc Endo], Synth Sub, NQ 127, 416
ØSPBØ[Ø,3,4,5,7,9,B, J,K]Z	Rmvl/Hip Jt, Lt, Opn, [Drain Dev, Inf Dev, Int Fix Dev, Ext Fix Dev, Auto Tissue Sub, Liner, Resurfacing Dev, Synth Sub, Nonauto Tissue Sub], NQ 352
ØSPB4[Ø,3,4,5,7,J,K]Z	Rmvl/Hip Jt, Lt, Perc Endo, [Drain Dev, Inf Dev, Int Fix Dev, Ext Fix Dev, Auto Tissue Sub, Synth Sub, Nonauto Tissue Sub], NQ 352
ØSPB3[Ø,3,4,5,7,J,K]Z	Rmvl/Hip Jt, Lt, Perc, [Drain Dev, Inf Dev, Int Fix Dev, Ext Fix Dev, Auto Tissue Sub, Synth Sub, Nonauto Tissue Sub], NQ 352
ØSP9[Ø,3,4] [Ø,3,4,5,7,K]Z	Rmvl/Hip Jt, Rt, [Opn, Perc, Perc Endo], [Drain Dev, Inf Dev, Int Fix Dev, Ext Fix Dev, Auto Tissue Sub, Nonauto Tissue Sub], NQ 131
ØSP9[Ø,3,4]JZ	Rmvl/Hip Jt, Rt, [Opn, Perc, Perc Endo], Synth Sub, NQ 127, 416
ØSP9Ø[Ø,3,4,5,7,9,B, J,K]Z	Rmvl/Hip Jt, Rt, Opn, [Drain Dev, Inf Dev, Int Fix Dev, Ext Fix Dev, Auto Tissue Sub, Liner, Resurfacing Dev, Synth Sub, Nonauto Tissue Sub], NQ 352
ØSP94[Ø,3,4,5,7,J,K]Z	Rmvl/Hip Jt, Rt, Perc Endo, [Drain Dev, Inf Dev, Int Fix Dev, Ext Fix Dev, Auto Tissue Sub, Synth Sub, Nonauto Tissue Sub], NQ 352
ØSP93[Ø,3,4,5,7,J,K]Z	Rmvl/Hip Jt, Rt, Perc, [Drain Dev, Inf Dev, Int Fix Dev, Ext Fix Dev, Auto Tissue Sub, Synth Sub, Nonauto Tissue Sub], NQ 352
ØPPD[Ø,3,4] [4,5,7,J,K]Z	Rmvl/Humeral Head, Lt, [Opn, Perc, Perc Endo], [Int Fix Dev, Ext Fix Dev, Auto Tissue Sub, Synth Sub, Nonauto Tissue Sub], NQ 134, 346, 455
ØPPC[Ø,3,4][4,5,7,J,K]Z	Rmvl/Humeral Head, Rt, [Opn, Perc, Perc Endo], [Int Fix Dev, Ext Fix Dev, Auto Tissue Sub, Synth Sub, Nonauto Tissue Sub], NQ 134, 346, 455
ØPPG[Ø,3,4] [4,5,7,J,K]Z	Rmvl/Humeral Shaft, Lt, [Opn, Perc, Perc Endo], [Int Fix Dev, Ext Fix Dev, Auto Tissue Sub, Synth Sub, Nonauto Tissue Sub], NQ 134, 346, 455
ØPPF[Ø,3,4][4,5,7,J,K]Z	Rmvl/Humeral Shaft, Rt, [Opn, Perc, Perc Endo], [Int Fix Dev, Ext Fix Dev, Auto Tissue Sub, Synth Sub, Nonauto Tissue Sub], NQ 134, 346, 455
Ø9PE*	Rmvl/Inner Ear, Lt 52
Ø9PD*	Rmvl/Inner Ear, Rt 52
ØTP5[Ø,3,4,7,8] [Ø,2,3,7,C,D,J,K]Z	Rmvl/Kidney, [Opn, Perc, Perc Endo, Via Natrl or Artfcl Opng, Via Natrl or Artfcl Opng Endo], [Drain Dev, Monitoring Dev, Inf Dev, Auto Tissue Sub, Extralum Dev, Intralum Dev, Synth Sub, Nonauto Tissue Sub], NQ 249, 354
ØSPD[Ø,3,4] [Ø,3,4,5,7,K]Z	Rmvl/Knee Jt, Lt, [Opn, Perc, Perc Endo], [Drain Dev, Inf Dev, Int Fix Dev, Ext Fix Dev, Auto Tissue Sub, Nonauto Tissue Sub], NQ 132, 457
ØSPD[Ø,3,4] [Ø,3,4,5,7,J,K]Z	Rmvl/Knee Jt, Lt, [Opn, Perc, Perc Endo], [Drain Dev, Inf Dev, Int Fix Dev, Ext Fix Dev, Auto Tissue Sub, Synth Sub, Nonauto Tissue Sub], NQ 352
ØSPD[Ø,3,4]JZ	Rmvl/Knee Jt, Lt, [Opn, Perc, Perc Endo], Synth Sub, NQ 127
ØSPC[Ø,3,4] [Ø,3,4,5,7,K]Z	Rmvl/Knee Jt, Rt, [Opn, Perc, Perc Endo], [Drain Dev, Inf Dev, Int Fix Dev, Ext Fix Dev, Auto Tissue Sub, Nonauto Tissue Sub], NQ 132, 457
ØSPC[Ø,3,4] [Ø,3,4,5,7,J,K]Z	Rmvl/Knee Jt, Rt, [Opn, Perc, Perc Endo], [Drain Dev, Inf Dev, Int Fix Dev, Ext Fix Dev, Auto Tissue Sub, Synth Sub, Nonauto Tissue Sub], NQ 352
ØSPC[Ø,3,4]JZ	Rmvl/Knee Jt, Rt, [Opn, Perc, Perc Endo], Synth Sub, NQ 127
ØCPS[Ø,3,7,8] [Ø,7,D,J,K]Z	Rmvl/Larynx, [Opn, Perc, Via Natrl or Artfcl Opng, Via Natrl or Artfcl Opng Endo], [Drain Dev, Auto Tissue Sub, Intralum Dev, Synth Sub, Nonauto Tissue Sub], NQ 53
ØCPS[Ø,3,7,8]JZ	Rmvl/Larynx, [Opn, Perc, Via Natrl or Artfcl Opng, Via Natrl or Artfcl Opng Endo], Synth Sub, NQ 65, 448
ØFPØ[Ø,3,4][Ø,2,3]Z	Rmvl/Liver, [Opn, Perc, Perc Endo], [Drain Dev, Monitoring Dev, Inf Dev], NQ 119, 335
ØSP2[Ø,3,4][Ø,3,7,K]Z	Rmvl/Lumbar Vert Disc, [Opn, Perc, Perc Endo], [Drain Dev, Inf Dev, Auto Tissue Sub, Nonauto Tissue Sub], NQ 157
ØSP2[Ø,3,4]JZ	Rmvl/Lumbar Vert Disc, [Opn, Perc, Perc Endo], Synth Sub, NQ 136, 352
ØSPØ[Ø,3,4] [Ø,3,4,7,A,K]Z	Rmvl/Lumbar Vert Jt, [Opn, Perc, Perc Endo], [Drain Dev, Inf Dev, Int Fix Dev, Auto Tissue Sub, Interbody Fusion Dev, Nonauto Tissue Sub], NQ 157
ØSPØ[Ø,3,4]JZ	Rmvl/Lumbar Vert Jt, [Opn, Perc, Perc Endo], Synth Sub, NQ 136, 352
ØQPØ[Ø,3,4][4,7,J,K]Z	Rmvl/Lumbar Vertebra, [Opn, Perc, Perc Endo], [Int Fix Dev, Auto Tissue Sub, Synth Sub, Nonauto Tissue Sub], NQ 135, 347, 456
ØSP4[Ø,3,4][Ø,3,7,K]Z	Rmvl/Lumbosacral Disc, [Opn, Perc, Perc Endo], [Drain Dev, Inf Dev, Auto Tissue Sub, Nonauto Tissue Sub], NQ 157
ØSP4[Ø,3,4]JZ	Rmvl/Lumbosacral Disc, [Opn, Perc, Perc Endo], Synth Sub, NQ 136, 352
ØSP3[Ø,3,4] [Ø,3,4,7,A,K]Z	Rmvl/Lumbosacral Jt, [Opn, Perc, Perc Endo], [Drain Dev, Inf Dev, Int Fix Dev, Auto Tissue Sub, Interbody Fusion Dev, Nonauto Tissue Sub], NQ 157
ØSP3[Ø,3,4]JZ	Rmvl/Lumbosacral Jt, [Opn, Perc, Perc Endo], Synth Sub, NQ 136, 352
ØBPL[Ø,3,4,7,8] [Ø,1,2,3]Z	Rmvl/Lung, Lt, [Opn, Perc, Perc Endo, Via Natrl or Artfcl Opng, Via Natrl or Artfcl Opng Endo], [Drain Dev, Radioact Elmt, Monitoring Dev, Inf Dev], NQ 62, 331
ØBPK[Ø,3,4,7,8] [Ø,1,2,3]Z	Rmvl/Lung, Rt, [Opn, Perc, Perc Endo, Via Natrl or Artfcl Opng, Via Natrl or Artfcl Opng Endo], [Drain Dev, Radioact Elmt, Monitoring Dev, Inf Dev], NQ 62, 331
Ø4PY[Ø,3,4][7,J,K]Z	Rmvl/Lwr Artery, [Opn, Perc, Perc Endo], [Auto Tissue Sub, Synth Sub, Nonauto Tissue Sub], NQ 442
Ø4PY[Ø,3,4] [Ø,2,3,7,C,D,J,K]Z	Rmvl/Lwr Artery, [Opn, Perc, Perc Endo], [Drain Dev, Monitoring Dev, Inf Dev, Auto Tissue Sub, Extralum Dev, Intralum Dev, Synth Sub, Nonauto Tissue Sub], NQ 84
Ø4PY[Ø,3,4] [Ø,2,3,C,D]Z	Rmvl/Lwr Artery, [Opn, Perc, Perc Endo], [Drain Dev, Monitoring Dev, Inf Dev, Extralum Dev, Intralum Dev], NQ 240, 297, 324
ØQPY[Ø,3,4][Ø,M]Z	Rmvl/Lwr Bone, [Opn, Perc, Perc Endo], [Drain Dev, Bone Growth Stimulator], NQ 135, 457
ØQPY[Ø,3,4]MZ	Rmvl/Lwr Bone, [Opn, Perc, Perc Endo], Bone Growth Stimulator, NQ 348
ØMPY[Ø,3,4][7,K]Z	Rmvl/Lwr Bursa & Lgmt, [Opn, Perc, Perc Endo], [Auto Tissue Sub, Nonauto Tissue Sub], NQ 144, 343, 454
ØMPY[Ø,3,4][Ø,J]Z	Rmvl/Lwr Bursa & Lgmt, [Opn, Perc, Perc Endo], [Drain Dev, Synth Sub], NQ 153

Code	Description
0QPC[0,3,4][4,5,7,J,K]Z	Rmvl/Lwr Femur, Lt, [Opn, Perc, Perc Endo], [Int Fix Dev, Ext Fix Dev, Auto Tissue Sub, Synth Sub, Nonauto Tissue Sub], NQ **137, 244, 347, 456**
0QPB[0,3,4][4,5,7,J,K]Z	Rmvl/Lwr Femur, Rt, [Opn, Perc, Perc Endo], [Int Fix Dev, Ext Fix Dev, Auto Tissue Sub, Synth Sub, Nonauto Tissue Sub], NQ **137, 244, 347, 456**
0DPD[0,3,4,7,8][0,2,3,7,C,D,J,K,U]Z	Rmvl/Lwr Intestinal Tract, [Opn, Perc, Perc Endo, Via Natrl or Artfcl Opng, Via Natrl or Artfcl Opng Endo], [Drain Dev, Monitoring Dev, Inf Dev, Auto Tissue Sub, Extralum Dev, Intralum Dev, Synth Sub, Nonauto Tissue Sub, Feeding Dev], NQ **109, 334**
0KPY[0,3,4][0,7,J,K,M]Z	Rmvl/Lwr Muscle, [Opn, Perc, Perc Endo], [Drain Dev, Auto Tissue Sub, Synth Sub, Nonauto Tissue Sub, Stimulator Lead], NQ **140, 339**
0KPY[0,3,4][0,7,J,K]Z	Rmvl/Lwr Muscle, [Opn, Perc, Perc Endo], [Drain Dev, Auto Tissue Sub, Synth Sub, Nonauto Tissue Sub], NQ **215, 452**
0KPY[0,3,4]MZ	Rmvl/Lwr Muscle, [Opn, Perc, Perc Endo], Stimulator Lead, NQ **27**
0LPY[0,3,4][0,7,J,K]Z	Rmvl/Lwr Tndn, [Opn, Perc, Perc Endo], [Drain Dev, Auto Tissue Sub, Synth Sub, Nonauto Tissue Sub], NQ **142, 341, 453**
06PY[0,3,4][7,J,K]Z	Rmvl/Lwr Vein, [Opn, Perc, Perc Endo], [Auto Tissue Sub, Synth Sub, Nonauto Tissue Sub], NQ **87**
06PY[0,3,4][0,2,3,7,C,D,J,K]Z	Rmvl/Lwr Vein, [Opn, Perc, Perc Endo], [Drain Dev, Monitoring Dev, Inf Dev, Auto Tissue Sub, Extralum Dev, Intralum Dev, Synth Sub, Nonauto Tissue Sub], NQ **443**
06PY[0,3,4][0,2,3,C,D]Z	Rmvl/Lwr Vein, [Opn, Perc, Perc Endo], [Drain Dev, Monitoring Dev, Inf Dev, Extralum Dev, Intralum Dev], NQ **89, 327**
07PN[0,3,4][7,J,K]Z	Rmvl/Lymphatic, [Opn, Perc, Perc Endo], [Auto Tissue Sub, Synth Sub, Nonauto Tissue Sub], NQ **298, 328**
07PN[0,3,4][0,3,7,C,D,J,K]Z	Rmvl/Lymphatic, [Opn, Perc, Perc Endo], [Drain Dev, Inf Dev, Auto Tissue Sub, Extralum Dev, Intralum Dev, Synth Sub, Nonauto Tissue Sub], NQ **291**
07PN[0,3,4][0,3,C,D]Z	Rmvl/Lymphatic, [Opn, Perc, Perc Endo], [Drain Dev, Inf Dev, Extralum Dev, Intralum Dev], NQ **210, 443**
0WPC[0,3,4][0,1,3,7,J,K,Y]Z	Rmvl/Mediastinum, [Opn, Perc, Perc Endo], [Drain Dev, Radioact Elmt, Inf Dev, Auto Tissue Sub, Synth Sub, Nonauto Tissue Sub, Oth Dev], NQ **66, 91, 356**
0DPV*	Rmvl/Mesentery **112**
0PPQ[0,3,4][4,5,7,J,K]Z	Rmvl/Metacarpal, Lt, [Opn, Perc, Perc Endo], [Int Fix Dev, Ext Fix Dev, Auto Tissue Sub, Synth Sub, Nonauto Tissue Sub], NQ **134, 315, 455**
0PPP[0,3,4][4,5,7,J,K]Z	Rmvl/Metacarpal, Rt, [Opn, Perc, Perc Endo], [Int Fix Dev, Ext Fix Dev, Auto Tissue Sub, Synth Sub, Nonauto Tissue Sub], NQ **134, 315, 455**
0RPT[0,3,4][0,3,4,5,7,K]Z	Rmvl/Metacarpocarpal Jt, Lt, [Opn, Perc, Perc Endo], [Drain Dev, Inf Dev, Int Fix Dev, Ext Fix Dev, Auto Tissue Sub, Nonauto Tissue Sub], NQ **147**
0RPT[0,3,4][0,3,4,5,7,J,K]Z	Rmvl/Metacarpocarpal Jt, Lt, [Opn, Perc, Perc Endo], [Drain Dev, Inf Dev, Int Fix Dev, Ext Fix Dev, Auto Tissue Sub, Synth Sub, Nonauto Tissue Sub], NQ **316**
0RPT[0,3,4]JZ	Rmvl/Metacarpocarpal Jt, Lt, [Opn, Perc, Perc Endo], Synth Sub, NQ **136**
0RPS[0,3,4][0,3,4,5,7,K]Z	Rmvl/Metacarpocarpal Jt, Rt, [Opn, Perc, Perc Endo], [Drain Dev, Inf Dev, Int Fix Dev, Ext Fix Dev, Auto Tissue Sub, Nonauto Tissue Sub], NQ **147**
0RPS[0,3,4][0,3,4,5,7,J,K]Z	Rmvl/Metacarpocarpal Jt, Rt, [Opn, Perc, Perc Endo], [Drain Dev, Inf Dev, Int Fix Dev, Ext Fix Dev, Auto Tissue Sub, Synth Sub, Nonauto Tissue Sub], NQ **316**
0RPS[0,3,4]JZ	Rmvl/Metacarpocarpal Jt, Rt, [Opn, Perc, Perc Endo], Synth Sub, NQ **136**
0RPV[0,3,4][0,3,4,5,7,K]Z	Rmvl/Metacarpophalangeal Jt, Lt, [Opn, Perc, Perc Endo], [Drain Dev, Inf Dev, Int Fix Dev, Ext Fix Dev, Auto Tissue Sub, Nonauto Tissue Sub], NQ **147**
0RPV[0,3,4][0,3,4,5,7,J,K]Z	Rmvl/Metacarpophalangeal Jt, Lt, [Opn, Perc, Perc Endo], [Drain Dev, Inf Dev, Int Fix Dev, Ext Fix Dev, Auto Tissue Sub, Synth Sub, Nonauto Tissue Sub], NQ **316**
0RPV[0,3,4]JZ	Rmvl/Metacarpophalangeal Jt, Lt, [Opn, Perc, Perc Endo], Synth Sub, NQ **136**
0RPU[0,3,4][0,3,4,5,7,K]Z	Rmvl/Metacarpophalangeal Jt, Rt, [Opn, Perc, Perc Endo], [Drain Dev, Inf Dev, Int Fix Dev, Ext Fix Dev, Auto Tissue Sub, Nonauto Tissue Sub], NQ **147**
0RPU[0,3,4][0,3,4,5,7,J,K]Z	Rmvl/Metacarpophalangeal Jt, Rt, [Opn, Perc, Perc Endo], [Drain Dev, Inf Dev, Int Fix Dev, Ext Fix Dev, Auto Tissue Sub, Synth Sub, Nonauto Tissue Sub], NQ **316**
0RPU[0,3,4]JZ	Rmvl/Metacarpophalangeal Jt, Rt, [Opn, Perc, Perc Endo], Synth Sub, NQ **136**
0SPN[0,3,4][0,3,4,5,7,K]Z	Rmvl/Metatarsal-Phalangeal Jt, Lt, [Opn, Perc, Perc Endo], [Drain Dev, Inf Dev, Int Fix Dev, Ext Fix Dev, Auto Tissue Sub, Nonauto Tissue Sub], NQ **146, 457**
0SPN[0,3,4][0,3,4,5,7,J,K]Z	Rmvl/Metatarsal-Phalangeal Jt, Lt, [Opn, Perc, Perc Endo], [Drain Dev, Inf Dev, Int Fix Dev, Ext Fix Dev, Auto Tissue Sub, Synth Sub, Nonauto Tissue Sub], NQ **352**
0SPN[0,3,4]JZ	Rmvl/Metatarsal-Phalangeal Jt, Lt, [Opn, Perc, Perc Endo], Synth Sub, NQ **136**
0SPM[0,3,4][0,3,4,5,7,K]Z	Rmvl/Metatarsal-Phalangeal Jt, Rt, [Opn, Perc, Perc Endo], [Drain Dev, Inf Dev, Int Fix Dev, Ext Fix Dev, Auto Tissue Sub, Nonauto Tissue Sub], NQ **146, 457**
0SPM[0,3,4][0,3,4,5,7,J,K]Z	Rmvl/Metatarsal-Phalangeal Jt, Rt, [Opn, Perc, Perc Endo], [Drain Dev, Inf Dev, Int Fix Dev, Ext Fix Dev, Auto Tissue Sub, Synth Sub, Nonauto Tissue Sub], NQ **352**
0SPM[0,3,4]JZ	Rmvl/Metatarsal-Phalangeal Jt, Rt, [Opn, Perc, Perc Endo], Synth Sub, NQ **136**
0SPL[0,3,4][0,3,4,5,7,K]Z	Rmvl/Metatarsal-Tarsal Jt, Lt, [Opn, Perc, Perc Endo], [Drain Dev, Inf Dev, Int Fix Dev, Ext Fix Dev, Auto Tissue Sub, Nonauto Tissue Sub], NQ **146, 457**
0SPL[0,3,4][0,3,4,5,7,J,K]Z	Rmvl/Metatarsal-Tarsal Jt, Lt, [Opn, Perc, Perc Endo], [Drain Dev, Inf Dev, Int Fix Dev, Ext Fix Dev, Auto Tissue Sub, Synth Sub, Nonauto Tissue Sub], NQ **352**
0SPL[0,3,4]JZ	Rmvl/Metatarsal-Tarsal Jt, Lt, [Opn, Perc, Perc Endo], Synth Sub, NQ **136**
0SPK[0,3,4][0,3,4,5,7,K]Z	Rmvl/Metatarsal-Tarsal Jt, Rt, [Opn, Perc, Perc Endo], [Drain Dev, Inf Dev, Int Fix Dev, Ext Fix Dev, Auto Tissue Sub, Nonauto Tissue Sub], NQ **146, 457**
0SPK[0,3,4][0,3,4,5,7,J,K]Z	Rmvl/Metatarsal-Tarsal Jt, Rt, [Opn, Perc, Perc Endo], [Drain Dev, Inf Dev, Int Fix Dev, Ext Fix Dev, Auto Tissue Sub, Synth Sub, Nonauto Tissue Sub], NQ **352**
0SPK[0,3,4]JZ	Rmvl/Metatarsal-Tarsal Jt, Rt, [Opn, Perc, Perc Endo], Synth Sub, NQ **136**
0QPP[0,3,4][4,5,7,J,K]Z	Rmvl/Metatarsal, Lt, [Opn, Perc, Perc Endo], [Int Fix Dev, Ext Fix Dev, Auto Tissue Sub, Synth Sub, Nonauto Tissue Sub], NQ **135, 348, 456**
0QPN[0,3,4][4,5,7,J,K]Z	Rmvl/Metatarsal, Rt, [Opn, Perc, Perc Endo], [Int Fix Dev, Ext Fix Dev, Auto Tissue Sub, Synth Sub, Nonauto Tissue Sub], NQ **135, 348, 456**
0CPY[0,3][0,1,7,D,J,K]Z	Rmvl/Mouth and Throat, [Opn, Perc], [Drain Dev, Radioact Elmt, Auto Tissue Sub, Intralum Dev, Synth Sub, Nonauto Tissue Sub], NQ **56, 211, 332, 448**
0CPY[7,8][1,7,J,K]Z	Rmvl/Mouth and Throat, [Via Natrl or Artfcl Opng, Via Natrl or Artfcl Opng Endo], [Radioact Elmt, Auto Tissue Sub, Synth Sub, Nonauto Tissue Sub], NQ **53**
0CPY8[1,7,J,K]Z	Rmvl/Mouth and Throat, Via Natrl or Artfcl Opng Endo, [Radioact Elmt, Auto Tissue Sub, Synth Sub, Nonauto Tissue Sub], NQ **332**
0CPY7[1,7,J,K]Z	Rmvl/Mouth and Throat, Via Natrl or Artfcl Opng, [Radioact Elmt, Auto Tissue Sub, Synth Sub, Nonauto Tissue Sub], NQ **332**
0RP0[0,3,4,7,A,K]Z	Rmvl/Occipital-cervical Jt, [Opn, Perc, Perc Endo], [Drain Dev, Inf Dev, Int Fix Dev, Auto Tissue Sub, Interbody Fusion Dev, Nonauto Tissue Sub], NQ **156**
0RP0[0,3,4]JZ	Rmvl/Occipital-cervical Jt, [Opn, Perc, Perc Endo], Synth Sub, NQ **136, 350**
0DPU*	Rmvl/Omentum **112**
0UP3[0,3,4][0,3]Z	Rmvl/Ovary, [Opn, Perc, Perc Endo], [Drain Dev, Inf Dev], NQ **263, 264, 266**
0FPG[0,3,4][0,2,3,D]Z	Rmvl/Pancreas, [Opn, Perc, Perc Endo], [Drain Dev, Monitoring Dev, Inf Dev, Intralum Dev], NQ **119**
0FPD[0,3,4,7,8][0,1,2,3,7,C,D,J,K]Z	Rmvl/Pancreatic Duct, [Opn, Perc, Perc Endo, Via Natrl or Artfcl Opng, Via Natrl or Artfcl Opng Endo], [Drain Dev, Radioact Elmt, Monitoring Dev, Inf Dev, Auto Tissue Sub, Extralum Dev, Intralum Dev, Synth Sub, Nonauto Tissue Sub], NQ **119**
0GPR[0,3,4]0Z	Rmvl/Parathyroid Gland, [Opn, Perc, Perc Endo], Drain Dev, NQ **53, 211, 238, 336**
0QPF[0,3,4][4,5,7,J,K]Z	Rmvl/Patella, Lt, [Opn, Perc, Perc Endo], [Int Fix Dev, Ext Fix Dev, Auto Tissue Sub, Synth Sub, Nonauto Tissue Sub], NQ **135, 348, 456**
0QPD[0,3,4][4,5,7,J,K]Z	Rmvl/Patella, Rt, [Opn, Perc, Perc Endo], [Int Fix Dev, Ext Fix Dev, Auto Tissue Sub, Synth Sub, Nonauto Tissue Sub], NQ **135, 348, 456**
0QP3[0,3,4][4,5,7,J,K]Z	Rmvl/Pelvic Bone, Lt, [Opn, Perc, Perc Endo], [Int Fix Dev, Ext Fix Dev, Auto Tissue Sub, Synth Sub, Nonauto Tissue Sub], NQ **135, 347, 456**

0QP2[0,3,4] [4,5,7,J,K]Z Rmvl/Pelvic Bone, Rt, [Opn, Perc, Perc Endo], [Int Fix Dev, Ext Fix Dev, Auto Tissue Sub, Synth Sub, Nonauto Tissue Sub], NQ **135, 347, 456**

0VPS[0,3,4,7,8] [0,3,7,J,K]Z Rmvl/Penis, [Opn, Perc, Perc Endo, Via Natrl or Artfcl Opng, Via Natrl or Artfcl Opng Endo], [Drain Dev, Inf Dev, Auto Tissue Sub, Synth Sub, Nonauto Tissue Sub], NQ **257, 459**

0VPS[0,3,4,7,8]JZ Rmvl/Penis, [Opn, Perc, Perc Endo, Via Natrl or Artfcl Opng, Via Natrl or Artfcl Opng Endo], Synth Sub, NQ **254**

0WPD[0,3,4][0,1,3,Y] Z Rmvl/Pericardial Cavity, [Opn, Perc, Perc Endo], [Drain Dev, Radioact Elmt, Inf Dev, Oth Dev], NQ **62, 98, 303, 356**

0WPN[0,3,4] [0,1,3,7,J,K,Y]Z Rmvl/Perineum, Female, [Opn, Perc, Perc Endo], [Drain Dev, Radioact Elmt, Inf Dev, Auto Tissue Sub, Synth Sub, Nonauto Tissue Sub, Oth Dev], NQ **217, 267, 275**

0WPN[0,3,4] [0,1,3,7,J,K,Y]Z Rmvl/Perineum, Female, [Opn, Perc, Perc Endo], [Drain Dev, Radioact Elmt, Inf Dev, Auto Tissue Sub, Synth Sub, Nonauto Tissue Sub, Oth Dev], NQ **460**

0WPM[0,3,4,X][7,K]Z Rmvl/Perineum, Male, [Opn, Perc, Perc Endo, Ext], [Auto Tissue Sub, Nonauto Tissue Sub], NQ **460**

01PY[0,3,4,X]MZ Rmvl/Peripheral Nerve, [Opn, Perc, Perc Endo, Ext], Neurostimulator Lead, NQ **50, 152, 258, 267, 319**

01PY[0,3,4][0,2,7,M] Z Rmvl/Peripheral Nerve, [Opn, Perc, Perc Endo], [Drain Dev, Monitoring Dev, Auto Tissue Sub, Neurostimulator Lead], NQ **24**

0WPG[0,3,4] [0,1,3,J,Y]Z Rmvl/Peritoneal Cavity, [Opn, Perc, Perc Endo], [Drain Dev, Radioact Elmt, Inf Dev, Synth Sub, Oth Dev], NQ **114**

0DPW* Rmvl/Peritoneum **112**

0GP1[0,3,4]0Z Rmvl/Pineal Body, [Opn, Perc, Perc Endo], Drain Dev, NQ **9, 13, 17, 235**

0GP0[0,3,4]0Z Rmvl/Pituitary Gland, [Opn, Perc, Perc Endo], Drain Dev, NQ **9, 13, 17, 211, 235**

0VP4[0,3,4,7,8] [0,1,3,7,J,K]Z Rmvl/Prostate and Seminal Vesicles, [Opn, Perc, Perc Endo, Via Natrl or Artfcl Opng, Via Natrl or Artfcl Opng Endo], [Drain Dev, Radioact Elmt, Inf Dev, Auto Tissue Sub, Synth Sub, Nonauto Tissue Sub], NQ **260**

0PPJ[0,3,4][4,5,7,J,K] Z Rmvl/Radius, Lt, [Opn, Perc, Perc Endo], [Int Fix Dev, Ext Fix Dev, Auto Tissue Sub, Synth Sub, Nonauto Tissue Sub], NQ **134, 346, 455**

0PPH[0,3,4] [4,5,7,J,K]Z Rmvl/Radius, Rt, [Opn, Perc, Perc Endo], [Int Fix Dev, Ext Fix Dev, Auto Tissue Sub, Synth Sub, Nonauto Tissue Sub], NQ **134, 346, 455**

0DPP[0,3,4]1Z Rmvl/Rectum, [Opn, Perc, Perc Endo], Radioact Elmt, NQ **109, 334**

0WPQ[3,4,7][1,3,Y]Z Rmvl/Respiratory Tract, [Perc, Perc Endo, Via Natrl or Artfcl Opng], [Radioact Elmt, Inf Dev, Oth Dev], NQ **66, 356**

0WPH[0,3,4][0,1,3,Y] Z Rmvl/Retroperitoneum, [Opn, Perc, Perc Endo], [Drain Dev, Radioact Elmt, Inf Dev, Oth Dev], NQ **114**

0PP2[0,3,4][4,7,J,K]Z Rmvl/Rib, Lt, [Opn, Perc, Perc Endo], [Int Fix Dev, Auto Tissue Sub, Synth Sub, Nonauto Tissue Sub], NQ **134, 345, 455**

0PP1[0,3,4][4,7,J,K]Z Rmvl/Rib, Rt, [Opn, Perc, Perc Endo], [Int Fix Dev, Auto Tissue Sub, Synth Sub, Nonauto Tissue Sub], NQ **134, 345, 455**

0SP5[0,3,4] [0,3,4,7,K]Z Rmvl/Sacrococcygeal Jt, [Opn, Perc, Perc Endo], [Drain Dev, Inf Dev, Int Fix Dev, Auto Tissue Sub, Nonauto Tissue Sub], NQ **157**

0SP5[0,3,4]JZ Rmvl/Sacrococcygeal Jt, [Opn, Perc, Perc Endo], Synth Sub, NQ **136, 352**

0SP8[0,3,4] [0,3,4,7,K]Z Rmvl/Sacroiliac Jt, Lt, [Opn, Perc, Perc Endo], [Drain Dev, Inf Dev, Int Fix Dev, Auto Tissue Sub, Nonauto Tissue Sub], NQ **157**

0SP8[0,3,4]JZ Rmvl/Sacroiliac Jt, Lt, [Opn, Perc, Perc Endo], Synth Sub, NQ **136, 352**

0SP7[0,3,4] [0,3,4,7,K]Z Rmvl/Sacroiliac Jt, Rt, [Opn, Perc, Perc Endo], [Drain Dev, Inf Dev, Int Fix Dev, Auto Tissue Sub, Nonauto Tissue Sub], NQ **157**

0SP7[0,3,4]JZ Rmvl/Sacroiliac Jt, Rt, [Opn, Perc, Perc Endo], Synth Sub, NQ **136, 352**

0QP1[0,3,4][4,7,J,K]Z Rmvl/Sacrum, [Opn, Perc, Perc Endo], [Int Fix Dev, Auto Tissue Sub, Synth Sub, Nonauto Tissue Sub], NQ **135, 347, 456**

0PP6[0,3,4][4,7,J,K]Z Rmvl/Scapula, Lt, [Opn, Perc, Perc Endo], [Int Fix Dev, Auto Tissue Sub, Synth Sub, Nonauto Tissue Sub], NQ **134, 346, 455**

0PP5[0,3,4][4,7,J,K]Z Rmvl/Scapula, Rt, [Opn, Perc, Perc Endo], [Int Fix Dev, Auto Tissue Sub, Synth Sub, Nonauto Tissue Sub], NQ **134, 345, 455**

0RPK[0,3,4] [0,3,4,7,K]Z Rmvl/Shldr Jt, Lt, [Opn, Perc, Perc Endo], [Drain Dev, Inf Dev, Int Fix Dev, Auto Tissue Sub, Nonauto Tissue Sub], NQ **148**

0RPK[0,3,4] [0,3,4,7,J,K]Z Rmvl/Shldr Jt, Lt, [Opn, Perc, Perc Endo], [Drain Dev, Inf Dev, Int Fix Dev, Auto Tissue Sub, Synth Sub, Nonauto Tissue Sub], NQ **350**

0RPK[0,3,4]JZ Rmvl/Shldr Jt, Lt, [Opn, Perc, Perc Endo], Synth Sub, NQ **136**

0RPJ[0,3,4][0,3,4,7,K] Z Rmvl/Shldr Jt, Rt, [Opn, Perc, Perc Endo], [Drain Dev, Inf Dev, Int Fix Dev, Auto Tissue Sub, Nonauto Tissue Sub], NQ **148**

0RPJ[0,3,4] [0,3,4,7,J,K]Z Rmvl/Shldr Jt, Rt, [Opn, Perc, Perc Endo], [Drain Dev, Inf Dev, Int Fix Dev, Auto Tissue Sub, Synth Sub, Nonauto Tissue Sub], NQ **350**

0RPJ[0,3,4]JZ Rmvl/Shldr Jt, Rt, [Opn, Perc, Perc Endo], Synth Sub, NQ **136**

09PY[0,3,4]0Z Rmvl/Sinus, [Opn, Perc, Perc Endo], Drain Dev, NQ **56**

0NP0[0,3,4,X]MZ Rmvl/Skull, [Opn, Perc, Perc Endo, Ext], Bone Growth Stimulator, NQ **301**

0NP0[0,3,4] [0,4,7,J,K,M,S]Z Rmvl/Skull, [Opn, Perc, Perc Endo], [Drain Dev, Int Fix Dev, Auto Tissue Sub, Synth Sub, Nonauto Tissue Sub, Bone Growth Stimulator, Hearing Dev], NQ **10, 14, 18**

0NP0[0,3,4]JZ Rmvl/Skull, [Opn, Perc, Perc Endo], Synth Sub, NQ **49, 154, 344**

0NP0X[4,M,S]Z Rmvl/Skull, Ext, [Int Fix Dev, Bone Growth Stimulator, Bone Conduction Hearing Dev], NQ **14, 18**

00PU[0,3,4] [0,2,3,J,M]Z Rmvl/Spinal Canal, [Opn, Perc, Perc Endo], [Drain Dev, Monitoring Dev, Inf Dev, Synth Sub, Neurostimulator Lead], NQ **159, 160, 318**

00PU[0,3,4] [0,2,3,J,M]Z Rmvl/Spinal Canal, [Opn, Perc, Perc Endo], [Drain Dev, Monitoring Dev, Inf Dev, Synth Sub, Neurostimulator Lead], NQ **19**

00PU[0,3,4][0,2,3]Z Rmvl/Spinal Canal, [Opn, Perc, Perc Endo], [Drain Dev, Monitoring Dev, Inf Dev], NQ **296**

00PU[0,3,4]MZ Rmvl/Spinal Canal, [Opn, Perc, Perc Endo], Neurostimulator Lead, NQ **251, 258, 267**

00PV[0,3,4] [0,2,3,7,J,K,M]Z Rmvl/Spinal Cord, [Opn, Perc, Perc Endo], [Drain Dev, Monitoring Dev, Inf Dev, Auto Tissue Sub, Synth Sub, Nonauto Tissue Sub, Neurostimulator Lead], NQ **19, 318**

00PV[0,3,4] [0,2,3,7,J,K]Z Rmvl/Spinal Cord, [Opn, Perc, Perc Endo], [Drain Dev, Monitoring Dev, Inf Dev, Auto Tissue Sub, Synth Sub, Nonauto Tissue Sub], NQ **121, 296**

00PV[0,3,4]MZ Rmvl/Spinal Cord, [Opn, Perc, Perc Endo], Neurostimulator Lead, NQ **159, 160, 251, 258, 267**

07PP[0,3,4][0,3]Z Rmvl/Spleen, [Opn, Perc, Perc Endo], [Drain Dev, Inf Dev], NQ **290, 298, 328**

0JPT[0,3]PZ Rmvl/SQ Tissue & Fascia, Trunk, [Opn, Perc], Cardiac Rhythm Related Dev, NQ **26, 29, 30, 77, 78, 88, 337, 358, 450**

0RPF[0,3,4] [0,3,4,7,K]Z Rmvl/Sternoclavicular Jt, Lt, [Opn, Perc, Perc Endo], [Drain Dev, Inf Dev, Int Fix Dev, Auto Tissue Sub, Nonauto Tissue Sub], NQ **148**

0RPF[0,3,4] [0,3,4,7,J,K]Z Rmvl/Sternoclavicular Jt, Lt, [Opn, Perc, Perc Endo], [Drain Dev, Inf Dev, Int Fix Dev, Auto Tissue Sub, Synth Sub, Nonauto Tissue Sub], NQ **350**

0RPF[0,3,4]JZ Rmvl/Sternoclavicular Jt, Lt, [Opn, Perc, Perc Endo], Synth Sub, NQ **136**

0RPE[0,3,4] [0,3,4,7,K]Z Rmvl/Sternoclavicular Jt, Rt, [Opn, Perc, Perc Endo], [Drain Dev, Inf Dev, Int Fix Dev, Auto Tissue Sub, Nonauto Tissue Sub], NQ **148**

0RPE[0,3,4] [0,3,4,7,J,K]Z Rmvl/Sternoclavicular Jt, Rt, [Opn, Perc, Perc Endo], [Drain Dev, Inf Dev, Int Fix Dev, Auto Tissue Sub, Synth Sub, Nonauto Tissue Sub], NQ **350**

0RPE[0,3,4]JZ Rmvl/Sternoclavicular Jt, Rt, [Opn, Perc, Perc Endo], Synth Sub, NQ **136**

0PP0[0,3,4][4,7,J,K]Z Rmvl/Sternum, [Opn, Perc, Perc Endo], [Int Fix Dev, Auto Tissue Sub, Synth Sub, Nonauto Tissue Sub], NQ **134, 345, 455**

0DP6[0,3,4]MZ Rmvl/Stomach, [Opn, Perc, Perc Endo], Stimulator Lead, NQ **25, 53, 153, 259, 268**

0DP6[0,3,7,8] [0,2,3,7,C,J,K,U]Z Rmvl/Stomach, [Opn, Perc, Via Natrl or Artfcl Opng, Via Natrl or Artfcl Opng Endo], [Drain Dev, Monitoring Dev, Inf Dev, Auto Tissue Sub, Extralum Dev, Synth Sub, Nonauto Tissue Sub, Feeding Dev], NQ **106**

0DP6[0,3] [0,2,3,7,C,D,J,K,M,U] Z Rmvl/Stomach, [Opn, Perc], [Drain Dev, Monitoring Dev, Inf Dev, Auto Tissue Sub, Extralum Dev, Intralum Dev, Synth Sub, Nonauto Tissue Sub, Stimulator Lead, Feeding Dev], NQ **334**

0DP6[0,3]DZ Rmvl/Stomach, [Opn, Perc], Intralum Dev, NQ **106**

0DP64[0,2,7,D,J,K,U] Z Rmvl/Stomach, Perc Endo, [Drain Dev, Monitoring Dev, Auto Tissue Sub, Intralum Dev, Synth Sub, Nonauto Tissue Sub, Feeding Dev], NQ **106**

0DP64[0,2,7,D,J,K,M, U]Z Rmvl/Stomach, Perc Endo, [Drain Dev, Monitoring Dev, Auto Tissue Sub, Intralum Dev, Synth Sub, Nonauto Tissue Sub, Stimulator Lead, Feeding Dev], NQ **334**

0DP64[3,C]Z Rmvl/Stomach, Perc Endo, [Inf Dev, Extralum Dev], NQ **235, 449**

0DP68[0,2,3,7,C,J,K, U]Z Rmvl/Stomach, Via Natrl or Artfcl Opng Endo, [Drain Dev, Monitoring Dev, Inf Dev, Auto Tissue Sub, Extralum Dev, Synth Sub, Nonauto Tissue Sub, Feeding Dev], NQ **334**

0DP67[0,2,3,7,C,J,K,U]Z Rmvl/Stomach, Via Natrl or Artfcl Opng, [Drain Dev, Monitoring Dev, Inf Dev, Auto Tissue Sub, Extralum Dev, Synth Sub, Nonauto Tissue Sub, Feeding Dev], NQ 334

0SPJ[0,3,4][0,3,4,5,7,K]Z Rmvl/Tarsal Jt, Lt, [Opn, Perc, Perc Endo], [Drain Dev, Inf Dev, Int Fix Dev, Ext Fix Dev, Auto Tissue Sub, Nonauto Tissue Sub], NQ 146, 457

0SPJ[0,3,4][0,3,4,5,7,J,K]Z Rmvl/Tarsal Jt, Lt, [Opn, Perc, Perc Endo], [Drain Dev, Inf Dev, Int Fix Dev, Ext Fix Dev, Auto Tissue Sub, Synth Sub, Nonauto Tissue Sub], NQ 352

0SPJ[0,3,4]JZ Rmvl/Tarsal Jt, Lt, [Opn, Perc, Perc Endo], Synth Sub, NQ 136

0SPH[0,3,4][0,3,4,5,7,K]Z Rmvl/Tarsal Jt, Rt, [Opn, Perc, Perc Endo], [Drain Dev, Inf Dev, Int Fix Dev, Ext Fix Dev, Auto Tissue Sub, Nonauto Tissue Sub], NQ 146, 457

0SPH[0,3,4][0,3,4,5,7,J,K]Z Rmvl/Tarsal Jt, Rt, [Opn, Perc, Perc Endo], [Drain Dev, Inf Dev, Int Fix Dev, Ext Fix Dev, Auto Tissue Sub, Synth Sub, Nonauto Tissue Sub], NQ 352

0SPH[0,3,4]JZ Rmvl/Tarsal Jt, Rt, [Opn, Perc, Perc Endo], Synth Sub, NQ 136

0QPM[0,3,4][4,5,7,J,K]Z Rmvl/Tarsal, Lt, [Opn, Perc, Perc Endo], [Int Fix Dev, Ext Fix Dev, Auto Tissue Sub, Synth Sub, Nonauto Tissue Sub], NQ 135, 348, 456

0QPL[0,3,4][4,5,7,J,K]Z Rmvl/Tarsal, Rt, [Opn, Perc, Perc Endo], [Int Fix Dev, Ext Fix Dev, Auto Tissue Sub, Synth Sub, Nonauto Tissue Sub], NQ 135, 348, 456

0RPD[0,3,4,X]4Z Rmvl/Temporomandibular Jt, Lt, [Opn, Perc, Perc Endo, Ext], Int Fix Dev, NQ 49, 350

0RPD[0,3,4][0,3,7,J,K]Z Rmvl/Temporomandibular Jt, Lt, [Opn, Perc, Perc Endo], [Drain Dev, Inf Dev, Auto Tissue Sub, Synth Sub, Nonauto Tissue Sub], NQ 55

0RPC[0,3,4,X]4Z Rmvl/Temporomandibular Jt, Rt, [Opn, Perc, Perc Endo, Ext], Int Fix Dev, NQ 49, 350

0RPC[0,3,4][0,3,7,J,K]Z Rmvl/Temporomandibular Jt, Rt, [Opn, Perc, Perc Endo], [Drain Dev, Inf Dev, Auto Tissue Sub, Synth Sub, Nonauto Tissue Sub], NQ 55

0VPD[0,3,4,7,8][0,3,7,J,K]Z Rmvl/Testis, [Opn, Perc, Perc Endo, Via Natrl or Artfcl Opng, Via Natrl or Artfcl Opng Endo], [Drain Dev, Inf Dev, Auto Tissue Sub, Synth Sub, Nonauto Tissue Sub], NQ 258

0VPD[0,3,4,7,8][0,3,7,J,K]Z Rmvl/Testis, [Opn, Perc, Perc Endo, Via Natrl or Artfcl Opng, Via Natrl or Artfcl Opng Endo], [Drain Dev, Inf Dev, Auto Tissue Sub, Synth Sub, Nonauto Tissue Sub], NQ 355

07PK[0,3,4][7,J,K]Z Rmvl/Thoracic Duct, [Opn, Perc, Perc Endo], [Auto Tissue Sub, Synth Sub, Nonauto Tissue Sub], NQ 291, 298, 328

07PK[0,3,4][0,3,C,D]Z Rmvl/Thoracic Duct, [Opn, Perc, Perc Endo], [Drain Dev, Inf Dev, Extralum Dev, Intralum Dev], NQ 60

0RP9[0,3,4][0,3,7,K]Z Rmvl/Thoracic Vert Disc, [Opn, Perc, Perc Endo], [Drain Dev, Inf Dev, Auto Tissue Sub, Nonauto Tissue Sub], NQ 156

0RP9[0,3,4]JZ Rmvl/Thoracic Vert Disc, [Opn, Perc, Perc Endo], Synth Sub, NQ 136, 350

0RP6[0,3,4][0,3,4,7,A,K]Z Rmvl/Thoracic Vert Jt, [Opn, Perc, Perc Endo], [Drain Dev, Inf Dev, Int Fix Dev, Auto Tissue Sub, Interbody Fusion Dev, Nonauto Tissue Sub], NQ 156

0RP6[0,3,4]JZ Rmvl/Thoracic Vert Jt, [Opn, Perc, Perc Endo], Synth Sub, NQ 136, 350

0PP4[0,3,4][4,7,J,K]Z Rmvl/Thoracic Vertebra, [Opn, Perc, Perc Endo], [Int Fix Dev, Auto Tissue Sub, Synth Sub, Nonauto Tissue Sub], NQ 134, 345, 455

0RPB[0,3,4][0,3,7,K]Z Rmvl/Thoracolumbar Vert Disc, [Opn, Perc, Perc Endo], [Drain Dev, Inf Dev, Auto Tissue Sub, Nonauto Tissue Sub], NQ 157

0RPB[0,3,4]JZ Rmvl/Thoracolumbar Vert Disc, [Opn, Perc, Perc Endo], Synth Sub, NQ 136, 350

0RPA[0,3,4][0,3,4,7,A,K]Z Rmvl/Thoracolumbar Vert Jt, [Opn, Perc, Perc Endo], [Drain Dev, Inf Dev, Int Fix Dev, Auto Tissue Sub, Interbody Fusion Dev, Nonauto Tissue Sub], NQ 156

0RPA[0,3,4]JZ Rmvl/Thoracolumbar Vert Jt, [Opn, Perc, Perc Endo], Synth Sub, NQ 136, 350

0PPS[0,3,4][4,5,7,J,K]Z Rmvl/Thumb Phalanx, Lt, [Opn, Perc, Perc Endo], [Int Fix Dev, Ext Fix Dev, Auto Tissue Sub, Synth Sub, Nonauto Tissue Sub], NQ 134, 346, 455

0PPR[0,3,4][4,5,7,J,K]Z Rmvl/Thumb Phalanx, Rt, [Opn, Perc, Perc Endo], [Int Fix Dev, Ext Fix Dev, Auto Tissue Sub, Synth Sub, Nonauto Tissue Sub], NQ 134, 346, 455

07PM[0,3,4][0,3]Z Rmvl/Thymus, [Opn, Perc, Perc Endo], [Drain Dev, Inf Dev], NQ 60, 241, 291, 298, 328

0GPK[0,3,4]0Z Rmvl/Thyroid Gland, [Opn, Perc, Perc Endo], Drain Dev, NQ 53, 211, 238, 336

0QPH[0,3,4][4,5,7,J,K]Z Rmvl/Tibia, Lt, [Opn, Perc, Perc Endo], [Int Fix Dev, Ext Fix Dev, Auto Tissue Sub, Synth Sub, Nonauto Tissue Sub], NQ 135, 348, 456

0QPG[0,3,4][4,5,7,J,K]Z Rmvl/Tibia, Rt, [Opn, Perc, Perc Endo], [Int Fix Dev, Ext Fix Dev, Auto Tissue Sub, Synth Sub, Nonauto Tissue Sub], NQ 135, 348, 456

0SPQ[0,3,4][0,3,4,5,7,K]Z Rmvl/Toe Phalangeal Jt, Lt, [Opn, Perc, Perc Endo], [Drain Dev, Inf Dev, Int Fix Dev, Ext Fix Dev, Auto Tissue Sub, Nonauto Tissue Sub], NQ 146, 458

0SPQ[0,3,4][0,3,4,5,7,J,K]Z Rmvl/Toe Phalangeal Jt, Lt, [Opn, Perc, Perc Endo], [Drain Dev, Inf Dev, Int Fix Dev, Ext Fix Dev, Auto Tissue Sub, Synth Sub, Nonauto Tissue Sub], NQ 352

0SPQ[0,3,4]JZ Rmvl/Toe Phalangeal Jt, Lt, [Opn, Perc, Perc Endo], Synth Sub, NQ 136

0SPP[0,3,4][0,3,4,5,7,K]Z Rmvl/Toe Phalangeal Jt, Rt, [Opn, Perc, Perc Endo], [Drain Dev, Inf Dev, Int Fix Dev, Ext Fix Dev, Auto Tissue Sub, Nonauto Tissue Sub], NQ 146, 457

0SPP[0,3,4][0,3,4,5,7,J,K]Z Rmvl/Toe Phalangeal Jt, Rt, [Opn, Perc, Perc Endo], [Drain Dev, Inf Dev, Int Fix Dev, Ext Fix Dev, Auto Tissue Sub, Synth Sub, Nonauto Tissue Sub], NQ 352

0SPP[0,3,4]JZ Rmvl/Toe Phalangeal Jt, Rt, [Opn, Perc, Perc Endo], Synth Sub, NQ 136

0QPR[0,3,4][4,5,7,J,K]Z Rmvl/Toe Phalanx, Lt, [Opn, Perc, Perc Endo], [Int Fix Dev, Ext Fix Dev, Auto Tissue Sub, Synth Sub, Nonauto Tissue Sub], NQ 135, 456

0QPR[0,3,4][4,5,7,J,K]Z Rmvl/Toe Phalanx, Lt, [Opn, Perc, Perc Endo], [Int Fix Dev, Ext Fix Dev, Auto Tissue Sub, Synth Sub, Nonauto Tissue Sub], NQ 348

0QPQ[0,3,4][4,5,7,J,K]Z Rmvl/Toe Phalanx, Rt, [Opn, Perc, Perc Endo], [Int Fix Dev, Ext Fix Dev, Auto Tissue Sub, Synth Sub, Nonauto Tissue Sub], NQ 135, 348, 456

0BP1[0,3,4,7,8][0,2,7,C,D,F,J,K]Z Rmvl/Trachea, [Opn, Perc, Perc Endo, Via Natrl or Artfcl Opng, Via Natrl or Artfcl Opng Endo], [Drain Dev, Monitoring Dev, Auto Tissue Sub, Extralum Dev, Intralum Dev, Tracheostomy Dev, Synth Sub, Nonauto Tissue Sub], NQ 65

0BP0[0,3,4][0,1,2,C,D,J,K]Z Rmvl/Tracheobronchial Tree, [Opn, Perc, Perc Endo], [Drain Dev, Radioact Elmt, Monitoring Dev, Extralum Dev, Intralum Dev, Synth Sub, Nonauto Tissue Sub], NQ 62

0BP0[7,8][3,7,C,J,K]Z Rmvl/Tracheobronchial Tree, [Via Natrl or Artfcl Opng, Via Natrl or Artfcl Opng Endo], [Inf Dev, Auto Tissue Sub, Extralum Dev, Synth Sub, Nonauto Tissue Sub], NQ 65

0BP00[3,7]Z Rmvl/Tracheobronchial Tree, Opn, [Inf Dev, Auto Tissue Sub], NQ 64

0BP04[3,7]Z Rmvl/Tracheobronchial Tree, Perc Endo, [Inf Dev, Auto Tissue Sub], NQ 65

0BP03[3,7]Z Rmvl/Tracheobronchial Tree, Perc, [Inf Dev, Auto Tissue Sub], NQ 65

0BP08[0,1,2,D]Z Rmvl/Tracheobronchial Tree, Via Natrl or Artfcl Opng Endo, [Drain Dev, Radioact Elmt, Monitoring Dev, Intralum Dev], NQ 62

0BP07[0,1,2,D]Z Rmvl/Tracheobronchial Tree, Via Natrl or Artfcl Opng, [Drain Dev, Radioact Elmt, Monitoring Dev, Intralum Dev], NQ 62

0PPL[0,3,4][4,5,7,J,K]Z Rmvl/Ulna, Lt, [Opn, Perc, Perc Endo], [Int Fix Dev, Ext Fix Dev, Auto Tissue Sub, Synth Sub, Nonauto Tissue Sub], NQ 134, 346, 455

0PPK[0,3,4][4,5,7,J,K]Z Rmvl/Ulna, Rt, [Opn, Perc, Perc Endo], [Int Fix Dev, Ext Fix Dev, Auto Tissue Sub, Synth Sub, Nonauto Tissue Sub], NQ 134, 346, 455

03PY[0,3,4][7,J,K]Z Rmvl/Upr Artery, [Opn, Perc, Perc Endo], [Auto Tissue Sub, Synth Sub, Nonauto Tissue Sub], NQ 89, 251, 321

03PY[0,3,4][0,2,3,C,D,M]Z Rmvl/Upr Artery, [Opn, Perc, Perc Endo], [Drain Dev, Monitoring Dev, Inf Dev, Extralum Dev, Intralum Dev, Stimulator Lead], NQ 82

0PPY[0,3,4][0,M]Z Rmvl/Upr Bone, [Opn, Perc, Perc Endo], [Drain Dev, Bone Growth Stimulator], NQ 135, 455

0PPY[0,3,4]MZ Rmvl/Upr Bone, [Opn, Perc, Perc Endo], Bone Growth Stimulator, NQ 346

0MPX[0,3,4][7,K]Z Rmvl/Upr Bursa & Lgmt, [Opn, Perc, Perc Endo], [Auto Tissue Sub, Nonauto Tissue Sub], NQ 144, 343, 454

0MPX[0,3,4][0,J]Z Rmvl/Upr Bursa & Lgmt, [Opn, Perc, Perc Endo], [Drain Dev, Synth Sub], NQ 153

0QP7[0,3,4][4,5,7,J,K]Z Rmvl/Upr Femur, Lt, [Opn, Perc, Perc Endo], [Int Fix Dev, Ext Fix Dev, Auto Tissue Sub, Synth Sub, Nonauto Tissue Sub], NQ 137, 244, 347, 456

0QP6[0,3,4][4,5,7,J,K]Z Rmvl/Upr Femur, Rt, [Opn, Perc, Perc Endo], [Int Fix Dev, Ext Fix Dev, Auto Tissue Sub, Synth Sub, Nonauto Tissue Sub], NQ 137, 244, 347, 456

0DQ5[0,3,4,7,8]ZZ	Rpr/Esophagus, [Opn, Perc, Perc Endo, Via Natrl or Artfcl Opng, Via Natrl or Artfcl Opng Endo] 300
09Q4[0,3,4,7,8]ZZ	Rpr/Ext Auditory Canal, Lt, [Opn, Perc, Perc Endo, Via Natrl or Artfcl Opng, Via Natrl or Artfcl Opng Endo] 52, 210, 330, 447
09Q3[0,3,4,7,8]ZZ	Rpr/Ext Auditory Canal, Rt, [Opn, Perc, Perc Endo, Via Natrl or Artfcl Opng, Via Natrl or Artfcl Opng Endo] 52, 210, 330, 447
09Q2[0,3,4]ZZ	Rpr/Ext Ear, Bilat, [Opn, Perc, Perc Endo] 52, 210, 330, 447
09Q1[0,3,4]ZZ	Rpr/Ext Ear, Lt, [Opn, Perc, Perc Endo] 52, 210, 330, 447
09Q0[0,3,4]ZZ	Rpr/Ext Ear, Rt, [Opn, Perc, Perc Endo] 52, 210, 330, 447
04QJ[0,3,4]ZZ	Rpr/Ext Iliac Artery, Lt, [Opn, Perc, Perc Endo] 209
04QH[0,3,4]ZZ	Rpr/Ext Iliac Artery, Rt, [Opn, Perc, Perc Endo] 209
08QM[0,3]ZZ	Rpr/Extraocular Muscle, Lt, [Opn, Perc] 445
08QL[0,3]ZZ	Rpr/Extraocular Muscle, Rt, [Opn, Perc] 445
0WQ2[0,3,4,X]ZZ	Rpr/Face, [Opn, Perc, Perc Endo, Ext] 217, 460
0KQ1[0,3,4]ZZ	Rpr/Facial Muscle, [Opn, Perc, Perc Endo] 215, 452
04QL[0,3,4]ZZ	Rpr/Femor Artery, Lt, [Opn, Perc, Perc Endo] 209
04QK[0,3,4]ZZ	Rpr/Femor Artery, Rt, [Opn, Perc, Perc Endo] 209
0YQE[0,3,4]ZZ	Rpr/Femor Rgn, Bilat, [Opn, Perc, Perc Endo] 110, 462
0YQ8[0,3,4]ZZ	Rpr/Femor Rgn, Lt, [Opn, Perc, Perc Endo] 110, 462
0YQ7[0,3,4]ZZ	Rpr/Femor Rgn, Rt, [Opn, Perc, Perc Endo] 110, 462
0RQX[0,3,4,X]ZZ	Rpr/Finger Phalangeal Jt, Lt, [Opn, Perc, Perc Endo, Ext] 316
0RQW[0,3,4,X]ZZ	Rpr/Finger Phalangeal Jt, Rt, [Opn, Perc, Perc Endo, Ext] 316
04QW[0,3,4]ZZ	Rpr/Foot Artery, Lt, [Opn, Perc, Perc Endo] 209
04QV[0,3,4]ZZ	Rpr/Foot Artery, Rt, [Opn, Perc, Perc Endo] 209
0MQT[0,3,4]ZZ	Rpr/Foot Bursa & Lgmt, Lt, [Opn, Perc, Perc Endo] 462
0MQS[0,3,4]ZZ	Rpr/Foot Bursa & Lgmt, Rt, [Opn, Perc, Perc Endo] 462
0KQW[0,3,4]ZZ	Rpr/Foot Muscle, Lt, [Opn, Perc, Perc Endo] 215, 452
0KQV[0,3,4]ZZ	Rpr/Foot Muscle, Rt, [Opn, Perc, Perc Endo] 215, 452
0LQW[0,3,4]ZZ	Rpr/Foot Tndn, Lt, [Opn, Perc, Perc Endo] 216
0LQV[0,3,4]ZZ	Rpr/Foot Tndn, Rt, [Opn, Perc, Perc Endo] 216
0NQ2[0,3,4,X]ZZ	Rpr/Frontal Bone, Lt, [Opn, Perc, Perc Endo, Ext] 14, 18
0NQ1[0,3,4,X]ZZ	Rpr/Frontal Bone, Rt, [Opn, Perc, Perc Endo, Ext] 14, 18
0FQ4[0,3,4]ZZ	Rpr/Gallbladder, [Opn, Perc, Perc Endo] 301
03QF[0,3,4]ZZ	Rpr/Hand Artery, Lt, [Opn, Perc, Perc Endo] 208
03QD[0,3,4]ZZ	Rpr/Hand Artery, Rt, [Opn, Perc, Perc Endo] 208
0KQD[0,3,4]ZZ	Rpr/Hand Muscle, Lt, [Opn, Perc, Perc Endo] 314, 452
0KQC[0,3,4]ZZ	Rpr/Hand Muscle, Rt, [Opn, Perc, Perc Endo] 314, 452
0LQ8[0,3,4]ZZ	Rpr/Hand Tndn, Lt, [Opn, Perc, Perc Endo] 216, 315, 453
0LQ7[0,3,4]ZZ	Rpr/Hand Tndn, Rt, [Opn, Perc, Perc Endo] 216, 315, 453
0CQ2[0,3,X]ZZ	Rpr/Hard Palate, [Opn, Perc, Ext] 211
0LQ0[0,3,4]ZZ	Rpr/Head and Neck Tndn, [Opn, Perc, Perc Endo] 216
0KQ0[0,3,4]ZZ	Rpr/Head Muscle, [Opn, Perc, Perc Endo] 215, 452
0WQ0[0,3,4,X]ZZ	Rpr/Head, [Opn, Perc, Perc Endo, Ext] 217, 460
02QA[0,3,4]ZZ	Rpr/Heart, [Opn, Perc, Perc Endo] 93
02QC[0,3,4]ZZ	Rpr/Heart, Lt, [Opn, Perc, Perc Endo] 75
02QB[0,3,4]ZZ	Rpr/Heart, Rt, [Opn, Perc, Perc Endo] 75
0FQ6[0,3,4,7,8]ZZ	Rpr/Hepatic Duct, Lt, [Opn, Perc, Perc Endo, Via Natrl or Artfcl Opng, Via Natrl or Artfcl Opng Endo] 301
0FQ5[0,3,4,7,8]ZZ	Rpr/Hepatic Duct, Rt, [Opn, Perc, Perc Endo, Via Natrl or Artfcl Opng, Via Natrl or Artfcl Opng Endo] 301
0KQP[0,3,4]ZZ	Rpr/Hip Muscle, Lt, [Opn, Perc, Perc Endo] 215, 452
0KQN[0,3,4]ZZ	Rpr/Hip Muscle, Rt, [Opn, Perc, Perc Endo] 215, 452
0LQK[0,3,4]ZZ	Rpr/Hip Tndn, Lt, [Opn, Perc, Perc Endo] 216
0LQJ[0,3,4]ZZ	Rpr/Hip Tndn, Rt, [Opn, Perc, Perc Endo] 216
0UQK[0,3,4,7,8]ZZ	Rpr/Hymen, [Opn, Perc, Perc Endo, Via Natrl or Artfcl Opng, Via Natrl or Artfcl Opng Endo] 459
00QA[0,3,4]ZZ	Rpr/Hypothalamus, [Opn, Perc, Perc Endo] 8, 12, 17, 296
0YQA[0,3,4]ZZ	Rpr/Inguinal Rgn, Bilat, [Opn, Perc, Perc Endo] 110, 462
0YQ6[0,3,4]ZZ	Rpr/Inguinal Rgn, Lt, [Opn, Perc, Perc Endo] 110, 462
0YQ5[0,3,4]ZZ	Rpr/Inguinal Rgn, Rt, [Opn, Perc, Perc Endo] 110, 462
04QF[0,3,4]ZZ	Rpr/Int Iliac Artery, Lt, [Opn, Perc, Perc Endo] 209
04QE[0,3,4]ZZ	Rpr/Int Iliac Artery, Rt, [Opn, Perc, Perc Endo] 209
0TQ1[0,3,4,7,8]ZZ	Rpr/Kidney, Lt, [Opn, Perc, Perc Endo, Via Natrl or Artfcl Opng, Via Natrl or Artfcl Opng Endo] 302
0TQ0[0,3,4,7,8]ZZ	Rpr/Kidney, Rt, [Opn, Perc, Perc Endo, Via Natrl or Artfcl Opng, Via Natrl or Artfcl Opng Endo] 302
0LQR[0,3,4]ZZ	Rpr/Knee Tndn, Lt, [Opn, Perc, Perc Endo] 453
0LQQ[0,3,4]ZZ	Rpr/Knee Tndn, Rt, [Opn, Perc, Perc Endo] 453
08QY[0,3,7,8]ZZ	Rpr/Lacrimal Duct, Lt, [Opn, Perc, Via Natrl or Artfcl Opng, Via Natrl or Artfcl Opng Endo] 445
08QY[7,8]ZZ	Rpr/Lacrimal Duct, Lt, [Via Natrl or Artfcl Opng, Via Natrl or Artfcl Opng Endo] 210
08QX[0,3,7,8]ZZ	Rpr/Lacrimal Duct, Rt, [Opn, Perc, Via Natrl or Artfcl Opng, Via Natrl or Artfcl Opng Endo] 445
08QX[7,8]ZZ	Rpr/Lacrimal Duct, Rt, [Via Natrl or Artfcl Opng, Via Natrl or Artfcl Opng Endo] 210
08QW[0,3]ZZ	Rpr/Lacrimal Gland, Lt, [Opn, Perc] 445
08QV[0,3]ZZ	Rpr/Lacrimal Gland, Rt, [Opn, Perc] 445
0DQG[3,4,7,8]ZZ	Rpr/Lg Intestine, Lt, [Perc, Perc Endo, Via Natrl or Artfcl Opng, Via Natrl or Artfcl Opng Endo] 107, 334
0DQF[3,4,7,8]ZZ	Rpr/Lg Intestine, Rt, [Perc, Perc Endo, Via Natrl or Artfcl Opng, Via Natrl or Artfcl Opng Endo] 107, 334
00QY[0,3,4]ZZ	Rpr/Lumbar Spinal Cord, [Opn, Perc, Perc Endo] 19, 296
0SQ2[3,4,X]ZZ	Rpr/Lumbar Vert Disc, [Perc, Perc Endo, Ext] 157
0SQ4[3,4,X]ZZ	Rpr/Lumbosacral Disc, [Perc, Perc Endo, Ext] 157
0KQB[0,3,4]ZZ	Rpr/Lwr Arm and Wrist Muscle, Lt, [Opn, Perc, Perc Endo] 215, 452
0KQ9[0,3,4]ZZ	Rpr/Lwr Arm and Wrist Muscle, Rt, [Opn, Perc, Perc Endo] 215, 452
0LQ6[0,3,4]ZZ	Rpr/Lwr Arm and Wrist Tndn, Lt, [Opn, Perc, Perc Endo] 216
0LQ5[0,3,4]ZZ	Rpr/Lwr Arm and Wrist Tndn, Rt, [Opn, Perc, Perc Endo] 216
0WQL[0,3,4,X]ZZ	Rpr/Lwr Back, [Opn, Perc, Perc Endo, Ext] 217, 460
0WQ5[0,3,4,X]ZZ	Rpr/Lwr Jaw, [Opn, Perc, Perc Endo, Ext] 217, 460
0KQT[0,3,4]ZZ	Rpr/Lwr Leg Muscle, Lt, [Opn, Perc, Perc Endo] 215, 452
0KQS[0,3,4]ZZ	Rpr/Lwr Leg Muscle, Rt, [Opn, Perc, Perc Endo] 215, 452
0LQP[0,3,4]ZZ	Rpr/Lwr Leg Tndn, Lt, [Opn, Perc, Perc Endo] 216
0LQN[0,3,4]ZZ	Rpr/Lwr Leg Tndn, Rt, [Opn, Perc, Perc Endo] 216
0CQ1[0,3]ZZ	Rpr/Lwr Lip, [Opn, Perc] 56, 211, 332, 448
07QD[0,3,4]ZZ	Rpr/Lymphatic, Aortic, [Opn, Perc, Perc Endo] 291, 298
07Q0[0,3,4]ZZ	Rpr/Lymphatic, Head, [Opn, Perc, Perc Endo] 291, 298
07Q9[0,3,4]ZZ	Rpr/Lymphatic, Int Mammary, Lt, [Opn, Perc, Perc Endo] 291, 298
07Q8[0,3,4]ZZ	Rpr/Lymphatic, Int Mammary, Rt, [Opn, Perc, Perc Endo] 291, 298
07Q6[0,3,4]ZZ	Rpr/Lymphatic, Lt Axillary, [Opn, Perc, Perc Endo] 291, 298
07QJ[0,3,4]ZZ	Rpr/Lymphatic, Lt Inguinal, [Opn, Perc, Perc Endo] 291, 298
07QG[0,3,4]ZZ	Rpr/Lymphatic, Lt Lwr Extr, [Opn, Perc, Perc Endo] 291, 298
07Q2[0,3,4]ZZ	Rpr/Lymphatic, Lt Neck, [Opn, Perc, Perc Endo] 291, 298
07Q4[0,3,4]ZZ	Rpr/Lymphatic, Lt Upr Extr, [Opn, Perc, Perc Endo] 291, 298
07QB[0,3,4]ZZ	Rpr/Lymphatic, Mesenteric, [Opn, Perc, Perc Endo] 291, 298
07QC[0,3,4]ZZ	Rpr/Lymphatic, Pelvis, [Opn, Perc, Perc Endo] 291, 298
07Q5[0,3,4]ZZ	Rpr/Lymphatic, Rt Axillary, [Opn, Perc, Perc Endo] 291, 298
07QH[0,3,4]ZZ	Rpr/Lymphatic, Rt Inguinal, [Opn, Perc, Perc Endo] 291, 298
07QF[0,3,4]ZZ	Rpr/Lymphatic, Rt Lwr Extr, [Opn, Perc, Perc Endo] 291, 298
07Q1[0,3,4]ZZ	Rpr/Lymphatic, Rt Neck, [Opn, Perc, Perc Endo] 291, 298
07Q3[0,3,4]ZZ	Rpr/Lymphatic, Rt Upr Extr, [Opn, Perc, Perc Endo] 291, 298
07Q7[0,3,4]ZZ	Rpr/Lymphatic, Thorax, [Opn, Perc, Perc Endo] 291, 298
00Q0[0,3,4]ZZ	Rpr/Medulla Oblongata, [Opn, Perc, Perc Endo] 8, 12, 17
0DQV[0,3,4]ZZ	Rpr/Mesentery, [Opn, Perc, Perc Endo] 300
0PQQ[0,3,4,X]ZZ	Rpr/Metacarpal, Lt, [Opn, Perc, Perc Endo, Ext] 315
0PQP[0,3,4,X]ZZ	Rpr/Metacarpal, Rt, [Opn, Perc, Perc Endo, Ext] 315
0RQT[0,3,4,X]ZZ	Rpr/Metacarpocarpal Jt, Lt, [Opn, Perc, Perc Endo, Ext] 316
0RQS[0,3,4,X]ZZ	Rpr/Metacarpocarpal Jt, Rt, [Opn, Perc, Perc Endo, Ext] 316
0RQV[0,3,4,X]ZZ	Rpr/Metacarpophalangeal Jt, Lt, [Opn, Perc, Perc Endo, Ext] 316
0RQU[0,3,4,X]ZZ	Rpr/Metacarpophalangeal Jt, Rt, [Opn, Perc, Perc Endo, Ext] 316
0NQB[0,3,4,X]ZZ	Rpr/Nasal Bone, [Opn, Perc, Perc Endo, Ext] 216, 454
09QM[0,3,4]ZZ	Rpr/Nasal Septum, [Opn, Perc, Perc Endo] 210, 447
09QL[0,3,4,7,8]ZZ	Rpr/Nasal Turbinate, [Opn, Perc, Perc Endo, Via Natrl or Artfcl Opng, Via Natrl or Artfcl Opng Endo] 210, 447
0KQ3[0,3,4]ZZ	Rpr/Neck Muscle, Lt, [Opn, Perc, Perc Endo] 215, 452
0KQ2[0,3,4]ZZ	Rpr/Neck Muscle, Rt, [Opn, Perc, Perc Endo] 215, 452
0WQ6[0,3,4,X]ZZ	Rpr/Neck, [Opn, Perc, Perc Endo, Ext] 217, 460
09QK[0,3,4,X]ZZ	Rpr/Nose, [Opn, Perc, Perc Endo, Ext] 210, 447
0NQ8[0,3,4,X]ZZ	Rpr/Occipital Bone, Lt, [Opn, Perc, Perc Endo, Ext] 14, 18
0NQ7[0,3,4,X]ZZ	Rpr/Occipital Bone, Rt, [Opn, Perc, Perc Endo, Ext] 14, 18
0NQQ[0,3,4,X]ZZ	Rpr/Orbit, Lt, [Opn, Perc, Perc Endo, Ext] 454
0NQP[0,3,4,X]ZZ	Rpr/Orbit, Rt, [Opn, Perc, Perc Endo, Ext] 454
02QD[0,3,4]ZZ	Rpr/Papillary Muscle, [Opn, Perc, Perc Endo] 75
0NQ4[0,3,4,X]ZZ	Rpr/Parietal Bone, Lt, [Opn, Perc, Perc Endo, Ext] 14, 18

ØNQ3[Ø,3,4,X]ZZ	Rpr/Parietal Bone, Rt, [Opn, Perc, Perc Endo, Ext] 14, 18
ØQQF[Ø,4,X]ZZ	Rpr/Patella, Lt, [Opn, Perc Endo, Ext] 132, 348
ØQQD[Ø,4,X]ZZ	Rpr/Patella, Rt, [Opn, Perc Endo, Ext] 132, 348
ØVQS[Ø,3,4]ZZ	Rpr/Penis, [Opn, Perc, Perc Endo] 217, 459
Ø2QN[Ø,3,4]ZZ	Rpr/Pericardium, [Opn, Perc, Perc Endo] 93
ØKQM[Ø,3,4]ZZ	Rpr/Perineum Muscle, [Opn, Perc, Perc Endo] 215, 452
ØLQH[Ø,3,4]ZZ	Rpr/Perineum Tndn, [Opn, Perc, Perc Endo] 216
ØWQN[Ø,3,4]ZZ	Rpr/Perineum, Female, [Opn, Perc, Perc Endo] 267, 275, 356, 460
ØWQM[Ø,3,4,X]ZZ	Rpr/Perineum, Male, [Opn, Perc, Perc Endo, Ext] 218, 460
ØDQW[Ø,3,4]ZZ	Rpr/Peritoneum, [Opn, Perc, Perc Endo] 300, 449
Ø4QU[Ø,3,4]ZZ	Rpr/Peroneal Artery, Lt, [Opn, Perc, Perc Endo] 209
Ø4QT[Ø,3,4]ZZ	Rpr/Peroneal Artery, Rt, [Opn, Perc, Perc Endo] 209
ØCQM[Ø,3,4,7,8]ZZ	Rpr/Pharynx, [Opn, Perc, Perc Endo, Via Natrl or Artfcl Opng, Via Natrl or Artfcl Opng Endo] 211
ØGQ1[Ø,3,4]ZZ	Rpr/Pineal Body, [Opn, Perc, Perc Endo] 9, 13, 17
ØGQØ[Ø,3,4]ZZ	Rpr/Pituitary Gland, [Opn, Perc, Perc Endo] 9, 13, 17, 211
ØØQB[Ø,3,4]ZZ	Rpr/Pons, [Opn, Perc, Perc Endo] 8, 12, 17
Ø4QN[Ø,3,4]ZZ	Rpr/Popliteal Artery, Lt, [Opn, Perc, Perc Endo] 209
Ø4QM[Ø,3,4]ZZ	Rpr/Popliteal Artery, Rt, [Opn, Perc, Perc Endo] 209
Ø4QS[Ø,3,4]ZZ	Rpr/Post Tibial Artery, Lt, [Opn, Perc, Perc Endo] 209
Ø4QR[Ø,3,4]ZZ	Rpr/Post Tibial Artery, Rt, [Opn, Perc, Perc Endo] 209
ØVQT[Ø,3,4,X]ZZ	Rpr/Prepuce, [Opn, Perc, Perc Endo, Ext] 217, 459
Ø3QC[Ø,3,4]ZZ	Rpr/Radial Artery, Lt, [Opn, Perc, Perc Endo] 208
Ø3QB[Ø,3,4]ZZ	Rpr/Radial Artery, Rt, [Opn, Perc, Perc Endo] 208
ØDQP[Ø,3,4,7,8]ZZ	Rpr/Rectum, [Opn, Perc, Perc Endo, Via Natrl or Artfcl Opng, Via Natrl or Artfcl Opng Endo] 211
ØRQK[Ø,3,4,X]ZZ	Rpr/Shldr Jt, Lt, [Opn, Perc, Perc Endo, Ext] 457
ØRQJ[Ø,3,4,X]ZZ	Rpr/Shldr Jt, Rt, [Opn, Perc, Perc Endo, Ext] 457
ØKQ6[Ø,3,4]ZZ	Rpr/Shldr Muscle, Lt, [Opn, Perc, Perc Endo] 215, 452
ØKQ5[Ø,3,4]ZZ	Rpr/Shldr Muscle, Rt, [Opn, Perc, Perc Endo] 215, 452
ØLQ2[Ø,3,4]ZZ	Rpr/Shldr Tndn, Lt, [Opn, Perc, Perc Endo] 453
ØLQ1[Ø,3,4]ZZ	Rpr/Shldr Tndn, Rt, [Opn, Perc, Perc Endo] 453
ØNQØ[Ø,3,4,X]ZZ	Rpr/Skull, [Opn, Perc, Perc Endo, Ext] 14, 18
ØCQ3[Ø,3,X]ZZ	Rpr/Soft Palate, [Opn, Perc, Ext] 211
ØØQT[Ø,3,4]ZZ	Rpr/Spinal Meninges, [Opn, Perc, Perc Endo] 19, 296
Ø7QP[Ø,3,4]ZZ	Rpr/Spleen, [Opn, Perc, Perc Endo] 298
ØJQ8[Ø,3]ZZ	Rpr/SQ Tissue & Fascia, Abd, [Opn, Perc] 213, 450
ØJQ4[Ø,3]ZZ	Rpr/SQ Tissue & Fascia, Ant Neck, [Opn, Perc] 212, 450
ØJQ7[Ø,3]ZZ	Rpr/SQ Tissue & Fascia, Back, [Opn, Perc] 212, 450
ØJQ9[Ø,3]ZZ	Rpr/SQ Tissue & Fascia, Buttock, [Opn, Perc] 213, 450
ØJQ6[Ø,3]ZZ	Rpr/SQ Tissue & Fascia, Chest, [Opn, Perc] 212, 450
ØJQ1[Ø,3]ZZ	Rpr/SQ Tissue & Fascia, Face, [Opn, Perc] 212, 450
ØJQC[Ø,3]ZZ	Rpr/SQ Tissue & Fascia, Genitalia, [Opn, Perc] 213
ØJQR[Ø,3]ZZ	Rpr/SQ Tissue & Fascia, Lt Foot, [Opn, Perc] 213, 451
ØJQK[Ø,3]ZZ	Rpr/SQ Tissue & Fascia, Lt Hand, [Opn, Perc] 213, 314, 450
ØJQH[Ø,3]ZZ	Rpr/SQ Tissue & Fascia, Lt Lwr Arm, [Opn, Perc] 213, 450
ØJQP[Ø,3]ZZ	Rpr/SQ Tissue & Fascia, Lt Lwr Leg, [Opn, Perc] 213, 451
ØJQF[Ø,3]ZZ	Rpr/SQ Tissue & Fascia, Lt Upr Arm, [Opn, Perc] 213, 450
ØJQM[Ø,3]ZZ	Rpr/SQ Tissue & Fascia, Lt Upr Leg, [Opn, Perc] 213, 451
ØJQB[Ø,3]ZZ	Rpr/SQ Tissue & Fascia, Perineum, [Opn, Perc] 213, 450
ØJQ5[Ø,3]ZZ	Rpr/SQ Tissue & Fascia, Post Neck, [Opn, Perc] 212, 450
ØJQQ[Ø,3]ZZ	Rpr/SQ Tissue & Fascia, Rt Foot, [Opn, Perc] 213, 451
ØJQJ[Ø,3]ZZ	Rpr/SQ Tissue & Fascia, Rt Hand, [Opn, Perc] 213, 314, 450
ØJQG[Ø,3]ZZ	Rpr/SQ Tissue & Fascia, Rt Lwr Arm, [Opn, Perc] 213, 450
ØJQN[Ø,3]ZZ	Rpr/SQ Tissue & Fascia, Rt Lwr Leg, [Opn, Perc] 213, 451
ØJQD[Ø,3]ZZ	Rpr/SQ Tissue & Fascia, Rt Upr Arm, [Opn, Perc] 213, 450
ØJQL[Ø,3]ZZ	Rpr/SQ Tissue & Fascia, Rt Upr Leg, [Opn, Perc] 213, 450
ØJQØ[Ø,3]ZZ	Rpr/SQ Tissue & Fascia, Scalp, [Opn, Perc] 212
ØRQF[Ø,3,4,X]ZZ	Rpr/Sternoclavicular Jt, Lt, [Opn, Perc, Perc Endo, Ext] 457
ØRQE[Ø,3,4,X]ZZ	Rpr/Sternoclavicular Jt, Rt, [Opn, Perc, Perc Endo, Ext] 457
ØDQ6[Ø,3,7,8]ZZ	Rpr/Stomach, [Opn, Perc, Via Natrl or Artfcl Opng, Via Natrl or Artfcl Opng Endo] 123, 300
ØHQY[Ø,3,7,8]ZZ	Rpr/Supernumerary Breast, [Opn, Perc, Via Natrl or Artfcl Opng, Via Natrl or Artfcl Opng Endo] 222
ØNQ6[Ø,3,4,X]ZZ	Rpr/Temporal Bone, Lt, [Opn, Perc, Perc Endo, Ext] 14, 18
ØNQ5[Ø,3,4,X]ZZ	Rpr/Temporal Bone, Rt, [Opn, Perc, Perc Endo, Ext] 14, 18
ØRQD[Ø,3,4]ZZ	Rpr/Temporomandibular Jt, Lt, [Opn, Perc, Perc Endo] 55, 157, 350
ØRQC[Ø,3,4]ZZ	Rpr/Temporomandibular Jt, Rt, [Opn, Perc, Perc Endo] 55, 157, 350
ØØQ9[Ø,3,4]ZZ	Rpr/Thalamus, [Opn, Perc, Perc Endo] 8, 12, 17, 296
Ø2QW[Ø,3,4]ZZ	Rpr/Thoracic Aorta, [Opn, Perc, Perc Endo] 92
ØØQX[Ø,3,4]ZZ	Rpr/Thoracic Spinal Cord, [Opn, Perc, Perc Endo] 19, 296
ØRQ9[3,4,X]ZZ	Rpr/Thoracic Vert Disc, [Perc, Perc Endo, Ext] 157
ØRQB[3,4,X]ZZ	Rpr/Thoracolumbar Vert Disc, [Perc, Perc Endo, Ext] 157
ØKQJ[Ø,3,4]ZZ	Rpr/Thorax Muscle, Lt, [Opn, Perc, Perc Endo] 215, 452
ØKQH[Ø,3,4]ZZ	Rpr/Thorax Muscle, Rt, [Opn, Perc, Perc Endo] 215, 452
ØLQD[Ø,3,4]ZZ	Rpr/Thorax Tndn, Lt, [Opn, Perc, Perc Endo] 216
ØLQC[Ø,3,4]ZZ	Rpr/Thorax Tndn, Rt, [Opn, Perc, Perc Endo] 216
Ø7QM[Ø,3,4]ZZ	Rpr/Thymus, [Opn, Perc, Perc Endo] 291, 298
ØKQ4[Ø,3,4]ZZ	Rpr/Tongue, Palate, Pharynx Muscle, [Opn, Perc, Perc Endo] 215, 452
ØBQ1[Ø,3,4,7,8]ZZ	Rpr/Trachea, [Opn, Perc, Perc Endo, Via Natrl or Artfcl Opng, Via Natrl or Artfcl Opng Endo] 210
ØDQL[3,4,7,8]ZZ	Rpr/Transv Colon, [Perc, Perc Endo, Via Natrl or Artfcl Opng, Via Natrl or Artfcl Opng Endo] 107, 334
ØKQG[Ø,3,4]ZZ	Rpr/Trunk Muscle, Lt, [Opn, Perc, Perc Endo] 215, 452
ØKQF[Ø,3,4]ZZ	Rpr/Trunk Muscle, Rt, [Opn, Perc, Perc Endo] 215, 452
ØLQB[Ø,3,4]ZZ	Rpr/Trunk Tndn, Lt, [Opn, Perc, Perc Endo] 216
ØLQ9[Ø,3,4]ZZ	Rpr/Trunk Tndn, Rt, [Opn, Perc, Perc Endo] 216
Ø9Q8[Ø,3,4,7,8]ZZ	Rpr/Tympanic Membrane, Lt, [Opn, Perc, Perc Endo, Via Natrl or Artfcl Opng, Via Natrl or Artfcl Opng Endo] 447
Ø9Q7[Ø,3,4,7,8]ZZ	Rpr/Tympanic Membrane, Rt, [Opn, Perc, Perc Endo, Via Natrl or Artfcl Opng, Via Natrl or Artfcl Opng Endo] 447
Ø3QA[Ø,3,4]ZZ	Rpr/Ulnar Artery, Lt, [Opn, Perc, Perc Endo] 208
Ø3Q9[Ø,3,4]ZZ	Rpr/Ulnar Artery, Rt, [Opn, Perc, Perc Endo] 208
ØKQ8[Ø,3,4]ZZ	Rpr/Upr Arm Muscle, Lt, [Opn, Perc, Perc Endo] 215, 452
ØKQ7[Ø,3,4]ZZ	Rpr/Upr Arm Muscle, Rt, [Opn, Perc, Perc Endo] 215, 452
ØLQ4[Ø,3,4]ZZ	Rpr/Upr Arm Tndn, Lt, [Opn, Perc, Perc Endo] 216
ØLQ3[Ø,3,4]ZZ	Rpr/Upr Arm Tndn, Rt, [Opn, Perc, Perc Endo] 216
ØWQK[Ø,3,4,X]ZZ	Rpr/Upr Back, [Opn, Perc, Perc Endo, Ext] 217, 460
ØWQ4[Ø,3,4,X]ZZ	Rpr/Upr Jaw, [Opn, Perc, Perc Endo, Ext] 217, 460
ØLQM[Ø,3,4]ZZ	Rpr/Upr Leg Tndn, Lt, [Opn, Perc, Perc Endo] 216
ØLQL[Ø,3,4]ZZ	Rpr/Upr Leg Tndn, Rt, [Opn, Perc, Perc Endo] 216
ØCQØ[Ø,3]ZZ	Rpr/Upr Lip, [Opn, Perc] 56, 211, 332, 448
Ø7Q7[Ø,3,4,7,8]ZZ	Rpr/Ureter, Lt, [Opn, Perc, Perc Endo, Via Natrl or Artfcl Opng, Via Natrl or Artfcl Opng Endo] 302
ØTQD[Ø,3,4,7,8,X]ZZ	Rpr/Urethra, [Opn, Perc, Perc Endo, Via Natrl or Artfcl Opng, Via Natrl or Artfcl Opng Endo, Ext] 302
ØTQD[Ø,3,4]ZZ	Rpr/Urethra, [Opn, Perc, Perc Endo] 250
ØTQD[7,8,X]ZZ	Rpr/Urethra, [Via Natrl or Artfcl Opng, Via Natrl or Artfcl Opng Endo, Ext] 250
ØCQN[Ø,3,X]ZZ	Rpr/Uvula, [Opn, Perc, Ext] 448
ØUQG[Ø,3,4,7,8,X]ZZ	Rpr/Vagina, [Opn, Perc, Perc Endo, Via Natrl or Artfcl Opng, Via Natrl or Artfcl Opng Endo, Ext] 272, 302
ØUQG[Ø,3,4]ZZ	Rpr/Vagina, [Opn, Perc, Perc Endo] 107, 267
ØUQG[7,8,X]ZZ	Rpr/Vagina, [Via Natrl or Artfcl Opng, Via Natrl or Artfcl Opng Endo, Ext] 217
Ø2QL[Ø,3,4]ZZ	Rpr/Ventricle, Lt, [Opn, Perc, Perc Endo] 93
Ø2QK[Ø,3,4]ZZ	Rpr/Ventricle, Rt, [Opn, Perc, Perc Endo] 93
Ø2QM[Ø,3,4]ZZ	Rpr/Ventricular Septum, [Opn, Perc, Perc Endo] 75
ØUQL[Ø,X]ZZ	Rpr/Vestibular Gland, [Opn, Ext] 459
ØUQM[Ø,X]ZZ	Rpr/Vulva, [Opn, Ext] 217, 272
ØRQP[Ø,3,4,X]ZZ	Rpr/Wrist Jt, Lt, [Opn, Perc, Perc Endo, Ext] 316
ØRQN[Ø,3,4,X]ZZ	Rpr/Wrist Jt, Rt, [Opn, Perc, Perc Endo, Ext] 316
ØHØ*	Skin and Breast, Alter 222
ØHH*	Skin and Breast, Insert 336
ØHU*	Skin and Breast, Supl 222
ØHX*	Skin and Breast, Transfer 53
ØJØ*	SQ Tissue & Fascia, Alter 337
DW23[D,H,J]ZZ	Stereotactic Radiosurgery/Abd, [Stereotactic Oth Photon Radiosurgery, Stereotactic Particulate Radiosurgery, Stereotactic Gamma Beam Radiosurgery], None, None 31
DG22[D,H,J]ZZ	Stereotactic Radiosurgery/Adrenal Glands, [Stereotactic Oth Photon Radiosurgery, Stereotactic Particulate Radiosurgery, Stereotactic Gamma Beam Radiosurgery], None, None 31
DF22[D,H,J]ZZ	Stereotactic Radiosurgery/Bile Ducts, [Stereotactic Oth Photon Radiosurgery, Stereotactic Particulate Radiosurgery, Stereotactic Gamma Beam Radiosurgery], None, None 31
DT22[D,H,J]ZZ	Stereotactic Radiosurgery/Bladder, [Stereotactic Oth Photon Radiosurgery, Stereotactic Particulate Radiosurgery, Stereotactic Gamma Beam Radiosurgery], None, None 31

D720[D,H,J]ZZ Stereotactic Radiosurgery/Bone Marrow, [Stereotactic Oth Photon Radiosurgery, Stereotactic Particulate Radiosurgery, Stereotactic Gamma Beam Radiosurgery], None, None 30

D021[D,H,J]ZZ Stereotactic Radiosurgery/Brain Stem, [Stereotactic Oth Photon Radiosurgery, Stereotactic Particulate Radiosurgery, Stereotactic Gamma Beam Radiosurgery], None, None 30

D020[D,H,J]ZZ Stereotactic Radiosurgery/Brain, [Stereotactic Oth Photon Radiosurgery, Stereotactic Particulate Radiosurgery, Stereotactic Gamma Beam Radiosurgery], None, None 30

DM20[D,H,J]ZZ Stereotactic Radiosurgery/Breast, Lt, [Stereotactic Oth Photon Radiosurgery, Stereotactic Particulate Radiosurgery, Stereotactic Gamma Beam Radiosurgery], None, None 31

DM21[D,H,J]ZZ Stereotactic Radiosurgery/Breast, Rt, [Stereotactic Oth Photon Radiosurgery, Stereotactic Particulate Radiosurgery, Stereotactic Gamma Beam Radiosurgery], None, None 31

DB21[D,H,J]ZZ Stereotactic Radiosurgery/Bronchus, [Stereotactic Oth Photon Radiosurgery, Stereotactic Particulate Radiosurgery, Stereotactic Gamma Beam Radiosurgery], None, None 31

DU21[D,H,J]ZZ Stereotactic Radiosurgery/Cervix, [Stereotactic Oth Photon Radiosurgery, Stereotactic Particulate Radiosurgery, Stereotactic Gamma Beam Radiosurgery], None, None 31

DB27[D,H,J]ZZ Stereotactic Radiosurgery/Chest Wall, [Stereotactic Oth Photon Radiosurgery, Stereotactic Particulate Radiosurgery, Stereotactic Gamma Beam Radiosurgery], None, None 31

DW22[D,H,J]ZZ Stereotactic Radiosurgery/Chest, [Stereotactic Oth Photon Radiosurgery, Stereotactic Particulate Radiosurgery, Stereotactic Gamma Beam Radiosurgery], None, None 31

DD25[D,H,J]ZZ Stereotactic Radiosurgery/Colon, [Stereotactic Oth Photon Radiosurgery, Stereotactic Particulate Radiosurgery, Stereotactic Gamma Beam Radiosurgery], None, None 31

DB28[D,H,J]ZZ Stereotactic Radiosurgery/Diaphragm, [Stereotactic Oth Photon Radiosurgery, Stereotactic Particulate Radiosurgery, Stereotactic Gamma Beam Radiosurgery], None, None 31

DD22[D,H,J]ZZ Stereotactic Radiosurgery/Duodenum, [Stereotactic Oth Photon Radiosurgery, Stereotactic Particulate Radiosurgery, Stereotactic Gamma Beam Radiosurgery], None, None 31

D920[D,H,J]ZZ Stereotactic Radiosurgery/Ear, [Stereotactic Oth Photon Radiosurgery, Stereotactic Particulate Radiosurgery, Stereotactic Gamma Beam Radiosurgery], None, None 30

DD20[D,H,J]ZZ Stereotactic Radiosurgery/Esophagus, [Stereotactic Oth Photon Radiosurgery, Stereotactic Particulate Radiosurgery, Stereotactic Gamma Beam Radiosurgery], None, None 31

D820[D,H,J]ZZ Stereotactic Radiosurgery/Eye, [Stereotactic Oth Photon Radiosurgery, Stereotactic Particulate Radiosurgery, Stereotactic Gamma Beam Radiosurgery], None, None 30

DF21[D,H,J]ZZ Stereotactic Radiosurgery/Gallbladder, [Stereotactic Oth Photon Radiosurgery, Stereotactic Particulate Radiosurgery, Stereotactic Gamma Beam Radiosurgery], None, None 31

D928[D,H,J]ZZ Stereotactic Radiosurgery/Hard Palate, [Stereotactic Oth Photon Radiosurgery, Stereotactic Particulate Radiosurgery, Stereotactic Gamma Beam Radiosurgery], None, None 30

DW21[D,H,J]ZZ Stereotactic Radiosurgery/Head and Neck, [Stereotactic Oth Photon Radiosurgery, Stereotactic Particulate Radiosurgery, Stereotactic Gamma Beam Radiosurgery], None, None 31

DD24[D,H,J]ZZ Stereotactic Radiosurgery/Ileum, [Stereotactic Oth Photon Radiosurgery, Stereotactic Particulate Radiosurgery, Stereotactic Gamma Beam Radiosurgery], None, None 31

DD23[D,H,J]ZZ Stereotactic Radiosurgery/Jejunum, [Stereotactic Oth Photon Radiosurgery, Stereotactic Particulate Radiosurgery, Stereotactic Gamma Beam Radiosurgery], None, None 31

DT20[D,H,J]ZZ Stereotactic Radiosurgery/Kidney, [Stereotactic Oth Photon Radiosurgery, Stereotactic Particulate Radiosurgery, Stereotactic Gamma Beam Radiosurgery], None, None 31

D92B[D,H,J]ZZ Stereotactic Radiosurgery/Larynx, [Stereotactic Oth Photon Radiosurgery, Stereotactic Particulate Radiosurgery, Stereotactic Gamma Beam Radiosurgery], None, None 30

DF20[D,H,J]ZZ Stereotactic Radiosurgery/Liver, [Stereotactic Oth Photon Radiosurgery, Stereotactic Particulate Radiosurgery, Stereotactic Gamma Beam Radiosurgery], None, None 31

DB22[D,H,J]ZZ Stereotactic Radiosurgery/Lung, [Stereotactic Oth Photon Radiosurgery, Stereotactic Particulate Radiosurgery, Stereotactic Gamma Beam Radiosurgery], None, None 31

D726[D,H,J]ZZ Stereotactic Radiosurgery/Lymphatics, Abd, [Stereotactic Oth Photon Radiosurgery, Stereotactic Particulate Radiosurgery, Stereotactic Gamma Beam Radiosurgery], None, None 30

D724[D,H,J]ZZ Stereotactic Radiosurgery/Lymphatics, Axillary, [Stereotactic Oth Photon Radiosurgery, Stereotactic Particulate Radiosurgery, Stereotactic Gamma Beam Radiosurgery], None, None 30

D728[D,H,J]ZZ Stereotactic Radiosurgery/Lymphatics, Inguinal, [Stereotactic Oth Photon Radiosurgery, Stereotactic Particulate Radiosurgery, Stereotactic Gamma Beam Radiosurgery], None, None 30

D723[D,H,J]ZZ Stereotactic Radiosurgery/Lymphatics, Neck, [Stereotactic Oth Photon Radiosurgery, Stereotactic Particulate Radiosurgery, Stereotactic Gamma Beam Radiosurgery], None, None 30

D727[D,H,J]ZZ Stereotactic Radiosurgery/Lymphatics, Pelvis, [Stereotactic Oth Photon Radiosurgery, Stereotactic Particulate Radiosurgery, Stereotactic Gamma Beam Radiosurgery], None, None 30

D725[D,H,J]ZZ Stereotactic Radiosurgery/Lymphatics, Thorax, [Stereotactic Oth Photon Radiosurgery, Stereotactic Particulate Radiosurgery, Stereotactic Gamma Beam Radiosurgery], None, None 30

DB26[D,H,J]ZZ Stereotactic Radiosurgery/Mediastinum, [Stereotactic Oth Photon Radiosurgery, Stereotactic Particulate Radiosurgery, Stereotactic Gamma Beam Radiosurgery], None, None 31

D924[D,H,J]ZZ Stereotactic Radiosurgery/Mouth, [Stereotactic Oth Photon Radiosurgery, Stereotactic Particulate Radiosurgery, Stereotactic Gamma Beam Radiosurgery], None, None 30

D92D[D,H,J]ZZ Stereotactic Radiosurgery/Nasopharynx, [Stereotactic Oth Photon Radiosurgery, Stereotactic Particulate Radiosurgery, Stereotactic Gamma Beam Radiosurgery], None, None 30

D921[D,H,J]ZZ Stereotactic Radiosurgery/Nose, [Stereotactic Oth Photon Radiosurgery, Stereotactic Particulate Radiosurgery, Stereotactic Gamma Beam Radiosurgery], None, None 30

DU20[D,H,J]ZZ Stereotactic Radiosurgery/Ovary, [Stereotactic Oth Photon Radiosurgery, Stereotactic Particulate Radiosurgery, Stereotactic Gamma Beam Radiosurgery], None, None 31

DF23[D,H,J]ZZ Stereotactic Radiosurgery/Pancreas, [Stereotactic Oth Photon Radiosurgery, Stereotactic Particulate Radiosurgery, Stereotactic Gamma Beam Radiosurgery], None, None 31

DG24[D,H,J]ZZ Stereotactic Radiosurgery/Parathyroid Glands, [Stereotactic Oth Photon Radiosurgery, Stereotactic Particulate Radiosurgery, Stereotactic Gamma Beam Radiosurgery], None, None 31

DW26[D,H,J]ZZ Stereotactic Radiosurgery/Pelvic Rgn, [Stereotactic Oth Photon Radiosurgery, Stereotactic Particulate Radiosurgery, Stereotactic Gamma Beam Radiosurgery], None, None 31

D027[D,H,J]ZZ Stereotactic Radiosurgery/Peripheral Nerve, [Stereotactic Oth Photon Radiosurgery, Stereotactic Particulate Radiosurgery, Stereotactic Gamma Beam Radiosurgery], None, None 30

D92C[D,H,J]ZZ Stereotactic Radiosurgery/Pharynx, [Stereotactic Oth Photon Radiosurgery, Stereotactic Particulate Radiosurgery, Stereotactic Gamma Beam Radiosurgery], None, None 30

DG21[D,H,J]ZZ Stereotactic Radiosurgery/Pineal Body, [Stereotactic Oth Photon Radiosurgery, Stereotactic Particulate Radiosurgery, Stereotactic Gamma Beam Radiosurgery], None, None 31

DG20[D,H,J]ZZ Stereotactic Radiosurgery/Pituitary Gland, [Stereotactic Oth Photon Radiosurgery, Stereotactic Particulate Radiosurgery, Stereotactic Gamma Beam Radiosurgery], None, None 31

DB25[D,H,J]ZZ Stereotactic Radiosurgery/Pleura, [Stereotactic Oth Photon Radiosurgery, Stereotactic Particulate Radiosurgery, Stereotactic Gamma Beam Radiosurgery], None, None 31

DV20[D,H,J]ZZ Stereotactic Radiosurgery/Prostate, [Stereotactic Oth Photon Radiosurgery, Stereotactic Particulate Radiosurgery, Stereotactic Gamma Beam Radiosurgery], None, None 31

DD27[D,H,J]ZZ Stereotactic Radiosurgery/Rectum, [Stereotactic Oth Photon Radiosurgery, Stereotactic Particulate Radiosurgery, Stereotactic Gamma Beam Radiosurgery], None, None 31

D926[D,H,J]ZZ Stereotactic Radiosurgery/Salivary Glands, [Stereotactic Oth Photon Radiosurgery, Stereotactic Particulate Radiosurgery, Stereotactic Gamma Beam Radiosurgery], None, None 30

D927[D,H,J]ZZ Stereotactic Radiosurgery/Sinuses, [Stereotactic Oth Photon Radiosurgery, Stereotactic Particulate Radiosurgery, Stereotactic Gamma Beam Radiosurgery], None, None 30

D929[D,H,J]ZZ Stereotactic Radiosurgery/Soft Palate, [Stereotactic Oth Photon Radiosurgery, Stereotactic Particulate Radiosurgery, Stereotactic Gamma Beam Radiosurgery], None, None 30

D026[D,H,J]ZZ Stereotactic Radiosurgery/Spinal Cord, [Stereotactic Oth Photon Radiosurgery, Stereotactic Particulate Radiosurgery, Stereotactic Gamma Beam Radiosurgery], None, None 30

D722[D,H,J]ZZ	Stereotactic Radiosurgery/Spleen, [Stereotactic Oth Photon Radiosurgery, Stereotactic Particulate Radiosurgery, Stereotactic Gamma Beam Radiosurgery], None, None 30
DD21[D,H,J]ZZ	Stereotactic Radiosurgery/Stomach, [Stereotactic Oth Photon Radiosurgery, Stereotactic Particulate Radiosurgery, Stereotactic Gamma Beam Radiosurgery], None, None 31
DV21[D,H,J]ZZ	Stereotactic Radiosurgery/Testis, [Stereotactic Oth Photon Radiosurgery, Stereotactic Particulate Radiosurgery, Stereotactic Gamma Beam Radiosurgery], None, None 31
D721[D,H,J]ZZ	Stereotactic Radiosurgery/Thymus, [Stereotactic Oth Photon Radiosurgery, Stereotactic Particulate Radiosurgery, Stereotactic Gamma Beam Radiosurgery], None, None 30
DG25[D,H,J]ZZ	Stereotactic Radiosurgery/Thyroid, [Stereotactic Oth Photon Radiosurgery, Stereotactic Particulate Radiosurgery, Stereotactic Gamma Beam Radiosurgery], None, None 31
D925[D,H,J]ZZ	Stereotactic Radiosurgery/Tongue, [Stereotactic Oth Photon Radiosurgery, Stereotactic Particulate Radiosurgery, Stereotactic Gamma Beam Radiosurgery], None, None 30
DB20[D,H,J]ZZ	Stereotactic Radiosurgery/Trachea, [Stereotactic Oth Photon Radiosurgery, Stereotactic Particulate Radiosurgery, Stereotactic Gamma Beam Radiosurgery], None, None 30
DT21[D,H,J]ZZ	Stereotactic Radiosurgery/Ureter, [Stereotactic Oth Photon Radiosurgery, Stereotactic Particulate Radiosurgery, Stereotactic Gamma Beam Radiosurgery], None, None 31
DT23[D,H,J]ZZ	Stereotactic Radiosurgery/Urethra, [Stereotactic Oth Photon Radiosurgery, Stereotactic Particulate Radiosurgery, Stereotactic Gamma Beam Radiosurgery], None, None 31
DU22[D,H,J]ZZ	Stereotactic Radiosurgery/Uterus, [Stereotactic Oth Photon Radiosurgery, Stereotactic Particulate Radiosurgery, Stereotactic Gamma Beam Radiosurgery], None, None 31
08U[8,9]X7Z	Supl [Rt, Lt] Cornea w/ Auto Tissue Sub, Ext Appr 43
0SU[R,S]09Z	Supl [Rt, Lt] Hip Jt, Femor Surface w/ Liner, Opn Appr 158
0SU[R,S]0BZ	Supl [Rt, Lt] Hip Jt, Femor Surface w/ Resurfacing Dev, Opn Appr 128
0SU[T,U]09Z	Supl [Rt, Lt] Knee Jt, Femor Surface w/ Liner, Opn Appr 158
0SU[V,W]09Z	Supl [Rt, Lt] Knee Jt, Tibial Surface w/ Liner, Opn Appr 158
04U00JZ	Supl Abd Aorta with Synth Sub, Opn Appr 84
04U03JZ	Supl Abd Aorta with Synth Sub, Perc Appr 92
04U04JZ	Supl Abd Aorta with Synth Sub, Perc Endo Appr 92
02U50JZ	Supl Atrial Septum with Synth Sub, Opn Appr 75
0RU40JZ	Supl C-thor Jt with Synth Sub, Opn Appr 159
0RU43JZ	Supl C-thor Jt with Synth Sub, Perc Appr 159
0RU44JZ	Supl C-thor Jt with Synth Sub, Perc Endo Appr 159
0RU10JZ	Supl Cerv Jt with Synth Sub, Opn Appr 159
0RU13JZ	Supl Cerv Jt with Synth Sub, Perc Appr 159
0RU14JZ	Supl Cerv Jt with Synth Sub, Perc Endo Appr 159
0PU347Z	Supl Cervcal Vertebra w Autol Sub, Perc Endo 155
0PU34KZ	Supl Cervcal Vertebra w Nonaut Sub, Perc Endo 155
0PU34JZ	Supl Cervcal Vertebra w Synth Sub, Perc Endo 155
0PU307Z	Supl Cervical Vertebra with Autol Sub, Opn Appr 155
0PU337Z	Supl Cervical Vertebra with Autol Sub, Perc Appr 155
0PU30KZ	Supl Cervical Vertebra with Nonaut Sub, Opn Appr 155
0PU33KZ	Supl Cervical Vertebra with Nonaut Sub, Perc Appr 155
0PU30JZ	Supl Cervical Vertebra with Synth Sub, Opn Appr 155
0PU33JZ	Supl Cervical Vertebra with Synth Sub, Perc Appr 155, 158
0QUS3JZ	Supl Coccyx with Synth Sub, Perc Appr 158
0CU2XJZ	Supl Hard Palate with Synth Sub, Extern Appr 25, 53
02UA0JZ	Supl Heart with Synth Sub, Opn Appr 92
02UA3JZ	Supl Heart with Synth Sub, Perc Appr 92
02UA4JZ	Supl Heart with Synth Sub, Perc Endo Appr 92
02U70JZ	Supl Lt Atrium with Synth Sub, Opn Appr 93, 320
02U73JZ	Supl Lt Atrium with Synth Sub, Perc Appr 80
02U74JZ	Supl Lt Atrium with Synth Sub, Perc Endo Appr 80
0SU[B,E]0BZ	Supl Lt Hip Jt [w/ Resurfacing Dev, Acetabular Surface w/ Resurfacing Dev], Opn Appr 128
0SUB09Z	Supl Lt Hip Jt with Liner, Opn Appr 128, 158, 245
0SUB0BZ	Supl Lt Hip Jt with Resurf Dev, Opn Appr 126, 352, 416
0SUE09Z	Supl Lt Hip Jt, Acetab with Liner, Opn Appr 128, 158, 245
0SUE0BZ	Supl Lt Hip Jt, Acetab with Resurf Dev, Opn Appr 126, 244, 352, 416
0SUS09Z	Supl Lt Hip Jt, Femor with Liner, Opn Appr 128, 245
0SUS0BZ	Supl Lt Hip Jt, Femor with Resurf Dev, Opn Appr 126, 244, 416
0SUW09Z	Supl Lt Knee Jt, Tibial with Liner, Opn Appr 132, 352

0SU00JZ	Supl Lum Jt with Synth Sub, Opn Appr 160
0SU03JZ	Supl Lum Jt with Synth Sub, Perc Appr 160
0SU04JZ	Supl Lum Jt with Synth Sub, Perc Endo Appr 160
0QU03JZ	Supl Lumbar Vertebra with Synth Sub, Perc Appr 158
0SU30JZ	Supl Lumbosacral Jt with Synth Sub, Opn Appr 160
0SU33JZ	Supl Lumbosacral Jt with Synth Sub, Perc Appr 160
0SU34JZ	Supl Lumsac Jt with Synth Sub, Perc Endo Appr 160
02UG07Z	Supl Mitral Valve with Autol Sub, Opn Appr 71, 72
02UG37Z	Supl Mitral Valve with Autol Sub, Perc Appr 71, 72
02UG47Z	Supl Mitral Valve with Autol Sub, Perc Endo Appr 71, 72
02UG0KZ	Supl Mitral Valve with Nonaut Sub, Opn Appr 71, 72
02UG3KZ	Supl Mitral Valve with Nonaut Sub, Perc Appr 71, 72
02UG4KZ	Supl Mitral Valve with Nonaut Sub, Perc Endo Appr 71, 72
02UG0JZ	Supl Mitral Valve with Synth Sub, Opn Appr 71, 72
02UG3JZ	Supl Mitral Valve with Synth Sub, Perc Appr 75, 98
02UG4JZ	Supl Mitral Valve with Synth Sub, Perc Endo Appr 71, 72
02UG08Z	Supl Mitral Valve with Zooplastic, Opn Appr 71, 72
02UG38Z	Supl Mitral Valve with Zooplastic, Perc Appr 71, 72
02UG48Z	Supl Mitral Valve with Zooplastic, Perc Endo Appr 71, 72
0RU00JZ	Supl Occip Jt with Synth Sub, Opn Appr 159
0RU03JZ	Supl Occip Jt with Synth Sub, Perc Appr 159
0RU04JZ	Supl Occip Jt with Synth Sub, Perc Endo Appr 159
02U60JZ	Supl Rt Atrium with Synth Sub, Opn Appr 93, 320
0SU[9,A]0BZ	Supl Rt Hip Jt [w/ Resurfacing Dev, Acetabular Surface w/ Resurfacing Dev], Opn Appr 128
0SU909Z	Supl Rt Hip Jt with Liner, Opn Appr 128, 158, 245
0SU90BZ	Supl Rt Hip Jt with Resurf Dev, Opn Appr 126, 352, 416
0SUA09Z	Supl Rt Hip Jt, Acetab with Liner, Opn Appr 128, 158, 245
0SUA0BZ	Supl Rt Hip Jt, Acetab with Resurf Dev, Opn Appr 126, 244, 352, 416
0SUR09Z	Supl Rt Hip Jt, Femor with Liner, Opn Appr 128, 245
0SUR0BZ	Supl Rt Hip Jt, Femor with Resurf Dev, Opn Appr 126, 244, 416
0SUV09Z	Supl Rt Knee Jt, Tibial with Liner, Opn Appr 132, 352
0NU347Z	Supl Rt Parietal Bone w Autol Sub, Perc Endo 10
0NU34KZ	Supl Rt Parietal Bone w Nonaut Sub, Perc Endo 10
0NU34JZ	Supl Rt Parietal Bone w Synth Sub, Perc Endo 10
0NU307Z	Supl Rt Parietal Bone with Autol Sub, Opn Appr 10
0NU337Z	Supl Rt Parietal Bone with Autol Sub, Perc Appr 10
0NU30KZ	Supl Rt Parietal Bone with Nonaut Sub, Opn Appr 10
0NU33KZ	Supl Rt Parietal Bone with Nonaut Sub, Perc Appr 10
0NU30JZ	Supl Rt Parietal Bone with Synth Sub, Opn Appr 10
0NU33JZ	Supl Rt Parietal Bone with Synth Sub, Perc Appr 10
0QU13JZ	Supl Sacrum with Synth Sub, Perc Appr 158
0RUA0JZ	Supl T-lum Jt with Synth Sub, Opn Appr 159
0RUA3JZ	Supl T-lum Jt with Synth Sub, Perc Appr 159
0RUA4JZ	Supl T-lum Jt with Synth Sub, Perc Endo Appr 159
0RU60JZ	Supl Thor Jt with Synth Sub, Opn Appr 159
0RU63JZ	Supl Thor Jt with Synth Sub, Perc Appr 159
0RU64JZ	Supl Thor Jt with Synth Sub, Perc Endo Appr 159
02UW0JZ	Supl Thoracic Aorta with Synth Sub, Opn Appr 80
0PU43JZ	Supl Thoracic Vertebra with Synth Sub, Perc Appr 158
02UM08Z	Supl Ventricular Septum with Zooplastic, Opn Appr 93, 320
0YUQ*	Supl/1st Toe, Lt 357
0YUQ[0,4][7,J,K]Z	Supl/1st Toe, Lt, [Opn, Perc Endo], [Auto Tissue Sub, Synth Sub, Nonauto Tissue Sub], NQ 219, 462
0YUP*	Supl/1st Toe, Rt 357
0YUP[0,4][7,J,K]Z	Supl/1st Toe, Rt, [Opn, Perc Endo], [Auto Tissue Sub, Synth Sub, Nonauto Tissue Sub], NQ 219, 462
0YUS*	Supl/2nd Toe, Lt 357
0YUS[0,4][7,J,K]Z	Supl/2nd Toe, Lt, [Opn, Perc Endo], [Auto Tissue Sub, Synth Sub, Nonauto Tissue Sub], NQ 219, 462
0YUR*	Supl/2nd Toe, Rt 357
0YUR[0,4][7,J,K]Z	Supl/2nd Toe, Rt, [Opn, Perc Endo], [Auto Tissue Sub, Synth Sub, Nonauto Tissue Sub], NQ 219, 462
0YUU*	Supl/3rd Toe, Lt 357
0YUU[0,4][7,J,K]Z	Supl/3rd Toe, Lt, [Opn, Perc Endo], [Auto Tissue Sub, Synth Sub, Nonauto Tissue Sub], NQ 219, 462
0YUT*	Supl/3rd Toe, Rt 357
0YUT[0,4][7,J,K]Z	Supl/3rd Toe, Rt, [Opn, Perc Endo], [Auto Tissue Sub, Synth Sub, Nonauto Tissue Sub], NQ 219, 462
0YUW*	Supl/4th Toe, Lt 357

ØYUW[Ø,4][7,J,K]Z	Supl/4th Toe, Lt, [Opn, Perc Endo], [Auto Tissue Sub, Synth Sub, Nonauto Tissue Sub], NQ 219, 462
ØYUV*	Supl/4th Toe, Rt 357
ØYUV[Ø,4][7,J,K]Z	Supl/4th Toe, Rt, [Opn, Perc Endo], [Auto Tissue Sub, Synth Sub, Nonauto Tissue Sub], NQ 219, 462
ØYUY*	Supl/5th Toe, Lt 357
ØYUY[Ø,4][7,J,K]Z	Supl/5th Toe, Lt, [Opn, Perc Endo], [Auto Tissue Sub, Synth Sub, Nonauto Tissue Sub], NQ 219, 462
ØYUX*	Supl/5th Toe, Rt 357
ØYUX[Ø,4][7,J,K]Z	Supl/5th Toe, Rt, [Opn, Perc Endo], [Auto Tissue Sub, Synth Sub, Nonauto Tissue Sub], NQ 219, 462
04UØ[Ø,3,4][7,K]Z	Supl/Abd Aorta, [Opn, Perc, Perc Endo], [Auto Tissue Sub, Nonauto Tissue Sub], NQ 84
04UØ[Ø,3,4][7,J]Z	Supl/Abd Aorta, [Opn, Perc, Perc Endo], [Auto Tissue Sub, Synth Sub], NQ 324
04UØ[3,4]JZ	Supl/Abd Aorta, [Perc, Perc Endo], Synth Sub, NQ 252
ØMUJ*	Supl/Abd Bursa & Lgmt, Lt 153
ØMUH*	Supl/Abd Bursa & Lgmt, Rt 153
ØKUL*	Supl/Abd Muscle, Lt 140, 340
ØKUL[Ø,4][7,J,K]Z	Supl/Abd Muscle, Lt, [Opn, Perc Endo], [Auto Tissue Sub, Synth Sub, Nonauto Tissue Sub], NQ 215
ØKUK*	Supl/Abd Muscle, Rt 140, 340
ØKUK[Ø,4][7,J,K]Z	Supl/Abd Muscle, Rt, [Opn, Perc Endo], [Auto Tissue Sub, Synth Sub, Nonauto Tissue Sub], NQ 215
ØLUG*	Supl/Abd Tndn, Lt 142, 342
ØLUF*	Supl/Abd Tndn, Rt 142, 342
ØWUF*	Supl/Abd Wall 110, 356
ØWUF[7,J,K]Z	Supl/Abd Wall, Opn, [Auto Tissue Sub, Synth Sub, Nonauto Tissue Sub], NQ 460
ØØUL*	Supl/Abducens Nerve 23
ØØUR*	Supl/Accessory Nerve 24
ØQU5[Ø,3,4]JZ	Supl/Acetab, Lt, [Opn, Perc, Perc Endo], Synth Sub, NQ 348
ØQU4[Ø,3,4]JZ	Supl/Acetab, Rt, [Opn, Perc, Perc Endo], Synth Sub, NQ 348
ØQU5*	Supl/Acetabulum, Lt 156
ØQU4*	Supl/Acetabulum, Rt 156
ØØUN*	Supl/Acoustic Nerve 23
ØRUH*	Supl/Acromioclavicular Jt, Lt 148, 350
ØRUH[Ø,3,4][7,J,K]Z	Supl/Acromioclavicular Jt, Lt, [Opn, Perc, Perc Endo], [Auto Tissue Sub, Synth Sub, Nonauto Tissue Sub], NQ 457
ØRUG*	Supl/Acromioclavicular Jt, Rt 148, 350
ØRUG[Ø,3,4][7,J,K]Z	Supl/Acromioclavicular Jt, Rt, [Opn, Perc, Perc Endo], [Auto Tissue Sub, Synth Sub, Nonauto Tissue Sub], NQ 457
ØFUC*	Supl/Ampulla of Vater 120
ØDUR*	Supl/Anal Sphincter 110, 334
ØDUR[Ø,4][7,J,K]Z	Supl/Anal Sphincter, [Opn, Perc Endo], [Auto Tissue Sub, Synth Sub, Nonauto Tissue Sub], NQ 211, 449
ØMUR*	Supl/Ankle Bursa & Lgmt, Lt 154
ØMUQ*	Supl/Ankle Bursa & Lgmt, Rt 154
ØSUG*	Supl/Ankle Jt, Lt 158
ØSUF*	Supl/Ankle Jt, Rt 158
ØYUL*	Supl/Ankle Region, Lt 357
ØYUK*	Supl/Ankle Region, Rt 357
ØYUL[Ø,4][7,J,K]Z	Supl/Ankle Rgn, Lt, [Opn, Perc Endo], [Auto Tissue Sub, Synth Sub, Nonauto Tissue Sub], NQ 219, 462
ØYUK[Ø,4][7,J,K]Z	Supl/Ankle Rgn, Rt, [Opn, Perc Endo], [Auto Tissue Sub, Synth Sub, Nonauto Tissue Sub], NQ 219, 462
ØLUT*	Supl/Ankle Tndn, Lt 142, 342
ØLUS*	Supl/Ankle Tndn, Rt 142, 342
04UQ*	Supl/Ant Tibial Artery, Lt 84
04UQ[Ø,3,4][7,J]Z	Supl/Ant Tibial Artery, Lt, [Opn, Perc, Perc Endo], [Auto Tissue Sub, Synth Sub], NQ 324
04UP*	Supl/Ant Tibial Artery, Rt 84
04UP[Ø,3,4][7,J]Z	Supl/Ant Tibial Artery, Rt, [Opn, Perc, Perc Endo], [Auto Tissue Sub, Synth Sub], NQ 324
ØDUQ*	Supl/Anus 110, 334
Ø2UF*	Supl/Aortic Valve 71, 72
ØDUK*	Supl/Ascending Colon 107, 334
Ø2U5[Ø,3,4][7,8,K]Z	Supl/Atrial Septum, [Opn, Perc, Perc Endo], [Auto Tissue Sub, Zooplastic Tissue, Nonauto Tissue Sub], NQ 75
Ø2U5[3,4]JZ	Supl/Atrial Septum, [Perc, Perc Endo], Synth Sub, NQ 98
Ø2U7[Ø,3,4][7,8,K]Z	Supl/Atrium, Lt, [Opn, Perc, Perc Endo], [Auto Tissue Sub, Zooplastic Tissue, Nonauto Tissue Sub], NQ 75

Ø2U6[3,4][7,8,J,K]Z	Supl/Atrium, Rt, [Perc, Perc Endo], [Auto Tissue Sub, Zooplastic Tissue, Synth Sub, Nonauto Tissue Sub], NQ 93, 320
Ø2U6Ø[7,8,K]Z	Supl/Atrium, Rt, Opn, [Auto Tissue Sub, Zooplastic Tissue, Nonauto Tissue Sub], NQ 75
Ø9UAØ[7,J,K]Z	Supl/Auditory Ossicle, Lt, Opn, [Auto Tissue Sub, Synth Sub, Nonauto Tissue Sub], NQ 447
Ø9U9Ø[7,J,K]Z	Supl/Auditory Ossicle, Rt, Opn, [Auto Tissue Sub, Synth Sub, Nonauto Tissue Sub], NQ 447
ØXU5[Ø,4][7,J,K]Z	Supl/Axilla, Lt, [Opn, Perc Endo], [Auto Tissue Sub, Synth Sub, Nonauto Tissue Sub], NQ 461
ØXU5[Ø,4][J,K]Z	Supl/Axilla, Lt, [Opn, Perc Endo], [Synth Sub, Nonauto Tissue Sub], NQ 218, 356
ØXU5[Ø,4]7Z	Supl/Axilla, Lt, [Opn, Perc Endo], Auto Tissue Sub, NQ 127, 379, 380
ØXU4[Ø,4][7,J,K]Z	Supl/Axilla, Rt, [Opn, Perc Endo], [Auto Tissue Sub, Synth Sub, Nonauto Tissue Sub], NQ 461
ØXU4[Ø,4][J,K]Z	Supl/Axilla, Rt, [Opn, Perc Endo], [Synth Sub, Nonauto Tissue Sub], NQ 218, 356
ØXU4[Ø,4]7Z	Supl/Axilla, Rt, [Opn, Perc Endo], Auto Tissue Sub, NQ 127, 379, 380
Ø3U6[Ø,3,4][7,J]Z	Supl/Axillary Artery, Lt, [Opn, Perc, Perc Endo], [Auto Tissue Sub, Synth Sub], NQ 322
Ø3U5[Ø,3,4][7,J]Z	Supl/Axillary Artery, Rt, [Opn, Perc, Perc Endo], [Auto Tissue Sub, Synth Sub], NQ 322
Ø5U8[Ø,3,4][7,J]Z	Supl/Axillary Vein, Lt, [Opn, Perc, Perc Endo], [Auto Tissue Sub, Synth Sub], NQ 326
Ø5U7[Ø,3,4][7,J]Z	Supl/Axillary Vein, Rt, [Opn, Perc, Perc Endo], [Auto Tissue Sub, Synth Sub], NQ 326
Ø5UØ[Ø,3,4][7,J]Z	Supl/Azygos Vein, [Opn, Perc, Perc Endo], [Auto Tissue Sub, Synth Sub], NQ 326
Ø5UC[Ø,3,4][7,J]Z	Supl/Basilic Vein, Lt, [Opn, Perc, Perc Endo], [Auto Tissue Sub, Synth Sub], NQ 326
Ø5UB[Ø,3,4][7,J]Z	Supl/Basilic Vein, Rt, [Opn, Perc, Perc Endo], [Auto Tissue Sub, Synth Sub], NQ 326
ØTUB*	Supl/Bladder 248, 354
ØTUC*	Supl/Bladder Neck 250, 267
ØTUC[Ø,4,7,8]JZ	Supl/Bladder Neck, [Opn, Perc Endo, Via Natrl or Artfcl Opng, Via Natrl or Artfcl Opng Endo], Synth Sub, NQ 458
Ø3U8[Ø,3,4][7,J]Z	Supl/Brachial Artery, Lt, [Opn, Perc, Perc Endo], [Auto Tissue Sub, Synth Sub], NQ 322
Ø3U7[Ø,3,4][7,J]Z	Supl/Brachial Artery, Rt, [Opn, Perc, Perc Endo], [Auto Tissue Sub, Synth Sub], NQ 322
Ø5UA[Ø,3,4][7,J]Z	Supl/Brachial Vein, Lt, [Opn, Perc, Perc Endo], [Auto Tissue Sub, Synth Sub], NQ 326
Ø5U9[Ø,3,4][7,J]Z	Supl/Brachial Vein, Rt, [Opn, Perc, Perc Endo], [Auto Tissue Sub, Synth Sub], NQ 326
ØCU4*	Supl/Buccal Mucosa 56, 332
ØCU4[Ø,3,X][7,J,K]Z	Supl/Buccal Mucosa, [Opn, Perc, Ext], [Auto Tissue Sub, Synth Sub, Nonauto Tissue Sub], NQ 211, 448
ØYU1*	Supl/Buttock, Lt 357
ØYU1[Ø,4][7,J,K]Z	Supl/Buttock, Lt, [Opn, Perc Endo], [Auto Tissue Sub, Synth Sub, Nonauto Tissue Sub], NQ 219, 462
ØYUØ*	Supl/Buttock, Rt 357
ØYUØ[Ø,4][7,J,K]Z	Supl/Buttock, Rt, [Opn, Perc Endo], [Auto Tissue Sub, Synth Sub, Nonauto Tissue Sub], NQ 219, 462
ØBU2*	Supl/Carina 52, 331
ØRUR*	Supl/Carpal Jt, Lt 28, 147
ØRUR[Ø,3,4][7,J,K]Z	Supl/Carpal Jt, Lt, [Opn, Perc, Perc Endo], [Auto Tissue Sub, Synth Sub, Nonauto Tissue Sub], NQ 317
ØRUQ*	Supl/Carpal Jt, Rt 28, 147
ØRUQ[Ø,3,4][7,J,K]Z	Supl/Carpal Jt, Rt, [Opn, Perc, Perc Endo], [Auto Tissue Sub, Synth Sub, Nonauto Tissue Sub], NQ 317
ØPUN*	Supl/Carpal, Lt 150
ØPUN[Ø,3,4][7,J,K]Z	Supl/Carpal, Lt, [Opn, Perc, Perc Endo], [Auto Tissue Sub, Synth Sub, Nonauto Tissue Sub], NQ 315
ØPUM*	Supl/Carpal, Rt 150
ØPUM[Ø,3,4][7,J,K]Z	Supl/Carpal, Rt, [Opn, Perc, Perc Endo], [Auto Tissue Sub, Synth Sub, Nonauto Tissue Sub], NQ 315
ØDUH*	Supl/Cecum 107, 334
04U1*	Supl/Celiac Artery 84
04U1[Ø,3,4][7,J]Z	Supl/Celiac Artery, [Opn, Perc, Perc Endo], [Auto Tissue Sub, Synth Sub], NQ 324
Ø5UF[Ø,3,4][7,J]Z	Supl/Cephalic Vein, Lt, [Opn, Perc, Perc Endo], [Auto Tissue Sub, Synth Sub], NQ 326

04UJ*	Supl/Ext Iliac Artery, Lt 84
04UJ[0,3,4][7,J]Z	Supl/Ext Iliac Artery, Lt, [Opn, Perc, Perc Endo], [Auto Tissue Sub, Synth Sub], NQ 324
04UH*	Supl/Ext Iliac Artery, Rt 84
04UH[0,3,4][7,J]Z	Supl/Ext Iliac Artery, Rt, [Opn, Perc, Perc Endo], [Auto Tissue Sub, Synth Sub], NQ 324
06UG[0,3,4][7,J]Z	Supl/Ext Iliac Vein, Lt, [Opn, Perc, Perc Endo], [Auto Tissue Sub, Synth Sub], NQ 328
06UF[0,3,4][7,J]Z	Supl/Ext Iliac Vein, Rt, [Opn, Perc, Perc Endo], [Auto Tissue Sub, Synth Sub], NQ 328
05UQ[0,3,4][7,J]Z	Supl/Ext Jugular Vein, Lt, [Opn, Perc, Perc Endo], [Auto Tissue Sub, Synth Sub], NQ 326
05UP[0,3,4][7,J]Z	Supl/Ext Jugular Vein, Rt, [Opn, Perc, Perc Endo], [Auto Tissue Sub, Synth Sub], NQ 326
08UM*	Supl/Extraocular Muscle, Lt 43, 330
08UM[0,3][7,J,K]Z	Supl/Extraocular Muscle, Lt, [Opn, Perc], [Auto Tissue Sub, Synth Sub, Nonauto Tissue Sub], NQ 446
08UL*	Supl/Extraocular Muscle, Rt 43, 330
08UL[0,3][7,J,K]Z	Supl/Extraocular Muscle, Rt, [Opn, Perc], [Auto Tissue Sub, Synth Sub, Nonauto Tissue Sub], NQ 446
08U1*	Supl/Eye, Lt 43, 241, 330
08U1[0,3][7,J,K]Z	Supl/Eye, Lt, [Opn, Perc], [Auto Tissue Sub, Synth Sub, Nonauto Tissue Sub], NQ 446
08U0*	Supl/Eye, Rt 43, 241, 330
08U0[0,3][7,J,K]Z	Supl/Eye, Rt, [Opn, Perc], [Auto Tissue Sub, Synth Sub, Nonauto Tissue Sub], NQ 446
0WU2*	Supl/Face 356
03UR[0,3,4][7,J]Z	Supl/Face Artery, [Opn, Perc, Perc Endo], [Auto Tissue Sub, Synth Sub], NQ 322
05UV[0,3,4][7,J]Z	Supl/Face Vein, Lt, [Opn, Perc, Perc Endo], [Auto Tissue Sub, Synth Sub], NQ 326
05UT[0,3,4][7,J]Z	Supl/Face Vein, Rt, [Opn, Perc, Perc Endo], [Auto Tissue Sub, Synth Sub], NQ 326
0WU2[0,4][7,J,K]Z	Supl/Face, [Opn, Perc Endo], [Auto Tissue Sub, Synth Sub, Nonauto Tissue Sub], NQ 218
0WU2[0,4][J,K]Z	Supl/Face, [Opn, Perc Endo], [Synth Sub, Nonauto Tissue Sub] , NQ 55, 460
0WU2[0,4]7Z	Supl/Face, [Opn, Perc Endo], Auto Tissue Sub, NQ 28, 127, 378, 380
0KU1*	Supl/Facial Muscle 140, 340
0KU1[0,4][7,J]Z	Supl/Facial Muscle, [Opn, Perc Endo], [Auto Tissue Sub, Synth Sub, Nonauto Tissue Sub], NQ 215
00UM*	Supl/Facial Nerve 23
0UU6*	Supl/Fallopian Tube, Lt 263, 264, 266
0UU6[0,4,7,8][7,K]Z	Supl/Fallopian Tube, Lt, [Opn, Perc Endo, Via Natrl or Artfcl Opng, Via Natrl or Artfcl Opng Endo], [Auto Tissue Sub, Nonauto Tissue Sub], NQ 354
0UU5*	Supl/Fallopian Tube, Rt 263, 264, 266
0UU5[0,4,7,8][7,K]Z	Supl/Fallopian Tube, Rt, [Opn, Perc Endo, Via Natrl or Artfcl Opng, Via Natrl or Artfcl Opng Endo], [Auto Tissue Sub, Nonauto Tissue Sub], NQ 354
0UU7*	Supl/Fallopian Tubes, Bilat 263, 264, 266
0UU7[0,4,7,8][7,K]Z	Supl/Fallopian Tubes, Bilat, [Opn, Perc Endo, Via Natrl or Artfcl Opng, Via Natrl or Artfcl Opng Endo], [Auto Tissue Sub, Nonauto Tissue Sub], NQ 354
04UL*	Supl/Femor Artery, Lt 84
04UL[0,3,4][7,J]Z	Supl/Femor Artery, Lt, [Opn, Perc, Perc Endo], [Auto Tissue Sub, Synth Sub], NQ 324
04UK*	Supl/Femor Artery, Rt 84
04UK[0,3,4][7,J]Z	Supl/Femor Artery, Rt, [Opn, Perc, Perc Endo], [Auto Tissue Sub, Synth Sub], NQ 324
0YUE*	Supl/Femor Region, Bilat 110
0YU8*	Supl/Femor Region, Lt 110
0YU7*	Supl/Femor Region, Rt 110
0YUE[0,4][7,J,K]Z	Supl/Femor Rgn, Bilat, [Opn, Perc Endo], [Auto Tissue Sub, Synth Sub, Nonauto Tissue Sub], NQ 462
0YU8[0,4][7,J,K]Z	Supl/Femor Rgn, Lt, [Opn, Perc Endo], [Auto Tissue Sub, Synth Sub, Nonauto Tissue Sub], NQ 462
0YU7[0,4][7,J,K]Z	Supl/Femor Rgn, Rt, [Opn, Perc Endo], [Auto Tissue Sub, Synth Sub, Nonauto Tissue Sub], NQ 462
0QU9*	Supl/Femor Shaft, Lt 131, 348, 416
0QU8*	Supl/Femor Shaft, Rt 131, 348, 416
06UN[0,3,4][7,J]Z	Supl/Femor Vein, Lt, [Opn, Perc, Perc Endo], [Auto Tissue Sub, Synth Sub], NQ 328
06UM[0,3,4][7,J]Z	Supl/Femor Vein, Rt, [Opn, Perc, Perc Endo], [Auto Tissue Sub, Synth Sub], NQ 328
0QUK*	Supl/Fibula, Lt 133, 349
0QUJ*	Supl/Fibula, Rt 133, 349
0RUX*	Supl/Finger Phalangeal Jt, Lt 28, 147
0RUX[0,3,4][7,J,K]Z	Supl/Finger Phalangeal Jt, Lt, [Opn, Perc, Perc Endo], [Auto Tissue Sub, Synth Sub, Nonauto Tissue Sub], NQ 317
0RUW*	Supl/Finger Phalangeal Jt, Rt 28, 147
0RUW[0,3,4][7,J,K]Z	Supl/Finger Phalangeal Jt, Rt, [Opn, Perc, Perc Endo], [Auto Tissue Sub, Synth Sub, Nonauto Tissue Sub], NQ 317
0PUV*	Supl/Finger Phalanx, Lt 156
0PUT*	Supl/Finger Phalanx, Rt 156
04UW*	Supl/Foot Artery, Lt 84
04UW[0,3,4][7,J]Z	Supl/Foot Artery, Lt, [Opn, Perc, Perc Endo], [Auto Tissue Sub, Synth Sub], NQ 324
04UV*	Supl/Foot Artery, Rt 84
04UV[0,3,4][7,J]Z	Supl/Foot Artery, Rt, [Opn, Perc, Perc Endo], [Auto Tissue Sub, Synth Sub], NQ 324
0MUT*	Supl/Foot Bursa & Lgmt, Lt 154
0MUS*	Supl/Foot Bursa & Lgmt, Rt 154
0KUW*	Supl/Foot Muscle, Lt 140, 340
0KUW[0,4][7,J,K]Z	Supl/Foot Muscle, Lt, [Opn, Perc Endo], [Auto Tissue Sub, Synth Sub, Nonauto Tissue Sub], NQ 215
0KUV*	Supl/Foot Muscle, Rt 140, 340
0KUV[0,4][7,J,K]Z	Supl/Foot Muscle, Rt, [Opn, Perc Endo], [Auto Tissue Sub, Synth Sub, Nonauto Tissue Sub], NQ 215
0LUW*	Supl/Foot Tndn, Lt 142, 342
0LUV*	Supl/Foot Tndn, Rt 142, 342
06UV[0,3,4][7,J]Z	Supl/Foot Vein, Lt, [Opn, Perc, Perc Endo], [Auto Tissue Sub, Synth Sub], NQ 328
06UT[0,3,4][7,J]Z	Supl/Foot Vein, Rt, [Opn, Perc, Perc Endo], [Auto Tissue Sub, Synth Sub], NQ 328
0YUN*	Supl/Foot, Lt 357
0YUN[0,4][7,J,K]Z	Supl/Foot, Lt, [Opn, Perc Endo], [Auto Tissue Sub, Synth Sub, Nonauto Tissue Sub], NQ 219, 462
0YUM*	Supl/Foot, Rt 357
0YUM[0,4][7,J,K]Z	Supl/Foot, Rt, [Opn, Perc Endo], [Auto Tissue Sub, Synth Sub, Nonauto Tissue Sub], NQ 219, 462
0NU2*	Supl/Frontal Bone, Lt 10, 49, 154
0NU2[0,3,4][7,J,K]Z	Supl/Frontal Bone, Lt, [Opn, Perc, Perc Endo], [Auto Tissue Sub, Synth Sub, Nonauto Tissue Sub], NQ 14, 18
0NU2[0,3,4]JZ	Supl/Frontal Bone, Lt, [Opn, Perc, Perc Endo], Synth Sub, NQ 344, 415
0NU1*	Supl/Frontal Bone, Rt 10, 49, 154
0NU1[0,3,4][7,J,K]Z	Supl/Frontal Bone, Rt, [Opn, Perc, Perc Endo], [Auto Tissue Sub, Synth Sub, Nonauto Tissue Sub], NQ 14, 18
0NU1[0,3,4]JZ	Supl/Frontal Bone, Rt, [Opn, Perc, Perc Endo], Synth Sub, NQ 344, 415
04U2*	Supl/Gastric Artery 84
04U2[0,3,4][7,J]Z	Supl/Gastric Artery, [Opn, Perc, Perc Endo], [Auto Tissue Sub, Synth Sub], NQ 324
06U2[0,3,4][7,J]Z	Supl/Gastric Vein, [Opn, Perc, Perc Endo], [Auto Tissue Sub, Synth Sub], NQ 327
0PU8*	Supl/Glenoid Cavity, Lt 156
0PU8[0,3,4]JZ	Supl/Glenoid Cavity, Lt, [Opn, Perc, Perc Endo], Synth Sub, NQ 66, 347
0PU7*	Supl/Glenoid Cavity, Rt 156
0PU7[0,3,4]JZ	Supl/Glenoid Cavity, Rt, [Opn, Perc, Perc Endo], Synth Sub, NQ 66, 347
00UP*	Supl/Glossopharyngeal Nerve 24
0DUS*	Supl/Greater Omentum 112, 123, 334
0DUS[0,4][7,J,K]Z	Supl/Greater Omentum, [Opn, Perc Endo], [Auto Tissue Sub, Synth Sub, Nonauto Tissue Sub], NQ 300
06UQ[0,3,4][7,J]Z	Supl/Greater Saphenous Vein, Lt, [Opn, Perc, Perc Endo], [Auto Tissue Sub, Synth Sub], NQ 328
06UP[0,3,4][7,J]Z	Supl/Greater Saphenous Vein, Rt, [Opn, Perc, Perc Endo], [Auto Tissue Sub, Synth Sub], NQ 328
03UF[0,3,4][7,J]Z	Supl/Hand Artery, Lt, [Opn, Perc, Perc Endo], [Auto Tissue Sub, Synth Sub], NQ 322
03UD[0,3,4][7,J]Z	Supl/Hand Artery, Rt, [Opn, Perc, Perc Endo], [Auto Tissue Sub, Synth Sub], NQ 322
0MU8*	Supl/Hand Bursa & Lgmt, Lt 153
0MU7*	Supl/Hand Bursa & Lgmt, Rt 153

Code	Description
ØTU3*	Supl/Kidney Pelvis, Rt 249
ØMUP*	Supl/Knee Bursa & Lgmt, Lt 154
ØMUN*	Supl/Knee Bursa & Lgmt, Rt 154
ØSUD*	Supl/Knee Jt, Lt 158
ØSUC*	Supl/Knee Jt, Rt 158
ØYUG*	Supl/Knee Region, Lt 357
ØYUF*	Supl/Knee Region, Rt 357
ØYUG[Ø,4][7,J,K]Z	Supl/Knee Rgn, Lt, [Opn, Perc Endo], [Auto Tissue Sub, Synth Sub, Nonauto Tissue Sub], NQ 219, 462
ØYUF[Ø,4][7,J,K]Z	Supl/Knee Rgn, Rt, [Opn, Perc Endo], [Auto Tissue Sub, Synth Sub, Nonauto Tissue Sub], NQ 219, 462
ØLUR*	Supl/Knee Tndn, Lt 142, 342
ØLUQ*	Supl/Knee Tndn, Rt 142, 342
ØNUJ*	Supl/Lacrimal Bone, Lt 49
ØNUJ[Ø,3,4]JZ	Supl/Lacrimal Bone, Lt, [Opn, Perc, Perc Endo], Synth Sub, NQ 42, 154, 344
ØNUH*	Supl/Lacrimal Bone, Rt 49
ØNUH[Ø,3,4]JZ	Supl/Lacrimal Bone, Rt, [Opn, Perc, Perc Endo], Synth Sub, NQ 42, 154, 344
Ø8UY*	Supl/Lacrimal Duct, Lt 43, 330
Ø8UY[Ø,3,7,8][7,J,K]Z	Supl/Lacrimal Duct, Lt, [Opn, Perc, Via Natrl or Artfcl Opng, Via Natrl or Artfcl Opng Endo], [Auto Tissue Sub, Synth Sub, Nonauto Tissue Sub], NQ 210, 446
Ø8UX*	Supl/Lacrimal Duct, Rt 43, 330
Ø8UX[Ø,3,7,8][7,J,K]Z	Supl/Lacrimal Duct, Rt, [Opn, Perc, Via Natrl or Artfcl Opng, Via Natrl or Artfcl Opng Endo], [Auto Tissue Sub, Synth Sub, Nonauto Tissue Sub], NQ 210, 446
ØDUE*	Supl/Large Intestine 107, 334
ØDUG*	Supl/Large Intestine, Lt 107, 334
ØDUF*	Supl/Large Intestine, Rt 107, 334
ØCUS*	Supl/Larynx 53, 65, 332
ØDUT*	Supl/Lesser Omentum 112, 123, 334
ØDUT[Ø,4][7,J,K]Z	Supl/Lesser Omentum, [Opn, Perc Endo], [Auto Tissue Sub, Synth Sub, Nonauto Tissue Sub], NQ 300
Ø6US[Ø,3,4][7,J]Z	Supl/Lesser Saphenous Vein, Lt, [Opn, Perc, Perc Endo], [Auto Tissue Sub, Synth Sub], NQ 328
Ø6UR[Ø,3,4][7,J]Z	Supl/Lesser Saphenous Vein, Rt, [Opn, Perc, Perc Endo], [Auto Tissue Sub, Synth Sub], NQ 328
ØXUW[Ø,4][7,J,K]Z	Supl/Little Finger, Lt, [Opn, Perc Endo], [Auto Tissue Sub, Synth Sub, Nonauto Tissue Sub], NQ 461
ØXUW[Ø,4][J,K]Z	Supl/Little Finger, Lt, [Opn, Perc Endo], [Synth Sub, Nonauto Tissue Sub], NQ 218, 357
ØXUW[Ø,4]7Z	Supl/Little Finger, Lt, [Opn, Perc Endo], Auto Tissue Sub, NQ 29, 92, 151, 207, 317, 379, 381
ØXUV[Ø,4][7,J,K]Z	Supl/Little Finger, Rt, [Opn, Perc Endo], [Auto Tissue Sub, Synth Sub, Nonauto Tissue Sub], NQ 461
ØXUV[Ø,4][J,K]Z	Supl/Little Finger, Rt, [Opn, Perc Endo], [Synth Sub, Nonauto Tissue Sub], NQ 218, 357
ØXUV[Ø,4]7Z	Supl/Little Finger, Rt, [Opn, Perc Endo], Auto Tissue Sub, NQ 29, 92, 151, 207, 317, 379, 381
ØSU2*	Supl/Lumbar Vert Disc 160, 161, 352
ØSU2[Ø,3,4][7,J,K]Z	Supl/Lumbar Vert Disc, [Opn, Perc, Perc Endo], [Auto Tissue Sub, Synth Sub, Nonauto Tissue Sub], NQ 20, 302
ØSUØ[Ø,3,4][7,K]Z	Supl/Lumbar Vert Jt, [Opn, Perc, Perc Endo], [Auto Tissue Sub, Nonauto Tissue Sub], NQ 158
ØSUØ[Ø,3,4]JZ	Supl/Lumbar Vert Jt, [Opn, Perc, Perc Endo], Synth Sub, NQ 20, 160, 161, 352
ØQUØ*	Supl/Lumbar Vertebra 156
ØQUØ[Ø,3,4]JZ	Supl/Lumbar Vertebra, [Opn, Perc, Perc Endo], Synth Sub, NQ 348
ØSU4*	Supl/Lumbosacral Disc 160, 161, 352
ØSU4[Ø,3,4][7,J,K]Z	Supl/Lumbosacral Disc, [Opn, Perc, Perc Endo], [Auto Tissue Sub, Synth Sub, Nonauto Tissue Sub], NQ 20, 302
ØSU3[Ø,3,4][7,K]Z	Supl/Lumbosacral Jt, [Opn, Perc, Perc Endo], [Auto Tissue Sub, Nonauto Tissue Sub], NQ 158
ØSU3[Ø,3,4]JZ	Supl/Lumbosacral Jt, [Opn, Perc, Perc Endo], Synth Sub, NQ 20, 160, 161, 352
ØKUB*	Supl/Lwr Arm and Wrist Muscle, Lt 140, 340
ØKUB[Ø,4][7,J,K]Z	Supl/Lwr Arm and Wrist Muscle, Lt, [Opn, Perc Endo], [Auto Tissue Sub, Synth Sub, Nonauto Tissue Sub], NQ 215
ØKU9*	Supl/Lwr Arm and Wrist Muscle, Rt 140, 340
ØKU9[Ø,4][7,J,K]Z	Supl/Lwr Arm and Wrist Muscle, Rt, [Opn, Perc Endo], [Auto Tissue Sub, Synth Sub, Nonauto Tissue Sub], NQ 215
ØLU6*	Supl/Lwr Arm and Wrist Tndn, Lt 142, 342
ØLU5*	Supl/Lwr Arm and Wrist Tndn, Rt 142, 342
ØXUF[Ø,4][7,J,K]Z	Supl/Lwr Arm, Lt, [Opn, Perc Endo], [Auto Tissue Sub, Synth Sub, Nonauto Tissue Sub], NQ 461
ØXUF[Ø,4][J,K]Z	Supl/Lwr Arm, Lt, [Opn, Perc Endo], [Synth Sub, Nonauto Tissue Sub], NQ 218, 356
ØXUF[Ø,4]7Z	Supl/Lwr Arm, Lt, [Opn, Perc Endo], Auto Tissue Sub, NQ 127, 379, 381
ØXUD[Ø,4][7,J,K]Z	Supl/Lwr Arm, Rt, [Opn, Perc Endo], [Auto Tissue Sub, Synth Sub, Nonauto Tissue Sub], NQ 461
ØXUD[Ø,4][J,K]Z	Supl/Lwr Arm, Rt, [Opn, Perc Endo], [Synth Sub, Nonauto Tissue Sub], NQ 218, 356
ØXUD[Ø,4]7Z	Supl/Lwr Arm, Rt, [Opn, Perc Endo], Auto Tissue Sub, NQ 127, 379, 381
Ø4UY*	Supl/Lwr Artery 84
Ø4UY[Ø,3,4][7,J]Z	Supl/Lwr Artery, [Opn, Perc, Perc Endo], [Auto Tissue Sub, Synth Sub], NQ 324
ØWUL[Ø,4][7,J,K]Z	Supl/Lwr Back, [Opn, Perc Endo], [Auto Tissue Sub, Synth Sub, Nonauto Tissue Sub], NQ 460
ØWUL[Ø,4][J,K]Z	Supl/Lwr Back, [Opn, Perc Endo], [Synth Sub, Nonauto Tissue Sub], NQ 218, 356
ØWUL[Ø,4]7Z	Supl/Lwr Back, [Opn, Perc Endo], Auto Tissue Sub, NQ 127, 378, 380
ØMUW*	Supl/Lwr Extr Bursa & Lgmt, Lt 144
ØMUV*	Supl/Lwr Extr Bursa & Lgmt, Rt 144
ØYUB*	Supl/Lwr Extr, Lt 357
ØYUB[Ø,4][7,J,K]Z	Supl/Lwr Extr, Lt, [Opn, Perc Endo], [Auto Tissue Sub, Synth Sub, Nonauto Tissue Sub], NQ 219, 462
ØYU9*	Supl/Lwr Extr, Rt 357
ØYU9[Ø,4][7,J,K]Z	Supl/Lwr Extr, Rt, [Opn, Perc Endo], [Auto Tissue Sub, Synth Sub, Nonauto Tissue Sub], NQ 219, 462
Ø8UR*	Supl/Lwr Eyelid, Lt 43, 330
Ø8UR[Ø,3,X][7,J,K]Z	Supl/Lwr Eyelid, Lt, [Opn, Perc, Ext], [Auto Tissue Sub, Synth Sub, Nonauto Tissue Sub], NQ 210, 446
Ø8UR[Ø,3,X]JZ	Supl/Lwr Eyelid, Lt, [Opn, Perc, Ext], Synth Sub, NQ 241
Ø8UQ*	Supl/Lwr Eyelid, Rt 43, 330
Ø8UQ[Ø,3,X][7,J,K]Z	Supl/Lwr Eyelid, Rt, [Opn, Perc, Ext], [Auto Tissue Sub, Synth Sub, Nonauto Tissue Sub], NQ 210, 446
Ø8UQ[Ø,3,X]JZ	Supl/Lwr Eyelid, Rt, [Opn, Perc, Ext], Synth Sub, NQ 241
ØQUC*	Supl/Lwr Femur, Lt 131, 349, 416
ØQUB*	Supl/Lwr Femur, Rt 131, 349, 416
ØCU6*	Supl/Lwr Gingiva 56, 332
ØWU5*	Supl/Lwr Jaw 49, 158, 356
ØWU5[Ø,4]7Z	Supl/Lwr Jaw, [Opn, Perc Endo], Auto Tissue Sub, NQ 28, 218
ØKUT*	Supl/Lwr Leg Muscle, Lt 140, 340
ØKUT[Ø,4][7,J,K]Z	Supl/Lwr Leg Muscle, Lt, [Opn, Perc Endo], [Auto Tissue Sub, Synth Sub, Nonauto Tissue Sub], NQ 215
ØKUS*	Supl/Lwr Leg Muscle, Rt 140, 340
ØKUS[Ø,4][7,J,K]Z	Supl/Lwr Leg Muscle, Rt, [Opn, Perc Endo], [Auto Tissue Sub, Synth Sub, Nonauto Tissue Sub], NQ 215
ØLUP*	Supl/Lwr Leg Tndn, Lt 142, 342
ØLUN*	Supl/Lwr Leg Tndn, Rt 142, 342
ØYUJ*	Supl/Lwr Leg, Lt 357
ØYUJ[Ø,4][7,J,K]Z	Supl/Lwr Leg, Lt, [Opn, Perc Endo], [Auto Tissue Sub, Synth Sub, Nonauto Tissue Sub], NQ 219, 462
ØYUH*	Supl/Lwr Leg, Rt 357
ØYUH[Ø,4][7,J,K]Z	Supl/Lwr Leg, Rt, [Opn, Perc Endo], [Auto Tissue Sub, Synth Sub, Nonauto Tissue Sub], NQ 219, 462
ØCU1*	Supl/Lwr Lip 56, 332
ØCU1[Ø,3,X][7,J,K]Z	Supl/Lwr Lip, [Opn, Perc, Ext], [Auto Tissue Sub, Synth Sub, Nonauto Tissue Sub], NQ 211, 448
Ø6UY[Ø,3,4][7,J]Z	Supl/Lwr Vein, [Opn, Perc, Perc Endo], [Auto Tissue Sub, Synth Sub], NQ 328
Ø7UD*	Supl/Lymphatic, Aortic 329
Ø7UD[Ø,4][7,J,K]Z	Supl/Lymphatic, Aortic, [Opn, Perc Endo], [Auto Tissue Sub, Synth Sub, Nonauto Tissue Sub], NQ 291, 298
Ø7UØ*	Supl/Lymphatic, Head 329
Ø7UØ[Ø,4][7,J,K]Z	Supl/Lymphatic, Head, [Opn, Perc Endo], [Auto Tissue Sub, Synth Sub, Nonauto Tissue Sub], NQ 291, 298
Ø7U9*	Supl/Lymphatic, Int Mammary, Lt 329
Ø7U9[Ø,4][7,J,K]Z	Supl/Lymphatic, Int Mammary, Lt, [Opn, Perc Endo], [Auto Tissue Sub, Synth Sub, Nonauto Tissue Sub], NQ 291, 298
Ø7U8*	Supl/Lymphatic, Int Mammary, Rt 329

07U8[0,4][7,J,K]Z	Supl/Lymphatic, Int Mammary, Rt, [Opn, Perc Endo], [Auto Tissue Sub, Synth Sub, Nonauto Tissue Sub], NQ 291, 298
07U6*	Supl/Lymphatic, Lt Axillary 329
07U6[0,4][7,J,K]Z	Supl/Lymphatic, Lt Axillary, [Opn, Perc Endo], [Auto Tissue Sub, Synth Sub, Nonauto Tissue Sub], NQ 291, 298
07UJ*	Supl/Lymphatic, Lt Inguinal 329
07UJ[0,4][7,J,K]Z	Supl/Lymphatic, Lt Inguinal, [Opn, Perc Endo], [Auto Tissue Sub, Synth Sub, Nonauto Tissue Sub], NQ 291, 298
07UG*	Supl/Lymphatic, Lt Lwr Extr 329
07UG[0,4][7,J,K]Z	Supl/Lymphatic, Lt Lwr Extr, [Opn, Perc Endo], [Auto Tissue Sub, Synth Sub, Nonauto Tissue Sub], NQ 291, 298
07U2*	Supl/Lymphatic, Lt Neck 329
07U2[0,4][7,J,K]Z	Supl/Lymphatic, Lt Neck, [Opn, Perc Endo], [Auto Tissue Sub, Synth Sub, Nonauto Tissue Sub], NQ 291, 298
07U4*	Supl/Lymphatic, Lt Upr Extr 329
07U4[0,4][7,J,K]Z	Supl/Lymphatic, Lt Upr Extr, [Opn, Perc Endo], [Auto Tissue Sub, Synth Sub, Nonauto Tissue Sub], NQ 291, 298
07UB*	Supl/Lymphatic, Mesenteric 329
07UB[0,4][7,J,K]Z	Supl/Lymphatic, Mesenteric, [Opn, Perc Endo], [Auto Tissue Sub, Synth Sub, Nonauto Tissue Sub], NQ 291, 298
07UC*	Supl/Lymphatic, Pelvis 329
07UC[0,4][7,J,K]Z	Supl/Lymphatic, Pelvis, [Opn, Perc Endo], [Auto Tissue Sub, Synth Sub, Nonauto Tissue Sub], NQ 291, 298
07U5*	Supl/Lymphatic, Rt Axillary 329
07U5[0,4][7,J,K]Z	Supl/Lymphatic, Rt Axillary, [Opn, Perc Endo], [Auto Tissue Sub, Synth Sub, Nonauto Tissue Sub], NQ 291, 298
07UH*	Supl/Lymphatic, Rt Inguinal 329
07UH[0,4][7,J,K]Z	Supl/Lymphatic, Rt Inguinal, [Opn, Perc Endo], [Auto Tissue Sub, Synth Sub, Nonauto Tissue Sub], NQ 291, 298
07UF*	Supl/Lymphatic, Rt Lwr Extr 329
07UF[0,4][7,J,K]Z	Supl/Lymphatic, Rt Lwr Extr, [Opn, Perc Endo], [Auto Tissue Sub, Synth Sub, Nonauto Tissue Sub], NQ 291, 298
07U1*	Supl/Lymphatic, Rt Neck 329
07U1[0,4][7,J,K]Z	Supl/Lymphatic, Rt Neck, [Opn, Perc Endo], [Auto Tissue Sub, Synth Sub, Nonauto Tissue Sub], NQ 291, 298
07U3*	Supl/Lymphatic, Rt Upr Extr 329
07U3[0,4][7,J,K]Z	Supl/Lymphatic, Rt Upr Extr, [Opn, Perc Endo], [Auto Tissue Sub, Synth Sub, Nonauto Tissue Sub], NQ 291, 298
07U7*	Supl/Lymphatic, Thorax 329
07U7[0,4][7,J,K]Z	Supl/Lymphatic, Thorax, [Opn, Perc Endo], [Auto Tissue Sub, Synth Sub, Nonauto Tissue Sub], NQ 291, 298
0NUV*	Supl/Mandible, Lt 49, 155, 344
0NUV[0,3,4][7,J,K]Z	Supl/Mandible, Lt, [Opn, Perc, Perc Endo], [Auto Tissue Sub, Synth Sub, Nonauto Tissue Sub], NQ 216
0NUT*	Supl/Mandible, Rt 49, 155, 344
0NUT[0,3,4][7,J,K]Z	Supl/Mandible, Rt, [Opn, Perc, Perc Endo], [Auto Tissue Sub, Synth Sub, Nonauto Tissue Sub], NQ 216
0NUS*	Supl/Maxilla, Lt 49, 344
0NUR*	Supl/Maxilla, Rt 49, 344
0WUC*	Supl/Mediastinum 66, 356
0DUV*	Supl/Mesentery 112, 123, 334
0DUV[0,4][7,J,K]Z	Supl/Mesentery, [Opn, Perc Endo], [Auto Tissue Sub, Synth Sub, Nonauto Tissue Sub], NQ 300
0PUQ*	Supl/Metacarpal, Lt 150
0PUQ[0,3,4][7,J,K]Z	Supl/Metacarpal, Lt, [Opn, Perc, Perc Endo], [Auto Tissue Sub, Synth Sub, Nonauto Tissue Sub], NQ 315
0PUP*	Supl/Metacarpal, Rt 150
0PUP[0,3,4][7,J,K]Z	Supl/Metacarpal, Rt, [Opn, Perc, Perc Endo], [Auto Tissue Sub, Synth Sub, Nonauto Tissue Sub], NQ 315
0RUT*	Supl/Metacarpocarpal Jt, Lt 28, 147
0RUT[0,3,4][7,J,K]Z	Supl/Metacarpocarpal Jt, Lt, [Opn, Perc, Perc Endo], [Auto Tissue Sub, Synth Sub, Nonauto Tissue Sub], NQ 317
0RUS*	Supl/Metacarpocarpal Jt, Rt 28, 147
0RUS[0,3,4][7,J,K]Z	Supl/Metacarpocarpal Jt, Rt, [Opn, Perc, Perc Endo], [Auto Tissue Sub, Synth Sub, Nonauto Tissue Sub], NQ 317
0RUV*	Supl/Metacarpophalangeal Jt, Lt 28, 147
0RUV[0,3,4][7,J,K]Z	Supl/Metacarpophalangeal Jt, Lt, [Opn, Perc, Perc Endo], [Auto Tissue Sub, Synth Sub, Nonauto Tissue Sub], NQ 317
0RUU*	Supl/Metacarpophalangeal Jt, Rt 28, 147
0RUU[0,3,4][7,J,K]Z	Supl/Metacarpophalangeal Jt, Rt, [Opn, Perc, Perc Endo], [Auto Tissue Sub, Synth Sub, Nonauto Tissue Sub], NQ 317
0SUN*	Supl/Metatarsal-Phalangeal Jt, Lt 158
0SUM*	Supl/Metatarsal-Phalangeal Jt, Rt 158

0SUL*	Supl/Metatarsal-Tarsal Jt, Lt 158
0SUK*	Supl/Metatarsal-Tarsal Jt, Rt 158
0QUP*	Supl/Metatarsal, Lt 145, 349
0QUN*	Supl/Metatarsal, Rt 145, 349
09U60[7,J,K]Z	Supl/Mid Ear, Lt, Opn, [Auto Tissue Sub, Synth Sub, Nonauto Tissue Sub], NQ 447
09U50[7,J,K]Z	Supl/Mid Ear, Rt, Opn, [Auto Tissue Sub, Synth Sub, Nonauto Tissue Sub], NQ 447
0XUR[0,4][7,J,K]Z	Supl/Mid Finger, Lt, [Opn, Perc Endo], [Auto Tissue Sub, Synth Sub, Nonauto Tissue Sub], NQ 461
0XUR[0,4][J,K]Z	Supl/Mid Finger, Lt, [Opn, Perc Endo], [Synth Sub, Nonauto Tissue Sub], NQ 218, 357
0XUR[0,4]7Z	Supl/Mid Finger, Lt, [Opn, Perc Endo], Auto Tissue Sub, NQ 29, 92, 151, 207, 317, 379, 381
0XUQ[0,4][7,J,K]Z	Supl/Mid Finger, Rt, [Opn, Perc Endo], [Auto Tissue Sub, Synth Sub, Nonauto Tissue Sub], NQ 461
0XUQ[0,4][J,K]Z	Supl/Mid Finger, Rt, [Opn, Perc Endo], [Synth Sub, Nonauto Tissue Sub], NQ 218, 357
0XUQ[0,4]7Z	Supl/Mid Finger, Rt, [Opn, Perc Endo], Auto Tissue Sub, NQ 29, 92, 151, 207, 317, 379, 381
0NUB*	Supl/Nasal Bone 54, 154, 344
0NUB[0,3,4][7,J,K]Z	Supl/Nasal Bone, [Opn, Perc, Perc Endo], [Auto Tissue Sub, Synth Sub, Nonauto Tissue Sub], NQ 216, 455
09UM*	Supl/Nasal Septum 153, 331
09UM[0,3,4][7,J,K]Z	Supl/Nasal Septum, [Opn, Perc, Perc Endo], [Auto Tissue Sub, Synth Sub, Nonauto Tissue Sub], NQ 210, 447
09UL*	Supl/Nasal Turbinate 331
09UL[0,3,4,7,8][7,J,K]Z	Supl/Nasal Turbinate, [Opn, Perc, Perc Endo, Via Natrl or Artfcl Opng, Via Natrl or Artfcl Opng Endo], [Auto Tissue Sub, Synth Sub, Nonauto Tissue Sub], NQ 210, 447
09UN*	Supl/Nasopharynx 25, 331
09UN[0,7,8][7,J,K]Z	Supl/Nasopharynx, [Opn, Via Natrl or Artfcl Opng, Via Natrl or Artfcl Opng Endo], [Auto Tissue Sub, Synth Sub, Nonauto Tissue Sub], NQ 447
0KU3*	Supl/Neck Muscle, Lt 140, 340
0KU3[0,4][7,J,K]Z	Supl/Neck Muscle, Lt, [Opn, Perc Endo], [Auto Tissue Sub, Synth Sub, Nonauto Tissue Sub], NQ 215
0KU2*	Supl/Neck Muscle, Rt 140, 340
0KU2[0,4][7,J,K]Z	Supl/Neck Muscle, Rt, [Opn, Perc Endo], [Auto Tissue Sub, Synth Sub, Nonauto Tissue Sub], NQ 215
0WU6[0,4][7,J,K]Z	Supl/Neck, [Opn, Perc Endo], [Auto Tissue Sub, Synth Sub, Nonauto Tissue Sub], NQ 460
0WU6[0,4][J,K]Z	Supl/Neck, [Opn, Perc Endo], [Synth Sub, Nonauto Tissue Sub], NQ 55, 218, 356
0WU6[0,4]7Z	Supl/Neck, [Opn, Perc Endo], Auto Tissue Sub, NQ 127, 378, 380
0HUX*	Supl/Nipple, Lt 337
0HUW*	Supl/Nipple, Rt 337
09UK*	Supl/Nose 153, 331
09UK[0,X][7,J,K]Z	Supl/Nose, [Opn, Ext], [Auto Tissue Sub, Synth Sub, Nonauto Tissue Sub], NQ 210, 447
0NU8*	Supl/Occipital Bone, Lt 10, 49, 154
0NU8[0,3,4][7,J,K]Z	Supl/Occipital Bone, Lt, [Opn, Perc, Perc Endo], [Auto Tissue Sub, Synth Sub, Nonauto Tissue Sub], NQ 14, 18
0NU8[0,3,4]JZ	Supl/Occipital Bone, Lt, [Opn, Perc, Perc Endo], Synth Sub, NQ 344, 415
0NU7*	Supl/Occipital Bone, Rt 10, 49, 154
0NU7[0,3,4][7,J,K]Z	Supl/Occipital Bone, Rt, [Opn, Perc, Perc Endo], [Auto Tissue Sub, Synth Sub, Nonauto Tissue Sub], NQ 14
0NU7[0,3,4][7,J,K]Z	Supl/Occipital Bone, Rt, [Opn, Perc, Perc Endo], [Auto Tissue Sub, Synth Sub, Nonauto Tissue Sub], NQ 18
0NU7[0,3,4]JZ	Supl/Occipital Bone, Rt, [Opn, Perc, Perc Endo], Synth Sub, NQ 344, 415
0RU0[0,3,4][7,K]Z	Supl/Occipital-cervical Jt, [Opn, Perc, Perc Endo], [Auto Tissue Sub, Nonauto Tissue Sub], NQ 157
0RU0[0,3,4]JZ	Supl/Occipital-cervical Jt, [Opn, Perc, Perc Endo], Synth Sub, NQ 20, 160, 161, 350
00UH*	Supl/Oculomotor Nerve 23
00UF*	Supl/Olfactory Nerve 23
00UG*	Supl/Optic Nerve 23
0NUQ*	Supl/Orbit, Lt 49
0NUQ[0,3,4]JZ	Supl/Orbit, Lt, [Opn, Perc, Perc Endo], Synth Sub, NQ 42, 344, 455
0NUP*	Supl/Orbit, Rt 49

ØNUP[Ø,3,4]JZ	Supl/Orbit, Rt, [Opn, Perc, Perc Endo], Synth Sub, NQ 42, 344, 455
ØNUL*	Supl/Palatine Bone, Lt 49
ØNUL[Ø,3,4]JZ	Supl/Palatine Bone, Lt, [Opn, Perc, Perc Endo], Synth Sub, NQ 42, 154, 344
ØNUK*	Supl/Palatine Bone, Rt 49
ØNUK[Ø,3,4]JZ	Supl/Palatine Bone, Rt, [Opn, Perc, Perc Endo], Synth Sub, NQ 42, 154, 344
ØFUD*	Supl/Pancreatic Duct 119
ØFUD[3,4]7Z	Supl/Pancreatic Duct, [Perc, Perc Endo], Auto Tissue Sub, NQ 113, 301
ØFUF*	Supl/Pancreatic Duct, Accessory 119
Ø2UD[Ø,3,4][7,8,J,K]Z	Supl/Papillary Muscle, [Opn, Perc, Perc Endo], [Auto Tissue Sub, Zooplastic Tissue, Synth Sub, Nonauto Tissue Sub], NQ 75
ØNU4*	Supl/Parietal Bone, Lt 10, 49, 154
ØNU4[Ø,3,4][7,J,K]Z	Supl/Parietal Bone, Lt, [Opn, Perc, Perc Endo], [Auto Tissue Sub, Synth Sub, Nonauto Tissue Sub], NQ 14, 18
ØNU4[Ø,3,4]JZ	Supl/Parietal Bone, Lt, [Opn, Perc, Perc Endo], Synth Sub, NQ 344, 415
ØNU3*	Supl/Parietal Bone, Rt 49, 154
ØNU3[Ø,3,4][7,J,K]Z	Supl/Parietal Bone, Rt, [Opn, Perc, Perc Endo], [Auto Tissue Sub, Synth Sub, Nonauto Tissue Sub], NQ 14
ØNU3[Ø,3,4][7,J,K]Z	Supl/Parietal Bone, Rt, [Opn, Perc, Perc Endo], [Auto Tissue Sub, Synth Sub, Nonauto Tissue Sub], NQ 18
ØNU3[Ø,3,4]JZ	Supl/Parietal Bone, Rt, [Opn, Perc, Perc Endo], Synth Sub, NQ 344, 415
ØQUF*	Supl/Patella, Lt 132, 349
ØQUD*	Supl/Patella, Rt 132, 349
ØQU3*	Supl/Pelvic Bone, Lt 156
ØQU2*	Supl/Pelvic Bone, Rt 156
ØVUS[Ø,4][7,K]Z	Supl/Penis, [Opn, Perc Endo], [Auto Tissue Sub, Nonauto Tissue Sub], NQ 355
ØVUS[Ø,4][7,J,K]Z	Supl/Penis, [Opn, Perc Endo], [Auto Tissue Sub, Synth Sub, Nonauto Tissue Sub], NQ 257
ØVUS[Ø,4]JZ	Supl/Penis, [Opn, Perc Endo], Synth Sub, NQ 254, 459
Ø2UN*	Supl/Pericardium 320
Ø2UN[Ø,3,4][7,8,J,K]Z	Supl/Pericardium, [Opn, Perc, Perc Endo], [Auto Tissue Sub, Zooplastic Tissue, Synth Sub, Nonauto Tissue Sub], NQ 93
ØMUK*	Supl/Perineum Bursa & Lgmt 154
ØKUM*	Supl/Perineum Muscle 140, 340
ØKUM[Ø,4][7,J,K]Z	Supl/Perineum Muscle, [Opn, Perc Endo], [Auto Tissue Sub, Synth Sub, Nonauto Tissue Sub], NQ 215
ØLUH*	Supl/Perineum Tndn 142, 342
ØWUN*	Supl/Perineum, Female 267, 275, 356
ØWUN[Ø,4][7,J,K]Z	Supl/Perineum, Female, [Opn, Perc Endo], [Auto Tissue Sub, Synth Sub, Nonauto Tissue Sub], NQ 460
ØWUM[Ø,4][7,J,K]Z	Supl/Perineum, Male, [Opn, Perc Endo], [Auto Tissue Sub, Synth Sub, Nonauto Tissue Sub], NQ 460
ØWUM[Ø,4][J,K]Z	Supl/Perineum, Male, [Opn, Perc Endo], [Synth Sub, Nonauto Tissue Sub], NQ 218, 356
ØWUM[Ø,4]7Z	Supl/Perineum, Male, [Opn, Perc Endo], Auto Tissue Sub, NQ 257
ØDUW*	Supl/Peritoneum 112, 123, 334
ØDUW[Ø,4][7,J,K]Z	Supl/Peritoneum, [Opn, Perc Endo], [Auto Tissue Sub, Synth Sub, Nonauto Tissue Sub], NQ 300
Ø4UU*	Supl/Peroneal Artery, Lt 84
Ø4UU[Ø,3,4][7,J]Z	Supl/Peroneal Artery, Lt, [Opn, Perc, Perc Endo], [Auto Tissue Sub, Synth Sub], NQ 324
Ø4UT*	Supl/Peroneal Artery, Rt 84
Ø4UT[Ø,3,4][7,J]Z	Supl/Peroneal Artery, Rt, [Opn, Perc, Perc Endo], [Auto Tissue Sub, Synth Sub], NQ 324
ØCUM*	Supl/Pharynx 25, 53, 332
ØCUM[Ø,7,8][7,J,K]Z	Supl/Pharynx, [Opn, Via Natrl or Artfcl Opng, Via Natrl or Artfcl Opng Endo], [Auto Tissue Sub, Synth Sub, Nonauto Tissue Sub], NQ 448
Ø4UN*	Supl/Popliteal Artery, Lt 84
Ø4UN[Ø,3,4][7,J]Z	Supl/Popliteal Artery, Lt, [Opn, Perc, Perc Endo], [Auto Tissue Sub, Synth Sub], NQ 324
Ø4UM*	Supl/Popliteal Artery, Rt 84
Ø4UM[Ø,3,4][7,J]Z	Supl/Popliteal Artery, Rt, [Opn, Perc, Perc Endo], [Auto Tissue Sub, Synth Sub], NQ 324
Ø6U8[Ø,3,4][7,J]Z	Supl/Portal Vein, [Opn, Perc, Perc Endo], [Auto Tissue Sub, Synth Sub], NQ 327

Ø4US[Ø,3,4][7,J]Z	Supl/Post Tibial Artery, Lt, [Opn, Perc, Perc Endo], [Auto Tissue Sub, Synth Sub], NQ 324
Ø4UR[Ø,3,4][7,J]Z	Supl/Post Tibial Artery, Rt, [Opn, Perc, Perc Endo], [Auto Tissue Sub, Synth Sub], NQ 324
Ø4US*	Supl/Posterior Tibial Artery, Lt 84
Ø4UR*	Supl/Posterior Tibial Artery, Rt 84
ØVUT*	Supl/Prepuce 355
ØVUT[Ø,4,X][7,J,K]Z	Supl/Prepuce, [Opn, Perc Endo, Ext], [Auto Tissue Sub, Synth Sub, Nonauto Tissue Sub], NQ 217, 257, 459
Ø2UR*	Supl/Pulmn Artery, Lt 80, 320
Ø2UQ*	Supl/Pulmn Artery, Rt 80, 320
Ø2UP*	Supl/Pulmn Trunk 80, 320
Ø2UH*	Supl/Pulmn Valve 71, 72
Ø2UT*	Supl/Pulmn Vein, Lt 80, 320
Ø2US*	Supl/Pulmn Vein, Rt 80, 320
Ø3UC[Ø,3,4][7,J]Z	Supl/Radial Artery, Lt, [Opn, Perc, Perc Endo], [Auto Tissue Sub, Synth Sub], NQ 322
Ø3UB[Ø,3,4][7,J]Z	Supl/Radial Artery, Rt, [Opn, Perc, Perc Endo], [Auto Tissue Sub, Synth Sub], NQ 322
ØPUJ*	Supl/Radius, Lt 149, 347
ØPUJ[Ø,3,4][7,K]Z	Supl/Radius, Lt, [Opn, Perc, Perc Endo], [Auto Tissue Sub, Nonauto Tissue Sub], NQ 456
ØPUH*	Supl/Radius, Rt 149, 347
ØPUH[Ø,3,4][7,K]Z	Supl/Radius, Rt, [Opn, Perc, Perc Endo], [Auto Tissue Sub, Nonauto Tissue Sub], NQ 456
ØDUP*	Supl/Rectum 110, 271, 334
Ø4UA*	Supl/Renal Artery, Lt 84
Ø4UA[Ø,3,4][7,J]Z	Supl/Renal Artery, Lt, [Opn, Perc, Perc Endo], [Auto Tissue Sub, Synth Sub], NQ 252, 324
Ø4U9*	Supl/Renal Artery, Rt 84
Ø4U9[Ø,3,4][7,J]Z	Supl/Renal Artery, Rt, [Opn, Perc, Perc Endo], [Auto Tissue Sub, Synth Sub], NQ 252, 324
Ø6UB[Ø,3,4][7,J]Z	Supl/Renal Vein, Lt, [Opn, Perc, Perc Endo], [Auto Tissue Sub, Synth Sub], NQ 252, 327
Ø6U9[Ø,3,4][7,J]Z	Supl/Renal Vein, Rt, [Opn, Perc, Perc Endo], [Auto Tissue Sub, Synth Sub], NQ 252, 327
Ø8UF*	Supl/Retina, Lt 44
Ø8UF[Ø,3][7,J,K]Z	Supl/Retina, Lt, [Opn, Perc], [Auto Tissue Sub, Synth Sub, Nonauto Tissue Sub], NQ 446
Ø8UF[Ø,3]JZ	Supl/Retina, Lt, [Opn, Perc], Synth Sub, NQ 330
Ø8UE*	Supl/Retina, Rt 44
Ø8UE[Ø,3][7,J,K]Z	Supl/Retina, Rt, [Opn, Perc], [Auto Tissue Sub, Synth Sub, Nonauto Tissue Sub], NQ 446
Ø8UE[Ø,3]JZ	Supl/Retina, Rt, [Opn, Perc], Synth Sub, NQ 330
Ø8UH*	Supl/Retinal Vessel, Lt 44, 330
Ø8UH[Ø,3][7,J,K]Z	Supl/Retinal Vessel, Lt, [Opn, Perc], [Auto Tissue Sub, Synth Sub, Nonauto Tissue Sub], NQ 446
Ø8UG*	Supl/Retinal Vessel, Rt 44, 330
Ø8UG[Ø,3][7,J,K]Z	Supl/Retinal Vessel, Rt, [Opn, Perc], [Auto Tissue Sub, Synth Sub, Nonauto Tissue Sub], NQ 446
ØPU2*	Supl/Rib, Lt 155
ØPU2[Ø,3,4]JZ	Supl/Rib, Lt, [Opn, Perc, Perc Endo], Synth Sub, NQ 66, 347
ØPU1*	Supl/Rib, Rt 155
ØPU1[Ø,3,4]JZ	Supl/Rib, Rt, [Opn, Perc, Perc Endo], Synth Sub, NQ 66, 347
ØXUT[Ø,4][7,J,K]Z	Supl/Ring Finger, Lt, [Opn, Perc Endo], [Auto Tissue Sub, Synth Sub, Nonauto Tissue Sub], NQ 461
ØXUT[Ø,4][J,K]Z	Supl/Ring Finger, Lt, [Opn, Perc Endo], [Synth Sub, Nonauto Tissue Sub], NQ 218, 357
ØXUT[Ø,4]7Z	Supl/Ring Finger, Lt, [Opn, Perc Endo], Auto Tissue Sub, NQ 29, 92, 151, 207, 317, 379, 381
ØXUS[Ø,4][7,J,K]Z	Supl/Ring Finger, Rt, [Opn, Perc Endo], [Auto Tissue Sub, Synth Sub, Nonauto Tissue Sub], NQ 461
ØXUS[Ø,4][J,K]Z	Supl/Ring Finger, Rt, [Opn, Perc Endo], [Synth Sub, Nonauto Tissue Sub], NQ 218, 357
ØXUS[Ø,4]7Z	Supl/Ring Finger, Rt, [Opn, Perc Endo], Auto Tissue Sub, NQ 29, 92, 151, 207, 317, 379, 381
ØSU5[Ø,3,4][7,K]Z	Supl/Sacrococcygeal Jt, [Opn, Perc, Perc Endo], [Auto Tissue Sub, Nonauto Tissue Sub], NQ 158
ØSU5[Ø,3,4]JZ	Supl/Sacrococcygeal Jt, [Opn, Perc, Perc Endo], Synth Sub, NQ 20, 160, 161, 352
ØSU8*	Supl/Sacroiliac Jt, Lt 158
ØSU7*	Supl/Sacroiliac Jt, Rt 158
ØQU1*	Supl/Sacrum 156

03U3[0,3,4][7,J]Z	Supl/Subclavian Artery, Rt, [Opn, Perc, Perc Endo], [Auto Tissue Sub, Synth Sub], NQ **322**
05U6[0,3,4][7,J]Z	Supl/Subclavian Vein, Lt, [Opn, Perc, Perc Endo], [Auto Tissue Sub, Synth Sub], NQ **326**
05U5[0,3,4][7,J]Z	Supl/Subclavian Vein, Rt, [Opn, Perc, Perc Endo], [Auto Tissue Sub, Synth Sub], NQ **326**
04U5*	Supl/Superior Mesenteric Artery **84**
04U5[0,3,4][7,J]Z	Supl/Superior Mesenteric Artery, [Opn, Perc, Perc Endo], [Auto Tissue Sub, Synth Sub], NQ **324**
06U5[0,3,4][7,J]Z	Supl/Superior Mesenteric Vein, [Opn, Perc, Perc Endo], [Auto Tissue Sub, Synth Sub], NQ **327**
02UV*	Supl/Superior Vena Cava **80, 320**
0SUJ*	Supl/Tarsal Jt, Lt **158**
0SUJ[0,3,4]JZ	Supl/Tarsal Jt, Lt, [Opn, Perc, Perc Endo], Synth Sub, NQ **352**
0SUH*	Supl/Tarsal Jt, Rt **158**
0SUH[0,3,4]JZ	Supl/Tarsal Jt, Rt, [Opn, Perc, Perc Endo], Synth Sub, NQ **352**
0QUM*	Supl/Tarsal, Lt **145, 349**
0QUL*	Supl/Tarsal, Rt **145, 349**
03UT[0,3,4][7,J]Z	Supl/Temporal Artery, Lt, [Opn, Perc, Perc Endo], [Auto Tissue Sub, Synth Sub], NQ **322**
03US[0,3,4][7,J]Z	Supl/Temporal Artery, Rt, [Opn, Perc, Perc Endo], [Auto Tissue Sub, Synth Sub], NQ **322**
0NU6*	Supl/Temporal Bone, Lt **10, 49, 154**
0NU6[0,3,4][7,J,K]Z	Supl/Temporal Bone, Lt, [Opn, Perc, Perc Endo], [Auto Tissue Sub, Synth Sub, Nonauto Tissue Sub], NQ **14, 18**
0NU6[0,3,4]JZ	Supl/Temporal Bone, Lt, [Opn, Perc, Perc Endo], Synth Sub, NQ **344, 415**
0NU5*	Supl/Temporal Bone, Rt **10, 49, 154**
0NU5[0,3,4][7,J,K]Z	Supl/Temporal Bone, Rt, [Opn, Perc, Perc Endo], [Auto Tissue Sub, Synth Sub, Nonauto Tissue Sub], NQ **14, 18**
0NU5[0,3,4]JZ	Supl/Temporal Bone, Rt, [Opn, Perc, Perc Endo], Synth Sub, NQ **344, 415**
0RUD*	Supl/Temporomandibular Jt, Lt **55, 157, 350**
0RUC*	Supl/Temporomandibular Jt, Rt **55, 157, 350**
0VUC*	Supl/Testes, Bilat **258, 355**
0VUB*	Supl/Testis, Lt **258, 355**
0VU9*	Supl/Testis, Rt **258, 355**
02UW*	Supl/Thoracic Aorta **320**
02UW[0,3,4][7,8,K]Z	Supl/Thoracic Aorta, [Opn, Perc, Perc Endo], [Auto Tissue Sub, Zooplastic Tissue, Nonauto Tissue Sub], NQ **80**
02UW[3,4]JZ	Supl/Thoracic Aorta, [Perc, Perc Endo], Synth Sub, NQ **71, 72, 251**
07UK*	Supl/Thoracic Duct **60**
0RU9*	Supl/Thoracic Vert Disc **159, 161, 350**
0RU9[0,3,4][7,J,K]Z	Supl/Thoracic Vert Disc, [Opn, Perc, Perc Endo], [Auto Tissue Sub, Synth Sub, Nonauto Tissue Sub], NQ **20, 302**
0RU6[0,3,4][7,K]Z	Supl/Thoracic Vert Jt, [Opn, Perc, Perc Endo], [Auto Tissue Sub, Nonauto Tissue Sub], NQ **157**
0RU6[0,3,4]JZ	Supl/Thoracic Vert Jt, [Opn, Perc, Perc Endo], Synth Sub, NQ **20, 160, 161, 350**
0PU4*	Supl/Thoracic Vertebra **155**
0PU4[0,3,4]JZ	Supl/Thoracic Vertebra, [Opn, Perc, Perc Endo], Synth Sub, NQ **347**
0RUB*	Supl/Thoracolumbar Vert Disc **159, 161, 350**
0RUB[0,3,4][7,J,K]Z	Supl/Thoracolumbar Vert Disc, [Opn, Perc, Perc Endo], [Auto Tissue Sub, Synth Sub, Nonauto Tissue Sub], NQ **20, 302**
0RUA[0,3,4][7,K]Z	Supl/Thoracolumbar Vert Jt, [Opn, Perc, Perc Endo], [Auto Tissue Sub, Nonauto Tissue Sub], NQ **157**
0RUA[0,3,4]JZ	Supl/Thoracolumbar Vert Jt, [Opn, Perc, Perc Endo], Synth Sub, NQ **20, 160, 161, 350**
0MUG*	Supl/Thorax Bursa & Lgmt, Lt **153**
0MUF*	Supl/Thorax Bursa & Lgmt, Rt **153**
0KUJ*	Supl/Thorax Muscle, Lt **140, 340**
0KUJ[0,4][7,J,K]Z	Supl/Thorax Muscle, Lt, [Opn, Perc Endo], [Auto Tissue Sub, Synth Sub, Nonauto Tissue Sub], NQ **215**
0KUH*	Supl/Thorax Muscle, Rt **140, 340**
0KUH[0,4][7,J,K]Z	Supl/Thorax Muscle, Rt, [Opn, Perc Endo], [Auto Tissue Sub, Synth Sub, Nonauto Tissue Sub], NQ **215**
0LUD*	Supl/Thorax Tndn, Lt **142, 342**
0LUC*	Supl/Thorax Tndn, Rt **142, 342**
0PUS*	Supl/Thumb Phalanx, Lt **156**
0PUR*	Supl/Thumb Phalanx, Rt **156**
0XUM[0,4][7,J,K]Z	Supl/Thumb, Lt, [Opn, Perc Endo], [Auto Tissue Sub, Synth Sub, Nonauto Tissue Sub], NQ **461**
0XUM[0,4][J,K]Z	Supl/Thumb, Lt, [Opn, Perc Endo], [Synth Sub, Nonauto Tissue Sub], NQ **218, 357**
0XUM[0,4]7Z	Supl/Thumb, Lt, [Opn, Perc Endo], Auto Tissue Sub, NQ **29, 92, 151, 207, 317, 379, 381**
0XUL[0,4][7,J,K]Z	Supl/Thumb, Rt, [Opn, Perc Endo], [Auto Tissue Sub, Synth Sub, Nonauto Tissue Sub], NQ **461**
0XUL[0,4][J,K]Z	Supl/Thumb, Rt, [Opn, Perc Endo], [Synth Sub, Nonauto Tissue Sub], NQ **218, 357**
0XUL[0,4]7Z	Supl/Thumb, Rt, [Opn, Perc Endo], Auto Tissue Sub, NQ **29, 92, 151, 207, 317, 379, 381**
03UV[0,3,4][7,J]Z	Supl/Thyroid Artery, Lt, [Opn, Perc, Perc Endo], [Auto Tissue Sub, Synth Sub], NQ **322**
03UU[0,3,4][7,J]Z	Supl/Thyroid Artery, Rt, [Opn, Perc, Perc Endo], [Auto Tissue Sub, Synth Sub], NQ **322**
0QUH*	Supl/Tibia, Lt **133, 349**
0QUG*	Supl/Tibia, Rt **133, 349**
0SUQ*	Supl/Toe Phalangeal Jt, Lt **158**
0SUP*	Supl/Toe Phalangeal Jt, Rt **158**
0QUR*	Supl/Toe Phalanx, Lt **156**
0QUQ*	Supl/Toe Phalanx, Rt **156**
0CU7*	Supl/Tongue **56, 332**
0KU4*	Supl/Tongue, Palate, Pharynx Muscle **140, 340**
0KU4[0,4][7,J,K]Z	Supl/Tongue, Palate, Pharynx Muscle, [Opn, Perc Endo], [Auto Tissue Sub, Synth Sub, Nonauto Tissue Sub], NQ **215**
0BU1*	Supl/Trachea **52, 331**
0DUL*	Supl/Transv Colon **107, 334**
02UJ*	Supl/Tricuspid Valve **71, 72**
00UK*	Supl/Trigeminal Nerve **23**
00UJ*	Supl/Trochlear Nerve **23**
0MUD*	Supl/Trunk Bursa & Lgmt, Lt **153**
0MUC*	Supl/Trunk Bursa & Lgmt, Rt **153**
0KUG*	Supl/Trunk Muscle, Lt **140, 340**
0KUG[0,4][7,J,K]Z	Supl/Trunk Muscle, Lt, [Opn, Perc Endo], [Auto Tissue Sub, Synth Sub, Nonauto Tissue Sub], NQ **215**
0KUF*	Supl/Trunk Muscle, Rt **140, 340**
0KUF[0,4][7,J,K]Z	Supl/Trunk Muscle, Rt, [Opn, Perc Endo], [Auto Tissue Sub, Synth Sub, Nonauto Tissue Sub], NQ **215**
0LUB*	Supl/Trunk Tndn, Lt **142, 342**
0LU9*	Supl/Trunk Tndn, Rt **142, 342**
0VU7*	Supl/Tunica Vaginalis, Lt **258, 355**
0VU6*	Supl/Tunica Vaginalis, Rt **258, 355**
09U8[0,7,8][7,J,K]Z	Supl/Tympanic Membrane, Lt, [Opn, Via Natrl or Artfcl Opng, Via Natrl or Artfcl Opng Endo], [Auto Tissue Sub, Synth Sub, Nonauto Tissue Sub], NQ **447**
09U7[0,7,8][7,J,K]Z	Supl/Tympanic Membrane, Rt, [Opn, Via Natrl or Artfcl Opng, Via Natrl or Artfcl Opng Endo], [Auto Tissue Sub, Synth Sub, Nonauto Tissue Sub], NQ **447**
0PUL*	Supl/Ulna, Lt **149, 347**
0PUL[0,3,4][7,K]Z	Supl/Ulna, Lt, [Opn, Perc, Perc Endo], [Auto Tissue Sub, Nonauto Tissue Sub], NQ **456**
0PUK*	Supl/Ulna, Rt **149, 347**
0PUK[0,3,4][7,K]Z	Supl/Ulna, Rt, [Opn, Perc, Perc Endo], [Auto Tissue Sub, Nonauto Tissue Sub], NQ **456**
03UA[0,3,4][7,J]Z	Supl/Ulnar Artery, Lt, [Opn, Perc, Perc Endo], [Auto Tissue Sub, Synth Sub], NQ **322**
03U9[0,3,4][7,J]Z	Supl/Ulnar Artery, Rt, [Opn, Perc, Perc Endo], [Auto Tissue Sub, Synth Sub], NQ **322**
0KU8*	Supl/Upr Arm Muscle, Lt **140, 340**
0KU8[0,4][7,J,K]Z	Supl/Upr Arm Muscle, Lt, [Opn, Perc Endo], [Auto Tissue Sub, Synth Sub, Nonauto Tissue Sub], NQ **215**
0KU7*	Supl/Upr Arm Muscle, Rt **140, 340**
0KU7[0,4][7,J,K]Z	Supl/Upr Arm Muscle, Rt, [Opn, Perc Endo], [Auto Tissue Sub, Synth Sub, Nonauto Tissue Sub], NQ **215**
0LU4*	Supl/Upr Arm Tndn, Lt **142, 342**
0LU3*	Supl/Upr Arm Tndn, Rt **142, 342**
0XU9[0,4][7,J,K]Z	Supl/Upr Arm, Lt, [Opn, Perc Endo], [Auto Tissue Sub, Synth Sub, Nonauto Tissue Sub], NQ **461**
0XU9[0,4][J,K]Z	Supl/Upr Arm, Lt, [Opn, Perc Endo], [Synth Sub, Nonauto Tissue Sub], NQ **218, 356**
0XU9[0,4]7Z	Supl/Upr Arm, Lt, [Opn, Perc Endo], Auto Tissue Sub, NQ **127, 379, 381**

0HXCXZZ	Transfer Lt Upr Arm Skin, Ext Appr 237, 313, 378, 380
0HXJXZZ	Transfer Lt Upr Leg Skin, Ext Appr 237, 313, 378, 380
0HX4XZZ	Transfer Neck Skin, Ext Appr 237, 313, 378, 380
0HX9XZZ	Transfer Perineum Skin, Ext Appr 237, 313, 378, 380
0HX2XZZ	Transfer Rt Ear Skin, Ext Appr 212, 337, 450
0HXMXZZ	Transfer Rt Foot Skin, Ext Appr 237, 313, 378, 380
0HXFXZZ	Transfer Rt Hand Skin, Ext Appr 237, 313, 378, 380
0XXN0ZL	Transfer Rt Index Finger to Rt Thumb, Opn Appr 147, 317
0HXDXZZ	Transfer Rt Lwr Arm Skin, Ext Appr 237, 313, 378, 380
0HXKXZZ	Transfer Rt Lwr Leg Skin, Ext Appr 237, 313, 378, 380
0HXBXZZ	Transfer Rt Upr Arm Skin, Ext Appr 237, 313, 378, 380
0HXHXZZ	Transfer Rt Upr Leg Skin, Ext Appr 237, 313, 378, 380
0HX0XZZ	Transfer Scalp Skin, Ext Appr 237, 313, 378, 380
0KXL[0,4]Z[0,1,2,Z]	Transfer/Abd Muscle, Lt, [Opn, Perc Endo], No Dev, [Skin, SQ Tissue, Skin and SQ Tissue, NQ] 28, 140
0KXL[0,4]Z6	Transfer/Abd Muscle, Lt, [Opn, Perc Endo], No Dev, Transv Rectus Abdominis Myocutaneous Flap 221, 222, 340
0KXK[0,4]Z[0,1,2,Z]	Transfer/Abd Muscle, Rt, [Opn, Perc Endo], No Dev, [Skin, SQ Tissue, Skin and SQ Tissue, NQ] 28, 140
0KXK[0,4]Z6	Transfer/Abd Muscle, Rt, [Opn, Perc Endo], No Dev, Transv Rectus Abdominis Myocutaneous Flap 221, 222, 340
0LXG*	Transfer/Abd Tndn, Lt 143, 243, 342
0LXF*	Transfer/Abd Tndn, Rt 143, 243, 342
00XR[0,4]Z[M,S]	Transfer/Accessory Nerve, [Opn, Perc Endo], No Dev, [Facial Nerve, Hypoglossal Nerve] 50
0LXT*	Transfer/Ankle Tndn, Lt 143, 243, 342
0LXS*	Transfer/Ankle Tndn, Rt 143, 243, 342
0CX4[0,X]ZZ	Transfer/Buccal Mucosa, [Opn, Ext] 211, 448
08XM[0,3]ZZ	Transfer/Extraocular Muscle, Lt, [Opn, Perc] 446
08XL[0,3]ZZ	Transfer/Extraocular Muscle, Rt, [Opn, Perc] 446
0KX1*	Transfer/Facial Muscle 27, 140
0KXW*	Transfer/Foot Muscle, Lt 28, 141
0KXV*	Transfer/Foot Muscle, Rt 28, 141
0LXW*	Transfer/Foot Tndn, Lt 143, 243, 342
0LXV*	Transfer/Foot Tndn, Rt 143, 243, 342
0KXD*	Transfer/Hand Muscle, Lt 28, 149
0KXD[0,4]Z[0,1,2,Z]	Transfer/Hand Muscle, Lt, [Opn, Perc Endo], No Dev, [Skin, SQ Tissue, Skin and SQ Tissue, NQ] 314
0KXC*	Transfer/Hand Muscle, Rt 28, 149
0KXC[0,4]Z[0,1,2,Z]	Transfer/Hand Muscle, Rt, [Opn, Perc Endo], No Dev, [Skin, SQ Tissue, Skin and SQ Tissue, NQ] 314
0LX8*	Transfer/Hand Tndn, Lt 150
0LX8[0,4]ZZ	Transfer/Hand Tndn, Lt, [Opn, Perc Endo] 315
0LX7*	Transfer/Hand Tndn, Rt 150
0LX7[0,4]ZZ	Transfer/Hand Tndn, Rt, [Opn, Perc Endo] 315
0LX0*	Transfer/Head and Neck Tndn 143, 243, 342
0KX0*	Transfer/Head Muscle 27, 140
0KXP*	Transfer/Hip Muscle, Lt 28, 140
0KXN*	Transfer/Hip Muscle, Rt 28, 140
0LXK*	Transfer/Hip Tndn, Lt 143, 243, 342
0LXJ*	Transfer/Hip Tndn, Rt 143, 243, 342
00XS[0,4]ZM	Transfer/Hypoglossal Nerve, [Opn, Perc Endo], No Dev, Facial Nerve 50
0LXR*	Transfer/Knee Tndn, Lt 143, 243, 342
0LXQ*	Transfer/Knee Tndn, Rt 143, 243, 342
0DXE[0,4]Z5	Transfer/Lg Intestine, [Opn, Perc Endo], No Dev, Esophagus 301
0KXB*	Transfer/Lwr Arm and Wrist Muscle, Lt 28, 140
0KX9*	Transfer/Lwr Arm and Wrist Muscle, Rt 28, 140
0LX6*	Transfer/Lwr Arm and Wrist Tndn, Lt 143, 243, 342
0LX5*	Transfer/Lwr Arm and Wrist Tndn, Rt 143, 243, 342
0CX6[0,X]ZZ	Transfer/Lwr Gingiva, [Opn, Ext] 211, 448
0KXT*	Transfer/Lwr Leg Muscle, Lt 28, 140
0KXS*	Transfer/Lwr Leg Muscle, Rt 28, 140
0LXP*	Transfer/Lwr Leg Tndn, Lt 143, 243, 342
0LXN*	Transfer/Lwr Leg Tndn, Rt 143, 243, 342
0CX1[0,X]ZZ	Transfer/Lwr Lip, [Opn, Ext] 211, 448
0KX3*	Transfer/Neck Muscle, Lt 27, 140
0KX2*	Transfer/Neck Muscle, Rt 27, 140
0KXM*	Transfer/Perineum Muscle 28, 140
0LXH*	Transfer/Perineum Tndn 143, 243, 342

0KX6*	Transfer/Shldr Muscle, Lt 28, 140
0KX5*	Transfer/Shldr Muscle, Rt 28, 140
0LX2*	Transfer/Shldr Tndn, Lt 143, 243, 342
0LX1*	Transfer/Shldr Tndn, Rt 143, 243, 342
0DX8[0,4]Z5	Transfer/Sm Intestine, [Opn, Perc Endo], No Dev, Esophagus 301
0CX3[0,X]ZZ	Transfer/Soft Palate, [Opn, Ext] 211, 448
0JX8[0,3]ZZ	Transfer/SQ Tissue & Fascia, Abd, [Opn, Perc] 138, 213, 338
0JX8[0,3]Z[B,C]	Transfer/SQ Tissue & Fascia, Abd, [Opn, Perc], No Dev, [Skin and SQ Tissue, Skin, SQ Tissue & Fascia] 26, 91, 113, 127, 207, 237, 314, 378, 380
0JX4[0,3]ZZ	Transfer/SQ Tissue & Fascia, Ant Neck, [Opn, Perc] 138, 213, 338
0JX4[0,3]Z[B,C]	Transfer/SQ Tissue & Fascia, Ant Neck, [Opn, Perc], No Dev, [Skin and SQ Tissue, Skin, SQ Tissue & Fascia] 26, 54, 91, 113, 127, 207, 237, 314, 378, 380
0JX7[0,3]ZZ	Transfer/SQ Tissue & Fascia, Back, [Opn, Perc] 138, 213, 338
0JX7[0,3]Z[B,C]	Transfer/SQ Tissue & Fascia, Back, [Opn, Perc], No Dev, [Skin and SQ Tissue, Skin, SQ Tissue & Fascia] 26, 91, 113, 127, 207, 237, 314, 378, 380
0JX9[0,3]ZZ	Transfer/SQ Tissue & Fascia, Buttock, [Opn, Perc] 138, 213, 338
0JX9[0,3]Z[B,C]	Transfer/SQ Tissue & Fascia, Buttock, [Opn, Perc], No Dev, [Skin and SQ Tissue, Skin, SQ Tissue & Fascia] 26, 91, 113, 127, 207, 237, 314, 378, 380
0JX6[0,3]ZZ	Transfer/SQ Tissue & Fascia, Chest, [Opn, Perc] 138, 213, 338
0JX6[0,3]Z[B,C]	Transfer/SQ Tissue & Fascia, Chest, [Opn, Perc], No Dev, [Skin and SQ Tissue, Skin, SQ Tissue & Fascia] 26, 91, 113, 127, 207, 237, 314, 378, 380
0JX1[0,3]ZZ	Transfer/SQ Tissue & Fascia, Face, [Opn, Perc] 138, 213, 338
0JX1[0,3]Z[B,C]	Transfer/SQ Tissue & Fascia, Face, [Opn, Perc], No Dev, [Skin and SQ Tissue, Skin, SQ Tissue & Fascia] 26, 54, 91, 113, 127, 207, 237, 314, 378, 380
0JXC[0,3]ZZ	Transfer/SQ Tissue & Fascia, Genitalia, [Opn, Perc] 138, 213, 338
0JXC[0,3]Z[B,C]	Transfer/SQ Tissue & Fascia, Genitalia, [Opn, Perc], No Dev, [Skin and SQ Tissue, Skin, SQ Tissue & Fascia] 26, 91, 113, 127, 207, 237, 314, 378, 380
0JXR[0,3]ZZ	Transfer/SQ Tissue & Fascia, Lt Foot, [Opn, Perc] 138, 213, 338
0JXR[0,3]Z[B,C]	Transfer/SQ Tissue & Fascia, Lt Foot, [Opn, Perc], No Dev, [Skin and SQ Tissue, Skin, SQ Tissue & Fascia] 27, 91, 113, 127, 207, 237, 314, 378, 380
0JXK[0,3]ZZ	Transfer/SQ Tissue & Fascia, Lt Hand, [Opn, Perc] 138, 338
0JXK[0,3]Z[B,C]	Transfer/SQ Tissue & Fascia, Lt Hand, [Opn, Perc], No Dev, [Skin and SQ Tissue, Skin, SQ Tissue & Fascia] 149, 207, 314, 378, 380
0JXH[0,3]ZZ	Transfer/SQ Tissue & Fascia, Lt Lwr Arm, [Opn, Perc] 138, 213, 338
0JXH[0,3]Z[B,C]	Transfer/SQ Tissue & Fascia, Lt Lwr Arm, [Opn, Perc], No Dev, [Skin and SQ Tissue, Skin, SQ Tissue & Fascia] 26, 91, 113, 127, 207, 237, 314, 378, 380
0JXP[0,3]ZZ	Transfer/SQ Tissue & Fascia, Lt Lwr Leg, [Opn, Perc] 138, 213, 338
0JXP[0,3]Z[B,C]	Transfer/SQ Tissue & Fascia, Lt Lwr Leg, [Opn, Perc], No Dev, [Skin and SQ Tissue, Skin, SQ Tissue & Fascia] 27, 91, 113, 127, 207, 237, 314, 378, 380
0JXF[0,3]ZZ	Transfer/SQ Tissue & Fascia, Lt Upr Arm, [Opn, Perc] 138, 213, 338
0JXF[0,3]Z[B,C]	Transfer/SQ Tissue & Fascia, Lt Upr Arm, [Opn, Perc], No Dev, [Skin and SQ Tissue, Skin, SQ Tissue & Fascia] 26, 91, 113, 127, 207, 237, 314, 378, 380
0JXM[0,3]ZZ	Transfer/SQ Tissue & Fascia, Lt Upr Leg, [Opn, Perc] 138, 213, 338
0JXM[0,3]Z[B,C]	Transfer/SQ Tissue & Fascia, Lt Upr Leg, [Opn, Perc], No Dev, [Skin and SQ Tissue, Skin, SQ Tissue & Fascia] 27, 91, 113, 127, 207, 237, 314, 378, 380
0JXB[0,3]ZZ	Transfer/SQ Tissue & Fascia, Perineum, [Opn, Perc] 138, 213, 338
0JXB[0,3]Z[B,C]	Transfer/SQ Tissue & Fascia, Perineum, [Opn, Perc], No Dev, [Skin and SQ Tissue, Skin, SQ Tissue & Fascia] 26, 91, 113, 127, 207, 237, 314, 378, 380
0JX5[0,3]ZZ	Transfer/SQ Tissue & Fascia, Post Neck, [Opn, Perc] 138, 213, 338
0JX5[0,3]Z[B,C]	Transfer/SQ Tissue & Fascia, Post Neck, [Opn, Perc], No Dev, [Skin and SQ Tissue, Skin, SQ Tissue & Fascia] 26, 54, 91, 113, 127, 207, 237, 314, 378, 380
0JXQ[0,3]ZZ	Transfer/SQ Tissue & Fascia, Rt Foot, [Opn, Perc] 138, 213, 338

ØJXQ[Ø,3]Z[B,C]	Transfer/SQ Tissue & Fascia, Rt Foot, [Opn, Perc], No Dev, [Skin and SQ Tissue, Skin, SQ Tissue & Fascia] 27, 91, 113, 127, 207, 237, 314, 378, 380
ØJXJ[Ø,3]ZZ	Transfer/SQ Tissue & Fascia, Rt Hand, [Opn, Perc] 27, 138, 213, 338
ØJXJ[Ø,3]Z[B,C]	Transfer/SQ Tissue & Fascia, Rt Hand, [Opn, Perc], No Dev, [Skin and SQ Tissue, Skin, SQ Tissue & Fascia] 149, 207, 314, 378, 380
ØJXG[Ø,3]ZZ	Transfer/SQ Tissue & Fascia, Rt Lwr Arm, [Opn, Perc] 138, 213, 338
ØJXG[Ø,3]Z[B,C]	Transfer/SQ Tissue & Fascia, Rt Lwr Arm, [Opn, Perc], No Dev, [Skin and SQ Tissue, Skin, SQ Tissue & Fascia] 26, 91, 113, 127, 207, 237, 314, 378, 380
ØJXN[Ø,3]ZZ	Transfer/SQ Tissue & Fascia, Rt Lwr Leg, [Opn, Perc] 138, 213, 338
ØJXN[Ø,3]Z[B,C]	Transfer/SQ Tissue & Fascia, Rt Lwr Leg, [Opn, Perc], No Dev, [Skin and SQ Tissue, Skin, SQ Tissue & Fascia] 27, 91, 113, 127, 207, 237, 314, 378, 380
ØJXD[Ø,3]ZZ	Transfer/SQ Tissue & Fascia, Rt Upr Arm, [Opn, Perc] 138, 213, 338
ØJXD[Ø,3]Z[B,C]	Transfer/SQ Tissue & Fascia, Rt Upr Arm, [Opn, Perc], No Dev, [Skin and SQ Tissue, Skin, SQ Tissue & Fascia] 26, 91, 113, 127, 207, 237, 314, 378, 380
ØJXL[Ø,3]ZZ	Transfer/SQ Tissue & Fascia, Rt Upr Leg, [Opn, Perc] 138, 213, 338
ØJXL[Ø,3]Z[B,C]	Transfer/SQ Tissue & Fascia, Rt Upr Leg, [Opn, Perc], No Dev, [Skin and SQ Tissue, Skin, SQ Tissue & Fascia] 27, 91, 113, 127, 207, 237, 314, 378, 380
ØJXØ[Ø,3]ZZ	Transfer/SQ Tissue & Fascia, Scalp, [Opn, Perc] 138, 213, 338
ØJXØ[Ø,3]Z[B,C]	Transfer/SQ Tissue & Fascia, Scalp, [Opn, Perc], No Dev, [Skin and SQ Tissue, Skin, SQ Tissue & Fascia] 26, 54, 91, 113, 127, 207, 237, 314, 378, 380
ØDX6[Ø,4]Z5	Transfer/Stomach, [Opn, Perc Endo], No Dev, Esophagus 300
ØKXJ[Ø,4]ZZ	Transfer/Thorax Muscle, Lt, [Opn, Perc Endo] 207, 340
ØKXJ[Ø,4]Z[Ø,1,2]	Transfer/Thorax Muscle, Lt, [Opn, Perc Endo], No Dev, [Skin, SQ Tissue, Skin and SQ Tissue] 28, 140
ØKXH[Ø,4]ZZ	Transfer/Thorax Muscle, Rt, [Opn, Perc Endo] 207, 340
ØKXH[Ø,4]Z[Ø,1,2]	Transfer/Thorax Muscle, Rt, [Opn, Perc Endo], No Dev, [Skin, SQ Tissue, Skin and SQ Tissue] 28, 140
ØLXD*	Transfer/Thorax Tndn, Lt 143, 243, 342
ØLXC*	Transfer/Thorax Tndn, Rt 143, 243, 342
ØKX4*	Transfer/Tongue, Palate, Pharynx Muscle 27, 140
ØKXG*	Transfer/Trunk Muscle, Lt 28, 140
ØKXF*	Transfer/Trunk Muscle, Rt 28, 140
ØLXB*	Transfer/Trunk Tndn, Lt 143, 243, 342
ØLX9*	Transfer/Trunk Tndn, Rt 143, 243, 342
ØKX8*	Transfer/Upr Arm Muscle, Lt 28, 140
ØKX7*	Transfer/Upr Arm Muscle, Rt 28, 140
ØLX4*	Transfer/Upr Arm Tndn, Lt 143, 243, 342
ØLX3*	Transfer/Upr Arm Tndn, Rt 143, 243, 342
ØCX5[Ø,X]ZZ	Transfer/Upr Gingiva, [Opn, Ext] 211, 448
ØKXR*	Transfer/Upr Leg Muscle, Lt 28, 140
ØKXQ*	Transfer/Upr Leg Muscle, Rt 28, 140
ØLXM*	Transfer/Upr Leg Tndn, Lt 143, 243, 342
ØLXL*	Transfer/Upr Leg Tndn, Rt 143, 243, 342
ØCXØ[Ø,X]ZZ	Transfer/Upr Lip, [Opn, Ext] 211, 448
30240AZ	Transfusion of Embr Stem Cell into Central Vein, Opn Appr 6
30243AZ	Transfusion of Embr Stem Cell into Central Vein, Perc Appr 6
30230AZ	Transfusion of Embr Stem Cell into Periph Vein, Opn Appr 6
30233AZ	Transfusion of Embr Stem Cell into Periph Vein, Perc Appr 6
3026[Ø,3][G,X,Y]1	Transfusion/Central Artery, [Opn, Perc], [Bone Marrow, Stem Cells, Cord Bld, Stem Cells, Hematopoietic], Nonauto 6
3026[Ø,3][G,Y]Ø	Transfusion/Central Artery, [Opn, Perc], [Bone Marrow, Stem Cells, Hematopoietic], Auto 6
3026[Ø,3]XØ	Transfusion/Central Artery, [Opn, Perc], Stem Cells, Cord Bld, Auto 6
3024[Ø,3][G,X,Y]1	Transfusion/Central Vein, [Opn, Perc], [Bone Marrow, Stem Cells, Cord Bld, Stem Cells, Hematopoietic], Nonauto 6
3024[Ø,3]XØ	Transfusion/Central Vein, [Opn, Perc], Stem Cells, Cord Bld, Auto 6
30240[G,Y]Ø	Transfusion/Central Vein, Opn, [Bone Marrow, Stem Cells, Hematopoietic], Auto 6
30243[G,Y]Ø	Transfusion/Central Vein, Perc, [Bone Marrow, Stem Cells, Hematopoietic], Auto 6

3025[Ø,3][G,X,Y]1	Transfusion/Peripheral Artery, [Opn, Perc], [Bone Marrow, Stem Cells, Cord Bld, Stem Cells, Hematopoietic], Nonauto 6
3025[Ø,3][G,Y]Ø	Transfusion/Peripheral Artery, [Opn, Perc], [Bone Marrow, Stem Cells, Hematopoietic], Auto 6
3025[Ø,3]XØ	Transfusion/Peripheral Artery, [Opn, Perc], Stem Cells, Cord Bld, Auto 6
3023[Ø,3][G,X,Y]1	Transfusion/Peripheral Vein, [Opn, Perc], [Bone Marrow, Stem Cells, Cord Bld, Stem Cells, Hematopoietic], Nonauto 6
3023[Ø,3]XØ	Transfusion/Peripheral Vein, [Opn, Perc], Stem Cells, Cord Bld, Auto 6
30230[G,Y]Ø	Transfusion/Peripheral Vein, Opn, [Bone Marrow, Stem Cells, Hematopoietic], Auto 6
30233[G,Y]Ø	Transfusion/Peripheral Vein, Perc, [Bone Marrow, Stem Cells, Hematopoietic], Auto 6
02YAØZ[Ø,1,2]	Transplantation/Heart, Opn, No Dev, [Allogeneic, Syngeneic, Zooplastic]
ØTY1ØZ[Ø,1,2]	Transplantation/Kidney, Lt, Opn, No Dev, [Allogeneic, Syngeneic, Zooplastic] 2
ØTYØØZ[Ø,1,2]	Transplantation/Kidney, Rt, Opn, No Dev, [Allogeneic, Syngeneic, Zooplastic] 2
ØDYEØZ[Ø,1,2]	Transplantation/Lg Intestine, Opn, No Dev, [Allogeneic, Syngeneic, Zooplastic] 1
ØFYØØZ[Ø,1,2]	Transplantation/Liver, Opn, No Dev, [Allogeneic, Syngeneic, Zooplastic] 1
ØBYHØZ[Ø,1,2]	Transplantation/Lung Lingula, Opn, No Dev, [Allogeneic, Syngeneic, Zooplastic] 1
ØBYLØZ[Ø,1,2]	Transplantation/Lung, Lt, Opn, No Dev, [Allogeneic, Syngeneic, Zooplastic] 1
ØBYKØZ[Ø,1,2]	Transplantation/Lung, Rt, Opn, No Dev, [Allogeneic, Syngeneic, Zooplastic] 1
ØBYMØZ[Ø,1,2]	Transplantation/Lungs, Bilat, Opn, No Dev, [Allogeneic, Syngeneic, Zooplastic] 1
ØBYJØZ[Ø,1,2]	Transplantation/Lwr Lung Lobe, Lt, Opn, No Dev, [Allogeneic, Syngeneic, Zooplastic] 1
ØBYFØZ[Ø,1,2]	Transplantation/Lwr Lung Lobe, Rt, Opn, No Dev, [Allogeneic, Syngeneic, Zooplastic] 1
ØBYDØZ[Ø,1,2]	Transplantation/Mid Lung Lobe, Rt, Opn, No Dev, [Allogeneic, Syngeneic, Zooplastic] 1
ØFYG*	Transplantation/Pancreas 2, 119, 242
ØDY8ØZ[Ø,1,2]	Transplantation/Sm Intestine, Opn, No Dev, [Allogeneic, Syngeneic, Zooplastic] 1
07YP*	Transplantation/Spleen 290
07YPØZ[Ø,1,2]	Transplantation/Spleen, Opn, No Dev, [Allogeneic, Syngeneic, Zooplastic] 299
ØDY6*	Transplantation/Stomach 106, 236, 335
07YM*	Transplantation/Thymus 60, 241
07YMØZ[Ø,1,2]	Transplantation/Thymus, Opn, No Dev, [Allogeneic, Syngeneic, Zooplastic] 292, 299
ØBYGØZ[Ø,1,2]	Transplantation/Upr Lung Lobe, Lt, Opn, No Dev, [Allogeneic, Syngeneic, Zooplastic] 1
ØBYCØZ[Ø,1,2]	Transplantation/Upr Lung Lobe, Rt, Opn, No Dev, [Allogeneic, Syngeneic, Zooplastic] 1
037*	Upr Arteries, Dilation 81
03C*	Upr Arteries, Extir 321
03Q*	Upr Arteries, Repair 82, 321
03S*	Upr Arteries, Repos 82, 321
03N*	Upr Arteries, Rls 82
03U*	Upr Arteries, Supl 82
057*	Upr Veins, Dilation 85
05D*	Upr Veins, Extract 88
05L*	Upr Veins, Occlsn 326
05Q*	Upr Veins, Repair 326
05S*	Upr Veins, Repos 86, 326
05N*	Upr Veins, Rls 86
05U*	Upr Veins, Supl 86
ØTY*	Urinary Sys, Transplantation 248

Numeric Index to Procedures

Code	Page
001*	295
0016[0,3][7,J,K][0,1,2,3,4,5,6,7,8]	20
0016[0,3][7,J,K]B	414
0016*	317
0016O[7,J,K]B	7, 12, 16
0016³[7,J,K]B	7, 12, 16
001U[0,3][7,J,K][4,6,7,9]	19
0050[0,3,4]ZZ	12, 16, 295
0050*	7, 317, 414
0051[0,3,4]ZZ	12, 16, 295
0051*	7, 414
0052[0,3,4]ZZ	12, 16, 295
0052*	7, 414
0056[0,3,4]ZZ	12, 16
0056*	7, 414
0057[0,3,4]ZZ	12, 16, 295
0057*	7, 317, 414
0058[0,3,4]ZZ	12, 16, 295
0058*	7, 414
0059[0,3,4]ZZ	12, 16, 295
0059*	7, 317, 414
005A[0,3,4]ZZ	12, 16, 295
005A*	7, 317, 414
005B[0,3,4]ZZ	12, 16, 295
005B*	7, 317, 414
005C[0,3,4]ZZ	12, 16, 295
005C*	8, 317, 414
005D[0,3,4]ZZ	12, 16, 295
005D*	8, 317, 414
005T[0,3,4]ZZ	19, 295
005T*	159, 160
005W[0,3,4]ZZ	19, 295
005W*	159, 160
005X[0,3,4]ZZ	19, 295
005X*	159, 160
005Y[0,3,4]ZZ	19, 295
005Y*	159, 160
0080[0,3,4]ZZ	12, 16, 295
0080*	8, 317, 414
0087[0,3,4]ZZ	12, 16, 295
0087*	8, 317, 414
0088[0,3,4]ZZ	12, 16, 295
0088*	8, 414
008F*	23, 50, 151, 317
008G*	23, 50, 151, 317
008H*	23, 50, 151, 317
008J*	23, 50, 151, 317
008K*	23, 50, 317
008L*	23, 50, 151, 317
008M*	23, 50, 151, 317
008N*	23, 50, 151, 317
008P[0,3,4]ZZ	12, 16
008P*	8, 50
008Q*	23, 50, 63, 105
008R*	23, 50, 151, 317
008S*	23, 50, 151, 317
008W[0,3,4]ZZ	19, 295
008W*	121, 317
008X[0,3,4]ZZ	19, 295
008X*	121, 317
008Y[0,3,4]ZZ	19, 295
008Y*	121, 317
009[F,G,H,J]0ZX	50, 151
009[K,L,M,N]0ZX	50, 151
009[P,Q,R,S]0ZX	50, 151
0090[0,3,4][0,Z]Z	8, 12, 16, 317, 414

Code	Page
00900ZX	8, 12, 16, 295
00910[0,Z]Z	8, 12, 16, 295, 317, 414
00910ZX	8, 12, 16, 295
00920[0,Z]Z	8, 12, 16, 295, 317, 414
00920ZX	8, 12, 16, 295
0093[0,3,4][0,Z]Z	8, 12, 16, 317, 414
00930ZX	8, 12, 16, 295
00940[0,Z]Z	8, 12, 16, 295, 317, 414
00940ZX	8, 12, 16, 295
00950[0,Z]Z	8, 12, 16, 295, 317, 414
00950ZX	8, 12, 16, 295
0096[0,3,4]0Z	8, 295, 317, 414
00960[0,Z]Z	12, 16
00960ZX	8, 12, 16, 295
00960ZZ	8, 317, 414
009630Z	12, 16
009640Z	12, 16
0097[0,3,4][0,Z]Z	8, 12, 16, 317, 414
00970ZX	8, 12, 16, 295
0098[0,3,4][0,Z]Z	8, 12, 16, 295, 414
00980ZX	8, 12, 16, 295
0099[0,3,4][0,Z]Z	8, 12, 16, 295, 317, 414
00990ZX	8, 12, 16, 295
009A[0,3,4][0,Z]Z	8, 12, 16, 295, 317, 414
009A0ZX	8, 12, 16, 295
009B[0,3,4][0,Z]Z	8, 12, 16, 317, 414
009B0ZX	8, 12, 16, 295
009C[0,3,4][0,Z]Z	8, 12, 16, 317, 414
009C0ZX	8, 12, 16, 295
009D[0,3,4][0,Z]Z	8, 12, 16, 318, 414
009D0ZX	8, 12, 16, 295
009F[0,3,4][0,Z]Z	23
009F0ZX	23, 318
009G[0,3,4][0,Z]Z	23
009G0ZX	23, 318
009H[0,3,4][0,Z]Z	23
009H0ZX	23, 318
009J[0,3,4][0,Z]Z	23
009J0ZX	23, 318
009K[0,3,4][0,Z]Z	23
009K0ZX	23, 318
009L[0,3,4][0,Z]Z	23
009L0ZX	23, 318
009M[0,3,4][0,Z]Z	23
009M0ZX	23, 318
009N[0,3,4][0,Z]Z	23
009N0ZX	23, 318
009P[0,3,4][0,Z]Z	23
009P0ZX	23, 318
009Q[0,3,4][0,Z]Z	23
009Q0ZX	23, 318
009R[0,3,4][0,Z]Z	23
009R0ZX	23, 318
009S[0,3,4][0,Z]Z	23
009S0ZX	23, 318
009T[0,3,4][0,Z]Z	19, 295, 318
009T[0,3,4]ZX	19, 295
009T*	159, 160
009U0[0,Z]Z	318
009U00Z	19, 159, 160, 295
009U0ZX	19, 159, 160, 295
009U0ZZ	19, 159, 160, 295
009W[0,3,4][0,Z]Z	19, 295, 318
009W[0,3,4]ZX	19, 295
009W*	159, 160

Code	Page
009X[0,3,4][0,Z]Z	19, 295, 318
009X[0,3,4]ZX	19, 295
009X*	159, 160
009Y[0,3,4][0,Z]Z	19, 295, 318
009Y[0,3,4]ZX	19, 295
009Y*	159, 160
00B0[0,3,4]ZZ	8, 12, 16, 295, 318, 414
00B00ZX	8, 12, 16, 295
00B1[0,3,4]ZZ	8, 12, 16, 295, 414
00B10ZX	8, 12, 16, 295
00B2[0,3,4]ZZ	8, 12, 16, 295, 414
00B20ZX	8, 12, 16, 295
00B6[0,3,4]ZZ	8, 12, 16, 295, 318, 414
00B60ZX	8, 12, 16, 295
00B7[0,3,4]ZZ	8, 12, 16, 295, 318, 414
00B70ZX	8, 12, 16, 295
00B8[0,3,4]ZZ	8, 12, 16, 295, 414
00B80ZX	8, 12, 16, 295
00B9[0,3,4]ZZ	8, 12, 16, 295, 318, 414
00B90ZX	8, 12, 16, 295
00BA[0,3,4]ZZ	8, 12, 16, 295, 318, 414
00BA0ZX	8, 12, 16, 295
00BB[0,3,4]ZZ	8, 12, 16, 295, 318, 414
00BB0ZX	8, 12, 16, 295
00BC[0,3,4]ZZ	8, 12, 16, 295, 318, 414
00BC0ZX	8, 12, 16, 295
00BD[0,3,4]ZZ	8, 12, 16, 295, 318, 414
00BD0ZX	8, 12, 16, 295
00BF[0,3,4]ZZ	23, 50, 151, 318, 440
00BF0ZX	23, 50, 151, 318
00BG[0,3,4]ZZ	23, 50, 151, 318, 440
00BG0ZX	23, 50, 151, 318
00BH[0,3,4]ZZ	23, 50, 151, 318, 440
00BH0ZX	23, 50, 151, 318
00BJ[0,3,4]ZZ	23, 50, 151, 318, 440
00BJ0ZX	23, 50, 151, 318
00BK[0,3,4]ZZ	23, 50, 151, 318, 440
00BK0ZX	23, 50, 151, 318
00BL[0,3,4]ZZ	23, 50, 151, 318, 440
00BL0ZX	23, 50, 151, 318
00BM[0,3,4]ZZ	23, 50, 151, 318, 440
00BM0ZX	23, 50, 151, 318
00BN[0,3,4]ZZ	50
00BN[3,4]ZZ	23, 151, 318, 440
00BN0ZX	23, 50, 151, 318
00BN0ZZ	8, 12, 16
00BP[0,3,4]ZZ	23, 50, 151, 318, 440
00BP0ZX	23, 50, 151, 318
00BQ[0,3,4]ZZ	23, 50, 151, 318, 440
00BQ0ZX	23, 50, 151, 318
00BR[0,3,4]ZZ	23, 50, 151, 318, 440
00BR0ZX	23, 50, 151, 318
00BS[0,3,4]ZZ	23, 50, 151, 318, 440
00BS0ZX	23, 50, 151, 318
00BT[0,3,4]Z[X,Z]	19, 295
00BT*	159, 160
00BW[0,3,4]Z[X,Z]	19, 295
00BW*	159, 160
00BX[0,3,4]Z[X,Z]	19, 295
00BX*	159, 160
00BY[0,3,4]Z[X,Z]	19, 295
00BY*	159, 160
00C0[0,3,4]ZZ	8, 12, 16
00C0*	318, 414
00C1[0,3,4]ZZ	8, 12, 16, 295
00C1*	318, 414

Code	Page
00C2[0,3,4]ZZ	8, 12, 16, 295
00C2*	318, 414
00C3[0,3,4]ZZ	8, 12, 16
00C3*	318
00C4[0,3,4]ZZ	8, 12, 16, 295
00C4*	318, 414
00C5[0,3,4]ZZ	8, 12, 16, 295
00C5*	318, 414
00C6[0,3,4]ZZ	8, 12, 16
00C6*	318, 414
00C7[0,3,4]ZZ	8, 12, 16
00C7*	318, 414
00C8[0,3,4]ZZ	8, 12, 16, 295
00C8*	414
00C9[0,3,4]ZZ	8, 12, 16, 295
00C9*	318, 414
00CA[0,3,4]ZZ	8, 12, 16, 295
00CA*	318, 414
00CB[0,3,4]ZZ	8, 12, 16
00CB*	318, 414
00CC[0,3,4]ZZ	8, 12, 16
00CC*	318, 414
00CD[0,3,4]ZZ	8, 12, 16
00CD*	318, 414
00CF*	23
00CG*	23
00CH*	23
00CJ*	23
00CK*	23
00CL*	23
00CM*	23
00CN*	23
00CP*	23
00CQ*	23
00CR*	23
00CS*	23
00CT[0,3,4]ZZ	19
00CT*	318
00CW[0,3,4]ZZ	19
00CW*	318
00CX[0,3,4]ZZ	19
00CX*	318
00CY[0,3,4]ZZ	19
00CY*	318
00D1[0,3,4]ZZ	8, 12, 16, 295
00D1*	414
00D2[0,3,4]ZZ	8, 12, 16, 295
00D2*	414
00DF[0,3,4]ZZ	440
00DF*	23, 50, 151, 318
00DG[0,3,4]ZZ	440
00DG*	23, 50, 151, 318
00DH[0,3,4]ZZ	440
00DH*	23, 50, 151, 318
00DJ[0,3,4]ZZ	440
00DJ*	23, 50, 151, 318
00DK[0,3,4]ZZ	440
00DK*	23, 50, 151, 318
00DL[0,3,4]ZZ	440
00DL*	23, 50, 151, 318
00DM[0,3,4]ZZ	440
00DM*	23, 50, 151, 318
00DN[0,3,4]ZZ	440
00DN*	23, 50, 151, 318
00DP[0,3,4]ZZ	440
00DP*	23, 50, 151, 318

Code	Page	Code	Page	Code	Page	Code	Page
0198[0,3,4][0,Z]Z	24	01BM*	24	01N3[0,3,4]ZZ	441	021K0A[P,Q,R]	74
01980ZX	24, 319	01BN[0,3,4]ZZ	89, 441	01N3*	152, 319	021K0J[P,Q,R]	74
0199[0,3,4][0,Z]Z	24	01BN*	24	01N4[0,3,4]ZZ	441	021K0K[P,Q,R]	74
01990ZX	24, 319	01BP[0,3,4]ZZ	89, 267	01N4*	152, 319	021K0Z[5,8,9,C,F,P,Q,R,W]	74
019A[0,3,4][0,Z]Z	24	01BP*	24	01N5[0,3,4]ZZ	314, 441	021K49[P,Q,R]	74
019A0ZX	24, 319	01BQ[0,3,4]ZZ	24, 151, 319, 441	01N5*	149	021K4A[P,Q,R]	74
019B[0,3,4][0,Z]Z	24	01BQ0ZX	24, 151, 319	01N6[0,3,4]ZZ	441	021K4J[P,Q,R]	74
019B0ZX	24, 319	01BR[0,3,4]ZZ	24, 151, 319, 441	01N6*	152, 319	021K4K[P,Q,R]	74
019C[0,3,4][0,Z]Z	24	01BR0ZX	24, 151, 319	01N8[0,3,4]ZZ	441	021K4Z[5,8,9,C,F,P,Q,R,W]	74
019C0ZX	24, 319	01C*	24	01N8*	152, 319	021L09[P,Q,R]	74
019D[0,3,4][0,Z]Z	24	01CK*	89	01N9[0,3,4]ZZ	441	021L0A[P,Q,R]	74
019D0ZX	24, 319	01CL*	89	01N9*	152, 319	021L0J[P,Q,R]	74
019F[0,3,4][0,Z]Z	24	01CM*	89	01NA[0,3,4]ZZ	441	021L0K[P,Q,R]	74
019F0ZX	24, 319	01CN*	89	01NA*	152, 319	021L0Z[5,8,9,C,F,P,Q,R,W]	74
019G[0,3,4][0,Z]Z	24	01CP*	89	01NB[0,3,4]ZZ	441	021L49[P,Q,R]	74
019G0ZX	24, 319	01D*	24	01NB*	152, 319	021L4A[P,Q,R]	74
019H[0,3,4][0,Z]Z	24	01D0[0,3,4]ZZ	441	01NC[0,3,4]ZZ	441	021L4J[P,Q,R]	74
019H0ZX	24, 319	01D0*	151, 319	01NC*	152, 319	021L4K[P,Q,R]	74
019K[0,3,4][0,Z]Z	89	01D1[0,3,4]ZZ	441	01ND[0,3,4]ZZ	441	021L4Z[5,8,9,C,F,P,Q,R,W]	74
019K*	24	01D1*	151, 319	01ND*	152, 319	021V[0,4][9,A,J,K,Z][P,Q,R]	92
019L[0,3,4][0,Z]Z	89	01D2[0,3,4]ZZ	441	01NF[0,3,4]ZZ	441	021W[0,4][9,A,J,K,Z][B,D,P,Q,R]	92
019L*	24	01D2*	151, 319	01NF*	152, 319	021W[0,4][9,A,J,K,Z][B,D]	21, 319
019M[0,3,4][0,Z]Z	89	01D3[0,3,4]ZZ	441	01NG[0,3,4]ZZ	441	0254[0,3,4]ZZ	74
019M*	24	01D3*	152, 319	01NG*	145, 319	0255[0,4]ZZ	74
019N[0,3,4][0,Z]Z	89	01D4[0,3,4]ZZ	441	01NH[0,3,4]ZZ	441	02553ZZ	98
019N*	24	01D4*	152, 319	01NH*	152, 319	0256[0,4]ZZ	74
019P[0,3,4][0,Z]Z	89	01D5[0,3,4]ZZ	441	01NQ[0,3,4]ZZ	441	02563ZZ	98
019P*	24	01D5*	152, 319	01NQ*	152, 319	0257[0,4]ZZ	74
019Q[0,3,4][0,Z]Z	24	01D6[0,3,4]ZZ	441	01NR[0,3,4]ZZ	441	02570ZK	80
019Q0ZX	24, 319	01D6*	152, 319	01NR*	152, 319	02573ZK	98
019R[0,3,4][0,Z]Z	24	01D8[0,3,4]ZZ	441	01PY[0,3,4,X]MZ	50, 152, 258, 267, 319	02573ZZ	98
019R0ZX	24, 319	01D8*	152, 319	01PY[0,3,4][0,2,7,M]Z	24	02574ZK	98
01B0[0,3,4]ZZ	24, 151, 319, 440	01D9[0,3,4]ZZ	441	01PYXMZ	24	0258[0,4]ZZ	74
01B00ZX	24, 151, 319	01D9*	152, 319	01Q*	24	02583ZZ	98
01B1[0,3,4]ZZ	24, 151, 319, 440	01DA[0,3,4]ZZ	441	01Q0*	152, 319	0259[0,4]ZZ	74
01B10ZX	24, 151, 319	01DA*	152, 319	01Q1*	152, 319	02593ZZ	98
01B2[0,3,4]ZZ	24, 151, 319, 440	01DB[0,3,4]ZZ	441	01Q2*	152, 319	025D[0,3,4]ZZ	74
01B20ZX	24, 151, 319	01DB*	152, 319	01Q3*	152, 319	025F[0,4]ZZ	74
01B3[0,3,4]ZZ	24, 151, 319, 440	01DC[0,3,4]ZZ	441	01Q4*	152, 319	025F3ZZ	98
01B30ZX	24, 151, 319	01DC*	152, 319	01Q5*	152, 319	025G[0,4]ZZ	74
01B4[0,3,4]ZZ	24, 151, 319, 440	01DD[0,3,4]ZZ	441	01Q6*	152, 319	025G3ZZ	98
01B40ZX	24, 151, 319	01DD*	152, 319	01Q8*	152, 319	025H[0,4]ZZ	74
01B5[0,3,4]ZZ	24, 151, 319, 440	01DF[0,3,4]ZZ	441	01Q9*	152, 319	025H3ZZ	98
01B50ZX	24, 151, 319	01DF*	152, 319	01QA*	152, 319	025J[0,4]ZZ	74
01B6[0,3,4]ZZ	24, 151, 319, 440	01DG[0,3,4]ZZ	441	01QB*	152, 319	025J3ZZ	98
01B60ZX	24, 151, 319	01DG*	152, 319	01QC*	152, 319	025K[0,4]ZZ	74
01B8[0,3,4]ZZ	24, 151, 319, 440	01DH[0,3,4]ZZ	441	01QD*	152, 319	025K3ZZ	98
01B80ZX	24, 151, 319	01DH*	152, 319	01QF*	152, 319	025L[0,4]ZZ	74
01B9[0,3,4]ZZ	24, 151, 319, 440	01DK*	50, 89	01QG*	152, 319	025L3ZZ	98
01B90ZX	24, 151, 319	01DL*	89	01QH*	152, 319	025M[0,4]ZZ	74
01BA[0,3,4]ZZ	24, 151, 319, 440	01DM*	89	01QQ*	152, 319	025M3ZZ	98
01BA0ZX	24, 151, 319	01DN[0,3,4]ZZ	441	01QR*	319	025N[0,3,4]ZZ	92, 296
01BB[0,3,4]ZZ	24, 151, 319, 440	01DN*	89	01S*	24	025N*	60, 319
01BB0ZX	24, 151, 319	01DP*	89, 267	01U*	24, 319	025P[0,3,4]ZZ	92
01BC[0,3,4]ZZ	24, 151, 319, 440	01DQ[0,3,4]ZZ	441	01WY[0,3,4][0,2,7,M]Z	24	025P*	60
01BC0ZX	24, 151, 319	01DQ*	152, 319	01X*	24	025Q[0,3,4]ZZ	92
01BD[0,3,4]ZZ	24, 151, 319, 440	01DR[0,3,4]ZZ	441	0210[0,4][9,A,J,K,Z][3,8,9,C,F]	75, 76	025Q*	60
01BD0ZX	24, 151, 319	01DR*	152, 319	0210[0,4][9,A,J,K]W	75, 76, 76	025R[0,3,4]ZZ	92
01BF[0,3,4]ZZ	24, 151, 319, 440	01H*	24	0211[0,4][9,A,J,K,Z][3,8,9,C,F]		025R*	60
01BF0ZX	24, 151, 319	01HY[0,3,4]MZ	31, 50, 80, 152, 251, 258, 267, 319		75, 76, 76	025S[0,3,4]ZZ	93
01BG[0,3,4]ZZ	24, 151, 319, 440			0211[0,4][9,A,J,K]W	75, 76	025S*	60
01BG0ZX	24, 151, 319	01J*	24	0212[0,4][9,A,J,K,Z][3,8,9,C,F]	75, 76	025T[0,3,4]ZZ	93
01BH[0,3,4]ZZ	24, 151, 319, 441	01N*	24	0212[0,4][9,A,J,K]W	75, 76, 76	025T*	60
01BH0ZX	24, 151, 319	01N0[0,3,4]ZZ	441	0213[0,4][9,A,J,K,Z][3,8,9,C,F]	75, 76	025V[0,3,4]ZZ	93
01BK[0,3,4]ZZ	50, 89	01N0*	152, 319	0213[0,4][9,A,J,K]W	75, 76, 76	025V*	60
01BK*	24	01N1[0,3,4]ZZ	441	0216[0,4][9,A,J,K,Z][P,Q,R]	74	025W[0,3,4]ZZ	93
01BL[0,3,4]ZZ	89	01N1*	152, 319	0216[0,4]Z7	92, 319	025W*	60
01BL*	24	01N2[0,3,4]ZZ	441	0217[0,4][9,A,J,K,Z][P,Q,R]	74	0270[0,3,4][4,D,T][6,Z]	78, 79
01BM[0,3,4]ZZ	89	01N2*	152, 319	021K09[P,Q,R]	74	0270[0,3,4][D,T][6,Z]	79, 79

Code	Page	Code	Page	Code	Page	Code	Page
0270[0,3,4]4[6,Z]	78, 79	02BH[0,4]ZZ	74	02CR[0,3,4]ZZ	93	02HL[0,3,4]0Z	89
0270[3,4][4,D,T,Z][6,Z]	75	02BH3ZZ	98	02CR*	60, 319	02HL[0,3,4]2Z	319
0270[3,4][4,D,T][6,Z]	78, 79	02BJ[0,4]ZZ	74	02CS[0,3,4]ZZ	93	02HL[0,3,4]JZ	76
0270[3,4]Z[6,Z]	80	02BJ3ZZ	98	02CS*	60, 319	02HL[0,3,4]KZ	72, 73, 74, 92
02700[4,D,T,Z][6,Z]	74	02BK[0,3,4]ZZ	74	02CT[0,3,4]ZZ	93	02HL[0,3,4]MZ	72, 73
0271[0,3,4][4,D,T][6,Z]	78, 79, 80	02BL[0,3,4]ZZ	74	02CT*	60, 319	02HL3JZ	24, 29, 30, 77, 78, 88, 319, 358
0271[0,3,4][D,T][6,Z]	79, 79	02BM[0,4]ZZ	74	02CV[0,3,4]ZZ	93	02HN[0,3,4][0,2,J,M]Z	319
0271[0,3,4]4[6,Z]	78, 79	02BM3ZZ	98	02CV*	60, 319	02HN[0,3,4][0,2]Z	60, 93, 296
0271[3,4][4,D,T,Z][6,Z]	75	02BN[0,3,4]Z[X,Z]	93, 296	02CW[0,3,4]ZZ	92	02HN[0,3,4][J,K,M]Z	73, 73, 74
0271[3,4][4,D,T][6,Z]	78, 79	02BN[0,3,4]ZZ	319	02CW*	110, 319	02HN[0,3,4][J,M]Z	24, 29, 30, 77, 88, 358
0271[3,4]Z[6,Z]	80	02BN*	60	02FN[0,3,4]ZZ	93, 319	02HN[0,3,4]KZ	92
02710[4,D,T,Z][6,Z]	74	02BP[0,3,4]ZX	80, 441	02H4[0,3,4][2,3,D]Z	74	02HP[0,3,4]DZ	93
0272[0,3,4][4,D,T][6,Z]	78, 79, 80	02BP[0,3,4]ZZ	60, 93	02H4[0,3,4][J,M]Z	78	02HQ[0,3,4]DZ	93
0272[0,3,4][D,T][6,Z]	79	02BP3ZZ	105, 319	02H4[0,3,4]0Z	89	02HQ00Z	89
0272[0,3,4]4[6,Z]	78, 79	02BQ[0,3,4]ZX	80, 441	02H4[0,4][J,M]Z	29, 77, 357, 358	02HQ30Z	89
0272[3,4][4,D,T,Z][6,Z]	75	02BQ[0,3,4]ZZ	60, 93	02H4[0,4]KZ	73, 74	02HQ40Z	89
0272[3,4][4,D,T][6,Z]	78, 79	02BQ3ZZ	319	02H40KZ	73, 92	02HR[0,3,4]DZ	93
0272[3,4]Z[6,Z]	80	02BR[0,3,4]ZX	80, 441	02H43[J,K,M]Z	73, 92	02HR00Z	89
02720[4,D,T,Z][6,Z]	74	02BR[0,3,4]ZZ	60, 93	02H43KZ	78	02HR30Z	89
0273[0,3,4][4,D,T][6,Z]	78, 79	02BR3ZZ	319	02H44KZ	73, 92	02HR40Z	89
0273[0,3,4][D,T][6,Z]	79, 79	02BS[0,3,4]ZX	80, 441	02H6[0,3,4]0Z	89	02HS[0,3,4][2,D]Z	93
0273[0,3,4]4[6,Z]	78, 79	02BS[0,3,4]ZZ	60, 93	02H6[0,3,4]2Z	74	02HS[0,3,4]0Z	89
0273[3,4][4,D,T,Z][6,Z]	75	02BS3ZZ	319	02H6[0,3,4]JZ	29, 77, 78, 357, 358	02HT[0,3,4][2,D]Z	93
0273[3,4][4,D,T][6,Z]	78, 79	02BT[0,3,4]ZX	80, 441	02H6[0,3,4]KZ	73, 74, 92	02HT[0,3,4]0Z	89
0273[3,4]Z[6,Z]	80	02BT[0,3,4]ZZ	60, 93	02H6[0,4]MZ	29, 77, 78, 357, 358	02HV[0,3,4][2,D]Z	24, 63, 80, 110, 121,
02730[4,D,T,Z][6,Z]	74	02BT3ZZ	319	02H6[3,4]JZ	29, 77, 358		152, 238, 251, 258, 268, 290, 319
027F[3,4][4,D,Z]Z	75, 98	02BV[0,3,4]ZX	80, 441	02H602Z	319	02HV[0,3,4]0Z	89
027F0[4,D,Z]Z	71, 72	02BV[0,3,4]ZZ	60, 93	02H603Z	74	02HV[0,3,4]DZ	271
027G[3,4][4,D,Z]Z	75, 98	02BV3ZZ	319	02H60DZ	74	02HV[3,4]2Z	271
027G0[4,D,Z]Z	71, 72	02BW[0,3,4]ZX	80, 441	02H63[2,J,M]Z	319	02HV02Z	271
027H[3,4][4,D,Z]Z	75, 98	02BW[0,3,4]ZZ	319	02H63[J,M]Z	24	02HW[0,3,4][2,D]Z	93
027H0[4,D,Z]Z	71, 72	02BW[0,4]ZZ	92, 110	02H63DZ	74	02J[A,Y]4ZZ	50, 63, 290
027J[3,4][4,D,Z]Z	75, 98	02BW3ZZ	60, 93	02H63JZ	30, 77, 78, 88, 358	02JA[0,4]ZZ	89, 296
027J0[4,D,Z]Z	71, 72	02C0[3,4]ZZ	78, 79, 80	02H63MZ	30, 77, 88, 358	02JA0ZZ	60, 251, 319
027K[0,3,4][4,D,Z]Z	93	02C00ZZ	74	02H642Z	319	02JY[0,4]ZZ	296
027K*	319	02C03ZZ	75	02H643Z	74	02JY0ZZ	60, 89, 251, 319
027P*	80	02C1[3,4]ZZ	78, 79, 80	02H64DZ	74	02JY4ZZ	89
027Q*	80	02C10ZZ	74	02H64MZ	29, 77, 358	02K80ZZ	78, 79, 80
027R[0,3,4][4,D,Z]T	93, 319	02C13ZZ	75	02H7[0,3,4][2,3,D]Z	74	02K83ZZ	98
027R[0,3,4][4,D,Z]Z	80	02C2[3,4]ZZ	78, 79, 80	02H7[0,3,4]0Z	89	02K84ZZ	98
027S*	80	02C20ZZ	74	02H7[0,3,4]JZ	29, 77, 78, 357, 358	02L70CK	80
027T*	80	02C23ZZ	75	02H7[0,3,4]KZ	73, 74, 92	02L70DK	80
027V*	80	02C3[3,4]ZZ	78, 79, 80	02H7[0,4]MZ	29, 77, 78, 357, 358	02L70ZK	80
027W*	80	02C30ZZ	74	02H702Z	319	02L73CK	98
0288[0,3,4]ZZ	93	02C33ZZ	75	02H73[2,J,M]Z	319	02L73DK	98
0289[0,3,4]ZZ	74	02C4[0,3,4]ZZ	74	02H73[J,M]Z	24	02L73ZK	98
028D[0,3,4]ZZ	74	02C5[0,3,4]ZZ	74	02H73JZ	30, 77, 78, 88, 358	02L74CK	98
02B[Q,R]3ZZ	105	02C6[0,3,4]ZZ	74	02H73MZ	30, 77, 88, 358	02L74DK	98
02B[S,T]3ZZ	105	02C7[0,3,4]ZZ	74	02H742Z	319	02L74ZK	98
02B[V,W]3ZZ	105	02C8[0,3,4]ZZ	74	02HA[0,3,4]QZ	1	02LR[0,3,4][C,D,Z]T	93, 319
02B4[0,3,4]ZZ	74	02C9[0,3,4]ZZ	74	02HA0RS	1, 71	02LS[0,3,4][C,D,Z]Z	93, 320
02B5[0,4]ZZ	74	02CD[0,3,4]ZZ	74	02HA0RZ	1, 71	02LT[0,3,4][C,D,Z]Z	93, 320
02B53ZZ	98	02CF[3,4]ZZ	93	02HA3RS	1, 71	02LV[0,3,4][C,D,Z]Z	320
02B6[0,4]ZZ	74	02CF0ZZ	74	02HA3RZ	71	02LV*	24, 63, 80, 110, 121, 152, 238,
02B63ZZ	98	02CG[3,4]ZZ	93	02HA4RS	1, 71		251, 258, 268, 271, 290
02B7[0,4]ZZ	74	02CG0ZZ	74	02HA4RZ	1, 71	02N4[0,3,4]ZZ	93
02B70ZK	80	02CH[3,4]ZZ	93	02HK[0,3,4][0,2]Z	88, 92	02N4*	320
02B73ZK	98	02CH0ZZ	74	02HK[0,3,4][J,M]Z	29, 77, 78, 357, 358	02N5[0,3,4]ZZ	75
02B73ZZ	98	02CJ[3,4]ZZ	93	02HK[0,3,4]JZ	76	02N6[0,3,4]ZZ	75
02B74ZK	98	02CJ0ZZ	74	02HK[0,3,4]KZ	72, 73, 74, 92	02N7[0,3,4]ZZ	75
02B8[0,4]ZZ	74	02CK[0,3,4]ZZ	74	02HK[3,4][J,M]Z	29, 77, 358	02N8[0,3,4]ZZ	93
02B83ZZ	98	02CL[0,3,4]ZZ	74	02HK03Z	74	02N8*	320
02B9[0,4]ZZ	74	02CM[0,3,4]ZZ	74	02HK0DZ	74	02N9[0,3,4]ZZ	75
02B93ZZ	98	02CN[0,3,4]ZZ	93, 296	02HK3DZ	74	02ND[0,3,4]ZZ	75
02BD[0,3,4]ZZ	74	02CN*	60, 319	02HK3JZ	24, 29, 30, 77, 78, 88, 319, 358	02NF[3,4]ZZ	93
02BF[0,4]ZZ	74	02CP[0,3,4]ZZ	93	02HK43Z	74	02NF0ZZ	71, 72
02BF3ZZ	98	02CP*	60, 319	02HK4DZ	74	02NG[3,4]ZZ	93
02BG[0,4]ZZ	74	02CQ[0,3,4]ZZ	93	02HL[0,3,4][2,3,D]Z	75	02NG0ZZ	71, 72
02BG3ZZ	98	02CQ*	60, 319	02HL[0,3,4][J,M]Z	29, 77, 78, 357, 358	02NH[3,4]ZZ	93

Code	Page	Code	Page	Code	Page	Code	Page
02NH0ZZ	71, 72	02RF0JZ	71, 72	02UF*	71, 72	02W5[0,4]JZ	75
02NJ[3,4]ZZ	93	02RF0KZ	71, 72	02UG07Z	71, 72	02WA[0,3,4][2,3,7,8,C,D,K]Z	75
02NJ0ZZ	71, 72	02RF3[7,8,J,K]H	92	02UG08Z	71, 72	02WA[0,3,4][K,M]Z	320
02NK[0,3,4]ZZ	75	02RF3[7,8,J,K]Z	92	02UG0JZ	71, 72	02WA[0,3,4][Q,R]Z	1
02NL[0,3,4]ZZ	75	02RF47Z	71, 72	02UG0KZ	71, 72	02WA[0,3,4]MZ	24, 88
02NM[0,3,4]ZZ	75	02RF48Z	71, 72	02UG37Z	71, 72	02WA[3,4]JZ	75, 320
02NN[0,3,4]ZZ	93, 296	02RF4JZ	71, 72	02UG38Z	71, 72	02WA0JZ	71
02NN*	60, 320	02RF4KZ	71, 72	02UG3JZ	75, 98	02WA0QZ	71
02NP*	80	02RG[0,3,4][7,8,J,K]Z	71, 72	02UG3KZ	71, 72	02WA0RZ	71
02NQ*	80	02RG3[7,8,J,K]H	92	02UG47Z	71, 72	02WA3QZ	71
02NR*	80	02RH07Z	71, 72	02UG48Z	71, 72	02WA3RZ	71
02NS*	80	02RH08Z	71, 72	02UG4JZ	71, 72	02WA4QZ	71
02NT*	80	02RH0JZ	71, 72	02UG4KZ	71, 72	02WA4RZ	71
02NV*	80	02RH0KZ	71, 72	02UH*	71, 72	02WF[0,4][7,8,J,K]Z	75
02NW*	80	02RH3[7,8,J,K]H	92	02UJ*	71, 72	02WG[0,4][7,8,J,K]Z	75
02PA[0,3,4,X]MZ	24, 30, 77, 78, 88, 320, 358	02RH3[7,8,J,K]Z	92	02UK[0,3,4][7,8,J]Z	93, 320	02WH[0,4][7,8,J,K]Z	75
02PA[0,3,4][2,3,7,8,C,D,J,K]Z	75	02RH47Z	71, 72	02UK[0,3,4]KZ	75	02WJ[0,4][7,8,J,K]Z	75
02PA[0,3,4][Q,R]Z	92	02RH48Z	71, 72	02UL[0,3,4][7,8,J]Z	93, 320	02WM[0,4]JZ	75
02PA[0,3,4]RZ	1	02RH4JZ	71, 72	02UL[0,3,4]KZ	75	02WY[0,3,4][2,3,7,8,C,D,J,K]Z	93
02PY[0,3,4][2,3,7,8,C,D,J,K]Z	93	02RH4KZ	71, 72	02UM[0,3,4][7,J,K]Z	75	02YA0Z[0,1,2]	1
02Q0[0,3,4]ZZ	75	02RJ*	71, 72	02UM[3,4]8Z	75	031[3,4]0ZD	110
02Q1[0,3,4]ZZ	75	02RK[0,4][7,K]Z	75	02UM08Z	93, 320	031[5,6]0ZD	110
02Q2[0,3,4]ZZ	75	02RK[0,4][8,J]Z	93, 320	02UN[0,3,4][7,8,J,K]Z	93	031[7,8]0ZD	110
02Q3[0,3,4]ZZ	75	02RL[0,4][7,K]Z	75	02UN*	320	0312*	80
02Q4[0,3,4]ZZ	75	02RL[0,4][8,J]Z	93, 320	02UP*	80, 320	03130[9,A,J,K,Z][0,1,2,3,4,5,6,7,8,9,B,C,D,F,J,K]	80
02Q5[0,3,4]ZZ	75	02RM[0,4][7,J,K]Z	75	02UQ*	80, 320	03130[9,A,J,K,Z][M,N]	93
02Q6[0,3,4]ZZ	93	02RM[0,4]8Z	93, 320	02UR*	80, 320	03130ZD	238, 251, 320
02Q6*	320	02RN[0,4][7,8,J,K]Z	93	02US*	80, 320	03140[9,A,J,K,Z][0,1,2,3,4,5,6,7,8,9,B,C,D,F,J,K]	80
02Q7[0,3,4]ZZ	93	02RN*	320	02UT*	80, 320	03140[9,A,J,K,Z][M,N]	93
02Q7*	320	02RP[0,4][7,8,J,K]Z	71, 72	02UV*	80, 320	03140ZD	238, 251, 320
02Q8[0,3,4]ZZ	93	02RP*	60, 320	02UW[0,3,4][7,8,K]Z	80	0315*	80
02Q8*	320	02RQ[0,4][7,8,J,K]Z	71, 72	02UW[3,4]JZ	71, 72, 251	03150[9,A,J,K,Z]0	21, 63, 121, 207, 238, 320
02Q9[0,3,4]ZZ	75	02RQ*	60, 320	02UW*	320	03150ZD	238, 251, 320
02QA[0,3,4]ZZ	93	02RR[0,4][7,8,J,K]Z	71, 72	02UW0JZ	80	0316*	80
02QA*	320	02RR*	60, 320	02VA[0,3,4][C,Z]Z	93	03160[9,A,J,K,Z]1	21, 63, 121, 207, 238, 320
02QA0ZZ	60, 296	02RS[0,4][7,8,J,K]Z	71, 72	02VA*	320	03160ZD	238, 251, 320
02QB[0,3,4]ZZ	75	02RS*	60, 320	02VP[0,3,4][D,Z]Z	93, 320	03170[9,A,J,K,Z][0,3]	80
02QC[0,3,4]ZZ	75	02RT[0,4][7,8,J,K]Z	71, 72	02VP[0,3,4]CZ	80	03170[9,A,J,K,Z][D,F]	
02QD[0,3,4]ZZ	75	02RT*	60, 320	02VQ[0,3,4][D,Z]Z	93, 320	03170[9,A,J,K,Z][D,F]	89, 238, 251, 320
02QF*	71, 72	02RV[0,4][7,8,J,K]Z	71, 72	02VQ[0,3,4]CZ	93	03180[9,A,J,K,Z][1,4]	80
02QG*	71, 72	02RV*	60, 320	02VR[0,3,4][D,Z][T,Z]	320	03180[9,A,J,K,Z][D,F]	89, 238, 251320
02QH*	71, 72	02RW[0,4][7,8,J,K]Z	71, 72	02VR0CT	80	03190[9,A,J,K,Z]3	80
02QJ*	71, 72	02RW*	60, 320	02VR0CZ	93	03190[9,A,J,K,Z]F	89, 238, 251, 320
02QK[0,3,4]ZZ	93	02S*	80, 320	02VR0DT	93	03190ZF	110
02QK*	320	02T5[0,3,4]ZZ	75	02VR0DZ	93	031A0[9,A,J,K,Z]4	80
02QL[0,3,4]ZZ	93	02T8[0,4]ZZ	75	02VR0ZT	93	031A0[9,A,J,K,Z]F	89, 238, 251, 320
02QL*	320	02T83ZZ	98	02VR0ZZ	93	031A0ZF	110
02QM[0,3,4]ZZ	75	02T9[0,3,4]ZZ	75	02VR3CT	80	031B0[9,A,J,K,Z]3	80
02QN[0,3,4]ZZ	93	02TD[0,3,4]ZZ	75	02VR3CZ	93	031B0[9,A,J,K,Z]F	89, 238, 251, 320
02QN*	320	02TH[0,3,4]ZZ	75	02VR3DT	93	031B0ZF	110
02QP*	63, 80, 320	02TM[0,3,4]ZZ	75	02VR3DZ	93	031C0[9,A,J,K,Z]4	80
02QQ*	63, 80, 320	02TN[0,3,4]ZZ	93, 296	02VR3ZT	93	031C0[9,A,J,K,Z]F	89, 238, 251, 320
02QR*	63, 80, 320	02TN*	60, 320	02VR3ZZ	93	031C0ZF	110
02QS*	88, 320	02U5[0,3,4][7,8,K]Z	75	02VR4CT	80	031G*	80
02QT*	88, 320	02U5[3,4]JZ	98	02VR4CZ	93	031H*	320
02QV*	88, 320	02U50JZ	75	02VR4DT	93	031H0[9,A,J,K,Z]G	7, 8, 12, 17
02QW[0,3,4]ZZ	92	02U6[3,4][7,8,J,K]Z	93, 320	02VR4DZ	93	031H0[9,A,J,K,Z]J	21, 63, 80, 121, 207, 238
02QW*	63, 320	02U60[7,8,K]Z	75	02VR4ZT	93		
02R5[0,4][7,8,J,K]Z	93	02U60JZ	93, 320	02VR4ZZ	93	031J*	320
02R5*	320	02U7[0,3,4][7,8,K]Z	75	02VS[0,3,4][D,Z]Z	93, 320	031J0[9,A,J,K,Z]G	7, 8, 13, 17
02R6[0,4][7,8,J,K]Z	93	02U70JZ	93, 320	02VS[0,3,4]CZ	80	031J0[9,A,J,K,Z]K	21, 63, 122, 80, 207, 238
02R6*	320	02U73JZ	80	02VT[0,3,4][D,Z]Z	93, 320		
02R7[0,4][7,8,J,K]Z	93	02U74JZ	80	02VT[0,3,4]CZ	80	031K*	320
02R7*	320	02U9[0,3,4][7,8,J,K]Z	75	02VV*	24, 63, 80, 110, 121, 152, 238, 251, 258, 268, 271, 290, 320	031K0[9,A,J,K,Z]J	21, 63, 80, 121, 207, 238
02R9[0,4][7,8,J,K]Z	75	02UA[0,3,4][7,8,K]Z	93, 320				
02RD[0,4][7,8,J,K]Z	75	02UA0JZ	92	02VW[0,3,4][D,Z]Z	320	031L*	320
02RF07Z	71, 72	02UA3JZ	92	02VW[0,3,4]CZ	80		
02RF08Z	71, 72	02UA4JZ	92	02VW[0,3,4]DZ	71, 72, 251		
		02UD[0,3,4][7,8,J,K]Z	75	02VW[0,3,4]ZZ	93		

Numeric Index to Procedures

Code	Page	Code	Page	Code	Page	Code	Page
03VM[0,3,4][B,D,Z]Z	94, 322	04100AH	94	0410499	95	04104ZB	95
03VM[0,3,4][B,D]Z	7, 9, 13, 17, 251	04100AJ	94	041049B	95	04104ZC	95
03VM[0,3,4]CZ	82	04100AK	94	041049C	95	04104ZD	95
03VN[0,3,4][B,D,Z]Z	94, 322	04100AQ	94	041049D	95	04104ZF	95
03VN[0,3,4][B,D]Z	7, 9, 13, 17, 251	04100AR	94	041049F	95	04104ZG	95
03VN[0,3,4]CZ	82	04100J[1,2,3,4,5]	248	041049G	95	04104ZH	95
03VP[0,3,4][B,D,Z]Z	94, 322	04100J0	94	041049H	95	04104ZJ	95
03VP[0,3,4][B,D]Z	7, 9, 13, 17, 251	04100J1	94	041049J	95	04104ZK	95
03VP[0,3,4]CZ	82	04100J2	94	041049K	95	04104ZQ	95
03VQ[0,3,4][B,D,Z]Z	94, 322	04100J6	94	041049Q	95	04104ZR	95
03VQ[0,3,4][B,D]Z	7, 9, 13, 17, 251	04100J7	94	041049R	95	0414[0,4][9,A,J,K,Z][3,4,5]	95
03VQ[0,3,4]CZ	82	04100J8	94	04104A0	95	041C[0,4][9,A,J,K,Z][H,J,K]	208, 322
03VR[0,3,4][D,Z]Z	94, 322	04100J9	94	04104A1	95	041C[0,4][J,Z][3,4,5]	110, 248
03VR[0,3,4]CZ	82	04100JB	94	04104A2	95	041C*	95
03VR[0,3,4]DZ	7, 9, 13, 17, 251	04100JC	94	04104A6	95	041D[0,4][9,A,J,K,Z][H,J,K]	208, 322
03VS[0,3,4][D,Z]Z	94, 322	04100JD	94	04104A7	95	041D[0,4][J,Z][3,4,5]	110, 248
03VS[0,3,4]CZ	82	04100JF	94	04104A8	95	041D*	95
03VS[0,3,4]DZ	7, 9, 13, 17, 251	04100JG	94	04104A9	95	041E[0,4][9,A,J,K,Z][H,J,K]	208, 322
03VT[0,3,4][D,Z]Z	94, 322	04100JH	94	04104AB	95	041E*	95
03VT[0,3,4]CZ	82	04100JJ	94	04104AC	95	041F[0,4][9,A,J,K,Z][H,J,K]	208, 322
03VT[0,3,4]DZ	7, 9, 13, 17, 251	04100JK	94	04104AD	95	041F*	95
03VU[0,3,4][D,Z]Z	94, 322	04100JQ	94	04104AF	95	041H[0,4][9,A,J,K,Z][H,J,K]	208, 322
03VU[0,3,4]CZ	82	04100JR	94	04104AG	95	041H*	95
03VU[0,3,4]DZ	7, 9, 13, 17, 251	04100K[3,4,5]	248	04104AH	95	041J[0,4][9,A,J,K,Z][H,J,K]	208, 322
03VV[0,3,4][D,Z]Z	94, 322	04100K0	94	04104AJ	95	041J*	95
03VV[0,3,4]CZ	82	04100K1	94	04104AK	95	041K[0,4][9,A,J,K,Z]	22, 63, 122, 208,
03VV[0,3,4]DZ	7, 9, 13, 17, 251	04100K2	94	04104AQ	95	[H,J,K,L]	22, 63, 122, 208, 239, 322
03VY[0,3,4][D,Z]Z	94, 322	04100K6	94	04104AR	95	041K*	82
03VY[0,3,4]CZ	82	04100K7	94	04104J0	95	041L[0,4][9,A,J,K,Z]	22, 63, 122, 208,
03WY[0,3,4][0,2,3,7,C,D,J,K,M]Z	82	04100K8	94	04104J1	95	[H,J,K,L]	239, 322
03WY[0,3,4][7,K]Z	441	04100K9	94	04104J2	95	041L*	82
03WY[0,3,4]JZ	251	04100KB	94	04104J6	95	041M*	82
0410[0,4][9,A,J,K,Z][3,4,5]	322	04100KC	94	04104J7	95	041N*	82
0410[0,4][9,A,J,K,Z][6,7,8,9,		04100KD	94	04104J8	95	0450[0,3,4]ZZ	92
B,C,D,F,G,H,J,K,Q,R]	208, 322	04100KF	94	04104J9	95	0450*	110, 322
04100[9,A,J,K,Z]3	92	04100KG	94	04104JB	95	0451[0,3,4]ZZ	95
04100[9,A,J,K,Z]4	92	04100KH	94	04104JC	95	0452[0,3,4]ZZ	95
04100[9,A,J,K,Z]5	92	04100KJ	94	04104JD	95	0453[0,3,4]ZZ	95
04100[9,A][3,4,5]	248	04100KK	94	04104JF	95	0454[0,3,4]ZZ	95
04100[J,Z][1,2]	110	04100KQ	94	04104JG	95	0455[0,3,4]ZZ	95
0410090	94	04100KR	94	04104JH	95	0456[0,3,4]ZZ	95
0410091	94	04100Z[1,2,3,4,5]	248	04104JJ	95	0457[0,3,4]ZZ	95
0410092	94	04100Z0	94	04104JK	95	0458[0,3,4]ZZ	95
0410096	94	04100Z1	94	04104JQ	95	0459[0,3,4]ZZ	95
0410097	94	04100Z2	94	04104JR	95	0459*	251
0410098	94	04100Z6	94	04104K0	95	045A[0,3,4]ZZ	95
0410099	94	04100Z7	94	04104K1	95	045A*	251
041009B	94	04100Z8	94	04104K2	95	045B[0,3,4]ZZ	95
041009C	94	04100Z9	94	04104K6	95	045C[0,3,4]ZZ	95
041009D	94	04100ZB	95	04104K7	95	045D[0,3,4]ZZ	95
041009F	94	04100ZC	95	04104K8	95	045E[0,3,4]ZZ	95
041009G	94	04100ZD	95	04104K9	95	045F[0,3,4]ZZ	95
041009H	94	04100ZF	95	04104KB	95	045H[0,3,4]ZZ	95
041009J	94	04100ZG	95	04104KC	95	045J[0,3,4]ZZ	95
041009K	94	04100ZH	95	04104KD	95	045K*	82, 239, 322
041009Q	94	04100ZJ	95	04104KF	95	045L*	82, 239, 322
041009R	94	04100ZK	95	04104KG	95	045M*	82, 239, 323
04100A0	94	04100ZQ	95	04104KH	95	045N*	82, 239, 323
04100A1	94	04100ZR	95	04104KJ	95	045P*	82, 239, 323
04100A2	94	04104[9,A,J,K,Z][3,4,5]	248	04104KK	95	045Q*	82, 239, 323
04100A6	94	04104[9,A,J,K,Z]3	92	04104KQ	95	045R*	82, 239, 323
04100A7	94	04104[9,A,J,K,Z]4	92	04104KR	95	045S*	82, 239, 323
04100A8	94	04104[9,A,J,K,Z]5	92	04104Z0	95	045T*	82, 239, 323
04100A9	94	0410490	95	04104Z1	95	045U*	82, 239, 323
04100AB	94	0410491	95	04104Z2	95	045V*	82, 239, 323
04100AC	94	0410492	95	04104Z6	95	045W*	82, 239, 323
04100AD	94	0410496	95	04104Z7	95	045Y*	82, 239, 323
04100AF	94	0410497	95	04104Z8	95	047*	82
04100AG	94	0410498	95	04104Z9	95		

Code	Page	Code	Page	Code	Page	Code	Page
04703[4,D,Z]Z	22, 63, 110, 122, 152, 208, 239, 251, 323	047L4Z1	22, 63, 83, 111, 122, 152, 208, 240, 252, 323	04B0[0,3,4]ZZ	92, 111, 323	04BW[0,3,4]ZZ	240, 323
04713[4,D,Z]Z	22, 63, 110, 122, 152, 208, 239, 251, 323	047M041	22, 63, 83, 111, 122, 152, 208, 240, 252, 323	04B1[0,3,4]ZX	83, 441	04BW*	83
04723[4,D,Z]Z	22, 63, 110, 122, 152, 208, 239, 251, 323	047M0D1	22, 63, 83, 111, 122, 152, 208, 240, 252, 323	04B1[0,3,4]ZZ	95	04BY[0,3,4]ZX	442
04733[4,D,Z]Z	22, 63, 110, 122, 152, 208, 239, 251, 323	047M0Z1	22, 63, 83, 111, 122, 152, 208, 240, 252, 323	04B2[0,3,4]ZX	83, 441	04BY[0,3,4]ZZ	240, 323
04743[4,D,Z]Z	22, 63, 110, 122, 152, 208, 239, 251, 323	047M341	22, 63, 83, 111, 122, 152, 208, 240, 252, 323	04B2[0,3,4]ZZ	95	04BY*	83
04753[4,D,Z]Z	22, 63, 110, 122, 152, 208, 239, 251, 323	047M3D1	22, 63, 83, 111, 122, 152, 208, 240, 252, 323	04B3[0,3,4]ZX	83, 441	04C*	323
04763[4,D,Z]Z	22, 63, 110, 122, 152, 208, 239, 251, 323	047M3Z1	22, 64, 83, 111, 122, 152, 208, 240, 252, 323	04B3[0,3,4]ZZ	95	04C0[0,3,4]ZZ	92
04773[4,D,Z]Z	22, 63, 110, 122, 152, 208, 239, 251, 323	047M441	22, 64, 83, 111, 122, 152, 208, 240, 252, 323	04B4[0,3,4]ZX	83, 441	04C0*	111
04783[4,D,Z]Z	22, 63, 110, 122, 152, 208, 239, 251, 323	047M4D1	22, 64, 83, 111, 122, 152, 208, 240, 252, 323	04B4[0,3,4]ZZ	95	04C1[0,3,4]ZZ	95
04793[4,D,Z]Z	22, 63, 110, 122, 152, 208, 239, 251, 323	047M4Z1	22, 64, 83, 111, 122, 152, 208, 240, 252, 323	04B5[0,3,4]ZX	83, 441	04C1*	111, 252
047A3[4,D,Z]Z	22, 63, 110, 122, 152, 208, 239, 251, 323	047N041	22, 64, 83, 111, 122, 152, 208, 240, 252, 323	04B5[0,3,4]ZZ	95	04C2[0,3,4]ZZ	95
047B3[4,D,Z]Z	22, 63, 110, 122, 152, 208, 239, 251, 323	047N0D1	22, 64, 83, 111, 122, 152, 208, 240, 252, 323	04B6[0,3,4]ZX	83, 441	04C2*	111, 252
047C3[4,D,Z]Z	22, 63, 110, 122, 152, 208, 239, 251, 323	047N0Z1	22, 64, 83, 111, 122, 152, 208, 240, 252, 323	04B6[0,3,4]ZZ	95	04C3[0,3,4]ZZ	95
047D3[4,D,Z]Z	22, 63, 110, 122, 152, 208, 239, 251, 323	047N341	22, 64, 83, 111, 122, 152, 208, 240, 252, 323	04B7[0,3,4]ZX	83, 441	04C3*	111, 252
047E3[4,D,Z]Z	22, 63, 110, 122, 152, 208, 239, 251, 323	047N3D1	22, 64, 83, 111, 122, 152, 208, 240, 252, 323	04B7[0,3,4]ZZ	95	04C4[0,3,4]ZZ	95
047F3[4,D,Z]Z	22, 63, 110, 122, 152, 208, 239, 251, 323	047N3Z1	22, 64, 83, 111, 122, 152, 208, 240, 252, 323	04B8[0,3,4]ZX	83, 441	04C4*	111, 252
047H3[4,D,Z]Z	22, 63, 110, 122, 152, 208, 239, 252, 323	047N441	22, 64, 83, 111, 122, 152, 208, 240, 252, 323	04B8[0,3,4]ZZ	95	04C5[0,3,4]ZZ	95
047J3[4,D,Z]Z	22, 63, 110, 122, 152, 208, 239, 252, 323	047N4D1	22, 64, 83, 111, 122, 152, 208, 240, 252, 323	04B9[0,3,4]ZX	83, 441	04C5*	111, 252
047K041	22, 63, 83, 110, 122, 152, 208, 239, 252, 323	047N4Z1	22, 64, 83, 111, 122, 152, 208, 240, 252, 323	04B9[0,3,4]ZZ	95	04C6[0,3,4]ZZ	95
047K0D1	22, 63, 83, 110, 122, 152, 208, 239, 252, 323	047Y3[4,D,Z]Z	22, 64, 111, 122, 152, 208, 240, 252, 323	04BA[0,3,4]ZX	83, 441	04C6*	111, 252
047K0Z1	22, 63, 83, 111, 122, 152, 208, 239, 252, 323	0490[0,3,4]ZX	83, 441	04BA[0,3,4]ZZ	95	04C7[0,3,4]ZZ	95
047K3[4,D,Z]Z	22, 63, 111, 122, 152, 208, 239, 252, 323	0491[0,3,4]ZX	83, 441	04BB[0,3,4]ZX	83, 441	04C7*	111, 252
047K341	22, 63, 83, 111, 122, 152, 208, 239, 252, 323	0492[0,3,4]ZX	83, 441	04BB[0,3,4]ZZ	95	04C8[0,3,4]ZZ	95
047K3D1	22, 63, 83, 111, 122, 152, 208, 239, 252, 323	0493[0,3,4]ZX	83, 441	04BC[0,3,4]ZX	83, 441	04C8*	111, 252
047K3Z1	22, 63, 83, 111, 122, 152, 208, 239, 252, 323	0494[0,3,4]ZX	83, 441	04BC[0,3,4]ZZ	95	04C9[0,3,4]ZZ	95
047K441	22, 63, 83, 111, 122, 152, 208, 240, 252, 323	0495[0,3,4]ZX	83, 441	04BD[0,3,4]ZX	83, 441	04C9*	111, 252
047K4D1	22, 63, 83, 111, 122, 152, 208, 240, 252, 323	0496[0,3,4]ZX	83, 441	04BD[0,3,4]ZZ	95	04CA[0,3,4]ZZ	95
047K4Z1	22, 63, 83, 111, 122, 152, 208, 240, 252, 323	0497[0,3,4]ZX	83, 441	04BE[0,3,4]ZX	83, 441	04CA*	111, 252
047L041	22, 63, 83, 111, 122, 152, 208, 240, 252, 323	0498[0,3,4]ZX	83, 441	04BE[0,3,4]ZZ	95	04CB[0,3,4]ZZ	95
047L0D1	22, 63, 83, 111, 122, 152, 208, 240, 252, 323	0499[0,3,4]ZX	83, 441	04BF[0,3,4]ZX	83, 441	04CB*	111, 252
047L0Z1	22, 63, 83, 111, 122, 152, 208, 240, 252, 323	049A[0,3,4]ZX	83, 441	04BF[0,3,4]ZZ	95	04CC[0,3,4]ZZ	95
047L3[4,D,Z]Z	22, 63, 111, 122, 152, 208, 240, 252, 323	049B[0,3,4]ZX	83, 441	04BH[0,3,4]ZX	83, 441	04CC*	111, 252
047L341	22, 63, 83, 111, 122, 152, 208, 240, 252, 323	049C[0,3,4]ZX	83, 441	04BH[0,3,4]ZZ	95	04CD[0,3,4]ZZ	95
047L3D1	22, 63, 83, 111, 122, 152, 208, 240, 252, 323	049D[0,3,4]ZX	83, 441	04BJ[0,3,4]ZX	83, 441	04CD*	111, 252
047L3Z1	22, 63, 83, 111, 122, 152, 208, 240, 252, 323	049E[0,3,4]ZX	83, 441	04BJ[0,3,4]ZZ	95	04CE[0,3,4]ZZ	95
047L441	22, 63, 83, 111, 122, 152, 208, 240, 252, 323	049F[0,3,4]ZX	83, 441	04BK[0,3,4]ZX	441	04CE*	111, 252
047L4D1	22, 63, 83, 111, 122, 152, 208, 240, 252, 323	049H[0,3,4]ZX	83, 441	04BK[0,3,4]ZZ	240, 323	04CF[0,3,4]ZZ	95
		049J[0,3,4]ZX	83, 441	04BK*	83	04CF*	111, 252
		049K[0,3,4]ZX	83, 441	04BL[0,3,4]ZX	442	04CH[0,3,4]ZZ	95
		049L[0,3,4]ZX	83, 441	04BL[0,3,4]ZZ	240, 323	04CH*	111, 252
		049M[0,3,4]ZX	83, 441	04BL*	83	04CJ[0,3,4]ZZ	95
		049N[0,3,4]ZX	83, 441	04BM[0,3,4]ZX	442	04CJ*	111, 252
		049P[0,3,4]ZX	83, 441	04BM[0,3,4]ZZ	240, 323	04CK[0,3,4]ZZ	296
		049Q[0,3,4]ZX	83, 441	04BM*	83	04CK*	83, 240
		049R[0,3,4]ZX	83, 441	04BN[0,3,4]ZX	442	04CL[0,3,4]ZZ	296
		049S[0,3,4]ZX	83, 441	04BN[0,3,4]ZZ	240, 323	04CL*	83, 240
		049T[0,3,4]ZX	83, 441	04BN*	83	04CM[0,3,4]ZZ	296
		049U[0,3,4]ZX	83, 441	04BP[0,3,4]ZX	442	04CM*	83, 240
		049V[0,3,4]ZX	83, 441	04BP[0,3,4]ZZ	240, 323	04CN[0,3,4]ZZ	296
		049W[0,3,4]ZX	83, 441	04BP*	83	04CN*	83, 240
		049Y[0,3,4]ZX	83, 441	04BQ[0,3,4]ZX	442	04CP[0,3,4]ZZ	296
		04B0[0,3,4]ZX	83, 441	04BQ[0,3,4]ZZ	240, 323	04CP*	83, 240
				04BQ*	83	04CQ[0,3,4]ZZ	296
				04BR[0,3,4]ZX	442	04CQ*	83, 240
				04BR[0,3,4]ZZ	240, 323	04CR[0,3,4]ZZ	296
				04BR*	83	04CR*	83, 240
				04BS[0,3,4]ZX	442	04CS[0,3,4]ZZ	296
				04BS[0,3,4]ZZ	240, 323	04CS*	83, 240
				04BS*	83	04CT[0,3,4]ZZ	296
				04BT[0,3,4]ZX	442	04CT*	83, 240
				04BT[0,3,4]ZZ	240, 323	04CU[0,3,4]ZZ	296
				04BT*	83	04CU*	83, 240
				04BU[0,3,4]ZX	442	04CV[0,3,4]ZZ	296
				04BU[0,3,4]ZZ	240, 323	04CV*	83, 240
				04BU*	83	04CW[0,3,4]ZZ	296
				04BV[0,3,4]ZX	442	04CW*	83, 240
				04BV[0,3,4]ZZ	240, 323	04CY[0,3,4]ZZ	296
				04BV*	83	04CY*	22, 83, 111, 122, 240, 252
				04BW[0,3,4]ZX	442	04H0[0,3,4]DZ	83, 111, 296, 323

Code	Page	Code	Page	Code	Page	Code	Page
04H1[0,3,4]DZ	83, 296, 323	04LH[0,3,4][C,D,Z]Z	96	04QL[0,3,4]ZZ	209	04RV*	84, 240, 324
04H2[0,3,4]DZ	83, 296, 323	04LH[0,3,4][C,Z]Z	111, 442	04QL*	240	04RW*	84, 240, 324
04H3[0,3,4]DZ	83, 296, 323	04LH*	324	04QM[0,3,4]ZZ	209	04RY*	84, 240, 324
04H4[0,3,4]DZ	83, 296, 323	04LJ[0,3,4][C,D,Z]Z	96	04QM*	240	04S*	84
04H5[0,3,4]DZ	83, 296, 323	04LJ[0,3,4][C,Z]Z	111, 442	04QN[0,3,4]ZZ	209	04S0*	240, 252, 324
04H6[0,3,4]DZ	83, 296, 323	04LJ*	324	04QN*	240	04S1*	240, 252, 324
04H7[0,3,4]DZ	83, 296, 323	04LK[0,3,4][C,D,Z]Z	84	04QP[0,3,4]ZZ	209	04S2*	240, 252, 324
04H8[0,3,4]DZ	83, 296, 323	04LK*	324	04QP*	240	04S3*	240, 252, 324
04H9[0,3,4]DZ	83, 297, 323	04LL[0,3,4][C,D,Z]Z	84	04QQ[0,3,4]ZZ	209	04S4*	240, 252, 324
04HA[0,3,4]DZ	83, 297, 323	04LL*	324	04QQ*	240	04S5*	240, 252, 324
04HB[0,3,4]DZ	83, 297, 323	04LM[0,3,4][C,D,Z]Z	84	04QR[0,3,4]ZZ	209	04S6*	240, 252, 324
04HC[0,3,4]DZ	83, 297, 323	04LM*	324	04QR*	240	04S7*	240, 252, 324
04HD[0,3,4]DZ	83, 297, 323	04LN[0,3,4][C,D,Z]Z	84	04QS[0,3,4]ZZ	209	04S8*	240, 252, 324
04HE[0,3,4]DZ	83, 297, 323	04LN*	324	04QS*	240	04S9*	248
04HF[0,3,4]DZ	83, 297, 323	04LP[0,3,4][C,D,Z]Z	84	04QT[0,3,4]ZZ	209	04SA*	248
04HH[0,3,4]DZ	83, 297, 323	04LP*	324	04QT*	240	04SB*	240, 252, 324
04HJ[0,3,4]DZ	83, 297, 323	04LQ[0,3,4][C,D,Z]Z	84	04QU[0,3,4]ZZ	209	04SC*	324
04HK[0,3,4]DZ	83, 297, 323	04LQ*	324	04QU*	240	04SD*	324
04HL[0,3,4]DZ	83, 297, 323	04LR[0,3,4][C,D,Z]Z	84	04QV[0,3,4]ZZ	209	04SE*	324
04HM[0,3,4]DZ	83, 297, 323	04LR*	324	04QV*	240	04SF*	324
04HN[0,3,4]DZ	83, 297, 323	04LS[0,3,4][C,D,Z]Z	84	04QW[0,3,4]ZZ	209	04SH*	324
04HP[0,3,4]DZ	83, 297, 323	04LS*	324	04QW*	240	04SJ*	324
04HQ[0,3,4]DZ	83, 297, 323	04LT[0,3,4][C,D,Z]Z	84	04QY*	111, 122, 240, 252	04SK[0,3,4]ZZ	209
04HR[0,3,4]DZ	83, 297, 323	04LT*	324	04R0[0,4][7,J,K]Z	92	04SK*	324
04HS[0,3,4]DZ	83, 297, 323	04LU[0,3,4][C,D,Z]Z	84	04R0*	324	04SL[0,3,4]ZZ	209
04HT[0,3,4]DZ	84, 297, 323	04LU*	324	04R1[0,4][7,J,K]Z	96	04SL*	324
04HU[0,3,4]DZ	84, 297, 323	04LV[0,3,4][C,D,Z]Z	84	04R1*	324	04SM[0,3,4]ZZ	209
04HV[0,3,4]DZ	84, 297, 323	04LV*	324	04R2[0,4][7,J,K]Z	96	04SM*	324
04HW[0,3,4]DZ	84, 297, 323	04LW[0,3,4][C,D,Z]Z	84	04R2*	324	04SN[0,3,4]ZZ	209
04HY[0,3,4][2,D]Z	84, 297, 324	04LW*	324	04R3[0,4][7,J,K]Z	96	04SN*	324
04HY[0,3,4]2Z	240	04LY[0,3,4][C,D,Z]Z	84	04R3*	324	04SP[0,3,4]ZZ	209
04JY[0,3]ZZ	84	04LY*	324	04R4[0,4][7,J,K]Z	96	04SP*	324
04L0[0,3,4][C,D,Z]Z	92	04N*	84	04R4*	324	04SQ[0,3,4]ZZ	209
04L0*	111, 324	04N0[0,4]ZZ	111	04R5[0,4][7,J,K]Z	96	04SQ*	324
04L1[0,3,4][C,D,Z]Z	95, 442	04N1[0,4]ZZ	111	04R5*	324	04SR[0,3,4]ZZ	209
04L1*	111, 324	04N2[0,4]ZZ	111	04R6[0,4][7,J,K]Z	96	04SR*	324
04L2[0,3,4][C,Z]Z	95, 111, 324, 442	04N3[0,4]ZZ	111	04R6*	324	04SS[0,3,4]ZZ	209
04L2[0,4]DZ	95, 111, 324, 442	04N4[0,4]ZZ	111	04R7[0,4][7,J,K]Z	96	04SS*	324
04L3[0,3,4][C,D,Z]Z	96, 442	04N5[0,4]ZZ	111	04R7*	324	04ST[0,3,4]ZZ	209
04L3*	111, 324	04N6[0,4]ZZ	111	04R8[0,4][7,J,K]Z	96	04ST*	324
04L4[0,3,4][C,D,Z]Z	96, 442	04N7[0,4]ZZ	111	04R8*	324	04SU[0,3,4]ZZ	209
04L4*	111, 324	04N8[0,4]ZZ	111	04R9[0,4][7,J,K]Z	96	04SU*	324
04L5[0,3,4][C,D,Z]Z	96, 442	04N9[0,4]ZZ	111	04R9*	252	04SV[0,3,4]ZZ	209
04L5*	111, 324	04NA[0,4]ZZ	111	04RA[0,4][7,J,K]Z	96	04SV*	324
04L6[0,3,4][C,D,Z]Z	96, 442	04NB[0,4]ZZ	111	04RA*	252	04SW[0,3,4]ZZ	209
04L6*	111, 324	04NC[0,4]ZZ	111	04RB[0,4][7,J,K]Z	96	04SW*	324
04L7[0,3,4][C,D,Z]Z	96, 442	04ND[0,4]ZZ	111	04RB*	324	04SY[0,3,4]ZZ	209
04L7*	111, 324	04NE[0,4]ZZ	111	04RC[0,4][7,J,K]Z	96	04SY*	324
04L8[0,3,4][C,D,Z]Z	96, 442	04NF[0,4]ZZ	111	04RC*	324	04U0[0,3,4][7,J]Z	324
04L8*	111, 324	04NH[0,4]ZZ	111	04RD[0,4][7,J,K]Z	96	04U0[0,3,4][7,K]Z	84
04L9[0,3,4][C,D,Z]Z	96, 442	04NJ[0,4]ZZ	111	04RD*	324	04U0[3,4]JZ	252
04L9*	111, 252, 324	04PY[0,3,4][0,2,3,7,C,D,J,K]Z	84	04RE[0,4][7,J,K]Z	96	04U00JZ	84
04LA[0,3,4][C,D,Z]Z	96, 442	04PY[0,3,4][0,2,3,C,D]Z	240, 297, 324	04RE*	324	04U03JZ	92
04LA*	111, 252, 324	04PY[0,3,4][7,J,K]Z	442	04RF[0,4][7,J,K]Z	96	04U04JZ	92
04LB[0,3,4][C,D,Z]Z		04Q*	84, 324	04RF*	324	04U1[0,3,4][7,J]Z	324
04LB[0,3,4][C,D,Z]Z	96, 442	04QC[0,3,4]ZZ	208	04RH[0,4][7,J,K]Z	96	04U1*	84
04LB*	111, 324	04QC*	240	04RH*	324	04U2[0,3,4][7,J]Z	324
04LC[0,3,4][C,D,Z]Z	96	04QD[0,3,4]ZZ	208	04RJ[0,4][7,J,K]Z	96	04U2*	84
04LC[0,3,4][C,Z]Z	111, 442	04QD*	240	04RJ*	324	04U3[0,3,4][7,J]Z	324
04LC*	324	04QE[0,3,4]ZZ	209	04RK*	84, 240, 324	04U3*	84
04LD[0,3,4][C,D,Z]Z	96	04QE*	240	04RL*	84, 240, 324	04U4[0,3,4][7,J]Z	324
04LD[0,3,4][C,Z]Z	111, 442	04QF[0,3,4]ZZ	209	04RM*	84, 240, 324	04U4*	84
04LD*	324	04QF*	240	04RN*	84, 240, 324	04U5[0,3,4][7,J]Z	324
04LE[0,3,4][C,D,Z]T	268	04QH[0,3,4]ZZ	209	04RP*	84, 240, 324	04U5*	84
04LE[0,3,4][C,D,Z]Z	96, 324	04QH*	240	04RQ*	84, 240, 324	04U6[0,3,4][7,J]Z	324
04LE[0,3,4][C,Z]Z	111, 442	04QJ[0,3,4]ZZ	209	04RR*	84, 240, 324	04U6*	84
04LF[0,3,4][C,D,Z]U	268	04QJ*	240	04RS*	84, 240, 324	04U7[0,3,4][7,J]Z	324
04LF[0,3,4][C,D,Z]Z	96, 324	04QK[0,3,4]ZZ	209	04RT*	84, 240, 324	04U7*	84
04LF[0,3,4][C,Z]Z	111, 442	04QK*	240	04RU*	84, 240, 324	04U8[0,3,4][7,J]Z	324

Code	Page	Code	Page	Code	Page	Code	Page
04U8*	84	04V6[0,3,4][D,Z]Z	96, 325	0517*	84	057Q[3,4]DZ	21, 22, 325
04U9[0,3,4][7,J]Z	252, 324	04V6[0,3,4]CZ	84	0518*	84	057R[3,4]DZ	21, 22, 325
04U9*	84	04V6[0,3,4]ZZ	252	0519*	84	057S[3,4]DZ	21, 22, 325
04UA[0,3,4][7,J]Z	252, 324	04V7[0,3,4][D,Z]Z	96, 325	051A*	84	057T[3,4]DZ	21, 22, 325
04UA*	84	04V7[0,3,4]CZ	84	051B*	84	0590[0,3,4]ZX	85, 442
04UB[0,3,4][7,J]Z	324	04V7[0,3,4]ZZ	252	051C*	84	0591[0,3,4]ZX	85, 442
04UB*	84	04V8[0,3,4][D,Z]Z	96, 325	051D*	84	0593[0,3,4]ZX	85, 442
04UC[0,3,4][7,J]Z	324	04V8[0,3,4]CZ	84	051F*	85	0594[0,3,4]ZX	85, 442
04UC*	84	04V8[0,3,4]ZZ	252	051G*	85	0595[0,3,4]ZX	85, 442
04UD[0,3,4][7,J]Z	324	04V9[0,3,4][D,Z]Z	96, 252, 325	051H*	85	0596[0,3,4]ZX	85, 442
04UD*	84	04V9[0,3,4]CZ	84	051L*	85	0597[0,3,4]ZX	85, 442
04UE[0,3,4][7,J]Z	324	04VA[0,3,4][D,Z]Z	96, 252, 325	051M*	85	0598[0,3,4]ZX	85, 442
04UE*	84	04VA[0,3,4]CZ	84	051N*	85	0599[0,3,4]ZX	85, 442
04UF[0,3,4][7,J]Z	324	04VB[0,3,4][D,Z]Z	96, 325	051P*	85	059A[0,3,4]ZX	85, 442
04UF*	84	04VB[0,3,4]CZ	84	051Q*	85	059B[0,3,4]ZX	85, 442
04UH[0,3,4][7,J]Z	324	04VB[0,3,4]ZZ	252	051R*	85	059C[0,3,4]ZX	85, 442
04UH*	84	04VC[0,3,4][D,Z]Z	96, 325	051S*	85	059D[0,3,4]ZX	85, 442
04UJ[0,3,4][7,J]Z	324	04VC[0,3,4]CZ	84	051T*	85	059F[0,3,4]ZX	85, 442
04UJ*	84	04VD[0,3,4][D,Z]Z	96, 325	051V*	85	059G[0,3,4]ZX	85, 442
04UK[0,3,4][7,J]Z	324	04VD[0,3,4]CZ	84	0550[0,3,4]ZZ	96	059H[0,3,4]ZX	85, 442
04UK*	84	04VE[0,3,4][D,Z]Z	96, 325	0550*	60	059L[0,3,4]ZX	85, 442
04UL[0,3,4][7,J]Z	324	04VE[0,3,4]CZ	84	0551[0,3,4]ZZ	96	059M[0,3,4]ZX	85, 442
04UL*	84	04VF[0,3,4][D,Z]Z	96, 325	0551*	60	059N[0,3,4]ZX	85, 442
04UM[0,3,4][7,J]Z	324	04VF[0,3,4]CZ	84	0553[0,3,4]ZZ	96	059P[0,3,4]ZX	85, 442
04UM*	84	04VH[0,3,4][D,Z]Z	96, 325	0553*	60	059Q[0,3,4]ZX	85, 442
04UN[0,3,4][7,J]Z	324	04VH[0,3,4]CZ	84	0554[0,3,4]ZZ	96	059R[0,3,4]ZX	85, 442
04UN*	84	04VJ[0,3,4][D,Z]Z	96, 325	0554*	60	059S[0,3,4]ZX	85, 442
04UP[0,3,4][7,J]Z	324	04VJ[0,3,4]CZ	84	0555[0,3,4]ZZ	96	059T[0,3,4]ZX	85, 442
04UP*	84	04VK[0,3,4][D,Z]Z	96, 325	0555*	60	059V[0,3,4]ZX	85, 442
04UQ[0,3,4][7,J]Z	324	04VK[0,3,4]CZ	84	0556[0,3,4]ZZ	96	059Y[0,3,4]ZX	85, 442
04UQ*	84	04VL[0,3,4][D,Z]Z	96, 325	0556*	60	05B0[0,3,4]ZX	85, 442
04UR[0,3,4][7,J]Z	324	04VL[0,3,4]CZ	84	0557*	85, 240, 325	05B0[0,3,4]ZZ	60, 96
04UR*	84	04VM[0,3,4][D,Z]Z	96, 325	0558*	85, 240, 325	05B1[0,3,4]ZX	85, 442
04US[0,3,4][7,J]Z	324	04VM[0,3,4]CZ	84	0559*	85, 240, 325	05B1[0,3,4]ZZ	60, 96
04US*	84	04VN[0,3,4][D,Z]Z	96, 325	055A*	85, 240, 325	05B3[0,3,4]ZX	85, 442
04UT[0,3,4][7,J]Z	324	04VN[0,3,4]CZ	84	055B*	85, 240, 325	05B3[0,3,4]ZZ	60, 96
04UT*	84	04VP[0,3,4][D,Z]Z	96, 325	055C*	85, 240, 325	05B4[0,3,4]ZX	85, 442
04UU[0,3,4][7,J]Z	324	04VP[0,3,4]CZ	84	055D*	85, 240, 325	05B4[0,3,4]ZZ	60, 96
04UU*	84	04VQ[0,3,4][D,Z]Z	96, 325	055F*	85, 240, 325	05B5[0,3,4]ZX	85, 442
04UV[0,3,4][7,J]Z	324	04VQ[0,3,4]CZ	84	055G*	85, 240, 325	05B5[0,3,4]ZZ	60, 96
04UV*	84	04VR[0,3,4][D,Z]Z	96, 325	055H*	85, 240, 325	05B6[0,3,4]ZX	85, 442
04UW[0,3,4][7,J]Z	324	04VR[0,3,4]CZ	84	055L[0,3,4]ZZ	7, 9, 13, 17	05B6[0,3,4]ZZ	60, 96
04UW*	84	04VS[0,3,4][D,Z]Z	96, 325	055L*	325	05B7[0,3,4]ZX	442
04UY[0,3,4][7,J]Z	324	04VS[0,3,4]CZ	84	055M*	22, 85, 325	05B7[0,3,4]ZZ	240, 325
04UY*	84	04VT[0,3,4][D,Z]Z	96, 325	055N*	22, 85, 325	05B7*	85
04V0[0,3,4][D,Z]Z	252, 325	04VT[0,3,4]CZ	84	055P*	22, 85, 325	05B8[0,3,4]ZX	442
04V0[0,3,4]CZ	84	04VU[0,3,4][D,Z]Z	96, 325	055Q*	22, 85, 325	05B8[0,3,4]ZZ	240, 325
04V0[0,3,4]DJ	22, 84, 325	04VU[0,3,4]CZ	84	055R*	22, 85, 325	05B8*	85
04V00DZ	96	04VV[0,3,4][D,Z]Z	96, 325	055S*	22, 85, 325	05B9[0,3,4]ZX	442
04V00ZZ	96	04VV[0,3,4]CZ	84	055T*	22, 85, 325	05B9[0,3,4]ZZ	240, 325
04V03DZ	92	04VW[0,3,4][D,Z]Z	96, 325	055V*	22, 85, 325	05B9*	85
04V03ZZ	96	04VW[0,3,4]CZ	84	055Y*	85, 240, 325	05BA[0,3,4]ZX	442
04V04DZ	92	04VY[0,3,4][D,Z]Z	96, 325	057*	85	05BA[0,3,4]ZZ	240, 325
04V04ZZ	96	04VY[0,3,4]CZ	84	05793[D,Z]Z	22, 64, 111, 122, 152, 209, 240, 252, 325	05BA*	85
04V1[0,3,4][D,Z]Z	96, 325	04WY[0,3,4][0,2,3,7,C,D,J,K]Z	84	057A3[D,Z]Z	22, 64, 111, 122, 152, 209, 240, 252, 325	05BB[0,3,4]ZX	442
04V1[0,3,4]CZ	84	04WY[0,3,4][0,2,3,C,D]Z	240, 297, 325			05BB[0,3,4]ZZ	240, 325
04V1[0,3,4]ZZ	252	04WY[0,3,4][7,J,K]Z	442	057B3[D,Z]Z	22, 64, 111, 122, 152, 209, 240, 252, 325	05BB*	85
04V2[0,3,4][D,Z]Z	96, 325	0510[0,4][7,9,A,J,K,Z]Y	96	057C3[D,Z]Z	22, 64, 111, 122, 152, 209, 240, 252, 325	05BC[0,3,4]ZX	442
04V2[0,3,4]CZ	84	0510*	325			05BC[0,3,4]ZZ	240, 325
04V2[0,3,4]ZZ	252	0511[0,4][7,9,A,J,K,Z]Y	96	057D3[D,Z]Z	22, 64, 111, 122, 152, 209, 240, 252, 325	05BC*	85
04V3[0,3,4][D,Z]Z	96, 325	0511*	325			05BD[0,3,4]ZX	442
04V3[0,3,4]CZ	84	0513[0,4][7,9,A,J,K,Z]Y	96	057F3[D,Z]Z	22, 64, 111, 122, 152, 209, 240, 252, 325	05BD[0,3,4]ZZ	240, 325
04V3[0,3,4]ZZ	252	0513*	325			05BD*	85
04V4[0,3,4][D,Z]Z	96, 325	0514[0,4][7,9,A,J,K,Z]Y	96	057L[3,4]DZ	9, 13, 17, 325	05BF[0,3,4]ZX	442
04V4[0,3,4]CZ	84	0514*	325	057M[3,4]DZ	21, 22, 325	05BF[0,3,4]ZZ	240, 325
04V4[0,3,4]ZZ	252	0515[0,4][7,9,A,J,K,Z]Y	96	057N[3,4]DZ	21, 22, 325	05BF*	85
04V5[0,3,4][D,Z]Z	96, 325	0515*	325	057P[3,4]DZ	21, 22, 325	05BG[0,3,4]ZX	442
04V5[0,3,4]CZ	84	0516[0,4][7,9,A,J,K,Z]Y	96			05BG[0,3,4]ZZ	240, 325
04V5[0,3,4]ZZ	252	0516*	325			05BG*	85

Numeric Index to Procedures

Code	Page
06LC*	327
06LD[0,3,4][C,D,Z]Z	97
06LD[0,3,4][C,Z]Z	111
06LD*	327
06LF[0,3,4][C,D,Z]Z	97
06LF[0,3,4][C,Z]Z	111
06LF*	327
06LG[0,3,4][C,D,Z]Z	97
06LG[0,3,4][C,Z]Z	111
06LG*	327
06LH[0,3,4][C,D,Z]Z	97
06LH*	111, 327
06LJ[0,3,4][C,D,Z]Z	97
06LJ*	111, 327
06LM[0,3,4][C,D,Z]Z	89
06LM*	327
06LN[0,3,4][C,D,Z]Z	89
06LN*	327
06LP[0,3,4][C,D,Z]Z	89
06LP*	327
06LQ[0,3,4][C,D,Z]Z	89
06LQ*	327
06LR[0,3,4][C,D,Z]Z	89
06LR*	327
06LS[0,3,4][C,D,Z]Z	89
06LS*	327
06LT[0,3,4][C,D,Z]Z	89
06LT*	327
06LV[0,3,4][C,D,Z]Z	89
06LV*	327
06LY[0,3,4][C,D,Z]C	109
06LY[0,3,4][C,D,Z]C	443
06LY[0,3,4][C,D,Z]Z	327
06LY[0,3,4][C,Z]Z	87
06LY[0,3,4]DZ	89
06N*	87
06N0[0,4]ZZ	111
06N1[0,4]ZZ	111
06N2[0,4]ZZ	111
06N3[0,4]ZZ	111
06N4[0,4]ZZ	111
06N5[0,4]ZZ	112
06N6[0,4]ZZ	112
06N7[0,4]ZZ	112
06N8[0,4]ZZ	112
06N9[0,4]ZZ	112
06NB[0,4]ZZ	112
06NC[0,4]ZZ	112
06ND[0,4]ZZ	112
06NF[0,4]ZZ	112
06NG[0,4]ZZ	112
06NH[0,4]ZZ	112
06NJ[0,4]ZZ	112
06PY[0,3,4][0,2,3,7,C,D,J,K]Z	443
06PY[0,3,4][0,2,3,C,D]Z	89, 327
06PY[0,3,4][7,J,K]Z	87
06Q*	327
06Q0*	89
06Q1*	89
06Q2*	89
06Q3*	89
06Q4*	89
06Q5*	89
06Q6*	89
06Q7*	89
06Q8*	89
06Q9*	89
06QB*	89
06QC*	89

Code	Page
06QD*	89
06QF*	89
06QG*	89
06QH*	89
06QJ*	89
06QM*	89
06QN*	89
06QP*	89
06QQ*	89
06QR*	89
06QS*	89
06QT*	89
06QV*	89
06QY*	87, 112, 122, 241, 252
06R0[0,4][7,J,K]Z	98
06R1[0,4][7,J,K]Z	98
06R2[0,4][7,J,K]Z	98
06R3*	25, 87
06R4[0,4][7,J,K]Z	98
06R5[0,4][7,J,K]Z	98
06R6[0,4][7,J,K]Z	98
06R7[0,4][7,J,K]Z	98
06R8[0,4][7,J,K]Z	98
06R9[0,4][7,J,K]Z	98
06RB[0,4][7,J,K]Z	98
06RC[0,4][7,J,K]Z	98
06RD[0,4][7,J,K]Z	98
06RF[0,4][7,J,K]Z	98
06RG[0,4][7,J,K]Z	98
06RH[0,4][7,J,K]Z	98
06RJ[0,4][7,J,K]Z	98
06RM*	89, 327
06RN*	89, 327
06RP*	89, 327
06RQ*	89, 327
06RR*	89, 327
06RS*	89, 327
06RT*	89, 327
06RV*	89, 327
06RY*	89, 327
06S*	87
06S0*	241, 252, 327
06S1*	241, 252, 327
06S2*	241, 252, 327
06S3*	241, 252, 327
06S4*	241, 252, 327
06S5*	241, 252, 327
06S6*	241, 252, 327
06S7*	241, 252, 327
06S8*	241, 252, 327
06S9*	248
06SB*	248
06SC*	327
06SD*	327
06SF*	327
06SG*	327
06SH*	327
06SJ*	327
06SM[0,3,4]ZZ	209
06SM*	327
06SN[0,3,4]ZZ	209
06SN*	327
06SP[0,3,4]ZZ	209
06SP*	327
06SQ[0,3,4]ZZ	209
06SQ*	327
06SR[0,3,4]ZZ	209
06SR*	327
06SS[0,3,4]ZZ	209

Code	Page
06SS*	327
06ST[0,3,4]ZZ	209
06ST*	327
06SV[0,3,4]ZZ	209
06SV*	327
06SY[0,3,4]ZZ	209
06SY*	327
06U*	87
06U0[0,3,4][7,J]Z	327
06U1[0,3,4][7,J]Z	327
06U2[0,3,4][7,J]Z	327
06U3[0,3,4][7,J]Z	327
06U4[0,3,4][7,J]Z	327
06U5[0,3,4][7,J]Z	327
06U6[0,3,4][7,J]Z	327
06U7[0,3,4][7,J]Z	327
06U8[0,3,4][7,J]Z	327
06U9[0,3,4][7,J]Z	252, 327
06UB[0,3,4][7,J]Z	252, 327
06UC[0,3,4][7,J]Z	328
06UD[0,3,4][7,J]Z	328
06UF[0,3,4][7,J]Z	328
06UG[0,3,4][7,J]Z	328
06UH[0,3,4][7,J]Z	328
06UJ[0,3,4][7,J]Z	328
06UM[0,3,4][7,J]Z	328
06UN[0,3,4][7,J]Z	328
06UP[0,3,4][7,J]Z	328
06UQ[0,3,4][7,J]Z	328
06UR[0,3,4][7,J]Z	328
06US[0,3,4][7,J]Z	328
06UT[0,3,4][7,J]Z	328
06UV[0,3,4][7,J]Z	328
06UY[0,3,4][7,J]Z	328
06V0*	25, 64, 87, 112, 122, 153, 241, 252, 258, 268, 271, 290, 328
06V1[0,3,4][D,Z]Z	98, 328
06V1[0,3,4]CZ	87
06V1[0,3,4]ZZ	252
06V2[0,3,4][D,Z]Z	98, 328
06V2[0,3,4]CZ	87
06V2[0,3,4]ZZ	252
06V3[0,3,4][D,Z]Z	98, 328
06V3[0,3,4]CZ	87
06V3[0,3,4]ZZ	252
06V4[0,3,4][D,Z]Z	98, 328
06V4[0,3,4]CZ	87
06V4[0,3,4]ZZ	252
06V5[0,3,4][D,Z]Z	98, 328
06V5[0,3,4]CZ	87
06V5[0,3,4]ZZ	252
06V6[0,3,4][D,Z]Z	98, 328
06V6[0,3,4]CZ	87
06V6[0,3,4]ZZ	252
06V7[0,3,4][D,Z]Z	98, 328
06V7[0,3,4]CZ	87
06V7[0,3,4]ZZ	252
06V8[0,3,4][D,Z]Z	98, 328
06V8[0,3,4]CZ	87
06V8[0,3,4]ZZ	252
06V9[0,3,4][D,Z]Z	98, 252, 328
06V9[0,3,4]CZ	87
06VB[0,3,4][D,Z]Z	98, 252, 328
06VB[0,3,4]CZ	87
06VC[0,3,4][D,Z]Z	98, 328
06VC[0,3,4]CZ	87
06VD[0,3,4][D,Z]Z	98, 328
06VD[0,3,4]CZ	87
06VF[0,3,4][D,Z]Z	98, 328

Code	Page
06VF[0,3,4]CZ	87
06VG[0,3,4][D,Z]Z	98, 328
06VG[0,3,4]CZ	87
06VH[0,3,4][D,Z]Z	98, 328
06VH[0,3,4]CZ	87
06VJ[0,3,4][D,Z]Z	98, 328
06VJ[0,3,4]CZ	87
06VM[0,3,4][D,Z]Z	98, 328
06VM[0,3,4]CZ	87
06VN[0,3,4][D,Z]Z	98, 328
06VN[0,3,4]CZ	87
06VP[0,3,4][D,Z]Z	98, 328
06VP[0,3,4]CZ	87
06VQ[0,3,4][D,Z]Z	98, 328
06VQ[0,3,4]CZ	87
06VR[0,3,4][D,Z]Z	98, 328
06VR[0,3,4]CZ	87
06VS[0,3,4][D,Z]Z	98, 328
06VS[0,3,4]CZ	87
06VT[0,3,4][D,Z]Z	98, 328
06VT[0,3,4]CZ	87
06VV[0,3,4][D,Z]Z	98, 328
06VV[0,3,4]CZ	87
06VY[0,3,4][D,Z]Z	98, 328
06VY[0,3,4]CZ	87
06WY[0,3,4][0,2,3,7,C,D,J,K]Z	443
06WY[0,3,4][0,2,3,C,D]Z	89, 328
06WY[0,3,4][7,J,K]Z	87
0750[0,3,4]ZZ	297
0750*	290, 328
0751[0,3,4]ZZ	297
0751*	290, 328
0752[0,3,4]ZZ	297
0752*	290, 328
0753[0,3,4]ZZ	297
0753*	290, 328
0754[0,3,4]ZZ	297
0754*	290, 328
0755[0,3,4]ZZ	297
0755*	290, 328
0756[0,3,4]ZZ	297
0756*	290, 328
0757[0,3,4]ZZ	297
0757*	290, 328
0758[0,3,4]ZZ	297
0758*	290, 328
0759[0,3,4]ZZ	297
0759*	290, 328
075B[0,3,4]ZZ	297
075B*	290, 328
075C[0,3,4]ZZ	297
075C*	290, 328
075D[0,3,4]ZZ	297
075D*	290, 328
075F[0,3,4]ZZ	297
075F*	290, 328
075G[0,3,4]ZZ	297
075G*	290, 328
075H[0,3,4]ZZ	297
075H*	290, 328
075J[0,3,4]ZZ	297
075J*	290, 328
075K*	60
075L*	60
075M[0,3,4]ZZ	297
075M*	25, 60, 241, 290, 328
075P[0,3,4]ZZ	297
075P*	290, 328
0790[0,3,4][0,Z]Z	209, 443

Code	Page	Code	Page	Code	Page	Code	Page
079Ø[Ø,3,4]ZX	25, 51, 89, 153, 209, 241, 443	079L[Ø,3,4]ZX	25, 90, 112, 122, 153, 209, 241, 252, 290, 443	07BH[Ø,3,4]ZX	25, 241	07LK*	60
079Ø*	290			07BH[Ø,3,4]ZZ	64, 112, 252, 271	07LL*	60
0791[Ø,3,4][Ø,Z]Z	209, 443	079M[Ø,3,4][Ø,Z]Z	297, 328	07BH[Ø,4]ZZ	262	07NØ[Ø,3,4]ZZ	291, 298
0791[Ø,3,4]ZX	25, 51, 89, 153, 209, 241, 443	079M[Ø,3,4]ZX	297	07BH*	90, 153, 258, 268, 290	07NØ*	328
		079M*	60, 241, 290	07BJ[Ø,3,4]Z[X,Z]	209, 443	07N1[Ø,3,4]ZZ	291, 298
0791*	290	079M4ZZ	25	07BJ[Ø,3,4]ZX	25, 241	07N1*	328
0792[Ø,3,4][Ø,Z]Z	209, 443	079PØ[Ø,Z]Z	290, 297, 328	07BJ[Ø,3,4]ZZ	64, 112, 252, 271	07N2[Ø,3,4]ZZ	291, 298
0792[Ø,3,4]ZX	25, 51, 89, 153, 209, 241, 443	079PØZX	290, 297	07BJ[Ø,4]ZZ	262	07N2*	328
0792*	290	07BØ[Ø,3,4]Z[X,Z]	209, 443	07BJ*	90, 153, 258, 268, 290	07N3[Ø,3,4]ZZ	291, 298
0793[Ø,3,4][Ø,Z]Z	209, 443	07BØ[Ø,3,4]ZX	25, 51, 90, 153, 241	07BK[Ø,3,4]ZX	25, 64, 90, 153, 209, 241, 290, 443	07N3*	328
0793[Ø,3,4]ZX	25, 89, 153, 209, 241, 443	07BØ[Ø,4]ZZ	51, 297			07N4[Ø,3,4]ZZ	291, 298
		07BØ*	290	07BK[Ø,3,4]ZZ	60	07N4*	328
0793*	290	07B1[Ø,3,4]Z[X,Z]	209, 443	07BL[Ø,3,4]ZX	25, 90, 112, 122, 153, 209, 241, 252, 290, 443	07N5[Ø,3,4]ZZ	291, 298
0794[Ø,3,4][Ø,Z]Z	209, 443	07B1[Ø,3,4]ZX	25			07N5*	328
0794[Ø,3,4]ZX	25, 89, 153, 209, 241, 443	07B1[Ø,3,4]ZZ	64, 112	07BL[Ø,3,4]ZZ	60	07N6[Ø,3,4]ZZ	291, 298
0794*	290	07B1*	51, 90, 153, 241, 290	07BM[Ø,3,4]Z[X,Z]	290, 297	07N6*	328
0795[Ø,3,4][Ø,Z]Z	209, 443	07B2[Ø,3,4]Z[X,Z]	209, 443	07BM[Ø,3,4]ZZ	25, 328	07N7[Ø,3,4]ZZ	291, 298
0795[Ø,3,4]ZX	25, 89, 153, 209, 241, 443	07B2[Ø,3,4]ZX	25	07BM*	60, 241	07N7*	328
		07B2[Ø,3,4]ZZ	64, 112	07BP[Ø,3,4]ZZ	153, 290, 298, 328	07N8[Ø,3,4]ZZ	291, 298
0795*	290	07B2*	51, 90, 153, 241, 290	07BPØZX	290, 297	07N8*	328
0796[Ø,3,4][Ø,Z]Z	209, 443	07B3[Ø,3,4]Z[X,Z]	209, 443	07CØ[Ø,3,4]ZZ	209, 290, 443	07N9[Ø,3,4]ZZ	291, 298
0796[Ø,3,4]ZX	25, 89, 153, 209, 241, 443	07B3[Ø,3,4]ZX	25, 90, 153, 241	07C1[Ø,3,4]ZZ	209, 290, 443	07N9*	328
		07B3[Ø,4]ZZ	90, 153, 241, 297	07C2[Ø,3,4]ZZ	209, 290, 443	07NB[Ø,3,4]ZZ	291, 298
0796*	290	07B3*	290	07C3[Ø,3,4]ZZ	209, 290, 443	07NB*	328
0797[Ø,3,4][Ø,Z]Z	209, 443	07B4[Ø,3,4]Z[X,Z]	209, 443	07C4[Ø,3,4]ZZ	209, 290, 443	07NC[Ø,3,4]ZZ	291, 298
0797[Ø,3,4]ZX	25, 64, 89, 153, 209, 241, 443	07B4[Ø,3,4]ZX	25, 90, 153, 241	07C5[Ø,3,4]ZZ	209, 290, 443	07NC*	328
		07B4[Ø,4]ZZ	90, 153, 241, 297	07C6[Ø,3,4]ZZ	209, 290, 443	07ND[Ø,3,4]ZZ	291, 298
0797*	290	07B4*	290	07C7[Ø,3,4]ZZ	209, 290, 443	07ND*	328
0798[Ø,3,4][Ø,Z]Z	209, 443	07B5[Ø,3,4]Z[X,Z]	209, 443	07C8[Ø,3,4]ZZ	209, 290, 443	07NF[Ø,3,4]ZZ	291, 298
0798[Ø,3,4]ZX	25, 89, 153, 209, 241, 443	07B5[Ø,3,4]ZX	25, 241	07C9[Ø,3,4]ZZ	209, 290, 443	07NF*	328
		07B5[Ø,3,4]ZZ	51, 64, 112	07CB[Ø,3,4]ZZ	209, 290, 443	07NG[Ø,3,4]ZZ	291, 298
0798*	290	07B5*	90, 153, 290	07CC[Ø,3,4]ZZ	209, 290, 443	07NG*	328
0799[Ø,3,4][Ø,Z]Z	209, 443	07B6[Ø,3,4]Z[X,Z]	209, 443	07CD[Ø,3,4]ZZ	209, 290, 443	07NH[Ø,3,4]ZZ	291, 298
0799[Ø,3,4]ZX	25, 89, 153, 209, 241, 443	07B6[Ø,3,4]ZX	25, 241	07CF[Ø,3,4]ZZ	209, 290, 443	07NH*	328
		07B6[Ø,3,4]ZZ	51, 64, 112	07CG[Ø,3,4]ZZ	209, 290, 443	07NJ[Ø,3,4]ZZ	291, 298
0799*	290	07B6*	90, 153, 290	07CH[Ø,3,4]ZZ	209, 290, 443	07NJ*	328
079B[Ø,3,4][Ø,Z]Z	209, 443	07B7[Ø,3,4]Z[X,Z]	209, 443	07CJ[Ø,3,4]ZZ	209, 290, 443	07NK*	60
079B[Ø,3,4]ZX	25, 89, 112, 122, 153, 209, 241, 443	07B7[Ø,3,4]ZX	25, 90, 153, 241	07CK[Ø,3,4]ZZ	209, 290, 443	07NL*	60
		07B7[Ø,4]ZZ	64, 90, 153, 241, 297	07CL[Ø,3,4]ZZ	210, 290, 443	07NM[Ø,3,4]ZZ	291, 298
079B*	290	07B7*	290	07CM[Ø,3,4]ZZ	290, 298	07NM*	60, 241, 328
079C[Ø,3,4][Ø,Z]Z	209, 443	07B8[Ø,3,4]Z[X,Z]	209	07CM*	60, 241, 328	07NM4ZZ	25
079C[Ø,3,4]ZX	25, 90, 112, 122, 153, 209, 241, 252, 258, 268, 443	07B8[Ø,3,4]ZX	25, 90, 153, 241, 443	07CM4ZZ	25	07NP[Ø,3,4]ZZ	298
		07B8[Ø,3,4]ZZ	60	07CPØZZ	290, 298, 328	07NP*	290, 328
079C*	290	07B8*	290	07JK[Ø,3,4]ZZ	210, 290, 443	07PK[Ø,3,4][Ø,3,C,D]Z	60
079D[Ø,3,4][Ø,Z]Z	209, 443	07B9[Ø,3,4]Z[X,Z]	209	07JL[Ø,3,4]ZZ	210, 290, 443	07PK[Ø,3,4][7,J,K]Z	291, 298, 328
079D[Ø,3,4]ZX	25, 90, 112, 122, 153, 209, 241, 252, 443	07B9[Ø,3,4]ZX	25, 90, 153, 241, 443	07JM[Ø,4]ZZ	60, 241, 290, 298, 328	07PL[Ø,3,4][Ø,3,C,D]Z	60
		07B9[Ø,3,4]ZZ	60	07JM[3,4]ZZ	25	07PL[Ø,3,4][7,J,K]Z	291, 298, 328
079D*	290	07B9*	290	07JM3ZZ	235	07PM[Ø,3,4][Ø,3]Z	60, 241, 291, 298, 328
079F[Ø,3,4][Ø,Z]Z	209, 443	07BB[Ø,3,4]Z[X,Z]	209, 443	07JN[Ø,3,4]ZZ	112, 210, 290, 443		
079F[Ø,3,4]ZX	25, 90, 153, 209, 241, 443	07BB[Ø,3,4]ZX	25, 90, 122, 153, 241	07JPØZZ	64, 90, 112, 121, 210, 241, 252, 257, 268, 271, 290, 298, 328	07PN[Ø,3,4][Ø,3,7,C,D,J,K]Z	291
		07BB[Ø,4]ZZ	241, 297			07PN[Ø,3,4][Ø,3,C,D]Z	210, 443
079F*	290	07BB*	112, 290	07L*	328	07PN[Ø,3,4][7,J,K]Z	298, 328
079G[Ø,3,4][Ø,Z]Z	209, 443	07BC[Ø,3,4]Z[X,Z]	209, 443	07LØ[Ø,3,4][C,D,Z]Z	290, 298	07PP[Ø,3,4][Ø,3]Z	290, 298, 328
079G[Ø,3,4]ZX	25, 90, 153, 209, 241, 443	07BC[Ø,3,4]ZX	25, 90, 122, 153, 241, 252, 258, 268	07L1[Ø,3,4][C,D,Z]Z	290, 298	07QØ[Ø,3,4]ZZ	291, 298
				07L2[Ø,3,4][C,D,Z]Z	290, 298	07QØ*	328
079G*	290	07BC*	112, 290	07L3[Ø,3,4][C,D,Z]Z	290, 298	07Q1[Ø,3,4]ZZ	291, 298
079H[Ø,3,4][Ø,Z]Z	209, 443	07BD[Ø,3,4]Z[X,Z]	209, 443	07L4[Ø,3,4][C,D,Z]Z	290, 298	07Q1*	328
079H[Ø,3,4]ZX	25, 90, 153, 209, 241, 258, 268, 443	07BD[Ø,3,4]ZX	25, 90, 122, 153, 241, 252	07L5[Ø,3,4][C,D,Z]Z	290, 298	07Q2[Ø,3,4]ZZ	291, 298
				07L6[Ø,3,4][C,D,Z]Z	290, 298	07Q2*	328
079H*	290	07BD*	112, 290	07L7[Ø,3,4][C,D,Z]Z	291, 298	07Q3[Ø,3,4]ZZ	291, 298
079J[Ø,3,4][Ø,Z]Z	209, 443	07BF[Ø,3,4]Z[X,Z]	209, 443	07L8[Ø,3,4][C,D,Z]Z	291, 298	07Q3*	328
079J[Ø,3,4]ZX	25, 90, 153, 209, 241, 258, 268, 443	07BF[Ø,3,4]ZX	25, 90, 153, 241	07L9[Ø,3,4][C,D,Z]Z	291, 298	07Q4[Ø,3,4]ZZ	291, 298
		07BF[Ø,4]ZZ	90, 153, 241, 297	07LB[Ø,3,4][C,D,Z]Z	291, 298	07Q4*	328
079J*	290	07BF*	290	07LC[Ø,3,4][C,D,Z]Z	291, 298	07Q5[Ø,3,4]ZZ	291, 298
079K[Ø,3,4][Ø,Z]Z	60, 328	07BG[Ø,3,4]Z[X,Z]	209, 443	07LD[Ø,3,4][C,D,Z]Z	291, 298	07Q5*	328
079K[Ø,3,4]ZX	25, 64, 90, 153, 209, 241, 290, 443	07BG[Ø,3,4]ZX	25, 90, 153, 241	07LF[Ø,3,4][C,D,Z]Z	291, 298	07Q6[Ø,3,4]ZZ	291, 298
		07BG[Ø,4]ZZ	90, 153, 241, 297	07LG[Ø,3,4][C,D,Z]Z	291, 298	07Q6*	328
079L[Ø,3,4][Ø,Z]Z	60, 328	07BG*	290	07LH[Ø,3,4][C,D,Z]Z	291, 298	07Q7[Ø,3,4]ZZ	291, 298
		07BH[Ø,3,4]Z[X,Z]	209, 443	07LJ[Ø,3,4][C,D,Z]Z	291, 298	07Q7*	328

Code	Page	Code	Page	Code	Page	Code	Page
0997[0,3,4,7,8]0Z	51, 446	09BT0ZX	55	09N3[0,3,4,7,8,X]ZZ	210, 447	09R*	52
0997[0,3,4,7,8]ZX	51, 446	09BU[0,3,4]ZZ	55, 446	09N3*	51, 330	09R0[0,X][7,J,K]Z	210, 447
0998[0,3,4,7,8]0Z	51, 446	09BU0ZX	55	09N4[0,3,4,7,8,X]ZZ	210, 447	09R0*	330
0998[0,3,4,7,8]ZX	51, 446	09BV[0,3,4]ZZ	55, 446	09N4*	51, 330	09R1[0,X][7,J,K]Z	210, 447
0999*	51	09BV0ZX	55	09N50ZZ	447	09R1*	331
09990ZX	446	09BW[0,3,4]ZZ	55	09N60ZZ	447	09R2[0,X][7,J,K]Z	210, 447
099A*	51	09BW0ZX	55	09N7*	51	09R2*	331
099A0ZX	446	09BX[0,3,4]ZZ	55	09N8*	51	09R50[7,J,K]Z	447
099B[0,3,4][0,Z]Z	55, 446	09BX0ZX	55	09NB*	51	09R60[7,J,K]Z	447
099B[0,3,4]ZX	51, 446	09C[5,6,9,A,D,E]0ZZ	51	09NC*	51	09R90[7,J,K]Z	447
099C[0,3,4][0,Z]Z	55, 446	09C50ZZ	446	09NN*	51	09RA0[7,J,K]Z	447
099C[0,3,4]ZX	51, 446	09C60ZZ	446	09NP*	55	09RK[0,X][7,J,K]Z	210, 447
099D*	51	09CB[0,3,4]ZZ	446	09NQ*	56	09RK*	153, 331
099D0ZX	446	09CB*	55	09NR*	56	09RK07Z	90
099E*	51	09CC[0,3,4]ZZ	446	09NS*	56	09RL[0,3,4,7,8][7,J,K]Z	210, 447
099E0ZX	446	09CC*	55	09NT*	56	09RL*	331
099F[0,3,4,7,8]ZX	51, 446	09CN*	51, 330	09NU*	56	09RM[0,3,4][7,J,K]Z	210, 447
099G[0,3,4,7,8]ZX	51, 446	09CP*	55	09NV*	56	09RM*	153, 331
099N[0,3,4,7,8][0,Z]Z	51, 330	09CQ*	55	09NW*	56	09RN[0,7,8][7,J,K]Z	447
099P0[0,Z]Z	55	09CR*	55	09NX*	56	09RN*	25, 331
099P0ZX	55	09CS*	55	09PD*	52	09S0[0,4,X]ZZ	210, 447
099Q0[0,Z]Z	55	09CT*	55	09PE*	52	09S0*	52, 331
099Q0ZX	55	09CU*	55	09PH[0,7,8][7,J,K]Z	52	09S1[0,4,X]ZZ	210, 447
099R0[0,Z]Z	55	09CV*	55	09PH00Z	52	09S1*	52, 331
099R0ZX	55	09CW*	55	09PH0DZ	52	09S2[0,4,X]ZZ	210, 447
099S0[0,Z]Z	55	09CX*	55	09PH37Z	52	09S2*	52, 331
099S0ZX	55	09D[9,A]0ZZ	51	09PH3DZ	52	09S7[0,4,7,8]ZZ	447
099T0[0,Z]Z	55	09D7*	51	09PH47Z	52	09S7*	52
099T0ZX	55	09D8*	51	09PH4DZ	52	09S8[0,4,7,8]ZZ	447
099U0[0,Z]Z	55	09D90ZZ	446	09PJ[0,7,8][7,J,K]Z	52	09S8*	52
099U0ZX	55	09DA0ZZ	446	09PJ00Z	52	09S9*	52
099V0[0,Z]Z	55	09DB*	55	09PJ0DZ	52	09SA*	52
099V0ZX	55	09DC*	55	09PJ37Z	52	09SK[0,4,X]ZZ	210, 447
099W0[0,Z]Z	55	09DL[0,3,4,7,8]ZZ	447	09PJ3DZ	52	09SK*	52, 153, 331
099W0ZX	55	09DL*	51, 330	09PJ47Z	52	09SL[0,4,7,8]ZZ	447
099X0[0,Z]Z	55	09DM[0,3,4]ZZ	210, 447	09PJ4DZ	52	09SL*	52, 331
099X0ZX	55	09DM*	51, 330	09PY[0,3,4]0Z	56	09SM[0,4]ZZ	210, 447
09B5*	51	09DP*	55	09Q[5,6]0ZZ	52	09SM*	52, 153, 331
09B50Z[X,Z]	446	09DQ*	55	09Q[9,A,D,E]0ZZ	52	09T[5,6]0ZZ	52
09B6*	51	09DR*	55	09Q0[0,3,4]ZZ	52, 210, 330, 447	09T[9,A,D,E]0ZZ	52
09B60Z[X,Z]	446	09DS*	55	09Q1[0,3,4]ZZ	52, 210, 330, 447	09T0[0,4,X]ZZ	210, 447
09B7[0,3,4,7,8]Z[X,Z]	446	09DT*	55	09Q2[0,3,4]ZZ	52, 210, 330, 447	09T0*	52, 331
09B7*	51	09DU[0,3,4]ZZ	447	09Q3[0,3,4,7,8]ZZ	52, 210, 330, 447	09T1[0,4,X]ZZ	210, 447
09B8[0,3,4,7,8]Z[X,Z]	446	09DU*	55	09Q4[0,3,4,7,8]ZZ	52, 210, 330, 447	09T1*	52, 331
09B8*	51	09DV[0,3,4]ZZ	447	09Q50ZZ	447	09T7*	52
09B9*	51	09DV*	55	09Q60ZZ	447	09T8*	52
09B90Z[X,Z]	446	09DW*	55	09Q7[0,3,4,7,8]ZZ	447	09T90ZZ	447
09BA*	51	09DX*	55	09Q7*	52	09TA0ZZ	447
09BA0Z[X,Z]	446	09HD[0,3,4][5,6,S]Z	48	09Q8[0,3,4,7,8]ZZ	447	09TB*	56
09BB[0,3,4]ZX	51, 446	09HD[0,3,4]4Z	51	09Q8*	52	09TC*	56
09BB[0,3,4]ZZ	55	09HE[0,3,4][5,6,S]Z	48, 48	09QB*	56	09TK[0,4,X]ZZ	210
09BC[0,3,4]ZX	51, 446	09HE[0,3,4]4Z	51	09QC*	56	09TK*	48, 331
09BC[0,3,4]ZZ	55	09J7[0,3,4,7,X]ZZ	51, 447	09QK[0,3,4,X]ZZ	210, 447	09TL[0,4,7,8]ZZ	447
09BD*	51	09J8[0,3,4,7,X]ZZ	51, 447	09QK*	52, 153, 330	09TL*	52, 331
09BD0ZX	446	09JD[0,3,4,X]ZZ	447	09QKXZZ	90	09TM[0,4]ZZ	447
09BE*	51	09JD*	51	09QL[0,3,4,7,8]ZZ	210, 447	09TM*	52, 331
09BE0ZX	446	09JE[0,3,4,X]ZZ	447	09QL*	52, 330	09TN*	52, 105
09BL[0,3,4,7,8]ZZ	51, 330, 446	09JE*	51	09QM[0,3,4]ZZ	210, 447	09TP*	56
09BM[0,3,4]ZZ	51, 330, 446	09M*	51, 330	09QM*	52, 153, 330	09TQ*	56, 153
09BN[0,3,4,7,8]ZZ	51, 105	09M0XZZ	447	09QN*	25, 52, 330	09TR*	56, 153
09BP[0,3,4]ZZ	55	09M1XZZ	447	09QP*	56	09TS*	56
09BP0ZX	55	09MKXZZ	153, 210, 447	09QQ*	56	09TT*	56
09BQ[0,3,4]ZZ	55, 153	09N[5,6]0ZZ	51	09QR*	56	09TU[0,4]ZZ	447
09BQ0ZX	55	09N[9,A]0ZZ	52	09QS*	56	09TU*	56
09BR[0,3,4]ZZ	55, 153	09N[D,E]0ZZ	52	09QT*	56	09TV[0,4]ZZ	447
09BR0ZX	55	09N0[0,3,4,X]ZZ	210, 447	09QU*	56	09TV*	56
09BS[0,3,4]ZZ	55	09N0*	51, 330	09QV*	56	09TW*	56
09BS0ZZ	55	09N1[0,3,4,X]ZZ	210, 447	09QW*	56	09TX*	56
09BT[0,3,4]ZZ	55	09N1*	51, 330	09QX*	56	09U*	52

Code	Page	Code	Page	Code	Page	Code	Page
ØBH3[Ø,3,4,7]GZ	62	ØBP04[3,7]Z	65	ØBW1[Ø,3,4]FZ	52, 90, 210, 331	ØC93[Ø,3,X]ZX	448
ØBH4[Ø,3,4,7]GZ	62	ØBP07[Ø,1,2,D]Z	62	ØBWK[Ø,3,4,7,8][Ø,2,3]Z	62, 331	ØC93*	56
ØBH5[Ø,3,4,7]GZ	62	ØBP08[Ø,1,2,D]Z	62	ØBWL[Ø,3,4,7,8][Ø,2,3]Z	62, 331	ØC94[Ø,3,X][Ø,Z]Z	56, 210, 331
ØBH6[Ø,3,4,7]GZ	62	ØBP1[Ø,3,4,7,8][Ø,2,7,C,D,F,J,K]Z	65	ØBWT[Ø,3,4,7,8][Ø,2,7,J,K,M]Z	62	ØC97[Ø,3,X][Ø,Z]Z	56
ØBH7[Ø,3,4,7]GZ	62	ØBPK[Ø,3,4,7,8][Ø,1,2,3]Z	62, 331	ØBYCØZ[Ø,1,2]	1	ØC97ØZX	56
ØBH8[Ø,3,4,7]GZ	62	ØBPL[Ø,3,4,7,8][Ø,1,2,3]Z	62, 331	ØBYDØZ[Ø,1,2]	1	ØC98ØZX	448
ØBH9[Ø,3,4,7]GZ	62	ØBPT[Ø,3,4,7,8][Ø,2,7,J,K,M]Z	62	ØBYFØZ[Ø,1,2]	1	ØC99ØZX	448
ØBHB[Ø,3,4,7]GZ	62	ØBQ*	62	ØBYGØZ[Ø,1,2]	1	ØC9BØZX	448
ØBHK[Ø,3,4,7,8][2,3]Z	62	ØBQ1[Ø,3,4,7,8]ZZ	210	ØBYHØZ[Ø,1,2]	1	ØC9CØZX	448
ØBHK[Ø,3,4,7,8]1Z	64, 447	ØBQ1*	52, 90, 331	ØBYJØZ[Ø,1,2]	1	ØC9DØZX	448
ØBHK*	331	ØBQ2*	52, 331	ØBYKØZ[Ø,1,2]	1	ØC9FØZX	448
ØBHL[Ø,3,4,7,8][2,3]Z	62	ØBQ3*	331	ØBYLØZ[Ø,1,2]	1	ØC9GØZX	448
ØBHL[Ø,3,4,7,8]1Z	64, 447	ØBQ4*	331	ØBYMØZ[Ø,1,2]	1	ØC9HØZX	448
ØBHL*	331	ØBQ5*	331	ØCØ*	56, 331	ØC9JØZX	56, 448
ØBHR[Ø,3,4]MZ	331	ØBQ6*	331	ØCØØX[7,J,K,Z]Z	210, 447	ØC9M[Ø,3,4,7,8][Ø,Z]Z	52, 331
ØBHR*	62	ØBQ7*	331	ØCØ1X[7,J,K,Z]Z	210, 447	ØC9N[Ø,3,X][Ø,Z]Z	448
ØBHS[Ø,3,4]MZ	331	ØBQ8*	331	ØC5Ø[Ø,3,X]ZZ	210, 447	ØC9N[Ø,3,X]ZX	448
ØBHS*	62	ØBQ9*	331	ØC5Ø*	56	ØC9N*	56
ØBJ[Ø,K,L]4ZZ	90	ØBQB*	331	ØC51[Ø,3,X]ZZ	210, 447	ØC9P[Ø,3,X]ZX	448
ØBJØ[Ø,3,4,7,X]ZZ	64	ØBQK*	331	ØC51*	56	ØC9P*	52
ØBJØ4ZZ	331	ØBQL*	331	ØC52[Ø,3,X]ZZ	447	ØC9Q[Ø,3,X]ZX	448
ØBJ1ØZZ	64	ØBQM*	331	ØC52*	56	ØC9Q*	52
ØBJK[Ø,3,4,7,X]ZZ	64	ØBQN*	331	ØC53[Ø,3,X]ZZ	447	ØC9R[Ø,3,4,7,8][Ø,Z]Z	52
ØBJK4ZZ	331	ØBQP*	331	ØC53*	56, 331	ØC9RØZX	52
ØBJL[Ø,3,4,7,X]ZZ	64	ØBQR*	105, 331	ØC54[Ø,3,X]ZZ	447	ØC9S[Ø,3,4,7,8][Ø,Z]Z	52
ØBJL4ZZ	331	ØBQS*	105, 331	ØC54*	56, 331	ØC9SØZX	52
ØBJQ*	64	ØBS[1,2]ØZZ	52	ØC57[Ø,3,X]ZZ	447	ØC9T[Ø,3,4,7,8][Ø,Z]Z	52
ØBJT*	64	ØBS*	62	ØC57*	56, 90	ØC9TØZX	52
ØBL1*	52, 64, 331	ØBS1ØZZ	331	ØC58[Ø,3]ZZ	447	ØC9V[Ø,3,4,7,8][Ø,Z]Z	52
ØBL2*	52, 64, 331	ØBS2ØZZ	331	ØC58*	56	ØC9VØZX	52
ØBL3*	62	ØBT*	331	ØC59[Ø,3]ZZ	447	ØCBØ[Ø,3,X]ZZ	56, 210, 448
ØBL4*	62	ØBT1*	52, 62	ØC59*	56	ØCB1[Ø,3,X]ZZ	56, 211, 448
ØBL5*	62	ØBT2*	52, 62	ØC5B[Ø,3]ZZ	447	ØCB2[Ø,3,X]Z[X,Z]	448
ØBL6*	62	ØBT3*	62	ØC5B*	56	ØCB2*	56
ØBL7*	62	ØBT4*	62	ØC5C[Ø,3]ZZ	448	ØCB3[Ø,3,X]Z[X,Z]	448
ØBL8*	62	ØBT5*	62	ØC5C*	56	ØCB3[Ø,3,X]ZZ	331
ØBL9*	62	ØBT6*	62	ØC5D[Ø,3]ZZ	448	ØCB3*	56
ØBLB*	62	ØBT7*	62	ØC5D*	56	ØCB4[Ø,3,X]ZZ	56, 331, 448
ØBM[1,2]ØZZ	52	ØBT8*	62	ØC5F[Ø,3]ZZ	448	ØCB7[Ø,3,X]ZZ	56, 237
ØBM*	62	ØBT9*	62	ØC5F*	56	ØCB7ØZX	56
ØBM1ØZZ	331	ØBTB*	62	ØC5G[Ø,3]ZZ	448	ØCB8[Ø,3]ZZ	56, 448
ØBM2ØZZ	331	ØBTC*	62	ØC5G*	56	ØCB8ØZX	56, 448
ØBN1*	52, 64, 331	ØBTD*	62	ØC5H[Ø,3]ZZ	448	ØCB9[Ø,3]ZZ	56, 448
ØBN2*	52, 64, 331	ØBTF*	62	ØC5H*	56	ØCB9ØZX	56, 448
ØBN3*	62	ØBTG*	62	ØC5J[Ø,3]ZZ	448	ØCBB[Ø,3]ZZ	56, 448
ØBN4*	62	ØBTH[Ø,4]ZZ	299	ØC5J*	56	ØCBBØZX	56, 448
ØBN5*	62	ØBTH*	62	ØC5M*	52, 105	ØCBC[Ø,3]ZZ	56, 448
ØBN6*	62	ØBTJ*	62	ØC5N[Ø,3,X]ZZ	448	ØCBCØZX	56, 448
ØBN7*	62	ØBTK*	62	ØC5N*	56	ØCBD[Ø,3]ZZ	57, 448
ØBN8*	62	ØBTL*	62	ØC5P*	52	ØCBDØZX	56, 448
ØBN9*	62	ØBTM*	62	ØC5Q*	52	ØCBF[Ø,3]ZZ	57, 448
ØBNB*	62	ØBTR*	65	ØC5R*	52, 65, 331	ØCBFØZX	57, 448
ØBNC*	62	ØBTS*	65	ØC5S[Ø,3,4,7,8]ZZ	448	ØCBG[Ø,3]ZZ	57, 448
ØBND*	62	ØBU*	62	ØC5S*	52, 65	ØCBGØZX	57, 448
ØBNF*	62	ØBU1*	52, 331	ØC5T[Ø,3,4,7,8]ZZ	448	ØCBH[Ø,3]ZZ	57, 448
ØBNG*	62	ØBU2*	52, 331	ØC5T*	52, 65	ØCBHØZX	57, 448
ØBNH*	62	ØBUR*	105, 331	ØC5V[Ø,3,4,7,8]ZZ	448	ØCBJ[Ø,3]ZZ	57, 448
ØBNJ*	62	ØBUS*	105, 331	ØC5V*	52, 65	ØCBJØZX	57, 448
ØBNK*	62	ØBV*	62	ØC7S[Ø,3,4,7,8][D,Z]Z	448	ØCBM[Ø,3,4,7,8]ZZ	52, 105
ØBNL*	62	ØBV1*	52, 331	ØC7S*	52, 65	ØCBN[Ø,3,X]Z[X,Z]	448
ØBNM*	62	ØBV2*	52, 331	ØC9[8,9]ØZX	56	ØCBN*	56
ØBNN*	64, 331	ØBWØ[Ø,3,4][Ø,2,C,D,J,K]Z	62	ØC9[B,C]ØZX	56	ØCBP[Ø,3,X]ZX	448
ØBNP*	64, 331	ØBWØ[7,8][3,7,C,J,K]Z	65	ØC9[D,F]ØZX	56	ØCBP*	52
ØBNR*	62	ØBWØØ[3,7]Z	65	ØC9[G,H]ØZX	56	ØCBQ[Ø,3,X]ZX	448
ØBNS*	62	ØBWØ3[3,7]Z	65	ØC9[R,S,T,V]ØZX	65	ØCBQ*	52
ØBPØ[Ø,3,4][Ø,1,2,C,D,J,K]Z	62	ØBWØ4[3,7]Z	65	ØC9Ø[Ø,3,X][Ø,Z]Z	56, 210, 331	ØCBR[Ø,3,4,7,8]ZZ	52, 65, 331
ØBPØ[7,8][3,7,C,J,K]Z	65	ØBWØ7[Ø,2,D]Z	62	ØC91[Ø,3,X][Ø,Z]Z	56, 210, 331	ØCBRØZX	52, 65
ØBPØØ[3,7]Z	64	ØBWØ8[Ø,2,D]Z	62	ØC92[Ø,3,X]ZX	448	ØCBS[Ø,3,4,7,8]ZZ	48, 65, 331
ØBPØ3[3,7]Z	65	ØBW1[Ø,3,4,7,8][Ø,2,7,C,D,F,J,K]Z	65	ØC92*	56	ØCBSØZX	52, 65

Code	Page	Code	Page	Code	Page	Code	Page
ØDH573Z	105	ØDM8*	107	ØDP6[Ø,3,4]MZ	25, 53, 153, 259, 268	ØDQV*	112, 123, 334
ØDH582Z	106	ØDM9*	107	ØDP6[Ø,3,7,8][Ø,2,3,7,C,J,K,U]Z	106	ØDQW[Ø,3,4]ZZ	300, 449
ØDH583Z	106	ØDMA*	107	ØDP6[Ø,3][Ø,2,3,7,C,D,J,K,M,U]Z	334	ØDQW*	112, 123, 334
ØDH6[Ø,3,4,7,8][2,3,D]Z	106, 333	ØDMB*	107	ØDP6[Ø,3]DZ	106	ØDR*	334
ØDH6[Ø,3,4,7,8]DZ	235	ØDME*	107	ØDP64[Ø,2,7,D,J,K,M,U]Z	334	ØDR5[Ø,4,7,8][7,J,K]Z	300
ØDH6[Ø,3,4]MZ	25, 31, 53, 87, 153, 253, 259, 268, 333	ØDMF*	107	ØDP64[Ø,2,7,D,J,K,U]Z	106	ØDR5*	53, 106
ØDH60UZ	106, 333	ØDMG*	107	ØDP64[3,C]Z	235, 449	ØDRR[Ø,4][7,J,K]Z	211, 449
ØDH8[Ø,3,4,7,8][2,3]Z	109, 333	ØDMH*	107	ØDP67[Ø,2,3,7,C,J,K,U]Z	334	ØDRR*	110
ØDH9[Ø,3,4,7,8][2,3]Z	106, 123, 333	ØDMK*	107	ØDP68[Ø,2,3,7,C,J,K,U]Z	334	ØDRS[Ø,4][7,J,K]Z	300
ØDHA[Ø,3,4,7,8][2,3]Z	109, 333	ØDML*	107	ØDPD[Ø,3,4,7,8] [Ø,2,3,7,C,D,J,K,U]Z	109, 334	ØDRS*	112, 123
ØDHB[Ø,3,4,7,8][2,3]Z	109, 333	ØDMM*	107	ØDPP[Ø,3,4]1Z	109, 334	ØDRT[Ø,4][7,J,K]Z	300
ØDHP[Ø,3,4,7,8]1Z	112, 333, 449	ØDMN*	107	ØDPQ[Ø,3,4,7,8]LZ	211	ØDRT*	112, 123
ØDHQ[Ø,3,4,7,8]DZ	109	ØDMP*	107	ØDPQ*	107, 334	ØDRV[Ø,4][7,J,K]Z	300
ØDHQ[Ø,3,4]LZ	107, 211	ØDN1*	106, 333	ØDPR*	25, 53, 153, 259, 268, 334	ØDRV*	112, 123
ØDHQ*	333	ØDN2*	106, 333	ØDPU*	112	ØDRW[Ø,4][7,J,K]Z	300
ØDHR*	109	ØDN3*	106, 333	ØDPV*	112	ØDRW*	112, 123
ØDJ[Ø,6,D,U,V,W]ØZZ	65, 90	ØDN4*	106, 333	ØDPW*	112	ØDS5*	106, 334
ØDJ[Ø,6,D]ØZZ	112	ØDN5*	53, 106, 333	ØDQ1*	106, 334	ØDS6[7,8]ZZ	123, 242
ØDJ[Ø,6]4ZZ	106	ØDN6*	106, 235, 333	ØDQ2*	106, 334	ØDS60ZZ	106, 334
ØDJØ[Ø,4]ZZ	300, 333	ØDN7*	106	ØDQ3*	106, 334	ØDS64ZZ	106, 334
ØDJ00ZZ	121, 211, 242, 253, 257, 268, 271, 292	ØDN8[Ø,3,4]ZZ	107, 123, 253, 268, 333	ØDQ4*	106, 334	ØDS67ZZ	106, 334
ØDJ04ZZ	53	ØDN8[Ø,3]ZZ	242	ØDQ5[Ø,3,4,7,8]ZZ	300	ØDS68ZZ	106, 334
ØDJ6[Ø,4]ZZ	121, 300, 333	ØDN9[Ø,3,4]ZZ	107, 123, 253, 268, 333	ØDQ5*	53, 62, 106, 334	ØDS9[Ø,4,7,8]ZZ	109
ØDJ60ZZ	211, 242, 253, 257, 268, 271, 292	ØDN9[Ø,3]ZZ	242	ØDQ6[Ø,3,7,8]ZZ	123, 300	ØDSA[Ø,4,7,8]ZZ	109
ØDJD[Ø,4]ZZ	300, 333	ØDNA[Ø,3,4]ZZ	108, 123, 253, 268, 333	ØDQ6*	106, 236, 334	ØDSB[Ø,4,7,8]ZZ	107, 123, 300, 334
ØDJDØZZ	121, 211, 242, 253, 257, 268, 271, 292	ØDNA[Ø,3]ZZ	242	ØDQ64ZZ	449	ØDSH[Ø,4,7,8]ZZ	107, 123, 300, 334
ØDJD4ZZ	109, 449	ØDNB[Ø,3,4]ZZ	108, 123, 253, 268, 333	ØDQ7*	106	ØDSK[Ø,4,7,8]ZZ	109
ØDJU[Ø,3,4]ZZ	112, 121, 292, 333	ØDNB[Ø,3]ZZ	242	ØDQ8*	107, 334	ØDSL[Ø,4,7,8]ZZ	109
ØDJU[Ø,3]ZZ	268, 300	ØDNC[Ø,3,4]ZZ	108, 123, 253, 268	ØDQ80ZZ	109	ØDSM[Ø,4,7,8]ZZ	109
ØDJU[Ø,4]ZZ	211, 253, 271	ØDNC[Ø,3]ZZ	242	ØDQ9*	106, 334	ØDSN[Ø,4,7,8]ZZ	109
ØDJU[3,4]ZZ	449	ØDNC[7,8]ZZ	107	ØDQ90ZZ	109	ØDSP[Ø,4,7,8]ZZ	107, 334
ØDJUØZZ	242, 257	ØDNC*	334	ØDQA*	107, 334	ØDSQ*	110
ØDJU4ZZ	266	ØDNE[Ø,3,4]ZZ	108, 123, 253, 268, 334	ØDQA0ZZ	109	ØDT1[Ø,4,7,8]ZZ	300
ØDJV[Ø,3,4]ZZ	112, 121, 292, 333	ØDNE[Ø,3]ZZ	242	ØDQB*	107, 334	ØDT1*	53, 106, 334
ØDJV[Ø,3]ZZ	268, 300	ØDNF[Ø,3,4]ZZ	108, 123, 253, 268, 334	ØDQB0ZZ	109	ØDT2[Ø,4,7,8]ZZ	300
ØDJV[Ø,4]ZZ	211, 253, 271	ØDNF[Ø,3]ZZ	242	ØDQC*	107, 334	ØDT2*	53, 106, 334
ØDJV[3,4]ZZ	449	ØDNG[Ø,3,4]ZZ	108, 123, 253, 268, 334	ØDQE*	107, 334	ØDT3[Ø,4,7,8]ZZ	300
ØDJVØZZ	242, 257	ØDNG[Ø,3]ZZ	242	ØDQE0ZZ	109	ØDT3*	53, 106, 334
ØDJV4ZZ	266	ØDNH[Ø,3,4]ZZ	108, 123, 253, 268, 334	ØDQF[3,4,7,8]ZZ	107, 334	ØDT4[Ø,4,7,8]ZZ	300
ØDJW[Ø,3,4]ZZ	112, 121, 292, 333	ØDNH[Ø,3]ZZ	242	ØDQF0ZZ	109	ØDT4*	106, 334
ØDJW[Ø,3]ZZ	268, 300	ØDNJ[Ø,3,4]ZZ	108, 123, 253, 268, 334	ØDQG[3,4,7,8]ZZ	107, 334	ØDT5[Ø,4,7,8]ZZ	300
ØDJW[Ø,4]ZZ	211, 253, 271	ØDNJ[Ø,3]ZZ	242	ØDQG0ZZ	109	ØDT5*	53, 106, 334
ØDJW[3,4]ZZ	449	ØDNJ[7,8]ZZ	108	ØDQH*	107, 334	ØDT6[Ø,4,7,8]ZZ	300
ØDJWØZZ	242, 257	ØDNK[Ø,3,4]ZZ	108, 123, 253, 268, 334	ØDQH0ZZ	109	ØDT6*	90, 106, 334
ØDJW4ZZ	266	ØDNK[Ø,3]ZZ	242	ØDQJ*	108, 334	ØDT7[Ø,4,7,8]ZZ	300
ØDL6*	106, 235, 333	ØDNL[Ø,3,4]ZZ	108, 123, 253, 268, 334	ØDQK*	107, 334	ØDT7*	90, 106, 334
ØDL7*	106, 235, 333	ØDNL[Ø,3]ZZ	242	ØDQK0ZZ	109	ØDT8[Ø,4,7,8]ZZ	300
ØDL8*	107, 123	ØDNM[Ø,3,4]ZZ	108, 123, 253, 268, 334	ØDQL[3,4,7,8]ZZ	107, 334	ØDT8*	107, 334
ØDL9*	107, 123	ØDNM[Ø,3]ZZ	242	ØDQL0ZZ	109	ØDT9[Ø,4,7,8]ZZ	300
ØDLA*	107	ØDNN[Ø,3,4]ZZ	108, 123, 253, 268, 334	ØDQM[3,4,7,8]ZZ	107, 334	ØDT9*	90, 107, 242, 334
ØDLB*	107	ØDNN[Ø,3]ZZ	242	ØDQM0ZZ	109	ØDT90ZZ	106
ØDLC*	107	ØDNP[Ø,3,4,7,8]ZZ	211, 449	ØDQN*	107, 334	ØDTA[Ø,4,7,8]ZZ	300
ØDLE*	107	ØDNP*	109, 334	ØDQN0ZZ	109	ØDTA*	90, 107, 242, 334
ØDLF*	107	ØDNQ*	109	ØDQP[Ø,3,4,7,8]ZZ	211	ØDTB[Ø,4,7,8]ZZ	300
ØDLG*	107	ØDNR[Ø,3,4]ZZ	211, 449	ØDQP*	107, 334	ØDTB*	90, 107, 242, 334
ØDLH*	107	ØDNR*	109, 334	ØDQP0ZZ	274	ØDTC[Ø,4,7,8]ZZ	300
ØDLK*	107	ØDNS[Ø,3]ZZ	242	ØDQP3ZZ	274	ØDTC*	90, 107, 242, 334
ØDLL*	107	ØDNS*	108, 123, 253, 268, 334	ØDQP4ZZ	274	ØDTE[Ø,4,7,8]ZZ	300
ØDLM*	107	ØDNT[Ø,3]ZZ	242	ØDQP7ZZ	271, 272, 273, 274, 275	ØDTE*	90, 107, 334
ØDLN*	107	ØDNT*	108, 123, 253, 268, 334	ØDQP8ZZ	274	ØDTF[Ø,4,7,8]ZZ	300
ØDLP*	109	ØDNV[Ø,3]ZZ	242	ØDQQ[Ø,3,4,7,8,X]ZZ	211	ØDTF*	90, 107, 334
ØDLQ*	109, 333	ØDNV*	108, 123, 253, 268, 334	ØDQQ*	109, 334	ØDTG[Ø,4,7,8]ZZ	300
ØDM*	333	ØDNW[Ø,3]ZZ	242	ØDQQXZZ	272	ØDTG*	90, 107, 242, 334
ØDM5*	106	ØDNW*	108, 123, 253, 268, 334	ØDQR[Ø,3,4]ZZ	211, 449	ØDTH*	90, 107, 334
ØDM6*	106, 235	ØDPØ[Ø,3,4,7,8] [Ø,2,3,7,C,D,J,K,U]Z	109, 334	ØDQR*	109, 334	ØDTJ[Ø,7,8]ZZ	90
		ØDP5[Ø,3,4][1,2,3,U]Z	106, 334	ØDQS*	110	ØDTJ*	108, 268, 334
		ØDP57DZ	106, 334	ØDQT*	110	ØDTK[Ø,4,7,8]ZZ	300
		ØDP58DZ	106, 334	ØDQV[Ø,3,4]ZZ	300	ØDTK*	90, 107, 334
						ØDTL[Ø,4,7,8]ZZ	300

Code	Page	Code	Page	Code	Page	Code	Page
ØFJG[Ø,3,4]ZZ	113, 121, 335	ØFQ9*	120	ØG5Ø*	235	ØGBM[Ø,3,4]ZX	153
ØFJG[Ø,3]ZZ	242, 301	ØFQC*	106, 119	ØG51[Ø,3,4]ZZ	9, 13, 17	ØGBM[Ø,3,4]ZZ	253
ØFJG4ZZ	211, 253, 266, 271, 292, 449	ØFQD*	119	ØG51*	235	ØGBM*	238
ØFL5Ø[C,D,Z]Z	120, 301, 335, 449	ØFQF*	119	ØG52*	235	ØGBN[Ø,3,4]ZX	153
ØFL6Ø[C,D,Z]Z	120, 301, 335, 449	ØFQG*	119	ØG53*	235	ØGBN[Ø,3,4]ZZ	253
ØFL8Ø[C,D,Z]Z	120, 301, 335, 449	ØFR*	335	ØG54*	235	ØGBN*	238
ØFL9Ø[C,D,Z]Z	120, 301, 335, 449	ØFR5[Ø,4]JZ	301, 449	ØG5G*	237	ØGBP[Ø,3,4]ZX	153
ØFLC*	120, 335	ØFR5*	120	ØG5H*	237	ØGBP[Ø,3,4]ZZ	253
ØFLD*	113, 119, 335	ØFR6[Ø,4]JZ	301, 449	ØG5K*	237	ØGBP*	238
ØFLF*	113, 119, 335	ØFR6*	120	ØG5L*	237, 253	ØGBQ[Ø,3,4]ZX	153
ØFMØ*	119, 335	ØFR8[Ø,4]JZ	301, 449	ØG5M*	237, 253	ØGBQ[Ø,3,4]ZZ	253
ØFM1*	119, 335	ØFR8*	120	ØG5N*	237, 253	ØGBQ*	238
ØFM2*	119, 335	ØFR9[Ø,4]JZ	301, 449	ØG5P*	237, 253	ØGBR[Ø,3,4]ZX	153
ØFM4ØZZ	120, 301, 335, 449	ØFR9*	120	ØG5Q*	237, 253	ØGBR[Ø,3,4]ZZ	253
ØFM5ØZZ	120, 335	ØFRC*	120	ØG5R*	237, 253	ØGBR*	238
ØFM6ØZZ	120, 335	ØFRD*	119	ØG8Ø[Ø,3,4]ZZ	9, 13, 17	ØGCØ[Ø,3,4]ZZ	9, 13, 17, 211
ØFM8ØZZ	120, 335	ØFRF*	119	ØG8Ø*	235	ØGCØ*	235
ØFM9ØZZ	120, 335	ØFSØ*	119, 335	ØG8J*	237	ØGC1[Ø,3,4]ZZ	9, 13, 17
ØFMC*	120, 335	ØFS4[Ø,4]ZZ	301, 449	ØG9Ø[Ø,3,4][Ø,Z]Z	9, 13, 17, 211	ØGC1*	235
ØFMD*	119, 335	ØFS4*	120, 335	ØG9Ø[Ø,3,4]ZX	9, 13, 17	ØGC2*	235
ØFMF*	119, 335	ØFS5*	120, 335	ØG9Ø*	235	ØGC3*	235
ØFMG*	119, 335	ØFS6*	120, 335	ØG91[Ø,3,4][Ø,Z]Z	9, 13, 17, 211	ØGC4*	235
ØFN*	108, 123, 253, 335	ØFS8*	120, 335	ØG91[Ø,3,4]ZX	9, 13, 17	ØGCG[Ø,3,4]ZZ	211
ØFNØ[Ø,3]ZZ	242	ØFS9*	120, 335	ØG91*	235	ØGCG*	53, 238, 336
ØFNØ*	268	ØFSC*	120, 335	ØG92[Ø,3,4][Ø,Z]Z	235	ØGCH[Ø,3,4]ZZ	211
ØFN1[Ø,3]ZZ	242	ØFSD*	119, 335	ØG92ØZX	235	ØGCH*	53, 238, 336
ØFN1*	268	ØFSF*	119, 335	ØG93[Ø,3,4][Ø,Z]Z	235	ØGCK[Ø,3,4]ZZ	211
ØFN2[Ø,3]ZZ	242	ØFSG*	119	ØG93ØZX	235	ØGCK*	53, 238, 336
ØFN2*	268	ØFTØ*	119, 335	ØG94[Ø,3,4][Ø,Z]Z	235	ØGCL[Ø,3,4]ZZ	211
ØFN4[Ø,3]ZZ	242	ØFT1*	119, 335	ØG94ØZX	235	ØGCL*	53, 238, 336
ØFN4*	268	ØFT2*	119, 335	ØG9GØ[Ø,Z]Z	53, 211, 336	ØGCM[Ø,3,4]ZZ	211
ØFN5[Ø,3,7,8]ZZ	242	ØFT4[Ø,4]ZZ	301	ØG9GØØZ	237	ØGCM*	53, 238, 336
ØFN5*	268	ØFT4*	113, 120, 335	ØG9GØZ[X,Z]	237	ØGCN[Ø,3,4]ZZ	211
ØFN6[Ø,3,7,8]ZZ	242	ØFT4ØZZ	121	ØG9HØ[Ø,Z]Z	53, 211, 336	ØGCN*	53, 238, 336
ØFN6*	268	ØFT44ZZ	121, 449	ØG9HØØZ	237	ØGCP[Ø,3,4]ZZ	211
ØFN8[Ø,3,7,8]ZZ	242	ØFT5*	113, 120	ØG9HØZ[X,Z]	237	ØGCP*	53, 238, 336
ØFN8*	268	ØFT6*	113, 120	ØG9KØ[Ø,Z]Z	53, 211, 336	ØGCQ[Ø,3,4]ZZ	211
ØFN9[Ø,3,7,8]ZZ	242	ØFT8*	113, 120	ØG9KØØZ	237	ØGCQ*	53, 238, 336
ØFN9*	268	ØFT9*	113, 120	ØG9KØZ[X,Z]	237	ØGCR[Ø,3,4]ZZ	211
ØFNC[Ø,3,7,8]ZZ	242	ØFTC*	113, 120	ØG9L[Ø,3,4]ZX	153, 238	ØGCR*	53, 238, 336
ØFNC*	268	ØFTD[Ø,7]ZZ	119, 242	ØG9LØ[Ø,Z]Z	53, 211, 238, 336	ØGH*	53, 238, 336
ØFND[Ø,3,7,8]ZZ	242	ØFTF[Ø,7]ZZ	119, 242	ØG9M[Ø,3,4]ZX	153, 238	ØGHS[Ø,3,4][2,3]Z	211
ØFND*	268	ØFTG*	119, 335	ØG9MØ[Ø,Z]Z	53, 211, 238, 336	ØGJ[K,R,S]ØZZ	53
ØFNF[Ø,3,7,8]ZZ	242	ØFTGØZZ	106	ØG9N[Ø,3,4]ZX	153, 238	ØGJØ[Ø,3,4]ZZ	9, 13, 17
ØFNF*	268	ØFU*	335	ØG9NØ[Ø,Z]Z	53, 211, 238, 336	ØGJØ*	235
ØFNG[Ø,3]ZZ	242	ØFU5*	120	ØG9P[Ø,3,4]ZX	153, 238	ØGJ1[Ø,3,4]ZZ	9, 13, 17
ØFNG*	268	ØFU6*	120	ØG9PØ[Ø,Z]Z	53, 211, 238, 336	ØGJ1*	235
ØFPØ[Ø,3,4][Ø,2,3]Z	119, 335	ØFU8*	120	ØG9Q[Ø,3,4]ZX	153, 238	ØGJ5*	235
ØFP4[Ø,3,4][Ø,2,3,D]Z	120	ØFU9*	120	ØG9QØ[Ø,Z]Z	53, 211, 238, 336	ØGJK[3,4]ZZ	153
ØFP4[Ø,3,4]DZ	301, 335	ØFUC*	120	ØG9R[Ø,3,4]ZX	153, 238	ØGJK*	238
ØFPB[Ø,3,4,7,8] [Ø,1,2,3,7,C,D,J,K]Z	120, 335	ØFUD[3,4]7Z	113, 301	ØG9RØ[Ø,Z]Z	53, 211, 238, 336	ØGJKØZZ	211, 336
ØFPD[Ø,3,4,7,8] [Ø,1,2,3,7,C,D,J,K]Z	119	ØFUD*	119	ØGBØ[Ø,3,4]Z[X,Z]	9, 13, 17	ØGJR[3,4]ZZ	153
ØFPG[Ø,3,4][Ø,2,3,D]Z	119	ØFUF*	119	ØGBØ[Ø,3,4]ZZ	211	ØGJR*	238
ØFPGXDZ	119	ØFV5Ø[C,D,Z]Z	120, 301, 335, 449	ØGBØ*	235	ØGJRØZZ	211, 336
ØFQ*	335	ØFV6Ø[C,D,Z]Z	120, 301, 335, 449	ØGB1[Ø,3,4]Z[X,Z]	9, 13, 17	ØGJS*	238
ØFQØ*	119	ØFV8Ø[C,D,Z]Z	120, 301, 335, 449	ØGB1*	235	ØGJSØZZ	211, 336
ØFQ1*	119	ØFV9Ø[C,D,Z]Z	120, 301, 335, 449	ØGB2[Ø,3,4]ZZ	235	ØGJS3ZZ	153
ØFQ2*	119	ØFVC*	120, 335	ØGB2ØZX	235	ØGJS4ZZ	153
ØFQ4[Ø,3,4]ZZ	301	ØFVD*	119, 335	ØGB3[Ø,3,4]ZZ	235	ØGM2*	235, 336
ØFQ4*	120	ØFVF*	119, 335	ØGB3ØZX	235	ØGM3*	235, 336
ØFQ5[Ø,3,4,7,8]ZZ	301	ØFWØ[Ø,3,4][Ø,2,3]Z	119, 335	ØGB4[Ø,3,4]ZZ	235	ØGMG*	238
ØFQ5*	120	ØFW4[Ø,3,4][Ø,2,3,D]Z	120	ØGB4ØZX	235	ØGMH*	238
ØFQ6[Ø,3,4,7,8]ZZ	301	ØFWB[Ø,3,4,7,8] [Ø,2,3,7,C,D,J,K]Z	120, 336	ØGBG[Ø,3,4]ZZ	238	ØGML*	238
ØFQ6*	120	ØFWD[Ø,3,4,7,8][Ø,2,3,7,C,D,J,K]Z	119	ØGBGØZX	238	ØGMM*	238
ØFQ8[Ø,3,4,7,8]ZZ	301	ØFWG[Ø,3,4][Ø,2,3,D]Z	119	ØGBH[Ø,3,4]ZZ	238	ØGMN*	238
ØFQ8*	120	ØFYØØZ[Ø,1,2]	1	ØGBHØZX	238	ØGMP*	238
ØFQ9[Ø,3,4,7,8]ZZ	301	ØFYG*	2, 119, 242	ØGBL[Ø,3,4]ZX	153	ØGMQ*	238
		ØG5Ø[Ø,3,4]ZZ	9, 13, 17, 211	ØGBL[Ø,3,4]ZZ	253	ØGMR*	238
				ØGBL*	238	ØGNØ[Ø,3,4]ZZ	9, 13, 17, 211

Numeric Index to Procedures

Code	Page	Code	Page	Code	Page	Code	Page
ØK53*	138, 338	ØK8L*	27, 138, 338	ØK9DØZX	214, 292, 451	ØKB1[Ø,3,4]ZZ	27, 214, 339
ØK54[Ø,3,4]ZZ	213, 451	ØK8M*	27, 138, 338	ØK9DØZZ	149, 314	ØKB1*	139
ØK54*	138, 338	ØK8N*	27, 138, 338	ØK9D3ØZ	149	ØKB1ØZX	27, 214, 292, 451
ØK55[Ø,3,4]ZZ	213, 451	ØK8P*	27, 138, 338	ØK9D4ØZ	149	ØKB2[Ø,3,4]ZZ	27, 214, 339
ØK55*	138, 338	ØK8Q*	27, 138, 338	ØK9F[Ø,3,4]ØZ	139, 214, 338, 451	ØKB2*	139
ØK56[Ø,3,4]ZZ	213, 451	ØK8R*	27, 138, 338	ØK9F[Ø,3,4]ZX	139	ØKB2ØZX	27, 214, 292, 451
ØK56*	138, 338	ØK8S*	27, 138, 338	ØK9F[Ø,4]ZZ	139, 214, 338, 451	ØKB3[Ø,3,4]ZZ	27, 214, 339
ØK57[Ø,3,4]ZZ	213, 451	ØK8T*	27, 138, 338	ØK9FØZX	214, 292, 451	ØKB3*	139
ØK57*	138, 338	ØK8V*	27, 138, 338	ØK9G[Ø,3,4]ØZ	139, 214, 338, 451	ØKB3ØZX	27, 214, 292, 451
ØK58[Ø,3,4]ZZ	213, 451	ØK8W*	27, 138, 338	ØK9G[Ø,3,4]ZX	139	ØKB4[Ø,3,4]ZZ	27, 214, 339
ØK58*	138, 338	ØK9[Ø,1,2,3,4,5,6]ØZX	27	ØK9G[Ø,4]ZZ	139, 214, 338, 451	ØKB4*	139
ØK59[Ø,3,4]ZZ	213, 451	ØK9[7,8,9,B,C,D]ØZX	27	ØK9GØZX	214, 292, 451	ØKB4ØZX	27, 214, 292, 451
ØK59*	138, 338	ØK9[F,G,H,J,K,L,M,N,P]ØZX	27	ØK9H[Ø,3,4]ØZ	139, 214, 338, 451	ØKB5[Ø,3,4]ZZ	27, 214, 339
ØK5B[Ø,3,4]ZZ	213, 451	ØK9[H,J]ØZX	65	ØK9H[Ø,3,4]ZX	139	ØKB5*	139
ØK5B*	138, 338	ØK9[Q,R,S,T,V,W]ØZX	27	ØK9H[Ø,4]ZZ	139, 214, 338, 451	ØKB5ØZX	27, 214, 292, 451
ØK5C[Ø,3,4]ZZ	314	ØK9Ø[Ø,3,4]ØZ	54, 138, 213, 338, 451	ØK9HØZX	214, 292, 451	ØKB6[Ø,3,4]ZZ	27, 214, 339
ØK5C*	149	ØK9Ø[Ø,3,4]ZX	138	ØK9J[Ø,3,4]ØZ	139, 214, 338, 451	ØKB6*	139
ØK5D[Ø,3,4]ZZ	314	ØK9Ø[Ø,4]ZZ	54, 138, 213, 338, 451	ØK9J[Ø,3,4]ZX	139	ØKB6ØZX	27, 214, 292, 451
ØK5D*	149	ØK9ØØZX	213, 292, 451	ØK9J[Ø,4]ZZ	139, 214, 338, 451	ØKB7[Ø,3,4]ZZ	27, 214, 339
ØK5F[Ø,3,4]ZZ	213, 451	ØK91[Ø,3,4]ØZ	54, 138, 213, 338, 451	ØK9JØZX	214, 292, 451	ØKB7*	139
ØK5F*	138, 338	ØK91[Ø,3,4]ZX	138	ØK9K[Ø,3,4]ØZ	139, 214, 338, 451	ØKB7ØZX	27, 214, 292, 451
ØK5G[Ø,3,4]ZZ	213, 451	ØK91[Ø,4]ZZ	54, 138, 213, 338, 451	ØK9K[Ø,3,4]ZX	139	ØKB8[Ø,3,4]ZZ	27, 214, 339
ØK5G*	138, 338	ØK91ØZX	213, 292, 451	ØK9K[Ø,4]ZZ	139, 214, 338, 451	ØKB8*	139
ØK5H[Ø,3,4]ZZ	213, 451	ØK92[Ø,3,4]ØZ	54, 138, 214, 338, 451	ØK9KØZX	214, 292, 451	ØKB8ØZX	27, 214, 292, 451
ØK5H*	138, 338	ØK92[Ø,3,4]ZX	138	ØK9L[Ø,3,4]ØZ	139, 214, 338, 451	ØKB9[Ø,3,4]ZZ	27, 214, 339
ØK5J[Ø,3,4]ZZ	213, 451	ØK92[Ø,4]ZZ	54, 138, 214, 338, 451	ØK9L[Ø,3,4]ZX	139	ØKB9*	139
ØK5J*	138, 338	ØK92ØZX	213, 292, 451	ØK9L[Ø,4]ZZ	139, 214, 338, 451	ØKB9ØZX	27, 214, 292, 451
ØK5K[Ø,3,4]ZZ	213, 451	ØK93[Ø,3,4]ØZ	54, 138, 214, 338, 451	ØK9LØZX	214, 292, 451	ØKBB[Ø,3,4]ZZ	27, 214, 339
ØK5K*	138, 338	ØK93[Ø,3,4]ZX	138	ØK9M[Ø,3,4]ØZ	139, 214, 338, 451	ØKBB*	139
ØK5L[Ø,3,4]ZZ	213, 451	ØK93[Ø,4]ZZ	54, 138, 214, 338, 451	ØK9M[Ø,3,4]ZX	139	ØKBBØZX	27, 214, 292, 451
ØK5L*	138, 338	ØK93ØZX	214, 292, 451	ØK9M[Ø,4]ZZ	139, 214, 338, 451	ØKBC[Ø,3,4]ZX	139
ØK5M[Ø,3,4]ZZ	213, 451	ØK94[Ø,3,4]ØZ	138, 214, 338, 451	ØK9MØZX	214, 292, 451	ØKBC[Ø,3,4]ZZ	149, 314
ØK5M*	138, 338	ØK94[Ø,3,4]ZX	138	ØK9N[Ø,3,4]ØZ	139, 214, 338, 451	ØKBCØZX	214, 292, 451
ØK5N[Ø,3,4]ZZ	213, 451	ØK94[Ø,4]ZZ	138, 214, 338, 451	ØK9N[Ø,3,4]ZX	139	ØKBD[Ø,3,4]ZX	139
ØK5N*	138, 338	ØK94ØZX	214, 292, 451	ØK9N[Ø,4]ZZ	139, 214, 338, 451	ØKBD[Ø,3,4]ZZ	149, 314
ØK5P[Ø,3,4]ZZ	213, 451	ØK95[Ø,3,4]ØZ	138, 214, 338, 451	ØK9NØZX	214, 292, 451	ØKBDØZX	214, 292, 451
ØK5P*	138, 338	ØK95[Ø,3,4]ZX	138	ØK9P[Ø,3,4]ØZ	139, 214, 338, 451	ØKBF[Ø,3,4]ZZ	27, 214, 339
ØK5Q[Ø,3,4]ZZ	213, 451	ØK95[Ø,4]ZZ	138, 214, 338, 451	ØK9P[Ø,3,4]ZX	139	ØKBF*	139
ØK5Q*	138, 338	ØK95ØZX	214, 292, 451	ØK9P[Ø,4]ZZ	139, 214, 338, 451	ØKBFØZX	27, 214, 292, 451
ØK5R[Ø,3,4]ZZ	213, 451	ØK96[Ø,3,4]ØZ	138, 214, 338, 451	ØK9PØZX	214, 292, 451	ØKBG[Ø,3,4]ZZ	27, 214, 339
ØK5R*	138, 338	ØK96[Ø,3,4]ZX	138	ØK9Q[Ø,3,4]ØZ	139, 214, 338, 451	ØKBG*	139
ØK5S[Ø,3,4]ZZ	213, 451	ØK96[Ø,4]ZZ	138, 214, 338, 451	ØK9Q[Ø,3,4]ZX	139	ØKBGØZX	27, 214, 292, 451
ØK5S*	138, 338	ØK96ØZX	214, 292, 451	ØK9Q[Ø,4]ZZ	139, 214, 338, 451	ØKBH[Ø,3,4]ZZ	27, 214, 339
ØK5T[Ø,3,4]ZZ	213, 451	ØK97[Ø,3,4]ØZ	139, 214, 338, 451	ØK9QØZX	214, 292, 451	ØKBH*	139
ØK5T*	138, 338	ØK97[Ø,3,4]ZX	139	ØK9R[Ø,3,4]ØZ	139, 214, 338, 451	ØKBHØZX	27, 214, 292, 451
ØK5V[Ø,3,4]ZZ	213, 451	ØK97[Ø,4]ZZ	139, 214, 338, 451	ØK9R[Ø,3,4]ZX	139	ØKBJ[Ø,3,4]ZZ	27, 214, 339
ØK5V*	138, 338	ØK97ØZX	214, 292, 451	ØK9R[Ø,4]ZZ	139, 214, 338, 451	ØKBJ*	139
ØK5W[Ø,3,4]ZZ	213, 451	ØK98[Ø,3,4]ØZ	139, 214, 338, 451	ØK9RØZX	214, 292, 451	ØKBJØZX	27, 214, 292, 451
ØK5W*	138, 338	ØK98[Ø,3,4]ZX	139	ØK9S[Ø,3,4]ØZ	139, 214, 338, 451	ØKBK[Ø,3,4]ZZ	27, 214, 339
ØK8Ø*	27, 138, 338	ØK98[Ø,4]ZZ	139, 214, 338, 451	ØK9S[Ø,3,4]ZX	139	ØKBK*	139
ØK81*	27, 138, 338	ØK98ØZX	214, 292, 451	ØK9S[Ø,4]ZZ	139, 214, 338, 451	ØKBKØZX	27, 214, 292, 451
ØK82*	27, 138, 338	ØK99[Ø,3,4]ØZ	139, 214, 338, 451	ØK9SØZX	214, 292, 451	ØKBL[Ø,3,4]ZZ	27, 214, 339
ØK83*	27, 138, 338	ØK99[Ø,3,4]ZX	139	ØK9T[Ø,3,4]ØZ	139, 214, 339, 451	ØKBL*	139
ØK84*	54, 106	ØK99[Ø,4]ZZ	139, 214, 338, 451	ØK9T[Ø,3,4]ZX	139	ØKBLØZX	27, 214, 292, 451
ØK85*	27, 138, 338	ØK99ØZX	214, 292, 451	ØK9T[Ø,4]ZZ	139, 214, 339, 451	ØKBM[Ø,3,4]ZZ	27, 214, 339
ØK86*	27, 138, 338	ØK9B[Ø,3,4]ØZ	139, 214, 338, 451	ØK9TØZX	214, 292, 451	ØKBM*	139
ØK87*	27, 138, 338	ØK9B[Ø,3,4]ZX	139	ØK9V[Ø,3,4]ØZ	139, 214, 339, 451	ØKBMØZX	27, 214, 292, 451
ØK88*	27, 138, 338	ØK9B[Ø,4]ZZ	139, 214, 338, 451	ØK9V[Ø,3,4]ZX	139	ØKBN[Ø,3,4]ZZ	27, 214, 339
ØK89*	27, 138, 338	ØK9BØZX	214, 292, 451	ØK9V[Ø,4]ZZ	139, 214, 339, 451	ØKBN*	139
ØK8B*	27, 138, 338	ØK9C[Ø,3,4]ØZ	314	ØK9VØZX	214, 292, 451	ØKBNØZX	27, 214, 292, 451
ØK8C[Ø,3,4]ZZ	314	ØK9C[Ø,3,4]ZX	139	ØK9W[Ø,3,4]ØZ	139, 214, 339, 451	ØKBP[Ø,3,4]ZZ	27, 214, 339
ØK8C*	149	ØK9CØØZ	149	ØK9W[Ø,3,4]ZX	139	ØKBP*	139
ØK8D[Ø,3,4]ZZ	314	ØK9CØZX	214, 292, 451	ØK9W[Ø,4]ZZ	139, 214, 339, 451	ØKBPØZX	27, 214, 292, 451
ØK8D*	149	ØK9CØZZ	149, 314	ØK9WØZX	214, 292, 451	ØKBQ[Ø,3,4]ZZ	27, 214, 339
ØK8F*	27, 138, 338	ØK9C3ØZ	149	ØKB[C,D]ØZX	27	ØKBQ*	139
ØK8G*	27, 138, 338	ØK9C4ØZ	149	ØKB[H,J]ØZX	65	ØKBQØZX	27, 214, 292, 451
ØK8H*	27, 138, 338	ØK9D[Ø,3,4]ØZ	314	ØKBØ[Ø,3,4]ZZ	27, 214, 339	ØKBR[Ø,3,4]ZZ	27, 214, 339
ØK8J*	27, 138, 338	ØK9D[Ø,3,4]ZX	139	ØKBØ*	139	ØKBR*	139
ØK8K*	27, 138, 338	ØK9DØØZ	149	ØKBØØZX	27, 214, 292, 451	ØKBRØZX	27, 214, 292, 451

Numeric Index to Procedures

Code	Page
0KBS[0,3,4]ZZ	27, 214, 339
0KBS*	139
0KBS0ZX	27, 214, 292, 451
0KBT[0,3,4]ZZ	27, 214, 339
0KBT*	139
0KBT0ZX	27, 214, 292, 451
0KBV[0,3,4]ZZ	27, 214, 339
0KBV*	139
0KBV0ZX	27, 214, 292, 451
0KBW[0,3,4]ZZ	27, 214, 339
0KBW*	139
0KBW0ZX	27, 214, 292, 451
0KC0[0,3,4]ZZ	214, 451
0KC0*	54, 139, 339
0KC1[0,3,4]ZZ	214, 451
0KC1*	54, 139, 339
0KC2[0,3,4]ZZ	214, 451
0KC2*	54, 139, 339
0KC3[0,3,4]ZZ	214, 451
0KC3*	54, 139, 339
0KC4[0,3,4]ZZ	214, 451
0KC4*	139, 339
0KC5[0,3,4]ZZ	214, 451
0KC5*	139, 339
0KC6[0,3,4]ZZ	214, 451
0KC6*	139, 339
0KC7[0,3,4]ZZ	214, 451
0KC7*	139, 339
0KC8[0,3,4]ZZ	214, 451
0KC8*	139, 339
0KC9[0,3,4]ZZ	214, 451
0KC9*	139, 339
0KCB[0,3,4]ZZ	214, 451
0KCB*	139, 339
0KCC[0,3,4]ZZ	314
0KCC*	149
0KCD[0,3,4]ZZ	314
0KCD*	149
0KCF[0,3,4]ZZ	214, 451
0KCF*	139, 339
0KCG[0,3,4]ZZ	214, 452
0KCG*	139, 339
0KCH[0,3,4]ZZ	214, 452
0KCH*	139, 339
0KCJ[0,3,4]ZZ	214, 452
0KCJ*	139, 339
0KCK[0,3,4]ZZ	214, 452
0KCK*	139, 339
0KCL[0,3,4]ZZ	214, 452
0KCL*	139, 339
0KCM[0,3,4]ZZ	214, 452
0KCM*	139, 339
0KCN[0,3,4]ZZ	214, 452
0KCN*	139, 339
0KCP[0,3,4]ZZ	214, 452
0KCP*	139, 339
0KCQ[0,3,4]ZZ	214, 452
0KCQ*	139, 339
0KCR[0,3,4]ZZ	214, 452
0KCR*	139, 339
0KCS[0,3,4]ZZ	214, 452
0KCS*	139, 339
0KCT[0,3,4]ZZ	214, 452
0KCT*	139, 339
0KCV[0,3,4]ZZ	215, 452
0KCV*	139, 339
0KCW[0,3,4]ZZ	215, 452
0KCW*	139, 339
0KH*	27, 139, 339
0KJX[0,3,4]ZZ	139
0KJY[0,3,4]ZZ	139
0KM*	27
0KM0*	139, 339
0KM1*	139, 339
0KM2*	139, 339
0KM3*	139, 339
0KM4*	139, 339
0KM5*	139, 339
0KM6*	139, 339
0KM7*	139, 339
0KM8*	139, 339
0KM9*	139, 339
0KMB*	139, 339
0KMC[0,4]ZZ	314
0KMC*	149
0KMD[0,4]ZZ	314
0KMD*	149
0KMF*	139, 339
0KMG*	139, 339
0KMH*	139, 339
0KMJ*	139, 339
0KMK*	139, 339
0KML*	139, 339
0KMM*	139, 339
0KMN*	139, 339
0KMP*	139, 339
0KMQ*	139, 339
0KMR*	139, 339
0KMS*	139, 339
0KMT*	139, 339
0KMV*	139, 339
0KMW*	139, 339
0KN0[0,3,4]ZZ	139
0KN1[0,3,4]ZZ	139
0KN2[0,3,4]ZZ	139
0KN3[0,3,4]ZZ	139
0KN4[0,3,4]ZZ	139
0KN5[0,3,4]ZZ	139
0KN6[0,3,4]ZZ	139
0KN7[0,3,4]ZZ	139
0KN8[0,3,4]ZZ	139
0KN9[0,3,4]ZZ	139
0KNB[0,3,4]ZZ	140
0KNC[0,3,4]ZZ	149, 215, 314
0KND[0,3,4]ZZ	149, 215, 314
0KNF[0,3,4]ZZ	140
0KNG[0,3,4]ZZ	140
0KNH[0,3,4]ZZ	140
0KNJ[0,3,4]ZZ	140
0KNK[0,3,4]ZZ	140
0KNL[0,3,4]ZZ	140
0KNM[0,3,4]ZZ	140
0KNN[0,3,4]ZZ	140
0KNP[0,3,4]ZZ	140
0KNQ[0,3,4]ZZ	140
0KNR[0,3,4]ZZ	140
0KNS[0,3,4]ZZ	140
0KNT[0,3,4]ZZ	140
0KNV[0,3,4]ZZ	140
0KNW[0,3,4]ZZ	140
0KPX[0,3,4][0,7,J,K,M]Z	140, 339
0KPX[0,3,4][0,7,J,K]Z	215, 452
0KPX[0,3,4]MZ	27
0KPY[0,3,4][0,7,J,K,M]Z	140, 339
0KPY[0,3,4][0,7,J,K]Z	215, 452
0KPY[0,3,4]MZ	27
0KQ0[0,3,4]ZZ	215, 452
0KQ0*	27, 140, 339
0KQ1[0,3,4]ZZ	215, 452
0KQ1*	27, 140, 339
0KQ2[0,3,4]ZZ	215, 452
0KQ2*	27, 140, 339
0KQ3[0,3,4]ZZ	215, 452
0KQ3*	27, 140, 339
0KQ4[0,3,4]ZZ	215, 452
0KQ4*	27, 140, 339
0KQ5[0,3,4]ZZ	215, 452
0KQ5*	27, 140, 242, 339
0KQ6[0,3,4]ZZ	215, 452
0KQ6*	27, 140, 242, 339
0KQ7[0,3,4]ZZ	215, 452
0KQ7*	27, 140, 242, 339
0KQ8[0,3,4]ZZ	215, 452
0KQ8*	27, 140, 242, 339
0KQ9[0,3,4]ZZ	215, 452
0KQ9*	27, 140, 242, 339
0KQB[0,3,4]ZZ	215, 452
0KQB*	27, 140, 242, 339
0KQC[0,3,4]ZZ	314, 452
0KQC*	149
0KQD[0,3,4]ZZ	314, 452
0KQD*	149
0KQF[0,3,4]ZZ	215, 452
0KQF*	27, 140, 339
0KQG[0,3,4]ZZ	215, 452
0KQG*	27, 140, 339
0KQH[0,3,4]ZZ	215, 452
0KQH*	27, 140, 339
0KQJ[0,3,4]ZZ	215, 452
0KQJ*	27, 140, 339
0KQK[0,3,4]ZZ	215, 452
0KQK*	27, 140, 339
0KQL[0,3,4]ZZ	215, 452
0KQL*	27, 140, 339
0KQM[0,3,4]ZZ	215, 452
0KQM*	27, 140, 339
0KQN[0,3,4]ZZ	215, 452
0KQN*	27, 140, 242, 339
0KQP[0,3,4]ZZ	215, 452
0KQP*	27, 140, 242, 339
0KQQ*	140, 339
0KQR*	140, 339
0KQS[0,3,4]ZZ	215, 452
0KQS*	27, 140, 242, 339
0KQT[0,3,4]ZZ	215, 452
0KQT*	27, 140, 242, 339
0KQV[0,3,4]ZZ	215, 452
0KQV*	27, 140, 242, 339
0KQW[0,3,4]ZZ	215, 452
0KQW*	27, 140, 242, 339
0KS*	27
0KS0*	140, 243, 339
0KS1*	44, 140, 339
0KS2*	140, 243, 339
0KS3*	140, 243, 339
0KS4*	140, 243, 339
0KS5*	140, 243, 339
0KS6*	140, 243, 339
0KS7*	140, 243, 339
0KS8*	140, 243, 339
0KS9*	140, 243, 339
0KSB*	140, 243, 339
0KSC[0,4]ZZ	314
0KSC*	149
0KSD[0,4]ZZ	314
0KSD*	149
0KSF*	140, 243, 339
0KSG*	140, 243, 339
0KSH*	140, 243, 339
0KSJ*	140, 243, 339
0KSK*	140, 243, 339
0KSL*	140, 243, 339
0KSM*	140, 243, 339
0KSN*	140, 243, 339
0KSP*	140, 243, 339
0KSQ*	140, 243, 339
0KSR*	140, 243, 339
0KSS*	140, 243, 339
0KST*	140, 243, 339
0KSV*	140, 243, 339
0KSW*	140, 243, 339
0KT0[0,4]ZZ	215
0KT0*	27, 140, 339
0KT1[0,4]ZZ	215
0KT1*	27, 140, 339
0KT2[0,4]ZZ	215
0KT2*	27, 140, 339
0KT3[0,4]ZZ	215
0KT3*	27, 140, 339
0KT4[0,4]ZZ	215
0KT4*	27, 140, 339
0KT5[0,4]ZZ	215
0KT5*	27, 140, 339
0KT6[0,4]ZZ	215
0KT6*	27, 140, 339
0KT7[0,4]ZZ	215
0KT7*	27, 140, 339
0KT8[0,4]ZZ	215
0KT8*	27, 140, 339
0KT9[0,4]ZZ	215
0KT9*	27, 140, 339
0KTB[0,4]ZZ	215
0KTB*	27, 140, 339
0KTC[0,4]ZZ	314
0KTC*	149
0KTD[0,4]ZZ	314
0KTD*	149
0KTF[0,4]ZZ	215
0KTF*	27, 140, 339
0KTG[0,4]ZZ	215
0KTG*	27, 140, 339
0KTH[0,4]ZZ	215
0KTH*	27, 140, 339
0KTH0ZZ	221, 222, 223
0KTJ[0,4]ZZ	215
0KTJ*	27, 140, 339
0KTJ0ZZ	221, 222, 223
0KTK[0,4]ZZ	215
0KTK*	27, 140, 339
0KTL[0,4]ZZ	215
0KTL*	27, 140, 340
0KTM[0,4]ZZ	215
0KTM*	27, 140, 340
0KTN[0,4]ZZ	215
0KTN*	27, 140, 340
0KTP[0,4]ZZ	215
0KTP*	27, 140, 340
0KTQ[0,4]ZZ	215
0KTQ*	27, 140, 340
0KTR[0,4]ZZ	215
0KTR*	27, 140, 340
0KTS[0,4]ZZ	215
0KTS*	27, 140, 340
0KTT[0,4]ZZ	215
0KTT*	27, 140, 340
0KTV[0,4]ZZ	215

Code	Page	Code	Page	Code	Page	Code	Page
0N9M[0,3,4]ZX	129, 454	0NBM[0,3,4]ZX	54, 129, 454	0NHG*	54	0NPW30Z	134
0N9M*	54	0NBM[0,3,4]ZZ	48, 154, 343	0NHH*	54	0NPW34Z	134
0N9N[0,3,4]ZX	129, 454	0NBN[0,3,4]ZX	54, 129, 454	0NHJ*	54	0NPW37Z	134
0N9N*	54	0NBN[0,3,4]ZZ	48, 154, 343	0NHK*	54	0NPW3KZ	134
0N9P[0,3,4]0Z	42, 48, 343, 454	0NBP[0,3,4]Z[X,Z]	454	0NHL*	54	0NPW3MZ	134
0N9P[0,3,4]ZX	42, 454	0NBP[0,3,4]ZZ	48, 343	0NHM*	54	0NPW40Z	134
0N9P[0,4]ZZ	42, 48, 343, 454	0NBP*	42	0NHN*	54	0NPW44Z	134
0N9Q[0,3,4]0Z	42, 48, 343, 454	0NBQ[0,3,4]Z[X,Z]	454	0NHP*	54	0NPW47Z	134
0N9Q[0,3,4]ZX	42, 454	0NBQ[0,3,4]ZZ	48, 343	0NHQ*	54	0NPW4KZ	134
0N9Q[0,4]ZZ	42, 48, 343, 454	0NBQ*	42	0NHR*	54	0NPW4MZ	134
0N9R[0,3,4]ZX	54, 129, 454	0NBR[0,3,4]ZZ	48, 154, 343	0NHS*	54	0NPWX4Z	134
0N9S[0,3,4]ZX	54, 129, 454	0NBS[0,3,4]ZZ	48, 154, 343	0NHT*	54	0NQ*	344
0N9T[0,3,4]ZX	54, 129, 454	0NBT[0,3,4]ZZ	48, 154, 343	0NHV*	54	0NQ0[0,3,4,X]ZZ	14, 18
0N9V[0,3,4]ZX	54, 129, 454	0NBV[0,3,4]ZZ	48, 154, 344	0NHW*	54	0NQ0*	10, 49, 154, 415
0N9X[0,3,4]ZX	129, 454	0NBX[0,3,4]ZX	54, 129, 454	0NHX*	54	0NQ0XZZ	301
0N9X*	54	0NBX[0,3,4]ZZ	48, 154, 344	0NJ0[0,3,4]ZZ	10, 14, 18, 129, 344	0NQ1[0,3,4,X]ZZ	14, 18
0NB0[0,3,4]Z[X,Z]	14, 18	0NC1[0,3,4]ZZ	14, 18, 301	0NJB[0,3,4]ZZ	48, 129, 344	0NQ1*	10, 49, 154, 415
0NB0[0,3,4]ZX	129, 243	0NC1*	9, 48, 344, 415	0NJW[0,3,4]ZZ	48, 129, 344	0NQ2[0,3,4,X]ZZ	14, 18
0NB0[0,3,4]ZZ	48, 154, 301, 343, 415	0NC2[0,3,4]ZZ	14, 18, 301	0NN1[0,3,4]ZZ	14, 18	0NQ2*	10, 49, 154, 415
0NB0*	9	0NC2*	9, 48, 344, 415	0NN1*	10, 48, 154, 344, 415	0NQ3[0,3,4,X]ZZ	14, 18
0NB1[0,3,4]Z[X,Z]	14, 18	0NC3[0,3,4]ZZ	14, 18, 301	0NN2[0,3,4]ZZ	14, 18	0NQ3*	10, 49, 154, 415
0NB1[0,3,4]ZX	129, 243	0NC3*	9, 48, 344, 415	0NN2*	10, 48, 154, 344, 415	0NQ4[0,3,4,X]ZZ	14, 18
0NB1[0,3,4]ZZ	48, 154, 301, 343, 415	0NC4[0,3,4]ZZ	14, 18, 301	0NN3[0,3,4]ZZ	14, 18	0NQ4*	10, 49, 154, 415
0NB1*	9	0NC4*	9, 48, 344, 415	0NN3*	10, 48, 154, 344, 415	0NQ5[0,3,4,X]ZZ	14, 18
0NB2[0,3,4]Z[X,Z]	14, 18	0NC5[0,3,4]ZZ	14, 18, 301	0NN4[0,3,4]ZZ	14, 18	0NQ5*	10, 49, 154, 415
0NB2[0,3,4]ZX	129, 243	0NC5*	9, 48, 344, 415	0NN4*	10, 48, 154, 344, 415	0NQ6[0,3,4,X]ZZ	14, 18
0NB2[0,3,4]ZZ	48, 154, 301, 343, 415	0NC6[0,3,4]ZZ	14, 18, 301	0NN5[0,3,4]ZZ	14, 18	0NQ6*	10, 49, 154, 415
0NB2*	9	0NC6*	9, 48, 344, 415	0NN5*	10, 48, 154, 344, 415	0NQ7[0,3,4,X]ZZ	14, 18
0NB3[0,3,4]Z[X,Z]	14, 18	0NC7[0,3,4]ZZ	14, 18, 301	0NN6[0,3,4]ZZ	14, 18	0NQ7*	10, 49, 154, 415
0NB3[0,3,4]ZX	129, 243	0NC7*	10, 48, 344, 415	0NN6*	10, 48, 154, 344, 415	0NQ8[0,3,4,X]ZZ	14, 18
0NB3[0,3,4]ZZ	48, 154, 301, 343, 415	0NC8[0,3,4]ZZ	14, 18, 301	0NN7[0,3,4]ZZ	14, 18	0NQ8*	10, 49, 154, 415
0NB3*	9	0NC8*	10, 48, 344, 415	0NN7*	10, 48, 154, 344, 415	0NQB[0,3,4,X]ZZ	216, 454
0NB4[0,3,4]Z[X,Z]	14, 18	0NCC*	54	0NN8[0,3,4]ZZ	14, 18	0NQB*	54, 154
0NB4[0,3,4]ZX	129, 243	0NCD*	54	0NN8*	10, 48, 154, 344, 415	0NQC*	49
0NB4[0,3,4]ZZ	48, 154, 301, 343, 415	0NCF*	54	0NNC*	48, 344	0NQD*	49
0NB4*	9	0NCG*	54	0NND*	48, 344	0NQF*	49
0NB5[0,3,4]Z[X,Z]	14, 18	0NCH*	54	0NNF*	48, 344	0NQG*	49
0NB5[0,3,4]ZX	129, 243	0NCJ*	54	0NNG*	49, 344	0NQH*	49
0NB5[0,3,4]ZZ	48, 154, 301, 343, 415	0NCK*	54	0NNH*	49, 344	0NQJ*	49
0NB5*	9	0NCL*	54	0NNJ*	49, 344	0NQK*	49
0NB6[0,3,4]Z[X,Z]	14, 18	0NCM*	54	0NNK*	49, 344	0NQL*	49
0NB6[0,3,4]ZX	129, 243	0NCN*	54	0NNL*	49, 344	0NQM*	49
0NB6[0,3,4]ZZ	48, 154, 301, 343, 415	0NCP*	54	0NNM*	49, 344	0NQN*	49
0NB6*	9	0NCQ*	54	0NNN*	49, 344	0NQP[0,3,4,X]ZZ	454
0NB7[0,3,4]Z[X,Z]	14, 18	0NCX*	54	0NNP*	49, 344	0NQP*	42, 49
0NB7[0,3,4]ZX	129, 243	0NH0[0,3,4][4,M]Z	10, 14, 18	0NNQ*	49, 344	0NQQ[0,3,4,X]ZZ	454
0NB7[0,3,4]ZZ	48, 154, 301, 343, 415	0NH0[0,3,4]4Z	154, 344, 415	0NNR*	49, 344	0NQQ*	42, 49
0NB7*	9	0NH00NZ	11, 16, 28	0NNS*	49, 344	0NQR*	49, 154
0NB8[0,3,4]Z[X,Z]	14, 18	0NH1[0,3,4]4Z	14, 18	0NNT*	49, 344	0NQS*	49, 154
0NB8[0,3,4]ZX	129, 243	0NH1*	10, 48, 154, 344, 415	0NNV*	49, 344	0NQT*	49, 154
0NB8[0,3,4]ZZ	48, 154, 301, 343, 415	0NH2[0,3,4]4Z	14, 18	0NNX[0,3,4]ZZ	216, 454	0NQV*	49, 154
0NB8*	9	0NH2*	10, 48, 154, 344, 415	0NNX*	56, 344	0NQX*	49
0NBB[0,3,4]ZZ	48, 154, 343	0NH3[0,3,4]4Z	14, 18	0NP0[0,3,4,X]MZ	301	0NR0[0,3,4][7,J,K]Z	14, 18
0NBC[0,3,4]ZX	54, 129, 454	0NH3*	10, 48, 154, 344, 415	0NP0[0,3,4][0,4,7,J,K,M,S]Z	10, 14, 18	0NR0*	10, 49, 154, 344, 415
0NBC[0,3,4]ZZ	48, 154, 343	0NH4[0,3,4]4Z	14, 18	0NP0[0,3,4]JZ	49, 154, 344	0NR1[0,3,4][7,J,K]Z	14, 18
0NBD[0,3,4]ZX	54, 129, 454	0NH4*	10, 48, 154, 344, 415	0NP005Z	10, 14, 18	0NR1[0,3,4]JZ	344, 415
0NBD[0,3,4]ZZ	48, 154, 343	0NH5[0,3,4]4Z	10, 14, 18, 48, 154, 344, 415	0NP00NZ	28	0NR1*	10, 49, 154
0NBF[0,3,4]ZX	54, 129, 454	0NH5[0,3,4]SZ	54	0NP0X[4,M,S]Z	14, 18	0NR2[0,3,4][7,J,K]Z	14, 18
0NBF[0,3,4]ZZ	48, 154, 343	0NH6[0,3,4]4Z	10, 14, 18, 48, 154, 344, 415	0NP0X4Z	10	0NR2[0,3,4]JZ	344, 415
0NBG[0,3,4]ZX	54, 129, 454	0NH6[0,3,4]SZ	54	0NP0XMZ	10	0NR2*	10, 49, 154
0NBG[0,3,4]ZZ	48, 154, 343	0NH7[0,3,4]4Z	14, 18	0NP0XSZ	10	0NR3[0,3,4][7,J,K]Z	14, 18
0NBH[0,3,4]ZX	54, 129, 454	0NH7*	10, 48, 154, 344, 415	0NPW[0,3,4,X]4Z	49, 344	0NR3[0,3,4]JZ	344, 415
0NBH[0,3,4]ZZ	48, 154, 343	0NH8[0,3,4]4Z	14, 18	0NPW[0,3,4][0,7,K,M]Z	54	0NR3*	10, 49, 154
0NBJ[0,3,4]ZX	54, 129, 454	0NH8*	10, 48, 154, 344, 415	0NPW[0,3,4]JZ	42, 344, 454	0NR4[0,3,4][7,J,K]Z	14, 18
0NBJ[0,3,4]ZZ	48, 154, 343	0NHC*	54	0NPW00Z	134	0NR4[0,3,4]JZ	344, 415
0NBK[0,3,4]ZX	54, 129, 454	0NHD*	54	0NPW04Z	134	0NR4*	10, 49, 154
0NBK[0,3,4]ZZ	48, 154, 343	0NHF*	54	0NPW07Z	134	0NR5[0,3,4][7,J,K]Z	14, 18
0NBL[0,3,4]ZX	54, 129, 454			0NPW0KZ	134	0NR5[0,3,4]JZ	344, 415
0NBL[0,3,4]ZZ	48, 154, 343			0NPW0MZ	134	0NR5*	10, 49, 154

Code	Page	Code	Page	Code	Page	Code	Page
ØPP4[Ø,3,4][4,7,J,K]Z	134, 345, 455	ØPR7[Ø,3,4]JZ	66, 346	ØPSBØZZ	155, 346	ØPTQØZZ	315
ØPP5[Ø,3,4][4,7,J,K]Z	134, 345, 455	ØPR7*	155	ØPSC[Ø,3,4][4,5,6,B,C,D]Z	133, 346	ØPTRØZZ	347
ØPP6[Ø,3,4][4,7,J,K]Z	134, 346, 455	ØPR8[Ø,3,4]JZ	66, 346	ØPSCØZZ	133, 346	ØPTSØZZ	347
ØPP7[Ø,3,4][4,7,J,K]Z	455	ØPR8*	155	ØPSD[Ø,3,4][4,5,6,B,C,D]Z	133, 346	ØPTTØZZ	347
ØPP7[Ø,3,4][4,7,J,K]Z	134, 346	ØPR9[Ø,3,4]JZ	66, 346	ØPSDØZZ	133, 346	ØPTVØZZ	347
ØPP8[Ø,3,4][4,7,J,K]Z	134, 346, 455	ØPR9*	155	ØPSF[Ø,3,4][4,5,6,B,C,D]Z	133, 346	ØPUØ[Ø,3,4]JZ	66, 347
ØPP9[Ø,3,4][4,7,J,K]Z	134, 346, 455	ØPRB[Ø,3,4]JZ	66, 346	ØPSFØZZ	133, 346	ØPUØ*	155
ØPPB[Ø,3,4][4,7,J,K]Z	134, 346, 455	ØPRB*	155	ØPSG[Ø,3,4][4,5,6,B,C,D]Z	133, 346	ØPU1[Ø,3,4]JZ	66, 347
ØPPC[Ø,3,4][4,5,7,J,K]Z	134, 346, 455	ØPRC[Ø,3,4][7,K]Z	133, 346	ØPSGØZZ	133, 346	ØPU1*	155
ØPPD[Ø,3,4][4,5,7,J,K]Z	134, 346, 455	ØPRC[3,4]JZ	133, 346	ØPSH[Ø,3,4][4,5,6,B,C,D]Z	149, 346	ØPU2[Ø,3,4]JZ	66, 347
ØPPF[Ø,3,4][4,5,7,J,K]Z	134, 346, 455	ØPRD[Ø,3,4][7,K]Z	133, 346	ØPSH[3,4][4,6]Z	456	ØPU2*	155
ØPPG[Ø,3,4][4,5,7,J,K]Z	134, 346, 455	ØPRD[3,4]JZ	133, 346	ØPSHØZZ	149, 346	ØPU3[Ø,3,4]JZ	347
ØPPH[Ø,3,4][4,5,7,J,K]Z	134, 346, 455	ØPRF*	133, 346	ØPSJ[Ø,3,4][4,5,6,B,C,D]Z	149, 346	ØPU3Ø7Z	155
ØPPJ[Ø,3,4][4,5,7,J,K]Z	134, 346, 455	ØPRG*	133, 346	ØPSJ[3,4][4,6]Z	456	ØPU3ØJZ	155
ØPPK[Ø,3,4][4,5,7,J,K]Z	134, 346, 455	ØPRH[Ø,3,4][7,K]Z	455	ØPSJØZZ	149, 346	ØPU3ØKZ	155
ØPPL[Ø,3,4][4,5,7,J,K]Z	134, 346, 455	ØPRH*	148, 346	ØPSK[Ø,3,4][4,5,6,B,C,D]Z	149, 346	ØPU337Z	155
ØPPM[Ø,3,4][4,5,7,J,K]Z	134, 315, 455	ØPRJ[Ø,3,4][7,K]Z	455	ØPSK[3,4][4,6]Z	456	ØPU33JZ	155, 158
ØPPN[Ø,3,4][4,5,7,J,K]Z	134, 315, 455	ØPRJ*	148, 346	ØPSKØZZ	149, 346	ØPU33KZ	155
ØPPP[Ø,3,4][4,5,7,J,K]Z	134, 315, 455	ØPRK[Ø,3,4][7,K]Z	455	ØPSL[Ø,3,4][4,5,6,B,C,D]Z	149, 346	ØPU347Z	155
ØPPQ[Ø,3,4][4,5,7,J,K]Z	134, 315, 455	ØPRK*	148, 346	ØPSL[3,4][4,6]Z	456	ØPU34JZ	155
ØPPR[Ø,3,4][4,5,7,J,K]Z	134, 346, 455	ØPRL[Ø,3,4][7,K]Z	456	ØPSLØZZ	149, 346	ØPU34KZ	155
ØPPS[Ø,3,4][4,5,7,J,K]Z	134, 346, 455	ØPRL*	148, 346	ØPSM[Ø,3,4][4,5]Z	150, 315	ØPU4[Ø,3,4]JZ	347
ØPPT[Ø,3,4][4,5,7,J,K]Z	135, 346, 455	ØPRM[Ø,3,4][7,J,K]Z	315	ØPSMØZZ	150, 315	ØPU4*	155
ØPPV[Ø,3,4][4,5,7,J,K]Z	135, 346, 455	ØPRM*	150	ØPSN[Ø,3,4][4,5]Z	150, 315	ØPU43JZ	158
ØPPY[Ø,3,4][Ø,M]Z	135, 455	ØPRN[Ø,3,4][7,J,K]Z	315	ØPSNØZZ	150, 315	ØPU5[Ø,3,4]JZ	66, 347
ØPPY[Ø,3,4]MZ	346	ØPRN*	150	ØPSP[Ø,3,4][4,5]Z	150, 315	ØPU5*	156
ØPQØ*	66, 155, 346	ØPRP[Ø,3,4][7,J,K]Z	315	ØPSPØZZ	150, 315	ØPU6[Ø,3,4]JZ	66, 347
ØPQ1*	66, 155, 346	ØPRP*	150	ØPSQ[Ø,3,4][4,5]Z	150, 315	ØPU6*	156
ØPQ2*	66, 155, 346	ØPRQ[Ø,3,4][7,J,K]Z	315	ØPSQØZZ	150, 315	ØPU7[Ø,3,4]JZ	66, 347
ØPQ3*	155	ØPRQ*	150	ØPSR[Ø,3,4]4Z	150, 315	ØPU7*	156
ØPQ4*	155	ØPRR*	155	ØPSR[Ø,3,4]5Z	155, 346	ØPU8[Ø,3,4]JZ	66, 347
ØPQ5*	66, 155, 346	ØPRS*	155	ØPSRØZZ	150, 315	ØPU8*	156
ØPQ6*	66, 155, 346	ØPRT*	155	ØPSS[Ø,3,4]4Z	150, 315	ØPU9[Ø,3,4]JZ	66, 347
ØPQ7*	66, 155, 346	ØPRV*	155	ØPSS[Ø,3,4]5Z	155, 346	ØPU9*	156
ØPQ8*	66, 155, 346	ØPSØ[Ø,3,4][Ø,4]Z	155, 346	ØPSSØZZ	150, 315	ØPUB[Ø,3,4]JZ	66, 347
ØPQ9*	66, 155, 346	ØPSØ[Ø,3,4]ØZ	66, 91	ØPST[Ø,3,4]4Z	150, 315	ØPUB*	156
ØPQB*	66, 155, 346	ØPSØØ[4,Z]Z	54	ØPST[Ø,3,4]5Z	155, 346	ØPUC*	133, 347
ØPQC*	133, 346	ØPSØØZZ	155, 346	ØPSTØZZ	150, 315	ØPUD*	133, 347
ØPQD*	133, 346	ØPS1[Ø,3,4]4Z	155, 346	ØPSV[Ø,3,4]4Z	150, 315	ØPUF*	133, 347
ØPQF*	133, 346	ØPS1Ø[4,Z]Z	54	ØPSV[Ø,3,4]5Z	155, 346	ØPUG*	133, 347
ØPQG*	133, 346	ØPS1ØZZ	155, 346	ØPSVØZZ	150, 315	ØPUH[Ø,3,4][7,K]Z	456
ØPQH*	148, 346	ØPS2[Ø,3,4]4Z	155, 346	ØPT[Ø,1,2,5,6,7,8,9,B]ØZZ	19	ØPUH*	149, 347
ØPQJ*	148, 346	ØPS2Ø[4,Z]Z	54	ØPT[Ø,1,2,5,6]ØZZ	66, 155	ØPUJ[Ø,3,4][7,K]Z	456
ØPQK*	148, 346	ØPS2ØZZ	155, 346	ØPT[7,8,9,B]ØZZ	66, 155	ØPUJ*	149, 347
ØPQL*	148, 346	ØPS3[Ø,3,4]4Z	19, 159, 160, 301, 346	ØPT[C,D]ØZZ	133	ØPUK[Ø,3,4][7,K]Z	456
ØPQM[Ø,3,4,X]ZZ	315	ØPS3[Ø,4]ZZ	19, 159, 160, 301, 346	ØPT[F,G]ØZZ	133	ØPUK*	149, 347
ØPQM*	150	ØPS33ZZ	155, 158	ØPT[H,J,K,L]ØZZ	149	ØPUL[Ø,3,4][7,K]Z	456
ØPQN[Ø,3,4,X]ZZ	315	ØPS3XZZ	19, 159, 160, 301, 346	ØPT[M,N,P,Q]ØZZ	150	ØPUL*	149, 347
ØPQN*	150	ØPS4[Ø,3,4]4Z	19, 159, 160, 301, 346	ØPT[R,S,T,V]ØZZ	54, 155	ØPUM[Ø,3,4][7,J,K]Z	315
ØPQP[Ø,3,4,X]ZZ	315	ØPS4[Ø,4]ZZ	19, 159, 160, 301, 346	ØPTØØZZ	346	ØPUM*	150
ØPQP*	150	ØPS43ZZ	158	ØPT1ØZZ	346	ØPUN[Ø,3,4][7,J,K]Z	315
ØPQQ[Ø,3,4,X]ZZ	315	ØPS4XZZ	19, 159, 160, 301, 346	ØPT2ØZZ	346	ØPUN*	150
ØPQQ*	150	ØPS5[Ø,3,4]4Z	155, 346	ØPT5ØZZ	346	ØPUP[Ø,3,4][7,J,K]Z	315
ØPQR*	155	ØPS5Ø[4,Z]Z	54	ØPT6ØZZ	346	ØPUP*	150
ØPQS*	155	ØPS5ØZZ	155, 346	ØPT7ØZZ	346	ØPUQ[Ø,3,4][7,J,K]Z	315
ØPQT*	155	ØPS6[Ø,3,4]4Z	155, 346	ØPT8ØZZ	346	ØPUQ*	150
ØPQV*	155	ØPS6Ø[4,Z]Z	54	ØPT9ØZZ	347	ØPUR*	156
ØPRØ[Ø,3,4]JZ	66, 346	ØPS6ØZZ	155, 346	ØPTBØZZ	347	ØPUS*	156
ØPRØ*	155	ØPS7[Ø,3,4]4Z	155, 346	ØPTCØZZ	347	ØPUT*	156
ØPR1[Ø,3,4]JZ	66, 346	ØPS7Ø[4,Z]Z	54	ØPTDØZZ	347	ØPUV*	156
ØPR1*	155	ØPS7ØZZ	155, 346	ØPTFØZZ	347	ØPWØ[Ø,3,4][4,7,J,K]Z	135
ØPR2[Ø,3,4]JZ	66, 346	ØPS8[Ø,3,4]4Z	155, 346	ØPTGØZZ	347	ØPW1[Ø,3,4][4,7,J,K]Z	135
ØPR2*	155	ØPS8Ø[4,Z]Z	54	ØPTHØZZ	347	ØPW2[Ø,3,4][4,7,J,K]Z	135
ØPR3*	155	ØPS8ØZZ	155, 346	ØPTJØZZ	347	ØPW3[Ø,3,4][4,7,J,K]Z	135
ØPR4*	155	ØPS9[Ø,3,4]4Z	155, 346	ØPTKØZZ	347	ØPW4[Ø,3,4][4,7,J,K]Z	135
ØPR5[Ø,3,4]JZ	66, 346	ØPS9Ø[4,Z]Z	54	ØPTLØZZ	347	ØPW5[Ø,3,4][4,7,J,K]Z	135
ØPR5*	155	ØPS9ØZZ	155, 346	ØPTMØZZ	315	ØPW6[Ø,3,4][4,7,J,K]Z	135
ØPR6[Ø,3,4]JZ	66, 346	ØPSB[Ø,3,4]4Z	155, 346	ØPTNØZZ	315	ØPW7[Ø,3,4][4,7,J,K]Z	135
ØPR6*	155	ØPSBØ[4,Z]Z	54	ØPTPØZZ	315	ØPW8[Ø,3,4][4,7,J,K]Z	135

Numeric Index to Procedures

Code	Page	Code	Page	Code	Page	Code	Page
ØRRL*	131, 350	ØRTMØZZ	350	ØRUS*	28, 147	ØRWX[Ø,3,4][Ø,3,4,5,7,8,K]Z	147, 317
ØRRM*	131, 350	ØRTNØZZ	317	ØRUT*[7,J,K]Z	317	ØRWX[Ø,3,4]JZ	157, 351
ØRRN*	131, 350	ØRTPØZZ	317	ØRUT*	28, 147	ØS5*	351
ØRRP*	131, 350	ØRTQØZZ	317	ØRUU[Ø,3,4][7,J,K]Z	317	ØS5Ø*	136
ØRRQ*	28, 147	ØRTRØZZ	317	ØRUU*	28, 147	ØS52[Ø,3,4]ZZ	20
ØRRQØ[7,J,K]Z	316	ØRTSØZZ	317	ØRUV[Ø,3,4][7,J,K]Z	317	ØS52*	159, 161
ØRRR*	28, 147	ØRTTØZZ	317	ØRUV*	28, 147	ØS53*	136
ØRRRØ[7,J,K]Z	316	ØRTUØZZ	317	ØRUW[Ø,3,4][7,J,K]Z	317	ØS54[Ø,3,4]ZZ	20
ØRRS*	28, 147	ØRTVØZZ	317	ØRUW*	28, 147	ØS54*	159, 161
ØRRSØ[7,J,K]Z	316	ØRTWØZZ	317	ØRUX[Ø,3,4][7,J,K]Z	317	ØS55*	136
ØRRT*	28, 147	ØRTXØZZ	317	ØRUX*	28, 147	ØS56*	136
ØRRTØ[7,J,K]Z	316	ØRUØ[Ø,3,4][7,K]Z	157	ØRWØ[Ø,3,4][Ø,3,4,7,8,A,J,K]Z	157	ØS57*	136
ØRRU*	28, 147	ØRUØ[Ø,3,4]JZ	20, 160, 161, 350	ØRWØ[Ø,3,4][4,J]Z	350	ØS58*	136
ØRRUØ[7,J,K]Z	316	ØRUØØJZ	159	ØRW1[Ø,3,4][Ø,3,4,7,8,A,J,K]Z	157	ØS59*	137
ØRRV*	28, 147	ØRUØ3JZ	159	ØRW1[Ø,3,4][4,J]Z	350	ØS5B*	137
ØRRVØ[7,J,K]Z	316	ØRUØ4JZ	159	ØRW3[Ø,3,4][Ø,3,7,K]Z	157	ØS5C[Ø,3,4]ZZ	457
ØRRW*	28, 147	ØRU1[Ø,3,4][7,K]Z	157	ØRW3[Ø,3,4]JZ	20, 159, 161, 350	ØS5C*	136
ØRRWØ[7,J,K]Z	316	ØRU1[Ø,3,4]JZ	20, 160, 161, 350	ØRW4[Ø,3,4][Ø,3,4,7,8,A,J,K]Z	157	ØS5D[Ø,3,4]ZZ	457
ØRRX*	28, 147	ØRU1ØJZ	159	ØRW4[Ø,3,4][4,J]Z	350	ØS5D*	136
ØRRXØ[7,J,K]Z	316	ØRU13JZ	159	ØRW5[Ø,3,4][Ø,3,7,K]Z	157	ØS5F*	133
ØRSØØ[4,Z]Z	157, 350	ØRU14JZ	159	ØRW5[Ø,3,4]JZ	20, 159, 161, 350	ØS5G*	133
ØRS1Ø[4,Z]Z	157, 350	ØRU3[Ø,3,4][7,J,K]Z	20, 302	ØRW6[Ø,3,4][Ø,3,4,7,8,A,J,K]Z	157	ØS5H[Ø,3,4]ZZ	457
ØRS4Ø[4,Z]Z	157, 350	ØRU3*	159, 161, 350	ØRW6[Ø,3,4][4,J]Z	350	ØS5H*	145, 244
ØRS6Ø[4,Z]Z	157, 350	ØRU4[Ø,3,4][7,K]Z	157	ØRW9[Ø,3,4][Ø,3,7,K]Z	157	ØS5J[Ø,3,4]ZZ	457
ØRSAØ[4,Z]Z	157, 350	ØRU4[Ø,3,4]JZ	20, 160, 161, 350	ØRW9[Ø,3,4]JZ	20, 159, 161, 350	ØS5J*	145, 244
ØRSCØ[4,Z]Z	49, 157, 350	ØRU4ØJZ	159	ØRWA[Ø,3,4][Ø,3,4,7,8,A,J,K]Z	157	ØS5K[Ø,3,4]ZZ	457
ØRSDØ[4,Z]Z	49, 157, 350	ØRU43JZ	159	ØRWA[Ø,3,4][4,J]Z	350	ØS5K*	145, 244
ØRSEØ[4,Z]Z	149, 350	ØRU44JZ	159	ØRWB[Ø,3,4][Ø,3,7,K]Z	157	ØS5L[Ø,3,4]ZZ	457
ØRSFØ[4,Z]Z	149, 350	ØRU5[Ø,3,4][7,K]Z	157	ØRWB[Ø,3,4]JZ	20, 159, 161, 350	ØS5L*	145, 244
ØRSGØ[4,Z]Z	149, 350	ØRU5[Ø,3,4]JZ	20, 159, 160, 161, 350	ØRWC[Ø,3,4][Ø,3,4,7,8,J,K]Z	55	ØS5M[Ø,3,4]ZZ	457
ØRSHØ[4,Z]Z	149, 350	ØRU6[Ø,3,4][7,K]Z	157	ØRWD[Ø,3,4][Ø,3,4,7,8,J,K]Z	55	ØS5M*	145, 244
ØRSJØ[4,Z]Z	149, 350	ØRU6[Ø,3,4]JZ	20, 160, 161, 350	ØRWE[Ø,3,4][Ø,3,4,7,8,J,K]Z	148, 350	ØS5N[Ø,3,4]ZZ	457
ØRSKØ[4,Z]Z	149, 350	ØRU6ØJZ	159	ØRWF[Ø,3,4][Ø,3,4,7,8,J,K]Z	148, 350	ØS5N*	145, 244
ØRSLØ[4,5,Z]Z	149, 350	ØRU63JZ	159	ØRWG[Ø,3,4][Ø,3,4,7,8,J,K]Z	350	ØS5P[Ø,3,4]ZZ	457
ØRSMØ[4,5,Z]Z	149, 350	ØRU64JZ	159	ØRWG[Ø,3,4][Ø,3,4,7,8,K]Z	148	ØS5P*	145, 244
ØRSNØ[4,5,Z]Z	150, 316	ØRU9[Ø,3,4][7,J,K]Z	20, 302	ØRWG[Ø,3,4]JZ	157	ØS5Q[Ø,3,4]ZZ	457
ØRSPØ[4,5,Z]Z	150, 316	ØRU9*	159, 161, 350	ØRWH[Ø,3,4][Ø,3,4,7,8,J,K]Z	350	ØS5Q*	145, 244
ØRSQØ[4,5,Z]Z	150, 316	ØRUA[Ø,3,4][7,K]Z	157	ØRWH[Ø,3,4][Ø,3,4,7,8,K]Z	148	ØS9ØØ[Ø,Z]Z	157
ØRSRØ[4,5,Z]Z	150, 316	ØRUA[Ø,3,4]JZ	20, 160, 161, 350	ØRWH[Ø,3,4]JZ	157	ØS92Ø[Ø,Z]Z	157
ØRSSØ[4,5,Z]Z	150, 316	ØRUAØJZ	159	ØRWJ[Ø,3,4][Ø,3,4,7,8,J,K]Z	350	ØS93Ø[Ø,Z]Z	157
ØRSTØ[4,5,Z]Z	150, 316	ØRUA3JZ	159	ØRWJ[Ø,3,4][Ø,3,4,7,8,K]Z	148	ØS94Ø[Ø,Z]Z	157
ØRSUØ[4,5,Z]Z	150, 316	ØRUA4JZ	159	ØRWJ[Ø,3,4]JZ	157	ØS95Ø[Ø,Z]Z	157
ØRSVØ[4,5,Z]Z	150, 317	ØRUB[Ø,3,4][7,J,K]Z	20, 302	ØRWK[Ø,3,4][Ø,3,4,7,8,J,K]Z	351	ØS96Ø[Ø,Z]Z	157
ØRSWØ[4,5,Z]Z	150, 317	ØRUB*	159, 161, 350	ØRWK[Ø,3,4][Ø,3,4,7,8,K]Z	148	ØS97Ø[Ø,Z]Z	157
ØRSXØ[4,5,Z]Z	150, 317	ØRUC*	55, 157, 350	ØRWK[Ø,3,4]JZ	157	ØS98Ø[Ø,Z]Z	157
ØRT[3,4,5,9,B]ØZZ	20, 159, 161	ØRUD*	55, 157, 350	ØRWL[Ø,3,4][Ø,3,4,5,7,8,J,K]Z	351	ØS99Ø[Ø,Z]Z	131, 351
ØRT[C,D]ØZZ	49, 157	ØRUE[Ø,3,4][7,J,K]Z	457	ØRWL[Ø,3,4][Ø,3,4,5,7,8,K]Z	148	ØS9BØ[Ø,Z]Z	131, 351
ØRT[E,F]ØZZ	149	ØRUE*	148, 350	ØRWL[Ø,3,4]JZ	157	ØS9CØ[Ø,Z]Z	132, 244, 351, 457
ØRT[G,H]ØZZ	149	ØRUF[Ø,3,4][7,J,K]Z	457	ØRWM[Ø,3,4][Ø,3,4,5,7,8,J,K]Z	351	ØS9DØ[Ø,Z]Z	132, 244, 351, 457
ØRT[J,K,L,M]ØZZ	149	ØRUF*	148, 350	ØRWM[Ø,3,4][Ø,3,4,5,7,8,K]Z	148	ØS9FØ[Ø,Z]Z	133, 351
ØRT[N,P]ØZZ	151	ØRUG[Ø,3,4][7,J,K]Z	457	ØRWM[Ø,3,4]JZ	157	ØS9GØ[Ø,Z]Z	133, 351
ØRT[Q,R]ØZZ	151	ØRUG*	148, 350	ØRWN[Ø,3,4][Ø,3,4,5,7,8,K]Z	147, 317	ØS9HØ[Ø,Z]Z	145, 351, 457
ØRT[S,T]ØZZ	151	ØRUH[Ø,3,4][7,J,K]Z	457	ØRWN[Ø,3,4]JZ	157, 351	ØS9JØ[Ø,Z]Z	145, 351, 457
ØRT[U,V]ØZZ	151	ØRUH*	148, 350	ØRWP[Ø,3,4][Ø,3,4,5,7,8,K]Z	147, 317	ØS9KØ[Ø,Z]Z	145, 351, 457
ØRT[W,X]ØZZ	151	ØRUJ[Ø,3,4][7,J,K]Z	457	ØRWP[Ø,3,4]JZ	157, 351	ØS9LØ[Ø,Z]Z	145, 351, 457
ØRT3ØZZ	350	ØRUJ*	148, 350	ØRWQ[Ø,3,4][Ø,3,4,5,7,8,K]Z	147, 317	ØS9MØ[Ø,Z]Z	145, 351, 457
ØRT4ØZZ	350	ØRUK[Ø,3,4][7,J,K]Z	457	ØRWQ[Ø,3,4]JZ	157, 351	ØS9NØ[Ø,Z]Z	145, 351, 457
ØRT5ØZZ	350	ØRUK*	148, 350	ØRWR[Ø,3,4][Ø,3,4,5,7,8,K]Z	147, 317	ØS9PØ[Ø,Z]Z	145, 351, 457
ØRT9ØZZ	350	ØRUL*	148, 350	ØRWR[Ø,3,4]JZ	157, 351	ØS9QØ[Ø,Z]Z	145, 351, 457
ØRTBØZZ	350	ØRUM*	148, 350	ØRWS[Ø,3,4][Ø,3,4,5,7,8,K]Z	147, 317	ØSBØ[Ø,3,4]ZZ	20, 159, 161, 302, 351
ØRTCØZZ	350	ØRUN[Ø,3,4][7,J,K]Z	317	ØRWS[Ø,3,4]JZ	157, 351	ØSB2[Ø,3,4]ZZ	20, 159, 161, 351
ØRTDØZZ	350	ØRUN*	28, 147	ØRWT[Ø,3,4][Ø,3,4,5,7,8,K]Z	147, 317	ØSB3[Ø,3,4]ZZ	20, 159, 161, 302, 351
ØRTEØZZ	350	ØRUP[Ø,3,4][7,J,K]Z	317	ØRWT[Ø,3,4]JZ	157, 351	ØSB4[Ø,3,4]ZZ	20, 159, 161, 351
ØRTFØZZ	350	ØRUP*	28, 147	ØRWU[Ø,3,4][Ø,3,4,5,7,8,K]Z	147, 317	ØSB5[Ø,3,4]ZZ	20, 159, 161, 302, 351
ØRTGØZZ	350	ØRUQ[Ø,3,4][7,J,K]Z	317	ØRWU[Ø,3,4]JZ	157, 351	ØSB6[Ø,3,4]ZZ	20, 159, 161, 302, 351
ØRTHØZZ	350	ØRUQ*	28, 147	ØRWV[Ø,3,4][Ø,3,4,5,7,8,K]Z	147, 317	ØSB7[Ø,3,4]ZZ	20, 159, 161, 302, 351
ØRTJØZZ	350	ØRUR[Ø,3,4][7,J,K]Z	317	ØRWV[Ø,3,4]JZ	157, 351	ØSB8[Ø,3,4]ZZ	20, 159, 161, 302, 351
ØRTKØZZ	350	ØRUR*	28, 147	ØRWW[Ø,3,4][Ø,3,4,5,7,8,K]Z	147, 317	ØSB9[Ø,3,4]ZZ	131, 351, 416
ØRTLØZZ	350	ØRUS[Ø,3,4][7,J,K]Z	317	ØRWW[Ø,3,4]JZ	157, 351	ØSBB[Ø,3,4]ZZ	131, 351, 416

Numeric Index to Procedures

Code	Page	Code	Page	Code	Page	Code	Page
0UTG0ZZ	107, 262	0V5J*	257	0VC9*	257, 354	0VQF*	258, 355
0UTJ[0,X]ZZ	459	0V5K[0,3,4]ZZ	459	0VCB*	257, 354	0VQG*	258, 355
0UTJ*	267	0V5K*	257	0VCC*	257, 354	0VQH*	258, 355
0UTK[0,4,7,8]ZZ	459	0V5L[0,3,4]ZZ	459	0VCF*	257	0VQJ*	258, 355
0UTK*	267, 275	0V5L*	257	0VCG*	257	0VQK*	258, 355
0UTKXZZ	459	0V5S[0,3,4,X]ZZ	217, 459	0VCH*	257	0VQL*	258, 355
0UTL[0,X]ZZ	217, 459	0V5S*	257	0VCJ*	257	0VQN*	258, 355
0UTL*	267, 272	0V5T[0,3,4,X]ZZ	217, 459	0VCK*	257	0VQP*	258, 355
0UTM[0,X]ZZ	217	0V5T*	257	0VCL*	258	0VQQ*	258, 355
0UTM*	262, 267	0V7*	257, 354	0VCS[0,3,4]ZZ	257, 459	0VQS[0,3,4]ZZ	217, 459
0UU4*	267, 354	0V90[0,7,8][0,Z]Z	260	0VCT[0,3,4,X]ZZ	459	0VQS*	257, 355
0UU5[0,4,7,8][7,K]Z	354	0V90[0,7,8]0Z	440	0VCT*	257	0VQT[0,3,4,X]ZZ	217, 459
0UU5*	263, 264, 266	0V90[0,7,8]ZZ	440	0VH0[0,3,4,7,8]1Z	459	0VQT*	257, 355
0UU6[0,4,7,8][7,K]Z	354	0V900ZX	250, 260, 440	0VH0*	260, 354	0VR*	244, 258
0UU6*	263, 264, 266	0V910[0,Z]Z	260	0VJ4[0,3,4]ZZ	260, 440	0VS*	258
0UU7[0,4,7,8][7,K]Z	354	0V910ZX	260	0VJD[0,3,4]ZZ	258	0VSF*	355
0UU7*	263, 264, 266	0V920[0,Z]Z	260	0VJM[0,3,4]ZZ	258, 459	0VSG*	355
0UUF*	267	0V920ZX	260	0VJR[0,3,4]ZZ	258, 459	0VSH*	355
0UUG*	267, 354	0V930[0,Z]Z	260	0VLN[0,3,4]DZ	258, 354	0VT0[0,4]ZZ	257
0UUJ[0,X][7,J,K]Z	459	0V930ZX	260	0VLP[0,3,4]DZ	258, 354	0VT0[4,7,8]ZZ	440
0UUJ*	267	0V990[0,Z]Z	257, 354	0VLQ[0,3,4]DZ	258, 354	0VT0[7,8]ZZ	258
0UUK*	269	0V990ZX	257	0VM*	354	0VT0*	250, 257
0UUM[0,X][7,J,K]Z	459	0V9B0[0,Z]Z	257, 354	0VM5XZZ	258	0VT1*	260
0UUM*	267, 275, 354	0V9B0ZX	257	0VM6*	258	0VT2*	260
0UV*	267, 354	0V9C0[0,Z]Z	257, 354	0VM7*	258	0VT3*	250, 257, 260
0UVC0CZ	274	0V9C0ZX	257	0VM9*	258	0VT6*	258
0UVC0DZ	274	0V9J[0,3,4][0,Z]Z	257	0VMB*	258	0VT7*	258
0UVC0ZZ	274	0V9K[0,3,4][0,Z]Z	257	0VMC*	258	0VT9*	258, 355
0UVC3CZ	274	0V9L[0,3,4][0,Z]Z	257	0VMF*	258	0VTB*	258, 355
0UVC3DZ	274	0V9S[0,3,4,X][0,Z]Z	459	0VMG*	258	0VTC*	158, 258, 355
0UVC3ZZ	274	0V9S[0,3,4,X]ZX	217, 459	0VMH*	258	0VTF[0,4]ZZ	459
0UVC4CZ	274	0V9S*	257	0VMSXZZ	257	0VTF*	258
0UVC4DZ	274	0V9T[0,3,4,X][0,Z]Z	459	0VN0*	260, 354, 440	0VTG[0,4]ZZ	459
0UVC4ZZ	274	0V9T[0,3,4,X]ZX	217, 459	0VN1*	260	0VTG*	258
0UVC7DZ	274	0V9T*	257	0VN2*	260	0VTH[0,4]ZZ	459
0UVC7ZZ	274	0VB0[0,3,4,7,8]ZZ	440	0VN3*	260	0VTH*	258
0UVC8DZ	274	0VB0[0,3,4]ZZ	260	0VN5*	258, 354	0VTJ*	258
0UVC8ZZ	274	0VB0[7,8]ZZ	250, 258	0VN6*	258, 354	0VTK*	258
0UW3[0,3,4][0,3]Z	263, 264, 266	0VB00ZX	250, 260, 440	0VN7*	258, 354	0VTL*	258
0UW8[0,3,4,7,8][0,3,7,C,D,J,K]Z	263, 264, 266	0VB1[0,3,4]ZZ	260	0VNF*	258, 354	0VTS*	257
0UWD[0,3,4,7,8][0,1,3,7,C,D,H,J,K]Z	272	0VB10ZX	260	0VNG*	258, 354	0VU1*	260
0UWD[0,3,4,7,8][0,1,3,7,D,H,J,K]Z	263, 264, 266, 354	0VB2[0,3,4]ZZ	260	0VNH*	258, 354	0VU2*	260
0UWD[0,3,4,7,8]CZ	267, 459	0VB20ZX	260	0VNJ*	258, 354	0VU3*	260
0UWH[0,3,4,7,8][0,1,3,7,D,J,K]Z	267, 275, 459	0VB3[0,3,4]ZZ	260	0VNK*	258, 354	0VU5*	258, 355
0UWM0[0,7,J,K]Z	217, 267, 275, 459	0VB30ZX	260	0VNL*	258, 354	0VU6*	258, 355
0UY*	263, 264, 266	0VB6[0,3,4]ZZ	257	0VNN*	258, 355	0VU7*	258, 355
0V1*	257	0VB60ZZ	459	0VNP*	258, 355	0VU9*	258, 355
0V50[0,3,4]ZZ	257	0VB7[0,3,4]ZZ	257	0VNQ*	258, 355	0VUB*	258, 355
0V50[7,8]ZZ	258, 440	0VB70ZZ	459	0VNS[0,3,4]ZZ	459	0VUC*	258, 355
0V50*	250	0VB9[0,3,4]ZZ	257	0VNS*	257	0VUF*	258, 355
0V51*	260	0VB90ZX	257	0VP4[0,3,4,7,8][0,1,3,7,J,K]Z	260	0VUG*	258, 355
0V52*	260	0VBB[0,3,4]ZZ	257	0VP40[0,1,3,7,J,K]	440	0VUH*	258, 355
0V53*	260	0VBB0ZZ	257	0VP43[0,1,3,7,J,K]Z	440	0VUJ*	258, 355
0V56*	257	0VBC[0,3,4]ZZ	257	0VP44[0,1,3,7,J,K]Z	440	0VUK*	258, 355
0V57*	257	0VBC0ZX	257	0VP47[0,1,3,7,J,K]Z	440	0VUL*	258, 355
0V59*	257	0VBF[0,3,4]ZZ	257, 459	0VP48[0,1,3,7,J,K]Z	440	0VUN*	258, 355
0V5B*	257	0VBG[0,3,4]ZZ	257, 459	0VPD[0,3,4,7,8][0,3,7,J,K]Z	355	0VUP*	258, 355
0V5C*	257	0VBH[0,3,4]ZZ	257, 459	0VPD[0,3,4,7,8][0,3,7,J,K]Z	258	0VUQ*	258, 355
0V5F[0,3,4]ZZ	459	0VBJ[0,3,4]ZZ	257, 459	0VPM[0,3,4,7,8][0,3,7,C,J,K]Z	258	0VUS[0,4][7,J,K]Z	257
0V5F*	257	0VBK[0,3,4]ZZ	257, 459	0VPR[0,3,4,7,8]DZ	258	0VUS[0,4][7,K]Z	355
0V5G[0,3,4]ZZ	459	0VBL[0,3,4]ZZ	257, 459	0VPS[0,3,4,7,8][0,3,7,J,K]Z	257, 459	0VUS[0,4]JZ	254, 459
0V5G*	257	0VBS[0,3,4,X]Z[X,Z]	217, 459	0VPS[0,3,4,7,8]JZ	254	0VUT[0,4,X][7,J,K]Z	217, 257, 459
0V5H[0,3,4]ZZ	459	0VBS*	257	0VQ0*	260, 355, 440	0VUT*	355
0V5H*	257	0VBT[0,3,4,X]Z[X,Z]	217, 459	0VQ1*	260	0VW4[0,3,4,7,8][0,3,7,J,K]Z	260
0V5J[0,3,4]ZZ	459	0VBT*	257	0VQ2*	260	0VW40[0,3,7,J,K]Z	440
		0VC0*	260, 440	0VQ3*	260	0VW43[0,3,7,J,K]Z	440
		0VC1*	260	0VQ9*	258, 355	0VW44[0,3,7,J,K]Z	440
		0VC2*	260	0VQB*	258, 355	0VW47[0,3,7,J,K]Z	440
		0VC3*	260	0VQC*	258, 355	0VW48[0,3,7,J,K]Z	440

© 2015 Optum360, LLC

Code	Page
ØWJKØZZ	220
ØWJLØZZ	220
ØWJM[Ø,4]ZZ	220
ØWJN[Ø,3,4]ZZ	269
ØWJP[Ø,3,4,7,8]ZZ	293
ØWJP[Ø,3,7,8]ZZ	269, 303
ØWJP[Ø,4]ZZ	217, 254, 272
ØWJP[3,4,7,8]ZZ	460
ØWJP*	114, 121, 356
ØWJPØZZ	66, 245, 257
ØWJP4ZZ	266
ØWJQ[Ø,4]ZZ	356
ØWJQ[3,4,7,8]ZZ	66
ØWJQØZZ	62, 91, 254, 303
ØWJQ4ZZ	91
ØWJR[Ø,3,4,7,8]ZZ	293
ØWJR[Ø,3,7,8]ZZ	269, 303
ØWJR[Ø,4]ZZ	217, 254, 272
ØWJR[3,4,7,8]ZZ	460
ØWJR*	114, 121, 356
ØWJRØZZ	66, 91, 245, 257
ØWJR4ZZ	266
ØWM[2,4,5,6]ØZZ	55
ØWM*	356
ØWM2ØZZ	217, 460
ØWM4ØZZ	217, 460
ØWM5ØZZ	217, 460
ØWM6ØZZ	217, 460
ØWM8ØZZ	66, 158, 217
ØWMFØZZ	110, 123, 217, 303
ØWMKØZZ	217, 460
ØWMLØZZ	217, 460
ØWMMØZZ	217, 460
ØWMNØZZ	267, 275, 460
ØWP1[Ø,3,4][Ø,1,J,Y]Z	10, 14, 19
ØWPC[Ø,3,4][Ø,1,3,7,J,K,Y]Z	66, 91, 356
ØWPD[Ø,3,4][Ø,1,3,Y]Z	62, 98, 303, 356
ØWPF[Ø,3,4][Ø,1,3,7,J,K,Y]Z	114, 356
ØWPG[Ø,3,4][Ø,1,3,J,Y]Z	114
ØWPH[Ø,3,4][Ø,1,3,Y]Z	114
ØWPM[Ø,3,4,X][7,K]Z	460
ØWPM[Ø,3,4][7,K]Z	257
ØWPMX7Z	257
ØWPMXJZ	257, 460
ØWPMXKZ	257
ØWPN[Ø,3,4][Ø,1,3,7,J,K,Y]Z	217, 267, 275
ØWPN[Ø,3,4][Ø,1,3,7,J,K,Y]Z	460
ØWPPØ[1,3,Y]Z	114
ØWPQ[3,4,7][1,3,Y]Z	66, 356
ØWPQ81Z	66, 356
ØWQØ[Ø,3,4,X]ZZ	217, 460
ØWQØ*	356
ØWQ2[Ø,3,4,X]ZZ	217, 460
ØWQ2*	55, 356
ØWQ2XZZ	42
ØWQ4[Ø,3,4,X]ZZ	217, 460
ØWQ4*	55, 356
ØWQ5[Ø,3,4,X]ZZ	217, 460
ØWQ5*	55, 356
ØWQ6[Ø,3,4,X]ZZ	217, 460
ØWQ6*	55, 356
ØWQ6XZ2	66, 91, 106, 217, 303
ØWQ8[Ø,3,4,X]ZZ	217
ØWQ8*	66, 158, 356
ØWQC*	66, 356
ØWQF[Ø,3,4,X]ZZ	110, 260, 303
ØWQF[Ø,3,4]ZZ	249
ØWQF[3,4,X]ZZ	123, 217
ØWQF*	269, 356
ØWQFØZZ	460
ØWQFXZ[2,Z]	250
ØWQFXZ2	109, 110, 260, 303, 460
ØWQK[Ø,3,4,X]ZZ	217, 460
ØWQK*	356
ØWQL[Ø,3,4,X]ZZ	217, 460
ØWQL*	356
ØWQM[Ø,3,4,X]ZZ	218, 460
ØWQM*	356
ØWQN[Ø,3,4]ZZ	267, 275, 356, 460
ØWUØ[Ø,4][7,J,K]Z	460
ØWUØ[Ø,4][J,K]Z	218, 356
ØWUØ[Ø,4]7Z	127, 378, 380
ØWU2[Ø,4][7,J,K]Z	218
ØWU2[Ø,4][J,K]Z	55, 460
ØWU2[Ø,4]7Z	28, 127, 378, 380
ØWU2*	356
ØWU4[Ø,4]7Z	28
ØWU4*	49, 158, 356
ØWU5[Ø,4]7Z	28, 218
ØWU5*	49, 158, 356
ØWU6[Ø,4][7,J,K]Z	460
ØWU6[Ø,4][J,K]Z	55, 218, 356
ØWU6[Ø,4]7Z	127, 378, 380
ØWU8[Ø,4]JZ	158
ØWU8*	62
ØWUC*	66, 356
ØWUF*	110, 356
ØWUFØ[7,J,K]Z	460
ØWUK[Ø,4][7,J,K]Z	460
ØWUK[Ø,4][J,K]Z	218, 356
ØWUK[Ø,4]7Z	127, 378, 380
ØWUL[Ø,4][7,J,K]Z	460
ØWUL[Ø,4][J,K]Z	218, 356
ØWUL[Ø,4]7Z	127, 378, 380
ØWUM[Ø,4][7,J,K]Z	460
ØWUM[Ø,4][J,K]Z	218, 356
ØWUM[Ø,4]7Z	257
ØWUN[Ø,4][7,J,K]Z	460
ØWUN*	267, 275, 356
ØWWØ[Ø,3,4][Ø,1,3,7,J,K,Y]Z	220
ØWW1[Ø,3,4][Ø,1,3,J,Y]Z	19
ØWW1[Ø,3,4][Ø,1,3,J,Y]Z	10, 14
ØWW2[Ø,3,4][Ø,1,3,7,J,K,Y]Z	220
ØWW4[Ø,3,4][Ø,1,3,7,J,K,Y]Z	220
ØWW5[Ø,3,4][Ø,1,3,7,J,K,Y]Z	220
ØWW6[Ø,3,4][Ø,1,3,7,J,K,Y]Z	220
ØWWC[Ø,3,4][Ø,1,3,7,J,K,Y]Z	66, 91, 356
ØWWD[Ø,3,4][Ø,1,3,Y]Z	62, 98, 303, 356
ØWWF[Ø,3,4][Ø,1,3,7,J,K,Y]Z	114, 356
ØWWG[Ø,3,4][Ø,1,3,J,Y]Z	114
ØWWH[Ø,3,4][Ø,1,3,Y]Z	114
ØWWJ[Ø,3,4][Ø,1,3,J,Y]Z	114
ØWWK[Ø,3,4][Ø,1,3,7,J,K,Y]Z	220
ØWWL[Ø,3,4][Ø,1,3,7,J,K,Y]Z	220
ØWWM[Ø,3,4][Ø,1,3,J,Y]Z	220
ØWWM[Ø,3,4][7,K]Z	257, 460
ØWWN[Ø,3,4][Ø,1,3,7,J,K,Y]Z	218, 267, 275, 460
ØWWPØ[1,3,Y]Z	114
ØWWQ[3,4,7,8][1,3,Y]Z	66, 356
ØXØ*	356
ØXØ2[Ø,3,4][7,J,K,Z]Z	218, 460
ØXØ3[Ø,3,4][7,J,K,Z]Z	218, 460
ØXØ4[Ø,3,4][7,J,K,Z]Z	218, 460
ØXØ5[Ø,3,4][7,J,K,Z]Z	218, 460
ØXØ6[Ø,3,4][7,J,K,Z]Z	218, 460
ØXØ7[Ø,3,4][7,J,K,Z]Z	460
ØXØ7[Ø,3,4][7,J,K,Z]Z	218
ØXØ8[Ø,3,4][7,J,K,Z]Z	218 460
ØXØ9[Ø,3,4][7,J,K,Z]Z	218, 460
ØXØB[Ø,3,4][7,J,K,Z]Z	218, 460
ØXØC[Ø,3,4][7,J,K,Z]Z	218, 460
ØXØD[Ø,3,4][7,J,K,Z]Z	218, 460
ØXØF[Ø,3,4][7,J,K,Z]Z	218 460
ØXØG[Ø,3,4][7,J,K,Z]Z	218, 460
ØXØH[Ø,3,4][7,J,K,Z]Z	218, 460
ØX3*	91, 158, 356
ØX32[Ø,3,4]ZZ	218, 303
ØX33[Ø,3,4]ZZ	218, 303
ØX34[Ø,3,4]ZZ	218, 303
ØX35[Ø,3,4]ZZ	218, 303
ØX36[Ø,3,4]ZZ	218, 303
ØX37[Ø,3,4]ZZ	218, 303
ØX38[Ø,3,4]ZZ	218, 303
ØX39[Ø,3,4]ZZ	218, 303
ØX3B[Ø,3,4]ZZ	218, 303
ØX3C[Ø,3,4]ZZ	218, 303
ØX3D[Ø,3,4]ZZ	218, 303
ØX3F[Ø,3,4]ZZ	218, 303
ØX3G[Ø,3,4]ZZ	218, 303
ØX3H[Ø,3,4]ZZ	218, 303
ØX3J[Ø,3,4]ZZ	218, 303
ØX3K[Ø,3,4]ZZ	218, 303
ØX6[Ø,1]ØZZ	129
ØX6[2,3]ØZZ	129
ØX6[B,C]ØZZ	129
ØX6*	87
ØX6ØØZZ	218, 356
ØX61ØZZ	218, 356
ØX62ØZZ	218, 356
ØX63ØZZ	218, 356
ØX68*	129, 356
ØX68ØZ[1,2,3]	218
ØX69*	129, 356
ØX69ØZ[1,2,3]	218
ØX6BØZZ	218, 356
ØX6CØZZ	218, 356
ØX6D*	129, 356
ØX6DØZ[1,2,3]	218
ØX6F*	129, 356
ØX6FØZ[1,2,3]	218
ØX6J*	129, 356
ØX6JØZ[Ø,4,5,6,7,8,9,B,C,D,F]	218
ØX6K*	129, 356
ØX6KØZ[Ø,4,5,6,7,8,9,B,C,D,F]	218
ØX6L*	151
ØX6LØZ[Ø,1,2,3]	218, 317
ØX6M*	151
ØX6MØZ[Ø,1,2,3]	218, 317
ØX6N*	151
ØX6NØZ[Ø,1,2,3]	218, 317, 460
ØX6P*	151
ØX6PØZ[Ø,1,2,3]	218, 317, 460
ØX6Q*	151
ØX6QØZ[Ø,1,2,3]	218, 317, 460
ØX6R*	151
ØX6RØZ[Ø,1,2,3]	218, 317, 460
ØX6S*	151
ØX6SØZ[Ø,1,2,3]	218, 317, 460
ØX6T*	151
ØX6TØZ[Ø,1,2,3]	218, 317, 461
ØX6V*	151
ØX6VØZ[Ø,1,2,3]	218, 317, 461
ØX6W*	151
ØX6WØZ[Ø,1,2,3]	218, 317, 461
ØXB2[Ø,3,4]ZZ	28, 91, 144, 207, 356, 461
ØXB3[Ø,3,4]ZZ	28, 91, 144, 207, 356, 461
ØXB4[Ø,3,4]ZZ	28, 91, 144, 207, 356, 461
ØXB5[Ø,3,4]ZZ	28, 91, 144, 207, 356, 461
ØXB6[Ø,3,4]ZZ	28, 91, 144, 207, 356, 461
ØXB7[Ø,3,4]ZZ	28, 91, 144, 207, 356, 461
ØXB8[Ø,3,4]ZZ	28, 91, 144, 207, 356, 461
ØXB9[Ø,3,4]ZZ	28, 91, 144, 207, 356, 461
ØXBB[Ø,3,4]ZZ	28, 91, 144, 207, 356, 461
ØXBC[Ø,3,4]ZZ	28, 91, 144, 207, 356, 461
ØXBD[Ø,3,4]ZZ	29, 91, 144, 207, 356, 461
ØXBF[Ø,3,4]ZZ	29, 92, 144, 207, 356, 461
ØXBG[Ø,3,4]ZZ	29, 92, 144, 207, 356, 461
ØXBH[Ø,3,4]ZZ	29, 92, 144, 207, 356, 461
ØXBJ[Ø,3,4]ZZ	29, 92, 144, 207, 356, 461
ØXBK[Ø,3,4]ZZ	29, 92, 144, 207, 356, 461
ØXH2[Ø,3,4][3,Y]Z	220
ØXH2[Ø,3,4]1Z	356, 461
ØXH3[Ø,3,4][3,Y]Z	220
ØXH3[Ø,3,4]1Z	356, 461
ØXH4[Ø,3,4][3,Y]Z	220
ØXH4[Ø,3,4]1Z	356, 461
ØXH5[Ø,3,4][3,Y]Z	220
ØXH5[Ø,3,4]1Z	356, 461
ØXH6[Ø,3,4][3,Y]Z	220
ØXH6[Ø,3,4]1Z	356, 461
ØXH7[Ø,3,4][3,Y]Z	220
ØXH7[Ø,3,4]1Z	356, 461
ØXH8[Ø,3,4][3,Y]Z	220
ØXH8[Ø,3,4]1Z	356, 461
ØXH9[Ø,3,4][3,Y]Z	220
ØXH9[Ø,3,4]1Z	356, 461
ØXHB[Ø,3,4][3,Y]Z	220
ØXHB[Ø,3,4]1Z	356, 461
ØXHC[Ø,3,4][3,Y]Z	220
ØXHC[Ø,3,4]1Z	356, 461
ØXHD[Ø,3,4][3,Y]Z	220
ØXHD[Ø,3,4]1Z	356, 461
ØXHF[Ø,3,4][3,Y]Z	220
ØXHF[Ø,3,4]1Z	356, 461
ØXHG[Ø,3,4][3,Y]Z	220
ØXHG[Ø,3,4]1Z	356, 461
ØXHH[Ø,3,4][3,Y]Z	220
ØXHH[Ø,3,4]1Z	356, 461
ØXHJ[Ø,3,4][3,Y]Z	220
ØXHJ[Ø,3,4]1Z	356, 461
ØXHK[Ø,3,4][3,Y]Z	220
ØXHK[Ø,3,4]1Z	356, 461
ØXJ2ØZZ	220
ØXJ3ØZZ	220
ØXJ4ØZZ	220
ØXJ5ØZZ	220
ØXJ6ØZZ	220
ØXJ7ØZZ	220
ØXJ8ØZZ	220
ØXJ9ØZZ	220
ØXJBØZZ	220
ØXJCØZZ	220
ØXJDØZZ	220
ØXJFØZZ	220
ØXJGØZZ	220
ØXJHØZZ	220
ØXJJ[3,4]ZZ	144
ØXJJØZZ	220
ØXJK[3,4]ZZ	144
ØXJKØZZ	220
ØXM[Ø,1]ØZZ	131
ØXM[2,3]ØZZ	131
ØXM[4,5]ØZZ	131
ØXM[6,7]ØZZ	131

Numeric Index to Procedures

Code	Page	Code	Page	Code	Page	Code	Page
5A1945Z	70	D927[D,H,J]ZZ	30	DG2*	246, 304	HZ30ZZZ	312
5A1955Z	1, 70, 309, 377, 382	D928[D,H,J]ZZ	30	DG20[D,H,J]ZZ	31	HZ31ZZZ	312
B20*	71, 73, 76, 99	D929[D,H,J]ZZ	30	DG21[D,H,J]ZZ	31	HZ32ZZZ	312
B210[0,1,Y]ZZ	71, 73, 76, 99	D92B[D,H,J]ZZ	30	DG22[D,H,J]ZZ	31	HZ33ZZZ	312
B211[0,1,Y]ZZ	71, 73, 76, 99	D92C[D,H,J]ZZ	30	DG24[D,H,J]ZZ	31	HZ34ZZZ	312
B212[0,1,Y]ZZ	71, 73, 76, 99	D92D[D,H,J]ZZ	30	DG25[D,H,J]ZZ	31	HZ35ZZZ	312
B213[0,1,Y]ZZ	71, 73, 76, 99	DB2*	246, 304	DGY[0,1,4,5]KZZ	238	HZ36ZZZ	312
B214*	71, 73, 76, 99	DB20[D,H,J]ZZ	30	DGY0KZZ	303	HZ37ZZZ	312
B215*	71, 73, 76, 99	DB21[D,H,J]ZZ	31	DGY1KZZ	303	HZ38ZZZ	312
B216*	71, 73, 76, 99	DB22[D,H,J]ZZ	31	DGY2KZZ	63, 260, 303	HZ39ZZZ	312
B217*	71, 73, 76, 99	DB25[D,H,J]ZZ	31	DGY4KZZ	303	HZ3BZZZ	312
B218*	71, 73, 76, 99	DB26[D,H,J]ZZ	31	DGY5KZZ	303	HZ40ZZZ	312
B21F*	71, 73, 76, 99	DB27[D,H,J]ZZ	31	DM2*	246, 304	HZ41ZZZ	312
BF03[0,1,Y]ZZ	121	DB28[D,H,J]ZZ	31	DM20[D,H,J]ZZ	31	HZ42ZZZ	312
BF030ZZ	462	DBY0KZZ	62, 223, 260, 303	DM21[D,H,J]ZZ	31	HZ43ZZZ	312
BF031ZZ	462	DBY1KZZ	62, 223, 260, 303	DMY0KZZ	63, 223, 260, 303	HZ44ZZZ	312
BF03YZZ	462	DBY2KZZ	62, 223, 260, 303	DMY1KZZ	63, 223, 260, 303	HZ45ZZZ	312
BF0C[0,1,Y]ZZ	121	DBY5KZZ	62, 223, 260, 303	DT2*	246, 304	HZ46ZZZ	312
BF0C0ZZ	462	DBY6KZZ	62, 223, 260, 303	DT20[D,H,J]ZZ	31	HZ47ZZZ	312
BF0C1ZZ	462	DBY7KZZ	62, 223, 260, 303	DT21[D,H,J]ZZ	31	HZ48ZZZ	312
BF0CYZZ	462	DBY8KZZ	62, 223, 260, 303	DT22[D,H,J]ZZ	31	HZ49ZZZ	312
D02*	246, 304	DD2*	246, 304	DT23[D,H,J]ZZ	31	HZ4BZZZ	312
D020[D,H,J]ZZ	30	DD20[D,H,J]ZZ	31	DU2*	246, 304	HZ50ZZZ	312
D021[D,H,J]ZZ	30	DD21[D,H,J]ZZ	31	DU20[D,H,J]ZZ	31	HZ51ZZZ	312
D026[D,H,J]ZZ	30	DD22[D,H,J]ZZ	31	DU21[D,H,J]ZZ	31	HZ52ZZZ	312
D027[D,H,J]ZZ	30	DD23[D,H,J]ZZ	31	DU22[D,H,J]ZZ	31	HZ53ZZZ	312
D0Y0KZZ	10, 14, 19	DD24[D,H,J]ZZ	31	DV2*	246, 304	HZ54ZZZ	312
D0Y1KZZ	10, 14, 19	DD25[D,H,J]ZZ	31	DV20[D,H,J]ZZ	31	HZ55ZZZ	312
D0Y6KZZ	62, 260, 303	DD27[D,H,J]ZZ	31	DV21[D,H,J]ZZ	31	HZ56ZZZ	312
D0Y7KZZ	62, 260, 303	DDY[0,1,2,3,4,5,7,8]KZZ	260, 303	DVY0KZZ	63, 223, 260, 303	HZ57ZZZ	312
D72*	246, 304	DDY0KZZ	62	DW2*	246, 304	HZ58ZZZ	312
D720[D,H,J]ZZ	30	DDY1KZZ	62	DW21[D,H,J]ZZ	31	HZ59ZZZ	312
D721[D,H,J]ZZ	30	DDY2KZZ	62	DW22[D,H,J]ZZ	31	HZ5BZZZ	312
D722[D,H,J]ZZ	30	DDY3KZZ	62	DW23[D,H,J]ZZ	31	HZ5CZZZ	312
D723[D,H,J]ZZ	30	DDY4KZZ	62	DW26[D,H,J]ZZ	31	HZ5DZZZ	312
D724[D,H,J]ZZ	30	DDY5KZZ	62	F00*	385	X2C0361	75, 78, 79, 80
D725[D,H,J]ZZ	30	DDY7KZZ	62	F01*	385	X2C1361	75, 78, 79, 80
D726[D,H,J]ZZ	30	DDY8KZZ	62	F02*	385	X2C2361	75, 78, 79, 80
D727[D,H,J]ZZ	30	DF2*	246, 304	F06*	385	X2C3361	75, 78, 79, 80
D728[D,H,J]ZZ	30	DF20[D,H,J]ZZ	31	F07*	385	XR2G021	132, 462
D82*	246, 304	DF21[D,H,J]ZZ	31	F08*	385	XR2H021	132, 462
D820[D,H,J]ZZ	30	DF22[D,H,J]ZZ	31	F09*	385		
D92*	246, 304	DF23[D,H,J]ZZ	31	F0B*	385		
D920[D,H,J]ZZ	30	DFY[1,2,3]KZZ	260, 303	F0C*	385		
D921[D,H,J]ZZ	30	DFY0KZZ	114, 119	F0D*	385		
D924[D,H,J]ZZ	30	DFY1KZZ	62	F0DZ8ZZ	158, 357		
D925[D,H,J]ZZ	30	DFY2KZZ	62	F0DZ9[E,F,U,Z]Z	158, 357		
D926[D,H,J]ZZ	30	DFY3KZZ	62	F0F*	385		

Appendix A — Lists of Principal Diagnoses That Are Their Own CC and Their Own MCC

Principal Diagnoses That Are Their Own CC

B25.1	I70.349	I70.539	I70.669	K50.912	K57.40	M02.359	M05.471	M90.559
B52.0	I70.361	I70.541	I70.731	K50.913	K57.41	M02.361	M05.472	M90.561
D57.211	I70.362	I70.542	I70.732	K50.914	K57.52	M02.362	M05.479	M90.562
D57.411	I70.363	I70.543	I70.733	K51.012	K57.80	M02.369	M05.49	M90.569
E08.52	I70.368	I70.544	I70.734	K51.013	K57.81	M02.371	M32.11	M90.571
E09.52	I70.369	I70.548	I70.738	K51.014	K80.30	M02.372	M32.12	M90.572
E10.52	I70.431	I70.549	I70.739	K51.212	K80.31	M02.379	M33.02	M90.579
E11.52	I70.432	I70.561	I70.741	K51.213	K80.32	M02.38	M33.12	M90.58
E13.52	I70.433	I70.562	I70.742	K51.214	K80.33	M02.39	M33.22	M90.59
I25.110	I70.434	I70.563	I70.743	K51.312	K80.34	M05.40	M33.92	N11.1
I25.700	I70.438	I70.568	I70.744	K51.313	K80.35	M05.411	M34.81	N13.1
I25.710	I70.439	I70.569	I70.748	K51.314	K80.36	M05.412	M34.82	N13.2
I25.720	I70.441	I70.631	I70.749	K51.412	K80.37	M05.419	M35.03	O12.21
I25.730	I70.442	I70.632	I70.761	K51.413	M02.30	M05.421	M90.50	O12.22
I25.750	I70.443	I70.633	I70.762	K51.414	M02.311	M05.422	M90.511	O12.23
I25.760	I70.444	I70.634	I70.763	K51.512	M02.312	M05.429	M90.512	T86.30
I25.790	I70.448	I70.638	I70.768	K51.513	M02.319	M05.431	M90.519	T86.31
I70.331	I70.449	I70.639	I70.769	K51.514	M02.321	M05.432	M90.521	T86.32
I70.332	I70.461	I70.641	I73.01	K51.812	M02.322	M05.439	M90.522	T86.33
I70.333	I70.462	I70.642	K50.012	K51.813	M02.329	M05.441	M90.529	T86.39
I70.334	I70.463	I70.643	K50.013	K51.814	M02.331	M05.442	M90.531	Z48.21
I70.338	I70.468	I70.644	K50.014	K51.912	M02.332	M05.449	M90.532	Z48.22
I70.339	I70.469	I70.648	K50.112	K51.913	M02.339	M05.451	M90.539	Z48.23
I70.341	I70.531	I70.649	K50.113	K51.914	M02.341	M05.452	M90.541	Z48.24
I70.342	I70.532	I70.661	K50.114	K57.00	M02.342	M05.459	M90.542	Z48.280
I70.343	I70.533	I70.662	K50.812	K57.01	M02.349	M05.461	M90.549	Z48.290
I70.344	I70.534	I70.663	K50.813	K57.20	M02.351	M05.462	M90.551	Z94.3
I70.348	I70.538	I70.668	K50.814	K57.21	M02.352	M05.469	M90.552	

Principal Diagnoses That Are Their Own MCC

A22.7	B37.7	K72.11	L89.114	L89.204	L89.324	L89.604	L89.94	S06.1X8A
A26.7	B44.0	L89.003	L89.123	L89.213	L89.43	L89.613	R65.21	S06.1X9A
A32.7	B45.1	L89.004	L89.124	L89.214	L89.44	L89.614	S06.1X0A	
A37.01	B77.81	L89.013	L89.133	L89.223	L89.503	L89.623	S06.1X1A	
A37.11	I26.01	L89.014	L89.134	L89.224	L89.504	L89.624	S06.1X2A	
A37.81	I26.02	L89.023	L89.143	L89.303	L89.513	L89.813	S06.1X3A	
A37.91	I26.09	L89.024	L89.144	L89.304	L89.514	L89.814	S06.1X4A	
A54.86	K70.41	L89.103	L89.153	L89.313	L89.523	L89.893	S06.1X5A	
B25.0	K71.11	L89.104	L89.154	L89.314	L89.524	L89.894	S06.1X6A	
B25.2	K72.01	L89.113	L89.203	L89.323	L89.603	L89.93	S06.1X7A	

Alphabetic CC List

S42.222A	2-part disp fx of surg neck of lt humerus, init enc for clsd fx
S42.222P	2-part disp fx of surg neck of lt humerus, subsq enc for fx w/ malu
S42.222K	2-part disp fx of surg neck of lt humerus, subsq enc for fx w/ nonu
S42.221A	2-part disp fx of surg neck of rt humerus, init enc for clsd fx
S42.221P	2-part disp fx of surg neck of rt humerus, subsq enc for fx w/ malu
S42.221K	2-part disp fx of surg neck of rt humerus, subsq enc for fx w/ nonu
S42.223A	2-part disp fx of surg neck of unsp humerus, init enc for clsd fx
S42.223P	2-part disp fx of surg neck of unsp humerus, subsq enc for fx w/ malu
S42.223K	2-part disp fx of surg neck of unsp humerus, subsq enc for fx w/ nonu
S42.225A	2-part nondisp fx of surg neck of lt humerus, init enc for clsd fx
S42.225P	2-part nondisp fx of surg neck of lt humerus, subsq enc for fx w/ malu
S42.225K	2-part nondisp fx of surg neck of lt humerus, subsq enc for fx w/ nonu
S42.224A	2-part nondisp fx of surg neck of rt humerus, init enc for clsd fx
S42.224P	2-part nondisp fx of surg neck of rt humerus, subsq enc for fx w/ malu
S42.224K	2-part nondisp fx of surg neck of rt humerus, subsq enc for fx w/ nonu
S42.226A	2-part nondisp fx of surg neck of unsp humerus, init enc for clsd fx
S42.226P	2-part nondisp fx of surg neck of unsp humerus, subsq enc for fx w/ malu
S42.226K	2-part nondisp fx of surg neck of unsp humerus, subsq enc for fx w/ nonu
E71.111	3-methylglutaconic aciduria
S42.232A	3-part fx of surg neck of lt humerus, init enc for clsd fx
S42.232P	3-part fx of surg neck of lt humerus, subsq enc for fx w/ malu
S42.232K	3-part fx of surg neck of lt humerus, subsq enc for fx w/ nonu
S42.231A	3-part fx of surg neck of rt humerus, init enc for clsd fx
S42.231P	3-part fx of surg neck of rt humerus, subsq enc for fx w/ malu
S42.231K	3-part fx of surg neck of rt humerus, subsq enc for fx w/ nonu
S42.239A	3-part fx of surg neck of unsp humerus, init enc for clsd fx
S42.239P	3-part fx of surg neck of unsp humerus, subsq enc for fx w/ malu
S42.239K	3-part fx of surg neck of unsp humerus, subsq enc for fx w/ nonu
O70.2	3rd degree perineal lac during delivery
O72.0	3rd-stage hemor
S42.242A	4-part fx of surg neck of lt humerus, init enc for clsd fx
S42.242P	4-part fx of surg neck of lt humerus, subsq enc for fx w/ malu
S42.242K	4-part fx of surg neck of lt humerus, subsq enc for fx w/ nonu
S42.241A	4-part fx of surg neck of rt humerus, init enc for clsd fx
S42.241P	4-part fx of surg neck of rt humerus, subsq enc for fx w/ malu
S42.241K	4-part fx of surg neck of rt humerus, subsq enc for fx w/ nonu
S42.249A	4-part fx of surg neck of unsp humerus, init enc for clsd fx
S42.249P	4-part fx of surg neck of unsp humerus, subsq enc for fx w/ malu
S42.249K	4-part fx of surg neck of unsp humerus, subsq enc for fx w/ nonu
O70.3	4th degree perineal lac during delivery
A42.1	Abd actinomycosis
O00.0	Abd preg
T80.30XA	ABO incompatibility reaction d/t transfusion of blood or blood products, unsp, init enc
T80.310A	ABO incompatibility w/ acute hemolytic transfusion reaction, init enc
T80.311A	ABO incompatibility w/ delayed hemolytic transfusion reaction, init enc
T80.319A	ABO incompatibility w/ hemolytic transfusion reaction, unsp, init enc
N75.1	Abscess of Bartholin's gland
N45.4	Abscess of epididymis or testis
K63.0	Abscess of intestine
N41.2	Abscess of prostate
K11.3	Abscess of salivary gland
E32.1	Abscess of thymus
N76.4	Abscess of vulva
G40.A11	Absence epileptic synd, intractable, w/ status epilepticus
G40.A19	Absence epileptic synd, intractable, w/o status epilepticus
B60.10	Acanthamebiasis, unsp
I97.51	Accid punc & lac of a circulatory sys organ or structure during a circulatory sys procedure
I97.52	Accid punc & lac of a circulatory sys organ or structure during oth procedure
K91.71	Accid punc & lac of a digestive sys organ or structure during a digestive sys procedure
K91.72	Accid punc & lac of a digestive sys organ or structure during oth procedure
N99.71	Accid punc & lac of a genitourinary sys organ or structure during a genitourinary sys procedure
N99.72	Accid punc & lac of a genitourinary sys organ or structure during oth procedure

M96.820	Accid punc & lac of a musculoskeletal structure during a musculoskeletal sys procedure
M96.821	Accid punc & lac of a musculoskeletal structure during oth procedure
J95.71	Accid punc & lac of a respiratory sys organ or structure during a respiratory sys procedure
J95.72	Accid punc & lac of a respiratory sys organ or structure during oth procedure
E36.11	Accid punc & lac of an endocrine sys organ or structure during an endocrine sys procedure
E36.12	Accid punc & lac of an endocrine sys organ or structure during oth procedure
H59.213	Accid punc & lac of eye & adnexa during an ophthalmic procedure, bilat
H59.223	Accid punc & lac of eye & adnexa during oth procedure, bilat
H59.212	Accid punc & lac of lt eye & adnexa during an ophthalmic procedure
H59.222	Accid punc & lac of lt eye & adnexa during oth procedure
G97.48	Accid punc & lac of oth nervous sys organ or structure during a nervous sys procedure
G97.49	Accid punc & lac of oth nervous sys organ or structure during oth procedure
H59.211	Accid punc & lac of rt eye & adnexa during an ophthalmic procedure
H59.221	Accid punc & lac of rt eye & adnexa during oth procedure
L76.11	Accid punc & lac of skin & SQ tissue during a dermatologic procedure
L76.12	Accid punc & lac of skin & SQ tissue during oth procedure
H95.31	Accid punc & lac of the ear & mastoid process during a procedure on the ear & mastoid process
H95.32	Accid punc & lac of the ear & mastoid process during oth procedure
D78.11	Accid punc & lac of the spleen during a procedure on the spleen
D78.12	Accid punc & lac of the spleen during oth procedure
H59.219	Accid punc & lac of unsp eye & adnexa during an ophthalmic procedure
H59.229	Accid punc & lac of unsp eye & adnexa during oth procedure
G97.41	Accid punc or lac of dura during a procedure
E87.2	Acidosis
D68.4	Acquired coagulation factor deficiency
L12.30	Acquired epidermolysis bullosa, unsp
D59.9	Acquired hemolytic anemia, unsp
D68.311	Acquired hemophilia
B47.1	Actinomycetoma
A42.9	Actinomycosis, unsp
A42.82	Actinomycotic encephalitis
A42.81	Actinomycotic meningitis
D68.51	Activated protein C resistance
A24.1	Acute & fulminating melioidosis
G36.1	Acute & subacute hemorrhagic leukoencephalitis [Hurst]
A06.0	Acute amebic dysentery
H40.213	Acute angle-closure glaucoma, bilat
H40.212	Acute angle-closure glaucoma, lt eye
H40.211	Acute angle-closure glaucoma, rt eye
H40.219	Acute angle-closure glaucoma, unsp eye
K04.4	Acute apical periodontitis of pulpal origin
J21.1	Acute bronchiolitis d/t human metapneumovirus
J21.8	Acute bronchiolitis d/t oth spec organisms
J21.0	Acute bronchiolitis d/t respiratory syncytial virus
J21.9	Acute bronchiolitis, unsp
I67.81	Acute cerebrovascular insufficiency
B57.0	Acute Chagas' disease w/ heart involvement
B57.1	Acute Chagas' disease w/o heart involvement
K81.0	Acute cholecystitis
K81.2	Acute cholecystitis w/ chr cholecystitis
I24.0	Acute coronary thrombosis not resulting in myocardial infarction
N30.01	Acute cystitis w/ hematuria
N30.00	Acute cystitis w/o hematuria
B17.0	Acute delta-(super) infxn of hepatitis B carrier
K31.0	Acute dilatation of stomach
G36.9	Acute disseminated demyelination, unsp
K26.3	Acute duodenal ulcer w/o hemor or perforation
I82.A13	Acute embolism & thrombosis of axillary vein, bilat
I82.622	Acute embolism & thrombosis of deep veins of lt upr extr
I82.621	Acute embolism & thrombosis of deep veins of rt upr extr
I82.629	Acute embolism & thrombosis of deep veins of unsp upr extr
I82.623	Acute embolism & thrombosis of deep veins of upr extr, bilat
I82.413	Acute embolism & thrombosis of femoral vein, bilat
I82.423	Acute embolism & thrombosis of iliac vein, bilat

I82.C13	Acute embolism & thrombosis of int jugular vein, bilat	M86.051	Acute hematogenous osteomyelitis, rt femur
I82.A12	Acute embolism & thrombosis of lt axillary vein	M86.041	Acute hematogenous osteomyelitis, rt hand
I82.412	Acute embolism & thrombosis of lt femoral vein	M86.021	Acute hematogenous osteomyelitis, rt humerus
I82.422	Acute embolism & thrombosis of lt iliac vein	M86.031	Acute hematogenous osteomyelitis, rt radius & ulna
I82.C12	Acute embolism & thrombosis of lt int jugular vein	M86.011	Acute hematogenous osteomyelitis, rt shldr
I82.432	Acute embolism & thrombosis of lt popliteal vein	M86.061	Acute hematogenous osteomyelitis, rt tibia & fibula
I82.B12	Acute embolism & thrombosis of lt subclavian vein	M86.079	Acute hematogenous osteomyelitis, unsp ankle & foot
I82.442	Acute embolism & thrombosis of lt tibial vein	M86.059	Acute hematogenous osteomyelitis, unsp femur
I82.492	Acute embolism & thrombosis of oth spec deep vein of lt lwr extr	M86.049	Acute hematogenous osteomyelitis, unsp hand
I82.493	Acute embolism & thrombosis of oth spec deep vein of lwr extr, bilat	M86.029	Acute hematogenous osteomyelitis, unsp humerus
I82.491	Acute embolism & thrombosis of oth spec deep vein of rt lwr extr	M86.039	Acute hematogenous osteomyelitis, unsp radius & ulna
I82.499	Acute embolism & thrombosis of oth spec deep vein of unsp lwr extr	M86.019	Acute hematogenous osteomyelitis, unsp shldr
I82.890	Acute embolism & thrombosis of oth spec veins	M86.00	Acute hematogenous osteomyelitis, unsp site
I82.290	Acute embolism & thrombosis of oth thoracic veins	M86.069	Acute hematogenous osteomyelitis, unsp tibia & fibula
I82.433	Acute embolism & thrombosis of popliteal vein, bilat	T80.910A	Acute hemolytic transfusion reaction, unsp incompatibility, init enc
I82.A11	Acute embolism & thrombosis of rt axillary vein	B16.1	Acute hepatitis B w/ delta-agent w/o hepatic coma
I82.411	Acute embolism & thrombosis of rt femoral vein	B16.9	Acute hepatitis B w/o delta-agent & w/o hepatic coma
I82.421	Acute embolism & thrombosis of rt iliac vein	B17.10	Acute hepatitis C w/o hepatic coma
I82.C11	Acute embolism & thrombosis of rt int jugular vein	B17.2	Acute hepatitis E
I82.431	Acute embolism & thrombosis of rt popliteal vein	R04.81	Acute idiopathic pulmn hemor in infants
I82.B11	Acute embolism & thrombosis of rt subclavian vein	N71.0	Acute inflam disease of uterus
I82.441	Acute embolism & thrombosis of rt tibial vein	T80.22XA	Acute infxn following transfusion, inf, or injection of blood & blood products, init enc
I82.B13	Acute embolism & thrombosis of subclavian vein, bilat		
I82.612	Acute embolism & thrombosis of superf veins of lt upr extr	E80.21	Acute intermittent (hepatic) porphyria
I82.611	Acute embolism & thrombosis of superf veins of rt upr extr	J84.114	Acute interstitial pneumonitis
I82.619	Acute embolism & thrombosis of superf veins of unsp upr extr	I24.9	Acute ischemic heart disease, unsp
I82.613	Acute embolism & thrombosis of superf veins of upr extr, bilat	N17.9	Acute kidney failure, unsp
I82.210	Acute embolism & thrombosis of superior vena cava	C95.00	Acute leukemia of unsp cell type not having achieved remission
I82.443	Acute embolism & thrombosis of tibial vein, bilat	C95.02	Acute leukemia of unsp cell type, in relapse
I82.A19	Acute embolism & thrombosis of unsp axillary vein	C95.01	Acute leukemia of unsp cell type, in remission
I82.4Z3	Acute embolism & thrombosis of unsp deep veins of distal lwr extr, bilat	L03.321	Acute lymphangitis of abd wall
I82.4Z2	Acute embolism & thrombosis of unsp deep veins of lt distal lwr extr	L03.322	Acute lymphangitis of back [any part except buttock]
I82.402	Acute embolism & thrombosis of unsp deep veins of lt lwr extr	L03.327	Acute lymphangitis of buttock
I82.4Y2	Acute embolism & thrombosis of unsp deep veins of lt proximal lwr extr	L03.323	Acute lymphangitis of chest wall
I82.403	Acute embolism & thrombosis of unsp deep veins of lwr extr, bilat	L03.212	Acute lymphangitis of face
I82.4Y3	Acute embolism & thrombosis of unsp deep veins of proximal lwr extr, bilat	L03.324	Acute lymphangitis of groin
		L03.891	Acute lymphangitis of head [any part, except face]
I82.4Z1	Acute embolism & thrombosis of unsp deep veins of rt distal lwr extr	L03.122	Acute lymphangitis of lt axilla
I82.401	Acute embolism & thrombosis of unsp deep veins of rt lwr extr	L03.126	Acute lymphangitis of lt lwr limb
I82.4Y1	Acute embolism & thrombosis of unsp deep veins of rt proximal lwr extr	L03.124	Acute lymphangitis of lt upr limb
I82.4Z9	Acute embolism & thrombosis of unsp deep veins of unsp distal lwr extr	L03.222	Acute lymphangitis of neck
I82.409	Acute embolism & thrombosis of unsp deep veins of unsp lwr extr	L03.898	Acute lymphangitis of oth sites
I82.4Y9	Acute embolism & thrombosis of unsp deep veins of unsp proximal lwr extr	L03.325	Acute lymphangitis of perineum
		L03.121	Acute lymphangitis of rt axilla
I82.419	Acute embolism & thrombosis of unsp femoral vein	L03.125	Acute lymphangitis of rt lwr limb
I82.429	Acute embolism & thrombosis of unsp iliac vein	L03.123	Acute lymphangitis of rt upr limb
I82.C19	Acute embolism & thrombosis of unsp int jugular vein	L03.329	Acute lymphangitis of trunk, unsp
I82.439	Acute embolism & thrombosis of unsp popliteal vein	L03.326	Acute lymphangitis of umbilicus
I82.B19	Acute embolism & thrombosis of unsp subclavian vein	L03.129	Acute lymphangitis of unsp part of limb
I82.449	Acute embolism & thrombosis of unsp tibial vein	L03.91	Acute lymphangitis, unsp
I82.90	Acute embolism & thrombosis of unsp vein	C91.00	Acute lymphoblastic leukemia not having achieved remission
I82.602	Acute embolism & thrombosis of unsp veins of lt upr extr	C91.02	Acute lymphoblastic leukemia, in relapse
I82.601	Acute embolism & thrombosis of unsp veins of rt upr extr	C91.01	Acute lymphoblastic leukemia, in remission
I82.609	Acute embolism & thrombosis of unsp veins of unsp upr extr	H70.093	Acute mastoiditis w/ oth comp, bilat
I82.603	Acute embolism & thrombosis of unsp veins of upr extr, bilat	H70.092	Acute mastoiditis w/ oth comp, lt ear
J05.10	Acute epiglottitis w/o obstruction	H70.091	Acute mastoiditis w/ oth comp, rt ear
C94.02	Acute erythroid leukemia, in relapse	H70.099	Acute mastoiditis w/ oth comp, unsp ear
C94.01	Acute erythroid leukemia, in remission	H70.003	Acute mastoiditis w/o comp, bilat
C94.00	Acute erythroid leukemia, not having achieved remission	H70.002	Acute mastoiditis w/o comp, lt ear
K25.3	Acute gastric ulcer w/o hemor or perforation	H70.001	Acute mastoiditis w/o comp, rt ear
A08.11	Acute gastroenteropathy d/t Norwalk agent	H70.009	Acute mastoiditis w/o comp, unsp ear
A08.19	Acute gastroenteropathy d/t oth sm round viruses	C94.20	Acute megakaryoblastic leukemia not having achieved remission
K28.3	Acute gastrojejunal ulcer w/o hemor or perforation	C94.22	Acute megakaryoblastic leukemia, in relapse
D89.810	Acute graft-versus-host disease	C94.21	Acute megakaryoblastic leukemia, in remission
M86.072	Acute hematogenous osteomyelitis, lt ankle & foot	C93.02	Acute monoblastic/monocytic leukemia, in relapse
M86.052	Acute hematogenous osteomyelitis, lt femur	C93.01	Acute monoblastic/monocytic leukemia, in remission
M86.042	Acute hematogenous osteomyelitis, lt hand	C93.00	Acute monoblastic/monocytic leukemia, not having achieved remission
M86.022	Acute hematogenous osteomyelitis, lt humerus	C92.02	Acute myeloblastic leukemia, in relapse
M86.032	Acute hematogenous osteomyelitis, lt radius & ulna	C92.01	Acute myeloblastic leukemia, in remission
M86.012	Acute hematogenous osteomyelitis, lt shldr	C92.00	Acute myeloblastic leukemia, not having achieved remission
M86.062	Acute hematogenous osteomyelitis, lt tibia & fibula	C92.62	Acute myeloid leukemia w/ 11q23-abnormality in relapse
M86.09	Acute hematogenous osteomyelitis, multi sites	C92.61	Acute myeloid leukemia w/ 11q23-abnormality in remission
M86.08	Acute hematogenous osteomyelitis, oth sites	C92.60	Acute myeloid leukemia w/ 11q23-abnormality not having achieved remission
M86.071	Acute hematogenous osteomyelitis, rt ankle & foot		

C92.A2	Acute myeloid leukemia w/ multilineage dysplasia, in relapse
C92.A1	Acute myeloid leukemia w/ multilineage dysplasia, in remission
C92.A0	Acute myeloid leukemia w/ multilineage dysplasia, not having achieved remission
C92.52	Acute myelomonocytic leukemia, in relapse
C92.51	Acute myelomonocytic leukemia, in remission
C92.50	Acute myelomonocytic leukemia, not having achieved remission
I30.0	Acute nonspecific idiopathic pericarditis
D89.812	Acute on chr graft-versus-host disease
N70.02	Acute oophoritis
C94.40	Acute panmyelosis w/ myelofibrosis not having achieved remission
C94.42	Acute panmyelosis w/ myelofibrosis, in relapse
C94.41	Acute panmyelosis w/ myelofibrosis, in remission
N73.0	Acute parametritis & pelvic cellulitis
K27.3	Acute peptic ulcer, site unsp, w/o hemor or perforation
I30.9	Acute pericarditis, unsp
H30.143	Acute post multifocal placoid pigment epitheliopathy, bilat
H30.142	Acute post multifocal placoid pigment epitheliopathy, lt eye
H30.141	Acute post multifocal placoid pigment epitheliopathy, rt eye
H30.149	Acute post multifocal placoid pigment epitheliopathy, unsp eye
D62	Acute posthemorrhagic anemia
C92.42	Acute promyelocytic leukemia, in relapse
C92.41	Acute promyelocytic leukemia, in remission
C92.40	Acute promyelocytic leukemia, not having achieved remission
N41.0	Acute prostatitis
B40.0	Acute pulmn blastomycosis
B38.0	Acute pulmn coccidioidomycosis
J70.0	Acute pulmn manifestations d/t radiation
J80	Acute respiratory distress synd
I01.1	Acute rheumatic endocarditis
I01.9	Acute rheumatic heart disease, unsp
I01.2	Acute rheumatic myocarditis
I01.0	Acute rheumatic pericarditis
N70.01	Acute salpingitis
N70.03	Acute salpingitis & oophoritis
E06.0	Acute thyroiditis
G37.3	Acute transv myelitis in demyelinating disease of central nervous sys
N10	Acute tubulo-interstitial nephritis
B17.9	Acute viral hepatitis, unsp
E27.2	Addisonian crisis
D81.3	Adenosine deaminase [ADA] deficiency
A85.1	Adenoviral encephalitis
A08.2	Adenoviral enteritis
A87.1	Adenoviral meningitis
T81.516A	Adhesions d/t FB accidentally lt in body following aspiration, punc or oth catheterization, init enc
T81.514A	Adhesions d/t FB accidentally lt in body following endo exam, init enc
T81.515A	Adhesions d/t FB accidentally lt in body following heart catheterization, init enc
T81.511A	Adhesions d/t FB accidentally lt in body following inf or transfusion, init enc
T81.513A	Adhesions d/t FB accidentally lt in body following injection or immunization, init enc
T81.512A	Adhesions d/t FB accidentally lt in body following kidney dialysis, init enc
T81.518A	Adhesions d/t FB accidentally lt in body following oth procedure, init enc
T81.517A	Adhesions d/t FB accidentally lt in body following rmvl of catheter or packing, init enc
T81.510A	Adhesions d/t FB accidentally lt in body following surg operation, init enc
T81.519A	Adhesions d/t FB accidentally lt in body following unsp procedure, init enc
E71.521	Adolescent X-linked adrenoleukodystrophy
E27.5	Adrenomedullary hyperfunction
E71.522	Adrenomyeloneuropathy
K31.1	Adult hypertrophic pyloric stenosis
T74.01XA	Adult neglect or abandonment, confirmed, init enc
T76.01XA	Adult neglect or abandonment, suspected, init enc
T74.11XA	Adult physical abuse, confirmed, init enc
T76.11XA	Adult physical abuse, suspected, init enc
J84.82	Adult pulmn Langerhans cell histiocytosis
T74.21XA	Adult sexual abuse, confirmed, init enc
T76.21XA	Adult sexual abuse, suspected, init enc

C91.50	Adult T-cell lymphoma/leukemia (HTLV-1-associated) not having achieved remission
C91.52	Adult T-cell lymphoma/leukemia (HTLV-1-associated), in relapse
C91.51	Adult T-cell lymphoma/leukemia (HTLV-1-associated), in remission
B56.9	African trypanosomiasis, unsp
M80.072A	Age-related osteoporosis w/ current path fx, lt ankle & foot, init enc for fx
M80.072P	Age-related osteoporosis w/ current path fx, lt ankle & foot, subsq enc for fx w/ malu
M80.072K	Age-related osteoporosis w/ current path fx, lt ankle & foot, subsq enc for fx w/ nonu
M80.052A	Age-related osteoporosis w/ current path fx, lt femur, init enc for fx
M80.052P	Age-related osteoporosis w/ current path fx, lt femur, subsq enc for fx w/ malu
M80.052K	Age-related osteoporosis w/ current path fx, lt femur, subsq enc for fx w/ nonu
M80.032A	Age-related osteoporosis w/ current path fx, lt forearm, init enc for fx
M80.032P	Age-related osteoporosis w/ current path fx, lt forearm, subsq enc for fx w/ malu
M80.032K	Age-related osteoporosis w/ current path fx, lt forearm, subsq enc for fx w/ nonu
M80.042A	Age-related osteoporosis w/ current path fx, lt hand, init enc for fx
M80.042P	Age-related osteoporosis w/ current path fx, lt hand, subsq enc for fx w/ malu
M80.042K	Age-related osteoporosis w/ current path fx, lt hand, subsq enc for fx w/ nonu
M80.022A	Age-related osteoporosis w/ current path fx, lt humerus, init enc for fx
M80.022P	Age-related osteoporosis w/ current path fx, lt humerus, subsq enc for fx w/ malu
M80.022K	Age-related osteoporosis w/ current path fx, lt humerus, subsq enc for fx w/ nonu
M80.062A	Age-related osteoporosis w/ current path fx, lt lwr leg, init enc for fx
M80.062P	Age-related osteoporosis w/ current path fx, lt lwr leg, subsq enc for fx w/ malu
M80.062K	Age-related osteoporosis w/ current path fx, lt lwr leg, subsq enc for fx w/ nonu
M80.012A	Age-related osteoporosis w/ current path fx, lt shldr, init enc for fx
M80.012P	Age-related osteoporosis w/ current path fx, lt shldr, subsq enc for fx w/ malu
M80.012K	Age-related osteoporosis w/ current path fx, lt shldr, subsq enc for fx w/ nonu
M80.071A	Age-related osteoporosis w/ current path fx, rt ankle & foot, init enc for fx
M80.071P	Age-related osteoporosis w/ current path fx, rt ankle & foot, subsq enc for fx w/ malu
M80.071K	Age-related osteoporosis w/ current path fx, rt ankle & foot, subsq enc for fx w/ nonu
M80.051A	Age-related osteoporosis w/ current path fx, rt femur, init enc for fx
M80.051P	Age-related osteoporosis w/ current path fx, rt femur, subsq enc for fx w/ malu
M80.051K	Age-related osteoporosis w/ current path fx, rt femur, subsq enc for fx w/ nonu
M80.031A	Age-related osteoporosis w/ current path fx, rt forearm, init enc for fx
M80.031P	Age-related osteoporosis w/ current path fx, rt forearm, subsq enc for fx w/ malu
M80.031K	Age-related osteoporosis w/ current path fx, rt forearm, subsq enc for fx w/ nonu
M80.041A	Age-related osteoporosis w/ current path fx, rt hand, init enc for fx
M80.041P	Age-related osteoporosis w/ current path fx, rt hand, subsq enc for fx w/ malu
M80.041K	Age-related osteoporosis w/ current path fx, rt hand, subsq enc for fx w/ nonu
M80.021A	Age-related osteoporosis w/ current path fx, rt humerus, init enc for fx
M80.021P	Age-related osteoporosis w/ current path fx, rt humerus, subsq enc for fx w/ malu
M80.021K	Age-related osteoporosis w/ current path fx, rt humerus, subsq enc for fx w/ nonu
M80.061A	Age-related osteoporosis w/ current path fx, rt lwr leg, init enc for fx
M80.061P	Age-related osteoporosis w/ current path fx, rt lwr leg, subsq enc for fx w/ malu
M80.061K	Age-related osteoporosis w/ current path fx, rt lwr leg, subsq enc for fx w/ nonu
M80.011A	Age-related osteoporosis w/ current path fx, rt shldr, init enc for fx
M80.011P	Age-related osteoporosis w/ current path fx, rt shldr, subsq enc for fx w/ malu
M80.011K	Age-related osteoporosis w/ current path fx, rt shldr, subsq enc for fx w/ nonu
M80.079A	Age-related osteoporosis w/ current path fx, unsp ankle & foot, init enc for fx

Code	Description
M80.079P	Age-related osteoporosis w/ current path fx, unsp ankle & foot, subsq enc for fx w/ malu
M80.079K	Age-related osteoporosis w/ current path fx, unsp ankle & foot, subsq enc for fx w/ nonu
M80.059A	Age-related osteoporosis w/ current path fx, unsp femur, init enc for fx
M80.059P	Age-related osteoporosis w/ current path fx, unsp femur, subsq enc for fx w/ malu
M80.059K	Age-related osteoporosis w/ current path fx, unsp femur, subsq enc for fx w/ nonu
M80.039A	Age-related osteoporosis w/ current path fx, unsp forearm, init enc for fx
M80.039P	Age-related osteoporosis w/ current path fx, unsp forearm, subsq enc for fx w/ malu
M80.039K	Age-related osteoporosis w/ current path fx, unsp forearm, subsq enc for fx w/ nonu
M80.049A	Age-related osteoporosis w/ current path fx, unsp hand, init enc for fx
M80.049P	Age-related osteoporosis w/ current path fx, unsp hand, subsq enc for fx w/ malu
M80.049K	Age-related osteoporosis w/ current path fx, unsp hand, subsq enc for fx w/ nonu
M80.029A	Age-related osteoporosis w/ current path fx, unsp humerus, init enc for fx
M80.029P	Age-related osteoporosis w/ current path fx, unsp humerus, subsq enc for fx w/ malu
M80.029K	Age-related osteoporosis w/ current path fx, unsp humerus, subsq enc for fx w/ nonu
M80.069A	Age-related osteoporosis w/ current path fx, unsp lwr leg, init enc for fx
M80.069P	Age-related osteoporosis w/ current path fx, unsp lwr leg, subsq enc for fx w/ malu
M80.069K	Age-related osteoporosis w/ current path fx, unsp lwr leg, subsq enc for fx w/ nonu
M80.019A	Age-related osteoporosis w/ current path fx, unsp shldr, init enc for fx
M80.019P	Age-related osteoporosis w/ current path fx, unsp shldr, subsq enc for fx w/ malu
M80.019K	Age-related osteoporosis w/ current path fx, unsp shldr, subsq enc for fx w/ nonu
M80.00XA	Age-related osteoporosis w/ current path fx, unsp site, init enc for fx
M80.00XP	Age-related osteoporosis w/ current path fx, unsp site, subsq enc for fx w/ malu
M80.00XK	Age-related osteoporosis w/ current path fx, unsp site, subsq enc for fx w/ nonu
M80.08XA	Age-related osteoporosis w/ current path fx, vertebra(e), init enc for fx
M80.08XP	Age-related osteoporosis w/ current path fx, vertebra(e), subsq enc for fx w/ malu
M80.08XK	Age-related osteoporosis w/ current path fx, vertebra(e), subsq enc for fx w/ nonu
Q44.0	Agenesis, aplasia & hypoplasia of gallbladder
Q45.0	Agenesis, aplasia & hypoplasia of pancreas
J67.7	Air conditioner & humidifier lung
E70.339	Albinism w/ hematologic abnormality, unsp
E70.30	Albinism, unsp
F10.180	Alcohol abuse w/ alcohol-induced anxiety d/o
F10.14	Alcohol abuse w/ alcohol-induced mood d/o
F10.151	Alcohol abuse w/ alcohol-induced psychotic d/o w/ hallucinations
F10.159	Alcohol abuse w/ alcohol-induced psychotic d/o, unsp
F10.181	Alcohol abuse w/ alcohol-induced sexual dysfunction
F10.121	Alcohol abuse w/ intoxication delirium
F10.188	Alcohol abuse w/ oth alcohol-induced d/o
F10.19	Alcohol abuse w/ unsp alcohol-induced d/o
F10.280	Alcohol dependence w/ alcohol-induced anxiety d/o
F10.24	Alcohol dependence w/ alcohol-induced mood d/o
F10.27	Alcohol dependence w/ alcohol-induced persisting dementia
F10.251	Alcohol dependence w/ alcohol-induced psychotic d/o w/ hallucinations
F10.259	Alcohol dependence w/ alcohol-induced psychotic d/o, unsp
F10.281	Alcohol dependence w/ alcohol-induced sexual dysfunction
F10.221	Alcohol dependence w/ intoxication delirium
F10.288	Alcohol dependence w/ oth alcohol-induced d/o
F10.29	Alcohol dependence w/ unsp alcohol-induced d/o
F10.231	Alcohol dependence w/ withdrawal delirium
F10.232	Alcohol dependence w/ withdrawal w/ perceptual disturbance
F10.230	Alcohol dependence w/ withdrawal, uncomplicated
F10.239	Alcohol dependence w/ withdrawal, unsp
F10.980	Alcohol use, unsp w/ alcohol-induced anxiety d/o
F10.94	Alcohol use, unsp w/ alcohol-induced mood d/o
F10.951	Alcohol use, unsp w/ alcohol-induced psychotic d/o w/ hallucinations
F10.959	Alcohol use, unsp w/ alcohol-induced psychotic d/o, unsp

Code	Description
F10.981	Alcohol use, unsp w/ alcohol-induced sexual dysfunction
F10.921	Alcohol use, unsp w/ intoxication delirium
F10.988	Alcohol use, unsp w/ oth alcohol-induced d/o
F10.99	Alcohol use, unsp w/ unsp alcohol-induced d/o
K86.0	Alcohol-induced chr pancreatitis
E24.4	Alcohol-induced pseudo-Cushing's synd
I42.6	Alcoholic cardiomyopathy
G72.1	Alcoholic myopathy
E87.3	Alkalosis
B44.81	Allergic bronchopulmonary aspergillosis
D69.0	Allergic purpura
B48.2	Allescheriasis
G31.81	Alpers disease
Q87.81	Alport synd
J84.01	Alveolar proteinosis
G45.3	Amaurosis fugax
A06.81	Amebic cystitis
A06.2	Amebic nondysenteric colitis
A06.3	Ameboma of intestine
E85.9	Amyloidosis, unsp
G12.21	Amyotrophic lat sclerosis
K61.0	Anal abscess
O70.4	Anal sphincter tear comp delivery, not associated w/ 3rd degree lac
T80.51XA	Anaphylactic reaction d/t administration of blood & blood products, init enc
T88.6XXA	Anaphylactic reaction d/t adverse effect of correct drug or medicament properly administered, init enc
T78.08XA	Anaphylactic reaction d/t eggs, init enc
T78.06XA	Anaphylactic reaction d/t food additives, init enc
T78.04XA	Anaphylactic reaction d/t fruits & vegetables, init enc
T78.07XA	Anaphylactic reaction d/t milk & dairy products, init enc
T78.03XA	Anaphylactic reaction d/t oth fish, init enc
T78.09XA	Anaphylactic reaction d/t oth food products, init enc
T80.59XA	Anaphylactic reaction d/t oth serum, init enc
T78.01XA	Anaphylactic reaction d/t peanuts, init enc
T78.02XA	Anaphylactic reaction d/t shellfish (crustaceans), init enc
T78.05XA	Anaphylactic reaction d/t tree nuts & seeds, init enc
T78.00XA	Anaphylactic reaction d/t unsp food, init enc
T80.52XA	Anaphylactic reaction d/t vaccination, init enc
T78.2XXA	Anaphylactic shock, unsp, init enc
C84.79	Anaplastic lg cell lymphoma, ALK-negative, extranodal & solid organ sites
C84.73	Anaplastic lg cell lymphoma, ALK-negative, intra-abd lymph nodes
C84.76	Anaplastic lg cell lymphoma, ALK-negative, intrapelvic lymph nodes
C84.72	Anaplastic lg cell lymphoma, ALK-negative, intrathoracic lymph nodes
C84.74	Anaplastic lg cell lymphoma, ALK-negative, lymph nodes of axilla & upr limb
C84.71	Anaplastic lg cell lymphoma, ALK-negative, lymph nodes of head, face, & neck
C84.75	Anaplastic lg cell lymphoma, ALK-negative, lymph nodes of inguinal rgn & lwr limb
C84.78	Anaplastic lg cell lymphoma, ALK-negative, lymph nodes of multi sites
C84.77	Anaplastic lg cell lymphoma, ALK-negative, spleen
C84.70	Anaplastic lg cell lymphoma, ALK-negative, unsp site
C84.69	Anaplastic lg cell lymphoma, ALK-positive, extranodal & solid organ sites
C84.63	Anaplastic lg cell lymphoma, ALK-positive, intra-abd lymph nodes
C84.66	Anaplastic lg cell lymphoma, ALK-positive, intrapelvic lymph nodes
C84.62	Anaplastic lg cell lymphoma, ALK-positive, intrathoracic lymph nodes
C84.64	Anaplastic lg cell lymphoma, ALK-positive, lymph nodes of axilla & upr limb
C84.61	Anaplastic lg cell lymphoma, ALK-positive, lymph nodes of head, face, & neck
C84.65	Anaplastic lg cell lymphoma, ALK-positive, lymph nodes of inguinal rgn & lwr limb
C84.68	Anaplastic lg cell lymphoma, ALK-positive, lymph nodes of multi sites
C84.67	Anaplastic lg cell lymphoma, ALK-positive, spleen
C84.60	Anaplastic lg cell lymphoma, ALK-positive, unsp site
B76.0	Ancylostomiasis
P61.2	Anemia of prematurity
I25.3	Aneurysm of heart
I28.1	Aneurysm of pulmn artery
I20.1	Angina pectoris w/ documented spasm
C86.5	Angioimmunoblastic T-cell lymphoma
C22.3	Angiosarcoma of liver

B81.0	Anisakiasis
Q45.1	Annular pancreas
Q26.4	Anomalous pulmn venous connection, unsp
K61.2	Anorectal abscess
F50.02	Anorexia nervosa, binge eating/purging type
F50.01	Anorexia nervosa, restricting type
F50.00	Anorexia nervosa, unsp
G93.1	Anoxic brain damage, NEC
G46.1	Ant cerebral artery synd
S43.215A	Ant disloc of lt sternoclavicular jt, init enc
S43.214A	Ant disloc of rt sternoclavicular jt, init enc
S43.216A	Ant disloc of unsp sternoclavicular jt, init enc
S42.012B	Ant disp fx of sternal end of lt clavicle, init enc for opn fx
S42.012P	Ant disp fx of sternal end of lt clavicle, subsq enc for fx w/ malu
S42.012K	Ant disp fx of sternal end of lt clavicle, subsq enc for fx w/ nonu
S42.011B	Ant disp fx of sternal end of rt clavicle, init enc for opn fx
S42.011P	Ant disp fx of sternal end of rt clavicle, subsq enc for fx w/ malu
S42.011K	Ant disp fx of sternal end of rt clavicle, subsq enc for fx w/ nonu
S42.013B	Ant disp fx of sternal end of unsp clavicle, init enc for opn fx
S42.013P	Ant disp fx of sternal end of unsp clavicle, subsq enc for fx w/ malu
S42.013K	Ant disp fx of sternal end of unsp clavicle, subsq enc for fx w/ nonu
S12.110A	Ant disp Type II dens fx, init enc for clsd fx
S12.110K	Ant disp Type II dens fx, subsq enc for fx w/ nonu
M47.012	Ant spinal artery compression syndromes, cervical rgn
M47.013	Ant spinal artery compression syndromes, cervicothoracic rgn
M47.016	Ant spinal artery compression syndromes, lumbar rgn
M47.011	Ant spinal artery compression syndromes, occipito-atlanto-axial rgn
M47.019	Ant spinal artery compression syndromes, site unsp
M47.014	Ant spinal artery compression syndromes, thoracic rgn
M47.015	Ant spinal artery compression syndromes, thoracolumbar rgn
S43.212A	Ant sublux of lt sternoclavicular jt, init enc
S43.211A	Ant sublux of rt sternoclavicular jt, init enc
S43.213A	Ant sublux of unsp sternoclavicular jt, init enc
A22.9	Anthrax, unsp
D80.6	Antibody deficiency w/ near-normal immunoglobulins or w/ hyperimmunoglobulinemia
D68.312	Antiphospholipid antibody w/ hemorrhagic d/o
D68.61	Antiphospholipid synd
M31.4	Aortic arch synd [Takayasu]
R47.01	Aphasia
D61.9	Aplastic anemia, unsp
A96.9	Arenaviral hemorrhagic fever, unsp
E72.21	Argininemia
E72.22	Arginosuccinic aciduria
Q07.02	Arnold-Chiari synd w/ hydrocephalus
Q07.03	Arnold-Chiari synd w/ spina bifida & hydrocephalus
I28.0	Arteriovenous fistula of pulmn vessels
Q28.0	Arteriovenous malformation of precerebral vessels
Q27.30	Arteriovenous malformation, site unsp
A69.23	Arthritis d/t Lyme disease
M00.872	Arthritis d/t oth bacteria, lt ankle & foot
M00.822	Arthritis d/t oth bacteria, lt elbow
M00.842	Arthritis d/t oth bacteria, lt hand
M00.852	Arthritis d/t oth bacteria, lt hip
M00.862	Arthritis d/t oth bacteria, lt knee
M00.812	Arthritis d/t oth bacteria, lt shldr
M00.832	Arthritis d/t oth bacteria, lt wrist
M00.871	Arthritis d/t oth bacteria, rt ankle & foot
M00.821	Arthritis d/t oth bacteria, rt elbow
M00.841	Arthritis d/t oth bacteria, rt hand
M00.851	Arthritis d/t oth bacteria, rt hip
M00.861	Arthritis d/t oth bacteria, rt knee
M00.811	Arthritis d/t oth bacteria, rt shldr
M00.831	Arthritis d/t oth bacteria, rt wrist
M00.879	Arthritis d/t oth bacteria, unsp ankle & foot
M00.829	Arthritis d/t oth bacteria, unsp elbow
M00.849	Arthritis d/t oth bacteria, unsp hand
M00.859	Arthritis d/t oth bacteria, unsp hip
M00.80	Arthritis d/t oth bacteria, unsp jt
M00.869	Arthritis d/t oth bacteria, unsp knee
M00.819	Arthritis d/t oth bacteria, unsp shldr
M00.839	Arthritis d/t oth bacteria, unsp wrist
M00.88	Arthritis d/t oth bacteria, vertebrae

Q74.3	Arthrogryposis multiplex congenita
B77.0	Ascariasis w/ intestinal comp
B77.89	Ascariasis w/ oth comp
B77.9	Ascariasis, unsp
T81.61XA	Aseptic peritonitis d/t foreign substance accidentally lt during a procedure, init enc
F84.5	Asperger's synd
B44.9	Aspergillosis, unsp
R09.01	Asphyxia
T71.231A	Asphyxiation d/t being trapped in a (discarded) refrigerator, accid, init enc
T71.233A	Asphyxiation d/t being trapped in a (discarded) refrigerator, assault, init enc
T71.232A	Asphyxiation d/t being trapped in a (discarded) refrigerator, intentional self-harm, init enc
T71.234A	Asphyxiation d/t being trapped in a (discarded) refrigerator, undetermined, init enc
T71.221A	Asphyxiation d/t being trapped in a car trunk, accid, init enc
T71.223A	Asphyxiation d/t being trapped in a car trunk, assault, init enc
T71.222A	Asphyxiation d/t being trapped in a car trunk, intentional self-harm, init enc
T71.224A	Asphyxiation d/t being trapped in a car trunk, undetermined, init enc
T71.131A	Asphyxiation d/t being trapped in bed linens, accid, init enc
T71.133A	Asphyxiation d/t being trapped in bed linens, assault, init enc
T71.132A	Asphyxiation d/t being trapped in bed linens, intentional self-harm, init enc
T71.134A	Asphyxiation d/t being trapped in bed linens, undetermined, init enc
T71.29XA	Asphyxiation d/t being trapped in oth low oxygen environment, init enc
T71.21XA	Asphyxiation d/t cave-in or falling earth, init enc
T71.161A	Asphyxiation d/t hanging, accid, init enc
T71.163A	Asphyxiation d/t hanging, assault, init enc
T71.162A	Asphyxiation d/t hanging, intentional self-harm, init enc
T71.164A	Asphyxiation d/t hanging, undetermined, init enc
T71.191A	Asphyxiation d/t mech threat to breathing d/t oth causes, accid, init enc
T71.193A	Asphyxiation d/t mech threat to breathing d/t oth causes, assault, init enc
T71.192A	Asphyxiation d/t mech threat to breathing d/t oth causes, intentional self-harm, init enc
T71.194A	Asphyxiation d/t mech threat to breathing d/t oth causes, undetermined, init enc
T71.121A	Asphyxiation d/t plastic bag, accid, init enc
T71.123A	Asphyxiation d/t plastic bag, assault, init enc
T71.122A	Asphyxiation d/t plastic bag, intentional self-harm, init enc
T71.124A	Asphyxiation d/t plastic bag, undetermined, init enc
T71.151A	Asphyxiation d/t smothering in furniture, accid, init enc
T71.153A	Asphyxiation d/t smothering in furniture, assault, init enc
T71.152A	Asphyxiation d/t smothering in furniture, intentional self-harm, init enc
T71.154A	Asphyxiation d/t smothering in furniture, undetermined, init enc
T71.141A	Asphyxiation d/t smothering under another person's body (in bed), accid, init enc
T71.143A	Asphyxiation d/t smothering under another person's body (in bed), assault, init enc
T71.144A	Asphyxiation d/t smothering under another person's body (in bed), undetermined, init enc
T71.111A	Asphyxiation d/t smothering under pillow, accid, init enc
T71.113A	Asphyxiation d/t smothering under pillow, assault, init enc
T71.112A	Asphyxiation d/t smothering under pillow, intentional self-harm, init enc
T71.114A	Asphyxiation d/t smothering under pillow, undetermined, init enc
T71.20XA	Asphyxiation d/t systemic oxygen deficiency d/t low oxygen content in ambient air d/t unsp cause, init enc
T71.9XXA	Asphyxiation d/t unsp cause, init enc
Q89.01	Asplenia (congenital)
A08.32	Astrovirus enteritis
A52.2	Asymptomatic neurosyphilis
J98.11	Atelectasis
I75.023	Atheroembolism of bilat lwr extremities
I75.013	Atheroembolism of bilat upr extremities
I75.81	Atheroembolism of kidney
I75.022	Atheroembolism of lt lwr extr
I75.012	Atheroembolism of lt upr extr
I75.89	Atheroembolism of oth site
I75.021	Atheroembolism of rt lwr extr
I75.011	Atheroembolism of rt upr extr
I75.029	Atheroembolism of unsp lwr extr
I75.019	Atheroembolism of unsp upr extr

I25.721	Athscl of auto artery coronary artery bypass graft(s) w/ angina pectoris w/ documented spasm
I25.728	Athscl of auto artery coronary artery bypass graft(s) w/ oth forms of angina pectoris
I25.729	Athscl of auto artery coronary artery bypass graft(s) w/ unsp angina pectoris
I25.720	Athscl of auto artery coronary artery bypass graft(s) w/ unstable angina pectoris
I70.463	Athscl of auto vein bypass graft(s) of the extremities w/ gangrene, bilat legs
I70.462	Athscl of auto vein bypass graft(s) of the extremities w/ gangrene, lt leg
I70.468	Athscl of auto vein bypass graft(s) of the extremities w/ gangrene, oth extr
I70.461	Athscl of auto vein bypass graft(s) of the extremities w/ gangrene, rt leg
I70.469	Athscl of auto vein bypass graft(s) of the extremities w/ gangrene, unsp extr
I70.443	Athscl of auto vein bypass graft(s) of the lt leg w/ ulceration of ankle
I70.442	Athscl of auto vein bypass graft(s) of the lt leg w/ ulceration of calf
I70.444	Athscl of auto vein bypass graft(s) of the lt leg w/ ulceration of heel & midfoot
I70.448	Athscl of auto vein bypass graft(s) of the lt leg w/ ulceration of oth part of lwr leg
I70.441	Athscl of auto vein bypass graft(s) of the lt leg w/ ulceration of thigh
I70.449	Athscl of auto vein bypass graft(s) of the lt leg w/ ulceration of unsp site
I70.433	Athscl of auto vein bypass graft(s) of the rt leg w/ ulceration of ankle
I70.432	Athscl of auto vein bypass graft(s) of the rt leg w/ ulceration of calf
I70.434	Athscl of auto vein bypass graft(s) of the rt leg w/ ulceration of heel & midfoot
I70.438	Athscl of auto vein bypass graft(s) of the rt leg w/ ulceration of oth part of lwr leg
I70.431	Athscl of auto vein bypass graft(s) of the rt leg w/ ulceration of thigh
I70.439	Athscl of auto vein bypass graft(s) of the rt leg w/ ulceration of unsp site
I25.711	Athscl of auto vein coronary artery bypass graft(s) w/ angina pectoris w/ documented spasm
I25.718	Athscl of auto vein coronary artery bypass graft(s) w/ oth forms of angina pectoris
I25.719	Athscl of auto vein coronary artery bypass graft(s) w/ unsp angina pectoris
I25.710	Athscl of auto vein coronary artery bypass graft(s) w/ unstable angina pectoris
I25.761	Athscl of bypass graft of coronary artery of transplanted heart w/ angina pectoris w/ documented spasm
I25.768	Athscl of bypass graft of coronary artery of transplanted heart w/ oth forms of angina pectoris
I25.769	Athscl of bypass graft of coronary artery of transplanted heart w/ unsp angina pectoris
I25.760	Athscl of bypass graft of coronary artery of transplanted heart w/ unstable angina
I25.812	Athscl of bypass graft of coronary artery of transplanted heart w/o angina pectoris
I25.810	Athscl of coronary artery bypass graft(s) w/o angina pectoris
I25.700	Athscl of coronary artery bypass graft(s), unsp, w/ unstable angina pectoris
I70.263	Athscl of native arteries of extremities w/ gangrene, bilat legs
I70.262	Athscl of native arteries of extremities w/ gangrene, lt leg
I70.268	Athscl of native arteries of extremities w/ gangrene, oth extr
I70.261	Athscl of native arteries of extremities w/ gangrene, rt leg
I70.269	Athscl of native arteries of extremities w/ gangrene, unsp extr
I25.751	Athscl of native coronary artery of transplanted heart w/ angina pectoris w/ documented spasm
I25.758	Athscl of native coronary artery of transplanted heart w/ oth forms of angina pectoris
I25.759	Athscl of native coronary artery of transplanted heart w/ unsp angina pectoris
I25.750	Athscl of native coronary artery of transplanted heart w/ unstable angina
I25.811	Athscl of native coronary artery of transplanted heart w/o angina pectoris
I70.563	Athscl of nonauto biological bypass graft(s) of the extremities w/ gangrene, bilat legs
I70.562	Athscl of nonauto biological bypass graft(s) of the extremities w/ gangrene, lt leg
I70.568	Athscl of nonauto biological bypass graft(s) of the extremities w/ gangrene, oth extr
I70.561	Athscl of nonauto biological bypass graft(s) of the extremities w/ gangrene, rt leg
I70.569	Athscl of nonauto biological bypass graft(s) of the extremities w/ gangrene, unsp extr

I70.543	Athscl of nonauto biological bypass graft(s) of the lt leg w/ ulceration of ankle
I70.542	Athscl of nonauto biological bypass graft(s) of the lt leg w/ ulceration of calf
I70.544	Athscl of nonauto biological bypass graft(s) of the lt leg w/ ulceration of heel & midfoot
I70.548	Athscl of nonauto biological bypass graft(s) of the lt leg w/ ulceration of oth part of lwr leg
I70.541	Athscl of nonauto biological bypass graft(s) of the lt leg w/ ulceration of thigh
I70.549	Athscl of nonauto biological bypass graft(s) of the lt leg w/ ulceration of unsp site
I70.533	Athscl of nonauto biological bypass graft(s) of the rt leg w/ ulceration of ankle
I70.532	Athscl of nonauto biological bypass graft(s) of the rt leg w/ ulceration of calf
I70.534	Athscl of nonauto biological bypass graft(s) of the rt leg w/ ulceration of heel & midfoot
I70.538	Athscl of nonauto biological bypass graft(s) of the rt leg w/ ulceration of oth part of lwr leg
I70.531	Athscl of nonauto biological bypass graft(s) of the rt leg w/ ulceration of thigh
I70.539	Athscl of nonauto biological bypass graft(s) of the rt leg w/ ulceration of unsp site
I25.731	Athscl of nonauto biological coronary artery bypass graft(s) w/ angina pectoris w/ documented spasm
I25.738	Athscl of nonauto biological coronary artery bypass graft(s) w/ oth forms of angina pectoris
I25.739	Athscl of nonauto biological coronary artery bypass graft(s) w/ unsp angina pectoris
I25.730	Athscl of nonauto biological coronary artery bypass graft(s) w/ unstable angina pectoris
I70.663	Athscl of nonbiological bypass graft(s) of the extremities w/ gangrene, bilat legs
I70.662	Athscl of nonbiological bypass graft(s) of the extremities w/ gangrene, lt leg
I70.668	Athscl of nonbiological bypass graft(s) of the extremities w/ gangrene, oth extr
I70.661	Athscl of nonbiological bypass graft(s) of the extremities w/ gangrene, rt leg
I70.669	Athscl of nonbiological bypass graft(s) of the extremities w/ gangrene, unsp extr
I70.643	Athscl of nonbiological bypass graft(s) of the lt leg w/ ulceration of ankle
I70.642	Athscl of nonbiological bypass graft(s) of the lt leg w/ ulceration of calf
I70.644	Athscl of nonbiological bypass graft(s) of the lt leg w/ ulceration of heel & midfoot
I70.648	Athscl of nonbiological bypass graft(s) of the lt leg w/ ulceration of oth part of lwr leg
I70.641	Athscl of nonbiological bypass graft(s) of the lt leg w/ ulceration of thigh
I70.649	Athscl of nonbiological bypass graft(s) of the lt leg w/ ulceration of unsp site
I70.633	Athscl of nonbiological bypass graft(s) of the rt leg w/ ulceration of ankle
I70.632	Athscl of nonbiological bypass graft(s) of the rt leg w/ ulceration of calf
I70.634	Athscl of nonbiological bypass graft(s) of the rt leg w/ ulceration of heel & midfoot
I70.638	Athscl of nonbiological bypass graft(s) of the rt leg w/ ulceration of oth part of lwr leg
I70.631	Athscl of nonbiological bypass graft(s) of the rt leg w/ ulceration of thigh
I70.639	Athscl of nonbiological bypass graft(s) of the rt leg w/ ulceration of unsp site
I25.791	Athscl of oth coronary artery bypass graft(s) w/ angina pectoris w/ documented spasm
I25.798	Athscl of oth coronary artery bypass graft(s) w/ oth forms of angina pectoris
I25.799	Athscl of oth coronary artery bypass graft(s) w/ unsp angina pectoris
I25.790	Athscl of oth coronary artery bypass graft(s) w/ unstable angina pectoris
I70.763	Athscl of oth type of bypass graft(s) of the extremities w/ gangrene, bilat legs
I70.762	Athscl of oth type of bypass graft(s) of the extremities w/ gangrene, lt leg
I70.768	Athscl of oth type of bypass graft(s) of the extremities w/ gangrene, oth extr
I70.761	Athscl of oth type of bypass graft(s) of the extremities w/ gangrene, rt leg
I70.769	Athscl of oth type of bypass graft(s) of the extremities w/ gangrene, unsp extr
I70.743	Athscl of oth type of bypass graft(s) of the lt leg w/ ulceration of ankle
I70.742	Athscl of oth type of bypass graft(s) of the lt leg w/ ulceration of calf

I70.744	Athscl of oth type of bypass graft(s) of the lt leg w/ ulceration of heel & midfoot
I70.748	Athscl of oth type of bypass graft(s) of the lt leg w/ ulceration of oth part of lwr leg
I70.741	Athscl of oth type of bypass graft(s) of the lt leg w/ ulceration of thigh
I70.749	Athscl of oth type of bypass graft(s) of the lt leg w/ ulceration of unsp site
I70.733	Athscl of oth type of bypass graft(s) of the rt leg w/ ulceration of ankle
I70.732	Athscl of oth type of bypass graft(s) of the rt leg w/ ulceration of calf
I70.734	Athscl of oth type of bypass graft(s) of the rt leg w/ ulceration of heel & midfoot
I70.738	Athscl of oth type of bypass graft(s) of the rt leg w/ ulceration of oth part of lwr leg
I70.731	Athscl of oth type of bypass graft(s) of the rt leg w/ ulceration of thigh
I70.739	Athscl of oth type of bypass graft(s) of the rt leg w/ ulceration of unsp site
I70.363	Athscl of unsp type of bypass graft(s) of the extremities w/ gangrene, bilat legs
I70.362	Athscl of unsp type of bypass graft(s) of the extremities w/ gangrene, lt leg
I70.368	Athscl of unsp type of bypass graft(s) of the extremities w/ gangrene, oth extr
I70.361	Athscl of unsp type of bypass graft(s) of the extremities w/ gangrene, rt leg
I70.369	Athscl of unsp type of bypass graft(s) of the extremities w/ gangrene, unsp extr
I70.343	Athscl of unsp type of bypass graft(s) of the lt leg w/ ulceration of ankle
I70.342	Athscl of unsp type of bypass graft(s) of the lt leg w/ ulceration of calf
I70.344	Athscl of unsp type of bypass graft(s) of the lt leg w/ ulceration of heel & midfoot
I70.348	Athscl of unsp type of bypass graft(s) of the lt leg w/ ulceration of oth part of lwr leg
I70.341	Athscl of unsp type of bypass graft(s) of the lt leg w/ ulceration of thigh
I70.349	Athscl of unsp type of bypass graft(s) of the lt leg w/ ulceration of unsp site
I70.333	Athscl of unsp type of bypass graft(s) of the rt leg w/ ulceration of ankle
I70.332	Athscl of unsp type of bypass graft(s) of the rt leg w/ ulceration of calf
I70.334	Athscl of unsp type of bypass graft(s) of the rt leg w/ ulceration of heel & midfoot
I70.338	Athscl of unsp type of bypass graft(s) of the rt leg w/ ulceration of oth part of lwr leg
I70.331	Athscl of unsp type of bypass graft(s) of the rt leg w/ ulceration of thigh
I70.339	Athscl of unsp type of bypass graft(s) of the rt leg w/ ulceration of unsp site
I25.110	Atherosclerotic heart disease of native coronary artery w/ unstable angina pectoris
G80.3	Athetoid cerebral palsy
Q25.2	Atresia of aorta
Q21.1	Atrial septal defect
I23.1	Atrial septal defect as current comp following acute myocardial infarction
I44.2	Atrioventricular block, complete
Q21.2	Atrioventricular septal defect
I48.4	Atypical atrial flutter
C92.22	Atypical chr myeloid leukemia, BCR/ABL-negative, in relapse
C92.21	Atypical chr myeloid leukemia, BCR/ABL-negative, in remission
C92.20	Atypical chr myeloid leukemia, BCR/ABL-negative, not having achieved remission
A81.9	Atypical virus infxn of central nervous sys, unsp
R44.0	Auditory hallucinations
F84.0	Autistic d/o
G99.0	Autonomic neuropathy in diseases classified elsw
E70.311	Autosomal recessive ocular albinism
S05.72XA	Avulsion of lt eye, init enc
S05.71XA	Avulsion of rt eye, init enc
S05.70XA	Avulsion of unsp eye, init enc
B60.0	Babesiosis
R78.81	Bacteremia
A04.9	Bacterial intestinal infxn, unsp
E78.71	Barth synd
S52.562A	Barton's fx of lt radius, init enc for clsd fx
S52.562P	Barton's fx of lt radius, subsq enc for clsd fx w/ malu
S52.562K	Barton's fx of lt radius, subsq enc for clsd fx w/ nonu
S52.562Q	Barton's fx of lt radius, subsq enc for opn fx type I or II w/ malu
S52.562M	Barton's fx of lt radius, subsq enc for opn fx type I or II w/ nonu
S52.562R	Barton's fx of lt radius, subsq enc for opn fx type IIIA, IIIB, or IIIC w/ malu
S52.562N	Barton's fx of lt radius, subsq enc for opn fx type IIIA, IIIB, or IIIC w/ nonu

S52.561A	Barton's fx of rt radius, init enc for clsd fx
S52.561P	Barton's fx of rt radius, subsq enc for clsd fx w/ malu
S52.561K	Barton's fx of rt radius, subsq enc for clsd fx w/ nonu
S52.561Q	Barton's fx of rt radius, subsq enc for opn fx type I or II w/ malu
S52.561M	Barton's fx of rt radius, subsq enc for opn fx type I or II w/ nonu
S52.561R	Barton's fx of rt radius, subsq enc for opn fx type IIIA, IIIB, or IIIC w/ malu
S52.561N	Barton's fx of rt radius, subsq enc for opn fx type IIIA, IIIB, or IIIC w/ nonu
S52.569A	Barton's fx of unsp radius, init enc for clsd fx
S52.569P	Barton's fx of unsp radius, subsq enc for clsd fx w/ malu
S52.569K	Barton's fx of unsp radius, subsq enc for clsd fx w/ nonu
S52.569Q	Barton's fx of unsp radius, subsq enc for opn fx type I or II w/ malu
S52.569M	Barton's fx of unsp radius, subsq enc for opn fx type I or II w/ nonu
S52.569R	Barton's fx of unsp radius, subsq enc for opn fx type IIIA, IIIB, or IIIC w/ malu
S52.569N	Barton's fx of unsp radius, subsq enc for opn fx type IIIA, IIIB, or IIIC w/ nonu
A44.9	Bartonellosis, unsp
M35.2	Behcet's disease
G03.2	Benign recurrent meningitis [Mollaret]
S62.212B	Bennett's fx, lt hand, init enc for opn fx
S62.212P	Bennett's fx, lt hand, subsq enc for fx w/ malu
S62.212K	Bennett's fx, lt hand, subsq enc for fx w/ nonu
S62.211B	Bennett's fx, rt hand, init enc for opn fx
S62.211P	Bennett's fx, rt hand, subsq enc for fx w/ malu
S62.211K	Bennett's fx, rt hand, subsq enc for fx w/ nonu
S62.213B	Bennett's fx, unsp hand, init enc for opn fx
S62.213P	Bennett's fx, unsp hand, subsq enc for fx w/ malu
S62.213K	Bennett's fx, unsp hand, subsq enc for fx w/ nonu
S52.382A	Bent bone of lt radius, init enc for clsd fx
S52.382P	Bent bone of lt radius, subsq enc for clsd fx w/ malu
S52.382K	Bent bone of lt radius, subsq enc for clsd fx w/ nonu
S52.382Q	Bent bone of lt radius, subsq enc for opn fx type I or II w/ malu
S52.382M	Bent bone of lt radius, subsq enc for opn fx type I or II w/ nonu
S52.382R	Bent bone of lt radius, subsq enc for opn fx type IIIA, IIIB, or IIIC w/ malu
S52.382N	Bent bone of lt radius, subsq enc for opn fx type IIIA, IIIB, or IIIC w/ nonu
S52.282A	Bent bone of lt ulna, init enc for clsd fx
S52.282P	Bent bone of lt ulna, subsq enc for clsd fx w/ malu
S52.282K	Bent bone of lt ulna, subsq enc for clsd fx w/ nonu
S52.282Q	Bent bone of lt ulna, subsq enc for opn fx type I or II w/ malu
S52.282M	Bent bone of lt ulna, subsq enc for opn fx type I or II w/ nonu
S52.282R	Bent bone of lt ulna, subsq enc for opn fx type IIIA, IIIB, or IIIC w/ malu
S52.282N	Bent bone of lt ulna, subsq enc for opn fx type IIIA, IIIB, or IIIC w/ nonu
S52.381A	Bent bone of rt radius, init enc for clsd fx
S52.381P	Bent bone of rt radius, subsq enc for clsd fx w/ malu
S52.381K	Bent bone of rt radius, subsq enc for clsd fx w/ nonu
S52.381Q	Bent bone of rt radius, subsq enc for opn fx type I or II w/ malu
S52.381M	Bent bone of rt radius, subsq enc for opn fx type I or II w/ nonu
S52.381R	Bent bone of rt radius, subsq enc for opn fx type IIIA, IIIB, or IIIC w/ malu
S52.381N	Bent bone of rt radius, subsq enc for opn fx type IIIA, IIIB, or IIIC w/ nonu
S52.281A	Bent bone of rt ulna, init enc for clsd fx
S52.281P	Bent bone of rt ulna, subsq enc for clsd fx w/ malu
S52.281K	Bent bone of rt ulna, subsq enc for clsd fx w/ nonu
S52.281Q	Bent bone of rt ulna, subsq enc for opn fx type I or II w/ malu
S52.281M	Bent bone of rt ulna, subsq enc for opn fx type I or II w/ nonu
S52.281R	Bent bone of rt ulna, subsq enc for opn fx type IIIA, IIIB, or IIIC w/ malu
S52.281N	Bent bone of rt ulna, subsq enc for opn fx type IIIA, IIIB, or IIIC w/ nonu
S52.389A	Bent bone of unsp radius, init enc for clsd fx
S52.389P	Bent bone of unsp radius, subsq enc for clsd fx w/ malu
S52.389K	Bent bone of unsp radius, subsq enc for clsd fx w/ nonu
S52.389Q	Bent bone of unsp radius, subsq enc for opn fx type I or II w/ malu
S52.389M	Bent bone of unsp radius, subsq enc for opn fx type I or II w/ nonu
S52.389R	Bent bone of unsp radius, subsq enc for opn fx type IIIA, IIIB, or IIIC w/ malu
S52.389N	Bent bone of unsp radius, subsq enc for opn fx type IIIA, IIIB, or IIIC w/ nonu
S52.283A	Bent bone of unsp ulna, init enc for clsd fx
S52.283P	Bent bone of unsp ulna, subsq enc for clsd fx w/ malu
S52.283K	Bent bone of unsp ulna, subsq enc for clsd fx w/ nonu
S52.283Q	Bent bone of unsp ulna, subsq enc for opn fx type I or II w/ malu
S52.283M	Bent bone of unsp ulna, subsq enc for opn fx type I or II w/ nonu
S52.283R	Bent bone of unsp ulna, subsq enc for opn fx type IIIA, IIIB, or IIIC w/ malu
S52.283N	Bent bone of unsp ulna, subsq enc for opn fx type IIIA, IIIB, or IIIC w/ nonu
I45.2	Bifascicular block
K41.00	Bilat femoral hernia, w/ obstruction, w/o gangrene, not spec as recurrent

K41.01	Bilat femoral hernia, w/ obstruction, w/o gangrene, recurrent
K40.00	Bilat inguinal hernia, w/ obstruction, w/o gangrene, not spec as recurrent
K40.01	Bilat inguinal hernia, w/ obstruction, w/o gangrene, recurrent
F31.31	Bipolar d/o, current episode depressed, mild
F31.30	Bipolar d/o, current episode depressed, mild or mod severity, unsp
F31.32	Bipolar d/o, current episode depressed, mod
F31.5	Bipolar d/o, current episode depressed, severe, w/ psychotic features
F31.4	Bipolar d/o, current episode depressed, severe, w/o psychotic features
F31.0	Bipolar d/o, current episode hypomanic
F31.2	Bipolar d/o, current episode manic severe w/ psychotic features
F31.11	Bipolar d/o, current episode manic w/o psychotic features, mild
F31.12	Bipolar d/o, current episode manic w/o psychotic features, mod
F31.13	Bipolar d/o, current episode manic w/o psychotic features, severe
F31.10	Bipolar d/o, current episode manic w/o psychotic features, unsp
F31.61	Bipolar d/o, current episode mixed, mild
F31.62	Bipolar d/o, current episode mixed, mod
F31.64	Bipolar d/o, current episode mixed, severe, w/ psychotic features
F31.63	Bipolar d/o, current episode mixed, severe, w/o psychotic features
F31.60	Bipolar d/o, current episode mixed, unsp
F31.81	Bipolar II d/o
C86.4	Blastic NK-cell lymphoma
B40.9	Blastomycosis, unsp
B40.81	Blastomycotic meningoencephalitis
K90.2	Blind loop synd, NEC
T80.211A	Bloodstream infxn d/t central venous catheter, init enc
Z68.1	Body mass index (BMI) 19 or less, adult
Z68.41	Body mass index (BMI) 40.0-44.9, adult
Z68.42	Body mass index (BMI) 45.0-49.9, adult
Z68.43	Body mass index (BMI) 50-59.9 , adult
Z68.44	Body mass index (BMI) 60.0-69.9, adult
Z68.45	Body mass index (BMI) 70 or greater, adult
T86.831	Bone graft failure
T86.832	Bone graft infxn
T86.830	Bone graft rejection
T86.02	Bone marrow transplant failure
T86.03	Bone marrow transplant infxn
T86.01	Bone marrow transplant rejection
Z94.81	Bone marrow transplant status
A30.4	Borderline lepromatous leprosy
A30.3	Borderline leprosy
A30.2	Borderline tuberculoid leprosy
A05.1	Botulism food poison
L10.3	Brazilian pemphigus [fogo selvagem]
T82.310A	Breakdown (mech) of aortic (bifurcation) graft (replace), init enc
T82.512A	Breakdown (mech) of artfcl heart, init enc
T85.613A	Breakdown (mech) of artfcl skin graft & decellularized allodermis, init enc
T82.513A	Breakdown (mech) of balloon (counterpulsation) dev, init enc
T85.510A	Breakdown (mech) of bile duct prosthesis, init enc
T82.221A	Breakdown (mech) of biological heart valve graft, init enc
T85.41XA	Breakdown (mech) of breast prosthesis & implant, init enc
T82.110A	Breakdown (mech) of cardiac electrode, init enc
T82.111A	Breakdown (mech) of cardiac pulse generator (battery), init enc
T82.311A	Breakdown (mech) of carotid arterial graft (bypass), init enc
T82.211A	Breakdown (mech) of coronary artery bypass graft, init enc
T83.010A	Breakdown (mech) of cystostomy catheter, init enc
T84.310A	Breakdown (mech) of electronic bone stimulator, init enc
T85.610A	Breakdown (mech) of epidural & subdural inf catheter, init enc
T85.511A	Breakdown (mech) of esophageal anti-reflux dev, init enc
T82.312A	Breakdown (mech) of femoral arterial graft (bypass), init enc
T83.21XA	Breakdown (mech) of graft of urinary organ, init enc
T82.01XA	Breakdown (mech) of heart valve prosthesis, init enc
T85.110A	Breakdown (mech) of implanted electronic neurostimulator (electrode) of brain, init enc
T85.111A	Breakdown (mech) of implanted electronic neurostimulator (electrode) of peripheral nerve, init enc
T85.112A	Breakdown (mech) of implanted electronic neurostimulator (electrode) of spinal cord, init enc
T82.514A	Breakdown (mech) of inf catheter, init enc
T85.614A	Breakdown (mech) of insulin pump, init enc
T84.113A	Breakdown (mech) of int fix dev of bone of lt forearm, init enc
T84.117A	Breakdown (mech) of int fix dev of bone of lt lwr leg, init enc
T84.112A	Breakdown (mech) of int fix dev of bone of rt forearm, init enc
T84.116A	Breakdown (mech) of int fix dev of bone of rt lwr leg, init enc
T84.213A	Breakdown (mech) of int fix dev of bones of foot & toes, init enc
T84.210A	Breakdown (mech) of int fix dev of bones of hand & fingers, init enc
T84.115A	Breakdown (mech) of int fix dev of lt femur, init enc
T84.111A	Breakdown (mech) of int fix dev of lt humerus, init enc
T84.218A	Breakdown (mech) of int fix dev of oth bones, init enc
T84.114A	Breakdown (mech) of int fix dev of rt femur, init enc
T84.110A	Breakdown (mech) of int fix dev of rt humerus, init enc
T84.119A	Breakdown (mech) of int fix dev of unsp bone of limb, init enc
T84.216A	Breakdown (mech) of int fix dev of vertebrae, init enc
T85.21XA	Breakdown (mech) of intraocular lens, init enc
T85.611A	Breakdown (mech) of intraperitoneal dialysis catheter, init enc
T84.410A	Breakdown (mech) of muscle & tndn graft, init enc
T84.318A	Breakdown (mech) of oth bone devices, implants & grafts, init enc
T82.518A	Breakdown (mech) of oth cardiac & vascular devices & implants, init enc
T82.118A	Breakdown (mech) of oth cardiac electronic dev, init enc
T85.518A	Breakdown (mech) of oth gastrointestinal prosthetic devices, implants & grafts, init enc
T85.118A	Breakdown (mech) of oth implanted electronic stimulator of nervous sys, init enc
T84.418A	Breakdown (mech) of oth int orthopedic devices, implants & grafts, init enc
T83.418A	Breakdown (mech) of oth prosthetic devices, implants & grafts of genital tract, init enc
T85.618A	Breakdown (mech) of oth spec int prosthetic devices, implants & grafts, init enc
T83.118A	Breakdown (mech) of oth urinary devices & implants, init enc
T82.318A	Breakdown (mech) of oth vascular grafts, init enc
T83.410A	Breakdown (mech) of penile (implanted) prosthesis, init enc
T85.612A	Breakdown (mech) of permanent sutures, init enc
T85.311A	Breakdown (mech) of prosthetic orbit of lt eye, init enc
T85.310A	Breakdown (mech) of prosthetic orbit of rt eye, init enc
T82.510A	Breakdown (mech) of surgly created arteriovenous fistula, init enc
T82.511A	Breakdown (mech) of surgly created arteriovenous shunt, init enc
T82.515A	Breakdown (mech) of umbrella dev, init enc
T82.519A	Breakdown (mech) of unsp cardiac & vascular devices & implants, init enc
T82.119A	Breakdown (mech) of unsp cardiac electronic dev, init enc
T82.319A	Breakdown (mech) of unsp vascular grafts, init enc
T83.110A	Breakdown (mech) of urinary electronic stimulator dev, init enc
T83.111A	Breakdown (mech) of urinary sphincter implant, init enc
T83.112A	Breakdown (mech) of urinary stent, init enc
T82.41XA	Breakdown (mech) of vascular dialysis catheter, init enc
T85.01XA	Breakdown (mech) of ventricular intracranial (communicating) shunt, init enc
F23	Brief psychotic d/o
T84.018A	Broken int jt prosthesis, oth site, init enc
T84.019A	Broken int jt prosthesis, unsp site, init enc
T84.011A	Broken int lt hip prosthesis, init enc
T84.013A	Broken int lt knee prosthesis, init enc
T84.010A	Broken int rt hip prosthesis, init enc
T84.012A	Broken int rt knee prosthesis, init enc
J47.1	Bronchiectasis w/ (acute) exacerbation
J47.0	Bronchiectasis w/ acute lwr respiratory infxn
J68.0	Bronchitis & pneumonitis d/t chemicals, gases, fumes & vapors
A23.9	Brucellosis, unsp
F50.2	Bulimia nervosa
L12.0	Bullous pemphigoid
C83.79	Burkitt lymphoma, extranodal & solid organ sites
C83.73	Burkitt lymphoma, intra-abd lymph nodes
C83.76	Burkitt lymphoma, intrapelvic lymph nodes
C83.72	Burkitt lymphoma, intrathoracic lymph nodes
C83.74	Burkitt lymphoma, lymph nodes of axilla & upr limb
C83.71	Burkitt lymphoma, lymph nodes of head, face, & neck
C83.75	Burkitt lymphoma, lymph nodes of inguinal rgn & lwr limb
C83.78	Burkitt lymphoma, lymph nodes of multi sites
C83.77	Burkitt lymphoma, spleen
C83.70	Burkitt lymphoma, unsp site
T27.1XXA	Burn involving larynx & trachea w/ lung, init enc
T21.32XA	Burn of 3rd degree of abd wall, init enc
T23.362A	Burn of 3rd degree of back of lt hand, init enc
T23.361A	Burn of 3rd degree of back of rt hand, init enc
T23.369A	Burn of 3rd degree of back of unsp hand, init enc
T21.35XA	Burn of 3rd degree of buttock, init enc

T21.31XA	Burn of 3rd degree of chest wall, init enc
T20.33XA	Burn of 3rd degree of chin, init enc
T21.37XA	Burn of 3rd degree of female genital rgn, init enc
T20.36XA	Burn of 3rd degree of forehead & cheek, init enc
T20.30XA	Burn of 3rd degree of head, face, & neck, unsp site, init enc
T20.32XA	Burn of 3rd degree of lip(s), init enc
T25.312A	Burn of 3rd degree of lt ankle, init enc
T22.342A	Burn of 3rd degree of lt axilla, init enc
T20.312A	Burn of 3rd degree of lt ear [any part, except ear drum], init enc
T22.322A	Burn of 3rd degree of lt elbow, init enc
T25.322A	Burn of 3rd degree of lt foot, init enc
T22.312A	Burn of 3rd degree of lt forearm, init enc
T23.302A	Burn of 3rd degree of lt hand, unsp site, init enc
T24.322A	Burn of 3rd degree of lt knee, init enc
T24.332A	Burn of 3rd degree of lt lwr leg, init enc
T23.352A	Burn of 3rd degree of lt palm, init enc
T22.362A	Burn of 3rd degree of lt scapular rgn, init enc
T22.352A	Burn of 3rd degree of lt shldr, init enc
T24.312A	Burn of 3rd degree of lt thigh, init enc
T23.312A	Burn of 3rd degree of lt thumb (nail), init enc
T25.332A	Burn of 3rd degree of lt toe(s) (nail), init enc
T22.332A	Burn of 3rd degree of lt upr arm, init enc
T23.372A	Burn of 3rd degree of lt wrist, init enc
T21.34XA	Burn of 3rd degree of lwr back, init enc
T21.36XA	Burn of 3rd degree of male genital rgn, init enc
T23.342A	Burn of 3rd degree of multi lt fingers (nail), incl thumb, init enc
T23.332A	Burn of 3rd degree of multi lt fingers (nail), not incl thumb, init enc
T23.341A	Burn of 3rd degree of multi rt fingers (nail), incl thumb, init enc
T23.331A	Burn of 3rd degree of multi rt fingers (nail), not incl thumb, init enc
T20.39XA	Burn of 3rd degree of multi sites of head, face, & neck, init enc
T25.392A	Burn of 3rd degree of multi sites of lt ankle & foot, init enc
T24.392A	Burn of 3rd degree of multi sites of lt lwr limb, except ankle & foot, init enc
T22.392A	Burn of 3rd degree of multi sites of lt shldr & upr limb, except wrist & hand, init enc
T23.392A	Burn of 3rd degree of multi sites of lt wrist & hand, init enc
T25.391A	Burn of 3rd degree of multi sites of rt ankle & foot, init enc
T24.391A	Burn of 3rd degree of multi sites of rt lwr limb, except ankle & foot, init enc
T22.391A	Burn of 3rd degree of multi sites of rt shldr & upr limb, except wrist & hand, init enc
T23.391A	Burn of 3rd degree of multi sites of rt wrist & hand, init enc
T25.399A	Burn of 3rd degree of multi sites of unsp ankle & foot, init enc
T24.399A	Burn of 3rd degree of multi sites of unsp lwr limb, except ankle & foot, init enc
T22.399A	Burn of 3rd degree of multi sites of unsp shldr & upr limb, except wrist & hand, init enc
T23.399A	Burn of 3rd degree of multi sites of unsp wrist & hand, init enc
T20.37XA	Burn of 3rd degree of neck, init enc
T20.34XA	Burn of 3rd degree of nose (septum), init enc
T21.39XA	Burn of 3rd degree of oth site of trunk, init enc
T25.311A	Burn of 3rd degree of rt ankle, init enc
T22.341A	Burn of 3rd degree of rt axilla, init enc
T20.311A	Burn of 3rd degree of rt ear [any part, except ear drum], init enc
T22.321A	Burn of 3rd degree of rt elbow, init enc
T25.321A	Burn of 3rd degree of rt foot, init enc
T22.311A	Burn of 3rd degree of rt forearm, init enc
T23.301A	Burn of 3rd degree of rt hand, unsp site, init enc
T24.321A	Burn of 3rd degree of rt knee, init enc
T24.331A	Burn of 3rd degree of rt lwr leg, init enc
T23.351A	Burn of 3rd degree of rt palm, init enc
T22.361A	Burn of 3rd degree of rt scapular rgn, init enc
T22.351A	Burn of 3rd degree of rt shldr, init enc
T24.311A	Burn of 3rd degree of rt thigh, init enc
T23.311A	Burn of 3rd degree of rt thumb (nail), init enc
T25.331A	Burn of 3rd degree of rt toe(s) (nail), init enc
T22.331A	Burn of 3rd degree of rt upr arm, init enc
T23.371A	Burn of 3rd degree of rt wrist, init enc
T20.35XA	Burn of 3rd degree of scalp [any part], init enc
T22.30XA	Burn of 3rd degree of shldr & upr limb, except wrist & hand, unsp site, init enc
T23.322A	Burn of 3rd degree of single lt finger (nail) except thumb, init enc
T23.321A	Burn of 3rd degree of single rt finger (nail) except thumb, init enc
T21.30XA	Burn of 3rd degree of trunk, unsp site, init enc
T25.319A	Burn of 3rd degree of unsp ankle, init enc
T22.349A	Burn of 3rd degree of unsp axilla, init enc
T20.319A	Burn of 3rd degree of unsp ear [any part, except ear drum], init enc
T22.329A	Burn of 3rd degree of unsp elbow, init enc
T25.329A	Burn of 3rd degree of unsp foot, init enc
T22.319A	Burn of 3rd degree of unsp forearm, init enc
T23.309A	Burn of 3rd degree of unsp hand, unsp site, init enc
T24.329A	Burn of 3rd degree of unsp knee, init enc
T24.339A	Burn of 3rd degree of unsp lwr leg, init enc
T23.349A	Burn of 3rd degree of unsp multi fingers (nail), incl thumb, init enc
T23.339A	Burn of 3rd degree of unsp multi fingers (nail), not incl thumb, init enc
T23.359A	Burn of 3rd degree of unsp palm, init enc
T22.369A	Burn of 3rd degree of unsp scapular rgn, init enc
T22.359A	Burn of 3rd degree of unsp shldr, init enc
T23.329A	Burn of 3rd degree of unsp single finger (nail) except thumb, init enc
T24.302A	Burn of 3rd degree of unsp site of lt lwr limb, except ankle & foot, init enc
T24.301A	Burn of 3rd degree of unsp site of rt lwr limb, except ankle & foot, init enc
T24.309A	Burn of 3rd degree of unsp site of unsp lwr limb, except ankle & foot, init enc
T24.319A	Burn of 3rd degree of unsp thigh, init enc
T23.319A	Burn of 3rd degree of unsp thumb (nail), init enc
T25.339A	Burn of 3rd degree of unsp toe(s) (nail), init enc
T22.339A	Burn of 3rd degree of unsp upr arm, init enc
T23.379A	Burn of 3rd degree of unsp wrist, init enc
T21.33XA	Burn of 3rd degree of upr back, init enc
T28.1XXA	Burn of esophagus, init enc
T27.0XXA	Burn of larynx & trachea, init enc
T28.2XXA	Burn of oth parts of alimentary tract, init enc
T27.2XXA	Burn of oth parts of respiratory tract, init enc
T27.3XXA	Burn of respiratory tract, part unsp, init enc
T26.22XA	Burn w/ resulting rupture & destr of lt eyeball, init enc
T26.21XA	Burn w/ resulting rupture & destr of rt eyeball, init enc
T26.20XA	Burn w/ resulting rupture & destr of unsp eyeball, init enc
T31.10	Burns involving 10-19% of body surface w/ 0% to 9% 3rd degree burns
T31.11	Burns involving 10-19% of body surface w/ 10-19% 3rd degree burns
T31.20	Burns involving 20-29% of body surface w/ 0% to 9% 3rd degree burns
T31.30	Burns involving 30-39% of body surface w/ 0% to 9% 3rd degree burns
T31.40	Burns involving 40-49% of body surface w/ 0% to 9% 3rd degree burns
T31.50	Burns involving 50-59% of body surface w/ 0% to 9% 3rd degree burns
T31.60	Burns involving 60-69% of body surface w/ 0% to 9% 3rd degree burns
T31.70	Burns involving 70-79% of body surface w/ 0% to 9% 3rd degree burns
T31.80	Burns involving 80-89% of body surface w/ 0% to 9% 3rd degree burns
T31.90	Burns involving 90% or more of body surface w/ 0% to 9% 3rd degree burns
R64	Cachexia
T70.3XXA	Caisson disease [decompression sickness], init enc
K80.37	Calculus of bile duct w/ acute & chr cholangitis w/ obstruction
K80.36	Calculus of bile duct w/ acute & chr cholangitis w/o obstruction
K80.47	Calculus of bile duct w/ acute & chr cholecystitis w/ obstruction
K80.46	Calculus of bile duct w/ acute & chr cholecystitis w/o obstruction
K80.33	Calculus of bile duct w/ acute cholangitis w/ obstruction
K80.32	Calculus of bile duct w/ acute cholangitis w/o obstruction
K80.43	Calculus of bile duct w/ acute cholecystitis w/ obstruction
K80.42	Calculus of bile duct w/ acute cholecystitis w/o obstruction
K80.31	Calculus of bile duct w/ cholangitis, unsp, w/ obstruction
K80.30	Calculus of bile duct w/ cholangitis, unsp, w/o obstruction
K80.41	Calculus of bile duct w/ cholecystitis, unsp, w/ obstruction
K80.40	Calculus of bile duct w/ cholecystitis, unsp, w/o obstruction
K80.35	Calculus of bile duct w/ chr cholangitis w/ obstruction
K80.34	Calculus of bile duct w/ chr cholangitis w/o obstruction
K80.45	Calculus of bile duct w/ chr cholecystitis w/ obstruction
K80.44	Calculus of bile duct w/ chr cholecystitis w/o obstruction
K80.51	Calculus of bile duct w/o cholangitis or cholecystitis w/ obstruction
K80.66	Calculus of gallbladder & bile duct w/ acute & chr cholecystitis w/o obstruction
K80.63	Calculus of gallbladder & bile duct w/ acute cholecystitis w/ obstruction
K80.62	Calculus of gallbladder & bile duct w/ acute cholecystitis w/o obstruction
K80.61	Calculus of gallbladder & bile duct w/ cholecystitis, unsp, w/ obstruction
K80.60	Calculus of gallbladder & bile duct w/ cholecystitis, unsp, w/o obstruction
K80.65	Calculus of gallbladder & bile duct w/ chr cholecystitis w/ obstruction
K80.64	Calculus of gallbladder & bile duct w/ chr cholecystitis w/o obstruction
K80.71	Calculus of gallbladder & bile duct w/o cholecystitis w/ obstruction
K80.13	Calculus of gallbladder w/ acute & chr cholecystitis w/ obstruction

K80.12	Calculus of gallbladder w/ acute & chr cholecystitis w/o obstruction
K80.01	Calculus of gallbladder w/ acute cholecystitis w/ obstruction
K80.00	Calculus of gallbladder w/ acute cholecystitis w/o obstruction
K80.11	Calculus of gallbladder w/ chr cholecystitis w/ obstruction
K80.10	Calculus of gallbladder w/ chr cholecystitis w/o obstruction
K80.19	Calculus of gallbladder w/ oth cholecystitis w/ obstruction
K80.18	Calculus of gallbladder w/ oth cholecystitis w/o obstruction
K80.21	Calculus of gallbladder w/o cholecystitis w/ obstruction
N20.2	Calculus of kidney w/ calculus of ureter
N20.1	Calculus of ureter
A08.31	Calicivirus enteritis
A04.5	Campylobacter enteritis
B37.83	Candidal cheilitis
B37.41	Candidal cystitis & urethritis
B37.82	Candidal enteritis
B37.81	Candidal esophagitis
B37.84	Candidal otitis externa
B37.0	Candidal stomatitis
F12.121	Cannabis abuse w/ intoxication delirium
F12.150	Cannabis abuse w/ psychotic d/o w/ delusions
F12.151	Cannabis abuse w/ psychotic d/o w/ hallucinations
F12.221	Cannabis dependence w/ intoxication delirium
F12.250	Cannabis dependence w/ psychotic d/o w/ delusions
F12.251	Cannabis dependence w/ psychotic d/o w/ hallucinations
F12.921	Cannabis use, unsp w/ intoxication delirium
F12.950	Cannabis use, unsp w/ psychotic d/o w/ delusions
F12.951	Cannabis use, unsp w/ psychotic d/o w/ hallucinations
T85.44XA	Capsular contracture of breast implant, init enc
E34.0	Carcinoid synd
T86.290	Cardiac allograft vasculopathy
O04.86	Cardiac arrest following (induced) termination of pregnancy
O08.81	Cardiac arrest following an ectopic & molar pregnancy
O03.86	Cardiac arrest following complete or unsp spontaneous abortion
O07.36	Cardiac arrest following failed attempted termination of pregnancy
O03.36	Cardiac arrest following incomplete spontaneous abortion
I51.0	Cardiac septal defect, acquired
I31.4	Cardiac tamponade
I42.7	Cardiomyopathy d/t drug & ext agent
I43	Cardiomyopathy in diseases classified elsw
I42.9	Cardiomyopathy, unsp
A52.00	Cardiovascular syphilis, unsp
G45.1	Carotid artery synd (hemispheric)
A28.1	Cat-scratch disease
F20.2	Catatonic schizophrenia
G83.4	Cauda equina synd
Q62.32	Cecoureterocele
I77.4	Celiac artery compression synd
K12.2	Cellulitis & abscess of mouth
L03.311	Cellulitis of abd wall
L03.312	Cellulitis of back [any part except buttock]
H05.013	Cellulitis of bilat orbits
L03.317	Cellulitis of buttock
L03.313	Cellulitis of chest wall
L03.211	Cellulitis of face
L03.314	Cellulitis of groin
L03.811	Cellulitis of head [any part, except face]
L03.112	Cellulitis of lt axilla
L03.116	Cellulitis of lt lwr limb
H05.012	Cellulitis of lt orbit
L03.114	Cellulitis of lt upr limb
L03.221	Cellulitis of neck
L03.818	Cellulitis of oth sites
L03.315	Cellulitis of perineum
L03.111	Cellulitis of rt axilla
L03.115	Cellulitis of rt lwr limb
H05.011	Cellulitis of rt orbit
L03.113	Cellulitis of rt upr limb
L03.319	Cellulitis of trunk, unsp
L03.316	Cellulitis of umbilicus
H05.019	Cellulitis of unsp orbit
L03.119	Cellulitis of unsp part of limb
L03.90	Cellulitis, unsp
G37.1	Central demyelination of corpus callosum

S73.045A	Central disloc of lt hip, init enc
S73.044A	Central disloc of rt hip, init enc
S73.046A	Central disloc of unsp hip, init enc
G37.2	Central pontine myelinolysis
H34.13	Central retinal artery occlsn, bilat
H34.12	Central retinal artery occlsn, lt eye
H34.11	Central retinal artery occlsn, rt eye
H34.10	Central retinal artery occlsn, unsp eye
H34.813	Central retinal vein occlsn, bilat
H34.812	Central retinal vein occlsn, lt eye
H34.811	Central retinal vein occlsn, rt eye
H34.819	Central retinal vein occlsn, unsp eye
S73.042A	Central sublux of lt hip, init enc
S73.041A	Central sublux of rt hip, init enc
S73.043A	Central sublux of unsp hip, init enc
B65.3	Cercarial dermatitis
G32.81	Cerebellar ataxia in diseases classified elsw
G11.3	Cerebellar ataxia w/ defective DNA rpr
I68.2	Cerebral arteritis in oth diseases classified elsw
I67.7	Cerebral arteritis, NEC
I67.82	Cerebral ischemia
O22.51	Cerebral venous thrombosis in pregnancy, 1st trmstr
O22.52	Cerebral venous thrombosis in pregnancy, 2nd trmstr
O22.53	Cerebral venous thrombosis in pregnancy, 3rd trmstr
O22.50	Cerebral venous thrombosis in pregnancy, unsp trmstr
O87.3	Cerebral venous thrombosis in the puerperium
G96.0	Cerebrospinal fluid leak
G97.0	Cerebrospinal fluid leak from spinal punc
M50.03	Cervical disc d/o w/ myelopathy, cervicothoracic rgn
M50.01	Cervical disc d/o w/ myelopathy, high cervical rgn
M50.02	Cervical disc d/o w/ myelopathy, mid-cervical rgn
M50.00	Cervical disc d/o w/ myelopathy, unsp cervical rgn
O26.872	Cervical shortening, 2nd trmstr
O26.873	Cervical shortening, 3rd trmstr
O26.879	Cervical shortening, unsp trmstr
Q05.0	Cervical spina bifida w/ hydrocephalus
O86.11	Cervicitis following delivery
A42.2	Cervicofacial actinomycosis
B57.2	Chagas' disease (chr) w/ heart involvement
B57.5	Chagas' disease (chr) w/ oth organ involvement
B57.30	Chagas' disease w/ digestive sys involvement, unsp
B57.40	Chagas' disease w/ nervous sys involvement, unsp
A52.16	Charcot's arthropathy (tabetic)
E70.330	Chediak-Higashi synd
J95.4	Chemical pneumonitis d/t anesthesia
A92.0	Chikungunya virus disease
T74.02XA	Child neglect or abandonment, confirmed, init enc
T76.02XA	Child neglect or abandonment, suspected, init enc
T74.12XA	Child physical abuse, confirmed, init enc
T76.12XA	Child physical abuse, suspected, init enc
T74.32XA	Child psychological abuse, confirmed, init enc
T76.32XA	Child psychological abuse, suspected, init enc
T74.22XA	Child sexual abuse, confirmed, init enc
T76.22XA	Child sexual abuse, suspected, init enc
E71.520	Childhood cerebral X-linked adrenoleukodystrophy
A70	Chlamydia psittaci infections
K83.0	Cholangitis
Q44.4	Choledochal cyst
A00.0	Cholera d/t Vibrio cholerae 01, biovar cholerae
A00.1	Cholera d/t Vibrio cholerae 01, biovar eltor
A00.9	Cholera, unsp
H59.813	Chorioretinal scars after surgery for detach, bilat
H59.812	Chorioretinal scars after surgery for detach, lt eye
H59.811	Chorioretinal scars after surgery for detach, rt eye
H59.819	Chorioretinal scars after surgery for detach, unsp eye
H31.323	Choroidal rupture, bilat
H31.322	Choroidal rupture, lt eye
H31.321	Choroidal rupture, rt eye
H31.329	Choroidal rupture, unsp eye
J70.1	Chr & oth pulmn manifestations d/t radiation
I31.0	Chr adhesive pericarditis
I50.42	Chr combined systolic (congestive) & diastolic (congestive) heart failure
I31.1	Chr constrictive pericarditis

I50.32	Chr diastolic (congestive) heart failure
I82.A23	Chr embolism & thrombosis of axillary vein, bilat
I82.722	Chr embolism & thrombosis of deep veins of lt upr extr
I82.721	Chr embolism & thrombosis of deep veins of rt upr extr
I82.729	Chr embolism & thrombosis of deep veins of unsp upr extr
I82.723	Chr embolism & thrombosis of deep veins of upr extr, bilat
I82.513	Chr embolism & thrombosis of femoral vein, bilat
I82.523	Chr embolism & thrombosis of iliac vein, bilat
I82.C23	Chr embolism & thrombosis of int jugular vein, bilat
I82.A22	Chr embolism & thrombosis of lt axillary vein
I82.512	Chr embolism & thrombosis of lt femoral vein
I82.522	Chr embolism & thrombosis of lt iliac vein
I82.C22	Chr embolism & thrombosis of lt int jugular vein
I82.532	Chr embolism & thrombosis of lt popliteal vein
I82.B22	Chr embolism & thrombosis of lt subclavian vein
I82.542	Chr embolism & thrombosis of lt tibial vein
I82.592	Chr embolism & thrombosis of oth spec deep vein of lt lwr extr
I82.593	Chr embolism & thrombosis of oth spec deep vein of lwr extr, bilat
I82.591	Chr embolism & thrombosis of oth spec deep vein of rt lwr extr
I82.599	Chr embolism & thrombosis of oth spec deep vein of unsp lwr extr
I82.891	Chr embolism & thrombosis of oth spec veins
I82.291	Chr embolism & thrombosis of oth thoracic veins
I82.533	Chr embolism & thrombosis of popliteal vein, bilat
I82.A21	Chr embolism & thrombosis of rt axillary vein
I82.511	Chr embolism & thrombosis of rt femoral vein
I82.521	Chr embolism & thrombosis of rt iliac vein
I82.C21	Chr embolism & thrombosis of rt int jugular vein
I82.531	Chr embolism & thrombosis of rt popliteal vein
I82.B21	Chr embolism & thrombosis of rt subclavian vein
I82.541	Chr embolism & thrombosis of rt tibial vein
I82.B23	Chr embolism & thrombosis of subclavian vein, bilat
I82.712	Chr embolism & thrombosis of superf veins of lt upr extr
I82.711	Chr embolism & thrombosis of superf veins of rt upr extr
I82.719	Chr embolism & thrombosis of superf veins of unsp upr extr
I82.713	Chr embolism & thrombosis of superf veins of upr extr, bilat
I82.211	Chr embolism & thrombosis of superior vena cava
I82.543	Chr embolism & thrombosis of tibial vein, bilat
I82.A29	Chr embolism & thrombosis of unsp axillary vein
I82.5Z3	Chr embolism & thrombosis of unsp deep veins of distal lwr extr, bilat
I82.5Z2	Chr embolism & thrombosis of unsp deep veins of lt distal lwr extr
I82.502	Chr embolism & thrombosis of unsp deep veins of lt lwr extr
I82.5Y2	Chr embolism & thrombosis of unsp deep veins of lt proximal lwr extr
I82.503	Chr embolism & thrombosis of unsp deep veins of lwr extr, bilat
I82.5Y3	Chr embolism & thrombosis of unsp deep veins of proximal lwr extr, bilat
I82.5Z1	Chr embolism & thrombosis of unsp deep veins of rt distal lwr extr
I82.501	Chr embolism & thrombosis of unsp deep veins of rt lwr extr
I82.5Y1	Chr embolism & thrombosis of unsp deep veins of rt proximal lwr extr
I82.5Z9	Chr embolism & thrombosis of unsp deep veins of unsp distal lwr extr
I82.509	Chr embolism & thrombosis of unsp deep veins of unsp lwr extr
I82.5Y9	Chr embolism & thrombosis of unsp deep veins of unsp proximal lwr extr
I82.519	Chr embolism & thrombosis of unsp femoral vein
I82.529	Chr embolism & thrombosis of unsp iliac vein
I82.C29	Chr embolism & thrombosis of unsp int jugular vein
I82.539	Chr embolism & thrombosis of unsp popliteal vein
I82.B29	Chr embolism & thrombosis of unsp subclavian vein
I82.549	Chr embolism & thrombosis of unsp tibial vein
I82.91	Chr embolism & thrombosis of unsp vein
I82.702	Chr embolism & thrombosis of unsp veins of lt upr extr
I82.701	Chr embolism & thrombosis of unsp veins of rt upr extr
I82.709	Chr embolism & thrombosis of unsp veins of unsp upr extr
I82.703	Chr embolism & thrombosis of unsp veins of upr extr, bilat
D89.811	Chr graft-versus-host disease
G61.81	Chr inflam demyelinating polyneuritis
A06.1	Chr intestinal amebiasis
N18.4	Chr kidney disease, stage 4 (severe)
N18.5	Chr kidney disease, stage 5
C95.10	Chr leukemia of unsp cell type not having achieved remission
C95.12	Chr leukemia of unsp cell type, in relapse
C95.11	Chr leukemia of unsp cell type, in remission
C91.12	Chr lymphocytic leukemia of B-cell type in relapse
C91.11	Chr lymphocytic leukemia of B-cell type in remission
C91.10	Chr lymphocytic leukemia of B-cell type not having achieved remission
G03.1	Chr meningitis

M86.372	Chr multifocal osteomyelitis, lt ankle & foot
M86.352	Chr multifocal osteomyelitis, lt femur
M86.342	Chr multifocal osteomyelitis, lt hand
M86.322	Chr multifocal osteomyelitis, lt humerus
M86.332	Chr multifocal osteomyelitis, lt radius & ulna
M86.312	Chr multifocal osteomyelitis, lt shldr
M86.362	Chr multifocal osteomyelitis, lt tibia & fibula
M86.39	Chr multifocal osteomyelitis, multi sites
M86.38	Chr multifocal osteomyelitis, oth site
M86.371	Chr multifocal osteomyelitis, rt ankle & foot
M86.351	Chr multifocal osteomyelitis, rt femur
M86.341	Chr multifocal osteomyelitis, rt hand
M86.321	Chr multifocal osteomyelitis, rt humerus
M86.331	Chr multifocal osteomyelitis, rt radius & ulna
M86.311	Chr multifocal osteomyelitis, rt shldr
M86.361	Chr multifocal osteomyelitis, rt tibia & fibula
M86.379	Chr multifocal osteomyelitis, unsp ankle & foot
M86.359	Chr multifocal osteomyelitis, unsp femur
M86.349	Chr multifocal osteomyelitis, unsp hand
M86.329	Chr multifocal osteomyelitis, unsp humerus
M86.339	Chr multifocal osteomyelitis, unsp radius & ulna
M86.319	Chr multifocal osteomyelitis, unsp shldr
M86.30	Chr multifocal osteomyelitis, unsp site
M86.369	Chr multifocal osteomyelitis, unsp tibia & fibula
C92.12	Chr myeloid leukemia, BCR/ABL-positive, in relapse
C92.11	Chr myeloid leukemia, BCR/ABL-positive, in remission
C92.10	Chr myeloid leukemia, BCR/ABL-positive, not having achieved remission
C93.10	Chr myelomonocytic leukemia not having achieved remission
C93.12	Chr myelomonocytic leukemia, in relapse
C93.11	Chr myelomonocytic leukemia, in remission
D47.1	Chr myeloproliferative disease
N03.6	Chr nephritic synd w/ dense deposit disease
N03.7	Chr nephritic synd w/ diffuse crescentic glomerulonephritis
N03.4	Chr nephritic synd w/ diffuse endocapillary proliferative glomerulonephritis
N03.2	Chr nephritic synd w/ diffuse membranous glomerulonephritis
N03.3	Chr nephritic synd w/ diffuse mesangial proliferative glomerulonephritis
N03.5	Chr nephritic synd w/ diffuse mesangiocapillary glomerulonephritis
N03.1	Chr nephritic synd w/ focal & segmental glomerular lesions
N03.0	Chr nephritic synd w/ minor glomerular abnormality
N03.8	Chr nephritic synd w/ oth morphologic changes
N03.9	Chr nephritic synd w/ unsp morphologic changes
J44.1	Chr obstructive pulmn disease w/ (acute) exacerbation
J44.0	Chr obstructive pulmn disease w/ acute lwr respiratory infxn
N11.1	Chr obstructive pyelonephritis
M86.472	Chr osteomyelitis w/ draining sinus, lt ankle & foot
M86.452	Chr osteomyelitis w/ draining sinus, lt femur
M86.442	Chr osteomyelitis w/ draining sinus, lt hand
M86.422	Chr osteomyelitis w/ draining sinus, lt humerus
M86.432	Chr osteomyelitis w/ draining sinus, lt radius & ulna
M86.412	Chr osteomyelitis w/ draining sinus, lt shldr
M86.462	Chr osteomyelitis w/ draining sinus, lt tibia & fibula
M86.49	Chr osteomyelitis w/ draining sinus, multi sites
M86.48	Chr osteomyelitis w/ draining sinus, oth site
M86.471	Chr osteomyelitis w/ draining sinus, rt ankle & foot
M86.451	Chr osteomyelitis w/ draining sinus, rt femur
M86.441	Chr osteomyelitis w/ draining sinus, rt hand
M86.421	Chr osteomyelitis w/ draining sinus, rt humerus
M86.431	Chr osteomyelitis w/ draining sinus, rt radius & ulna
M86.411	Chr osteomyelitis w/ draining sinus, rt shldr
M86.461	Chr osteomyelitis w/ draining sinus, rt tibia & fibula
M86.479	Chr osteomyelitis w/ draining sinus, unsp ankle & foot
M86.459	Chr osteomyelitis w/ draining sinus, unsp femur
M86.449	Chr osteomyelitis w/ draining sinus, unsp hand
M86.429	Chr osteomyelitis w/ draining sinus, unsp humerus
M86.439	Chr osteomyelitis w/ draining sinus, unsp radius & ulna
M86.419	Chr osteomyelitis w/ draining sinus, unsp shldr
M86.40	Chr osteomyelitis w/ draining sinus, unsp site
M86.469	Chr osteomyelitis w/ draining sinus, unsp tibia & fibula
J93.81	Chr pneumothorax
B40.1	Chr pulmn blastomycosis
B38.1	Chr pulmn coccidioidomycosis
J81.1	Chr pulmn edema

I27.82	Chr pulmn embolism
J96.12	Chr respiratory failure w/ hypercapnia
J96.11	Chr respiratory failure w/ hypoxia
J96.10	Chr respiratory failure, unsp whether w/ hypoxia or hypercapnia
I09.2	Chr rheumatic pericarditis
I50.22	Chr systolic (congestive) heart failure
I70.92	Chr total occlsn of artery of the extremities
N11.9	Chr tubulo-interstitial nephritis, unsp
K55.1	Chr vascular d/o of intestine
I87.333	Chr venous hypertension (idiopathic) w/ ulcer & inflam of bilat lwr extr
I87.332	Chr venous hypertension (idiopathic) w/ ulcer & inflam of lt lwr extr
I87.331	Chr venous hypertension (idiopathic) w/ ulcer & inflam of rt lwr extr
I87.339	Chr venous hypertension (idiopathic) w/ ulcer & inflam of unsp lwr extr
I87.313	Chr venous hypertension (idiopathic) w/ ulcer of bilat lwr extr
I87.312	Chr venous hypertension (idiopathic) w/ ulcer of lt lwr extr
I87.311	Chr venous hypertension (idiopathic) w/ ulcer of rt lwr extr
I87.319	Chr venous hypertension (idiopathic) w/ ulcer of unsp lwr extr
B18.0	Chr viral hepatitis B w/ delta-agent
B18.1	Chr viral hepatitis B w/o delta-agent
B18.9	Chr viral hepatitis, unsp
J94.0	Chylous effusion
R82.0	Chyluria
E72.23	Citrullinemia
E70.0	Classical phenylketonuria
Q64.12	Cloacal extrophy of urinary bladder
B66.1	Clonorchiasis
A50.51	Clutton's joints
D68.9	Coagulation defect, unsp
Q25.1	Coarctation of aorta
F14.150	Cocaine abuse w/ cocaine-induced psychotic d/o w/ delusions
F14.151	Cocaine abuse w/ cocaine-induced psychotic d/o w/ hallucinations
F14.121	Cocaine abuse w/ intoxication w/ delirium
F14.280	Cocaine dependence w/ cocaine-induced anxiety d/o
F14.250	Cocaine dependence w/ cocaine-induced psychotic d/o w/ delusions
F14.251	Cocaine dependence w/ cocaine-induced psychotic d/o w/ hallucinations
F14.259	Cocaine dependence w/ cocaine-induced psychotic d/o, unsp
F14.281	Cocaine dependence w/ cocaine-induced sexual dysfunction
F14.282	Cocaine dependence w/ cocaine-induced sleep d/o
F14.221	Cocaine dependence w/ intoxication delirium
F14.222	Cocaine dependence w/ intoxication w/ perceptual disturbance
F14.229	Cocaine dependence w/ intoxication, unsp
F14.288	Cocaine dependence w/ oth cocaine-induced d/o
F14.23	Cocaine dependence w/ withdrawal
F14.20	Cocaine dependence, uncomplicated
F14.950	Cocaine use, unsp w/ cocaine-induced psychotic d/o w/ delusions
F14.951	Cocaine use, unsp w/ cocaine-induced psychotic d/o w/ hallucinations
F14.921	Cocaine use, unsp w/ intoxication delirium
B38.9	Coccidioidomycosis, unsp
M48.52XA	Collapsed vertebra, NEC, cervical rgn, init enc for fx
M48.53XA	Collapsed vertebra, NEC, cervicothoracic rgn, init enc for fx
M48.56XA	Collapsed vertebra, NEC, lumbar rgn, init enc for fx
M48.57XA	Collapsed vertebra, NEC, lumbosacral rgn, init enc for fx
M48.51XA	Collapsed vertebra, NEC, occipito-atlanto-axial rgn, init enc for fx
M48.58XA	Collapsed vertebra, NEC, sacral & sacrococcygeal rgn, init enc for fx
M48.50XA	Collapsed vertebra, NEC, site unsp, init enc for fx
M48.54XA	Collapsed vertebra, NEC, thoracic rgn, init enc for fx
M48.55XA	Collapsed vertebra, NEC, thoracolumbar rgn, init enc for fx
S52.532A	Colles' fx of lt radius, init enc for clsd fx
S52.532P	Colles' fx of lt radius, subsq enc for clsd fx w/ malu
S52.532K	Colles' fx of lt radius, subsq enc for clsd fx w/ nonu
S52.532Q	Colles' fx of lt radius, subsq enc for opn fx type I or II w/ malu
S52.532M	Colles' fx of lt radius, subsq enc for opn fx type I or II w/ nonu
S52.532R	Colles' fx of lt radius, subsq enc for opn fx type IIIA, IIIB, or IIIC w/ malu
S52.532N	Colles' fx of lt radius, subsq enc for opn fx type IIIA, IIIB, or IIIC w/ nonu
S52.531A	Colles' fx of rt radius, init enc for clsd fx
S52.531P	Colles' fx of rt radius, subsq enc for clsd fx w/ malu
S52.531K	Colles' fx of rt radius, subsq enc for clsd fx w/ nonu
S52.531Q	Colles' fx of rt radius, subsq enc for opn fx type I or II w/ malu
S52.531M	Colles' fx of rt radius, subsq enc for opn fx type I or II w/ nonu
S52.531R	Colles' fx of rt radius, subsq enc for opn fx type IIIA, IIIB, or IIIC w/ malu
S52.531N	Colles' fx of rt radius, subsq enc for opn fx type IIIA, IIIB, or IIIC w/ nonu
S52.539A	Colles' fx of unsp radius, init enc for clsd fx

S52.539P	Colles' fx of unsp radius, subsq enc for clsd fx w/ malu
S52.539K	Colles' fx of unsp radius, subsq enc for clsd fx w/ nonu
S52.539Q	Colles' fx of unsp radius, subsq enc for opn fx type I or II w/ malu
S52.539M	Colles' fx of unsp radius, subsq enc for opn fx type I or II w/ nonu
S52.539R	Colles' fx of unsp radius, subsq enc for opn fx type IIIA, IIIB, or IIIC w/ malu
S52.539N	Colles' fx of unsp radius, subsq enc for opn fx type IIIA, IIIB, or IIIC w/ nonu
A93.2	Colorado tick fever
K94.01	Colostomy hemor
K94.02	Colostomy infxn
K94.03	Colostomy malfunction
D81.9	Combined immunodeficiency, unsp
D83.2	Common variable immunodeficiency w/ autoantibodies to B- or T-cells
D83.0	Common variable immunodeficiency w/ predominant abnormalities of B-cell numbers & function
D83.1	Common variable immunodeficiency w/ predominant immunoregulatory T-cell d/o
D83.9	Common variable immunodeficiency, unsp
G91.0	Communicating hydrocephalus
N98.9	Comp associated w/ artfcl fertilization, unsp
N98.3	Comp of attempted introduction of embryo in embryo transfer
N98.2	Comp of attempted introduction of fertilized ovum following in vitro fertilization
T81.710A	Comp of mesenteric artery following a procedure, NEC, init enc
T81.718A	Comp of oth artery following a procedure, NEC, init enc
T87.2	Comp of oth reattached body part
T87.1X2	Comp of reattached (part of) lt lwr extr
T87.0X2	Comp of reattached (part of) lt upr extr
T87.1X1	Comp of reattached (part of) rt lwr extr
T87.0X1	Comp of reattached (part of) rt upr extr
T87.1X9	Comp of reattached (part of) unsp lwr extr
T87.0X9	Comp of reattached (part of) unsp upr extr
T81.711A	Comp of renal artery following a procedure, NEC, init enc
T86.5	Comp of stem cell transplant
T81.719A	Comp of unsp artery following a procedure, NEC, init enc
T81.72XA	Comp of vein following a procedure, NEC, init enc
T79.A0XA	Compartment synd, unsp, init enc
O03.89	Complete or unsp spontaneous abortion w/ oth comp
S58.012A	Complete traum amp at elbow lvl, lt arm, init enc
S58.011A	Complete traum amp at elbow lvl, rt arm, init enc
S58.019A	Complete traum amp at elbow lvl, unsp arm, init enc
S88.012A	Complete traum amp at knee lvl, lt lwr leg, init enc
S88.011A	Complete traum amp at knee lvl, rt lwr leg, init enc
S88.019A	Complete traum amp at knee lvl, unsp lwr leg, init enc
S78.012A	Complete traum amp at lt hip jt, init enc
S48.012A	Complete traum amp at lt shldr jt, init enc
S58.112A	Complete traum amp at lvl between elbow & wrist, lt arm, init enc
S58.111A	Complete traum amp at lvl between elbow & wrist, rt arm, init enc
S58.119A	Complete traum amp at lvl between elbow & wrist, unsp arm, init enc
S88.112A	Complete traum amp at lvl between knee & ankle, lt lwr leg, init enc
S88.111A	Complete traum amp at lvl between knee & ankle, rt lwr leg, init enc
S88.119A	Complete traum amp at lvl between knee & ankle, unsp lwr leg, init enc
S78.112A	Complete traum amp at lvl between lt hip & knee, init enc
S48.112A	Complete traum amp at lvl between lt shldr & elbow, init enc
S78.111A	Complete traum amp at lvl between rt hip & knee, init enc
S48.111A	Complete traum amp at lvl between rt shldr & elbow, init enc
S78.119A	Complete traum amp at lvl between unsp hip & knee, init enc
S48.119A	Complete traum amp at lvl between unsp shldr & elbow, init enc
S78.011A	Complete traum amp at rt hip jt, init enc
S48.011A	Complete traum amp at rt shldr jt, init enc
S78.019A	Complete traum amp at unsp hip jt, init enc
S48.019A	Complete traum amp at unsp shldr jt, init enc
S98.012A	Complete traum amp of lt foot at ankle lvl, init enc
S98.912A	Complete traum amp of lt foot, lvl unsp, init enc
S58.912A	Complete traum amp of lt forearm, lvl unsp, init enc
S68.412A	Complete traum amp of lt hand at wrist lvl, init enc
S78.912A	Complete traum amp of lt hip & thigh, lvl unsp, init enc
S88.912A	Complete traum amp of lt lwr leg, lvl unsp, init enc
S98.312A	Complete traum amp of lt midfoot, init enc
S48.912A	Complete traum amp of lt shldr & upr arm, lvl unsp, init enc
S98.011A	Complete traum amp of rt foot at ankle lvl, init enc
S98.911A	Complete traum amp of rt foot, lvl unsp, init enc
S58.911A	Complete traum amp of rt forearm, lvl unsp, init enc
S68.411A	Complete traum amp of rt hand at wrist lvl, init enc
S78.911A	Complete traum amp of rt hip & thigh, lvl unsp, init enc

S88.911A	Complete traum amp of rt lwr leg, lvl unsp, init enc
S98.311A	Complete traum amp of rt midfoot, init enc
S48.911A	Complete traum amp of rt shldr & upr arm, lvl unsp, init enc
S98.019A	Complete traum amp of unsp foot at ankle lvl, init enc
S98.919A	Complete traum amp of unsp foot, lvl unsp, init enc
S58.919A	Complete traum amp of unsp forearm, lvl unsp, init enc
S68.419A	Complete traum amp of unsp hand at wrist lvl, init enc
S78.919A	Complete traum amp of unsp hip & thigh, lvl unsp, init enc
S88.919A	Complete traum amp of unsp lwr leg, lvl unsp, init enc
S98.319A	Complete traum amp of unsp midfoot, init enc
S48.919A	Complete traum amp of unsp shldr & upr arm, lvl unsp, init enc
S68.712A	Complete traum transmetacarpal amp of lt hand, init enc
S68.711A	Complete traum transmetacarpal amp of rt hand, init enc
S68.719A	Complete traum transmetacarpal amp of unsp hand, init enc
R56.01	Complex febrile convulsions
G90.522	Complex regional pain synd I of lt lwr limb
G90.512	Complex regional pain synd I of lt upr limb
G90.523	Complex regional pain synd I of lwr limb, bilat
G90.59	Complex regional pain synd I of oth spec site
G90.521	Complex regional pain synd I of rt lwr limb
G90.511	Complex regional pain synd I of rt upr limb
G90.529	Complex regional pain synd I of unsp lwr limb
G90.519	Complex regional pain synd I of unsp upr limb
G90.513	Complex regional pain synd I of upr limb, bilat
G90.50	Complex regional pain synd I, unsp
I87.1	Compression of vein
G37.5	Concentric sclerosis [Balo] of central nervous sys
S06.0X5A	Concussion w/ loss of cnscness > 24 hrs w/ return to pre-existing conscious lvl, init enc
S06.0X3A	Concussion w/ loss of cnscness of 1 hr to 5 hrs 59 mins, init enc
S06.0X1A	Concussion w/ loss of cnscness of 30 mins or less, init enc
S06.0X2A	Concussion w/ loss of cnscness of 31 mins to 59 mins, init enc
S06.0X4A	Concussion w/ loss of cnscness of 6 hrs to 24 hrs, init enc
S06.0X7A	Concussion w/ loss of cnscness of any dur w/ death d/t brain inj prior to regain cnscness, init enc
S06.0X8A	Concussion w/ loss of cnscness of any dur w/ death d/t oth cause prior to regain cnscness, init enc
S06.0X9A	Concussion w/ loss of cnscness of unsp dur, init enc
A51.31	Condyloma latum
D69.42	Congenital & hereditary thrombocytopenia purpura
Q42.2	Congenital absence, atresia & stenosis of anus w/ fistula
Q42.3	Congenital absence, atresia & stenosis of anus w/o fistula
Q41.0	Congenital absence, atresia & stenosis of duodenum
Q41.2	Congenital absence, atresia & stenosis of ileum
Q41.1	Congenital absence, atresia & stenosis of jejunum
Q42.9	Congenital absence, atresia & stenosis of lg intestine, part unsp
Q42.8	Congenital absence, atresia & stenosis of oth parts of lg intestine
Q41.8	Congenital absence, atresia & stenosis of oth spec parts of sm intestine
Q42.0	Congenital absence, atresia & stenosis of rectum w/ fistula
Q42.1	Congenital absence, atresia & stenosis of rectum w/o fistula
Q41.9	Congenital absence, atresia & stenosis of sm intestine, part unsp
P61.3	Congenital anemia from fetal blood loss
Q64.31	Congenital bladder neck obstruction
Q33.4	Congenital bronchiectasis
Q32.2	Congenital bronchomalacia
Q04.6	Congenital cerebral cysts
Q33.0	Congenital cystic lung
Q68.1	Congenital deformity of finger(s) & hand
Q67.5	Congenital deformity of spine
Q39.5	Congenital dilatation of esophagus
Q39.6	Congenital diverticulum of esophagus
Q43.6	Congenital fistula of rectum & anus
Q62.0	Congenital hydronephrosis
Q23.1	Congenital insufficiency of aortic valve
Q31.5	Congenital laryngomalacia
Q76.426	Congenital lordosis, lumbar rgn
Q76.427	Congenital lordosis, lumbosacral rgn
Q76.428	Congenital lordosis, sacral & sacrococcygeal rgn
Q76.425	Congenital lordosis, thoracolumbar rgn
Q76.429	Congenital lordosis, unsp rgn
Q76.9	Congenital malformation of bony thorax, unsp
Q28.9	Congenital malformation of circulatory sys, unsp
Q39.9	Congenital malformation of esophagus, unsp
Q25.9	Congenital malformation of great arteries, unsp

Q26.9	Congenital malformation of great vein, unsp
Q43.9	Congenital malformation of intestine, unsp
Q31.9	Congenital malformation of larynx, unsp
Q76.7	Congenital malformation of sternum
Q87.3	Congenital malformation syndromes involving early overgrowth
Q87.1	Congenital malformation syndromes predominantly associated w/ short stature
Q87.2	Congenital malformation syndromes predominantly involving limbs
Q43.3	Congenital malformations of intestinal fix
Q89.09	Congenital malformations of spleen
Q62.2	Congenital megaureter
D74.0	Congenital methemoglobinemia
Q23.3	Congenital mitral insufficiency
Q23.2	Congenital mitral stenosis
Q61.02	Congenital multi renal cysts
G71.2	Congenital myopathies
G11.0	Congenital nonprogressive ataxia
Q62.10	Congenital occlsn of ureter, unsp
Q62.11	Congenital occlsn of ureteropelvic junction
Q62.12	Congenital occlsn of ureterovesical orifice
Q45.2	Congenital pancreatic cyst
Q27.4	Congenital phlebectasia
Q64.2	Congenital post urethral valves
Q22.2	Congenital pulmn valve insufficiency
Q22.1	Congenital pulmn valve stenosis
Q61.00	Congenital renal cyst, unsp
P35.0	Congenital rubella synd
Q76.3	Congenital scoliosis d/t congenital bony malformation
Q61.01	Congenital single renal cyst
Q23.0	Congenital stenosis of aortic valve
Q32.3	Congenital stenosis of bronchus
Q26.0	Congenital stenosis of vena cava
Q64.32	Congenital stricture of urethra
Q64.33	Congenital stricture of urinary meatus
Q31.1	Congenital subglottic stenosis
Q32.0	Congenital tracheomalacia
Q62.31	Congenital ureterocele, orthotopic
D61.01	Constitutional (pure) red blood cell aplasia
S37.812A	Contsn of adrenal gland, init enc
S36.520A	Contsn of ascending [rt] colon, init enc
S37.22XA	Contsn of bladder, init enc
S36.221A	Contsn of body of pancreas, init enc
S36.522A	Contsn of descending [lt] colon, init enc
S27.802A	Contsn of diaphragm, init enc
S36.420A	Contsn of duodenum, init enc
S36.122A	Contsn of gallbladder, init enc
S36.220A	Contsn of head of pancreas, init enc
S26.01XA	Contsn of heart w/ hemopericardium, init enc
S26.11XA	Contsn of heart w/o hemopericardium, init enc
S26.91XA	Contsn of heart, unsp w/ or w/o hemopericardium, init enc
S36.112A	Contsn of liver, init enc
S27.322A	Contsn of lung, bilat, init enc
S27.321A	Contsn of lung, unilat, init enc
S27.329A	Contsn of lung, unsp, init enc
S36.892A	Contsn of oth intra-abd organs, init enc
S36.528A	Contsn of oth part of colon, init enc
S36.428A	Contsn of oth part of sm intestine, init enc
S27.892A	Contsn of oth spec intrathoracic organs, init enc
S37.892A	Contsn of oth urinary & pelvic organ, init enc
S36.62XA	Contsn of rectum, init enc
S36.523A	Contsn of sigmoid colon, init enc
S36.32XA	Contsn of stomach, init enc
S36.222A	Contsn of tail of pancreas, init enc
S27.52XA	Contsn of thoracic trachea, init enc
S36.521A	Contsn of transv colon, init enc
S36.92XA	Contsn of unsp intra-abd organ, init enc
S36.529A	Contsn of unsp part of colon, init enc
S36.229A	Contsn of unsp part of pancreas, init enc
S36.429A	Contsn of unsp part of sm intestine, init enc
S37.92XA	Contsn of unsp urinary & pelvic organ, init enc
S37.12XA	Contsn of ureter, init enc
S37.32XA	Contsn of urethra, init enc
S37.62XA	Contsn of uterus, init enc

S06.385A	Contsn, lac, & hemor of brainstem w/ loss of cnscness > 24 hrs w/ return to pre-existing conscious lvl, init enc
S06.383A	Contsn, lac, & hemor of brainstem w/ loss of cnscness of 1 hr to 5 hrs 59 mins, init enc
S06.381A	Contsn, lac, & hemor of brainstem w/ loss of cnscness of 30 mins or less, init enc
S06.382A	Contsn, lac, & hemor of brainstem w/ loss of cnscness of 31 mins to 59 mins, init enc
S06.384A	Contsn, lac, & hemor of brainstem w/ loss of cnscness of 6 hrs to 24 hrs, init enc
S06.389A	Contsn, lac, & hemor of brainstem w/ loss of cnscness of unsp dur, init enc
S06.375A	Contsn, lac, & hemor of cerebellum w/ loss of cnscness > 24 hrs w/ return to pre-existing conscious lvl, init enc
S06.373A	Contsn, lac, & hemor of cerebellum w/ loss of cnscness of 1 hr to 5 hrs 59 mins, init enc
S06.371A	Contsn, lac, & hemor of cerebellum w/ loss of cnscness of 30 mins or less, init enc
S06.372A	Contsn, lac, & hemor of cerebellum w/ loss of cnscness of 31 mins to 59 mins, init enc
S06.374A	Contsn, lac, & hemor of cerebellum w/ loss of cnscness of 6 hrs to 24 hrs, init enc
S06.379A	Contsn, lac, & hemor of cerebellum w/ loss of cnscness of unsp dur, init enc
G95.81	Conus medullaris synd
E74.03	Cori disease
T86.841	Corneal transplant failure
T86.842	Corneal transplant infxn
T86.840	Corneal transplant rejection
T27.5XXA	Corrosion involving larynx & trachea w/ lung, init enc
T23.769A	Corrosion of 3rd degree back of unsp hand, init enc
T21.72XA	Corrosion of 3rd degree of abd wall, init enc
T23.762A	Corrosion of 3rd degree of back of lt hand, init enc
T23.761A	Corrosion of 3rd degree of back of rt hand, init enc
T21.75XA	Corrosion of 3rd degree of buttock, init enc
T21.71XA	Corrosion of 3rd degree of chest wall, init enc
T20.73XA	Corrosion of 3rd degree of chin, init enc
T21.77XA	Corrosion of 3rd degree of female genital rgn, init enc
T20.76XA	Corrosion of 3rd degree of forehead & cheek, init enc
T20.70XA	Corrosion of 3rd degree of head, face, & neck, unsp site, init enc
T20.72XA	Corrosion of 3rd degree of lip(s), init enc
T25.712A	Corrosion of 3rd degree of lt ankle, init enc
T22.742A	Corrosion of 3rd degree of lt axilla, init enc
T20.712A	Corrosion of 3rd degree of lt ear [any part, except ear drum], init enc
T22.722A	Corrosion of 3rd degree of lt elbow, init enc
T25.722A	Corrosion of 3rd degree of lt foot, init enc
T22.712A	Corrosion of 3rd degree of lt forearm, init enc
T23.702A	Corrosion of 3rd degree of lt hand, unsp site, init enc
T24.722A	Corrosion of 3rd degree of lt knee, init enc
T24.732A	Corrosion of 3rd degree of lt lwr leg, init enc
T23.752A	Corrosion of 3rd degree of lt palm, init enc
T22.762A	Corrosion of 3rd degree of lt scapular rgn, init enc
T22.752A	Corrosion of 3rd degree of lt shldr, init enc
T24.712A	Corrosion of 3rd degree of lt thigh, init enc
T23.712A	Corrosion of 3rd degree of lt thumb (nail), init enc
T25.732A	Corrosion of 3rd degree of lt toe(s) (nail), init enc
T22.732A	Corrosion of 3rd degree of lt upr arm, init enc
T23.772A	Corrosion of 3rd degree of lt wrist, init enc
T21.74XA	Corrosion of 3rd degree of lwr back, init enc
T21.76XA	Corrosion of 3rd degree of male genital rgn, init enc
T23.742A	Corrosion of 3rd degree of multi lt fingers (nail), incl thumb, init enc
T23.732A	Corrosion of 3rd degree of multi lt fingers (nail), not incl thumb, init enc
T23.741A	Corrosion of 3rd degree of multi rt fingers (nail), incl thumb, init enc
T23.731A	Corrosion of 3rd degree of multi rt fingers (nail), not incl thumb, init enc
T20.79XA	Corrosion of 3rd degree of multi sites of head, face, & neck, init enc
T25.792A	Corrosion of 3rd degree of multi sites of lt ankle & foot, init enc
T24.792A	Corrosion of 3rd degree of multi sites of lt lwr limb, except ankle & foot, init enc
T22.792A	Corrosion of 3rd degree of multi sites of lt shldr & upr limb, except wrist & hand, init enc
T23.792A	Corrosion of 3rd degree of multi sites of lt wrist & hand, init enc
T25.791A	Corrosion of 3rd degree of multi sites of rt ankle & foot, init enc
T24.791A	Corrosion of 3rd degree of multi sites of rt lwr limb, except ankle & foot, init enc
T22.791A	Corrosion of 3rd degree of multi sites of rt shldr & upr limb, except wrist & hand, init enc
T23.791A	Corrosion of 3rd degree of multi sites of rt wrist & hand, init enc
T25.799A	Corrosion of 3rd degree of multi sites of unsp ankle & foot, init enc
T24.799A	Corrosion of 3rd degree of multi sites of unsp lwr limb, except ankle & foot, init enc
T22.799A	Corrosion of 3rd degree of multi sites of unsp shldr & upr limb, except wrist & hand, init enc
T23.799A	Corrosion of 3rd degree of multi sites of unsp wrist & hand, init enc
T20.77XA	Corrosion of 3rd degree of neck, init enc
T20.74XA	Corrosion of 3rd degree of nose (septum), init enc
T21.79XA	Corrosion of 3rd degree of oth site of trunk, init enc
T25.711A	Corrosion of 3rd degree of rt ankle, init enc
T22.741A	Corrosion of 3rd degree of rt axilla, init enc
T20.711A	Corrosion of 3rd degree of rt ear [any part, except ear drum], init enc
T22.721A	Corrosion of 3rd degree of rt elbow, init enc
T25.721A	Corrosion of 3rd degree of rt foot, init enc
T22.711A	Corrosion of 3rd degree of rt forearm, init enc
T23.701A	Corrosion of 3rd degree of rt hand, unsp site, init enc
T24.721A	Corrosion of 3rd degree of rt knee, init enc
T24.731A	Corrosion of 3rd degree of rt lwr leg, init enc
T23.751A	Corrosion of 3rd degree of rt palm, init enc
T22.761A	Corrosion of 3rd degree of rt scapular rgn, init enc
T22.751A	Corrosion of 3rd degree of rt shldr, init enc
T24.711A	Corrosion of 3rd degree of rt thigh, init enc
T23.711A	Corrosion of 3rd degree of rt thumb (nail), init enc
T25.731A	Corrosion of 3rd degree of rt toe(s) (nail), init enc
T22.731A	Corrosion of 3rd degree of rt upr arm, init enc
T23.771A	Corrosion of 3rd degree of rt wrist, init enc
T20.75XA	Corrosion of 3rd degree of scalp [any part], init enc
T22.70XA	Corrosion of 3rd degree of shldr & upr limb, except wrist & hand, unsp site, init enc
T23.722A	Corrosion of 3rd degree of single lt finger (nail) except thumb, init enc
T23.721A	Corrosion of 3rd degree of single rt finger (nail) except thumb, init enc
T21.70XA	Corrosion of 3rd degree of trunk, unsp site, init enc
T25.719A	Corrosion of 3rd degree of unsp ankle, init enc
T22.749A	Corrosion of 3rd degree of unsp axilla, init enc
T20.719A	Corrosion of 3rd degree of unsp ear [any part, except ear drum], init enc
T22.729A	Corrosion of 3rd degree of unsp elbow, init enc
T25.729A	Corrosion of 3rd degree of unsp foot, init enc
T22.719A	Corrosion of 3rd degree of unsp forearm, init enc
T23.709A	Corrosion of 3rd degree of unsp hand, unsp site, init enc
T24.729A	Corrosion of 3rd degree of unsp knee, init enc
T24.739A	Corrosion of 3rd degree of unsp lwr leg, init enc
T23.749A	Corrosion of 3rd degree of unsp multi fingers (nail), incl thumb, init enc
T23.739A	Corrosion of 3rd degree of unsp multi fingers (nail), not incl thumb, init enc
T23.759A	Corrosion of 3rd degree of unsp palm, init enc
T22.769A	Corrosion of 3rd degree of unsp scapular rgn, init enc
T22.759A	Corrosion of 3rd degree of unsp shldr, init enc
T23.729A	Corrosion of 3rd degree of unsp single finger (nail) except thumb, init enc
T24.702A	Corrosion of 3rd degree of unsp site of lt lwr limb, except ankle & foot, init enc
T24.701A	Corrosion of 3rd degree of unsp site of rt lwr limb, except ankle & foot, init enc
T24.709A	Corrosion of 3rd degree of unsp site of unsp lwr limb, except ankle & foot, init enc
T24.719A	Corrosion of 3rd degree of unsp thigh, init enc
T23.719A	Corrosion of 3rd degree of unsp thumb (nail), init enc
T25.739A	Corrosion of 3rd degree of unsp toe(s) (nail), init enc
T22.739A	Corrosion of 3rd degree of unsp upr arm, init enc
T23.779A	Corrosion of 3rd degree of unsp wrist, init enc
T21.73XA	Corrosion of 3rd degree of upr back, init enc
T28.6XXA	Corrosion of esophagus, init enc
T27.4XXA	Corrosion of larynx & trachea, init enc
T28.7XXA	Corrosion of oth parts of alimentary tract, init enc
T27.6XXA	Corrosion of oth parts of respiratory tract, init enc
T27.7XXA	Corrosion of respiratory tract, part unsp, init enc
T26.72XA	Corrosion w/ resulting rupture & destr of lt eyeball, init enc
T26.71XA	Corrosion w/ resulting rupture & destr of rt eyeball, init enc
T26.70XA	Corrosion w/ resulting rupture & destr of unsp eyeball, init enc
T32.10	Corrosions involving 10-19% of body surface w/ 0% to 9% 3rd degree corrosion

T32.11	Corrosions involving 10-19% of body surface w/ 10-19% 3rd degree corrosion	**L02.214**	Cutaneous abscess of groin
T32.20	Corrosions involving 20-29% of body surface w/ 0% to 9% 3rd degree corrosion	**L02.811**	Cutaneous abscess of head [any part, except face]
		L02.419	Cutaneous abscess of limb, unsp
T32.30	Corrosions involving 30-39% of body surface w/ 0% to 9% 3rd degree corrosion	**L02.412**	Cutaneous abscess of lt axilla
		L02.612	Cutaneous abscess of lt foot
T32.40	Corrosions involving 40-49% of body surface w/ 0% to 9% 3rd degree corrosion	**L02.512**	Cutaneous abscess of lt hand
		L02.416	Cutaneous abscess of lt lwr limb
T32.50	Corrosions involving 50-59% of body surface w/ 0% to 9% 3rd degree corrosion	**L02.414**	Cutaneous abscess of lt upr limb
		L02.11	Cutaneous abscess of neck
T32.60	Corrosions involving 60-69% of body surface w/ 0% to 9% 3rd degree corrosion	**L02.818**	Cutaneous abscess of oth sites
		L02.215	Cutaneous abscess of perineum
T32.70	Corrosions involving 70-79% of body surface w/ 0% to 9% 3rd degree corrosion	**L02.411**	Cutaneous abscess of rt axilla
		L02.611	Cutaneous abscess of rt foot
T32.80	Corrosions involving 80-89% of body surface w/ 0% to 9% 3rd degree corrosion	**L02.511**	Cutaneous abscess of rt hand
		L02.415	Cutaneous abscess of rt lwr limb
T32.90	Corrosions involving 90% or more of body surface w/ 0% to 9% 3rd degree corrosion	**L02.413**	Cutaneous abscess of rt upr limb
		L02.219	Cutaneous abscess of trunk, unsp
		L02.216	Cutaneous abscess of umbilicus
P71.0	Cow's milk hypocalcemia in newborn	**L02.619**	Cutaneous abscess of unsp foot
A81.00	Creutzfeldt-Jakob disease, unsp	**L02.519**	Cutaneous abscess of unsp hand
A98.0	Crimean-Congo hemorrhagic fever	**L02.91**	Cutaneous abscess, unsp
G72.81	Critical illness myopathy	**A22.0**	Cutaneous anthrax
G62.81	Critical illness polyneuropathy	**B40.3**	Cutaneous blastomycosis
K50.814	Crohn's disease of both sm & lg intestine w/ abscess	**B38.3**	Cutaneous coccidioidomycosis
K50.813	Crohn's disease of both sm & lg intestine w/ fistula	**B45.2**	Cutaneous cryptococcosis
K50.812	Crohn's disease of both sm & lg intestine w/ intestinal obstruction	**A36.3**	Cutaneous diphtheria
K50.818	Crohn's disease of both sm & lg intestine w/ oth comp	**C82.69**	Cutaneous follicle center lymphoma, extranodal & solid organ sites
K50.811	Crohn's disease of both sm & lg intestine w/ rectal bleeding	**C82.63**	Cutaneous follicle center lymphoma, intra-abd lymph nodes
K50.819	Crohn's disease of both sm & lg intestine w/ unsp comp	**C82.66**	Cutaneous follicle center lymphoma, intrapelvic lymph nodes
K50.80	Crohn's disease of both sm & lg intestine w/o comp	**C82.62**	Cutaneous follicle center lymphoma, intrathoracic lymph nodes
K50.114	Crohn's disease of lg intestine w/ abscess	**C82.64**	Cutaneous follicle center lymphoma, lymph nodes of axilla & upr limb
K50.113	Crohn's disease of lg intestine w/ fistula	**C82.61**	Cutaneous follicle center lymphoma, lymph nodes of head, face, & neck
K50.112	Crohn's disease of lg intestine w/ intestinal obstruction	**C82.65**	Cutaneous follicle center lymphoma, lymph nodes of inguinal rgn & lwr limb
K50.118	Crohn's disease of lg intestine w/ oth comp		
K50.111	Crohn's disease of lg intestine w/ rectal bleeding	**C82.68**	Cutaneous follicle center lymphoma, lymph nodes of multi sites
K50.119	Crohn's disease of lg intestine w/ unsp comp	**C82.67**	Cutaneous follicle center lymphoma, spleen
K50.10	Crohn's disease of lg intestine w/o comp	**C82.60**	Cutaneous follicle center lymphoma, unsp site
K50.014	Crohn's disease of sm intestine w/ abscess	**B55.1**	Cutaneous leishmaniasis
K50.013	Crohn's disease of sm intestine w/ fistula	**A32.0**	Cutaneous listeriosis
K50.012	Crohn's disease of sm intestine w/ intestinal obstruction	**A31.1**	Cutaneous mycobacterial infxn
K50.018	Crohn's disease of sm intestine w/ oth comp	**A43.1**	Cutaneous nocardiosis
K50.011	Crohn's disease of sm intestine w/ rectal bleeding	**C84.A1**	Cutaneous T-cell lymphoma, unsp lymph nodes of head, face, & neck
K50.019	Crohn's disease of sm intestine w/ unsp comp	**C84.A9**	Cutaneous T-cell lymphoma, unsp, extranodal & solid organ sites
K50.00	Crohn's disease of sm intestine w/o comp	**C84.A3**	Cutaneous T-cell lymphoma, unsp, intra-abd lymph nodes
K50.914	Crohn's disease, unsp, w/ abscess	**C84.A6**	Cutaneous T-cell lymphoma, unsp, intrapelvic lymph nodes
K50.913	Crohn's disease, unsp, w/ fistula	**C84.A2**	Cutaneous T-cell lymphoma, unsp, intrathoracic lymph nodes
K50.912	Crohn's disease, unsp, w/ intestinal obstruction	**C84.A4**	Cutaneous T-cell lymphoma, unsp, lymph nodes of axilla & upr limb
K50.918	Crohn's disease, unsp, w/ oth comp	**C84.A5**	Cutaneous T-cell lymphoma, unsp, lymph nodes of inguinal rgn & lwr limb
K50.911	Crohn's disease, unsp, w/ rectal bleeding		
K50.919	Crohn's disease, unsp, w/ unsp comp	**C84.A8**	Cutaneous T-cell lymphoma, unsp, lymph nodes of multi sites
K50.90	Crohn's disease, unsp, w/o comp	**C84.A7**	Cutaneous T-cell lymphoma, unsp, spleen
S07.0XXA	Crushing inj of face, init enc	**C84.A0**	Cutaneous T-cell lymphoma, unsp, unsp site
S07.9XXA	Crushing inj of head, part unsp, init enc	**P28.2**	Cyanotic attacks of newborn
S17.0XXA	Crushing inj of larynx & trachea, init enc	**A07.4**	Cyclosporiasis
S77.02XA	Crushing inj of lt hip, init enc	**K86.2**	Cyst of pancreas
S77.12XA	Crushing inj of lt thigh, init enc	**Q61.11**	Cystic dilatation of collecting ducts
S17.9XXA	Crushing inj of neck, part unsp, init enc	**Q44.6**	Cystic disease of liver
S07.8XXA	Crushing inj of oth parts of head, init enc	**E84.19**	Cystic fibrosis w/ oth intestinal manifestations
S17.8XXA	Crushing inj of oth spec parts of neck, init enc	**E84.8**	Cystic fibrosis w/ oth manifestations
S77.01XA	Crushing inj of rt hip, init enc	**E84.9**	Cystic fibrosis, unsp
S77.11XA	Crushing inj of rt thigh, init enc	**Q61.9**	Cystic kidney disease, unsp
S07.1XXA	Crushing inj of skull, init enc	**B69.0**	Cysticercosis of central nervous sys
S77.00XA	Crushing inj of unsp hip, init enc	**B69.1**	Cysticercosis of eye
S77.10XA	Crushing inj of unsp thigh, init enc	**B69.89**	Cysticercosis of oth sites
B45.9	Cryptococcosis, unsp	**B69.9**	Cysticercosis, unsp
J84.116	Cryptogenic organizing pneumonia	**E72.04**	Cystinosis
A07.2	Cryptosporidiosis	**E72.01**	Cystinuria
E24.9	Cushing's synd, unsp	**H59.033**	Cystoid macular edema following cataract surgery, bilat
A44.1	Cutaneous & mucocutaneous bartonellosis	**H59.032**	Cystoid macular edema following cataract surgery, lt eye
L02.211	Cutaneous abscess of abd wall	**H59.031**	Cystoid macular edema following cataract surgery, rt eye
L02.212	Cutaneous abscess of back [any part, except buttock]	**H59.039**	Cystoid macular edema following cataract surgery, unsp eye
L02.31	Cutaneous abscess of buttock	**N99.510**	Cystostomy hemor
L02.213	Cutaneous abscess of chest wall	**N99.511**	Cystostomy infxn
L02.01	Cutaneous abscess of face	**N99.512**	Cystostomy malfunction

B25.9	Cytomegaloviral disease, unsp
B25.1	Cytomegaloviral hepatitis
E72.9	D/o of amino-acid metabolism, unsp
E72.00	D/o of amino-acid transport, unsp
E70.9	D/o of aromatic amino-acid metabolism, unsp
E71.2	D/o of branched-chain amino-acid metabolism, unsp
E74.20	D/o of galactose metabolism, unsp
E72.50	D/o of glycine metabolism, unsp
E70.40	D/o of histidine metabolism, unsp
E71.32	D/o of ketone metabolism
E72.3	D/o of lysine & hydroxylysine metabolism
H47.41	D/o of optic chiasm in (d/t) inflam d/o
H47.42	D/o of optic chiasm in (d/t) neoplasm
H47.49	D/o of optic chiasm in (d/t) oth d/o
H47.43	D/o of optic chiasm in (d/t) vascular d/o
E72.4	D/o of ornithine metabolism
E79.9	D/o of purine & pyrimidine metabolism, unsp
E74.4	D/o of pyruvate metabolism & gluconeogenesis
E72.10	D/o of sulfur-bearing amino-acid metabolism, unsp
E70.5	D/o of tryptophan metabolism
E70.20	D/o of tyrosine metabolism, unsp
E72.20	D/o of urea cycle metabolism, unsp
H47.622	D/o of visual cortex in (d/t) inflam d/o, lt side of brain
H47.621	D/o of visual cortex in (d/t) inflam d/o, rt side of brain
H47.629	D/o of visual cortex in (d/t) inflam d/o, unsp side of brain
H47.632	D/o of visual cortex in (d/t) neoplasm, lt side of brain
H47.631	D/o of visual cortex in (d/t) neoplasm, rt side of brain
H47.639	D/o of visual cortex in (d/t) neoplasm, unsp side of brain
H47.642	D/o of visual cortex in (d/t) vascular d/o, lt side of brain
H47.641	D/o of visual cortex in (d/t) vascular d/o, rt side of brain
H47.649	D/o of visual cortex in (d/t) vascular d/o, unsp side of brain
H47.512	D/o of visual pathways in (d/t) inflam d/o, lt side
H47.511	D/o of visual pathways in (d/t) inflam d/o, rt side
H47.519	D/o of visual pathways in (d/t) inflam d/o, unsp side
H47.522	D/o of visual pathways in (d/t) neoplasm, lt side
H47.521	D/o of visual pathways in (d/t) neoplasm, rt side
H47.529	D/o of visual pathways in (d/t) neoplasm, unsp side
H47.532	D/o of visual pathways in (d/t) vascular d/o, lt side
H47.531	D/o of visual pathways in (d/t) vascular d/o, rt side
H47.539	D/o of visual pathways in (d/t) vascular d/o, unsp side
O08.6	Damage to pelvic organs & tissues following an ectopic & molar pregnancy
O04.84	Damage to pelvic organs following (induced) termination of pregnancy
O03.84	Damage to pelvic organs following complete or unsp spontaneous abortion
O07.34	Damage to pelvic organs following failed attempted termination of pregnancy
O03.34	Damage to pelvic organs following incomplete spontaneous abortion
O22.30	Deep phlebothrombosis in pregnancy, unsp trmstr
E80.3	Defects of catalase & peroxidase
G23.9	Degenerative disease of basal ganglia, unsp
O72.2	Delayed & secondary postpartum hemor
T80.911A	Delayed hemolytic transfusion reaction, unsp incompatibility, init enc
O08.1	Delayed or excessive hemor following ectopic & molar pregnancy
O07.1	Delayed or excessive hemor following failed attempted termination of pregnancy
Q93.9	Deletion from autosomes, unsp
Q93.3	Deletion of short arm of chromosome 4
Q93.4	Deletion of short arm of chromosome 5
Q93.7	Deletions w/ oth complex rearrangements
F05	Delirium d/t known physiological condition
F02.81	Dementia in oth diseases classified elsw w/ behavioral disturbance
G37.9	Demyelinating disease of central nervous sys, unsp
A90	Dengue fever [classical dengue]
A91	Dengue hemorrhagic fever
Z99.11	Dependence on respirator [ventilator] status
M36.0	Dermato(poly)myositis in neoplastic disease
M33.92	Dermatopolymyositis, unsp w/ myopathy
M33.99	Dermatopolymyositis, unsp w/ oth organ involvement
M33.91	Dermatopolymyositis, unsp w/ respiratory involvement
M33.90	Dermatopolymyositis, unsp, organ involvement unsp
J84.117	Desquamative interstitial pneumonia
Q24.0	Dextrocardia
D82.1	Di George's synd

E23.2	Diabetes insipidus
E08.52	Diabetes mellitus d/t underlying condition w/ diabetic peripheral angiopathy w/ gangrene
K44.0	Diaphragmatic hernia w/ obstruction, w/o gangrene
B66.2	Dicroceliasis
C82.59	Diffuse follicle center lymphoma, extranodal & solid organ sites
C82.53	Diffuse follicle center lymphoma, intra-abd lymph nodes
C82.56	Diffuse follicle center lymphoma, intrapelvic lymph nodes
C82.52	Diffuse follicle center lymphoma, intrathoracic lymph nodes
C82.54	Diffuse follicle center lymphoma, lymph nodes of axilla & upr limb
C82.51	Diffuse follicle center lymphoma, lymph nodes of head, face, & neck
C82.55	Diffuse follicle center lymphoma, lymph nodes of inguinal rgn & lwr limb
C82.58	Diffuse follicle center lymphoma, lymph nodes of multi sites
C82.57	Diffuse follicle center lymphoma, spleen
C82.50	Diffuse follicle center lymphoma, unsp site
C83.39	Diffuse lg B-cell lymphoma, extranodal & solid organ sites
C83.33	Diffuse lg B-cell lymphoma, intra-abd lymph nodes
C83.36	Diffuse lg B-cell lymphoma, intrapelvic lymph nodes
C83.32	Diffuse lg B-cell lymphoma, intrathoracic lymph nodes
C83.34	Diffuse lg B-cell lymphoma, lymph nodes of axilla & upr limb
C83.31	Diffuse lg B-cell lymphoma, lymph nodes of head, face, & neck
C83.35	Diffuse lg B-cell lymphoma, lymph nodes of inguinal rgn & lwr limb
C83.38	Diffuse lg B-cell lymphoma, lymph nodes of multi sites
C83.37	Diffuse lg B-cell lymphoma, spleen
C83.30	Diffuse lg B-cell lymphoma, unsp site
G37.0	Diffuse sclerosis of central nervous sys
S06.2X5A	Diffuse traum brain inj w/ loss of cnscness > 24 hrs w/ return to pre-existing conscious lvls, init enc
S06.2X3A	Diffuse traum brain inj w/ loss of cnscness of 1 hr to 5 hrs 59 mins, init enc
S06.2X1A	Diffuse traum brain inj w/ loss of cnscness of 30 mins or less, init enc
S06.2X2A	Diffuse traum brain inj w/ loss of cnscness of 31 mins to 59 mins, init enc
S06.2X4A	Diffuse traum brain inj w/ loss of cnscness of 6 hrs to 24 hrs, init enc
S06.2X9A	Diffuse traum brain inj w/ loss of cnscness of unsp dur, init enc
I42.0	Dilated cardiomyopathy
A36.9	Diphtheria, unsp
A36.81	Diphtheritic cardiomyopathy
A36.86	Diphtheritic conjunctivitis
A36.85	Diphtheritic cystitis
A36.83	Diphtheritic polyneuritis
A36.82	Diphtheritic radiculomyelitis
A36.84	Diphtheritic tubulo-interstitial nephropathy
B70.0	Diphyllobothriasis
G83.0	Diplegia of upr limbs
B71.1	Dipylidiasis
M01.X72	Direct infxn of lt ankle & foot in infectious & parasitic diseases classified elsw
M01.X22	Direct infxn of lt elbow in infectious & parasitic diseases classified elsw
M01.X42	Direct infxn of lt hand in infectious & parasitic diseases classified elsw
M01.X52	Direct infxn of lt hip in infectious & parasitic diseases classified elsw
M01.X62	Direct infxn of lt knee in infectious & parasitic diseases classified elsw
M01.X12	Direct infxn of lt shldr in infectious & parasitic diseases classified elsw
M01.X32	Direct infxn of lt wrist in infectious & parasitic diseases classified elsw
M01.X9	Direct infxn of multi joints in infectious & parasitic diseases classified elsw
M01.X71	Direct infxn of rt ankle & foot in infectious & parasitic diseases classified elsw
M01.X21	Direct infxn of rt elbow in infectious & parasitic diseases classified elsw
M01.X41	Direct infxn of rt hand in infectious & parasitic diseases classified elsw
M01.X51	Direct infxn of rt hip in infectious & parasitic diseases classified elsw
M01.X61	Direct infxn of rt knee in infectious & parasitic diseases classified elsw
M01.X11	Direct infxn of rt shldr in infectious & parasitic diseases classified elsw
M01.X31	Direct infxn of rt wrist in infectious & parasitic diseases classified elsw
M01.X79	Direct infxn of unsp ankle & foot in infectious & parasitic diseases classified elsw
M01.X29	Direct infxn of unsp elbow in infectious & parasitic diseases classified elsw
M01.X49	Direct infxn of unsp hand in infectious & parasitic diseases classified elsw
M01.X59	Direct infxn of unsp hip in infectious & parasitic diseases classified elsw
M01.X0	Direct infxn of unsp jt in infectious & parasitic diseases classified elsw
M01.X69	Direct infxn of unsp knee in infectious & parasitic diseases classified elsw
M01.X19	Direct infxn of unsp shldr in infectious & parasitic diseases classified elsw
M01.X39	Direct infxn of unsp wrist in infectious & parasitic diseases classified elsw
M01.X8	Direct infxn of vertebrae in infectious & parasitic diseases classified elsw
Q20.5	Discordant atrioventricular connection

I31.9	Disease of pericardium, unsp
G95.9	Disease of spinal cord, unsp
O99.411	Diseases of the circulatory sys comp pregnancy, 1st trmstr
O99.412	Diseases of the circulatory sys comp pregnancy, 2nd trmstr
O99.413	Diseases of the circulatory sys comp pregnancy, 3rd trmstr
O99.43	Diseases of the circulatory sys comp the puerperium
O99.354	Diseases of the nervous sys comp childbirth
O99.355	Diseases of the nervous sys comp the puerperium
S13.111A	Disloc of C0/C1 cervical vertebrae, init enc
S13.121A	Disloc of C1/C2 cervical vertebrae, init enc
S13.131A	Disloc of C2/C3 cervical vertebrae, init enc
S13.141A	Disloc of C3/C4 cervical vertebrae, init enc
S13.151A	Disloc of C4/C5 cervical vertebrae, init enc
S13.161A	Disloc of C5/C6 cervical vertebrae, init enc
S13.171A	Disloc of C6/C7 cervical vertebrae, init enc
S13.181A	Disloc of C7/T1 cervical vertebrae, init enc
T84.021A	Disloc of int lt hip prosthesis, init enc
T84.020A	Disloc of int rt hip prosthesis, init enc
T84.028A	Disloc of oth int jt prosthesis, init enc
S13.29XA	Disloc of oth parts of neck, init enc
S13.101A	Disloc of unsp cervical vertebrae, init enc
T84.029A	Disloc of unsp int jt prosthesis, init enc
S13.20XA	Disloc of unsp parts of neck, init enc
F20.1	Disorganized schizophrenia
S72.132P	Disp apophyseal fx of lt femur, subsq enc for clsd fx w/ malu
S72.132K	Disp apophyseal fx of lt femur, subsq enc for clsd fx w/ nonu
S72.132Q	Disp apophyseal fx of lt femur, subsq enc for opn fx type I or II w/ malu
S72.132M	Disp apophyseal fx of lt femur, subsq enc for opn fx type I or II w/ nonu
S72.132R	Disp apophyseal fx of lt femur, subsq enc for opn fx type IIIA, IIIB, or IIIC w/ malu
S72.132N	Disp apophyseal fx of lt femur, subsq enc for opn fx type IIIA, IIIB, or IIIC w/ nonu
S72.131P	Disp apophyseal fx of rt femur, subsq enc for clsd fx w/ malu
S72.131K	Disp apophyseal fx of rt femur, subsq enc for clsd fx w/ nonu
S72.131Q	Disp apophyseal fx of rt femur, subsq enc for opn fx type I or II w/ malu
S72.131M	Disp apophyseal fx of rt femur, subsq enc for opn fx type I or II w/ nonu
S72.131R	Disp apophyseal fx of rt femur, subsq enc for opn fx type IIIA, IIIB, or IIIC w/ malu
S72.131N	Disp apophyseal fx of rt femur, subsq enc for opn fx type IIIA, IIIB, or IIIC w/ nonu
S72.133P	Disp apophyseal fx of unsp femur, subsq enc for clsd fx w/ malu
S72.133K	Disp apophyseal fx of unsp femur, subsq enc for clsd fx w/ nonu
S72.133Q	Disp apophyseal fx of unsp femur, subsq enc for opn fx type I or II w/ malu
S72.133M	Disp apophyseal fx of unsp femur, subsq enc for opn fx type I or II w/ nonu
S72.133R	Disp apophyseal fx of unsp femur, subsq enc for opn fx type IIIA, IIIB, or IIIC w/ malu
S72.133N	Disp apophyseal fx of unsp femur, subsq enc for opn fx type IIIA, IIIB, or IIIC w/ nonu
S72.062P	Disp articular fx of head of lt femur, subsq enc for clsd fx w/ malu
S72.062K	Disp articular fx of head of lt femur, subsq enc for clsd fx w/ nonu
S72.062Q	Disp articular fx of head of lt femur, subsq enc for opn fx type I or II w/ malu
S72.062M	Disp articular fx of head of lt femur, subsq enc for opn fx type I or II w/ nonu
S72.062R	Disp articular fx of head of lt femur, subsq enc for opn fx type IIIA, IIIB, or IIIC w/ malu
S72.062N	Disp articular fx of head of lt femur, subsq enc for opn fx type IIIA, IIIB, or IIIC w/ nonu
S72.061P	Disp articular fx of head of rt femur, subsq enc for clsd fx w/ malu
S72.061K	Disp articular fx of head of rt femur, subsq enc for clsd fx w/ nonu
S72.061Q	Disp articular fx of head of rt femur, subsq enc for opn fx type I or II w/ malu
S72.061M	Disp articular fx of head of rt femur, subsq enc for opn fx type I or II w/ nonu
S72.061R	Disp articular fx of head of rt femur, subsq enc for opn fx type IIIA, IIIB, or IIIC w/ malu
S72.061N	Disp articular fx of head of rt femur, subsq enc for opn fx type IIIA, IIIB, or IIIC w/ nonu
S72.063P	Disp articular fx of head of unsp femur, subsq enc for clsd fx w/ malu
S72.063K	Disp articular fx of head of unsp femur, subsq enc for clsd fx w/ nonu
S72.063Q	Disp articular fx of head of unsp femur, subsq enc for opn fx type I or II w/ malu

S72.063M	Disp articular fx of head of unsp femur, subsq enc for opn fx type I or II w/ nonu
S72.063R	Disp articular fx of head of unsp femur, subsq enc for opn fx type IIIA, IIIB, or IIIC w/ malu
S72.063N	Disp articular fx of head of unsp femur, subsq enc for opn fx type IIIA, IIIB, or IIIC w/ nonu
S32.462K	Disp associated transv-post fx of lt acetab, subsq enc for fx w/ nonu
S32.461K	Disp associated transv-post fx of rt acetab, subsq enc for fx w/ nonu
S32.463K	Disp associated transv-post fx of unsp acetab, subsq enc for fx w/ nonu
S92.152B	Disp avulsion fx (chip fx) of lt talus, init enc for opn fx
S92.152P	Disp avulsion fx (chip fx) of lt talus, subsq enc for fx w/ malu
S92.152K	Disp avulsion fx (chip fx) of lt talus, subsq enc for fx w/ nonu
S92.151B	Disp avulsion fx (chip fx) of rt talus, init enc for opn fx
S92.151P	Disp avulsion fx (chip fx) of rt talus, subsq enc for fx w/ malu
S92.151K	Disp avulsion fx (chip fx) of rt talus, subsq enc for fx w/ nonu
S92.153B	Disp avulsion fx (chip fx) of unsp talus, init enc for opn fx
S92.153P	Disp avulsion fx (chip fx) of unsp talus, subsq enc for fx w/ malu
S92.153K	Disp avulsion fx (chip fx) of unsp talus, subsq enc for fx w/ nonu
S32.312A	Disp avulsion fx of lt ilium, init enc for clsd fx
S32.312K	Disp avulsion fx of lt ilium, subsq enc for fx w/ nonu
S32.612A	Disp avulsion fx of lt ischium, init enc for clsd fx
S32.612K	Disp avulsion fx of lt ischium, subsq enc for fx w/ nonu
S32.311A	Disp avulsion fx of rt ilium, init enc for clsd fx
S32.311K	Disp avulsion fx of rt ilium, subsq enc for fx w/ nonu
S32.611A	Disp avulsion fx of rt ischium, init enc for clsd fx
S32.611K	Disp avulsion fx of rt ischium, subsq enc for fx w/ nonu
S92.032B	Disp avulsion fx of tuberosity of lt calcaneus, init enc for opn fx
S92.032P	Disp avulsion fx of tuberosity of lt calcaneus, subsq enc for fx w/ malu
S92.032K	Disp avulsion fx of tuberosity of lt calcaneus, subsq enc for fx w/ nonu
S92.031B	Disp avulsion fx of tuberosity of rt calcaneus, init enc for opn fx
S92.031P	Disp avulsion fx of tuberosity of rt calcaneus, subsq enc for fx w/ malu
S92.031K	Disp avulsion fx of tuberosity of rt calcaneus, subsq enc for fx w/ nonu
S92.033B	Disp avulsion fx of tuberosity of unsp calcaneus, init enc for opn fx
S92.033P	Disp avulsion fx of tuberosity of unsp calcaneus, subsq enc for fx w/ malu
S92.033K	Disp avulsion fx of tuberosity of unsp calcaneus, subsq enc for fx w/ nonu
S32.313A	Disp avulsion fx of unsp ilium, init enc for clsd fx
S32.313K	Disp avulsion fx of unsp ilium, subsq enc for fx w/ nonu
S32.613A	Disp avulsion fx of unsp ischium, init enc for clsd fx
S32.613K	Disp avulsion fx of unsp ischium, subsq enc for fx w/ nonu
S82.142A	Disp bicondylar fx of lt tibia, init enc for clsd fx
S82.142P	Disp bicondylar fx of lt tibia, subsq enc for clsd fx w/ malu
S82.142K	Disp bicondylar fx of lt tibia, subsq enc for clsd fx w/ nonu
S82.142Q	Disp bicondylar fx of lt tibia, subsq enc for opn fx type I or II w/ malu
S82.142M	Disp bicondylar fx of lt tibia, subsq enc for opn fx type I or II w/ nonu
S82.142R	Disp bicondylar fx of lt tibia, subsq enc for opn fx type IIIA, IIIB, or IIIC w/ malu
S82.142N	Disp bicondylar fx of lt tibia, subsq enc for opn fx type IIIA, IIIB, or IIIC w/ nonu
S82.141A	Disp bicondylar fx of rt tibia, init enc for clsd fx
S82.141P	Disp bicondylar fx of rt tibia, subsq enc for clsd fx w/ malu
S82.141K	Disp bicondylar fx of rt tibia, subsq enc for clsd fx w/ nonu
S82.141Q	Disp bicondylar fx of rt tibia, subsq enc for opn fx type I or II w/ malu
S82.141M	Disp bicondylar fx of rt tibia, subsq enc for opn fx type I or II w/ nonu
S82.141R	Disp bicondylar fx of rt tibia, subsq enc for opn fx type IIIA, IIIB, or IIIC w/ malu
S82.141N	Disp bicondylar fx of rt tibia, subsq enc for opn fx type IIIA, IIIB, or IIIC w/ nonu
S82.143A	Disp bicondylar fx of unsp tibia, init enc for clsd fx
S82.143P	Disp bicondylar fx of unsp tibia, subsq enc for clsd fx w/ malu
S82.143K	Disp bicondylar fx of unsp tibia, subsq enc for clsd fx w/ nonu
S82.143Q	Disp bicondylar fx of unsp tibia, subsq enc for opn fx type I or II w/ malu
S82.143M	Disp bicondylar fx of unsp tibia, subsq enc for opn fx type I or II w/ nonu
S82.143R	Disp bicondylar fx of unsp tibia, subsq enc for opn fx type IIIA, IIIB, or IIIC w/ malu
S82.143N	Disp bicondylar fx of unsp tibia, subsq enc for opn fx type IIIA, IIIB, or IIIC w/ nonu
S82.842B	Disp bimalleolar fx of lt lwr leg, init enc for opn fx type I or II
S82.842C	Disp bimalleolar fx of lt lwr leg, init enc for opn fx type IIIA, IIIB, or IIIC
S82.842P	Disp bimalleolar fx of lt lwr leg, subsq enc for clsd fx w/ malu
S82.842K	Disp bimalleolar fx of lt lwr leg, subsq enc for clsd fx w/ nonu
S82.842Q	Disp bimalleolar fx of lt lwr leg, subsq enc for opn fx type I or II w/ malu
S82.842M	Disp bimalleolar fx of lt lwr leg, subsq enc for opn fx type I or II w/ nonu
S82.842R	Disp bimalleolar fx of lt lwr leg, subsq enc for opn fx type IIIA, IIIB, or IIIC w/ malu

S82.842N	Disp bimalleolar fx of lt lwr leg, subsq enc for opn fx type IIIA, IIIB, or IIIC w/ nonu
S82.841B	Disp bimalleolar fx of rt lwr leg, init enc for opn fx type I or II
S82.841C	Disp bimalleolar fx of rt lwr leg, init enc for opn fx type IIIA, IIIB, or IIIC
S82.841P	Disp bimalleolar fx of rt lwr leg, subsq enc for clsd fx w/ malu
S82.841K	Disp bimalleolar fx of rt lwr leg, subsq enc for clsd fx w/ nonu
S82.841Q	Disp bimalleolar fx of rt lwr leg, subsq enc for opn fx type I or II w/ malu
S82.841M	Disp bimalleolar fx of rt lwr leg, subsq enc for opn fx type I or II w/ nonu
S82.841R	Disp bimalleolar fx of rt lwr leg, subsq enc for opn fx type IIIA, IIIB, or IIIC w/ malu
S82.841N	Disp bimalleolar fx of rt lwr leg, subsq enc for opn fx type IIIA, IIIB, or IIIC w/ nonu
S82.843B	Disp bimalleolar fx of unsp lwr leg, init enc for opn fx type I or II
S82.843C	Disp bimalleolar fx of unsp lwr leg, init enc for opn fx type IIIA, IIIB, or IIIC
S82.843P	Disp bimalleolar fx of unsp lwr leg, subsq enc for clsd fx w/ malu
S82.843K	Disp bimalleolar fx of unsp lwr leg, subsq enc for clsd fx w/ nonu
S82.843Q	Disp bimalleolar fx of unsp lwr leg, subsq enc for opn fx type I or II w/ malu
S82.843M	Disp bimalleolar fx of unsp lwr leg, subsq enc for opn fx type I or II w/ nonu
S82.843R	Disp bimalleolar fx of unsp lwr leg, subsq enc for opn fx type IIIA, IIIB, or IIIC w/ malu
S82.843N	Disp bimalleolar fx of unsp lwr leg, subsq enc for opn fx type IIIA, IIIB, or IIIC w/ nonu
S82.042A	Disp comm fx of lt patella, init enc for clsd fx
S82.042B	Disp comm fx of lt patella, init enc for opn fx type I or II
S82.042C	Disp comm fx of lt patella, init enc for opn fx type IIIA, IIIB, or IIIC
S82.042P	Disp comm fx of lt patella, subsq enc for clsd fx w/ malu
S82.042K	Disp comm fx of lt patella, subsq enc for clsd fx w/ nonu
S82.042Q	Disp comm fx of lt patella, subsq enc for opn fx type I or II w/ malu
S82.042M	Disp comm fx of lt patella, subsq enc for opn fx type I or II w/ nonu
S82.042R	Disp comm fx of lt patella, subsq enc for opn fx type IIIA, IIIB, or IIIC w/ malu
S82.042N	Disp comm fx of lt patella, subsq enc for opn fx type IIIA, IIIB, or IIIC w/ nonu
S82.041A	Disp comm fx of rt patella, init enc for clsd fx
S82.041B	Disp comm fx of rt patella, init enc for opn fx type I or II
S82.041C	Disp comm fx of rt patella, init enc for opn fx type IIIA, IIIB, or IIIC
S82.041P	Disp comm fx of rt patella, subsq enc for clsd fx w/ malu
S82.041K	Disp comm fx of rt patella, subsq enc for clsd fx w/ nonu
S82.041Q	Disp comm fx of rt patella, subsq enc for opn fx type I or II w/ malu
S82.041M	Disp comm fx of rt patella, subsq enc for opn fx type I or II w/ nonu
S82.041R	Disp comm fx of rt patella, subsq enc for opn fx type IIIA, IIIB, or IIIC w/ malu
S82.041N	Disp comm fx of rt patella, subsq enc for opn fx type IIIA, IIIB, or IIIC w/ nonu
S42.352A	Disp comm fx of shaft of humerus, lt arm, init enc for clsd fx
S42.352P	Disp comm fx of shaft of humerus, lt arm, subsq enc for fx w/ malu
S42.352K	Disp comm fx of shaft of humerus, lt arm, subsq enc for fx w/ nonu
S42.351A	Disp comm fx of shaft of humerus, rt arm, init enc for clsd fx
S42.351P	Disp comm fx of shaft of humerus, rt arm, subsq enc for fx w/ malu
S42.351K	Disp comm fx of shaft of humerus, rt arm, subsq enc for fx w/ nonu
S42.353A	Disp comm fx of shaft of humerus, unsp arm, init enc for clsd fx
S42.353P	Disp comm fx of shaft of humerus, unsp arm, subsq enc for fx w/ malu
S42.353K	Disp comm fx of shaft of humerus, unsp arm, subsq enc for fx w/ nonu
S72.352P	Disp comm fx of shaft of lt femur, subsq enc for clsd fx w/ malu
S72.352K	Disp comm fx of shaft of lt femur, subsq enc for clsd fx w/ nonu
S72.352Q	Disp comm fx of shaft of lt femur, subsq enc for opn fx type I or II w/ malu
S72.352M	Disp comm fx of shaft of lt femur, subsq enc for opn fx type I or II w/ nonu
S72.352R	Disp comm fx of shaft of lt femur, subsq enc for opn fx type IIIA, IIIB, or IIIC w/ malu
S72.352N	Disp comm fx of shaft of lt femur, subsq enc for opn fx type IIIA, IIIB, or IIIC w/ nonu
S82.452P	Disp comm fx of shaft of lt fibula, subsq enc for clsd fx w/ malu
S82.452K	Disp comm fx of shaft of lt fibula, subsq enc for clsd fx w/ nonu
S82.452Q	Disp comm fx of shaft of lt fibula, subsq enc for opn fx type I or II w/ malu
S82.452M	Disp comm fx of shaft of lt fibula, subsq enc for opn fx type I or II w/ nonu
S82.452R	Disp comm fx of shaft of lt fibula, subsq enc for opn fx type IIIA, IIIB, or IIIC w/ malu
S82.452N	Disp comm fx of shaft of lt fibula, subsq enc for opn fx type IIIA, IIIB, or IIIC w/ nonu
S82.252A	Disp comm fx of shaft of lt tibia, init enc for clsd fx
S82.252P	Disp comm fx of shaft of lt tibia, subsq enc for clsd fx w/ malu
S82.252K	Disp comm fx of shaft of lt tibia, subsq enc for clsd fx w/ nonu
S82.252Q	Disp comm fx of shaft of lt tibia, subsq enc for opn fx type I or II w/ malu
S82.252M	Disp comm fx of shaft of lt tibia, subsq enc for opn fx type I or II w/ nonu
S82.252R	Disp comm fx of shaft of lt tibia, subsq enc for opn fx type IIIA, IIIB, or IIIC w/ malu
S82.252N	Disp comm fx of shaft of lt tibia, subsq enc for opn fx type IIIA, IIIB, or IIIC w/ nonu
S52.352A	Disp comm fx of shaft of radius, lt arm, init enc for clsd fx
S52.352P	Disp comm fx of shaft of radius, lt arm, subsq enc for clsd fx w/ malu
S52.352K	Disp comm fx of shaft of radius, lt arm, subsq enc for clsd fx w/ nonu
S52.352Q	Disp comm fx of shaft of radius, lt arm, subsq enc for opn fx type I or II w/ malu
S52.352M	Disp comm fx of shaft of radius, lt arm, subsq enc for opn fx type I or II w/ nonu
S52.352R	Disp comm fx of shaft of radius, lt arm, subsq enc for opn fx type IIIA, IIIB, or IIIC w/ malu
S52.352N	Disp comm fx of shaft of radius, lt arm, subsq enc for opn fx type IIIA, IIIB, or IIIC w/ nonu
S52.351A	Disp comm fx of shaft of radius, rt arm, init enc for clsd fx
S52.351P	Disp comm fx of shaft of radius, rt arm, subsq enc for clsd fx w/ malu
S52.351K	Disp comm fx of shaft of radius, rt arm, subsq enc for clsd fx w/ nonu
S52.351Q	Disp comm fx of shaft of radius, rt arm, subsq enc for opn fx type I or II w/ malu
S52.351M	Disp comm fx of shaft of radius, rt arm, subsq enc for opn fx type I or II w/ nonu
S52.351R	Disp comm fx of shaft of radius, rt arm, subsq enc for opn fx type IIIA, IIIB, or IIIC w/ malu
S52.351N	Disp comm fx of shaft of radius, rt arm, subsq enc for opn fx type IIIA, IIIB, or IIIC w/ nonu
S52.353A	Disp comm fx of shaft of radius, unsp arm, init enc for clsd fx
S52.353P	Disp comm fx of shaft of radius, unsp arm, subsq enc for clsd fx w/ malu
S52.353K	Disp comm fx of shaft of radius, unsp arm, subsq enc for clsd fx w/ nonu
S52.353Q	Disp comm fx of shaft of radius, unsp arm, subsq enc for opn fx type I or II w/ malu
S52.353M	Disp comm fx of shaft of radius, unsp arm, subsq enc for opn fx type I or II w/ nonu
S52.353R	Disp comm fx of shaft of radius, unsp arm, subsq enc for opn fx type IIIA, IIIB, or IIIC w/ malu
S52.353N	Disp comm fx of shaft of radius, unsp arm, subsq enc for opn fx type IIIA, IIIB, or IIIC w/ nonu
S72.351P	Disp comm fx of shaft of rt femur, subsq enc for clsd fx w/ malu
S72.351K	Disp comm fx of shaft of rt femur, subsq enc for clsd fx w/ nonu
S72.351Q	Disp comm fx of shaft of rt femur, subsq enc for opn fx type I or II w/ malu
S72.351M	Disp comm fx of shaft of rt femur, subsq enc for opn fx type I or II w/ nonu
S72.351R	Disp comm fx of shaft of rt femur, subsq enc for opn fx type IIIA, IIIB, or IIIC w/ malu
S72.351N	Disp comm fx of shaft of rt femur, subsq enc for opn fx type IIIA, IIIB, or IIIC w/ nonu
S82.451P	Disp comm fx of shaft of rt fibula, subsq enc for clsd fx w/ malu
S82.451K	Disp comm fx of shaft of rt fibula, subsq enc for clsd fx w/ nonu
S82.451Q	Disp comm fx of shaft of rt fibula, subsq enc for opn fx type I or II w/ malu
S82.451M	Disp comm fx of shaft of rt fibula, subsq enc for opn fx type I or II w/ nonu
S82.451R	Disp comm fx of shaft of rt fibula, subsq enc for opn fx type IIIA, IIIB, or IIIC w/ malu
S82.451N	Disp comm fx of shaft of rt fibula, subsq enc for opn fx type IIIA, IIIB, or IIIC w/ nonu
S82.251A	Disp comm fx of shaft of rt tibia, init enc for clsd fx
S82.251P	Disp comm fx of shaft of rt tibia, subsq enc for clsd fx w/ malu
S82.251K	Disp comm fx of shaft of rt tibia, subsq enc for clsd fx w/ nonu
S82.251Q	Disp comm fx of shaft of rt tibia, subsq enc for opn fx type I or II w/ malu
S82.251M	Disp comm fx of shaft of rt tibia, subsq enc for opn fx type I or II w/ nonu
S82.251R	Disp comm fx of shaft of rt tibia, subsq enc for opn fx type IIIA, IIIB, or IIIC w/ malu
S82.251N	Disp comm fx of shaft of rt tibia, subsq enc for opn fx type IIIA, IIIB, or IIIC w/ nonu
S52.252A	Disp comm fx of shaft of ulna, lt arm, init enc for clsd fx
S52.252P	Disp comm fx of shaft of ulna, lt arm, subsq enc for clsd fx w/ malu
S52.252K	Disp comm fx of shaft of ulna, lt arm, subsq enc for clsd fx w/ nonu
S52.252Q	Disp comm fx of shaft of ulna, lt arm, subsq enc for opn fx type I or II w/ malu
S52.252M	Disp comm fx of shaft of ulna, lt arm, subsq enc for opn fx type I or II w/ nonu
S52.252R	Disp comm fx of shaft of ulna, lt arm, subsq enc for opn fx type IIIA, IIIB, or IIIC w/ malu
S52.252N	Disp comm fx of shaft of ulna, lt arm, subsq enc for opn fx type IIIA, IIIB, or IIIC w/ nonu
S52.251A	Disp comm fx of shaft of ulna, rt arm, init enc for clsd fx
S52.251P	Disp comm fx of shaft of ulna, rt arm, subsq enc for clsd fx w/ malu

S52.251K	Disp comm fx of shaft of ulna, rt arm, subsq enc for clsd fx w/ nonu
S52.251Q	Disp comm fx of shaft of ulna, rt arm, subsq enc for opn fx type I or II w/ malu
S52.251M	Disp comm fx of shaft of ulna, rt arm, subsq enc for opn fx type I or II w/ nonu
S52.251R	Disp comm fx of shaft of ulna, rt arm, subsq enc for opn fx type IIIA, IIIB, or IIIC w/ malu
S52.251N	Disp comm fx of shaft of ulna, rt arm, subsq enc for opn fx type IIIA, IIIB, or IIIC w/ nonu
S52.253A	Disp comm fx of shaft of ulna, unsp arm, init enc for clsd fx
S52.253P	Disp comm fx of shaft of ulna, unsp arm, subsq enc for clsd fx w/ malu
S52.253K	Disp comm fx of shaft of ulna, unsp arm, subsq enc for clsd fx w/ nonu
S52.253Q	Disp comm fx of shaft of ulna, unsp arm, subsq enc for opn fx type I or II w/ malu
S52.253M	Disp comm fx of shaft of ulna, unsp arm, subsq enc for opn fx type I or II w/ nonu
S52.253R	Disp comm fx of shaft of ulna, unsp arm, subsq enc for opn fx type IIIA, IIIB, or IIIC w/ malu
S52.253N	Disp comm fx of shaft of ulna, unsp arm, subsq enc for opn fx type IIIA, IIIB, or IIIC w/ nonu
S72.353P	Disp comm fx of shaft of unsp femur, subsq enc for clsd fx w/ malu
S72.353K	Disp comm fx of shaft of unsp femur, subsq enc for clsd fx w/ nonu
S72.353Q	Disp comm fx of shaft of unsp femur, subsq enc for opn fx type I or II w/ malu
S72.353M	Disp comm fx of shaft of unsp femur, subsq enc for opn fx type I or II w/ nonu
S72.353R	Disp comm fx of shaft of unsp femur, subsq enc for opn fx type IIIA, IIIB, or IIIC w/ malu
S72.353N	Disp comm fx of shaft of unsp femur, subsq enc for opn fx type IIIA, IIIB, or IIIC w/ nonu
S82.453P	Disp comm fx of shaft of unsp fibula, subsq enc for clsd fx w/ malu
S82.453K	Disp comm fx of shaft of unsp fibula, subsq enc for clsd fx w/ nonu
S82.453Q	Disp comm fx of shaft of unsp fibula, subsq enc for opn fx type I or II w/ malu
S82.453M	Disp comm fx of shaft of unsp fibula, subsq enc for opn fx type I or II w/ nonu
S82.453R	Disp comm fx of shaft of unsp fibula, subsq enc for opn fx type IIIA, IIIB, or IIIC w/ malu
S82.453N	Disp comm fx of shaft of unsp fibula, subsq enc for opn fx type IIIA, IIIB, or IIIC w/ nonu
S82.253A	Disp comm fx of shaft of unsp tibia, init enc for clsd fx
S82.253P	Disp comm fx of shaft of unsp tibia, subsq enc for clsd fx w/ malu
S82.253K	Disp comm fx of shaft of unsp tibia, subsq enc for clsd fx w/ nonu
S82.253Q	Disp comm fx of shaft of unsp tibia, subsq enc for opn fx type I or II w/ malu
S82.253M	Disp comm fx of shaft of unsp tibia, subsq enc for opn fx type I or II w/ nonu
S82.253R	Disp comm fx of shaft of unsp tibia, subsq enc for opn fx type IIIA, IIIB, or IIIC w/ malu
S82.253N	Disp comm fx of shaft of unsp tibia, subsq enc for opn fx type IIIA, IIIB, or IIIC w/ nonu
S82.043A	Disp comm fx of unsp patella, init enc for clsd fx
S82.043B	Disp comm fx of unsp patella, init enc for opn fx type I or II
S82.043C	Disp comm fx of unsp patella, init enc for opn fx type IIIA, IIIB, or IIIC
S82.043P	Disp comm fx of unsp patella, subsq enc for clsd fx w/ malu
S82.043K	Disp comm fx of unsp patella, subsq enc for clsd fx w/ nonu
S82.043Q	Disp comm fx of unsp patella, subsq enc for opn fx type I or II w/ malu
S82.043M	Disp comm fx of unsp patella, subsq enc for opn fx type I or II w/ nonu
S82.043R	Disp comm fx of unsp patella, subsq enc for opn fx type IIIA, IIIB, or IIIC w/ malu
S82.043N	Disp comm fx of unsp patella, subsq enc for opn fx type IIIA, IIIB, or IIIC w/ nonu
S42.422A	Disp comm supracondylar fx w/o intercondylar fx of lt humerus, init enc for clsd fx
S42.422P	Disp comm supracondylar fx w/o intercondylar fx of lt humerus, subsq enc for fx w/ malu
S42.422K	Disp comm supracondylar fx w/o intercondylar fx of lt humerus, subsq enc for fx w/ nonu
S42.421A	Disp comm supracondylar fx w/o intercondylar fx of rt humerus, init enc for clsd fx
S42.421P	Disp comm supracondylar fx w/o intercondylar fx of rt humerus, subsq enc for fx w/ malu
S42.421K	Disp comm supracondylar fx w/o intercondylar fx of rt humerus, subsq enc for fx w/ nonu
S42.423A	Disp comm supracondylar fx w/o intercondylar fx of unsp humerus, init enc for clsd fx
S42.423P	Disp comm supracondylar fx w/o intercondylar fx of unsp humerus, subsq enc for fx w/ malu
S42.423K	Disp comm supracondylar fx w/o intercondylar fx of unsp humerus, subsq enc for fx w/ nonu
S32.482K	Disp dome fx of lt acetab, subsq enc for fx w/ nonu
S92.142B	Disp dome fx of lt talus, init enc for opn fx
S92.142P	Disp dome fx of lt talus, subsq enc for fx w/ malu
S92.142K	Disp dome fx of lt talus, subsq enc for fx w/ nonu
S32.481K	Disp dome fx of rt acetab, subsq enc for fx w/ nonu
S92.141B	Disp dome fx of rt talus, init enc for opn fx
S92.141P	Disp dome fx of rt talus, subsq enc for fx w/ malu
S92.141K	Disp dome fx of rt talus, subsq enc for fx w/ nonu
S32.483K	Disp dome fx of unsp acetab, subsq enc for fx w/ nonu
S92.143B	Disp dome fx of unsp talus, init enc for opn fx
S92.143P	Disp dome fx of unsp talus, subsq enc for fx w/ malu
S92.143K	Disp dome fx of unsp talus, subsq enc for fx w/ nonu
S42.432A	Disp fx (avulsion) of lat epicondyle of lt humerus, init enc for clsd fx
S42.432P	Disp fx (avulsion) of lat epicondyle of lt humerus, subsq enc for fx w/ malu
S42.432K	Disp fx (avulsion) of lat epicondyle of lt humerus, subsq enc for fx w/ nonu
S42.431A	Disp fx (avulsion) of lat epicondyle of rt humerus, init enc for clsd fx
S42.431P	Disp fx (avulsion) of lat epicondyle of rt humerus, subsq enc for fx w/ malu
S42.431K	Disp fx (avulsion) of lat epicondyle of rt humerus, subsq enc for fx w/ nonu
S42.433A	Disp fx (avulsion) of lat epicondyle of unsp humerus, init enc for clsd fx
S42.433P	Disp fx (avulsion) of lat epicondyle of unsp humerus, subsq enc for fx w/ malu
S42.433K	Disp fx (avulsion) of lat epicondyle of unsp humerus, subsq enc for fx w/ nonu
S42.442A	Disp fx (avulsion) of med epicondyle of lt humerus, init enc for clsd fx
S42.442P	Disp fx (avulsion) of med epicondyle of lt humerus, subsq enc for fx w/ malu
S42.442K	Disp fx (avulsion) of med epicondyle of lt humerus, subsq enc for fx w/ nonu
S42.441A	Disp fx (avulsion) of med epicondyle of rt humerus, init enc for clsd fx
S42.441P	Disp fx (avulsion) of med epicondyle of rt humerus, subsq enc for fx w/ malu
S42.441K	Disp fx (avulsion) of med epicondyle of rt humerus, subsq enc for fx w/ nonu
S42.443A	Disp fx (avulsion) of med epicondyle of unsp humerus, init enc for clsd fx
S42.443P	Disp fx (avulsion) of med epicondyle of unsp humerus, subsq enc for fx w/ malu
S42.443K	Disp fx (avulsion) of med epicondyle of unsp humerus, subsq enc for fx w/ nonu
S92.312B	Disp fx of 1st metatarsal bone, lt foot, init enc for opn fx
S92.312P	Disp fx of 1st metatarsal bone, lt foot, subsq enc for fx w/ malu
S92.312K	Disp fx of 1st metatarsal bone, lt foot, subsq enc for fx w/ nonu
S92.311B	Disp fx of 1st metatarsal bone, rt foot, init enc for opn fx
S92.311P	Disp fx of 1st metatarsal bone, rt foot, subsq enc for fx w/ malu
S92.311K	Disp fx of 1st metatarsal bone, rt foot, subsq enc for fx w/ nonu
S92.313B	Disp fx of 1st metatarsal bone, unsp foot, init enc for opn fx
S92.313P	Disp fx of 1st metatarsal bone, unsp foot, subsq enc for fx w/ malu
S92.313K	Disp fx of 1st metatarsal bone, unsp foot, subsq enc for fx w/ nonu
S92.322B	Disp fx of 2nd metatarsal bone, lt foot, init enc for opn fx
S92.322P	Disp fx of 2nd metatarsal bone, lt foot, subsq enc for fx w/ malu
S92.322K	Disp fx of 2nd metatarsal bone, lt foot, subsq enc for fx w/ nonu
S92.321B	Disp fx of 2nd metatarsal bone, rt foot, init enc for opn fx
S92.321P	Disp fx of 2nd metatarsal bone, rt foot, subsq enc for fx w/ malu
S92.321K	Disp fx of 2nd metatarsal bone, rt foot, subsq enc for fx w/ nonu
S92.323B	Disp fx of 2nd metatarsal bone, unsp foot, init enc for opn fx
S92.323P	Disp fx of 2nd metatarsal bone, unsp foot, subsq enc for fx w/ malu
S92.323K	Disp fx of 2nd metatarsal bone, unsp foot, subsq enc for fx w/ nonu
S92.332B	Disp fx of 3rd metatarsal bone, lt foot, init enc for opn fx
S92.332P	Disp fx of 3rd metatarsal bone, lt foot, subsq enc for fx w/ malu
S92.332K	Disp fx of 3rd metatarsal bone, lt foot, subsq enc for fx w/ nonu
S92.331B	Disp fx of 3rd metatarsal bone, rt foot, init enc for opn fx
S92.331P	Disp fx of 3rd metatarsal bone, rt foot, subsq enc for fx w/ malu
S92.331K	Disp fx of 3rd metatarsal bone, rt foot, subsq enc for fx w/ nonu
S92.333B	Disp fx of 3rd metatarsal bone, unsp foot, init enc for opn fx
S92.333P	Disp fx of 3rd metatarsal bone, unsp foot, subsq enc for fx w/ malu
S92.333K	Disp fx of 3rd metatarsal bone, unsp foot, subsq enc for fx w/ nonu
S92.342B	Disp fx of 4th metatarsal bone, lt foot, init enc for opn fx
S92.342P	Disp fx of 4th metatarsal bone, lt foot, subsq enc for fx w/ malu

Code	Description
S92.342K	Disp fx of 4th metatarsal bone, lt foot, subsq enc for fx w/ nonu
S92.341B	Disp fx of 4th metatarsal bone, rt foot, init enc for opn fx
S92.341P	Disp fx of 4th metatarsal bone, rt foot, subsq enc for fx w/ malu
S92.341K	Disp fx of 4th metatarsal bone, rt foot, subsq enc for fx w/ nonu
S92.343B	Disp fx of 4th metatarsal bone, unsp foot, init enc for opn fx
S92.343P	Disp fx of 4th metatarsal bone, unsp foot, subsq enc for fx w/ malu
S92.343K	Disp fx of 4th metatarsal bone, unsp foot, subsq enc for fx w/ nonu
S92.352B	Disp fx of 5th metatarsal bone, lt foot, init enc for opn fx
S92.352P	Disp fx of 5th metatarsal bone, lt foot, subsq enc for fx w/ malu
S92.352K	Disp fx of 5th metatarsal bone, lt foot, subsq enc for fx w/ nonu
S92.351B	Disp fx of 5th metatarsal bone, rt foot, init enc for opn fx
S92.351P	Disp fx of 5th metatarsal bone, rt foot, subsq enc for fx w/ malu
S92.351K	Disp fx of 5th metatarsal bone, rt foot, subsq enc for fx w/ nonu
S92.353B	Disp fx of 5th metatarsal bone, unsp foot, init enc for opn fx
S92.353P	Disp fx of 5th metatarsal bone, unsp foot, subsq enc for fx w/ malu
S92.353K	Disp fx of 5th metatarsal bone, unsp foot, subsq enc for fx w/ nonu
S42.122B	Disp fx of acromial process, lt shldr, init enc for opn fx
S42.122P	Disp fx of acromial process, lt shldr, subsq enc for fx w/ malu
S42.122K	Disp fx of acromial process, lt shldr, subsq enc for fx w/ nonu
S42.121B	Disp fx of acromial process, rt shldr, init enc for opn fx
S42.121P	Disp fx of acromial process, rt shldr, subsq enc for fx w/ malu
S42.121K	Disp fx of acromial process, rt shldr, subsq enc for fx w/ nonu
S42.123B	Disp fx of acromial process, unsp shldr, init enc for opn fx
S42.123P	Disp fx of acromial process, unsp shldr, subsq enc for fx w/ malu
S42.123K	Disp fx of acromial process, unsp shldr, subsq enc for fx w/ nonu
S32.432K	Disp fx of ant column [iliopubic] of lt acetab, subsq enc for fx w/ nonu
S32.431K	Disp fx of ant column [iliopubic] of rt acetab, subsq enc for fx w/ nonu
S32.433K	Disp fx of ant column [iliopubic] of unsp acetab, subsq enc for fx w/ nonu
S92.022B	Disp fx of ant process of lt calcaneus, init enc for opn fx
S92.022P	Disp fx of ant process of lt calcaneus, subsq enc for fx w/ malu
S92.022K	Disp fx of ant process of lt calcaneus, subsq enc for fx w/ nonu
S92.021B	Disp fx of ant process of rt calcaneus, init enc for opn fx
S92.021P	Disp fx of ant process of rt calcaneus, subsq enc for fx w/ malu
S92.021K	Disp fx of ant process of rt calcaneus, subsq enc for fx w/ nonu
S92.023B	Disp fx of ant process of unsp calcaneus, init enc for opn fx
S92.023P	Disp fx of ant process of unsp calcaneus, subsq enc for fx w/ malu
S92.023K	Disp fx of ant process of unsp calcaneus, subsq enc for fx w/ nonu
S32.412K	Disp fx of ant wall of lt acetab, subsq enc for fx w/ nonu
S32.411K	Disp fx of ant wall of rt acetab, subsq enc for fx w/ nonu
S32.413K	Disp fx of ant wall of unsp acetab, subsq enc for fx w/ nonu
S62.310B	Disp fx of base of 2nd metacarpal bone, rt hand, init enc for opn fx
S62.310P	Disp fx of base of 2nd metacarpal bone, rt hand, subsq enc for fx w/ malu
S62.310K	Disp fx of base of 2nd metacarpal bone, rt hand, subsq enc for fx w/ nonu
S62.311B	Disp fx of base of 2nd metacarpal bone. lt hand, init enc for opn fx
S62.311P	Disp fx of base of 2nd metacarpal bone. lt hand, subsq enc for fx w/ malu
S62.311K	Disp fx of base of 2nd metacarpal bone. lt hand, subsq enc for fx w/ nonu
S62.313B	Disp fx of base of 3rd metacarpal bone, lt hand, init enc for opn fx
S62.313P	Disp fx of base of 3rd metacarpal bone, lt hand, subsq enc for fx w/ malu
S62.313K	Disp fx of base of 3rd metacarpal bone, lt hand, subsq enc for fx w/ nonu
S62.312B	Disp fx of base of 3rd metacarpal bone, rt hand, init enc for opn fx
S62.312P	Disp fx of base of 3rd metacarpal bone, rt hand, subsq enc for fx w/ malu
S62.312K	Disp fx of base of 3rd metacarpal bone, rt hand, subsq enc for fx w/ nonu
S62.315B	Disp fx of base of 4th metacarpal bone, lt hand, init enc for opn fx
S62.315P	Disp fx of base of 4th metacarpal bone, lt hand, subsq enc for fx w/ malu
S62.315K	Disp fx of base of 4th metacarpal bone, lt hand, subsq enc for fx w/ nonu
S62.314B	Disp fx of base of 4th metacarpal bone, rt hand, init enc for opn fx
S62.314P	Disp fx of base of 4th metacarpal bone, rt hand, subsq enc for fx w/ malu
S62.314K	Disp fx of base of 4th metacarpal bone, rt hand, subsq enc for fx w/ nonu
S62.316B	Disp fx of base of 5th metacarpal bone, rt hand, init enc for opn fx
S62.316P	Disp fx of base of 5th metacarpal bone, rt hand, subsq enc for fx w/ malu
S62.316K	Disp fx of base of 5th metacarpal bone, rt hand, subsq enc for fx w/ nonu
S62.317B	Disp fx of base of 5th metacarpal bone. lt hand, init enc for opn fx
S62.317P	Disp fx of base of 5th metacarpal bone. lt hand, subsq enc for fx w/ malu
S62.317K	Disp fx of base of 5th metacarpal bone. lt hand, subsq enc for fx w/ nonu
S72.042P	Disp fx of base of neck of lt femur, subsq enc for clsd fx w/ malu
S72.042K	Disp fx of base of neck of lt femur, subsq enc for clsd fx w/ nonu
S72.042Q	Disp fx of base of neck of lt femur, subsq enc for opn fx type I or II w/ malu
S72.042M	Disp fx of base of neck of lt femur, subsq enc for opn fx type I or II w/ nonu
S72.042R	Disp fx of base of neck of lt femur, subsq enc for opn fx type IIIA, IIIB, or IIIC w/ malu
S72.042N	Disp fx of base of neck of lt femur, subsq enc for opn fx type IIIA, IIIB, or IIIC w/ nonu
S72.041P	Disp fx of base of neck of rt femur, subsq enc for clsd fx w/ malu
S72.041K	Disp fx of base of neck of rt femur, subsq enc for clsd fx w/ nonu

Code	Description
S72.041Q	Disp fx of base of neck of rt femur, subsq enc for opn fx type I or II w/ malu
S72.041M	Disp fx of base of neck of rt femur, subsq enc for opn fx type I or II w/ nonu
S72.041R	Disp fx of base of neck of rt femur, subsq enc for opn fx type IIIA, IIIB, or IIIC w/ malu
S72.041N	Disp fx of base of neck of rt femur, subsq enc for opn fx type IIIA, IIIB, or IIIC w/ nonu
S72.043P	Disp fx of base of neck of unsp femur, subsq enc for clsd fx w/ malu
S72.043K	Disp fx of base of neck of unsp femur, subsq enc for clsd fx w/ nonu
S72.043Q	Disp fx of base of neck of unsp femur, subsq enc for opn fx type I or II w/ malu
S72.043M	Disp fx of base of neck of unsp femur, subsq enc for opn fx type I or II w/ nonu
S72.043R	Disp fx of base of neck of unsp femur, subsq enc for opn fx type IIIA, IIIB, or IIIC w/ malu
S72.043N	Disp fx of base of neck of unsp femur, subsq enc for opn fx type IIIA, IIIB, or IIIC w/ nonu
S62.318B	Disp fx of base of oth metacarpal bone, init enc for opn fx
S62.318P	Disp fx of base of oth metacarpal bone, subsq enc for fx w/ malu
S62.318K	Disp fx of base of oth metacarpal bone, subsq enc for fx w/ nonu
S62.319B	Disp fx of base of unsp metacarpal bone, init enc for opn fx
S62.319P	Disp fx of base of unsp metacarpal bone, subsq enc for fx w/ malu
S62.319K	Disp fx of base of unsp metacarpal bone, subsq enc for fx w/ nonu
S62.142B	Disp fx of body of hamate [unciform] bone, lt wrist, init enc for opn fx
S62.142P	Disp fx of body of hamate [unciform] bone, lt wrist, subsq enc for fx w/ malu
S62.142K	Disp fx of body of hamate [unciform] bone, lt wrist, subsq enc for fx w/ nonu
S62.141B	Disp fx of body of hamate [unciform] bone, rt wrist, init enc for opn fx
S62.141P	Disp fx of body of hamate [unciform] bone, rt wrist, subsq enc for fx w/ malu
S62.141K	Disp fx of body of hamate [unciform] bone, rt wrist, subsq enc for fx w/ nonu
S62.143B	Disp fx of body of hamate [unciform] bone, unsp wrist, init enc for opn fx
S62.143P	Disp fx of body of hamate [unciform] bone, unsp wrist, subsq enc for fx w/ malu
S62.143K	Disp fx of body of hamate [unciform] bone, unsp wrist, subsq enc for fx w/ nonu
S92.012B	Disp fx of body of lt calcaneus, init enc for opn fx
S92.012P	Disp fx of body of lt calcaneus, subsq enc for fx w/ malu
S92.012K	Disp fx of body of lt calcaneus, subsq enc for fx w/ nonu
S92.122B	Disp fx of body of lt talus, init enc for opn fx
S92.122P	Disp fx of body of lt talus, subsq enc for fx w/ malu
S92.122K	Disp fx of body of lt talus, subsq enc for fx w/ nonu
S92.011B	Disp fx of body of rt calcaneus, init enc for opn fx
S92.011P	Disp fx of body of rt calcaneus, subsq enc for fx w/ malu
S92.011K	Disp fx of body of rt calcaneus, subsq enc for fx w/ nonu
S92.121B	Disp fx of body of rt talus, init enc for opn fx
S92.121P	Disp fx of body of rt talus, subsq enc for fx w/ malu
S92.121K	Disp fx of body of rt talus, subsq enc for fx w/ nonu
S42.112B	Disp fx of body of scapula, lt shldr, init enc for opn fx
S42.112P	Disp fx of body of scapula, lt shldr, subsq enc for fx w/ malu
S42.112K	Disp fx of body of scapula, lt shldr, subsq enc for fx w/ nonu
S42.111B	Disp fx of body of scapula, rt shldr, init enc for opn fx
S42.111P	Disp fx of body of scapula, rt shldr, subsq enc for fx w/ malu
S42.111K	Disp fx of body of scapula, rt shldr, subsq enc for fx w/ nonu
S42.113B	Disp fx of body of scapula, unsp shldr, init enc for opn fx
S42.113P	Disp fx of body of scapula, unsp shldr, subsq enc for fx w/ malu
S42.113K	Disp fx of body of scapula, unsp shldr, subsq enc for fx w/ nonu
S92.013B	Disp fx of body of unsp calcaneus, init enc for opn fx
S92.013P	Disp fx of body of unsp calcaneus, subsq enc for fx w/ malu
S92.013K	Disp fx of body of unsp calcaneus, subsq enc for fx w/ nonu
S92.123B	Disp fx of body of unsp talus, init enc for opn fx
S92.123P	Disp fx of body of unsp talus, subsq enc for fx w/ malu
S92.123K	Disp fx of body of unsp talus, subsq enc for fx w/ nonu
S62.132B	Disp fx of capitate [os magnum] bone, lt wrist, init enc for opn fx
S62.132P	Disp fx of capitate [os magnum] bone, lt wrist, subsq enc for fx w/ malu
S62.132K	Disp fx of capitate [os magnum] bone, lt wrist, subsq enc for fx w/ nonu
S62.131B	Disp fx of capitate [os magnum] bone, rt wrist, init enc for opn fx
S62.131P	Disp fx of capitate [os magnum] bone, rt wrist, subsq enc for fx w/ malu
S62.131K	Disp fx of capitate [os magnum] bone, rt wrist, subsq enc for fx w/ nonu
S62.133B	Disp fx of capitate [os magnum] bone, unsp wrist, init enc for opn fx
S62.133P	Disp fx of capitate [os magnum] bone, unsp wrist, subsq enc for fx w/ malu

S62.133K	Disp fx of capitate [os magnum] bone, unsp wrist, subsq enc for fx w/ nonu
S42.132B	Disp fx of coracoid process, lt shldr, init enc for opn fx
S42.132P	Disp fx of coracoid process, lt shldr, subsq enc for fx w/ malu
S42.132K	Disp fx of coracoid process, lt shldr, subsq enc for fx w/ nonu
S42.131B	Disp fx of coracoid process, rt shldr, init enc for opn fx
S42.131P	Disp fx of coracoid process, rt shldr, subsq enc for fx w/ malu
S42.131K	Disp fx of coracoid process, rt shldr, subsq enc for fx w/ nonu
S42.133B	Disp fx of coracoid process, unsp shldr, init enc for opn fx
S42.133P	Disp fx of coracoid process, unsp shldr, subsq enc for fx w/ malu
S42.133K	Disp fx of coracoid process, unsp shldr, subsq enc for fx w/ nonu
S52.042P	Disp fx of coronoid process of lt ulna, subsq enc for clsd fx w/ malu
S52.042K	Disp fx of coronoid process of lt ulna, subsq enc for clsd fx w/ nonu
S52.042Q	Disp fx of coronoid process of lt ulna, subsq enc for opn fx type I or II w/ malu
S52.042M	Disp fx of coronoid process of lt ulna, subsq enc for opn fx type I or II w/ nonu
S52.042R	Disp fx of coronoid process of lt ulna, subsq enc for opn fx type IIIA, IIIB, or IIIC w/ malu
S52.042N	Disp fx of coronoid process of lt ulna, subsq enc for opn fx type IIIA, IIIB, or IIIC w/ nonu
S52.041P	Disp fx of coronoid process of rt ulna, subsq enc for clsd fx w/ malu
S52.041K	Disp fx of coronoid process of rt ulna, subsq enc for clsd fx w/ nonu
S52.041Q	Disp fx of coronoid process of rt ulna, subsq enc for opn fx type I or II w/ malu
S52.041M	Disp fx of coronoid process of rt ulna, subsq enc for opn fx type I or II w/ nonu
S52.041R	Disp fx of coronoid process of rt ulna, subsq enc for opn fx type IIIA, IIIB, or IIIC w/ malu
S52.041N	Disp fx of coronoid process of rt ulna, subsq enc for opn fx type IIIA, IIIB, or IIIC w/ nonu
S52.043P	Disp fx of coronoid process of unsp ulna, subsq enc for clsd fx w/ malu
S52.043K	Disp fx of coronoid process of unsp ulna, subsq enc for clsd fx w/ nonu
S52.043Q	Disp fx of coronoid process of unsp ulna, subsq enc for opn fx type I or II w/ malu
S52.043M	Disp fx of coronoid process of unsp ulna, subsq enc for opn fx type I or II w/ nonu
S52.043R	Disp fx of coronoid process of unsp ulna, subsq enc for opn fx type IIIA, IIIB, or IIIC w/ malu
S52.043N	Disp fx of coronoid process of unsp ulna, subsq enc for opn fx type IIIA, IIIB, or IIIC w/ nonu
S92.212B	Disp fx of cuboid bone of lt foot, init enc for opn fx
S92.212P	Disp fx of cuboid bone of lt foot, subsq enc for fx w/ malu
S92.212K	Disp fx of cuboid bone of lt foot, subsq enc for fx w/ nonu
S92.211B	Disp fx of cuboid bone of rt foot, init enc for opn fx
S92.211P	Disp fx of cuboid bone of rt foot, subsq enc for fx w/ malu
S92.211K	Disp fx of cuboid bone of rt foot, subsq enc for fx w/ nonu
S92.213B	Disp fx of cuboid bone of unsp foot, init enc for opn fx
S92.213P	Disp fx of cuboid bone of unsp foot, subsq enc for fx w/ malu
S92.213K	Disp fx of cuboid bone of unsp foot, subsq enc for fx w/ nonu
S92.422P	Disp fx of distal phalanx of lt great toe, subsq enc for fx w/ malu
S92.422K	Disp fx of distal phalanx of lt great toe, subsq enc for fx w/ nonu
S62.631B	Disp fx of distal phalanx of lt index finger, init enc for opn fx
S62.631P	Disp fx of distal phalanx of lt index finger, subsq enc for fx w/ malu
S62.631K	Disp fx of distal phalanx of lt index finger, subsq enc for fx w/ nonu
S92.532P	Disp fx of distal phalanx of lt lesser toe(s), subsq enc for fx w/ malu
S92.532K	Disp fx of distal phalanx of lt lesser toe(s), subsq enc for fx w/ nonu
S62.637B	Disp fx of distal phalanx of lt little finger, init enc for opn fx
S62.637P	Disp fx of distal phalanx of lt little finger, subsq enc for fx w/ malu
S62.637K	Disp fx of distal phalanx of lt little finger, subsq enc for fx w/ nonu
S62.633B	Disp fx of distal phalanx of lt mid finger, init enc for opn fx
S62.633P	Disp fx of distal phalanx of lt mid finger, subsq enc for fx w/ malu
S62.633K	Disp fx of distal phalanx of lt mid finger, subsq enc for fx w/ nonu
S62.635B	Disp fx of distal phalanx of lt ring finger, init enc for opn fx
S62.635P	Disp fx of distal phalanx of lt ring finger, subsq enc for fx w/ malu
S62.635K	Disp fx of distal phalanx of lt ring finger, subsq enc for fx w/ nonu
S62.522B	Disp fx of distal phalanx of lt thumb, init enc for opn fx
S62.522P	Disp fx of distal phalanx of lt thumb, subsq enc for fx w/ malu
S62.522K	Disp fx of distal phalanx of lt thumb, subsq enc for fx w/ nonu
S62.638B	Disp fx of distal phalanx of oth finger, init enc for opn fx
S62.638P	Disp fx of distal phalanx of oth finger, subsq enc for fx w/ malu
S62.638K	Disp fx of distal phalanx of oth finger, subsq enc for fx w/ nonu
S92.421P	Disp fx of distal phalanx of rt great toe, subsq enc for fx w/ malu
S92.421K	Disp fx of distal phalanx of rt great toe, subsq enc for fx w/ nonu
S62.630B	Disp fx of distal phalanx of rt index finger, init enc for opn fx

S62.630P	Disp fx of distal phalanx of rt index finger, subsq enc for fx w/ malu
S62.630K	Disp fx of distal phalanx of rt index finger, subsq enc for fx w/ nonu
S92.531P	Disp fx of distal phalanx of rt lesser toe(s), subsq enc for fx w/ malu
S92.531K	Disp fx of distal phalanx of rt lesser toe(s), subsq enc for fx w/ nonu
S62.636B	Disp fx of distal phalanx of rt little finger, init enc for opn fx
S62.636P	Disp fx of distal phalanx of rt little finger, subsq enc for fx w/ malu
S62.636K	Disp fx of distal phalanx of rt little finger, subsq enc for fx w/ nonu
S62.632B	Disp fx of distal phalanx of rt mid finger, init enc for opn fx
S62.632P	Disp fx of distal phalanx of rt mid finger, subsq enc for fx w/ malu
S62.632K	Disp fx of distal phalanx of rt mid finger, subsq enc for fx w/ nonu
S62.634B	Disp fx of distal phalanx of rt ring finger, init enc for opn fx
S62.634P	Disp fx of distal phalanx of rt ring finger, subsq enc for fx w/ malu
S62.634K	Disp fx of distal phalanx of rt ring finger, subsq enc for fx w/ nonu
S62.521B	Disp fx of distal phalanx of rt thumb, init enc for opn fx
S62.521P	Disp fx of distal phalanx of rt thumb, subsq enc for fx w/ malu
S62.521K	Disp fx of distal phalanx of rt thumb, subsq enc for fx w/ nonu
S62.639B	Disp fx of distal phalanx of unsp finger, init enc for opn fx
S62.639P	Disp fx of distal phalanx of unsp finger, subsq enc for fx w/ malu
S62.639K	Disp fx of distal phalanx of unsp finger, subsq enc for fx w/ nonu
S92.423P	Disp fx of distal phalanx of unsp great toe, subsq enc for fx w/ malu
S92.423K	Disp fx of distal phalanx of unsp great toe, subsq enc for fx w/ nonu
S92.533P	Disp fx of distal phalanx of unsp lesser toe(s), subsq enc for fx w/ malu
S92.533K	Disp fx of distal phalanx of unsp lesser toe(s), subsq enc for fx w/ nonu
S62.523B	Disp fx of distal phalanx of unsp thumb, init enc for opn fx
S62.523P	Disp fx of distal phalanx of unsp thumb, subsq enc for fx w/ malu
S62.523K	Disp fx of distal phalanx of unsp thumb, subsq enc for fx w/ nonu
S62.012B	Disp fx of distal pole of navicular [scaphoid] bone of lt wrist, init enc for opn fx
S62.012P	Disp fx of distal pole of navicular [scaphoid] bone of lt wrist, subsq enc for fx w/ malu
S62.012K	Disp fx of distal pole of navicular [scaphoid] bone of lt wrist, subsq enc for fx w/ nonu
S62.011B	Disp fx of distal pole of navicular [scaphoid] bone of rt wrist, init enc for opn fx
S62.011P	Disp fx of distal pole of navicular [scaphoid] bone of rt wrist, subsq enc for fx w/ malu
S62.011K	Disp fx of distal pole of navicular [scaphoid] bone of rt wrist, subsq enc for fx w/ nonu
S62.013B	Disp fx of distal pole of navicular [scaphoid] bone of unsp wrist, init enc for opn fx
S62.013P	Disp fx of distal pole of navicular [scaphoid] bone of unsp wrist, subsq enc for fx w/ malu
S62.013K	Disp fx of distal pole of navicular [scaphoid] bone of unsp wrist, subsq enc for fx w/ nonu
S72.022P	Disp fx of epiphysis (separation) (upr) of lt femur, subsq enc for clsd fx w/ malu
S72.022K	Disp fx of epiphysis (separation) (upr) of lt femur, subsq enc for clsd fx w/ nonu
S72.022Q	Disp fx of epiphysis (separation) (upr) of lt femur, subsq enc for opn fx type I or II w/ malu
S72.022M	Disp fx of epiphysis (separation) (upr) of lt femur, subsq enc for opn fx type I or II w/ nonu
S72.022R	Disp fx of epiphysis (separation) (upr) of lt femur, subsq enc for opn fx type IIIA, IIIB, or IIIC w/ malu
S72.022N	Disp fx of epiphysis (separation) (upr) of lt femur, subsq enc for opn fx type IIIA, IIIB, or IIIC w/ nonu
S72.021P	Disp fx of epiphysis (separation) (upr) of rt femur, subsq enc for clsd fx w/ malu
S72.021K	Disp fx of epiphysis (separation) (upr) of rt femur, subsq enc for clsd fx w/ nonu
S72.021Q	Disp fx of epiphysis (separation) (upr) of rt femur, subsq enc for opn fx type I or II w/ malu
S72.021M	Disp fx of epiphysis (separation) (upr) of rt femur, subsq enc for opn fx type I or II w/ nonu
S72.021R	Disp fx of epiphysis (separation) (upr) of rt femur, subsq enc for opn fx type IIIA, IIIB, or IIIC w/ malu
S72.021N	Disp fx of epiphysis (separation) (upr) of rt femur, subsq enc for opn fx type IIIA, IIIB, or IIIC w/ nonu
S72.023P	Disp fx of epiphysis (separation) (upr) of unsp femur, subsq enc for clsd fx w/ malu
S72.023K	Disp fx of epiphysis (separation) (upr) of unsp femur, subsq enc for clsd fx w/ nonu
S72.023Q	Disp fx of epiphysis (separation) (upr) of unsp femur, subsq enc for opn fx type I or II w/ malu
S72.023M	Disp fx of epiphysis (separation) (upr) of unsp femur, subsq enc for opn fx type I or II w/ nonu

S72.023R	Disp fx of epiphysis (separation) (upr) of unsp femur, subsq enc for opn fx type IIIA, IIIB, or IIIC w/ malu
S72.023N	Disp fx of epiphysis (separation) (upr) of unsp femur, subsq enc for opn fx type IIIA, IIIB, or IIIC w/ nonu
S42.142B	Disp fx of glenoid cavity of scapula, lt shldr, init enc for opn fx
S42.142P	Disp fx of glenoid cavity of scapula, lt shldr, subsq enc for fx w/ malu
S42.142K	Disp fx of glenoid cavity of scapula, lt shldr, subsq enc for fx w/ nonu
S42.141B	Disp fx of glenoid cavity of scapula, rt shldr, init enc for opn fx
S42.141P	Disp fx of glenoid cavity of scapula, rt shldr, subsq enc for fx w/ malu
S42.141K	Disp fx of glenoid cavity of scapula, rt shldr, subsq enc for fx w/ nonu
S42.143B	Disp fx of glenoid cavity of scapula, unsp shldr, init enc for opn fx
S42.143P	Disp fx of glenoid cavity of scapula, unsp shldr, subsq enc for fx w/ malu
S42.143K	Disp fx of glenoid cavity of scapula, unsp shldr, subsq enc for fx w/ nonu
S72.112P	Disp fx of greater trochanter of lt femur, subsq enc for clsd fx w/ malu
S72.112K	Disp fx of greater trochanter of lt femur, subsq enc for clsd fx w/ nonu
S72.112Q	Disp fx of greater trochanter of lt femur, subsq enc for opn fx type I or II w/ malu
S72.112M	Disp fx of greater trochanter of lt femur, subsq enc for opn fx type I or II w/ nonu
S72.112R	Disp fx of greater trochanter of lt femur, subsq enc for opn fx type IIIA, IIIB, or IIIC w/ malu
S72.112N	Disp fx of greater trochanter of lt femur, subsq enc for opn fx type IIIA, IIIB, or IIIC w/ nonu
S72.111P	Disp fx of greater trochanter of rt femur, subsq enc for clsd fx w/ malu
S72.111K	Disp fx of greater trochanter of rt femur, subsq enc for clsd fx w/ nonu
S72.111Q	Disp fx of greater trochanter of rt femur, subsq enc for opn fx type I or II w/ malu
S72.111M	Disp fx of greater trochanter of rt femur, subsq enc for opn fx type I or II w/ nonu
S72.111R	Disp fx of greater trochanter of rt femur, subsq enc for opn fx type IIIA, IIIB, or IIIC w/ malu
S72.111N	Disp fx of greater trochanter of rt femur, subsq enc for opn fx type IIIA, IIIB, or IIIC w/ nonu
S72.113P	Disp fx of greater trochanter of unsp femur, subsq enc for clsd fx w/ malu
S72.113K	Disp fx of greater trochanter of unsp femur, subsq enc for clsd fx w/ nonu
S72.113Q	Disp fx of greater trochanter of unsp femur, subsq enc for opn fx type I or II w/ malu
S72.113M	Disp fx of greater trochanter of unsp femur, subsq enc for opn fx type I or II w/ nonu
S72.113R	Disp fx of greater trochanter of unsp femur, subsq enc for opn fx type IIIA, IIIB, or IIIC w/ malu
S72.113N	Disp fx of greater trochanter of unsp femur, subsq enc for opn fx type IIIA, IIIB, or IIIC w/ nonu
S42.252A	Disp fx of greater tuberosity of lt humerus, init enc for clsd fx
S42.252P	Disp fx of greater tuberosity of lt humerus, subsq enc for fx w/ malu
S42.252K	Disp fx of greater tuberosity of lt humerus, subsq enc for fx w/ nonu
S42.251A	Disp fx of greater tuberosity of rt humerus, init enc for clsd fx
S42.251P	Disp fx of greater tuberosity of rt humerus, subsq enc for fx w/ malu
S42.251K	Disp fx of greater tuberosity of rt humerus, subsq enc for fx w/ nonu
S42.253A	Disp fx of greater tuberosity of unsp humerus, init enc for clsd fx
S42.253P	Disp fx of greater tuberosity of unsp humerus, subsq enc for fx w/ malu
S42.253K	Disp fx of greater tuberosity of unsp humerus, subsq enc for fx w/ nonu
S52.122P	Disp fx of head of lt radius, subsq enc for clsd fx w/ malu
S52.122K	Disp fx of head of lt radius, subsq enc for clsd fx w/ nonu
S52.122Q	Disp fx of head of lt radius, subsq enc for opn fx type I or II w/ malu
S52.122M	Disp fx of head of lt radius, subsq enc for opn fx type I or II w/ nonu
S52.122R	Disp fx of head of lt radius, subsq enc for opn fx type IIIA, IIIB, or IIIC w/ malu
S52.122N	Disp fx of head of lt radius, subsq enc for opn fx type IIIA, IIIB, or IIIC w/ nonu
S52.121P	Disp fx of head of rt radius, subsq enc for clsd fx w/ malu
S52.121K	Disp fx of head of rt radius, subsq enc for clsd fx w/ nonu
S52.121Q	Disp fx of head of rt radius, subsq enc for opn fx type I or II w/ malu
S52.121M	Disp fx of head of rt radius, subsq enc for opn fx type I or II w/ nonu
S52.121R	Disp fx of head of rt radius, subsq enc for opn fx type IIIA, IIIB, or IIIC w/ malu
S52.121N	Disp fx of head of rt radius, subsq enc for opn fx type IIIA, IIIB, or IIIC w/ nonu
S52.123P	Disp fx of head of unsp radius, subsq enc for clsd fx w/ malu
S52.123K	Disp fx of head of unsp radius, subsq enc for clsd fx w/ nonu
S52.123Q	Disp fx of head of unsp radius, subsq enc for opn fx type I or II w/ malu
S52.123M	Disp fx of head of unsp radius, subsq enc for opn fx type I or II w/ nonu
S52.123R	Disp fx of head of unsp radius, subsq enc for opn fx type IIIA, IIIB, or IIIC w/ malu
S52.123N	Disp fx of head of unsp radius, subsq enc for opn fx type IIIA, IIIB, or IIIC w/ nonu
S62.152B	Disp fx of hook process of hamate [unciform] bone, lt wrist, init enc for opn fx
S62.152P	Disp fx of hook process of hamate [unciform] bone, lt wrist, subsq enc for fx w/ malu
S62.152K	Disp fx of hook process of hamate [unciform] bone, lt wrist, subsq enc for fx w/ nonu
S62.151B	Disp fx of hook process of hamate [unciform] bone, rt wrist, init enc for opn fx
S62.151P	Disp fx of hook process of hamate [unciform] bone, rt wrist, subsq enc for fx w/ malu
S62.151K	Disp fx of hook process of hamate [unciform] bone, rt wrist, subsq enc for fx w/ nonu
S62.153B	Disp fx of hook process of hamate [unciform] bone, unsp wrist, init enc for opn fx
S62.153P	Disp fx of hook process of hamate [unciform] bone, unsp wrist, subsq enc for fx w/ malu
S62.153K	Disp fx of hook process of hamate [unciform] bone, unsp wrist, subsq enc for fx w/ nonu
S92.232B	Disp fx of intermediate cuneiform of lt foot, init enc for opn fx
S92.232P	Disp fx of intermediate cuneiform of lt foot, subsq enc for fx w/ malu
S92.232K	Disp fx of intermediate cuneiform of lt foot, subsq enc for fx w/ nonu
S92.231B	Disp fx of intermediate cuneiform of rt foot, init enc for opn fx
S92.231P	Disp fx of intermediate cuneiform of rt foot, subsq enc for fx w/ malu
S92.231K	Disp fx of intermediate cuneiform of rt foot, subsq enc for fx w/ nonu
S92.233B	Disp fx of intermediate cuneiform of unsp foot, init enc for opn fx
S92.233P	Disp fx of intermediate cuneiform of unsp foot, subsq enc for fx w/ malu
S92.233K	Disp fx of intermediate cuneiform of unsp foot, subsq enc for fx w/ nonu
S72.422A	Disp fx of lat condyle of lt femur, init enc for clsd fx
S72.422P	Disp fx of lat condyle of lt femur, subsq enc for clsd fx w/ malu
S72.422K	Disp fx of lat condyle of lt femur, subsq enc for clsd fx w/ nonu
S72.422Q	Disp fx of lat condyle of lt femur, subsq enc for opn fx type I or II w/ malu
S72.422M	Disp fx of lat condyle of lt femur, subsq enc for opn fx type I or II w/ nonu
S72.422R	Disp fx of lat condyle of lt femur, subsq enc for opn fx type IIIA, IIIB, or IIIC w/ malu
S72.422N	Disp fx of lat condyle of lt femur, subsq enc for opn fx type IIIA, IIIB, or IIIC w/ nonu
S42.452A	Disp fx of lat condyle of lt humerus, init enc for clsd fx
S42.452P	Disp fx of lat condyle of lt humerus, subsq enc for fx w/ malu
S42.452K	Disp fx of lat condyle of lt humerus, subsq enc for fx w/ nonu
S82.122A	Disp fx of lat condyle of lt tibia, init enc for clsd fx
S82.122P	Disp fx of lat condyle of lt tibia, subsq enc for clsd fx w/ malu
S82.122K	Disp fx of lat condyle of lt tibia, subsq enc for clsd fx w/ nonu
S82.122Q	Disp fx of lat condyle of lt tibia, subsq enc for opn fx type I or II w/ malu
S82.122M	Disp fx of lat condyle of lt tibia, subsq enc for opn fx type I or II w/ nonu
S82.122R	Disp fx of lat condyle of lt tibia, subsq enc for opn fx type IIIA, IIIB, or IIIC w/ malu
S82.122N	Disp fx of lat condyle of lt tibia, subsq enc for opn fx type IIIA, IIIB, or IIIC w/ nonu
S72.421A	Disp fx of lat condyle of rt femur, init enc for clsd fx
S72.421P	Disp fx of lat condyle of rt femur, subsq enc for clsd fx w/ malu
S72.421K	Disp fx of lat condyle of rt femur, subsq enc for clsd fx w/ nonu
S72.421Q	Disp fx of lat condyle of rt femur, subsq enc for opn fx type I or II w/ malu
S72.421M	Disp fx of lat condyle of rt femur, subsq enc for opn fx type I or II w/ nonu
S72.421R	Disp fx of lat condyle of rt femur, subsq enc for opn fx type IIIA, IIIB, or IIIC w/ malu
S72.421N	Disp fx of lat condyle of rt femur, subsq enc for opn fx type IIIA, IIIB, or IIIC w/ nonu
S42.451A	Disp fx of lat condyle of rt humerus, init enc for clsd fx
S42.451P	Disp fx of lat condyle of rt humerus, subsq enc for fx w/ malu
S42.451K	Disp fx of lat condyle of rt humerus, subsq enc for fx w/ nonu
S82.121A	Disp fx of lat condyle of rt tibia, init enc for clsd fx
S82.121P	Disp fx of lat condyle of rt tibia, subsq enc for clsd fx w/ malu
S82.121K	Disp fx of lat condyle of rt tibia, subsq enc for clsd fx w/ nonu
S82.121Q	Disp fx of lat condyle of rt tibia, subsq enc for opn fx type I or II w/ malu
S82.121M	Disp fx of lat condyle of rt tibia, subsq enc for opn fx type I or II w/ nonu
S82.121R	Disp fx of lat condyle of rt tibia, subsq enc for opn fx type IIIA, IIIB, or IIIC w/ malu
S82.121N	Disp fx of lat condyle of rt tibia, subsq enc for opn fx type IIIA, IIIB, or IIIC w/ nonu
S72.423A	Disp fx of lat condyle of unsp femur, init enc for clsd fx
S72.423P	Disp fx of lat condyle of unsp femur, subsq enc for clsd fx w/ malu
S72.423K	Disp fx of lat condyle of unsp femur, subsq enc for clsd fx w/ nonu
S72.423Q	Disp fx of lat condyle of unsp femur, subsq enc for opn fx type I or II w/ malu

S72.423M	Disp fx of lat condyle of unsp femur, subsq enc for opn fx type I or II w/ nonu
S72.423R	Disp fx of lat condyle of unsp femur, subsq enc for opn fx type IIIA, IIIB, or IIIC w/ malu
S72.423N	Disp fx of lat condyle of unsp femur, subsq enc for opn fx type IIIA, IIIB, or IIIC w/ nonu
S42.453A	Disp fx of lat condyle of unsp humerus, init enc for clsd fx
S42.453P	Disp fx of lat condyle of unsp humerus, subsq enc for fx w/ malu
S42.453K	Disp fx of lat condyle of unsp humerus, subsq enc for fx w/ nonu
S82.123A	Disp fx of lat condyle of unsp tibia, init enc for clsd fx
S82.123P	Disp fx of lat condyle of unsp tibia, subsq enc for clsd fx w/ malu
S82.123K	Disp fx of lat condyle of unsp tibia, subsq enc for clsd fx w/ nonu
S82.123Q	Disp fx of lat condyle of unsp tibia, subsq enc for opn fx type I or II w/ malu
S82.123M	Disp fx of lat condyle of unsp tibia, subsq enc for opn fx type I or II w/ nonu
S82.123R	Disp fx of lat condyle of unsp tibia, subsq enc for opn fx type IIIA, IIIB, or IIIC w/ malu
S82.123N	Disp fx of lat condyle of unsp tibia, subsq enc for opn fx type IIIA, IIIB, or IIIC w/ nonu
S92.222B	Disp fx of lat cuneiform of lt foot, init enc for opn fx
S92.222P	Disp fx of lat cuneiform of lt foot, subsq enc for fx w/ malu
S92.222K	Disp fx of lat cuneiform of lt foot, subsq enc for fx w/ nonu
S92.221B	Disp fx of lat cuneiform of rt foot, init enc for opn fx
S92.221P	Disp fx of lat cuneiform of rt foot, subsq enc for fx w/ malu
S92.221K	Disp fx of lat cuneiform of rt foot, subsq enc for fx w/ nonu
S92.223B	Disp fx of lat cuneiform of unsp foot, init enc for opn fx
S92.223P	Disp fx of lat cuneiform of unsp foot, subsq enc for fx w/ malu
S92.223K	Disp fx of lat cuneiform of unsp foot, subsq enc for fx w/ nonu
S42.032B	Disp fx of lat end of lt clavicle, init enc for opn fx
S42.032P	Disp fx of lat end of lt clavicle, subsq enc for fx w/ malu
S42.032K	Disp fx of lat end of lt clavicle, subsq enc for fx w/ nonu
S42.031B	Disp fx of lat end of rt clavicle, init enc for opn fx
S42.031P	Disp fx of lat end of rt clavicle, subsq enc for fx w/ malu
S42.031K	Disp fx of lat end of rt clavicle, subsq enc for fx w/ nonu
S42.033B	Disp fx of lat end of unsp clavicle, init enc for opn fx
S42.033P	Disp fx of lat end of unsp clavicle, subsq enc for fx w/ malu
S42.033K	Disp fx of lat end of unsp clavicle, subsq enc for fx w/ nonu
S82.62XB	Disp fx of lat malleolus of lt fibula, init enc for opn fx type I or II
S82.62XC	Disp fx of lat malleolus of lt fibula, init enc for opn fx type IIIA, IIIB, or IIIC
S82.62XP	Disp fx of lat malleolus of lt fibula, subsq enc for clsd fx w/ malu
S82.62XK	Disp fx of lat malleolus of lt fibula, subsq enc for clsd fx w/ nonu
S82.62XQ	Disp fx of lat malleolus of lt fibula, subsq enc for opn fx type I or II w/ malu
S82.62XM	Disp fx of lat malleolus of lt fibula, subsq enc for opn fx type I or II w/ nonu
S82.62XR	Disp fx of lat malleolus of lt fibula, subsq enc for opn fx type IIIA, IIIB, or IIIC w/ malu
S82.62XN	Disp fx of lat malleolus of lt fibula, subsq enc for opn fx type IIIA, IIIB, or IIIC w/ nonu
S82.61XB	Disp fx of lat malleolus of rt fibula, init enc for opn fx type I or II
S82.61XC	Disp fx of lat malleolus of rt fibula, init enc for opn fx type IIIA, IIIB, or IIIC
S82.61XP	Disp fx of lat malleolus of rt fibula, subsq enc for clsd fx w/ malu
S82.61XK	Disp fx of lat malleolus of rt fibula, subsq enc for clsd fx w/ nonu
S82.61XQ	Disp fx of lat malleolus of rt fibula, subsq enc for opn fx type I or II w/ malu
S82.61XM	Disp fx of lat malleolus of rt fibula, subsq enc for opn fx type I or II w/ nonu
S82.61XR	Disp fx of lat malleolus of rt fibula, subsq enc for opn fx type IIIA, IIIB, or IIIC w/ malu
S82.61XN	Disp fx of lat malleolus of rt fibula, subsq enc for opn fx type IIIA, IIIB, or IIIC w/ nonu
S82.63XB	Disp fx of lat malleolus of unsp fibula, init enc for opn fx type I or II
S82.63XC	Disp fx of lat malleolus of unsp fibula, init enc for opn fx type IIIA, IIIB, or IIIC
S82.63XP	Disp fx of lat malleolus of unsp fibula, subsq enc for clsd fx w/ malu
S82.63XK	Disp fx of lat malleolus of unsp fibula, subsq enc for clsd fx w/ nonu
S82.63XQ	Disp fx of lat malleolus of unsp fibula, subsq enc for opn fx type I or II w/ malu
S82.63XM	Disp fx of lat malleolus of unsp fibula, subsq enc for opn fx type I or II w/ nonu
S82.63XR	Disp fx of lat malleolus of unsp fibula, subsq enc for opn fx type IIIA, IIIB, or IIIC w/ malu
S82.63XN	Disp fx of lat malleolus of unsp fibula, subsq enc for opn fx type IIIA, IIIB, or IIIC w/ nonu
S72.122P	Disp fx of lesser trochanter of lt femur, subsq enc for clsd fx w/ malu
S72.122K	Disp fx of lesser trochanter of lt femur, subsq enc for clsd fx w/ nonu
S72.122Q	Disp fx of lesser trochanter of lt femur, subsq enc for opn fx type I or II w/ malu
S72.122M	Disp fx of lesser trochanter of lt femur, subsq enc for opn fx type I or II w/ nonu
S72.122R	Disp fx of lesser trochanter of lt femur, subsq enc for opn fx type IIIA, IIIB, or IIIC w/ malu
S72.122N	Disp fx of lesser trochanter of lt femur, subsq enc for opn fx type IIIA, IIIB, or IIIC w/ nonu
S72.121P	Disp fx of lesser trochanter of rt femur, subsq enc for clsd fx w/ malu
S72.121K	Disp fx of lesser trochanter of rt femur, subsq enc for clsd fx w/ nonu
S72.121Q	Disp fx of lesser trochanter of rt femur, subsq enc for opn fx type I or II w/ malu
S72.121M	Disp fx of lesser trochanter of rt femur, subsq enc for opn fx type I or II w/ nonu
S72.121R	Disp fx of lesser trochanter of rt femur, subsq enc for opn fx type IIIA, IIIB, or IIIC w/ malu
S72.121N	Disp fx of lesser trochanter of rt femur, subsq enc for opn fx type IIIA, IIIB, or IIIC w/ nonu
S72.123P	Disp fx of lesser trochanter of unsp femur, subsq enc for clsd fx w/ malu
S72.123K	Disp fx of lesser trochanter of unsp femur, subsq enc for clsd fx w/ nonu
S72.123Q	Disp fx of lesser trochanter of unsp femur, subsq enc for opn fx type I or II w/ malu
S72.123M	Disp fx of lesser trochanter of unsp femur, subsq enc for opn fx type I or II w/ nonu
S72.123R	Disp fx of lesser trochanter of unsp femur, subsq enc for opn fx type IIIA, IIIB, or IIIC w/ malu
S72.123N	Disp fx of lesser trochanter of unsp femur, subsq enc for opn fx type IIIA, IIIB, or IIIC w/ nonu
S42.262A	Disp fx of lesser tuberosity of lt humerus, init enc for clsd fx
S42.262P	Disp fx of lesser tuberosity of lt humerus, subsq enc for fx w/ malu
S42.262K	Disp fx of lesser tuberosity of lt humerus, subsq enc for fx w/ nonu
S42.261A	Disp fx of lesser tuberosity of rt humerus, init enc for clsd fx
S42.261P	Disp fx of lesser tuberosity of rt humerus, subsq enc for fx w/ malu
S42.261K	Disp fx of lesser tuberosity of rt humerus, subsq enc for fx w/ nonu
S42.263A	Disp fx of lesser tuberosity of unsp humerus, init enc for clsd fx
S42.263P	Disp fx of lesser tuberosity of unsp humerus, subsq enc for fx w/ malu
S42.263K	Disp fx of lesser tuberosity of unsp humerus, subsq enc for fx w/ nonu
S52.512A	Disp fx of lt radial styloid process, init enc for clsd fx
S52.512P	Disp fx of lt radial styloid process, subsq enc for clsd fx w/ malu
S52.512K	Disp fx of lt radial styloid process, subsq enc for clsd fx w/ nonu
S52.512Q	Disp fx of lt radial styloid process, subsq enc for opn fx type I or II w/ malu
S52.512M	Disp fx of lt radial styloid process, subsq enc for opn fx type I or II w/ nonu
S52.512R	Disp fx of lt radial styloid process, subsq enc for opn fx type IIIA, IIIB, or IIIC w/ malu
S52.512N	Disp fx of lt radial styloid process, subsq enc for opn fx type IIIA, IIIB, or IIIC w/ nonu
S82.112A	Disp fx of lt tibial spine, init enc for clsd fx
S82.112P	Disp fx of lt tibial spine, subsq enc for clsd fx w/ malu
S82.112K	Disp fx of lt tibial spine, subsq enc for clsd fx w/ nonu
S82.112Q	Disp fx of lt tibial spine, subsq enc for opn fx type I or II w/ malu
S82.112M	Disp fx of lt tibial spine, subsq enc for opn fx type I or II w/ nonu
S82.112R	Disp fx of lt tibial spine, subsq enc for opn fx type IIIA, IIIB, or IIIC w/ malu
S82.112N	Disp fx of lt tibial spine, subsq enc for opn fx type IIIA, IIIB, or IIIC w/ nonu
S82.152A	Disp fx of lt tibial tuberosity, init enc for clsd fx
S82.152P	Disp fx of lt tibial tuberosity, subsq enc for clsd fx w/ malu
S82.152K	Disp fx of lt tibial tuberosity, subsq enc for clsd fx w/ nonu
S82.152Q	Disp fx of lt tibial tuberosity, subsq enc for opn fx type I or II w/ malu
S82.152M	Disp fx of lt tibial tuberosity, subsq enc for opn fx type I or II w/ nonu
S82.152R	Disp fx of lt tibial tuberosity, subsq enc for opn fx type IIIA, IIIB, or IIIC w/ malu
S82.152N	Disp fx of lt tibial tuberosity, subsq enc for opn fx type IIIA, IIIB, or IIIC w/ nonu
S52.612A	Disp fx of lt ulna styloid process, init enc for clsd fx
S52.612P	Disp fx of lt ulna styloid process, subsq enc for clsd fx w/ malu
S52.612K	Disp fx of lt ulna styloid process, subsq enc for clsd fx w/ nonu
S52.612Q	Disp fx of lt ulna styloid process, subsq enc for opn fx type I or II w/ malu
S52.612M	Disp fx of lt ulna styloid process, subsq enc for opn fx type I or II w/ nonu
S52.612R	Disp fx of lt ulna styloid process, subsq enc for opn fx type IIIA, IIIB, or IIIC w/ malu
S52.612N	Disp fx of lt ulna styloid process, subsq enc for opn fx type IIIA, IIIB, or IIIC w/ nonu
S62.122B	Disp fx of lunate [semilunar], lt wrist, init enc for opn fx
S62.122P	Disp fx of lunate [semilunar], lt wrist, subsq enc for fx w/ malu
S62.122K	Disp fx of lunate [semilunar], lt wrist, subsq enc for fx w/ nonu

S62.121B	Disp fx of lunate [semilunar], rt wrist, init enc for opn fx
S62.121P	Disp fx of lunate [semilunar], rt wrist, subsq enc for fx w/ malu
S62.121K	Disp fx of lunate [semilunar], rt wrist, subsq enc for fx w/ nonu
S62.123B	Disp fx of lunate [semilunar], unsp wrist, init enc for opn fx
S62.123P	Disp fx of lunate [semilunar], unsp wrist, subsq enc for fx w/ malu
S62.123K	Disp fx of lunate [semilunar], unsp wrist, subsq enc for fx w/ nonu
S72.442A	Disp fx of lwr epiphysis (separation) of lt femur, init enc for clsd fx
S72.442P	Disp fx of lwr epiphysis (separation) of lt femur, subsq enc for clsd fx w/ malu
S72.442K	Disp fx of lwr epiphysis (separation) of lt femur, subsq enc for clsd fx w/ nonu
S72.442Q	Disp fx of lwr epiphysis (separation) of lt femur, subsq enc for opn fx type I or II w/ malu
S72.442M	Disp fx of lwr epiphysis (separation) of lt femur, subsq enc for opn fx type I or II w/ nonu
S72.442R	Disp fx of lwr epiphysis (separation) of lt femur, subsq enc for opn fx type IIIA, IIIB, or IIIC w/ malu
S72.442N	Disp fx of lwr epiphysis (separation) of lt femur, subsq enc for opn fx type IIIA, IIIB, or IIIC w/ nonu
S72.441A	Disp fx of lwr epiphysis (separation) of rt femur, init enc for clsd fx
S72.441P	Disp fx of lwr epiphysis (separation) of rt femur, subsq enc for clsd fx w/ malu
S72.441K	Disp fx of lwr epiphysis (separation) of rt femur, subsq enc for clsd fx w/ nonu
S72.441Q	Disp fx of lwr epiphysis (separation) of rt femur, subsq enc for opn fx type I or II w/ malu
S72.441M	Disp fx of lwr epiphysis (separation) of rt femur, subsq enc for opn fx type I or II w/ nonu
S72.441R	Disp fx of lwr epiphysis (separation) of rt femur, subsq enc for opn fx type IIIA, IIIB, or IIIC w/ malu
S72.441N	Disp fx of lwr epiphysis (separation) of rt femur, subsq enc for opn fx type IIIA, IIIB, or IIIC w/ nonu
S72.443A	Disp fx of lwr epiphysis (separation) of unsp femur, init enc for clsd fx
S72.443P	Disp fx of lwr epiphysis (separation) of unsp femur, subsq enc for clsd fx w/ malu
S72.443K	Disp fx of lwr epiphysis (separation) of unsp femur, subsq enc for clsd fx w/ nonu
S72.443Q	Disp fx of lwr epiphysis (separation) of unsp femur, subsq enc for opn fx type I or II w/ malu
S72.443M	Disp fx of lwr epiphysis (separation) of unsp femur, subsq enc for opn fx type I or II w/ nonu
S72.443R	Disp fx of lwr epiphysis (separation) of unsp femur, subsq enc for opn fx type IIIA, IIIB, or IIIC w/ malu
S72.443N	Disp fx of lwr epiphysis (separation) of unsp femur, subsq enc for opn fx type IIIA, IIIB, or IIIC w/ nonu
S72.432A	Disp fx of med condyle of lt femur, init enc for clsd fx
S72.432P	Disp fx of med condyle of lt femur, subsq enc for clsd fx w/ malu
S72.432K	Disp fx of med condyle of lt femur, subsq enc for clsd fx w/ nonu
S72.432Q	Disp fx of med condyle of lt femur, subsq enc for opn fx type I or II w/ malu
S72.432M	Disp fx of med condyle of lt femur, subsq enc for opn fx type I or II w/ nonu
S72.432R	Disp fx of med condyle of lt femur, subsq enc for opn fx type IIIA, IIIB, or IIIC w/ malu
S72.432N	Disp fx of med condyle of lt femur, subsq enc for opn fx type IIIA, IIIB, or IIIC w/ nonu
S42.462A	Disp fx of med condyle of lt humerus, init enc for clsd fx
S42.462P	Disp fx of med condyle of lt humerus, subsq enc for fx w/ malu
S42.462K	Disp fx of med condyle of lt humerus, subsq enc for fx w/ nonu
S82.132A	Disp fx of med condyle of lt tibia, init enc for clsd fx
S82.132P	Disp fx of med condyle of lt tibia, subsq enc for clsd fx w/ malu
S82.132K	Disp fx of med condyle of lt tibia, subsq enc for clsd fx w/ nonu
S82.132Q	Disp fx of med condyle of lt tibia, subsq enc for opn fx type I or II w/ malu
S82.132M	Disp fx of med condyle of lt tibia, subsq enc for opn fx type I or II w/ nonu
S82.132R	Disp fx of med condyle of lt tibia, subsq enc for opn fx type IIIA, IIIB, or IIIC w/ malu
S82.132N	Disp fx of med condyle of lt tibia, subsq enc for opn fx type IIIA, IIIB, or IIIC w/ nonu
S72.431A	Disp fx of med condyle of rt femur, init enc for clsd fx
S72.431P	Disp fx of med condyle of rt femur, subsq enc for clsd fx w/ malu
S72.431K	Disp fx of med condyle of rt femur, subsq enc for clsd fx w/ nonu
S72.431Q	Disp fx of med condyle of rt femur, subsq enc for opn fx type I or II w/ malu
S72.431M	Disp fx of med condyle of rt femur, subsq enc for opn fx type I or II w/ nonu
S72.431R	Disp fx of med condyle of rt femur, subsq enc for opn fx type IIIA, IIIB, or IIIC w/ malu
S72.431N	Disp fx of med condyle of rt femur, subsq enc for opn fx type IIIA, IIIB, or IIIC w/ nonu
S42.461A	Disp fx of med condyle of rt humerus, init enc for clsd fx
S42.461P	Disp fx of med condyle of rt humerus, subsq enc for fx w/ malu
S42.461K	Disp fx of med condyle of rt humerus, subsq enc for fx w/ nonu
S82.131A	Disp fx of med condyle of rt tibia, init enc for clsd fx
S82.131P	Disp fx of med condyle of rt tibia, subsq enc for clsd fx w/ malu
S82.131K	Disp fx of med condyle of rt tibia, subsq enc for clsd fx w/ nonu
S82.131Q	Disp fx of med condyle of rt tibia, subsq enc for opn fx type I or II w/ malu
S82.131M	Disp fx of med condyle of rt tibia, subsq enc for opn fx type I or II w/ nonu
S82.131R	Disp fx of med condyle of rt tibia, subsq enc for opn fx type IIIA, IIIB, or IIIC w/ malu
S82.131N	Disp fx of med condyle of rt tibia, subsq enc for opn fx type IIIA, IIIB, or IIIC w/ nonu
S72.433A	Disp fx of med condyle of unsp femur, init enc for clsd fx
S72.433P	Disp fx of med condyle of unsp femur, subsq enc for clsd fx w/ malu
S72.433K	Disp fx of med condyle of unsp femur, subsq enc for clsd fx w/ nonu
S72.433Q	Disp fx of med condyle of unsp femur, subsq enc for opn fx type I or II w/ malu
S72.433M	Disp fx of med condyle of unsp femur, subsq enc for opn fx type I or II w/ nonu
S72.433R	Disp fx of med condyle of unsp femur, subsq enc for opn fx type IIIA, IIIB, or IIIC w/ malu
S72.433N	Disp fx of med condyle of unsp femur, subsq enc for opn fx type IIIA, IIIB, or IIIC w/ nonu
S42.463A	Disp fx of med condyle of unsp humerus, init enc for clsd fx
S42.463P	Disp fx of med condyle of unsp humerus, subsq enc for fx w/ malu
S42.463K	Disp fx of med condyle of unsp humerus, subsq enc for fx w/ nonu
S82.133A	Disp fx of med condyle of unsp tibia, init enc for clsd fx
S82.133P	Disp fx of med condyle of unsp tibia, subsq enc for clsd fx w/ malu
S82.133K	Disp fx of med condyle of unsp tibia, subsq enc for clsd fx w/ nonu
S82.133Q	Disp fx of med condyle of unsp tibia, subsq enc for opn fx type I or II w/ malu
S82.133M	Disp fx of med condyle of unsp tibia, subsq enc for opn fx type I or II w/ nonu
S82.133R	Disp fx of med condyle of unsp tibia, subsq enc for opn fx type IIIA, IIIB, or IIIC w/ malu
S82.133N	Disp fx of med condyle of unsp tibia, subsq enc for opn fx type IIIA, IIIB, or IIIC w/ nonu
S92.242B	Disp fx of med cuneiform of lt foot, init enc for opn fx
S92.242P	Disp fx of med cuneiform of lt foot, subsq enc for fx w/ malu
S92.242K	Disp fx of med cuneiform of lt foot, subsq enc for fx w/ nonu
S92.241B	Disp fx of med cuneiform of rt foot, init enc for opn fx
S92.241P	Disp fx of med cuneiform of rt foot, subsq enc for fx w/ malu
S92.241K	Disp fx of med cuneiform of rt foot, subsq enc for fx w/ nonu
S92.243B	Disp fx of med cuneiform of unsp foot, init enc for opn fx
S92.243P	Disp fx of med cuneiform of unsp foot, subsq enc for fx w/ malu
S92.243K	Disp fx of med cuneiform of unsp foot, subsq enc for fx w/ nonu
S82.52XB	Disp fx of med malleolus of lt tibia, init enc for opn fx type I or II
S82.52XC	Disp fx of med malleolus of lt tibia, init enc for opn fx type IIIA, IIIB, or IIIC
S82.52XP	Disp fx of med malleolus of lt tibia, subsq enc for clsd fx w/ malu
S82.52XK	Disp fx of med malleolus of lt tibia, subsq enc for clsd fx w/ nonu
S82.52XQ	Disp fx of med malleolus of lt tibia, subsq enc for opn fx type I or II w/ malu
S82.52XM	Disp fx of med malleolus of lt tibia, subsq enc for opn fx type I or II w/ nonu
S82.52XR	Disp fx of med malleolus of lt tibia, subsq enc for opn fx type IIIA, IIIB, or IIIC w/ malu
S82.52XN	Disp fx of med malleolus of lt tibia, subsq enc for opn fx type IIIA, IIIB, or IIIC w/ nonu
S82.51XB	Disp fx of med malleolus of rt tibia, init enc for opn fx type I or II
S82.51XC	Disp fx of med malleolus of rt tibia, init enc for opn fx type IIIA, IIIB, or IIIC
S82.51XP	Disp fx of med malleolus of rt tibia, subsq enc for clsd fx w/ malu
S82.51XK	Disp fx of med malleolus of rt tibia, subsq enc for clsd fx w/ nonu
S82.51XQ	Disp fx of med malleolus of rt tibia, subsq enc for opn fx type I or II w/ malu
S82.51XM	Disp fx of med malleolus of rt tibia, subsq enc for opn fx type I or II w/ nonu
S82.51XR	Disp fx of med malleolus of rt tibia, subsq enc for opn fx type IIIA, IIIB, or IIIC w/ malu
S82.51XN	Disp fx of med malleolus of rt tibia, subsq enc for opn fx type IIIA, IIIB, or IIIC w/ nonu
S82.53XB	Disp fx of med malleolus of unsp tibia, init enc for opn fx type I or II

Code	Description
S82.53XC	Disp fx of med malleolus of unsp tibia, init enc for opn fx type IIIA, IIIB, or IIIC
S82.53XP	Disp fx of med malleolus of unsp tibia, subsq enc for clsd fx w/ malu
S82.53XK	Disp fx of med malleolus of unsp tibia, subsq enc for clsd fx w/ nonu
S82.53XQ	Disp fx of med malleolus of unsp tibia, subsq enc for opn fx type I or II w/ malu
S82.53XM	Disp fx of med malleolus of unsp tibia, subsq enc for opn fx type I or II w/ nonu
S82.53XR	Disp fx of med malleolus of unsp tibia, subsq enc for opn fx type IIIA, IIIB, or IIIC w/ malu
S82.53XN	Disp fx of med malleolus of unsp tibia, subsq enc for opn fx type IIIA, IIIB, or IIIC w/ nonu
S62.621B	Disp fx of med phalanx of lt index finger, init enc for opn fx
S62.621P	Disp fx of med phalanx of lt index finger, subsq enc for fx w/ malu
S62.621K	Disp fx of med phalanx of lt index finger, subsq enc for fx w/ nonu
S92.522P	Disp fx of med phalanx of lt lesser toe(s), subsq enc for fx w/ malu
S92.522K	Disp fx of med phalanx of lt lesser toe(s), subsq enc for fx w/ nonu
S62.627B	Disp fx of med phalanx of lt little finger, init enc for opn fx
S62.627P	Disp fx of med phalanx of lt little finger, subsq enc for fx w/ malu
S62.627K	Disp fx of med phalanx of lt little finger, subsq enc for fx w/ nonu
S62.623B	Disp fx of med phalanx of lt mid finger, init enc for opn fx
S62.623P	Disp fx of med phalanx of lt mid finger, subsq enc for fx w/ malu
S62.623K	Disp fx of med phalanx of lt mid finger, subsq enc for fx w/ nonu
S62.625B	Disp fx of med phalanx of lt ring finger, init enc for opn fx
S62.625P	Disp fx of med phalanx of lt ring finger, subsq enc for fx w/ malu
S62.625K	Disp fx of med phalanx of lt ring finger, subsq enc for fx w/ nonu
S62.628B	Disp fx of med phalanx of oth finger, init enc for opn fx
S62.628P	Disp fx of med phalanx of oth finger, subsq enc for fx w/ malu
S62.628K	Disp fx of med phalanx of oth finger, subsq enc for fx w/ nonu
S62.620B	Disp fx of med phalanx of rt index finger, init enc for opn fx
S62.620P	Disp fx of med phalanx of rt index finger, subsq enc for fx w/ malu
S62.620K	Disp fx of med phalanx of rt index finger, subsq enc for fx w/ nonu
S92.521P	Disp fx of med phalanx of rt lesser toe(s), subsq enc for fx w/ malu
S92.521K	Disp fx of med phalanx of rt lesser toe(s), subsq enc for fx w/ nonu
S62.626B	Disp fx of med phalanx of rt little finger, init enc for opn fx
S62.626P	Disp fx of med phalanx of rt little finger, subsq enc for fx w/ malu
S62.626K	Disp fx of med phalanx of rt little finger, subsq enc for fx w/ nonu
S62.622B	Disp fx of med phalanx of rt mid finger, init enc for opn fx
S62.622P	Disp fx of med phalanx of rt mid finger, subsq enc for fx w/ malu
S62.622K	Disp fx of med phalanx of rt mid finger, subsq enc for fx w/ nonu
S62.624B	Disp fx of med phalanx of rt ring finger, init enc for opn fx
S62.624P	Disp fx of med phalanx of rt ring finger, subsq enc for fx w/ malu
S62.624K	Disp fx of med phalanx of rt ring finger, subsq enc for fx w/ nonu
S62.629B	Disp fx of med phalanx of unsp finger, init enc for opn fx
S62.629P	Disp fx of med phalanx of unsp finger, subsq enc for fx w/ malu
S62.629K	Disp fx of med phalanx of unsp finger, subsq enc for fx w/ nonu
S92.523P	Disp fx of med phalanx of unsp lesser toe(s), subsq enc for fx w/ malu
S92.523K	Disp fx of med phalanx of unsp lesser toe(s), subsq enc for fx w/ nonu
S32.472K	Disp fx of med wall of lt acetab, subsq enc for fx w/ nonu
S32.471K	Disp fx of med wall of rt acetab, subsq enc for fx w/ nonu
S32.473K	Disp fx of med wall of unsp acetab, subsq enc for fx w/ nonu
S62.022B	Disp fx of mid 3rd of navicular [scaphoid] bone of lt wrist, init enc for opn fx
S62.022P	Disp fx of mid 3rd of navicular [scaphoid] bone of lt wrist, subsq enc for fx w/ malu
S62.022K	Disp fx of mid 3rd of navicular [scaphoid] bone of lt wrist, subsq enc for fx w/ nonu
S62.021B	Disp fx of mid 3rd of navicular [scaphoid] bone of rt wrist, init enc for opn fx
S62.021P	Disp fx of mid 3rd of navicular [scaphoid] bone of rt wrist, subsq enc for fx w/ malu
S62.021K	Disp fx of mid 3rd of navicular [scaphoid] bone of rt wrist, subsq enc for fx w/ nonu
S62.023B	Disp fx of mid 3rd of navicular [scaphoid] bone of unsp wrist, init enc for opn fx
S62.023P	Disp fx of mid 3rd of navicular [scaphoid] bone of unsp wrist, subsq enc for fx w/ malu
S62.023K	Disp fx of mid 3rd of navicular [scaphoid] bone of unsp wrist, subsq enc for fx w/ nonu
S92.252B	Disp fx of navicular [scaphoid] of lt foot, init enc for opn fx
S92.252P	Disp fx of navicular [scaphoid] of lt foot, subsq enc for fx w/ malu
S92.252K	Disp fx of navicular [scaphoid] of lt foot, subsq enc for fx w/ nonu
S92.251B	Disp fx of navicular [scaphoid] of rt foot, init enc for opn fx
S92.251P	Disp fx of navicular [scaphoid] of rt foot, subsq enc for fx w/ malu
S92.251K	Disp fx of navicular [scaphoid] of rt foot, subsq enc for fx w/ nonu
S92.253B	Disp fx of navicular [scaphoid] of unsp foot, init enc for opn fx
S92.253P	Disp fx of navicular [scaphoid] of unsp foot, subsq enc for fx w/ malu
S92.253K	Disp fx of navicular [scaphoid] of unsp foot, subsq enc for fx w/ nonu
S62.252B	Disp fx of neck of 1st metacarpal bone, lt hand, init enc for opn fx
S62.252P	Disp fx of neck of 1st metacarpal bone, lt hand, subsq enc for fx w/ malu
S62.252K	Disp fx of neck of 1st metacarpal bone, lt hand, subsq enc for fx w/ nonu
S62.251B	Disp fx of neck of 1st metacarpal bone, rt hand, init enc for opn fx
S62.251P	Disp fx of neck of 1st metacarpal bone, rt hand, subsq enc for fx w/ malu
S62.251K	Disp fx of neck of 1st metacarpal bone, rt hand, subsq enc for fx w/ nonu
S62.253B	Disp fx of neck of 1st metacarpal bone, unsp hand, init enc for opn fx
S62.253P	Disp fx of neck of 1st metacarpal bone, unsp hand, subsq enc for fx w/ malu
S62.253K	Disp fx of neck of 1st metacarpal bone, unsp hand, subsq enc for fx w/ nonu
S62.331B	Disp fx of neck of 2nd metacarpal bone, lt hand, init enc for opn fx
S62.331P	Disp fx of neck of 2nd metacarpal bone, lt hand, subsq enc for fx w/ malu
S62.331K	Disp fx of neck of 2nd metacarpal bone, lt hand, subsq enc for fx w/ nonu
S62.330B	Disp fx of neck of 2nd metacarpal bone, rt hand, init enc for opn fx
S62.330P	Disp fx of neck of 2nd metacarpal bone, rt hand, subsq enc for fx w/ malu
S62.330K	Disp fx of neck of 2nd metacarpal bone, rt hand, subsq enc for fx w/ nonu
S62.333B	Disp fx of neck of 3rd metacarpal bone, lt hand, init enc for opn fx
S62.333P	Disp fx of neck of 3rd metacarpal bone, lt hand, subsq enc for fx w/ malu
S62.333K	Disp fx of neck of 3rd metacarpal bone, lt hand, subsq enc for fx w/ nonu
S62.332B	Disp fx of neck of 3rd metacarpal bone, rt hand, init enc for opn fx
S62.332P	Disp fx of neck of 3rd metacarpal bone, rt hand, subsq enc for fx w/ malu
S62.332K	Disp fx of neck of 3rd metacarpal bone, rt hand, subsq enc for fx w/ nonu
S62.335B	Disp fx of neck of 4th metacarpal bone, lt hand, init enc for opn fx
S62.335P	Disp fx of neck of 4th metacarpal bone, lt hand, subsq enc for fx w/ malu
S62.335K	Disp fx of neck of 4th metacarpal bone, lt hand, subsq enc for fx w/ nonu
S62.334B	Disp fx of neck of 4th metacarpal bone, rt hand, init enc for opn fx
S62.334P	Disp fx of neck of 4th metacarpal bone, rt hand, subsq enc for fx w/ malu
S62.334K	Disp fx of neck of 4th metacarpal bone, rt hand, subsq enc for fx w/ nonu
S62.337B	Disp fx of neck of 5th metacarpal bone, lt hand, init enc for opn fx
S62.337P	Disp fx of neck of 5th metacarpal bone, lt hand, subsq enc for fx w/ malu
S62.337K	Disp fx of neck of 5th metacarpal bone, lt hand, subsq enc for fx w/ nonu
S62.336B	Disp fx of neck of 5th metacarpal bone, rt hand, init enc for opn fx
S62.336P	Disp fx of neck of 5th metacarpal bone, rt hand, subsq enc for fx w/ malu
S62.336K	Disp fx of neck of 5th metacarpal bone, rt hand, subsq enc for fx w/ nonu
S52.132P	Disp fx of neck of lt radius, subsq enc for clsd fx w/ malu
S52.132K	Disp fx of neck of lt radius, subsq enc for clsd fx w/ nonu
S52.132Q	Disp fx of neck of lt radius, subsq enc for opn fx type I or II w/ malu
S52.132M	Disp fx of neck of lt radius, subsq enc for opn fx type I or II w/ nonu
S52.132R	Disp fx of neck of lt radius, subsq enc for opn fx type IIIA, IIIB, or IIIC w/ malu
S52.132N	Disp fx of neck of lt radius, subsq enc for opn fx type IIIA, IIIB, or IIIC w/ nonu
S92.112B	Disp fx of neck of lt talus, init enc for opn fx
S92.112P	Disp fx of neck of lt talus, subsq enc for fx w/ malu
S92.112K	Disp fx of neck of lt talus, subsq enc for fx w/ nonu
S62.338B	Disp fx of neck of oth metacarpal bone, init enc for opn fx
S62.338P	Disp fx of neck of oth metacarpal bone, subsq enc for fx w/ malu
S62.338K	Disp fx of neck of oth metacarpal bone, subsq enc for fx w/ nonu
S52.131P	Disp fx of neck of rt radius, subsq enc for clsd fx w/ malu
S52.131K	Disp fx of neck of rt radius, subsq enc for clsd fx w/ nonu
S52.131Q	Disp fx of neck of rt radius, subsq enc for opn fx type I or II w/ malu
S52.131M	Disp fx of neck of rt radius, subsq enc for opn fx type I or II w/ nonu
S52.131R	Disp fx of neck of rt radius, subsq enc for opn fx type IIIA, IIIB, or IIIC w/ malu
S52.131N	Disp fx of neck of rt radius, subsq enc for opn fx type IIIA, IIIB, or IIIC w/ nonu
S92.111B	Disp fx of neck of rt talus, init enc for opn fx
S92.111P	Disp fx of neck of rt talus, subsq enc for fx w/ malu
S92.111K	Disp fx of neck of rt talus, subsq enc for fx w/ nonu
S42.152B	Disp fx of neck of scapula, lt shldr, init enc for opn fx
S42.152P	Disp fx of neck of scapula, lt shldr, subsq enc for fx w/ malu
S42.152K	Disp fx of neck of scapula, lt shldr, subsq enc for fx w/ nonu
S42.151B	Disp fx of neck of scapula, rt shldr, init enc for opn fx
S42.151P	Disp fx of neck of scapula, rt shldr, subsq enc for fx w/ malu
S42.151K	Disp fx of neck of scapula, rt shldr, subsq enc for fx w/ nonu
S42.153B	Disp fx of neck of scapula, unsp shldr, init enc for opn fx
S42.153P	Disp fx of neck of scapula, unsp shldr, subsq enc for fx w/ malu
S42.153K	Disp fx of neck of scapula, unsp shldr, subsq enc for fx w/ nonu
S62.339B	Disp fx of neck of unsp metacarpal bone, init enc for opn fx
S62.339P	Disp fx of neck of unsp metacarpal bone, subsq enc for fx w/ malu

S62.339K	Disp fx of neck of unsp metacarpal bone, subsq enc for fx w/ nonu
S52.133P	Disp fx of neck of unsp radius, subsq enc for clsd fx w/ malu
S52.133K	Disp fx of neck of unsp radius, subsq enc for clsd fx w/ nonu
S52.133Q	Disp fx of neck of unsp radius, subsq enc for opn fx type I or II w/ malu
S52.133M	Disp fx of neck of unsp radius, subsq enc for opn fx type I or II w/ nonu
S52.133R	Disp fx of neck of unsp radius, subsq enc for opn fx type IIIA, IIIB, or IIIC w/ malu
S52.133N	Disp fx of neck of unsp radius, subsq enc for opn fx type IIIA, IIIB, or IIIC w/ nonu
S92.113B	Disp fx of neck of unsp talus, init enc for opn fx
S92.113P	Disp fx of neck of unsp talus, subsq enc for fx w/ malu
S92.113K	Disp fx of neck of unsp talus, subsq enc for fx w/ nonu
S52.032P	Disp fx of olecranon process w/ intraarticular extension of lt ulna, subsq enc for clsd fx w/ malu
S52.032K	Disp fx of olecranon process w/ intraarticular extension of lt ulna, subsq enc for clsd fx w/ nonu
S52.032Q	Disp fx of olecranon process w/ intraarticular extension of lt ulna, subsq enc for opn fx type I or II w/ malu
S52.032M	Disp fx of olecranon process w/ intraarticular extension of lt ulna, subsq enc for opn fx type I or II w/ nonu
S52.032R	Disp fx of olecranon process w/ intraarticular extension of lt ulna, subsq enc for opn fx type IIIA, IIIB, or IIIC w/ malu
S52.032N	Disp fx of olecranon process w/ intraarticular extension of lt ulna, subsq enc for opn fx type IIIA, IIIB, or IIIC w/ nonu
S52.031P	Disp fx of olecranon process w/ intraarticular extension of rt ulna, subsq enc for clsd fx w/ malu
S52.031K	Disp fx of olecranon process w/ intraarticular extension of rt ulna, subsq enc for clsd fx w/ nonu
S52.031Q	Disp fx of olecranon process w/ intraarticular extension of rt ulna, subsq enc for opn fx type I or II w/ malu
S52.031M	Disp fx of olecranon process w/ intraarticular extension of rt ulna, subsq enc for opn fx type I or II w/ nonu
S52.031R	Disp fx of olecranon process w/ intraarticular extension of rt ulna, subsq enc for opn fx type IIIA, IIIB, or IIIC w/ malu
S52.031N	Disp fx of olecranon process w/ intraarticular extension of rt ulna, subsq enc for opn fx type IIIA, IIIB, or IIIC w/ nonu
S52.033P	Disp fx of olecranon process w/ intraarticular extension of unsp ulna, subsq enc for clsd fx w/ malu
S52.033K	Disp fx of olecranon process w/ intraarticular extension of unsp ulna, subsq enc for clsd fx w/ nonu
S52.033Q	Disp fx of olecranon process w/ intraarticular extension of unsp ulna, subsq enc for opn fx type I or II w/ malu
S52.033M	Disp fx of olecranon process w/ intraarticular extension of unsp ulna, subsq enc for opn fx type I or II w/ nonu
S52.033R	Disp fx of olecranon process w/ intraarticular extension of unsp ulna, subsq enc for opn fx type IIIA, IIIB, or IIIC w/ malu
S52.033N	Disp fx of olecranon process w/ intraarticular extension of unsp ulna, subsq enc for opn fx type IIIA, IIIB, or IIIC w/ nonu
S52.022P	Disp fx of olecranon process w/o intraarticular extension of lt ulna, subsq enc for clsd fx w/ malu
S52.022K	Disp fx of olecranon process w/o intraarticular extension of lt ulna, subsq enc for clsd fx w/ nonu
S52.022Q	Disp fx of olecranon process w/o intraarticular extension of lt ulna, subsq enc for opn fx type I or II w/ malu
S52.022M	Disp fx of olecranon process w/o intraarticular extension of lt ulna, subsq enc for opn fx type I or II w/ nonu
S52.022R	Disp fx of olecranon process w/o intraarticular extension of lt ulna, subsq enc for opn fx type IIIA, IIIB, or IIIC w/ malu
S52.022N	Disp fx of olecranon process w/o intraarticular extension of lt ulna, subsq enc for opn fx type IIIA, IIIB, or IIIC w/ nonu
S52.021P	Disp fx of olecranon process w/o intraarticular extension of rt ulna, subsq enc for clsd fx w/ malu
S52.021K	Disp fx of olecranon process w/o intraarticular extension of rt ulna, subsq enc for clsd fx w/ nonu
S52.021Q	Disp fx of olecranon process w/o intraarticular extension of rt ulna, subsq enc for opn fx type I or II w/ malu
S52.021M	Disp fx of olecranon process w/o intraarticular extension of rt ulna, subsq enc for opn fx type I or II w/ nonu
S52.021R	Disp fx of olecranon process w/o intraarticular extension of rt ulna, subsq enc for opn fx type IIIA, IIIB, or IIIC w/ malu
S52.021N	Disp fx of olecranon process w/o intraarticular extension of rt ulna, subsq enc for opn fx type IIIA, IIIB, or IIIC w/ nonu
S52.023P	Disp fx of olecranon process w/o intraarticular extension of unsp ulna, subsq enc for clsd fx w/ malu
S52.023K	Disp fx of olecranon process w/o intraarticular extension of unsp ulna, subsq enc for clsd fx w/ nonu

S52.023Q	Disp fx of olecranon process w/o intraarticular extension of unsp ulna, subsq enc for opn fx type I or II w/ malu
S52.023M	Disp fx of olecranon process w/o intraarticular extension of unsp ulna, subsq enc for opn fx type I or II w/ nonu
S52.023R	Disp fx of olecranon process w/o intraarticular extension of unsp ulna, subsq enc for opn fx type IIIA, IIIB, or IIIC w/ malu
S52.023N	Disp fx of olecranon process w/o intraarticular extension of unsp ulna, subsq enc for opn fx type IIIA, IIIB, or IIIC w/ nonu
S62.162B	Disp fx of pisiform, lt wrist, init enc for opn fx
S62.162P	Disp fx of pisiform, lt wrist, subsq enc for fx w/ malu
S62.162K	Disp fx of pisiform, lt wrist, subsq enc for fx w/ nonu
S62.161B	Disp fx of pisiform, rt wrist, init enc for opn fx
S62.161P	Disp fx of pisiform, rt wrist, subsq enc for fx w/ malu
S62.161K	Disp fx of pisiform, rt wrist, subsq enc for fx w/ nonu
S62.163B	Disp fx of pisiform, unsp wrist, init enc for opn fx
S62.163P	Disp fx of pisiform, unsp wrist, subsq enc for fx w/ malu
S62.163K	Disp fx of pisiform, unsp wrist, subsq enc for fx w/ nonu
S32.442K	Disp fx of post column [ilioischial] of lt acetab, subsq enc for fx w/ nonu
S32.441K	Disp fx of post column [ilioischial] of rt acetab, subsq enc for fx w/ nonu
S32.443K	Disp fx of post column [ilioischial] of unsp acetab, subsq enc for fx w/ nonu
S92.132B	Disp fx of post process of lt talus, init enc for opn fx
S92.132P	Disp fx of post process of lt talus, subsq enc for fx w/ malu
S92.132K	Disp fx of post process of lt talus, subsq enc for fx w/ nonu
S92.131B	Disp fx of post process of rt talus, init enc for opn fx
S92.131P	Disp fx of post process of rt talus, subsq enc for fx w/ malu
S92.131K	Disp fx of post process of rt talus, subsq enc for fx w/ nonu
S92.133B	Disp fx of post process of unsp talus, init enc for opn fx
S92.133P	Disp fx of post process of unsp talus, subsq enc for fx w/ malu
S92.133K	Disp fx of post process of unsp talus, subsq enc for fx w/ nonu
S32.422K	Disp fx of post wall of lt acetab, subsq enc for fx w/ nonu
S32.421K	Disp fx of post wall of rt acetab, subsq enc for fx w/ nonu
S32.423K	Disp fx of post wall of unsp acetab, subsq enc for fx w/ nonu
S62.032B	Disp fx of proximal 3rd of navicular [scaphoid] bone of lt wrist, init enc for opn fx
S62.032P	Disp fx of proximal 3rd of navicular [scaphoid] bone of lt wrist, subsq enc for fx w/ malu
S62.032K	Disp fx of proximal 3rd of navicular [scaphoid] bone of lt wrist, subsq enc for fx w/ nonu
S62.031B	Disp fx of proximal 3rd of navicular [scaphoid] bone of rt wrist, init enc for opn fx
S62.031P	Disp fx of proximal 3rd of navicular [scaphoid] bone of rt wrist, subsq enc for fx w/ malu
S62.031K	Disp fx of proximal 3rd of navicular [scaphoid] bone of rt wrist, subsq enc for fx w/ nonu
S62.033B	Disp fx of proximal 3rd of navicular [scaphoid] bone of unsp wrist, init enc for opn fx
S62.033P	Disp fx of proximal 3rd of navicular [scaphoid] bone of unsp wrist, subsq enc for fx w/ malu
S62.033K	Disp fx of proximal 3rd of navicular [scaphoid] bone of unsp wrist, subsq enc for fx w/ nonu
S92.412P	Disp fx of proximal phalanx of lt great toe, subsq enc for fx w/ malu
S92.412K	Disp fx of proximal phalanx of lt great toe, subsq enc for fx w/ nonu
S62.611B	Disp fx of proximal phalanx of lt index finger, init enc for opn fx
S62.611P	Disp fx of proximal phalanx of lt index finger, subsq enc for fx w/ malu
S62.611K	Disp fx of proximal phalanx of lt index finger, subsq enc for fx w/ nonu
S92.512P	Disp fx of proximal phalanx of lt lesser toe(s), subsq enc for fx w/ malu
S92.512K	Disp fx of proximal phalanx of lt lesser toe(s), subsq enc for fx w/ nonu
S62.617B	Disp fx of proximal phalanx of lt little finger, init enc for opn fx
S62.617P	Disp fx of proximal phalanx of lt little finger, subsq enc for fx w/ malu
S62.617K	Disp fx of proximal phalanx of lt little finger, subsq enc for fx w/ nonu
S62.613B	Disp fx of proximal phalanx of lt mid finger, init enc for opn fx
S62.613P	Disp fx of proximal phalanx of lt mid finger, subsq enc for fx w/ malu
S62.613K	Disp fx of proximal phalanx of lt mid finger, subsq enc for fx w/ nonu
S62.615B	Disp fx of proximal phalanx of lt ring finger, init enc for opn fx
S62.615P	Disp fx of proximal phalanx of lt ring finger, subsq enc for fx w/ malu
S62.615K	Disp fx of proximal phalanx of lt ring finger, subsq enc for fx w/ nonu
S62.512B	Disp fx of proximal phalanx of lt thumb, init enc for opn fx
S62.512P	Disp fx of proximal phalanx of lt thumb, subsq enc for fx w/ malu
S62.512K	Disp fx of proximal phalanx of lt thumb, subsq enc for fx w/ nonu
S62.618B	Disp fx of proximal phalanx of oth finger, init enc for opn fx
S62.618P	Disp fx of proximal phalanx of oth finger, subsq enc for fx w/ malu
S62.618K	Disp fx of proximal phalanx of oth finger, subsq enc for fx w/ nonu
S92.411P	Disp fx of proximal phalanx of rt great toe, subsq enc for fx w/ malu
S92.411K	Disp fx of proximal phalanx of rt great toe, subsq enc for fx w/ nonu

Code	Description
S62.610B	Disp fx of proximal phalanx of rt index finger, init enc for opn fx
S62.610P	Disp fx of proximal phalanx of rt index finger, subsq enc for fx w/ malu
S62.610K	Disp fx of proximal phalanx of rt index finger, subsq enc for fx w/ nonu
S92.511P	Disp fx of proximal phalanx of rt lesser toe(s), subsq enc for fx w/ malu
S92.511K	Disp fx of proximal phalanx of rt lesser toe(s), subsq enc for fx w/ nonu
S62.616B	Disp fx of proximal phalanx of rt little finger, init enc for opn fx
S62.616P	Disp fx of proximal phalanx of rt little finger, subsq enc for fx w/ malu
S62.616K	Disp fx of proximal phalanx of rt little finger, subsq enc for fx w/ nonu
S62.612B	Disp fx of proximal phalanx of rt mid finger, init enc for opn fx
S62.612P	Disp fx of proximal phalanx of rt mid finger, subsq enc for fx w/ malu
S62.612K	Disp fx of proximal phalanx of rt mid finger, subsq enc for fx w/ nonu
S62.614B	Disp fx of proximal phalanx of rt ring finger, init enc for opn fx
S62.614P	Disp fx of proximal phalanx of rt ring finger, subsq enc for fx w/ malu
S62.614K	Disp fx of proximal phalanx of rt ring finger, subsq enc for fx w/ nonu
S62.511B	Disp fx of proximal phalanx of rt thumb, init enc for opn fx
S62.511P	Disp fx of proximal phalanx of rt thumb, subsq enc for fx w/ malu
S62.511K	Disp fx of proximal phalanx of rt thumb, subsq enc for fx w/ nonu
S62.619B	Disp fx of proximal phalanx of unsp finger, init enc for opn fx
S62.619P	Disp fx of proximal phalanx of unsp finger, subsq enc for fx w/ malu
S62.619K	Disp fx of proximal phalanx of unsp finger, subsq enc for fx w/ nonu
S92.413P	Disp fx of proximal phalanx of unsp great toe, subsq enc for fx w/ malu
S92.413K	Disp fx of proximal phalanx of unsp great toe, subsq enc for fx w/ nonu
S92.513P	Disp fx of proximal phalanx of unsp lesser toe(s), subsq enc for fx w/ malu
S92.513K	Disp fx of proximal phalanx of unsp lesser toe(s), subsq enc for fx w/ nonu
S62.513B	Disp fx of proximal phalanx of unsp thumb, init enc for opn fx
S62.513P	Disp fx of proximal phalanx of unsp thumb, subsq enc for fx w/ malu
S62.513K	Disp fx of proximal phalanx of unsp thumb, subsq enc for fx w/ nonu
S52.511A	Disp fx of rt radial styloid process, init enc for clsd fx
S52.511P	Disp fx of rt radial styloid process, subsq enc for clsd fx w/ malu
S52.511K	Disp fx of rt radial styloid process, subsq enc for clsd fx w/ nonu
S52.511Q	Disp fx of rt radial styloid process, subsq enc for opn fx type I or II w/ malu
S52.511M	Disp fx of rt radial styloid process, subsq enc for opn fx type I or II w/ nonu
S52.511R	Disp fx of rt radial styloid process, subsq enc for opn fx type IIIA, IIIB, or IIIC w/ malu
S52.511N	Disp fx of rt radial styloid process, subsq enc for opn fx type IIIA, IIIB, or IIIC w/ nonu
S82.111A	Disp fx of rt tibial spine, init enc for clsd fx
S82.111P	Disp fx of rt tibial spine, subsq enc for clsd fx w/ malu
S82.111K	Disp fx of rt tibial spine, subsq enc for clsd fx w/ nonu
S82.111Q	Disp fx of rt tibial spine, subsq enc for opn fx type I or II w/ malu
S82.111M	Disp fx of rt tibial spine, subsq enc for opn fx type I or II w/ nonu
S82.111R	Disp fx of rt tibial spine, subsq enc for opn fx type IIIA, IIIB, or IIIC w/ malu
S82.111N	Disp fx of rt tibial spine, subsq enc for opn fx type IIIA, IIIB, or IIIC w/ nonu
S82.151A	Disp fx of rt tibial tuberosity, init enc for clsd fx
S82.151P	Disp fx of rt tibial tuberosity, subsq enc for clsd fx w/ malu
S82.151K	Disp fx of rt tibial tuberosity, subsq enc for clsd fx w/ nonu
S82.151Q	Disp fx of rt tibial tuberosity, subsq enc for opn fx type I or II w/ malu
S82.151M	Disp fx of rt tibial tuberosity, subsq enc for opn fx type I or II w/ nonu
S82.151R	Disp fx of rt tibial tuberosity, subsq enc for opn fx type IIIA, IIIB, or IIIC w/ malu
S82.151N	Disp fx of rt tibial tuberosity, subsq enc for opn fx type IIIA, IIIB, or IIIC w/ nonu
S52.611A	Disp fx of rt ulna styloid process, init enc for clsd fx
S52.611P	Disp fx of rt ulna styloid process, subsq enc for clsd fx w/ malu
S52.611K	Disp fx of rt ulna styloid process, subsq enc for clsd fx w/ nonu
S52.611Q	Disp fx of rt ulna styloid process, subsq enc for opn fx type I or II w/ malu
S52.611M	Disp fx of rt ulna styloid process, subsq enc for opn fx type I or II w/ nonu
S52.611R	Disp fx of rt ulna styloid process, subsq enc for opn fx type IIIA, IIIB, or IIIC w/ malu
S52.611N	Disp fx of rt ulna styloid process, subsq enc for opn fx type IIIA, IIIB, or IIIC w/ nonu
S62.242B	Disp fx of shaft of 1st metacarpal bone, lt hand, init enc for opn fx
S62.242P	Disp fx of shaft of 1st metacarpal bone, lt hand, subsq enc for fx w/ malu
S62.242K	Disp fx of shaft of 1st metacarpal bone, lt hand, subsq enc for fx w/ nonu
S62.241B	Disp fx of shaft of 1st metacarpal bone, rt hand, init enc for opn fx
S62.241P	Disp fx of shaft of 1st metacarpal bone, rt hand, subsq enc for fx w/ malu
S62.241K	Disp fx of shaft of 1st metacarpal bone, rt hand, subsq enc for fx w/ nonu
S62.243B	Disp fx of shaft of 1st metacarpal bone, unsp hand, init enc for opn fx
S62.243P	Disp fx of shaft of 1st metacarpal bone, unsp hand, subsq enc for fx w/ malu
S62.243K	Disp fx of shaft of 1st metacarpal bone, unsp hand, subsq enc for fx w/ nonu
S62.321B	Disp fx of shaft of 2nd metacarpal bone, lt hand, init enc for opn fx
S62.321P	Disp fx of shaft of 2nd metacarpal bone, lt hand, subsq enc for fx w/ malu
S62.321K	Disp fx of shaft of 2nd metacarpal bone, lt hand, subsq enc for fx w/ nonu
S62.320B	Disp fx of shaft of 2nd metacarpal bone, rt hand, init enc for opn fx
S62.320P	Disp fx of shaft of 2nd metacarpal bone, rt hand, subsq enc for fx w/ malu
S62.320K	Disp fx of shaft of 2nd metacarpal bone, rt hand, subsq enc for fx w/ nonu
S62.323B	Disp fx of shaft of 3rd metacarpal bone, lt hand, init enc for opn fx
S62.323P	Disp fx of shaft of 3rd metacarpal bone, lt hand, subsq enc for fx w/ malu
S62.323K	Disp fx of shaft of 3rd metacarpal bone, lt hand, subsq enc for fx w/ nonu
S62.322B	Disp fx of shaft of 3rd metacarpal bone, rt hand, init enc for opn fx
S62.322P	Disp fx of shaft of 3rd metacarpal bone, rt hand, subsq enc for fx w/ malu
S62.322K	Disp fx of shaft of 3rd metacarpal bone, rt hand, subsq enc for fx w/ nonu
S62.325B	Disp fx of shaft of 4th metacarpal bone, lt hand, init enc for opn fx
S62.325P	Disp fx of shaft of 4th metacarpal bone, lt hand, subsq enc for fx w/ malu
S62.325K	Disp fx of shaft of 4th metacarpal bone, lt hand, subsq enc for fx w/ nonu
S62.324B	Disp fx of shaft of 4th metacarpal bone, rt hand, init enc for opn fx
S62.324P	Disp fx of shaft of 4th metacarpal bone, rt hand, subsq enc for fx w/ malu
S62.324K	Disp fx of shaft of 4th metacarpal bone, rt hand, subsq enc for fx w/ nonu
S62.327B	Disp fx of shaft of 5th metacarpal bone, lt hand, init enc for opn fx
S62.327P	Disp fx of shaft of 5th metacarpal bone, lt hand, subsq enc for fx w/ malu
S62.327K	Disp fx of shaft of 5th metacarpal bone, lt hand, subsq enc for fx w/ nonu
S62.326B	Disp fx of shaft of 5th metacarpal bone, rt hand, init enc for opn fx
S62.326P	Disp fx of shaft of 5th metacarpal bone, rt hand, subsq enc for fx w/ malu
S62.326K	Disp fx of shaft of 5th metacarpal bone, rt hand, subsq enc for fx w/ nonu
S42.022B	Disp fx of shaft of lt clavicle, init enc for opn fx
S42.022P	Disp fx of shaft of lt clavicle, subsq enc for fx w/ malu
S42.022K	Disp fx of shaft of lt clavicle, subsq enc for fx w/ nonu
S62.328B	Disp fx of shaft of oth metacarpal bone, init enc for opn fx
S62.328P	Disp fx of shaft of oth metacarpal bone, subsq enc for fx w/ malu
S62.328K	Disp fx of shaft of oth metacarpal bone, subsq enc for fx w/ nonu
S42.021B	Disp fx of shaft of rt clavicle, init enc for opn fx
S42.021P	Disp fx of shaft of rt clavicle, subsq enc for fx w/ malu
S42.021K	Disp fx of shaft of rt clavicle, subsq enc for fx w/ nonu
S42.023B	Disp fx of shaft of unsp clavicle, init enc for opn fx
S42.023P	Disp fx of shaft of unsp clavicle, subsq enc for fx w/ malu
S42.023K	Disp fx of shaft of unsp clavicle, subsq enc for fx w/ nonu
S62.329B	Disp fx of shaft of unsp metacarpal bone, init enc for opn fx
S62.329P	Disp fx of shaft of unsp metacarpal bone, subsq enc for fx w/ malu
S62.329K	Disp fx of shaft of unsp metacarpal bone, subsq enc for fx w/ nonu
S62.172B	Disp fx of trapezium [larger multangular], lt wrist, init enc for opn fx
S62.172P	Disp fx of trapezium [larger multangular], lt wrist, subsq enc for fx w/ malu
S62.172K	Disp fx of trapezium [larger multangular], lt wrist, subsq enc for fx w/ nonu
S62.171B	Disp fx of trapezium [larger multangular], rt wrist, init enc for opn fx
S62.171P	Disp fx of trapezium [larger multangular], rt wrist, subsq enc for fx w/ malu
S62.171K	Disp fx of trapezium [larger multangular], rt wrist, subsq enc for fx w/ nonu
S62.173B	Disp fx of trapezium [larger multangular], unsp wrist, init enc for opn fx
S62.173P	Disp fx of trapezium [larger multangular], unsp wrist, subsq enc for fx w/ malu
S62.173K	Disp fx of trapezium [larger multangular], unsp wrist, subsq enc for fx w/ nonu
S62.182B	Disp fx of trapezoid [smaller multangular], lt wrist, init enc for opn fx
S62.182P	Disp fx of trapezoid [smaller multangular], lt wrist, subsq enc for fx w/ malu
S62.182K	Disp fx of trapezoid [smaller multangular], lt wrist, subsq enc for fx w/ nonu
S62.181B	Disp fx of trapezoid [smaller multangular], rt wrist, init enc for opn fx
S62.181P	Disp fx of trapezoid [smaller multangular], rt wrist, subsq enc for fx w/ malu
S62.181K	Disp fx of trapezoid [smaller multangular], rt wrist, subsq enc for fx w/ nonu
S62.183B	Disp fx of trapezoid [smaller multangular], unsp wrist, init enc for opn fx
S62.183P	Disp fx of trapezoid [smaller multangular], unsp wrist, subsq enc for fx w/ malu
S62.183K	Disp fx of trapezoid [smaller multangular], unsp wrist, subsq enc for fx w/ nonu
S62.112B	Disp fx of triquetrum [cuneiform] bone, lt wrist, init enc for opn fx
S62.112P	Disp fx of triquetrum [cuneiform] bone, lt wrist, subsq enc for fx w/ malu
S62.112K	Disp fx of triquetrum [cuneiform] bone, lt wrist, subsq enc for fx w/ nonu
S62.111B	Disp fx of triquetrum [cuneiform] bone, rt wrist, init enc for opn fx
S62.111P	Disp fx of triquetrum [cuneiform] bone, rt wrist, subsq enc for fx w/ malu
S62.111K	Disp fx of triquetrum [cuneiform] bone, rt wrist, subsq enc for fx w/ nonu
S62.113B	Disp fx of triquetrum [cuneiform] bone, unsp wrist, init enc for opn fx

Code	Description
S62.113P	Disp fx of triquetrum [cuneiform] bone, unsp wrist, subsq enc for fx w/ malu
S62.113K	Disp fx of triquetrum [cuneiform] bone, unsp wrist, subsq enc for fx w/ malu
S52.513A	Disp fx of unsp radial styloid process, init enc for clsd fx
S52.513P	Disp fx of unsp radial styloid process, subsq enc for clsd fx w/ malu
S52.513K	Disp fx of unsp radial styloid process, subsq enc for clsd fx w/ nonu
S52.513Q	Disp fx of unsp radial styloid process, subsq enc for opn fx type I or II w/ malu
S52.513M	Disp fx of unsp radial styloid process, subsq enc for opn fx type I or II w/ nonu
S52.513R	Disp fx of unsp radial styloid process, subsq enc for opn fx type IIIA, IIIB, or IIIC w/ malu
S52.513N	Disp fx of unsp radial styloid process, subsq enc for opn fx type IIIA, IIIB, or IIIC w/ nonu
S82.113A	Disp fx of unsp tibial spine, init enc for clsd fx
S82.113P	Disp fx of unsp tibial spine, subsq enc for clsd fx w/ malu
S82.113K	Disp fx of unsp tibial spine, subsq enc for clsd fx w/ nonu
S82.113Q	Disp fx of unsp tibial spine, subsq enc for opn fx type I or II w/ malu
S82.113M	Disp fx of unsp tibial spine, subsq enc for opn fx type I or II w/ nonu
S82.113R	Disp fx of unsp tibial spine, subsq enc for opn fx type IIIA, IIIB, or IIIC w/ malu
S82.113N	Disp fx of unsp tibial spine, subsq enc for opn fx type IIIA, IIIB, or IIIC w/ nonu
S82.153A	Disp fx of unsp tibial tuberosity, init enc for clsd fx
S82.153P	Disp fx of unsp tibial tuberosity, subsq enc for clsd fx w/ malu
S82.153K	Disp fx of unsp tibial tuberosity, subsq enc for clsd fx w/ nonu
S82.153Q	Disp fx of unsp tibial tuberosity, subsq enc for opn fx type I or II w/ malu
S82.153M	Disp fx of unsp tibial tuberosity, subsq enc for opn fx type I or II w/ nonu
S82.153R	Disp fx of unsp tibial tuberosity, subsq enc for opn fx type IIIA, IIIB, or IIIC w/ malu
S82.153N	Disp fx of unsp tibial tuberosity, subsq enc for opn fx type IIIA, IIIB, or IIIC w/ nonu
S52.613A	Disp fx of unsp ulna styloid process, init enc for clsd fx
S52.613P	Disp fx of unsp ulna styloid process, subsq enc for clsd fx w/ malu
S52.613K	Disp fx of unsp ulna styloid process, subsq enc for clsd fx w/ nonu
S52.613Q	Disp fx of unsp ulna styloid process, subsq enc for opn fx type I or II w/ malu
S52.613M	Disp fx of unsp ulna styloid process, subsq enc for opn fx type I or II w/ nonu
S52.613R	Disp fx of unsp ulna styloid process, subsq enc for opn fx type IIIA, IIIB, or IIIC w/ malu
S52.613N	Disp fx of unsp ulna styloid process, subsq enc for opn fx type IIIA, IIIB, or IIIC w/ nonu
S72.142P	Disp intertrochanteric fx of lt femur, subsq enc for clsd fx w/ malu
S72.142K	Disp intertrochanteric fx of lt femur, subsq enc for clsd fx w/ nonu
S72.142Q	Disp intertrochanteric fx of lt femur, subsq enc for opn fx type I or II w/ malu
S72.142M	Disp intertrochanteric fx of lt femur, subsq enc for opn fx type I or II w/ nonu
S72.142R	Disp intertrochanteric fx of lt femur, subsq enc for opn fx type IIIA, IIIB, or IIIC w/ malu
S72.142N	Disp intertrochanteric fx of lt femur, subsq enc for opn fx type IIIA, IIIB, or IIIC w/ nonu
S72.141P	Disp intertrochanteric fx of rt femur, subsq enc for clsd fx w/ malu
S72.141K	Disp intertrochanteric fx of rt femur, subsq enc for clsd fx w/ nonu
S72.141Q	Disp intertrochanteric fx of rt femur, subsq enc for opn fx type I or II w/ malu
S72.141M	Disp intertrochanteric fx of rt femur, subsq enc for opn fx type I or II w/ nonu
S72.141R	Disp intertrochanteric fx of rt femur, subsq enc for opn fx type IIIA, IIIB, or IIIC w/ malu
S72.141N	Disp intertrochanteric fx of rt femur, subsq enc for opn fx type IIIA, IIIB, or IIIC w/ nonu
S72.143P	Disp intertrochanteric fx of unsp femur, subsq enc for clsd fx w/ malu
S72.143K	Disp intertrochanteric fx of unsp femur, subsq enc for clsd fx w/ nonu
S72.143Q	Disp intertrochanteric fx of unsp femur, subsq enc for opn fx type I or II w/ malu
S72.143M	Disp intertrochanteric fx of unsp femur, subsq enc for opn fx type I or II w/ nonu
S72.143R	Disp intertrochanteric fx of unsp femur, subsq enc for opn fx type IIIA, IIIB, or IIIC w/ malu
S72.143N	Disp intertrochanteric fx of unsp femur, subsq enc for opn fx type IIIA, IIIB, or IIIC w/ nonu
S92.062B	Disp intraarticular fx of lt calcaneus, init enc for opn fx
S92.062P	Disp intraarticular fx of lt calcaneus, subsq enc for fx w/ malu
S92.062K	Disp intraarticular fx of lt calcaneus, subsq enc for fx w/ nonu
S92.061B	Disp intraarticular fx of rt calcaneus, init enc for opn fx
S92.061P	Disp intraarticular fx of rt calcaneus, subsq enc for fx w/ malu
S92.061K	Disp intraarticular fx of rt calcaneus, subsq enc for fx w/ nonu
S92.063B	Disp intraarticular fx of unsp calcaneus, init enc for opn fx
S92.063P	Disp intraarticular fx of unsp calcaneus, subsq enc for fx w/ malu
S92.063K	Disp intraarticular fx of unsp calcaneus, subsq enc for fx w/ nonu
S12.040A	Disp lat mass fx of 1st cervical vertebra, init enc for clsd fx
S12.040K	Disp lat mass fx of 1st cervical vertebra, subsq enc for fx w/ nonu
S82.022A	Disp longitudinal fx of lt patella, init enc for clsd fx
S82.022B	Disp longitudinal fx of lt patella, init enc for opn fx type I or II
S82.022C	Disp longitudinal fx of lt patella, init enc for opn fx type IIIA, IIIB, or IIIC
S82.022P	Disp longitudinal fx of lt patella, subsq enc for clsd fx w/ malu
S82.022K	Disp longitudinal fx of lt patella, subsq enc for clsd fx w/ nonu
S82.022Q	Disp longitudinal fx of lt patella, subsq enc for opn fx type I or II w/ malu
S82.022M	Disp longitudinal fx of lt patella, subsq enc for opn fx type I or II w/ nonu
S82.022R	Disp longitudinal fx of lt patella, subsq enc for opn fx type IIIA, IIIB, or IIIC w/ malu
S82.022N	Disp longitudinal fx of lt patella, subsq enc for opn fx type IIIA, IIIB, or IIIC w/ nonu
S82.021A	Disp longitudinal fx of rt patella, init enc for clsd fx
S82.021B	Disp longitudinal fx of rt patella, init enc for opn fx type I or II
S82.021C	Disp longitudinal fx of rt patella, init enc for opn fx type IIIA, IIIB, or IIIC
S82.021P	Disp longitudinal fx of rt patella, subsq enc for clsd fx w/ malu
S82.021K	Disp longitudinal fx of rt patella, subsq enc for clsd fx w/ nonu
S82.021Q	Disp longitudinal fx of rt patella, subsq enc for opn fx type I or II w/ malu
S82.021M	Disp longitudinal fx of rt patella, subsq enc for opn fx type I or II w/ nonu
S82.021R	Disp longitudinal fx of rt patella, subsq enc for opn fx type IIIA, IIIB, or IIIC w/ malu
S82.021N	Disp longitudinal fx of rt patella, subsq enc for opn fx type IIIA, IIIB, or IIIC w/ nonu
S82.023A	Disp longitudinal fx of unsp patella, init enc for clsd fx
S82.023B	Disp longitudinal fx of unsp patella, init enc for opn fx type I or II
S82.023C	Disp longitudinal fx of unsp patella, init enc for opn fx type IIIA, IIIB, or IIIC
S82.023P	Disp longitudinal fx of unsp patella, subsq enc for clsd fx w/ malu
S82.023K	Disp longitudinal fx of unsp patella, subsq enc for clsd fx w/ nonu
S82.023Q	Disp longitudinal fx of unsp patella, subsq enc for opn fx type I or II w/ malu
S82.023M	Disp longitudinal fx of unsp patella, subsq enc for opn fx type I or II w/ nonu
S82.023R	Disp longitudinal fx of unsp patella, subsq enc for opn fx type IIIA, IIIB, or IIIC w/ malu
S82.023N	Disp longitudinal fx of unsp patella, subsq enc for opn fx type IIIA, IIIB, or IIIC w/ nonu
S82.862P	Disp Maisonneuve's fx of lt leg, subsq enc for clsd fx w/ malu
S82.862K	Disp Maisonneuve's fx of lt leg, subsq enc for clsd fx w/ nonu
S82.862Q	Disp Maisonneuve's fx of lt leg, subsq enc for opn fx type I or II w/ malu
S82.862M	Disp Maisonneuve's fx of lt leg, subsq enc for opn fx type I or II w/ nonu
S82.862R	Disp Maisonneuve's fx of lt leg, subsq enc for opn fx type IIIA, IIIB, or IIIC w/ malu
S82.862N	Disp Maisonneuve's fx of lt leg, subsq enc for opn fx type IIIA, IIIB, or IIIC w/ nonu
S82.861P	Disp Maisonneuve's fx of rt leg, subsq enc for clsd fx w/ malu
S82.861K	Disp Maisonneuve's fx of rt leg, subsq enc for clsd fx w/ nonu
S82.861Q	Disp Maisonneuve's fx of rt leg, subsq enc for opn fx type I or II w/ malu
S82.861M	Disp Maisonneuve's fx of rt leg, subsq enc for opn fx type I or II w/ nonu
S82.861R	Disp Maisonneuve's fx of rt leg, subsq enc for opn fx type IIIA, IIIB, or IIIC w/ malu
S82.861N	Disp Maisonneuve's fx of rt leg, subsq enc for opn fx type IIIA, IIIB, or IIIC w/ nonu
S82.863P	Disp Maisonneuve's fx of unsp leg, subsq enc for clsd fx w/ malu
S82.863K	Disp Maisonneuve's fx of unsp leg, subsq enc for clsd fx w/ nonu
S82.863Q	Disp Maisonneuve's fx of unsp leg, subsq enc for opn fx type I or II w/ malu
S82.863M	Disp Maisonneuve's fx of unsp leg, subsq enc for opn fx type I or II w/ nonu
S82.863R	Disp Maisonneuve's fx of unsp leg, subsq enc for opn fx type IIIA, IIIB, or IIIC w/ malu
S82.863N	Disp Maisonneuve's fx of unsp leg, subsq enc for opn fx type IIIA, IIIB, or IIIC w/ nonu
S72.032P	Disp midcervical fx of lt femur, subsq enc for clsd fx w/ malu
S72.032K	Disp midcervical fx of lt femur, subsq enc for clsd fx w/ nonu
S72.032Q	Disp midcervical fx of lt femur, subsq enc for opn fx type I or II w/ malu
S72.032M	Disp midcervical fx of lt femur, subsq enc for opn fx type I or II w/ nonu

Code	Description
S72.032R	Disp midcervical fx of lt femur, subsq enc for opn fx type IIIA, IIIB, or IIIC w/ malu
S72.032N	Disp midcervical fx of lt femur, subsq enc for opn fx type IIIA, IIIB, or IIIC w/ nonu
S72.031P	Disp midcervical fx of rt femur, subsq enc for clsd fx w/ malu
S72.031K	Disp midcervical fx of rt femur, subsq enc for clsd fx w/ nonu
S72.031Q	Disp midcervical fx of rt femur, subsq enc for opn fx type I or II w/ malu
S72.031M	Disp midcervical fx of rt femur, subsq enc for opn fx type I or II w/ nonu
S72.031R	Disp midcervical fx of rt femur, subsq enc for opn fx type IIIA, IIIB, or IIIC w/ malu
S72.031N	Disp midcervical fx of rt femur, subsq enc for opn fx type IIIA, IIIB, or IIIC w/ nonu
S72.033P	Disp midcervical fx of unsp femur, subsq enc for clsd fx w/ malu
S72.033K	Disp midcervical fx of unsp femur, subsq enc for clsd fx w/ nonu
S72.033Q	Disp midcervical fx of unsp femur, subsq enc for opn fx type I or II w/ malu
S72.033M	Disp midcervical fx of unsp femur, subsq enc for opn fx type I or II w/ nonu
S72.033R	Disp midcervical fx of unsp femur, subsq enc for opn fx type IIIA, IIIB, or IIIC w/ malu
S72.033N	Disp midcervical fx of unsp femur, subsq enc for opn fx type IIIA, IIIB, or IIIC w/ nonu
S42.332A	Disp oblique fx of shaft of humerus, lt arm, init enc for clsd fx
S42.332P	Disp oblique fx of shaft of humerus, lt arm, subsq enc for fx w/ malu
S42.332K	Disp oblique fx of shaft of humerus, lt arm, subsq enc for fx w/ nonu
S42.331A	Disp oblique fx of shaft of humerus, rt arm, init enc for clsd fx
S42.331P	Disp oblique fx of shaft of humerus, rt arm, subsq enc for fx w/ malu
S42.331K	Disp oblique fx of shaft of humerus, rt arm, subsq enc for fx w/ nonu
S42.333A	Disp oblique fx of shaft of humerus, unsp arm, init enc for clsd fx
S42.333P	Disp oblique fx of shaft of humerus, unsp arm, subsq enc for fx w/ malu
S42.333K	Disp oblique fx of shaft of humerus, unsp arm, subsq enc for fx w/ nonu
S72.332P	Disp oblique fx of shaft of lt femur, subsq enc for clsd fx w/ malu
S72.332K	Disp oblique fx of shaft of lt femur, subsq enc for clsd fx w/ nonu
S72.332Q	Disp oblique fx of shaft of lt femur, subsq enc for opn fx type I or II w/ malu
S72.332M	Disp oblique fx of shaft of lt femur, subsq enc for opn fx type I or II w/ nonu
S72.332R	Disp oblique fx of shaft of lt femur, subsq enc for opn fx type IIIA, IIIB, or IIIC w/ malu
S72.332N	Disp oblique fx of shaft of lt femur, subsq enc for opn fx type IIIA, IIIB, or IIIC w/ nonu
S82.432P	Disp oblique fx of shaft of lt fibula, subsq enc for clsd fx w/ malu
S82.432K	Disp oblique fx of shaft of lt fibula, subsq enc for clsd fx w/ nonu
S82.432Q	Disp oblique fx of shaft of lt fibula, subsq enc for opn fx type I or II w/ malu
S82.432M	Disp oblique fx of shaft of lt fibula, subsq enc for opn fx type I or II w/ nonu
S82.432R	Disp oblique fx of shaft of lt fibula, subsq enc for opn fx type IIIA, IIIB, or IIIC w/ malu
S82.432N	Disp oblique fx of shaft of lt fibula, subsq enc for opn fx type IIIA, IIIB, or IIIC w/ nonu
S52.332A	Disp oblique fx of shaft of lt radius, init enc for clsd fx
S52.332P	Disp oblique fx of shaft of lt radius, subsq enc for clsd fx w/ malu
S52.332K	Disp oblique fx of shaft of lt radius, subsq enc for clsd fx w/ nonu
S52.332Q	Disp oblique fx of shaft of lt radius, subsq enc for opn fx type I or II w/ malu
S52.332M	Disp oblique fx of shaft of lt radius, subsq enc for opn fx type I or II w/ nonu
S52.332R	Disp oblique fx of shaft of lt radius, subsq enc for opn fx type IIIA, IIIB, or IIIC w/ malu
S52.332N	Disp oblique fx of shaft of lt radius, subsq enc for opn fx type IIIA, IIIB, or IIIC w/ nonu
S82.232A	Disp oblique fx of shaft of lt tibia, init enc for clsd fx
S82.232P	Disp oblique fx of shaft of lt tibia, subsq enc for clsd fx w/ malu
S82.232K	Disp oblique fx of shaft of lt tibia, subsq enc for clsd fx w/ nonu
S82.232Q	Disp oblique fx of shaft of lt tibia, subsq enc for opn fx type I or II w/ malu
S82.232M	Disp oblique fx of shaft of lt tibia, subsq enc for opn fx type I or II w/ nonu
S82.232R	Disp oblique fx of shaft of lt tibia, subsq enc for opn fx type IIIA, IIIB, or IIIC w/ malu
S82.232N	Disp oblique fx of shaft of lt tibia, subsq enc for opn fx type IIIA, IIIB, or IIIC w/ nonu
S52.232A	Disp oblique fx of shaft of lt ulna, init enc for clsd fx
S52.232P	Disp oblique fx of shaft of lt ulna, subsq enc for clsd fx w/ malu
S52.232K	Disp oblique fx of shaft of lt ulna, subsq enc for clsd fx w/ nonu
S52.232Q	Disp oblique fx of shaft of lt ulna, subsq enc for opn fx type I or II w/ malu
S52.232M	Disp oblique fx of shaft of lt ulna, subsq enc for opn fx type I or II w/ nonu
S52.232R	Disp oblique fx of shaft of lt ulna, subsq enc for opn fx type IIIA, IIIB, or IIIC w/ malu
S52.232N	Disp oblique fx of shaft of lt ulna, subsq enc for opn fx type IIIA, IIIB, or IIIC w/ nonu
S72.331P	Disp oblique fx of shaft of rt femur, subsq enc for clsd fx w/ malu
S72.331K	Disp oblique fx of shaft of rt femur, subsq enc for clsd fx w/ nonu
S72.331Q	Disp oblique fx of shaft of rt femur, subsq enc for opn fx type I or II w/ malu
S72.331M	Disp oblique fx of shaft of rt femur, subsq enc for opn fx type I or II w/ nonu
S72.331R	Disp oblique fx of shaft of rt femur, subsq enc for opn fx type IIIA, IIIB, or IIIC w/ malu
S72.331N	Disp oblique fx of shaft of rt femur, subsq enc for opn fx type IIIA, IIIB, or IIIC w/ nonu
S82.431P	Disp oblique fx of shaft of rt fibula, subsq enc for clsd fx w/ malu
S82.431K	Disp oblique fx of shaft of rt fibula, subsq enc for clsd fx w/ nonu
S82.431Q	Disp oblique fx of shaft of rt fibula, subsq enc for opn fx type I or II w/ malu
S82.431M	Disp oblique fx of shaft of rt fibula, subsq enc for opn fx type I or II w/ nonu
S82.431R	Disp oblique fx of shaft of rt fibula, subsq enc for opn fx type IIIA, IIIB, or IIIC w/ malu
S82.431N	Disp oblique fx of shaft of rt fibula, subsq enc for opn fx type IIIA, IIIB, or IIIC w/ nonu
S52.331A	Disp oblique fx of shaft of rt radius, init enc for clsd fx
S52.331P	Disp oblique fx of shaft of rt radius, subsq enc for clsd fx w/ malu
S52.331K	Disp oblique fx of shaft of rt radius, subsq enc for clsd fx w/ nonu
S52.331Q	Disp oblique fx of shaft of rt radius, subsq enc for opn fx type I or II w/ malu
S52.331M	Disp oblique fx of shaft of rt radius, subsq enc for opn fx type I or II w/ nonu
S52.331R	Disp oblique fx of shaft of rt radius, subsq enc for opn fx type IIIA, IIIB, or IIIC w/ malu
S52.331N	Disp oblique fx of shaft of rt radius, subsq enc for opn fx type IIIA, IIIB, or IIIC w/ nonu
S82.231A	Disp oblique fx of shaft of rt tibia, init enc for clsd fx
S82.231P	Disp oblique fx of shaft of rt tibia, subsq enc for clsd fx w/ malu
S82.231K	Disp oblique fx of shaft of rt tibia, subsq enc for clsd fx w/ nonu
S82.231Q	Disp oblique fx of shaft of rt tibia, subsq enc for opn fx type I or II w/ malu
S82.231M	Disp oblique fx of shaft of rt tibia, subsq enc for opn fx type I or II w/ nonu
S82.231R	Disp oblique fx of shaft of rt tibia, subsq enc for opn fx type IIIA, IIIB, or IIIC w/ malu
S82.231N	Disp oblique fx of shaft of rt tibia, subsq enc for opn fx type IIIA, IIIB, or IIIC w/ nonu
S52.231A	Disp oblique fx of shaft of rt ulna, init enc for clsd fx
S52.231P	Disp oblique fx of shaft of rt ulna, subsq enc for clsd fx w/ malu
S52.231K	Disp oblique fx of shaft of rt ulna, subsq enc for clsd fx w/ nonu
S52.231Q	Disp oblique fx of shaft of rt ulna, subsq enc for opn fx type I or II w/ malu
S52.231M	Disp oblique fx of shaft of rt ulna, subsq enc for opn fx type I or II w/ nonu
S52.231R	Disp oblique fx of shaft of rt ulna, subsq enc for opn fx type IIIA, IIIB, or IIIC w/ malu
S52.231N	Disp oblique fx of shaft of rt ulna, subsq enc for opn fx type IIIA, IIIB, or IIIC w/ nonu
S72.333P	Disp oblique fx of shaft of unsp femur, subsq enc for clsd fx w/ malu
S72.333K	Disp oblique fx of shaft of unsp femur, subsq enc for clsd fx w/ nonu
S72.333Q	Disp oblique fx of shaft of unsp femur, subsq enc for opn fx type I or II w/ malu
S72.333M	Disp oblique fx of shaft of unsp femur, subsq enc for opn fx type I or II w/ nonu
S72.333R	Disp oblique fx of shaft of unsp femur, subsq enc for opn fx type IIIA, IIIB, or IIIC w/ malu
S72.333N	Disp oblique fx of shaft of unsp femur, subsq enc for opn fx type IIIA, IIIB, or IIIC w/ nonu
S82.433P	Disp oblique fx of shaft of unsp fibula, subsq enc for clsd fx w/ malu
S82.433K	Disp oblique fx of shaft of unsp fibula, subsq enc for clsd fx w/ nonu
S82.433Q	Disp oblique fx of shaft of unsp fibula, subsq enc for opn fx type I or II w/ malu
S82.433M	Disp oblique fx of shaft of unsp fibula, subsq enc for opn fx type I or II w/ nonu
S82.433R	Disp oblique fx of shaft of unsp fibula, subsq enc for opn fx type IIIA, IIIB, or IIIC w/ malu
S82.433N	Disp oblique fx of shaft of unsp fibula, subsq enc for opn fx type IIIA, IIIB, or IIIC w/ nonu
S52.333A	Disp oblique fx of shaft of unsp radius, init enc for clsd fx
S52.333P	Disp oblique fx of shaft of unsp radius, subsq enc for clsd fx w/ malu
S52.333K	Disp oblique fx of shaft of unsp radius, subsq enc for clsd fx w/ nonu

S52.333Q	Disp oblique fx of shaft of unsp radius, subsq enc for opn fx type I or II w/ malu
S52.333M	Disp oblique fx of shaft of unsp radius, subsq enc for opn fx type I or II w/ nonu
S52.333R	Disp oblique fx of shaft of unsp radius, subsq enc for opn fx type IIIA, IIIB, or IIIC w/ malu
S52.333N	Disp oblique fx of shaft of unsp radius, subsq enc for opn fx type IIIA, IIIB, or IIIC w/ nonu
S82.233A	Disp oblique fx of shaft of unsp tibia, init enc for clsd fx
S82.233P	Disp oblique fx of shaft of unsp tibia, subsq enc for clsd fx w/ malu
S82.233K	Disp oblique fx of shaft of unsp tibia, subsq enc for clsd fx w/ nonu
S82.233Q	Disp oblique fx of shaft of unsp tibia, subsq enc for opn fx type I or II w/ malu
S82.233M	Disp oblique fx of shaft of unsp tibia, subsq enc for opn fx type I or II w/ nonu
S82.233R	Disp oblique fx of shaft of unsp tibia, subsq enc for opn fx type IIIA, IIIB, or IIIC w/ malu
S82.233N	Disp oblique fx of shaft of unsp tibia, subsq enc for opn fx type IIIA, IIIB, or IIIC w/ nonu
S52.233A	Disp oblique fx of shaft of unsp ulna, init enc for clsd fx
S52.233P	Disp oblique fx of shaft of unsp ulna, subsq enc for clsd fx w/ malu
S52.233K	Disp oblique fx of shaft of unsp ulna, subsq enc for clsd fx w/ nonu
S52.233Q	Disp oblique fx of shaft of unsp ulna, subsq enc for opn fx type I or II w/ malu
S52.233M	Disp oblique fx of shaft of unsp ulna, subsq enc for opn fx type I or II w/ nonu
S52.233R	Disp oblique fx of shaft of unsp ulna, subsq enc for opn fx type IIIA, IIIB, or IIIC w/ malu
S52.233N	Disp oblique fx of shaft of unsp ulna, subsq enc for opn fx type IIIA, IIIB, or IIIC w/ nonu
S82.012A	Disp osteochondral fx of lt patella, init enc for clsd fx
S82.012B	Disp osteochondral fx of lt patella, init enc for opn fx type I or II
S82.012C	Disp osteochondral fx of lt patella, init enc for opn fx type IIIA, IIIB, or IIIC
S82.012P	Disp osteochondral fx of lt patella, subsq enc for clsd fx w/ malu
S82.012K	Disp osteochondral fx of lt patella, subsq enc for clsd fx w/ nonu
S82.012Q	Disp osteochondral fx of lt patella, subsq enc for opn fx type I or II w/ malu
S82.012M	Disp osteochondral fx of lt patella, subsq enc for opn fx type I or II w/ nonu
S82.012R	Disp osteochondral fx of lt patella, subsq enc for opn fx type IIIA, IIIB, or IIIC w/ malu
S82.012N	Disp osteochondral fx of lt patella, subsq enc for opn fx type IIIA, IIIB, or IIIC w/ nonu
S82.011A	Disp osteochondral fx of rt patella, init enc for clsd fx
S82.011B	Disp osteochondral fx of rt patella, init enc for opn fx type I or II
S82.011C	Disp osteochondral fx of rt patella, init enc for opn fx type IIIA, IIIB, or IIIC
S82.011P	Disp osteochondral fx of rt patella, subsq enc for clsd fx w/ malu
S82.011K	Disp osteochondral fx of rt patella, subsq enc for clsd fx w/ nonu
S82.011Q	Disp osteochondral fx of rt patella, subsq enc for opn fx type I or II w/ malu
S82.011M	Disp osteochondral fx of rt patella, subsq enc for opn fx type I or II w/ nonu
S82.011R	Disp osteochondral fx of rt patella, subsq enc for opn fx type IIIA, IIIB, or IIIC w/ malu
S82.011N	Disp osteochondral fx of rt patella, subsq enc for opn fx type IIIA, IIIB, or IIIC w/ nonu
S82.013A	Disp osteochondral fx of unsp patella, init enc for clsd fx
S82.013B	Disp osteochondral fx of unsp patella, init enc for opn fx type I or II
S82.013C	Disp osteochondral fx of unsp patella, init enc for opn fx type IIIA, IIIB, or IIIC
S82.013P	Disp osteochondral fx of unsp patella, subsq enc for clsd fx w/ malu
S82.013K	Disp osteochondral fx of unsp patella, subsq enc for clsd fx w/ nonu
S82.013Q	Disp osteochondral fx of unsp patella, subsq enc for opn fx type I or II w/ malu
S82.013M	Disp osteochondral fx of unsp patella, subsq enc for opn fx type I or II w/ nonu
S82.013R	Disp osteochondral fx of unsp patella, subsq enc for opn fx type IIIA, IIIB, or IIIC w/ malu
S82.013N	Disp osteochondral fx of unsp patella, subsq enc for opn fx type IIIA, IIIB, or IIIC w/ nonu
S92.052B	Disp oth extraarticular fx of lt calcaneus, init enc for opn fx
S92.052P	Disp oth extraarticular fx of lt calcaneus, subsq enc for fx w/ malu
S92.052K	Disp oth extraarticular fx of lt calcaneus, subsq enc for fx w/ nonu
S92.051B	Disp oth extraarticular fx of rt calcaneus, init enc for opn fx
S92.051P	Disp oth extraarticular fx of rt calcaneus, subsq enc for fx w/ malu
S92.051K	Disp oth extraarticular fx of rt calcaneus, subsq enc for fx w/ nonu

S92.053B	Disp oth extraarticular fx of unsp calcaneus, init enc for opn fx
S92.053P	Disp oth extraarticular fx of unsp calcaneus, subsq enc for fx w/ malu
S92.053K	Disp oth extraarticular fx of unsp calcaneus, subsq enc for fx w/ nonu
S92.042B	Disp oth fx of tuberosity of lt calcaneus, init enc for opn fx
S92.042P	Disp oth fx of tuberosity of lt calcaneus, subsq enc for fx w/ malu
S92.042K	Disp oth fx of tuberosity of lt calcaneus, subsq enc for fx w/ nonu
S92.041B	Disp oth fx of tuberosity of rt calcaneus, init enc for opn fx
S92.041P	Disp oth fx of tuberosity of rt calcaneus, subsq enc for fx w/ malu
S92.041K	Disp oth fx of tuberosity of rt calcaneus, subsq enc for fx w/ nonu
S92.043B	Disp oth fx of tuberosity of unsp calcaneus, init enc for opn fx
S92.043P	Disp oth fx of tuberosity of unsp calcaneus, subsq enc for fx w/ malu
S92.043K	Disp oth fx of tuberosity of unsp calcaneus, subsq enc for fx w/ nonu
S82.872B	Disp pilon fx of lt tibia, init enc for opn fx type I or II
S82.872C	Disp pilon fx of lt tibia, init enc for opn fx type IIIA, IIIB, or IIIC
S82.872P	Disp pilon fx of lt tibia, subsq enc for clsd fx w/ malu
S82.872K	Disp pilon fx of lt tibia, subsq enc for clsd fx w/ nonu
S82.872Q	Disp pilon fx of lt tibia, subsq enc for opn fx type I or II w/ malu
S82.872M	Disp pilon fx of lt tibia, subsq enc for opn fx type I or II w/ nonu
S82.872R	Disp pilon fx of lt tibia, subsq enc for opn fx type IIIA, IIIB, or IIIC w/ malu
S82.872N	Disp pilon fx of lt tibia, subsq enc for opn fx type IIIA, IIIB, or IIIC w/ nonu
S82.871B	Disp pilon fx of rt tibia, init enc for opn fx type I or II
S82.871C	Disp pilon fx of rt tibia, init enc for opn fx type IIIA, IIIB, or IIIC
S82.871P	Disp pilon fx of rt tibia, subsq enc for clsd fx w/ malu
S82.871K	Disp pilon fx of rt tibia, subsq enc for clsd fx w/ nonu
S82.871Q	Disp pilon fx of rt tibia, subsq enc for opn fx type I or II w/ malu
S82.871M	Disp pilon fx of rt tibia, subsq enc for opn fx type I or II w/ nonu
S82.871R	Disp pilon fx of rt tibia, subsq enc for opn fx type IIIA, IIIB, or IIIC w/ malu
S82.871N	Disp pilon fx of rt tibia, subsq enc for opn fx type IIIA, IIIB, or IIIC w/ nonu
S82.873B	Disp pilon fx of unsp tibia, init enc for opn fx type I or II
S82.873C	Disp pilon fx of unsp tibia, init enc for opn fx type IIIA, IIIB, or IIIC
S82.873P	Disp pilon fx of unsp tibia, subsq enc for clsd fx w/ malu
S82.873K	Disp pilon fx of unsp tibia, subsq enc for clsd fx w/ nonu
S82.873Q	Disp pilon fx of unsp tibia, subsq enc for opn fx type I or II w/ malu
S82.873M	Disp pilon fx of unsp tibia, subsq enc for opn fx type I or II w/ nonu
S82.873R	Disp pilon fx of unsp tibia, subsq enc for opn fx type IIIA, IIIB, or IIIC w/ malu
S82.873N	Disp pilon fx of unsp tibia, subsq enc for opn fx type IIIA, IIIB, or IIIC w/ nonu
S12.030A	Disp post arch fx of 1st cervical vertebra, init enc for clsd fx
S12.030K	Disp post arch fx of 1st cervical vertebra, subsq enc for fx w/ nonu
S62.222B	Disp Rolando's fx, lt hand, init enc for opn fx
S62.222P	Disp Rolando's fx, lt hand, subsq enc for fx w/ malu
S62.222K	Disp Rolando's fx, lt hand, subsq enc for fx w/ nonu
S62.221B	Disp Rolando's fx, rt hand, init enc for opn fx
S62.221P	Disp Rolando's fx, rt hand, subsq enc for fx w/ malu
S62.221K	Disp Rolando's fx, rt hand, subsq enc for fx w/ nonu
S62.223B	Disp Rolando's fx, unsp hand, init enc for opn fx
S62.223P	Disp Rolando's fx, unsp hand, subsq enc for fx w/ malu
S62.223K	Disp Rolando's fx, unsp hand, subsq enc for fx w/ nonu
S42.362A	Disp segmental fx of shaft of humerus, lt arm, init enc for clsd fx
S42.362P	Disp segmental fx of shaft of humerus, lt arm, subsq enc for fx w/ malu
S42.362K	Disp segmental fx of shaft of humerus, lt arm, subsq enc for fx w/ nonu
S42.361A	Disp segmental fx of shaft of humerus, rt arm, init enc for clsd fx
S42.361P	Disp segmental fx of shaft of humerus, rt arm, subsq enc for fx w/ malu
S42.361K	Disp segmental fx of shaft of humerus, rt arm, subsq enc for fx w/ nonu
S42.363A	Disp segmental fx of shaft of humerus, unsp arm, init enc for clsd fx
S42.363P	Disp segmental fx of shaft of humerus, unsp arm, subsq enc for fx w/ malu
S42.363K	Disp segmental fx of shaft of humerus, unsp arm, subsq enc for fx w/ nonu
S72.362P	Disp segmental fx of shaft of lt femur, subsq enc for clsd fx w/ malu
S72.362K	Disp segmental fx of shaft of lt femur, subsq enc for clsd fx w/ nonu
S72.362Q	Disp segmental fx of shaft of lt femur, subsq enc for opn fx type I or II w/ malu
S72.362M	Disp segmental fx of shaft of lt femur, subsq enc for opn fx type I or II w/ nonu
S72.362R	Disp segmental fx of shaft of lt femur, subsq enc for opn fx type IIIA, IIIB, or IIIC w/ malu
S72.362N	Disp segmental fx of shaft of lt femur, subsq enc for opn fx type IIIA, IIIB, or IIIC w/ nonu
S82.462P	Disp segmental fx of shaft of lt fibula, subsq enc for clsd fx w/ malu
S82.462K	Disp segmental fx of shaft of lt fibula, subsq enc for clsd fx w/ nonu
S82.462Q	Disp segmental fx of shaft of lt fibula, subsq enc for opn fx type I or II w/ malu

S82.462M	Disp segmental fx of shaft of lt fibula, subsq enc for opn fx type I or II w/ nonu
S82.462R	Disp segmental fx of shaft of lt fibula, subsq enc for opn fx type IIIA, IIIB, or IIIC w/ malu
S82.462N	Disp segmental fx of shaft of lt fibula, subsq enc for opn fx type IIIA, IIIB, or IIIC w/ nonu
S82.262A	Disp segmental fx of shaft of lt tibia, init enc for clsd fx
S82.262P	Disp segmental fx of shaft of lt tibia, subsq enc for clsd fx w/ malu
S82.262K	Disp segmental fx of shaft of lt tibia, subsq enc for clsd fx w/ nonu
S82.262Q	Disp segmental fx of shaft of lt tibia, subsq enc for opn fx type I or II w/ malu
S82.262M	Disp segmental fx of shaft of lt tibia, subsq enc for opn fx type I or II w/ nonu
S82.262R	Disp segmental fx of shaft of lt tibia, subsq enc for opn fx type IIIA, IIIB, or IIIC w/ malu
S82.262N	Disp segmental fx of shaft of lt tibia, subsq enc for opn fx type IIIA, IIIB, or IIIC w/ nonu
S52.362A	Disp segmental fx of shaft of radius, lt arm, init enc for clsd fx
S52.362P	Disp segmental fx of shaft of radius, lt arm, subsq enc for clsd fx w/ malu
S52.362K	Disp segmental fx of shaft of radius, lt arm, subsq enc for clsd fx w/ nonu
S52.362Q	Disp segmental fx of shaft of radius, lt arm, subsq enc for opn fx type I or II w/ malu
S52.362M	Disp segmental fx of shaft of radius, lt arm, subsq enc for opn fx type I or II w/ nonu
S52.362R	Disp segmental fx of shaft of radius, lt arm, subsq enc for opn fx type IIIA, IIIB, or IIIC w/ malu
S52.362N	Disp segmental fx of shaft of radius, lt arm, subsq enc for opn fx type IIIA, IIIB, or IIIC w/ nonu
S52.361A	Disp segmental fx of shaft of radius, rt arm, init enc for clsd fx
S52.361P	Disp segmental fx of shaft of radius, rt arm, subsq enc for clsd fx w/ malu
S52.361K	Disp segmental fx of shaft of radius, rt arm, subsq enc for clsd fx w/ nonu
S52.361Q	Disp segmental fx of shaft of radius, rt arm, subsq enc for opn fx type I or II w/ malu
S52.361M	Disp segmental fx of shaft of radius, rt arm, subsq enc for opn fx type I or II w/ nonu
S52.361R	Disp segmental fx of shaft of radius, rt arm, subsq enc for opn fx type IIIA, IIIB, or IIIC w/ malu
S52.361N	Disp segmental fx of shaft of radius, rt arm, subsq enc for opn fx type IIIA, IIIB, or IIIC w/ nonu
S52.363A	Disp segmental fx of shaft of radius, unsp arm, init enc for clsd fx
S52.363P	Disp segmental fx of shaft of radius, unsp arm, subsq enc for clsd fx w/ malu
S52.363K	Disp segmental fx of shaft of radius, unsp arm, subsq enc for clsd fx w/ nonu
S52.363Q	Disp segmental fx of shaft of radius, unsp arm, subsq enc for opn fx type I or II w/ malu
S52.363M	Disp segmental fx of shaft of radius, unsp arm, subsq enc for opn fx type I or II w/ nonu
S52.363R	Disp segmental fx of shaft of radius, unsp arm, subsq enc for opn fx type IIIA, IIIB, or IIIC w/ malu
S52.363N	Disp segmental fx of shaft of radius, unsp arm, subsq enc for opn fx type IIIA, IIIB, or IIIC w/ nonu
S72.361P	Disp segmental fx of shaft of rt femur, subsq enc for clsd fx w/ malu
S72.361K	Disp segmental fx of shaft of rt femur, subsq enc for clsd fx w/ nonu
S72.361Q	Disp segmental fx of shaft of rt femur, subsq enc for opn fx type I or II w/ malu
S72.361M	Disp segmental fx of shaft of rt femur, subsq enc for opn fx type I or II w/ nonu
S72.361R	Disp segmental fx of shaft of rt femur, subsq enc for opn fx type IIIA, IIIB, or IIIC w/ malu
S72.361N	Disp segmental fx of shaft of rt femur, subsq enc for opn fx type IIIA, IIIB, or IIIC w/ nonu
S82.461P	Disp segmental fx of shaft of rt fibula, subsq enc for clsd fx w/ malu
S82.461K	Disp segmental fx of shaft of rt fibula, subsq enc for clsd fx w/ nonu
S82.461Q	Disp segmental fx of shaft of rt fibula, subsq enc for opn fx type I or II w/ malu
S82.461M	Disp segmental fx of shaft of rt fibula, subsq enc for opn fx type I or II w/ nonu
S82.461R	Disp segmental fx of shaft of rt fibula, subsq enc for opn fx type IIIA, IIIB, or IIIC w/ malu
S82.461N	Disp segmental fx of shaft of rt fibula, subsq enc for opn fx type IIIA, IIIB, or IIIC w/ nonu
S82.261A	Disp segmental fx of shaft of rt tibia, init enc for clsd fx
S82.261P	Disp segmental fx of shaft of rt tibia, subsq enc for clsd fx w/ malu
S82.261K	Disp segmental fx of shaft of rt tibia, subsq enc for clsd fx w/ nonu
S82.261Q	Disp segmental fx of shaft of rt tibia, subsq enc for opn fx type I or II w/ malu
S82.261M	Disp segmental fx of shaft of rt tibia, subsq enc for opn fx type I or II w/ nonu
S82.261R	Disp segmental fx of shaft of rt tibia, subsq enc for opn fx type IIIA, IIIB, or IIIC w/ malu
S82.261N	Disp segmental fx of shaft of rt tibia, subsq enc for opn fx type IIIA, IIIB, or IIIC w/ nonu
S52.262A	Disp segmental fx of shaft of ulna, lt arm, init enc for clsd fx
S52.262P	Disp segmental fx of shaft of ulna, lt arm, subsq enc for clsd fx w/ malu
S52.262K	Disp segmental fx of shaft of ulna, lt arm, subsq enc for clsd fx w/ nonu
S52.262Q	Disp segmental fx of shaft of ulna, lt arm, subsq enc for opn fx type I or II w/ malu
S52.262M	Disp segmental fx of shaft of ulna, lt arm, subsq enc for opn fx type I or II w/ nonu
S52.262R	Disp segmental fx of shaft of ulna, lt arm, subsq enc for opn fx type IIIA, IIIB, or IIIC w/ malu
S52.262N	Disp segmental fx of shaft of ulna, lt arm, subsq enc for opn fx type IIIA, IIIB, or IIIC w/ nonu
S52.261A	Disp segmental fx of shaft of ulna, rt arm, init enc for clsd fx
S52.261P	Disp segmental fx of shaft of ulna, rt arm, subsq enc for clsd fx w/ malu
S52.261K	Disp segmental fx of shaft of ulna, rt arm, subsq enc for clsd fx w/ nonu
S52.261Q	Disp segmental fx of shaft of ulna, rt arm, subsq enc for opn fx type I or II w/ malu
S52.261M	Disp segmental fx of shaft of ulna, rt arm, subsq enc for opn fx type I or II w/ nonu
S52.261R	Disp segmental fx of shaft of ulna, rt arm, subsq enc for opn fx type IIIA, IIIB, or IIIC w/ malu
S52.261N	Disp segmental fx of shaft of ulna, rt arm, subsq enc for opn fx type IIIA, IIIB, or IIIC w/ nonu
S52.263A	Disp segmental fx of shaft of ulna, unsp arm, init enc for clsd fx
S52.263P	Disp segmental fx of shaft of ulna, unsp arm, subsq enc for clsd fx w/ malu
S52.263K	Disp segmental fx of shaft of ulna, unsp arm, subsq enc for clsd fx w/ nonu
S52.263Q	Disp segmental fx of shaft of ulna, unsp arm, subsq enc for opn fx type I or II w/ malu
S52.263M	Disp segmental fx of shaft of ulna, unsp arm, subsq enc for opn fx type I or II w/ nonu
S52.263R	Disp segmental fx of shaft of ulna, unsp arm, subsq enc for opn fx type IIIA, IIIB, or IIIC w/ malu
S52.263N	Disp segmental fx of shaft of ulna, unsp arm, subsq enc for opn fx type IIIA, IIIB, or IIIC w/ nonu
S72.363P	Disp segmental fx of shaft of unsp femur, subsq enc for clsd fx w/ malu
S72.363K	Disp segmental fx of shaft of unsp femur, subsq enc for clsd fx w/ nonu
S72.363Q	Disp segmental fx of shaft of unsp femur, subsq enc for opn fx type I or II w/ malu
S72.363M	Disp segmental fx of shaft of unsp femur, subsq enc for opn fx type I or II w/ nonu
S72.363R	Disp segmental fx of shaft of unsp femur, subsq enc for opn fx type IIIA, IIIB, or IIIC w/ malu
S72.363N	Disp segmental fx of shaft of unsp femur, subsq enc for opn fx type IIIA, IIIB, or IIIC w/ nonu
S82.463P	Disp segmental fx of shaft of unsp fibula, subsq enc for clsd fx w/ malu
S82.463K	Disp segmental fx of shaft of unsp fibula, subsq enc for clsd fx w/ nonu
S82.463Q	Disp segmental fx of shaft of unsp fibula, subsq enc for opn fx type I or II w/ malu
S82.463M	Disp segmental fx of shaft of unsp fibula, subsq enc for opn fx type I or II w/ nonu
S82.463R	Disp segmental fx of shaft of unsp fibula, subsq enc for opn fx type IIIA, IIIB, or IIIC w/ malu
S82.463N	Disp segmental fx of shaft of unsp fibula, subsq enc for opn fx type IIIA, IIIB, or IIIC w/ nonu
S82.263A	Disp segmental fx of shaft of unsp tibia, init enc for clsd fx
S82.263P	Disp segmental fx of shaft of unsp tibia, subsq enc for clsd fx w/ malu
S82.263K	Disp segmental fx of shaft of unsp tibia, subsq enc for clsd fx w/ nonu
S82.263Q	Disp segmental fx of shaft of unsp tibia, subsq enc for opn fx type I or II w/ malu
S82.263M	Disp segmental fx of shaft of unsp tibia, subsq enc for opn fx type I or II w/ nonu
S82.263R	Disp segmental fx of shaft of unsp tibia, subsq enc for opn fx type IIIA, IIIB, or IIIC w/ malu
S82.263N	Disp segmental fx of shaft of unsp tibia, subsq enc for opn fx type IIIA, IIIB, or IIIC w/ nonu
S42.412A	Disp simple supracondylar fx w/o intercondylar fx of lt humerus, init enc for clsd fx
S42.412P	Disp simple supracondylar fx w/o intercondylar fx of lt humerus, subsq enc for fx w/ malu

S42.412K	Disp simple supracondylar fx w/o intercondylar fx of lt humerus, subsq enc for fx w/ nonu
S42.411A	Disp simple supracondylar fx w/o intercondylar fx of rt humerus, init enc for clsd fx
S42.411P	Disp simple supracondylar fx w/o intercondylar fx of rt humerus, subsq enc for fx w/ malu
S42.411K	Disp simple supracondylar fx w/o intercondylar fx of rt humerus, subsq enc for fx w/ nonu
S42.413A	Disp simple supracondylar fx w/o intercondylar fx of unsp humerus, init enc for clsd fx
S42.413P	Disp simple supracondylar fx w/o intercondylar fx of unsp humerus, subsq enc for fx w/ malu
S42.413K	Disp simple supracondylar fx w/o intercondylar fx of unsp humerus, subsq enc for fx w/ nonu
S42.342A	Disp spiral fx of shaft of humerus, lt arm, init enc for clsd fx
S42.342P	Disp spiral fx of shaft of humerus, lt arm, subsq enc for fx w/ malu
S42.342K	Disp spiral fx of shaft of humerus, lt arm, subsq enc for fx w/ nonu
S42.341A	Disp spiral fx of shaft of humerus, rt arm, init enc for clsd fx
S42.341P	Disp spiral fx of shaft of humerus, rt arm, subsq enc for fx w/ malu
S42.341K	Disp spiral fx of shaft of humerus, rt arm, subsq enc for fx w/ nonu
S42.343A	Disp spiral fx of shaft of humerus, unsp arm, init enc for clsd fx
S42.343P	Disp spiral fx of shaft of humerus, unsp arm, subsq enc for fx w/ malu
S42.343K	Disp spiral fx of shaft of humerus, unsp arm, subsq enc for fx w/ nonu
S72.342P	Disp spiral fx of shaft of lt femur, subsq enc for clsd fx w/ malu
S72.342K	Disp spiral fx of shaft of lt femur, subsq enc for clsd fx w/ nonu
S72.342Q	Disp spiral fx of shaft of lt femur, subsq enc for opn fx type I or II w/ malu
S72.342M	Disp spiral fx of shaft of lt femur, subsq enc for opn fx type I or II w/ nonu
S72.342R	Disp spiral fx of shaft of lt femur, subsq enc for opn fx type IIIA, IIIB, or IIIC w/ malu
S72.342N	Disp spiral fx of shaft of lt femur, subsq enc for opn fx type IIIA, IIIB, or IIIC w/ nonu
S82.442P	Disp spiral fx of shaft of lt fibula, subsq enc for clsd fx w/ malu
S82.442K	Disp spiral fx of shaft of lt fibula, subsq enc for clsd fx w/ nonu
S82.442Q	Disp spiral fx of shaft of lt fibula, subsq enc for opn fx type I or II w/ malu
S82.442M	Disp spiral fx of shaft of lt fibula, subsq enc for opn fx type I or II w/ nonu
S82.442R	Disp spiral fx of shaft of lt fibula, subsq enc for opn fx type IIIA, IIIB, or IIIC w/ malu
S82.442N	Disp spiral fx of shaft of lt fibula, subsq enc for opn fx type IIIA, IIIB, or IIIC w/ nonu
S82.242A	Disp spiral fx of shaft of lt tibia, init enc for clsd fx
S82.242P	Disp spiral fx of shaft of lt tibia, subsq enc for clsd fx w/ malu
S82.242K	Disp spiral fx of shaft of lt tibia, subsq enc for clsd fx w/ nonu
S82.242Q	Disp spiral fx of shaft of lt tibia, subsq enc for opn fx type I or II w/ malu
S82.242M	Disp spiral fx of shaft of lt tibia, subsq enc for opn fx type I or II w/ nonu
S82.242R	Disp spiral fx of shaft of lt tibia, subsq enc for opn fx type IIIA, IIIB, or IIIC w/ malu
S82.242N	Disp spiral fx of shaft of lt tibia, subsq enc for opn fx type IIIA, IIIB, or IIIC w/ nonu
S52.342A	Disp spiral fx of shaft of radius, lt arm, init enc for clsd fx
S52.342P	Disp spiral fx of shaft of radius, lt arm, subsq enc for clsd fx w/ malu
S52.342K	Disp spiral fx of shaft of radius, lt arm, subsq enc for clsd fx w/ nonu
S52.342Q	Disp spiral fx of shaft of radius, lt arm, subsq enc for opn fx type I or II w/ malu
S52.342M	Disp spiral fx of shaft of radius, lt arm, subsq enc for opn fx type I or II w/ nonu
S52.342R	Disp spiral fx of shaft of radius, lt arm, subsq enc for opn fx type IIIA, IIIB, or IIIC w/ malu
S52.342N	Disp spiral fx of shaft of radius, lt arm, subsq enc for opn fx type IIIA, IIIB, or IIIC w/ nonu
S52.341A	Disp spiral fx of shaft of radius, rt arm, init enc for clsd fx
S52.341P	Disp spiral fx of shaft of radius, rt arm, subsq enc for clsd fx w/ malu
S52.341K	Disp spiral fx of shaft of radius, rt arm, subsq enc for clsd fx w/ nonu
S52.341Q	Disp spiral fx of shaft of radius, rt arm, subsq enc for opn fx type I or II w/ malu
S52.341M	Disp spiral fx of shaft of radius, rt arm, subsq enc for opn fx type I or II w/ nonu
S52.341R	Disp spiral fx of shaft of radius, rt arm, subsq enc for opn fx type IIIA, IIIB, or IIIC w/ malu
S52.341N	Disp spiral fx of shaft of radius, rt arm, subsq enc for opn fx type IIIA, IIIB, or IIIC w/ nonu
S52.343A	Disp spiral fx of shaft of radius, unsp arm, init enc for clsd fx
S52.343P	Disp spiral fx of shaft of radius, unsp arm, subsq enc for clsd fx w/ malu
S52.343K	Disp spiral fx of shaft of radius, unsp arm, subsq enc for clsd fx w/ nonu
S52.343Q	Disp spiral fx of shaft of radius, unsp arm, subsq enc for opn fx type I or II w/ malu

S52.343M	Disp spiral fx of shaft of radius, unsp arm, subsq enc for opn fx type I or II w/ nonu
S52.343R	Disp spiral fx of shaft of radius, unsp arm, subsq enc for opn fx type IIIA, IIIB, or IIIC w/ malu
S52.343N	Disp spiral fx of shaft of radius, unsp arm, subsq enc for opn fx type IIIA, IIIB, or IIIC w/ nonu
S72.341P	Disp spiral fx of shaft of rt femur, subsq enc for clsd fx w/ malu
S72.341K	Disp spiral fx of shaft of rt femur, subsq enc for clsd fx w/ nonu
S72.341Q	Disp spiral fx of shaft of rt femur, subsq enc for opn fx type I or II w/ malu
S72.341M	Disp spiral fx of shaft of rt femur, subsq enc for opn fx type I or II w/ nonu
S72.341R	Disp spiral fx of shaft of rt femur, subsq enc for opn fx type IIIA, IIIB, or IIIC w/ malu
S72.341N	Disp spiral fx of shaft of rt femur, subsq enc for opn fx type IIIA, IIIB, or IIIC w/ nonu
S82.441P	Disp spiral fx of shaft of rt fibula, subsq enc for clsd fx w/ malu
S82.441K	Disp spiral fx of shaft of rt fibula, subsq enc for clsd fx w/ nonu
S82.441Q	Disp spiral fx of shaft of rt fibula, subsq enc for opn fx type I or II w/ malu
S82.441M	Disp spiral fx of shaft of rt fibula, subsq enc for opn fx type I or II w/ nonu
S82.441R	Disp spiral fx of shaft of rt fibula, subsq enc for opn fx type IIIA, IIIB, or IIIC w/ malu
S82.441N	Disp spiral fx of shaft of rt fibula, subsq enc for opn fx type IIIA, IIIB, or IIIC w/ nonu
S82.241A	Disp spiral fx of shaft of rt tibia, init enc for clsd fx
S82.241P	Disp spiral fx of shaft of rt tibia, subsq enc for clsd fx w/ malu
S82.241K	Disp spiral fx of shaft of rt tibia, subsq enc for clsd fx w/ nonu
S82.241Q	Disp spiral fx of shaft of rt tibia, subsq enc for opn fx type I or II w/ malu
S82.241M	Disp spiral fx of shaft of rt tibia, subsq enc for opn fx type I or II w/ nonu
S82.241R	Disp spiral fx of shaft of rt tibia, subsq enc for opn fx type IIIA, IIIB, or IIIC w/ malu
S82.241N	Disp spiral fx of shaft of rt tibia, subsq enc for opn fx type IIIA, IIIB, or IIIC w/ nonu
S52.242A	Disp spiral fx of shaft of ulna, lt arm, init enc for clsd fx
S52.242P	Disp spiral fx of shaft of ulna, lt arm, subsq enc for clsd fx w/ malu
S52.242K	Disp spiral fx of shaft of ulna, lt arm, subsq enc for clsd fx w/ nonu
S52.242Q	Disp spiral fx of shaft of ulna, lt arm, subsq enc for opn fx type I or II w/ malu
S52.242M	Disp spiral fx of shaft of ulna, lt arm, subsq enc for opn fx type I or II w/ nonu
S52.242R	Disp spiral fx of shaft of ulna, lt arm, subsq enc for opn fx type IIIA, IIIB, or IIIC w/ malu
S52.242N	Disp spiral fx of shaft of ulna, lt arm, subsq enc for opn fx type IIIA, IIIB, or IIIC w/ nonu
S52.241A	Disp spiral fx of shaft of ulna, rt arm, init enc for clsd fx
S52.241P	Disp spiral fx of shaft of ulna, rt arm, subsq enc for clsd fx w/ malu
S52.241K	Disp spiral fx of shaft of ulna, rt arm, subsq enc for clsd fx w/ nonu
S52.241Q	Disp spiral fx of shaft of ulna, rt arm, subsq enc for opn fx type I or II w/ malu
S52.241M	Disp spiral fx of shaft of ulna, rt arm, subsq enc for opn fx type I or II w/ nonu
S52.241R	Disp spiral fx of shaft of ulna, rt arm, subsq enc for opn fx type IIIA, IIIB, or IIIC w/ malu
S52.241N	Disp spiral fx of shaft of ulna, rt arm, subsq enc for opn fx type IIIA, IIIB, or IIIC w/ nonu
S52.243A	Disp spiral fx of shaft of ulna, unsp arm, init enc for clsd fx
S52.243P	Disp spiral fx of shaft of ulna, unsp arm, subsq enc for clsd fx w/ malu
S52.243K	Disp spiral fx of shaft of ulna, unsp arm, subsq enc for clsd fx w/ nonu
S52.243Q	Disp spiral fx of shaft of ulna, unsp arm, subsq enc for opn fx type I or II w/ malu
S52.243M	Disp spiral fx of shaft of ulna, unsp arm, subsq enc for opn fx type I or II w/ nonu
S52.243R	Disp spiral fx of shaft of ulna, unsp arm, subsq enc for opn fx type IIIA, IIIB, or IIIC w/ malu
S52.243N	Disp spiral fx of shaft of ulna, unsp arm, subsq enc for opn fx type IIIA, IIIB, or IIIC w/ nonu
S72.343P	Disp spiral fx of shaft of unsp femur, subsq enc for clsd fx w/ malu
S72.343K	Disp spiral fx of shaft of unsp femur, subsq enc for clsd fx w/ nonu
S72.343Q	Disp spiral fx of shaft of unsp femur, subsq enc for opn fx type I or II w/ malu
S72.343M	Disp spiral fx of shaft of unsp femur, subsq enc for opn fx type I or II w/ nonu
S72.343R	Disp spiral fx of shaft of unsp femur, subsq enc for opn fx type IIIA, IIIB, or IIIC w/ malu
S72.343N	Disp spiral fx of shaft of unsp femur, subsq enc for opn fx type IIIA, IIIB, or IIIC w/ nonu
S82.443P	Disp spiral fx of shaft of unsp fibula, subsq enc for clsd fx w/ malu
S82.443K	Disp spiral fx of shaft of unsp fibula, subsq enc for clsd fx w/ nonu

Code	Description
S82.443Q	Disp spiral fx of shaft of unsp fibula, subsq enc for opn fx type I or II w/ malu
S82.443M	Disp spiral fx of shaft of unsp fibula, subsq enc for opn fx type I or II w/ nonu
S82.443R	Disp spiral fx of shaft of unsp fibula, subsq enc for opn fx type IIIA, IIIB, or IIIC w/ malu
S82.443N	Disp spiral fx of shaft of unsp fibula, subsq enc for opn fx type IIIA, IIIB, or IIIC w/ nonu
S82.243A	Disp spiral fx of shaft of unsp tibia, init enc for clsd fx
S82.243P	Disp spiral fx of shaft of unsp tibia, subsq enc for clsd fx w/ malu
S82.243K	Disp spiral fx of shaft of unsp tibia, subsq enc for clsd fx w/ nonu
S82.243Q	Disp spiral fx of shaft of unsp tibia, subsq enc for opn fx type I or II w/ malu
S82.243M	Disp spiral fx of shaft of unsp tibia, subsq enc for opn fx type I or II w/ nonu
S82.243R	Disp spiral fx of shaft of unsp tibia, subsq enc for opn fx type IIIA, IIIB, or IIIC w/ malu
S82.243N	Disp spiral fx of shaft of unsp tibia, subsq enc for opn fx type IIIA, IIIB, or IIIC w/ nonu
S72.22XP	Disp subtrochanteric fx of lt femur, subsq enc for clsd fx w/ malu
S72.22XK	Disp subtrochanteric fx of lt femur, subsq enc for clsd fx w/ nonu
S72.22XQ	Disp subtrochanteric fx of lt femur, subsq enc for opn fx type I or II w/ malu
S72.22XM	Disp subtrochanteric fx of lt femur, subsq enc for opn fx type I or II w/ nonu
S72.22XR	Disp subtrochanteric fx of lt femur, subsq enc for opn fx type IIIA, IIIB, or IIIC w/ malu
S72.22XN	Disp subtrochanteric fx of lt femur, subsq enc for opn fx type IIIA, IIIB, or IIIC w/ nonu
S72.21XP	Disp subtrochanteric fx of rt femur, subsq enc for clsd fx w/ malu
S72.21XK	Disp subtrochanteric fx of rt femur, subsq enc for clsd fx w/ nonu
S72.21XQ	Disp subtrochanteric fx of rt femur, subsq enc for opn fx type I or II w/ malu
S72.21XM	Disp subtrochanteric fx of rt femur, subsq enc for opn fx type I or II w/ nonu
S72.21XR	Disp subtrochanteric fx of rt femur, subsq enc for opn fx type IIIA, IIIB, or IIIC w/ malu
S72.21XN	Disp subtrochanteric fx of rt femur, subsq enc for opn fx type IIIA, IIIB, or IIIC w/ nonu
S72.23XP	Disp subtrochanteric fx of unsp femur, subsq enc for clsd fx w/ malu
S72.23XK	Disp subtrochanteric fx of unsp femur, subsq enc for clsd fx w/ nonu
S72.23XQ	Disp subtrochanteric fx of unsp femur, subsq enc for opn fx type I or II w/ malu
S72.23XM	Disp subtrochanteric fx of unsp femur, subsq enc for opn fx type I or II w/ nonu
S72.23XR	Disp subtrochanteric fx of unsp femur, subsq enc for opn fx type IIIA, IIIB, or IIIC w/ malu
S72.23XN	Disp subtrochanteric fx of unsp femur, subsq enc for opn fx type IIIA, IIIB, or IIIC w/ nonu
S72.462A	Disp supracondylar fx w/ intracondylar extension of lwr end of lt femur, init enc for clsd fx
S72.462P	Disp supracondylar fx w/ intracondylar extension of lwr end of lt femur, subsq enc for clsd fx w/ malu
S72.462K	Disp supracondylar fx w/ intracondylar extension of lwr end of lt femur, subsq enc for clsd fx w/ nonu
S72.462Q	Disp supracondylar fx w/ intracondylar extension of lwr end of lt femur, subsq enc for opn fx type I or II w/ malu
S72.462M	Disp supracondylar fx w/ intracondylar extension of lwr end of lt femur, subsq enc for opn fx type I or II w/ nonu
S72.462R	Disp supracondylar fx w/ intracondylar extension of lwr end of lt femur, subsq enc for opn fx type IIIA, IIIB, or IIIC w/ malu
S72.462N	Disp supracondylar fx w/ intracondylar extension of lwr end of lt femur, subsq enc for opn fx type IIIA, IIIB, or IIIC w/ nonu
S72.461A	Disp supracondylar fx w/ intracondylar extension of lwr end of rt femur, init enc for clsd fx
S72.461P	Disp supracondylar fx w/ intracondylar extension of lwr end of rt femur, subsq enc for clsd fx w/ malu
S72.461K	Disp supracondylar fx w/ intracondylar extension of lwr end of rt femur, subsq enc for clsd fx w/ nonu
S72.461Q	Disp supracondylar fx w/ intracondylar extension of lwr end of rt femur, subsq enc for opn fx type I or II w/ malu
S72.461M	Disp supracondylar fx w/ intracondylar extension of lwr end of rt femur, subsq enc for opn fx type I or II w/ nonu
S72.461R	Disp supracondylar fx w/ intracondylar extension of lwr end of rt femur, subsq enc for opn fx type IIIA, IIIB, or IIIC w/ malu
S72.461N	Disp supracondylar fx w/ intracondylar extension of lwr end of rt femur, subsq enc for opn fx type IIIA, IIIB, or IIIC w/ nonu
S72.463A	Disp supracondylar fx w/ intracondylar extension of lwr end of unsp femur, init enc for clsd fx
S72.463P	Disp supracondylar fx w/ intracondylar extension of lwr end of unsp femur, subsq enc for clsd fx w/ malu
S72.463K	Disp supracondylar fx w/ intracondylar extension of lwr end of unsp femur, subsq enc for clsd fx w/ nonu
S72.463Q	Disp supracondylar fx w/ intracondylar extension of lwr end of unsp femur, subsq enc for opn fx type I or II w/ malu
S72.463M	Disp supracondylar fx w/ intracondylar extension of lwr end of unsp femur, subsq enc for opn fx type I or II w/ nonu
S72.463R	Disp supracondylar fx w/ intracondylar extension of lwr end of unsp femur, subsq enc for opn fx type IIIA, IIIB, or IIIC w/ malu
S72.463N	Disp supracondylar fx w/ intracondylar extension of lwr end of unsp femur, subsq enc for opn fx type IIIA, IIIB, or IIIC w/ nonu
S72.452A	Disp supracondylar fx w/o intracondylar extension of lwr end of lt femur, init enc for clsd fx
S72.452P	Disp supracondylar fx w/o intracondylar extension of lwr end of lt femur, subsq enc for clsd fx w/ malu
S72.452K	Disp supracondylar fx w/o intracondylar extension of lwr end of lt femur, subsq enc for clsd fx w/ nonu
S72.452Q	Disp supracondylar fx w/o intracondylar extension of lwr end of lt femur, subsq enc for opn fx type I or II w/ malu
S72.452M	Disp supracondylar fx w/o intracondylar extension of lwr end of lt femur, subsq enc for opn fx type I or II w/ nonu
S72.452R	Disp supracondylar fx w/o intracondylar extension of lwr end of lt femur, subsq enc for opn fx type IIIA, IIIB, or IIIC w/ malu
S72.452N	Disp supracondylar fx w/o intracondylar extension of lwr end of lt femur, subsq enc for opn fx type IIIA, IIIB, or IIIC w/ nonu
S72.451A	Disp supracondylar fx w/o intracondylar extension of lwr end of rt femur, init enc for clsd fx
S72.451P	Disp supracondylar fx w/o intracondylar extension of lwr end of rt femur, subsq enc for clsd fx w/ malu
S72.451K	Disp supracondylar fx w/o intracondylar extension of lwr end of rt femur, subsq enc for clsd fx w/ nonu
S72.451Q	Disp supracondylar fx w/o intracondylar extension of lwr end of rt femur, subsq enc for opn fx type I or II w/ malu
S72.451M	Disp supracondylar fx w/o intracondylar extension of lwr end of rt femur, subsq enc for opn fx type I or II w/ nonu
S72.451R	Disp supracondylar fx w/o intracondylar extension of lwr end of rt femur, subsq enc for opn fx type IIIA, IIIB, or IIIC w/ malu
S72.451N	Disp supracondylar fx w/o intracondylar extension of lwr end of rt femur, subsq enc for opn fx type IIIA, IIIB, or IIIC w/ nonu
S72.453A	Disp supracondylar fx w/o intracondylar extension of lwr end of unsp femur, init enc for clsd fx
S72.453P	Disp supracondylar fx w/o intracondylar extension of lwr end of unsp femur, subsq enc for clsd fx w/ malu
S72.453K	Disp supracondylar fx w/o intracondylar extension of lwr end of unsp femur, subsq enc for clsd fx w/ nonu
S72.453Q	Disp supracondylar fx w/o intracondylar extension of lwr end of unsp femur, subsq enc for opn fx type I or II w/ malu
S72.453M	Disp supracondylar fx w/o intracondylar extension of lwr end of unsp femur, subsq enc for opn fx type I or II w/ nonu
S72.453R	Disp supracondylar fx w/o intracondylar extension of lwr end of unsp femur, subsq enc for opn fx type IIIA, IIIB, or IIIC w/ malu
S72.453N	Disp supracondylar fx w/o intracondylar extension of lwr end of unsp femur, subsq enc for opn fx type IIIA, IIIB, or IIIC w/ nonu
S42.472A	Disp transcondylar fx of lt humerus, init enc for clsd fx
S42.472P	Disp transcondylar fx of lt humerus, subsq enc for fx w/ malu
S42.472K	Disp transcondylar fx of lt humerus, subsq enc for fx w/ nonu
S42.471A	Disp transcondylar fx of rt humerus, init enc for clsd fx
S42.471P	Disp transcondylar fx of rt humerus, subsq enc for fx w/ malu
S42.471K	Disp transcondylar fx of rt humerus, subsq enc for fx w/ nonu
S42.473A	Disp transcondylar fx of unsp humerus, init enc for clsd fx
S42.473P	Disp transcondylar fx of unsp humerus, subsq enc for fx w/ malu
S42.473K	Disp transcondylar fx of unsp humerus, subsq enc for fx w/ nonu
S32.452K	Disp transv fx of lt acetab, subsq enc for fx w/ nonu
S82.032A	Disp transv fx of lt patella, init enc for clsd fx
S82.032B	Disp transv fx of lt patella, init enc for opn fx type I or II
S82.032C	Disp transv fx of lt patella, init enc for opn fx type IIIA, IIIB, or IIIC
S82.032P	Disp transv fx of lt patella, subsq enc for clsd fx w/ malu
S82.032K	Disp transv fx of lt patella, subsq enc for clsd fx w/ nonu
S82.032Q	Disp transv fx of lt patella, subsq enc for opn fx type I or II w/ malu
S82.032M	Disp transv fx of lt patella, subsq enc for opn fx type I or II w/ nonu
S82.032R	Disp transv fx of lt patella, subsq enc for opn fx type IIIA, IIIB, or IIIC w/ malu
S82.032N	Disp transv fx of lt patella, subsq enc for opn fx type IIIA, IIIB, or IIIC w/ nonu

S32.451K	Disp transv fx of rt acetab, subsq enc for fx w/ nonu
S82.031A	Disp transv fx of rt patella, init enc for clsd fx
S82.031B	Disp transv fx of rt patella, init enc for opn fx type I or II
S82.031C	Disp transv fx of rt patella, init enc for opn fx type IIIA, IIIB, or IIIC
S82.031P	Disp transv fx of rt patella, subsq enc for clsd fx w/ malu
S82.031K	Disp transv fx of rt patella, subsq enc for clsd fx w/ nonu
S82.031Q	Disp transv fx of rt patella, subsq enc for opn fx type I or II w/ malu
S82.031M	Disp transv fx of rt patella, subsq enc for opn fx type I or II w/ nonu
S82.031R	Disp transv fx of rt patella, subsq enc for opn fx type IIIA, IIIB, or IIIC w/ malu
S82.031N	Disp transv fx of rt patella, subsq enc for opn fx type IIIA, IIIB, or IIIC w/ nonu
S42.322A	Disp transv fx of shaft of humerus, lt arm, init enc for clsd fx
S42.322P	Disp transv fx of shaft of humerus, lt arm, subsq enc for fx w/ malu
S42.322K	Disp transv fx of shaft of humerus, lt arm, subsq enc for fx w/ nonu
S42.321A	Disp transv fx of shaft of humerus, rt arm, init enc for clsd fx
S42.321P	Disp transv fx of shaft of humerus, rt arm, subsq enc for fx w/ malu
S42.321K	Disp transv fx of shaft of humerus, rt arm, subsq enc for fx w/ nonu
S42.323A	Disp transv fx of shaft of humerus, unsp arm, init enc for clsd fx
S42.323P	Disp transv fx of shaft of humerus, unsp arm, subsq enc for fx w/ malu
S42.323K	Disp transv fx of shaft of humerus, unsp arm, subsq enc for fx w/ nonu
S72.322P	Disp transv fx of shaft of lt femur, subsq enc for clsd fx w/ malu
S72.322K	Disp transv fx of shaft of lt femur, subsq enc for clsd fx w/ nonu
S72.322Q	Disp transv fx of shaft of lt femur, subsq enc for opn fx type I or II w/ malu
S72.322M	Disp transv fx of shaft of lt femur, subsq enc for opn fx type I or II w/ nonu
S72.322R	Disp transv fx of shaft of lt femur, subsq enc for opn fx type IIIA, IIIB, or IIIC w/ malu
S72.322N	Disp transv fx of shaft of lt femur, subsq enc for opn fx type IIIA, IIIB, or IIIC w/ nonu
S82.422P	Disp transv fx of shaft of lt fibula, subsq enc for clsd fx w/ malu
S82.422K	Disp transv fx of shaft of lt fibula, subsq enc for clsd fx w/ nonu
S82.422Q	Disp transv fx of shaft of lt fibula, subsq enc for opn fx type I or II w/ malu
S82.422M	Disp transv fx of shaft of lt fibula, subsq enc for opn fx type I or II w/ nonu
S82.422R	Disp transv fx of shaft of lt fibula, subsq enc for opn fx type IIIA, IIIB, or IIIC w/ malu
S82.422N	Disp transv fx of shaft of lt fibula, subsq enc for opn fx type IIIA, IIIB, or IIIC w/ nonu
S52.322A	Disp transv fx of shaft of lt radius, init enc for clsd fx
S52.322P	Disp transv fx of shaft of lt radius, subsq enc for clsd fx w/ malu
S52.322K	Disp transv fx of shaft of lt radius, subsq enc for clsd fx w/ nonu
S52.322Q	Disp transv fx of shaft of lt radius, subsq enc for opn fx type I or II w/ malu
S52.322M	Disp transv fx of shaft of lt radius, subsq enc for opn fx type I or II w/ nonu
S52.322R	Disp transv fx of shaft of lt radius, subsq enc for opn fx type IIIA, IIIB, or IIIC w/ malu
S52.322N	Disp transv fx of shaft of lt radius, subsq enc for opn fx type IIIA, IIIB, or IIIC w/ nonu
S82.222A	Disp transv fx of shaft of lt tibia, init enc for clsd fx
S82.222P	Disp transv fx of shaft of lt tibia, subsq enc for clsd fx w/ malu
S82.222K	Disp transv fx of shaft of lt tibia, subsq enc for clsd fx w/ nonu
S82.222Q	Disp transv fx of shaft of lt tibia, subsq enc for opn fx type I or II w/ malu
S82.222M	Disp transv fx of shaft of lt tibia, subsq enc for opn fx type I or II w/ nonu
S82.222R	Disp transv fx of shaft of lt tibia, subsq enc for opn fx type IIIA, IIIB, or IIIC w/ malu
S82.222N	Disp transv fx of shaft of lt tibia, subsq enc for opn fx type IIIA, IIIB, or IIIC w/ nonu
S52.222A	Disp transv fx of shaft of lt ulna, init enc for clsd fx
S52.222P	Disp transv fx of shaft of lt ulna, subsq enc for clsd fx w/ malu
S52.222K	Disp transv fx of shaft of lt ulna, subsq enc for clsd fx w/ nonu
S52.222Q	Disp transv fx of shaft of lt ulna, subsq enc for opn fx type I or II w/ malu
S52.222M	Disp transv fx of shaft of lt ulna, subsq enc for opn fx type I or II w/ nonu
S52.222R	Disp transv fx of shaft of lt ulna, subsq enc for opn fx type IIIA, IIIB, or IIIC w/ malu
S52.222N	Disp transv fx of shaft of lt ulna, subsq enc for opn fx type IIIA, IIIB, or IIIC w/ nonu
S72.321P	Disp transv fx of shaft of rt femur, subsq enc for clsd fx w/ malu
S72.321K	Disp transv fx of shaft of rt femur, subsq enc for clsd fx w/ nonu
S72.321Q	Disp transv fx of shaft of rt femur, subsq enc for opn fx type I or II w/ malu
S72.321M	Disp transv fx of shaft of rt femur, subsq enc for opn fx type I or II w/ nonu
S72.321R	Disp transv fx of shaft of rt femur, subsq enc for opn fx type IIIA, IIIB, or IIIC w/ malu
S72.321N	Disp transv fx of shaft of rt femur, subsq enc for opn fx type IIIA, IIIB, or IIIC w/ nonu
S82.421P	Disp transv fx of shaft of rt fibula, subsq enc for clsd fx w/ malu
S82.421K	Disp transv fx of shaft of rt fibula, subsq enc for clsd fx w/ nonu
S82.421Q	Disp transv fx of shaft of rt fibula, subsq enc for opn fx type I or II w/ malu

S82.421M	Disp transv fx of shaft of rt fibula, subsq enc for opn fx type I or II w/ nonu
S82.421R	Disp transv fx of shaft of rt fibula, subsq enc for opn fx type IIIA, IIIB, or IIIC w/ malu
S82.421N	Disp transv fx of shaft of rt fibula, subsq enc for opn fx type IIIA, IIIB, or IIIC w/ nonu
S52.321A	Disp transv fx of shaft of rt radius, init enc for clsd fx
S52.321P	Disp transv fx of shaft of rt radius, subsq enc for clsd fx w/ malu
S52.321K	Disp transv fx of shaft of rt radius, subsq enc for clsd fx w/ nonu
S52.321Q	Disp transv fx of shaft of rt radius, subsq enc for opn fx type I or II w/ malu
S52.321M	Disp transv fx of shaft of rt radius, subsq enc for opn fx type I or II w/ nonu
S52.321R	Disp transv fx of shaft of rt radius, subsq enc for opn fx type IIIA, IIIB, or IIIC w/ malu
S52.321N	Disp transv fx of shaft of rt radius, subsq enc for opn fx type IIIA, IIIB, or IIIC w/ nonu
S82.221A	Disp transv fx of shaft of rt tibia, init enc for clsd fx
S82.221P	Disp transv fx of shaft of rt tibia, subsq enc for clsd fx w/ malu
S82.221K	Disp transv fx of shaft of rt tibia, subsq enc for clsd fx w/ nonu
S82.221Q	Disp transv fx of shaft of rt tibia, subsq enc for opn fx type I or II w/ malu
S82.221M	Disp transv fx of shaft of rt tibia, subsq enc for opn fx type I or II w/ nonu
S82.221R	Disp transv fx of shaft of rt tibia, subsq enc for opn fx type IIIA, IIIB, or IIIC w/ malu
S82.221N	Disp transv fx of shaft of rt tibia, subsq enc for opn fx type IIIA, IIIB, or IIIC w/ nonu
S52.221A	Disp transv fx of shaft of rt ulna, init enc for clsd fx
S52.221P	Disp transv fx of shaft of rt ulna, subsq enc for clsd fx w/ malu
S52.221K	Disp transv fx of shaft of rt ulna, subsq enc for clsd fx w/ nonu
S52.221Q	Disp transv fx of shaft of rt ulna, subsq enc for opn fx type I or II w/ malu
S52.221M	Disp transv fx of shaft of rt ulna, subsq enc for opn fx type I or II w/ nonu
S52.221R	Disp transv fx of shaft of rt ulna, subsq enc for opn fx type IIIA, IIIB, or IIIC w/ malu
S52.221N	Disp transv fx of shaft of rt ulna, subsq enc for opn fx type IIIA, IIIB, or IIIC w/ nonu
S72.323P	Disp transv fx of shaft of unsp femur, subsq enc for clsd fx w/ malu
S72.323K	Disp transv fx of shaft of unsp femur, subsq enc for clsd fx w/ nonu
S72.323Q	Disp transv fx of shaft of unsp femur, subsq enc for opn fx type I or II w/ malu
S72.323M	Disp transv fx of shaft of unsp femur, subsq enc for opn fx type I or II w/ nonu
S72.323R	Disp transv fx of shaft of unsp femur, subsq enc for opn fx type IIIA, IIIB, or IIIC w/ malu
S72.323N	Disp transv fx of shaft of unsp femur, subsq enc for opn fx type IIIA, IIIB, or IIIC w/ nonu
S82.423P	Disp transv fx of shaft of unsp fibula, subsq enc for clsd fx w/ malu
S82.423K	Disp transv fx of shaft of unsp fibula, subsq enc for clsd fx w/ nonu
S82.423Q	Disp transv fx of shaft of unsp fibula, subsq enc for opn fx type I or II w/ malu
S82.423M	Disp transv fx of shaft of unsp fibula, subsq enc for opn fx type I or II w/ nonu
S82.423R	Disp transv fx of shaft of unsp fibula, subsq enc for opn fx type IIIA, IIIB, or IIIC w/ malu
S82.423N	Disp transv fx of shaft of unsp fibula, subsq enc for opn fx type IIIA, IIIB, or IIIC w/ nonu
S52.323A	Disp transv fx of shaft of unsp radius, init enc for clsd fx
S52.323P	Disp transv fx of shaft of unsp radius, subsq enc for clsd fx w/ malu
S52.323K	Disp transv fx of shaft of unsp radius, subsq enc for clsd fx w/ nonu
S52.323Q	Disp transv fx of shaft of unsp radius, subsq enc for opn fx type I or II w/ malu
S52.323M	Disp transv fx of shaft of unsp radius, subsq enc for opn fx type I or II w/ nonu
S52.323R	Disp transv fx of shaft of unsp radius, subsq enc for opn fx type IIIA, IIIB, or IIIC w/ malu
S52.323N	Disp transv fx of shaft of unsp radius, subsq enc for opn fx type IIIA, IIIB, or IIIC w/ nonu
S82.223A	Disp transv fx of shaft of unsp tibia, init enc for clsd fx
S82.223P	Disp transv fx of shaft of unsp tibia, subsq enc for clsd fx w/ malu
S82.223K	Disp transv fx of shaft of unsp tibia, subsq enc for clsd fx w/ nonu
S82.223Q	Disp transv fx of shaft of unsp tibia, subsq enc for opn fx type I or II w/ malu
S82.223M	Disp transv fx of shaft of unsp tibia, subsq enc for opn fx type I or II w/ nonu
S82.223R	Disp transv fx of shaft of unsp tibia, subsq enc for opn fx type IIIA, IIIB, or IIIC w/ malu
S82.223N	Disp transv fx of shaft of unsp tibia, subsq enc for opn fx type IIIA, IIIB, or IIIC w/ nonu
S52.223A	Disp transv fx of shaft of unsp ulna, init enc for clsd fx
S52.223P	Disp transv fx of shaft of unsp ulna, subsq enc for clsd fx w/ malu

S52.223K	Disp transv fx of shaft of unsp ulna, subsq enc for clsd fx w/ nonu		**S72.413P**	Disp unsp condyle fx of lwr end of unsp femur, subsq enc for clsd fx w/ malu
S52.223Q	Disp transv fx of shaft of unsp ulna, subsq enc for opn fx type I or II w/ malu		**S72.413K**	Disp unsp condyle fx of lwr end of unsp femur, subsq enc for clsd fx w/ nonu
S52.223M	Disp transv fx of shaft of unsp ulna, subsq enc for opn fx type I or II w/ nonu		**S72.413Q**	Disp unsp condyle fx of lwr end of unsp femur, subsq enc for opn fx type I or II w/ malu
S52.223R	Disp transv fx of shaft of unsp ulna, subsq enc for opn fx type IIIA, IIIB, or IIIC w/ malu		**S72.413M**	Disp unsp condyle fx of lwr end of unsp femur, subsq enc for opn fx type I or II w/ nonu
S52.223N	Disp transv fx of shaft of unsp ulna, subsq enc for opn fx type IIIA, IIIB, or IIIC w/ nonu		**S72.413R**	Disp unsp condyle fx of lwr end of unsp femur, subsq enc for opn fx type IIIA, IIIB, or IIIC w/ malu
S32.453K	Disp transv fx of unsp acetab, subsq enc for fx w/ nonu		**S72.413N**	Disp unsp condyle fx of lwr end of unsp femur, subsq enc for opn fx type IIIA, IIIB, or IIIC w/ nonu
S82.033A	Disp transv fx of unsp patella, init enc for clsd fx		**S92.402P**	Disp unsp fx of lt great toe, subsq enc for fx w/ malu
S82.033B	Disp transv fx of unsp patella, init enc for opn fx type I or II		**S92.402K**	Disp unsp fx of lt great toe, subsq enc for fx w/ nonu
S82.033C	Disp transv fx of unsp patella, init enc for opn fx type IIIA, IIIB, or IIIC		**S92.502P**	Disp unsp fx of lt lesser toe(s), subsq enc for fx w/ malu
S82.033P	Disp transv fx of unsp patella, subsq enc for clsd fx w/ malu		**S92.502K**	Disp unsp fx of lt lesser toe(s), subsq enc for fx w/ nonu
S82.033K	Disp transv fx of unsp patella, subsq enc for clsd fx w/ nonu		**S92.401P**	Disp unsp fx of rt great toe, subsq enc for fx w/ malu
S82.033Q	Disp transv fx of unsp patella, subsq enc for opn fx type I or II w/ malu		**S92.401K**	Disp unsp fx of rt great toe, subsq enc for fx w/ nonu
S82.033M	Disp transv fx of unsp patella, subsq enc for opn fx type I or II w/ nonu		**S92.501P**	Disp unsp fx of rt lesser toe(s), subsq enc for fx w/ malu
S82.033R	Disp transv fx of unsp patella, subsq enc for opn fx type IIIA, IIIB, or IIIC w/ malu		**S92.501K**	Disp unsp fx of rt lesser toe(s), subsq enc for fx w/ nonu
S82.033N	Disp transv fx of unsp patella, subsq enc for opn fx type IIIA, IIIB, or IIIC w/ nonu		**S92.403P**	Disp unsp fx of unsp great toe, subsq enc for fx w/ malu
S82.852B	Disp trimalleolar fx of lt lwr leg, init enc for opn fx type I or II		**S92.403K**	Disp unsp fx of unsp great toe, subsq enc for fx w/ nonu
S82.852C	Disp trimalleolar fx of lt lwr leg, init enc for opn fx type IIIA, IIIB, or IIIC		**S92.503P**	Disp unsp fx of unsp lesser toe(s), subsq enc for fx w/ malu
S82.852P	Disp trimalleolar fx of lt lwr leg, subsq enc for clsd fx w/ malu		**S92.503K**	Disp unsp fx of unsp lesser toe(s), subsq enc for fx w/ nonu
S82.852K	Disp trimalleolar fx of lt lwr leg, subsq enc for clsd fx w/ nonu		**T82.320A**	Displac of aortic (bifurcation) graft (replace), init enc
S82.852Q	Disp trimalleolar fx of lt lwr leg, subsq enc for opn fx type I or II w/ malu		**T82.522A**	Displac of artfcl heart, init enc
S82.852M	Disp trimalleolar fx of lt lwr leg, subsq enc for opn fx type I or II w/ nonu		**T85.623A**	Displac of artfcl skin graft & decellularized allodermis, init enc
S82.852R	Disp trimalleolar fx of lt lwr leg, subsq enc for opn fx type IIIA, IIIB, or IIIC w/ malu		**T82.523A**	Displac of balloon (counterpulsation) dev, init enc
S82.852N	Disp trimalleolar fx of lt lwr leg, subsq enc for opn fx type IIIA, IIIB, or IIIC w/ nonu		**T85.520A**	Displac of bile duct prosthesis, init enc
S82.851B	Disp trimalleolar fx of rt lwr leg, init enc for opn fx type I or II		**T82.222A**	Displac of biological heart valve graft, init enc
S82.851C	Disp trimalleolar fx of rt lwr leg, init enc for opn fx type IIIA, IIIB, or IIIC		**T85.42XA**	Displac of breast prosthesis & implant, init enc
S82.851P	Disp trimalleolar fx of rt lwr leg, subsq enc for clsd fx w/ malu		**T82.120A**	Displac of cardiac electrode, init enc
S82.851K	Disp trimalleolar fx of rt lwr leg, subsq enc for clsd fx w/ nonu		**T82.121A**	Displac of cardiac pulse generator (battery), init enc
S82.851Q	Disp trimalleolar fx of rt lwr leg, subsq enc for opn fx type I or II w/ malu		**T82.321A**	Displac of carotid arterial graft (bypass), init enc
S82.851M	Disp trimalleolar fx of rt lwr leg, subsq enc for opn fx type I or II w/ nonu		**T82.212A**	Displac of coronary artery bypass graft, init enc
S82.851R	Disp trimalleolar fx of rt lwr leg, subsq enc for opn fx type IIIA, IIIB, or IIIC w/ malu		**T83.020A**	Displac of cystostomy catheter, init enc
S82.851N	Disp trimalleolar fx of rt lwr leg, subsq enc for opn fx type IIIA, IIIB, or IIIC w/ nonu		**T84.320A**	Displac of electronic bone stimulator, init enc
S82.853B	Disp trimalleolar fx of unsp lwr leg, init enc for opn fx type I or II		**T85.620A**	Displac of epidural & subdural inf catheter, init enc
S82.853C	Disp trimalleolar fx of unsp lwr leg, init enc for opn fx type IIIA, IIIB, or IIIC		**T85.521A**	Displac of esophageal anti-reflux dev, init enc
S82.853P	Disp trimalleolar fx of unsp lwr leg, subsq enc for clsd fx w/ malu		**T82.322A**	Displac of femoral arterial graft (bypass), init enc
S82.853K	Disp trimalleolar fx of unsp lwr leg, subsq enc for clsd fx w/ nonu		**T83.22XA**	Displac of graft of urinary organ, init enc
S82.853Q	Disp trimalleolar fx of unsp lwr leg, subsq enc for opn fx type I or II w/ malu		**T82.02XA**	Displac of heart valve prosthesis, init enc
S82.853M	Disp trimalleolar fx of unsp lwr leg, subsq enc for opn fx type I or II w/ nonu		**T85.120A**	Displac of implanted electronic neurostimulator (electrode) of brain, init enc
S82.853R	Disp trimalleolar fx of unsp lwr leg, subsq enc for opn fx type IIIA, IIIB, or IIIC w/ malu		**T85.121A**	Displac of implanted electronic neurostimulator (electrode) of peripheral nerve, init enc
S82.853N	Disp trimalleolar fx of unsp lwr leg, subsq enc for opn fx type IIIA, IIIB, or IIIC w/ nonu		**T85.122A**	Displac of implanted electronic neurostimulator (electrode) of spinal cord, init enc
S72.412A	Disp unsp condyle fx of lwr end of lt femur, init enc for clsd fx		**T82.524A**	Displac of inf catheter, init enc
S72.412P	Disp unsp condyle fx of lwr end of lt femur, subsq enc for clsd fx w/ malu		**T85.624A**	Displac of insulin pump, init enc
S72.412K	Disp unsp condyle fx of lwr end of lt femur, subsq enc for clsd fx w/ nonu		**T84.123A**	Displac of int fix dev of bone of lt forearm, init enc
S72.412Q	Disp unsp condyle fx of lwr end of lt femur, subsq enc for opn fx type I or II w/ malu		**T84.127A**	Displac of int fix dev of bone of lt lwr leg, init enc
S72.412M	Disp unsp condyle fx of lwr end of lt femur, subsq enc for opn fx type I or II w/ nonu		**T84.122A**	Displac of int fix dev of bone of rt forearm, init enc
			T84.126A	Displac of int fix dev of bone of rt lwr leg, init enc
S72.412R	Disp unsp condyle fx of lwr end of lt femur, subsq enc for opn fx type IIIA, IIIB, or IIIC w/ malu		**T84.223A**	Displac of int fix dev of bones of foot & toes, init enc
S72.412N	Disp unsp condyle fx of lwr end of lt femur, subsq enc for opn fx type IIIA, IIIB, or IIIC w/ nonu		**T84.220A**	Displac of int fix dev of bones of hand & fingers, init enc
S72.411A	Disp unsp condyle fx of lwr end of rt femur, init enc for clsd fx		**T84.125A**	Displac of int fix dev of lt femur, init enc
S72.411P	Disp unsp condyle fx of lwr end of rt femur, subsq enc for clsd fx w/ malu		**T84.121A**	Displac of int fix dev of lt humerus, init enc
S72.411K	Disp unsp condyle fx of lwr end of rt femur, subsq enc for clsd fx w/ nonu		**T84.228A**	Displac of int fix dev of oth bones, init enc
S72.411Q	Disp unsp condyle fx of lwr end of rt femur, subsq enc for opn fx type I or II w/ malu		**T84.124A**	Displac of int fix dev of rt femur, init enc
S72.411M	Disp unsp condyle fx of lwr end of rt femur, subsq enc for opn fx type I or II w/ nonu		**T84.120A**	Displac of int fix dev of rt humerus, init enc
			T84.129A	Displac of int fix dev of unsp bone of limb, init enc
S72.411R	Disp unsp condyle fx of lwr end of rt femur, subsq enc for opn fx type IIIA, IIIB, or IIIC w/ malu		**T84.226A**	Displac of int fix dev of vertebrae, init enc
			T85.22XA	Displac of intraocular lens, init enc
S72.411N	Disp unsp condyle fx of lwr end of rt femur, subsq enc for opn fx type IIIA, IIIB, or IIIC w/ nonu		**T85.621A**	Displac of intraperitoneal dialysis catheter, init enc
			T84.420A	Displac of muscle & tndn graft, init enc
S72.413A	Disp unsp condyle fx of lwr end of unsp femur, init enc for clsd fx		**T84.328A**	Displac of oth bone devices, implants & grafts, init enc
			T82.528A	Displac of oth cardiac & vascular devices & implants, init enc
			T82.128A	Displac of oth cardiac electronic dev, init enc
			T85.528A	Displac of oth gastrointestinal prosthetic devices, implants & grafts, init enc
			T85.128A	Displac of oth implanted electronic stimulator of nervous sys, init enc
			T84.428A	Displac of oth int orthopedic devices, implants & grafts, init enc
			T83.428A	Displac of oth prosthetic devices, implants & grafts of genital tract, init enc

Code	Description
T85.628A	Displac of oth spec int prosthetic devices, implants & grafts, init enc
T83.128A	Displac of oth urinary devices & implants, init enc
T82.328A	Displac of oth vascular grafts, init enc
T83.420A	Displac of penile (implanted) prosthesis, init enc
T85.622A	Displac of permanent sutures, init enc
T85.321A	Displac of prosthetic orbit of lt eye, init enc
T85.320A	Displac of prosthetic orbit of rt eye, init enc
T82.520A	Displac of surgly created arteriovenous fistula, init enc
T82.521A	Displac of surgly created arteriovenous shunt, init enc
T82.525A	Displac of umbrella dev, init enc
T82.529A	Displac of unsp cardiac & vascular devices & implants, init enc
T82.129A	Displac of unsp cardiac electronic dev, init enc
T82.329A	Displac of unsp vascular grafts, init enc
T83.120A	Displac of urinary electronic stimulator dev, init enc
T83.121A	Displac of urinary sphincter implant, init enc
T83.122A	Displac of urinary stent, init enc
T82.42XA	Displac of vascular dialysis catheter, init enc
T85.02XA	Displac of ventricular intracranial (communicating) shunt, init enc
T81.31XA	Disruption of ext operation (surg) wnd, NEC, init enc
T81.32XA	Disruption of int operation (surg) wnd, NEC, init enc
T81.33XA	Disruption of traum inj wnd rpr, init enc
T81.30XA	Disruption of wnd, unsp, init enc
B44.7	Disseminated aspergillosis
B40.7	Disseminated blastomycosis
H30.113	Disseminated chorioretinal inflam of post pole, bilat
H30.112	Disseminated chorioretinal inflam of post pole, lt eye
H30.111	Disseminated chorioretinal inflam of post pole, rt eye
H30.119	Disseminated chorioretinal inflam of post pole, unsp eye
H30.133	Disseminated chorioretinal inflam, generalized, bilat
H30.132	Disseminated chorioretinal inflam, generalized, lt eye
H30.131	Disseminated chorioretinal inflam, generalized, rt eye
H30.139	Disseminated chorioretinal inflam, generalized, unsp eye
H30.121	Disseminated chorioretinal inflam, peripheral rt eye
H30.123	Disseminated chorioretinal inflam, peripheral, bilat
H30.122	Disseminated chorioretinal inflam, peripheral, lt eye
H30.129	Disseminated chorioretinal inflam, peripheral, unsp eye
B38.7	Disseminated coccidioidomycosis
B45.7	Disseminated cryptococcosis
B39.3	Disseminated histoplasmosis capsulati
C80.0	Disseminated malig neoplasm, unsp
A31.2	Disseminated mycobacterium avium-intracellulare complex (DMAC)
B41.7	Disseminated paracoccidioidomycosis
B78.7	Disseminated strongyloidiasis
B02.7	Disseminated zoster
K57.40	Diverticulitis of both sm & lg intestine w/ perforation & abscess w/o bleeding
K57.52	Diverticulitis of both sm & lg intestine w/o perforation or abscess w/o bleeding
K57.80	Diverticulitis of intestine, part unsp, w/ perforation & abscess w/o bleeding
K57.92	Diverticulitis of intestine, part unsp, w/o perforation or abscess w/o bleeding
K57.20	Diverticulitis of lg intestine w/ perforation & abscess w/o bleeding
K57.32	Diverticulitis of lg intestine w/o perforation or abscess w/o bleeding
K57.00	Diverticulitis of sm intestine w/ perforation & abscess w/o bleeding
K57.12	Diverticulitis of sm intestine w/o perforation or abscess w/o bleeding
B72	Dracunculiasis
I24.1	Dressler's synd
G24.02	Drug induced acute dystonia
E09.52	Drug or chemical induced diabetes mellitus w/ diabetic peripheral angiopathy w/ gangrene
O99.324	Drug use comp childbirth
O99.321	Drug use comp pregnancy, 1st trmstr
O99.322	Drug use comp pregnancy, 2nd trmstr
O99.323	Drug use comp pregnancy, 3rd trmstr
O99.325	Drug use comp the puerperium
E27.3	Drug-induced adrenocortical insufficiency
D59.0	Drug-induced autoimmune hemolytic anemia
E24.2	Drug-induced Cushing's synd
G72.0	Drug-induced myopathy
D59.2	Drug-induced nonautoimmune hemolytic anemia
L10.5	Drug-induced pemphigus
E51.11	Dry beriberi
Q43.4	Duplication of intestine
G96.11	Dural tear
A50.2	Early congenital syphilis, unsp
A50.01	Early congenital syphilitic oculopathy
A50.02	Early congenital syphilitic osteochondropathy
A50.03	Early congenital syphilitic pharyngitis
A50.04	Early congenital syphilitic pneumonia
A50.05	Early congenital syphilitic rhinitis
A50.06	Early cutaneous congenital syphilis
A50.07	Early mucocutaneous congenital syphilis
A50.08	Early visceral congenital syphilis
G11.1	Early-onset cerebellar ataxia
B67.90	Echinococcosis, unsp
B67.8	Echinococcosis, unsp, of liver
B67.2	Echinococcus granulosus infxn of bone
B67.0	Echinococcus granulosus infxn of liver
B67.1	Echinococcus granulosus infxn of lung
B67.32	Echinococcus granulosus infxn, multi sites
B67.39	Echinococcus granulosus infxn, oth sites
B67.31	Echinococcus granulosus infxn, thyroid gland
B67.4	Echinococcus granulosus infxn, unsp
B67.5	Echinococcus multilocularis infxn of liver
B67.61	Echinococcus multilocularis infxn, multi sites
B67.69	Echinococcus multilocularis infxn, oth sites
B67.7	Echinococcus multilocularis infxn, unsp
E24.3	Ectopic ACTH synd
Q43.5	Ectopic anus
O00.9	Ectopic pregnancy, unsp
Q79.6	Ehlers-Danlos synd
A77.41	Ehrlichiosis chafeensis [E. chafeensis]
A77.40	Ehrlichiosis, unsp
I74.4	Embolism & thrombosis of arteries of extremities, unsp
I74.3	Embolism & thrombosis of arteries of the lwr extremities
I74.2	Embolism & thrombosis of arteries of the upr extremities
I74.5	Embolism & thrombosis of iliac artery
I74.8	Embolism & thrombosis of oth arteries
I74.19	Embolism & thrombosis of oth parts of aorta
I82.3	Embolism & thrombosis of renal vein
I82.812	Embolism & thrombosis of superf veins of lt lwr extremities
I82.813	Embolism & thrombosis of superf veins of lwr extremities, bilat
I82.811	Embolism & thrombosis of superf veins of rt lwr extremities
I82.819	Embolism & thrombosis of superf veins of unsp lwr extremities
I74.11	Embolism & thrombosis of thoracic aorta
I74.9	Embolism & thrombosis of unsp artery
I74.10	Embolism & thrombosis of unsp parts of aorta
T84.81XA	Embolism d/t int orthopedic prosthetic devices, implants & grafts, init enc
T85.81XA	Embolism d/t int prosthetic devices, implants & grafts, NEC, init enc
O03.7	Embolism following complete or unsp spontaneous abortion
T82.817A	Embolism of cardiac prosthetic devices, implants & grafts, init enc
T83.81XA	Embolism of genitourinary prosthetic devices, implants & grafts, init enc
T82.818A	Embolism of vascular prosthetic devices, implants & grafts, init enc
Z48.290	Enc for aftercare following bone marrow transplant
Z48.21	Enc for aftercare following heart transplant
Z48.280	Enc for aftercare following heart-lung transplant
Z48.22	Enc for aftercare following kidney transplant
Z48.23	Enc for aftercare following liver transplant
Z48.24	Enc for aftercare following lung transplant
Z43.1	Enc for attention to gastrostomy
Z99.12	Enc for respirator [ventilator] dependence during power failure
Q01.8	Encephalocele of oth sites
Q01.9	Encephalocele, unsp
I42.4	Endocardial fibroelastosis
I39	Endocarditis & heart valve d/o in diseases classified elsw
M32.11	Endocarditis in systemic lupus erythematosus
I38	Endocarditis, valve unsp
O86.12	Endometritis following delivery
I42.3	Endomyocardial (eosinophilic) disease
A04.6	Enteritis d/t Yersinia enterocolitica
B80	Enterobiasis
A04.7	Enterocolitis d/t Clostridium difficile
A04.3	Enterohemorrhagic Escherichia coli infxn
A04.2	Enteroinvasive Escherichia coli infxn
A04.0	Enteropathogenic Escherichia coli infxn

C86.2	Enteropathy-type (intestinal) T-cell lymphoma		N82.9	Female genital tract fistula, unsp
K94.11	Enterostomy hemor		N82.5	Female genital tract-skin fistulae
K94.12	Enterostomy infxn		T84.82XA	Fibrosis d/t int orthopedic prosthetic devices, implants & grafts, init enc
K94.13	Enterostomy malfunction		T85.82XA	Fibrosis d/t int prosthetic devices, implants & grafts, NEC, init enc
A04.1	Enterotoxigenic Escherichia coli infxn		T82.827A	Fibrosis of cardiac prosthetic devices, implants & grafts, init enc
A85.0	Enteroviral encephalitis		T83.82XA	Fibrosis of genitourinary prosthetic devices, implants & grafts, init enc
A88.0	Enteroviral exanthematous fever [Boston exanthem]		T82.828A	Fibrosis of vascular prosthetic devices, implants & grafts, init enc
A87.0	Enteroviral meningitis		B74.1	Filariasis d/t Brugia malayi
L98.3	Eosinophilic cellulitis [Wells]		B74.2	Filariasis d/t Brugia timori
P12.2	Epicranial subaponeurotic hemor d/t birth inj		B74.0	Filariasis d/t Wuchereria bancrofti
A75.0	Epidemic louse-borne typhus fever d/t Rickettsia prowazekii		B74.9	Filariasis, unsp
L12.31	Epidermolysis bullosa d/t drug		K83.3	Fistula of bile duct
G40.911	Epilepsy, unsp, intractable, w/ status epilepticus		K82.3	Fistula of gallbladder
G40.919	Epilepsy, unsp, intractable, w/o status epilepticus		K63.2	Fistula of intestine
G40.501	Epileptic seizures related to ext causes, not intractable, w/ status epilepticus		K11.4	Fistula of salivary gland
			K31.6	Fistula of stomach & duodenum
G40.509	Epileptic seizures related to ext causes, not intractable, w/o status epilepticus		N82.3	Fistula of vagina to lg intestine
			N82.2	Fistula of vagina to sm intestine
G40.823	Epileptic spasms, intractable, w/ status epilepticus		G81.02	Flaccid hemiplegia affecting lt dominant side
G40.824	Epileptic spasms, intractable, w/o status epilepticus		G81.04	Flaccid hemiplegia affecting lt nondominant side
G40.821	Epileptic spasms, not intractable, w/ status epilepticus		G81.01	Flaccid hemiplegia affecting rt dominant side
G40.822	Epileptic spasms, not intractable, w/o status epilepticus		G81.03	Flaccid hemiplegia affecting rt nondominant side
T83.718A	Erosion of oth implanted mesh & oth prosthetic materials to surrounding organ or tissue, init enc		G81.00	Flaccid hemiplegia affecting unsp side
			S22.5XXK	Flail chest, subsq enc for fx w/ nonu
L53.1	Erythema annulare centrifugum		C82.09	Follicular lymphoma grade I, extranodal & solid organ sites
B08.3	Erythema infectiosum [5th disease]		C82.03	Follicular lymphoma grade I, intra-abd lymph nodes
L53.2	Erythema marginatum		C82.06	Follicular lymphoma grade I, intrapelvic lymph nodes
L08.1	Erythrasma		C82.02	Follicular lymphoma grade I, intrathoracic lymph nodes
I85.00	Esophageal varices w/o bleeding		C82.04	Follicular lymphoma grade I, lymph nodes of axilla & upr limb
K94.30	Esophagostomy comp, unsp		C82.01	Follicular lymphoma grade I, lymph nodes of head, face, & neck
K94.31	Esophagostomy hemor		C82.05	Follicular lymphoma grade I, lymph nodes of inguinal rgn & lwr limb
K94.32	Esophagostomy infxn		C82.08	Follicular lymphoma grade I, lymph nodes of multi sites
K94.33	Esophagostomy malfunction		C82.07	Follicular lymphoma grade I, spleen
B47.0	Eumycetoma		C82.00	Follicular lymphoma grade I, unsp site
D69.41	Evans synd		C82.19	Follicular lymphoma grade II, extranodal & solid organ sites
L49.3	Exfoliation d/t erythematous condition involving 30-39 percent of body surface		C82.13	Follicular lymphoma grade II, intra-abd lymph nodes
			C82.16	Follicular lymphoma grade II, intrapelvic lymph nodes
L49.4	Exfoliation d/t erythematous condition involving 40-49 percent of body surface		C82.12	Follicular lymphoma grade II, intrathoracic lymph nodes
			C82.14	Follicular lymphoma grade II, lymph nodes of axilla & upr limb
L49.5	Exfoliation d/t erythematous condition involving 50-59 percent of body surface		C82.11	Follicular lymphoma grade II, lymph nodes of head, face, & neck
			C82.15	Follicular lymphoma grade II, lymph nodes of inguinal rgn & lwr limb
L49.6	Exfoliation d/t erythematous condition involving 60-69 percent of body surface		C82.18	Follicular lymphoma grade II, lymph nodes of multi sites
			C82.17	Follicular lymphoma grade II, spleen
L49.7	Exfoliation d/t erythematous condition involving 70-79 percent of body surface		C82.10	Follicular lymphoma grade II, unsp site
			C82.29	Follicular lymphoma grade III, unsp, extranodal & solid organ sites
L49.8	Exfoliation d/t erythematous condition involving 80-89 percent of body surface		C82.23	Follicular lymphoma grade III, unsp, intra-abd lymph nodes
			C82.26	Follicular lymphoma grade III, unsp, intrapelvic lymph nodes
L49.9	Exfoliation d/t erythematous condition involving 90 or more percent of body surface		C82.22	Follicular lymphoma grade III, unsp, intrathoracic lymph nodes
			C82.24	Follicular lymphoma grade III, unsp, lymph nodes of axilla & upr limb
T83.728A	Exposure of oth implanted mesh & oth prosthetic materials to surrounding organ or tissue, init enc		C82.21	Follicular lymphoma grade III, unsp, lymph nodes of head, face, & neck
			C82.25	Follicular lymphoma grade III, unsp, lymph nodes of inguinal rgn & lwr limb
Q64.10	Exstrophy of urinary bladder, unsp			
A28.2	Extraintestinal yersiniosis		C82.28	Follicular lymphoma grade III, unsp, lymph nodes of multi sites
C90.22	Extramedullary plasmacytoma in relapse		C82.27	Follicular lymphoma grade III, unsp, spleen
C90.21	Extramedullary plasmacytoma in remission		C82.20	Follicular lymphoma grade III, unsp, unsp site
C90.20	Extramedullary plasmacytoma not having achieved remission		C82.39	Follicular lymphoma grade IIIa, extranodal & solid organ sites
C88.4	Extranodal marginal zone B-cell lymphoma of mucosa-associated lymphoid tissue [MALT-lymphoma]		C82.33	Follicular lymphoma grade IIIa, intra-abd lymph nodes
			C82.36	Follicular lymphoma grade IIIa, intrapelvic lymph nodes
C86.0	Extranodal NK/T-cell lymphoma, nasal type		C82.32	Follicular lymphoma grade IIIa, intrathoracic lymph nodes
G25.9	Extrapyramidal & movement d/o, unsp		C82.34	Follicular lymphoma grade IIIa, lymph nodes of axilla & upr limb
N44.01	Extravaginal torsion of spermatic cord		C82.31	Follicular lymphoma grade IIIa, lymph nodes of head, face, & neck
T80.818A	Extravasation of oth vesicant agent, init enc		C82.35	Follicular lymphoma grade IIIa, lymph nodes of inguinal rgn & lwr limb
R39.0	Extravasation of urine		C82.38	Follicular lymphoma grade IIIa, lymph nodes of multi sites
T80.810A	Extravasation of vesicant antineoplastic chemotherapy, init enc		C82.37	Follicular lymphoma grade IIIa, spleen
			C82.30	Follicular lymphoma grade IIIa, unsp site
F68.12	Factitious d/o w/ predominantly physical signs & symptoms		C82.49	Follicular lymphoma grade IIIb, extranodal & solid organ sites
F68.10	Factitious d/o, unsp		C82.43	Follicular lymphoma grade IIIb, intra-abd lymph nodes
O07.39	Failed attempted termination of pregnancy w/ oth comp		C82.46	Follicular lymphoma grade IIIb, intrapelvic lymph nodes
O07.30	Failed attempted termination of pregnancy w/ unsp comp		C82.42	Follicular lymphoma grade IIIb, intrathoracic lymph nodes
O47.1	False labor at or after 37 completed weeks of gestation		C82.44	Follicular lymphoma grade IIIb, lymph nodes of axilla & upr limb
O47.02	False labor before 37 completed weeks of gestation, 2nd trmstr		C82.41	Follicular lymphoma grade IIIb, lymph nodes of head, face, & neck
O47.03	False labor before 37 completed weeks of gestation, 3rd trmstr		C82.45	Follicular lymphoma grade IIIb, lymph nodes of inguinal rgn & lwr limb
B66.3	Fascioliasis		C82.48	Follicular lymphoma grade IIIb, lymph nodes of multi sites
B66.5	Fasciolopsiasis			
A81.83	Fatal familial insomnia			
N73.4	Female chr pelvic peritonitis			

C82.47	Follicular lymphoma grade IIIb, spleen
C82.40	Follicular lymphoma grade IIIb, unsp site
C82.99	Follicular lymphoma, unsp, extranodal & solid organ sites
C82.93	Follicular lymphoma, unsp, intra-abd lymph nodes
C82.96	Follicular lymphoma, unsp, intrapelvic lymph nodes
C82.92	Follicular lymphoma, unsp, intrathoracic lymph nodes
C82.94	Follicular lymphoma, unsp, lymph nodes of axilla & upr limb
C82.91	Follicular lymphoma, unsp, lymph nodes of head, face, & neck
C82.95	Follicular lymphoma, unsp, lymph nodes of inguinal rgn & lwr limb
C82.98	Follicular lymphoma, unsp, lymph nodes of multi sites
C82.97	Follicular lymphoma, unsp, spleen
C82.90	Follicular lymphoma, unsp, unsp site
T17.520A	Food in bronchus causing asphyxiation, init enc
T17.528A	Food in bronchus causing oth inj, init enc
T17.820A	Food in oth parts of respiratory tract causing asphyxiation, init enc
T17.828A	Food in oth parts of respiratory tract causing oth inj, init enc
T17.420A	Food in trachea causing asphyxiation, init enc
T17.428A	Food in trachea causing oth inj, init enc
A05.4	Foodborne Bacillus cereus intoxication
A05.2	Foodborne Clostridium perfringens [Clostridium welchii] intoxication
A05.0	Foodborne staphylococcal intoxication
A05.3	Foodborne Vibrio parahaemolyticus intoxication
A05.5	Foodborne Vibrio vulnificus intoxication
S02.8XXA	Fractures of oth spec skull & facial bones, init enc for clsd fx
S02.8XXB	Fractures of oth spec skull & facial bones, init enc for opn fx
S02.8XXK	Fractures of oth spec skull & facial bones, subsq enc for fx w/ nonu
Q01.0	Frontal encephalocele
T34.3XXA	Frostbite w/ tissue necrosis of abd wall, lwr back & pelvis, init enc
T34.812A	Frostbite w/ tissue necrosis of lt ankle, init enc
T34.42XA	Frostbite w/ tissue necrosis of lt arm, init enc
T34.012A	Frostbite w/ tissue necrosis of lt ear, init enc
T34.532A	Frostbite w/ tissue necrosis of lt finger(s), init enc
T34.822A	Frostbite w/ tissue necrosis of lt foot, init enc
T34.522A	Frostbite w/ tissue necrosis of lt hand, init enc
T34.62XA	Frostbite w/ tissue necrosis of lt hip & thigh, init enc
T34.72XA	Frostbite w/ tissue necrosis of lt knee & lwr leg, init enc
T34.832A	Frostbite w/ tissue necrosis of lt toe(s), init enc
T34.512A	Frostbite w/ tissue necrosis of lt wrist, init enc
T34.1XXA	Frostbite w/ tissue necrosis of neck, init enc
T34.02XA	Frostbite w/ tissue necrosis of nose, init enc
T34.09XA	Frostbite w/ tissue necrosis of oth part of head, init enc
T34.99XA	Frostbite w/ tissue necrosis of oth sites, init enc
T34.811A	Frostbite w/ tissue necrosis of rt ankle, init enc
T34.41XA	Frostbite w/ tissue necrosis of rt arm, init enc
T34.011A	Frostbite w/ tissue necrosis of rt ear, init enc
T34.531A	Frostbite w/ tissue necrosis of rt finger(s), init enc
T34.821A	Frostbite w/ tissue necrosis of rt foot, init enc
T34.521A	Frostbite w/ tissue necrosis of rt hand, init enc
T34.61XA	Frostbite w/ tissue necrosis of rt hip & thigh, init enc
T34.71XA	Frostbite w/ tissue necrosis of rt knee & lwr leg, init enc
T34.831A	Frostbite w/ tissue necrosis of rt toe(s), init enc
T34.511A	Frostbite w/ tissue necrosis of rt wrist, init enc
T34.2XXA	Frostbite w/ tissue necrosis of thorax, init enc
T34.819A	Frostbite w/ tissue necrosis of unsp ankle, init enc
T34.40XA	Frostbite w/ tissue necrosis of unsp arm, init enc
T34.019A	Frostbite w/ tissue necrosis of unsp ear, init enc
T34.539A	Frostbite w/ tissue necrosis of unsp finger(s), init enc
T34.829A	Frostbite w/ tissue necrosis of unsp foot, init enc
T34.529A	Frostbite w/ tissue necrosis of unsp hand, init enc
T34.60XA	Frostbite w/ tissue necrosis of unsp hip & thigh, init enc
T34.70XA	Frostbite w/ tissue necrosis of unsp knee & lwr leg, init enc
T34.90XA	Frostbite w/ tissue necrosis of unsp sites, init enc
T34.839A	Frostbite w/ tissue necrosis of unsp toe(s), init enc
T34.519A	Frostbite w/ tissue necrosis of unsp wrist, init enc
S02.67XA	Fx of alveolus of mandible, init enc for clsd fx
S02.67XB	Fx of alveolus of mandible, init enc for opn fx
S02.67XK	Fx of alveolus of mandible, subsq enc for fx w/ nonu
S02.42XA	Fx of alveolus of maxilla, init enc for clsd fx
S02.42XB	Fx of alveolus of maxilla, init enc for opn fx
S02.42XK	Fx of alveolus of maxilla, subsq enc for fx w/ nonu
S02.65XA	Fx of angle of mandible, init enc for clsd fx
S02.65XB	Fx of angle of mandible, init enc for opn fx
S02.65XK	Fx of angle of mandible, subsq enc for fx w/ nonu
S22.22XA	Fx of body of sternum, init enc for clsd fx
S22.22XK	Fx of body of sternum, subsq enc for fx w/ nonu
S22.9XXA	Fx of bony thorax, part unsp, init enc for clsd fx
S22.9XXK	Fx of bony thorax, part unsp, subsq enc for fx w/ nonu
S32.2XXA	Fx of coccyx, init enc for clsd fx
S32.2XXK	Fx of coccyx, subsq enc for fx w/ nonu
S02.61XA	Fx of condylar process of mandible, init enc for clsd fx
S02.61XB	Fx of condylar process of mandible, init enc for opn fx
S02.61XK	Fx of condylar process of mandible, subsq enc for fx w/ nonu
S02.63XA	Fx of coronoid process of mandible, init enc for clsd fx
S02.63XB	Fx of coronoid process of mandible, init enc for opn fx
S02.63XK	Fx of coronoid process of mandible, subsq enc for fx w/ nonu
M96.662	Fx of femur following insert of orthopedic implant, jt prosthesis, or bone plate, lt leg
M96.661	Fx of femur following insert of orthopedic implant, jt prosthesis, or bone plate, rt leg
M96.669	Fx of femur following insert of orthopedic implant, jt prosthesis, or bone plate, unsp leg
M96.622	Fx of humerus following insert of orthopedic implant, jt prosthesis, or bone plate, lt arm
M96.621	Fx of humerus following insert of orthopedic implant, jt prosthesis, or bone plate, rt arm
M96.629	Fx of humerus following insert of orthopedic implant, jt prosthesis, or bone plate, unsp arm
S42.92XA	Fx of lt shldr girdle, part unsp, init enc for clsd fx
S42.92XP	Fx of lt shldr girdle, part unsp, subsq enc for fx w/ malu
S42.92XK	Fx of lt shldr girdle, part unsp, subsq enc for fx w/ nonu
S02.69XA	Fx of mandible of oth spec site, init enc for clsd fx
S02.69XB	Fx of mandible of oth spec site, init enc for opn fx
S02.69XK	Fx of mandible of oth spec site, subsq enc for fx w/ nonu
S02.609A	Fx of mandible, unsp, init enc for clsd fx
S02.609B	Fx of mandible, unsp, init enc for opn fx
S02.609K	Fx of mandible, unsp, subsq enc for fx w/ nonu
S22.21XA	Fx of manubrium, init enc for clsd fx
S22.21XK	Fx of manubrium, subsq enc for fx w/ nonu
S02.2XXB	Fx of nasal bones, init enc for opn fx
S02.2XXK	Fx of nasal bones, subsq enc for fx w/ nonu
S12.9XXA	Fx of neck, unsp, init enc
S22.32XA	Fx of one rib, lt side, init enc for clsd fx
S22.32XK	Fx of one rib, lt side, subsq enc for fx w/ nonu
S22.31XA	Fx of one rib, rt side, init enc for clsd fx
S22.31XK	Fx of one rib, rt side, subsq enc for fx w/ nonu
S22.39XA	Fx of one rib, unsp side, init enc for clsd fx
S22.39XK	Fx of one rib, unsp side, subsq enc for fx w/ nonu
S02.3XXA	Fx of orbital floor, init enc for clsd fx
S02.3XXB	Fx of orbital floor, init enc for opn fx
S02.3XXK	Fx of orbital floor, subsq enc for fx w/ nonu
M96.69	Fx of oth bone following insert of orthopedic implant, jt prosthesis, or bone plate
S42.192B	Fx of oth part of scapula, lt shldr, init enc for opn fx
S42.192P	Fx of oth part of scapula, lt shldr, subsq enc for fx w/ malu
S42.192K	Fx of oth part of scapula, lt shldr, subsq enc for fx w/ nonu
S42.191B	Fx of oth part of scapula, rt shldr, init enc for opn fx
S42.191P	Fx of oth part of scapula, rt shldr, subsq enc for fx w/ malu
S42.191K	Fx of oth part of scapula, rt shldr, subsq enc for fx w/ nonu
S42.199B	Fx of oth part of scapula, unsp shldr, init enc for opn fx
S42.199P	Fx of oth part of scapula, unsp shldr, subsq enc for fx w/ malu
S42.199K	Fx of oth part of scapula, unsp shldr, subsq enc for fx w/ nonu
S32.89XA	Fx of oth parts of pelvis, init enc for clsd fx
S32.89XK	Fx of oth parts of pelvis, subsq enc for fx w/ nonu
M96.65	Fx of pelvis following insert of orthopedic implant, jt prosthesis, or bone plate
M96.632	Fx of radius or ulna following insert of orthopedic implant, jt prosthesis, or bone plate, lt arm
M96.631	Fx of radius or ulna following insert of orthopedic implant, jt prosthesis, or bone plate, rt arm
M96.639	Fx of radius or ulna following insert of orthopedic implant, jt prosthesis, or bone plate, unsp arm
S02.64XA	Fx of ramus of mandible, init enc for clsd fx
S02.64XB	Fx of ramus of mandible, init enc for opn fx
S02.64XK	Fx of ramus of mandible, subsq enc for fx w/ nonu
S42.91XA	Fx of rt shldr girdle, part unsp, init enc for clsd fx
S42.91XP	Fx of rt shldr girdle, part unsp, subsq enc for fx w/ malu
S42.91XK	Fx of rt shldr girdle, part unsp, subsq enc for fx w/ nonu
S02.62XA	Fx of subcondylar process of mandible, init enc for clsd fx

Code	Description
S02.62XB	Fx of subcondylar process of mandible, init enc for opn fx
S02.62XK	Fx of subcondylar process of mandible, subsq enc for fx w/ nonu
S32.512A	Fx of superior rim of lt pubis, init enc for clsd fx
S32.512K	Fx of superior rim of lt pubis, subsq enc for fx w/ nonu
S32.511A	Fx of superior rim of rt pubis, init enc for clsd fx
S32.511K	Fx of superior rim of rt pubis, subsq enc for fx w/ nonu
S32.519A	Fx of superior rim of unsp pubis, init enc for clsd fx
S32.519K	Fx of superior rim of unsp pubis, subsq enc for fx w/ nonu
S02.66XA	Fx of symphysis of mandible, init enc for clsd fx
S02.66XB	Fx of symphysis of mandible, init enc for opn fx
S02.66XK	Fx of symphysis of mandible, subsq enc for fx w/ nonu
M96.672	Fx of tibia or fibula following insert of orthopedic implant, jt prosthesis, or bone plate, lt leg
M96.671	Fx of tibia or fibula following insert of orthopedic implant, jt prosthesis, or bone plate, rt leg
M96.679	Fx of tibia or fibula following insert of orthopedic implant, jt prosthesis, or bone plate, unsp leg
S02.5XXK	Fx of tooth (traum), subsq enc for fx w/ nonu
S62.102B	Fx of unsp carpal bone, lt wrist, init enc for opn fx
S62.102P	Fx of unsp carpal bone, lt wrist, subsq enc for fx w/ malu
S62.102K	Fx of unsp carpal bone, lt wrist, subsq enc for fx w/ nonu
S62.101B	Fx of unsp carpal bone, rt wrist, init enc for opn fx
S62.101P	Fx of unsp carpal bone, rt wrist, subsq enc for fx w/ malu
S62.101K	Fx of unsp carpal bone, rt wrist, subsq enc for fx w/ nonu
S62.109B	Fx of unsp carpal bone, unsp wrist, init enc for opn fx
S62.109P	Fx of unsp carpal bone, unsp wrist, subsq enc for fx w/ malu
S62.109K	Fx of unsp carpal bone, unsp wrist, subsq enc for fx w/ nonu
S92.302B	Fx of unsp metatarsal bone(s), lt foot, init enc for opn fx
S92.302P	Fx of unsp metatarsal bone(s), lt foot, subsq enc for fx w/ malu
S92.302K	Fx of unsp metatarsal bone(s), lt foot, subsq enc for fx w/ nonu
S92.301B	Fx of unsp metatarsal bone(s), rt foot, init enc for opn fx
S92.301P	Fx of unsp metatarsal bone(s), rt foot, subsq enc for fx w/ malu
S92.301K	Fx of unsp metatarsal bone(s), rt foot, subsq enc for fx w/ nonu
S92.309B	Fx of unsp metatarsal bone(s), unsp foot, init enc for opn fx
S92.309P	Fx of unsp metatarsal bone(s), unsp foot, subsq enc for fx w/ malu
S92.309K	Fx of unsp metatarsal bone(s), unsp foot, subsq enc for fx w/ nonu
S02.600A	Fx of unsp part of body of mandible, init enc for clsd fx
S02.600B	Fx of unsp part of body of mandible, init enc for opn fx
S02.600K	Fx of unsp part of body of mandible, subsq enc for fx w/ nonu
S42.002B	Fx of unsp part of lt clavicle, init enc for opn fx
S42.002P	Fx of unsp part of lt clavicle, subsq enc for fx w/ malu
S42.002K	Fx of unsp part of lt clavicle, subsq enc for fx w/ nonu
S72.002P	Fx of unsp part of neck of lt femur, subsq enc for clsd fx w/ malu
S72.002K	Fx of unsp part of neck of lt femur, subsq enc for clsd fx w/ nonu
S72.002Q	Fx of unsp part of neck of lt femur, subsq enc for opn fx type I or II w/ malu
S72.002M	Fx of unsp part of neck of lt femur, subsq enc for opn fx type I or II w/ nonu
S72.002R	Fx of unsp part of neck of lt femur, subsq enc for opn fx type IIIA, IIIB, or IIIC w/ malu
S72.002N	Fx of unsp part of neck of lt femur, subsq enc for opn fx type IIIA, IIIB, or IIIC w/ nonu
S72.001P	Fx of unsp part of neck of rt femur, subsq enc for clsd fx w/ malu
S72.001K	Fx of unsp part of neck of rt femur, subsq enc for clsd fx w/ nonu
S72.001Q	Fx of unsp part of neck of rt femur, subsq enc for opn fx type I or II w/ malu
S72.001M	Fx of unsp part of neck of rt femur, subsq enc for opn fx type I or II w/ nonu
S72.001R	Fx of unsp part of neck of rt femur, subsq enc for opn fx type IIIA, IIIB, or IIIC w/ malu
S72.001N	Fx of unsp part of neck of rt femur, subsq enc for opn fx type IIIA, IIIB, or IIIC w/ nonu
S72.009P	Fx of unsp part of neck of unsp femur, subsq enc for clsd fx w/ malu
S72.009K	Fx of unsp part of neck of unsp femur, subsq enc for clsd fx w/ nonu
S72.009Q	Fx of unsp part of neck of unsp femur, subsq enc for opn fx type I or II w/ malu
S72.009M	Fx of unsp part of neck of unsp femur, subsq enc for opn fx type I or II w/ nonu
S72.009R	Fx of unsp part of neck of unsp femur, subsq enc for opn fx type IIIA, IIIB, or IIIC w/ malu
S72.009N	Fx of unsp part of neck of unsp femur, subsq enc for opn fx type IIIA, IIIB, or IIIC w/ nonu
S42.001B	Fx of unsp part of rt clavicle, init enc for opn fx
S42.001P	Fx of unsp part of rt clavicle, subsq enc for fx w/ malu
S42.001K	Fx of unsp part of rt clavicle, subsq enc for fx w/ nonu
S42.102B	Fx of unsp part of scapula, lt shldr, init enc for opn fx
S42.102P	Fx of unsp part of scapula, lt shldr, subsq enc for fx w/ malu
S42.102K	Fx of unsp part of scapula, lt shldr, subsq enc for fx w/ nonu
S42.101B	Fx of unsp part of scapula, rt shldr, init enc for opn fx
S42.101P	Fx of unsp part of scapula, rt shldr, subsq enc for fx w/ malu
S42.101K	Fx of unsp part of scapula, rt shldr, subsq enc for fx w/ nonu
S42.109B	Fx of unsp part of scapula, unsp shldr, init enc for opn fx
S42.109P	Fx of unsp part of scapula, unsp shldr, subsq enc for fx w/ malu
S42.109K	Fx of unsp part of scapula, unsp shldr, subsq enc for fx w/ nonu
S42.009B	Fx of unsp part of unsp clavicle, init enc for opn fx
S42.009P	Fx of unsp part of unsp clavicle, subsq enc for fx w/ malu
S42.009K	Fx of unsp part of unsp clavicle, subsq enc for fx w/ nonu
S32.9XXA	Fx of unsp parts of lumbosacral spine & pelvis, init enc for clsd fx
S32.9XXK	Fx of unsp parts of lumbosacral spine & pelvis, subsq enc for fx w/ nonu
S62.601B	Fx of unsp phalanx of lt index finger, init enc for opn fx
S62.601P	Fx of unsp phalanx of lt index finger, subsq enc for fx w/ malu
S62.601K	Fx of unsp phalanx of lt index finger, subsq enc for fx w/ nonu
S62.607B	Fx of unsp phalanx of lt little finger, init enc for opn fx
S62.607P	Fx of unsp phalanx of lt little finger, subsq enc for fx w/ malu
S62.607K	Fx of unsp phalanx of lt little finger, subsq enc for fx w/ nonu
S62.603B	Fx of unsp phalanx of lt mid finger, init enc for opn fx
S62.603P	Fx of unsp phalanx of lt mid finger, subsq enc for fx w/ malu
S62.603K	Fx of unsp phalanx of lt mid finger, subsq enc for fx w/ nonu
S62.605B	Fx of unsp phalanx of lt ring finger, init enc for opn fx
S62.605P	Fx of unsp phalanx of lt ring finger, subsq enc for fx w/ malu
S62.605K	Fx of unsp phalanx of lt ring finger, subsq enc for fx w/ nonu
S62.502B	Fx of unsp phalanx of lt thumb, init enc for opn fx
S62.502P	Fx of unsp phalanx of lt thumb, subsq enc for fx w/ malu
S62.502K	Fx of unsp phalanx of lt thumb, subsq enc for fx w/ nonu
S62.608B	Fx of unsp phalanx of oth finger, init enc for opn fx
S62.608P	Fx of unsp phalanx of oth finger, subsq enc for fx w/ malu
S62.608K	Fx of unsp phalanx of oth finger, subsq enc for fx w/ nonu
S62.600B	Fx of unsp phalanx of rt index finger, init enc for opn fx
S62.600P	Fx of unsp phalanx of rt index finger, subsq enc for fx w/ malu
S62.600K	Fx of unsp phalanx of rt index finger, subsq enc for fx w/ nonu
S62.606B	Fx of unsp phalanx of rt little finger, init enc for opn fx
S62.606P	Fx of unsp phalanx of rt little finger, subsq enc for fx w/ malu
S62.606K	Fx of unsp phalanx of rt little finger, subsq enc for fx w/ nonu
S62.602B	Fx of unsp phalanx of rt mid finger, init enc for opn fx
S62.602P	Fx of unsp phalanx of rt mid finger, subsq enc for fx w/ malu
S62.602K	Fx of unsp phalanx of rt mid finger, subsq enc for fx w/ nonu
S62.604B	Fx of unsp phalanx of rt ring finger, init enc for opn fx
S62.604P	Fx of unsp phalanx of rt ring finger, subsq enc for fx w/ malu
S62.604K	Fx of unsp phalanx of rt ring finger, subsq enc for fx w/ nonu
S62.501B	Fx of unsp phalanx of rt thumb, init enc for opn fx
S62.501P	Fx of unsp phalanx of rt thumb, subsq enc for fx w/ malu
S62.501K	Fx of unsp phalanx of rt thumb, subsq enc for fx w/ nonu
S62.609B	Fx of unsp phalanx of unsp finger, init enc for opn fx
S62.609P	Fx of unsp phalanx of unsp finger, subsq enc for fx w/ malu
S62.609K	Fx of unsp phalanx of unsp finger, subsq enc for fx w/ nonu
S62.509B	Fx of unsp phalanx of unsp thumb, init enc for opn fx
S62.509P	Fx of unsp phalanx of unsp thumb, subsq enc for fx w/ malu
S62.509K	Fx of unsp phalanx of unsp thumb, subsq enc for fx w/ nonu
S42.90XA	Fx of unsp shldr girdle, part unsp, init enc for clsd fx
S42.90XP	Fx of unsp shldr girdle, part unsp, subsq enc for fx w/ malu
S42.90XK	Fx of unsp shldr girdle, part unsp, subsq enc for fx w/ nonu
S92.202B	Fx of unsp tarsal bone(s) of lt foot, init enc for opn fx
S92.202P	Fx of unsp tarsal bone(s) of lt foot, subsq enc for fx w/ malu
S92.202K	Fx of unsp tarsal bone(s) of lt foot, subsq enc for fx w/ nonu
S92.201B	Fx of unsp tarsal bone(s) of rt foot, init enc for opn fx
S92.201P	Fx of unsp tarsal bone(s) of rt foot, subsq enc for fx w/ malu
S92.201K	Fx of unsp tarsal bone(s) of rt foot, subsq enc for fx w/ nonu
S92.209B	Fx of unsp tarsal bone(s) of unsp foot, init enc for opn fx
S92.209P	Fx of unsp tarsal bone(s) of unsp foot, subsq enc for fx w/ malu
S92.209K	Fx of unsp tarsal bone(s) of unsp foot, subsq enc for fx w/ nonu
S02.0XXA	Fx of vault of skull, init enc for clsd fx
S02.0XXK	Fx of vault of skull, subsq enc for fx w/ nonu
S22.24XA	Fx of xiphoid process, init enc for clsd fx
S22.24XK	Fx of xiphoid process, subsq enc for fx w/ nonu
E74.21	Galactosemia
S52.372A	Galeazzi's fx of lt radius, init enc for clsd fx
S52.372P	Galeazzi's fx of lt radius, subsq enc for clsd fx w/ malu
S52.372K	Galeazzi's fx of lt radius, subsq enc for clsd fx w/ nonu

S52.372Q	Galeazzi's fx of lt radius, subsq enc for opn fx type I or II w/ malu
S52.372M	Galeazzi's fx of lt radius, subsq enc for opn fx type I or II w/ nonu
S52.372R	Galeazzi's fx of lt radius, subsq enc for opn fx type IIIA, IIIB, or IIIC w/ malu
S52.372N	Galeazzi's fx of lt radius, subsq enc for opn fx type IIIA, IIIB, or IIIC w/ nonu
S52.371A	Galeazzi's fx of rt radius, init enc for clsd fx
S52.371P	Galeazzi's fx of rt radius, subsq enc for clsd fx w/ malu
S52.371K	Galeazzi's fx of rt radius, subsq enc for clsd fx w/ nonu
S52.371Q	Galeazzi's fx of rt radius, subsq enc for opn fx type I or II w/ malu
S52.371M	Galeazzi's fx of rt radius, subsq enc for opn fx type I or II w/ nonu
S52.371R	Galeazzi's fx of rt radius, subsq enc for opn fx type IIIA, IIIB, or IIIC w/ malu
S52.371N	Galeazzi's fx of rt radius, subsq enc for opn fx type IIIA, IIIB, or IIIC w/ nonu
S52.379A	Galeazzi's fx of unsp radius, init enc for clsd fx
S52.379P	Galeazzi's fx of unsp radius, subsq enc for clsd fx w/ malu
S52.379K	Galeazzi's fx of unsp radius, subsq enc for clsd fx w/ nonu
S52.379Q	Galeazzi's fx of unsp radius, subsq enc for opn fx type I or II w/ malu
S52.379M	Galeazzi's fx of unsp radius, subsq enc for opn fx type I or II w/ nonu
S52.379R	Galeazzi's fx of unsp radius, subsq enc for opn fx type IIIA, IIIB, or IIIC w/ malu
S52.379N	Galeazzi's fx of unsp radius, subsq enc for opn fx type IIIA, IIIB, or IIIC w/ nonu
K56.3	Gallstone ileus
B56.0	Gambiense trypanosomiasis
I96	Gangrene, NEC
T17.510A	Gastric contents in bronchus causing asphyxiation, init enc
T17.518A	Gastric contents in bronchus causing oth inj, init enc
T17.810A	Gastric contents in oth parts of respiratory tract causing asphyxiation, init enc
T17.818A	Gastric contents in oth parts of respiratory tract causing oth inj, init enc
T17.410A	Gastric contents in trachea causing asphyxiation, init enc
T17.418A	Gastric contents in trachea causing oth inj, init enc
K52.0	Gastroenteritis & colitis d/t radiation
A22.2	Gastrointestinal anthrax
K92.2	Gastrointestinal hemor, unsp
K92.81	Gastrointestinal mucositis (ulcerative)
A21.3	Gastrointestinal tularemia
K94.22	Gastrostomy infxn
K94.23	Gastrostomy malfunction
A52.17	General paresis
A21.7	Generalized tularemia
O04.5	Genital tract & pelvic infxn following (induced) termination of pregnancy
O03.5	Genital tract & pelvic infxn following complete or unsp spontaneous abortion
O08.0	Genital tract & pelvic infxn following ectopic & molar pregnancy
O07.0	Genital tract & pelvic infxn following failed attempted termination of pregnancy
O03.0	Genital tract & pelvic infxn following incomplete spontaneous abortion
B48.3	Geotrichosis
A81.82	Gerstmann-Straussler-Scheinker synd
O12.21	Gestational edema w/ proteinuria, 1st trmstr
O12.22	Gestational edema w/ proteinuria, 2nd trmstr
O12.23	Gestational edema w/ proteinuria, 3rd trmstr
O12.11	Gestational proteinuria, 1st trmstr
O12.12	Gestational proteinuria, 2nd trmstr
O12.13	Gestational proteinuria, 3rd trmstr
A07.1	Giardiasis [lambliasis]
A24.0	Glanders
E76.9	Glucosaminoglycan metabolism d/o, unsp
E71.313	Glutaric aciduria type II
E74.00	Glycogen storage disease, unsp
E75.00	GM2 gangliosidosis, unsp
A54.42	Gonococcal arthritis
A54.82	Gonococcal brain abscess
A54.03	Gonococcal cervicitis, unsp
A54.31	Gonococcal conjunctivitis
A54.01	Gonococcal cystitis & urethritis, unsp
A54.24	Gonococcal female pelvic inflam disease
A54.83	Gonococcal heart infxn
A54.30	Gonococcal infxn of eye, unsp
A54.21	Gonococcal infxn of kidney & ureter
A54.1	Gonococcal infxn of lwr genitourinary tract w/ periurethral & accessory gland abscess
A54.00	Gonococcal infxn of lwr genitourinary tract, unsp
A54.40	Gonococcal infxn of musculoskeletal sys, unsp
A54.23	Gonococcal infxn of oth male genital organs
A54.49	Gonococcal infxn of oth musculoskeletal tissue
A54.9	Gonococcal infxn, unsp
A54.32	Gonococcal iridocyclitis
A54.33	Gonococcal keratitis
A54.43	Gonococcal osteomyelitis
A54.85	Gonococcal peritonitis
A54.84	Gonococcal pneumonia
A54.22	Gonococcal prostatitis
A54.41	Gonococcal spondylopathy
A54.02	Gonococcal vulvovaginitis, unsp
O98.22	Gonorrhea comp childbirth
O98.211	Gonorrhea comp pregnancy, 1st trmstr
O98.212	Gonorrhea comp pregnancy, 2nd trmstr
O98.213	Gonorrhea comp pregnancy, 3rd trmstr
O98.23	Gonorrhea comp the puerperium
D89.813	Graft-versus-host disease, unsp
S42.312A	Greenstick fx of shaft of humerus, lt arm, init enc for clsd fx
S42.312P	Greenstick fx of shaft of humerus, lt arm, subsq enc for fx w/ malu
S42.312K	Greenstick fx of shaft of humerus, lt arm, subsq enc for fx w/ nonu
S42.311A	Greenstick fx of shaft of humerus, rt arm, init enc for clsd fx
S42.311P	Greenstick fx of shaft of humerus, rt arm, subsq enc for fx w/ malu
S42.311K	Greenstick fx of shaft of humerus, rt arm, subsq enc for fx w/ nonu
S42.319A	Greenstick fx of shaft of humerus, unsp arm, init enc for clsd fx
S42.319P	Greenstick fx of shaft of humerus, unsp arm, subsq enc for fx w/ malu
S42.319K	Greenstick fx of shaft of humerus, unsp arm, subsq enc for fx w/ nonu
S52.212A	Greenstick fx of shaft of lt ulna, init enc for clsd fx
S52.212P	Greenstick fx of shaft of lt ulna, subsq enc for fx w/ malu
S52.212K	Greenstick fx of shaft of lt ulna, subsq enc for fx w/ nonu
S52.312A	Greenstick fx of shaft of radius, lt arm, init enc for clsd fx
S52.312P	Greenstick fx of shaft of radius, lt arm, subsq enc for fx w/ malu
S52.312K	Greenstick fx of shaft of radius, lt arm, subsq enc for fx w/ nonu
S52.311A	Greenstick fx of shaft of radius, rt arm, init enc for clsd fx
S52.311P	Greenstick fx of shaft of radius, rt arm, subsq enc for fx w/ malu
S52.311K	Greenstick fx of shaft of radius, rt arm, subsq enc for fx w/ nonu
S52.319A	Greenstick fx of shaft of radius, unsp arm, init enc for clsd fx
S52.319P	Greenstick fx of shaft of radius, unsp arm, subsq enc for fx w/ malu
S52.319K	Greenstick fx of shaft of radius, unsp arm, subsq enc for fx w/ nonu
S52.211A	Greenstick fx of shaft of rt ulna, init enc for clsd fx
S52.211P	Greenstick fx of shaft of rt ulna, subsq enc for fx w/ malu
S52.211K	Greenstick fx of shaft of rt ulna, subsq enc for fx w/ nonu
S52.219A	Greenstick fx of shaft of unsp ulna, init enc for clsd fx
S52.219P	Greenstick fx of shaft of unsp ulna, subsq enc for fx w/ malu
S52.219K	Greenstick fx of shaft of unsp ulna, subsq enc for fx w/ nonu
P93.0	Grey baby synd
G61.0	Guillain-Barre synd
C91.40	Hairy cell leukemia not having achieved remission
C91.42	Hairy cell leukemia, in relapse
C91.41	Hairy cell leukemia, in remission
G23.0	Hallervorden-Spatz disease
R44.3	Hallucinations, unsp
F16.150	Hallucinogen abuse w/ hallucinogen-induced psychotic d/o w/ delusions
F16.151	Hallucinogen abuse w/ hallucinogen-induced psychotic d/o w/ hallucinations
F16.121	Hallucinogen abuse w/ intoxication w/ delirium
F16.283	Hallucinogen dependence w/ hallucinogen persisting perception d/o (flashbacks)
F16.280	Hallucinogen dependence w/ hallucinogen-induced anxiety d/o
F16.250	Hallucinogen dependence w/ hallucinogen-induced psychotic d/o w/ delusions
F16.251	Hallucinogen dependence w/ hallucinogen-induced psychotic d/o w/ hallucinations
F16.259	Hallucinogen dependence w/ hallucinogen-induced psychotic d/o, unsp
F16.221	Hallucinogen dependence w/ intoxication w/ delirium
F16.288	Hallucinogen dependence w/ oth hallucinogen-induced d/o
F16.20	Hallucinogen dependence, uncomplicated
F16.950	Hallucinogen use, unsp w/ hallucinogen-induced psychotic d/o w/ delusions
F16.951	Hallucinogen use, unsp w/ hallucinogen-induced psychotic d/o w/ hallucinations
F16.921	Hallucinogen use, unsp w/ intoxication w/ delirium
B33.4	Hantavirus (cardio)-pulmn synd [HPS] [HCPS]
E72.02	Hartnup's disease

Z94.3	Heart & lungs transplant status		I69.859	Hemiplegia & hemiparesis following oth cerebrovascular disease affecting unsp side
T86.22	Heart transplant failure		I69.252	Hemiplegia & hemiparesis following oth nontraumatic intracranial hemor affecting lt dominant side
T86.23	Heart transplant infxn			
T86.21	Heart transplant rejection		I69.254	Hemiplegia & hemiparesis following oth nontraumatic intracranial hemor affecting lt non-dominant side
Z94.1	Heart transplant status			
T86.32	Heart-lung transplant failure		I69.251	Hemiplegia & hemiparesis following oth nontraumatic intracranial hemor affecting rt dominant side
T86.33	Heart-lung transplant infxn			
T86.31	Heart-lung transplant rejection		I69.253	Hemiplegia & hemiparesis following oth nontraumatic intracranial hemor affecting rt non-dominant side
T67.0XXA	Heatstroke & sunstroke, init enc			
C88.2	Heavy chain disease		I69.259	Hemiplegia & hemiparesis following oth nontraumatic intracranial hemor affecting unsp side
M25.072	Hemarthrosis, lt ankle			
M25.022	Hemarthrosis, lt elbow		I69.952	Hemiplegia & hemiparesis following unsp cerebrovascular disease affecting lt dominant side
M25.075	Hemarthrosis, lt foot			
M25.042	Hemarthrosis, lt hand		I69.954	Hemiplegia & hemiparesis following unsp cerebrovascular disease affecting lt non-dominant side
M25.052	Hemarthrosis, lt hip			
M25.062	Hemarthrosis, lt knee		I69.951	Hemiplegia & hemiparesis following unsp cerebrovascular disease affecting rt dominant side
M25.012	Hemarthrosis, lt shldr			
M25.032	Hemarthrosis, lt wrist		I69.953	Hemiplegia & hemiparesis following unsp cerebrovascular disease affecting rt non-dominant side
M25.08	Hemarthrosis, oth spec site			
M25.071	Hemarthrosis, rt ankle		I69.959	Hemiplegia & hemiparesis following unsp cerebrovascular disease affecting unsp side
M25.021	Hemarthrosis, rt elbow			
M25.074	Hemarthrosis, rt foot		G81.92	Hemiplegia, unsp affecting lt dominant side
M25.041	Hemarthrosis, rt hand		G81.94	Hemiplegia, unsp affecting lt nondominant side
M25.051	Hemarthrosis, rt hip		G81.91	Hemiplegia, unsp affecting rt dominant side
M25.061	Hemarthrosis, rt knee		G81.93	Hemiplegia, unsp affecting rt nondominant side
M25.011	Hemarthrosis, rt shldr		G81.90	Hemiplegia, unsp affecting unsp side
M25.031	Hemarthrosis, rt wrist		T80.919A	Hemolytic transfusion reaction, unsp incompatibility, unsp as acute or delayed, init enc
M25.073	Hemarthrosis, unsp ankle			
M25.029	Hemarthrosis, unsp elbow		I23.0	Hemopericardium as current comp following acute myocardial infarction
M25.076	Hemarthrosis, unsp foot			
M25.049	Hemarthrosis, unsp hand		I31.2	Hemopericardium, NEC
M25.059	Hemarthrosis, unsp hip		D76.1	Hemophagocytic lymphohistiocytosis
M25.00	Hemarthrosis, unsp jt		D76.2	Hemophagocytic synd, infxn-associated
M25.069	Hemarthrosis, unsp knee		R04.2	Hemoptysis
M25.019	Hemarthrosis, unsp shldr		T84.83XA	Hemor d/t int orthopedic prosthetic devices, implants & grafts, init enc
M25.039	Hemarthrosis, unsp wrist			
K92.0	Hematemesis		T85.83XA	Hemor d/t int prosthetic devices, implants & grafts, NEC, init enc
I69.352	Hemiplegia & hemiparesis following cerebral infarction affecting lt dominant side		R04.89	Hemor from oth sites in respiratory passages
			R04.9	Hemor from respiratory passages, unsp
I69.354	Hemiplegia & hemiparesis following cerebral infarction affecting lt non-dominant side		J95.01	Hemor from tracheostomy stoma
			O20.9	Hemor in early pregnancy, unsp
I69.351	Hemiplegia & hemiparesis following cerebral infarction affecting rt dominant side		K62.5	Hemor of anus & rectum
			T82.837A	Hemor of cardiac prosthetic devices, implants & grafts, init enc
I69.353	Hemiplegia & hemiparesis following cerebral infarction affecting rt non-dominant side		T83.83XA	Hemor of genitourinary prosthetic devices, implants & grafts, init enc
			T82.838A	Hemor of vascular prosthetic devices, implants & grafts, init enc
I69.359	Hemiplegia & hemiparesis following cerebral infarction affecting unsp side		H31.413	Hemorrhagic choroidal detach, bilat
			H31.412	Hemorrhagic choroidal detach, lt eye
I69.152	Hemiplegia & hemiparesis following nontraumatic intracerebral hemor affecting lt dominant side		H31.411	Hemorrhagic choroidal detach, rt eye
			H31.419	Hemorrhagic choroidal detach, unsp eye
I69.154	Hemiplegia & hemiparesis following nontraumatic intracerebral hemor affecting lt non-dominant side		D68.32	Hemorrhagic d/o d/t extrinsic circulating anticoagulants
			H35.733	Hemorrhagic detach of retinal pigment epithelium, bilat
I69.151	Hemiplegia & hemiparesis following nontraumatic intracerebral hemor affecting rt dominant side		H35.732	Hemorrhagic detach of retinal pigment epithelium, lt eye
			H35.731	Hemorrhagic detach of retinal pigment epithelium, rt eye
I69.153	Hemiplegia & hemiparesis following nontraumatic intracerebral hemor affecting rt non-dominant side		H35.739	Hemorrhagic detach of retinal pigment epithelium, unsp eye
			P53	Hemorrhagic disease of newborn
I69.159	Hemiplegia & hemiparesis following nontraumatic intracerebral hemor affecting unsp side		A98.5	Hemorrhagic fever w/ renal synd
			O22.41	Hemorrhoids in pregnancy, 1st trmstr
I69.052	Hemiplegia & hemiparesis following nontraumatic subarachnoid hemor affecting lt dominant side		O22.42	Hemorrhoids in pregnancy, 2nd trmstr
			O22.43	Hemorrhoids in pregnancy, 3rd trmstr
I69.054	Hemiplegia & hemiparesis following nontraumatic subarachnoid hemor affecting lt non-dominant side		O22.40	Hemorrhoids in pregnancy, unsp trmstr
			O87.2	Hemorrhoids in the puerperium
I69.051	Hemiplegia & hemiparesis following nontraumatic subarachnoid hemor affecting rt dominant side		J94.2	Hemothorax
			B15.9	Hepatitis A w/o hepatic coma
I69.053	Hemiplegia & hemiparesis following nontraumatic subarachnoid hemor affecting rt non-dominant side		C22.2	Hepatoblastoma
			C86.1	Hepatosplenic T-cell lymphoma
I69.059	Hemiplegia & hemiparesis following nontraumatic subarachnoid hemor affecting unsp side		G11.9	Hereditary ataxia, unsp
			D68.2	Hereditary deficiency of oth clotting factors
I69.852	Hemiplegia & hemiparesis following oth cerebrovascular disease affecting lt dominant side		E80.0	Hereditary erythropoietic porphyria
			D68.1	Hereditary factor XI deficiency
I69.854	Hemiplegia & hemiparesis following oth cerebrovascular disease affecting lt non-dominant side		D58.9	Hereditary hemolytic anemia, unsp
			D80.0	Hereditary hypogammaglobulinemia
I69.851	Hemiplegia & hemiparesis following oth cerebrovascular disease affecting rt dominant side		N07.4	Hereditary nephropathy, NEC w/ diffuse endocapillary proliferative glomerulonephritis
I69.853	Hemiplegia & hemiparesis following oth cerebrovascular disease affecting rt non-dominant side		N07.2	Hereditary nephropathy, NEC w/ diffuse membranous glomerulonephritis

N07.3	Hereditary nephropathy, NEC w/ diffuse mesangial proliferative glomerulonephritis
N07.5	Hereditary nephropathy, NEC w/ diffuse mesangiocapillary glomerulonephritis
G11.4	Hereditary spastic paraplegia
E85.2	Heredofamilial amyloidosis, unsp
E70.331	Hermansky-Pudlak synd
B00.53	Herpesviral conjunctivitis
B00.2	Herpesviral gingivostomatitis & pharyngotonsillitis
B00.81	Herpesviral hepatitis
B00.51	Herpesviral iridocyclitis
B00.52	Herpesviral keratitis
B00.50	Herpesviral ocular disease, unsp
Q43.1	Hirschsprung's disease
E70.41	Histidinemia
D47.0	Histiocytic & mast cell tumors of uncertain behavior
C96.A	Histiocytic sarcoma
C81.99	Hodgkin lymphoma, unsp, extranodal & solid organ sites
C81.93	Hodgkin lymphoma, unsp, intra-abd lymph nodes
C81.96	Hodgkin lymphoma, unsp, intrapelvic lymph nodes
C81.92	Hodgkin lymphoma, unsp, intrathoracic lymph nodes
C81.94	Hodgkin lymphoma, unsp, lymph nodes of axilla & upr limb
C81.91	Hodgkin lymphoma, unsp, lymph nodes of head, face, & neck
C81.95	Hodgkin lymphoma, unsp, lymph nodes of inguinal rgn & lwr limb
C81.98	Hodgkin lymphoma, unsp, lymph nodes of multi sites
C81.97	Hodgkin lymphoma, unsp, spleen
C81.90	Hodgkin lymphoma, unsp, unsp site
E72.11	Homocystinuria
B76.9	Hookworm disease, unsp
O98.72	Human immunodeficiency virus [HIV] disease comp childbirth
O98.711	Human immunodeficiency virus [HIV] disease comp pregnancy, 1st trmstr
O98.712	Human immunodeficiency virus [HIV] disease comp pregnancy, 2nd trmstr
O98.713	Human immunodeficiency virus [HIV] disease comp pregnancy, 3rd trmstr
O98.73	Human immunodeficiency virus [HIV] disease comp the puerperium
B97.35	Human immunodeficiency virus, type 2 [HIV 2] as the cause of diseases classified elsw
B97.33	Human T-cell lymphotrophic virus, type I [HTLV-I] as the cause of diseases classified elsw
B97.34	Human T-cell lymphotrophic virus, type II [HTLV-II] as the cause of diseases classified elsw
G10	Huntington's disease
E76.02	Hurler-Scheie synd
E76.01	Hurler's synd
A50.52	Hutchinson's teeth
A50.53	Hutchinson's triad
G91.9	Hydrocephalus, unsp
N13.2	Hydronephrosis w/ renal & ureteral calculus obstruction
N13.1	Hydronephrosis w/ ureteral stricture, NEC
K82.1	Hydrops of gallbladder
N13.4	Hydroureter
B71.0	Hymenolepiasis
E22.9	Hyperfunction of pituitary gland, unsp
E87.0	Hyperosmolality & hypernatremia
E72.53	Hyperoxaluria
E22.1	Hyperprolactinemia
M31.0	Hypersensitivity angiitis
J67.8	Hypersensitivity pneumonitis d/t oth organic dusts
J67.9	Hypersensitivity pneumonitis d/t unsp organic dust
N98.1	Hyperstimulation of ovaries
I12.0	Hypertensive chr kidney disease w/ stage 5 chr kidney disease or end stage renal disease
I67.4	Hypertensive encephalopathy
I13.0	Hypertensive heart & chr kidney disease w/ heart failure & stage 1 through stage 4 chr kidney disease, or unsp chr kidney disease
I13.2	Hypertensive heart & chr kidney disease w/ heart failure & w/ stage 5 chr kidney disease, or end stage renal disease
I13.11	Hypertensive heart & chr kidney disease w/o heart failure, w/ stage 5 chr kidney disease, or end stage renal disease
E87.1	Hypo-osmolality & hyponatremia
E23.0	Hypopituitarism
J18.2	Hypostatic pneumonia, unsp organism
P91.60	Hypoxic ischemic encephalopathy [HIE], unsp

M87.09	Idiopathic aseptic necrosis of bone, multi sites
M87.08	Idiopathic aseptic necrosis of bone, oth site
M87.072	Idiopathic aseptic necrosis of lt ankle
M87.038	Idiopathic aseptic necrosis of lt carpus
M87.052	Idiopathic aseptic necrosis of lt femur
M87.065	Idiopathic aseptic necrosis of lt fibula
M87.045	Idiopathic aseptic necrosis of lt finger(s)
M87.075	Idiopathic aseptic necrosis of lt foot
M87.042	Idiopathic aseptic necrosis of lt hand
M87.022	Idiopathic aseptic necrosis of lt humerus
M87.032	Idiopathic aseptic necrosis of lt radius
M87.012	Idiopathic aseptic necrosis of lt shldr
M87.062	Idiopathic aseptic necrosis of lt tibia
M87.078	Idiopathic aseptic necrosis of lt toe(s)
M87.035	Idiopathic aseptic necrosis of lt ulna
M87.050	Idiopathic aseptic necrosis of pelvis
M87.071	Idiopathic aseptic necrosis of rt ankle
M87.037	Idiopathic aseptic necrosis of rt carpus
M87.051	Idiopathic aseptic necrosis of rt femur
M87.064	Idiopathic aseptic necrosis of rt fibula
M87.044	Idiopathic aseptic necrosis of rt finger(s)
M87.074	Idiopathic aseptic necrosis of rt foot
M87.041	Idiopathic aseptic necrosis of rt hand
M87.021	Idiopathic aseptic necrosis of rt humerus
M87.031	Idiopathic aseptic necrosis of rt radius
M87.011	Idiopathic aseptic necrosis of rt shldr
M87.061	Idiopathic aseptic necrosis of rt tibia
M87.077	Idiopathic aseptic necrosis of rt toe(s)
M87.034	Idiopathic aseptic necrosis of rt ulna
M87.073	Idiopathic aseptic necrosis of unsp ankle
M87.00	Idiopathic aseptic necrosis of unsp bone
M87.039	Idiopathic aseptic necrosis of unsp carpus
M87.059	Idiopathic aseptic necrosis of unsp femur
M87.066	Idiopathic aseptic necrosis of unsp fibula
M87.046	Idiopathic aseptic necrosis of unsp finger(s)
M87.076	Idiopathic aseptic necrosis of unsp foot
M87.043	Idiopathic aseptic necrosis of unsp hand
M87.029	Idiopathic aseptic necrosis of unsp humerus
M87.033	Idiopathic aseptic necrosis of unsp radius
M87.019	Idiopathic aseptic necrosis of unsp shldr
M87.063	Idiopathic aseptic necrosis of unsp tibia
M87.079	Idiopathic aseptic necrosis of unsp toe(s)
M87.036	Idiopathic aseptic necrosis of unsp ulna
G24.2	Idiopathic nonfamilial dystonia
G91.2	(Idiopathic) normal pressure hydrocephalus
J84.03	Idiopathic pulmn hemosiderosis
K56.7	Ileus, unsp
T69.022A	Immersion foot, lt foot, init enc
T69.021A	Immersion foot, rt foot, init enc
T69.029A	Immersion foot, unsp foot, init enc
D69.3	Immune thrombocytopenic purpura
D80.5	Immunodeficiency w/ increased immunoglobulin M [IgM]
D80.9	Immunodeficiency w/ predominantly antibody defects, unsp
D84.9	Immunodeficiency, unsp
C88.3	Immunoproliferative sm intestinal disease
S42.448A	Incarcerated fx (avulsion) of med epicondyle of lt humerus, init enc for clsd fx
S42.448P	Incarcerated fx (avulsion) of med epicondyle of lt humerus, subsq enc for fx w/ malu
S42.448K	Incarcerated fx (avulsion) of med epicondyle of lt humerus, subsq enc for fx w/ nonu
S42.447A	Incarcerated fx (avulsion) of med epicondyle of rt humerus, init enc for clsd fx
S42.447P	Incarcerated fx (avulsion) of med epicondyle of rt humerus, subsq enc for fx w/ malu
S42.447K	Incarcerated fx (avulsion) of med epicondyle of rt humerus, subsq enc for fx w/ nonu
S42.449A	Incarcerated fx (avulsion) of med epicondyle of unsp humerus, init enc for clsd fx
S42.449P	Incarcerated fx (avulsion) of med epicondyle of unsp humerus, subsq enc for fx w/ malu
S42.449K	Incarcerated fx (avulsion) of med epicondyle of unsp humerus, subsq enc for fx w/ nonu
K43.0	Incisional hernia w/ obstruction, w/o gangrene

O03.39	Incomplete spontaneous abortion w/ oth comp
A30.0	Indeterminate leprosy
O04.89	(Induced) termination of pregnancy w/ oth comp
O04.80	(Induced) termination of pregnancy w/ unsp comp
A48.51	Infant botulism
G12.0	Infantile spinal muscular atrophy, type I [Werdnig-Hoffman]
N43.1	Infected hydrocele
O23.11	Infections of bladder in pregnancy, 1st trmstr
O23.12	Infections of bladder in pregnancy, 2nd trmstr
O23.13	Infections of bladder in pregnancy, 3rd trmstr
O23.511	Infections of cervix in pregnancy, 1st trmstr
O23.512	Infections of cervix in pregnancy, 2nd trmstr
O23.513	Infections of cervix in pregnancy, 3rd trmstr
O23.01	Infections of kidney in pregnancy, 1st trmstr
O23.02	Infections of kidney in pregnancy, 2nd trmstr
O23.03	Infections of kidney in pregnancy, 3rd trmstr
O23.31	Infections of oth parts of urinary tract in pregnancy, 1st trmstr
O23.32	Infections of oth parts of urinary tract in pregnancy, 2nd trmstr
O23.33	Infections of oth parts of urinary tract in pregnancy, 3rd trmstr
O23.21	Infections of urethra in pregnancy, 1st trmstr
O23.22	Infections of urethra in pregnancy, 2nd trmstr
O23.23	Infections of urethra in pregnancy, 3rd trmstr
A09	Infectious gastroenteritis & colitis, unsp
M60.071	Infective myositis, lt ankle
M60.045	Infective myositis, lt finger(s)
M60.074	Infective myositis, lt foot
M60.032	Infective myositis, lt forearm
M60.042	Infective myositis, lt hand
M60.062	Infective myositis, lt lwr leg
M60.012	Infective myositis, lt shldr
M60.052	Infective myositis, lt thigh
M60.077	Infective myositis, lt toe(s)
M60.022	Infective myositis, lt upr arm
M60.09	Infective myositis, multi sites
M60.08	Infective myositis, oth site
M60.070	Infective myositis, rt ankle
M60.044	Infective myositis, rt finger(s)
M60.073	Infective myositis, rt foot
M60.031	Infective myositis, rt forearm
M60.041	Infective myositis, rt hand
M60.061	Infective myositis, rt lwr leg
M60.011	Infective myositis, rt shldr
M60.051	Infective myositis, rt thigh
M60.076	Infective myositis, rt toe(s)
M60.021	Infective myositis, rt upr arm
M60.072	Infective myositis, unsp ankle
M60.002	Infective myositis, unsp arm
M60.046	Infective myositis, unsp finger(s)
M60.075	Infective myositis, unsp foot
M60.039	Infective myositis, unsp forearm
M60.043	Infective myositis, unsp hand
M60.005	Infective myositis, unsp leg
M60.001	Infective myositis, unsp lt arm
M60.004	Infective myositis, unsp lt leg
M60.069	Infective myositis, unsp lwr leg
M60.000	Infective myositis, unsp rt arm
M60.003	Infective myositis, unsp rt leg
M60.019	Infective myositis, unsp shldr
M60.009	Infective myositis, unsp site
M60.059	Infective myositis, unsp thigh
M60.078	Infective myositis, unsp toe(s)
M60.029	Infective myositis, unsp upr arm
I30.1	Infective pericarditis
K51.414	Inflam polyps of colon w/ abscess
K51.413	Inflam polyps of colon w/ fistula
K51.412	Inflam polyps of colon w/ intestinal obstruction
K51.418	Inflam polyps of colon w/ oth comp
K51.411	Inflam polyps of colon w/ rectal bleeding
K51.419	Inflam polyps of colon w/ unsp comp
K51.40	Inflam polyps of colon w/o comp
T82.6XXA	Infxn & inflam reaction d/t cardiac valve prosthesis, init enc
T83.51XA	Infxn & inflam reaction d/t indwelling urinary catheter, init enc
T85.72XA	Infxn & inflam reaction d/t insulin pump, init enc

T84.621A	Infxn & inflam reaction d/t int fix dev of lt femur, init enc
T84.625A	Infxn & inflam reaction d/t int fix dev of lt fibula, init enc
T84.611A	Infxn & inflam reaction d/t int fix dev of lt humerus, init enc
T84.613A	Infxn & inflam reaction d/t int fix dev of lt radius, init enc
T84.623A	Infxn & inflam reaction d/t int fix dev of lt tibia, init enc
T84.615A	Infxn & inflam reaction d/t int fix dev of lt ulna, init enc
T84.69XA	Infxn & inflam reaction d/t int fix dev of oth site, init enc
T84.620A	Infxn & inflam reaction d/t int fix dev of rt femur, init enc
T84.624A	Infxn & inflam reaction d/t int fix dev of rt fibula, init enc
T84.610A	Infxn & inflam reaction d/t int fix dev of rt humerus, init enc
T84.612A	Infxn & inflam reaction d/t int fix dev of rt radius, init enc
T84.622A	Infxn & inflam reaction d/t int fix dev of rt tibia, init enc
T84.614A	Infxn & inflam reaction d/t int fix dev of rt ulna, init enc
T84.63XA	Infxn & inflam reaction d/t int fix dev of spine, init enc
T84.619A	Infxn & inflam reaction d/t int fix dev of unsp bone of arm, init enc
T84.629A	Infxn & inflam reaction d/t int fix dev of unsp bone of leg, init enc
T84.60XA	Infxn & inflam reaction d/t int fix dev of unsp site, init enc
T84.52XA	Infxn & inflam reaction d/t int lt hip prosthesis, init enc
T84.54XA	Infxn & inflam reaction d/t int lt knee prosthesis, init enc
T84.51XA	Infxn & inflam reaction d/t int rt hip prosthesis, init enc
T84.53XA	Infxn & inflam reaction d/t int rt knee prosthesis, init enc
T82.7XXA	Infxn & inflam reaction d/t oth cardiac & vascular devices, implants & grafts, init enc
T84.59XA	Infxn & inflam reaction d/t oth int jt prosthesis, init enc
T84.7XXA	Infxn & inflam reaction d/t oth int orthopedic prosthetic devices, implants & grafts, init enc
T85.79XA	Infxn & inflam reaction d/t oth int prosthetic devices, implants & grafts, init enc
T85.71XA	Infxn & inflam reaction d/t peritoneal dialysis catheter, init enc
T83.6XXA	Infxn & inflam reaction d/t prosthetic dev, implant & graft in genital tract, init enc
T83.59XA	Infxn & inflam reaction d/t prosthetic dev, implant & graft in urinary sys, init enc
T84.50XA	Infxn & inflam reaction d/t unsp int jt prosthesis, init enc
N98.0	Infxn associated w/ artfcl insemination
K95.01	Infxn d/t gastric band procedure
K95.81	Infxn d/t oth bariatric procedure
T81.4XXA	Infxn following a procedure, init enc
T88.0XXA	Infxn following immunization, init enc
T80.29XA	Infxn following oth inf, transfusion & therapeutic injection, init enc
T87.44	Infxn of amp stump, lt lwr extr
T87.42	Infxn of amp stump, lt upr extr
T87.43	Infxn of amp stump, rt lwr extr
T87.41	Infxn of amp stump, rt upr extr
T87.40	Infxn of amp stump, unsp extr
O86.22	Infxn of bladder following delivery
M46.32	Infxn of interv disc (pyogenic), cervical rgn
M46.33	Infxn of interv disc (pyogenic), cervicothoracic rgn
M46.36	Infxn of interv disc (pyogenic), lumbar rgn
M46.37	Infxn of interv disc (pyogenic), lumbosacral rgn
M46.39	Infxn of interv disc (pyogenic), multi sites in spine
M46.31	Infxn of interv disc (pyogenic), occipito-atlanto-axial rgn
M46.38	Infxn of interv disc (pyogenic), sacral & sacrococcygeal rgn
M46.30	Infxn of interv disc (pyogenic), site unsp
M46.34	Infxn of interv disc (pyogenic), thoracic rgn
M46.35	Infxn of interv disc (pyogenic), thoracolumbar rgn
O86.21	Infxn of kidney following delivery
O23.591	Infxn of oth part of genital tract in pregnancy, 1st trmstr
O23.592	Infxn of oth part of genital tract in pregnancy, 2nd trmstr
O23.593	Infxn of oth part of genital tract in pregnancy, 3rd trmstr
J95.02	Infxn of tracheostomy stoma
P39.9	Infxn specific to the perinatal period, unsp
F18.17	Inhalant abuse w/ inhalant-induced dementia
F18.150	Inhalant abuse w/ inhalant-induced psychotic d/o w/ delusions
F18.151	Inhalant abuse w/ inhalant-induced psychotic d/o w/ hallucinations
F18.121	Inhalant abuse w/ intoxication delirium
F18.280	Inhalant dependence w/ inhalant-induced anxiety d/o
F18.27	Inhalant dependence w/ inhalant-induced dementia
F18.250	Inhalant dependence w/ inhalant-induced psychotic d/o w/ delusions
F18.251	Inhalant dependence w/ inhalant-induced psychotic d/o w/ hallucinations
F18.259	Inhalant dependence w/ inhalant-induced psychotic d/o, unsp
F18.221	Inhalant dependence w/ intoxication delirium
F18.288	Inhalant dependence w/ oth inhalant-induced d/o

F18.20	Inhalant dependence, uncomplicated
F18.97	Inhalant use, unsp w/ inhalant-induced persisting dementia
F18.950	Inhalant use, unsp w/ inhalant-induced psychotic d/o w/ delusions
F18.951	Inhalant use, unsp w/ inhalant-induced psychotic d/o w/ hallucinations
F18.921	Inhalant use, unsp w/ intoxication w/ delirium
S04.42XA	Inj of abducent nerve, lt side, init enc
S04.41XA	Inj of abducent nerve, rt side, init enc
S04.40XA	Inj of abducent nerve, unsp side, init enc
S04.72XA	Inj of accessory nerve, lt side, init enc
S04.71XA	Inj of accessory nerve, rt side, init enc
S04.70XA	Inj of accessory nerve, unsp side, init enc
S04.62XA	Inj of acoustic nerve, lt side, init enc
S04.61XA	Inj of acoustic nerve, rt side, init enc
S04.60XA	Inj of acoustic nerve, unsp side, init enc
S36.13XA	Inj of bile duct, init enc
S09.0XXA	Inj of blood vessels of head, NEC, init enc
S04.52XA	Inj of facial nerve, lt side, init enc
S04.51XA	Inj of facial nerve, rt side, init enc
S04.50XA	Inj of facial nerve, unsp side, init enc
S06.825A	Inj of lt int carotid artery, intracranial portion, NEC w/ loss of cnscness > 24 hrs w/ return to pre-existing conscious lvl, init enc
S06.823A	Inj of lt int carotid artery, intracranial portion, NEC w/ loss of cnscness of 1 hr to 5 hrs 59 mins, init enc
S06.821A	Inj of lt int carotid artery, intracranial portion, NEC w/ loss of cnscness of 30 mins or less, init enc
S06.822A	Inj of lt int carotid artery, intracranial portion, NEC w/ loss of cnscness of 31 mins to 59 mins, init enc
S06.824A	Inj of lt int carotid artery, intracranial portion, NEC w/ loss of cnscness of 6 hrs to 24 hrs, init enc
S06.829A	Inj of lt int carotid artery, intracranial portion, NEC w/ loss of cnscness of unsp dur, init enc
S35.532A	Inj of lt uterine artery, init enc
S35.535A	Inj of lt uterine vein, init enc
S04.12XA	Inj of oculomotor nerve, lt side, init enc
S04.11XA	Inj of oculomotor nerve, rt side, init enc
S04.10XA	Inj of oculomotor nerve, unsp side, init enc
S04.812A	Inj of olfactory [1st] nerve, lt side, init enc
S04.811A	Inj of olfactory [1st] nerve, rt side, init enc
S04.819A	Inj of olfactory [1st] nerve, unsp side, init enc
S04.02XA	Inj of optic chiasm, init enc
S04.012A	Inj of optic nerve, lt eye, init enc
S04.011A	Inj of optic nerve, rt eye, init enc
S04.019A	Inj of optic nerve, unsp eye, init enc
S04.032A	Inj of optic tract & pathways, lt eye, init enc
S04.031A	Inj of optic tract & pathways, rt eye, init enc
S04.039A	Inj of optic tract & pathways, unsp eye, init enc
S04.892A	Inj of oth cranial nerves, lt side, init enc
S04.891A	Inj of oth cranial nerves, rt side, init enc
S04.899A	Inj of oth cranial nerves, unsp side, init enc
S15.8XXA	Inj of oth spec blood vessels at neck lvl, init enc
S36.81XA	Inj of peritoneum, init enc
S06.815A	Inj of rt int carotid artery, intracranial portion, NEC w/ loss of cnscness > 24 hrs w/ return to pre-existing conscious lvl, init enc
S06.813A	Inj of rt int carotid artery, intracranial portion, NEC w/ loss of cnscness of 1 hr to 5 hrs 59 mins, init enc
S06.811A	Inj of rt int carotid artery, intracranial portion, NEC w/ loss of cnscness of 30 mins or less, init enc
S06.812A	Inj of rt int carotid artery, intracranial portion, NEC w/ loss of cnscness of 31 mins to 59 mins, init enc
S06.814A	Inj of rt int carotid artery, intracranial portion, NEC w/ loss of cnscness of 6 hrs to 24 hrs, init enc
S06.819A	Inj of rt int carotid artery, intracranial portion, NEC w/ loss of cnscness of unsp dur, init enc
S35.531A	Inj of rt uterine artery, init enc
S35.534A	Inj of rt uterine vein, init enc
S04.32XA	Inj of trigeminal nerve, lt side, init enc
S04.31XA	Inj of trigeminal nerve, rt side, init enc
S04.30XA	Inj of trigeminal nerve, unsp side, init enc
S04.22XA	Inj of trochlear nerve, lt side, init enc
S04.21XA	Inj of trochlear nerve, rt side, init enc
S04.20XA	Inj of trochlear nerve, unsp side, init enc
S15.9XXA	Inj of unsp blood vessel at neck lvl, init enc
S04.9XXA	Inj of unsp cranial nerve, init enc
S27.9XXA	Inj of unsp intrathoracic organ, init enc
S35.533A	Inj of unsp uterine artery, init enc

S35.536A	Inj of unsp uterine vein, init enc
S04.042A	Inj of visual cortex, lt eye, init enc
S04.041A	Inj of visual cortex, rt eye, init enc
S04.049A	Inj of visual cortex, unsp eye, init enc
T84.023A	Instability of int lt knee prosthesis, init enc
T84.022A	Instability of int rt knee prosthesis, init enc
J84.9	Interstitial pulmn disease, unsp
M51.06	Interv disc d/o w/ myelopathy, lumbar rgn
M51.04	Interv disc d/o w/ myelopathy, thoracic rgn
M51.05	Interv disc d/o w/ myelopathy, thoracolumbar rgn
K56.5	Intestinal adhesions [bands] w/ obstruction (postprocedural) (postinfection)
B81.3	Intestinal angiostrongyliasis
B81.1	Intestinal capillariasis
B82.0	Intestinal helminthiasis, unsp
K90.9	Intestinal malabsorption, unsp
B78.0	Intestinal strongyloidiasis
T86.851	Intestine transplant failure
T86.852	Intestine transplant infxn
T86.850	Intestine transplant rejection
Z94.82	Intestine transplant status
P39.2	Intra-amniotic infxn affecting newborn, NEC
G97.2	Intracranial hypotension following ventricular shunting
C22.1	Intrahepatic bile duct ca
I97.710	Intraoperative cardiac arrest during cardiac surgery
I97.711	Intraoperative cardiac arrest during oth surgery
I97.810	Intraoperative cerebrovascular infarction during cardiac surgery
I97.811	Intraoperative cerebrovascular infarction during oth surgery
I97.411	Intraoperative hemor & hematoma of a circulatory sys organ or structure comp a cardiac bypass
I97.410	Intraoperative hemor & hematoma of a circulatory sys organ or structure comp a cardiac catheterization
I97.418	Intraoperative hemor & hematoma of a circulatory sys organ or structure comp oth circulatory sys procedure
I97.42	Intraoperative hemor & hematoma of a circulatory sys organ or structure comp oth procedure
K91.61	Intraoperative hemor & hematoma of a digestive sys organ or structure comp a digestive sytem procedure
K91.62	Intraoperative hemor & hematoma of a digestive sys organ or structure comp oth procedure
N99.61	Intraoperative hemor & hematoma of a genitourinary sys organ or structure comp a genitourinary sys procedure
N99.62	Intraoperative hemor & hematoma of a genitourinary sys organ or structure comp oth procedure
M96.810	Intraoperative hemor & hematoma of a musculoskeletal structure comp a musculoskeletal sys procedure
M96.811	Intraoperative hemor & hematoma of a musculoskeletal structure comp oth procedure
G97.31	Intraoperative hemor & hematoma of a nervous sys organ or structure comp a nervous sys procedure
G97.32	Intraoperative hemor & hematoma of a nervous sys organ or structure comp oth procedure
J95.61	Intraoperative hemor & hematoma of a respiratory sys organ or structure comp a respiratory sys procedure
J95.62	Intraoperative hemor & hematoma of a respiratory sys organ or structure comp oth procedure
E36.01	Intraoperative hemor & hematoma of an endocrine sys organ or structure comp an endocrine sys procedure
E36.02	Intraoperative hemor & hematoma of an endocrine sys organ or structure comp oth procedure
H95.21	Intraoperative hemor & hematoma of ear & mastoid process comp a procedure on the ear & mastoid process
H95.22	Intraoperative hemor & hematoma of ear & mastoid process comp oth procedure
H59.113	Intraoperative hemor & hematoma of eye & adnexa comp an ophthalmic procedure, bilat
H59.123	Intraoperative hemor & hematoma of eye & adnexa comp oth procedure, bilat
H59.112	Intraoperative hemor & hematoma of lt eye & adnexa comp an ophthalmic procedure
H59.122	Intraoperative hemor & hematoma of lt eye & adnexa comp oth procedure
H59.111	Intraoperative hemor & hematoma of rt eye & adnexa comp an ophthalmic procedure
H59.121	Intraoperative hemor & hematoma of rt eye & adnexa comp oth procedure

L76.01	Intraoperative hemor & hematoma of skin & SQ tissue comp a dermatologic procedure	S37.813A	Lac of adrenal gland, init enc
L76.02	Intraoperative hemor & hematoma of skin & SQ tissue comp oth procedure	S85.142A	Lac of ant tibial artery, lt leg, init enc
D78.01	Intraoperative hemor & hematoma of the spleen comp a procedure on the spleen	S85.141A	Lac of ant tibial artery, rt leg, init enc
		S85.149A	Lac of ant tibial artery, unsp leg, init enc
		S36.530A	Lac of ascending [rt] colon, init enc
D78.02	Intraoperative hemor & hematoma of the spleen comp oth procedure	S45.212A	Lac of axillary or brachial vein, lt side, init enc
H59.119	Intraoperative hemor & hematoma of unsp eye & adnexa comp an ophthalmic procedure	S45.211A	Lac of axillary or brachial vein, rt side, init enc
		S45.219A	Lac of axillary or brachial vein, unsp side, init enc
H59.129	Intraoperative hemor & hematoma of unsp eye & adnexa comp oth procedure	S37.23XA	Lac of bladder, init enc
		S65.511A	Lac of blood vessel of lt index finger, init enc
K61.4	Intrasphincteric abscess	S65.517A	Lac of blood vessel of lt little finger, init enc
N44.02	Intravaginal torsion of spermatic cord	S65.513A	Lac of blood vessel of lt mid finger, init enc
P52.0	Intraventricular (nontraumatic) hemor, grade 1, of newborn	S65.515A	Lac of blood vessel of lt ring finger, init enc
P52.1	Intraventricular (nontraumatic) hemor, grade 2, of newborn	S65.412A	Lac of blood vessel of lt thumb, init enc
P10.2	Intraventricular hemor d/t birth inj	S65.518A	Lac of blood vessel of oth finger, init enc
K56.1	Intussusception	S65.510A	Lac of blood vessel of rt index finger, init enc
N30.41	Irradiation cystitis w/ hematuria	S65.516A	Lac of blood vessel of rt little finger, init enc
N30.40	Irradiation cystitis w/o hematuria	S65.512A	Lac of blood vessel of rt mid finger, init enc
N28.0	Ischemia & infarction of kidney	S65.514A	Lac of blood vessel of rt ring finger, init enc
K61.3	Ischiorectal abscess	S65.411A	Lac of blood vessel of rt thumb, init enc
N06.4	Isolated proteinuria w/ diffuse endocapillary proliferative glomerulonephritis	S65.519A	Lac of blood vessel of unsp finger, init enc
		S65.419A	Lac of blood vessel of unsp thumb, init enc
N06.2	Isolated proteinuria w/ diffuse membranous glomerulonephritis	S36.231A	Lac of body of pancreas, unsp degree, init enc
N06.3	Isolated proteinuria w/ diffuse mesangial proliferative glomerulonephritis	S45.112A	Lac of brachial artery, lt side, init enc
		S45.111A	Lac of brachial artery, rt side, init enc
		S45.119A	Lac of brachial artery, unsp side, init enc
N06.5	Isolated proteinuria w/ diffuse mesangiocapillary glomerulonephritis	S65.312A	Lac of deep palmar arch of lt hand, init enc
A07.3	Isosporiasis	S65.311A	Lac of deep palmar arch of rt hand, init enc
E71.110	Isovaleric acidemia	S65.319A	Lac of deep palmar arch of unsp hand, init enc
I49.2	Junctional premature depolarization	S36.532A	Lac of descending [lt] colon, init enc
A96.0	Junin hemorrhagic fever	S27.803A	Lac of diaphragm, init enc
M33.02	Juvenile dermatopolymyositis w/ myopathy	S95.012A	Lac of dorsal artery of lt foot, init enc
M33.09	Juvenile dermatopolymyositis w/ oth organ involvement	S95.011A	Lac of dorsal artery of rt foot, init enc
M33.01	Juvenile dermatopolymyositis w/ respiratory involvement	S95.019A	Lac of dorsal artery of unsp foot, init enc
M33.00	Juvenile dermatopolymyositis, organ involvement unsp	S95.212A	Lac of dorsal vein of lt foot, init enc
A50.45	Juvenile general paresis	S95.211A	Lac of dorsal vein of rt foot, init enc
C93.32	Juvenile myelomonocytic leukemia, in relapse	S95.219A	Lac of dorsal vein of unsp foot, init enc
C93.31	Juvenile myelomonocytic leukemia, in remission	S36.430A	Lac of duodenum, init enc
C93.30	Juvenile myelomonocytic leukemia, not having achieved remission	S56.422A	Lac of extensor muscle, fascia & tndn of lt index finger at forearm lvl, init enc
G40.B11	Juvenile myoclonic epilepsy, intractable, w/ status epilepticus	S66.321A	Lac of extensor muscle, fascia & tndn of lt index finger at wrist & hand lvl, init enc
G40.B19	Juvenile myoclonic epilepsy, intractable, w/o status epilepticus	S56.428A	Lac of extensor muscle, fascia & tndn of lt little finger at forearm lvl, init enc
G40.B01	Juvenile myoclonic epilepsy, not intractable, w/ status epilepticus	S66.327A	Lac of extensor muscle, fascia & tndn of lt little finger at wrist & hand lvl, init enc
G40.B09	Juvenile myoclonic epilepsy, not intractable, w/o status epilepticus	S56.424A	Lac of extensor muscle, fascia & tndn of lt mid finger at forearm lvl, init enc
M30.2	Juvenile polyarteritis	S66.323A	Lac of extensor muscle, fascia & tndn of lt mid finger at wrist & hand lvl, init enc
C46.4	Kaposi's sarcoma of gastrointestinal sites	S56.426A	Lac of extensor muscle, fascia & tndn of lt ring finger at forearm lvl, init enc
C46.52	Kaposi's sarcoma of lt lung	S66.325A	Lac of extensor muscle, fascia & tndn of lt ring finger at wrist & hand lvl, init enc
C46.3	Kaposi's sarcoma of lymph nodes		
C46.7	Kaposi's sarcoma of oth sites	S66.222A	Lac of extensor muscle, fascia & tndn of lt thumb at wrist & hand lvl, init enc
C46.2	Kaposi's sarcoma of palate		
C46.51	Kaposi's sarcoma of rt lung	S66.328A	Lac of extensor muscle, fascia & tndn of oth finger at wrist & hand lvl, init enc
C46.0	Kaposi's sarcoma of skin		
C46.1	Kaposi's sarcoma of soft tissue	S56.421A	Lac of extensor muscle, fascia & tndn of rt index finger at forearm lvl, init enc
C46.50	Kaposi's sarcoma of unsp lung		
C46.9	Kaposi's sarcoma, unsp	S66.320A	Lac of extensor muscle, fascia & tndn of rt index finger at wrist & hand lvl, init enc
H49.813	Kearns-Sayre synd, bilat		
H49.812	Kearns-Sayre synd, lt eye	S56.427A	Lac of extensor muscle, fascia & tndn of rt little finger at forearm lvl, init enc
H49.811	Kearns-Sayre synd, rt eye		
H49.819	Kearns-Sayre synd, unsp eye	S66.326A	Lac of extensor muscle, fascia & tndn of rt little finger at wrist & hand lvl, init enc
H59.013	Keratopathy (bullous aphakic) following cataract surgery, bilat		
H59.012	Keratopathy (bullous aphakic) following cataract surgery, lt eye	S56.423A	Lac of extensor muscle, fascia & tndn of rt mid finger at forearm lvl, init enc
H59.011	Keratopathy (bullous aphakic) following cataract surgery, rt eye	S66.322A	Lac of extensor muscle, fascia & tndn of rt mid finger at wrist & hand lvl, init enc
H59.019	Keratopathy (bullous aphakic) following cataract surgery, unsp eye		
T86.12	Kidney transplant failure	S56.425A	Lac of extensor muscle, fascia & tndn of rt ring finger at forearm lvl, init enc
T86.13	Kidney transplant infxn		
T86.11	Kidney transplant rejection	S66.324A	Lac of extensor muscle, fascia & tndn of rt ring finger at wrist & hand lvl, init enc
Z94.0	Kidney transplant status		
E75.23	Krabbe disease		
A81.81	Kuru		
A98.2	Kyasanur Forest disease		
I27.1	Kyphoscoliotic heart disease		
O68	Labor & delivery complicated by abnormality of fetal acid-base balance		
S76.222A	Lac of adductor muscle, fascia & tndn of lt thigh, init enc		
S76.221A	Lac of adductor muscle, fascia & tndn of rt thigh, init enc		
S76.229A	Lac of adductor muscle, fascia & tndn of unsp thigh, init enc		

S66.221A	Lac of extensor muscle, fascia & tndn of rt thumb at wrist & hand lvl, init enc
S56.429A	Lac of extensor muscle, fascia & tndn of unsp finger at forearm lvl, init enc
S66.329A	Lac of extensor muscle, fascia & tndn of unsp finger at wrist & hand lvl, init enc
S66.229A	Lac of extensor muscle, fascia & tndn of unsp thumb at wrist & hand lvl, init enc
S56.322A	Lac of extensor or abductor muscles, fascia & tendons of lt thumb at forearm lvl, init enc
S56.321A	Lac of extensor or abductor muscles, fascia & tendons of rt thumb at forearm lvl, init enc
S56.329A	Lac of extensor or abductor muscles, fascia & tendons of unsp thumb at forearm lvl, init enc
S56.122A	Lac of flexor muscle, fascia & tndn of lt index finger at forearm lvl, init enc
S66.121A	Lac of flexor muscle, fascia & tndn of lt index finger at wrist & hand lvl, init enc
S56.128A	Lac of flexor muscle, fascia & tndn of lt little finger at forearm lvl, init enc
S66.127A	Lac of flexor muscle, fascia & tndn of lt little finger at wrist & hand lvl, init enc
S56.124A	Lac of flexor muscle, fascia & tndn of lt mid finger at forearm lvl, init enc
S66.123A	Lac of flexor muscle, fascia & tndn of lt mid finger at wrist & hand lvl, init enc
S56.126A	Lac of flexor muscle, fascia & tndn of lt ring finger at forearm lvl, init enc
S66.125A	Lac of flexor muscle, fascia & tndn of lt ring finger at wrist & hand lvl, init enc
S56.022A	Lac of flexor muscle, fascia & tndn of lt thumb at forearm lvl, init enc
S66.128A	Lac of flexor muscle, fascia & tndn of oth finger at wrist & hand lvl, init enc
S56.121A	Lac of flexor muscle, fascia & tndn of rt index finger at forearm lvl, init enc
S66.120A	Lac of flexor muscle, fascia & tndn of rt index finger at wrist & hand lvl, init enc
S56.127A	Lac of flexor muscle, fascia & tndn of rt little finger at forearm lvl, init enc
S66.126A	Lac of flexor muscle, fascia & tndn of rt little finger at wrist & hand lvl, init enc
S56.123A	Lac of flexor muscle, fascia & tndn of rt mid finger at forearm lvl, init enc
S66.122A	Lac of flexor muscle, fascia & tndn of rt mid finger at wrist & hand lvl, init enc
S56.125A	Lac of flexor muscle, fascia & tndn of rt ring finger at forearm lvl, init enc
S66.124A	Lac of flexor muscle, fascia & tndn of rt ring finger at wrist & hand lvl, init enc
S56.021A	Lac of flexor muscle, fascia & tndn of rt thumb at forearm lvl, init enc
S56.129A	Lac of flexor muscle, fascia & tndn of unsp finger at forearm lvl, init enc
S66.129A	Lac of flexor muscle, fascia & tndn of unsp finger at wrist & hand lvl, init enc
S56.029A	Lac of flexor muscle, fascia & tndn of unsp thumb at forearm lvl, init enc
S36.123A	Lac of gallbladder, init enc
S85.312A	Lac of greater saphenous vein at lwr leg lvl, lt leg, init enc
S85.311A	Lac of greater saphenous vein at lwr leg lvl, rt leg, init enc
S85.319A	Lac of greater saphenous vein at lwr leg lvl, unsp leg, init enc
S36.230A	Lac of head of pancreas, unsp degree, init enc
S25.512A	Lac of intercostal blood vessels, lt side, init enc
S25.511A	Lac of intercostal blood vessels, rt side, init enc
S25.519A	Lac of intercostal blood vessels, unsp side, init enc
S96.222A	Lac of intrinsic muscle & tndn at ankle & foot lvl, lt foot, init enc
S96.221A	Lac of intrinsic muscle & tndn at ankle & foot lvl, rt foot, init enc
S96.229A	Lac of intrinsic muscle & tndn at ankle & foot lvl, unsp foot, init enc
S66.521A	Lac of intrinsic muscle, fascia & tndn of lt index finger at wrist & hand lvl, init enc
S66.527A	Lac of intrinsic muscle, fascia & tndn of lt little finger at wrist & hand lvl, init enc
S66.523A	Lac of intrinsic muscle, fascia & tndn of lt mid finger at wrist & hand lvl, init enc
S66.525A	Lac of intrinsic muscle, fascia & tndn of lt ring finger at wrist & hand lvl, init enc
S66.422A	Lac of intrinsic muscle, fascia & tndn of lt thumb at wrist & hand lvl, init enc
S66.528A	Lac of intrinsic muscle, fascia & tndn of oth finger at wrist & hand lvl, init enc
S66.520A	Lac of intrinsic muscle, fascia & tndn of rt index finger at wrist & hand lvl, init enc
S66.526A	Lac of intrinsic muscle, fascia & tndn of rt little finger at wrist & hand lvl, init enc
S66.522A	Lac of intrinsic muscle, fascia & tndn of rt mid finger at wrist & hand lvl, init enc

S66.524A	Lac of intrinsic muscle, fascia & tndn of rt ring finger at wrist & hand lvl, init enc
S66.421A	Lac of intrinsic muscle, fascia & tndn of rt thumb at wrist & hand lvl, init enc
S66.529A	Lac of intrinsic muscle, fascia & tndn of unsp finger at wrist & hand lvl, init enc
S66.429A	Lac of intrinsic muscle, fascia & tndn of unsp thumb at wrist & hand lvl, init enc
S85.412A	Lac of lesser saphenous vein at lwr leg lvl, lt leg, init enc
S85.411A	Lac of lesser saphenous vein at lwr leg lvl, rt leg, init enc
S85.419A	Lac of lesser saphenous vein at lwr leg lvl, unsp leg, init enc
S36.113A	Lac of liver, unsp degree, init enc
S66.022A	Lac of long flexor muscle, fascia & tndn of lt thumb at wrist & hand lvl, init enc
S66.021A	Lac of long flexor muscle, fascia & tndn of rt thumb at wrist & hand lvl, init enc
S66.029A	Lac of long flexor muscle, fascia & tndn of unsp thumb at wrist & hand lvl, init enc
S86.022A	Lac of lt Achilles tndn, init enc
S37.032A	Lac of lt kidney, unsp degree, init enc
S76.122A	Lac of lt quadriceps muscle, fascia & tndn, init enc
S29.021A	Lac of muscle & tndn of front wall of thorax, init enc
S96.122A	Lac of muscle & tndn of long extensor muscle of toe at ankle & foot lvl, lt foot, init enc
S96.121A	Lac of muscle & tndn of long extensor muscle of toe at ankle & foot lvl, rt foot, init enc
S96.129A	Lac of muscle & tndn of long extensor muscle of toe at ankle & foot lvl, unsp foot, init enc
S96.022A	Lac of muscle & tndn of long flexor muscle of toe at ankle & foot lvl, lt foot, init enc
S96.021A	Lac of muscle & tndn of long flexor muscle of toe at ankle & foot lvl, rt foot, init enc
S96.029A	Lac of muscle & tndn of long flexor muscle of toe at ankle & foot lvl, unsp foot, init enc
S29.029A	Lac of muscle & tndn of unsp wall of thorax, init enc
S46.122A	Lac of muscle, fascia & tndn of long head of biceps, lt arm, init enc
S46.121A	Lac of muscle, fascia & tndn of long head of biceps, rt arm, init enc
S46.129A	Lac of muscle, fascia & tndn of long head of biceps, unsp arm, init enc
S76.022A	Lac of muscle, fascia & tndn of lt hip, init enc
S46.222A	Lac of muscle, fascia & tndn of oth parts of biceps, lt arm, init enc
S46.221A	Lac of muscle, fascia & tndn of oth parts of biceps, rt arm, init enc
S46.229A	Lac of muscle, fascia & tndn of oth parts of biceps, unsp arm, init enc
S76.021A	Lac of muscle, fascia & tndn of rt hip, init enc
S76.322A	Lac of muscle, fascia & tndn of the post muscle group at thigh lvl, lt thigh, init enc
S76.321A	Lac of muscle, fascia & tndn of the post muscle group at thigh lvl, rt thigh, init enc
S76.329A	Lac of muscle, fascia & tndn of the post muscle group at thigh lvl, unsp thigh, init enc
S46.322A	Lac of muscle, fascia & tndn of triceps, lt arm, init enc
S46.321A	Lac of muscle, fascia & tndn of triceps, rt arm, init enc
S46.329A	Lac of muscle, fascia & tndn of triceps, unsp arm, init enc
S76.029A	Lac of muscle, fascia & tndn of unsp hip, init enc
S86.222A	Lac of muscle(s) & tndn(s) of ant muscle group at lwr leg lvl, lt leg, init enc
S86.221A	Lac of muscle(s) & tndn(s) of ant muscle group at lwr leg lvl, rt leg, init enc
S86.229A	Lac of muscle(s) & tndn(s) of ant muscle group at lwr leg lvl, unsp leg, init enc
S86.322A	Lac of muscle(s) & tndn(s) of peroneal muscle group at lwr leg lvl, lt leg, init enc
S86.321A	Lac of muscle(s) & tndn(s) of peroneal muscle group at lwr leg lvl, rt leg, init enc
S86.329A	Lac of muscle(s) & tndn(s) of peroneal muscle group at lwr leg lvl, unsp leg, init enc
S46.022A	Lac of muscle(s) & tndn(s) of the rotator cuff of lt shldr, init enc
S46.021A	Lac of muscle(s) & tndn(s) of the rotator cuff of rt shldr, init enc
S46.029A	Lac of muscle(s) & tndn(s) of the rotator cuff of unsp shldr, init enc
S35.8X1A	Lac of oth blood vessels at abd, lwr back & pelvis lvl, init enc
S95.812A	Lac of oth blood vessels at ankle & foot lvl, lt leg, init enc
S95.811A	Lac of oth blood vessels at ankle & foot lvl, rt leg, init enc
S95.819A	Lac of oth blood vessels at ankle & foot lvl, unsp leg, init enc
S55.812A	Lac of oth blood vessels at forearm lvl, lt arm, init enc
S55.811A	Lac of oth blood vessels at forearm lvl, rt arm, init enc
S55.819A	Lac of oth blood vessels at forearm lvl, unsp arm, init enc
S75.812A	Lac of oth blood vessels at hip & thigh lvl, lt leg, init enc
S75.811A	Lac of oth blood vessels at hip & thigh lvl, rt leg, init enc

S75.819A	Lac of oth blood vessels at hip & thigh lvl, unsp leg, init enc
S85.812A	Lac of oth blood vessels at lwr leg lvl, lt leg, init enc
S85.811A	Lac of oth blood vessels at lwr leg lvl, rt leg, init enc
S85.819A	Lac of oth blood vessels at lwr leg lvl, unsp leg, init enc
S65.812A	Lac of oth blood vessels at wrist & hand lvl of lt arm, init enc
S65.811A	Lac of oth blood vessels at wrist & hand lvl of rt arm, init enc
S65.819A	Lac of oth blood vessels at wrist & hand lvl of unsp arm, init enc
S25.812A	Lac of oth blood vessels of thorax, lt side, init enc
S25.811A	Lac of oth blood vessels of thorax, rt side, init enc
S25.819A	Lac of oth blood vessels of thorax, unsp side, init enc
S56.522A	Lac of oth extensor muscle, fascia & tndn at forearm lvl, lt arm, init enc
S56.521A	Lac of oth extensor muscle, fascia & tndn at forearm lvl, rt arm, init enc
S56.529A	Lac of oth extensor muscle, fascia & tndn at forearm lvl, unsp arm, init enc
S56.222A	Lac of oth flexor muscle, fascia & tndn at forearm lvl, lt arm, init enc
S56.221A	Lac of oth flexor muscle, fascia & tndn at forearm lvl, rt arm, init enc
S56.229A	Lac of oth flexor muscle, fascia & tndn at forearm lvl, unsp arm, init enc
S36.893A	Lac of oth intra-abd organs, init enc
S86.822A	Lac of oth muscle(s) & tndn(s) at lwr leg lvl, lt leg, init enc
S86.821A	Lac of oth muscle(s) & tndn(s) at lwr leg lvl, rt leg, init enc
S86.829A	Lac of oth muscle(s) & tndn(s) at lwr leg lvl, unsp leg, init enc
S86.122A	Lac of oth muscle(s) & tndn(s) of post muscle group at lwr leg lvl, lt leg, init enc
S86.121A	Lac of oth muscle(s) & tndn(s) of post muscle group at lwr leg lvl, rt leg, init enc
S86.129A	Lac of oth muscle(s) & tndn(s) of post muscle group at lwr leg lvl, unsp leg, init enc
S56.822A	Lac of oth muscles, fascia & tendons at forearm lvl, lt arm, init enc
S56.821A	Lac of oth muscles, fascia & tendons at forearm lvl, rt arm, init enc
S56.829A	Lac of oth muscles, fascia & tendons at forearm lvl, unsp arm, init enc
S46.822A	Lac of oth muscles, fascia & tendons at shldr & upr arm lvl, lt arm, init enc
S46.821A	Lac of oth muscles, fascia & tendons at shldr & upr arm lvl, rt arm, init enc
S46.829A	Lac of oth muscles, fascia & tendons at shldr & upr arm lvl, unsp arm, init enc
S36.538A	Lac of oth part of colon, init enc
S36.438A	Lac of oth part of sm intestine, init enc
S45.812A	Lac of oth spec blood vessels at shldr & upr arm lvl, lt arm, init enc
S45.811A	Lac of oth spec blood vessels at shldr & upr arm lvl, rt arm, init enc
S45.819A	Lac of oth spec blood vessels at shldr & upr arm lvl, unsp arm, init enc
S27.893A	Lac of oth spec intrathoracic organs, init enc
S96.822A	Lac of oth spec muscles & tendons at ankle & foot lvl, lt foot, init enc
S96.821A	Lac of oth spec muscles & tendons at ankle & foot lvl, rt foot, init enc
S96.829A	Lac of oth spec muscles & tendons at ankle & foot lvl, unsp foot, init enc
S76.822A	Lac of oth spec muscles, fascia & tendons at thigh lvl, lt thigh, init enc
S76.821A	Lac of oth spec muscles, fascia & tendons at thigh lvl, rt thigh, init enc
S76.829A	Lac of oth spec muscles, fascia & tendons at thigh lvl, unsp thigh, init enc
S66.822A	Lac of oth spec muscles, fascia & tendons at wrist & hand lvl, lt hand, init enc
S66.821A	Lac of oth spec muscles, fascia & tendons at wrist & hand lvl, rt hand, init enc
S66.829A	Lac of oth spec muscles, fascia & tendons at wrist & hand lvl, unsp hand, init enc
S37.893A	Lac of oth urinary & pelvic organ, init enc
S85.212A	Lac of peroneal artery, lt leg, init enc
S85.211A	Lac of peroneal artery, rt leg, init enc
S85.219A	Lac of peroneal artery, unsp leg, init enc
S95.112A	Lac of plantar artery of lt foot, init enc
S95.111A	Lac of plantar artery of rt foot, init enc
S95.119A	Lac of plantar artery of unsp foot, init enc
S27.63XA	Lac of pleura, init enc
S85.172A	Lac of post tibial artery, lt leg, init enc
S85.171A	Lac of post tibial artery, rt leg, init enc
S85.179A	Lac of post tibial artery, unsp leg, init enc
S55.112A	Lac of radial artery at forearm lvl, lt arm, init enc
S55.111A	Lac of radial artery at forearm lvl, rt arm, init enc
S55.119A	Lac of radial artery at forearm lvl, unsp arm, init enc
S65.112A	Lac of radial artery at wrist & hand lvl of lt arm, init enc
S65.111A	Lac of radial artery at wrist & hand lvl of rt arm, init enc
S65.119A	Lac of radial artery at wrist & hand lvl of unsp arm, init enc
S36.63XA	Lac of rectum, init enc
S86.021A	Lac of rt Achilles tndn, init enc
S37.031A	Lac of rt kidney, unsp degree, init enc
S76.121A	Lac of rt quadriceps muscle, fascia & tndn, init enc
S36.533A	Lac of sigmoid colon, init enc
S36.33XA	Lac of stomach, init enc
S65.212A	Lac of superf palmar arch of lt hand, init enc
S65.211A	Lac of superf palmar arch of rt hand, init enc
S65.219A	Lac of superf palmar arch of unsp hand, init enc
S45.312A	Lac of superf vein at shldr & upr arm lvl, lt arm, init enc
S45.311A	Lac of superf vein at shldr & upr arm lvl, rt arm, init enc
S45.319A	Lac of superf vein at shldr & upr arm lvl, unsp arm, init enc
S36.232A	Lac of tail of pancreas, unsp degree, init enc
S27.53XA	Lac of thoracic trachea, init enc
S36.531A	Lac of transv colon, init enc
S55.012A	Lac of ulnar artery at forearm lvl, lt arm, init enc
S55.011A	Lac of ulnar artery at forearm lvl, rt arm, init enc
S55.019A	Lac of ulnar artery at forearm lvl, unsp arm, init enc
S65.012A	Lac of ulnar artery at wrist & hand lvl of lt arm, init enc
S65.011A	Lac of ulnar artery at wrist & hand lvl of rt arm, init enc
S65.019A	Lac of ulnar artery at wrist & hand lvl of unsp arm, init enc
S86.029A	Lac of unsp Achilles tndn, init enc
S35.91XA	Lac of unsp blood vessel at abd, lwr back & pelvis lvl, init enc
S95.912A	Lac of unsp blood vessel at ankle & foot lvl, lt leg, init enc
S95.911A	Lac of unsp blood vessel at ankle & foot lvl, rt leg, init enc
S95.919A	Lac of unsp blood vessel at ankle & foot lvl, unsp leg, init enc
S55.912A	Lac of unsp blood vessel at forearm lvl, lt arm, init enc
S55.911A	Lac of unsp blood vessel at forearm lvl, rt arm, init enc
S55.919A	Lac of unsp blood vessel at forearm lvl, unsp arm, init enc
S75.912A	Lac of unsp blood vessel at hip & thigh lvl, lt leg, init enc
S75.911A	Lac of unsp blood vessel at hip & thigh lvl, rt leg, init enc
S75.919A	Lac of unsp blood vessel at hip & thigh lvl, unsp leg, init enc
S85.912A	Lac of unsp blood vessel at lwr leg lvl, lt leg, init enc
S85.911A	Lac of unsp blood vessel at lwr leg lvl, rt leg, init enc
S85.919A	Lac of unsp blood vessel at lwr leg lvl, unsp leg, init enc
S45.912A	Lac of unsp blood vessel at shldr & upr arm lvl, lt arm, init enc
S45.911A	Lac of unsp blood vessel at shldr & upr arm lvl, rt arm, init enc
S45.919A	Lac of unsp blood vessel at shldr & upr arm lvl, unsp arm, init enc
S65.912A	Lac of unsp blood vessel at wrist & hand lvl of lt arm, init enc
S65.911A	Lac of unsp blood vessel at wrist & hand lvl of rt arm, init enc
S65.919A	Lac of unsp blood vessel at wrist & hand lvl of unsp arm, init enc
S25.91XA	Lac of unsp blood vessel of thorax, init enc
S36.93XA	Lac of unsp intra-abd organ, init enc
S37.039A	Lac of unsp kidney, unsp degree, init enc
S96.922A	Lac of unsp muscle & tndn at ankle & foot lvl, lt foot, init enc
S96.921A	Lac of unsp muscle & tndn at ankle & foot lvl, rt foot, init enc
S96.929A	Lac of unsp muscle & tndn at ankle & foot lvl, unsp foot, init enc
S46.922A	Lac of unsp muscle, fascia & tndn at shldr & upr arm lvl, lt arm, init enc
S46.921A	Lac of unsp muscle, fascia & tndn at shldr & upr arm lvl, rt arm, init enc
S46.929A	Lac of unsp muscle, fascia & tndn at shldr & upr arm lvl, unsp arm, init enc
S66.922A	Lac of unsp muscle, fascia & tndn at wrist & hand lvl, lt hand, init enc
S66.921A	Lac of unsp muscle, fascia & tndn at wrist & hand lvl, rt hand, init enc
S66.929A	Lac of unsp muscle, fascia & tndn at wrist & hand lvl, unsp hand, init enc
S86.922A	Lac of unsp muscle(s) & tndn(s) at lwr leg lvl, lt leg, init enc
S86.921A	Lac of unsp muscle(s) & tndn(s) at lwr leg lvl, rt leg, init enc
S86.929A	Lac of unsp muscle(s) & tndn(s) at lwr leg lvl, unsp leg, init enc
S56.922A	Lac of unsp muscles, fascia & tendons at forearm lvl, lt arm, init enc
S56.921A	Lac of unsp muscles, fascia & tendons at forearm lvl, rt arm, init enc
S56.929A	Lac of unsp muscles, fascia & tendons at forearm lvl, unsp arm, init enc
S76.922A	Lac of unsp muscles, fascia & tendons at thigh lvl, lt thigh, init enc
S76.921A	Lac of unsp muscles, fascia & tendons at thigh lvl, rt thigh, init enc
S76.929A	Lac of unsp muscles, fascia & tendons at thigh lvl, unsp thigh, init enc
S36.539A	Lac of unsp part of colon, init enc
S36.239A	Lac of unsp part of pancreas, unsp degree, init enc
S36.439A	Lac of unsp part of sm intestine, init enc
S76.129A	Lac of unsp quadriceps muscle, fascia & tndn, init enc
S85.112A	Lac of unsp tibial artery, lt leg, init enc
S85.111A	Lac of unsp tibial artery, rt leg, init enc
S85.119A	Lac of unsp tibial artery, unsp leg, init enc
S37.93XA	Lac of unsp urinary & pelvic organ, init enc
S37.13XA	Lac of ureter, init enc
S37.33XA	Lac of urethra, init enc
S37.63XA	Lac of uterus, init enc
S55.212A	Lac of vein at forearm lvl, lt arm, init enc
S55.211A	Lac of vein at forearm lvl, rt arm, init enc
S55.219A	Lac of vein at forearm lvl, unsp arm, init enc
S21.122A	Lac w/ FB of lt front wall of thorax w/o penetration into thoracic cavity, init enc

Appendix B — Alphabetic CC List

S11.22XA	Lac w/ FB of pharynx & cervical esophagus, init enc
S21.121A	Lac w/ FB of rt front wall of thorax w/o penetration into thoracic cavity, init enc
S11.12XA	Lac w/ FB of thyroid gland, init enc
S21.129A	Lac w/ FB of unsp front wall of thorax w/o penetration into thoracic cavity, init enc
S21.92XA	Lac w/ FB of unsp part of thorax, init enc
S21.112A	Lac w/o FB of lt front wall of thorax w/o penetration into thoracic cavity, init enc
S11.21XA	Lac w/o FB of pharynx & cervical esophagus, init enc
S21.111A	Lac w/o FB of rt front wall of thorax w/o penetration into thoracic cavity, init enc
S11.11XA	Lac w/o FB of thyroid gland, init enc
S21.119A	Lac w/o FB of unsp front wall of thorax w/o penetration into thoracic cavity, init enc
S21.91XA	Lac w/o FB of unsp part of thorax, init enc
G70.81	Lambert-Eaton synd in disease classified elsw
G73.1	Lambert-Eaton synd in neoplastic disease
G70.80	Lambert-Eaton synd, unsp
A36.2	Laryngeal diphtheria
Q31.2	Laryngeal hypoplasia
Q31.3	Laryngocele
A50.54	Late congenital cardiovascular syphilis
A50.40	Late congenital neurosyphilis, unsp
A50.55	Late congenital syphilitic arthropathy
A50.32	Late congenital syphilitic chorioretinitis
A50.31	Late congenital syphilitic interstitial keratitis
A50.30	Late congenital syphilitic oculopathy, unsp
A50.44	Late congenital syphilitic optic nerve atrophy
A50.56	Late congenital syphilitic osteochondropathy
A50.43	Late congenital syphilitic polyneuropathy
A52.15	Late syphilitic neuropathy
A52.71	Late syphilitic oculopathy
G11.2	Late-onset cerebellar ataxia
T82.330A	Leakage of aortic (bifurcation) graft (replace), init enc
T82.532A	Leakage of artfcl heart, init enc
T82.533A	Leakage of balloon (counterpulsation) dev, init enc
T82.223A	Leakage of biological heart valve graft, init enc
T85.43XA	Leakage of breast prosthesis & implant, init enc
T82.331A	Leakage of carotid arterial graft (bypass), init enc
T82.213A	Leakage of coronary artery bypass graft, init enc
T83.030A	Leakage of cystostomy catheter, init enc
T85.630A	Leakage of epidural & subdural inf catheter, init enc
T82.332A	Leakage of femoral arterial graft (bypass), init enc
T83.23XA	Leakage of graft of urinary organ, init enc
T82.03XA	Leakage of heart valve prosthesis, init enc
T82.534A	Leakage of inf catheter, init enc
T85.633A	Leakage of insulin pump, init enc
T85.631A	Leakage of intraperitoneal dialysis catheter, init enc
T82.538A	Leakage of oth cardiac & vascular devices & implants, init enc
T85.638A	Leakage of oth spec int prosthetic devices, implants & grafts, init enc
T82.338A	Leakage of oth vascular grafts, init enc
T82.530A	Leakage of surgly created arteriovenous fistula, init enc
T82.531A	Leakage of surgly created arteriovenous shunt, init enc
T82.535A	Leakage of umbrella dev, init enc
T82.539A	Leakage of unsp cardiac & vascular devices & implants, init enc
T82.339A	Leakage of unsp vascular graft, init enc
T82.43XA	Leakage of vascular dialysis catheter, init enc
T85.03XA	Leakage of ventricular intracranial (communicating) shunt, init enc
S02.411A	LeFort I fx, init enc for clsd fx
S02.411B	LeFort I fx, init enc for opn fx
S02.411K	LeFort I fx, subsq enc for fx w/ nonu
S02.412A	LeFort II fx, init enc for clsd fx
S02.412B	LeFort II fx, init enc for opn fx
S02.412K	LeFort II fx, subsq enc for fx w/ nonu
S02.413A	LeFort III fx, init enc for clsd fx
S02.413B	LeFort III fx, init enc for opn fx
S02.413K	LeFort III fx, subsq enc for fx w/ nonu
G31.82	Leigh's disease
B55.9	Leishmaniasis, unsp
G40.813	Lennox-Gastaut synd, intractable, w/ status epilepticus
G40.814	Lennox-Gastaut synd, intractable, w/o status epilepticus
G40.811	Lennox-Gastaut synd, not intractable, w/ status epilepticus
G40.812	Lennox-Gastaut synd, not intractable, w/o status epilepticus

A30.5	Lepromatous leprosy
A30.9	Leprosy, unsp
A27.0	Leptospirosis icterohemorrhagica
A27.9	Leptospirosis, unsp
E79.1	Lesch-Nyhan synd
M31.2	Lethal midline granuloma
C95.90	Leukemia, unsp not having achieved remission
C95.92	Leukemia, unsp, in relapse
C95.91	Leukemia, unsp, in remission
Q24.1	Levocardia
A32.82	Listerial endocarditis
A32.11	Listerial meningitis
A32.12	Listerial meningoencephalitis
A32.9	Listeriosis, unsp
O26.62	Liver & biliary tract d/o in childbirth
O26.611	Liver & biliary tract d/o in pregnancy, 1st trmstr
O26.612	Liver & biliary tract d/o in pregnancy, 2nd trmstr
O26.613	Liver & biliary tract d/o in pregnancy, 3rd trmstr
C22.0	Liver cell ca
K77	Liver d/o in diseases classified elsw
T86.42	Liver transplant failure
T86.43	Liver transplant infxn
T86.41	Liver transplant rejection
Z94.4	Liver transplant status
T80.212A	Local infxn d/t central venous catheter, init enc
G40.011	Localization-related (focal) (partial) idiopathic epilepsy & epileptic syndromes w/ seizures of localized onset, intractable, w/ status epilepticus
G40.019	Localization-related (focal) (partial) idiopathic epilepsy & epileptic syndromes w/ seizures of localized onset, intractable, w/o status epilepticus
G40.001	Localization-related (focal) (partial) idiopathic epilepsy & epileptic syndromes w/ seizures of localized onset, not intractable, w/ status epilepticus
G40.009	Localization-related (focal) (partial) idiopathic epilepsy & epileptic syndromes w/ seizures of localized onset, not intractable, w/o status epilepticus
G40.211	Localization-related (focal) (partial) symptomatic epilepsy & epileptic syndromes w/ complex partial seizures, intractable, w/ status epilepticus
G40.219	Localization-related (focal) (partial) symptomatic epilepsy & epileptic syndromes w/ complex partial seizures, intractable, w/o status epilepticus
G40.201	Localization-related (focal) (partial) symptomatic epilepsy & epileptic syndromes w/ complex partial seizures, not intractable, w/ status epilepticus
G40.209	Localization-related (focal) (partial) symptomatic epilepsy & epileptic syndromes w/ complex partial seizures, not intractable, w/o status epilepticus
G40.111	Localization-related (focal) (partial) symptomatic epilepsy & epileptic syndromes w/ simple partial seizures, intractable, w/ status epilepticus
G40.119	Localization-related (focal) (partial) symptomatic epilepsy & epileptic syndromes w/ simple partial seizures, intractable, w/o status epilepticus
G40.101	Localization-related (focal) (partial) symptomatic epilepsy & epileptic syndromes w/ simple partial seizures, not intractable, w/ status epilepticus
G40.109	Localization-related (focal) (partial) symptomatic epilepsy & epileptic syndromes w/ simple partial seizures, not intractable, w/o status epilepticus
B74.3	Loiasis
E71.310	Long chain/very long chain acyl CoA dehydrogenase deficiency
O63.9	Long labor, unsp
A68.0	Louse-borne relapsing fever
E72.03	Lowe's synd
K51.514	Lt sided colitis w/ abscess
K51.513	Lt sided colitis w/ fistula
K51.512	Lt sided colitis w/ intestinal obstruction
K51.518	Lt sided colitis w/ oth comp
K51.511	Lt sided colitis w/ rectal bleeding
K51.519	Lt sided colitis w/ unsp comp
K51.50	Lt sided colitis w/o comp
I50.1	Lt ventricular failure
Q05.2	Lumbar spina bifida w/ hydrocephalus
T86.811	Lung transplant failure
T86.812	Lung transplant infxn
T86.810	Lung transplant rejection
Z94.2	Lung transplant status

D68.62	Lupus anticoagulant synd		S15.222A	Major lac of lt ext jugular vein, init enc
A69.20	Lyme disease, unsp		S15.322A	Major lac of lt int jugular vein, init enc
C83.59	Lymphoblastic (diffuse) lymphoma, extranodal & solid organ sites		S15.122A	Major lac of lt vert artery, init enc
C83.53	Lymphoblastic (diffuse) lymphoma, intra-abd lymph nodes		S15.021A	Major lac of rt carotid artery, init enc
C83.56	Lymphoblastic (diffuse) lymphoma, intrapelvic lymph nodes		S15.221A	Major lac of rt ext jugular vein, init enc
C83.52	Lymphoblastic (diffuse) lymphoma, intrathoracic lymph nodes		S15.321A	Major lac of rt int jugular vein, init enc
C83.54	Lymphoblastic (diffuse) lymphoma, lymph nodes of axilla & upr limb		S15.121A	Major lac of rt vert artery, init enc
C83.51	Lymphoblastic (diffuse) lymphoma, lymph nodes of head, face, & neck		S36.262A	Major lac of tail of pancreas, init enc
C83.55	Lymphoblastic (diffuse) lymphoma, lymph nodes of inguinal rgn & lwr limb		S15.029A	Major lac of unsp carotid artery, init enc
			S15.229A	Major lac of unsp ext jugular vein, init enc
C83.58	Lymphoblastic (diffuse) lymphoma, lymph nodes of multi sites		S15.329A	Major lac of unsp int jugular vein, init enc
C83.57	Lymphoblastic (diffuse) lymphoma, spleen		S36.269A	Major lac of unsp part of pancreas, init enc
C83.50	Lymphoblastic (diffuse) lymphoma, unsp site		S15.129A	Major lac of unsp vert artery, init enc
C81.39	Lymphocyte depleted classical Hodgkin lymphoma, extranodal & solid organ sites		K90.4	Malabsorption d/t intolerance, NEC
			S02.400A	Malar fx unsp, init enc for clsd fx
C81.33	Lymphocyte depleted classical Hodgkin lymphoma, intra-abd lymph nodes		S02.400B	Malar fx unsp, init enc for opn fx
			S02.400K	Malar fx unsp, subsq enc for fx w/ nonu
C81.36	Lymphocyte depleted classical Hodgkin lymphoma, intrapelvic lymph nodes		B53.1	Malaria d/t simian plasmodia
			Q24.5	Malformation of coronary vessels
C81.32	Lymphocyte depleted classical Hodgkin lymphoma, intrathoracic lymph nodes		J95.03	Malfunction of tracheostomy stoma
			R18.0	Malig ascites
C81.34	Lymphocyte depleted classical Hodgkin lymphoma, lymph nodes of axilla & upr limb		C7A.020	Malig carcinoid tumor of the appendix
			C7A.022	Malig carcinoid tumor of the ascending colon
C81.31	Lymphocyte depleted classical Hodgkin lymphoma, lymph nodes of head, face, & neck		C7A.090	Malig carcinoid tumor of the bronchus & lung
			C7A.021	Malig carcinoid tumor of the cecum
C81.35	Lymphocyte depleted classical Hodgkin lymphoma, lymph nodes of inguinal rgn & lwr limb		C7A.024	Malig carcinoid tumor of the descending colon
			C7A.010	Malig carcinoid tumor of the duodenum
C81.38	Lymphocyte depleted classical Hodgkin lymphoma, lymph nodes of multi sites		C7A.094	Malig carcinoid tumor of the foregut NOS
			C7A.096	Malig carcinoid tumor of the hindgut NOS
C81.37	Lymphocyte depleted classical Hodgkin lymphoma, spleen		C7A.012	Malig carcinoid tumor of the ileum
C81.30	Lymphocyte depleted classical Hodgkin lymphoma, unsp site		C7A.011	Malig carcinoid tumor of the jejunum
			C7A.093	Malig carcinoid tumor of the kidney
C81.49	Lymphocyte-rich classical Hodgkin lymphoma, extranodal & solid organ sites		C7A.029	Malig carcinoid tumor of the lg intestine, unsp portion
			C7A.095	Malig carcinoid tumor of the midgut NOS
C81.43	Lymphocyte-rich classical Hodgkin lymphoma, intra-abd lymph nodes		C7A.026	Malig carcinoid tumor of the rectum
C81.46	Lymphocyte-rich classical Hodgkin lymphoma, intrapelvic lymph nodes		C7A.025	Malig carcinoid tumor of the sigmoid colon
C81.42	Lymphocyte-rich classical Hodgkin lymphoma, intrathoracic lymph nodes		C7A.019	Malig carcinoid tumor of the sm intestine, unsp portion
			C7A.092	Malig carcinoid tumor of the stomach
C81.44	Lymphocyte-rich classical Hodgkin lymphoma, lymph nodes of axilla & upr limb		C7A.091	Malig carcinoid tumor of the thymus
			C7A.023	Malig carcinoid tumor of the transv colon
C81.41	Lymphocyte-rich classical Hodgkin lymphoma, lymph nodes of head, face, & neck		C7A.00	Malig carcinoid tumor of unsp site
			C7A.098	Malig carcinoid tumors of oth sites
C81.45	Lymphocyte-rich classical Hodgkin lymphoma, lymph nodes of inguinal rgn & lwr limb		T88.3XXA	Malig hyperthermia d/t anesthesia, init enc
			C88.9	Malig immunoproliferative disease, unsp
C81.48	Lymphocyte-rich classical Hodgkin lymphoma, lymph nodes of multi sites		C96.2	Malig mast cell tumor
			C80.2	Malig neoplasm associated w/ transplanted organ
C81.47	Lymphocyte-rich classical Hodgkin lymphoma, spleen		C24.1	Malig neoplasm of ampulla of Vater
C81.40	Lymphocyte-rich classical Hodgkin lymphoma, unsp site		C21.1	Malig neoplasm of anal canal
A87.2	Lymphocytic choriomeningitis		C38.1	Malig neoplasm of ant mediastinum
J84.2	Lymphoid interstitial pneumonia		C21.0	Malig neoplasm of anus, unsp
C91.90	Lymphoid leukemia, unsp not having achieved remission		C75.5	Malig neoplasm of aortic body & oth paraganglia
			C18.1	Malig neoplasm of appendix
C91.92	Lymphoid leukemia, unsp, in relapse		C18.2	Malig neoplasm of ascending colon
C91.91	Lymphoid leukemia, unsp, in remission		C24.9	Malig neoplasm of biliary tract, unsp
A96.1	Machupo hemorrhagic fever		C25.1	Malig neoplasm of body of pancreas
S37.022A	Major contsn of lt kidney, init enc		C16.2	Malig neoplasm of body of stomach
S37.021A	Major contsn of rt kidney, init enc		C41.9	Malig neoplasm of bone & articular cartilage, unsp
S36.021A	Major contsn of spleen, init enc		C41.0	Malig neoplasm of bones of skull & face
S37.029A	Major contsn of unsp kidney, init enc		C71.7	Malig neoplasm of brain stem
F33.2	Major depressive d/o, recurrent severe w/o psychotic features		C71.9	Malig neoplasm of brain, unsp
			C16.0	Malig neoplasm of cardia
F33.40	Major depressive d/o, recurrent, in remission, unsp		C75.4	Malig neoplasm of carotid body
F33.0	Major depressive d/o, recurrent, mild		C72.1	Malig neoplasm of cauda equina
F33.1	Major depressive d/o, recurrent, mod		C18.0	Malig neoplasm of cecum
F33.3	Major depressive d/o, recurrent, severe w/ psychotic symptoms		C72.9	Malig neoplasm of central nervous sys, unsp
			C71.6	Malig neoplasm of cerebellum
F33.9	Major depressive d/o, recurrent, unsp		C70.0	Malig neoplasm of cerebral meninges
F32.0	Major depressive d/o, single episode, mild		C71.5	Malig neoplasm of cerebral ventricle
F32.1	Major depressive d/o, single episode, mod		C71.0	Malig neoplasm of cerebrum, except lobes & ventricles
F32.3	Major depressive d/o, single episode, severe w/ psychotic features		C21.2	Malig neoplasm of cloacogenic zone
			C18.9	Malig neoplasm of colon, unsp
F32.2	Major depressive d/o, single episode, severe w/o psychotic features		C49.4	Malig neoplasm of connective & soft tissue of abd
D81.6	Major histocompatibility complex class I deficiency		C49.0	Malig neoplasm of connective & soft tissue of head, face & neck
D81.7	Major histocompatibility complex class II deficiency			
S36.261A	Major lac of body of pancreas, init enc			
S75.222A	Major lac of greater saphenous vein at hip & thigh lvl, lt leg, init enc			
S75.221A	Major lac of greater saphenous vein at hip & thigh lvl, rt leg, init enc			
S75.229A	Major lac of greater saphenous vein at hip & thigh lvl, unsp leg, init enc			
S36.260A	Major lac of head of pancreas, init enc			
S15.022A	Major lac of lt carotid artery, init enc			

Code	Description
C49.22	Malig neoplasm of connective & soft tissue of lt lwr limb, incl hip
C49.12	Malig neoplasm of connective & soft tissue of lt upr limb, incl shldr
C49.5	Malig neoplasm of connective & soft tissue of pelvis
C49.21	Malig neoplasm of connective & soft tissue of rt lwr limb, incl hip
C49.11	Malig neoplasm of connective & soft tissue of rt upr limb, incl shldr
C49.3	Malig neoplasm of connective & soft tissue of thorax
C49.6	Malig neoplasm of connective & soft tissue of trunk, unsp
C49.20	Malig neoplasm of connective & soft tissue of unsp lwr limb, incl hip
C49.10	Malig neoplasm of connective & soft tissue of unsp upr limb, incl shldr
C49.9	Malig neoplasm of connective & soft tissue, unsp
C74.02	Malig neoplasm of cortex of lt adrenal gland
C74.01	Malig neoplasm of cortex of rt adrenal gland
C74.00	Malig neoplasm of cortex of unsp adrenal gland
C75.2	Malig neoplasm of craniopharyngeal duct
C18.6	Malig neoplasm of descending colon
C17.0	Malig neoplasm of duodenum
C75.9	Malig neoplasm of endocrine gland, unsp
C25.4	Malig neoplasm of endocrine pancreas
C15.9	Malig neoplasm of esophagus, unsp
C24.0	Malig neoplasm of extrahepatic bile duct
C71.1	Malig neoplasm of frontal lobe
C16.1	Malig neoplasm of fundus of stomach
C23	Malig neoplasm of gallbladder
C16.6	Malig neoplasm of greater curvature of stomach, unsp
C25.0	Malig neoplasm of head of pancreas
C38.0	Malig neoplasm of heart
C18.3	Malig neoplasm of hepatic flexure
C17.2	Malig neoplasm of ileum
C17.1	Malig neoplasm of jejunum
C16.5	Malig neoplasm of lesser curvature of stomach, unsp
C22.9	Malig neoplasm of liver, not spec as primary or secondary
C22.8	Malig neoplasm of liver, primary, unsp as to type
C40.22	Malig neoplasm of long bones of lt lwr limb
C40.21	Malig neoplasm of long bones of rt lwr limb
C40.20	Malig neoplasm of long bones of unsp lwr limb
C72.42	Malig neoplasm of lt acoustic nerve
C64.2	Malig neoplasm of lt kidney, except renal pelvis
C34.02	Malig neoplasm of lt main bronchus
C72.22	Malig neoplasm of lt olfactory nerve
C72.32	Malig neoplasm of lt optic nerve
C56.2	Malig neoplasm of lt ovary
C65.2	Malig neoplasm of lt renal pelvis
C66.2	Malig neoplasm of lt ureter
C15.5	Malig neoplasm of lwr 3rd of esophagus
C34.32	Malig neoplasm of lwr lobe, lt bronchus or lung
C34.31	Malig neoplasm of lwr lobe, rt bronchus or lung
C34.30	Malig neoplasm of lwr lobe, unsp bronchus or lung
C96.9	Malig neoplasm of lymphoid, hematopoietic & related tissue, unsp
C41.1	Malig neoplasm of mandible
C38.3	Malig neoplasm of mediastinum, part unsp
C74.12	Malig neoplasm of medulla of lt adrenal gland
C74.11	Malig neoplasm of medulla of rt adrenal gland
C74.10	Malig neoplasm of medulla of unsp adrenal gland
C70.9	Malig neoplasm of meninges, unsp
C15.4	Malig neoplasm of mid 3rd of esophagus
C34.2	Malig neoplasm of mid lobe, bronchus or lung
C71.4	Malig neoplasm of occipital lobe
C72.59	Malig neoplasm of oth cranial nerves
C25.7	Malig neoplasm of oth parts of pancreas
C24.8	Malig neoplasm of overlapping sites of biliary tract
C40.82	Malig neoplasm of overlapping sites of bone & articular cartilage of lt limb
C40.81	Malig neoplasm of overlapping sites of bone & articular cartilage of rt limb
C40.80	Malig neoplasm of overlapping sites of bone & articular cartilage of unsp limb
C71.8	Malig neoplasm of overlapping sites of brain
C18.8	Malig neoplasm of overlapping sites of colon
C49.8	Malig neoplasm of overlapping sites of connective & soft tissue
C15.8	Malig neoplasm of overlapping sites of esophagus
C38.8	Malig neoplasm of overlapping sites of heart, mediastinum & pleura
C34.82	Malig neoplasm of overlapping sites of lt bronchus & lung
C25.8	Malig neoplasm of overlapping sites of pancreas
C47.8	Malig neoplasm of overlapping sites of peripheral nerves & autonomic nervous sys
C21.8	Malig neoplasm of overlapping sites of rectum, anus & anal canal
C48.8	Malig neoplasm of overlapping sites of retroperitoneum & peritoneum
C34.81	Malig neoplasm of overlapping sites of rt bronchus & lung
C17.8	Malig neoplasm of overlapping sites of sm intestine
C16.8	Malig neoplasm of overlapping sites of stomach
C34.80	Malig neoplasm of overlapping sites of unsp bronchus & lung
C68.8	Malig neoplasm of overlapping sites of urinary organs
C25.9	Malig neoplasm of pancreas, unsp
C25.3	Malig neoplasm of pancreatic duct
C75.0	Malig neoplasm of parathyroid gland
C68.1	Malig neoplasm of paraurethral glands
C71.3	Malig neoplasm of parietal lobe
C41.4	Malig neoplasm of pelvic bones, sacrum & coccyx
C47.9	Malig neoplasm of peripheral nerves & autonomic nervous sys, unsp
C47.4	Malig neoplasm of peripheral nerves of abd
C47.0	Malig neoplasm of peripheral nerves of head, face & neck
C47.22	Malig neoplasm of peripheral nerves of lt lwr limb, incl hip
C47.12	Malig neoplasm of peripheral nerves of lt upr limb, incl shldr
C47.5	Malig neoplasm of peripheral nerves of pelvis
C47.21	Malig neoplasm of peripheral nerves of rt lwr limb, incl hip
C47.11	Malig neoplasm of peripheral nerves of rt upr limb, incl shldr
C47.3	Malig neoplasm of peripheral nerves of thorax
C47.6	Malig neoplasm of peripheral nerves of trunk, unsp
C47.20	Malig neoplasm of peripheral nerves of unsp lwr limb, incl hip
C47.10	Malig neoplasm of peripheral nerves of unsp upr limb, incl shldr
C48.2	Malig neoplasm of peritoneum, unsp
C75.3	Malig neoplasm of pineal gland
C75.1	Malig neoplasm of pituitary gland
C38.4	Malig neoplasm of pleura
C38.2	Malig neoplasm of post mediastinum
C16.3	Malig neoplasm of pyloric antrum
C16.4	Malig neoplasm of pylorus
C19	Malig neoplasm of rectosigmoid junction
C20	Malig neoplasm of rectum
C48.0	Malig neoplasm of retroperitoneum
C41.3	Malig neoplasm of ribs, sternum & clavicle
C72.41	Malig neoplasm of rt acoustic nerve
C64.1	Malig neoplasm of rt kidney, except renal pelvis
C34.01	Malig neoplasm of rt main bronchus
C72.21	Malig neoplasm of rt olfactory nerve
C72.31	Malig neoplasm of rt optic nerve
C56.1	Malig neoplasm of rt ovary
C65.1	Malig neoplasm of rt renal pelvis
C66.1	Malig neoplasm of rt ureter
C40.02	Malig neoplasm of scapula & long bones of lt upr limb
C40.01	Malig neoplasm of scapula & long bones of rt upr limb
C40.00	Malig neoplasm of scapula & long bones of unsp upr limb
C40.32	Malig neoplasm of short bones of lt lwr limb
C40.12	Malig neoplasm of short bones of lt upr limb
C40.31	Malig neoplasm of short bones of rt lwr limb
C40.11	Malig neoplasm of short bones of rt upr limb
C40.30	Malig neoplasm of short bones of unsp lwr limb
C40.10	Malig neoplasm of short bones of unsp upr limb
C18.7	Malig neoplasm of sigmoid colon
C17.9	Malig neoplasm of sm intestine, unsp
C48.1	Malig neoplasm of spec parts of peritoneum
C72.0	Malig neoplasm of spinal cord
C70.1	Malig neoplasm of spinal meninges
C18.5	Malig neoplasm of splenic flexure
C16.9	Malig neoplasm of stomach, unsp
C25.2	Malig neoplasm of tail of pancreas
C71.2	Malig neoplasm of temporal lobe
C37	Malig neoplasm of thymus
C33	Malig neoplasm of trachea
C18.4	Malig neoplasm of transv colon
C72.40	Malig neoplasm of unsp acoustic nerve
C40.92	Malig neoplasm of unsp bones & articular cartilage of lt limb
C40.91	Malig neoplasm of unsp bones & articular cartilage of rt limb
C40.90	Malig neoplasm of unsp bones & articular cartilage of unsp limb
C72.50	Malig neoplasm of unsp cranial nerve
C64.9	Malig neoplasm of unsp kidney, except renal pelvis

C34.00	Malig neoplasm of unsp main bronchus
C72.20	Malig neoplasm of unsp olfactory nerve
C72.30	Malig neoplasm of unsp optic nerve
C56.9	Malig neoplasm of unsp ovary
C74.92	Malig neoplasm of unsp part of lt adrenal gland
C34.92	Malig neoplasm of unsp part of lt bronchus or lung
C74.91	Malig neoplasm of unsp part of rt adrenal gland
C34.91	Malig neoplasm of unsp part of rt bronchus or lung
C74.90	Malig neoplasm of unsp part of unsp adrenal gland
C34.90	Malig neoplasm of unsp part of unsp bronchus or lung
C65.9	Malig neoplasm of unsp renal pelvis
C66.9	Malig neoplasm of unsp ureter
C15.3	Malig neoplasm of upr 3rd of esophagus
C34.12	Malig neoplasm of upr lobe, lt bronchus or lung
C34.11	Malig neoplasm of upr lobe, rt bronchus or lung
C34.10	Malig neoplasm of upr lobe, unsp bronchus or lung
C68.0	Malig neoplasm of urethra
C68.9	Malig neoplasm of urinary organ, unsp
C41.2	Malig neoplasm of vert column
C75.8	Malig neoplasm w/ pluriglandular involvement, unsp
H60.23	Malig otitis externa, bilat
H60.22	Malig otitis externa, lt ear
H60.21	Malig otitis externa, rt ear
H60.20	Malig otitis externa, unsp ear
J91.0	Malig pleural effusion
C7A.1	Malig poorly differentiated neuroendocrine tumors
F30.11	Manic episode w/o psychotic symptoms, mild
F30.12	Manic episode w/o psychotic symptoms, mod
F30.10	Manic episode w/o psychotic symptoms, unsp
F30.2	Manic episode, severe w/ psychotic symptoms
F30.13	Manic episode, severe, w/o psychotic symptoms
F30.9	Manic episode, unsp
B74.4	Mansonelliasis
C83.19	Mantle cell lymphoma, extranodal & solid organ sites
C83.13	Mantle cell lymphoma, intra-abd lymph nodes
C83.16	Mantle cell lymphoma, intrapelvic lymph nodes
C83.12	Mantle cell lymphoma, intrathoracic lymph nodes
C83.14	Mantle cell lymphoma, lymph nodes of axilla & upr limb
C83.11	Mantle cell lymphoma, lymph nodes of head, face, & neck
C83.15	Mantle cell lymphoma, lymph nodes of inguinal rgn & lwr limb
C83.18	Mantle cell lymphoma, lymph nodes of multi sites
C83.17	Mantle cell lymphoma, spleen
C83.10	Mantle cell lymphoma, unsp site
E71.0	Maple-syrup-urine disease
Q87.410	Marfan's synd w/ aortic dilation
Q87.42	Marfan's synd w/ ocular manifestations
Q87.418	Marfan's synd w/ oth cardiovascular manifestations
Q87.43	Marfan's synd w/ skeletal manifestation
Q87.40	Marfan's synd, unsp
C94.30	Mast cell leukemia not having achieved remission
C94.32	Mast cell leukemia, in relapse
C94.31	Mast cell leukemia, in remission
O36.0111	Maternal care for anti-D [Rh] antibodies, 1st trmstr, fetus 1
O36.0112	Maternal care for anti-D [Rh] antibodies, 1st trmstr, fetus 2
O36.0113	Maternal care for anti-D [Rh] antibodies, 1st trmstr, fetus 3
O36.0114	Maternal care for anti-D [Rh] antibodies, 1st trmstr, fetus 4
O36.0115	Maternal care for anti-D [Rh] antibodies, 1st trmstr, fetus 5
O36.0110	Maternal care for anti-D [Rh] antibodies, 1st trmstr, N/A or unsp
O36.0119	Maternal care for anti-D [Rh] antibodies, 1st trmstr, oth fetus
O36.0121	Maternal care for anti-D [Rh] antibodies, 2nd trmstr, fetus 1
O36.0122	Maternal care for anti-D [Rh] antibodies, 2nd trmstr, fetus 2
O36.0123	Maternal care for anti-D [Rh] antibodies, 2nd trmstr, fetus 3
O36.0124	Maternal care for anti-D [Rh] antibodies, 2nd trmstr, fetus 4
O36.0125	Maternal care for anti-D [Rh] antibodies, 2nd trmstr, fetus 5
O36.0120	Maternal care for anti-D [Rh] antibodies, 2nd trmstr, N/A or unsp
O36.0129	Maternal care for anti-D [Rh] antibodies, 2nd trmstr, oth fetus
O36.0131	Maternal care for anti-D [Rh] antibodies, 3rd trmstr, fetus 1
O36.0132	Maternal care for anti-D [Rh] antibodies, 3rd trmstr, fetus 2
O36.0133	Maternal care for anti-D [Rh] antibodies, 3rd trmstr, fetus 3
O36.0134	Maternal care for anti-D [Rh] antibodies, 3rd trmstr, fetus 4
O36.0135	Maternal care for anti-D [Rh] antibodies, 3rd trmstr, fetus 5
O36.0130	Maternal care for anti-D [Rh] antibodies, 3rd trmstr, N/A or unsp
O36.0139	Maternal care for anti-D [Rh] antibodies, 3rd trmstr, oth fetus

O33.0	Maternal care for disproportion d/t deformity of maternal pelvic bones
O36.4XX1	Maternal care for intrauterine death, fetus 1
O36.4XX2	Maternal care for intrauterine death, fetus 2
O36.4XX3	Maternal care for intrauterine death, fetus 3
O36.4XX4	Maternal care for intrauterine death, fetus 4
O36.4XX5	Maternal care for intrauterine death, fetus 5
O36.4XX0	Maternal care for intrauterine death, N/A or unsp
O36.4XX9	Maternal care for intrauterine death, oth fetus
O36.0911	Maternal care for oth rhesus isoimmunization, 1st trmstr, fetus 1
O36.0912	Maternal care for oth rhesus isoimmunization, 1st trmstr, fetus 2
O36.0913	Maternal care for oth rhesus isoimmunization, 1st trmstr, fetus 3
O36.0914	Maternal care for oth rhesus isoimmunization, 1st trmstr, fetus 4
O36.0915	Maternal care for oth rhesus isoimmunization, 1st trmstr, fetus 5
O36.0910	Maternal care for oth rhesus isoimmunization, 1st trmstr, N/A or unsp
O36.0919	Maternal care for oth rhesus isoimmunization, 1st trmstr, oth fetus
O36.0921	Maternal care for oth rhesus isoimmunization, 2nd trmstr, fetus 1
O36.0922	Maternal care for oth rhesus isoimmunization, 2nd trmstr, fetus 2
O36.0923	Maternal care for oth rhesus isoimmunization, 2nd trmstr, fetus 3
O36.0924	Maternal care for oth rhesus isoimmunization, 2nd trmstr, fetus 4
O36.0925	Maternal care for oth rhesus isoimmunization, 2nd trmstr, fetus 5
O36.0920	Maternal care for oth rhesus isoimmunization, 2nd trmstr, N/A or unsp
O36.0929	Maternal care for oth rhesus isoimmunization, 2nd trmstr, oth fetus
O36.0931	Maternal care for oth rhesus isoimmunization, 3rd trmstr, fetus 1
O36.0932	Maternal care for oth rhesus isoimmunization, 3rd trmstr, fetus 2
O36.0933	Maternal care for oth rhesus isoimmunization, 3rd trmstr, fetus 3
O36.0934	Maternal care for oth rhesus isoimmunization, 3rd trmstr, fetus 4
O36.0935	Maternal care for oth rhesus isoimmunization, 3rd trmstr, fetus 5
O36.0930	Maternal care for oth rhesus isoimmunization, 3rd trmstr, N/A or unsp
O36.0939	Maternal care for oth rhesus isoimmunization, 3rd trmstr, oth fetus
C91.A0	Mature B-cell leukemia Burkitt-type not having achieved remission
C91.A2	Mature B-cell leukemia Burkitt-type, in relapse
C91.A1	Mature B-cell leukemia Burkitt-type, in remission
C84.99	Mature T/NK-cell lymphomas, unsp, extranodal & solid organ sites
C84.93	Mature T/NK-cell lymphomas, unsp, intra-abd lymph nodes
C84.96	Mature T/NK-cell lymphomas, unsp, intrapelvic lymph nodes
C84.92	Mature T/NK-cell lymphomas, unsp, intrathoracic lymph nodes
C84.94	Mature T/NK-cell lymphomas, unsp, lymph nodes of axilla & upr limb
C84.91	Mature T/NK-cell lymphomas, unsp, lymph nodes of head, face, & neck
C84.95	Mature T/NK-cell lymphomas, unsp, lymph nodes of inguinal rgn & lwr limb
C84.98	Mature T/NK-cell lymphomas, unsp, lymph nodes of multi sites
C84.97	Mature T/NK-cell lymphomas, unsp, spleen
C84.90	Mature T/NK-cell lymphomas, unsp, unsp site
S02.401A	Maxillary fx, unsp, init enc for clsd fx
S02.401B	Maxillary fx, unsp, init enc for opn fx
S02.401K	Maxillary fx, unsp, subsq enc for fx w/ nonu
E74.04	McArdle disease
B05.1	Measles complicated by meningitis
B05.81	Measles keratitis & keratoconjunctivitis
B05.4	Measles w/ intestinal comp
J95.850	Mech comp of respirator
T84.031A	Mech loosening of int lt hip prosthetic jt, init enc
T84.033A	Mech loosening of int lt knee prosthetic jt, init enc
T84.030A	Mech loosening of int rt hip prosthetic jt, init enc
T84.032A	Mech loosening of int rt knee prosthetic jt, init enc
T84.038A	Mech loosening of oth int prosthetic jt, init enc
T84.039A	Mech loosening of unsp int prosthetic jt, init enc
C17.3	Meckel's diverticulum, malig
C85.29	Mediastinal (thymic) lg B-cell lymphoma, extranodal & solid organ sites
C85.23	Mediastinal (thymic) lg B-cell lymphoma, intra-abd lymph nodes
C85.26	Mediastinal (thymic) lg B-cell lymphoma, intrapelvic lymph nodes
C85.22	Mediastinal (thymic) lg B-cell lymphoma, intrathoracic lymph nodes
C85.24	Mediastinal (thymic) lg B-cell lymphoma, lymph nodes of axilla & upr limb
C85.21	Mediastinal (thymic) lg B-cell lymphoma, lymph nodes of head, face, & neck
C85.25	Mediastinal (thymic) lg B-cell lymphoma, lymph nodes of inguinal rgn & lwr limb
C85.28	Mediastinal (thymic) lg B-cell lymphoma, lymph nodes of multi sites
C85.27	Mediastinal (thymic) lg B-cell lymphoma, spleen
C85.20	Mediastinal (thymic) lg B-cell lymphoma, unsp site
E71.311	Medium chain acyl CoA dehydrogenase deficiency
Q61.5	Medullary cystic kidney
B57.32	Megacolon in Chagas' disease

K59.3	Megacolon, NEC
B57.31	Megaesophagus in Chagas' disease
Q04.5	Megalencephaly
E88.41	MELAS synd
K92.1	Melena
A24.9	Melioidosis, unsp
R29.1	Meningismus
A69.21	Meningitis d/t Lyme disease
B57.41	Meningitis in Chagas' disease
A39.83	Meningococcal arthritis
A39.9	Meningococcal infxn, unsp
A39.82	Meningococcal retrobulbar neuritis
B57.42	Meningoencephalitis in Chagas' disease
E88.42	MERRF synd
C45.2	Mesothelioma of pericardium
C45.1	Mesothelioma of peritoneum
C45.0	Mesothelioma of pleura
O04.83	Metabolic d/o following (induced) termination of pregnancy
O08.5	Metabolic d/o following an ectopic & molar pregnancy
O03.83	Metabolic d/o following complete or unsp spontaneous abortion
O07.33	Metabolic d/o following failed attempted termination of pregnancy
O03.33	Metabolic d/o following incomplete spontaneous abortion
E75.25	Metachromatic leukodystrophy
D74.9	Methemoglobinemia, unsp
E72.12	Methylenetetrahydrofolate reductase deficiency
E71.120	Methylmalonic acidemia
M31.7	Microscopic polyangiitis
G46.0	Mid cerebral artery synd
P91.61	Mild hypoxic ischemic encephalopathy [HIE]
J45.21	Mild intermittent asthma w/ (acute) exacerbation
J45.22	Mild intermittent asthma w/ status asthmaticus
J45.31	Mild persistent asthma w/ (acute) exacerbation
J45.32	Mild persistent asthma w/ status asthmaticus
E44.1	Mild protein-calorie malnutrition
O14.02	Mild to mod pre-eclampsia, 2nd trmstr
O14.03	Mild to mod pre-eclampsia, 3rd trmstr
S32.111A	Minimally disp Zone I fx of sacrum, init enc for clsd fx
S32.111K	Minimally disp Zone I fx of sacrum, subsq enc for fx w/ nonu
S32.121A	Minimally disp Zone II fx of sacrum, init enc for clsd fx
S32.121K	Minimally disp Zone II fx of sacrum, subsq enc for fx w/ nonu
S32.131A	Minimally disp Zone III fx of sacrum, init enc for clsd fx
S32.131K	Minimally disp Zone III fx of sacrum, subsq enc for fx w/ nonu
S37.012A	Minor contsn of lt kidney, init enc
S37.011A	Minor contsn of rt kidney, init enc
S36.020A	Minor contsn of spleen, init enc
S37.019A	Minor contsn of unsp kidney, init enc
S36.241A	Minor lac of body of pancreas, init enc
S75.212A	Minor lac of greater saphenous vein at hip & thigh lvl, lt leg, init enc
S75.211A	Minor lac of greater saphenous vein at hip & thigh lvl, rt leg, init enc
S75.219A	Minor lac of greater saphenous vein at hip & thigh lvl, unsp leg, init enc
S36.240A	Minor lac of head of pancreas, init enc
S36.114A	Minor lac of liver, init enc
S15.012A	Minor lac of lt carotid artery, init enc
S15.212A	Minor lac of lt ext jugular vein, init enc
S15.312A	Minor lac of lt int jugular vein, init enc
S37.042A	Minor lac of lt kidney, init enc
S15.112A	Minor lac of lt vert artery, init enc
S15.011A	Minor lac of rt carotid artery, init enc
S15.211A	Minor lac of rt ext jugular vein, init enc
S15.311A	Minor lac of rt int jugular vein, init enc
S37.041A	Minor lac of rt kidney, init enc
S15.111A	Minor lac of rt vert artery, init enc
S36.242A	Minor lac of tail of pancreas, init enc
S15.019A	Minor lac of unsp carotid artery, init enc
S15.219A	Minor lac of unsp ext jugular vein, init enc
S15.319A	Minor lac of unsp int jugular vein, init enc
S37.049A	Minor lac of unsp kidney, init enc
S36.249A	Minor lac of unsp part of pancreas, init enc
S15.119A	Minor lac of unsp vert artery, init enc
E88.40	Mitochondrial metabolism d/o, unsp
C81.29	Mixed cellularity classical Hodgkin lymphoma, extranodal & solid organ sites
C81.23	Mixed cellularity classical Hodgkin lymphoma, intra-abd lymph nodes
C81.26	Mixed cellularity classical Hodgkin lymphoma, intrapelvic lymph nodes
C81.22	Mixed cellularity classical Hodgkin lymphoma, intrathoracic lymph nodes
C81.24	Mixed cellularity classical Hodgkin lymphoma, lymph nodes of axilla & upr limb
C81.21	Mixed cellularity classical Hodgkin lymphoma, lymph nodes of head, face, & neck
C81.25	Mixed cellularity classical Hodgkin lymphoma, lymph nodes of inguinal rgn & lwr limb
C81.28	Mixed cellularity classical Hodgkin lymphoma, lymph nodes of multi sites
C81.27	Mixed cellularity classical Hodgkin lymphoma, spleen
C81.20	Mixed cellularity classical Hodgkin lymphoma, unsp site
E87.4	Mixed d/o of acid-base balance
B81.4	Mixed intestinal helminthiases
P91.62	Mod hypoxic ischemic encephalopathy [HIE]
S36.251A	Mod lac of body of pancreas, init enc
S36.250A	Mod lac of head of pancreas, init enc
S37.052A	Mod lac of lt kidney, init enc
S37.051A	Mod lac of rt kidney, init enc
S36.252A	Mod lac of tail of pancreas, init enc
S37.059A	Mod lac of unsp kidney, init enc
S36.259A	Mod lac of unsp part of pancreas, init enc
J45.41	Mod persistent asthma w/ (acute) exacerbation
J45.42	Mod persistent asthma w/ status asthmaticus
E44.0	Mod protein-calorie malnutrition
B04	Monkeypox
C93.92	Monocytic leukemia, unsp in relapse
C93.91	Monocytic leukemia, unsp in remission
C93.90	Monocytic leukemia, unsp, not having achieved remission
S52.272P	Monteggia's fx of lt ulna, subsq enc for clsd fx w/ malu
S52.272K	Monteggia's fx of lt ulna, subsq enc for clsd fx w/ nonu
S52.272Q	Monteggia's fx of lt ulna, subsq enc for opn fx type I or II w/ malu
S52.272M	Monteggia's fx of lt ulna, subsq enc for opn fx type I or II w/ nonu
S52.272R	Monteggia's fx of lt ulna, subsq enc for opn fx type IIIA, IIIB, or IIIC w/ malu
S52.272N	Monteggia's fx of lt ulna, subsq enc for opn fx type IIIA, IIIB, or IIIC w/ nonu
S52.271P	Monteggia's fx of rt ulna, subsq enc for clsd fx w/ malu
S52.271K	Monteggia's fx of rt ulna, subsq enc for clsd fx w/ nonu
S52.271Q	Monteggia's fx of rt ulna, subsq enc for opn fx type I or II w/ malu
S52.271M	Monteggia's fx of rt ulna, subsq enc for opn fx type I or II w/ nonu
S52.271R	Monteggia's fx of rt ulna, subsq enc for opn fx type IIIA, IIIB, or IIIC w/ malu
S52.271N	Monteggia's fx of rt ulna, subsq enc for opn fx type IIIA, IIIB, or IIIC w/ nonu
S52.279P	Monteggia's fx of unsp ulna, subsq enc for clsd fx w/ malu
S52.279K	Monteggia's fx of unsp ulna, subsq enc for clsd fx w/ nonu
S52.279Q	Monteggia's fx of unsp ulna, subsq enc for opn fx type I or II w/ malu
S52.279M	Monteggia's fx of unsp ulna, subsq enc for opn fx type I or II w/ nonu
S52.279R	Monteggia's fx of unsp ulna, subsq enc for opn fx type IIIA, IIIB, or IIIC w/ malu
S52.279N	Monteggia's fx of unsp ulna, subsq enc for opn fx type IIIA, IIIB, or IIIC w/ nonu
E66.2	Morbid (severe) obesity w/ alveolar hypoventilation
E76.210	Morquio A mucopolysaccharidoses
E76.211	Morquio B mucopolysaccharidoses
E76.219	Morquio mucopolysaccharidoses, unsp
A92.9	Mosquito-borne viral fever, unsp
G12.20	Motor neuron disease, unsp
I67.5	Moyamoya disease
B55.2	Mucocutaneous leishmaniasis
M30.3	Mucocutaneous lymph node synd [Kawasaki]
E75.11	Mucolipidosis IV
E76.1	Mucopolysaccharidosis, type II
E76.3	Mucopolysaccharidosis, unsp
N76.81	Mucositis (ulcerative) of vagina & vulva
G45.2	Multi & bilat precerebral artery syndromes
Q89.7	Multi congenital malformations, NEC
S32.810A	Multi fractures of pelvis w/ stable disruption of pelvic ring, init enc for clsd fx
S32.810K	Multi fractures of pelvis w/ stable disruption of pelvic ring, subsq enc for fx w/ nonu
S32.811A	Multi fractures of pelvis w/ unstable disruption of pelvic ring, init enc for clsd fx

S32.811K	Multi fractures of pelvis w/ unstable disruption of pelvic ring, subsq enc for fx w/ nonu
S32.82XA	Multi fractures of pelvis w/o disruption of pelvic ring, init enc for clsd fx
S32.82XK	Multi fractures of pelvis w/o disruption of pelvic ring, subsq enc for fx w/ nonu
S22.43XA	Multi fractures of ribs, bilat, init enc for clsd fx
S22.43XK	Multi fractures of ribs, bilat, subsq enc for fx w/ nonu
S22.42XA	Multi fractures of ribs, lt side, init enc for clsd fx
S22.42XK	Multi fractures of ribs, lt side, subsq enc for fx w/ nonu
S22.41XA	Multi fractures of ribs, rt side, init enc for clsd fx
S22.41XK	Multi fractures of ribs, rt side, subsq enc for fx w/ nonu
S22.49XA	Multi fractures of ribs, unsp side, init enc for clsd fx
S22.49XK	Multi fractures of ribs, unsp side, subsq enc for fx w/ nonu
C90.02	Multi myeloma in relapse
C90.01	Multi myeloma in remission
C90.00	Multi myeloma not having achieved remission
G90.3	Multi-sys degeneration of the autonomic nervous sys
C96.0	Multifocal & multisystemic (disseminated) Langerhans-cell histiocytosis
C96.5	Multifocal & unisystemic Langerhans-cell histiocytosis
M35.5	Multifocal fibrosclerosis
B26.85	Mumps arthritis
B26.81	Mumps hepatitis
B26.82	Mumps myocarditis
B26.83	Mumps nephritis
B26.0	Mumps orchitis
B26.3	Mumps pancreatitis
B26.84	Mumps polyneuropathy
E71.314	Muscle carnitine palmitoyltransferase deficiency
G71.0	Muscular dystrophy
G73.3	Myasthenic syndromes in oth diseases classified elsw
B47.9	Mycetoma, unsp
A31.9	Mycobacterial infxn, unsp
C84.09	Mycosis fungoides, extranodal & solid organ sites
C84.03	Mycosis fungoides, intra-abd lymph nodes
C84.06	Mycosis fungoides, intrapelvic lymph nodes
C84.02	Mycosis fungoides, intrathoracic lymph nodes
C84.04	Mycosis fungoides, lymph nodes of axilla & upr limb
C84.01	Mycosis fungoides, lymph nodes of head, face, & neck
C84.05	Mycosis fungoides, lymph nodes of inguinal rgn & lwr limb
C84.08	Mycosis fungoides, lymph nodes of multi sites
C84.07	Mycosis fungoides, spleen
C84.00	Mycosis fungoides, unsp site
C94.6	Myelodysplastic disease, not classified
D46.C	Myelodysplastic synd w/ isolated del(5q) chromosomal abnormality
D75.81	Myelofibrosis
C92.92	Myeloid leukemia, unsp in relapse
C92.91	Myeloid leukemia, unsp in remission
C92.90	Myeloid leukemia, unsp, not having achieved remission
C92.32	Myeloid sarcoma, in relapse
C92.31	Myeloid sarcoma, in remission
C92.30	Myeloid sarcoma, not having achieved remission
G99.2	Myelopathy in diseases classified elsw
D61.82	Myelophthisis
E79.2	Myoadenylate deaminase deficiency
R82.1	Myoglobinuria
G72.2	Myopathy d/t oth toxic agents
B69.81	Myositis in cysticercosis
B60.2	Naegleriasis
Q01.1	Nasofrontal encephalocele
A36.1	Nasopharyngeal diphtheria
B76.1	Necatoriasis
I77.5	Necrosis of artery
M31.9	Necrotizing vasculopathy, unsp
P54.4	Neonatal adrenal hemor
E71.511	Neonatal adrenoleukodystrophy
P70.2	Neonatal diabetes mellitus
P72.0	Neonatal goiter, NEC
P71.2	Neonatal hypomagnesemia
P39.0	Neonatal infective mastitis
P39.4	Neonatal skin infxn
P71.3	Neonatal tetany w/o calcium or magnesium deficiency
P39.3	Neonatal urinary tract infxn
P96.1	Neonatal withdrawal symptoms from maternal use of drugs of addiction

D47.9	Neoplasm of uncertain behavior of lymphoid, hematopoietic & related tissue, unsp
N25.1	Nephrogenic diabetes insipidus
N04.6	Nephrotic synd w/ dense deposit disease
N04.7	Nephrotic synd w/ diffuse crescentic glomerulonephritis
N04.4	Nephrotic synd w/ diffuse endocapillary proliferative glomerulonephritis
N04.2	Nephrotic synd w/ diffuse membranous glomerulonephritis
N04.3	Nephrotic synd w/ diffuse mesangial proliferative glomerulonephritis
N04.5	Nephrotic synd w/ diffuse mesangiocapillary glomerulonephritis
N04.1	Nephrotic synd w/ focal & segmental glomerular lesions
N04.0	Nephrotic synd w/ minor glomerular abnormality
N04.8	Nephrotic synd w/ oth morphologic changes
N04.9	Nephrotic synd w/ unsp morphologic changes
K59.2	Neurogenic bowel, NEC
G21.11	Neuroleptic induced parkinsonism
R41.4	Neurologic neglect synd
G36.0	Neuromyelitis optica [Devic]
E75.4	Neuronal ceroid lipofuscinosis
E85.1	Neuropathic heredofamilial amyloidosis
A52.3	Neurosyphilis, unsp
D81.4	Nezelof's synd
F17.203	Nicotine dependence unsp, w/ withdrawal
F17.223	Nicotine dependence, chewing tobacco, w/ withdrawal
F17.213	Nicotine dependence, cigarettes, w/ withdrawal
F17.293	Nicotine dependence, oth tobacco product, w/ withdrawal
A43.9	Nocardiosis, unsp
C81.09	Nodular lymphocyte predominant Hodgkin lymphoma, extranodal & solid organ sites
C81.03	Nodular lymphocyte predominant Hodgkin lymphoma, intra-abd lymph nodes
C81.06	Nodular lymphocyte predominant Hodgkin lymphoma, intrapelvic lymph nodes
C81.02	Nodular lymphocyte predominant Hodgkin lymphoma, intrathoracic lymph nodes
C81.04	Nodular lymphocyte predominant Hodgkin lymphoma, lymph nodes of axilla & upr limb
C81.01	Nodular lymphocyte predominant Hodgkin lymphoma, lymph nodes of head, face, & neck
C81.05	Nodular lymphocyte predominant Hodgkin lymphoma, lymph nodes of inguinal rgn & lwr limb
C81.08	Nodular lymphocyte predominant Hodgkin lymphoma, lymph nodes of multi sites
C81.07	Nodular lymphocyte predominant Hodgkin lymphoma, spleen
C81.00	Nodular lymphocyte predominant Hodgkin lymphoma, unsp site
C81.19	Nodular sclerosis classical Hodgkin lymphoma, extranodal & solid organ sites
C81.13	Nodular sclerosis classical Hodgkin lymphoma, intra-abd lymph nodes
C81.16	Nodular sclerosis classical Hodgkin lymphoma, intrapelvic lymph nodes
C81.12	Nodular sclerosis classical Hodgkin lymphoma, intrathoracic lymph nodes
C81.14	Nodular sclerosis classical Hodgkin lymphoma, lymph nodes of axilla & upr limb
C81.11	Nodular sclerosis classical Hodgkin lymphoma, lymph nodes of head, face, & neck
C81.15	Nodular sclerosis classical Hodgkin lymphoma, lymph nodes of inguinal rgn & lwr limb
C81.18	Nodular sclerosis classical Hodgkin lymphoma, lymph nodes of multi sites
C81.17	Nodular sclerosis classical Hodgkin lymphoma, spleen
C81.10	Nodular sclerosis classical Hodgkin lymphoma, unsp site
T80.A0XA	Non-ABO incompatibility reaction d/t transfusion of blood or blood products, unsp, init enc
T80.A10A	Non-ABO incompatibility w/ acute hemolytic transfusion reaction, init enc
T80.A11A	Non-ABO incompatibility w/ delayed hemolytic transfusion reaction, init enc
T80.A19A	Non-ABO incompatibility w/ hemolytic transfusion reaction, unsp, init enc
C83.99	Non-follicular (diffuse) lymphoma, unsp, extranodal & solid organ sites
C83.93	Non-follicular (diffuse) lymphoma, unsp, intra-abd lymph nodes
C83.96	Non-follicular (diffuse) lymphoma, unsp, intrapelvic lymph nodes
C83.92	Non-follicular (diffuse) lymphoma, unsp, intrathoracic lymph nodes
C83.94	Non-follicular (diffuse) lymphoma, unsp, lymph nodes of axilla & upr limb

C83.91	Non-follicular (diffuse) lymphoma, unsp, lymph nodes of head, face, & neck
C83.95	Non-follicular (diffuse) lymphoma, unsp, lymph nodes of inguinal rgn & lwr limb
C83.98	Non-follicular (diffuse) lymphoma, unsp, lymph nodes of multi sites
C83.97	Non-follicular (diffuse) lymphoma, unsp, spleen
C83.90	Non-follicular (diffuse) lymphoma, unsp, unsp site
C85.99	Non-Hodgkin lymphoma, unsp, extranodal & solid organ sites
C85.93	Non-Hodgkin lymphoma, unsp, intra-abd lymph nodes
C85.96	Non-Hodgkin lymphoma, unsp, intrapelvic lymph nodes
C85.92	Non-Hodgkin lymphoma, unsp, intrathoracic lymph nodes
C85.94	Non-Hodgkin lymphoma, unsp, lymph nodes of axilla & upr limb
C85.91	Non-Hodgkin lymphoma, unsp, lymph nodes of head, face, & neck
C85.95	Non-Hodgkin lymphoma, unsp, lymph nodes of inguinal rgn & lwr limb
C85.98	Non-Hodgkin lymphoma, unsp, lymph nodes of multi sites
C85.97	Non-Hodgkin lymphoma, unsp, spleen
C85.90	Non-Hodgkin lymphoma, unsp, unsp site
E72.51	Non-ketotic hyperglycinemia
E85.0	Non-neuropathic heredofamilial amyloidosis
L97.321	Non-pressure chr ulcer of lt ankle limited to breakdown of skin
L97.322	Non-pressure chr ulcer of lt ankle w/ fat layer exposed
L97.324	Non-pressure chr ulcer of lt ankle w/ necrosis of bone
L97.323	Non-pressure chr ulcer of lt ankle w/ necrosis of muscle
L97.329	Non-pressure chr ulcer of lt ankle w/ unsp severity
L97.221	Non-pressure chr ulcer of lt calf limited to breakdown of skin
L97.222	Non-pressure chr ulcer of lt calf w/ fat layer exposed
L97.224	Non-pressure chr ulcer of lt calf w/ necrosis of bone
L97.223	Non-pressure chr ulcer of lt calf w/ necrosis of muscle
L97.229	Non-pressure chr ulcer of lt calf w/ unsp severity
L97.421	Non-pressure chr ulcer of lt heel & midfoot limited to breakdown of skin
L97.422	Non-pressure chr ulcer of lt heel & midfoot w/ fat layer exposed
L97.424	Non-pressure chr ulcer of lt heel & midfoot w/ necrosis of bone
L97.423	Non-pressure chr ulcer of lt heel & midfoot w/ necrosis of muscle
L97.429	Non-pressure chr ulcer of lt heel & midfoot w/ unsp severity
L97.121	Non-pressure chr ulcer of lt thigh limited to breakdown of skin
L97.122	Non-pressure chr ulcer of lt thigh w/ fat layer exposed
L97.124	Non-pressure chr ulcer of lt thigh w/ necrosis of bone
L97.123	Non-pressure chr ulcer of lt thigh w/ necrosis of muscle
L97.129	Non-pressure chr ulcer of lt thigh w/ unsp severity
L97.821	Non-pressure chr ulcer of oth part of lt lwr leg limited to breakdown of skin
L97.822	Non-pressure chr ulcer of oth part of lt lwr leg w/ fat layer exposed
L97.824	Non-pressure chr ulcer of oth part of lt lwr leg w/ necrosis of bone
L97.823	Non-pressure chr ulcer of oth part of lt lwr leg w/ necrosis of muscle
L97.829	Non-pressure chr ulcer of oth part of lt lwr leg w/ unsp severity
L97.811	Non-pressure chr ulcer of oth part of rt lwr leg limited to breakdown of skin
L97.812	Non-pressure chr ulcer of oth part of rt lwr leg w/ fat layer exposed
L97.814	Non-pressure chr ulcer of oth part of rt lwr leg w/ necrosis of bone
L97.813	Non-pressure chr ulcer of oth part of rt lwr leg w/ necrosis of muscle
L97.819	Non-pressure chr ulcer of oth part of rt lwr leg w/ unsp severity
L97.801	Non-pressure chr ulcer of oth part of unsp lwr leg limited to breakdown of skin
L97.802	Non-pressure chr ulcer of oth part of unsp lwr leg w/ fat layer exposed
L97.804	Non-pressure chr ulcer of oth part of unsp lwr leg w/ necrosis of bone
L97.803	Non-pressure chr ulcer of oth part of unsp lwr leg w/ necrosis of muscle
L97.809	Non-pressure chr ulcer of oth part of unsp lwr leg w/ unsp severity
L97.311	Non-pressure chr ulcer of rt ankle limited to breakdown of skin
L97.312	Non-pressure chr ulcer of rt ankle w/ fat layer exposed
L97.314	Non-pressure chr ulcer of rt ankle w/ necrosis of bone
L97.313	Non-pressure chr ulcer of rt ankle w/ necrosis of muscle
L97.319	Non-pressure chr ulcer of rt ankle w/ unsp severity
L97.211	Non-pressure chr ulcer of rt calf limited to breakdown of skin
L97.212	Non-pressure chr ulcer of rt calf w/ fat layer exposed
L97.214	Non-pressure chr ulcer of rt calf w/ necrosis of bone
L97.213	Non-pressure chr ulcer of rt calf w/ necrosis of muscle
L97.219	Non-pressure chr ulcer of rt calf w/ unsp severity
L97.411	Non-pressure chr ulcer of rt heel & midfoot limited to breakdown of skin
L97.412	Non-pressure chr ulcer of rt heel & midfoot w/ fat layer exposed
L97.414	Non-pressure chr ulcer of rt heel & midfoot w/ necrosis of bone
L97.413	Non-pressure chr ulcer of rt heel & midfoot w/ necrosis of muscle
L97.419	Non-pressure chr ulcer of rt heel & midfoot w/ unsp severity
L97.111	Non-pressure chr ulcer of rt thigh limited to breakdown of skin
L97.112	Non-pressure chr ulcer of rt thigh w/ fat layer exposed

L97.114	Non-pressure chr ulcer of rt thigh w/ necrosis of bone
L97.113	Non-pressure chr ulcer of rt thigh w/ necrosis of muscle
L97.119	Non-pressure chr ulcer of rt thigh w/ unsp severity
L97.301	Non-pressure chr ulcer of unsp ankle limited to breakdown of skin
L97.302	Non-pressure chr ulcer of unsp ankle w/ fat layer exposed
L97.304	Non-pressure chr ulcer of unsp ankle w/ necrosis of bone
L97.303	Non-pressure chr ulcer of unsp ankle w/ necrosis of muscle
L97.309	Non-pressure chr ulcer of unsp ankle w/ unsp severity
L97.201	Non-pressure chr ulcer of unsp calf limited to breakdown of skin
L97.202	Non-pressure chr ulcer of unsp calf w/ fat layer exposed
L97.204	Non-pressure chr ulcer of unsp calf w/ necrosis of bone
L97.203	Non-pressure chr ulcer of unsp calf w/ necrosis of muscle
L97.209	Non-pressure chr ulcer of unsp calf w/ unsp severity
L97.401	Non-pressure chr ulcer of unsp heel & midfoot limited to breakdown of skin
L97.402	Non-pressure chr ulcer of unsp heel & midfoot w/ fat layer exposed
L97.404	Non-pressure chr ulcer of unsp heel & midfoot w/ necrosis of bone
L97.403	Non-pressure chr ulcer of unsp heel & midfoot w/ necrosis of muscle
L97.409	Non-pressure chr ulcer of unsp heel & midfoot w/ unsp severity
L97.921	Non-pressure chr ulcer of unsp part of lt lwr leg limited to breakdown of skin
L97.922	Non-pressure chr ulcer of unsp part of lt lwr leg w/ fat layer exposed
L97.924	Non-pressure chr ulcer of unsp part of lt lwr leg w/ necrosis of bone
L97.923	Non-pressure chr ulcer of unsp part of lt lwr leg w/ necrosis of muscle
L97.929	Non-pressure chr ulcer of unsp part of lt lwr leg w/ unsp severity
L97.911	Non-pressure chr ulcer of unsp part of rt lwr leg limited to breakdown of skin
L97.912	Non-pressure chr ulcer of unsp part of rt lwr leg w/ fat layer exposed
L97.914	Non-pressure chr ulcer of unsp part of rt lwr leg w/ necrosis of bone
L97.913	Non-pressure chr ulcer of unsp part of rt lwr leg w/ necrosis of muscle
L97.919	Non-pressure chr ulcer of unsp part of rt lwr leg w/ unsp severity
L97.901	Non-pressure chr ulcer of unsp part of unsp lwr leg limited to breakdown of skin
L97.902	Non-pressure chr ulcer of unsp part of unsp lwr leg w/ fat layer exposed
L97.904	Non-pressure chr ulcer of unsp part of unsp lwr leg w/ necrosis of bone
L97.903	Non-pressure chr ulcer of unsp part of unsp lwr leg w/ necrosis of muscle
L97.909	Non-pressure chr ulcer of unsp part of unsp lwr leg w/ unsp severity
L97.101	Non-pressure chr ulcer of unsp thigh limited to breakdown of skin
L97.102	Non-pressure chr ulcer of unsp thigh w/ fat layer exposed
L97.104	Non-pressure chr ulcer of unsp thigh w/ necrosis of bone
L97.103	Non-pressure chr ulcer of unsp thigh w/ necrosis of muscle
L97.109	Non-pressure chr ulcer of unsp thigh w/ unsp severity
E15	Nondiabetic hypoglycemic coma
S72.135P	Nondisp apophyseal fx of lt femur, subsq enc for clsd fx w/ malu
S72.135K	Nondisp apophyseal fx of lt femur, subsq enc for clsd fx w/ nonu
S72.135Q	Nondisp apophyseal fx of lt femur, subsq enc for opn fx type I or II w/ malu
S72.135M	Nondisp apophyseal fx of lt femur, subsq enc for opn fx type I or II w/ nonu
S72.135R	Nondisp apophyseal fx of lt femur, subsq enc for opn fx type IIIA, IIIB, or IIIC w/ malu
S72.135N	Nondisp apophyseal fx of lt femur, subsq enc for opn fx type IIIA, IIIB, or IIIC w/ nonu
S72.134P	Nondisp apophyseal fx of rt femur, subsq enc for clsd fx w/ malu
S72.134K	Nondisp apophyseal fx of rt femur, subsq enc for clsd fx w/ nonu
S72.134Q	Nondisp apophyseal fx of rt femur, subsq enc for opn fx type I or II w/ malu
S72.134M	Nondisp apophyseal fx of rt femur, subsq enc for opn fx type I or II w/ nonu
S72.134R	Nondisp apophyseal fx of rt femur, subsq enc for opn fx type IIIA, IIIB, or IIIC w/ malu
S72.134N	Nondisp apophyseal fx of rt femur, subsq enc for opn fx type IIIA, IIIC w/ nonu
S72.136P	Nondisp apophyseal fx of unsp femur, subsq enc for clsd fx w/ malu
S72.136K	Nondisp apophyseal fx of unsp femur, subsq enc for clsd fx w/ nonu
S72.136Q	Nondisp apophyseal fx of unsp femur, subsq enc for opn fx type I or II w/ malu
S72.136M	Nondisp apophyseal fx of unsp femur, subsq enc for opn fx type I or II w/ nonu
S72.136R	Nondisp apophyseal fx of unsp femur, subsq enc for opn fx type IIIA, IIIB, or IIIC w/ malu
S72.136N	Nondisp apophyseal fx of unsp femur, subsq enc for opn fx type IIIA, IIIB, or IIIC w/ nonu
S72.065P	Nondisp articular fx of head of lt femur, subsq enc for clsd fx w/ malu
S72.065K	Nondisp articular fx of head of lt femur, subsq enc for clsd fx w/ nonu

S72.065Q	Nondisp articular fx of head of lt femur, subsq enc for opn fx type I or II w/ malu
S72.065M	Nondisp articular fx of head of lt femur, subsq enc for opn fx type I or II w/ nonu
S72.065R	Nondisp articular fx of head of lt femur, subsq enc for opn fx type IIIA, IIIB, or IIIC w/ malu
S72.065N	Nondisp articular fx of head of lt femur, subsq enc for opn fx type IIIA, IIIB, or IIIC w/ nonu
S72.064P	Nondisp articular fx of head of rt femur, subsq enc for clsd fx w/ malu
S72.064K	Nondisp articular fx of head of rt femur, subsq enc for clsd fx w/ nonu
S72.064Q	Nondisp articular fx of head of rt femur, subsq enc for opn fx type I or II w/ malu
S72.064M	Nondisp articular fx of head of rt femur, subsq enc for opn fx type I or II w/ nonu
S72.064R	Nondisp articular fx of head of rt femur, subsq enc for opn fx type IIIA, IIIB, or IIIC w/ malu
S72.064N	Nondisp articular fx of head of rt femur, subsq enc for opn fx type IIIA, IIIB, or IIIC w/ nonu
S72.066P	Nondisp articular fx of head of unsp femur, subsq enc for clsd fx w/ malu
S72.066K	Nondisp articular fx of head of unsp femur, subsq enc for clsd fx w/ nonu
S72.066Q	Nondisp articular fx of head of unsp femur, subsq enc for opn fx type I or II w/ malu
S72.066M	Nondisp articular fx of head of unsp femur, subsq enc for opn fx type I or II w/ nonu
S72.066R	Nondisp articular fx of head of unsp femur, subsq enc for opn fx type IIIA, IIIB, or IIIC w/ malu
S72.066N	Nondisp articular fx of head of unsp femur, subsq enc for opn fx type IIIA, IIIB, or IIIC w/ nonu
S32.465K	Nondisp associated transv-post fx of lt acetab, subsq enc for fx w/ nonu
S32.464K	Nondisp associated transv-post fx of rt acetab, subsq enc for fx w/ nonu
S32.466K	Nondisp associated transv-post fx of unsp acetab, subsq enc for fx w/ nonu
S92.155B	Nondisp avulsion fx (chip fx) of lt talus, init enc for opn fx
S92.155P	Nondisp avulsion fx (chip fx) of lt talus, subsq enc for fx w/ malu
S92.155K	Nondisp avulsion fx (chip fx) of lt talus, subsq enc for fx w/ nonu
S92.154B	Nondisp avulsion fx (chip fx) of rt talus, init enc for opn fx
S92.154P	Nondisp avulsion fx (chip fx) of rt talus, subsq enc for fx w/ malu
S92.154K	Nondisp avulsion fx (chip fx) of rt talus, subsq enc for fx w/ nonu
S92.156B	Nondisp avulsion fx (chip fx) of unsp talus, init enc for opn fx
S92.156P	Nondisp avulsion fx (chip fx) of unsp talus, subsq enc for fx w/ malu
S92.156K	Nondisp avulsion fx (chip fx) of unsp talus, subsq enc for fx w/ nonu
S32.315A	Nondisp avulsion fx of lt ilium, init enc for clsd fx
S32.315K	Nondisp avulsion fx of lt ilium, subsq enc for fx w/ nonu
S32.615A	Nondisp avulsion fx of lt ischium, init enc for clsd fx
S32.615K	Nondisp avulsion fx of lt ischium, subsq enc for fx w/ nonu
S32.314A	Nondisp avulsion fx of rt ilium, init enc for clsd fx
S32.314K	Nondisp avulsion fx of rt ilium, subsq enc for fx w/ nonu
S32.614A	Nondisp avulsion fx of rt ischium, init enc for clsd fx
S32.614K	Nondisp avulsion fx of rt ischium, subsq enc for fx w/ nonu
S92.035B	Nondisp avulsion fx of tuberosity of lt calcaneus, init enc for opn fx
S92.035P	Nondisp avulsion fx of tuberosity of lt calcaneus, subsq enc for fx w/ malu
S92.035K	Nondisp avulsion fx of tuberosity of lt calcaneus, subsq enc for fx w/ nonu
S92.034B	Nondisp avulsion fx of tuberosity of rt calcaneus, init enc for opn fx
S92.034P	Nondisp avulsion fx of tuberosity of rt calcaneus, subsq enc for fx w/ malu
S92.034K	Nondisp avulsion fx of tuberosity of rt calcaneus, subsq enc for fx w/ nonu
S92.036B	Nondisp avulsion fx of tuberosity of unsp calcaneus, init enc for opn fx
S92.036P	Nondisp avulsion fx of tuberosity of unsp calcaneus, subsq enc for fx w/ malu
S92.036K	Nondisp avulsion fx of tuberosity of unsp calcaneus, subsq enc for fx w/ nonu
S32.316A	Nondisp avulsion fx of unsp ilium, init enc for clsd fx
S32.316K	Nondisp avulsion fx of unsp ilium, subsq enc for fx w/ nonu
S32.616A	Nondisp avulsion fx of unsp ischium, init enc for clsd fx
S32.616K	Nondisp avulsion fx of unsp ischium, subsq enc for fx w/ nonu
S82.145A	Nondisp bicondylar fx of lt tibia, init enc for clsd fx
S82.145P	Nondisp bicondylar fx of lt tibia, subsq enc for clsd fx w/ malu
S82.145K	Nondisp bicondylar fx of lt tibia, subsq enc for clsd fx w/ nonu
S82.145Q	Nondisp bicondylar fx of lt tibia, subsq enc for opn fx type I or II w/ malu
S82.145M	Nondisp bicondylar fx of lt tibia, subsq enc for opn fx type I or II w/ nonu
S82.145R	Nondisp bicondylar fx of lt tibia, subsq enc for opn fx type IIIA, IIIB, or IIIC w/ malu

S82.145N	Nondisp bicondylar fx of lt tibia, subsq enc for opn fx type IIIA, IIIB, or IIIC w/ nonu
S82.144A	Nondisp bicondylar fx of rt tibia, init enc for clsd fx
S82.144P	Nondisp bicondylar fx of rt tibia, subsq enc for clsd fx w/ malu
S82.144K	Nondisp bicondylar fx of rt tibia, subsq enc for clsd fx w/ nonu
S82.144Q	Nondisp bicondylar fx of rt tibia, subsq enc for opn fx type I or II w/ malu
S82.144M	Nondisp bicondylar fx of rt tibia, subsq enc for opn fx type I or II w/ nonu
S82.144R	Nondisp bicondylar fx of rt tibia, subsq enc for opn fx type IIIA, IIIB, or IIIC w/ malu
S82.144N	Nondisp bicondylar fx of rt tibia, subsq enc for opn fx type IIIA, IIIB, or IIIC w/ nonu
S82.146A	Nondisp bicondylar fx of unsp tibia, init enc for clsd fx
S82.146P	Nondisp bicondylar fx of unsp tibia, subsq enc for clsd fx w/ malu
S82.146K	Nondisp bicondylar fx of unsp tibia, subsq enc for clsd fx w/ nonu
S82.146Q	Nondisp bicondylar fx of unsp tibia, subsq enc for opn fx type I or II w/ malu
S82.146M	Nondisp bicondylar fx of unsp tibia, subsq enc for opn fx type I or II w/ nonu
S82.146R	Nondisp bicondylar fx of unsp tibia, subsq enc for opn fx type IIIA, IIIB, or IIIC w/ malu
S82.146N	Nondisp bicondylar fx of unsp tibia, subsq enc for opn fx type IIIA, IIIB, or IIIC w/ nonu
S82.845B	Nondisp bimalleolar fx of lt lwr leg, init enc for opn fx type I or II
S82.845C	Nondisp bimalleolar fx of lt lwr leg, init enc for opn fx type IIIA, IIIB, or IIIC
S82.845P	Nondisp bimalleolar fx of lt lwr leg, subsq enc for clsd fx w/ malu
S82.845K	Nondisp bimalleolar fx of lt lwr leg, subsq enc for clsd fx w/ nonu
S82.845Q	Nondisp bimalleolar fx of lt lwr leg, subsq enc for opn fx type I or II w/ malu
S82.845M	Nondisp bimalleolar fx of lt lwr leg, subsq enc for opn fx type I or II w/ nonu
S82.845R	Nondisp bimalleolar fx of lt lwr leg, subsq enc for opn fx type IIIA, IIIB, or IIIC w/ malu
S82.845N	Nondisp bimalleolar fx of lt lwr leg, subsq enc for opn fx type IIIA, IIIB, or IIIC w/ nonu
S82.844B	Nondisp bimalleolar fx of rt lwr leg, init enc for opn fx type I or II
S82.844C	Nondisp bimalleolar fx of rt lwr leg, init enc for opn fx type IIIA, IIIB, or IIIC
S82.844P	Nondisp bimalleolar fx of rt lwr leg, subsq enc for clsd fx w/ malu
S82.844K	Nondisp bimalleolar fx of rt lwr leg, subsq enc for clsd fx w/ nonu
S82.844Q	Nondisp bimalleolar fx of rt lwr leg, subsq enc for opn fx type I or II w/ malu
S82.844M	Nondisp bimalleolar fx of rt lwr leg, subsq enc for opn fx type I or II w/ nonu
S82.844R	Nondisp bimalleolar fx of rt lwr leg, subsq enc for opn fx type IIIA, IIIB, or IIIC w/ malu
S82.844N	Nondisp bimalleolar fx of rt lwr leg, subsq enc for opn fx type IIIA, IIIB, or IIIC w/ nonu
S82.846B	Nondisp bimalleolar fx of unsp lwr leg, init enc for opn fx type I or II
S82.846C	Nondisp bimalleolar fx of unsp lwr leg, init enc for opn fx type IIIA, IIIB, or IIIC
S82.846P	Nondisp bimalleolar fx of unsp lwr leg, subsq enc for clsd fx w/ malu
S82.846K	Nondisp bimalleolar fx of unsp lwr leg, subsq enc for clsd fx w/ nonu
S82.846Q	Nondisp bimalleolar fx of unsp lwr leg, subsq enc for opn fx type I or II w/ malu
S82.846M	Nondisp bimalleolar fx of unsp lwr leg, subsq enc for opn fx type I or II w/ nonu
S82.846R	Nondisp bimalleolar fx of unsp lwr leg, subsq enc for opn fx type IIIA, IIIB, or IIIC w/ malu
S82.846N	Nondisp bimalleolar fx of unsp lwr leg, subsq enc for opn fx type IIIA, IIIB, or IIIC w/ nonu
S82.045A	Nondisp comm fx of lt patella, init enc for clsd fx
S82.045B	Nondisp comm fx of lt patella, init enc for opn fx type I or II
S82.045C	Nondisp comm fx of lt patella, init enc for opn fx type IIIA, IIIB, or IIIC
S82.045P	Nondisp comm fx of lt patella, subsq enc for clsd fx w/ malu
S82.045K	Nondisp comm fx of lt patella, subsq enc for clsd fx w/ nonu
S82.045Q	Nondisp comm fx of lt patella, subsq enc for opn fx type I or II w/ malu
S82.045M	Nondisp comm fx of lt patella, subsq enc for opn fx type I or II w/ nonu
S82.045R	Nondisp comm fx of lt patella, subsq enc for opn fx type IIIA, IIIB, or IIIC w/ malu
S82.045N	Nondisp comm fx of lt patella, subsq enc for opn fx type IIIA, IIIB, or IIIC w/ nonu
S82.044A	Nondisp comm fx of rt patella, init enc for clsd fx
S82.044B	Nondisp comm fx of rt patella, init enc for opn fx type I or II
S82.044C	Nondisp comm fx of rt patella, init enc for opn fx type IIIA, IIIB, or IIIC
S82.044P	Nondisp comm fx of rt patella, subsq enc for clsd fx w/ malu
S82.044K	Nondisp comm fx of rt patella, subsq enc for clsd fx w/ nonu
S82.044Q	Nondisp comm fx of rt patella, subsq enc for opn fx type I or II w/ malu

S82.044M	Nondisp comm fx of rt patella, subsq enc for opn fx type I or II w/ nonu
S82.044R	Nondisp comm fx of rt patella, subsq enc for opn fx type IIIA, IIIB, or IIIC w/ malu
S82.044N	Nondisp comm fx of rt patella, subsq enc for opn fx type IIIA, IIIB, or IIIC w/ nonu
S42.355A	Nondisp comm fx of shaft of humerus, lt arm, init enc for clsd fx
S42.355P	Nondisp comm fx of shaft of humerus, lt arm, subsq enc for fx w/ malu
S42.355K	Nondisp comm fx of shaft of humerus, lt arm, subsq enc for fx w/ nonu
S42.354A	Nondisp comm fx of shaft of humerus, rt arm, init enc for clsd fx
S42.354P	Nondisp comm fx of shaft of humerus, rt arm, subsq enc for fx w/ malu
S42.354K	Nondisp comm fx of shaft of humerus, rt arm, subsq enc for fx w/ nonu
S42.356A	Nondisp comm fx of shaft of humerus, unsp arm, init enc for clsd fx
S42.356P	Nondisp comm fx of shaft of humerus, unsp arm, subsq enc for fx w/ malu
S42.356K	Nondisp comm fx of shaft of humerus, unsp arm, subsq enc for fx w/ nonu
S72.355P	Nondisp comm fx of shaft of lt femur, subsq enc for clsd fx w/ malu
S72.355K	Nondisp comm fx of shaft of lt femur, subsq enc for clsd fx w/ nonu
S72.355Q	Nondisp comm fx of shaft of lt femur, subsq enc for opn fx type I or II w/ malu
S72.355M	Nondisp comm fx of shaft of lt femur, subsq enc for opn fx type I or II w/ nonu
S72.355R	Nondisp comm fx of shaft of lt femur, subsq enc for opn fx type IIIA, IIIB, or IIIC w/ malu
S72.355N	Nondisp comm fx of shaft of lt femur, subsq enc for opn fx type IIIA, IIIB, or IIIC w/ nonu
S82.455P	Nondisp comm fx of shaft of lt fibula, subsq enc for clsd fx w/ malu
S82.455K	Nondisp comm fx of shaft of lt fibula, subsq enc for clsd fx w/ nonu
S82.455Q	Nondisp comm fx of shaft of lt fibula, subsq enc for opn fx type I or II w/ malu
S82.455M	Nondisp comm fx of shaft of lt fibula, subsq enc for opn fx type I or II w/ nonu
S82.455R	Nondisp comm fx of shaft of lt fibula, subsq enc for opn fx type IIIA, IIIB, or IIIC w/ malu
S82.455N	Nondisp comm fx of shaft of lt fibula, subsq enc for opn fx type IIIA, IIIB, or IIIC w/ nonu
S82.255A	Nondisp comm fx of shaft of lt tibia, init enc for clsd fx
S82.255P	Nondisp comm fx of shaft of lt tibia, subsq enc for clsd fx w/ malu
S82.255K	Nondisp comm fx of shaft of lt tibia, subsq enc for clsd fx w/ nonu
S82.255Q	Nondisp comm fx of shaft of lt tibia, subsq enc for opn fx type I or II w/ malu
S82.255M	Nondisp comm fx of shaft of lt tibia, subsq enc for opn fx type I or II w/ nonu
S82.255R	Nondisp comm fx of shaft of lt tibia, subsq enc for opn fx type IIIA, IIIB, or IIIC w/ malu
S82.255N	Nondisp comm fx of shaft of lt tibia, subsq enc for opn fx type IIIA, IIIB, or IIIC w/ nonu
S52.355A	Nondisp comm fx of shaft of radius, lt arm, init enc for clsd fx
S52.355P	Nondisp comm fx of shaft of radius, lt arm, subsq enc for clsd fx w/ malu
S52.355K	Nondisp comm fx of shaft of radius, lt arm, subsq enc for clsd fx w/ nonu
S52.355Q	Nondisp comm fx of shaft of radius, lt arm, subsq enc for opn fx type I or II w/ malu
S52.355M	Nondisp comm fx of shaft of radius, lt arm, subsq enc for opn fx type I or II w/ nonu
S52.355R	Nondisp comm fx of shaft of radius, lt arm, subsq enc for opn fx type IIIA, IIIB, or IIIC w/ malu
S52.355N	Nondisp comm fx of shaft of radius, lt arm, subsq enc for opn fx type IIIA, IIIB, or IIIC w/ nonu
S52.354A	Nondisp comm fx of shaft of radius, rt arm, init enc for clsd fx
S52.354P	Nondisp comm fx of shaft of radius, rt arm, subsq enc for clsd fx w/ malu
S52.354K	Nondisp comm fx of shaft of radius, rt arm, subsq enc for clsd fx w/ nonu
S52.354Q	Nondisp comm fx of shaft of radius, rt arm, subsq enc for opn fx type I or II w/ malu
S52.354M	Nondisp comm fx of shaft of radius, rt arm, subsq enc for opn fx type I or II w/ nonu
S52.354R	Nondisp comm fx of shaft of radius, rt arm, subsq enc for opn fx type IIIA, IIIB, or IIIC w/ malu
S52.354N	Nondisp comm fx of shaft of radius, rt arm, subsq enc for opn fx type IIIA, IIIB, or IIIC w/ nonu
S52.356A	Nondisp comm fx of shaft of radius, unsp arm, init enc for clsd fx
S52.356P	Nondisp comm fx of shaft of radius, unsp arm, subsq enc for clsd fx w/ malu
S52.356K	Nondisp comm fx of shaft of radius, unsp arm, subsq enc for clsd fx w/ nonu
S52.356Q	Nondisp comm fx of shaft of radius, unsp arm, subsq enc for opn fx type I or II w/ malu

S52.356M	Nondisp comm fx of shaft of radius, unsp arm, subsq enc for opn fx type I or II w/ nonu
S52.356R	Nondisp comm fx of shaft of radius, unsp arm, subsq enc for opn fx type IIIA, IIIB, or IIIC w/ malu
S52.356N	Nondisp comm fx of shaft of radius, unsp arm, subsq enc for opn fx type IIIA, IIIB, or IIIC w/ nonu
S72.354P	Nondisp comm fx of shaft of rt femur, subsq enc for clsd fx w/ malu
S72.354K	Nondisp comm fx of shaft of rt femur, subsq enc for clsd fx w/ nonu
S72.354Q	Nondisp comm fx of shaft of rt femur, subsq enc for opn fx type I or II w/ malu
S72.354M	Nondisp comm fx of shaft of rt femur, subsq enc for opn fx type I or II w/ nonu
S72.354R	Nondisp comm fx of shaft of rt femur, subsq enc for opn fx type IIIA, IIIB, or IIIC w/ malu
S72.354N	Nondisp comm fx of shaft of rt femur, subsq enc for opn fx type IIIA, IIIB, or IIIC w/ nonu
S82.454P	Nondisp comm fx of shaft of rt fibula, subsq enc for clsd fx w/ malu
S82.454K	Nondisp comm fx of shaft of rt fibula, subsq enc for clsd fx w/ nonu
S82.454Q	Nondisp comm fx of shaft of rt fibula, subsq enc for opn fx type I or II w/ malu
S82.454M	Nondisp comm fx of shaft of rt fibula, subsq enc for opn fx type I or II w/ nonu
S82.454R	Nondisp comm fx of shaft of rt fibula, subsq enc for opn fx type IIIA, IIIB, or IIIC w/ malu
S82.454N	Nondisp comm fx of shaft of rt fibula, subsq enc for opn fx type IIIA, IIIB, or IIIC w/ nonu
S82.254A	Nondisp comm fx of shaft of rt tibia, init enc for clsd fx
S82.254P	Nondisp comm fx of shaft of rt tibia, subsq enc for clsd fx w/ malu
S82.254K	Nondisp comm fx of shaft of rt tibia, subsq enc for clsd fx w/ nonu
S82.254Q	Nondisp comm fx of shaft of rt tibia, subsq enc for opn fx type I or II w/ malu
S82.254M	Nondisp comm fx of shaft of rt tibia, subsq enc for opn fx type I or II w/ nonu
S82.254R	Nondisp comm fx of shaft of rt tibia, subsq enc for opn fx type IIIA, IIIB, or IIIC w/ malu
S82.254N	Nondisp comm fx of shaft of rt tibia, subsq enc for opn fx type IIIA, IIIB, or IIIC w/ nonu
S52.255A	Nondisp comm fx of shaft of ulna, lt arm, init enc for clsd fx
S52.255P	Nondisp comm fx of shaft of ulna, lt arm, subsq enc for clsd fx w/ malu
S52.255K	Nondisp comm fx of shaft of ulna, lt arm, subsq enc for clsd fx w/ nonu
S52.255Q	Nondisp comm fx of shaft of ulna, lt arm, subsq enc for opn fx type I or II w/ malu
S52.255M	Nondisp comm fx of shaft of ulna, lt arm, subsq enc for opn fx type I or II w/ nonu
S52.255R	Nondisp comm fx of shaft of ulna, lt arm, subsq enc for opn fx type IIIA, IIIB, or IIIC w/ malu
S52.255N	Nondisp comm fx of shaft of ulna, lt arm, subsq enc for opn fx type IIIA, IIIB, or IIIC w/ nonu
S52.254A	Nondisp comm fx of shaft of ulna, rt arm, init enc for clsd fx
S52.254P	Nondisp comm fx of shaft of ulna, rt arm, subsq enc for clsd fx w/ malu
S52.254K	Nondisp comm fx of shaft of ulna, rt arm, subsq enc for clsd fx w/ nonu
S52.254Q	Nondisp comm fx of shaft of ulna, rt arm, subsq enc for opn fx type I or II w/ malu
S52.254M	Nondisp comm fx of shaft of ulna, rt arm, subsq enc for opn fx type I or II w/ nonu
S52.254R	Nondisp comm fx of shaft of ulna, rt arm, subsq enc for opn fx type IIIA, IIIB, or IIIC w/ malu
S52.254N	Nondisp comm fx of shaft of ulna, rt arm, subsq enc for opn fx type IIIA, IIIB, or IIIC w/ nonu
S52.256A	Nondisp comm fx of shaft of ulna, unsp arm, init enc for clsd fx
S52.256P	Nondisp comm fx of shaft of ulna, unsp arm, subsq enc for clsd fx w/ malu
S52.256K	Nondisp comm fx of shaft of ulna, unsp arm, subsq enc for clsd fx w/ nonu
S52.256Q	Nondisp comm fx of shaft of ulna, unsp arm, subsq enc for opn fx type I or II w/ malu
S52.256M	Nondisp comm fx of shaft of ulna, unsp arm, subsq enc for opn fx type I or II w/ nonu
S52.256R	Nondisp comm fx of shaft of ulna, unsp arm, subsq enc for opn fx type IIIA, IIIB, or IIIC w/ malu
S52.256N	Nondisp comm fx of shaft of ulna, unsp arm, subsq enc for opn fx type IIIA, IIIB, or IIIC w/ nonu
S72.356P	Nondisp comm fx of shaft of unsp femur, subsq enc for clsd fx w/ malu
S72.356K	Nondisp comm fx of shaft of unsp femur, subsq enc for clsd fx w/ nonu
S72.356Q	Nondisp comm fx of shaft of unsp femur, subsq enc for opn fx type I or II w/ malu

Code	Description
S72.356M	Nondisp comm fx of shaft of unsp femur, subsq enc for opn fx type I or II w/ nonu
S72.356R	Nondisp comm fx of shaft of unsp femur, subsq enc for opn fx type IIIA, IIIB, or IIIC w/ malu
S72.356N	Nondisp comm fx of shaft of unsp femur, subsq enc for opn fx type IIIA, IIIB, or IIIC w/ nonu
S82.456P	Nondisp comm fx of shaft of unsp fibula, subsq enc for clsd fx w/ malu
S82.456K	Nondisp comm fx of shaft of unsp fibula, subsq enc for clsd fx w/ nonu
S82.456Q	Nondisp comm fx of shaft of unsp fibula, subsq enc for opn fx type I or II w/ malu
S82.456M	Nondisp comm fx of shaft of unsp fibula, subsq enc for opn fx type I or II w/ nonu
S82.456R	Nondisp comm fx of shaft of unsp fibula, subsq enc for opn fx type IIIA, IIIB, or IIIC w/ malu
S82.456N	Nondisp comm fx of shaft of unsp fibula, subsq enc for opn fx type IIIA, IIIB, or IIIC w/ nonu
S82.256A	Nondisp comm fx of shaft of unsp tibia, init enc for clsd fx
S82.256P	Nondisp comm fx of shaft of unsp tibia, subsq enc for clsd fx w/ malu
S82.256K	Nondisp comm fx of shaft of unsp tibia, subsq enc for clsd fx w/ nonu
S82.256Q	Nondisp comm fx of shaft of unsp tibia, subsq enc for opn fx type I or II w/ malu
S82.256M	Nondisp comm fx of shaft of unsp tibia, subsq enc for opn fx type I or II w/ nonu
S82.256R	Nondisp comm fx of shaft of unsp tibia, subsq enc for opn fx type IIIA, IIIB, or IIIC w/ malu
S82.256N	Nondisp comm fx of shaft of unsp tibia, subsq enc for opn fx type IIIA, IIIB, or IIIC w/ nonu
S82.046A	Nondisp comm fx of unsp patella, init enc for clsd fx
S82.046B	Nondisp comm fx of unsp patella, init enc for opn fx type I or II
S82.046C	Nondisp comm fx of unsp patella, init enc for opn fx type IIIA, IIIB, or IIIC
S82.046P	Nondisp comm fx of unsp patella, subsq enc for clsd fx w/ malu
S82.046K	Nondisp comm fx of unsp patella, subsq enc for clsd fx w/ nonu
S82.046Q	Nondisp comm fx of unsp patella, subsq enc for opn fx type I or II w/ malu
S82.046M	Nondisp comm fx of unsp patella, subsq enc for opn fx type I or II w/ nonu
S82.046R	Nondisp comm fx of unsp patella, subsq enc for opn fx type IIIA, IIIB, or IIIC w/ malu
S82.046N	Nondisp comm fx of unsp patella, subsq enc for opn fx type IIIA, IIIB, or IIIC w/ nonu
S42.425A	Nondisp comm supracondylar fx w/o intercondylar fx of lt humerus, init enc for clsd fx
S42.425P	Nondisp comm supracondylar fx w/o intercondylar fx of lt humerus, subsq enc for fx w/ malu
S42.425K	Nondisp comm supracondylar fx w/o intercondylar fx of lt humerus, subsq enc for fx w/ nonu
S42.424A	Nondisp comm supracondylar fx w/o intercondylar fx of rt humerus, init enc for clsd fx
S42.424P	Nondisp comm supracondylar fx w/o intercondylar fx of rt humerus, subsq enc for fx w/ malu
S42.424K	Nondisp comm supracondylar fx w/o intercondylar fx of rt humerus, subsq enc for fx w/ nonu
S42.426A	Nondisp comm supracondylar fx w/o intercondylar fx of unsp humerus, init enc for clsd fx
S42.426P	Nondisp comm supracondylar fx w/o intercondylar fx of unsp humerus, subsq enc for fx w/ malu
S42.426K	Nondisp comm supracondylar fx w/o intercondylar fx of unsp humerus, subsq enc for fx w/ nonu
S32.485K	Nondisp dome fx of lt acetab, subsq enc for fx w/ nonu
S92.145B	Nondisp dome fx of lt talus, init enc for opn fx
S92.145P	Nondisp dome fx of lt talus, subsq enc for fx w/ malu
S92.145K	Nondisp dome fx of lt talus, subsq enc for fx w/ nonu
S32.484K	Nondisp dome fx of rt acetab, subsq enc for fx w/ nonu
S92.144B	Nondisp dome fx of rt talus, init enc for opn fx
S92.144P	Nondisp dome fx of rt talus, subsq enc for fx w/ malu
S92.144K	Nondisp dome fx of rt talus, subsq enc for fx w/ nonu
S32.486K	Nondisp dome fx of unsp acetab, subsq enc for fx w/ nonu
S92.146B	Nondisp dome fx of unsp talus, init enc for opn fx
S92.146P	Nondisp dome fx of unsp talus, subsq enc for fx w/ malu
S92.146K	Nondisp dome fx of unsp talus, subsq enc for fx w/ nonu
S42.435A	Nondisp fx (avulsion) of lat epicondyle of lt humerus, init enc for clsd fx
S42.435P	Nondisp fx (avulsion) of lat epicondyle of lt humerus, subsq enc for fx w/ malu
S42.435K	Nondisp fx (avulsion) of lat epicondyle of lt humerus, subsq enc for fx w/ nonu
S42.434A	Nondisp fx (avulsion) of lat epicondyle of rt humerus, init enc for clsd fx

Code	Description
S42.434P	Nondisp fx (avulsion) of lat epicondyle of rt humerus, subsq enc for fx w/ malu
S42.434K	Nondisp fx (avulsion) of lat epicondyle of rt humerus, subsq enc for fx w/ nonu
S42.436A	Nondisp fx (avulsion) of lat epicondyle of unsp humerus, init enc for clsd fx
S42.436P	Nondisp fx (avulsion) of lat epicondyle of unsp humerus, subsq enc for fx w/ malu
S42.436K	Nondisp fx (avulsion) of lat epicondyle of unsp humerus, subsq enc for fx w/ nonu
S42.445A	Nondisp fx (avulsion) of med epicondyle of lt humerus, init enc for clsd fx
S42.445P	Nondisp fx (avulsion) of med epicondyle of lt humerus, subsq enc for fx w/ malu
S42.445K	Nondisp fx (avulsion) of med epicondyle of lt humerus, subsq enc for fx w/ nonu
S42.444A	Nondisp fx (avulsion) of med epicondyle of rt humerus, init enc for clsd fx
S42.444P	Nondisp fx (avulsion) of med epicondyle of rt humerus, subsq enc for fx w/ malu
S42.444K	Nondisp fx (avulsion) of med epicondyle of rt humerus, subsq enc for fx w/ nonu
S42.446A	Nondisp fx (avulsion) of med epicondyle of unsp humerus, init enc for clsd fx
S42.446P	Nondisp fx (avulsion) of med epicondyle of unsp humerus, subsq enc for fx w/ malu
S42.446K	Nondisp fx (avulsion) of med epicondyle of unsp humerus, subsq enc for fx w/ nonu
S92.315B	Nondisp fx of 1st metatarsal bone, lt foot, init enc for opn fx
S92.315P	Nondisp fx of 1st metatarsal bone, lt foot, subsq enc for fx w/ malu
S92.315K	Nondisp fx of 1st metatarsal bone, lt foot, subsq enc for fx w/ nonu
S92.314B	Nondisp fx of 1st metatarsal bone, rt foot, init enc for opn fx
S92.314P	Nondisp fx of 1st metatarsal bone, rt foot, subsq enc for fx w/ malu
S92.314K	Nondisp fx of 1st metatarsal bone, rt foot, subsq enc for fx w/ nonu
S92.316B	Nondisp fx of 1st metatarsal bone, unsp foot, init enc for opn fx
S92.316P	Nondisp fx of 1st metatarsal bone, unsp foot, subsq enc for fx w/ malu
S92.316K	Nondisp fx of 1st metatarsal bone, unsp foot, subsq enc for fx w/ nonu
S92.325B	Nondisp fx of 2nd metatarsal bone, lt foot, init enc for opn fx
S92.325P	Nondisp fx of 2nd metatarsal bone, lt foot, subsq enc for fx w/ malu
S92.325K	Nondisp fx of 2nd metatarsal bone, lt foot, subsq enc for fx w/ nonu
S92.324B	Nondisp fx of 2nd metatarsal bone, rt foot, init enc for opn fx
S92.324P	Nondisp fx of 2nd metatarsal bone, rt foot, subsq enc for fx w/ malu
S92.324K	Nondisp fx of 2nd metatarsal bone, rt foot, subsq enc for fx w/ nonu
S92.326B	Nondisp fx of 2nd metatarsal bone, unsp foot, init enc for opn fx
S92.326P	Nondisp fx of 2nd metatarsal bone, unsp foot, subsq enc for fx w/ malu
S92.326K	Nondisp fx of 2nd metatarsal bone, unsp foot, subsq enc for fx w/ nonu
S92.335B	Nondisp fx of 3rd metatarsal bone, lt foot, init enc for opn fx
S92.335P	Nondisp fx of 3rd metatarsal bone, lt foot, subsq enc for fx w/ malu
S92.335K	Nondisp fx of 3rd metatarsal bone, lt foot, subsq enc for fx w/ nonu
S92.334B	Nondisp fx of 3rd metatarsal bone, rt foot, init enc for opn fx
S92.334P	Nondisp fx of 3rd metatarsal bone, rt foot, subsq enc for fx w/ malu
S92.334K	Nondisp fx of 3rd metatarsal bone, rt foot, subsq enc for fx w/ nonu
S92.336B	Nondisp fx of 3rd metatarsal bone, unsp foot, init enc for opn fx
S92.336P	Nondisp fx of 3rd metatarsal bone, unsp foot, subsq enc for fx w/ malu
S92.336K	Nondisp fx of 3rd metatarsal bone, unsp foot, subsq enc for fx w/ nonu
S92.345B	Nondisp fx of 4th metatarsal bone, lt foot, init enc for opn fx
S92.345P	Nondisp fx of 4th metatarsal bone, lt foot, subsq enc for fx w/ malu
S92.345K	Nondisp fx of 4th metatarsal bone, lt foot, subsq enc for fx w/ nonu
S92.344B	Nondisp fx of 4th metatarsal bone, rt foot, init enc for opn fx
S92.344P	Nondisp fx of 4th metatarsal bone, rt foot, subsq enc for fx w/ malu
S92.344K	Nondisp fx of 4th metatarsal bone, rt foot, subsq enc for fx w/ nonu
S92.346B	Nondisp fx of 4th metatarsal bone, unsp foot, init enc for opn fx
S92.346P	Nondisp fx of 4th metatarsal bone, unsp foot, subsq enc for fx w/ malu
S92.346K	Nondisp fx of 4th metatarsal bone, unsp foot, subsq enc for fx w/ nonu
S92.355B	Nondisp fx of 5th metatarsal bone, lt foot, init enc for opn fx
S92.355P	Nondisp fx of 5th metatarsal bone, lt foot, subsq enc for fx w/ malu
S92.355K	Nondisp fx of 5th metatarsal bone, lt foot, subsq enc for fx w/ nonu
S92.354B	Nondisp fx of 5th metatarsal bone, rt foot, init enc for opn fx
S92.354P	Nondisp fx of 5th metatarsal bone, rt foot, subsq enc for fx w/ malu
S92.354K	Nondisp fx of 5th metatarsal bone, rt foot, subsq enc for fx w/ nonu
S92.356B	Nondisp fx of 5th metatarsal bone, unsp foot, init enc for opn fx
S92.356P	Nondisp fx of 5th metatarsal bone, unsp foot, subsq enc for fx w/ malu
S92.356K	Nondisp fx of 5th metatarsal bone, unsp foot, subsq enc for fx w/ nonu
S42.125B	Nondisp fx of acromial process, lt shldr, init enc for opn fx
S42.125P	Nondisp fx of acromial process, lt shldr, subsq enc for fx w/ malu
S42.125K	Nondisp fx of acromial process, lt shldr, subsq enc for fx w/ nonu
S42.124B	Nondisp fx of acromial process, rt shldr, init enc for opn fx

S42.124P	Nondisp fx of acromial process, rt shldr, subsq enc for fx w/ malu
S42.124K	Nondisp fx of acromial process, rt shldr, subsq enc for fx w/ nonu
S42.126B	Nondisp fx of acromial process, unsp shldr, init enc for opn fx
S42.126P	Nondisp fx of acromial process, unsp shldr, subsq enc for fx w/ malu
S42.126K	Nondisp fx of acromial process, unsp shldr, subsq enc for fx w/ nonu
S32.435K	Nondisp fx of ant column [iliopubic] of lt acetab, subsq enc for fx w/ nonu
S32.434K	Nondisp fx of ant column [iliopubic] of rt acetab, subsq enc for fx w/ nonu
S32.436K	Nondisp fx of ant column [iliopubic] of unsp acetab, subsq enc for fx w/ nonu
S92.025B	Nondisp fx of ant process of lt calcaneus, init enc for opn fx
S92.025P	Nondisp fx of ant process of lt calcaneus, subsq enc for fx w/ malu
S92.025K	Nondisp fx of ant process of lt calcaneus, subsq enc for fx w/ nonu
S92.024B	Nondisp fx of ant process of rt calcaneus, init enc for opn fx
S92.024P	Nondisp fx of ant process of rt calcaneus, subsq enc for fx w/ malu
S92.024K	Nondisp fx of ant process of rt calcaneus, subsq enc for fx w/ nonu
S92.026B	Nondisp fx of ant process of unsp calcaneus, init enc for opn fx
S92.026P	Nondisp fx of ant process of unsp calcaneus, subsq enc for fx w/ malu
S92.026K	Nondisp fx of ant process of unsp calcaneus, subsq enc for fx w/ nonu
S32.415K	Nondisp fx of ant wall of lt acetab, subsq enc for fx w/ nonu
S32.414K	Nondisp fx of ant wall of rt acetab, subsq enc for fx w/ nonu
S32.416K	Nondisp fx of ant wall of unsp acetab, subsq enc for fx w/ nonu
S62.340B	Nondisp fx of base of 2nd metacarpal bone, rt hand, init enc for opn fx
S62.340P	Nondisp fx of base of 2nd metacarpal bone, rt hand, subsq enc for fx w/ malu
S62.340K	Nondisp fx of base of 2nd metacarpal bone, rt hand, subsq enc for fx w/ nonu
S62.341B	Nondisp fx of base of 2nd metacarpal bone. lt hand, init enc for opn fx
S62.341P	Nondisp fx of base of 2nd metacarpal bone. lt hand, subsq enc for fx w/ malu
S62.341K	Nondisp fx of base of 2nd metacarpal bone. lt hand, subsq enc for fx w/ nonu
S62.343B	Nondisp fx of base of 3rd metacarpal bone, lt hand, init enc for opn fx
S62.343P	Nondisp fx of base of 3rd metacarpal bone, lt hand, subsq enc for fx w/ malu
S62.343K	Nondisp fx of base of 3rd metacarpal bone, lt hand, subsq enc for fx w/ nonu
S62.342B	Nondisp fx of base of 3rd metacarpal bone, rt hand, init enc for opn fx
S62.342P	Nondisp fx of base of 3rd metacarpal bone, rt hand, subsq enc for fx w/ malu
S62.342K	Nondisp fx of base of 3rd metacarpal bone, rt hand, subsq enc for fx w/ nonu
S62.345B	Nondisp fx of base of 4th metacarpal bone, lt hand, init enc for opn fx
S62.345P	Nondisp fx of base of 4th metacarpal bone, lt hand, subsq enc for fx w/ malu
S62.345K	Nondisp fx of base of 4th metacarpal bone, lt hand, subsq enc for fx w/ nonu
S62.344B	Nondisp fx of base of 4th metacarpal bone, rt hand, init enc for opn fx
S62.344P	Nondisp fx of base of 4th metacarpal bone, rt hand, subsq enc for fx w/ malu
S62.344K	Nondisp fx of base of 4th metacarpal bone, rt hand, subsq enc for fx w/ nonu
S62.346B	Nondisp fx of base of 5th metacarpal bone, rt hand, init enc for opn fx
S62.346P	Nondisp fx of base of 5th metacarpal bone, rt hand, subsq enc for fx w/ malu
S62.346K	Nondisp fx of base of 5th metacarpal bone, rt hand, subsq enc for fx w/ nonu
S62.347B	Nondisp fx of base of 5th metacarpal bone. lt hand, init enc for opn fx
S62.347P	Nondisp fx of base of 5th metacarpal bone. lt hand, subsq enc for fx w/ malu
S62.347K	Nondisp fx of base of 5th metacarpal bone. lt hand, subsq enc for fx w/ nonu
S72.045P	Nondisp fx of base of neck of lt femur, subsq enc for clsd fx w/ malu
S72.045K	Nondisp fx of base of neck of lt femur, subsq enc for clsd fx w/ nonu
S72.045Q	Nondisp fx of base of neck of lt femur, subsq enc for opn fx type I or II w/ malu
S72.045M	Nondisp fx of base of neck of lt femur, subsq enc for opn fx type I or II w/ nonu
S72.045R	Nondisp fx of base of neck of lt femur, subsq enc for opn fx type IIIA, IIIB, or IIIC w/ malu
S72.045N	Nondisp fx of base of neck of lt femur, subsq enc for opn fx type IIIA, IIIB, or IIIC w/ nonu
S72.044P	Nondisp fx of base of neck of rt femur, subsq enc for clsd fx w/ malu
S72.044K	Nondisp fx of base of neck of rt femur, subsq enc for clsd fx w/ nonu
S72.044Q	Nondisp fx of base of neck of rt femur, subsq enc for opn fx type I or II w/ malu

S72.044M	Nondisp fx of base of neck of rt femur, subsq enc for opn fx type I or II w/ nonu
S72.044R	Nondisp fx of base of neck of rt femur, subsq enc for opn fx type IIIA, IIIB, or IIIC w/ malu
S72.044N	Nondisp fx of base of neck of rt femur, subsq enc for opn fx type IIIA, IIIB, or IIIC w/ nonu
S72.046P	Nondisp fx of base of neck of unsp femur, subsq enc for clsd fx w/ malu
S72.046K	Nondisp fx of base of neck of unsp femur, subsq enc for clsd fx w/ nonu
S72.046Q	Nondisp fx of base of neck of unsp femur, subsq enc for opn fx type I or II w/ malu
S72.046M	Nondisp fx of base of neck of unsp femur, subsq enc for opn fx type I or II w/ nonu
S72.046R	Nondisp fx of base of neck of unsp femur, subsq enc for opn fx type IIIA, IIIB, or IIIC w/ malu
S72.046N	Nondisp fx of base of neck of unsp femur, subsq enc for opn fx type IIIA, IIIB, or IIIC w/ nonu
S62.348B	Nondisp fx of base of oth metacarpal bone, init enc for opn fx
S62.348P	Nondisp fx of base of oth metacarpal bone, subsq enc for fx w/ malu
S62.348K	Nondisp fx of base of oth metacarpal bone, subsq enc for fx w/ nonu
S62.349B	Nondisp fx of base of unsp metacarpal bone, init enc for opn fx
S62.349P	Nondisp fx of base of unsp metacarpal bone, subsq enc for fx w/ malu
S62.349K	Nondisp fx of base of unsp metacarpal bone, subsq enc for fx w/ nonu
S62.145B	Nondisp fx of body of hamate [unciform] bone, lt wrist, init enc for opn fx
S62.145P	Nondisp fx of body of hamate [unciform] bone, lt wrist, subsq enc for fx w/ malu
S62.145K	Nondisp fx of body of hamate [unciform] bone, lt wrist, subsq enc for fx w/ nonu
S62.144B	Nondisp fx of body of hamate [unciform] bone, rt wrist, init enc for opn fx
S62.144P	Nondisp fx of body of hamate [unciform] bone, rt wrist, subsq enc for fx w/ malu
S62.144K	Nondisp fx of body of hamate [unciform] bone, rt wrist, subsq enc for fx w/ nonu
S62.146B	Nondisp fx of body of hamate [unciform] bone, unsp wrist, init enc for opn fx
S62.146P	Nondisp fx of body of hamate [unciform] bone, unsp wrist, subsq enc for fx w/ malu
S62.146K	Nondisp fx of body of hamate [unciform] bone, unsp wrist, subsq enc for fx w/ nonu
S92.015B	Nondisp fx of body of lt calcaneus, init enc for opn fx
S92.015P	Nondisp fx of body of lt calcaneus, subsq enc for fx w/ malu
S92.015K	Nondisp fx of body of lt calcaneus, subsq enc for fx w/ nonu
S92.125B	Nondisp fx of body of lt talus, init enc for opn fx
S92.125P	Nondisp fx of body of lt talus, subsq enc for fx w/ malu
S92.125K	Nondisp fx of body of lt talus, subsq enc for fx w/ nonu
S92.014B	Nondisp fx of body of rt calcaneus, init enc for opn fx
S92.014P	Nondisp fx of body of rt calcaneus, subsq enc for fx w/ malu
S92.014K	Nondisp fx of body of rt calcaneus, subsq enc for fx w/ nonu
S92.124B	Nondisp fx of body of rt talus, init enc for opn fx
S92.124P	Nondisp fx of body of rt talus, subsq enc for fx w/ malu
S92.124K	Nondisp fx of body of rt talus, subsq enc for fx w/ nonu
S42.115B	Nondisp fx of body of scapula, lt shldr, init enc for opn fx
S42.115P	Nondisp fx of body of scapula, lt shldr, subsq enc for fx w/ malu
S42.115K	Nondisp fx of body of scapula, lt shldr, subsq enc for fx w/ nonu
S42.114B	Nondisp fx of body of scapula, rt shldr, init enc for opn fx
S42.114P	Nondisp fx of body of scapula, rt shldr, subsq enc for fx w/ malu
S42.114K	Nondisp fx of body of scapula, rt shldr, subsq enc for fx w/ nonu
S42.116B	Nondisp fx of body of scapula, unsp shldr, init enc for opn fx
S42.116P	Nondisp fx of body of scapula, unsp shldr, subsq enc for fx w/ malu
S42.116K	Nondisp fx of body of scapula, unsp shldr, subsq enc for fx w/ nonu
S92.016B	Nondisp fx of body of unsp calcaneus, init enc for opn fx
S92.016P	Nondisp fx of body of unsp calcaneus, subsq enc for fx w/ malu
S92.016K	Nondisp fx of body of unsp calcaneus, subsq enc for fx w/ nonu
S92.126B	Nondisp fx of body of unsp talus, init enc for opn fx
S92.126P	Nondisp fx of body of unsp talus, subsq enc for fx w/ malu
S92.126K	Nondisp fx of body of unsp talus, subsq enc for fx w/ nonu
S62.135B	Nondisp fx of capitate [os magnum] bone, lt wrist, init enc for opn fx
S62.135P	Nondisp fx of capitate [os magnum] bone, lt wrist, subsq enc for fx w/ malu
S62.135K	Nondisp fx of capitate [os magnum] bone, lt wrist, subsq enc for fx w/ nonu
S62.134B	Nondisp fx of capitate [os magnum] bone, rt wrist, init enc for opn fx
S62.134P	Nondisp fx of capitate [os magnum] bone, rt wrist, subsq enc for fx w/ malu
S62.134K	Nondisp fx of capitate [os magnum] bone, rt wrist, subsq enc for fx w/ nonu

S62.136B	Nondisp fx of capitate [os magnum] bone, unsp wrist, init enc for opn fx
S62.136P	Nondisp fx of capitate [os magnum] bone, unsp wrist, subsq enc for fx w/ malu
S62.136K	Nondisp fx of capitate [os magnum] bone, unsp wrist, subsq enc for fx w/ nonu
S42.135B	Nondisp fx of coracoid process, lt shldr, init enc for opn fx
S42.135P	Nondisp fx of coracoid process, lt shldr, subsq enc for fx w/ malu
S42.135K	Nondisp fx of coracoid process, lt shldr, subsq enc for fx w/ nonu
S42.134B	Nondisp fx of coracoid process, rt shldr, init enc for opn fx
S42.134P	Nondisp fx of coracoid process, rt shldr, subsq enc for fx w/ malu
S42.134K	Nondisp fx of coracoid process, rt shldr, subsq enc for fx w/ nonu
S42.136B	Nondisp fx of coracoid process, unsp shldr, init enc for opn fx
S42.136P	Nondisp fx of coracoid process, unsp shldr, subsq enc for fx w/ malu
S42.136K	Nondisp fx of coracoid process, unsp shldr, subsq enc for fx w/ nonu
S52.045P	Nondisp fx of coronoid process of lt ulna, subsq enc for clsd fx w/ malu
S52.045K	Nondisp fx of coronoid process of lt ulna, subsq enc for clsd fx w/ nonu
S52.045Q	Nondisp fx of coronoid process of lt ulna, subsq enc for opn fx type I or II w/ malu
S52.045M	Nondisp fx of coronoid process of lt ulna, subsq enc for opn fx type I or II w/ nonu
S52.045R	Nondisp fx of coronoid process of lt ulna, subsq enc for opn fx type IIIA, IIIB, or IIIC w/ malu
S52.045N	Nondisp fx of coronoid process of lt ulna, subsq enc for opn fx type IIIA, IIIB, or IIIC w/ nonu
S52.044P	Nondisp fx of coronoid process of rt ulna, subsq enc for clsd fx w/ malu
S52.044K	Nondisp fx of coronoid process of rt ulna, subsq enc for clsd fx w/ nonu
S52.044Q	Nondisp fx of coronoid process of rt ulna, subsq enc for opn fx type I or II w/ malu
S52.044M	Nondisp fx of coronoid process of rt ulna, subsq enc for opn fx type I or II w/ nonu
S52.044R	Nondisp fx of coronoid process of rt ulna, subsq enc for opn fx type IIIA, IIIB, or IIIC w/ malu
S52.044N	Nondisp fx of coronoid process of rt ulna, subsq enc for opn fx type IIIA, IIIB, or IIIC w/ nonu
S52.046P	Nondisp fx of coronoid process of unsp ulna, subsq enc for clsd fx w/ malu
S52.046K	Nondisp fx of coronoid process of unsp ulna, subsq enc for clsd fx w/ nonu
S52.046Q	Nondisp fx of coronoid process of unsp ulna, subsq enc for opn fx type I or II w/ malu
S52.046M	Nondisp fx of coronoid process of unsp ulna, subsq enc for opn fx type I or II w/ nonu
S52.046R	Nondisp fx of coronoid process of unsp ulna, subsq enc for opn fx type IIIA, IIIB, or IIIC w/ malu
S52.046N	Nondisp fx of coronoid process of unsp ulna, subsq enc for opn fx type IIIA, IIIB, or IIIC w/ nonu
S92.215B	Nondisp fx of cuboid bone of lt foot, init enc for opn fx
S92.215P	Nondisp fx of cuboid bone of lt foot, subsq enc for fx w/ malu
S92.215K	Nondisp fx of cuboid bone of lt foot, subsq enc for fx w/ nonu
S92.214B	Nondisp fx of cuboid bone of rt foot, init enc for opn fx
S92.214P	Nondisp fx of cuboid bone of rt foot, subsq enc for fx w/ malu
S92.214K	Nondisp fx of cuboid bone of rt foot, subsq enc for fx w/ nonu
S92.216B	Nondisp fx of cuboid bone of unsp foot, init enc for opn fx
S92.216P	Nondisp fx of cuboid bone of unsp foot, subsq enc for fx w/ malu
S92.216K	Nondisp fx of cuboid bone of unsp foot, subsq enc for fx w/ nonu
S92.425P	Nondisp fx of distal phalanx of lt great toe, subsq enc for fx w/ malu
S92.425K	Nondisp fx of distal phalanx of lt great toe, subsq enc for fx w/ nonu
S62.661B	Nondisp fx of distal phalanx of lt index finger, init enc for opn fx
S62.661P	Nondisp fx of distal phalanx of lt index finger, subsq enc for fx w/ malu
S62.661K	Nondisp fx of distal phalanx of lt index finger, subsq enc for fx w/ nonu
S92.535P	Nondisp fx of distal phalanx of lt lesser toe(s), subsq enc for fx w/ malu
S92.535K	Nondisp fx of distal phalanx of lt lesser toe(s), subsq enc for fx w/ nonu
S62.667B	Nondisp fx of distal phalanx of lt little finger, init enc for opn fx
S62.667P	Nondisp fx of distal phalanx of lt little finger, subsq enc for fx w/ malu
S62.667K	Nondisp fx of distal phalanx of lt little finger, subsq enc for fx w/ nonu
S62.663B	Nondisp fx of distal phalanx of lt mid finger, init enc for opn fx
S62.663P	Nondisp fx of distal phalanx of lt mid finger, subsq enc for fx w/ malu
S62.663K	Nondisp fx of distal phalanx of lt mid finger, subsq enc for fx w/ nonu
S62.665B	Nondisp fx of distal phalanx of lt ring finger, init enc for opn fx
S62.665P	Nondisp fx of distal phalanx of lt ring finger, subsq enc for fx w/ malu
S62.665K	Nondisp fx of distal phalanx of lt ring finger, subsq enc for fx w/ nonu
S62.525B	Nondisp fx of distal phalanx of lt thumb, init enc for opn fx
S62.525P	Nondisp fx of distal phalanx of lt thumb, subsq enc for fx w/ malu
S62.525K	Nondisp fx of distal phalanx of lt thumb, subsq enc for fx w/ nonu
S62.668B	Nondisp fx of distal phalanx of oth finger, init enc for opn fx
S62.668P	Nondisp fx of distal phalanx of oth finger, subsq enc for fx w/ malu
S62.668K	Nondisp fx of distal phalanx of oth finger, subsq enc for fx w/ nonu
S92.424P	Nondisp fx of distal phalanx of rt great toe, subsq enc for fx w/ malu
S92.424K	Nondisp fx of distal phalanx of rt great toe, subsq enc for fx w/ nonu
S62.660B	Nondisp fx of distal phalanx of rt index finger, init enc for opn fx
S62.660P	Nondisp fx of distal phalanx of rt index finger, subsq enc for fx w/ malu
S62.660K	Nondisp fx of distal phalanx of rt index finger, subsq enc for fx w/ nonu
S92.534P	Nondisp fx of distal phalanx of rt lesser toe(s), subsq enc for fx w/ malu
S92.534K	Nondisp fx of distal phalanx of rt lesser toe(s), subsq enc for fx w/ nonu
S62.666B	Nondisp fx of distal phalanx of rt little finger, init enc for opn fx
S62.666P	Nondisp fx of distal phalanx of rt little finger, subsq enc for fx w/ malu
S62.666K	Nondisp fx of distal phalanx of rt little finger, subsq enc for fx w/ nonu
S62.662B	Nondisp fx of distal phalanx of rt mid finger, init enc for opn fx
S62.662P	Nondisp fx of distal phalanx of rt mid finger, subsq enc for fx w/ malu
S62.662K	Nondisp fx of distal phalanx of rt mid finger, subsq enc for fx w/ nonu
S62.664B	Nondisp fx of distal phalanx of rt ring finger, init enc for opn fx
S62.664P	Nondisp fx of distal phalanx of rt ring finger, subsq enc for fx w/ malu
S62.664K	Nondisp fx of distal phalanx of rt ring finger, subsq enc for fx w/ nonu
S62.524B	Nondisp fx of distal phalanx of rt thumb, init enc for opn fx
S62.524P	Nondisp fx of distal phalanx of rt thumb, subsq enc for fx w/ malu
S62.524K	Nondisp fx of distal phalanx of rt thumb, subsq enc for fx w/ nonu
S62.669B	Nondisp fx of distal phalanx of unsp finger, init enc for opn fx
S62.669P	Nondisp fx of distal phalanx of unsp finger, subsq enc for fx w/ malu
S62.669K	Nondisp fx of distal phalanx of unsp finger, subsq enc for fx w/ nonu
S92.426P	Nondisp fx of distal phalanx of unsp great toe, subsq enc for fx w/ malu
S92.426K	Nondisp fx of distal phalanx of unsp great toe, subsq enc for fx w/ nonu
S92.536P	Nondisp fx of distal phalanx of unsp lesser toe(s), subsq enc for fx w/ malu
S92.536K	Nondisp fx of distal phalanx of unsp lesser toe(s), subsq enc for fx w/ nonu
S62.526B	Nondisp fx of distal phalanx of unsp thumb, init enc for opn fx
S62.526P	Nondisp fx of distal phalanx of unsp thumb, subsq enc for fx w/ malu
S62.526K	Nondisp fx of distal phalanx of unsp thumb, subsq enc for fx w/ nonu
S62.015B	Nondisp fx of distal pole of navicular [scaphoid] bone of lt wrist, init enc for opn fx
S62.015P	Nondisp fx of distal pole of navicular [scaphoid] bone of lt wrist, subsq enc for fx w/ malu
S62.015K	Nondisp fx of distal pole of navicular [scaphoid] bone of lt wrist, subsq enc for fx w/ nonu
S62.014B	Nondisp fx of distal pole of navicular [scaphoid] bone of rt wrist, init enc for opn fx
S62.014P	Nondisp fx of distal pole of navicular [scaphoid] bone of rt wrist, subsq enc for fx w/ malu
S62.014K	Nondisp fx of distal pole of navicular [scaphoid] bone of rt wrist, subsq enc for fx w/ nonu
S62.016B	Nondisp fx of distal pole of navicular [scaphoid] bone of unsp wrist, init enc for opn fx
S62.016P	Nondisp fx of distal pole of navicular [scaphoid] bone of unsp wrist, subsq enc for fx w/ malu
S62.016K	Nondisp fx of distal pole of navicular [scaphoid] bone of unsp wrist, subsq enc for fx w/ nonu
S72.025P	Nondisp fx of epiphysis (separation) (upr) of lt femur, subsq enc for clsd fx w/ malu
S72.025K	Nondisp fx of epiphysis (separation) (upr) of lt femur, subsq enc for clsd fx w/ nonu
S72.025Q	Nondisp fx of epiphysis (separation) (upr) of lt femur, subsq enc for opn fx type I or II w/ malu
S72.025M	Nondisp fx of epiphysis (separation) (upr) of lt femur, subsq enc for opn fx type I or II w/ nonu
S72.025R	Nondisp fx of epiphysis (separation) (upr) of lt femur, subsq enc for opn fx type IIIA, IIIB, or IIIC w/ malu
S72.025N	Nondisp fx of epiphysis (separation) (upr) of lt femur, subsq enc for opn fx type IIIA, IIIB, or IIIC w/ nonu
S72.024P	Nondisp fx of epiphysis (separation) (upr) of rt femur, subsq enc for clsd fx w/ malu
S72.024K	Nondisp fx of epiphysis (separation) (upr) of rt femur, subsq enc for clsd fx w/ nonu
S72.024Q	Nondisp fx of epiphysis (separation) (upr) of rt femur, subsq enc for opn fx type I or II w/ malu
S72.024M	Nondisp fx of epiphysis (separation) (upr) of rt femur, subsq enc for opn fx type I or II w/ nonu
S72.024R	Nondisp fx of epiphysis (separation) (upr) of rt femur, subsq enc for opn fx type IIIA, IIIB, or IIIC w/ malu
S72.024N	Nondisp fx of epiphysis (separation) (upr) of rt femur, subsq enc for opn fx type IIIA, IIIB, or IIIC w/ nonu

S72.026P	Nondisp fx of epiphysis (separation) (upr) of unsp femur, subsq enc for clsd fx w/ malu
S72.026K	Nondisp fx of epiphysis (separation) (upr) of unsp femur, subsq enc for clsd fx w/ nonu
S72.026Q	Nondisp fx of epiphysis (separation) (upr) of unsp femur, subsq enc for opn fx type I or II w/ malu
S72.026M	Nondisp fx of epiphysis (separation) (upr) of unsp femur, subsq enc for opn fx type I or II w/ nonu
S72.026R	Nondisp fx of epiphysis (separation) (upr) of unsp femur, subsq enc for opn fx type IIIA, IIIB, or IIIC w/ malu
S72.026N	Nondisp fx of epiphysis (separation) (upr) of unsp femur, subsq enc for opn fx type IIIA, IIIB, or IIIC w/ nonu
S42.145B	Nondisp fx of glenoid cavity of scapula, lt shldr, init enc for opn fx
S42.145P	Nondisp fx of glenoid cavity of scapula, lt shldr, subsq enc for fx w/ malu
S42.145K	Nondisp fx of glenoid cavity of scapula, lt shldr, subsq enc for fx w/ nonu
S42.144B	Nondisp fx of glenoid cavity of scapula, rt shldr, init enc for opn fx
S42.144P	Nondisp fx of glenoid cavity of scapula, rt shldr, subsq enc for fx w/ malu
S42.144K	Nondisp fx of glenoid cavity of scapula, rt shldr, subsq enc for fx w/ nonu
S42.146B	Nondisp fx of glenoid cavity of scapula, unsp shldr, init enc for opn fx
S42.146P	Nondisp fx of glenoid cavity of scapula, unsp shldr, subsq enc for fx w/ malu
S42.146K	Nondisp fx of glenoid cavity of scapula, unsp shldr, subsq enc for fx w/ nonu
S72.115P	Nondisp fx of greater trochanter of lt femur, subsq enc for clsd fx w/ malu
S72.115K	Nondisp fx of greater trochanter of lt femur, subsq enc for clsd fx w/ nonu
S72.115Q	Nondisp fx of greater trochanter of lt femur, subsq enc for opn fx type I or II w/ malu
S72.115M	Nondisp fx of greater trochanter of lt femur, subsq enc for opn fx type I or II w/ nonu
S72.115R	Nondisp fx of greater trochanter of lt femur, subsq enc for opn fx type IIIA, IIIB, or IIIC w/ malu
S72.115N	Nondisp fx of greater trochanter of lt femur, subsq enc for opn fx type IIIA, IIIB, or IIIC w/ nonu
S72.114P	Nondisp fx of greater trochanter of rt femur, subsq enc for clsd fx w/ malu
S72.114K	Nondisp fx of greater trochanter of rt femur, subsq enc for clsd fx w/ nonu
S72.114Q	Nondisp fx of greater trochanter of rt femur, subsq enc for opn fx type I or II w/ malu
S72.114M	Nondisp fx of greater trochanter of rt femur, subsq enc for opn fx type I or II w/ nonu
S72.114R	Nondisp fx of greater trochanter of rt femur, subsq enc for opn fx type IIIA, IIIB, or IIIC w/ malu
S72.114N	Nondisp fx of greater trochanter of rt femur, subsq enc for opn fx type IIIA, IIIB, or IIIC w/ nonu
S72.116P	Nondisp fx of greater trochanter of unsp femur, subsq enc for clsd fx w/ malu
S72.116K	Nondisp fx of greater trochanter of unsp femur, subsq enc for clsd fx w/ nonu
S72.116Q	Nondisp fx of greater trochanter of unsp femur, subsq enc for opn fx type I or II w/ malu
S72.116M	Nondisp fx of greater trochanter of unsp femur, subsq enc for opn fx type I or II w/ nonu
S72.116R	Nondisp fx of greater trochanter of unsp femur, subsq enc for opn fx type IIIA, IIIB, or IIIC w/ malu
S72.116N	Nondisp fx of greater trochanter of unsp femur, subsq enc for opn fx type IIIA, IIIB, or IIIC w/ nonu
S42.255A	Nondisp fx of greater tuberosity of lt humerus, init enc for clsd fx
S42.255P	Nondisp fx of greater tuberosity of lt humerus, subsq enc for fx w/ malu
S42.255K	Nondisp fx of greater tuberosity of lt humerus, subsq enc for fx w/ nonu
S42.254A	Nondisp fx of greater tuberosity of rt humerus, init enc for clsd fx
S42.254P	Nondisp fx of greater tuberosity of rt humerus, subsq enc for fx w/ malu
S42.254K	Nondisp fx of greater tuberosity of rt humerus, subsq enc for fx w/ nonu
S42.256A	Nondisp fx of greater tuberosity of unsp humerus, init enc for clsd fx
S42.256P	Nondisp fx of greater tuberosity of unsp humerus, subsq enc for fx w/ malu
S42.256K	Nondisp fx of greater tuberosity of unsp humerus, subsq enc for fx w/ nonu
S52.125P	Nondisp fx of head of lt radius, subsq enc for clsd fx w/ malu
S52.125K	Nondisp fx of head of lt radius, subsq enc for clsd fx w/ nonu
S52.125Q	Nondisp fx of head of lt radius, subsq enc for opn fx type I or II w/ malu
S52.125M	Nondisp fx of head of lt radius, subsq enc for opn fx type I or II w/ nonu
S52.125R	Nondisp fx of head of lt radius, subsq enc for opn fx type IIIA, IIIB, or IIIC w/ malu
S52.125N	Nondisp fx of head of lt radius, subsq enc for opn fx type IIIA, IIIB, or IIIC w/ nonu
S52.124P	Nondisp fx of head of rt radius, subsq enc for clsd fx w/ malu
S52.124K	Nondisp fx of head of rt radius, subsq enc for clsd fx w/ nonu
S52.124Q	Nondisp fx of head of rt radius, subsq enc for opn fx type I or II w/ malu
S52.124M	Nondisp fx of head of rt radius, subsq enc for opn fx type I or II w/ nonu
S52.124R	Nondisp fx of head of rt radius, subsq enc for opn fx type IIIA, IIIB, or IIIC w/ malu
S52.124N	Nondisp fx of head of rt radius, subsq enc for opn fx type IIIA, IIIB, or IIIC w/ nonu
S52.126P	Nondisp fx of head of unsp radius, subsq enc for clsd fx w/ malu
S52.126K	Nondisp fx of head of unsp radius, subsq enc for clsd fx w/ nonu
S52.126Q	Nondisp fx of head of unsp radius, subsq enc for opn fx type I or II w/ malu
S52.126M	Nondisp fx of head of unsp radius, subsq enc for opn fx type I or II w/ nonu
S52.126R	Nondisp fx of head of unsp radius, subsq enc for opn fx type IIIA, IIIB, or IIIC w/ malu
S52.126N	Nondisp fx of head of unsp radius, subsq enc for opn fx type IIIA, IIIB, or IIIC w/ nonu
S62.155B	Nondisp fx of hook process of hamate [unciform] bone, lt wrist, init enc for opn fx
S62.155P	Nondisp fx of hook process of hamate [unciform] bone, lt wrist, subsq enc for fx w/ malu
S62.155K	Nondisp fx of hook process of hamate [unciform] bone, lt wrist, subsq enc for fx w/ nonu
S62.154B	Nondisp fx of hook process of hamate [unciform] bone, rt wrist, init enc for opn fx
S62.154P	Nondisp fx of hook process of hamate [unciform] bone, rt wrist, subsq enc for fx w/ malu
S62.154K	Nondisp fx of hook process of hamate [unciform] bone, rt wrist, subsq enc for fx w/ nonu
S62.156B	Nondisp fx of hook process of hamate [unciform] bone, unsp wrist, init enc for opn fx
S62.156P	Nondisp fx of hook process of hamate [unciform] bone, unsp wrist, subsq enc for fx w/ malu
S62.156K	Nondisp fx of hook process of hamate [unciform] bone, unsp wrist, subsq enc for fx w/ nonu
S92.235B	Nondisp fx of intermediate cuneiform of lt foot, init enc for opn fx
S92.235P	Nondisp fx of intermediate cuneiform of lt foot, subsq enc for fx w/ malu
S92.235K	Nondisp fx of intermediate cuneiform of lt foot, subsq enc for fx w/ nonu
S92.234B	Nondisp fx of intermediate cuneiform of rt foot, init enc for opn fx
S92.234P	Nondisp fx of intermediate cuneiform of rt foot, subsq enc for fx w/ malu
S92.234K	Nondisp fx of intermediate cuneiform of rt foot, subsq enc for fx w/ nonu
S92.236B	Nondisp fx of intermediate cuneiform of unsp foot, init enc for opn fx
S92.236P	Nondisp fx of intermediate cuneiform of unsp foot, subsq enc for fx w/ malu
S92.236K	Nondisp fx of intermediate cuneiform of unsp foot, subsq enc for fx w/ nonu
S72.425A	Nondisp fx of lat condyle of lt femur, init enc for clsd fx
S72.425P	Nondisp fx of lat condyle of lt femur, subsq enc for clsd fx w/ malu
S72.425K	Nondisp fx of lat condyle of lt femur, subsq enc for clsd fx w/ nonu
S72.425Q	Nondisp fx of lat condyle of lt femur, subsq enc for opn fx type I or II w/ malu
S72.425M	Nondisp fx of lat condyle of lt femur, subsq enc for opn fx type I or II w/ nonu
S72.425R	Nondisp fx of lat condyle of lt femur, subsq enc for opn fx type IIIA, IIIB, or IIIC w/ malu
S72.425N	Nondisp fx of lat condyle of lt femur, subsq enc for opn fx type IIIA, IIIB, or IIIC w/ nonu
S42.455A	Nondisp fx of lat condyle of lt humerus, init enc for clsd fx
S42.455P	Nondisp fx of lat condyle of lt humerus, subsq enc for fx w/ malu
S42.455K	Nondisp fx of lat condyle of lt humerus, subsq enc for fx w/ nonu
S82.125A	Nondisp fx of lat condyle of lt tibia, init enc for clsd fx
S82.125P	Nondisp fx of lat condyle of lt tibia, subsq enc for clsd fx w/ malu
S82.125K	Nondisp fx of lat condyle of lt tibia, subsq enc for clsd fx w/ nonu
S82.125Q	Nondisp fx of lat condyle of lt tibia, subsq enc for opn fx type I or II w/ malu
S82.125M	Nondisp fx of lat condyle of lt tibia, subsq enc for opn fx type I or II w/ nonu
S82.125R	Nondisp fx of lat condyle of lt tibia, subsq enc for opn fx type IIIA, IIIB, or IIIC w/ malu
S82.125N	Nondisp fx of lat condyle of lt tibia, subsq enc for opn fx type IIIA, IIIB, or IIIC w/ nonu
S72.424A	Nondisp fx of lat condyle of rt femur, init enc for clsd fx
S72.424P	Nondisp fx of lat condyle of rt femur, subsq enc for clsd fx w/ malu

S72.424K	Nondisp fx of lat condyle of rt femur, subsq enc for clsd fx w/ nonu
S72.424Q	Nondisp fx of lat condyle of rt femur, subsq enc for opn fx type I or II w/ malu
S72.424M	Nondisp fx of lat condyle of rt femur, subsq enc for opn fx type I or II w/ nonu
S72.424R	Nondisp fx of lat condyle of rt femur, subsq enc for opn fx type IIIA, IIIB, or IIIC w/ malu
S72.424N	Nondisp fx of lat condyle of rt femur, subsq enc for opn fx type IIIA, IIIB, or IIIC w/ nonu
S42.454A	Nondisp fx of lat condyle of rt humerus, init enc for clsd fx
S42.454P	Nondisp fx of lat condyle of rt humerus, subsq enc for fx w/ malu
S42.454K	Nondisp fx of lat condyle of rt humerus, subsq enc for fx w/ nonu
S82.124A	Nondisp fx of lat condyle of rt tibia, init enc for clsd fx
S82.124P	Nondisp fx of lat condyle of rt tibia, subsq enc for clsd fx w/ malu
S82.124K	Nondisp fx of lat condyle of rt tibia, subsq enc for clsd fx w/ nonu
S82.124Q	Nondisp fx of lat condyle of rt tibia, subsq enc for opn fx type I or II w/ malu
S82.124M	Nondisp fx of lat condyle of rt tibia, subsq enc for opn fx type I or II w/ nonu
S82.124R	Nondisp fx of lat condyle of rt tibia, subsq enc for opn fx type IIIA, IIIB, or IIIC w/ malu
S82.124N	Nondisp fx of lat condyle of rt tibia, subsq enc for opn fx type IIIA, IIIB, or IIIC w/ nonu
S72.426A	Nondisp fx of lat condyle of unsp femur, init enc for clsd fx
S72.426P	Nondisp fx of lat condyle of unsp femur, subsq enc for clsd fx w/ malu
S72.426K	Nondisp fx of lat condyle of unsp femur, subsq enc for clsd fx w/ nonu
S72.426Q	Nondisp fx of lat condyle of unsp femur, subsq enc for opn fx type I or II w/ malu
S72.426M	Nondisp fx of lat condyle of unsp femur, subsq enc for opn fx type I or II w/ nonu
S72.426R	Nondisp fx of lat condyle of unsp femur, subsq enc for opn fx type IIIA, IIIB, or IIIC w/ malu
S72.426N	Nondisp fx of lat condyle of unsp femur, subsq enc for opn fx type IIIA, IIIB, or IIIC w/ nonu
S42.456A	Nondisp fx of lat condyle of unsp humerus, init enc for clsd fx
S42.456P	Nondisp fx of lat condyle of unsp humerus, subsq enc for fx w/ malu
S42.456K	Nondisp fx of lat condyle of unsp humerus, subsq enc for fx w/ nonu
S82.126A	Nondisp fx of lat condyle of unsp tibia, init enc for clsd fx
S82.126P	Nondisp fx of lat condyle of unsp tibia, subsq enc for clsd fx w/ malu
S82.126K	Nondisp fx of lat condyle of unsp tibia, subsq enc for clsd fx w/ nonu
S82.126Q	Nondisp fx of lat condyle of unsp tibia, subsq enc for opn fx type I or II w/ malu
S82.126M	Nondisp fx of lat condyle of unsp tibia, subsq enc for opn fx type I or II w/ nonu
S82.126R	Nondisp fx of lat condyle of unsp tibia, subsq enc for opn fx type IIIA, IIIB, or IIIC w/ malu
S82.126N	Nondisp fx of lat condyle of unsp tibia, subsq enc for opn fx type IIIA, IIIB, or IIIC w/ nonu
S92.225B	Nondisp fx of lat cuneiform of lt foot, init enc for opn fx
S92.225P	Nondisp fx of lat cuneiform of lt foot, subsq enc for fx w/ malu
S92.225K	Nondisp fx of lat cuneiform of lt foot, subsq enc for fx w/ nonu
S92.224B	Nondisp fx of lat cuneiform of rt foot, init enc for opn fx
S92.224P	Nondisp fx of lat cuneiform of rt foot, subsq enc for fx w/ malu
S92.224K	Nondisp fx of lat cuneiform of rt foot, subsq enc for fx w/ nonu
S92.226B	Nondisp fx of lat cuneiform of unsp foot, init enc for opn fx
S92.226P	Nondisp fx of lat cuneiform of unsp foot, subsq enc for fx w/ malu
S92.226K	Nondisp fx of lat cuneiform of unsp foot, subsq enc for fx w/ nonu
S42.035B	Nondisp fx of lat end of lt clavicle, init enc for opn fx
S42.035P	Nondisp fx of lat end of lt clavicle, subsq enc for fx w/ malu
S42.035K	Nondisp fx of lat end of lt clavicle, subsq enc for fx w/ nonu
S42.034B	Nondisp fx of lat end of rt clavicle, init enc for opn fx
S42.034P	Nondisp fx of lat end of rt clavicle, subsq enc for fx w/ malu
S42.034K	Nondisp fx of lat end of rt clavicle, subsq enc for fx w/ nonu
S42.036B	Nondisp fx of lat end of unsp clavicle, init enc for opn fx
S42.036P	Nondisp fx of lat end of unsp clavicle, subsq enc for fx w/ malu
S42.036K	Nondisp fx of lat end of unsp clavicle, subsq enc for fx w/ nonu
S82.65XB	Nondisp fx of lat malleolus of lt fibula, init enc for opn fx type I or II
S82.65XC	Nondisp fx of lat malleolus of lt fibula, init enc for opn fx type IIIA, IIIB, or IIIC
S82.65XP	Nondisp fx of lat malleolus of lt fibula, subsq enc for clsd fx w/ malu
S82.65XK	Nondisp fx of lat malleolus of lt fibula, subsq enc for clsd fx w/ nonu
S82.65XQ	Nondisp fx of lat malleolus of lt fibula, subsq enc for opn fx type I or II w/ malu
S82.65XM	Nondisp fx of lat malleolus of lt fibula, subsq enc for opn fx type I or II w/ nonu
S82.65XR	Nondisp fx of lat malleolus of lt fibula, subsq enc for opn fx type IIIA, IIIB, or IIIC w/ malu
S82.65XN	Nondisp fx of lat malleolus of lt fibula, subsq enc for opn fx type IIIA, IIIB, or IIIC w/ nonu
S82.64XB	Nondisp fx of lat malleolus of rt fibula, init enc for opn fx type I or II
S82.64XC	Nondisp fx of lat malleolus of rt fibula, init enc for opn fx type IIIA, IIIB, or IIIC
S82.64XP	Nondisp fx of lat malleolus of rt fibula, subsq enc for clsd fx w/ malu
S82.64XK	Nondisp fx of lat malleolus of rt fibula, subsq enc for clsd fx w/ nonu
S82.64XQ	Nondisp fx of lat malleolus of rt fibula, subsq enc for opn fx type I or II w/ malu
S82.64XM	Nondisp fx of lat malleolus of rt fibula, subsq enc for opn fx type I or II w/ nonu
S82.64XR	Nondisp fx of lat malleolus of rt fibula, subsq enc for opn fx type IIIA, IIIB, or IIIC w/ malu
S82.64XN	Nondisp fx of lat malleolus of rt fibula, subsq enc for opn fx type IIIA, IIIB, or IIIC w/ nonu
S82.66XB	Nondisp fx of lat malleolus of unsp fibula, init enc for opn fx type I or II
S82.66XC	Nondisp fx of lat malleolus of unsp fibula, init enc for opn fx type IIIA, IIIB, or IIIC
S82.66XP	Nondisp fx of lat malleolus of unsp fibula, subsq enc for clsd fx w/ malu
S82.66XK	Nondisp fx of lat malleolus of unsp fibula, subsq enc for clsd fx w/ nonu
S82.66XQ	Nondisp fx of lat malleolus of unsp fibula, subsq enc for opn fx type I or II w/ malu
S82.66XM	Nondisp fx of lat malleolus of unsp fibula, subsq enc for opn fx type I or II w/ nonu
S82.66XR	Nondisp fx of lat malleolus of unsp fibula, subsq enc for opn fx type IIIA, IIIB, or IIIC w/ malu
S82.66XN	Nondisp fx of lat malleolus of unsp fibula, subsq enc for opn fx type IIIA, IIIB, or IIIC w/ nonu
S72.125P	Nondisp fx of lesser trochanter of lt femur, subsq enc for clsd fx w/ malu
S72.125K	Nondisp fx of lesser trochanter of lt femur, subsq enc for clsd fx w/ nonu
S72.125Q	Nondisp fx of lesser trochanter of lt femur, subsq enc for opn fx type I or II w/ malu
S72.125M	Nondisp fx of lesser trochanter of lt femur, subsq enc for opn fx type I or II w/ nonu
S72.125R	Nondisp fx of lesser trochanter of lt femur, subsq enc for opn fx type IIIA, IIIB, or IIIC w/ malu
S72.125N	Nondisp fx of lesser trochanter of lt femur, subsq enc for opn fx type IIIA, IIIB, or IIIC w/ nonu
S72.124P	Nondisp fx of lesser trochanter of rt femur, subsq enc for clsd fx w/ malu
S72.124K	Nondisp fx of lesser trochanter of rt femur, subsq enc for clsd fx w/ nonu
S72.124Q	Nondisp fx of lesser trochanter of rt femur, subsq enc for opn fx type I or II w/ malu
S72.124M	Nondisp fx of lesser trochanter of rt femur, subsq enc for opn fx type I or II w/ nonu
S72.124R	Nondisp fx of lesser trochanter of rt femur, subsq enc for opn fx type IIIA, IIIB, or IIIC w/ malu
S72.124N	Nondisp fx of lesser trochanter of rt femur, subsq enc for opn fx type IIIA, IIIB, or IIIC w/ nonu
S72.126P	Nondisp fx of lesser trochanter of unsp femur, subsq enc for clsd fx w/ malu
S72.126K	Nondisp fx of lesser trochanter of unsp femur, subsq enc for clsd fx w/ nonu
S72.126Q	Nondisp fx of lesser trochanter of unsp femur, subsq enc for opn fx type I or II w/ malu
S72.126M	Nondisp fx of lesser trochanter of unsp femur, subsq enc for opn fx type I or II w/ nonu
S72.126R	Nondisp fx of lesser trochanter of unsp femur, subsq enc for opn fx type IIIA, IIIB, or IIIC w/ malu
S72.126N	Nondisp fx of lesser trochanter of unsp femur, subsq enc for opn fx type IIIA, IIIB, or IIIC w/ nonu
S42.265A	Nondisp fx of lesser tuberosity of lt humerus, init enc for clsd fx
S42.265P	Nondisp fx of lesser tuberosity of lt humerus, subsq enc for fx w/ malu
S42.265K	Nondisp fx of lesser tuberosity of lt humerus, subsq enc for fx w/ nonu
S42.264A	Nondisp fx of lesser tuberosity of rt humerus, init enc for clsd fx
S42.264P	Nondisp fx of lesser tuberosity of rt humerus, subsq enc for fx w/ malu
S42.264K	Nondisp fx of lesser tuberosity of rt humerus, subsq enc for fx w/ nonu
S42.266A	Nondisp fx of lesser tuberosity of unsp humerus, init enc for clsd fx
S42.266P	Nondisp fx of lesser tuberosity of unsp humerus, subsq enc for fx w/ malu
S42.266K	Nondisp fx of lesser tuberosity of unsp humerus, subsq enc for fx w/ nonu
S52.515A	Nondisp fx of lt radial styloid process, init enc for clsd fx
S52.515P	Nondisp fx of lt radial styloid process, subsq enc for clsd fx w/ malu
S52.515K	Nondisp fx of lt radial styloid process, subsq enc for clsd fx w/ nonu

S52.515Q	Nondisp fx of lt radial styloid process, subsq enc for opn fx type I or II w/ malu
S52.515M	Nondisp fx of lt radial styloid process, subsq enc for opn fx type I or II w/ nonu
S52.515R	Nondisp fx of lt radial styloid process, subsq enc for opn fx type IIIA, IIIB, or IIIC w/ malu
S52.515N	Nondisp fx of lt radial styloid process, subsq enc for opn fx type IIIA, IIIB, or IIIC w/ nonu
S82.115A	Nondisp fx of lt tibial spine, init enc for clsd fx
S82.115P	Nondisp fx of lt tibial spine, subsq enc for clsd fx w/ malu
S82.115K	Nondisp fx of lt tibial spine, subsq enc for clsd fx w/ nonu
S82.115Q	Nondisp fx of lt tibial spine, subsq enc for opn fx type I or II w/ malu
S82.115M	Nondisp fx of lt tibial spine, subsq enc for opn fx type I or II w/ nonu
S82.115R	Nondisp fx of lt tibial spine, subsq enc for opn fx type IIIA, IIIB, or IIIC w/ malu
S82.115N	Nondisp fx of lt tibial spine, subsq enc for opn fx type IIIA, IIIB, or IIIC w/ nonu
S82.155A	Nondisp fx of lt tibial tuberosity, init enc for clsd fx
S82.155P	Nondisp fx of lt tibial tuberosity, subsq enc for clsd fx w/ malu
S82.155K	Nondisp fx of lt tibial tuberosity, subsq enc for clsd fx w/ nonu
S82.155Q	Nondisp fx of lt tibial tuberosity, subsq enc for opn fx type I or II w/ malu
S82.155M	Nondisp fx of lt tibial tuberosity, subsq enc for opn fx type I or II w/ nonu
S82.155R	Nondisp fx of lt tibial tuberosity, subsq enc for opn fx type IIIA, IIIB, or IIIC w/ malu
S82.155N	Nondisp fx of lt tibial tuberosity, subsq enc for opn fx type IIIA, IIIB, or IIIC w/ nonu
S52.615A	Nondisp fx of lt ulna styloid process, init enc for clsd fx
S52.615P	Nondisp fx of lt ulna styloid process, subsq enc for clsd fx w/ malu
S52.615K	Nondisp fx of lt ulna styloid process, subsq enc for clsd fx w/ nonu
S52.615Q	Nondisp fx of lt ulna styloid process, subsq enc for opn fx type I or II w/ malu
S52.615M	Nondisp fx of lt ulna styloid process, subsq enc for opn fx type I or II w/ nonu
S52.615R	Nondisp fx of lt ulna styloid process, subsq enc for opn fx type IIIA, IIIB, or IIIC w/ malu
S52.615N	Nondisp fx of lt ulna styloid process, subsq enc for opn fx type IIIA, IIIB, or IIIC w/ nonu
S62.125B	Nondisp fx of lunate [semilunar], lt wrist, init enc for opn fx
S62.125P	Nondisp fx of lunate [semilunar], lt wrist, subsq enc for fx w/ malu
S62.125K	Nondisp fx of lunate [semilunar], lt wrist, subsq enc for fx w/ nonu
S62.124B	Nondisp fx of lunate [semilunar], rt wrist, init enc for opn fx
S62.124P	Nondisp fx of lunate [semilunar], rt wrist, subsq enc for fx w/ malu
S62.124K	Nondisp fx of lunate [semilunar], rt wrist, subsq enc for fx w/ nonu
S62.126B	Nondisp fx of lunate [semilunar], unsp wrist, init enc for opn fx
S62.126P	Nondisp fx of lunate [semilunar], unsp wrist, subsq enc for fx w/ malu
S62.126K	Nondisp fx of lunate [semilunar], unsp wrist, subsq enc for fx w/ nonu
S72.445A	Nondisp fx of lwr epiphysis (separation) of lt femur, init enc for clsd fx
S72.445P	Nondisp fx of lwr epiphysis (separation) of lt femur, subsq enc for clsd fx w/ malu
S72.445K	Nondisp fx of lwr epiphysis (separation) of lt femur, subsq enc for clsd fx w/ nonu
S72.445Q	Nondisp fx of lwr epiphysis (separation) of lt femur, subsq enc for opn fx type I or II w/ malu
S72.445M	Nondisp fx of lwr epiphysis (separation) of lt femur, subsq enc for opn fx type I or II w/ nonu
S72.445R	Nondisp fx of lwr epiphysis (separation) of lt femur, subsq enc for opn fx type IIIA, IIIB, or IIIC w/ malu
S72.445N	Nondisp fx of lwr epiphysis (separation) of lt femur, subsq enc for opn fx type IIIA, IIIB, or IIIC w/ nonu
S72.444A	Nondisp fx of lwr epiphysis (separation) of rt femur, init enc for clsd fx
S72.444P	Nondisp fx of lwr epiphysis (separation) of rt femur, subsq enc for clsd fx w/ malu
S72.444K	Nondisp fx of lwr epiphysis (separation) of rt femur, subsq enc for clsd fx w/ nonu
S72.444Q	Nondisp fx of lwr epiphysis (separation) of rt femur, subsq enc for opn fx type I or II w/ malu
S72.444M	Nondisp fx of lwr epiphysis (separation) of rt femur, subsq enc for opn fx type I or II w/ nonu
S72.444R	Nondisp fx of lwr epiphysis (separation) of rt femur, subsq enc for opn fx type IIIA, IIIB, or IIIC w/ malu
S72.444N	Nondisp fx of lwr epiphysis (separation) of rt femur, subsq enc for opn fx type IIIA, IIIB, or IIIC w/ nonu
S72.446A	Nondisp fx of lwr epiphysis (separation) of unsp femur, init enc for clsd fx
S72.446P	Nondisp fx of lwr epiphysis (separation) of unsp femur, subsq enc for clsd fx w/ malu

S72.446K	Nondisp fx of lwr epiphysis (separation) of unsp femur, subsq enc for clsd fx w/ nonu
S72.446Q	Nondisp fx of lwr epiphysis (separation) of unsp femur, subsq enc for opn fx type I or II w/ malu
S72.446M	Nondisp fx of lwr epiphysis (separation) of unsp femur, subsq enc for opn fx type I or II w/ nonu
S72.446R	Nondisp fx of lwr epiphysis (separation) of unsp femur, subsq enc for opn fx type IIIA, IIIB, or IIIC w/ malu
S72.446N	Nondisp fx of lwr epiphysis (separation) of unsp femur, subsq enc for opn fx type IIIA, IIIB, or IIIC w/ nonu
S72.435A	Nondisp fx of med condyle of lt femur, init enc for clsd fx
S72.435P	Nondisp fx of med condyle of lt femur, subsq enc for clsd fx w/ malu
S72.435K	Nondisp fx of med condyle of lt femur, subsq enc for clsd fx w/ nonu
S72.435Q	Nondisp fx of med condyle of lt femur, subsq enc for opn fx type I or II w/ malu
S72.435M	Nondisp fx of med condyle of lt femur, subsq enc for opn fx type I or II w/ nonu
S72.435R	Nondisp fx of med condyle of lt femur, subsq enc for opn fx type IIIA, IIIB, or IIIC w/ malu
S72.435N	Nondisp fx of med condyle of lt femur, subsq enc for opn fx type IIIA, IIIB, or IIIC w/ nonu
S42.465A	Nondisp fx of med condyle of lt humerus, init enc for clsd fx
S42.465P	Nondisp fx of med condyle of lt humerus, subsq enc for fx w/ malu
S42.465K	Nondisp fx of med condyle of lt humerus, subsq enc for fx w/ nonu
S82.135A	Nondisp fx of med condyle of lt tibia, init enc for clsd fx
S82.135P	Nondisp fx of med condyle of lt tibia, subsq enc for clsd fx w/ malu
S82.135K	Nondisp fx of med condyle of lt tibia, subsq enc for clsd fx w/ nonu
S82.135Q	Nondisp fx of med condyle of lt tibia, subsq enc for opn fx type I or II w/ malu
S82.135M	Nondisp fx of med condyle of lt tibia, subsq enc for opn fx type I or II w/ nonu
S82.135R	Nondisp fx of med condyle of lt tibia, subsq enc for opn fx type IIIA, IIIB, or IIIC w/ malu
S82.135N	Nondisp fx of med condyle of lt tibia, subsq enc for opn fx type IIIA, IIIB, or IIIC w/ nonu
S72.434A	Nondisp fx of med condyle of rt femur, init enc for clsd fx
S72.434P	Nondisp fx of med condyle of rt femur, subsq enc for clsd fx w/ malu
S72.434K	Nondisp fx of med condyle of rt femur, subsq enc for clsd fx w/ nonu
S72.434Q	Nondisp fx of med condyle of rt femur, subsq enc for opn fx type I or II w/ malu
S72.434M	Nondisp fx of med condyle of rt femur, subsq enc for opn fx type I or II w/ nonu
S72.434R	Nondisp fx of med condyle of rt femur, subsq enc for opn fx type IIIA, IIIB, or IIIC w/ malu
S72.434N	Nondisp fx of med condyle of rt femur, subsq enc for opn fx type IIIA, IIIB, or IIIC w/ nonu
S42.464A	Nondisp fx of med condyle of rt humerus, init enc for clsd fx
S42.464P	Nondisp fx of med condyle of rt humerus, subsq enc for fx w/ malu
S42.464K	Nondisp fx of med condyle of rt humerus, subsq enc for fx w/ nonu
S82.134A	Nondisp fx of med condyle of rt tibia, init enc for clsd fx
S82.134P	Nondisp fx of med condyle of rt tibia, subsq enc for clsd fx w/ malu
S82.134K	Nondisp fx of med condyle of rt tibia, subsq enc for clsd fx w/ nonu
S82.134Q	Nondisp fx of med condyle of rt tibia, subsq enc for opn fx type I or II w/ malu
S82.134M	Nondisp fx of med condyle of rt tibia, subsq enc for opn fx type I or II w/ nonu
S82.134R	Nondisp fx of med condyle of rt tibia, subsq enc for opn fx type IIIA, IIIB, or IIIC w/ malu
S82.134N	Nondisp fx of med condyle of rt tibia, subsq enc for opn fx type IIIA, IIIB, or IIIC w/ nonu
S72.436A	Nondisp fx of med condyle of unsp femur, init enc for clsd fx
S72.436P	Nondisp fx of med condyle of unsp femur, subsq enc for clsd fx w/ malu
S72.436K	Nondisp fx of med condyle of unsp femur, subsq enc for clsd fx w/ nonu
S72.436Q	Nondisp fx of med condyle of unsp femur, subsq enc for opn fx type I or II w/ malu
S72.436M	Nondisp fx of med condyle of unsp femur, subsq enc for opn fx type I or II w/ nonu
S72.436R	Nondisp fx of med condyle of unsp femur, subsq enc for opn fx type IIIA, IIIB, or IIIC w/ malu
S72.436N	Nondisp fx of med condyle of unsp femur, subsq enc for opn fx type IIIA, IIIB, or IIIC w/ nonu
S42.466A	Nondisp fx of med condyle of unsp humerus, init enc for clsd fx
S42.466P	Nondisp fx of med condyle of unsp humerus, subsq enc for fx w/ malu
S42.466K	Nondisp fx of med condyle of unsp humerus, subsq enc for fx w/ nonu
S82.136A	Nondisp fx of med condyle of unsp tibia, init enc for clsd fx
S82.136P	Nondisp fx of med condyle of unsp tibia, subsq enc for clsd fx w/ malu

Code	Description
S82.136K	Nondisp fx of med condyle of unsp tibia, subsq enc for clsd fx w/ nonu
S82.136Q	Nondisp fx of med condyle of unsp tibia, subsq enc for opn fx type I or II w/ malu
S82.136M	Nondisp fx of med condyle of unsp tibia, subsq enc for opn fx type I or II w/ nonu
S82.136R	Nondisp fx of med condyle of unsp tibia, subsq enc for opn fx type IIIA, IIIB, or IIIC w/ malu
S82.136N	Nondisp fx of med condyle of unsp tibia, subsq enc for opn fx type IIIA, IIIB, or IIIC w/ nonu
S92.245B	Nondisp fx of med cuneiform of lt foot, init enc for opn fx
S92.245P	Nondisp fx of med cuneiform of lt foot, subsq enc for fx w/ malu
S92.245K	Nondisp fx of med cuneiform of lt foot, subsq enc for fx w/ nonu
S92.244B	Nondisp fx of med cuneiform of rt foot, init enc for opn fx
S92.244P	Nondisp fx of med cuneiform of rt foot, subsq enc for fx w/ malu
S92.244K	Nondisp fx of med cuneiform of rt foot, subsq enc for fx w/ nonu
S92.246B	Nondisp fx of med cuneiform of unsp foot, init enc for opn fx
S92.246P	Nondisp fx of med cuneiform of unsp foot, subsq enc for fx w/ malu
S92.246K	Nondisp fx of med cuneiform of unsp foot, subsq enc for fx w/ nonu
S82.55XB	Nondisp fx of med malleolus of lt tibia, init enc for opn fx type I or II
S82.55XC	Nondisp fx of med malleolus of lt tibia, init enc for opn fx type IIIA, IIIB, or IIIC
S82.55XP	Nondisp fx of med malleolus of lt tibia, subsq enc for clsd fx w/ malu
S82.55XK	Nondisp fx of med malleolus of lt tibia, subsq enc for clsd fx w/ nonu
S82.55XQ	Nondisp fx of med malleolus of lt tibia, subsq enc for opn fx type I or II w/ malu
S82.55XM	Nondisp fx of med malleolus of lt tibia, subsq enc for opn fx type I or II w/ nonu
S82.55XR	Nondisp fx of med malleolus of lt tibia, subsq enc for opn fx type IIIA, IIIB, or IIIC w/ malu
S82.55XN	Nondisp fx of med malleolus of lt tibia, subsq enc for opn fx type IIIA, IIIB, or IIIC w/ nonu
S82.54XB	Nondisp fx of med malleolus of rt tibia, init enc for opn fx type I or II
S82.54XC	Nondisp fx of med malleolus of rt tibia, init enc for opn fx type IIIA, IIIB, or IIIC
S82.54XP	Nondisp fx of med malleolus of rt tibia, subsq enc for clsd fx w/ malu
S82.54XK	Nondisp fx of med malleolus of rt tibia, subsq enc for clsd fx w/ nonu
S82.54XQ	Nondisp fx of med malleolus of rt tibia, subsq enc for opn fx type I or II w/ malu
S82.54XM	Nondisp fx of med malleolus of rt tibia, subsq enc for opn fx type I or II w/ nonu
S82.54XR	Nondisp fx of med malleolus of rt tibia, subsq enc for opn fx type IIIA, IIIB, or IIIC w/ malu
S82.54XN	Nondisp fx of med malleolus of rt tibia, subsq enc for opn fx type IIIA, IIIB, or IIIC w/ nonu
S82.56XB	Nondisp fx of med malleolus of unsp tibia, init enc for opn fx type I or II
S82.56XC	Nondisp fx of med malleolus of unsp tibia, init enc for opn fx type IIIA, IIIB, or IIIC
S82.56XP	Nondisp fx of med malleolus of unsp tibia, subsq enc for clsd fx w/ malu
S82.56XK	Nondisp fx of med malleolus of unsp tibia, subsq enc for clsd fx w/ nonu
S82.56XQ	Nondisp fx of med malleolus of unsp tibia, subsq enc for opn fx type I or II w/ malu
S82.56XM	Nondisp fx of med malleolus of unsp tibia, subsq enc for opn fx type I or II w/ nonu
S82.56XR	Nondisp fx of med malleolus of unsp tibia, subsq enc for opn fx type IIIA, IIIB, or IIIC w/ malu
S82.56XN	Nondisp fx of med malleolus of unsp tibia, subsq enc for opn fx type IIIA, IIIB, or IIIC w/ nonu
S62.651B	Nondisp fx of med phalanx of lt index finger, init enc for opn fx
S62.651P	Nondisp fx of med phalanx of lt index finger, subsq enc for fx w/ malu
S62.651K	Nondisp fx of med phalanx of lt index finger, subsq enc for fx w/ nonu
S92.525P	Nondisp fx of med phalanx of lt lesser toe(s), subsq enc for fx w/ malu
S92.525K	Nondisp fx of med phalanx of lt lesser toe(s), subsq enc for fx w/ nonu
S62.657B	Nondisp fx of med phalanx of lt little finger, init enc for opn fx
S62.657P	Nondisp fx of med phalanx of lt little finger, subsq enc for fx w/ malu
S62.657K	Nondisp fx of med phalanx of lt little finger, subsq enc for fx w/ nonu
S62.653B	Nondisp fx of med phalanx of lt mid finger, init enc for opn fx
S62.653P	Nondisp fx of med phalanx of lt mid finger, subsq enc for fx w/ malu
S62.653K	Nondisp fx of med phalanx of lt mid finger, subsq enc for fx w/ nonu
S62.655B	Nondisp fx of med phalanx of lt ring finger, init enc for opn fx
S62.655P	Nondisp fx of med phalanx of lt ring finger, subsq enc for fx w/ malu
S62.655K	Nondisp fx of med phalanx of lt ring finger, subsq enc for fx w/ nonu
S62.658B	Nondisp fx of med phalanx of oth finger, init enc for opn fx
S62.658P	Nondisp fx of med phalanx of oth finger, subsq enc for fx w/ malu
S62.658K	Nondisp fx of med phalanx of oth finger, subsq enc for fx w/ nonu
S62.650B	Nondisp fx of med phalanx of rt index finger, init enc for opn fx
S62.650P	Nondisp fx of med phalanx of rt index finger, subsq enc for fx w/ malu
S62.650K	Nondisp fx of med phalanx of rt index finger, subsq enc for fx w/ nonu
S92.524P	Nondisp fx of med phalanx of rt lesser toe(s), subsq enc for fx w/ malu
S92.524K	Nondisp fx of med phalanx of rt lesser toe(s), subsq enc for fx w/ nonu
S62.656B	Nondisp fx of med phalanx of rt little finger, init enc for opn fx
S62.656P	Nondisp fx of med phalanx of rt little finger, subsq enc for fx w/ malu
S62.656K	Nondisp fx of med phalanx of rt little finger, subsq enc for fx w/ nonu
S62.652B	Nondisp fx of med phalanx of rt mid finger, init enc for opn fx
S62.652P	Nondisp fx of med phalanx of rt mid finger, subsq enc for fx w/ malu
S62.652K	Nondisp fx of med phalanx of rt mid finger, subsq enc for fx w/ nonu
S62.654B	Nondisp fx of med phalanx of rt ring finger, init enc for opn fx
S62.654P	Nondisp fx of med phalanx of rt ring finger, subsq enc for fx w/ malu
S62.654K	Nondisp fx of med phalanx of rt ring finger, subsq enc for fx w/ nonu
S62.659B	Nondisp fx of med phalanx of unsp finger, init enc for opn fx
S62.659P	Nondisp fx of med phalanx of unsp finger, subsq enc for fx w/ malu
S62.659K	Nondisp fx of med phalanx of unsp finger, subsq enc for fx w/ nonu
S92.526P	Nondisp fx of med phalanx of unsp lesser toe(s), subsq enc for fx w/ malu
S92.526K	Nondisp fx of med phalanx of unsp lesser toe(s), subsq enc for fx w/ nonu
S32.475K	Nondisp fx of med wall of lt acetab, subsq enc for fx w/ nonu
S32.474K	Nondisp fx of med wall of rt acetab, subsq enc for fx w/ nonu
S32.476K	Nondisp fx of med wall of unsp acetab, subsq enc for fx w/ nonu
S62.025B	Nondisp fx of mid 3rd of navicular [scaphoid] bone of lt wrist, init enc for opn fx
S62.025P	Nondisp fx of mid 3rd of navicular [scaphoid] bone of lt wrist, subsq enc for fx w/ malu
S62.025K	Nondisp fx of mid 3rd of navicular [scaphoid] bone of lt wrist, subsq enc for fx w/ nonu
S62.024B	Nondisp fx of mid 3rd of navicular [scaphoid] bone of rt wrist, init enc for opn fx
S62.024P	Nondisp fx of mid 3rd of navicular [scaphoid] bone of rt wrist, subsq enc for fx w/ malu
S62.024K	Nondisp fx of mid 3rd of navicular [scaphoid] bone of rt wrist, subsq enc for fx w/ nonu
S62.026B	Nondisp fx of mid 3rd of navicular [scaphoid] bone of unsp wrist, init enc for opn fx
S62.026P	Nondisp fx of mid 3rd of navicular [scaphoid] bone of unsp wrist, subsq enc for fx w/ malu
S62.026K	Nondisp fx of mid 3rd of navicular [scaphoid] bone of unsp wrist, subsq enc for fx w/ nonu
S92.255B	Nondisp fx of navicular [scaphoid] of lt foot, init enc for opn fx
S92.255P	Nondisp fx of navicular [scaphoid] of lt foot, subsq enc for fx w/ malu
S92.255K	Nondisp fx of navicular [scaphoid] of lt foot, subsq enc for fx w/ nonu
S92.254B	Nondisp fx of navicular [scaphoid] of rt foot, init enc for opn fx
S92.254P	Nondisp fx of navicular [scaphoid] of rt foot, subsq enc for fx w/ malu
S92.254K	Nondisp fx of navicular [scaphoid] of rt foot, subsq enc for fx w/ nonu
S92.256B	Nondisp fx of navicular [scaphoid] of unsp foot, init enc for opn fx
S92.256P	Nondisp fx of navicular [scaphoid] of unsp foot, subsq enc for fx w/ malu
S92.256K	Nondisp fx of navicular [scaphoid] of unsp foot, subsq enc for fx w/ nonu
S62.255B	Nondisp fx of neck of 1st metacarpal bone, lt hand, init enc for opn fx
S62.255P	Nondisp fx of neck of 1st metacarpal bone, lt hand, subsq enc for fx w/ malu
S62.255K	Nondisp fx of neck of 1st metacarpal bone, lt hand, subsq enc for fx w/ nonu
S62.254B	Nondisp fx of neck of 1st metacarpal bone, rt hand, init enc for opn fx
S62.254P	Nondisp fx of neck of 1st metacarpal bone, rt hand, subsq enc for fx w/ malu
S62.254K	Nondisp fx of neck of 1st metacarpal bone, rt hand, subsq enc for fx w/ nonu
S62.256B	Nondisp fx of neck of 1st metacarpal bone, unsp hand, init enc for opn fx
S62.256P	Nondisp fx of neck of 1st metacarpal bone, unsp hand, subsq enc for fx w/ malu
S62.256K	Nondisp fx of neck of 1st metacarpal bone, unsp hand, subsq enc for fx w/ nonu
S62.361B	Nondisp fx of neck of 2nd metacarpal bone, lt hand, init enc for opn fx
S62.361P	Nondisp fx of neck of 2nd metacarpal bone, lt hand, subsq enc for fx w/ malu
S62.361K	Nondisp fx of neck of 2nd metacarpal bone, lt hand, subsq enc for fx w/ nonu
S62.360B	Nondisp fx of neck of 2nd metacarpal bone, rt hand, init enc for opn fx
S62.360P	Nondisp fx of neck of 2nd metacarpal bone, rt hand, subsq enc for fx w/ malu
S62.360K	Nondisp fx of neck of 2nd metacarpal bone, rt hand, subsq enc for fx w/ nonu
S62.363B	Nondisp fx of neck of 3rd metacarpal bone, lt hand, init enc for opn fx
S62.363P	Nondisp fx of neck of 3rd metacarpal bone, lt hand, subsq enc for fx w/ malu

S62.363K	Nondisp fx of neck of 3rd metacarpal bone, lt hand, subsq enc for fx w/ nonu
S62.362B	Nondisp fx of neck of 3rd metacarpal bone, rt hand, init enc for opn fx
S62.362P	Nondisp fx of neck of 3rd metacarpal bone, rt hand, subsq enc for fx w/ malu
S62.362K	Nondisp fx of neck of 3rd metacarpal bone, rt hand, subsq enc for fx w/ nonu
S62.365B	Nondisp fx of neck of 4th metacarpal bone, lt hand, init enc for opn fx
S62.365P	Nondisp fx of neck of 4th metacarpal bone, lt hand, subsq enc for fx w/ malu
S62.365K	Nondisp fx of neck of 4th metacarpal bone, lt hand, subsq enc for fx w/ nonu
S62.364B	Nondisp fx of neck of 4th metacarpal bone, rt hand, init enc for opn fx
S62.364P	Nondisp fx of neck of 4th metacarpal bone, rt hand, subsq enc for fx w/ malu
S62.364K	Nondisp fx of neck of 4th metacarpal bone, rt hand, subsq enc for fx w/ nonu
S62.367B	Nondisp fx of neck of 5th metacarpal bone, lt hand, init enc for opn fx
S62.367P	Nondisp fx of neck of 5th metacarpal bone, lt hand, subsq enc for fx w/ malu
S62.367K	Nondisp fx of neck of 5th metacarpal bone, lt hand, subsq enc for fx w/ nonu
S62.366B	Nondisp fx of neck of 5th metacarpal bone, rt hand, init enc for opn fx
S62.366P	Nondisp fx of neck of 5th metacarpal bone, rt hand, subsq enc for fx w/ malu
S62.366K	Nondisp fx of neck of 5th metacarpal bone, rt hand, subsq enc for fx w/ nonu
S52.135P	Nondisp fx of neck of lt radius, subsq enc for clsd fx w/ malu
S52.135K	Nondisp fx of neck of lt radius, subsq enc for clsd fx w/ nonu
S52.135Q	Nondisp fx of neck of lt radius, subsq enc for opn fx type I or II w/ malu
S52.135M	Nondisp fx of neck of lt radius, subsq enc for opn fx type I or II w/ nonu
S52.135R	Nondisp fx of neck of lt radius, subsq enc for opn fx type IIIA, IIIB, or IIIC w/ malu
S52.135N	Nondisp fx of neck of lt radius, subsq enc for opn fx type IIIA, IIIB, or IIIC w/ nonu
S92.115B	Nondisp fx of neck of lt talus, init enc for opn fx
S92.115P	Nondisp fx of neck of lt talus, subsq enc for fx w/ malu
S92.115K	Nondisp fx of neck of lt talus, subsq enc for fx w/ nonu
S62.368B	Nondisp fx of neck of oth metacarpal bone, init enc for opn fx
S62.368P	Nondisp fx of neck of oth metacarpal bone, subsq enc for fx w/ malu
S62.368K	Nondisp fx of neck of oth metacarpal bone, subsq enc for fx w/ nonu
S52.134P	Nondisp fx of neck of rt radius, subsq enc for clsd fx w/ malu
S52.134K	Nondisp fx of neck of rt radius, subsq enc for clsd fx w/ nonu
S52.134Q	Nondisp fx of neck of rt radius, subsq enc for opn fx type I or II w/ malu
S52.134M	Nondisp fx of neck of rt radius, subsq enc for opn fx type I or II w/ nonu
S52.134R	Nondisp fx of neck of rt radius, subsq enc for opn fx type IIIA, IIIB, or IIIC w/ malu
S52.134N	Nondisp fx of neck of rt radius, subsq enc for opn fx type IIIA, IIIB, or IIIC w/ nonu
S92.114B	Nondisp fx of neck of rt talus, init enc for opn fx
S92.114P	Nondisp fx of neck of rt talus, subsq enc for fx w/ malu
S92.114K	Nondisp fx of neck of rt talus, subsq enc for fx w/ nonu
S42.155B	Nondisp fx of neck of scapula, lt shldr, init enc for opn fx
S42.155P	Nondisp fx of neck of scapula, lt shldr, subsq enc for fx w/ malu
S42.155K	Nondisp fx of neck of scapula, lt shldr, subsq enc for fx w/ nonu
S42.154B	Nondisp fx of neck of scapula, rt shldr, init enc for opn fx
S42.154P	Nondisp fx of neck of scapula, rt shldr, subsq enc for fx w/ malu
S42.154K	Nondisp fx of neck of scapula, rt shldr, subsq enc for fx w/ nonu
S42.156B	Nondisp fx of neck of scapula, unsp shldr, init enc for opn fx
S42.156P	Nondisp fx of neck of scapula, unsp shldr, subsq enc for fx w/ malu
S42.156K	Nondisp fx of neck of scapula, unsp shldr, subsq enc for fx w/ nonu
S62.369B	Nondisp fx of neck of unsp metacarpal bone, init enc for opn fx
S62.369P	Nondisp fx of neck of unsp metacarpal bone, subsq enc for fx w/ malu
S62.369K	Nondisp fx of neck of unsp metacarpal bone, subsq enc for fx w/ nonu
S52.136P	Nondisp fx of neck of unsp radius, subsq enc for clsd fx w/ malu
S52.136K	Nondisp fx of neck of unsp radius, subsq enc for clsd fx w/ nonu
S52.136Q	Nondisp fx of neck of unsp radius, subsq enc for opn fx type I or II w/ malu
S52.136M	Nondisp fx of neck of unsp radius, subsq enc for opn fx type I or II w/ nonu
S52.136R	Nondisp fx of neck of unsp radius, subsq enc for opn fx type IIIA, IIIB, or IIIC w/ malu
S52.136N	Nondisp fx of neck of unsp radius, subsq enc for opn fx type IIIA, IIIB, or IIIC w/ nonu
S92.116B	Nondisp fx of neck of unsp talus, init enc for opn fx
S92.116P	Nondisp fx of neck of unsp talus, subsq enc for fx w/ malu
S92.116K	Nondisp fx of neck of unsp talus, subsq enc for fx w/ nonu
S52.035P	Nondisp fx of olecranon process w/ intraarticular extension of lt ulna, subsq enc for clsd fx w/ malu
S52.035K	Nondisp fx of olecranon process w/ intraarticular extension of lt ulna, subsq enc for clsd fx w/ nonu
S52.035Q	Nondisp fx of olecranon process w/ intraarticular extension of lt ulna, subsq enc for opn fx type I or II w/ malu
S52.035M	Nondisp fx of olecranon process w/ intraarticular extension of lt ulna, subsq enc for opn fx type I or II w/ nonu
S52.035R	Nondisp fx of olecranon process w/ intraarticular extension of lt ulna, subsq enc for opn fx type IIIA, IIIB, or IIIC w/ malu
S52.035N	Nondisp fx of olecranon process w/ intraarticular extension of lt ulna, subsq enc for opn fx type IIIA, IIIB, or IIIC w/ nonu
S52.034P	Nondisp fx of olecranon process w/ intraarticular extension of rt ulna, subsq enc for clsd fx w/ malu
S52.034K	Nondisp fx of olecranon process w/ intraarticular extension of rt ulna, subsq enc for clsd fx w/ nonu
S52.034Q	Nondisp fx of olecranon process w/ intraarticular extension of rt ulna, subsq enc for opn fx type I or II w/ malu
S52.034M	Nondisp fx of olecranon process w/ intraarticular extension of rt ulna, subsq enc for opn fx type I or II w/ nonu
S52.034R	Nondisp fx of olecranon process w/ intraarticular extension of rt ulna, subsq enc for opn fx type IIIA, IIIB, or IIIC w/ malu
S52.034N	Nondisp fx of olecranon process w/ intraarticular extension of rt ulna, subsq enc for opn fx type IIIA, IIIB, or IIIC w/ nonu
S52.036P	Nondisp fx of olecranon process w/ intraarticular extension of unsp ulna, subsq enc for clsd fx w/ malu
S52.036K	Nondisp fx of olecranon process w/ intraarticular extension of unsp ulna, subsq enc for clsd fx w/ nonu
S52.036Q	Nondisp fx of olecranon process w/ intraarticular extension of unsp ulna, subsq enc for opn fx type I or II w/ malu
S52.036M	Nondisp fx of olecranon process w/ intraarticular extension of unsp ulna, subsq enc for opn fx type I or II w/ nonu
S52.036R	Nondisp fx of olecranon process w/ intraarticular extension of unsp ulna, subsq enc for opn fx type IIIA, IIIB, or IIIC w/ malu
S52.036N	Nondisp fx of olecranon process w/ intraarticular extension of unsp ulna, subsq enc for opn fx type IIIA, IIIB, or IIIC w/ nonu
S52.025P	Nondisp fx of olecranon process w/o intraarticular extension of lt ulna, subsq enc for clsd fx w/ malu
S52.025K	Nondisp fx of olecranon process w/o intraarticular extension of lt ulna, subsq enc for clsd fx w/ nonu
S52.025Q	Nondisp fx of olecranon process w/o intraarticular extension of lt ulna, subsq enc for opn fx type I or II w/ malu
S52.025M	Nondisp fx of olecranon process w/o intraarticular extension of lt ulna, subsq enc for opn fx type I or II w/ nonu
S52.025R	Nondisp fx of olecranon process w/o intraarticular extension of lt ulna, subsq enc for opn fx type IIIA, IIIB, or IIIC w/ malu
S52.025N	Nondisp fx of olecranon process w/o intraarticular extension of lt ulna, subsq enc for opn fx type IIIA, IIIB, or IIIC w/ nonu
S52.024P	Nondisp fx of olecranon process w/o intraarticular extension of rt ulna, subsq enc for clsd fx w/ malu
S52.024K	Nondisp fx of olecranon process w/o intraarticular extension of rt ulna, subsq enc for clsd fx w/ nonu
S52.024Q	Nondisp fx of olecranon process w/o intraarticular extension of rt ulna, subsq enc for opn fx type I or II w/ malu
S52.024M	Nondisp fx of olecranon process w/o intraarticular extension of rt ulna, subsq enc for opn fx type I or II w/ nonu
S52.024R	Nondisp fx of olecranon process w/o intraarticular extension of rt ulna, subsq enc for opn fx type IIIA, IIIB, or IIIC w/ malu
S52.024N	Nondisp fx of olecranon process w/o intraarticular extension of rt ulna, subsq enc for opn fx type IIIA, IIIB, or IIIC w/ nonu
S52.026P	Nondisp fx of olecranon process w/o intraarticular extension of unsp ulna, subsq enc for clsd fx w/ malu
S52.026K	Nondisp fx of olecranon process w/o intraarticular extension of unsp ulna, subsq enc for clsd fx w/ nonu
S52.026Q	Nondisp fx of olecranon process w/o intraarticular extension of unsp ulna, subsq enc for opn fx type I or II w/ malu
S52.026M	Nondisp fx of olecranon process w/o intraarticular extension of unsp ulna, subsq enc for opn fx type I or II w/ nonu
S52.026R	Nondisp fx of olecranon process w/o intraarticular extension of unsp ulna, subsq enc for opn fx type IIIA, IIIB, or IIIC w/ malu
S52.026N	Nondisp fx of olecranon process w/o intraarticular extension of unsp ulna, subsq enc for opn fx type IIIA, IIIB, or IIIC w/ nonu
S62.165B	Nondisp fx of pisiform, lt wrist, init enc for opn fx
S62.165P	Nondisp fx of pisiform, lt wrist, subsq enc for fx w/ malu
S62.165K	Nondisp fx of pisiform, lt wrist, subsq enc for fx w/ nonu
S62.164B	Nondisp fx of pisiform, rt wrist, init enc for opn fx

S62.164P	Nondisp fx of pisiform, rt wrist, subsq enc for fx w/ malu
S62.164K	Nondisp fx of pisiform, rt wrist, subsq enc for fx w/ nonu
S62.166B	Nondisp fx of pisiform, unsp wrist, init enc for opn fx
S62.166P	Nondisp fx of pisiform, unsp wrist, subsq enc for fx w/ malu
S62.166K	Nondisp fx of pisiform, unsp wrist, subsq enc for fx w/ nonu
S32.445K	Nondisp fx of post column [ilioischial] of lt acetab, subsq enc for fx w/ nonu
S32.444K	Nondisp fx of post column [ilioischial] of rt acetab, subsq enc for fx w/ nonu
S32.446K	Nondisp fx of post column [ilioischial] of unsp acetab, subsq enc for fx w/ nonu
S92.135B	Nondisp fx of post process of lt talus, init enc for opn fx
S92.135P	Nondisp fx of post process of lt talus, subsq enc for fx w/ malu
S92.135K	Nondisp fx of post process of lt talus, subsq enc for fx w/ nonu
S92.134B	Nondisp fx of post process of rt talus, init enc for opn fx
S92.134P	Nondisp fx of post process of rt talus, subsq enc for fx w/ malu
S92.134K	Nondisp fx of post process of rt talus, subsq enc for fx w/ nonu
S92.136B	Nondisp fx of post process of unsp talus, init enc for opn fx
S92.136P	Nondisp fx of post process of unsp talus, subsq enc for fx w/ malu
S92.136K	Nondisp fx of post process of unsp talus, subsq enc for fx w/ nonu
S32.425K	Nondisp fx of post wall of lt acetab, subsq enc for fx w/ nonu
S32.424K	Nondisp fx of post wall of rt acetab, subsq enc for fx w/ nonu
S32.426K	Nondisp fx of post wall of unsp acetab, subsq enc for fx w/ nonu
S62.035B	Nondisp fx of proximal 3rd of navicular [scaphoid] bone of lt wrist, init enc for opn fx
S62.035P	Nondisp fx of proximal 3rd of navicular [scaphoid] bone of lt wrist, subsq enc for fx w/ malu
S62.035K	Nondisp fx of proximal 3rd of navicular [scaphoid] bone of lt wrist, subsq enc for fx w/ nonu
S62.034B	Nondisp fx of proximal 3rd of navicular [scaphoid] bone of rt wrist, init enc for opn fx
S62.034P	Nondisp fx of proximal 3rd of navicular [scaphoid] bone of rt wrist, subsq enc for fx w/ malu
S62.034K	Nondisp fx of proximal 3rd of navicular [scaphoid] bone of rt wrist, subsq enc for fx w/ nonu
S62.036B	Nondisp fx of proximal 3rd of navicular [scaphoid] bone of unsp wrist, init enc for opn fx
S62.036P	Nondisp fx of proximal 3rd of navicular [scaphoid] bone of unsp wrist, subsq enc for fx w/ malu
S62.036K	Nondisp fx of proximal 3rd of navicular [scaphoid] bone of unsp wrist, subsq enc for fx w/ nonu
S92.415P	Nondisp fx of proximal phalanx of lt great toe, subsq enc for fx w/ malu
S92.415K	Nondisp fx of proximal phalanx of lt great toe, subsq enc for fx w/ nonu
S62.641B	Nondisp fx of proximal phalanx of lt index finger, init enc for opn fx
S62.641P	Nondisp fx of proximal phalanx of lt index finger, subsq enc for fx w/ malu
S62.641K	Nondisp fx of proximal phalanx of lt index finger, subsq enc for fx w/ nonu
S92.515P	Nondisp fx of proximal phalanx of lt lesser toe(s), subsq enc for fx w/ malu
S92.515K	Nondisp fx of proximal phalanx of lt lesser toe(s), subsq enc for fx w/ nonu
S62.647B	Nondisp fx of proximal phalanx of lt little finger, init enc for opn fx
S62.647P	Nondisp fx of proximal phalanx of lt little finger, subsq enc for fx w/ malu
S62.647K	Nondisp fx of proximal phalanx of lt little finger, subsq enc for fx w/ nonu
S62.643B	Nondisp fx of proximal phalanx of lt mid finger, init enc for opn fx
S62.643P	Nondisp fx of proximal phalanx of lt mid finger, subsq enc for fx w/ malu
S62.643K	Nondisp fx of proximal phalanx of lt mid finger, subsq enc for fx w/ nonu
S62.645B	Nondisp fx of proximal phalanx of lt ring finger, init enc for opn fx
S62.645P	Nondisp fx of proximal phalanx of lt ring finger, subsq enc for fx w/ malu
S62.645K	Nondisp fx of proximal phalanx of lt ring finger, subsq enc for fx w/ nonu
S62.515B	Nondisp fx of proximal phalanx of lt thumb, init enc for opn fx
S62.515P	Nondisp fx of proximal phalanx of lt thumb, subsq enc for fx w/ malu
S62.515K	Nondisp fx of proximal phalanx of lt thumb, subsq enc for fx w/ nonu
S62.648B	Nondisp fx of proximal phalanx of oth finger, init enc for opn fx
S62.648P	Nondisp fx of proximal phalanx of oth finger, subsq enc for fx w/ malu
S62.648K	Nondisp fx of proximal phalanx of oth finger, subsq enc for fx w/ nonu
S92.414P	Nondisp fx of proximal phalanx of rt great toe, subsq enc for fx w/ malu
S92.414K	Nondisp fx of proximal phalanx of rt great toe, subsq enc for fx w/ nonu
S62.640B	Nondisp fx of proximal phalanx of rt index finger, init enc for opn fx
S62.640P	Nondisp fx of proximal phalanx of rt index finger, subsq enc for fx w/ malu
S62.640K	Nondisp fx of proximal phalanx of rt index finger, subsq enc for fx w/ nonu
S92.514P	Nondisp fx of proximal phalanx of rt lesser toe(s), subsq enc for fx w/ malu
S92.514K	Nondisp fx of proximal phalanx of rt lesser toe(s), subsq enc for fx w/ nonu
S62.646B	Nondisp fx of proximal phalanx of rt little finger, init enc for opn fx
S62.646P	Nondisp fx of proximal phalanx of rt little finger, subsq enc for fx w/ malu
S62.646K	Nondisp fx of proximal phalanx of rt little finger, subsq enc for fx w/ nonu
S62.642B	Nondisp fx of proximal phalanx of rt mid finger, init enc for opn fx
S62.642P	Nondisp fx of proximal phalanx of rt mid finger, subsq enc for fx w/ malu
S62.642K	Nondisp fx of proximal phalanx of rt mid finger, subsq enc for fx w/ nonu
S62.644B	Nondisp fx of proximal phalanx of rt ring finger, init enc for opn fx
S62.644P	Nondisp fx of proximal phalanx of rt ring finger, subsq enc for fx w/ malu
S62.644K	Nondisp fx of proximal phalanx of rt ring finger, subsq enc for fx w/ nonu
S62.514B	Nondisp fx of proximal phalanx of rt thumb, init enc for opn fx
S62.514P	Nondisp fx of proximal phalanx of rt thumb, subsq enc for fx w/ malu
S62.514K	Nondisp fx of proximal phalanx of rt thumb, subsq enc for fx w/ nonu
S62.649B	Nondisp fx of proximal phalanx of unsp finger, init enc for opn fx
S62.649P	Nondisp fx of proximal phalanx of unsp finger, subsq enc for fx w/ malu
S62.649K	Nondisp fx of proximal phalanx of unsp finger, subsq enc for fx w/ nonu
S92.416P	Nondisp fx of proximal phalanx of unsp great toe, subsq enc for fx w/ malu
S92.416K	Nondisp fx of proximal phalanx of unsp great toe, subsq enc for fx w/ nonu
S92.516P	Nondisp fx of proximal phalanx of unsp lesser toe(s), subsq enc for fx w/ malu
S92.516K	Nondisp fx of proximal phalanx of unsp lesser toe(s), subsq enc for fx w/ nonu
S62.516B	Nondisp fx of proximal phalanx of unsp thumb, init enc for opn fx
S62.516P	Nondisp fx of proximal phalanx of unsp thumb, subsq enc for fx w/ malu
S62.516K	Nondisp fx of proximal phalanx of unsp thumb, subsq enc for fx w/ nonu
S52.514A	Nondisp fx of rt radial styloid process, init enc for clsd fx
S52.514P	Nondisp fx of rt radial styloid process, subsq enc for clsd fx w/ malu
S52.514K	Nondisp fx of rt radial styloid process, subsq enc for clsd fx w/ nonu
S52.514Q	Nondisp fx of rt radial styloid process, subsq enc for opn fx type I or II w/ malu
S52.514M	Nondisp fx of rt radial styloid process, subsq enc for opn fx type I or II w/ nonu
S52.514R	Nondisp fx of rt radial styloid process, subsq enc for opn fx type IIIA, IIIB, or IIIC w/ malu
S52.514N	Nondisp fx of rt radial styloid process, subsq enc for opn fx type IIIA, IIIB, or IIIC w/ nonu
S82.114A	Nondisp fx of rt tibial spine, init enc for clsd fx
S82.114P	Nondisp fx of rt tibial spine, subsq enc for clsd fx w/ malu
S82.114K	Nondisp fx of rt tibial spine, subsq enc for clsd fx w/ nonu
S82.114Q	Nondisp fx of rt tibial spine, subsq enc for opn fx type I or II w/ malu
S82.114M	Nondisp fx of rt tibial spine, subsq enc for opn fx type I or II w/ nonu
S82.114R	Nondisp fx of rt tibial spine, subsq enc for opn fx type IIIA, IIIB, or IIIC w/ malu
S82.114N	Nondisp fx of rt tibial spine, subsq enc for opn fx type IIIA, IIIB, or IIIC w/ nonu
S82.154A	Nondisp fx of rt tibial tuberosity, init enc for clsd fx
S82.154P	Nondisp fx of rt tibial tuberosity, subsq enc for clsd fx w/ malu
S82.154K	Nondisp fx of rt tibial tuberosity, subsq enc for clsd fx w/ nonu
S82.154Q	Nondisp fx of rt tibial tuberosity, subsq enc for opn fx type I or II w/ malu
S82.154M	Nondisp fx of rt tibial tuberosity, subsq enc for opn fx type I or II w/ nonu
S82.154R	Nondisp fx of rt tibial tuberosity, subsq enc for opn fx type IIIA, IIIB, or IIIC w/ malu
S82.154N	Nondisp fx of rt tibial tuberosity, subsq enc for opn fx type IIIA, IIIB, or IIIC w/ nonu
S52.614A	Nondisp fx of rt ulna styloid process, init enc for clsd fx
S52.614P	Nondisp fx of rt ulna styloid process, subsq enc for clsd fx w/ malu
S52.614K	Nondisp fx of rt ulna styloid process, subsq enc for clsd fx w/ nonu
S52.614Q	Nondisp fx of rt ulna styloid process, subsq enc for opn fx type I or II w/ malu
S52.614M	Nondisp fx of rt ulna styloid process, subsq enc for opn fx type I or II w/ nonu
S52.614R	Nondisp fx of rt ulna styloid process, subsq enc for opn fx type IIIA, IIIB, or IIIC w/ malu
S52.614N	Nondisp fx of rt ulna styloid process, subsq enc for opn fx type IIIA, IIIB, or IIIC w/ nonu
S62.245B	Nondisp fx of shaft of 1st metacarpal bone, lt hand, init enc for opn fx
S62.245P	Nondisp fx of shaft of 1st metacarpal bone, lt hand, subsq enc for fx w/ malu
S62.245K	Nondisp fx of shaft of 1st metacarpal bone, lt hand, subsq enc for fx w/ nonu
S62.244B	Nondisp fx of shaft of 1st metacarpal bone, rt hand, init enc for opn fx

S62.244P	Nondisp fx of shaft of 1st metacarpal bone, rt hand, subsq enc for fx w/ malu
S62.244K	Nondisp fx of shaft of 1st metacarpal bone, rt hand, subsq enc for fx w/ nonu
S62.246B	Nondisp fx of shaft of 1st metacarpal bone, unsp hand, init enc for opn fx
S62.246P	Nondisp fx of shaft of 1st metacarpal bone, unsp hand, subsq enc for fx w/ malu
S62.246K	Nondisp fx of shaft of 1st metacarpal bone, unsp hand, subsq enc for fx w/ nonu
S62.351B	Nondisp fx of shaft of 2nd metacarpal bone, lt hand, init enc for opn fx
S62.351P	Nondisp fx of shaft of 2nd metacarpal bone, lt hand, subsq enc for fx w/ malu
S62.351K	Nondisp fx of shaft of 2nd metacarpal bone, lt hand, subsq enc for fx w/ nonu
S62.350B	Nondisp fx of shaft of 2nd metacarpal bone, rt hand, init enc for opn fx
S62.350P	Nondisp fx of shaft of 2nd metacarpal bone, rt hand, subsq enc for fx w/ malu
S62.350K	Nondisp fx of shaft of 2nd metacarpal bone, rt hand, subsq enc for fx w/ nonu
S62.353B	Nondisp fx of shaft of 3rd metacarpal bone, lt hand, init enc for opn fx
S62.353P	Nondisp fx of shaft of 3rd metacarpal bone, lt hand, subsq enc for fx w/ malu
S62.353K	Nondisp fx of shaft of 3rd metacarpal bone, lt hand, subsq enc for fx w/ nonu
S62.352B	Nondisp fx of shaft of 3rd metacarpal bone, rt hand, init enc for opn fx
S62.352P	Nondisp fx of shaft of 3rd metacarpal bone, rt hand, subsq enc for fx w/ malu
S62.352K	Nondisp fx of shaft of 3rd metacarpal bone, rt hand, subsq enc for fx w/ nonu
S62.355B	Nondisp fx of shaft of 4th metacarpal bone, lt hand, init enc for opn fx
S62.355P	Nondisp fx of shaft of 4th metacarpal bone, lt hand, subsq enc for fx w/ malu
S62.355K	Nondisp fx of shaft of 4th metacarpal bone, lt hand, subsq enc for fx w/ nonu
S62.354B	Nondisp fx of shaft of 4th metacarpal bone, rt hand, init enc for opn fx
S62.354P	Nondisp fx of shaft of 4th metacarpal bone, rt hand, subsq enc for fx w/ malu
S62.354K	Nondisp fx of shaft of 4th metacarpal bone, rt hand, subsq enc for fx w/ nonu
S62.357B	Nondisp fx of shaft of 5th metacarpal bone, lt hand, init enc for opn fx
S62.357P	Nondisp fx of shaft of 5th metacarpal bone, lt hand, subsq enc for fx w/ malu
S62.357K	Nondisp fx of shaft of 5th metacarpal bone, lt hand, subsq enc for fx w/ nonu
S62.356B	Nondisp fx of shaft of 5th metacarpal bone, rt hand, init enc for opn fx
S62.356P	Nondisp fx of shaft of 5th metacarpal bone, rt hand, subsq enc for fx w/ malu
S62.356K	Nondisp fx of shaft of 5th metacarpal bone, rt hand, subsq enc for fx w/ nonu
S42.025B	Nondisp fx of shaft of lt clavicle, init enc for opn fx
S42.025P	Nondisp fx of shaft of lt clavicle, subsq enc for fx w/ malu
S42.025K	Nondisp fx of shaft of lt clavicle, subsq enc for fx w/ nonu
S62.358B	Nondisp fx of shaft of oth metacarpal bone, init enc for opn fx
S62.358P	Nondisp fx of shaft of oth metacarpal bone, subsq enc for fx w/ malu
S62.358K	Nondisp fx of shaft of oth metacarpal bone, subsq enc for fx w/ nonu
S42.024B	Nondisp fx of shaft of rt clavicle, init enc for opn fx
S42.024P	Nondisp fx of shaft of rt clavicle, subsq enc for fx w/ malu
S42.024K	Nondisp fx of shaft of rt clavicle, subsq enc for fx w/ nonu
S42.026B	Nondisp fx of shaft of unsp clavicle, init enc for opn fx
S42.026P	Nondisp fx of shaft of unsp clavicle, subsq enc for fx w/ malu
S42.026K	Nondisp fx of shaft of unsp clavicle, subsq enc for fx w/ nonu
S62.359B	Nondisp fx of shaft of unsp metacarpal bone, init enc for opn fx
S62.359P	Nondisp fx of shaft of unsp metacarpal bone, subsq enc for fx w/ malu
S62.359K	Nondisp fx of shaft of unsp metacarpal bone, subsq enc for fx w/ nonu
S42.018B	Nondisp fx of sternal end of lt clavicle, init enc for opn fx
S42.018P	Nondisp fx of sternal end of lt clavicle, subsq enc for fx w/ malu
S42.018K	Nondisp fx of sternal end of lt clavicle, subsq enc for fx w/ nonu
S42.017B	Nondisp fx of sternal end of rt clavicle, init enc for opn fx
S42.017P	Nondisp fx of sternal end of rt clavicle, subsq enc for fx w/ malu
S42.017K	Nondisp fx of sternal end of rt clavicle, subsq enc for fx w/ nonu
S42.019B	Nondisp fx of sternal end of unsp clavicle, init enc for opn fx
S42.019P	Nondisp fx of sternal end of unsp clavicle, subsq enc for fx w/ malu
S42.019K	Nondisp fx of sternal end of unsp clavicle, subsq enc for fx w/ nonu
S62.175B	Nondisp fx of trapezium [larger multangular], lt wrist, init enc for opn fx
S62.175P	Nondisp fx of trapezium [larger multangular], lt wrist, subsq enc for fx w/ malu

S62.175K	Nondisp fx of trapezium [larger multangular], lt wrist, subsq enc for fx w/ nonu
S62.174B	Nondisp fx of trapezium [larger multangular], rt wrist, init enc for opn fx
S62.174P	Nondisp fx of trapezium [larger multangular], rt wrist, subsq enc for fx w/ malu
S62.174K	Nondisp fx of trapezium [larger multangular], rt wrist, subsq enc for fx w/ nonu
S62.176B	Nondisp fx of trapezium [larger multangular], unsp wrist, init enc for opn fx
S62.176P	Nondisp fx of trapezium [larger multangular], unsp wrist, subsq enc for fx w/ malu
S62.176K	Nondisp fx of trapezium [larger multangular], unsp wrist, subsq enc for fx w/ nonu
S62.185B	Nondisp fx of trapezoid [smaller multangular], lt wrist, init enc for opn fx
S62.185P	Nondisp fx of trapezoid [smaller multangular], lt wrist, subsq enc for fx w/ malu
S62.185K	Nondisp fx of trapezoid [smaller multangular], lt wrist, subsq enc for fx w/ nonu
S62.184B	Nondisp fx of trapezoid [smaller multangular], rt wrist, init enc for opn fx
S62.184P	Nondisp fx of trapezoid [smaller multangular], rt wrist, subsq enc for fx w/ malu
S62.184K	Nondisp fx of trapezoid [smaller multangular], rt wrist, subsq enc for fx w/ nonu
S62.186B	Nondisp fx of trapezoid [smaller multangular], unsp wrist, init enc for opn fx
S62.186P	Nondisp fx of trapezoid [smaller multangular], unsp wrist, subsq enc for fx w/ malu
S62.186K	Nondisp fx of trapezoid [smaller multangular], unsp wrist, subsq enc for fx w/ nonu
S62.115B	Nondisp fx of triquetrum [cuneiform] bone, lt wrist, init enc for opn fx
S62.115P	Nondisp fx of triquetrum [cuneiform] bone, lt wrist, subsq enc for fx w/ malu
S62.115K	Nondisp fx of triquetrum [cuneiform] bone, lt wrist, subsq enc for fx w/ nonu
S62.114B	Nondisp fx of triquetrum [cuneiform] bone, rt wrist, init enc for opn fx
S62.114P	Nondisp fx of triquetrum [cuneiform] bone, rt wrist, subsq enc for fx w/ malu
S62.114K	Nondisp fx of triquetrum [cuneiform] bone, rt wrist, subsq enc for fx w/ nonu
S62.116B	Nondisp fx of triquetrum [cuneiform] bone, unsp wrist, init enc for opn fx
S62.116P	Nondisp fx of triquetrum [cuneiform] bone, unsp wrist, subsq enc for fx w/ malu
S62.116K	Nondisp fx of triquetrum [cuneiform] bone, unsp wrist, subsq enc for fx w/ nonu
S52.516A	Nondisp fx of unsp radial styloid process, init enc for clsd fx
S52.516P	Nondisp fx of unsp radial styloid process, subsq enc for clsd fx w/ malu
S52.516K	Nondisp fx of unsp radial styloid process, subsq enc for clsd fx w/ nonu
S52.516Q	Nondisp fx of unsp radial styloid process, subsq enc for opn fx type I or II w/ malu
S52.516M	Nondisp fx of unsp radial styloid process, subsq enc for opn fx type I or II w/ nonu
S52.516R	Nondisp fx of unsp radial styloid process, subsq enc for opn fx type IIIA, IIIB, or IIIC w/ malu
S52.516N	Nondisp fx of unsp radial styloid process, subsq enc for opn fx type IIIA, IIIB, or IIIC w/ nonu
S82.116A	Nondisp fx of unsp tibial spine, init enc for clsd fx
S82.116P	Nondisp fx of unsp tibial spine, subsq enc for clsd fx w/ malu
S82.116K	Nondisp fx of unsp tibial spine, subsq enc for clsd fx w/ nonu
S82.116Q	Nondisp fx of unsp tibial spine, subsq enc for opn fx type I or II w/ malu
S82.116M	Nondisp fx of unsp tibial spine, subsq enc for opn fx type I or II w/ nonu
S82.116R	Nondisp fx of unsp tibial spine, subsq enc for opn fx type IIIA, IIIB, or IIIC w/ malu
S82.116N	Nondisp fx of unsp tibial spine, subsq enc for opn fx type IIIA, IIIB, or IIIC w/ nonu
S82.156A	Nondisp fx of unsp tibial tuberosity, init enc for clsd fx
S82.156P	Nondisp fx of unsp tibial tuberosity, subsq enc for clsd fx w/ malu
S82.156K	Nondisp fx of unsp tibial tuberosity, subsq enc for clsd fx w/ nonu
S82.156Q	Nondisp fx of unsp tibial tuberosity, subsq enc for opn fx type I or II w/ malu
S82.156M	Nondisp fx of unsp tibial tuberosity, subsq enc for opn fx type I or II w/ nonu
S82.156R	Nondisp fx of unsp tibial tuberosity, subsq enc for opn fx type IIIA, IIIB, or IIIC w/ malu
S82.156N	Nondisp fx of unsp tibial tuberosity, subsq enc for opn fx type IIIA, IIIB, or IIIC w/ nonu
S52.616A	Nondisp fx of unsp ulna styloid process, init enc for clsd fx

S52.616P	Nondisp fx of unsp ulna styloid process, subsq enc for clsd fx w/ malu
S52.616K	Nondisp fx of unsp ulna styloid process, subsq enc for clsd fx w/ nonu
S52.616Q	Nondisp fx of unsp ulna styloid process, subsq enc for opn fx type I or II w/ malu
S52.616M	Nondisp fx of unsp ulna styloid process, subsq enc for opn fx type I or II w/ nonu
S52.616R	Nondisp fx of unsp ulna styloid process, subsq enc for opn fx type IIIA, IIIB, or IIIC w/ malu
S52.616N	Nondisp fx of unsp ulna styloid process, subsq enc for opn fx type IIIA, IIIB, or IIIC w/ nonu
S72.145P	Nondisp intertrochanteric fx of lt femur, subsq enc for clsd fx w/ malu
S72.145K	Nondisp intertrochanteric fx of lt femur, subsq enc for clsd fx w/ nonu
S72.145Q	Nondisp intertrochanteric fx of lt femur, subsq enc for opn fx type I or II w/ malu
S72.145M	Nondisp intertrochanteric fx of lt femur, subsq enc for opn fx type I or II w/ nonu
S72.145R	Nondisp intertrochanteric fx of lt femur, subsq enc for opn fx type IIIA, IIIB, or IIIC w/ malu
S72.145N	Nondisp intertrochanteric fx of lt femur, subsq enc for opn fx type IIIA, IIIB, or IIIC w/ nonu
S72.144P	Nondisp intertrochanteric fx of rt femur, subsq enc for clsd fx w/ malu
S72.144K	Nondisp intertrochanteric fx of rt femur, subsq enc for clsd fx w/ nonu
S72.144Q	Nondisp intertrochanteric fx of rt femur, subsq enc for opn fx type I or II w/ malu
S72.144M	Nondisp intertrochanteric fx of rt femur, subsq enc for opn fx type I or II w/ nonu
S72.144R	Nondisp intertrochanteric fx of rt femur, subsq enc for opn fx type IIIA, IIIB, or IIIC w/ malu
S72.144N	Nondisp intertrochanteric fx of rt femur, subsq enc for opn fx type IIIA, IIIB, or IIIC w/ nonu
S72.146P	Nondisp intertrochanteric fx of unsp femur, subsq enc for clsd fx w/ malu
S72.146K	Nondisp intertrochanteric fx of unsp femur, subsq enc for clsd fx w/ nonu
S72.146Q	Nondisp intertrochanteric fx of unsp femur, subsq enc for opn fx type I or II w/ malu
S72.146M	Nondisp intertrochanteric fx of unsp femur, subsq enc for opn fx type I or II w/ nonu
S72.146R	Nondisp intertrochanteric fx of unsp femur, subsq enc for opn fx type IIIA, IIIB, or IIIC w/ malu
S72.146N	Nondisp intertrochanteric fx of unsp femur, subsq enc for opn fx type IIIA, IIIB, or IIIC w/ nonu
S92.065B	Nondisp intraarticular fx of lt calcaneus, init enc for opn fx
S92.065P	Nondisp intraarticular fx of lt calcaneus, subsq enc for fx w/ malu
S92.065K	Nondisp intraarticular fx of lt calcaneus, subsq enc for fx w/ nonu
S92.064B	Nondisp intraarticular fx of rt calcaneus, init enc for opn fx
S92.064P	Nondisp intraarticular fx of rt calcaneus, subsq enc for fx w/ malu
S92.064K	Nondisp intraarticular fx of rt calcaneus, subsq enc for fx w/ nonu
S92.066B	Nondisp intraarticular fx of unsp calcaneus, init enc for opn fx
S92.066P	Nondisp intraarticular fx of unsp calcaneus, subsq enc for fx w/ malu
S92.066K	Nondisp intraarticular fx of unsp calcaneus, subsq enc for fx w/ nonu
S12.041A	Nondisp lat mass fx of 1st cervical vertebra, init enc for clsd fx
S12.041K	Nondisp lat mass fx of 1st cervical vertebra, subsq enc for fx w/ nonu
S82.025A	Nondisp longitudinal fx of lt patella, init enc for clsd fx
S82.025B	Nondisp longitudinal fx of lt patella, init enc for opn fx type I or II
S82.025C	Nondisp longitudinal fx of lt patella, init enc for opn fx type IIIA, IIIB, or IIIC
S82.025P	Nondisp longitudinal fx of lt patella, subsq enc for clsd fx w/ malu
S82.025K	Nondisp longitudinal fx of lt patella, subsq enc for clsd fx w/ nonu
S82.025Q	Nondisp longitudinal fx of lt patella, subsq enc for opn fx type I or II w/ malu
S82.025M	Nondisp longitudinal fx of lt patella, subsq enc for opn fx type I or II w/ nonu
S82.025R	Nondisp longitudinal fx of lt patella, subsq enc for opn fx type IIIA, IIIB, or IIIC w/ malu
S82.025N	Nondisp longitudinal fx of lt patella, subsq enc for opn fx type IIIA, IIIB, or IIIC w/ nonu
S82.024A	Nondisp longitudinal fx of rt patella, init enc for clsd fx
S82.024B	Nondisp longitudinal fx of rt patella, init enc for opn fx type I or II
S82.024C	Nondisp longitudinal fx of rt patella, init enc for opn fx type IIIA, IIIB, or IIIC
S82.024P	Nondisp longitudinal fx of rt patella, subsq enc for clsd fx w/ malu
S82.024K	Nondisp longitudinal fx of rt patella, subsq enc for clsd fx w/ nonu
S82.024Q	Nondisp longitudinal fx of rt patella, subsq enc for opn fx type I or II w/ malu
S82.024M	Nondisp longitudinal fx of rt patella, subsq enc for opn fx type I or II w/ nonu
S82.024R	Nondisp longitudinal fx of rt patella, subsq enc for opn fx type IIIA, IIIB, or IIIC w/ malu
S82.024N	Nondisp longitudinal fx of rt patella, subsq enc for opn fx type IIIA, IIIB, or IIIC w/ nonu
S82.026A	Nondisp longitudinal fx of unsp patella, init enc for clsd fx
S82.026B	Nondisp longitudinal fx of unsp patella, init enc for opn fx type I or II
S82.026C	Nondisp longitudinal fx of unsp patella, init enc for opn fx type IIIA, IIIB, or IIIC
S82.026P	Nondisp longitudinal fx of unsp patella, subsq enc for clsd fx w/ malu
S82.026K	Nondisp longitudinal fx of unsp patella, subsq enc for clsd fx w/ nonu
S82.026Q	Nondisp longitudinal fx of unsp patella, subsq enc for opn fx type I or II w/ malu
S82.026M	Nondisp longitudinal fx of unsp patella, subsq enc for opn fx type I or II w/ nonu
S82.026R	Nondisp longitudinal fx of unsp patella, subsq enc for opn fx type IIIA, IIIB, or IIIC w/ malu
S82.026N	Nondisp longitudinal fx of unsp patella, subsq enc for opn fx type IIIA, IIIB, or IIIC w/ nonu
S82.865P	Nondisp Maisonneuve's fx of lt leg, subsq enc for clsd fx w/ malu
S82.865K	Nondisp Maisonneuve's fx of lt leg, subsq enc for clsd fx w/ nonu
S82.865Q	Nondisp Maisonneuve's fx of lt leg, subsq enc for opn fx type I or II w/ malu
S82.865M	Nondisp Maisonneuve's fx of lt leg, subsq enc for opn fx type I or II w/ nonu
S82.865R	Nondisp Maisonneuve's fx of lt leg, subsq enc for opn fx type IIIA, IIIB, or IIIC w/ malu
S82.865N	Nondisp Maisonneuve's fx of lt leg, subsq enc for opn fx type IIIA, IIIB, or IIIC w/ nonu
S82.864P	Nondisp Maisonneuve's fx of rt leg, subsq enc for clsd fx w/ malu
S82.864K	Nondisp Maisonneuve's fx of rt leg, subsq enc for clsd fx w/ nonu
S82.864Q	Nondisp Maisonneuve's fx of rt leg, subsq enc for opn fx type I or II w/ malu
S82.864M	Nondisp Maisonneuve's fx of rt leg, subsq enc for opn fx type I or II w/ nonu
S82.864R	Nondisp Maisonneuve's fx of rt leg, subsq enc for opn fx type IIIA, IIIB, or IIIC w/ malu
S82.864N	Nondisp Maisonneuve's fx of rt leg, subsq enc for opn fx type IIIA, IIIB, or IIIC w/ nonu
S82.866P	Nondisp Maisonneuve's fx of unsp leg, subsq enc for clsd fx w/ malu
S82.866K	Nondisp Maisonneuve's fx of unsp leg, subsq enc for clsd fx w/ nonu
S82.866Q	Nondisp Maisonneuve's fx of unsp leg, subsq enc for opn fx type I or II w/ malu
S82.866M	Nondisp Maisonneuve's fx of unsp leg, subsq enc for opn fx type I or II w/ nonu
S82.866R	Nondisp Maisonneuve's fx of unsp leg, subsq enc for opn fx type IIIA, IIIB, or IIIC w/ malu
S82.866N	Nondisp Maisonneuve's fx of unsp leg, subsq enc for opn fx type IIIA, IIIB, or IIIC w/ nonu
S72.035P	Nondisp midcervical fx of lt femur, subsq enc for clsd fx w/ malu
S72.035K	Nondisp midcervical fx of lt femur, subsq enc for clsd fx w/ nonu
S72.035Q	Nondisp midcervical fx of lt femur, subsq enc for opn fx type I or II w/ malu
S72.035M	Nondisp midcervical fx of lt femur, subsq enc for opn fx type I or II w/ nonu
S72.035R	Nondisp midcervical fx of lt femur, subsq enc for opn fx type IIIA, IIIB, or IIIC w/ malu
S72.035N	Nondisp midcervical fx of lt femur, subsq enc for opn fx type IIIA, IIIB, or IIIC w/ nonu
S72.034P	Nondisp midcervical fx of rt femur, subsq enc for clsd fx w/ malu
S72.034K	Nondisp midcervical fx of rt femur, subsq enc for clsd fx w/ nonu
S72.034Q	Nondisp midcervical fx of rt femur, subsq enc for opn fx type I or II w/ malu
S72.034M	Nondisp midcervical fx of rt femur, subsq enc for opn fx type I or II w/ nonu
S72.034R	Nondisp midcervical fx of rt femur, subsq enc for opn fx type IIIA, IIIB, or IIIC w/ malu
S72.034N	Nondisp midcervical fx of rt femur, subsq enc for opn fx type IIIA, IIIB, or IIIC w/ nonu
S72.036P	Nondisp midcervical fx of unsp femur, subsq enc for clsd fx w/ malu
S72.036K	Nondisp midcervical fx of unsp femur, subsq enc for clsd fx w/ nonu
S72.036Q	Nondisp midcervical fx of unsp femur, subsq enc for opn fx type I or II w/ malu
S72.036M	Nondisp midcervical fx of unsp femur, subsq enc for opn fx type I or II w/ nonu
S72.036R	Nondisp midcervical fx of unsp femur, subsq enc for opn fx type IIIA, IIIB, or IIIC w/ malu

S72.036N	Nondisp midcervical fx of unsp femur, subsq enc for opn fx type IIIA, IIIB, or IIIC w/ nonu
S42.335A	Nondisp oblique fx of shaft of humerus, lt arm, init enc for clsd fx
S42.335P	Nondisp oblique fx of shaft of humerus, lt arm, subsq enc for fx w/ malu
S42.335K	Nondisp oblique fx of shaft of humerus, lt arm, subsq enc for fx w/ nonu
S42.334A	Nondisp oblique fx of shaft of humerus, rt arm, init enc for clsd fx
S42.334P	Nondisp oblique fx of shaft of humerus, rt arm, subsq enc for fx w/ malu
S42.334K	Nondisp oblique fx of shaft of humerus, rt arm, subsq enc for fx w/ nonu
S42.336A	Nondisp oblique fx of shaft of humerus, unsp arm, init enc for clsd fx
S42.336P	Nondisp oblique fx of shaft of humerus, unsp arm, subsq enc for fx w/ malu
S42.336K	Nondisp oblique fx of shaft of humerus, unsp arm, subsq enc for fx w/ nonu
S72.335P	Nondisp oblique fx of shaft of lt femur, subsq enc for clsd fx w/ malu
S72.335K	Nondisp oblique fx of shaft of lt femur, subsq enc for clsd fx w/ nonu
S72.335Q	Nondisp oblique fx of shaft of lt femur, subsq enc for opn fx type I or II w/ malu
S72.335M	Nondisp oblique fx of shaft of lt femur, subsq enc for opn fx type I or II w/ nonu
S72.335R	Nondisp oblique fx of shaft of lt femur, subsq enc for opn fx type IIIA, IIIB, or IIIC w/ malu
S72.335N	Nondisp oblique fx of shaft of lt femur, subsq enc for opn fx type IIIA, IIIB, or IIIC w/ nonu
S82.435P	Nondisp oblique fx of shaft of lt fibula, subsq enc for clsd fx w/ malu
S82.435K	Nondisp oblique fx of shaft of lt fibula, subsq enc for clsd fx w/ nonu
S82.435Q	Nondisp oblique fx of shaft of lt fibula, subsq enc for opn fx type I or II w/ malu
S82.435M	Nondisp oblique fx of shaft of lt fibula, subsq enc for opn fx type I or II w/ nonu
S82.435R	Nondisp oblique fx of shaft of lt fibula, subsq enc for opn fx type IIIA, IIIB, or IIIC w/ malu
S82.435N	Nondisp oblique fx of shaft of lt fibula, subsq enc for opn fx type IIIA, IIIB, or IIIC w/ nonu
S52.335A	Nondisp oblique fx of shaft of lt radius, init enc for clsd fx
S52.335P	Nondisp oblique fx of shaft of lt radius, subsq enc for clsd fx w/ malu
S52.335K	Nondisp oblique fx of shaft of lt radius, subsq enc for clsd fx w/ nonu
S52.335Q	Nondisp oblique fx of shaft of lt radius, subsq enc for opn fx type I or II w/ malu
S52.335M	Nondisp oblique fx of shaft of lt radius, subsq enc for opn fx type I or II w/ nonu
S52.335R	Nondisp oblique fx of shaft of lt radius, subsq enc for opn fx type IIIA, IIIB, or IIIC w/ malu
S52.335N	Nondisp oblique fx of shaft of lt radius, subsq enc for opn fx type IIIA, IIIB, or IIIC w/ nonu
S82.235A	Nondisp oblique fx of shaft of lt tibia, init enc for clsd fx
S82.235P	Nondisp oblique fx of shaft of lt tibia, subsq enc for clsd fx w/ malu
S82.235K	Nondisp oblique fx of shaft of lt tibia, subsq enc for clsd fx w/ nonu
S82.235Q	Nondisp oblique fx of shaft of lt tibia, subsq enc for opn fx type I or II w/ malu
S82.235M	Nondisp oblique fx of shaft of lt tibia, subsq enc for opn fx type I or II w/ nonu
S82.235R	Nondisp oblique fx of shaft of lt tibia, subsq enc for opn fx type IIIA, IIIB, or IIIC w/ malu
S82.235N	Nondisp oblique fx of shaft of lt tibia, subsq enc for opn fx type IIIA, IIIB, or IIIC w/ nonu
S52.235A	Nondisp oblique fx of shaft of lt ulna, init enc for clsd fx
S52.235P	Nondisp oblique fx of shaft of lt ulna, subsq enc for clsd fx w/ malu
S52.235K	Nondisp oblique fx of shaft of lt ulna, subsq enc for clsd fx w/ nonu
S52.235Q	Nondisp oblique fx of shaft of lt ulna, subsq enc for opn fx type I or II w/ malu
S52.235M	Nondisp oblique fx of shaft of lt ulna, subsq enc for opn fx type I or II w/ nonu
S52.235R	Nondisp oblique fx of shaft of lt ulna, subsq enc for opn fx type IIIA, IIIB, or IIIC w/ malu
S52.235N	Nondisp oblique fx of shaft of lt ulna, subsq enc for opn fx type IIIA, IIIB, or IIIC w/ nonu
S72.334P	Nondisp oblique fx of shaft of rt femur, subsq enc for clsd fx w/ malu
S72.334K	Nondisp oblique fx of shaft of rt femur, subsq enc for clsd fx w/ nonu
S72.334Q	Nondisp oblique fx of shaft of rt femur, subsq enc for opn fx type I or II w/ malu
S72.334M	Nondisp oblique fx of shaft of rt femur, subsq enc for opn fx type I or II w/ nonu
S72.334R	Nondisp oblique fx of shaft of rt femur, subsq enc for opn fx type IIIA, IIIB, or IIIC w/ malu
S72.334N	Nondisp oblique fx of shaft of rt femur, subsq enc for opn fx type IIIA, IIIB, or IIIC w/ nonu
S82.434P	Nondisp oblique fx of shaft of rt fibula, subsq enc for clsd fx w/ malu
S82.434K	Nondisp oblique fx of shaft of rt fibula, subsq enc for clsd fx w/ nonu
S82.434Q	Nondisp oblique fx of shaft of rt fibula, subsq enc for opn fx type I or II w/ malu
S82.434M	Nondisp oblique fx of shaft of rt fibula, subsq enc for opn fx type I or II w/ nonu
S82.434R	Nondisp oblique fx of shaft of rt fibula, subsq enc for opn fx type IIIA, IIIB, or IIIC w/ malu
S82.434N	Nondisp oblique fx of shaft of rt fibula, subsq enc for opn fx type IIIA, IIIB, or IIIC w/ nonu
S52.334A	Nondisp oblique fx of shaft of rt radius, init enc for clsd fx
S52.334P	Nondisp oblique fx of shaft of rt radius, subsq enc for clsd fx w/ malu
S52.334K	Nondisp oblique fx of shaft of rt radius, subsq enc for clsd fx w/ nonu
S52.334Q	Nondisp oblique fx of shaft of rt radius, subsq enc for opn fx type I or II w/ malu
S52.334M	Nondisp oblique fx of shaft of rt radius, subsq enc for opn fx type I or II w/ nonu
S52.334R	Nondisp oblique fx of shaft of rt radius, subsq enc for opn fx type IIIA, IIIB, or IIIC w/ malu
S52.334N	Nondisp oblique fx of shaft of rt radius, subsq enc for opn fx type IIIA, IIIB, or IIIC w/ nonu
S82.234A	Nondisp oblique fx of shaft of rt tibia, init enc for clsd fx
S82.234P	Nondisp oblique fx of shaft of rt tibia, subsq enc for clsd fx w/ malu
S82.234K	Nondisp oblique fx of shaft of rt tibia, subsq enc for clsd fx w/ nonu
S82.234Q	Nondisp oblique fx of shaft of rt tibia, subsq enc for opn fx type I or II w/ malu
S82.234M	Nondisp oblique fx of shaft of rt tibia, subsq enc for opn fx type I or II w/ nonu
S82.234R	Nondisp oblique fx of shaft of rt tibia, subsq enc for opn fx type IIIA, IIIB, or IIIC w/ malu
S82.234N	Nondisp oblique fx of shaft of rt tibia, subsq enc for opn fx type IIIA, IIIB, or IIIC w/ nonu
S52.234A	Nondisp oblique fx of shaft of rt ulna, init enc for clsd fx
S52.234P	Nondisp oblique fx of shaft of rt ulna, subsq enc for clsd fx w/ malu
S52.234K	Nondisp oblique fx of shaft of rt ulna, subsq enc for clsd fx w/ nonu
S52.234Q	Nondisp oblique fx of shaft of rt ulna, subsq enc for opn fx type I or II w/ malu
S52.234M	Nondisp oblique fx of shaft of rt ulna, subsq enc for opn fx type I or II w/ nonu
S52.234R	Nondisp oblique fx of shaft of rt ulna, subsq enc for opn fx type IIIA, IIIB, or IIIC w/ malu
S52.234N	Nondisp oblique fx of shaft of rt ulna, subsq enc for opn fx type IIIA, IIIB, or IIIC w/ nonu
S72.336P	Nondisp oblique fx of shaft of unsp femur, subsq enc for clsd fx w/ malu
S72.336K	Nondisp oblique fx of shaft of unsp femur, subsq enc for clsd fx w/ nonu
S72.336Q	Nondisp oblique fx of shaft of unsp femur, subsq enc for opn fx type I or II w/ malu
S72.336M	Nondisp oblique fx of shaft of unsp femur, subsq enc for opn fx type I or II w/ nonu
S72.336R	Nondisp oblique fx of shaft of unsp femur, subsq enc for opn fx type IIIA, IIIB, or IIIC w/ malu
S72.336N	Nondisp oblique fx of shaft of unsp femur, subsq enc for opn fx type IIIA, IIIB, or IIIC w/ nonu
S82.436P	Nondisp oblique fx of shaft of unsp fibula, subsq enc for clsd fx w/ malu
S82.436K	Nondisp oblique fx of shaft of unsp fibula, subsq enc for clsd fx w/ nonu
S82.436Q	Nondisp oblique fx of shaft of unsp fibula, subsq enc for opn fx type I or II w/ malu
S82.436M	Nondisp oblique fx of shaft of unsp fibula, subsq enc for opn fx type I or II w/ nonu
S82.436R	Nondisp oblique fx of shaft of unsp fibula, subsq enc for opn fx type IIIA, IIIB, or IIIC w/ malu
S82.436N	Nondisp oblique fx of shaft of unsp fibula, subsq enc for opn fx type IIIA, IIIB, or IIIC w/ nonu
S52.336A	Nondisp oblique fx of shaft of unsp radius, init enc for clsd fx
S52.336P	Nondisp oblique fx of shaft of unsp radius, subsq enc for clsd fx w/ malu
S52.336K	Nondisp oblique fx of shaft of unsp radius, subsq enc for clsd fx w/ nonu
S52.336Q	Nondisp oblique fx of shaft of unsp radius, subsq enc for opn fx type I or II w/ malu
S52.336M	Nondisp oblique fx of shaft of unsp radius, subsq enc for opn fx type I or II w/ nonu
S52.336R	Nondisp oblique fx of shaft of unsp radius, subsq enc for opn fx type IIIA, IIIB, or IIIC w/ malu
S52.336N	Nondisp oblique fx of shaft of unsp radius, subsq enc for opn fx type IIIA, IIIB, or IIIC w/ nonu
S82.236A	Nondisp oblique fx of shaft of unsp tibia, init enc for clsd fx
S82.236P	Nondisp oblique fx of shaft of unsp tibia, subsq enc for clsd fx w/ malu

S82.236K	Nondisp oblique fx of shaft of unsp tibia, subsq enc for clsd fx w/ nonu
S82.236Q	Nondisp oblique fx of shaft of unsp tibia, subsq enc for opn fx type I or II w/ malu
S82.236M	Nondisp oblique fx of shaft of unsp tibia, subsq enc for opn fx type I or II w/ nonu
S82.236R	Nondisp oblique fx of shaft of unsp tibia, subsq enc for opn fx type IIIA, IIIB, or IIIC w/ malu
S82.236N	Nondisp oblique fx of shaft of unsp tibia, subsq enc for opn fx type IIIA, IIIB, or IIIC w/ nonu
S52.236A	Nondisp oblique fx of shaft of unsp ulna, init enc for clsd fx
S52.236P	Nondisp oblique fx of shaft of unsp ulna, subsq enc for clsd fx w/ malu
S52.236K	Nondisp oblique fx of shaft of unsp ulna, subsq enc for clsd fx w/ nonu
S52.236Q	Nondisp oblique fx of shaft of unsp ulna, subsq enc for opn fx type I or II w/ malu
S52.236M	Nondisp oblique fx of shaft of unsp ulna, subsq enc for opn fx type I or II w/ nonu
S52.236R	Nondisp oblique fx of shaft of unsp ulna, subsq enc for opn fx type IIIA, IIIB, or IIIC w/ malu
S52.236N	Nondisp oblique fx of shaft of unsp ulna, subsq enc for opn fx type IIIA, IIIB, or IIIC w/ nonu
S82.015A	Nondisp osteochondral fx of lt patella, init enc for clsd fx
S82.015B	Nondisp osteochondral fx of lt patella, init enc for opn fx type I or II
S82.015C	Nondisp osteochondral fx of lt patella, init enc for opn fx type IIIA, IIIB, or IIIC
S82.015P	Nondisp osteochondral fx of lt patella, subsq enc for clsd fx w/ malu
S82.015K	Nondisp osteochondral fx of lt patella, subsq enc for clsd fx w/ nonu
S82.015Q	Nondisp osteochondral fx of lt patella, subsq enc for opn fx type I or II w/ malu
S82.015M	Nondisp osteochondral fx of lt patella, subsq enc for opn fx type I or II w/ nonu
S82.015R	Nondisp osteochondral fx of lt patella, subsq enc for opn fx type IIIA, IIIB, or IIIC w/ malu
S82.015N	Nondisp osteochondral fx of lt patella, subsq enc for opn fx type IIIA, IIIB, or IIIC w/ nonu
S82.014A	Nondisp osteochondral fx of rt patella, init enc for clsd fx
S82.014B	Nondisp osteochondral fx of rt patella, init enc for opn fx type I or II
S82.014C	Nondisp osteochondral fx of rt patella, init enc for opn fx type IIIA, IIIB, or IIIC
S82.014P	Nondisp osteochondral fx of rt patella, subsq enc for clsd fx w/ malu
S82.014K	Nondisp osteochondral fx of rt patella, subsq enc for clsd fx w/ nonu
S82.014Q	Nondisp osteochondral fx of rt patella, subsq enc for opn fx type I or II w/ malu
S82.014M	Nondisp osteochondral fx of rt patella, subsq enc for opn fx type I or II w/ nonu
S82.014R	Nondisp osteochondral fx of rt patella, subsq enc for opn fx type IIIA, IIIB, or IIIC w/ malu
S82.014N	Nondisp osteochondral fx of rt patella, subsq enc for opn fx type IIIA, IIIB, or IIIC w/ nonu
S82.016A	Nondisp osteochondral fx of unsp patella, init enc for clsd fx
S82.016B	Nondisp osteochondral fx of unsp patella, init enc for opn fx type I or II
S82.016C	Nondisp osteochondral fx of unsp patella, init enc for opn fx type IIIA, IIIB, or IIIC
S82.016P	Nondisp osteochondral fx of unsp patella, subsq enc for clsd fx w/ malu
S82.016K	Nondisp osteochondral fx of unsp patella, subsq enc for clsd fx w/ nonu
S82.016Q	Nondisp osteochondral fx of unsp patella, subsq enc for opn fx type I or II w/ malu
S82.016M	Nondisp osteochondral fx of unsp patella, subsq enc for opn fx type I or II w/ nonu
S82.016R	Nondisp osteochondral fx of unsp patella, subsq enc for opn fx type IIIA, IIIB, or IIIC w/ malu
S82.016N	Nondisp osteochondral fx of unsp patella, subsq enc for opn fx type IIIA, IIIB, or IIIC w/ nonu
S92.055B	Nondisp oth extraarticular fx of lt calcaneus, init enc for opn fx
S92.055P	Nondisp oth extraarticular fx of lt calcaneus, subsq enc for fx w/ malu
S92.055K	Nondisp oth extraarticular fx of lt calcaneus, subsq enc for fx w/ nonu
S92.054B	Nondisp oth extraarticular fx of rt calcaneus, init enc for opn fx
S92.054P	Nondisp oth extraarticular fx of rt calcaneus, subsq enc for fx w/ malu
S92.054K	Nondisp oth extraarticular fx of rt calcaneus, subsq enc for fx w/ nonu
S92.056B	Nondisp oth extraarticular fx of unsp calcaneus, init enc for opn fx
S92.056P	Nondisp oth extraarticular fx of unsp calcaneus, subsq enc for fx w/ malu
S92.056K	Nondisp oth extraarticular fx of unsp calcaneus, subsq enc for fx w/ nonu
S92.045B	Nondisp oth fx of tuberosity of lt calcaneus, init enc for opn fx
S92.045P	Nondisp oth fx of tuberosity of lt calcaneus, subsq enc for fx w/ malu
S92.045K	Nondisp oth fx of tuberosity of lt calcaneus, subsq enc for fx w/ nonu
S92.044B	Nondisp oth fx of tuberosity of rt calcaneus, init enc for opn fx
S92.044P	Nondisp oth fx of tuberosity of rt calcaneus, subsq enc for fx w/ malu

S92.044K	Nondisp oth fx of tuberosity of rt calcaneus, subsq enc for fx w/ nonu
S92.046B	Nondisp oth fx of tuberosity of unsp calcaneus, init enc for opn fx
S92.046P	Nondisp oth fx of tuberosity of unsp calcaneus, subsq enc for fx w/ malu
S92.046K	Nondisp oth fx of tuberosity of unsp calcaneus, subsq enc for fx w/ nonu
S82.875B	Nondisp pilon fx of lt tibia, init enc for opn fx type I or II
S82.875C	Nondisp pilon fx of lt tibia, init enc for opn fx type IIIA, IIIB, or IIIC
S82.875P	Nondisp pilon fx of lt tibia, subsq enc for clsd fx w/ malu
S82.875K	Nondisp pilon fx of lt tibia, subsq enc for clsd fx w/ nonu
S82.875Q	Nondisp pilon fx of lt tibia, subsq enc for opn fx type I or II w/ malu
S82.875M	Nondisp pilon fx of lt tibia, subsq enc for opn fx type I or II w/ nonu
S82.875R	Nondisp pilon fx of lt tibia, subsq enc for opn fx type IIIA, IIIB, or IIIC w/ malu
S82.875N	Nondisp pilon fx of lt tibia, subsq enc for opn fx type IIIA, IIIB, or IIIC w/ nonu
S82.874B	Nondisp pilon fx of rt tibia, init enc for opn fx type I or II
S82.874C	Nondisp pilon fx of rt tibia, init enc for opn fx type IIIA, IIIB, or IIIC
S82.874P	Nondisp pilon fx of rt tibia, subsq enc for clsd fx w/ malu
S82.874K	Nondisp pilon fx of rt tibia, subsq enc for clsd fx w/ nonu
S82.874Q	Nondisp pilon fx of rt tibia, subsq enc for opn fx type I or II w/ malu
S82.874M	Nondisp pilon fx of rt tibia, subsq enc for opn fx type I or II w/ nonu
S82.874R	Nondisp pilon fx of rt tibia, subsq enc for opn fx type IIIA, IIIB, or IIIC w/ malu
S82.874N	Nondisp pilon fx of rt tibia, subsq enc for opn fx type IIIA, IIIB, or IIIC w/ nonu
S82.876B	Nondisp pilon fx of unsp tibia, init enc for opn fx type I or II
S82.876C	Nondisp pilon fx of unsp tibia, init enc for opn fx type IIIA, IIIB, or IIIC
S82.876P	Nondisp pilon fx of unsp tibia, subsq enc for clsd fx w/ malu
S82.876K	Nondisp pilon fx of unsp tibia, subsq enc for clsd fx w/ nonu
S82.876Q	Nondisp pilon fx of unsp tibia, subsq enc for opn fx type I or II w/ malu
S82.876M	Nondisp pilon fx of unsp tibia, subsq enc for opn fx type I or II w/ nonu
S82.876R	Nondisp pilon fx of unsp tibia, subsq enc for opn fx type IIIA, IIIB, or IIIC w/ malu
S82.876N	Nondisp pilon fx of unsp tibia, subsq enc for opn fx type IIIA, IIIB, or IIIC w/ nonu
S12.031A	Nondisp post arch fx of 1st cervical vertebra, init enc for clsd fx
S12.031K	Nondisp post arch fx of 1st cervical vertebra, subsq enc for fx w/ nonu
S62.225B	Nondisp Rolando's fx, lt hand, init enc for opn fx
S62.225P	Nondisp Rolando's fx, lt hand, subsq enc for fx w/ malu
S62.225K	Nondisp Rolando's fx, lt hand, subsq enc for fx w/ nonu
S62.224B	Nondisp Rolando's fx, rt hand, init enc for opn fx
S62.224P	Nondisp Rolando's fx, rt hand, subsq enc for fx w/ malu
S62.224K	Nondisp Rolando's fx, rt hand, subsq enc for fx w/ nonu
S62.226B	Nondisp Rolando's fx, unsp hand, init enc for opn fx
S62.226P	Nondisp Rolando's fx, unsp hand, subsq enc for fx w/ malu
S62.226K	Nondisp Rolando's fx, unsp hand, subsq enc for fx w/ nonu
S42.365A	Nondisp segmental fx of shaft of humerus, lt arm, init enc for clsd fx
S42.365P	Nondisp segmental fx of shaft of humerus, lt arm, subsq enc for fx w/ malu
S42.365K	Nondisp segmental fx of shaft of humerus, lt arm, subsq enc for fx w/ nonu
S42.364A	Nondisp segmental fx of shaft of humerus, rt arm, init enc for clsd fx
S42.364P	Nondisp segmental fx of shaft of humerus, rt arm, subsq enc for fx w/ malu
S42.364K	Nondisp segmental fx of shaft of humerus, rt arm, subsq enc for fx w/ nonu
S42.366A	Nondisp segmental fx of shaft of humerus, unsp arm, init enc for clsd fx
S42.366P	Nondisp segmental fx of shaft of humerus, unsp arm, subsq enc for fx w/ malu
S42.366K	Nondisp segmental fx of shaft of humerus, unsp arm, subsq enc for fx w/ nonu
S72.365P	Nondisp segmental fx of shaft of lt femur, subsq enc for clsd fx w/ malu
S72.365K	Nondisp segmental fx of shaft of lt femur, subsq enc for clsd fx w/ nonu
S72.365Q	Nondisp segmental fx of shaft of lt femur, subsq enc for opn fx type I or II w/ malu
S72.365M	Nondisp segmental fx of shaft of lt femur, subsq enc for opn fx type I or II w/ nonu
S72.365R	Nondisp segmental fx of shaft of lt femur, subsq enc for opn fx type IIIA, IIIB, or IIIC w/ malu
S72.365N	Nondisp segmental fx of shaft of lt femur, subsq enc for opn fx type IIIA, IIIB, or IIIC w/ nonu
S82.465P	Nondisp segmental fx of shaft of lt fibula, subsq enc for clsd fx w/ malu
S82.465K	Nondisp segmental fx of shaft of lt fibula, subsq enc for clsd fx w/ nonu
S82.465Q	Nondisp segmental fx of shaft of lt fibula, subsq enc for opn fx type I or II w/ malu

S82.465M	Nondisp segmental fx of shaft of lt fibula, subsq enc for opn fx type I or II w/ nonu
S82.465R	Nondisp segmental fx of shaft of lt fibula, subsq enc for opn fx type IIIA, IIIB, or IIIC w/ malu
S82.465N	Nondisp segmental fx of shaft of lt fibula, subsq enc for opn fx type IIIA, IIIB, or IIIC w/ nonu
S82.265A	Nondisp segmental fx of shaft of lt tibia, init enc for clsd fx
S82.265P	Nondisp segmental fx of shaft of lt tibia, subsq enc for clsd fx w/ malu
S82.265K	Nondisp segmental fx of shaft of lt tibia, subsq enc for clsd fx w/ nonu
S82.265Q	Nondisp segmental fx of shaft of lt tibia, subsq enc for opn fx type I or II w/ malu
S82.265M	Nondisp segmental fx of shaft of lt tibia, subsq enc for opn fx type I or II w/ nonu
S82.265R	Nondisp segmental fx of shaft of lt tibia, subsq enc for opn fx type IIIA, IIIB, or IIIC w/ malu
S82.265N	Nondisp segmental fx of shaft of lt tibia, subsq enc for opn fx type IIIA, IIIB, or IIIC w/ nonu
S52.365A	Nondisp segmental fx of shaft of radius, lt arm, init enc for clsd fx
S52.365P	Nondisp segmental fx of shaft of radius, lt arm, subsq enc for clsd fx w/ malu
S52.365K	Nondisp segmental fx of shaft of radius, lt arm, subsq enc for clsd fx w/ nonu
S52.365Q	Nondisp segmental fx of shaft of radius, lt arm, subsq enc for opn fx type I or II w/ malu
S52.365M	Nondisp segmental fx of shaft of radius, lt arm, subsq enc for opn fx type I or II w/ nonu
S52.365R	Nondisp segmental fx of shaft of radius, lt arm, subsq enc for opn fx type IIIA, IIIB, or IIIC w/ malu
S52.365N	Nondisp segmental fx of shaft of radius, lt arm, subsq enc for opn fx type IIIA, IIIB, or IIIC w/ nonu
S52.364A	Nondisp segmental fx of shaft of radius, rt arm, init enc for clsd fx
S52.364P	Nondisp segmental fx of shaft of radius, rt arm, subsq enc for clsd fx w/ malu
S52.364K	Nondisp segmental fx of shaft of radius, rt arm, subsq enc for clsd fx w/ nonu
S52.364Q	Nondisp segmental fx of shaft of radius, rt arm, subsq enc for opn fx type I or II w/ malu
S52.364M	Nondisp segmental fx of shaft of radius, rt arm, subsq enc for opn fx type I or II w/ nonu
S52.364R	Nondisp segmental fx of shaft of radius, rt arm, subsq enc for opn fx type IIIA, IIIB, or IIIC w/ malu
S52.364N	Nondisp segmental fx of shaft of radius, rt arm, subsq enc for opn fx type IIIA, IIIB, or IIIC w/ nonu
S52.366A	Nondisp segmental fx of shaft of radius, unsp arm, init enc for clsd fx
S52.366P	Nondisp segmental fx of shaft of radius, unsp arm, subsq enc for clsd fx w/ malu
S52.366K	Nondisp segmental fx of shaft of radius, unsp arm, subsq enc for clsd fx w/ nonu
S52.366Q	Nondisp segmental fx of shaft of radius, unsp arm, subsq enc for opn fx type I or II w/ malu
S52.366M	Nondisp segmental fx of shaft of radius, unsp arm, subsq enc for opn fx type I or II w/ nonu
S52.366R	Nondisp segmental fx of shaft of radius, unsp arm, subsq enc for opn fx type IIIA, IIIB, or IIIC w/ malu
S52.366N	Nondisp segmental fx of shaft of radius, unsp arm, subsq enc for opn fx type IIIA, IIIB, or IIIC w/ nonu
S72.364P	Nondisp segmental fx of shaft of rt femur, subsq enc for clsd fx w/ malu
S72.364K	Nondisp segmental fx of shaft of rt femur, subsq enc for clsd fx w/ nonu
S72.364Q	Nondisp segmental fx of shaft of rt femur, subsq enc for opn fx type I or II w/ malu
S72.364M	Nondisp segmental fx of shaft of rt femur, subsq enc for opn fx type I or II w/ nonu
S72.364R	Nondisp segmental fx of shaft of rt femur, subsq enc for opn fx type IIIA, IIIB, or IIIC w/ malu
S72.364N	Nondisp segmental fx of shaft of rt femur, subsq enc for opn fx type IIIA, IIIB, or IIIC w/ nonu
S82.464P	Nondisp segmental fx of shaft of rt fibula, subsq enc for clsd fx w/ malu
S82.464K	Nondisp segmental fx of shaft of rt fibula, subsq enc for clsd fx w/ nonu
S82.464Q	Nondisp segmental fx of shaft of rt fibula, subsq enc for opn fx type I or II w/ malu
S82.464M	Nondisp segmental fx of shaft of rt fibula, subsq enc for opn fx type I or II w/ nonu
S82.464R	Nondisp segmental fx of shaft of rt fibula, subsq enc for opn fx type IIIA, IIIB, or IIIC w/ malu
S82.464N	Nondisp segmental fx of shaft of rt fibula, subsq enc for opn fx type IIIA, IIIB, or IIIC w/ nonu
S82.264A	Nondisp segmental fx of shaft of rt tibia, init enc for clsd fx

S82.264P	Nondisp segmental fx of shaft of rt tibia, subsq enc for clsd fx w/ malu
S82.264K	Nondisp segmental fx of shaft of rt tibia, subsq enc for clsd fx w/ nonu
S82.264Q	Nondisp segmental fx of shaft of rt tibia, subsq enc for opn fx type I or II w/ malu
S82.264M	Nondisp segmental fx of shaft of rt tibia, subsq enc for opn fx type I or II w/ nonu
S82.264R	Nondisp segmental fx of shaft of rt tibia, subsq enc for opn fx type IIIA, IIIB, or IIIC w/ malu
S82.264N	Nondisp segmental fx of shaft of rt tibia, subsq enc for opn fx type IIIA, IIIB, or IIIC w/ nonu
S52.265A	Nondisp segmental fx of shaft of ulna, lt arm, init enc for clsd fx
S52.265P	Nondisp segmental fx of shaft of ulna, lt arm, subsq enc for clsd fx w/ malu
S52.265K	Nondisp segmental fx of shaft of ulna, lt arm, subsq enc for clsd fx w/ nonu
S52.265Q	Nondisp segmental fx of shaft of ulna, lt arm, subsq enc for opn fx type I or II w/ malu
S52.265M	Nondisp segmental fx of shaft of ulna, lt arm, subsq enc for opn fx type I or II w/ nonu
S52.265R	Nondisp segmental fx of shaft of ulna, lt arm, subsq enc for opn fx type IIIA, IIIB, or IIIC w/ malu
S52.265N	Nondisp segmental fx of shaft of ulna, lt arm, subsq enc for opn fx type IIIA, IIIB, or IIIC w/ nonu
S52.264A	Nondisp segmental fx of shaft of ulna, rt arm, init enc for clsd fx
S52.264P	Nondisp segmental fx of shaft of ulna, rt arm, subsq enc for clsd fx w/ malu
S52.264K	Nondisp segmental fx of shaft of ulna, rt arm, subsq enc for clsd fx w/ nonu
S52.264Q	Nondisp segmental fx of shaft of ulna, rt arm, subsq enc for opn fx type I or II w/ malu
S52.264M	Nondisp segmental fx of shaft of ulna, rt arm, subsq enc for opn fx type I or II w/ nonu
S52.264R	Nondisp segmental fx of shaft of ulna, rt arm, subsq enc for opn fx type IIIA, IIIB, or IIIC w/ malu
S52.264N	Nondisp segmental fx of shaft of ulna, rt arm, subsq enc for opn fx type IIIA, IIIB, or IIIC w/ nonu
S52.266A	Nondisp segmental fx of shaft of ulna, unsp arm, init enc for clsd fx
S52.266P	Nondisp segmental fx of shaft of ulna, unsp arm, subsq enc for clsd fx w/ malu
S52.266K	Nondisp segmental fx of shaft of ulna, unsp arm, subsq enc for clsd fx w/ nonu
S52.266Q	Nondisp segmental fx of shaft of ulna, unsp arm, subsq enc for opn fx type I or II w/ malu
S52.266M	Nondisp segmental fx of shaft of ulna, unsp arm, subsq enc for opn fx type I or II w/ nonu
S52.266R	Nondisp segmental fx of shaft of ulna, unsp arm, subsq enc for opn fx type IIIA, IIIB, or IIIC w/ malu
S52.266N	Nondisp segmental fx of shaft of ulna, unsp arm, subsq enc for opn fx type IIIA, IIIB, or IIIC w/ nonu
S72.366P	Nondisp segmental fx of shaft of unsp femur, subsq enc for clsd fx w/ malu
S72.366K	Nondisp segmental fx of shaft of unsp femur, subsq enc for clsd fx w/ nonu
S72.366Q	Nondisp segmental fx of shaft of unsp femur, subsq enc for opn fx type I or II w/ malu
S72.366M	Nondisp segmental fx of shaft of unsp femur, subsq enc for opn fx type I or II w/ nonu
S72.366R	Nondisp segmental fx of shaft of unsp femur, subsq enc for opn fx type IIIA, IIIB, or IIIC w/ malu
S72.366N	Nondisp segmental fx of shaft of unsp femur, subsq enc for opn fx type IIIA, IIIB, or IIIC w/ nonu
S82.466P	Nondisp segmental fx of shaft of unsp fibula, subsq enc for clsd fx w/ malu
S82.466K	Nondisp segmental fx of shaft of unsp fibula, subsq enc for clsd fx w/ nonu
S82.466Q	Nondisp segmental fx of shaft of unsp fibula, subsq enc for opn fx type I or II w/ malu
S82.466M	Nondisp segmental fx of shaft of unsp fibula, subsq enc for opn fx type I or II w/ nonu
S82.466R	Nondisp segmental fx of shaft of unsp fibula, subsq enc for opn fx type IIIA, IIIB, or IIIC w/ malu
S82.466N	Nondisp segmental fx of shaft of unsp fibula, subsq enc for opn fx type IIIA, IIIB, or IIIC w/ nonu
S82.266A	Nondisp segmental fx of shaft of unsp tibia, init enc for clsd fx
S82.266P	Nondisp segmental fx of shaft of unsp tibia, subsq enc for clsd fx w/ malu
S82.266K	Nondisp segmental fx of shaft of unsp tibia, subsq enc for clsd fx w/ nonu

Code	Description
S82.266Q	Nondisp segmental fx of shaft of unsp tibia, subsq enc for opn fx type I or II w/ malu
S82.266M	Nondisp segmental fx of shaft of unsp tibia, subsq enc for opn fx type I or II w/ nonu
S82.266R	Nondisp segmental fx of shaft of unsp tibia, subsq enc for opn fx type IIIA, IIIB, or IIIC w/ malu
S82.266N	Nondisp segmental fx of shaft of unsp tibia, subsq enc for opn fx type IIIA, IIIB, or IIIC w/ nonu
S42.415A	Nondisp simple supracondylar fx w/o intercondylar fx of lt humerus, init enc for clsd fx
S42.415P	Nondisp simple supracondylar fx w/o intercondylar fx of lt humerus, subsq enc for fx w/ malu
S42.415K	Nondisp simple supracondylar fx w/o intercondylar fx of lt humerus, subsq enc for fx w/ nonu
S42.414A	Nondisp simple supracondylar fx w/o intercondylar fx of rt humerus, init enc for clsd fx
S42.414P	Nondisp simple supracondylar fx w/o intercondylar fx of rt humerus, subsq enc for fx w/ malu
S42.414K	Nondisp simple supracondylar fx w/o intercondylar fx of rt humerus, subsq enc for fx w/ nonu
S42.416A	Nondisp simple supracondylar fx w/o intercondylar fx of unsp humerus, init enc for clsd fx
S42.416P	Nondisp simple supracondylar fx w/o intercondylar fx of unsp humerus, subsq enc for fx w/ malu
S42.416K	Nondisp simple supracondylar fx w/o intercondylar fx of unsp humerus, subsq enc for fx w/ nonu
S42.345A	Nondisp spiral fx of shaft of humerus, lt arm, init enc for clsd fx
S42.345P	Nondisp spiral fx of shaft of humerus, lt arm, subsq enc for fx w/ malu
S42.345K	Nondisp spiral fx of shaft of humerus, lt arm, subsq enc for fx w/ nonu
S42.344A	Nondisp spiral fx of shaft of humerus, rt arm, init enc for clsd fx
S42.344P	Nondisp spiral fx of shaft of humerus, rt arm, subsq enc for fx w/ malu
S42.344K	Nondisp spiral fx of shaft of humerus, rt arm, subsq enc for fx w/ nonu
S42.346A	Nondisp spiral fx of shaft of humerus, unsp arm, init enc for clsd fx
S42.346P	Nondisp spiral fx of shaft of humerus, unsp arm, subsq enc for fx w/ malu
S42.346K	Nondisp spiral fx of shaft of humerus, unsp arm, subsq enc for fx w/ nonu
S72.345P	Nondisp spiral fx of shaft of lt femur, subsq enc for clsd fx w/ malu
S72.345K	Nondisp spiral fx of shaft of lt femur, subsq enc for clsd fx w/ nonu
S72.345Q	Nondisp spiral fx of shaft of lt femur, subsq enc for opn fx type I or II w/ malu
S72.345M	Nondisp spiral fx of shaft of lt femur, subsq enc for opn fx type I or II w/ nonu
S72.345R	Nondisp spiral fx of shaft of lt femur, subsq enc for opn fx type IIIA, IIIB, or IIIC w/ malu
S72.345N	Nondisp spiral fx of shaft of lt femur, subsq enc for opn fx type IIIA, IIIB, or IIIC w/ nonu
S82.445P	Nondisp spiral fx of shaft of lt fibula, subsq enc for clsd fx w/ malu
S82.445K	Nondisp spiral fx of shaft of lt fibula, subsq enc for clsd fx w/ nonu
S82.445Q	Nondisp spiral fx of shaft of lt fibula, subsq enc for opn fx type I or II w/ malu
S82.445M	Nondisp spiral fx of shaft of lt fibula, subsq enc for opn fx type I or II w/ nonu
S82.445R	Nondisp spiral fx of shaft of lt fibula, subsq enc for opn fx type IIIA, IIIB, or IIIC w/ malu
S82.445N	Nondisp spiral fx of shaft of lt fibula, subsq enc for opn fx type IIIA, IIIB, or IIIC w/ nonu
S82.245A	Nondisp spiral fx of shaft of lt tibia, init enc for clsd fx
S82.245P	Nondisp spiral fx of shaft of lt tibia, subsq enc for clsd fx w/ malu
S82.245K	Nondisp spiral fx of shaft of lt tibia, subsq enc for clsd fx w/ nonu
S82.245Q	Nondisp spiral fx of shaft of lt tibia, subsq enc for opn fx type I or II w/ malu
S82.245M	Nondisp spiral fx of shaft of lt tibia, subsq enc for opn fx type I or II w/ nonu
S82.245R	Nondisp spiral fx of shaft of lt tibia, subsq enc for opn fx type IIIA, IIIB, or IIIC w/ malu
S82.245N	Nondisp spiral fx of shaft of lt tibia, subsq enc for opn fx type IIIA, IIIB, or IIIC w/ nonu
S52.345A	Nondisp spiral fx of shaft of radius, lt arm, init enc for clsd fx
S52.345P	Nondisp spiral fx of shaft of radius, lt arm, subsq enc for clsd fx w/ malu
S52.345K	Nondisp spiral fx of shaft of radius, lt arm, subsq enc for clsd fx w/ nonu
S52.345Q	Nondisp spiral fx of shaft of radius, lt arm, subsq enc for opn fx type I or II w/ malu
S52.345M	Nondisp spiral fx of shaft of radius, lt arm, subsq enc for opn fx type I or II w/ nonu
S52.345R	Nondisp spiral fx of shaft of radius, lt arm, subsq enc for opn fx type IIIA, IIIB, or IIIC w/ malu
S52.345N	Nondisp spiral fx of shaft of radius, lt arm, subsq enc for opn fx type IIIA, IIIB, or IIIC w/ nonu
S52.344A	Nondisp spiral fx of shaft of radius, rt arm, init enc for clsd fx
S52.344P	Nondisp spiral fx of shaft of radius, rt arm, subsq enc for clsd fx w/ malu
S52.344K	Nondisp spiral fx of shaft of radius, rt arm, subsq enc for clsd fx w/ nonu
S52.344Q	Nondisp spiral fx of shaft of radius, rt arm, subsq enc for opn fx type I or II w/ malu
S52.344M	Nondisp spiral fx of shaft of radius, rt arm, subsq enc for opn fx type I or II w/ nonu
S52.344R	Nondisp spiral fx of shaft of radius, rt arm, subsq enc for opn fx type IIIA, IIIB, or IIIC w/ malu
S52.344N	Nondisp spiral fx of shaft of radius, rt arm, subsq enc for opn fx type IIIA, IIIB, or IIIC w/ nonu
S52.346A	Nondisp spiral fx of shaft of radius, unsp arm, init enc for clsd fx
S52.346P	Nondisp spiral fx of shaft of radius, unsp arm, subsq enc for clsd fx w/ malu
S52.346K	Nondisp spiral fx of shaft of radius, unsp arm, subsq enc for clsd fx w/ nonu
S52.346Q	Nondisp spiral fx of shaft of radius, unsp arm, subsq enc for opn fx type I or II w/ malu
S52.346M	Nondisp spiral fx of shaft of radius, unsp arm, subsq enc for opn fx type I or II w/ nonu
S52.346R	Nondisp spiral fx of shaft of radius, unsp arm, subsq enc for opn fx type IIIA, IIIB, or IIIC w/ malu
S52.346N	Nondisp spiral fx of shaft of radius, unsp arm, subsq enc for opn fx type IIIA, IIIB, or IIIC w/ nonu
S72.344P	Nondisp spiral fx of shaft of rt femur, subsq enc for clsd fx w/ malu
S72.344K	Nondisp spiral fx of shaft of rt femur, subsq enc for clsd fx w/ nonu
S72.344Q	Nondisp spiral fx of shaft of rt femur, subsq enc for opn fx type I or II w/ malu
S72.344M	Nondisp spiral fx of shaft of rt femur, subsq enc for opn fx type I or II w/ nonu
S72.344R	Nondisp spiral fx of shaft of rt femur, subsq enc for opn fx type IIIA, IIIB, or IIIC w/ malu
S72.344N	Nondisp spiral fx of shaft of rt femur, subsq enc for opn fx type IIIA, IIIB, or IIIC w/ nonu
S82.444P	Nondisp spiral fx of shaft of rt fibula, subsq enc for clsd fx w/ malu
S82.444K	Nondisp spiral fx of shaft of rt fibula, subsq enc for clsd fx w/ nonu
S82.444Q	Nondisp spiral fx of shaft of rt fibula, subsq enc for opn fx type I or II w/ malu
S82.444M	Nondisp spiral fx of shaft of rt fibula, subsq enc for opn fx type I or II w/ nonu
S82.444R	Nondisp spiral fx of shaft of rt fibula, subsq enc for opn fx type IIIA, IIIB, or IIIC w/ malu
S82.444N	Nondisp spiral fx of shaft of rt fibula, subsq enc for opn fx type IIIA, IIIB, or IIIC w/ nonu
S82.244A	Nondisp spiral fx of shaft of rt tibia, init enc for clsd fx
S82.244P	Nondisp spiral fx of shaft of rt tibia, subsq enc for clsd fx w/ malu
S82.244K	Nondisp spiral fx of shaft of rt tibia, subsq enc for clsd fx w/ nonu
S82.244Q	Nondisp spiral fx of shaft of rt tibia, subsq enc for opn fx type I or II w/ malu
S82.244M	Nondisp spiral fx of shaft of rt tibia, subsq enc for opn fx type I or II w/ nonu
S82.244R	Nondisp spiral fx of shaft of rt tibia, subsq enc for opn fx type IIIA, IIIB, or IIIC w/ malu
S82.244N	Nondisp spiral fx of shaft of rt tibia, subsq enc for opn fx type IIIA, IIIB, or IIIC w/ nonu
S52.245A	Nondisp spiral fx of shaft of ulna, lt arm, init enc for clsd fx
S52.245P	Nondisp spiral fx of shaft of ulna, lt arm, subsq enc for clsd fx w/ malu
S52.245K	Nondisp spiral fx of shaft of ulna, lt arm, subsq enc for clsd fx w/ nonu
S52.245Q	Nondisp spiral fx of shaft of ulna, lt arm, subsq enc for opn fx type I or II w/ malu
S52.245M	Nondisp spiral fx of shaft of ulna, lt arm, subsq enc for opn fx type I or II w/ nonu
S52.245R	Nondisp spiral fx of shaft of ulna, lt arm, subsq enc for opn fx type IIIA, IIIB, or IIIC w/ malu
S52.245N	Nondisp spiral fx of shaft of ulna, lt arm, subsq enc for opn fx type IIIA, IIIB, or IIIC w/ nonu
S52.244A	Nondisp spiral fx of shaft of ulna, rt arm, init enc for clsd fx
S52.244P	Nondisp spiral fx of shaft of ulna, rt arm, subsq enc for clsd fx w/ malu
S52.244K	Nondisp spiral fx of shaft of ulna, rt arm, subsq enc for clsd fx w/ nonu
S52.244Q	Nondisp spiral fx of shaft of ulna, rt arm, subsq enc for opn fx type I or II w/ malu
S52.244M	Nondisp spiral fx of shaft of ulna, rt arm, subsq enc for opn fx type I or II w/ nonu
S52.244R	Nondisp spiral fx of shaft of ulna, rt arm, subsq enc for opn fx type IIIA, IIIB, or IIIC w/ malu

S52.244N	Nondisp spiral fx of shaft of ulna, rt arm, subsq enc for opn fx type IIIA, IIIB, or IIIC w/ nonu
S52.246A	Nondisp spiral fx of shaft of ulna, unsp arm, init enc for clsd fx
S52.246P	Nondisp spiral fx of shaft of ulna, unsp arm, subsq enc for clsd fx w/ malu
S52.246K	Nondisp spiral fx of shaft of ulna, unsp arm, subsq enc for clsd fx w/ nonu
S52.246Q	Nondisp spiral fx of shaft of ulna, unsp arm, subsq enc for opn fx type I or II w/ malu
S52.246M	Nondisp spiral fx of shaft of ulna, unsp arm, subsq enc for opn fx type I or II w/ nonu
S52.246R	Nondisp spiral fx of shaft of ulna, unsp arm, subsq enc for opn fx type IIIA, IIIB, or IIIC w/ malu
S52.246N	Nondisp spiral fx of shaft of ulna, unsp arm, subsq enc for opn fx type IIIA, IIIB, or IIIC w/ nonu
S72.346P	Nondisp spiral fx of shaft of unsp femur, subsq enc for clsd fx w/ malu
S72.346K	Nondisp spiral fx of shaft of unsp femur, subsq enc for clsd fx w/ nonu
S72.346Q	Nondisp spiral fx of shaft of unsp femur, subsq enc for opn fx type I or II w/ malu
S72.346M	Nondisp spiral fx of shaft of unsp femur, subsq enc for opn fx type I or II w/ nonu
S72.346R	Nondisp spiral fx of shaft of unsp femur, subsq enc for opn fx type IIIA, IIIB, or IIIC w/ malu
S72.346N	Nondisp spiral fx of shaft of unsp femur, subsq enc for opn fx type IIIA, IIIB, or IIIC w/ nonu
S82.446P	Nondisp spiral fx of shaft of unsp fibula, subsq enc for clsd fx w/ malu
S82.446K	Nondisp spiral fx of shaft of unsp fibula, subsq enc for clsd fx w/ nonu
S82.446Q	Nondisp spiral fx of shaft of unsp fibula, subsq enc for opn fx type I or II w/ malu
S82.446M	Nondisp spiral fx of shaft of unsp fibula, subsq enc for opn fx type I or II w/ nonu
S82.446R	Nondisp spiral fx of shaft of unsp fibula, subsq enc for opn fx type IIIA, IIIB, or IIIC w/ malu
S82.446N	Nondisp spiral fx of shaft of unsp fibula, subsq enc for opn fx type IIIA, IIIB, or IIIC w/ nonu
S82.246A	Nondisp spiral fx of shaft of unsp tibia, init enc for clsd fx
S82.246P	Nondisp spiral fx of shaft of unsp tibia, subsq enc for clsd fx w/ malu
S82.246K	Nondisp spiral fx of shaft of unsp tibia, subsq enc for clsd fx w/ nonu
S82.246Q	Nondisp spiral fx of shaft of unsp tibia, subsq enc for opn fx type I or II w/ malu
S82.246M	Nondisp spiral fx of shaft of unsp tibia, subsq enc for opn fx type I or II w/ nonu
S82.246R	Nondisp spiral fx of shaft of unsp tibia, subsq enc for opn fx type IIIA, IIIB, or IIIC w/ malu
S82.246N	Nondisp spiral fx of shaft of unsp tibia, subsq enc for opn fx type IIIA, IIIB, or IIIC w/ nonu
S72.25XP	Nondisp subtrochanteric fx of lt femur, subsq enc for clsd fx w/ malu
S72.25XK	Nondisp subtrochanteric fx of lt femur, subsq enc for clsd fx w/ nonu
S72.25XQ	Nondisp subtrochanteric fx of lt femur, subsq enc for opn fx type I or II w/ malu
S72.25XM	Nondisp subtrochanteric fx of lt femur, subsq enc for opn fx type I or II w/ nonu
S72.25XR	Nondisp subtrochanteric fx of lt femur, subsq enc for opn fx type IIIA, IIIB, or IIIC w/ malu
S72.25XN	Nondisp subtrochanteric fx of lt femur, subsq enc for opn fx type IIIA, IIIB, or IIIC w/ nonu
S72.24XP	Nondisp subtrochanteric fx of rt femur, subsq enc for clsd fx w/ malu
S72.24XK	Nondisp subtrochanteric fx of rt femur, subsq enc for clsd fx w/ nonu
S72.24XQ	Nondisp subtrochanteric fx of rt femur, subsq enc for opn fx type I or II w/ malu
S72.24XM	Nondisp subtrochanteric fx of rt femur, subsq enc for opn fx type I or II w/ nonu
S72.24XR	Nondisp subtrochanteric fx of rt femur, subsq enc for opn fx type IIIA, IIIB, or IIIC w/ malu
S72.24XN	Nondisp subtrochanteric fx of rt femur, subsq enc for opn fx type IIIA, IIIB, or IIIC w/ nonu
S72.26XP	Nondisp subtrochanteric fx of unsp femur, subsq enc for clsd fx w/ malu
S72.26XK	Nondisp subtrochanteric fx of unsp femur, subsq enc for clsd fx w/ nonu
S72.26XQ	Nondisp subtrochanteric fx of unsp femur, subsq enc for opn fx type I or II w/ malu
S72.26XM	Nondisp subtrochanteric fx of unsp femur, subsq enc for opn fx type I or II w/ nonu
S72.26XR	Nondisp subtrochanteric fx of unsp femur, subsq enc for opn fx type IIIA, IIIB, or IIIC w/ malu
S72.26XN	Nondisp subtrochanteric fx of unsp femur, subsq enc for opn fx type IIIA, IIIB, or IIIC w/ nonu
S72.465A	Nondisp supracondylar fx w/ intracondylar extension of lwr end of lt femur, init enc for clsd fx
S72.465P	Nondisp supracondylar fx w/ intracondylar extension of lwr end of lt femur, subsq enc for clsd fx w/ malu
S72.465K	Nondisp supracondylar fx w/ intracondylar extension of lwr end of lt femur, subsq enc for clsd fx w/ nonu
S72.465Q	Nondisp supracondylar fx w/ intracondylar extension of lwr end of lt femur, subsq enc for opn fx type I or II w/ malu
S72.465M	Nondisp supracondylar fx w/ intracondylar extension of lwr end of lt femur, subsq enc for opn fx type I or II w/ nonu
S72.465R	Nondisp supracondylar fx w/ intracondylar extension of lwr end of lt femur, subsq enc for opn fx type IIIA, IIIB, or IIIC w/ malu
S72.465N	Nondisp supracondylar fx w/ intracondylar extension of lwr end of lt femur, subsq enc for opn fx type IIIA, IIIB, or IIIC w/ nonu
S72.464A	Nondisp supracondylar fx w/ intracondylar extension of lwr end of rt femur, init enc for clsd fx
S72.464P	Nondisp supracondylar fx w/ intracondylar extension of lwr end of rt femur, subsq enc for clsd fx w/ malu
S72.464K	Nondisp supracondylar fx w/ intracondylar extension of lwr end of rt femur, subsq enc for clsd fx w/ nonu
S72.464Q	Nondisp supracondylar fx w/ intracondylar extension of lwr end of rt femur, subsq enc for opn fx type I or II w/ malu
S72.464M	Nondisp supracondylar fx w/ intracondylar extension of lwr end of rt femur, subsq enc for opn fx type I or II w/ nonu
S72.464R	Nondisp supracondylar fx w/ intracondylar extension of lwr end of rt femur, subsq enc for opn fx type IIIA, IIIB, or IIIC w/ malu
S72.464N	Nondisp supracondylar fx w/ intracondylar extension of lwr end of rt femur, subsq enc for opn fx type IIIA, IIIB, or IIIC w/ nonu
S72.466A	Nondisp supracondylar fx w/ intracondylar extension of lwr end of unsp femur, init enc for clsd fx
S72.466P	Nondisp supracondylar fx w/ intracondylar extension of lwr end of unsp femur, subsq enc for clsd fx w/ malu
S72.466K	Nondisp supracondylar fx w/ intracondylar extension of lwr end of unsp femur, subsq enc for clsd fx w/ nonu
S72.466Q	Nondisp supracondylar fx w/ intracondylar extension of lwr end of unsp femur, subsq enc for opn fx type I or II w/ malu
S72.466M	Nondisp supracondylar fx w/ intracondylar extension of lwr end of unsp femur, subsq enc for opn fx type I or II w/ nonu
S72.466R	Nondisp supracondylar fx w/ intracondylar extension of lwr end of unsp femur, subsq enc for opn fx type IIIA, IIIB, or IIIC w/ malu
S72.466N	Nondisp supracondylar fx w/ intracondylar extension of lwr end of unsp femur, subsq enc for opn fx type IIIA, IIIB, or IIIC w/ nonu
S72.455A	Nondisp supracondylar fx w/o intracondylar extension of lwr end of lt femur, init enc for clsd fx
S72.455P	Nondisp supracondylar fx w/o intracondylar extension of lwr end of lt femur, subsq enc for clsd fx w/ malu
S72.455K	Nondisp supracondylar fx w/o intracondylar extension of lwr end of lt femur, subsq enc for clsd fx w/ nonu
S72.455Q	Nondisp supracondylar fx w/o intracondylar extension of lwr end of lt femur, subsq enc for opn fx type I or II w/ malu
S72.455M	Nondisp supracondylar fx w/o intracondylar extension of lwr end of lt femur, subsq enc for opn fx type I or II w/ nonu
S72.455R	Nondisp supracondylar fx w/o intracondylar extension of lwr end of lt femur, subsq enc for opn fx type IIIA, IIIB, or IIIC w/ malu
S72.455N	Nondisp supracondylar fx w/o intracondylar extension of lwr end of lt femur, subsq enc for opn fx type IIIA, IIIB, or IIIC w/ nonu
S72.454A	Nondisp supracondylar fx w/o intracondylar extension of lwr end of rt femur, init enc for clsd fx
S72.454P	Nondisp supracondylar fx w/o intracondylar extension of lwr end of rt femur, subsq enc for clsd fx w/ malu
S72.454K	Nondisp supracondylar fx w/o intracondylar extension of lwr end of rt femur, subsq enc for clsd fx w/ nonu
S72.454Q	Nondisp supracondylar fx w/o intracondylar extension of lwr end of rt femur, subsq enc for opn fx type I or II w/ malu
S72.454M	Nondisp supracondylar fx w/o intracondylar extension of lwr end of rt femur, subsq enc for opn fx type I or II w/ nonu
S72.454R	Nondisp supracondylar fx w/o intracondylar extension of lwr end of rt femur, subsq enc for opn fx type IIIA, IIIB, or IIIC w/ malu
S72.454N	Nondisp supracondylar fx w/o intracondylar extension of lwr end of rt femur, subsq enc for opn fx type IIIA, IIIB, or IIIC w/ nonu
S72.456A	Nondisp supracondylar fx w/o intracondylar extension of lwr end of unsp femur, init enc for clsd fx
S72.456P	Nondisp supracondylar fx w/o intracondylar extension of lwr end of unsp femur, subsq enc for clsd fx w/ malu
S72.456K	Nondisp supracondylar fx w/o intracondylar extension of lwr end of unsp femur, subsq enc for clsd fx w/ nonu
S72.456Q	Nondisp supracondylar fx w/o intracondylar extension of lwr end of unsp femur, subsq enc for opn fx type I or II w/ malu
S72.456M	Nondisp supracondylar fx w/o intracondylar extension of lwr end of unsp femur, subsq enc for opn fx type I or II w/ nonu

S72.456R	Nondisp supracondylar fx w/o intracondylar extension of lwr end of unsp femur, subsq enc for opn fx type IIIA, IIIB, or IIIC w/ malu
S72.456N	Nondisp supracondylar fx w/o intracondylar extension of lwr end of unsp femur, subsq enc for opn fx type IIIA, IIIB, or IIIC w/ nonu
S42.475A	Nondisp transcondylar fx of lt humerus, init enc for clsd fx
S42.475P	Nondisp transcondylar fx of lt humerus, subsq enc for fx w/ malu
S42.475K	Nondisp transcondylar fx of lt humerus, subsq enc for fx w/ nonu
S42.474A	Nondisp transcondylar fx of rt humerus, init enc for clsd fx
S42.474P	Nondisp transcondylar fx of rt humerus, subsq enc for fx w/ malu
S42.474K	Nondisp transcondylar fx of rt humerus, subsq enc for fx w/ nonu
S42.476A	Nondisp transcondylar fx of unsp humerus, init enc for clsd fx
S42.476P	Nondisp transcondylar fx of unsp humerus, subsq enc for fx w/ malu
S42.476K	Nondisp transcondylar fx of unsp humerus, subsq enc for fx w/ nonu
S32.455K	Nondisp transv fx of lt acetab, subsq enc for fx w/ nonu
S82.035A	Nondisp transv fx of lt patella, init enc for clsd fx
S82.035B	Nondisp transv fx of lt patella, init enc for opn fx type I or II
S82.035C	Nondisp transv fx of lt patella, init enc for opn fx type IIIA, IIIB, or IIIC
S82.035P	Nondisp transv fx of lt patella, subsq enc for clsd fx w/ malu
S82.035K	Nondisp transv fx of lt patella, subsq enc for clsd fx w/ nonu
S82.035Q	Nondisp transv fx of lt patella, subsq enc for opn fx type I or II w/ malu
S82.035M	Nondisp transv fx of lt patella, subsq enc for opn fx type I or II w/ nonu
S82.035R	Nondisp transv fx of lt patella, subsq enc for opn fx type IIIA, IIIB, or IIIC w/ malu
S82.035N	Nondisp transv fx of lt patella, subsq enc for opn fx type IIIA, IIIB, or IIIC w/ nonu
S32.454K	Nondisp transv fx of rt acetab, subsq enc for fx w/ nonu
S82.034A	Nondisp transv fx of rt patella, init enc for clsd fx
S82.034B	Nondisp transv fx of rt patella, init enc for opn fx type I or II
S82.034C	Nondisp transv fx of rt patella, init enc for opn fx type IIIA, IIIB, or IIIC
S82.034P	Nondisp transv fx of rt patella, subsq enc for clsd fx w/ malu
S82.034K	Nondisp transv fx of rt patella, subsq enc for clsd fx w/ nonu
S82.034Q	Nondisp transv fx of rt patella, subsq enc for opn fx type I or II w/ malu
S82.034M	Nondisp transv fx of rt patella, subsq enc for opn fx type I or II w/ nonu
S82.034R	Nondisp transv fx of rt patella, subsq enc for opn fx type IIIA, IIIB, or IIIC w/ malu
S82.034N	Nondisp transv fx of rt patella, subsq enc for opn fx type IIIA, IIIB, or IIIC w/ nonu
S42.325A	Nondisp transv fx of shaft of humerus, lt arm, init enc for clsd fx
S42.325P	Nondisp transv fx of shaft of humerus, lt arm, subsq enc for fx w/ malu
S42.325K	Nondisp transv fx of shaft of humerus, lt arm, subsq enc for fx w/ nonu
S42.324A	Nondisp transv fx of shaft of humerus, rt arm, init enc for clsd fx
S42.324P	Nondisp transv fx of shaft of humerus, rt arm, subsq enc for fx w/ malu
S42.324K	Nondisp transv fx of shaft of humerus, rt arm, subsq enc for fx w/ nonu
S42.326A	Nondisp transv fx of shaft of humerus, unsp arm, init enc for clsd fx
S42.326P	Nondisp transv fx of shaft of humerus, unsp arm, subsq enc for fx w/ malu
S42.326K	Nondisp transv fx of shaft of humerus, unsp arm, subsq enc for fx w/ nonu
S72.325P	Nondisp transv fx of shaft of lt femur, subsq enc for clsd fx w/ malu
S72.325K	Nondisp transv fx of shaft of lt femur, subsq enc for clsd fx w/ nonu
S72.325Q	Nondisp transv fx of shaft of lt femur, subsq enc for opn fx type I or II w/ malu
S72.325M	Nondisp transv fx of shaft of lt femur, subsq enc for opn fx type I or II w/ nonu
S72.325R	Nondisp transv fx of shaft of lt femur, subsq enc for opn fx type IIIA, IIIB, or IIIC w/ malu
S72.325N	Nondisp transv fx of shaft of lt femur, subsq enc for opn fx type IIIA, IIIB, or IIIC w/ nonu
S82.425P	Nondisp transv fx of shaft of lt fibula, subsq enc for clsd fx w/ malu
S82.425K	Nondisp transv fx of shaft of lt fibula, subsq enc for clsd fx w/ nonu
S82.425Q	Nondisp transv fx of shaft of lt fibula, subsq enc for opn fx type I or II w/ malu
S82.425M	Nondisp transv fx of shaft of lt fibula, subsq enc for opn fx type I or II w/ nonu
S82.425R	Nondisp transv fx of shaft of lt fibula, subsq enc for opn fx type IIIA, IIIB, or IIIC w/ malu
S82.425N	Nondisp transv fx of shaft of lt fibula, subsq enc for opn fx type IIIA, IIIB, or IIIC w/ nonu
S52.325A	Nondisp transv fx of shaft of lt radius, init enc for clsd fx
S52.325P	Nondisp transv fx of shaft of lt radius, subsq enc for clsd fx w/ malu
S52.325K	Nondisp transv fx of shaft of lt radius, subsq enc for clsd fx w/ nonu
S52.325Q	Nondisp transv fx of shaft of lt radius, subsq enc for opn fx type I or II w/ malu
S52.325M	Nondisp transv fx of shaft of lt radius, subsq enc for opn fx type I or II w/ nonu
S52.325R	Nondisp transv fx of shaft of lt radius, subsq enc for opn fx type IIIA, IIIB, or IIIC w/ malu
S52.325N	Nondisp transv fx of shaft of lt radius, subsq enc for opn fx type IIIA, IIIB, or IIIC w/ nonu
S82.225A	Nondisp transv fx of shaft of lt tibia, init enc for clsd fx
S82.225P	Nondisp transv fx of shaft of lt tibia, subsq enc for clsd fx w/ malu
S82.225K	Nondisp transv fx of shaft of lt tibia, subsq enc for clsd fx w/ nonu
S82.225Q	Nondisp transv fx of shaft of lt tibia, subsq enc for opn fx type I or II w/ malu
S82.225M	Nondisp transv fx of shaft of lt tibia, subsq enc for opn fx type I or II w/ nonu
S82.225R	Nondisp transv fx of shaft of lt tibia, subsq enc for opn fx type IIIA, IIIB, or IIIC w/ malu
S82.225N	Nondisp transv fx of shaft of lt tibia, subsq enc for opn fx type IIIA, IIIB, or IIIC w/ nonu
S52.225A	Nondisp transv fx of shaft of lt ulna, init enc for clsd fx
S52.225P	Nondisp transv fx of shaft of lt ulna, subsq enc for clsd fx w/ malu
S52.225K	Nondisp transv fx of shaft of lt ulna, subsq enc for clsd fx w/ nonu
S52.225Q	Nondisp transv fx of shaft of lt ulna, subsq enc for opn fx type I or II w/ malu
S52.225M	Nondisp transv fx of shaft of lt ulna, subsq enc for opn fx type I or II w/ nonu
S52.225R	Nondisp transv fx of shaft of lt ulna, subsq enc for opn fx type IIIA, IIIB, or IIIC w/ malu
S52.225N	Nondisp transv fx of shaft of lt ulna, subsq enc for opn fx type IIIA, IIIB, or IIIC w/ nonu
S72.324P	Nondisp transv fx of shaft of rt femur, subsq enc for clsd fx w/ malu
S72.324K	Nondisp transv fx of shaft of rt femur, subsq enc for clsd fx w/ nonu
S72.324Q	Nondisp transv fx of shaft of rt femur, subsq enc for opn fx type I or II w/ malu
S72.324M	Nondisp transv fx of shaft of rt femur, subsq enc for opn fx type I or II w/ nonu
S72.324R	Nondisp transv fx of shaft of rt femur, subsq enc for opn fx type IIIA, IIIB, or IIIC w/ malu
S72.324N	Nondisp transv fx of shaft of rt femur, subsq enc for opn fx type IIIA, IIIB, or IIIC w/ nonu
S82.424P	Nondisp transv fx of shaft of rt fibula, subsq enc for clsd fx w/ malu
S82.424K	Nondisp transv fx of shaft of rt fibula, subsq enc for clsd fx w/ nonu
S82.424Q	Nondisp transv fx of shaft of rt fibula, subsq enc for opn fx type I or II w/ malu
S82.424M	Nondisp transv fx of shaft of rt fibula, subsq enc for opn fx type I or II w/ nonu
S82.424R	Nondisp transv fx of shaft of rt fibula, subsq enc for opn fx type IIIA, IIIB, or IIIC w/ malu
S82.424N	Nondisp transv fx of shaft of rt fibula, subsq enc for opn fx type IIIA, IIIB, or IIIC w/ nonu
S52.324A	Nondisp transv fx of shaft of rt radius, init enc for clsd fx
S52.324P	Nondisp transv fx of shaft of rt radius, subsq enc for clsd fx w/ malu
S52.324K	Nondisp transv fx of shaft of rt radius, subsq enc for clsd fx w/ nonu
S52.324Q	Nondisp transv fx of shaft of rt radius, subsq enc for opn fx type I or II w/ malu
S52.324M	Nondisp transv fx of shaft of rt radius, subsq enc for opn fx type I or II w/ nonu
S52.324R	Nondisp transv fx of shaft of rt radius, subsq enc for opn fx type IIIA, IIIB, or IIIC w/ malu
S52.324N	Nondisp transv fx of shaft of rt radius, subsq enc for opn fx type IIIA, IIIB, or IIIC w/ nonu
S82.224A	Nondisp transv fx of shaft of rt tibia, init enc for clsd fx
S82.224P	Nondisp transv fx of shaft of rt tibia, subsq enc for clsd fx w/ malu
S82.224K	Nondisp transv fx of shaft of rt tibia, subsq enc for clsd fx w/ nonu
S82.224Q	Nondisp transv fx of shaft of rt tibia, subsq enc for opn fx type I or II w/ malu
S82.224M	Nondisp transv fx of shaft of rt tibia, subsq enc for opn fx type I or II w/ nonu
S82.224R	Nondisp transv fx of shaft of rt tibia, subsq enc for opn fx type IIIA, IIIB, or IIIC w/ malu
S82.224N	Nondisp transv fx of shaft of rt tibia, subsq enc for opn fx type IIIA, IIIB, or IIIC w/ nonu
S52.224A	Nondisp transv fx of shaft of rt ulna, init enc for clsd fx
S52.224P	Nondisp transv fx of shaft of rt ulna, subsq enc for clsd fx w/ malu
S52.224K	Nondisp transv fx of shaft of rt ulna, subsq enc for clsd fx w/ nonu
S52.224Q	Nondisp transv fx of shaft of rt ulna, subsq enc for opn fx type I or II w/ malu
S52.224M	Nondisp transv fx of shaft of rt ulna, subsq enc for opn fx type I or II w/ nonu

S52.224R	Nondisp transv fx of shaft of rt ulna, subsq enc for opn fx type IIIA, IIIB, or IIIC w/ malu
S52.224N	Nondisp transv fx of shaft of rt ulna, subsq enc for opn fx type IIIA, IIIB, or IIIC w/ nonu
S72.326P	Nondisp transv fx of shaft of unsp femur, subsq enc for clsd fx w/ malu
S72.326K	Nondisp transv fx of shaft of unsp femur, subsq enc for clsd fx w/ nonu
S72.326Q	Nondisp transv fx of shaft of unsp femur, subsq enc for opn fx type I or II w/ malu
S72.326M	Nondisp transv fx of shaft of unsp femur, subsq enc for opn fx type I or II w/ nonu
S72.326R	Nondisp transv fx of shaft of unsp femur, subsq enc for opn fx type IIIA, IIIB, or IIIC w/ malu
S72.326N	Nondisp transv fx of shaft of unsp femur, subsq enc for opn fx type IIIA, IIIB, or IIIC w/ nonu
S82.426P	Nondisp transv fx of shaft of unsp fibula, subsq enc for clsd fx w/ malu
S82.426K	Nondisp transv fx of shaft of unsp fibula, subsq enc for clsd fx w/ nonu
S82.426Q	Nondisp transv fx of shaft of unsp fibula, subsq enc for opn fx type I or II w/ malu
S82.426M	Nondisp transv fx of shaft of unsp fibula, subsq enc for opn fx type I or II w/ nonu
S82.426R	Nondisp transv fx of shaft of unsp fibula, subsq enc for opn fx type IIIA, IIIB, or IIIC w/ malu
S82.426N	Nondisp transv fx of shaft of unsp fibula, subsq enc for opn fx type IIIA, IIIB, or IIIC w/ nonu
S52.326A	Nondisp transv fx of shaft of unsp radius, init enc for clsd fx
S52.326P	Nondisp transv fx of shaft of unsp radius, subsq enc for clsd fx w/ malu
S52.326K	Nondisp transv fx of shaft of unsp radius, subsq enc for clsd fx w/ nonu
S52.326Q	Nondisp transv fx of shaft of unsp radius, subsq enc for opn fx type I or II w/ malu
S52.326M	Nondisp transv fx of shaft of unsp radius, subsq enc for opn fx type I or II w/ nonu
S52.326R	Nondisp transv fx of shaft of unsp radius, subsq enc for opn fx type IIIA, IIIB, or IIIC w/ malu
S52.326N	Nondisp transv fx of shaft of unsp radius, subsq enc for opn fx type IIIA, IIIB, or IIIC w/ nonu
S82.226A	Nondisp transv fx of shaft of unsp tibia, init enc for clsd fx
S82.226P	Nondisp transv fx of shaft of unsp tibia, subsq enc for clsd fx w/ malu
S82.226K	Nondisp transv fx of shaft of unsp tibia, subsq enc for clsd fx w/ nonu
S82.226Q	Nondisp transv fx of shaft of unsp tibia, subsq enc for opn fx type I or II w/ malu
S82.226M	Nondisp transv fx of shaft of unsp tibia, subsq enc for opn fx type I or II w/ nonu
S82.226R	Nondisp transv fx of shaft of unsp tibia, subsq enc for opn fx type IIIA, IIIB, or IIIC w/ malu
S82.226N	Nondisp transv fx of shaft of unsp tibia, subsq enc for opn fx type IIIA, IIIB, or IIIC w/ nonu
S52.226A	Nondisp transv fx of shaft of unsp ulna, init enc for clsd fx
S52.226P	Nondisp transv fx of shaft of unsp ulna, subsq enc for clsd fx w/ malu
S52.226K	Nondisp transv fx of shaft of unsp ulna, subsq enc for clsd fx w/ nonu
S52.226Q	Nondisp transv fx of shaft of unsp ulna, subsq enc for opn fx type I or II w/ malu
S52.226M	Nondisp transv fx of shaft of unsp ulna, subsq enc for opn fx type I or II w/ nonu
S52.226R	Nondisp transv fx of shaft of unsp ulna, subsq enc for opn fx type IIIA, IIIB, or IIIC w/ malu
S52.226N	Nondisp transv fx of shaft of unsp ulna, subsq enc for opn fx type IIIA, IIIB, or IIIC w/ nonu
S32.456K	Nondisp transv fx of unsp acetab, subsq enc for fx w/ nonu
S82.036A	Nondisp transv fx of unsp patella, init enc for clsd fx
S82.036B	Nondisp transv fx of unsp patella, init enc for opn fx type I or II
S82.036C	Nondisp transv fx of unsp patella, init enc for opn fx type IIIA, IIIB, or IIIC
S82.036P	Nondisp transv fx of unsp patella, subsq enc for clsd fx w/ malu
S82.036K	Nondisp transv fx of unsp patella, subsq enc for clsd fx w/ nonu
S82.036Q	Nondisp transv fx of unsp patella, subsq enc for opn fx type I or II w/ malu
S82.036M	Nondisp transv fx of unsp patella, subsq enc for opn fx type I or II w/ nonu
S82.036R	Nondisp transv fx of unsp patella, subsq enc for opn fx type IIIA, IIIB, or IIIC w/ malu
S82.036N	Nondisp transv fx of unsp patella, subsq enc for opn fx type IIIA, IIIB, or IIIC w/ nonu
S82.855B	Nondisp trimalleolar fx of lt lwr leg, init enc for opn fx type I or II
S82.855C	Nondisp trimalleolar fx of lt lwr leg, init enc for opn fx type IIIA, IIIB, or IIIC
S82.855P	Nondisp trimalleolar fx of lt lwr leg, subsq enc for clsd fx w/ malu
S82.855K	Nondisp trimalleolar fx of lt lwr leg, subsq enc for clsd fx w/ nonu
S82.855Q	Nondisp trimalleolar fx of lt lwr leg, subsq enc for opn fx type I or II w/ malu

S82.855M	Nondisp trimalleolar fx of lt lwr leg, subsq enc for opn fx type I or II w/ nonu
S82.855R	Nondisp trimalleolar fx of lt lwr leg, subsq enc for opn fx type IIIA, IIIB, or IIIC w/ malu
S82.855N	Nondisp trimalleolar fx of lt lwr leg, subsq enc for opn fx type IIIA, IIIB, or IIIC w/ nonu
S82.854B	Nondisp trimalleolar fx of rt lwr leg, init enc for opn fx type I or II
S82.854C	Nondisp trimalleolar fx of rt lwr leg, init enc for opn fx type IIIA, IIIB, or IIIC
S82.854P	Nondisp trimalleolar fx of rt lwr leg, subsq enc for clsd fx w/ malu
S82.854K	Nondisp trimalleolar fx of rt lwr leg, subsq enc for clsd fx w/ nonu
S82.854Q	Nondisp trimalleolar fx of rt lwr leg, subsq enc for opn fx type I or II w/ malu
S82.854M	Nondisp trimalleolar fx of rt lwr leg, subsq enc for opn fx type I or II w/ nonu
S82.854R	Nondisp trimalleolar fx of rt lwr leg, subsq enc for opn fx type IIIA, IIIB, or IIIC w/ malu
S82.854N	Nondisp trimalleolar fx of rt lwr leg, subsq enc for opn fx type IIIA, IIIB, or IIIC w/ nonu
S82.856B	Nondisp trimalleolar fx of unsp lwr leg, init enc for opn fx type I or II
S82.856C	Nondisp trimalleolar fx of unsp lwr leg, init enc for opn fx type IIIA, IIIB, or IIIC
S82.856P	Nondisp trimalleolar fx of unsp lwr leg, subsq enc for clsd fx w/ malu
S82.856K	Nondisp trimalleolar fx of unsp lwr leg, subsq enc for clsd fx w/ nonu
S82.856Q	Nondisp trimalleolar fx of unsp lwr leg, subsq enc for opn fx type I or II w/ malu
S82.856M	Nondisp trimalleolar fx of unsp lwr leg, subsq enc for opn fx type I or II w/ nonu
S82.856R	Nondisp trimalleolar fx of unsp lwr leg, subsq enc for opn fx type IIIA, IIIB, or IIIC w/ malu
S82.856N	Nondisp trimalleolar fx of unsp lwr leg, subsq enc for opn fx type IIIA, IIIB, or IIIC w/ nonu
S12.112A	Nondisp Type II dens fx, init enc for clsd fx
S12.112K	Nondisp Type II dens fx, subsq enc for fx w/ nonu
S72.415A	Nondisp unsp condyle fx of lwr end of lt femur, init enc for clsd fx
S72.415P	Nondisp unsp condyle fx of lwr end of lt femur, subsq enc for clsd fx w/ malu
S72.415K	Nondisp unsp condyle fx of lwr end of lt femur, subsq enc for clsd fx w/ nonu
S72.415Q	Nondisp unsp condyle fx of lwr end of lt femur, subsq enc for opn fx type I or II w/ malu
S72.415M	Nondisp unsp condyle fx of lwr end of lt femur, subsq enc for opn fx type I or II w/ nonu
S72.415R	Nondisp unsp condyle fx of lwr end of lt femur, subsq enc for opn fx type IIIA, IIIB, or IIIC w/ malu
S72.415N	Nondisp unsp condyle fx of lwr end of lt femur, subsq enc for opn fx type IIIA, IIIB, or IIIC w/ nonu
S72.414A	Nondisp unsp condyle fx of lwr end of rt femur, init enc for clsd fx
S72.414P	Nondisp unsp condyle fx of lwr end of rt femur, subsq enc for clsd fx w/ malu
S72.414K	Nondisp unsp condyle fx of lwr end of rt femur, subsq enc for clsd fx w/ nonu
S72.414Q	Nondisp unsp condyle fx of lwr end of rt femur, subsq enc for opn fx type I or II w/ malu
S72.414M	Nondisp unsp condyle fx of lwr end of rt femur, subsq enc for opn fx type I or II w/ nonu
S72.414R	Nondisp unsp condyle fx of lwr end of rt femur, subsq enc for opn fx type IIIA, IIIB, or IIIC w/ malu
S72.414N	Nondisp unsp condyle fx of lwr end of rt femur, subsq enc for opn fx type IIIA, IIIB, or IIIC w/ nonu
S72.416A	Nondisp unsp condyle fx of lwr end of unsp femur, init enc for clsd fx
S72.416P	Nondisp unsp condyle fx of lwr end of unsp femur, subsq enc for clsd fx w/ malu
S72.416K	Nondisp unsp condyle fx of lwr end of unsp femur, subsq enc for clsd fx w/ nonu
S72.416Q	Nondisp unsp condyle fx of lwr end of unsp femur, subsq enc for opn fx type I or II w/ malu
S72.416M	Nondisp unsp condyle fx of lwr end of unsp femur, subsq enc for opn fx type I or II w/ nonu
S72.416R	Nondisp unsp condyle fx of lwr end of unsp femur, subsq enc for opn fx type IIIA, IIIB, or IIIC w/ malu
S72.416N	Nondisp unsp condyle fx of lwr end of unsp femur, subsq enc for opn fx type IIIA, IIIB, or IIIC w/ nonu
S92.405P	Nondisp unsp fx of lt great toe, subsq enc for fx w/ malu
S92.405K	Nondisp unsp fx of lt great toe, subsq enc for fx w/ nonu
S92.505P	Nondisp unsp fx of lt lesser toe(s), subsq enc for fx w/ malu
S92.505K	Nondisp unsp fx of lt lesser toe(s), subsq enc for fx w/ nonu
S92.404P	Nondisp unsp fx of rt great toe, subsq enc for fx w/ malu

S92.404K	Nondisp unsp fx of rt great toe, subsq enc for fx w/ nonu
S92.504P	Nondisp unsp fx of rt lesser toe(s), subsq enc for fx w/ malu
S92.504K	Nondisp unsp fx of rt lesser toe(s), subsq enc for fx w/ nonu
S92.406P	Nondisp unsp fx of unsp great toe, subsq enc for fx w/ malu
S92.406K	Nondisp unsp fx of unsp great toe, subsq enc for fx w/ nonu
S92.506P	Nondisp unsp fx of unsp lesser toe(s), subsq enc for fx w/ malu
S92.506K	Nondisp unsp fx of unsp lesser toe(s), subsq enc for fx w/ nonu
S32.110A	Nondisp Zone I fx of sacrum, init enc for clsd fx
S32.110K	Nondisp Zone I fx of sacrum, subsq enc for fx w/ nonu
S32.120A	Nondisp Zone II fx of sacrum, init enc for clsd fx
S32.120K	Nondisp Zone II fx of sacrum, subsq enc for fx w/ nonu
S32.130A	Nondisp Zone III fx of sacrum, init enc for clsd fx
S32.130K	Nondisp Zone III fx of sacrum, subsq enc for fx w/ nonu
D80.1	Nonfamilial hypogammaglobulinemia
I67.6	Nonpyogenic thrombosis of intracranial venous sys
M79.A3	Nontraumatic compartment synd of abd
M79.A22	Nontraumatic compartment synd of lt lwr extr
M79.A12	Nontraumatic compartment synd of lt upr extr
M79.A9	Nontraumatic compartment synd of oth sites
M79.A21	Nontraumatic compartment synd of rt lwr extr
M79.A11	Nontraumatic compartment synd of rt upr extr
M79.A29	Nontraumatic compartment synd of unsp lwr extr
M79.A19	Nontraumatic compartment synd of unsp upr extr
I62.9	Nontraumatic intracranial hemor, unsp
A92.1	O'nyong-nyong fever
O71.6	Obstetric damage to pelvic joints & lgmts
O71.7	Obstetric hematoma of pelvis
O71.4	Obstetric high vaginal lac alone
O71.3	Obstetric lac of cervix
A34	Obstetrical tetanus
T81.526A	Obstruction d/t FB accidentally lt in body following aspiration, punc or oth catheterization, init enc
T81.524A	Obstruction d/t FB accidentally lt in body following endo exam, init enc
T81.525A	Obstruction d/t FB accidentally lt in body following heart catheterization, init enc
T81.521A	Obstruction d/t FB accidentally lt in body following inf or transfusion, init enc
T81.523A	Obstruction d/t FB accidentally lt in body following injection or immunization, init enc
T81.522A	Obstruction d/t FB accidentally lt in body following kidney dialysis, init enc
T81.528A	Obstruction d/t FB accidentally lt in body following oth procedure, init enc
T81.527A	Obstruction d/t FB accidentally lt in body following rmvl of catheter or packing, init enc
T81.520A	Obstruction d/t FB accidentally lt in body following surg operation, init enc
T81.529A	Obstruction d/t FB accidentally lt in body following unsp procedure, init enc
K31.5	Obstruction of duodenum
K82.0	Obstruction of gallbladder
G91.1	Obstructive hydrocephalus
I42.1	Obstructive hypertrophic cardiomyopathy
S73.025A	Obturator disloc of lt hip, init enc
S73.024A	Obturator disloc of rt hip, init enc
S73.026A	Obturator disloc of unsp hip, init enc
S73.022A	Obturator sublux of lt hip, init enc
S73.021A	Obturator sublux of rt hip, init enc
S73.023A	Obturator sublux of unsp hip, init enc
Q01.2	Occipital encephalocele
E70.319	Ocular albinism, unsp
S05.22XA	Ocular lac & rupture w/ prolapse or loss of intraocular tissue, lt eye, init enc
S05.21XA	Ocular lac & rupture w/ prolapse or loss of intraocular tissue, rt eye, init enc
S05.20XA	Ocular lac & rupture w/ prolapse or loss of intraocular tissue, unsp eye, init enc
S05.32XA	Ocular lac w/o prolapse or loss of intraocular tissue, lt eye, init enc
S05.31XA	Ocular lac w/o prolapse or loss of intraocular tissue, rt eye, init enc
S05.30XA	Ocular lac w/o prolapse or loss of intraocular tissue, unsp eye, init enc
E70.329	Oculocutaneous albinism, unsp
A32.81	Oculoglandular listeriosis
A21.1	Oculoglandular tularemia
O41.01X1	Oligohydramnios, 1st trmstr, fetus 1
O41.01X2	Oligohydramnios, 1st trmstr, fetus 2

O41.01X3	Oligohydramnios, 1st trmstr, fetus 3
O41.01X4	Oligohydramnios, 1st trmstr, fetus 4
O41.01X5	Oligohydramnios, 1st trmstr, fetus 5
O41.01X0	Oligohydramnios, 1st trmstr, N/A or unsp
O41.01X9	Oligohydramnios, 1st trmstr, oth fetus
O41.02X1	Oligohydramnios, 2nd trmstr, fetus 1
O41.02X2	Oligohydramnios, 2nd trmstr, fetus 2
O41.02X3	Oligohydramnios, 2nd trmstr, fetus 3
O41.02X4	Oligohydramnios, 2nd trmstr, fetus 4
O41.02X5	Oligohydramnios, 2nd trmstr, fetus 5
O41.02X0	Oligohydramnios, 2nd trmstr, N/A or unsp
O41.02X9	Oligohydramnios, 2nd trmstr, oth fetus
O41.03X1	Oligohydramnios, 3rd trmstr, fetus 1
O41.03X2	Oligohydramnios, 3rd trmstr, fetus 2
O41.03X3	Oligohydramnios, 3rd trmstr, fetus 3
O41.03X4	Oligohydramnios, 3rd trmstr, fetus 4
O41.03X5	Oligohydramnios, 3rd trmstr, fetus 5
O41.03X0	Oligohydramnios, 3rd trmstr, N/A or unsp
O41.03X9	Oligohydramnios, 3rd trmstr, oth fetus
P38.1	Omphalitis w/ mild hemor
P38.9	Omphalitis w/o hemor
A98.1	Omsk hemorrhagic fever
B73.01	Onchocerciasis w/ endophthalmitis
B73.00	Onchocerciasis w/ eye involvement, unsp
B73.02	Onchocerciasis w/ glaucoma
B73.09	Onchocerciasis w/ oth eye involvement
B73.1	Onchocerciasis w/o eye disease
F11.121	Opioid abuse w/ intoxication delirium
F11.150	Opioid abuse w/ opioid-induced psychotic d/o w/ delusions
F11.151	Opioid abuse w/ opioid-induced psychotic d/o w/ hallucinations
F11.221	Opioid dependence w/ intoxication delirium
F11.222	Opioid dependence w/ intoxication w/ perceptual disturbance
F11.250	Opioid dependence w/ opioid-induced psychotic d/o w/ delusions
F11.251	Opioid dependence w/ opioid-induced psychotic d/o w/ hallucinations
F11.259	Opioid dependence w/ opioid-induced psychotic d/o, unsp
F11.281	Opioid dependence w/ opioid-induced sexual dysfunction
F11.282	Opioid dependence w/ opioid-induced sleep d/o
F11.288	Opioid dependence w/ oth opioid-induced d/o
F11.23	Opioid dependence w/ withdrawal
F11.20	Opioid dependence, uncomplicated
F11.921	Opioid use, unsp w/ intoxication delirium
F11.950	Opioid use, unsp w/ opioid-induced psychotic d/o w/ delusions
F11.951	Opioid use, unsp w/ opioid-induced psychotic d/o w/ hallucinations
F11.93	Opioid use, unsp w/ withdrawal
B66.0	Opisthorchiasis
S21.152A	Opn bite of lt front wall of thorax w/o penetration into thoracic cavity, init enc
S11.25XA	Opn bite of pharynx & cervical esophagus, init enc
S21.151A	Opn bite of rt front wall of thorax w/o penetration into thoracic cavity, init enc
S11.15XA	Opn bite of thyroid gland, init enc
S21.159A	Opn bite of unsp front wall of thorax w/o penetration into thoracic cavity, init enc
S21.95XA	Opn bite of unsp part of thorax, init enc
H46.03	Optic papillitis, bilat
H46.02	Optic papillitis, lt eye
H46.01	Optic papillitis, rt eye
H46.00	Optic papillitis, unsp eye
E85.4	Organ-limited amyloidosis
A93.0	Oropouche virus disease
B45.3	Osseous cryptococcosis
Q78.0	Osteogenesis imperfecta
H05.023	Osteomyelitis of bilat orbits
H05.022	Osteomyelitis of lt orbit
H05.021	Osteomyelitis of rt orbit
H05.029	Osteomyelitis of unsp orbit
M46.22	Osteomyelitis of vertebra, cervical rgn
M46.23	Osteomyelitis of vertebra, cervicothoracic rgn
M46.26	Osteomyelitis of vertebra, lumbar rgn
M46.27	Osteomyelitis of vertebra, lumbosacral rgn
M46.21	Osteomyelitis of vertebra, occipito-atlanto-axial rgn
M46.28	Osteomyelitis of vertebra, sacral & sacrococcygeal rgn
M46.20	Osteomyelitis of vertebra, site unsp
M46.24	Osteomyelitis of vertebra, thoracic rgn

Appendix B — Alphabetic CC List

M46.25	Osteomyelitis of vertebra, thoracolumbar rgn
M86.9	Osteomyelitis, unsp
M87.138	Osteonecrosis d/t drugs of lt carpus
M87.132	Osteonecrosis d/t drugs of lt radius
M87.135	Osteonecrosis d/t drugs of lt ulna
M87.137	Osteonecrosis d/t drugs of rt carpus
M87.131	Osteonecrosis d/t drugs of rt radius
M87.134	Osteonecrosis d/t drugs of rt ulna
M87.139	Osteonecrosis d/t drugs of unsp carpus
M87.133	Osteonecrosis d/t drugs of unsp radius
M87.136	Osteonecrosis d/t drugs of unsp ulna
M87.180	Osteonecrosis d/t drugs, jaw
M87.172	Osteonecrosis d/t drugs, lt ankle
M87.152	Osteonecrosis d/t drugs, lt femur
M87.165	Osteonecrosis d/t drugs, lt fibula
M87.145	Osteonecrosis d/t drugs, lt finger(s)
M87.175	Osteonecrosis d/t drugs, lt foot
M87.142	Osteonecrosis d/t drugs, lt hand
M87.122	Osteonecrosis d/t drugs, lt humerus
M87.112	Osteonecrosis d/t drugs, lt shldr
M87.162	Osteonecrosis d/t drugs, lt tibia
M87.178	Osteonecrosis d/t drugs, lt toe(s)
M87.19	Osteonecrosis d/t drugs, multi sites
M87.188	Osteonecrosis d/t drugs, oth site
M87.150	Osteonecrosis d/t drugs, pelvis
M87.171	Osteonecrosis d/t drugs, rt ankle
M87.151	Osteonecrosis d/t drugs, rt femur
M87.164	Osteonecrosis d/t drugs, rt fibula
M87.144	Osteonecrosis d/t drugs, rt finger(s)
M87.174	Osteonecrosis d/t drugs, rt foot
M87.141	Osteonecrosis d/t drugs, rt hand
M87.121	Osteonecrosis d/t drugs, rt humerus
M87.111	Osteonecrosis d/t drugs, rt shldr
M87.161	Osteonecrosis d/t drugs, rt tibia
M87.177	Osteonecrosis d/t drugs, rt toe(s)
M87.173	Osteonecrosis d/t drugs, unsp ankle
M87.10	Osteonecrosis d/t drugs, unsp bone
M87.159	Osteonecrosis d/t drugs, unsp femur
M87.166	Osteonecrosis d/t drugs, unsp fibula
M87.146	Osteonecrosis d/t drugs, unsp finger(s)
M87.176	Osteonecrosis d/t drugs, unsp foot
M87.143	Osteonecrosis d/t drugs, unsp hand
M87.129	Osteonecrosis d/t drugs, unsp humerus
M87.119	Osteonecrosis d/t drugs, unsp shldr
M87.163	Osteonecrosis d/t drugs, unsp tibia
M87.179	Osteonecrosis d/t drugs, unsp toe(s)
M87.238	Osteonecrosis d/t previous trauma of lt carpus
M87.232	Osteonecrosis d/t previous trauma of lt radius
M87.235	Osteonecrosis d/t previous trauma of lt ulna
M87.237	Osteonecrosis d/t previous trauma of rt carpus
M87.231	Osteonecrosis d/t previous trauma of rt radius
M87.234	Osteonecrosis d/t previous trauma of rt ulna
M87.239	Osteonecrosis d/t previous trauma of unsp carpus
M87.233	Osteonecrosis d/t previous trauma of unsp radius
M87.236	Osteonecrosis d/t previous trauma of unsp ulna
M87.272	Osteonecrosis d/t previous trauma, lt ankle
M87.252	Osteonecrosis d/t previous trauma, lt femur
M87.265	Osteonecrosis d/t previous trauma, lt fibula
M87.245	Osteonecrosis d/t previous trauma, lt finger(s)
M87.275	Osteonecrosis d/t previous trauma, lt foot
M87.242	Osteonecrosis d/t previous trauma, lt hand
M87.222	Osteonecrosis d/t previous trauma, lt humerus
M87.212	Osteonecrosis d/t previous trauma, lt shldr
M87.262	Osteonecrosis d/t previous trauma, lt tibia
M87.278	Osteonecrosis d/t previous trauma, lt toe(s)
M87.29	Osteonecrosis d/t previous trauma, multi sites
M87.28	Osteonecrosis d/t previous trauma, oth site
M87.250	Osteonecrosis d/t previous trauma, pelvis
M87.271	Osteonecrosis d/t previous trauma, rt ankle
M87.251	Osteonecrosis d/t previous trauma, rt femur
M87.264	Osteonecrosis d/t previous trauma, rt fibula
M87.244	Osteonecrosis d/t previous trauma, rt finger(s)
M87.274	Osteonecrosis d/t previous trauma, rt foot
M87.241	Osteonecrosis d/t previous trauma, rt hand
M87.221	Osteonecrosis d/t previous trauma, rt humerus
M87.211	Osteonecrosis d/t previous trauma, rt shldr
M87.261	Osteonecrosis d/t previous trauma, rt tibia
M87.277	Osteonecrosis d/t previous trauma, rt toe(s)
M87.273	Osteonecrosis d/t previous trauma, unsp ankle
M87.20	Osteonecrosis d/t previous trauma, unsp bone
M87.256	Osteonecrosis d/t previous trauma, unsp femur
M87.266	Osteonecrosis d/t previous trauma, unsp fibula
M87.246	Osteonecrosis d/t previous trauma, unsp finger(s)
M87.276	Osteonecrosis d/t previous trauma, unsp foot
M87.243	Osteonecrosis d/t previous trauma, unsp hand
M87.229	Osteonecrosis d/t previous trauma, unsp humerus
M87.219	Osteonecrosis d/t previous trauma, unsp shldr
M87.263	Osteonecrosis d/t previous trauma, unsp tibia
M87.279	Osteonecrosis d/t previous trauma, unsp toe(s)
M90.572	Osteonecrosis in diseases classified elsw, lt ankle & foot
M90.532	Osteonecrosis in diseases classified elsw, lt forearm
M90.542	Osteonecrosis in diseases classified elsw, lt hand
M90.562	Osteonecrosis in diseases classified elsw, lt lwr leg
M90.512	Osteonecrosis in diseases classified elsw, lt shldr
M90.552	Osteonecrosis in diseases classified elsw, lt thigh
M90.522	Osteonecrosis in diseases classified elsw, lt upr arm
M90.59	Osteonecrosis in diseases classified elsw, multi sites
M90.58	Osteonecrosis in diseases classified elsw, oth site
M90.571	Osteonecrosis in diseases classified elsw, rt ankle & foot
M90.531	Osteonecrosis in diseases classified elsw, rt forearm
M90.541	Osteonecrosis in diseases classified elsw, rt hand
M90.561	Osteonecrosis in diseases classified elsw, rt lwr leg
M90.511	Osteonecrosis in diseases classified elsw, rt shldr
M90.551	Osteonecrosis in diseases classified elsw, rt thigh
M90.521	Osteonecrosis in diseases classified elsw, rt upr arm
M90.579	Osteonecrosis in diseases classified elsw, unsp ankle & foot
M90.539	Osteonecrosis in diseases classified elsw, unsp forearm
M90.549	Osteonecrosis in diseases classified elsw, unsp hand
M90.569	Osteonecrosis in diseases classified elsw, unsp lwr leg
M90.519	Osteonecrosis in diseases classified elsw, unsp shldr
M90.50	Osteonecrosis in diseases classified elsw, unsp site
M90.559	Osteonecrosis in diseases classified elsw, unsp thigh
M90.529	Osteonecrosis in diseases classified elsw, unsp upr arm
M87.9	Osteonecrosis, unsp
Q78.2	Osteopetrosis
K43.6	Oth & unsp ventral hernia w/ obstruction, w/o gangrene
T80.39XA	Oth ABO incompatibility reaction d/t transfusion of blood or blood products, init enc
J39.1	Oth abscess of pharynx
B60.19	Oth acanthamebic disease
L12.35	Oth acquired epidermolysis bullosa
K35.89	Oth acute appendicitis
N17.8	Oth acute kidney failure
M86.172	Oth acute osteomyelitis, lt ankle & foot
M86.152	Oth acute osteomyelitis, lt femur
M86.142	Oth acute osteomyelitis, lt hand
M86.122	Oth acute osteomyelitis, lt humerus
M86.132	Oth acute osteomyelitis, lt radius & ulna
M86.112	Oth acute osteomyelitis, lt shldr
M86.162	Oth acute osteomyelitis, lt tibia & fibula
M86.19	Oth acute osteomyelitis, multi sites
M86.18	Oth acute osteomyelitis, oth site
M86.171	Oth acute osteomyelitis, rt ankle & foot
M86.151	Oth acute osteomyelitis, rt femur
M86.141	Oth acute osteomyelitis, rt hand
M86.121	Oth acute osteomyelitis, rt humerus
M86.131	Oth acute osteomyelitis, rt radius & ulna
M86.111	Oth acute osteomyelitis, rt shldr
M86.161	Oth acute osteomyelitis, rt tibia & fibula
M86.179	Oth acute osteomyelitis, unsp ankle & foot
M86.159	Oth acute osteomyelitis, unsp femur
M86.149	Oth acute osteomyelitis, unsp hand
M86.129	Oth acute osteomyelitis, unsp humerus
M86.139	Oth acute osteomyelitis, unsp radius & ulna
M86.119	Oth acute osteomyelitis, unsp shldr
M86.10	Oth acute osteomyelitis, unsp site

M86.169	Oth acute osteomyelitis, unsp tibia & fibula
T81.69XA	Oth acute reaction to foreign substance accidentally lt during a procedure, init enc
I01.8	Oth acute rheumatic heart disease
E27.49	Oth adrenocortical insufficiency
E27.0	Oth adrenocortical overactivity
J93.82	Oth air leak
E70.338	Oth albinism w/ hematologic abnormality
J84.09	Oth alveolar & parieto-alveolar conditions
A06.82	Oth amebic genitourinary infections
A06.89	Oth amebic infections
E85.8	Oth amyloidosis
S73.035A	Oth ant disloc of lt hip, init enc
S73.034A	Oth ant disloc of rt hip, init enc
S73.036A	Oth ant disloc of unsp hip, init enc
S73.032A	Oth ant sublux of lt hip, init enc
S73.031A	Oth ant sublux of rt hip, init enc
S73.033A	Oth ant sublux of unsp hip, init enc
P28.4	Oth apnea of newborn
A96.8	Oth arenaviral hemorrhagic fevers
I74.09	Oth arterial embolism & thrombosis of abd aorta
R18.8	Oth ascites
P28.19	Oth atelectasis of newborn
Q64.39	Oth atresia & stenosis of urethra & bladder neck
A81.89	Oth atypical virus infections of central nervous sys
D59.1	Oth autoimmune hemolytic anemias
F31.89	Oth bipolar d/o
E71.118	Oth branched-chain organic acidurias
A23.8	Oth brucellosis
I42.8	Oth cardiomyopathies
A52.09	Oth cardiovascular syphilis
A52.12	Oth cerebrospinal syphilis
I67.89	Oth cerebrovascular disease
A52.05	Oth cerebrovascular syphilis
I67.848	Oth cerebrovascular vasospasm & vasoconstriction
F84.3	Oth childhood disintegrative d/o
K80.81	Oth cholelithiasis w/ obstruction
H30.893	Oth chorioretinal inflammations, bilat
H30.892	Oth chorioretinal inflammations, lt eye
H30.891	Oth chorioretinal inflammations, rt eye
H30.899	Oth chorioretinal inflammations, unsp eye
L53.3	Oth chr figurate erythema
M86.572	Oth chr hematogenous osteomyelitis, lt ankle & foot
M86.552	Oth chr hematogenous osteomyelitis, lt femur
M86.542	Oth chr hematogenous osteomyelitis, lt hand
M86.522	Oth chr hematogenous osteomyelitis, lt humerus
M86.532	Oth chr hematogenous osteomyelitis, lt radius & ulna
M86.512	Oth chr hematogenous osteomyelitis, lt shldr
M86.562	Oth chr hematogenous osteomyelitis, lt tibia & fibula
M86.59	Oth chr hematogenous osteomyelitis, multi sites
M86.58	Oth chr hematogenous osteomyelitis, oth site
M86.571	Oth chr hematogenous osteomyelitis, rt ankle & foot
M86.551	Oth chr hematogenous osteomyelitis, rt femur
M86.541	Oth chr hematogenous osteomyelitis, rt hand
M86.521	Oth chr hematogenous osteomyelitis, rt humerus
M86.531	Oth chr hematogenous osteomyelitis, rt radius & ulna
M86.511	Oth chr hematogenous osteomyelitis, rt shldr
M86.561	Oth chr hematogenous osteomyelitis, rt tibia & fibula
M86.579	Oth chr hematogenous osteomyelitis, unsp ankle & foot
M86.559	Oth chr hematogenous osteomyelitis, unsp femur
M86.549	Oth chr hematogenous osteomyelitis, unsp hand
M86.529	Oth chr hematogenous osteomyelitis, unsp humerus
M86.539	Oth chr hematogenous osteomyelitis, unsp radius & ulna
M86.519	Oth chr hematogenous osteomyelitis, unsp shldr
M86.50	Oth chr hematogenous osteomyelitis, unsp site
M86.569	Oth chr hematogenous osteomyelitis, unsp tibia & fibula
M86.672	Oth chr osteomyelitis, lt ankle & foot
M86.642	Oth chr osteomyelitis, lt hand
M86.622	Oth chr osteomyelitis, lt humerus
M86.632	Oth chr osteomyelitis, lt radius & ulna
M86.612	Oth chr osteomyelitis, lt shldr
M86.652	Oth chr osteomyelitis, lt thigh
M86.662	Oth chr osteomyelitis, lt tibia & fibula
M86.69	Oth chr osteomyelitis, multi sites
M86.68	Oth chr osteomyelitis, oth site
M86.671	Oth chr osteomyelitis, rt ankle & foot
M86.641	Oth chr osteomyelitis, rt hand
M86.621	Oth chr osteomyelitis, rt humerus
M86.631	Oth chr osteomyelitis, rt radius & ulna
M86.611	Oth chr osteomyelitis, rt shldr
M86.651	Oth chr osteomyelitis, rt thigh
M86.661	Oth chr osteomyelitis, rt tibia & fibula
M86.679	Oth chr osteomyelitis, unsp ankle & foot
M86.649	Oth chr osteomyelitis, unsp hand
M86.629	Oth chr osteomyelitis, unsp humerus
M86.639	Oth chr osteomyelitis, unsp radius & ulna
M86.619	Oth chr osteomyelitis, unsp shldr
M86.60	Oth chr osteomyelitis, unsp site
M86.659	Oth chr osteomyelitis, unsp thigh
M86.669	Oth chr osteomyelitis, unsp tibia & fibula
K86.1	Oth chr pancreatitis
N11.8	Oth chr tubulo-interstitial nephritis
B18.8	Oth chr viral hepatitis
C81.79	Oth classical Hodgkin lymphoma, extranodal & solid organ sites
C81.73	Oth classical Hodgkin lymphoma, intra-abd lymph nodes
C81.76	Oth classical Hodgkin lymphoma, intrapelvic lymph nodes
C81.72	Oth classical Hodgkin lymphoma, intrathoracic lymph nodes
C81.74	Oth classical Hodgkin lymphoma, lymph nodes of axilla & upr limb
C81.71	Oth classical Hodgkin lymphoma, lymph nodes of head, face, & neck
C81.75	Oth classical Hodgkin lymphoma, lymph nodes of inguinal rgn & lwr limb
C81.78	Oth classical Hodgkin lymphoma, lymph nodes of multi sites
C81.77	Oth classical Hodgkin lymphoma, spleen
C81.70	Oth classical Hodgkin lymphoma, unsp site
D81.89	Oth combined immunodeficiencies
D83.8	Oth common variable immunodeficiencies
N98.8	Oth comp associated w/ artfcl fertilization
O08.89	Oth comp following an ectopic & molar pregnancy
T88.1XXA	Oth comp following immunization, NEC, init enc
T86.838	Oth comp of bone graft
T86.09	Oth comp of bone marrow transplant
K94.09	Oth comp of colostomy
T86.848	Oth comp of corneal transplant
K94.19	Oth comp of enterostomy
K94.39	Oth comp of esophagostomy
T81.596A	Oth comp of FB accidentally lt in body following aspiration, punc or oth catheterization, init enc
T81.594A	Oth comp of FB accidentally lt in body following endo exam, init enc
T81.595A	Oth comp of FB accidentally lt in body following heart catheterization, init enc
T81.591A	Oth comp of FB accidentally lt in body following inf or transfusion, init enc
T81.593A	Oth comp of FB accidentally lt in body following injection or immunization, init enc
T81.592A	Oth comp of FB accidentally lt in body following kidney dialysis, init enc
T81.598A	Oth comp of FB accidentally lt in body following oth procedure, init enc
T81.597A	Oth comp of FB accidentally lt in body following rmvl of catheter or packing, init enc
T81.590A	Oth comp of FB accidentally lt in body following surg operation, init enc
T81.599A	Oth comp of FB accidentally lt in body following unsp procedure, init enc
K95.09	Oth comp of gastric band procedure
T86.298	Oth comp of heart transplant
T86.39	Oth comp of heart-lung transplant
K91.858	Oth comp of intestinal pouch
T86.858	Oth comp of intestine transplant
T86.19	Oth comp of kidney transplant
T86.49	Oth comp of liver transplant
T86.818	Oth comp of lung transplant
K95.89	Oth comp of oth bariatric procedure
T86.898	Oth comp of oth transplanted tissue
J95.859	Oth comp of respirator [ventilator]
T86.828	Oth comp of skin graft (allograft) (autograft)
T86.99	Oth comp of unsp transplanted organ & tissue
T82.49XA	Oth comp of vascular dialysis catheter, init enc
O31.8X11	Oth comp specific to multi gestation, 1st trmstr, fetus 1
O31.8X12	Oth comp specific to multi gestation, 1st trmstr, fetus 2
O31.8X13	Oth comp specific to multi gestation, 1st trmstr, fetus 3
O31.8X14	Oth comp specific to multi gestation, 1st trmstr, fetus 4

O31.8X15	Oth comp specific to multi gestation, 1st trmstr, fetus 5
O31.8X10	Oth comp specific to multi gestation, 1st trmstr, N/A or unsp
O31.8X19	Oth comp specific to multi gestation, 1st trmstr, oth fetus
O31.8X21	Oth comp specific to multi gestation, 2nd trmstr, fetus 1
O31.8X22	Oth comp specific to multi gestation, 2nd trmstr, fetus 2
O31.8X23	Oth comp specific to multi gestation, 2nd trmstr, fetus 3
O31.8X24	Oth comp specific to multi gestation, 2nd trmstr, fetus 4
O31.8X25	Oth comp specific to multi gestation, 2nd trmstr, fetus 5
O31.8X20	Oth comp specific to multi gestation, 2nd trmstr, N/A or unsp
O31.8X29	Oth comp specific to multi gestation, 2nd trmstr, oth fetus
O31.8X31	Oth comp specific to multi gestation, 3rd trmstr, fetus 1
O31.8X32	Oth comp specific to multi gestation, 3rd trmstr, fetus 2
O31.8X33	Oth comp specific to multi gestation, 3rd trmstr, fetus 3
O31.8X34	Oth comp specific to multi gestation, 3rd trmstr, fetus 4
O31.8X35	Oth comp specific to multi gestation, 3rd trmstr, fetus 5
O31.8X30	Oth comp specific to multi gestation, 3rd trmstr, N/A or unsp
O31.8X39	Oth comp specific to multi gestation, 3rd trmstr, oth fetus
A69.29	Oth conditions associated w/ Lyme disease
M30.8	Oth conditions related to polyarteritis nodosa
P61.4	Oth congenital anemias, NEC
Q67.8	Oth congenital deformities of chest
Q43.2	Oth congenital functional d/o of colon
Q87.5	Oth congenital malformation syndromes w/ oth skeletal changes
Q25.4	Oth congenital malformations of aorta
Q44.5	Oth congenital malformations of bile ducts
Q76.8	Oth congenital malformations of bony thorax
Q32.4	Oth congenital malformations of bronchus
Q39.8	Oth congenital malformations of esophagus
Q44.1	Oth congenital malformations of gallbladder
Q26.8	Oth congenital malformations of great veins
Q31.8	Oth congenital malformations of larynx
Q44.7	Oth congenital malformations of liver
Q25.8	Oth congenital malformations of oth great arteries
Q45.3	Oth congenital malformations of pancreas & pancreatic duct
Q22.3	Oth congenital malformations of pulmn valve
Q76.6	Oth congenital malformations of ribs
Q32.1	Oth congenital malformations of trachea
D61.09	Oth constitutional aplastic anemia
G95.29	Oth cord compression
A81.09	Oth Creutzfeldt-Jakob disease
I23.8	Oth current comp following acute myocardial infarction
E24.8	Oth Cushing's synd
Q61.8	Oth cystic kidney diseases
N99.518	Oth cystostomy comp
B25.8	Oth cytomegaloviral diseases
E72.09	Oth d/o of amino-acid transport
E70.8	Oth d/o of aromatic amino-acid metabolism
E71.19	Oth d/o of branched-chain amino-acid metabolism
E71.39	Oth d/o of fatty-acid metabolism
E71.318	Oth d/o of fatty-acid oxidation
E74.29	Oth d/o of galactose metabolism
E76.8	Oth d/o of glucosaminoglycan metabolism
E72.59	Oth d/o of glycine metabolism
E70.49	Oth d/o of histidine metabolism
E71.518	Oth d/o of peroxisome biogenesis
E71.128	Oth d/o of propionate metabolism
E79.8	Oth d/o of purine & pyrimidine metabolism
E72.19	Oth d/o of sulfur-bearing amino-acid metabolism
H59.093	Oth d/o of the eye following cataract surgery, bilat
H59.092	Oth d/o of the lt eye following cataract surgery
H59.091	Oth d/o of the rt eye following cataract surgery
E70.29	Oth d/o of tyrosine metabolism
H59.099	Oth d/o of unsp eye following cataract surgery
E72.29	Oth d/o of urea cycle metabolism
Q93.89	Oth deletions from the autosomes
Q93.5	Oth deletions of part of a chromosome
M33.12	Oth dermatopolymyositis w/ myopathy
M33.19	Oth dermatopolymyositis w/ oth organ involvement
M33.11	Oth dermatopolymyositis w/ respiratory involvement
M33.10	Oth dermatopolymyositis, organ involvement unsp
B57.39	Oth digestive sys involvement in Chagas' disease
A36.89	Oth diphtheritic comp
O99.12	Oth diseases of the blood & blood-forming organs & certain d/o involving the immune mech comp childbirth
O99.111	Oth diseases of the blood & blood-forming organs & certain d/o involving the immune mech comp pregnancy, 1st trmstr
O99.112	Oth diseases of the blood & blood-forming organs & certain d/o involving the immune mech comp pregnancy, 2nd trmstr
O99.113	Oth diseases of the blood & blood-forming organs & certain d/o involving the immune mech comp pregnancy, 3rd trmstr
O99.119	Oth diseases of the blood & blood-forming organs & certain d/o involving the immune mech comp pregnancy, unsp trmstr
O99.13	Oth diseases of the blood & blood-forming organs & certain d/o involving the immune mech comp the puerperium
S12.120A	Oth disp dens fx, init enc for clsd fx
S12.120K	Oth disp dens fx, subsq enc for fx w/ nonu
S12.090A	Oth disp fx of 1st cervical vertebra, init enc for clsd fx
S12.090K	Oth disp fx of 1st cervical vertebra, subsq enc for fx w/ nonu
S12.190A	Oth disp fx of 2nd cervical vertebra, init enc for clsd fx
S12.190K	Oth disp fx of 2nd cervical vertebra, subsq enc for fx w/ nonu
S12.290A	Oth disp fx of 3rd cervical vertebra, init enc for clsd fx
S12.290K	Oth disp fx of 3rd cervical vertebra, subsq enc for fx w/ nonu
S12.390A	Oth disp fx of 4th cervical vertebra, init enc for clsd fx
S12.390K	Oth disp fx of 4th cervical vertebra, subsq enc for fx w/ nonu
S12.490A	Oth disp fx of 5th cervical vertebra, init enc for clsd fx
S12.490K	Oth disp fx of 5th cervical vertebra, subsq enc for fx w/ nonu
S12.590A	Oth disp fx of 6th cervical vertebra, init enc for clsd fx
S12.590K	Oth disp fx of 6th cervical vertebra, subsq enc for fx w/ nonu
S12.690A	Oth disp fx of 7th cervical vertebra, init enc for clsd fx
S12.690K	Oth disp fx of 7th cervical vertebra, subsq enc for fx w/ nonu
S62.232B	Oth disp fx of base of 1st metacarpal bone, lt hand, init enc for opn fx
S62.232P	Oth disp fx of base of 1st metacarpal bone, lt hand, subsq enc for fx w/ malu
S62.232K	Oth disp fx of base of 1st metacarpal bone, lt hand, subsq enc for fx w/ nonu
S62.231B	Oth disp fx of base of 1st metacarpal bone, rt hand, init enc for opn fx
S62.231P	Oth disp fx of base of 1st metacarpal bone, rt hand, subsq enc for fx w/ malu
S62.231K	Oth disp fx of base of 1st metacarpal bone, rt hand, subsq enc for fx w/ nonu
S62.233B	Oth disp fx of base of 1st metacarpal bone, unsp hand, init enc for opn fx
S62.233P	Oth disp fx of base of 1st metacarpal bone, unsp hand, subsq enc for fx w/ malu
S62.233K	Oth disp fx of base of 1st metacarpal bone, unsp hand, subsq enc for fx w/ nonu
S42.492A	Oth disp fx of lwr end of lt humerus, init enc for clsd fx
S42.492P	Oth disp fx of lwr end of lt humerus, subsq enc for fx w/ malu
S42.492K	Oth disp fx of lwr end of lt humerus, subsq enc for fx w/ nonu
S42.491A	Oth disp fx of lwr end of rt humerus, init enc for clsd fx
S42.491P	Oth disp fx of lwr end of rt humerus, subsq enc for fx w/ malu
S42.491K	Oth disp fx of lwr end of rt humerus, subsq enc for fx w/ nonu
S42.493A	Oth disp fx of lwr end of unsp humerus, init enc for clsd fx
S42.493P	Oth disp fx of lwr end of unsp humerus, subsq enc for fx w/ malu
S42.493K	Oth disp fx of lwr end of unsp humerus, subsq enc for fx w/ nonu
S42.292A	Oth disp fx of upr end of lt humerus, init enc for clsd fx
S42.292P	Oth disp fx of upr end of lt humerus, subsq enc for fx w/ malu
S42.292K	Oth disp fx of upr end of lt humerus, subsq enc for fx w/ nonu
S42.291A	Oth disp fx of upr end of rt humerus, init enc for clsd fx
S42.291P	Oth disp fx of upr end of rt humerus, subsq enc for fx w/ malu
S42.291K	Oth disp fx of upr end of rt humerus, subsq enc for fx w/ nonu
S42.293A	Oth disp fx of upr end of unsp humerus, init enc for clsd fx
S42.293P	Oth disp fx of upr end of unsp humerus, subsq enc for fx w/ malu
S42.293K	Oth disp fx of upr end of unsp humerus, subsq enc for fx w/ nonu
G24.09	Oth drug induced dystonia
G21.19	Oth drug induced secondary parkinsonism
G24.8	Oth dystonia
A50.09	Oth early congenital syphilis, symptomatic
B67.99	Oth echinococcosis
O00.8	Oth ectopic pregnancy
P83.39	Oth edema specific to newborn
A77.49	Oth ehrlichiosis
H44.19	Oth endophthalmitis
G40.803	Oth epilepsy, intractable, w/ status epilepticus
G40.804	Oth epilepsy, intractable, w/o status epilepticus
G40.801	Oth epilepsy, not intractable, w/ status epilepticus
G40.802	Oth epilepsy, not intractable, w/o status epilepticus
Q64.19	Oth exstrophy of urinary bladder

Code	Description
S52.552A	Oth extraarticular fx of lwr end of lt radius, init enc for clsd fx
S52.552P	Oth extraarticular fx of lwr end of lt radius, subsq enc for clsd fx w/ malu
S52.552K	Oth extraarticular fx of lwr end of lt radius, subsq enc for clsd fx w/ nonu
S52.552Q	Oth extraarticular fx of lwr end of lt radius, subsq enc for opn fx type I or II w/ malu
S52.552M	Oth extraarticular fx of lwr end of lt radius, subsq enc for opn fx type I or II w/ nonu
S52.552R	Oth extraarticular fx of lwr end of lt radius, subsq enc for opn fx type IIIA, IIIB, or IIIC w/ malu
S52.552N	Oth extraarticular fx of lwr end of lt radius, subsq enc for opn fx type IIIA, IIIB, or IIIC w/ nonu
S52.551A	Oth extraarticular fx of lwr end of rt radius, init enc for clsd fx
S52.551P	Oth extraarticular fx of lwr end of rt radius, subsq enc for clsd fx w/ malu
S52.551K	Oth extraarticular fx of lwr end of rt radius, subsq enc for clsd fx w/ nonu
S52.551Q	Oth extraarticular fx of lwr end of rt radius, subsq enc for opn fx type I or II w/ malu
S52.551M	Oth extraarticular fx of lwr end of rt radius, subsq enc for opn fx type I or II w/ nonu
S52.551R	Oth extraarticular fx of lwr end of rt radius, subsq enc for opn fx type IIIA, IIIB, or IIIC w/ malu
S52.551N	Oth extraarticular fx of lwr end of rt radius, subsq enc for opn fx type IIIA, IIIB, or IIIC w/ nonu
S52.559A	Oth extraarticular fx of lwr end of unsp radius, init enc for clsd fx
S52.559P	Oth extraarticular fx of lwr end of unsp radius, subsq enc for clsd fx w/ malu
S52.559K	Oth extraarticular fx of lwr end of unsp radius, subsq enc for clsd fx w/ nonu
S52.559Q	Oth extraarticular fx of lwr end of unsp radius, subsq enc for opn fx type I or II w/ malu
S52.559M	Oth extraarticular fx of lwr end of unsp radius, subsq enc for opn fx type I or II w/ nonu
S52.559R	Oth extraarticular fx of lwr end of unsp radius, subsq enc for opn fx type IIIA, IIIB, or IIIC w/ malu
S52.559N	Oth extraarticular fx of lwr end of unsp radius, subsq enc for opn fx type IIIA, IIIB, or IIIC w/ nonu
N82.8	Oth female genital tract fistulae
N82.4	Oth female intestinal-genital tract fistulae
N82.1	Oth female urinary-genital tract fistulae
B74.8	Oth filariases
T17.590A	Oth foreign object in bronchus causing asphyxiation, init enc
T17.598A	Oth foreign object in bronchus causing oth inj, init enc
T17.890A	Oth foreign object in oth parts of respiratory tract causing asphyxiation, init enc
T17.898A	Oth foreign object in oth parts of respiratory tract causing oth inj, init enc
T17.490A	Oth foreign object in trachea causing asphyxiation, init enc
T17.498A	Oth foreign object in trachea causing oth inj, init enc
A42.89	Oth forms of actinomycosis
I24.8	Oth forms of acute ischemic heart disease
I30.8	Oth forms of acute pericarditis
A22.8	Oth forms of anthrax
B44.89	Oth forms of aspergillosis
A44.8	Oth forms of bartonellosis
B40.89	Oth forms of blastomycosis
B38.89	Oth forms of coccidioidomycosis
B45.8	Oth forms of cryptococcosis
A30.8	Oth forms of leprosy
A27.89	Oth forms of leptospirosis
A32.89	Oth forms of listeriosis
A43.8	Oth forms of nocardiosis
B41.8	Oth forms of paracoccidioidomycosis
A21.8	Oth forms of tularemia
S52.592A	Oth fractures of lwr end of lt radius, init enc for clsd fx
S52.592P	Oth fractures of lwr end of lt radius, subsq enc for clsd fx w/ malu
S52.592K	Oth fractures of lwr end of lt radius, subsq enc for clsd fx w/ nonu
S52.592Q	Oth fractures of lwr end of lt radius, subsq enc for opn fx type I or II w/ malu
S52.592M	Oth fractures of lwr end of lt radius, subsq enc for opn fx type I or II w/ nonu
S52.592R	Oth fractures of lwr end of lt radius, subsq enc for opn fx type IIIA, IIIB, or IIIC w/ malu
S52.592N	Oth fractures of lwr end of lt radius, subsq enc for opn fx type IIIA, IIIB, or IIIC w/ nonu
S52.591A	Oth fractures of lwr end of rt radius, init enc for clsd fx
S52.591P	Oth fractures of lwr end of rt radius, subsq enc for clsd fx w/ malu
S52.591K	Oth fractures of lwr end of rt radius, subsq enc for clsd fx w/ nonu
S52.591Q	Oth fractures of lwr end of rt radius, subsq enc for opn fx type I or II w/ malu
S52.591M	Oth fractures of lwr end of rt radius, subsq enc for opn fx type I or II w/ nonu
S52.591R	Oth fractures of lwr end of rt radius, subsq enc for opn fx type IIIA, IIIB, or IIIC w/ malu
S52.591N	Oth fractures of lwr end of rt radius, subsq enc for opn fx type IIIA, IIIB, or IIIC w/ nonu
S52.599A	Oth fractures of lwr end of unsp radius, init enc for clsd fx
S52.599P	Oth fractures of lwr end of unsp radius, subsq enc for clsd fx w/ malu
S52.599K	Oth fractures of lwr end of unsp radius, subsq enc for clsd fx w/ nonu
S52.599Q	Oth fractures of lwr end of unsp radius, subsq enc for opn fx type I or II w/ malu
S52.599M	Oth fractures of lwr end of unsp radius, subsq enc for opn fx type I or II w/ nonu
S52.599R	Oth fractures of lwr end of unsp radius, subsq enc for opn fx type IIIA, IIIB, or IIIC w/ malu
S52.599N	Oth fractures of lwr end of unsp radius, subsq enc for opn fx type IIIA, IIIB, or IIIC w/ nonu
S32.018A	Oth fx of 1st lumbar vertebra, init enc for clsd fx
S32.018K	Oth fx of 1st lumbar vertebra, subsq enc for fx w/ nonu
S62.292B	Oth fx of 1st metacarpal bone, lt hand, init enc for opn fx
S62.292P	Oth fx of 1st metacarpal bone, lt hand, subsq enc for fx w/ malu
S62.292K	Oth fx of 1st metacarpal bone, lt hand, subsq enc for fx w/ nonu
S62.291B	Oth fx of 1st metacarpal bone, rt hand, init enc for opn fx
S62.291P	Oth fx of 1st metacarpal bone, rt hand, subsq enc for fx w/ malu
S62.291K	Oth fx of 1st metacarpal bone, rt hand, subsq enc for fx w/ nonu
S62.299B	Oth fx of 1st metacarpal bone, unsp hand, init enc for opn fx
S62.299P	Oth fx of 1st metacarpal bone, unsp hand, subsq enc for fx w/ malu
S62.299K	Oth fx of 1st metacarpal bone, unsp hand, subsq enc for fx w/ nonu
S22.018A	Oth fx of 1st thoracic vertebra, init enc for clsd fx
S22.018K	Oth fx of 1st thoracic vertebra, subsq enc for fx w/ nonu
S32.028A	Oth fx of 2nd lumbar vertebra, init enc for clsd fx
S32.028K	Oth fx of 2nd lumbar vertebra, subsq enc for fx w/ nonu
S62.391B	Oth fx of 2nd metacarpal bone, lt hand, init enc for opn fx
S62.391P	Oth fx of 2nd metacarpal bone, lt hand, subsq enc for fx w/ malu
S62.391K	Oth fx of 2nd metacarpal bone, lt hand, subsq enc for fx w/ nonu
S62.390B	Oth fx of 2nd metacarpal bone, rt hand, init enc for opn fx
S62.390P	Oth fx of 2nd metacarpal bone, rt hand, subsq enc for fx w/ malu
S62.390K	Oth fx of 2nd metacarpal bone, rt hand, subsq enc for fx w/ nonu
S22.028A	Oth fx of 2nd thoracic vertebra, init enc for clsd fx
S22.028K	Oth fx of 2nd thoracic vertebra, subsq enc for fx w/ nonu
S32.038A	Oth fx of 3rd lumbar vertebra, init enc for clsd fx
S32.038K	Oth fx of 3rd lumbar vertebra, subsq enc for fx w/ nonu
S62.393B	Oth fx of 3rd metacarpal bone, lt hand, init enc for opn fx
S62.393P	Oth fx of 3rd metacarpal bone, lt hand, subsq enc for fx w/ malu
S62.393K	Oth fx of 3rd metacarpal bone, lt hand, subsq enc for fx w/ nonu
S62.392B	Oth fx of 3rd metacarpal bone, rt hand, init enc for opn fx
S62.392P	Oth fx of 3rd metacarpal bone, rt hand, subsq enc for fx w/ malu
S62.392K	Oth fx of 3rd metacarpal bone, rt hand, subsq enc for fx w/ nonu
S22.038A	Oth fx of 3rd thoracic vertebra, init enc for clsd fx
S22.038K	Oth fx of 3rd thoracic vertebra, subsq enc for fx w/ nonu
S32.048A	Oth fx of 4th lumbar vertebra, init enc for clsd fx
S32.048K	Oth fx of 4th lumbar vertebra, subsq enc for fx w/ nonu
S62.395B	Oth fx of 4th metacarpal bone, lt hand, init enc for opn fx
S62.395P	Oth fx of 4th metacarpal bone, lt hand, subsq enc for fx w/ malu
S62.395K	Oth fx of 4th metacarpal bone, lt hand, subsq enc for fx w/ nonu
S62.394B	Oth fx of 4th metacarpal bone, rt hand, init enc for opn fx
S62.394P	Oth fx of 4th metacarpal bone, rt hand, subsq enc for fx w/ malu
S62.394K	Oth fx of 4th metacarpal bone, rt hand, subsq enc for fx w/ nonu
S22.048A	Oth fx of 4th thoracic vertebra, init enc for clsd fx
S22.048K	Oth fx of 4th thoracic vertebra, subsq enc for fx w/ nonu
S32.058A	Oth fx of 5th lumbar vertebra, init enc for clsd fx
S32.058K	Oth fx of 5th lumbar vertebra, subsq enc for fx w/ nonu
S62.397B	Oth fx of 5th metacarpal bone, lt hand, init enc for opn fx
S62.397P	Oth fx of 5th metacarpal bone, lt hand, subsq enc for fx w/ malu
S62.397K	Oth fx of 5th metacarpal bone, lt hand, subsq enc for fx w/ nonu
S62.396B	Oth fx of 5th metacarpal bone, rt hand, init enc for opn fx
S62.396P	Oth fx of 5th metacarpal bone, rt hand, subsq enc for fx w/ malu
S62.396K	Oth fx of 5th metacarpal bone, rt hand, subsq enc for fx w/ nonu
S02.19XA	Oth fx of base of skull, init enc for clsd fx
S02.19XK	Oth fx of base of skull, subsq enc for fx w/ nonu
S72.092P	Oth fx of head & neck of lt femur, subsq enc for clsd fx w/ malu
S72.092K	Oth fx of head & neck of lt femur, subsq enc for clsd fx w/ nonu

Code	Description
S72.092Q	Oth fx of head & neck of lt femur, subsq enc for opn fx type I or II w/ malu
S72.092M	Oth fx of head & neck of lt femur, subsq enc for opn fx type I or II w/ nonu
S72.092R	Oth fx of head & neck of lt femur, subsq enc for opn fx type IIIA, IIIB, or IIIC w/ malu
S72.092N	Oth fx of head & neck of lt femur, subsq enc for opn fx type IIIA, IIIB, or IIIC w/ nonu
S72.091P	Oth fx of head & neck of rt femur, subsq enc for clsd fx w/ malu
S72.091K	Oth fx of head & neck of rt femur, subsq enc for clsd fx w/ nonu
S72.091Q	Oth fx of head & neck of rt femur, subsq enc for opn fx type I or II w/ malu
S72.091M	Oth fx of head & neck of rt femur, subsq enc for opn fx type I or II w/ nonu
S72.091R	Oth fx of head & neck of rt femur, subsq enc for opn fx type IIIA, IIIB, or IIIC w/ malu
S72.091N	Oth fx of head & neck of rt femur, subsq enc for opn fx type IIIA, IIIB, or IIIC w/ nonu
S72.099P	Oth fx of head & neck of unsp femur, subsq enc for clsd fx w/ malu
S72.099K	Oth fx of head & neck of unsp femur, subsq enc for clsd fx w/ nonu
S72.099Q	Oth fx of head & neck of unsp femur, subsq enc for opn fx type I or II w/ malu
S72.099M	Oth fx of head & neck of unsp femur, subsq enc for opn fx type I or II w/ nonu
S72.099R	Oth fx of head & neck of unsp femur, subsq enc for opn fx type IIIA, IIIB, or IIIC w/ malu
S72.099N	Oth fx of head & neck of unsp femur, subsq enc for opn fx type IIIA, IIIB, or IIIC w/ nonu
S72.8X2P	Oth fx of lt femur, subsq enc for clsd fx w/ malu
S72.8X2K	Oth fx of lt femur, subsq enc for clsd fx w/ nonu
S72.8X2Q	Oth fx of lt femur, subsq enc for opn fx type I or II w/ malu
S72.8X2M	Oth fx of lt femur, subsq enc for opn fx type I or II w/ nonu
S72.8X2R	Oth fx of lt femur, subsq enc for opn fx type IIIA, IIIB, or IIIC w/ malu
S72.8X2N	Oth fx of lt femur, subsq enc for opn fx type IIIA, IIIB, or IIIC w/ nonu
S92.492P	Oth fx of lt great toe, subsq enc for fx w/ malu
S92.492K	Oth fx of lt great toe, subsq enc for fx w/ nonu
S32.392A	Oth fx of lt ilium, init enc for clsd fx
S32.392K	Oth fx of lt ilium, subsq enc for fx w/ nonu
S92.592P	Oth fx of lt lesser toe(s), subsq enc for fx w/ malu
S92.592K	Oth fx of lt lesser toe(s), subsq enc for fx w/ nonu
S82.892B	Oth fx of lt lwr leg, init enc for opn fx type I or II
S82.892C	Oth fx of lt lwr leg, init enc for opn fx type IIIA, IIIB, or IIIC
S82.892P	Oth fx of lt lwr leg, subsq enc for clsd fx w/ malu
S82.892K	Oth fx of lt lwr leg, subsq enc for clsd fx w/ nonu
S82.892Q	Oth fx of lt lwr leg, subsq enc for opn fx type I or II w/ malu
S82.892M	Oth fx of lt lwr leg, subsq enc for opn fx type I or II w/ nonu
S82.892R	Oth fx of lt lwr leg, subsq enc for opn fx type IIIA, IIIB, or IIIC w/ malu
S82.892N	Oth fx of lt lwr leg, subsq enc for opn fx type IIIA, IIIB, or IIIC w/ nonu
S82.092A	Oth fx of lt patella, init enc for clsd fx
S82.092B	Oth fx of lt patella, init enc for opn fx type I or II
S82.092C	Oth fx of lt patella, init enc for opn fx type IIIA, IIIB, or IIIC
S82.092P	Oth fx of lt patella, subsq enc for clsd fx w/ malu
S82.092K	Oth fx of lt patella, subsq enc for clsd fx w/ nonu
S82.092Q	Oth fx of lt patella, subsq enc for opn fx type I or II w/ malu
S82.092M	Oth fx of lt patella, subsq enc for opn fx type I or II w/ nonu
S82.092R	Oth fx of lt patella, subsq enc for opn fx type IIIA, IIIB, or IIIC w/ malu
S82.092N	Oth fx of lt patella, subsq enc for opn fx type IIIA, IIIB, or IIIC w/ nonu
S92.192B	Oth fx of lt talus, init enc for opn fx
S92.192P	Oth fx of lt talus, subsq enc for fx w/ malu
S92.192K	Oth fx of lt talus, subsq enc for fx w/ nonu
S72.492A	Oth fx of lwr end of lt femur, init enc for clsd fx
S72.492P	Oth fx of lwr end of lt femur, subsq enc for clsd fx w/ malu
S72.492K	Oth fx of lwr end of lt femur, subsq enc for clsd fx w/ nonu
S72.492Q	Oth fx of lwr end of lt femur, subsq enc for opn fx type I or II w/ malu
S72.492M	Oth fx of lwr end of lt femur, subsq enc for opn fx type I or II w/ nonu
S72.492R	Oth fx of lwr end of lt femur, subsq enc for opn fx type IIIA, IIIB, or IIIC w/ malu
S72.492N	Oth fx of lwr end of lt femur, subsq enc for opn fx type IIIA, IIIB, or IIIC w/ nonu
S82.392B	Oth fx of lwr end of lt tibia, init enc for opn fx type I or II
S82.392C	Oth fx of lwr end of lt tibia, init enc for opn fx type IIIA, IIIB, or IIIC
S82.392P	Oth fx of lwr end of lt tibia, subsq enc for clsd fx w/ malu
S82.392K	Oth fx of lwr end of lt tibia, subsq enc for clsd fx w/ nonu
S82.392Q	Oth fx of lwr end of lt tibia, subsq enc for opn fx type I or II w/ malu
S82.392M	Oth fx of lwr end of lt tibia, subsq enc for opn fx type I or II w/ nonu
S82.392R	Oth fx of lwr end of lt tibia, subsq enc for opn fx type IIIA, IIIB, or IIIC w/ malu
S82.392N	Oth fx of lwr end of lt tibia, subsq enc for opn fx type IIIA, IIIB, or IIIC w/ nonu
S52.692A	Oth fx of lwr end of lt ulna, init enc for clsd fx
S52.692P	Oth fx of lwr end of lt ulna, subsq enc for clsd fx w/ malu
S52.692K	Oth fx of lwr end of lt ulna, subsq enc for clsd fx w/ nonu
S52.692Q	Oth fx of lwr end of lt ulna, subsq enc for opn fx type I or II w/ malu
S52.692M	Oth fx of lwr end of lt ulna, subsq enc for opn fx type I or II w/ nonu
S52.692R	Oth fx of lwr end of lt ulna, subsq enc for opn fx type IIIA, IIIB, or IIIC w/ malu
S52.692N	Oth fx of lwr end of lt ulna, subsq enc for opn fx type IIIA, IIIB, or IIIC w/ nonu
S72.491A	Oth fx of lwr end of rt femur, init enc for clsd fx
S72.491P	Oth fx of lwr end of rt femur, subsq enc for clsd fx w/ malu
S72.491K	Oth fx of lwr end of rt femur, subsq enc for clsd fx w/ nonu
S72.491Q	Oth fx of lwr end of rt femur, subsq enc for opn fx type I or II w/ malu
S72.491M	Oth fx of lwr end of rt femur, subsq enc for opn fx type I or II w/ nonu
S72.491R	Oth fx of lwr end of rt femur, subsq enc for opn fx type IIIA, IIIB, or IIIC w/ malu
S72.491N	Oth fx of lwr end of rt femur, subsq enc for opn fx type IIIA, IIIB, or IIIC w/ nonu
S82.391B	Oth fx of lwr end of rt tibia, init enc for opn fx type I or II
S82.391C	Oth fx of lwr end of rt tibia, init enc for opn fx type IIIA, IIIB, or IIIC
S82.391P	Oth fx of lwr end of rt tibia, subsq enc for clsd fx w/ malu
S82.391K	Oth fx of lwr end of rt tibia, subsq enc for clsd fx w/ nonu
S82.391Q	Oth fx of lwr end of rt tibia, subsq enc for opn fx type I or II w/ malu
S82.391M	Oth fx of lwr end of rt tibia, subsq enc for opn fx type I or II w/ nonu
S82.391R	Oth fx of lwr end of rt tibia, subsq enc for opn fx type IIIA, IIIB, or IIIC w/ malu
S82.391N	Oth fx of lwr end of rt tibia, subsq enc for opn fx type IIIA, IIIB, or IIIC w/ nonu
S52.691A	Oth fx of lwr end of rt ulna, init enc for clsd fx
S52.691P	Oth fx of lwr end of rt ulna, subsq enc for clsd fx w/ malu
S52.691K	Oth fx of lwr end of rt ulna, subsq enc for clsd fx w/ nonu
S52.691Q	Oth fx of lwr end of rt ulna, subsq enc for opn fx type I or II w/ malu
S52.691M	Oth fx of lwr end of rt ulna, subsq enc for opn fx type I or II w/ nonu
S52.691R	Oth fx of lwr end of rt ulna, subsq enc for opn fx type IIIA, IIIB, or IIIC w/ malu
S52.691N	Oth fx of lwr end of rt ulna, subsq enc for opn fx type IIIA, IIIB, or IIIC w/ nonu
S72.499A	Oth fx of lwr end of unsp femur, init enc for clsd fx
S72.499P	Oth fx of lwr end of unsp femur, subsq enc for clsd fx w/ malu
S72.499K	Oth fx of lwr end of unsp femur, subsq enc for clsd fx w/ nonu
S72.499Q	Oth fx of lwr end of unsp femur, subsq enc for opn fx type I or II w/ malu
S72.499M	Oth fx of lwr end of unsp femur, subsq enc for opn fx type I or II w/ nonu
S72.499R	Oth fx of lwr end of unsp femur, subsq enc for opn fx type IIIA, IIIB, or IIIC w/ malu
S72.499N	Oth fx of lwr end of unsp femur, subsq enc for opn fx type IIIA, IIIB, or IIIC w/ nonu
S82.399B	Oth fx of lwr end of unsp tibia, init enc for opn fx type I or II
S82.399C	Oth fx of lwr end of unsp tibia, init enc for opn fx type IIIA, IIIB, or IIIC
S82.399P	Oth fx of lwr end of unsp tibia, subsq enc for clsd fx w/ malu
S82.399K	Oth fx of lwr end of unsp tibia, subsq enc for clsd fx w/ nonu
S82.399Q	Oth fx of lwr end of unsp tibia, subsq enc for opn fx type I or II w/ malu
S82.399M	Oth fx of lwr end of unsp tibia, subsq enc for opn fx type I or II w/ nonu
S82.399R	Oth fx of lwr end of unsp tibia, subsq enc for opn fx type IIIA, IIIB, or IIIC w/ malu
S82.399N	Oth fx of lwr end of unsp tibia, subsq enc for opn fx type IIIA, IIIB, or IIIC w/ nonu
S52.699A	Oth fx of lwr end of unsp ulna, init enc for clsd fx
S52.699P	Oth fx of lwr end of unsp ulna, subsq enc for clsd fx w/ malu
S52.699K	Oth fx of lwr end of unsp ulna, subsq enc for clsd fx w/ nonu
S52.699Q	Oth fx of lwr end of unsp ulna, subsq enc for opn fx type I or II w/ malu
S52.699M	Oth fx of lwr end of unsp ulna, subsq enc for opn fx type I or II w/ nonu
S52.699R	Oth fx of lwr end of unsp ulna, subsq enc for opn fx type IIIA, IIIB, or IIIC w/ malu
S52.699N	Oth fx of lwr end of unsp ulna, subsq enc for opn fx type IIIA, IIIB, or IIIC w/ nonu
S02.118A	Oth fx of occiput, init enc for clsd fx
S02.118K	Oth fx of occiput, subsq enc for fx w/ nonu
S62.398B	Oth fx of oth metacarpal bone, init enc for opn fx
S62.398P	Oth fx of oth metacarpal bone, subsq enc for fx w/ malu
S62.398K	Oth fx of oth metacarpal bone, subsq enc for fx w/ nonu
S72.8X1P	Oth fx of rt femur, subsq enc for clsd fx w/ malu
S72.8X1K	Oth fx of rt femur, subsq enc for clsd fx w/ nonu
S72.8X1Q	Oth fx of rt femur, subsq enc for opn fx type I or II w/ malu
S72.8X1M	Oth fx of rt femur, subsq enc for opn fx type I or II w/ nonu
S72.8X1R	Oth fx of rt femur, subsq enc for opn fx type IIIA, IIIB, or IIIC w/ malu

S72.8X1N	Oth fx of rt femur, subsq enc for opn fx type IIIA, IIIB, or IIIC w/ nonu
S92.491P	Oth fx of rt great toe, subsq enc for fx w/ malu
S92.491K	Oth fx of rt great toe, subsq enc for fx w/ nonu
S32.391A	Oth fx of rt ilium, init enc for clsd fx
S32.391K	Oth fx of rt ilium, subsq enc for fx w/ nonu
S92.591P	Oth fx of rt lesser toe(s), subsq enc for fx w/ malu
S92.591K	Oth fx of rt lesser toe(s), subsq enc for fx w/ nonu
S82.891B	Oth fx of rt lwr leg, init enc for opn fx type I or II
S82.891C	Oth fx of rt lwr leg, init enc for opn fx type IIIA, IIIB, or IIIC
S82.891P	Oth fx of rt lwr leg, subsq enc for clsd fx w/ malu
S82.891K	Oth fx of rt lwr leg, subsq enc for clsd fx w/ nonu
S82.891Q	Oth fx of rt lwr leg, subsq enc for opn fx type I or II w/ malu
S82.891M	Oth fx of rt lwr leg, subsq enc for opn fx type I or II w/ nonu
S82.891R	Oth fx of rt lwr leg, subsq enc for opn fx type IIIA, IIIB, or IIIC w/ malu
S82.891N	Oth fx of rt lwr leg, subsq enc for opn fx type IIIA, IIIB, or IIIC w/ nonu
S82.091A	Oth fx of rt patella, init enc for clsd fx
S82.091B	Oth fx of rt patella, init enc for opn fx type I or II
S82.091C	Oth fx of rt patella, init enc for opn fx type IIIA, IIIB, or IIIC
S82.091P	Oth fx of rt patella, subsq enc for clsd fx w/ malu
S82.091K	Oth fx of rt patella, subsq enc for clsd fx w/ nonu
S82.091Q	Oth fx of rt patella, subsq enc for opn fx type I or II w/ malu
S82.091M	Oth fx of rt patella, subsq enc for opn fx type I or II w/ nonu
S82.091R	Oth fx of rt patella, subsq enc for opn fx type IIIA, IIIB, or IIIC w/ malu
S82.091N	Oth fx of rt patella, subsq enc for opn fx type IIIA, IIIB, or IIIC w/ nonu
S92.191B	Oth fx of rt talus, init enc for opn fx
S92.191P	Oth fx of rt talus, subsq enc for fx w/ malu
S92.191K	Oth fx of rt talus, subsq enc for fx w/ nonu
S32.19XA	Oth fx of sacrum, init enc for clsd fx
S32.19XK	Oth fx of sacrum, subsq enc for fx w/ nonu
S72.392P	Oth fx of shaft of lt femur, subsq enc for clsd fx w/ malu
S72.392K	Oth fx of shaft of lt femur, subsq enc for clsd fx w/ nonu
S72.392Q	Oth fx of shaft of lt femur, subsq enc for opn fx type I or II w/ malu
S72.392M	Oth fx of shaft of lt femur, subsq enc for opn fx type I or II w/ nonu
S72.392R	Oth fx of shaft of lt femur, subsq enc for opn fx type IIIA, IIIB, or IIIC w/ malu
S72.392N	Oth fx of shaft of lt femur, subsq enc for opn fx type IIIA, IIIB, or IIIC w/ nonu
S82.492P	Oth fx of shaft of lt fibula, subsq enc for clsd fx w/ malu
S82.492K	Oth fx of shaft of lt fibula, subsq enc for clsd fx w/ nonu
S82.492Q	Oth fx of shaft of lt fibula, subsq enc for opn fx type I or II w/ malu
S82.492M	Oth fx of shaft of lt fibula, subsq enc for opn fx type I or II w/ nonu
S82.492R	Oth fx of shaft of lt fibula, subsq enc for opn fx type IIIA, IIIB, or IIIC w/ malu
S82.492N	Oth fx of shaft of lt fibula, subsq enc for opn fx type IIIA, IIIB, or IIIC w/ nonu
S42.392A	Oth fx of shaft of lt humerus, init enc for clsd fx
S42.392P	Oth fx of shaft of lt humerus, subsq enc for fx w/ malu
S42.392K	Oth fx of shaft of lt humerus, subsq enc for fx w/ nonu
S82.292A	Oth fx of shaft of lt tibia, init enc for clsd fx
S82.292P	Oth fx of shaft of lt tibia, subsq enc for clsd fx w/ malu
S82.292K	Oth fx of shaft of lt tibia, subsq enc for clsd fx w/ nonu
S82.292Q	Oth fx of shaft of lt tibia, subsq enc for opn fx type I or II w/ malu
S82.292M	Oth fx of shaft of lt tibia, subsq enc for opn fx type I or II w/ nonu
S82.292R	Oth fx of shaft of lt tibia, subsq enc for opn fx type IIIA, IIIB, or IIIC w/ malu
S82.292N	Oth fx of shaft of lt tibia, subsq enc for opn fx type IIIA, IIIB, or IIIC w/ nonu
S52.292A	Oth fx of shaft of lt ulna, init enc for clsd fx
S52.292P	Oth fx of shaft of lt ulna, subsq enc for clsd fx w/ malu
S52.292K	Oth fx of shaft of lt ulna, subsq enc for clsd fx w/ nonu
S52.292Q	Oth fx of shaft of lt ulna, subsq enc for opn fx type I or II w/ malu
S52.292M	Oth fx of shaft of lt ulna, subsq enc for opn fx type I or II w/ nonu
S52.292R	Oth fx of shaft of lt ulna, subsq enc for opn fx type IIIA, IIIB, or IIIC w/ malu
S52.292N	Oth fx of shaft of lt ulna, subsq enc for opn fx type IIIA, IIIB, or IIIC w/ nonu
S52.392A	Oth fx of shaft of radius, lt arm, init enc for clsd fx
S52.392P	Oth fx of shaft of radius, lt arm, subsq enc for clsd fx w/ malu
S52.392K	Oth fx of shaft of radius, lt arm, subsq enc for clsd fx w/ nonu
S52.392Q	Oth fx of shaft of radius, lt arm, subsq enc for opn fx type I or II w/ malu
S52.392M	Oth fx of shaft of radius, lt arm, subsq enc for opn fx type I or II w/ nonu
S52.392R	Oth fx of shaft of radius, lt arm, subsq enc for opn fx type IIIA, IIIB, or IIIC w/ malu
S52.392N	Oth fx of shaft of radius, lt arm, subsq enc for opn fx type IIIA, IIIB, or IIIC w/ nonu
S52.391A	Oth fx of shaft of radius, rt arm, init enc for clsd fx
S52.391P	Oth fx of shaft of radius, rt arm, subsq enc for clsd fx w/ malu
S52.391K	Oth fx of shaft of radius, rt arm, subsq enc for clsd fx w/ nonu

S52.391Q	Oth fx of shaft of radius, rt arm, subsq enc for opn fx type I or II w/ malu
S52.391M	Oth fx of shaft of radius, rt arm, subsq enc for opn fx type I or II w/ nonu
S52.391R	Oth fx of shaft of radius, rt arm, subsq enc for opn fx type IIIA, IIIB, or IIIC w/ malu
S52.391N	Oth fx of shaft of radius, rt arm, subsq enc for opn fx type IIIA, IIIB, or IIIC w/ nonu
S52.399A	Oth fx of shaft of radius, unsp arm, init enc for clsd fx
S52.399P	Oth fx of shaft of radius, unsp arm, subsq enc for clsd fx w/ malu
S52.399K	Oth fx of shaft of radius, unsp arm, subsq enc for clsd fx w/ nonu
S52.399Q	Oth fx of shaft of radius, unsp arm, subsq enc for opn fx type I or II w/ malu
S52.399M	Oth fx of shaft of radius, unsp arm, subsq enc for opn fx type I or II w/ nonu
S52.399R	Oth fx of shaft of radius, unsp arm, subsq enc for opn fx type IIIA, IIIB, or IIIC w/ malu
S52.399N	Oth fx of shaft of radius, unsp arm, subsq enc for opn fx type IIIA, IIIB, or IIIC w/ nonu
S72.391P	Oth fx of shaft of rt femur, subsq enc for clsd fx w/ malu
S72.391K	Oth fx of shaft of rt femur, subsq enc for clsd fx w/ nonu
S72.391Q	Oth fx of shaft of rt femur, subsq enc for opn fx type I or II w/ malu
S72.391M	Oth fx of shaft of rt femur, subsq enc for opn fx type I or II w/ nonu
S72.391R	Oth fx of shaft of rt femur, subsq enc for opn fx type IIIA, IIIB, or IIIC w/ malu
S72.391N	Oth fx of shaft of rt femur, subsq enc for opn fx type IIIA, IIIB, or IIIC w/ nonu
S82.491P	Oth fx of shaft of rt fibula, subsq enc for clsd fx w/ malu
S82.491K	Oth fx of shaft of rt fibula, subsq enc for clsd fx w/ nonu
S82.491Q	Oth fx of shaft of rt fibula, subsq enc for opn fx type I or II w/ malu
S82.491M	Oth fx of shaft of rt fibula, subsq enc for opn fx type I or II w/ nonu
S82.491R	Oth fx of shaft of rt fibula, subsq enc for opn fx type IIIA, IIIB, or IIIC w/ malu
S82.491N	Oth fx of shaft of rt fibula, subsq enc for opn fx type IIIA, IIIB, or IIIC w/ nonu
S42.391A	Oth fx of shaft of rt humerus, init enc for clsd fx
S42.391P	Oth fx of shaft of rt humerus, subsq enc for fx w/ malu
S42.391K	Oth fx of shaft of rt humerus, subsq enc for fx w/ nonu
S82.291A	Oth fx of shaft of rt tibia, init enc for clsd fx
S82.291P	Oth fx of shaft of rt tibia, subsq enc for clsd fx w/ malu
S82.291K	Oth fx of shaft of rt tibia, subsq enc for clsd fx w/ nonu
S82.291Q	Oth fx of shaft of rt tibia, subsq enc for opn fx type I or II w/ malu
S82.291M	Oth fx of shaft of rt tibia, subsq enc for opn fx type I or II w/ nonu
S82.291R	Oth fx of shaft of rt tibia, subsq enc for opn fx type IIIA, IIIB, or IIIC w/ malu
S82.291N	Oth fx of shaft of rt tibia, subsq enc for opn fx type IIIA, IIIB, or IIIC w/ nonu
S52.291A	Oth fx of shaft of rt ulna, init enc for clsd fx
S52.291P	Oth fx of shaft of rt ulna, subsq enc for clsd fx w/ malu
S52.291K	Oth fx of shaft of rt ulna, subsq enc for clsd fx w/ nonu
S52.291Q	Oth fx of shaft of rt ulna, subsq enc for opn fx type I or II w/ malu
S52.291M	Oth fx of shaft of rt ulna, subsq enc for opn fx type I or II w/ nonu
S52.291R	Oth fx of shaft of rt ulna, subsq enc for opn fx type IIIA, IIIB, or IIIC w/ malu
S52.291N	Oth fx of shaft of rt ulna, subsq enc for opn fx type IIIA, IIIB, or IIIC w/ nonu
S72.399P	Oth fx of shaft of unsp femur, subsq enc for clsd fx w/ malu
S72.399K	Oth fx of shaft of unsp femur, subsq enc for clsd fx w/ nonu
S72.399Q	Oth fx of shaft of unsp femur, subsq enc for opn fx type I or II w/ malu
S72.399M	Oth fx of shaft of unsp femur, subsq enc for opn fx type I or II w/ nonu
S72.399R	Oth fx of shaft of unsp femur, subsq enc for opn fx type IIIA, IIIB, or IIIC w/ malu
S72.399N	Oth fx of shaft of unsp femur, subsq enc for opn fx type IIIA, IIIB, or IIIC w/ nonu
S82.499P	Oth fx of shaft of unsp fibula, subsq enc for clsd fx w/ malu
S82.499K	Oth fx of shaft of unsp fibula, subsq enc for clsd fx w/ nonu
S82.499Q	Oth fx of shaft of unsp fibula, subsq enc for opn fx type I or II w/ malu
S82.499M	Oth fx of shaft of unsp fibula, subsq enc for opn fx type I or II w/ nonu
S82.499R	Oth fx of shaft of unsp fibula, subsq enc for opn fx type IIIA, IIIB, or IIIC w/ malu
S82.499N	Oth fx of shaft of unsp fibula, subsq enc for opn fx type IIIA, IIIB, or IIIC w/ nonu
S42.399A	Oth fx of shaft of unsp humerus, init enc for clsd fx
S42.399P	Oth fx of shaft of unsp humerus, subsq enc for fx w/ malu
S42.399K	Oth fx of shaft of unsp humerus, subsq enc for fx w/ nonu
S82.299A	Oth fx of shaft of unsp tibia, init enc for clsd fx
S82.299P	Oth fx of shaft of unsp tibia, subsq enc for clsd fx w/ malu
S82.299K	Oth fx of shaft of unsp tibia, subsq enc for clsd fx w/ nonu
S82.299Q	Oth fx of shaft of unsp tibia, subsq enc for opn fx type I or II w/ malu
S82.299M	Oth fx of shaft of unsp tibia, subsq enc for opn fx type I or II w/ nonu

S82.299R	Oth fx of shaft of unsp tibia, subsq enc for opn fx type IIIA, IIIB, or IIIC w/ malu
S82.299N	Oth fx of shaft of unsp tibia, subsq enc for opn fx type IIIA, IIIB, or IIIC w/ nonu
S52.299A	Oth fx of shaft of unsp ulna, init enc for clsd fx
S52.299P	Oth fx of shaft of unsp ulna, subsq enc for clsd fx w/ malu
S52.299K	Oth fx of shaft of unsp ulna, subsq enc for clsd fx w/ nonu
S52.299Q	Oth fx of shaft of unsp ulna, subsq enc for opn fx type I or II w/ malu
S52.299M	Oth fx of shaft of unsp ulna, subsq enc for opn fx type I or II w/ nonu
S52.299R	Oth fx of shaft of unsp ulna, subsq enc for opn fx type IIIA, IIIB, or IIIC w/ malu
S52.299N	Oth fx of shaft of unsp ulna, subsq enc for opn fx type IIIA, IIIB, or IIIC w/ nonu
S22.088A	Oth fx of T11-T12 vertebra, init enc for clsd fx
S22.088K	Oth fx of T11-T12 vertebra, subsq enc for fx w/ nonu
S22.058A	Oth fx of T5-T6 vertebra, init enc for clsd fx
S22.058K	Oth fx of T5-T6 vertebra, subsq enc for fx w/ nonu
S22.068A	Oth fx of T7-T8 thoracic vertebra, init enc for clsd fx
S22.068K	Oth fx of T7-T8 thoracic vertebra, subsq enc for fx w/ nonu
S22.078A	Oth fx of T9-T10 vertebra, init enc for clsd fx
S22.078K	Oth fx of T9-T10 vertebra, subsq enc for fx w/ nonu
S72.8X9P	Oth fx of unsp femur, subsq enc for clsd fx w/ malu
S72.8X9K	Oth fx of unsp femur, subsq enc for clsd fx w/ nonu
S72.8X9Q	Oth fx of unsp femur, subsq enc for opn fx type I or II w/ malu
S72.8X9M	Oth fx of unsp femur, subsq enc for opn fx type I or II w/ nonu
S72.8X9R	Oth fx of unsp femur, subsq enc for opn fx type IIIA, IIIB, or IIIC w/ malu
S72.8X9N	Oth fx of unsp femur, subsq enc for opn fx type IIIA, IIIB, or IIIC w/ nonu
S92.499P	Oth fx of unsp great toe, subsq enc for fx w/ malu
S92.499K	Oth fx of unsp great toe, subsq enc for fx w/ nonu
S32.399A	Oth fx of unsp ilium, init enc for clsd fx
S32.399K	Oth fx of unsp ilium, subsq enc for fx w/ nonu
S92.599P	Oth fx of unsp lesser toe(s), subsq enc for fx w/ malu
S92.599K	Oth fx of unsp lesser toe(s), subsq enc for fx w/ nonu
S32.008A	Oth fx of unsp lumbar vertebra, init enc for clsd fx
S32.008K	Oth fx of unsp lumbar vertebra, subsq enc for fx w/ nonu
S82.899B	Oth fx of unsp lwr leg, init enc for opn fx type I or II
S82.899C	Oth fx of unsp lwr leg, init enc for opn fx type IIIA, IIIB, or IIIC
S82.899P	Oth fx of unsp lwr leg, subsq enc for clsd fx w/ malu
S82.899K	Oth fx of unsp lwr leg, subsq enc for clsd fx w/ nonu
S82.899Q	Oth fx of unsp lwr leg, subsq enc for opn fx type I or II w/ malu
S82.899M	Oth fx of unsp lwr leg, subsq enc for opn fx type I or II w/ nonu
S82.899R	Oth fx of unsp lwr leg, subsq enc for opn fx type IIIA, IIIB, or IIIC w/ malu
S82.899N	Oth fx of unsp lwr leg, subsq enc for opn fx type IIIA, IIIB, or IIIC w/ nonu
S62.399B	Oth fx of unsp metacarpal bone, init enc for opn fx
S62.399P	Oth fx of unsp metacarpal bone, subsq enc for fx w/ malu
S62.399K	Oth fx of unsp metacarpal bone, subsq enc for fx w/ nonu
S82.099A	Oth fx of unsp patella, init enc for clsd fx
S82.099B	Oth fx of unsp patella, init enc for opn fx type I or II
S82.099C	Oth fx of unsp patella, init enc for opn fx type IIIA, IIIB, or IIIC
S82.099P	Oth fx of unsp patella, subsq enc for clsd fx w/ malu
S82.099K	Oth fx of unsp patella, subsq enc for clsd fx w/ nonu
S82.099Q	Oth fx of unsp patella, subsq enc for opn fx type I or II w/ malu
S82.099M	Oth fx of unsp patella, subsq enc for opn fx type I or II w/ nonu
S82.099R	Oth fx of unsp patella, subsq enc for opn fx type IIIA, IIIB, or IIIC w/ malu
S82.099N	Oth fx of unsp patella, subsq enc for opn fx type IIIA, IIIB, or IIIC w/ nonu
S92.199B	Oth fx of unsp talus, init enc for opn fx
S92.199P	Oth fx of unsp talus, subsq enc for fx w/ malu
S92.199K	Oth fx of unsp talus, subsq enc for fx w/ nonu
S22.008A	Oth fx of unsp thoracic vertebra, init enc for clsd fx
S22.008K	Oth fx of unsp thoracic vertebra, subsq enc for fx w/ nonu
S82.832P	Oth fx of upr & lwr end of lt fibula, subsq enc for clsd fx w/ malu
S82.832K	Oth fx of upr & lwr end of lt fibula, subsq enc for clsd fx w/ nonu
S82.832Q	Oth fx of upr & lwr end of lt fibula, subsq enc for opn fx type I or II w/ malu
S82.832M	Oth fx of upr & lwr end of lt fibula, subsq enc for opn fx type I or II w/ nonu
S82.832R	Oth fx of upr & lwr end of lt fibula, subsq enc for opn fx type IIIA, IIIB, or IIIC w/ malu
S82.832N	Oth fx of upr & lwr end of lt fibula, subsq enc for opn fx type IIIA, IIIB, or IIIC w/ nonu
S82.831P	Oth fx of upr & lwr end of rt fibula, subsq enc for clsd fx w/ malu
S82.831K	Oth fx of upr & lwr end of rt fibula, subsq enc for clsd fx w/ nonu
S82.831Q	Oth fx of upr & lwr end of rt fibula, subsq enc for opn fx type I or II w/ malu
S82.831M	Oth fx of upr & lwr end of rt fibula, subsq enc for opn fx type I or II w/ nonu

S82.831R	Oth fx of upr & lwr end of rt fibula, subsq enc for opn fx type IIIA, IIIB, or IIIC w/ malu
S82.831N	Oth fx of upr & lwr end of rt fibula, subsq enc for opn fx type IIIA, IIIB, or IIIC w/ nonu
S82.839P	Oth fx of upr & lwr end of unsp fibula, subsq enc for clsd fx w/ malu
S82.839K	Oth fx of upr & lwr end of unsp fibula, subsq enc for clsd fx w/ nonu
S82.839Q	Oth fx of upr & lwr end of unsp fibula, subsq enc for opn fx type I or II w/ malu
S82.839M	Oth fx of upr & lwr end of unsp fibula, subsq enc for opn fx type I or II w/ nonu
S82.839R	Oth fx of upr & lwr end of unsp fibula, subsq enc for opn fx type IIIA, IIIB, or IIIC w/ malu
S82.839N	Oth fx of upr & lwr end of unsp fibula, subsq enc for opn fx type IIIA, IIIB, or IIIC w/ nonu
S52.182P	Oth fx of upr end of lt radius, subsq enc for clsd fx w/ malu
S52.182K	Oth fx of upr end of lt radius, subsq enc for clsd fx w/ nonu
S52.182Q	Oth fx of upr end of lt radius, subsq enc for opn fx type I or II w/ malu
S52.182M	Oth fx of upr end of lt radius, subsq enc for opn fx type I or II w/ nonu
S52.182R	Oth fx of upr end of lt radius, subsq enc for opn fx type IIIA, IIIB, or IIIC w/ malu
S52.182N	Oth fx of upr end of lt radius, subsq enc for opn fx type IIIA, IIIB, or IIIC w/ nonu
S82.192A	Oth fx of upr end of lt tibia, init enc for clsd fx
S82.192P	Oth fx of upr end of lt tibia, subsq enc for clsd fx w/ malu
S82.192K	Oth fx of upr end of lt tibia, subsq enc for clsd fx w/ nonu
S82.192Q	Oth fx of upr end of lt tibia, subsq enc for opn fx type I or II w/ malu
S82.192M	Oth fx of upr end of lt tibia, subsq enc for opn fx type I or II w/ nonu
S82.192R	Oth fx of upr end of lt tibia, subsq enc for opn fx type IIIA, IIIB, or IIIC w/ malu
S82.192N	Oth fx of upr end of lt tibia, subsq enc for opn fx type IIIA, IIIB, or IIIC w/ nonu
S52.092P	Oth fx of upr end of lt ulna, subsq enc for clsd fx w/ malu
S52.092K	Oth fx of upr end of lt ulna, subsq enc for clsd fx w/ nonu
S52.092Q	Oth fx of upr end of lt ulna, subsq enc for opn fx type I or II w/ malu
S52.092M	Oth fx of upr end of lt ulna, subsq enc for opn fx type I or II w/ nonu
S52.092R	Oth fx of upr end of lt ulna, subsq enc for opn fx type IIIA, IIIB, or IIIC w/ malu
S52.092N	Oth fx of upr end of lt ulna, subsq enc for opn fx type IIIA, IIIB, or IIIC w/ nonu
S52.181P	Oth fx of upr end of rt radius, subsq enc for clsd fx w/ malu
S52.181K	Oth fx of upr end of rt radius, subsq enc for clsd fx w/ nonu
S52.181Q	Oth fx of upr end of rt radius, subsq enc for opn fx type I or II w/ malu
S52.181M	Oth fx of upr end of rt radius, subsq enc for opn fx type I or II w/ nonu
S52.181R	Oth fx of upr end of rt radius, subsq enc for opn fx type IIIA, IIIB, or IIIC w/ malu
S52.181N	Oth fx of upr end of rt radius, subsq enc for opn fx type IIIA, IIIB, or IIIC w/ nonu
S82.191A	Oth fx of upr end of rt tibia, init enc for clsd fx
S82.191P	Oth fx of upr end of rt tibia, subsq enc for clsd fx w/ malu
S82.191K	Oth fx of upr end of rt tibia, subsq enc for clsd fx w/ nonu
S82.191Q	Oth fx of upr end of rt tibia, subsq enc for opn fx type I or II w/ malu
S82.191M	Oth fx of upr end of rt tibia, subsq enc for opn fx type I or II w/ nonu
S82.191R	Oth fx of upr end of rt tibia, subsq enc for opn fx type IIIA, IIIB, or IIIC w/ malu
S82.191N	Oth fx of upr end of rt tibia, subsq enc for opn fx type IIIA, IIIB, or IIIC w/ nonu
S52.091P	Oth fx of upr end of rt ulna, subsq enc for clsd fx w/ malu
S52.091K	Oth fx of upr end of rt ulna, subsq enc for clsd fx w/ nonu
S52.091Q	Oth fx of upr end of rt ulna, subsq enc for opn fx type I or II w/ malu
S52.091M	Oth fx of upr end of rt ulna, subsq enc for opn fx type I or II w/ nonu
S52.091R	Oth fx of upr end of rt ulna, subsq enc for opn fx type IIIA, IIIB, or IIIC w/ malu
S52.091N	Oth fx of upr end of rt ulna, subsq enc for opn fx type IIIA, IIIB, or IIIC w/ nonu
S52.189P	Oth fx of upr end of unsp radius, subsq enc for clsd fx w/ malu
S52.189K	Oth fx of upr end of unsp radius, subsq enc for clsd fx w/ nonu
S52.189Q	Oth fx of upr end of unsp radius, subsq enc for opn fx type I or II w/ malu
S52.189M	Oth fx of upr end of unsp radius, subsq enc for opn fx type I or II w/ nonu
S52.189R	Oth fx of upr end of unsp radius, subsq enc for opn fx type IIIA, IIIB, or IIIC w/ malu
S52.189N	Oth fx of upr end of unsp radius, subsq enc for opn fx type IIIA, IIIB, or IIIC w/ nonu
S82.199A	Oth fx of upr end of unsp tibia, init enc for clsd fx
S82.199P	Oth fx of upr end of unsp tibia, subsq enc for clsd fx w/ malu
S82.199K	Oth fx of upr end of unsp tibia, subsq enc for clsd fx w/ nonu
S82.199Q	Oth fx of upr end of unsp tibia, subsq enc for opn fx type I or II w/ malu

S82.199M	Oth fx of upr end of unsp tibia, subsq enc for opn fx type I or II w/ nonu
S82.199R	Oth fx of upr end of unsp tibia, subsq enc for opn fx type IIIA, IIIB, or IIIC w/ malu
S82.199N	Oth fx of upr end of unsp tibia, subsq enc for opn fx type IIIA, IIIB, or IIIC w/ nonu
S52.099P	Oth fx of upr end of unsp ulna, subsq enc for clsd fx w/ malu
S52.099K	Oth fx of upr end of unsp ulna, subsq enc for clsd fx w/ nonu
S52.099Q	Oth fx of upr end of unsp ulna, subsq enc for opn fx type I or II w/ malu
S52.099M	Oth fx of upr end of unsp ulna, subsq enc for opn fx type I or II w/ nonu
S52.099R	Oth fx of upr end of unsp ulna, subsq enc for opn fx type IIIA, IIIB, or IIIC w/ malu
S52.099N	Oth fx of upr end of unsp ulna, subsq enc for opn fx type IIIA, IIIB, or IIIC w/ nonu
E75.19	Oth gangliosidosis
G40.411	Oth generalized epilepsy & epileptic syndromes, intractable, w/ status epilepticus
G40.419	Oth generalized epilepsy & epileptic syndromes, intractable, w/o status epilepticus
A52.76	Oth genitourinary symptomatic late syphilis
E74.09	Oth glycogen storage disease
E75.09	Oth GM2 gangliosidosis
A54.39	Oth gonococcal eye infxn
A54.29	Oth gonococcal genitourinary infections
A54.89	Oth gonococcal infections
A54.09	Oth gonococcal infxn of lwr genitourinary tract
E71.53	Oth group 2 peroxisomal d/o
E71.542	Oth group 3 peroxisomal d/o
R44.2	Oth hallucinations
D68.318	Oth hemorrhagic d/o d/t intrinsic circulating anticoagulants, antibodies, or inhibitors
G11.8	Oth hereditary ataxias
B02.39	Oth herpes zoster eye disease
B00.59	Oth herpesviral disease of eye
B00.89	Oth herpesviral infxn
D76.3	Oth histiocytosis syndromes
B76.8	Oth hookworm diseases
G91.8	Oth hydrocephalus
N13.39	Oth hydronephrosis
E22.8	Oth hyperfunction of pituitary gland
E70.1	Oth hyperphenylalaninemias
I42.2	Oth hypertrophic cardiomyopathy
O72.1	Oth immediate postpartum hemor
D80.8	Oth immunodeficiencies w/ predominantly antibody defects
K56.49	Oth impaction of intestine
O98.32	Oth infections w/ a predominantly sexual mode of transmission comp childbirth
O98.311	Oth infections w/ a predominantly sexual mode of transmission comp pregnancy, 1st trmstr
O98.312	Oth infections w/ a predominantly sexual mode of transmission comp pregnancy, 2nd trmstr
O98.313	Oth infections w/ a predominantly sexual mode of transmission comp pregnancy, 3rd trmstr
O98.33	Oth infections w/ a predominantly sexual mode of transmission comp the puerperium
O99.834	Oth infxn carrier state comp childbirth
O99.830	Oth infxn carrier state comp pregnancy
O99.835	Oth infxn carrier state comp the puerperium
T80.218A	Oth infxn d/t central venous catheter, init enc
O86.19	Oth infxn of genital tract following delivery
G12.1	Oth inherited spinal muscular atrophy
S37.818A	Oth inj of adrenal gland, init enc
S36.590A	Oth inj of ascending [rt] colon, init enc
S37.29XA	Oth inj of bladder, init enc
S36.291A	Oth inj of body of pancreas, init enc
S36.592A	Oth inj of descending [lt] colon, init enc
S27.808A	Oth inj of diaphragm, init enc
S36.490A	Oth inj of duodenum, init enc
S36.128A	Oth inj of gallbladder, init enc
S36.290A	Oth inj of head of pancreas, init enc
S26.09XA	Oth inj of heart w/ hemopericardium, init enc
S26.19XA	Oth inj of heart w/o hemopericardium, init enc
S26.99XA	Oth inj of heart, unsp w/ or w/o hemopericardium, init enc
S36.118A	Oth inj of liver, init enc
S36.898A	Oth inj of oth intra-abd organs, init enc
S36.598A	Oth inj of oth part of colon, init enc

S36.498A	Oth inj of oth part of sm intestine, init enc
S27.898A	Oth inj of oth spec intrathoracic organs, init enc
S37.898A	Oth inj of oth urinary & pelvic organ, init enc
S27.69XA	Oth inj of pleura, init enc
S36.69XA	Oth inj of rectum, init enc
S36.593A	Oth inj of sigmoid colon, init enc
S36.09XA	Oth inj of spleen, init enc
S36.39XA	Oth inj of stomach, init enc
S36.292A	Oth inj of tail of pancreas, init enc
S27.59XA	Oth inj of thoracic trachea, init enc
S36.591A	Oth inj of transv colon, init enc
S36.99XA	Oth inj of unsp intra-abd organ, init enc
S36.599A	Oth inj of unsp part of colon, init enc
S36.299A	Oth inj of unsp part of pancreas, init enc
S36.499A	Oth inj of unsp part of sm intestine, init enc
S37.99XA	Oth inj of unsp urinary & pelvic organ, init enc
S37.19XA	Oth inj of ureter, init enc
S37.39XA	Oth inj of urethra, init enc
S37.69XA	Oth inj of uterus, init enc
S05.8X2A	Oth injuries of lt eye & orbit, init enc
S27.392A	Oth injuries of lung, bilat, init enc
S27.391A	Oth injuries of lung, unilat, init enc
S27.399A	Oth injuries of lung, unsp, init enc
S05.8X1A	Oth injuries of rt eye & orbit, init enc
S05.8X9A	Oth injuries of unsp eye & orbit, init enc
A04.4	Oth intestinal Escherichia coli infections
K90.89	Oth intestinal malabsorption
K56.69	Oth intestinal obstruction
S52.572A	Oth intraarticular fx of lwr end of lt radius, init enc for clsd fx
S52.572P	Oth intraarticular fx of lwr end of lt radius, subsq enc for clsd fx w/ malu
S52.572K	Oth intraarticular fx of lwr end of lt radius, subsq enc for clsd fx w/ nonu
S52.572Q	Oth intraarticular fx of lwr end of lt radius, subsq enc for opn fx type I or II w/ malu
S52.572M	Oth intraarticular fx of lwr end of lt radius, subsq enc for opn fx type I or II w/ nonu
S52.572R	Oth intraarticular fx of lwr end of lt radius, subsq enc for opn fx type IIIA, IIIB, or IIIC w/ malu
S52.572N	Oth intraarticular fx of lwr end of lt radius, subsq enc for opn fx type IIIA, IIIB, or IIIC w/ nonu
S52.571A	Oth intraarticular fx of lwr end of rt radius, init enc for clsd fx
S52.571P	Oth intraarticular fx of lwr end of rt radius, subsq enc for clsd fx w/ malu
S52.571K	Oth intraarticular fx of lwr end of rt radius, subsq enc for clsd fx w/ nonu
S52.571Q	Oth intraarticular fx of lwr end of rt radius, subsq enc for opn fx type I or II w/ malu
S52.571M	Oth intraarticular fx of lwr end of rt radius, subsq enc for opn fx type I or II w/ nonu
S52.571R	Oth intraarticular fx of lwr end of rt radius, subsq enc for opn fx type IIIA, IIIB, or IIIC w/ malu
S52.571N	Oth intraarticular fx of lwr end of rt radius, subsq enc for opn fx type IIIA, IIIB, or IIIC w/ nonu
S52.579A	Oth intraarticular fx of lwr end of unsp radius, init enc for clsd fx
S52.579P	Oth intraarticular fx of lwr end of unsp radius, subsq enc for clsd fx w/ malu
S52.579K	Oth intraarticular fx of lwr end of unsp radius, subsq enc for clsd fx w/ nonu
S52.579Q	Oth intraarticular fx of lwr end of unsp radius, subsq enc for opn fx type I or II w/ malu
S52.579M	Oth intraarticular fx of lwr end of unsp radius, subsq enc for opn fx type I or II w/ nonu
S52.579R	Oth intraarticular fx of lwr end of unsp radius, subsq enc for opn fx type IIIA, IIIB, or IIIC w/ malu
S52.579N	Oth intraarticular fx of lwr end of unsp radius, subsq enc for opn fx type IIIA, IIIB, or IIIC w/ nonu
M96.89	Oth intraoperative & postprocedural comp & d/o of the musculoskeletal sys
I97.790	Oth intraoperative cardiac functional disturbances during cardiac surgery
I97.791	Oth intraoperative cardiac functional disturbances during oth surgery
H95.88	Oth intraoperative comp & d/o of the ear & mastoid process, NEC
K91.81	Oth intraoperative comp of digestive sys
H59.88	Oth intraoperative comp of eye & adnexa, NEC
G97.81	Oth intraoperative comp of nervous sys
J95.88	Oth intraoperative comp of respiratory sys, NEC
I97.88	Oth intraoperative comp of the circulatory sys, NEC
D78.81	Oth intraoperative comp of the spleen

A50.49	Oth late congenital neurosyphilis
A50.59	Oth late congenital syphilis, symptomatic
A50.39	Oth late congenital syphilitic oculopathy
C91.Z0	Oth lymphoid leukemia not having achieved remission
C91.Z2	Oth lymphoid leukemia, in relapse
C91.Z1	Oth lymphoid leukemia, in remission
B53.8	Oth malaria, NEC
Q28.1	Oth malformations of precerebral vessels
C88.8	Oth malig immunoproliferative diseases
C7A.8	Oth malig neuroendocrine tumors
E51.8	Oth manifestations of thiamine deficiency
O98.82	Oth maternal infectious & parasitic diseases comp childbirth
O98.811	Oth maternal infectious & parasitic diseases comp pregnancy, 1st trmstr
O98.812	Oth maternal infectious & parasitic diseases comp pregnancy, 2nd trmstr
O98.813	Oth maternal infectious & parasitic diseases comp pregnancy, 3rd trmstr
O98.83	Oth maternal infectious & parasitic diseases comp the puerperium
C84.Z9	Oth mature T/NK-cell lymphomas, extranodal & solid organ sites
C84.Z3	Oth mature T/NK-cell lymphomas, intra-abd lymph nodes
C84.Z6	Oth mature T/NK-cell lymphomas, intrapelvic lymph nodes
C84.Z2	Oth mature T/NK-cell lymphomas, intrathoracic lymph nodes
C84.Z4	Oth mature T/NK-cell lymphomas, lymph nodes of axilla & upr limb
C84.Z1	Oth mature T/NK-cell lymphomas, lymph nodes of head, face, & neck
C84.Z5	Oth mature T/NK-cell lymphomas, lymph nodes of inguinal rgn & lwr limb
C84.Z8	Oth mature T/NK-cell lymphomas, lymph nodes of multi sites
C84.Z7	Oth mature T/NK-cell lymphomas, spleen
C84.Z0	Oth mature T/NK-cell lymphomas, unsp site
B05.89	Oth measles comp
T82.390A	Oth mech comp of aortic (bifurcation) graft (replace), init enc
T82.592A	Oth mech comp of artfcl heart, init enc
T85.693A	Oth mech comp of artfcl skin graft & decellularized allodermis, init enc
T82.593A	Oth mech comp of balloon (counterpulsation) dev, init enc
T85.590A	Oth mech comp of bile duct prosthesis, init enc
T82.228A	Oth mech comp of biological heart valve graft, init enc
T85.49XA	Oth mech comp of breast prosthesis & implant, init enc
T82.190A	Oth mech comp of cardiac electrode, init enc
T82.191A	Oth mech comp of cardiac pulse generator (battery), init enc
T82.391A	Oth mech comp of carotid arterial graft (bypass), init enc
T82.218A	Oth mech comp of coronary artery bypass graft, init enc
T83.090A	Oth mech comp of cystostomy catheter, init enc
T84.390A	Oth mech comp of electronic bone stimulator, init enc
T85.690A	Oth mech comp of epidural & subdural inf catheter, init enc
T85.591A	Oth mech comp of esophageal anti-reflux dev, init enc
T82.392A	Oth mech comp of femoral arterial graft (bypass), init enc
T83.29XA	Oth mech comp of graft of urinary organ, init enc
T82.09XA	Oth mech comp of heart valve prosthesis, init enc
T85.190A	Oth mech comp of implanted electronic neurostimulator (electrode) of brain, init enc
T85.191A	Oth mech comp of implanted electronic neurostimulator (electrode) of peripheral nerve, init enc
T85.192A	Oth mech comp of implanted electronic neurostimulator (electrode) of spinal cord, init enc
T82.594A	Oth mech comp of inf catheter, init enc
T85.694A	Oth mech comp of insulin pump, init enc
T84.193A	Oth mech comp of int fix dev of bone of lt forearm, init enc
T84.197A	Oth mech comp of int fix dev of bone of lt lwr leg, init enc
T84.192A	Oth mech comp of int fix dev of bone of rt forearm, init enc
T84.196A	Oth mech comp of int fix dev of bone of rt lwr leg, init enc
T84.293A	Oth mech comp of int fix dev of bones of foot & toes, init enc
T84.290A	Oth mech comp of int fix dev of bones of hand & fingers, init enc
T84.195A	Oth mech comp of int fix dev of lt femur, init enc
T84.191A	Oth mech comp of int fix dev of lt humerus, init enc
T84.298A	Oth mech comp of int fix dev of oth bones, init enc
T84.194A	Oth mech comp of int fix dev of rt femur, init enc
T84.190A	Oth mech comp of int fix dev of rt humerus, init enc
T84.199A	Oth mech comp of int fix dev of unsp bone of limb, init enc
T84.296A	Oth mech comp of int fix dev of vertebrae, init enc
T84.091A	Oth mech comp of int lt hip prosthesis, init enc
T84.093A	Oth mech comp of int lt knee prosthesis, init enc
T84.090A	Oth mech comp of int rt hip prosthesis, init enc
T84.092A	Oth mech comp of int rt knee prosthesis, init enc
T85.29XA	Oth mech comp of intraocular lens, init enc
T85.691A	Oth mech comp of intraperitoneal dialysis catheter, init enc
T84.490A	Oth mech comp of muscle & tndn graft, init enc
T84.398A	Oth mech comp of oth bone devices, implants & grafts, init enc
T82.598A	Oth mech comp of oth cardiac & vascular devices & implants, init enc
T82.198A	Oth mech comp of oth cardiac electronic dev, init enc
T85.598A	Oth mech comp of oth gastrointestinal prosthetic devices, implants & grafts, init enc
T85.199A	Oth mech comp of oth implanted electronic stimulator of nervous sys, init enc
T84.098A	Oth mech comp of oth int jt prosthesis, init enc
T84.498A	Oth mech comp of oth int orthopedic devices, implants & grafts, init enc
T83.498A	Oth mech comp of oth prosthetic devices, implants & grafts of genital tract, init enc
T85.698A	Oth mech comp of oth spec int prosthetic devices, implants & grafts, init enc
T83.198A	Oth mech comp of oth urinary devices & implants, init enc
T82.398A	Oth mech comp of oth vascular grafts, init enc
T83.490A	Oth mech comp of penile (implanted) prosthesis, init enc
T85.692A	Oth mech comp of permanent sutures, init enc
T85.391A	Oth mech comp of prosthetic orbit of lt eye, init enc
T85.390A	Oth mech comp of prosthetic orbit of rt eye, init enc
T82.590A	Oth mech comp of surgly created arteriovenous fistula, init enc
T82.591A	Oth mech comp of surgly created arteriovenous shunt, init enc
T82.595A	Oth mech comp of umbrella dev, init enc
T82.599A	Oth mech comp of unsp cardiac & vascular devices & implants, init enc
T82.199A	Oth mech comp of unsp cardiac dev, init enc
T84.099A	Oth mech comp of unsp int jt prosthesis, init enc
T82.399A	Oth mech comp of unsp vascular grafts, init enc
T83.190A	Oth mech comp of urinary electronic stimulator dev, init enc
T83.191A	Oth mech comp of urinary sphincter implant, init enc
T83.192A	Oth mech comp of urinary stent, init enc
T85.09XA	Oth mech comp of ventricular intracranial (communicating) shunt, init enc
A24.3	Oth melioidosis
A39.89	Oth meningococcal infections
D74.8	Oth methemoglobinemias
Q93.88	Oth microdeletions
E88.49	Oth mitochondrial metabolism d/o
C93.Z2	Oth monocytic leukemia, in relapse
C93.Z1	Oth monocytic leukemia, in remission
C93.Z0	Oth monocytic leukemia, not having achieved remission
G12.29	Oth motor neuron disease
E76.29	Oth mucopolysaccharidoses
B26.89	Oth mumps comp
A18.09	Oth musculoskeletal tuberculosis
A31.8	Oth mycobacterial infections
C92.Z0	Oth myeloid leukemia not having achieved remission
C92.Z2	Oth myeloid leukemia, in relapse
C92.Z1	Oth myeloid leukemia, in remission
P71.1	Oth neonatal hypocalcemia
B57.49	Oth nervous sys involvement in Chagas' disease
A69.22	Oth neurologic d/o in Lyme disease
B06.09	Oth neurological comp of rubella
T80.A9XA	Oth non-ABO incompatibility reaction d/t transfusion of blood or blood products, init enc
C83.89	Oth non-follicular lymphoma, extranodal & solid organ sites
C83.83	Oth non-follicular lymphoma, intra-abd lymph nodes
C83.86	Oth non-follicular lymphoma, intrapelvic lymph nodes
C83.82	Oth non-follicular lymphoma, intrathoracic lymph nodes
C83.84	Oth non-follicular lymphoma, lymph nodes of axilla & upr limb
C83.81	Oth non-follicular lymphoma, lymph nodes of head, face, & neck
C83.85	Oth non-follicular lymphoma, lymph nodes of inguinal rgn & lwr limb
C83.88	Oth non-follicular lymphoma, lymph nodes of multi sites
C83.87	Oth non-follicular lymphoma, spleen
C83.80	Oth non-follicular lymphoma, unsp site
D59.4	Oth nonautoimmune hemolytic anemias
S12.121A	Oth nondisp dens fx, init enc for clsd fx
S12.121K	Oth nondisp dens fx, subsq enc for fx w/ nonu
S12.091A	Oth nondisp fx of 1st cervical vertebra, init enc for clsd fx
S12.091K	Oth nondisp fx of 1st cervical vertebra, subsq enc for fx w/ nonu
S12.191A	Oth nondisp fx of 2nd cervical vertebra, init enc for clsd fx
S12.191K	Oth nondisp fx of 2nd cervical vertebra, subsq enc for fx w/ nonu
S12.291A	Oth nondisp fx of 3rd cervical vertebra, init enc for clsd fx
S12.291K	Oth nondisp fx of 3rd cervical vertebra, subsq enc for fx w/ nonu
S12.391A	Oth nondisp fx of 4th cervical vertebra, init enc for clsd fx
S12.391K	Oth nondisp fx of 4th cervical vertebra, subsq enc for fx w/ nonu

S12.491A	Oth nondisp fx of 5th cervical vertebra, init enc for clsd fx
S12.491K	Oth nondisp fx of 5th cervical vertebra, subsq enc for fx w/ nonu
S12.591A	Oth nondisp fx of 6th cervical vertebra, init enc for clsd fx
S12.591K	Oth nondisp fx of 6th cervical vertebra, subsq enc for fx w/ nonu
S12.691A	Oth nondisp fx of 7th cervical vertebra, init enc for clsd fx
S12.691K	Oth nondisp fx of 7th cervical vertebra, subsq enc for fx w/ nonu
S62.235B	Oth nondisp fx of base of 1st metacarpal bone, lt hand, init enc for opn fx
S62.235P	Oth nondisp fx of base of 1st metacarpal bone, lt hand, subsq enc for fx w/ malu
S62.235K	Oth nondisp fx of base of 1st metacarpal bone, lt hand, subsq enc for fx w/ nonu
S62.234B	Oth nondisp fx of base of 1st metacarpal bone, rt hand, init enc for opn fx
S62.234P	Oth nondisp fx of base of 1st metacarpal bone, rt hand, subsq enc for fx w/ malu
S62.234K	Oth nondisp fx of base of 1st metacarpal bone, rt hand, subsq enc for fx w/ nonu
S62.236B	Oth nondisp fx of base of 1st metacarpal bone, unsp hand, init enc for opn fx
S62.236P	Oth nondisp fx of base of 1st metacarpal bone, unsp hand, subsq enc for fx w/ malu
S62.236K	Oth nondisp fx of base of 1st metacarpal bone, unsp hand, subsq enc for fx w/ nonu
S42.495A	Oth nondisp fx of lwr end of lt humerus, init enc for clsd fx
S42.495P	Oth nondisp fx of lwr end of lt humerus, subsq enc for fx w/ malu
S42.495K	Oth nondisp fx of lwr end of lt humerus, subsq enc for fx w/ nonu
S42.494A	Oth nondisp fx of lwr end of rt humerus, init enc for clsd fx
S42.494P	Oth nondisp fx of lwr end of rt humerus, subsq enc for fx w/ malu
S42.494K	Oth nondisp fx of lwr end of rt humerus, subsq enc for fx w/ nonu
S42.496A	Oth nondisp fx of lwr end of unsp humerus, init enc for clsd fx
S42.496P	Oth nondisp fx of lwr end of unsp humerus, subsq enc for fx w/ malu
S42.496K	Oth nondisp fx of lwr end of unsp humerus, subsq enc for fx w/ nonu
S42.295A	Oth nondisp fx of upr end of lt humerus, init enc for clsd fx
S42.295P	Oth nondisp fx of upr end of lt humerus, subsq enc for fx w/ malu
S42.295K	Oth nondisp fx of upr end of lt humerus, subsq enc for fx w/ nonu
S42.294A	Oth nondisp fx of upr end of rt humerus, init enc for clsd fx
S42.294P	Oth nondisp fx of upr end of rt humerus, subsq enc for fx w/ malu
S42.294K	Oth nondisp fx of upr end of rt humerus, subsq enc for fx w/ nonu
S42.296A	Oth nondisp fx of upr end of unsp humerus, init enc for clsd fx
S42.296P	Oth nondisp fx of upr end of unsp humerus, subsq enc for fx w/ malu
S42.296K	Oth nondisp fx of upr end of unsp humerus, subsq enc for fx w/ nonu
O71.5	Oth obstetric inj to pelvic organs
N13.8	Oth obstructive & reflux uropathy
Q62.39	Oth obstructive defects of renal pelvis & ureter
E70.318	Oth ocular albinism
E70.328	Oth oculocutaneous albinism
H46.8	Oth optic neuritis
M86.8X7	Oth osteomyelitis, ankle & foot
M86.8X3	Oth osteomyelitis, forearm
M86.8X4	Oth osteomyelitis, hand
M86.8X6	Oth osteomyelitis, lwr leg
M86.8X0	Oth osteomyelitis, multi sites
M86.8X8	Oth osteomyelitis, oth site
M86.8X1	Oth osteomyelitis, shldr
M86.8X5	Oth osteomyelitis, thigh
M86.8X9	Oth osteomyelitis, unsp sites
M86.8X2	Oth osteomyelitis, upr arm
M87.838	Oth osteonecrosis of lt carpus
M87.832	Oth osteonecrosis of lt radius
M87.835	Oth osteonecrosis of lt ulna
M87.837	Oth osteonecrosis of rt carpus
M87.831	Oth osteonecrosis of rt radius
M87.834	Oth osteonecrosis of rt ulna
M87.839	Oth osteonecrosis of unsp carpus
M87.833	Oth osteonecrosis of unsp radius
M87.836	Oth osteonecrosis of unsp ulna
M87.872	Oth osteonecrosis, lt ankle
M87.852	Oth osteonecrosis, lt femur
M87.865	Oth osteonecrosis, lt fibula
M87.845	Oth osteonecrosis, lt finger(s)
M87.875	Oth osteonecrosis, lt foot
M87.842	Oth osteonecrosis, lt hand
M87.822	Oth osteonecrosis, lt humerus
M87.812	Oth osteonecrosis, lt shldr
M87.862	Oth osteonecrosis, lt tibia

M87.878	Oth osteonecrosis, lt toe(s)
M87.89	Oth osteonecrosis, multi sites
M87.88	Oth osteonecrosis, oth site
M87.850	Oth osteonecrosis, pelvis
M87.871	Oth osteonecrosis, rt ankle
M87.851	Oth osteonecrosis, rt femur
M87.864	Oth osteonecrosis, rt fibula
M87.844	Oth osteonecrosis, rt finger(s)
M87.874	Oth osteonecrosis, rt foot
M87.841	Oth osteonecrosis, rt hand
M87.821	Oth osteonecrosis, rt humerus
M87.811	Oth osteonecrosis, rt shldr
M87.861	Oth osteonecrosis, rt tibia
M87.877	Oth osteonecrosis, rt toe(s)
M87.873	Oth osteonecrosis, unsp ankle
M87.80	Oth osteonecrosis, unsp bone
M87.859	Oth osteonecrosis, unsp femur
M87.869	Oth osteonecrosis, unsp fibula
M87.849	Oth osteonecrosis, unsp finger(s)
M87.876	Oth osteonecrosis, unsp foot
M87.843	Oth osteonecrosis, unsp hand
M87.829	Oth osteonecrosis, unsp humerus
M87.819	Oth osteonecrosis, unsp shldr
M87.863	Oth osteonecrosis, unsp tibia
M87.879	Oth osteonecrosis, unsp toe(s)
M80.872A	Oth osteoporosis w/ current path fx, lt ankle & foot, init enc for fx
M80.872P	Oth osteoporosis w/ current path fx, lt ankle & foot, subsq enc for fx w/ malu
M80.872K	Oth osteoporosis w/ current path fx, lt ankle & foot, subsq enc for fx w/ nonu
M80.852A	Oth osteoporosis w/ current path fx, lt femur, init enc for fx
M80.852P	Oth osteoporosis w/ current path fx, lt femur, subsq enc for fx w/ malu
M80.852K	Oth osteoporosis w/ current path fx, lt femur, subsq enc for fx w/ nonu
M80.832A	Oth osteoporosis w/ current path fx, lt forearm, init enc for fx
M80.832P	Oth osteoporosis w/ current path fx, lt forearm, subsq enc for fx w/ malu
M80.832K	Oth osteoporosis w/ current path fx, lt forearm, subsq enc for fx w/ nonu
M80.842A	Oth osteoporosis w/ current path fx, lt hand, init enc for fx
M80.842P	Oth osteoporosis w/ current path fx, lt hand, subsq enc for fx w/ malu
M80.842K	Oth osteoporosis w/ current path fx, lt hand, subsq enc for fx w/ nonu
M80.822A	Oth osteoporosis w/ current path fx, lt humerus, init enc for fx
M80.822P	Oth osteoporosis w/ current path fx, lt humerus, subsq enc for fx w/ malu
M80.822K	Oth osteoporosis w/ current path fx, lt humerus, subsq enc for fx w/ nonu
M80.862A	Oth osteoporosis w/ current path fx, lt lwr leg, init enc for fx
M80.862P	Oth osteoporosis w/ current path fx, lt lwr leg, subsq enc for fx w/ malu
M80.862K	Oth osteoporosis w/ current path fx, lt lwr leg, subsq enc for fx w/ nonu
M80.812A	Oth osteoporosis w/ current path fx, lt shldr, init enc for fx
M80.812P	Oth osteoporosis w/ current path fx, lt shldr, subsq enc for fx w/ malu
M80.812K	Oth osteoporosis w/ current path fx, lt shldr, subsq enc for fx w/ nonu
M80.871A	Oth osteoporosis w/ current path fx, rt ankle & foot, init enc for fx
M80.871P	Oth osteoporosis w/ current path fx, rt ankle & foot, subsq enc for fx w/ malu
M80.871K	Oth osteoporosis w/ current path fx, rt ankle & foot, subsq enc for fx w/ nonu
M80.851A	Oth osteoporosis w/ current path fx, rt femur, init enc for fx
M80.851P	Oth osteoporosis w/ current path fx, rt femur, subsq enc for fx w/ malu
M80.851K	Oth osteoporosis w/ current path fx, rt femur, subsq enc for fx w/ nonu
M80.831A	Oth osteoporosis w/ current path fx, rt forearm, init enc for fx
M80.831P	Oth osteoporosis w/ current path fx, rt forearm, subsq enc for fx w/ malu
M80.831K	Oth osteoporosis w/ current path fx, rt forearm, subsq enc for fx w/ nonu
M80.841A	Oth osteoporosis w/ current path fx, rt hand, init enc for fx
M80.841P	Oth osteoporosis w/ current path fx, rt hand, subsq enc for fx w/ malu
M80.841K	Oth osteoporosis w/ current path fx, rt hand, subsq enc for fx w/ nonu
M80.821A	Oth osteoporosis w/ current path fx, rt humerus, init enc for fx
M80.821P	Oth osteoporosis w/ current path fx, rt humerus, subsq enc for fx w/ malu
M80.821K	Oth osteoporosis w/ current path fx, rt humerus, subsq enc for fx w/ nonu
M80.861A	Oth osteoporosis w/ current path fx, rt lwr leg, init enc for fx
M80.861P	Oth osteoporosis w/ current path fx, rt lwr leg, subsq enc for fx w/ malu
M80.861K	Oth osteoporosis w/ current path fx, rt lwr leg, subsq enc for fx w/ nonu
M80.811A	Oth osteoporosis w/ current path fx, rt shldr, init enc for fx
M80.811P	Oth osteoporosis w/ current path fx, rt shldr, subsq enc for fx w/ malu
M80.811K	Oth osteoporosis w/ current path fx, rt shldr, subsq enc for fx w/ nonu
M80.879A	Oth osteoporosis w/ current path fx, unsp ankle & foot, init enc for fx

Code	Description
M80.879P	Oth osteoporosis w/ current path fx, unsp ankle & foot, subsq enc for fx w/ malu
M80.879K	Oth osteoporosis w/ current path fx, unsp ankle & foot, subsq enc for fx w/ nonu
M80.859A	Oth osteoporosis w/ current path fx, unsp femur, init enc for fx
M80.859P	Oth osteoporosis w/ current path fx, unsp femur, subsq enc for fx w/ malu
M80.859K	Oth osteoporosis w/ current path fx, unsp femur, subsq enc for fx w/ nonu
M80.839A	Oth osteoporosis w/ current path fx, unsp forearm, init enc for fx
M80.839P	Oth osteoporosis w/ current path fx, unsp forearm, subsq enc for fx w/ malu
M80.839K	Oth osteoporosis w/ current path fx, unsp forearm, subsq enc for fx w/ nonu
M80.849A	Oth osteoporosis w/ current path fx, unsp hand, init enc for fx
M80.849P	Oth osteoporosis w/ current path fx, unsp hand, subsq enc for fx w/ malu
M80.849K	Oth osteoporosis w/ current path fx, unsp hand, subsq enc for fx w/ nonu
M80.829A	Oth osteoporosis w/ current path fx, unsp humerus, init enc for fx
M80.829P	Oth osteoporosis w/ current path fx, unsp humerus, subsq enc for fx w/ malu
M80.829K	Oth osteoporosis w/ current path fx, unsp humerus, subsq enc for fx w/ nonu
M80.869A	Oth osteoporosis w/ current path fx, unsp lwr leg, init enc for fx
M80.869P	Oth osteoporosis w/ current path fx, unsp lwr leg, subsq enc for fx w/ malu
M80.869K	Oth osteoporosis w/ current path fx, unsp lwr leg, subsq enc for fx w/ nonu
M80.819A	Oth osteoporosis w/ current path fx, unsp shldr, init enc for fx
M80.819P	Oth osteoporosis w/ current path fx, unsp shldr, subsq enc for fx w/ malu
M80.819K	Oth osteoporosis w/ current path fx, unsp shldr, subsq enc for fx w/ nonu
M80.80XA	Oth osteoporosis w/ current path fx, unsp site, init enc for fx
M80.80XP	Oth osteoporosis w/ current path fx, unsp site, subsq enc for fx w/ malu
M80.80XK	Oth osteoporosis w/ current path fx, unsp site, subsq enc for fx w/ nonu
M80.88XA	Oth osteoporosis w/ current path fx, vertebra(e), init enc for fx
M80.88XP	Oth osteoporosis w/ current path fx, vertebra(e), subsq enc for fx w/ malu
M80.88XK	Oth osteoporosis w/ current path fx, vertebra(e), subsq enc for fx w/ nonu
M35.1	Oth overlap syndromes
D61.818	Oth pancytopenia
L12.8	Oth pemphigoid
L10.89	Oth pemphigus
E71.548	Oth peroxisomal d/o
F34.8	Oth persistent mood [affective] d/o
F84.8	Oth pervasive developmental d/o
Q85.8	Oth phakomatoses, NEC
S49.192A	Oth physeal fx of lwr end of humerus, lt arm, init enc for clsd fx
S49.192P	Oth physeal fx of lwr end of humerus, lt arm, subsq enc for fx w/ malu
S49.192K	Oth physeal fx of lwr end of humerus, lt arm, subsq enc for fx w/ nonu
S49.191A	Oth physeal fx of lwr end of humerus, rt arm, init enc for clsd fx
S49.191P	Oth physeal fx of lwr end of humerus, rt arm, subsq enc for fx w/ malu
S49.191K	Oth physeal fx of lwr end of humerus, rt arm, subsq enc for fx w/ nonu
S49.199A	Oth physeal fx of lwr end of humerus, unsp arm, init enc for clsd fx
S49.199P	Oth physeal fx of lwr end of humerus, unsp arm, subsq enc for fx w/ malu
S49.199K	Oth physeal fx of lwr end of humerus, unsp arm, subsq enc for fx w/ nonu
S79.192A	Oth physeal fx of lwr end of lt femur, init enc for clsd fx
S79.192P	Oth physeal fx of lwr end of lt femur, subsq enc for fx w/ malu
S79.192K	Oth physeal fx of lwr end of lt femur, subsq enc for fx w/ nonu
S89.392P	Oth physeal fx of lwr end of lt fibula, subsq enc for fx w/ malu
S89.392K	Oth physeal fx of lwr end of lt fibula, subsq enc for fx w/ nonu
S89.192P	Oth physeal fx of lwr end of lt tibia, subsq enc for fx w/ malu
S89.192K	Oth physeal fx of lwr end of lt tibia, subsq enc for fx w/ nonu
S59.292A	Oth physeal fx of lwr end of radius, lt arm, init enc for clsd fx
S59.292P	Oth physeal fx of lwr end of radius, lt arm, subsq enc for fx w/ malu
S59.292K	Oth physeal fx of lwr end of radius, lt arm, subsq enc for fx w/ nonu
S59.291A	Oth physeal fx of lwr end of radius, rt arm, init enc for clsd fx
S59.291P	Oth physeal fx of lwr end of radius, rt arm, subsq enc for fx w/ malu
S59.291K	Oth physeal fx of lwr end of radius, rt arm, subsq enc for fx w/ nonu
S59.299A	Oth physeal fx of lwr end of radius, unsp arm, init enc for clsd fx
S59.299P	Oth physeal fx of lwr end of radius, unsp arm, subsq enc for fx w/ malu
S59.299K	Oth physeal fx of lwr end of radius, unsp arm, subsq enc for fx w/ nonu
S79.191A	Oth physeal fx of lwr end of rt femur, init enc for clsd fx
S79.191P	Oth physeal fx of lwr end of rt femur, subsq enc for fx w/ malu
S79.191K	Oth physeal fx of lwr end of rt femur, subsq enc for fx w/ nonu
S89.391P	Oth physeal fx of lwr end of rt fibula, subsq enc for fx w/ malu
S89.391K	Oth physeal fx of lwr end of rt fibula, subsq enc for fx w/ nonu
S89.191P	Oth physeal fx of lwr end of rt tibia, subsq enc for fx w/ malu
S89.191K	Oth physeal fx of lwr end of rt tibia, subsq enc for fx w/ nonu
S59.092A	Oth physeal fx of lwr end of ulna, lt arm, init enc for clsd fx
S59.092P	Oth physeal fx of lwr end of ulna, lt arm, subsq enc for fx w/ malu
S59.092K	Oth physeal fx of lwr end of ulna, lt arm, subsq enc for fx w/ nonu
S59.091A	Oth physeal fx of lwr end of ulna, rt arm, init enc for clsd fx
S59.091P	Oth physeal fx of lwr end of ulna, rt arm, subsq enc for fx w/ malu
S59.091K	Oth physeal fx of lwr end of ulna, rt arm, subsq enc for fx w/ nonu
S59.099A	Oth physeal fx of lwr end of ulna, unsp arm, init enc for clsd fx
S59.099P	Oth physeal fx of lwr end of ulna, unsp arm, subsq enc for fx w/ malu
S59.099K	Oth physeal fx of lwr end of ulna, unsp arm, subsq enc for fx w/ nonu
S79.199A	Oth physeal fx of lwr end of unsp femur, init enc for clsd fx
S79.199P	Oth physeal fx of lwr end of unsp femur, subsq enc for fx w/ malu
S79.199K	Oth physeal fx of lwr end of unsp femur, subsq enc for fx w/ nonu
S89.399P	Oth physeal fx of lwr end of unsp fibula, subsq enc for fx w/ malu
S89.399K	Oth physeal fx of lwr end of unsp fibula, subsq enc for fx w/ nonu
S89.199P	Oth physeal fx of lwr end of unsp tibia, subsq enc for fx w/ malu
S89.199K	Oth physeal fx of lwr end of unsp tibia, subsq enc for fx w/ nonu
S49.092A	Oth physeal fx of upr end of humerus, lt arm, init enc for clsd fx
S49.092P	Oth physeal fx of upr end of humerus, lt arm, subsq enc for fx w/ malu
S49.092K	Oth physeal fx of upr end of humerus, lt arm, subsq enc for fx w/ nonu
S49.091A	Oth physeal fx of upr end of humerus, rt arm, init enc for clsd fx
S49.091P	Oth physeal fx of upr end of humerus, rt arm, subsq enc for fx w/ malu
S49.091K	Oth physeal fx of upr end of humerus, rt arm, subsq enc for fx w/ nonu
S49.099A	Oth physeal fx of upr end of humerus, unsp arm, init enc for clsd fx
S49.099P	Oth physeal fx of upr end of humerus, unsp arm, subsq enc for fx w/ malu
S49.099K	Oth physeal fx of upr end of humerus, unsp arm, subsq enc for fx w/ nonu
S79.092P	Oth physeal fx of upr end of lt femur, subsq enc for fx w/ malu
S79.092K	Oth physeal fx of upr end of lt femur, subsq enc for fx w/ nonu
S89.292P	Oth physeal fx of upr end of lt fibula, subsq enc for fx w/ malu
S89.292K	Oth physeal fx of upr end of lt fibula, subsq enc for fx w/ nonu
S89.092A	Oth physeal fx of upr end of lt tibia, init enc for clsd fx
S89.092P	Oth physeal fx of upr end of lt tibia, subsq enc for fx w/ malu
S89.092K	Oth physeal fx of upr end of lt tibia, subsq enc for fx w/ nonu
S59.192P	Oth physeal fx of upr end of radius, lt arm, subsq enc for fx w/ malu
S59.192K	Oth physeal fx of upr end of radius, lt arm, subsq enc for fx w/ nonu
S59.191P	Oth physeal fx of upr end of radius, rt arm, subsq enc for fx w/ malu
S59.191K	Oth physeal fx of upr end of radius, rt arm, subsq enc for fx w/ nonu
S59.199P	Oth physeal fx of upr end of radius, unsp arm, subsq enc for fx w/ malu
S59.199K	Oth physeal fx of upr end of radius, unsp arm, subsq enc for fx w/ nonu
S79.091P	Oth physeal fx of upr end of rt femur, subsq enc for fx w/ malu
S79.091K	Oth physeal fx of upr end of rt femur, subsq enc for fx w/ nonu
S89.291P	Oth physeal fx of upr end of rt fibula, subsq enc for fx w/ malu
S89.291K	Oth physeal fx of upr end of rt fibula, subsq enc for fx w/ nonu
S89.091A	Oth physeal fx of upr end of rt tibia, init enc for clsd fx
S89.091P	Oth physeal fx of upr end of rt tibia, subsq enc for fx w/ malu
S89.091K	Oth physeal fx of upr end of rt tibia, subsq enc for fx w/ nonu
S79.099P	Oth physeal fx of upr end of unsp femur, subsq enc for fx w/ malu
S79.099K	Oth physeal fx of upr end of unsp femur, subsq enc for fx w/ nonu
S89.299P	Oth physeal fx of upr end of unsp fibula, subsq enc for fx w/ malu
S89.299K	Oth physeal fx of upr end of unsp fibula, subsq enc for fx w/ nonu
S89.099A	Oth physeal fx of upr end of unsp tibia, init enc for clsd fx
S89.099P	Oth physeal fx of upr end of unsp tibia, subsq enc for fx w/ malu
S89.099K	Oth physeal fx of upr end of unsp tibia, subsq enc for fx w/ nonu
J93.83	Oth pneumothorax
Q61.19	Oth polycystic kidney, infantile type
E80.29	Oth porphyria
B02.29	Oth postherpetic nervous sys involvement
I97.190	Oth postprocedural cardiac functional disturbances following cardiac surgery
I97.191	Oth postprocedural cardiac functional disturbances following oth surgery
K91.89	Oth postprocedural comp & d/o of digestive sys
H59.89	Oth postprocedural comp & d/o of eye & adnexa, NEC
G97.82	Oth postprocedural comp & d/o of nervous sys
J95.89	Oth postprocedural comp & d/o of respiratory sys, NEC
I97.89	Oth postprocedural comp & d/o of the circulatory sys, NEC
H95.89	Oth postprocedural comp & d/o of the ear & mastoid process, NEC
D78.89	Oth postprocedural comp of the spleen
E89.89	Oth postprocedural endocrine & metabolic comp & d/o
O24.811	Oth pre-existing diabetes mellitus in pregnancy, 1st trmstr
O24.812	Oth pre-existing diabetes mellitus in pregnancy, 2nd trmstr
O24.813	Oth pre-existing diabetes mellitus in pregnancy, 3rd trmstr

O24.819	Oth pre-existing diabetes mellitus in pregnancy, unsp trmstr
O24.83	Oth pre-existing diabetes mellitus in the puerperium
N48.39	Oth priapism
D68.59	Oth primary thrombophilia
F19.121	Oth psychoactive substance abuse w/ intoxication delirium
F19.17	Oth psychoactive substance abuse w/ psychoactive substance-induced persisting dementia
F19.150	Oth psychoactive substance abuse w/ psychoactive substance-induced psychotic d/o w/ delusions
F19.151	Oth psychoactive substance abuse w/ psychoactive substance-induced psychotic d/o w/ hallucinations
F19.221	Oth psychoactive substance dependence w/ intoxication delirium
F19.222	Oth psychoactive substance dependence w/ intoxication w/ perceptual disturbance
F19.288	Oth psychoactive substance dependence w/ oth psychoactive substance-induced d/o
F19.280	Oth psychoactive substance dependence w/ psychoactive substance-induced anxiety d/o
F19.26	Oth psychoactive substance dependence w/ psychoactive substance-induced persisting amnestic d/o
F19.27	Oth psychoactive substance dependence w/ psychoactive substance-induced persisting dementia
F19.250	Oth psychoactive substance dependence w/ psychoactive substance-induced psychotic d/o w/ delusions
F19.251	Oth psychoactive substance dependence w/ psychoactive substance-induced psychotic d/o w/ hallucinations
F19.259	Oth psychoactive substance dependence w/ psychoactive substance-induced psychotic d/o, unsp
F19.281	Oth psychoactive substance dependence w/ psychoactive substance-induced sexual dysfunction
F19.282	Oth psychoactive substance dependence w/ psychoactive substance-induced sleep d/o
F19.231	Oth psychoactive substance dependence w/ withdrawal delirium
F19.232	Oth psychoactive substance dependence w/ withdrawal w/ perceptual disturbance
F19.230	Oth psychoactive substance dependence w/ withdrawal, uncomplicated
F19.239	Oth psychoactive substance dependence w/ withdrawal, unsp
F19.20	Oth psychoactive substance dependence, uncomplicated
F19.921	Oth psychoactive substance use, unsp w/ intoxication w/ delirium
F19.97	Oth psychoactive substance use, unsp w/ psychoactive substance-induced persisting dementia
F19.950	Oth psychoactive substance use, unsp w/ psychoactive substance-induced psychotic d/o w/ delusions
F19.951	Oth psychoactive substance use, unsp w/ psychoactive substance-induced psychotic d/o w/ hallucinations
F19.931	Oth psychoactive substance use, unsp w/ withdrawal delirium
F19.932	Oth psychoactive substance use, unsp w/ withdrawal w/ perceptual disturbance
F19.930	Oth psychoactive substance use, unsp w/ withdrawal, uncomplicated
F19.939	Oth psychoactive substance use, unsp w/ withdrawal, unsp
B44.1	Oth pulmn aspergillosis
J98.19	Oth pulmn collapse
P93.8	Oth reactions & intoxications d/t drugs administered to newborn
M02.872	Oth reactive arthropathies, lt ankle & foot
M02.822	Oth reactive arthropathies, lt elbow
M02.842	Oth reactive arthropathies, lt hand
M02.852	Oth reactive arthropathies, lt hip
M02.862	Oth reactive arthropathies, lt knee
M02.812	Oth reactive arthropathies, lt shldr
M02.832	Oth reactive arthropathies, lt wrist
M02.89	Oth reactive arthropathies, multi sites
M02.871	Oth reactive arthropathies, rt ankle & foot
M02.821	Oth reactive arthropathies, rt elbow
M02.841	Oth reactive arthropathies, rt hand
M02.851	Oth reactive arthropathies, rt hip
M02.861	Oth reactive arthropathies, rt knee
M02.811	Oth reactive arthropathies, rt shldr
M02.831	Oth reactive arthropathies, rt wrist
M02.879	Oth reactive arthropathies, unsp ankle & foot
M02.829	Oth reactive arthropathies, unsp elbow
M02.849	Oth reactive arthropathies, unsp hand
M02.859	Oth reactive arthropathies, unsp hip
M02.869	Oth reactive arthropathies, unsp knee
M02.819	Oth reactive arthropathies, unsp shldr
M02.80	Oth reactive arthropathies, unsp site

M02.839	Oth reactive arthropathies, unsp wrist
M02.88	Oth reactive arthropathies, vertebrae
F33.8	Oth recurrent depressive d/o
A15.8	Oth respiratory tuberculosis
I42.5	Oth restrictive cardiomyopathy
H33.8	Oth retinal detachments
T80.49XA	Oth Rh incompatibility reaction d/t transfusion of blood or blood products, init enc
B06.89	Oth rubella comp
C22.4	Oth sarcomas of liver
B65.8	Oth schistosomiasis
F20.89	Oth schizophrenia
C7B.8	Oth secondary neuroendocrine tumors
M87.338	Oth secondary osteonecrosis of lt carpus
M87.332	Oth secondary osteonecrosis of lt radius
M87.335	Oth secondary osteonecrosis of lt ulna
M87.337	Oth secondary osteonecrosis of rt carpus
M87.331	Oth secondary osteonecrosis of rt radius
M87.334	Oth secondary osteonecrosis of rt ulna
M87.339	Oth secondary osteonecrosis of unsp carpus
M87.333	Oth secondary osteonecrosis of unsp radius
M87.336	Oth secondary osteonecrosis of unsp ulna
M87.372	Oth secondary osteonecrosis, lt ankle
M87.352	Oth secondary osteonecrosis, lt femur
M87.365	Oth secondary osteonecrosis, lt fibula
M87.345	Oth secondary osteonecrosis, lt finger(s)
M87.375	Oth secondary osteonecrosis, lt foot
M87.342	Oth secondary osteonecrosis, lt hand
M87.322	Oth secondary osteonecrosis, lt humerus
M87.312	Oth secondary osteonecrosis, lt shldr
M87.362	Oth secondary osteonecrosis, lt tibia
M87.378	Oth secondary osteonecrosis, lt toe(s)
M87.39	Oth secondary osteonecrosis, multi sites
M87.38	Oth secondary osteonecrosis, oth site
M87.350	Oth secondary osteonecrosis, pelvis
M87.371	Oth secondary osteonecrosis, rt ankle
M87.351	Oth secondary osteonecrosis, rt femur
M87.364	Oth secondary osteonecrosis, rt fibula
M87.344	Oth secondary osteonecrosis, rt finger(s)
M87.374	Oth secondary osteonecrosis, rt foot
M87.341	Oth secondary osteonecrosis, rt hand
M87.321	Oth secondary osteonecrosis, rt humerus
M87.311	Oth secondary osteonecrosis, rt shldr
M87.361	Oth secondary osteonecrosis, rt tibia
M87.377	Oth secondary osteonecrosis, rt toe(s)
M87.373	Oth secondary osteonecrosis, unsp ankle
M87.30	Oth secondary osteonecrosis, unsp bone
M87.353	Oth secondary osteonecrosis, unsp femur
M87.366	Oth secondary osteonecrosis, unsp fibula
M87.346	Oth secondary osteonecrosis, unsp finger(s)
M87.376	Oth secondary osteonecrosis, unsp foot
M87.343	Oth secondary osteonecrosis, unsp hand
M87.329	Oth secondary osteonecrosis, unsp humerus
M87.319	Oth secondary osteonecrosis, unsp shldr
M87.363	Oth secondary osteonecrosis, unsp tibia
M87.379	Oth secondary osteonecrosis, unsp toe(s)
G21.8	Oth secondary parkinsonism
A51.39	Oth secondary syphilis of skin
A51.49	Oth secondary syphilitic conditions
G40.89	Oth seizures
T80.61XA	Oth serum reaction d/t administration of blood & blood products, init enc
T80.69XA	Oth serum reaction d/t oth serum, init enc
T80.62XA	Oth serum reaction d/t vaccination, init enc
B50.8	Oth severe & complicated Plasmodium falciparum malaria
B37.89	Oth sites of candidiasis
K45.0	Oth spec abd hernia w/ obstruction, w/o gangrene
G36.8	Oth spec acute disseminated demyelination
B17.8	Oth spec acute viral hepatitis
E70.39	Oth spec albinism
A93.8	Oth spec arthropod-borne viral fevers
A05.8	Oth spec bacterial foodborne intoxications
A04.8	Oth spec bacterial intestinal infections
C22.7	Oth spec carcinomas of liver

Code	Description
B71.8	Oth spec cestode infections
D68.8	Oth spec coagulation defects
T82.897A	Oth spec comp of cardiac prosthetic devices, implants & grafts, init enc
T83.89XA	Oth spec comp of genitourinary prosthetic devices, implants & grafts, init enc
T84.89XA	Oth spec comp of int orthopedic prosthetic devices, implants & grafts, init enc
T85.89XA	Oth spec comp of int prosthetic devices, implants & grafts, NEC, init enc
T82.898A	Oth spec comp of vascular prosthetic devices, implants & grafts, init enc
I45.89	Oth spec conduction d/o
Q87.89	Oth spec congenital malformation syndromes, NEC
Q89.8	Oth spec congenital malformations
Q04.8	Oth spec congenital malformations of brain
Q28.8	Oth spec congenital malformations of circulatory sys
Q43.8	Oth spec congenital malformations of intestine
E72.8	Oth spec d/o of amino-acid metabolism
E74.8	Oth spec d/o of carbohydrate metabolism
G23.8	Oth spec degenerative diseases of basal ganglia
G37.8	Oth spec demyelinating diseases of central nervous sys
E13.52	Oth spec diabetes mellitus w/ diabetic peripheral angiopathy w/ gangrene
I31.8	Oth spec diseases of pericardium
G95.89	Oth spec diseases of spinal cord
B66.8	Oth spec fluke infections
S32.492K	Oth spec fx of lt acetab, subsq enc for fx w/ nonu
S32.692A	Oth spec fx of lt ischium, init enc for clsd fx
S32.692K	Oth spec fx of lt ischium, subsq enc for fx w/ nonu
S32.592A	Oth spec fx of lt pubis, init enc for clsd fx
S32.592K	Oth spec fx of lt pubis, subsq enc for fx w/ nonu
S32.491K	Oth spec fx of rt acetab, subsq enc for fx w/ nonu
S32.691A	Oth spec fx of rt ischium, init enc for clsd fx
S32.691K	Oth spec fx of rt ischium, subsq enc for fx w/ nonu
S32.591A	Oth spec fx of rt pubis, init enc for clsd fx
S32.591K	Oth spec fx of rt pubis, subsq enc for fx w/ nonu
S32.499K	Oth spec fx of unsp acetab, subsq enc for fx w/ nonu
S32.699A	Oth spec fx of unsp ischium, init enc for clsd fx
S32.699K	Oth spec fx of unsp ischium, subsq enc for fx w/ nonu
S32.599A	Oth spec fx of unsp pubis, init enc for clsd fx
S32.599K	Oth spec fx of unsp pubis, subsq enc for fx w/ nonu
D58.8	Oth spec hereditary hemolytic anemias
D84.8	Oth spec immunodeficiencies
P39.8	Oth spec infections specific to the perinatal period
S85.152A	Oth spec inj of ant tibial artery, lt leg, init enc
S85.151A	Oth spec inj of ant tibial artery, rt leg, init enc
S85.159A	Oth spec inj of ant tibial artery, unsp leg, init enc
S45.292A	Oth spec inj of axillary or brachial vein, lt side, init enc
S45.291A	Oth spec inj of axillary or brachial vein, rt side, init enc
S45.299A	Oth spec inj of axillary or brachial vein, unsp side, init enc
S65.591A	Oth spec inj of blood vessel of lt index finger, init enc
S65.597A	Oth spec inj of blood vessel of lt little finger, init enc
S65.593A	Oth spec inj of blood vessel of lt mid finger, init enc
S65.595A	Oth spec inj of blood vessel of lt ring finger, init enc
S65.492A	Oth spec inj of blood vessel of lt thumb, init enc
S65.598A	Oth spec inj of blood vessel of oth finger, init enc
S65.590A	Oth spec inj of blood vessel of rt index finger, init enc
S65.596A	Oth spec inj of blood vessel of rt little finger, init enc
S65.592A	Oth spec inj of blood vessel of rt mid finger, init enc
S65.594A	Oth spec inj of blood vessel of rt ring finger, init enc
S65.491A	Oth spec inj of blood vessel of rt thumb, init enc
S65.599A	Oth spec inj of blood vessel of unsp finger, init enc
S65.499A	Oth spec inj of blood vessel of unsp thumb, init enc
S45.192A	Oth spec inj of brachial artery, lt side, init enc
S45.191A	Oth spec inj of brachial artery, rt side, init enc
S45.199A	Oth spec inj of brachial artery, unsp side, init enc
S65.392A	Oth spec inj of deep palmar arch of lt hand, init enc
S65.391A	Oth spec inj of deep palmar arch of rt hand, init enc
S65.399A	Oth spec inj of deep palmar arch of unsp hand, init enc
S95.092A	Oth spec inj of dorsal artery of lt foot, init enc
S95.091A	Oth spec inj of dorsal artery of rt foot, init enc
S95.099A	Oth spec inj of dorsal artery of unsp foot, init enc
S95.292A	Oth spec inj of dorsal vein of lt foot, init enc
S95.291A	Oth spec inj of dorsal vein of rt foot, init enc
S95.299A	Oth spec inj of dorsal vein of unsp foot, init enc
S75.292A	Oth spec inj of greater saphenous vein at hip & thigh lvl, lt leg, init enc
S75.291A	Oth spec inj of greater saphenous vein at hip & thigh lvl, rt leg, init enc
S75.299A	Oth spec inj of greater saphenous vein at hip & thigh lvl, unsp leg, init enc
S85.392A	Oth spec inj of greater saphenous vein at lwr leg lvl, lt leg, init enc
S85.391A	Oth spec inj of greater saphenous vein at lwr leg lvl, rt leg, init enc
S85.399A	Oth spec inj of greater saphenous vein at lwr leg lvl, unsp leg, init enc
S25.592A	Oth spec inj of intercostal blood vessels, lt side, init enc
S25.591A	Oth spec inj of intercostal blood vessels, rt side, init enc
S25.599A	Oth spec inj of intercostal blood vessels, unsp side, init enc
S85.492A	Oth spec inj of lesser saphenous vein at lwr leg lvl, lt leg, init enc
S85.491A	Oth spec inj of lesser saphenous vein at lwr leg lvl, rt leg, init enc
S85.499A	Oth spec inj of lesser saphenous vein at lwr leg lvl, unsp leg, init enc
S15.092A	Oth spec inj of lt carotid artery, init enc
S15.292A	Oth spec inj of lt ext jugular vein, init enc
S15.392A	Oth spec inj of lt int jugular vein, init enc
S09.392A	Oth spec inj of lt mid & inner ear, init enc
S15.192A	Oth spec inj of lt vert artery, init enc
S35.8X8A	Oth spec inj of oth blood vessels at abd, lwr back & pelvis lvl, init enc
S95.892A	Oth spec inj of oth blood vessels at ankle & foot lvl, lt leg, init enc
S95.891A	Oth spec inj of oth blood vessels at ankle & foot lvl, rt leg, init enc
S95.899A	Oth spec inj of oth blood vessels at ankle & foot lvl, unsp leg, init enc
S55.892A	Oth spec inj of oth blood vessels at forearm lvl, lt arm, init enc
S55.891A	Oth spec inj of oth blood vessels at forearm lvl, rt arm, init enc
S55.899A	Oth spec inj of oth blood vessels at forearm lvl, unsp arm, init enc
S75.892A	Oth spec inj of oth blood vessels at hip & thigh lvl, lt leg, init enc
S75.891A	Oth spec inj of oth blood vessels at hip & thigh lvl, rt leg, init enc
S75.899A	Oth spec inj of oth blood vessels at hip & thigh lvl, unsp leg, init enc
S85.892A	Oth spec inj of oth blood vessels at lwr leg lvl, lt leg, init enc
S85.891A	Oth spec inj of oth blood vessels at lwr leg lvl, rt leg, init enc
S85.899A	Oth spec inj of oth blood vessels at lwr leg lvl, unsp leg, init enc
S65.892A	Oth spec inj of oth blood vessels at wrist & hand lvl of lt arm, init enc
S65.891A	Oth spec inj of oth blood vessels at wrist & hand lvl of rt arm, init enc
S65.899A	Oth spec inj of oth blood vessels at wrist & hand lvl of unsp arm, init enc
S25.892A	Oth spec inj of oth blood vessels of thorax, lt side, init enc
S25.891A	Oth spec inj of oth blood vessels of thorax, rt side, init enc
S25.899A	Oth spec inj of oth blood vessels of thorax, unsp side, init enc
S45.892A	Oth spec inj of oth spec blood vessels at shldr & upr arm lvl, lt arm, init enc
S45.891A	Oth spec inj of oth spec blood vessels at shldr & upr arm lvl, rt arm, init enc
S45.899A	Oth spec inj of oth spec blood vessels at shldr & upr arm lvl, unsp arm, init enc
S85.292A	Oth spec inj of peroneal artery, lt leg, init enc
S85.291A	Oth spec inj of peroneal artery, rt leg, init enc
S85.299A	Oth spec inj of peroneal artery, unsp leg, init enc
S95.192A	Oth spec inj of plantar artery of lt foot, init enc
S95.191A	Oth spec inj of plantar artery of rt foot, init enc
S95.199A	Oth spec inj of plantar artery of unsp foot, init enc
S85.182A	Oth spec inj of post tibial artery, lt leg, init enc
S85.181A	Oth spec inj of post tibial artery, rt leg, init enc
S85.189A	Oth spec inj of post tibial artery, unsp leg, init enc
S55.192A	Oth spec inj of radial artery at forearm lvl, lt arm, init enc
S55.191A	Oth spec inj of radial artery at forearm lvl, rt arm, init enc
S55.199A	Oth spec inj of radial artery at forearm lvl, unsp arm, init enc
S65.192A	Oth spec inj of radial artery at wrist & hand lvl of lt arm, init enc
S65.191A	Oth spec inj of radial artery at wrist & hand lvl of rt arm, init enc
S65.199A	Oth spec inj of radial artery at wrist & hand lvl of unsp arm, init enc
S15.091A	Oth spec inj of rt carotid artery, init enc
S15.291A	Oth spec inj of rt ext jugular vein, init enc
S15.391A	Oth spec inj of rt int jugular vein, init enc
S09.391A	Oth spec inj of rt mid & inner ear, init enc
S15.191A	Oth spec inj of rt vert artery, init enc
S65.292A	Oth spec inj of superf palmar arch of lt hand, init enc
S65.291A	Oth spec inj of superf palmar arch of rt hand, init enc
S65.299A	Oth spec inj of superf palmar arch of unsp hand, init enc
S45.392A	Oth spec inj of superf vein at shldr & upr arm lvl, lt arm, init enc
S45.391A	Oth spec inj of superf vein at shldr & upr arm lvl, rt arm, init enc
S45.399A	Oth spec inj of superf vein at shldr & upr arm lvl, unsp arm, init enc
S55.092A	Oth spec inj of ulnar artery at forearm lvl, lt arm, init enc
S55.091A	Oth spec inj of ulnar artery at forearm lvl, rt arm, init enc
S55.099A	Oth spec inj of ulnar artery at forearm lvl, unsp arm, init enc
S65.092A	Oth spec inj of ulnar artery at wrist & hand lvl of lt arm, init enc
S65.091A	Oth spec inj of ulnar artery at wrist & hand lvl of rt arm, init enc
S65.099A	Oth spec inj of ulnar artery at wrist & hand lvl of unsp arm, init enc

S35.99XA	Oth spec inj of unsp blood vessel at abd, lwr back & pelvis lvl, init enc
S95.992A	Oth spec inj of unsp blood vessel at ankle & foot lvl, lt leg, init enc
S95.991A	Oth spec inj of unsp blood vessel at ankle & foot lvl, rt leg, init enc
S95.999A	Oth spec inj of unsp blood vessel at ankle & foot lvl, unsp leg, init enc
S55.992A	Oth spec inj of unsp blood vessel at forearm lvl, lt arm, init enc
S55.991A	Oth spec inj of unsp blood vessel at forearm lvl, rt arm, init enc
S55.999A	Oth spec inj of unsp blood vessel at forearm lvl, unsp arm, init enc
S75.992A	Oth spec inj of unsp blood vessel at hip & thigh lvl, lt leg, init enc
S75.991A	Oth spec inj of unsp blood vessel at hip & thigh lvl, rt leg, init enc
S75.999A	Oth spec inj of unsp blood vessel at hip & thigh lvl, unsp leg, init enc
S85.992A	Oth spec inj of unsp blood vessel at lwr leg lvl, lt leg, init enc
S85.991A	Oth spec inj of unsp blood vessel at lwr leg lvl, rt leg, init enc
S85.999A	Oth spec inj of unsp blood vessel at lwr leg lvl, unsp leg, init enc
S45.992A	Oth spec inj of unsp blood vessel at shldr & upr arm lvl, lt arm, init enc
S45.991A	Oth spec inj of unsp blood vessel at shldr & upr arm lvl, rt arm, init enc
S45.999A	Oth spec inj of unsp blood vessel at shldr & upr arm lvl, unsp arm, init enc
S65.992A	Oth spec inj of unsp blood vessel at wrist & hand of lt arm, init enc
S65.991A	Oth spec inj of unsp blood vessel at wrist & hand of rt arm, init enc
S65.999A	Oth spec inj of unsp blood vessel at wrist & hand of unsp arm, init enc
S25.99XA	Oth spec inj of unsp blood vessel of thorax, init enc
S15.099A	Oth spec inj of unsp carotid artery, init enc
S15.299A	Oth spec inj of unsp ext jugular vein, init enc
S15.399A	Oth spec inj of unsp int jugular vein, init enc
S09.399A	Oth spec inj of unsp mid & inner ear, init enc
S85.122A	Oth spec inj of unsp tibial artery, lt leg, init enc
S85.121A	Oth spec inj of unsp tibial artery, rt leg, init enc
S85.129A	Oth spec inj of unsp tibial artery, unsp leg, init enc
S15.199A	Oth spec inj of unsp vert artery, init enc
S55.292A	Oth spec inj of vein at forearm lvl, lt arm, init enc
S55.291A	Oth spec inj of vein at forearm lvl, rt arm, init enc
S55.299A	Oth spec inj of vein at forearm lvl, unsp arm, init enc
B81.8	Oth spec intestinal helminthiases
S06.895A	Oth spec intracranial inj w/ loss of cnscness > 24 hrs w/ return to pre-existing conscious lvl, init enc
S06.893A	Oth spec intracranial inj w/ loss of cnscness of 1 hr to 5 hrs 59 mins, init enc
S06.891A	Oth spec intracranial inj w/ loss of cnscness of 30 mins or less, init enc
S06.892A	Oth spec intracranial inj w/ loss of cnscness of 31 mins to 59 mins, init enc
S06.894A	Oth spec intracranial inj w/ loss of cnscness of 6 hrs to 24 hrs, init enc
S06.899A	Oth spec intracranial inj w/ loss of cnscness of unsp dur, init enc
C94.80	Oth spec leukemias not having achieved remission
C94.82	Oth spec leukemias, in relapse
C94.81	Oth spec leukemias, in remission
C96.Z	Oth spec malig neoplasms of lymphoid, hematopoietic & related tissue
A92.8	Oth spec mosquito-borne viral fevers
O30.821	Oth spec multi gestation w/ two or more monoamniotic fetuses, 1st trmstr
O30.822	Oth spec multi gestation w/ two or more monoamniotic fetuses, 2nd trmstr
O30.823	Oth spec multi gestation w/ two or more monoamniotic fetuses, 3rd trmstr
O30.811	Oth spec multi gestation w/ two or more monochorionic fetuses, 1st trmstr
O30.812	Oth spec multi gestation w/ two or more monochorionic fetuses, 2nd trmstr
O30.813	Oth spec multi gestation w/ two or more monochorionic fetuses, 3rd trmstr
O30.891	Oth spec multi gestation, unable to determine number of placenta & number of amniotic sacs, 1st trmstr
O30.892	Oth spec multi gestation, unable to determine number of placenta & number of amniotic sacs, 2nd trmstr
O30.893	Oth spec multi gestation, unable to determine number of placenta & number of amniotic sacs, 3rd trmstr
O30.801	Oth spec multi gestation, unsp number of placenta & unsp number of amniotic sacs, 1st trmstr
O30.802	Oth spec multi gestation, unsp number of placenta & unsp number of amniotic sacs, 2nd trmstr
O30.803	Oth spec multi gestation, unsp number of placenta & unsp number of amniotic sacs, 3rd trmstr
B48.8	Oth spec mycoses
M31.8	Oth spec necrotizing vasculopathies
D47.Z9	Oth spec neoplasms of uncertain behavior of lymphoid, hematopoietic & related tissue
J94.8	Oth spec pleural conditions
A07.8	Oth spec protozoal intestinal diseases
A79.89	Oth spec rickettsioses
A02.8	Oth spec salmonella infections
M35.8	Oth spec systemic involvement of connective tissue
P72.8	Oth spec transitory neonatal endocrine d/o
C85.89	Oth spec types of non-Hodgkin lymphoma, extranodal & solid organ sites
C85.83	Oth spec types of non-Hodgkin lymphoma, intra-abd lymph nodes
C85.86	Oth spec types of non-Hodgkin lymphoma, intrapelvic lymph nodes
C85.82	Oth spec types of non-Hodgkin lymphoma, intrathoracic lymph nodes
C85.84	Oth spec types of non-Hodgkin lymphoma, lymph nodes of axilla & upr limb
C85.81	Oth spec types of non-Hodgkin lymphoma, lymph nodes of head, face, & neck
C85.85	Oth spec types of non-Hodgkin lymphoma, lymph nodes of inguinal rgn & lwr limb
C85.88	Oth spec types of non-Hodgkin lymphoma, lymph nodes of multi sites
C85.87	Oth spec types of non-Hodgkin lymphoma, spleen
C85.80	Oth spec types of non-Hodgkin lymphoma, unsp site
A85.8	Oth spec viral encephalitis
A98.8	Oth spec viral hemorrhagic fevers
A88.8	Oth spec viral infections of central nervous sys
A28.8	Oth spec zoonotic bacterial diseases, NEC
E75.29	Oth sphingolipidosis
G12.8	Oth spinal muscular atrophies & related syndromes
M47.12	Oth spondylosis w/ myelopathy, cervical rgn
M47.13	Oth spondylosis w/ myelopathy, cervicothoracic rgn
M47.16	Oth spondylosis w/ myelopathy, lumbar rgn
M47.11	Oth spondylosis w/ myelopathy, occipito-atlanto-axial rgn
M47.10	Oth spondylosis w/ myelopathy, site unsp
M47.14	Oth spondylosis w/ myelopathy, thoracic rgn
M47.15	Oth spondylosis w/ myelopathy, thoracolumbar rgn
A77.8	Oth spotted fevers
F15.121	Oth stimulant abuse w/ intoxication delirium
F15.150	Oth stimulant abuse w/ stimulant-induced psychotic d/o w/ delusions
F15.151	Oth stimulant abuse w/ stimulant-induced psychotic d/o w/ hallucinations
F15.221	Oth stimulant dependence w/ intoxication delirium
F15.222	Oth stimulant dependence w/ intoxication w/ perceptual disturbance
F15.288	Oth stimulant dependence w/ oth stimulant-induced d/o
F15.280	Oth stimulant dependence w/ stimulant-induced anxiety d/o
F15.250	Oth stimulant dependence w/ stimulant-induced psychotic d/o w/ delusions
F15.251	Oth stimulant dependence w/ stimulant-induced psychotic d/o w/ hallucinations
F15.259	Oth stimulant dependence w/ stimulant-induced psychotic d/o, unsp
F15.281	Oth stimulant dependence w/ stimulant-induced sexual dysfunction
F15.282	Oth stimulant dependence w/ stimulant-induced sleep d/o
F15.23	Oth stimulant dependence w/ withdrawal
F15.20	Oth stimulant dependence, uncomplicated
F15.921	Oth stimulant use, unsp w/ intoxication delirium
F15.950	Oth stimulant use, unsp w/ stimulant-induced psychotic d/o w/ delusions
F15.951	Oth stimulant use, unsp w/ stimulant-induced psychotic d/o w/ hallucinations
F15.93	Oth stimulant use, unsp w/ withdrawal
M00.272	Oth streptococcal arthritis, lt ankle & foot
M00.222	Oth streptococcal arthritis, lt elbow
M00.242	Oth streptococcal arthritis, lt hand
M00.252	Oth streptococcal arthritis, lt hip
M00.262	Oth streptococcal arthritis, lt knee
M00.212	Oth streptococcal arthritis, lt shldr
M00.232	Oth streptococcal arthritis, lt wrist
M00.271	Oth streptococcal arthritis, rt ankle & foot
M00.221	Oth streptococcal arthritis, rt elbow
M00.241	Oth streptococcal arthritis, rt hand
M00.251	Oth streptococcal arthritis, rt hip
M00.261	Oth streptococcal arthritis, rt knee
M00.211	Oth streptococcal arthritis, rt shldr
M00.231	Oth streptococcal arthritis, rt wrist
M00.279	Oth streptococcal arthritis, unsp ankle & foot
M00.229	Oth streptococcal arthritis, unsp elbow
M00.249	Oth streptococcal arthritis, unsp hand
M00.259	Oth streptococcal arthritis, unsp hip
M00.20	Oth streptococcal arthritis, unsp jt

M00.269	Oth streptococcal arthritis, unsp knee
M00.219	Oth streptococcal arthritis, unsp shldr
M00.239	Oth streptococcal arthritis, unsp wrist
M00.28	Oth streptococcal arthritis, vertebrae
M00.29	Oth streptococcal polyarthritis
A52.79	Oth symptomatic late syphilis
A52.19	Oth symptomatic neurosyphilis
A52.06	Oth syphilitic heart involvement
D68.69	Oth thrombophilia
B58.09	Oth toxoplasma oculopathy
J95.09	Oth tracheostomy comp
G45.8	Oth transient cerebral ischemic attacks & related syndromes
P61.6	Oth transient neonatal d/o of coagulation
P70.8	Oth transitory d/o of carbohydrate metabolism of newborn
P74.8	Oth transitory metabolic disturbances of newborn
P71.8	Oth transitory neonatal d/o of calcium & magnesium metabolism
P72.2	Oth transitory neonatal d/o of thyroid function, NEC
T86.891	Oth transplanted tissue failure
T86.892	Oth transplanted tissue infxn
T86.890	Oth transplanted tissue rejection
S12.150A	Oth traum disp spondylolisthesis of 2nd cervical vertebra, init enc for clsd fx
S12.150K	Oth traum disp spondylolisthesis of 2nd cervical vertebra, subsq enc for fx w/ nonu
S12.250A	Oth traum disp spondylolisthesis of 3rd cervical vertebra, init enc for clsd fx
S12.250K	Oth traum disp spondylolisthesis of 3rd cervical vertebra, subsq enc for fx w/ nonu
S12.350A	Oth traum disp spondylolisthesis of 4th cervical vertebra, init enc for clsd fx
S12.350K	Oth traum disp spondylolisthesis of 4th cervical vertebra, subsq enc for fx w/ nonu
S12.450A	Oth traum disp spondylolisthesis of 5th cervical vertebra, init enc for clsd fx
S12.450K	Oth traum disp spondylolisthesis of 5th cervical vertebra, subsq enc for fx w/ nonu
S12.550A	Oth traum disp spondylolisthesis of 6th cervical vertebra, init enc for clsd fx
S12.550K	Oth traum disp spondylolisthesis of 6th cervical vertebra, subsq enc for fx w/ nonu
S12.650A	Oth traum disp spondylolisthesis of 7th cervical vertebra, init enc for clsd fx
S12.650K	Oth traum disp spondylolisthesis of 7th cervical vertebra, subsq enc for fx w/ nonu
S12.151A	Oth traum nondisp spondylolisthesis of 2nd cervical vertebra, init enc for clsd fx
S12.151K	Oth traum nondisp spondylolisthesis of 2nd cervical vertebra, subsq enc for fx w/ nonu
S12.251A	Oth traum nondisp spondylolisthesis of 3rd cervical vertebra, init enc for clsd fx
S12.251K	Oth traum nondisp spondylolisthesis of 3rd cervical vertebra, subsq enc for fx w/ nonu
S12.351A	Oth traum nondisp spondylolisthesis of 4th cervical vertebra, init enc for clsd fx
S12.351K	Oth traum nondisp spondylolisthesis of 4th cervical vertebra, subsq enc for fx w/ nonu
S12.451A	Oth traum nondisp spondylolisthesis of 5th cervical vertebra, init enc for clsd fx
S12.451K	Oth traum nondisp spondylolisthesis of 5th cervical vertebra, subsq enc for fx w/ nonu
S12.551A	Oth traum nondisp spondylolisthesis of 6th cervical vertebra, init enc for clsd fx
S12.551K	Oth traum nondisp spondylolisthesis of 6th cervical vertebra, subsq enc for fx w/ nonu
S12.651A	Oth traum nondisp spondylolisthesis of 7th cervical vertebra, init enc for clsd fx
S12.651K	Oth traum nondisp spondylolisthesis of 7th cervical vertebra, subsq enc for fx w/ nonu
A18.59	Oth tuberculosis of eye
C82.89	Oth types of follicular lymphoma, extranodal & solid organ sites
C82.83	Oth types of follicular lymphoma, intra-abd lymph nodes
C82.86	Oth types of follicular lymphoma, intrapelvic lymph nodes
C82.82	Oth types of follicular lymphoma, intrathoracic lymph nodes
C82.84	Oth types of follicular lymphoma, lymph nodes of axilla & upr limb
C82.81	Oth types of follicular lymphoma, lymph nodes of head, face, & neck
C82.85	Oth types of follicular lymphoma, lymph nodes of inguinal rgn & lwr limb
C82.88	Oth types of follicular lymphoma, lymph nodes of multi sites
C82.87	Oth types of follicular lymphoma, spleen
C82.80	Oth types of follicular lymphoma, unsp site
K51.814	Oth ulcerative colitis w/ abscess
K51.813	Oth ulcerative colitis w/ fistula
K51.812	Oth ulcerative colitis w/ intestinal obstruction
K51.818	Oth ulcerative colitis w/ oth comp
K51.811	Oth ulcerative colitis w/ rectal bleeding
K51.819	Oth ulcerative colitis w/ unsp comp
K51.80	Oth ulcerative colitis w/o comp
O86.29	Oth urinary tract infxn following delivery
B37.49	Oth urogenital candidiasis
B01.89	Oth varicella comp
K55.8	Oth vascular d/o of intestine
O04.85	Oth venous comp following (induced) termination of pregnancy
O08.7	Oth venous comp following an ectopic & molar pregnancy
O03.85	Oth venous comp following complete or unsp spontaneous abortion
O07.35	Oth venous comp following failed attempted termination of pregnancy
O03.35	Oth venous comp following incomplete spontaneous abortion
O22.8X1	Oth venous comp in pregnancy, 1st trmstr
O22.8X2	Oth venous comp in pregnancy, 2nd trmstr
O22.8X3	Oth venous comp in pregnancy, 3rd trmstr
O22.8X9	Oth venous comp in pregnancy, unsp trmstr
O87.8	Oth venous comp in the puerperium
A69.1	Oth Vincent's infections
O98.52	Oth viral diseases comp childbirth
O98.511	Oth viral diseases comp pregnancy, 1st trmstr
O98.512	Oth viral diseases comp pregnancy, 2nd trmstr
O98.513	Oth viral diseases comp pregnancy, 3rd trmstr
O98.53	Oth viral diseases comp the puerperium
A08.39	Oth viral enteritis
A87.8	Oth viral meningitis
E71.528	Oth X-linked adrenoleukodystrophy
O00.2	Ovarian pregnancy
T84.84XA	Pain d/t int orthopedic prosthetic devices, implants & grafts, init enc
T85.84XA	Pain d/t int prosthetic devices, implants & grafts, NEC, init enc
T82.847A	Pain from cardiac prosthetic devices, implants & grafts, init enc
T83.84XA	Pain from genitourinary prosthetic devices, implants & grafts, init enc
T82.848A	Pain from vascular prosthetic devices, implants & grafts, init enc
Z94.83	Pancreas transplant status
K90.3	Pancreatic steatorrhea
H44.013	Panophthalmitis (acute), bilat
H44.012	Panophthalmitis (acute), lt eye
H44.011	Panophthalmitis (acute), rt eye
H44.019	Panophthalmitis (acute), unsp eye
H44.113	Panuveitis, bilat
H44.112	Panuveitis, lt eye
H44.111	Panuveitis, rt eye
H44.119	Panuveitis, unsp eye
H47.11	Papilledema associated w/ increased intracranial pressure
B41.9	Paracoccidioidomycosis, unsp
B66.4	Paragonimiasis
K56.0	Paralytic ileus
L10.81	Paraneoplastic pemphigus
F20.0	Paranoid schizophrenia
G82.21	Paraplegia, complete
G82.22	Paraplegia, incomplete
G82.20	Paraplegia, unsp
H21.333	Parasitic cyst of iris, ciliary body or ant chamber, bilat
H21.332	Parasitic cyst of iris, ciliary body or ant chamber, lt eye
H21.331	Parasitic cyst of iris, ciliary body or ant chamber, rt eye
H21.339	Parasitic cyst of iris, ciliary body or ant chamber, unsp eye
H33.123	Parasitic cyst of retina, bilat
H33.122	Parasitic cyst of retina, lt eye
H33.121	Parasitic cyst of retina, rt eye
H33.129	Parasitic cyst of retina, unsp eye
H44.123	Parasitic endophthalmitis, unsp, bilat
H44.122	Parasitic endophthalmitis, unsp, lt eye
H44.121	Parasitic endophthalmitis, unsp, rt eye
H44.129	Parasitic endophthalmitis, unsp, unsp eye
K43.3	Parastomal hernia w/ obstruction, w/o gangrene
A01.1	Paratyphoid fever A
A01.2	Paratyphoid fever B

A01.3	Paratyphoid fever C	M84.575A	Path fx in neoplastic disease, lt foot, init enc for fx
A01.4	Paratyphoid fever, unsp	M84.575P	Path fx in neoplastic disease, lt foot, subsq enc for fx w/ malu
Q26.3	Partial anomalous pulmn venous connection	M84.575K	Path fx in neoplastic disease, lt foot, subsq enc for fx w/ nonu
H34.213	Partial retinal artery occlsn, bilat	M84.542A	Path fx in neoplastic disease, lt hand, init enc for fx
H34.212	Partial retinal artery occlsn, lt eye	M84.542P	Path fx in neoplastic disease, lt hand, subsq enc for fx w/ malu
H34.211	Partial retinal artery occlsn, rt eye	M84.542K	Path fx in neoplastic disease, lt hand, subsq enc for fx w/ nonu
H34.219	Partial retinal artery occlsn, unsp eye	M84.522A	Path fx in neoplastic disease, lt humerus, init enc for fx
S58.022A	Partial traum amp at elbow lvl, lt arm, init enc	M84.522P	Path fx in neoplastic disease, lt humerus, subsq enc for fx w/ malu
S58.021A	Partial traum amp at elbow lvl, rt arm, init enc	M84.522K	Path fx in neoplastic disease, lt humerus, subsq enc for fx w/ nonu
S58.029A	Partial traum amp at elbow lvl, unsp arm, init enc	M84.534A	Path fx in neoplastic disease, lt radius, init enc for fx
S88.022A	Partial traum amp at knee lvl, lt lwr leg, init enc	M84.534P	Path fx in neoplastic disease, lt radius, subsq enc for fx w/ malu
S88.021A	Partial traum amp at knee lvl, rt lwr leg, init enc	M84.534K	Path fx in neoplastic disease, lt radius, subsq enc for fx w/ nonu
S88.029A	Partial traum amp at knee lvl, unsp lwr leg, init enc	M84.512A	Path fx in neoplastic disease, lt shldr, init enc for fx
S78.022A	Partial traum amp at lt hip jt, init enc	M84.512P	Path fx in neoplastic disease, lt shldr, subsq enc for fx w/ malu
S48.022A	Partial traum amp at lt shldr jt, init enc	M84.512K	Path fx in neoplastic disease, lt shldr, subsq enc for fx w/ nonu
S58.122A	Partial traum amp at lvl between elbow & wrist, lt arm, init enc	M84.562A	Path fx in neoplastic disease, lt tibia, init enc for fx
S58.121A	Partial traum amp at lvl between elbow & wrist, rt arm, init enc	M84.562P	Path fx in neoplastic disease, lt tibia, subsq enc for fx w/ malu
S58.129A	Partial traum amp at lvl between elbow & wrist, unsp arm, init enc	M84.562K	Path fx in neoplastic disease, lt tibia, subsq enc for fx w/ nonu
S88.122A	Partial traum amp at lvl between knee & ankle, lt lwr leg, init enc	M84.532A	Path fx in neoplastic disease, lt ulna, init enc for fx
S88.121A	Partial traum amp at lvl between knee & ankle, rt lwr leg, init enc	M84.532P	Path fx in neoplastic disease, lt ulna, subsq enc for fx w/ malu
S88.129A	Partial traum amp at lvl between knee & ankle, unsp lwr leg, init enc	M84.532K	Path fx in neoplastic disease, lt ulna, subsq enc for fx w/ nonu
S78.122A	Partial traum amp at lvl between lt hip & knee, init enc	M84.58XA	Path fx in neoplastic disease, oth spec site, init enc for fx
S48.122A	Partial traum amp at lvl between lt shldr & elbow, init enc	M84.58XP	Path fx in neoplastic disease, oth spec site, subsq enc for fx w/ malu
S78.121A	Partial traum amp at lvl between rt hip & knee, init enc	M84.58XK	Path fx in neoplastic disease, oth spec site, subsq enc for fx w/ nonu
S48.121A	Partial traum amp at lvl between rt shldr & elbow, init enc	M84.550A	Path fx in neoplastic disease, pelvis, init enc for fx
S78.129A	Partial traum amp at lvl between unsp hip & knee, init enc	M84.550P	Path fx in neoplastic disease, pelvis, subsq enc for fx w/ malu
S48.129A	Partial traum amp at lvl between unsp shldr & elbow, init enc	M84.550K	Path fx in neoplastic disease, pelvis, subsq enc for fx w/ nonu
S78.021A	Partial traum amp at rt hip jt, init enc	M84.571A	Path fx in neoplastic disease, rt ankle, init enc for fx
S48.021A	Partial traum amp at rt shldr jt, init enc	M84.571P	Path fx in neoplastic disease, rt ankle, subsq enc for fx w/ malu
S78.029A	Partial traum amp at unsp hip jt, init enc	M84.571K	Path fx in neoplastic disease, rt ankle, subsq enc for fx w/ nonu
S48.029A	Partial traum amp at unsp shldr jt, init enc	M84.551A	Path fx in neoplastic disease, rt femur, init enc for fx
S98.022A	Partial traum amp of lt foot at ankle lvl, init enc	M84.551P	Path fx in neoplastic disease, rt femur, subsq enc for fx w/ malu
S98.922A	Partial traum amp of lt foot, lvl unsp, init enc	M84.551K	Path fx in neoplastic disease, rt femur, subsq enc for fx w/ nonu
S58.922A	Partial traum amp of lt forearm, lvl unsp, init enc	M84.563A	Path fx in neoplastic disease, rt fibula, init enc for fx
S68.422A	Partial traum amp of lt hand at wrist lvl, init enc	M84.563P	Path fx in neoplastic disease, rt fibula, subsq enc for fx w/ malu
S78.922A	Partial traum amp of lt hip & thigh, lvl unsp, init enc	M84.563K	Path fx in neoplastic disease, rt fibula, subsq enc for fx w/ nonu
S88.922A	Partial traum amp of lt lwr leg, lvl unsp, init enc	M84.574A	Path fx in neoplastic disease, rt foot, init enc for fx
S98.322A	Partial traum amp of lt midfoot, init enc	M84.574P	Path fx in neoplastic disease, rt foot, subsq enc for fx w/ malu
S48.922A	Partial traum amp of lt shldr & upr arm, lvl unsp, init enc	M84.574K	Path fx in neoplastic disease, rt foot, subsq enc for fx w/ nonu
S98.021A	Partial traum amp of rt foot at ankle lvl, init enc	M84.541A	Path fx in neoplastic disease, rt hand, init enc for fx
S98.921A	Partial traum amp of rt foot, lvl unsp, init enc	M84.541P	Path fx in neoplastic disease, rt hand, subsq enc for fx w/ malu
S58.921A	Partial traum amp of rt forearm, lvl unsp, init enc	M84.541K	Path fx in neoplastic disease, rt hand, subsq enc for fx w/ nonu
S68.421A	Partial traum amp of rt hand at wrist lvl, init enc	M84.521A	Path fx in neoplastic disease, rt humerus, init enc for fx
S78.921A	Partial traum amp of rt hip & thigh, lvl unsp, init enc	M84.521P	Path fx in neoplastic disease, rt humerus, subsq enc for fx w/ malu
S88.921A	Partial traum amp of rt lwr leg, lvl unsp, init enc	M84.521K	Path fx in neoplastic disease, rt humerus, subsq enc for fx w/ nonu
S98.321A	Partial traum amp of rt midfoot, init enc	M84.533A	Path fx in neoplastic disease, rt radius, init enc for fx
S48.921A	Partial traum amp of rt shldr & upr arm, lvl unsp, init enc	M84.533P	Path fx in neoplastic disease, rt radius, subsq enc for fx w/ malu
S98.029A	Partial traum amp of unsp foot at ankle lvl, init enc	M84.533K	Path fx in neoplastic disease, rt radius, subsq enc for fx w/ nonu
S98.929A	Partial traum amp of unsp foot, lvl unsp, init enc	M84.511A	Path fx in neoplastic disease, rt shldr, init enc for fx
S58.929A	Partial traum amp of unsp forearm, lvl unsp, init enc	M84.511P	Path fx in neoplastic disease, rt shldr, subsq enc for fx w/ malu
S68.429A	Partial traum amp of unsp hand at wrist lvl, init enc	M84.511K	Path fx in neoplastic disease, rt shldr, subsq enc for fx w/ nonu
S78.929A	Partial traum amp of unsp hip & thigh, lvl unsp, init enc	M84.561A	Path fx in neoplastic disease, rt tibia, init enc for fx
S88.929A	Partial traum amp of unsp lwr leg, lvl unsp, init enc	M84.561P	Path fx in neoplastic disease, rt tibia, subsq enc for fx w/ malu
S98.329A	Partial traum amp of unsp midfoot, init enc	M84.561K	Path fx in neoplastic disease, rt tibia, subsq enc for fx w/ nonu
S48.929A	Partial traum amp of unsp shldr & upr arm, lvl unsp, init enc	M84.531A	Path fx in neoplastic disease, rt ulna, init enc for fx
S68.722A	Partial traum transmetacarpal amp of lt hand, init enc	M84.531P	Path fx in neoplastic disease, rt ulna, subsq enc for fx w/ malu
S68.721A	Partial traum transmetacarpal amp of rt hand, init enc	M84.531K	Path fx in neoplastic disease, rt ulna, subsq enc for fx w/ nonu
S68.729A	Partial traum transmetacarpal amp of unsp hand, init enc	M84.573A	Path fx in neoplastic disease, unsp ankle, init enc for fx
B34.3	Parvovirus infxn, unsp	M84.573P	Path fx in neoplastic disease, unsp ankle, subsq enc for fx w/ malu
A28.0	Pasteurellosis	M84.573K	Path fx in neoplastic disease, unsp ankle, subsq enc for fx w/ nonu
Q25.0	Patent ductus arteriosus	M84.553A	Path fx in neoplastic disease, unsp femur, init enc for fx
M84.559A	Path fx in neoplastic disease, hip, unsp, init enc for fx	M84.553P	Path fx in neoplastic disease, unsp femur, subsq enc for fx w/ malu
M84.559P	Path fx in neoplastic disease, hip, unsp, subsq enc for fx w/ malu	M84.553K	Path fx in neoplastic disease, unsp femur, subsq enc for fx w/ nonu
M84.559K	Path fx in neoplastic disease, hip, unsp, subsq enc for fx w/ nonu	M84.576A	Path fx in neoplastic disease, unsp foot, init enc for fx
M84.572A	Path fx in neoplastic disease, lt ankle, init enc for fx	M84.576P	Path fx in neoplastic disease, unsp foot, subsq enc for fx w/ malu
M84.572P	Path fx in neoplastic disease, lt ankle, subsq enc for fx w/ malu	M84.576K	Path fx in neoplastic disease, unsp foot, subsq enc for fx w/ nonu
M84.572K	Path fx in neoplastic disease, lt ankle, subsq enc for fx w/ nonu	M84.549A	Path fx in neoplastic disease, unsp hand, init enc for fx
M84.552A	Path fx in neoplastic disease, lt femur, init enc for fx	M84.549P	Path fx in neoplastic disease, unsp hand, subsq enc for fx w/ malu
M84.552P	Path fx in neoplastic disease, lt femur, subsq enc for fx w/ malu	M84.549K	Path fx in neoplastic disease, unsp hand, subsq enc for fx w/ nonu
M84.552K	Path fx in neoplastic disease, lt femur, subsq enc for fx w/ nonu	M84.529A	Path fx in neoplastic disease, unsp humerus, init enc for fx
M84.564A	Path fx in neoplastic disease, lt fibula, init enc for fx	M84.529P	Path fx in neoplastic disease, unsp humerus, subsq enc for fx w/ malu
M84.564P	Path fx in neoplastic disease, lt fibula, subsq enc for fx w/ malu	M84.529K	Path fx in neoplastic disease, unsp humerus, subsq enc for fx w/ nonu
M84.564K	Path fx in neoplastic disease, lt fibula, subsq enc for fx w/ nonu	M84.519A	Path fx in neoplastic disease, unsp shldr, init enc for fx

© 2015 Optum360, LLC

Code	Description
M84.519P	Path fx in neoplastic disease, unsp shldr, subsq enc for fx w/ malu
M84.519K	Path fx in neoplastic disease, unsp shldr, subsq enc for fx w/ nonu
M84.50XA	Path fx in neoplastic disease, unsp site, init enc for fx
M84.50XP	Path fx in neoplastic disease, unsp site, subsq enc for fx w/ malu
M84.50XK	Path fx in neoplastic disease, unsp site, subsq enc for fx w/ nonu
M84.569A	Path fx in neoplastic disease, unsp tibia & fibula, init enc for fx
M84.569P	Path fx in neoplastic disease, unsp tibia & fibula, subsq enc for fx w/ malu
M84.569K	Path fx in neoplastic disease, unsp tibia & fibula, subsq enc for fx w/ nonu
M84.539A	Path fx in neoplastic disease, unsp ulna & radius, init enc for fx
M84.539P	Path fx in neoplastic disease, unsp ulna & radius, subsq enc for fx w/ malu
M84.539K	Path fx in neoplastic disease, unsp ulna & radius, subsq enc for fx w/ nonu
M84.659A	Path fx in oth disease, hip, unsp, init enc for fx
M84.659P	Path fx in oth disease, hip, unsp, subsq enc for fx w/ malu
M84.659K	Path fx in oth disease, hip, unsp, subsq enc for fx w/ nonu
M84.672A	Path fx in oth disease, lt ankle, init enc for fx
M84.672P	Path fx in oth disease, lt ankle, subsq enc for fx w/ malu
M84.672K	Path fx in oth disease, lt ankle, subsq enc for fx w/ nonu
M84.652A	Path fx in oth disease, lt femur, init enc for fx
M84.652P	Path fx in oth disease, lt femur, subsq enc for fx w/ malu
M84.652K	Path fx in oth disease, lt femur, subsq enc for fx w/ nonu
M84.664A	Path fx in oth disease, lt fibula, init enc for fx
M84.664P	Path fx in oth disease, lt fibula, subsq enc for fx w/ malu
M84.664K	Path fx in oth disease, lt fibula, subsq enc for fx w/ nonu
M84.675A	Path fx in oth disease, lt foot, init enc for fx
M84.675P	Path fx in oth disease, lt foot, subsq enc for fx w/ malu
M84.675K	Path fx in oth disease, lt foot, subsq enc for fx w/ nonu
M84.642A	Path fx in oth disease, lt hand, init enc for fx
M84.642P	Path fx in oth disease, lt hand, subsq enc for fx w/ malu
M84.642K	Path fx in oth disease, lt hand, subsq enc for fx w/ nonu
M84.622A	Path fx in oth disease, lt humerus, init enc for fx
M84.622P	Path fx in oth disease, lt humerus, subsq enc for fx w/ malu
M84.622K	Path fx in oth disease, lt humerus, subsq enc for fx w/ nonu
M84.634A	Path fx in oth disease, lt radius, init enc for fx
M84.634P	Path fx in oth disease, lt radius, subsq enc for fx w/ malu
M84.634K	Path fx in oth disease, lt radius, subsq enc for fx w/ nonu
M84.612A	Path fx in oth disease, lt shldr, init enc for fx
M84.612P	Path fx in oth disease, lt shldr, subsq enc for fx w/ malu
M84.612K	Path fx in oth disease, lt shldr, subsq enc for fx w/ nonu
M84.662A	Path fx in oth disease, lt tibia, init enc for fx
M84.662P	Path fx in oth disease, lt tibia, subsq enc for fx w/ malu
M84.662K	Path fx in oth disease, lt tibia, subsq enc for fx w/ nonu
M84.632A	Path fx in oth disease, lt ulna, init enc for fx
M84.632P	Path fx in oth disease, lt ulna, subsq enc for fx w/ malu
M84.632K	Path fx in oth disease, lt ulna, subsq enc for fx w/ nonu
M84.68XA	Path fx in oth disease, oth site, init enc for fx
M84.68XP	Path fx in oth disease, oth site, subsq enc for fx w/ malu
M84.68XK	Path fx in oth disease, oth site, subsq enc for fx w/ nonu
M84.650A	Path fx in oth disease, pelvis, init enc for fx
M84.650P	Path fx in oth disease, pelvis, subsq enc for fx w/ malu
M84.650K	Path fx in oth disease, pelvis, subsq enc for fx w/ nonu
M84.671A	Path fx in oth disease, rt ankle, init enc for fx
M84.671P	Path fx in oth disease, rt ankle, subsq enc for fx w/ malu
M84.671K	Path fx in oth disease, rt ankle, subsq enc for fx w/ nonu
M84.651A	Path fx in oth disease, rt femur, init enc for fx
M84.651P	Path fx in oth disease, rt femur, subsq enc for fx w/ malu
M84.651K	Path fx in oth disease, rt femur, subsq enc for fx w/ nonu
M84.663A	Path fx in oth disease, rt fibula, init enc for fx
M84.663P	Path fx in oth disease, rt fibula, subsq enc for fx w/ malu
M84.663K	Path fx in oth disease, rt fibula, subsq enc for fx w/ nonu
M84.674A	Path fx in oth disease, rt foot, init enc for fx
M84.674P	Path fx in oth disease, rt foot, subsq enc for fx w/ malu
M84.674K	Path fx in oth disease, rt foot, subsq enc for fx w/ nonu
M84.641A	Path fx in oth disease, rt hand, init enc for fx
M84.641P	Path fx in oth disease, rt hand, subsq enc for fx w/ malu
M84.641K	Path fx in oth disease, rt hand, subsq enc for fx w/ nonu
M84.621A	Path fx in oth disease, rt humerus, init enc for fx
M84.621P	Path fx in oth disease, rt humerus, subsq enc for fx w/ malu
M84.621K	Path fx in oth disease, rt humerus, subsq enc for fx w/ nonu
M84.633A	Path fx in oth disease, rt radius, init enc for fx
M84.633P	Path fx in oth disease, rt radius, subsq enc for fx w/ malu
M84.633K	Path fx in oth disease, rt radius, subsq enc for fx w/ nonu
M84.611A	Path fx in oth disease, rt shldr, init enc for fx
M84.611P	Path fx in oth disease, rt shldr, subsq enc for fx w/ malu
M84.611K	Path fx in oth disease, rt shldr, subsq enc for fx w/ nonu
M84.661A	Path fx in oth disease, rt tibia, init enc for fx
M84.661P	Path fx in oth disease, rt tibia, subsq enc for fx w/ malu
M84.661K	Path fx in oth disease, rt tibia, subsq enc for fx w/ nonu
M84.631A	Path fx in oth disease, rt ulna, init enc for fx
M84.631P	Path fx in oth disease, rt ulna, subsq enc for fx w/ malu
M84.631K	Path fx in oth disease, rt ulna, subsq enc for fx w/ nonu
M84.673A	Path fx in oth disease, unsp ankle, init enc for fx
M84.673P	Path fx in oth disease, unsp ankle, subsq enc for fx w/ malu
M84.673K	Path fx in oth disease, unsp ankle, subsq enc for fx w/ nonu
M84.653A	Path fx in oth disease, unsp femur, init enc for fx
M84.653P	Path fx in oth disease, unsp femur, subsq enc for fx w/ malu
M84.653K	Path fx in oth disease, unsp femur, subsq enc for fx w/ nonu
M84.676A	Path fx in oth disease, unsp foot, init enc for fx
M84.676P	Path fx in oth disease, unsp foot, subsq enc for fx w/ malu
M84.676K	Path fx in oth disease, unsp foot, subsq enc for fx w/ nonu
M84.649A	Path fx in oth disease, unsp hand, init enc for fx
M84.649P	Path fx in oth disease, unsp hand, subsq enc for fx w/ malu
M84.649K	Path fx in oth disease, unsp hand, subsq enc for fx w/ nonu
M84.629A	Path fx in oth disease, unsp humerus, init enc for fx
M84.629P	Path fx in oth disease, unsp humerus, subsq enc for fx w/ malu
M84.629K	Path fx in oth disease, unsp humerus, subsq enc for fx w/ nonu
M84.619A	Path fx in oth disease, unsp shldr, init enc for fx
M84.619P	Path fx in oth disease, unsp shldr, subsq enc for fx w/ malu
M84.619K	Path fx in oth disease, unsp shldr, subsq enc for fx w/ nonu
M84.60XA	Path fx in oth disease, unsp site, init enc for fx
M84.60XP	Path fx in oth disease, unsp site, subsq enc for fx w/ malu
M84.60XK	Path fx in oth disease, unsp site, subsq enc for fx w/ nonu
M84.669A	Path fx in oth disease, unsp tibia & fibula, init enc for fx
M84.669P	Path fx in oth disease, unsp tibia & fibula, subsq enc for fx w/ malu
M84.669K	Path fx in oth disease, unsp tibia & fibula, subsq enc for fx w/ nonu
M84.639A	Path fx in oth disease, unsp ulna & radius, init enc for fx
M84.639P	Path fx in oth disease, unsp ulna & radius, subsq enc for fx w/ malu
M84.639K	Path fx in oth disease, unsp ulna & radius, subsq enc for fx w/ nonu
M84.459A	Path fx, hip, unsp, init enc for fx
M84.459P	Path fx, hip, unsp, subsq enc for fx w/ malu
M84.459K	Path fx, hip, unsp, subsq enc for fx w/ nonu
M84.472A	Path fx, lt ankle, init enc for fx
M84.472P	Path fx, lt ankle, subsq enc for fx w/ malu
M84.472K	Path fx, lt ankle, subsq enc for fx w/ nonu
M84.452A	Path fx, lt femur, init enc for fx
M84.452P	Path fx, lt femur, subsq enc for fx w/ malu
M84.452K	Path fx, lt femur, subsq enc for fx w/ nonu
M84.464A	Path fx, lt fibula, init enc for fx
M84.464P	Path fx, lt fibula, subsq enc for fx w/ malu
M84.464K	Path fx, lt fibula, subsq enc for fx w/ nonu
M84.445A	Path fx, lt finger(s), init enc for fx
M84.445P	Path fx, lt finger(s), subsq enc for fx w/ malu
M84.445K	Path fx, lt finger(s), subsq enc for fx w/ nonu
M84.475A	Path fx, lt foot, init enc for fx
M84.475P	Path fx, lt foot, subsq enc for fx w/ malu
M84.475K	Path fx, lt foot, subsq enc for fx w/ nonu
M84.442A	Path fx, lt hand, init enc for fx
M84.442P	Path fx, lt hand, subsq enc for fx w/ malu
M84.442K	Path fx, lt hand, subsq enc for fx w/ nonu
M84.422A	Path fx, lt humerus, init enc for fx
M84.422P	Path fx, lt humerus, subsq enc for fx w/ malu
M84.422K	Path fx, lt humerus, subsq enc for fx w/ nonu
M84.434A	Path fx, lt radius, init enc for fx
M84.434P	Path fx, lt radius, subsq enc for fx w/ malu
M84.434K	Path fx, lt radius, subsq enc for fx w/ nonu
M84.412A	Path fx, lt shldr, init enc for fx
M84.412P	Path fx, lt shldr, subsq enc for fx w/ malu
M84.412K	Path fx, lt shldr, subsq enc for fx w/ nonu
M84.462A	Path fx, lt tibia, init enc for fx
M84.462P	Path fx, lt tibia, subsq enc for fx w/ malu
M84.462K	Path fx, lt tibia, subsq enc for fx w/ nonu
M84.478A	Path fx, lt toe(s), init enc for fx
M84.478P	Path fx, lt toe(s), subsq enc for fx w/ malu
M84.478K	Path fx, lt toe(s), subsq enc for fx w/ nonu
M84.432A	Path fx, lt ulna, init enc for fx
M84.432P	Path fx, lt ulna, subsq enc for fx w/ malu

Code	Description
M84.432K	Path fx, lt ulna, subsq enc for fx w/ nonu
M84.48XA	Path fx, oth site, init enc for fx
M84.48XP	Path fx, oth site, subsq enc for fx w/ malu
M84.48XK	Path fx, oth site, subsq enc for fx w/ nonu
M84.454A	Path fx, pelvis, init enc for fx
M84.454P	Path fx, pelvis, subsq enc for fx w/ malu
M84.454K	Path fx, pelvis, subsq enc for fx w/ nonu
M84.471A	Path fx, rt ankle, init enc for fx
M84.471P	Path fx, rt ankle, subsq enc for fx w/ malu
M84.471K	Path fx, rt ankle, subsq enc for fx w/ nonu
M84.451A	Path fx, rt femur, init enc for fx
M84.451P	Path fx, rt femur, subsq enc for fx w/ malu
M84.451K	Path fx, rt femur, subsq enc for fx w/ nonu
M84.463A	Path fx, rt fibula, init enc for fx
M84.463P	Path fx, rt fibula, subsq enc for fx w/ malu
M84.463K	Path fx, rt fibula, subsq enc for fx w/ nonu
M84.444A	Path fx, rt finger(s), init enc for fx
M84.444P	Path fx, rt finger(s), subsq enc for fx w/ malu
M84.444K	Path fx, rt finger(s), subsq enc for fx w/ nonu
M84.474A	Path fx, rt foot, init enc for fx
M84.474P	Path fx, rt foot, subsq enc for fx w/ malu
M84.474K	Path fx, rt foot, subsq enc for fx w/ nonu
M84.441A	Path fx, rt hand, init enc for fx
M84.441P	Path fx, rt hand, subsq enc for fx w/ malu
M84.441K	Path fx, rt hand, subsq enc for fx w/ nonu
M84.421A	Path fx, rt humerus, init enc for fx
M84.421P	Path fx, rt humerus, subsq enc for fx w/ malu
M84.421K	Path fx, rt humerus, subsq enc for fx w/ nonu
M84.433A	Path fx, rt radius, init enc for fx
M84.433P	Path fx, rt radius, subsq enc for fx w/ malu
M84.433K	Path fx, rt radius, subsq enc for fx w/ nonu
M84.411A	Path fx, rt shldr, init enc for fx
M84.411P	Path fx, rt shldr, subsq enc for fx w/ malu
M84.411K	Path fx, rt shldr, subsq enc for fx w/ nonu
M84.461A	Path fx, rt tibia, init enc for fx
M84.461P	Path fx, rt tibia, subsq enc for fx w/ malu
M84.461K	Path fx, rt tibia, subsq enc for fx w/ nonu
M84.477A	Path fx, rt toe(s), init enc for fx
M84.477P	Path fx, rt toe(s), subsq enc for fx w/ malu
M84.477K	Path fx, rt toe(s), subsq enc for fx w/ nonu
M84.431A	Path fx, rt ulna, init enc for fx
M84.431P	Path fx, rt ulna, subsq enc for fx w/ malu
M84.431K	Path fx, rt ulna, subsq enc for fx w/ nonu
M84.473A	Path fx, unsp ankle, init enc for fx
M84.473P	Path fx, unsp ankle, subsq enc for fx w/ malu
M84.473K	Path fx, unsp ankle, subsq enc for fx w/ nonu
M84.453A	Path fx, unsp femur, init enc for fx
M84.453P	Path fx, unsp femur, subsq enc for fx w/ malu
M84.453K	Path fx, unsp femur, subsq enc for fx w/ nonu
M84.446A	Path fx, unsp finger(s), init enc for fx
M84.446P	Path fx, unsp finger(s), subsq enc for fx w/ malu
M84.446K	Path fx, unsp finger(s), subsq enc for fx w/ nonu
M84.476A	Path fx, unsp foot, init enc for fx
M84.476P	Path fx, unsp foot, subsq enc for fx w/ malu
M84.476K	Path fx, unsp foot, subsq enc for fx w/ nonu
M84.443A	Path fx, unsp hand, init enc for fx
M84.443P	Path fx, unsp hand, subsq enc for fx w/ malu
M84.443K	Path fx, unsp hand, subsq enc for fx w/ nonu
M84.429A	Path fx, unsp humerus, init enc for fx
M84.429P	Path fx, unsp humerus, subsq enc for fx w/ malu
M84.429K	Path fx, unsp humerus, subsq enc for fx w/ nonu
M84.419A	Path fx, unsp shldr, init enc for fx
M84.419P	Path fx, unsp shldr, subsq enc for fx w/ malu
M84.419K	Path fx, unsp shldr, subsq enc for fx w/ nonu
M84.40XA	Path fx, unsp site, init enc for fx
M84.40XP	Path fx, unsp site, subsq enc for fx w/ malu
M84.40XK	Path fx, unsp site, subsq enc for fx w/ nonu
M84.469A	Path fx, unsp tibia & fibula, init enc for fx
M84.469P	Path fx, unsp tibia & fibula, subsq enc for fx w/ malu
M84.469K	Path fx, unsp tibia & fibula, subsq enc for fx w/ nonu
M84.479A	Path fx, unsp toe(s), init enc for fx
M84.479P	Path fx, unsp toe(s), subsq enc for fx w/ malu
M84.479K	Path fx, unsp toe(s), subsq enc for fx w/ nonu
M84.439A	Path fx, unsp ulna & radius, init enc for fx
M84.439P	Path fx, unsp ulna & radius, subsq enc for fx w/ malu
M84.439K	Path fx, unsp ulna & radius, subsq enc for fx w/ nonu
L12.9	Pemphigoid, unsp
L10.4	Pemphigus erythematosus
L10.2	Pemphigus foliaceous
L10.1	Pemphigus vegetans
L10.0	Pemphigus vulgaris
L10.9	Pemphigus, unsp
S05.42XA	Penetrating wnd of orbit w/ or w/o FB, lt eye, init enc
S05.41XA	Penetrating wnd of orbit w/ or w/o FB, rt eye, init enc
S05.40XA	Penetrating wnd of orbit w/ or w/o FB, unsp eye, init enc
S05.52XA	Penetrating wnd w/ FB of lt eyeball, init enc
S05.51XA	Penetrating wnd w/ FB of rt eyeball, init enc
S05.50XA	Penetrating wnd w/ FB of unsp eyeball, init enc
B48.4	Penicillosis
T81.536A	Perforation d/t FB accidentally lt in body following aspiration, punc or oth catheterization, init enc
T81.534A	Perforation d/t FB accidentally lt in body following endo exam, init enc
T81.535A	Perforation d/t FB accidentally lt in body following heart catheterization, init enc
T81.531A	Perforation d/t FB accidentally lt in body following inf or transfusion, init enc
T81.533A	Perforation d/t FB accidentally lt in body following injection or immunization, init enc
T81.532A	Perforation d/t FB accidentally lt in body following kidney dialysis, init enc
T81.538A	Perforation d/t FB accidentally lt in body following oth procedure, init enc
T81.537A	Perforation d/t FB accidentally lt in body following rmvl of catheter or packing, init enc
T81.530A	Perforation d/t FB accidentally lt in body following surg operation, init enc
T81.539A	Perforation d/t FB accidentally lt in body following unsp procedure, init enc
I31.3	Pericardial effusion (noninflammatory)
I32	Pericarditis in diseases classified elsw
M32.12	Pericarditis in systemic lupus erythematosus
R06.3	Periodic breathing
H05.033	Periostitis of bilat orbits
H05.032	Periostitis of lt orbit
H05.031	Periostitis of rt orbit
H05.039	Periostitis of unsp orbit
C84.49	Peripheral T-cell lymphoma, not classified, extranodal & solid organ sites
C84.43	Peripheral T-cell lymphoma, not classified, intra-abd lymph nodes
C84.46	Peripheral T-cell lymphoma, not classified, intrapelvic lymph nodes
C84.42	Peripheral T-cell lymphoma, not classified, intrathoracic lymph nodes
C84.44	Peripheral T-cell lymphoma, not classified, lymph nodes of axilla & upr limb
C84.41	Peripheral T-cell lymphoma, not classified, lymph nodes of head, face, & neck
C84.45	Peripheral T-cell lymphoma, not classified, lymph nodes of inguinal rgn & lwr limb
C84.48	Peripheral T-cell lymphoma, not classified, lymph nodes of multi sites
C84.47	Peripheral T-cell lymphoma, not classified, spleen
C84.40	Peripheral T-cell lymphoma, not classified, unsp site
T84.041A	Periprosthetic fx around int prosthetic lt hip jt, init enc
T84.043A	Periprosthetic fx around int prosthetic lt knee jt, init enc
T84.040A	Periprosthetic fx around int prosthetic rt hip jt, init enc
T84.042A	Periprosthetic fx around int prosthetic rt knee jt, init enc
T84.048A	Periprosthetic fx around oth int prosthetic jt, init enc
T84.049A	Periprosthetic fx around unsp int prosthetic jt, init enc
T84.051A	Periprosthetic osteolysis of int prosthetic lt hip jt, init enc
T84.053A	Periprosthetic osteolysis of int prosthetic lt knee jt, init enc
T84.050A	Periprosthetic osteolysis of int prosthetic rt hip jt, init enc
T84.052A	Periprosthetic osteolysis of int prosthetic rt knee jt, init enc
T84.058A	Periprosthetic osteolysis of oth int prosthetic jt, init enc
T84.059A	Periprosthetic osteolysis of unsp int prosthetic jt, init enc
J36	Peritonsillar abscess
E71.50	Peroxisomal d/o, unsp
I48.1	Persistent atrial fibrillation
Q43.7	Persistent cloaca
Q26.1	Persistent lt superior vena cava
G43.611	Persistent migraine aura w/ cerebral infarction, intractable, w/ status migrainosus

G43.619	Persistent migraine aura w/ cerebral infarction, intractable, w/o status migrainosus
G43.601	Persistent migraine aura w/ cerebral infarction, not intractable, w/ status migrainosus
G43.609	Persistent migraine aura w/ cerebral infarction, not intractable, w/o status migrainosus
F34.9	Persistent mood [affective] d/o, unsp
T81.83XA	Persistent postprocedural fistula, init enc
R40.3	Persistent vegetative state
F84.9	Pervasive developmental d/o, unsp
Q85.9	Phakomatosis, unsp
A36.0	Pharyngeal diphtheria
I80.13	Phlebitis & thrombophlebitis of femoral vein, bilat
I80.213	Phlebitis & thrombophlebitis of iliac vein, bilat
I80.12	Phlebitis & thrombophlebitis of lt femoral vein
I80.212	Phlebitis & thrombophlebitis of lt iliac vein
I80.222	Phlebitis & thrombophlebitis of lt popliteal vein
I80.232	Phlebitis & thrombophlebitis of lt tibial vein
I80.292	Phlebitis & thrombophlebitis of oth deep vessels of lt lwr extr
I80.293	Phlebitis & thrombophlebitis of oth deep vessels of lwr extr, bilat
I80.291	Phlebitis & thrombophlebitis of oth deep vessels of rt lwr extr
I80.299	Phlebitis & thrombophlebitis of oth deep vessels of unsp lwr extr
I80.223	Phlebitis & thrombophlebitis of popliteal vein, bilat
I80.11	Phlebitis & thrombophlebitis of rt femoral vein
I80.211	Phlebitis & thrombophlebitis of rt iliac vein
I80.221	Phlebitis & thrombophlebitis of rt popliteal vein
I80.231	Phlebitis & thrombophlebitis of rt tibial vein
I80.233	Phlebitis & thrombophlebitis of tibial vein, bilat
I80.202	Phlebitis & thrombophlebitis of unsp deep vessels of lt lwr extr
I80.203	Phlebitis & thrombophlebitis of unsp deep vessels of lwr extremities, bilat
I80.201	Phlebitis & thrombophlebitis of unsp deep vessels of rt lwr extr
I80.209	Phlebitis & thrombophlebitis of unsp deep vessels of unsp lwr extr
I80.10	Phlebitis & thrombophlebitis of unsp femoral vein
I80.219	Phlebitis & thrombophlebitis of unsp iliac vein
I80.229	Phlebitis & thrombophlebitis of unsp popliteal vein
I80.239	Phlebitis & thrombophlebitis of unsp tibial vein
L05.01	Pilonidal cyst w/ abscess
L05.02	Pilonidal sinus w/ abscess
E24.0	Pituitary-dependent Cushing's disease
O44.01	Placenta previa spec as w/o hemor, 1st trmstr
O44.02	Placenta previa spec as w/o hemor, 2nd trmstr
O44.03	Placenta previa spec as w/o hemor, 3rd trmstr
C90.12	Plasma cell leukemia in relapse
C90.11	Plasma cell leukemia in remission
C90.10	Plasma cell leukemia not having achieved remission
B50.0	Plasmodium falciparum malaria w/ cerebral comp
B52.0	Plasmodium malariae malaria w/ nephropathy
B52.8	Plasmodium malariae malaria w/ oth comp
B52.9	Plasmodium malariae malaria w/o comp
B53.0	Plasmodium ovale malaria
B51.8	Plasmodium vivax malaria w/ oth comp
B51.0	Plasmodium vivax malaria w/ rupture of spleen
B51.9	Plasmodium vivax malaria w/o comp
J91.8	Pleural effusion in oth conditions classified elsw
J90	Pleural effusion, NEC
M00.172	Pneumococcal arthritis, lt ankle & foot
M00.122	Pneumococcal arthritis, lt elbow
M00.142	Pneumococcal arthritis, lt hand
M00.152	Pneumococcal arthritis, lt hip
M00.162	Pneumococcal arthritis, lt knee
M00.112	Pneumococcal arthritis, lt shldr
M00.132	Pneumococcal arthritis, lt wrist
M00.171	Pneumococcal arthritis, rt ankle & foot
M00.121	Pneumococcal arthritis, rt elbow
M00.141	Pneumococcal arthritis, rt hand
M00.151	Pneumococcal arthritis, rt hip
M00.161	Pneumococcal arthritis, rt knee
M00.111	Pneumococcal arthritis, rt shldr
M00.131	Pneumococcal arthritis, rt wrist
M00.179	Pneumococcal arthritis, unsp ankle & foot
M00.129	Pneumococcal arthritis, unsp elbow
M00.149	Pneumococcal arthritis, unsp hand
M00.159	Pneumococcal arthritis, unsp hip
M00.10	Pneumococcal arthritis, unsp jt
M00.169	Pneumococcal arthritis, unsp knee
M00.119	Pneumococcal arthritis, unsp shldr
M00.139	Pneumococcal arthritis, unsp wrist
M00.18	Pneumococcal arthritis, vertebrae
M00.19	Pneumococcal polyarthritis
J93.9	Pneumothorax, unsp
M30.0	Polyarteritis nodosa
M30.1	Polyarteritis w/ lung involvement [Churg-Strauss]
M00.89	Polyarthritis d/t oth bacteria
Q61.2	Polycystic kidney, adult type
Q61.3	Polycystic kidney, unsp
M33.22	Polymyositis w/ myopathy
M33.29	Polymyositis w/ oth organ involvement
M33.21	Polymyositis w/ respiratory involvement
M33.20	Polymyositis, organ involvement unsp
E74.02	Pompe disease
E80.1	Porphyria cutanea tarda
K76.6	Portal hypertension
G46.2	Post cerebral artery synd
S73.015A	Post disloc of lt hip, init enc
S43.225A	Post disloc of lt sternoclavicular jt, init enc
S73.014A	Post disloc of rt hip, init enc
S43.224A	Post disloc of rt sternoclavicular jt, init enc
S73.016A	Post disloc of unsp hip, init enc
S43.226A	Post disloc of unsp sternoclavicular jt, init enc
S42.015B	Post disp fx of sternal end of lt clavicle, init enc for opn fx
S42.015P	Post disp fx of sternal end of lt clavicle, subsq enc for fx w/ malu
S42.015K	Post disp fx of sternal end of lt clavicle, subsq enc for fx w/ nonu
S42.014B	Post disp fx of sternal end of rt clavicle, init enc for opn fx
S42.014P	Post disp fx of sternal end of rt clavicle, subsq enc for fx w/ malu
S42.014K	Post disp fx of sternal end of rt clavicle, subsq enc for fx w/ nonu
S42.016B	Post disp fx of sternal end of unsp clavicle, init enc for opn fx
S42.016P	Post disp fx of sternal end of unsp clavicle, subsq enc for fx w/ malu
S42.016K	Post disp fx of sternal end of unsp clavicle, subsq enc for fx w/ nonu
S12.111A	Post disp Type II dens fx, init enc for clsd fx
S12.111K	Post disp Type II dens fx, subsq enc for fx w/ nonu
S73.012A	Post sublux of lt hip, init enc
S43.222A	Post sublux of lt sternoclavicular jt, init enc
S73.011A	Post sublux of rt hip, init enc
S43.221A	Post sublux of rt sternoclavicular jt, init enc
S73.013A	Post sublux of unsp hip, init enc
S43.223A	Post sublux of unsp sternoclavicular jt, init enc
R56.1	Post traum seizures
D47.Z1	Post-transplant lymphoproliferative d/o (PTLD)
G91.3	Post-traum hydrocephalus, unsp
M02.172	Postdysenteric arthropathy, lt ankle & foot
M02.122	Postdysenteric arthropathy, lt elbow
M02.142	Postdysenteric arthropathy, lt hand
M02.152	Postdysenteric arthropathy, lt hip
M02.162	Postdysenteric arthropathy, lt knee
M02.112	Postdysenteric arthropathy, lt shldr
M02.132	Postdysenteric arthropathy, lt wrist
M02.19	Postdysenteric arthropathy, multi sites
M02.171	Postdysenteric arthropathy, rt ankle & foot
M02.121	Postdysenteric arthropathy, rt elbow
M02.141	Postdysenteric arthropathy, rt hand
M02.151	Postdysenteric arthropathy, rt hip
M02.161	Postdysenteric arthropathy, rt knee
M02.111	Postdysenteric arthropathy, rt shldr
M02.131	Postdysenteric arthropathy, rt wrist
M02.179	Postdysenteric arthropathy, unsp ankle & foot
M02.129	Postdysenteric arthropathy, unsp elbow
M02.149	Postdysenteric arthropathy, unsp hand
M02.159	Postdysenteric arthropathy, unsp hip
M02.169	Postdysenteric arthropathy, unsp knee
M02.119	Postdysenteric arthropathy, unsp shldr
M02.10	Postdysenteric arthropathy, unsp site
M02.139	Postdysenteric arthropathy, unsp wrist
M02.18	Postdysenteric arthropathy, vertebrae
G21.3	Postencephalitic parkinsonism
B02.21	Postherpetic geniculate ganglionitis
B02.23	Postherpetic polyneuropathy

B02.22	Postherpetic trigeminal neuralgia
I23.7	Postinfarction angina
A39.84	Postmeningococcal arthritis
O71.2	Postpartum inversion of uterus
E89.6	Postprocedural adrenocortical (-medullary) hypofunction
J95.812	Postprocedural air leak
I97.120	Postprocedural cardiac arrest following cardiac surgery
I97.121	Postprocedural cardiac arrest following oth surgery
I97.110	Postprocedural cardiac insufficiency following cardiac surgery
I97.111	Postprocedural cardiac insufficiency following oth surgery
I97.820	Postprocedural cerebrovascular infarction during cardiac surgery
I97.821	Postprocedural cerebrovascular infarction during oth surgery
I97.130	Postprocedural heart failure following cardiac surgery
I97.131	Postprocedural heart failure following oth surgery
I97.610	Postprocedural hemor & hematoma of a circulatory sys organ or structure following a cardiac catheterization
I97.611	Postprocedural hemor & hematoma of a circulatory sys organ or structure following cardiac bypass
I97.618	Postprocedural hemor & hematoma of a circulatory sys organ or structure following oth circulatory sys procedure
I97.62	Postprocedural hemor & hematoma of a circulatory sys organ or structure following oth procedure
K91.840	Postprocedural hemor & hematoma of a digestive sys organ or structure following a digestive sys procedure
K91.841	Postprocedural hemor & hematoma of a digestive sys organ or structure following oth procedure
N99.820	Postprocedural hemor & hematoma of a genitourinary sys organ or structure following a genitourinary sys procedure
N99.821	Postprocedural hemor & hematoma of a genitourinary sys organ or structure following oth procedure
M96.830	Postprocedural hemor & hematoma of a musculoskeletal structure following a musculoskeletal sys procedure
M96.831	Postprocedural hemor & hematoma of a musculoskeletal structure following oth procedure
G97.51	Postprocedural hemor & hematoma of a nervous sys organ or structure following a nervous sys procedure
G97.52	Postprocedural hemor & hematoma of a nervous sys organ or structure following oth procedure
J95.830	Postprocedural hemor & hematoma of a respiratory sys organ or structure following a respiratory sys procedure
J95.831	Postprocedural hemor & hematoma of a respiratory sys organ or structure following oth procedure
E89.810	Postprocedural hemor & hematoma of an endocrine sys organ or structure following an endocrine sys procedure
E89.811	Postprocedural hemor & hematoma of an endocrine sys organ or structure following oth procedure
H95.41	Postprocedural hemor & hematoma of ear & mastoid process following a procedure on the ear & mastoid process
H95.42	Postprocedural hemor & hematoma of ear & mastoid process following oth procedure
H59.313	Postprocedural hemor & hematoma of eye & adnexa following an ophthalmic procedure, bilat
H59.323	Postprocedural hemor & hematoma of eye & adnexa following oth procedure, bilat
H59.312	Postprocedural hemor & hematoma of lt eye & adnexa following an ophthalmic procedure
H59.322	Postprocedural hemor & hematoma of lt eye & adnexa following oth procedure
H59.311	Postprocedural hemor & hematoma of rt eye & adnexa following an ophthalmic procedure
H59.321	Postprocedural hemor & hematoma of rt eye & adnexa following oth procedure
L76.21	Postprocedural hemor & hematoma of skin & SQ tissue following a dermatologic procedure
L76.22	Postprocedural hemor & hematoma of skin & SQ tissue following oth procedure
D78.21	Postprocedural hemor & hematoma of the spleen following a procedure on the spleen
D78.22	Postprocedural hemor & hematoma of the spleen following oth procedure
H59.319	Postprocedural hemor & hematoma of unsp eye & adnexa following an ophthalmic procedure
H59.329	Postprocedural hemor & hematoma of unsp eye & adnexa following oth procedure
K91.82	Postprocedural hepatic failure
K91.83	Postprocedural hepatorenal synd
E89.1	Postprocedural hypoinsulinemia

K91.3	Postprocedural intestinal obstruction
J95.811	Postprocedural pneumothorax
K68.11	Postprocedural retroperitoneal abscess
T81.10XA	Postprocedural shock unsp, init enc
H95.813	Postprocedural stenosis of ext ear canal, bilat
H95.812	Postprocedural stenosis of lt ext ear canal
H95.811	Postprocedural stenosis of rt ext ear canal
H95.819	Postprocedural stenosis of unsp ext ear canal
J95.5	Postprocedural subglottic stenosis
K91.2	Postsurg malabsorption, NEC
I87.033	Postthrombotic synd w/ ulcer & inflam of bilat lwr extr
I87.032	Postthrombotic synd w/ ulcer & inflam of lt lwr extr
I87.031	Postthrombotic synd w/ ulcer & inflam of rt lwr extr
I87.039	Postthrombotic synd w/ ulcer & inflam of unsp lwr extr
I87.013	Postthrombotic synd w/ ulcer of bilat lwr extr
I87.012	Postthrombotic synd w/ ulcer of lt lwr extr
I87.011	Postthrombotic synd w/ ulcer of rt lwr extr
I87.019	Postthrombotic synd w/ ulcer of unsp lwr extr
Q60.6	Potter's synd
K91.850	Pouchitis
O24.011	Pre-existing diabetes mellitus, type 1, in pregnancy, 1st trmstr
O24.012	Pre-existing diabetes mellitus, type 1, in pregnancy, 2nd trmstr
O24.013	Pre-existing diabetes mellitus, type 1, in pregnancy, 3rd trmstr
O24.019	Pre-existing diabetes mellitus, type 1, in pregnancy, unsp trmstr
O24.03	Pre-existing diabetes mellitus, type 1, in the puerperium
O24.111	Pre-existing diabetes mellitus, type 2, in pregnancy, 1st trmstr
O24.112	Pre-existing diabetes mellitus, type 2, in pregnancy, 2nd trmstr
O24.113	Pre-existing diabetes mellitus, type 2, in pregnancy, 3rd trmstr
O24.119	Pre-existing diabetes mellitus, type 2, in pregnancy, unsp trmstr
O24.13	Pre-existing diabetes mellitus, type 2, in the puerperium
O10.02	Pre-existing essential hypertension comp childbirth
O10.011	Pre-existing essential hypertension comp pregnancy, 1st trmstr
O10.012	Pre-existing essential hypertension comp pregnancy, 2nd trmstr
O10.013	Pre-existing essential hypertension comp pregnancy, 3rd trmstr
O10.411	Pre-existing secondary hypertension comp pregnancy, 1st trmstr
O10.412	Pre-existing secondary hypertension comp pregnancy, 2nd trmstr
O10.413	Pre-existing secondary hypertension comp pregnancy, 3rd trmstr
O10.43	Pre-existing secondary hypertension comp the puerperium
R71.0	Precipitous drop in hematocrit
O26.831	Pregnancy related renal disease, 1st trmstr
O26.832	Pregnancy related renal disease, 2nd trmstr
O26.833	Pregnancy related renal disease, 3rd trmstr
Z95.812	Presence of fully implantable artfcl heart
Z95.811	Presence of heart assist dev
O60.10X1	Preterm labor w/ preterm delivery, unsp trmstr, fetus 1
O60.10X2	Preterm labor w/ preterm delivery, unsp trmstr, fetus 2
O60.10X3	Preterm labor w/ preterm delivery, unsp trmstr, fetus 3
O60.10X4	Preterm labor w/ preterm delivery, unsp trmstr, fetus 4
O60.10X5	Preterm labor w/ preterm delivery, unsp trmstr, fetus 5
O60.10X0	Preterm labor w/ preterm delivery, unsp trmstr, N/A or unsp
O60.10X9	Preterm labor w/ preterm delivery, unsp trmstr, oth fetus
N48.32	Priapism d/t disease classified elsw
N48.31	Priapism d/t trauma
N48.33	Priapism, drug-induced
N48.30	Priapism, unsp
E27.1	Primary adrenocortical insufficiency
P28.0	Primary atelectasis of newborn
S36.510A	Primary blast inj of ascending [rt] colon, init enc
S36.512A	Primary blast inj of descending [lt] colon, init enc
S36.410A	Primary blast inj of duodenum, init enc
S09.313A	Primary blast inj of ear, bilat, init enc
S09.312A	Primary blast inj of lt ear, init enc
S27.312A	Primary blast inj of lung, bilat, init enc
S27.311A	Primary blast inj of lung, unilat, init enc
S27.319A	Primary blast inj of lung, unsp, init enc
S36.518A	Primary blast inj of oth part of colon, init enc
S36.418A	Primary blast inj of oth part of sm intestine, init enc
S36.61XA	Primary blast inj of rectum, init enc
S09.311A	Primary blast inj of rt ear, init enc
S36.513A	Primary blast inj of sigmoid colon, init enc
S27.51XA	Primary blast inj of thoracic trachea, init enc
S36.511A	Primary blast inj of transv colon, init enc
S09.319A	Primary blast inj of unsp ear, init enc

S36.519A	Primary blast inj of unsp part of colon, init enc
S36.419A	Primary blast inj of unsp part of sm intestine, init enc
C86.6	Primary cutaneous CD30-positive T-cell proliferations
H20.013	Primary iridocyclitis, bilat
H20.012	Primary iridocyclitis, lt eye
H20.011	Primary iridocyclitis, rt eye
H20.019	Primary iridocyclitis, unsp eye
I27.0	Primary pulmn hypertension
A15.7	Primary respiratory tuberculosis
P28.3	Primary sleep apnea of newborn
J93.11	Primary spontaneous pneumothorax
F73	Profound intellectual disabilities
G12.22	Progressive bulbar palsy
A81.2	Progressive multifocal leukoencephalopathy
G23.1	Progressive supranuclear ophthalmoplegia [Steele-Richardson-Olszewski]
I67.3	Progressive vascular leukoencephalopathy
C91.30	Prolymphocytic leukemia of B-cell type not having achieved remission
C91.32	Prolymphocytic leukemia of B-cell type, in relapse
C91.31	Prolymphocytic leukemia of B-cell type, in remission
C91.60	Prolymphocytic leukemia of T-cell type not having achieved remission
C91.62	Prolymphocytic leukemia of T-cell type, in relapse
C91.61	Prolymphocytic leukemia of T-cell type, in remission
E71.121	Propionic acidemia
B38.81	Prostatic coccidioidomycosis
D68.52	Prothrombin gene mutation
O98.62	Protozoal diseases comp childbirth
O98.611	Protozoal diseases comp pregnancy, 1st trmstr
O98.612	Protozoal diseases comp pregnancy, 2nd trmstr
O98.613	Protozoal diseases comp pregnancy, 3rd trmstr
O98.63	Protozoal diseases comp the puerperium
A07.9	Protozoal intestinal disease, unsp
M96.0	Pseudarthrosis after fusion or arthrodesis
K86.3	Pseudocyst of pancreas
F06.2	Psychotic d/o w/ delusions d/t known physiological condition
F06.0	Psychotic d/o w/ hallucinations d/t known physiological condition
A42.0	Pulmn actinomycosis
J84.02	Pulmn alveolar microlithiasis
B40.2	Pulmn blastomycosis, unsp
B38.2	Pulmn coccidioidomycosis, unsp
B45.0	Pulmn cryptococcosis
J82	Pulmn eosinophilia, NEC
Q24.3	Pulmn infundibular stenosis
A31.0	Pulmn mycobacterial infxn
A43.0	Pulmn nocardiosis
B41.0	Pulmn paracoccidioidomycosis
A21.2	Pulmn tularemia
K04.0	Pulpitis
S21.142A	Punc wnd w/ FB of lt front wall of thorax w/o penetration into thoracic cavity, init enc
S11.24XA	Punc wnd w/ FB of pharynx & cervical esophagus, init enc
S21.141A	Punc wnd w/ FB of rt front wall of thorax w/o penetration into thoracic cavity, init enc
S11.14XA	Punc wnd w/ FB of thyroid gland, init enc
S21.149A	Punc wnd w/ FB of unsp front wall of thorax w/o penetration into thoracic cavity, init enc
S21.94XA	Punc wnd w/ FB of unsp part of thorax, init enc
S21.132A	Punc wnd w/o FB of lt front wall of thorax w/o penetration into thoracic cavity, init enc
S11.23XA	Punc wnd w/o FB of pharynx & cervical esophagus, init enc
S21.131A	Punc wnd w/o FB of rt front wall of thorax w/o penetration into thoracic cavity, init enc
S11.13XA	Punc wnd w/o FB of thyroid gland, init enc
S21.139A	Punc wnd w/o FB of unsp front wall of thorax w/o penetration into thoracic cavity, init enc
S21.93XA	Punc wnd w/o FB of unsp part of thorax, init enc
D81.5	Purine nucleoside phosphorylase [PNP] deficiency
N28.84	Pyelitis cystica
N28.85	Pyeloureteritis cystica
O88.319	Pyemic & septic embolism in pregnancy, unsp trmstr
L88	Pyoderma gangrenosum
M00.9	Pyogenic arthritis, unsp
N13.6	Pyonephrosis
O75.2	Pyrexia during labor, NEC

O86.4	Pyrexia of unknown origin following delivery
A78	Q fever
O30.221	Quadruplet pregnancy w/ two or more monoamniotic fetuses, 1st trmstr
O30.222	Quadruplet pregnancy w/ two or more monoamniotic fetuses, 2nd trmstr
O30.223	Quadruplet pregnancy w/ two or more monoamniotic fetuses, 3rd trmstr
O30.211	Quadruplet pregnancy w/ two or more monochorionic fetuses, 1st trmstr
O30.212	Quadruplet pregnancy w/ two or more monochorionic fetuses, 2nd trmstr
O30.213	Quadruplet pregnancy w/ two or more monochorionic fetuses, 3rd trmstr
O30.291	Quadruplet pregnancy, unable to determine number of placenta & number of amniotic sacs, 1st trmstr
O30.292	Quadruplet pregnancy, unable to determine number of placenta & number of amniotic sacs, 2nd trmstr
O30.293	Quadruplet pregnancy, unable to determine number of placenta & number of amniotic sacs, 3rd trmstr
O30.201	Quadruplet pregnancy, unsp number of placenta & unsp number of amniotic sacs, 1st trmstr
O30.202	Quadruplet pregnancy, unsp number of placenta & unsp number of amniotic sacs, 2nd trmstr
O30.203	Quadruplet pregnancy, unsp number of placenta & unsp number of amniotic sacs, 3rd trmstr
A82.9	Rabies, unsp
A25.9	Rat-bite fever, unsp
I73.01	Raynaud's synd w/ gangrene
I47.0	Re-entry ventricular arrhythmia
A75.1	Recrudescent typhus [Brill's disease]
K61.1	Rectal abscess
N02.6	Recurrent & persistent hematuria w/ dense deposit disease
N02.7	Recurrent & persistent hematuria w/ diffuse crescentic glomerulonephritis
N02.4	Recurrent & persistent hematuria w/ diffuse endocapillary proliferative glomerulonephritis
N02.2	Recurrent & persistent hematuria w/ diffuse membranous glomerulonephritis
N02.3	Recurrent & persistent hematuria w/ diffuse mesangial proliferative glomerulonephritis
N02.5	Recurrent & persistent hematuria w/ diffuse mesangiocapillary glomerulonephritis
N02.1	Recurrent & persistent hematuria w/ focal & segmental glomerular lesions
N02.0	Recurrent & persistent hematuria w/ minor glomerular abnormality
N02.8	Recurrent & persistent hematuria w/ oth morphologic changes
N02.9	Recurrent & persistent hematuria w/ unsp morphologic changes
H20.023	Recurrent acute iridocyclitis, bilat
H20.022	Recurrent acute iridocyclitis, lt eye
H20.021	Recurrent acute iridocyclitis, rt eye
H20.029	Recurrent acute iridocyclitis, unsp eye
D46.22	Refractory anemia w/ excess of blasts 2
G60.1	Refsum's disease
M02.372	Reiter's disease, lt ankle & foot
M02.322	Reiter's disease, lt elbow
M02.342	Reiter's disease, lt hand
M02.352	Reiter's disease, lt hip
M02.362	Reiter's disease, lt knee
M02.312	Reiter's disease, lt shldr
M02.332	Reiter's disease, lt wrist
M02.39	Reiter's disease, multi sites
M02.371	Reiter's disease, rt ankle & foot
M02.321	Reiter's disease, rt elbow
M02.341	Reiter's disease, rt hand
M02.351	Reiter's disease, rt hip
M02.361	Reiter's disease, rt knee
M02.311	Reiter's disease, rt shldr
M02.331	Reiter's disease, rt wrist
M02.379	Reiter's disease, unsp ankle & foot
M02.329	Reiter's disease, unsp elbow
M02.349	Reiter's disease, unsp hand
M02.359	Reiter's disease, unsp hip
M02.369	Reiter's disease, unsp knee
M02.319	Reiter's disease, unsp shldr
M02.30	Reiter's disease, unsp site

M02.339	Reiter's disease, unsp wrist
M02.38	Reiter's disease, vertebrae
A68.9	Relapsing fever, unsp
Q60.1	Renal agenesis, bilat
Q60.0	Renal agenesis, unilat
Q60.2	Renal agenesis, unsp
Q61.4	Renal dysplasia
Q60.4	Renal hypoplasia, bilat
Q60.3	Renal hypoplasia, unilat
Q60.5	Renal hypoplasia, unsp
F20.5	Residual schizophrenia
P28.11	Resorption atelectasis w/o respiratory distress synd
A15.9	Respiratory tuberculosis unsp
K91.86	Retained cholelithiasis following cholecystectomy
E45	Retarded development following protein-calorie malnutrition
H34.233	Retinal artery branch occlsn, bilat
H34.232	Retinal artery branch occlsn, lt eye
H34.231	Retinal artery branch occlsn, rt eye
H34.239	Retinal artery branch occlsn, unsp eye
H35.82	Retinal ischemia
H46.13	Retrobulbar neuritis, bilat
H46.12	Retrobulbar neuritis, lt eye
H46.11	Retrobulbar neuritis, rt eye
H46.10	Retrobulbar neuritis, unsp eye
A18.39	Retroperitoneal tuberculosis
J39.0	Retropharyngeal & parapharyngeal abscess
F84.2	Rett's synd
I67.841	Reversible cerebrovascular vasoconstriction synd
T80.40XA	Rh incompatibility reaction d/t transfusion of blood or blood products, unsp init enc
T80.410A	Rh incompatibility w/ acute hemolytic transfusion reaction, init enc
T80.411A	Rh incompatibility w/ delayed hemolytic transfusion reaction, init enc
T80.419A	Rh incompatibility w/ hemolytic transfusion reaction, unsp, init enc
M62.82	Rhabdomyolysis
I02.0	Rheumatic chorea w/ heart involvement
I02.9	Rheumatic chorea w/o heart involvement
I09.81	Rheumatic heart failure
I09.0	Rheumatic myocarditis
M05.472	Rheumatoid myopathy w/ rheumatoid arthritis of lt ankle & foot
M05.422	Rheumatoid myopathy w/ rheumatoid arthritis of lt elbow
M05.442	Rheumatoid myopathy w/ rheumatoid arthritis of lt hand
M05.452	Rheumatoid myopathy w/ rheumatoid arthritis of lt hip
M05.462	Rheumatoid myopathy w/ rheumatoid arthritis of lt knee
M05.412	Rheumatoid myopathy w/ rheumatoid arthritis of lt shldr
M05.432	Rheumatoid myopathy w/ rheumatoid arthritis of lt wrist
M05.49	Rheumatoid myopathy w/ rheumatoid arthritis of multi sites
M05.471	Rheumatoid myopathy w/ rheumatoid arthritis of rt ankle & foot
M05.421	Rheumatoid myopathy w/ rheumatoid arthritis of rt elbow
M05.441	Rheumatoid myopathy w/ rheumatoid arthritis of rt hand
M05.451	Rheumatoid myopathy w/ rheumatoid arthritis of rt hip
M05.461	Rheumatoid myopathy w/ rheumatoid arthritis of rt knee
M05.411	Rheumatoid myopathy w/ rheumatoid arthritis of rt shldr
M05.431	Rheumatoid myopathy w/ rheumatoid arthritis of rt wrist
M05.479	Rheumatoid myopathy w/ rheumatoid arthritis of unsp ankle & foot
M05.429	Rheumatoid myopathy w/ rheumatoid arthritis of unsp elbow
M05.449	Rheumatoid myopathy w/ rheumatoid arthritis of unsp hand
M05.459	Rheumatoid myopathy w/ rheumatoid arthritis of unsp hip
M05.469	Rheumatoid myopathy w/ rheumatoid arthritis of unsp knee
M05.419	Rheumatoid myopathy w/ rheumatoid arthritis of unsp shldr
M05.40	Rheumatoid myopathy w/ rheumatoid arthritis of unsp site
M05.439	Rheumatoid myopathy w/ rheumatoid arthritis of unsp wrist
E71.540	Rhizomelic chondrodysplasia punctata
B56.1	Rhodesiense trypanosomiasis
E53.0	Riboflavin deficiency
E55.0	Rickets, active
A79.1	Rickettsialpox d/t Rickettsia akari
A79.81	Rickettsiosis d/t Ehrlichia sennetsu
A79.9	Rickettsiosis, unsp
A92.4	Rift Valley fever
B33.1	Ross River disease
A08.0	Rotaviral enteritis
B06.82	Rubella arthritis
B06.02	Rubella meningitis

B06.81	Rubella pneumonia
B06.00	Rubella w/ neurological comp, unsp
I77.2	Rupture of artery
I23.3	Rupture of cardiac wall w/o hemopericardium as current comp following acute myocardial infarction
Q05.3	Sacral spina bifida w/ hydrocephalus
A02.23	Salmonella arthritis
A02.0	Salmonella enteritis
A02.9	Salmonella infxn, unsp
A02.24	Salmonella osteomyelitis
A02.25	Salmonella pyelonephritis
A02.29	Salmonella w/ oth localized infxn
O23.521	Salpingo-oophoritis in pregnancy, 1st trmstr
O23.522	Salpingo-oophoritis in pregnancy, 2nd trmstr
O23.523	Salpingo-oophoritis in pregnancy, 3rd trmstr
S49.132A	Salter Harris Type III physeal fx of lwr end of humerus, lt arm, init enc for clsd fx
S49.132P	Salter Harris Type III physeal fx of lwr end of humerus, lt arm, subsq enc for fx w/ malu
S49.132K	Salter Harris Type III physeal fx of lwr end of humerus, lt arm, subsq enc for fx w/ nonu
S49.131A	Salter Harris Type III physeal fx of lwr end of humerus, rt arm, init enc for clsd fx
S49.131P	Salter Harris Type III physeal fx of lwr end of humerus, rt arm, subsq enc for fx w/ malu
S49.131K	Salter Harris Type III physeal fx of lwr end of humerus, rt arm, subsq enc for fx w/ nonu
S49.139A	Salter Harris Type III physeal fx of lwr end of humerus, unsp arm, init enc for clsd fx
S49.139P	Salter Harris Type III physeal fx of lwr end of humerus, unsp arm, subsq enc for fx w/ malu
S49.139K	Salter Harris Type III physeal fx of lwr end of humerus, unsp arm, subsq enc for fx w/ nonu
S49.032A	Salter Harris Type III physeal fx of upr end of humerus, lt arm, init enc for clsd fx
S49.032P	Salter Harris Type III physeal fx of upr end of humerus, lt arm, subsq enc for fx w/ malu
S49.032K	Salter Harris Type III physeal fx of upr end of humerus, lt arm, subsq enc for fx w/ nonu
S49.031A	Salter Harris Type III physeal fx of upr end of humerus, rt arm, init enc for clsd fx
S49.031P	Salter Harris Type III physeal fx of upr end of humerus, rt arm, subsq enc for fx w/ malu
S49.031K	Salter Harris Type III physeal fx of upr end of humerus, rt arm, subsq enc for fx w/ nonu
S49.039A	Salter Harris Type III physeal fx of upr end of humerus, unsp arm, init enc for clsd fx
S49.039P	Salter Harris Type III physeal fx of upr end of humerus, unsp arm, subsq enc for fx w/ malu
S49.039K	Salter Harris Type III physeal fx of upr end of humerus, unsp arm, subsq enc for fx w/ nonu
S49.112A	Salter-Harris Type I physeal fx of lwr end of humerus, lt arm, init enc for clsd fx
S49.112P	Salter-Harris Type I physeal fx of lwr end of humerus, lt arm, subsq enc for fx w/ malu
S49.112K	Salter-Harris Type I physeal fx of lwr end of humerus, lt arm, subsq enc for fx w/ nonu
S49.111A	Salter-Harris Type I physeal fx of lwr end of humerus, rt arm, init enc for clsd fx
S49.111P	Salter-Harris Type I physeal fx of lwr end of humerus, rt arm, subsq enc for fx w/ malu
S49.111K	Salter-Harris Type I physeal fx of lwr end of humerus, rt arm, subsq enc for fx w/ nonu
S49.119A	Salter-Harris Type I physeal fx of lwr end of humerus, unsp arm, init enc for clsd fx
S49.119P	Salter-Harris Type I physeal fx of lwr end of humerus, unsp arm, subsq enc for fx w/ malu
S49.119K	Salter-Harris Type I physeal fx of lwr end of humerus, unsp arm, subsq enc for fx w/ nonu
S79.112A	Salter-Harris Type I physeal fx of lwr end of lt femur, init enc for clsd fx
S79.112P	Salter-Harris Type I physeal fx of lwr end of lt femur, subsq enc for fx w/ malu
S79.112K	Salter-Harris Type I physeal fx of lwr end of lt femur, subsq enc for fx w/ nonu
S89.312P	Salter-Harris Type I physeal fx of lwr end of lt fibula, subsq enc for fx w/ malu

Code	Description
S89.312K	Salter-Harris Type I physeal fx of lwr end of lt fibula, subsq enc for fx w/ nonu
S89.112P	Salter-Harris Type I physeal fx of lwr end of lt tibia, subsq enc for fx w/ malu
S89.112K	Salter-Harris Type I physeal fx of lwr end of lt tibia, subsq enc for fx w/ nonu
S59.212A	Salter-Harris Type I physeal fx of lwr end of radius, lt arm, init enc for clsd fx
S59.212P	Salter-Harris Type I physeal fx of lwr end of radius, lt arm, subsq enc for fx w/ malu
S59.212K	Salter-Harris Type I physeal fx of lwr end of radius, lt arm, subsq enc for fx w/ nonu
S59.211A	Salter-Harris Type I physeal fx of lwr end of radius, rt arm, init enc for clsd fx
S59.211P	Salter-Harris Type I physeal fx of lwr end of radius, rt arm, subsq enc for fx w/ malu
S59.211K	Salter-Harris Type I physeal fx of lwr end of radius, rt arm, subsq enc for fx w/ nonu
S59.219A	Salter-Harris Type I physeal fx of lwr end of radius, unsp arm, init enc for clsd fx
S59.219P	Salter-Harris Type I physeal fx of lwr end of radius, unsp arm, subsq enc for fx w/ malu
S59.219K	Salter-Harris Type I physeal fx of lwr end of radius, unsp arm, subsq enc for fx w/ nonu
S79.111A	Salter-Harris Type I physeal fx of lwr end of rt femur, init enc for clsd fx
S79.111P	Salter-Harris Type I physeal fx of lwr end of rt femur, subsq enc for fx w/ malu
S79.111K	Salter-Harris Type I physeal fx of lwr end of rt femur, subsq enc for fx w/ nonu
S89.311P	Salter-Harris Type I physeal fx of lwr end of rt fibula, subsq enc for fx w/ malu
S89.311K	Salter-Harris Type I physeal fx of lwr end of rt fibula, subsq enc for fx w/ nonu
S89.111P	Salter-Harris Type I physeal fx of lwr end of rt tibia, subsq enc for fx w/ malu
S89.111K	Salter-Harris Type I physeal fx of lwr end of rt tibia, subsq enc for fx w/ nonu
S59.012A	Salter-Harris Type I physeal fx of lwr end of ulna, lt arm, init enc for clsd fx
S59.012P	Salter-Harris Type I physeal fx of lwr end of ulna, lt arm, subsq enc for fx w/ malu
S59.012K	Salter-Harris Type I physeal fx of lwr end of ulna, lt arm, subsq enc for fx w/ nonu
S59.011A	Salter-Harris Type I physeal fx of lwr end of ulna, rt arm, init enc for clsd fx
S59.011P	Salter-Harris Type I physeal fx of lwr end of ulna, rt arm, subsq enc for fx w/ malu
S59.011K	Salter-Harris Type I physeal fx of lwr end of ulna, rt arm, subsq enc for fx w/ nonu
S59.019A	Salter-Harris Type I physeal fx of lwr end of ulna, unsp arm, init enc for clsd fx
S59.019P	Salter-Harris Type I physeal fx of lwr end of ulna, unsp arm, subsq enc for fx w/ malu
S59.019K	Salter-Harris Type I physeal fx of lwr end of ulna, unsp arm, subsq enc for fx w/ nonu
S79.119A	Salter-Harris Type I physeal fx of lwr end of unsp femur, init enc for clsd fx
S79.119P	Salter-Harris Type I physeal fx of lwr end of unsp femur, subsq enc for fx w/ malu
S79.119K	Salter-Harris Type I physeal fx of lwr end of unsp femur, subsq enc for fx w/ nonu
S89.319P	Salter-Harris Type I physeal fx of lwr end of unsp fibula, subsq enc for fx w/ malu
S89.319K	Salter-Harris Type I physeal fx of lwr end of unsp fibula, subsq enc for fx w/ nonu
S89.119P	Salter-Harris Type I physeal fx of lwr end of unsp tibia, subsq enc for fx w/ malu
S89.119K	Salter-Harris Type I physeal fx of lwr end of unsp tibia, subsq enc for fx w/ nonu
S49.012A	Salter-Harris Type I physeal fx of upr end of humerus, lt arm, init enc for clsd fx
S49.012P	Salter-Harris Type I physeal fx of upr end of humerus, lt arm, subsq enc for fx w/ malu
S49.012K	Salter-Harris Type I physeal fx of upr end of humerus, lt arm, subsq enc for fx w/ nonu
S49.011A	Salter-Harris Type I physeal fx of upr end of humerus, rt arm, init enc for clsd fx
S49.011P	Salter-Harris Type I physeal fx of upr end of humerus, rt arm, subsq enc for fx w/ malu
S49.011K	Salter-Harris Type I physeal fx of upr end of humerus, rt arm, subsq enc for fx w/ nonu
S49.019A	Salter-Harris Type I physeal fx of upr end of humerus, unsp arm, init enc for clsd fx
S49.019P	Salter-Harris Type I physeal fx of upr end of humerus, unsp arm, subsq enc for fx w/ malu
S49.019K	Salter-Harris Type I physeal fx of upr end of humerus, unsp arm, subsq enc for fx w/ nonu
S79.012P	Salter-Harris Type I physeal fx of upr end of lt femur, subsq enc for fx w/ malu
S79.012K	Salter-Harris Type I physeal fx of upr end of lt femur, subsq enc for fx w/ nonu
S89.212P	Salter-Harris Type I physeal fx of upr end of lt fibula, subsq enc for fx w/ malu
S89.212K	Salter-Harris Type I physeal fx of upr end of lt fibula, subsq enc for fx w/ nonu
S89.012A	Salter-Harris Type I physeal fx of upr end of lt tibia, init enc for clsd fx
S89.012P	Salter-Harris Type I physeal fx of upr end of lt tibia, subsq enc for fx w/ malu
S89.012K	Salter-Harris Type I physeal fx of upr end of lt tibia, subsq enc for fx w/ nonu
S59.112P	Salter-Harris Type I physeal fx of upr end of radius, lt arm, subsq enc for fx w/ malu
S59.112K	Salter-Harris Type I physeal fx of upr end of radius, lt arm, subsq enc for fx w/ nonu
S59.111P	Salter-Harris Type I physeal fx of upr end of radius, rt arm, subsq enc for fx w/ malu
S59.111K	Salter-Harris Type I physeal fx of upr end of radius, rt arm, subsq enc for fx w/ nonu
S59.119P	Salter-Harris Type I physeal fx of upr end of radius, unsp arm, subsq enc for fx w/ malu
S59.119K	Salter-Harris Type I physeal fx of upr end of radius, unsp arm, subsq enc for fx w/ nonu
S79.011P	Salter-Harris Type I physeal fx of upr end of rt femur, subsq enc for fx w/ malu
S79.011K	Salter-Harris Type I physeal fx of upr end of rt femur, subsq enc for fx w/ nonu
S89.211P	Salter-Harris Type I physeal fx of upr end of rt fibula, subsq enc for fx w/ malu
S89.211K	Salter-Harris Type I physeal fx of upr end of rt fibula, subsq enc for fx w/ nonu
S89.011A	Salter-Harris Type I physeal fx of upr end of rt tibia, init enc for clsd fx
S89.011P	Salter-Harris Type I physeal fx of upr end of rt tibia, subsq enc for fx w/ malu
S89.011K	Salter-Harris Type I physeal fx of upr end of rt tibia, subsq enc for fx w/ nonu
S79.019P	Salter-Harris Type I physeal fx of upr end of unsp femur, subsq enc for fx w/ malu
S79.019K	Salter-Harris Type I physeal fx of upr end of unsp femur, subsq enc for fx w/ nonu
S89.219P	Salter-Harris Type I physeal fx of upr end of unsp fibula, subsq enc for fx w/ malu
S89.219K	Salter-Harris Type I physeal fx of upr end of unsp fibula, subsq enc for fx w/ nonu
S89.019A	Salter-Harris Type I physeal fx of upr end of unsp tibia, init enc for clsd fx
S89.019P	Salter-Harris Type I physeal fx of upr end of unsp tibia, subsq enc for fx w/ malu
S89.019K	Salter-Harris Type I physeal fx of upr end of unsp tibia, subsq enc for fx w/ nonu
S49.122A	Salter-Harris Type II physeal fx of lwr end of humerus, lt arm, init enc for clsd fx
S49.122P	Salter-Harris Type II physeal fx of lwr end of humerus, lt arm, subsq enc for fx w/ malu
S49.122K	Salter-Harris Type II physeal fx of lwr end of humerus, lt arm, subsq enc for fx w/ nonu
S49.121A	Salter-Harris Type II physeal fx of lwr end of humerus, rt arm, init enc for clsd fx
S49.121P	Salter-Harris Type II physeal fx of lwr end of humerus, rt arm, subsq enc for fx w/ malu
S49.121K	Salter-Harris Type II physeal fx of lwr end of humerus, rt arm, subsq enc for fx w/ nonu
S49.129A	Salter-Harris Type II physeal fx of lwr end of humerus, unsp arm, init enc for clsd fx
S49.129P	Salter-Harris Type II physeal fx of lwr end of humerus, unsp arm, subsq enc for fx w/ malu
S49.129K	Salter-Harris Type II physeal fx of lwr end of humerus, unsp arm, subsq enc for fx w/ nonu

S79.122A	Salter-Harris Type II physeal fx of lwr end of lt femur, init enc for clsd fx
S79.122P	Salter-Harris Type II physeal fx of lwr end of lt femur, subsq enc for fx w/ malu
S79.122K	Salter-Harris Type II physeal fx of lwr end of lt femur, subsq enc for fx w/ nonu
S89.322P	Salter-Harris Type II physeal fx of lwr end of lt fibula, subsq enc for fx w/ malu
S89.322K	Salter-Harris Type II physeal fx of lwr end of lt fibula, subsq enc for fx w/ nonu
S89.122P	Salter-Harris Type II physeal fx of lwr end of lt tibia, subsq enc for fx w/ malu
S89.122K	Salter-Harris Type II physeal fx of lwr end of lt tibia, subsq enc for fx w/ nonu
S59.222A	Salter-Harris Type II physeal fx of lwr end of radius, lt arm, init enc for clsd fx
S59.222P	Salter-Harris Type II physeal fx of lwr end of radius, lt arm, subsq enc for fx w/ malu
S59.222K	Salter-Harris Type II physeal fx of lwr end of radius, lt arm, subsq enc for fx w/ nonu
S59.221A	Salter-Harris Type II physeal fx of lwr end of radius, rt arm, init enc for clsd fx
S59.221P	Salter-Harris Type II physeal fx of lwr end of radius, rt arm, subsq enc for fx w/ malu
S59.221K	Salter-Harris Type II physeal fx of lwr end of radius, rt arm, subsq enc for fx w/ nonu
S59.229A	Salter-Harris Type II physeal fx of lwr end of radius, unsp arm, init enc for clsd fx
S59.229P	Salter-Harris Type II physeal fx of lwr end of radius, unsp arm, subsq enc for fx w/ malu
S59.229K	Salter-Harris Type II physeal fx of lwr end of radius, unsp arm, subsq enc for fx w/ nonu
S79.121A	Salter-Harris Type II physeal fx of lwr end of rt femur, init enc for clsd fx
S79.121P	Salter-Harris Type II physeal fx of lwr end of rt femur, subsq enc for fx w/ malu
S79.121K	Salter-Harris Type II physeal fx of lwr end of rt femur, subsq enc for fx w/ nonu
S89.321P	Salter-Harris Type II physeal fx of lwr end of rt fibula, subsq enc for fx w/ malu
S89.321K	Salter-Harris Type II physeal fx of lwr end of rt fibula, subsq enc for fx w/ nonu
S89.121P	Salter-Harris Type II physeal fx of lwr end of rt tibia, subsq enc for fx w/ malu
S89.121K	Salter-Harris Type II physeal fx of lwr end of rt tibia, subsq enc for fx w/ nonu
S59.022A	Salter-Harris Type II physeal fx of lwr end of ulna, lt arm, init enc for clsd fx
S59.022P	Salter-Harris Type II physeal fx of lwr end of ulna, lt arm, subsq enc for fx w/ malu
S59.022K	Salter-Harris Type II physeal fx of lwr end of ulna, lt arm, subsq enc for fx w/ nonu
S59.021A	Salter-Harris Type II physeal fx of lwr end of ulna, rt arm, init enc for clsd fx
S59.021P	Salter-Harris Type II physeal fx of lwr end of ulna, rt arm, subsq enc for fx w/ malu
S59.021K	Salter-Harris Type II physeal fx of lwr end of ulna, rt arm, subsq enc for fx w/ nonu
S59.029A	Salter-Harris Type II physeal fx of lwr end of ulna, unsp arm, init enc for clsd fx
S59.029P	Salter-Harris Type II physeal fx of lwr end of ulna, unsp arm, subsq enc for fx w/ malu
S59.029K	Salter-Harris Type II physeal fx of lwr end of ulna, unsp arm, subsq enc for fx w/ nonu
S79.129A	Salter-Harris Type II physeal fx of lwr end of unsp femur, init enc for clsd fx
S79.129P	Salter-Harris Type II physeal fx of lwr end of unsp femur, subsq enc for fx w/ malu
S79.129K	Salter-Harris Type II physeal fx of lwr end of unsp femur, subsq enc for fx w/ nonu
S89.329P	Salter-Harris Type II physeal fx of lwr end of unsp fibula, subsq enc for fx w/ malu
S89.329K	Salter-Harris Type II physeal fx of lwr end of unsp fibula, subsq enc for fx w/ nonu
S89.129P	Salter-Harris Type II physeal fx of lwr end of unsp tibia, subsq enc for fx w/ malu
S89.129K	Salter-Harris Type II physeal fx of lwr end of unsp tibia, subsq enc for fx w/ nonu
S49.022A	Salter-Harris Type II physeal fx of upr end of humerus, lt arm, init enc for clsd fx
S49.022P	Salter-Harris Type II physeal fx of upr end of humerus, lt arm, subsq enc for fx w/ malu
S49.022K	Salter-Harris Type II physeal fx of upr end of humerus, lt arm, subsq enc for fx w/ nonu
S49.021A	Salter-Harris Type II physeal fx of upr end of humerus, rt arm, init enc for clsd fx
S49.021P	Salter-Harris Type II physeal fx of upr end of humerus, rt arm, subsq enc for fx w/ malu
S49.021K	Salter-Harris Type II physeal fx of upr end of humerus, rt arm, subsq enc for fx w/ nonu
S49.029A	Salter-Harris Type II physeal fx of upr end of humerus, unsp arm, init enc for clsd fx
S49.029P	Salter-Harris Type II physeal fx of upr end of humerus, unsp arm, subsq enc for fx w/ malu
S49.029K	Salter-Harris Type II physeal fx of upr end of humerus, unsp arm, subsq enc for fx w/ nonu
S89.222P	Salter-Harris Type II physeal fx of upr end of lt fibula, subsq enc for fx w/ malu
S89.222K	Salter-Harris Type II physeal fx of upr end of lt fibula, subsq enc for fx w/ nonu
S89.022A	Salter-Harris Type II physeal fx of upr end of lt tibia, init enc for clsd fx
S89.022P	Salter-Harris Type II physeal fx of upr end of lt tibia, subsq enc for fx w/ malu
S89.022K	Salter-Harris Type II physeal fx of upr end of lt tibia, subsq enc for fx w/ nonu
S59.122P	Salter-Harris Type II physeal fx of upr end of radius, lt arm, subsq enc for fx w/ malu
S59.122K	Salter-Harris Type II physeal fx of upr end of radius, lt arm, subsq enc for fx w/ nonu
S59.121P	Salter-Harris Type II physeal fx of upr end of radius, rt arm, subsq enc for fx w/ malu
S59.121K	Salter-Harris Type II physeal fx of upr end of radius, rt arm, subsq enc for fx w/ nonu
S59.129P	Salter-Harris Type II physeal fx of upr end of radius, unsp arm, subsq enc for fx w/ malu
S59.129K	Salter-Harris Type II physeal fx of upr end of radius, unsp arm, subsq enc for fx w/ nonu
S89.221P	Salter-Harris Type II physeal fx of upr end of rt fibula, subsq enc for fx w/ malu
S89.221K	Salter-Harris Type II physeal fx of upr end of rt fibula, subsq enc for fx w/ nonu
S89.021A	Salter-Harris Type II physeal fx of upr end of rt tibia, init enc for clsd fx
S89.021P	Salter-Harris Type II physeal fx of upr end of rt tibia, subsq enc for fx w/ malu
S89.021K	Salter-Harris Type II physeal fx of upr end of rt tibia, subsq enc for fx w/ nonu
S89.229P	Salter-Harris Type II physeal fx of upr end of unsp fibula, subsq enc for fx w/ malu
S89.229K	Salter-Harris Type II physeal fx of upr end of unsp fibula, subsq enc for fx w/ nonu
S89.029A	Salter-Harris Type II physeal fx of upr end of unsp tibia, init enc for clsd fx
S89.029P	Salter-Harris Type II physeal fx of upr end of unsp tibia, subsq enc for fx w/ malu
S89.029K	Salter-Harris Type II physeal fx of upr end of unsp tibia, subsq enc for fx w/ nonu
S79.132A	Salter-Harris Type III physeal fx of lwr end of lt femur, init enc for clsd fx
S79.132P	Salter-Harris Type III physeal fx of lwr end of lt femur, subsq enc for fx w/ malu
S79.132K	Salter-Harris Type III physeal fx of lwr end of lt femur, subsq enc for fx w/ nonu
S89.132P	Salter-Harris Type III physeal fx of lwr end of lt tibia, subsq enc for fx w/ malu
S89.132K	Salter-Harris Type III physeal fx of lwr end of lt tibia, subsq enc for fx w/ nonu
S59.232A	Salter-Harris Type III physeal fx of lwr end of radius, lt arm, init enc for clsd fx
S59.232P	Salter-Harris Type III physeal fx of lwr end of radius, lt arm, subsq enc for fx w/ malu
S59.232K	Salter-Harris Type III physeal fx of lwr end of radius, lt arm, subsq enc for fx w/ nonu
S59.231A	Salter-Harris Type III physeal fx of lwr end of radius, rt arm, init enc for clsd fx
S59.231P	Salter-Harris Type III physeal fx of lwr end of radius, rt arm, subsq enc for fx w/ malu
S59.231K	Salter-Harris Type III physeal fx of lwr end of radius, rt arm, subsq enc for fx w/ nonu

S59.239A	Salter-Harris Type III physeal fx of lwr end of radius, unsp arm, init enc for clsd fx
S59.239P	Salter-Harris Type III physeal fx of lwr end of radius, unsp arm, subsq enc for fx w/ malu
S59.239K	Salter-Harris Type III physeal fx of lwr end of radius, unsp arm, subsq enc for fx w/ nonu
S79.131A	Salter-Harris Type III physeal fx of lwr end of rt femur, init enc for clsd fx
S79.131P	Salter-Harris Type III physeal fx of lwr end of rt femur, subsq enc for fx w/ malu
S79.131K	Salter-Harris Type III physeal fx of lwr end of rt femur, subsq enc for fx w/ nonu
S89.131P	Salter-Harris Type III physeal fx of lwr end of rt tibia, subsq enc for fx w/ malu
S89.131K	Salter-Harris Type III physeal fx of lwr end of rt tibia, subsq enc for fx w/ nonu
S59.032A	Salter-Harris Type III physeal fx of lwr end of ulna, lt arm, init enc for clsd fx
S59.032P	Salter-Harris Type III physeal fx of lwr end of ulna, lt arm, subsq enc for fx w/ malu
S59.032K	Salter-Harris Type III physeal fx of lwr end of ulna, lt arm, subsq enc for fx w/ nonu
S59.031A	Salter-Harris Type III physeal fx of lwr end of ulna, rt arm, init enc for clsd fx
S59.031P	Salter-Harris Type III physeal fx of lwr end of ulna, rt arm, subsq enc for fx w/ malu
S59.031K	Salter-Harris Type III physeal fx of lwr end of ulna, rt arm, subsq enc for fx w/ nonu
S59.039A	Salter-Harris Type III physeal fx of lwr end of ulna, unsp arm, init enc for clsd fx
S59.039P	Salter-Harris Type III physeal fx of lwr end of ulna, unsp arm, subsq enc for fx w/ malu
S59.039K	Salter-Harris Type III physeal fx of lwr end of ulna, unsp arm, subsq enc for fx w/ nonu
S79.139A	Salter-Harris Type III physeal fx of lwr end of unsp femur, init enc for clsd fx
S79.139P	Salter-Harris Type III physeal fx of lwr end of unsp femur, subsq enc for fx w/ malu
S79.139K	Salter-Harris Type III physeal fx of lwr end of unsp femur, subsq enc for fx w/ nonu
S89.139P	Salter-Harris Type III physeal fx of lwr end of unsp tibia, subsq enc for fx w/ malu
S89.139K	Salter-Harris Type III physeal fx of lwr end of unsp tibia, subsq enc for fx w/ nonu
S89.032A	Salter-Harris Type III physeal fx of upr end of lt tibia, init enc for clsd fx
S89.032P	Salter-Harris Type III physeal fx of upr end of lt tibia, subsq enc for fx w/ malu
S89.032K	Salter-Harris Type III physeal fx of upr end of lt tibia, subsq enc for fx w/ nonu
S59.132P	Salter-Harris Type III physeal fx of upr end of radius, lt arm, subsq enc for fx w/ malu
S59.132K	Salter-Harris Type III physeal fx of upr end of radius, lt arm, subsq enc for fx w/ nonu
S59.131P	Salter-Harris Type III physeal fx of upr end of radius, rt arm, subsq enc for fx w/ malu
S59.131K	Salter-Harris Type III physeal fx of upr end of radius, rt arm, subsq enc for fx w/ nonu
S59.139P	Salter-Harris Type III physeal fx of upr end of radius, unsp arm, subsq enc for fx w/ malu
S59.139K	Salter-Harris Type III physeal fx of upr end of radius, unsp arm, subsq enc for fx w/ nonu
S89.031A	Salter-Harris Type III physeal fx of upr end of rt tibia, init enc for clsd fx
S89.031P	Salter-Harris Type III physeal fx of upr end of rt tibia, subsq enc for fx w/ malu
S89.031K	Salter-Harris Type III physeal fx of upr end of rt tibia, subsq enc for fx w/ nonu
S89.039A	Salter-Harris Type III physeal fx of upr end of unsp tibia, init enc for clsd fx
S89.039P	Salter-Harris Type III physeal fx of upr end of unsp tibia, subsq enc for fx w/ malu
S89.039K	Salter-Harris Type III physeal fx of upr end of unsp tibia, subsq enc for fx w/ nonu
S49.142A	Salter-Harris Type IV physeal fx of lwr end of humerus, lt arm, init enc for clsd fx
S49.142P	Salter-Harris Type IV physeal fx of lwr end of humerus, lt arm, subsq enc for fx w/ malu
S49.142K	Salter-Harris Type IV physeal fx of lwr end of humerus, lt arm, subsq enc for fx w/ nonu

S49.141A	Salter-Harris Type IV physeal fx of lwr end of humerus, rt arm, init enc for clsd fx
S49.141P	Salter-Harris Type IV physeal fx of lwr end of humerus, rt arm, subsq enc for fx w/ malu
S49.141K	Salter-Harris Type IV physeal fx of lwr end of humerus, rt arm, subsq enc for fx w/ nonu
S49.149A	Salter-Harris Type IV physeal fx of lwr end of humerus, unsp arm, init enc for clsd fx
S49.149P	Salter-Harris Type IV physeal fx of lwr end of humerus, unsp arm, subsq enc for fx w/ malu
S49.149K	Salter-Harris Type IV physeal fx of lwr end of humerus, unsp arm, subsq enc for fx w/ nonu
S79.142A	Salter-Harris Type IV physeal fx of lwr end of lt femur, init enc for clsd fx
S79.142P	Salter-Harris Type IV physeal fx of lwr end of lt femur, subsq enc for fx w/ malu
S79.142K	Salter-Harris Type IV physeal fx of lwr end of lt femur, subsq enc for fx w/ nonu
S89.142P	Salter-Harris Type IV physeal fx of lwr end of lt tibia, subsq enc for fx w/ malu
S89.142K	Salter-Harris Type IV physeal fx of lwr end of lt tibia, subsq enc for fx w/ nonu
S59.242A	Salter-Harris Type IV physeal fx of lwr end of radius, lt arm, init enc for clsd fx
S59.242P	Salter-Harris Type IV physeal fx of lwr end of radius, lt arm, subsq enc for fx w/ malu
S59.242K	Salter-Harris Type IV physeal fx of lwr end of radius, lt arm, subsq enc for fx w/ nonu
S59.241A	Salter-Harris Type IV physeal fx of lwr end of radius, rt arm, init enc for clsd fx
S59.241P	Salter-Harris Type IV physeal fx of lwr end of radius, rt arm, subsq enc for fx w/ malu
S59.241K	Salter-Harris Type IV physeal fx of lwr end of radius, rt arm, subsq enc for fx w/ nonu
S59.249A	Salter-Harris Type IV physeal fx of lwr end of radius, unsp arm, init enc for clsd fx
S59.249P	Salter-Harris Type IV physeal fx of lwr end of radius, unsp arm, subsq enc for fx w/ malu
S59.249K	Salter-Harris Type IV physeal fx of lwr end of radius, unsp arm, subsq enc for fx w/ nonu
S79.141A	Salter-Harris Type IV physeal fx of lwr end of rt femur, init enc for clsd fx
S79.141P	Salter-Harris Type IV physeal fx of lwr end of rt femur, subsq enc for fx w/ malu
S79.141K	Salter-Harris Type IV physeal fx of lwr end of rt femur, subsq enc for fx w/ nonu
S89.141P	Salter-Harris Type IV physeal fx of lwr end of rt tibia, subsq enc for fx w/ malu
S89.141K	Salter-Harris Type IV physeal fx of lwr end of rt tibia, subsq enc for fx w/ nonu
S59.042A	Salter-Harris Type IV physeal fx of lwr end of ulna, lt arm, init enc for clsd fx
S59.042P	Salter-Harris Type IV physeal fx of lwr end of ulna, lt arm, subsq enc for fx w/ malu
S59.042K	Salter-Harris Type IV physeal fx of lwr end of ulna, lt arm, subsq enc for fx w/ nonu
S59.041A	Salter-Harris Type IV physeal fx of lwr end of ulna, rt arm, init enc for clsd fx
S59.041P	Salter-Harris Type IV physeal fx of lwr end of ulna, rt arm, subsq enc for fx w/ malu
S59.041K	Salter-Harris Type IV physeal fx of lwr end of ulna, rt arm, subsq enc for fx w/ nonu
S59.049A	Salter-Harris Type IV physeal fx of lwr end of ulna, unsp arm, init enc for clsd fx
S59.049P	Salter-Harris Type IV physeal fx of lwr end of ulna, unsp arm, subsq enc for fx w/ malu
S59.049K	Salter-Harris Type IV physeal fx of lwr end of ulna, unsp arm, subsq enc for fx w/ nonu
S79.149A	Salter-Harris Type IV physeal fx of lwr end of unsp femur, init enc for clsd fx
S79.149P	Salter-Harris Type IV physeal fx of lwr end of unsp femur, subsq enc for fx w/ malu
S79.149K	Salter-Harris Type IV physeal fx of lwr end of unsp femur, subsq enc for fx w/ nonu
S89.149P	Salter-Harris Type IV physeal fx of lwr end of unsp tibia, subsq enc for fx w/ malu
S89.149K	Salter-Harris Type IV physeal fx of lwr end of unsp tibia, subsq enc for fx w/ nonu

S49.042A	Salter-Harris Type IV physeal fx of upr end of humerus, lt arm, init enc for clsd fx
S49.042P	Salter-Harris Type IV physeal fx of upr end of humerus, lt arm, subsq enc for fx w/ malu
S49.042K	Salter-Harris Type IV physeal fx of upr end of humerus, lt arm, subsq enc for fx w/ nonu
S49.041A	Salter-Harris Type IV physeal fx of upr end of humerus, rt arm, init enc for clsd fx
S49.041P	Salter-Harris Type IV physeal fx of upr end of humerus, rt arm, subsq enc for fx w/ malu
S49.041K	Salter-Harris Type IV physeal fx of upr end of humerus, rt arm, subsq enc for fx w/ nonu
S49.049A	Salter-Harris Type IV physeal fx of upr end of humerus, unsp arm, init enc for clsd fx
S49.049P	Salter-Harris Type IV physeal fx of upr end of humerus, unsp arm, subsq enc for fx w/ malu
S49.049K	Salter-Harris Type IV physeal fx of upr end of humerus, unsp arm, subsq enc for fx w/ nonu
S89.042A	Salter-Harris Type IV physeal fx of upr end of lt tibia, init enc for clsd fx
S89.042P	Salter-Harris Type IV physeal fx of upr end of lt tibia, subsq enc for fx w/ malu
S89.042K	Salter-Harris Type IV physeal fx of upr end of lt tibia, subsq enc for fx w/ nonu
S59.142P	Salter-Harris Type IV physeal fx of upr end of radius, lt arm, subsq enc for fx w/ malu
S59.142K	Salter-Harris Type IV physeal fx of upr end of radius, lt arm, subsq enc for fx w/ nonu
S59.141P	Salter-Harris Type IV physeal fx of upr end of radius, rt arm, subsq enc for fx w/ malu
S59.141K	Salter-Harris Type IV physeal fx of upr end of radius, rt arm, subsq enc for fx w/ nonu
S59.149P	Salter-Harris Type IV physeal fx of upr end of radius, unsp arm, subsq enc for fx w/ malu
S59.149K	Salter-Harris Type IV physeal fx of upr end of radius, unsp arm, subsq enc for fx w/ nonu
S89.041A	Salter-Harris Type IV physeal fx of upr end of rt tibia, init enc for clsd fx
S89.041P	Salter-Harris Type IV physeal fx of upr end of rt tibia, subsq enc for fx w/ malu
S89.041K	Salter-Harris Type IV physeal fx of upr end of rt tibia, subsq enc for fx w/ nonu
S89.049A	Salter-Harris Type IV physeal fx of upr end of unsp tibia, init enc for clsd fx
S89.049P	Salter-Harris Type IV physeal fx of upr end of unsp tibia, subsq enc for fx w/ malu
S89.049K	Salter-Harris Type IV physeal fx of upr end of unsp tibia, subsq enc for fx w/ nonu
A93.1	Sandfly fever
E75.01	Sandhoff disease
E76.22	Sanfilippo mucopolysaccharidoses
C96.4	Sarcoma of dendritic cells (accessory cells)
B97.21	SARS-associated coronavirus as the cause of diseases classified elsw
A38.1	Scarlet fever w/ myocarditis
A38.8	Scarlet fever w/ oth comp
A38.0	Scarlet fever w/ otitis media
A38.9	Scarlet fever, uncomplicated
E76.03	Scheie's synd
B65.0	Schistosomiasis d/t Schistosoma haematobium [urinary schistosomiasis]
B65.2	Schistosomiasis d/t Schistosoma japonicum
B65.1	Schistosomiasis d/t Schistosoma mansoni [intestinal schistosomiasis]
B65.9	Schistosomiasis, unsp
F20.81	Schizophreniform d/o
P83.0	Sclerema neonatorum
K65.4	Sclerosing mesenteritis
C77.3	Secondary & unsp malig neoplasm of axilla & upr limb lymph nodes
C77.4	Secondary & unsp malig neoplasm of inguinal & lwr limb lymph nodes
C77.2	Secondary & unsp malig neoplasm of intra-abd lymph nodes
C77.5	Secondary & unsp malig neoplasm of intrapelvic lymph nodes
C77.1	Secondary & unsp malig neoplasm of intrathoracic lymph nodes
C77.9	Secondary & unsp malig neoplasm of lymph node, unsp
C77.0	Secondary & unsp malig neoplasm of lymph nodes of head, face & neck
C77.8	Secondary & unsp malig neoplasm of lymph nodes of multi regions
C7B.03	Secondary carcinoid tumors of bone
C7B.01	Secondary carcinoid tumors of distant lymph nodes
C7B.02	Secondary carcinoid tumors of liver
C7B.09	Secondary carcinoid tumors of oth sites
C7B.04	Secondary carcinoid tumors of peritoneum

I85.10	Secondary esophageal varices w/o bleeding
N25.81	Secondary hyperparathyroidism of renal origin
H20.033	Secondary infectious iridocyclitis, bilat
H20.032	Secondary infectious iridocyclitis, lt eye
H20.031	Secondary infectious iridocyclitis, rt eye
H20.039	Secondary infectious iridocyclitis, unsp eye
C79.11	Secondary malig neoplasm of bladder
C79.51	Secondary malig neoplasm of bone
C79.52	Secondary malig neoplasm of bone marrow
C79.31	Secondary malig neoplasm of brain
C79.81	Secondary malig neoplasm of breast
C79.32	Secondary malig neoplasm of cerebral meninges
C79.82	Secondary malig neoplasm of genital organs
C78.5	Secondary malig neoplasm of lg intestine & rectum
C78.7	Secondary malig neoplasm of liver & intrahepatic bile duct
C79.72	Secondary malig neoplasm of lt adrenal gland
C79.02	Secondary malig neoplasm of lt kidney & renal pelvis
C78.02	Secondary malig neoplasm of lt lung
C79.62	Secondary malig neoplasm of lt ovary
C78.1	Secondary malig neoplasm of mediastinum
C78.89	Secondary malig neoplasm of oth digestive organs
C79.49	Secondary malig neoplasm of oth parts of nervous sys
C78.39	Secondary malig neoplasm of oth respiratory organs
C79.89	Secondary malig neoplasm of oth spec sites
C79.19	Secondary malig neoplasm of oth urinary organs
C78.2	Secondary malig neoplasm of pleura
C78.6	Secondary malig neoplasm of retroperitoneum & peritoneum
C79.71	Secondary malig neoplasm of rt adrenal gland
C79.01	Secondary malig neoplasm of rt kidney & renal pelvis
C78.01	Secondary malig neoplasm of rt lung
C79.61	Secondary malig neoplasm of rt ovary
C79.2	Secondary malig neoplasm of skin
C78.4	Secondary malig neoplasm of sm intestine
C79.70	Secondary malig neoplasm of unsp adrenal gland
C78.80	Secondary malig neoplasm of unsp digestive organ
C79.00	Secondary malig neoplasm of unsp kidney & renal pelvis
C78.00	Secondary malig neoplasm of unsp lung
C79.60	Secondary malig neoplasm of unsp ovary
C79.40	Secondary malig neoplasm of unsp part of nervous sys
C78.30	Secondary malig neoplasm of unsp respiratory organ
C79.9	Secondary malig neoplasm of unsp site
C79.10	Secondary malig neoplasm of unsp urinary organs
G21.2	Secondary parkinsonism d/t oth ext agents
G21.9	Secondary parkinsonism, unsp
J93.12	Secondary spontaneous pneumothorax
A51.42	Secondary syphilitic female pelvic disease
A51.45	Secondary syphilitic hepatitis
A51.44	Secondary syphilitic nephritis
A51.43	Secondary syphilitic oculopathy
A51.46	Secondary syphilitic osteopathy
E85.3	Secondary systemic amyloidosis
F13.121	Sedative, hypnotic or anxiolytic abuse w/ intoxication delirium
F13.150	Sedative, hypnotic or anxiolytic abuse w/ sedative, hypnotic or anxiolytic-induced psychotic d/o w/ delusions
F13.151	Sedative, hypnotic or anxiolytic abuse w/ sedative, hypnotic or anxiolytic-induced psychotic d/o w/ hallucinations
F13.221	Sedative, hypnotic or anxiolytic dependence w/ intoxication delirium
F13.288	Sedative, hypnotic or anxiolytic dependence w/ oth sedative, hypnotic or anxiolytic-induced d/o
F13.280	Sedative, hypnotic or anxiolytic dependence w/ sedative, hypnotic or anxiolytic-induced anxiety d/o
F13.26	Sedative, hypnotic or anxiolytic dependence w/ sedative, hypnotic or anxiolytic-induced persisting amnestic d/o
F13.27	Sedative, hypnotic or anxiolytic dependence w/ sedative, hypnotic or anxiolytic-induced persisting dementia
F13.250	Sedative, hypnotic or anxiolytic dependence w/ sedative, hypnotic or anxiolytic-induced psychotic d/o w/ delusions
F13.251	Sedative, hypnotic or anxiolytic dependence w/ sedative, hypnotic or anxiolytic-induced psychotic d/o w/ hallucinations
F13.259	Sedative, hypnotic or anxiolytic dependence w/ sedative, hypnotic or anxiolytic-induced psychotic d/o, unsp
F13.281	Sedative, hypnotic or anxiolytic dependence w/ sedative, hypnotic or anxiolytic-induced sexual dysfunction
F13.282	Sedative, hypnotic or anxiolytic dependence w/ sedative, hypnotic or anxiolytic-induced sleep d/o

F13.231	Sedative, hypnotic or anxiolytic dependence w/ withdrawal delirium
F13.232	Sedative, hypnotic or anxiolytic dependence w/ withdrawal w/ perceptual disturbance
F13.230	Sedative, hypnotic or anxiolytic dependence w/ withdrawal, uncomplicated
F13.239	Sedative, hypnotic or anxiolytic dependence w/ withdrawal, unsp
F13.20	Sedative, hypnotic or anxiolytic dependence, uncomplicated
F13.921	Sedative, hypnotic or anxiolytic use, unsp w/ intoxication delirium
F13.97	Sedative, hypnotic or anxiolytic use, unsp w/ sedative, hypnotic or anxiolytic-induced persisting dementia
F13.950	Sedative, hypnotic or anxiolytic use, unsp w/ sedative, hypnotic or anxiolytic-induced psychotic d/o w/ delusions
F13.951	Sedative, hypnotic or anxiolytic use, unsp w/ sedative, hypnotic or anxiolytic-induced psychotic d/o w/ hallucinations
F13.931	Sedative, hypnotic or anxiolytic use, unsp w/ withdrawal delirium
F13.932	Sedative, hypnotic or anxiolytic use, unsp w/ withdrawal w/ perceptual disturbances
F13.930	Sedative, hypnotic or anxiolytic use, unsp w/ withdrawal, uncomplicated
F13.939	Sedative, hypnotic or anxiolytic use, unsp w/ withdrawal, unsp
D80.2	Selective deficiency of immunoglobulin A [IgA]
D80.3	Selective deficiency of immunoglobulin G [IgG] subclasses
D80.4	Selective deficiency of immunoglobulin M [IgM]
O04.87	Sepsis following (induced) termination of pregnancy
O03.87	Sepsis following complete or unsp spontaneous abortion
O08.82	Sepsis following ectopic & molar pregnancy
O07.37	Sepsis following failed attempted termination of pregnancy
O03.37	Sepsis following incomplete spontaneous abortion
I76	Septic arterial embolism
Q04.4	Septo-optic dysplasia of brain
E64.0	Sequelae of protein-calorie malnutrition
H31.423	Serous choroidal detach, bilat
H31.422	Serous choroidal detach, lt eye
H31.421	Serous choroidal detach, rt eye
H31.429	Serous choroidal detach, unsp eye
H35.723	Serous detach of retinal pigment epithelium, bilat
H35.722	Serous detach of retinal pigment epithelium, lt eye
H35.721	Serous detach of retinal pigment epithelium, rt eye
H35.729	Serous detach of retinal pigment epithelium, unsp eye
H33.23	Serous retinal detach, bilat
H33.22	Serous retinal detach, lt eye
H33.21	Serous retinal detach, rt eye
H33.20	Serous retinal detach, unsp eye
D81.2	Severe combined immunodeficiency [SCID] w/ low or normal B-cell numbers
D81.1	Severe combined immunodeficiency [SCID] w/ low T- & B-cell numbers
D81.0	Severe combined immunodeficiency [SCID] w/ reticular dysgenesis
F72	Severe intellectual disabilities
J45.51	Severe persistent asthma w/ (acute) exacerbation
J45.52	Severe persistent asthma w/ status asthmaticus
S32.112A	Severely disp Zone I fx of sacrum, init enc for clsd fx
S32.112K	Severely disp Zone I fx of sacrum, subsq enc for fx w/ nonu
S32.122A	Severely disp Zone II fx of sacrum, init enc for clsd fx
S32.122K	Severely disp Zone II fx of sacrum, subsq enc for fx w/ nonu
S32.132A	Severely disp Zone III fx of sacrum, init enc for clsd fx
S32.132K	Severely disp Zone III fx of sacrum, subsq enc for fx w/ nonu
C84.19	Sezary disease, extranodal & solid organ sites
C84.13	Sezary disease, intra-abd lymph nodes
C84.16	Sezary disease, intrapelvic lymph nodes
C84.12	Sezary disease, intrathoracic lymph nodes
C84.14	Sezary disease, lymph nodes of axilla & upr limb
C84.11	Sezary disease, lymph nodes of head, face, & neck
C84.15	Sezary disease, lymph nodes of inguinal rgn & lwr limb
C84.18	Sezary disease, lymph nodes of multi sites
C84.17	Sezary disease, spleen
C84.10	Sezary disease, unsp site
T74.4XXA	Shaken infant synd, init enc
A03.0	Shigellosis d/t Shigella dysenteriae
T88.2XXA	Shock d/t anesthesia, init enc
R57.9	Shock, unsp
E71.312	Short chain acyl CoA dehydrogenase deficiency
Q77.2	Short rib synd
M35.03	Sicca synd w/ myopathy
R56.00	Simple febrile convulsions
Q89.3	Situs inversus
T86.821	Skin graft (allograft) (autograft) failure
T86.822	Skin graft (allograft) (autograft) infxn
T86.820	Skin graft (allograft) rejection
C83.09	Sm cell B-cell lymphoma, extranodal & solid organ sites
C83.03	Sm cell B-cell lymphoma, intra-abd lymph nodes
C83.06	Sm cell B-cell lymphoma, intrapelvic lymph nodes
C83.02	Sm cell B-cell lymphoma, intrathoracic lymph nodes
C83.04	Sm cell B-cell lymphoma, lymph nodes of axilla & upr limb
C83.01	Sm cell B-cell lymphoma, lymph nodes of head, face, & neck
C83.05	Sm cell B-cell lymphoma, lymph nodes of inguinal rgn & lwr limb
C83.08	Sm cell B-cell lymphoma, lymph nodes of multi sites
C83.07	Sm cell B-cell lymphoma, spleen
C83.00	Sm cell B-cell lymphoma, unsp site
B03	Smallpox
E78.72	Smith-Lemli-Opitz synd
S52.542A	Smith's fx of lt radius, init enc for clsd fx
S52.542P	Smith's fx of lt radius, subsq enc for clsd fx w/ malu
S52.542K	Smith's fx of lt radius, subsq enc for clsd fx w/ nonu
S52.542Q	Smith's fx of lt radius, subsq enc for opn fx type I or II w/ malu
S52.542M	Smith's fx of lt radius, subsq enc for opn fx type I or II w/ nonu
S52.542R	Smith's fx of lt radius, subsq enc for opn fx type IIIA, IIIB, or IIIC w/ malu
S52.542N	Smith's fx of lt radius, subsq enc for opn fx type IIIA, IIIB, or IIIC w/ nonu
S52.541A	Smith's fx of rt radius, init enc for clsd fx
S52.541P	Smith's fx of rt radius, subsq enc for clsd fx w/ malu
S52.541K	Smith's fx of rt radius, subsq enc for clsd fx w/ nonu
S52.541Q	Smith's fx of rt radius, subsq enc for opn fx type I or II w/ malu
S52.541M	Smith's fx of rt radius, subsq enc for opn fx type I or II w/ nonu
S52.541R	Smith's fx of rt radius, subsq enc for opn fx type IIIA, IIIB, or IIIC w/ malu
S52.541N	Smith's fx of rt radius, subsq enc for opn fx type IIIA, IIIB, or IIIC w/ nonu
S52.549A	Smith's fx of unsp radius, init enc for clsd fx
S52.549P	Smith's fx of unsp radius, subsq enc for clsd fx w/ malu
S52.549K	Smith's fx of unsp radius, subsq enc for clsd fx w/ nonu
S52.549Q	Smith's fx of unsp radius, subsq enc for opn fx type I or II w/ malu
S52.549M	Smith's fx of unsp radius, subsq enc for opn fx type I or II w/ nonu
S52.549R	Smith's fx of unsp radius, subsq enc for opn fx type IIIA, IIIB, or IIIC w/ malu
S52.549N	Smith's fx of unsp radius, subsq enc for opn fx type IIIA, IIIB, or IIIC w/ nonu
C90.32	Solitary plasmacytoma in relapse
C90.31	Solitary plasmacytoma in remission
C90.30	Solitary plasmacytoma not having achieved remission
B70.1	Sparganosis
G80.1	Spastic diplegic cerebral palsy
G81.12	Spastic hemiplegia affecting lt dominant side
G81.14	Spastic hemiplegia affecting lt nondominant side
G81.11	Spastic hemiplegia affecting rt dominant side
G81.13	Spastic hemiplegia affecting rt nondominant side
G81.10	Spastic hemiplegia affecting unsp side
G80.2	Spastic hemiplegic cerebral palsy
G12.9	Spinal muscular atrophy, unsp
A25.0	Spirillosis
A77.3	Spotted fever d/t Rickettsia australis
A77.1	Spotted fever d/t Rickettsia conorii
A77.0	Spotted fever d/t Rickettsia rickettsii
A77.2	Spotted fever d/t Rickettsia siberica
A77.9	Spotted fever, unsp
C86.3	SQ panniculitis-like T-cell lymphoma
S12.01XA	Stable burst fx of 1st cervical vertebra, init enc for clsd fx
S12.01XK	Stable burst fx of 1st cervical vertebra, subsq enc for fx w/ nonu
S32.011A	Stable burst fx of 1st lumbar vertebra, init enc for clsd fx
S32.011K	Stable burst fx of 1st lumbar vertebra, subsq enc for fx w/ nonu
S22.011A	Stable burst fx of 1st thoracic vertebra, init enc for clsd fx
S22.011K	Stable burst fx of 1st thoracic vertebra, subsq enc for fx w/ nonu
S32.021A	Stable burst fx of 2nd lumbar vertebra, init enc for clsd fx
S32.021K	Stable burst fx of 2nd lumbar vertebra, subsq enc for fx w/ nonu
S22.021A	Stable burst fx of 2nd thoracic vertebra, init enc for clsd fx
S22.021K	Stable burst fx of 2nd thoracic vertebra, subsq enc for fx w/ nonu
S32.031A	Stable burst fx of 3rd lumbar vertebra, init enc for clsd fx
S32.031K	Stable burst fx of 3rd lumbar vertebra, subsq enc for fx w/ nonu
S22.031A	Stable burst fx of 3rd thoracic vertebra, init enc for clsd fx
S22.031K	Stable burst fx of 3rd thoracic vertebra, subsq enc for fx w/ nonu
S32.041A	Stable burst fx of 4th lumbar vertebra, init enc for clsd fx
S32.041K	Stable burst fx of 4th lumbar vertebra, subsq enc for fx w/ nonu
S22.041A	Stable burst fx of 4th thoracic vertebra, init enc for clsd fx

S22.041K	Stable burst fx of 4th thoracic vertebra, subsq enc for fx w/ nonu
S32.051A	Stable burst fx of 5th lumbar vertebra, init enc for clsd fx
S32.051K	Stable burst fx of 5th lumbar vertebra, subsq enc for fx w/ nonu
S22.081A	Stable burst fx of T11-T12 vertebra, init enc for clsd fx
S22.081K	Stable burst fx of T11-T12 vertebra, subsq enc for fx w/ nonu
S22.051A	Stable burst fx of T5-T6 vertebra, init enc for clsd fx
S22.051K	Stable burst fx of T5-T6 vertebra, subsq enc for fx w/ nonu
S22.061A	Stable burst fx of T7-T8 vertebra, init enc for clsd fx
S22.061K	Stable burst fx of T7-T8 vertebra, subsq enc for fx w/ nonu
S22.071A	Stable burst fx of T9-T10 vertebra, init enc for clsd fx
S22.071K	Stable burst fx of T9-T10 vertebra, subsq enc for fx w/ nonu
S32.001A	Stable burst fx of unsp lumbar vertebra, init enc for clsd fx
S32.001K	Stable burst fx of unsp lumbar vertebra, subsq enc for fx w/ nonu
S22.001A	Stable burst fx of unsp thoracic vertebra, init enc for clsd fx
S22.001K	Stable burst fx of unsp thoracic vertebra, subsq enc for fx w/ nonu
M00.079	Staphylococcal arthritis, unsp ankle & foot
M00.029	Staphylococcal arthritis, unsp elbow
M00.049	Staphylococcal arthritis, unsp hand
M00.059	Staphylococcal arthritis, unsp hip
M00.00	Staphylococcal arthritis, unsp jt
M00.069	Staphylococcal arthritis, unsp knee
M00.019	Staphylococcal arthritis, unsp shldr
M00.039	Staphylococcal arthritis, unsp wrist
M00.08	Staphylococcal arthritis, vertebrae
M00.09	Staphylococcal polyarthritis
Z94.84	Stem cells transplant status
T84.85XA	Stenosis d/t int orthopedic prosthetic devices, implants & grafts, init enc
T85.85XA	Stenosis d/t int prosthetic devices, implants & grafts, NEC, init enc
T82.857A	Stenosis of cardiac prosthetic devices, implants & grafts, init enc
T83.85XA	Stenosis of genitourinary prosthetic devices, implants & grafts, init enc
T82.858A	Stenosis of vascular prosthetic devices, implants & grafts, init enc
S22.23XA	Sternal manubrial dissociation, init enc for clsd fx
S22.23XK	Sternal manubrial dissociation, subsq enc for fx w/ nonu
L51.1	Stevens-Johnson synd
L51.3	Stevens-Johnson synd-toxic epidermal necrolysis overlap synd
G25.82	Stiff-man synd
A25.1	Streptobacillosis
M84.359P	Stress fx, hip, unsp, subsq enc for fx w/ malu
M84.359K	Stress fx, hip, unsp, subsq enc for fx w/ nonu
M84.372P	Stress fx, lt ankle, subsq enc for fx w/ malu
M84.372K	Stress fx, lt ankle, subsq enc for fx w/ nonu
M84.352P	Stress fx, lt femur, subsq enc for fx w/ malu
M84.352K	Stress fx, lt femur, subsq enc for fx w/ nonu
M84.364P	Stress fx, lt fibula, subsq enc for fx w/ malu
M84.364K	Stress fx, lt fibula, subsq enc for fx w/ nonu
M84.345P	Stress fx, lt finger(s), subsq enc for fx w/ malu
M84.345K	Stress fx, lt finger(s), subsq enc for fx w/ nonu
M84.375P	Stress fx, lt foot, subsq enc for fx w/ malu
M84.375K	Stress fx, lt foot, subsq enc for fx w/ nonu
M84.342P	Stress fx, lt hand, subsq enc for fx w/ malu
M84.342K	Stress fx, lt hand, subsq enc for fx w/ nonu
M84.322P	Stress fx, lt humerus, subsq enc for fx w/ malu
M84.322K	Stress fx, lt humerus, subsq enc for fx w/ nonu
M84.334P	Stress fx, lt radius, subsq enc for fx w/ malu
M84.334K	Stress fx, lt radius, subsq enc for fx w/ nonu
M84.312P	Stress fx, lt shldr, subsq enc for fx w/ malu
M84.312K	Stress fx, lt shldr, subsq enc for fx w/ nonu
M84.362P	Stress fx, lt tibia, subsq enc for fx w/ malu
M84.362K	Stress fx, lt tibia, subsq enc for fx w/ nonu
M84.378P	Stress fx, lt toe(s), subsq enc for fx w/ malu
M84.378K	Stress fx, lt toe(s), subsq enc for fx w/ nonu
M84.332P	Stress fx, lt ulna, subsq enc for fx w/ malu
M84.332K	Stress fx, lt ulna, subsq enc for fx w/ nonu
M84.38XP	Stress fx, oth site, subsq enc for fx w/ malu
M84.38XK	Stress fx, oth site, subsq enc for fx w/ nonu
M84.350P	Stress fx, pelvis, subsq enc for fx w/ malu
M84.350K	Stress fx, pelvis, subsq enc for fx w/ nonu
M84.371P	Stress fx, rt ankle, subsq enc for fx w/ malu
M84.371K	Stress fx, rt ankle, subsq enc for fx w/ nonu
M84.351P	Stress fx, rt femur, subsq enc for fx w/ malu
M84.351K	Stress fx, rt femur, subsq enc for fx w/ nonu
M84.363P	Stress fx, rt fibula, subsq enc for fx w/ malu
M84.363K	Stress fx, rt fibula, subsq enc for fx w/ nonu

M84.344P	Stress fx, rt finger(s), subsq enc for fx w/ malu
M84.344K	Stress fx, rt finger(s), subsq enc for fx w/ nonu
M84.374P	Stress fx, rt foot, subsq enc for fx w/ malu
M84.374K	Stress fx, rt foot, subsq enc for fx w/ nonu
M84.341P	Stress fx, rt hand, subsq enc for fx w/ malu
M84.341K	Stress fx, rt hand, subsq enc for fx w/ nonu
M84.321P	Stress fx, rt humerus, subsq enc for fx w/ malu
M84.321K	Stress fx, rt humerus, subsq enc for fx w/ nonu
M84.333P	Stress fx, rt radius, subsq enc for fx w/ malu
M84.333K	Stress fx, rt radius, subsq enc for fx w/ nonu
M84.311P	Stress fx, rt shldr, subsq enc for fx w/ malu
M84.311K	Stress fx, rt shldr, subsq enc for fx w/ nonu
M84.361P	Stress fx, rt tibia, subsq enc for fx w/ malu
M84.361K	Stress fx, rt tibia, subsq enc for fx w/ nonu
M84.377P	Stress fx, rt toe(s), subsq enc for fx w/ malu
M84.377K	Stress fx, rt toe(s), subsq enc for fx w/ nonu
M84.331P	Stress fx, rt ulna, subsq enc for fx w/ malu
M84.331K	Stress fx, rt ulna, subsq enc for fx w/ nonu
M84.373P	Stress fx, unsp ankle, subsq enc for fx w/ malu
M84.373K	Stress fx, unsp ankle, subsq enc for fx w/ nonu
M84.353P	Stress fx, unsp femur, subsq enc for fx w/ malu
M84.353K	Stress fx, unsp femur, subsq enc for fx w/ nonu
M84.346P	Stress fx, unsp finger(s), subsq enc for fx w/ malu
M84.346K	Stress fx, unsp finger(s), subsq enc for fx w/ nonu
M84.376P	Stress fx, unsp foot, subsq enc for fx w/ malu
M84.376K	Stress fx, unsp foot, subsq enc for fx w/ nonu
M84.343P	Stress fx, unsp hand, subsq enc for fx w/ malu
M84.343K	Stress fx, unsp hand, subsq enc for fx w/ nonu
M84.329P	Stress fx, unsp humerus, subsq enc for fx w/ malu
M84.329K	Stress fx, unsp humerus, subsq enc for fx w/ nonu
M84.319P	Stress fx, unsp shldr, subsq enc for fx w/ malu
M84.319K	Stress fx, unsp shldr, subsq enc for fx w/ nonu
M84.30XP	Stress fx, unsp site, subsq enc for fx w/ malu
M84.30XK	Stress fx, unsp site, subsq enc for fx w/ nonu
M84.369P	Stress fx, unsp tibia & fibula, subsq enc for fx w/ malu
M84.369K	Stress fx, unsp tibia & fibula, subsq enc for fx w/ nonu
M84.379P	Stress fx, unsp toe(s), subsq enc for fx w/ malu
M84.379K	Stress fx, unsp toe(s), subsq enc for fx w/ nonu
M84.339P	Stress fx, unsp ulna & radius, subsq enc for fx w/ malu
M84.339K	Stress fx, unsp ulna & radius, subsq enc for fx w/ nonu
G23.2	Striatonigral degeneration
B78.9	Strongyloidiasis, unsp
A24.2	Subacute & chr melioidosis
G32.0	Subacute combined degeneration of spinal cord in diseases classified elsw
M86.272	Subacute osteomyelitis, lt ankle & foot
M86.252	Subacute osteomyelitis, lt femur
M86.242	Subacute osteomyelitis, lt hand
M86.222	Subacute osteomyelitis, lt humerus
M86.232	Subacute osteomyelitis, lt radius & ulna
M86.212	Subacute osteomyelitis, lt shldr
M86.262	Subacute osteomyelitis, lt tibia & fibula
M86.29	Subacute osteomyelitis, multi sites
M86.28	Subacute osteomyelitis, oth site
M86.271	Subacute osteomyelitis, rt ankle & foot
M86.251	Subacute osteomyelitis, rt femur
M86.241	Subacute osteomyelitis, rt hand
M86.221	Subacute osteomyelitis, rt humerus
M86.231	Subacute osteomyelitis, rt radius & ulna
M86.211	Subacute osteomyelitis, rt shldr
M86.261	Subacute osteomyelitis, rt tibia & fibula
M86.279	Subacute osteomyelitis, unsp ankle & foot
M86.259	Subacute osteomyelitis, unsp femur
M86.249	Subacute osteomyelitis, unsp hand
M86.229	Subacute osteomyelitis, unsp humerus
M86.239	Subacute osteomyelitis, unsp radius & ulna
M86.219	Subacute osteomyelitis, unsp shldr
M86.20	Subacute osteomyelitis, unsp site
M86.269	Subacute osteomyelitis, unsp tibia & fibula
A81.1	Subacute sclerosing panencephalitis
M99.11	Sublux complex (vert) of cervical rgn
M99.10	Sublux complex (vert) of head rgn
M99.18	Sublux complex (vert) of rib cage

Appendix B — Alphabetic CC List

S13.110A	Sublux of C0/C1 cervical vertebrae, init enc
S13.120A	Sublux of C1/C2 cervical vertebrae, init enc
S13.130A	Sublux of C2/C3 cervical vertebrae, init enc
S13.140A	Sublux of C3/C4 cervical vertebrae, init enc
S13.150A	Sublux of C4/C5 cervical vertebrae, init enc
S13.160A	Sublux of C5/C6 cervical vertebrae, init enc
S13.170A	Sublux of C6/C7 cervical vertebrae, init enc
S13.180A	Sublux of C7/T1 cervical vertebrae, init enc
S13.100A	Sublux of unsp cervical vertebrae, init enc
H70.013	Subperiosteal abscess of mastoid, bilat
H70.012	Subperiosteal abscess of mastoid, lt ear
H70.011	Subperiosteal abscess of mastoid, rt ear
H70.019	Subperiosteal abscess of mastoid, unsp ear
H53.133	Sudden visual loss, bilat
H53.132	Sudden visual loss, lt eye
H53.131	Sudden visual loss, rt eye
H53.139	Sudden visual loss, unsp eye
R45.851	Suicidal ideations
S36.030A	Superf (capsular) lac of spleen, init enc
T33.3XXA	Superf frostbite of abd wall, lwr back & pelvis, init enc
T33.812A	Superf frostbite of lt ankle, init enc
T33.42XA	Superf frostbite of lt arm, init enc
T33.012A	Superf frostbite of lt ear, init enc
T33.532A	Superf frostbite of lt finger(s), init enc
T33.822A	Superf frostbite of lt foot, init enc
T33.522A	Superf frostbite of lt hand, init enc
T33.62XA	Superf frostbite of lt hip & thigh, init enc
T33.72XA	Superf frostbite of lt knee & lwr leg, init enc
T33.832A	Superf frostbite of lt toe(s), init enc
T33.512A	Superf frostbite of lt wrist, init enc
T33.1XXA	Superf frostbite of neck, init enc
T33.02XA	Superf frostbite of nose, init enc
T33.09XA	Superf frostbite of oth part of head, init enc
T33.99XA	Superf frostbite of oth sites, init enc
T33.811A	Superf frostbite of rt ankle, init enc
T33.41XA	Superf frostbite of rt arm, init enc
T33.011A	Superf frostbite of rt ear, init enc
T33.531A	Superf frostbite of rt finger(s), init enc
T33.821A	Superf frostbite of rt foot, init enc
T33.521A	Superf frostbite of rt hand, init enc
T33.61XA	Superf frostbite of rt hip & thigh, init enc
T33.71XA	Superf frostbite of rt knee & lwr leg, init enc
T33.831A	Superf frostbite of rt toe(s), init enc
T33.511A	Superf frostbite of rt wrist, init enc
T33.2XXA	Superf frostbite of thorax, init enc
T33.819A	Superf frostbite of unsp ankle, init enc
T33.40XA	Superf frostbite of unsp arm, init enc
T33.019A	Superf frostbite of unsp ear, init enc
T33.539A	Superf frostbite of unsp finger(s), init enc
T33.829A	Superf frostbite of unsp foot, init enc
T33.529A	Superf frostbite of unsp hand, init enc
T33.60XA	Superf frostbite of unsp hip & thigh, init enc
T33.70XA	Superf frostbite of unsp knee & lwr leg, init enc
T33.90XA	Superf frostbite of unsp sites, init enc
T33.839A	Superf frostbite of unsp toe(s), init enc
T33.519A	Superf frostbite of unsp wrist, init enc
O22.21	Superf thrombophlebitis in pregnancy, 1st trmstr
O22.22	Superf thrombophlebitis in pregnancy, 2nd trmstr
O22.23	Superf thrombophlebitis in pregnancy, 3rd trmstr
O22.20	Superf thrombophlebitis in pregnancy, unsp trmstr
O87.0	Superf thrombophlebitis in the puerperium
Q25.3	Supravalvular aortic stenosis
I47.1	Supraventricular tachycardia
Q64.11	Supravesical fissure of urinary bladder
A82.0	Sylvatic rabies
A95.0	Sylvatic yellow fever
H44.133	Sympathetic uveitis, bilat
H44.132	Sympathetic uveitis, lt eye
H44.131	Sympathetic uveitis, rt eye
H44.139	Sympathetic uveitis, unsp eye
A52.73	Symptomatic late syphilis of oth respiratory organs
A52.10	Symptomatic neurosyphilis, unsp
E22.2	Synd of inappropriate secretion of antidiuretic hormone
O98.12	Syphilis comp childbirth
O98.111	Syphilis comp pregnancy, 1st trmstr
O98.112	Syphilis comp pregnancy, 2nd trmstr
O98.113	Syphilis comp pregnancy, 3rd trmstr
O98.13	Syphilis comp the puerperium
A52.77	Syphilis of bone & jt
A52.75	Syphilis of kidney & ureter
A52.74	Syphilis of liver & oth viscera
A52.72	Syphilis of lung & bronchus
A52.78	Syphilis of oth musculoskeletal tissue
A51.32	Syphilitic alopecia
A52.01	Syphilitic aneurysm of aorta
A52.02	Syphilitic aortitis
A52.04	Syphilitic cerebral arteritis
A52.03	Syphilitic endocarditis
A50.57	Syphilitic saddle nose
G95.0	Syringomyelia & syringobulbia
A44.0	Systemic bartonellosis
R65.10	Systemic inflam response synd (SIRS) of non-infectious origin w/o acute organ dysfunction
M34.81	Systemic sclerosis w/ lung involvement
M34.82	Systemic sclerosis w/ myopathy
A52.11	Tabes dorsalis
B68.1	Taenia saginata taeniasis
B68.0	Taenia solium taeniasis
B68.9	Taeniasis, unsp
I51.81	Takotsubo synd
B08.71	Tanapox virus disease
E75.02	Tay-Sachs disease
O60.20X1	Term delivery w/ preterm labor, unsp trmstr, fetus 1
O60.20X2	Term delivery w/ preterm labor, unsp trmstr, fetus 2
O60.20X3	Term delivery w/ preterm labor, unsp trmstr, fetus 3
O60.20X4	Term delivery w/ preterm labor, unsp trmstr, fetus 4
O60.20X5	Term delivery w/ preterm labor, unsp trmstr, fetus 5
O60.20X0	Term delivery w/ preterm labor, unsp trmstr, N/A or unsp
O60.20X9	Term delivery w/ preterm labor, unsp trmstr, oth fetus
R29.0	Tetany
E51.9	Thiamine deficiency, unsp
Q05.1	Thoracic spina bifida w/ hydrocephalus
O20.0	Threatened abortion
I82.1	Thrombophlebitis migrans
T84.86XA	Thrombosis d/t int orthopedic prosthetic devices, implants & grafts, init enc
T85.86XA	Thrombosis d/t int prosthetic devices, implants & grafts, NEC, init enc
I23.6	Thrombosis of atrium, auricular appendage, & ventricle as current comp following acute myocardial infarction
T82.867A	Thrombosis of cardiac prosthetic devices, implants & grafts, init enc
T83.86XA	Thrombosis of genitourinary prosthetic devices, implants & grafts, init enc
T82.868A	Thrombosis of vascular prosthetic devices, implants & grafts, init enc
A68.1	Tick-borne relapsing fever
B44.2	Tonsillar aspergillosis
N44.04	Torsion of appendix epididymis
N44.03	Torsion of appendix testis
N83.52	Torsion of fallopian tube
N83.51	Torsion of ovary & ovarian pedicle
N83.53	Torsion of ovary, ovarian pedicle & fallopian tube
N44.00	Torsion of testis, unsp
S72.472A	Torus fx of lwr end of lt femur, init enc for clsd fx
S72.472P	Torus fx of lwr end of lt femur, subsq enc for fx w/ malu
S72.472K	Torus fx of lwr end of lt femur, subsq enc for fx w/ nonu
S82.822A	Torus fx of lwr end of lt fibula, subsq enc for fx w/ malu
S82.822K	Torus fx of lwr end of lt fibula, subsq enc for fx w/ nonu
S42.482A	Torus fx of lwr end of lt humerus, init enc for clsd fx
S42.482P	Torus fx of lwr end of lt humerus, subsq enc for fx w/ malu
S42.482K	Torus fx of lwr end of lt humerus, subsq enc for fx w/ nonu
S52.522A	Torus fx of lwr end of lt radius, init enc for clsd fx
S52.522P	Torus fx of lwr end of lt radius, subsq enc for fx w/ malu
S52.522K	Torus fx of lwr end of lt radius, subsq enc for fx w/ nonu
S82.312A	Torus fx of lwr end of lt tibia, init enc for clsd fx
S82.312P	Torus fx of lwr end of lt tibia, subsq enc for fx w/ malu
S82.312K	Torus fx of lwr end of lt tibia, subsq enc for fx w/ nonu
S52.622A	Torus fx of lwr end of lt ulna, init enc for clsd fx
S52.622P	Torus fx of lwr end of lt ulna, subsq enc for fx w/ malu

Code	Description
S52.622K	Torus fx of lwr end of lt ulna, subsq enc for fx w/ nonu
S72.471A	Torus fx of lwr end of rt femur, init enc for clsd fx
S72.471P	Torus fx of lwr end of rt femur, subsq enc for fx w/ malu
S72.471K	Torus fx of lwr end of rt femur, subsq enc for fx w/ nonu
S82.821P	Torus fx of lwr end of rt fibula, subsq enc for fx w/ malu
S82.821K	Torus fx of lwr end of rt fibula, subsq enc for fx w/ nonu
S42.481A	Torus fx of lwr end of rt humerus, init enc for clsd fx
S42.481P	Torus fx of lwr end of rt humerus, subsq enc for fx w/ malu
S42.481K	Torus fx of lwr end of rt humerus, subsq enc for fx w/ nonu
S52.521A	Torus fx of lwr end of rt radius, init enc for clsd fx
S52.521P	Torus fx of lwr end of rt radius, subsq enc for fx w/ malu
S52.521K	Torus fx of lwr end of rt radius, subsq enc for fx w/ nonu
S82.311A	Torus fx of lwr end of rt tibia, init enc for clsd fx
S82.311P	Torus fx of lwr end of rt tibia, subsq enc for fx w/ malu
S82.311K	Torus fx of lwr end of rt tibia, subsq enc for fx w/ nonu
S52.621A	Torus fx of lwr end of rt ulna, init enc for clsd fx
S52.621P	Torus fx of lwr end of rt ulna, subsq enc for fx w/ malu
S52.621K	Torus fx of lwr end of rt ulna, subsq enc for fx w/ nonu
S72.479A	Torus fx of lwr end of unsp femur, init enc for clsd fx
S72.479P	Torus fx of lwr end of unsp femur, subsq enc for fx w/ malu
S72.479K	Torus fx of lwr end of unsp femur, subsq enc for fx w/ nonu
S82.829P	Torus fx of lwr end of unsp fibula, subsq enc for fx w/ malu
S82.829K	Torus fx of lwr end of unsp fibula, subsq enc for fx w/ nonu
S42.489A	Torus fx of lwr end of unsp humerus, init enc for clsd fx
S42.489P	Torus fx of lwr end of unsp humerus, subsq enc for fx w/ malu
S42.489K	Torus fx of lwr end of unsp humerus, subsq enc for fx w/ nonu
S52.529A	Torus fx of lwr end of unsp radius, init enc for clsd fx
S52.529P	Torus fx of lwr end of unsp radius, subsq enc for fx w/ malu
S52.529K	Torus fx of lwr end of unsp radius, subsq enc for fx w/ nonu
S82.319A	Torus fx of lwr end of unsp tibia, init enc for clsd fx
S82.319P	Torus fx of lwr end of unsp tibia, subsq enc for fx w/ malu
S82.319K	Torus fx of lwr end of unsp tibia, subsq enc for fx w/ nonu
S52.629A	Torus fx of lwr end of unsp ulna, init enc for clsd fx
S52.629P	Torus fx of lwr end of unsp ulna, subsq enc for fx w/ malu
S52.629K	Torus fx of lwr end of unsp ulna, subsq enc for fx w/ nonu
S82.812P	Torus fx of upr end of lt fibula, subsq enc for fx w/ malu
S82.812K	Torus fx of upr end of lt fibula, subsq enc for fx w/ nonu
S42.272A	Torus fx of upr end of lt humerus, init enc for clsd fx
S42.272P	Torus fx of upr end of lt humerus, subsq enc for fx w/ malu
S42.272K	Torus fx of upr end of lt humerus, subsq enc for fx w/ nonu
S52.112A	Torus fx of upr end of lt radius, init enc for clsd fx
S52.112P	Torus fx of upr end of lt radius, subsq enc for fx w/ malu
S52.112K	Torus fx of upr end of lt radius, subsq enc for fx w/ nonu
S82.162A	Torus fx of upr end of lt tibia, init enc for clsd fx
S82.162P	Torus fx of upr end of lt tibia, subsq enc for fx w/ malu
S82.162K	Torus fx of upr end of lt tibia, subsq enc for fx w/ nonu
S52.012A	Torus fx of upr end of lt ulna, init enc for clsd fx
S52.012P	Torus fx of upr end of lt ulna, subsq enc for fx w/ malu
S52.012K	Torus fx of upr end of lt ulna, subsq enc for fx w/ nonu
S82.811P	Torus fx of upr end of rt fibula, subsq enc for fx w/ malu
S82.811K	Torus fx of upr end of rt fibula, subsq enc for fx w/ nonu
S42.271A	Torus fx of upr end of rt humerus, init enc for clsd fx
S42.271P	Torus fx of upr end of rt humerus, subsq enc for fx w/ malu
S42.271K	Torus fx of upr end of rt humerus, subsq enc for fx w/ nonu
S52.111A	Torus fx of upr end of rt radius, init enc for clsd fx
S52.111P	Torus fx of upr end of rt radius, subsq enc for fx w/ malu
S52.111K	Torus fx of upr end of rt radius, subsq enc for fx w/ nonu
S82.161A	Torus fx of upr end of rt tibia, init enc for clsd fx
S82.161P	Torus fx of upr end of rt tibia, subsq enc for fx w/ malu
S82.161K	Torus fx of upr end of rt tibia, subsq enc for fx w/ nonu
S52.011A	Torus fx of upr end of rt ulna, init enc for clsd fx
S52.011P	Torus fx of upr end of rt ulna, subsq enc for fx w/ malu
S52.011K	Torus fx of upr end of rt ulna, subsq enc for fx w/ nonu
S82.819P	Torus fx of upr end of unsp fibula, subsq enc for fx w/ malu
S82.819K	Torus fx of upr end of unsp fibula, subsq enc for fx w/ nonu
S42.279A	Torus fx of upr end of unsp humerus, init enc for clsd fx
S42.279P	Torus fx of upr end of unsp humerus, subsq enc for fx w/ malu
S42.279K	Torus fx of upr end of unsp humerus, subsq enc for fx w/ nonu
S52.119A	Torus fx of upr end of unsp radius, init enc for clsd fx
S52.119P	Torus fx of upr end of unsp radius, subsq enc for fx w/ malu
S52.119K	Torus fx of upr end of unsp radius, subsq enc for fx w/ nonu
S82.169A	Torus fx of upr end of unsp tibia, init enc for clsd fx
S82.169P	Torus fx of upr end of unsp tibia, subsq enc for fx w/ malu
S82.169K	Torus fx of upr end of unsp tibia, subsq enc for fx w/ nonu
S52.019A	Torus fx of upr end of unsp ulna, init enc for clsd fx
S52.019P	Torus fx of upr end of unsp ulna, subsq enc for fx w/ malu
S52.019K	Torus fx of upr end of unsp ulna, subsq enc for fx w/ nonu
Q26.2	Total anomalous pulmn venous connection
L51.2	Toxic epidermal necrolysis [Lyell]
L53.0	Toxic erythema
K52.1	Toxic gastroenteritis & colitis
B58.01	Toxoplasma chorioretinitis
B58.1	Toxoplasma hepatitis
B58.82	Toxoplasma myositis
B58.00	Toxoplasma oculopathy, unsp
B58.83	Toxoplasma tubulo-interstitial nephropathy
B58.89	Toxoplasmosis w/ oth organ involvement
B58.9	Toxoplasmosis, unsp
J95.04	Tracheo-esophageal fistula following tracheostomy
H33.43	Traction detach of retina, bilat
H33.42	Traction detach of retina, lt eye
H33.41	Traction detach of retina, rt eye
H33.40	Traction detach of retina, unsp eye
J95.84	Transfusion-related acute lung inj (TRALI)
G45.9	Transient cerebral ischemic attack, unsp
D80.7	Transient hypogammaglobulinemia of infancy
P94.0	Transient neonatal myasthenia gravis
R29.5	Transient paralysis
H34.03	Transient retinal artery occlsn, bilat
H34.02	Transient retinal artery occlsn, lt eye
H34.01	Transient retinal artery occlsn, rt eye
H34.00	Transient retinal artery occlsn, unsp eye
H53.123	Transient visual loss, bilat
H53.122	Transient visual loss, lt eye
H53.121	Transient visual loss, rt eye
H53.129	Transient visual loss, unsp eye
P74.6	Transitory hyperammonemia of newborn
P76.1	Transitory ileus of newborn
P71.9	Transitory neonatal d/o of calcium & magnesium metabolism, unsp
P72.1	Transitory neonatal hyperthyroidism
P71.4	Transitory neonatal hypoparathyroidism
P74.5	Transitory tyrosinemia of newborn
S28.1XXA	Traum amp (partial) of part of thorax, except breast, init enc
T79.A3XA	Traum compartment synd of abd, init enc
T79.A22A	Traum compartment synd of lt lwr extr, init enc
T79.A12A	Traum compartment synd of lt upr extr, init enc
T79.A9XA	Traum compartment synd of oth sites, init enc
T79.A21A	Traum compartment synd of rt lwr extr, init enc
T79.A11A	Traum compartment synd of rt upr extr, init enc
T79.A29A	Traum compartment synd of unsp lwr extr, init enc
T79.A19A	Traum compartment synd of unsp upr extr, init enc
S27.0XXA	Traum pneumothorax, init enc
S13.0XXA	Traum rupture of cervical interv disc, init enc
S09.22XA	Traum rupture of lt ear drum, init enc
S09.21XA	Traum rupture of rt ear drum, init enc
S09.20XA	Traum rupture of unsp ear drum, init enc
T79.2XXA	Traum secondary & recurrent hemor & seroma, init enc
M48.32	Traum spondylopathy, cervical rgn
M48.33	Traum spondylopathy, cervicothoracic rgn
M48.36	Traum spondylopathy, lumbar rgn
M48.37	Traum spondylopathy, lumbosacral rgn
M48.31	Traum spondylopathy, occipito-atlanto-axial rgn
M48.38	Traum spondylopathy, sacral & sacrococcygeal rgn
M48.30	Traum spondylopathy, site unsp
M48.34	Traum spondylopathy, thoracic rgn
M48.35	Traum spondylopathy, thoracolumbar rgn
T79.7XXA	Traum SQ emphysema, init enc
A79.0	Trench fever
B75	Trichinellosis
B81.2	Trichostrongyliasis
B79	Trichuriasis
I45.3	Trifascicular block
E72.52	Trimethylaminuria
O30.121	Triplet pregnancy w/ two or more monoamniotic fetuses, 1st trmstr
O30.122	Triplet pregnancy w/ two or more monoamniotic fetuses, 2nd trmstr
O30.123	Triplet pregnancy w/ two or more monoamniotic fetuses, 3rd trmstr

O30.111	Triplet pregnancy w/ two or more monochorionic fetuses, 1st trmstr
O30.112	Triplet pregnancy w/ two or more monochorionic fetuses, 2nd trmstr
O30.113	Triplet pregnancy w/ two or more monochorionic fetuses, 3rd trmstr
O30.191	Triplet pregnancy, unable to determine number of placenta & number of amniotic sacs, 1st trmstr
O30.192	Triplet pregnancy, unable to determine number of placenta & number of amniotic sacs, 2nd trmstr
O30.193	Triplet pregnancy, unable to determine number of placenta & number of amniotic sacs, 3rd trmstr
O30.101	Triplet pregnancy, unsp number of placenta & unsp number of amniotic sacs, 1st trmstr
O30.102	Triplet pregnancy, unsp number of placenta & unsp number of amniotic sacs, 2nd trmstr
O30.103	Triplet pregnancy, unsp number of placenta & unsp number of amniotic sacs, 3rd trmstr
Q91.5	Trisomy 13, mosaicism (mitotic nondisjunction)
Q91.4	Trisomy 13, nonmosaicism (meiotic nondisjunction)
Q91.6	Trisomy 13, translocation
Q91.7	Trisomy 13, unsp
Q91.1	Trisomy 18, mosaicism (mitotic nondisjunction)
Q91.0	Trisomy 18, nonmosaicism (meiotic nondisjunction)
Q91.2	Trisomy 18, translocation
Q91.3	Trisomy 18, unsp
G04.1	Tropical spastic paraplegia
K90.1	Tropical sprue
O00.1	Tubal pregnancy
A30.1	Tuberculoid leprosy
O98.02	Tuberculosis comp childbirth
O98.011	Tuberculosis comp pregnancy, 1st trmstr
O98.012	Tuberculosis comp pregnancy, 2nd trmstr
O98.013	Tuberculosis comp pregnancy, 3rd trmstr
O98.03	Tuberculosis comp the puerperium
A18.6	Tuberculosis of (inner) (mid) ear
A18.7	Tuberculosis of adrenal glands
A18.12	Tuberculosis of bladder
A18.16	Tuberculosis of cervix
A18.83	Tuberculosis of digestive tract organs, NEC
A18.50	Tuberculosis of eye, unsp
A18.10	Tuberculosis of genitourinary sys, unsp
A18.84	Tuberculosis of heart
A15.4	Tuberculosis of intrathoracic lymph nodes
A18.11	Tuberculosis of kidney & ureter
A15.5	Tuberculosis of larynx, trachea & bronchus
A15.0	Tuberculosis of lung
A17.9	Tuberculosis of nervous sys, unsp
A18.03	Tuberculosis of oth bones
A18.82	Tuberculosis of oth endocrine glands
A18.18	Tuberculosis of oth female genital organs
A18.15	Tuberculosis of oth male genital organs
A18.89	Tuberculosis of oth sites
A18.13	Tuberculosis of oth urinary organs
A18.14	Tuberculosis of prostate
A18.4	Tuberculosis of skin & SQ tissue
A18.01	Tuberculosis of spine
A18.85	Tuberculosis of spleen
A18.81	Tuberculosis of thyroid gland
A18.02	Tuberculous arthritis of oth joints
A18.53	Tuberculous chorioretinitis
A18.32	Tuberculous enteritis
A18.51	Tuberculous episcleritis
A18.17	Tuberculous female pelvic inflam disease
A18.54	Tuberculous iridocyclitis
A18.52	Tuberculous keratitis
A18.2	Tuberculous peripheral lymphadenopathy
A15.6	Tuberculous pleurisy
Q85.1	Tuberous sclerosis
N12	Tubulo-interstitial nephritis, not spec as acute or chr
A21.9	Tularemia, unsp
E10.52	Type 1 diabetes mellitus w/ diabetic peripheral angiopathy w/ gangrene
S32.14XA	Type 1 fx of sacrum, init enc for clsd fx
S32.14XK	Type 1 fx of sacrum, subsq enc for fx w/ nonu
E11.52	Type 2 diabetes mellitus w/ diabetic peripheral angiopathy w/ gangrene
S32.15XA	Type 2 fx of sacrum, init enc for clsd fx
S32.15XK	Type 2 fx of sacrum, subsq enc for fx w/ nonu
S32.16XA	Type 3 fx of sacrum, init enc for clsd fx
S32.16XK	Type 3 fx of sacrum, subsq enc for fx w/ nonu
S32.17XA	Type 4 fx of sacrum, init enc for clsd fx
S32.17XK	Type 4 fx of sacrum, subsq enc for fx w/ nonu
S02.110A	Type I occipital condyle fx, init enc for clsd fx
S02.110K	Type I occipital condyle fx, subsq enc for fx w/ nonu
S02.111A	Type II occipital condyle fx, init enc for clsd fx
S02.111K	Type II occipital condyle fx, subsq enc for fx w/ nonu
S02.112A	Type III occipital condyle fx, init enc for clsd fx
S02.112K	Type III occipital condyle fx, subsq enc for fx w/ nonu
S12.14XA	Type III traum spondylolisthesis of 2nd cervical vertebra, init enc for clsd fx
S12.14XK	Type III traum spondylolisthesis of 2nd cervical vertebra, subsq enc for fx w/ nonu
S12.24XA	Type III traum spondylolisthesis of 3rd cervical vertebra, init enc for clsd fx
S12.24XK	Type III traum spondylolisthesis of 3rd cervical vertebra, subsq enc for fx w/ nonu
S12.34XA	Type III traum spondylolisthesis of 4th cervical vertebra, init enc for clsd fx
S12.34XK	Type III traum spondylolisthesis of 4th cervical vertebra, subsq enc for fx w/ nonu
S12.44XA	Type III traum spondylolisthesis of 5th cervical vertebra, init enc for clsd fx
S12.44XK	Type III traum spondylolisthesis of 5th cervical vertebra, subsq enc for fx w/ nonu
S12.54XA	Type III traum spondylolisthesis of 6th cervical vertebra, init enc for clsd fx
S12.54XK	Type III traum spondylolisthesis of 6th cervical vertebra, subsq enc for fx w/ nonu
S12.64XA	Type III traum spondylolisthesis of 7th cervical vertebra, init enc for clsd fx
S12.64XK	Type III traum spondylolisthesis of 7th cervical vertebra, subsq enc for fx w/ nonu
A01.04	Typhoid arthritis
A01.02	Typhoid fever w/ heart involvement
A01.09	Typhoid fever w/ oth comp
A01.00	Typhoid fever, unsp
A01.01	Typhoid meningitis
A01.05	Typhoid osteomyelitis
A01.03	Typhoid pneumonia
A75.3	Typhus fever d/t Rickettsia tsutsugamushi
A75.2	Typhus fever d/t Rickettsia typhi
A75.9	Typhus fever, unsp
I48.3	Typical atrial flutter
E70.320	Tyrosinase negative oculocutaneous albinism
E70.321	Tyrosinase positive oculocutaneous albinism
E70.21	Tyrosinemia
K62.6	Ulcer of anus & rectum
K22.10	Ulcer of esophagus w/o bleeding
K63.3	Ulcer of intestine
K51.014	Ulcerative (chr) pancolitis w/ abscess
K51.013	Ulcerative (chr) pancolitis w/ fistula
K51.012	Ulcerative (chr) pancolitis w/ intestinal obstruction
K51.018	Ulcerative (chr) pancolitis w/ oth comp
K51.011	Ulcerative (chr) pancolitis w/ rectal bleeding
K51.019	Ulcerative (chr) pancolitis w/ unsp comp
K51.00	Ulcerative (chr) pancolitis w/o comp
K51.214	Ulcerative (chr) proctitis w/ abscess
K51.213	Ulcerative (chr) proctitis w/ fistula
K51.212	Ulcerative (chr) proctitis w/ intestinal obstruction
K51.218	Ulcerative (chr) proctitis w/ oth comp
K51.211	Ulcerative (chr) proctitis w/ rectal bleeding
K51.219	Ulcerative (chr) proctitis w/ unsp comp
K51.20	Ulcerative (chr) proctitis w/o comp
K51.314	Ulcerative (chr) rectosigmoiditis w/ abscess
K51.313	Ulcerative (chr) rectosigmoiditis w/ fistula
K51.312	Ulcerative (chr) rectosigmoiditis w/ intestinal obstruction
K51.318	Ulcerative (chr) rectosigmoiditis w/ oth comp
K51.311	Ulcerative (chr) rectosigmoiditis w/ rectal bleeding
K51.319	Ulcerative (chr) rectosigmoiditis w/ unsp comp
K51.30	Ulcerative (chr) rectosigmoiditis w/o comp
K51.914	Ulcerative colitis, unsp w/ abscess
K51.913	Ulcerative colitis, unsp w/ fistula
K51.912	Ulcerative colitis, unsp w/ intestinal obstruction

K51.918	Ulcerative colitis, unsp w/ oth comp
K51.911	Ulcerative colitis, unsp w/ rectal bleeding
K51.919	Ulcerative colitis, unsp w/ unsp comp
K51.90	Ulcerative colitis, unsp, w/o comp
A21.0	Ulceroglandular tularemia
K42.0	Umbilical hernia w/ obstruction, w/o gangrene
C96.6	Unifocal Langerhans-cell histiocytosis
K41.30	Unilat femoral hernia, w/ obstruction, w/o gangrene, not spec as recurrent
K41.31	Unilat femoral hernia, w/ obstruction, w/o gangrene, recurrent
K40.30	Unilat inguinal hernia, w/ obstruction, w/o gangrene, not spec as recurrent
K40.31	Unilat inguinal hernia, w/ obstruction, w/o gangrene, recurrent
K46.0	Unsp abd hernia w/ obstruction, w/o gangrene
H20.00	Unsp acute & subacute iridocyclitis
K35.80	Unsp acute appendicitis
T81.60XA	Unsp acute reaction to foreign substance accidentally lt during a procedure, init enc
E27.40	Unsp adrenocortical insufficiency
T74.91XA	Unsp adult maltreatment, confirmed, init enc
T76.91XA	Unsp adult maltreatment, suspected, init enc
A94	Unsp arthropod-borne viral fever
J45.901	Unsp asthma w/ (acute) exacerbation
J45.902	Unsp asthma w/ status asthmaticus
P28.10	Unsp atelectasis of newborn
I48.92	Unsp atrial flutter
C85.19	Unsp B-cell lymphoma, extranodal & solid organ sites
C85.13	Unsp B-cell lymphoma, intra-abd lymph nodes
C85.16	Unsp B-cell lymphoma, intrapelvic lymph nodes
C85.12	Unsp B-cell lymphoma, intrathoracic lymph nodes
C85.14	Unsp B-cell lymphoma, lymph nodes of axilla & upr limb
C85.11	Unsp B-cell lymphoma, lymph nodes of head, face, & neck
C85.15	Unsp B-cell lymphoma, lymph nodes of inguinal rgn & lwr limb
C85.18	Unsp B-cell lymphoma, lymph nodes of multi sites
C85.17	Unsp B-cell lymphoma, spleen
C85.10	Unsp B-cell lymphoma, unsp site
T74.92XA	Unsp child maltreatment, confirmed, init enc
T76.92XA	Unsp child maltreatment, suspected, init enc
H30.93	Unsp chorioretinal inflam, bilat
H30.92	Unsp chorioretinal inflam, lt eye
H30.91	Unsp chorioretinal inflam, rt eye
H30.90	Unsp chorioretinal inflam, unsp eye
H31.403	Unsp choroidal detach, bilat
H31.402	Unsp choroidal detach, lt eye
H31.401	Unsp choroidal detach, rt eye
H31.409	Unsp choroidal detach, unsp eye
I50.40	Unsp combined systolic (congestive) & diastolic (congestive) heart failure
O08.9	Unsp comp following an ectopic & molar pregnancy
O03.80	Unsp comp following complete or unsp spontaneous abortion
O03.30	Unsp comp following incomplete spontaneous abortion
T86.839	Unsp comp of bone graft
T86.00	Unsp comp of bone marrow transplant
T82.9XXA	Unsp comp of cardiac & vascular prosthetic dev, implant & graft, init enc
T86.849	Unsp comp of corneal transplant
T81.506A	Unsp comp of FB accidentally lt in body following aspiration, punc or oth catheterization, init enc
T81.504A	Unsp comp of FB accidentally lt in body following endo exam, init enc
T81.505A	Unsp comp of FB accidentally lt in body following heart catheterization, init enc
T81.501A	Unsp comp of FB accidentally lt in body following inf or transfusion, init enc
T81.503A	Unsp comp of FB accidentally lt in body following injection or immunization, init enc
T81.502A	Unsp comp of FB accidentally lt in body following kidney dialysis, init enc
T81.508A	Unsp comp of FB accidentally lt in body following oth procedure, init enc
T81.507A	Unsp comp of FB accidentally lt in body following rmvl of catheter or packing, init enc
T81.500A	Unsp comp of FB accidentally lt in body following surg operation, init enc
T81.509A	Unsp comp of FB accidentally lt in body following unsp procedure, init enc
T83.9XXA	Unsp comp of genitourinary prosthetic dev, implant & graft, init enc
T86.20	Unsp comp of heart transplant
T86.30	Unsp comp of heart-lung transplant

T84.9XXA	Unsp comp of int orthopedic prosthetic dev, implant & graft, init enc
T86.859	Unsp comp of intestine transplant
T86.10	Unsp comp of kidney transplant
T86.40	Unsp comp of liver transplant
T86.819	Unsp comp of lung transplant
T86.899	Unsp comp of oth transplanted tissue
T86.829	Unsp comp of skin graft (allograft) (autograft)
T86.90	Unsp comp of unsp transplanted organ & tissue
S36.029A	Unsp contsn of spleen, init enc
G95.20	Unsp cord compression
F03.91	Unsp dementia w/ behavioral disturbance
O24.911	Unsp diabetes mellitus in pregnancy, 1st trmstr
O24.912	Unsp diabetes mellitus in pregnancy, 2nd trmstr
O24.913	Unsp diabetes mellitus in pregnancy, 3rd trmstr
O24.919	Unsp diabetes mellitus in pregnancy, unsp trmstr
O24.93	Unsp diabetes mellitus in the puerperium
I50.30	Unsp diastolic (congestive) heart failure
S73.005A	Unsp disloc of lt hip, init enc
S43.205A	Unsp disloc of lt sternoclavicular jt, init enc
S73.004A	Unsp disloc of rt hip, init enc
S43.204A	Unsp disloc of rt sternoclavicular jt, init enc
S73.006A	Unsp disloc of unsp hip, init enc
S43.206A	Unsp disloc of unsp sternoclavicular jt, init enc
S12.000A	Unsp disp fx of 1st cervical vertebra, init enc for clsd fx
S12.000K	Unsp disp fx of 1st cervical vertebra, subsq enc for fx w/ nonu
S12.100A	Unsp disp fx of 2nd cervical vertebra, init enc for clsd fx
S12.100K	Unsp disp fx of 2nd cervical vertebra, subsq enc for fx w/ nonu
S12.200A	Unsp disp fx of 3rd cervical vertebra, init enc for clsd fx
S12.200K	Unsp disp fx of 3rd cervical vertebra, subsq enc for fx w/ nonu
S12.300A	Unsp disp fx of 4th cervical vertebra, init enc for clsd fx
S12.300K	Unsp disp fx of 4th cervical vertebra, subsq enc for fx w/ nonu
S12.400A	Unsp disp fx of 5th cervical vertebra, init enc for clsd fx
S12.400K	Unsp disp fx of 5th cervical vertebra, subsq enc for fx w/ nonu
S12.500A	Unsp disp fx of 6th cervical vertebra, init enc for clsd fx
S12.500K	Unsp disp fx of 6th cervical vertebra, subsq enc for fx w/ nonu
S12.600A	Unsp disp fx of 7th cervical vertebra, init enc for clsd fx
S12.600K	Unsp disp fx of 7th cervical vertebra, subsq enc for fx w/ nonu
S42.212A	Unsp disp fx of surg neck of lt humerus, init enc for clsd fx
S42.212P	Unsp disp fx of surg neck of lt humerus, subsq enc for fx w/ malu
S42.212K	Unsp disp fx of surg neck of lt humerus, subsq enc for fx w/ nonu
S42.211A	Unsp disp fx of surg neck of rt humerus, init enc for clsd fx
S42.211P	Unsp disp fx of surg neck of rt humerus, subsq enc for fx w/ malu
S42.211K	Unsp disp fx of surg neck of rt humerus, subsq enc for fx w/ nonu
S42.213A	Unsp disp fx of surg neck of unsp humerus, init enc for clsd fx
S42.213P	Unsp disp fx of surg neck of unsp humerus, subsq enc for fx w/ malu
S42.213K	Unsp disp fx of surg neck of unsp humerus, subsq enc for fx w/ nonu
H30.103	Unsp disseminated chorioretinal inflam, bilat
H30.102	Unsp disseminated chorioretinal inflam, lt eye
H30.101	Unsp disseminated chorioretinal inflam, rt eye
H30.109	Unsp disseminated chorioretinal inflam, unsp eye
P83.30	Unsp edema specific to newborn
T75.1XXA	Unsp effects of drowning & nonfatal submersion, init enc
T17.500A	Unsp FB in bronchus causing asphyxiation, init enc
T17.508A	Unsp FB in bronchus causing oth inj, init enc
T17.800A	Unsp FB in oth parts of respiratory tract causing asphyxiation, init enc
T17.808A	Unsp FB in oth parts of respiratory tract causing oth inj, init enc
T17.400A	Unsp FB in trachea causing asphyxiation, init enc
T17.408A	Unsp FB in trachea causing oth inj, init enc
S06.305A	Unsp focal traum brain inj w/ loss of cnscness > 24 hrs w/ return to pre-existing conscious lvl, init enc
S06.303A	Unsp focal traum brain inj w/ loss of cnscness of 1 hr to 5 hrs 59 mins, init enc
S06.301A	Unsp focal traum brain inj w/ loss of cnscness of 30 mins or less, init enc
S06.302A	Unsp focal traum brain inj w/ loss of cnscness of 31 mins to 59 mins, init enc
S06.304A	Unsp focal traum brain inj w/ loss of cnscness of 6 hrs to 24 hrs, init enc
S06.309A	Unsp focal traum brain inj w/ loss of cnscness of unsp dur, init enc
S32.019A	Unsp fx of 1st lumbar vertebra, init enc for clsd fx
S32.019K	Unsp fx of 1st lumbar vertebra, subsq enc for fx w/ nonu
S62.202B	Unsp fx of 1st metacarpal bone, lt hand, init enc for opn fx
S62.202P	Unsp fx of 1st metacarpal bone, lt hand, subsq enc for fx w/ malu
S62.202K	Unsp fx of 1st metacarpal bone, lt hand, subsq enc for fx w/ nonu
S62.201B	Unsp fx of 1st metacarpal bone, rt hand, init enc for opn fx
S62.201P	Unsp fx of 1st metacarpal bone, rt hand, subsq enc for fx w/ malu

S62.201K	Unsp fx of 1st metacarpal bone, rt hand, subsq enc for fx w/ nonu
S62.209B	Unsp fx of 1st metacarpal bone, unsp hand, init enc for opn fx
S62.209P	Unsp fx of 1st metacarpal bone, unsp hand, subsq enc for fx w/ malu
S62.209K	Unsp fx of 1st metacarpal bone, unsp hand, subsq enc for fx w/ nonu
S22.019A	Unsp fx of 1st thoracic vertebra, init enc for clsd fx
S22.019K	Unsp fx of 1st thoracic vertebra, subsq enc for fx w/ nonu
S32.029A	Unsp fx of 2nd lumbar vertebra, init enc for clsd fx
S32.029K	Unsp fx of 2nd lumbar vertebra, subsq enc for fx w/ nonu
S62.301B	Unsp fx of 2nd metacarpal bone, lt hand, init enc for opn fx
S62.301P	Unsp fx of 2nd metacarpal bone, lt hand, subsq enc for fx w/ malu
S62.301K	Unsp fx of 2nd metacarpal bone, lt hand, subsq enc for fx w/ nonu
S62.300B	Unsp fx of 2nd metacarpal bone, rt hand, init enc for opn fx
S62.300P	Unsp fx of 2nd metacarpal bone, rt hand, subsq enc for fx w/ malu
S62.300K	Unsp fx of 2nd metacarpal bone, rt hand, subsq enc for fx w/ nonu
S22.029A	Unsp fx of 2nd thoracic vertebra, init enc for clsd fx
S22.029K	Unsp fx of 2nd thoracic vertebra, subsq enc for fx w/ nonu
S32.039A	Unsp fx of 3rd lumbar vertebra, init enc for clsd fx
S32.039K	Unsp fx of 3rd lumbar vertebra, subsq enc for fx w/ nonu
S62.303B	Unsp fx of 3rd metacarpal bone, lt hand, init enc for opn fx
S62.303P	Unsp fx of 3rd metacarpal bone, lt hand, subsq enc for fx w/ malu
S62.303K	Unsp fx of 3rd metacarpal bone, lt hand, subsq enc for fx w/ nonu
S62.302B	Unsp fx of 3rd metacarpal bone, rt hand, init enc for opn fx
S62.302P	Unsp fx of 3rd metacarpal bone, rt hand, subsq enc for fx w/ malu
S62.302K	Unsp fx of 3rd metacarpal bone, rt hand, subsq enc for fx w/ nonu
S22.039A	Unsp fx of 3rd thoracic vertebra, init enc for clsd fx
S22.039K	Unsp fx of 3rd thoracic vertebra, subsq enc for fx w/ nonu
S32.049A	Unsp fx of 4th lumbar vertebra, init enc for clsd fx
S32.049K	Unsp fx of 4th lumbar vertebra, subsq enc for fx w/ nonu
S62.305B	Unsp fx of 4th metacarpal bone, lt hand, init enc for opn fx
S62.305P	Unsp fx of 4th metacarpal bone, lt hand, subsq enc for fx w/ malu
S62.305K	Unsp fx of 4th metacarpal bone, lt hand, subsq enc for fx w/ nonu
S62.304B	Unsp fx of 4th metacarpal bone, rt hand, init enc for opn fx
S62.304P	Unsp fx of 4th metacarpal bone, rt hand, subsq enc for fx w/ malu
S62.304K	Unsp fx of 4th metacarpal bone, rt hand, subsq enc for fx w/ nonu
S22.049A	Unsp fx of 4th thoracic vertebra, init enc for clsd fx
S22.049K	Unsp fx of 4th thoracic vertebra, subsq enc for fx w/ nonu
S32.059A	Unsp fx of 5th lumbar vertebra, init enc for clsd fx
S32.059K	Unsp fx of 5th lumbar vertebra, subsq enc for fx w/ nonu
S62.307B	Unsp fx of 5th metacarpal bone, lt hand, init enc for opn fx
S62.307P	Unsp fx of 5th metacarpal bone, lt hand, subsq enc for fx w/ malu
S62.307K	Unsp fx of 5th metacarpal bone, lt hand, subsq enc for fx w/ nonu
S62.306B	Unsp fx of 5th metacarpal bone, rt hand, init enc for opn fx
S62.306P	Unsp fx of 5th metacarpal bone, rt hand, subsq enc for fx w/ malu
S62.306K	Unsp fx of 5th metacarpal bone, rt hand, subsq enc for fx w/ nonu
S02.10XA	Unsp fx of base of skull, init enc for clsd fx
S02.10XK	Unsp fx of base of skull, subsq enc for fx w/ nonu
S02.92XA	Unsp fx of facial bones, init enc for clsd fx
S02.92XB	Unsp fx of facial bones, init enc for opn fx
S02.92XK	Unsp fx of facial bones, subsq enc for fx w/ nonu
S72.052P	Unsp fx of head of lt femur, subsq enc for clsd fx w/ malu
S72.052K	Unsp fx of head of lt femur, subsq enc for clsd fx w/ nonu
S72.052Q	Unsp fx of head of lt femur, subsq enc for opn fx type I or II w/ malu
S72.052M	Unsp fx of head of lt femur, subsq enc for opn fx type I or II w/ nonu
S72.052R	Unsp fx of head of lt femur, subsq enc for opn fx type IIIA, IIIB, or IIIC w/ malu
S72.052N	Unsp fx of head of lt femur, subsq enc for opn fx type IIIA, IIIB, or IIIC w/ nonu
S72.051P	Unsp fx of head of rt femur, subsq enc for clsd fx w/ malu
S72.051K	Unsp fx of head of rt femur, subsq enc for clsd fx w/ nonu
S72.051Q	Unsp fx of head of rt femur, subsq enc for opn fx type I or II w/ malu
S72.051M	Unsp fx of head of rt femur, subsq enc for opn fx type I or II w/ nonu
S72.051R	Unsp fx of head of rt femur, subsq enc for opn fx type IIIA, IIIB, or IIIC w/ malu
S72.051N	Unsp fx of head of rt femur, subsq enc for opn fx type IIIA, IIIB, or IIIC w/ nonu
S72.059P	Unsp fx of head of unsp femur, subsq enc for clsd fx w/ malu
S72.059K	Unsp fx of head of unsp femur, subsq enc for clsd fx w/ nonu
S72.059Q	Unsp fx of head of unsp femur, subsq enc for opn fx type I or II w/ malu
S72.059M	Unsp fx of head of unsp femur, subsq enc for opn fx type I or II w/ nonu
S72.059R	Unsp fx of head of unsp femur, subsq enc for opn fx type IIIA, IIIB, or IIIC w/ malu
S72.059N	Unsp fx of head of unsp femur, subsq enc for opn fx type IIIA, IIIB, or IIIC w/ nonu
S32.402K	Unsp fx of lt acetab, subsq enc for fx w/ nonu
S92.002B	Unsp fx of lt calcaneus, init enc for opn fx
S92.002P	Unsp fx of lt calcaneus, subsq enc for fx w/ malu
S92.002K	Unsp fx of lt calcaneus, subsq enc for fx w/ nonu
S72.92XP	Unsp fx of lt femur, subsq enc for clsd fx w/ malu
S72.92XK	Unsp fx of lt femur, subsq enc for clsd fx w/ nonu
S72.92XQ	Unsp fx of lt femur, subsq enc for opn fx type I or II w/ malu
S72.92XM	Unsp fx of lt femur, subsq enc for opn fx type I or II w/ nonu
S72.92XR	Unsp fx of lt femur, subsq enc for opn fx type IIIA, IIIB, or IIIC w/ malu
S72.92XN	Unsp fx of lt femur, subsq enc for opn fx type IIIA, IIIB, or IIIC w/ nonu
S92.902B	Unsp fx of lt foot, init enc for opn fx
S92.902P	Unsp fx of lt foot, subsq enc for fx w/ malu
S92.902K	Unsp fx of lt foot, subsq enc for fx w/ nonu
S52.92XA	Unsp fx of lt forearm, init enc for clsd fx
S52.92XP	Unsp fx of lt forearm, subsq enc for clsd fx w/ malu
S52.92XK	Unsp fx of lt forearm, subsq enc for clsd fx w/ nonu
S52.92XQ	Unsp fx of lt forearm, subsq enc for opn fx type I or II w/ malu
S52.92XM	Unsp fx of lt forearm, subsq enc for opn fx type I or II w/ nonu
S52.92XR	Unsp fx of lt forearm, subsq enc for opn fx type IIIA, IIIB, or IIIC w/ malu
S52.92XN	Unsp fx of lt forearm, subsq enc for opn fx type IIIA, IIIB, or IIIC w/ nonu
S32.302A	Unsp fx of lt ilium, init enc for clsd fx
S32.302K	Unsp fx of lt ilium, subsq enc for fx w/ nonu
S32.602A	Unsp fx of lt ischium, init enc for clsd fx
S32.602K	Unsp fx of lt ischium, subsq enc for fx w/ nonu
S82.92XB	Unsp fx of lt lwr leg, init enc for opn fx type I or II
S82.92XC	Unsp fx of lt lwr leg, init enc for opn fx type IIIA, IIIB, or IIIC
S82.92XP	Unsp fx of lt lwr leg, subsq enc for clsd fx w/ malu
S82.92XK	Unsp fx of lt lwr leg, subsq enc for clsd fx w/ nonu
S82.92XQ	Unsp fx of lt lwr leg, subsq enc for opn fx type I or II w/ malu
S82.92XM	Unsp fx of lt lwr leg, subsq enc for opn fx type I or II w/ nonu
S82.92XR	Unsp fx of lt lwr leg, subsq enc for opn fx type IIIA, IIIB, or IIIC w/ malu
S82.92XN	Unsp fx of lt lwr leg, subsq enc for opn fx type IIIA, IIIB, or IIIC w/ nonu
S82.002A	Unsp fx of lt patella, init enc for clsd fx
S82.002B	Unsp fx of lt patella, init enc for opn fx type I or II
S82.002C	Unsp fx of lt patella, init enc for opn fx type IIIA, IIIB, or IIIC
S82.002P	Unsp fx of lt patella, subsq enc for clsd fx w/ malu
S82.002K	Unsp fx of lt patella, subsq enc for clsd fx w/ nonu
S82.002Q	Unsp fx of lt patella, subsq enc for opn fx type I or II w/ malu
S82.002M	Unsp fx of lt patella, subsq enc for opn fx type I or II w/ nonu
S82.002R	Unsp fx of lt patella, subsq enc for opn fx type IIIA, IIIB, or IIIC w/ malu
S82.002N	Unsp fx of lt patella, subsq enc for opn fx type IIIA, IIIB, or IIIC w/ nonu
S32.502A	Unsp fx of lt pubis, init enc for clsd fx
S32.502K	Unsp fx of lt pubis, subsq enc for fx w/ nonu
S92.102B	Unsp fx of lt talus, init enc for opn fx
S92.102P	Unsp fx of lt talus, subsq enc for fx w/ malu
S92.102K	Unsp fx of lt talus, subsq enc for fx w/ nonu
S92.912P	Unsp fx of lt toe(s), subsq enc for fx w/ malu
S92.912K	Unsp fx of lt toe(s), subsq enc for fx w/ nonu
S62.92XB	Unsp fx of lt wrist & hand, init enc for opn fx
S62.92XP	Unsp fx of lt wrist & hand, subsq enc for fx w/ malu
S62.92XK	Unsp fx of lt wrist & hand, subsq enc for fx w/ nonu
S72.402A	Unsp fx of lwr end of lt femur, init enc for clsd fx
S72.402P	Unsp fx of lwr end of lt femur, subsq enc for clsd fx w/ malu
S72.402K	Unsp fx of lwr end of lt femur, subsq enc for clsd fx w/ nonu
S72.402Q	Unsp fx of lwr end of lt femur, subsq enc for opn fx type I or II w/ malu
S72.402M	Unsp fx of lwr end of lt femur, subsq enc for opn fx type I or II w/ nonu
S72.402R	Unsp fx of lwr end of lt femur, subsq enc for opn fx type IIIA, IIIB, or IIIC w/ malu
S72.402N	Unsp fx of lwr end of lt femur, subsq enc for opn fx type IIIA, IIIB, or IIIC w/ nonu
S42.402A	Unsp fx of lwr end of lt humerus, init enc for clsd fx
S42.402P	Unsp fx of lwr end of lt humerus, subsq enc for fx w/ malu
S42.402K	Unsp fx of lwr end of lt humerus, subsq enc for fx w/ nonu
S82.302B	Unsp fx of lwr end of lt tibia, init enc for opn fx type I or II
S82.302C	Unsp fx of lwr end of lt tibia, init enc for opn fx type IIIA, IIIB, or IIIC
S82.302P	Unsp fx of lwr end of lt tibia, subsq enc for clsd fx w/ malu
S82.302K	Unsp fx of lwr end of lt tibia, subsq enc for clsd fx w/ nonu
S82.302Q	Unsp fx of lwr end of lt tibia, subsq enc for opn fx type I or II w/ malu
S82.302M	Unsp fx of lwr end of lt tibia, subsq enc for opn fx type I or II w/ nonu
S82.302R	Unsp fx of lwr end of lt tibia, subsq enc for opn fx type IIIA, IIIB, or IIIC w/ malu
S82.302N	Unsp fx of lwr end of lt tibia, subsq enc for opn fx type IIIA, IIIB, or IIIC w/ nonu
S52.602A	Unsp fx of lwr end of lt ulna, init enc for clsd fx
S52.602P	Unsp fx of lwr end of lt ulna, subsq enc for clsd fx w/ malu

S52.602K	Unsp fx of lwr end of lt ulna, subsq enc for clsd fx w/ nonu
S52.602Q	Unsp fx of lwr end of lt ulna, subsq enc for opn fx type I or II w/ malu
S52.602M	Unsp fx of lwr end of lt ulna, subsq enc for opn fx type I or II w/ nonu
S52.602R	Unsp fx of lwr end of lt ulna, subsq enc for opn fx type IIIA, IIIB, or IIIC w/ malu
S52.602N	Unsp fx of lwr end of lt ulna, subsq enc for opn fx type IIIA, IIIB, or IIIC w/ nonu
S72.401A	Unsp fx of lwr end of rt femur, init enc for clsd fx
S72.401P	Unsp fx of lwr end of rt femur, subsq enc for clsd fx w/ malu
S72.401K	Unsp fx of lwr end of rt femur, subsq enc for clsd fx w/ nonu
S72.401Q	Unsp fx of lwr end of rt femur, subsq enc for opn fx type I or II w/ malu
S72.401M	Unsp fx of lwr end of rt femur, subsq enc for opn fx type I or II w/ nonu
S72.401R	Unsp fx of lwr end of rt femur, subsq enc for opn fx type IIIA, IIIB, or IIIC w/ malu
S72.401N	Unsp fx of lwr end of rt femur, subsq enc for opn fx type IIIA, IIIB, or IIIC w/ nonu
S42.401A	Unsp fx of lwr end of rt humerus, init enc for clsd fx
S42.401P	Unsp fx of lwr end of rt humerus, subsq enc for fx w/ malu
S42.401K	Unsp fx of lwr end of rt humerus, subsq enc for fx w/ nonu
S82.301B	Unsp fx of lwr end of rt tibia, init enc for opn fx type I or II
S82.301C	Unsp fx of lwr end of rt tibia, init enc for opn fx type IIIA, IIIB, or IIIC
S82.301P	Unsp fx of lwr end of rt tibia, subsq enc for clsd fx w/ malu
S82.301K	Unsp fx of lwr end of rt tibia, subsq enc for clsd fx w/ nonu
S82.301Q	Unsp fx of lwr end of rt tibia, subsq enc for opn fx type I or II w/ malu
S82.301M	Unsp fx of lwr end of rt tibia, subsq enc for opn fx type I or II w/ nonu
S82.301R	Unsp fx of lwr end of rt tibia, subsq enc for opn fx type IIIA, IIIB, or IIIC w/ malu
S82.301N	Unsp fx of lwr end of rt tibia, subsq enc for opn fx type IIIA, IIIB, or IIIC w/ nonu
S52.601A	Unsp fx of lwr end of rt ulna, init enc for clsd fx
S52.601P	Unsp fx of lwr end of rt ulna, subsq enc for clsd fx w/ malu
S52.601K	Unsp fx of lwr end of rt ulna, subsq enc for clsd fx w/ nonu
S52.601Q	Unsp fx of lwr end of rt ulna, subsq enc for opn fx type I or II w/ malu
S52.601M	Unsp fx of lwr end of rt ulna, subsq enc for opn fx type I or II w/ nonu
S52.601R	Unsp fx of lwr end of rt ulna, subsq enc for opn fx type IIIA, IIIB, or IIIC w/ malu
S52.601N	Unsp fx of lwr end of rt ulna, subsq enc for opn fx type IIIA, IIIB, or IIIC w/ nonu
S72.409A	Unsp fx of lwr end of unsp femur, init enc for clsd fx
S72.409P	Unsp fx of lwr end of unsp femur, subsq enc for clsd fx w/ malu
S72.409K	Unsp fx of lwr end of unsp femur, subsq enc for clsd fx w/ nonu
S72.409Q	Unsp fx of lwr end of unsp femur, subsq enc for opn fx type I or II w/ malu
S72.409M	Unsp fx of lwr end of unsp femur, subsq enc for opn fx type I or II w/ nonu
S72.409R	Unsp fx of lwr end of unsp femur, subsq enc for opn fx type IIIA, IIIB, or IIIC w/ malu
S72.409N	Unsp fx of lwr end of unsp femur, subsq enc for opn fx type IIIA, IIIB, or IIIC w/ nonu
S42.409A	Unsp fx of lwr end of unsp humerus, init enc for clsd fx
S42.409P	Unsp fx of lwr end of unsp humerus, subsq enc for fx w/ malu
S42.409K	Unsp fx of lwr end of unsp humerus, subsq enc for fx w/ nonu
S82.309B	Unsp fx of lwr end of unsp tibia, init enc for opn fx type I or II
S82.309C	Unsp fx of lwr end of unsp tibia, init enc for opn fx type IIIA, IIIB, or IIIC
S82.309P	Unsp fx of lwr end of unsp tibia, subsq enc for clsd fx w/ malu
S82.309K	Unsp fx of lwr end of unsp tibia, subsq enc for clsd fx w/ nonu
S82.309Q	Unsp fx of lwr end of unsp tibia, subsq enc for opn fx type I or II w/ malu
S82.309M	Unsp fx of lwr end of unsp tibia, subsq enc for opn fx type I or II w/ nonu
S82.309R	Unsp fx of lwr end of unsp tibia, subsq enc for opn fx type IIIA, IIIB, or IIIC w/ malu
S82.309N	Unsp fx of lwr end of unsp tibia, subsq enc for opn fx type IIIA, IIIB, or IIIC w/ nonu
S52.609A	Unsp fx of lwr end of unsp ulna, init enc for clsd fx
S52.609P	Unsp fx of lwr end of unsp ulna, subsq enc for clsd fx w/ malu
S52.609K	Unsp fx of lwr end of unsp ulna, subsq enc for clsd fx w/ nonu
S52.609Q	Unsp fx of lwr end of unsp ulna, subsq enc for opn fx type I or II w/ malu
S52.609M	Unsp fx of lwr end of unsp ulna, subsq enc for opn fx type I or II w/ nonu
S52.609R	Unsp fx of lwr end of unsp ulna, subsq enc for opn fx type IIIA, IIIB, or IIIC w/ malu
S52.609N	Unsp fx of lwr end of unsp ulna, subsq enc for opn fx type IIIA, IIIB, or IIIC w/ nonu
S62.002B	Unsp fx of navicular [scaphoid] bone of lt wrist, init enc for opn fx
S62.002P	Unsp fx of navicular [scaphoid] bone of lt wrist, subsq enc for fx w/ malu
S62.002K	Unsp fx of navicular [scaphoid] bone of lt wrist, subsq enc for fx w/ nonu
S62.001B	Unsp fx of navicular [scaphoid] bone of rt wrist, init enc for opn fx
S62.001P	Unsp fx of navicular [scaphoid] bone of rt wrist, subsq enc for fx w/ malu
S62.001K	Unsp fx of navicular [scaphoid] bone of rt wrist, subsq enc for fx w/ nonu

S62.009B	Unsp fx of navicular [scaphoid] bone of unsp wrist, init enc for opn fx
S62.009P	Unsp fx of navicular [scaphoid] bone of unsp wrist, subsq enc for fx w/ malu
S62.009K	Unsp fx of navicular [scaphoid] bone of unsp wrist, subsq enc for fx w/ nonu
S02.119A	Unsp fx of occiput, init enc for clsd fx
S02.119K	Unsp fx of occiput, subsq enc for fx w/ nonu
S62.308B	Unsp fx of oth metacarpal bone, init enc for opn fx
S62.308P	Unsp fx of oth metacarpal bone, subsq enc for fx w/ malu
S62.308K	Unsp fx of oth metacarpal bone, subsq enc for fx w/ nonu
S32.401K	Unsp fx of rt acetab, subsq enc for fx w/ nonu
S92.001B	Unsp fx of rt calcaneus, init enc for opn fx
S92.001P	Unsp fx of rt calcaneus, subsq enc for fx w/ malu
S92.001K	Unsp fx of rt calcaneus, subsq enc for fx w/ nonu
S72.91XP	Unsp fx of rt femur, subsq enc for clsd fx w/ malu
S72.91XK	Unsp fx of rt femur, subsq enc for clsd fx w/ nonu
S72.91XQ	Unsp fx of rt femur, subsq enc for opn fx type I or II w/ malu
S72.91XM	Unsp fx of rt femur, subsq enc for opn fx type I or II w/ nonu
S72.91XR	Unsp fx of rt femur, subsq enc for opn fx type IIIA, IIIB, or IIIC w/ malu
S72.91XN	Unsp fx of rt femur, subsq enc for opn fx type IIIA, IIIB, or IIIC w/ nonu
S92.901B	Unsp fx of rt foot, init enc for opn fx
S92.901P	Unsp fx of rt foot, subsq enc for fx w/ malu
S92.901K	Unsp fx of rt foot, subsq enc for fx w/ nonu
S52.91XA	Unsp fx of rt forearm, init enc for clsd fx
S52.91XP	Unsp fx of rt forearm, subsq enc for clsd fx w/ malu
S52.91XK	Unsp fx of rt forearm, subsq enc for clsd fx w/ nonu
S52.91XQ	Unsp fx of rt forearm, subsq enc for opn fx type I or II w/ malu
S52.91XM	Unsp fx of rt forearm, subsq enc for opn fx type I or II w/ nonu
S52.91XR	Unsp fx of rt forearm, subsq enc for opn fx type IIIA, IIIB, or IIIC w/ malu
S52.91XN	Unsp fx of rt forearm, subsq enc for opn fx type IIIA, IIIB, or IIIC w/ nonu
S32.301A	Unsp fx of rt ilium, init enc for clsd fx
S32.301K	Unsp fx of rt ilium, subsq enc for fx w/ nonu
S32.601A	Unsp fx of rt ischium, init enc for clsd fx
S32.601K	Unsp fx of rt ischium, subsq enc for fx w/ nonu
S82.91XB	Unsp fx of rt lwr leg, init enc for opn fx type I or II
S82.91XC	Unsp fx of rt lwr leg, init enc for opn fx type IIIA, IIIB, or IIIC
S82.91XP	Unsp fx of rt lwr leg, subsq enc for clsd fx w/ malu
S82.91XK	Unsp fx of rt lwr leg, subsq enc for clsd fx w/ nonu
S82.91XQ	Unsp fx of rt lwr leg, subsq enc for opn fx type I or II w/ malu
S82.91XM	Unsp fx of rt lwr leg, subsq enc for opn fx type I or II w/ nonu
S82.91XR	Unsp fx of rt lwr leg, subsq enc for opn fx type IIIA, IIIB, or IIIC w/ malu
S82.91XN	Unsp fx of rt lwr leg, subsq enc for opn fx type IIIA, IIIB, or IIIC w/ nonu
S82.001A	Unsp fx of rt patella, init enc for clsd fx
S82.001B	Unsp fx of rt patella, init enc for opn fx type I or II
S82.001C	Unsp fx of rt patella, init enc for opn fx type IIIA, IIIB, or IIIC
S82.001P	Unsp fx of rt patella, subsq enc for clsd fx w/ malu
S82.001K	Unsp fx of rt patella, subsq enc for clsd fx w/ nonu
S82.001Q	Unsp fx of rt patella, subsq enc for opn fx type I or II w/ malu
S82.001M	Unsp fx of rt patella, subsq enc for opn fx type I or II w/ nonu
S82.001R	Unsp fx of rt patella, subsq enc for opn fx type IIIA, IIIB, or IIIC w/ malu
S82.001N	Unsp fx of rt patella, subsq enc for opn fx type IIIA, IIIB, or IIIC w/ nonu
S32.501A	Unsp fx of rt pubis, init enc for clsd fx
S32.501K	Unsp fx of rt pubis, subsq enc for fx w/ nonu
S92.101B	Unsp fx of rt talus, init enc for opn fx
S92.101P	Unsp fx of rt talus, subsq enc for fx w/ malu
S92.101K	Unsp fx of rt talus, subsq enc for fx w/ nonu
S92.911P	Unsp fx of rt toe(s), subsq enc for fx w/ malu
S92.911K	Unsp fx of rt toe(s), subsq enc for fx w/ nonu
S62.91XB	Unsp fx of rt wrist & hand, init enc for opn fx
S62.91XP	Unsp fx of rt wrist & hand, subsq enc for fx w/ malu
S62.91XK	Unsp fx of rt wrist & hand, subsq enc for fx w/ nonu
S32.10XA	Unsp fx of sacrum, init enc for clsd fx
S32.10XK	Unsp fx of sacrum, subsq enc for fx w/ nonu
S42.302A	Unsp fx of shaft of humerus, lt arm, init enc for clsd fx
S42.302P	Unsp fx of shaft of humerus, lt arm, subsq enc for fx w/ malu
S42.302K	Unsp fx of shaft of humerus, lt arm, subsq enc for fx w/ nonu
S42.301A	Unsp fx of shaft of humerus, rt arm, init enc for clsd fx
S42.301P	Unsp fx of shaft of humerus, rt arm, subsq enc for fx w/ malu
S42.301K	Unsp fx of shaft of humerus, rt arm, subsq enc for fx w/ nonu
S42.309A	Unsp fx of shaft of humerus, unsp arm, init enc for clsd fx
S42.309P	Unsp fx of shaft of humerus, unsp arm, subsq enc for fx w/ malu
S42.309K	Unsp fx of shaft of humerus, unsp arm, subsq enc for fx w/ nonu
S72.302P	Unsp fx of shaft of lt femur, subsq enc for clsd fx w/ malu
S72.302K	Unsp fx of shaft of lt femur, subsq enc for clsd fx w/ nonu

S72.302Q	Unsp fx of shaft of lt femur, subsq enc for opn fx type I or II w/ malu
S72.302M	Unsp fx of shaft of lt femur, subsq enc for opn fx type I or II w/ nonu
S72.302R	Unsp fx of shaft of lt femur, subsq enc for opn fx type IIIA, IIIB, or IIIC w/ malu
S72.302N	Unsp fx of shaft of lt femur, subsq enc for opn fx type IIIA, IIIB, or IIIC w/ nonu
S82.402P	Unsp fx of shaft of lt fibula, subsq enc for clsd fx w/ malu
S82.402K	Unsp fx of shaft of lt fibula, subsq enc for clsd fx w/ nonu
S82.402Q	Unsp fx of shaft of lt fibula, subsq enc for opn fx type I or II w/ malu
S82.402M	Unsp fx of shaft of lt fibula, subsq enc for opn fx type I or II w/ nonu
S82.402R	Unsp fx of shaft of lt fibula, subsq enc for opn fx type IIIA, IIIB, or IIIC w/ malu
S82.402N	Unsp fx of shaft of lt fibula, subsq enc for opn fx type IIIA, IIIB, or IIIC w/ nonu
S52.302A	Unsp fx of shaft of lt radius, init enc for clsd fx
S52.302P	Unsp fx of shaft of lt radius, subsq enc for clsd fx w/ malu
S52.302K	Unsp fx of shaft of lt radius, subsq enc for clsd fx w/ nonu
S52.302Q	Unsp fx of shaft of lt radius, subsq enc for opn fx type I or II w/ malu
S52.302M	Unsp fx of shaft of lt radius, subsq enc for opn fx type I or II w/ nonu
S52.302R	Unsp fx of shaft of lt radius, subsq enc for opn fx type IIIA, IIIB, or IIIC w/ malu
S52.302N	Unsp fx of shaft of lt radius, subsq enc for opn fx type IIIA, IIIB, or IIIC w/ nonu
S82.202A	Unsp fx of shaft of lt tibia, init enc for clsd fx
S82.202P	Unsp fx of shaft of lt tibia, subsq enc for clsd fx w/ malu
S82.202K	Unsp fx of shaft of lt tibia, subsq enc for clsd fx w/ nonu
S82.202Q	Unsp fx of shaft of lt tibia, subsq enc for opn fx type I or II w/ malu
S82.202M	Unsp fx of shaft of lt tibia, subsq enc for opn fx type I or II w/ nonu
S82.202R	Unsp fx of shaft of lt tibia, subsq enc for opn fx type IIIA, IIIB, or IIIC w/ malu
S82.202N	Unsp fx of shaft of lt tibia, subsq enc for opn fx type IIIA, IIIB, or IIIC w/ nonu
S52.202A	Unsp fx of shaft of lt ulna, init enc for clsd fx
S52.202P	Unsp fx of shaft of lt ulna, subsq enc for clsd fx w/ malu
S52.202K	Unsp fx of shaft of lt ulna, subsq enc for clsd fx w/ nonu
S52.202Q	Unsp fx of shaft of lt ulna, subsq enc for opn fx type I or II w/ malu
S52.202M	Unsp fx of shaft of lt ulna, subsq enc for opn fx type I or II w/ nonu
S52.202R	Unsp fx of shaft of lt ulna, subsq enc for opn fx type IIIA, IIIB, or IIIC w/ malu
S52.202N	Unsp fx of shaft of lt ulna, subsq enc for opn fx type IIIA, IIIB, or IIIC w/ nonu
S72.301P	Unsp fx of shaft of rt femur, subsq enc for clsd fx w/ malu
S72.301K	Unsp fx of shaft of rt femur, subsq enc for clsd fx w/ nonu
S72.301Q	Unsp fx of shaft of rt femur, subsq enc for opn fx type I or II w/ malu
S72.301M	Unsp fx of shaft of rt femur, subsq enc for opn fx type I or II w/ nonu
S72.301R	Unsp fx of shaft of rt femur, subsq enc for opn fx type IIIA, IIIB, or IIIC w/ malu
S72.301N	Unsp fx of shaft of rt femur, subsq enc for opn fx type IIIA, IIIB, or IIIC w/ nonu
S82.401P	Unsp fx of shaft of rt fibula, subsq enc for clsd fx w/ malu
S82.401K	Unsp fx of shaft of rt fibula, subsq enc for clsd fx w/ nonu
S82.401Q	Unsp fx of shaft of rt fibula, subsq enc for opn fx type I or II w/ malu
S82.401M	Unsp fx of shaft of rt fibula, subsq enc for opn fx type I or II w/ nonu
S82.401R	Unsp fx of shaft of rt fibula, subsq enc for opn fx type IIIA, IIIB, or IIIC w/ malu
S82.401N	Unsp fx of shaft of rt fibula, subsq enc for opn fx type IIIA, IIIB, or IIIC w/ nonu
S52.301A	Unsp fx of shaft of rt radius, init enc for clsd fx
S52.301P	Unsp fx of shaft of rt radius, subsq enc for clsd fx w/ malu
S52.301K	Unsp fx of shaft of rt radius, subsq enc for clsd fx w/ nonu
S52.301Q	Unsp fx of shaft of rt radius, subsq enc for opn fx type I or II w/ malu
S52.301M	Unsp fx of shaft of rt radius, subsq enc for opn fx type I or II w/ nonu
S52.301R	Unsp fx of shaft of rt radius, subsq enc for opn fx type IIIA, IIIB, or IIIC w/ malu
S52.301N	Unsp fx of shaft of rt radius, subsq enc for opn fx type IIIA, IIIB, or IIIC w/ nonu
S82.201A	Unsp fx of shaft of rt tibia, init enc for clsd fx
S82.201P	Unsp fx of shaft of rt tibia, subsq enc for clsd fx w/ malu
S82.201K	Unsp fx of shaft of rt tibia, subsq enc for clsd fx w/ nonu
S82.201Q	Unsp fx of shaft of rt tibia, subsq enc for opn fx type I or II w/ malu
S82.201M	Unsp fx of shaft of rt tibia, subsq enc for opn fx type I or II w/ nonu
S82.201R	Unsp fx of shaft of rt tibia, subsq enc for opn fx type IIIA, IIIB, or IIIC w/ malu
S82.201N	Unsp fx of shaft of rt tibia, subsq enc for opn fx type IIIA, IIIB, or IIIC w/ nonu
S52.201A	Unsp fx of shaft of rt ulna, init enc for clsd fx
S52.201P	Unsp fx of shaft of rt ulna, subsq enc for clsd fx w/ malu
S52.201K	Unsp fx of shaft of rt ulna, subsq enc for clsd fx w/ nonu
S52.201Q	Unsp fx of shaft of rt ulna, subsq enc for opn fx type I or II w/ malu
S52.201M	Unsp fx of shaft of rt ulna, subsq enc for opn fx type I or II w/ nonu
S52.201R	Unsp fx of shaft of rt ulna, subsq enc for opn fx type IIIA, IIIB, or IIIC w/ malu
S52.201N	Unsp fx of shaft of rt ulna, subsq enc for opn fx type IIIA, IIIB, or IIIC w/ nonu
S72.309P	Unsp fx of shaft of unsp femur, subsq enc for clsd fx w/ malu
S72.309K	Unsp fx of shaft of unsp femur, subsq enc for clsd fx w/ nonu
S72.309Q	Unsp fx of shaft of unsp femur, subsq enc for opn fx type I or II w/ malu
S72.309M	Unsp fx of shaft of unsp femur, subsq enc for opn fx type I or II w/ nonu
S72.309R	Unsp fx of shaft of unsp femur, subsq enc for opn fx type IIIA, IIIB, or IIIC w/ malu
S72.309N	Unsp fx of shaft of unsp femur, subsq enc for opn fx type IIIA, IIIB, or IIIC w/ nonu
S82.409P	Unsp fx of shaft of unsp fibula, subsq enc for clsd fx w/ malu
S82.409K	Unsp fx of shaft of unsp fibula, subsq enc for clsd fx w/ nonu
S82.409Q	Unsp fx of shaft of unsp fibula, subsq enc for opn fx type I or II w/ malu
S82.409M	Unsp fx of shaft of unsp fibula, subsq enc for opn fx type I or II w/ nonu
S82.409R	Unsp fx of shaft of unsp fibula, subsq enc for opn fx type IIIA, IIIB, or IIIC w/ malu
S82.409N	Unsp fx of shaft of unsp fibula, subsq enc for opn fx type IIIA, IIIB, or IIIC w/ nonu
S52.309A	Unsp fx of shaft of unsp radius, init enc for clsd fx
S52.309P	Unsp fx of shaft of unsp radius, subsq enc for clsd fx w/ malu
S52.309K	Unsp fx of shaft of unsp radius, subsq enc for clsd fx w/ nonu
S52.309Q	Unsp fx of shaft of unsp radius, subsq enc for opn fx type I or II w/ malu
S52.309M	Unsp fx of shaft of unsp radius, subsq enc for opn fx type I or II w/ nonu
S52.309R	Unsp fx of shaft of unsp radius, subsq enc for opn fx type IIIA, IIIB, or IIIC w/ malu
S52.309N	Unsp fx of shaft of unsp radius, subsq enc for opn fx type IIIA, IIIB, or IIIC w/ nonu
S82.209A	Unsp fx of shaft of unsp tibia, init enc for clsd fx
S82.209P	Unsp fx of shaft of unsp tibia, subsq enc for clsd fx w/ malu
S82.209K	Unsp fx of shaft of unsp tibia, subsq enc for clsd fx w/ nonu
S82.209Q	Unsp fx of shaft of unsp tibia, subsq enc for opn fx type I or II w/ malu
S82.209M	Unsp fx of shaft of unsp tibia, subsq enc for opn fx type I or II w/ nonu
S82.209R	Unsp fx of shaft of unsp tibia, subsq enc for opn fx type IIIA, IIIB, or IIIC w/ malu
S82.209N	Unsp fx of shaft of unsp tibia, subsq enc for opn fx type IIIA, IIIB, or IIIC w/ nonu
S52.209A	Unsp fx of shaft of unsp ulna, init enc for clsd fx
S52.209P	Unsp fx of shaft of unsp ulna, subsq enc for clsd fx w/ malu
S52.209K	Unsp fx of shaft of unsp ulna, subsq enc for clsd fx w/ nonu
S52.209Q	Unsp fx of shaft of unsp ulna, subsq enc for opn fx type I or II w/ malu
S52.209M	Unsp fx of shaft of unsp ulna, subsq enc for opn fx type I or II w/ nonu
S52.209R	Unsp fx of shaft of unsp ulna, subsq enc for opn fx type IIIA, IIIB, or IIIC w/ malu
S52.209N	Unsp fx of shaft of unsp ulna, subsq enc for opn fx type IIIA, IIIB, or IIIC w/ nonu
S02.91XA	Unsp fx of skull, init enc for clsd fx
S02.91XK	Unsp fx of skull, subsq enc for fx w/ nonu
S22.20XA	Unsp fx of sternum, init enc for clsd fx
S22.20XK	Unsp fx of sternum, subsq enc for fx w/ nonu
S22.089A	Unsp fx of T11-T12 vertebra, init enc for clsd fx
S22.089K	Unsp fx of T11-T12 vertebra, subsq enc for fx w/ nonu
S22.059A	Unsp fx of T5-T6 vertebra, init enc for clsd fx
S22.059K	Unsp fx of T5-T6 vertebra, subsq enc for fx w/ nonu
S22.069A	Unsp fx of T7-T8 vertebra, init enc for clsd fx
S22.069K	Unsp fx of T7-T8 vertebra, subsq enc for fx w/ nonu
S22.079A	Unsp fx of T9-T10 vertebra, init enc for clsd fx
S22.079K	Unsp fx of T9-T10 vertebra, subsq enc for fx w/ nonu
S52.502A	Unsp fx of the lwr end of lt radius, init enc for clsd fx
S52.502P	Unsp fx of the lwr end of lt radius, subsq enc for clsd fx w/ malu
S52.502K	Unsp fx of the lwr end of lt radius, subsq enc for clsd fx w/ nonu
S52.502Q	Unsp fx of the lwr end of lt radius, subsq enc for opn fx type I or II w/ malu
S52.502M	Unsp fx of the lwr end of lt radius, subsq enc for opn fx type I or II w/ nonu
S52.502R	Unsp fx of the lwr end of lt radius, subsq enc for opn fx type IIIA, IIIB, or IIIC w/ malu
S52.502N	Unsp fx of the lwr end of lt radius, subsq enc for opn fx type IIIA, IIIB, or IIIC w/ nonu
S52.501A	Unsp fx of the lwr end of rt radius, init enc for clsd fx
S52.501P	Unsp fx of the lwr end of rt radius, subsq enc for clsd fx w/ malu

S52.501K	Unsp fx of the lwr end of rt radius, subsq enc for clsd fx w/ nonu
S52.501Q	Unsp fx of the lwr end of rt radius, subsq enc for opn fx type I or II w/ malu
S52.501M	Unsp fx of the lwr end of rt radius, subsq enc for opn fx type I or II w/ nonu
S52.501R	Unsp fx of the lwr end of rt radius, subsq enc for opn fx type IIIA, IIIB, or IIIC w/ malu
S52.501N	Unsp fx of the lwr end of rt radius, subsq enc for opn fx type IIIA, IIIB, or IIIC w/ nonu
S52.509A	Unsp fx of the lwr end of unsp radius, init enc for clsd fx
S52.509P	Unsp fx of the lwr end of unsp radius, subsq enc for clsd fx w/ malu
S52.509K	Unsp fx of the lwr end of unsp radius, subsq enc for clsd fx w/ nonu
S52.509Q	Unsp fx of the lwr end of unsp radius, subsq enc for opn fx type I or II w/ malu
S52.509M	Unsp fx of the lwr end of unsp radius, subsq enc for opn fx type I or II w/ nonu
S52.509R	Unsp fx of the lwr end of unsp radius, subsq enc for opn fx type IIIA, IIIB, or IIIC w/ malu
S52.509N	Unsp fx of the lwr end of unsp radius, subsq enc for opn fx type IIIA, IIIB, or IIIC w/ nonu
S32.409K	Unsp fx of unsp acetab, subsq enc for fx w/ nonu
S92.009B	Unsp fx of unsp calcaneus, init enc for opn fx
S92.009P	Unsp fx of unsp calcaneus, subsq enc for fx w/ malu
S92.009K	Unsp fx of unsp calcaneus, subsq enc for fx w/ nonu
S72.90XP	Unsp fx of unsp femur, subsq enc for clsd fx w/ malu
S72.90XK	Unsp fx of unsp femur, subsq enc for clsd fx w/ nonu
S72.90XQ	Unsp fx of unsp femur, subsq enc for opn fx type I or II w/ malu
S72.90XM	Unsp fx of unsp femur, subsq enc for opn fx type I or II w/ nonu
S72.90XR	Unsp fx of unsp femur, subsq enc for opn fx type IIIA, IIIB, or IIIC w/ malu
S72.90XN	Unsp fx of unsp femur, subsq enc for opn fx type IIIA, IIIB, or IIIC w/ nonu
S92.909B	Unsp fx of unsp foot, init enc for opn fx
S92.909P	Unsp fx of unsp foot, subsq enc for fx w/ malu
S92.909K	Unsp fx of unsp foot, subsq enc for fx w/ nonu
S52.90XA	Unsp fx of unsp forearm, init enc for clsd fx
S52.90XP	Unsp fx of unsp forearm, subsq enc for clsd fx w/ malu
S52.90XK	Unsp fx of unsp forearm, subsq enc for clsd fx w/ nonu
S52.90XQ	Unsp fx of unsp forearm, subsq enc for opn fx type I or II w/ malu
S52.90XM	Unsp fx of unsp forearm, subsq enc for opn fx type I or II w/ nonu
S52.90XR	Unsp fx of unsp forearm, subsq enc for opn fx type IIIA, IIIB, or IIIC w/ malu
S52.90XN	Unsp fx of unsp forearm, subsq enc for opn fx type IIIA, IIIB, or IIIC w/ nonu
S32.309A	Unsp fx of unsp ilium, init enc for clsd fx
S32.309K	Unsp fx of unsp ilium, subsq enc for fx w/ nonu
S32.609A	Unsp fx of unsp ischium, init enc for clsd fx
S32.609K	Unsp fx of unsp ischium, subsq enc for fx w/ nonu
S32.009A	Unsp fx of unsp lumbar vertebra, init enc for clsd fx
S32.009K	Unsp fx of unsp lumbar vertebra, subsq enc for fx w/ nonu
S82.90XB	Unsp fx of unsp lwr leg, init enc for opn fx type I or II
S82.90XC	Unsp fx of unsp lwr leg, init enc for opn fx type IIIA, IIIB, or IIIC
S82.90XP	Unsp fx of unsp lwr leg, subsq enc for clsd fx w/ malu
S82.90XK	Unsp fx of unsp lwr leg, subsq enc for clsd fx w/ nonu
S82.90XQ	Unsp fx of unsp lwr leg, subsq enc for opn fx type I or II w/ malu
S82.90XM	Unsp fx of unsp lwr leg, subsq enc for opn fx type I or II w/ nonu
S82.90XR	Unsp fx of unsp lwr leg, subsq enc for opn fx type IIIA, IIIB, or IIIC w/ malu
S82.90XN	Unsp fx of unsp lwr leg, subsq enc for opn fx type IIIA, IIIB, or IIIC w/ nonu
S62.309B	Unsp fx of unsp metacarpal bone, init enc for opn fx
S62.309P	Unsp fx of unsp metacarpal bone, subsq enc for fx w/ malu
S62.309K	Unsp fx of unsp metacarpal bone, subsq enc for fx w/ nonu
S82.009A	Unsp fx of unsp patella, init enc for clsd fx
S82.009B	Unsp fx of unsp patella, init enc for opn fx type I or II
S82.009C	Unsp fx of unsp patella, init enc for opn fx type IIIA, IIIB, or IIIC
S82.009P	Unsp fx of unsp patella, subsq enc for clsd fx w/ malu
S82.009K	Unsp fx of unsp patella, subsq enc for clsd fx w/ nonu
S82.009Q	Unsp fx of unsp patella, subsq enc for opn fx type I or II w/ malu
S82.009M	Unsp fx of unsp patella, subsq enc for opn fx type I or II w/ nonu
S82.009R	Unsp fx of unsp patella, subsq enc for opn fx type IIIA, IIIB, or IIIC w/ malu
S82.009N	Unsp fx of unsp patella, subsq enc for opn fx type IIIA, IIIB, or IIIC w/ nonu
S32.509A	Unsp fx of unsp pubis, init enc for clsd fx
S32.509K	Unsp fx of unsp pubis, subsq enc for fx w/ nonu
S92.109B	Unsp fx of unsp talus, init enc for opn fx
S92.109P	Unsp fx of unsp talus, subsq enc for fx w/ malu
S92.109K	Unsp fx of unsp talus, subsq enc for fx w/ nonu
S22.009A	Unsp fx of unsp thoracic vertebra, init enc for clsd fx
S22.009K	Unsp fx of unsp thoracic vertebra, subsq enc for fx w/ nonu
S92.919P	Unsp fx of unsp toe(s), subsq enc for fx w/ malu

S92.919K	Unsp fx of unsp toe(s), subsq enc for fx w/ nonu
S62.90XB	Unsp fx of unsp wrist & hand, init enc for opn fx
S62.90XP	Unsp fx of unsp wrist & hand, subsq enc for fx w/ malu
S62.90XK	Unsp fx of unsp wrist & hand, subsq enc for fx w/ nonu
S42.202A	Unsp fx of upr end of lt humerus, init enc for clsd fx
S42.202P	Unsp fx of upr end of lt humerus, subsq enc for fx w/ malu
S42.202K	Unsp fx of upr end of lt humerus, subsq enc for fx w/ nonu
S52.102P	Unsp fx of upr end of lt radius, subsq enc for clsd fx w/ malu
S52.102K	Unsp fx of upr end of lt radius, subsq enc for clsd fx w/ nonu
S52.102Q	Unsp fx of upr end of lt radius, subsq enc for opn fx type I or II w/ malu
S52.102M	Unsp fx of upr end of lt radius, subsq enc for opn fx type I or II w/ nonu
S52.102R	Unsp fx of upr end of lt radius, subsq enc for opn fx type IIIA, IIIB, or IIIC w/ malu
S52.102N	Unsp fx of upr end of lt radius, subsq enc for opn fx type IIIA, IIIB, or IIIC w/ nonu
S82.102A	Unsp fx of upr end of lt tibia, init enc for clsd fx
S82.102P	Unsp fx of upr end of lt tibia, subsq enc for clsd fx w/ malu
S82.102K	Unsp fx of upr end of lt tibia, subsq enc for clsd fx w/ nonu
S82.102Q	Unsp fx of upr end of lt tibia, subsq enc for opn fx type I or II w/ malu
S82.102M	Unsp fx of upr end of lt tibia, subsq enc for opn fx type I or II w/ nonu
S82.102R	Unsp fx of upr end of lt tibia, subsq enc for opn fx type IIIA, IIIB, or IIIC w/ malu
S82.102N	Unsp fx of upr end of lt tibia, subsq enc for opn fx type IIIA, IIIB, or IIIC w/ nonu
S52.002P	Unsp fx of upr end of lt ulna, subsq enc for clsd fx w/ malu
S52.002K	Unsp fx of upr end of lt ulna, subsq enc for clsd fx w/ nonu
S52.002Q	Unsp fx of upr end of lt ulna, subsq enc for opn fx type I or II w/ malu
S52.002M	Unsp fx of upr end of lt ulna, subsq enc for opn fx type I or II w/ nonu
S52.002R	Unsp fx of upr end of lt ulna, subsq enc for opn fx type IIIA, IIIB, or IIIC w/ malu
S52.002N	Unsp fx of upr end of lt ulna, subsq enc for opn fx type IIIA, IIIB, or IIIC w/ nonu
S42.201A	Unsp fx of upr end of rt humerus, init enc for clsd fx
S42.201P	Unsp fx of upr end of rt humerus, subsq enc for fx w/ malu
S42.201K	Unsp fx of upr end of rt humerus, subsq enc for fx w/ nonu
S52.101P	Unsp fx of upr end of rt radius, subsq enc for clsd fx w/ malu
S52.101K	Unsp fx of upr end of rt radius, subsq enc for clsd fx w/ nonu
S52.101Q	Unsp fx of upr end of rt radius, subsq enc for opn fx type I or II w/ malu
S52.101M	Unsp fx of upr end of rt radius, subsq enc for opn fx type I or II w/ nonu
S52.101R	Unsp fx of upr end of rt radius, subsq enc for opn fx type IIIA, IIIB, or IIIC w/ malu
S52.101N	Unsp fx of upr end of rt radius, subsq enc for opn fx type IIIA, IIIB, or IIIC w/ nonu
S82.101A	Unsp fx of upr end of rt tibia, init enc for clsd fx
S82.101P	Unsp fx of upr end of rt tibia, subsq enc for clsd fx w/ malu
S82.101K	Unsp fx of upr end of rt tibia, subsq enc for clsd fx w/ nonu
S82.101Q	Unsp fx of upr end of rt tibia, subsq enc for opn fx type I or II w/ malu
S82.101M	Unsp fx of upr end of rt tibia, subsq enc for opn fx type I or II w/ nonu
S82.101R	Unsp fx of upr end of rt tibia, subsq enc for opn fx type IIIA, IIIB, or IIIC w/ malu
S82.101N	Unsp fx of upr end of rt tibia, subsq enc for opn fx type IIIA, IIIB, or IIIC w/ nonu
S52.001P	Unsp fx of upr end of rt ulna, subsq enc for clsd fx w/ malu
S52.001K	Unsp fx of upr end of rt ulna, subsq enc for clsd fx w/ nonu
S52.001Q	Unsp fx of upr end of rt ulna, subsq enc for opn fx type I or II w/ malu
S52.001M	Unsp fx of upr end of rt ulna, subsq enc for opn fx type I or II w/ nonu
S52.001R	Unsp fx of upr end of rt ulna, subsq enc for opn fx type IIIA, IIIB, or IIIC w/ malu
S52.001N	Unsp fx of upr end of rt ulna, subsq enc for opn fx type IIIA, IIIB, or IIIC w/ nonu
S42.209A	Unsp fx of upr end of unsp humerus, init enc for clsd fx
S42.209P	Unsp fx of upr end of unsp humerus, subsq enc for fx w/ malu
S42.209K	Unsp fx of upr end of unsp humerus, subsq enc for fx w/ nonu
S52.109P	Unsp fx of upr end of unsp radius, subsq enc for clsd fx w/ malu
S52.109K	Unsp fx of upr end of unsp radius, subsq enc for clsd fx w/ nonu
S52.109Q	Unsp fx of upr end of unsp radius, subsq enc for opn fx type I or II w/ malu
S52.109M	Unsp fx of upr end of unsp radius, subsq enc for opn fx type I or II w/ nonu
S52.109R	Unsp fx of upr end of unsp radius, subsq enc for opn fx type IIIA, IIIB, or IIIC w/ malu
S52.109N	Unsp fx of upr end of unsp radius, subsq enc for opn fx type IIIA, IIIB, or IIIC w/ nonu
S82.109A	Unsp fx of upr end of unsp tibia, init enc for clsd fx
S82.109P	Unsp fx of upr end of unsp tibia, subsq enc for clsd fx w/ malu
S82.109K	Unsp fx of upr end of unsp tibia, subsq enc for clsd fx w/ nonu
S82.109Q	Unsp fx of upr end of unsp tibia, subsq enc for opn fx type I or II w/ malu

S82.109M	Unsp fx of upr end of unsp tibia, subsq enc for opn fx type I or II w/ nonu
S82.109R	Unsp fx of upr end of unsp tibia, subsq enc for opn fx type IIIA, IIIB, or IIIC w/ malu
S82.109N	Unsp fx of upr end of unsp tibia, subsq enc for opn fx type IIIA, IIIB, or IIIC w/ nonu
S52.009P	Unsp fx of upr end of unsp ulna, subsq enc for clsd fx w/ malu
S52.009K	Unsp fx of upr end of unsp ulna, subsq enc for clsd fx w/ nonu
S52.009Q	Unsp fx of upr end of unsp ulna, subsq enc for opn fx type I or II w/ malu
S52.009M	Unsp fx of upr end of unsp ulna, subsq enc for opn fx type I or II w/ nonu
S52.009R	Unsp fx of upr end of unsp ulna, subsq enc for opn fx type IIIA, IIIB, or IIIC w/ malu
S52.009N	Unsp fx of upr end of unsp ulna, subsq enc for opn fx type IIIA, IIIB, or IIIC w/ nonu
E75.10	Unsp gangliosidosis
O23.91	Unsp genitourinary tract infxn in pregnancy, 1st trmstr
O23.92	Unsp genitourinary tract infxn in pregnancy, 2nd trmstr
O23.93	Unsp genitourinary tract infxn in pregnancy, 3rd trmstr
N13.30	Unsp hydronephrosis
T80.219A	Unsp infxn d/t central venous catheter, init enc
O23.41	Unsp infxn of urinary tract in pregnancy, 1st trmstr
O23.42	Unsp infxn of urinary tract in pregnancy, 2nd trmstr
O23.43	Unsp infxn of urinary tract in pregnancy, 3rd trmstr
S37.819A	Unsp inj of adrenal gland, init enc
S85.132A	Unsp inj of ant tibial artery, lt leg, init enc
S85.131A	Unsp inj of ant tibial artery, rt leg, init enc
S85.139A	Unsp inj of ant tibial artery, unsp leg, init enc
S36.500A	Unsp inj of ascending [rt] colon, init enc
S45.202A	Unsp inj of axillary or brachial vein, lt side, init enc
S45.201A	Unsp inj of axillary or brachial vein, rt side, init enc
S45.209A	Unsp inj of axillary or brachial vein, unsp side, init enc
S37.20XA	Unsp inj of bladder, init enc
S65.501A	Unsp inj of blood vessel of lt index finger, init enc
S65.507A	Unsp inj of blood vessel of lt little finger, init enc
S65.503A	Unsp inj of blood vessel of lt mid finger, init enc
S65.505A	Unsp inj of blood vessel of lt ring finger, init enc
S65.402A	Unsp inj of blood vessel of lt thumb, init enc
S65.508A	Unsp inj of blood vessel of oth finger, init enc
S65.500A	Unsp inj of blood vessel of rt index finger, init enc
S65.506A	Unsp inj of blood vessel of rt little finger, init enc
S65.502A	Unsp inj of blood vessel of rt mid finger, init enc
S65.504A	Unsp inj of blood vessel of rt ring finger, init enc
S65.401A	Unsp inj of blood vessel of rt thumb, init enc
S65.509A	Unsp inj of blood vessel of unsp finger, init enc
S65.409A	Unsp inj of blood vessel of unsp thumb, init enc
S36.201A	Unsp inj of body of pancreas, init enc
S45.102A	Unsp inj of brachial artery, lt side, init enc
S45.101A	Unsp inj of brachial artery, rt side, init enc
S45.109A	Unsp inj of brachial artery, unsp side, init enc
S65.302A	Unsp inj of deep palmar arch of lt hand, init enc
S65.301A	Unsp inj of deep palmar arch of rt hand, init enc
S65.309A	Unsp inj of deep palmar arch of unsp hand, init enc
S36.502A	Unsp inj of descending [lt] colon, init enc
S27.809A	Unsp inj of diaphragm, init enc
S95.002A	Unsp inj of dorsal artery of lt foot, init enc
S95.001A	Unsp inj of dorsal artery of rt foot, init enc
S95.009A	Unsp inj of dorsal artery of unsp foot, init enc
S95.202A	Unsp inj of dorsal vein of lt foot, init enc
S95.201A	Unsp inj of dorsal vein of rt foot, init enc
S95.209A	Unsp inj of dorsal vein of unsp foot, init enc
S36.400A	Unsp inj of duodenum, init enc
S36.129A	Unsp inj of gallbladder, init enc
S75.202A	Unsp inj of greater saphenous vein at hip & thigh lvl, lt leg, init enc
S75.201A	Unsp inj of greater saphenous vein at hip & thigh lvl, rt leg, init enc
S75.209A	Unsp inj of greater saphenous vein at hip & thigh lvl, unsp leg, init enc
S85.302A	Unsp inj of greater saphenous vein at lwr leg lvl, lt leg, init enc
S85.301A	Unsp inj of greater saphenous vein at lwr leg lvl, rt leg, init enc
S85.309A	Unsp inj of greater saphenous vein at lwr leg lvl, unsp leg, init enc
S36.200A	Unsp inj of head of pancreas, init enc
S26.00XA	Unsp inj of heart w/ hemopericardium, init enc
S26.10XA	Unsp inj of heart w/o hemopericardium, init enc
S26.90XA	Unsp inj of heart, unsp w/ or w/o hemopericardium, init enc
S25.502A	Unsp inj of intercostal blood vessels, lt side, init enc
S25.501A	Unsp inj of intercostal blood vessels, rt side, init enc
S25.509A	Unsp inj of intercostal blood vessels, unsp side, init enc
S85.402A	Unsp inj of lesser saphenous vein at lwr leg lvl, lt leg, init enc
S85.401A	Unsp inj of lesser saphenous vein at lwr leg lvl, rt leg, init enc
S85.409A	Unsp inj of lesser saphenous vein at lwr leg lvl, unsp leg, init enc
S36.119A	Unsp inj of liver, init enc
S15.002A	Unsp inj of lt carotid artery, init enc
S15.202A	Unsp inj of lt ext jugular vein, init enc
S05.92XA	Unsp inj of lt eye & orbit, init enc
S15.302A	Unsp inj of lt int jugular vein, init enc
S37.002A	Unsp inj of lt kidney, init enc
S09.302A	Unsp inj of lt mid & inner ear, init enc
S15.102A	Unsp inj of lt vert artery, init enc
S27.302A	Unsp inj of lung, bilat, init enc
S27.301A	Unsp inj of lung, unilat, init enc
S27.309A	Unsp inj of lung, unsp, init enc
S35.8X9A	Unsp inj of oth blood vessels at abd, lwr back & pelvis lvl, init enc
S95.802A	Unsp inj of oth blood vessels at ankle & foot lvl, lt leg, init enc
S95.801A	Unsp inj of oth blood vessels at ankle & foot lvl, rt leg, init enc
S95.809A	Unsp inj of oth blood vessels at ankle & foot lvl, unsp leg, init enc
S55.802A	Unsp inj of oth blood vessels at forearm lvl, lt arm, init enc
S55.801A	Unsp inj of oth blood vessels at forearm lvl, rt arm, init enc
S55.809A	Unsp inj of oth blood vessels at forearm lvl, unsp arm, init enc
S75.802A	Unsp inj of oth blood vessels at hip & thigh lvl, lt leg, init enc
S75.801A	Unsp inj of oth blood vessels at hip & thigh lvl, rt leg, init enc
S75.809A	Unsp inj of oth blood vessels at hip & thigh lvl, unsp leg, init enc
S85.802A	Unsp inj of oth blood vessels at lwr leg lvl, lt leg, init enc
S85.801A	Unsp inj of oth blood vessels at lwr leg lvl, rt leg, init enc
S85.809A	Unsp inj of oth blood vessels at lwr leg lvl, unsp leg, init enc
S65.802A	Unsp inj of oth blood vessels at wrist & hand lvl of lt arm, init enc
S65.801A	Unsp inj of oth blood vessels at wrist & hand lvl of rt arm, init enc
S65.809A	Unsp inj of oth blood vessels at wrist & hand lvl of unsp arm, init enc
S25.802A	Unsp inj of oth blood vessels of thorax, lt side, init enc
S25.801A	Unsp inj of oth blood vessels of thorax, rt side, init enc
S25.809A	Unsp inj of oth blood vessels of thorax, unsp side, init enc
S36.899A	Unsp inj of oth intra-abd organs, init enc
S36.508A	Unsp inj of oth part of colon, init enc
S36.408A	Unsp inj of oth part of sm intestine, init enc
S45.802A	Unsp inj of oth spec blood vessels at shldr & upr arm lvl, lt arm, init enc
S45.801A	Unsp inj of oth spec blood vessels at shldr & upr arm lvl, rt arm, init enc
S45.809A	Unsp inj of oth spec blood vessels at shldr & upr arm lvl, unsp arm, init enc
S27.899A	Unsp inj of oth spec intrathoracic organs, init enc
S37.899A	Unsp inj of oth urinary & pelvic organ, init enc
S85.202A	Unsp inj of peroneal artery, lt leg, init enc
S85.201A	Unsp inj of peroneal artery, rt leg, init enc
S85.209A	Unsp inj of peroneal artery, unsp leg, init enc
S95.102A	Unsp inj of plantar artery of lt foot, init enc
S95.101A	Unsp inj of plantar artery of rt foot, init enc
S95.109A	Unsp inj of plantar artery of unsp foot, init enc
S27.60XA	Unsp inj of pleura, init enc
S85.162A	Unsp inj of post tibial artery, lt leg, init enc
S85.161A	Unsp inj of post tibial artery, rt leg, init enc
S85.169A	Unsp inj of post tibial artery, unsp leg, init enc
S55.102A	Unsp inj of radial artery at forearm lvl, lt arm, init enc
S55.101A	Unsp inj of radial artery at forearm lvl, rt arm, init enc
S55.109A	Unsp inj of radial artery at forearm lvl, unsp arm, init enc
S65.102A	Unsp inj of radial artery at wrist & hand lvl of lt arm, init enc
S65.101A	Unsp inj of radial artery at wrist & hand lvl of rt arm, init enc
S65.109A	Unsp inj of radial artery at wrist & hand lvl of unsp arm, init enc
S36.60XA	Unsp inj of rectum, init enc
S15.001A	Unsp inj of rt carotid artery, init enc
S15.201A	Unsp inj of rt ext jugular vein, init enc
S05.91XA	Unsp inj of rt eye & orbit, init enc
S15.301A	Unsp inj of rt int jugular vein, init enc
S37.001A	Unsp inj of rt kidney, init enc
S09.301A	Unsp inj of rt mid & inner ear, init enc
S15.101A	Unsp inj of rt vert artery, init enc
S36.503A	Unsp inj of sigmoid colon, init enc
S36.00XA	Unsp inj of spleen, init enc
S36.30XA	Unsp inj of stomach, init enc
S65.202A	Unsp inj of superf palmar arch of lt hand, init enc
S65.201A	Unsp inj of superf palmar arch of rt hand, init enc
S65.209A	Unsp inj of superf palmar arch of unsp hand, init enc
S45.302A	Unsp inj of superf vein at shldr & upr arm lvl, lt arm, init enc

S45.301A	Unsp inj of superf vein at shldr & upr arm lvl, rt arm, init enc
S45.309A	Unsp inj of superf vein at shldr & upr arm lvl, unsp arm, init enc
S36.202A	Unsp inj of tail of pancreas, init enc
S27.50XA	Unsp inj of thoracic trachea, init enc
S36.501A	Unsp inj of transv colon, init enc
S55.002A	Unsp inj of ulnar artery at forearm lvl, lt arm, init enc
S55.001A	Unsp inj of ulnar artery at forearm lvl, rt arm, init enc
S55.009A	Unsp inj of ulnar artery at forearm lvl, unsp arm, init enc
S65.002A	Unsp inj of ulnar artery at wrist & hand lvl of lt arm, init enc
S65.001A	Unsp inj of ulnar artery at wrist & hand lvl of rt arm, init enc
S65.009A	Unsp inj of ulnar artery at wrist & hand lvl of unsp arm, init enc
S35.90XA	Unsp inj of unsp blood vessel at abd, lwr back & pelvis lvl, init enc
S95.902A	Unsp inj of unsp blood vessel at ankle & foot lvl, lt leg, init enc
S95.901A	Unsp inj of unsp blood vessel at ankle & foot lvl, rt leg, init enc
S95.909A	Unsp inj of unsp blood vessel at ankle & foot lvl, unsp leg, init enc
S55.902A	Unsp inj of unsp blood vessel at forearm lvl, lt arm, init enc
S55.901A	Unsp inj of unsp blood vessel at forearm lvl, rt arm, init enc
S55.909A	Unsp inj of unsp blood vessel at forearm lvl, unsp arm, init enc
S75.902A	Unsp inj of unsp blood vessel at hip & thigh lvl, lt leg, init enc
S75.901A	Unsp inj of unsp blood vessel at hip & thigh lvl, rt leg, init enc
S75.909A	Unsp inj of unsp blood vessel at hip & thigh lvl, unsp leg, init enc
S85.902A	Unsp inj of unsp blood vessel at lwr leg lvl, lt leg, init enc
S85.901A	Unsp inj of unsp blood vessel at lwr leg lvl, rt leg, init enc
S85.909A	Unsp inj of unsp blood vessel at lwr leg lvl, unsp leg, init enc
S45.902A	Unsp inj of unsp blood vessel at shldr & upr arm lvl, lt arm, init enc
S45.901A	Unsp inj of unsp blood vessel at shldr & upr arm lvl, rt arm, init enc
S45.909A	Unsp inj of unsp blood vessel at shldr & upr arm lvl, unsp arm, init enc
S65.902A	Unsp inj of unsp blood vessel at wrist & hand lvl of lt arm, init enc
S65.901A	Unsp inj of unsp blood vessel at wrist & hand lvl of rt arm, init enc
S65.909A	Unsp inj of unsp blood vessel at wrist & hand lvl of unsp arm, init enc
S25.90XA	Unsp inj of unsp blood vessel of thorax, init enc
S15.009A	Unsp inj of unsp carotid artery, init enc
S15.209A	Unsp inj of unsp ext jugular vein, init enc
S15.309A	Unsp inj of unsp int jugular vein, init enc
S36.90XA	Unsp inj of unsp intra-abd organ, init enc
S37.009A	Unsp inj of unsp kidney, init enc
S09.309A	Unsp inj of unsp mid & inner ear, init enc
S36.509A	Unsp inj of unsp part of colon, init enc
S36.209A	Unsp inj of unsp part of pancreas, init enc
S36.409A	Unsp inj of unsp part of sm intestine, init enc
S85.102A	Unsp inj of unsp tibial artery, lt leg, init enc
S85.101A	Unsp inj of unsp tibial artery, rt leg, init enc
S85.109A	Unsp inj of unsp tibial artery, unsp leg, init enc
S37.90XA	Unsp inj of unsp urinary & pelvic organ, init enc
S15.109A	Unsp inj of unsp vert artery, init enc
S37.10XA	Unsp inj of ureter, init enc
S37.30XA	Unsp inj of urethra, init enc
S37.60XA	Unsp inj of uterus, init enc
S55.202A	Unsp inj of vein at forearm lvl, lt arm, init enc
S55.201A	Unsp inj of vein at forearm lvl, rt arm, init enc
S55.209A	Unsp inj of vein at forearm lvl, unsp arm, init enc
K56.60	Unsp intestinal obstruction
S72.012P	Unsp intracapsular fx of lt femur, subsq enc for clsd fx w/ malu
S72.012K	Unsp intracapsular fx of lt femur, subsq enc for clsd fx w/ nonu
S72.012Q	Unsp intracapsular fx of lt femur, subsq enc for opn fx type I or II w/ malu
S72.012M	Unsp intracapsular fx of lt femur, subsq enc for opn fx type I or II w/ nonu
S72.012R	Unsp intracapsular fx of lt femur, subsq enc for opn fx type IIIA, IIIB, or IIIC w/ malu
S72.012N	Unsp intracapsular fx of lt femur, subsq enc for opn fx type IIIA, IIIB, or IIIC w/ nonu
S72.011P	Unsp intracapsular fx of rt femur, subsq enc for clsd fx w/ malu
S72.011K	Unsp intracapsular fx of rt femur, subsq enc for clsd fx w/ nonu
S72.011Q	Unsp intracapsular fx of rt femur, subsq enc for opn fx type I or II w/ malu
S72.011M	Unsp intracapsular fx of rt femur, subsq enc for opn fx type I or II w/ nonu
S72.011R	Unsp intracapsular fx of rt femur, subsq enc for opn fx type IIIA, IIIB, or IIIC w/ malu
S72.011N	Unsp intracapsular fx of rt femur, subsq enc for opn fx type IIIA, IIIB, or IIIC w/ nonu
S72.019P	Unsp intracapsular fx of unsp femur, subsq enc for clsd fx w/ malu
S72.019K	Unsp intracapsular fx of unsp femur, subsq enc for clsd fx w/ nonu
S72.019Q	Unsp intracapsular fx of unsp femur, subsq enc for opn fx type I or II w/ malu
S72.019M	Unsp intracapsular fx of unsp femur, subsq enc for opn fx type I or II w/ nonu

S72.019R	Unsp intracapsular fx of unsp femur, subsq enc for opn fx type IIIA, IIIB, or IIIC w/ malu
S72.019N	Unsp intracapsular fx of unsp femur, subsq enc for opn fx type IIIA, IIIB, or IIIC w/ nonu
S06.9X5A	Unsp intracranial inj w/ loss of cnscness > 24 hrs w/ return to pre-existing conscious lvl, init enc
S06.9X3A	Unsp intracranial inj w/ loss of cnscness of 1 hr to 5 hrs 59 mins, init enc
S06.9X1A	Unsp intracranial inj w/ loss of cnscness of 30 mins or less, init enc
S06.9X2A	Unsp intracranial inj w/ loss of cnscness of 31 mins to 59 mins, init enc
S06.9X4A	Unsp intracranial inj w/ loss of cnscness of 6 hrs to 24 hrs, init enc
S06.9X9A	Unsp intracranial inj w/ loss of cnscness of unsp dur, init enc
P52.3	Unsp intraventricular (nontraumatic) hemor of newborn
H20.9	Unsp iridocyclitis
R17	Unsp jaundice
S36.039A	Unsp lac of spleen, init enc
B54	Unsp malaria
O16.1	Unsp maternal hypertension, 1st trmstr
O16.2	Unsp maternal hypertension, 2nd trmstr
O16.3	Unsp maternal hypertension, 3rd trmstr
O98.92	Unsp maternal infectious & parasitic disease comp childbirth
O98.911	Unsp maternal infectious & parasitic disease comp pregnancy, 1st trmstr
O98.912	Unsp maternal infectious & parasitic disease comp pregnancy, 2nd trmstr
O98.913	Unsp maternal infectious & parasitic disease comp pregnancy, 3rd trmstr
O98.93	Unsp maternal infectious & parasitic disease comp the puerperium
B49	Unsp mycosis
N05.4	Unsp nephritic synd w/ diffuse endocapillary proliferative glomerulonephritis
N05.2	Unsp nephritic synd w/ diffuse membranous glomerulonephritis
N05.3	Unsp nephritic synd w/ diffuse mesangial proliferative glomerulonephritis
N05.5	Unsp nephritic synd w/ diffuse mesangiocapillary glomerulonephritis
S12.001A	Unsp nondisp fx of 1st cervical vertebra, init enc for clsd fx
S12.001K	Unsp nondisp fx of 1st cervical vertebra, subsq enc for fx w/ nonu
S12.101A	Unsp nondisp fx of 2nd cervical vertebra, init enc for clsd fx
S12.101K	Unsp nondisp fx of 2nd cervical vertebra, subsq enc for fx w/ nonu
S12.201A	Unsp nondisp fx of 3rd cervical vertebra, init enc for clsd fx
S12.201K	Unsp nondisp fx of 3rd cervical vertebra, subsq enc for fx w/ nonu
S12.301A	Unsp nondisp fx of 4th cervical vertebra, init enc for clsd fx
S12.301K	Unsp nondisp fx of 4th cervical vertebra, subsq enc for fx w/ nonu
S12.401A	Unsp nondisp fx of 5th cervical vertebra, init enc for clsd fx
S12.401K	Unsp nondisp fx of 5th cervical vertebra, subsq enc for fx w/ nonu
S12.501A	Unsp nondisp fx of 6th cervical vertebra, init enc for clsd fx
S12.501K	Unsp nondisp fx of 6th cervical vertebra, subsq enc for fx w/ nonu
S12.601A	Unsp nondisp fx of 7th cervical vertebra, init enc for clsd fx
S12.601K	Unsp nondisp fx of 7th cervical vertebra, subsq enc for fx w/ nonu
S42.215A	Unsp nondisp fx of surg neck of lt humerus, init enc for clsd fx
S42.215P	Unsp nondisp fx of surg neck of lt humerus, subsq enc for fx w/ malu
S42.215K	Unsp nondisp fx of surg neck of lt humerus, subsq enc for fx w/ nonu
S42.214A	Unsp nondisp fx of surg neck of rt humerus, init enc for clsd fx
S42.214P	Unsp nondisp fx of surg neck of rt humerus, subsq enc for fx w/ malu
S42.214K	Unsp nondisp fx of surg neck of rt humerus, subsq enc for fx w/ nonu
S42.216A	Unsp nondisp fx of surg neck of unsp humerus, init enc for clsd fx
S42.216P	Unsp nondisp fx of surg neck of unsp humerus, subsq enc for fx w/ malu
S42.216K	Unsp nondisp fx of surg neck of unsp humerus, subsq enc for fx w/ nonu
S02.113A	Unsp occipital condyle fx, init enc for clsd fx
S02.113K	Unsp occipital condyle fx, subsq enc for fx w/ nonu
S01.102A	Unsp opn wnd of lt eyelid & periocular area, init enc
S21.102A	Unsp opn wnd of lt front wall of thorax w/o penetration into thoracic cavity, init enc
S11.20XA	Unsp opn wnd of pharynx & cervical esophagus, init enc
S01.101A	Unsp opn wnd of rt eyelid & periocular area, init enc
S21.101A	Unsp opn wnd of rt front wall of thorax w/o penetration into thoracic cavity, init enc
S11.10XA	Unsp opn wnd of thyroid gland, init enc
S01.109A	Unsp opn wnd of unsp eyelid & periocular area, init enc
S21.109A	Unsp opn wnd of unsp front wall of thorax w/o penetration into thoracic cavity, init enc
S21.90XA	Unsp opn wnd of unsp part of thorax, init enc
H46.9	Unsp optic neuritis
H47.10	Unsp papilledema
S49.102A	Unsp physeal fx of lwr end of humerus, lt arm, init enc for clsd fx
S49.102P	Unsp physeal fx of lwr end of humerus, lt arm, subsq enc for fx w/ malu
S49.102K	Unsp physeal fx of lwr end of humerus, lt arm, subsq enc for fx w/ nonu

S49.101A	Unsp physeal fx of lwr end of humerus, rt arm, init enc for clsd fx
S49.101P	Unsp physeal fx of lwr end of humerus, rt arm, subsq enc for fx w/ malu
S49.101K	Unsp physeal fx of lwr end of humerus, rt arm, subsq enc for fx w/ nonu
S49.109A	Unsp physeal fx of lwr end of humerus, unsp arm, init enc for clsd fx
S49.109P	Unsp physeal fx of lwr end of humerus, unsp arm, subsq enc for fx w/ malu
S49.109K	Unsp physeal fx of lwr end of humerus, unsp arm, subsq enc for fx w/ nonu
S79.102A	Unsp physeal fx of lwr end of lt femur, init enc for clsd fx
S79.102P	Unsp physeal fx of lwr end of lt femur, subsq enc for fx w/ malu
S79.102K	Unsp physeal fx of lwr end of lt femur, subsq enc for fx w/ nonu
S89.302P	Unsp physeal fx of lwr end of lt fibula, subsq enc for fx w/ malu
S89.302K	Unsp physeal fx of lwr end of lt fibula, subsq enc for fx w/ nonu
S89.102P	Unsp physeal fx of lwr end of lt tibia, subsq enc for fx w/ malu
S89.102K	Unsp physeal fx of lwr end of lt tibia, subsq enc for fx w/ nonu
S59.202A	Unsp physeal fx of lwr end of radius, lt arm, init enc for clsd fx
S59.202P	Unsp physeal fx of lwr end of radius, lt arm, subsq enc for fx w/ malu
S59.202K	Unsp physeal fx of lwr end of radius, lt arm, subsq enc for fx w/ nonu
S59.201A	Unsp physeal fx of lwr end of radius, rt arm, init enc for clsd fx
S59.201P	Unsp physeal fx of lwr end of radius, rt arm, subsq enc for fx w/ malu
S59.201K	Unsp physeal fx of lwr end of radius, rt arm, subsq enc for fx w/ nonu
S59.209A	Unsp physeal fx of lwr end of radius, unsp arm, init enc for clsd fx
S59.209P	Unsp physeal fx of lwr end of radius, unsp arm, subsq enc for fx w/ malu
S59.209K	Unsp physeal fx of lwr end of radius, unsp arm, subsq enc for fx w/ nonu
S79.101A	Unsp physeal fx of lwr end of rt femur, init enc for clsd fx
S79.101P	Unsp physeal fx of lwr end of rt femur, subsq enc for fx w/ malu
S79.101K	Unsp physeal fx of lwr end of rt femur, subsq enc for fx w/ nonu
S89.301P	Unsp physeal fx of lwr end of rt fibula, subsq enc for fx w/ malu
S89.301K	Unsp physeal fx of lwr end of rt fibula, subsq enc for fx w/ nonu
S89.101P	Unsp physeal fx of lwr end of rt tibia, subsq enc for fx w/ malu
S89.101K	Unsp physeal fx of lwr end of rt tibia, subsq enc for fx w/ nonu
S59.002A	Unsp physeal fx of lwr end of ulna, lt arm, init enc for clsd fx
S59.002P	Unsp physeal fx of lwr end of ulna, lt arm, subsq enc for fx w/ malu
S59.002K	Unsp physeal fx of lwr end of ulna, lt arm, subsq enc for fx w/ nonu
S59.001A	Unsp physeal fx of lwr end of ulna, rt arm, init enc for clsd fx
S59.001P	Unsp physeal fx of lwr end of ulna, rt arm, subsq enc for fx w/ malu
S59.001K	Unsp physeal fx of lwr end of ulna, rt arm, subsq enc for fx w/ nonu
S59.009A	Unsp physeal fx of lwr end of ulna, unsp arm, init enc for clsd fx
S59.009P	Unsp physeal fx of lwr end of ulna, unsp arm, subsq enc for fx w/ malu
S59.009K	Unsp physeal fx of lwr end of ulna, unsp arm, subsq enc for fx w/ nonu
S79.109A	Unsp physeal fx of lwr end of unsp femur, init enc for clsd fx
S79.109P	Unsp physeal fx of lwr end of unsp femur, subsq enc for fx w/ malu
S79.109K	Unsp physeal fx of lwr end of unsp femur, subsq enc for fx w/ nonu
S89.309P	Unsp physeal fx of lwr end of unsp fibula, subsq enc for fx w/ malu
S89.309K	Unsp physeal fx of lwr end of unsp fibula, subsq enc for fx w/ nonu
S89.109P	Unsp physeal fx of lwr end of unsp tibia, subsq enc for fx w/ malu
S89.109K	Unsp physeal fx of lwr end of unsp tibia, subsq enc for fx w/ nonu
S49.002A	Unsp physeal fx of upr end of humerus, lt arm, init enc for clsd fx
S49.002P	Unsp physeal fx of upr end of humerus, lt arm, subsq enc for fx w/ malu
S49.002K	Unsp physeal fx of upr end of humerus, lt arm, subsq enc for fx w/ nonu
S49.001A	Unsp physeal fx of upr end of humerus, rt arm, init enc for clsd fx
S49.001P	Unsp physeal fx of upr end of humerus, rt arm, subsq enc for fx w/ malu
S49.001K	Unsp physeal fx of upr end of humerus, rt arm, subsq enc for fx w/ nonu
S49.009A	Unsp physeal fx of upr end of humerus, unsp arm, init enc for clsd fx
S49.009P	Unsp physeal fx of upr end of humerus, unsp arm, subsq enc for fx w/ malu
S49.009K	Unsp physeal fx of upr end of humerus, unsp arm, subsq enc for fx w/ nonu
S79.002P	Unsp physeal fx of upr end of lt femur, subsq enc for fx w/ malu
S79.002K	Unsp physeal fx of upr end of lt femur, subsq enc for fx w/ nonu
S89.202P	Unsp physeal fx of upr end of lt fibula, subsq enc for fx w/ malu
S89.202K	Unsp physeal fx of upr end of lt fibula, subsq enc for fx w/ nonu
S89.002A	Unsp physeal fx of upr end of lt tibia, init enc for clsd fx
S89.002P	Unsp physeal fx of upr end of lt tibia, subsq enc for fx w/ malu
S89.002K	Unsp physeal fx of upr end of lt tibia, subsq enc for fx w/ nonu
S59.102P	Unsp physeal fx of upr end of radius, lt arm, subsq enc for fx w/ malu
S59.102K	Unsp physeal fx of upr end of radius, lt arm, subsq enc for fx w/ nonu
S59.101P	Unsp physeal fx of upr end of radius, rt arm, subsq enc for fx w/ malu
S59.101K	Unsp physeal fx of upr end of radius, rt arm, subsq enc for fx w/ nonu
S59.109P	Unsp physeal fx of upr end of radius, unsp arm, subsq enc for fx w/ malu
S59.109K	Unsp physeal fx of upr end of radius, unsp arm, subsq enc for fx w/ nonu
S79.001P	Unsp physeal fx of upr end of rt femur, subsq enc for fx w/ malu
S79.001K	Unsp physeal fx of upr end of rt femur, subsq enc for fx w/ nonu
S89.201P	Unsp physeal fx of upr end of rt fibula, subsq enc for fx w/ malu

S89.201K	Unsp physeal fx of upr end of rt fibula, subsq enc for fx w/ nonu
S89.001A	Unsp physeal fx of upr end of rt tibia, init enc for clsd fx
S89.001P	Unsp physeal fx of upr end of rt tibia, subsq enc for fx w/ malu
S89.001K	Unsp physeal fx of upr end of rt tibia, subsq enc for fx w/ nonu
S79.009P	Unsp physeal fx of upr end of unsp femur, subsq enc for fx w/ malu
S79.009K	Unsp physeal fx of upr end of unsp femur, subsq enc for fx w/ nonu
S89.209P	Unsp physeal fx of upr end of unsp fibula, subsq enc for fx w/ malu
S89.209K	Unsp physeal fx of upr end of unsp fibula, subsq enc for fx w/ nonu
S89.009A	Unsp physeal fx of upr end of unsp tibia, init enc for clsd fx
S89.009P	Unsp physeal fx of upr end of unsp tibia, subsq enc for fx w/ malu
S89.009K	Unsp physeal fx of upr end of unsp tibia, subsq enc for fx w/ nonu
E80.20	Unsp porphyria
O14.92	Unsp pre-eclampsia, 2nd trmstr
O14.93	Unsp pre-eclampsia, 3rd trmstr
O24.311	Unsp pre-existing diabetes mellitus in pregnancy, 1st trmstr
O24.312	Unsp pre-existing diabetes mellitus in pregnancy, 2nd trmstr
O24.313	Unsp pre-existing diabetes mellitus in pregnancy, 3rd trmstr
O24.319	Unsp pre-existing diabetes mellitus in pregnancy, unsp trmstr
O24.33	Unsp pre-existing diabetes mellitus in the puerperium
O10.92	Unsp pre-existing hypertension comp childbirth
O10.911	Unsp pre-existing hypertension comp pregnancy, 1st trmstr
O10.912	Unsp pre-existing hypertension comp pregnancy, 2nd trmstr
O10.913	Unsp pre-existing hypertension comp pregnancy, 3rd trmstr
E46	Unsp protein-calorie malnutrition
H44.003	Unsp purulent endophthalmitis, bilat
H44.002	Unsp purulent endophthalmitis, lt eye
H44.001	Unsp purulent endophthalmitis, rt eye
H44.009	Unsp purulent endophthalmitis, unsp eye
H34.9	Unsp retinal vascular occlsn
H35.70	Unsp separation of retinal layers
Q05.4	Unsp spina bifida w/ hydrocephalus
S73.002A	Unsp sublux of lt hip, init enc
S43.202A	Unsp sublux of lt sternoclavicular jt, init enc
S73.001A	Unsp sublux of rt hip, init enc
S43.201A	Unsp sublux of rt sternoclavicular jt, init enc
S73.003A	Unsp sublux of unsp hip, init enc
S43.203A	Unsp sublux of unsp sternoclavicular jt, init enc
I50.20	Unsp systolic (congestive) heart failure
J95.00	Unsp tracheostomy comp
T86.92	Unsp transplanted organ & tissue failure
T86.93	Unsp transplanted organ & tissue infxn
T86.91	Unsp transplanted organ & tissue rejection
S12.130A	Unsp traum disp spondylolisthesis of 2nd cervical vertebra, init enc for clsd fx
S12.130K	Unsp traum disp spondylolisthesis of 2nd cervical vertebra, subsq enc for fx w/ nonu
S12.230A	Unsp traum disp spondylolisthesis of 3rd cervical vertebra, init enc for clsd fx
S12.230K	Unsp traum disp spondylolisthesis of 3rd cervical vertebra, subsq enc for fx w/ nonu
S12.330A	Unsp traum disp spondylolisthesis of 4th cervical vertebra, init enc for clsd fx
S12.330K	Unsp traum disp spondylolisthesis of 4th cervical vertebra, subsq enc for fx w/ nonu
S12.430A	Unsp traum disp spondylolisthesis of 5th cervical vertebra, init enc for clsd fx
S12.430K	Unsp traum disp spondylolisthesis of 5th cervical vertebra, subsq enc for fx w/ nonu
S12.530A	Unsp traum disp spondylolisthesis of 6th cervical vertebra, init enc for clsd fx
S12.530K	Unsp traum disp spondylolisthesis of 6th cervical vertebra, subsq enc for fx w/ nonu
S12.630A	Unsp traum disp spondylolisthesis of 7th cervical vertebra, init enc for clsd fx
S12.630K	Unsp traum disp spondylolisthesis of 7th cervical vertebra, subsq enc for fx w/ nonu
S12.131A	Unsp traum nondisp spondylolisthesis of 2nd cervical vertebra, init enc for clsd fx
S12.131K	Unsp traum nondisp spondylolisthesis of 2nd cervical vertebra, subsq enc for fx w/ nonu
S12.231A	Unsp traum nondisp spondylolisthesis of 3rd cervical vertebra, init enc for clsd fx
S12.231K	Unsp traum nondisp spondylolisthesis of 3rd cervical vertebra, subsq enc for fx w/ nonu

S12.331A	Unsp traum nondisp spondylolisthesis of 4th cervical vertebra, init enc for clsd fx
S12.331K	Unsp traum nondisp spondylolisthesis of 4th cervical vertebra, subsq enc for fx w/ nonu
S12.431A	Unsp traum nondisp spondylolisthesis of 5th cervical vertebra, init enc for clsd fx
S12.431K	Unsp traum nondisp spondylolisthesis of 5th cervical vertebra, subsq enc for fx w/ nonu
S12.531A	Unsp traum nondisp spondylolisthesis of 6th cervical vertebra, init enc for clsd fx
S12.531K	Unsp traum nondisp spondylolisthesis of 6th cervical vertebra, subsq enc for fx w/ nonu
S12.631A	Unsp traum nondisp spondylolisthesis of 7th cervical vertebra, init enc for clsd fx
S12.631K	Unsp traum nondisp spondylolisthesis of 7th cervical vertebra, subsq enc for fx w/ nonu
S72.102P	Unsp trochanteric fx of lt femur, subsq enc for clsd fx w/ malu
S72.102K	Unsp trochanteric fx of lt femur, subsq enc for clsd fx w/ nonu
S72.102Q	Unsp trochanteric fx of lt femur, subsq enc for opn fx type I or II w/ malu
S72.102M	Unsp trochanteric fx of lt femur, subsq enc for opn fx type I or II w/ nonu
S72.102R	Unsp trochanteric fx of lt femur, subsq enc for opn fx type IIIA, IIIB, or IIIC w/ malu
S72.102N	Unsp trochanteric fx of lt femur, subsq enc for opn fx type IIIA, IIIB, or IIIC w/ nonu
S72.101P	Unsp trochanteric fx of rt femur, subsq enc for clsd fx w/ malu
S72.101K	Unsp trochanteric fx of rt femur, subsq enc for clsd fx w/ nonu
S72.101Q	Unsp trochanteric fx of rt femur, subsq enc for opn fx type I or II w/ malu
S72.101M	Unsp trochanteric fx of rt femur, subsq enc for opn fx type I or II w/ nonu
S72.101R	Unsp trochanteric fx of rt femur, subsq enc for opn fx type IIIA, IIIB, or IIIC w/ malu
S72.101N	Unsp trochanteric fx of rt femur, subsq enc for opn fx type IIIA, IIIB, or IIIC w/ nonu
S72.109P	Unsp trochanteric fx of unsp femur, subsq enc for clsd fx w/ malu
S72.109K	Unsp trochanteric fx of unsp femur, subsq enc for clsd fx w/ nonu
S72.109Q	Unsp trochanteric fx of unsp femur, subsq enc for opn fx type I or II w/ malu
S72.109M	Unsp trochanteric fx of unsp femur, subsq enc for opn fx type I or II w/ nonu
S72.109R	Unsp trochanteric fx of unsp femur, subsq enc for opn fx type IIIA, IIIB, or IIIC w/ malu
S72.109N	Unsp trochanteric fx of unsp femur, subsq enc for opn fx type IIIA, IIIB, or IIIC w/ nonu
A86	Unsp viral encephalitis
A99	Unsp viral hemorrhagic fever
B19.10	Unsp viral hepatitis B w/o hepatic coma
B19.9	Unsp viral hepatitis w/o hepatic coma
A89	Unsp viral infxn of central nervous sys
S32.119A	Unsp Zone I fx of sacrum, init enc for clsd fx
S32.119K	Unsp Zone I fx of sacrum, subsq enc for fx w/ nonu
S32.129A	Unsp Zone II fx of sacrum, init enc for clsd fx
S32.129K	Unsp Zone II fx of sacrum, subsq enc for fx w/ nonu
S32.139A	Unsp Zone III fx of sacrum, init enc for clsd fx
S32.139K	Unsp Zone III fx of sacrum, subsq enc for fx w/ nonu
I20.0	Unstable angina
S12.02XA	Unstable burst fx of 1st cervical vertebra, init enc for clsd fx
S12.02XK	Unstable burst fx of 1st cervical vertebra, subsq enc for fx w/ nonu
S32.012A	Unstable burst fx of 1st lumbar vertebra, init enc for clsd fx
S32.012K	Unstable burst fx of 1st lumbar vertebra, subsq enc for fx w/ nonu
S22.012A	Unstable burst fx of 1st thoracic vertebra, init enc for clsd fx
S22.012K	Unstable burst fx of 1st thoracic vertebra, subsq enc for fx w/ nonu
S32.022A	Unstable burst fx of 2nd lumbar vertebra, init enc for clsd fx
S32.022K	Unstable burst fx of 2nd lumbar vertebra, subsq enc for fx w/ nonu
S22.022A	Unstable burst fx of 2nd thoracic vertebra, init enc for clsd fx
S22.022K	Unstable burst fx of 2nd thoracic vertebra, subsq enc for fx w/ nonu
S32.032A	Unstable burst fx of 3rd lumbar vertebra, init enc for clsd fx
S32.032K	Unstable burst fx of 3rd lumbar vertebra, subsq enc for fx w/ nonu
S22.032A	Unstable burst fx of 3rd thoracic vertebra, init enc for clsd fx
S22.032K	Unstable burst fx of 3rd thoracic vertebra, subsq enc for fx w/ nonu
S32.042A	Unstable burst fx of 4th lumbar vertebra, init enc for clsd fx
S32.042K	Unstable burst fx of 4th lumbar vertebra, subsq enc for fx w/ nonu
S22.042A	Unstable burst fx of 4th thoracic vertebra, init enc for clsd fx
S22.042K	Unstable burst fx of 4th thoracic vertebra, subsq enc for fx w/ nonu
S32.052A	Unstable burst fx of 5th lumbar vertebra, init enc for clsd fx
S32.052K	Unstable burst fx of 5th lumbar vertebra, subsq enc for fx w/ nonu
S22.082A	Unstable burst fx of T11-T12 vertebra, init enc for clsd fx
S22.082K	Unstable burst fx of T11-T12 vertebra, subsq enc for fx w/ nonu
S22.052A	Unstable burst fx of T5-T6 vertebra, init enc for clsd fx
S22.052K	Unstable burst fx of T5-T6 vertebra, subsq enc for fx w/ nonu
S22.062A	Unstable burst fx of T7-T8 vertebra, init enc for clsd fx
S22.062K	Unstable burst fx of T7-T8 vertebra, subsq enc for fx w/ nonu
S22.072A	Unstable burst fx of T9-T10 vertebra, init enc for clsd fx
S22.072K	Unstable burst fx of T9-T10 vertebra, subsq enc for fx w/ nonu
S32.002A	Unstable burst fx of unsp lumbar vertebra, init enc for clsd fx
S32.002K	Unstable burst fx of unsp lumbar vertebra, subsq enc for fx w/ nonu
S22.002A	Unstable burst fx of unsp thoracic vertebra, init enc for clsd fx
S22.002K	Unstable burst fx of unsp thoracic vertebra, subsq enc for fx w/ nonu
A82.1	Urban rabies
A95.1	Urban yellow fever
N28.86	Ureteritis cystica
N34.0	Urethral abscess
N36.0	Urethral fistula
O04.88	Urinary tract infxn following (induced) termination of pregnancy
O08.83	Urinary tract infxn following an ectopic & molar pregnancy
O03.88	Urinary tract infxn following complete or unsp spontaneous abortion
O86.20	Urinary tract infxn following delivery, unsp
O07.38	Urinary tract infxn following failed attempted termination of pregnancy
O03.38	Urinary tract infxn following incomplete spontaneous abortion
N39.0	Urinary tract infxn, site not spec
O86.13	Vaginitis following delivery
A81.01	Variant Creutzfeldt-Jakob disease
B01.81	Varicella keratitis
B01.0	Varicella meningitis
B01.9	Varicella w/o comp
I83.223	Varicose veins of lt lwr extr w/ both ulcer of ankle & inflam
I83.222	Varicose veins of lt lwr extr w/ both ulcer of calf & inflam
I83.224	Varicose veins of lt lwr extr w/ both ulcer of heel & midfoot & inflam
I83.228	Varicose veins of lt lwr extr w/ both ulcer of oth part of lwr extr & inflam
I83.221	Varicose veins of lt lwr extr w/ both ulcer of thigh & inflam
I83.229	Varicose veins of lt lwr extr w/ both ulcer of unsp site & inflam
I83.225	Varicose veins of lt lwr extr w/ both ulcer oth part of foot & inflam
I83.213	Varicose veins of rt lwr extr w/ both ulcer of ankle & inflam
I83.212	Varicose veins of rt lwr extr w/ both ulcer of calf & inflam
I83.214	Varicose veins of rt lwr extr w/ both ulcer of heel & midfoot & inflam
I83.218	Varicose veins of rt lwr extr w/ both ulcer of oth part of lwr extr & inflam
I83.211	Varicose veins of rt lwr extr w/ both ulcer of thigh & inflam
I83.219	Varicose veins of rt lwr extr w/ both ulcer of unsp site & inflam
I83.215	Varicose veins of rt lwr extr w/ both ulcer oth part of foot & inflam
I83.203	Varicose veins of unsp lwr extr w/ both ulcer of ankle & inflam
I83.202	Varicose veins of unsp lwr extr w/ both ulcer of calf & inflam
I83.204	Varicose veins of unsp lwr extr w/ both ulcer of heel & midfoot & inflam
I83.208	Varicose veins of unsp lwr extr w/ both ulcer of oth part of lwr extr & inflam
I83.201	Varicose veins of unsp lwr extr w/ both ulcer of thigh & inflam
I83.209	Varicose veins of unsp lwr extr w/ both ulcer of unsp site & inflam
I83.205	Varicose veins of unsp lwr extr w/ both ulcer oth part of foot & inflam
T80.1XXA	Vascular comp following inf, transfusion & therapeutic injection, init enc
K55.9	Vascular d/o of intestine, unsp
F01.51	Vascular dementia w/ behavioral disturbance
A92.2	Venezuelan equine fever
O22.90	Venous comp in pregnancy, unsp, unsp trmstr
J95.851	Ventilator associated pneumonia
Q21.0	Ventricular septal defect
I23.2	Ventricular septal defect as current comp following acute myocardial infarction
I47.2	Ventricular tachycardia
M47.022	Vert artery compression syndromes, cervical rgn
M47.021	Vert artery compression syndromes, occipito-atlanto-axial rgn
M47.029	Vert artery compression syndromes, site unsp
G45.0	Vertebro-basilar artery synd
N32.2	Vesical fistula, NEC
N32.1	Vesicointestinal fistula
N82.0	Vesicovaginal fistula
B33.20	Viral carditis, unsp
B33.21	Viral endocarditis
O98.42	Viral hepatitis comp childbirth
O98.411	Viral hepatitis comp pregnancy, 1st trmstr
O98.412	Viral hepatitis comp pregnancy, 2nd trmstr
O98.413	Viral hepatitis comp pregnancy, 3rd trmstr
O98.43	Viral hepatitis comp the puerperium

A87.9	Viral meningitis, unsp
B33.22	Viral myocarditis
B33.23	Viral pericarditis
B55.0	Visceral leishmaniasis
H44.023	Vitreous abscess (chr), bilat
H44.022	Vitreous abscess (chr), lt eye
H44.021	Vitreous abscess (chr), rt eye
H44.029	Vitreous abscess (chr), unsp eye
E74.01	von Gierke disease
D68.0	Von Willebrand's disease
T84.061A	Wear of articular bearing surface of int prosthetic lt hip jt, init enc
T84.063A	Wear of articular bearing surface of int prosthetic lt knee jt, init enc
T84.060A	Wear of articular bearing surface of int prosthetic rt hip jt, init enc
T84.062A	Wear of articular bearing surface of int prosthetic rt knee jt, init enc
T84.068A	Wear of articular bearing surface of oth int prosthetic jt, init enc
T84.069A	Wear of articular bearing surface of unsp int prosthetic jt, init enc
S32.010A	Wedge compression fx of 1st lumbar vertebra, init enc for clsd fx
S32.010K	Wedge compression fx of 1st lumbar vertebra, subsq enc for fx w/ nonu
S22.010A	Wedge compression fx of 1st thoracic vertebra, init enc for clsd fx
S22.010K	Wedge compression fx of 1st thoracic vertebra, subsq enc for fx w/ nonu
S32.020A	Wedge compression fx of 2nd lumbar vertebra, init enc for clsd fx
S32.020K	Wedge compression fx of 2nd lumbar vertebra, subsq enc for fx w/ nonu
S22.020A	Wedge compression fx of 2nd thoracic vertebra, init enc for clsd fx
S22.020K	Wedge compression fx of 2nd thoracic vertebra, subsq enc for fx w/ nonu
S32.030A	Wedge compression fx of 3rd lumbar vertebra, init enc for clsd fx
S32.030K	Wedge compression fx of 3rd lumbar vertebra, subsq enc for fx w/ nonu
S22.030A	Wedge compression fx of 3rd thoracic vertebra, init enc for clsd fx
S22.030K	Wedge compression fx of 3rd thoracic vertebra, subsq enc for fx w/ nonu
S32.040A	Wedge compression fx of 4th lumbar vertebra, init enc for clsd fx
S32.040K	Wedge compression fx of 4th lumbar vertebra, subsq enc for fx w/ nonu
S22.040A	Wedge compression fx of 4th thoracic vertebra, init enc for clsd fx
S22.040K	Wedge compression fx of 4th thoracic vertebra, subsq enc for fx w/ nonu
S32.050A	Wedge compression fx of 5th lumbar vertebra, init enc for clsd fx
S32.050K	Wedge compression fx of 5th lumbar vertebra, subsq enc for fx w/ nonu
S22.080A	Wedge compression fx of T11-T12 vertebra, init enc for clsd fx
S22.080K	Wedge compression fx of T11-T12 vertebra, subsq enc for fx w/ nonu
S22.050A	Wedge compression fx of T5-T6 vertebra, init enc for clsd fx
S22.050K	Wedge compression fx of T5-T6 vertebra, subsq enc for fx w/ nonu
S22.060A	Wedge compression fx of T7-T8 vertebra, init enc for clsd fx
S22.060K	Wedge compression fx of T7-T8 vertebra, subsq enc for fx w/ nonu
S22.070A	Wedge compression fx of T9-T10 vertebra, init enc for clsd fx
S22.070K	Wedge compression fx of T9-T10 vertebra, subsq enc for fx w/ nonu
S32.000A	Wedge compression fx of unsp lumbar vertebra, init enc for clsd fx
S32.000K	Wedge compression fx of unsp lumbar vertebra, subsq enc for fx w/ nonu
S22.000A	Wedge compression fx of unsp thoracic vertebra, init enc for clsd fx
S22.000K	Wedge compression fx of unsp thoracic vertebra, subsq enc for fx w/ nonu
M31.31	Wegener's granulomatosis w/ renal involvement
M31.30	Wegener's granulomatosis w/o renal involvement
E51.2	Wernicke's encephalopathy
E51.12	Wet beriberi
K90.81	Whipple's disease
A37.10	Whooping cough d/t Bordetella parapertussis w/o pneumonia
A37.00	Whooping cough d/t Bordetella pertussis w/o pneumonia
A37.80	Whooping cough d/t oth Bordetella species w/o pneumonia
A37.90	Whooping cough, unsp species w/o pneumonia
D82.0	Wiskott-Aldrich synd
P96.2	Withdrawal symptoms from therapeutic use of drugs in newborn
A48.52	Wnd botulism
E71.529	X-linked adrenoleukodystrophy, unsp type
E70.310	X-linked ocular albinism
A95.9	Yellow fever, unsp
E71.510	Zellweger synd
E71.541	Zellweger-like synd
A28.9	Zoonotic bacterial disease, unsp
B02.31	Zoster conjunctivitis
B02.0	Zoster encephalitis
B02.32	Zoster iridocyclitis
B02.33	Zoster keratitis
B02.30	Zoster ocular disease, unsp
B02.34	Zoster scleritis
B02.8	Zoster w/ oth comp

S02.402A	Zygomatic fx, unsp, init enc for clsd fx
S02.402B	Zygomatic fx, unsp, init enc for opn fx
S02.402K	Zygomatic fx, unsp, subsq enc for fx w/ nonu

Alphabetic MCC List

S42.222B	2-part disp fx of surg neck of lt humerus, init enc for opn fx
S42.221B	2-part disp fx of surg neck of rt humerus, init enc for opn fx
S42.223B	2-part disp fx of surg neck of unsp humerus, init enc for opn fx
S42.225B	2-part nondisp fx of surg neck of lt humerus, init enc for opn fx
S42.224B	2-part nondisp fx of surg neck of rt humerus, init enc for opn fx
S42.226B	2-part nondisp fx of surg neck of unsp humerus, init enc for opn fx
S42.232B	3-part fx of surg neck of lt humerus, init enc for opn fx
S42.231B	3-part fx of surg neck of rt humerus, init enc for opn fx
S42.239B	3-part fx of surg neck of unsp humerus, init enc for opn fx
S42.242B	4-part fx of surg neck of lt humerus, init enc for opn fx
S42.241B	4-part fx of surg neck of rt humerus, init enc for opn fx
S42.249B	4-part fx of surg neck of unsp humerus, init enc for opn fx
I71.3	Abd aortic aneurysm, ruptured
K75.0	Abscess of liver
J85.1	Abscess of lung w/ pneumonia
J85.2	Abscess of lung w/o pneumonia
J85.3	Abscess of mediastinum
P91.1	Acquired periventricular cysts of newborn
D60.9	Acquired pure red cell aplasia, unsp
A42.7	Actinomycotic sepsis
J95.822	Acute & chr postprocedural respiratory failure
J96.22	Acute & chr respiratory failure w/ hypercapnia
J96.21	Acute & chr respiratory failure w/ hypoxia
J96.20	Acute & chr respiratory failure, unsp whether w/ hypoxia or hypercapnia
I33.9	Acute & subacute endocarditis, unsp
K72.01	Acute & subacute hepatic failure w/ coma
K72.00	Acute & subacute hepatic failure w/o coma
I33.0	Acute & subacute infective endocarditis
K35.2	Acute appendicitis w/ generalized peritonitis
K35.3	Acute appendicitis w/ localized peritonitis
I50.41	Acute combined systolic (congestive) & diastolic (congestive) heart failure
I50.31	Acute diastolic (congestive) heart failure
G04.00	Acute disseminated encephalitis & encephalomyelitis, unsp
K26.2	Acute duodenal ulcer w/ both hemor & perforation
K26.0	Acute duodenal ulcer w/ hemor
K26.1	Acute duodenal ulcer w/ perforation
I82.220	Acute embolism & thrombosis of inferior vena cava
J05.11	Acute epiglottitis w/ obstruction
K25.2	Acute gastric ulcer w/ both hemor & perforation
K25.0	Acute gastric ulcer w/ hemor
K25.1	Acute gastric ulcer w/ perforation
K29.01	Acute gastritis w/ bleeding
K28.2	Acute gastrojejunal ulcer w/ both hemor & perforation
K28.0	Acute gastrojejunal ulcer w/ hemor
K28.1	Acute gastrojejunal ulcer w/ perforation
B16.0	Acute hepatitis B w/ delta-agent w/ hepatic coma
B16.2	Acute hepatitis B w/o delta-agent w/ hepatic coma
B17.11	Acute hepatitis C w/ hepatic coma
G95.11	Acute infarction of spinal cord (embolic) (nonembolic)
N17.1	Acute kidney failure w/ acute cortical necrosis
N17.2	Acute kidney failure w/ medullary necrosis
N17.0	Acute kidney failure w/ tubular necrosis
A39.2	Acute meningococcemia
A19.0	Acute miliary tuberculosis of a single spec site
A19.1	Acute miliary tuberculosis of multi sites
A19.2	Acute miliary tuberculosis, unsp
I40.9	Acute myocarditis, unsp
G04.30	Acute necrotizing hemorrhagic encephalopathy, unsp
N00.6	Acute nephritic synd w/ dense deposit disease
N00.7	Acute nephritic synd w/ diffuse crescentic glomerulonephritis
N00.4	Acute nephritic synd w/ diffuse endocapillary proliferative glomerulonephritis
N00.2	Acute nephritic synd w/ diffuse membranous glomerulonephritis
N00.3	Acute nephritic synd w/ diffuse mesangial proliferative glomerulonephritis
N00.5	Acute nephritic synd w/ diffuse mesangiocapillary glomerulonephritis
N00.1	Acute nephritic synd w/ focal & segmental glomerular lesions
N00.0	Acute nephritic synd w/ minor glomerular abnormality
N00.8	Acute nephritic synd w/ oth morphologic changes
N00.9	Acute nephritic synd w/ unsp morphologic changes
I50.43	Acute on chr combined systolic (congestive) & diastolic (congestive) heart failure
I50.33	Acute on chr diastolic (congestive) heart failure
I50.23	Acute on chr systolic (congestive) heart failure
K85.9	Acute pancreatitis, unsp
A80.30	Acute paralytic poliomyelitis, unsp
A80.0	Acute paralytic poliomyelitis, vaccine-associated
A80.1	Acute paralytic poliomyelitis, wild virus, imported
A80.2	Acute paralytic poliomyelitis, wild virus, indigenous
K27.2	Acute peptic ulcer, site unsp, w/ both hemor & perforation
K27.0	Acute peptic ulcer, site unsp, w/ hemor
K27.1	Acute peptic ulcer, site unsp, w/ perforation
J95.821	Acute postprocedural respiratory failure
J81.0	Acute pulmn edema
B39.0	Acute pulmn histoplasmosis capsulati
J95.2	Acute pulmn insufficiency following nonthoracic surgery
J95.1	Acute pulmn insufficiency following thoracic surgery
J96.02	Acute respiratory failure w/ hypercapnia
J96.01	Acute respiratory failure w/ hypoxia
J96.00	Acute respiratory failure, unsp whether w/ hypoxia or hypercapnia
I50.21	Acute systolic (congestive) heart failure
J04.11	Acute tracheitis w/ obstruction
K55.0	Acute vascular d/o of intestine
J12.0	Adenoviral pneumonia
Q33.3	Agenesis of lung
T79.0XXA	Air embolism (traum), init enc
T80.0XXA	Air embolism following inf, transfusion & therapeutic injection, init enc
O88.02	Air embolism in childbirth
O88.011	Air embolism in pregnancy, 1st trmstr
O88.012	Air embolism in pregnancy, 2nd trmstr
O88.013	Air embolism in pregnancy, 3rd trmstr
O88.03	Air embolism in the puerperium
K85.2	Alcohol induced acute pancreatitis
K29.21	Alcoholic gastritis w/ bleeding
K70.41	Alcoholic hepatic failure w/ coma
J84.843	Alveolar capillary dysplasia w/ vein misalignment
A06.6	Amebic brain abscess
A06.4	Amebic liver abscess
A06.5	Amebic lung abscess
O88.12	Amniotic fluid embolism in childbirth
O88.111	Amniotic fluid embolism in pregnancy, 1st trmstr
O88.112	Amniotic fluid embolism in pregnancy, 2nd trmstr
O88.113	Amniotic fluid embolism in pregnancy, 3rd trmstr
O88.13	Amniotic fluid embolism in the puerperium
Q00.0	Anencephaly
K55.21	Angiodysplasia of colon w/ hemor
K31.811	Angiodysplasia of stomach & duodenum w/ bleeding
S14.131A	Ant cord synd at C1 lvl of cervical spinal cord, init enc
S14.132A	Ant cord synd at C2 lvl of cervical spinal cord, init enc
S14.133A	Ant cord synd at C3 lvl of cervical spinal cord, init enc
S14.134A	Ant cord synd at C4 lvl of cervical spinal cord, init enc
S14.135A	Ant cord synd at C5 lvl of cervical spinal cord, init enc
S14.136A	Ant cord synd at C6 lvl of cervical spinal cord, init enc
S14.137A	Ant cord synd at C7 lvl of cervical spinal cord, init enc
S14.138A	Ant cord synd at C8 lvl of cervical spinal cord, init enc
S24.131A	Ant cord synd at T1 lvl of thoracic spinal cord, init enc
S24.134A	Ant cord synd at T11-T12 lvl of thoracic spinal cord, init enc
S24.132A	Ant cord synd at T2-T6 lvl of thoracic spinal cord, init enc
S24.133A	Ant cord synd at T7-T10 lvl of thoracic spinal cord, init enc
S12.110B	Ant disp Type II dens fx, init enc for opn fx
O46.011	Antepartum hemor w/ afibrinogenemia, 1st trmstr
O46.012	Antepartum hemor w/ afibrinogenemia, 2nd trmstr
O46.013	Antepartum hemor w/ afibrinogenemia, 3rd trmstr
O46.001	Antepartum hemor w/ coagulation defect, unsp, 1st trmstr
O46.002	Antepartum hemor w/ coagulation defect, unsp, 2nd trmstr
O46.003	Antepartum hemor w/ coagulation defect, unsp, 3rd trmstr
O46.021	Antepartum hemor w/ disseminated intravascular coagulation, 1st trmstr
O46.022	Antepartum hemor w/ disseminated intravascular coagulation, 2nd trmstr
O46.023	Antepartum hemor w/ disseminated intravascular coagulation, 3rd trmstr
O46.091	Antepartum hemor w/ oth coagulation defect, 1st trmstr
O46.092	Antepartum hemor w/ oth coagulation defect, 2nd trmstr
O46.093	Antepartum hemor w/ oth coagulation defect, 3rd trmstr
A22.7	Anthrax sepsis

D61.810	Antineoplastic chemotherapy induced pancytopenia
I71.8	Aortic aneurysm of unsp site, ruptured
D61.2	Aplastic anemia d/t oth ext agents
Q04.1	Arhinencephaly
Q28.2	Arteriovenous malformation of cerebral vessels
A85.2	Arthropod-borne viral encephalitis, unsp
B77.81	Ascariasis pneumonia
A27.81	Aseptic meningitis in leptospirosis
Q44.2	Atresia of bile ducts
Q39.1	Atresia of esophagus w/ tracheo-esophageal fistula
Q39.0	Atresia of esophagus w/o fistula
Q25.5	Atresia of pulmn artery
A83.4	Australian encephalitis
G00.9	Bacterial meningitis, unsp
G04.2	Bacterial meningoencephalitis & meningomyelitis, NEC
P36.9	Bacterial sepsis of newborn, unsp
S52.562B	Barton's fx of lt radius, init enc for opn fx type I or II
S52.562C	Barton's fx of lt radius, init enc for opn fx type IIIA, IIIB, or IIIC
S52.561B	Barton's fx of rt radius, init enc for opn fx type I or II
S52.561C	Barton's fx of rt radius, init enc for opn fx type IIIA, IIIB, or IIIC
S52.569B	Barton's fx of unsp radius, init enc for opn fx type I or II
S52.569C	Barton's fx of unsp radius, init enc for opn fx type IIIA, IIIB, or IIIC
S52.382B	Bent bone of lt radius, init enc for opn fx type I or II
S52.382C	Bent bone of lt radius, init enc for opn fx type IIIA, IIIB, or IIIC
S52.282B	Bent bone of lt ulna, init enc for opn fx type I or II
S52.282C	Bent bone of lt ulna, init enc for opn fx type IIIA, IIIB, or IIIC
S52.381B	Bent bone of rt radius, init enc for opn fx type I or II
S52.381C	Bent bone of rt radius, init enc for opn fx type IIIA, IIIB, or IIIC
S52.281B	Bent bone of rt ulna, init enc for opn fx type I or II
S52.281C	Bent bone of rt ulna, init enc for opn fx type IIIA, IIIB, or IIIC
S52.389B	Bent bone of unsp radius, init enc for opn fx type I or II
S52.389C	Bent bone of unsp radius, init enc for opn fx type IIIA, IIIB, or IIIC
S52.283B	Bent bone of unsp ulna, init enc for opn fx type I or II
S52.283C	Bent bone of unsp ulna, init enc for opn fx type IIIA, IIIB, or IIIC
K41.10	Bilat femoral hernia, w/ gangrene, not spec as recurrent
K41.11	Bilat femoral hernia, w/ gangrene, recurrent
K40.10	Bilat inguinal hernia, w/ gangrene, not spec as recurrent
K40.11	Bilat inguinal hernia, w/ gangrene, recurrent
K85.1	Biliary acute pancreatitis
P92.01	Bilious vomiting of newborn
P11.9	Birth inj to central nervous sys, unsp
G93.82	Brain death
J18.0	Bronchopneumonia, unsp organism
P27.1	Bronchopulmonary dysplasia originating in the perinatal period
S14.141A	Brown-Sequard synd at C1 lvl of cervical spinal cord, init enc
S14.142A	Brown-Sequard synd at C2 lvl of cervical spinal cord, init enc
S14.143A	Brown-Sequard synd at C3 lvl of cervical spinal cord, init enc
S14.144A	Brown-Sequard synd at C4 lvl of cervical spinal cord, init enc
S14.145A	Brown-Sequard synd at C5 lvl of cervical spinal cord, init enc
S14.146A	Brown-Sequard synd at C6 lvl of cervical spinal cord, init enc
S14.147A	Brown-Sequard synd at C7 lvl of cervical spinal cord, init enc
S14.148A	Brown-Sequard synd at C8 lvl of cervical spinal cord, init enc
S24.141A	Brown-Sequard synd at T1 lvl of thoracic spinal cord, init enc
S24.144A	Brown-Sequard synd at T11-T12 lvl of thoracic spinal cord, init enc
S24.142A	Brown-Sequard synd at T2-T6 lvl of thoracic spinal cord, init enc
S24.143A	Brown-Sequard synd at T7-T10 lvl of thoracic spinal cord, init enc
A20.0	Bubonic plague
I82.0	Budd-Chiari synd
T31.21	Burns involving 20-29% of body surface w/ 10-19% 3rd degree burns
T31.22	Burns involving 20-29% of body surface w/ 20-29% 3rd degree burns
T31.31	Burns involving 30-39% of body surface w/ 10-19% 3rd degree burns
T31.32	Burns involving 30-39% of body surface w/ 20-29% 3rd degree burns
T31.33	Burns involving 30-39% of body surface w/ 30-39% 3rd degree burns
T31.41	Burns involving 40-49% of body surface w/ 10-19% 3rd degree burns
T31.42	Burns involving 40-49% of body surface w/ 20-29% 3rd degree burns
T31.43	Burns involving 40-49% of body surface w/ 30-39% 3rd degree burns
T31.44	Burns involving 40-49% of body surface w/ 40-49% 3rd degree burns
T31.51	Burns involving 50-59% of body surface w/ 10-19% 3rd degree burns
T31.52	Burns involving 50-59% of body surface w/ 20-29% 3rd degree burns
T31.53	Burns involving 50-59% of body surface w/ 30-39% 3rd degree burns
T31.54	Burns involving 50-59% of body surface w/ 40-49% 3rd degree burns
T31.55	Burns involving 50-59% of body surface w/ 50-59% 3rd degree burns
T31.61	Burns involving 60-69% of body surface w/ 10-19% 3rd degree burns
T31.62	Burns involving 60-69% of body surface w/ 20-29% 3rd degree burns
T31.63	Burns involving 60-69% of body surface w/ 30-39% 3rd degree burns
T31.64	Burns involving 60-69% of body surface w/ 40-49% 3rd degree burns
T31.65	Burns involving 60-69% of body surface w/ 50-59% 3rd degree burns
T31.66	Burns involving 60-69% of body surface w/ 60-69% 3rd degree burns
T31.71	Burns involving 70-79% of body surface w/ 10-19% 3rd degree burns
T31.72	Burns involving 70-79% of body surface w/ 20-29% 3rd degree burns
T31.73	Burns involving 70-79% of body surface w/ 30-39% 3rd degree burns
T31.74	Burns involving 70-79% of body surface w/ 40-49% 3rd degree burns
T31.75	Burns involving 70-79% of body surface w/ 50-59% 3rd degree burns
T31.76	Burns involving 70-79% of body surface w/ 60-69% 3rd degree burns
T31.77	Burns involving 70-79% of body surface w/ 70-79% 3rd degree burns
T31.81	Burns involving 80-89% of body surface w/ 10-19% 3rd degree burns
T31.82	Burns involving 80-89% of body surface w/ 20-29% 3rd degree burns
T31.83	Burns involving 80-89% of body surface w/ 30-39% 3rd degree burns
T31.84	Burns involving 80-89% of body surface w/ 40-49% 3rd degree burns
T31.85	Burns involving 80-89% of body surface w/ 50-59% 3rd degree burns
T31.86	Burns involving 80-89% of body surface w/ 60-69% 3rd degree burns
T31.87	Burns involving 80-89% of body surface w/ 70-79% 3rd degree burns
T31.88	Burns involving 80-89% of body surface w/ 80-89% 3rd degree burns
T31.91	Burns involving 90% or more of body surface w/ 10-19% 3rd degree burns
T31.92	Burns involving 90% or more of body surface w/ 20-29% 3rd degree burns
T31.93	Burns involving 90% or more of body surface w/ 30-39% 3rd degree burns
T31.94	Burns involving 90% or more of body surface w/ 40-49% 3rd degree burns
T31.95	Burns involving 90% or more of body surface w/ 50-59% 3rd degree burns
T31.96	Burns involving 90% or more of body surface w/ 60-69% 3rd degree burns
T31.97	Burns involving 90% or more of body surface w/ 70-79% 3rd degree burns
T31.98	Burns involving 90% or more of body surface w/ 80-89% 3rd degree burns
T31.99	Burns involving 90% or more of body surface w/ 90% or more 3rd degree burns
K80.67	Calculus of gallbladder & bile duct w/ acute & chr cholecystitis w/ obstruction
A83.5	California encephalitis
B37.6	Candidal endocarditis
B37.5	Candidal meningitis
B37.7	Candidal sepsis
I46.8	Cardiac arrest d/t oth underlying condition
I46.2	Cardiac arrest d/t underlying cardiac condition
P29.81	Cardiac arrest of newborn
I46.9	Cardiac arrest, cause unsp
R57.0	Cardiogenic shock
A20.1	Cellulocutaneous plague
S14.121A	Central cord synd at C1 lvl of cervical spinal cord, init enc
S14.122A	Central cord synd at C2 lvl of cervical spinal cord, init enc
S14.123A	Central cord synd at C3 lvl of cervical spinal cord, init enc
S14.124A	Central cord synd at C4 lvl of cervical spinal cord, init enc
S14.125A	Central cord synd at C5 lvl of cervical spinal cord, init enc
S14.126A	Central cord synd at C6 lvl of cervical spinal cord, init enc
S14.127A	Central cord synd at C7 lvl of cervical spinal cord, init enc
S14.128A	Central cord synd at C8 lvl of cervical spinal cord, init enc
A84.1	Central European tick-borne encephalitis
K76.2	Central hemorrhagic necrosis of liver
P52.6	Cerebellar (nontraumatic) & post fossa hemor of newborn
B45.1	Cerebral cryptococcosis
G93.6	Cerebral edema
P11.0	Cerebral edema d/t birth inj
P10.1	Cerebral hemor d/t birth inj
I63.6	Cerebral infarction d/t cerebral venous thrombosis, nonpyogenic
I63.12	Cerebral infarction d/t embolism of basilar artery
I63.422	Cerebral infarction d/t embolism of lt ant cerebral artery
I63.132	Cerebral infarction d/t embolism of lt carotid artery
I63.442	Cerebral infarction d/t embolism of lt cerebellar artery
I63.412	Cerebral infarction d/t embolism of lt mid cerebral artery
I63.432	Cerebral infarction d/t embolism of lt post cerebral artery
I63.112	Cerebral infarction d/t embolism of lt vert artery
I63.49	Cerebral infarction d/t embolism of oth cerebral artery

I63.19	Cerebral infarction d/t embolism of oth precerebral artery
I63.421	Cerebral infarction d/t embolism of rt ant cerebral artery
I63.131	Cerebral infarction d/t embolism of rt carotid artery
I63.441	Cerebral infarction d/t embolism of rt cerebellar artery
I63.411	Cerebral infarction d/t embolism of rt mid cerebral artery
I63.431	Cerebral infarction d/t embolism of rt post cerebral artery
I63.111	Cerebral infarction d/t embolism of rt vert artery
I63.429	Cerebral infarction d/t embolism of unsp ant cerebral artery
I63.139	Cerebral infarction d/t embolism of unsp carotid artery
I63.449	Cerebral infarction d/t embolism of unsp cerebellar artery
I63.40	Cerebral infarction d/t embolism of unsp cerebral artery
I63.419	Cerebral infarction d/t embolism of unsp mid cerebral artery
I63.439	Cerebral infarction d/t embolism of unsp post cerebral artery
I63.10	Cerebral infarction d/t embolism of unsp precerebral artery
I63.119	Cerebral infarction d/t embolism of unsp vert artery
I63.02	Cerebral infarction d/t thrombosis of basilar artery
I63.322	Cerebral infarction d/t thrombosis of lt ant cerebral artery
I63.032	Cerebral infarction d/t thrombosis of lt carotid artery
I63.342	Cerebral infarction d/t thrombosis of lt cerebellar artery
I63.312	Cerebral infarction d/t thrombosis of lt mid cerebral artery
I63.332	Cerebral infarction d/t thrombosis of lt post cerebral artery
I63.012	Cerebral infarction d/t thrombosis of lt vert artery
I63.39	Cerebral infarction d/t thrombosis of oth cerebral artery
I63.09	Cerebral infarction d/t thrombosis of oth precerebral artery
I63.321	Cerebral infarction d/t thrombosis of rt ant cerebral artery
I63.031	Cerebral infarction d/t thrombosis of rt carotid artery
I63.341	Cerebral infarction d/t thrombosis of rt cerebellar artery
I63.311	Cerebral infarction d/t thrombosis of rt mid cerebral artery
I63.331	Cerebral infarction d/t thrombosis of rt post cerebral artery
I63.011	Cerebral infarction d/t thrombosis of rt vert artery
I63.329	Cerebral infarction d/t thrombosis of unsp ant cerebral artery
I63.039	Cerebral infarction d/t thrombosis of unsp carotid artery
I63.349	Cerebral infarction d/t thrombosis of unsp cerebellar artery
I63.30	Cerebral infarction d/t thrombosis of unsp cerebral artery
I63.319	Cerebral infarction d/t thrombosis of unsp mid cerebral artery
I63.339	Cerebral infarction d/t thrombosis of unsp post cerebral artery
I63.00	Cerebral infarction d/t thrombosis of unsp precerebral artery
I63.019	Cerebral infarction d/t thrombosis of unsp vert artery
I63.22	Cerebral infarction d/t unsp occlsn or stenosis of basilar arteries
I63.522	Cerebral infarction d/t unsp occlsn or stenosis of lt ant cerebral artery
I63.232	Cerebral infarction d/t unsp occlsn or stenosis of lt carotid arteries
I63.542	Cerebral infarction d/t unsp occlsn or stenosis of lt cerebellar artery
I63.512	Cerebral infarction d/t unsp occlsn or stenosis of lt mid cerebral artery
I63.532	Cerebral infarction d/t unsp occlsn or stenosis of lt post cerebral artery
I63.212	Cerebral infarction d/t unsp occlsn or stenosis of lt vert arteries
I63.59	Cerebral infarction d/t unsp occlsn or stenosis of oth cerebral artery
I63.29	Cerebral infarction d/t unsp occlsn or stenosis of oth precerebral arteries
I63.521	Cerebral infarction d/t unsp occlsn or stenosis of rt ant cerebral artery
I63.231	Cerebral infarction d/t unsp occlsn or stenosis of rt carotid arteries
I63.541	Cerebral infarction d/t unsp occlsn or stenosis of rt cerebellar artery
I63.511	Cerebral infarction d/t unsp occlsn or stenosis of rt mid cerebral artery
I63.531	Cerebral infarction d/t unsp occlsn or stenosis of rt post cerebral artery
I63.211	Cerebral infarction d/t unsp occlsn or stenosis of rt vert arteries
I63.529	Cerebral infarction d/t unsp occlsn or stenosis of unsp ant cerebral artery
I63.239	Cerebral infarction d/t unsp occlsn or stenosis of unsp carotid arteries
I63.549	Cerebral infarction d/t unsp occlsn or stenosis of unsp cerebellar artery
I63.50	Cerebral infarction d/t unsp occlsn or stenosis of unsp cerebral artery
I63.519	Cerebral infarction d/t unsp occlsn or stenosis of unsp mid cerebral artery
I63.539	Cerebral infarction d/t unsp occlsn or stenosis of unsp post cerebral artery
I63.20	Cerebral infarction d/t unsp occlsn or stenosis of unsp precerebral arteries
I63.219	Cerebral infarction d/t unsp occlsn or stenosis of unsp vert arteries
I63.9	Cerebral infarction, unsp
J16.0	Chlamydial pneumonia
K65.3	Choleperitonitis
O41.1211	Chorioamnionitis, 1st trmstr, fetus 1
O41.1212	Chorioamnionitis, 1st trmstr, fetus 2
O41.1213	Chorioamnionitis, 1st trmstr, fetus 3
O41.1214	Chorioamnionitis, 1st trmstr, fetus 4
O41.1215	Chorioamnionitis, 1st trmstr, fetus 5
O41.1210	Chorioamnionitis, 1st trmstr, N/A or unsp
O41.1219	Chorioamnionitis, 1st trmstr, oth fetus

O41.1221	Chorioamnionitis, 2nd trmstr, fetus 1
O41.1222	Chorioamnionitis, 2nd trmstr, fetus 2
O41.1223	Chorioamnionitis, 2nd trmstr, fetus 3
O41.1224	Chorioamnionitis, 2nd trmstr, fetus 4
O41.1225	Chorioamnionitis, 2nd trmstr, fetus 5
O41.1220	Chorioamnionitis, 2nd trmstr, N/A or unsp
O41.1229	Chorioamnionitis, 2nd trmstr, oth fetus
O41.1231	Chorioamnionitis, 3rd trmstr, fetus 1
O41.1232	Chorioamnionitis, 3rd trmstr, fetus 2
O41.1233	Chorioamnionitis, 3rd trmstr, fetus 3
O41.1234	Chorioamnionitis, 3rd trmstr, fetus 4
O41.1235	Chorioamnionitis, 3rd trmstr, fetus 5
O41.1230	Chorioamnionitis, 3rd trmstr, N/A or unsp
O41.1239	Chorioamnionitis, 3rd trmstr, oth fetus
D60.0	Chr acquired pure red cell aplasia
K29.41	Chr atrophic gastritis w/ bleeding
I82.221	Chr embolism & thrombosis of inferior vena cava
K72.11	Chr hepatic failure w/ coma
A39.3	Chr meningococcemia
K26.6	Chr or unsp duodenal ulcer w/ both hemor & perforation
K26.4	Chr or unsp duodenal ulcer w/ hemor
K26.5	Chr or unsp duodenal ulcer w/ perforation
K25.6	Chr or unsp gastric ulcer w/ both hemor & perforation
K25.4	Chr or unsp gastric ulcer w/ hemor
K25.5	Chr or unsp gastric ulcer w/ perforation
K28.6	Chr or unsp gastrojejunal ulcer w/ both hemor & perforation
K28.4	Chr or unsp gastrojejunal ulcer w/ hemor
K28.5	Chr or unsp gastrojejunal ulcer w/ perforation
K27.6	Chr or unsp peptic ulcer, site unsp, w/ both hemor & perforation
K27.4	Chr or unsp peptic ulcer, site unsp, w/ hemor
K27.5	Chr or unsp peptic ulcer, site unsp, w/ perforation
B39.1	Chr pulmn histoplasmosis capsulati
J95.3	Chr pulmn insufficiency following surgery
K29.31	Chr superf gastritis w/ bleeding
Q25.71	Coarctation of pulmn artery
B38.4	Coccidioidomycosis meningitis
S52.532B	Colles' fx of lt radius, init enc for opn fx type I or II
S52.532C	Colles' fx of lt radius, init enc for opn fx type IIIA, IIIB, or IIIC
S52.531B	Colles' fx of rt radius, init enc for opn fx type I or II
S52.531C	Colles' fx of rt radius, init enc for opn fx type IIIA, IIIB, or IIIC
S52.539B	Colles' fx of unsp radius, init enc for opn fx type I or II
S52.539C	Colles' fx of unsp radius, init enc for opn fx type IIIA, IIIB, or IIIC
R40.2320	Coma scale, best motor response, extension
R40.2321	Coma scale, best motor response, extension
R40.2322	Coma scale, best motor response, extension
R40.2323	Coma scale, best motor response, extension
R40.2324	Coma scale, best motor response, extension
R40.2340	Coma scale, best motor response, flexion withdrawal
R40.2341	Coma scale, best motor response, flexion withdrawal
R40.2342	Coma scale, best motor response, flexion withdrawal
R40.2343	Coma scale, best motor response, flexion withdrawal
R40.2344	Coma scale, best motor response, flexion withdrawal
R40.2310	Coma scale, best motor response, none
R40.2311	Coma scale, best motor response, none
R40.2312	Coma scale, best motor response, none
R40.2313	Coma scale, best motor response, none
R40.2314	Coma scale, best motor response, none
R40.2220	Coma scale, best verbal response, incomprehensible words
R40.2221	Coma scale, best verbal response, incomprehensible words
R40.2222	Coma scale, best verbal response, incomprehensible words
R40.2223	Coma scale, best verbal response, incomprehensible words
R40.2224	Coma scale, best verbal response, incomprehensible words
R40.2210	Coma scale, best verbal response, none
R40.2211	Coma scale, best verbal response, none
R40.2212	Coma scale, best verbal response, none
R40.2213	Coma scale, best verbal response, none
R40.2214	Coma scale, best verbal response, none
R40.2110	Coma scale, eyes opn, never
R40.2111	Coma scale, eyes opn, never
R40.2112	Coma scale, eyes opn, never
R40.2113	Coma scale, eyes opn, never
R40.2114	Coma scale, eyes opn, never
R40.2120	Coma scale, eyes opn, to pain

R40.2121	Coma scale, eyes opn, to pain
R40.2122	Coma scale, eyes opn, to pain
R40.2123	Coma scale, eyes opn, to pain
R40.2124	Coma scale, eyes opn, to pain
Q20.0	Common arterial trunk
S14.111A	Complete lesion at C1 lvl of cervical spinal cord, init enc
S14.112A	Complete lesion at C2 lvl of cervical spinal cord, init enc
S14.113A	Complete lesion at C3 lvl of cervical spinal cord, init enc
S14.114A	Complete lesion at C4 lvl of cervical spinal cord, init enc
S14.115A	Complete lesion at C5 lvl of cervical spinal cord, init enc
S14.116A	Complete lesion at C6 lvl of cervical spinal cord, init enc
S14.117A	Complete lesion at C7 lvl of cervical spinal cord, init enc
S14.118A	Complete lesion at C8 lvl of cervical spinal cord, init enc
S24.111A	Complete lesion at T1 lvl of thoracic spinal cord, init enc
S24.114A	Complete lesion at T11-T12 lvl of thoracic spinal cord, init enc
S24.112A	Complete lesion at T2-T6 lvl of thoracic spinal cord, init enc
S24.113A	Complete lesion at T7-T10 lvl of thoracic spinal cord, init enc
S34.111A	Complete lesion of L1 lvl of lumbar spinal cord, init enc
S34.112A	Complete lesion of L2 lvl of lumbar spinal cord, init enc
S34.113A	Complete lesion of L3 lvl of lumbar spinal cord, init enc
S34.114A	Complete lesion of L4 lvl of lumbar spinal cord, init enc
S34.115A	Complete lesion of L5 lvl of lumbar spinal cord, init enc
S34.131A	Complete lesion of sacral spinal cord, init enc
S34.119A	Complete lesion of unsp lvl of lumbar spinal cord, init enc
G93.5	Compression of brain
S14.0XXA	Concussion & edema of cervical spinal cord, init enc
S34.01XA	Concussion & edema of lumbar spinal cord, init enc
S34.02XA	Concussion & edema of sacral spinal cord, init enc
S24.0XXA	Concussion & edema of thoracic spinal cord, init enc
S06.0X6A	Concussion w/ loss of cnscness > 24 hrs w/o return to pre-existing conscious lvl w/ patient surviving, init enc
P35.1	Congenital cytomegalovirus infxn
Q79.0	Congenital diaphragmatic hernia
P37.3	Congenital falciparum malaria
Q24.6	Congenital heart block
Q79.51	Congenital hernia of bladder
P35.2	Congenital herpesviral [herpes simplex] infxn
Q33.6	Congenital hypoplasia & dysplasia of lung
P37.9	Congenital infectious or parasitic disease, unsp
Q22.9	Congenital malformation of tricuspid valve, unsp
Q04.0	Congenital malformations of corpus callosum
P23.1	Congenital pneumonia d/t Chlamydia
P23.4	Congenital pneumonia d/t Escherichia coli
P23.6	Congenital pneumonia d/t oth bacterial agents
P23.8	Congenital pneumonia d/t oth organisms
P23.5	Congenital pneumonia d/t Pseudomonas
P23.2	Congenital pneumonia d/t staphylococcus
P23.3	Congenital pneumonia d/t streptococcus, group B
P23.0	Congenital pneumonia d/t viral agent
P23.9	Congenital pneumonia, unsp
Q25.72	Congenital pulmn arteriovenous malformation
Q44.3	Congenital stenosis & stricture of bile ducts
Q39.3	Congenital stenosis & stricture of esophagus
Q24.4	Congenital subaortic stenosis
P37.1	Congenital toxoplasmosis
Q39.2	Congenital tracheo-esophageal fistula w/o atresia
Q22.4	Congenital tricuspid stenosis
P37.0	Congenital tuberculosis
P35.9	Congenital viral disease, unsp
P35.3	Congenital viral hepatitis
Q89.4	Conjoined twins
S06.335A	Contsn & lac of cerebrum, unsp, w/ loss of cnscness > 24 hrs w/ return to pre-existing conscious lvl, init enc
S06.336A	Contsn & lac of cerebrum, unsp, w/ loss of cnscness > 24 hrs w/o return to pre-existing conscious lvl w/ patient surviving, init enc
S06.333A	Contsn & lac of cerebrum, unsp, w/ loss of cnscness of 1 hr to 5 hrs 59 mins, init enc
S06.331A	Contsn & lac of cerebrum, unsp, w/ loss of cnscness of 30 mins or less, init enc
S06.332A	Contsn & lac of cerebrum, unsp, w/ loss of cnscness of 31 mins to 59 mins, init enc
S06.334A	Contsn & lac of cerebrum, unsp, w/ loss of cnscness of 6 hrs to 24 hrs, init enc
S06.337A	Contsn & lac of cerebrum, unsp, w/ loss of cnscness of any dur w/ death d/t brain inj prior to regain cnscness, init enc
S06.338A	Contsn & lac of cerebrum, unsp, w/ loss of cnscness of any dur w/ death d/t oth cause prior to regain cnscness, init enc
S06.339A	Contsn & lac of cerebrum, unsp, w/ loss of cnscness of unsp dur, init enc
S06.330A	Contsn & lac of cerebrum, unsp, w/o loss of cnscness, init enc
S06.325A	Contsn & lac of lt cerebrum w/ loss of cnscness > 24 hrs w/ return to pre-existing conscious lvl, init enc
S06.326A	Contsn & lac of lt cerebrum w/ loss of cnscness > 24 hrs w/o return to pre-existing conscious lvl w/ patient surviving, init enc
S06.323A	Contsn & lac of lt cerebrum w/ loss of cnscness of 1 hr to 5 hrs 59 mins, init enc
S06.321A	Contsn & lac of lt cerebrum w/ loss of cnscness of 30 mins or less, init enc
S06.322A	Contsn & lac of lt cerebrum w/ loss of cnscness of 31 mins to 59 mins, init enc
S06.324A	Contsn & lac of lt cerebrum w/ loss of cnscness of 6 hrs to 24 hrs, init enc
S06.327A	Contsn & lac of lt cerebrum w/ loss of cnscness of any dur w/ death d/t brain inj prior to regain cnscness, init enc
S06.328A	Contsn & lac of lt cerebrum w/ loss of cnscness of any dur w/ death d/t oth cause prior to regain cnscness, init enc
S06.329A	Contsn & lac of lt cerebrum w/ loss of cnscness of unsp dur, init enc
S06.320A	Contsn & lac of lt cerebrum w/o loss of cnscness, init enc
S06.315A	Contsn & lac of rt cerebrum w/ loss of cnscness > 24 hrs w/ return to pre-existing conscious lvl, init enc
S06.316A	Contsn & lac of rt cerebrum w/ loss of cnscness > 24 hrs w/o return to pre-existing conscious lvl w/ patient surviving, init enc
S06.313A	Contsn & lac of rt cerebrum w/ loss of cnscness of 1 hr to 5 hrs 59 mins, init enc
S06.311A	Contsn & lac of rt cerebrum w/ loss of cnscness of 30 mins or less, init enc
S06.312A	Contsn & lac of rt cerebrum w/ loss of cnscness of 31 mins to 59 mins, init enc
S06.314A	Contsn & lac of rt cerebrum w/ loss of cnscness of 6 hrs to 24 hrs, init enc
S06.317A	Contsn & lac of rt cerebrum w/ loss of cnscness of any dur w/ death d/t brain inj prior to regain cnscness, init enc
S06.318A	Contsn & lac of rt cerebrum w/ loss of cnscness of any dur w/ death d/t oth cause prior to regain cnscness, init enc
S06.319A	Contsn & lac of rt cerebrum w/ loss of cnscness of unsp dur, init enc
S06.310A	Contsn & lac of rt cerebrum w/o loss of cnscness, init enc
S27.422A	Contsn of bronchus, bilat, init enc
S27.421A	Contsn of bronchus, unilat, init enc
S27.429A	Contsn of bronchus, unsp, init enc
S27.812A	Contsn of esophagus (thoracic part), init enc
S06.386A	Contsn, lac, & hemor of brainstem w/ loss of cnscness > 24 hrs w/o return to pre-existing conscious lvl w/ patient surviving, init enc
S06.387A	Contsn, lac, & hemor of brainstem w/ loss of cnscness of any dur w/ death d/t brain inj prior to regain cnscness, init enc
S06.388A	Contsn, lac, & hemor of brainstem w/ loss of cnscness of any dur w/ death d/t oth cause prior to regain cnscness, init enc
S06.380A	Contsn, lac, & hemor of brainstem w/o loss of cnscness, init enc
S06.376A	Contsn, lac, & hemor of cerebellum w/ loss of cnscness > 24 hrs w/o return to pre-existing conscious lvl w/ patient surviving, init enc
S06.377A	Contsn, lac, & hemor of cerebellum w/ loss of cnscness of any dur w/ death d/t brain inj prior to regain cnscness, init enc
S06.378A	Contsn, lac, & hemor of cerebellum w/ loss of cnscness of any dur w/ death d/t oth cause prior to regain cnscness, init enc
S06.370A	Contsn, lac, & hemor of cerebellum w/o loss of cnscness, init enc
P90	Convulsions of newborn
Q24.2	Cor triatriatum
I25.42	Coronary artery dissection
T32.21	Corrosions involving 20-29% of body surface w/ 10-19% 3rd degree corrosion
T32.22	Corrosions involving 20-29% of body surface w/ 20-29% 3rd degree corrosion
T32.31	Corrosions involving 30-39% of body surface w/ 10-19% 3rd degree corrosion
T32.32	Corrosions involving 30-39% of body surface w/ 20-29% 3rd degree corrosion
T32.33	Corrosions involving 30-39% of body surface w/ 30-39% 3rd degree corrosion
T32.41	Corrosions involving 40-49% of body surface w/ 10-19% 3rd degree corrosion
T32.42	Corrosions involving 40-49% of body surface w/ 20-29% 3rd degree corrosion
T32.43	Corrosions involving 40-49% of body surface w/ 30-39% 3rd degree corrosion

T32.44	Corrosions involving 40-49% of body surface w/ 40-49% 3rd degree corrosion
T32.51	Corrosions involving 50-59% of body surface w/ 10-19% 3rd degree corrosion
T32.52	Corrosions involving 50-59% of body surface w/ 20-29% 3rd degree corrosion
T32.53	Corrosions involving 50-59% of body surface w/ 30-39% 3rd degree corrosion
T32.54	Corrosions involving 50-59% of body surface w/ 40-49% 3rd degree corrosion
T32.55	Corrosions involving 50-59% of body surface w/ 50-59% 3rd degree corrosion
T32.61	Corrosions involving 60-69% of body surface w/ 10-19% 3rd degree corrosion
T32.62	Corrosions involving 60-69% of body surface w/ 20-29% 3rd degree corrosion
T32.63	Corrosions involving 60-69% of body surface w/ 30-39% 3rd degree corrosion
T32.64	Corrosions involving 60-69% of body surface w/ 40-49% 3rd degree corrosion
T32.65	Corrosions involving 60-69% of body surface w/ 50-59% 3rd degree corrosion
T32.66	Corrosions involving 60-69% of body surface w/ 60-69% 3rd degree corrosion
T32.71	Corrosions involving 70-79% of body surface w/ 10-19% 3rd degree corrosion
T32.72	Corrosions involving 70-79% of body surface w/ 20-29% 3rd degree corrosion
T32.73	Corrosions involving 70-79% of body surface w/ 30-39% 3rd degree corrosion
T32.74	Corrosions involving 70-79% of body surface w/ 40-49% 3rd degree corrosion
T32.75	Corrosions involving 70-79% of body surface w/ 50-59% 3rd degree corrosion
T32.76	Corrosions involving 70-79% of body surface w/ 60-69% 3rd degree corrosion
T32.77	Corrosions involving 70-79% of body surface w/ 70-79% 3rd degree corrosion
T32.81	Corrosions involving 80-89% of body surface w/ 10-19% 3rd degree corrosion
T32.82	Corrosions involving 80-89% of body surface w/ 20-29% 3rd degree corrosion
T32.83	Corrosions involving 80-89% of body surface w/ 30-39% 3rd degree corrosion
T32.84	Corrosions involving 80-89% of body surface w/ 40-49% 3rd degree corrosion
T32.85	Corrosions involving 80-89% of body surface w/ 50-59% 3rd degree corrosion
T32.86	Corrosions involving 80-89% of body surface w/ 60-69% 3rd degree corrosion
T32.87	Corrosions involving 80-89% of body surface w/ 70-79% 3rd degree corrosion
T32.88	Corrosions involving 80-89% of body surface w/ 80-89% 3rd degree corrosion
T32.91	Corrosions involving 90% or more of body surface w/ 10-19% 3rd degree corrosion
T32.92	Corrosions involving 90% or more of body surface w/ 20-29% 3rd degree corrosion
T32.93	Corrosions involving 90% or more of body surface w/ 30-39% 3rd degree corrosion
T32.94	Corrosions involving 90% or more of body surface w/ 40-49% 3rd degree corrosion
T32.95	Corrosions involving 90% or more of body surface w/ 50-59% 3rd degree corrosion
T32.96	Corrosions involving 90% or more of body surface w/ 60-69% 3rd degree corrosion
T32.97	Corrosions involving 90% or more of body surface w/ 70-79% 3rd degree corrosion
T32.98	Corrosions involving 90% or more of body surface w/ 80-89% 3rd degree corrosion
T32.99	Corrosions involving 90% or more of body surface w/ 90% or more 3rd degree corrosion
Q00.1	Craniorachischisis
B46.3	Cutaneous mucormycosis
E84.0	Cystic fibrosis w/ pulmn manifestations
B25.2	Cytomegaloviral pancreatitis
B25.0	Cytomegaloviral pneumonitis

K67	D/o of peritoneum in infectious diseases classified elsw
O22.31	Deep phlebothrombosis in pregnancy, 1st trmstr
O22.32	Deep phlebothrombosis in pregnancy, 2nd trmstr
O22.33	Deep phlebothrombosis in pregnancy, 3rd trmstr
O87.1	Deep phlebothrombosis in the puerperium
E08.01	Diabetes mellitus d/t underlying condition w/ hyperosmolarity w/ coma
E08.00	Diabetes mellitus d/t underlying condition w/ hyperosmolarity w/o nonketotic hyperglycemic-hyperosmolar coma (NKHHC)
E08.641	Diabetes mellitus d/t underlying condition w/ hypoglycemia w/ coma
E08.11	Diabetes mellitus d/t underlying condition w/ ketoacidosis w/ coma
E08.10	Diabetes mellitus d/t underlying condition w/ ketoacidosis w/o coma
K44.1	Diaphragmatic hernia w/ gangrene
K31.82	Dieulafoy lesion (hemorrhagic) of stomach & duodenum
K63.81	Dieulafoy lesion of intestine
S06.2X6A	Diffuse traum brain inj w/ loss of cnscness > 24 hrs w/o return to pre-existing conscious lvl w/ patient surviving, init enc
S06.2X7A	Diffuse traum brain inj w/ loss of cnscness of any dur w/ death d/t brain inj prior to regain cnscness, init enc
S06.2X8A	Diffuse traum brain inj w/ loss of cnscness of any dur w/ death d/t oth cause prior to regain cnscness, init enc
Q20.3	Discordant ventriculoarterial connection
J98.5	Diseases of mediastinum, NEC
O99.42	Diseases of the circulatory sys comp childbirth
S72.132A	Disp apophyseal fx of lt femur, init enc for clsd fx
S72.132B	Disp apophyseal fx of lt femur, init enc for opn fx type I or II
S72.132C	Disp apophyseal fx of lt femur, init enc for opn fx type IIIA, IIIB, or IIIC
S72.131A	Disp apophyseal fx of rt femur, init enc for clsd fx
S72.131B	Disp apophyseal fx of rt femur, init enc for opn fx type I or II
S72.131C	Disp apophyseal fx of rt femur, init enc for opn fx type IIIA, IIIB, or IIIC
S72.133A	Disp apophyseal fx of unsp femur, init enc for clsd fx
S72.133B	Disp apophyseal fx of unsp femur, init enc for opn fx type I or II
S72.133C	Disp apophyseal fx of unsp femur, init enc for opn fx type IIIA, IIIB, or IIIC
S72.062A	Disp articular fx of head of lt femur, init enc for clsd fx
S72.062B	Disp articular fx of head of lt femur, init enc for opn fx type I or II
S72.062C	Disp articular fx of head of lt femur, init enc for opn fx type IIIA, IIIB, or IIIC
S72.061A	Disp articular fx of head of rt femur, init enc for clsd fx
S72.061B	Disp articular fx of head of rt femur, init enc for opn fx type I or II
S72.061C	Disp articular fx of head of rt femur, init enc for opn fx type IIIA, IIIB, or IIIC
S72.063A	Disp articular fx of head of unsp femur, init enc for clsd fx
S72.063B	Disp articular fx of head of unsp femur, init enc for opn fx type I or II
S72.063C	Disp articular fx of head of unsp femur, init enc for opn fx type IIIA, IIIB, or IIIC
S32.462A	Disp associated transv-post fx of lt acetab, init enc for clsd fx
S32.462B	Disp associated transv-post fx of lt acetab, init enc for opn fx
S32.461A	Disp associated transv-post fx of rt acetab, init enc for clsd fx
S32.461B	Disp associated transv-post fx of rt acetab, init enc for opn fx
S32.463A	Disp associated transv-post fx of unsp acetab, init enc for clsd fx
S32.463B	Disp associated transv-post fx of unsp acetab, init enc for opn fx
S32.312B	Disp avulsion fx of lt ilium, init enc for opn fx
S32.612B	Disp avulsion fx of lt ischium, init enc for opn fx
S32.311B	Disp avulsion fx of rt ilium, init enc for opn fx
S32.611B	Disp avulsion fx of rt ischium, init enc for opn fx
S32.313B	Disp avulsion fx of unsp ilium, init enc for opn fx
S32.613B	Disp avulsion fx of unsp ischium, init enc for opn fx
S82.142B	Disp bicondylar fx of lt tibia, init enc for opn fx type I or II
S82.142C	Disp bicondylar fx of lt tibia, init enc for opn fx type IIIA, IIIB, or IIIC
S82.141B	Disp bicondylar fx of rt tibia, init enc for opn fx type I or II
S82.141C	Disp bicondylar fx of rt tibia, init enc for opn fx type IIIA, IIIB, or IIIC
S82.143B	Disp bicondylar fx of unsp tibia, init enc for opn fx type I or II
S82.143C	Disp bicondylar fx of unsp tibia, init enc for opn fx type IIIA, IIIB, or IIIC
S42.352B	Disp comm fx of shaft of humerus, lt arm, init enc for opn fx
S42.351B	Disp comm fx of shaft of humerus, rt arm, init enc for opn fx
S42.353B	Disp comm fx of shaft of humerus, unsp arm, init enc for opn fx
S72.352A	Disp comm fx of shaft of lt femur, init enc for clsd fx
S72.352B	Disp comm fx of shaft of lt femur, init enc for opn fx type I or II
S72.352C	Disp comm fx of shaft of lt femur, init enc for opn fx type IIIA, IIIB, or IIIC
S82.452B	Disp comm fx of shaft of lt fibula, init enc for opn fx type I or II
S82.452C	Disp comm fx of shaft of lt fibula, init enc for opn fx type IIIA, IIIB, or IIIC
S82.252B	Disp comm fx of shaft of lt tibia, init enc for opn fx type I or II
S82.252C	Disp comm fx of shaft of lt tibia, init enc for opn fx type IIIA, IIIB, or IIIC
S52.352B	Disp comm fx of shaft of radius, lt arm, init enc for opn fx type I or II
S52.352C	Disp comm fx of shaft of radius, lt arm, init enc for opn fx type IIIA, IIIB, or IIIC
S52.351B	Disp comm fx of shaft of radius, rt arm, init enc for opn fx type I or II

S52.351C	Disp comm fx of shaft of radius, rt arm, init enc for opn fx type IIIA, IIIB, or IIIC
S52.353B	Disp comm fx of shaft of radius, unsp arm, init enc for opn fx type I or II
S52.353C	Disp comm fx of shaft of radius, unsp arm, init enc for opn fx type IIIA, IIIB, or IIIC
S72.351A	Disp comm fx of shaft of rt femur, init enc for clsd fx
S72.351B	Disp comm fx of shaft of rt femur, init enc for opn fx type I or II
S72.351C	Disp comm fx of shaft of rt femur, init enc for opn fx type IIIA, IIIB, or IIIC
S82.451B	Disp comm fx of shaft of rt fibula, init enc for opn fx type I or II
S82.451C	Disp comm fx of shaft of rt fibula, init enc for opn fx type IIIA, IIIB, or IIIC
S82.251B	Disp comm fx of shaft of rt tibia, init enc for opn fx type I or II
S82.251C	Disp comm fx of shaft of rt tibia, init enc for opn fx type IIIA, IIIB, or IIIC
S52.252B	Disp comm fx of shaft of ulna, lt arm, init enc for opn fx type I or II
S52.252C	Disp comm fx of shaft of ulna, lt arm, init enc for opn fx type IIIA, IIIB, or IIIC
S52.251B	Disp comm fx of shaft of ulna, rt arm, init enc for opn fx type I or II
S52.251C	Disp comm fx of shaft of ulna, rt arm, init enc for opn fx type IIIA, IIIB, or IIIC
S52.253B	Disp comm fx of shaft of ulna, unsp arm, init enc for opn fx type I or II
S52.253C	Disp comm fx of shaft of ulna, unsp arm, init enc for opn fx type IIIA, IIIB, or IIIC
S72.353A	Disp comm fx of shaft of unsp femur, init enc for clsd fx
S72.353B	Disp comm fx of shaft of unsp femur, init enc for opn fx type I or II
S72.353C	Disp comm fx of shaft of unsp femur, init enc for opn fx type IIIA, IIIB, or IIIC
S82.453B	Disp comm fx of shaft of unsp fibula, init enc for opn fx type I or II
S82.453C	Disp comm fx of shaft of unsp fibula, init enc for opn fx type IIIA, IIIB, or IIIC
S82.253B	Disp comm fx of shaft of unsp tibia, init enc for opn fx type I or II
S82.253C	Disp comm fx of shaft of unsp tibia, init enc for opn fx type IIIA, IIIB, or IIIC
S42.422B	Disp comm supracondylar fx w/o intercondylar fx of lt humerus, init enc for opn fx
S42.421B	Disp comm supracondylar fx w/o intercondylar fx of rt humerus, init enc for opn fx
S42.423B	Disp comm supracondylar fx w/o intercondylar fx of unsp humerus, init enc for opn fx
S32.482A	Disp dome fx of lt acetab, init enc for clsd fx
S32.482B	Disp dome fx of lt acetab, init enc for opn fx
S32.481A	Disp dome fx of rt acetab, init enc for clsd fx
S32.481B	Disp dome fx of rt acetab, init enc for opn fx
S32.483A	Disp dome fx of unsp acetab, init enc for clsd fx
S32.483B	Disp dome fx of unsp acetab, init enc for opn fx
S42.432B	Disp fx (avulsion) of lat epicondyle of lt humerus, init enc for opn fx
S42.431B	Disp fx (avulsion) of lat epicondyle of rt humerus, init enc for opn fx
S42.433B	Disp fx (avulsion) of lat epicondyle of unsp humerus, init enc for opn fx
S42.442B	Disp fx (avulsion) of med epicondyle of lt humerus, init enc for opn fx
S42.441B	Disp fx (avulsion) of med epicondyle of rt humerus, init enc for opn fx
S42.443B	Disp fx (avulsion) of med epicondyle of unsp humerus, init enc for opn fx
S32.432A	Disp fx of ant column [iliopubic] of lt acetab, init enc for clsd fx
S32.432B	Disp fx of ant column [iliopubic] of lt acetab, init enc for opn fx
S32.431A	Disp fx of ant column [iliopubic] of rt acetab, init enc for clsd fx
S32.431B	Disp fx of ant column [iliopubic] of rt acetab, init enc for opn fx
S32.433A	Disp fx of ant column [iliopubic] of unsp acetab, init enc for clsd fx
S32.433B	Disp fx of ant column [iliopubic] of unsp acetab, init enc for opn fx
S32.412A	Disp fx of ant wall of lt acetab, init enc for clsd fx
S32.412B	Disp fx of ant wall of lt acetab, init enc for opn fx
S32.411A	Disp fx of ant wall of rt acetab, init enc for clsd fx
S32.411B	Disp fx of ant wall of rt acetab, init enc for opn fx
S32.413A	Disp fx of ant wall of unsp acetab, init enc for clsd fx
S32.413B	Disp fx of ant wall of unsp acetab, init enc for opn fx
S72.042A	Disp fx of base of neck of lt femur, init enc for clsd fx
S72.042B	Disp fx of base of neck of lt femur, init enc for opn fx type I or II
S72.042C	Disp fx of base of neck of lt femur, init enc for opn fx type IIIA, IIIB, or IIIC
S72.041A	Disp fx of base of neck of rt femur, init enc for clsd fx
S72.041B	Disp fx of base of neck of rt femur, init enc for opn fx type I or II
S72.041C	Disp fx of base of neck of rt femur, init enc for opn fx type IIIA, IIIB, or IIIC
S72.043A	Disp fx of base of neck of unsp femur, init enc for clsd fx
S72.043B	Disp fx of base of neck of unsp femur, init enc for opn fx type I or II
S72.043C	Disp fx of base of neck of unsp femur, init enc for opn fx type IIIA, IIIB, or IIIC
S52.042B	Disp fx of coronoid process of lt ulna, init enc for opn fx type I or II
S52.042C	Disp fx of coronoid process of lt ulna, init enc for opn fx type IIIA, IIIB, or IIIC
S52.041B	Disp fx of coronoid process of rt ulna, init enc for opn fx type I or II
S52.041C	Disp fx of coronoid process of rt ulna, init enc for opn fx type IIIA, IIIB, or IIIC
S52.043B	Disp fx of coronoid process of unsp ulna, init enc for opn fx type I or II
S52.043C	Disp fx of coronoid process of unsp ulna, init enc for opn fx type IIIA, IIIB, or IIIC
S72.022A	Disp fx of epiphysis (separation) (upr) of lt femur, init enc for clsd fx
S72.022B	Disp fx of epiphysis (separation) (upr) of lt femur, init enc for opn fx type I or II
S72.022C	Disp fx of epiphysis (separation) (upr) of lt femur, init enc for opn fx type IIIA, IIIB, or IIIC
S72.021A	Disp fx of epiphysis (separation) (upr) of rt femur, init enc for clsd fx
S72.021B	Disp fx of epiphysis (separation) (upr) of rt femur, init enc for opn fx type I or II
S72.021C	Disp fx of epiphysis (separation) (upr) of rt femur, init enc for opn fx type IIIA, IIIB, or IIIC
S72.023A	Disp fx of epiphysis (separation) (upr) of unsp femur, init enc for clsd fx
S72.023B	Disp fx of epiphysis (separation) (upr) of unsp femur, init enc for opn fx type I or II
S72.023C	Disp fx of epiphysis (separation) (upr) of unsp femur, init enc for opn fx type IIIA, IIIB, or IIIC
S72.112A	Disp fx of greater trochanter of lt femur, init enc for clsd fx
S72.112B	Disp fx of greater trochanter of lt femur, init enc for opn fx type I or II
S72.112C	Disp fx of greater trochanter of lt femur, init enc for opn fx type IIIA, IIIB, or IIIC
S72.111A	Disp fx of greater trochanter of rt femur, init enc for clsd fx
S72.111B	Disp fx of greater trochanter of rt femur, init enc for opn fx type I or II
S72.111C	Disp fx of greater trochanter of rt femur, init enc for opn fx type IIIA, IIIB, or IIIC
S72.113A	Disp fx of greater trochanter of unsp femur, init enc for clsd fx
S72.113B	Disp fx of greater trochanter of unsp femur, init enc for opn fx type I or II
S72.113C	Disp fx of greater trochanter of unsp femur, init enc for opn fx type IIIA, IIIB, or IIIC
S42.252B	Disp fx of greater tuberosity of lt humerus, init enc for opn fx
S42.251B	Disp fx of greater tuberosity of rt humerus, init enc for opn fx
S42.253B	Disp fx of greater tuberosity of unsp humerus, init enc for opn fx
S52.122B	Disp fx of head of lt radius, init enc for opn fx type I or II
S52.122C	Disp fx of head of lt radius, init enc for opn fx type IIIA, IIIB, or IIIC
S52.121B	Disp fx of head of rt radius, init enc for opn fx type I or II
S52.121C	Disp fx of head of rt radius, init enc for opn fx type IIIA, IIIB, or IIIC
S52.123B	Disp fx of head of unsp radius, init enc for opn fx type I or II
S52.123C	Disp fx of head of unsp radius, init enc for opn fx type IIIA, IIIB, or IIIC
S72.422B	Disp fx of lat condyle of lt femur, init enc for opn fx type I or II
S72.422C	Disp fx of lat condyle of lt femur, init enc for opn fx type IIIA, IIIB, or IIIC
S42.452B	Disp fx of lat condyle of lt humerus, init enc for opn fx
S82.122B	Disp fx of lat condyle of lt tibia, init enc for opn fx type I or II
S82.122C	Disp fx of lat condyle of lt tibia, init enc for opn fx type IIIA, IIIB, or IIIC
S72.421B	Disp fx of lat condyle of rt femur, init enc for opn fx type I or II
S72.421C	Disp fx of lat condyle of rt femur, init enc for opn fx type IIIA, IIIB, or IIIC
S42.451B	Disp fx of lat condyle of rt humerus, init enc for opn fx
S82.121B	Disp fx of lat condyle of rt tibia, init enc for opn fx type I or II
S82.121C	Disp fx of lat condyle of rt tibia, init enc for opn fx type IIIA, IIIB, or IIIC
S72.423B	Disp fx of lat condyle of unsp femur, init enc for opn fx type I or II
S72.423C	Disp fx of lat condyle of unsp femur, init enc for opn fx type IIIA, IIIB, or IIIC
S42.453B	Disp fx of lat condyle of unsp humerus, init enc for opn fx
S82.123B	Disp fx of lat condyle of unsp tibia, init enc for opn fx type I or II
S82.123C	Disp fx of lat condyle of unsp tibia, init enc for opn fx type IIIA, IIIB, or IIIC
S72.122A	Disp fx of lesser trochanter of lt femur, init enc for clsd fx
S72.122B	Disp fx of lesser trochanter of lt femur, init enc for opn fx type I or II
S72.122C	Disp fx of lesser trochanter of lt femur, init enc for opn fx type IIIA, IIIB, or IIIC
S72.121A	Disp fx of lesser trochanter of rt femur, init enc for clsd fx
S72.121B	Disp fx of lesser trochanter of rt femur, init enc for opn fx type I or II
S72.121C	Disp fx of lesser trochanter of rt femur, init enc for opn fx type IIIA, IIIB, or IIIC
S72.123A	Disp fx of lesser trochanter of unsp femur, init enc for clsd fx
S72.123B	Disp fx of lesser trochanter of unsp femur, init enc for opn fx type I or II
S72.123C	Disp fx of lesser trochanter of unsp femur, init enc for opn fx type IIIA, IIIB, or IIIC
S42.262B	Disp fx of lesser tuberosity of lt humerus, init enc for opn fx
S42.261B	Disp fx of lesser tuberosity of rt humerus, init enc for opn fx
S42.263B	Disp fx of lesser tuberosity of unsp humerus, init enc for opn fx
S52.512B	Disp fx of lt radial styloid process, init enc for opn fx type I or II
S52.512C	Disp fx of lt radial styloid process, init enc for opn fx type IIIA, IIIB, or IIIC
S82.112B	Disp fx of lt tibial spine, init enc for opn fx type I or II

S82.112C	Disp fx of lt tibial spine, init enc for opn fx type IIIA, IIIB, or IIIC
S82.152B	Disp fx of lt tibial tuberosity, init enc for opn fx type I or II
S82.152C	Disp fx of lt tibial tuberosity, init enc for opn fx type IIIA, IIIB, or IIIC
S52.612B	Disp fx of lt ulna styloid process, init enc for opn fx type I or II
S52.612C	Disp fx of lt ulna styloid process, init enc for opn fx type IIIA, IIIB, or IIIC
S72.442B	Disp fx of lwr epiphysis (separation) of lt femur, init enc for opn fx type I or II
S72.442C	Disp fx of lwr epiphysis (separation) of lt femur, init enc for opn fx type IIIA, IIIB, or IIIC
S72.441B	Disp fx of lwr epiphysis (separation) of rt femur, init enc for opn fx type I or II
S72.441C	Disp fx of lwr epiphysis (separation) of rt femur, init enc for opn fx type IIIA, IIIB, or IIIC
S72.443B	Disp fx of lwr epiphysis (separation) of unsp femur, init enc for opn fx type I or II
S72.443C	Disp fx of lwr epiphysis (separation) of unsp femur, init enc for opn fx type IIIA, IIIB, or IIIC
S72.432B	Disp fx of med condyle of lt femur, init enc for opn fx type I or II
S72.432C	Disp fx of med condyle of lt femur, init enc for opn fx type IIIA, IIIB, or IIIC
S42.462B	Disp fx of med condyle of lt humerus, init enc for opn fx
S82.132B	Disp fx of med condyle of lt tibia, init enc for opn fx type I or II
S82.132C	Disp fx of med condyle of lt tibia, init enc for opn fx type IIIA, IIIB, or IIIC
S72.431B	Disp fx of med condyle of rt femur, init enc for opn fx type I or II
S72.431C	Disp fx of med condyle of rt femur, init enc for opn fx type IIIA, IIIB, or IIIC
S42.461B	Disp fx of med condyle of rt humerus, init enc for opn fx
S82.131B	Disp fx of med condyle of rt tibia, init enc for opn fx type I or II
S82.131C	Disp fx of med condyle of rt tibia, init enc for opn fx type IIIA, IIIB, or IIIC
S72.433B	Disp fx of med condyle of unsp femur, init enc for opn fx type I or II
S72.433C	Disp fx of med condyle of unsp femur, init enc for opn fx type IIIA, IIIB, or IIIC
S42.463B	Disp fx of med condyle of unsp humerus, init enc for opn fx
S82.133B	Disp fx of med condyle of unsp tibia, init enc for opn fx type I or II
S82.133C	Disp fx of med condyle of unsp tibia, init enc for opn fx type IIIA, IIIB, or IIIC
S32.472A	Disp fx of med wall of lt acetab, init enc for clsd fx
S32.472B	Disp fx of med wall of lt acetab, init enc for opn fx
S32.471A	Disp fx of med wall of rt acetab, init enc for clsd fx
S32.471B	Disp fx of med wall of rt acetab, init enc for opn fx
S32.473A	Disp fx of med wall of unsp acetab, init enc for clsd fx
S32.473B	Disp fx of med wall of unsp acetab, init enc for opn fx
S52.132B	Disp fx of neck of lt radius, init enc for opn fx type I or II
S52.132C	Disp fx of neck of lt radius, init enc for opn fx type IIIA, IIIB, or IIIC
S52.131B	Disp fx of neck of rt radius, init enc for opn fx type I or II
S52.131C	Disp fx of neck of rt radius, init enc for opn fx type IIIA, IIIB, or IIIC
S52.133B	Disp fx of neck of unsp radius, init enc for opn fx type I or II
S52.133C	Disp fx of neck of unsp radius, init enc for opn fx type IIIA, IIIB, or IIIC
S52.032B	Disp fx of olecranon process w/ intraarticular extension of lt ulna, init enc for opn fx type I or II
S52.032C	Disp fx of olecranon process w/ intraarticular extension of lt ulna, init enc for opn fx type IIIA, IIIB, or IIIC
S52.031B	Disp fx of olecranon process w/ intraarticular extension of rt ulna, init enc for opn fx type I or II
S52.031C	Disp fx of olecranon process w/ intraarticular extension of rt ulna, init enc for opn fx type IIIA, IIIB, or IIIC
S52.033B	Disp fx of olecranon process w/ intraarticular extension of unsp ulna, init enc for opn fx type I or II
S52.033C	Disp fx of olecranon process w/ intraarticular extension of unsp ulna, init enc for opn fx type IIIA, IIIB, or IIIC
S52.022B	Disp fx of olecranon process w/o intraarticular extension of lt ulna, init enc for opn fx type I or II
S52.022C	Disp fx of olecranon process w/o intraarticular extension of lt ulna, init enc for opn fx type IIIA, IIIB, or IIIC
S52.021B	Disp fx of olecranon process w/o intraarticular extension of rt ulna, init enc for opn fx type I or II
S52.021C	Disp fx of olecranon process w/o intraarticular extension of rt ulna, init enc for opn fx type IIIA, IIIB, or IIIC
S52.023B	Disp fx of olecranon process w/o intraarticular extension of unsp ulna, init enc for opn fx type I or II
S52.023C	Disp fx of olecranon process w/o intraarticular extension of unsp ulna, init enc for opn fx type IIIA, IIIB, or IIIC
S32.442A	Disp fx of post column [ilioischial] of lt acetab, init enc for clsd fx
S32.442B	Disp fx of post column [ilioischial] of lt acetab, init enc for opn fx
S32.441A	Disp fx of post column [ilioischial] of rt acetab, init enc for clsd fx
S32.441B	Disp fx of post column [ilioischial] of rt acetab, init enc for opn fx
S32.443A	Disp fx of post column [ilioischial] of unsp acetab, init enc for clsd fx
S32.443B	Disp fx of post column [ilioischial] of unsp acetab, init enc for opn fx

S32.422A	Disp fx of post wall of lt acetab, init enc for clsd fx
S32.422B	Disp fx of post wall of lt acetab, init enc for opn fx
S32.421A	Disp fx of post wall of rt acetab, init enc for clsd fx
S32.421B	Disp fx of post wall of rt acetab, init enc for opn fx
S32.423A	Disp fx of post wall of unsp acetab, init enc for clsd fx
S32.423B	Disp fx of post wall of unsp acetab, init enc for opn fx
S52.511B	Disp fx of rt radial styloid process, init enc for opn fx type I or II
S52.511C	Disp fx of rt radial styloid process, init enc for opn fx type IIIA, IIIB, or IIIC
S82.111B	Disp fx of rt tibial spine, init enc for opn fx type I or II
S82.111C	Disp fx of rt tibial spine, init enc for opn fx type IIIA, IIIB, or IIIC
S82.151B	Disp fx of rt tibial tuberosity, init enc for opn fx type I or II
S82.151C	Disp fx of rt tibial tuberosity, init enc for opn fx type IIIA, IIIB, or IIIC
S52.611B	Disp fx of rt ulna styloid process, init enc for opn fx type I or II
S52.611C	Disp fx of rt ulna styloid process, init enc for opn fx type IIIA, IIIB, or IIIC
S52.513B	Disp fx of unsp radial styloid process, init enc for opn fx type I or II
S52.513C	Disp fx of unsp radial styloid process, init enc for opn fx type IIIA, IIIB, or IIIC
S82.113B	Disp fx of unsp tibial spine, init enc for opn fx type I or II
S82.113C	Disp fx of unsp tibial spine, init enc for opn fx type IIIA, IIIB, or IIIC
S82.153B	Disp fx of unsp tibial tuberosity, init enc for opn fx type I or II
S82.153C	Disp fx of unsp tibial tuberosity, init enc for opn fx type IIIA, IIIB, or IIIC
S52.613B	Disp fx of unsp ulna styloid process, init enc for opn fx type I or II
S52.613C	Disp fx of unsp ulna styloid process, init enc for opn fx type IIIA, IIIB, or IIIC
S72.142A	Disp intertrochanteric fx of lt femur, init enc for clsd fx
S72.142B	Disp intertrochanteric fx of lt femur, init enc for opn fx type I or II
S72.142C	Disp intertrochanteric fx of lt femur, init enc for opn fx type IIIA, IIIB, or IIIC
S72.141A	Disp intertrochanteric fx of rt femur, init enc for clsd fx
S72.141B	Disp intertrochanteric fx of rt femur, init enc for opn fx type I or II
S72.141C	Disp intertrochanteric fx of rt femur, init enc for opn fx type IIIA, IIIB, or IIIC
S72.143A	Disp intertrochanteric fx of unsp femur, init enc for clsd fx
S72.143B	Disp intertrochanteric fx of unsp femur, init enc for opn fx type I or II
S72.143C	Disp intertrochanteric fx of unsp femur, init enc for opn fx type IIIA, IIIB, or IIIC
S12.040B	Disp lat mass fx of 1st cervical vertebra, init enc for opn fx
S82.862B	Disp Maisonneuve's fx of lt leg, init enc for opn fx type I or II
S82.862C	Disp Maisonneuve's fx of lt leg, init enc for opn fx type IIIA, IIIB, or IIIC
S82.861B	Disp Maisonneuve's fx of rt leg, init enc for opn fx type I or II
S82.861C	Disp Maisonneuve's fx of rt leg, init enc for opn fx type IIIA, IIIB, or IIIC
S82.863B	Disp Maisonneuve's fx of unsp leg, init enc for opn fx type I or II
S82.863C	Disp Maisonneuve's fx of unsp leg, init enc for opn fx type IIIA, IIIB, or IIIC
S72.032A	Disp midcervical fx of lt femur, init enc for clsd fx
S72.032B	Disp midcervical fx of lt femur, init enc for opn fx type I or II
S72.032C	Disp midcervical fx of lt femur, init enc for opn fx type IIIA, IIIB, or IIIC
S72.031A	Disp midcervical fx of rt femur, init enc for clsd fx
S72.031B	Disp midcervical fx of rt femur, init enc for opn fx type I or II
S72.031C	Disp midcervical fx of rt femur, init enc for opn fx type IIIA, IIIB, or IIIC
S72.033A	Disp midcervical fx of unsp femur, init enc for clsd fx
S72.033B	Disp midcervical fx of unsp femur, init enc for opn fx type I or II
S72.033C	Disp midcervical fx of unsp femur, init enc for opn fx type IIIA, IIIB, or IIIC
S42.332B	Disp oblique fx of shaft of humerus, lt arm, init enc for opn fx
S42.331B	Disp oblique fx of shaft of humerus, rt arm, init enc for opn fx
S42.333B	Disp oblique fx of shaft of humerus, unsp arm, init enc for opn fx
S72.332A	Disp oblique fx of shaft of lt femur, init enc for clsd fx
S72.332B	Disp oblique fx of shaft of lt femur, init enc for opn fx type I or II
S72.332C	Disp oblique fx of shaft of lt femur, init enc for opn fx type IIIA, IIIB, or IIIC
S82.432B	Disp oblique fx of shaft of lt fibula, init enc for opn fx type I or II
S82.432C	Disp oblique fx of shaft of lt fibula, init enc for opn fx type IIIA, IIIB, or IIIC
S52.332B	Disp oblique fx of shaft of lt radius, init enc for opn fx type I or II
S52.332C	Disp oblique fx of shaft of lt radius, init enc for opn fx type IIIA, IIIB, or IIIC
S82.232B	Disp oblique fx of shaft of lt tibia, init enc for opn fx type I or II
S82.232C	Disp oblique fx of shaft of lt tibia, init enc for opn fx type IIIA, IIIB, or IIIC
S52.232B	Disp oblique fx of shaft of lt ulna, init enc for opn fx type I or II
S52.232C	Disp oblique fx of shaft of lt ulna, init enc for opn fx type IIIA, IIIB, or IIIC
S72.331A	Disp oblique fx of shaft of rt femur, init enc for clsd fx
S72.331B	Disp oblique fx of shaft of rt femur, init enc for opn fx type I or II
S72.331C	Disp oblique fx of shaft of rt femur, init enc for opn fx type IIIA, IIIB, or IIIC
S82.431B	Disp oblique fx of shaft of rt fibula, init enc for opn fx type I or II
S82.431C	Disp oblique fx of shaft of rt fibula, init enc for opn fx type IIIA, IIIB, or IIIC
S52.331B	Disp oblique fx of shaft of rt radius, init enc for opn fx type I or II
S52.331C	Disp oblique fx of shaft of rt radius, init enc for opn fx type IIIA, IIIB, or IIIC
S82.231B	Disp oblique fx of shaft of rt tibia, init enc for opn fx type I or II
S82.231C	Disp oblique fx of shaft of rt tibia, init enc for opn fx type IIIA, IIIB, or IIIC

S52.231B	Disp oblique fx of shaft of rt ulna, init enc for opn fx type I or II
S52.231C	Disp oblique fx of shaft of rt ulna, init enc for opn fx type IIIA, IIIB, or IIIC
S72.333A	Disp oblique fx of shaft of unsp femur, init enc for clsd fx
S72.333B	Disp oblique fx of shaft of unsp femur, init enc for opn fx type I or II
S72.333C	Disp oblique fx of shaft of unsp femur, init enc for opn fx type IIIA, IIIB, or IIIC
S82.433B	Disp oblique fx of shaft of unsp fibula, init enc for opn fx type I or II
S82.433C	Disp oblique fx of shaft of unsp fibula, init enc for opn fx type IIIA, IIIB, or IIIC
S52.333B	Disp oblique fx of shaft of unsp radius, init enc for opn fx type I or II
S52.333C	Disp oblique fx of shaft of unsp radius, init enc for opn fx type IIIA, IIIB, or IIIC
S82.233B	Disp oblique fx of shaft of unsp tibia, init enc for opn fx type I or II
S82.233C	Disp oblique fx of shaft of unsp tibia, init enc for opn fx type IIIA, IIIB, or IIIC
S52.233B	Disp oblique fx of shaft of unsp ulna, init enc for opn fx type I or II
S52.233C	Disp oblique fx of shaft of unsp ulna, init enc for opn fx type IIIA, IIIB, or IIIC
S12.030B	Disp post arch fx of 1st cervical vertebra, init enc for opn fx
S42.362B	Disp segmental fx of shaft of humerus, lt arm, init enc for opn fx
S42.361B	Disp segmental fx of shaft of humerus, rt arm, init enc for opn fx
S42.363B	Disp segmental fx of shaft of humerus, unsp arm, init enc for opn fx
S72.362A	Disp segmental fx of shaft of lt femur, init enc for clsd fx
S72.362B	Disp segmental fx of shaft of lt femur, init enc for opn fx type I or II
S72.362C	Disp segmental fx of shaft of lt femur, init enc for opn fx type IIIA, IIIB, or IIIC
S82.462B	Disp segmental fx of shaft of lt fibula, init enc for opn fx type I or II
S82.462C	Disp segmental fx of shaft of lt fibula, init enc for opn fx type IIIA, IIIB, or IIIC
S82.262B	Disp segmental fx of shaft of lt tibia, init enc for opn fx type I or II
S82.262C	Disp segmental fx of shaft of lt tibia, init enc for opn fx type IIIA, IIIB, or IIIC
S52.362B	Disp segmental fx of shaft of radius, lt arm, init enc for opn fx type I or II
S52.362C	Disp segmental fx of shaft of radius, lt arm, init enc for opn fx type IIIA, IIIB, or IIIC
S52.361B	Disp segmental fx of shaft of radius, rt arm, init enc for opn fx type I or II
S52.361C	Disp segmental fx of shaft of radius, rt arm, init enc for opn fx type IIIA, IIIB, or IIIC
S52.363B	Disp segmental fx of shaft of radius, unsp arm, init enc for opn fx type I or II
S52.363C	Disp segmental fx of shaft of radius, unsp arm, init enc for opn fx type IIIA, IIIB, or IIIC
S72.361A	Disp segmental fx of shaft of rt femur, init enc for clsd fx
S72.361B	Disp segmental fx of shaft of rt femur, init enc for opn fx type I or II
S72.361C	Disp segmental fx of shaft of rt femur, init enc for opn fx type IIIA, IIIB, or IIIC
S82.461B	Disp segmental fx of shaft of rt fibula, init enc for opn fx type I or II
S82.461C	Disp segmental fx of shaft of rt fibula, init enc for opn fx type IIIA, IIIB, or IIIC
S82.261B	Disp segmental fx of shaft of rt tibia, init enc for opn fx type I or II
S82.261C	Disp segmental fx of shaft of rt tibia, init enc for opn fx type IIIA, IIIB, or IIIC
S52.262B	Disp segmental fx of shaft of ulna, lt arm, init enc for opn fx type I or II
S52.262C	Disp segmental fx of shaft of ulna, lt arm, init enc for opn fx type IIIA, IIIB, or IIIC
S52.261B	Disp segmental fx of shaft of ulna, rt arm, init enc for opn fx type I or II
S52.261C	Disp segmental fx of shaft of ulna, rt arm, init enc for opn fx type IIIA, IIIB, or IIIC
S52.263B	Disp segmental fx of shaft of ulna, unsp arm, init enc for opn fx type I or II
S52.263C	Disp segmental fx of shaft of ulna, unsp arm, init enc for opn fx type IIIA, IIIB, or IIIC
S72.363A	Disp segmental fx of shaft of unsp femur, init enc for clsd fx
S72.363B	Disp segmental fx of shaft of unsp femur, init enc for opn fx type I or II
S72.363C	Disp segmental fx of shaft of unsp femur, init enc for opn fx type IIIA, IIIB, or IIIC
S82.463B	Disp segmental fx of shaft of unsp fibula, init enc for opn fx type I or II
S82.463C	Disp segmental fx of shaft of unsp fibula, init enc for opn fx type IIIA, IIIB, or IIIC
S82.263B	Disp segmental fx of shaft of unsp tibia, init enc for opn fx type I or II
S82.263C	Disp segmental fx of shaft of unsp tibia, init enc for opn fx type IIIA, IIIB, or IIIC
S42.412B	Disp simple supracondylar fx w/o intercondylar fx of lt humerus, init enc for opn fx
S42.411B	Disp simple supracondylar fx w/o intercondylar fx of rt humerus, init enc for opn fx
S42.413B	Disp simple supracondylar fx w/o intercondylar fx of unsp humerus, init enc for opn fx

S42.342B	Disp spiral fx of shaft of humerus, lt arm, init enc for opn fx
S42.341B	Disp spiral fx of shaft of humerus, rt arm, init enc for opn fx
S42.343B	Disp spiral fx of shaft of humerus, unsp arm, init enc for opn fx
S72.342A	Disp spiral fx of shaft of lt femur, init enc for clsd fx
S72.342B	Disp spiral fx of shaft of lt femur, init enc for opn fx type I or II
S72.342C	Disp spiral fx of shaft of lt femur, init enc for opn fx type IIIA, IIIB, or IIIC
S82.442B	Disp spiral fx of shaft of lt fibula, init enc for opn fx type I or II
S82.442C	Disp spiral fx of shaft of lt fibula, init enc for opn fx type IIIA, IIIB, or IIIC
S82.242B	Disp spiral fx of shaft of lt tibia, init enc for opn fx type I or II
S82.242C	Disp spiral fx of shaft of lt tibia, init enc for opn fx type IIIA, IIIB, or IIIC
S52.342B	Disp spiral fx of shaft of radius, lt arm, init enc for opn fx type I or II
S52.342C	Disp spiral fx of shaft of radius, lt arm, init enc for opn fx type IIIA, IIIB, or IIIC
S52.341B	Disp spiral fx of shaft of radius, rt arm, init enc for opn fx type I or II
S52.341C	Disp spiral fx of shaft of radius, rt arm, init enc for opn fx type IIIA, IIIB, or IIIC
S52.343B	Disp spiral fx of shaft of radius, unsp arm, init enc for opn fx type I or II
S52.343C	Disp spiral fx of shaft of radius, unsp arm, init enc for opn fx type IIIA, IIIB, or IIIC
S72.341A	Disp spiral fx of shaft of rt femur, init enc for clsd fx
S72.341B	Disp spiral fx of shaft of rt femur, init enc for opn fx type I or II
S72.341C	Disp spiral fx of shaft of rt femur, init enc for opn fx type IIIA, IIIB, or IIIC
S82.441B	Disp spiral fx of shaft of rt fibula, init enc for opn fx type I or II
S82.441C	Disp spiral fx of shaft of rt fibula, init enc for opn fx type IIIA, IIIB, or IIIC
S82.241B	Disp spiral fx of shaft of rt tibia, init enc for opn fx type I or II
S82.241C	Disp spiral fx of shaft of rt tibia, init enc for opn fx type IIIA, IIIB, or IIIC
S52.242B	Disp spiral fx of shaft of ulna, lt arm, init enc for opn fx type I or II
S52.242C	Disp spiral fx of shaft of ulna, lt arm, init enc for opn fx type IIIA, IIIB, or IIIC
S52.241B	Disp spiral fx of shaft of ulna, rt arm, init enc for opn fx type I or II
S52.241C	Disp spiral fx of shaft of ulna, rt arm, init enc for opn fx type IIIA, IIIB, or IIIC
S52.243B	Disp spiral fx of shaft of ulna, unsp arm, init enc for opn fx type I or II
S52.243C	Disp spiral fx of shaft of ulna, unsp arm, init enc for opn fx type IIIA, IIIB, or IIIC
S72.343A	Disp spiral fx of shaft of unsp femur, init enc for clsd fx
S72.343B	Disp spiral fx of shaft of unsp femur, init enc for opn fx type I or II
S72.343C	Disp spiral fx of shaft of unsp femur, init enc for opn fx type IIIA, IIIB, or IIIC
S82.443B	Disp spiral fx of shaft of unsp fibula, init enc for opn fx type I or II
S82.443C	Disp spiral fx of shaft of unsp fibula, init enc for opn fx type IIIA, IIIB, or IIIC
S82.243B	Disp spiral fx of shaft of unsp tibia, init enc for opn fx type I or II
S82.243C	Disp spiral fx of shaft of unsp tibia, init enc for opn fx type IIIA, IIIB, or IIIC
S72.22XA	Disp subtrochanteric fx of lt femur, init enc for clsd fx
S72.22XB	Disp subtrochanteric fx of lt femur, init enc for opn fx type I or II
S72.22XC	Disp subtrochanteric fx of lt femur, init enc for opn fx type IIIA, IIIB, or IIIC
S72.21XA	Disp subtrochanteric fx of rt femur, init enc for clsd fx
S72.21XB	Disp subtrochanteric fx of rt femur, init enc for opn fx type I or II
S72.21XC	Disp subtrochanteric fx of rt femur, init enc for opn fx type IIIA, IIIB, or IIIC
S72.23XA	Disp subtrochanteric fx of unsp femur, init enc for clsd fx
S72.23XB	Disp subtrochanteric fx of unsp femur, init enc for opn fx type I or II
S72.23XC	Disp subtrochanteric fx of unsp femur, init enc for opn fx type IIIA, IIIB, or IIIC
S72.462B	Disp supracondylar fx w/ intracondylar extension of lwr end of lt femur, init enc for opn fx type I or II
S72.462C	Disp supracondylar fx w/ intracondylar extension of lwr end of lt femur, init enc for opn fx type IIIA, IIIB, or IIIC
S72.461B	Disp supracondylar fx w/ intracondylar extension of lwr end of rt femur, init enc for opn fx type I or II
S72.461C	Disp supracondylar fx w/ intracondylar extension of lwr end of rt femur, init enc for opn fx type IIIA, IIIB, or IIIC
S72.463B	Disp supracondylar fx w/ intracondylar extension of lwr end of unsp femur, init enc for opn fx type I or II
S72.463C	Disp supracondylar fx w/ intracondylar extension of lwr end of unsp femur, init enc for opn fx type IIIA, IIIB, or IIIC
S72.452B	Disp supracondylar fx w/o intracondylar extension of lwr end of lt femur, init enc for opn fx type I or II
S72.452C	Disp supracondylar fx w/o intracondylar extension of lwr end of lt femur, init enc for opn fx type IIIA, IIIB, or IIIC
S72.451B	Disp supracondylar fx w/o intracondylar extension of lwr end of rt femur, init enc for opn fx type I or II
S72.451C	Disp supracondylar fx w/o intracondylar extension of lwr end of rt femur, init enc for opn fx type IIIA, IIIB, or IIIC
S72.453B	Disp supracondylar fx w/o intracondylar extension of lwr end of unsp femur, init enc for opn fx type I or II
S72.453C	Disp supracondylar fx w/o intracondylar extension of lwr end of unsp femur, init enc for opn fx type IIIA, IIIB, or IIIC
S42.472B	Disp transcondylar fx of lt humerus, init enc for opn fx

S42.471B	Disp transcondylar fx of rt humerus, init enc for opn fx
S42.473B	Disp transcondylar fx of unsp humerus, init enc for opn fx
S32.452A	Disp transv fx of lt acetab, init enc for clsd fx
S32.452B	Disp transv fx of lt acetab, init enc for opn fx
S32.451A	Disp transv fx of rt acetab, init enc for clsd fx
S32.451B	Disp transv fx of rt acetab, init enc for opn fx
S42.322B	Disp transv fx of shaft of humerus, lt arm, init enc for opn fx
S42.321B	Disp transv fx of shaft of humerus, rt arm, init enc for opn fx
S42.323B	Disp transv fx of shaft of humerus, unsp arm, init enc for opn fx
S72.322A	Disp transv fx of shaft of lt femur, init enc for clsd fx
S72.322B	Disp transv fx of shaft of lt femur, init enc for opn fx type I or II
S72.322C	Disp transv fx of shaft of lt femur, init enc for opn fx type IIIA, IIIB, or IIIC
S82.422B	Disp transv fx of shaft of lt fibula, init enc for opn fx type I or II
S82.422C	Disp transv fx of shaft of lt fibula, init enc for opn fx type IIIA, IIIB, or IIIC
S52.322B	Disp transv fx of shaft of lt radius, init enc for opn fx type I or II
S52.322C	Disp transv fx of shaft of lt radius, init enc for opn fx type IIIA, IIIB, or IIIC
S82.222B	Disp transv fx of shaft of lt tibia, init enc for opn fx type I or II
S82.222C	Disp transv fx of shaft of lt tibia, init enc for opn fx type IIIA, IIIB, or IIIC
S52.222B	Disp transv fx of shaft of lt ulna, init enc for opn fx type I or II
S52.222C	Disp transv fx of shaft of lt ulna, init enc for opn fx type IIIA, IIIB, or IIIC
S72.321A	Disp transv fx of shaft of rt femur, init enc for clsd fx
S72.321B	Disp transv fx of shaft of rt femur, init enc for opn fx type I or II
S72.321C	Disp transv fx of shaft of rt femur, init enc for opn fx type IIIA, IIIB, or IIIC
S82.421B	Disp transv fx of shaft of rt fibula, init enc for opn fx type I or II
S82.421C	Disp transv fx of shaft of rt fibula, init enc for opn fx type IIIA, IIIB, or IIIC
S52.321B	Disp transv fx of shaft of rt radius, init enc for opn fx type I or II
S52.321C	Disp transv fx of shaft of rt radius, init enc for opn fx type IIIA, IIIB, or IIIC
S82.221B	Disp transv fx of shaft of rt tibia, init enc for opn fx type I or II
S82.221C	Disp transv fx of shaft of rt tibia, init enc for opn fx type IIIA, IIIB, or IIIC
S52.221B	Disp transv fx of shaft of rt ulna, init enc for opn fx type I or II
S52.221C	Disp transv fx of shaft of rt ulna, init enc for opn fx type IIIA, IIIB, or IIIC
S72.323A	Disp transv fx of shaft of unsp femur, init enc for clsd fx
S72.323B	Disp transv fx of shaft of unsp femur, init enc for opn fx type I or II
S72.323C	Disp transv fx of shaft of unsp femur, init enc for opn fx type IIIA, IIIB, or IIIC
S82.423B	Disp transv fx of shaft of unsp fibula, init enc for opn fx type I or II
S82.423C	Disp transv fx of shaft of unsp fibula, init enc for opn fx type IIIA, IIIB, or IIIC
S52.323B	Disp transv fx of shaft of unsp radius, init enc for opn fx type I or II
S52.323C	Disp transv fx of shaft of unsp radius, init enc for opn fx type IIIA, IIIB, or IIIC
S82.223B	Disp transv fx of shaft of unsp tibia, init enc for opn fx type I or II
S82.223C	Disp transv fx of shaft of unsp tibia, init enc for opn fx type IIIA, IIIB, or IIIC
S52.223B	Disp transv fx of shaft of unsp ulna, init enc for opn fx type I or II
S52.223C	Disp transv fx of shaft of unsp ulna, init enc for opn fx type IIIA, IIIB, or IIIC
S32.453A	Disp transv fx of unsp acetab, init enc for clsd fx
S32.453B	Disp transv fx of unsp acetab, init enc for opn fx
S72.412B	Disp unsp condyle fx of lwr end of lt femur, init enc for opn fx type I or II
S72.412C	Disp unsp condyle fx of lwr end of lt femur, init enc for opn fx type IIIA, IIIB, or IIIC
S72.411B	Disp unsp condyle fx of lwr end of rt femur, init enc for opn fx type I or II
S72.411C	Disp unsp condyle fx of lwr end of rt femur, init enc for opn fx type IIIA, IIIB, or IIIC
S72.413B	Disp unsp condyle fx of lwr end of unsp femur, init enc for opn fx type I or II
S72.413C	Disp unsp condyle fx of lwr end of unsp femur, init enc for opn fx type IIIA, IIIB, or IIIC
I71.02	Dissection of abd aorta
I77.71	Dissection of carotid artery
I67.0	Dissection of cerebral arteries, nonruptured
I77.72	Dissection of iliac artery
I77.79	Dissection of oth artery
I77.73	Dissection of renal artery
I71.01	Dissection of thoracic aorta
I71.03	Dissection of thoracoabdominal aorta
I71.00	Dissection of unsp site of aorta
I77.74	Dissection of vert artery
B00.7	Disseminated herpesviral disease
D65	Disseminated intravascular coagulation [defibrination synd]
P60	Disseminated intravascular coagulation of newborn
B46.4	Disseminated mucormycosis
K57.41	Diverticulitis of both sm & lg intestine w/ perforation & abscess w/ bleeding

K57.53	Diverticulitis of both sm & lg intestine w/o perforation or abscess w/ bleeding
K57.81	Diverticulitis of intestine, part unsp, w/ perforation & abscess w/ bleeding
K57.93	Diverticulitis of intestine, part unsp, w/o perforation or abscess w/ bleeding
K57.21	Diverticulitis of lg intestine w/ perforation & abscess w/ bleeding
K57.33	Diverticulitis of lg intestine w/o perforation or abscess w/ bleeding
K57.01	Diverticulitis of sm intestine w/ perforation & abscess w/ bleeding
K57.13	Diverticulitis of sm intestine w/o perforation or abscess w/ bleeding
K57.51	Diverticulosis of both sm & lg intestine w/o perforation or abscess w/ bleeding
K57.91	Diverticulosis of intestine, part unsp, w/o perforation or abscess w/ bleeding
K57.31	Diverticulosis of lg intestine w/o perforation or abscess w/ bleeding
K57.11	Diverticulosis of sm intestine w/o perforation or abscess w/ bleeding
Q20.4	Double inlet ventricle
Q20.2	Double outlet lt ventricle
Q20.1	Double outlet rt ventricle
K85.3	Drug induced acute pancreatitis
E09.01	Drug or chemical induced diabetes mellitus w/ hyperosmolarity w/ coma
E09.00	Drug or chemical induced diabetes mellitus w/ hyperosmolarity w/o nonketotic hyperglycemic-hyperosmolar coma (NKHHC)
E09.641	Drug or chemical induced diabetes mellitus w/ hypoglycemia w/ coma
E09.11	Drug or chemical induced diabetes mellitus w/ ketoacidosis w/ coma
E09.10	Drug or chemical induced diabetes mellitus w/ ketoacidosis w/o coma
D61.1	Drug-induced aplastic anemia
K29.81	Duodenitis w/ bleeding
A83.2	Eastern equine encephalitis
Q22.5	Ebstein's anomaly
O15.1	Eclampsia in labor
O15.02	Eclampsia in pregnancy, 2nd trmstr
O15.03	Eclampsia in pregnancy, 3rd trmstr
O15.2	Eclampsia in the puerperium
O04.7	Embolism following (induced) termination of pregnancy
O08.2	Embolism following ectopic & molar pregnancy
O07.2	Embolism following failed attempted termination of pregnancy
O03.2	Embolism following incomplete spontaneous abortion
G05.3	Encephalitis & encephalomyelitis in diseases classified elsw
G04.90	Encephalitis & encephalomyelitis, unsp
G93.40	Encephalopathy, unsp
N18.6	End stage renal disease
S06.4X5A	Epidural hemor w/ loss of cnscness > 24 hrs w/ return to pre-existing conscious lvl, init enc
S06.4X6A	Epidural hemor w/ loss of cnscness > 24 hrs w/o return to pre-existing conscious lvl w/ patient surviving, init enc
S06.4X3A	Epidural hemor w/ loss of cnscness of 1 hr to 5 hrs 59 mins, init enc
S06.4X1A	Epidural hemor w/ loss of cnscness of 30 mins or less, init enc
S06.4X2A	Epidural hemor w/ loss of cnscness of 31 mins to 59 mins, init enc
S06.4X4A	Epidural hemor w/ loss of cnscness of 6 hrs to 24 hrs, init enc
S06.4X7A	Epidural hemor w/ loss of cnscness of any dur w/ death d/t brain inj prior to regain cnscness, init enc
S06.4X8A	Epidural hemor w/ loss of cnscness of any dur w/ death d/t oth causes prior to regain cnscness, init enc
S06.4X9A	Epidural hemor w/ loss of cnscness of unsp dur, init enc
S06.4X0A	Epidural hemor w/o loss of cnscness, init enc
A26.7	Erysipelothrix sepsis
I85.01	Esophageal varices w/ bleeding
Q39.4	Esophageal web
Q79.2	Exomphalos
G06.2	Extradural & subdural abscess, unsp
A84.0	Far Eastern tick-borne encephalitis [Russian spring-summer encephalitis]
T79.1XXA	Fat embolism (traum), init enc
N73.3	Female acute pelvic peritonitis
S22.5XXA	Flail chest, init enc for clsd fx
S22.5XXB	Flail chest, init enc for opn fx
J09.X1	Flu d/t identified novel flu A virus w/ pneumonia
J10.08	Flu d/t oth identified flu virus w/ oth spec pneumonia
J10.01	Flu d/t oth identified flu virus w/ the same oth identified flu virus pneumonia
J10.00	Flu d/t oth identified flu virus w/ unsp type of pneumonia
J11.08	Flu d/t unidentified flu virus w/ spec pneumonia
J11.00	Flu d/t unidentified flu virus w/ unsp type of pneumonia

R53.2	Functional quadriplegia
S22.22XB	Fx of body of sternum, init enc for opn fx
S22.9XXB	Fx of bony thorax, part unsp, init enc for opn fx
S32.2XXB	Fx of coccyx, init enc for opn fx
S42.92XB	Fx of lt shldr girdle, part unsp, init enc for opn fx
S22.21XB	Fx of manubrium, init enc for opn fx
S22.32XB	Fx of one rib, lt side, init enc for opn fx
S22.31XB	Fx of one rib, rt side, init enc for opn fx
S22.39XB	Fx of one rib, unsp side, init enc for opn fx
S12.8XXA	Fx of oth parts of neck, init enc
S32.89XB	Fx of oth parts of pelvis, init enc for opn fx
S42.91XB	Fx of rt shldr girdle, part unsp, init enc for opn fx
S32.512B	Fx of superior rim of lt pubis, init enc for opn fx
S32.511B	Fx of superior rim of rt pubis, init enc for opn fx
S32.519B	Fx of superior rim of unsp pubis, init enc for opn fx
S72.002A	Fx of unsp part of neck of lt femur, init enc for clsd fx
S72.002B	Fx of unsp part of neck of lt femur, init enc for opn fx type I or II
S72.002C	Fx of unsp part of neck of lt femur, init enc for opn fx type IIIA, IIIB, or IIIC
S72.001A	Fx of unsp part of neck of rt femur, init enc for clsd fx
S72.001B	Fx of unsp part of neck of rt femur, init enc for opn fx type I or II
S72.001C	Fx of unsp part of neck of rt femur, init enc for opn fx type IIIA, IIIB, or IIIC
S72.009A	Fx of unsp part of neck of unsp femur, init enc for clsd fx
S72.009B	Fx of unsp part of neck of unsp femur, init enc for opn fx type I or II
S72.009C	Fx of unsp part of neck of unsp femur, init enc for opn fx type IIIA, IIIB, or IIIC
S32.9XXB	Fx of unsp parts of lumbosacral spine & pelvis, init enc for opn fx
S42.90XB	Fx of unsp shldr girdle, part unsp, init enc for opn fx
S02.0XXB	Fx of vault of skull, init enc for opn fx
S22.24XB	Fx of xiphoid process, init enc for opn fx
S52.372B	Galeazzi's fx of lt radius, init enc for opn fx type I or II
S52.372C	Galeazzi's fx of lt radius, init enc for opn fx type IIIA, IIIB, or IIIC
S52.371B	Galeazzi's fx of rt radius, init enc for opn fx type I or II
S52.371C	Galeazzi's fx of rt radius, init enc for opn fx type IIIA, IIIB, or IIIC
S52.379B	Galeazzi's fx of unsp radius, init enc for opn fx type I or II
S52.379C	Galeazzi's fx of unsp radius, init enc for opn fx type IIIA, IIIB, or IIIC
J85.0	Gangrene & necrosis of lung
A48.0	Gas gangrene
K29.71	Gastritis, unsp, w/ bleeding
K22.6	Gastro-esophageal lac-hemor synd
K29.91	Gastroduodenitis, unsp, w/ bleeding
B46.2	Gastrointestinal mucormycosis
Q79.3	Gastroschisis
K65.0	Generalized (acute) peritonitis
G40.311	Generalized idiopathic epilepsy & epileptic syndromes, intractable, w/ status epilepticus
G40.319	Generalized idiopathic epilepsy & epileptic syndromes, intractable, w/o status epilepticus
G40.301	Generalized idiopathic epilepsy & epileptic syndromes, not intractable, w/ status epilepticus
A54.81	Gonococcal meningitis
A54.86	Gonococcal sepsis
A41.50	Gram-negative sepsis, unsp
D57.01	Hb-SS disease w/ acute chest synd
D57.00	Hb-SS disease w/ crisis, unsp
D57.02	Hb-SS disease w/ splenic sequestration
O14.22	HELLP synd (HELLP), 2nd trmstr
O14.23	HELLP synd (HELLP), 3rd trmstr
D59.3	Hemolytic-uremic synd
K66.1	Hemoperitoneum
G00.0	Hemophilus meningitis
K72.91	Hepatic failure, unsp w/ coma
B15.0	Hepatitis A w/ hepatic coma
K76.7	Hepatorenal synd
D67	Hereditary factor IX deficiency
D66	Hereditary factor VIII deficiency
B00.82	Herpes simplex myelitis
B00.4	Herpesviral encephalitis
B00.3	Herpesviral meningitis
Q04.2	Holoprosencephaly
B10.01	Human herpesvirus 6 encephalitis
B20	Human immunodeficiency virus [HIV] disease
J12.3	Human metapneumovirus pneumonia
P56.0	Hydrops fetalis d/t isoimmunization
P56.99	Hydrops fetalis d/t oth hemolytic disease
P56.90	Hydrops fetalis d/t unsp hemolytic disease
P83.2	Hydrops fetalis not d/t hemolytic disease
Q23.4	Hypoplastic lt heart synd
Q22.6	Hypoplastic rt heart synd
R57.1	Hypovolemic shock
K85.0	Idiopathic acute pancreatitis
D61.3	Idiopathic aplastic anemia
S42.448B	Incarcerated fx (avulsion) of med epicondyle of lt humerus, init enc for opn fx
S42.447B	Incarcerated fx (avulsion) of med epicondyle of rt humerus, init enc for opn fx
S42.449B	Incarcerated fx (avulsion) of med epicondyle of unsp humerus, init enc for opn fx
K43.1	Incisional hernia w/ gangrene
S34.121A	Incomplete lesion of L1 lvl of lumbar spinal cord, init enc
S34.122A	Incomplete lesion of L2 lvl of lumbar spinal cord, init enc
S34.123A	Incomplete lesion of L3 lvl of lumbar spinal cord, init enc
S34.124A	Incomplete lesion of L4 lvl of lumbar spinal cord, init enc
S34.125A	Incomplete lesion of L5 lvl of lumbar spinal cord, init enc
S34.132A	Incomplete lesion of sacral spinal cord, init enc
S34.129A	Incomplete lesion of unsp lvl of lumbar spinal cord, init enc
K76.3	Infarction of liver
I40.0	Infective myocarditis
O41.1011	Infxn of amniotic sac & membranes, unsp, 1st trmstr, fetus 1
O41.1012	Infxn of amniotic sac & membranes, unsp, 1st trmstr, fetus 2
O41.1013	Infxn of amniotic sac & membranes, unsp, 1st trmstr, fetus 3
O41.1014	Infxn of amniotic sac & membranes, unsp, 1st trmstr, fetus 4
O41.1015	Infxn of amniotic sac & membranes, unsp, 1st trmstr, fetus 5
O41.1010	Infxn of amniotic sac & membranes, unsp, 1st trmstr, N/A or unsp
O41.1019	Infxn of amniotic sac & membranes, unsp, 1st trmstr, oth fetus
O41.1021	Infxn of amniotic sac & membranes, unsp, 2nd trmstr, fetus 1
O41.1022	Infxn of amniotic sac & membranes, unsp, 2nd trmstr, fetus 2
O41.1023	Infxn of amniotic sac & membranes, unsp, 2nd trmstr, fetus 3
O41.1024	Infxn of amniotic sac & membranes, unsp, 2nd trmstr, fetus 4
O41.1025	Infxn of amniotic sac & membranes, unsp, 2nd trmstr, fetus 5
O41.1020	Infxn of amniotic sac & membranes, unsp, 2nd trmstr, N/A or unsp
O41.1029	Infxn of amniotic sac & membranes, unsp, 2nd trmstr, oth fetus
O41.1031	Infxn of amniotic sac & membranes, unsp, 3rd trmstr, fetus 1
O41.1032	Infxn of amniotic sac & membranes, unsp, 3rd trmstr, fetus 2
O41.1033	Infxn of amniotic sac & membranes, unsp, 3rd trmstr, fetus 3
O41.1034	Infxn of amniotic sac & membranes, unsp, 3rd trmstr, fetus 4
O41.1035	Infxn of amniotic sac & membranes, unsp, 3rd trmstr, fetus 5
O41.1030	Infxn of amniotic sac & membranes, unsp, 3rd trmstr, N/A or unsp
O41.1039	Infxn of amniotic sac & membranes, unsp, 3rd trmstr, oth fetus
Q00.2	Iniencephaly
S34.3XXA	Inj of cauda equina, init enc
S35.512A	Inj of lt iliac artery, init enc
S35.515A	Inj of lt iliac vein, init enc
S06.826A	Inj of lt int carotid artery, intracranial portion, NEC w/ loss of cnscness > 24 hrs w/o return to pre-existing conscious lvl w/ patient surviving, init enc
S06.827A	Inj of lt int carotid artery, intracranial portion, NEC w/ loss of cnscness of any dur w/ death d/t brain inj prior to regain cnscness, init enc
S06.828A	Inj of lt int carotid artery, intracranial portion, NEC w/ loss of cnscness of any dur w/ death d/t oth cause prior to regain cnscness, init enc
S35.59XA	Inj of oth iliac blood vessels, init enc
S35.511A	Inj of rt iliac artery, init enc
S35.514A	Inj of rt iliac vein, init enc
S06.816A	Inj of rt int carotid artery, intracranial portion, NEC w/ loss of cnscness > 24 hrs w/o return to pre-existing conscious lvl w/ patient surviving, init enc
S06.817A	Inj of rt int carotid artery, intracranial portion, NEC w/ loss of cnscness of any dur w/ death d/t brain inj prior to regain cnscness, init enc
S06.818A	Inj of rt int carotid artery, intracranial portion, NEC w/ loss of cnscness of any dur w/ death d/t oth cause prior to regain cnscness, init enc
S35.513A	Inj of unsp iliac artery, init enc
S35.50XA	Inj of unsp iliac blood vessel(s), init enc
S35.516A	Inj of unsp iliac vein, init enc
P59.1	Inspissated bile synd
P25.0	Interstitial emphysema originating in the perinatal period
P52.4	Intracerebral (nontraumatic) hemor of newborn
P52.9	Intracranial (nontraumatic) hemor of newborn, unsp
G07	Intracranial & intraspinal abscess & granuloma in diseases classified elsw
G08	Intracranial & intraspinal phlebitis & thrombophlebitis
G06.0	Intracranial abscess & granuloma

O67.0	Intrapartum hemor w/ coagulation defect
G06.1	Intraspinal abscess & granuloma
P52.21	Intraventricular (nontraumatic) hemor, grade 3, of newborn
P52.22	Intraventricular (nontraumatic) hemor, grade 4, of newborn
B44.0	Invasive pulmn aspergillosis
I40.1	Isolated myocarditis
A83.0	Japanese encephalitis
P57.0	Kernicterus d/t isoimmunization
P57.9	Kernicterus, unsp
E40	Kwashiorkor
S45.012A	Lac of axillary artery, lt side, init enc
S45.011A	Lac of axillary artery, rt side, init enc
S45.019A	Lac of axillary artery, unsp side, init enc
S27.432A	Lac of bronchus, bilat, init enc
S27.431A	Lac of bronchus, unilat, init enc
S27.439A	Lac of bronchus, unsp, init enc
S27.813A	Lac of esophagus (thoracic part), init enc
S26.12XA	Lac of heart w/o hemopericardium, init enc
S26.92XA	Lac of heart, unsp w/ or w/o hemopericardium, init enc
S35.341A	Lac of inferior mesenteric vein, init enc
S35.412A	Lac of lt renal artery, init enc
S35.415A	Lac of lt renal vein, init enc
S27.332A	Lac of lung, bilat, init enc
S27.331A	Lac of lung, unilat, init enc
S27.339A	Lac of lung, unsp, init enc
S85.012A	Lac of popliteal artery, lt leg, init enc
S85.011A	Lac of popliteal artery, rt leg, init enc
S85.019A	Lac of popliteal artery, unsp leg, init enc
S85.512A	Lac of popliteal vein, lt leg, init enc
S85.511A	Lac of popliteal vein, rt leg, init enc
S85.519A	Lac of popliteal vein, unsp leg, init enc
S35.311A	Lac of portal vein, init enc
S35.411A	Lac of rt renal artery, init enc
S35.414A	Lac of rt renal vein, init enc
S35.321A	Lac of splenic vein, init enc
S35.331A	Lac of superior mesenteric vein, init enc
S35.413A	Lac of unsp renal artery, init enc
S35.416A	Lac of unsp renal vein, init enc
S31.622A	Lac w/ FB of abd wall, epigastric rgn w/ penetration into peritoneal cavity, init enc
S31.624A	Lac w/ FB of abd wall, lt lwr quadrant w/ penetration into peritoneal cavity, init enc
S31.621A	Lac w/ FB of abd wall, lt upr quadrant w/ penetration into peritoneal cavity, init enc
S31.625A	Lac w/ FB of abd wall, periumbilic rgn w/ penetration into peritoneal cavity, init enc
S31.623A	Lac w/ FB of abd wall, rt lwr quadrant w/ penetration into peritoneal cavity, init enc
S31.620A	Lac w/ FB of abd wall, rt upr quadrant w/ penetration into peritoneal cavity, init enc
S31.629A	Lac w/ FB of abd wall, unsp quadrant w/ penetration into peritoneal cavity, init enc
S11.012A	Lac w/ FB of larynx, init enc
S21.422A	Lac w/ FB of lt back wall of thorax w/ penetration into thoracic cavity, init enc
S21.322A	Lac w/ FB of lt front wall of thorax w/ penetration into thoracic cavity, init enc
S31.021A	Lac w/ FB of lwr back & pelvis w/ penetration into retroperitoneum, init enc
S21.421A	Lac w/ FB of rt back wall of thorax w/ penetration into thoracic cavity, init enc
S21.321A	Lac w/ FB of rt front wall of thorax w/ penetration into thoracic cavity, init enc
S11.022A	Lac w/ FB of trachea, init enc
S21.429A	Lac w/ FB of unsp back wall of thorax w/ penetration into thoracic cavity, init enc
S21.329A	Lac w/ FB of unsp front wall of thorax w/ penetration into thoracic cavity, init enc
S11.032A	Lac w/ FB of vocal cord, init enc
S31.612A	Lac w/o FB of abd wall, epigastric rgn w/ penetration into peritoneal cavity, init enc
S31.614A	Lac w/o FB of abd wall, lt lwr quadrant w/ penetration into peritoneal cavity, init enc
S31.611A	Lac w/o FB of abd wall, lt upr quadrant w/ penetration into peritoneal cavity, init enc
S31.615A	Lac w/o FB of abd wall, periumbilic rgn w/ penetration into peritoneal cavity, init enc
S31.613A	Lac w/o FB of abd wall, rt lwr quadrant w/ penetration into peritoneal cavity, init enc
S31.610A	Lac w/o FB of abd wall, rt upr quadrant w/ penetration into peritoneal cavity, init enc
S31.619A	Lac w/o FB of abd wall, unsp quadrant w/ penetration into peritoneal cavity, init enc
S11.011A	Lac w/o FB of larynx, init enc
S21.412A	Lac w/o FB of lt back wall of thorax w/ penetration into thoracic cavity, init enc
S21.312A	Lac w/o FB of lt front wall of thorax w/ penetration into thoracic cavity, init enc
S31.011A	Lac w/o FB of lwr back & pelvis w/ penetration into retroperitoneum, init enc
S21.411A	Lac w/o FB of rt back wall of thorax w/ penetration into thoracic cavity, init enc
S21.311A	Lac w/o FB of rt front wall of thorax w/ penetration into thoracic cavity, init enc
S11.021A	Lac w/o FB of trachea, init enc
S21.419A	Lac w/o FB of unsp back wall of thorax w/ penetration into thoracic cavity, init enc
S21.319A	Lac w/o FB of unsp front wall of thorax w/ penetration into thoracic cavity, init enc
S11.031A	Lac w/o FB of vocal cord, init enc
A50.42	Late congenital syphilitic encephalitis
A50.41	Late congenital syphilitic meningitis
P74.0	Late metabolic acidosis of newborn
A52.14	Late syphilitic encephalitis
A52.13	Late syphilitic meningitis
A48.1	Legionnaires' disease
A32.7	Listerial sepsis
J18.1	Lobar pneumonia, unsp organism
G83.5	Locked-in state
J84.81	Lymphangioleiomyomatosis
S35.02XA	Major lac of abd aorta, init enc
S35.292A	Major lac of branches of celiac & mesenteric artery, init enc
S35.212A	Major lac of celiac artery, init enc
S75.022A	Major lac of femoral artery, lt leg, init enc
S75.021A	Major lac of femoral artery, rt leg, init enc
S75.029A	Major lac of femoral artery, unsp leg, init enc
S75.122A	Major lac of femoral vein at hip & thigh lvl, lt leg, init enc
S75.121A	Major lac of femoral vein at hip & thigh lvl, rt leg, init enc
S75.129A	Major lac of femoral vein at hip & thigh lvl, unsp leg, init enc
S26.022A	Major lac of heart w/ hemopericardium, init enc
S35.232A	Major lac of inferior mesenteric artery, init enc
S35.12XA	Major lac of inferior vena cava, init enc
S36.116A	Major lac of liver, init enc
S25.122A	Major lac of lt innominate or subclavian artery, init enc
S25.322A	Major lac of lt innominate or subclavian vein, init enc
S37.062A	Major lac of lt kidney, init enc
S25.422A	Major lac of lt pulmn blood vessels, init enc
S25.121A	Major lac of rt innominate or subclavian artery, init enc
S25.321A	Major lac of rt innominate or subclavian vein, init enc
S37.061A	Major lac of rt kidney, init enc
S25.421A	Major lac of rt pulmn blood vessels, init enc
S36.032A	Major lac of spleen, init enc
S35.222A	Major lac of superior mesenteric artery, init enc
S25.22XA	Major lac of superior vena cava, init enc
S25.02XA	Major lac of thoracic aorta, init enc
S25.129A	Major lac of unsp innominate or subclavian artery, init enc
S25.329A	Major lac of unsp innominate or subclavian vein, init enc
S37.069A	Major lac of unsp kidney, init enc
S25.429A	Major lac of unsp pulmn blood vessels, init enc
G21.0	Malig neuroleptic synd
E42	Marasmic kwashiorkor
P26.1	Massive pulmn hemor originating in the perinatal period
O34.31	Maternal care for cervical incompetence, 1st trmstr
O34.32	Maternal care for cervical incompetence, 2nd trmstr
O34.33	Maternal care for cervical incompetence, 3rd trmstr
B05.0	Measles complicated by encephalitis
B05.2	Measles complicated by pneumonia
P24.01	Meconium aspiration w/ respiratory symptoms
E84.11	Meconium ileus in cystic fibrosis
A17.1	Meningeal tuberculoma

G03.8	Meningitis d/t oth spec causes
G01	Meningitis in bacterial diseases classified elsw
G02	Meningitis in oth infectious & parasitic diseases classified elsw
G03.9	Meningitis, unsp
A39.50	Meningococcal carditis, unsp
A39.81	Meningococcal encephalitis
A39.51	Meningococcal endocarditis
A39.0	Meningococcal meningitis
A39.52	Meningococcal myocarditis
A39.53	Meningococcal pericarditis
A39.4	Meningococcemia, unsp
G93.41	Metabolic encephalopathy
S26.020A	Mild lac of heart w/ hemopericardium, init enc
A19.9	Miliary tuberculosis, unsp
S32.111B	Minimally disp Zone I fx of sacrum, init enc for opn fx
S32.121B	Minimally disp Zone II fx of sacrum, init enc for opn fx
S32.131B	Minimally disp Zone III fx of sacrum, init enc for opn fx
S35.01XA	Minor lac of abd aorta, init enc
S35.291A	Minor lac of branches of celiac & mesenteric artery, init enc
S35.211A	Minor lac of celiac artery, init enc
S75.012A	Minor lac of femoral artery, lt leg, init enc
S75.011A	Minor lac of femoral artery, rt leg, init enc
S75.019A	Minor lac of femoral artery, unsp leg, init enc
S75.112A	Minor lac of femoral vein at hip & thigh lvl, lt leg, init enc
S75.111A	Minor lac of femoral vein at hip & thigh lvl, rt leg, init enc
S75.119A	Minor lac of femoral vein at hip & thigh lvl, unsp leg, init enc
S35.231A	Minor lac of inferior mesenteric artery, init enc
S35.11XA	Minor lac of inferior vena cava, init enc
S25.112A	Minor lac of lt innominate or subclavian artery, init enc
S25.312A	Minor lac of lt innominate or subclavian vein, init enc
S25.412A	Minor lac of lt pulmn blood vessels, init enc
S25.111A	Minor lac of rt innominate or subclavian artery, init enc
S25.311A	Minor lac of rt innominate or subclavian vein, init enc
S25.411A	Minor lac of rt pulmn blood vessels, init enc
S35.221A	Minor lac of superior mesenteric artery, init enc
S25.21XA	Minor lac of superior vena cava, init enc
S25.01XA	Minor lac of thoracic aorta, init enc
S25.119A	Minor lac of unsp innominate or subclavian artery, init enc
S25.319A	Minor lac of unsp innominate or subclavian vein, init enc
S25.419A	Minor lac of unsp pulmn blood vessels, init enc
S26.021A	Mod lac of heart w/ hemopericardium, init enc
S36.115A	Mod lac of liver, init enc
S36.031A	Mod lac of spleen, init enc
S52.272B	Monteggia's fx of lt ulna, init enc for opn fx type I or II
S52.272C	Monteggia's fx of lt ulna, init enc for opn fx type IIIA, IIIB, or IIIC
S52.271B	Monteggia's fx of rt ulna, init enc for opn fx type I or II
S52.271C	Monteggia's fx of rt ulna, init enc for opn fx type IIIA, IIIB, or IIIC
S52.279B	Monteggia's fx of unsp ulna, init enc for opn fx type I or II
S52.279C	Monteggia's fx of unsp ulna, init enc for opn fx type IIIA, IIIB, or IIIC
A83.9	Mosquito-borne viral encephalitis, unsp
B46.5	Mucormycosis, unsp
S32.810B	Multi fractures of pelvis w/ stable disruption of pelvic ring, init enc for opn fx
S32.811B	Multi fractures of pelvis w/ unstable disruption of pelvic ring, init enc for opn fx
S32.82XB	Multi fractures of pelvis w/o disruption of pelvic ring, init enc for opn fx
S22.43XB	Multi fractures of ribs, bilat, init enc for opn fx
S22.42XB	Multi fractures of ribs, lt side, init enc for opn fx
S22.41XB	Multi fractures of ribs, rt side, init enc for opn fx
S22.49XB	Multi fractures of ribs, unsp side, init enc for opn fx
B26.2	Mumps encephalitis
B26.1	Mumps meningitis
G70.01	Myasthenia gravis w/ (acute) exacerbation
G05.4	Myelitis in diseases classified elsw
G04.91	Myelitis, unsp
I41	Myocarditis in diseases classified elsw
E03.5	Myxedema coma
P77.9	Necrotizing enterocolitis in newborn, unsp
M72.6	Necrotizing fasciitis
P37.2	Neonatal (disseminated) listeriosis
P24.11	Neonatal aspiration of (clear) amniotic fluid & mucus w/ respiratory symptoms
P24.21	Neonatal aspiration of blood w/ respiratory symptoms

P24.31	Neonatal aspiration of milk & regurgitated food w/ respiratory symptoms
P91.4	Neonatal cerebral depression
P91.3	Neonatal cerebral irritability
P91.0	Neonatal cerebral ischemia
P91.2	Neonatal cerebral leukomalacia
P91.5	Neonatal coma
P59.29	Neonatal jaundice from oth hepatocellular damage
P59.20	Neonatal jaundice from unsp hepatocellular damage
P54.1	Neonatal melena
P54.2	Neonatal rectal hemor
J84.841	Neuroendocrine cell hyperplasia of infancy
I21.4	Non-ST elevation (NSTEMI) myocardial infarction
S72.135A	Nondisp apophyseal fx of lt femur, init enc for clsd fx
S72.135B	Nondisp apophyseal fx of lt femur, init enc for opn fx type I or II
S72.135C	Nondisp apophyseal fx of lt femur, init enc for opn fx type IIIA, IIIB, or IIIC
S72.134A	Nondisp apophyseal fx of rt femur, init enc for clsd fx
S72.134B	Nondisp apophyseal fx of rt femur, init enc for opn fx type I or II
S72.134C	Nondisp apophyseal fx of rt femur, init enc for opn fx type IIIA, IIIB, or IIIC
S72.136A	Nondisp apophyseal fx of unsp femur, init enc for clsd fx
S72.136B	Nondisp apophyseal fx of unsp femur, init enc for opn fx type I or II
S72.136C	Nondisp apophyseal fx of unsp femur, init enc for opn fx type IIIA, IIIB, or IIIC
S72.065A	Nondisp articular fx of head of lt femur, init enc for clsd fx
S72.065B	Nondisp articular fx of head of lt femur, init enc for opn fx type I or II
S72.065C	Nondisp articular fx of head of lt femur, init enc for opn fx type IIIA, IIIB, or IIIC
S72.064A	Nondisp articular fx of head of rt femur, init enc for clsd fx
S72.064B	Nondisp articular fx of head of rt femur, init enc for opn fx type I or II
S72.064C	Nondisp articular fx of head of rt femur, init enc for opn fx type IIIA, IIIB, or IIIC
S72.066A	Nondisp articular fx of head of unsp femur, init enc for clsd fx
S72.066B	Nondisp articular fx of head of unsp femur, init enc for opn fx type I or II
S72.066C	Nondisp articular fx of head of unsp femur, init enc for opn fx type IIIA, IIIB, or IIIC
S32.465A	Nondisp associated transv-post fx of lt acetab, init enc for clsd fx
S32.465B	Nondisp associated transv-post fx of lt acetab, init enc for opn fx
S32.464A	Nondisp associated transv-post fx of rt acetab, init enc for clsd fx
S32.464B	Nondisp associated transv-post fx of rt acetab, init enc for opn fx
S32.466A	Nondisp associated transv-post fx of unsp acetab, init enc for clsd fx
S32.466B	Nondisp associated transv-post fx of unsp acetab, init enc for opn fx
S32.315B	Nondisp avulsion fx of lt ilium, init enc for opn fx
S32.615B	Nondisp avulsion fx of lt ischium, init enc for opn fx
S32.314B	Nondisp avulsion fx of rt ilium, init enc for opn fx
S32.614B	Nondisp avulsion fx of rt ischium, init enc for opn fx
S32.316B	Nondisp avulsion fx of unsp ilium, init enc for opn fx
S32.616B	Nondisp avulsion fx of unsp ischium, init enc for opn fx
S82.145B	Nondisp bicondylar fx of lt tibia, init enc for opn fx type I or II
S82.145C	Nondisp bicondylar fx of lt tibia, init enc for opn fx type IIIA, IIIB, or IIIC
S82.144B	Nondisp bicondylar fx of rt tibia, init enc for opn fx type I or II
S82.144C	Nondisp bicondylar fx of rt tibia, init enc for opn fx type IIIA, IIIB, or IIIC
S82.146B	Nondisp bicondylar fx of unsp tibia, init enc for opn fx type I or II
S82.146C	Nondisp bicondylar fx of unsp tibia, init enc for opn fx type IIIA, IIIB, or IIIC
S42.355B	Nondisp comm fx of shaft of humerus, lt arm, init enc for opn fx
S42.354B	Nondisp comm fx of shaft of humerus, rt arm, init enc for opn fx
S42.356B	Nondisp comm fx of shaft of humerus, unsp arm, init enc for opn fx
S72.355A	Nondisp comm fx of shaft of lt femur, init enc for clsd fx
S72.355B	Nondisp comm fx of shaft of lt femur, init enc for opn fx type I or II
S72.355C	Nondisp comm fx of shaft of lt femur, init enc for opn fx type IIIA, IIIB, or IIIC
S82.455B	Nondisp comm fx of shaft of lt fibula, init enc for opn fx type I or II
S82.455C	Nondisp comm fx of shaft of lt fibula, init enc for opn fx type IIIA, IIIB, or IIIC
S82.255B	Nondisp comm fx of shaft of lt tibia, init enc for opn fx type I or II
S82.255C	Nondisp comm fx of shaft of lt tibia, init enc for opn fx type IIIA, IIIB, or IIIC
S52.355B	Nondisp comm fx of shaft of radius, lt arm, init enc for opn fx type I or II
S52.355C	Nondisp comm fx of shaft of radius, lt arm, init enc for opn fx type IIIA, IIIB, or IIIC
S52.354B	Nondisp comm fx of shaft of radius, rt arm, init enc for opn fx type I or II
S52.354C	Nondisp comm fx of shaft of radius, rt arm, init enc for opn fx type IIIA, IIIB, or IIIC
S52.356B	Nondisp comm fx of shaft of radius, unsp arm, init enc for opn fx type I or II
S52.356C	Nondisp comm fx of shaft of radius, unsp arm, init enc for opn fx type IIIA, IIIB, or IIIC

S72.354A	Nondisp comm fx of shaft of rt femur, init enc for clsd fx
S72.354B	Nondisp comm fx of shaft of rt femur, init enc for opn fx type I or II
S72.354C	Nondisp comm fx of shaft of rt femur, init enc for opn fx type IIIA, IIIB, or IIIC
S82.454B	Nondisp comm fx of shaft of rt fibula, init enc for opn fx type I or II
S82.454C	Nondisp comm fx of shaft of rt fibula, init enc for opn fx type IIIA, IIIB, or IIIC
S82.254B	Nondisp comm fx of shaft of rt tibia, init enc for opn fx type I or II
S82.254C	Nondisp comm fx of shaft of rt tibia, init enc for opn fx type IIIA, IIIB, or IIIC
S52.255B	Nondisp comm fx of shaft of ulna, lt arm, init enc for opn fx type I or II
S52.255C	Nondisp comm fx of shaft of ulna, lt arm, init enc for opn fx type IIIA, IIIB, or IIIC
S52.254B	Nondisp comm fx of shaft of ulna, rt arm, init enc for opn fx type I or II
S52.254C	Nondisp comm fx of shaft of ulna, rt arm, init enc for opn fx type IIIA, IIIB, or IIIC
S52.256B	Nondisp comm fx of shaft of ulna, unsp arm, init enc for opn fx type I or II
S52.256C	Nondisp comm fx of shaft of ulna, unsp arm, init enc for opn fx type IIIA, IIIB, or IIIC
S72.356A	Nondisp comm fx of shaft of unsp femur, init enc for clsd fx
S72.356B	Nondisp comm fx of shaft of unsp femur, init enc for opn fx type I or II
S72.356C	Nondisp comm fx of shaft of unsp femur, init enc for opn fx type IIIA, IIIB, or IIIC
S82.456B	Nondisp comm fx of shaft of unsp fibula, init enc for opn fx type I or II
S82.456C	Nondisp comm fx of shaft of unsp fibula, init enc for opn fx type IIIA, IIIB, or IIIC
S82.256B	Nondisp comm fx of shaft of unsp tibia, init enc for opn fx type I or II
S82.256C	Nondisp comm fx of shaft of unsp tibia, init enc for opn fx type IIIA, IIIB, or IIIC
S42.425B	Nondisp comm supracondylar fx w/o intercondylar fx of lt humerus, init enc for opn fx
S42.424B	Nondisp comm supracondylar fx w/o intercondylar fx of rt humerus, init enc for opn fx
S42.426B	Nondisp comm supracondylar fx w/o intercondylar fx of unsp humerus, init enc for opn fx
S32.485A	Nondisp dome fx of lt acetab, init enc for clsd fx
S32.485B	Nondisp dome fx of lt acetab, init enc for opn fx
S32.484A	Nondisp dome fx of rt acetab, init enc for clsd fx
S32.484B	Nondisp dome fx of rt acetab, init enc for opn fx
S32.486A	Nondisp dome fx of unsp acetab, init enc for clsd fx
S32.486B	Nondisp dome fx of unsp acetab, init enc for opn fx
S42.435B	Nondisp fx (avulsion) of lat epicondyle of lt humerus, init enc for opn fx
S42.434B	Nondisp fx (avulsion) of lat epicondyle of rt humerus, init enc for opn fx
S42.436B	Nondisp fx (avulsion) of lat epicondyle of unsp humerus, init enc for opn fx
S42.445B	Nondisp fx (avulsion) of med epicondyle of lt humerus, init enc for opn fx
S42.444B	Nondisp fx (avulsion) of med epicondyle of rt humerus, init enc for opn fx
S42.446B	Nondisp fx (avulsion) of med epicondyle of unsp humerus, init enc for opn fx
S32.435A	Nondisp fx of ant column [iliopubic] of lt acetab, init enc for clsd fx
S32.435B	Nondisp fx of ant column [iliopubic] of lt acetab, init enc for opn fx
S32.434A	Nondisp fx of ant column [iliopubic] of rt acetab, init enc for clsd fx
S32.434B	Nondisp fx of ant column [iliopubic] of rt acetab, init enc for opn fx
S32.436A	Nondisp fx of ant column [iliopubic] of unsp acetab, init enc for clsd fx
S32.436B	Nondisp fx of ant column [iliopubic] of unsp acetab, init enc for opn fx
S32.415A	Nondisp fx of ant wall of lt acetab, init enc for clsd fx
S32.415B	Nondisp fx of ant wall of lt acetab, init enc for opn fx
S32.414A	Nondisp fx of ant wall of rt acetab, init enc for clsd fx
S32.414B	Nondisp fx of ant wall of rt acetab, init enc for opn fx
S32.416A	Nondisp fx of ant wall of unsp acetab, init enc for clsd fx
S32.416B	Nondisp fx of ant wall of unsp acetab, init enc for opn fx
S72.045A	Nondisp fx of base of neck of lt femur, init enc for clsd fx
S72.045B	Nondisp fx of base of neck of lt femur, init enc for opn fx type I or II
S72.045C	Nondisp fx of base of neck of lt femur, init enc for opn fx type IIIA, IIIB, or IIIC
S72.044A	Nondisp fx of base of neck of rt femur, init enc for clsd fx
S72.044B	Nondisp fx of base of neck of rt femur, init enc for opn fx type I or II
S72.044C	Nondisp fx of base of neck of rt femur, init enc for opn fx type IIIA, IIIC
S72.046A	Nondisp fx of base of neck of unsp femur, init enc for clsd fx
S72.046B	Nondisp fx of base of neck of unsp femur, init enc for opn fx type I or II
S72.046C	Nondisp fx of base of neck of unsp femur, init enc for opn fx type IIIA, IIIB, or IIIC
S52.045B	Nondisp fx of coronoid process of lt ulna, init enc for opn fx type I or II
S52.045C	Nondisp fx of coronoid process of lt ulna, init enc for opn fx type IIIA, IIIB, or IIIC
S52.044B	Nondisp fx of coronoid process of rt ulna, init enc for opn fx type I or II
S52.044C	Nondisp fx of coronoid process of rt ulna, init enc for opn fx type IIIA, IIIB, or IIIC
S52.046B	Nondisp fx of coronoid process of unsp ulna, init enc for opn fx type I or II
S52.046C	Nondisp fx of coronoid process of unsp ulna, init enc for opn fx type IIIA, IIIB, or IIIC
S72.025A	Nondisp fx of epiphysis (separation) (upr) of lt femur, init enc for clsd fx
S72.025B	Nondisp fx of epiphysis (separation) (upr) of lt femur, init enc for opn fx type I or II
S72.025C	Nondisp fx of epiphysis (separation) (upr) of lt femur, init enc for opn fx type IIIA, IIIB, or IIIC
S72.024A	Nondisp fx of epiphysis (separation) (upr) of rt femur, init enc for clsd fx
S72.024B	Nondisp fx of epiphysis (separation) (upr) of rt femur, init enc for opn fx type I or II
S72.024C	Nondisp fx of epiphysis (separation) (upr) of rt femur, init enc for opn fx type IIIA, IIIB, or IIIC
S72.026A	Nondisp fx of epiphysis (separation) (upr) of unsp femur, init enc for clsd fx
S72.026B	Nondisp fx of epiphysis (separation) (upr) of unsp femur, init enc for opn fx type I or II
S72.026C	Nondisp fx of epiphysis (separation) (upr) of unsp femur, init enc for opn fx type IIIA, IIIB, or IIIC
S72.115A	Nondisp fx of greater trochanter of lt femur, init enc for clsd fx
S72.115B	Nondisp fx of greater trochanter of lt femur, init enc for opn fx type I or II
S72.115C	Nondisp fx of greater trochanter of lt femur, init enc for opn fx type IIIA, IIIB, or IIIC
S72.114A	Nondisp fx of greater trochanter of rt femur, init enc for clsd fx
S72.114B	Nondisp fx of greater trochanter of rt femur, init enc for opn fx type I or II
S72.114C	Nondisp fx of greater trochanter of rt femur, init enc for opn fx type IIIA, IIIB, or IIIC
S72.116A	Nondisp fx of greater trochanter of unsp femur, init enc for clsd fx
S72.116B	Nondisp fx of greater trochanter of unsp femur, init enc for opn fx type I or II
S72.116C	Nondisp fx of greater trochanter of unsp femur, init enc for opn fx type IIIA, IIIB, or IIIC
S42.255B	Nondisp fx of greater tuberosity of lt humerus, init enc for opn fx
S42.254B	Nondisp fx of greater tuberosity of rt humerus, init enc for opn fx
S42.256B	Nondisp fx of greater tuberosity of unsp humerus, init enc for opn fx
S52.125B	Nondisp fx of head of lt radius, init enc for opn fx type I or II
S52.125C	Nondisp fx of head of lt radius, init enc for opn fx type IIIA, IIIB, or IIIC
S52.124B	Nondisp fx of head of rt radius, init enc for opn fx type I or II
S52.124C	Nondisp fx of head of rt radius, init enc for opn fx type IIIA, IIIB, or IIIC
S52.126B	Nondisp fx of head of unsp radius, init enc for opn fx type I or II
S52.126C	Nondisp fx of head of unsp radius, init enc for opn fx type IIIA, IIIB, or IIIC
S72.425B	Nondisp fx of lat condyle of lt femur, init enc for opn fx type I or II
S72.425C	Nondisp fx of lat condyle of lt femur, init enc for opn fx type IIIA, IIIB, or IIIC
S42.455B	Nondisp fx of lat condyle of lt humerus, init enc for opn fx
S82.125B	Nondisp fx of lat condyle of lt tibia, init enc for opn fx type I or II
S82.125C	Nondisp fx of lat condyle of lt tibia, init enc for opn fx type IIIA, IIIB, or IIIC
S72.424B	Nondisp fx of lat condyle of rt femur, init enc for opn fx type I or II
S72.424C	Nondisp fx of lat condyle of rt femur, init enc for opn fx type IIIA, IIIB, or IIIC
S42.454B	Nondisp fx of lat condyle of rt humerus, init enc for opn fx
S82.124B	Nondisp fx of lat condyle of rt tibia, init enc for opn fx type I or II
S82.124C	Nondisp fx of lat condyle of rt tibia, init enc for opn fx type IIIA, IIIB, or IIIC
S72.426B	Nondisp fx of lat condyle of unsp femur, init enc for opn fx type I or II
S72.426C	Nondisp fx of lat condyle of unsp femur, init enc for opn fx type IIIA, IIIB, or IIIC
S42.456B	Nondisp fx of lat condyle of unsp humerus, init enc for opn fx
S82.126B	Nondisp fx of lat condyle of unsp tibia, init enc for opn fx type I or II
S82.126C	Nondisp fx of lat condyle of unsp tibia, init enc for opn fx type IIIA, IIIB, or IIIC
S72.125A	Nondisp fx of lesser trochanter of lt femur, init enc for clsd fx
S72.125B	Nondisp fx of lesser trochanter of lt femur, init enc for opn fx type I or II
S72.125C	Nondisp fx of lesser trochanter of lt femur, init enc for opn fx type IIIA, IIIB, or IIIC
S72.124A	Nondisp fx of lesser trochanter of rt femur, init enc for clsd fx
S72.124B	Nondisp fx of lesser trochanter of rt femur, init enc for opn fx type I or II
S72.124C	Nondisp fx of lesser trochanter of rt femur, init enc for opn fx type IIIA, IIIB, or IIIC
S72.126A	Nondisp fx of lesser trochanter of unsp femur, init enc for clsd fx
S72.126B	Nondisp fx of lesser trochanter of unsp femur, init enc for opn fx type I or II
S72.126C	Nondisp fx of lesser trochanter of unsp femur, init enc for opn fx type IIIA, IIIB, or IIIC

S42.265B	Nondisp fx of lesser tuberosity of lt humerus, init enc for opn fx
S42.264B	Nondisp fx of lesser tuberosity of rt humerus, init enc for opn fx
S42.266B	Nondisp fx of lesser tuberosity of unsp humerus, init enc for opn fx
S52.515B	Nondisp fx of lt radial styloid process, init enc for opn fx type I or II
S52.515C	Nondisp fx of lt radial styloid process, init enc for opn fx type IIIA, IIIB, or IIIC
S82.115B	Nondisp fx of lt tibial spine, init enc for opn fx type I or II
S82.115C	Nondisp fx of lt tibial spine, init enc for opn fx type IIIA, IIIB, or IIIC
S82.155B	Nondisp fx of lt tibial tuberosity, init enc for opn fx type I or II
S82.155C	Nondisp fx of lt tibial tuberosity, init enc for opn fx type IIIA, IIIB, or IIIC
S52.615B	Nondisp fx of lt ulna styloid process, init enc for opn fx type I or II
S52.615C	Nondisp fx of lt ulna styloid process, init enc for opn fx type IIIA, IIIB, or IIIC
S72.445B	Nondisp fx of lwr epiphysis (separation) of lt femur, init enc for opn fx type I or II
S72.445C	Nondisp fx of lwr epiphysis (separation) of lt femur, init enc for opn fx type IIIA, IIIB, or IIIC
S72.444B	Nondisp fx of lwr epiphysis (separation) of rt femur, init enc for opn fx type I or II
S72.444C	Nondisp fx of lwr epiphysis (separation) of rt femur, init enc for opn fx type IIIA, IIIB, or IIIC
S72.446B	Nondisp fx of lwr epiphysis (separation) of unsp femur, init enc for opn fx type I or II
S72.446C	Nondisp fx of lwr epiphysis (separation) of unsp femur, init enc for opn fx type IIIA, IIIB, or IIIC
S72.435B	Nondisp fx of med condyle of lt femur, init enc for opn fx type I or II
S72.435C	Nondisp fx of med condyle of lt femur, init enc for opn fx type IIIA, IIIB, or IIIC
S42.465B	Nondisp fx of med condyle of lt humerus, init enc for opn fx
S82.135B	Nondisp fx of med condyle of lt tibia, init enc for opn fx type I or II
S82.135C	Nondisp fx of med condyle of lt tibia, init enc for opn fx type IIIA, IIIB, or IIIC
S72.434B	Nondisp fx of med condyle of rt femur, init enc for opn fx type I or II
S72.434C	Nondisp fx of med condyle of rt femur, init enc for opn fx type IIIA, IIIB, or IIIC
S42.464B	Nondisp fx of med condyle of rt humerus, init enc for opn fx
S82.134B	Nondisp fx of med condyle of rt tibia, init enc for opn fx type I or II
S82.134C	Nondisp fx of med condyle of rt tibia, init enc for opn fx type IIIA, IIIB, or IIIC
S72.436B	Nondisp fx of med condyle of unsp femur, init enc for opn fx type I or II
S72.436C	Nondisp fx of med condyle of unsp femur, init enc for opn fx type IIIA, IIIB, or IIIC
S42.466B	Nondisp fx of med condyle of unsp humerus, init enc for opn fx
S82.136B	Nondisp fx of med condyle of unsp tibia, init enc for opn fx type I or II
S82.136C	Nondisp fx of med condyle of unsp tibia, init enc for opn fx type IIIA, IIIB, or IIIC
S32.475A	Nondisp fx of med wall of lt acetab, init enc for clsd fx
S32.475B	Nondisp fx of med wall of lt acetab, init enc for opn fx
S32.474A	Nondisp fx of med wall of rt acetab, init enc for clsd fx
S32.474B	Nondisp fx of med wall of rt acetab, init enc for opn fx
S32.476A	Nondisp fx of med wall of unsp acetab, init enc for clsd fx
S32.476B	Nondisp fx of med wall of unsp acetab, init enc for opn fx
S52.135B	Nondisp fx of neck of lt radius, init enc for opn fx type I or II
S52.135C	Nondisp fx of neck of lt radius, init enc for opn fx type IIIA, IIIB, or IIIC
S52.134B	Nondisp fx of neck of rt radius, init enc for opn fx type I or II
S52.134C	Nondisp fx of neck of rt radius, init enc for opn fx type IIIA, IIIB, or IIIC
S52.136B	Nondisp fx of neck of unsp radius, init enc for opn fx type I or II
S52.136C	Nondisp fx of neck of unsp radius, init enc for opn fx type IIIA, IIIB, or IIIC
S52.035B	Nondisp fx of olecranon process w/ intraarticular extension of lt ulna, init enc for opn fx type I or II
S52.035C	Nondisp fx of olecranon process w/ intraarticular extension of lt ulna, init enc for opn fx type IIIA, IIIB, or IIIC
S52.034B	Nondisp fx of olecranon process w/ intraarticular extension of rt ulna, init enc for opn fx type I or II
S52.034C	Nondisp fx of olecranon process w/ intraarticular extension of rt ulna, init enc for opn fx type IIIA, IIIB, or IIIC
S52.036B	Nondisp fx of olecranon process w/ intraarticular extension of unsp ulna, init enc for opn fx type I or II
S52.036C	Nondisp fx of olecranon process w/ intraarticular extension of unsp ulna, init enc for opn fx type IIIA, IIIB, or IIIC
S52.025B	Nondisp fx of olecranon process w/o intraarticular extension of lt ulna, init enc for opn fx type I or II
S52.025C	Nondisp fx of olecranon process w/o intraarticular extension of lt ulna, init enc for opn fx type IIIA, IIIB, or IIIC
S52.024B	Nondisp fx of olecranon process w/o intraarticular extension of rt ulna, init enc for opn fx type I or II
S52.024C	Nondisp fx of olecranon process w/o intraarticular extension of rt ulna, init enc for opn fx type IIIA, IIIB, or IIIC
S52.026B	Nondisp fx of olecranon process w/o intraarticular extension of unsp ulna, init enc for opn fx type I or II
S52.026C	Nondisp fx of olecranon process w/o intraarticular extension of unsp ulna, init enc for opn fx type IIIA, IIIB, or IIIC
S32.445A	Nondisp fx of post column [ilioischial] of lt acetab, init enc for clsd fx
S32.445B	Nondisp fx of post column [ilioischial] of lt acetab, init enc for opn fx
S32.444A	Nondisp fx of post column [ilioischial] of rt acetab, init enc for clsd fx
S32.444B	Nondisp fx of post column [ilioischial] of rt acetab, init enc for opn fx
S32.446A	Nondisp fx of post column [ilioischial] of unsp acetab, init enc for clsd fx
S32.446B	Nondisp fx of post column [ilioischial] of unsp acetab, init enc for opn fx
S32.425A	Nondisp fx of post wall of lt acetab, init enc for clsd fx
S32.425B	Nondisp fx of post wall of lt acetab, init enc for opn fx
S32.424A	Nondisp fx of post wall of rt acetab, init enc for clsd fx
S32.424B	Nondisp fx of post wall of rt acetab, init enc for opn fx
S32.426A	Nondisp fx of post wall of unsp acetab, init enc for clsd fx
S32.426B	Nondisp fx of post wall of unsp acetab, init enc for opn fx
S52.514B	Nondisp fx of rt radial styloid process, init enc for opn fx type I or II
S52.514C	Nondisp fx of rt radial styloid process, init enc for opn fx type IIIA, IIIB, or IIIC
S82.114B	Nondisp fx of rt tibial spine, init enc for opn fx type I or II
S82.114C	Nondisp fx of rt tibial spine, init enc for opn fx type IIIA, IIIB, or IIIC
S82.154B	Nondisp fx of rt tibial tuberosity, init enc for opn fx type I or II
S82.154C	Nondisp fx of rt tibial tuberosity, init enc for opn fx type IIIA, IIIB, or IIIC
S52.614B	Nondisp fx of rt ulna styloid process, init enc for opn fx type I or II
S52.614C	Nondisp fx of rt ulna styloid process, init enc for opn fx type IIIA, IIIB, or IIIC
S52.516B	Nondisp fx of unsp radial styloid process, init enc for opn fx type I or II
S52.516C	Nondisp fx of unsp radial styloid process, init enc for opn fx type IIIA, IIIB, or IIIC
S82.116B	Nondisp fx of unsp tibial spine, init enc for opn fx type I or II
S82.116C	Nondisp fx of unsp tibial spine, init enc for opn fx type IIIA, IIIB, or IIIC
S82.156B	Nondisp fx of unsp tibial tuberosity, init enc for opn fx type I or II
S82.156C	Nondisp fx of unsp tibial tuberosity, init enc for opn fx type IIIA, IIIB, or IIIC
S52.616B	Nondisp fx of unsp ulna styloid process, init enc for opn fx type I or II
S52.616C	Nondisp fx of unsp ulna styloid process, init enc for opn fx type IIIA, IIIB, or IIIC
S72.145A	Nondisp intertrochanteric fx of lt femur, init enc for clsd fx
S72.145B	Nondisp intertrochanteric fx of lt femur, init enc for opn fx type I or II
S72.145C	Nondisp intertrochanteric fx of lt femur, init enc for opn fx type IIIA, IIIB, or IIIC
S72.144A	Nondisp intertrochanteric fx of rt femur, init enc for clsd fx
S72.144B	Nondisp intertrochanteric fx of rt femur, init enc for opn fx type I or II
S72.144C	Nondisp intertrochanteric fx of rt femur, init enc for opn fx type IIIA, IIIB, or IIIC
S72.146A	Nondisp intertrochanteric fx of unsp femur, init enc for clsd fx
S72.146B	Nondisp intertrochanteric fx of unsp femur, init enc for opn fx type I or II
S72.146C	Nondisp intertrochanteric fx of unsp femur, init enc for opn fx type IIIA, IIIB, or IIIC
S12.041B	Nondisp lat mass fx of 1st cervical vertebra, init enc for opn fx
S82.865B	Nondisp Maisonneuve's fx of lt leg, init enc for opn fx type I or II
S82.865C	Nondisp Maisonneuve's fx of lt leg, init enc for opn fx type IIIA, IIIB, or IIIC
S82.864B	Nondisp Maisonneuve's fx of rt leg, init enc for opn fx type I or II
S82.864C	Nondisp Maisonneuve's fx of rt leg, init enc for opn fx type IIIA, IIIB, or IIIC
S82.866B	Nondisp Maisonneuve's fx of unsp leg, init enc for opn fx type I or II
S82.866C	Nondisp Maisonneuve's fx of unsp leg, init enc for opn fx type IIIA, IIIB, or IIIC
S72.035A	Nondisp midcervical fx of lt femur, init enc for clsd fx
S72.035B	Nondisp midcervical fx of lt femur, init enc for opn fx type I or II
S72.035C	Nondisp midcervical fx of lt femur, init enc for opn fx type IIIA, IIIB, or IIIC
S72.034A	Nondisp midcervical fx of rt femur, init enc for clsd fx
S72.034B	Nondisp midcervical fx of rt femur, init enc for opn fx type I or II
S72.034C	Nondisp midcervical fx of rt femur, init enc for opn fx type IIIA, IIIB, or IIIC
S72.036A	Nondisp midcervical fx of unsp femur, init enc for clsd fx
S72.036B	Nondisp midcervical fx of unsp femur, init enc for opn fx type I or II
S72.036C	Nondisp midcervical fx of unsp femur, init enc for opn fx type IIIA, IIIB, or IIIC
S42.335B	Nondisp oblique fx of shaft of humerus, lt arm, init enc for opn fx
S42.334B	Nondisp oblique fx of shaft of humerus, rt arm, init enc for opn fx
S42.336B	Nondisp oblique fx of shaft of humerus, unsp arm, init enc for opn fx
S72.335A	Nondisp oblique fx of shaft of lt femur, init enc for clsd fx
S72.335B	Nondisp oblique fx of shaft of lt femur, init enc for opn fx type I or II
S72.335C	Nondisp oblique fx of shaft of lt femur, init enc for opn fx type IIIA, IIIB, or IIIC

S82.435B	Nondisp oblique fx of shaft of lt fibula, init enc for opn fx type I or II
S82.435C	Nondisp oblique fx of shaft of lt fibula, init enc for opn fx type IIIA, IIIB, or IIIC
S52.335B	Nondisp oblique fx of shaft of lt radius, init enc for opn fx type I or II
S52.335C	Nondisp oblique fx of shaft of lt radius, init enc for opn fx type IIIA, IIIB, or IIIC
S82.235B	Nondisp oblique fx of shaft of lt tibia, init enc for opn fx type I or II
S82.235C	Nondisp oblique fx of shaft of lt tibia, init enc for opn fx type IIIA, IIIB, or IIIC
S52.235B	Nondisp oblique fx of shaft of lt ulna, init enc for opn fx type I or II
S52.235C	Nondisp oblique fx of shaft of lt ulna, init enc for opn fx type IIIA, IIIB, or IIIC
S72.334A	Nondisp oblique fx of shaft of rt femur, init enc for clsd fx
S72.334B	Nondisp oblique fx of shaft of rt femur, init enc for opn fx type I or II
S72.334C	Nondisp oblique fx of shaft of rt femur, init enc for opn fx type IIIA, IIIB, or IIIC
S82.434B	Nondisp oblique fx of shaft of rt fibula, init enc for opn fx type I or II
S82.434C	Nondisp oblique fx of shaft of rt fibula, init enc for opn fx type IIIA, IIIB, or IIIC
S52.334B	Nondisp oblique fx of shaft of rt radius, init enc for opn fx type I or II
S52.334C	Nondisp oblique fx of shaft of rt radius, init enc for opn fx type IIIA, IIIB, or IIIC
S82.234B	Nondisp oblique fx of shaft of rt tibia, init enc for opn fx type I or II
S82.234C	Nondisp oblique fx of shaft of rt tibia, init enc for opn fx type IIIA, IIIB, or IIIC
S52.234B	Nondisp oblique fx of shaft of rt ulna, init enc for opn fx type I or II
S52.234C	Nondisp oblique fx of shaft of rt ulna, init enc for opn fx type IIIA, IIIB, or IIIC
S72.336A	Nondisp oblique fx of shaft of unsp femur, init enc for clsd fx
S72.336B	Nondisp oblique fx of shaft of unsp femur, init enc for opn fx type I or II
S72.336C	Nondisp oblique fx of shaft of unsp femur, init enc for opn fx type IIIA, IIIB, or IIIC
S82.436B	Nondisp oblique fx of shaft of unsp fibula, init enc for opn fx type I or II
S82.436C	Nondisp oblique fx of shaft of unsp fibula, init enc for opn fx type IIIA, IIIB, or IIIC
S52.336B	Nondisp oblique fx of shaft of unsp radius, init enc for opn fx type I or II
S52.336C	Nondisp oblique fx of shaft of unsp radius, init enc for opn fx type IIIA, IIIB, or IIIC
S82.236B	Nondisp oblique fx of shaft of unsp tibia, init enc for opn fx type I or II
S82.236C	Nondisp oblique fx of shaft of unsp tibia, init enc for opn fx type IIIA, IIIB, or IIIC
S52.236B	Nondisp oblique fx of shaft of unsp ulna, init enc for opn fx type I or II
S52.236C	Nondisp oblique fx of shaft of unsp ulna, init enc for opn fx type IIIA, IIIB, or IIIC
S12.031B	Nondisp post arch fx of 1st cervical vertebra, init enc for opn fx
S42.365B	Nondisp segmental fx of shaft of humerus, lt arm, init enc for opn fx
S42.364B	Nondisp segmental fx of shaft of humerus, rt arm, init enc for opn fx
S42.366B	Nondisp segmental fx of shaft of humerus, unsp arm, init enc for opn fx
S72.365A	Nondisp segmental fx of shaft of lt femur, init enc for clsd fx
S72.365B	Nondisp segmental fx of shaft of lt femur, init enc for opn fx type I or II
S72.365C	Nondisp segmental fx of shaft of lt femur, init enc for opn fx type IIIA, IIIB, or IIIC
S82.465B	Nondisp segmental fx of shaft of lt fibula, init enc for opn fx type I or II
S82.465C	Nondisp segmental fx of shaft of lt fibula, init enc for opn fx type IIIA, IIIB, or IIIC
S82.265B	Nondisp segmental fx of shaft of lt tibia, init enc for opn fx type I or II
S82.265C	Nondisp segmental fx of shaft of lt tibia, init enc for opn fx type IIIA, IIIB, or IIIC
S52.365B	Nondisp segmental fx of shaft of radius, lt arm, init enc for opn fx type I or II
S52.365C	Nondisp segmental fx of shaft of radius, lt arm, init enc for opn fx type IIIA, IIIB, or IIIC
S52.364B	Nondisp segmental fx of shaft of radius, rt arm, init enc for opn fx type I or II
S52.364C	Nondisp segmental fx of shaft of radius, rt arm, init enc for opn fx type IIIA, IIIB, or IIIC
S52.366B	Nondisp segmental fx of shaft of radius, unsp arm, init enc for opn fx type I or II
S52.366C	Nondisp segmental fx of shaft of radius, unsp arm, init enc for opn fx type IIIA, IIIB, or IIIC
S72.364A	Nondisp segmental fx of shaft of rt femur, init enc for clsd fx
S72.364B	Nondisp segmental fx of shaft of rt femur, init enc for opn fx type I or II
S72.364C	Nondisp segmental fx of shaft of rt femur, init enc for opn fx type IIIA, IIIB, or IIIC
S82.464B	Nondisp segmental fx of shaft of rt fibula, init enc for opn fx type I or II
S82.464C	Nondisp segmental fx of shaft of rt fibula, init enc for opn fx type IIIA, IIIB, or IIIC
S82.264B	Nondisp segmental fx of shaft of rt tibia, init enc for opn fx type I or II
S82.264C	Nondisp segmental fx of shaft of rt tibia, init enc for opn fx type IIIA, IIIB, or IIIC
S52.265B	Nondisp segmental fx of shaft of ulna, lt arm, init enc for opn fx type I or II
S52.265C	Nondisp segmental fx of shaft of ulna, lt arm, init enc for opn fx type IIIA, IIIB, or IIIC
S52.264B	Nondisp segmental fx of shaft of ulna, rt arm, init enc for opn fx type I or II
S52.264C	Nondisp segmental fx of shaft of ulna, rt arm, init enc for opn fx type IIIA, IIIB, or IIIC
S52.266B	Nondisp segmental fx of shaft of ulna, unsp arm, init enc for opn fx type I or II
S52.266C	Nondisp segmental fx of shaft of ulna, unsp arm, init enc for opn fx type IIIA, IIIB, or IIIC
S72.366A	Nondisp segmental fx of shaft of unsp femur, init enc for clsd fx
S72.366B	Nondisp segmental fx of shaft of unsp femur, init enc for opn fx type I or II
S72.366C	Nondisp segmental fx of shaft of unsp femur, init enc for opn fx type IIIA, IIIB, or IIIC
S82.466B	Nondisp segmental fx of shaft of unsp fibula, init enc for opn fx type I or II
S82.466C	Nondisp segmental fx of shaft of unsp fibula, init enc for opn fx type IIIA, IIIB, or IIIC
S82.266B	Nondisp segmental fx of shaft of unsp tibia, init enc for opn fx type I or II
S82.266C	Nondisp segmental fx of shaft of unsp tibia, init enc for opn fx type IIIA, IIIB, or IIIC
S42.415B	Nondisp simple supracondylar fx w/o intercondylar fx of lt humerus, init enc for opn fx
S42.414B	Nondisp simple supracondylar fx w/o intercondylar fx of rt humerus, init enc for opn fx
S42.416B	Nondisp simple supracondylar fx w/o intercondylar fx of unsp humerus, init enc for opn fx
S42.345B	Nondisp spiral fx of shaft of humerus, lt arm, init enc for opn fx
S42.344B	Nondisp spiral fx of shaft of humerus, rt arm, init enc for opn fx
S42.346B	Nondisp spiral fx of shaft of humerus, unsp arm, init enc for opn fx
S72.345A	Nondisp spiral fx of shaft of lt femur, init enc for clsd fx
S72.345B	Nondisp spiral fx of shaft of lt femur, init enc for opn fx type I or II
S72.345C	Nondisp spiral fx of shaft of lt femur, init enc for opn fx type IIIA, IIIB, or IIIC
S82.445B	Nondisp spiral fx of shaft of lt fibula, init enc for opn fx type I or II
S82.445C	Nondisp spiral fx of shaft of lt fibula, init enc for opn fx type IIIA, IIIB, or IIIC
S82.245B	Nondisp spiral fx of shaft of lt tibia, init enc for opn fx type I or II
S82.245C	Nondisp spiral fx of shaft of lt tibia, init enc for opn fx type IIIA, IIIB, or IIIC
S52.345B	Nondisp spiral fx of shaft of radius, lt arm, init enc for opn fx type I or II
S52.345C	Nondisp spiral fx of shaft of radius, lt arm, init enc for opn fx type IIIA, IIIB, or IIIC
S52.344B	Nondisp spiral fx of shaft of radius, rt arm, init enc for opn fx type I or II
S52.344C	Nondisp spiral fx of shaft of radius, rt arm, init enc for opn fx type IIIA, IIIB, or IIIC
S52.346B	Nondisp spiral fx of shaft of radius, unsp arm, init enc for opn fx type I or II
S52.346C	Nondisp spiral fx of shaft of radius, unsp arm, init enc for opn fx type IIIA, IIIB, or IIIC
S72.344A	Nondisp spiral fx of shaft of rt femur, init enc for clsd fx
S72.344B	Nondisp spiral fx of shaft of rt femur, init enc for opn fx type I or II
S72.344C	Nondisp spiral fx of shaft of rt femur, init enc for opn fx type IIIA, IIIB, or IIIC
S82.444B	Nondisp spiral fx of shaft of rt fibula, init enc for opn fx type I or II
S82.444C	Nondisp spiral fx of shaft of rt fibula, init enc for opn fx type IIIA, IIIB, or IIIC
S82.244B	Nondisp spiral fx of shaft of rt tibia, init enc for opn fx type I or II
S82.244C	Nondisp spiral fx of shaft of rt tibia, init enc for opn fx type IIIA, IIIB, or IIIC
S52.245B	Nondisp spiral fx of shaft of ulna, lt arm, init enc for opn fx type I or II
S52.245C	Nondisp spiral fx of shaft of ulna, lt arm, init enc for opn fx type IIIA, IIIB, or IIIC
S52.244B	Nondisp spiral fx of shaft of ulna, rt arm, init enc for opn fx type I or II
S52.244C	Nondisp spiral fx of shaft of ulna, rt arm, init enc for opn fx type IIIA, IIIB, or IIIC
S52.246B	Nondisp spiral fx of shaft of ulna, unsp arm, init enc for opn fx type I or II
S52.246C	Nondisp spiral fx of shaft of ulna, unsp arm, init enc for opn fx type IIIA, IIIB, or IIIC
S72.346A	Nondisp spiral fx of shaft of unsp femur, init enc for clsd fx
S72.346B	Nondisp spiral fx of shaft of unsp femur, init enc for opn fx type I or II
S72.346C	Nondisp spiral fx of shaft of unsp femur, init enc for opn fx type IIIA, IIIB, or IIIC
S82.446B	Nondisp spiral fx of shaft of unsp fibula, init enc for opn fx type I or II
S82.446C	Nondisp spiral fx of shaft of unsp fibula, init enc for opn fx type IIIA, IIIB, or IIIC

S82.246B	Nondisp spiral fx of shaft of unsp tibia, init enc for opn fx type I or II
S82.246C	Nondisp spiral fx of shaft of unsp tibia, init enc for opn fx type IIIA, IIIB, or IIIC
S72.25XA	Nondisp subtrochanteric fx of lt femur, init enc for clsd fx
S72.25XB	Nondisp subtrochanteric fx of lt femur, init enc for opn fx type I or II
S72.25XC	Nondisp subtrochanteric fx of lt femur, init enc for opn fx type IIIA, IIIB, or IIIC
S72.24XA	Nondisp subtrochanteric fx of rt femur, init enc for clsd fx
S72.24XB	Nondisp subtrochanteric fx of rt femur, init enc for opn fx type I or II
S72.24XC	Nondisp subtrochanteric fx of rt femur, init enc for opn fx type IIIA, IIIB, or IIIC
S72.26XA	Nondisp subtrochanteric fx of unsp femur, init enc for clsd fx
S72.26XB	Nondisp subtrochanteric fx of unsp femur, init enc for opn fx type I or II
S72.26XC	Nondisp subtrochanteric fx of unsp femur, init enc for opn fx type IIIA, IIIB, or IIIC
S72.465B	Nondisp supracondylar fx w/ intracondylar extension of lwr end of lt femur, init enc for opn fx type I or II
S72.465C	Nondisp supracondylar fx w/ intracondylar extension of lwr end of lt femur, init enc for opn fx type IIIA, IIIB, or IIIC
S72.464B	Nondisp supracondylar fx w/ intracondylar extension of lwr end of rt femur, init enc for opn fx type I or II
S72.464C	Nondisp supracondylar fx w/ intracondylar extension of lwr end of rt femur, init enc for opn fx type IIIA, IIIB, or IIIC
S72.466B	Nondisp supracondylar fx w/ intracondylar extension of lwr end of unsp femur, init enc for opn fx type I or II
S72.466C	Nondisp supracondylar fx w/ intracondylar extension of lwr end of unsp femur, init enc for opn fx type IIIA, IIIB, or IIIC
S72.455B	Nondisp supracondylar fx w/o intracondylar extension of lwr end of lt femur, init enc for opn fx type I or II
S72.455C	Nondisp supracondylar fx w/o intracondylar extension of lwr end of lt femur, init enc for opn fx type IIIA, IIIB, or IIIC
S72.454B	Nondisp supracondylar fx w/o intracondylar extension of lwr end of rt femur, init enc for opn fx type I or II
S72.454C	Nondisp supracondylar fx w/o intracondylar extension of lwr end of rt femur, init enc for opn fx type IIIA, IIIB, or IIIC
S72.456B	Nondisp supracondylar fx w/o intracondylar extension of lwr end of unsp femur, init enc for opn fx type I or II
S72.456C	Nondisp supracondylar fx w/o intracondylar extension of lwr end of unsp femur, init enc for opn fx type IIIA, IIIB, or IIIC
S42.475B	Nondisp transcondylar fx of lt humerus, init enc for opn fx
S42.474B	Nondisp transcondylar fx of rt humerus, init enc for opn fx
S42.476B	Nondisp transcondylar fx of unsp humerus, init enc for opn fx
S32.455A	Nondisp transv fx of lt acetab, init enc for clsd fx
S32.455B	Nondisp transv fx of lt acetab, init enc for opn fx
S32.454A	Nondisp transv fx of rt acetab, init enc for clsd fx
S32.454B	Nondisp transv fx of rt acetab, init enc for opn fx
S42.325B	Nondisp transv fx of shaft of humerus, lt arm, init enc for opn fx
S42.324B	Nondisp transv fx of shaft of humerus, rt arm, init enc for opn fx
S42.326B	Nondisp transv fx of shaft of humerus, unsp arm, init enc for opn fx
S72.325A	Nondisp transv fx of shaft of lt femur, init enc for clsd fx
S72.325B	Nondisp transv fx of shaft of lt femur, init enc for opn fx type I or II
S72.325C	Nondisp transv fx of shaft of lt femur, init enc for opn fx type IIIA, IIIB, or IIIC
S82.425B	Nondisp transv fx of shaft of lt fibula, init enc for opn fx type I or II
S82.425C	Nondisp transv fx of shaft of lt fibula, init enc for opn fx type IIIA, IIIB, or IIIC
S52.325B	Nondisp transv fx of shaft of lt radius, init enc for opn fx type I or II
S52.325C	Nondisp transv fx of shaft of lt radius, init enc for opn fx type IIIA, IIIB, or IIIC
S82.225B	Nondisp transv fx of shaft of lt tibia, init enc for opn fx type I or II
S82.225C	Nondisp transv fx of shaft of lt tibia, init enc for opn fx type IIIA, IIIB, or IIIC
S52.225B	Nondisp transv fx of shaft of lt ulna, init enc for opn fx type I or II
S52.225C	Nondisp transv fx of shaft of lt ulna, init enc for opn fx type IIIA, IIIB, or IIIC
S72.324A	Nondisp transv fx of shaft of rt femur, init enc for clsd fx
S72.324B	Nondisp transv fx of shaft of rt femur, init enc for opn fx type I or II
S72.324C	Nondisp transv fx of shaft of rt femur, init enc for opn fx type IIIA, IIIB, or IIIC
S82.424B	Nondisp transv fx of shaft of rt fibula, init enc for opn fx type I or II
S82.424C	Nondisp transv fx of shaft of rt fibula, init enc for opn fx type IIIA, IIIB, or IIIC
S52.324B	Nondisp transv fx of shaft of rt radius, init enc for opn fx type I or II
S52.324C	Nondisp transv fx of shaft of rt radius, init enc for opn fx type IIIA, IIIB, or IIIC
S82.224B	Nondisp transv fx of shaft of rt tibia, init enc for opn fx type I or II
S82.224C	Nondisp transv fx of shaft of rt tibia, init enc for opn fx type IIIA, IIIB, or IIIC
S52.224B	Nondisp transv fx of shaft of rt ulna, init enc for opn fx type I or II

S52.224C	Nondisp transv fx of shaft of rt ulna, init enc for opn fx type IIIA, IIIB, or IIIC
S72.326A	Nondisp transv fx of shaft of unsp femur, init enc for clsd fx
S72.326B	Nondisp transv fx of shaft of unsp femur, init enc for opn fx type I or II
S72.326C	Nondisp transv fx of shaft of unsp femur, init enc for opn fx type IIIA, IIIB, or IIIC
S82.426B	Nondisp transv fx of shaft of unsp fibula, init enc for opn fx type I or II
S82.426C	Nondisp transv fx of shaft of unsp fibula, init enc for opn fx type IIIA, IIIB, or IIIC
S52.326B	Nondisp transv fx of shaft of unsp radius, init enc for opn fx type I or II
S52.326C	Nondisp transv fx of shaft of unsp radius, init enc for opn fx type IIIA, IIIB, or IIIC
S82.226B	Nondisp transv fx of shaft of unsp tibia, init enc for opn fx type I or II
S82.226C	Nondisp transv fx of shaft of unsp tibia, init enc for opn fx type IIIA, IIIB, or IIIC
S52.226B	Nondisp transv fx of shaft of unsp ulna, init enc for opn fx type I or II
S52.226C	Nondisp transv fx of shaft of unsp ulna, init enc for opn fx type IIIA, IIIB, or IIIC
S32.456A	Nondisp transv fx of unsp acetab, init enc for clsd fx
S32.456B	Nondisp transv fx of unsp acetab, init enc for opn fx
S12.112B	Nondisp Type II dens fx, init enc for opn fx
S72.415B	Nondisp unsp condyle fx of lwr end of lt femur, init enc for opn fx type I or II
S72.415C	Nondisp unsp condyle fx of lwr end of lt femur, init enc for opn fx type IIIA, IIIB, or IIIC
S72.414B	Nondisp unsp condyle fx of lwr end of rt femur, init enc for opn fx type I or II
S72.414C	Nondisp unsp condyle fx of lwr end of rt femur, init enc for opn fx type IIIA, IIIB, or IIIC
S72.416B	Nondisp unsp condyle fx of lwr end of unsp femur, init enc for opn fx type I or II
S72.416C	Nondisp unsp condyle fx of lwr end of unsp femur, init enc for opn fx type IIIA, IIIB, or IIIC
S32.110B	Nondisp Zone I fx of sacrum, init enc for opn fx
S32.120B	Nondisp Zone II fx of sacrum, init enc for opn fx
S32.130B	Nondisp Zone III fx of sacrum, init enc for opn fx
G03.0	Nonpyogenic meningitis
I62.01	Nontraumatic acute subdural hemor
I62.03	Nontraumatic chr subdural hemor
I62.1	Nontraumatic extradural hemor
I61.3	Nontraumatic intracerebral hemor in brain stem
I61.4	Nontraumatic intracerebral hemor in cerebellum
I61.1	Nontraumatic intracerebral hemor in hemisphere, cortical
I61.0	Nontraumatic intracerebral hemor in hemisphere, subcortical
I61.2	Nontraumatic intracerebral hemor in hemisphere, unsp
I61.5	Nontraumatic intracerebral hemor, intraventricular
I61.6	Nontraumatic intracerebral hemor, multi localized
I61.9	Nontraumatic intracerebral hemor, unsp
I62.02	Nontraumatic subacute subdural hemor
I60.4	Nontraumatic subarachnoid hemor from basilar artery
I60.22	Nontraumatic subarachnoid hemor from lt ant communicating artery
I60.02	Nontraumatic subarachnoid hemor from lt carotid siphon & bifurcation
I60.12	Nontraumatic subarachnoid hemor from lt mid cerebral artery
I60.32	Nontraumatic subarachnoid hemor from lt post communicating artery
I60.52	Nontraumatic subarachnoid hemor from lt vert artery
I60.6	Nontraumatic subarachnoid hemor from oth intracranial arteries
I60.21	Nontraumatic subarachnoid hemor from rt ant communicating artery
I60.01	Nontraumatic subarachnoid hemor from rt carotid siphon & bifurcation
I60.11	Nontraumatic subarachnoid hemor from rt mid cerebral artery
I60.31	Nontraumatic subarachnoid hemor from rt post communicating artery
I60.51	Nontraumatic subarachnoid hemor from rt vert artery
I60.20	Nontraumatic subarachnoid hemor from unsp ant communicating artery
I60.00	Nontraumatic subarachnoid hemor from unsp carotid siphon & bifurcation
I60.7	Nontraumatic subarachnoid hemor from unsp intracranial artery
I60.10	Nontraumatic subarachnoid hemor from unsp mid cerebral artery
I60.30	Nontraumatic subarachnoid hemor from unsp post communicating artery
I60.50	Nontraumatic subarachnoid hemor from unsp vert artery
I60.9	Nontraumatic subarachnoid hemor, unsp
I62.00	Nontraumatic subdural hemor, unsp
E41	Nutritional marasmus
K83.1	Obstruction of bile duct
S31.652A	Opn bite of abd wall, epigastric rgn w/ penetration into peritoneal cavity, init enc

S31.654A	Opn bite of abd wall, lt lwr quadrant w/ penetration into peritoneal cavity, init enc	S52.551C	Oth extraarticular fx of lwr end of rt radius, init enc for opn fx type IIIA, IIIB, or IIIC
S31.651A	Opn bite of abd wall, lt upr quadrant w/ penetration into peritoneal cavity, init enc	S52.559B	Oth extraarticular fx of lwr end of unsp radius, init enc for opn fx type I or II
S31.655A	Opn bite of abd wall, periumbilic rgn w/ penetration into peritoneal cavity, init enc	S52.559C	Oth extraarticular fx of lwr end of unsp radius, init enc for opn fx type IIIA, IIIB, or IIIC
S31.653A	Opn bite of abd wall, rt lwr quadrant w/ penetration into peritoneal cavity, init enc	A20.8	Oth forms of plague
		S52.592B	Oth fractures of lwr end of lt radius, init enc for opn fx type I or II
S31.650A	Opn bite of abd wall, rt upr quadrant w/ penetration into peritoneal cavity, init enc	S52.592C	Oth fractures of lwr end of lt radius, init enc for opn fx type IIIA, IIIB, or IIIC
S31.659A	Opn bite of abd wall, unsp quadrant w/ penetration into peritoneal cavity, init enc	S52.591B	Oth fractures of lwr end of rt radius, init enc for opn fx type I or II
S11.015A	Opn bite of larynx, init enc	S52.591C	Oth fractures of lwr end of rt radius, init enc for opn fx type IIIA, IIIB, or IIIC
S21.452A	Opn bite of lt back wall of thorax w/ penetration into thoracic cavity, init enc	S52.599B	Oth fractures of lwr end of unsp radius, init enc for opn fx type I or II
S21.352A	Opn bite of lt front wall of thorax w/ penetration into thoracic cavity, init enc	S52.599C	Oth fractures of lwr end of unsp radius, init enc for opn fx type IIIA, IIIB, or IIIC
S31.051A	Opn bite of lwr back & pelvis w/ penetration into retroperitoneum, init enc	S32.018B	Oth fx of 1st lumbar vertebra, init enc for opn fx
		S22.018B	Oth fx of 1st thoracic vertebra, init enc for opn fx
S21.451A	Opn bite of rt back wall of thorax w/ penetration into thoracic cavity, init enc	S32.028B	Oth fx of 2nd lumbar vertebra, init enc for opn fx
		S22.028B	Oth fx of 2nd thoracic vertebra, init enc for opn fx
S21.351A	Opn bite of rt front wall of thorax w/ penetration into thoracic cavity, init enc	S32.038B	Oth fx of 3rd lumbar vertebra, init enc for opn fx
		S22.038B	Oth fx of 3rd thoracic vertebra, init enc for opn fx
S11.025A	Opn bite of trachea, init enc	S32.048B	Oth fx of 4th lumbar vertebra, init enc for opn fx
S21.459A	Opn bite of unsp back wall of thorax w/ penetration into thoracic cavity, init enc	S22.048B	Oth fx of 4th thoracic vertebra, init enc for opn fx
		S32.058B	Oth fx of 5th lumbar vertebra, init enc for opn fx
S21.359A	Opn bite of unsp front wall of thorax w/ penetration into thoracic cavity, init enc	S02.19XB	Oth fx of base of skull, init enc for opn fx
		S72.092A	Oth fx of head & neck of lt femur, init enc for clsd fx
S11.035A	Opn bite of vocal cord, init enc	S72.092B	Oth fx of head & neck of lt femur, init enc for opn fx type I or II
K43.7	Oth & unsp ventral hernia w/ gangrene	S72.092C	Oth fx of head & neck of lt femur, init enc for opn fx type IIIA, IIIB, or IIIC
D60.8	Oth acquired pure red cell aplasias	S72.091A	Oth fx of head & neck of rt femur, init enc for clsd fx
I40.8	Oth acute myocarditis	S72.091B	Oth fx of head & neck of rt femur, init enc for opn fx type I or II
G04.39	Oth acute necrotizing hemorrhagic encephalopathy	S72.091C	Oth fx of head & neck of rt femur, init enc for opn fx type IIIA, IIIB, or IIIC
K85.8	Oth acute pancreatitis	S72.099A	Oth fx of head & neck of unsp femur, init enc for clsd fx
A80.39	Oth acute paralytic poliomyelitis	S72.099B	Oth fx of head & neck of unsp femur, init enc for opn fx type I or II
G00.8	Oth bacterial meningitis	S72.099C	Oth fx of head & neck of unsp femur, init enc for opn fx type IIIA, IIIB, or IIIC
P36.8	Oth bacterial sepsis of newborn		
I63.8	Oth cerebral infarction	S72.8X2A	Oth fx of lt femur, init enc for clsd fx
P27.8	Oth chr respiratory diseases originating in the perinatal period	S72.8X2B	Oth fx of lt femur, init enc for opn fx type I or II
		S72.8X2C	Oth fx of lt femur, init enc for opn fx type IIIA, IIIB, or IIIC
P25.8	Oth conditions related to interstitial emphysema originating in the perinatal period	S32.392B	Oth fx of lt ilium, init enc for opn fx
		S72.492B	Oth fx of lwr end of lt femur, init enc for opn fx type I or II
P37.4	Oth congenital malaria	S72.492C	Oth fx of lwr end of lt femur, init enc for opn fx type IIIA, IIIB, or IIIC
Q79.59	Oth congenital malformations of abd wall	S52.692B	Oth fx of lwr end of lt ulna, init enc for opn fx type I or II
Q79.1	Oth congenital malformations of diaphragm	S52.692C	Oth fx of lwr end of lt ulna, init enc for opn fx type IIIA, IIIB, or IIIC
Q25.79	Oth congenital malformations of pulmn artery	S72.491B	Oth fx of lwr end of rt femur, init enc for opn fx type I or II
Q22.8	Oth congenital malformations of tricuspid valve	S72.491C	Oth fx of lwr end of rt femur, init enc for opn fx type IIIA, IIIB, or IIIC
P35.8	Oth congenital viral diseases	S52.691B	Oth fx of lwr end of rt ulna, init enc for opn fx type I or II
K68.9	Oth d/o of retroperitoneum	S52.691C	Oth fx of lwr end of rt ulna, init enc for opn fx type IIIA, IIIB, or IIIC
S12.120B	Oth disp dens fx, init enc for opn fx	S72.499B	Oth fx of lwr end of unsp femur, init enc for opn fx type I or II
S12.090B	Oth disp fx of 1st cervical vertebra, init enc for opn fx	S72.499C	Oth fx of lwr end of unsp femur, init enc for opn fx type IIIA, IIIB, or IIIC
S12.190B	Oth disp fx of 2nd cervical vertebra, init enc for opn fx	S52.699B	Oth fx of lwr end of unsp ulna, init enc for opn fx type I or II
S12.290B	Oth disp fx of 3rd cervical vertebra, init enc for opn fx	S52.699C	Oth fx of lwr end of unsp ulna, init enc for opn fx type IIIA, IIIB, or IIIC
S12.390B	Oth disp fx of 4th cervical vertebra, init enc for opn fx	S02.118B	Oth fx of occiput, init enc for opn fx
S12.490B	Oth disp fx of 5th cervical vertebra, init enc for opn fx	S72.8X1A	Oth fx of rt femur, init enc for clsd fx
S12.590B	Oth disp fx of 6th cervical vertebra, init enc for opn fx	S72.8X1B	Oth fx of rt femur, init enc for opn fx type I or II
S12.690B	Oth disp fx of 7th cervical vertebra, init enc for opn fx	S72.8X1C	Oth fx of rt femur, init enc for opn fx type IIIA, IIIB, or IIIC
S42.492B	Oth disp fx of lwr end of lt humerus, init enc for opn fx	S32.391B	Oth fx of rt ilium, init enc for opn fx
S42.491B	Oth disp fx of lwr end of rt humerus, init enc for opn fx	S32.19XB	Oth fx of sacrum, init enc for opn fx
S42.493B	Oth disp fx of lwr end of unsp humerus, init enc for opn fx	S72.392A	Oth fx of shaft of lt femur, init enc for clsd fx
S42.292B	Oth disp fx of upr end of lt humerus, init enc for opn fx	S72.392B	Oth fx of shaft of lt femur, init enc for opn fx type I or II
S42.291B	Oth disp fx of upr end of rt humerus, init enc for opn fx	S72.392C	Oth fx of shaft of lt femur, init enc for opn fx type IIIA, IIIB, or IIIC
S42.293B	Oth disp fx of upr end of unsp humerus, init enc for opn fx	S82.492B	Oth fx of shaft of lt fibula, init enc for opn fx type I or II
D61.811	Oth drug-induced pancytopenia	S82.492C	Oth fx of shaft of lt fibula, init enc for opn fx type IIIA, IIIB, or IIIC
O88.82	Oth embolism in childbirth	S42.392B	Oth fx of shaft of lt humerus, init enc for opn fx
O88.811	Oth embolism in pregnancy, 1st trmstr	S82.292B	Oth fx of shaft of lt tibia, init enc for opn fx type I or II
O88.812	Oth embolism in pregnancy, 2nd trmstr	S82.292C	Oth fx of shaft of lt tibia, init enc for opn fx type IIIA, IIIB, or IIIC
O88.813	Oth embolism in pregnancy, 3rd trmstr	S52.292B	Oth fx of shaft of lt ulna, init enc for opn fx type I or II
O88.83	Oth embolism in the puerperium	S52.292C	Oth fx of shaft of lt ulna, init enc for opn fx type IIIA, IIIB, or IIIC
G04.81	Oth encephalitis & encephalomyelitis	S52.392B	Oth fx of shaft of radius, lt arm, init enc for opn fx type I or II
G93.49	Oth encephalopathy	S52.392C	Oth fx of shaft of radius, lt arm, init enc for opn fx type IIIA, IIIB, or IIIC
S52.552B	Oth extraarticular fx of lwr end of lt radius, init enc for opn fx type I or II	S52.391B	Oth fx of shaft of radius, rt arm, init enc for opn fx type I or II
S52.552C	Oth extraarticular fx of lwr end of lt radius, init enc for opn fx type IIIA, IIIB, or IIIC	S52.391C	Oth fx of shaft of radius, rt arm, init enc for opn fx type IIIA, IIIB, or IIIC
		S52.399B	Oth fx of shaft of radius, unsp arm, init enc for opn fx type I or II
		S52.399C	Oth fx of shaft of radius, unsp arm, init enc for opn fx type IIIA, IIIB, or IIIC
S52.551B	Oth extraarticular fx of lwr end of rt radius, init enc for opn fx type I or II	S72.391A	Oth fx of shaft of rt femur, init enc for clsd fx
		S72.391B	Oth fx of shaft of rt femur, init enc for opn fx type I or II

S72.391C	Oth fx of shaft of rt femur, init enc for opn fx type IIIA, IIIB, or IIIC
S82.491B	Oth fx of shaft of rt fibula, init enc for opn fx type I or II
S82.491C	Oth fx of shaft of rt fibula, init enc for opn fx type IIIA, IIIB, or IIIC
S42.391B	Oth fx of shaft of rt humerus, init enc for opn fx
S82.291B	Oth fx of shaft of rt tibia, init enc for opn fx type I or II
S82.291C	Oth fx of shaft of rt tibia, init enc for opn fx type IIIA, IIIB, or IIIC
S52.291B	Oth fx of shaft of rt ulna, init enc for opn fx type I or II
S52.291C	Oth fx of shaft of rt ulna, init enc for opn fx type IIIA, IIIB, or IIIC
S72.399A	Oth fx of shaft of unsp femur, init enc for clsd fx
S72.399B	Oth fx of shaft of unsp femur, init enc for opn fx type I or II
S72.399C	Oth fx of shaft of unsp femur, init enc for opn fx type IIIA, IIIB, or IIIC
S82.499B	Oth fx of shaft of unsp fibula, init enc for opn fx type I or II
S82.499C	Oth fx of shaft of unsp fibula, init enc for opn fx type IIIA, IIIB, or IIIC
S42.399B	Oth fx of shaft of unsp humerus, init enc for opn fx
S82.299B	Oth fx of shaft of unsp tibia, init enc for opn fx type I or II
S82.299C	Oth fx of shaft of unsp tibia, init enc for opn fx type IIIA, IIIB, or IIIC
S52.299B	Oth fx of shaft of unsp ulna, init enc for opn fx type I or II
S52.299C	Oth fx of shaft of unsp ulna, init enc for opn fx type IIIA, IIIB, or IIIC
S22.088B	Oth fx of T11-T12 vertebra, init enc for opn fx
S22.058B	Oth fx of T5-T6 vertebra, init enc for opn fx
S22.068B	Oth fx of T7-T8 thoracic vertebra, init enc for opn fx
S22.078B	Oth fx of T9-T10 vertebra, init enc for opn fx
S72.8X9A	Oth fx of unsp femur, init enc for clsd fx
S72.8X9B	Oth fx of unsp femur, init enc for opn fx type I or II
S72.8X9C	Oth fx of unsp femur, init enc for opn fx type IIIA, IIIB, or IIIC
S32.399B	Oth fx of unsp ilium, init enc for opn fx
S32.008B	Oth fx of unsp lumbar vertebra, init enc for opn fx
S22.008B	Oth fx of unsp thoracic vertebra, init enc for opn fx
S82.832B	Oth fx of upr & lwr end of lt fibula, init enc for opn fx type I or II
S82.832C	Oth fx of upr & lwr end of lt fibula, init enc for opn fx type IIIA, IIIB, or IIIC
S82.831B	Oth fx of upr & lwr end of rt fibula, init enc for opn fx type I or II
S82.831C	Oth fx of upr & lwr end of rt fibula, init enc for opn fx type IIIA, IIIB, or IIIC
S82.839B	Oth fx of upr & lwr end of unsp fibula, init enc for opn fx type I or II
S82.839C	Oth fx of upr & lwr end of unsp fibula, init enc for opn fx type IIIA, IIIB, or IIIC
S52.182B	Oth fx of upr end of lt radius, init enc for opn fx type I or II
S52.182C	Oth fx of upr end of lt radius, init enc for opn fx type IIIA, IIIB, or IIIC
S82.192B	Oth fx of upr end of lt tibia, init enc for opn fx type I or II
S82.192C	Oth fx of upr end of lt tibia, init enc for opn fx type IIIA, IIIB, or IIIC
S52.092B	Oth fx of upr end of lt ulna, init enc for opn fx type I or II
S52.092C	Oth fx of upr end of lt ulna, init enc for opn fx type IIIA, IIIB, or IIIC
S52.181B	Oth fx of upr end of rt radius, init enc for opn fx type I or II
S52.181C	Oth fx of upr end of rt radius, init enc for opn fx type IIIA, IIIB, or IIIC
S82.191B	Oth fx of upr end of rt tibia, init enc for opn fx type I or II
S82.191C	Oth fx of upr end of rt tibia, init enc for opn fx type IIIA, IIIB, or IIIC
S52.091B	Oth fx of upr end of rt ulna, init enc for opn fx type I or II
S52.091C	Oth fx of upr end of rt ulna, init enc for opn fx type IIIA, IIIB, or IIIC
S52.189B	Oth fx of upr end of unsp radius, init enc for opn fx type I or II
S52.189C	Oth fx of upr end of unsp radius, init enc for opn fx type IIIA, IIIB, or IIIC
S82.199B	Oth fx of upr end of unsp tibia, init enc for opn fx type I or II
S82.199C	Oth fx of upr end of unsp tibia, init enc for opn fx type IIIA, IIIB, or IIIC
S52.099B	Oth fx of upr end of unsp ulna, init enc for opn fx type I or II
S52.099C	Oth fx of upr end of unsp ulna, init enc for opn fx type IIIA, IIIB, or IIIC
K29.61	Oth gastritis w/ bleeding
A41.59	Oth Gram-negative sepsis
B10.09	Oth human herpesvirus encephalitis
S14.151A	Oth incomplete lesion at C1 lvl of cervical spinal cord, init enc
S14.152A	Oth incomplete lesion at C2 lvl of cervical spinal cord, init enc
S14.153A	Oth incomplete lesion at C3 lvl of cervical spinal cord, init enc
S14.154A	Oth incomplete lesion at C4 lvl of cervical spinal cord, init enc
S14.155A	Oth incomplete lesion at C5 lvl of cervical spinal cord, init enc
S14.156A	Oth incomplete lesion at C6 lvl of cervical spinal cord, init enc
S14.157A	Oth incomplete lesion at C7 lvl of cervical spinal cord, init enc
S14.158A	Oth incomplete lesion at C8 lvl of cervical spinal cord, init enc
S24.151A	Oth incomplete lesion at T1 lvl of thoracic spinal cord, init enc
S24.154A	Oth incomplete lesion at T11-T12 lvl of thoracic spinal cord, init enc
S24.152A	Oth incomplete lesion at T2-T6 lvl of thoracic spinal cord, init enc
S24.153A	Oth incomplete lesion at T7-T10 lvl of thoracic spinal cord, init enc
O75.3	Oth infxn during labor
S35.09XA	Oth inj of abd aorta, init enc
S35.298A	Oth inj of branches of celiac & mesenteric artery, init enc
S27.492A	Oth inj of bronchus, bilat, init enc
S27.491A	Oth inj of bronchus, unilat, init enc
S27.499A	Oth inj of bronchus, unsp, init enc
S35.218A	Oth inj of celiac artery, init enc
S27.818A	Oth inj of esophagus (thoracic part), init enc
S35.238A	Oth inj of inferior mesenteric artery, init enc
S35.19XA	Oth inj of inferior vena cava, init enc
S37.092A	Oth inj of lt kidney, init enc
S37.091A	Oth inj of rt kidney, init enc
S35.228A	Oth inj of superior mesenteric artery, init enc
S37.099A	Oth inj of unsp kidney, init enc
J84.848	Oth interstitial lung diseases of childhood
S52.572B	Oth intraarticular fx of lwr end of lt radius, init enc for opn fx type I or II
S52.572C	Oth intraarticular fx of lwr end of lt radius, init enc for opn fx type IIIA, IIIB, or IIIC
S52.571B	Oth intraarticular fx of lwr end of rt radius, init enc for opn fx type I or II
S52.571C	Oth intraarticular fx of lwr end of rt radius, init enc for opn fx type IIIA, IIIB, or IIIC
S52.579B	Oth intraarticular fx of lwr end of unsp radius, init enc for opn fx type I or II
S52.579C	Oth intraarticular fx of lwr end of unsp radius, init enc for opn fx type IIIA, IIIB, or IIIC
P52.8	Oth intracranial (nontraumatic) hemorrhages of newborn
P10.8	Oth intracranial lacerations & hemorrhages d/t birth inj
Q28.3	Oth malformations of cerebral vessels
A19.8	Oth miliary tuberculosis
A83.8	Oth mosquito-borne viral encephalitis
G04.89	Oth myelitis
P24.81	Oth neonatal aspiration w/ respiratory symptoms
P54.3	Oth neonatal gastrointestinal hemor
S12.121B	Oth nondisp dens fx, init enc for opn fx
S12.091B	Oth nondisp fx of 1st cervical vertebra, init enc for opn fx
S12.191B	Oth nondisp fx of 2nd cervical vertebra, init enc for opn fx
S12.291B	Oth nondisp fx of 3rd cervical vertebra, init enc for opn fx
S12.391B	Oth nondisp fx of 4th cervical vertebra, init enc for opn fx
S12.491B	Oth nondisp fx of 5th cervical vertebra, init enc for opn fx
S12.591B	Oth nondisp fx of 6th cervical vertebra, init enc for opn fx
S12.691B	Oth nondisp fx of 7th cervical vertebra, init enc for opn fx
S42.495B	Oth nondisp fx of lwr end of lt humerus, init enc for opn fx
S42.494B	Oth nondisp fx of lwr end of rt humerus, init enc for opn fx
S42.496B	Oth nondisp fx of lwr end of unsp humerus, init enc for opn fx
S42.295B	Oth nondisp fx of upr end of lt humerus, init enc for opn fx
S42.294B	Oth nondisp fx of upr end of rt humerus, init enc for opn fx
S42.296B	Oth nondisp fx of upr end of unsp humerus, init enc for opn fx
I61.8	Oth nontraumatic intracerebral hemor
I60.8	Oth nontraumatic subarachnoid hemor
K65.8	Oth peritonitis
S79.092A	Oth physeal fx of upr end of lt femur, init enc for clsd fx
S79.091A	Oth physeal fx of upr end of rt femur, init enc for clsd fx
S79.099A	Oth physeal fx of upr end of unsp femur, init enc for clsd fx
J18.8	Oth pneumonia, unsp organism
T81.19XA	Oth postprocedural shock, init enc
O24.82	Oth pre-existing diabetes mellitus in childbirth
O45.8X1	Oth premature separation of placenta, 1st trmstr
O45.8X2	Oth premature separation of placenta, 2nd trmstr
O45.8X3	Oth premature separation of placenta, 3rd trmstr
I26.09	Oth pulmn embolism w/ acute cor pulmonale
I26.99	Oth pulmn embolism w/o acute cor pulmonale
P26.8	Oth pulmn hemorrhages originating in the perinatal period
Q04.3	Oth reduction deformities of brain
K68.19	Oth retroperitoneal abscess
R57.8	Oth shock
D57.811	Oth sickle-cell d/o w/ acute chest synd
D57.819	Oth sickle-cell d/o w/ crisis, unsp
D57.812	Oth sickle-cell d/o w/ splenic sequestration
K45.1	Oth spec abd hernia w/ gangrene
D61.89	Oth spec aplastic anemias & oth bone marrow failure syndromes
P37.8	Oth spec congenital infectious & parasitic diseases
E13.01	Oth spec diabetes mellitus w/ hyperosmolarity w/ coma
E13.00	Oth spec diabetes mellitus w/ hyperosmolarity w/o nonketotic hyperglycemic-hyperosmolar coma (NKHHC)
E13.641	Oth spec diabetes mellitus w/ hypoglycemia w/ coma
E13.11	Oth spec diabetes mellitus w/ ketoacidosis w/ coma
E13.10	Oth spec diabetes mellitus w/ ketoacidosis w/o coma
S32.492A	Oth spec fx of lt acetab, init enc for clsd fx
S32.492B	Oth spec fx of lt acetab, init enc for opn fx

S32.692B	Oth spec fx of lt ischium, init enc for opn fx
S32.592B	Oth spec fx of lt pubis, init enc for opn fx
S32.491A	Oth spec fx of rt acetab, init enc for clsd fx
S32.491B	Oth spec fx of rt acetab, init enc for opn fx
S32.691B	Oth spec fx of rt ischium, init enc for opn fx
S32.591B	Oth spec fx of rt pubis, init enc for opn fx
S32.499A	Oth spec fx of unsp acetab, init enc for clsd fx
S32.499B	Oth spec fx of unsp acetab, init enc for opn fx
S32.699B	Oth spec fx of unsp ischium, init enc for opn fx
S32.599B	Oth spec fx of unsp pubis, init enc for opn fx
S45.092A	Oth spec inj of axillary artery, lt side, init enc
S45.091A	Oth spec inj of axillary artery, rt side, init enc
S45.099A	Oth spec inj of axillary artery, unsp side, init enc
S75.092A	Oth spec inj of femoral artery, lt leg, init enc
S75.091A	Oth spec inj of femoral artery, rt leg, init enc
S75.099A	Oth spec inj of femoral artery, unsp leg, init enc
S75.192A	Oth spec inj of femoral vein at hip & thigh lvl, lt leg, init enc
S75.191A	Oth spec inj of femoral vein at hip & thigh lvl, rt leg, init enc
S75.199A	Oth spec inj of femoral vein at hip & thigh lvl, unsp leg, init enc
S35.348A	Oth spec inj of inferior mesenteric vein, init enc
S25.192A	Oth spec inj of lt innominate or subclavian artery, init enc
S25.392A	Oth spec inj of lt innominate or subclavian vein, init enc
S25.492A	Oth spec inj of lt pulmn blood vessels, init enc
S35.492A	Oth spec inj of lt renal artery, init enc
S35.495A	Oth spec inj of lt renal vein, init enc
S85.092A	Oth spec inj of popliteal artery, lt leg, init enc
S85.091A	Oth spec inj of popliteal artery, rt leg, init enc
S85.099A	Oth spec inj of popliteal artery, unsp leg, init enc
S85.592A	Oth spec inj of popliteal vein, lt leg, init enc
S85.591A	Oth spec inj of popliteal vein, rt leg, init enc
S85.599A	Oth spec inj of popliteal vein, unsp leg, init enc
S35.318A	Oth spec inj of portal vein, init enc
S25.191A	Oth spec inj of rt innominate or subclavian artery, init enc
S25.391A	Oth spec inj of rt innominate or subclavian vein, init enc
S25.491A	Oth spec inj of rt pulmn blood vessels, init enc
S35.491A	Oth spec inj of rt renal artery, init enc
S35.494A	Oth spec inj of rt renal vein, init enc
S35.328A	Oth spec inj of splenic vein, init enc
S35.338A	Oth spec inj of superior mesenteric vein, init enc
S25.29XA	Oth spec inj of superior vena cava, init enc
S25.09XA	Oth spec inj of thoracic aorta, init enc
S25.199A	Oth spec inj of unsp innominate or subclavian artery, init enc
S25.399A	Oth spec inj of unsp innominate or subclavian vein, init enc
S25.499A	Oth spec inj of unsp pulmn blood vessels, init enc
S35.493A	Oth spec inj of unsp renal artery, init enc
S35.496A	Oth spec inj of unsp renal vein, init enc
S06.896A	Oth spec intracranial inj w/ loss of cnscness > 24 hrs w/o return to pre-existing conscious lvl w/ patient surviving, init enc
S06.897A	Oth spec intracranial inj w/ loss of cnscness of any dur w/ death d/t brain inj prior to regain cnscness, init enc
S06.898A	Oth spec intracranial inj w/ loss of cnscness of any dur w/ death d/t oth cause prior to regain cnscness, init enc
P57.8	Oth spec kernicterus
O86.89	Oth spec puerperal infections
A41.89	Oth spec sepsis
A40.8	Oth streptococcal sepsis
A35	Oth tetanus
E05.81	Oth thyrotoxicosis w/ thyrotoxic crisis or storm
A84.8	Oth tick-borne viral encephalitis
S12.150B	Oth traum disp spondylolisthesis of 2nd cervical vertebra, init enc for opn fx
S12.250B	Oth traum disp spondylolisthesis of 3rd cervical vertebra, init enc for opn fx
S12.350B	Oth traum disp spondylolisthesis of 4th cervical vertebra, init enc for opn fx
S12.450B	Oth traum disp spondylolisthesis of 5th cervical vertebra, init enc for opn fx
S12.550B	Oth traum disp spondylolisthesis of 6th cervical vertebra, init enc for opn fx
S12.650B	Oth traum disp spondylolisthesis of 7th cervical vertebra, init enc for opn fx
S12.151B	Oth traum nondisp spondylolisthesis of 2nd cervical vertebra, init enc for opn fx
S12.251B	Oth traum nondisp spondylolisthesis of 3rd cervical vertebra, init enc for opn fx

S12.351B	Oth traum nondisp spondylolisthesis of 4th cervical vertebra, init enc for opn fx
S12.451B	Oth traum nondisp spondylolisthesis of 5th cervical vertebra, init enc for opn fx
S12.551B	Oth traum nondisp spondylolisthesis of 6th cervical vertebra, init enc for opn fx
S12.651B	Oth traum nondisp spondylolisthesis of 7th cervical vertebra, init enc for opn fx
A17.89	Oth tuberculosis of nervous sys
G95.19	Oth vascular myelopathies
J12.89	Oth viral pneumonia
B46.8	Oth zygomycoses
J12.2	Parainfluenza virus pneumonia
K43.4	Parastomal hernia w/ gangrene
K83.2	Perforation of bile duct
K22.3	Perforation of esophagus
K82.2	Perforation of gallbladder
K63.1	Perforation of intestine (nontraumatic)
P78.0	Perinatal intestinal perforation
O90.3	Peripartum cardiomyopathy
K65.1	Peritoneal abscess
K65.9	Peritonitis, unsp
P29.3	Persistent fetal circulation
K75.1	Phlebitis of portal vein
O44.11	Placenta previa w/ hemor, 1st trmstr
O44.12	Placenta previa w/ hemor, 2nd trmstr
O44.13	Placenta previa w/ hemor, 3rd trmstr
O41.1411	Placentitis, 1st trmstr, fetus 1
O41.1412	Placentitis, 1st trmstr, fetus 2
O41.1413	Placentitis, 1st trmstr, fetus 3
O41.1414	Placentitis, 1st trmstr, fetus 4
O41.1415	Placentitis, 1st trmstr, fetus 5
O41.1410	Placentitis, 1st trmstr, N/A or unsp
O41.1419	Placentitis, 1st trmstr, oth fetus
O41.1421	Placentitis, 2nd trmstr, fetus 1
O41.1422	Placentitis, 2nd trmstr, fetus 2
O41.1423	Placentitis, 2nd trmstr, fetus 3
O41.1424	Placentitis, 2nd trmstr, fetus 4
O41.1425	Placentitis, 2nd trmstr, fetus 5
O41.1420	Placentitis, 2nd trmstr, N/A or unsp
O41.1429	Placentitis, 2nd trmstr, oth fetus
O41.1431	Placentitis, 3rd trmstr, fetus 1
O41.1432	Placentitis, 3rd trmstr, fetus 2
O41.1433	Placentitis, 3rd trmstr, fetus 3
O41.1434	Placentitis, 3rd trmstr, fetus 4
O41.1435	Placentitis, 3rd trmstr, fetus 5
O41.1430	Placentitis, 3rd trmstr, N/A or unsp
O41.1439	Placentitis, 3rd trmstr, oth fetus
A20.3	Plague meningitis
A20.9	Plague, unsp
B50.9	Plasmodium falciparum malaria, unsp
G00.1	Pneumococcal meningitis
B59	Pneumocystosis
P25.2	Pneumomediastinum originating in the perinatal period
J15.5	Pneumonia d/t Escherichia coli
J14	Pneumonia d/t Hemophilus influenzae
J15.0	Pneumonia d/t Klebsiella pneumoniae
J15.212	Pneumonia d/t Methicillin resistant Staphylococcus aureus
J15.211	Pneumonia d/t Methicillin susceptible Staphylococcus aureus
J15.7	Pneumonia d/t Mycoplasma pneumoniae
J15.6	Pneumonia d/t oth aerobic Gram-negative bacteria
J15.8	Pneumonia d/t oth spec bacteria
J16.8	Pneumonia d/t oth spec infectious organisms
J15.29	Pneumonia d/t oth staphylococcus
J15.4	Pneumonia d/t oth streptococci
J15.1	Pneumonia d/t Pseudomonas
J12.81	Pneumonia d/t SARS-associated coronavirus
J15.20	Pneumonia d/t staphylococcus, unsp
J13	Pneumonia d/t Streptococcus pneumoniae
J15.3	Pneumonia d/t streptococcus, group B
J17	Pneumonia in diseases classified elsw
J18.9	Pneumonia, unsp organism
A20.2	Pneumonic plague
J69.0	Pneumonitis d/t inhalation of food & vomit

J69.1	Pneumonitis d/t inhalation of oils & essences
J69.8	Pneumonitis d/t inhalation of oth solids & liquids
P25.3	Pneumopericardium originating in the perinatal period
P25.1	Pneumothorax originating in the perinatal period
I81	Portal vein thrombosis
S12.111B	Post disp Type II dens fx, init enc for opn fx
I67.83	Post reversible encephalopathy synd
B02.24	Postherpetic myelitis
G04.02	Postimmunization acute disseminated encephalitis, myelitis & encephalomyelitis
G04.32	Postimmunization acute necrotizing hemorrhagic encephalopathy
G04.01	Postinfectious acute disseminated encephalitis & encephalomyelitis (postinfectious ADEM)
G04.31	Postinfectious acute necrotizing hemorrhagic encephalopathy
O90.4	Postpartum acute kidney failure
T81.11XA	Postprocedural cardiogenic shock, init enc
T81.12XA	Postprocedural septic shock, init enc
O24.02	Pre-existing diabetes mellitus, type 1, in childbirth
O24.12	Pre-existing diabetes mellitus, type 2, in childbirth
O11.1	Pre-existing hypertension w/ pre-eclampsia, 1st trmstr
O11.2	Pre-existing hypertension w/ pre-eclampsia, 2nd trmstr
O11.3	Pre-existing hypertension w/ pre-eclampsia, 3rd trmstr
O10.42	Pre-existing secondary hypertension comp childbirth
O45.011	Premature separation of placenta w/ afibrinogenemia, 1st trmstr
O45.012	Premature separation of placenta w/ afibrinogenemia, 2nd trmstr
O45.013	Premature separation of placenta w/ afibrinogenemia, 3rd trmstr
O45.001	Premature separation of placenta w/ coagulation defect, unsp, 1st trmstr
O45.002	Premature separation of placenta w/ coagulation defect, unsp, 2nd trmstr
O45.003	Premature separation of placenta w/ coagulation defect, unsp, 3rd trmstr
O45.021	Premature separation of placenta w/ disseminated intravascular coagulation, 1st trmstr
O45.022	Premature separation of placenta w/ disseminated intravascular coagulation, 2nd trmstr
O45.023	Premature separation of placenta w/ disseminated intravascular coagulation, 3rd trmstr
O45.091	Premature separation of placenta w/ oth coagulation defect, 1st trmstr
O45.092	Premature separation of placenta w/ oth coagulation defect, 2nd trmstr
O45.093	Premature separation of placenta w/ oth coagulation defect, 3rd trmstr
O45.91	Premature separation of placenta, unsp, 1st trmstr
O45.92	Premature separation of placenta, unsp, 2nd trmstr
O45.93	Premature separation of placenta, unsp, 3rd trmstr
L89.43	Pressure ulcer of contiguous site of back, buttock & hip, stage 3
L89.44	Pressure ulcer of contiguous site of back, buttock & hip, stage 4
L89.813	Pressure ulcer of head, stage 3
L89.814	Pressure ulcer of head, stage 4
L89.523	Pressure ulcer of lt ankle, stage 3
L89.524	Pressure ulcer of lt ankle, stage 4
L89.323	Pressure ulcer of lt buttock, stage 3
L89.324	Pressure ulcer of lt buttock, stage 4
L89.023	Pressure ulcer of lt elbow, stage 3
L89.024	Pressure ulcer of lt elbow, stage 4
L89.623	Pressure ulcer of lt heel, stage 3
L89.624	Pressure ulcer of lt heel, stage 4
L89.223	Pressure ulcer of lt hip, stage 3
L89.224	Pressure ulcer of lt hip, stage 4
L89.143	Pressure ulcer of lt lwr back, stage 3
L89.144	Pressure ulcer of lt lwr back, stage 4
L89.123	Pressure ulcer of lt upr back, stage 3
L89.124	Pressure ulcer of lt upr back, stage 4
L89.893	Pressure ulcer of oth site, stage 3
L89.894	Pressure ulcer of oth site, stage 4
L89.513	Pressure ulcer of rt ankle, stage 3
L89.514	Pressure ulcer of rt ankle, stage 4
L89.313	Pressure ulcer of rt buttock, stage 3
L89.314	Pressure ulcer of rt buttock, stage 4
L89.013	Pressure ulcer of rt elbow, stage 3
L89.014	Pressure ulcer of rt elbow, stage 4
L89.613	Pressure ulcer of rt heel, stage 3
L89.614	Pressure ulcer of rt heel, stage 4
L89.213	Pressure ulcer of rt hip, stage 3
L89.214	Pressure ulcer of rt hip, stage 4
L89.133	Pressure ulcer of rt lwr back, stage 3

L89.134	Pressure ulcer of rt lwr back, stage 4
L89.113	Pressure ulcer of rt upr back, stage 3
L89.114	Pressure ulcer of rt upr back, stage 4
L89.153	Pressure ulcer of sacral rgn, stage 3
L89.154	Pressure ulcer of sacral rgn, stage 4
L89.503	Pressure ulcer of unsp ankle, stage 3
L89.504	Pressure ulcer of unsp ankle, stage 4
L89.303	Pressure ulcer of unsp buttock, stage 3
L89.304	Pressure ulcer of unsp buttock, stage 4
L89.003	Pressure ulcer of unsp elbow, stage 3
L89.004	Pressure ulcer of unsp elbow, stage 4
L89.603	Pressure ulcer of unsp heel, stage 3
L89.604	Pressure ulcer of unsp heel, stage 4
L89.203	Pressure ulcer of unsp hip, stage 3
L89.204	Pressure ulcer of unsp hip, stage 4
L89.103	Pressure ulcer of unsp part of back, stage 3
L89.104	Pressure ulcer of unsp part of back, stage 4
L89.93	Pressure ulcer of unsp site, stage 3
L89.94	Pressure ulcer of unsp site, stage 4
O60.12X1	Preterm labor 2nd trmstr w/ preterm delivery 2nd trmstr, fetus 1
O60.12X2	Preterm labor 2nd trmstr w/ preterm delivery 2nd trmstr, fetus 2
O60.12X3	Preterm labor 2nd trmstr w/ preterm delivery 2nd trmstr, fetus 3
O60.12X4	Preterm labor 2nd trmstr w/ preterm delivery 2nd trmstr, fetus 4
O60.12X5	Preterm labor 2nd trmstr w/ preterm delivery 2nd trmstr, fetus 5
O60.12X0	Preterm labor 2nd trmstr w/ preterm delivery 2nd trmstr, N/A or unsp
O60.12X9	Preterm labor 2nd trmstr w/ preterm delivery 2nd trmstr, oth fetus
O60.13X1	Preterm labor 2nd trmstr w/ preterm delivery 3rd trmstr, fetus 1
O60.13X2	Preterm labor 2nd trmstr w/ preterm delivery 3rd trmstr, fetus 2
O60.13X3	Preterm labor 2nd trmstr w/ preterm delivery 3rd trmstr, fetus 3
O60.13X4	Preterm labor 2nd trmstr w/ preterm delivery 3rd trmstr, fetus 4
O60.13X5	Preterm labor 2nd trmstr w/ preterm delivery 3rd trmstr, fetus 5
O60.13X0	Preterm labor 2nd trmstr w/ preterm delivery 3rd trmstr, N/A or unsp
O60.13X9	Preterm labor 2nd trmstr w/ preterm delivery 3rd trmstr, oth fetus
O60.14X1	Preterm labor 3rd trmstr w/ preterm delivery 3rd trmstr, fetus 1
O60.14X2	Preterm labor 3rd trmstr w/ preterm delivery 3rd trmstr, fetus 2
O60.14X3	Preterm labor 3rd trmstr w/ preterm delivery 3rd trmstr, fetus 3
O60.14X4	Preterm labor 3rd trmstr w/ preterm delivery 3rd trmstr, fetus 4
O60.14X5	Preterm labor 3rd trmstr w/ preterm delivery 3rd trmstr, fetus 5
O60.14X0	Preterm labor 3rd trmstr w/ preterm delivery 3rd trmstr, N/A or unsp
O60.14X9	Preterm labor 3rd trmstr w/ preterm delivery 3rd trmstr, oth fetus
O60.02	Preterm labor w/o delivery, 2nd trmstr
O60.03	Preterm labor w/o delivery, 3rd trmstr
S27.412A	Primary blast inj of bronchus, bilat, init enc
S27.411A	Primary blast inj of bronchus, unilat, init enc
S27.419A	Primary blast inj of bronchus, unsp, init enc
Q79.4	Prune belly synd
K68.12	Psoas muscle abscess
O85	Puerperal sepsis
O86.81	Puerperal septic thrombophlebitis
A22.1	Pulmn anthrax
B37.1	Pulmn candidiasis
J68.1	Pulmn edema d/t chemicals, gases, fumes & vapors
B39.2	Pulmn histoplasmosis capsulati, unsp
J84.842	Pulmn interstitial glycogenosis
B46.0	Pulmn mucormycosis
B58.3	Pulmn toxoplasmosis
Q22.0	Pulmn valve atresia
S31.642A	Punc wnd w/ FB of abd wall, epigastric rgn w/ penetration into peritoneal cavity, init enc
S31.644A	Punc wnd w/ FB of abd wall, lt lwr quadrant w/ penetration into peritoneal cavity, init enc
S31.641A	Punc wnd w/ FB of abd wall, lt upr quadrant w/ penetration into peritoneal cavity, init enc
S31.645A	Punc wnd w/ FB of abd wall, periumbilic rgn w/ penetration into peritoneal cavity, init enc
S31.643A	Punc wnd w/ FB of abd wall, rt lwr quadrant w/ penetration into peritoneal cavity, init enc
S31.640A	Punc wnd w/ FB of abd wall, rt upr quadrant w/ penetration into peritoneal cavity, init enc
S31.649A	Punc wnd w/ FB of abd wall, unsp quadrant w/ penetration into peritoneal cavity, init enc
S11.014A	Punc wnd w/ FB of larynx, init enc
S21.442A	Punc wnd w/ FB of lt back wall of thorax w/ penetration into thoracic cavity, init enc

S21.342A	Punc wnd w/ FB of lt front wall of thorax w/ penetration into thoracic cavity, init enc
S31.041A	Punc wnd w/ FB of lwr back & pelvis w/ penetration into retroperitoneum, init enc
S21.441A	Punc wnd w/ FB of rt back wall of thorax w/ penetration into thoracic cavity, init enc
S21.341A	Punc wnd w/ FB of rt front wall of thorax w/ penetration into thoracic cavity, init enc
S11.024A	Punc wnd w/ FB of trachea, init enc
S21.449A	Punc wnd w/ FB of unsp back wall of thorax w/ penetration into thoracic cavity, init enc
S21.349A	Punc wnd w/ FB of unsp front wall of thorax w/ penetration into thoracic cavity, init enc
S11.034A	Punc wnd w/ FB of vocal cord, init enc
S31.632A	Punc wnd w/o FB of abd wall, epigastric rgn w/ penetration into peritoneal cavity, init enc
S31.634A	Punc wnd w/o FB of abd wall, lt lwr quadrant w/ penetration into peritoneal cavity, init enc
S31.631A	Punc wnd w/o FB of abd wall, lt upr quadrant w/ penetration into peritoneal cavity, init enc
S31.635A	Punc wnd w/o FB of abd wall, periumbilic rgn w/ penetration into peritoneal cavity, init enc
S31.633A	Punc wnd w/o FB of abd wall, rt lwr quadrant w/ penetration into peritoneal cavity, init enc
S31.630A	Punc wnd w/o FB of abd wall, rt upr quadrant w/ penetration into peritoneal cavity, init enc
S31.639A	Punc wnd w/o FB of abd wall, unsp quadrant w/ penetration into peritoneal cavity, init enc
S11.013A	Punc wnd w/o FB of larynx, init enc
S21.432A	Punc wnd w/o FB of lt back wall of thorax w/ penetration into thoracic cavity, init enc
S21.332A	Punc wnd w/o FB of lt front wall of thorax w/ penetration into thoracic cavity, init enc
S31.031A	Punc wnd w/o FB of lwr back & pelvis w/ penetration into retroperitoneum, init enc
S21.431A	Punc wnd w/o FB of rt back wall of thorax w/ penetration into thoracic cavity, init enc
S21.331A	Punc wnd w/o FB of rt front wall of thorax w/ penetration into thoracic cavity, init enc
S11.023A	Punc wnd w/o FB of trachea, init enc
S21.439A	Punc wnd w/o FB of unsp back wall of thorax w/ penetration into thoracic cavity, init enc
S21.339A	Punc wnd w/o FB of unsp front wall of thorax w/ penetration into thoracic cavity, init enc
S11.033A	Punc wnd w/o FB of vocal cord, init enc
O88.32	Pyemic & septic embolism in childbirth
O88.311	Pyemic & septic embolism in preg, 1st trmstr
O88.312	Pyemic & septic embolism in preg, 2nd trmstr
O88.313	Pyemic & septic embolism in preg, 3rd trmstr
O88.33	Pyemic & septic embolism in the puerperium
J86.0	Pyothorax w/ fistula
J86.9	Pyothorax w/o fistula
G82.51	Quadriplegia, C1-C4 complete
G82.52	Quadriplegia, C1-C4 incomplete
G82.53	Quadriplegia, C5-C7 complete
G82.54	Quadriplegia, C5-C7 incomplete
G82.50	Quadriplegia, unsp
N01.6	Rapidly progressive nephritic synd w/ dense deposit disease
N01.7	Rapidly progressive nephritic synd w/ diffuse crescentic glomerulonephritis
N01.4	Rapidly progressive nephritic synd w/ diffuse endocapillary proliferative glomerulonephritis
N01.2	Rapidly progressive nephritic synd w/ diffuse membranous glomerulonephritis
N01.3	Rapidly progressive nephritic synd w/ diffuse mesangial proliferative glomerulonephritis
N01.5	Rapidly progressive nephritic synd w/ diffuse mesangiocapillary glomerulonephritis
N01.1	Rapidly progressive nephritic synd w/ focal & segmental glomerular lesions
N01.0	Rapidly progressive nephritic synd w/ minor glomerular abnormality
N01.8	Rapidly progressive nephritic synd w/ oth morphologic changes
N01.9	Rapidly progressive nephritic synd w/ unsp morphologic changes
N15.1	Renal & perinephric abscess
O04.82	Renal failure following (induced) termination of preg
O03.82	Renal failure following complete or unsp spontaneous abortion
O08.4	Renal failure following ectopic & molar preg
O07.32	Renal failure following failed attempted termination of preg
O03.32	Renal failure following incomplete spontaneous abortion
R09.2	Respiratory arrest
P28.81	Respiratory arrest of newborn
P22.0	Respiratory distress synd of newborn
P28.5	Respiratory failure of newborn
J96.92	Respiratory failure, unsp w/ hypercapnia
J96.91	Respiratory failure, unsp w/ hypoxia
J96.90	Respiratory failure, unsp, unsp whether w/ hypoxia or hypercapnia
J12.1	Respiratory syncytial virus pneumonia
G93.7	Reye's synd
B46.1	Rhinocerebral mucormycosis
A83.6	Rocio virus disease
B06.01	Rubella encephalitis
I23.4	Rupture of chordae tendineae as current comp following acute myocardial infarction
I51.1	Rupture of chordae tendineae, NEC
I23.5	Rupture of papillary muscle as current comp following acute myocardial infarction
I51.2	Rupture of papillary muscle, NEC
O71.02	Rupture of uterus before onset of labor, 2nd trmstr
O71.03	Rupture of uterus before onset of labor, 3rd trmstr
O71.1	Rupture of uterus during labor
I74.01	Saddle embolus of abd aorta
I26.02	Saddle embolus of pulmn artery w/ acute cor pulmonale
I26.92	Saddle embolus of pulmn artery w/o acute cor pulmonale
A02.21	Salmonella meningitis
A02.22	Salmonella pneumonia
A02.1	Salmonella sepsis
S79.012A	Salter-Harris Type I physeal fx of upr end of lt femur, init enc for clsd fx
S79.011A	Salter-Harris Type I physeal fx of upr end of rt femur, init enc for clsd fx
S79.019A	Salter-Harris Type I physeal fx of upr end of unsp femur, init enc for clsd fx
I85.11	Secondary esophageal varices w/ bleeding
A51.41	Secondary syphilitic meningitis
A41.4	Sepsis d/t anaerobes
A41.81	Sepsis d/t Enterococcus
A41.51	Sepsis d/t Escherichia coli [E. coli]
A41.3	Sepsis d/t Hemophilus influenzae
A41.02	Sepsis d/t Methicillin resistant Staphylococcus aureus
A41.01	Sepsis d/t Methicillin susceptible Staphylococcus aureus
A41.1	Sepsis d/t oth spec staphylococcus
A41.52	Sepsis d/t Pseudomonas
A41.53	Sepsis d/t Serratia
A40.3	Sepsis d/t Streptococcus pneumoniae
A40.0	Sepsis d/t streptococcus, group A
A40.1	Sepsis d/t streptococcus, group B
A41.2	Sepsis d/t unsp staphylococcus
P36.5	Sepsis of newborn d/t anaerobes
P36.4	Sepsis of newborn d/t Escherichia coli
P36.39	Sepsis of newborn d/t oth staphylococci
P36.19	Sepsis of newborn d/t oth streptococci
P36.2	Sepsis of newborn d/t Staphylococcus aureus
P36.0	Sepsis of newborn d/t streptococcus, group B
P36.30	Sepsis of newborn d/t unsp staphylococci
P36.10	Sepsis of newborn d/t unsp streptococci
A41.9	Sepsis, unsp organism
I26.01	Septic pulmn embolism w/ acute cor pulmonale
I26.90	Septic pulmn embolism w/o acute cor pulmonale
A20.7	Septicemic plague
Q33.2	Sequestration of lung
P91.63	Severe hypoxic ischemic encephalopathy [HIE]
O14.12	Severe pre-eclampsia, 2nd trmstr
O14.13	Severe pre-eclampsia, 3rd trmstr
R65.21	Severe sepsis w/ septic shock
R65.20	Severe sepsis w/o septic shock
S32.112B	Severely disp Zone I fx of sacrum, init enc for opn fx
S32.122B	Severely disp Zone II fx of sacrum, init enc for opn fx
S32.132B	Severely disp Zone III fx of sacrum, init enc for opn fx
O75.1	Shock during or following labor & delivery
O04.81	Shock following (induced) termination of preg
O03.81	Shock following complete or unsp spontaneous abortion
O08.3	Shock following ectopic & molar preg
O07.31	Shock following failed attempted termination of preg

O03.31	Shock following incomplete spontaneous abortion
D57.411	Sickle-cell thalassemia w/ acute chest synd
D57.419	Sickle-cell thalassemia w/ crisis, unsp
D57.412	Sickle-cell thalassemia w/ splenic sequestration
D57.211	Sickle-cell/Hb-C disease w/ acute chest synd
D57.219	Sickle-cell/Hb-C disease w/ crisis, unsp
D57.212	Sickle-cell/Hb-C disease w/ splenic sequestration
S52.542B	Smith's fx of lt radius, init enc for opn fx type I or II
S52.542C	Smith's fx of lt radius, init enc for opn fx type IIIA, IIIB, or IIIC
S52.541B	Smith's fx of rt radius, init enc for opn fx type I or II
S52.541C	Smith's fx of rt radius, init enc for opn fx type IIIA, IIIB, or IIIC
S52.549B	Smith's fx of unsp radius, init enc for opn fx type I or II
S52.549C	Smith's fx of unsp radius, init enc for opn fx type IIIA, IIIB, or IIIC
G80.0	Spastic quadriplegic cerebral palsy
K65.2	Spontaneous bacterial peritonitis
J93.0	Spontaneous tension pneumothorax
I21.02	ST elevation (STEMI) myocardial infarction involving lt ant descending coronary artery
I21.21	ST elevation (STEMI) myocardial infarction involving lt circumflex coronary artery
I21.01	ST elevation (STEMI) myocardial infarction involving lt main coronary artery
I21.09	ST elevation (STEMI) myocardial infarction involving oth coronary artery of ant wall
I21.19	ST elevation (STEMI) myocardial infarction involving oth coronary artery of inferior wall
I21.29	ST elevation (STEMI) myocardial infarction involving oth sites
I21.11	ST elevation (STEMI) myocardial infarction involving rt coronary artery
I21.3	ST elevation (STEMI) myocardial infarction of unsp site
A83.3	St Louis encephalitis
S12.01XB	Stable burst fx of 1st cervical vertebra, init enc for opn fx
S32.011B	Stable burst fx of 1st lumbar vertebra, init enc for opn fx
S22.011B	Stable burst fx of 1st thoracic vertebra, init enc for opn fx
S32.021B	Stable burst fx of 2nd lumbar vertebra, init enc for opn fx
S22.021B	Stable burst fx of 2nd thoracic vertebra, init enc for opn fx
S32.031B	Stable burst fx of 3rd lumbar vertebra, init enc for opn fx
S22.031B	Stable burst fx of 3rd thoracic vertebra, init enc for opn fx
S32.041B	Stable burst fx of 4th lumbar vertebra, init enc for opn fx
S22.041B	Stable burst fx of 4th thoracic vertebra, init enc for opn fx
S32.051B	Stable burst fx of 5th lumbar vertebra, init enc for opn fx
S22.081B	Stable burst fx of T11-T12 vertebra, init enc for opn fx
S22.051B	Stable burst fx of T5-T6 vertebra, init enc for opn fx
S22.061B	Stable burst fx of T7-T8 vertebra, init enc for opn fx
S22.071B	Stable burst fx of T9-T10 vertebra, init enc for opn fx
S32.001B	Stable burst fx of unsp lumbar vertebra, init enc for opn fx
S22.001B	Stable burst fx of unsp thoracic vertebra, init enc for opn fx
P77.1	Stage 1 necrotizing enterocolitis in newborn
P77.2	Stage 2 necrotizing enterocolitis in newborn
P77.3	Stage 3 necrotizing enterocolitis in newborn
G00.3	Staphylococcal meningitis
Q25.6	Stenosis of pulmn artery
S22.23XB	Sternal manubrial dissociation, init enc for opn fx
G00.2	Streptococcal meningitis
A40.9	Streptococcal sepsis, unsp
G37.4	Subacute necrotizing myelitis of central nervous sys
P52.5	Subarachnoid (nontraumatic) hemor of newborn
P10.3	Subarachnoid hemor d/t birth inj
P10.0	Subdural hemor d/t birth inj
I22.2	Subsq non-ST elevation (NSTEMI) myocardial infarction
I22.0	Subsq ST elevation (STEMI) myocardial infarction of ant wall
I22.1	Subsq ST elevation (STEMI) myocardial infarction of inferior wall
I22.8	Subsq ST elevation (STEMI) myocardial infarction of oth sites
I22.9	Subsq ST elevation (STEMI) myocardial infarction of unsp site
J04.31	Supraglottitis, unsp, w/ obstruction
J84.83	Surfactant mutations of the lung
R65.11	Systemic inflam response synd (SIRS) of non-infectious origin w/ acute organ dysfunction
P10.4	Tentorial tear d/t birth inj
O60.22X1	Term delivery w/ preterm labor, 2nd trmstr, fetus 1
O60.22X2	Term delivery w/ preterm labor, 2nd trmstr, fetus 2
O60.22X3	Term delivery w/ preterm labor, 2nd trmstr, fetus 3
O60.22X4	Term delivery w/ preterm labor, 2nd trmstr, fetus 4
O60.22X5	Term delivery w/ preterm labor, 2nd trmstr, fetus 5
O60.22X0	Term delivery w/ preterm labor, 2nd trmstr, N/A or unsp

O60.22X9	Term delivery w/ preterm labor, 2nd trmstr, oth fetus
O60.23X1	Term delivery w/ preterm labor, 3rd trmstr, fetus 1
O60.23X2	Term delivery w/ preterm labor, 3rd trmstr, fetus 2
O60.23X3	Term delivery w/ preterm labor, 3rd trmstr, fetus 3
O60.23X4	Term delivery w/ preterm labor, 3rd trmstr, fetus 4
O60.23X5	Term delivery w/ preterm labor, 3rd trmstr, fetus 5
O60.23X0	Term delivery w/ preterm labor, 3rd trmstr, N/A or unsp
O60.23X9	Term delivery w/ preterm labor, 3rd trmstr, oth fetus
A33	Tetanus neonatorum
Q21.3	Tetralogy of Fallot
I71.1	Thoracic aortic aneurysm, ruptured
I71.5	Thoracoabdominal aortic aneurysm, ruptured
O88.22	Thromboembolism in childbirth
O88.211	Thromboembolism in preg, 1st trmstr
O88.212	Thromboembolism in preg, 2nd trmstr
O88.213	Thromboembolism in preg, 3rd trmstr
O88.23	Thromboembolism in the puerperium
M31.1	Thrombotic microangiopathy
E05.41	Thyrotoxicosis factitia w/ thyrotoxic crisis or storm
E05.31	Thyrotoxicosis from ectopic thyroid tissue w/ thyrotoxic crisis or storm
E05.01	Thyrotoxicosis w/ diffuse goiter w/ thyrotoxic crisis or storm
E05.21	Thyrotoxicosis w/ toxic multinodular goiter w/ thyrotoxic crisis or storm
E05.11	Thyrotoxicosis w/ toxic single thyroid nodule w/ thyrotoxic crisis or storm
E05.91	Thyrotoxicosis, unsp w/ thyrotoxic crisis or storm
A84.9	Tick-borne viral encephalitis, unsp
G92	Toxic encephalopathy
K71.11	Toxic liver disease w/ hepatic necrosis, w/ coma
A48.3	Toxic shock synd
B58.2	Toxoplasma meningoencephalitis
B58.81	Toxoplasma myocarditis
P26.0	Tracheobronchial hemor originating in the perinatal period
D60.1	Transient acquired pure red cell aplasia
P61.5	Transient neonatal neutropenia
P61.0	Transient neonatal thrombocytopenia
T79.5XXA	Traum anuria, init enc
S06.1X5A	Traum cerebral edema w/ loss of cnscness > 24 hrs w/ return to pre-existing conscious lvl, init enc
S06.1X6A	Traum cerebral edema w/ loss of cnscness > 24 hrs w/o return to pre-existing conscious lvl w/ patient surviving, init enc
S06.1X3A	Traum cerebral edema w/ loss of cnscness of 1 hr to 5 hrs 59 mins, init enc
S06.1X1A	Traum cerebral edema w/ loss of cnscness of 30 mins or less, init enc
S06.1X2A	Traum cerebral edema w/ loss of cnscness of 31 mins to 59 mins, init enc
S06.1X4A	Traum cerebral edema w/ loss of cnscness of 6 hrs to 24 hrs, init enc
S06.1X7A	Traum cerebral edema w/ loss of cnscness of any dur w/ death d/t brain inj prior to regain cnscness, init enc
S06.1X8A	Traum cerebral edema w/ loss of cnscness of any dur w/ death d/t oth cause prior to regain cnscness, init enc
S06.1X9A	Traum cerebral edema w/ loss of cnscness of unsp dur, init enc
S06.1X0A	Traum cerebral edema w/o loss of cnscness, init enc
S27.2XXA	Traum hemopneumothorax, init enc
S06.365A	Traum hemor of cerebrum, unsp, w/ loss of cnscness > 24 hrs w/ return to pre-existing conscious lvl, init enc
S06.366A	Traum hemor of cerebrum, unsp, w/ loss of cnscness > 24 hrs w/o return to pre-existing conscious lvl w/ patient surviving, init enc
S06.363A	Traum hemor of cerebrum, unsp, w/ loss of cnscness of 1 hrs to 5 hrs 59 mins, init enc
S06.361A	Traum hemor of cerebrum, unsp, w/ loss of cnscness of 30 mins or less, init enc
S06.362A	Traum hemor of cerebrum, unsp, w/ loss of cnscness of 31 mins to 59 mins, init enc
S06.364A	Traum hemor of cerebrum, unsp, w/ loss of cnscness of 6 hrs to 24 hrs, init enc
S06.367A	Traum hemor of cerebrum, unsp, w/ loss of cnscness of any dur w/ death d/t brain inj prior to regain cnscness, init enc
S06.368A	Traum hemor of cerebrum, unsp, w/ loss of cnscness of any dur w/ death d/t oth cause prior to regain cnscness, init enc
S06.369A	Traum hemor of cerebrum, unsp, w/ loss of cnscness of unsp dur, init enc
S06.360A	Traum hemor of cerebrum, unsp, w/o loss of cnscness, init enc
S06.355A	Traum hemor of lt cerebrum w/ loss of cnscness > 24 hrs w/ return to pre-existing conscious lvl, init enc
S06.356A	Traum hemor of lt cerebrum w/ loss of cnscness > 24 hrs w/o return to pre-existing conscious lvl w/ patient surviving, init enc

S06.353A	Traum hemor of lt cerebrum w/ loss of cnscness of 1 hrs to 5 hrs 59 mins, init enc
S06.351A	Traum hemor of lt cerebrum w/ loss of cnscness of 30 mins or less, init enc
S06.352A	Traum hemor of lt cerebrum w/ loss of cnscness of 31 mins to 59 mins, init enc
S06.354A	Traum hemor of lt cerebrum w/ loss of cnscness of 6 hrs to 24 hrs, init enc
S06.357A	Traum hemor of lt cerebrum w/ loss of cnscness of any dur w/ death d/t brain inj prior to regain cnscness, init enc
S06.358A	Traum hemor of lt cerebrum w/ loss of cnscness of any dur w/ death d/t oth cause prior to regain cnscness, init enc
S06.359A	Traum hemor of lt cerebrum w/ loss of cnscness of unsp dur, init enc
S06.350A	Traum hemor of lt cerebrum w/o loss of cnscness, init enc
S06.345A	Traum hemor of rt cerebrum w/ loss of cnscness > 24 hrs w/ return to pre-existing conscious lvl, init enc
S06.346A	Traum hemor of rt cerebrum w/ loss of cnscness > 24 hrs w/o return to pre-existing conscious lvl w/ patient surviving, init enc
S06.343A	Traum hemor of rt cerebrum w/ loss of cnscness of 1 hrs to 5 hrs 59 mins, init enc
S06.341A	Traum hemor of rt cerebrum w/ loss of cnscness of 30 mins or less, init enc
S06.342A	Traum hemor of rt cerebrum w/ loss of cnscness of 31 mins to 59 mins, init enc
S06.344A	Traum hemor of rt cerebrum w/ loss of cnscness of 6 hrs to 24 hrs, init enc
S06.347A	Traum hemor of rt cerebrum w/ loss of cnscness of any dur w/ death d/t brain inj prior to regain cnscness, init enc
S06.348A	Traum hemor of rt cerebrum w/ loss of cnscness of any dur w/ death d/t oth cause prior to regain cnscness, init enc
S06.349A	Traum hemor of rt cerebrum w/ loss of cnscness of unsp dur, init enc
S06.340A	Traum hemor of rt cerebrum w/o loss of cnscness, init enc
S27.1XXA	Traum hemothorax, init enc
T79.4XXA	Traum shock, init enc
S06.6X5A	Traum subarachnoid hemor w/ loss of cnscness > 24 hrs w/ return to pre-existing conscious lvl, init enc
S06.6X6A	Traum subarachnoid hemor w/ loss of cnscness > 24 hrs w/o return to pre-existing conscious lvl w/ patient surviving, init enc
S06.6X3A	Traum subarachnoid hemor w/ loss of cnscness of 1 hr to 5 hrs 59 mins, init enc
S06.6X1A	Traum subarachnoid hemor w/ loss of cnscness of 30 mins or less, init enc
S06.6X2A	Traum subarachnoid hemor w/ loss of cnscness of 31 mins to 59 mins, init enc
S06.6X4A	Traum subarachnoid hemor w/ loss of cnscness of 6 hrs to 24 hrs, init enc
S06.6X7A	Traum subarachnoid hemor w/ loss of cnscness of any dur w/ death d/t brain inj prior to regain cnscness, init enc
S06.6X8A	Traum subarachnoid hemor w/ loss of cnscness of any dur w/ death d/t oth cause prior to regain cnscness, init enc
S06.6X9A	Traum subarachnoid hemor w/ loss of cnscness of unsp dur, init enc
S06.6X0A	Traum subarachnoid hemor w/o loss of cnscness, init enc
S06.5X5A	Traum subdural hemor w/ loss of cnscness > 24 hrs w/ return to pre-existing conscious lvl, init enc
S06.5X6A	Traum subdural hemor w/ loss of cnscness > 24 hrs w/o return to pre-existing conscious lvl w/ patient surviving, init enc
S06.5X3A	Traum subdural hemor w/ loss of cnscness of 1 hr to 5 hrs 59 mins, init enc
S06.5X1A	Traum subdural hemor w/ loss of cnscness of 30 mins or less, init enc
S06.5X2A	Traum subdural hemor w/ loss of cnscness of 31 mins to 59 mins, init enc
S06.5X4A	Traum subdural hemor w/ loss of cnscness of 6 hrs to 24 hrs, init enc
S06.5X7A	Traum subdural hemor w/ loss of cnscness of any dur w/ death d/t brain inj before regain cnscness, init enc
S06.5X8A	Traum subdural hemor w/ loss of cnscness of any dur w/ death d/t oth cause before regain cnscness, init enc
S06.5X9A	Traum subdural hemor w/ loss of cnscness of unsp dur, init enc
S06.5X0A	Traum subdural hemor w/o loss of cnscness, init enc
A17.81	Tuberculoma of brain & spinal cord
A17.0	Tuberculous meningitis
A17.82	Tuberculous meningoencephalitis
A17.83	Tuberculous neuritis
A18.31	Tuberculous peritonitis
E88.3	Tumor lysis synd
E10.641	Type 1 diabetes mellitus w/ hypoglycemia w/ coma
E10.11	Type 1 diabetes mellitus w/ ketoacidosis w/ coma
E10.10	Type 1 diabetes mellitus w/ ketoacidosis w/o coma
S32.14XB	Type 1 fx of sacrum, init enc for opn fx
E11.01	Type 2 diabetes mellitus w/ hyperosmolarity w/ coma
E11.00	Type 2 diabetes mellitus w/ hyperosmolarity w/o nonketotic hyperglycemic-hyperosmolar coma (NKHHC)
E11.641	Type 2 diabetes mellitus w/ hypoglycemia w/ coma
S32.15XB	Type 2 fx of sacrum, init enc for opn fx
S32.16XB	Type 3 fx of sacrum, init enc for opn fx
S32.17XB	Type 4 fx of sacrum, init enc for opn fx
S02.110B	Type I occipital condyle fx, init enc for opn fx
S02.111B	Type II occipital condyle fx, init enc for opn fx
S02.112B	Type III occipital condyle fx, init enc for opn fx
S12.14XB	Type III traum spondylolisthesis of 2nd cervical vertebra, init enc for opn fx
S12.24XB	Type III traum spondylolisthesis of 3rd cervical vertebra, init enc for opn fx
S12.34XB	Type III traum spondylolisthesis of 4th cervical vertebra, init enc for opn fx
S12.44XB	Type III traum spondylolisthesis of 5th cervical vertebra, init enc for opn fx
S12.54XB	Type III traum spondylolisthesis of 6th cervical vertebra, init enc for opn fx
S12.64XB	Type III traum spondylolisthesis of 7th cervical vertebra, init enc for opn fx
K22.11	Ulcer of esophagus w/ bleeding
K42.1	Umbilical hernia w/ gangrene
K41.40	Unilat femoral hernia, w/ gangrene, not spec as recurrent
K41.41	Unilat femoral hernia, w/ gangrene, recurrent
K40.40	Unilat inguinal hernia, w/ gangrene, not spec as recurrent
K40.41	Unilat inguinal hernia, w/ gangrene, recurrent
K46.1	Unsp abd hernia w/ gangrene
J15.9	Unsp bacterial pneumonia
P11.2	Unsp brain damage d/t birth inj
K29.51	Unsp chr gastritis w/ bleeding
P27.9	Unsp chr respiratory disease originating in the perinatal period
R40.20	Unsp coma
S12.000B	Unsp disp fx of 1st cervical vertebra, init enc for opn fx
S12.100B	Unsp disp fx of 2nd cervical vertebra, init enc for opn fx
S12.200B	Unsp disp fx of 3rd cervical vertebra, init enc for opn fx
S12.300B	Unsp disp fx of 4th cervical vertebra, init enc for opn fx
S12.400B	Unsp disp fx of 5th cervical vertebra, init enc for opn fx
S12.500B	Unsp disp fx of 6th cervical vertebra, init enc for opn fx
S12.600B	Unsp disp fx of 7th cervical vertebra, init enc for opn fx
S42.212B	Unsp disp fx of surg neck of lt humerus, init enc for opn fx
S42.211B	Unsp disp fx of surg neck of rt humerus, init enc for opn fx
S42.213B	Unsp disp fx of surg neck of unsp humerus, init enc for opn fx
S06.306A	Unsp focal traum brain inj w/ loss of cnscness > 24 hrs w/o return to pre-existing conscious lvl w/ patient surviving, init enc
S06.307A	Unsp focal traum brain inj w/ loss of cnscness of any dur w/ death d/t brain inj prior to regain cnscness, init enc
S06.308A	Unsp focal traum brain inj w/ loss of cnscness of any dur w/ death d/t oth cause prior to regain cnscness, init enc
S32.019B	Unsp fx of 1st lumbar vertebra, init enc for opn fx
S22.019B	Unsp fx of 1st thoracic vertebra, init enc for opn fx
S32.029B	Unsp fx of 2nd lumbar vertebra, init enc for opn fx
S22.029B	Unsp fx of 2nd thoracic vertebra, init enc for opn fx
S32.039B	Unsp fx of 3rd lumbar vertebra, init enc for opn fx
S22.039B	Unsp fx of 3rd thoracic vertebra, init enc for opn fx
S32.049B	Unsp fx of 4th lumbar vertebra, init enc for opn fx
S22.049B	Unsp fx of 4th thoracic vertebra, init enc for opn fx
S32.059B	Unsp fx of 5th lumbar vertebra, init enc for opn fx
S02.10XB	Unsp fx of base of skull, init enc for opn fx
S72.052A	Unsp fx of head of lt femur, init enc for clsd fx
S72.052B	Unsp fx of head of lt femur, init enc for opn fx type I or II
S72.052C	Unsp fx of head of lt femur, init enc for opn fx type IIIA, IIIB, or IIIC
S72.051A	Unsp fx of head of rt femur, init enc for clsd fx
S72.051B	Unsp fx of head of rt femur, init enc for opn fx type I or II
S72.051C	Unsp fx of head of rt femur, init enc for opn fx type IIIA, IIIB, or IIIC
S72.059A	Unsp fx of head of unsp femur, init enc for clsd fx
S72.059B	Unsp fx of head of unsp femur, init enc for opn fx type I or II
S72.059C	Unsp fx of head of unsp femur, init enc for opn fx type IIIA, IIIB, or IIIC
S32.402A	Unsp fx of lt acetab, init enc for clsd fx
S32.402B	Unsp fx of lt acetab, init enc for opn fx
S72.92XA	Unsp fx of lt femur, init enc for clsd fx
S72.92XB	Unsp fx of lt femur, init enc for opn fx type I or II
S72.92XC	Unsp fx of lt femur, init enc for opn fx type IIIA, IIIB, or IIIC
S52.92XB	Unsp fx of lt forearm, init enc for opn fx type I or II

S52.92XC	Unsp fx of lt forearm, init enc for opn fx type IIIA, IIIB, or IIIC
S32.302B	Unsp fx of lt ilium, init enc for opn fx
S32.602B	Unsp fx of lt ischium, init enc for opn fx
S32.502B	Unsp fx of lt pubis, init enc for opn fx
S72.402B	Unsp fx of lwr end of lt femur, init enc for opn fx type I or II
S72.402C	Unsp fx of lwr end of lt femur, init enc for opn fx type IIIA, IIIB, or IIIC
S42.402B	Unsp fx of lwr end of lt humerus, init enc for opn fx
S52.602B	Unsp fx of lwr end of lt ulna, init enc for opn fx type I or II
S52.602C	Unsp fx of lwr end of lt ulna, init enc for opn fx type IIIA, IIIB, or IIIC
S72.401B	Unsp fx of lwr end of rt femur, init enc for opn fx type I or II
S72.401C	Unsp fx of lwr end of rt femur, init enc for opn fx type IIIA, IIIB, or IIIC
S42.401B	Unsp fx of lwr end of rt humerus, init enc for opn fx
S52.601B	Unsp fx of lwr end of rt ulna, init enc for opn fx type I or II
S52.601C	Unsp fx of lwr end of rt ulna, init enc for opn fx type IIIA, IIIB, or IIIC
S72.409B	Unsp fx of lwr end of unsp femur, init enc for opn fx type I or II
S72.409C	Unsp fx of lwr end of unsp femur, init enc for opn fx type IIIA, IIIB, or IIIC
S42.409B	Unsp fx of lwr end of unsp humerus, init enc for opn fx
S52.609B	Unsp fx of lwr end of unsp ulna, init enc for opn fx type I or II
S52.609C	Unsp fx of lwr end of unsp ulna, init enc for opn fx type IIIA, IIIB, or IIIC
S02.119B	Unsp fx of occiput, init enc for opn fx
S32.401A	Unsp fx of rt acetab, init enc for clsd fx
S32.401B	Unsp fx of rt acetab, init enc for opn fx
S72.91XA	Unsp fx of rt femur, init enc for clsd fx
S72.91XB	Unsp fx of rt femur, init enc for opn fx type I or II
S72.91XC	Unsp fx of rt femur, init enc for opn fx type IIIA, IIIB, or IIIC
S52.91XB	Unsp fx of rt forearm, init enc for opn fx type I or II
S52.91XC	Unsp fx of rt forearm, init enc for opn fx type IIIA, IIIB, or IIIC
S32.301B	Unsp fx of rt ilium, init enc for opn fx
S32.601B	Unsp fx of rt ischium, init enc for opn fx
S32.501B	Unsp fx of rt pubis, init enc for opn fx
S32.10XB	Unsp fx of sacrum, init enc for opn fx
S42.302B	Unsp fx of shaft of humerus, lt arm, init enc for opn fx
S42.301B	Unsp fx of shaft of humerus, rt arm, init enc for opn fx
S42.309B	Unsp fx of shaft of humerus, unsp arm, init enc for opn fx
S72.302A	Unsp fx of shaft of lt femur, init enc for clsd fx
S72.302B	Unsp fx of shaft of lt femur, init enc for opn fx type I or II
S72.302C	Unsp fx of shaft of lt femur, init enc for opn fx type IIIA, IIIB, or IIIC
S82.402B	Unsp fx of shaft of lt fibula, init enc for opn fx type I or II
S82.402C	Unsp fx of shaft of lt fibula, init enc for opn fx type IIIA, IIIB, or IIIC
S52.302B	Unsp fx of shaft of lt radius, init enc for opn fx type I or II
S52.302C	Unsp fx of shaft of lt radius, init enc for opn fx type IIIA, IIIB, or IIIC
S82.202B	Unsp fx of shaft of lt tibia, init enc for opn fx type I or II
S82.202C	Unsp fx of shaft of lt tibia, init enc for opn fx type IIIA, IIIB, or IIIC
S52.202B	Unsp fx of shaft of lt ulna, init enc for opn fx type I or II
S52.202C	Unsp fx of shaft of lt ulna, init enc for opn fx type IIIA, IIIB, or IIIC
S72.301A	Unsp fx of shaft of rt femur, init enc for clsd fx
S72.301B	Unsp fx of shaft of rt femur, init enc for opn fx type I or II
S72.301C	Unsp fx of shaft of rt femur, init enc for opn fx type IIIA, IIIB, or IIIC
S82.401B	Unsp fx of shaft of rt fibula, init enc for opn fx type I or II
S82.401C	Unsp fx of shaft of rt fibula, init enc for opn fx type IIIA, IIIB, or IIIC
S52.301B	Unsp fx of shaft of rt radius, init enc for opn fx type I or II
S52.301C	Unsp fx of shaft of rt radius, init enc for opn fx type IIIA, IIIB, or IIIC
S82.201B	Unsp fx of shaft of rt tibia, init enc for opn fx type I or II
S82.201C	Unsp fx of shaft of rt tibia, init enc for opn fx type IIIA, IIIB, or IIIC
S52.201B	Unsp fx of shaft of rt ulna, init enc for opn fx type I or II
S52.201C	Unsp fx of shaft of rt ulna, init enc for opn fx type IIIA, IIIB, or IIIC
S72.309A	Unsp fx of shaft of unsp femur, init enc for clsd fx
S72.309B	Unsp fx of shaft of unsp femur, init enc for opn fx type I or II
S72.309C	Unsp fx of shaft of unsp femur, init enc for opn fx type IIIA, IIIB, or IIIC
S82.409B	Unsp fx of shaft of unsp fibula, init enc for opn fx type I or II
S82.409C	Unsp fx of shaft of unsp fibula, init enc for opn fx type IIIA, IIIB, or IIIC
S52.309B	Unsp fx of shaft of unsp radius, init enc for opn fx type I or II
S52.309C	Unsp fx of shaft of unsp radius, init enc for opn fx type IIIA, IIIB, or IIIC
S82.209B	Unsp fx of shaft of unsp tibia, init enc for opn fx type I or II
S82.209C	Unsp fx of shaft of unsp tibia, init enc for opn fx type IIIA, IIIB, or IIIC
S52.209B	Unsp fx of shaft of unsp ulna, init enc for opn fx type I or II
S52.209C	Unsp fx of shaft of unsp ulna, init enc for opn fx type IIIA, IIIB, or IIIC
S02.91XB	Unsp fx of skull, init enc for opn fx
S22.20XB	Unsp fx of sternum, init enc for opn fx
S22.089B	Unsp fx of T11-T12 vertebra, init enc for opn fx
S22.059B	Unsp fx of T5-T6 vertebra, init enc for opn fx
S22.069B	Unsp fx of T7-T8 vertebra, init enc for opn fx
S22.079B	Unsp fx of T9-T10 vertebra, init enc for opn fx

S52.502B	Unsp fx of the lwr end of lt radius, init enc for opn fx type I or II
S52.502C	Unsp fx of the lwr end of lt radius, init enc for opn fx type IIIA, IIIB, or IIIC
S52.501B	Unsp fx of the lwr end of rt radius, init enc for opn fx type I or II
S52.501C	Unsp fx of the lwr end of rt radius, init enc for opn fx type IIIA, IIIB, or IIIC
S52.509B	Unsp fx of the lwr end of unsp radius, init enc for opn fx type I or II
S52.509C	Unsp fx of the lwr end of unsp radius, init enc for opn fx type IIIA, IIIB, or IIIC
S32.409A	Unsp fx of unsp acetab, init enc for clsd fx
S32.409B	Unsp fx of unsp acetab, init enc for opn fx
S72.90XA	Unsp fx of unsp femur, init enc for clsd fx
S72.90XB	Unsp fx of unsp femur, init enc for opn fx type I or II
S72.90XC	Unsp fx of unsp femur, init enc for opn fx type IIIA, IIIB, or IIIC
S52.90XB	Unsp fx of unsp forearm, init enc for opn fx type I or II
S52.90XC	Unsp fx of unsp forearm, init enc for opn fx type IIIA, IIIB, or IIIC
S32.309B	Unsp fx of unsp ilium, init enc for opn fx
S32.609B	Unsp fx of unsp ischium, init enc for opn fx
S32.009B	Unsp fx of unsp lumbar vertebra, init enc for opn fx
S32.509B	Unsp fx of unsp pubis, init enc for opn fx
S22.009B	Unsp fx of unsp thoracic vertebra, init enc for opn fx
S42.202B	Unsp fx of upr end of lt humerus, init enc for opn fx
S52.102B	Unsp fx of upr end of lt radius, init enc for opn fx type I or II
S52.102C	Unsp fx of upr end of lt radius, init enc for opn fx type IIIA, IIIB, or IIIC
S82.102B	Unsp fx of upr end of lt tibia, init enc for opn fx type I or II
S82.102C	Unsp fx of upr end of lt tibia, init enc for opn fx type IIIA, IIIB, or IIIC
S52.002B	Unsp fx of upr end of lt ulna, init enc for opn fx type I or II
S52.002C	Unsp fx of upr end of lt ulna, init enc for opn fx type IIIA, IIIB, or IIIC
S42.201B	Unsp fx of upr end of rt humerus, init enc for opn fx
S52.101B	Unsp fx of upr end of rt radius, init enc for opn fx type I or II
S52.101C	Unsp fx of upr end of rt radius, init enc for opn fx type IIIA, IIIB, or IIIC
S82.101B	Unsp fx of upr end of rt tibia, init enc for opn fx type I or II
S82.101C	Unsp fx of upr end of rt tibia, init enc for opn fx type IIIA, IIIB, or IIIC
S52.001B	Unsp fx of upr end of rt ulna, init enc for opn fx type I or II
S52.001C	Unsp fx of upr end of rt ulna, init enc for opn fx type IIIA, IIIB, or IIIC
S42.209B	Unsp fx of upr end of unsp humerus, init enc for opn fx
S52.109B	Unsp fx of upr end of unsp radius, init enc for opn fx type I or II
S52.109C	Unsp fx of upr end of unsp radius, init enc for opn fx type IIIA, IIIB, or IIIC
S82.109B	Unsp fx of upr end of unsp tibia, init enc for opn fx type I or II
S82.109C	Unsp fx of upr end of unsp tibia, init enc for opn fx type IIIA, IIIB, or IIIC
S52.009B	Unsp fx of upr end of unsp ulna, init enc for opn fx type I or II
S52.009C	Unsp fx of upr end of unsp ulna, init enc for opn fx type IIIA, IIIB, or IIIC
S14.101A	Unsp inj at C1 lvl of cervical spinal cord, init enc
S14.102A	Unsp inj at C2 lvl of cervical spinal cord, init enc
S14.103A	Unsp inj at C3 lvl of cervical spinal cord, init enc
S14.104A	Unsp inj at C4 lvl of cervical spinal cord, init enc
S14.105A	Unsp inj at C5 lvl of cervical spinal cord, init enc
S14.106A	Unsp inj at C6 lvl of cervical spinal cord, init enc
S14.107A	Unsp inj at C7 lvl of cervical spinal cord, init enc
S14.108A	Unsp inj at C8 lvl of cervical spinal cord, init enc
S24.101A	Unsp inj at T1 lvl of thoracic spinal cord, init enc
S24.104A	Unsp inj at T11-T12 lvl of thoracic spinal cord, init enc
S24.102A	Unsp inj at T2-T6 lvl of thoracic spinal cord, init enc
S24.103A	Unsp inj at T7-T10 lvl of thoracic spinal cord, init enc
S35.00XA	Unsp inj of abd aorta, init enc
S45.002A	Unsp inj of axillary artery, lt side, init enc
S45.001A	Unsp inj of axillary artery, rt side, init enc
S45.009A	Unsp inj of axillary artery, unsp side, init enc
S35.299A	Unsp inj of branches of celiac & mesenteric artery, init enc
S27.402A	Unsp inj of bronchus, bilat, init enc
S27.401A	Unsp inj of bronchus, unilat, init enc
S27.409A	Unsp inj of bronchus, unsp, init enc
S35.219A	Unsp inj of celiac artery, init enc
S27.819A	Unsp inj of esophagus (thoracic part), init enc
S75.002A	Unsp inj of femoral artery, lt leg, init enc
S75.001A	Unsp inj of femoral artery, rt leg, init enc
S75.009A	Unsp inj of femoral artery, unsp leg, init enc
S75.102A	Unsp inj of femoral vein at hip & thigh lvl, lt leg, init enc
S75.101A	Unsp inj of femoral vein at hip & thigh lvl, rt leg, init enc
S75.109A	Unsp inj of femoral vein at hip & thigh lvl, unsp leg, init enc
S35.239A	Unsp inj of inferior mesenteric artery, init enc
S35.349A	Unsp inj of inferior mesenteric vein, init enc
S35.10XA	Unsp inj of inferior vena cava, init enc
S25.102A	Unsp inj of lt innominate or subclavian artery, init enc
S25.302A	Unsp inj of lt innominate or subclavian vein, init enc

S25.402A	Unsp inj of lt pulmn blood vessels, init enc
S35.402A	Unsp inj of lt renal artery, init enc
S35.405A	Unsp inj of lt renal vein, init enc
S85.002A	Unsp inj of popliteal artery, lt leg, init enc
S85.001A	Unsp inj of popliteal artery, rt leg, init enc
S85.009A	Unsp inj of popliteal artery, unsp leg, init enc
S85.502A	Unsp inj of popliteal vein, lt leg, init enc
S85.501A	Unsp inj of popliteal vein, rt leg, init enc
S85.509A	Unsp inj of popliteal vein, unsp leg, init enc
S35.319A	Unsp inj of portal vein, init enc
S25.101A	Unsp inj of rt innominate or subclavian artery, init enc
S25.301A	Unsp inj of rt innominate or subclavian vein, init enc
S25.401A	Unsp inj of rt pulmn blood vessels, init enc
S35.401A	Unsp inj of rt renal artery, init enc
S35.404A	Unsp inj of rt renal vein, init enc
S35.329A	Unsp inj of splenic vein, init enc
S35.229A	Unsp inj of superior mesenteric artery, init enc
S35.339A	Unsp inj of superior mesenteric vein, init enc
S25.20XA	Unsp inj of superior vena cava, init enc
S25.00XA	Unsp inj of thoracic aorta, init enc
S25.109A	Unsp inj of unsp innominate or subclavian artery, init enc
S25.309A	Unsp inj of unsp innominate or subclavian vein, init enc
S25.409A	Unsp inj of unsp pulmn blood vessels, init enc
S35.403A	Unsp inj of unsp renal artery, init enc
S35.406A	Unsp inj of unsp renal vein, init enc
S34.101A	Unsp inj to L1 lvl of lumbar spinal cord, init enc
S34.102A	Unsp inj to L2 lvl of lumbar spinal cord, init enc
S34.103A	Unsp inj to L3 lvl of lumbar spinal cord, init enc
S34.104A	Unsp inj to L4 lvl of lumbar spinal cord, init enc
S34.105A	Unsp inj to L5 lvl of lumbar spinal cord, init enc
S34.139A	Unsp inj to sacral spinal cord, init enc
S34.109A	Unsp inj to unsp lvl of lumbar spinal cord, init enc
S72.012A	Unsp intracapsular fx of lt femur, init enc for clsd fx
S72.012B	Unsp intracapsular fx of lt femur, init enc for opn fx type I or II
S72.012C	Unsp intracapsular fx of lt femur, init enc for opn fx type IIIA, IIIB, or IIIC
S72.011A	Unsp intracapsular fx of rt femur, init enc for clsd fx
S72.011B	Unsp intracapsular fx of rt femur, init enc for opn fx type I or II
S72.011C	Unsp intracapsular fx of rt femur, init enc for opn fx type IIIA, IIIB, or IIIC
S72.019A	Unsp intracapsular fx of unsp femur, init enc for clsd fx
S72.019B	Unsp intracapsular fx of unsp femur, init enc for opn fx type I or II
S72.019C	Unsp intracapsular fx of unsp femur, init enc for opn fx type IIIA, IIIB, or IIIC
S06.9X6A	Unsp intracranial inj w/ loss of cnscness > 24 hrs w/o return to pre-existing conscious lvl w/ patient surviving, init enc
S06.9X7A	Unsp intracranial inj w/ loss of cnscness of any dur w/ death d/t brain inj prior to regain cnscness, init enc
S06.9X8A	Unsp intracranial inj w/ loss of cnscness of any dur w/ death d/t oth cause prior to regain cnscness, init enc
P10.9	Unsp intracranial lac & hemor d/t birth inj
S12.001B	Unsp nondisp fx of 1st cervical vertebra, init enc for opn fx
S12.101B	Unsp nondisp fx of 2nd cervical vertebra, init enc for opn fx
S12.201B	Unsp nondisp fx of 3rd cervical vertebra, init enc for opn fx
S12.301B	Unsp nondisp fx of 4th cervical vertebra, init enc for opn fx
S12.401B	Unsp nondisp fx of 5th cervical vertebra, init enc for opn fx
S12.501B	Unsp nondisp fx of 6th cervical vertebra, init enc for opn fx
S12.601B	Unsp nondisp fx of 7th cervical vertebra, init enc for opn fx
S42.215B	Unsp nondisp fx of surg neck of lt humerus, init enc for opn fx
S42.214B	Unsp nondisp fx of surg neck of rt humerus, init enc for opn fx
S42.216B	Unsp nondisp fx of surg neck of unsp humerus, init enc for opn fx
S02.113B	Unsp occipital condyle fx, init enc for opn fx
S31.602A	Unsp opn wnd of abd wall, epigastric rgn w/ penetration into peritoneal cavity, init enc
S31.604A	Unsp opn wnd of abd wall, lt lwr quadrant w/ penetration into peritoneal cavity, init enc
S31.601A	Unsp opn wnd of abd wall, lt upr quadrant w/ penetration into peritoneal cavity, init enc
S31.605A	Unsp opn wnd of abd wall, periumbilic rgn w/ penetration into peritoneal cavity, init enc
S31.603A	Unsp opn wnd of abd wall, rt lwr quadrant w/ penetration into peritoneal cavity, init enc
S31.600A	Unsp opn wnd of abd wall, rt upr quadrant w/ penetration into peritoneal cavity, init enc
S31.609A	Unsp opn wnd of abd wall, unsp quadrant w/ penetration into peritoneal cavity, init enc
S11.019A	Unsp opn wnd of larynx, init enc
S21.402A	Unsp opn wnd of lt back wall of thorax w/ penetration into thoracic cavity, init enc
S21.302A	Unsp opn wnd of lt front wall of thorax w/ penetration into thoracic cavity, init enc
S31.001A	Unsp opn wnd of lwr back & pelvis w/ penetration into retroperitoneum, init enc
S21.401A	Unsp opn wnd of rt back wall of thorax w/ penetration into thoracic cavity, init enc
S21.301A	Unsp opn wnd of rt front wall of thorax w/ penetration into thoracic cavity, init enc
S11.029A	Unsp opn wnd of trachea, init enc
S21.409A	Unsp opn wnd of unsp back wall of thorax w/ penetration into thoracic cavity, init enc
S21.309A	Unsp opn wnd of unsp front wall of thorax w/ penetration into thoracic cavity, init enc
S11.039A	Unsp opn wnd of vocal cord, init enc
S79.002A	Unsp physeal fx of upr end of lt femur, init enc for clsd fx
S79.001A	Unsp physeal fx of upr end of rt femur, init enc for clsd fx
S79.009A	Unsp physeal fx of upr end of unsp femur, init enc for clsd fx
O24.32	Unsp pre-existing diabetes mellitus in childbirth
P26.9	Unsp pulmn hemor originating in the perinatal period
E43	Unsp severe protein-calorie malnutrition
S12.130B	Unsp traum disp spondylolisthesis of 2nd cervical vertebra, init enc for opn fx
S12.230B	Unsp traum disp spondylolisthesis of 3rd cervical vertebra, init enc for opn fx
S12.330B	Unsp traum disp spondylolisthesis of 4th cervical vertebra, init enc for opn fx
S12.430B	Unsp traum disp spondylolisthesis of 5th cervical vertebra, init enc for opn fx
S12.530B	Unsp traum disp spondylolisthesis of 6th cervical vertebra, init enc for opn fx
S12.630B	Unsp traum disp spondylolisthesis of 7th cervical vertebra, init enc for opn fx
S12.131B	Unsp traum nondisp spondylolisthesis of 2nd cervical vertebra, init enc for opn fx
S12.231B	Unsp traum nondisp spondylolisthesis of 3rd cervical vertebra, init enc for opn fx
S12.331B	Unsp traum nondisp spondylolisthesis of 4th cervical vertebra, init enc for opn fx
S12.431B	Unsp traum nondisp spondylolisthesis of 5th cervical vertebra, init enc for opn fx
S12.531B	Unsp traum nondisp spondylolisthesis of 6th cervical vertebra, init enc for opn fx
S12.631B	Unsp traum nondisp spondylolisthesis of 7th cervical vertebra, init enc for opn fx
S72.102A	Unsp trochanteric fx of lt femur, init enc for clsd fx
S72.102B	Unsp trochanteric fx of lt femur, init enc for opn fx type I or II
S72.102C	Unsp trochanteric fx of lt femur, init enc for opn fx type IIIA, IIIB, or IIIC
S72.101A	Unsp trochanteric fx of rt femur, init enc for clsd fx
S72.101B	Unsp trochanteric fx of rt femur, init enc for opn fx type I or II
S72.101C	Unsp trochanteric fx of rt femur, init enc for opn fx type IIIA, IIIB, or IIIC
S72.109A	Unsp trochanteric fx of unsp femur, init enc for clsd fx
S72.109B	Unsp trochanteric fx of unsp femur, init enc for opn fx type I or II
S72.109C	Unsp trochanteric fx of unsp femur, init enc for opn fx type IIIA, IIIB, or IIIC
B19.11	Unsp viral hepatitis B w/ hepatic coma
B19.21	Unsp viral hepatitis C w/ hepatic coma
B19.0	Unsp viral hepatitis w/ hepatic coma
S32.119B	Unsp Zone I fx of sacrum, init enc for opn fx
S32.129B	Unsp Zone II fx of sacrum, init enc for opn fx
S32.139B	Unsp Zone III fx of sacrum, init enc for opn fx
S12.02XB	Unstable burst fx of 1st cervical vertebra, init enc for opn fx
S32.012B	Unstable burst fx of 1st lumbar vertebra, init enc for opn fx
S22.012B	Unstable burst fx of 1st thoracic vertebra, init enc for opn fx
S32.022B	Unstable burst fx of 2nd lumbar vertebra, init enc for opn fx
S22.022B	Unstable burst fx of 2nd thoracic vertebra, init enc for opn fx
S32.032B	Unstable burst fx of 3rd lumbar vertebra, init enc for opn fx
S22.032B	Unstable burst fx of 3rd thoracic vertebra, init enc for opn fx
S32.042B	Unstable burst fx of 4th lumbar vertebra, init enc for opn fx
S22.042B	Unstable burst fx of 4th thoracic vertebra, init enc for opn fx
S32.052B	Unstable burst fx of 5th lumbar vertebra, init enc for opn fx
S22.082B	Unstable burst fx of T11-T12 vertebra, init enc for opn fx
S22.052B	Unstable burst fx of T5-T6 vertebra, init enc for opn fx
S22.062B	Unstable burst fx of T7-T8 vertebra, init enc for opn fx
S22.072B	Unstable burst fx of T9-T10 vertebra, init enc for opn fx

S32.002B	Unstable burst fx of unsp lumbar vertebra, init enc for opn fx
S22.002B	Unstable burst fx of unsp thoracic vertebra, init enc for opn fx
B01.11	Varicella encephalitis & encephalomyelitis
B01.12	Varicella myelitis
B01.2	Varicella pneumonia
Q93.81	Velo-cardio-facial synd
I49.01	Ventricular fibrillation
I49.02	Ventricular flutter
J12.9	Viral pneumonia, unsp
K56.2	Volvulus
A39.1	Waterhouse-Friderichsen synd
S32.010B	Wedge compression fx of 1st lumbar vertebra, init enc for opn fx
S22.010B	Wedge compression fx of 1st thoracic vertebra, init enc for opn fx
S32.020B	Wedge compression fx of 2nd lumbar vertebra, init enc for opn fx
S22.020B	Wedge compression fx of 2nd thoracic vertebra, init enc for opn fx
S32.030B	Wedge compression fx of 3rd lumbar vertebra, init enc for opn fx
S22.030B	Wedge compression fx of 3rd thoracic vertebra, init enc for opn fx
S32.040B	Wedge compression fx of 4th lumbar vertebra, init enc for opn fx
S22.040B	Wedge compression fx of 4th thoracic vertebra, init enc for opn fx
S32.050B	Wedge compression fx of 5th lumbar vertebra, init enc for opn fx
S22.080B	Wedge compression fx of T11-T12 vertebra, init enc for opn fx
S22.050B	Wedge compression fx of T5-T6 vertebra, init enc for opn fx
S22.060B	Wedge compression fx of T7-T8 vertebra, init enc for opn fx
S22.070B	Wedge compression fx of T9-T10 vertebra, init enc for opn fx
S32.000B	Wedge compression fx of unsp lumbar vertebra, init enc for opn fx
S22.000B	Wedge compression fx of unsp thoracic vertebra, init enc for opn fx
A92.31	West Nile virus infxn w/ encephalitis
A92.39	West Nile virus infxn w/ oth comp
A92.32	West Nile virus infxn w/ oth neurologic manifestation
A92.30	West Nile virus infxn, unsp
A83.1	Western equine encephalitis
A37.11	Whooping cough d/t Bordetella parapertussis w/ pneumonia
A37.01	Whooping cough d/t Bordetella pertussis w/ pneumonia
A37.81	Whooping cough d/t oth Bordetella species w/ pneumonia
A37.91	Whooping cough, unsp species w/ pneumonia
P27.0	Wilson-Mikity synd
B02.1	Zoster meningitis
B46.9	Zygomycosis, unsp

Numeric Lists of CCs & MCCs

Numeric CC List

A00.0	A18.14	A36.3	A52.01	A78	B02.32	B40.9	B66.2	C16.2
A00.1	A18.15	A36.81	A52.02	A79.0	B02.33	B41.0	B66.3	C16.3
A00.9	A18.16	A36.82	A52.03	A79.1	B02.34	B41.7	B66.4	C16.4
A01.00	A18.17	A36.83	A52.04	A79.81	B02.39	B41.8	B66.5	C16.5
A01.01	A18.18	A36.84	A52.05	A79.89	B02.7	B41.9	B66.8	C16.6
A01.02	A18.2	A36.85	A52.06	A79.9	B02.8	B44.1	B67.0	C16.8
A01.03	A18.32	A36.86	A52.09	A81.00	B03	B44.2	B67.1	C16.9
A01.04	A18.39	A36.89	A52.10	A81.01	B04	B44.7	B67.2	C17.0
A01.05	A18.4	A36.9	A52.11	A81.09	B05.1	B44.81	B67.31	C17.1
A01.09	A18.50	A37.00	A52.12	A81.1	B05.4	B44.89	B67.32	C17.2
A01.1	A18.51	A37.10	A52.15	A81.2	B05.81	B44.9	B67.39	C17.3
A01.2	A18.52	A37.80	A52.16	A81.81	B05.89	B45.0	B67.4	C17.8
A01.3	A18.53	A37.90	A52.17	A81.82	B06.00	B45.2	B67.5	C17.9
A01.4	A18.54	A38.0	A52.19	A81.83	B06.02	B45.3	B67.61	C18.0
A02.0	A18.59	A38.1	A52.2	A81.89	B06.09	B45.7	B67.69	C18.1
A02.23	A18.6	A38.8	A52.3	A81.9	B06.81	B45.8	B67.7	C18.2
A02.24	A18.7	A38.9	A52.71	A82.0	B06.82	B45.9	B67.8	C18.3
A02.25	A18.81	A39.82	A52.72	A82.1	B06.89	B47.0	B67.90	C18.4
A02.29	A18.82	A39.83	A52.73	A82.9	B08.3	B47.1	B67.99	C18.5
A02.8	A18.83	A39.84	A52.74	A85.0	B08.71	B47.9	B68.0	C18.6
A02.9	A18.84	A39.89	A52.75	A85.1	B15.9	B48.2	B68.1	C18.7
A03.0	A18.85	A39.9	A52.76	A85.8	B16.1	B48.3	B68.9	C18.8
A04.0	A18.89	A42.0	A52.77	A86	B16.9	B48.4	B69.0	C18.9
A04.1	A21.0	A42.1	A52.78	A87.0	B17.0	B48.8	B69.1	C19
A04.2	A21.1	A42.2	A52.79	A87.1	B17.10	B49	B69.81	C20
A04.3	A21.2	A42.81	A54.00	A87.2	B17.2	B50.0	B69.89	C21.0
A04.4	A21.3	A42.82	A54.01	A87.8	B17.8	B50.8	B69.9	C21.1
A04.5	A21.7	A42.89	A54.02	A87.9	B17.9	B51.0	B70.0	C21.2
A04.6	A21.8	A42.9	A54.03	A88.0	B18.0	B51.8	B70.1	C21.8
A04.7	A21.9	A43.0	A54.09	A88.8	B18.1	B51.9	B71.0	C22.0
A04.8	A22.0	A43.1	A54.1	A89	B18.8	B52.0	B71.1	C22.1
A04.9	A22.2	A43.8	A54.21	A90	B18.9	B52.8	B71.8	C22.2
A05.0	A22.8	A43.9	A54.22	A91	B19.10	B52.9	B72	C22.3
A05.1	A22.9	A44.0	A54.23	A92.0	B19.9	B53.0	B73.00	C22.4
A05.2	A23.8	A44.1	A54.24	A92.1	B25.1	B53.1	B73.01	C22.7
A05.3	A23.9	A44.8	A54.29	A92.2	B25.8	B53.8	B73.02	C22.8
A05.4	A24.0	A44.9	A54.30	A92.4	B25.9	B54	B73.09	C22.9
A05.5	A24.1	A48.51	A54.31	A92.8	B26.0	B55.0	B73.1	C23
A05.8	A24.2	A48.52	A54.32	A92.9	B26.3	B55.1	B74.0	C24.0
A06.0	A24.3	A50.01	A54.33	A93.0	B26.81	B55.2	B74.1	C24.1
A06.1	A24.9	A50.02	A54.39	A93.1	B26.82	B55.9	B74.2	C24.8
A06.2	A25.0	A50.03	A54.40	A93.2	B26.83	B56.0	B74.3	C24.9
A06.3	A25.1	A50.04	A54.41	A93.8	B26.84	B56.1	B74.4	C25.0
A06.81	A25.9	A50.05	A54.42	A94	B26.85	B57.0	B74.8	C25.1
A06.82	A27.0	A50.06	A54.43	A95.0	B26.89	B57.1	B74.9	C25.2
A06.89	A27.89	A50.07	A54.49	A95.1	B33.1	B57.2	B75	C25.3
A07.1	A27.9	A50.08	A54.82	A95.9	B33.20	B57.30	B76.0	C25.4
A07.2	A28.0	A50.09	A54.83	A96.0	B33.21	B57.31	B76.1	C25.7
A07.3	A28.1	A50.2	A54.84	A96.1	B33.22	B57.32	B76.8	C25.8
A07.4	A28.2	A50.30	A54.85	A96.8	B33.23	B57.39	B76.9	C25.9
A07.8	A28.8	A50.31	A54.89	A96.9	B33.4	B57.40	B77.0	C33
A07.9	A28.9	A50.32	A54.9	A98.0	B34.3	B57.41	B77.89	C34.00
A08.0	A30.0	A50.39	A68.0	A98.1	B37.0	B57.42	B77.9	C34.01
A08.11	A30.1	A50.40	A68.1	A98.2	B37.41	B57.49	B78.0	C34.02
A08.19	A30.2	A50.43	A68.9	A98.5	B37.49	B57.5	B78.7	C34.10
A08.2	A30.3	A50.44	A69.1	A98.8	B37.81	B58.00	B78.9	C34.11
A08.31	A30.4	A50.45	A69.20	A99	B37.82	B58.01	B79	C34.12
A08.32	A30.5	A50.49	A69.21	B00.2	B37.83	B58.09	B80	C34.2
A08.39	A30.8	A50.51	A69.22	B00.50	B37.84	B58.1	B81.0	C34.30
A09	A30.9	A50.52	A69.23	B00.51	B37.89	B58.82	B81.1	C34.31
A15.0	A31.0	A50.53	A69.29	B00.52	B38.0	B58.83	B81.2	C34.32
A15.4	A31.1	A50.54	A70	B00.53	B38.1	B58.89	B81.3	C34.80
A15.5	A31.2	A50.55	A75.0	B00.59	B38.2	B58.9	B81.4	C34.81
A15.6	A31.8	A50.56	A75.1	B00.81	B38.3	B60.0	B81.8	C34.82
A15.7	A31.9	A50.57	A75.2	B00.89	B38.7	B60.10	B82.0	C34.90
A15.8	A32.0	A50.59	A75.3	B01.0	B38.81	B60.19	B97.21	C34.91
A15.9	A32.11	A51.31	A75.9	B01.81	B38.89	B60.2	B97.33	C34.92
A17.9	A32.12	A51.32	A77.0	B01.89	B38.9	B65.0	B97.34	C37
A18.01	A32.81	A51.39	A77.1	B01.9	B39.3	B65.1	B97.35	C38.0
A18.02	A32.82	A51.42	A77.2	B02.0	B40.0	B65.2	C15.3	C38.1
A18.03	A32.89	A51.43	A77.3	B02.21	B40.1	B65.3	C15.4	C38.2
A18.09	A32.9	A51.44	A77.40	B02.22	B40.2	B65.8	C15.5	C38.3
A18.10	A34	A51.45	A77.41	B02.23	B40.3	B65.9	C15.8	C38.4
A18.11	A36.0	A51.46	A77.49	B02.29	B40.7	B66.0	C15.9	C38.8
A18.12	A36.1	A51.49	A77.8	B02.30	B40.81	B66.1	C16.0	C40.00
A18.13	A36.2	A52.00	A77.9	B02.31	B40.89		C16.1	C40.01

C40.02	C70.1	C79.72	C81.46	C82.58	C83.80	C84.A2	C91.00	C94.41
C40.10	C70.9	C79.81	C81.47	C82.59	C83.81	C84.A3	C91.01	C94.42
C40.11	C71.0	C79.82	C81.48	C82.60	C83.82	C84.A4	C91.02	C94.6
C40.12	C71.1	C79.89	C81.49	C82.61	C83.83	C84.A5	C91.10	C94.80
C40.20	C71.2	C79.9	C81.70	C82.62	C83.84	C84.A6	C91.11	C94.81
C40.21	C71.3	C7A.00	C81.71	C82.63	C83.85	C84.A7	C91.12	C94.82
C40.22	C71.4	C7A.010	C81.72	C82.64	C83.86	C84.A8	C91.30	C95.00
C40.30	C71.5	C7A.011	C81.73	C82.65	C83.87	C84.A9	C91.31	C95.01
C40.31	C71.6	C7A.012	C81.74	C82.66	C83.88	C84.Z0	C91.32	C95.02
C40.32	C71.7	C7A.019	C81.75	C82.67	C83.89	C84.Z1	C91.40	C95.10
C40.80	C71.8	C7A.020	C81.76	C82.68	C83.90	C84.Z2	C91.41	C95.11
C40.81	C71.9	C7A.021	C81.77	C82.69	C83.91	C84.Z3	C91.42	C95.12
C40.82	C72.0	C7A.022	C81.78	C82.80	C83.92	C84.Z4	C91.50	C95.90
C40.90	C72.1	C7A.023	C81.79	C82.81	C83.93	C84.Z5	C91.51	C95.91
C40.91	C72.20	C7A.024	C81.90	C82.82	C83.94	C84.Z6	C91.52	C95.92
C40.92	C72.21	C7A.025	C81.91	C82.83	C83.95	C84.Z7	C91.60	C96.0
C41.0	C72.22	C7A.026	C81.92	C82.84	C83.96	C84.Z8	C91.61	C96.2
C41.1	C72.30	C7A.029	C81.93	C82.85	C83.97	C84.Z9	C91.62	C96.4
C41.2	C72.31	C7A.090	C81.94	C82.86	C83.98	C85.10	C91.90	C96.5
C41.3	C72.32	C7A.091	C81.95	C82.87	C83.99	C85.11	C91.91	C96.6
C41.4	C72.40	C7A.092	C81.96	C82.88	C84.00	C85.12	C91.92	C96.9
C41.9	C72.41	C7A.093	C81.97	C82.89	C84.01	C85.13	C91.A0	C96.A
C45.0	C72.42	C7A.094	C81.98	C82.90	C84.02	C85.14	C91.A1	C96.Z
C45.1	C72.50	C7A.095	C81.99	C82.91	C84.03	C85.15	C91.A2	D46.22
C45.2	C72.59	C7A.096	C82.00	C82.92	C84.04	C85.16	C91.Z0	D46.C
C46.0	C72.9	C7A.098	C82.01	C82.93	C84.05	C85.17	C91.Z1	D47.0
C46.1	C74.00	C7A.1	C82.02	C82.94	C84.06	C85.18	C91.Z2	D47.1
C46.2	C74.01	C7A.8	C82.03	C82.95	C84.07	C85.19	C92.00	D47.9
C46.3	C74.02	C7B.01	C82.04	C82.96	C84.08	C85.20	C92.01	D47.Z1
C46.4	C74.10	C7B.02	C82.05	C82.97	C84.09	C85.21	C92.02	D47.Z9
C46.50	C74.11	C7B.03	C82.06	C82.98	C84.10	C85.22	C92.10	D58.8
C46.51	C74.12	C7B.04	C82.07	C82.99	C84.11	C85.23	C92.11	D58.9
C46.52	C74.90	C7B.09	C82.08	C83.00	C84.12	C85.24	C92.12	D59.0
C46.7	C74.91	C7B.8	C82.09	C83.01	C84.13	C85.25	C92.20	D59.1
C46.9	C74.92	C80.0	C82.10	C83.02	C84.14	C85.26	C92.21	D59.2
C47.0	C75.0	C80.2	C82.11	C83.03	C84.15	C85.27	C92.22	D59.4
C47.10	C75.1	C81.00	C82.12	C83.04	C84.16	C85.28	C92.30	D59.9
C47.11	C75.2	C81.01	C82.13	C83.05	C84.17	C85.29	C92.31	D61.01
C47.12	C75.3	C81.02	C82.14	C83.06	C84.18	C85.80	C92.32	D61.09
C47.20	C75.4	C81.03	C82.15	C83.07	C84.19	C85.81	C92.40	D61.818
C47.21	C75.5	C81.04	C82.16	C83.08	C84.40	C85.82	C92.41	D61.82
C47.22	C75.8	C81.05	C82.17	C83.09	C84.41	C85.83	C92.42	D61.9
C47.3	C75.9	C81.06	C82.18	C83.10	C84.42	C85.84	C92.50	D62
C47.4	C77.0	C81.07	C82.19	C83.11	C84.43	C85.85	C92.51	D68.0
C47.5	C77.1	C81.08	C82.20	C83.12	C84.44	C85.86	C92.52	D68.1
C47.6	C77.2	C81.09	C82.21	C83.13	C84.45	C85.87	C92.60	D68.2
C47.8	C77.3	C81.10	C82.22	C83.14	C84.46	C85.88	C92.61	D68.311
C47.9	C77.4	C81.11	C82.23	C83.15	C84.47	C85.89	C92.62	D68.312
C48.0	C77.5	C81.12	C82.24	C83.16	C84.48	C85.90	C92.90	D68.318
C48.1	C77.8	C81.13	C82.25	C83.17	C84.49	C85.91	C92.91	D68.32
C48.2	C77.9	C81.14	C82.26	C83.18	C84.60	C85.92	C92.92	D68.51
C48.8	C78.00	C81.15	C82.27	C83.19	C84.61	C85.93	C92.A0	D68.52
C49.0	C78.01	C81.16	C82.28	C83.30	C84.62	C85.94	C92.A1	D68.59
C49.10	C78.02	C81.17	C82.29	C83.31	C84.63	C85.95	C92.A2	D68.61
C49.11	C78.1	C81.18	C82.30	C83.32	C84.64	C85.96	C92.Z0	D68.62
C49.12	C78.2	C81.19	C82.31	C83.33	C84.65	C85.97	C92.Z1	D68.69
C49.20	C78.30	C81.20	C82.32	C83.34	C84.66	C85.98	C92.Z2	D68.8
C49.21	C78.39	C81.21	C82.33	C83.35	C84.67	C85.99	C93.00	D68.9
C49.22	C78.4	C81.22	C82.34	C83.36	C84.68	C86.0	C93.01	D69.0
C49.3	C78.5	C81.23	C82.35	C83.37	C84.69	C86.1	C93.02	D69.3
C49.4	C78.6	C81.24	C82.36	C83.38	C84.70	C86.2	C93.10	D69.41
C49.5	C78.7	C81.25	C82.37	C83.39	C84.71	C86.3	C93.11	D69.42
C49.6	C78.80	C81.26	C82.38	C83.50	C84.72	C86.4	C93.12	D74.0
C49.8	C78.89	C81.27	C82.39	C83.51	C84.73	C86.5	C93.30	D74.8
C49.9	C79.00	C81.28	C82.40	C83.52	C84.74	C86.6	C93.31	D74.9
C56.1	C79.01	C81.29	C82.41	C83.53	C84.75	C88.2	C93.32	D75.81
C56.2	C79.02	C81.30	C82.42	C83.54	C84.76	C88.3	C93.90	D76.1
C56.9	C79.10	C81.31	C82.43	C83.55	C84.77	C88.4	C93.91	D76.2
C64.1	C79.11	C81.32	C82.44	C83.56	C84.78	C88.8	C93.92	D76.3
C64.2	C79.19	C81.33	C82.45	C83.57	C84.79	C88.9	C93.Z0	D78.01
C64.9	C79.2	C81.34	C82.46	C83.58	C84.90	C90.00	C93.Z1	D78.02
C65.1	C79.31	C81.35	C82.47	C83.59	C84.91	C90.01	C93.Z2	D78.11
C65.2	C79.32	C81.36	C82.48	C83.70	C84.92	C90.02	C94.00	D78.12
C65.9	C79.40	C81.37	C82.49	C83.71	C84.93	C90.10	C94.01	D78.21
C66.1	C79.49	C81.38	C82.50	C83.72	C84.94	C90.11	C94.02	D78.22
C66.2	C79.51	C81.39	C82.51	C83.73	C84.95	C90.12	C94.20	D78.81
C66.9	C79.52	C81.40	C82.52	C83.74	C84.96	C90.20	C94.21	D78.89
C68.0	C79.60	C81.41	C82.53	C83.75	C84.97	C90.21	C94.22	D80.0
C68.1	C79.61	C81.42	C82.54	C83.76	C84.98	C90.22	C94.30	D80.1
C68.8	C79.62	C81.43	C82.55	C83.77	C84.99	C90.30	C94.31	D80.2
C68.9	C79.70	C81.44	C82.56	C83.78	C84.A0	C90.31	C94.32	D80.3
C70.0	C79.71	C81.45	C82.57	C83.79	C84.A1	C90.32	C94.40	

© 2015 Optum360, LLC

D80.4	E70.318	E74.8	F10.27	F14.951	F20.1	G23.0	G71.0	H20.00
D80.5	E70.319	E75.00	F10.280	F15.121	F20.2	G23.1	G71.2	H20.011
D80.6	E70.320	E75.01	F10.281	F15.150	F20.5	G23.2	G72.0	H20.012
D80.7	E70.321	E75.02	F10.288	F15.151	F20.81	G23.8	G72.1	H20.013
D80.8	E70.328	E75.09	F10.29	F15.20	F20.89	G23.9	G72.2	H20.019
D80.9	E70.329	E75.10	F10.921	F15.221	F23	G24.02	G72.81	H20.021
D81.0	E70.330	E75.11	F10.94	F15.222	F30.10	G24.09	G73.1	H20.022
D81.1	E70.331	E75.19	F10.951	F15.23	F30.11	G24.2	G73.3	H20.023
D81.2	E70.338	E75.23	F10.959	F15.250	F30.12	G24.8	G80.1	H20.029
D81.3	E70.339	E75.25	F10.980	F15.251	F30.13	G25.82	G80.2	H20.031
D81.4	E70.39	E75.29	F10.981	F15.259	F30.2	G25.9	G80.3	H20.032
D81.5	E70.40	E75.4	F10.988	F15.280	F30.9	G31.81	G81.00	H20.033
D81.6	E70.41	E76.01	F10.99	F15.281	F31.0	G31.82	G81.01	H20.039
D81.7	E70.49	E76.02	F11.121	F15.282	F31.10	G32.0	G81.02	H20.9
D81.89	E70.5	E76.03	F11.150	F15.288	F31.11	G32.81	G81.03	H21.331
D81.9	E70.8	E76.1	F11.151	F15.921	F31.12	G36.0	G81.04	H21.332
D82.0	E70.9	E76.210	F11.20	F15.93	F31.13	G36.1	G81.10	H21.333
D82.1	E71.0	E76.211	F11.221	F15.950	F31.2	G36.8	G81.11	H21.339
D83.0	E71.110	E76.219	F11.222	F15.951	F31.30	G36.9	G81.12	H30.101
D83.1	E71.111	E76.22	F11.23	F16.121	F31.31	G37.0	G81.13	H30.102
D83.2	E71.118	E76.29	F11.250	F16.150	F31.32	G37.1	G81.14	H30.103
D83.8	E71.120	E76.3	F11.251	F16.151	F31.4	G37.2	G81.90	H30.109
D83.9	E71.121	E76.8	F11.259	F16.20	F31.5	G37.3	G81.91	H30.111
D84.8	E71.128	E76.9	F11.281	F16.221	F31.60	G37.5	G81.92	H30.112
D84.9	E71.19	E78.71	F11.282	F16.250	F31.61	G37.8	G81.93	H30.113
D89.810	E71.2	E78.72	F11.288	F16.251	F31.62	G37.9	G81.94	H30.119
D89.811	E71.310	E79.1	F11.921	F16.259	F31.63	G40.001	G82.20	H30.121
D89.812	E71.311	E79.2	F11.93	F16.280	F31.64	G40.009	G82.21	H30.122
D89.813	E71.312	E79.8	F11.950	F16.283	F31.81	G40.011	G82.22	H30.123
E06.0	E71.313	E79.9	F11.951	F16.288	F31.89	G40.019	G83.0	H30.129
E08.52	E71.314	E80.0	F12.121	F16.921	F32.0	G40.101	G83.4	H30.131
E09.52	E71.318	E80.1	F12.150	F16.950	F32.1	G40.109	G90.3	H30.132
E10.52	E71.32	E80.20	F12.151	F16.951	F32.2	G40.111	G90.50	H30.133
E11.52	E71.39	E80.21	F12.221	F17.203	F32.3	G40.119	G90.511	H30.139
E13.52	E71.50	E80.29	F12.250	F17.213	F33.0	G40.201	G90.512	H30.141
E15	E71.510	E80.3	F12.251	F17.223	F33.1	G40.209	G90.513	H30.142
E22.1	E71.511	E84.19	F12.921	F17.293	F33.2	G40.211	G90.519	H30.143
E22.2	E71.518	E84.8	F12.950	F18.121	F33.3	G40.219	G90.521	H30.149
E22.8	E71.520	E84.9	F12.951	F18.150	F33.40	G40.411	G90.522	H30.891
E22.9	E71.521	E85.0	F13.121	F18.151	F33.8	G40.419	G90.523	H30.892
E23.0	E71.522	E85.1	F13.150	F18.17	F33.9	G40.501	G90.529	H30.893
E23.2	E71.528	E85.2	F13.151	F18.20	F34.8	G40.509	G90.59	H30.899
E24.0	E71.529	E85.3	F13.20	F18.221	F34.9	G40.801	G91.0	H30.90
E24.2	E71.53	E85.4	F13.221	F18.250	F50.00	G40.802	G91.1	H30.91
E24.3	E71.540	E85.8	F13.230	F18.251	F50.01	G40.803	G91.2	H30.92
E24.4	E71.541	E85.9	F13.231	F18.259	F50.02	G40.804	G91.3	H30.93
E24.8	E71.542	E87.0	F13.232	F18.27	F50.2	G40.811	G91.8	H31.321
E24.9	E71.548	E87.1	F13.239	F18.280	F68.10	G40.812	G91.9	H31.322
E27.0	E72.00	E87.2	F13.250	F18.288	F68.12	G40.813	G93.1	H31.323
E27.1	E72.01	E87.3	F13.251	F18.921	F72	G40.814	G95.0	H31.329
E27.2	E72.02	E87.4	F13.259	F18.950	F73	G40.821	G95.20	H31.401
E27.3	E72.03	E88.40	F13.26	F18.951	F84.0	G40.822	G95.29	H31.402
E27.40	E72.04	E88.41	F13.27	F18.97	F84.2	G40.823	G95.81	H31.403
E27.49	E72.09	E88.42	F13.280	F19.121	F84.3	G40.824	G95.89	H31.409
E27.5	E72.10	E88.49	F13.281	F19.150	F84.5	G40.89	G95.9	H31.411
E32.1	E72.11	E89.1	F13.282	F19.151	F84.8	G40.911	G96.0	H31.412
E34.0	E72.12	E89.6	F13.288	F19.17	F84.9	G40.919	G96.11	H31.413
E36.01	E72.19	E89.810	F13.921	F19.20	G03.1	G40.A11	G97.0	H31.419
E36.02	E72.20	E89.811	F13.930	F19.221	G03.2	G40.A19	G97.2	H31.421
E36.11	E72.21	E89.89	F13.931	F19.222	G04.1	G40.B01	G97.31	H31.422
E36.12	E72.22	F01.51	F13.932	F19.230	G10	G40.B09	G97.32	H31.423
E44.0	E72.23	F02.81	F13.939	F19.231	G11.0	G40.B11	G97.41	H31.429
E44.1	E72.29	F03.91	F13.950	F19.232	G11.1	G40.B19	G97.48	H33.121
E45	E72.3	F05	F13.951	F19.239	G11.2	G43.601	G97.49	H33.122
E46	E72.4	F06.0	F13.97	F19.250	G11.3	G43.609	G97.51	H33.123
E51.11	E72.50	F06.2	F14.121	F19.251	G11.4	G43.611	G97.52	H33.129
E51.12	E72.51	F10.121	F14.150	F19.259	G11.8	G43.619	G97.81	H33.20
E51.2	E72.52	F10.14	F14.151	F19.26	G11.9	G45.0	G97.82	H33.21
E51.8	E72.53	F10.151	F14.20	F19.27	G12.1	G45.1	G99.0	H33.22
E51.9	E72.59	F10.159	F14.221	F19.280	G12.20	G45.2	G99.2	H33.23
E53.0	E72.8	F10.180	F14.222	F19.281	G12.21	G45.3	H05.011	H33.40
E55.0	E72.9	F10.181	F14.229	F19.282	G12.22	G45.8	H05.012	H33.41
E64.0	E74.00	F10.188	F14.23	F19.288	G12.29	G45.9	H05.013	H33.42
E66.2	E74.01	F10.19	F14.250	F19.921	G12.8	G46.0	H05.019	H33.43
E70.0	E74.02	F10.221	F14.251	F19.930	G12.9	G46.1	H05.021	H33.8
E70.1	E74.03	F10.230	F14.259	F19.931	G21.11	G46.2	H05.022	H34.00
E70.20	E74.04	F10.231	F14.280	F19.932	G21.19	G60.1	H05.023	H34.01
E70.21	E74.09	F10.232	F14.281	F19.939	G21.2	G61.0	H05.029	H34.02
E70.29	E74.20	F10.239	F14.282	F19.950	G21.3	G61.81	H05.031	H34.03
E70.30	E74.21	F10.24	F14.288	F19.951	G21.8	G62.81	H05.032	H34.10
E70.310	E74.29	F10.251	F14.921	F19.97	G21.9	G70.80	H05.033	H34.11
E70.311	E74.4	F10.259	F14.950	F20.0		G70.81	H05.039	H34.12

H34.13	H47.632	H95.812	I42.1	I70.338	I73.01	I82.4Y9	I82.B22	J21.0
H34.211	H47.639	H95.813	I42.2	I70.339	I74.09	I82.4Z1	I82.B23	J21.1
H34.212	H47.641	H95.819	I42.3	I70.341	I74.10	I82.4Z2	I82.B29	J21.8
H34.213	H47.642	H95.88	I42.4	I70.342	I74.11	I82.4Z3	I82.C11	J21.9
H34.219	H47.649	H95.89	I42.5	I70.343	I74.19	I82.4Z9	I82.C12	J36
H34.231	H49.811	I01.0	I42.6	I70.344	I74.2	I82.501	I82.C13	J39.0
H34.232	H49.812	I01.1	I42.7	I70.348	I74.3	I82.502	I82.C19	J39.1
H34.233	H49.813	I01.2	I42.8	I70.349	I74.4	I82.503	I82.C21	J44.0
H34.239	H49.819	I01.8	I42.9	I70.361	I74.5	I82.509	I82.C22	J44.1
H34.811	H53.121	I01.9	I43	I70.362	I74.8	I82.511	I82.C23	J45.21
H34.812	H53.122	I02.0	I44.2	I70.363	I74.9	I82.512	I82.C29	J45.22
H34.813	H53.123	I02.9	I45.2	I70.368	I75.011	I82.513	I83.201	J45.31
H34.819	H53.129	I09.0	I45.3	I70.369	I75.012	I82.519	I83.202	J45.32
H34.9	H53.131	I09.2	I45.89	I70.431	I75.013	I82.521	I83.203	J45.41
H35.70	H53.132	I09.81	I47.0	I70.432	I75.019	I82.522	I83.204	J45.42
H35.721	H53.133	I12.0	I47.1	I70.433	I75.021	I82.523	I83.205	J45.51
H35.722	H53.139	I13.0	I47.2	I70.434	I75.022	I82.529	I83.208	J45.52
H35.723	H59.011	I13.11	I48.1	I70.438	I75.023	I82.531	I83.209	J45.901
H35.729	H59.012	I13.2	I48.3	I70.439	I75.029	I82.532	I83.211	J45.902
H35.731	H59.013	I20.0	I48.4	I70.441	I75.81	I82.533	I83.212	J47.0
H35.732	H59.019	I20.1	I48.92	I70.442	I75.89	I82.539	I83.213	J47.1
H35.733	H59.031	I23.0	I49.2	I70.443	I76	I82.541	I83.214	J67.7
H35.739	H59.032	I23.1	I50.1	I70.444	I77.2	I82.542	I83.215	J67.8
H35.82	H59.033	I23.2	I50.20	I70.448	I77.4	I82.543	I83.218	J67.9
H40.211	H59.039	I23.3	I50.22	I70.449	I77.5	I82.549	I83.219	J68.0
H40.212	H59.091	I23.6	I50.30	I70.461	I80.10	I82.591	I83.221	J70.0
H40.213	H59.092	I23.7	I50.32	I70.462	I80.11	I82.592	I83.222	J70.1
H40.219	H59.093	I23.8	I50.40	I70.463	I80.12	I82.593	I83.223	J80
H44.001	H59.099	I24.0	I50.42	I70.468	I80.13	I82.599	I83.224	J81.1
H44.002	H59.111	I24.1	I51.0	I70.469	I80.201	I82.5Y1	I83.225	J82
H44.003	H59.112	I24.8	I51.81	I70.531	I80.202	I82.5Y2	I83.228	J84.01
H44.009	H59.113	I24.9	I62.9	I70.532	I80.203	I82.5Y3	I83.229	J84.02
H44.011	H59.119	I25.110	I67.3	I70.533	I80.209	I82.5Y9	I85.00	J84.03
H44.012	H59.121	I25.3	I67.4	I70.534	I80.211	I82.5Z1	I85.10	J84.09
H44.013	H59.122	I25.700	I67.5	I70.538	I80.212	I82.5Z2	I87.011	J84.114
H44.019	H59.123	I25.710	I67.6	I70.539	I80.213	I82.5Z3	I87.012	J84.116
H44.021	H59.129	I25.711	I67.7	I70.541	I80.219	I82.5Z9	I87.013	J84.117
H44.022	H59.211	I25.718	I67.81	I70.542	I80.221	I82.601	I87.019	J84.2
H44.023	H59.212	I25.719	I67.82	I70.543	I80.222	I82.602	I87.031	J84.82
H44.029	H59.219	I25.720	I67.841	I70.544	I80.223	I82.603	I87.032	J84.9
H44.111	H59.221	I25.721	I67.848	I70.548	I80.229	I82.609	I87.033	J90
H44.112	H59.222	I25.728	I67.89	I70.549	I80.231	I82.611	I87.039	J91.0
H44.113	H59.223	I25.729	I68.2	I70.561	I80.232	I82.612	I87.1	J91.8
H44.119	H59.229	I25.730	I69.051	I70.562	I80.233	I82.613	I87.311	J93.11
H44.121	H59.229	I25.731	I69.052	I70.563	I80.239	I82.619	I87.312	J93.12
H44.122	H59.311	I25.738	I69.053	I70.568	I80.291	I82.621	I87.313	J93.81
H44.123	H59.312	I25.739	I69.054	I70.569	I80.292	I82.622	I87.319	J93.82
H44.129	H59.313	I25.750	I69.059	I70.631	I80.293	I82.623	I87.331	J93.83
H44.131	H59.319	I25.751	I69.151	I70.632	I80.299	I82.629	I87.332	J93.9
H44.132	H59.321	I25.758	I69.152	I70.633	I82.1	I82.701	I87.333	J94.0
H44.133	H59.322	I25.759	I69.153	I70.634	I82.210	I82.702	I87.339	J94.2
H44.139	H59.323	I25.760	I69.154	I70.638	I82.211	I82.703	I96	J94.8
H44.19	H59.329	I25.761	I69.159	I70.639	I82.290	I82.709	I97.110	J95.00
H46.00	H59.811	I25.768	I69.251	I70.641	I82.291	I82.711	I97.111	J95.01
H46.01	H59.812	I25.769	I69.252	I70.642	I82.3	I82.712	I97.120	J95.02
H46.02	H59.813	I25.790	I69.253	I70.643	I82.401	I82.713	I97.121	J95.03
H46.03	H59.819	I25.791	I69.254	I70.644	I82.402	I82.719	I97.130	J95.04
H46.10	H59.88	I25.798	I69.259	I70.648	I82.403	I82.721	I97.131	J95.09
H46.11	H59.89	I25.799	I69.351	I70.649	I82.409	I82.722	I97.190	J95.4
H46.12	H60.20	I25.810	I69.352	I70.661	I82.411	I82.723	I97.191	J95.5
H46.13	H60.21	I25.811	I69.353	I70.662	I82.412	I82.729	I97.410	J95.61
H46.8	H60.22	I25.812	I69.354	I70.663	I82.413	I82.811	I97.411	J95.62
H46.9	H60.23	I27.0	I69.359	I70.668	I82.419	I82.812	I97.418	J95.71
H47.10	H70.001	I27.1	I69.851	I70.669	I82.421	I82.813	I97.42	J95.72
H47.11	H70.002	I27.82	I69.852	I70.731	I82.422	I82.819	I97.51	J95.811
H47.41	H70.003	I28.0	I69.853	I70.732	I82.423	I82.890	I97.52	J95.812
H47.42	H70.009	I28.1	I69.854	I70.733	I82.429	I82.891	I97.610	J95.830
H47.43	H70.011	I30.0	I69.859	I70.734	I82.431	I82.90	I97.611	J95.831
H47.49	H70.012	I30.1	I69.951	I70.738	I82.432	I82.91	I97.618	J95.84
H47.511	H70.013	I30.8	I69.952	I70.739	I82.433	I82.A11	I97.62	J95.850
H47.512	H70.019	I30.9	I69.953	I70.742	I82.439	I82.A12	I97.710	J95.851
H47.519	H70.091	I31.0	I69.954	I70.742	I82.441	I82.A13	I97.711	J95.859
H47.521	H70.092	I31.1	I69.959	I70.743	I82.442	I82.A19	I97.790	J95.88
H47.522	H70.093	I31.2	I70.261	I70.744	I82.443	I82.A21	I97.791	J95.89
H47.529	H70.099	I31.3	I70.262	I70.748	I82.449	I82.A22	I97.810	J96.10
H47.531	H95.21	I31.4	I70.263	I70.749	I82.491	I82.A23	I97.811	J96.11
H47.532	H95.22	I31.8	I70.268	I70.761	I82.492	I82.A29	I97.820	J96.12
H47.539	H95.31	I31.9	I70.269	I70.762	I82.493	I82.B11	I97.821	J98.11
H47.621	H95.32	I32	I70.331	I70.763	I82.499	I82.B12	I97.88	J98.19
H47.622	H95.41	I38	I70.332	I70.768	I82.4Y1	I82.B13	I97.89	K04.0
H47.629	H95.42	I39	I70.333	I70.769	I82.4Y2	I82.B19	J05.10	K04.4
H47.631	H95.811	I42.0	I70.334	I70.92	I82.4Y3	I82.B21	J18.2	K11.3

K11.4	K51.418	K80.45	L02.414	L53.1	L97.823	M00.822	M02.352	M25.08
K12.2	K51.419	K80.46	L02.415	L53.2	L97.824	M00.829	M02.359	M30.0
K22.10	K51.50	K80.47	L02.416	L53.3	L97.829	M00.831	M02.361	M30.2
K25.3	K51.511	K80.51	L02.419	L76.01	L97.901	M00.832	M02.362	M30.3
K26.3	K51.512	K80.60	L02.511	L76.02	L97.902	M00.839	M02.369	M30.8
K27.3	K51.513	K80.61	L02.512	L76.11	L97.903	M00.841	M02.371	M31.0
K28.3	K51.514	K80.62	L02.519	L76.12	L97.904	M00.842	M02.372	M31.2
K31.0	K51.518	K80.63	L02.611	L76.21	L97.909	M00.849	M02.379	M31.30
K31.1	K51.519	K80.64	L02.612	L76.22	L97.911	M00.851	M02.38	M31.31
K31.5	K51.80	K80.65	L02.619	L88	L97.912	M00.852	M02.39	M31.4
K31.6	K51.811	K80.66	L02.811	L97.101	L97.913	M00.859	M02.811	M31.7
K35.80	K51.812	K80.71	L02.818	L97.102	L97.914	M00.861	M02.812	M31.8
K35.89	K51.813	K80.81	L02.91	L97.103	L97.919	M00.862	M02.819	M31.9
K40.00	K51.814	K81.0	L03.111	L97.104	L97.921	M00.869	M02.821	M32.11
K40.01	K51.818	K81.2	L03.112	L97.109	L97.922	M00.872	M02.822	M32.12
K40.30	K51.819	K82.0	L03.113	L97.111	L97.923	M00.879	M02.829	M33.00
K40.31	K51.90	K82.1	L03.114	L97.112	L97.924	M00.88	M02.831	M33.01
K41.00	K51.911	K82.3	L03.115	L97.113	L97.929	M00.89	M02.832	M33.02
K41.01	K51.912	K83.0	L03.116	L97.114	L98.3	M00.9	M02.839	M33.09
K41.30	K51.913	K83.3	L03.119	L97.119	M00.00	M01.X0	M02.841	M33.10
K41.31	K51.914	K86.0	L03.121	L97.121	M00.019	M01.X11	M02.842	M33.11
K42.0	K51.918	K86.1	L03.122	L97.122	M00.029	M01.X12	M02.849	M33.12
K43.0	K51.919	K86.2	L03.123	L97.123	M00.039	M01.X19	M02.851	M33.19
K43.3	K52.0	K86.3	L03.124	L97.124	M00.049	M01.X21	M02.852	M33.20
K43.6	K52.1	K90.1	L03.125	L97.129	M00.059	M01.X22	M02.859	M33.21
K44.0	K55.1	K90.2	L03.126	L97.201	M00.069	M01.X29	M02.861	M33.22
K45.0	K55.8	K90.3	L03.211	L97.202	M00.079	M01.X31	M02.862	M33.29
K46.0	K55.9	K90.4	L03.212	L97.203	M00.08	M01.X32	M02.869	M33.90
K50.00	K56.0	K90.81	L03.221	L97.204	M00.09	M01.X39	M02.871	M33.91
K50.011	K56.1	K90.89	L03.222	L97.209	M00.10	M01.X41	M02.872	M33.92
K50.012	K56.3	K90.9	L03.311	L97.211	M00.111	M01.X42	M02.879	M33.99
K50.013	K56.49	K91.2	L03.312	L97.212	M00.112	M01.X49	M02.88	M34.81
K50.014	K56.5	K91.3	L03.313	L97.213	M00.119	M01.X51	M02.89	M34.82
K50.018	K56.60	K91.61	L03.314	L97.214	M00.121	M01.X52	M05.40	M35.03
K50.019	K56.69	K91.62	L03.315	L97.219	M00.122	M01.X59	M05.411	M35.1
K50.10	K56.7	K91.71	L03.316	L97.221	M00.129	M01.X61	M05.412	M35.2
K50.111	K57.00	K91.72	L03.317	L97.222	M00.131	M01.X62	M05.419	M35.5
K50.112	K57.12	K91.81	L03.319	L97.223	M00.132	M01.X69	M05.421	M35.8
K50.113	K57.20	K91.82	L03.321	L97.224	M00.139	M01.X71	M05.422	M36.0
K50.114	K57.32	K91.83	L03.322	L97.229	M00.141	M01.X72	M05.429	M46.20
K50.118	K57.40	K91.840	L03.323	L97.301	M00.142	M01.X79	M05.431	M46.21
K50.119	K57.52	K91.841	L03.324	L97.302	M00.149	M01.X8	M05.432	M46.22
K50.80	K57.80	K91.850	L03.325	L97.303	M00.151	M01.X9	M05.439	M46.23
K50.811	K57.92	K91.858	L03.326	L97.304	M00.152	M02.10	M05.441	M46.24
K50.812	K59.2	K91.86	L03.327	L97.309	M00.159	M02.111	M05.442	M46.25
K50.813	K59.3	K91.89	L03.329	L97.311	M00.161	M02.112	M05.449	M46.26
K50.814	K61.0	K92.0	L03.811	L97.312	M00.162	M02.119	M05.451	M46.27
K50.818	K61.1	K92.1	L03.818	L97.313	M00.169	M02.121	M05.452	M46.28
K50.819	K61.2	K92.2	L03.891	L97.314	M00.171	M02.122	M05.459	M46.30
K50.90	K61.3	K92.81	L03.898	L97.319	M00.172	M02.129	M05.461	M46.31
K50.911	K61.4	K94.01	L03.90	L97.321	M00.179	M02.131	M05.462	M46.32
K50.912	K62.5	K94.02	L03.91	L97.322	M00.18	M02.132	M05.469	M46.33
K50.913	K62.6	K94.03	L05.01	L97.323	M00.19	M02.139	M05.471	M46.34
K50.914	K63.0	K94.09	L05.02	L97.324	M00.20	M02.141	M05.472	M46.35
K50.918	K63.2	K94.11	L08.1	L97.329	M00.211	M02.142	M05.479	M46.36
K50.919	K63.3	K94.12	L10.0	L97.401	M00.212	M02.149	M05.49	M46.37
K51.00	K65.4	K94.13	L10.1	L97.402	M00.219	M02.151	M25.00	M46.38
K51.011	K68.11	K94.19	L10.2	L97.403	M00.221	M02.152	M25.011	M46.39
K51.012	K76.6	K94.22	L10.3	L97.404	M00.222	M02.159	M25.012	M47.011
K51.013	K77	K94.23	L10.4	L97.409	M00.229	M02.161	M25.019	M47.012
K51.014	K80.00	K94.30	L10.5	L97.411	M00.231	M02.162	M25.021	M47.013
K51.018	K80.01	K94.31	L10.81	L97.412	M00.232	M02.169	M25.022	M47.014
K51.019	K80.10	K94.32	L10.89	L97.413	M00.239	M02.171	M25.029	M47.015
K51.20	K80.11	K94.33	L10.9	L97.414	M00.241	M02.172	M25.031	M47.016
K51.211	K80.12	K94.39	L12.0	L97.419	M00.242	M02.179	M25.032	M47.019
K51.212	K80.13	K95.01	L12.30	L97.421	M00.249	M02.18	M25.039	M47.021
K51.213	K80.18	K95.09	L12.31	L97.422	M00.251	M02.19	M25.041	M47.022
K51.214	K80.19	K95.81	L12.35	L97.423	M00.252	M02.30	M25.042	M47.029
K51.218	K80.21	K95.89	L12.8	L97.424	M00.259	M02.311	M25.049	M47.11
K51.219	K80.30	L02.01	L12.9	L97.429	M00.261	M02.312	M25.051	M47.12
K51.30	K80.31	L02.11	L49.3	L97.801	M00.262	M02.319	M25.052	M47.13
K51.311	K80.32	L02.211	L49.4	L97.802	M00.269	M02.321	M25.059	M47.14
K51.312	K80.33	L02.212	L49.5	L97.803	M00.271	M02.322	M25.061	M47.15
K51.313	K80.34	L02.213	L49.6	L97.809	M00.272	M02.329	M25.062	M47.16
K51.314	K80.35	L02.214	L49.7	L97.811	M00.279	M02.331	M25.069	M48.30
K51.318	K80.36	L02.215	L49.8	L97.812	M00.28	M02.332	M25.071	M48.31
K51.319	K80.37	L02.216	L49.9	L97.813	M00.29	M02.339	M25.072	M48.32
K51.40	K80.40	L02.219	L51.1	L97.814	M00.80	M02.341	M25.073	M48.33
K51.411	K80.41	L02.31	L51.2	L97.819	M00.811	M02.342	M25.074	M48.34
K51.412	K80.42	L02.411	L51.3	L97.821	M00.812	M02.349	M25.075	M48.35
K51.413	K80.43	L02.412	L53.0	L97.822	M00.819	M02.351	M25.076	
K51.414	K80.44	L02.413			M00.821			

M48.36	M80.022A	M80.839K	M84.352P	M84.444P	M84.522A	M84.60XK	M84.673P	M86.279
M48.37	M80.022K	M80.839P	M84.353K	M84.445A	M84.522K	M84.60XP	M84.674A	M86.28
M48.38	M80.022P	M80.841A	M84.353P	M84.445K	M84.522P	M84.611A	M84.674K	M86.29
M48.50XA	M80.029A	M80.841K	M84.359K	M84.445P	M84.529A	M84.611K	M84.674P	M86.30
M48.51XA	M80.029K	M80.841P	M84.359P	M84.446A	M84.529K	M84.611P	M84.675A	M86.311
M48.52XA	M80.029P	M80.842A	M84.361K	M84.446K	M84.529P	M84.612A	M84.675K	M86.312
M48.53XA	M80.031A	M80.842K	M84.361P	M84.446P	M84.531A	M84.612K	M84.675P	M86.319
M48.54XA	M80.031K	M80.842P	M84.362K	M84.451A	M84.531K	M84.619A	M84.676A	M86.321
M48.55XA	M80.031P	M80.849A	M84.362P	M84.451K	M84.531P	M84.619K	M84.676K	M86.322
M48.56XA	M80.032A	M80.849K	M84.363K	M84.451P	M84.532A	M84.619P	M84.676P	M86.329
M48.57XA	M80.032K	M80.849P	M84.363P	M84.452A	M84.532K	M84.621A	M84.68XA	M86.331
M48.58XA	M80.032P	M80.851A	M84.364K	M84.452K	M84.532P	M84.621K	M84.68XK	M86.332
M50.00	M80.039A	M80.851K	M84.364P	M84.452P	M84.533A	M84.621P	M84.68XP	M86.339
M50.01	M80.039K	M80.851P	M84.369K	M84.453A	M84.533K	M84.622A	M86.00	M86.341
M50.02	M80.039P	M80.852A	M84.369P	M84.453K	M84.533P	M84.622K	M86.011	M86.342
M50.03	M80.041A	M80.852K	M84.371K	M84.453P	M84.534A	M84.622P	M86.012	M86.349
M51.04	M80.041K	M80.852P	M84.371P	M84.454A	M84.534K	M84.629A	M86.019	M86.351
M51.05	M80.041P	M80.859A	M84.372K	M84.454K	M84.534P	M84.629K	M86.021	M86.352
M51.06	M80.042A	M80.859K	M84.372P	M84.454P	M84.539A	M84.629P	M86.022	M86.359
M60.000	M80.042K	M80.859P	M84.373K	M84.459A	M84.539K	M84.631A	M86.029	M86.361
M60.001	M80.042P	M80.861A	M84.373P	M84.459K	M84.539P	M84.631K	M86.031	M86.362
M60.002	M80.049A	M80.861K	M84.374K	M84.459P	M84.541A	M84.631P	M86.032	M86.369
M60.003	M80.049K	M80.861P	M84.374P	M84.461A	M84.541K	M84.632A	M86.039	M86.371
M60.004	M80.049P	M80.862A	M84.375K	M84.461K	M84.541P	M84.632K	M86.041	M86.372
M60.005	M80.051A	M80.862K	M84.375P	M84.461P	M84.542A	M84.632P	M86.042	M86.379
M60.009	M80.051K	M80.862P	M84.376K	M84.462A	M84.542K	M84.633A	M86.049	M86.38
M60.011	M80.051P	M80.869A	M84.376P	M84.462K	M84.542P	M84.633K	M86.051	M86.39
M60.012	M80.052A	M80.869K	M84.377K	M84.462P	M84.549A	M84.633P	M86.052	M86.40
M60.019	M80.052K	M80.869P	M84.377P	M84.463A	M84.549K	M84.634A	M86.059	M86.411
M60.021	M80.052P	M80.871A	M84.378K	M84.463K	M84.549P	M84.634K	M86.061	M86.412
M60.022	M80.059A	M80.871K	M84.378P	M84.463P	M84.550A	M84.634P	M86.062	M86.419
M60.029	M80.059K	M80.871P	M84.379K	M84.464A	M84.550K	M84.639A	M86.069	M86.421
M60.031	M80.059P	M80.872A	M84.379P	M84.464K	M84.550P	M84.639K	M86.071	M86.422
M60.032	M80.061A	M80.872K	M84.38XK	M84.464P	M84.551A	M84.639P	M86.072	M86.429
M60.039	M80.061K	M80.872P	M84.38XP	M84.469A	M84.551K	M84.641A	M86.079	M86.431
M60.041	M80.061P	M80.879A	M84.40XA	M84.469K	M84.551P	M84.641K	M86.08	M86.432
M60.042	M80.062A	M80.879K	M84.40XK	M84.469P	M84.552A	M84.641P	M86.09	M86.439
M60.043	M80.062K	M80.879P	M84.40XP	M84.471A	M84.552K	M84.642A	M86.10	M86.441
M60.044	M80.062P	M80.88XA	M84.411A	M84.471K	M84.552P	M84.642K	M86.111	M86.442
M60.045	M80.069A	M80.88XK	M84.411K	M84.471P	M84.553A	M84.642P	M86.112	M86.449
M60.046	M80.069K	M80.88XP	M84.411P	M84.472A	M84.553K	M84.649A	M86.119	M86.451
M60.051	M80.069P	M84.30XK	M84.412A	M84.472K	M84.553P	M84.649K	M86.121	M86.452
M60.052	M80.071A	M84.30XP	M84.412K	M84.472P	M84.559A	M84.649P	M86.122	M86.459
M60.059	M80.071K	M84.311K	M84.412P	M84.473A	M84.559K	M84.650A	M86.129	M86.461
M60.061	M80.071P	M84.311P	M84.419A	M84.473K	M84.559P	M84.650K	M86.131	M86.462
M60.062	M80.072A	M84.312K	M84.419K	M84.473P	M84.561A	M84.650P	M86.132	M86.469
M60.069	M80.072K	M84.312P	M84.419P	M84.474A	M84.561K	M84.651A	M86.139	M86.471
M60.070	M80.072P	M84.319K	M84.421A	M84.474K	M84.561P	M84.651K	M86.141	M86.472
M60.071	M80.079A	M84.319P	M84.421K	M84.474P	M84.562A	M84.651P	M86.142	M86.479
M60.072	M80.079K	M84.321K	M84.421P	M84.475A	M84.562K	M84.652A	M86.149	M86.48
M60.073	M80.079P	M84.321P	M84.422A	M84.475K	M84.562P	M84.652K	M86.151	M86.49
M60.074	M80.08XA	M84.322K	M84.422K	M84.475P	M84.563A	M84.652P	M86.152	M86.50
M60.075	M80.08XK	M84.322P	M84.422P	M84.476A	M84.563K	M84.653A	M86.159	M86.511
M60.076	M80.08XP	M84.329K	M84.429A	M84.476K	M84.563P	M84.653K	M86.161	M86.512
M60.077	M80.80XA	M84.329P	M84.429K	M84.476P	M84.564A	M84.653P	M86.162	M86.519
M60.078	M80.80XK	M84.331K	M84.429P	M84.477A	M84.564K	M84.659A	M86.169	M86.521
M60.08	M80.80XP	M84.331P	M84.431A	M84.477K	M84.564P	M84.659K	M86.171	M86.522
M60.09	M80.811A	M84.332K	M84.431K	M84.477P	M84.569A	M84.659P	M86.172	M86.529
M62.82	M80.811K	M84.332P	M84.431P	M84.478A	M84.569K	M84.661A	M86.179	M86.531
M79.A11	M80.811P	M84.333K	M84.432A	M84.478K	M84.569P	M84.661K	M86.18	M86.532
M79.A12	M80.812A	M84.333P	M84.432K	M84.478P	M84.571A	M84.661P	M86.19	M86.539
M79.A19	M80.812K	M84.334K	M84.432P	M84.479A	M84.571K	M84.662A	M86.20	M86.541
M79.A21	M80.812P	M84.334P	M84.433A	M84.479K	M84.571P	M84.662K	M86.211	M86.542
M79.A22	M80.819A	M84.339K	M84.433K	M84.479P	M84.572A	M84.662P	M86.212	M86.549
M79.A29	M80.819K	M84.339P	M84.433P	M84.48XA	M84.572K	M84.663A	M86.219	M86.551
M79.A3	M80.819P	M84.341K	M84.434A	M84.48XK	M84.572P	M84.663K	M86.221	M86.552
M79.A9	M80.821A	M84.341P	M84.434K	M84.48XP	M84.573A	M84.663P	M86.222	M86.559
M80.00XA	M80.821K	M84.342K	M84.434P	M84.50XA	M84.573K	M84.664A	M86.229	M86.561
M80.00XK	M80.821P	M84.342P	M84.439A	M84.50XK	M84.573P	M84.664K	M86.231	M86.562
M80.00XP	M80.822A	M84.343K	M84.439K	M84.50XP	M84.574A	M84.664P	M86.232	M86.569
M80.011A	M80.822K	M84.343P	M84.439P	M84.511A	M84.574K	M84.669A	M86.239	M86.571
M80.011K	M80.822P	M84.344K	M84.441A	M84.511K	M84.574P	M84.669K	M86.241	M86.572
M80.011P	M80.829A	M84.344P	M84.441K	M84.511P	M84.575A	M84.669P	M86.242	M86.579
M80.012A	M80.829K	M84.345K	M84.441P	M84.512A	M84.575K	M84.671A	M86.249	M86.58
M80.012K	M80.829P	M84.345P	M84.442A	M84.512K	M84.575P	M84.671K	M86.251	M86.59
M80.012P	M80.831A	M84.346K	M84.442K	M84.512P	M84.576A	M84.671P	M86.252	M86.60
M80.019A	M80.831K	M84.346P	M84.442P	M84.519A	M84.576K	M84.672A	M86.259	M86.611
M80.019K	M80.831P	M84.350K	M84.443A	M84.519K	M84.576P	M84.672K	M86.261	M86.612
M80.019P	M80.832A	M84.350P	M84.443K	M84.519P	M84.58XA	M84.672P	M86.262	M86.619
M80.021A	M80.832K	M84.351K	M84.443P	M84.521A	M84.58XK	M84.673A	M86.269	M86.621
M80.021K	M80.832P	M84.351P	M84.444A	M84.521K	M84.58XP	M84.673K	M86.271	M86.622
M80.021P	M80.839A	M84.352K	M84.444K	M84.521P	M84.60XA	M84.673K	M86.272	M86.629

M86.631	M87.135	M87.329	M90.511	N06.2	N99.511	O14.92	O26.832	O36.0135
M86.632	M87.136	M87.331	M90.512	N06.3	N99.512	O14.93	O26.833	O36.0139
M86.639	M87.137	M87.332	M90.519	N06.4	N99.518	O16.1	O26.872	O36.0910
M86.641	M87.138	M87.333	M90.521	N06.5	N99.61	O16.2	O26.873	O36.0911
M86.642	M87.139	M87.334	M90.522	N07.2	N99.62	O16.3	O26.879	O36.0912
M86.649	M87.141	M87.335	M90.529	N07.3	N99.71	O20.0	O30.101	O36.0913
M86.651	M87.142	M87.336	M90.531	N07.4	N99.72	O20.9	O30.102	O36.0914
M86.652	M87.143	M87.337	M90.532	N07.5	N99.820	O22.20	O30.103	O36.0915
M86.659	M87.144	M87.338	M90.539	N10	N99.821	O22.21	O30.111	O36.0919
M86.661	M87.145	M87.339	M90.541	N11.1	O00.0	O22.22	O30.112	O36.0920
M86.662	M87.146	M87.341	M90.542	N11.8	O00.1	O22.23	O30.113	O36.0921
M86.669	M87.150	M87.342	M90.549	N11.9	O00.2	O22.30	O30.121	O36.0922
M86.671	M87.151	M87.343	M90.551	N12	O00.8	O22.40	O30.122	O36.0923
M86.672	M87.152	M87.344	M90.552	N13.1	O00.9	O22.41	O30.123	O36.0924
M86.679	M87.159	M87.345	M90.559	N13.2	O03.0	O22.42	O30.191	O36.0925
M86.68	M87.161	M87.346	M90.561	N13.30	O03.30	O22.43	O30.192	O36.0929
M86.69	M87.162	M87.350	M90.562	N13.39	O03.33	O22.50	O30.193	O36.0930
M86.8X0	M87.163	M87.351	M90.569	N13.4	O03.34	O22.51	O30.201	O36.0931
M86.8X1	M87.164	M87.352	M90.571	N13.6	O03.35	O22.52	O30.202	O36.0932
M86.8X2	M87.165	M87.353	M90.572	N13.8	O03.36	O22.53	O30.203	O36.0933
M86.8X3	M87.166	M87.361	M90.579	N17.8	O03.37	O22.8X1	O30.211	O36.0934
M86.8X4	M87.171	M87.362	M90.58	N17.9	O03.38	O22.8X2	O30.212	O36.0935
M86.8X5	M87.172	M87.363	M90.59	N18.4	O03.39	O22.8X3	O30.213	O36.0939
M86.8X6	M87.173	M87.364	M96.0	N18.5	O03.5	O22.8X9	O30.221	O36.4XX0
M86.8X7	M87.174	M87.365	M96.621	N20.1	O03.7	O22.90	O30.222	O36.4XX1
M86.8X8	M87.175	M87.366	M96.622	N20.2	O03.80	O23.01	O30.223	O36.4XX2
M86.8X9	M87.176	M87.371	M96.629	N25.1	O03.83	O23.02	O30.291	O36.4XX3
M86.9	M87.177	M87.372	M96.631	N25.81	O03.84	O23.03	O30.292	O36.4XX4
M87.00	M87.178	M87.373	M96.632	N28.0	O03.85	O23.11	O30.293	O36.4XX5
M87.011	M87.179	M87.374	M96.639	N28.84	O03.86	O23.12	O30.801	O36.4XX9
M87.012	M87.180	M87.375	M96.65	N28.85	O03.87	O23.13	O30.802	O41.01X0
M87.019	M87.188	M87.376	M96.661	N28.86	O03.88	O23.21	O30.803	O41.01X1
M87.021	M87.19	M87.377	M96.662	N30.00	O03.89	O23.22	O30.811	O41.01X2
M87.022	M87.20	M87.378	M96.669	N30.01	O04.5	O23.23	O30.812	O41.01X3
M87.029	M87.211	M87.379	M96.671	N30.40	O04.80	O23.31	O30.813	O41.01X4
M87.031	M87.212	M87.38	M96.672	N30.41	O04.83	O23.32	O30.821	O41.01X5
M87.032	M87.219	M87.39	M96.679	N32.1	O04.84	O23.33	O30.822	O41.01X9
M87.033	M87.221	M87.80	M96.69	N32.2	O04.85	O23.41	O30.823	O41.02X0
M87.034	M87.222	M87.811	M96.810	N34.0	O04.86	O23.42	O30.891	O41.02X1
M87.035	M87.229	M87.812	M96.811	N36.0	O04.87	O23.43	O30.892	O41.02X2
M87.036	M87.231	M87.819	M96.820	N39.0	O04.88	O23.511	O30.893	O41.02X3
M87.037	M87.232	M87.821	M96.821	N41.0	O04.89	O23.512	O31.8X10	O41.02X4
M87.038	M87.233	M87.822	M96.830	N41.2	O07.0	O23.513	O31.8X11	O41.02X5
M87.039	M87.234	M87.829	M96.831	N43.1	O07.1	O23.521	O31.8X12	O41.02X9
M87.041	M87.235	M87.831	M96.89	N44.00	O07.30	O23.522	O31.8X13	O41.03X0
M87.042	M87.236	M87.832	M99.10	N44.01	O07.33	O23.523	O31.8X14	O41.03X1
M87.043	M87.237	M87.833	M99.11	N44.02	O07.34	O23.591	O31.8X15	O41.03X2
M87.044	M87.238	M87.834	M99.18	N44.03	O07.35	O23.592	O31.8X19	O41.03X3
M87.045	M87.239	M87.835	N02.0	N44.04	O07.36	O23.593	O31.8X20	O41.03X4
M87.046	M87.241	M87.836	N02.1	N45.4	O07.37	O23.91	O31.8X21	O41.03X9
M87.050	M87.242	M87.837	N02.2	N48.30	O07.38	O23.92	O31.8X22	O44.01
M87.051	M87.243	M87.838	N02.3	N48.31	O07.39	O23.93	O31.8X23	O44.02
M87.052	M87.244	M87.839	N02.4	N48.32	O08.0	O24.011	O31.8X24	O44.03
M87.059	M87.245	M87.841	N02.5	N48.33	O08.1	O24.012	O31.8X25	O47.02
M87.061	M87.246	M87.842	N02.6	N48.39	O08.5	O24.019	O31.8X29	O47.03
M87.062	M87.250	M87.843	N02.7	N70.01	O08.6	O24.03	O31.8X30	O47.1
M87.063	M87.251	M87.844	N02.8	N70.02	O08.7	O24.111	O31.8X31	O60.10X0
M87.064	M87.252	M87.845	N02.9	N70.03	O08.81	O24.112	O31.8X32	O60.10X1
M87.065	M87.256	M87.849	N03.0	N71.0	O08.82	O24.113	O31.8X33	O60.10X2
M87.066	M87.261	M87.850	N03.1	N73.0	O08.83	O24.119	O31.8X34	O60.10X3
M87.071	M87.262	M87.851	N03.2	N73.4	O08.89	O24.13	O31.8X35	O60.10X4
M87.072	M87.263	M87.852	N03.3	N75.1	O08.9	O24.311	O31.8X39	O60.10X5
M87.073	M87.264	M87.859	N03.4	N76.4	O10.011	O24.312	O33.0	O60.10X9
M87.074	M87.265	M87.861	N03.5	N76.81	O10.012	O24.313	O36.0110	O60.20X0
M87.075	M87.266	M87.862	N03.6	N82.0	O10.013	O24.319	O36.0111	O60.20X1
M87.076	M87.271	M87.863	N03.7	N82.1	O10.02	O24.33	O36.0112	O60.20X2
M87.077	M87.272	M87.864	N03.8	N82.2	O10.411	O24.811	O36.0113	O60.20X3
M87.078	M87.273	M87.865	N03.9	N82.3	O10.412	O24.812	O36.0114	O60.20X4
M87.079	M87.274	M87.869	N04.0	N82.4	O10.413	O24.813	O36.0115	O60.20X5
M87.08	M87.275	M87.871	N04.1	N82.5	O10.43	O24.819	O36.0119	O60.20X9
M87.09	M87.276	M87.872	N04.2	N82.8	O10.911	O24.83	O36.0120	O63.9
M87.10	M87.277	M87.873	N04.3	N82.9	O10.912	O24.911	O36.0121	O68
M87.111	M87.278	M87.874	N04.4	N83.51	O10.913	O24.912	O36.0122	O70.2
M87.112	M87.279	M87.875	N04.5	N83.52	O10.92	O24.913	O36.0123	O70.3
M87.119	M87.28	M87.876	N04.6	N83.53	O12.11	O24.919	O36.0124	O70.4
M87.121	M87.29	M87.877	N04.7	N98.0	O12.12	O24.93	O36.0125	O71.2
M87.122	M87.30	M87.878	N04.8	N98.1	O12.13	O26.611	O36.0129	O71.3
M87.129	M87.311	M87.879	N04.9	N98.2	O12.21	O26.612	O36.0130	O71.4
M87.131	M87.312	M87.88	N05.2	N98.3	O12.22	O26.613	O36.0131	O71.5
M87.132	M87.319	M87.89	N05.3	N98.8	O12.23	O26.62	O36.0132	O71.6
M87.133	M87.321	M87.9	N05.4	N98.9	O14.02	O26.831	O36.0133	O71.7
M87.134	M87.322	M90.50	N05.5	N99.510	O14.03		O36.0134	

Appendix B—Numeric CC List

O72.0	O99.412	Q22.2	Q60.5	R04.2	S02.609B	S05.51XA	S09.392A	S12.301A
O72.1	O99.413	Q22.3	Q60.6	R04.81	S02.609K	S05.52XA	S09.399A	S12.301K
O72.2	O99.43	Q23.0	Q61.00	R04.89	S02.61XA	S05.70XA	S11.10XA	S12.330A
O75.2	O99.830	Q23.1	Q61.01	R04.9	S02.61XB	S05.71XA	S11.11XA	S12.330K
O86.11	O99.834	Q23.2	Q61.02	R06.3	S02.61XK	S05.72XA	S11.12XA	S12.331A
O86.12	O99.835	Q23.3	Q61.11	R09.01	S02.62XA	S05.8X1A	S11.13XA	S12.331K
O86.13	P10.2	Q24.0	Q61.19	R17	S02.62XB	S05.8X2A	S11.14XA	S12.34XA
O86.19	P12.2	Q24.1	Q61.2	R18.0	S02.62XK	S05.8X9A	S11.15XA	S12.34XK
O86.20	P28.0	Q24.4	Q61.3	R18.8	S02.63XA	S05.91XA	S11.20XA	S12.350A
O86.21	P28.10	Q24.5	Q61.4	R29.0	S02.63XB	S05.92XA	S11.21XA	S12.350K
O86.22	P28.11	Q25.0	Q61.5	R29.1	S02.63XK	S06.0X1A	S11.22XA	S12.351A
O86.29	P28.19	Q25.1	Q61.8	R29.5	S02.64XA	S06.0X2A	S11.23XA	S12.351K
O86.4	P28.2	Q25.2	Q61.9	R39.0	S02.64XB	S06.0X3A	S11.24XA	S12.390A
O87.0	P28.3	Q25.3	Q62.0	R40.3	S02.64XK	S06.0X4A	S11.25XA	S12.390K
O87.2	P28.4	Q25.4	Q62.10	R41.4	S02.65XA	S06.0X5A	S12.000A	S12.391A
O87.3	P35.0	Q25.8	Q62.11	R44.0	S02.65XB	S06.0X7A	S12.000K	S12.391K
O87.8	P38.1	Q25.9	Q62.12	R44.2	S02.65XK	S06.0X8A	S12.001A	S12.400A
O88.319	P38.9	Q26.0	Q62.31	R44.3	S02.66XA	S06.0X9A	S12.001K	S12.400K
O98.011	P39.0	Q26.1	Q62.32	R45.851	S02.66XB	S06.2X1A	S12.01XA	S12.401A
O98.012	P39.2	Q26.2	Q62.39	R47.01	S02.66XK	S06.2X2A	S12.01XK	S12.401K
O98.013	P39.3	Q26.3	Q64.10	R56.00	S02.67XA	S06.2X3A	S12.02XA	S12.430A
O98.02	P39.4	Q26.4	Q64.11	R56.01	S02.67XB	S06.2X4A	S12.02XK	S12.430K
O98.03	P39.8	Q26.8	Q64.12	R56.1	S02.67XK	S06.2X5A	S12.030A	S12.431A
O98.111	P39.9	Q26.9	Q64.19	R57.9	S02.69XA	S06.2X9A	S12.030K	S12.431K
O98.112	P52.0	Q27.30	Q64.2	R64	S02.69XB	S06.301A	S12.031A	S12.44XA
O98.113	P52.1	Q27.4	Q64.31	R65.10	S02.69XK	S06.302A	S12.031K	S12.44XK
O98.12	P52.3	Q28.0	Q64.32	R71.0	S02.8XXA	S06.303A	S12.040A	S12.450A
O98.13	P53	Q28.1	Q64.33	R78.81	S02.8XXB	S06.304A	S12.040K	S12.450K
O98.211	P54.4	Q28.8	Q64.39	R82.0	S02.8XXK	S06.305A	S12.041A	S12.451A
O98.212	P61.2	Q28.9	Q67.5	R82.1	S02.91XA	S06.309A	S12.041K	S12.451K
O98.213	P61.3	Q31.1	Q67.8	S01.101A	S02.91XK	S06.371A	S12.090A	S12.490A
O98.22	P61.4	Q31.2	Q68.1	S01.102A	S02.92XA	S06.372A	S12.090K	S12.490K
O98.23	P61.6	Q31.3	Q74.3	S01.109A	S02.92XB	S06.373A	S12.091A	S12.491A
O98.311	P70.2	Q31.5	Q76.3	S02.0XXA	S02.92XK	S06.374A	S12.091K	S12.491K
O98.312	P70.8	Q31.8	Q76.425	S02.0XXK	S04.011A	S06.375A	S12.100A	S12.500A
O98.313	P71.0	Q31.9	Q76.426	S02.10XA	S04.012A	S06.379A	S12.100K	S12.500K
O98.32	P71.1	Q32.0	Q76.427	S02.10XK	S04.019A	S06.381A	S12.101A	S12.501A
O98.33	P71.2	Q32.1	Q76.428	S02.110A	S04.02XA	S06.382A	S12.101K	S12.501K
O98.411	P71.3	Q32.2	Q76.429	S02.110K	S04.031A	S06.383A	S12.110A	S12.530A
O98.412	P71.4	Q32.3	Q76.6	S02.111A	S04.032A	S06.384A	S12.110K	S12.530K
O98.413	P71.8	Q32.4	Q76.7	S02.111K	S04.039A	S06.385A	S12.111A	S12.531A
O98.42	P71.9	Q33.0	Q76.8	S02.112A	S04.041A	S06.389A	S12.111K	S12.531K
O98.43	P72.0	Q33.4	Q76.9	S02.112K	S04.042A	S06.811A	S12.112A	S12.54XA
O98.511	P72.1	Q39.5	Q77.2	S02.113A	S04.049A	S06.812A	S12.112K	S12.54XK
O98.512	P72.2	Q39.6	Q78.0	S02.113K	S04.10XA	S06.813A	S12.120A	S12.550A
O98.513	P72.8	Q39.8	Q78.2	S02.118A	S04.11XA	S06.814A	S12.120K	S12.550K
O98.52	P74.5	Q39.9	Q79.6	S02.118K	S04.12XA	S06.815A	S12.121A	S12.551A
O98.53	P74.6	Q41.0	Q85.1	S02.119A	S04.20XA	S06.819A	S12.121K	S12.551K
O98.611	P74.8	Q41.1	Q85.8	S02.119K	S04.21XA	S06.821A	S12.130A	S12.590A
O98.612	P76.1	Q41.2	Q85.9	S02.19XA	S04.22XA	S06.822A	S12.130K	S12.590K
O98.613	P83.0	Q41.8	Q87.1	S02.19XK	S04.30XA	S06.823A	S12.131A	S12.591A
O98.62	P83.30	Q41.9	Q87.2	S02.2XXB	S04.31XA	S06.824A	S12.131K	S12.591K
O98.63	P83.39	Q42.0	Q87.3	S02.2XXK	S04.32XA	S06.825A	S12.14XA	S12.600A
O98.711	P91.60	Q42.1	Q87.40	S02.3XXA	S04.40XA	S06.829A	S12.14XK	S12.600K
O98.712	P91.61	Q42.2	Q87.410	S02.3XXB	S04.41XA	S06.891A	S12.150A	S12.601A
O98.713	P91.62	Q42.3	Q87.418	S02.3XXK	S04.42XA	S06.892A	S12.150K	S12.601K
O98.72	P93.0	Q42.8	Q87.42	S02.400A	S04.50XA	S06.893A	S12.151A	S12.630A
O98.73	P93.8	Q42.9	Q87.43	S02.400B	S04.51XA	S06.894A	S12.151K	S12.630K
O98.811	P94.0	Q43.1	Q87.5	S02.400K	S04.52XA	S06.895A	S12.190A	S12.631A
O98.812	P96.1	Q43.2	Q87.81	S02.401A	S04.60XA	S06.899A	S12.190K	S12.631K
O98.813	P96.2	Q43.3	Q87.89	S02.401B	S04.61XA	S06.9X1A	S12.191A	S12.64XA
O98.82	Q01.0	Q43.4	Q89.01	S02.401K	S04.62XA	S06.9X2A	S12.191K	S12.64XK
O98.83	Q01.1	Q43.5	Q89.09	S02.402A	S04.70XA	S06.9X3A	S12.200A	S12.650A
O98.911	Q01.2	Q43.6	Q89.3	S02.402B	S04.71XA	S06.9X4A	S12.200K	S12.650K
O98.912	Q01.8	Q43.7	Q89.7	S02.402K	S04.72XA	S06.9X5A	S12.201A	S12.651A
O98.913	Q01.9	Q43.8	Q89.8	S02.411A	S04.811A	S06.9X9A	S12.201K	S12.651K
O98.92	Q04.4	Q43.9	Q91.0	S02.411B	S04.812A	S07.0XXA	S12.230A	S12.690A
O98.93	Q04.5	Q44.0	Q91.1	S02.411K	S04.819A	S07.1XXA	S12.230K	S12.690K
O99.111	Q04.6	Q44.1	Q91.2	S02.412A	S04.891A	S07.8XXA	S12.231A	S12.691A
O99.112	Q04.8	Q44.4	Q91.3	S02.412B	S04.892A	S07.9XXA	S12.231K	S12.691K
O99.113	Q05.0	Q44.5	Q91.4	S02.412K	S04.899A	S09.0XXA	S12.24XA	S12.9XXA
O99.119	Q05.1	Q44.6	Q91.5	S02.413A	S04.9XXA	S09.20XA	S12.24XK	S13.0XXA
O99.12	Q05.2	Q44.7	Q91.6	S02.413B	S05.10XA	S09.21XA	S12.250A	S13.100A
O99.13	Q05.3	Q45.0	Q91.7	S02.413K	S05.21XA	S09.22XA	S12.250K	S13.101A
O99.321	Q05.4	Q45.1	Q93.3	S02.42XA	S05.22XA	S09.301A	S12.251A	S13.110A
O99.322	Q07.02	Q45.2	Q93.4	S02.42XB	S05.30XA	S09.302A	S12.251K	S13.111A
O99.323	Q07.03	Q45.3	Q93.5	S02.42XK	S05.31XA	S09.309A	S12.290A	S13.120A
O99.324	Q20.5	Q60.0	Q93.7	S02.5XXK	S05.32XA	S09.311A	S12.290K	S13.121A
O99.325	Q21.0	Q60.1	Q93.88	S02.600A	S05.40XA	S09.312A	S12.291A	S13.130A
O99.354	Q21.1	Q60.2	Q93.89	S02.600B	S05.41XA	S09.313A	S12.291K	S13.131A
O99.355	Q21.2	Q60.3	Q93.9	S02.600K	S05.42XA	S09.319A	S12.300A	S13.140A
O99.411	Q22.1	Q60.4		S02.609A	S05.50XA	S09.391A	S12.300K	S13.141A

S13.150A	S21.91XA	S22.078K	S27.399A	S32.10XK	S32.441K	S32.89XK	S36.503A	S37.899A
S13.151A	S21.92XA	S22.079A	S27.50XA	S32.110A	S32.442K	S32.9XXA	S36.508A	S37.90XA
S13.160A	S21.93XA	S22.079K	S27.51XA	S32.110K	S32.443K	S32.9XXK	S36.509A	S37.92XA
S13.161A	S21.94XA	S22.080A	S27.52XA	S32.111A	S32.444K	S35.531A	S36.510A	S37.93XA
S13.170A	S21.95XA	S22.080K	S27.53XA	S32.111K	S32.445K	S35.532A	S36.511A	S37.99XA
S13.171A	S22.000A	S22.081A	S27.59XA	S32.112A	S32.446K	S35.533A	S36.512A	S42.001B
S13.180A	S22.000K	S22.081K	S27.60XA	S32.112K	S32.451K	S35.534A	S36.513A	S42.001K
S13.181A	S22.001A	S22.082A	S27.63XA	S32.119A	S32.452K	S35.535A	S36.518A	S42.001P
S13.20XA	S22.001K	S22.082K	S27.69XA	S32.119K	S32.453K	S35.536A	S36.519A	S42.002B
S13.29XA	S22.002A	S22.088A	S27.802A	S32.120A	S32.454K	S35.8X1A	S36.520A	S42.002K
S15.001A	S22.002K	S22.088K	S27.803A	S32.120K	S32.455K	S35.8X8A	S36.521A	S42.002P
S15.002A	S22.008A	S22.089A	S27.808A	S32.121A	S32.456K	S35.8X9A	S36.522A	S42.009B
S15.009A	S22.008K	S22.089K	S27.809A	S32.121K	S32.461K	S35.90XA	S36.523A	S42.009K
S15.011A	S22.009A	S22.20XA	S27.892A	S32.122A	S32.462K	S35.91XA	S36.528A	S42.009P
S15.012A	S22.009K	S22.20XK	S27.893A	S32.122K	S32.463K	S35.99XA	S36.529A	S42.011B
S15.019A	S22.010A	S22.21XA	S27.898A	S32.129A	S32.464K	S36.00XA	S36.530A	S42.011K
S15.021A	S22.010K	S22.21XK	S27.899A	S32.129K	S32.465K	S36.020A	S36.531A	S42.011P
S15.022A	S22.011A	S22.22XA	S27.9XXA	S32.130A	S32.466K	S36.021A	S36.532A	S42.012B
S15.029A	S22.011K	S22.22XK	S28.1XXA	S32.130K	S32.471K	S36.029A	S36.533A	S42.012K
S15.091A	S22.012A	S22.23XA	S29.021A	S32.131A	S32.472K	S36.030A	S36.538A	S42.012P
S15.092A	S22.012K	S22.23XK	S29.029A	S32.131K	S32.473K	S36.039A	S36.539A	S42.013B
S15.099A	S22.018A	S22.24XA	S32.000A	S32.132A	S32.474K	S36.09XA	S36.590A	S42.013K
S15.101A	S22.018K	S22.24XK	S32.000K	S32.132K	S32.475K	S36.112A	S36.591A	S42.013P
S15.102A	S22.019A	S22.31XA	S32.001A	S32.139A	S32.476K	S36.113A	S36.592A	S42.014B
S15.109A	S22.019K	S22.31XK	S32.001K	S32.139K	S32.481K	S36.114A	S36.593A	S42.014K
S15.111A	S22.020A	S22.32XA	S32.002A	S32.14XA	S32.482K	S36.118A	S36.598A	S42.014P
S15.112A	S22.020K	S22.32XK	S32.002K	S32.14XK	S32.483K	S36.119A	S36.599A	S42.015B
S15.119A	S22.021A	S22.39XA	S32.008A	S32.15XA	S32.484K	S36.122A	S36.60XA	S42.015K
S15.121A	S22.021K	S22.39XK	S32.008K	S32.15XK	S32.485K	S36.123A	S36.61XA	S42.015P
S15.122A	S22.022A	S22.41XA	S32.009A	S32.16XA	S32.486K	S36.128A	S36.62XA	S42.016B
S15.129A	S22.022K	S22.41XK	S32.009K	S32.16XK	S32.491K	S36.129A	S36.63XA	S42.016K
S15.191A	S22.028A	S22.42XA	S32.010A	S32.17XA	S32.492K	S36.13XA	S36.69XA	S42.016P
S15.192A	S22.028K	S22.42XK	S32.010K	S32.17XK	S32.499K	S36.200A	S36.81XA	S42.017B
S15.199A	S22.029A	S22.43XA	S32.011A	S32.19XA	S32.501A	S36.201A	S36.892A	S42.017K
S15.201A	S22.029K	S22.43XK	S32.011K	S32.19XK	S32.501K	S36.202A	S36.893A	S42.017P
S15.202A	S22.030A	S22.49XA	S32.012A	S32.2XXA	S32.502A	S36.209A	S36.898A	S42.018B
S15.209A	S22.030K	S22.49XK	S32.012K	S32.2XXK	S32.502K	S36.220A	S36.899A	S42.018K
S15.211A	S22.031A	S22.5XXK	S32.018A	S32.301A	S32.509A	S36.221A	S36.90XA	S42.018P
S15.212A	S22.031K	S22.9XXA	S32.018K	S32.301K	S32.509K	S36.222A	S36.92XA	S42.019B
S15.219A	S22.032A	S22.9XXK	S32.019A	S32.302A	S32.511A	S36.229A	S36.93XA	S42.019K
S15.221A	S22.032K	S25.501A	S32.019K	S32.302K	S32.511K	S36.230A	S36.99XA	S42.019P
S15.222A	S22.038A	S25.502A	S32.020A	S32.309A	S32.512A	S36.231A	S37.001A	S42.021B
S15.229A	S22.038K	S25.509A	S32.020K	S32.309K	S32.512K	S36.232A	S37.002A	S42.021K
S15.291A	S22.039A	S25.511A	S32.021A	S32.311A	S32.519A	S36.239A	S37.009A	S42.021P
S15.292A	S22.039K	S25.512A	S32.021K	S32.311K	S32.519K	S36.240A	S37.011A	S42.022B
S15.299A	S22.040A	S25.519A	S32.022A	S32.312A	S32.591A	S36.241A	S37.012A	S42.022K
S15.301A	S22.040K	S25.591A	S32.022K	S32.312K	S32.591K	S36.242A	S37.019A	S42.022P
S15.302A	S22.041A	S25.592A	S32.028A	S32.313A	S32.592A	S36.249A	S37.021A	S42.023B
S15.309A	S22.041K	S25.599A	S32.028K	S32.313K	S32.592K	S36.250A	S37.022A	S42.023K
S15.311A	S22.042A	S25.801A	S32.029A	S32.314A	S32.599A	S36.251A	S37.029A	S42.023P
S15.312A	S22.042K	S25.802A	S32.029K	S32.314K	S32.599K	S36.252A	S37.031A	S42.024B
S15.319A	S22.048A	S25.809A	S32.030A	S32.315A	S32.601A	S36.259A	S37.032A	S42.024K
S15.321A	S22.048K	S25.811A	S32.030K	S32.315K	S32.601K	S36.260A	S37.039A	S42.024P
S15.322A	S22.049A	S25.812A	S32.031A	S32.316A	S32.602A	S36.261A	S37.041A	S42.025B
S15.329A	S22.049K	S25.819A	S32.031K	S32.316K	S32.602K	S36.262A	S37.042A	S42.025K
S15.391A	S22.050A	S25.891A	S32.032A	S32.391A	S32.609A	S36.269A	S37.049A	S42.025P
S15.392A	S22.050K	S25.892A	S32.032K	S32.391K	S32.609K	S36.290A	S37.051A	S42.026B
S15.399A	S22.051A	S25.899A	S32.038A	S32.392A	S32.611A	S36.291A	S37.052A	S42.026K
S15.8XXA	S22.051K	S25.90XA	S32.038K	S32.392K	S32.611K	S36.292A	S37.059A	S42.026P
S15.9XXA	S22.052A	S25.91XA	S32.039A	S32.399A	S32.612A	S36.299A	S37.10XA	S42.031B
S17.0XXA	S22.052K	S25.99XA	S32.039K	S32.399K	S32.612K	S36.30XA	S37.12XA	S42.031K
S17.8XXA	S22.058A	S26.00XA	S32.040A	S32.401K	S32.613A	S36.32XA	S37.13XA	S42.031P
S17.9XXA	S22.058K	S26.01XA	S32.040K	S32.402K	S32.613K	S36.33XA	S37.19XA	S42.032B
S21.101A	S22.059A	S26.09XA	S32.041A	S32.409K	S32.614A	S36.39XA	S37.20XA	S42.032K
S21.102A	S22.059K	S26.10XA	S32.041K	S32.411K	S32.614K	S36.400A	S37.22XA	S42.032P
S21.109A	S22.060A	S26.11XA	S32.042A	S32.412K	S32.615A	S36.408A	S37.23XA	S42.033B
S21.111A	S22.060K	S26.19XA	S32.042K	S32.413K	S32.615K	S36.409A	S37.29XA	S42.033K
S21.112A	S22.061A	S26.90XA	S32.048A	S32.414K	S32.616A	S36.410A	S37.30XA	S42.033P
S21.119A	S22.061K	S26.91XA	S32.048K	S32.415K	S32.616K	S36.418A	S37.32XA	S42.034B
S21.121A	S22.062A	S26.99XA	S32.049A	S32.416K	S32.691A	S36.419A	S37.33XA	S42.034K
S21.122A	S22.062K	S27.0XXA	S32.049K	S32.421K	S32.691K	S36.420A	S37.39XA	S42.034P
S21.129A	S22.068A	S27.301A	S32.050A	S32.422K	S32.692A	S36.428A	S37.60XA	S42.035B
S21.131A	S22.068K	S27.302A	S32.050K	S32.423K	S32.692K	S36.429A	S37.62XA	S42.035K
S21.132A	S22.069A	S27.309A	S32.051A	S32.424K	S32.699A	S36.430A	S37.63XA	S42.035P
S21.139A	S22.069K	S27.311A	S32.051K	S32.425K	S32.699K	S36.438A	S37.69XA	S42.036B
S21.141A	S22.070A	S27.312A	S32.052A	S32.426K	S32.810A	S36.439A	S37.812A	S42.036K
S21.142A	S22.070K	S27.319A	S32.052K	S32.431K	S32.810K	S36.490A	S37.813A	S42.036P
S21.149A	S22.071A	S27.321A	S32.058A	S32.432K	S32.811A	S36.498A	S37.818A	S42.101B
S21.151A	S22.071K	S27.322A	S32.058K	S32.433K	S32.811K	S36.499A	S37.819A	S42.101K
S21.152A	S22.072A	S27.329A	S32.059A	S32.434K	S32.82XA	S36.500A	S37.892A	S42.101P
S21.159A	S22.072K	S27.391A	S32.059K	S32.435K	S32.82XK	S36.501A	S37.893A	S42.102B
S21.90XA	S22.078A	S27.392A	S32.10XA	S32.436K	S32.89XA	S36.502A	S37.898A	S42.102K

S42.102P	S42.153B	S42.249K	S42.319P	S42.364A	S42.441K	S42.481P	S45.811A	S49.032K
S42.109B	S42.153K	S42.249P	S42.321A	S42.364K	S42.441P	S42.482A	S45.812A	S49.032P
S42.109K	S42.153P	S42.251A	S42.321K	S42.364P	S42.442A	S42.482K	S45.819A	S49.039A
S42.109P	S42.154B	S42.251K	S42.321P	S42.365A	S42.442K	S42.482P	S45.891A	S49.039K
S42.111B	S42.154K	S42.251P	S42.322A	S42.365K	S42.442P	S42.489A	S45.892A	S49.039P
S42.111K	S42.154P	S42.252A	S42.322K	S42.365P	S42.443A	S42.489K	S45.899A	S49.041A
S42.111P	S42.155B	S42.252K	S42.322P	S42.366A	S42.443K	S42.489P	S45.901A	S49.041K
S42.112B	S42.155K	S42.252P	S42.323A	S42.366K	S42.443P	S42.491A	S45.902A	S49.041P
S42.112K	S42.155P	S42.253A	S42.323K	S42.366P	S42.444A	S42.491K	S45.909A	S49.042A
S42.112P	S42.156B	S42.253K	S42.323P	S42.391A	S42.444K	S42.491P	S45.911A	S49.042K
S42.113B	S42.156K	S42.253P	S42.324A	S42.391K	S42.444P	S42.492A	S45.912A	S49.042P
S42.113K	S42.156P	S42.254A	S42.324K	S42.391P	S42.445A	S42.492K	S45.919A	S49.049A
S42.113P	S42.191B	S42.254K	S42.324P	S42.392A	S42.445K	S42.492P	S45.991A	S49.049K
S42.114B	S42.191K	S42.254P	S42.325A	S42.392K	S42.445P	S42.493A	S45.992A	S49.091A
S42.114K	S42.191P	S42.255A	S42.325K	S42.392P	S42.446A	S42.493K	S45.999A	S49.091K
S42.114P	S42.192B	S42.255K	S42.325P	S42.399A	S42.446K	S42.493P	S46.021A	S49.091P
S42.115B	S42.192K	S42.255P	S42.326A	S42.399K	S42.446P	S42.494A	S46.022A	S49.092A
S42.115K	S42.192P	S42.256A	S42.326K	S42.399P	S42.447A	S42.494K	S46.029A	S49.092K
S42.115P	S42.199B	S42.256K	S42.326P	S42.401A	S42.447K	S42.494P	S46.121A	S49.092P
S42.116B	S42.199K	S42.256P	S42.331A	S42.401K	S42.447P	S42.495A	S46.122A	S49.099A
S42.116K	S42.199P	S42.261A	S42.331K	S42.401P	S42.448A	S42.495K	S46.129A	S49.099K
S42.116P	S42.201A	S42.261K	S42.331P	S42.402A	S42.448K	S42.495P	S46.221A	S49.099P
S42.121B	S42.201K	S42.261P	S42.332A	S42.402K	S42.448P	S42.496A	S46.222A	S49.101A
S42.121K	S42.201P	S42.262A	S42.332K	S42.402P	S42.449A	S42.496K	S46.229A	S49.101K
S42.121P	S42.202A	S42.262K	S42.332P	S42.409A	S42.449K	S42.496P	S46.321A	S49.101P
S42.122B	S42.202K	S42.262P	S42.333A	S42.409K	S42.449P	S42.90XA	S46.322A	S49.102A
S42.122K	S42.202P	S42.263A	S42.333K	S42.409P	S42.451A	S42.90XK	S46.329A	S49.102K
S42.122P	S42.209A	S42.263K	S42.333P	S42.411A	S42.451K	S42.90XP	S46.821A	S49.102P
S42.123B	S42.209K	S42.263P	S42.334A	S42.411K	S42.451P	S42.91XA	S46.822A	S49.109A
S42.123K	S42.209P	S42.264A	S42.334K	S42.411P	S42.452A	S42.91XK	S46.829A	S49.109K
S42.123P	S42.211A	S42.264K	S42.334P	S42.412A	S42.452K	S42.91XP	S46.921A	S49.109P
S42.124B	S42.211K	S42.264P	S42.335A	S42.412K	S42.452P	S42.92XA	S46.922A	S49.111A
S42.124K	S42.211P	S42.265A	S42.335K	S42.412P	S42.453A	S42.92XK	S46.929A	S49.111K
S42.124P	S42.212A	S42.265K	S42.335P	S42.413A	S42.453K	S42.92XP	S48.011A	S49.111P
S42.125B	S42.212K	S42.265P	S42.336A	S42.413K	S42.453P	S43.201A	S48.012A	S49.112A
S42.125K	S42.212P	S42.266A	S42.336K	S42.413P	S42.454A	S43.202A	S48.019A	S49.112K
S42.125P	S42.213A	S42.266K	S42.336P	S42.414A	S42.454K	S43.203A	S48.021A	S49.112P
S42.126B	S42.213K	S42.266P	S42.341A	S42.414K	S42.454P	S43.204A	S48.022A	S49.119A
S42.126K	S42.213P	S42.271A	S42.341K	S42.414P	S42.455A	S43.205A	S48.029A	S49.119K
S42.126P	S42.214A	S42.271K	S42.341P	S42.415A	S42.455K	S43.206A	S48.111A	S49.119P
S42.131B	S42.214K	S42.271P	S42.342A	S42.415K	S42.455P	S43.211A	S48.112A	S49.121A
S42.131K	S42.214P	S42.272A	S42.342K	S42.415P	S42.456A	S43.212A	S48.119A	S49.121K
S42.131P	S42.215A	S42.272K	S42.342P	S42.416A	S42.456K	S43.213A	S48.121A	S49.121P
S42.132B	S42.215K	S42.272P	S42.343A	S42.416K	S42.456P	S43.214A	S48.122A	S49.122A
S42.132K	S42.215P	S42.279A	S42.343K	S42.416P	S42.461A	S43.215A	S48.129A	S49.122K
S42.132P	S42.216A	S42.279K	S42.343P	S42.421A	S42.461K	S43.216A	S48.911A	S49.122P
S42.133B	S42.216K	S42.279P	S42.344A	S42.421K	S42.461P	S43.221A	S48.912A	S49.129A
S42.133K	S42.216P	S42.291A	S42.344K	S42.421P	S42.462A	S43.222A	S48.919A	S49.129K
S42.133P	S42.221A	S42.291K	S42.344P	S42.422A	S42.462K	S43.223A	S48.921A	S49.129P
S42.134B	S42.221K	S42.291P	S42.345A	S42.422K	S42.462P	S43.224A	S48.922A	S49.131A
S42.134K	S42.221P	S42.292A	S42.345K	S42.422P	S42.463A	S43.225A	S48.929A	S49.131K
S42.134P	S42.222A	S42.292K	S42.345P	S42.423A	S42.463K	S43.226A	S49.001A	S49.131P
S42.135B	S42.222K	S42.292P	S42.346A	S42.423K	S42.463P	S45.101A	S49.001K	S49.132A
S42.135K	S42.222P	S42.293A	S42.346K	S42.423P	S42.464A	S45.102A	S49.001P	S49.132K
S42.135P	S42.223A	S42.293K	S42.346P	S42.424A	S42.464K	S45.109A	S49.002A	S49.132P
S42.136B	S42.223K	S42.293P	S42.351A	S42.424K	S42.464P	S45.111A	S49.002K	S49.139A
S42.136K	S42.223P	S42.294A	S42.351K	S42.424P	S42.465A	S45.112A	S49.002P	S49.139K
S42.136P	S42.224A	S42.294K	S42.351P	S42.425A	S42.465K	S45.119A	S49.009A	S49.139P
S42.141B	S42.224K	S42.294P	S42.352A	S42.425K	S42.465P	S45.191A	S49.009K	S49.141A
S42.141K	S42.224P	S42.295A	S42.352K	S42.425P	S42.466A	S45.192A	S49.009P	S49.141K
S42.141P	S42.225A	S42.295K	S42.352P	S42.426A	S42.466K	S45.199A	S49.011A	S49.141P
S42.142B	S42.225K	S42.295P	S42.353A	S42.426K	S42.466P	S45.201A	S49.011K	S49.142A
S42.142K	S42.225P	S42.296A	S42.353K	S42.426P	S42.471A	S45.202A	S49.011P	S49.142K
S42.142P	S42.226A	S42.296K	S42.353P	S42.431A	S42.471K	S45.209A	S49.012A	S49.142P
S42.143B	S42.226K	S42.296P	S42.354A	S42.431K	S42.471P	S45.211A	S49.012K	S49.149A
S42.143K	S42.226P	S42.301A	S42.354K	S42.431P	S42.472A	S45.212A	S49.012P	S49.149K
S42.143P	S42.231A	S42.301K	S42.354P	S42.432A	S42.472K	S45.219A	S49.019A	S49.149P
S42.144B	S42.231K	S42.301P	S42.355A	S42.432K	S42.472P	S45.291A	S49.019K	S49.191A
S42.144K	S42.231P	S42.302A	S42.355K	S42.432P	S42.473A	S45.292A	S49.019P	S49.191K
S42.144P	S42.232A	S42.302K	S42.355P	S42.433A	S42.473K	S45.299A	S49.021A	S49.191P
S42.145B	S42.232K	S42.302P	S42.356A	S42.433K	S42.473P	S45.301A	S49.021K	S49.192A
S42.145K	S42.232P	S42.309A	S42.356K	S42.433P	S42.474A	S45.302A	S49.021P	S49.192K
S42.145P	S42.239A	S42.309K	S42.356P	S42.434A	S42.474K	S45.309A	S49.022A	S49.192P
S42.146B	S42.239K	S42.309P	S42.361A	S42.434K	S42.474P	S45.311A	S49.022K	S49.199A
S42.146K	S42.239P	S42.311A	S42.361K	S42.434P	S42.475A	S45.312A	S49.022P	S49.199K
S42.146P	S42.241A	S42.311K	S42.361P	S42.435A	S42.475K	S45.319A	S49.029A	S49.199P
S42.151B	S42.241K	S42.311P	S42.362A	S42.435K	S42.475P	S45.391A	S49.029K	S52.001K
S42.151K	S42.241P	S42.312A	S42.362K	S42.435P	S42.476A	S45.392A	S49.029P	S52.001M
S42.151P	S42.242A	S42.312K	S42.362P	S42.436A	S42.476K	S45.399A	S49.031A	S52.001N
S42.152B	S42.242K	S42.312P	S42.363A	S42.436K	S42.476P	S45.801A	S49.031K	S52.001P
S42.152K	S42.242P	S42.319A	S42.363K	S42.436P	S42.481A	S45.802A	S49.031P	S52.001Q
S42.152P	S42.249A	S42.319K	S42.363P	S42.441A	S42.481K	S45.809A	S49.032A	

S52.001R	S52.035K	S52.109Q	S52.136R	S52.225Q	S52.245N	S52.265K	S52.302M	S52.333Q
S52.002K	S52.035M	S52.109R	S52.181K	S52.225R	S52.245P	S52.265M	S52.302N	S52.333R
S52.002M	S52.035N	S52.111A	S52.181M	S52.226A	S52.245Q	S52.265N	S52.302P	S52.334A
S52.002N	S52.035P	S52.111K	S52.181N	S52.226K	S52.245R	S52.265P	S52.302Q	S52.334K
S52.002P	S52.035Q	S52.111P	S52.181P	S52.226M	S52.246A	S52.265Q	S52.309A	S52.334M
S52.002Q	S52.035R	S52.112A	S52.181Q	S52.226N	S52.246K	S52.265R	S52.309K	S52.334N
S52.002R	S52.036K	S52.112K	S52.181R	S52.226P	S52.246M	S52.266A	S52.309M	S52.334P
S52.009K	S52.036M	S52.112P	S52.182K	S52.226Q	S52.246N	S52.266K	S52.309N	S52.334Q
S52.009M	S52.036N	S52.119A	S52.182N	S52.231A	S52.246P	S52.266M	S52.309P	S52.334R
S52.009N	S52.036P	S52.119K	S52.182P	S52.231K	S52.246Q	S52.266N	S52.309Q	S52.335A
S52.009P	S52.036Q	S52.119P	S52.182Q	S52.231M	S52.246R	S52.266P	S52.309R	S52.335K
S52.009Q	S52.036R	S52.121K	S52.182R	S52.231N	S52.251A	S52.266Q	S52.311A	S52.335M
S52.009R	S52.041K	S52.121M	S52.189K	S52.231P	S52.251K	S52.266R	S52.311K	S52.335N
S52.011A	S52.041M	S52.121N	S52.189M	S52.231Q	S52.251M	S52.271K	S52.311P	S52.335P
S52.011K	S52.041N	S52.121P	S52.189N	S52.231R	S52.251N	S52.271M	S52.312A	S52.335Q
S52.011P	S52.041P	S52.121Q	S52.189P	S52.232A	S52.251P	S52.271N	S52.312K	S52.335R
S52.012A	S52.041Q	S52.121R	S52.189Q	S52.232K	S52.251Q	S52.271P	S52.312P	S52.336A
S52.012K	S52.041R	S52.122K	S52.189R	S52.232M	S52.251R	S52.271Q	S52.319A	S52.336K
S52.012P	S52.042K	S52.122M	S52.201A	S52.232N	S52.252A	S52.271R	S52.319K	S52.336M
S52.019A	S52.042M	S52.122N	S52.201K	S52.232P	S52.252K	S52.272K	S52.319P	S52.336N
S52.019K	S52.042N	S52.122P	S52.201M	S52.232Q	S52.252M	S52.272M	S52.321A	S52.336P
S52.019P	S52.042P	S52.122Q	S52.201N	S52.232R	S52.252N	S52.272N	S52.321K	S52.336Q
S52.021K	S52.042Q	S52.122R	S52.201P	S52.233A	S52.252P	S52.272P	S52.321M	S52.336R
S52.021M	S52.042R	S52.123K	S52.201Q	S52.233K	S52.252Q	S52.272Q	S52.321N	S52.341A
S52.021N	S52.043K	S52.123M	S52.201R	S52.233M	S52.252R	S52.272R	S52.321P	S52.341K
S52.021P	S52.043M	S52.123N	S52.202A	S52.233N	S52.253A	S52.279K	S52.321Q	S52.341M
S52.021Q	S52.043N	S52.123P	S52.202K	S52.233P	S52.253K	S52.279M	S52.321R	S52.341N
S52.021R	S52.043P	S52.123Q	S52.202M	S52.233Q	S52.253M	S52.279N	S52.322A	S52.341P
S52.022K	S52.043Q	S52.123R	S52.202N	S52.233R	S52.253N	S52.279P	S52.322K	S52.341Q
S52.022M	S52.043R	S52.124K	S52.202P	S52.234A	S52.253P	S52.279Q	S52.322M	S52.341R
S52.022N	S52.044K	S52.124M	S52.202Q	S52.234K	S52.253Q	S52.279R	S52.322N	S52.342A
S52.022P	S52.044M	S52.124N	S52.202R	S52.234M	S52.253R	S52.281A	S52.322P	S52.342K
S52.022Q	S52.044N	S52.124P	S52.209A	S52.234N	S52.254A	S52.281K	S52.322Q	S52.342M
S52.022R	S52.044P	S52.124Q	S52.209K	S52.234P	S52.254K	S52.281M	S52.322R	S52.342N
S52.023K	S52.044Q	S52.124R	S52.209M	S52.234Q	S52.254M	S52.281N	S52.323A	S52.342P
S52.023M	S52.044R	S52.125K	S52.209N	S52.234R	S52.254N	S52.281P	S52.323K	S52.342Q
S52.023N	S52.045K	S52.125M	S52.209P	S52.235A	S52.254P	S52.281Q	S52.323M	S52.343A
S52.023P	S52.045M	S52.125N	S52.209Q	S52.235K	S52.254Q	S52.281R	S52.323N	S52.343K
S52.023Q	S52.045N	S52.125P	S52.209R	S52.235M	S52.254R	S52.282A	S52.323P	S52.343M
S52.023R	S52.045P	S52.125Q	S52.211A	S52.235N	S52.255A	S52.282K	S52.323Q	S52.343N
S52.024K	S52.045Q	S52.125R	S52.211K	S52.235P	S52.255K	S52.282M	S52.323R	S52.343P
S52.024M	S52.045R	S52.126K	S52.211P	S52.235Q	S52.255M	S52.282N	S52.324A	S52.343Q
S52.024N	S52.046K	S52.126M	S52.212A	S52.235R	S52.255N	S52.282P	S52.324K	S52.343R
S52.024P	S52.046M	S52.126N	S52.212K	S52.236A	S52.255P	S52.282Q	S52.324M	S52.344A
S52.024Q	S52.046N	S52.126P	S52.212P	S52.236K	S52.255Q	S52.282R	S52.324P	S52.344K
S52.024R	S52.046P	S52.126Q	S52.219A	S52.236M	S52.255R	S52.283A	S52.324Q	S52.344M
S52.025K	S52.046Q	S52.126R	S52.219K	S52.236N	S52.256A	S52.283K	S52.324R	S52.344N
S52.025M	S52.046R	S52.131K	S52.219P	S52.236P	S52.256K	S52.283M	S52.325A	S52.344P
S52.025N	S52.091K	S52.131M	S52.221A	S52.236Q	S52.256M	S52.283N	S52.325K	S52.344Q
S52.025P	S52.091M	S52.131N	S52.221K	S52.236R	S52.256N	S52.283P	S52.325M	S52.344R
S52.025Q	S52.091N	S52.131P	S52.221M	S52.241A	S52.256P	S52.283Q	S52.325N	S52.345A
S52.025R	S52.091P	S52.131Q	S52.221N	S52.241K	S52.256Q	S52.283R	S52.325P	S52.345K
S52.026K	S52.091Q	S52.131R	S52.221P	S52.241M	S52.256R	S52.291A	S52.325Q	S52.345M
S52.026M	S52.091R	S52.132K	S52.221Q	S52.241N	S52.261A	S52.291K	S52.325R	S52.345N
S52.026N	S52.092K	S52.132M	S52.221R	S52.241P	S52.261K	S52.291M	S52.326A	S52.345P
S52.026P	S52.092M	S52.132N	S52.222A	S52.241Q	S52.261M	S52.291N	S52.326K	S52.345Q
S52.026Q	S52.092N	S52.132P	S52.222K	S52.241R	S52.261N	S52.291P	S52.326N	S52.345R
S52.026R	S52.092P	S52.132Q	S52.222M	S52.242A	S52.261P	S52.291Q	S52.326P	S52.346A
S52.031K	S52.092Q	S52.132R	S52.222N	S52.242K	S52.261Q	S52.291R	S52.326Q	S52.346K
S52.031M	S52.092R	S52.133K	S52.222P	S52.242M	S52.261R	S52.292A	S52.326R	S52.346M
S52.031N	S52.099K	S52.133M	S52.222Q	S52.242N	S52.262A	S52.292K	S52.331A	S52.346N
S52.031P	S52.099M	S52.133N	S52.222R	S52.242P	S52.262K	S52.292M	S52.331K	S52.346P
S52.031Q	S52.099N	S52.133P	S52.223A	S52.242Q	S52.262M	S52.292N	S52.331M	S52.346Q
S52.031R	S52.099P	S52.133Q	S52.223K	S52.242R	S52.262N	S52.292P	S52.331N	S52.346R
S52.032K	S52.099Q	S52.133R	S52.223M	S52.243A	S52.262P	S52.292Q	S52.331P	S52.351A
S52.032M	S52.099R	S52.134K	S52.223N	S52.243K	S52.262Q	S52.292R	S52.331Q	S52.351K
S52.032N	S52.101K	S52.134M	S52.223P	S52.243M	S52.262R	S52.299A	S52.331R	S52.351M
S52.032P	S52.101M	S52.134N	S52.223Q	S52.243N	S52.263A	S52.299K	S52.332A	S52.351P
S52.032Q	S52.101N	S52.134P	S52.223R	S52.243P	S52.263K	S52.299M	S52.332K	S52.351Q
S52.032R	S52.101P	S52.134Q	S52.224A	S52.243Q	S52.263M	S52.299N	S52.332M	S52.351R
S52.033K	S52.101Q	S52.134R	S52.224K	S52.243R	S52.263N	S52.299P	S52.332N	S52.352A
S52.033M	S52.101R	S52.135K	S52.224M	S52.244A	S52.263P	S52.299Q	S52.332P	S52.352K
S52.033N	S52.102K	S52.135M	S52.224N	S52.244K	S52.263Q	S52.299R	S52.332Q	S52.352M
S52.033P	S52.102M	S52.135N	S52.224P	S52.244M	S52.263R	S52.301A	S52.332R	S52.352N
S52.033Q	S52.102N	S52.135P	S52.224Q	S52.244N	S52.264A	S52.301K	S52.333A	S52.352P
S52.033R	S52.102P	S52.135Q	S52.224R	S52.244P	S52.264K	S52.301M	S52.333K	S52.352Q
S52.034K	S52.102Q	S52.135R	S52.225A	S52.244Q	S52.264M	S52.301N	S52.333M	S52.352R
S52.034M	S52.102R	S52.136K	S52.225K	S52.244R	S52.264N	S52.301P	S52.333N	S52.353A
S52.034N	S52.109K	S52.136M	S52.225M	S52.245A	S52.264P	S52.301Q	S52.333P	S52.353K
S52.034P	S52.109M	S52.136N	S52.225N	S52.245K	S52.264Q	S52.301R		
S52.034Q	S52.109N	S52.136P	S52.225P	S52.245M	S52.264R	S52.302A		
S52.034R	S52.109P	S52.136Q			S52.265A	S52.302K		S52.353M

Appendix B—Numeric CC List

S52.353N	S52.379K	S52.512R	S52.551M	S52.601A	S52.692N	S56.123A	S59.039A	S59.229K
S52.353P	S52.379M	S52.513A	S52.551N	S52.601K	S52.692P	S56.124A	S59.039K	S59.229P
S52.353Q	S52.379N	S52.513K	S52.551P	S52.601M	S52.692Q	S56.125A	S59.039P	S59.231A
S52.353R	S52.379P	S52.513M	S52.551Q	S52.601N	S52.692R	S56.126A	S59.041A	S59.231K
S52.354A	S52.379Q	S52.513N	S52.551R	S52.601P	S52.699A	S56.127A	S59.041K	S59.231P
S52.354K	S52.379R	S52.513P	S52.552A	S52.601Q	S52.699K	S56.128A	S59.041P	S59.232A
S52.354M	S52.381A	S52.513Q	S52.552K	S52.601R	S52.699M	S56.129A	S59.042A	S59.232K
S52.354N	S52.381K	S52.513R	S52.552M	S52.602A	S52.699N	S56.221A	S59.042K	S59.232P
S52.354P	S52.381M	S52.514A	S52.552N	S52.602K	S52.699P	S56.222A	S59.042P	S59.239A
S52.354Q	S52.381N	S52.514K	S52.552P	S52.602M	S52.699Q	S56.229A	S59.049A	S59.239K
S52.354R	S52.381P	S52.514M	S52.552Q	S52.602N	S52.699R	S56.321A	S59.049K	S59.239P
S52.355A	S52.381Q	S52.514N	S52.552R	S52.602P	S52.90XA	S56.322A	S59.049P	S59.241A
S52.355K	S52.381R	S52.514P	S52.559A	S52.602Q	S52.90XK	S56.329A	S59.091A	S59.241K
S52.355M	S52.382A	S52.514Q	S52.559K	S52.602R	S52.90XM	S56.421A	S59.091K	S59.241P
S52.355N	S52.382K	S52.514R	S52.559M	S52.609A	S52.90XN	S56.422A	S59.091P	S59.242A
S52.355P	S52.382M	S52.515A	S52.559N	S52.609K	S52.90XP	S56.423A	S59.092A	S59.242K
S52.355Q	S52.382N	S52.515K	S52.559P	S52.609M	S52.90XQ	S56.424A	S59.092K	S59.242P
S52.355R	S52.382P	S52.515M	S52.559Q	S52.609N	S52.90XR	S56.425A	S59.092P	S59.249A
S52.356A	S52.382Q	S52.515N	S52.559R	S52.609P	S52.91XA	S56.426A	S59.099A	S59.249K
S52.356K	S52.382R	S52.515P	S52.561A	S52.609Q	S52.91XK	S56.427A	S59.099K	S59.249P
S52.356M	S52.389A	S52.515Q	S52.561K	S52.609R	S52.91XM	S56.428A	S59.099P	S59.291A
S52.356N	S52.389K	S52.515R	S52.561M	S52.611A	S52.91XN	S56.429A	S59.101K	S59.291K
S52.356P	S52.389M	S52.516A	S52.561N	S52.611K	S52.91XQ	S56.521A	S59.101P	S59.291P
S52.356Q	S52.389N	S52.516K	S52.561P	S52.611M	S52.91XR	S56.522A	S59.102K	S59.292A
S52.356R	S52.389P	S52.516M	S52.561Q	S52.611N	S52.92XA	S56.529A	S59.102P	S59.292K
S52.361A	S52.389Q	S52.516N	S52.561R	S52.611P	S52.92XK	S56.821A	S59.109K	S59.292P
S52.361K	S52.389R	S52.516P	S52.562A	S52.611Q	S52.92XM	S56.822A	S59.109P	S59.299A
S52.361M	S52.391A	S52.516Q	S52.562K	S52.611R	S52.92XN	S56.829A	S59.111K	S59.299K
S52.361N	S52.391K	S52.516R	S52.562M	S52.612A	S52.92XP	S56.921A	S59.111P	S59.299P
S52.361P	S52.391M	S52.521A	S52.562N	S52.612K	S52.92XQ	S56.922A	S59.112K	S62.001B
S52.361Q	S52.391N	S52.521K	S52.562P	S52.612M	S52.92XR	S56.929A	S59.112P	S62.001K
S52.361R	S52.391P	S52.521P	S52.562Q	S52.612N	S55.001A	S58.011A	S59.119K	S62.001P
S52.362A	S52.391Q	S52.522A	S52.562R	S52.612P	S55.002A	S58.012A	S59.119P	S62.002B
S52.362K	S52.391R	S52.522K	S52.569A	S52.612Q	S55.009A	S58.019A	S59.121K	S62.002K
S52.362M	S52.392A	S52.522P	S52.569K	S52.612R	S55.011A	S58.021A	S59.121P	S62.002P
S52.362N	S52.392K	S52.529A	S52.569M	S52.613A	S55.012A	S58.022A	S59.122K	S62.009B
S52.362P	S52.392M	S52.529K	S52.569N	S52.613K	S55.019A	S58.029A	S59.122P	S62.009K
S52.362Q	S52.392N	S52.529P	S52.569P	S52.613M	S55.091A	S58.111A	S59.129K	S62.009P
S52.362R	S52.392P	S52.531A	S52.569Q	S52.613N	S55.092A	S58.112A	S59.129P	S62.011B
S52.363A	S52.392Q	S52.531K	S52.569R	S52.613P	S55.099A	S58.119A	S59.131K	S62.011K
S52.363K	S52.392R	S52.531M	S52.571A	S52.613Q	S55.101A	S58.121A	S59.131P	S62.011P
S52.363M	S52.399A	S52.531N	S52.571K	S52.613R	S55.102A	S58.122A	S59.132K	S62.012B
S52.363N	S52.399K	S52.531P	S52.571M	S52.614A	S55.109A	S58.129A	S59.132P	S62.012K
S52.363P	S52.399M	S52.531Q	S52.571N	S52.614K	S55.111A	S58.911A	S59.139K	S62.012P
S52.363Q	S52.399N	S52.531R	S52.571P	S52.614M	S55.112A	S58.912A	S59.139P	S62.013B
S52.363R	S52.399P	S52.532A	S52.571Q	S52.614N	S55.119A	S58.919A	S59.141K	S62.013K
S52.364A	S52.399Q	S52.532K	S52.571R	S52.614P	S55.191A	S58.921A	S59.141P	S62.013P
S52.364K	S52.399R	S52.532M	S52.572A	S52.614Q	S55.192A	S58.922A	S59.142K	S62.014B
S52.364M	S52.501A	S52.532N	S52.572K	S52.614R	S55.199A	S58.929A	S59.142P	S62.014K
S52.364N	S52.501K	S52.532P	S52.572M	S52.615A	S55.201A	S59.001A	S59.149K	S62.014P
S52.364P	S52.501M	S52.532Q	S52.572N	S52.615K	S55.202A	S59.001P	S59.149P	S62.015B
S52.364Q	S52.501N	S52.532R	S52.572P	S52.615M	S55.209A	S59.002A	S59.191K	S62.015K
S52.364R	S52.501P	S52.539A	S52.572Q	S52.615N	S55.211A	S59.002K	S59.191P	S62.015P
S52.365A	S52.501Q	S52.539K	S52.572R	S52.615P	S55.212A	S59.002P	S59.192K	S62.016B
S52.365K	S52.501R	S52.539M	S52.579A	S52.615Q	S55.219A	S59.009A	S59.192P	S62.016K
S52.365M	S52.502A	S52.539N	S52.579K	S52.615R	S55.291A	S59.009K	S59.199K	S62.016P
S52.365N	S52.502K	S52.539P	S52.579M	S52.616A	S55.292A	S59.009P	S59.199P	S62.021B
S52.365P	S52.502M	S52.539Q	S52.579N	S52.616K	S55.299A	S59.011A	S59.201A	S62.021K
S52.365Q	S52.502N	S52.539R	S52.579P	S52.616M	S55.801A	S59.011K	S59.201K	S62.021P
S52.365R	S52.502P	S52.541A	S52.579Q	S52.616N	S55.802A	S59.011P	S59.201P	S62.022B
S52.366A	S52.502Q	S52.541K	S52.579R	S52.616Q	S55.809A	S59.012A	S59.202A	S62.022K
S52.366K	S52.502R	S52.541M	S52.591A	S52.616R	S55.811A	S59.012K	S59.202K	S62.022P
S52.366M	S52.509A	S52.541N	S52.591K	S52.621A	S55.812A	S59.012P	S59.202P	S62.023B
S52.366N	S52.509K	S52.541P	S52.591M	S52.621K	S55.819A	S59.019A	S59.209A	S62.023K
S52.366P	S52.509M	S52.541Q	S52.591N	S52.621P	S55.891A	S59.019K	S59.209K	S62.023P
S52.366Q	S52.509N	S52.541R	S52.591P	S52.622A	S55.892A	S59.019P	S59.209P	S62.024B
S52.366R	S52.509P	S52.542A	S52.591Q	S52.622K	S55.899A	S59.021A	S59.211A	S62.024K
S52.371A	S52.509Q	S52.542K	S52.591R	S52.622P	S55.901A	S59.021K	S59.211K	S62.024P
S52.371K	S52.509R	S52.542M	S52.592A	S52.629A	S55.902A	S59.021P	S59.211P	S62.025B
S52.371M	S52.511A	S52.542N	S52.592K	S52.629K	S55.909A	S59.022A	S59.212A	S62.025K
S52.371N	S52.511K	S52.542P	S52.592M	S52.629P	S55.911A	S59.022K	S59.212K	S62.025P
S52.371P	S52.511M	S52.542Q	S52.592N	S52.691A	S55.912A	S59.022P	S59.212P	S62.026B
S52.371Q	S52.511N	S52.542R	S52.592P	S52.691K	S55.919A	S59.029A	S59.219A	S62.026K
S52.371R	S52.511P	S52.549A	S52.592Q	S52.691M	S55.991A	S59.029K	S59.219K	S62.026P
S52.372A	S52.511Q	S52.549K	S52.592R	S52.691N	S55.992A	S59.029P	S59.219P	S62.031B
S52.372K	S52.511R	S52.549M	S52.599A	S52.691P	S55.999A	S59.031A	S59.221A	S62.031K
S52.372M	S52.512A	S52.549N	S52.599K	S52.691Q	S56.021A	S59.031K	S59.221K	S62.031P
S52.372N	S52.512K	S52.549P	S52.599M	S52.691R	S56.022A	S59.031P	S59.221P	S62.032B
S52.372P	S52.512M	S52.549Q	S52.599N	S52.692A	S56.029A	S59.032A	S59.222A	S62.032K
S52.372Q	S52.512N	S52.549R	S52.599P	S52.692K	S56.121A	S59.032K	S59.222K	S62.032P
S52.372R	S52.512P	S52.551A	S52.599Q	S52.692M	S56.122A	S59.032P	S59.222P	S62.033B
S52.379A	S52.512Q	S52.551K	S52.599R				S59.229A	S62.033K

S62.033P	S62.144B	S62.201K	S62.254P	S62.322B	S62.349K	S62.396P	S62.609B	S62.636K
S62.034B	S62.144K	S62.201P	S62.255B	S62.322K	S62.349P	S62.397B	S62.609K	S62.636P
S62.034K	S62.144P	S62.202B	S62.255K	S62.322P	S62.350B	S62.397K	S62.609P	S62.637K
S62.034P	S62.145B	S62.202K	S62.255P	S62.323B	S62.350K	S62.397P	S62.610B	S62.637P
S62.035B	S62.145K	S62.202P	S62.256B	S62.323K	S62.350P	S62.398B	S62.610K	S62.638B
S62.035K	S62.145P	S62.209B	S62.256K	S62.323P	S62.351B	S62.398K	S62.610P	S62.638K
S62.035P	S62.146B	S62.209K	S62.256P	S62.324B	S62.351K	S62.398P	S62.611B	S62.638P
S62.036B	S62.146K	S62.209P	S62.291B	S62.324K	S62.351P	S62.399B	S62.611K	S62.639B
S62.036K	S62.146P	S62.211B	S62.291K	S62.324P	S62.352B	S62.399K	S62.611P	S62.639K
S62.036P	S62.151B	S62.211K	S62.291P	S62.325B	S62.352K	S62.399P	S62.612B	S62.639P
S62.101B	S62.151K	S62.211P	S62.292B	S62.325K	S62.352P	S62.501B	S62.612K	S62.640B
S62.101K	S62.151P	S62.212B	S62.292K	S62.325P	S62.353B	S62.501K	S62.612P	S62.640K
S62.101P	S62.152B	S62.212K	S62.292P	S62.326B	S62.353K	S62.501P	S62.613B	S62.640P
S62.102B	S62.152K	S62.212P	S62.299B	S62.326K	S62.353P	S62.502B	S62.613K	S62.641B
S62.102K	S62.152P	S62.213B	S62.299K	S62.326P	S62.354B	S62.502K	S62.613P	S62.641K
S62.102P	S62.153B	S62.213K	S62.299P	S62.327B	S62.354K	S62.502P	S62.614B	S62.641P
S62.109B	S62.153K	S62.213P	S62.300B	S62.327K	S62.354P	S62.509B	S62.614K	S62.642B
S62.109K	S62.153P	S62.221B	S62.300K	S62.327P	S62.355B	S62.509K	S62.614P	S62.642K
S62.109P	S62.154B	S62.221K	S62.300P	S62.328B	S62.355K	S62.509P	S62.615B	S62.642P
S62.111B	S62.154K	S62.221P	S62.301B	S62.328K	S62.355P	S62.511B	S62.615K	S62.643B
S62.111K	S62.154P	S62.222B	S62.301K	S62.328P	S62.356B	S62.511K	S62.615P	S62.643K
S62.111P	S62.155B	S62.222K	S62.301P	S62.329B	S62.356K	S62.511P	S62.616B	S62.643P
S62.112B	S62.155K	S62.222P	S62.302B	S62.329K	S62.356P	S62.512B	S62.616K	S62.644B
S62.112K	S62.155P	S62.223B	S62.302K	S62.329P	S62.357B	S62.512K	S62.616P	S62.644K
S62.112P	S62.156B	S62.223K	S62.302P	S62.330B	S62.357K	S62.512P	S62.617B	S62.644P
S62.113B	S62.156K	S62.223P	S62.303B	S62.330K	S62.357P	S62.513B	S62.617K	S62.645B
S62.113K	S62.156P	S62.224B	S62.303K	S62.330P	S62.358B	S62.513K	S62.617P	S62.645K
S62.113P	S62.161B	S62.224K	S62.303P	S62.331B	S62.358K	S62.513P	S62.618B	S62.645P
S62.114B	S62.161K	S62.224P	S62.304B	S62.331K	S62.358P	S62.514B	S62.618K	S62.646B
S62.114K	S62.161P	S62.225B	S62.304K	S62.331P	S62.359B	S62.514K	S62.618P	S62.646K
S62.114P	S62.162B	S62.225K	S62.304P	S62.332B	S62.359K	S62.514P	S62.619B	S62.646P
S62.115B	S62.162K	S62.225P	S62.305B	S62.332K	S62.359P	S62.515B	S62.619K	S62.647B
S62.115K	S62.162P	S62.226B	S62.305K	S62.332P	S62.360B	S62.515K	S62.619P	S62.647K
S62.115P	S62.163B	S62.226K	S62.305P	S62.333B	S62.360K	S62.515P	S62.620B	S62.647P
S62.116B	S62.163K	S62.226P	S62.306B	S62.333K	S62.360P	S62.516B	S62.620K	S62.648B
S62.116K	S62.163P	S62.231B	S62.306K	S62.333P	S62.361B	S62.516K	S62.620P	S62.648K
S62.116P	S62.164B	S62.231K	S62.306P	S62.334B	S62.361K	S62.516P	S62.621B	S62.648P
S62.121B	S62.164K	S62.231P	S62.307B	S62.334K	S62.361P	S62.521B	S62.621K	S62.649B
S62.121K	S62.164P	S62.232B	S62.307K	S62.334P	S62.362B	S62.521K	S62.621P	S62.649K
S62.121P	S62.165B	S62.232K	S62.307P	S62.335B	S62.362K	S62.521P	S62.622B	S62.649P
S62.122B	S62.165K	S62.232P	S62.308B	S62.335K	S62.362P	S62.522B	S62.622K	S62.650B
S62.122K	S62.165P	S62.233B	S62.308K	S62.335P	S62.363B	S62.522K	S62.622P	S62.650K
S62.122P	S62.166B	S62.233K	S62.308P	S62.336B	S62.363K	S62.522P	S62.623B	S62.650P
S62.123B	S62.166K	S62.233P	S62.309B	S62.336K	S62.363P	S62.523B	S62.623K	S62.651B
S62.123K	S62.166P	S62.234B	S62.309K	S62.336P	S62.364B	S62.523K	S62.623P	S62.651K
S62.123P	S62.171B	S62.234K	S62.309P	S62.337B	S62.364K	S62.523P	S62.624B	S62.651P
S62.124B	S62.171K	S62.234P	S62.310B	S62.337K	S62.364P	S62.524B	S62.624K	S62.652B
S62.124K	S62.171P	S62.235B	S62.310K	S62.337P	S62.365B	S62.524K	S62.624P	S62.652K
S62.124P	S62.172B	S62.235K	S62.310P	S62.338B	S62.365K	S62.524P	S62.625B	S62.652P
S62.125B	S62.172K	S62.235P	S62.311B	S62.338K	S62.365P	S62.525B	S62.625K	S62.653B
S62.125K	S62.172P	S62.236B	S62.311K	S62.338P	S62.366B	S62.525K	S62.625P	S62.653K
S62.125P	S62.173B	S62.236K	S62.311P	S62.339B	S62.366K	S62.525P	S62.626B	S62.653P
S62.126B	S62.173K	S62.236P	S62.312B	S62.339K	S62.366P	S62.526B	S62.626K	S62.654B
S62.126K	S62.173P	S62.241B	S62.312K	S62.339P	S62.367B	S62.526K	S62.626P	S62.654K
S62.126P	S62.174B	S62.241K	S62.312P	S62.340B	S62.367K	S62.526P	S62.627B	S62.654P
S62.131B	S62.174K	S62.241P	S62.313B	S62.340K	S62.367P	S62.600B	S62.627K	S62.655B
S62.131K	S62.174P	S62.242B	S62.313K	S62.340P	S62.368B	S62.600K	S62.627P	S62.655K
S62.131P	S62.175B	S62.242K	S62.313P	S62.341B	S62.368K	S62.600P	S62.628B	S62.655P
S62.132B	S62.175K	S62.242P	S62.314B	S62.341K	S62.368P	S62.601B	S62.628K	S62.656B
S62.132K	S62.175P	S62.243B	S62.314K	S62.341P	S62.369B	S62.601K	S62.628P	S62.656K
S62.132P	S62.176B	S62.243K	S62.314P	S62.342B	S62.369K	S62.601P	S62.629B	S62.656P
S62.133B	S62.176K	S62.243P	S62.315B	S62.342K	S62.369P	S62.602B	S62.629K	S62.657B
S62.133K	S62.176P	S62.244B	S62.315K	S62.342P	S62.390B	S62.602K	S62.629P	S62.657K
S62.133P	S62.181B	S62.244K	S62.315P	S62.343B	S62.390K	S62.602P	S62.630B	S62.657P
S62.134B	S62.181K	S62.244P	S62.316B	S62.343K	S62.390P	S62.603B	S62.630K	S62.658B
S62.134K	S62.181P	S62.245B	S62.316K	S62.343P	S62.391B	S62.603K	S62.630P	S62.658K
S62.134P	S62.182B	S62.245K	S62.316P	S62.344B	S62.391K	S62.603P	S62.631B	S62.658P
S62.135B	S62.182K	S62.245P	S62.317B	S62.344K	S62.391P	S62.604B	S62.631K	S62.659B
S62.135K	S62.182P	S62.246B	S62.317K	S62.344P	S62.392B	S62.604K	S62.631P	S62.659K
S62.135P	S62.183B	S62.246K	S62.317P	S62.345B	S62.392K	S62.604P	S62.632B	S62.659P
S62.136B	S62.183K	S62.246P	S62.318B	S62.345K	S62.392P	S62.605B	S62.632K	S62.660B
S62.136K	S62.183P	S62.251B	S62.318K	S62.345P	S62.393B	S62.605K	S62.632P	S62.660K
S62.136P	S62.184B	S62.251K	S62.318P	S62.346B	S62.393K	S62.605P	S62.633B	S62.660P
S62.141B	S62.184K	S62.251P	S62.319B	S62.346K	S62.393P	S62.606B	S62.633K	S62.661B
S62.141K	S62.184P	S62.252B	S62.319K	S62.346P	S62.394B	S62.606K	S62.633P	S62.661K
S62.141P	S62.185B	S62.252K	S62.319P	S62.347B	S62.394K	S62.606P	S62.634B	S62.661P
S62.142B	S62.185K	S62.252P	S62.320B	S62.347K	S62.394P	S62.607B	S62.634K	S62.662B
S62.142K	S62.185P	S62.253B	S62.320K	S62.347P	S62.395B	S62.607K	S62.634P	S62.662K
S62.142P	S62.186B	S62.253K	S62.320P	S62.348B	S62.395K	S62.607P	S62.635B	S62.662P
S62.143B	S62.186K	S62.253P	S62.321B	S62.348K	S62.395P	S62.608B	S62.635K	S62.663B
S62.143K	S62.186P	S62.254B	S62.321K	S62.348P	S62.396B	S62.608K	S62.635P	S62.663K
S62.143P	S62.201B	S62.254K	S62.321P	S62.349B	S62.396K	S62.608P	S62.636B	

Appendix B—Numeric CC List

S62.663P	S65.509A	S66.922A	S72.026N	S72.052K	S72.109Q	S72.132N	S72.24XK	S72.332Q
S62.664B	S65.510A	S66.929A	S72.026P	S72.052M	S72.109R	S72.132P	S72.24XM	S72.332R
S62.664K	S65.511A	S68.411A	S72.026Q	S72.052N	S72.111K	S72.132Q	S72.24XN	S72.333K
S62.664P	S65.512A	S68.412A	S72.026R	S72.052P	S72.111M	S72.132R	S72.24XP	S72.333M
S62.665B	S65.513A	S68.419A	S72.031K	S72.052Q	S72.111N	S72.133K	S72.24XQ	S72.333N
S62.665K	S65.514A	S68.421A	S72.031M	S72.052R	S72.111P	S72.133M	S72.24XR	S72.333P
S62.665P	S65.515A	S68.422A	S72.031N	S72.059K	S72.111Q	S72.133N	S72.25XK	S72.333Q
S62.666B	S65.516A	S68.429A	S72.031P	S72.059M	S72.111R	S72.133P	S72.25XM	S72.333R
S62.666K	S65.517A	S68.711A	S72.031Q	S72.059N	S72.112K	S72.133Q	S72.25XN	S72.334K
S62.666P	S65.518A	S68.712A	S72.031R	S72.059P	S72.112M	S72.133R	S72.25XP	S72.334M
S62.667B	S65.519A	S68.719A	S72.032K	S72.059Q	S72.112N	S72.134K	S72.25XQ	S72.334N
S62.667K	S65.590A	S68.721A	S72.032M	S72.059R	S72.112P	S72.134M	S72.25XR	S72.334P
S62.667P	S65.591A	S68.722A	S72.032N	S72.061K	S72.112Q	S72.134N	S72.26XK	S72.334Q
S62.668B	S65.592A	S68.729A	S72.032P	S72.061M	S72.113K	S72.134P	S72.26XM	S72.334R
S62.668K	S65.593A	S72.001K	S72.032Q	S72.061N	S72.113M	S72.134Q	S72.26XN	S72.335K
S62.668P	S65.594A	S72.001M	S72.032R	S72.061P	S72.113N	S72.134R	S72.26XP	S72.335M
S62.669B	S65.595A	S72.001N	S72.033K	S72.061Q	S72.113P	S72.135K	S72.26XQ	S72.335N
S62.669K	S65.596A	S72.001P	S72.033M	S72.061R	S72.113Q	S72.135M	S72.26XR	S72.335P
S62.669P	S65.597A	S72.001Q	S72.033N	S72.062K	S72.113R	S72.135N	S72.301K	S72.335Q
S62.90XB	S65.598A	S72.001R	S72.033P	S72.062M	S72.114K	S72.135P	S72.301M	S72.335R
S62.90XK	S65.599A	S72.002K	S72.033Q	S72.062N	S72.114M	S72.135Q	S72.301N	S72.336K
S62.90XP	S65.801A	S72.002M	S72.033R	S72.062P	S72.114N	S72.135R	S72.301P	S72.336M
S62.91XB	S65.802A	S72.002N	S72.034K	S72.062Q	S72.114P	S72.136K	S72.301Q	S72.336N
S62.91XK	S65.809A	S72.002P	S72.034M	S72.062R	S72.114Q	S72.136M	S72.301R	S72.336P
S62.91XP	S65.811A	S72.002Q	S72.034N	S72.063K	S72.114R	S72.136N	S72.302K	S72.336Q
S62.92XB	S65.812A	S72.002R	S72.034P	S72.063M	S72.115K	S72.136P	S72.302M	S72.336R
S62.92XK	S65.819A	S72.009K	S72.034Q	S72.063N	S72.115M	S72.136Q	S72.302N	S72.341K
S62.92XP	S65.891A	S72.009M	S72.034R	S72.063P	S72.115N	S72.136R	S72.302P	S72.341M
S65.001A	S65.892A	S72.009N	S72.035K	S72.063Q	S72.115P	S72.141K	S72.302Q	S72.341N
S65.002A	S65.899A	S72.009P	S72.035M	S72.063R	S72.115Q	S72.141M	S72.302R	S72.341P
S65.009A	S65.901A	S72.009Q	S72.035N	S72.064K	S72.115R	S72.141N	S72.309K	S72.341Q
S65.011A	S65.902A	S72.009R	S72.035P	S72.064M	S72.116K	S72.141P	S72.309M	S72.341R
S65.012A	S65.909A	S72.011K	S72.035Q	S72.064N	S72.116M	S72.141Q	S72.309N	S72.342K
S65.019A	S65.911A	S72.011M	S72.035R	S72.064P	S72.116N	S72.141R	S72.309P	S72.342M
S65.091A	S65.912A	S72.011N	S72.036K	S72.064Q	S72.116P	S72.142K	S72.309Q	S72.342N
S65.092A	S65.919A	S72.011P	S72.036M	S72.064R	S72.116R	S72.142M	S72.309R	S72.342P
S65.099A	S65.991A	S72.011Q	S72.036N	S72.065K	S72.121K	S72.142N	S72.321K	S72.342Q
S65.101A	S65.992A	S72.011R	S72.036P	S72.065M	S72.121M	S72.142P	S72.321M	S72.342R
S65.102A	S65.999A	S72.012K	S72.036Q	S72.065N	S72.121N	S72.142Q	S72.321N	S72.343K
S65.109A	S66.021A	S72.012M	S72.036R	S72.065P	S72.121P	S72.142R	S72.321P	S72.343M
S65.111A	S66.022A	S72.012N	S72.041K	S72.065Q	S72.121Q	S72.143K	S72.321Q	S72.343N
S65.112A	S66.029A	S72.012P	S72.041M	S72.065R	S72.121R	S72.143M	S72.321R	S72.343P
S65.119A	S66.120A	S72.012Q	S72.041N	S72.066K	S72.122K	S72.143N	S72.322K	S72.343Q
S65.191A	S66.121A	S72.012R	S72.041P	S72.066M	S72.122M	S72.143P	S72.322M	S72.343R
S65.192A	S66.122A	S72.019K	S72.041Q	S72.066N	S72.122N	S72.143Q	S72.322N	S72.344K
S65.199A	S66.123A	S72.019M	S72.041R	S72.066P	S72.122P	S72.143R	S72.322P	S72.344M
S65.201A	S66.124A	S72.019N	S72.042K	S72.066Q	S72.122Q	S72.144K	S72.322Q	S72.344N
S65.202A	S66.125A	S72.019P	S72.042M	S72.066R	S72.122R	S72.144M	S72.322R	S72.344P
S65.209A	S66.126A	S72.019Q	S72.042N	S72.091K	S72.123K	S72.144N	S72.323K	S72.344Q
S65.211A	S66.127A	S72.019R	S72.042P	S72.091M	S72.123M	S72.144P	S72.323M	S72.344R
S65.212A	S66.128A	S72.021K	S72.042Q	S72.091N	S72.123N	S72.144Q	S72.323N	S72.345K
S65.219A	S66.129A	S72.021M	S72.042R	S72.091P	S72.123P	S72.144R	S72.323P	S72.345M
S65.291A	S66.221A	S72.021N	S72.043K	S72.091Q	S72.123Q	S72.145K	S72.323Q	S72.345N
S65.292A	S66.222A	S72.021P	S72.043M	S72.091R	S72.123R	S72.145M	S72.323R	S72.345P
S65.299A	S66.229A	S72.021Q	S72.043N	S72.092K	S72.124K	S72.145N	S72.324K	S72.345Q
S65.301A	S66.320A	S72.021R	S72.043P	S72.092M	S72.124M	S72.145P	S72.324M	S72.345R
S65.302A	S66.321A	S72.022K	S72.043Q	S72.092N	S72.124N	S72.145Q	S72.324N	S72.346K
S65.309A	S66.322A	S72.022M	S72.043R	S72.092P	S72.124P	S72.145R	S72.324P	S72.346M
S65.311A	S66.323A	S72.022N	S72.044K	S72.092Q	S72.124Q	S72.146K	S72.324Q	S72.346N
S65.312A	S66.324A	S72.022P	S72.044M	S72.092R	S72.124R	S72.146M	S72.324R	S72.346P
S65.319A	S66.325A	S72.022Q	S72.044N	S72.099K	S72.125K	S72.146N	S72.325K	S72.346Q
S65.391A	S66.326A	S72.022R	S72.044P	S72.099M	S72.125M	S72.146P	S72.325M	S72.346R
S65.392A	S66.327A	S72.023K	S72.044Q	S72.099N	S72.125N	S72.146Q	S72.325N	S72.351K
S65.399A	S66.328A	S72.023M	S72.044R	S72.099P	S72.125P	S72.146R	S72.325P	S72.351M
S65.401A	S66.329A	S72.023N	S72.045K	S72.099Q	S72.125Q	S72.21XK	S72.325Q	S72.351N
S65.402A	S66.421A	S72.023P	S72.045M	S72.099R	S72.125R	S72.21XM	S72.325R	S72.351P
S65.409A	S66.422A	S72.023Q	S72.045N	S72.101K	S72.126K	S72.21XN	S72.326K	S72.351Q
S65.411A	S66.429A	S72.023R	S72.045P	S72.101M	S72.126M	S72.21XP	S72.326M	S72.351R
S65.412A	S66.520A	S72.024K	S72.045Q	S72.101N	S72.126N	S72.21XQ	S72.326N	S72.352K
S65.419A	S66.521A	S72.024M	S72.045R	S72.101P	S72.126P	S72.21XR	S72.326P	S72.352M
S65.491A	S66.522A	S72.024N	S72.046K	S72.101Q	S72.126Q	S72.22XK	S72.326Q	S72.352N
S65.492A	S66.523A	S72.024P	S72.046M	S72.101R	S72.126R	S72.22XM	S72.326R	S72.352P
S65.499A	S66.524A	S72.024Q	S72.046N	S72.102K	S72.131K	S72.22XN	S72.331K	S72.352Q
S65.500A	S66.525A	S72.024R	S72.046P	S72.102M	S72.131M	S72.22XP	S72.331M	S72.352R
S65.501A	S66.526A	S72.025K	S72.046Q	S72.102N	S72.131N	S72.22XQ	S72.331N	S72.353K
S65.502A	S66.527A	S72.025M	S72.046R	S72.102P	S72.131P	S72.22XR	S72.331P	S72.353M
S65.503A	S66.528A	S72.025N	S72.051K	S72.102Q	S72.131Q	S72.23XK	S72.331Q	S72.353N
S65.504A	S66.529A	S72.025P	S72.051M	S72.102R	S72.131R	S72.23XM	S72.331R	S72.353P
S65.505A	S66.821A	S72.025Q	S72.051N	S72.109K	S72.132K	S72.23XN	S72.332K	S72.353Q
S65.506A	S66.822A	S72.025R	S72.051P	S72.109M	S72.132M	S72.23XP	S72.332M	S72.353R
S65.507A	S66.829A	S72.026K	S72.051Q	S72.109N	S72.132K	S72.23XQ	S72.332N	S72.354K
S65.508A	S66.921A	S72.026M	S72.051R	S72.109P	S72.132M	S72.23XR	S72.332P	S72.354M

S72.354N	S72.402Q	S72.425N	S72.445K	S72.464R	S73.002A	S77.12XA	S79.191A	S82.016B
S72.354P	S72.402R	S72.425P	S72.445M	S72.465A	S73.003A	S78.011A	S79.191K	S82.016C
S72.354Q	S72.409A	S72.425Q	S72.445N	S72.465K	S73.004A	S78.012A	S79.191P	S82.016K
S72.354R	S72.409K	S72.425R	S72.445P	S72.465M	S73.005A	S78.019A	S79.192A	S82.016M
S72.355K	S72.409M	S72.426A	S72.445Q	S72.465N	S73.006A	S78.021A	S79.192K	S82.016N
S72.355M	S72.409N	S72.426K	S72.445R	S72.465P	S73.011A	S78.022A	S79.192P	S82.016P
S72.355N	S72.409P	S72.426M	S72.446A	S72.465Q	S73.012A	S78.029A	S79.199A	S82.016Q
S72.355P	S72.409Q	S72.426N	S72.446K	S72.465R	S73.013A	S78.111A	S79.199K	S82.016R
S72.355Q	S72.409R	S72.426P	S72.446M	S72.466A	S73.014A	S78.112A	S79.199P	S82.021A
S72.355R	S72.411A	S72.426Q	S72.446N	S72.466K	S73.015A	S78.119A	S82.001A	S82.021B
S72.356K	S72.411K	S72.426R	S72.446P	S72.466M	S73.016A	S78.121A	S82.001B	S82.021C
S72.356M	S72.411M	S72.431A	S72.446Q	S72.466N	S73.021A	S78.122A	S82.001C	S82.021K
S72.356N	S72.411N	S72.431K	S72.446R	S72.466P	S73.022A	S78.129A	S82.001K	S82.021M
S72.356P	S72.411P	S72.431M	S72.451A	S72.466Q	S73.023A	S78.911A	S82.001M	S82.021N
S72.356Q	S72.411Q	S72.431N	S72.451K	S72.466R	S73.024A	S78.912A	S82.001N	S82.021P
S72.356R	S72.411R	S72.431P	S72.451M	S72.471A	S73.025A	S78.919A	S82.001P	S82.021Q
S72.361K	S72.412A	S72.431Q	S72.451N	S72.471K	S73.026A	S78.921A	S82.001Q	S82.021R
S72.361M	S72.412K	S72.431R	S72.451P	S72.471P	S73.031A	S78.922A	S82.001R	S82.022A
S72.361N	S72.412M	S72.432A	S72.451Q	S72.472A	S73.032A	S78.929A	S82.002A	S82.022B
S72.361P	S72.412N	S72.432K	S72.451R	S72.472K	S73.033A	S79.001K	S82.002B	S82.022C
S72.361Q	S72.412P	S72.432M	S72.452A	S72.472P	S73.034A	S79.001P	S82.002C	S82.022K
S72.361R	S72.412Q	S72.432N	S72.452K	S72.479A	S73.035A	S79.002K	S82.002K	S82.022M
S72.362K	S72.412R	S72.432P	S72.452M	S72.479K	S73.036A	S79.002P	S82.002M	S82.022N
S72.362M	S72.413A	S72.432Q	S72.452N	S72.479P	S73.041A	S79.009K	S82.002N	S82.022P
S72.362N	S72.413K	S72.432R	S72.452P	S72.491A	S73.042A	S79.009P	S82.002P	S82.022Q
S72.362P	S72.413M	S72.433A	S72.452Q	S72.491K	S73.043A	S79.011K	S82.002Q	S82.022R
S72.362Q	S72.413N	S72.433K	S72.452R	S72.491M	S73.044A	S79.011P	S82.002R	S82.023A
S72.362R	S72.413P	S72.433M	S72.453A	S72.491N	S73.045A	S79.012K	S82.009A	S82.023B
S72.363K	S72.413Q	S72.433N	S72.453K	S72.491P	S73.046A	S79.012P	S82.009B	S82.023C
S72.363M	S72.413R	S72.433P	S72.453M	S72.491Q	S75.201A	S79.019K	S82.009C	S82.023K
S72.363N	S72.414A	S72.433Q	S72.453N	S72.491R	S75.202A	S79.019P	S82.009K	S82.023M
S72.363P	S72.414K	S72.433R	S72.453P	S72.492A	S75.209A	S79.091K	S82.009M	S82.023N
S72.363Q	S72.414M	S72.434A	S72.453Q	S72.492K	S75.211A	S79.091P	S82.009N	S82.023P
S72.363R	S72.414N	S72.434K	S72.453R	S72.492M	S75.212A	S79.092K	S82.009P	S82.023Q
S72.364K	S72.414P	S72.434M	S72.454A	S72.492N	S75.219A	S79.092P	S82.009Q	S82.023R
S72.364M	S72.414Q	S72.434N	S72.454K	S72.492P	S75.221A	S79.099K	S82.009R	S82.024A
S72.364N	S72.414R	S72.434P	S72.454M	S72.492Q	S75.222A	S79.099P	S82.011A	S82.024B
S72.364P	S72.415A	S72.434Q	S72.454N	S72.492R	S75.229A	S79.101A	S82.011B	S82.024C
S72.364Q	S72.415K	S72.434R	S72.454P	S72.499A	S75.291A	S79.101K	S82.011C	S82.024K
S72.364R	S72.415M	S72.435A	S72.454Q	S72.499K	S75.292A	S79.101P	S82.011K	S82.024M
S72.365K	S72.415N	S72.435K	S72.454R	S72.499M	S75.299A	S79.102A	S82.011M	S82.024N
S72.365M	S72.415P	S72.435M	S72.455A	S72.499N	S75.801A	S79.102K	S82.011N	S82.024P
S72.365N	S72.415Q	S72.435N	S72.455K	S72.499P	S75.802A	S79.102P	S82.011P	S82.024Q
S72.365P	S72.415R	S72.435P	S72.455M	S72.499Q	S75.809A	S79.109A	S82.011Q	S82.024R
S72.365Q	S72.416A	S72.435Q	S72.455N	S72.499R	S75.811A	S79.109K	S82.011R	S82.025A
S72.365R	S72.416K	S72.435R	S72.455P	S72.8X1K	S75.812A	S79.109P	S82.012A	S82.025B
S72.366K	S72.416M	S72.436A	S72.455Q	S72.8X1M	S75.819A	S79.111A	S82.012B	S82.025C
S72.366M	S72.416N	S72.436K	S72.455R	S72.8X1N	S75.891A	S79.111K	S82.012C	S82.025K
S72.366N	S72.416P	S72.436M	S72.456A	S72.8X1P	S75.892A	S79.111P	S82.012K	S82.025M
S72.366P	S72.416Q	S72.436N	S72.456K	S72.8X1Q	S75.899A	S79.112A	S82.012M	S82.025N
S72.366Q	S72.416R	S72.436P	S72.456M	S72.8X1R	S75.901A	S79.112K	S82.012N	S82.025P
S72.366R	S72.421A	S72.436Q	S72.456N	S72.8X2K	S75.902A	S79.112P	S82.012P	S82.025Q
S72.391K	S72.421K	S72.436R	S72.456P	S72.8X2M	S75.909A	S79.119A	S82.012Q	S82.025R
S72.391M	S72.421M	S72.441A	S72.456Q	S72.8X2N	S75.911A	S79.119K	S82.012R	S82.026A
S72.391N	S72.421N	S72.441K	S72.456R	S72.8X2P	S75.912A	S79.119P	S82.013A	S82.026B
S72.391P	S72.421P	S72.441M	S72.461A	S72.8X2Q	S75.919A	S79.121A	S82.013B	S82.026C
S72.391Q	S72.421Q	S72.441N	S72.461K	S72.8X2R	S75.991A	S79.121K	S82.013C	S82.026K
S72.391R	S72.421R	S72.441P	S72.461M	S72.8X9K	S75.992A	S79.121P	S82.013K	S82.026M
S72.392K	S72.422A	S72.441Q	S72.461N	S72.8X9M	S75.999A	S79.122A	S82.013M	S82.026N
S72.392M	S72.422K	S72.441R	S72.461P	S72.8X9N	S76.021A	S79.122K	S82.013N	S82.026P
S72.392N	S72.422M	S72.442A	S72.461Q	S72.8X9P	S76.022A	S79.122P	S82.013P	S82.026Q
S72.392P	S72.422N	S72.442K	S72.461R	S72.8X9Q	S76.029A	S79.129A	S82.013Q	S82.026R
S72.392Q	S72.422P	S72.442M	S72.462A	S72.8X9R	S76.121A	S79.129K	S82.013R	S82.031A
S72.392R	S72.422Q	S72.442N	S72.462K	S72.90XK	S76.122A	S79.129P	S82.014A	S82.031B
S72.399K	S72.422R	S72.442P	S72.462M	S72.90XM	S76.129A	S79.131A	S82.014B	S82.031C
S72.399M	S72.423A	S72.442Q	S72.462N	S72.90XN	S76.221A	S79.131K	S82.014C	S82.031K
S72.399N	S72.423K	S72.442R	S72.462P	S72.90XP	S76.222A	S79.131P	S82.014K	S82.031M
S72.399P	S72.423M	S72.443A	S72.462Q	S72.90XQ	S76.229A	S79.132A	S82.014M	S82.031N
S72.399Q	S72.423N	S72.443K	S72.462R	S72.90XR	S76.321A	S79.132K	S82.014N	S82.031P
S72.399R	S72.423P	S72.443M	S72.463A	S72.91XK	S76.322A	S79.132P	S82.014P	S82.031Q
S72.401A	S72.423Q	S72.443N	S72.463K	S72.91XM	S76.329A	S79.139A	S82.014Q	S82.031R
S72.401K	S72.423R	S72.443P	S72.463M	S72.91XN	S76.821A	S79.139K	S82.014R	S82.032A
S72.401M	S72.424A	S72.443Q	S72.463N	S72.91XP	S76.822A	S79.139P	S82.015A	S82.032B
S72.401N	S72.424K	S72.443R	S72.463P	S72.91XQ	S76.829A	S79.141A	S82.015B	S82.032C
S72.401P	S72.424M	S72.444A	S72.463Q	S72.91XR	S76.921A	S79.141K	S82.015C	S82.032K
S72.401Q	S72.424N	S72.444K	S72.463R	S72.92XK	S76.922A	S79.141P	S82.015K	S82.032M
S72.401R	S72.424P	S72.444M	S72.464A	S72.92XM	S76.929A	S79.142A	S82.015M	S82.032N
S72.402A	S72.424Q	S72.444N	S72.464K	S72.92XN	S77.00XA	S79.142K	S82.015N	S82.032P
S72.402K	S72.424R	S72.444P	S72.464M	S72.92XP	S77.01XA	S79.142P	S82.015P	S82.032Q
S72.402M	S72.425A	S72.444Q	S72.464N	S72.92XQ	S77.02XA	S79.149A	S82.015Q	S82.032R
S72.402N	S72.425K	S72.444R	S72.464P	S72.92XR	S77.10XA	S79.149K	S82.015R	S82.033A
S72.402P	S72.425M	S72.445A	S72.464Q	S73.001A	S77.11XA	S79.149P	S82.016A	S82.033B

S82.033C	S82.046K	S82.115A	S82.134Q	S82.154N	S82.222R	S82.242P	S82.262M	S82.312K
S82.033K	S82.046M	S82.115K	S82.134R	S82.154P	S82.223A	S82.242Q	S82.262N	S82.312P
S82.033M	S82.046N	S82.115M	S82.135A	S82.154Q	S82.223K	S82.242R	S82.262P	S82.319A
S82.033N	S82.046P	S82.115N	S82.135M	S82.154R	S82.223M	S82.243A	S82.262Q	S82.319K
S82.033P	S82.046Q	S82.115P	S82.135N	S82.155A	S82.223N	S82.243K	S82.262R	S82.319P
S82.033Q	S82.046R	S82.115Q	S82.135P	S82.155K	S82.223P	S82.243M	S82.263A	S82.391B
S82.033R	S82.091A	S82.115R	S82.135Q	S82.155M	S82.223Q	S82.243N	S82.263K	S82.391C
S82.034A	S82.091B	S82.116A	S82.135R	S82.155N	S82.223R	S82.243P	S82.263M	S82.391K
S82.034B	S82.091C	S82.116K	S82.136A	S82.155P	S82.224A	S82.243Q	S82.263N	S82.391M
S82.034C	S82.091K	S82.116M	S82.136K	S82.155Q	S82.224K	S82.243R	S82.263P	S82.391N
S82.034K	S82.091M	S82.116N	S82.136M	S82.155R	S82.224M	S82.244A	S82.263Q	S82.391P
S82.034M	S82.091N	S82.116P	S82.136N	S82.156A	S82.224N	S82.244K	S82.263R	S82.391Q
S82.034N	S82.091P	S82.116Q	S82.136P	S82.156K	S82.224P	S82.244M	S82.264A	S82.391R
S82.034P	S82.091Q	S82.116R	S82.136Q	S82.156M	S82.224Q	S82.244N	S82.264K	S82.392B
S82.034Q	S82.091R	S82.121A	S82.136R	S82.156N	S82.224R	S82.244P	S82.264M	S82.392C
S82.034R	S82.092A	S82.121K	S82.141A	S82.156P	S82.225A	S82.244Q	S82.264N	S82.392K
S82.035A	S82.092B	S82.121M	S82.141M	S82.156Q	S82.225K	S82.244R	S82.264P	S82.392M
S82.035B	S82.092C	S82.121N	S82.141N	S82.156R	S82.225M	S82.245A	S82.264Q	S82.392N
S82.035C	S82.092K	S82.121P	S82.141P	S82.161A	S82.225N	S82.245K	S82.265A	S82.392P
S82.035K	S82.092M	S82.121Q	S82.141Q	S82.161K	S82.225P	S82.245M	S82.265K	S82.392Q
S82.035M	S82.092N	S82.121R	S82.141R	S82.161P	S82.225Q	S82.245N	S82.265M	S82.392R
S82.035N	S82.092P	S82.122A	S82.142A	S82.162A	S82.225R	S82.245P	S82.265N	S82.399B
S82.035P	S82.092Q	S82.122K	S82.142K	S82.162K	S82.226A	S82.245Q	S82.265P	S82.399C
S82.035Q	S82.092R	S82.122M	S82.142M	S82.162P	S82.226K	S82.245R	S82.265Q	S82.399M
S82.035R	S82.099A	S82.122N	S82.142N	S82.169A	S82.226M	S82.246A	S82.265R	S82.399N
S82.036A	S82.099B	S82.122P	S82.142P	S82.169K	S82.226N	S82.246K	S82.266A	S82.399P
S82.036B	S82.099C	S82.122R	S82.142Q	S82.169P	S82.226P	S82.246M	S82.266K	S82.399Q
S82.036C	S82.099K	S82.123A	S82.142R	S82.191A	S82.226Q	S82.246N	S82.266M	S82.399R
S82.036K	S82.099M	S82.123K	S82.143A	S82.191K	S82.226R	S82.246P	S82.266N	S82.401K
S82.036M	S82.099N	S82.123M	S82.143K	S82.191M	S82.231A	S82.246Q	S82.266P	S82.401M
S82.036N	S82.099P	S82.123N	S82.143M	S82.191N	S82.231K	S82.246R	S82.266Q	S82.401N
S82.036P	S82.099Q	S82.123P	S82.143N	S82.191P	S82.231M	S82.251A	S82.266R	S82.401P
S82.036Q	S82.099R	S82.123Q	S82.143P	S82.191Q	S82.231N	S82.251K	S82.291A	S82.401Q
S82.036R	S82.101A	S82.123R	S82.143Q	S82.191R	S82.231P	S82.251M	S82.291K	S82.401R
S82.041A	S82.101K	S82.124A	S82.143R	S82.192A	S82.231Q	S82.251N	S82.291M	S82.402K
S82.041B	S82.101M	S82.124K	S82.144A	S82.192K	S82.231R	S82.251P	S82.291N	S82.402M
S82.041C	S82.101N	S82.124M	S82.144K	S82.192M	S82.232A	S82.251Q	S82.291P	S82.402N
S82.041K	S82.101P	S82.124N	S82.144M	S82.192P	S82.232K	S82.251R	S82.291Q	S82.402P
S82.041M	S82.101Q	S82.124P	S82.144N	S82.192Q	S82.232M	S82.252A	S82.291R	S82.402Q
S82.041N	S82.101R	S82.124Q	S82.144P	S82.192R	S82.232N	S82.252K	S82.292A	S82.402R
S82.041P	S82.102A	S82.124R	S82.144Q	S82.199A	S82.232P	S82.252M	S82.292K	S82.409K
S82.041Q	S82.102K	S82.125A	S82.144R	S82.199K	S82.232Q	S82.252N	S82.292M	S82.409M
S82.041R	S82.102M	S82.125K	S82.145A	S82.199M	S82.232R	S82.252P	S82.292N	S82.409N
S82.042A	S82.102N	S82.125M	S82.145K	S82.199N	S82.233A	S82.252Q	S82.292P	S82.409P
S82.042B	S82.102P	S82.125N	S82.145M	S82.199P	S82.233K	S82.252R	S82.292Q	S82.409Q
S82.042C	S82.102Q	S82.125P	S82.145N	S82.199Q	S82.233M	S82.253A	S82.292R	S82.409R
S82.042K	S82.102R	S82.125Q	S82.145P	S82.199R	S82.233N	S82.253K	S82.299A	S82.421K
S82.042M	S82.109A	S82.125R	S82.145Q	S82.201A	S82.233P	S82.253M	S82.299K	S82.421M
S82.042N	S82.109K	S82.126A	S82.145R	S82.201K	S82.233Q	S82.253N	S82.299M	S82.421N
S82.042P	S82.109M	S82.126K	S82.146A	S82.201M	S82.233R	S82.253P	S82.299N	S82.421P
S82.042Q	S82.109N	S82.126M	S82.146K	S82.201N	S82.234A	S82.253Q	S82.299P	S82.421Q
S82.042R	S82.109P	S82.126N	S82.146M	S82.201P	S82.234K	S82.253R	S82.299Q	S82.421R
S82.043A	S82.109Q	S82.126P	S82.146N	S82.201Q	S82.234M	S82.254A	S82.299R	S82.422K
S82.043B	S82.109R	S82.126Q	S82.146P	S82.201R	S82.234N	S82.254K	S82.301B	S82.422M
S82.043C	S82.111A	S82.126R	S82.146Q	S82.202A	S82.234P	S82.254M	S82.301C	S82.422N
S82.043K	S82.111K	S82.131A	S82.146R	S82.202K	S82.234Q	S82.254N	S82.301K	S82.422P
S82.043M	S82.111M	S82.131K	S82.151A	S82.202M	S82.234R	S82.254P	S82.301M	S82.422Q
S82.043N	S82.111N	S82.131M	S82.151K	S82.202N	S82.235A	S82.254Q	S82.301N	S82.422R
S82.043P	S82.111P	S82.131N	S82.151M	S82.202P	S82.235K	S82.254R	S82.301P	S82.423K
S82.043Q	S82.111Q	S82.131P	S82.151N	S82.202Q	S82.235M	S82.255A	S82.301Q	S82.423M
S82.043R	S82.111R	S82.131Q	S82.151P	S82.202R	S82.235N	S82.255K	S82.301R	S82.423N
S82.044A	S82.112A	S82.131R	S82.151Q	S82.209A	S82.235P	S82.255M	S82.302B	S82.423P
S82.044B	S82.112K	S82.132A	S82.151R	S82.209K	S82.235Q	S82.255N	S82.302C	S82.423Q
S82.044C	S82.112M	S82.132K	S82.152A	S82.209N	S82.235R	S82.255P	S82.302K	S82.423R
S82.044K	S82.112N	S82.132M	S82.152K	S82.209P	S82.236A	S82.255Q	S82.302M	S82.424K
S82.044M	S82.112P	S82.132N	S82.152M	S82.209Q	S82.236K	S82.255R	S82.302N	S82.424M
S82.044N	S82.112Q	S82.132P	S82.152N	S82.209R	S82.236M	S82.256A	S82.302P	S82.424N
S82.044P	S82.112R	S82.132Q	S82.152P	S82.221A	S82.236N	S82.256K	S82.302Q	S82.424P
S82.044Q	S82.113A	S82.132R	S82.152Q	S82.221K	S82.236P	S82.256M	S82.302R	S82.424Q
S82.044R	S82.113K	S82.133A	S82.152R	S82.221M	S82.236Q	S82.256N	S82.309B	S82.424R
S82.045A	S82.113M	S82.133K	S82.153A	S82.221N	S82.236R	S82.256P	S82.309C	S82.425K
S82.045B	S82.113N	S82.133M	S82.153K	S82.221P	S82.241A	S82.256Q	S82.309K	S82.425M
S82.045C	S82.113P	S82.133N	S82.153M	S82.221Q	S82.241K	S82.256R	S82.309M	S82.425N
S82.045K	S82.113R	S82.133P	S82.153N	S82.221R	S82.241M	S82.261A	S82.309N	S82.425P
S82.045M	S82.114A	S82.133Q	S82.153P	S82.222A	S82.241N	S82.261K	S82.309P	S82.425Q
S82.045N	S82.114K	S82.133R	S82.153Q	S82.222K	S82.241P	S82.261M	S82.309Q	S82.425R
S82.045P	S82.114M	S82.134A	S82.153R	S82.222M	S82.241Q	S82.261N	S82.309R	S82.426K
S82.045Q	S82.114N	S82.134K	S82.154A	S82.222P	S82.241R	S82.261P	S82.311A	S82.426M
S82.045R	S82.114P	S82.134M	S82.154K	S82.222Q	S82.242A	S82.261Q	S82.311K	S82.426N
S82.046A	S82.114Q	S82.134N	S82.154M		S82.242K	S82.261R	S82.311P	S82.426P
S82.046B	S82.114R	S82.134P			S82.242M	S82.262A	S82.312A	S82.426Q
S82.046C					S82.242N	S82.262K		

S82.426R	S82.452P	S82.51XC	S82.65XM	S82.845R	S82.865M	S82.899R	S85.811A	S89.032K
S82.431K	S82.452Q	S82.51XK	S82.65XN	S82.846B	S82.865N	S82.90XB	S85.812A	S89.032P
S82.431M	S82.452R	S82.51XM	S82.65XP	S82.846C	S82.865P	S82.90XC	S85.819A	S89.039A
S82.431N	S82.453K	S82.51XN	S82.65XQ	S82.846K	S82.865Q	S82.90XK	S85.891A	S89.039K
S82.431P	S82.453M	S82.51XP	S82.65XR	S82.846M	S82.865R	S82.90XM	S85.892A	S89.039P
S82.431Q	S82.453N	S82.51XQ	S82.66XB	S82.846N	S82.866K	S82.90XN	S85.899A	S89.041A
S82.431R	S82.453P	S82.51XR	S82.66XC	S82.846P	S82.866M	S82.90XP	S85.901A	S89.041K
S82.432K	S82.453Q	S82.52XB	S82.66XK	S82.846Q	S82.866N	S82.90XQ	S85.902A	S89.041P
S82.432M	S82.453R	S82.52XC	S82.66XM	S82.846R	S82.866P	S82.90XR	S85.909A	S89.042A
S82.432N	S82.454K	S82.52XK	S82.66XN	S82.851B	S82.866Q	S82.91XB	S85.911A	S89.042K
S82.432P	S82.454M	S82.52XM	S82.66XP	S82.851C	S82.866R	S82.91XC	S85.912A	S89.042P
S82.432Q	S82.454N	S82.52XN	S82.66XQ	S82.851K	S82.871B	S82.91XK	S85.919A	S89.049A
S82.432R	S82.454P	S82.52XP	S82.66XR	S82.851M	S82.871C	S82.91XM	S85.991A	S89.049K
S82.433K	S82.454Q	S82.52XQ	S82.811K	S82.851N	S82.871K	S82.91XN	S85.992A	S89.049P
S82.433M	S82.454R	S82.52XR	S82.811P	S82.851P	S82.871M	S82.91XP	S85.999A	S89.091A
S82.433N	S82.455K	S82.53XB	S82.812K	S82.851Q	S82.871N	S82.91XQ	S86.021A	S89.091K
S82.433P	S82.455M	S82.53XC	S82.812P	S82.851R	S82.871P	S82.91XR	S86.022A	S89.091P
S82.433Q	S82.455N	S82.53XK	S82.819K	S82.852B	S82.871Q	S82.92XB	S86.029A	S89.092A
S82.433R	S82.455P	S82.53XM	S82.819P	S82.852C	S82.871R	S82.92XC	S86.121A	S89.092K
S82.434K	S82.455Q	S82.53XN	S82.821K	S82.852K	S82.872B	S82.92XK	S86.122A	S89.092P
S82.434M	S82.455R	S82.53XP	S82.821P	S82.852M	S82.872C	S82.92XM	S86.129A	S89.099A
S82.434N	S82.456K	S82.53XQ	S82.822K	S82.852N	S82.872K	S82.92XN	S86.221A	S89.099K
S82.434P	S82.456M	S82.53XR	S82.822P	S82.852P	S82.872M	S82.92XP	S86.222A	S89.099P
S82.434Q	S82.456N	S82.54XB	S82.829K	S82.852Q	S82.872N	S82.92XQ	S86.229A	S89.101K
S82.434R	S82.456P	S82.54XC	S82.829P	S82.852R	S82.872P	S82.92XR	S86.321A	S89.101P
S82.435K	S82.456Q	S82.54XK	S82.831K	S82.853B	S82.872Q	S85.101A	S86.322A	S89.102K
S82.435M	S82.456R	S82.54XM	S82.831M	S82.853C	S82.872R	S85.102A	S86.329A	S89.102P
S82.435N	S82.461K	S82.54XN	S82.831N	S82.853K	S82.873B	S85.109A	S86.821A	S89.109K
S82.435P	S82.461M	S82.54XP	S82.831P	S82.853M	S82.873C	S85.111A	S86.822A	S89.109P
S82.435Q	S82.461N	S82.54XQ	S82.831Q	S82.853N	S82.873K	S85.112A	S86.829A	S89.111K
S82.435R	S82.461P	S82.54XR	S82.831R	S82.853P	S82.873M	S85.119A	S86.921A	S89.111P
S82.436K	S82.461Q	S82.55XB	S82.832K	S82.853Q	S82.873N	S85.121A	S86.922A	S89.112K
S82.436M	S82.461R	S82.55XC	S82.832M	S82.853R	S82.873P	S85.122A	S86.929A	S89.112P
S82.436N	S82.462K	S82.55XK	S82.832N	S82.854B	S82.873Q	S85.129A	S88.011A	S89.119K
S82.436P	S82.462M	S82.55XM	S82.832P	S82.854C	S82.873R	S85.131A	S88.012A	S89.119P
S82.436Q	S82.462N	S82.55XN	S82.832Q	S82.854K	S82.874B	S85.132A	S88.019A	S89.121K
S82.436R	S82.462P	S82.55XP	S82.832R	S82.854M	S82.874C	S85.139A	S88.021A	S89.121P
S82.441K	S82.462Q	S82.55XQ	S82.839K	S82.854N	S82.874K	S85.141A	S88.022A	S89.122K
S82.441M	S82.462R	S82.55XR	S82.839M	S82.854P	S82.874M	S85.142A	S88.029A	S89.122P
S82.441N	S82.463K	S82.56XB	S82.839N	S82.854Q	S82.874N	S85.149A	S88.111A	S89.129K
S82.441P	S82.463M	S82.56XC	S82.839P	S82.854R	S82.874P	S85.151A	S88.112A	S89.129P
S82.441Q	S82.463N	S82.56XK	S82.839Q	S82.855B	S82.874Q	S85.152A	S88.119A	S89.131K
S82.441R	S82.463P	S82.56XM	S82.841B	S82.855C	S82.874R	S85.159A	S88.121A	S89.131P
S82.442K	S82.463Q	S82.56XN	S82.841C	S82.855K	S82.875B	S85.161A	S88.122A	S89.132K
S82.442M	S82.463R	S82.56XP	S82.841K	S82.855M	S82.875C	S85.162A	S88.129A	S89.132P
S82.442N	S82.464K	S82.56XQ	S82.841M	S82.855N	S82.875K	S85.169A	S88.911A	S89.139K
S82.442P	S82.464M	S82.56XR	S82.841N	S82.855P	S82.875M	S85.171A	S88.912A	S89.139P
S82.442Q	S82.464N	S82.61XB	S82.841P	S82.855Q	S82.875N	S85.172A	S88.919A	S89.141K
S82.442R	S82.464P	S82.61XC	S82.841Q	S82.855R	S82.875P	S85.179A	S88.921A	S89.141P
S82.443K	S82.464Q	S82.61XK	S82.841R	S82.856B	S82.875Q	S85.181A	S88.922A	S89.142K
S82.443M	S82.464R	S82.61XM	S82.842B	S82.856C	S82.875R	S85.182A	S88.929A	S89.142P
S82.443N	S82.465K	S82.61XN	S82.842C	S82.856K	S82.876B	S85.189A	S89.001A	S89.149K
S82.443P	S82.465M	S82.61XP	S82.842K	S82.856M	S82.876C	S85.201A	S89.001K	S89.149P
S82.443Q	S82.465N	S82.61XQ	S82.842M	S82.856N	S82.876K	S85.202A	S89.001P	S89.191K
S82.443R	S82.465P	S82.61XR	S82.842N	S82.856P	S82.876M	S85.209A	S89.002A	S89.191P
S82.444K	S82.465Q	S82.62XB	S82.842P	S82.856Q	S82.876N	S85.211A	S89.002K	S89.192K
S82.444M	S82.465R	S82.62XC	S82.842Q	S82.856R	S82.876P	S85.212A	S89.002P	S89.192P
S82.444N	S82.466K	S82.62XK	S82.842R	S82.861K	S82.876Q	S85.219A	S89.009A	S89.199K
S82.444P	S82.466M	S82.62XM	S82.843B	S82.861M	S82.876R	S85.291A	S89.009K	S89.199P
S82.444Q	S82.466N	S82.62XN	S82.843C	S82.861N	S82.891B	S85.292A	S89.009P	S89.201K
S82.444R	S82.466P	S82.62XP	S82.843K	S82.861P	S82.891C	S85.299A	S89.011A	S89.201P
S82.445K	S82.466Q	S82.62XQ	S82.843M	S82.861Q	S82.891K	S85.301A	S89.011K	S89.202K
S82.445M	S82.466R	S82.62XR	S82.843N	S82.861R	S82.891M	S85.302A	S89.011P	S89.202P
S82.445N	S82.491K	S82.63XB	S82.843P	S82.862K	S82.891N	S85.309A	S89.012A	S89.209K
S82.445P	S82.491M	S82.63XC	S82.843Q	S82.862M	S82.891P	S85.311A	S89.012K	S89.209P
S82.445Q	S82.491N	S82.63XK	S82.843R	S82.862N	S82.891Q	S85.312A	S89.012P	S89.211K
S82.445R	S82.491P	S82.63XM	S82.844B	S82.862P	S82.891R	S85.319A	S89.019A	S89.211P
S82.446K	S82.491Q	S82.63XN	S82.844C	S82.862Q	S82.892B	S85.391A	S89.019K	S89.212K
S82.446M	S82.491R	S82.63XP	S82.844K	S82.862R	S82.892C	S85.392A	S89.019P	S89.212P
S82.446N	S82.492K	S82.63XQ	S82.844M	S82.863K	S82.892K	S85.399A	S89.021A	S89.219K
S82.446P	S82.492M	S82.63XR	S82.844N	S82.863M	S82.892M	S85.401A	S89.021K	S89.219P
S82.446Q	S82.492N	S82.64XB	S82.844P	S82.863N	S82.892N	S85.402A	S89.021P	S89.221K
S82.446R	S82.492P	S82.64XC	S82.844Q	S82.863P	S82.892P	S85.409A	S89.022A	S89.221P
S82.451K	S82.492Q	S82.64XK	S82.844R	S82.863Q	S82.892Q	S85.411A	S89.022K	S89.222K
S82.451M	S82.492R	S82.64XM	S82.845B	S82.863R	S82.892R	S85.412A	S89.022P	S89.222P
S82.451N	S82.499K	S82.64XN	S82.845C	S82.864K	S82.899B	S85.419A	S89.029A	S89.229K
S82.451P	S82.499M	S82.64XP	S82.845K	S82.864M	S82.899C	S85.491A	S89.029K	S89.229P
S82.451Q	S82.499N	S82.64XQ	S82.845M	S82.864N	S82.899K	S85.492A	S89.029P	S89.291K
S82.451R	S82.499P	S82.64XR	S82.845N	S82.864P	S82.899M	S85.499A	S89.031A	S89.291P
S82.452K	S82.499Q	S82.65XB	S82.845P	S82.864Q	S82.899N	S85.801A	S89.031K	S89.292K
S82.452M	S82.499R	S82.65XC	S82.845Q	S82.864R	S82.899P	S85.802A	S89.031P	S89.292P
S82.452N	S82.51XB	S82.65XK		S82.865K	S82.899Q	S85.809A	S89.032A	S89.299K

S89.299P	S92.035B	S92.115K	S92.192P	S92.246B	S92.336K	S92.502K	S95.191A	T17.818A
S89.301K	S92.035K	S92.115P	S92.199B	S92.246K	S92.336P	S92.502P	S95.192A	T17.820A
S89.301P	S92.035P	S92.116B	S92.199K	S92.246P	S92.341B	S92.503K	S95.199A	T17.828A
S89.302K	S92.036B	S92.116K	S92.199P	S92.251B	S92.341K	S92.503P	S95.201A	T17.890A
S89.302P	S92.036K	S92.116P	S92.201B	S92.251K	S92.341P	S92.504K	S95.202A	T17.898A
S89.309K	S92.036P	S92.121B	S92.201K	S92.251P	S92.342B	S92.504P	S95.209A	T20.30XA
S89.309P	S92.041B	S92.121K	S92.201P	S92.252B	S92.342K	S92.505K	S95.211A	T20.311A
S89.311K	S92.041K	S92.121P	S92.202B	S92.252K	S92.342P	S92.505P	S95.212A	T20.312A
S89.311P	S92.041P	S92.122B	S92.202K	S92.252P	S92.343B	S92.506K	S95.219A	T20.319A
S89.312K	S92.042B	S92.122K	S92.202P	S92.253B	S92.343K	S92.506P	S95.291A	T20.32XA
S89.312P	S92.042K	S92.122P	S92.209B	S92.253K	S92.343P	S92.511K	S95.292A	T20.33XA
S89.319K	S92.042P	S92.123B	S92.209K	S92.253P	S92.344B	S92.511P	S95.299A	T20.34XA
S89.319P	S92.043B	S92.123K	S92.209P	S92.254B	S92.344K	S92.512K	S95.801A	T20.35XA
S89.321K	S92.043K	S92.123P	S92.211B	S92.254K	S92.344P	S92.512P	S95.802A	T20.36XA
S89.321P	S92.043P	S92.124B	S92.211K	S92.254P	S92.345B	S92.513K	S95.809A	T20.37XA
S89.322K	S92.044B	S92.124K	S92.211P	S92.255B	S92.345K	S92.513P	S95.811A	T20.39XA
S89.322P	S92.044K	S92.124P	S92.212B	S92.255K	S92.345P	S92.514K	S95.812A	T20.70XA
S89.329K	S92.044P	S92.125B	S92.212K	S92.255P	S92.346B	S92.514P	S95.819A	T20.711A
S89.329P	S92.045B	S92.125K	S92.212P	S92.256B	S92.346K	S92.515K	S95.891A	T20.712A
S89.391K	S92.045K	S92.125P	S92.213B	S92.256K	S92.346P	S92.515P	S95.892A	T20.719A
S89.391P	S92.045P	S92.126B	S92.213K	S92.256P	S92.351B	S92.516K	S95.899A	T20.72XA
S89.392K	S92.046B	S92.126K	S92.213P	S92.301B	S92.351K	S92.516P	S95.901A	T20.73XA
S89.392P	S92.046K	S92.126P	S92.214B	S92.301K	S92.351P	S92.521K	S95.902A	T20.74XA
S89.399K	S92.046P	S92.131B	S92.214K	S92.301P	S92.352B	S92.521P	S95.909A	T20.75XA
S89.399P	S92.051B	S92.131K	S92.214P	S92.302B	S92.352K	S92.522K	S95.911A	T20.76XA
S92.001B	S92.051K	S92.131P	S92.215B	S92.302K	S92.352P	S92.522P	S95.912A	T20.77XA
S92.001K	S92.051P	S92.132B	S92.215K	S92.302P	S92.353B	S92.523K	S95.919A	T20.79XA
S92.001P	S92.052B	S92.132K	S92.215P	S92.309B	S92.353K	S92.523P	S95.991A	T21.30XA
S92.002B	S92.052K	S92.132P	S92.216B	S92.309K	S92.353P	S92.524K	S95.992A	T21.31XA
S92.002K	S92.052P	S92.133B	S92.216K	S92.309P	S92.354B	S92.524P	S95.999A	T21.32XA
S92.002P	S92.053B	S92.133K	S92.216P	S92.311B	S92.354K	S92.525K	S96.021A	T21.33XA
S92.009B	S92.053K	S92.133P	S92.221B	S92.311K	S92.354P	S92.525P	S96.022A	T21.34XA
S92.009K	S92.053P	S92.134B	S92.221K	S92.311P	S92.355B	S92.526K	S96.029A	T21.35XA
S92.009P	S92.054B	S92.134K	S92.221P	S92.312B	S92.355K	S92.526P	S96.121A	T21.36XA
S92.011B	S92.054K	S92.134P	S92.222B	S92.312K	S92.355P	S92.531K	S96.122A	T21.37XA
S92.011K	S92.054P	S92.135B	S92.222K	S92.312P	S92.356B	S92.531P	S96.129A	T21.39XA
S92.011P	S92.055B	S92.135K	S92.222P	S92.313B	S92.356K	S92.532K	S96.221A	T21.70XA
S92.012B	S92.055K	S92.135P	S92.223B	S92.313K	S92.356P	S92.532P	S96.222A	T21.71XA
S92.012K	S92.055P	S92.136B	S92.223K	S92.313P	S92.401K	S92.533K	S96.229A	T21.72XA
S92.012P	S92.056B	S92.136K	S92.223P	S92.314B	S92.401P	S92.533P	S96.821A	T21.73XA
S92.013B	S92.056K	S92.136P	S92.224B	S92.314K	S92.402K	S92.534K	S96.822A	T21.74XA
S92.013K	S92.056P	S92.141B	S92.224K	S92.314P	S92.402P	S92.534P	S96.829A	T21.75XA
S92.013P	S92.061B	S92.141K	S92.224P	S92.315B	S92.403K	S92.535K	S96.921A	T21.76XA
S92.014B	S92.061K	S92.141P	S92.225B	S92.315K	S92.403P	S92.535P	S96.922A	T21.77XA
S92.014K	S92.061P	S92.142B	S92.225K	S92.315P	S92.404K	S92.536K	S96.929A	T21.79XA
S92.014P	S92.062B	S92.142K	S92.225P	S92.316B	S92.404P	S92.536P	S98.011A	T22.30XA
S92.015B	S92.062K	S92.142P	S92.226B	S92.316K	S92.405K	S92.591K	S98.012A	T22.311A
S92.015K	S92.062P	S92.143B	S92.226K	S92.316P	S92.405P	S92.591P	S98.019A	T22.312A
S92.015P	S92.063B	S92.143K	S92.226P	S92.321B	S92.406K	S92.592K	S98.021A	T22.319A
S92.016B	S92.063K	S92.143P	S92.231B	S92.321K	S92.406P	S92.592P	S98.022A	T22.321A
S92.016K	S92.063P	S92.144B	S92.231K	S92.321P	S92.411K	S92.599K	S98.029A	T22.322A
S92.016P	S92.064B	S92.144K	S92.231P	S92.322B	S92.411P	S92.599P	S98.311A	T22.329A
S92.021B	S92.064K	S92.144P	S92.232B	S92.322K	S92.412K	S92.901B	S98.312A	T22.331A
S92.021K	S92.064P	S92.145B	S92.232K	S92.322P	S92.412P	S92.901K	S98.319A	T22.332A
S92.021P	S92.065B	S92.145K	S92.232P	S92.323B	S92.413K	S92.901P	S98.321A	T22.339A
S92.022B	S92.065K	S92.145P	S92.233B	S92.323K	S92.413P	S92.902B	S98.322A	T22.341A
S92.022K	S92.065P	S92.146B	S92.233K	S92.323P	S92.414K	S92.902K	S98.329A	T22.342A
S92.022P	S92.066B	S92.146K	S92.233P	S92.324B	S92.414P	S92.902P	S98.911A	T22.349A
S92.023B	S92.066K	S92.146P	S92.234B	S92.324K	S92.415K	S92.909B	S98.912A	T22.351A
S92.023K	S92.066P	S92.151B	S92.234K	S92.324P	S92.415P	S92.909K	S98.919A	T22.352A
S92.023P	S92.101B	S92.151K	S92.234P	S92.325B	S92.416K	S92.909P	S98.921A	T22.359A
S92.024B	S92.101K	S92.151P	S92.235B	S92.325K	S92.416P	S92.911K	S98.922A	T22.361A
S92.024K	S92.101P	S92.152B	S92.235K	S92.325P	S92.421K	S92.911P	S98.929A	T22.362A
S92.024P	S92.102B	S92.152K	S92.235P	S92.326B	S92.421P	S92.912K	T17.400A	T22.369A
S92.025B	S92.102K	S92.152P	S92.236B	S92.326K	S92.422K	S92.912P	T17.408A	T22.391A
S92.025K	S92.102P	S92.153B	S92.236K	S92.326P	S92.422P	S92.919K	T17.410A	T22.392A
S92.025P	S92.109B	S92.153K	S92.236P	S92.331B	S92.423K	S92.919P	T17.418A	T22.399A
S92.026B	S92.109K	S92.153P	S92.241B	S92.331K	S92.423P	S95.001A	T17.420A	T22.70XA
S92.026K	S92.109P	S92.154B	S92.241K	S92.331P	S92.424K	S95.002A	T17.428A	T22.711A
S92.026P	S92.111B	S92.154K	S92.241P	S92.332B	S92.424P	S95.009A	T17.490A	T22.712A
S92.031B	S92.111K	S92.154P	S92.242B	S92.332K	S92.425K	S95.011A	T17.498A	T22.719A
S92.031K	S92.111P	S92.155B	S92.242K	S92.332P	S92.425P	S95.012A	T17.500A	T22.721A
S92.031P	S92.112B	S92.155K	S92.242P	S92.333B	S92.426K	S95.019A	T17.508A	T22.722A
S92.032B	S92.112K	S92.155P	S92.243B	S92.333K	S92.426P	S95.091A	T17.510A	T22.729A
S92.032K	S92.112P	S92.156B	S92.243K	S92.333P	S92.491K	S95.092A	T17.518A	T22.731A
S92.032P	S92.113B	S92.156K	S92.243P	S92.334B	S92.491P	S95.099A	T17.520A	T22.732A
S92.033B	S92.113K	S92.156P	S92.244B	S92.334K	S92.492K	S95.101A	T17.528A	T22.739A
S92.033K	S92.113P	S92.191B	S92.244K	S92.334P	S92.492P	S95.102A	T17.590A	T22.741A
S92.033P	S92.114B	S92.191K	S92.244P	S92.335B	S92.499K	S95.109A	T17.598A	T22.742A
S92.034B	S92.114K	S92.191P	S92.245B	S92.335K	S92.499P	S95.111A	T17.800A	T22.749A
S92.034K	S92.114P	S92.192B	S92.245K	S92.335P	S92.501K	S95.112A	T17.808A	T22.751A
S92.034P	S92.115B	S92.192K	S92.245P	S92.336B	S92.501P	S95.119A	T17.810A	T22.752A

T22.759A	T24.721A	T33.511A	T71.144A	T80.419A	T81.83XA	T82.7XXA	T84.053A	T84.622A
T22.761A	T24.722A	T33.512A	T71.151A	T80.49XA	T82.01XA	T82.817A	T84.058A	T84.623A
T22.762A	T24.729A	T33.519A	T71.152A	T80.51XA	T82.02XA	T82.818A	T84.059A	T84.624A
T22.769A	T24.731A	T33.521A	T71.153A	T80.52XA	T82.03XA	T82.827A	T84.060A	T84.625A
T22.791A	T24.732A	T33.522A	T71.154A	T80.59XA	T82.09XA	T82.828A	T84.061A	T84.629A
T22.792A	T24.739A	T33.529A	T71.161A	T80.61XA	T82.110A	T82.837A	T84.062A	T84.63XA
T22.799A	T24.791A	T33.531A	T71.162A	T80.62XA	T82.111A	T82.838A	T84.063A	T84.69XA
T23.301A	T24.792A	T33.532A	T71.163A	T80.69XA	T82.118A	T82.847A	T84.068A	T84.7XXA
T23.302A	T24.799A	T33.539A	T71.164A	T80.810A	T82.119A	T82.848A	T84.069A	T84.81XA
T23.309A	T25.311A	T33.60XA	T71.191A	T80.818A	T82.120A	T82.857A	T84.090A	T84.82XA
T23.311A	T25.312A	T33.61XA	T71.192A	T80.910A	T82.121A	T82.858A	T84.091A	T84.83XA
T23.312A	T25.319A	T33.62XA	T71.193A	T80.911A	T82.128A	T82.867A	T84.092A	T84.84XA
T23.319A	T25.321A	T33.70XA	T71.194A	T80.919A	T82.129A	T82.868A	T84.093A	T84.85XA
T23.321A	T25.322A	T33.71XA	T71.20XA	T80.A0XA	T82.190A	T82.897A	T84.098A	T84.86XA
T23.322A	T25.329A	T33.72XA	T71.21XA	T80.A10A	T82.191A	T82.898A	T84.099A	T84.89XA
T23.329A	T25.331A	T33.811A	T71.221A	T80.A11A	T82.198A	T82.9XXA	T84.110A	T84.9XXA
T23.331A	T25.332A	T33.812A	T71.222A	T80.A19A	T82.199A	T83.010A	T84.111A	T85.01XA
T23.332A	T25.339A	T33.819A	T71.223A	T80.A9XA	T82.211A	T83.020A	T84.112A	T85.02XA
T23.339A	T25.391A	T33.821A	T71.224A	T81.10XA	T82.212A	T83.030A	T84.113A	T85.03XA
T23.341A	T25.392A	T33.822A	T71.231A	T81.30XA	T82.213A	T83.090A	T84.114A	T85.09XA
T23.342A	T25.399A	T33.829A	T71.232A	T81.31XA	T82.218A	T83.110A	T84.115A	T85.110A
T23.349A	T25.711A	T33.831A	T71.233A	T81.32XA	T82.221A	T83.111A	T84.116A	T85.111A
T23.351A	T25.712A	T33.832A	T71.234A	T81.33XA	T82.222A	T83.112A	T84.117A	T85.112A
T23.352A	T25.719A	T33.839A	T71.29XA	T81.4XXA	T82.223A	T83.118A	T84.119A	T85.118A
T23.359A	T25.721A	T33.90XA	T71.9XXA	T81.500A	T82.228A	T83.120A	T84.120A	T85.120A
T23.361A	T25.722A	T33.99XA	T74.01XA	T81.501A	T82.310A	T83.121A	T84.121A	T85.121A
T23.362A	T25.729A	T34.011A	T74.02XA	T81.502A	T82.311A	T83.122A	T84.122A	T85.122A
T23.369A	T25.731A	T34.012A	T74.11XA	T81.503A	T82.312A	T83.128A	T84.123A	T85.128A
T23.371A	T25.732A	T34.019A	T74.12XA	T81.504A	T82.318A	T83.190A	T84.124A	T85.190A
T23.372A	T25.739A	T34.02XA	T74.21XA	T81.505A	T82.319A	T83.191A	T84.125A	T85.191A
T23.379A	T25.791A	T34.09XA	T74.22XA	T81.506A	T82.320A	T83.192A	T84.126A	T85.192A
T23.391A	T25.792A	T34.1XXA	T74.32XA	T81.507A	T82.321A	T83.198A	T84.127A	T85.199A
T23.392A	T25.799A	T34.2XXA	T74.4XXA	T81.508A	T82.322A	T83.21XA	T84.129A	T85.21XA
T23.399A	T26.20XA	T34.3XXA	T74.91XA	T81.509A	T82.328A	T83.22XA	T84.190A	T85.22XA
T23.701A	T26.21XA	T34.40XA	T74.92XA	T81.510A	T82.329A	T83.23XA	T84.191A	T85.29XA
T23.702A	T26.22XA	T34.41XA	T75.1XXA	T81.511A	T82.330A	T83.29XA	T84.192A	T85.310A
T23.709A	T26.70XA	T34.42XA	T76.01XA	T81.512A	T82.331A	T83.410A	T84.193A	T85.311A
T23.711A	T26.71XA	T34.511A	T76.02XA	T81.513A	T82.332A	T83.418A	T84.194A	T85.320A
T23.712A	T26.72XA	T34.512A	T76.11XA	T81.514A	T82.338A	T83.420A	T84.195A	T85.321A
T23.719A	T27.0XXA	T34.519A	T76.12XA	T81.515A	T82.339A	T83.428A	T84.196A	T85.390A
T23.721A	T27.1XXA	T34.521A	T76.21XA	T81.516A	T82.390A	T83.490A	T84.197A	T85.391A
T23.722A	T27.2XXA	T34.522A	T76.22XA	T81.517A	T82.391A	T83.498A	T84.199A	T85.41XA
T23.729A	T27.3XXA	T34.529A	T76.32XA	T81.518A	T82.392A	T83.51XA	T84.210A	T85.42XA
T23.731A	T27.4XXA	T34.531A	T76.91XA	T81.519A	T82.398A	T83.59XA	T84.213A	T85.43XA
T23.732A	T27.5XXA	T34.532A	T76.92XA	T81.520A	T82.399A	T83.6XXA	T84.216A	T85.44XA
T23.739A	T27.6XXA	T34.539A	T78.00XA	T81.521A	T82.41XA	T83.718A	T84.218A	T85.49XA
T23.741A	T27.7XXA	T34.60XA	T78.01XA	T81.522A	T82.42XA	T83.728A	T84.220A	T85.510A
T23.742A	T28.1XXA	T34.61XA	T78.02XA	T81.523A	T82.43XA	T83.81XA	T84.223A	T85.511A
T23.749A	T28.2XXA	T34.62XA	T78.03XA	T81.524A	T82.49XA	T83.82XA	T84.226A	T85.518A
T23.751A	T28.6XXA	T34.70XA	T78.04XA	T81.525A	T82.510A	T83.83XA	T84.228A	T85.520A
T23.752A	T28.7XXA	T34.71XA	T78.05XA	T81.526A	T82.511A	T83.84XA	T84.290A	T85.521A
T23.759A	T31.10	T34.72XA	T78.06XA	T81.527A	T82.512A	T83.85XA	T84.293A	T85.528A
T23.761A	T31.11	T34.811A	T78.07XA	T81.528A	T82.513A	T83.86XA	T84.296A	T85.590A
T23.762A	T31.20	T34.812A	T78.08XA	T81.529A	T82.514A	T83.89XA	T84.298A	T85.591A
T23.769A	T31.30	T34.819A	T78.09XA	T81.530A	T82.515A	T83.9XXA	T84.310A	T85.598A
T23.771A	T31.40	T34.821A	T78.2XXA	T81.531A	T82.518A	T84.010A	T84.318A	T85.610A
T23.772A	T31.50	T34.822A	T79.2XXA	T81.532A	T82.519A	T84.011A	T84.320A	T85.611A
T23.779A	T31.60	T34.829A	T79.7XXA	T81.533A	T82.520A	T84.012A	T84.328A	T85.612A
T23.791A	T31.70	T34.831A	T79.A0XA	T81.534A	T82.521A	T84.013A	T84.390A	T85.613A
T23.792A	T31.80	T34.832A	T79.A11A	T81.535A	T82.522A	T84.018A	T84.398A	T85.614A
T23.799A	T31.90	T34.839A	T79.A12A	T81.536A	T82.523A	T84.019A	T84.410A	T85.618A
T24.301A	T32.10	T34.90XA	T79.A19A	T81.537A	T82.524A	T84.020A	T84.418A	T85.620A
T24.302A	T32.11	T34.99XA	T79.A21A	T81.538A	T82.525A	T84.021A	T84.420A	T85.621A
T24.309A	T32.20	T67.0XXA	T79.A22A	T81.539A	T82.528A	T84.022A	T84.428A	T85.622A
T24.311A	T32.30	T69.021A	T79.A29A	T81.590A	T82.529A	T84.023A	T84.490A	T85.623A
T24.312A	T32.40	T69.022A	T79.A3XA	T81.591A	T82.530A	T84.028A	T84.498A	T85.624A
T24.319A	T32.50	T69.029A	T79.A9XA	T81.592A	T82.531A	T84.029A	T84.50XA	T85.628A
T24.321A	T32.60	T70.3XXA	T80.1XXA	T81.593A	T82.532A	T84.030A	T84.51XA	T85.630A
T24.322A	T32.70	T71.111A	T80.211A	T81.594A	T82.533A	T84.031A	T84.52XA	T85.631A
T24.329A	T32.80	T71.112A	T80.212A	T81.595A	T82.534A	T84.032A	T84.53XA	T85.633A
T24.331A	T32.90	T71.113A	T80.218A	T81.596A	T82.535A	T84.033A	T84.54XA	T85.638A
T24.332A	T33.011A	T71.114A	T80.219A	T81.597A	T82.538A	T84.038A	T84.59XA	T85.690A
T24.339A	T33.012A	T71.121A	T80.22XA	T81.598A	T82.539A	T84.039A	T84.60XA	T85.691A
T24.391A	T33.019A	T71.122A	T80.29XA	T81.599A	T82.590A	T84.040A	T84.610A	T85.692A
T24.392A	T33.02XA	T71.123A	T80.30XA	T81.60XA	T82.591A	T84.041A	T84.611A	T85.693A
T24.399A	T33.09XA	T71.124A	T80.310A	T81.61XA	T82.592A	T84.042A	T84.612A	T85.694A
T24.701A	T33.1XXA	T71.131A	T80.311A	T81.69XA	T82.593A	T84.043A	T84.613A	T85.698A
T24.702A	T33.2XXA	T71.132A	T80.319A	T81.710A	T82.594A	T84.048A	T84.614A	T85.71XA
T24.709A	T33.3XXA	T71.133A	T80.39XA	T81.711A	T82.595A	T84.049A	T84.615A	T85.72XA
T24.711A	T33.40XA	T71.134A	T80.40XA	T81.718A	T82.598A	T84.050A	T84.619A	T85.79XA
T24.712A	T33.41XA	T71.141A	T80.410A	T81.719A	T82.599A	T84.051A	T84.620A	T85.81XA
T24.719A	T33.42XA	T71.143A	T80.411A	T81.72XA	T82.6XXA	T84.052A	T84.621A	T85.82XA

T85.83XA	T86.13	T86.40	T86.822	T86.850	T86.93	T87.44	Z68.1	Z94.83
T85.84XA	T86.19	T86.41	T86.828	T86.851	T86.99	T88.0XXA	Z68.41	Z94.84
T85.85XA	T86.20	T86.42	T86.829	T86.852	T87.0X1	T88.1XXA	Z68.42	Z95.811
T85.86XA	T86.21	T86.43	T86.830	T86.858	T87.0X2	T88.2XXA	Z68.43	Z95.812
T85.89XA	T86.22	T86.49	T86.831	T86.859	T87.0X9	T88.3XXA	Z68.44	Z99.11
T86.00	T86.23	T86.5	T86.832	T86.890	T87.1X1	T88.6XXA	Z68.45	Z99.12
T86.01	T86.290	T86.810	T86.838	T86.891	T87.1X2	Z43.1	Z94.0	
T86.02	T86.298	T86.811	T86.839	T86.892	T87.1X9	Z48.21	Z94.1	
T86.03	T86.30	T86.812	T86.840	T86.898	T87.2	Z48.22	Z94.2	
T86.09	T86.31	T86.818	T86.841	T86.899	T87.40	Z48.23	Z94.3	
T86.10	T86.32	T86.819	T86.842	T86.90	T87.41	Z48.24	Z94.4	
T86.11	T86.33	T86.820	T86.848	T86.91	T87.42	Z48.280	Z94.81	
T86.12	T86.39	T86.821	T86.849	T86.92	T87.43	Z48.290	Z94.82	

Numeric MCC List

A02.1	A48.0	B39.2	E11.641	I21.01	I61.3	I63.50	J15.6	K28.1
A02.21	A48.1	B44.0	E13.00	I21.02	I61.4	I63.511	J15.7	K28.2
A02.22	A48.3	B45.1	E13.01	I21.09	I61.5	I63.512	J15.8	K28.4
A06.4	A50.41	B46.0	E13.10	I21.11	I61.6	I63.519	J15.9	K28.5
A06.5	A50.42	B46.1	E13.11	I21.19	I61.8	I63.521	J16.0	K28.6
A06.6	A51.41	B46.2	E13.641	I21.21	I61.9	I63.522	J16.8	K29.01
A17.0	A52.13	B46.3	E40	I21.29	I62.00	I63.529	J17	K29.21
A17.1	A52.14	B46.4	E41	I21.3	I62.01	I63.531	J18.0	K29.31
A17.81	A54.81	B46.5	E42	I21.4	I62.02	I63.532	J18.1	K29.41
A17.82	A54.86	B46.8	E43	I22.0	I62.03	I63.539	J18.8	K29.51
A17.83	A80.0	B46.9	E84.0	I22.1	I62.1	I63.541	J18.9	K29.61
A17.89	A80.1	B50.9	E84.11	I22.2	I63.00	I63.542	J68.1	K29.71
A18.31	A80.2	B58.2	E88.3	I22.8	I63.011	I63.549	J69.0	K29.81
A19.0	A80.30	B58.3	G00.0	I22.9	I63.012	I63.59	J69.1	K29.91
A19.1	A80.39	B58.81	G00.1	I23.4	I63.019	I63.6	J69.8	K31.811
A19.2	A83.0	B59	G00.2	I23.5	I63.02	I63.8	J81.0	K31.82
A19.8	A83.1	B77.81	G00.3	I25.42	I63.031	I63.9	J84.81	K35.2
A19.9	A83.2	D57.00	G00.8	I26.01	I63.032	I67.0	J84.83	K35.3
A20.0	A83.3	D57.01	G00.9	I26.02	I63.039	I67.83	J84.841	K40.10
A20.1	A83.4	D57.02	G01	I26.09	I63.09	I71.00	J84.842	K40.11
A20.2	A83.5	D57.211	G02	I26.90	I63.10	I71.01	J84.843	K40.40
A20.3	A83.6	D57.212	G03.0	I26.92	I63.111	I71.02	J84.848	K40.41
A20.7	A83.8	D57.219	G03.8	I26.99	I63.112	I71.03	J85.0	K41.10
A20.8	A83.9	D57.411	G03.9	I33.0	I63.119	I71.1	J85.1	K41.11
A20.9	A84.0	D57.412	G04.00	I33.9	I63.12	I71.3	J85.2	K41.40
A22.1	A84.1	D57.419	G04.01	I40.0	I63.131	I71.5	J85.3	K41.41
A22.7	A84.8	D57.811	G04.02	I40.1	I63.132	I71.8	J86.0	K42.1
A26.7	A84.9	D57.812	G04.2	I40.8	I63.139	I74.01	J86.9	K43.1
A27.81	A85.2	D57.819	G04.30	I40.9	I63.19	I77.71	J93.0	K43.4
A32.7	A92.30	D59.3	G04.31	I41	I63.20	I77.72	J95.1	K43.7
A33	A92.31	D60.0	G04.32	I46.2	I63.211	I77.73	J95.2	K44.1
A35	A92.32	D60.1	G04.39	I46.8	I63.212	I77.74	J95.3	K45.1
A37.01	A92.39	D60.8	G04.81	I46.9	I63.219	I77.79	J95.821	K46.1
A37.11	B00.3	D60.9	G04.89	I49.01	I63.22	I81	J95.822	K55.0
A37.81	B00.4	D61.1	G04.90	I49.02	I63.231	I82.0	J96.00	K55.21
A37.91	B00.7	D61.2	G04.91	I50.21	I63.232	I82.220	J96.01	K56.2
A39.0	B00.82	D61.3	G05.3	I50.23	I63.239	I82.221	J96.02	K57.01
A39.1	B01.11	D61.810	G05.4	I50.31	I63.29	I85.01	J96.20	K57.11
A39.2	B01.12	D61.811	G06.0	I50.33	I63.30	I85.11	J96.21	K57.13
A39.3	B01.2	D61.89	G06.1	I50.41	I63.311	J04.11	J96.22	K57.21
A39.4	B02.1	D65	G06.2	I50.43	I63.312	J04.31	J96.90	K57.31
A39.50	B02.24	D66	G07	I51.1	I63.319	J05.11	J96.91	K57.33
A39.51	B05.0	D67	G08	I51.2	I63.321	J09.X1	J96.92	K57.41
A39.52	B05.2	E03.5	G21.0	I60.00	I63.322	J10.00	J98.5	K57.51
A39.53	B06.01	E05.01	G37.4	I60.01	I63.329	J10.01	K22.11	K57.53
A39.81	B10.01	E05.11	G40.301	I60.02	I63.331	J10.08	K22.3	K57.81
A40.0	B10.09	E05.21	G40.311	I60.10	I63.332	J11.00	K22.6	K57.91
A40.1	B15.0	E05.31	G40.319	I60.11	I63.339	J11.08	K25.0	K57.93
A40.3	B16.0	E05.41	G70.01	I60.12	I63.341	J12.0	K25.1	K63.1
A40.8	B16.2	E05.81	G80.0	I60.20	I63.342	J12.1	K25.2	K63.81
A40.9	B17.11	E05.91	G82.50	I60.21	I63.349	J12.2	K25.4	K65.0
A41.01	B19.0	E08.00	G82.51	I60.22	I63.39	J12.3	K25.5	K65.1
A41.02	B19.11	E08.01	G82.52	I60.30	I63.40	J12.81	K25.6	K65.2
A41.1	B19.21	E08.10	G82.53	I60.31	I63.411	J12.89	K26.0	K65.3
A41.2	B20	E08.11	G82.54	I60.32	I63.412	J12.9	K26.1	K65.8
A41.3	B25.0	E08.641	G83.5	I60.4	I63.419	J13	K26.2	K65.9
A41.4	B25.2	E09.00	G92	I60.50	I63.421	J14	K26.4	K66.1
A41.50	B26.1	E09.01	G93.40	I60.51	I63.422	J15.0	K26.5	K67
A41.51	B26.2	E09.11	G93.41	I60.52	I63.429	J15.1	K26.6	K68.12
A41.52	B37.1	E09.641	G93.49	I60.6	I63.431	J15.20	K27.0	K68.19
A41.53	B37.5	E10.10	G93.5	I60.7	I63.432	J15.211	K27.1	K68.9
A41.59	B37.6	E10.11	G93.6	I60.8	I63.439	J15.212	K27.2	K70.41
A41.81	B37.7	E10.641	G93.7	I60.9	I63.441	J15.29	K27.4	K71.11
A41.89	B38.4	E11.00	G93.82	I61.0	I63.442	J15.3	K27.5	K72.00
A41.9	B39.0	E11.01	G95.11	I61.1	I63.449	J15.4	K27.6	K72.01
A42.7	B39.1		G95.19	I61.2	I63.49	J15.5	K28.0	K72.11

© 2015 Optum360, LLC

K72.91	N01.4	O41.1229	O60.14X4	P25.3	Q20.1	R65.11	S06.362A	S12.040B
K75.0	N01.5	O41.1230	O60.14X5	P25.8	Q20.2	R65.20	S06.363A	S12.041B
K75.1	N01.6	O41.1231	O60.14X9	P26.0	Q20.3	R65.21	S06.364A	S12.090B
K76.2	N01.7	O41.1232	O60.22X0	P26.1	Q20.4	S02.0XXB	S06.365A	S12.091B
K76.3	N01.8	O41.1233	O60.22X1	P26.8	Q21.3	S02.10XB	S06.366A	S12.100B
K76.7	N01.9	O41.1234	O60.22X2	P26.9	Q22.0	S02.110B	S06.367A	S12.101B
K80.67	N15.1	O41.1235	O60.22X3	P27.0	Q22.4	S02.111B	S06.368A	S12.110B
K82.2	N17.0	O41.1239	O60.22X4	P27.1	Q22.5	S02.112B	S06.369A	S12.111B
K83.1	N17.1	O41.1410	O60.22X5	P27.8	Q22.6	S02.113B	S06.370A	S12.112B
K83.2	N17.2	O41.1411	O60.22X9	P27.9	Q22.8	S02.118B	S06.376A	S12.120B
K85.0	N18.6	O41.1412	O60.23X0	P28.5	Q22.9	S02.119B	S06.377A	S12.121B
K85.1	N73.3	O41.1413	O60.23X1	P28.81	Q23.4	S02.19XB	S06.378A	S12.130B
K85.2	O03.2	O41.1414	O60.23X2	P29.3	Q24.2	S02.91XB	S06.380A	S12.131B
K85.3	O03.31	O41.1415	O60.23X3	P29.81	Q24.4	S06.0X6A	S06.386A	S12.14XB
K85.8	O03.32	O41.1419	O60.23X4	P35.1	Q24.6	S06.1X0A	S06.387A	S12.150B
K85.9	O03.81	O41.1420	O60.23X5	P35.2	Q25.5	S06.1X1A	S06.388A	S12.151B
L89.003	O03.82	O41.1421	O60.23X9	P35.3	Q25.6	S06.1X2A	S06.4X0A	S12.190B
L89.004	O04.7	O41.1422	O67.0	P35.8	Q25.71	S06.1X3A	S06.4X1A	S12.191B
L89.013	O04.81	O41.1423	O71.02	P35.9	Q25.72	S06.1X4A	S06.4X2A	S12.200B
L89.014	O04.82	O41.1424	O71.03	P36.0	Q25.79	S06.1X5A	S06.4X3A	S12.201B
L89.023	O07.2	O41.1425	O71.1	P36.10	Q28.2	S06.1X6A	S06.4X4A	S12.230B
L89.024	O07.31	O41.1429	O75.1	P36.19	Q28.3	S06.1X7A	S06.4X5A	S12.231B
L89.103	O07.32	O41.1430	O75.3	P36.2	Q33.2	S06.1X8A	S06.4X6A	S12.24XB
L89.104	O08.2	O41.1431	O85	P36.30	Q33.3	S06.1X9A	S06.4X7A	S12.250B
L89.113	O08.3	O41.1432	O86.81	P36.39	Q33.6	S06.2X6A	S06.4X8A	S12.251B
L89.114	O08.4	O41.1433	O86.89	P36.4	Q39.0	S06.2X7A	S06.4X9A	S12.290B
L89.123	O10.42	O41.1434	O87.1	P36.5	Q39.1	S06.2X8A	S06.5X0A	S12.291B
L89.124	O11.1	O41.1435	O88.011	P36.8	Q39.2	S06.306A	S06.5X1A	S12.300B
L89.133	O11.2	O41.1439	O88.012	P36.9	Q39.3	S06.307A	S06.5X2A	S12.301B
L89.134	O11.3	O44.11	O88.013	P37.0	Q39.4	S06.308A	S06.5X3A	S12.330B
L89.143	O14.12	O44.12	O88.02	P37.1	Q44.2	S06.310A	S06.5X4A	S12.331B
L89.144	O14.13	O45.001	O88.03	P37.2	Q44.3	S06.311A	S06.5X5A	S12.34XB
L89.153	O14.22	O45.002	O88.111	P37.3	Q79.0	S06.312A	S06.5X6A	S12.350B
L89.154	O14.23	O45.003	O88.112	P37.4	Q79.1	S06.313A	S06.5X7A	S12.351B
L89.203	O15.02	O45.011	O88.113	P37.8	Q79.2	S06.314A	S06.5X8A	S12.390B
L89.204	O15.03	O45.012	O88.12	P37.9	Q79.3	S06.315A	S06.5X9A	S12.391B
L89.213	O15.1	O45.013	O88.13	P52.21	Q79.4	S06.316A	S06.6X0A	S12.400B
L89.214	O15.2	O45.021	O88.211	P52.22	Q79.51	S06.317A	S06.6X1A	S12.401B
L89.223	O22.31	O45.022	O88.212	P52.4	Q79.59	S06.318A	S06.6X2A	S12.430B
L89.224	O22.32	O45.023	O88.213	P52.5	Q89.4	S06.319A	S06.6X3A	S12.431B
L89.303	O22.33	O45.091	O88.22	P52.6	Q93.81	S06.320A	S06.6X4A	S12.44XB
L89.304	O24.02	O45.092	O88.23	P52.8	R09.2	S06.321A	S06.6X5A	S12.450B
L89.313	O24.12	O45.093	O88.311	P52.9	R40.20	S06.322A	S06.6X6A	S12.451B
L89.314	O24.32	O45.8X1	O88.312	P54.1	R40.2110	S06.323A	S06.6X7A	S12.490B
L89.323	O24.82	O45.8X2	O88.313	P54.2	R40.2111	S06.324A	S06.6X8A	S12.491B
L89.324	O34.31	O45.8X3	O88.32	P54.3	R40.2112	S06.325A	S06.6X9A	S12.500B
L89.43	O34.32	O45.91	O88.33	P56.0	R40.2113	S06.326A	S06.816A	S12.501B
L89.44	O34.33	O45.92	O88.811	P56.90	R40.2114	S06.327A	S06.817A	S12.530B
L89.503	O41.1010	O45.93	O88.812	P56.99	R40.2120	S06.328A	S06.818A	S12.531B
L89.504	O41.1011	O46.001	O88.813	P57.0	R40.2121	S06.329A	S06.826A	S12.54XB
L89.513	O41.1012	O46.002	O88.82	P57.8	R40.2122	S06.330A	S06.827A	S12.550B
L89.514	O41.1013	O46.003	O88.83	P57.9	R40.2123	S06.331A	S06.828A	S12.551B
L89.523	O41.1014	O46.011	O90.3	P59.1	R40.2124	S06.332A	S06.896A	S12.590B
L89.524	O41.1015	O46.012	O90.4	P59.20	R40.2210	S06.333A	S06.897A	S12.591B
L89.603	O41.1019	O46.013	O99.42	P59.29	R40.2211	S06.334A	S06.898A	S12.600B
L89.604	O41.1020	O46.021	P10.0	P60	R40.2212	S06.335A	S06.9X6A	S12.601B
L89.613	O41.1021	O46.022	P10.1	P61.0	R40.2213	S06.336A	S06.9X7A	S12.630B
L89.614	O41.1022	O46.023	P10.3	P61.5	R40.2214	S06.337A	S06.9X8A	S12.631B
L89.623	O41.1023	O46.091	P10.4	P74.0	R40.2220	S06.338A	S11.011A	S12.64XB
L89.624	O41.1024	O46.092	P10.8	P77.1	R40.2221	S06.339A	S11.012A	S12.650B
L89.813	O41.1025	O46.093	P10.9	P77.2	R40.2222	S06.340A	S11.013A	S12.651B
L89.814	O41.1029	O60.02	P11.0	P77.3	R40.2223	S06.341A	S11.014A	S12.690B
L89.893	O41.1030	O60.03	P11.2	P77.9	R40.2224	S06.342A	S11.015A	S12.691B
L89.894	O41.1031	O60.12X0	P11.9	P78.0	R40.2310	S06.343A	S11.019A	S12.8XXA
L89.93	O41.1032	O60.12X1	P22.0	P83.2	R40.2311	S06.344A	S11.021A	S14.0XXA
L89.94	O41.1033	O60.12X2	P23.0	P90	R40.2312	S06.345A	S11.022A	S14.101A
M31.1	O41.1034	O60.12X3	P23.1	P91.0	R40.2313	S06.346A	S11.023A	S14.102A
M72.6	O41.1035	O60.12X4	P23.2	P91.1	R40.2314	S06.347A	S11.024A	S14.103A
N00.0	O41.1039	O60.12X5	P23.3	P91.2	R40.2320	S06.348A	S11.025A	S14.104A
N00.1	O41.1210	O60.12X9	P23.4	P91.3	R40.2321	S06.349A	S11.029A	S14.105A
N00.2	O41.1211	O60.13X0	P23.5	P91.4	R40.2322	S06.350A	S11.031A	S14.106A
N00.3	O41.1212	O60.13X1	P23.6	P91.5	R40.2323	S06.351A	S11.032A	S14.107A
N00.4	O41.1213	O60.13X2	P23.8	P91.63	R40.2324	S06.352A	S11.033A	S14.108A
N00.5	O41.1214	O60.13X3	P23.9	P92.01	R40.2340	S06.353A	S11.034A	S14.111A
N00.6	O41.1215	O60.13X4	P24.01	Q00.0	R40.2341	S06.354A	S11.035A	S14.112A
N00.7	O41.1219	O60.13X5	P24.11	Q00.1	R40.2342	S06.355A	S11.039A	S14.113A
N00.8	O41.1220	O60.13X9	P24.21	Q00.2	R40.2343	S06.356A	S12.000B	S14.114A
N00.9	O41.1221	O60.14X0	P24.31	Q04.0	R40.2344	S06.357A	S12.001B	S14.115A
N01.0	O41.1222	O60.14X1	P24.81	Q04.1	R53.2	S06.358A	S12.01XB	S14.116A
N01.1	O41.1223	O60.14X2	P25.0	Q04.2	R57.0	S06.359A	S12.02XB	S14.117A
N01.2	O41.1224	O60.14X3	P25.1	Q04.3	R57.1	S06.360A	S12.030B	S14.118A
N01.3	O41.1225		P25.2	Q20.0	R57.8	S06.361A	S12.031B	S14.121A

Appendix B—Numeric MCC List

S14.122A	S22.030B	S25.20XA	S31.625A	S32.392B	S32.472A	S35.10XA	S42.226B	S42.441B
S14.123A	S22.031B	S25.21XA	S31.629A	S32.399B	S32.472B	S35.11XA	S42.231B	S42.442B
S14.124A	S22.032B	S25.22XA	S31.630A	S32.401A	S32.473A	S35.12XA	S42.232B	S42.443B
S14.125A	S22.038B	S25.29XA	S31.631A	S32.401B	S32.473B	S35.19XA	S42.239B	S42.444B
S14.126A	S22.039B	S25.301A	S31.632A	S32.402A	S32.474A	S35.211A	S42.241B	S42.445B
S14.127A	S22.040B	S25.302A	S31.633A	S32.409A	S32.474B	S35.212A	S42.242B	S42.446B
S14.128A	S22.041B	S25.309A	S31.634A	S32.409B	S32.475A	S35.218A	S42.249B	S42.447B
S14.131A	S22.042B	S25.311A	S31.635A	S32.411A	S32.475B	S35.219A	S42.251B	S42.448B
S14.132A	S22.048B	S25.312A	S31.639A	S32.411B	S32.476A	S35.221A	S42.252B	S42.449B
S14.133A	S22.049B	S25.319A	S31.640A	S32.412A	S32.476B	S35.222A	S42.253B	S42.451B
S14.134A	S22.050B	S25.321A	S31.641A	S32.412B	S32.481A	S35.228A	S42.254B	S42.452B
S14.135A	S22.051B	S25.322A	S31.642A	S32.413A	S32.481B	S35.229A	S42.255B	S42.453B
S14.136A	S22.052B	S25.329A	S31.643A	S32.413B	S32.482A	S35.231A	S42.256B	S42.454B
S14.137A	S22.058B	S25.391A	S31.644A	S32.414A	S32.482B	S35.232A	S42.261B	S42.455B
S14.138A	S22.059B	S25.392A	S31.645A	S32.414B	S32.483A	S35.238A	S42.262B	S42.456B
S14.141A	S22.060B	S25.399A	S31.649A	S32.415A	S32.483B	S35.239A	S42.263B	S42.461B
S14.142A	S22.061B	S25.401A	S31.650A	S32.415B	S32.484A	S35.291A	S42.264B	S42.462B
S14.143A	S22.062B	S25.402A	S31.651A	S32.416A	S32.484B	S35.292A	S42.265B	S42.463B
S14.144A	S22.068B	S25.409A	S31.652A	S32.416B	S32.485A	S35.298A	S42.266B	S42.464B
S14.145A	S22.069B	S25.411A	S31.653A	S32.421A	S32.485B	S35.299A	S42.291B	S42.465B
S14.146A	S22.070B	S25.412A	S31.654A	S32.421B	S32.486A	S35.311A	S42.292B	S42.466B
S14.147A	S22.071B	S25.419A	S31.655A	S32.422A	S32.486B	S35.318A	S42.293B	S42.471B
S14.148A	S22.072B	S25.421A	S31.659A	S32.422B	S32.491A	S35.319A	S42.294B	S42.472B
S14.151A	S22.078B	S25.422A	S32.000B	S32.423A	S32.491B	S35.321A	S42.295B	S42.473B
S14.152A	S22.079B	S25.429A	S32.001B	S32.423B	S32.492A	S35.328A	S42.296B	S42.474B
S14.153A	S22.080B	S25.491A	S32.002B	S32.424A	S32.492B	S35.329A	S42.301B	S42.475B
S14.154A	S22.081B	S25.492A	S32.008B	S32.424B	S32.499A	S35.331A	S42.302B	S42.476B
S14.155A	S22.082B	S25.499A	S32.009B	S32.425A	S32.499B	S35.338A	S42.309B	S42.491B
S14.156A	S22.088B	S26.020A	S32.010B	S32.425B	S32.501B	S35.339A	S42.321B	S42.492B
S14.157A	S22.089B	S26.021A	S32.011B	S32.426A	S32.502B	S35.341A	S42.322B	S42.493B
S14.158A	S22.20XB	S26.022A	S32.012B	S32.426B	S32.509B	S35.348A	S42.323B	S42.494B
S21.301A	S22.21XB	S26.12XA	S32.018B	S32.431A	S32.511B	S35.349A	S42.324B	S42.495B
S21.302A	S22.22XB	S26.92XA	S32.019B	S32.431B	S32.512B	S35.401A	S42.325B	S42.496B
S21.309A	S22.23XB	S27.1XXA	S32.020B	S32.432A	S32.519B	S35.402A	S42.326B	S42.90XB
S21.311A	S22.24XB	S27.2XXA	S32.021B	S32.432B	S32.591B	S35.403A	S42.331B	S42.91XB
S21.312A	S22.31XB	S27.331A	S32.022B	S32.433A	S32.592B	S35.404A	S42.332B	S42.92XB
S21.319A	S22.32XB	S27.332A	S32.028B	S32.433B	S32.599B	S35.405A	S42.333B	S45.001A
S21.321A	S22.39XB	S27.339A	S32.029B	S32.434A	S32.601B	S35.406A	S42.334B	S45.002A
S21.322A	S22.41XB	S27.401A	S32.030B	S32.434B	S32.602B	S35.411A	S42.335B	S45.009A
S21.329A	S22.42XB	S27.402A	S32.031B	S32.435A	S32.609B	S35.412A	S42.336B	S45.011A
S21.331A	S22.43XB	S27.409A	S32.032B	S32.435B	S32.611B	S35.413A	S42.341B	S45.012A
S21.332A	S22.49XB	S27.411A	S32.038B	S32.436A	S32.612B	S35.414A	S42.342B	S45.019A
S21.339A	S22.5XXA	S27.412A	S32.039B	S32.436B	S32.613B	S35.415A	S42.343B	S45.091A
S21.341A	S22.5XXB	S27.419A	S32.040B	S32.441A	S32.614B	S35.416A	S42.344B	S45.092A
S21.342A	S22.9XXB	S27.421A	S32.041B	S32.441B	S32.615B	S35.491A	S42.345B	S45.099A
S21.349A	S24.0XXA	S27.422A	S32.042B	S32.442A	S32.616B	S35.492A	S42.346B	S52.001B
S21.351A	S24.101A	S27.429A	S32.048B	S32.442B	S32.691B	S35.493A	S42.351B	S52.001C
S21.352A	S24.102A	S27.431A	S32.049B	S32.443A	S32.692B	S35.494A	S42.352B	S52.002B
S21.359A	S24.103A	S27.432A	S32.050B	S32.443B	S32.699B	S35.495A	S42.353B	S52.002C
S21.401A	S24.104A	S27.439A	S32.051B	S32.444A	S32.810B	S35.496A	S42.354B	S52.009B
S21.402A	S24.111A	S27.491A	S32.052B	S32.444B	S32.811B	S35.50XA	S42.355B	S52.009C
S21.409A	S24.112A	S27.492A	S32.058B	S32.445A	S32.82XB	S35.511A	S42.356B	S52.021B
S21.411A	S24.113A	S27.499A	S32.059B	S32.445B	S32.89XB	S35.512A	S42.361B	S52.021C
S21.412A	S24.114A	S27.812A	S32.10XB	S32.446A	S32.9XXB	S35.513A	S42.362B	S52.022B
S21.419A	S24.131A	S27.813A	S32.110B	S32.446B	S34.01XA	S35.514A	S42.363B	S52.022C
S21.421A	S24.132A	S27.818A	S32.111B	S32.451A	S34.02XA	S35.515A	S42.364B	S52.023B
S21.422A	S24.133A	S27.819A	S32.112B	S32.451B	S34.101A	S35.516A	S42.365B	S52.023C
S21.429A	S24.134A	S31.001A	S32.119B	S32.452A	S34.102A	S35.59XA	S42.366B	S52.024B
S21.431A	S24.141A	S31.011A	S32.120B	S32.452B	S34.103A	S36.031A	S42.391B	S52.024C
S21.432A	S24.142A	S31.021A	S32.121B	S32.453A	S34.104A	S36.032A	S42.392B	S52.025B
S21.439A	S24.143A	S31.031A	S32.122B	S32.453B	S34.105A	S36.115A	S42.399B	S52.025C
S21.441A	S24.144A	S31.041A	S32.129B	S32.454A	S34.109A	S36.116A	S42.401B	S52.026B
S21.442A	S24.151A	S31.051A	S32.130B	S32.454B	S34.111A	S37.061A	S42.402B	S52.026C
S21.449A	S24.152A	S31.600A	S32.131B	S32.455A	S34.112A	S37.062A	S42.409B	S52.031B
S21.451A	S24.153A	S31.601A	S32.132B	S32.455B	S34.113A	S37.069A	S42.411B	S52.031C
S21.452A	S24.154A	S31.602A	S32.139B	S32.456A	S34.114A	S37.091A	S42.412B	S52.032B
S21.459A	S25.00XA	S31.603A	S32.14XB	S32.456B	S34.115A	S37.092A	S42.413B	S52.032C
S22.000B	S25.01XA	S31.604A	S32.15XB	S32.461A	S34.119A	S37.099A	S42.414B	S52.033B
S22.001B	S25.02XA	S31.605A	S32.16XB	S32.461B	S34.121A	S42.201B	S42.415B	S52.033C
S22.002B	S25.09XA	S31.609A	S32.17XB	S32.462A	S34.122A	S42.202B	S42.416B	S52.034B
S22.008B	S25.101A	S31.610A	S32.19XB	S32.462B	S34.123A	S42.209B	S42.421B	S52.034C
S22.009B	S25.102A	S31.611A	S32.2XXB	S32.463A	S34.124A	S42.211B	S42.422B	S52.035B
S22.010B	S25.109A	S31.612A	S32.301B	S32.463B	S34.125A	S42.212B	S42.423B	S52.035C
S22.011B	S25.111A	S31.613A	S32.302B	S32.464A	S34.129A	S42.213B	S42.424B	S52.036B
S22.012B	S25.112A	S31.614A	S32.309B	S32.464B	S34.131A	S42.214B	S42.425B	S52.036C
S22.018B	S25.119A	S31.615A	S32.311B	S32.465A	S34.132A	S42.215B	S42.426B	S52.041B
S22.019B	S25.121A	S31.619A	S32.312B	S32.465B	S34.139A	S42.216B	S42.431B	S52.041C
S22.020B	S25.122A	S31.620A	S32.313B	S32.466A	S34.3XXA	S42.221B	S42.432B	S52.042B
S22.021B	S25.129A	S31.621A	S32.314B	S32.466B	S35.00XA	S42.222B	S42.433B	S52.042C
S22.022B	S25.191A	S31.622A	S32.315B	S32.471A	S35.01XA	S42.223B	S42.434B	S52.043B
S22.028B	S25.192A	S31.623A	S32.316B	S32.471B	S35.02XA	S42.224B	S42.435B	S52.043C
S22.029B	S25.199A	S31.624A	S32.391B		S35.09XA	S42.225B	S42.436B	S52.044B

S52.044C	S52.243C	S52.342C	S52.551C	S72.024C	S72.102A	S72.22XB	S72.352C	S72.441B
S52.045B	S52.244B	S52.343B	S52.552B	S72.025A	S72.102B	S72.22XC	S72.353A	S72.441C
S52.045C	S52.244C	S52.343C	S52.552C	S72.025B	S72.102C	S72.23XA	S72.353B	S72.442B
S52.046B	S52.245B	S52.344B	S52.559B	S72.025C	S72.109A	S72.23XB	S72.353C	S72.442C
S52.046C	S52.245C	S52.344C	S52.559C	S72.026A	S72.109B	S72.23XC	S72.354A	S72.443B
S52.091B	S52.246B	S52.345B	S52.561B	S72.026B	S72.109C	S72.24XA	S72.354B	S72.443C
S52.091C	S52.246C	S52.345C	S52.561C	S72.026C	S72.111A	S72.24XB	S72.354C	S72.444B
S52.092B	S52.251B	S52.346B	S52.562B	S72.031A	S72.111B	S72.24XC	S72.355A	S72.444C
S52.092C	S52.251C	S52.346C	S52.562C	S72.031B	S72.111C	S72.25XA	S72.355B	S72.445B
S52.099B	S52.252B	S52.351B	S52.569B	S72.031C	S72.112A	S72.25XB	S72.355C	S72.445C
S52.099C	S52.252C	S52.351C	S52.569C	S72.032A	S72.112B	S72.25XC	S72.356A	S72.446B
S52.101B	S52.253B	S52.352B	S52.571B	S72.032B	S72.112C	S72.26XA	S72.356B	S72.446C
S52.101C	S52.253C	S52.352C	S52.571C	S72.032C	S72.113A	S72.26XB	S72.356C	S72.451B
S52.102B	S52.254B	S52.353B	S52.572B	S72.033A	S72.113B	S72.26XC	S72.361A	S72.451C
S52.102C	S52.254C	S52.353C	S52.572C	S72.033B	S72.113C	S72.301A	S72.361B	S72.452B
S52.109B	S52.255B	S52.354B	S52.579B	S72.033C	S72.114A	S72.301B	S72.361C	S72.452C
S52.109C	S52.255C	S52.354C	S52.579C	S72.034A	S72.114B	S72.301C	S72.362A	S72.453B
S52.121B	S52.256B	S52.355B	S52.591B	S72.034B	S72.114C	S72.302A	S72.362B	S72.453C
S52.121C	S52.256C	S52.355C	S52.591C	S72.034C	S72.115A	S72.302B	S72.362C	S72.454B
S52.122B	S52.261B	S52.356B	S52.592B	S72.035A	S72.115B	S72.302C	S72.363A	S72.454C
S52.122C	S52.261C	S52.356C	S52.592C	S72.035B	S72.115C	S72.309A	S72.363B	S72.455B
S52.123B	S52.262B	S52.361B	S52.599B	S72.035C	S72.116A	S72.309B	S72.363C	S72.455C
S52.123C	S52.262C	S52.361C	S52.599C	S72.036A	S72.116B	S72.309C	S72.364A	S72.456B
S52.124B	S52.263B	S52.362B	S52.601B	S72.036B	S72.116C	S72.321A	S72.364B	S72.456C
S52.124C	S52.263C	S52.362C	S52.601C	S72.036C	S72.121A	S72.321B	S72.364C	S72.461B
S52.125B	S52.264B	S52.363B	S52.602B	S72.041A	S72.121B	S72.321C	S72.365A	S72.461C
S52.125C	S52.264C	S52.363C	S52.602C	S72.041B	S72.121C	S72.322A	S72.365B	S72.462B
S52.126B	S52.265B	S52.364B	S52.609B	S72.041C	S72.122A	S72.322B	S72.365C	S72.462C
S52.126C	S52.265C	S52.364C	S52.609C	S72.042A	S72.122B	S72.322C	S72.366A	S72.463B
S52.131B	S52.266B	S52.365B	S52.611B	S72.042B	S72.122C	S72.323A	S72.366B	S72.463C
S52.131C	S52.266C	S52.365C	S52.611C	S72.042C	S72.123A	S72.323B	S72.366C	S72.464B
S52.132B	S52.271B	S52.366B	S52.612B	S72.043A	S72.123B	S72.323C	S72.391A	S72.464C
S52.132C	S52.271C	S52.366C	S52.612C	S72.043B	S72.123C	S72.324A	S72.391B	S72.465B
S52.133B	S52.272B	S52.371B	S52.613B	S72.043C	S72.124A	S72.324B	S72.391C	S72.465C
S52.133C	S52.272C	S52.371C	S52.613C	S72.044A	S72.124B	S72.324C	S72.392A	S72.466B
S52.134B	S52.279B	S52.372B	S52.614B	S72.044B	S72.124C	S72.325A	S72.392B	S72.466C
S52.134C	S52.279C	S52.372C	S52.614C	S72.044C	S72.125A	S72.325B	S72.392C	S72.491B
S52.135B	S52.281B	S52.379B	S52.615B	S72.045A	S72.125B	S72.325C	S72.399A	S72.491C
S52.135C	S52.281C	S52.379C	S52.615C	S72.045B	S72.125C	S72.326A	S72.399B	S72.492B
S52.136B	S52.282B	S52.381B	S52.616B	S72.045C	S72.126A	S72.326B	S72.399C	S72.492C
S52.136C	S52.282C	S52.381C	S52.616C	S72.046A	S72.126B	S72.326C	S72.401B	S72.499B
S52.181B	S52.283B	S52.382B	S52.691B	S72.046B	S72.126C	S72.331A	S72.401C	S72.499C
S52.181C	S52.283C	S52.382C	S52.691C	S72.046C	S72.131A	S72.331B	S72.402B	S72.8X1A
S52.182B	S52.291B	S52.389B	S52.692B	S72.051A	S72.131B	S72.331C	S72.402C	S72.8X1B
S52.182C	S52.291C	S52.389C	S52.692C	S72.051B	S72.131C	S72.332A	S72.409B	S72.8X1C
S52.189B	S52.292B	S52.391B	S52.699B	S72.051C	S72.132A	S72.332B	S72.409C	S72.8X2A
S52.189C	S52.292C	S52.391C	S52.699C	S72.052A	S72.132B	S72.332C	S72.411B	S72.8X2B
S52.201B	S52.299B	S52.392B	S52.90XB	S72.052B	S72.132C	S72.333A	S72.411C	S72.8X2C
S52.201C	S52.299C	S52.392C	S52.90XC	S72.052C	S72.133A	S72.333B	S72.412B	S72.8X9A
S52.202B	S52.301B	S52.399B	S52.91XB	S72.059A	S72.133B	S72.333C	S72.412C	S72.8X9B
S52.202C	S52.301C	S52.399C	S52.91XC	S72.059B	S72.133C	S72.334A	S72.413B	S72.8X9C
S52.209B	S52.302B	S52.501B	S52.92XB	S72.059C	S72.134A	S72.334B	S72.413C	S72.90XA
S52.209C	S52.302C	S52.501C	S52.92XC	S72.061A	S72.134B	S72.334C	S72.414B	S72.90XB
S52.221B	S52.309B	S52.502B	S72.001A	S72.061B	S72.134C	S72.335A	S72.414C	S72.90XC
S52.221C	S52.309C	S52.502C	S72.001B	S72.061C	S72.135A	S72.335B	S72.415B	S72.91XA
S52.222B	S52.321B	S52.509B	S72.001C	S72.062A	S72.135B	S72.335C	S72.415C	S72.91XB
S52.222C	S52.321C	S52.509C	S72.002A	S72.062B	S72.135C	S72.336A	S72.416B	S72.91XC
S52.223B	S52.322B	S52.511B	S72.002B	S72.062C	S72.136A	S72.336B	S72.416C	S72.92XA
S52.223C	S52.322C	S52.511C	S72.002C	S72.063A	S72.136B	S72.336C	S72.421B	S72.92XB
S52.224B	S52.323B	S52.512B	S72.009A	S72.063B	S72.136C	S72.341A	S72.421C	S72.92XC
S52.224C	S52.323C	S52.512C	S72.009B	S72.063C	S72.141A	S72.341B	S72.422B	S75.001A
S52.225B	S52.324B	S52.513B	S72.009C	S72.064A	S72.141B	S72.341C	S72.422C	S75.002A
S52.225C	S52.324C	S52.513C	S72.011A	S72.064B	S72.141C	S72.342A	S72.423B	S75.009A
S52.226B	S52.325B	S52.514B	S72.011B	S72.064C	S72.142A	S72.342B	S72.423C	S75.011A
S52.226C	S52.325C	S52.514C	S72.011C	S72.065A	S72.142B	S72.342C	S72.424B	S75.012A
S52.231B	S52.326B	S52.515B	S72.012A	S72.065B	S72.142C	S72.343A	S72.424C	S75.019A
S52.231C	S52.326C	S52.515C	S72.012B	S72.065C	S72.143A	S72.343B	S72.425B	S75.021A
S52.232B	S52.331B	S52.516B	S72.012C	S72.066A	S72.143B	S72.343C	S72.425C	S75.022A
S52.232C	S52.331C	S52.516C	S72.019A	S72.066B	S72.143C	S72.344A	S72.426B	S75.029A
S52.233B	S52.332B	S52.531B	S72.019B	S72.066C	S72.144A	S72.344B	S72.426C	S75.091A
S52.233C	S52.332C	S52.531C	S72.019C	S72.091A	S72.144B	S72.344C	S72.431B	S75.092A
S52.234B	S52.333B	S52.532B	S72.021A	S72.091B	S72.144C	S72.345A	S72.431C	S75.099A
S52.234C	S52.333C	S52.532C	S72.021B	S72.091C	S72.145A	S72.345B	S72.432B	S75.101A
S52.235B	S52.334B	S52.539B	S72.021C	S72.092A	S72.145B	S72.345C	S72.432C	S75.102A
S52.235C	S52.334C	S52.539C	S72.022A	S72.092B	S72.145C	S72.346A	S72.433B	S75.109A
S52.236B	S52.335B	S52.541B	S72.022B	S72.092C	S72.146A	S72.346B	S72.433C	S75.111A
S52.236C	S52.335C	S52.541C	S72.022C	S72.099A	S72.146B	S72.346C	S72.434B	S75.112A
S52.241B	S52.336B	S52.542B	S72.023A	S72.099B	S72.146C	S72.351A	S72.434C	S75.119A
S52.241C	S52.336C	S52.542C	S72.023B	S72.099C	S72.21XA	S72.351B	S72.435B	S75.121A
S52.242B	S52.341B	S52.549B	S72.023C	S72.101A	S72.21XB	S72.351C	S72.435C	S75.122A
S52.242C	S52.341C	S52.549C	S72.024A	S72.101B	S72.21XC	S72.352A	S72.436B	S75.129A
S52.243B	S52.342B	S52.551B	S72.024B	S72.101C	S72.22XA	S72.352B	S72.436C	S75.191A

S75.192A	S82.126C	S82.192C	S82.244C	S82.409C	S82.452C	S82.864C	T31.64	T32.55
S75.199A	S82.131B	S82.199B	S82.245B	S82.421B	S82.453B	S82.865B	T31.65	T32.61
S79.001A	S82.131C	S82.199C	S82.245C	S82.421C	S82.453C	S82.865C	T31.66	T32.62
S79.002A	S82.132B	S82.201B	S82.246B	S82.422B	S82.454B	S82.866B	T31.71	T32.63
S79.009A	S82.132C	S82.201C	S82.246C	S82.422C	S82.454C	S82.866C	T31.72	T32.64
S79.011A	S82.133B	S82.202B	S82.251B	S82.423B	S82.455B	S85.001A	T31.73	T32.65
S79.012A	S82.133C	S82.202C	S82.251C	S82.423C	S82.455C	S85.002A	T31.74	T32.66
S79.019A	S82.134B	S82.209B	S82.252B	S82.424B	S82.456B	S85.009A	T31.75	T32.71
S79.091A	S82.134C	S82.209C	S82.252C	S82.424C	S82.456C	S85.011A	T31.76	T32.72
S79.092A	S82.135B	S82.221B	S82.253B	S82.425B	S82.461B	S85.012A	T31.77	T32.73
S79.099A	S82.135C	S82.221C	S82.253C	S82.425C	S82.461C	S85.019A	T31.81	T32.74
S82.101B	S82.136B	S82.222B	S82.254B	S82.426B	S82.462B	S85.091A	T31.82	T32.75
S82.101C	S82.136C	S82.222C	S82.254C	S82.426C	S82.462C	S85.092A	T31.83	T32.76
S82.102B	S82.141B	S82.223B	S82.255B	S82.431B	S82.463B	S85.099A	T31.84	T32.77
S82.102C	S82.141C	S82.223C	S82.255C	S82.431C	S82.463C	S85.501A	T31.85	T32.81
S82.109B	S82.142B	S82.224B	S82.256B	S82.432B	S82.464B	S85.502A	T31.86	T32.82
S82.109C	S82.142C	S82.224C	S82.256C	S82.432C	S82.464C	S85.509A	T31.87	T32.83
S82.111B	S82.143B	S82.225B	S82.261B	S82.433B	S82.465B	S85.511A	T31.88	T32.84
S82.111C	S82.143C	S82.225C	S82.261C	S82.433C	S82.465C	S85.512A	T31.91	T32.85
S82.112B	S82.144B	S82.226B	S82.262B	S82.434B	S82.466B	S85.519A	T31.92	T32.86
S82.112C	S82.144C	S82.226C	S82.262C	S82.434C	S82.466C	S85.591A	T31.93	T32.87
S82.113B	S82.145B	S82.231B	S82.263B	S82.435B	S82.491B	S85.592A	T31.94	T32.88
S82.113C	S82.145C	S82.231C	S82.263C	S82.435C	S82.491C	S85.599A	T31.95	T32.91
S82.114B	S82.146B	S82.232B	S82.264B	S82.436B	S82.492B	T31.21	T31.96	T32.92
S82.114C	S82.146C	S82.232C	S82.264C	S82.436C	S82.492C	T31.22	T31.97	T32.93
S82.115B	S82.151B	S82.233B	S82.265B	S82.441B	S82.499B	T31.31	T31.98	T32.94
S82.115C	S82.151C	S82.233C	S82.265C	S82.441C	S82.499C	T31.32	T31.99	T32.95
S82.116B	S82.152B	S82.234B	S82.266B	S82.442B	S82.831B	T31.33	T32.21	T32.96
S82.116C	S82.152C	S82.234C	S82.266C	S82.442C	S82.831C	T31.41	T32.22	T32.97
S82.121B	S82.153B	S82.235B	S82.291B	S82.443B	S82.832B	T31.42	T32.31	T32.98
S82.121C	S82.153C	S82.235C	S82.291C	S82.443C	S82.832C	T31.43	T32.32	T32.99
S82.122B	S82.154B	S82.236B	S82.292B	S82.444B	S82.839B	T31.44	T32.33	T79.0XXA
S82.122C	S82.154C	S82.236C	S82.292C	S82.444C	S82.839C	T31.51	T32.41	T79.1XXA
S82.123B	S82.155B	S82.241B	S82.299B	S82.445B	S82.861B	T31.52	T32.42	T79.4XXA
S82.123C	S82.155C	S82.241C	S82.299C	S82.445C	S82.861C	T31.53	T32.43	T79.5XXA
S82.124B	S82.156B	S82.242B	S82.401B	S82.446B	S82.862B	T31.54	T32.44	T80.0XXA
S82.124C	S82.156C	S82.242C	S82.401C	S82.446C	S82.862C	T31.55	T32.51	T81.11XA
S82.125B	S82.191B	S82.243B	S82.402B	S82.451B	S82.863B	T31.61	T32.52	T81.12XA
S82.125C	S82.191C	S82.243C	S82.402C	S82.451C	S82.863C	T31.62	T32.53	T81.19XA
S82.126B	S82.192B	S82.244B	S82.409B	S82.452B	S82.864B	T31.63	T32.54	

Appendix C — MS-DRG Surgical Hierarchy Table

The surgical hierarchy reflects the relative resources requirement of the various surgical procedures of each major diagnostic category (MDC). The hierarchy is based upon variables such as principal diagnosis, surgical class, complications and comorbidities.

Arranging the surgical MS-DRGs in this manner allows for the assignment of patients with multiple procedures related to the principal diagnosis to a surgical MS-DRG that best reflects the resources used in the care of that patient. Since patients can be assigned to only one surgical class for each inpatient stay, patients with multiple procedures related to the principal diagnosis are assigned to the MS-DRG associated with the most resource-intensive surgical class.

Pre MDC

Heart transplant or implant of heart assist system w MCC; w/o MCC	001–002
ECMO or trach w MV 96+ hrs or PDX exc face, mouth & neck w maj O.R.; w/o maj O.R.	003–004
Liver transplant w MCC; w/o MCC or intestinal transplant	005–006
Allogeneic bone marrow transplant	014
Lung transplant	007
Simultaneous pancreas/kidney transplant	008
Autologous bone marrow transplant; w CC/MCC; w/o CC/MCC	016–017
Pancreas transplant	010
Tracheostomy for face, mouth & neck diagnoses w MCC; w CC; w/o CC/MCC	011–013

MDC 1   DISEASES & DISORDERS OF THE NERVOUS SYSTEM

Intracranial vascular procedures w PDX hemorrhage w MCC; w CC; w/o CC/MCC	020–022
Craniotomy	023–027
Spinal procedures w MCC; w CC or spinal neurostimulators; w/o CC/MCC	028–030
Ventricular shunt procedures w MCC; w CC; w/o CC/MCC	031–033
Carotid artery stent procedure w MCC; w CC; w/o CC/MCC	034–036
Extracranial procedures w MCC; w CC; w/o CC/MCC	037–039
Periph/cranial nerve & other nerv syst proc w MCC; w CC or periph neurostim; w/o CC/MCC	040–042

MDC 2   DISEASES & DISORDERS OF THE EYE

Orbital procedures w CC/MCC; w/o CC/MCC	113–114
Extraocular procedures except orbit	115
Intraocular procedures w CC/MCC; w/o CC/MCC	116–117

MDC 3   DISEASES & DISORDERS OF THE EAR, NOSE, MOUTH & THROAT

Major head & neck procedures w CC/MCC or major device; w/o CC/MCC	129–130
Cranial/facial procedures w CC/MCC; w/o CC/MCC	131–132
Other ear, nose, mouth & throat O.R. procedures w CC/MCC; w/o CC/MCC	133–134
Sinus & mastoid procedures w CC/MCC; w/o CC/MCC	135–136
Mouth procedures w CC/MCC; w/o CC/MCC	137–138
Salivary gland procedures	139

MDC 4   DISEASES & DISORDERS OF THE RESPIRATORY SYSTEM

Major chest procedures w MCC; w CC; w/o CC/MCC	163–165
Other resp system O.R. procedures w MCC; w CC; w/o CC/MCC	166–168

MDC 5   DISEASES & DISORDERS OF THE CIRCULATORY SYSTEM

Other heart assist system implant	215
Cardiac valve & oth maj cardiothoracic proc w or w/o card cath w MCC; w CC; w/o CC/MCC	216-221
Endovascular cardiac valve replacement w MCC; w/o MCC	266-267
Cardiac defibrillator implant	222-227
Other cardiothoracic procedures w MCC; w CC; w/o CC/MCC	228-230
Coronary bypass	231-236
Aortic & heart assist procedures exc pulsation balloon w MCC; w/o MCC	268-269
Other maj cardiovascular procedures w MCC; w CC; w/o CC/MCC	270-272
Amputation for circ sys disorders exc upper limb & toe w MCC; w CC; w/o CC/MCC	239-241
Permanent cardiac pacemaker implant w MCC; w CC; w/o CC/MCC	242-244
AICD generator procedures	245
AICD lead procedures	265
Percutaneous intracardiac procedures w MCC; w/o MCC	273-274
Percutaneous cardiovascular procedures; with coronary artery stent	246-249
Perc cardiovasc proc w/o coronary artery stent	250-251
Other vascular procedures w MCC; w CC; w/o CC/MCC	252-254
Upper limb & toe amputation for circ system disorders w MCC; w CC; w/o CC/MCC	255–257
Cardiac pacemaker device replacement w MCC; w/o MCC	258-259
Cardiac pacemaker revision except device replacement w MCC; w CC; w/o CC/MCC	260-262
Vein ligation & stripping	263
Other circulatory system O.R. procedures	264

MDC 6   DISEASES & DISORDERS OF THE DIGESTIVE SYSTEM

Stomach, esophageal & duodenal proc w MCC; w CC; w/o CC/MCC	326–328
Major small & large bowel procedures w MCC; w CC; w/o CC/MCC	329–331
Rectal resection w MCC; w CC; w/o CC/MCC	332–334
Peritoneal adhesiolysis w MCC; w CC; w/o CC/MCC	335–337
Appendectomy w; w/o complicated principal diag w MCC; w CC; w/o CC/MCC	338–343
Minor small & large bowel procedures w MCC; w CC; w/o CC/MCC	344–346
Anal & stomal procedures w MCC; w CC; w/o CC/MCC	347–349
Hernia procedures	350–355
Other digestive system O.R. procedures w MCC; w CC; w/o CC/MCC	356–358

MDC 7   DISEASES & DISORDERS OF THE HEPATOBILIARY SYSTEM & PANCREAS

Pancreas, liver & shunt procedures w MCC; w CC; w/o CC/MCC	405–407
Biliary tract procs except only cholecyst w or w/o c.d.e. w MCC; w CC; w/o CC/MCC	408–410
Cholecystectomy	411–419
Hepatobiliary diagnostic procedures w MCC; w CC; w/o CC/MCC	420–422
Other hepatobiliary or pancreas O.R. procedures w MCC; w CC; w/o CC/MCC	423–425

MDC 8 DISEASES & DISORDERS OF THE MUSCULOSKELETAL SYSTEM & CONNECTIVE TISSUE

Combined anterior/posterior spinal fusion w MCC; w CC; w/o CC/MCC	453–455
Spinal fus exc cerv w spinal curv/malig/infec or 9+ fus w MCC; w CC; w/o CC/MCC	456–458
Spinal fusion except cervical w MCC; w/o MCC	459–460
Bilateral or multiple major joint procs of lower extremity w MCC; w/o MCC	461–462
Wnd debrid & skn graft exc hand, for musculo-conn tiss dis w MCC; w CC; w/o CC/MCC	463–465
Revision of hip or knee replacement w MCC; w CC; w/o CC/MCC	466–468
Major joint replacement or reattachment of lower extremity w MCC; w/o MCC	469–470
Cervical spinal fusion w MCC; w CC; w/o CC/MCC	471–473
Amputation for musculoskeletal sys & conn tissue dis w MCC; w CC; w/o CC/MCC	474–476
Biopsies of musculoskeletal system & connective tissue w MCC; w CC; w/o CC/MCC	477–479
Hip & femur procedures except major joint w MCC; w CC; w/o CC/MCC	480–482
Major joint & limb reattachment procs of upper extremity	483
Knee procedures w pdx of infection w MCC; w CC; w/o CC/MCC	485–487
Knee procedures w/o pdx of infection w CC/MCC; w/o CC/MCC	488–489
Back & neck proc exc spinal fusion w MCC or disc device/neurostim; w CC; w/o CC/MCC	518–520
Lower extrem & humer procs except hip, foot, femur w MCC; w CC; w/o CC/MCC	492–494
Local excision & removal int fix devices exc hip & femur w MCC; w CC; w/o CC/MCC	495–497
Local excision & removal int fix devices of hip & femur w CC/MCC; w/o CC/MCC	498–499
Soft tissue procedures w MCC; w CC; w/o CC/MCC	500–502
Foot procedures w MCC; w CC; w/o CC/MCC	503–505
Major thumb or joint procedures	506
Major shoulder or elbow joint procedures w CC/MCC; w/o CC/MCC	507–508
Arthroscopy	509
Shoulder, elbow or forearm procs, exc major joint procs w MCC; w CC; w/o CC/MCC	510–512
Hand or wrist procs, except major thumb or joint procs w CC/MCC; w/o CC/MCC	513–514
Other musculoskelet sys & conn tiss O.R. procs w MCC; w CC; w/o CC/MCC	515–517

MDC 9 DISEASES & DISORDERS OF THE SKIN, SUBCUTANEOUS TISSUE, & BREAST

Skin graft	573–578
Skin debridement w MCC; w CC; w/o MCC/CC	570–572
Other skin, subcut tiss & breast procs w MCC; w CC; w/o CC/MCC	579–581
Mastectomy for malignancy w CC/MCC; w/o CC/MCC	582–583
Breast biopsy, local excision & other breast procedures w CC/MCC; w/o CC/MCC	584–585

MDC 10 ENDOCRINE, NUTRITIONAL, & METABOLIC DISEASES & DISORDERS

Amputat of lower limb for endocrine, nutrit, & metabol dis w MCC; w CC; w/o CC/MCC	616–618
O.R. procedures for obesity w MCC; w CC; w/o CC/MCC	619–621
Skin grafts & wound debrid for endoc, nutrit & metab dis w MCC; w CC; w/o CC/MCC	622–624
Adrenal & pituitary procedures w CC/MCC; w/o CC/MCC	614–615
Thyroid, parathyroid & thyroglossal procedures w MCC; w CC; w/o CC/MCC	625–627
Other endocrine, nutrit & metab O.R. procs w MCC; w CC; w/o CC/MCC	628–630

MDC 11 DISEASES AND DISORDERS OF THE KIDNEY & URINARY TRACT

Kidney transplant	652
Major bladder procedures w MCC; w CC; w/o CC/MCC	653–655
Kidney & ureter procedures for neoplasm or non-neoplasm w MCC; w CC; w/o CC/MCC	656–661
Minor bladder procedures w MCC; w CC; w/o CC/MCC	662–664
Prostatectomy w MCC; w CC; w/o CC/MCC	665–667
Transurethral procedures w MCC; w CC; w/o CC/MCC	668–670
Urethral procedures w CC/MCC; w/o CC/MCC	671–672
Other kidney & urinary tract procedures w MCC; w CC; w/o CC/MCC	673–675

MDC 12 DISEASES & DISORDERS OF THE MALE REPRODUCTIVE SYSTEM

Major male pelvic procedures w CC/MCC; w/o CC/MCC	707–708
Penis procedures w CC/MCC; w/o CC/MCC	709–710
Testes procedures w CC/MCC; w/o CC/MCC	711–712
Transurethral prostatectomy w CC/MCC; w/o CC/MCC	713–714
Other male reproductive system procs	715–718

MDC 13 DISEASES & DISORDERS OF THE FEMALE REPRODUCTIVE SYSTEM

Pelvic evisceration, rad hysterectomy & rad vulvectomy w CC/MCC; w/o CC/MCC	734–735
Uterine & adnexa procs for malignancy	736–741
Uterine & adnexa procs for non-malignancy	742–743
D&C, conization, laparoscopy & tubal interruption w CC/MCC; w/o CC/MCC	744–745
Vagina, cervix & vulva procedures w CC/MCC; w/o CC/MCC	746–747
Female reproductive system reconstructive procedures	748
Other female reproductive system O.R. procedures w CC/MCC; w/o CC/MCC	749–750

MDC 14 PREGNANCY, CHILDBIRTH, & THE PUERPERIUM

Cesarean section w CC/MCC; w/o CC/MCC	765–766
Postpartum & post abortion diagnoses w O.R. procedure	769
Abortion w D&C, aspiration curettage or hysterotomy	770
Vaginal delivery w sterilization &/or D&C	767
Vaginal delivery w O.R. proc except steril &/or D&C	768

MDC 15 NEWBORNS & OTHER NEONATES WITH CONDITIONS ORIGINATING IN THE PERINATAL PERIOD

None	

MDC 16   DISEASES & DISORDERS OF THE BLOOD AND BLOOD FORMING ORGANS & IMMUNOLOGICAL DISORDERS

Splenectomy w MCC; w CC; w/o CC/MCC	799–801
Other O.R. proc of the blood & blood forming organs w MCC; w CC; w/o CC/MCC	802–804

MDC 17   MYELOPROLIFERATIVE DISEASES & DISORDERS, POORLY DIFFERENTIATED NEOPLASMS

Lymphoma & leukemia w major O.R. procedure w MCC; w CC; w/o CC/MCC	820–822
Lymphoma & non-acute leukemia w other O.R. proc w MCC; w CC; w/o CC/MCC	823–825
Myeloprolif disord or poorly diff neopl w maj O.R. proc w MCC; w CC; w/o CC/MCC	826–828
Myeloprolif disord or poorly diff neopl w other O.R. proc w CC/MCC; w/o CC/MCC	829–830

MDC 18   INFECTIOUS & PARASITIC DISEASES, SYSTEMIC OR UNSPECIFIED SITES

Infectious & parasitic diseases w O.R. procedure w MCC; w CC; w/o CC/MCC	856–858
Postoperative or posttraumatic infections w O.R. proc w MCC; w CC; w/o CC/MCC	853–855

MDC 19   MENTAL DISEASES & DISORDERS

O.R. procedure w principal diagnoses of mental illness	876

MDC 20   ALCOHOL/DRUG USE & ALCOHOL/DRUG INDUCED ORGANIC MENTAL DISORDERS

None	

MDC 21   INJURIES, POISONINGS, & TOXIC EFFECTS OF DRUGS

Wound debridements for injuries w MCC; w CC; w/o CC/MCC	901–903
Skin grafts for injuries w CC/MCC; w/o CC/MCC	904–905
Hand procedures for injuries	906
Other O.R. procedures for injuries w MCC; w CC; w/o CC/MCC	907–909

MDC 22   BURNS

Extensive burns or full thickness burns w MV 96+ hrs w skin graft; w/o skin graft	927, 933
Full thickness burn w skin graft or inhal inj w CC/MCC; w/o CC/MCC	928–929

MDC 23   FACTORS INFLUENCING HEALTH STATUS & OTHER CONTACTS WITH HEALTH SERVICES

O.R. proc w diagnoses of other contact w health services w MCC; w CC; w/o CC/MCC	939–941

MDC 24   MULTIPLE SIGNIFICANT TRAUMA

Craniotomy for multiple significant trauma	955
Limb reattachment, hip & femur procs for multiple significant trauma	956
Other O.R. procedures for multiple significant trauma w MCC; w CC; w/o CC/MCC	957–959

MDC 25   HUMAN IMMUNODEFICIENCY VIRUS INFECTIONS

HIV w extensive O.R. procedure w MCC; w/o MCC	969–970

Appendix D — National Average Payment Table

The national average payment for each DRG is calculated by multiplying the current relative weight of the DRG by the national average hospital Medicare base rate. The national average hospital Medicare base rate is the sum of the full update labor-related and nonlabor-related amounts published in the *Federal Register*, FY 2016 Final Rule, Table 1A. National Adjusted Operating Standardized Amounts; Labor/Nonlabor (if wage index greater than 1) or Table 1B. National Adjusted Operating Standardized Amounts; Labor/Nonlabor (if wage index less than or equal to 1). This information is provided as a benchmark reference only. There is no official publication of the average hospital base rate; therefore the national average payments provided in this table are approximate.

DRG		Description	Relative Weight	GMLOS	AMLOS	National Payment Rate
	001	HEART TRANSPLANT OR IMPLANT OF HEART ASSIST SYSTEM W MCC	26.2466	29.4	38.8	$142,619.82
	002	HEART TRANSPLANT OR IMPLANT OF HEART ASSIST SYSTEM W/O MCC	14.6448	16.6	20.0	$79,577.50
T	003	ECMO OR TRACH W MV >96 HRS OR PDX EXC FACE, MOUTH & NECK W MAJ O.R.	17.6569	25.5	31.7	$95,944.77
T	004	TRACH W MV >96 HRS OR PDX EXC FACE, MOUTH & NECK W/O MAJ O.R.	10.9458	20.0	24.1	$59,477.73
	005	LIVER TRANSPLANT W MCC OR INTESTINAL TRANSPLANT	10.7263	15.3	21.0	$58,285.00
	006	LIVER TRANSPLANT W/O MCC	4.8330	7.9	8.8	$26,261.75
	007	LUNG TRANSPLANT	9.7007	15.8	18.8	$52,712.05
	008	SIMULTANEOUS PANCREAS/KIDNEY TRANSPLANT	5.4338	9.8	11.4	$29,526.40
	010	PANCREAS TRANSPLANT	4.3039	8.1	9.5	$23,386.70
	011	TRACHEOSTOMY FOR FACE,MOUTH & NECK DIAGNOSES W MCC	4.7501	11.3	13.8	$25,811.28
	012	TRACHEOSTOMY FOR FACE,MOUTH & NECK DIAGNOSES W CC	3.4047	8.4	9.8	$18,500.60
	013	TRACHEOSTOMY FOR FACE,MOUTH & NECK DIAGNOSES W/O CC/MCC	2.1906	5.8	6.6	$11,903.37
	014	ALLOGENEIC BONE MARROW TRANSPLANT	11.5928	22.7	27.5	$62,993.42
	016	AUTOLOGOUS BONE MARROW TRANSPLANT W CC/MCC	6.1746	17.8	19.2	$33,551.79
	017	AUTOLOGOUS BONE MARROW TRANSPLANT W/O CC/MCC	4.3721	10.0	12.8	$23,757.29
	020	INTRACRANIAL VASCULAR PROCEDURES W PDX HEMORRHAGE W MCC	9.7571	13.6	16.8	$53,018.52
	021	INTRACRANIAL VASCULAR PROCEDURES W PDX HEMORRHAGE W CC	7.1549	12.3	13.7	$38,878.58
	022	INTRACRANIAL VASCULAR PROCEDURES W PDX HEMORRHAGE W/O CC/MCC	4.9977	6.7	8.4	$27,156.70
T	023	CRANIO W MAJOR DEV IMPL/ACUTE COMPLEX CNS PDX W MCC OR CHEMO IMPLANT	5.3486	7.9	11.0	$29,063.44
T	024	CRANIO W MAJOR DEV IMPL/ACUTE COMPLEX CNS PDX W/O MCC	3.7976	4.2	5.9	$20,635.55
T	025	CRANIOTOMY & ENDOVASCULAR INTRACRANIAL PROCEDURES W MCC	4.2965	7.2	9.3	$23,346.49
T	026	CRANIOTOMY & ENDOVASCULAR INTRACRANIAL PROCEDURES W CC	2.9958	4.6	6.1	$16,278.70
T	027	CRANIOTOMY & ENDOVASCULAR INTRACRANIAL PROCEDURES W/O CC/MCC	2.2835	2.4	3.1	$12,408.17
SP	028	SPINAL PROCEDURES W MCC	5.3695	9.3	11.7	$29,177.00
SP	029	SPINAL PROCEDURES W CC OR SPINAL NEUROSTIMULATORS	3.0548	4.8	6.2	$16,599.29
SP	030	SPINAL PROCEDURES W/O CC/MCC	1.7982	2.6	3.3	$9,771.13
T	031	VENTRICULAR SHUNT PROCEDURES W MCC	3.7834	7.4	10.3	$20,558.39
T	032	VENTRICULAR SHUNT PROCEDURES W CC	2.0352	3.3	4.7	$11,058.95
T	033	VENTRICULAR SHUNT PROCEDURES W/O CC/MCC	1.5734	2.0	2.5	$8,549.60
	034	CAROTID ARTERY STENT PROCEDURE W MCC	3.6851	4.8	7.1	$20,024.24
	035	CAROTID ARTERY STENT PROCEDURE W CC	2.3048	2.1	3.2	$12,523.91
	036	CAROTID ARTERY STENT PROCEDURE W/O CC/MCC	1.7180	1.3	1.5	$9,335.34
	037	EXTRACRANIAL PROCEDURES W MCC	3.0888	5.3	7.8	$16,784.04
	038	EXTRACRANIAL PROCEDURES W CC	1.5560	2.3	3.2	$8,455.06

Calculated with an average hospital Medicare base rate of $5,433.84. Each hospital's base rate and corresponding payment will vary. The national average hospital Medicare base rate is the sum of the full update labor-related and nonlabor-related amounts published in the *Federal Register*, FY 2016 Final Rule, Table 1A. National Adjusted Operating Standardized Amounts; Labor/Nonlabor (if wage index greater than 1) or Table 1B. National Adjusted Operating Standardized Amounts; Labor/Nonlabor (if wage index less than or equal to 1).

MS-DRGs 998 and 999 contain cases that could not be assigned to valid DRGs.

Note: If there is no value in either the geometric mean length of stay or the arithmetic mean length of stay columns, the volume of cases is insufficient to determine a meaningful computation of these statistics.

T Transfer DRG   SP Special Payment

DRG		Description	Relative Weight	GMLOS	AMLOS	National Payment Rate
	039	EXTRACRANIAL PROCEDURES W/O CC/MCC	1.0609	1.3	1.6	$5,764.76
SP	040	PERIPH/CRANIAL NERVE & OTHER NERV SYST PROC W MCC	3.8044	8.2	10.8	$20,672.50
SP	041	PERIPH/CRANIAL NERVE & OTHER NERV SYST PROC W CC OR PERIPH NEUROSTIM	2.1354	4.7	6.0	$11,603.42
SP	042	PERIPH/CRANIAL NERVE & OTHER NERV SYST PROC W/O CC/MCC	1.9242	2.7	3.5	$10,455.79
	052	SPINAL DISORDERS & INJURIES W CC/MCC	1.4915	4.1	5.4	$8,104.57
	053	SPINAL DISORDERS & INJURIES W/O CC/MCC	0.8625	2.8	3.4	$4,686.69
T	054	NERVOUS SYSTEM NEOPLASMS W MCC	1.3570	4.0	5.4	$7,373.72
T	055	NERVOUS SYSTEM NEOPLASMS W/O MCC	1.0401	3.0	4.1	$5,651.74
T	056	DEGENERATIVE NERVOUS SYSTEM DISORDERS W MCC	1.8513	5.2	7.2	$10,059.67
T	057	DEGENERATIVE NERVOUS SYSTEM DISORDERS W/O MCC	1.0716	3.7	5.0	$5,822.90
	058	MULTIPLE SCLEROSIS & CEREBELLAR ATAXIA W MCC	1.7198	5.5	7.3	$9,345.12
	059	MULTIPLE SCLEROSIS & CEREBELLAR ATAXIA W CC	1.0134	3.7	4.5	$5,506.65
	060	MULTIPLE SCLEROSIS & CEREBELLAR ATAXIA W/O CC/MCC	0.8130	3.1	3.7	$4,417.71
	061	ACUTE ISCHEMIC STROKE W USE OF THROMBOLYTIC AGENT W MCC	2.6843	5.4	7.1	$14,586.06
	062	ACUTE ISCHEMIC STROKE W USE OF THROMBOLYTIC AGENT W CC	1.8918	3.9	4.6	$10,279.74
	063	ACUTE ISCHEMIC STROKE W USE OF THROMBOLYTIC AGENT W/O CC/MCC	1.5238	2.9	3.2	$8,280.09
T	064	INTRACRANIAL HEMORRHAGE OR CEREBRAL INFARCTION W MCC	1.7326	4.5	6.1	$9,414.67
T	065	INTRACRANIAL HEMORRHAGE OR CEREBRAL INFARCTION W CC OR TPA IN 24 HRS	1.0593	3.3	4.1	$5,756.07
T	066	INTRACRANIAL HEMORRHAGE OR CEREBRAL INFARCTION W/O CC/MCC	0.7574	2.4	2.8	$4,115.59
	067	NONSPECIFIC CVA & PRECEREBRAL OCCLUSION W/O INFARCT W MCC	1.4338	4.0	5.0	$7,791.04
	068	NONSPECIFIC CVA & PRECEREBRAL OCCLUSION W/O INFARCT W/O MCC	0.8731	2.4	2.9	$4,744.29
	069	TRANSIENT ISCHEMIA	0.7227	2.1	2.5	$3,927.04
T	070	NONSPECIFIC CEREBROVASCULAR DISORDERS W MCC	1.6283	4.7	6.3	$8,847.92
T	071	NONSPECIFIC CEREBROVASCULAR DISORDERS W CC	1.0079	3.5	4.4	$5,476.77
T	072	NONSPECIFIC CEREBROVASCULAR DISORDERS W/O CC/MCC	0.7329	2.4	3.0	$3,982.46
	073	CRANIAL & PERIPHERAL NERVE DISORDERS W MCC	1.3359	3.8	5.2	$7,259.07
	074	CRANIAL & PERIPHERAL NERVE DISORDERS W/O MCC	0.9063	3.0	3.8	$4,924.69
	075	VIRAL MENINGITIS W CC/MCC	1.6917	5.3	6.7	$9,192.43
	076	VIRAL MENINGITIS W/O CC/MCC	0.8302	2.9	3.4	$4,511.17
	077	HYPERTENSIVE ENCEPHALOPATHY W MCC	1.5448	4.4	5.6	$8,394.20
	078	HYPERTENSIVE ENCEPHALOPATHY W CC	0.9676	3.1	3.9	$5,257.78
	079	HYPERTENSIVE ENCEPHALOPATHY W/O CC/MCC	0.6862	2.3	2.8	$3,728.70
	080	NONTRAUMATIC STUPOR & COMA W MCC	1.2159	3.7	5.1	$6,607.01
	081	NONTRAUMATIC STUPOR & COMA W/O MCC	0.7651	2.7	3.5	$4,157.43
	082	TRAUMATIC STUPOR & COMA, COMA >1 HR W MCC	2.0170	3.4	5.8	$10,960.06
	083	TRAUMATIC STUPOR & COMA, COMA >1 HR W CC	1.3006	3.3	4.3	$7,067.25
	084	TRAUMATIC STUPOR & COMA, COMA >1 HR W/O CC/MCC	0.8469	2.1	2.6	$4,601.92
T	085	TRAUMATIC STUPOR & COMA, COMA <1 HR W MCC	2.0357	4.7	6.6	$11,061.67
T	086	TRAUMATIC STUPOR & COMA, COMA <1 HR W CC	1.1394	3.3	4.1	$6,191.32

Calculated with an average hospital Medicare base rate of $5,433.84. Each hospital's base rate and corresponding payment will vary. The national average hospital Medicare base rate is the sum of the full update labor-related and nonlabor-related amounts published in the *Federal Register*, FY 2016 Final Rule, Table 1A. National Adjusted Operating Standardized Amounts; Labor/Nonlabor (if wage index greater than 1) or Table 1B. National Adjusted Operating Standardized Amounts; Labor/Nonlabor (if wage index less than or equal to 1).

MS-DRGs 998 and 999 contain cases that could not be assigned to valid DRGs.

Note: If there is no value in either the geometric mean length of stay or the arithmetic mean length of stay columns, the volume of cases is insufficient to determine a meaningful computation of these statistics.

T Transfer DRG   SP Special Payment

DRG		Description	Relative Weight	GMLOS	AMLOS	National Payment Rate
T	087	TRAUMATIC STUPOR & COMA, COMA <1 HR W/O CC/MCC	0.7918	2.2	2.7	$4,302.51
	088	CONCUSSION W MCC	1.3653	3.7	4.7	$7,418.82
	089	CONCUSSION W CC	0.9759	2.8	3.4	$5,302.88
	090	CONCUSSION W/O CC/MCC	0.7394	1.9	2.3	$4,017.78
T	091	OTHER DISORDERS OF NERVOUS SYSTEM W MCC	1.5880	4.2	5.8	$8,628.94
T	092	OTHER DISORDERS OF NERVOUS SYSTEM W CC	0.9075	3.1	3.8	$4,931.21
T	093	OTHER DISORDERS OF NERVOUS SYSTEM W/O CC/MCC	0.6981	2.2	2.7	$3,793.36
	094	BACTERIAL & TUBERCULOUS INFECTIONS OF NERVOUS SYSTEM W MCC	3.4429	8.2	10.7	$18,708.17
	095	BACTERIAL & TUBERCULOUS INFECTIONS OF NERVOUS SYSTEM W CC	2.3282	5.7	7.2	$12,651.07
	096	BACTERIAL & TUBERCULOUS INFECTIONS OF NERVOUS SYSTEM W/O CC/MCC	2.1855	4.8	5.7	$11,875.66
	097	NON-BACTERIAL INFECT OF NERVOUS SYS EXC VIRAL MENINGITIS W MCC	3.1221	8.1	10.6	$16,964.99
	098	NON-BACTERIAL INFECT OF NERVOUS SYS EXC VIRAL MENINGITIS W CC	1.8410	5.7	7.3	$10,003.70
	099	NON-BACTERIAL INFECT OF NERVOUS SYS EXC VIRAL MENINGITIS W/O CC/MCC	1.2570	4.1	5.0	$6,830.34
T	100	SEIZURES W MCC	1.5639	4.2	5.6	$8,497.98
T	101	SEIZURES W/O MCC	0.7942	2.6	3.3	$4,315.56
	102	HEADACHES W MCC	1.0685	3.1	4.2	$5,806.06
	103	HEADACHES W/O MCC	0.7199	2.3	2.9	$3,911.82
	113	ORBITAL PROCEDURES W CC/MCC	2.0118	4.0	5.8	$10,931.80
	114	ORBITAL PROCEDURES W/O CC/MCC	1.2094	2.4	2.9	$6,571.69
	115	EXTRAOCULAR PROCEDURES EXCEPT ORBIT	1.3151	3.5	4.5	$7,146.04
	116	INTRAOCULAR PROCEDURES W CC/MCC	1.5015	3.5	5.2	$8,158.91
	117	INTRAOCULAR PROCEDURES W/O CC/MCC	0.8340	2.0	2.5	$4,531.82
	121	ACUTE MAJOR EYE INFECTIONS W CC/MCC	0.9934	3.8	4.7	$5,397.98
	122	ACUTE MAJOR EYE INFECTIONS W/O CC/MCC	0.5850	3.0	3.6	$3,178.80
	123	NEUROLOGICAL EYE DISORDERS	0.7171	2.1	2.6	$3,896.61
	124	OTHER DISORDERS OF THE EYE W MCC	1.2163	3.8	5.1	$6,609.18
	125	OTHER DISORDERS OF THE EYE W/O MCC	0.7256	2.5	3.2	$3,942.79
	129	MAJOR HEAD & NECK PROCEDURES W CC/MCC OR MAJOR DEVICE	2.2292	3.7	5.2	$12,113.12
	130	MAJOR HEAD & NECK PROCEDURES W/O CC/MCC	1.3596	2.3	2.8	$7,387.85
	131	CRANIAL/FACIAL PROCEDURES W CC/MCC	2.4094	4.3	6.0	$13,092.29
	132	CRANIAL/FACIAL PROCEDURES W/O CC/MCC	1.4401	2.2	2.8	$7,825.27
	133	OTHER EAR, NOSE, MOUTH & THROAT O.R. PROCEDURES W CC/MCC	1.8573	3.8	5.5	$10,092.27
	134	OTHER EAR, NOSE, MOUTH & THROAT O.R. PROCEDURES W/O CC/MCC	1.0635	1.9	2.4	$5,778.89
	135	SINUS & MASTOID PROCEDURES W CC/MCC	1.9100	4.1	5.6	$10,378.63
	136	SINUS & MASTOID PROCEDURES W/O CC/MCC	1.1905	1.9	2.6	$6,468.99
	137	MOUTH PROCEDURES W CC/MCC	1.4261	3.8	5.0	$7,749.20
	138	MOUTH PROCEDURES W/O CC/MCC	0.8272	2.0	2.5	$4,494.87
	139	SALIVARY GLAND PROCEDURES	0.9828	1.6	2.2	$5,340.38
	146	EAR, NOSE, MOUTH & THROAT MALIGNANCY W MCC	1.8740	5.7	8.0	$10,183.02

Calculated with an average hospital Medicare base rate of $5,433.84. Each hospital's base rate and corresponding payment will vary. The national average hospital Medicare base rate is the sum of the full update labor-related and nonlabor-related amounts published in the *Federal Register*, FY 2016 Final Rule, Table 1A. National Adjusted Operating Standardized Amounts; Labor/Nonlabor (if wage index greater than 1) or Table 1B. National Adjusted Operating Standardized Amounts; Labor/Nonlabor (if wage index less than or equal to 1).

MS-DRGs 998 and 999 contain cases that could not be assigned to valid DRGs.

Note: If there is no value in either the geometric mean length of stay or the arithmetic mean length of stay columns, the volume of cases is insufficient to determine a meaningful computation of these statistics.

T **Transfer DRG**   SP **Special Payment**

	DRG	Description	Relative Weight	GMLOS	AMLOS	National Payment Rate
	147	EAR, NOSE, MOUTH & THROAT MALIGNANCY W CC	1.2419	3.9	5.2	$6,748.29
	148	EAR, NOSE, MOUTH & THROAT MALIGNANCY W/O CC/MCC	0.8094	2.2	2.8	$4,398.15
	149	DYSEQUILIBRIUM	0.6707	2.1	2.5	$3,644.48
	150	EPISTAXIS W MCC	1.2560	3.6	4.7	$6,824.90
	151	EPISTAXIS W/O MCC	0.7033	2.3	2.8	$3,821.62
	152	OTITIS MEDIA & URI W MCC	1.0612	3.4	4.3	$5,766.39
	153	OTITIS MEDIA & URI W/O MCC	0.7042	2.5	3.0	$3,826.51
	154	OTHER EAR, NOSE, MOUTH & THROAT DIAGNOSES W MCC	1.4090	4.0	5.4	$7,656.28
	155	OTHER EAR, NOSE, MOUTH & THROAT DIAGNOSES W CC	0.8733	3.1	3.8	$4,745.37
	156	OTHER EAR, NOSE, MOUTH & THROAT DIAGNOSES W/O CC/MCC	0.6662	2.3	2.8	$3,620.02
	157	DENTAL & ORAL DISEASES W MCC	1.4949	4.5	6.1	$8,123.05
	158	DENTAL & ORAL DISEASES W CC	0.8582	3.0	3.8	$4,663.32
	159	DENTAL & ORAL DISEASES W/O CC/MCC	0.6176	2.1	2.6	$3,355.94
T	163	MAJOR CHEST PROCEDURES W MCC	5.0016	10.5	12.8	$27,177.89
T	164	MAJOR CHEST PROCEDURES W CC	2.5822	5.3	6.4	$14,031.26
T	165	MAJOR CHEST PROCEDURES W/O CC/MCC	1.8148	3.1	3.8	$9,861.33
T	166	OTHER RESP SYSTEM O.R. PROCEDURES W MCC	3.6796	8.5	10.9	$19,994.36
T	167	OTHER RESP SYSTEM O.R. PROCEDURES W CC	1.9367	5.0	6.2	$10,523.72
T	168	OTHER RESP SYSTEM O.R. PROCEDURES W/O CC/MCC	1.2950	2.9	3.8	$7,036.82
T	175	PULMONARY EMBOLISM W MCC	1.4839	4.9	5.9	$8,063.28
T	176	PULMONARY EMBOLISM W/O MCC	0.9375	3.3	4.0	$5,094.23
T	177	RESPIRATORY INFECTIONS & INFLAMMATIONS W MCC	1.9033	6.0	7.4	$10,342.23
T	178	RESPIRATORY INFECTIONS & INFLAMMATIONS W CC	1.3575	4.8	5.8	$7,376.44
T	179	RESPIRATORY INFECTIONS & INFLAMMATIONS W/O CC/MCC	0.9659	3.6	4.3	$5,248.55
	180	RESPIRATORY NEOPLASMS W MCC	1.6767	5.2	6.7	$9,110.92
	181	RESPIRATORY NEOPLASMS W CC	1.1775	3.7	4.8	$6,398.35
	182	RESPIRATORY NEOPLASMS W/O CC/MCC	0.8553	2.6	3.3	$4,647.56
	183	MAJOR CHEST TRAUMA W MCC	1.4723	4.7	5.8	$8,000.24
	184	MAJOR CHEST TRAUMA W CC	1.0125	3.4	4.0	$5,501.76
	185	MAJOR CHEST TRAUMA W/O CC/MCC	0.7182	2.5	2.9	$3,902.58
T	186	PLEURAL EFFUSION W MCC	1.5734	4.7	6.1	$8,549.60
T	187	PLEURAL EFFUSION W CC	1.0835	3.5	4.4	$5,887.57
T	188	PLEURAL EFFUSION W/O CC/MCC	0.7860	2.7	3.3	$4,271.00
	189	PULMONARY EDEMA & RESPIRATORY FAILURE	1.2265	3.9	5.0	$6,664.60
T	190	CHRONIC OBSTRUCTIVE PULMONARY DISEASE W MCC	1.1578	4.0	4.9	$6,291.30
T	191	CHRONIC OBSTRUCTIVE PULMONARY DISEASE W CC	0.9321	3.3	4.0	$5,064.88
T	192	CHRONIC OBSTRUCTIVE PULMONARY DISEASE W/O CC/MCC	0.7313	2.7	3.3	$3,973.77
T	193	SIMPLE PNEUMONIA & PLEURISY W MCC	1.4261	4.8	5.8	$7,749.20
T	194	SIMPLE PNEUMONIA & PLEURISY W CC	0.9695	3.7	4.4	$5,268.11

Calculated with an average hospital Medicare base rate of $5,433.84. Each hospital's base rate and corresponding payment will vary. The national average hospital Medicare base rate is the sum of the full update labor-related and nonlabor-related amounts published in the *Federal Register*, FY 2016 Final Rule, Table 1A. National Adjusted Operating Standardized Amounts; Labor/Nonlabor (if wage index greater than 1) or Table 1B. National Adjusted Operating Standardized Amounts; Labor/Nonlabor (if wage index less than or equal to 1).

MS-DRGs 998 and 999 contain cases that could not be assigned to valid DRGs.

Note: If there is no value in either the geometric mean length of stay or the arithmetic mean length of stay columns, the volume of cases is insufficient to determine a meaningful computation of these statistics.

T **Transfer DRG**   SP **Special Payment**

© 2015 Optum360, LLC

DRG		Description	Relative Weight	GMLOS	AMLOS	National Payment Rate
T	195	SIMPLE PNEUMONIA & PLEURISY W/O CC/MCC	0.7111	2.8	3.3	$3,864.00
T	196	INTERSTITIAL LUNG DISEASE W MCC	1.6315	5.2	6.6	$8,865.31
T	197	INTERSTITIAL LUNG DISEASE W CC	1.0406	3.6	4.4	$5,654.45
T	198	INTERSTITIAL LUNG DISEASE W/O CC/MCC	0.7775	2.8	3.4	$4,224.81
	199	PNEUMOTHORAX W MCC	1.7503	5.7	7.2	$9,510.85
	200	PNEUMOTHORAX W CC	1.0443	3.5	4.5	$5,674.56
	201	PNEUMOTHORAX W/O CC/MCC	0.7354	2.7	3.3	$3,996.05
	202	BRONCHITIS & ASTHMA W CC/MCC	0.8980	3.1	3.8	$4,879.59
	203	BRONCHITIS & ASTHMA W/O CC/MCC	0.6697	2.5	3.0	$3,639.04
	204	RESPIRATORY SIGNS & SYMPTOMS	0.7291	2.2	2.8	$3,961.81
T	205	OTHER RESPIRATORY SYSTEM DIAGNOSES W MCC	1.4478	4.1	5.4	$7,867.11
T	206	OTHER RESPIRATORY SYSTEM DIAGNOSES W/O MCC	0.8164	2.5	3.2	$4,436.19
T	207	RESPIRATORY SYSTEM DIAGNOSIS W VENTILATOR SUPPORT >96 HOURS	5.3498	12.2	14.1	$29,069.96
	208	RESPIRATORY SYSTEM DIAGNOSIS W VENTILATOR SUPPORT <96 HOURS	2.3055	4.9	6.7	$12,527.72
	215	OTHER HEART ASSIST SYSTEM IMPLANT	15.8738	12.0	18.4	$86,255.69
SP	216	CARDIAC VALVE & OTH MAJ CARDIOTHORACIC PROC W CARD CATH W MCC	9.4642	12.7	15.5	$51,426.95
SP	217	CARDIAC VALVE & OTH MAJ CARDIOTHORACIC PROC W CARD CATH W CC	6.2576	8.5	9.7	$34,002.80
SP	218	CARDIAC VALVE & OTH MAJ CARDIOTHORACIC PROC W CARD CATH W/O CC/MCC	5.4815	6.5	7.2	$29,785.59
SP	219	CARDIAC VALVE & OTH MAJ CARDIOTHORACIC PROC W/O CARD CATH W MCC	7.5590	9.6	11.5	$41,074.40
SP	220	CARDIAC VALVE & OTH MAJ CARDIOTHORACIC PROC W/O CARD CATH W CC	5.1074	6.5	7.1	$27,752.79
SP	221	CARDIAC VALVE & OTH MAJ CARDIOTHORACIC PROC W/O CARD CATH W/O CC/MCC	4.5406	4.8	5.4	$24,672.89
	222	CARDIAC DEFIB IMPLANT W CARDIAC CATH W AMI/HF/SHOCK W MCC	8.5188	10.2	12.1	$46,289.80
	223	CARDIAC DEFIB IMPLANT W CARDIAC CATH W AMI/HF/SHOCK W/O MCC	6.4026	5.4	6.6	$34,790.70
	224	CARDIAC DEFIB IMPLANT W CARDIAC CATH W/O AMI/HF/SHOCK W MCC	7.6140	8.0	9.9	$41,373.26
	225	CARDIAC DEFIB IMPLANT W CARDIAC CATH W/O AMI/HF/SHOCK W/O MCC	5.8561	4.1	4.9	$31,821.11
	226	CARDIAC DEFIBRILLATOR IMPLANT W/O CARDIAC CATH W MCC	6.9737	6.8	8.9	$37,893.97
	227	CARDIAC DEFIBRILLATOR IMPLANT W/O CARDIAC CATH W/O MCC	5.4816	3.1	4.3	$29,786.14
	228	OTHER CARDIOTHORACIC PROCEDURES W MCC	6.9512	10.8	12.8	$37,771.71
	229	OTHER CARDIOTHORACIC PROCEDURES W CC	4.5589	6.5	7.4	$24,772.33
	230	OTHER CARDIOTHORACIC PROCEDURES W/O CC/MCC	4.3018	4.3	4.9	$23,375.29
	231	CORONARY BYPASS W PTCA W MCC	7.8056	9.9	11.7	$42,414.38
	232	CORONARY BYPASS W PTCA W/O MCC	5.7779	7.9	8.6	$31,396.18
T	233	CORONARY BYPASS W CARDIAC CATH W MCC	7.3581	11.6	13.0	$39,982.74
T	234	CORONARY BYPASS W CARDIAC CATH W/O MCC	4.9076	8.0	8.6	$26,667.11
T	235	CORONARY BYPASS W/O CARDIAC CATH W MCC	5.8103	8.9	10.3	$31,572.24
T	236	CORONARY BYPASS W/O CARDIAC CATH W/O MCC	3.8013	6.0	6.5	$20,655.66
T	239	AMPUTATION FOR CIRC SYS DISORDERS EXC UPPER LIMB & TOE W MCC	4.8380	10.5	13.4	$26,288.92
T	240	AMPUTATION FOR CIRC SYS DISORDERS EXC UPPER LIMB & TOE W CC	2.6835	7.0	8.5	$14,581.71

Calculated with an average hospital Medicare base rate of $5,433.84. Each hospital's base rate and corresponding payment will vary. The national average hospital Medicare base rate is the sum of the full update labor-related and nonlabor-related amounts published in the *Federal Register*, FY 2016 Final Rule, Table 1A. National Adjusted Operating Standardized Amounts; Labor/Nonlabor (if wage index greater than 1) or Table 1B. National Adjusted Operating Standardized Amounts; Labor/Nonlabor (if wage index less than or equal to 1).

MS-DRGs 998 and 999 contain cases that could not be assigned to valid DRGs.

Note: If there is no value in either the geometric mean length of stay or the arithmetic mean length of stay columns, the volume of cases is insufficient to determine a meaningful computation of these statistics.

T **Transfer DRG**   SP **Special Payment**

	DRG	Description	Relative Weight	GMLOS	AMLOS	National Payment Rate
T	241	AMPUTATION FOR CIRC SYS DISORDERS EXC UPPER LIMB & TOE W/O CC/MCC	1.4476	4.5	5.3	$7,866.03
T	242	PERMANENT CARDIAC PACEMAKER IMPLANT W MCC	3.7836	5.7	7.4	$20,559.48
T	243	PERMANENT CARDIAC PACEMAKER IMPLANT W CC	2.6444	3.6	4.4	$14,369.25
T	244	PERMANENT CARDIAC PACEMAKER IMPLANT W/O CC/MCC	2.1394	2.5	2.9	$11,625.16
	245	AICD GENERATOR PROCEDURES	4.6864	4.0	5.5	$25,465.15
	246	PERC CARDIOVASC PROC W DRUG-ELUTING STENT W MCC OR 4+ VESSELS/STENTS	3.2494	4.1	5.5	$17,656.72
	247	PERC CARDIOVASC PROC W DRUG-ELUTING STENT W/O MCC	2.1307	2.2	2.7	$11,577.88
	248	PERC CARDIOVASC PROC W NON-DRUG-ELUTING STENT W MCC OR 4+ VES/STENTS	3.0696	4.8	6.3	$16,679.72
	249	PERC CARDIOVASC PROC W NON-DRUG-ELUTING STENT W/O MCC	1.9140	2.5	3.1	$10,400.37
	250	PERC CARDIOVASC PROC W/O CORONARY ARTERY STENT W MCC	2.6975	4.2	5.7	$14,657.78
	251	PERC CARDIOVASC PROC W/O CORONARY ARTERY STENT W/O MCC	1.6863	2.4	2.9	$9,163.08
	252	OTHER VASCULAR PROCEDURES W MCC	3.2872	5.5	7.9	$17,862.12
	253	OTHER VASCULAR PROCEDURES W CC	2.6028	4.3	5.7	$14,143.20
	254	OTHER VASCULAR PROCEDURES W/O CC/MCC	1.7232	2.4	3.0	$9,363.59
T	255	UPPER LIMB & TOE AMPUTATION FOR CIRC SYSTEM DISORDERS W MCC	2.6202	6.8	8.6	$14,237.75
T	256	UPPER LIMB & TOE AMPUTATION FOR CIRC SYSTEM DISORDERS W CC	1.6241	5.3	6.4	$8,825.10
T	257	UPPER LIMB & TOE AMPUTATION FOR CIRC SYSTEM DISORDERS W/O CC/MCC	1.0844	3.4	4.1	$5,892.46
	258	CARDIAC PACEMAKER DEVICE REPLACEMENT W MCC	2.8590	4.9	6.3	$15,535.35
	259	CARDIAC PACEMAKER DEVICE REPLACEMENT W/O MCC	1.9456	2.9	3.6	$10,572.08
	260	CARDIAC PACEMAKER REVISION EXCEPT DEVICE REPLACEMENT W MCC	3.7299	7.6	10.3	$20,267.68
	261	CARDIAC PACEMAKER REVISION EXCEPT DEVICE REPLACEMENT W CC	1.8639	3.5	4.4	$10,128.13
	262	CARDIAC PACEMAKER REVISION EXCEPT DEVICE REPLACEMENT W/O CC/MCC	1.5125	2.5	3.0	$8,218.68
	263	VEIN LIGATION & STRIPPING	2.0854	4.1	6.2	$11,331.73
T	264	OTHER CIRCULATORY SYSTEM O.R. PROCEDURES	2.8080	5.8	8.3	$15,258.22
	265	AICD LEAD PROCEDURES	2.9681	3.1	4.5	$16,128.18
SP	266	ENDOVASCULAR CARDIAC VALVE REPLACEMENT W MCC	8.5986	7.3	9.5	$46,723.42
SP	267	ENDOVASCULAR CARDIAC VALVE REPLACEMENT W/O MCC	6.5575	4.4	5.2	$35,632.41
	268	AORTIC AND HEART ASSIST PROCEDURES EXCEPT PULSATION BALLOON W MCC	6.2807	6.9	9.9	$34,128.32
	269	AORTIC AND HEART ASSIST PROCEDURES EXCEPT PULSATION BALLOON W/O MCC	3.9041	1.9	2.6	$21,214.25
	270	OTHER MAJOR CARDIOVASCULAR PROCEDURES W MCC	4.7349	6.5	9.3	$25,728.69
	271	OTHER MAJOR CARDIOVASCULAR PROCEDURES W CC	3.1426	4.5	6.0	$17,076.39
	272	OTHER MAJOR CARDIOVASCULAR PROCEDURES W/O CC/MCC	2.2508	2.3	3.1	$12,230.49
SP	273	PERCUTANEOUS INTRACARDIAC PROCEDURES W MCC	3.5499	6.0	8.0	$19,289.59
SP	274	PERCUTANEOUS INTRACARDIAC PROCEDURES W/O MCC	2.4197	2.7	3.4	$13,148.26
T	280	ACUTE MYOCARDIAL INFARCTION, DISCHARGED ALIVE W MCC	1.6971	4.5	5.8	$9,221.77
T	281	ACUTE MYOCARDIAL INFARCTION, DISCHARGED ALIVE W CC	1.0232	2.9	3.6	$5,559.91
T	282	ACUTE MYOCARDIAL INFARCTION, DISCHARGED ALIVE W/O CC/MCC	0.7557	2.0	2.4	$4,106.35

Calculated with an average hospital Medicare base rate of $5,433.84. Each hospital's base rate and corresponding payment will vary. The national average hospital Medicare base rate is the sum of the full update labor-related and nonlabor-related amounts published in the *Federal Register*, FY 2016 Final Rule, Table 1A. National Adjusted Operating Standardized Amounts; Labor/Nonlabor (if wage index greater than 1) or Table 1B. National Adjusted Operating Standardized Amounts; Labor/Nonlabor (if wage index less than or equal to 1).

MS-DRGs 998 and 999 contain cases that could not be assigned to valid DRGs.

Note: If there is no value in either the geometric mean length of stay or the arithmetic mean length of stay columns, the volume of cases is insufficient to determine a meaningful computation of these statistics.

T **Transfer DRG**   SP **Special Payment**

DRG		Description	Relative Weight	GMLOS	AMLOS	National Payment Rate
	283	ACUTE MYOCARDIAL INFARCTION, EXPIRED W MCC	1.6613	2.9	4.6	$9,027.24
	284	ACUTE MYOCARDIAL INFARCTION, EXPIRED W CC	0.7827	1.8	2.5	$4,253.07
	285	ACUTE MYOCARDIAL INFARCTION, EXPIRED W/O CC/MCC	0.5473	1.4	1.6	$2,973.94
	286	CIRCULATORY DISORDERS EXCEPT AMI, W CARD CATH W MCC	2.1775	5.1	6.9	$11,832.19
	287	CIRCULATORY DISORDERS EXCEPT AMI, W CARD CATH W/O MCC	1.1562	2.5	3.3	$6,282.61
T	288	ACUTE & SUBACUTE ENDOCARDITIS W MCC	2.7933	7.5	9.5	$15,178.35
T	289	ACUTE & SUBACUTE ENDOCARDITIS W CC	1.6969	5.6	6.9	$9,220.68
T	290	ACUTE & SUBACUTE ENDOCARDITIS W/O CC/MCC	1.0546	3.7	4.4	$5,730.53
T	291	HEART FAILURE & SHOCK W MCC	1.4809	4.6	5.8	$8,046.97
T	292	HEART FAILURE & SHOCK W CC	0.9707	3.6	4.4	$5,274.63
T	293	HEART FAILURE & SHOCK W/O CC/MCC	0.6737	2.6	3.1	$3,660.78
	294	DEEP VEIN THROMBOPHLEBITIS W CC/MCC	0.9826	3.8	4.7	$5,339.29
	295	DEEP VEIN THROMBOPHLEBITIS W/O CC/MCC	0.7427	3.2	3.7	$4,035.71
	296	CARDIAC ARREST, UNEXPLAINED W MCC	1.2864	1.9	2.8	$6,990.09
	297	CARDIAC ARREST, UNEXPLAINED W CC	0.6488	1.3	1.6	$3,525.48
	298	CARDIAC ARREST, UNEXPLAINED W/O CC/MCC	0.4477	1.1	1.2	$2,432.73
T	299	PERIPHERAL VASCULAR DISORDERS W MCC	1.4216	4.3	5.6	$7,724.75
T	300	PERIPHERAL VASCULAR DISORDERS W CC	0.9994	3.5	4.4	$5,430.58
T	301	PERIPHERAL VASCULAR DISORDERS W/O CC/MCC	0.7023	2.6	3.2	$3,816.19
	302	ATHEROSCLEROSIS W MCC	1.0590	2.9	3.9	$5,754.44
	303	ATHEROSCLEROSIS W/O MCC	0.6427	2.0	2.4	$3,492.33
	304	HYPERTENSION W MCC	1.0109	3.3	4.1	$5,493.07
	305	HYPERTENSION W/O MCC	0.6626	2.2	2.6	$3,600.46
	306	CARDIAC CONGENITAL & VALVULAR DISORDERS W MCC	1.4029	4.0	5.4	$7,623.13
	307	CARDIAC CONGENITAL & VALVULAR DISORDERS W/O MCC	0.8044	2.5	3.2	$4,370.98
	308	CARDIAC ARRHYTHMIA & CONDUCTION DISORDERS W MCC	1.2150	3.8	4.8	$6,602.12
	309	CARDIAC ARRHYTHMIA & CONDUCTION DISORDERS W CC	0.7851	2.6	3.3	$4,266.11
	310	CARDIAC ARRHYTHMIA & CONDUCTION DISORDERS W/O CC/MCC	0.5608	2.0	2.3	$3,047.30
	311	ANGINA PECTORIS	0.6091	1.8	2.3	$3,309.75
	312	SYNCOPE & COLLAPSE	0.7630	2.4	2.9	$4,146.02
	313	CHEST PAIN	0.6621	1.8	2.2	$3,597.75
T	314	OTHER CIRCULATORY SYSTEM DIAGNOSES W MCC	1.9334	4.9	6.7	$10,505.79
T	315	OTHER CIRCULATORY SYSTEM DIAGNOSES W CC	0.9722	3.1	3.9	$5,282.78
T	316	OTHER CIRCULATORY SYSTEM DIAGNOSES W/O CC/MCC	0.6498	2.0	2.5	$3,530.91
T	326	STOMACH, ESOPHAGEAL & DUODENAL PROC W MCC	5.4452	11.0	14.2	$29,588.35
T	327	STOMACH, ESOPHAGEAL & DUODENAL PROC W CC	2.6399	5.7	7.5	$14,344.79
T	328	STOMACH, ESOPHAGEAL & DUODENAL PROC W/O CC/MCC	1.5154	2.5	3.3	$8,234.44
T	329	MAJOR SMALL & LARGE BOWEL PROCEDURES W MCC	5.0709	11.5	14.2	$27,554.46
T	330	MAJOR SMALL & LARGE BOWEL PROCEDURES W CC	2.5511	7.0	8.2	$13,862.27

Calculated with an average hospital Medicare base rate of $5,433.84. Each hospital's base rate and corresponding payment will vary. The national average hospital Medicare base rate is the sum of the full update labor-related and nonlabor-related amounts published in the *Federal Register*, FY 2016 Final Rule, Table 1A. National Adjusted Operating Standardized Amounts; Labor/Nonlabor (if wage index greater than 1) or Table 1B. National Adjusted Operating Standardized Amounts; Labor/Nonlabor (if wage index less than or equal to 1).

MS-DRGs 998 and 999 contain cases that could not be assigned to valid DRGs.

Note: If there is no value in either the geometric mean length of stay or the arithmetic mean length of stay columns, the volume of cases is insufficient to determine a meaningful computation of these statistics.

T Transfer DRG   SP Special Payment

DRG		Description	Relative Weight	GMLOS	AMLOS	National Payment Rate
T	331	MAJOR SMALL & LARGE BOWEL PROCEDURES W/O CC/MCC	1.6491	4.1	4.6	$8,960.95
T	332	RECTAL RESECTION W MCC	4.5570	10.2	12.4	$24,762.01
T	333	RECTAL RESECTION W CC	2.4254	6.0	7.1	$13,179.24
T	334	RECTAL RESECTION W/O CC/MCC	1.6480	3.5	4.1	$8,954.97
T	335	PERITONEAL ADHESIOLYSIS W MCC	4.1261	10.4	12.6	$22,420.57
T	336	PERITONEAL ADHESIOLYSIS W CC	2.3340	6.7	8.1	$12,682.58
T	337	PERITONEAL ADHESIOLYSIS W/O CC/MCC	1.5675	4.0	4.9	$8,517.54
	338	APPENDECTOMY W COMPLICATED PRINCIPAL DIAG W MCC	2.9719	7.5	9.0	$16,148.83
	339	APPENDECTOMY W COMPLICATED PRINCIPAL DIAG W CC	1.7693	4.8	5.8	$9,614.09
	340	APPENDECTOMY W COMPLICATED PRINCIPAL DIAG W/O CC/MCC	1.1773	2.9	3.4	$6,397.26
	341	APPENDECTOMY W/O COMPLICATED PRINCIPAL DIAG W MCC	2.1523	4.5	6.2	$11,695.25
	342	APPENDECTOMY W/O COMPLICATED PRINCIPAL DIAG W CC	1.3275	2.7	3.5	$7,213.42
	343	APPENDECTOMY W/O COMPLICATED PRINCIPAL DIAG W/O CC/MCC	1.0099	1.7	2.0	$5,487.64
	344	MINOR SMALL & LARGE BOWEL PROCEDURES W MCC	3.1029	8.0	10.2	$16,860.66
	345	MINOR SMALL & LARGE BOWEL PROCEDURES W CC	1.6268	5.2	6.1	$8,839.77
	346	MINOR SMALL & LARGE BOWEL PROCEDURES W/O CC/MCC	1.2143	3.7	4.2	$6,598.31
	347	ANAL & STOMAL PROCEDURES W MCC	2.4457	6.1	8.3	$13,289.54
	348	ANAL & STOMAL PROCEDURES W CC	1.4486	4.0	5.1	$7,871.46
	349	ANAL & STOMAL PROCEDURES W/O CC/MCC	0.9265	2.4	2.9	$5,034.45
	350	INGUINAL & FEMORAL HERNIA PROCEDURES W MCC	2.4982	5.6	7.6	$13,574.82
	351	INGUINAL & FEMORAL HERNIA PROCEDURES W CC	1.4110	3.4	4.3	$7,667.15
	352	INGUINAL & FEMORAL HERNIA PROCEDURES W/O CC/MCC	0.9764	2.1	2.6	$5,305.60
	353	HERNIA PROCEDURES EXCEPT INGUINAL & FEMORAL W MCC	2.9142	6.2	8.1	$15,835.30
	354	HERNIA PROCEDURES EXCEPT INGUINAL & FEMORAL W CC	1.6640	3.9	4.8	$9,041.91
	355	HERNIA PROCEDURES EXCEPT INGUINAL & FEMORAL W/O CC/MCC	1.2366	2.5	3.0	$6,719.49
T	356	OTHER DIGESTIVE SYSTEM O.R. PROCEDURES W MCC	3.7588	8.2	10.9	$20,424.72
T	357	OTHER DIGESTIVE SYSTEM O.R. PROCEDURES W CC	2.0801	5.1	6.6	$11,302.93
T	358	OTHER DIGESTIVE SYSTEM O.R. PROCEDURES W/O CC/MCC	1.3515	3.1	3.8	$7,343.83
	368	MAJOR ESOPHAGEAL DISORDERS W MCC	1.7848	4.8	6.1	$9,698.32
	369	MAJOR ESOPHAGEAL DISORDERS W CC	1.0630	3.4	4.1	$5,776.17
	370	MAJOR ESOPHAGEAL DISORDERS W/O CC/MCC	0.7355	2.4	2.9	$3,996.59
T	371	MAJOR GASTROINTESTINAL DISORDERS & PERITONEAL INFECTIONS W MCC	1.7854	5.8	7.5	$9,701.58
T	372	MAJOR GASTROINTESTINAL DISORDERS & PERITONEAL INFECTIONS W CC	1.1090	4.4	5.4	$6,026.13
T	373	MAJOR GASTROINTESTINAL DISORDERS & PERITONEAL INFECTIONS W/O CC/MCC	0.7817	3.3	3.9	$4,247.63
T	374	DIGESTIVE MALIGNANCY W MCC	2.0345	5.9	7.9	$11,055.15
T	375	DIGESTIVE MALIGNANCY W CC	1.2302	4.0	5.1	$6,684.71
T	376	DIGESTIVE MALIGNANCY W/O CC/MCC	0.9093	2.8	3.5	$4,940.99
T	377	G.I. HEMORRHAGE W MCC	1.7509	4.7	5.9	$9,514.11

Calculated with an average hospital Medicare base rate of $5,433.84. Each hospital's base rate and corresponding payment will vary. The national average hospital Medicare base rate is the sum of the full update labor-related and nonlabor-related amounts published in the *Federal Register*, FY 2016 Final Rule, Table 1A. National Adjusted Operating Standardized Amounts; Labor/Nonlabor (if wage index greater than 1) or Table 1B. National Adjusted Operating Standardized Amounts; Labor/Nonlabor (if wage index less than or equal to 1).

MS-DRGs 998 and 999 contain cases that could not be assigned to valid DRGs.

Note: If there is no value in either the geometric mean length of stay or the arithmetic mean length of stay columns, the volume of cases is insufficient to determine a meaningful computation of these statistics.

T Transfer DRG   SP Special Payment

DRG		Description	Relative Weight	GMLOS	AMLOS	National Payment Rate
T	378	G.I. HEMORRHAGE W CC	0.9949	3.2	3.8	$5,406.13
T	379	G.I. HEMORRHAGE W/O CC/MCC	0.6712	2.3	2.7	$3,647.19
T	380	COMPLICATED PEPTIC ULCER W MCC	1.9549	5.3	7.0	$10,622.61
T	381	COMPLICATED PEPTIC ULCER W CC	1.0690	3.5	4.2	$5,808.77
T	382	COMPLICATED PEPTIC ULCER W/O CC/MCC	0.8238	2.7	3.3	$4,476.40
	383	UNCOMPLICATED PEPTIC ULCER W MCC	1.3545	4.2	5.1	$7,360.14
	384	UNCOMPLICATED PEPTIC ULCER W/O MCC	0.8481	2.8	3.3	$4,608.44
	385	INFLAMMATORY BOWEL DISEASE W MCC	1.7195	5.7	7.5	$9,343.49
	386	INFLAMMATORY BOWEL DISEASE W CC	0.9996	3.8	4.8	$5,431.67
	387	INFLAMMATORY BOWEL DISEASE W/O CC/MCC	0.7379	3.0	3.6	$4,009.63
T	388	G.I. OBSTRUCTION W MCC	1.5813	5.2	6.8	$8,592.53
T	389	G.I. OBSTRUCTION W CC	0.8707	3.5	4.3	$4,731.24
T	390	G.I. OBSTRUCTION W/O CC/MCC	0.6067	2.7	3.1	$3,296.71
	391	ESOPHAGITIS, GASTROENT & MISC DIGEST DISORDERS W MCC	1.1925	3.8	5.0	$6,479.85
	392	ESOPHAGITIS, GASTROENT & MISC DIGEST DISORDERS W/O MCC	0.7400	2.7	3.3	$4,021.04
	393	OTHER DIGESTIVE SYSTEM DIAGNOSES W MCC	1.6335	4.6	6.3	$8,876.18
	394	OTHER DIGESTIVE SYSTEM DIAGNOSES W CC	0.9502	3.3	4.2	$5,163.23
	395	OTHER DIGESTIVE SYSTEM DIAGNOSES W/O CC/MCC	0.6756	2.4	2.9	$3,671.10
T	405	PANCREAS, LIVER & SHUNT PROCEDURES W MCC	5.5888	10.5	14.2	$30,368.64
T	406	PANCREAS, LIVER & SHUNT PROCEDURES W CC	2.8075	5.9	7.4	$15,255.51
T	407	PANCREAS, LIVER & SHUNT PROCEDURES W/O CC/MCC	2.0026	4.1	5.0	$10,881.81
	408	BILIARY TRACT PROC EXCEPT ONLY CHOLECYST W OR W/O C.D.E. W MCC	3.6476	9.6	11.6	$19,820.47
	409	BILIARY TRACT PROC EXCEPT ONLY CHOLECYST W OR W/O C.D.E. W CC	2.4648	6.6	7.9	$13,393.33
	410	BILIARY TRACT PROC EXCEPT ONLY CHOLECYST W OR W/O C.D.E. W/O CC/MCC	1.5576	4.5	5.2	$8,463.75
	411	CHOLECYSTECTOMY W C.D.E. W MCC	3.5782	8.9	11.0	$19,443.37
	412	CHOLECYSTECTOMY W C.D.E. W CC	2.4981	6.6	7.6	$13,574.28
	413	CHOLECYSTECTOMY W C.D.E. W/O CC/MCC	1.7996	4.1	5.0	$9,778.74
T	414	CHOLECYSTECTOMY EXCEPT BY LAPAROSCOPE W/O C.D.E. W MCC	3.5283	8.5	10.3	$19,172.22
T	415	CHOLECYSTECTOMY EXCEPT BY LAPAROSCOPE W/O C.D.E. W CC	2.0071	5.5	6.4	$10,906.26
T	416	CHOLECYSTECTOMY EXCEPT BY LAPAROSCOPE W/O C.D.E. W/O CC/MCC	1.3342	3.4	4.0	$7,249.83
	417	LAPAROSCOPIC CHOLECYSTECTOMY W/O C.D.E. W MCC	2.4734	5.8	7.2	$13,440.06
	418	LAPAROSCOPIC CHOLECYSTECTOMY W/O C.D.E. W CC	1.6584	3.9	4.7	$9,011.48
	419	LAPAROSCOPIC CHOLECYSTECTOMY W/O C.D.E. W/O CC/MCC	1.2540	2.5	3.0	$6,814.04
	420	HEPATOBILIARY DIAGNOSTIC PROCEDURES W MCC	3.6609	8.1	11.1	$19,892.74
	421	HEPATOBILIARY DIAGNOSTIC PROCEDURES W CC	1.7451	4.1	5.3	$9,482.59
	422	HEPATOBILIARY DIAGNOSTIC PROCEDURES W/O CC/MCC	1.2941	2.8	3.4	$7,031.93
	423	OTHER HEPATOBILIARY OR PANCREAS O.R. PROCEDURES W MCC	4.2650	9.8	13.4	$23,175.33
	424	OTHER HEPATOBILIARY OR PANCREAS O.R. PROCEDURES W CC	2.3049	6.0	8.0	$12,524.46
	425	OTHER HEPATOBILIARY OR PANCREAS O.R. PROCEDURES W/O CC/MCC	1.6000	3.6	4.8	$8,694.14

Calculated with an average hospital Medicare base rate of $5,433.84. Each hospital's base rate and corresponding payment will vary. The national average hospital Medicare base rate is the sum of the full update labor-related and nonlabor-related amounts published in the *Federal Register*, FY 2016 Final Rule, Table 1A. National Adjusted Operating Standardized Amounts; Labor/Nonlabor (if wage index greater than 1) or Table 1B. National Adjusted Operating Standardized Amounts; Labor/Nonlabor (if wage index less than or equal to 1).

MS-DRGs 998 and 999 contain cases that could not be assigned to valid DRGs.

Note: If there is no value in either the geometric mean length of stay or the arithmetic mean length of stay columns, the volume of cases is insufficient to determine a meaningful computation of these statistics.

T Transfer DRG   SP Special Payment

DRG		Description	Relative Weight	GMLOS	AMLOS	National Payment Rate
	432	CIRRHOSIS & ALCOHOLIC HEPATITIS W MCC	1.6567	4.7	6.1	$9,002.24
	433	CIRRHOSIS & ALCOHOLIC HEPATITIS W CC	0.9164	3.2	4.0	$4,979.57
	434	CIRRHOSIS & ALCOHOLIC HEPATITIS W/O CC/MCC	0.6235	2.3	2.7	$3,388.00
	435	MALIGNANCY OF HEPATOBILIARY SYSTEM OR PANCREAS W MCC	1.7476	5.1	6.6	$9,496.18
	436	MALIGNANCY OF HEPATOBILIARY SYSTEM OR PANCREAS W CC	1.1686	3.8	4.9	$6,349.99
	437	MALIGNANCY OF HEPATOBILIARY SYSTEM OR PANCREAS W/O CC/MCC	0.9051	2.7	3.4	$4,918.17
	438	DISORDERS OF PANCREAS EXCEPT MALIGNANCY W MCC	1.6612	4.9	6.7	$9,026.70
	439	DISORDERS OF PANCREAS EXCEPT MALIGNANCY W CC	0.8823	3.5	4.3	$4,794.28
	440	DISORDERS OF PANCREAS EXCEPT MALIGNANCY W/O CC/MCC	0.6368	2.6	3.1	$3,460.27
T	441	DISORDERS OF LIVER EXCEPT MALIG,CIRR,ALC HEPA W MCC	1.8767	5.0	6.8	$10,197.69
T	442	DISORDERS OF LIVER EXCEPT MALIG,CIRR,ALC HEPA W CC	0.9371	3.4	4.3	$5,092.05
T	443	DISORDERS OF LIVER EXCEPT MALIG,CIRR,ALC HEPA W/O CC/MCC	0.6545	2.5	3.1	$3,556.45
	444	DISORDERS OF THE BILIARY TRACT W MCC	1.5895	4.5	5.9	$8,637.09
	445	DISORDERS OF THE BILIARY TRACT W CC	1.0553	3.3	4.0	$5,734.33
	446	DISORDERS OF THE BILIARY TRACT W/O CC/MCC	0.7633	2.4	2.8	$4,147.65
	453	COMBINED ANTERIOR/POSTERIOR SPINAL FUSION W MCC	11.4304	9.2	11.3	$62,110.96
	454	COMBINED ANTERIOR/POSTERIOR SPINAL FUSION W CC	8.0698	4.9	5.8	$43,850.00
	455	COMBINED ANTERIOR/POSTERIOR SPINAL FUSION W/O CC/MCC	6.1934	3.0	3.4	$33,653.94
	456	SPINAL FUS EXC CERV W SPINAL CURV/MALIG/INFEC OR EXT FUS W MCC	9.4061	9.8	12.0	$51,111.24
	457	SPINAL FUS EXC CERV W SPINAL CURV/MALIG/INFEC OR EXT FUS W CC	7.0741	5.5	6.5	$38,439.53
	458	SPINAL FUS EXC CERV W SPINAL CURV/MALIG/INFEC OR EXT FUS W/O CC/MCC	5.2986	3.3	3.7	$28,791.74
T	459	SPINAL FUSION EXCEPT CERVICAL W MCC	6.5455	6.7	8.3	$35,567.20
T	460	SPINAL FUSION EXCEPT CERVICAL W/O MCC	3.9717	2.9	3.4	$21,581.58
	461	BILATERAL OR MULTIPLE MAJOR JOINT PROCS OF LOWER EXTREMITY W MCC	5.0977	6.3	8.2	$27,700.09
	462	BILATERAL OR MULTIPLE MAJOR JOINT PROCS OF LOWER EXTREMITY W/O MCC	3.2145	3.2	3.5	$17,467.08
T	463	WND DEBRID & SKN GRFT EXC HAND, FOR MUSCULO-CONN TISS DIS W MCC	5.1028	10.2	13.4	$27,727.80
T	464	WND DEBRID & SKN GRFT EXC HAND, FOR MUSCULO-CONN TISS DIS W CC	3.0937	6.2	7.8	$16,810.67
T	465	WND DEBRID & SKN GRFT EXC HAND, FOR MUSCULO-CONN TISS DIS W/O CC/MCC	1.9349	3.8	4.7	$10,513.94
T	466	REVISION OF HIP OR KNEE REPLACEMENT W MCC	5.0394	6.6	8.1	$27,383.29
T	467	REVISION OF HIP OR KNEE REPLACEMENT W CC	3.4376	3.7	4.3	$18,679.37
T	468	REVISION OF HIP OR KNEE REPLACEMENT W/O CC/MCC	2.7513	2.7	3.0	$14,950.12
T	469	MAJOR JOINT REPLACEMENT OR REATTACHMENT OF LOWER EXTREMITY W MCC	3.2962	5.9	7.0	$17,911.02
T	470	MAJOR JOINT REPLACEMENT OR REATTACHMENT OF LOWER EXTREMITY W/O MCC	2.0816	2.8	3.1	$11,311.08
	471	CERVICAL SPINAL FUSION W MCC	4.9033	6.2	8.6	$26,643.75
	472	CERVICAL SPINAL FUSION W CC	2.9051	2.4	3.3	$15,785.85
	473	CERVICAL SPINAL FUSION W/O CC/MCC	2.2650	1.5	1.8	$12,307.65
T	474	AMPUTATION FOR MUSCULOSKELETAL SYS & CONN TISSUE DIS W MCC	3.6260	8.7	11.0	$19,703.10
T	475	AMPUTATION FOR MUSCULOSKELETAL SYS & CONN TISSUE DIS W CC	2.1001	5.7	7.2	$11,411.61

Calculated with an average hospital Medicare base rate of $5,433.84. Each hospital's base rate and corresponding payment will vary. The national average hospital Medicare base rate is the sum of the full update labor-related and nonlabor-related amounts published in the *Federal Register*, FY 2016 Final Rule, Table 1A. National Adjusted Operating Standardized Amounts; Labor/Nonlabor (if wage index greater than 1) or Table 1B. National Adjusted Operating Standardized Amounts; Labor/Nonlabor (if wage index less than or equal to 1).

MS-DRGs 998 and 999 contain cases that could not be assigned to valid DRGs.

Note: If there is no value in either the geometric mean length of stay or the arithmetic mean length of stay columns, the volume of cases is insufficient to determine a meaningful computation of these statistics.

T **Transfer DRG**   SP **Special Payment**

© 2015 Optum360, LLC

DRG		Description	Relative Weight	GMLOS	AMLOS	National Payment Rate
T	476	AMPUTATION FOR MUSCULOSKELETAL SYS & CONN TISSUE DIS W/O CC/MCC	1.1427	3.1	3.9	$6,209.25
SP	477	BIOPSIES OF MUSCULOSKELETAL SYSTEM & CONNECTIVE TISSUE W MCC	3.1211	8.3	10.2	$16,959.56
SP	478	BIOPSIES OF MUSCULOSKELETAL SYSTEM & CONNECTIVE TISSUE W CC	2.1992	5.4	6.6	$11,950.10
SP	479	BIOPSIES OF MUSCULOSKELETAL SYSTEM & CONNECTIVE TISSUE W/O CC/MCC	1.7158	3.5	4.3	$9,323.38
SP	480	HIP & FEMUR PROCEDURES EXCEPT MAJOR JOINT W MCC	2.9990	6.7	7.9	$16,296.09
SP	481	HIP & FEMUR PROCEDURES EXCEPT MAJOR JOINT W CC	1.9790	4.6	5.0	$10,753.57
SP	482	HIP & FEMUR PROCEDURES EXCEPT MAJOR JOINT W/O CC/MCC	1.6228	3.7	4.0	$8,818.04
	483	MAJOR JOINT/LIMB REATTACHMENT PROCEDURE OF UPPER EXTREMITIES	2.4127	1.9	2.3	$13,110.23
	485	KNEE PROCEDURES W PDX OF INFECTION W MCC	3.2132	8.1	9.8	$17,460.01
	486	KNEE PROCEDURES W PDX OF INFECTION W CC	2.0690	5.4	6.2	$11,242.61
	487	KNEE PROCEDURES W PDX OF INFECTION W/O CC/MCC	1.5484	3.9	4.5	$8,413.76
T	488	KNEE PROCEDURES W/O PDX OF INFECTION W CC/MCC	1.7591	3.4	4.2	$9,558.67
T	489	KNEE PROCEDURES W/O PDX OF INFECTION W/O CC/MCC	1.2991	2.3	2.6	$7,059.10
SP	492	LOWER EXTREM & HUMER PROC EXCEPT HIP,FOOT,FEMUR W MCC	3.1585	6.2	7.6	$17,162.78
SP	493	LOWER EXTREM & HUMER PROC EXCEPT HIP,FOOT,FEMUR W CC	2.0557	3.9	4.6	$11,170.34
SP	494	LOWER EXTREM & HUMER PROC EXCEPT HIP,FOOT,FEMUR W/O CC/MCC	1.5796	2.7	3.1	$8,583.29
SP	495	LOCAL EXCISION & REMOVAL INT FIX DEVICES EXC HIP & FEMUR W MCC	3.0151	7.3	9.3	$16,383.57
SP	496	LOCAL EXCISION & REMOVAL INT FIX DEVICES EXC HIP & FEMUR W CC	1.7451	4.0	5.1	$9,482.59
SP	497	LOCAL EXCISION & REMOVAL INT FIX DEVICES EXC HIP & FEMUR W/O CC/MCC	1.2436	2.1	2.6	$6,757.52
	498	LOCAL EXCISION & REMOVAL INT FIX DEVICES OF HIP & FEMUR W CC/MCC	2.2492	5.4	7.3	$12,221.79
	499	LOCAL EXCISION & REMOVAL INT FIX DEVICES OF HIP & FEMUR W/O CC/MCC	1.0512	2.2	2.7	$5,712.05
SP	500	SOFT TISSUE PROCEDURES W MCC	3.2024	7.4	10.1	$17,401.33
SP	501	SOFT TISSUE PROCEDURES W CC	1.6064	4.3	5.4	$8,728.92
SP	502	SOFT TISSUE PROCEDURES W/O CC/MCC	1.1752	2.4	2.9	$6,385.85
	503	FOOT PROCEDURES W MCC	2.2679	6.7	8.1	$12,323.41
	504	FOOT PROCEDURES W CC	1.5941	5.0	5.9	$8,662.08
	505	FOOT PROCEDURES W/O CC/MCC	1.2590	2.9	3.5	$6,841.20
	506	MAJOR THUMB OR JOINT PROCEDURES	1.3490	3.4	4.3	$7,330.25
	507	MAJOR SHOULDER OR ELBOW JOINT PROCEDURES W CC/MCC	1.8698	4.3	5.3	$10,160.19
	508	MAJOR SHOULDER OR ELBOW JOINT PROCEDURES W/O CC/MCC	1.6134	2.2	2.7	$8,766.96
	509	ARTHROSCOPY	1.6562	3.4	4.8	$8,999.53
T	510	SHOULDER,ELBOW OR FOREARM PROC,EXC MAJOR JOINT PROC W MCC	2.4420	4.8	5.9	$13,269.44
T	511	SHOULDER,ELBOW OR FOREARM PROC,EXC MAJOR JOINT PROC W CC	1.7018	3.3	3.9	$9,247.31
T	512	SHOULDER,ELBOW OR FOREARM PROC,EXC MAJOR JOINT PROC W/O CC/MCC	1.3531	2.1	2.5	$7,352.53
	513	HAND OR WRIST PROC, EXCEPT MAJOR THUMB OR JOINT PROC W CC/MCC	1.5025	3.8	4.9	$8,164.34
	514	HAND OR WRIST PROC, EXCEPT MAJOR THUMB OR JOINT PROC W/O CC/MCC	0.9055	2.3	2.8	$4,920.34
SP	515	OTHER MUSCULOSKELET SYS & CONN TISS O.R. PROC W MCC	3.1862	7.0	8.9	$17,313.30
SP	516	OTHER MUSCULOSKELET SYS & CONN TISS O.R. PROC W CC	2.0670	4.3	5.3	$11,231.75

Calculated with an average hospital Medicare base rate of $5,433.84. Each hospital's base rate and corresponding payment will vary. The national average hospital Medicare base rate is the sum of the full update labor-related and nonlabor-related amounts published in the *Federal Register*, FY 2016 Final Rule, Table 1A. National Adjusted Operating Standardized Amounts; Labor/Nonlabor (if wage index greater than 1) or Table 1B. National Adjusted Operating Standardized Amounts; Labor/Nonlabor (if wage index less than or equal to 1).

MS-DRGs 998 and 999 contain cases that could not be assigned to valid DRGs.

Note: If there is no value in either the geometric mean length of stay or the arithmetic mean length of stay columns, the volume of cases is insufficient to determine a meaningful computation of these statistics.

T Transfer DRG   SP Special Payment

Appendix D — National Average Payment Table

DRG		Description	Relative Weight	GMLOS	AMLOS	National Payment Rate
SP	517	OTHER MUSCULOSKELET SYS & CONN TISS O.R. PROC W/O CC/MCC	1.7716	2.6	3.2	$9,626.59
SP	518	BACK & NECK PROC EXC SPINAL FUSION W MCC OR DISC DEVICE/NEUROSTIM	2.9249	3.8	5.8	$15,893.44
SP	519	BACK & NECK PROC EXC SPINAL FUSION W CC	1.6805	3.1	4.0	$9,131.57
SP	520	BACK & NECK PROC EXC SPINAL FUSION W/O CC/MCC	1.1812	1.9	2.3	$6,418.45
T	533	FRACTURES OF FEMUR W MCC	1.4430	4.5	6.0	$7,841.03
T	534	FRACTURES OF FEMUR W/O MCC	0.7353	2.9	3.5	$3,995.50
T	535	FRACTURES OF HIP & PELVIS W MCC	1.2235	4.0	5.1	$6,648.30
T	536	FRACTURES OF HIP & PELVIS W/O MCC	0.7241	3.0	3.4	$3,934.64
	537	SPRAINS, STRAINS, & DISLOCATIONS OF HIP, PELVIS & THIGH W CC/MCC	0.9046	3.3	3.9	$4,915.45
	538	SPRAINS, STRAINS, & DISLOCATIONS OF HIP, PELVIS & THIGH W/O CC/MCC	0.6282	2.5	2.9	$3,413.54
T	539	OSTEOMYELITIS W MCC	1.8365	6.0	7.8	$9,979.25
T	540	OSTEOMYELITIS W CC	1.2832	4.7	5.9	$6,972.70
T	541	OSTEOMYELITIS W/O CC/MCC	0.9098	3.4	4.3	$4,943.71
T	542	PATHOLOGICAL FRACTURES & MUSCULOSKELET & CONN TISS MALIG W MCC	1.9100	5.7	7.5	$10,378.63
T	543	PATHOLOGICAL FRACTURES & MUSCULOSKELET & CONN TISS MALIG W CC	1.1171	4.0	5.0	$6,070.14
T	544	PATHOLOGICAL FRACTURES & MUSCULOSKELET & CONN TISS MALIG W/O CC/MCC	0.7805	3.1	3.5	$4,241.11
T	545	CONNECTIVE TISSUE DISORDERS W MCC	2.4409	5.9	8.3	$13,263.46
T	546	CONNECTIVE TISSUE DISORDERS W CC	1.1645	3.8	4.8	$6,327.71
T	547	CONNECTIVE TISSUE DISORDERS W/O CC/MCC	0.7882	2.7	3.3	$4,282.95
	548	SEPTIC ARTHRITIS W MCC	1.8733	6.0	7.4	$10,179.21
	549	SEPTIC ARTHRITIS W CC	1.1824	4.2	5.3	$6,424.97
	550	SEPTIC ARTHRITIS W/O CC/MCC	0.8129	2.9	3.6	$4,417.17
T	551	MEDICAL BACK PROBLEMS W MCC	1.5573	4.6	5.9	$8,462.12
T	552	MEDICAL BACK PROBLEMS W/O MCC	0.8648	3.1	3.7	$4,699.18
	553	BONE DISEASES & ARTHROPATHIES W MCC	1.2287	4.1	5.3	$6,676.56
	554	BONE DISEASES & ARTHROPATHIES W/O MCC	0.7337	2.8	3.4	$3,986.81
	555	SIGNS & SYMPTOMS OF MUSCULOSKELETAL SYSTEM & CONN TISSUE W MCC	1.2656	3.7	5.0	$6,877.07
	556	SIGNS & SYMPTOMS OF MUSCULOSKELETAL SYSTEM & CONN TISSUE W/O MCC	0.7440	2.6	3.2	$4,042.78
T	557	TENDONITIS, MYOSITIS & BURSITIS W MCC	1.4295	4.8	6.0	$7,767.67
T	558	TENDONITIS, MYOSITIS & BURSITIS W/O MCC	0.8457	3.3	3.9	$4,595.40
T	559	AFTERCARE, MUSCULOSKELETAL SYSTEM & CONNECTIVE TISSUE W MCC	1.9202	5.0	7.0	$10,434.06
T	560	AFTERCARE, MUSCULOSKELETAL SYSTEM & CONNECTIVE TISSUE W CC	1.0814	3.5	4.4	$5,876.15
T	561	AFTERCARE, MUSCULOSKELETAL SYSTEM & CONNECTIVE TISSUE W/O CC/MCC	0.6842	2.1	2.6	$3,717.83
T	562	FX, SPRN, STRN & DISL EXCEPT FEMUR, HIP, PELVIS & THIGH W MCC	1.3662	4.2	5.3	$7,423.71
T	563	FX, SPRN, STRN & DISL EXCEPT FEMUR, HIP, PELVIS & THIGH W/O MCC	0.7870	3.0	3.5	$4,276.43
	564	OTHER MUSCULOSKELETAL SYS & CONNECTIVE TISSUE DIAGNOSES W MCC	1.5225	4.7	6.1	$8,273.02
	565	OTHER MUSCULOSKELETAL SYS & CONNECTIVE TISSUE DIAGNOSES W CC	0.9598	3.5	4.3	$5,215.40
	566	OTHER MUSCULOSKELETAL SYS & CONNECTIVE TISSUE DIAGNOSES W/O CC/MCC	0.7159	2.5	3.1	$3,890.09

Calculated with an average hospital Medicare base rate of $5,433.84. Each hospital's base rate and corresponding payment will vary. The national average hospital Medicare base rate is the sum of the full update labor-related and nonlabor-related amounts published in the *Federal Register*, FY 2016 Final Rule, Table 1A. National Adjusted Operating Standardized Amounts; Labor/Nonlabor (if wage index greater than 1) or Table 1B. National Adjusted Operating Standardized Amounts; Labor/Nonlabor (if wage index less than or equal to 1).

MS-DRGs 998 and 999 contain cases that could not be assigned to valid DRGs.

Note: If there is no value in either the geometric mean length of stay or the arithmetic mean length of stay columns, the volume of cases is insufficient to determine a meaningful computation of these statistics.

T **Transfer DRG**   SP **Special Payment**

DRG		Description	Relative Weight	GMLOS	AMLOS	National Payment Rate
T	570	SKIN DEBRIDEMENT W MCC	2.4504	7.0	9.2	$13,315.08
T	571	SKIN DEBRIDEMENT W CC	1.4569	5.2	6.3	$7,916.56
T	572	SKIN DEBRIDEMENT W/O CC/MCC	1.0391	3.7	4.5	$5,646.30
T	573	SKIN GRAFT FOR SKIN ULCER OR CELLULITIS W MCC	3.9130	8.6	12.9	$21,262.62
T	574	SKIN GRAFT FOR SKIN ULCER OR CELLULITIS W CC	2.8430	7.4	9.5	$15,448.41
T	575	SKIN GRAFT FOR SKIN ULCER OR CELLULITIS W/O CC/MCC	1.6141	4.4	5.6	$8,770.76
	576	SKIN GRAFT EXC FOR SKIN ULCER OR CELLULITIS W MCC	5.3493	8.9	13.6	$29,067.24
	577	SKIN GRAFT EXC FOR SKIN ULCER OR CELLULITIS W CC	2.2579	4.4	6.4	$12,269.07
	578	SKIN GRAFT EXC FOR SKIN ULCER OR CELLULITIS W/O CC/MCC	1.3812	2.6	3.7	$7,505.22
	579	OTHER SKIN, SUBCUT TISS & BREAST PROC W MCC	2.6848	7.0	9.1	$14,588.77
T	580	OTHER SKIN, SUBCUT TISS & BREAST PROC W CC	1.6155	4.0	5.3	$8,778.37
T	581	OTHER SKIN, SUBCUT TISS & BREAST PROC W/O CC/MCC	1.1834	2.2	2.8	$6,430.41
	582	MASTECTOMY FOR MALIGNANCY W CC/MCC	1.3370	2.2	2.9	$7,265.04
	583	MASTECTOMY FOR MALIGNANCY W/O CC/MCC	1.1856	1.6	1.9	$6,442.36
	584	BREAST BIOPSY, LOCAL EXCISION & OTHER BREAST PROCEDURES W CC/MCC	1.6794	3.7	5.0	$9,125.59
	585	BREAST BIOPSY, LOCAL EXCISION & OTHER BREAST PROCEDURES W/O CC/MCC	1.5184	2.1	2.5	$8,250.74
T	592	SKIN ULCERS W MCC	1.4255	5.0	6.4	$7,745.94
T	593	SKIN ULCERS W CC	1.0198	4.2	5.1	$5,541.43
T	594	SKIN ULCERS W/O CC/MCC	0.7049	3.1	3.7	$3,830.31
	595	MAJOR SKIN DISORDERS W MCC	1.8480	5.4	7.3	$10,041.74
	596	MAJOR SKIN DISORDERS W/O MCC	0.9375	3.6	4.4	$5,094.23
	597	MALIGNANT BREAST DISORDERS W MCC	1.7397	5.3	7.0	$9,453.25
	598	MALIGNANT BREAST DISORDERS W CC	1.0617	3.7	4.7	$5,769.11
	599	MALIGNANT BREAST DISORDERS W/O CC/MCC	0.7211	2.3	3.0	$3,918.34
	600	NON-MALIGNANT BREAST DISORDERS W CC/MCC	0.9843	3.7	4.6	$5,348.53
	601	NON-MALIGNANT BREAST DISORDERS W/O CC/MCC	0.6799	2.8	3.3	$3,694.47
T	602	CELLULITIS W MCC	1.4371	4.9	6.1	$7,808.97
T	603	CELLULITIS W/O MCC	0.8429	3.5	4.1	$4,580.18
	604	TRAUMA TO THE SKIN, SUBCUT TISS & BREAST W MCC	1.3527	3.9	5.1	$7,350.36
	605	TRAUMA TO THE SKIN, SUBCUT TISS & BREAST W/O MCC	0.8019	2.6	3.2	$4,357.40
	606	MINOR SKIN DISORDERS W MCC	1.3708	4.3	5.9	$7,448.71
	607	MINOR SKIN DISORDERS W/O MCC	0.7258	2.8	3.6	$3,943.88
	614	ADRENAL & PITUITARY PROCEDURES W CC/MCC	2.3916	3.9	5.4	$12,995.57
	615	ADRENAL & PITUITARY PROCEDURES W/O CC/MCC	1.4254	2.1	2.5	$7,745.40
T	616	AMPUTAT OF LOWER LIMB FOR ENDOCRINE,NUTRIT,& METABOL DIS W MCC	4.0054	10.3	12.6	$21,764.70
T	617	AMPUTAT OF LOWER LIMB FOR ENDOCRINE,NUTRIT,& METABOL DIS W CC	2.0064	6.0	7.2	$10,902.46
T	618	AMPUTAT OF LOWER LIMB FOR ENDOCRINE,NUTRIT,& METABOL DIS W/O CC/MCC	1.1804	4.3	5.0	$6,414.10
	619	O.R. PROCEDURES FOR OBESITY W MCC	2.9418	3.8	5.7	$15,985.27
	620	O.R. PROCEDURES FOR OBESITY W CC	1.8407	2.5	3.0	$10,002.07

Calculated with an average hospital Medicare base rate of $5,433.84. Each hospital's base rate and corresponding payment will vary. The national average hospital Medicare base rate is the sum of the full update labor-related and nonlabor-related amounts published in the *Federal Register*, FY 2016 Final Rule, Table 1A. National Adjusted Operating Standardized Amounts; Labor/Nonlabor (if wage index greater than 1) or Table 1B. National Adjusted Operating Standardized Amounts; Labor/Nonlabor (if wage index less than or equal to 1).

MS-DRGs 998 and 999 contain cases that could not be assigned to valid DRGs.

Note: If there is no value in either the geometric mean length of stay or the arithmetic mean length of stay columns, the volume of cases is insufficient to determine a meaningful computation of these statistics.

T Transfer DRG   SP Special Payment

	DRG	Description	Relative Weight	GMLOS	AMLOS	National Payment Rate
	621	O.R. PROCEDURES FOR OBESITY W/O CC/MCC	1.5484	1.8	1.9	$8,413.76
T	622	SKIN GRAFTS & WOUND DEBRID FOR ENDOC, NUTRIT & METAB DIS W MCC	3.5239	8.6	11.5	$19,148.31
T	623	SKIN GRAFTS & WOUND DEBRID FOR ENDOC, NUTRIT & METAB DIS W CC	1.8623	5.6	6.8	$10,119.44
T	624	SKIN GRAFTS & WOUND DEBRID FOR ENDOC, NUTRIT & METAB DIS W/O CC/MCC	1.1292	3.7	4.5	$6,135.89
	625	THYROID, PARATHYROID & THYROGLOSSAL PROCEDURES W MCC	2.6133	4.9	7.5	$14,200.25
	626	THYROID, PARATHYROID & THYROGLOSSAL PROCEDURES W CC	1.3936	2.2	3.2	$7,572.60
	627	THYROID, PARATHYROID & THYROGLOSSAL PROCEDURES W/O CC/MCC	0.9108	1.3	1.5	$4,949.14
T	628	OTHER ENDOCRINE, NUTRIT & METAB O.R. PROC W MCC	3.4413	7.0	9.8	$18,699.47
T	629	OTHER ENDOCRINE, NUTRIT & METAB O.R. PROC W CC	2.1952	6.1	7.2	$11,928.37
T	630	OTHER ENDOCRINE, NUTRIT & METAB O.R. PROC W/O CC/MCC	1.3601	3.0	3.9	$7,390.57
T	637	DIABETES W MCC	1.3823	4.1	5.3	$7,511.20
T	638	DIABETES W CC	0.8463	3.0	3.7	$4,598.66
T	639	DIABETES W/O CC/MCC	0.6007	2.2	2.6	$3,264.11
T	640	MISC DISORDERS OF NUTRITION,METABOLISM,FLUIDS/ELECTROLYTES W MCC	1.1318	3.3	4.5	$6,150.02
T	641	MISC DISORDERS OF NUTRITION,METABOLISM,FLUIDS/ELECTROLYTES W/O MCC	0.7221	2.7	3.3	$3,923.78
	642	INBORN AND OTHER DISORDERS OF METABOLISM	1.2246	3.4	4.5	$6,654.28
T	643	ENDOCRINE DISORDERS W MCC	1.6249	5.3	6.7	$8,829.45
T	644	ENDOCRINE DISORDERS W CC	1.0123	3.7	4.6	$5,500.68
T	645	ENDOCRINE DISORDERS W/O CC/MCC	0.7255	2.8	3.4	$3,942.25
	652	KIDNEY TRANSPLANT	3.1540	5.5	6.5	$17,138.33
T	653	MAJOR BLADDER PROCEDURES W MCC	6.0456	11.9	14.8	$32,850.82
T	654	MAJOR BLADDER PROCEDURES W CC	3.0267	7.2	8.2	$16,446.60
T	655	MAJOR BLADDER PROCEDURES W/O CC/MCC	2.2796	4.8	5.4	$12,386.98
	656	KIDNEY & URETER PROCEDURES FOR NEOPLASM W MCC	3.4617	6.8	8.8	$18,810.32
	657	KIDNEY & URETER PROCEDURES FOR NEOPLASM W CC	2.0091	4.2	5.0	$10,917.13
	658	KIDNEY & URETER PROCEDURES FOR NEOPLASM W/O CC/MCC	1.5337	2.6	3.0	$8,333.88
T	659	KIDNEY & URETER PROCEDURES FOR NON-NEOPLASM W MCC	3.4848	7.5	10.1	$18,935.85
T	660	KIDNEY & URETER PROCEDURES FOR NON-NEOPLASM W CC	1.9030	4.1	5.5	$10,340.60
T	661	KIDNEY & URETER PROCEDURES FOR NON-NEOPLASM W/O CC/MCC	1.3981	2.3	2.7	$7,597.05
	662	MINOR BLADDER PROCEDURES W MCC	2.8897	7.6	10.0	$15,702.17
	663	MINOR BLADDER PROCEDURES W CC	1.6652	4.1	5.4	$9,048.43
	664	MINOR BLADDER PROCEDURES W/O CC/MCC	1.2987	2.0	2.5	$7,056.93
	665	PROSTATECTOMY W MCC	3.1132	8.9	11.2	$16,916.63
	666	PROSTATECTOMY W CC	1.7878	4.6	6.3	$9,714.62
	667	PROSTATECTOMY W/O CC/MCC	0.9964	2.3	3.0	$5,414.28
	668	TRANSURETHRAL PROCEDURES W MCC	2.4521	6.3	8.4	$13,324.32
	669	TRANSURETHRAL PROCEDURES W CC	1.3111	3.1	4.1	$7,124.31
	670	TRANSURETHRAL PROCEDURES W/O CC/MCC	0.9207	2.1	2.6	$5,002.94
	671	URETHRAL PROCEDURES W CC/MCC	1.5705	4.1	5.4	$8,533.85

Calculated with an average hospital Medicare base rate of $5,433.84. Each hospital's base rate and corresponding payment will vary. The national average hospital Medicare base rate is the sum of the full update labor-related and nonlabor-related amounts published in the *Federal Register*, FY 2016 Final Rule, Table 1A. National Adjusted Operating Standardized Amounts; Labor/Nonlabor (if wage index greater than 1) or Table 1B. National Adjusted Operating Standardized Amounts; Labor/Nonlabor (if wage index less than or equal to 1).

MS-DRGs 998 and 999 contain cases that could not be assigned to valid DRGs.

Note: If there is no value in either the geometric mean length of stay or the arithmetic mean length of stay columns, the volume of cases is insufficient to determine a meaningful computation of these statistics.

T Transfer DRG   SP Special Payment

DRG		Description	Relative Weight	GMLOS	AMLOS	National Payment Rate
	672	URETHRAL PROCEDURES W/O CC/MCC	0.8742	1.9	2.4	$4,750.26
	673	OTHER KIDNEY & URINARY TRACT PROCEDURES W MCC	3.3559	7.3	10.3	$18,235.42
	674	OTHER KIDNEY & URINARY TRACT PROCEDURES W CC	2.3148	5.4	7.1	$12,578.25
	675	OTHER KIDNEY & URINARY TRACT PROCEDURES W/O CC/MCC	1.5595	2.4	3.2	$8,474.07
T	682	RENAL FAILURE W MCC	1.5085	4.6	6.0	$8,196.95
T	683	RENAL FAILURE W CC	0.9406	3.5	4.3	$5,111.07
T	684	RENAL FAILURE W/O CC/MCC	0.6272	2.5	2.9	$3,408.10
	685	ADMIT FOR RENAL DIALYSIS	1.0369	2.9	3.8	$5,634.35
	686	KIDNEY & URINARY TRACT NEOPLASMS W MCC	1.6670	5.3	7.0	$9,058.21
	687	KIDNEY & URINARY TRACT NEOPLASMS W CC	1.0161	3.5	4.4	$5,521.32
	688	KIDNEY & URINARY TRACT NEOPLASMS W/O CC/MCC	0.6607	2.2	2.8	$3,590.14
T	689	KIDNEY & URINARY TRACT INFECTIONS W MCC	1.0821	4.0	5.0	$5,879.96
T	690	KIDNEY & URINARY TRACT INFECTIONS W/O MCC	0.7828	3.1	3.7	$4,253.61
	691	URINARY STONES W ESW LITHOTRIPSY W CC/MCC	1.5470	2.8	3.7	$8,406.15
	692	URINARY STONES W ESW LITHOTRIPSY W/O CC/MCC	1.2566	1.9	2.3	$6,828.16
	693	URINARY STONES W/O ESW LITHOTRIPSY W MCC	1.3323	3.8	4.9	$7,239.51
	694	URINARY STONES W/O ESW LITHOTRIPSY W/O MCC	0.7294	2.0	2.5	$3,963.44
	695	KIDNEY & URINARY TRACT SIGNS & SYMPTOMS W MCC	1.2494	4.1	5.2	$6,789.04
	696	KIDNEY & URINARY TRACT SIGNS & SYMPTOMS W/O MCC	0.6934	2.6	3.2	$3,767.82
	697	URETHRAL STRICTURE	0.9417	2.8	3.6	$5,117.05
T	698	OTHER KIDNEY & URINARY TRACT DIAGNOSES W MCC	1.5524	5.0	6.3	$8,435.49
T	699	OTHER KIDNEY & URINARY TRACT DIAGNOSES W CC	1.0246	3.5	4.4	$5,567.51
T	700	OTHER KIDNEY & URINARY TRACT DIAGNOSES W/O CC/MCC	0.7163	2.6	3.2	$3,892.26
	707	MAJOR MALE PELVIC PROCEDURES W CC/MCC	1.7753	2.8	3.8	$9,646.70
	708	MAJOR MALE PELVIC PROCEDURES W/O CC/MCC	1.3146	1.4	1.6	$7,143.33
	709	PENIS PROCEDURES W CC/MCC	1.9721	4.0	5.9	$10,716.08
	710	PENIS PROCEDURES W/O CC/MCC	1.4170	1.8	2.4	$7,699.75
	711	TESTES PROCEDURES W CC/MCC	1.9959	5.2	7.3	$10,845.40
	712	TESTES PROCEDURES W/O CC/MCC	0.9475	2.3	3.0	$5,148.56
	713	TRANSURETHRAL PROSTATECTOMY W CC/MCC	1.5077	3.4	4.7	$8,192.60
	714	TRANSURETHRAL PROSTATECTOMY W/O CC/MCC	0.8072	1.7	2.0	$4,386.20
	715	OTHER MALE REPRODUCTIVE SYSTEM O.R. PROC FOR MALIGNANCY W CC/MCC	1.8793	5.2	7.0	$10,211.82
	716	OTHER MALE REPRODUCTIVE SYSTEM O.R. PROC FOR MALIGNANCY W/O CC/MCC	1.1508	1.6	2.0	$6,253.26
	717	OTHER MALE REPRODUCTIVE SYSTEM O.R. PROC EXC MALIGNANCY W CC/MCC	1.7645	4.7	6.3	$9,588.01
	718	OTHER MALE REPRODUCTIVE SYSTEM O.R. PROC EXC MALIGNANCY W/O CC/MCC	0.9069	2.1	2.5	$4,927.95
	722	MALIGNANCY, MALE REPRODUCTIVE SYSTEM W MCC	1.7370	5.5	7.3	$9,438.58
	723	MALIGNANCY, MALE REPRODUCTIVE SYSTEM W CC	1.0979	3.8	4.8	$5,965.81
	724	MALIGNANCY, MALE REPRODUCTIVE SYSTEM W/O CC/MCC	0.6545	2.0	2.9	$3,556.45
	725	BENIGN PROSTATIC HYPERTROPHY W MCC	1.3198	4.5	5.8	$7,171.58

Calculated with an average hospital Medicare base rate of $5,433.84. Each hospital's base rate and corresponding payment will vary. The national average hospital Medicare base rate is the sum of the full update labor-related and nonlabor-related amounts published in the *Federal Register*, FY 2016 Final Rule, Table 1A. National Adjusted Operating Standardized Amounts; Labor/Nonlabor (if wage index greater than 1) or Table 1B. National Adjusted Operating Standardized Amounts; Labor/Nonlabor (if wage index less than or equal to 1).

MS-DRGs 998 and 999 contain cases that could not be assigned to valid DRGs.

Note: If there is no value in either the geometric mean length of stay or the arithmetic mean length of stay columns, the volume of cases is insufficient to determine a meaningful computation of these statistics.

T **Transfer DRG**   SP **Special Payment**

DRG	Description	Relative Weight	GMLOS	AMLOS	National Payment Rate
726	BENIGN PROSTATIC HYPERTROPHY W/O MCC	0.7406	2.7	3.3	$4,024.30
727	INFLAMMATION OF THE MALE REPRODUCTIVE SYSTEM W MCC	1.4461	4.9	6.2	$7,857.88
728	INFLAMMATION OF THE MALE REPRODUCTIVE SYSTEM W/O MCC	0.7838	3.1	3.8	$4,259.04
729	OTHER MALE REPRODUCTIVE SYSTEM DIAGNOSES W CC/MCC	1.1169	3.5	4.6	$6,069.06
730	OTHER MALE REPRODUCTIVE SYSTEM DIAGNOSES W/O CC/MCC	0.6036	2.3	2.9	$3,279.87
734	PELVIC EVISCERATION, RAD HYSTERECTOMY & RAD VULVECTOMY W CC/MCC	2.5255	4.5	6.4	$13,723.16
735	PELVIC EVISCERATION, RAD HYSTERECTOMY & RAD VULVECTOMY W/O CC/MCC	1.2207	1.8	2.2	$6,633.09
736	UTERINE & ADNEXA PROC FOR OVARIAN OR ADNEXAL MALIGNANCY W MCC	4.3286	9.9	12.3	$23,520.92
737	UTERINE & ADNEXA PROC FOR OVARIAN OR ADNEXAL MALIGNANCY W CC	2.0037	5.1	5.9	$10,887.79
738	UTERINE & ADNEXA PROC FOR OVARIAN OR ADNEXAL MALIGNANCY W/O CC/MCC	1.3498	3.0	3.4	$7,334.60
739	UTERINE,ADNEXA PROC FOR NON-OVARIAN/ADNEXAL MALIG W MCC	3.4082	6.6	9.0	$18,519.61
740	UTERINE,ADNEXA PROC FOR NON-OVARIAN/ADNEXAL MALIG W CC	1.6920	3.3	4.2	$9,194.06
741	UTERINE,ADNEXA PROC FOR NON-OVARIAN/ADNEXAL MALIG W/O CC/MCC	1.1973	1.8	2.2	$6,505.94
742	UTERINE & ADNEXA PROC FOR NON-MALIGNANCY W CC/MCC	1.5586	3.0	4.0	$8,469.18
743	UTERINE & ADNEXA PROC FOR NON-MALIGNANCY W/O CC/MCC	1.0090	1.8	2.0	$5,482.74
744	D&C, CONIZATION, LAPAROSCOPY & TUBAL INTERRUPTION W CC/MCC	1.6851	4.1	5.8	$9,156.56
745	D&C, CONIZATION, LAPAROSCOPY & TUBAL INTERRUPTION W/O CC/MCC	0.9719	2.0	2.4	$5,281.15
746	VAGINA, CERVIX & VULVA PROCEDURES W CC/MCC	1.4628	3.3	4.8	$7,948.62
747	VAGINA, CERVIX & VULVA PROCEDURES W/O CC/MCC	0.9099	1.6	1.9	$4,944.25
748	FEMALE REPRODUCTIVE SYSTEM RECONSTRUCTIVE PROCEDURES	1.1241	1.6	2.0	$6,108.18
749	OTHER FEMALE REPRODUCTIVE SYSTEM O.R. PROCEDURES W CC/MCC	2.6452	6.1	8.5	$14,373.59
750	OTHER FEMALE REPRODUCTIVE SYSTEM O.R. PROCEDURES W/O CC/MCC	1.3346	2.4	3.1	$7,252.00
754	MALIGNANCY, FEMALE REPRODUCTIVE SYSTEM W MCC	1.9204	5.8	7.9	$10,435.15
755	MALIGNANCY, FEMALE REPRODUCTIVE SYSTEM W CC	1.1325	3.7	4.9	$6,153.82
756	MALIGNANCY, FEMALE REPRODUCTIVE SYSTEM W/O CC/MCC	0.5908	2.2	2.8	$3,210.31
757	INFECTIONS, FEMALE REPRODUCTIVE SYSTEM W MCC	1.3717	5.2	6.4	$7,453.60
758	INFECTIONS, FEMALE REPRODUCTIVE SYSTEM W CC	1.0090	4.1	5.0	$5,482.74
759	INFECTIONS, FEMALE REPRODUCTIVE SYSTEM W/O CC/MCC	0.7595	3.2	3.8	$4,127.00
760	MENSTRUAL & OTHER FEMALE REPRODUCTIVE SYSTEM DISORDERS W CC/MCC	0.8524	2.8	3.6	$4,631.81
761	MENSTRUAL & OTHER FEMALE REPRODUCTIVE SYSTEM DISORDERS W/O CC/MCC	0.5355	1.9	2.2	$2,909.82
765	CESAREAN SECTION W CC/MCC	1.1442	3.7	4.7	$6,217.40
766	CESAREAN SECTION W/O CC/MCC	0.7807	2.8	3.0	$4,242.20
767	VAGINAL DELIVERY W STERILIZATION &/OR D&C	1.2965	2.7	3.8	$7,044.97
768	VAGINAL DELIVERY W O.R. PROC EXCEPT STERIL &/OR D&C	1.2618	3.6	4.3	$6,856.42
769	POSTPARTUM & POST ABORTION DIAGNOSES W O.R. PROCEDURE	2.1737	4.4	6.5	$11,811.54
770	ABORTION W D&C, ASPIRATION CURETTAGE OR HYSTEROTOMY	0.8272	1.9	2.4	$4,494.87
774	VAGINAL DELIVERY W COMPLICATING DIAGNOSES	0.7509	2.6	3.1	$4,080.27
775	VAGINAL DELIVERY W/O COMPLICATING DIAGNOSES	0.5865	2.1	2.3	$3,186.95
776	POSTPARTUM & POST ABORTION DIAGNOSES W/O O.R. PROCEDURE	0.6766	2.4	3.2	$3,676.54

Calculated with an average hospital Medicare base rate of $5,433.84. Each hospital's base rate and corresponding payment will vary. The national average hospital Medicare base rate is the sum of the full update labor-related and nonlabor-related amounts published in the *Federal Register*, FY 2016 Final Rule, Table 1A. National Adjusted Operating Standardized Amounts; Labor/Nonlabor (if wage index greater than 1) or Table 1B. National Adjusted Operating Standardized Amounts; Labor/Nonlabor (if wage index less than or equal to 1).

MS-DRGs 998 and 999 contain cases that could not be assigned to valid DRGs.

Note: If there is no value in either the geometric mean length of stay or the arithmetic mean length of stay columns, the volume of cases is insufficient to determine a meaningful computation of these statistics.

T Transfer DRG   SP Special Payment

DRG	Description	Relative Weight	GMLOS	AMLOS	National Payment Rate
777	ECTOPIC PREGNANCY	0.9386	1.9	2.3	$5,100.20
778	THREATENED ABORTION	0.5332	2.0	3.1	$2,897.32
779	ABORTION W/O D&C	0.6850	1.7	2.2	$3,722.18
780	FALSE LABOR	0.2062	1.1	1.1	$1,120.46
781	OTHER ANTEPARTUM DIAGNOSES W MEDICAL COMPLICATIONS	0.8182	2.7	4.0	$4,445.97
782	OTHER ANTEPARTUM DIAGNOSES W/O MEDICAL COMPLICATIONS	0.5454	1.7	2.5	$2,963.62
789	NEONATES, DIED OR TRANSFERRED TO ANOTHER ACUTE CARE FACILITY	1.5860	1.8	1.8	$8,618.07
790	EXTREME IMMATURITY OR RESPIRATORY DISTRESS SYNDROME, NEONATE	5.2300	17.9	17.9	$28,418.98
791	PREMATURITY W MAJOR PROBLEMS	3.5719	13.3	13.3	$19,409.13
792	PREMATURITY W/O MAJOR PROBLEMS	2.1552	8.6	8.6	$11,711.01
793	FULL TERM NEONATE W MAJOR PROBLEMS	3.6692	4.7	4.7	$19,937.85
794	NEONATE W OTHER SIGNIFICANT PROBLEMS	1.2987	3.4	3.4	$7,056.93
795	NORMAL NEWBORN	0.1758	3.1	3.1	$955.27
799	SPLENECTOMY W MCC	4.7569	9.2	11.6	$25,848.23
800	SPLENECTOMY W CC	2.7364	5.3	6.8	$14,869.16
801	SPLENECTOMY W/O CC/MCC	1.7458	2.8	3.7	$9,486.40
802	OTHER O.R. PROC OF THE BLOOD & BLOOD FORMING ORGANS W MCC	3.3880	8.1	11.1	$18,409.85
803	OTHER O.R. PROC OF THE BLOOD & BLOOD FORMING ORGANS W CC	1.8719	4.7	6.0	$10,171.61
804	OTHER O.R. PROC OF THE BLOOD & BLOOD FORMING ORGANS W/O CC/MCC	1.1715	2.3	3.0	$6,365.74
808	MAJOR HEMATOL/IMMUN DIAG EXC SICKLE CELL CRISIS & COAGUL W MCC	2.2346	6.0	8.0	$12,142.46
809	MAJOR HEMATOL/IMMUN DIAG EXC SICKLE CELL CRISIS & COAGUL W CC	1.2235	3.8	4.7	$6,648.30
810	MAJOR HEMATOL/IMMUN DIAG EXC SICKLE CELL CRISIS & COAGUL W/O CC/MCC	0.8644	2.7	3.3	$4,697.01
811	RED BLOOD CELL DISORDERS W MCC	1.2992	3.7	4.9	$7,059.64
812	RED BLOOD CELL DISORDERS W/O MCC	0.8572	2.8	3.5	$4,657.89
813	COAGULATION DISORDERS	1.7350	3.7	5.1	$9,427.71
814	RETICULOENDOTHELIAL & IMMUNITY DISORDERS W MCC	1.6622	4.7	6.4	$9,032.13
815	RETICULOENDOTHELIAL & IMMUNITY DISORDERS W CC	0.9803	3.2	4.1	$5,326.79
816	RETICULOENDOTHELIAL & IMMUNITY DISORDERS W/O CC/MCC	0.6962	2.4	2.9	$3,783.04
820	LYMPHOMA & LEUKEMIA W MAJOR O.R. PROCEDURE W MCC	5.9153	12.1	16.2	$32,142.79
821	LYMPHOMA & LEUKEMIA W MAJOR O.R. PROCEDURE W CC	2.3113	4.7	6.5	$12,559.23
822	LYMPHOMA & LEUKEMIA W MAJOR O.R. PROCEDURE W/O CC/MCC	1.2851	2.1	2.7	$6,983.03
823	LYMPHOMA & NON-ACUTE LEUKEMIA W OTHER O.R. PROC W MCC	4.4536	11.1	14.3	$24,200.15
824	LYMPHOMA & NON-ACUTE LEUKEMIA W OTHER O.R. PROC W CC	2.3467	6.0	7.9	$12,751.59
825	LYMPHOMA & NON-ACUTE LEUKEMIA W OTHER O.R. PROC W/O CC/MCC	1.3967	2.9	3.9	$7,589.44
826	MYELOPROLIF DISORD OR POORLY DIFF NEOPL W MAJ O.R. PROC W MCC	5.1814	10.8	14.3	$28,154.90
827	MYELOPROLIF DISORD OR POORLY DIFF NEOPL W MAJ O.R. PROC W CC	2.3141	5.0	6.5	$12,574.45
828	MYELOPROLIF DISORD OR POORLY DIFF NEOPL W MAJ O.R. PROC W/O CC/MCC	1.5139	2.8	3.5	$8,226.29
829	MYELOPROLIF DISORD OR POORLY DIFF NEOPL W OTHER O.R. PROC W CC/MCC	3.3241	6.8	10.2	$18,062.63
830	MYELOPROLIF DISORD OR POORLY DIFF NEOPL W OTHER O.R. PROC W/O CC/MCC	1.3670	2.6	3.5	$7,428.06

Calculated with an average hospital Medicare base rate of $5,433.84. Each hospital's base rate and corresponding payment will vary. The national average hospital Medicare base rate is the sum of the full update labor-related and nonlabor-related amounts published in the *Federal Register*, FY 2016 Final Rule, Table 1A. National Adjusted Operating Standardized Amounts; Labor/Nonlabor (if wage index greater than 1) or Table 1B. National Adjusted Operating Standardized Amounts; Labor/Nonlabor (if wage index less than or equal to 1).

MS-DRGs 998 and 999 contain cases that could not be assigned to valid DRGs.

Note: If there is no value in either the geometric mean length of stay or the arithmetic mean length of stay columns, the volume of cases is insufficient to determine a meaningful computation of these statistics.

Ⓣ **Transfer DRG**   ˢᴾ **Special Payment**

DRG		Description	Relative Weight	GMLOS	AMLOS	National Payment Rate
	834	ACUTE LEUKEMIA W/O MAJOR O.R. PROCEDURE W MCC	5.5990	10.4	17.2	$30,424.07
	835	ACUTE LEUKEMIA W/O MAJOR O.R. PROCEDURE W CC	2.3024	4.9	7.7	$12,510.87
	836	ACUTE LEUKEMIA W/O MAJOR O.R. PROCEDURE W/O CC/MCC	1.1381	2.9	4.0	$6,184.25
	837	CHEMO W ACUTE LEUKEMIA AS SDX OR W HIGH DOSE CHEMO AGENT W MCC	6.1348	15.7	21.6	$33,335.52
	838	CHEMO W ACUTE LEUKEMIA AS SDX W CC OR HIGH DOSE CHEMO AGENT	2.7707	7.0	9.8	$15,055.54
	839	CHEMO W ACUTE LEUKEMIA AS SDX W/O CC/MCC	1.3190	4.9	5.5	$7,167.23
T	840	LYMPHOMA & NON-ACUTE LEUKEMIA W MCC	3.1449	7.6	10.4	$17,088.88
T	841	LYMPHOMA & NON-ACUTE LEUKEMIA W CC	1.6118	4.7	6.6	$8,758.26
T	842	LYMPHOMA & NON-ACUTE LEUKEMIA W/O CC/MCC	1.1167	3.1	4.0	$6,067.97
	843	OTHER MYELOPROLIF DIS OR POORLY DIFF NEOPL DIAG W MCC	1.8464	5.6	7.6	$10,033.04
	844	OTHER MYELOPROLIF DIS OR POORLY DIFF NEOPL DIAG W CC	1.1233	4.0	5.1	$6,103.83
	845	OTHER MYELOPROLIF DIS OR POORLY DIFF NEOPL DIAG W/O CC/MCC	0.8261	2.8	3.6	$4,488.90
	846	CHEMOTHERAPY W/O ACUTE LEUKEMIA AS SECONDARY DIAGNOSIS W MCC	2.4618	5.9	8.0	$13,377.03
	847	CHEMOTHERAPY W/O ACUTE LEUKEMIA AS SECONDARY DIAGNOSIS W CC	1.1883	3.4	3.9	$6,457.03
	848	CHEMOTHERAPY W/O ACUTE LEUKEMIA AS SECONDARY DIAGNOSIS W/O CC/MCC	0.9352	2.8	3.3	$5,081.73
	849	RADIOTHERAPY	1.6745	4.9	6.5	$9,098.97
T	853	INFECTIOUS & PARASITIC DISEASES W O.R. PROCEDURE W MCC	5.1334	10.7	13.7	$27,894.07
T	854	INFECTIOUS & PARASITIC DISEASES W O.R. PROCEDURE W CC	2.3804	6.6	7.9	$12,934.71
T	855	INFECTIOUS & PARASITIC DISEASES W O.R. PROCEDURE W/O CC/MCC	1.5124	3.5	4.7	$8,218.14
T	856	POSTOPERATIVE OR POST-TRAUMATIC INFECTIONS W O.R. PROC W MCC	4.6569	9.8	12.8	$25,304.85
T	857	POSTOPERATIVE OR POST-TRAUMATIC INFECTIONS W O.R. PROC W CC	2.0516	5.6	7.0	$11,148.07
T	858	POSTOPERATIVE OR POST-TRAUMATIC INFECTIONS W O.R. PROC W/O CC/MCC	1.3300	3.8	4.5	$7,227.01
T	862	POSTOPERATIVE & POST-TRAUMATIC INFECTIONS W MCC	1.8550	5.5	7.1	$10,079.77
T	863	POSTOPERATIVE & POST-TRAUMATIC INFECTIONS W/O MCC	1.0089	3.7	4.5	$5,482.20
	864	FEVER	0.8481	2.8	3.5	$4,608.44
	865	VIRAL ILLNESS W MCC	1.5273	4.2	5.9	$8,299.10
	866	VIRAL ILLNESS W/O MCC	0.7739	2.8	3.4	$4,205.25
T	867	OTHER INFECTIOUS & PARASITIC DISEASES DIAGNOSES W MCC	2.6068	6.7	9.0	$14,164.93
T	868	OTHER INFECTIOUS & PARASITIC DISEASES DIAGNOSES W CC	1.0292	3.8	4.7	$5,592.51
T	869	OTHER INFECTIOUS & PARASITIC DISEASES DIAGNOSES W/O CC/MCC	0.7091	2.8	3.4	$3,853.14
T	870	SEPTICEMIA OR SEVERE SEPSIS W MV >96 HOURS	5.8782	12.6	14.6	$31,941.20
T	871	SEPTICEMIA OR SEVERE SEPSIS W/O MV >96 HOURS W MCC	1.7926	5.0	6.5	$9,740.70
T	872	SEPTICEMIA OR SEVERE SEPSIS W/O MV >96 HOURS W/O MCC	1.0427	3.9	4.6	$5,665.86
	876	O.R. PROCEDURE W PRINCIPAL DIAGNOSES OF MENTAL ILLNESS	3.0841	7.8	13.5	$16,758.51
	880	ACUTE ADJUSTMENT REACTION & PSYCHOSOCIAL DYSFUNCTION	0.7227	2.4	3.3	$3,927.04
	881	DEPRESSIVE NEUROSES	0.6618	3.4	4.5	$3,596.12
	882	NEUROSES EXCEPT DEPRESSIVE	0.6924	3.3	4.5	$3,762.39
	883	DISORDERS OF PERSONALITY & IMPULSE CONTROL	1.3737	4.6	8.0	$7,464.47

Calculated with an average hospital Medicare base rate of $5,433.84. Each hospital's base rate and corresponding payment will vary. The national average hospital Medicare base rate is the sum of the full update labor-related and nonlabor-related amounts published in the *Federal Register*, FY 2016 Final Rule, Table 1A. National Adjusted Operating Standardized Amounts; Labor/Nonlabor (if wage index greater than 1) or Table 1B. National Adjusted Operating Standardized Amounts; Labor/Nonlabor (if wage index less than or equal to 1).

MS-DRGs 998 and 999 contain cases that could not be assigned to valid DRGs.

Note: If there is no value in either the geometric mean length of stay or the arithmetic mean length of stay columns, the volume of cases is insufficient to determine a meaningful computation of these statistics.

T **Transfer DRG**   SP **Special Payment**

DRG		Description	Relative Weight	GMLOS	AMLOS	National Payment Rate
Ⓣ	884	ORGANIC DISTURBANCES & MENTAL RETARDATION	1.1483	4.3	6.3	$6,239.68
	885	PSYCHOSES	1.0575	5.6	7.7	$5,746.29
	886	BEHAVIORAL & DEVELOPMENTAL DISORDERS	0.8718	3.9	6.0	$4,737.22
	887	OTHER MENTAL DISORDER DIAGNOSES	0.9939	3.0	4.6	$5,400.69
	894	ALCOHOL/DRUG ABUSE OR DEPENDENCE, LEFT AMA	0.4859	2.1	3.1	$2,640.30
	895	ALCOHOL/DRUG ABUSE OR DEPENDENCE W REHABILITATION THERAPY	1.2435	9.3	12.0	$6,756.98
Ⓣ	896	ALCOHOL/DRUG ABUSE OR DEPENDENCE W/O REHABILITATION THERAPY W MCC	1.5678	4.8	6.6	$8,519.17
Ⓣ	897	ALCOHOL/DRUG ABUSE OR DEPENDENCE W/O REHABILITATION THERAPY W/O MCC	0.7231	3.3	4.1	$3,929.21
	901	WOUND DEBRIDEMENTS FOR INJURIES W MCC	3.9370	9.2	13.3	$21,393.03
	902	WOUND DEBRIDEMENTS FOR INJURIES W CC	1.8265	5.3	7.1	$9,924.91
	903	WOUND DEBRIDEMENTS FOR INJURIES W/O CC/MCC	1.1723	3.3	4.3	$6,370.09
	904	SKIN GRAFTS FOR INJURIES W CC/MCC	3.2140	7.1	10.4	$17,464.36
	905	SKIN GRAFTS FOR INJURIES W/O CC/MCC	1.4233	3.6	4.7	$7,733.98
	906	HAND PROCEDURES FOR INJURIES	1.5670	2.8	4.4	$8,514.83
Ⓣ	907	OTHER O.R. PROCEDURES FOR INJURIES W MCC	3.8073	7.5	10.3	$20,688.26
Ⓣ	908	OTHER O.R. PROCEDURES FOR INJURIES W CC	1.9904	4.3	5.7	$10,815.52
Ⓣ	909	OTHER O.R. PROCEDURES FOR INJURIES W/O CC/MCC	1.2992	2.6	3.3	$7,059.64
	913	TRAUMATIC INJURY W MCC	1.3561	3.8	5.1	$7,368.83
	914	TRAUMATIC INJURY W/O MCC	0.7317	2.5	3.1	$3,975.94
	915	ALLERGIC REACTIONS W MCC	1.6040	3.7	5.1	$8,715.88
	916	ALLERGIC REACTIONS W/O MCC	0.5582	1.8	2.2	$3,033.17
Ⓣ	917	POISONING & TOXIC EFFECTS OF DRUGS W MCC	1.4065	3.5	4.8	$7,642.70
Ⓣ	918	POISONING & TOXIC EFFECTS OF DRUGS W/O MCC	0.6859	2.2	2.9	$3,727.07
	919	COMPLICATIONS OF TREATMENT W MCC	1.7611	4.5	6.2	$9,569.54
	920	COMPLICATIONS OF TREATMENT W CC	0.9991	3.1	4.0	$5,428.95
	921	COMPLICATIONS OF TREATMENT W/O CC/MCC	0.6960	2.3	2.8	$3,781.95
	922	OTHER INJURY, POISONING & TOXIC EFFECT DIAG W MCC	1.5833	4.0	6.0	$8,603.40
	923	OTHER INJURY, POISONING & TOXIC EFFECT DIAG W/O MCC	0.8117	2.5	3.5	$4,410.65
	927	EXTENSIVE BURNS OR FULL THICKNESS BURNS W MV >96 HRS W SKIN GRAFT	15.9672	23.5	30.6	$86,763.21
	928	FULL THICKNESS BURN W SKIN GRAFT OR INHAL INJ W CC/MCC	5.7399	11.3	15.4	$31,189.70
	929	FULL THICKNESS BURN W SKIN GRAFT OR INHAL INJ W/O CC/MCC	2.4661	5.5	7.5	$13,400.39
	933	EXTENSIVE BURNS OR FULL THICKNESS BURNS W MV >96 HRS W/O SKIN GRAFT	2.8685	2.6	5.9	$15,586.97
	934	FULL THICKNESS BURN W/O SKIN GRFT OR INHAL INJ	1.6716	4.2	6.2	$9,083.21
	935	NON-EXTENSIVE BURNS	1.5141	3.4	5.1	$8,227.38
	939	O.R. PROC W DIAGNOSES OF OTHER CONTACT W HEALTH SERVICES W MCC	2.9866	6.2	9.1	$16,228.71
	940	O.R. PROC W DIAGNOSES OF OTHER CONTACT W HEALTH SERVICES W CC	1.9107	3.7	5.2	$10,382.44
	941	O.R. PROC W DIAGNOSES OF OTHER CONTACT W HEALTH SERVICES W/O CC/MCC	1.3589	2.1	2.7	$7,384.05
Ⓣ	945	REHABILITATION W CC/MCC	1.2781	8.8	10.9	$6,944.99

Calculated with an average hospital Medicare base rate of $5,433.84. Each hospital's base rate and corresponding payment will vary. The national average hospital Medicare base rate is the sum of the full update labor-related and nonlabor-related amounts published in the *Federal Register*, FY 2016 Final Rule, Table 1A. National Adjusted Operating Standardized Amounts; Labor/Nonlabor (if wage index greater than 1) or Table 1B. National Adjusted Operating Standardized Amounts; Labor/Nonlabor (if wage index less than or equal to 1).

MS-DRGs 998 and 999 contain cases that could not be assigned to valid DRGs.

Note: If there is no value in either the geometric mean length of stay or the arithmetic mean length of stay columns, the volume of cases is insufficient to determine a meaningful computation of these statistics.

Ⓣ **Transfer DRG**   SP **Special Payment**

DRG		Description	Relative Weight	GMLOS	AMLOS	National Payment Rate
T	946	REHABILITATION W/O CC/MCC	1.0151	6.8	7.8	$5,515.89
T	947	SIGNS & SYMPTOMS W MCC	1.1323	3.5	4.7	$6,152.74
T	948	SIGNS & SYMPTOMS W/O MCC	0.7356	2.7	3.3	$3,997.13
	949	AFTERCARE W CC/MCC	1.1197	3.3	5.1	$6,084.27
	950	AFTERCARE W/O CC/MCC	0.5798	2.3	2.9	$3,150.54
	951	OTHER FACTORS INFLUENCING HEALTH STATUS	0.9885	2.7	6.0	$5,371.35
	955	CRANIOTOMY FOR MULTIPLE SIGNIFICANT TRAUMA	5.6773	8.4	11.9	$30,849.54
T	956	LIMB REATTACHMENT, HIP & FEMUR PROC FOR MULTIPLE SIGNIFICANT TRAUMA	3.7116	6.4	7.8	$20,168.24
	957	OTHER O.R. PROCEDURES FOR MULTIPLE SIGNIFICANT TRAUMA W MCC	6.5504	9.4	13.3	$35,593.83
	958	OTHER O.R. PROCEDURES FOR MULTIPLE SIGNIFICANT TRAUMA W CC	3.8565	6.9	8.4	$20,955.60
	959	OTHER O.R. PROCEDURES FOR MULTIPLE SIGNIFICANT TRAUMA W/O CC/MCC	2.1705	4.2	4.8	$11,794.15
	963	OTHER MULTIPLE SIGNIFICANT TRAUMA W MCC	2.6295	5.4	8.0	$14,288.28
	964	OTHER MULTIPLE SIGNIFICANT TRAUMA W CC	1.4205	4.1	5.0	$7,718.77
	965	OTHER MULTIPLE SIGNIFICANT TRAUMA W/O CC/MCC	0.9217	3.0	3.5	$5,008.37
	969	HIV W EXTENSIVE O.R. PROCEDURE W MCC	5.0291	11.2	15.1	$27,327.32
	970	HIV W EXTENSIVE O.R. PROCEDURE W/O MCC	2.7871	5.1	6.9	$15,144.66
	974	HIV W MAJOR RELATED CONDITION W MCC	2.6531	6.6	9.2	$14,416.52
	975	HIV W MAJOR RELATED CONDITION W CC	1.3589	4.5	6.0	$7,384.05
	976	HIV W MAJOR RELATED CONDITION W/O CC/MCC	0.9073	3.3	4.1	$4,930.12
	977	HIV W OR W/O OTHER RELATED CONDITION	1.1577	3.5	4.7	$6,290.76
T	981	EXTENSIVE O.R. PROCEDURE UNRELATED TO PRINCIPAL DIAGNOSIS W MCC	4.8532	9.5	12.5	$26,371.51
T	982	EXTENSIVE O.R. PROCEDURE UNRELATED TO PRINCIPAL DIAGNOSIS W CC	2.7416	5.4	7.1	$14,897.42
T	983	EXTENSIVE O.R. PROCEDURE UNRELATED TO PRINCIPAL DIAGNOSIS W/O CC/MCC	1.7615	2.8	3.6	$9,571.71
	984	PROSTATIC O.R. PROCEDURE UNRELATED TO PRINCIPAL DIAGNOSIS W MCC	3.3844	9.3	12.2	$18,390.29
	985	PROSTATIC O.R. PROCEDURE UNRELATED TO PRINCIPAL DIAGNOSIS W CC	1.9339	4.8	6.7	$10,508.50
	986	PROSTATIC O.R. PROCEDURE UNRELATED TO PRINCIPAL DIAGNOSIS W/O CC/MCC	1.2079	2.4	3.4	$6,563.54
T	987	NON-EXTENSIVE O.R. PROC UNRELATED TO PRINCIPAL DIAGNOSIS W MCC	3.2123	8.0	10.5	$17,455.12
T	988	NON-EXTENSIVE O.R. PROC UNRELATED TO PRINCIPAL DIAGNOSIS W CC	1.7533	4.6	6.1	$9,527.15
T	989	NON-EXTENSIVE O.R. PROC UNRELATED TO PRINCIPAL DIAGNOSIS W/O CC/MCC	1.0425	2.2	3.0	$5,664.78
	998	PRINCIPAL DIAGNOSIS INVALID AS DISCHARGE DIAGNOSIS				
	999	UNGROUPABLE				

Calculated with an average hospital Medicare base rate of $5,433.84. Each hospital's base rate and corresponding payment will vary. The national average hospital Medicare base rate is the sum of the full update labor-related and nonlabor-related amounts published in the *Federal Register*, FY 2016 Final Rule, Table 1A. National Adjusted Operating Standardized Amounts; Labor/Nonlabor (if wage index greater than 1) or Table 1B. National Adjusted Operating Standardized Amounts; Labor/Nonlabor (if wage index less than or equal to 1).

MS-DRGs 998 and 999 contain cases that could not be assigned to valid DRGs.

Note: If there is no value in either the geometric mean length of stay or the arithmetic mean length of stay columns, the volume of cases is insufficient to determine a meaningful computation of these statistics.

T Transfer DRG   SP Special Payment

Appendix E — Abbreviations

abdomen or abdominal	abd	fixation	fix
accident or accidental	accid	foreign body	FB
acetabulum	acetab	fourth	4th
alteration	alter	fracture	fx
amputation	amp	fragmentation	fragmn
anterior	ant	greater than	>
approach	appr	hemorrhage	hemor
artificial	artfcl	hour, hours	hr
autologous	auto	including	incl*
bilateral	bilat	infection	infxn
blood	bld	inflammatory, inflammation	inflam
carcinoma	ca	influenza	flu
chronic	chr	infusion	inf
chronic kidney disease	CKD	initial	init
closed	clsd	injury	inj
comminuted	comm	insertion	insert
complication, complicated, complicated	comp	inspection	inspec
consciousness	cnscness	inspection	inspect
contusion	contsn	internal	int
destruction, destructive	destr	intervertebral	interv
detachment	detach	intraluminal	intralum
device	dev	joint	jt
diagnostic	dx	laceration	lac
disease, diseases	dz	large	lg
dislocation	disloc	lateral	lat
disorder	d/o	left	lt
displaced	disp	left lower quadrant	LLQ
displacement	displac	left upper quadrant	LUQ
division	div	less than	<
drainage	drain	level	lvl
due to	d/t	ligament, ligaments	lgmt
duration	dur	lower	lwr
element	elmt	malignant	malig
elsewhere	elsw	malunion	malu
encounter	enc	management	mgt
endoscopic	endo	mechanical, mechanism	mech
examination	exam	medial	med
excision	exc	middle	mid
external	ext	minutes	min
extirpation	Extir	moderate	mod
extraction	extract	monoplanar	monop
extraluminal	extralum	multiple	multi
extremity	extr	natural	natrl
fifth	5th	No Qual	NQ
first	1st	nonautologous	nonauto

nondisplaced	nondisp	seventh	7th
nonunion	nonu	shoulder	shldr
not applicable	N/A	sixth	6th
not elsewhere classified	NEC	small	sm
not otherwise specified	NOS	specified	spec
occlusion	occlsn	stabilization	stabliz
open	opn	stimulation	stimu
opening	opng	subcutaneous	SQ
other	oth	subluxation	sublux
pathological	path	subsequent	subsq
percutaneous	perc	substitute	sub
poisoning	poison	superficial	superf
posterior	post	supplement	supl
pregnancy	preg	syndrome	synd
pulmonary	pulmn	synthetic	synth
puncture	punc	system	sys
qualifier	qual	tempomandibular	tempom
radioactive	radioact	tendon	tndn
reattachment	reattach	third	3rd
regaining	regain	toxic effect	txc effct
region	rgn	transverse	transv
release	rls	traumatic	traum
removal	rmvl	treatment	tx
repair	rpr	trimester	trmstr
replacement	replace	unilateral	unilat
reposition	repos	unspecified	unsp
resection	resect	upper	upr
restriction	restrict	ventilation	vent
revision	rev	vertebral	vert
right	rt	with	w/
right lower quadrant	RLQ	without	w/o
right upper quadrant	RUQ	wound	wnd
second	2nd		
segmental	seg		
sequela	seq		

Glossary

against medical advice. Discharge status of patients who leave the hospital after signing a form that releases the hospital from responsibility, or those who leave the hospital premises without notifying hospital personnel.

arithmetic mean length of stay. Average number of days within a given DRG-stay in the hospital, also referred to as the average length of stay. The AMLOS is used to determine payment for outlier cases.

base rate. Payment weight assigned to hospitals to calculate diagnosis-related group (DRG) reimbursement. The base payment rate is divided into labor-related and nonlabor shares. The labor-related share is adjusted by the wage index applicable to the area where the hospital is located, and if the hospital is located in Alaska or Hawaii, the nonlabor share is adjusted by a cost of living adjustment factor. This base payment rate is multiplied by the DRG relative weight to calculate DRG reimbursement.

case mix index. Sum of all DRG relative weights for cases over a given period of time, divided by the number of Medicare cases.

charges. Dollar amount assigned to a service or procedure by a provider and reported to a payer.

code cluster. Group of two or more ICD-10-CM or ICD-10-PCS codes that must be used together to replicate the meaning of one ICD-9-CM code.

complication/comorbidity (CC). Condition that, when present, leads to substantially increased hospital resource use, such as intensive monitoring, expensive and technically complex services, and extensive care requiring a greater number of caregivers. Significant acute disease, acute exacerbations of significant chronic diseases, advanced or end stage chronic diseases, and chronic diseases associated with extensive debility are representative of CC conditions.

discharge. Situation in which the patient leaves an acute care (prospective payment) hospital after receiving complete acute care treatment.

discharge status. Disposition of the patient at discharge (e.g., left against medical advice, discharged home, transferred to an acute care hospital, expired).

GEM. General equivalence mapping. Translation tool that maps codes from one system (e.g., ICD-9-CM) to another (e.g., ICD-10-CM). The mappings are generally described as forward (mapping from ICD-9-CM to ICD-10-CM or ICD-10-PCS) or backwards (mapping ICD-10-CM or ICD-10-PCS to ICD-9-CM). Size, structure, and scope of the two systems may be completely different, which may require some decision making on the part of the user.

geometric mean length of stay. Statistically adjusted value for all cases for a given diagnosis-related group, allowing for the outliers, transfer cases, and negative outlier cases that would normally skew the data. The GMLOS is used to determine payment only for transfer cases (i.e., the per diem rate).

grouper. Software program that assigns diagnosis-related groups (DRGs).

homogeneous. Group of patients consuming similar types and amounts of hospital resources.

hospital-acquired condition (HAC). A significant, reasonably preventable condition determined to have occurred during a hospital visit, identified via the assignment of certain present on admission (POA) indicators. The MCC or CC status for the code for the HAC condition is invalidated when the POA indicator is N or U, thus potentially affecting DRG reimbursement.

major complication/comorbidity (MCC). Diagnosis codes that reflect the highest level of severity and have the potential to increase DRG reimbursement. See also complication/comorbidity.

major diagnostic category. Broad classification of diagnoses typically grouped by body system.

Medicare severity-adjusted diagnosis-related group (MS-DRG). One of the 758 classifications of diagnoses in which patients demonstrate similar resource consumption and length-of-stay patterns. MS-DRGs are a modification of the prior system that more accurately reflect the severity of a patient's illness and resources used.

nonoperating room procedure. Procedure that does not normally require the use of the operating room and that can affect MS-DRG assignment.

operating room (OR) procedure. Defined group of procedures that normally require the use of an operating room.

other diagnosis. All conditions (secondary) that exist at the time of admission or that develop subsequently that affect the treatment received and/or the length of stay. Diagnoses that relate to an earlier episode and that have no bearing on the current hospital stay are not to be reported.

outliers. There are two types of outliers: cost and day outliers. A cost outlier is a case in which the costs for treating the patient are extraordinarily high compared with other cases classified to the same MS-DRG. A cost outlier is paid an amount in excess of the cut-off threshold for a given MS-DRG. Payment for day outliers was eliminated with discharges occurring on or after October 1, 1997.

per diem rate. Payment made to the hospital from which a patient is transferred for each day of stay. It is determined by dividing the full MS-DRG payment by the GMLOS for the MS-DRG. The payment rate for the first day of stay is twice the per diem rate, and subsequent days are paid at the per diem rate up to the full DRG amount.

PMDC (Pre-major diagnostic category). Fifteen MS-DRGs to which cases are directly assigned based upon procedure codes before classification to an MDC, including MS-DRGs for the heart, liver, bone marrow transplants, simultaneous pancreas/kidney transplant, pancreas transplant, lung transplant, and five MS-DRGs for tracheostomies.

present on admission (POA). CMS-mandated assignment of indicators Y (Yes), N (No), U (Unknown), W (Clinically undetermined), or 1 (Exempt) to identify each condition as present or not present at the time the order for inpatient admission occurs for Medicare patients. A POA indicator should be listed for the principal diagnosis as well as secondary diagnoses and external cause of injury codes, unless present on the exempt list found in the ICD-9-CM Official Guidelines for Coding and Reporting.

principal diagnosis. Condition established after study to be chiefly responsible for occasioning the admission of the patient to the hospital for care.

principal procedure. Procedure performed for definitive treatment rather than for diagnostic or exploratory purposes, or that was necessary to treat a complication. Usually related to the principal diagnosis.

relative weight. Assigned weight that is intended to reflect the relative resource consumption associated with each MS-DRG. The higher the relative weight, the greater the payment to the hospital. The relative weights are calculated by CMS and published in the final prospective payment system rule.

surgical hierarchy. Ordering of surgical cases from most to least resource intensive. Application of this decision rule is necessary when patient stays involve multiple surgical procedures, each of which, occurring by itself, could result in assignment to a different MS-DRG. All patients must be assigned to only one MS-DRG per admission.

transfer. A situation in which the patient is transferred to another acute care hospital for related care.